This book is dedicated to my wife Karen and to my children, Jennifer Lynn, Judith Leslie, Joan Ellen, Charles John II, Daniel Arthur, and Thomas Mathew.

The Aldrich Library of Infrared Spectra

EDITION III

Charles J. Pouchert

PREFACE

(First Edition)

Whenever we think of the value of infrared spectra in structure determinations, we think of a classic book review by Professor R. B. Woodward [*J. Amer. Chem. Soc.*, **72**, 3327 (1950)], and can do no better than to quote him: "Infrared spectra have now become an asset of almost incomparable value to all chemists interested in structural problems in organic chemistry. The facility and certainty with which the presence, or absence, of a large number of structural features in a molecule may be established through infrared studies must defy the imagination of those unfamiliar with the method. Who does not remember occasions when Nature has been reluctant to afford him a crystalline derivative in the attempt to define the presence of a given group? Who has not at times thrown reagent after reagent into futile attack upon a function to which approach is barred by the gross bulk of hindering substituents? Light is not easily denied access, and more important, in the infrared region it is sensitive to the molecular vibrations of atomic groupings which are devoid of useful chemical reactivity . . ." "But we must remember, that in applying this very valuable tool, we enter the realm of the intellect, and once the simple fundamentals have been mastered, each investigator will find his own approach, and will have the opportunity to illumine the field and his own problems in uncounted different ways."

In the last several years a number of excellent works on infrared spectra have appeared, for instance, the works of L. J. Bellamy, K. Nakanishi, and N. B. Colthup. Although they all include empirical collections of band positions and intensities as well as theory, they lack a sufficient number of quality spectra. It is therefore the intention of this book to present a large number of spectra on each of the important organic functional groups along with a short written description and graphic representation of their spectral features for the *purpose of review* by the average chemist who is not a specialist in infrared spectroscopy.

ACKNOWLEDGMENTS

As with previous editions, a large number of people helped to produce this collection. The entire Quality Control, Data Processing and Printing Departments were instrumental in bringing their expertise together to make this book possible.

Of special mention are Shirley Bloomier, James Brien, Diana Docta, Ronnie Heaton, Jeffrey Kett, Anna Napiorkowski, Judy Pruss and Cathie Wyrobeck from Quality Control, who worked hard bringing together the many fragments of data. Milt Lathan of our Data Processing group and Wes Nosek of our Printing Department were of great help putting the indices together.

TABLE OF CONTENTS

INTRODUCTION

Location of Specific Compounds

For specific spectrum location, either the Alphabetical or Molecular Formula Indices should be used.

The sections are arranged in an order of increasing complexity. A multifunctional compound is found in the representative functional group located farthest down the list in the table of contents.

For example, 3,5-di-tert-butyl-2,6-dihydroxybenzoic acid, will be found under aromatic carboxylic acids and not under the other functional group heading represented (i.e., aromatic phenols).

Ten categories of compounds including heterocyclic N-oxides, oximes, alkynes, indicators and dyes, steroids and indole alkaloids, deuterated compounds, silanes, boranes, organometallics and polymers have been grouped separately from either the non-aromatics, the aromatic carbocycles or the aromatic heterocycles. Diphenylacetylene would therefore be found in the alkyne section rather than the aromatic hydrocarbon section.

Compounds which have both carbocyclic and heterocyclic aromatic rings, whether they are fused or not, will appear in the appropriate heterocyclic section. Functional groups which are not attached directly to an aromatic ring but do have an aromatic ring in their structure are still included in the corresponding aromatic section. For example, the spectra of benzoic acid and phenylacetic acid are both in the aromatic carboxylic acid section. The spectra of 3-hydroxypyridine and 3-pyridylcarbinol will be found in the 6-membered aromatic heterocyclic section.

Production of the Infrared Spectra

Most of the spectra were produced using a Beckman I.R.-8 grating spectrophotometer; some were run on a Beckman I.R.-5 sodium chloride prism spectrophotometer. Neither compensating sodium chloride plates nor reference beam attenuation were used in scanning the spectra.

Over 4,000 spectra have been added since the first edition. Each has been inserted within the appropriate section and position to retain the advantages of an order of functionality and molecular complexity.

The compounds were prepared for spectral analysis in the neat, melt or Nujol mull form as indicated on each of the spectra. A compound which is liquid at ambient temperatures was placed between two sodium chloride plates with the thickness adjusted so that the maximum absorption of the spectrum is close to 2-10% transmittance. Certain classes of compounds which are composed of long aliphatic chains and a weakly absorbing functional group were prepared so that the C-H stretch absorption at 3.4 μ (2940 cm^{-1}) is close to 0% transmittance while the weakly absorbing functional group has its main characteristic absorption near 10% transmittance. Because this is not an absolute rule throughout the collection, it is necessary that the spectra be read keeping in mind the relative intensities of each of the functional group absorptions, especially as they appear in the same molecule.

The melt method retains the advantages of the neat method with one exception. The presence of residual solvents in the material to be melted will probably be driven off, leaving the analyst with the wrong impression concerning the chemical's purity. In preparing a melt, both the sodium chloride plates and the holder were heated to a temperature 30-50° C. above the melting point of the material. The temperature selected was dependent upon the scanning period of the instrument being used. This period is 10 minutes for the I.R.-8 and 3.5 minutes for the I.R.-5. The maximum temperature with which this method can be used is approximately 70° C. (50° C. or lower is ideal). The thickness of the cell was adjusted in a manner similar to that of the neat method. It is necessary that the sample remains in the liquid phase during the entire scan to avoid shifts and splits of the absorptions at higher wavelengths as the material solidifies. This method obviously should not be used if the material boils near its melting point.

The Nujol spectra were prepared by grinding the sample to a very fine powder and then adding as little Nujol as possible in order to form a paste. The WIG-L-BUG manufactured by the Crescent Dental Manufacturing Company of Lyons, Illinois has been found to work ideally for this purpose. Approximately 50 to 150 mg. of material and an acrylic ball are placed in a one inch disposable polystyrene sample vial and pulverized for 30 seconds. A small amount of Nujol is then added and the material mixed for another 15 seconds in the WIG-L-BUG. The resulting paste is placed between 2 sodium chloride plates which are then rotated against each other to obtain the correct sample thickness. For this procedure, the maximum absorption is set at 2-10% transmittance with the additional requirement that the base line be maintained as high as possible near 2 μ (5000 cm^{-1}). In some cases, this is extremely difficult to do, particularly when the crystals are exceptionally hard or tend to stick together making pulverization difficult. Polycyclic aromatic mulls are usually the most difficult to prepare. A good indication of the quality of the mull is the degree of visible transparency obtained when the material is pressed between the plates. It should be close to that of a finely ground glass surface. The following spectra are of Nujol prepared in three different thicknesses between sodium chloride plates.

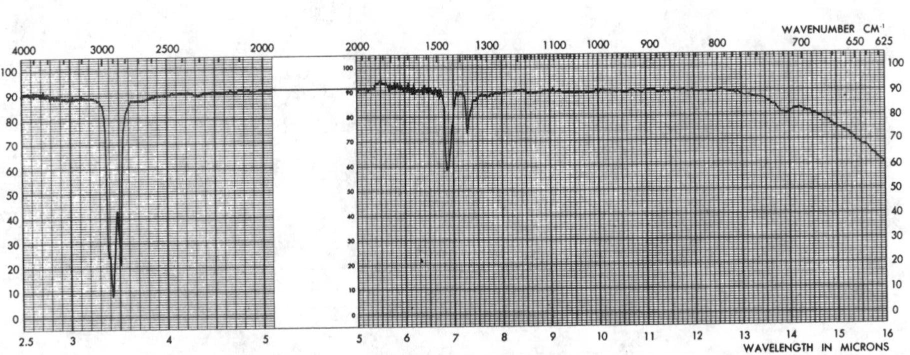

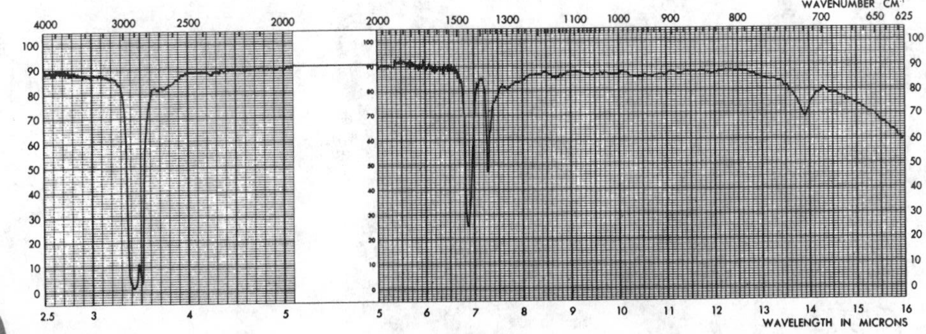

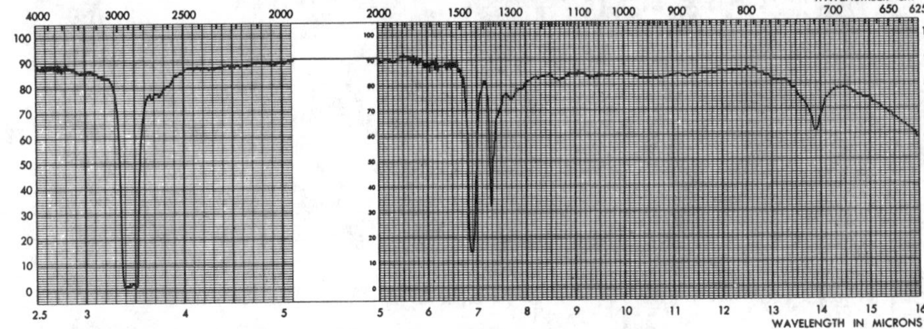

Except in a few instances, KBr pellets have been avoided for the following reasons:

1.) Spectrum reproducibility is difficult to regulate without careful weighing of both the KBr and the sample.

2.) KBr is hygroscopic. Therefore, when water bands do appear in the spectrum, one does not know whether the sample originally contained water of whether it was picked up by the KBr. If the KBr pellet is then dried, residual solvent impurities could also be driven off.

3.) Due to KBr interactions with amine salts, the spectra of a given compound may vary from sample to sample over the entire 2 to 16 μ (5000-625 cm^{-1}) range.

However, for the experienced analyst, the KBr method often can give better resolution, but as it presents such difficulties for routine analysis, we have not used it extensively.

The polymer spectra from the last section of this book were produced as films from appropriate solvents. The polymer was dissolved and then spread on to a NaCl plate. The solvent was then evaporated at ~100° C. and the spectrum run. Some of the spectra do show residual solvent when the solvent used would not totally evaporate. This should be kept in mind when the spectrum is observed.

The Preparation of the Book

The 12,000 spectra chosen as examples were picked from over 400,000 accumulated in our analytical department. The very best with regard to sample purity and over-all spectral appearance were chosen for the book. The chemical titles which include molecular weights, linear formulas and physical constants were taken from the Aldrich Chemical Company catalog computer file. The structures presented on each of the spectra are not intended to represent spatial configuration.

The indices were produced by computer through the facilities of the Aldrich Data Processing Department.

Both wavelength and wavenumber designations are used in describing band positions in the introductory descriptions of each of the functional group sections. The wavenumber values are rounded off to the nearest 5 units.

ALDRICH

NON-AROMATIC HYDROCARBONS

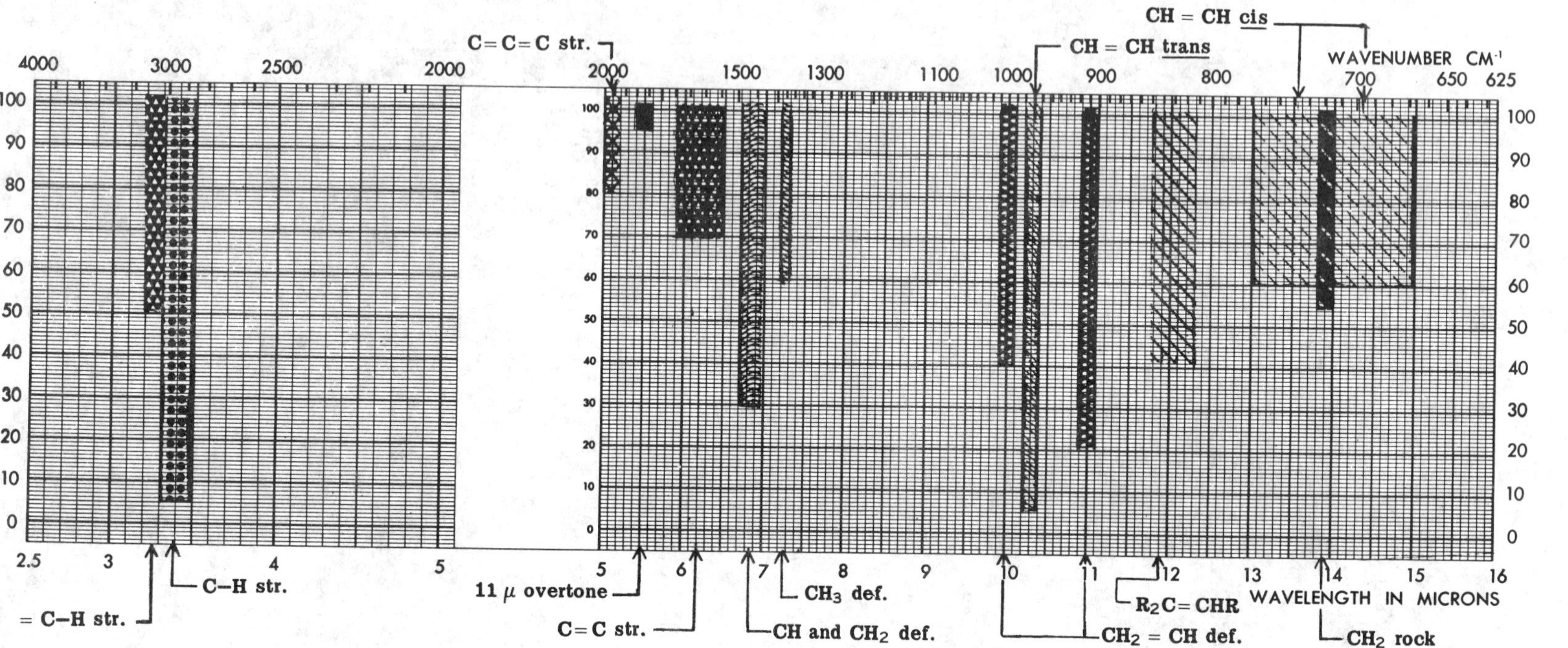

1.) Straight Chain 3A-5F
2.) Branched Chain 5G-10D
3.) Unsaturated Straight Chain 10E-14H
4.) Unsaturated Branched Chain 15A-21A
5.) Two or More Double Bonds 21B-25B
6.) Cyclic Saturated 25C-30D
7.) Cyclic Unsaturated . . 30E-39C

This section contains spectra of a group of organic chemicals with the simplest functions, the carbon-carbon and the carbon-hydrogen bonds. As we progress from the simple straight chain aliphatics through the branched to the unsaturated and finally to the cyclic unsaturated compounds, the spectra increase in complexity.

The straight chain aliphatic compounds (spectra 3A—5F) exhibit the basic absorptions seen in the remainder of the spectra of this section:

1.) the carbon-hydrogen stretch absorption at 3.4 – 3.5 μ (2940 – 2855 cm^{-1});
2.) the carbon-hydrogen bending band at 6.8 μ (1470 cm^{-1});
3.) the symmetric carbon-hydrogen bending band of the $-CH_3$ group at 7.25 μ (1380 cm^{-1});
4.) the CH_2 rocking absorption at 13.8 μ (725 cm^{-1}) which increases in intensity in direct proportion to the number of consecutive CH_2's in the chain; this band is split when observed in the solid state.

Branching of the chain adds a considerable number of absorptions due to skeletal vibrations between 8 and 11 μ (1250 – 910 cm^{-1}). Very weak bands also appear here in the spectra of the straight chain compounds, but are too weak to show significantly when run in the usual manner with the compounds between NaCl plates. Also significant is the split in the 7.25 μ (1380 cm^{-1}) absorption. This doublet is due to the gem–CH_3 group and presents a split very uniform in shape. When there are three CH_3 s on the same carbon atom, as in spectra 8D, 8H, 9D, 10B, etc., this absorption becomes very lopsided with the peak at higher wavelength, now shifted to 7.32 μ (1365 cm^{-1}), becoming the stronger.

The presence of a double bond in structures of this series introduces a number of significant absorptions. First, the carbon-hydrogen stretch absorption shifts to a lower wavelength when the carbon atom is double-bonded. The new position is usually between 3.2 and 3.3 μ (3125 – 3030 cm^{-1}) and shifts within that range depending on the neighboring atoms. The carbon-carbon double bond stretch shows itself as an absorption of medium intensity between 5.9 and 6.5 μ (1695 – 1540 cm^{-1}). This absorption will appear at a slightly higher wavelength when the double bond is conjugated or bears a halogen. The intensity is highly variable, ranging from nil for molecules having a center of symmetry in the double bond to very strong for vinyl ethers.

Aside from these two stretch vibrations there are the characteristic deformation bands of the vinyl group ($CH=CH_2$). Noteworthy is their consistent placement at 10 and 11 μ (1000 and 910 cm^{-1}) with an obvious overtone between 5.5 and 5.6 μ (1820 – 1785 cm^{-1}). The band at 10 μ (1000 cm^{-1}) disappears when the lone hydrogen of the vinyl group is substituted ($^{R'}_{R}{>}C=CH_2$, see spectra 18B, C, 18F, etc.). The 5.6 and 11 μ (1785 and 910 cm^{-1}) absorptions remain, although the 11 μ (910 cm^{-1}) band is shifted to about 11.3 μ (885 cm^{-1}). The replacement of the methylene protons of the vinyl group ($R–CH=C{<}^{R}_{R}$) results in an absorption in the vicinity of 12 μ (835 cm^{-1}). In general, this band is not as reliable for structure diagnosis as are the vinyl and methylene absorptions. The R–CH=CH–R′ group absorbs near 10.3 μ (970 cm^{-1}) in the *trans* form and between 13 and 15 μ (770 – 665 cm^{-1}) in the *cis* form.

The cumulated double bonds of an allene (C=C=C) absorb between 5 and 5.2 μ (2000 – 1925 cm^{-1}). (See spectrum 23B.) Tetramethylallene (spectrum 23C) does not exhibit this absorption, apparently because of its symmetry.

The saturated cyclic members of this collection display spectra very similar to those of branched open-chain hydrocarbons with the skeletal vibrations appearing between 8 and 11 μ (1250 – 910 cm^{-1}).

Additional complexity is introduced when a double bond is added to the ring. The additional absorptions are usually above 13 μ (770 cm^{-1}) and can be attributed to the *cis* configuration of the double bond. Note, however, in spectra 36A and B that the size of the ring allows the double bonds to be *trans* as can be seen in the absorptions around 10.3 μ (970 cm^{-1}) in addition to the *cis* bands at 14 μ (715 cm^{-1}).

A 15,894-1
Pentane, 98%
$CH_3(CH_2)_3CH_3$
M.W. 72.15 m.p. -147° b.p. 36° n_D^{20} 1.3580
d 0.626 Beil. 1,130

B 13,938-6 **n-Hexane**, 99.9 %
$CH_3(CH_2)_4CH_3$ M.W. 86.18 n_D^{20} 1.3749
b.p. 69°

C 17,891-8
Hexanes, A.C.S. reagent
C_6H_{14}
M.W. 86.18 b.p. 68-72° n_D^{20} 1.3788 d 0.68
Beil. 1,142

D H219-8 **Heptane, puriss.**
$CH_3(CH_2)_5CH_3$ M.W. 100.21 n_D^{20} 1.3860
b.p. 98.5°

E O-325-7 **Octane, puriss.**
$CH_3(CH_2)_6CH_3$ M.W. 114.23 n_D^{20} 1.3960
b.p. 124-126°

F N2940-6 **n-Nonane**
$CH_3(CH_2)_7CH_3$ M.W. 128.26 n_D^{20} 1.4028

G D90-1 **Decane, puriss.**
$CH_3(CH_2)_8CH_3$ M.W. 142.29 n_D^{20} 1.4113

H U40-7 **n-Undecane**
$CH_3(CH_2)_9CH_3$ M.W. 156.31 n_D^{20} 1.4169
b.p. 194-196°

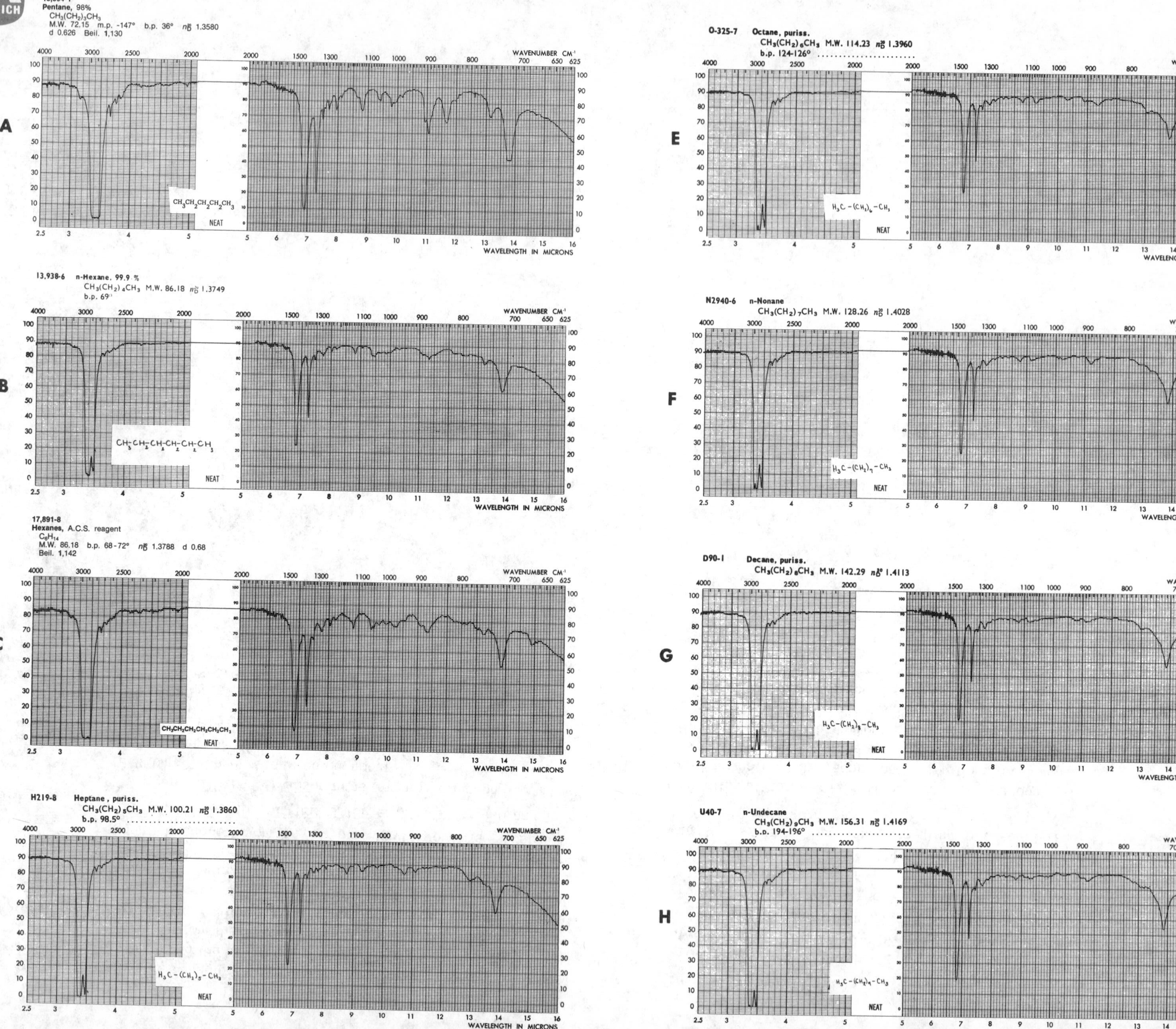

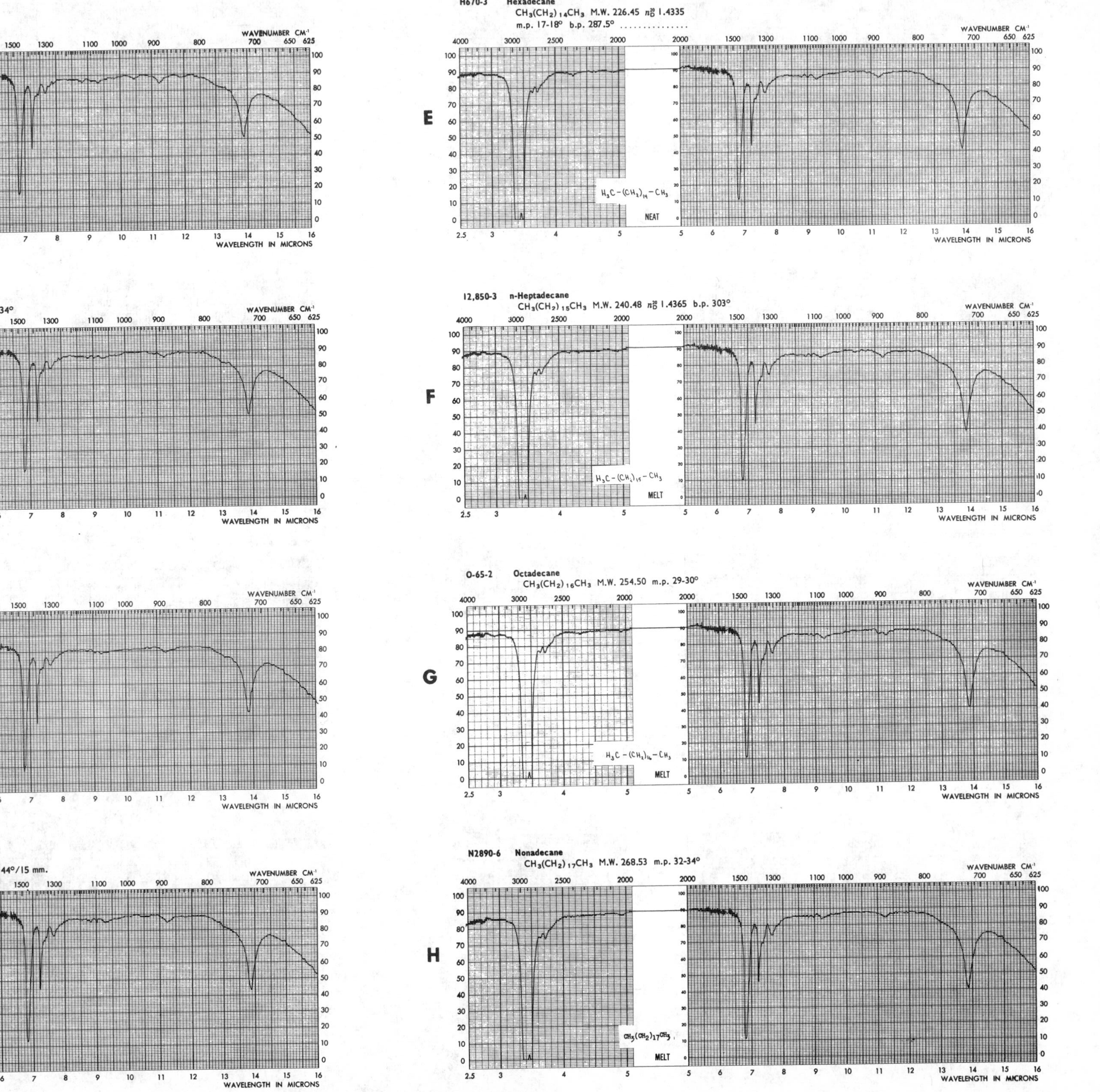
A
D22,110-4 Dodecane
$CH_3(CH_2)_{10}CH_3$ M.W. 170.34
n_D^{20} 1.4212
$H_3C-(CH_2)_{10}-CH_3$
NEAT
B
T5740-1 n-Tridecane
$CH_3(CH_2)_{11}CH_3$ M.W. 184.37 n_D^{20} 1.4253 b.p. 234°
$H_3C-(CH_2)_{11}-CH_3$
NEAT
C
17,245-6
Tetradecane
$CH_3(CH_2)_{12}CH_3$ FW 198.40 mp -6 to 5°
bp 252-254° n_D^{20} 1.4280 d 0.763 *Beil.* 1,171
Disp. C
$CH_3(CH_2)_{12}CH_3$
NEAT
D
P340-6 n-Pentadecane
$CH_3(CH_2)_{13}CH_3$ M.W. 212.42 n_D^{20} 1.4317 b.p. 144°/15 mm.
$H_3C-(CH_2)_{13}-CH_3$
NEAT
E
H670-3 Hexadecane
$CH_3(CH_2)_{14}CH_3$ M.W. 226.45 n_D^{20} 1.4335
m.p. 17-18° b.p. 287.5°
$H_3C-(CH_2)_{14}-CH_3$
NEAT
F
12,850-3 n-Heptadecane
$CH_3(CH_2)_{15}CH_3$ M.W. 240.48 n_D^{20} 1.4365 b.p. 303°
$H_3C-(CH_2)_{15}-CH_3$
MELT
G
O-65-2 Octadecane
$CH_3(CH_2)_{16}CH_3$ M.W. 254.50 m.p. 29-30°
$H_3C-(CH_2)_{16}-CH_3$
MELT
H
N2890-6 Nonadecane
$CH_3(CH_2)_{17}CH_3$ M.W. 268.53 m.p. 32-34°
$CH_3(CH_2)_{17}CH_3$
MELT
WAVENUMBER CM^{-1}
WAVELENGTH IN MICRONS

ALDRICH

NON-AROMATIC HYDROCARBONS

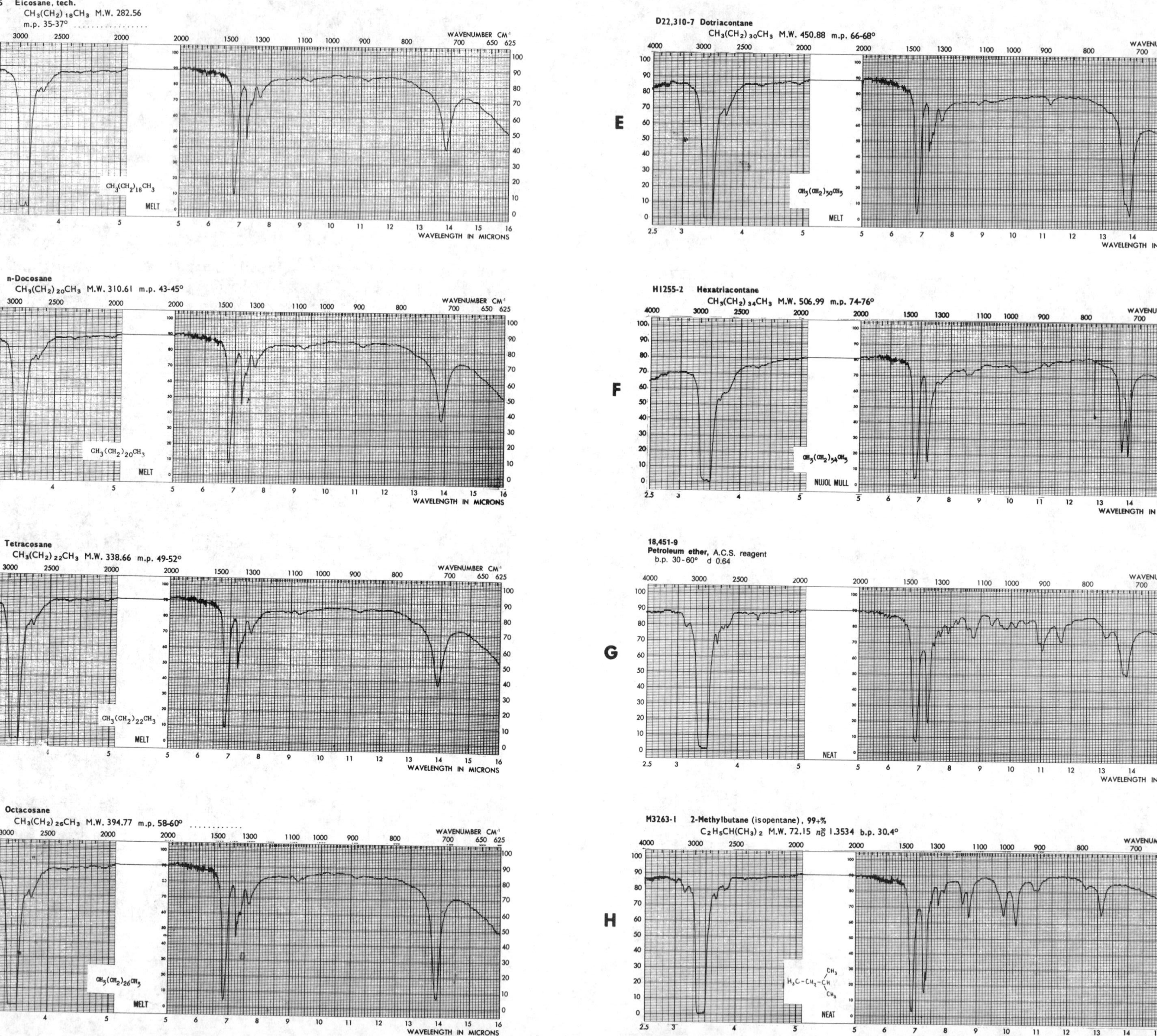
ALDRICH
A
11,776-5 Eicosane, tech.
$CH_3(CH_2)_{18}CH_3$ M.W. 282.56
m.p. 35-37°
MELT
B
13,445-7 n-Docosane
$CH_3(CH_2)_{20}CH_3$ M.W. 310.61 m.p. 43-45°
MELT
C
T875-2 Tetracosane
$CH_3(CH_2)_{22}CH_3$ M.W. 338.66 m.p. 49-52°
MELT
D
O-50-4 Octacosane
$CH_3(CH_2)_{26}CH_3$ M.W. 394.77 m.p. 58-60°
MELT
E
D22,310-7 Dotriacontane
$CH_3(CH_2)_{30}CH_3$ M.W. 450.88 m.p. 66-68°
MELT
F
H1255-2 Hexatriacontane
$CH_3(CH_2)_{34}CH_3$ M.W. 506.99 m.p. 74-76°
NUJOL MULL
G
18,451-9
Petroleum ether, A.C.S. reagent
b.p. 30-60° d 0.64
NEAT
H
M3263-1 2-Methylbutane (isopentane), 99+%
$C_2H_5CH(CH_3)_2$ M.W. 72.15 n_D^{20} 1.3534 b.p. 30.4°
NEAT
WAVENUMBER CM⁻¹
WAVELENGTH IN MICRONS

A

M6580-7 **2-Methylpentane, puriss.**
$CH_3CH_2CH_2CH(CH_3)_2$ M.W. 86.18 n_D^{20} 1.3716 b.p. 62°

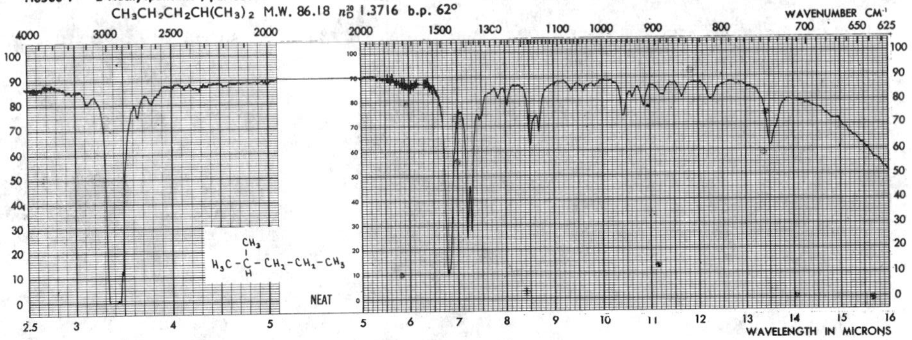

B

M6600-5 **3-Methylpentane, puriss.**
$C_2H_5CH(CH_3)C_2H_5$ M.W. 86.18 n_D^{20} 1.3755
b.p. 64°

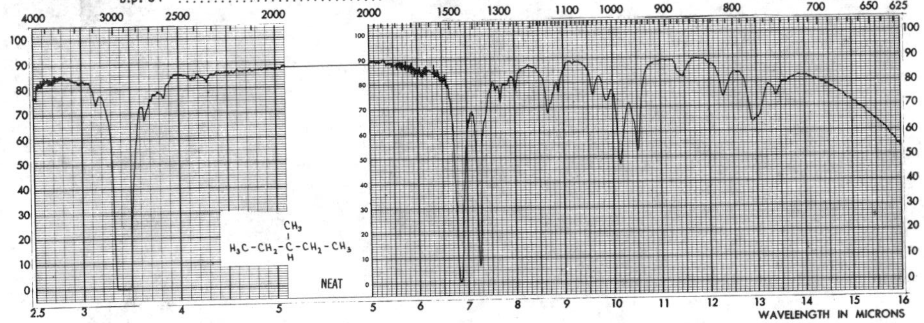

C

11,079-5 **3-Ethylpentane**
$(C_2H_5)_3CH$ M.W. 100.21 n_D^{20} 1.3931
b.p. 93°

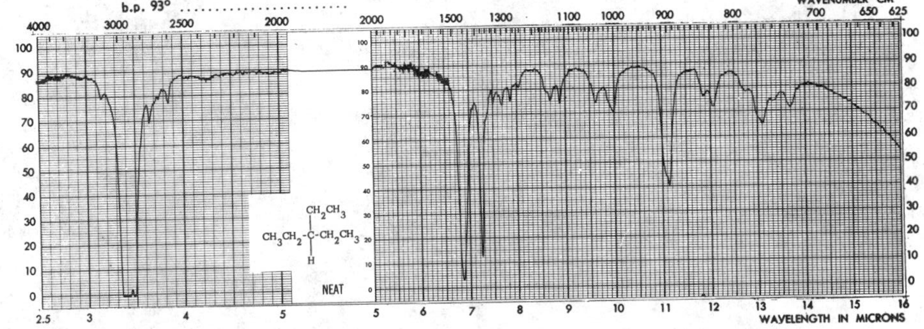

D

M4970-4 **2-Methylhexane**
$CH_3(CH_2)_3CH(CH_3)_2$ M.W. 100.21 n_D^{20} 1.3840

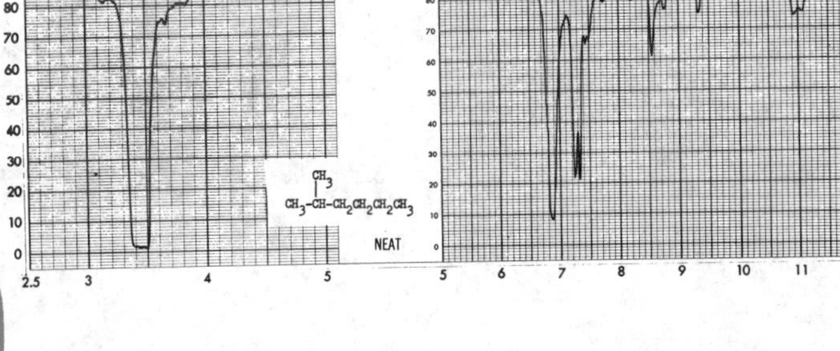
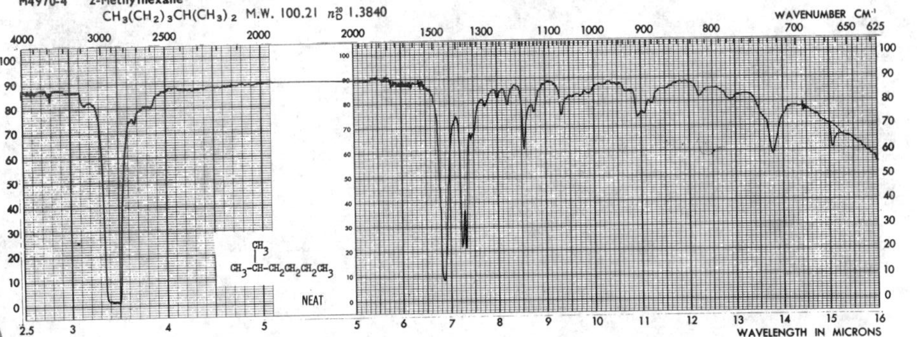

E

M4980-1 **3-Methylhexane**
$CH_3CH_2CH_2CH(CH_3)C_2H_5$ M.W. 100.21 n_D^{20} 1.3863
b.p. 91-92°

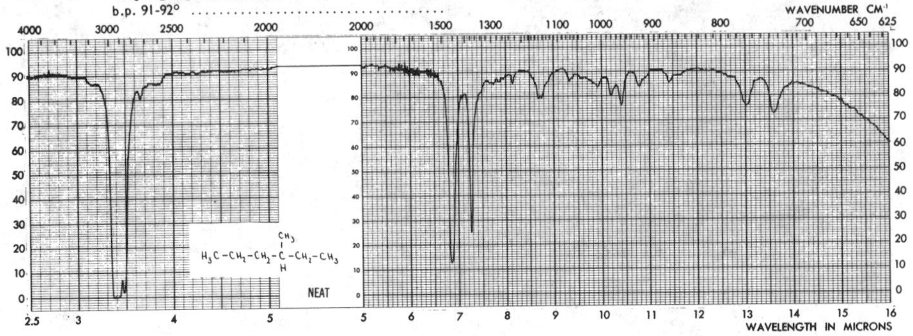

F

M4794-9 **2-Methylheptane**
$CH_3(CH_2)_4CH(CH_3)_2$ M.W. 114.23
n_D^{20} 1.3980

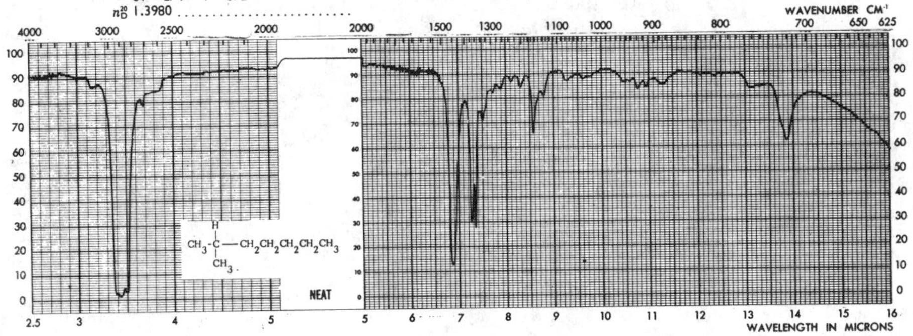

G

M4795-7 **3-Methylheptane**
$CH_3(CH_2)_3CH(CH_3)C_2H_5$ M.W. 114.23 n_D^{20} 1.3977
b.p. 118-120°

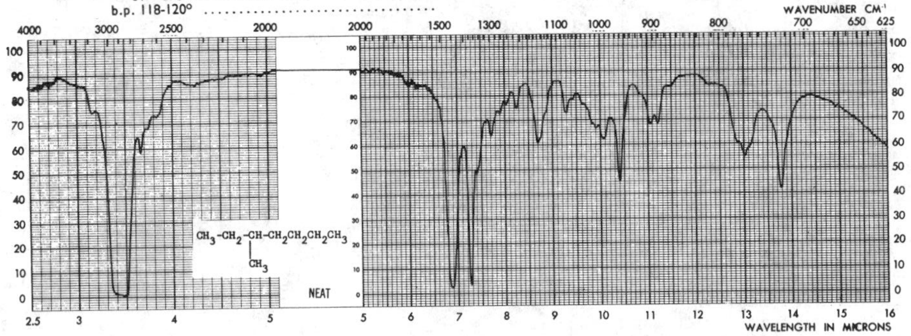

H

11,102-3 **4-Methylheptane**
$CH_3CH_2CH_2CH(CH_3)CH_2CH_2CH_3$ M.W. 114.23
n_D^{20} 1.3980 b.p. 118°

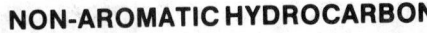

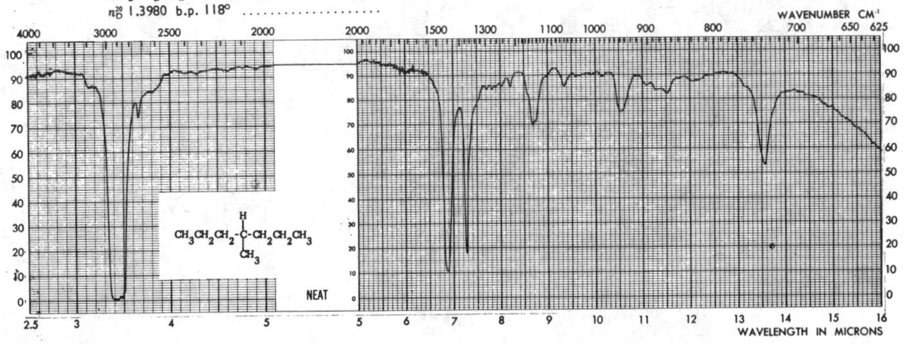

A 12,939-9 **3-Ethylheptane**
$CH_3(CH_2)_3CH(C_2H_5)_2$ M.W. 128.26
n_D^{20} 1.4090

B 11,172-4 **2-Methyloctane**
$CH_3(CH_2)_5CH(CH_3)_2$ M.W. 128.26 n_D^{20} 1.4005
b.p. 142°

C 11,173-2 **3-Methyloctane**
$CH_3(CH_2)_4CH(CH_3)C_2H_5$ M.W. 128.26 n_D^{20} 1.4068
b.p. 114°

D 11,174-0 **4-Methyloctane**
$CH_3(CH_2)_3CH(CH_3)CH_2CH_2CH_3$ M.W. 128.26
n_D^{20} 1.4052 b.p. 142°

E 11,168-6 **2-Methylnonane**
$CH_3(CH_2)_6CH(CH_3)_2$ M.W. 142.29
n_D^{20} 1.4088

F 11,170-8 **4-Methylnonane, puriss.**
$CH_3(CH_2)_4CH(CH_3)CH_2CH_2CH_3$ M.W. 142.29
n_D^{20} 1.4118

G 11,171-6 **5-Methylnonane**
$CH_3(CH_2)_3CH(CH_3)(CH_2)_3CH_3$ M.W. 142.29
n_D^{20} 1.4101

H 11,100-7 **2-Methyldecane**
$CH_3(CH_2)_7CH(CH_3)_2$ M.W. 156.31
n_D^{20} 1.4133

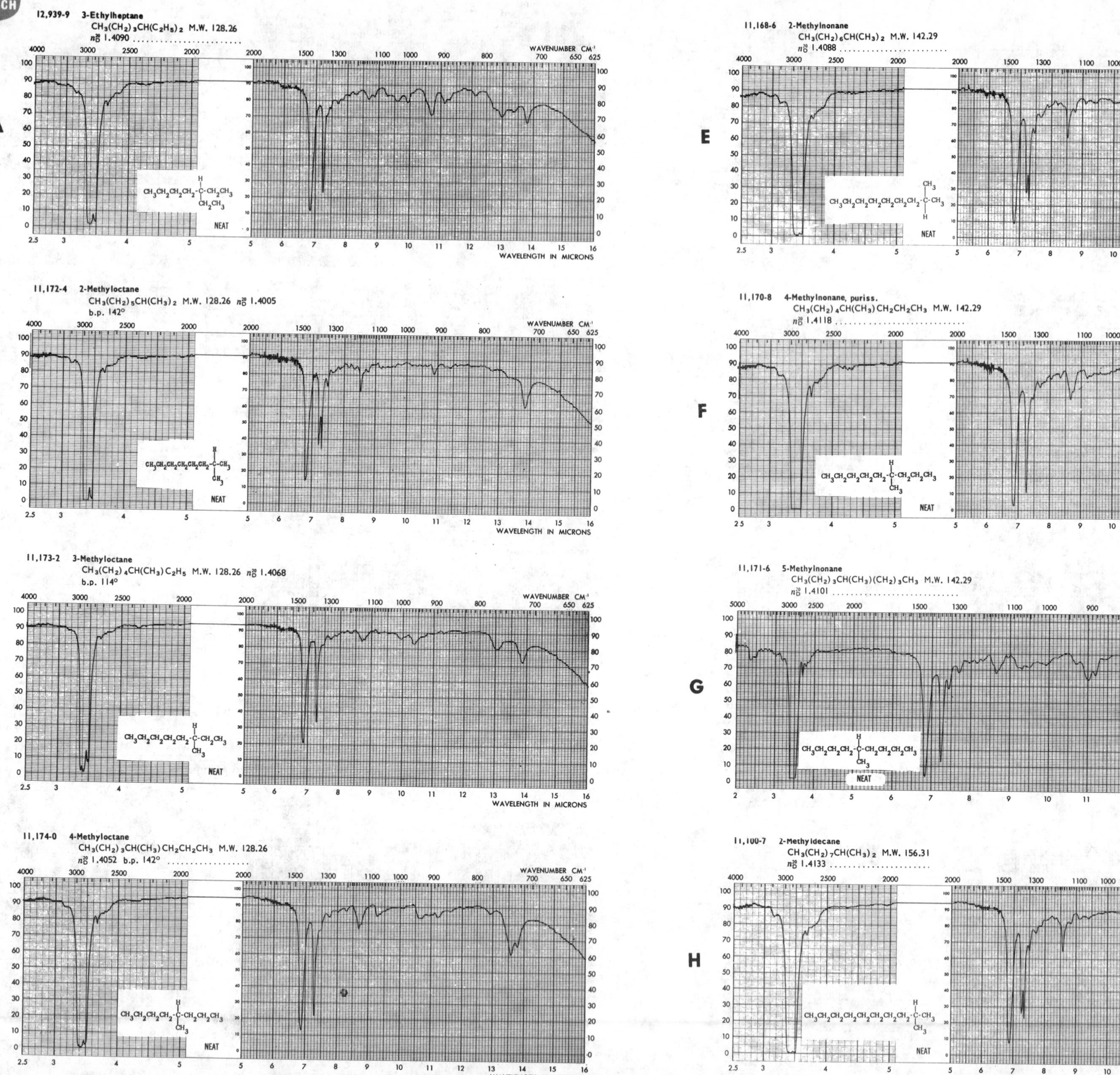

A

11,178-3 2-Methylundecane
$CH_3(CH_2)_8CH(CH_3)_2$ M.W. 170.34
n_D^{20} 1.4191

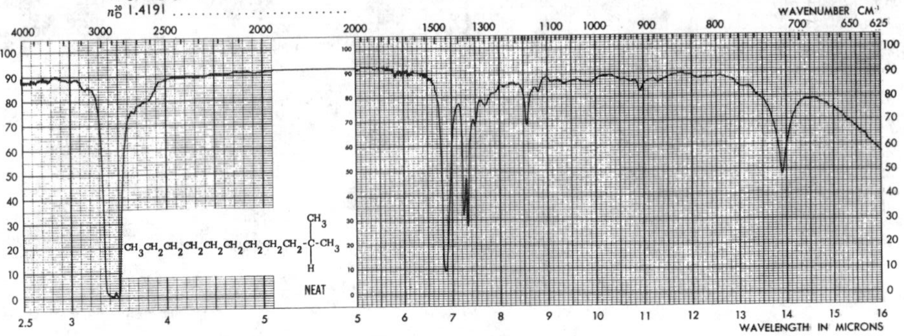

$CH_3CH_2CH_2CH_2CH_2CH_2CH_2CH_2CH_2$-C(H)($CH_3$)-$CH_3$ — NEAT

B

D15,140-8 2,2-Dimethylbutane (neohexane)
$C_2H_5C(CH_3)_3$ M.W. 86.18 n_D^{20} 1.3660

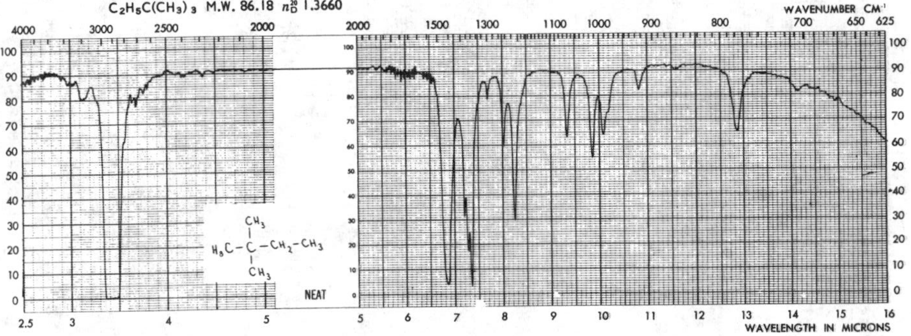

$H_3C-C(CH_3)_2-CH_2-CH_3$ — NEAT

C

D15,160-2 2,3-Dimethylbutane (diisopropyl)
$(CH_3)_2CHCH(CH_3)_2$ M.W. 86.18 n_D^{20} 1.3750

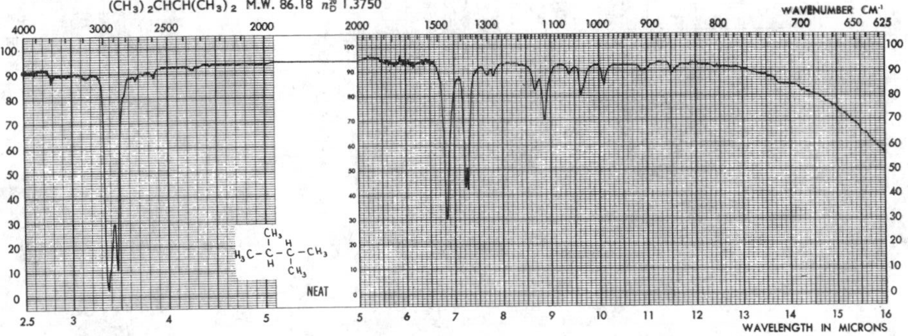

$H_3C-CH(CH_3)-CH(CH_3)-CH_3$ — NEAT

D

11,067-1 2,2-Dimethylpentane
$CH_3CH_2CH_2C(CH_3)_3$ M.W. 100.21 n_D^{20} 1.3824
b.p. 78°/743 mm.

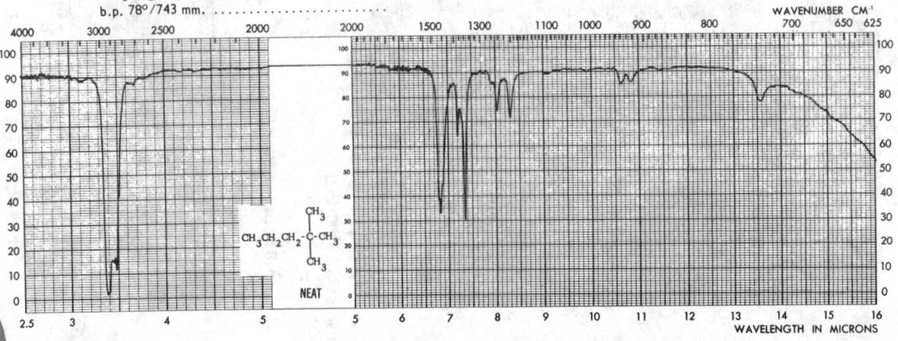

$CH_3CH_2CH_2-C(CH_3)_2-CH_3$ — NEAT

E

11,845-1 3,3-Dimethylpentane
$C_2H_5C(CH_3)_2C_2H_5$ M.W. 100.21 n_D^{20} 1.3921
b.p. 86°

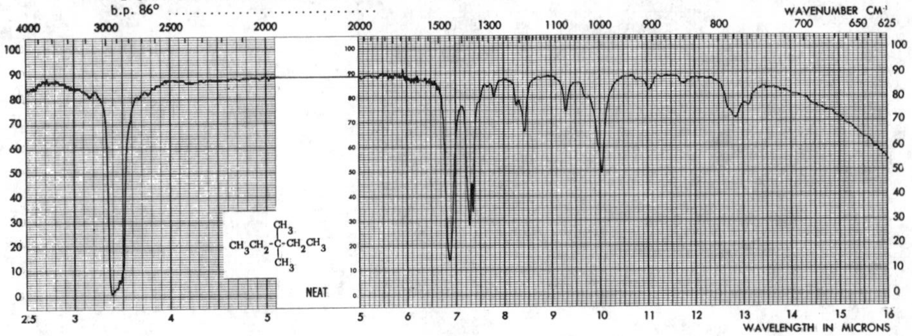

$CH_3CH_2-C(CH_3)_2-CH_2CH_3$ — NEAT

F

D17,320-7 2,3-Dimethylpentane
$C_2H_5CH(CH_3)CH(CH_3)_2$ M.W. 100.21
n_D^{20} 1.3899

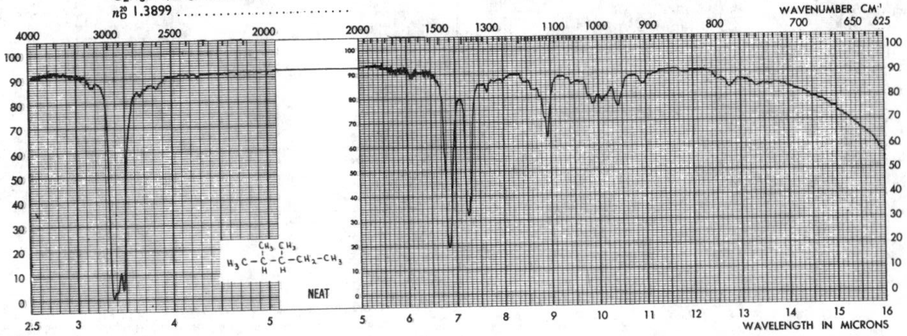

$H_3C-CH(CH_3)-CH(CH_3)-CH_2-CH_3$ — NEAT

G

D17,340-1 2,4-Dimethylpentane
$(CH_3)_2CHCH_2CH(CH_3)_2$ M.W. 100.21 n_D^{20} 1.3820

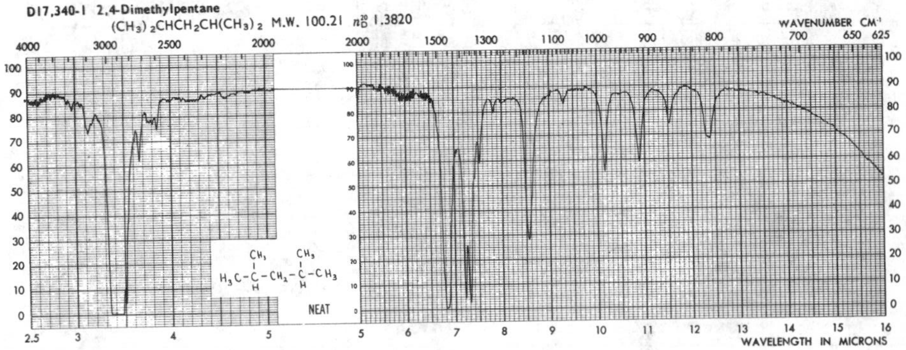

$H_3C-CH(CH_3)-CH_2-CH(CH_3)-CH_3$ — NEAT

H

11,145-7 2,2-Dimethylhexane
$CH_3(CH_2)_3C(CH_3)_3$ M.W. 114.23
n_D^{20} 1.3908

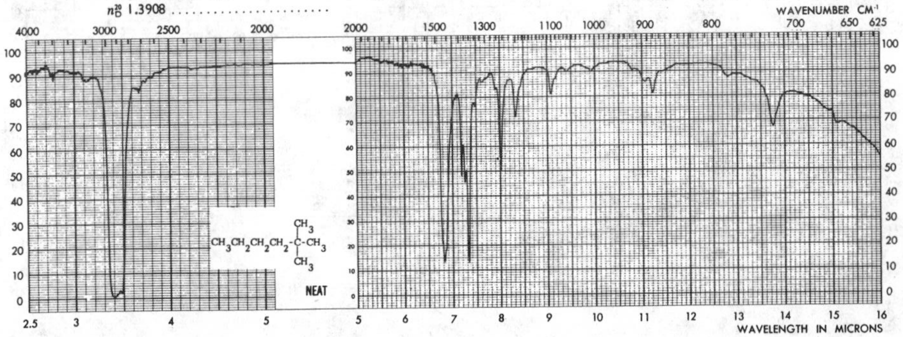

$CH_3CH_2CH_2CH_2-C(CH_3)_2-CH_3$ — NEAT

WAVENUMBER CM⁻¹ — WAVELENGTH IN MICRONS

A

11,057-4 **2,4-Dimethylhexane, puriss.**
$C_2H_5CH(CH_3)CH_2CH(CH_3)_2$ M.W. 114.23 n_D^{20} 1.3955

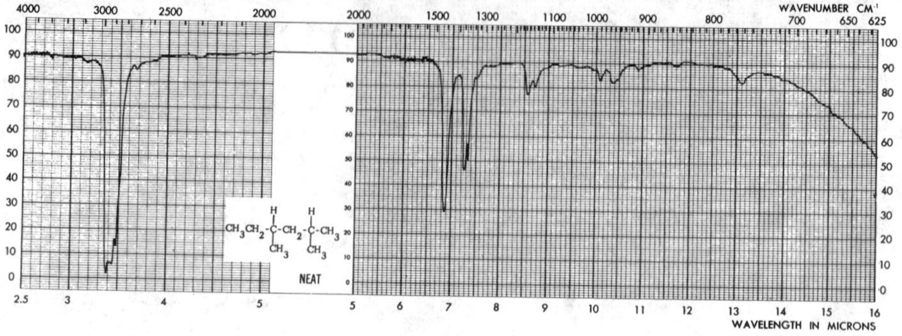

B

11,841-9 **3,4-Dimethylhexane, puriss.**
$C_2H_5CH(CH_3)CH(CH_3)C_2H_5$ M.W. 114.23 n_D^{20} 1.4013
b.p. 119°

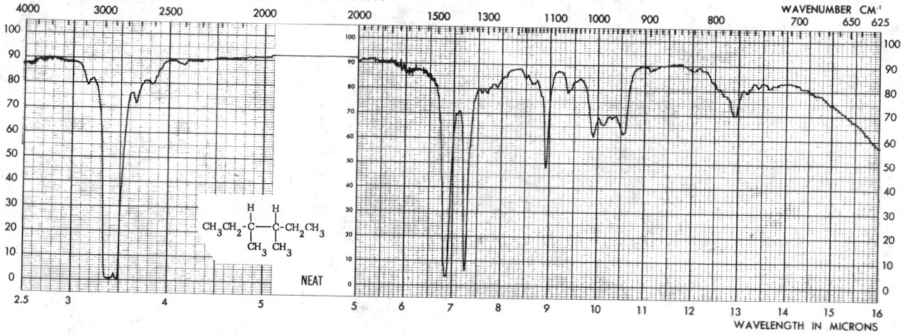

C

11,058-2 **2,5-Dimethylhexane**
$(CH_3)_2CHCH_2CH_2CH(CH_3)_2$ M.W. 114.23 n_D^{20} 1.3922
b.p. 108°

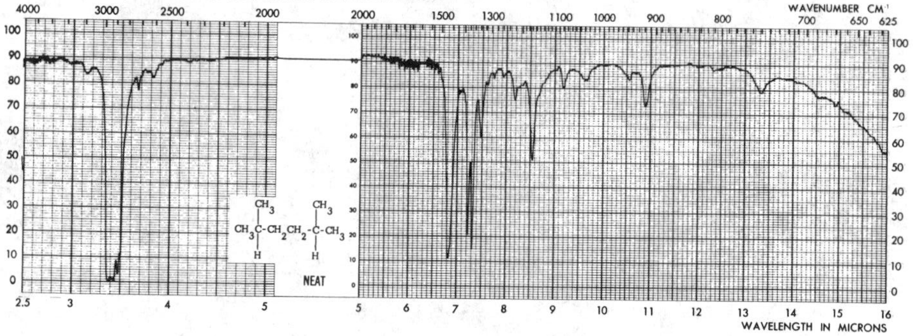

D

11,143-0 **2,2-Dimethylheptane, puriss.**
$CH_3(CH_2)_4C(CH_3)_3$ M.W. 128.26
n_D^{20} 1.4009

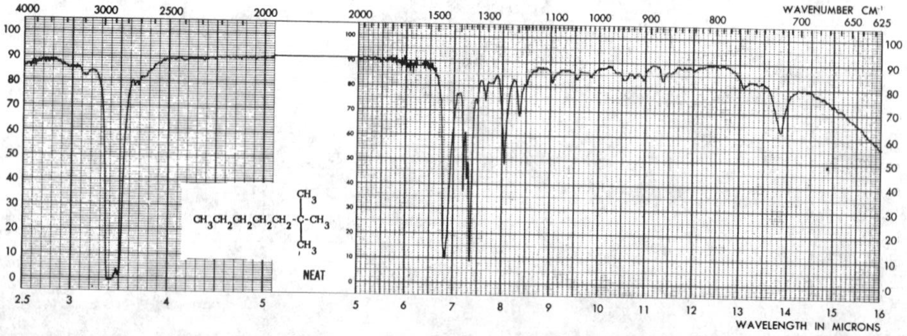

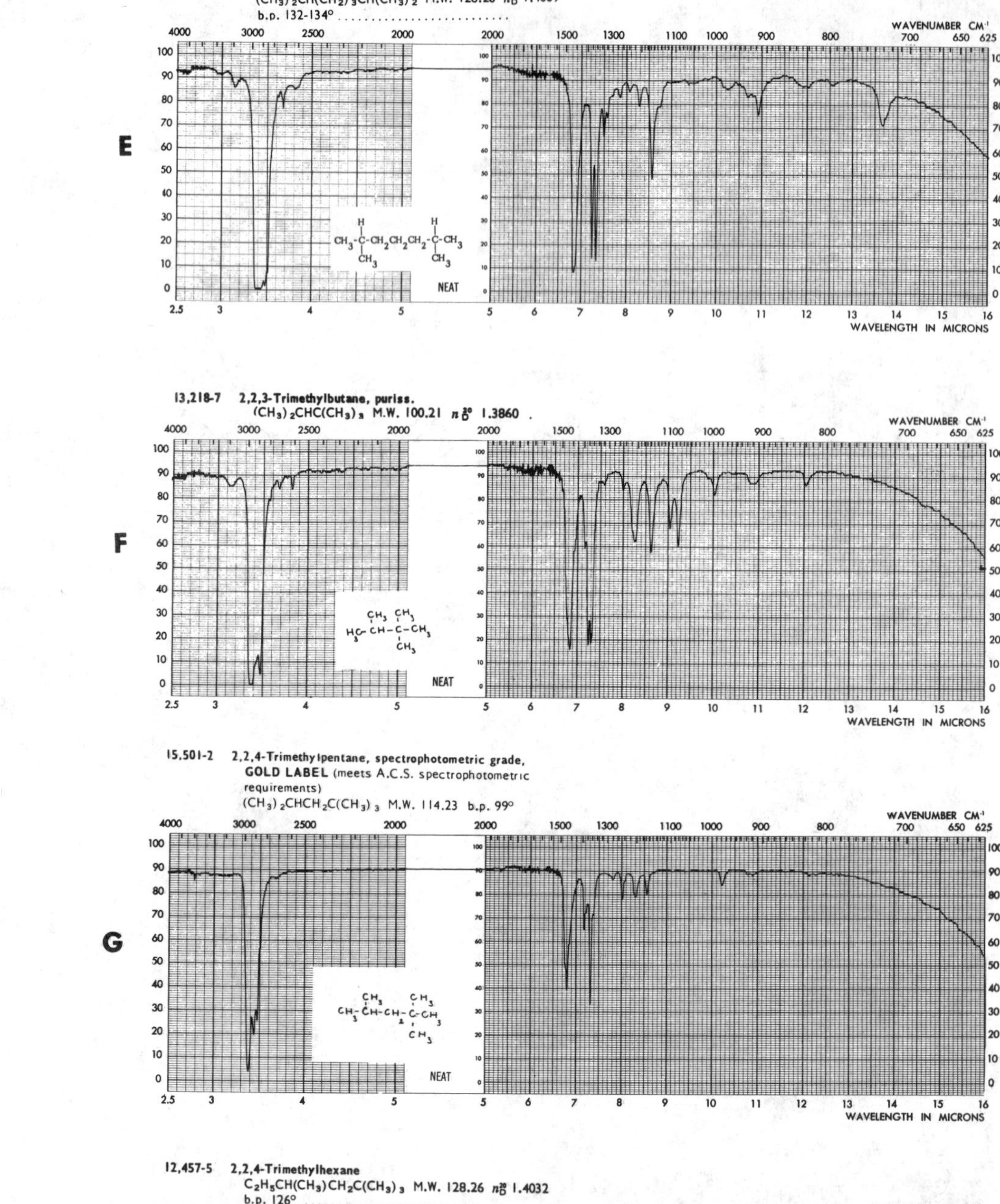

E

12,926-7 **2,6-Dimethylheptane, puriss.**
$(CH_3)_2CH(CH_2)_3CH(CH_3)_2$ M.W. 128.26 n_D^{20} 1.4009
b.p. 132-134°

F

13,218-7 **2,2,3-Trimethylbutane, puriss.**
$(CH_3)_2CHC(CH_3)_3$ M.W. 100.21 n_D^{20} 1.3860

G

15,501-2 **2,2,4-Trimethylpentane, spectrophotometric grade, GOLD LABEL** (meets A.C.S. spectrophotometric requirements)
$(CH_3)_2CHCH_2C(CH_3)_3$ M.W. 114.23 b.p. 99°

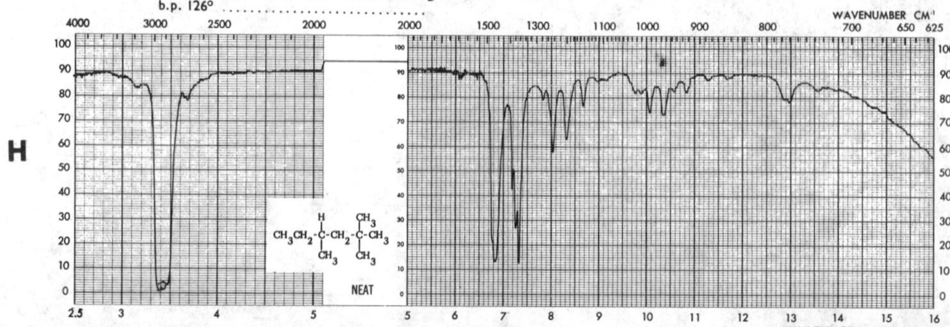

H

12,457-5 **2,2,4-Trimethylhexane**
$C_2H_5CH(CH_3)CH_2C(CH_3)_3$ M.W. 128.26 n_D^{20} 1.4032
b.p. 126°

A T2280-2 2,6,10,14-Tetramethylpentadecane
$(CH_3)_2CH(CH_2)_3CH(CH_3)(CH_2)_3CH(CH_3)(CH_2)_3CH(CH_3)_2$
M.W. 268.53 n_D^{20} 1.4379 b.p. 165-167°/11 mm.

B 11,330-1 2,2,4,6,6-Pentamethylheptane
$(CH_3)_3CCH_2CH(CH_3)CH_2C(CH_3)_3$ M.W. 170.34
n_D^{20} 1.4187

C H1,140-8 Hexamethylethane, 99% (2,2,3,3-tetramethylbutane)
$(CH_3)_3CC(CH_3)_3$ M.W. 114.23 m.p. 99 - 101°
b.p. 106 - 107°/765mm. *Beil.* 1,165 *IR* 9G

D 12,851-1 2,2,4,4,6,8,8-Heptamethylnonane
$(CH_3)_3CCH_2CH(CH_3)CH_2C(CH_3)_2CH_2C(CH_3)_3$
M.W. 226.45 n_D^{20} 1.4391

E H1260-9 1-Hexene
$CH_3(CH_2)_3CH{:}CH_2$ M.W. 84.16 n_D^{20} 1.3858
b.p. 67°

F H320-8 1-Heptene, puriss.
$CH_3(CH_2)_4CH{:}CH_2$ M.W. 98.19 n_D^{20} 1.3995

G O-480-6 1-Octene
$CH_3(CH_2)_5CH{:}CH_2$ M.W. 112.22 n_D^{20} 1.4064 b.p. 122-123°.

H N3040-4 1-Nonene
$CH_3(CH_2)_6CH{:}CH_2$ M.W. 126.24 n_D^{20} 1.4160

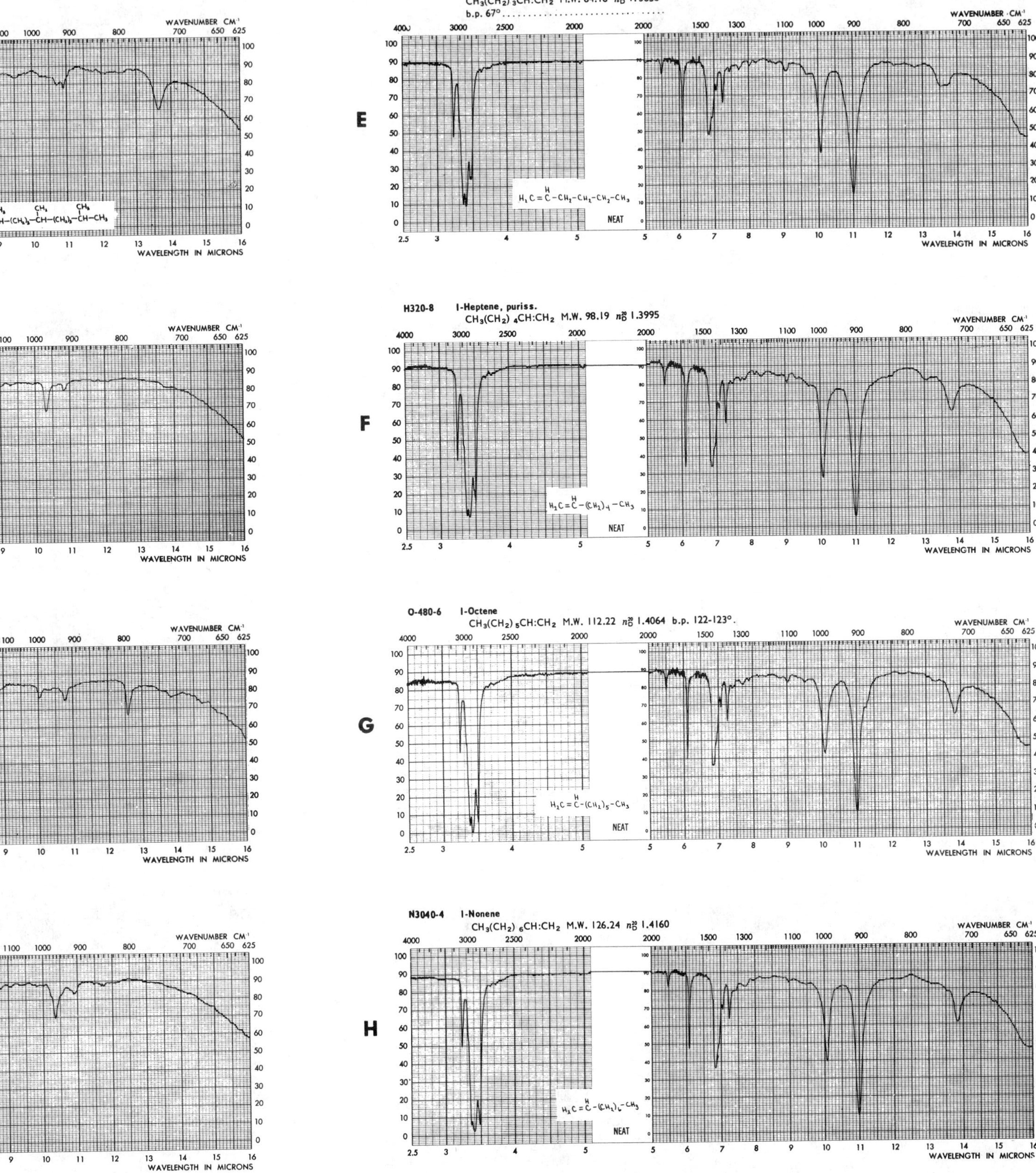

A D180-7 1-Decene
$CH_3(CH_2)_7CH{:}CH_2$ M.W. 140.27 n_D^{20} 1.4195

B U135-4 1-Undecene
$CH_3(CH_2)_8CH{:}CH_2$ M.W. 154.30 n_D^{20} 1.4261 b.p. 192-193°

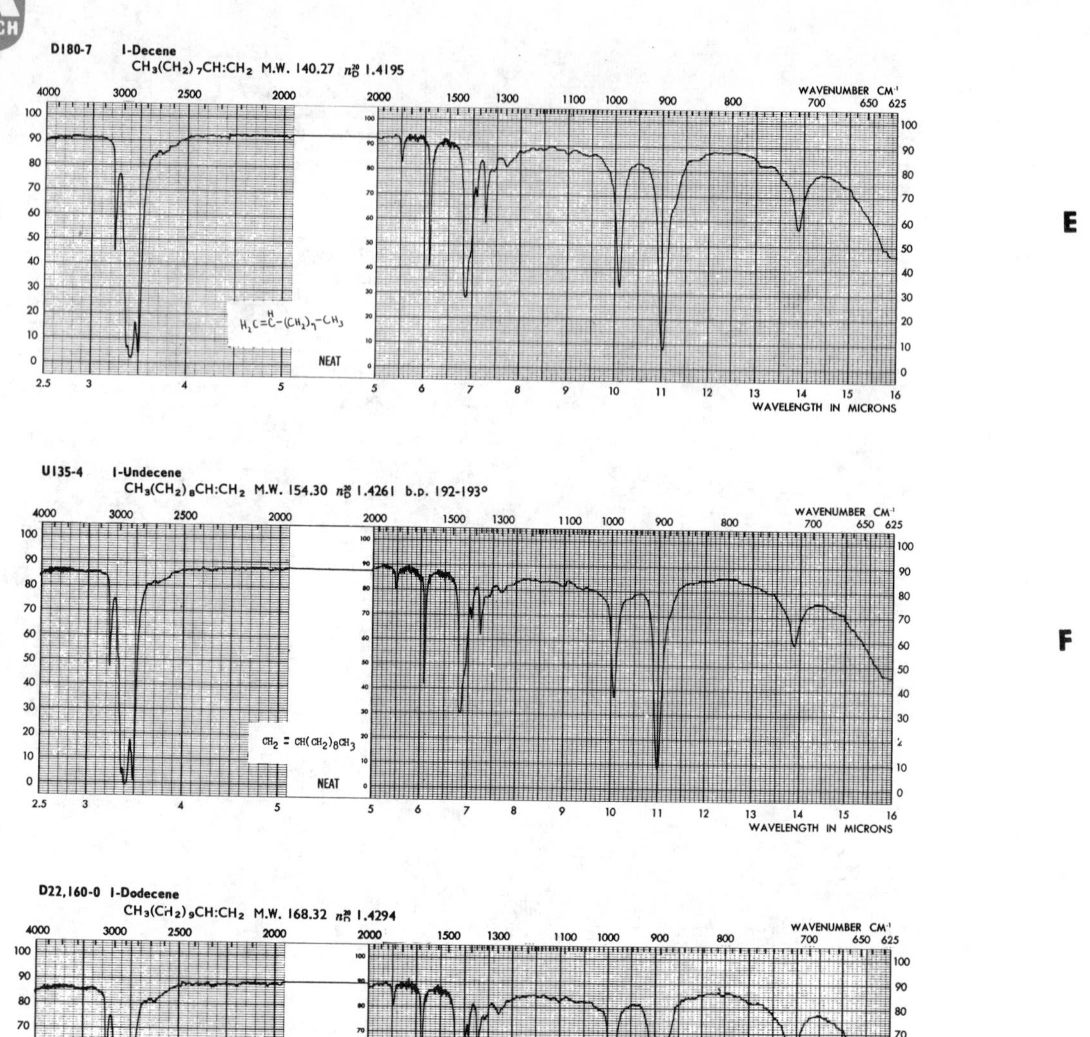

C D22,160-0 1-Dodecene
$CH_3(CH_2)_9CH{:}CH_2$ M.W. 168.32 n_D^{20} 1.4294

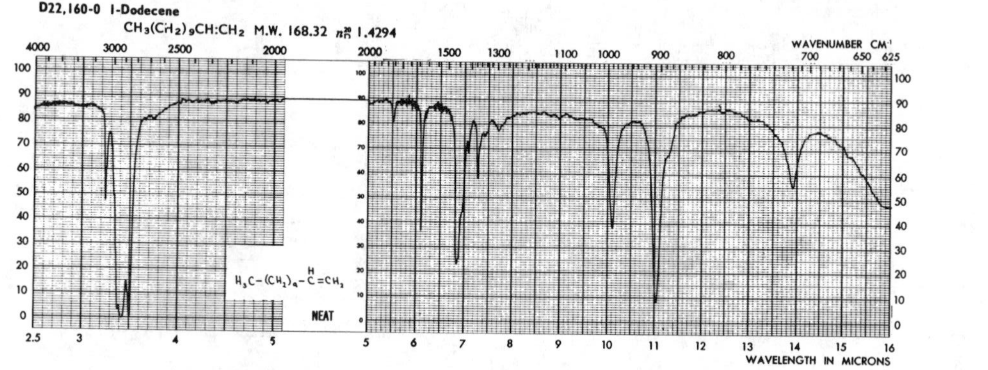

D T5770-3 1-Tridecene
$CH_3(CH_2)_{10}CH{:}CH_2$ M.W. 182.35 n_D^{20} 1.4329
b.p. 232-233°

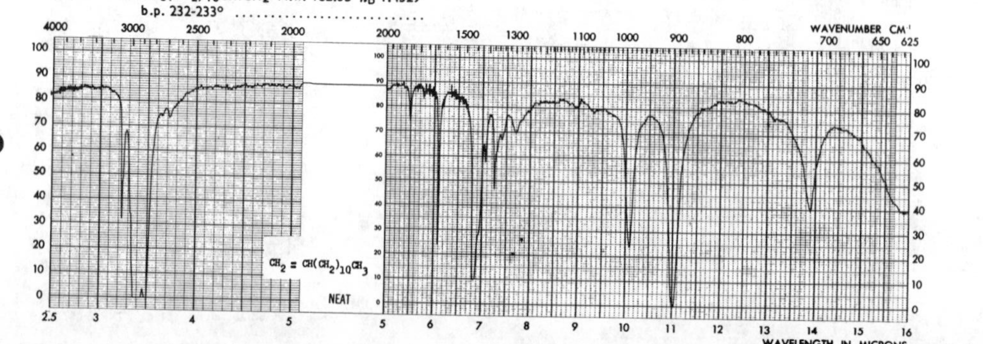

E T980-5 1-Tetradecene
$CH_3(CH_2)_{11}CH{:}CH_2$ M.W. 196.38 n_D^{20} 1.4351

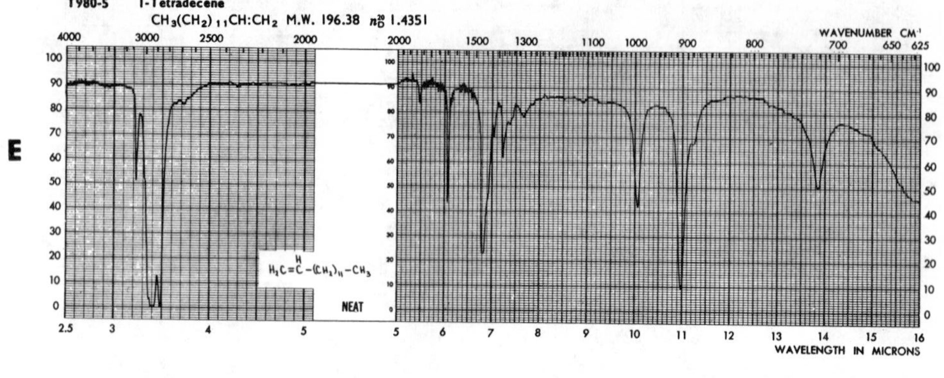

F P390-2 1-Pentadecene
$CH_3(CH_2)_{12}CH{:}CH_2$ M.W. 210.41 n_D^{20} 1.4390
b.p. 268-269°

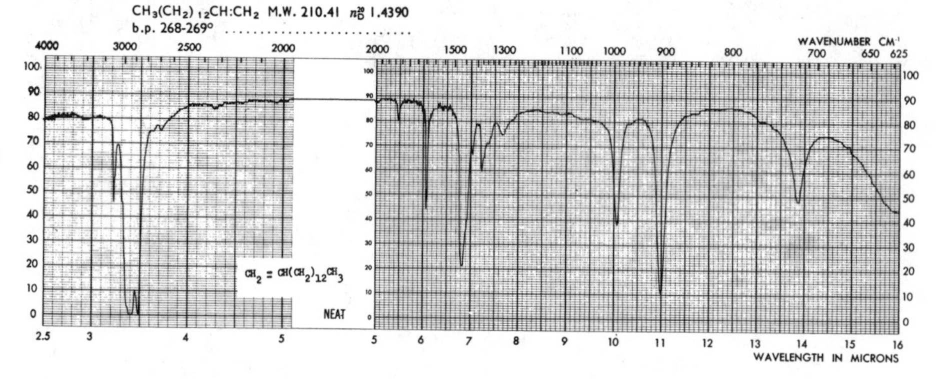

G H700-9 1-Hexadecene
$CH_3(CH_2)_{13}CH{:}CH_2$ M.W. 224.43 n_D^{20} 1.4401
b.p. 274°

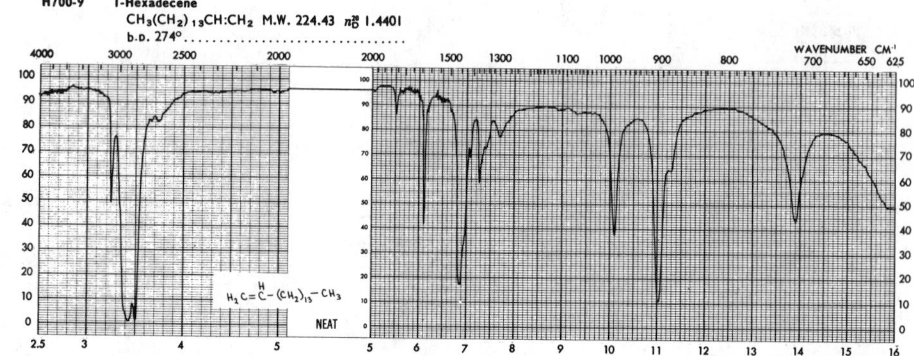

H H110-8 1-Heptadecene
$CH_3(CH_2)_{14}CH{:}CH_2$ M.W. 238.46 n_D^{20} 1.4442

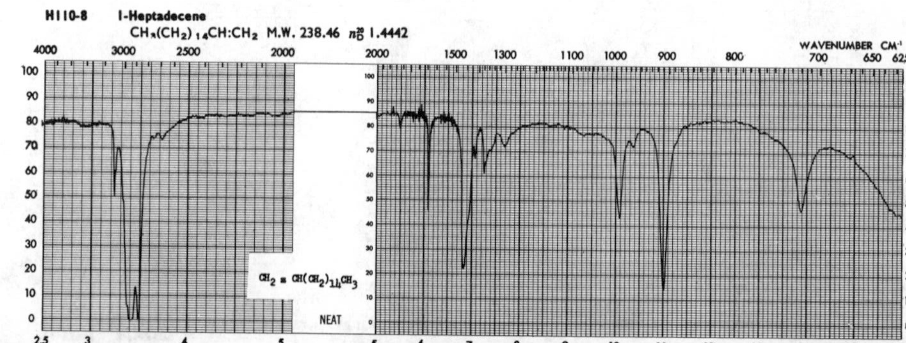

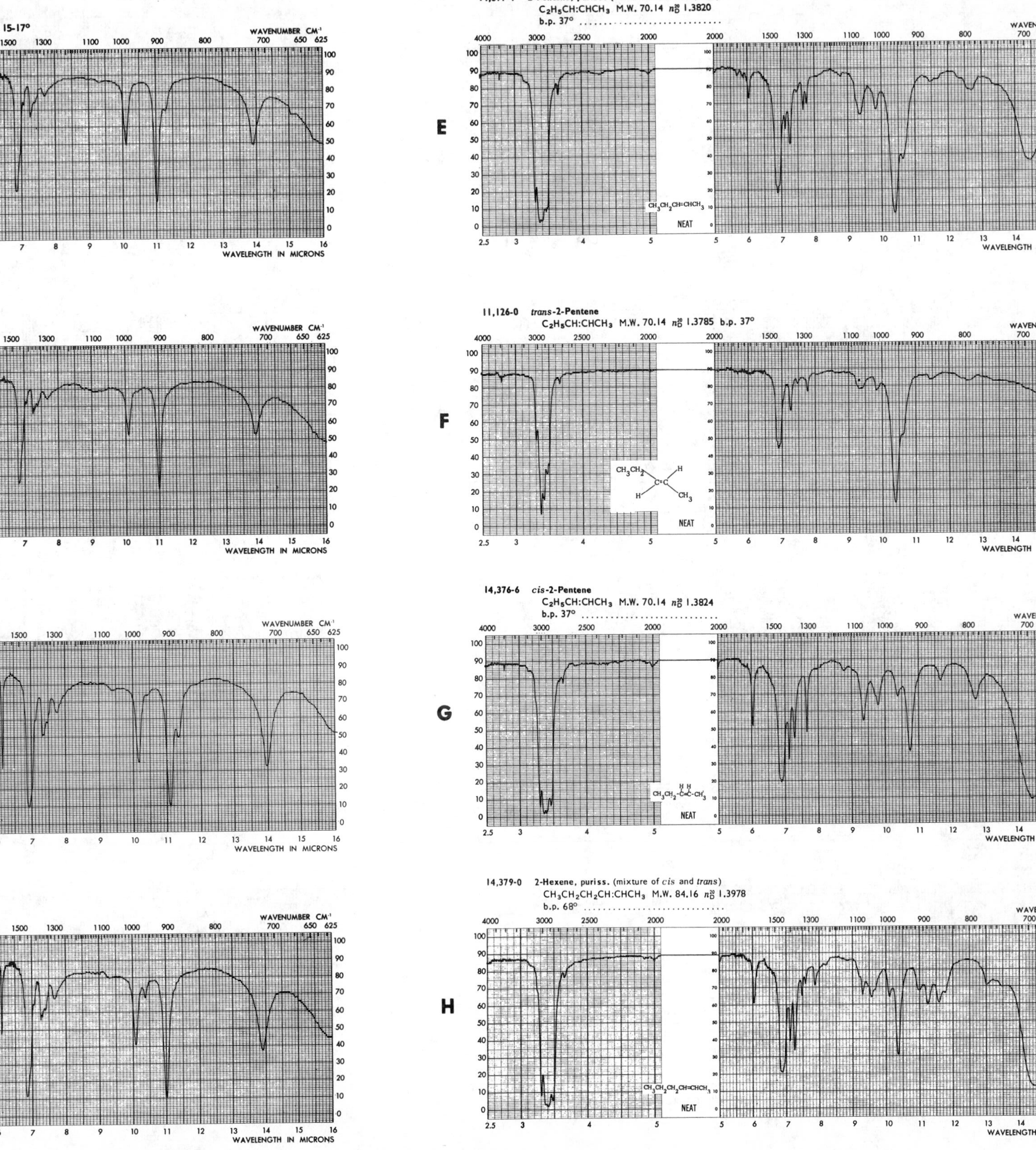

A — O-80-6 **1-Octadecene**
$CH_3(CH_2)_{15}CH{:}CH_2$ M.W. 252.49 n_D^{20} 1.4439 m.p. 15-17°
NEAT

B — N2930-9 **1-Nonadecene**
$CH_3(CH_2)_{16}CH{:}CH_2$ M.W. 266.51 m.p. 23.5-25°
MELT

C — 18,441-1 **1-Eicosene**, tech.
$CH_3(CH_2)_{17}CH{=}CH_2$
M.W. 280.54 m.p. 27-29° b.p. 151°/1.5mm.
Beil. 1(3),881
MELT

D — 13,446-5 **1-Docosene**
$CH_3(CH_2)_{19}CH{:}CH_2$ M.W. 308.60
m.p. 37.5-38.5°
MELT

E — 14,377-4 **2-Pentene, puriss.** (mixture of *cis* and *trans*)
$C_2H_5CH{:}CHCH_3$ M.W. 70.14 n_D^{20} 1.3820
b.p. 37°
NEAT

F — 11,126-0 ***trans*-2-Pentene**
$C_2H_5CH{:}CHCH_3$ M.W. 70.14 n_D^{20} 1.3785 b.p. 37°
NEAT

G — 14,376-6 ***cis*-2-Pentene**
$C_2H_5CH{:}CHCH_3$ M.W. 70.14 n_D^{20} 1.3824
b.p. 37°
NEAT

H — 14,379-0 **2-Hexene, puriss.** (mixture of *cis* and *trans*)
$CH_3CH_2CH_2CH{:}CHCH_3$ M.W. 84.16 n_D^{20} 1.3978
b.p. 68°
NEAT

A

11,089-2 *trans*-2-Hexene, puriss.
$CH_3CH_2CH_2CH{:}CHCH_3$ M.W. 84.16 n_D^{20} 1.3929
b.p. 68-69°

NEAT

B

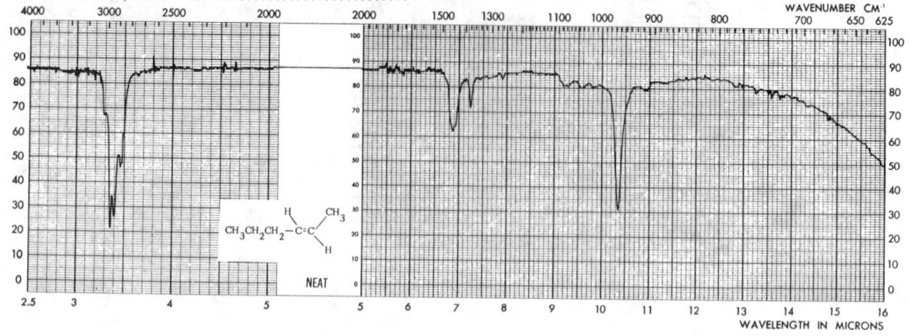

11,090-6 *trans*-3-Hexene, puriss.
$C_2H_5CH{:}CHC_2H_5$ M.W. 84.16 n_D^{20} 1.3940
b.p. 67°

NEAT

C

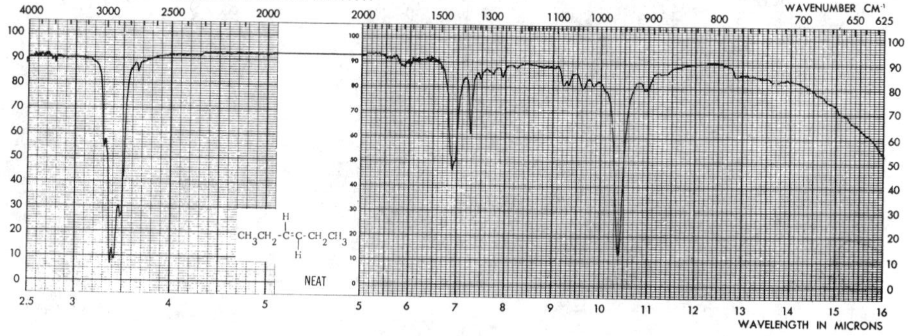

H341-0 *trans*-2-Heptene, puriss.
$CH_3(CH_2)_3CH{:}CHCH_3$ M.W. 98.19
n_D^{20} 1.4035

NEAT

D

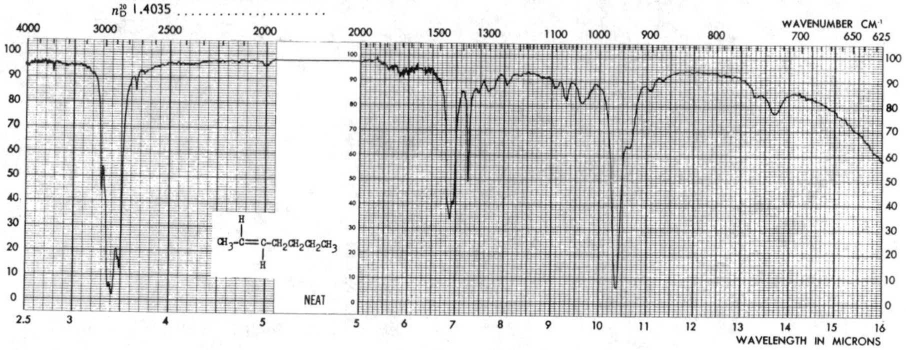

11,082-5 *trans*-3-Heptene
$CH_3(CH_2)_2CH{:}CHCH_2CH_3$ M.W. 98.19 n_D^{20} 1.4032 b.p. 94°

NEAT

E

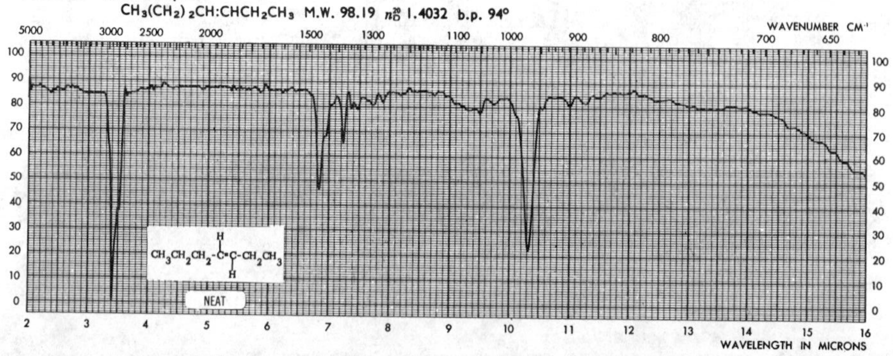

O-500-4 2-Octene
$CH_3(CH_2)_4CH{:}CHCH_3$ M.W. 112.22 n_D^{20} 1.4138

NEAT

F

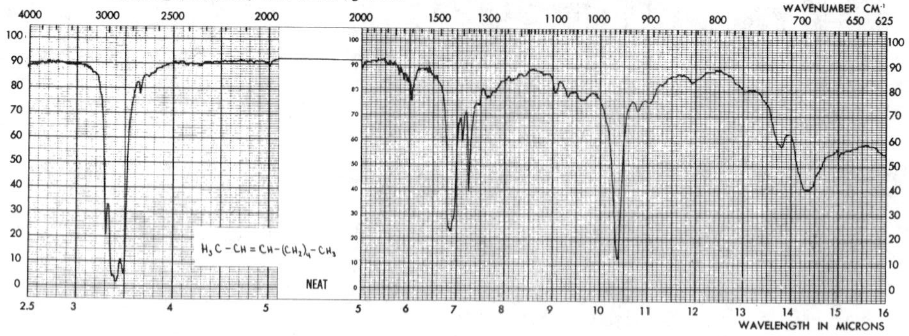

11,123-6 *trans*-2-Octene
$CH_3(CH_2)_4CH{:}CHCH_3$ M.W. 112.22 n_D^{20} 1.4130

NEAT

G

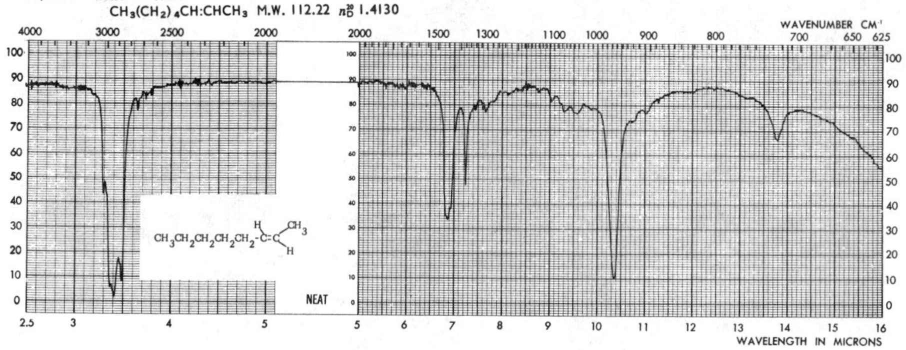

10,928-2 *cis*-2-Octene
$CH_3(CH_2)_4CH{:}CHCH_3$ M.W. 112.22 n_D^{20} 1.4163
b.p. 124.5-125.5°

NEAT

H

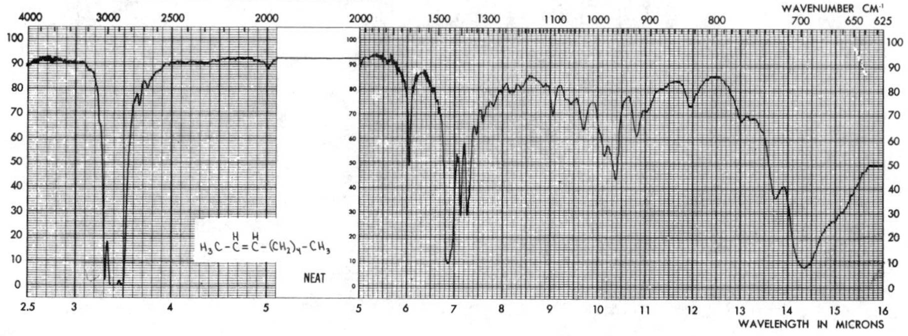

11,124-4 *trans*-3-Octene
$CH_3(CH_2)_3CH{:}CHC_2H_5$ M.W. 112.22
n_D^{20} 1.4122

NEAT

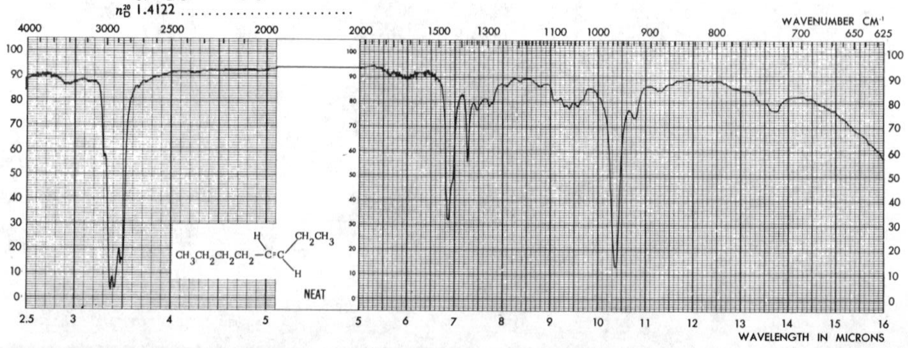

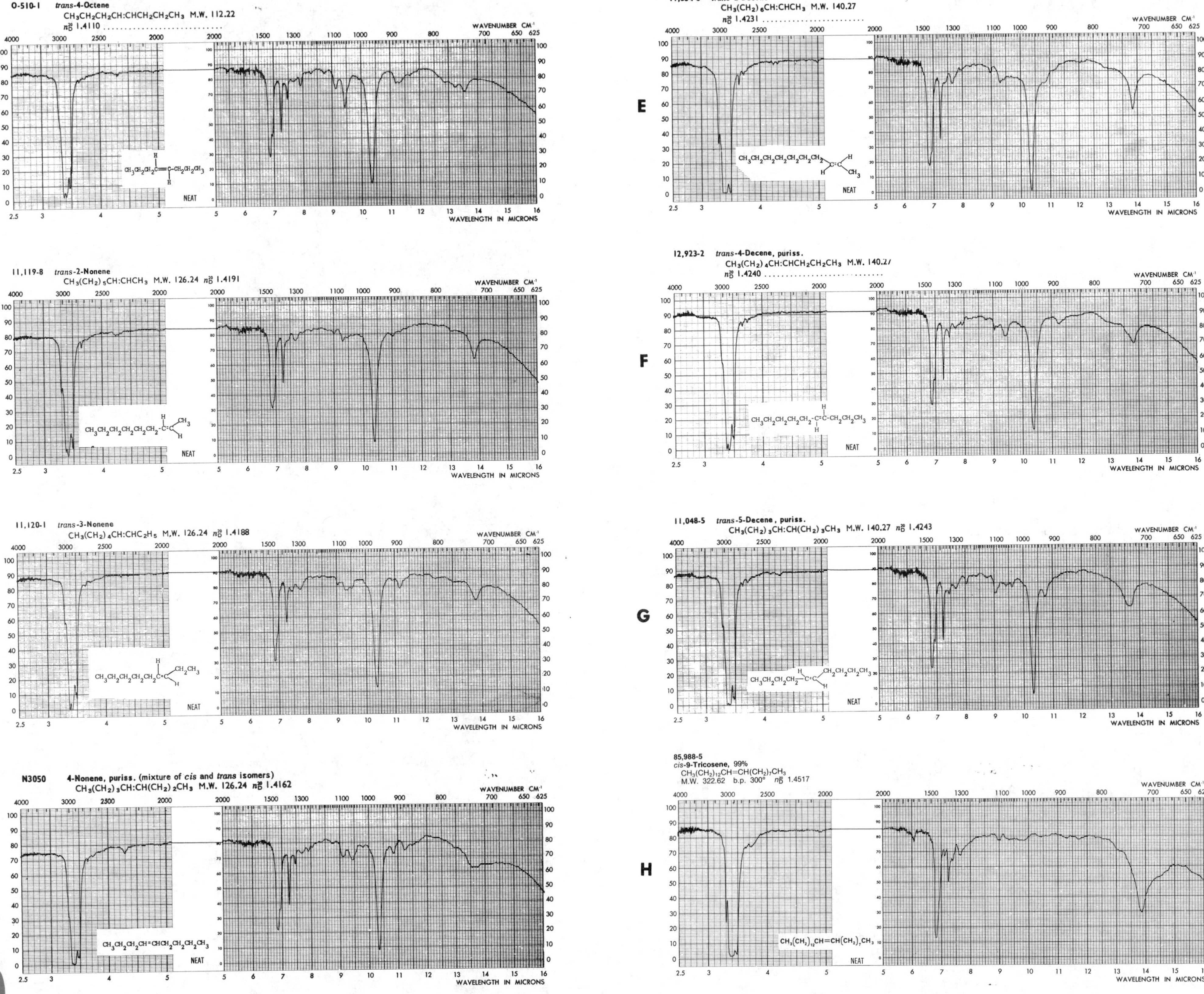

A
O-510-1 *trans*-4-Octene
$CH_3CH_2CH_2CH{:}CHCH_2CH_2CH_3$ M.W. 112.22
n_D^{20} 1.4110
NEAT
B
11,119-8 *trans*-2-Nonene
$CH_3(CH_2)_5CH{:}CHCH_3$ M.W. 126.24 n_D^{20} 1.4191
NEAT
C
11,120-1 *trans*-3-Nonene
$CH_3(CH_2)_4CH{:}CHC_2H_5$ M.W. 126.24 n_D^{20} 1.4188
NEAT
D
N3050 4-Nonene, puriss. (mixture of *cis* and *trans* isomers)
$CH_3(CH_2)_3CH{:}CH(CH_2)_2CH_3$ M.W. 126.24 n_D^{20} 1.4162
$CH_3CH_2CH_2CH{=}CHCH_2CH_2CH_2CH_3$
NEAT
E
11,834-6 *trans*-2-Decene
$CH_3(CH_2)_6CH{:}CHCH_3$ M.W. 140.27
n_D^{20} 1.4231
NEAT
F
12,923-2 *trans*-4-Decene, puriss.
$CH_3(CH_2)_4CH{:}CHCH_2CH_2CH_3$ M.W. 140.27
n_D^{20} 1.4240
NEAT
G
11,048-5 *trans*-5-Decene, puriss.
$CH_3(CH_2)_3CH{:}CH(CH_2)_3CH_3$ M.W. 140.27 n_D^{20} 1.4243
NEAT
H
85,988-5
cis-9-Tricosene, 99%
$CH_3(CH_2)_{12}CH{=}CH(CH_2)_7CH_3$
M.W. 322.62 b.p. 300° n_D^{20} 1.4517
$CH_3(CH_2)_{12}CH{=}CH(CH_2)_7CH_3$
NEAT
WAVENUMBER CM⁻¹
WAVELENGTH IN MICRONS

A

M3270-4 **2-Methyl-2-butene, 99+%**
$CH_3CH{:}C(CH_3)_2$ M.W. 70.14 n_D^{20} 1.3870 b.p. 35-38°

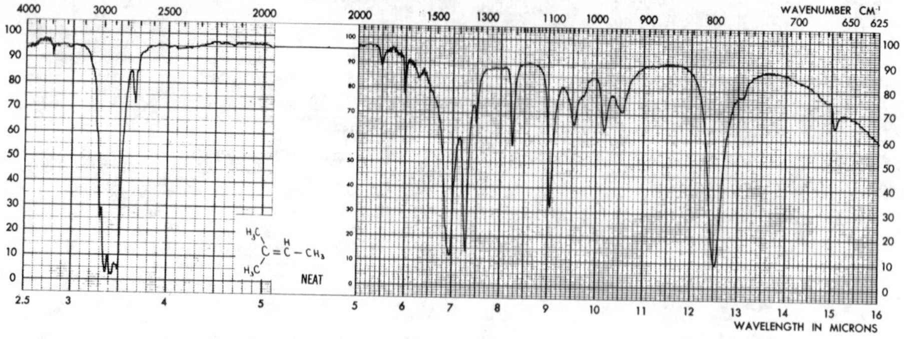

NEAT

B

19,040-3
2,3-Dimethyl-1-butene, 98+%
$(CH_3)_2CHC(CH_3){=}CH_2$ FW 84.16 bp 56°
n_D^{20} 1.3896 d 0.680 *Beil.* **1**(3),816 Disp. C

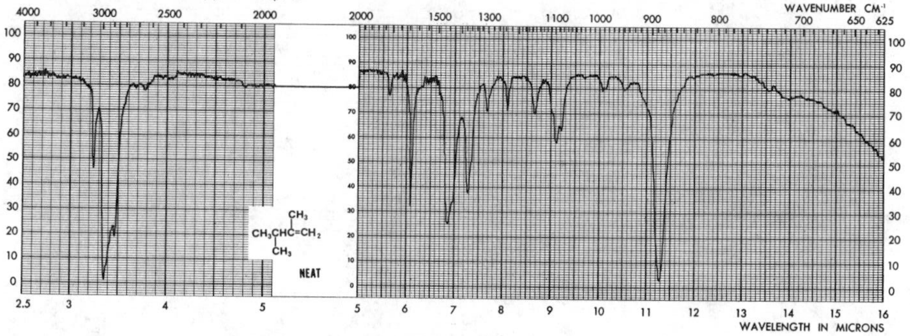

NEAT

C

E1470-5 **2-Ethyl-1-butene**
$(C_2H_5)_2C{:}CH_2$ M.W.84.16 N_D^{20} 1.3962

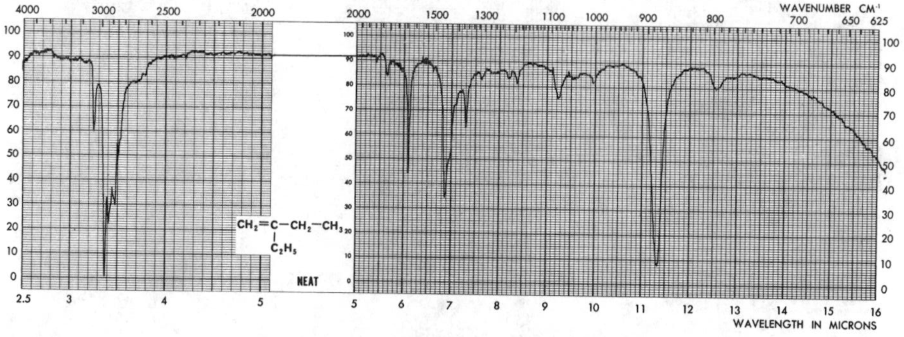

NEAT

D

M6720-6 **2-Methyl-1-pentene**
$CH_3CH_2CH_2C(CH_3){:}CH_2$ M.W. 84.16 n_D^{20} 1.3940
b.p. 62°

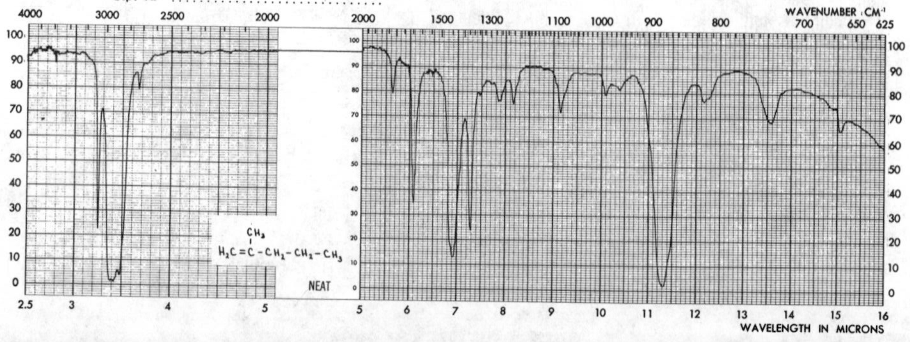

NEAT

E

11,114-7 **3-Methyl-1-pentene**
$C_2H_5CH(CH_3)CH{:}CH_2$ M.W. 84.16 n_D^{20} 1.3852

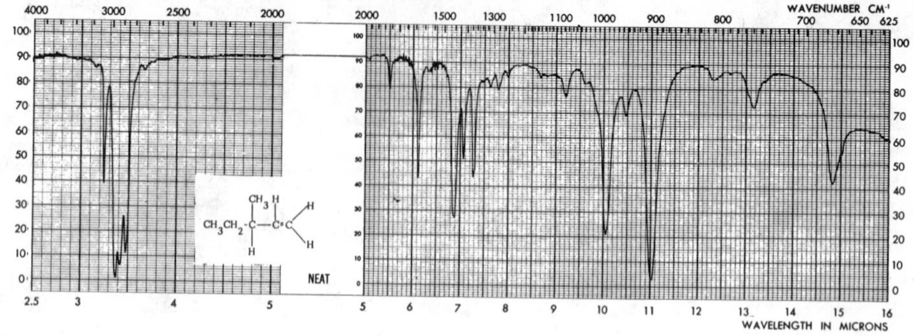

NEAT

F

M6740-0 **4-Methyl-1-pentene, puriss.**
$(CH_3)_2CHCH_2CH{:}CH_2$ M.W. 84.16 n_D^{20} 1.3820
b.p. 53.6-53.9°

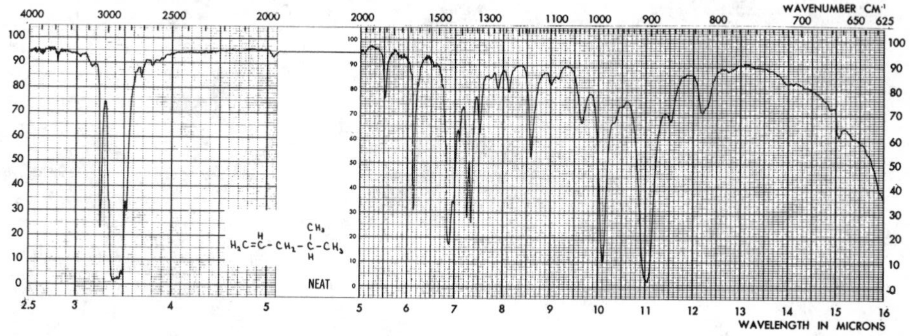

NEAT

G

M6730-3 **2-Methyl-2-pentene, puriss.**
$C_2H_5CH{:}C(CH_3)_2$ M.W. 84.16 n_D^{20} 1.3994

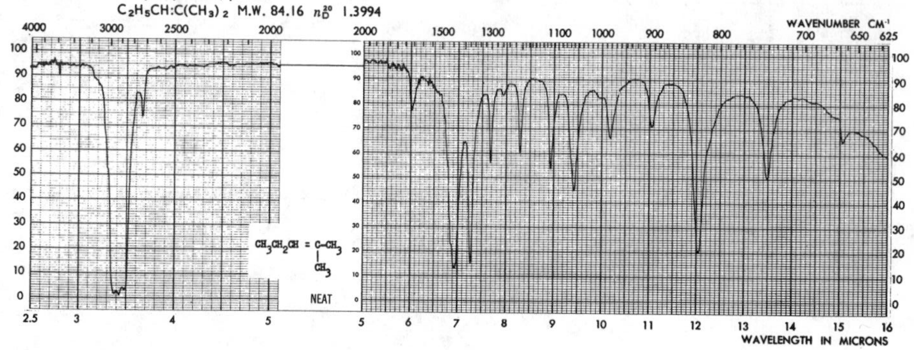

NEAT

H

11,177-5 **3-Methyl-2-pentene** (mixture of *cis* and *trans*)
$C_2H_5C(CH_3){:}CHCH_3$ M.W. 84.16 n_D^{20} 1.4042
b.p. 69°

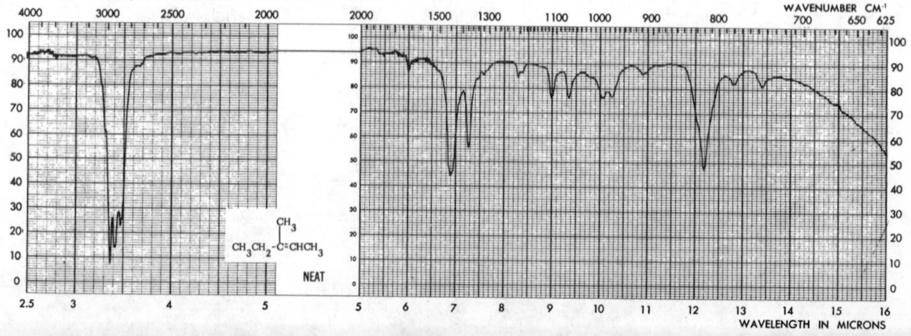

NEAT

A

M6737-0 *trans*-3-Methyl-2-pentene, puriss.
$C_2H_5C(CH_3):CHCH_3$ M.W. 84.16 n_D^{20} 1.4028

NEAT

B

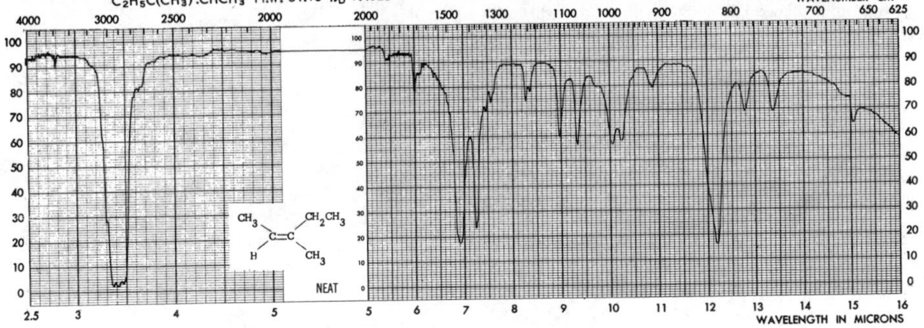

M6735-4 *cis*-3-Methyl-2-pentene, puriss.
$C_2H_5C(CH_3):CHCH_3$ M.W. 84.16
n_D^{20} 1.4007

NEAT

C

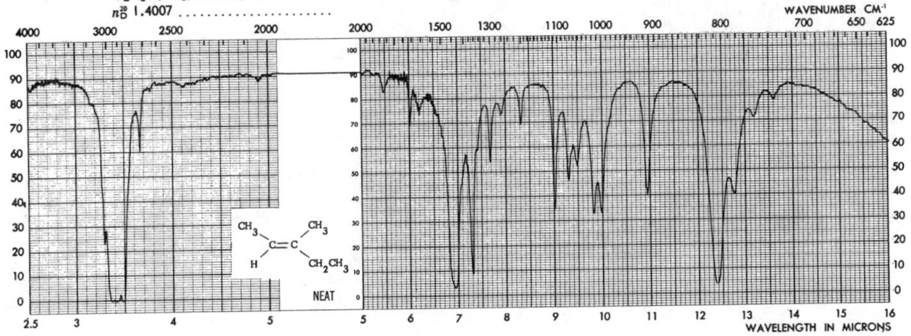

14,378-2 4-Methyl-2-pentene (mixture of *cis* and *trans*)
$(CH_3)_2CHCH:CHCH_3$ M.W. 84.16 n_D^{20} 1.3880
b.p. 57°

NEAT

D

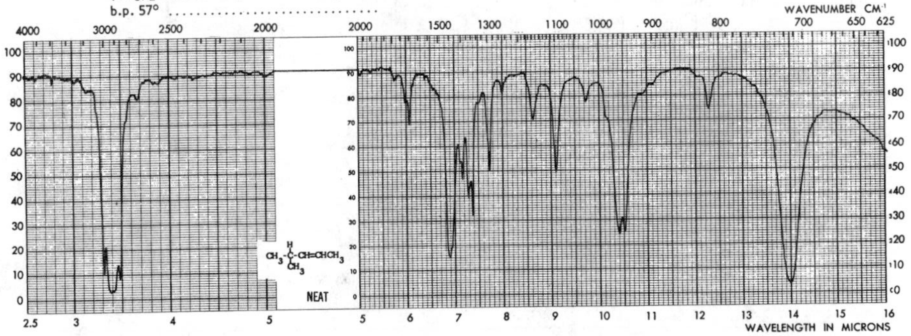

M6760-5 *cis*-4-Methyl-2-pentene
$(CH_3)_2CHCH:CHCH_3$ M.W. 84.16 n_D^{20} 1.3883
b.p. 57-58.5°

NEAT

E

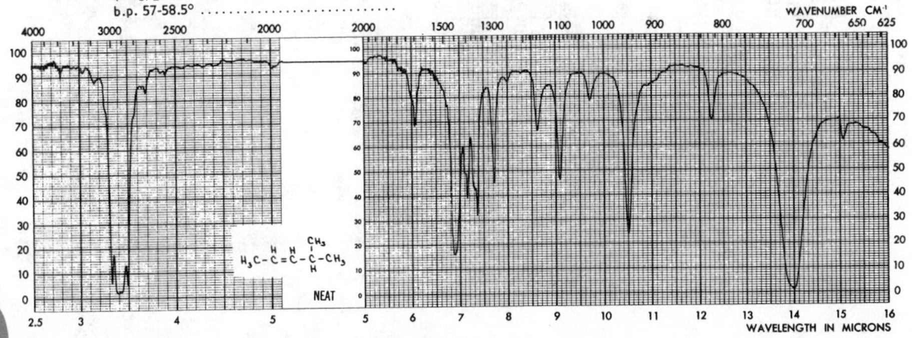

12,998-4 *trans*-4-Methyl-2-pentene
$(CH_3)_2CHCH:CHCH_3$ M.W. 84.16 n_D^{20} 1.3912
b.p. 57-58°

NEAT

F

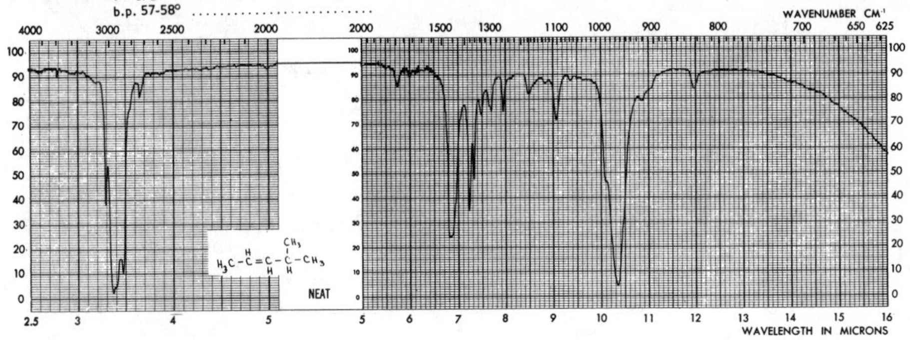

E4370-5 3-Ethyl-1-pentene, puriss.
$(C_2H_5)_2CHCH:CH_2$ M.W. 98.19 n_D^{20} 1.3956

NEAT

G

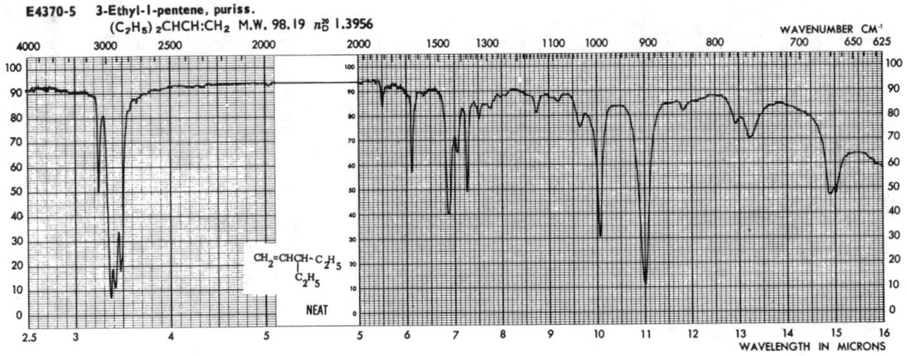

11,080-9 3-Ethyl-2-pentene
$(C_2H_5)_2C:CHCH_3$ M.W. 98.19 n_D^{20} 1.4141 b.p. 97-98°

NEAT

H

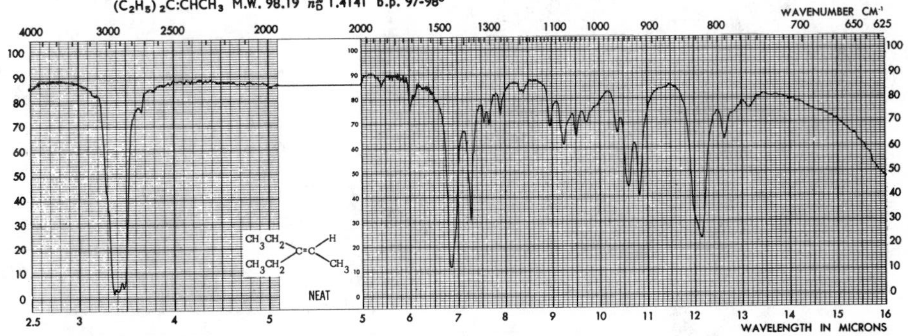

11,162-7 2-Methyl-1-hexene
$CH_3(CH_2)_3C(CH_3):CH_2$ M.W. 98.19
n_D^{20} 1.4025

NEAT

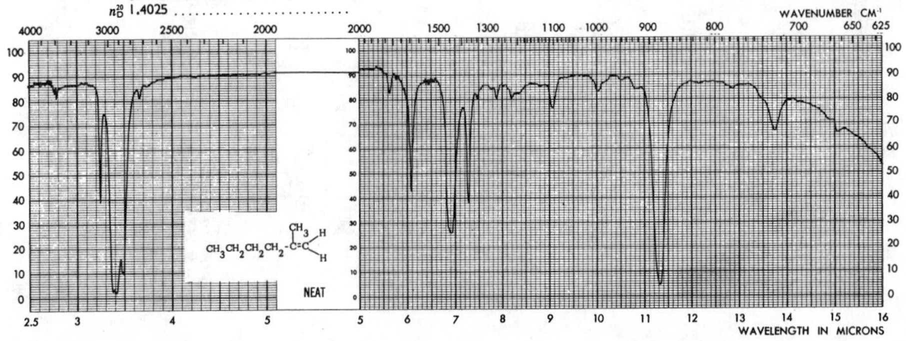

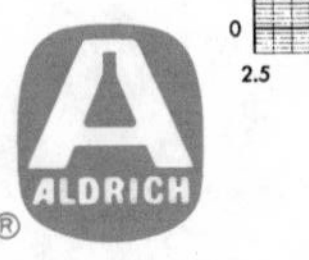

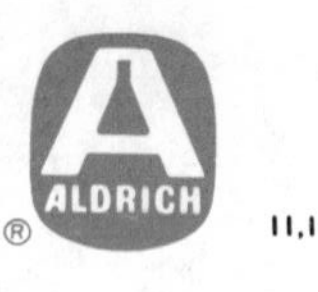

A 11,163-5 **3-Methyl-1-hexene**
$CH_3CH_2CH_2CH(CH_3)CH{:}CH_2$ M.W. 98.19
n_D^{20} 1.3963
NEAT

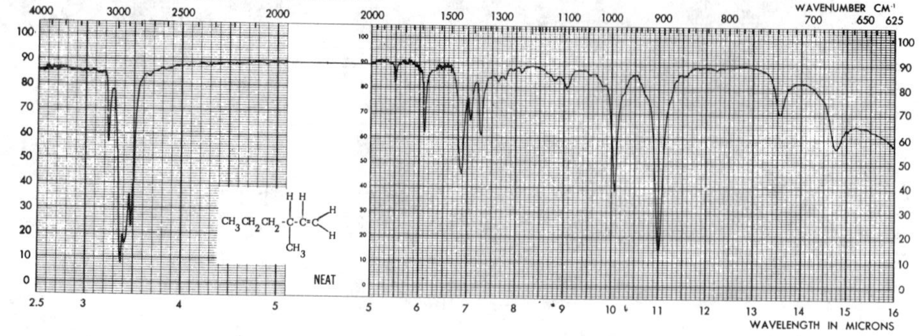

B 11,107-4 **4-Methyl-1-hexene**
$C_2H_5CH(CH_3)CH_2CH{:}CH_2$ M.W. 98.19
n_D^{20} 1.3992
NEAT

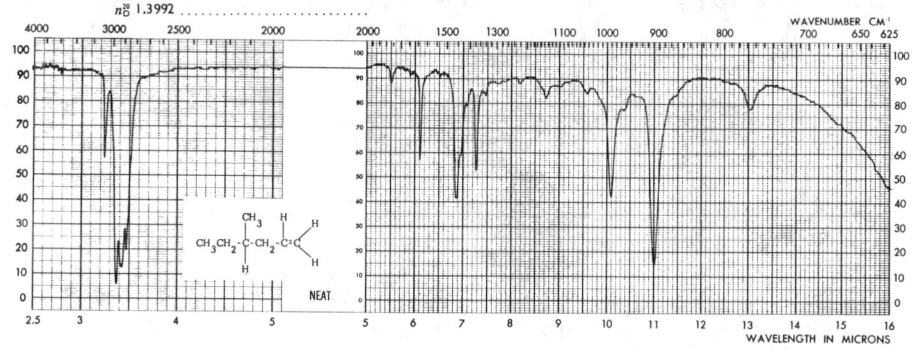

C 11,108-2 **5-Methyl-1-hexene**
$(CH_3)_2CHCH_2CH_2CH{:}CH_2$ M.W. 98.19
n_D^{20} 1.3953
NEAT

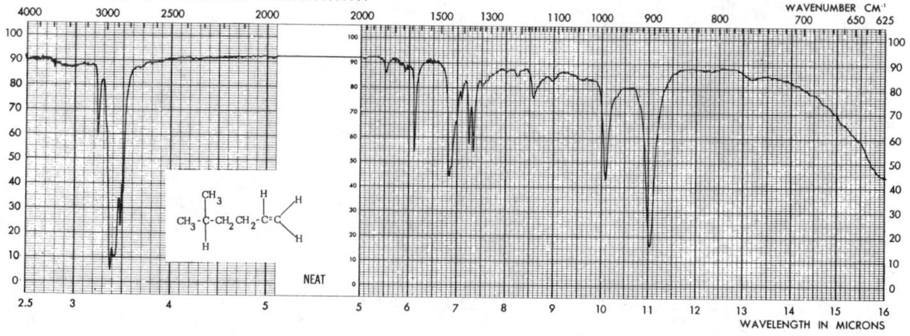

D 11,164-3 **2-Methyl-2-hexene**
$CH_3CH_2CH_2CH{:}C(CH_3)_2$ M.W. 98.19
n_D^{20} 1.4097
NEAT

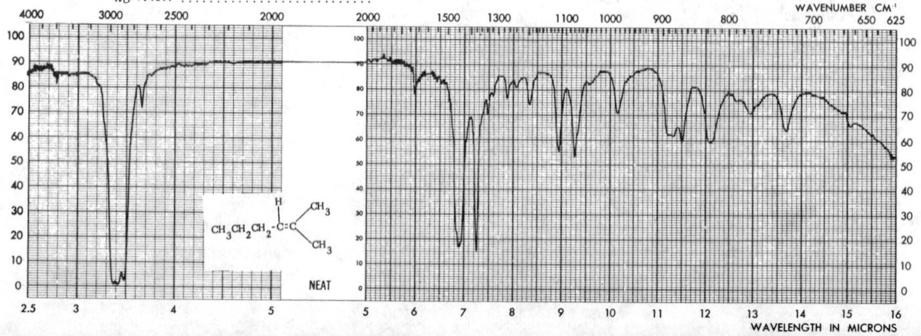

E 11,864-8 ***trans*-2-Methyl-3-hexene, puriss.**
$C_2H_5CH{:}CHCH(CH_3)_2$ M.W. 98.19
n_D^{20} 1.3965
NEAT

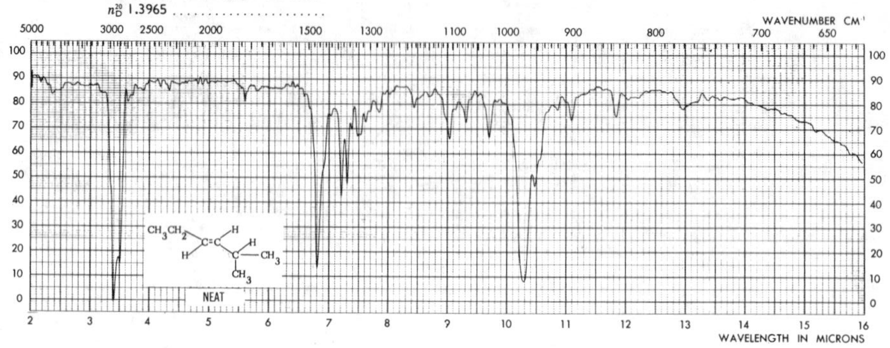

F 21,509-0
trans-**1,2-Di-*tert*-butylethylene**, 99% (*trans*-2,2,5,5-tetramethyl-3-hexene)
$(CH_3)_3CCH{=}CHC(CH_3)_3$ FW 140.27 mp -4.80°
bp 125-126° n_D^{20} 1.4120 d 0.717 *Beil.* **1**(3),865
Disp. C
NEAT

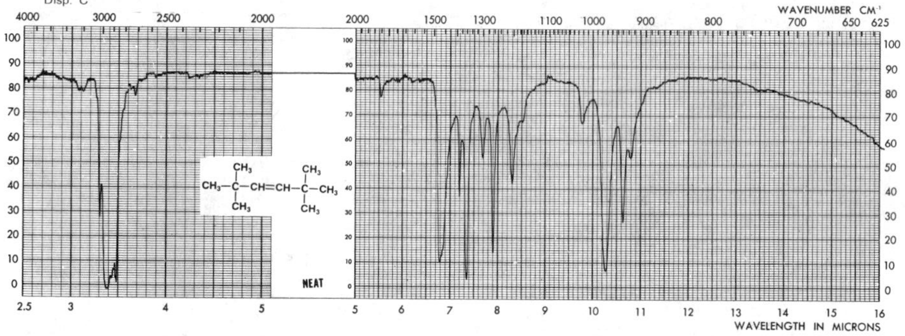

G 11,165-1 ***cis*-3-Methyl-2-hexene**
$CH_3CH_2CH_2C(CH_3){:}CHCH_3$ M.W. 98.19 n_D^{20} 1.4114
NEAT

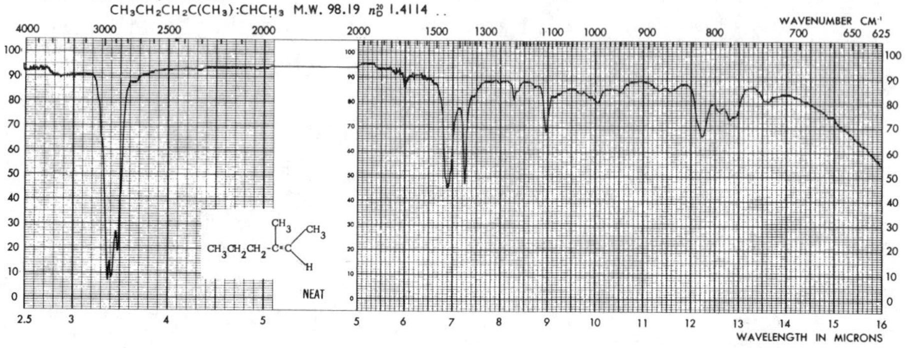

H 11,105-8 **2-Methyl-1-heptene**
$CH_3(CH_2)_4C(CH_3){:}CH_2$ M.W. 112.22
n_D^{20} 1.4110
NEAT

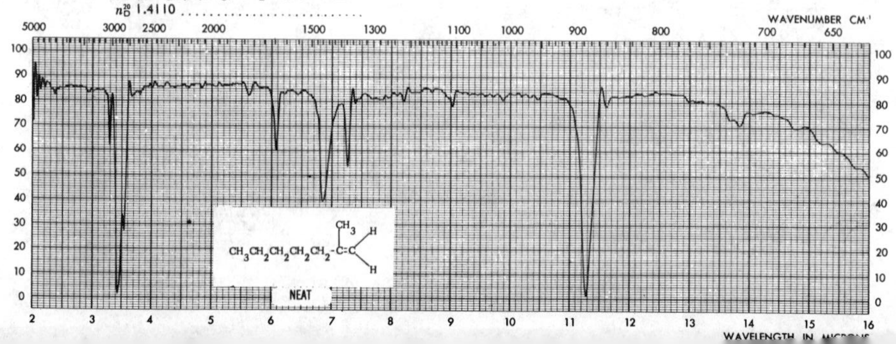

A

11,861-3 **2-Methyl-2-heptene**
$CH_3(CH_2)_3CH{:}C(CH_3)_2$ M.W. 112.22
n_D^{20} 1.4161

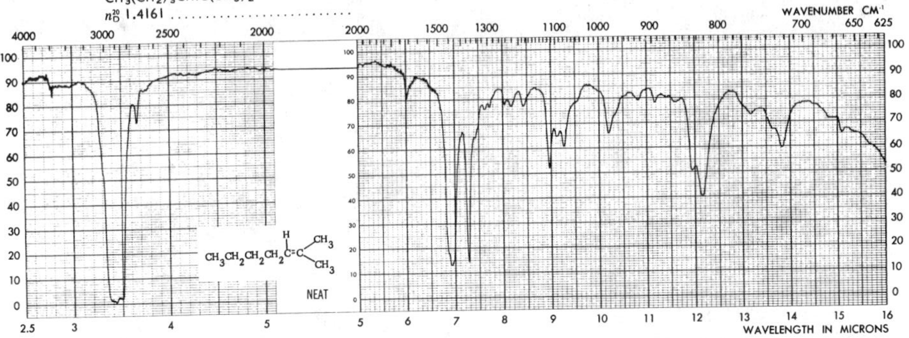

$CH_3CH_2CH_2CH_2CH{=}C(CH_3)_2$

NEAT

B

12,941-0 **2-Methyl-1-nonene**
$CH_3(CH_2)_6C(CH_3){:}CH_2$ M.W. 140.27
n_D^{20} 1.4240

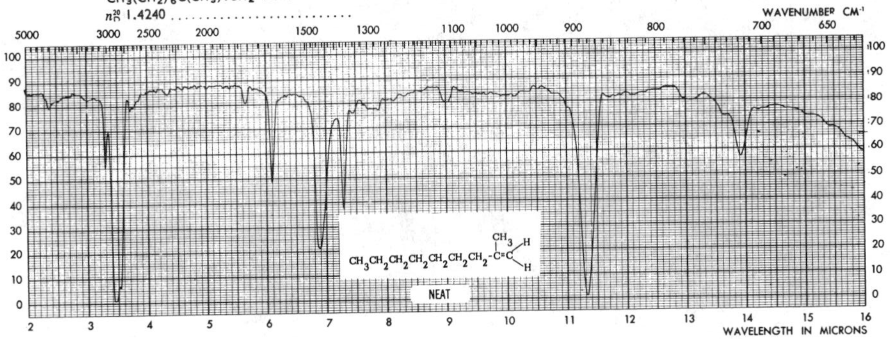

$CH_3CH_2CH_2CH_2CH_2CH_2CH_2C(CH_3){=}CH_2$

NEAT

C

10,137-0 **2-Methyl-1-undecene, puriss.**
$CH_3(CH_2)_8C(CH_3){:}CH_2$ M.W. 168.32
n_D^{20} 1.4320

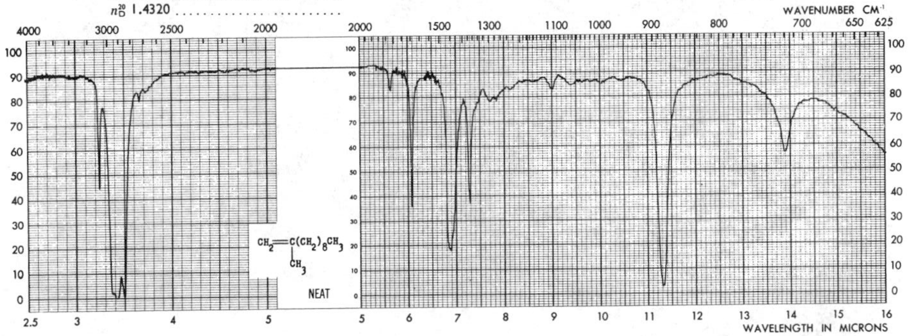

$CH_2{=}C(CH_2)_8CH_3$ with CH_3

NEAT

D

12,925-9 **2,3-Dimethyl-2-butene, puriss.**
$(CH_3)_2C{:}C(CH_3)_2$ M.W. 84.16 n_D^{20} 1.4124
b.p. 73°

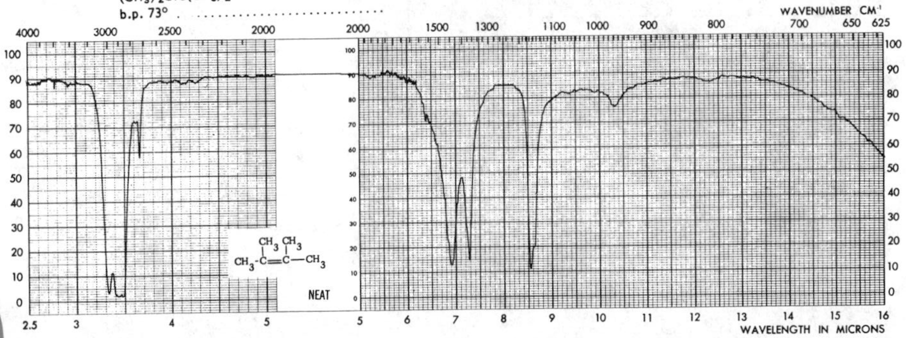

$CH_3C(CH_3){=}C(CH_3)CH_3$

NEAT

E

11,905-9 **3,3-Dimethyl-1-butene (neohexene)**
$(CH_3)_3CCH{:}CH_2$ M.W. 84.16 n_D^{20} 1.3760
b.p. 41°

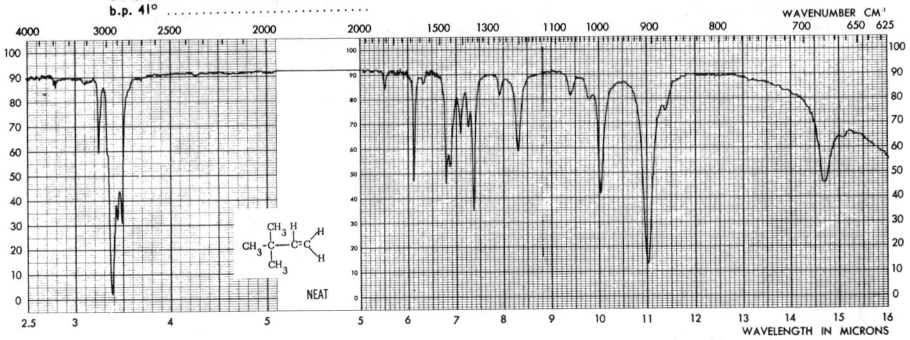

$CH_3C(CH_3)_2CH{=}CH_2$

NEAT

F

13,391-4 **2,3-Dimethyl-1-pentene**
$C_2H_5CH(CH_3)C(CH_3){:}CH_2$ M.W. 98.19 n_D^{20} 1.3997

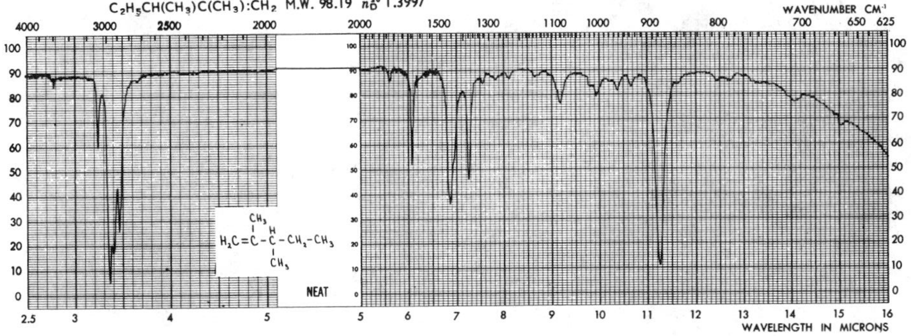

$H_2C{=}C(CH_3){-}CH(CH_3){-}CH_2{-}CH_3$

NEAT

G

11,151-1 **2,4-Dimethyl-1-pentene**
$(CH_3)_2CHCH_2C(CH_3){:}CH_2$ M.W. 98.19
n_D^{20} 1.3968

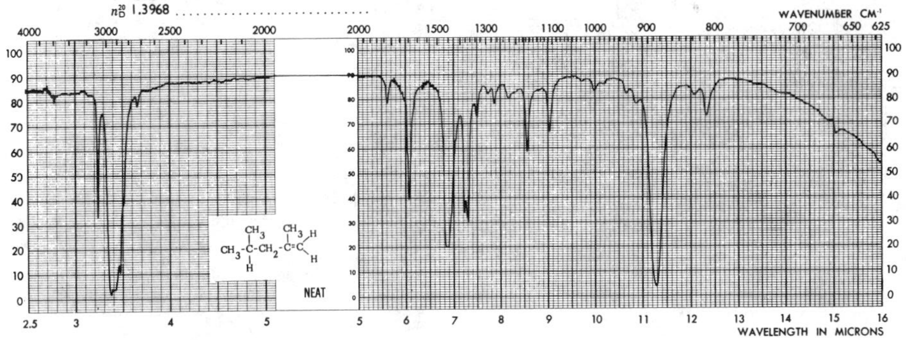

$CH_3CH(CH_3){-}CH_2{-}C(CH_3){=}CH_2$

NEAT

H

11,070-1 **4,4-Dimethyl-1-pentene, puriss.**
$(CH_3)_3CCH_2CH{:}CH_2$ M.W. 98.19 n_D^{20} 1.3900

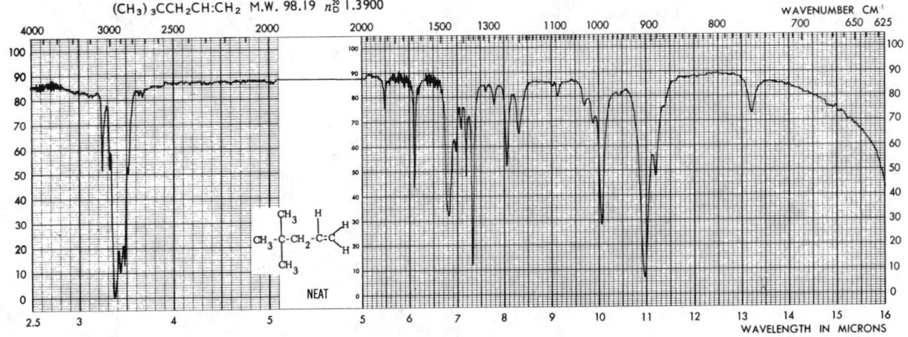

$CH_3C(CH_3)_2{-}CH_2{-}CH{=}CH_2$

NEAT

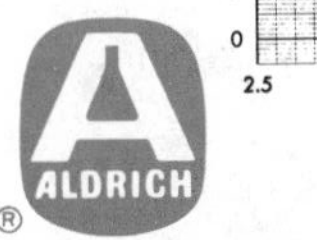

A 11,153-8 2,3-Dimethyl-2-pentene
$C_2H_5C(CH_3):C(CH_3)_2$ M.W. 98.19 n_D^{20} 1.4138
NEAT

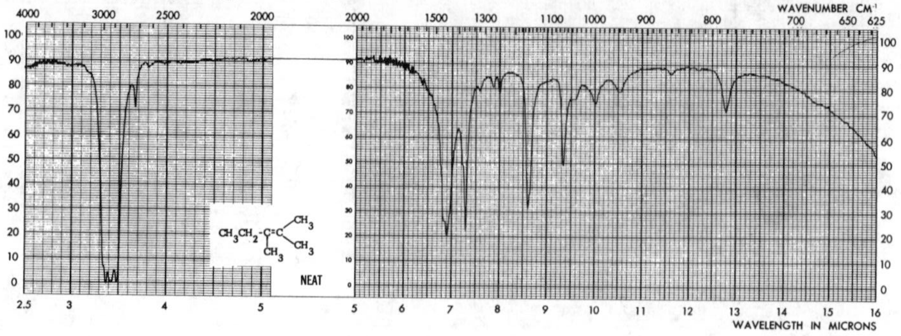

B 11,154-6 2,4-Dimethyl-2-pentene
$(CH_3)_2CHCH:C(CH_3)_2$ M.W. 98.19 n_D^{20} 1.4040
b.p. 83°
NEAT

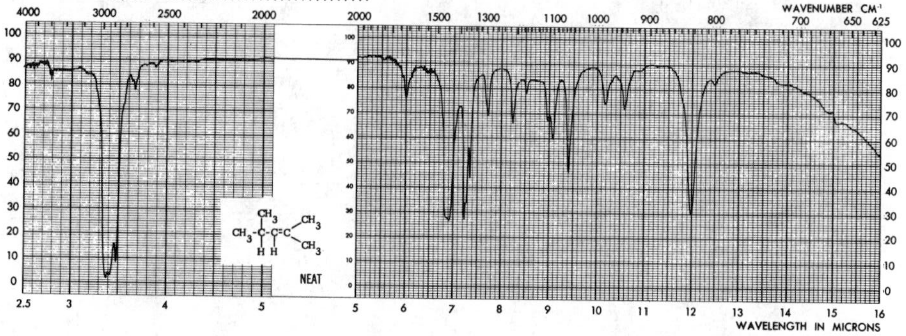

C D17,364-9 *trans*-4,4-Dimethyl-2-pentene
$(CH_3)_3CCH:CHCH_3$ M.W. 98.19 n_D^{20} 1.3966
NEAT

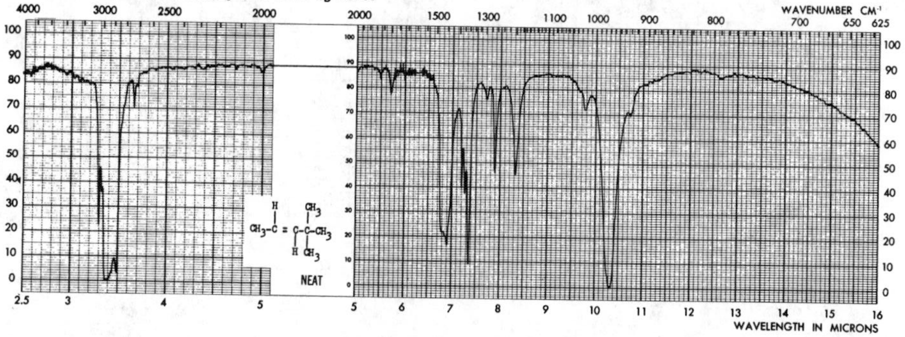

D 11,072-8 *cis*-4,4-Dimethyl-2-pentene
$(CH_3)_3CCH:CHCH_3$ M.W. 98.19 n_D^{20} 1.4020 b.p. 76°
NEAT

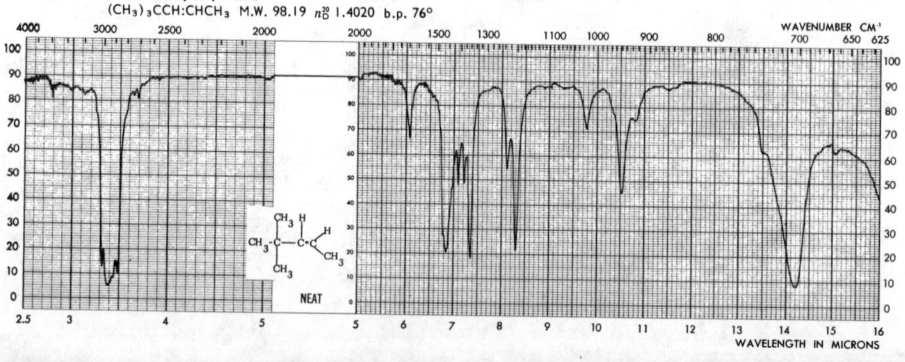

E 11,146-5 2,3-Dimethyl-1-hexene
$CH_3CH_2CH_2CH(CH_3)C(CH_3):CH_2$ M.W. 112.22 n_D^{20} 1.4120
NEAT

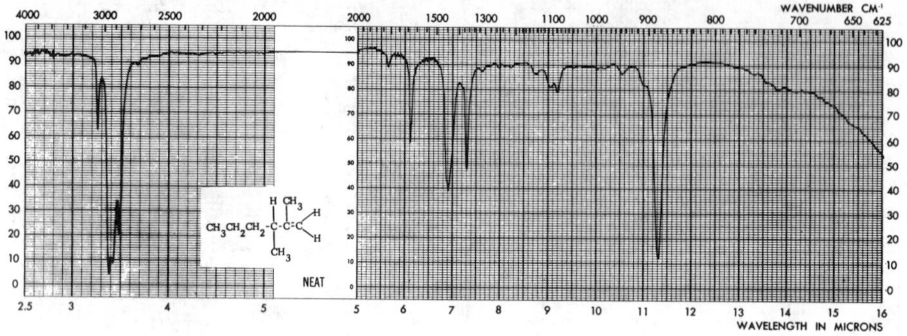

F 11,843-5 3,4-Dimethyl-1-hexene
$C_2H_5CH(CH_3)CH(CH_3)CH:CH_2$ M.W. 112.22
n_D^{20} 1.4103
NEAT

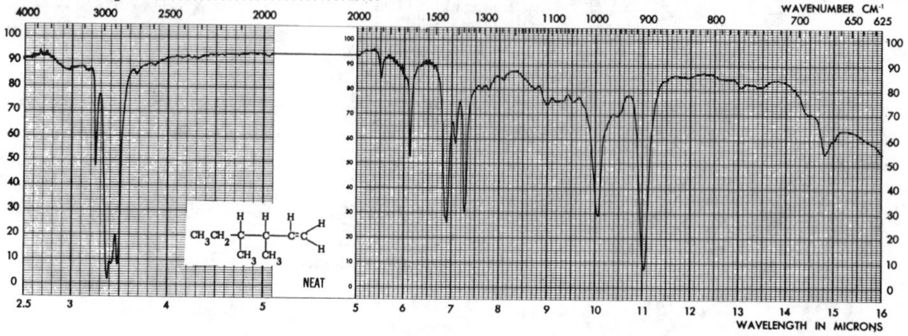

G 11,064-7 2,5-Dimethyl-2-hexene
$(CH_3)_2CHCH_2CH:C(CH_3)_2$ M.W. 112.22 n_D^{20} 1.4143
NEAT

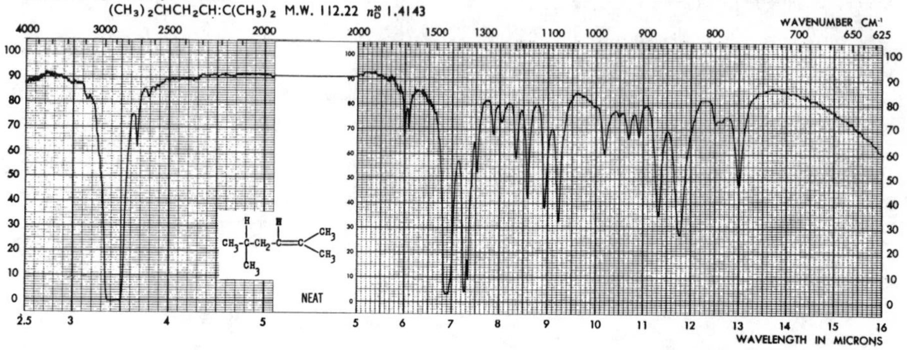

H 11,066-3 *trans*-2,5-Dimethyl-3-hexene
$(CH_3)_2CHCH:CHCH(CH_3)_2$ M.W. 112.22 n_D^{20} 1.4020
NEAT

WAVENUMBER CM⁻¹
WAVELENGTH IN MICRONS

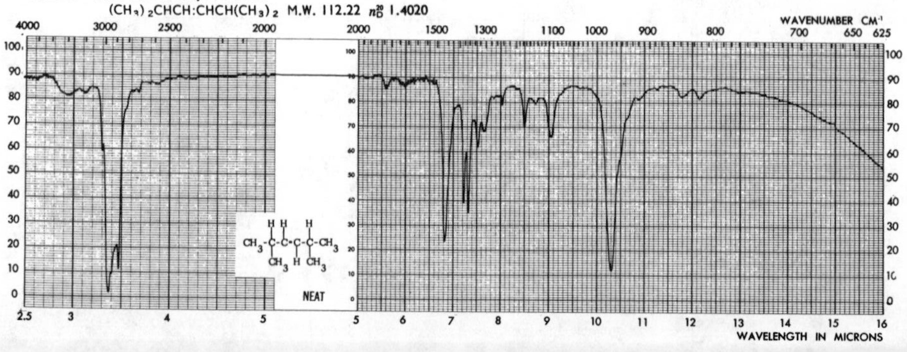

A 11,065-5 *trans*-2,2-Dimethyl-3-hexene, puriss.
$C_2H_5CH{:}CHC(CH_3)_3$ M.W. 112.22
n_D^{20} 1.4063

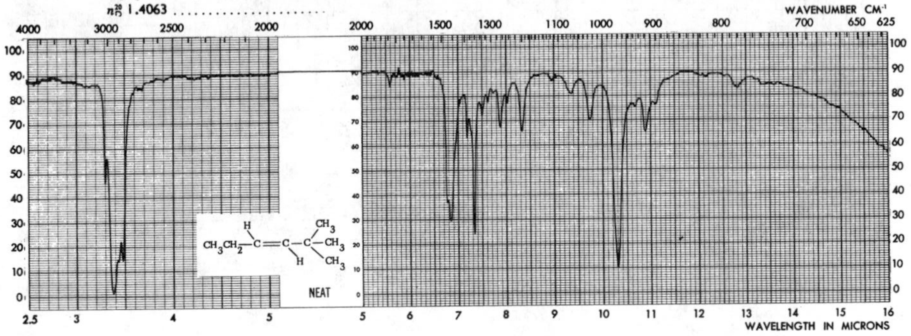

NEAT

B 11,147-3 *cis*-2,2-Dimethyl-3-hexene
$C_2H_5CH{:}CHC(CH_3)_3$ M.W. 112.22
n_D^{20} 1.4092

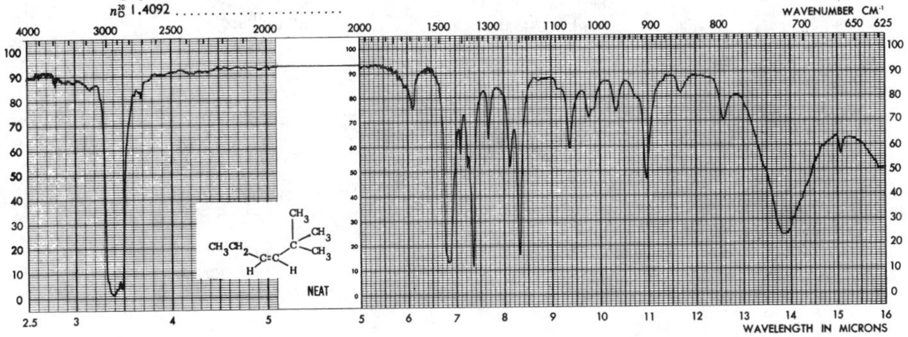

NEAT

C 11,840-0 3,5-Dimethyl-3-heptene (mixture of *cis* and *trans*)
$C_2H_5CH(CH_3)CH{:}C(CH_3)C_2H_5$ M.W. 126.24
n_D^{20} 1.4182

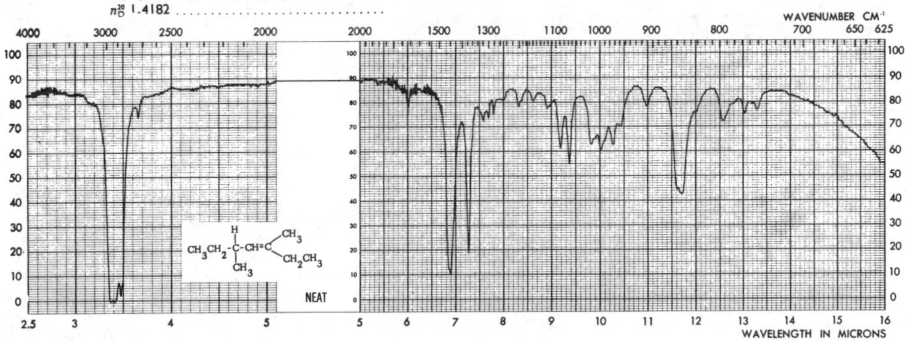

NEAT

D 11,327-1 1,1-Dineopentylethylene (4,4-dimethyl-2-neopentyl-1-pentene)
$[(CH_3)_3CCH_2]_2C{:}CH_2$ M.W. 168.33 n_D^{20} 1.4270

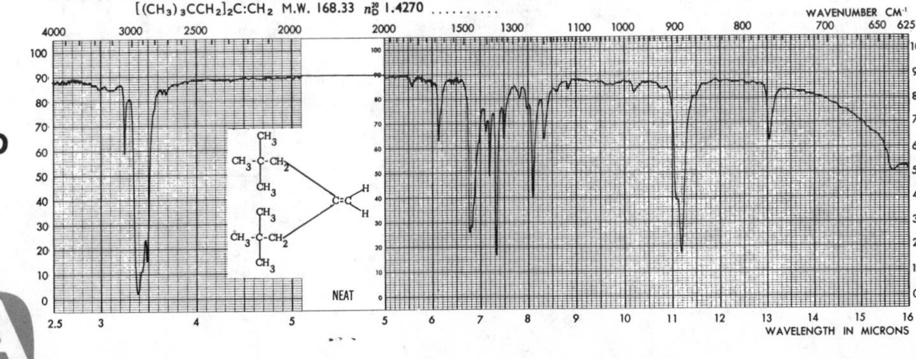

NEAT

E T7569-8 2,3,3-Trimethyl-1-butene, puriss.
$(CH_3)_3CC(CH_3){:}CH_2$ M.W. 98.19 n_D^{20} 1.4020

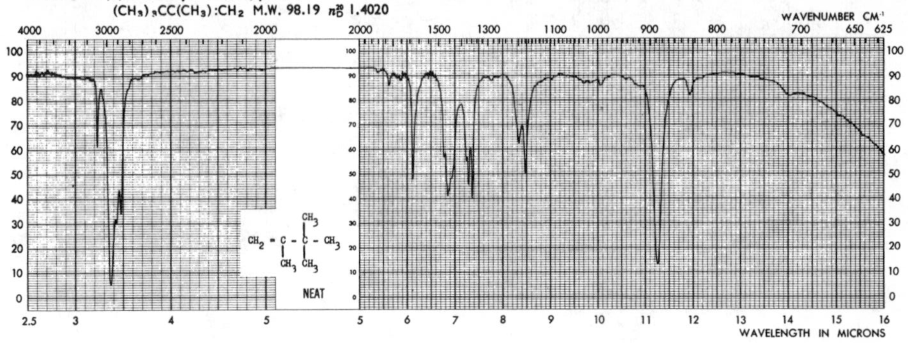

NEAT

F T7840-9 2,4,4-Trimethyl-1-pentene (diisobutylene)
$(CH_3)_3CCH_2C(CH_3){:}CH_2$ M.W. 112.22 n_D^{20} 1.4079 b.p. 81°

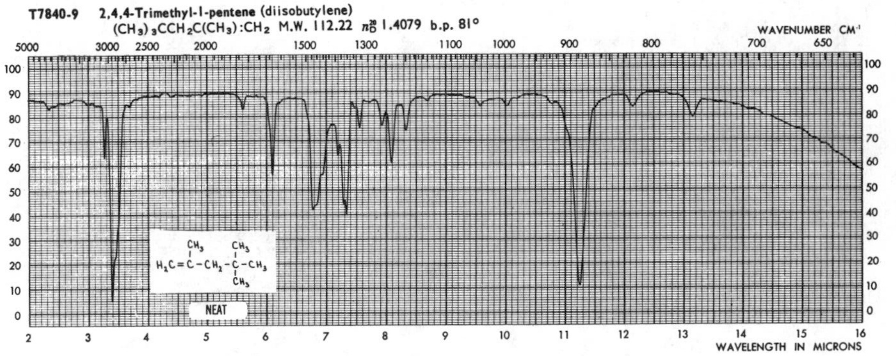

NEAT

G 14,382-0 2,4,4-Trimethyl-2-pentene
$(CH_3)_3CCH{:}C(CH_3)_2$ M.W. 112.22 n_D^{20} 1.4159
b.p. 104°

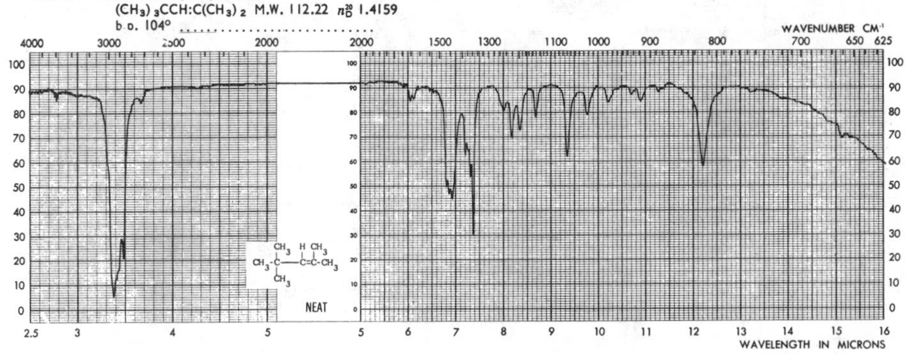

NEAT

H 11,137-6 3,5,5-Trimethyl-1-hexene
$(CH_3)_3CCH_2CH(CH_3)CH{:}CH_2$ M.W. 126.24
n_D^{20} 1.4100

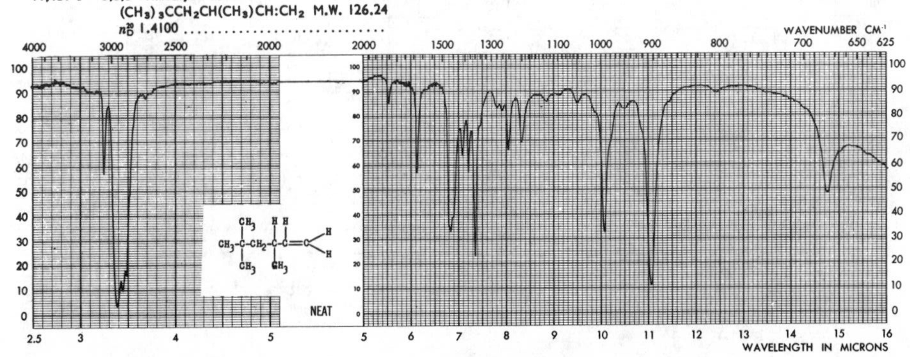

NEAT

A

11,329-8 **2,2,4,6,6-Pentamethyl-3-heptene**
$(CH_3)_3CCH_2C(CH_3):CHC(CH_3)_3$ M.W. 168.33 n_D^{20} 1.4295

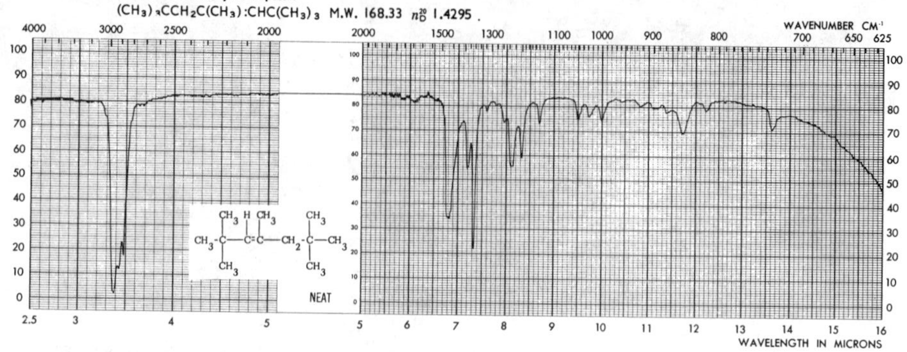

NEAT

B

P4985-6 **Piperylene** (1,3-pentadiene) (mixture of isomers)
$CH_3CH:CHCH:CH_2$ M.W. 68.12

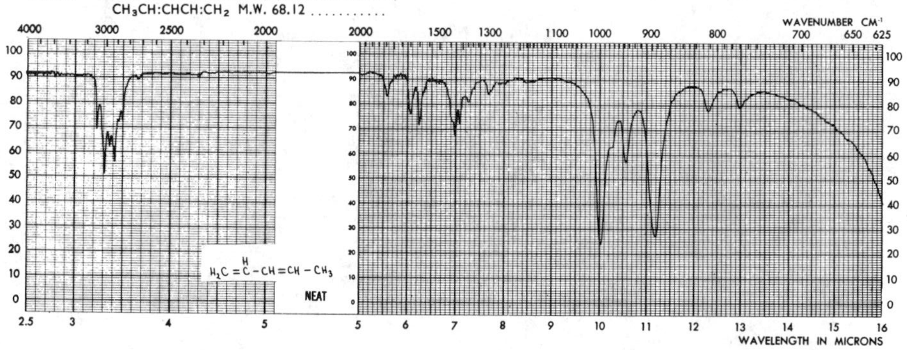

NEAT

C

11,180-5 ***trans*-Piperylene** (*trans*-1,3-pentadiene)
$CH_3CH:CHCH:CH_2$ M.W. 68.12 n_D^{20} 1.4331
b.p. 42°

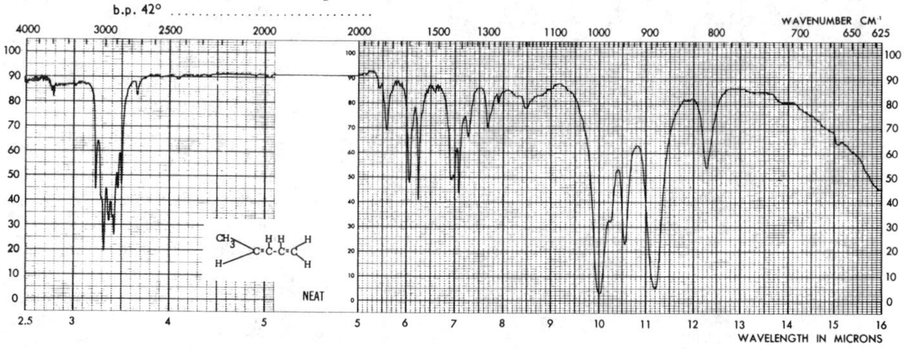

NEAT

D

P460-7 **1,4-Pentadiene**
$H_2C:CHCH_2CH:CH_2$ M.W. 68.12 n_D^{20} 1.3894
b.p. 26°

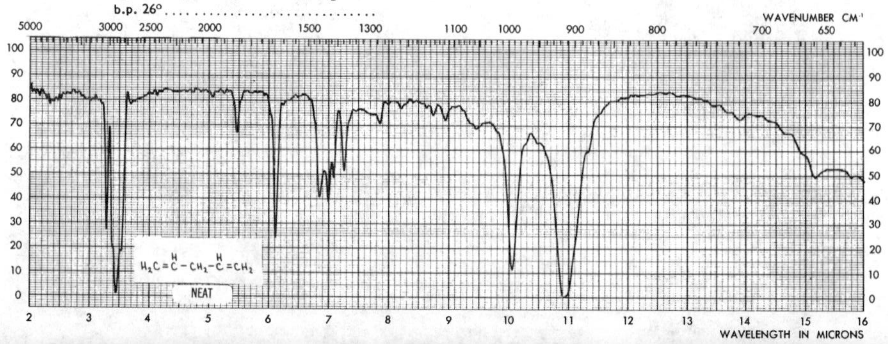

NEAT

E

11,083-3 **1,3-Hexadiene** (mixture of *cis* and *trans*)
$C_2H_5CH:CHCH:CH_2$ M.W. 82.15 n_D^{20} 1.4380
b.p. 72-75°

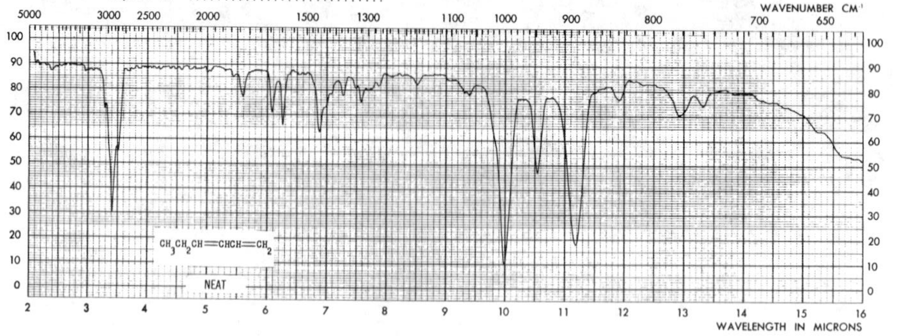

NEAT

F

12,918-6 **1,4-Hexadiene** (mixture of *cis* and *trans*)
$CH_3CH:CHCH_2CH:CH_2$ M.W. 82.15 n_D^{20} 1.410°
b.p. 64-66°

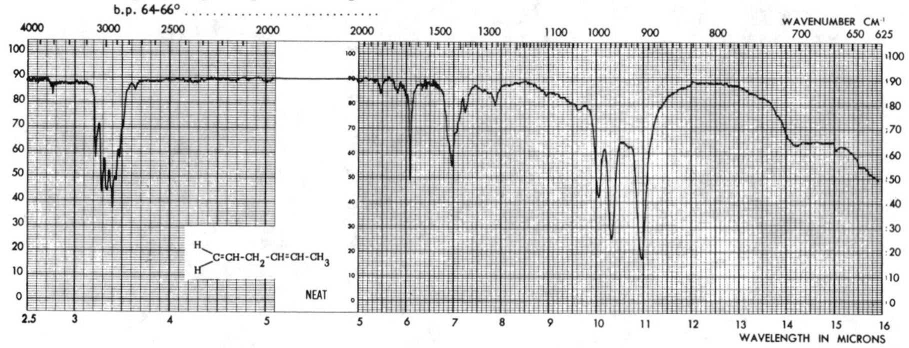

NEAT

G

11,084-1 **2,4-Hexadiene**
$CH_3CH:CHCH:CHCH_3$ M.W. 82.15 n_D^{20} 1.4529 b.p. 82°

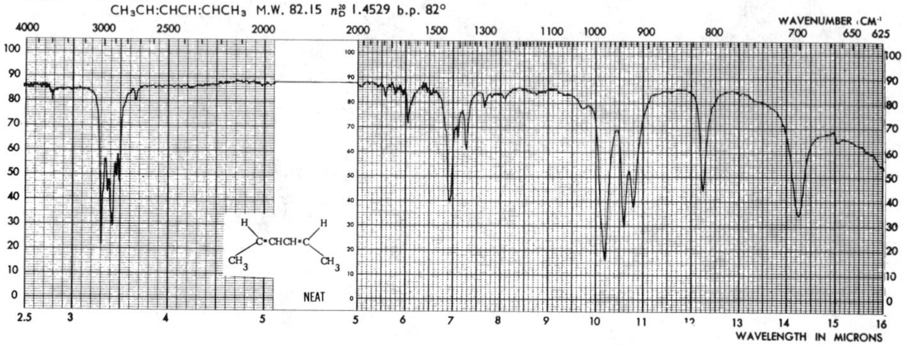

NEAT

H

11,088-4 ***trans*-2, *trans*-4-Hexadiene**
$CH_3CH:CHCH:CHCH_3$ M.W. 82.15
n_D^{20} 1.4479

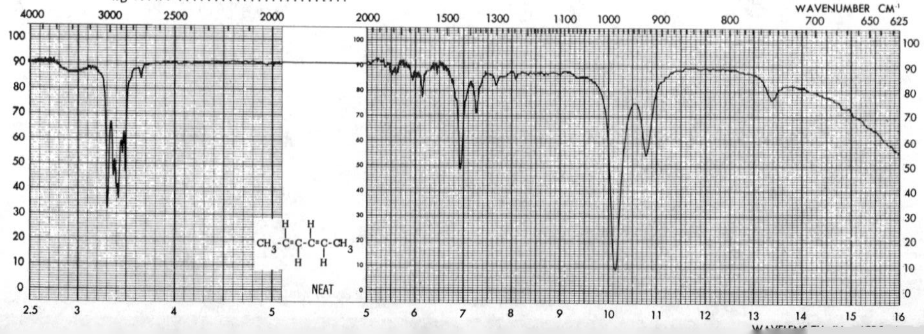

NEAT

A 11,087-6 *cis*-2, *trans*-4-Hexadiene
$CH_3CH{:}CHCH{:}CHCH_3$ M.W. 82.15 n_D^{20} 1.4553 b.p. 80-82°
NEAT

B 12,855-4 1,5-Hexadiene
$H_2C{:}CHCH_2CH_2CH{:}CH_2$ M.W. 82.15 n_D^{20} 1.4029
b.p. 59.6°
NEAT

C H130-2 1,5-Heptadiene, puriss.
$CH_3CH{:}CHCH_2CH_2CH{:}CH_2$ M.W. 96.17
n_D^{20} 1.4193
NEAT

D H1258-7 1,3,5-Hexatriene
$H_2C{:}CHCH{:}CHCH{:}CH_2$ M.W. 80.12
n_D^{20} 1.5135
NEAT

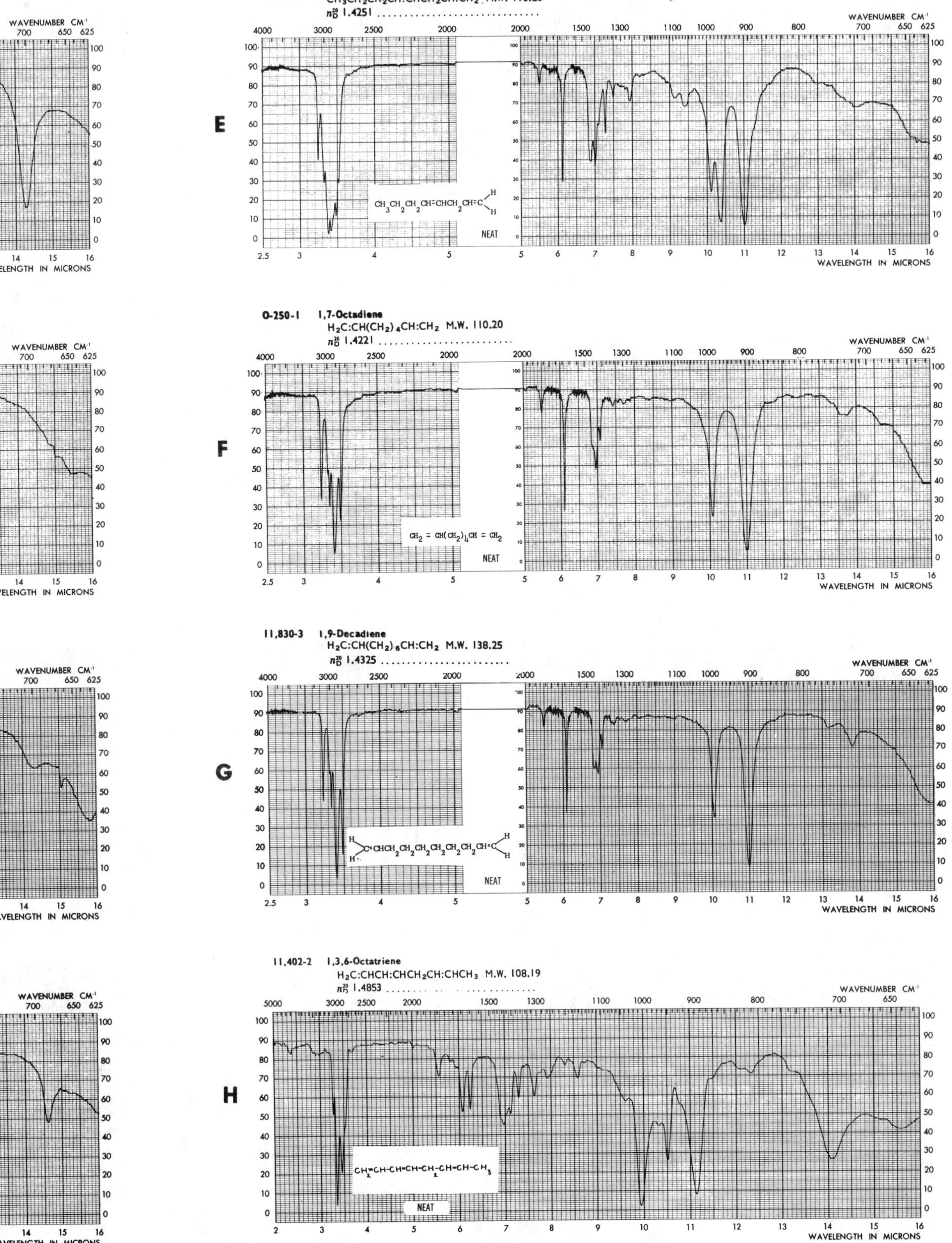

E 11,878-8 1,4-Octadiene (mixture of *cis* and *trans*)
$CH_3CH_2CH_2CH{:}CHCH_2CH{:}CH_2$ M.W. 110.20
n_D^{20} 1.4251
NEAT

F O-250-1 1,7-Octadiene
$H_2C{:}CH(CH_2)_4CH{:}CH_2$ M.W. 110.20
n_D^{20} 1.4221
NEAT

G 11,830-3 1,9-Decadiene
$H_2C{:}CH(CH_2)_6CH{:}CH_2$ M.W. 138.25
n_D^{20} 1.4325
NEAT

H 11,402-2 1,3,6-Octatriene
$H_2C{:}CHCH{:}CHCH_2CH{:}CHCH_3$ M.W. 108.19
n_D^{20} 1.4853
NEAT

A

15,043-6 1,*trans*-4,9-Decatriene
$H_2C:CHCH_2CH:CH(CH_2)_3CH:CH_2$ M.W. 136.24
n_D^{20} 1.4496 b.p. 164-166°

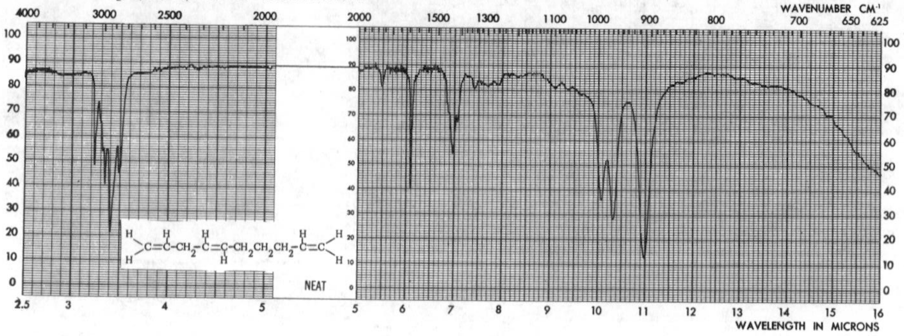

B

11,093-0 3-Methyl-1,2-butadiene (3,3-dimethylallene)
$(CH_3)_2C:C:CH_2$ M.W. 68.12 n_D^{20} 1.4179 b.p. 40.5-41.5°

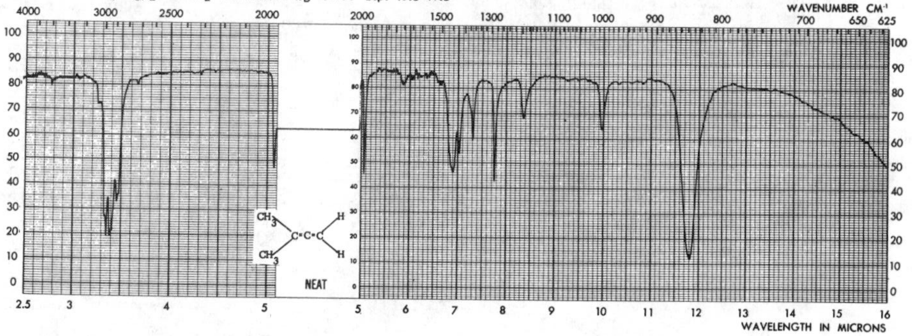

C

T1945-3 Tetramethylallene
$(CH_3)_2C:C:C(CH_3)_2$ M.W. 96.17 n_D^{20} 1.4415 b.p. 88-89°

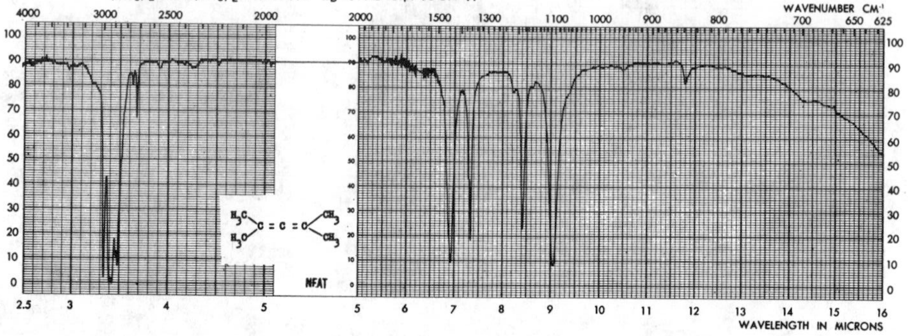

D

10,021-8 2-Ethyl-1,3-butadiene
$H_2C:CHC(C_2H_5):CH_2$ M.W. 82.15 n_D^{20} 1.4332

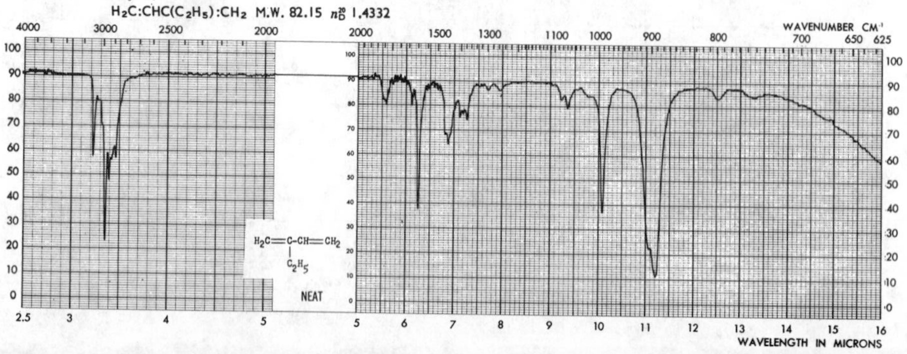

E

I-1955-1 Isoprene, puriss.
$H_2C:CHC(CH_3):CH_2$ M.W. 68.12 n_D^{20} 1.4217

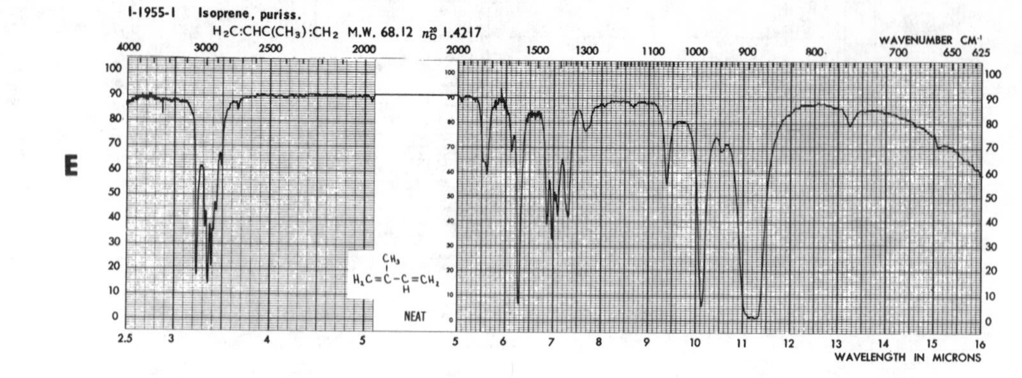

F

11,110-4 *trans*-2-Methyl-1,3-pentadiene
$CH_3CH:CHC(CH_3):CH_2$ M.W. 82.15 n_D^{20} 1.4439 b.p. 75-76°

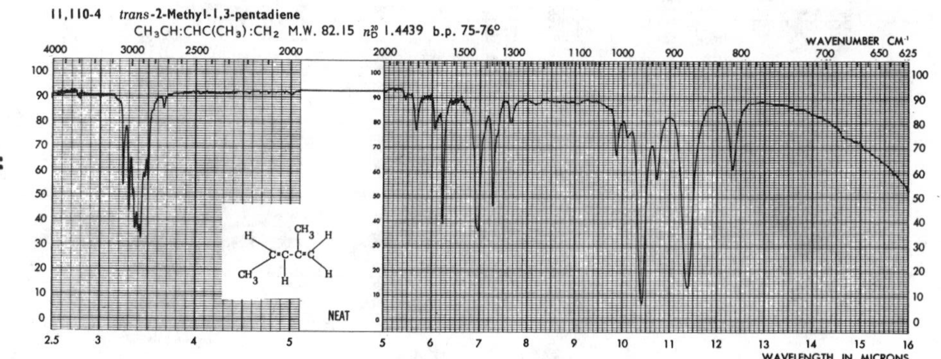

G

11,871-0 2-Methyl-1,4-pentadiene
$H_2C:CHCH_2C(CH_3):CH_2$ M.W. 82.15
n_D^{20} 1.4020

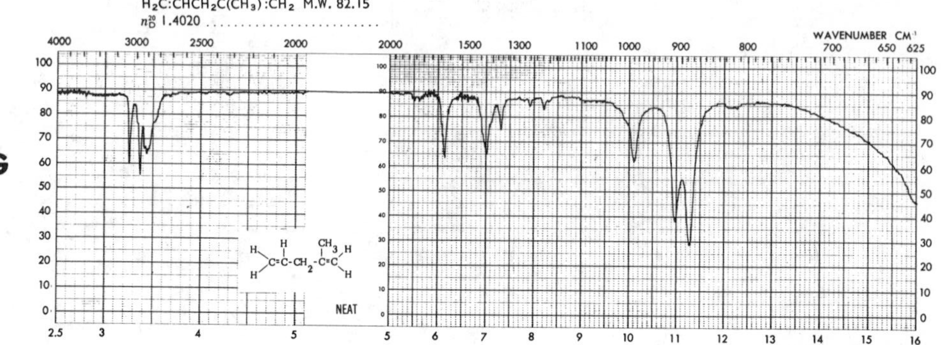

H

11,176-7 4-Methyl-1,3-pentadiene
$(CH_3)_2C:CHCH:CH_2$ M.W. 82.15 n_D^{20} 1.4524
b.p. 75.5-76°

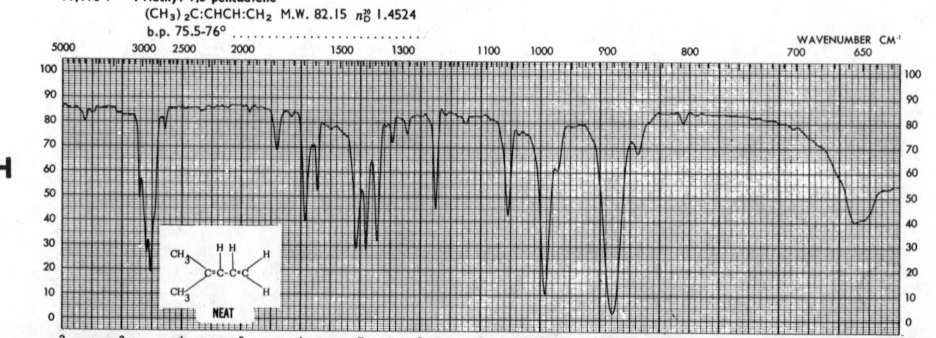

A

M4920-8 2-Methyl-1,5-hexadiene, puriss.
$H_2C:C(CH_3)CH_2CH_2CH:CH_2$ M.W. 96.17 n_D^{20} 1.4175
b.p. 92°

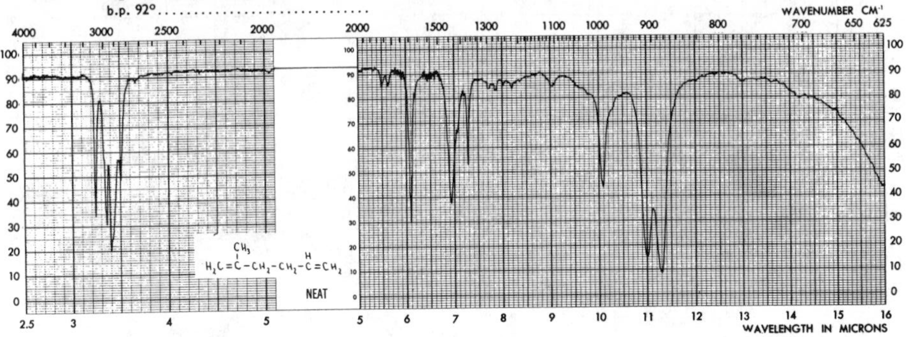

B

14,549-1 2,3-Dimethyl-1,3-butadiene
$H_2C:C(CH_3)C(CH_3):CH_2$ M.W. 82.15 n_D^{20} 1.4380
b.p. 68-69°

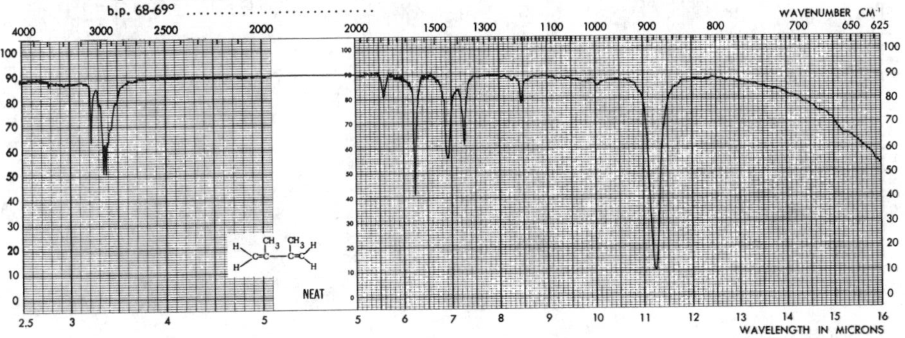

C

12,655-1 2,4-Dimethyl-1,3-pentadiene
$(CH_3)_2C:CHC(CH_3):CH_2$ M.W. 96.17 n_D^{20} 1.4412

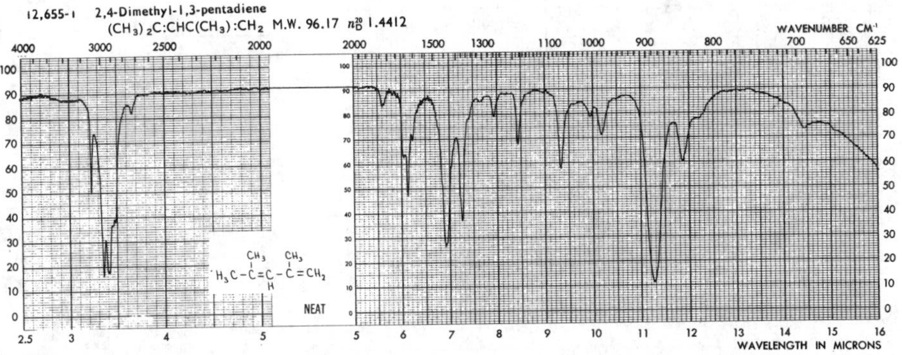

D

D16,080-6 2,5-Dimethyl-1,5-hexadiene
$H_2C:C(CH_3)CH_2CH_2C(CH_3):CH_2$ M.W. 110.20 n_D^{20} 1.4301

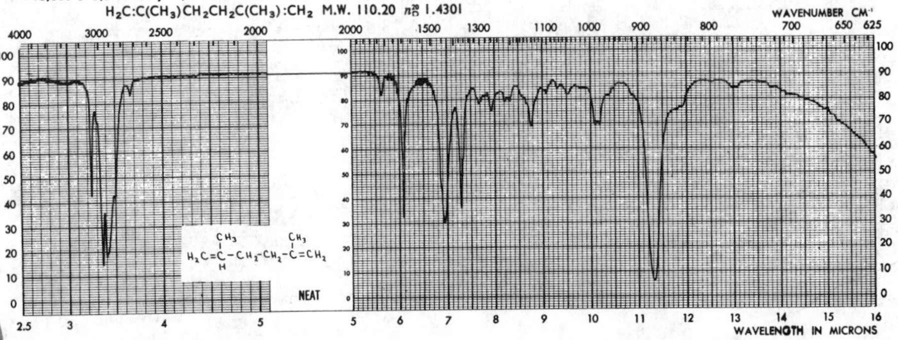

E

D16,100-4 2,5-Dimethyl-2,4-hexadiene
$(CH_3)_2C:CHCH:C(CH_3)_2$ M.W. 110.20 n_D^{20} 1.4741 m.p. 12-14°

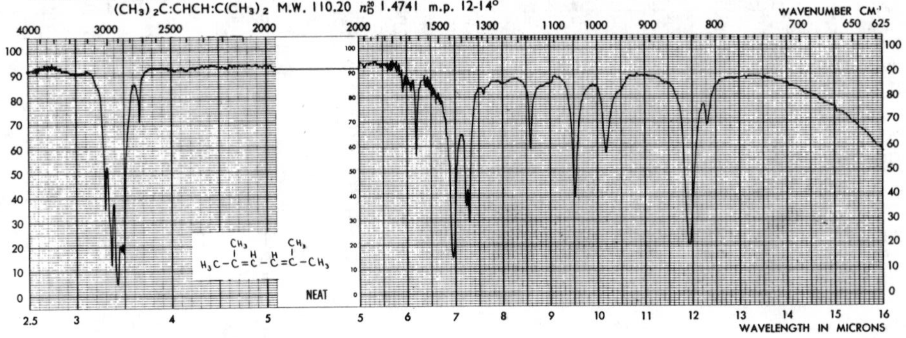

F

11,401-4 5-Methyl-1,3,6-heptatriene (butadiene dimer)
$H_2C:CHCH(CH_3)CH:CHCH:CH_2$ M.W. 108.19
n_D^{20} 1.4618 b.p. 117°

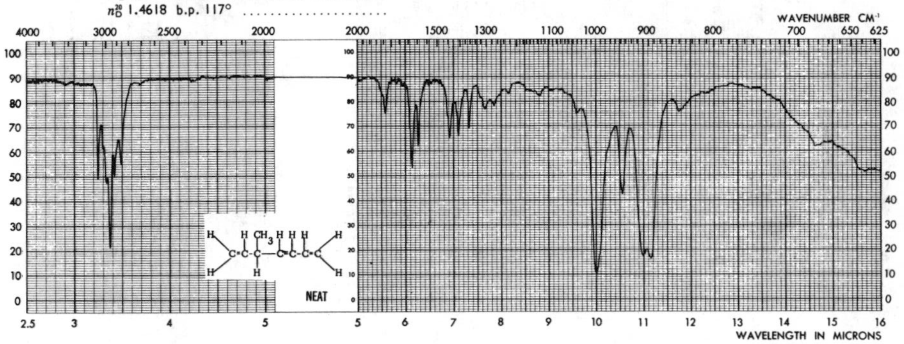

G

12,934-8 2,6-Dimethyl-2,*cis*-6-octadiene
$CH_3CH:C(CH_3)CH_2CH_2CH:C(CH_3)_2$ M.W. 138.25
n_D^{20} 1.4485

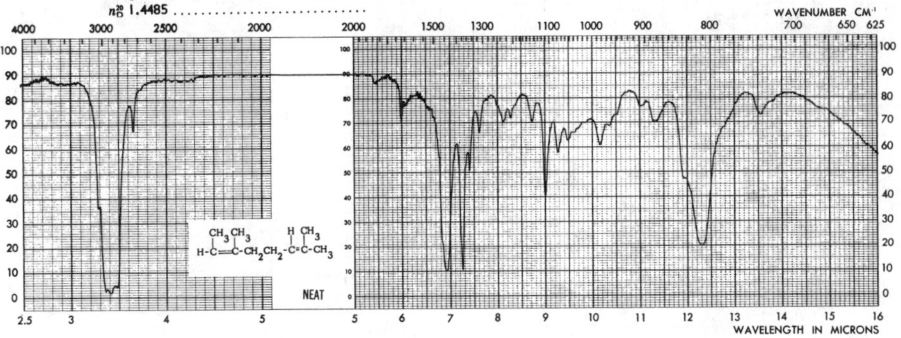

H

12,935-6 2,6-Dimethyl-2,*trans*-6-octadiene
$CH_3CH:C(CH_3)CH_2CH_2CH:C(CH_3)_2$ M.W. 138.25
n_D^{20} 1.4502

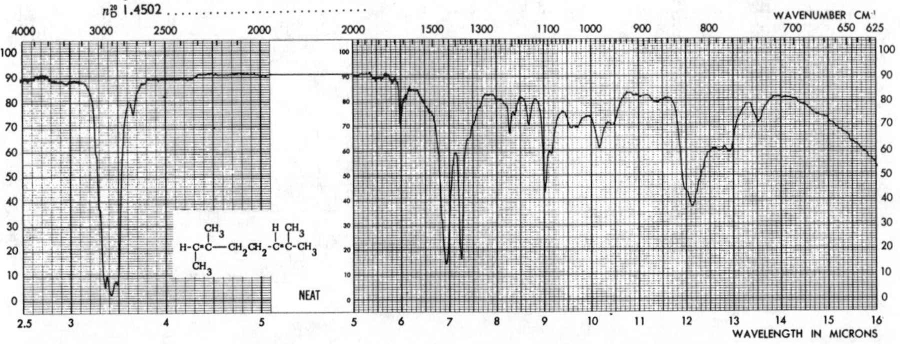

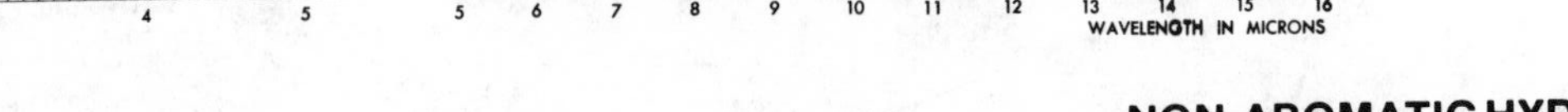

A

M10,000-5 **Myrcene, tech.**
$H_2C{:}CHC({:}CH_2)CH_2CH_2CH{:}C(CH_3)_2$ M.W. 136.24
n_D^{20} 1.4715 b.p. 167°

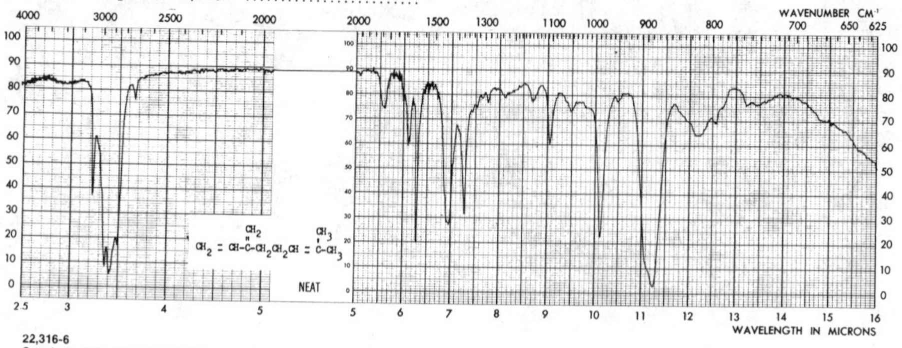

$CH_2=CH-C(=CH_2)-CH_2CH_2CH=C(CH_3)-CH_3$ NEAT

B

22,316-6
Squalene, 98% (2,6,10,15,19,23-hexamethyl-2,6,10,14,18,22-tetracosahexaene)
$[(CH_3)_2C[=CHCH_2CH_2C(CH_3)]_2=CHCH_2-]_2$
FW 410.73 mp -75° bp 285°/25mm. n_D^{20} 1.4945
d 0.858 *Beil.* **1**(1),130 Disp. C

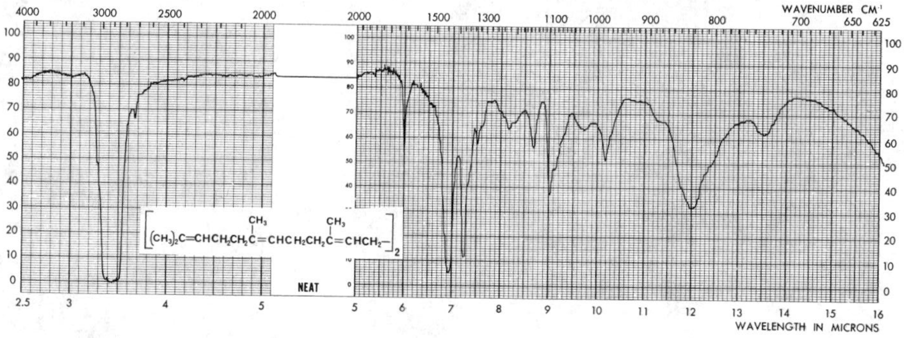

$[(CH_3)_2C=CHCH_2CH_2C(CH_3)=CHCH_2CH_2C(CH_3)=CHCH_2-]_2$ NEAT

C

C11,180-5 **Cyclopentane**
C_5H_{10} M.W. 70.14 n_D^{20} 1.4023

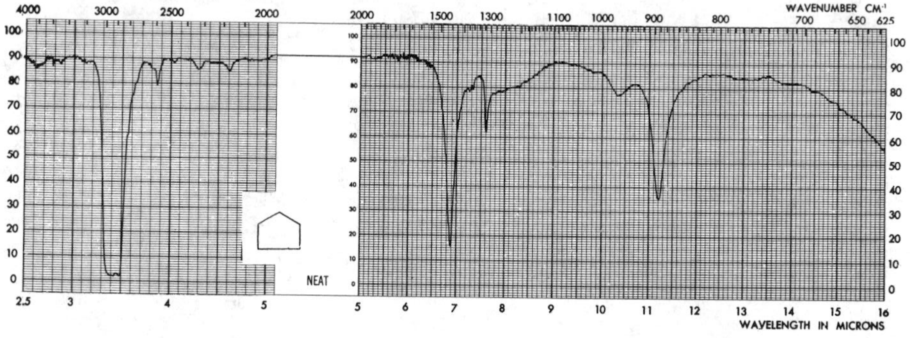

NEAT

D

C10,030-7 **Cyclohexane, 99 + %**
C_6H_{12} M.W. 84.16 n_D^{20} 1.4255 m.p. 4-6°

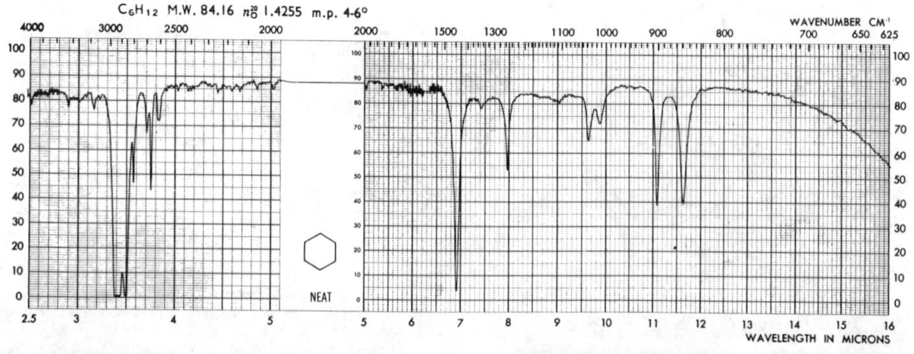

NEAT

E

C9840-3 **Cycloheptane**
C_7H_{14} M.W. 98.19 n_D^{20} 1.4455.

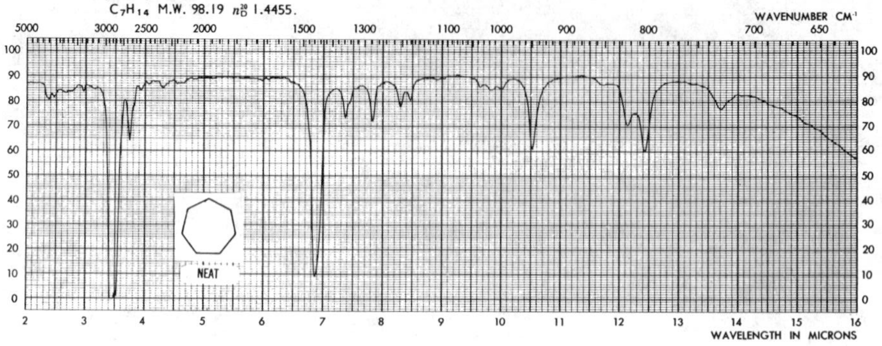

NEAT

F

C10,940-1 **Cyclooctane, puriss.**
C_8H_{16} M.W. 112.22 n_D^{20} 1.4574 m.p. 10-13°

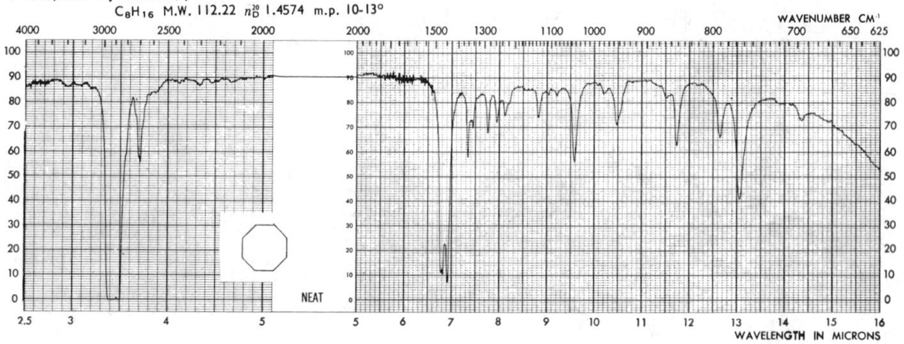

NEAT

G

15,533-0 **Cyclodecane**
$C_{10}H_{20}$ M.W. 140.27

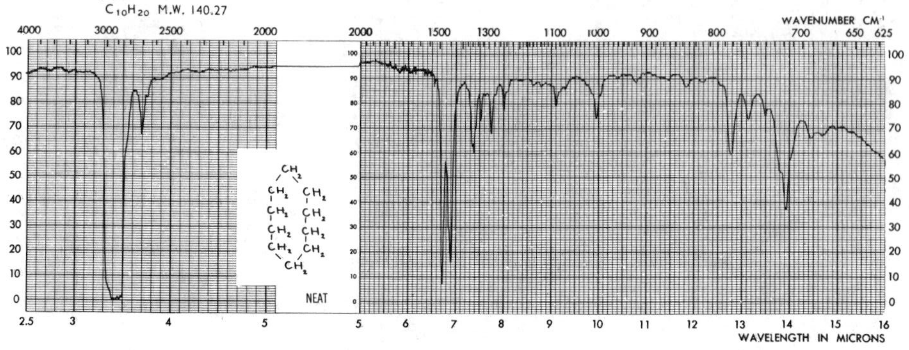

NEAT

H

C9700-8 **Cyclododecane**
$C_{12}H_{24}$ M.W. 168.32 m.p. 61-63°

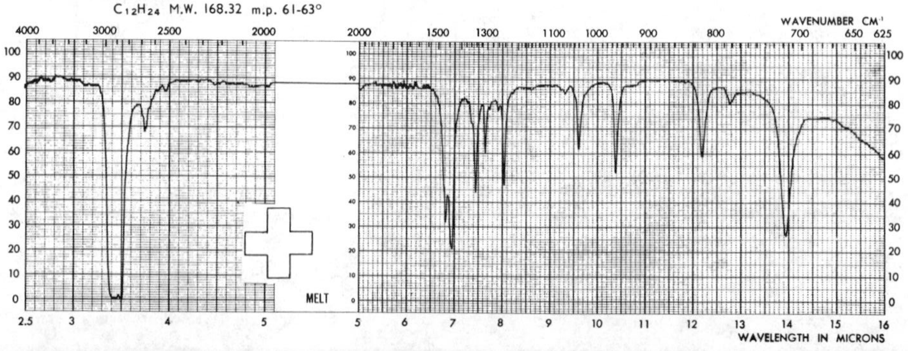

MELT

A M3940-7 Methylcyclopentane
$C_5H_9CH_3$ M.W. 84.16 n_D^{20} 1.4087 b.p. 71.8°
NEAT

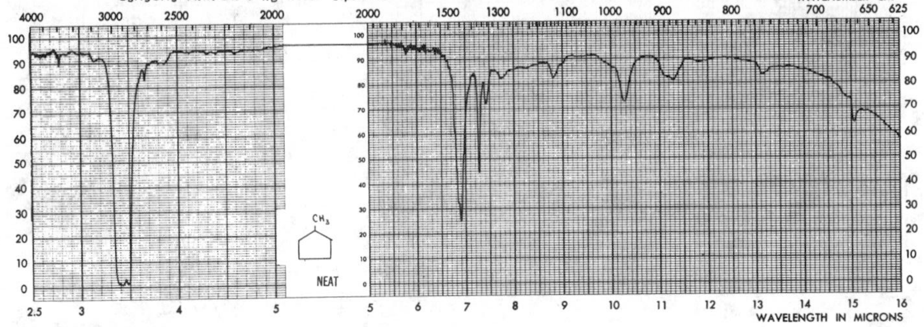

B 11,075-2 Ethylcyclopentane, puriss.
$C_5H_9C_2H_5$ M.W. 98.19 n_D^{20} 1.4195
b.p. 103°
NEAT

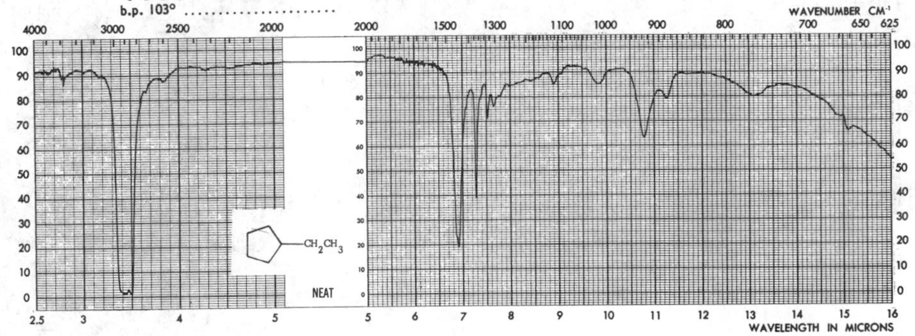

C 11,131-7 n-Propylcyclopentane
$C_5H_9CH_2CH_2CH_3$ M.W. 112.22 n_D^{20} 1.4225
NEAT

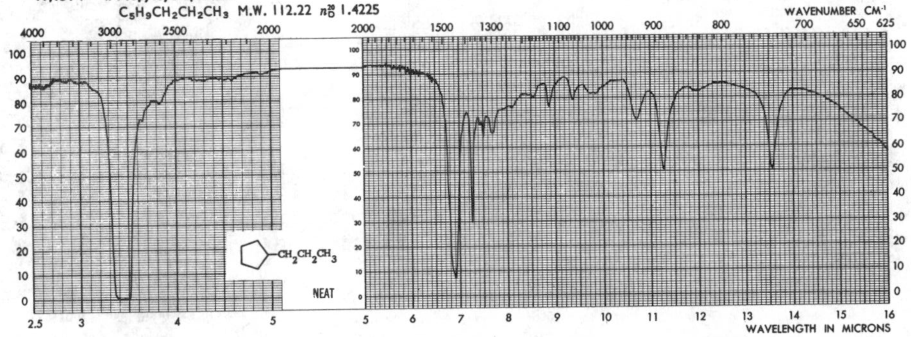

D M3788-9 Methylcyclohexane
$C_6H_{11}CH_3$ M.W. 98.19 n_D^{20} 1.4222
b.p. 100-101°
NEAT

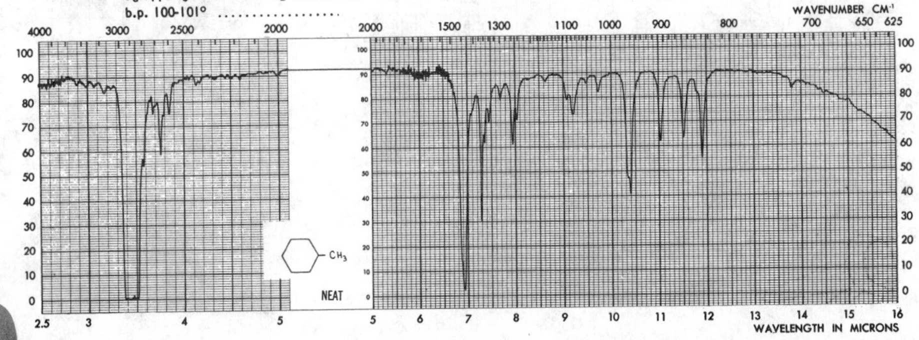

E E1915-4 Ethylcyclohexane
$C_6H_{11}C_2H_5$ M.W. 112.21
n_D^{20} 1.4321
NEAT

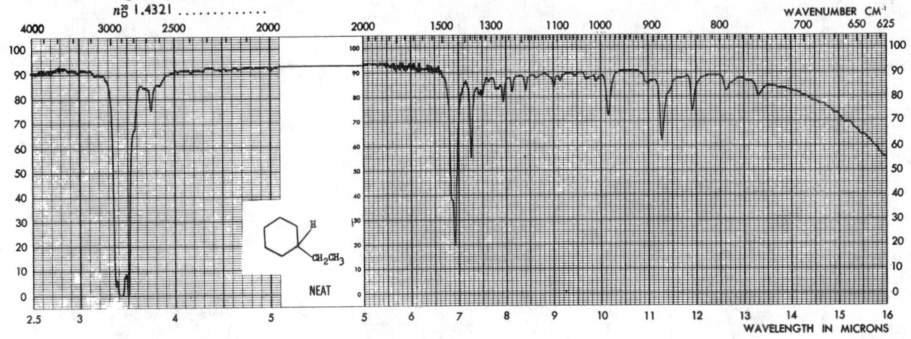

F 11,185-6 n-Propylcyclohexane
$C_6H_{11}CH_2CH_2CH_3$ M.W. 126.24
n_D^{20} 1.4359
NEAT

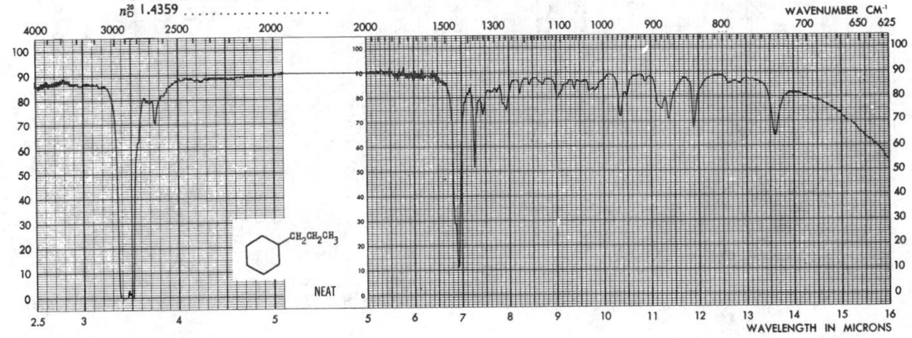

G I-2190-4 Isopropylcyclohexane
$C_6H_{11}CH(CH_3)_2$ M.W. 126.24 n_D^{20} 1.4399
b.p. 151°
NEAT

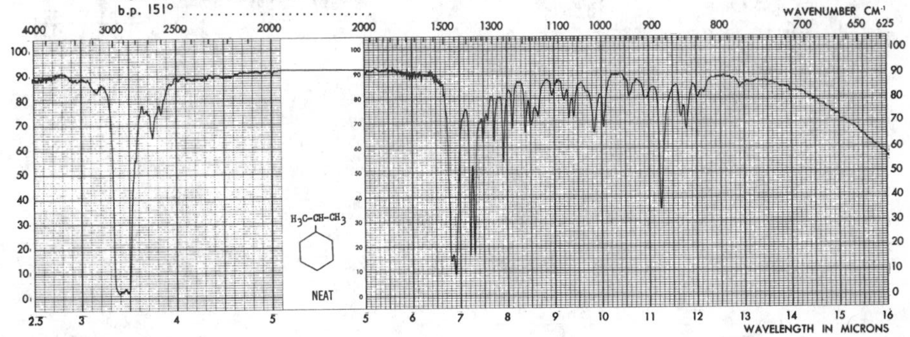

H 11,041-8 n-Butylcyclopentane
$C_5H_9(CH_2)_3CH_3$ M.W. 126.24 n_D^{20} 1.4304
NEAT

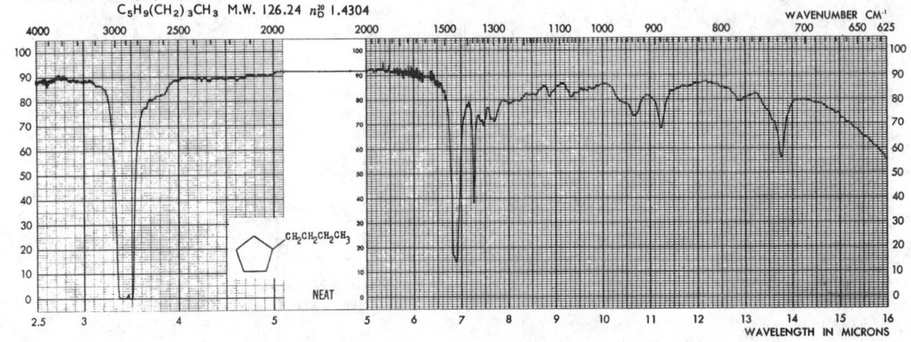

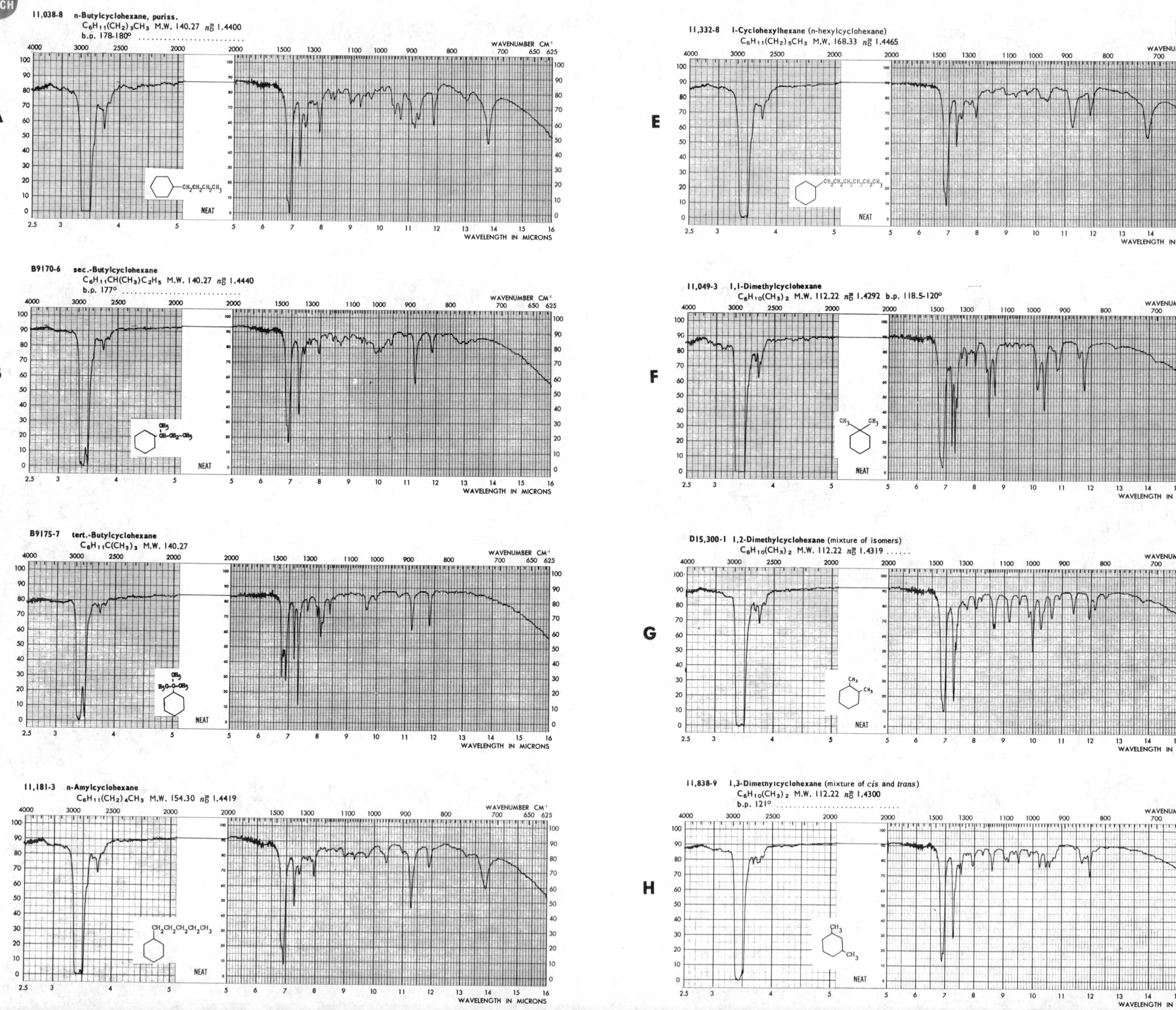
ALDRICH
A
11,038-8 n-Butylcyclohexane, puriss.
$C_6H_{11}(CH_2)_3CH_3$ M.W. 140.27 n_D^{20} 1.4400
b.p. 178-180°
NEAT
B
B9170-6 sec.-Butylcyclohexane
$C_6H_{11}CH(CH_3)C_2H_5$ M.W. 140.27 n_D^{20} 1.4440
b.p. 177°
NEAT
C
B9175-7 tert.-Butylcyclohexane
$C_6H_{11}C(CH_3)_3$ M.W. 140.27
NEAT
D
11,181-3 n-Amylcyclohexane
$C_6H_{11}(CH_2)_4CH_3$ M.W. 154.30 n_D^{20} 1.4419
NEAT
E
11,332-8 1-Cyclohexylhexane (n-hexylcyclohexane)
$C_6H_{11}(CH_2)_5CH_3$ M.W. 168.33 n_D^{20} 1.4465
NEAT
F
11,049-3 1,1-Dimethylcyclohexane
$C_6H_{10}(CH_3)_2$ M.W. 112.22 n_D^{20} 1.4292 b.p. 118.5-120°
NEAT
G
D15,300-1 1,2-Dimethylcyclohexane (mixture of isomers)
$C_6H_{10}(CH_3)_2$ M.W. 112.22 n_D^{20} 1.4319
NEAT
H
11,838-9 1,3-Dimethylcyclohexane (mixture of *cis* and *trans*)
$C_6H_{10}(CH_3)_2$ M.W. 112.22 n_D^{20} 1.4300
b.p. 121°
NEAT
WAVENUMBER CM⁻¹
WAVELENGTH IN MICRONS

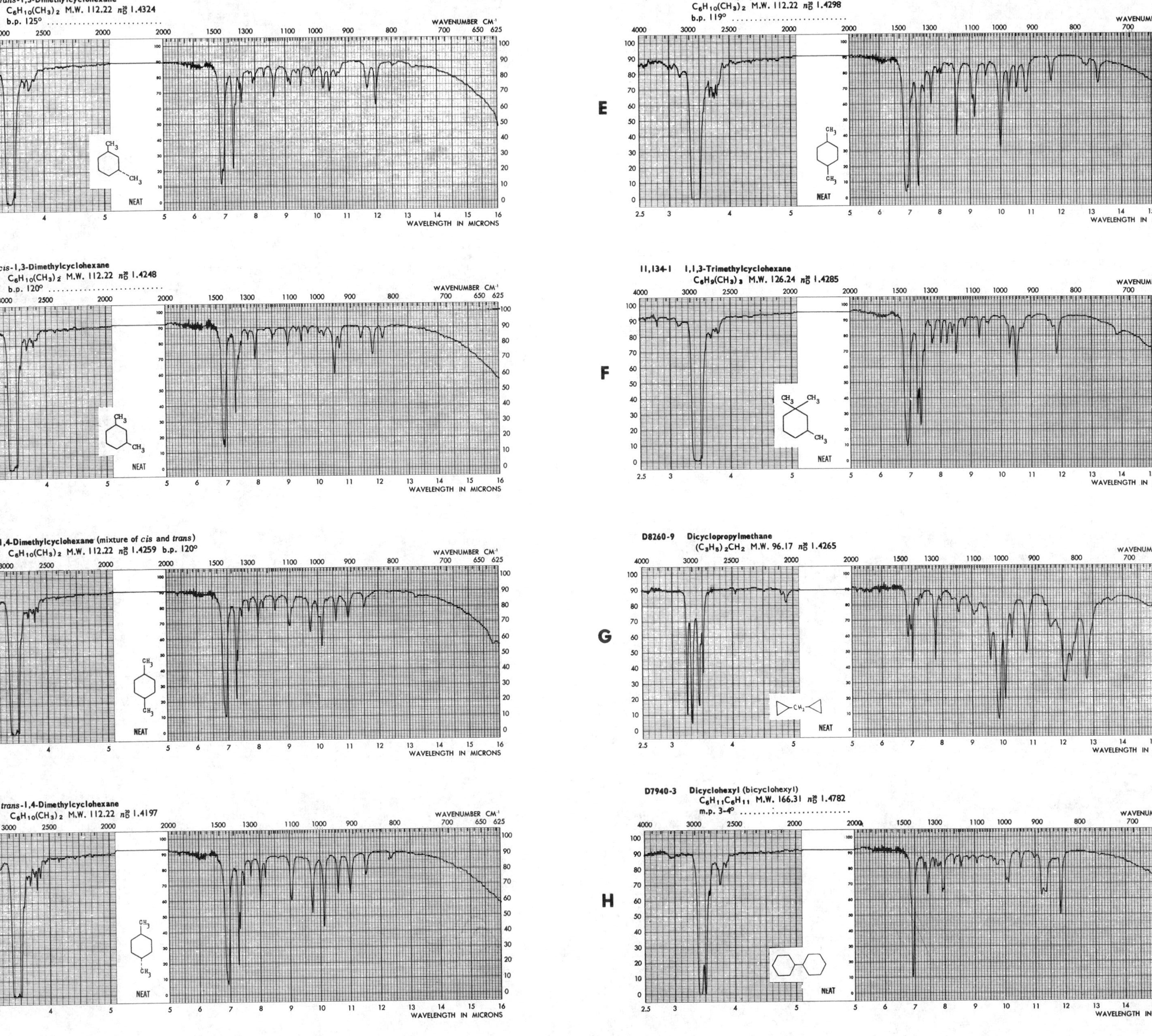
A
11,837-0 trans-1,3-Dimethylcyclohexane
$C_6H_{10}(CH_3)_2$ M.W. 112.22 n_D^{20} 1.4324
b.p. 125°
NEAT
B
11,836-2 cis-1,3-Dimethylcyclohexane
$C_6H_{10}(CH_3)_2$ M.W. 112.22 n_D^{20} 1.4248
b.p. 120°
NEAT
C
11,050-7 1,4-Dimethylcyclohexane (mixture of cis and trans)
$C_6H_{10}(CH_3)_2$ M.W. 112.22 n_D^{20} 1.4259 b.p. 120°
NEAT
D
11,052-3 trans-1,4-Dimethylcyclohexane
$C_6H_{10}(CH_3)_2$ M.W. 112.22 n_D^{20} 1.4197
NEAT
E
11,051-5 cis-1,4-Dimethylcyclohexane, puriss.
$C_6H_{10}(CH_3)_2$ M.W. 112.22 n_D^{20} 1.4298
b.p. 119°
NEAT
F
11,134-1 1,1,3-Trimethylcyclohexane
$C_6H_9(CH_3)_3$ M.W. 126.24 n_D^{20} 1.4285
NEAT
G
D8260-9 Dicyclopropylmethane
$(C_3H_5)_2CH_2$ M.W. 96.17 n_D^{20} 1.4265
NEAT
H
D7940-3 Dicyclohexyl (bicyclohexyl)
$C_6H_{11}C_6H_{11}$ M.W. 166.31 n_D^{20} 1.4782
m.p. 3-4°
NEAT
WAVENUMBER CM⁻¹
WAVELENGTH IN MICRONS

ALDRICH

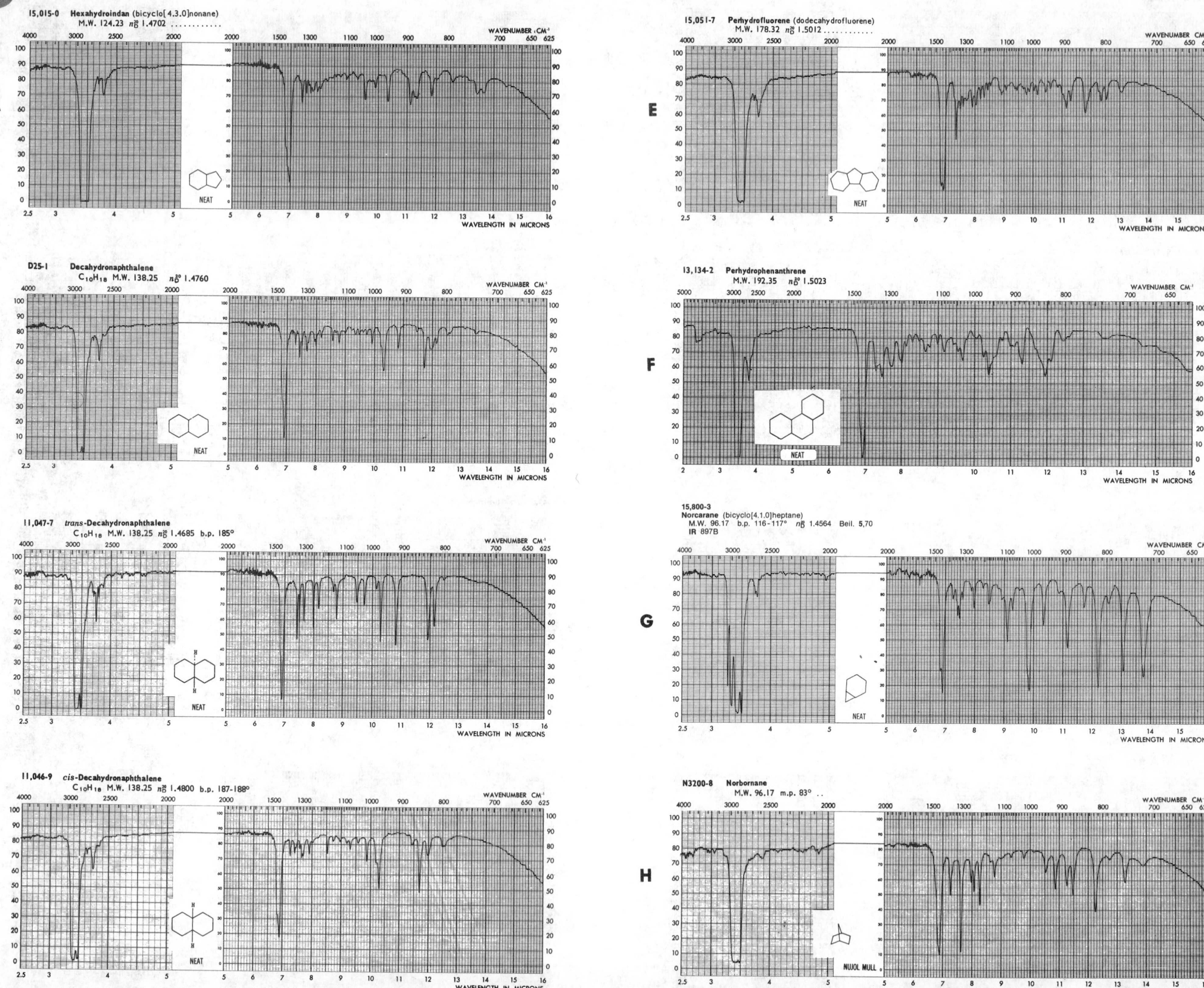
ALDRICH
A
15,015-0 Hexahydroindan (bicyclo[4.3.0]nonane)
M.W. 124.23 n_D^{20} 1.4702 ....
B
D25-1 Decahydronaphthalene
$C_{10}H_{18}$ M.W. 138.25 n_D^{20} 1.4760
C
11,047-7 *trans*-Decahydronaphthalene
$C_{10}H_{18}$ M.W. 138.25 n_D^{20} 1.4685 b.p. 185°
D
11,046-9 *cis*-Decahydronaphthalene
$C_{10}H_{18}$ M.W. 138.25 n_D^{20} 1.4800 b.p. 187-188°
E
15,051-7 Perhydrofluorene (dodecahydrofluorene)
M.W. 178.32 n_D^{20} 1.5012 ....
F
13,134-2 Perhydrophenanthrene
M.W. 192.35 n_D^{20} 1.5023
G
15,800-3
Norcarane (bicyclo[4.1.0]heptane)
M.W. 96.17 b.p. 116-117° n_D^{20} 1.4564 Beil. 5,70
IR 897B
H
N3200-8 Norbornane
M.W. 96.17 m.p. 83° ..

A

20,108-1
Quadricyclane (quadricyclo[2.2.1.0^2,6.0^3,5]heptane)
FW 92.14 bp 108°/740mm. n_D^{20} 1.4855 d 0.919
Disp. C

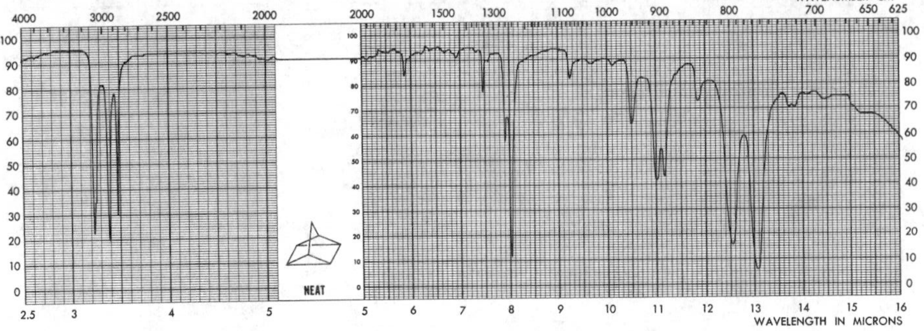

NEAT

B

T5720-7 **Tricyclo[5.2.1.0^2,6]decane** (tetrahydrodicyclopentadiene)
M.W. 136.24 m.p. 68-71°

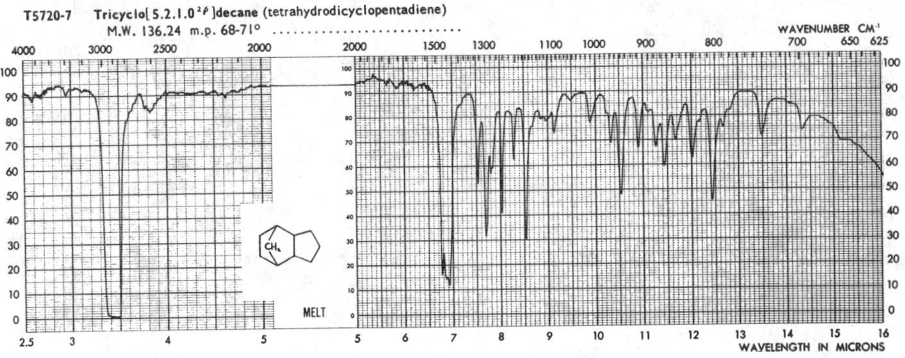

MELT

C

10,027-7 **Adamantane, puriss.**
M.W. 136.24 m.p. 205-210° (sublimes); 268° (sealed tube)

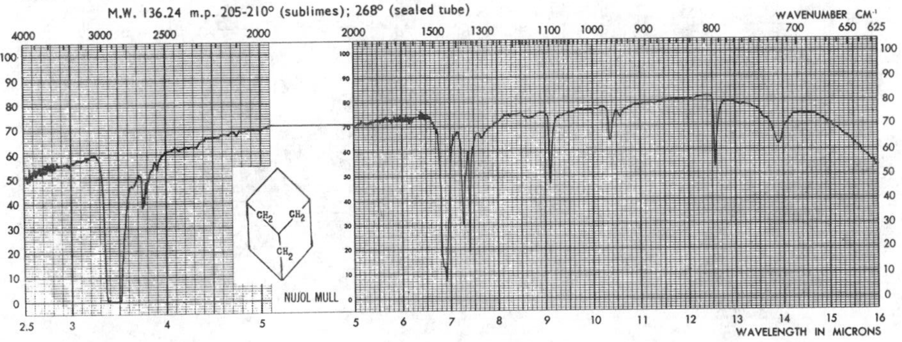

NUJOL MULL

D

18,783-6
1,3-Dimethyladamantane, 99+%
FW 164.29 n_D^{20} 1.4784 d 0.886 *NMR* 1,37D
Disp. C

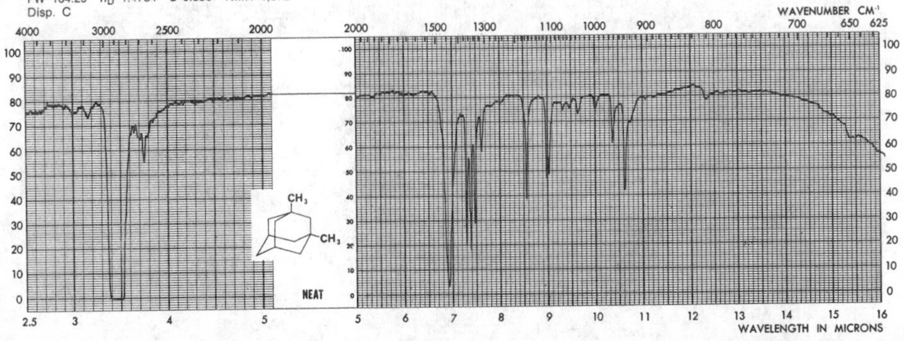

NEAT

E

C11,258-5 **Cyclopentene, puriss.**
C_5H_8 M.W. 68.12 n_D^{20} 1.4220

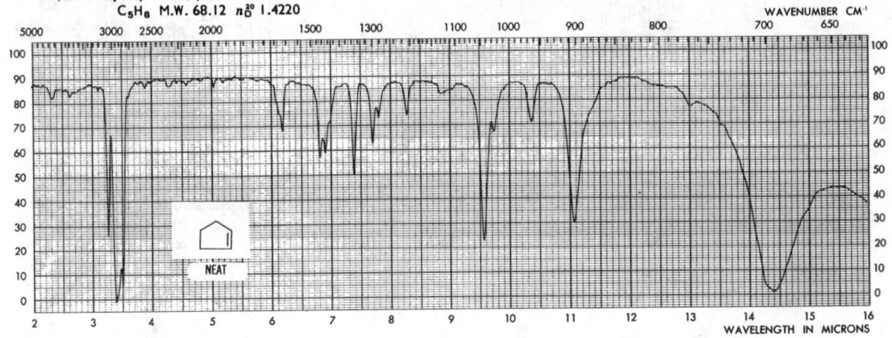

NEAT

F

12,543-1 **Cyclohexene**
C_6H_{10} M.W. 82.15 n_D^{20} 1.4450

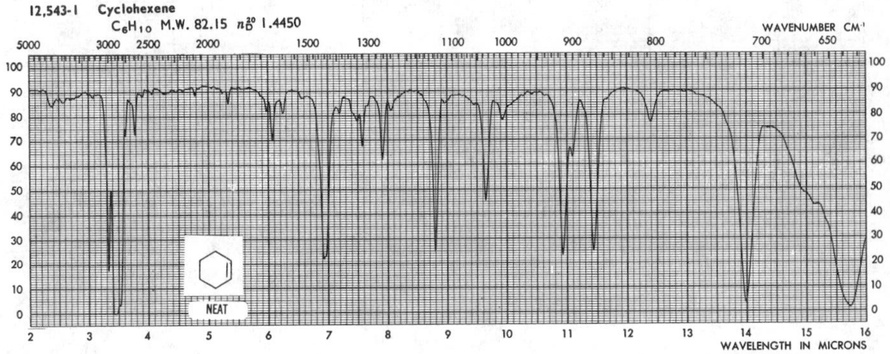

NEAT

G

14,172-0 **Cycloheptene, puriss.**
C_7H_{12} M.W. 96.17 n_D^{20} 1.4585 b.p. 112°

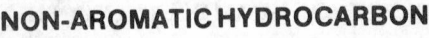

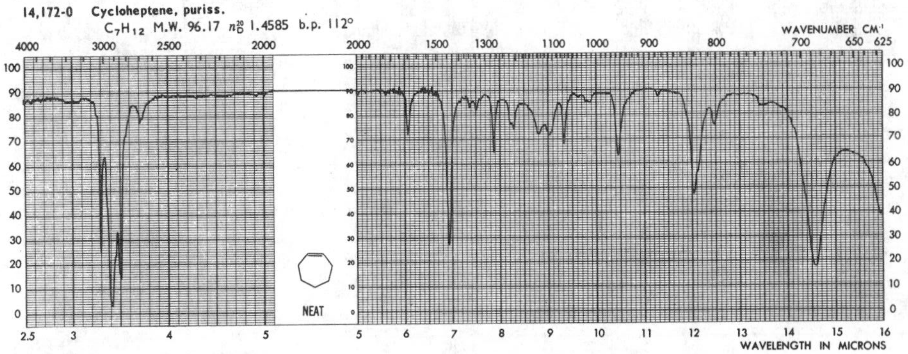

NEAT

H

12,548-2 **Cyclooctene**
C_8H_{14} M.W. 110.20 n_D^{20} 1.4698

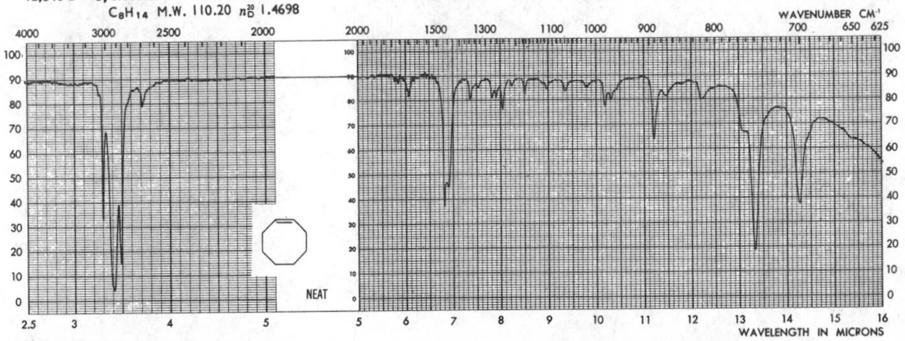

NEAT

A

C9760-1 Cyclododecene, tech.
$C_{12}H_{22}$ M.W. 166.31 n_D^{20} 1.4822

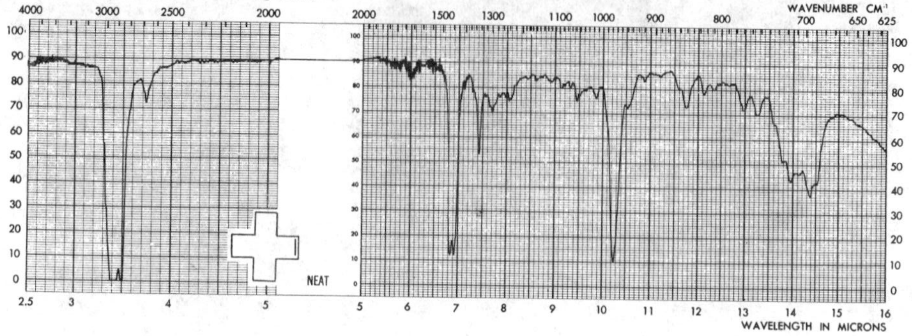

NEAT

B

M3980-6 1-Methyl-1-cyclopentene
$C_5H_7CH_3$ M.W. 82.15 n_D^{20} 1.4334 b.p. 72°/754 mm.

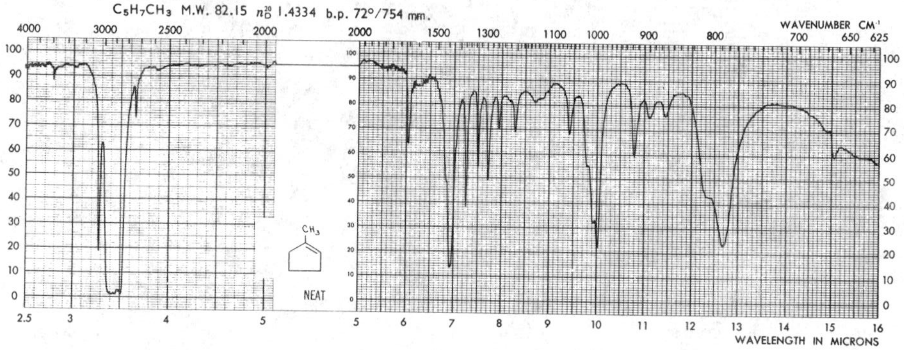

NEAT

C

11,076-0 1-Ethyl-1-cyclopentene
$C_5H_7C_2H_5$ M.W. 96.17 n_D^{20} 1.4392

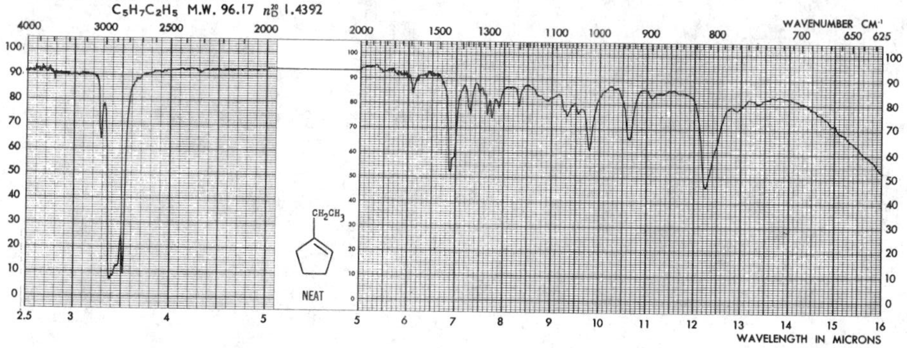

NEAT

D

E2110-8 3-Ethylcyclopentene, puriss.
$C_5H_7C_2H_5$ M.W. 96.17 n_D^{20} 1.4318

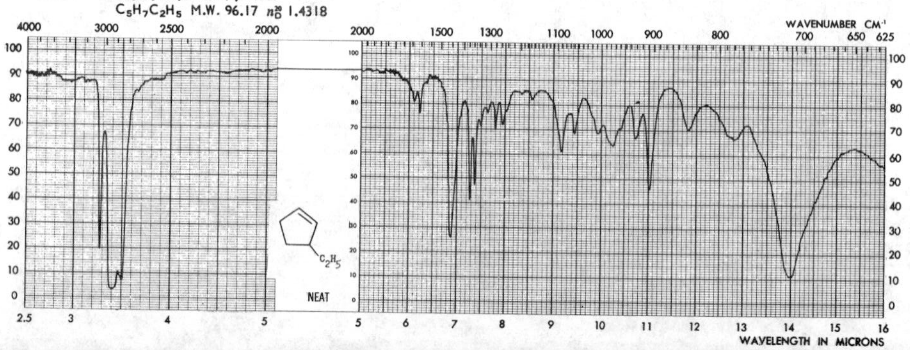

NEAT

E

21,402-7
1,2,3,4,5-Pentamethylcyclopentadiene
FW 136.24 bp 58°/13mm. n_D^{20} 1.4733 d 0.870
Disp. C

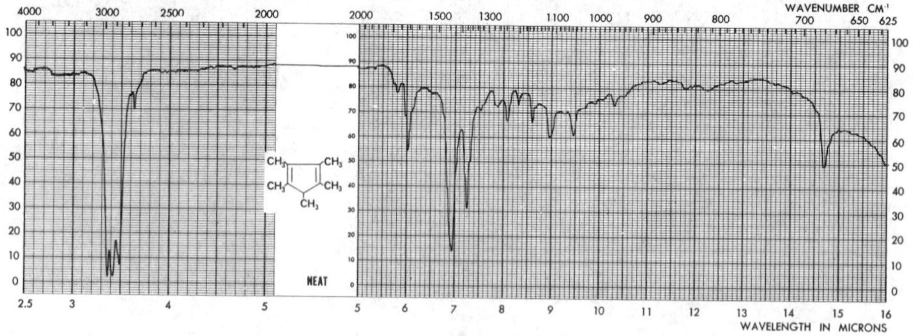

NEAT

F

12,980-1 1-Methyl-1-cyclohexene
$C_6H_9CH_3$ M.W. 96.17 n_D^{20} 1.4502 b.p. 110.5-111°

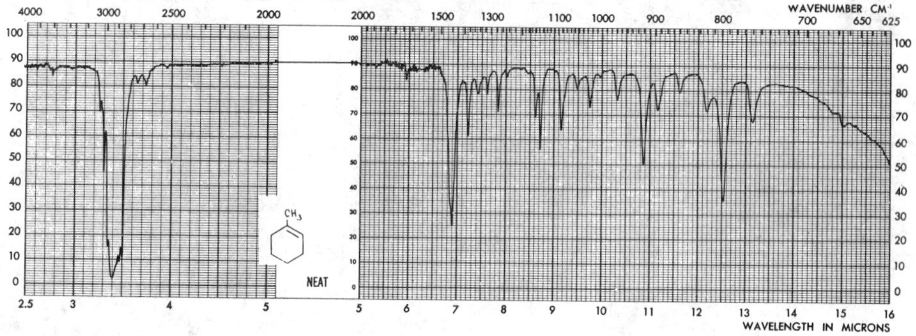

NEAT

G

M3890-7 3-Methyl-1-cyclohexene
$C_6H_9CH_3$ M.W. 96.17 n_D^{20} 1.4423

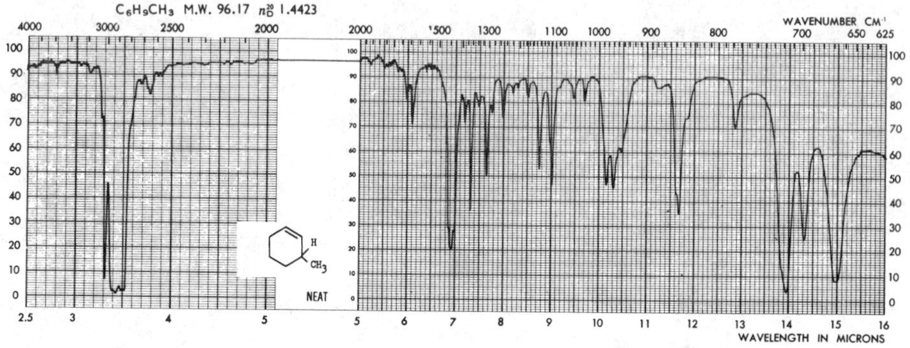

NEAT

H

M3900-8 4-Methyl-1-cyclohexene
$C_6H_9CH_3$ M.W. 96.17 n_D^{20} 1.3996
b.p. 101-102°

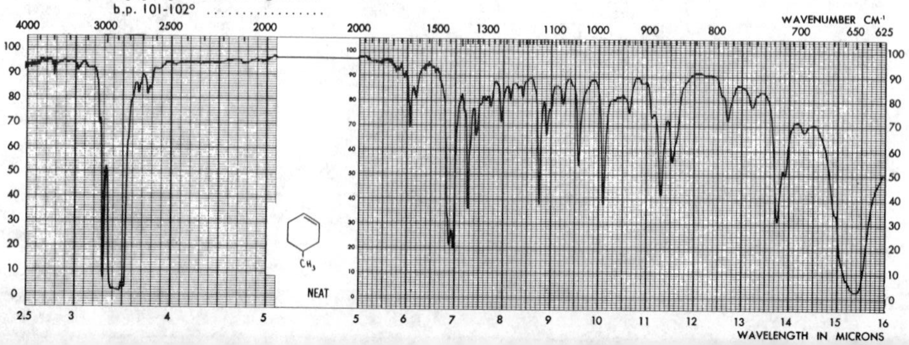

NEAT

WAVENUMBER CM^{-1} — WAVELENGTH IN MICRONS

A

18,786-0
3,5,5-Trimethylcyclohexene, 98%
$C_6H_7(CH_3)_3$ FW 124.23 bp 135°/690mm.
d 1.440 Disp. C

NEAT

B

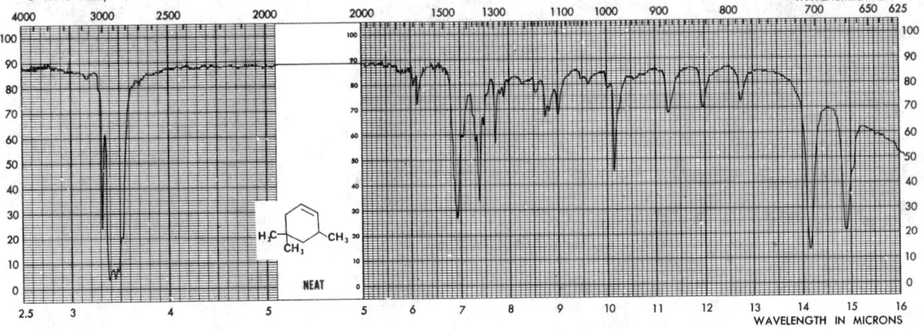

18,773-9
(+)-*p*-Menth-1-ene, tech., 90% (carvomenthene, 4-isopropyl-1-methylcyclohexene)
FW 138.25 bp 175-177° n_D^{20} 1.4570 d 0.825
$[\alpha]^{22}$ +82.6° (c=10.2, CH_3OH) Disp. C

NEAT

C

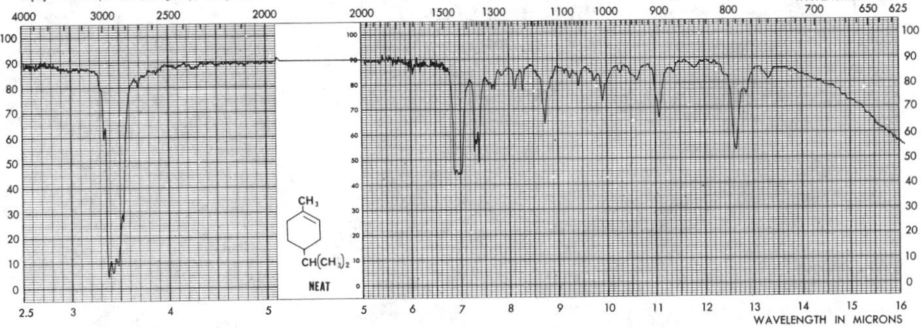

18,316-4
(+)-Limonene, 97%
M.W. 136.24 b.p. 175.5-176° n_D^{20} 1.4715 d 0.84
$[\alpha]^{24}$ +106° (c=1, CH_3OH) Beil. **5**,133

NEAT

D

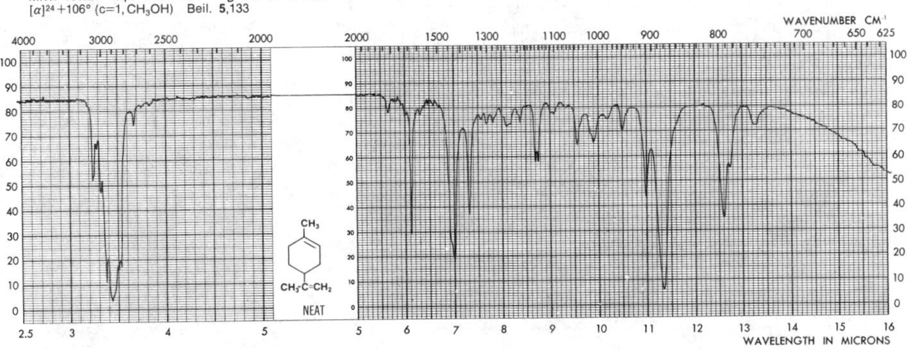

21,836-7
(-)-Limonene, 92%
$[\alpha]^{19}$ -100° (c=10, C_2H_5OH) FW 136.24
bp 175-177° n_D^{20} 1.4706 d 0.844 *Beil.* **5**,136
Disp. C

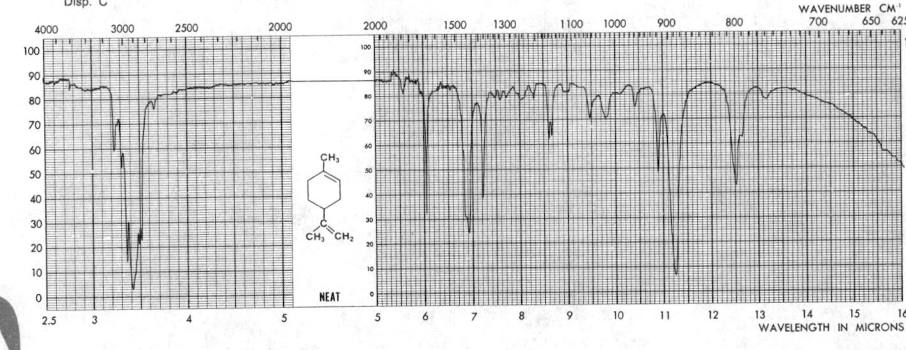

NEAT

E

M3780-3 **1-Methyl-1-cycloheptene**
$C_7H_{11}CH_3$ M.W. 110.20 n_D^{20} 1.4555 b.p. 137-138°

NEAT

F

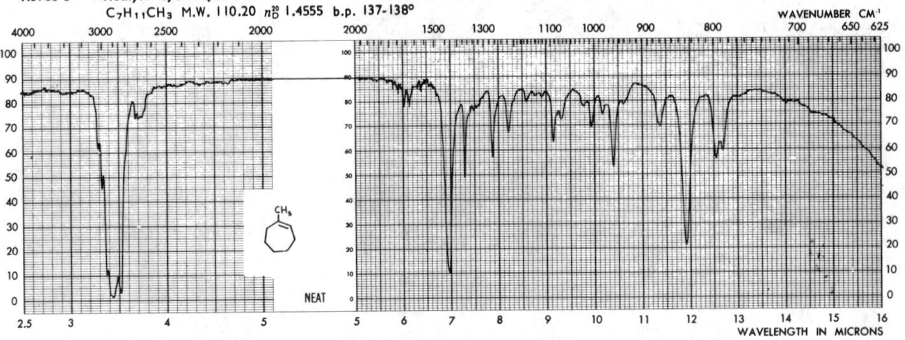

11,055-8 **4,4-Dimethyl-1-cyclohexene, puriss.**
$C_6H_8(CH_3)_2$ M.W. 110.20 n_D^{20} 1.4419

NEAT

G

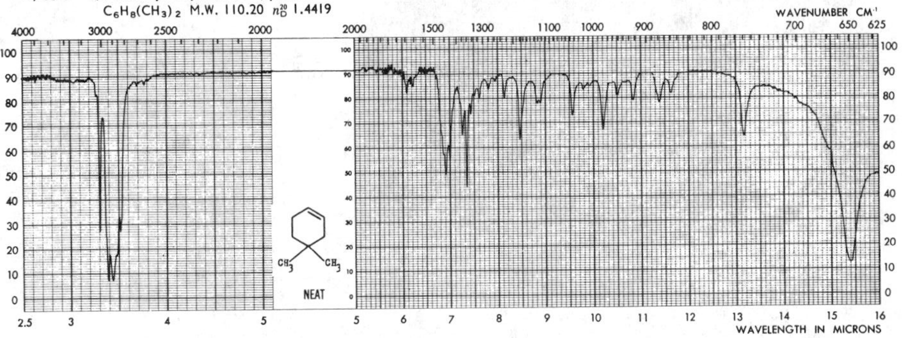

M4500-8 **Methylenecyclobutane, tech.**
$C_4H_6(:CH_2)$ M.W. 68.12 n_D^{20} 1.4156

NEAT

H

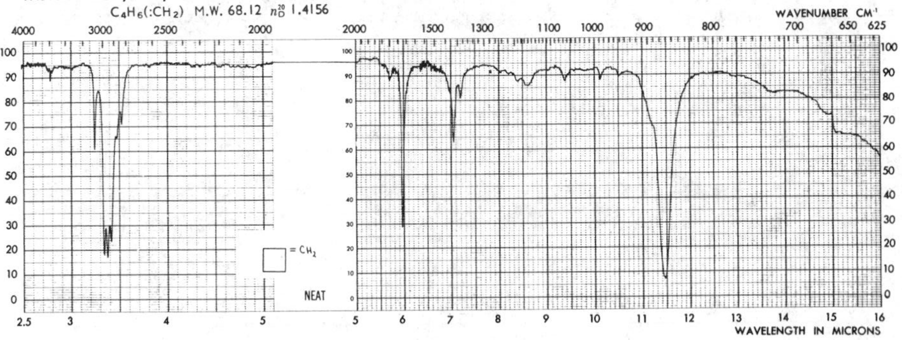

11,078-7 **Ethylidenecyclopentane**
$C_5H_8(:CHCH_3)$ M.W. 96.17 n_D^{20} 1.4483

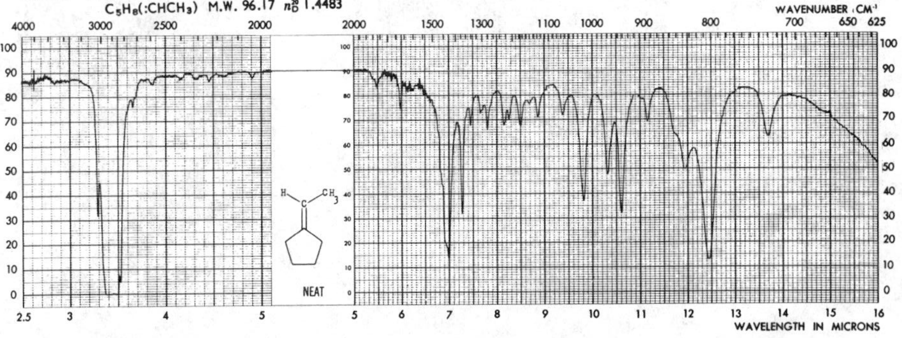

NEAT

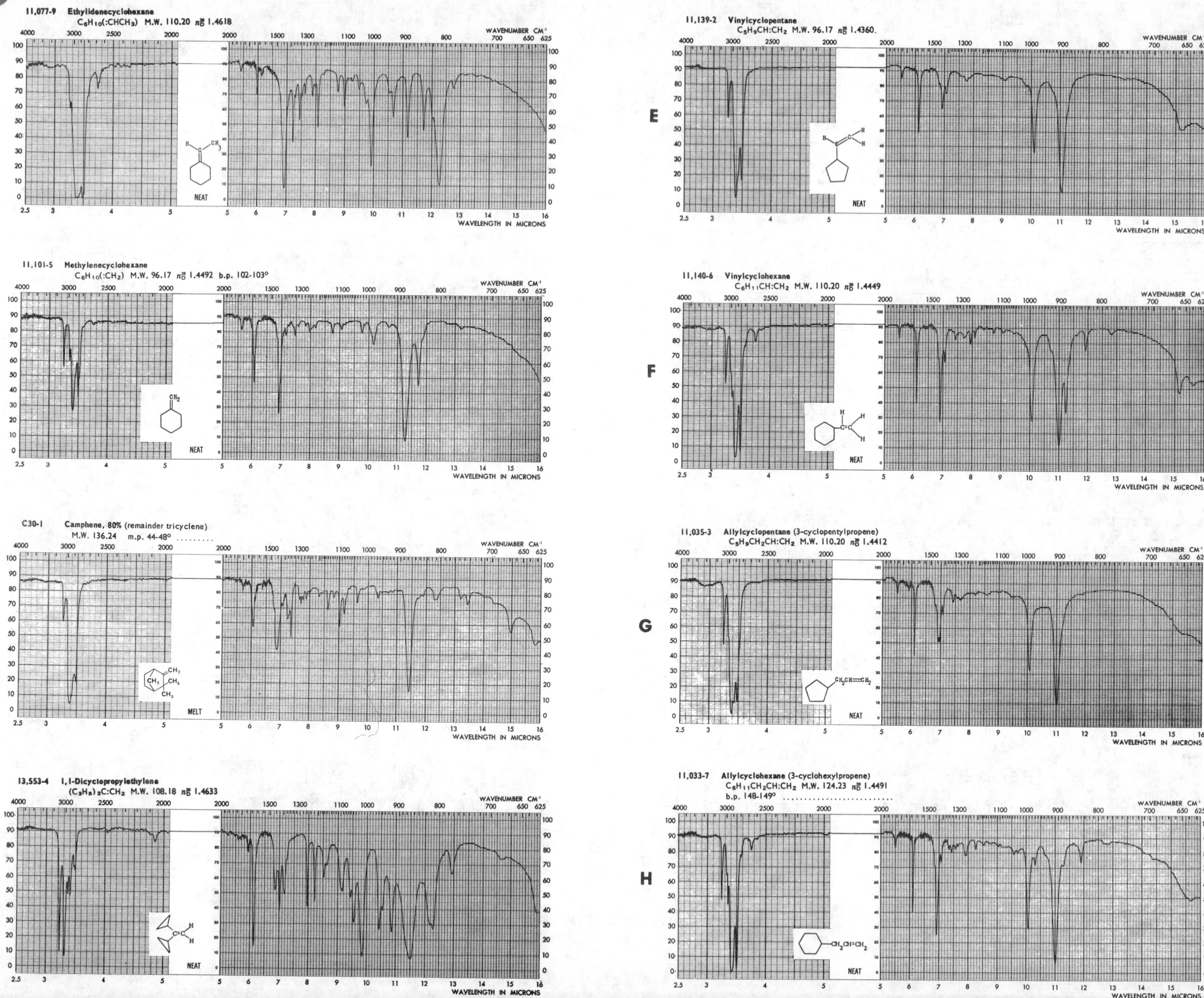
ALDRICH
A
11,077-9 Ethylidenecyclohexane
$C_6H_{10}(:CHCH_3)$ M.W. 110.20 n_D^{20} 1.4618
NEAT
B
11,101-5 Methylenecyclohexane
$C_6H_{10}(:CH_2)$ M.W. 96.17 n_D^{20} 1.4492 b.p. 102-103°
NEAT
C
C30-1 Camphene, 80% (remainder tricyclene)
M.W. 136.24 m.p. 44-48°
MELT
D
13,553-4 1,1-Dicyclopropylethylene
$(C_3H_5)_2C:CH_2$ M.W. 108.18 n_D^{20} 1.4633
NEAT
E
11,139-2 Vinylcyclopentane
$C_5H_9CH:CH_2$ M.W. 96.17 n_D^{20} 1.4360
NEAT
F
11,140-6 Vinylcyclohexane
$C_6H_{11}CH:CH_2$ M.W. 110.20 n_D^{20} 1.4449
NEAT
G
11,035-3 Allylcyclopentane (3-cyclopentylpropene)
$C_5H_9CH_2CH:CH_2$ M.W. 110.20 n_D^{20} 1.4412
NEAT
H
11,033-7 Allylcyclohexane (3-cyclohexylpropene)
$C_6H_{11}CH_2CH:CH_2$ M.W. 124.23 n_D^{20} 1.4491
b.p. 148-149°
NEAT
WAVENUMBER CM⁻¹
WAVELENGTH IN MICRONS

A

T8910-9 1,2,4-Trivinylcyclohexane
$C_6H_9(CH:CH_2)_3$ M.W. 162.28 n_D^{20} 1.4805 b.p. 85-88°/20 mm.

NEAT

B

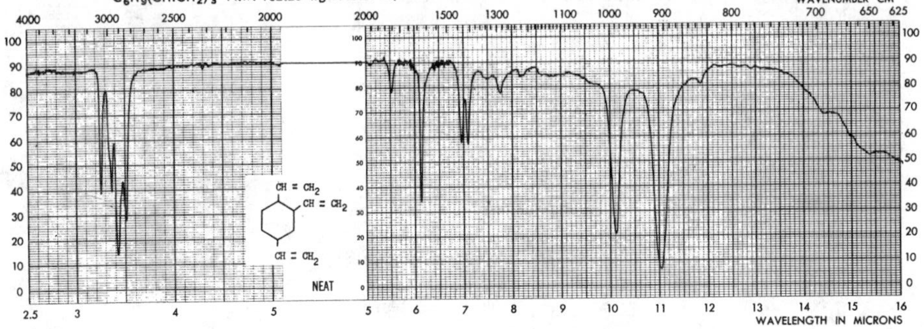

C10,000-5 1,3-Cyclohexadiene
M.W. 80.13 n_D^{20} 1.4741

NEAT

C

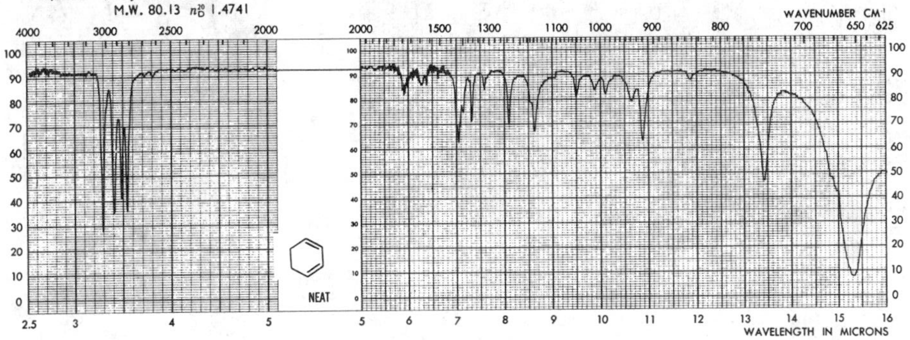

12,541-5 1,4-Cyclohexadiene
M.W. 80.13 .....

NEAT

D

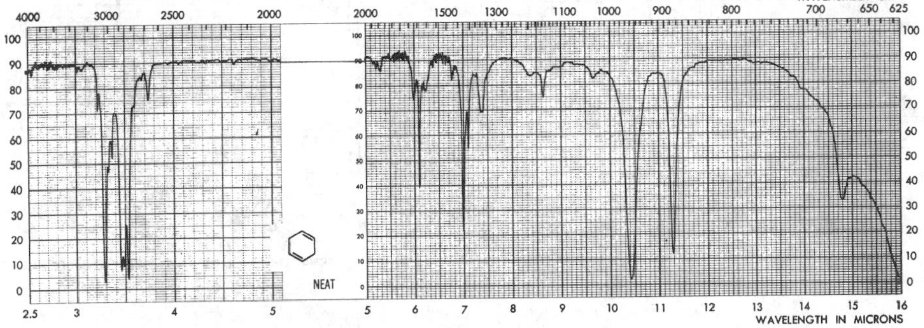

11,097-3 1-Methyl-1,4-cyclohexadiene
$C_6H_7CH_3$ M.W. 94.16 n_D^{20} 1.4702

NEAT

E

11,849-4 1-Ethyl-1,4-cyclohexadiene
M.W. 108.18 n_D^{20} 1.4729 ...

NEAT

F

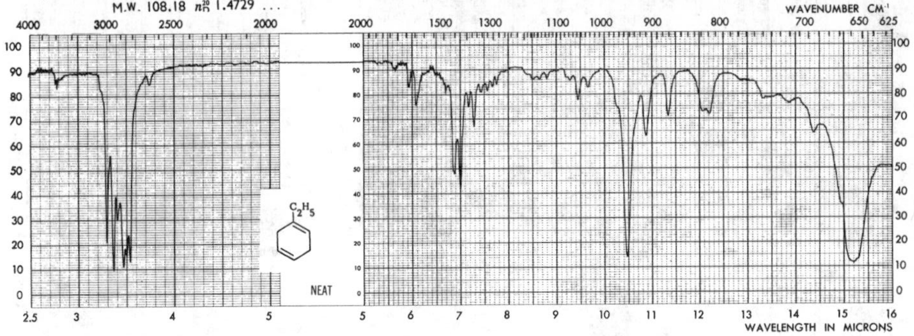

22,318-2
α-**Terpinene,** 98% (1-isopropyl-4-methyl-1,3-cyclohexadiene)
FW 136.24 bp 173-175° n_D^{20} 1.4775 d 0.837
Beil. 5,126 Disp. C

NEAT

G

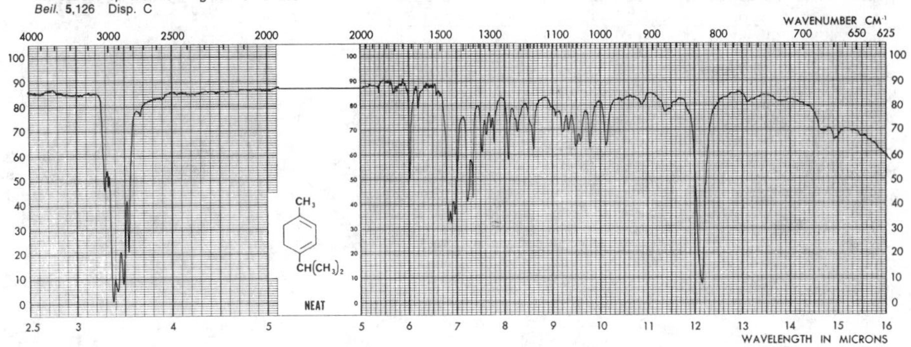

22,319-0
γ-**Terpinene,** 98% (1-isopropyl-4-methyl-1,4-cyclohexadiene)
FW 136.24 bp 182° n_D^{20} 1.4740 d 0.849
Beil. 5,128 Disp. C

NEAT

H

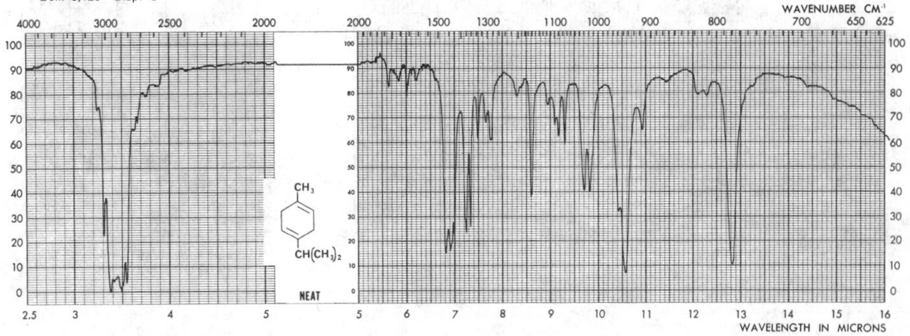

V220-8 4-Vinyl-1-cyclohexene
$C_6H_9CH:CH_2$ M.W. 108.18 n_D^{20} 1.4631
b.p. 126-127° ....

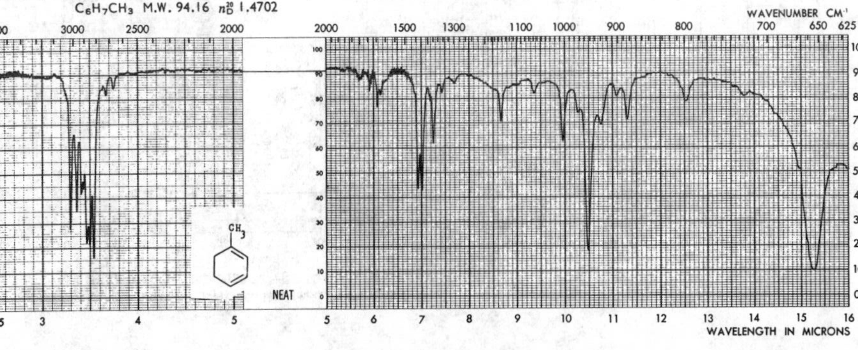

NEAT

ALDRICH®

NON-AROMATIC HYDROCARBONS

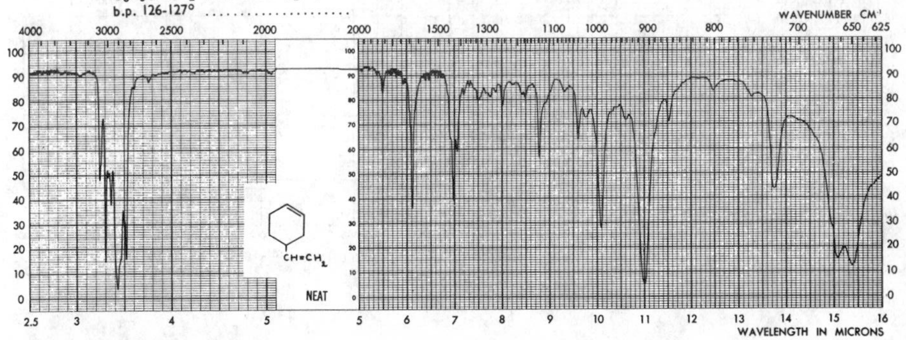

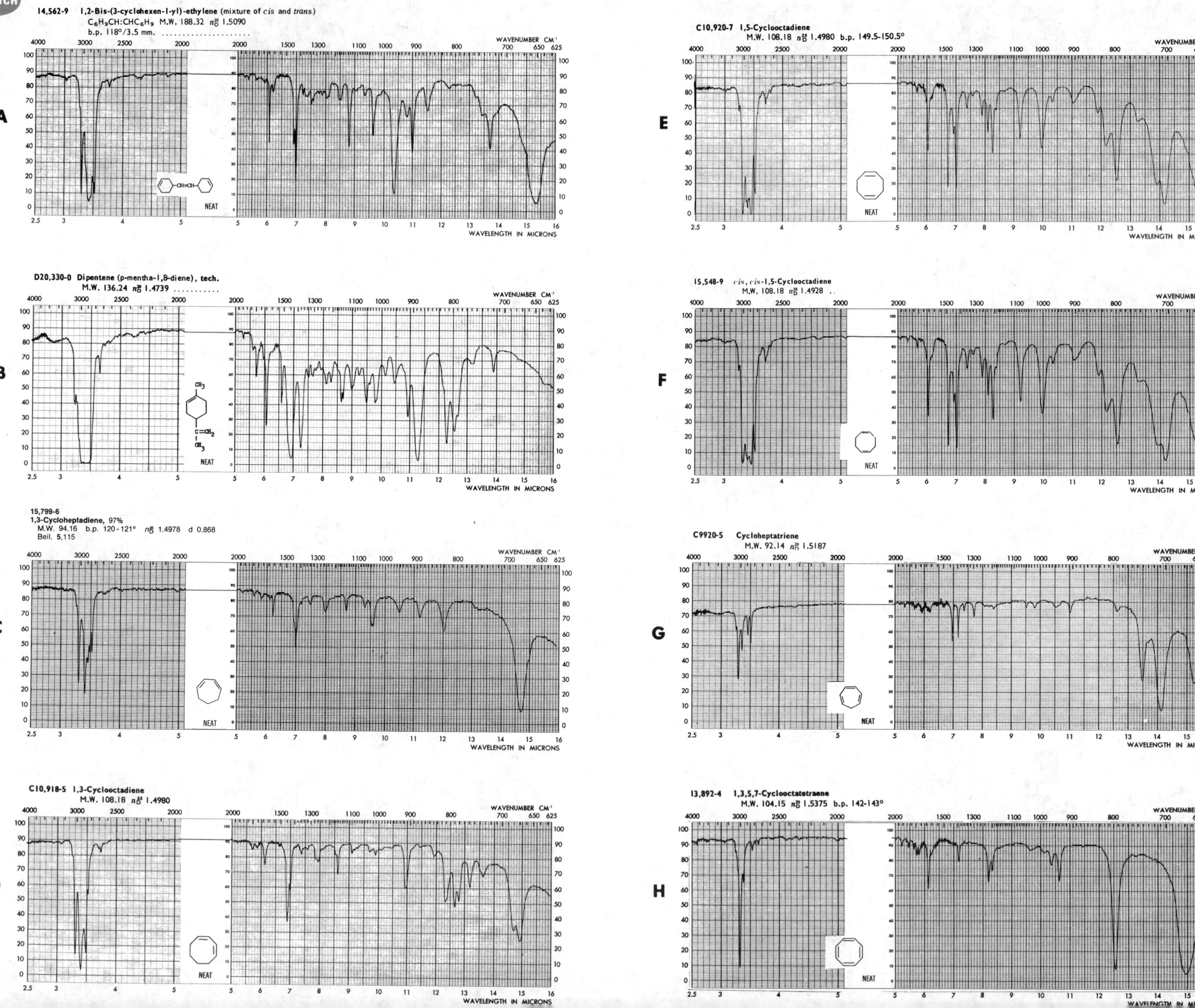
A
14,562-9 1,2-Bis-(3-cyclohexen-1-yl)-ethylene (mixture of *cis* and *trans*)
$C_6H_9CH{:}CHC_6H_9$ M.W. 188.32 n_D^{20} 1.5090
b.p. 118°/3.5 mm.
NEAT
B
D20,330-0 Dipentene (p-mentha-1,8-diene), tech.
M.W. 136.24 n_D^{20} 1.4739
NEAT
C
15,799-6
1,3-Cycloheptadiene, 97%
M.W. 94.16 b.p. 120-121° n_D^{20} 1.4978 d 0.868
Beil. 5,115
NEAT
D
C10,918-5 1,3-Cyclooctadiene
M.W. 108.18 n_D^{20} 1.4980
NEAT
E
C10,920-7 1,5-Cyclooctadiene
M.W. 108.18 n_D^{20} 1.4980 b.p. 149.5-150.5°
NEAT
F
15,548-9 *cis, cis*-1,5-Cyclooctadiene
M.W. 108.18 n_D^{20} 1.4928
NEAT
G
C9920-5 Cycloheptatriene
M.W. 92.14 n_D^{20} 1.5187
NEAT
H
13,892-4 1,3,5,7-Cyclooctatetraene
M.W. 104.15 n_D^{20} 1.5375 b.p. 142-143°
NEAT
WAVENUMBER CM⁻¹
WAVELENGTH IN MICRONS

A

C9750-4 **1,5,9-Cyclododecatriene** (mixture of isomers)
M.W. 162.28 n_D^{20} 1.5070 ....

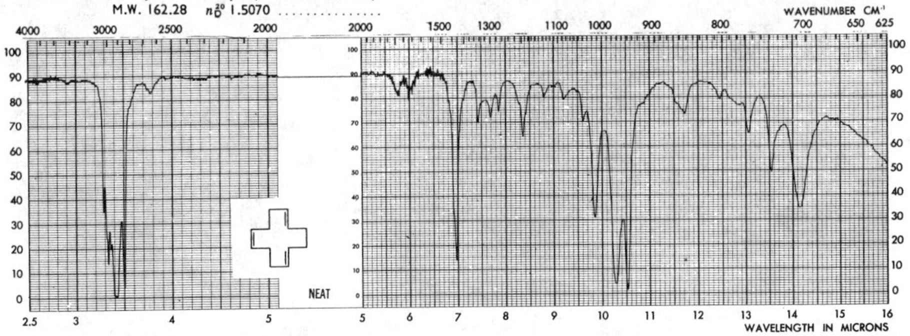

NEAT

B

C9748-2 *trans, trans, cis*-**1,5,9-Cyclododecatriene**
M.W. 162.28 n_D^{20} 1.5064 ....

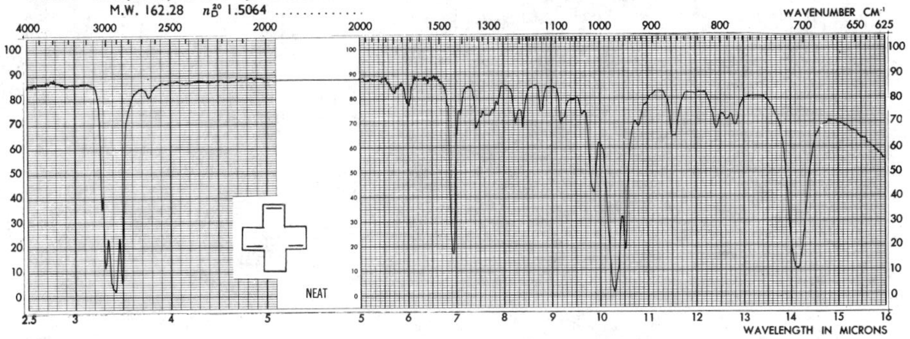

NEAT

C

14,758-3 **1,5,9-Trimethyl-1,5,9-cyclododecatriene** (mixture of isomers)
M.W. 204.36 n_D^{20} 1.5116 ....

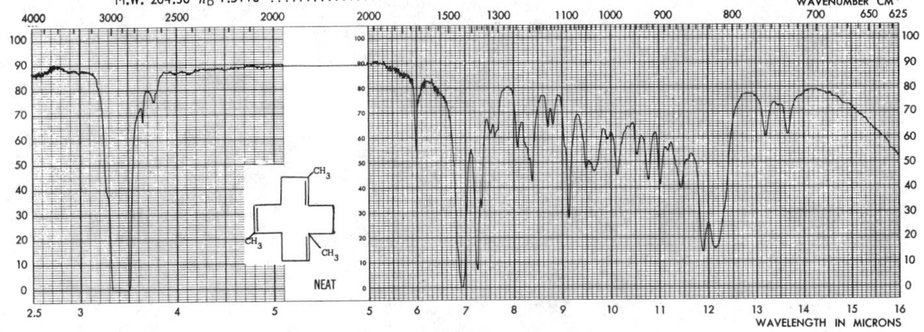

NEAT

D

N3240-7 **Norbornylene** (bicyclo[2.2.1]-2-heptene)
M.W. 94.16 m.p. 44-46° ....

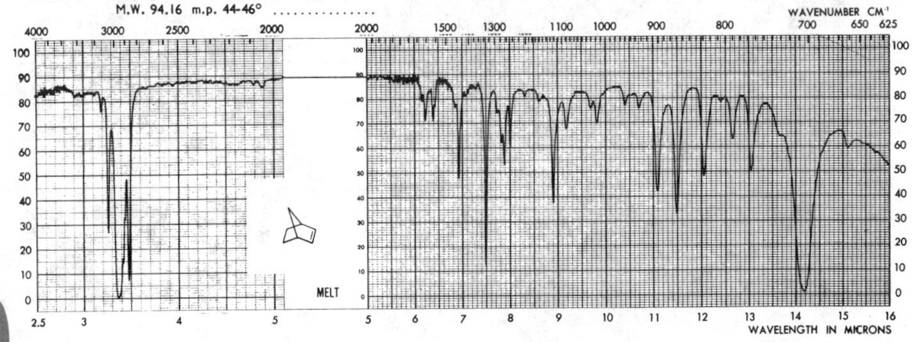

MELT

E

P4570-2 (-)-*α*-**Pinene**
M.W. 136.24 n_D^{20} 1.4645 $[\alpha]_D^{20}$ - 48.2° (neat)

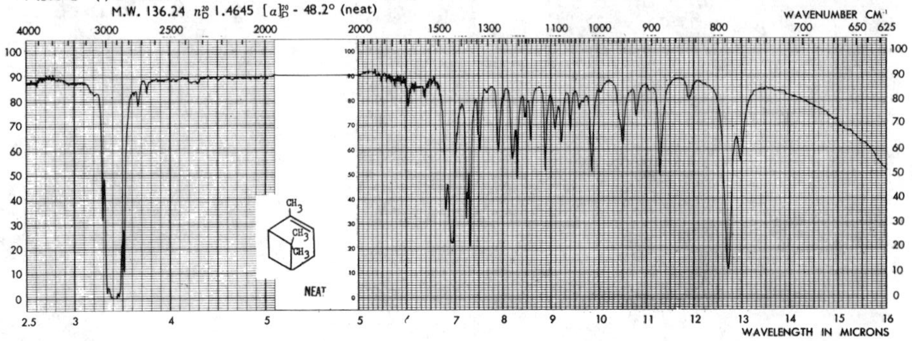

NEAT

F

P4568-0 (+)-*α*-**Pinene**
M.W. 136.24 n_D^{20} 1.4645 $[\alpha]_D^{20}$ + 35.3° (neat)

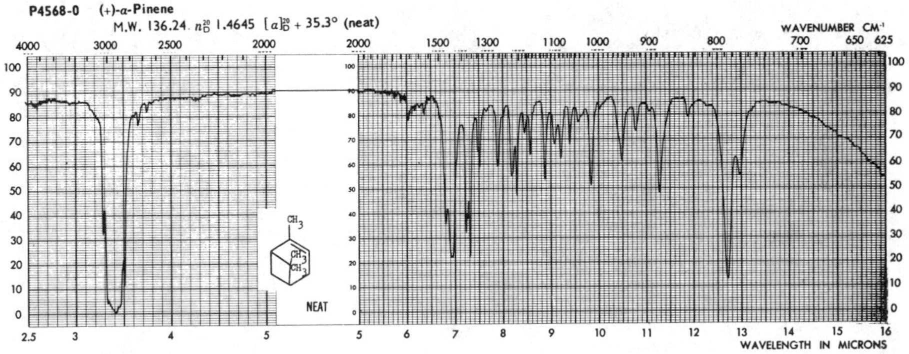

NEAT

G

14,752-4 *dl*-*α*-**Pinene**
M.W. 136.24 n_D^{20} 1.4652
b.p. 152° ....

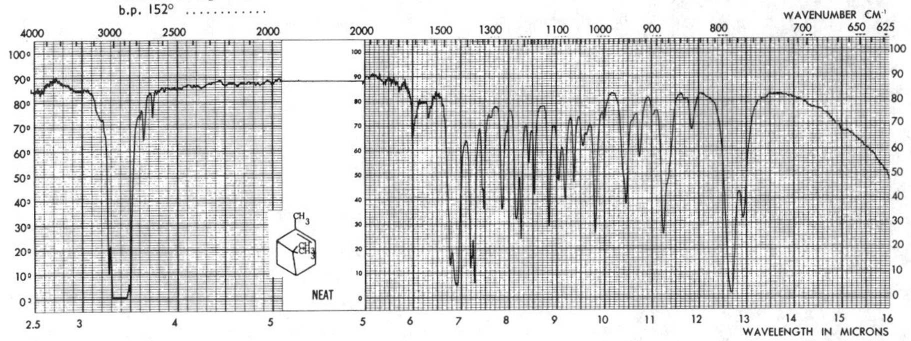

NEAT

H

11,208-9 (-)-*β*-**Pinene**
M.W. 136.24 n_D^{20} 1.4762 b.p. 165-167°

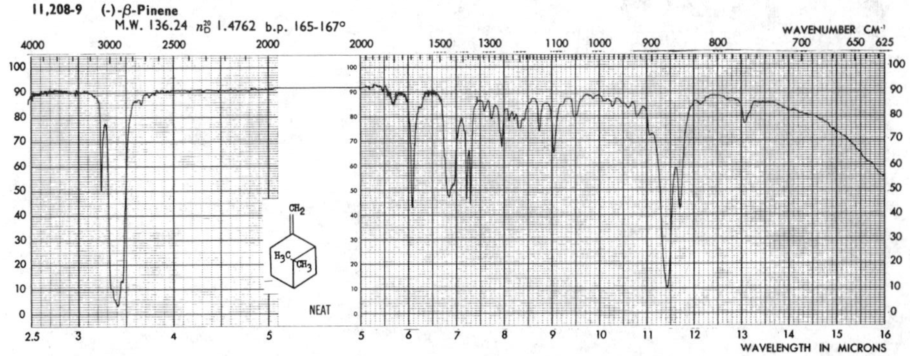

NEAT

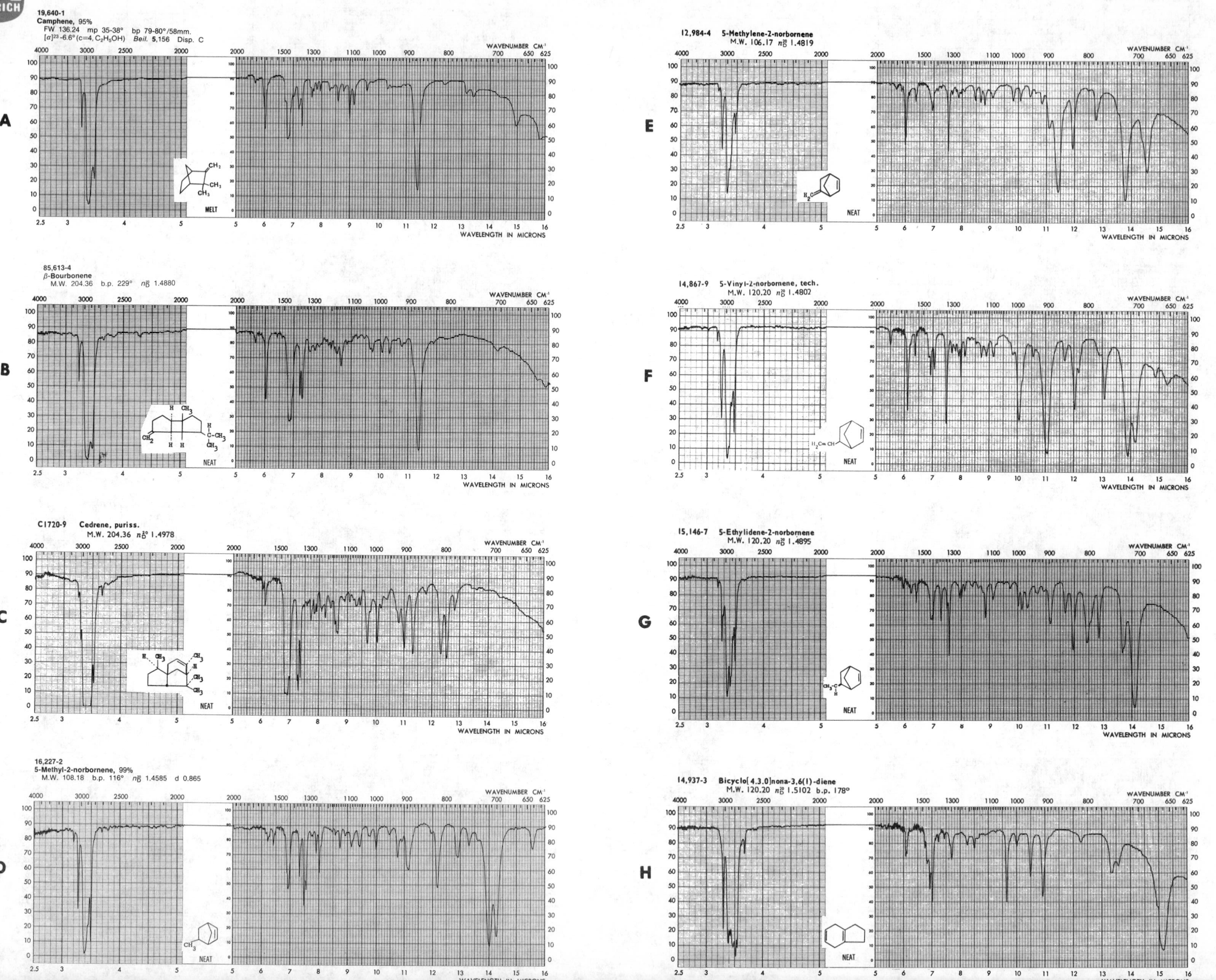
ALDRICH
A
19,640-1
Camphene, 95%
FW 136.24 mp 35-38° bp 79-80°/58mm.
[α]23 -6.6° (c=4, C2H5OH) Beil. 5,156 Disp. C
MELT
B
85,613-4
β-Bourbonene
M.W. 204.36 b.p. 229° nD 1.4880
NEAT
C
C1720-9 Cedrene, puriss.
M.W. 204.36 nD20 1.4978
NEAT
D
16,227-2
5-Methyl-2-norbornene, 99%
M.W. 108.18 b.p. 116° nD 1.4585 d 0.865
NEAT
E
12,984-4 5-Methylene-2-norbornene
M.W. 106.17 nD 1.4819
NEAT
F
14,867-9 5-Vinyl-2-norbornene, tech.
M.W. 120.20 nD 1.4802
NEAT
G
15,146-7 5-Ethylidene-2-norbornene
M.W. 120.20 nD 1.4895
NEAT
H
14,937-3 Bicyclo[4.3.0]nona-3,6(1)-diene
M.W. 120.20 nD 1.5102 b.p. 178°
NEAT
WAVENUMBER CM-1
WAVELENGTH IN MICRONS

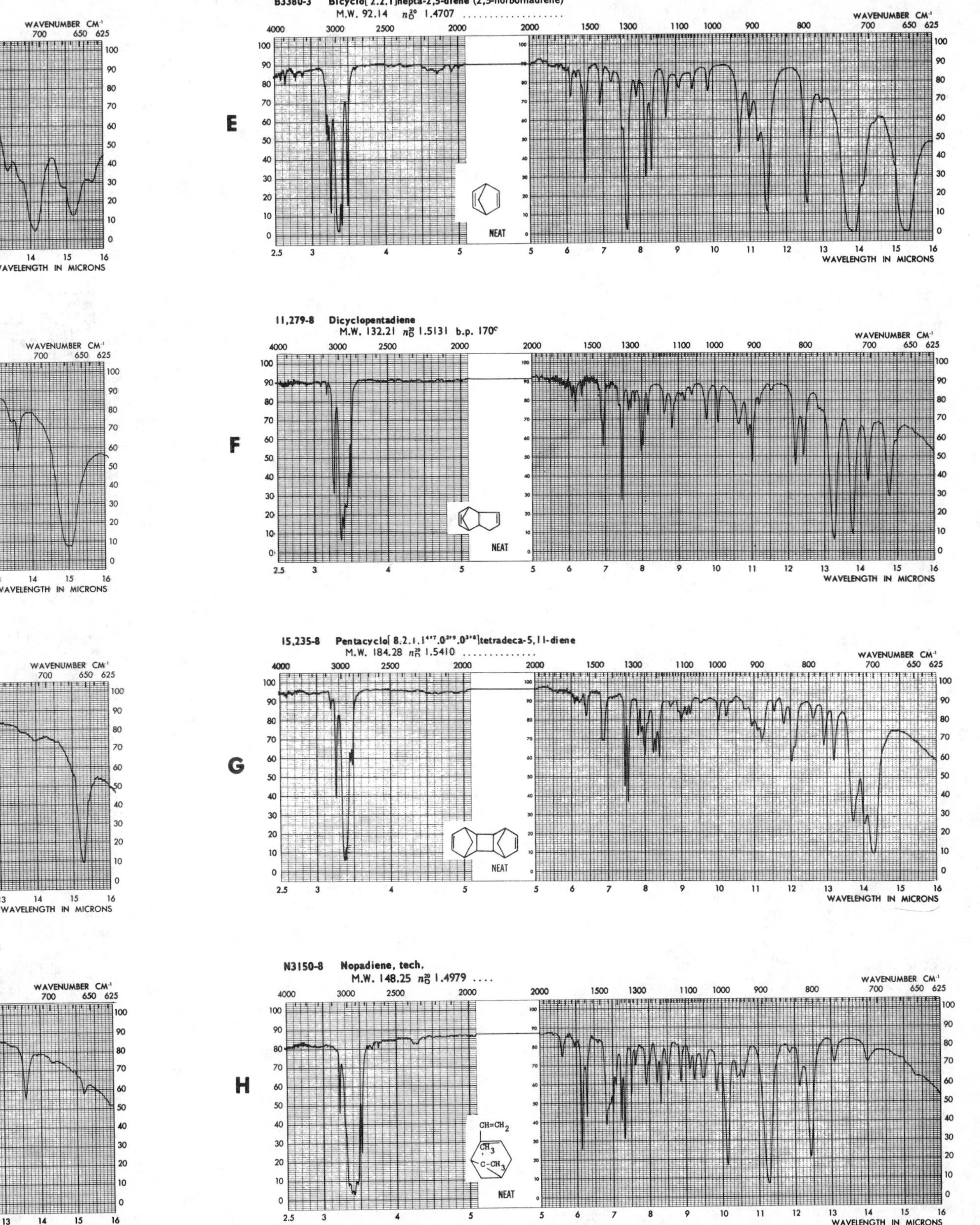

A 14,868-7 Bicyclo[4.3.0]nona-3,7-diene (3a,4,7,7a-tetrahydroindene)
M.W. 120.20 n_D^{20} 1.4966 . . . . NEAT

B 19,739-4 Isotetralin, 98+% (1,4,5,8-tetrahydronaphthalene)
FW 132.21 mp 54-57° Disp. C MELT

C 20,774-8 1,4,5,8,9,10-Hexahydroanthracene, 99%
FW 184.28 mp 147-150° Disp. C NUJOL MULL

D 13,669-7 Hexamethyldewarbenzene
M.W. 162.28 n_D^{20} .4478 MELT

E B3380-3 Bicyclo[2.2.1]hepta-2,5-diene (2,5-norbornadiene)
M.W. 92.14 n_D^{20} 1.4707 . . . . NEAT

F 11,279-8 Dicyclopentadiene
M.W. 132.21 n_D^{20} 1.5131 b.p. 170° NEAT

G 15,235-8 Pentacyclo[8.2.1.1^{4,7}.0^{2,9}.0^{3,8}]tetradeca-5,11-diene
M.W. 184.28 n_D^{20} 1.5410 . . . . NEAT

H N3150-8 Nopadiene, tech.
M.W. 148.25 n_D^{20} 1.4979 . . . . NEAT

A

G1120-9 Guaiene, tech.
M.W. 204.36

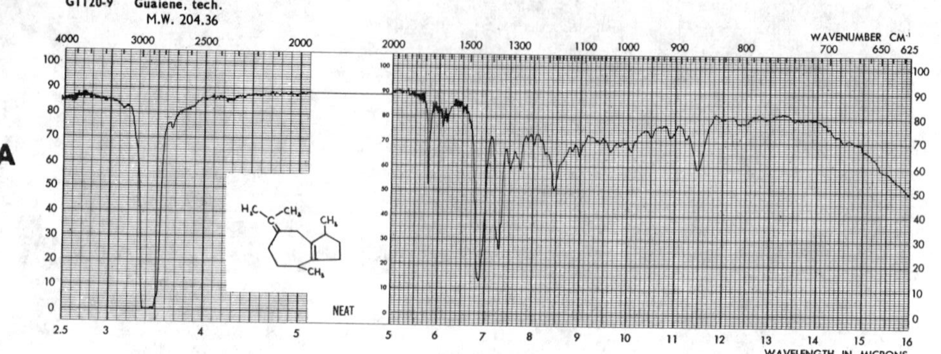

B

12,982-8 Methylcyclopentadiene dimer
M.W. 160.26 n_D^{20} 1.4976 .....

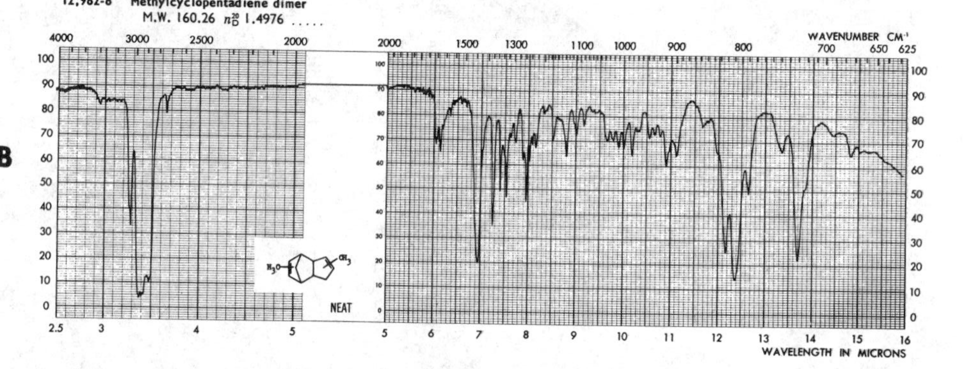

C

85,555-3
***trans*-β-Carotene**
M.W. 536.89 m.p. 178 - 179°

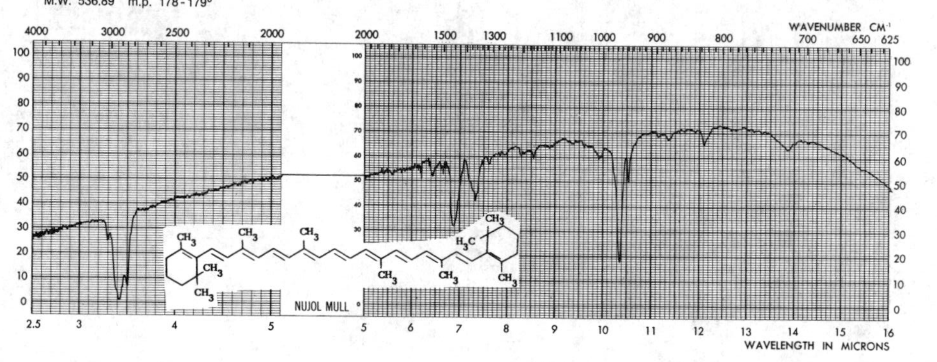

ALDRICH

NON-AROMATIC HALOGENATED HYDROCARBONS

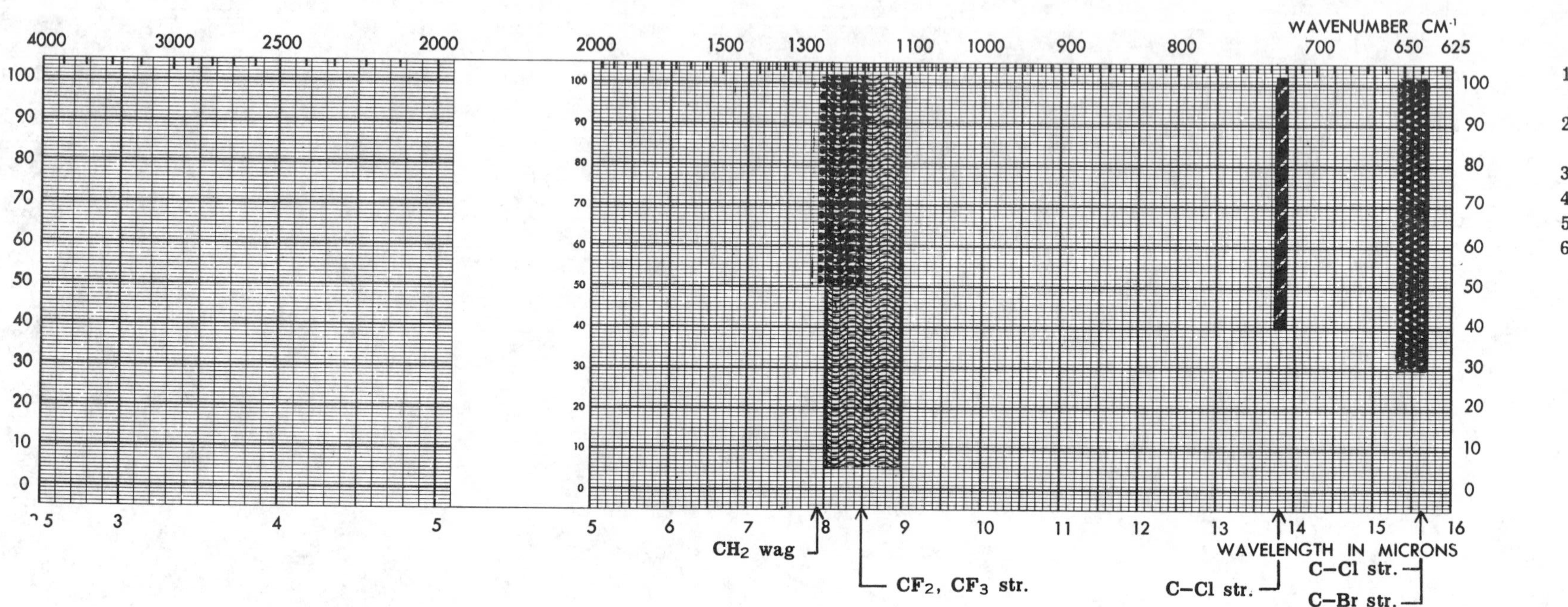

The outstanding absorptions attributable to the addition of Cl or Br in our order of increasing complexity appear near 8 μ (1250 cm^{-1}) (CH_2 deformation) and 15 μ (665 cm^{-1}) (carbon-halogen stretch). When looking at the shorter molecules in this series, note the profusion of absorptions throughout the region between 8 and 13 μ (1250 – 770 cm^{-1}). These absorptions gradually weaken as the chain length increases. When neither Cl or Br is terminal, the stretch absorptions, which appear practically without exception at 13.8 μ and 15.5 μ (725 and 645 cm^{-1}) for chlorine and at 15.5 μ (645 cm^{-1}) for bromine, shift beyond 16 μ (625 cm^{-1}). In the longer chain molecules the 13.8 μ (725 cm^{-1}) band overlaps the $(CH_2)_n$ absorption. As additional halogens are added, either in a vicinal position or on the same carbon atom, the stretch absorptions between 14 and 16 μ (715 – 625 cm^{-1}) reappear and the absorption at 8 μ (1250 cm^{-1}) becomes weaker and loses its broad appearance.

The carbon-iodine stretch band occurs beyond 16 μ (625 cm^{-1}) with the CH_2 wag band appearing between 8 and 8.5 μ (1250 – 1175 cm^{-1}). It is difficult to assign specific characteristic absorptions when several halogen atoms are introduced into any one molecule because of the broad range in which their halogen-carbon stretch bands appear. It is therefore important for the analyst actually to observe as many different combinations of the polyhalogenated compounds as possible when using this evidence in structural assignments.

The CF_2 and CF_3 groups absorb very strongly between 8 and 9 μ (1250 – 1110 cm^{-1}).

A I-850-7 **Iodomethane** (methyl iodide)
CH_3I M.W. 141.94 n_D^{20} 1.5304

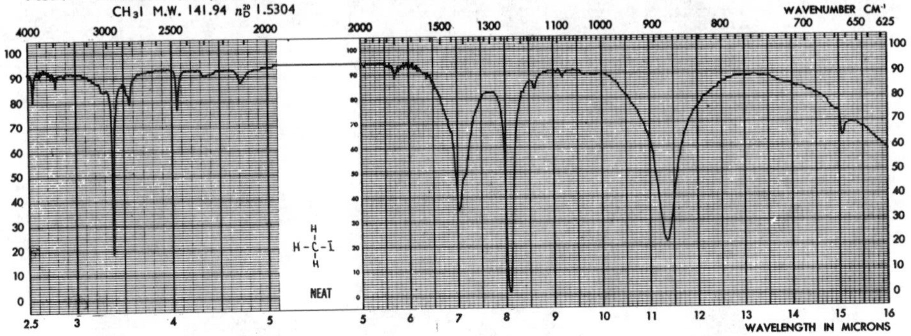

H–C(H)(H)–I
NEAT

B 12,405-2 **Bromoethane** (ethyl bromide)
C_2H_5Br M.W. 108.98 n_D^{20} 1.4236

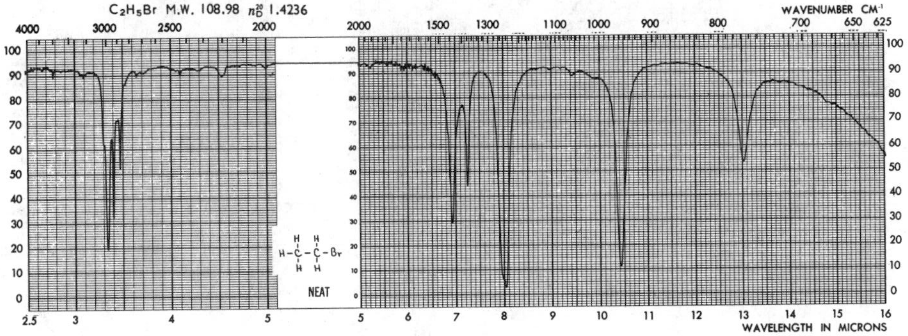

H–C(H)(H)–C(H)(H)–Br
NEAT

C I-778-0 **Iodoethane** (ethyl iodide)
C_2H_5I M.W. 155.97 n_D^{20} 1.5103 b.p. 72°

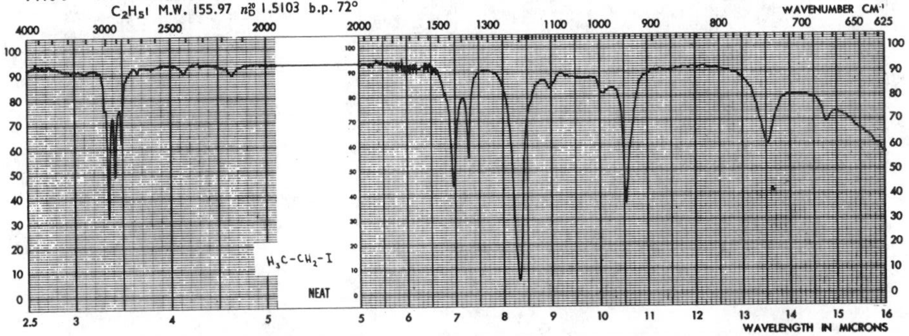

H_3C-CH_2-I
NEAT

D C6855-5 **1-Chloropropane** (n-propyl chloride)
$CH_3CH_2CH_2Cl$ M.W. 78.54 n_D^{20} 1.3859
b.p. 45-47°

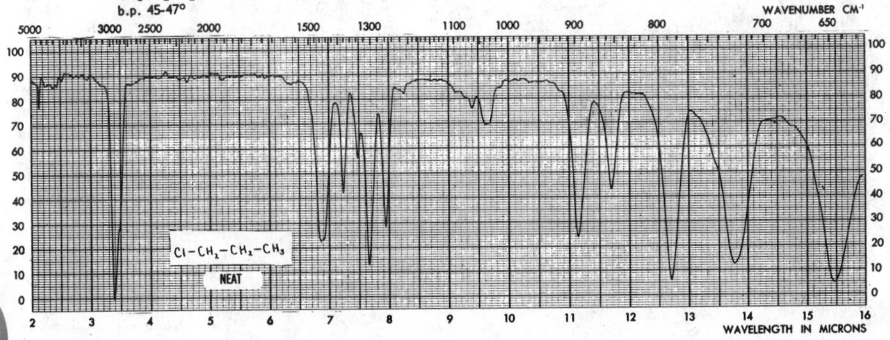

$Cl-CH_2-CH_2-CH_3$
NEAT

E B7810-6 **1-Bromopropane** (n-propyl bromide)
$CH_3CH_2CH_2Br$ M.W. 123.00 n_D^{20} 1.4336

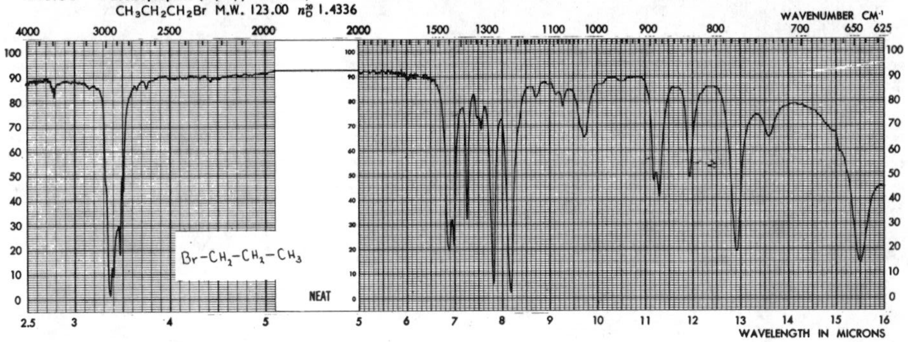

$Br-CH_2-CH_2-CH_3$
NEAT

F 17,188-3
1-Iodopropane, 99% (propyl iodide)
$CH_3CH_2CH_2I$
M.W. 169.99 b.p. 101-102° n_D^{20} 1.5040 d 1.743
Beil. 1,113

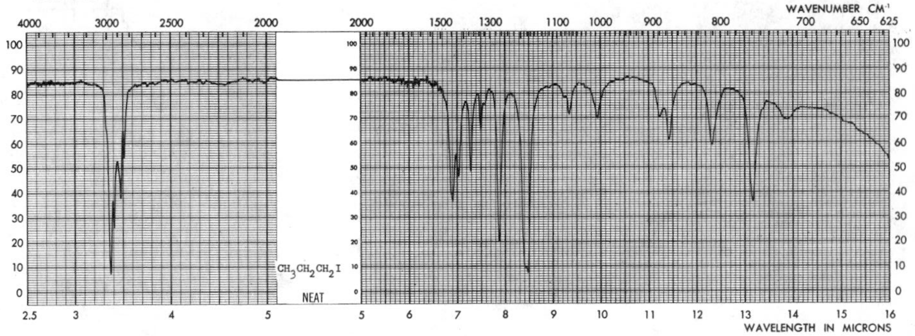

$CH_3CH_2CH_2I$
NEAT

G 12,500-8 **1-Chlorobutane** (n-butyl chloride)
$CH_3(CH_2)_3Cl$ M.W. 92.57 n_D^{20} 1.4018

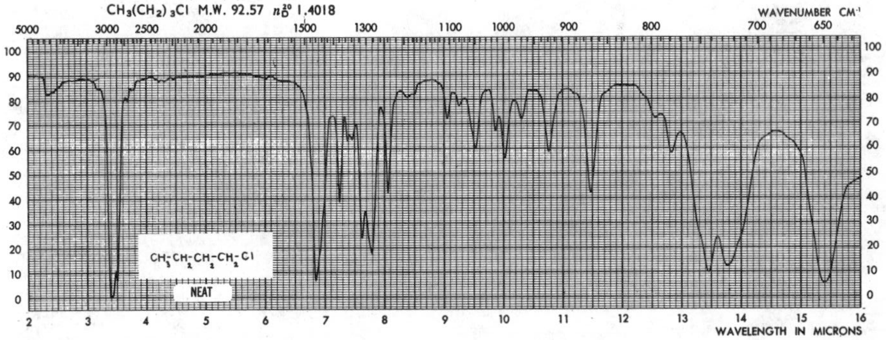

$CH_3-CH_2-CH_2-CH_2-Cl$
NEAT

H B5949-7 **1-Bromobutane** (n-butyl bromide), puriss.
$CH_3(CH_2)_3Br$ M.W. 137.03
n_D^{20} 1.4394

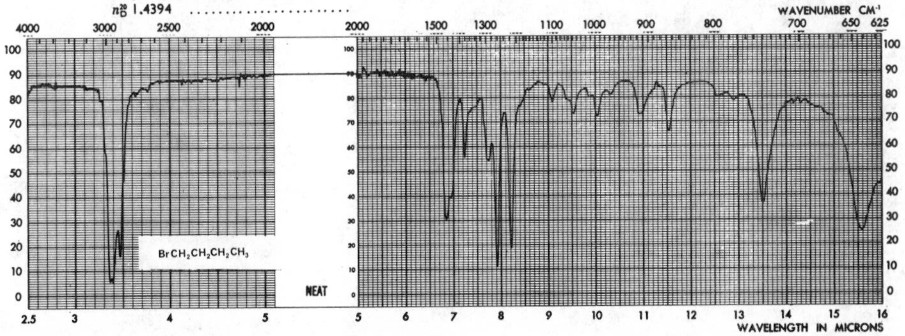

$BrCH_2CH_2CH_2CH_3$
NEAT

NON-AROMATIC HALOGENS

ALDRICH

NON-AROMATIC HALOGENS

A

16,730-4
1-Iodobutane, 99% (butyl iodide)
$CH_3(CH_2)_3I$
M.W. 184.02 b.p. 130-131° n_D^{20} 1.4979 d 1.617
Beil. 1,123

$CH_3CH_2CH_2CH_2I$
NEAT

B

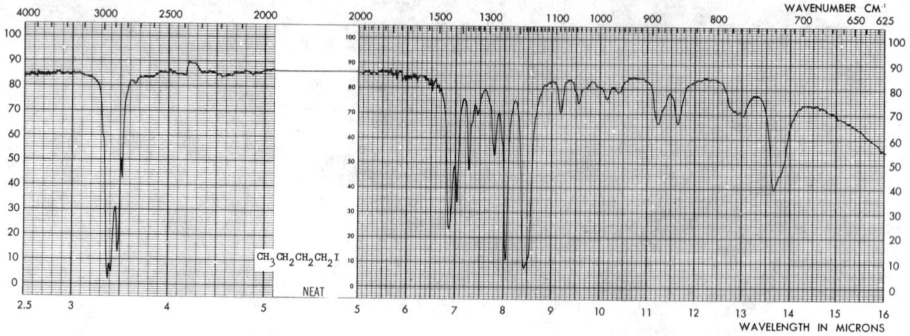

11,781-1 1-Bromopentane (n-amyl bromide)
$CH_3(CH_2)_4Br$ M.W. 151.05 n_D^{20} 1.4436
b.p. 130°

$CH_3CH_2CH_2CH_2CH_2Br$
NEAT

C

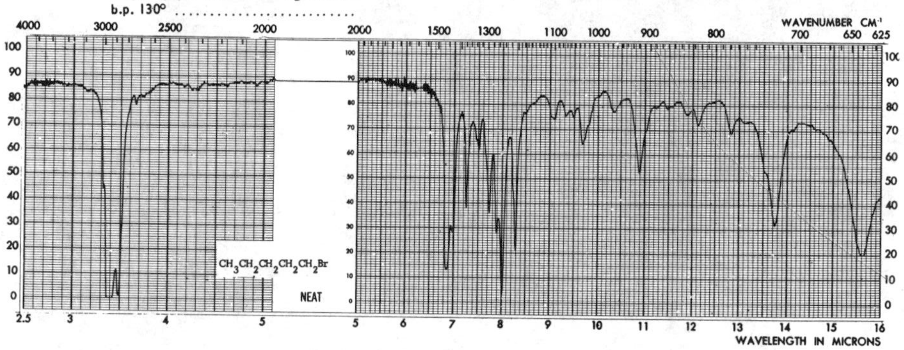

B6824-0 1-Bromohexane (n-hexyl bromide)
$CH_3(CH_2)_5Br$ M.W. 165.08 n_D^{20} 1.4475 b.p. 155°

$Br-CH_2-CH_2-CH_2-CH_2-CH_2-CH_3$
NEAT

D

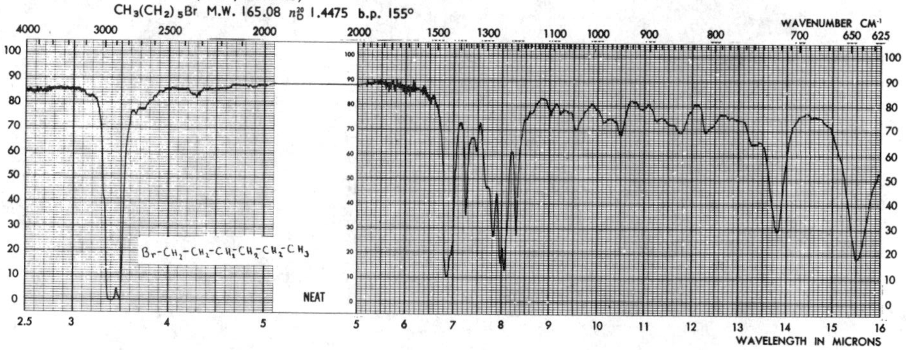

10,974-6 1-Chloroheptane
$CH_3(CH_2)_6Cl$ M.W. 134.65 n_D^{20} 1.4250
b.p. 159-161°

$CH_3CH_2CH_2CH_2CH_2CH_2CH_2Cl$
NEAT

E

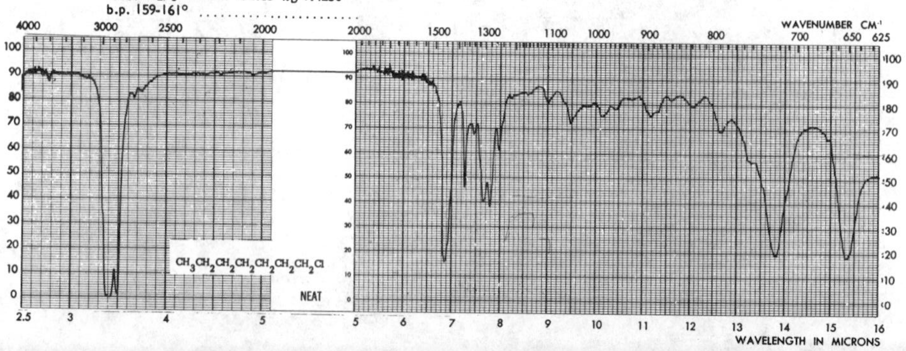

B6757-0 1-Bromoheptane
$CH_3(CH_2)_6Br$ M.W. 179.11 n_D^{20} 1.4499

$Br-CH_2-(CH_2)_5-CH_3$
NEAT

F

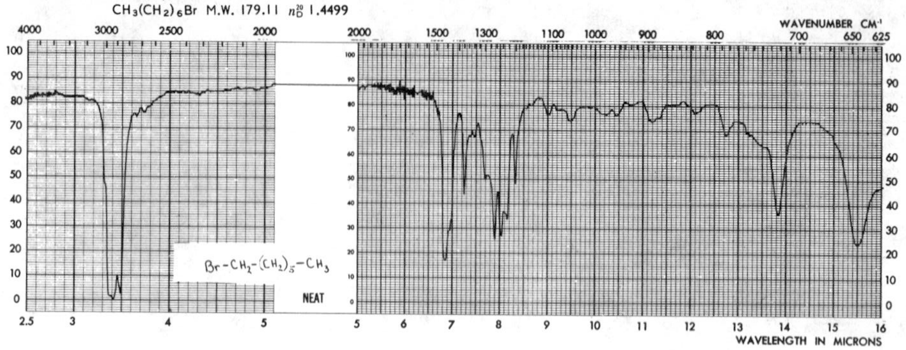

17,785-7
1-Iodoheptane, 98% (heptyl iodide)
$CH_3(CH_2)_6I$
M.W. 226.1 m.p. -48° b.p. 204° n_D^{20} 1.4900
d 1.379 Beil. 1,155

$CH_3CH_2CH_2CH_2CH_2CH_2CH_2I$
NEAT

G

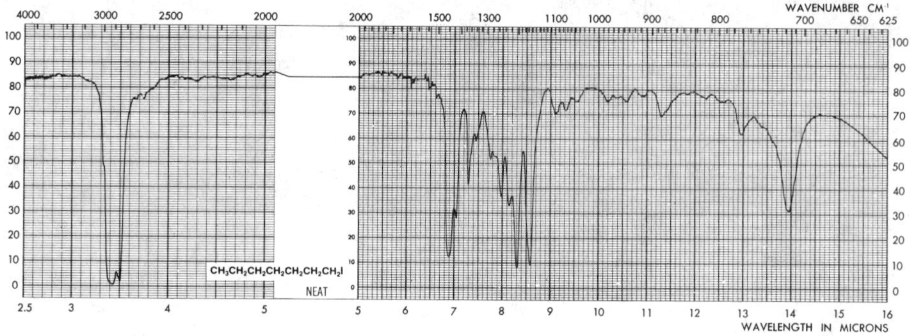

12,515-6 1-Chlorooctane
$CH_3(CH_2)_7Cl$ M.W. 148.68 n_D^{20} 1.4298

$H_3C-(CH_2)_6-CH_2-Cl$
NEAT

H

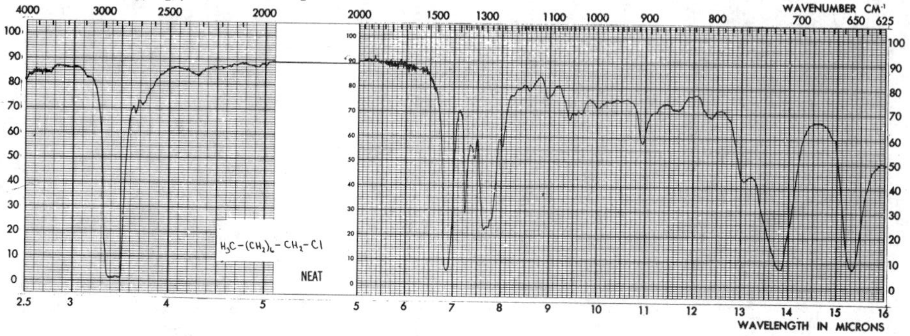

15,295-1 1-Bromooctane (octyl bromide)
$CH_3(CH_2)_7Br$ M.W. 193.13 n_D^{20} 1.4518
b.p. 201°

$CH_3CH_2CH_2CH_2CH_2CH_2CH_2CH_2Br$
NEAT

WAVENUMBER CM^{-1}
WAVELENGTH IN MICRONS

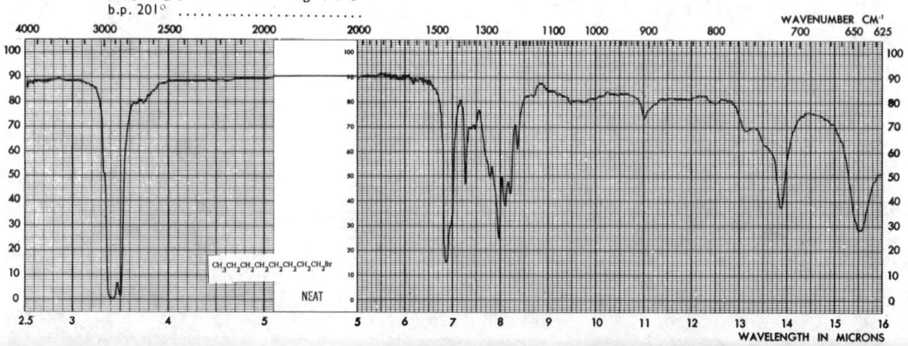

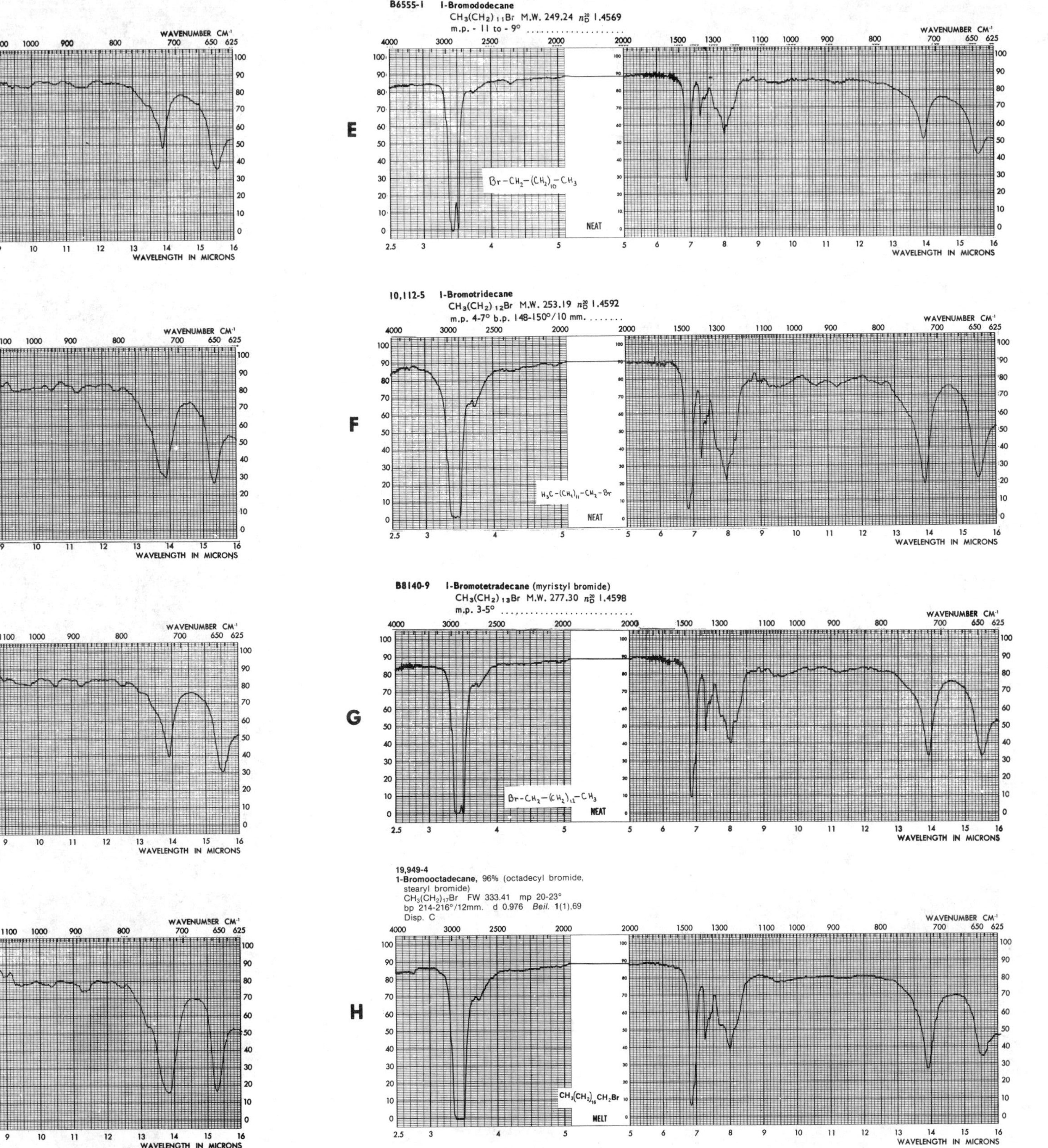

A
B7460-7 1-Bromononane
$CH_3(CH_2)_8Br$ M.W. 207.16 n_D^{20} 1.4526
$Br-CH_2-(CH_2)_7-CH_3$
NEAT
B
C3290-9 1-Chlorodecane (n-decyl chloride)
$CH_3(CH_2)_9Cl$ M.W. 176.73 n_D^{20} 1.4362
$Cl-CH_2-(CH_2)_8-CH_3$
NEAT
C
14,578-5 1-Bromodecane
$CH_3(CH_2)_9Br$ M.W. 221.19 n_D^{20} 1.4560
b.p. 238°
$CH_3-(CH_2)_9-Br$
NEAT
D
C3980-6 1-Chlorododecane (n-dodecyl chloride), tech.
$CH_3(CH_2)_{11}Cl$ M.W. 204.79 n_D^{20} 1.4420
$Cl-CH_2-(CH_2)_{10}-CH_3$
NEAT
E
B6555-1 1-Bromododecane
$CH_3(CH_2)_{11}Br$ M.W. 249.24 n_D^{20} 1.4569
m.p. - 11 to - 9°
$Br-CH_2-(CH_2)_{10}-CH_3$
NEAT
F
10,112-5 1-Bromotridecane
$CH_3(CH_2)_{12}Br$ M.W. 253.19 n_D^{20} 1.4592
m.p. 4-7° b.p. 148-150°/10 mm.
$H_3C-(CH_2)_{11}-CH_2-Br$
NEAT
G
B8140-9 1-Bromotetradecane (myristyl bromide)
$CH_3(CH_2)_{13}Br$ M.W. 277.30 n_D^{20} 1.4598
m.p. 3-5°
$Br-CH_2-(CH_2)_{12}-CH_3$
NEAT
H
19,949-4
1-Bromooctadecane, 96% (octadecyl bromide, stearyl bromide)
$CH_3(CH_2)_{17}Br$ FW 333.41 mp 20-23°
bp 214-216°/12mm. d 0.976 Beil. 1(1),69
Disp. C
$CH_3(CH_2)_{16}CH_2Br$
MELT
WAVENUMBER CM⁻¹
WAVELENGTH IN MICRONS

A

C3690-4 **1-Chloro-3,3-dimethylbutane**
$(CH_3)_3CCH_2CH_2Cl$ M.W. 120.62
n_D^{20} 1.4159

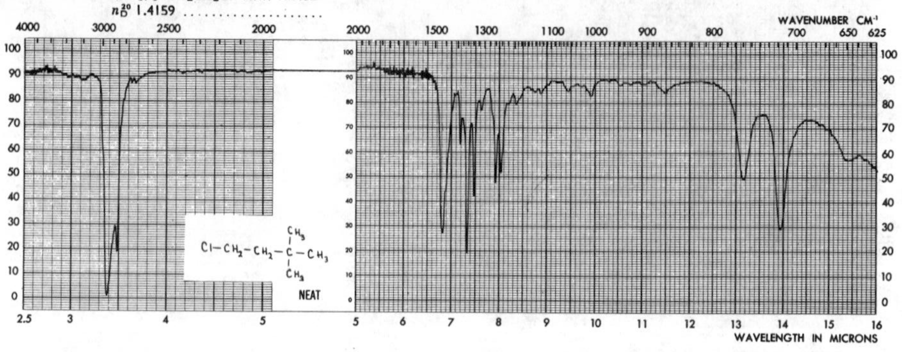

B

11,030-2 **3-(Chloromethyl)-heptane** (2-ethylhexyl chloride)
$CH_3(CH_2)_3CH(CH_2Cl)C_2H_5$ M.W. 148.68 n_D^{20} 1.4310
b.p. 174°

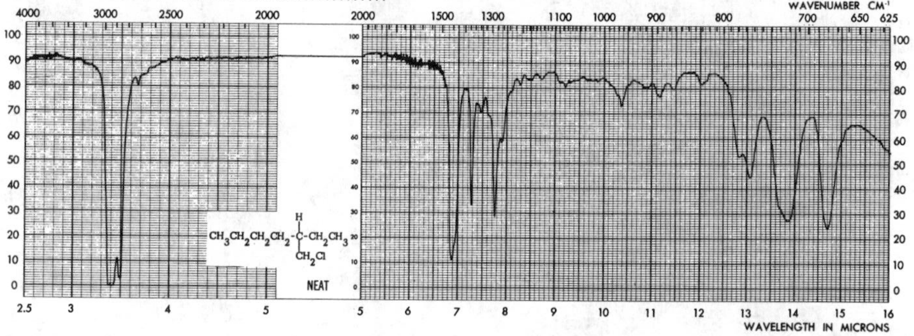

C

C6856-3 **2-Chloropropane** (isopropyl chloride)
$(CH_3)_2CHCl$ M.W. 78.54 n_D^{20} 1.3778

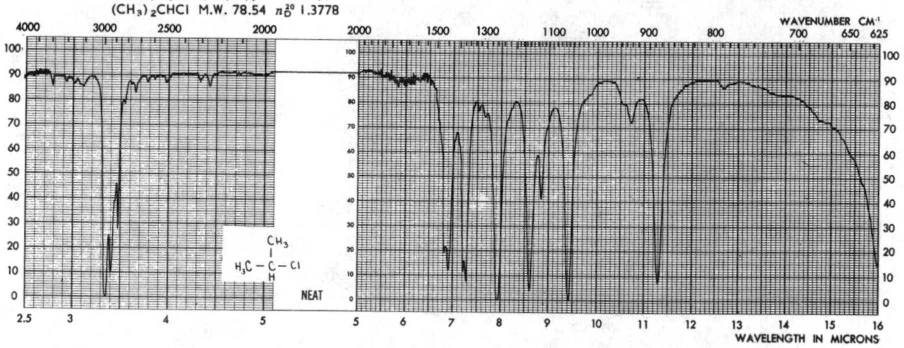

D

B7811-4 **2-Bromopropane** (isopropyl bromide)
$(CH_3)_2CHBr$ M.W. 123.00 n_D^{20} 1.4252

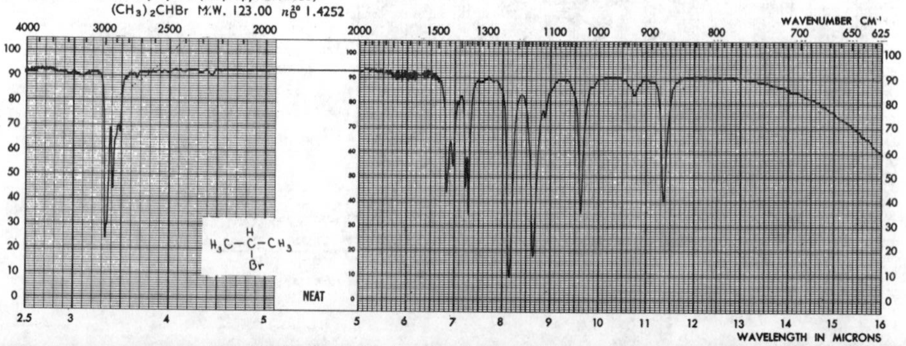

E

14,893-8
2-Iodopropane, 97% (isopropyl iodide)
$(CH_3)_2CHI$
M.W. 169.99 m.p. -90° b.p. 88-90° n_D^{20} 1.4982
d 1.703 Beil. 1,114

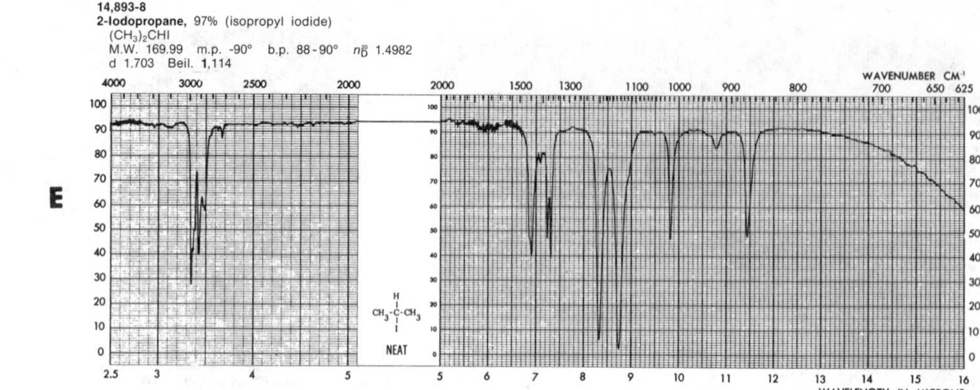

F

C2889-8 **2-Chlorobutane** (sec.-butyl chloride)
$C_2H_5CH(Cl)CH_3$ M.W. 92.57 n_D^{20} 1.3950

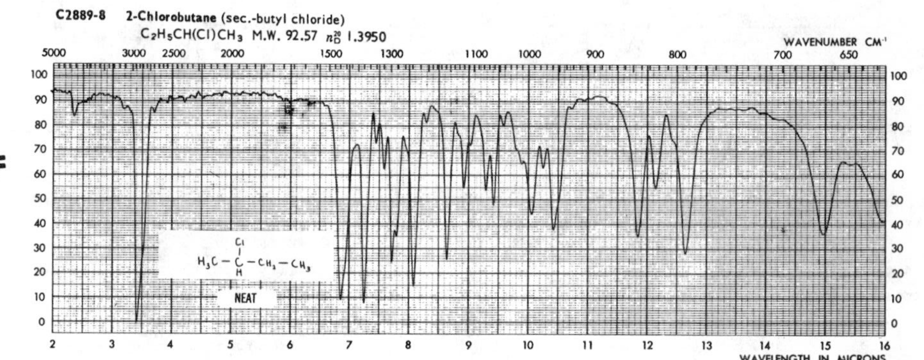

G

B5950-0 **2-Bromobutane** (sec.-butyl bromide)
$C_2H_5CH(Br)CH_3$ M.W. 137.03 n_D^{20} 1.4369

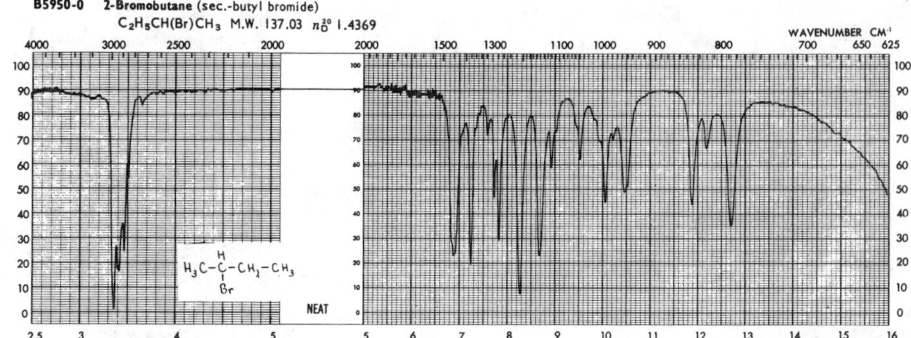

H

C5635-2 **2-Chloro-2-methylpropane** (tert.-butyl chloride)
$(CH_3)_3CCl$ M.W. 92.57 n_D^{20} 1.3848

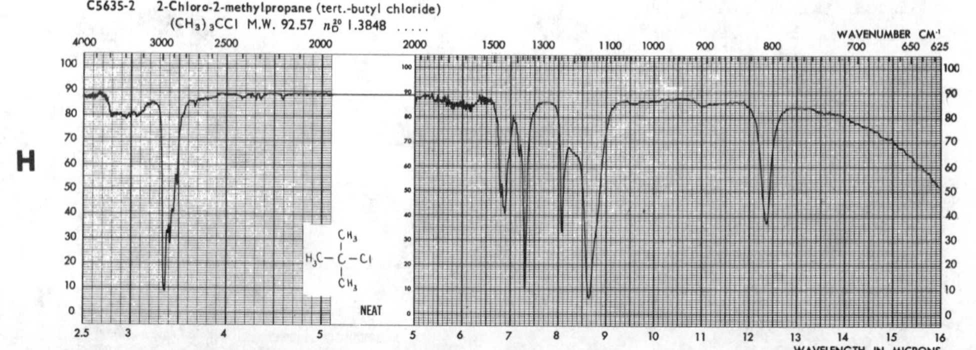

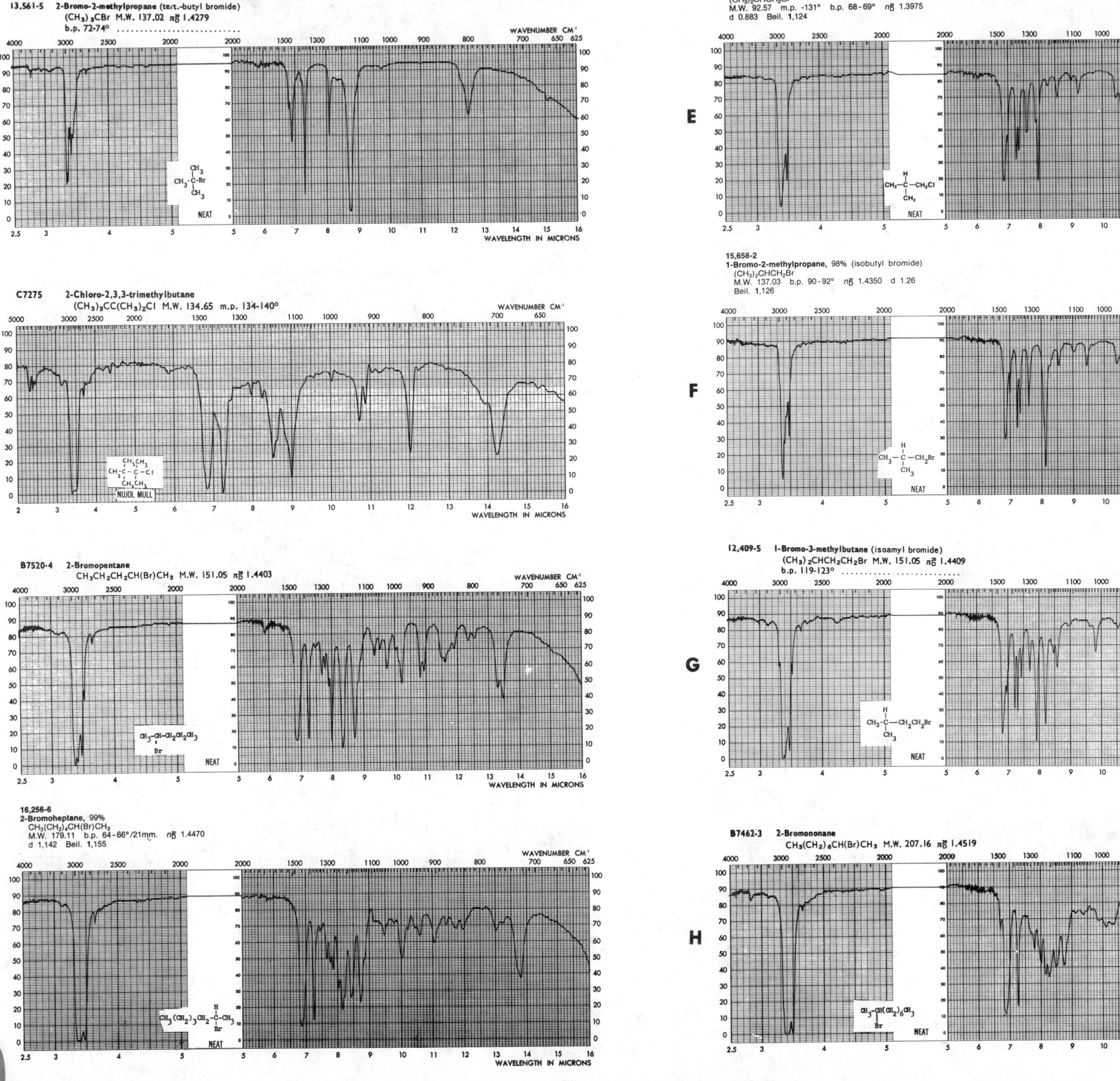

A 13,561-5 **2-Bromo-2-methylpropane** (tert.-butyl bromide)
$(CH_3)_3CBr$ M.W. 137.02 n_D^{20} 1.4279
b.p. 72-74°

B C7275 **2-Chloro-2,3,3-trimethylbutane**
$(CH_3)_3CC(CH_3)_2Cl$ M.W. 134.65 m.p. 134-140°

C B7520-4 **2-Bromopentane**
$CH_3CH_2CH_2CH(Br)CH_3$ M.W. 151.05 n_D^{20} 1.4403

D 16,256-6
2-Bromoheptane, 99%
$CH_3(CH_2)_4CH(Br)CH_3$
M.W. 179.11 b.p. 64-66°/21mm. n_D^{20} 1.4470
d 1.142 Beil. 1,155

E 17,800-4
1-Chloro-2-methylpropane, 98% (isobutyl chloride)
$(CH_3)_2CHCH_2Cl$
M.W. 92.57 m.p. -131° b.p. 68-69° n_D^{20} 1.3975
d 0.883 Beil. 1,124

F 15,658-2
1-Bromo-2-methylpropane, 98% (isobutyl bromide)
$(CH_3)_2CHCH_2Br$
M.W. 137.03 b.p. 90-92° n_D^{20} 1.4350 d 1.26
Beil. 1,126

G 12,409-5 **1-Bromo-3-methylbutane** (isoamyl bromide)
$(CH_3)_2CHCH_2CH_2Br$ M.W. 151.05 n_D^{20} 1.4409
b.p. 119-123°

H B7462-3 **2-Bromononane**
$CH_3(CH_2)_6CH(Br)CH_3$ M.W. 207.16 n_D^{20} 1.4519

A

10,850-2 **2-Bromodecane**
$CH_3(CH_2)_7CH(Br)CH_3$ M.W. 221.19
n_D^{20} 1.4530

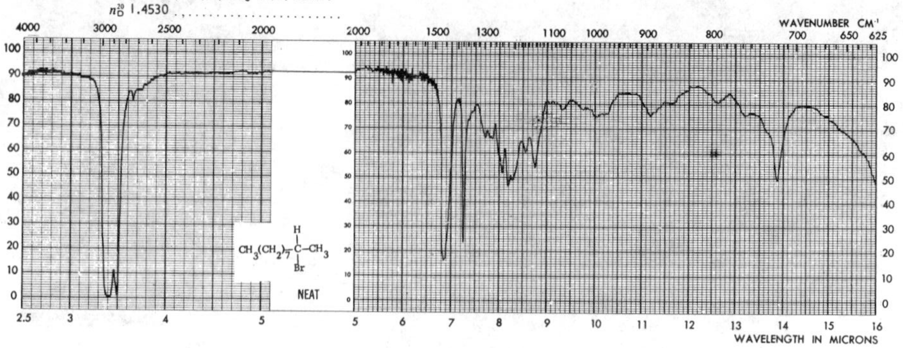

NEAT

B

B8277-4 **2-Bromoundecane**
$CH_3(CH_2)_8CH(Br)CH_3$ M.W. 235.22 n_D^{20} 1.4551

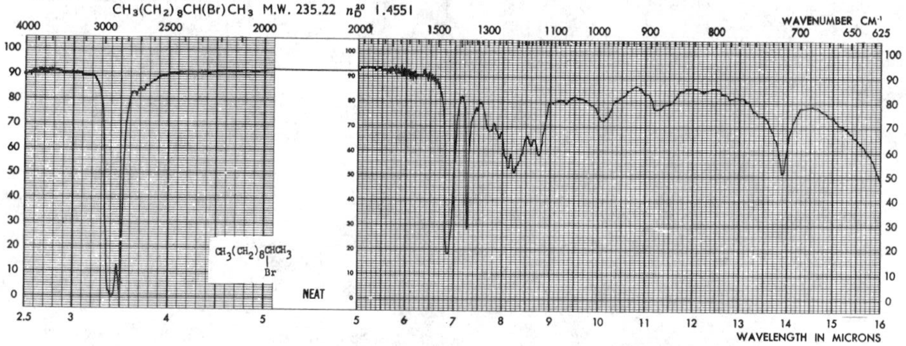

NEAT

C

10,849-9 **2-Bromododecane**
$CH_3(CH_2)_9CH(Br)CH_3$ M.W. 249.24
n_D^{20} 1.4555

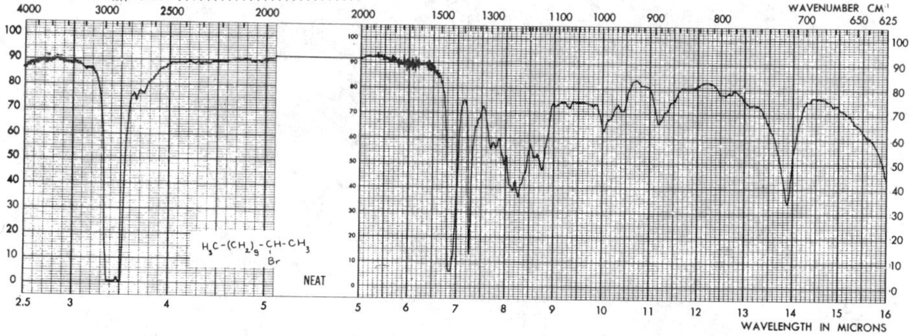

NEAT

D

B8230-8 **2-Bromotridecane**
$CH_3(CH_2)_{10}CH(Br)CH_3$ M.W. 253.19 n_D^{20} 1.4535

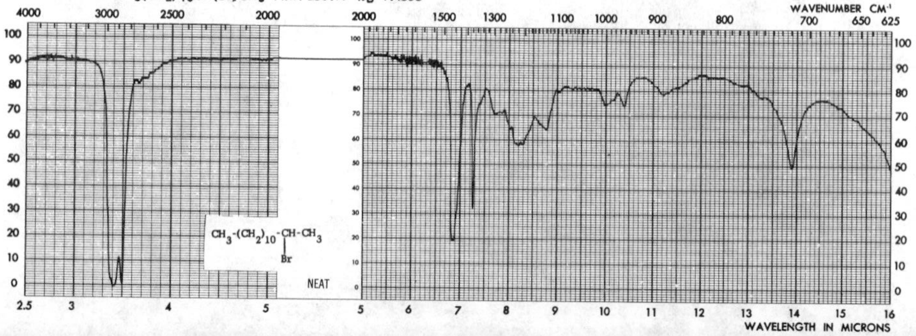

NEAT

E

D6510-0 **Dichloromethane** (methylene chloride) **A.C.S. reagent**
CH_2Cl_2 M.W. 84.93 n_D^{20} 1.4235

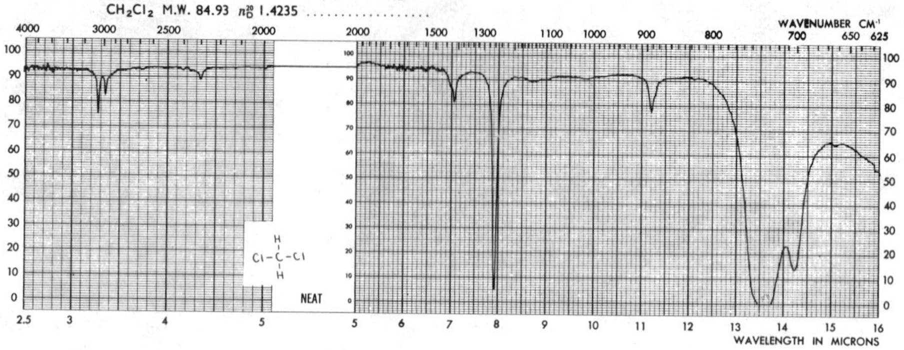

NEAT

F

D4168-6 **Dibromomethane** (methylene bromide)
CH_2Br_2 M.W. 173.85 n_D^{20} 1.5400

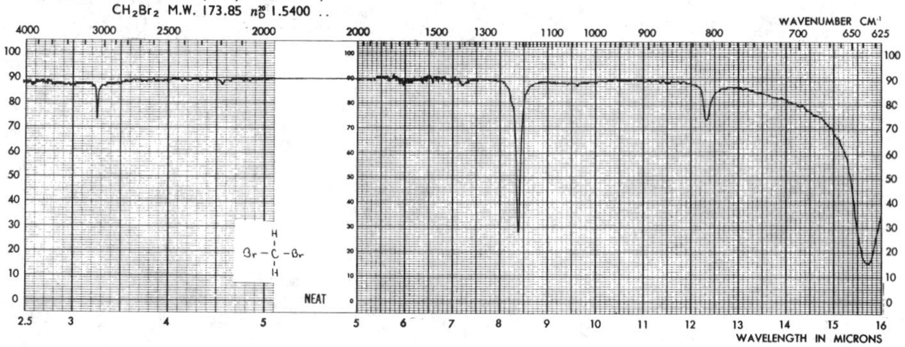

NEAT

G

13,526-7 **Bromochloromethane**
$BrCH_2Cl$ M.W. 129.39 n_D^{20} 1.4852 b.p. 66-68°

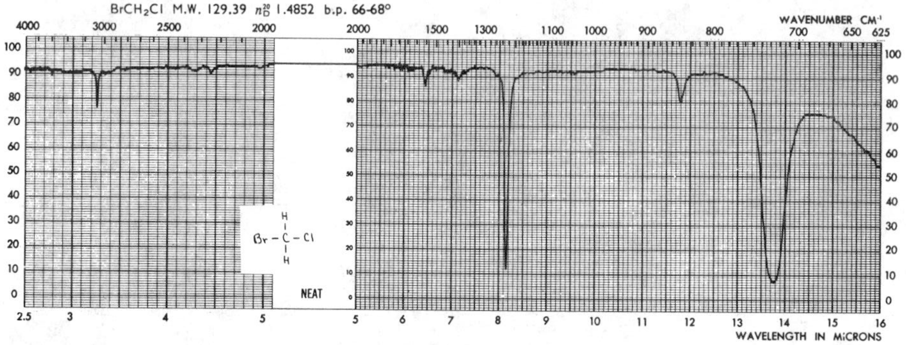

NEAT

H

15,842-9
Diiodomethane, 99% (methylene iodide)
CH_2I_2
M.W. 267.84 m.p. 6° b.p. 181° d 3.325
Beil. 1,71

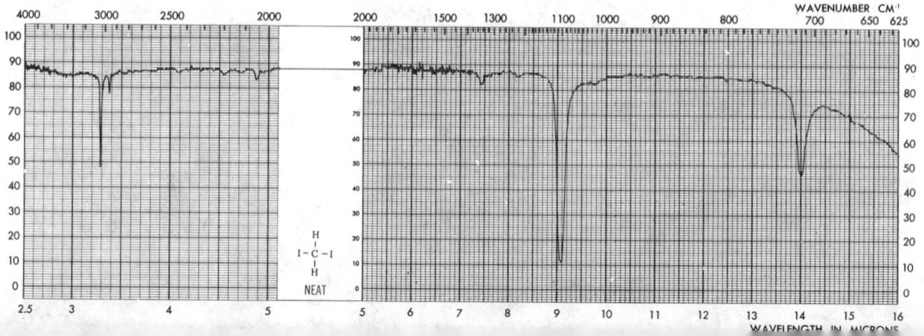

NEAT

A

D6156-3 1,2-Dichloroethane (ethylene dichloride)
$ClCH_2CH_2Cl$ M.W. 98.96 n_D^{20} 1.4434

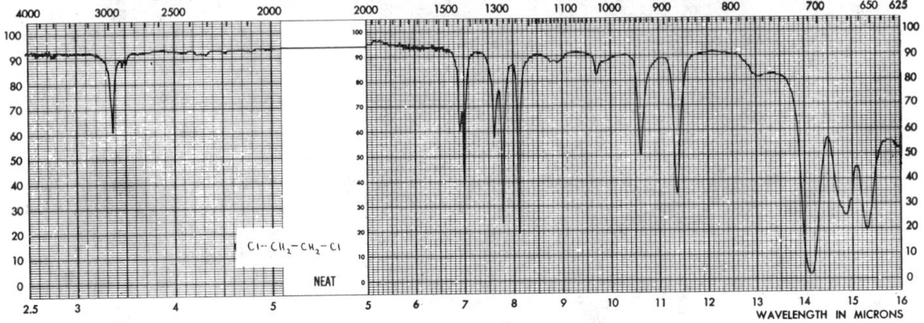

B

D4075-2 1,2-Dibromoethane (ethylene dibromide)
$BrCH_2CH_2Br$ M.W. 187.87 n_D^{20} 1.5375
m.p. 9-10° ....

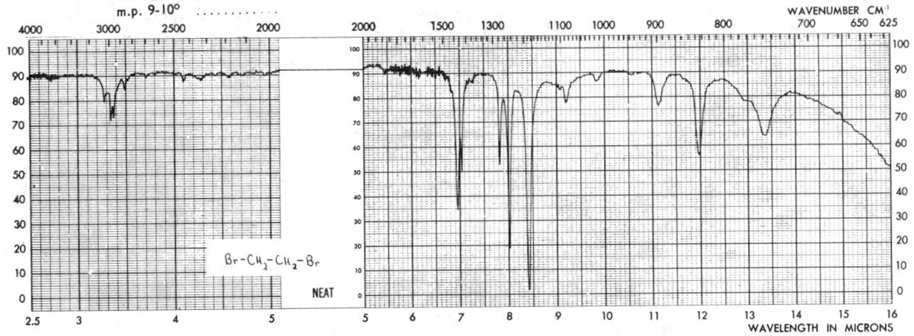

C

D12,280-7 1,2-Diiodoethane
ICH_2CH_2I M.W. 281.86 m.p. 81-84°

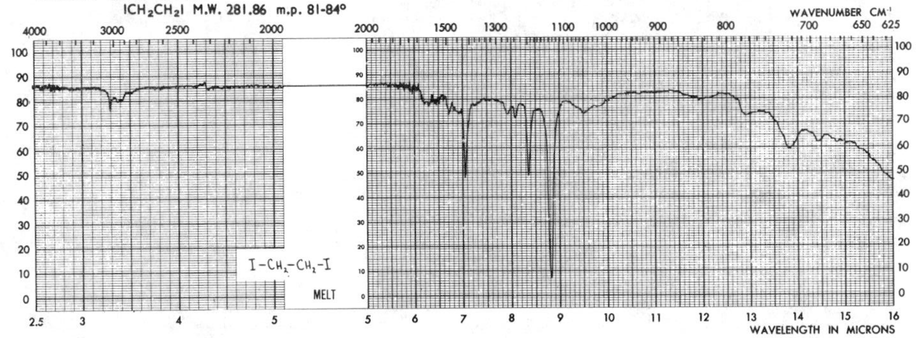

D

D7220-4 1,3-Dichloropropane
$Cl(CH_2)_3Cl$ M.W. 112.99 n_D^{20} 1.4481
b.p. 120-122° ....

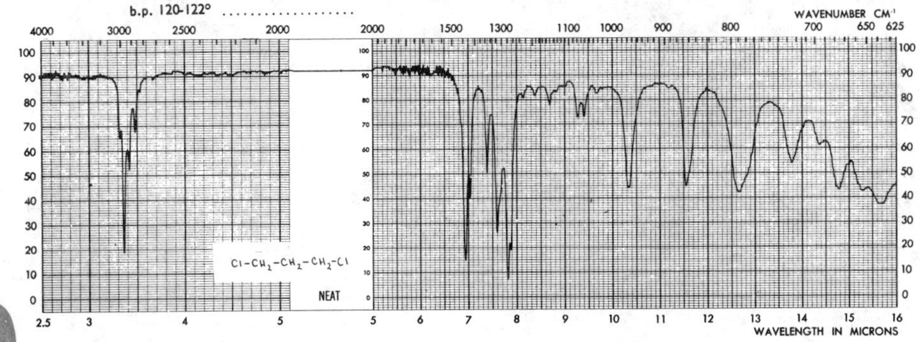

E

12,590-3 1,3-Dibromopropane
$Br(CH_2)_3Br$ M.W. 201.90 n_D^{20} 1.5214 .....

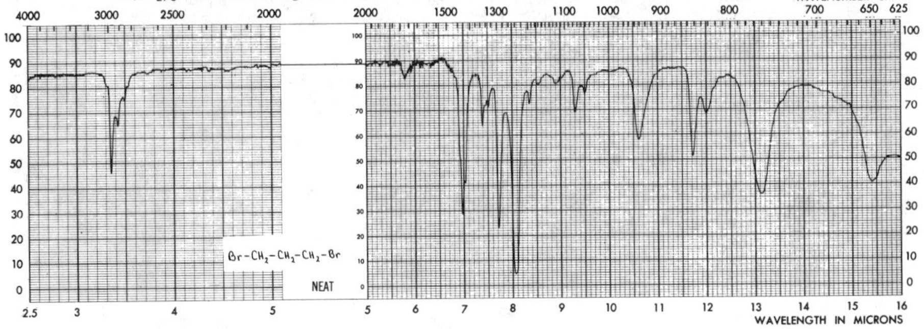

F

B6240-4 1-Bromo-3-chloropropane (trimethylene chlorobromide), **puriss.**
$Cl(CH_2)_3Br$ M.W. 157.44 n_D^{20} 1.4860 ....

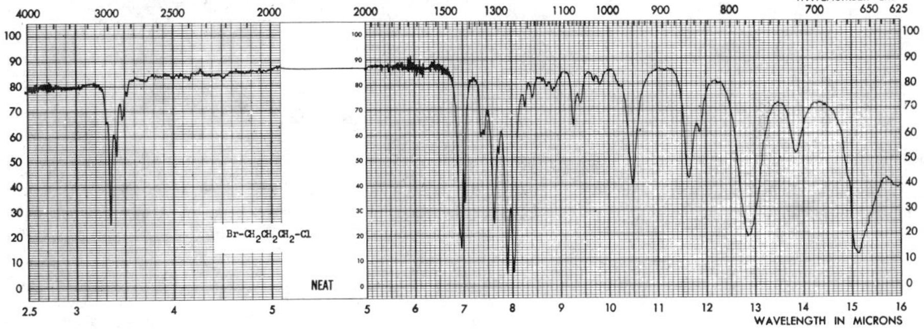

G

19,365-8
2,2-Dibromopropane, 98%
$CH_3CBr_2CH_3$ FW 201.90 bp 114°/740mm.
n_D^{20} 1.4984 d 1.782 *Beil.* 1,111 Disp. C

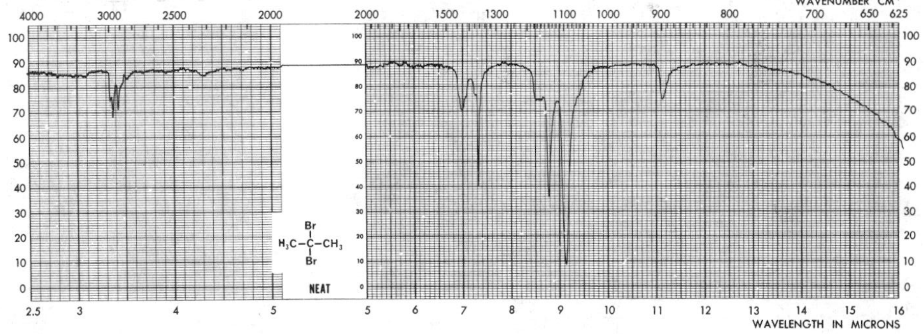

H

D5910-0 1,4-Dichlorobutane
$Cl(CH_2)_4Cl$ M.W. 127.01 n_D^{20} 1.4542

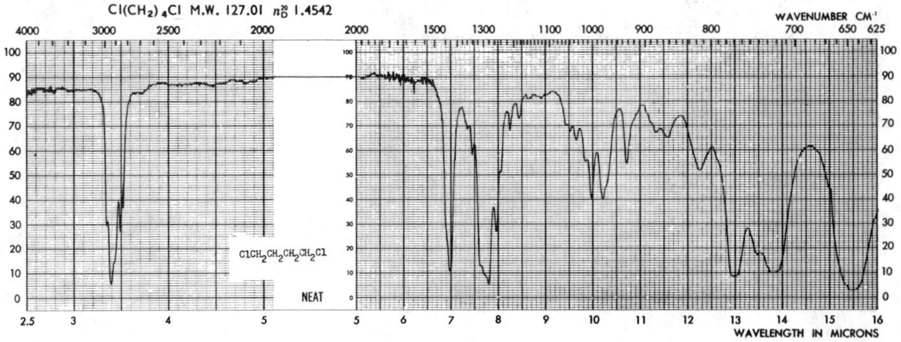

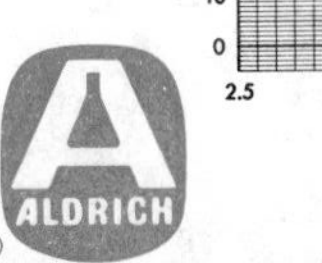

ALDRICH

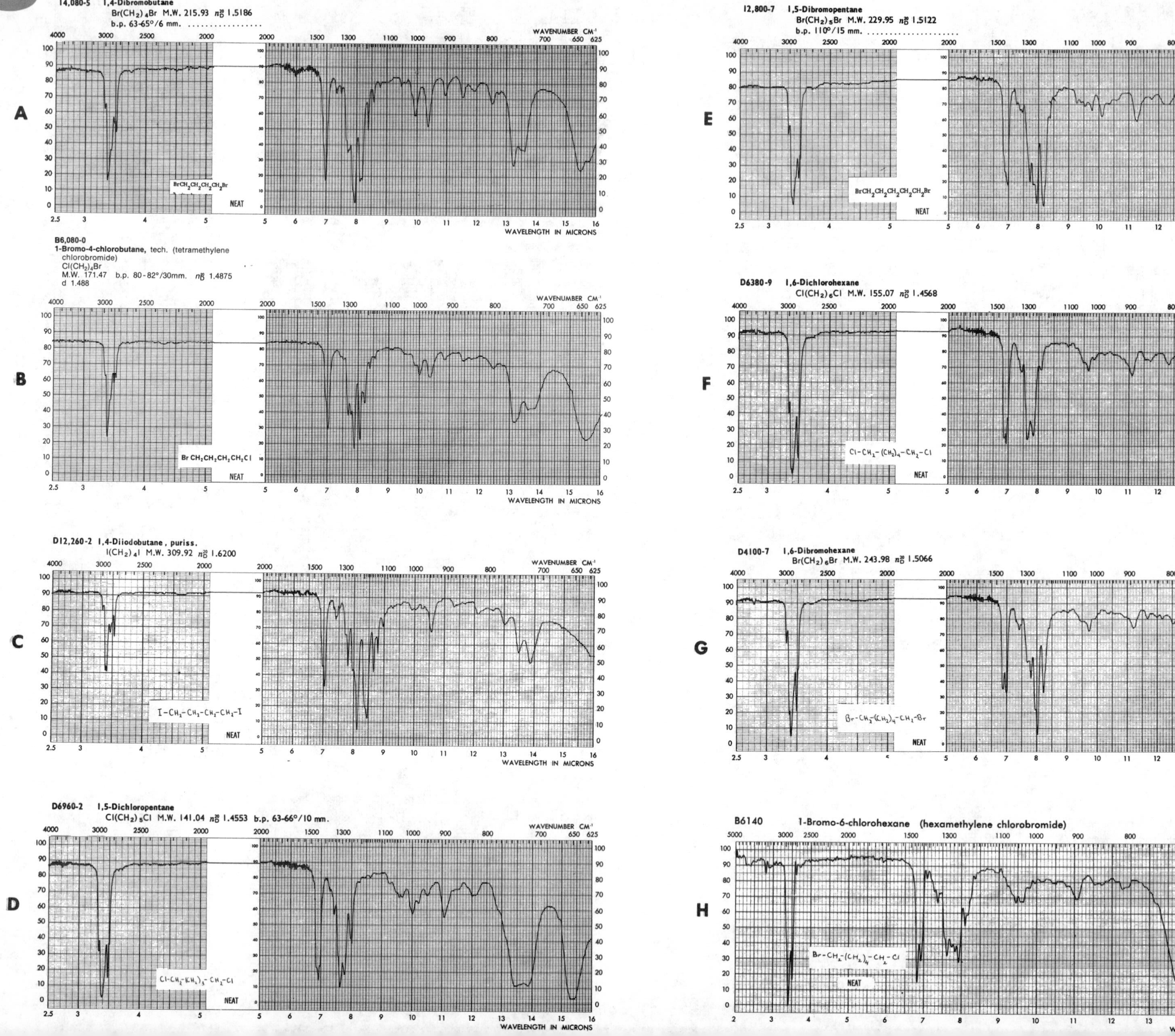

A 14,080-5 1,4-Dibromobutane
Br(CH$_2$)$_4$Br M.W. 215.93 n_D^{20} 1.5186
b.p. 63-65°/6 mm.

B B6,080-0
1-Bromo-4-chlorobutane, tech. (tetramethylene chlorobromide)
Cl(CH$_2$)$_4$Br
M.W. 171.47 b.p. 80-82°/30mm. n_D^{20} 1.4875
d 1.488

C D12,260-2 1,4-Diiodobutane, puriss.
I(CH$_2$)$_4$I M.W. 309.92 n_D^{20} 1.6200

D D6960-2 1,5-Dichloropentane
Cl(CH$_2$)$_5$Cl M.W. 141.04 n_D^{20} 1.4553 b.p. 63-66°/10 mm.

E 12,800-7 1,5-Dibromopentane
Br(CH$_2$)$_5$Br M.W. 229.95 n_D^{20} 1.5122
b.p. 110°/15 mm.

F D6380-9 1,6-Dichlorohexane
Cl(CH$_2$)$_6$Cl M.W. 155.07 n_D^{20} 1.4568

G D4100-7 1,6-Dibromohexane
Br(CH$_2$)$_6$Br M.W. 243.98 n_D^{20} 1.5066

H B6140 1-Bromo-6-chlorohexane (hexamethylene chlorobromide)

A

14,499-1 **1,7-Dibromoheptane**
$Br(CH_2)_7Br$ M.W. 258.01 n_D^{20} 1.5017
b.p. 255°

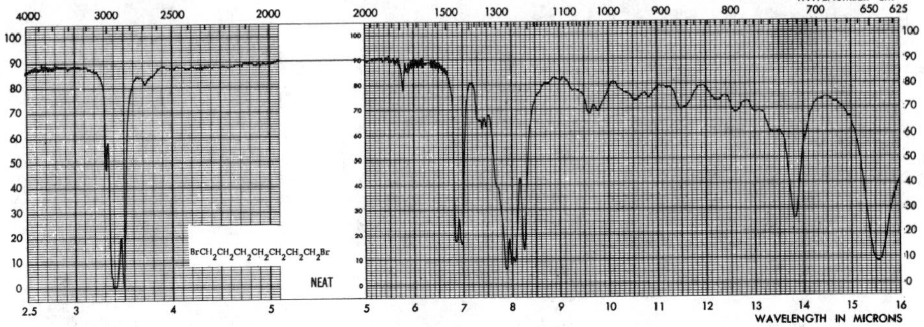

NEAT

B

D4260-7 **1,8-Dibromooctane**
$Br(CH_2)_8Br$ M.W. 272.03
n_D^{20} 1.4991

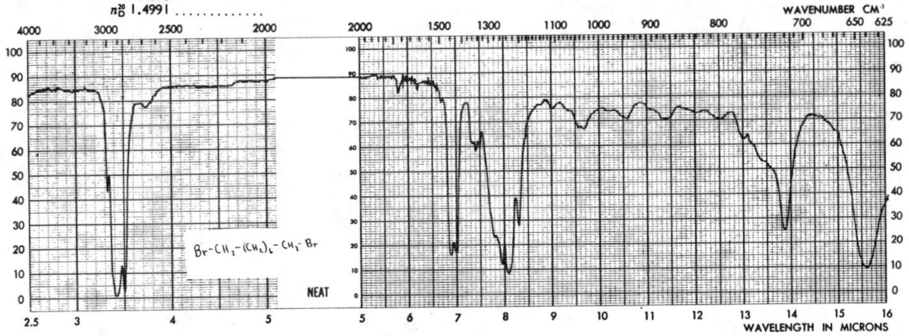

NEAT

C

D6940-8 **1,9-Dichlorononane**
$Cl(CH_2)_9Cl$ M.W. 197.15 n_D^{20} 1.4599
b.p. 258-262°

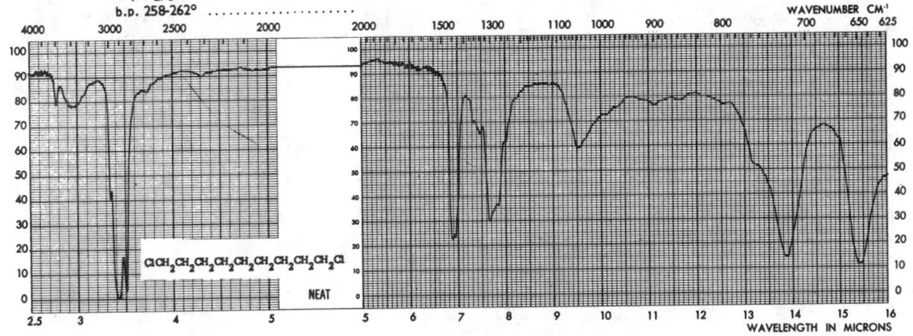

NEAT

D

D4240-2 **1,9-Dibromononane**
$Br(CH_2)_9Br$ M.W. 286.06 n_D^{20} 1.4955

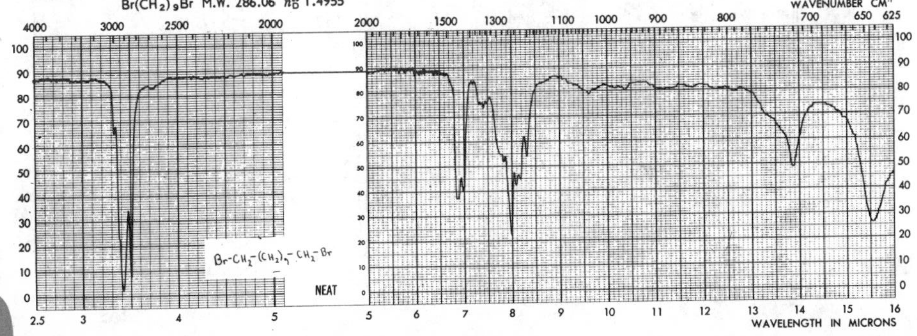

NEAT

E

D3980-0 **1,10-Dibromodecane**
$Br(CH_2)_{10}Br$ M.W. 300.09 m.p. < 30°

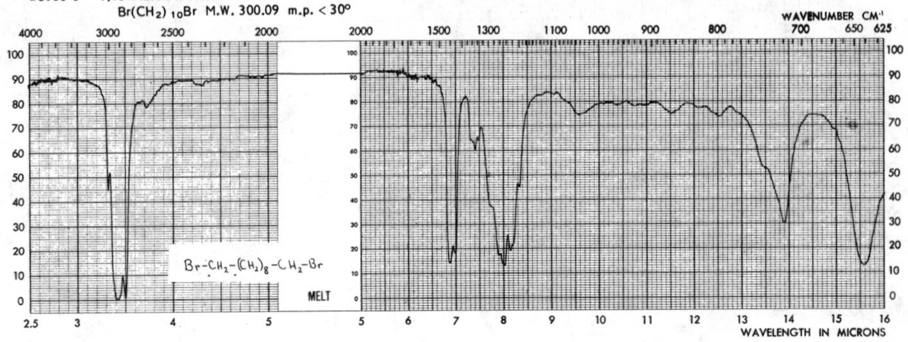

MELT

F

13,338-8 **1,12-Dibromododecane**
$Br(CH_2)_{12}Br$ M.W. 328.14 m.p. 37-39°

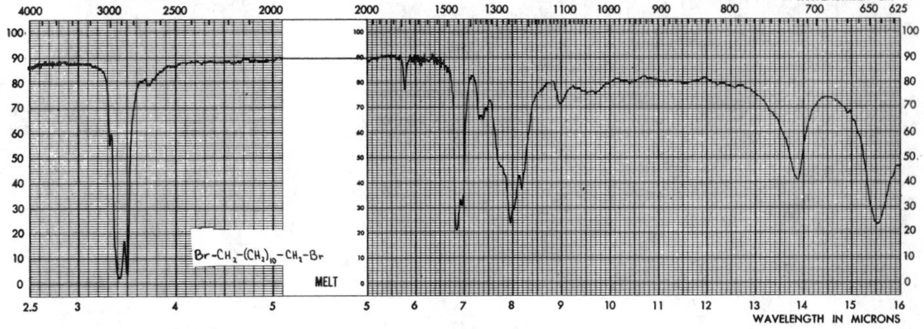

MELT

G

D6155-5 **1,1-Dichloroethane (ethylidene chloride)**
CH_3CHCl_2 M.W. 98.96 n_D^{20} 1.4140

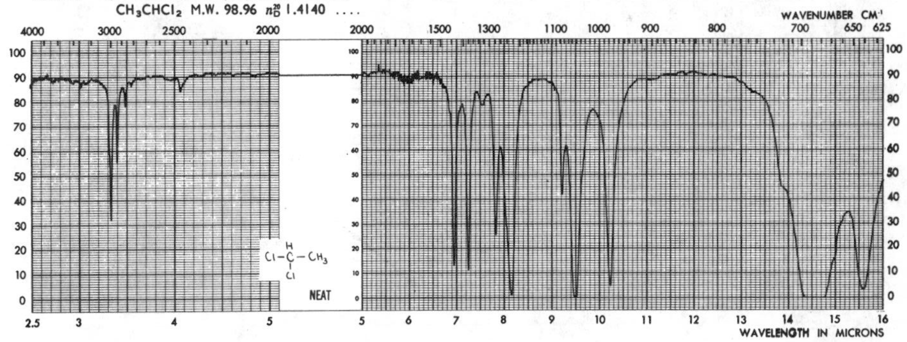

NEAT

H

D5940-2 **2,3-Dichlorobutane**
$CH_3CH(Cl)CH(Cl)CH_3$ M.W. 127.01 n_D^{20} 1.4420

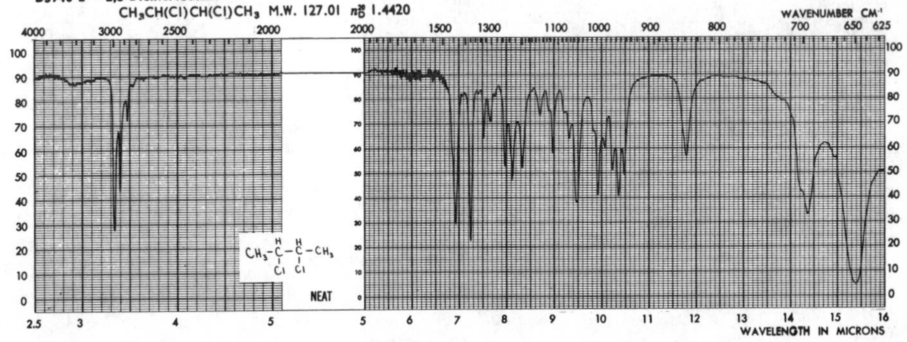

NEAT

ALDRICH ®

A

11,355-7 **1-Bromo-1-chloroethane**
$CH_3CH(Cl)Br$ M.W. 143.42 n_D^{20} 1.4660 b.p. 81-83°

$CH_3-\overset{H}{\underset{Cl}{C}}-Br$ NEAT

B

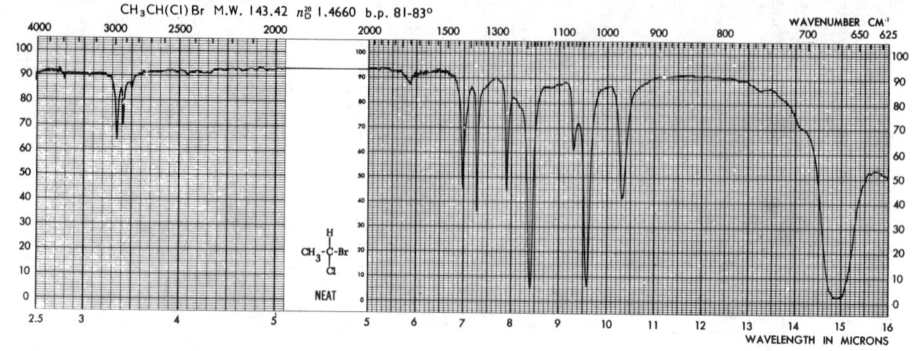

D7218-2 **1,2-Dichloropropane**
$CH_3CH(Cl)CH_2Cl$ M.W. 112.99
n_D^{20} 1.4384

$Cl-CH_2-\overset{Cl}{\underset{H}{C}}-CH_3$ NEAT

C

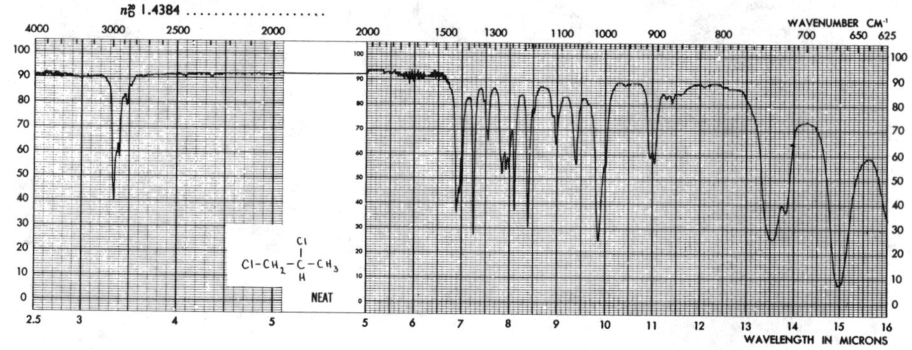

14,096-1 **1,2-Dibromopropane** (propylene dibromide)
$CH_3CH(Br)CH_2Br$ M.W. 201.90 n_D^{20} 1.5190
b.p. 140-142°

$CH_3-\overset{H}{\underset{Br}{C}}-CH_2Br$ NEAT

D

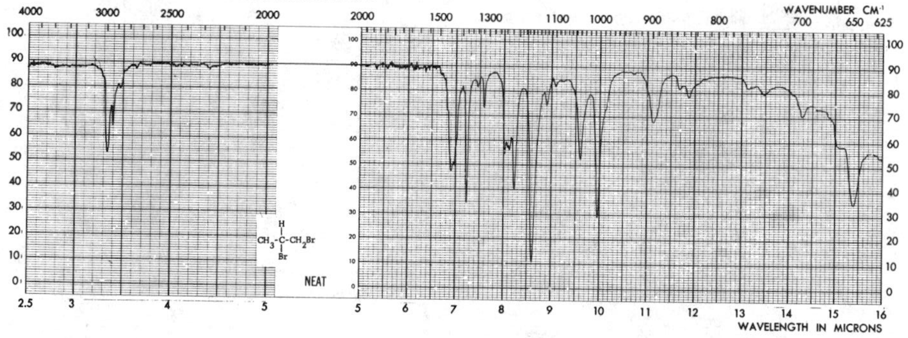

15,657-4
1,3-Dibromobutane
$CH_3CH(Br)CH_2CH_2Br$
M.W. 215.93 b.p. 175° n_D^{20} 1.5085 d 1.8
Beil. 1,120

$CH_3-\overset{H}{\underset{Br}{C}}-CH_2CH_2Br$ NEAT

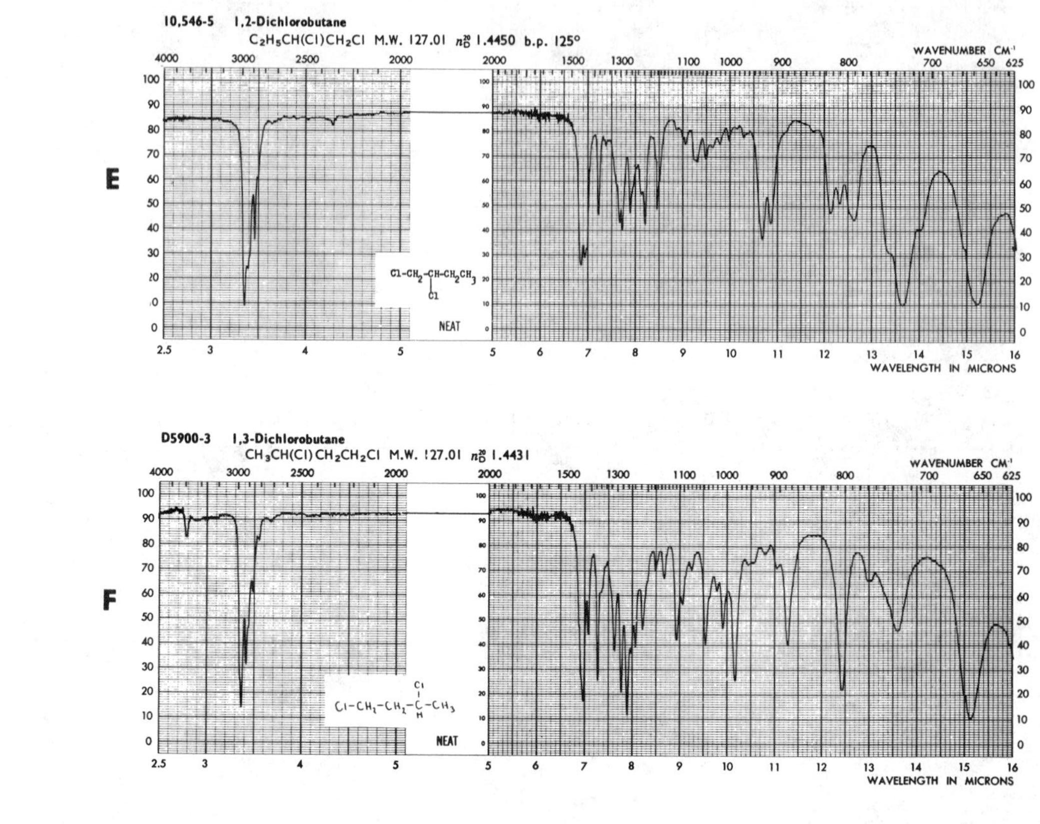

E

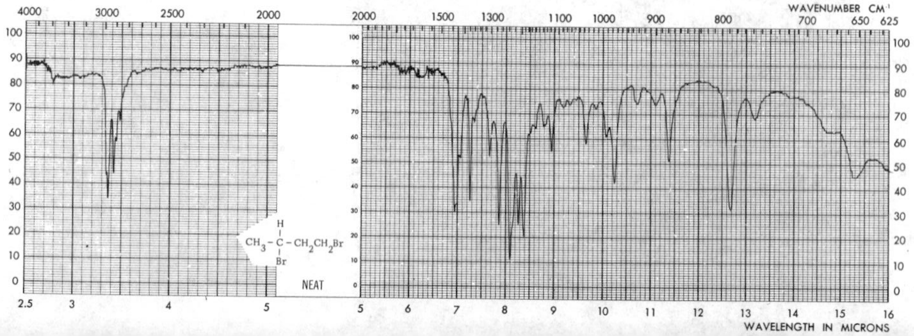

10,546-5 **1,2-Dichlorobutane**
$C_2H_5CH(Cl)CH_2Cl$ M.W. 127.01 n_D^{20} 1.4450 b.p. 125°

$Cl-CH_2-\underset{Cl}{CH}-CH_2CH_3$ NEAT

F

D5900-3 **1,3-Dichlorobutane**
$CH_3CH(Cl)CH_2CH_2Cl$ M.W. 127.01 n_D^{20} 1.4431

$Cl-CH_2-CH_2-\overset{Cl}{\underset{H}{C}}-CH_3$ NEAT

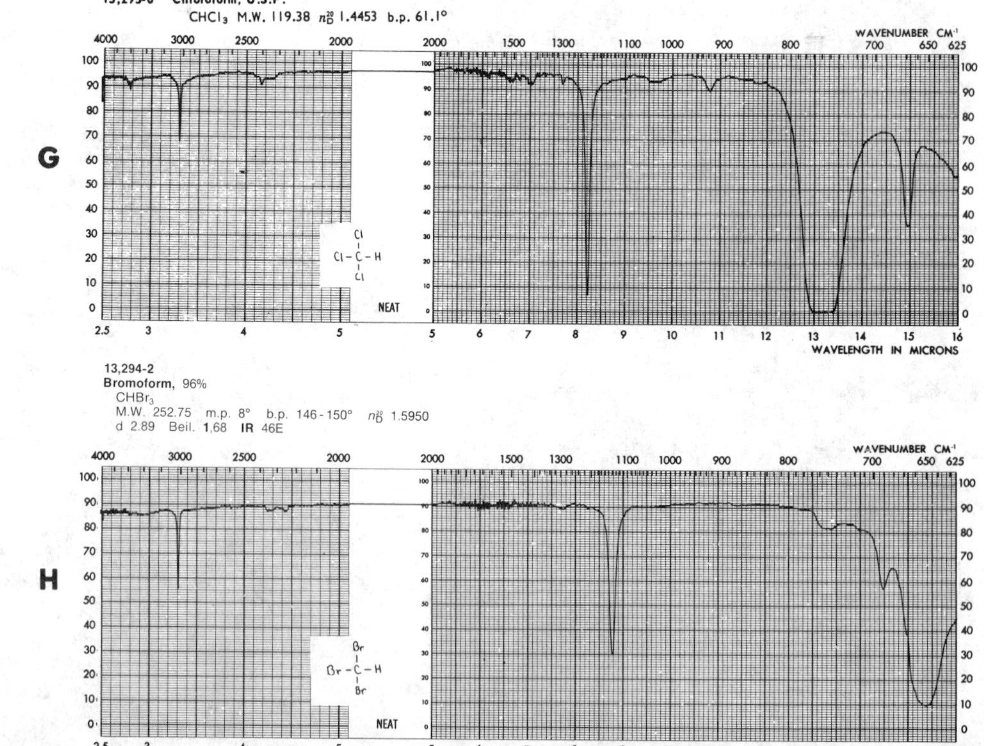

G

13,295-0 **Chloroform, U.S.P.**
$CHCl_3$ M.W. 119.38 n_D^{20} 1.4453 b.p. 61.1°

$Cl-\overset{Cl}{\underset{Cl}{C}}-H$ NEAT

H

13,294-2
Bromoform, 96%
$CHBr_3$
M.W. 252.75 m.p. 8° b.p. 146-150° n_D^{20} 1.5950
d 2.89 Beil. 1,68 IR 46E

$Br-\overset{Br}{\underset{Br}{C}}-H$ NEAT

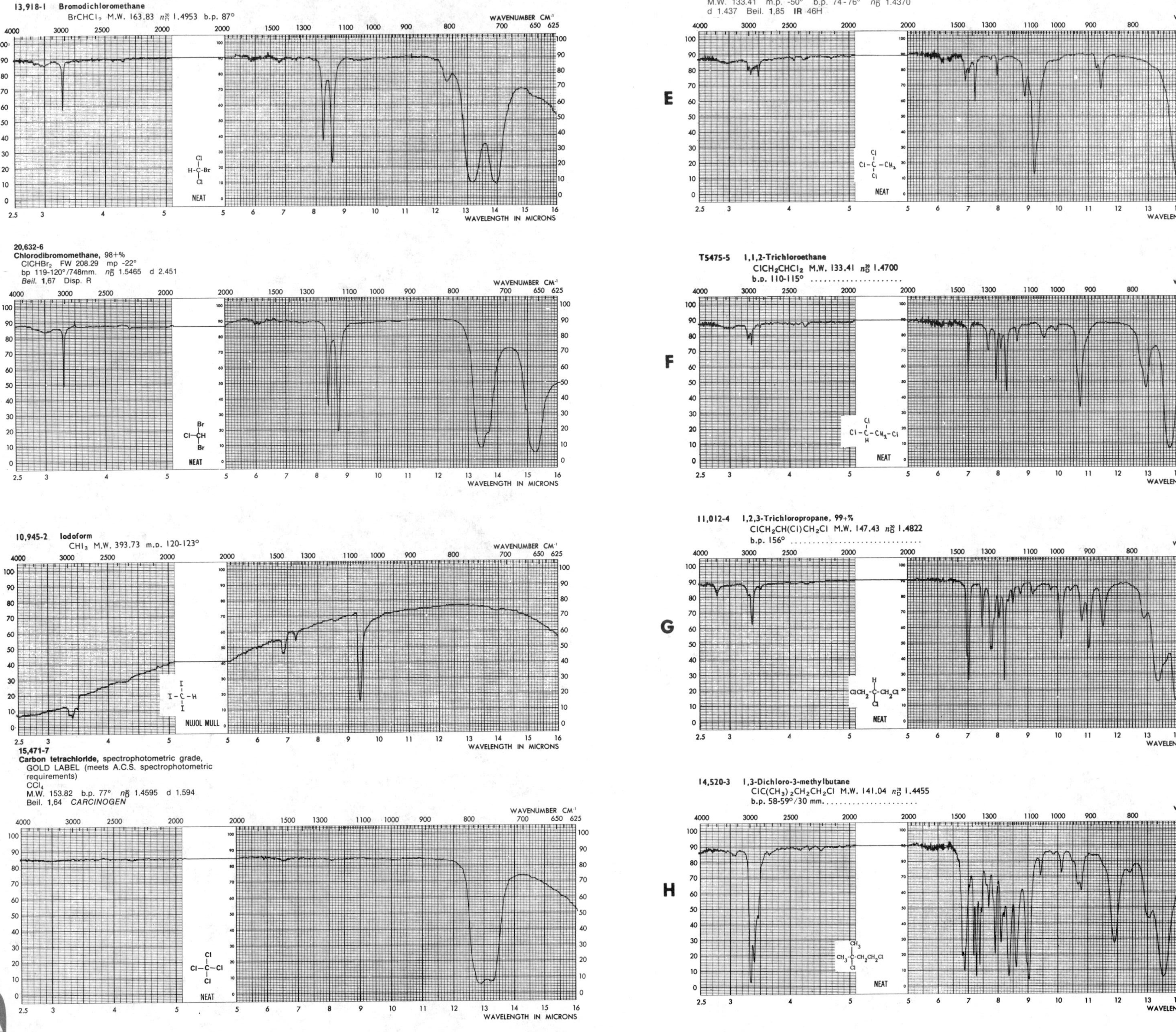

A 13,918-1 **Bromodichloromethane**
$BrCHCl_2$ M.W. 163.83 n_D^{20} 1.4953 b.p. 87°
NEAT

B 20,632-6
Chlorodibromomethane, 98+%
$ClCHBr_2$ FW 208.29 mp -22°
bp 119-120°/748mm. n_D^{20} 1.5465 d 2.451
Beil. 1,67 Disp. R
NEAT

C 10,945-2 **Iodoform**
CHI_3 M.W. 393.73 m.p. 120-123°
NUJOL MULL

D 15,471-7
Carbon tetrachloride, spectrophotometric grade, GOLD LABEL (meets A.C.S. spectrophotometric requirements)
CCl_4
M.W. 153.82 b.p. 77° n_D^{20} 1.4595 d 1.594
Beil. 1,64 *CARCINOGEN*
NEAT

E **1,1,1-Trichloroethane,** 97%, inhibited with 3% p-dioxane
CH_3CCl_3
M.W. 133.41 m.p. -50° b.p. 74-76° n_D^{20} 1.4370
d 1.437 Beil. 1,85 **IR** 46H
NEAT

F T5475-5 **1,1,2-Trichloroethane**
$ClCH_2CHCl_2$ M.W. 133.41 n_D^{20} 1.4700
b.p. 110-115°
NEAT

G 11,012-4 **1,2,3-Trichloropropane,** 99+%
$ClCH_2CH(Cl)CH_2Cl$ M.W. 147.43 n_D^{20} 1.4822
b.p. 156°
NEAT

H 14,520-3 **1,3-Dichloro-3-methylbutane**
$ClC(CH_3)_2CH_2CH_2Cl$ M.W. 141.04 n_D^{20} 1.4455
b.p. 58-59°/30 mm.
NEAT

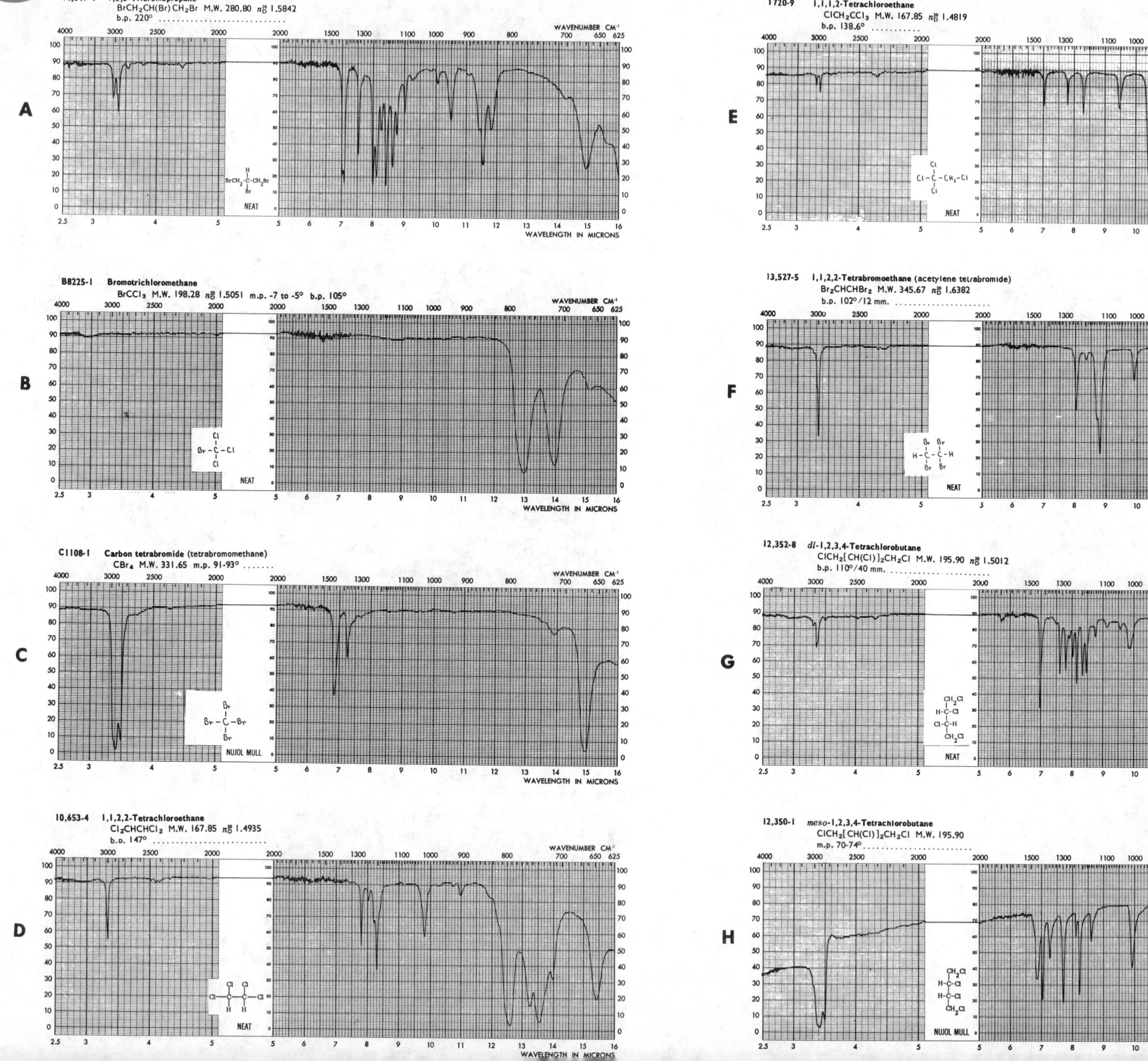
A
14,847-4 1,2,3-Tribromopropane
BrCH2CH(Br)CH2Br M.W. 280.80 n20/D 1.5842
b.p. 220°
NEAT
B
B8225-1 Bromotrichloromethane
BrCCl3 M.W. 198.28 n20/D 1.5051 m.p. -7 to -5° b.p. 105°
NEAT
C
C1108-1 Carbon tetrabromide (tetrabromomethane)
CBr4 M.W. 331.65 m.p. 91-93°
NUJOL MULL
D
10,653-4 1,1,2,2-Tetrachloroethane
Cl2CHCHCl2 M.W. 167.85 n20/D 1.4935
b.p. 147°
NEAT
E
T720-9 1,1,1,2-Tetrachloroethane
ClCH2CCl3 M.W. 167.85 n20/D 1.4819
b.p. 138.6°
NEAT
F
13,527-5 1,1,2,2-Tetrabromoethane (acetylene tetrabromide)
Br2CHCHBr2 M.W. 345.67 n20/D 1.6382
b.p. 102°/12 mm.
NEAT
G
12,352-8 dl-1,2,3,4-Tetrachlorobutane
ClCH2[CH(Cl)]2CH2Cl M.W. 195.90 n20/D 1.5012
b.p. 110°/40 mm.
NEAT
H
12,350-1 meso-1,2,3,4-Tetrachlorobutane
ClCH2[CH(Cl)]2CH2Cl M.W. 195.90
m.p. 70-74°
NUJOL MULL
WAVENUMBER CM-1
WAVELENGTH IN MICRONS

A

15,154-8 1,1,2,3,4,4-Hexachlorobutane
$Cl_2CHCH(Cl)CH(Cl)CHCl_2$ M.W. 264.79
m.p. 105-107°

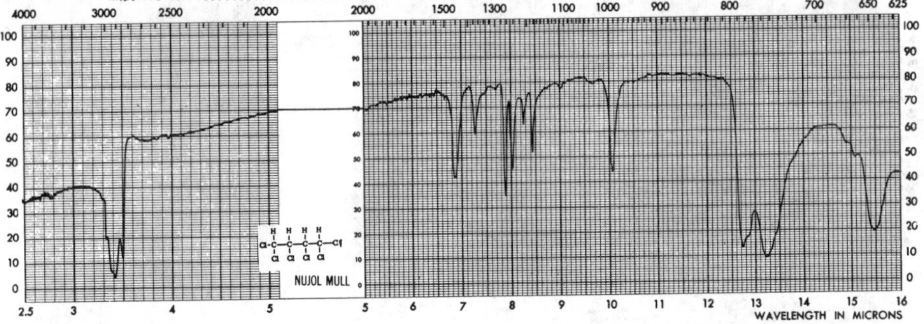

NUJOL MULL

B

14,213-1 1,2,3,4-Tetrabromobutane
$BrCH_2CH(Br)CH(Br)CH_2Br$ M.W. 373.73
m.p. 109-112°

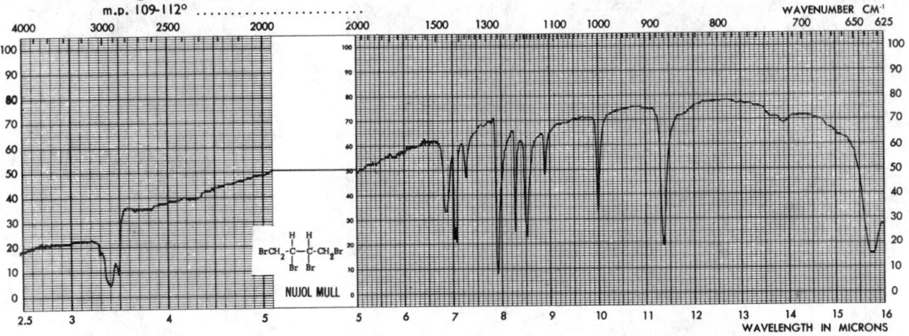

NUJOL MULL

C

13,042-7 2-Iodo-1,1,1-trifluoroethane
ICH_2CF_3 M.W. 209.94 n_D^{20} 1.4012
b.p. 55°

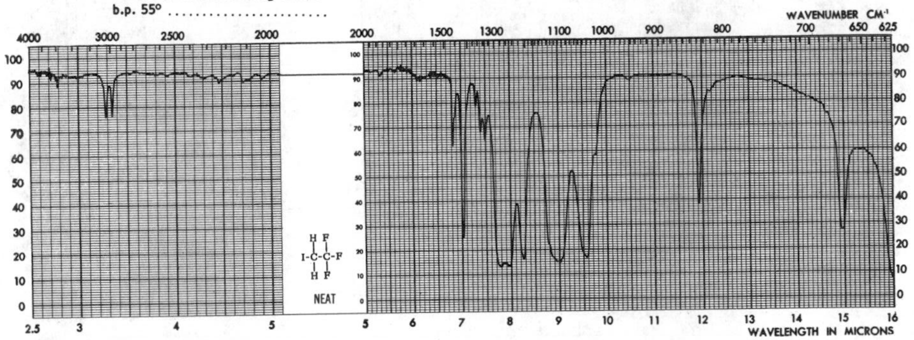

NEAT

D

D3990 1,2-Dibromo-2,3-dichloropropane
$BrCH_2C(Cl)(Br)CH_2Cl$ M.W. 270.79 n_D^{20} 1.5559

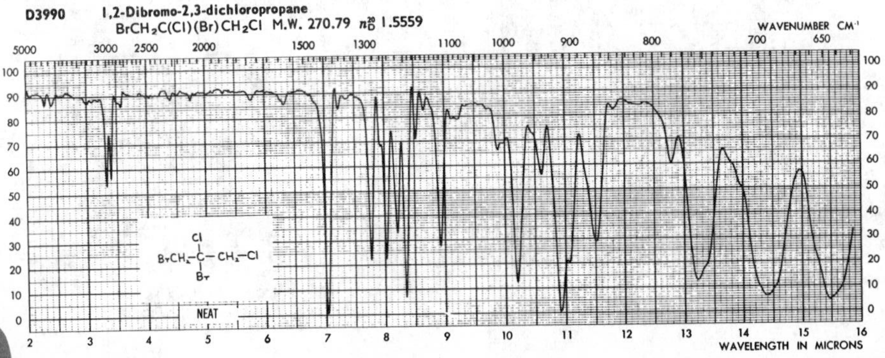

NEAT

E

P490-9 Pentaerythrityl tetrachloride
$C(CH_2Cl)_4$ M.W. 209.93 m.p. 95-96°

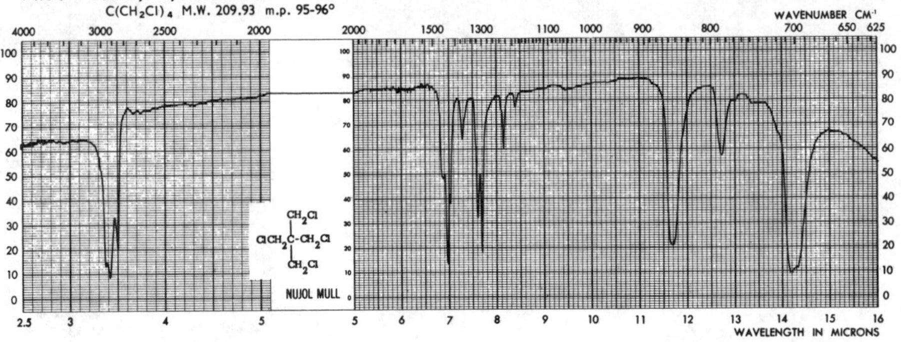

NUJOL MULL

F

P480-1 Pentaerythrityl tetrabromide
$C(CH_2Br)_4$ M.W. 387.76 m.p. 155-159°

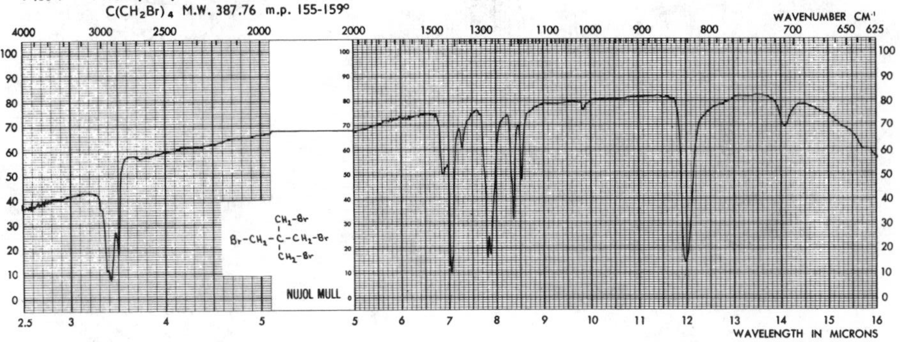

NUJOL MULL

G

13,133-4 Pentaerythrityl tetraiodide
$C(CH_2I)_4$ M.W. 575.74 m.p. 228-230°

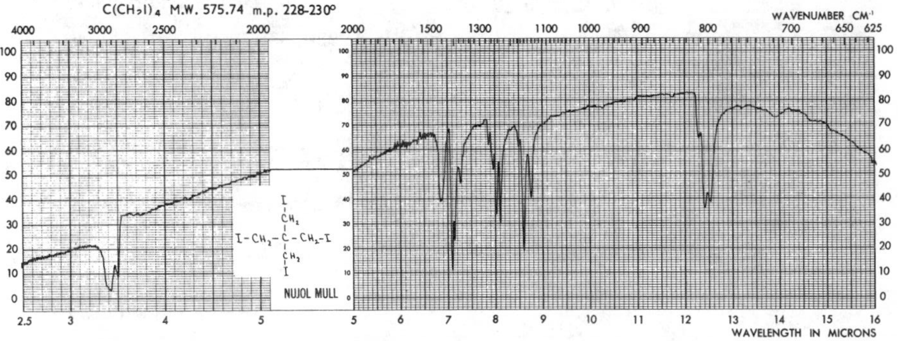

NUJOL MULL

H

P200-0 Pentachloroethane
Cl_2CHCCl_3 M.W. 202.30 n_D^{20} 1.5025

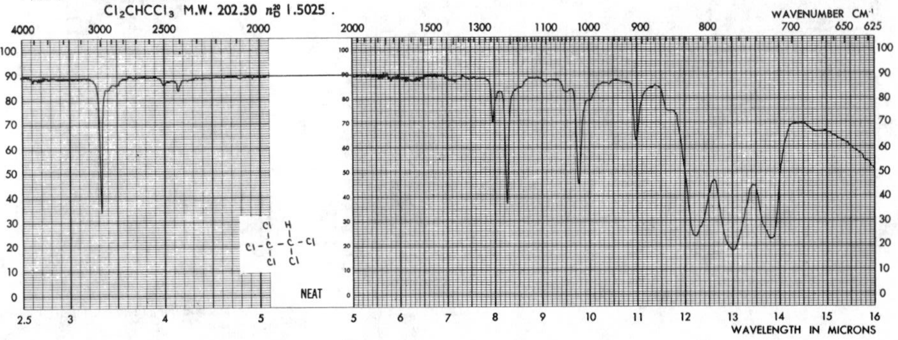

NEAT

ALDRICH

A

11,353-0 1,2-Dibromo-1,2-trichloroethane
$BrCCl_2CH(Cl)Br$ M.W. 291.21 n_D^{20} 1.5687
b.p. 94-95°/10 mm.

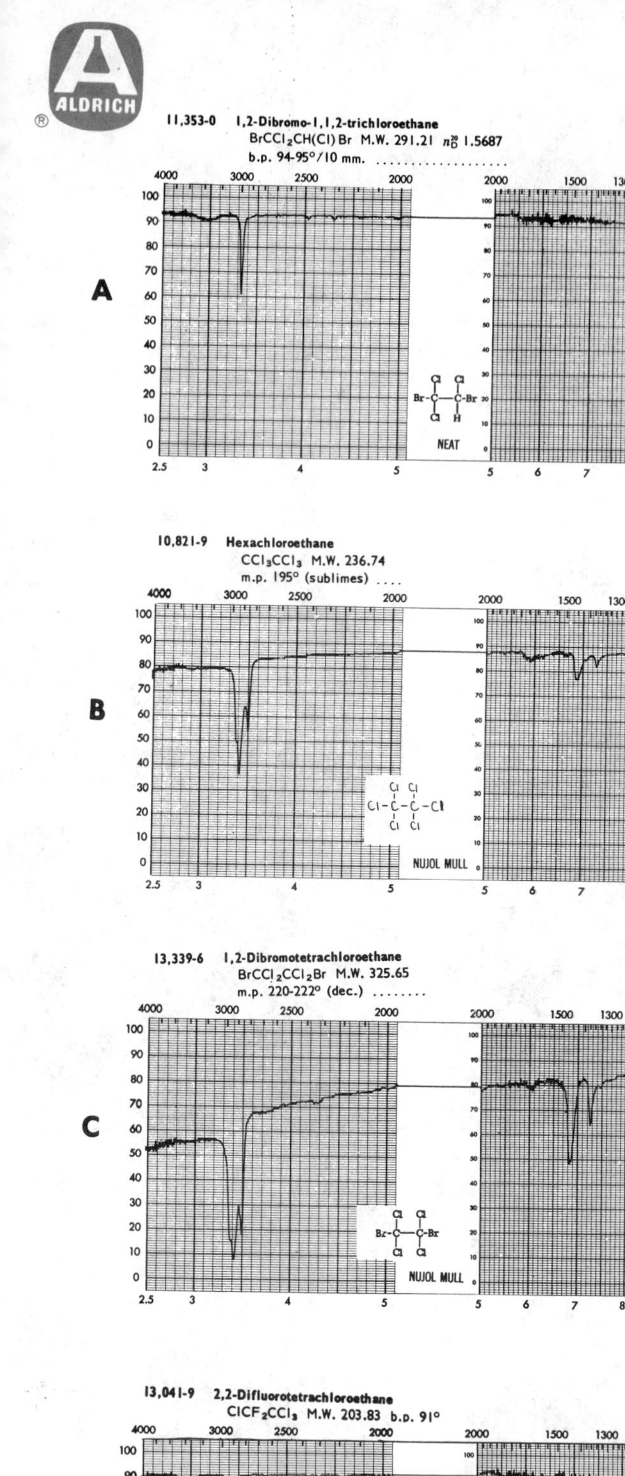

B

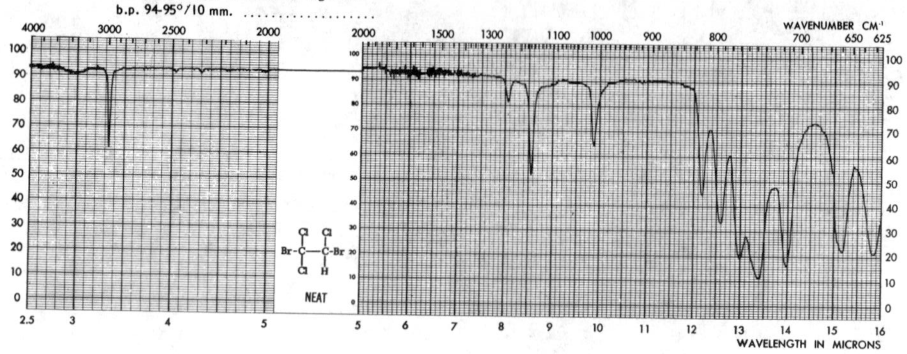

10,821-9 Hexachloroethane
CCl_3CCl_3 M.W. 236.74
m.p. 195° (sublimes)

NUJOL MULL

C

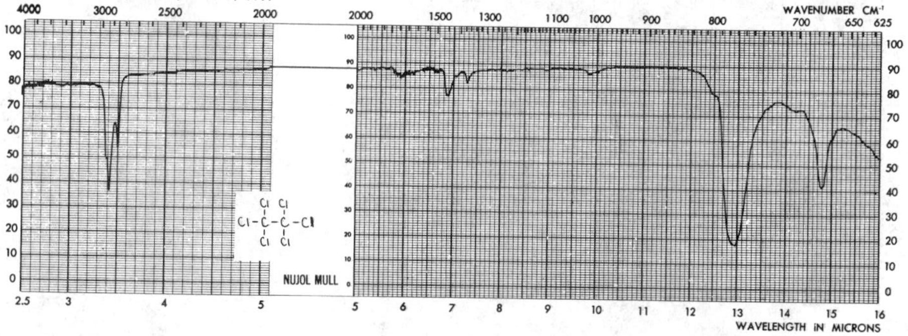

13,339-6 1,2-Dibromotetrachloroethane
$BrCCl_2CCl_2Br$ M.W. 325.65
m.p. 220-222° (dec.)

NUJOL MULL

D

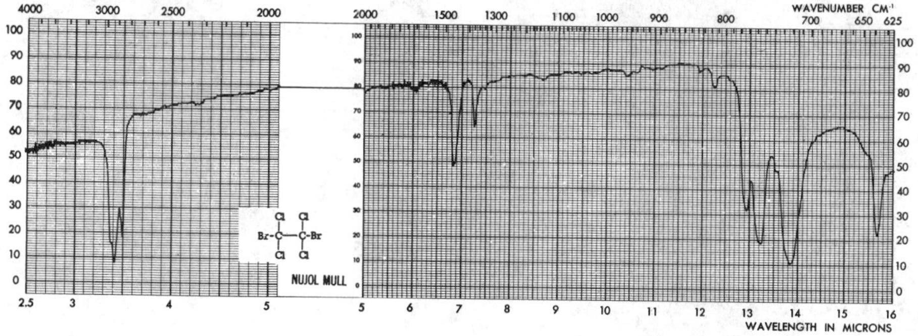

13,041-9 2,2-Difluorotetrachloroethane
$ClCF_2CCl_3$ M.W. 203.83 b.p. 91°

MELT

E

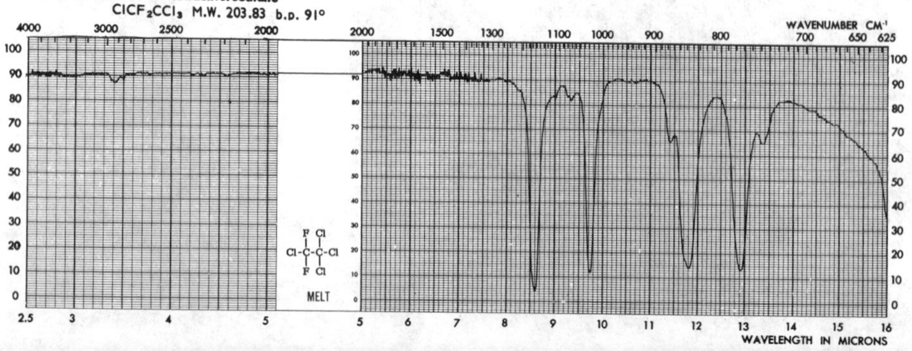

15,940-9
1,1,1,3-Tetrachlorotetrafluoropropane, 99%
$ClCF_2CF_2CCl_3$
M.W. 253.84 b.p. 112-113° n_D^{20} 1.3968

NEAT

F

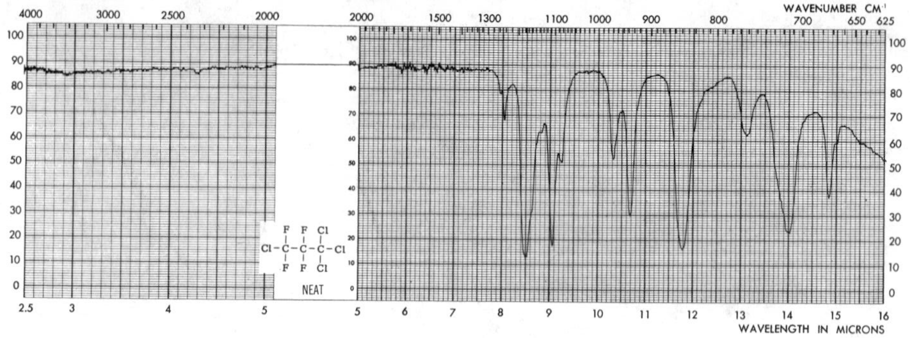

13,040-0 1,1,1-Trichlorotrifluoroethane
CF_3CCl_3 M.W. 187.38 n_D^{20}1.3599
b.p. 45.9°

NEAT

G

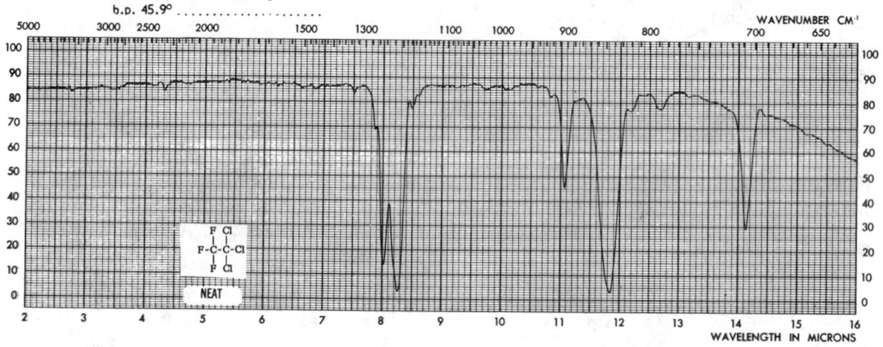

17,282-0
1,1,2-Trichlorotrifluoroethane, 99+%
$ClCF_2CCl_2F$ FW 187.38 mp -35° bp 45-47°
n_D^{20} 1.3592 d 1.564 *Beil.* 1(3),157 Disp. R,D

NEAT

H

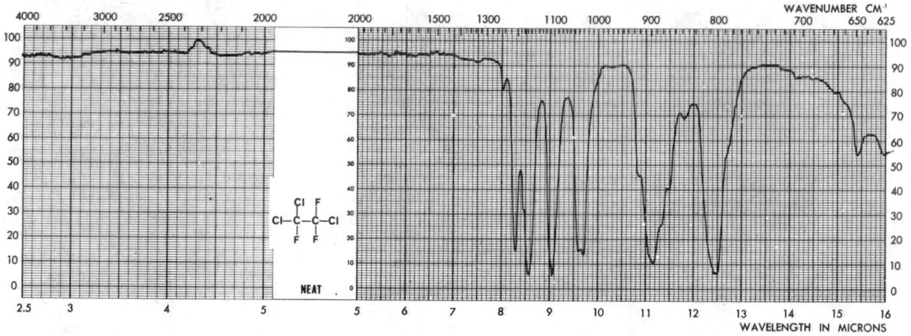

17,781-4
2-Iodo-1,1,1-trifluoroethane, 99% (2,2,2-trifluoroethyl iodide)
ICH_2CF_3
M.W. 209.94 b.p. 54.8° n_D^{20} 1.4009

NEAT

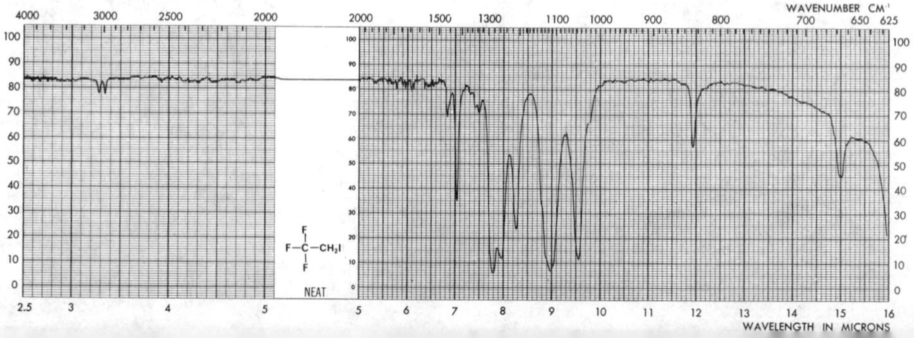

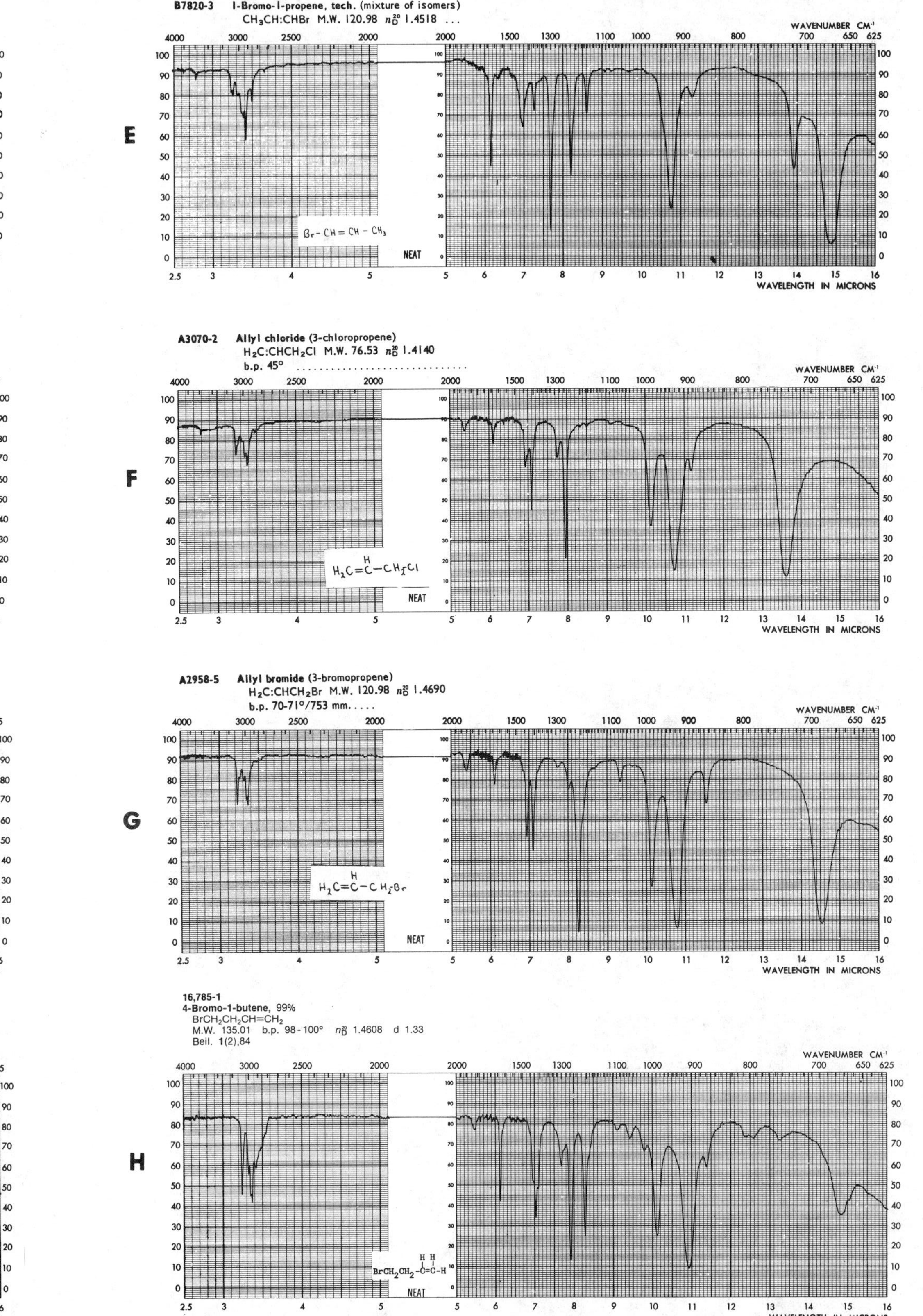

A D6370-1 **1,2-Dichlorohexafluoropropane**
$CF_3CF(Cl)CF_2Cl$ M.W. 220.93 n_D^{20} 1.3020
NEAT

B 15,554-3 1,3-Dichlorohexafluoropropane
$Cl(CF_2)_3Cl$ M.W. 220.93 n_D^{20} 1.3019
b.p. 36° ....
NEAT

C P1040-2 **Perfluoropropyl iodide**
$CF_3CF_2CF_2I$ M.W. 295.92 n_D^{20} 1.3269
b.p. 41° ....
NEAT

D V190-2 **Vinyl bromide** (bromoethylene)
$H_2C{:}CHBr$ M.W. 106.96 n_D^{20} 1.4323
b.p. 16°/750 mm. ....
NEAT

E B7820-3 **1-Bromo-1-propene, tech.** (mixture of isomers)
$CH_3CH{:}CHBr$ M.W. 120.98 n_D^{20} 1.4518 ...
NEAT

F A3070-2 **Allyl chloride** (3-chloropropene)
$H_2C{:}CHCH_2Cl$ M.W. 76.53 n_D^{20} 1.4140
b.p. 45° ....
NEAT

G A2958-5 **Allyl bromide** (3-bromopropene)
$H_2C{:}CHCH_2Br$ M.W. 120.98 n_D^{20} 1.4690
b.p. 70-71°/753 mm.....
NEAT

H 16,785-1
4-Bromo-1-butene, 99%
$BrCH_2CH_2CH{=}CH_2$
M.W. 135.01 b.p. 98-100° n_D^{20} 1.4608 d 1.33
Beil. 1(2),84
NEAT

A

12,533-4 **Crotyl chloride** (1-chloro-2-butene)
$CH_3CH{:}CHCH_2Cl$ M.W. 90.55
n_D^{20} 1.4350

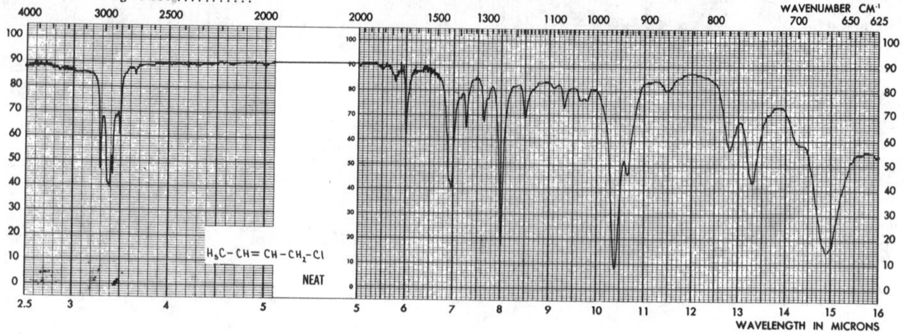

B

C8640-5 **Crotyl bromide** (1-bromo-2-butene), tech.
$CH_3CH{:}CHCH_2Br$ M.W. 135.01
n_D^{20} 1.4753

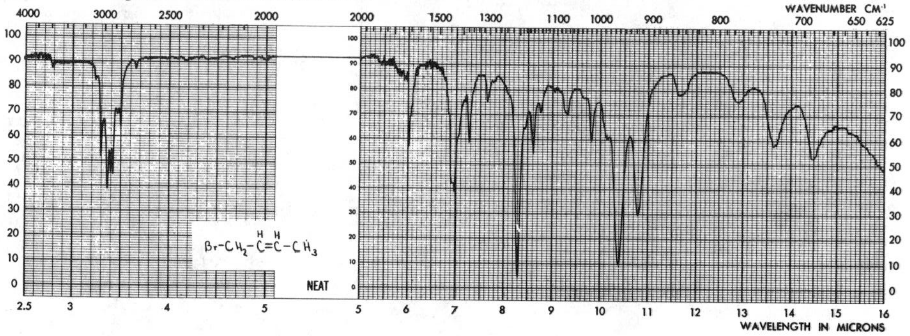

C

21,556-2
2-Bromo-2-butene, 98%, mixture of *cis* and *trans*
$CH_3CH{=}C(Br)CH_3$ FW 135.01 bp 82-90°/740mm.
n_D^{20} 1.4613 d 1.328 *Beil.* 1,205 Disp. C

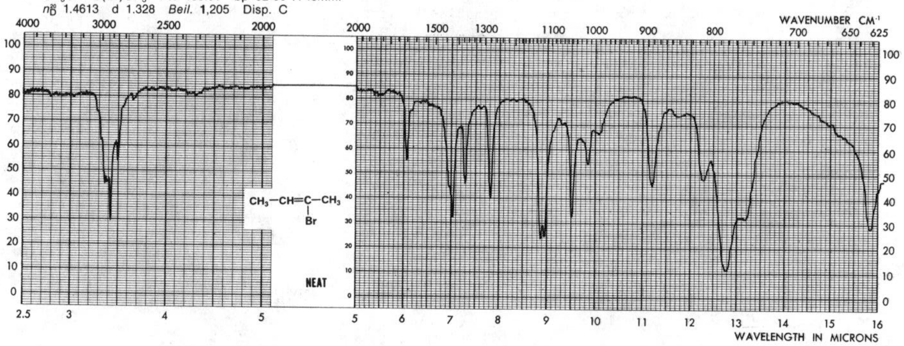

D

B7825-4 **2-Bromopropene, puriss.**
$CH_3C(Br){:}CH_2$ M.W. 120.98 n_D^{20} 1.4425

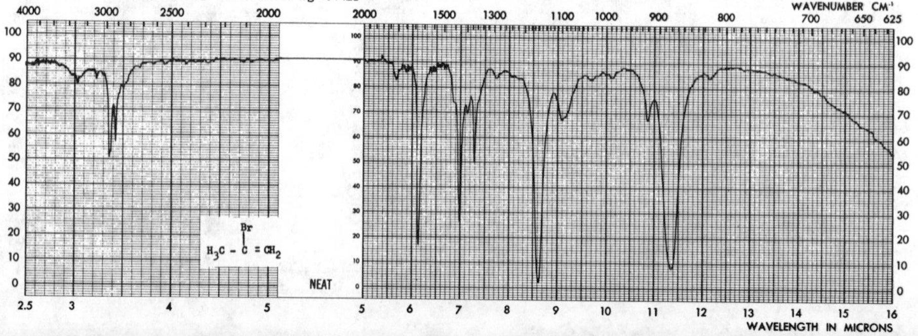

E

C2900-2 **3-Chloro-1-butene**
$CH_3CH(Cl)CH{:}CH_2$ M.W. 90.55 n_D^{20} 1.4155

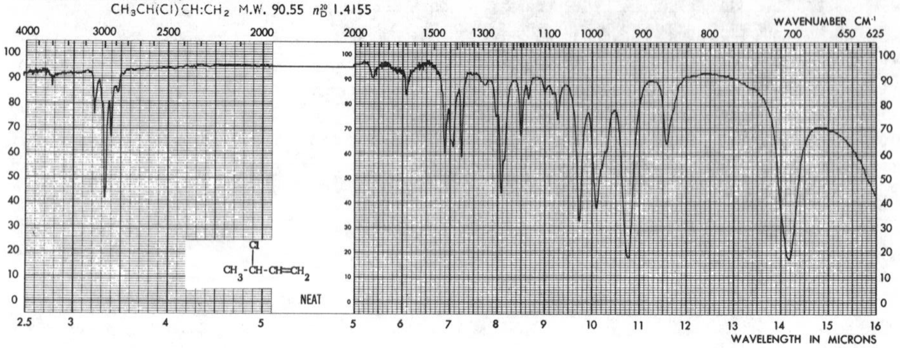

F

10,803-0 **3-Chloro-2-methylpropene** (methallyl chloride)
$H_2C{:}C(CH_3)CH_2Cl$ M.W. 90.55 n_D^{20} 1.4272 b.p. 71-72°

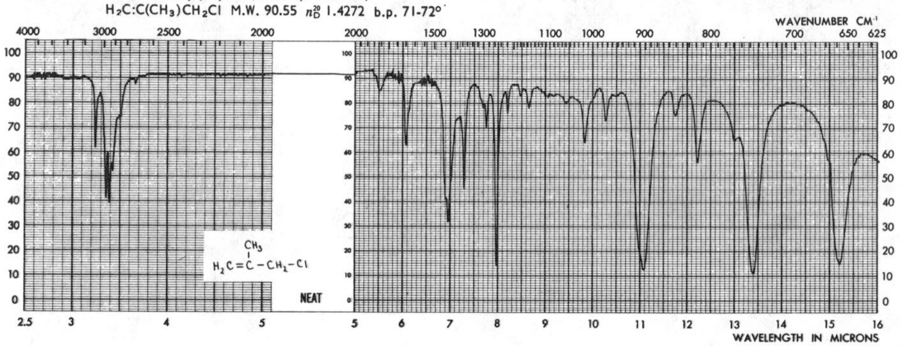

G

12,335-8 **1-Chloro-2-methylpropene**
$(CH_3)_2C{:}CHCl$ M.W. 90.55 n_D^{20} 1.4232
b.p. 68°

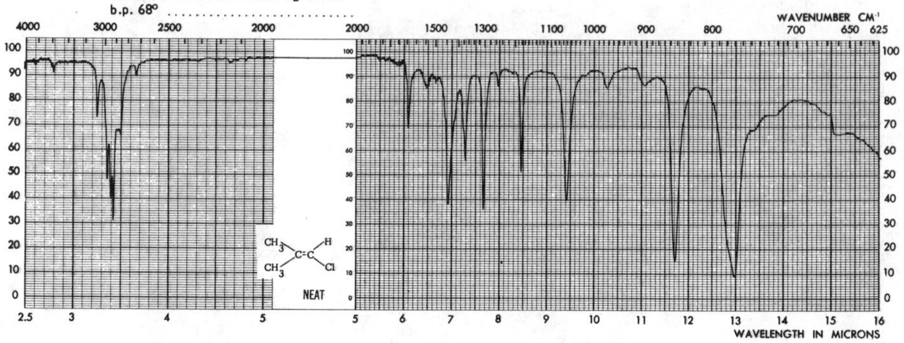

H

D6240-3 **1,2-Dichloroethylene** (mixture of isomers)
$ClCH{:}CHCl$ M.W. 96.94 n_D^{20} 1.4463

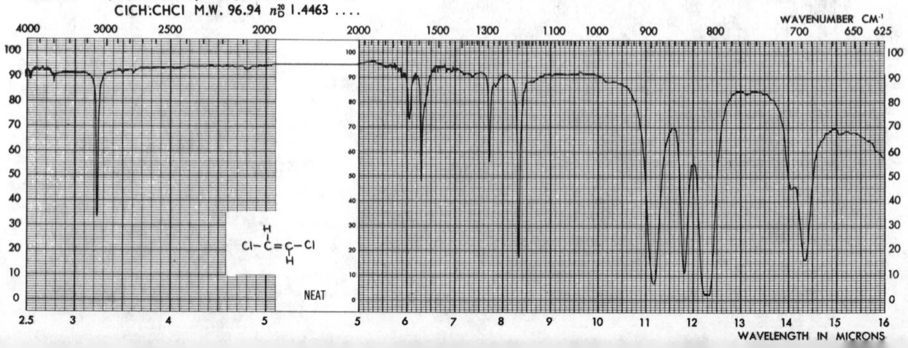

A

D6220-9 *trans*-1,2-Dichloroethylene
ClCH:CHCl M.W. 96.94 n_D^{20} 1.4456
NEAT

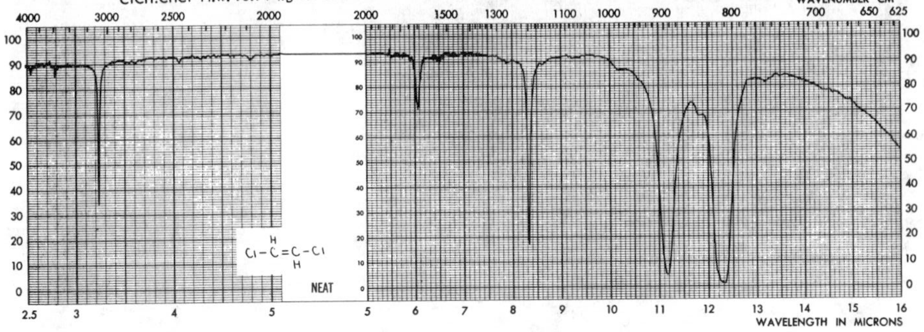

B

D6200-4 *cis*-1,2-Dichloroethylene
ClCH:CHCl M.W. 96.94 n_D^{20} 1.4481
NEAT

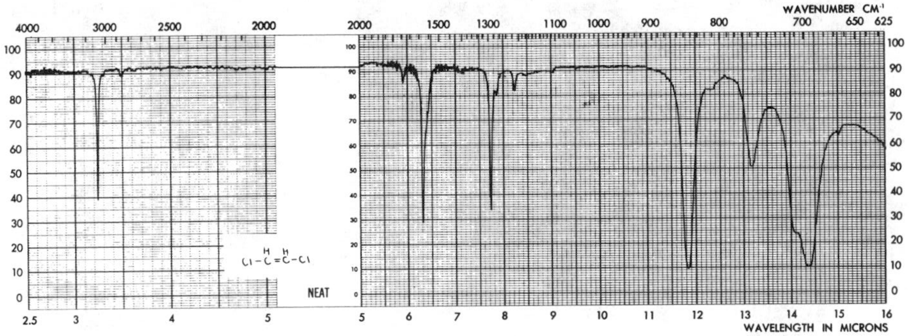

C

16,302-3
Vinylidene chloride, 99% (1,1-dichloroethylene)
$H_2C=CCl_2$
M.W. 96.94 b.p. 30-32° n_D^{20} 1.4254 d 1.213
Beil. 1,186
NEAT

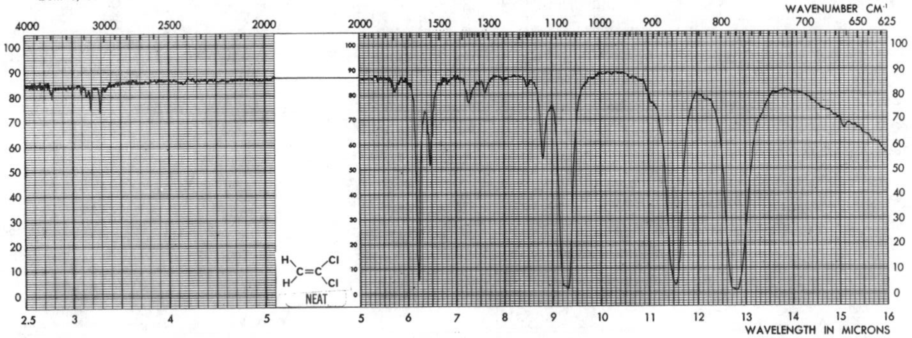

D

D4080-9 1,2-Dibromoethylene
BrCH:CHBr M.W. 185.86 n_D^{20} 1.5433
NEAT

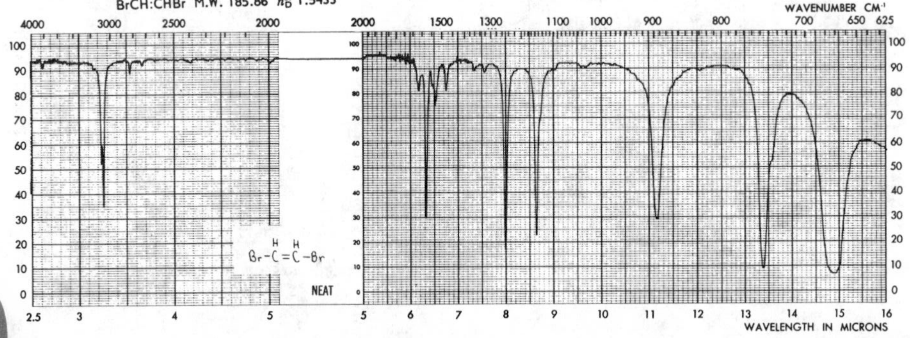

E

D7260-3 2,3-Dichloro-1-propene
$H_2C:C(Cl)CH_2Cl$ M.W. 110.97 n_D^{20} 1.4611
NEAT

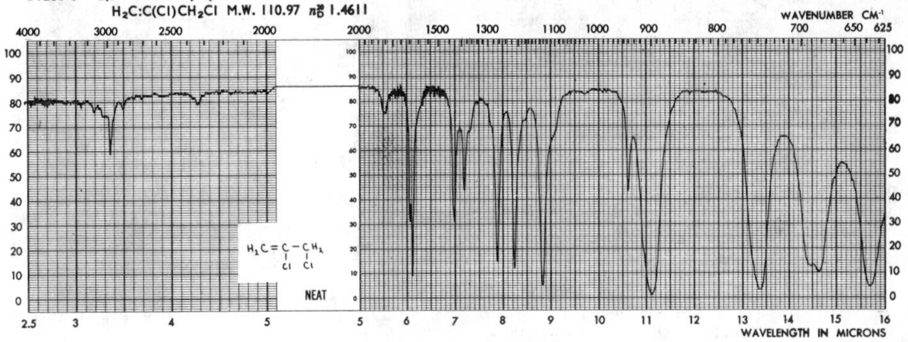

F

15,930-1
3,4-Dichloro-1-butene, 98%
$ClCH_2CH(Cl)CH=CH_2$
M.W. 125 m.p. -61° b.p. 123° n_D^{20} 1.4658
d 1.15 *IRRITANT*
NEAT

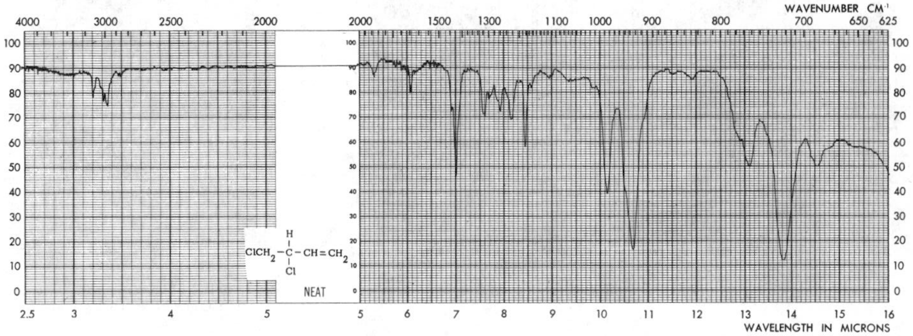

G

10,600-3 2,3-Dibromopropene
$BrCH_2C(Br):CH_2$ M.W. 199.88 n_D^{20} 1.5470
b.p. 42-44°/17 mm.
NEAT

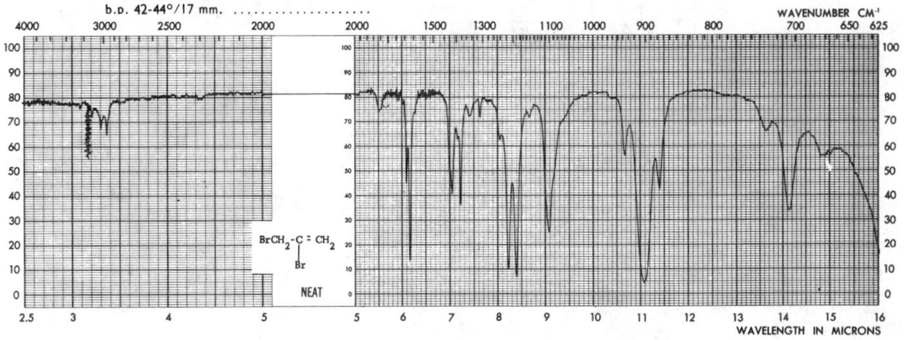

H

14,540-8 1,3-Dichloro-2-butene
$CH_3C(Cl):CHCH_2Cl$ M.W. 125.01
n_D^{20} 1.4720
NEAT

WAVENUMBER CM⁻¹ / WAVELENGTH IN MICRONS

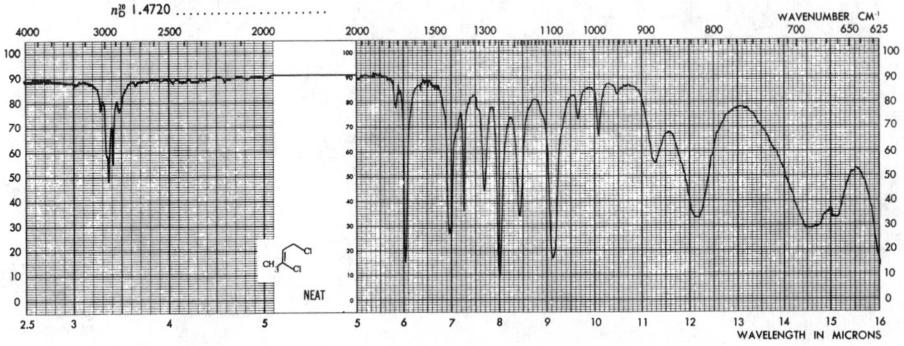

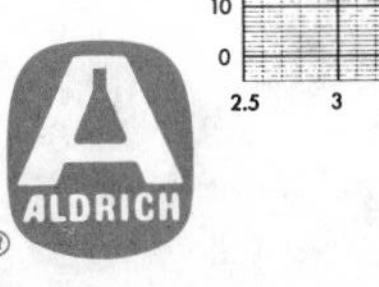

A

C3110-4 **3-Chloro-2-chloromethyl-1-propene**
$H_2C:C(CH_2Cl)_2$ M.W. 125.01 n_D^{20} 1.4753

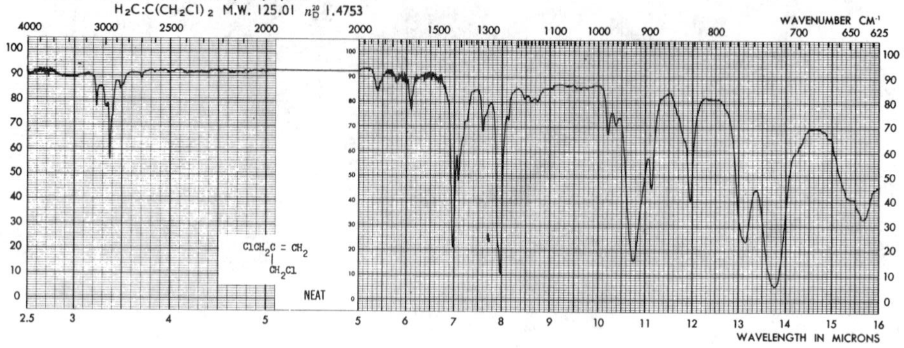

$ClCH_2C=CH_2$, CH_2Cl — NEAT

B

15,932-8
1,4-Dichloro-2-butene, 98%, mixture of cis and trans
$ClCH_2CH=CHCH_2Cl$
M.W. 125 b.p. 72-75°/40mm. n_D^{20} 1.4896
d 1.185 *IRRITANT*

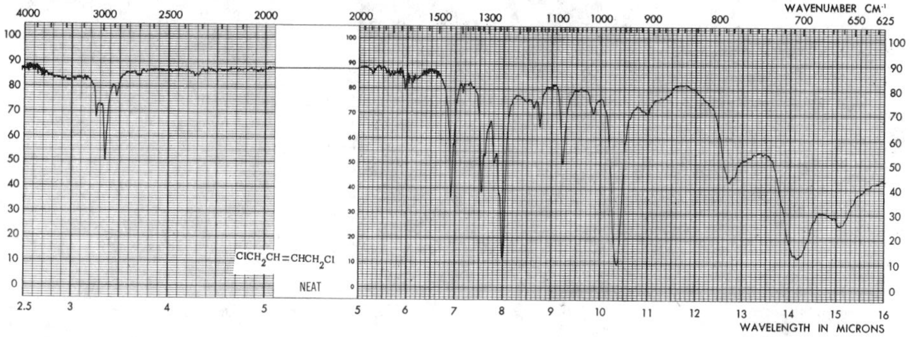

$ClCH_2CH=CHCH_2Cl$ — NEAT

C

19,570-7
cis-**1,4-Dichloro-2-butene,** 95%
$ClCH_2CH=CHCH_2Cl$ FW 125.00 mp -48°
bp 152°/758mm. n_D^{20} 1.4884 d 1.188
Beil. **1**(3),743 Disp. C

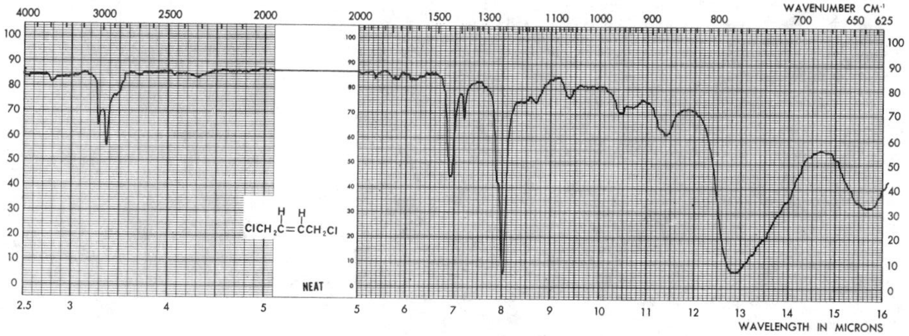

$ClCH_2C(H)=C(H)CH_2Cl$ — NEAT

D

21,508-2
trans-**1,4-Dichloro-2-butene,** tech., 85%
$ClCH_2CH=CHCH_2Cl$ FW 125.00 mp 1-3°
bp 74-76°/40mm. n_D^{20} 1.4900 d 1.183
Beil. **1**(3),743 Disp. C

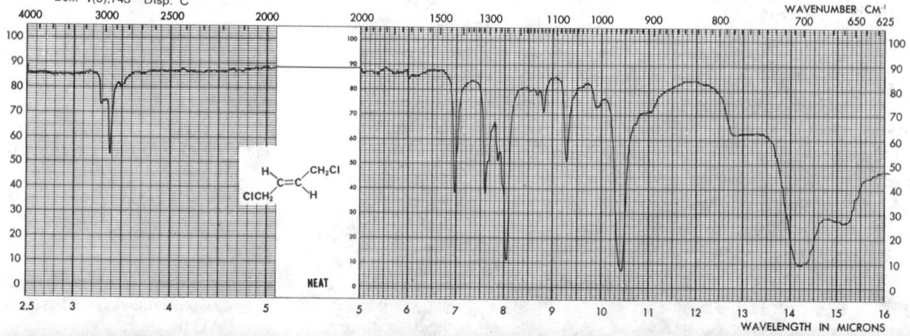

H, CH_2Cl, $ClCH_2$, H (C=C) — NEAT

E

21,556-2
2-Bromo-2-butene, 98%, mixture of *cis* and *trans*
$CH_3CH=C(Br)CH_3$ FW 135.01 bp 82-90°/740mm.
n_D^{20} 1.4613 d 1.328 *Beil.* **1**,205 Disp. C

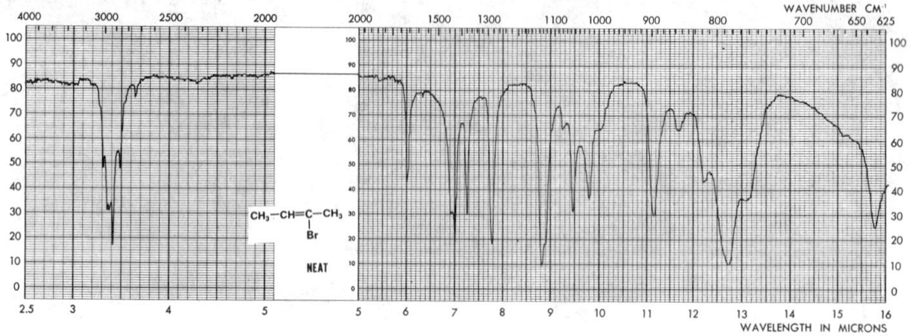

$CH_3-CH=C(Br)-CH_3$ — NEAT

F

D3920-7 **1,4-Dibromo-2-butene**
$BrCH_2CH:CHCH_2Br$ M.W. 213.91
m.p. 47-51°

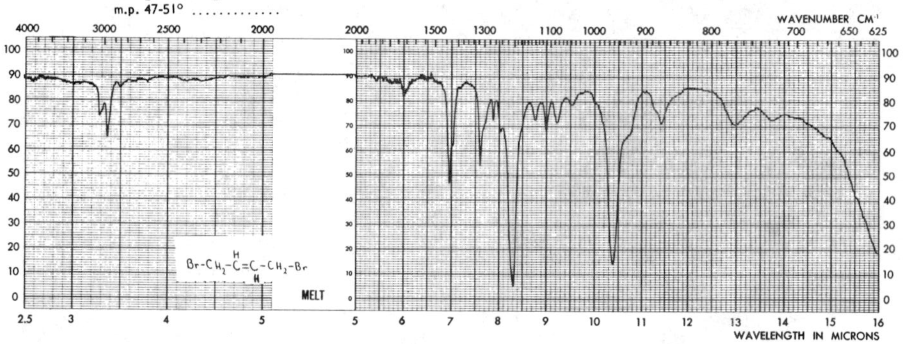

$Br-CH_2-C(H)=C(H)-CH_2-Br$ — MELT

G

11,379-4 **2,3-Bis-(bromomethyl)-1,4-dibromo-2-butene**
$(BrCH_2)_2C:C(CH_2Br)_2$ M.W. 399.77
m.p. 156-158°

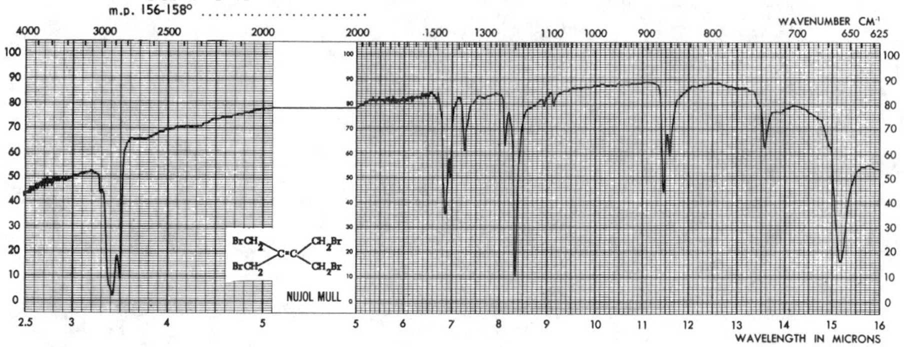

$(BrCH_2)_2C=C(CH_2Br)_2$ — NUJOL MULL

H

13,312-4 **Trichloroethylene**
$ClCH:CCl_2$ M.W. 131.39 n_D^{20} 1.4770
b.p. 87°

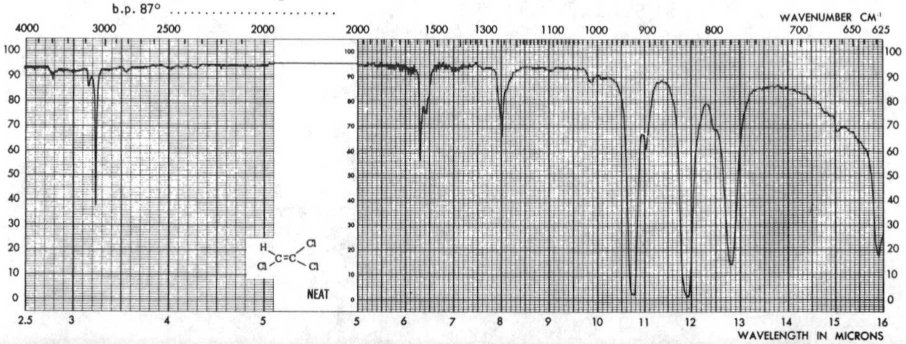

H, Cl, Cl, Cl (C=C) — NEAT

(Each spectrum: WAVENUMBER CM⁻¹ 4000–625; WAVELENGTH IN MICRONS 2.5–16; transmittance 0–100)

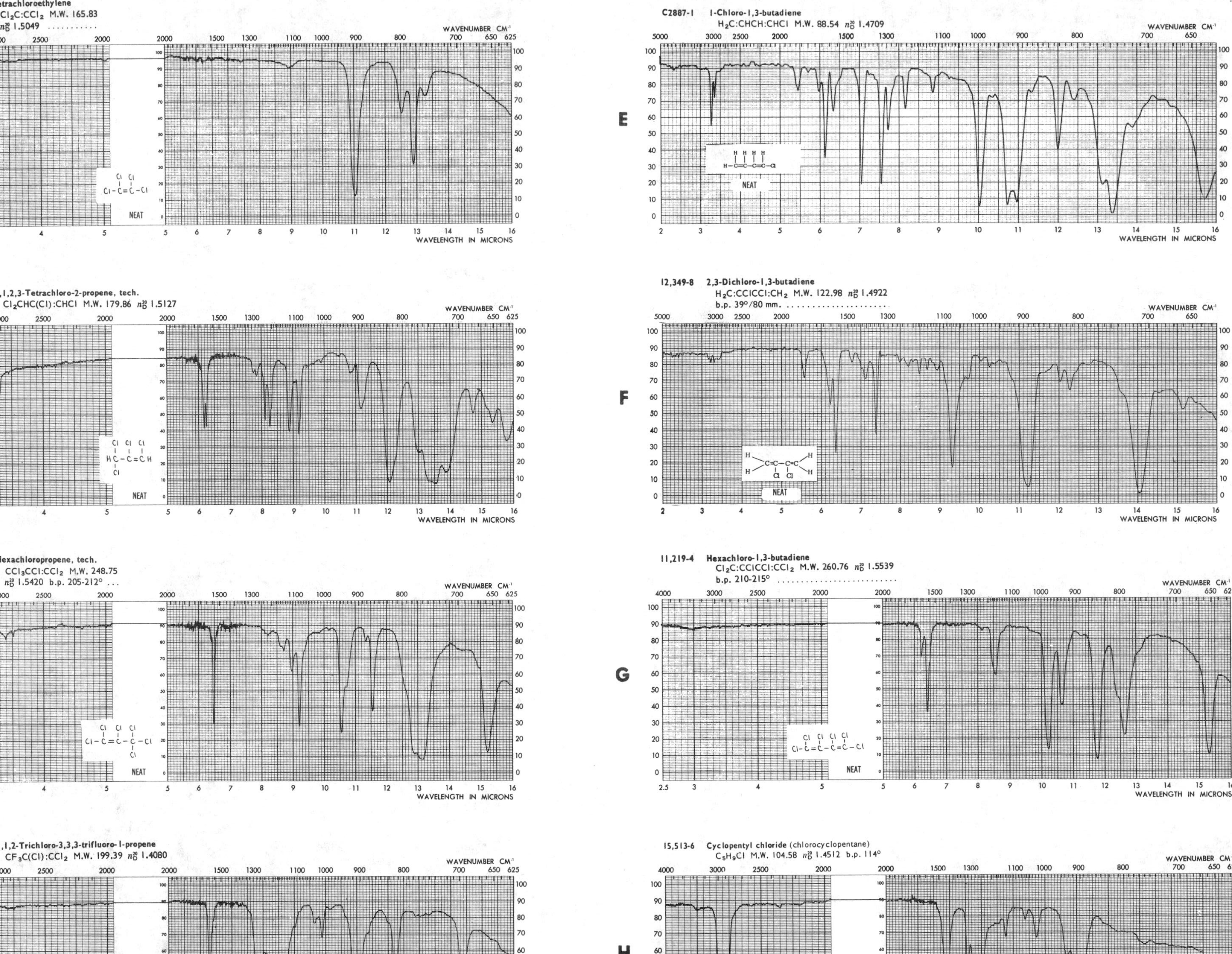

A — T750-0 Tetrachloroethylene
$Cl_2C:CCl_2$ M.W. 165.83
n_D^{20} 1.5049
NEAT

B — T800-0 1,1,2,3-Tetrachloro-2-propene, tech.
$Cl_2CHC(Cl):CHCl$ M.W. 179.86 n_D^{20} 1.5127
NEAT

C — H640-1 Hexachloropropene, tech.
$CCl_3CCl:CCl_2$ M.W. 248.75
n_D^{20} 1.5420 b.p. 205-212°
NEAT

D — 10,067-6 1,1,2-Trichloro-3,3,3-trifluoro-1-propene
$CF_3C(Cl):CCl_2$ M.W. 199.39 n_D^{20} 1.4080
NEAT

E — C2887-1 1-Chloro-1,3-butadiene
$H_2C:CHCH:CHCl$ M.W. 88.54 n_D^{20} 1.4709
NEAT

F — 12,349-8 2,3-Dichloro-1,3-butadiene
$H_2C:CClCCl:CH_2$ M.W. 122.98 n_D^{20} 1.4922
b.p. 39°/80 mm.
NEAT

G — 11,219-4 Hexachloro-1,3-butadiene
$Cl_2C:CClCCl:CCl_2$ M.W. 260.76 n_D^{20} 1.5539
b.p. 210-215°
NEAT

H — 15,513-6 Cyclopentyl chloride (chlorocyclopentane)
C_5H_9Cl M.W. 104.58 n_D^{20} 1.4512 b.p. 114°
NEAT

ALDRICH

A

18,466-7
(Chloromethyl)cyclopropane, 98%
$C_3H_5CH_2Cl$
M.W. 90.55

B

C11,730-7 Cyclopropyl bromide (bromocyclopropane)
C_3H_5Br M.W. 120.98
n_D^{20} 1.4568

C

C11,520-7 Cyclopentyl bromide (bromocyclopentane)
C_5H_9Br M.W. 149.04 n_D^{20} 1.4881

D

C10,505-8 Cyclohexyl chloride (chlorocyclohexane)
$C_6H_{11}Cl$ M.W. 118.61 n_D^{20} 1.4606

E

13,519-4 Cyclohexyl bromide (bromocyclohexane), 95%
$C_6H_{11}Br$ M.W. 163.06 n_D^{20} 1.4950
b.p. 166-168°

F

13,751-0 Cycloheptyl chloride (chlorocycloheptane)
$C_7H_{13}Cl$ M.W. 132.64 n_D^{20} 1.4750
b.p. 175-177°

G

C9970-1 Cycloheptyl bromide (bromocycloheptane)
$C_7H_{13}Br$ M.W. 177.09 n_D^{20} 1.5052

H

C10,600-3 Cyclohexylmethyl bromide (bromomethylcyclohexane)
$C_6H_{11}CH_2Br$ M.W. 177.09 n_D^{20} 1.4913

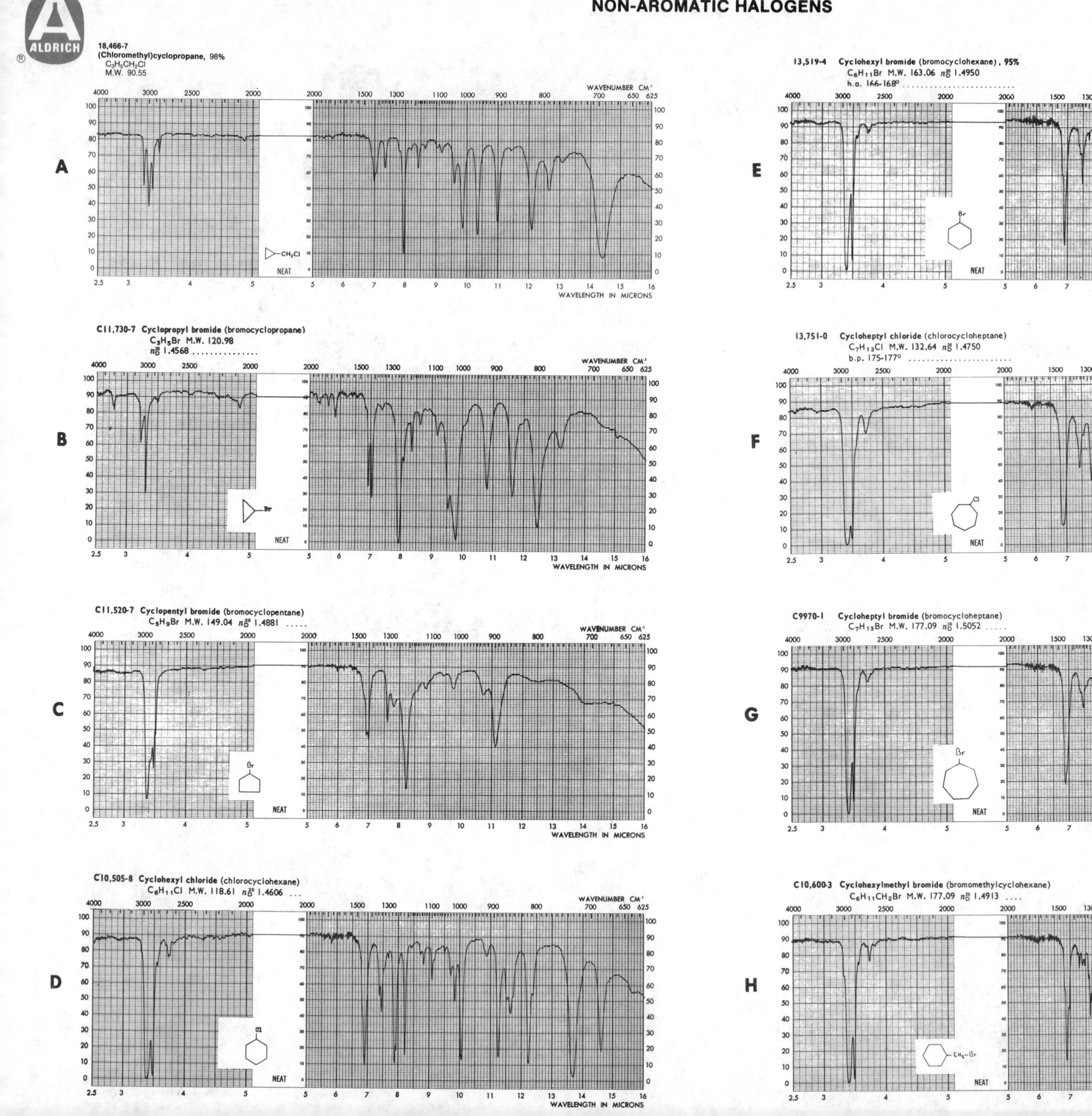

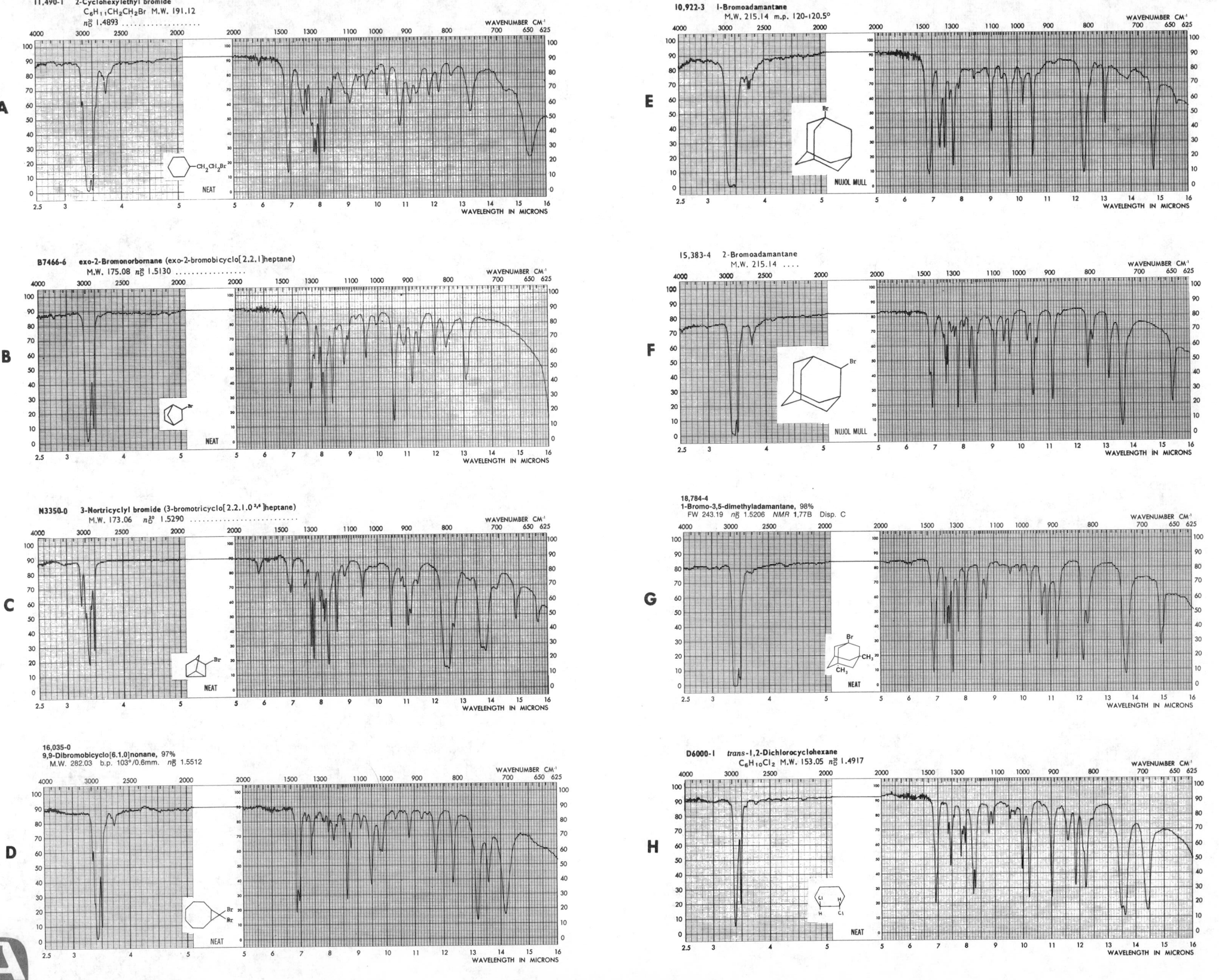

A
11,490-1 2-Cyclohexylethyl bromide
$C_6H_{11}CH_2CH_2Br$ M.W. 191.12
n_D^{20} 1.4893
NEAT
B
B7466-6 exo-2-Bromonorbornane (exo-2-bromobicyclo[2.2.1]heptane)
M.W. 175.08 n_D^{20} 1.5130
NEAT
C
N3350-0 3-Nortricyclyl bromide (3-bromotricyclo[2.2.1.0^{2,6}]heptane)
M.W. 173.06 n_D^{20} 1.5290
NEAT
D
16,035-0
9,9-Dibromobicyclo[6.1.0]nonane, 97%
M.W. 282.03 b.p. 103°/0.6mm. n_D^{20} 1.5512
NEAT
E
10,922-3 1-Bromoadamantane
M.W. 215.14 m.p. 120-120.5°
NUJOL MULL
F
15,383-4 2-Bromoadamantane
M.W. 215.14
NUJOL MULL
G
18,784-4
1-Bromo-3,5-dimethyladamantane, 98%
FW 243.19 n_D^{20} 1.5206 NMR 1,77B Disp. C
NEAT
H
D6000-1 trans-1,2-Dichlorocyclohexane
$C_6H_{10}Cl_2$ M.W. 153.05 n_D^{20} 1.4917
NEAT
WAVENUMBER CM⁻¹
WAVELENGTH IN MICRONS

A

D3960-6 *trans*-1,2-Dibromocyclohexane
$C_6H_{10}Br_2$ M.W. 241.96 n_D^{20} 1.5515 m.p. - 6 to - 4°
NEAT

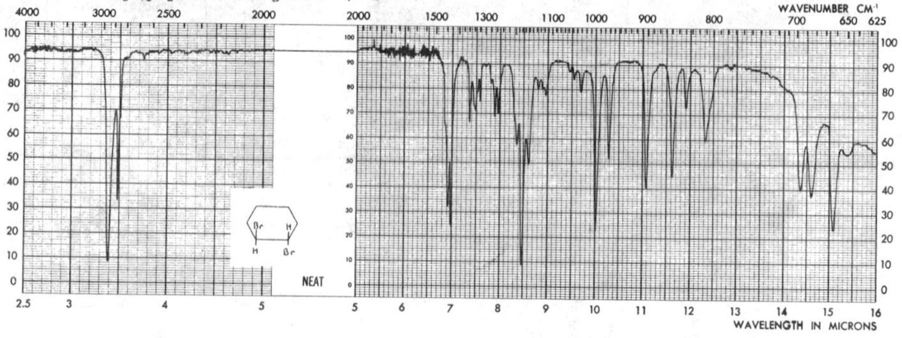

B

T5507-7 1-Trichloromethyl-*cis*-perhydropentalene
M.W. 227.56 n_D^{20} 1.5114 b.p. 120°/7 mm.
NEAT

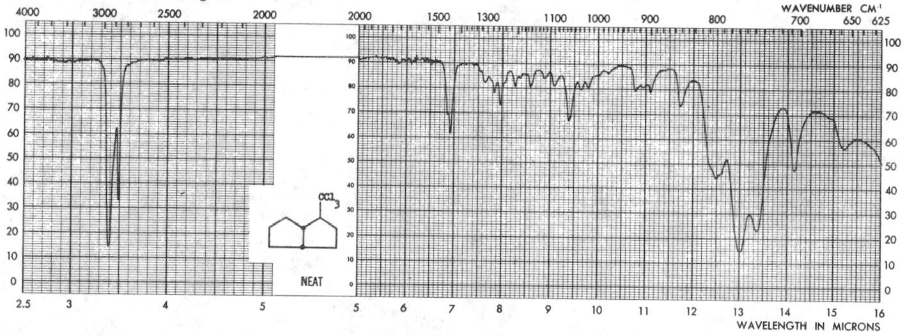

C

85,501-4
Cadinene dihydrochloride, 99%
M.W. 277.28 m.p. 115-119°
NUJOL MULL

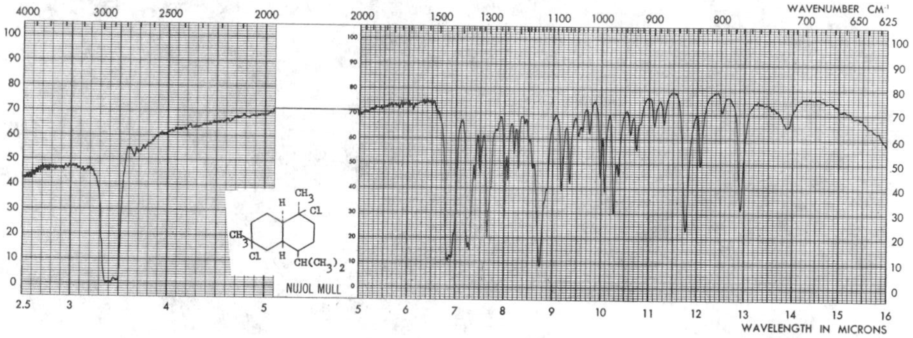

D

14,476-2 1,2,5,6,9,10-Hexabromocyclododecane, tech.
M.W. 641.73
NUJOL MULL

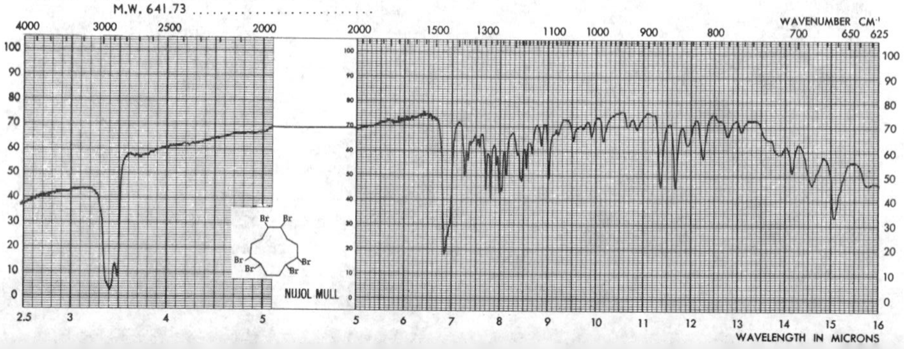

E

13,393-0 Dodecafluorocyclohexane (perfluorocyclohexane)
C_6F_{12} M.W. 300.04 m.p. 51° b.p. 52°
NUJOL MULL

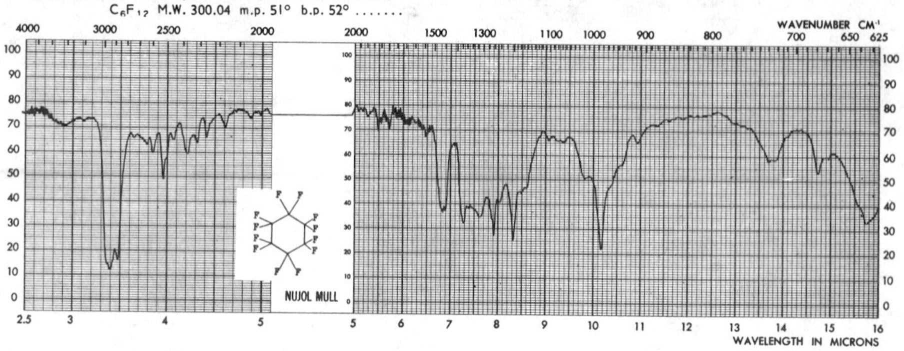

F

P1030-5 Perfluoro(methylcyclohexane)
$C_6F_{11}CF_3$ M.W. 350.05 n_D^{20} 1.2600 b.p. 76°
NEAT

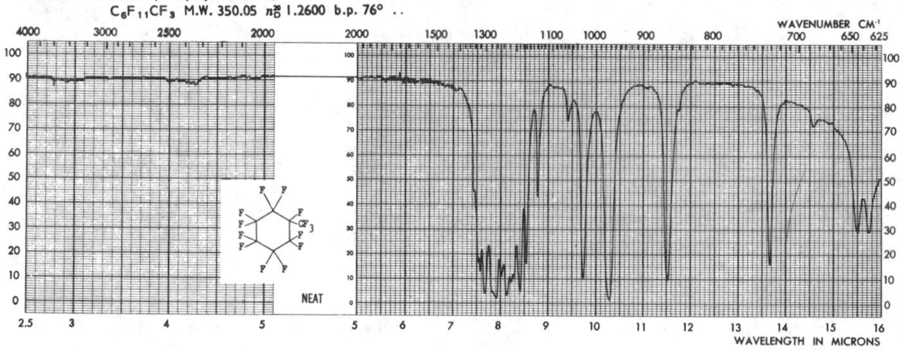

G

P990-0 Perfluorodecalin (octadecafluorodecahydronaphthalene) (mixture of *cis* and *trans*)
M.W. 462.07
NEAT

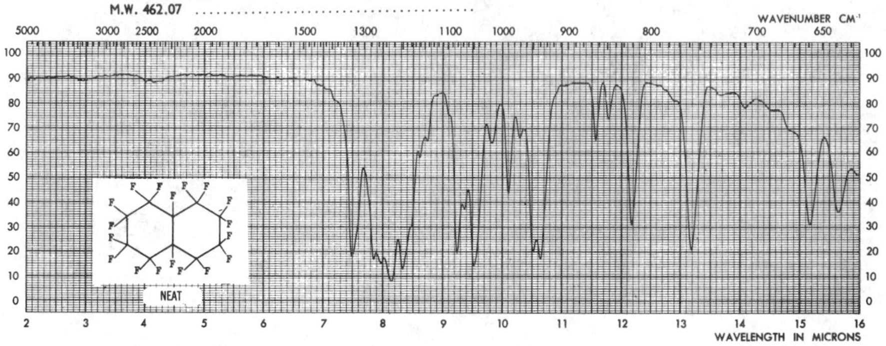

H

14,594-7 Tetrachlorocyclopropene
(send for data sheet)
M.W. 177.85 n_D^{20} 1.5063
b.p. 125-130° (under nitrogen)
NEAT

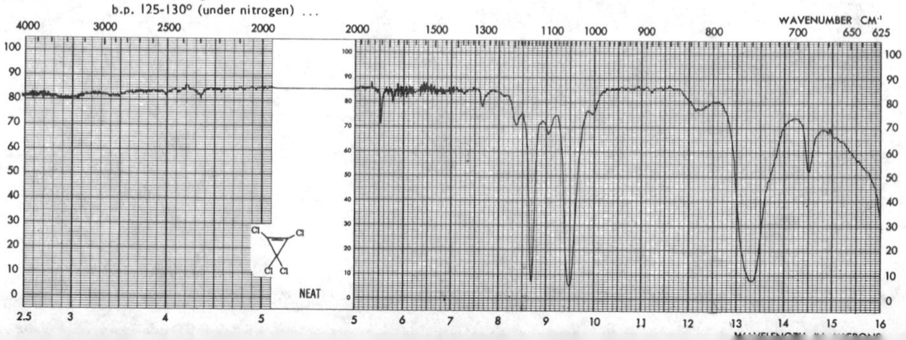

A

O-20-2 **Octachlorocyclopentene**
M.W. 343.68 m.p. 35-40°

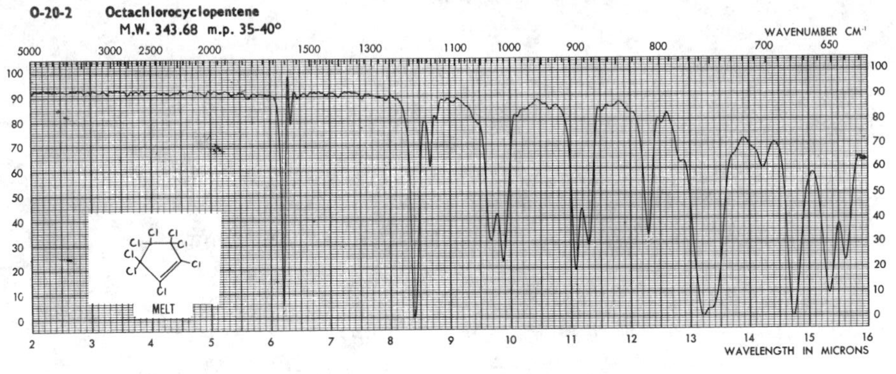

B

H600-2 **Hexachlorocyclopentadiene**
M.W. 272.77 n_D^{20} 1.5625 . . .

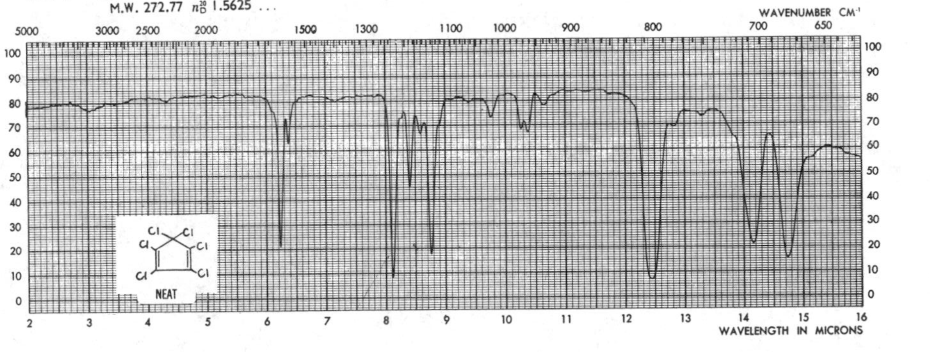

C

H540-5 **1,2,3,4,7,7-Hexachlorobicyclo[2.2.1]-2,5-heptadiene, tech.**
(shipped under water)
M.W. 298.81 . . . .

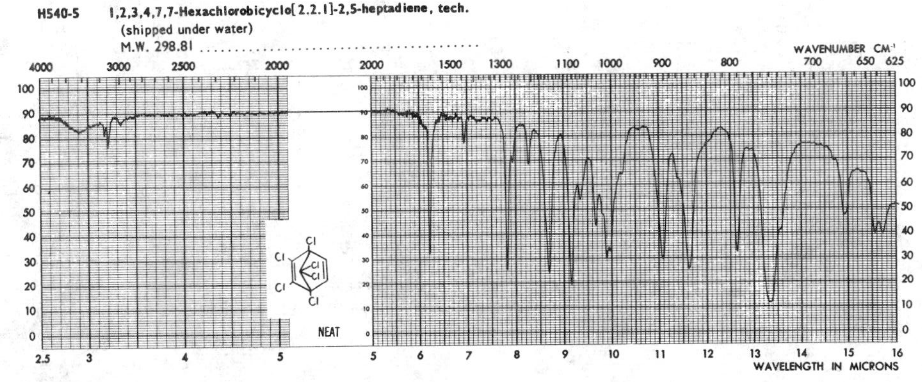

NON-AROMATIC ALCOHOLS

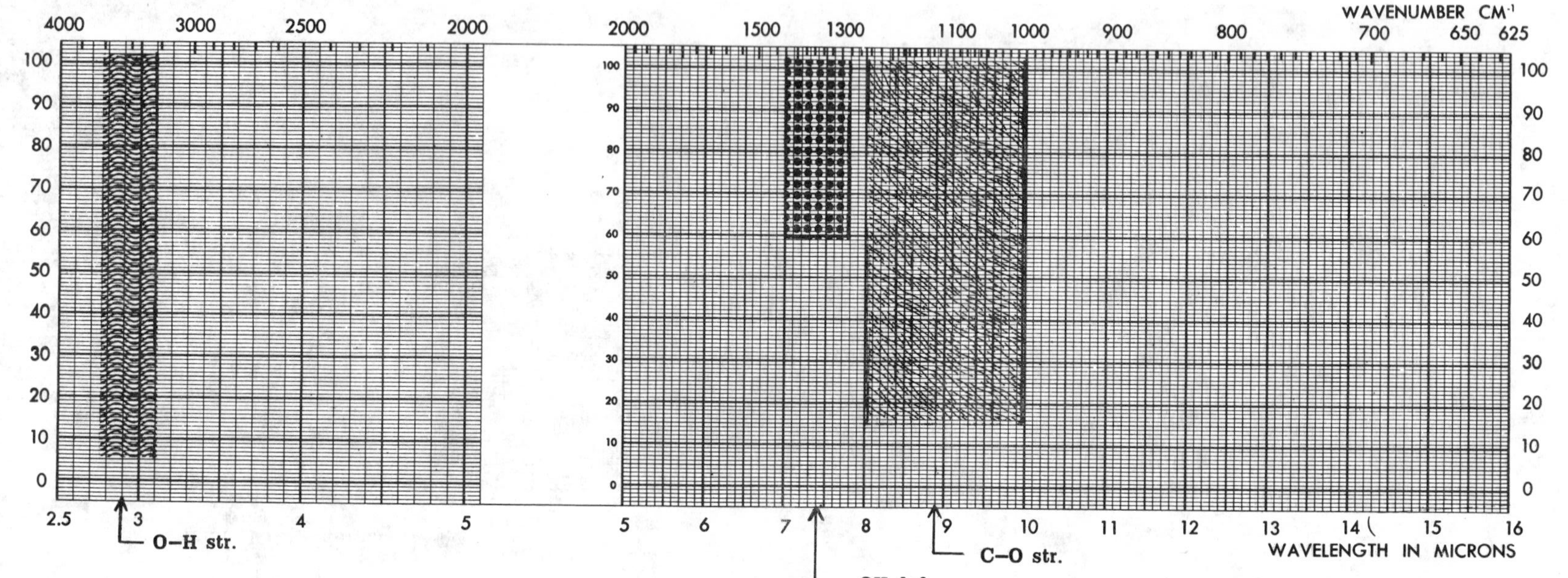

The stretch vibrations of the oxygen-hydrogen and the carbon-oxygen bonds are responsible for the characteristic absorptions in this section. The first vibration causes strong absorption close to 3 μ (3335 cm^{-1}). As can be seen from practically every example, the shape, intensity and position of the OH stretch absorption are very uniform. The broadness is due to hydrogen bonding. The sharp absorption appearing in some cases at 2.75 μ (3635 cm^{-1}) is attributable to the presence of molecules without this hydrogen bonding. (See spectra 67E-68A, 72H-73B, etc).

The carbon-oxygen stretch appears between 8 and 10 μ (1250 – 1000 cm^{-1}), depending on the substitution of the carbon atom. For simple saturated alcohols the absorption moves from the vicinity of 9.5 μ (1055 cm^{-1}) in primary alcohols to 9 μ (1110 cm^{-1}) in secondary alcohols and to 8.5 μ (1175 cm^{-1}) in tertiary alcohols. These absorptions can be split and shifted when viewed as nujol mulls. The CH_2–O absorption will shift above 9.5 μ (1055 cm^{-1}) to almost 10 μ (1000 cm^{-1}) when the methylene group is attached to an unsaturated carbon atom (see spectra 84 D, E, 90 F & H) or often when attached to a tertiary carbon. Although the principal absorption of the secondary and tertiary alcohols can be found in broad bands at 9 μ (1110 cm^{-1}) and 8.5 μ (1175 cm^{-1}) respectively, the bands are usually joined by a profusion of other absorptions of similar or of slightly less intensity from 9.5 to 12 μ (1055 – 835 cm^{-1}).

The absorptions observed in the various simple alcohols are combined into broad bands with various maxima in the polyalcohol and sugar spectra (see spectra 112G-121H). Of course sugars do not display an aldehyde carbonyl due to their cyclic hemiacetal structure.

A

Methyl alcohol, spectrophotometric grade, GOLD LABEL (meets A.C.S. spectrophotometric requirements) (methanol)
CH_3OH
M.W. 32.04 m.p. -98° b.p. 65° n_D^{20} 1.3290
d 0.791 Beil. **1**,273 **IR** 1087C *HYGROSCOPIC*

B

Ethyl alcohol, anhydrous
C_2H_5OH M.W. 46.07 b.p. 78.4° n_D^{20} 1.3612
d 0.785 f.p. 54°F *Merck Index* **8**,30 Disp C

C

11,003-5 1-Propanol, 99+%
$CH_3CH_2CH_2OH$ M.W. 60.10 n_D^{20} 1.3840
b.p. 97°

D

15,467-9
***n*-Butanol**, spectrophotometric grade, GOLD LABEL (meets A.C.S. specifications) (*n*-butyl alcohol)
$CH_3(CH_2)_3OH$
M.W. 74.12 m.p. -90 to -80° b.p. 117.7°
n_D^{20} 1.3985 d 0.81 Beil. **1**,367

E

13,897-5 1-Pentanol
$CH_3(CH_2)_4OH$ M.W. 88.15 n_D^{20} 1.4093
b.p. 136-138°

F

H1,330-3
Hexyl alcohol, 98% (1-hexanol)
$CH_3(CH_2)_5OH$
M.W. 102.18 m.p. -52° b.p. 156.5° n_D^{20} 1.4179
d 0.814 Beil. **1**,407

G

H280-5 1-Heptanol (heptyl alcohol)
$CH_3(CH_2)_6OH$ M.W. 116.20 n_D^{20} 1.4232 b.p. 176°

H

11,261-5 1-Octanol (capryl alcohol, octyl alcohol)
$CH_3(CH_2)_7OH$ M.W. 130.23 n_D^{20} 1.4297
b.p. 192°

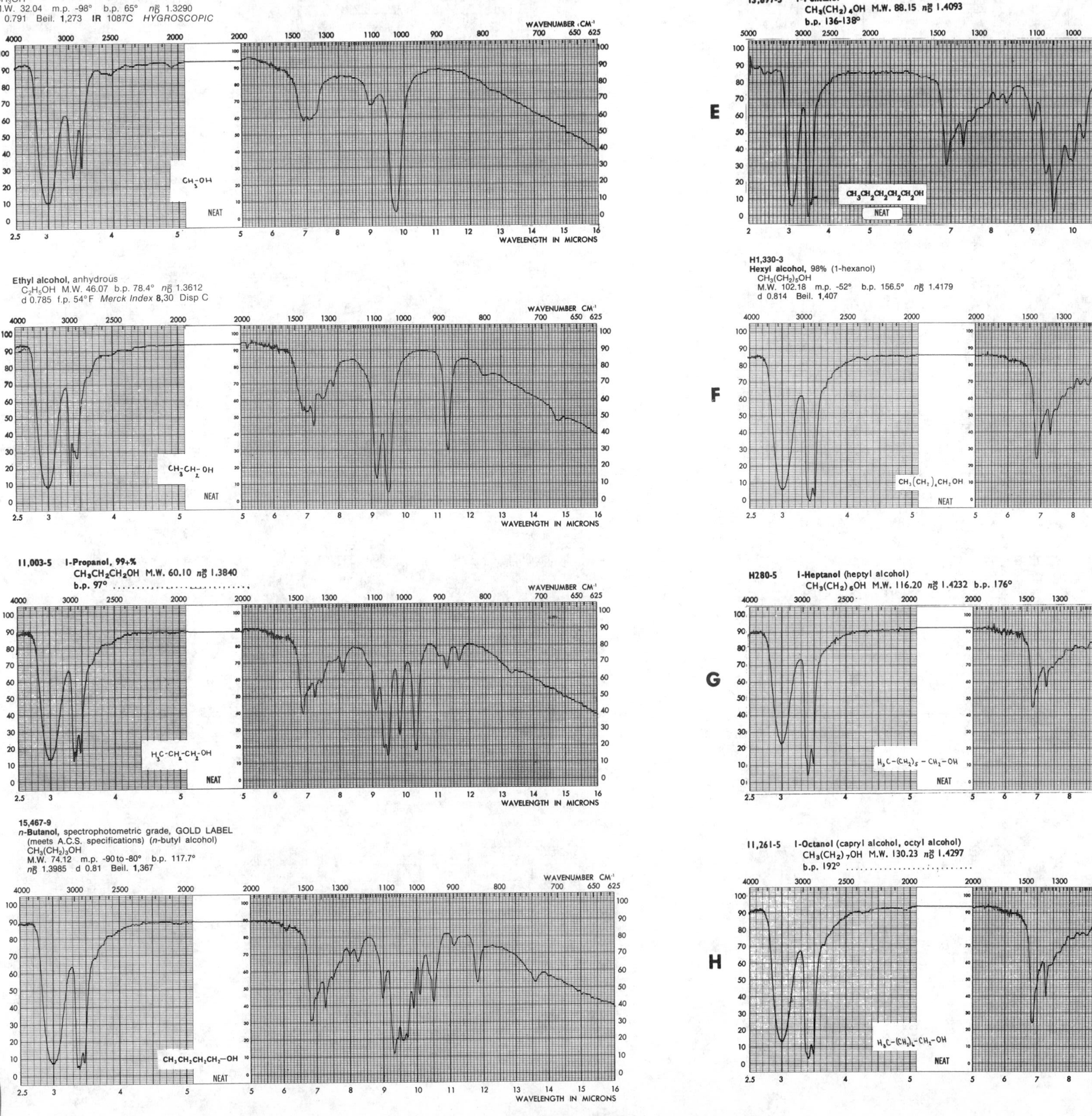

ALDRICH

A

13,121-0 **1-Nonanol** (nonyl alcohol)
$CH_3(CH_2)_8OH$ M.W. 144.26 n_D^{20} 1.4334 m.p. -8 to -6°

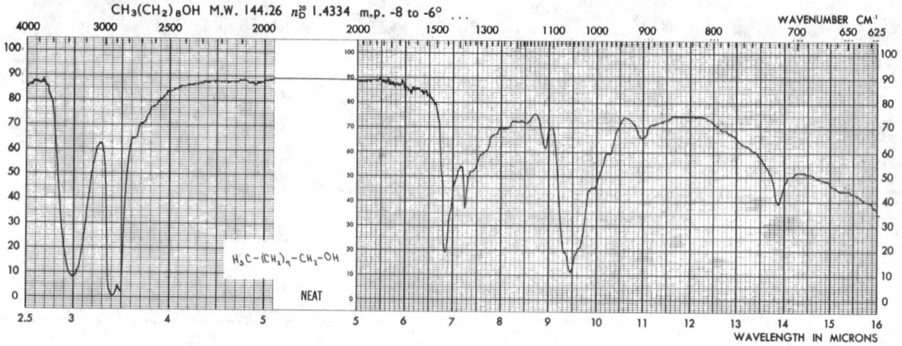

$H_3C-(CH_2)_7-CH_2-OH$ NEAT

B

15,058-4 **Decyl alcohol** (1-decanol)
$CH_3(CH_2)_9OH$ M.W. 158.29 n_D^{20} 1.4372
b.p. 231°

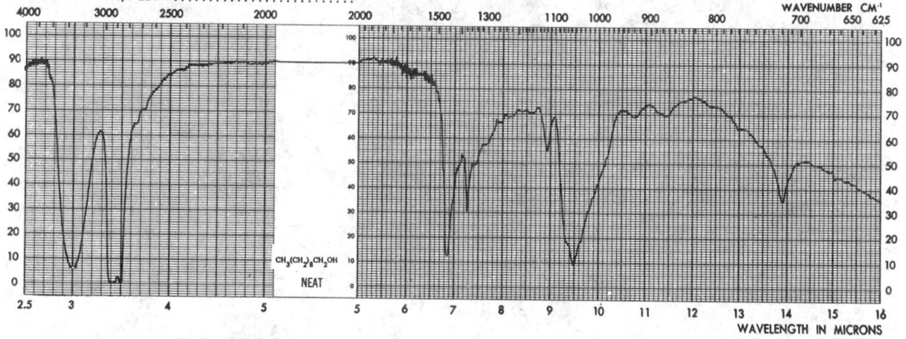

$CH_3(CH_2)_8CH_2OH$ NEAT

C

U100-1 **1-Undecanol** (undecyl alcohol)
$CH_3(CH_2)_9CH_2OH$ M.W. 172.31 n_D^{20} 1.4390
b.p. 146°/30 mm.

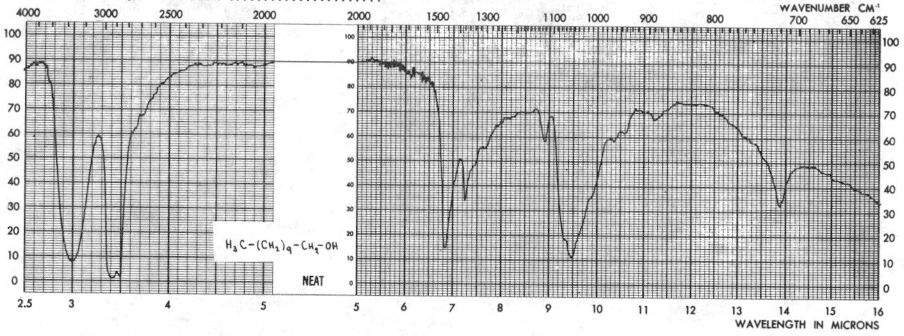

$H_3C-(CH_2)_9-CH_2-OH$ NEAT

D

12,679-9 **1-Dodecanol** (dodecyl alcohol)
$CH_3(CH_2)_{11}OH$ M.W. 186.34 m.p. 24-27°

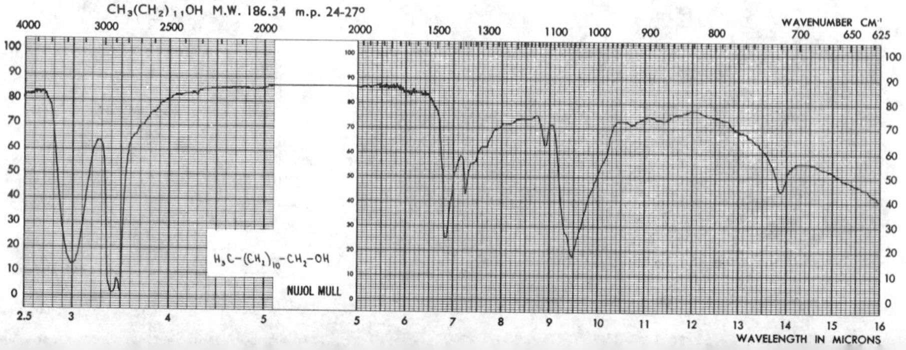

$H_3C-(CH_2)_{10}-CH_2-OH$ NUJOL MULL

E

T5763-0 **1-Tridecanol**
$CH_3(CH_2)_{12}OH$ M.W. 200.37 m.p. 32.5-33.5°

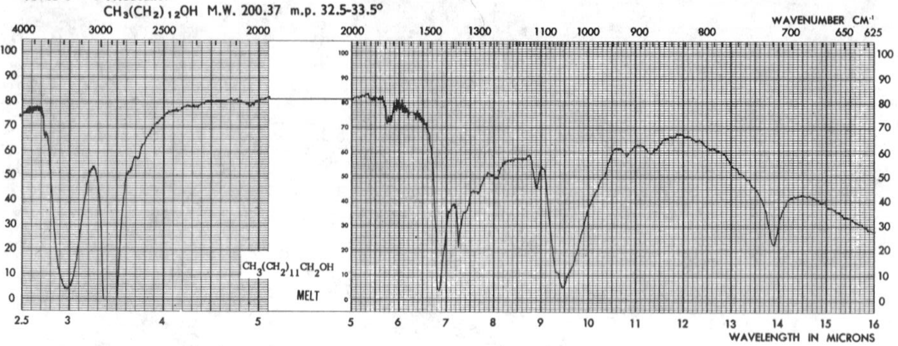

$CH_3(CH_2)_{11}CH_2OH$ MELT

F

T960-0 **1-Tetradecanol, tech.**
$CH_3(CH_2)_{13}OH$ M.W. 214.39 m.p. 38-40°

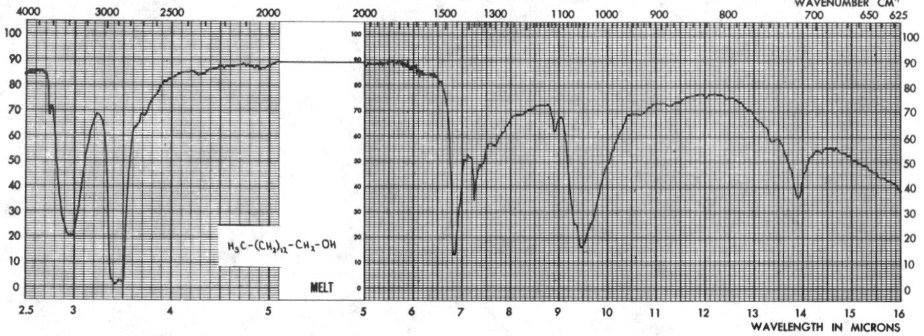

$H_3C-(CH_2)_{12}-CH_2-OH$ MELT

G

P380-5 **1-Pentadecanol**
$CH_3(CH_2)_{14}OH$ M.W. 228.42 m.p. 45-46°

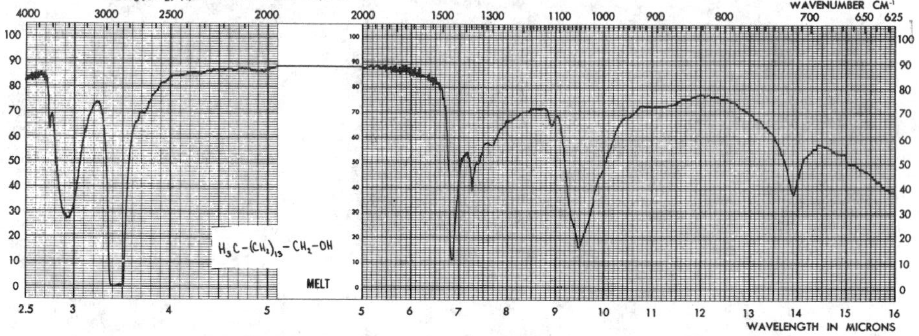

$H_3C-(CH_2)_{13}-CH_2-OH$ MELT

H

H680-0 **1-Hexadecanol, tech.**
$CH_3(CH_2)_{15}OH$ M.W. 242.45 m.p. 48-50°

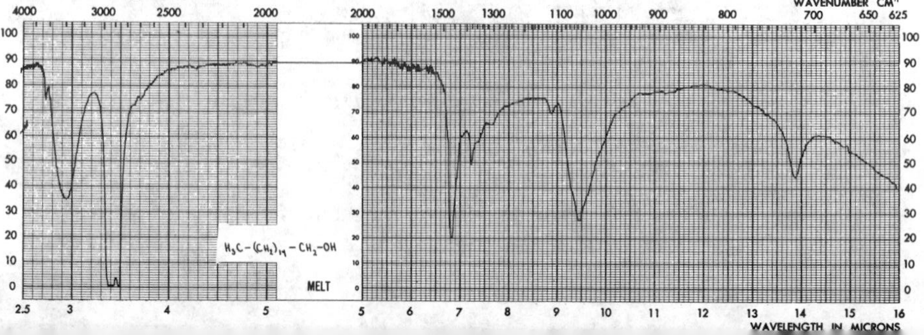

$H_3C-(CH_2)_{14}-CH_2-OH$ MELT

WAVENUMBER CM⁻¹ — WAVELENGTH IN MICRONS

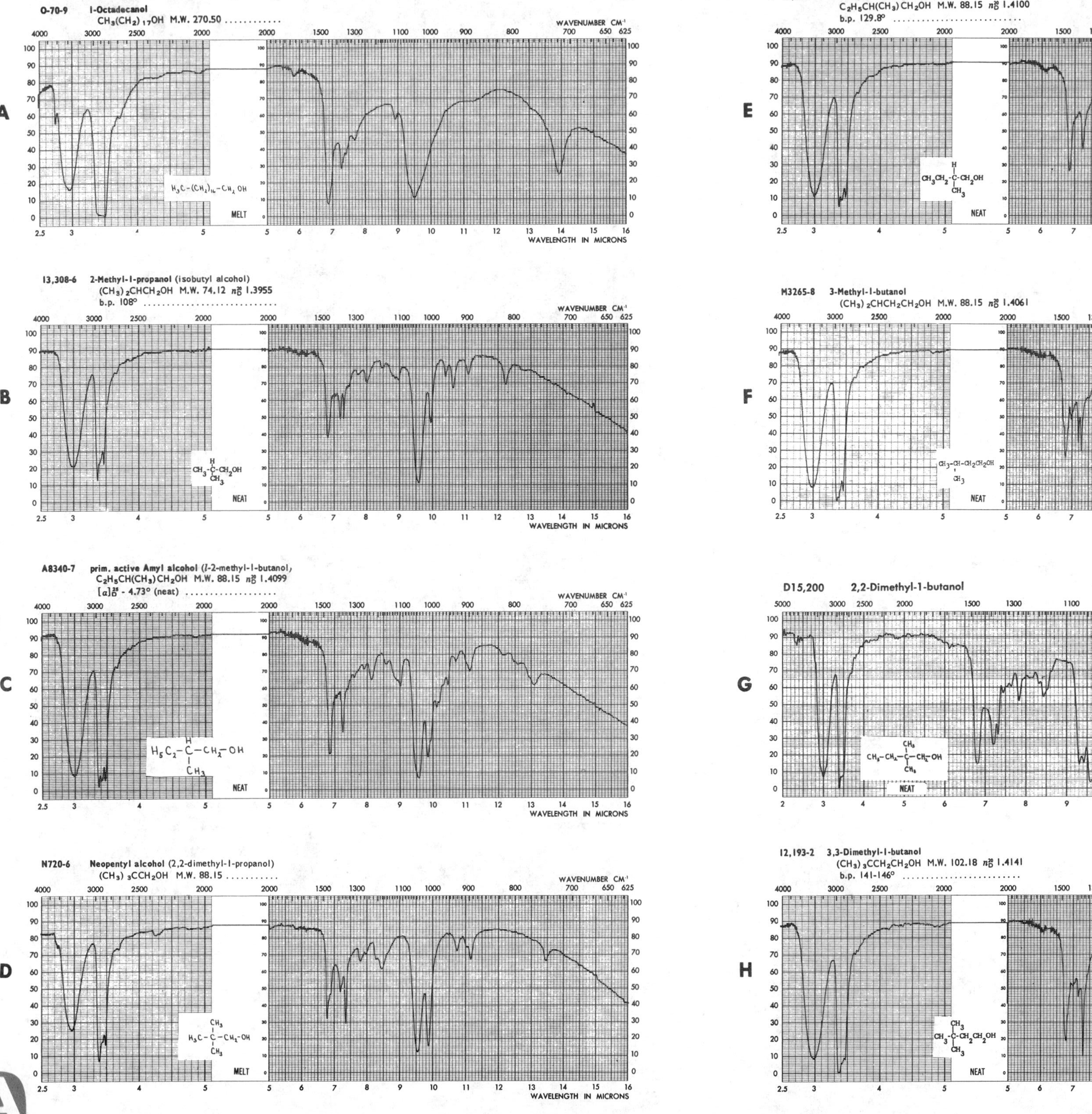
A
O-70-9 1-Octadecanol
$CH_3(CH_2)_{17}OH$ M.W. 270.50
$H_3C-(CH_2)_{16}-CH_2OH$
MELT
B
13,308-6 2-Methyl-1-propanol (isobutyl alcohol)
$(CH_3)_2CHCH_2OH$ M.W. 74.12 n_D^{20} 1.3955
b.p. 108°
NEAT
C
A8340-7 prim. active Amyl alcohol (*l*-2-methyl-1-butanol)
$C_2H_5CH(CH_3)CH_2OH$ M.W. 88.15 n_D^{20} 1.4099
$[\alpha]_D^{25}$ - 4.73° (neat)
NEAT
D
N720-6 Neopentyl alcohol (2,2-dimethyl-1-propanol)
$(CH_3)_3CCH_2OH$ M.W. 88.15
MELT
E
13,305-1 2-Methyl-1-butanol
$C_2H_5CH(CH_3)CH_2OH$ M.W. 88.15 n_D^{20} 1.4100
b.p. 129.8°
NEAT
F
M3265-8 3-Methyl-1-butanol
$(CH_3)_2CHCH_2CH_2OH$ M.W. 88.15 n_D^{20} 1.4061
NEAT
G
D15,200 2,2-Dimethyl-1-butanol
NEAT
H
12,193-2 3,3-Dimethyl-1-butanol
$(CH_3)_3CCH_2CH_2OH$ M.W. 102.18 n_D^{20} 1.4141
b.p. 141-146°
NEAT
WAVENUMBER CM⁻¹
WAVELENGTH IN MICRONS
ALDRICH

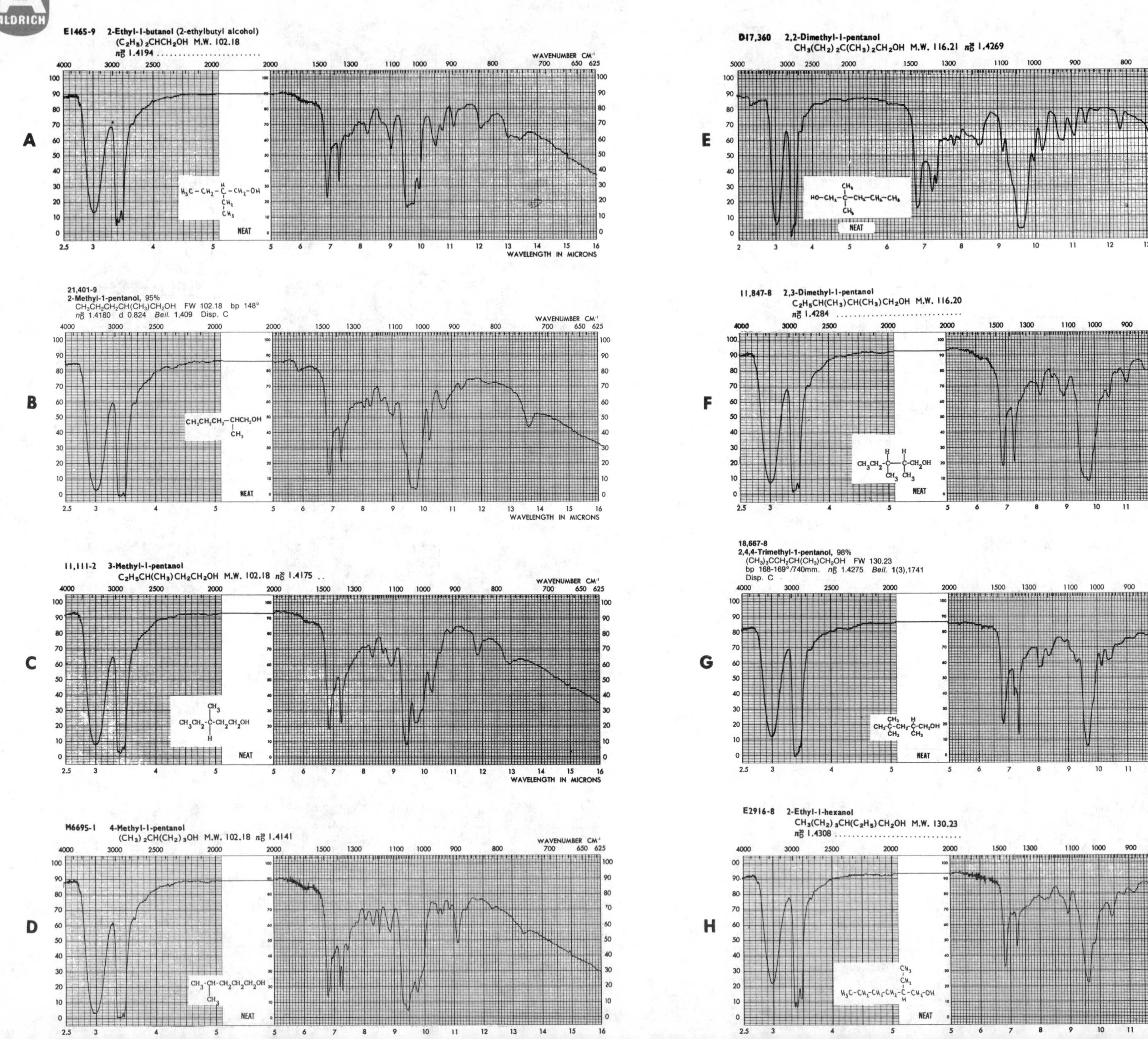

A E1465-9 2-Ethyl-1-butanol (2-ethylbutyl alcohol)
$(C_2H_5)_2CHCH_2OH$ M.W. 102.18
n_D^{20} 1.4194

B 21,401-9
2-Methyl-1-pentanol, 95%
$CH_3CH_2CH_2CH(CH_3)CH_2OH$ FW 102.18 bp 148°
n_D^{20} 1.4180 d 0.824 *Beil.* 1,409 Disp. C

C 11,111-2 3-Methyl-1-pentanol
$C_2H_5CH(CH_3)CH_2CH_2OH$ M.W. 102.18 n_D^{20} 1.4175

D M6695-1 4-Methyl-1-pentanol
$(CH_3)_2CH(CH_2)_3OH$ M.W. 102.18 n_D^{20} 1.4141

E D17,360 2,2-Dimethyl-1-pentanol
$CH_3(CH_2)_2C(CH_3)_2CH_2OH$ M.W. 116.21 n_D^{20} 1.4269

F 11,847-8 2,3-Dimethyl-1-pentanol
$C_2H_5CH(CH_3)CH(CH_3)CH_2OH$ M.W. 116.20
n_D^{20} 1.4284

G 18,667-8
2,4,4-Trimethyl-1-pentanol, 98%
$(CH_3)_3CCH_2CH(CH_3)CH_2OH$ FW 130.23
bp 168-169°/740mm. n_D^{20} 1.4275 *Beil.* 1(3),1741
Disp. C

H E2916-8 2-Ethyl-1-hexanol
$CH_3(CH_2)_3CH(C_2H_5)CH_2OH$ M.W. 130.23
n_D^{20} 1.4308

A

E4690 **2-Ethyl-2-propyl-1-hexanol**
$CH_3(CH_2)_3C(C_2H_5)[(CH_2)_2CH_3]CH_2OH$ M.W. 172.30
n_D^{20} 1.4452

NEAT

B

10,982-7 **Isopropanol** (isopropyl alcohol), 99+%, anhydrous
$(CH_3)_2CHOH$ M.W. 60.10 n_D^{20} 1.3770
b.p. 82.3°

NEAT

C

B8,591-9
sec.-**Butanol** (*sec.*-butyl alcohol)
$C_2H_5CH(OH)CH_3$
M.W. 74.12 m.p. -115° b.p. 98° n_D^{20} 1.3971
d 0.808 *IRRITANT*

NEAT

D

P801-7 **2-Pentanol**
$CH_3CH_2CH_2CH(OH)CH_3$ M.W. 88.15 n_D^{20} 1.4055
b.p. 118.5-119.5°

NEAT

E

P802-5 **3-Pentanol, puriss.**
$C_2H_5CH(OH)C_2H_5$ M.W. 88.15 n_D^{20} 1.4096

$CH_3CH_2CH(OH)CH_2CH_3$

NEAT

F

12,857-0 **2-Hexanol**
$CH_3(CH_2)_3CH(OH)CH_3$ M.W. 102.18 n_D^{20} 1.4115
b.p. 136-139°

NEAT

G

H1240-4 **3-Hexanol**
$CH_3CH_2CH_2CH(OH)C_2H_5$ M.W. 102.18 n_D^{20} 1.4150
b.p. 135°

NEAT

H

H300-3 **2-Heptanol**
$CH_3(CH_2)_4CH(OH)CH_3$ M.W. 116.20 n_D^{20} 1.4210
b.p. 160-162°

NEAT

ALDRICH

A

10,936-3 *dl*-3-Heptanol
$CH_3(CH_2)_3CH(OH)C_2H_5$ M.W. 116.20 n_D^{20} 1.4199
b.p. 66°/20 mm.

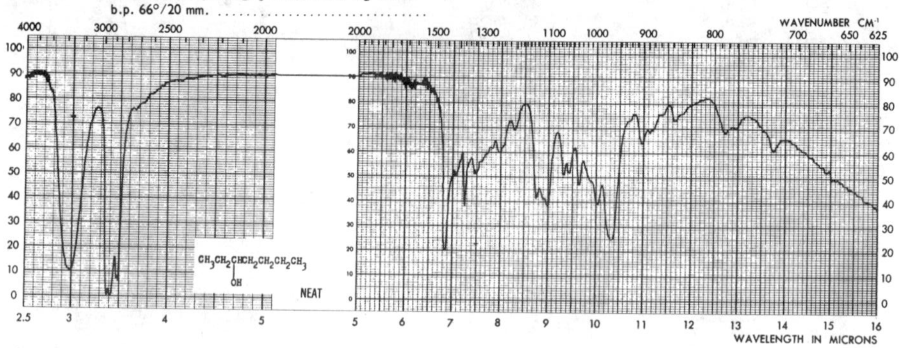

NEAT

B

11,081-7 4-Heptanol
$CH_3CH_2CH_2CH(OH)CH_2CH_2CH_3$ M.W. 116.20 n_D^{20} 1.4190
b.p. 156°

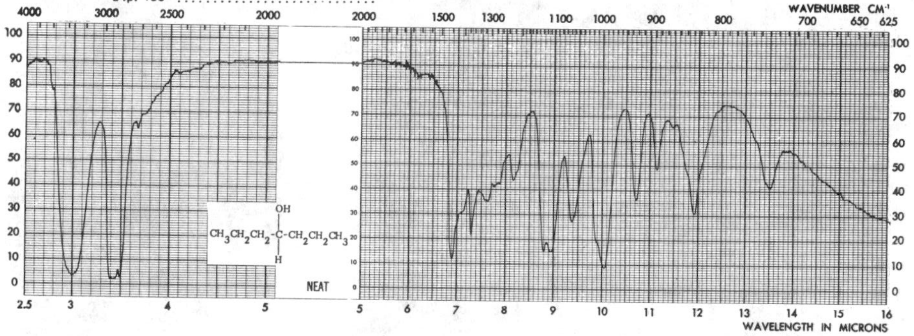

NEAT

C

14,799-0 *l*-2-Octanol
$CH_3(CH_2)_5CH(OH)CH_3$ M.W. 130.23 n_D^{20} 1.4254
b.p. 175° $[\alpha]_D^{17}$ -9.5° (neat)

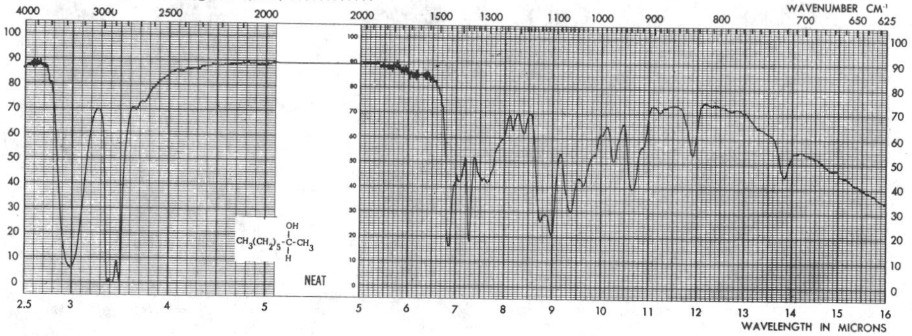

NEAT

D

14,798-2 *d*-2-Octanol
$CH_3(CH_2)_5CH(OH)CH_3$ M.W. 130.23 n_D^{20} 1.4258
b.p. 175° $[\alpha]_D^{17}$ +9.5° (neat)

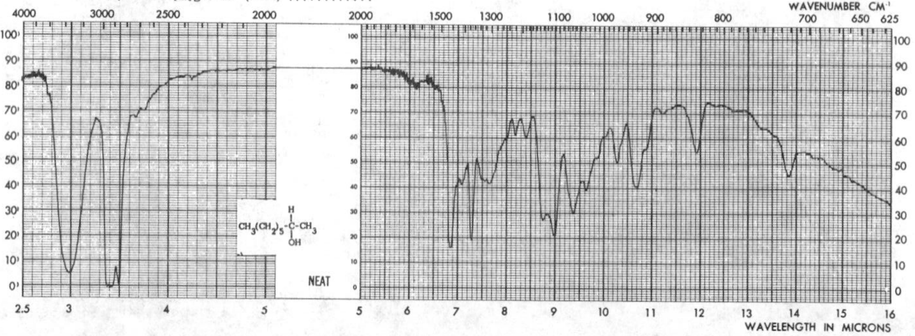

NEAT

E

15,260-9 3-Octanol
$CH_3(CH_2)_4CH(OH)C_2H_5$ M.W. 130.23 n_D^{20} 1.4257
b.p. 174°

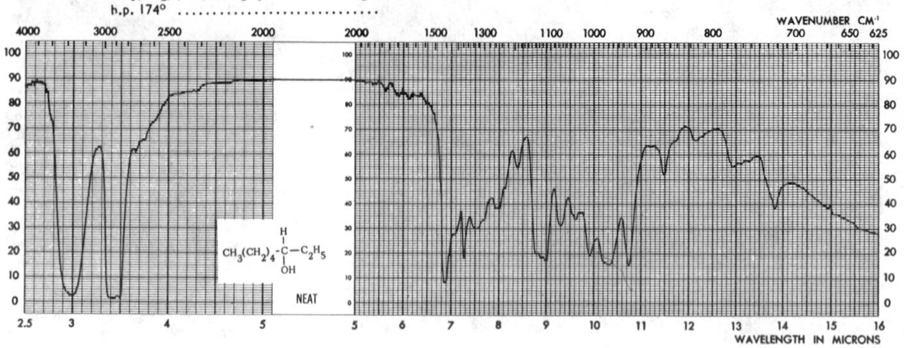

NEAT

F

O-460-1 4-Octanol
$CH_3(CH_2)_3CH(OH)CH_2CH_2CH_3$ M.W. 130.23
n_D^{20} 1.4242

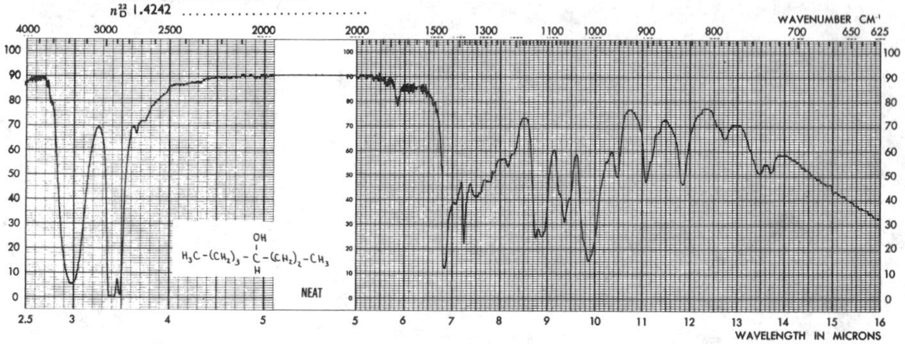

NEAT

G

N3030-7 2-Nonanol
$CH_3(CH_2)_6CH(OH)CH_3$ M.W. 144.26
n_D^{20} 1.4307

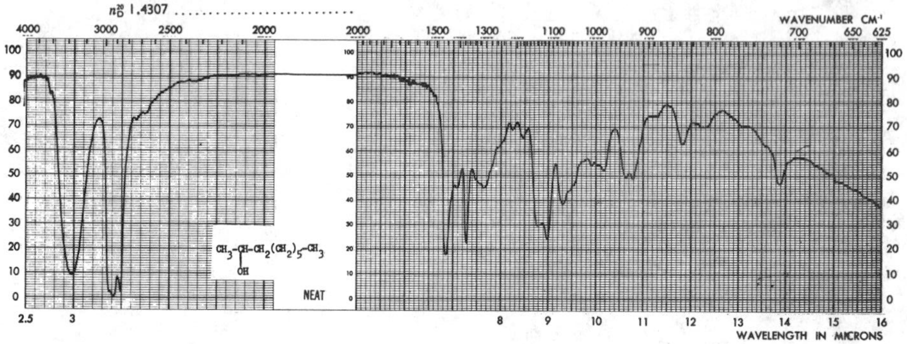

NEAT

H

11,874-5
4-Nonanol
$CH_3(CH_2)_4CH(OH)CH_2CH_2CH_3$ M.W. 144.26
n_D^{20} 1.4293 bp 192-193°

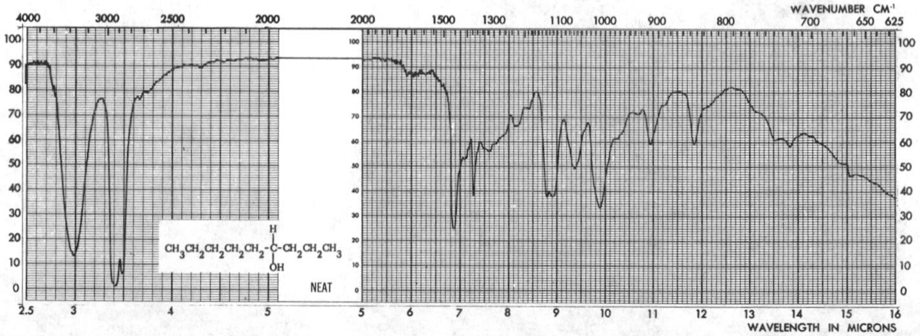

NEAT

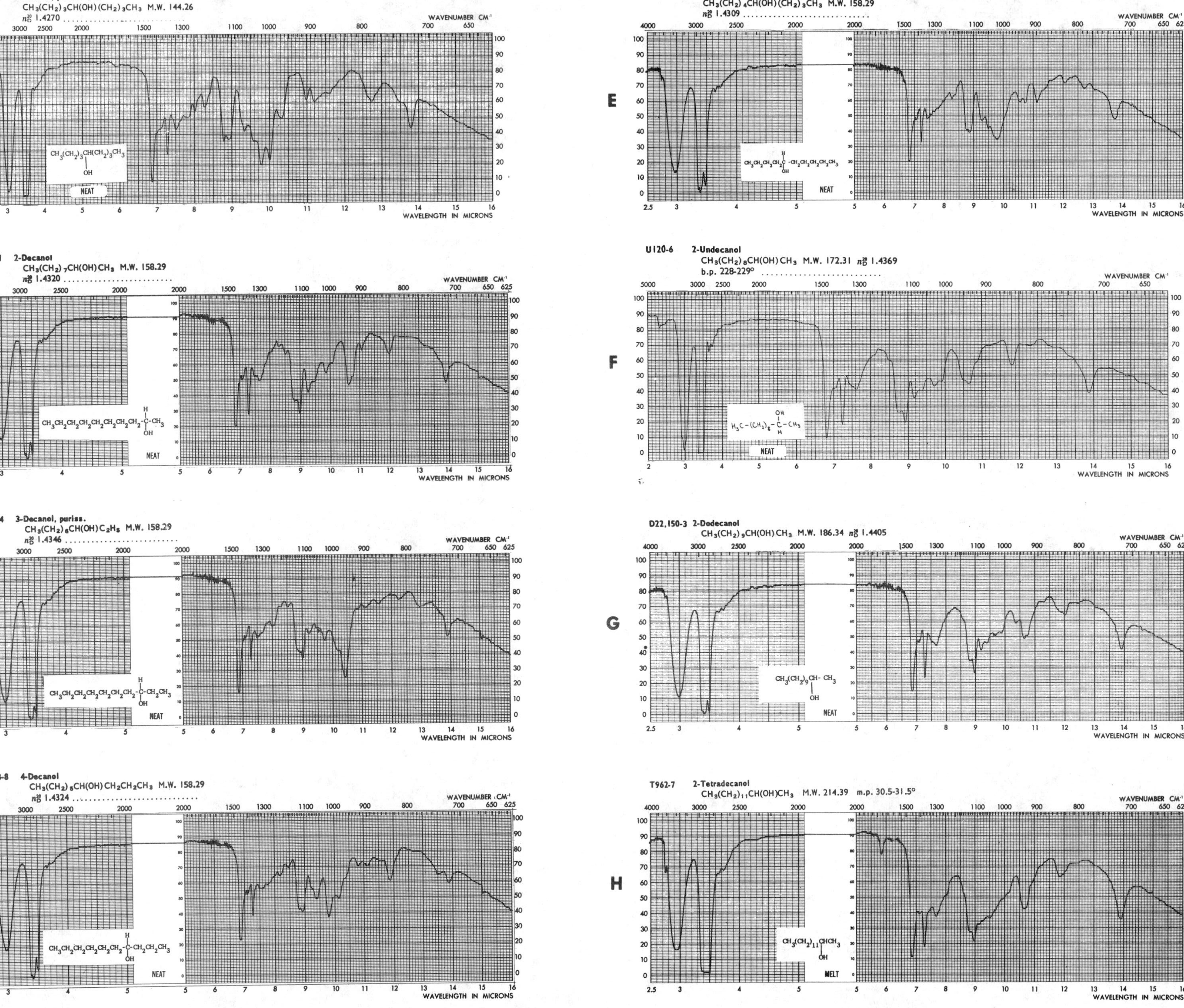

A
N3035-8 5-Nonanol, puriss.
$CH_3(CH_2)_3CH(OH)(CH_2)_3CH_3$ M.W. 144.26
n_D^{20} 1.4270
NEAT
B
11,831-1 2-Decanol
$CH_3(CH_2)_7CH(OH)CH_3$ M.W. 158.29
n_D^{20} 1.4320
NEAT
C
12,922-4 3-Decanol, puriss.
$CH_3(CH_2)_6CH(OH)C_2H_5$ M.W. 158.29
n_D^{20} 1.4346
NEAT
D
11,833-8 4-Decanol
$CH_3(CH_2)_5CH(OH)CH_2CH_2CH_3$ M.W. 158.29
n_D^{20} 1.4324
NEAT
E
D169-6 5-Decanol, puriss.
$CH_3(CH_2)_4CH(OH)(CH_2)_3CH_3$ M.W. 158.29
n_D^{20} 1.4309
NEAT
F
U120-6 2-Undecanol
$CH_3(CH_2)_8CH(OH)CH_3$ M.W. 172.31 n_D^{20} 1.4369
b.p. 228-229°
NEAT
G
D22,150-3 2-Dodecanol
$CH_3(CH_2)_9CH(OH)CH_3$ M.W. 186.34 n_D^{20} 1.4405
NEAT
H
T962-7 2-Tetradecanol
$CH_3(CH_2)_{11}CH(OH)CH_3$ M.W. 214.39 m.p. 30.5-31.5°
MELT
WAVENUMBER CM⁻¹
WAVELENGTH IN MICRONS
ALDRICH

NON-AROMATIC ALCOHOLS

A

P381-3 2-Pentadecanol
$CH_3(CH_2)_{12}CH(OH)CH_3$ M.W. 228.42 m.p. 34-35°

MELT

B

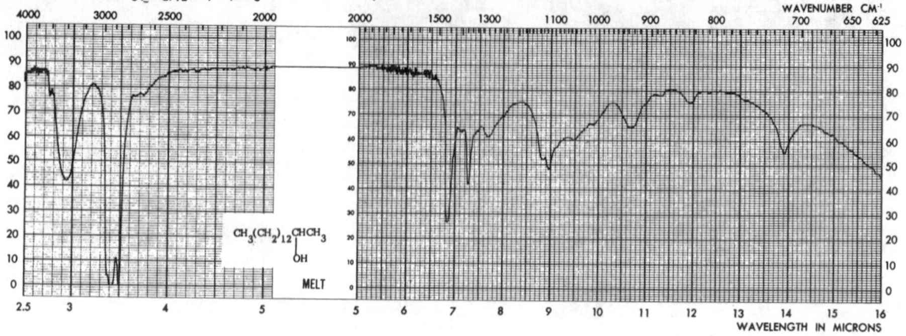

H682-7 2-Hexadecanol
$CH_3(CH_2)_{13}CH(OH)CH_3$ M.W. 242.45 m.p. 41-44°

MELT

C

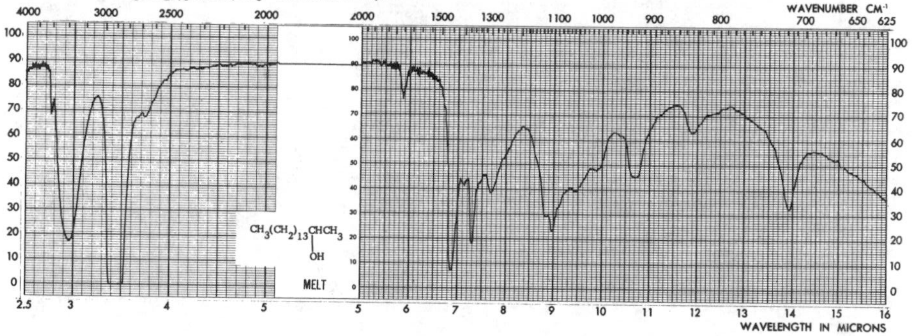

N2910-4 2-Nonadecanol, tech.
$CH_3(CH_2)_{16}CH(OH)CH_3$ M.W. 284.53 m.p. 42.5-43°

MELT

D

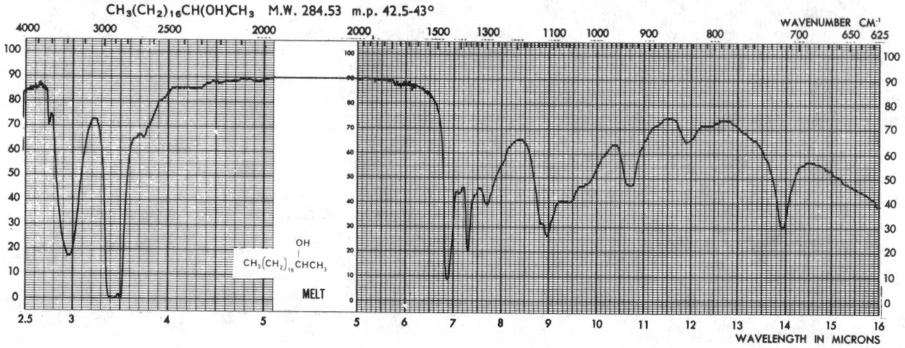

11,094-9 3-Methyl-2-butanol
$(CH_3)_2CHCH(OH)CH_3$ M.W. 88.15 n_D^{20} 1.4089
b.p. 112°

NEAT

E

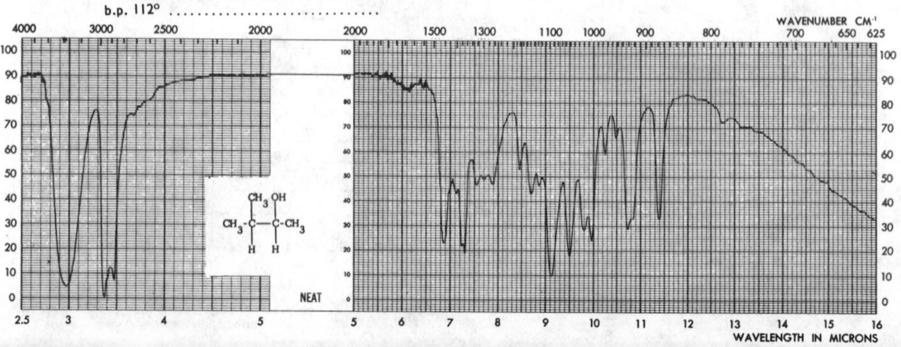

13,682-4 3,3-Dimethyl-2-butanol
$(CH_3)_3CCH(OH)CH_3$ M.W. 102.18 n_D^{20} 1.4148

NEAT

F

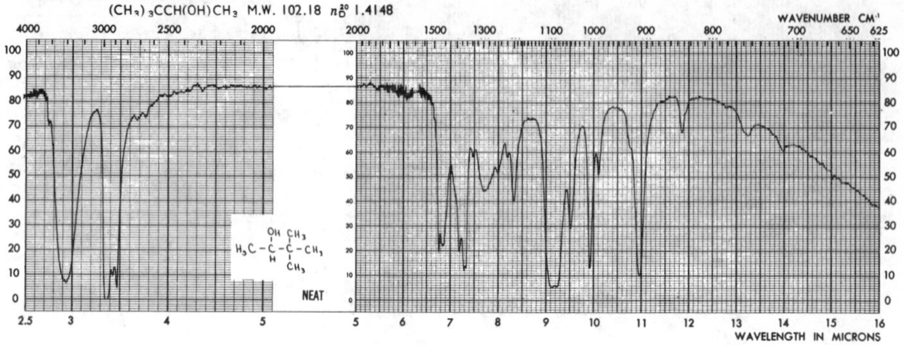

11,113-9 3-Methyl-2-pentanol
$C_2H_5CH(CH_3)CH(OH)CH_3$ M.W. 102.18 n_D^{20} 1.4182

NEAT

G

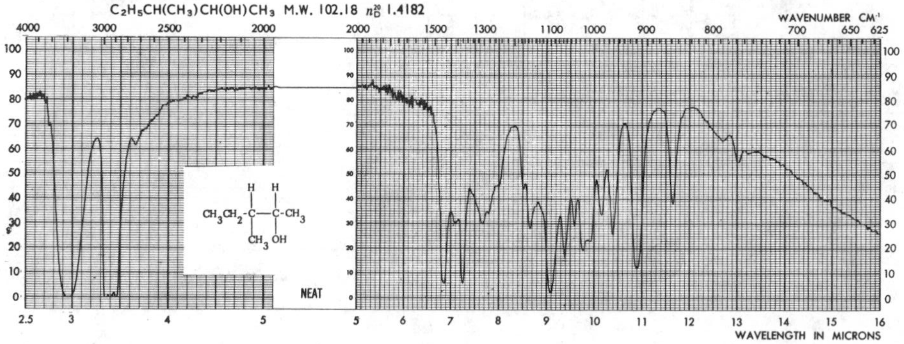

10,991-6 4-Methyl-2-pentanol, 99+%
$(CH_3)_2CHCH_2CH(OH)CH_3$ M.W. 102.18 n_D^{20} 1.4100
b.p. 132°

NEAT

H

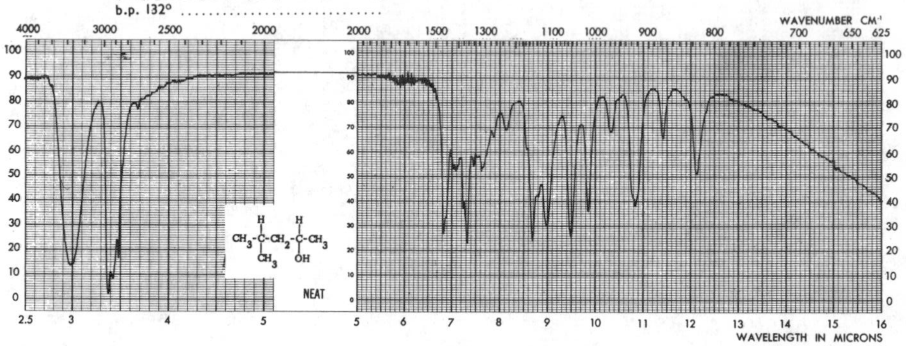

E4365 3-Ethyl-2-pentanol
$(C_2H_5)_2CHCH(OH)CH_3$ M.W. 116.20 n_D^{20} 1.4262

NEAT

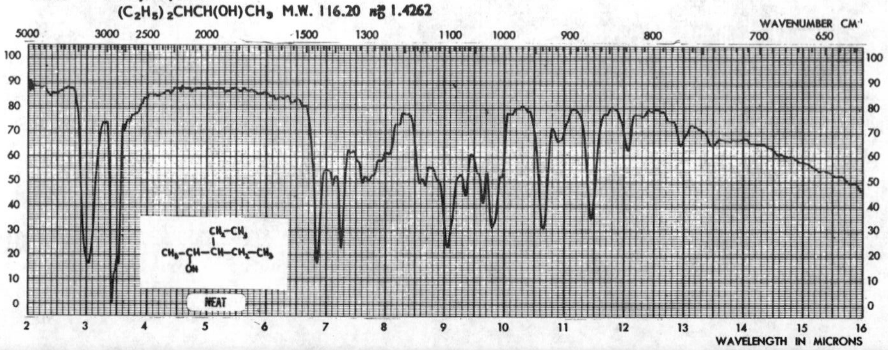

A 12,997-6 2-Methyl-3-pentanol, puriss.
$C_2H_5CH(OH)CH(CH_3)_2$ M.W. 102.18
n_D^{20} 1.4174

B 19,058-6
4,4-Dimethyl-2-pentanol, 99%
$(CH_3)_3CCH_2CH(OH)CH_3$ FW 116.20
bp 137-137°/736mm. n_D^{20} 1.4183 d 0.815
Disp. C

C D17,362-2 2,2-Dimethyl-3-pentanol
$C_2H_5CH(OH)C(CH_3)_3$ M.W. 116.20 n_D^{20} 1.4219

D 15,004-5
2,4-Dimethyl-3-pentanol, 99+% (diisopropylcarbinol)
$(CH_3)_2CHCH(OH)CH(CH_3)_2$
M.W. 116.2 b.p. 139-140° n_D^{20} 1.4254 d 0.829
Beil. 1,417

E 13,410-4 3-Methyl-2-hexanol
$CH_3CH_2CH_2CH(CH_3)CH(OH)CH_3$ M.W. 116.20 n_D^{20} 1.4225

F M4983-6 2-Methyl-3-hexanol
$CH_3CH_2CH_2CH(OH)CH(CH_3)_2$ M.W. 116.20
n_D^{20} 1.4215

G 18,973-1
5-Methyl-2-hexanol, 98%
$(CH_3)_2CHCH_2CH_2CH(OH)CH_3$ FW 116.20
bp 148-150° n_D^{20} 1.4176 d 0.819 *Beil.* 1,416
Disp. C

H 11,161-9 5-Methyl-3-hexanol
$(CH_3)_2CHCH_2CH(OH)C_2H_5$ M.W. 116.20 n_D^{20} 1.4169

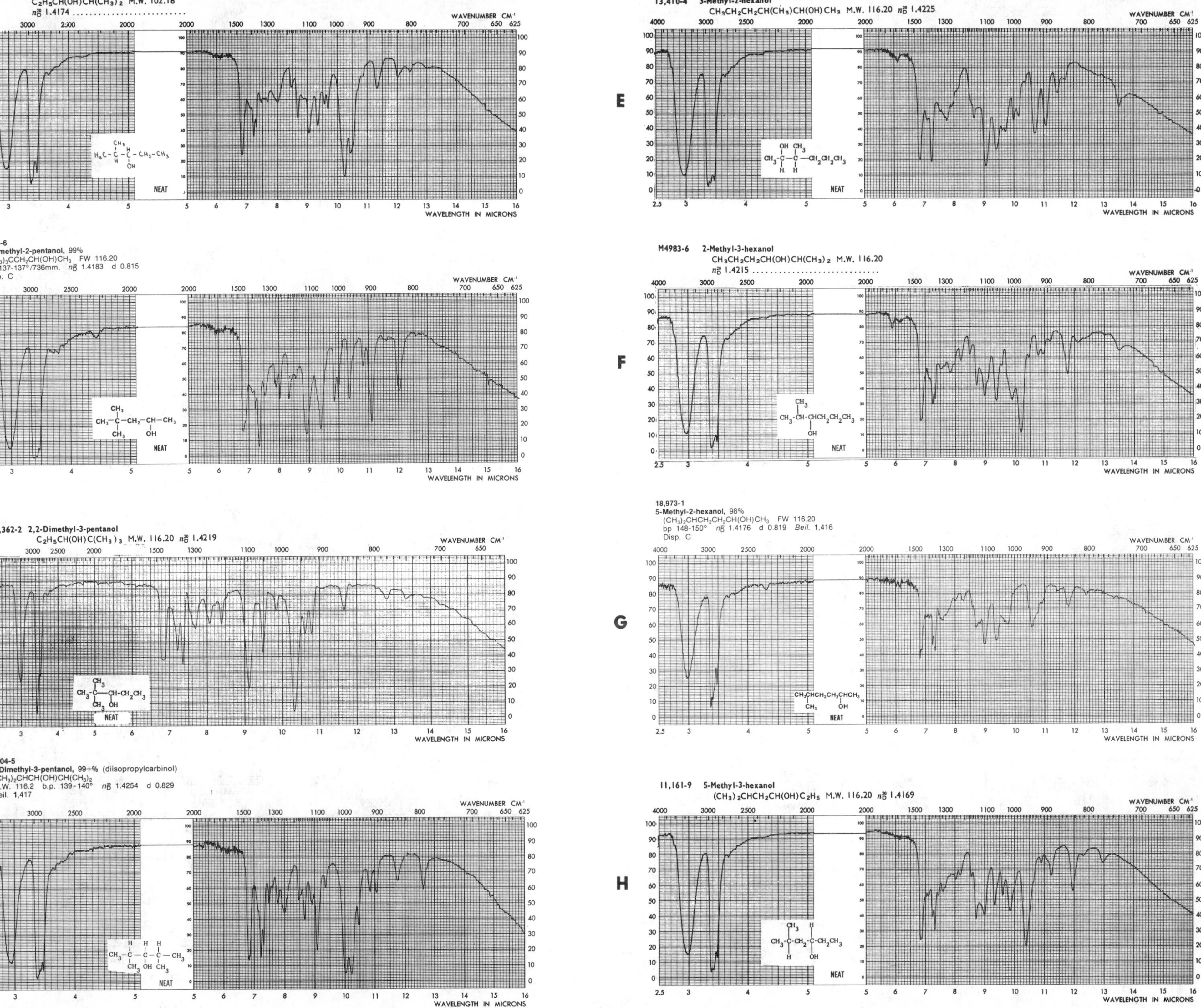

A — 11,156-2 **4-Ethyl-3-hexanol**
$(C_2H_5)_2CHCH(OH)C_2H_5$ M.W. 130.23
n_D^{20} 1.4312
NEAT

B — 11,059-0 **3,4-Dimethyl-2-hexanol** (mixture of isomers)
$C_2H_5CH(CH_3)CH(CH_3)CH(OH)CH_3$ M.W. 130.23
n_D^{20} 1.4343
NEAT

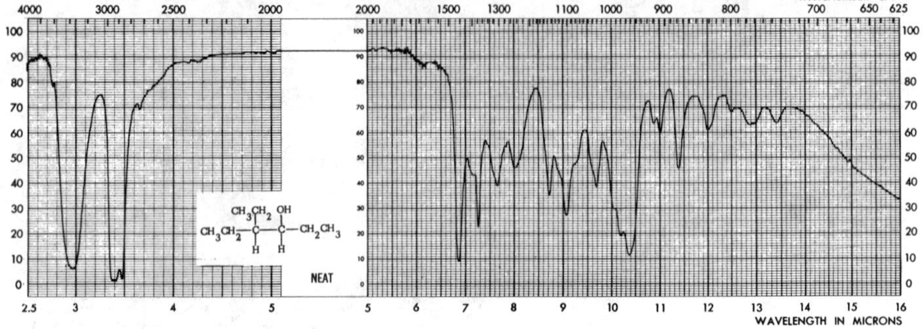

C — 11,060-4 **2,2-Dimethyl-3-hexanol, puriss.**
$CH_3CH_2CH_2CH(OH)C(CH_3)_3$ M.W. 130.23 n_D^{20} 1.4269
b.p. 155-157°
NEAT

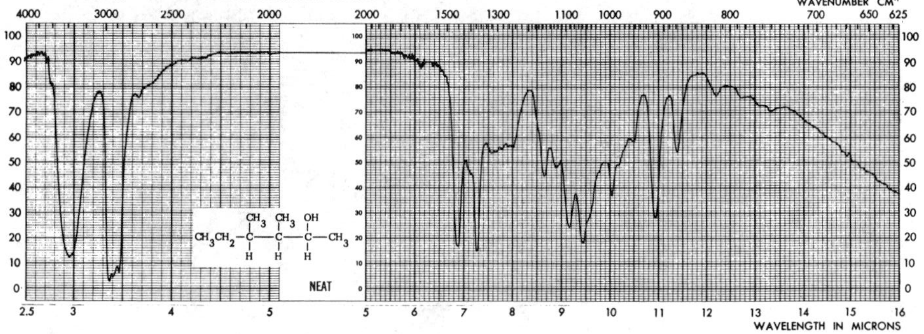

D — 11,061-2 **2,5-Dimethyl-3-hexanol, puriss.**
$(CH_3)_2CHCH_2CH(OH)CH(CH_3)_2$ M.W. 130.23
n_D^{20} 1.4247 b.p. 160-163°/755 mm.
NEAT

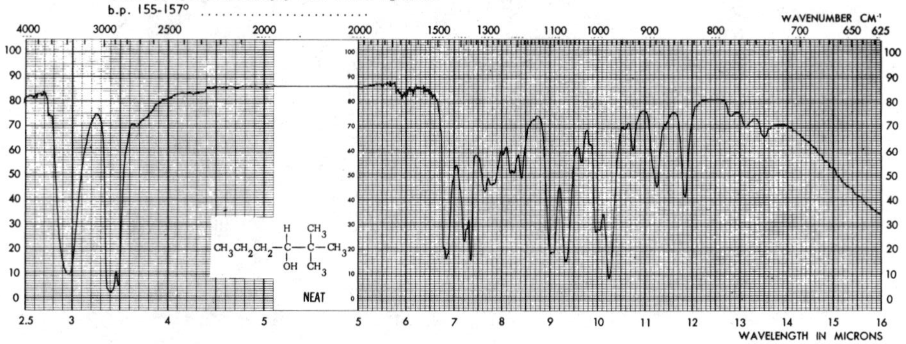

E — M4817-1 **6-Methyl-2-heptanol**
$(CH_3)_2CH(CH_2)_3CH(OH)CH_3$ M.W. 130.23
n_D^{20} 1.4221
NEAT

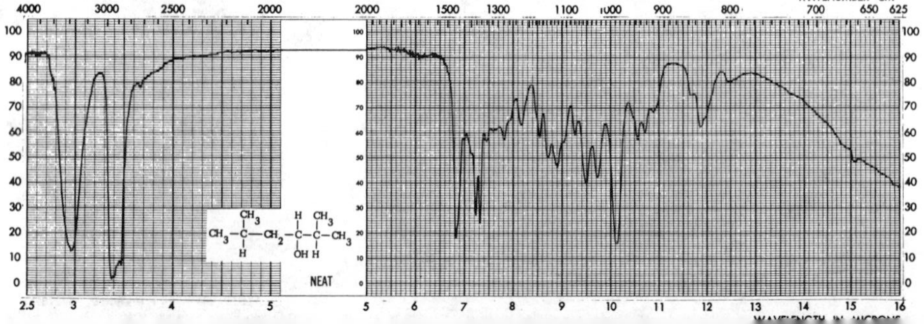

F — 12,341-2 **5-Ethyl-2-heptanol**
$(C_2H_5)_2CHCH_2CH_2CH(OH)CH_3$ M.W. 144.26 n_D^{20} 1.4343
b.p. 87°/15 mm.
NEAT

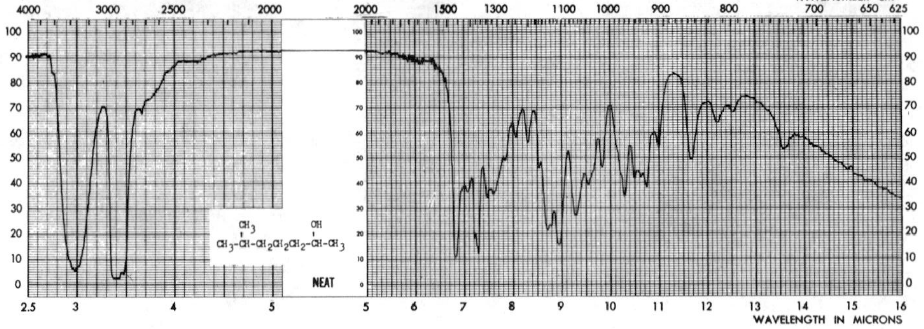

G — M4830-9 **4-Methyl-3-heptanol, puriss.**
$CH_3CH_2CH_2CH(CH_3)CH(OH)C_2H_5$ M.W. 130.23
n_D^{20} 1.4300
NEAT

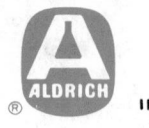

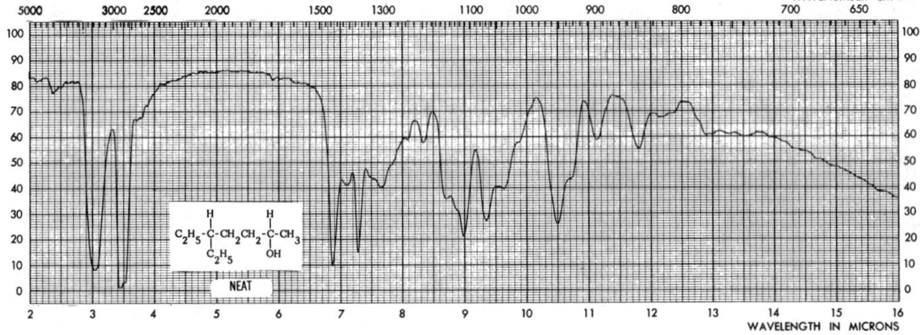

H — 11,970-9 **5-Methyl-3-heptanol**
$C_2H_5CH(CH_3)CH_2CH(OH)C_2H_5$ M.W. 130.23
n_D^{20} 1.4254 b.p. 167-168°
NEAT

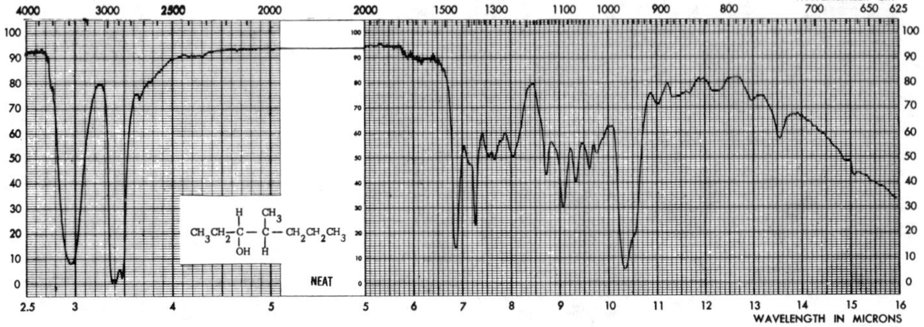

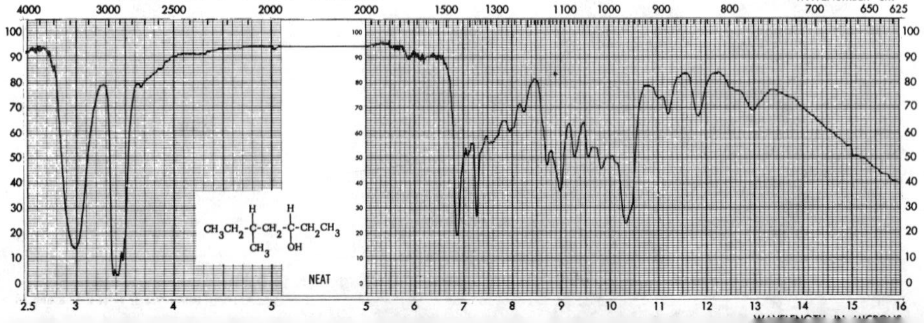

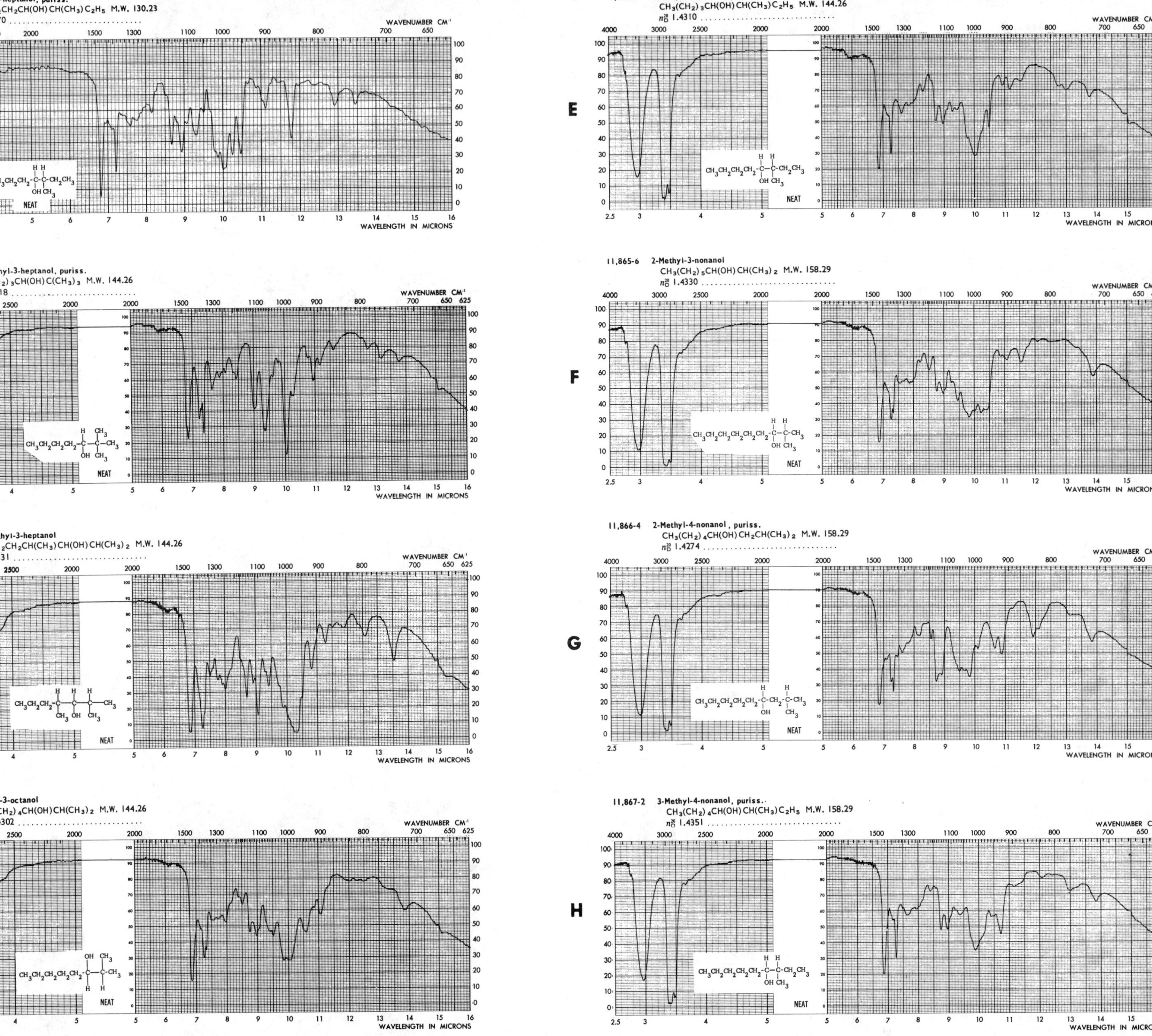

A 11,860-5 3-Methyl-4-heptanol, puriss.
$CH_3CH_2CH_2CH(OH)CH(CH_3)C_2H_5$ M.W. 130.23
n_D^{20} 1.4270

B 11,056-6 2,2-Dimethyl-3-heptanol, puriss.
$CH_3(CH_2)_3CH(OH)C(CH_3)_3$ M.W. 144.26
n_D^{20} 1.4318

C 11,839-7 2,4-Dimethyl-3-heptanol
$CH_3CH_2CH_2CH(CH_3)CH(OH)CH(CH_3)_2$ M.W. 144.26
n_D^{20} 1.4331

D 11,175-9 2-Methyl-3-octanol
$CH_3(CH_2)_4CH(OH)CH(CH_3)_2$ M.W. 144.26
n_D^{20} 1.4302

E 11,869-9 3-Methyl-4-octanol, puriss.
$CH_3(CH_2)_3CH(OH)CH(CH_3)C_2H_5$ M.W. 144.26
n_D^{20} 1.4310

F 11,865-6 2-Methyl-3-nonanol
$CH_3(CH_2)_5CH(OH)CH(CH_3)_2$ M.W. 158.29
n_D^{20} 1.4330

G 11,866-4 2-Methyl-4-nonanol, puriss.
$CH_3(CH_2)_4CH(OH)CH_2CH(CH_3)_2$ M.W. 158.29
n_D^{20} 1.4274

H 11,867-2 3-Methyl-4-nonanol, puriss.
$CH_3(CH_2)_4CH(OH)CH(CH_3)C_2H_5$ M.W. 158.29
n_D^{20} 1.4351

A

B8,592-7
tert.-Butanol, 99.5% (tert.-butyl alcohol)
$(CH_3)_3COH$
M.W. 74.12 m.p. 25-25.5° b.p. 83° n_D^{20} 1.3860
d 0.786 Beil. 1,379

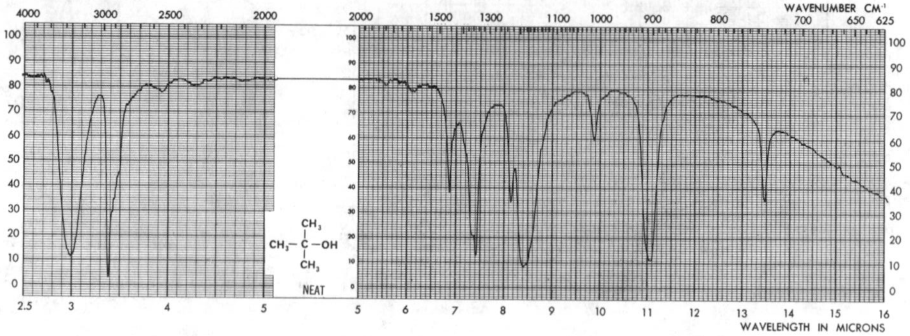

NEAT

B

18,471-3
tert.-Butyl hydroperoxide, tech.
$(CH_3)_3COOH$
M.W. 90.12 m.p. -8° n_D^{20} 1.3975 d 0.896

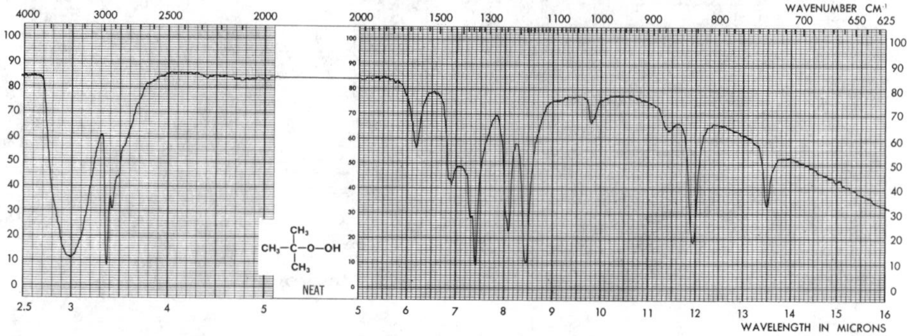

NEAT

C

15,246-3 **tert.-Amyl alcohol** (2-methyl-2-butanol)
$C_2H_5C(CH_3)_2OH$ M.W. 88.15 n_D^{20} 1.4038 b.p. 102°

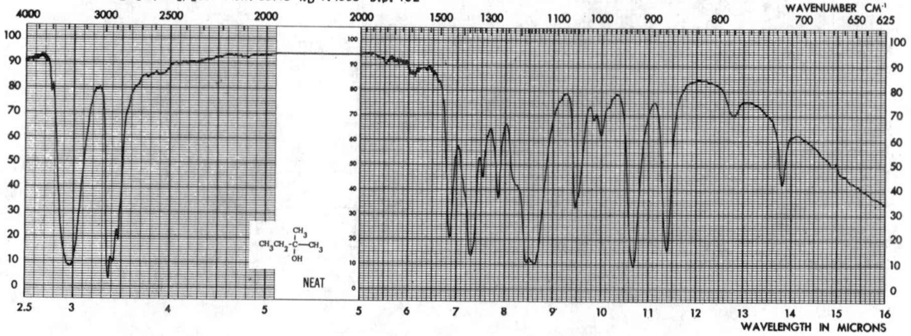

NEAT

D

12,924-0 **2,3-Dimethyl-2-butanol**, puriss.
$(CH_3)_2CHC(CH_3)_2OH$ M.W. 102.18 n_D^{20} 1.4172
b.p. 120-121°

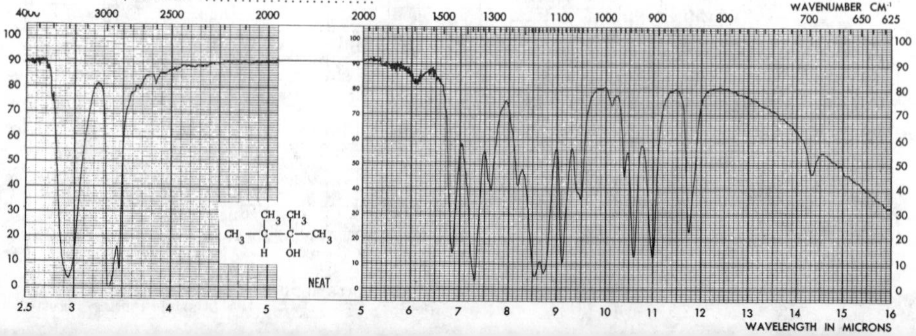

NEAT

E

11,112-0 **2-Methyl-2-pentanol**
$CH_3CH_2CH_2C(CH_3)_2OH$ M.W. 102.18 n_D^{20} 1.4100
b.p. 120-122°

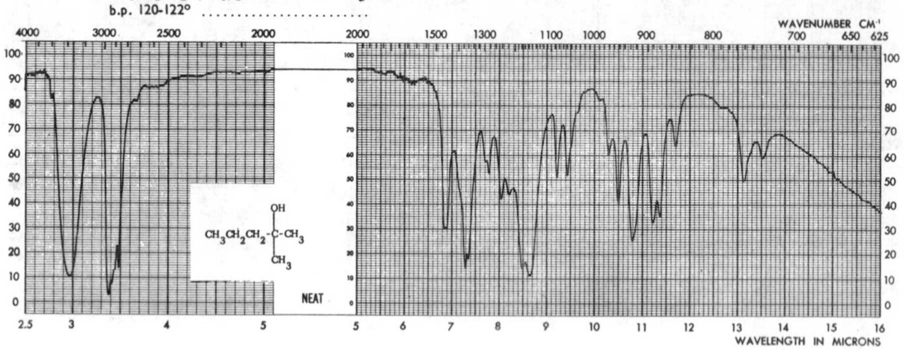

NEAT

F

M6690-0 **3-Methyl-3-pentanol**
$C_2H_5C(CH_3)(OH)C_2H_5$ M.W. 102.18
n_D^{20} 1.4142

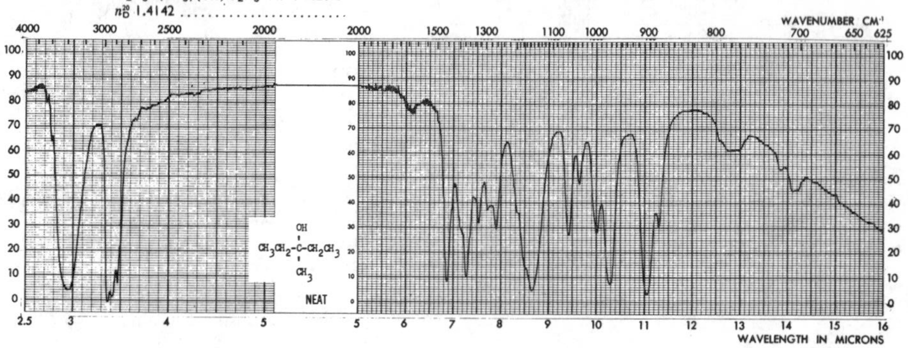

NEAT

G

11,157-0 **3-Ethyl-3-pentanol** (triethyl carbinol)
$(C_2H_5)_3COH$ M.W. 116.20 n_D^{20} 1.4289
b.p. 141°/743 mm.

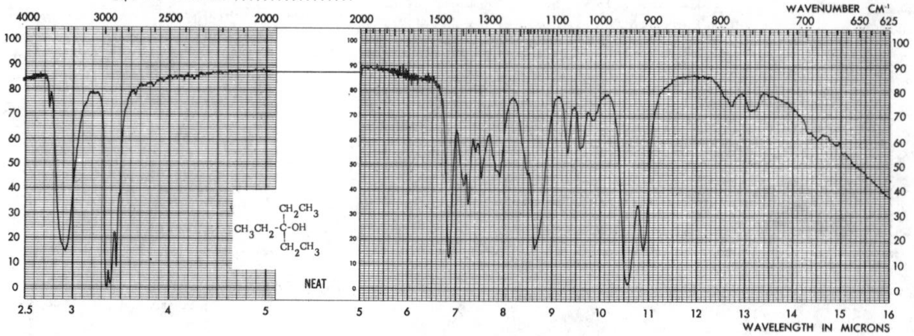

NEAT

H

D17,363 **2,4-Dimethyl-2-pentanol**
$(CH_3)_2C(OH)CH_2CH(CH_3)_2$ M.W. 116.21 n_D^{20} 1.4155

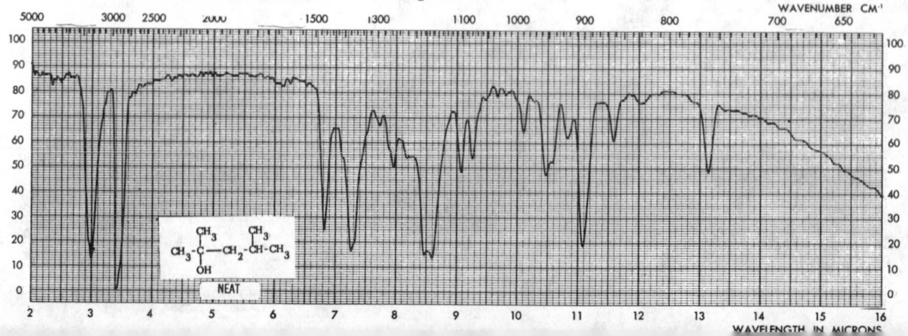

NEAT

A — 11,848-6 **2,3-Dimethyl-3-pentanol**
$C_2H_5C(CH_3)(OH)CH(CH_3)_2$ M.W. 116.20
n_D^{20} 1.4269
NEAT

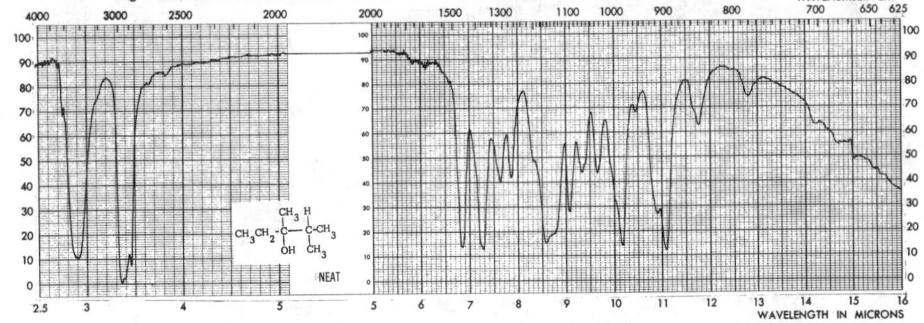

B — 11,138-4 **2,2,4-Trimethyl-3-pentanol**
$(CH_3)_2CHCH(OH)C(CH_3)_3$ M.W. 130.23
n_D^{20} 1.4275
NEAT

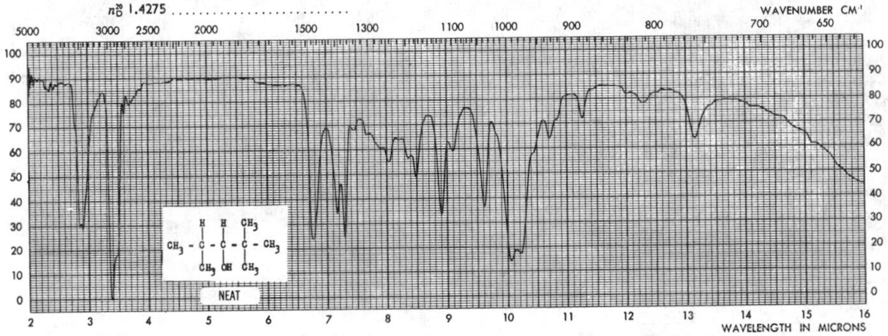

C — 11,160-0 **2-Methyl-2-hexanol**
$CH_3(CH_2)_3C(CH_3)_2OH$ M.W. 116.20 n_D^{20} 1.4166
b.p. 58-60°/20 mm.
NEAT

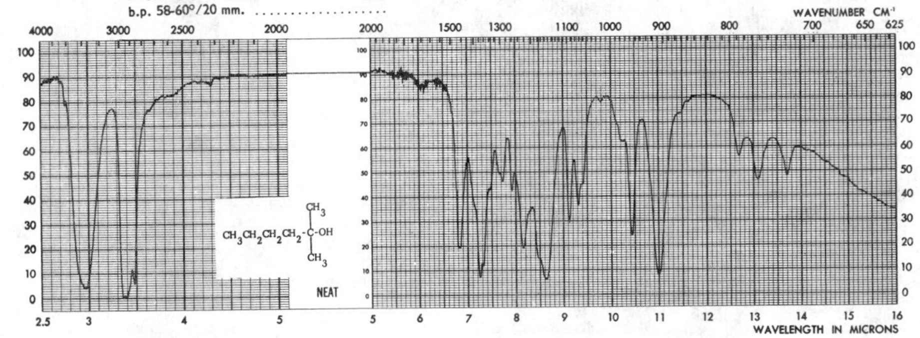

D — 11,106-6 **3-Methyl-3-hexanol**
$CH_3CH_2CH_2C(CH_3)(OH)C_2H_5$ M.W. 116.20
n_D^{20} 1.4216
NEAT

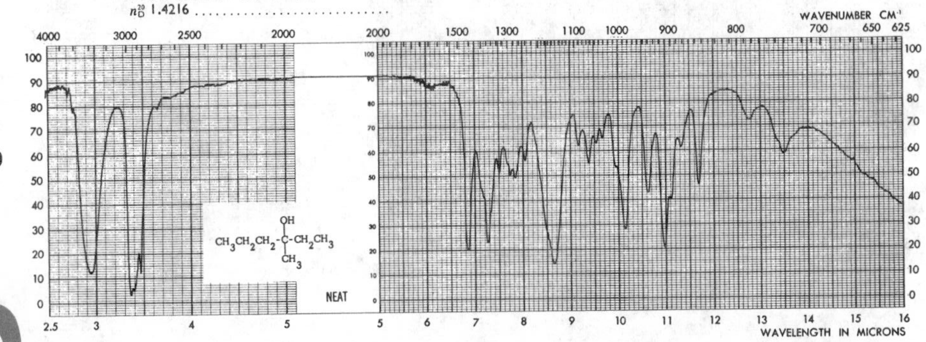

E — 12,931-3 **2,3-Dimethyl-2-hexanol, puriss.**
$CH_3CH_2CH_2CH(CH_3)C(CH_3)_2OH$ M.W. 130.23
n_D^{20} 1.4306
NEAT

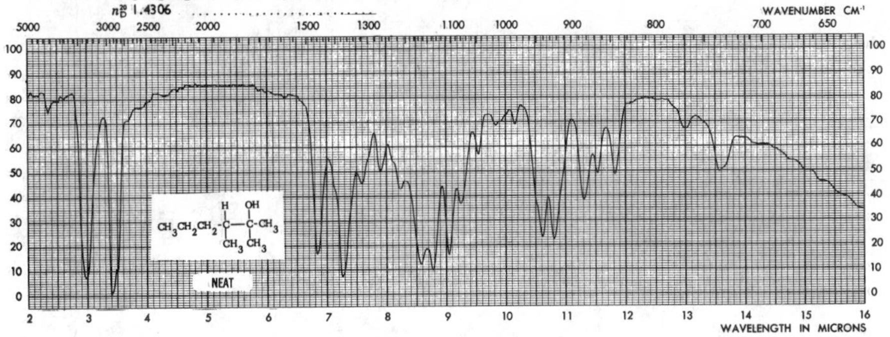

F — 11,842-7 **2,5-Dimethyl-2-hexanol**
$(CH_3)_2CHCH_2CH_2C(OH)(CH_3)_2$ M.W. 130.23
n_D^{20} 1.4197
NEAT

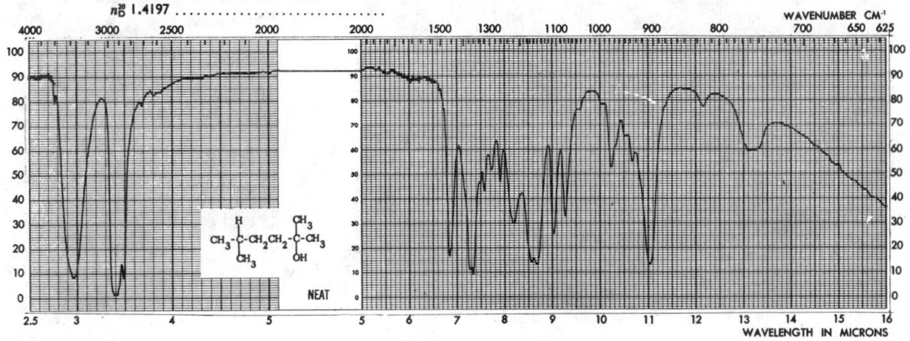

G — 11,062-0 **3,4-Dimethyl-3-hexanol**
$CH_3CH_2CH(CH_3)C(CH_3)(OH)CH_2CH_3$ M.W. 130.23
n_D^{20} 1.4347
NEAT

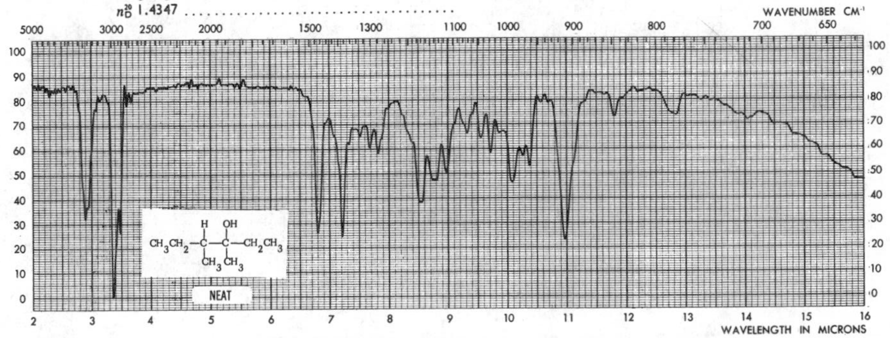

H — 11,063-9 **3,5-Dimethyl-3-hexanol**
$(CH_3)_2CHCH_2C(CH_3)(OH)CH_2CH_3$ M.W. 130.23
n_D^{20} 1.4258 b.p. 151°
NEAT

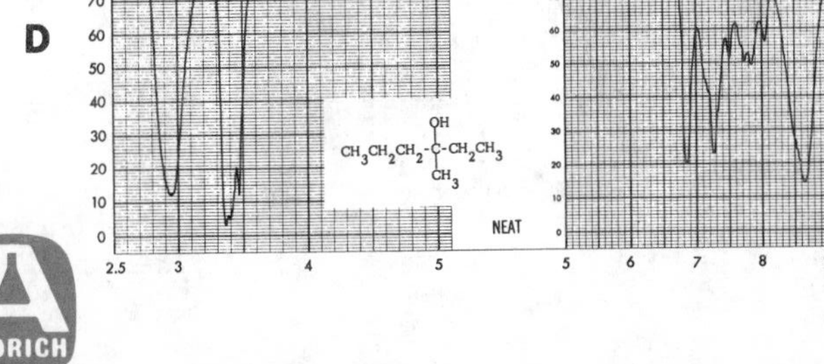

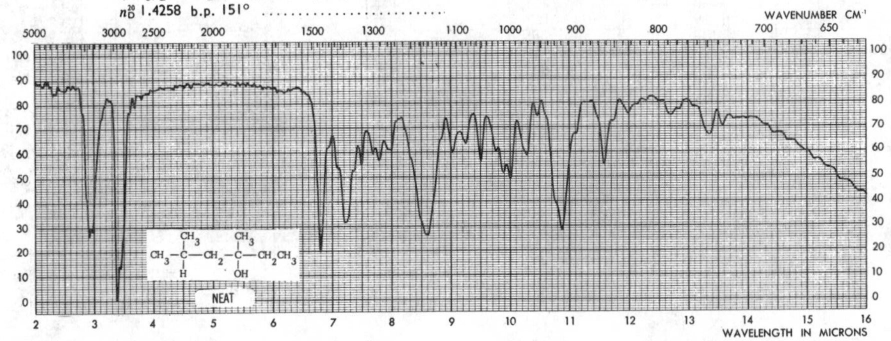

A 11,103-1 **2-Methyl-2-heptanol**
$CH_3(CH_2)_4C(CH_3)_2OH$ M.W. 130.23 n_D^{20} 1.4240

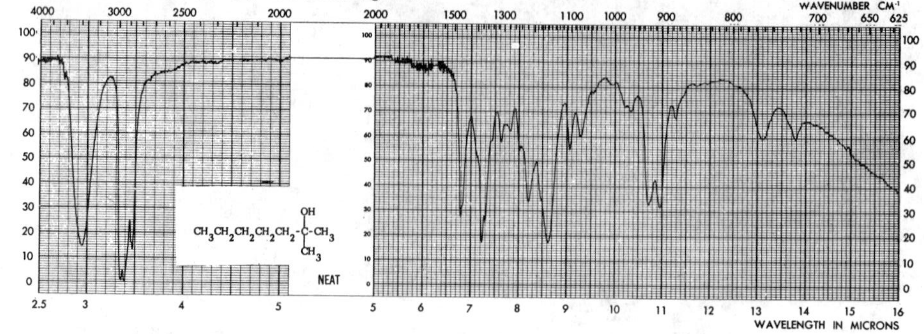

NEAT

B 12,987-9 **3-Methyl-3-heptanol, puriss.**
$CH_3(CH_2)_3C(CH_3)(OH)C_2H_5$ M.W. 130.23
n_D^{20} 1.4276

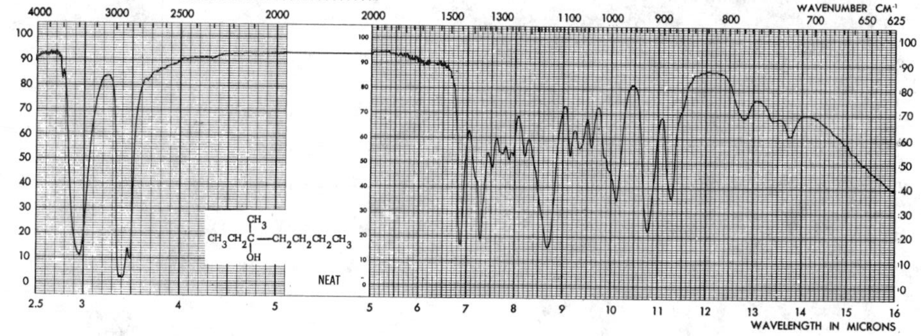

NEAT

C 11,155-4 **3-Ethyl-3-heptanol**
$CH_3(CH_2)_3C(C_2H_5)_2OH$ M.W. 144.26 n_D^{20} 1.4350
b.p. 119-121°/110 mm.

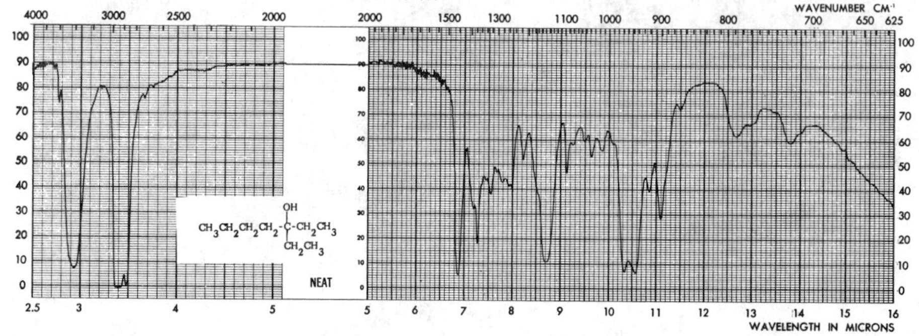

NEAT

D 11,159-7 **4-Methyl-4-heptanol**
$CH_3CH_2CH_2C(CH_3)(OH)CH_2CH_2CH_3$ M.W. 130.23
n_D^{20} 1.4249

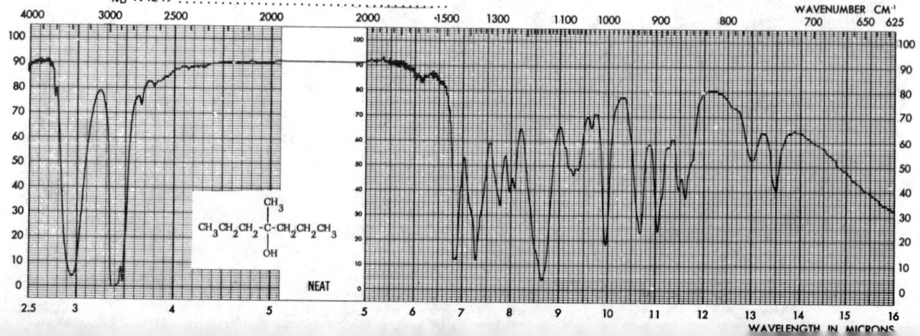

NEAT

E 11,870-2 **4-Methyl-4-octanol**
$CH_3(CH_2)_3C(CH_3)(OH)CH_2CH_2CH_3$ M.W. 144.26
n_D^{20} 1.4284

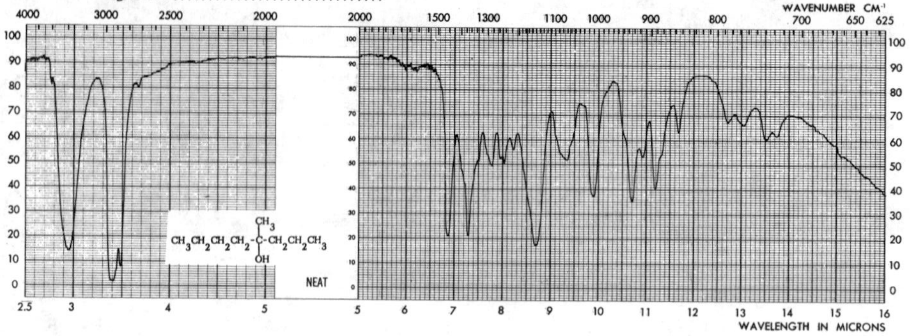

NEAT

F 11,868-0 **4-Methyl-4-nonanol**
$CH_3(CH_2)_4C(CH_3)(OH)CH_2CH_2CH_3$ M.W. 158.29
n_D^{20} 1.4315

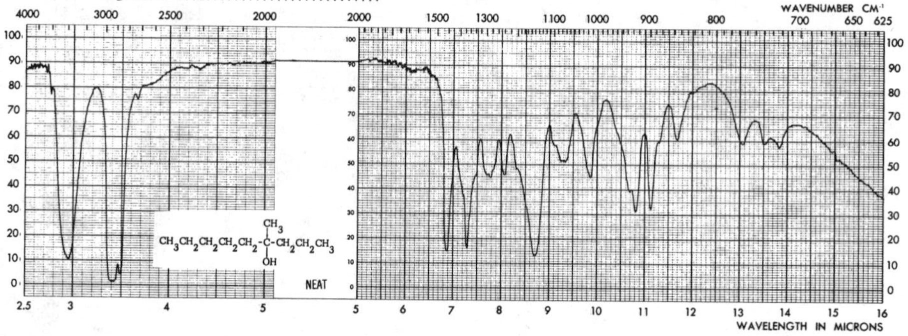

NEAT

G 18,060-2
9-Octyl-9-heptadecanol, tech. (tri-*n*-octylmethanol)
$[CH_3(CH_2)_7]_3COH$
M.W. 368.69 n_D^{20} 1.4538

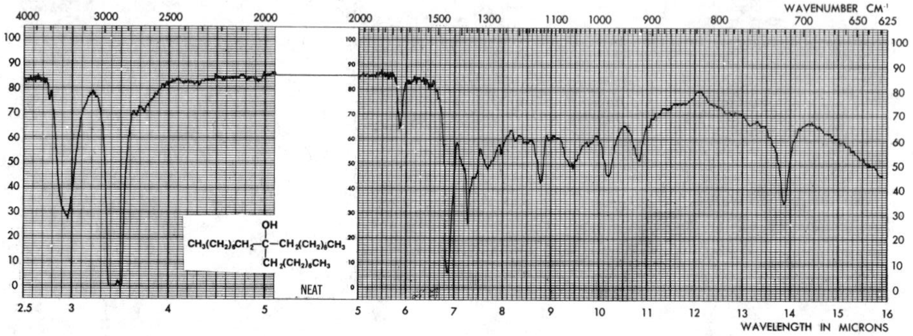

NEAT

H 10,246-6 **Ethylene glycol, puriss.**
$HOCH_2CH_2OH$ M.W. 62.07 n_D^{20} 1.4320
b.p. 196-198°

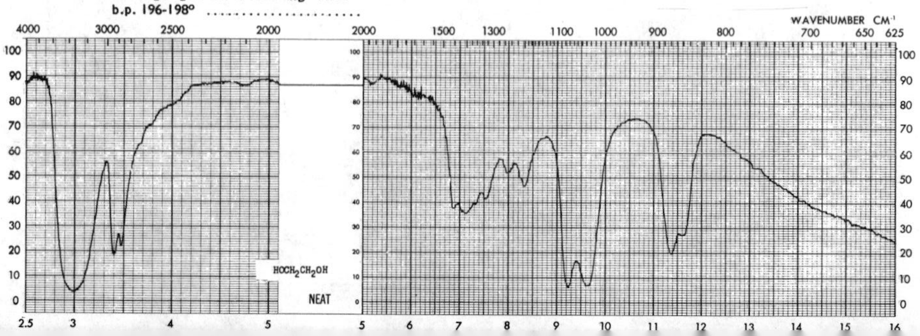

NEAT

A

P5040-4 1,3-Propanediol (trimethylene glycol)
$HO(CH_2)_3OH$ M.W. 76.10 n_D^{20} 1.4384
b.p. 214°

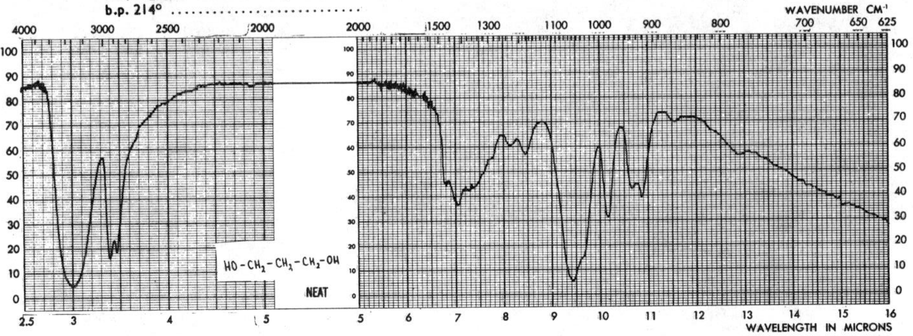

HO-CH₂-CH₂-CH₂-OH — NEAT

B

13,436-8 1,2-Propanediol (propylene glycol) U.S.P.
$CH_3CH(OH)CH_2OH$ M.W. 76.10 n_D^{20} 1.4319
b.p. 185-186°

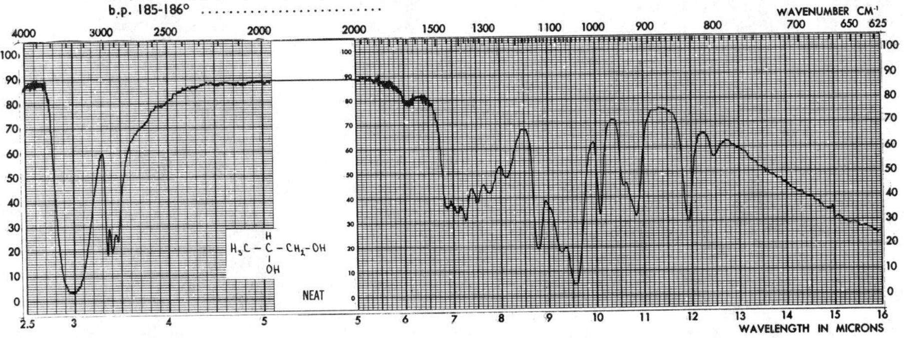

NEAT

C

P5039-0 *d*-1,2-Propanediol (*d*-1,2-propylene glycol) optically pure
$CH_3CH(OH)CH_2OH$ M.W. 76.10 n_D^{20} 1.4321 b.p. 82-85°/7 mm.
$[\alpha]_D^{20}$ + 15° (min.) (neat)

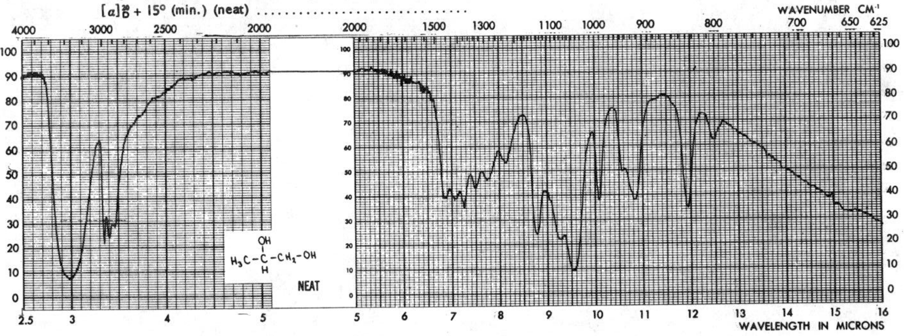

NEAT

D

12,658-6 2,2-Dimethyl-1,3-propanediol
$HOCH_2C(CH_3)_2CH_2OH$ M.W. 104.15 m.p. 127.5-130°

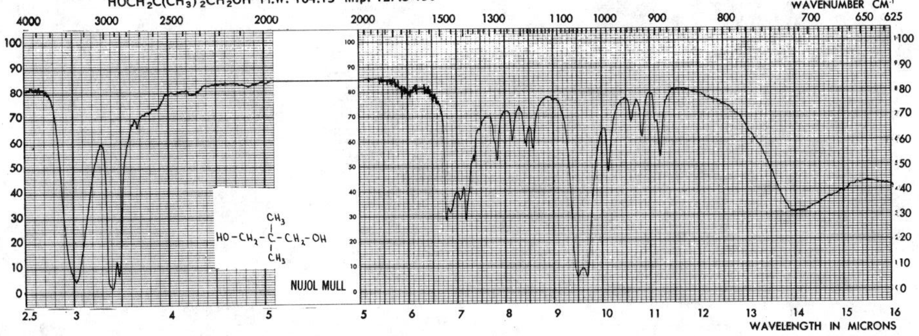

NUJOL MULL

E

D10,000-5 2,2-Diethyl-1,3-propanediol
$HOCH_2C(C_2H_5)_2CH_2OH$ M.W. 132.20
m.p. 60-62°

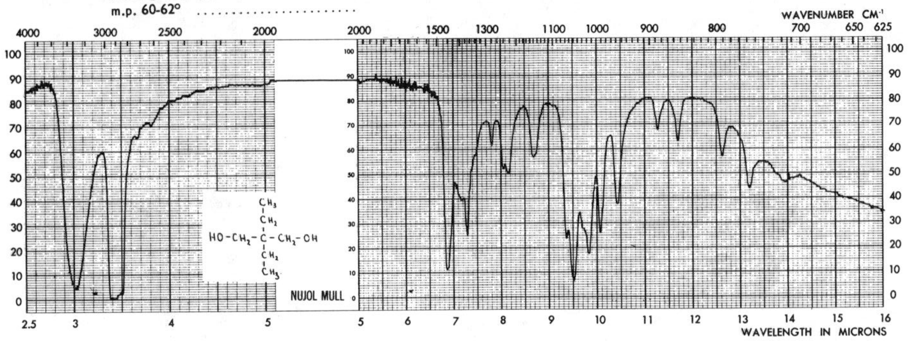

NUJOL MULL

F

E3835-3 2-Ethyl-2-methyl-1,3-propanediol
$HOCH_2C(C_2H_5)(CH_3)CH_2OH$ M.W. 118.18 m.p. 41-44°

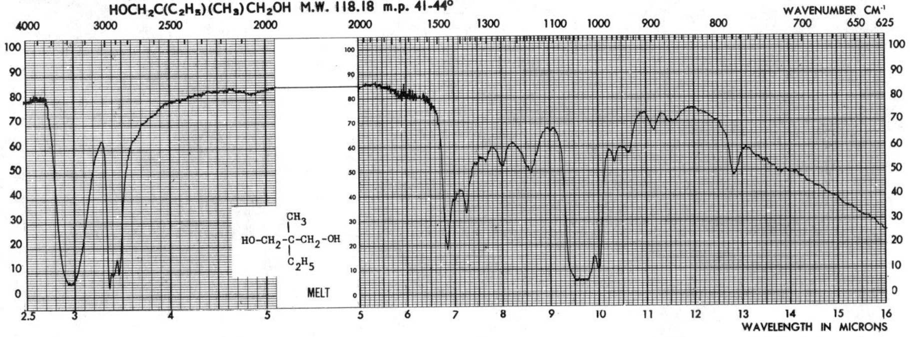

MELT

G

M7520-9 2-Methyl-2-propyl-1,3-propanediol
$HOCH_2C(CH_3)(CH_2CH_2CH_3)CH_2OH$ M.W. 132.20
m.p. 53-55°

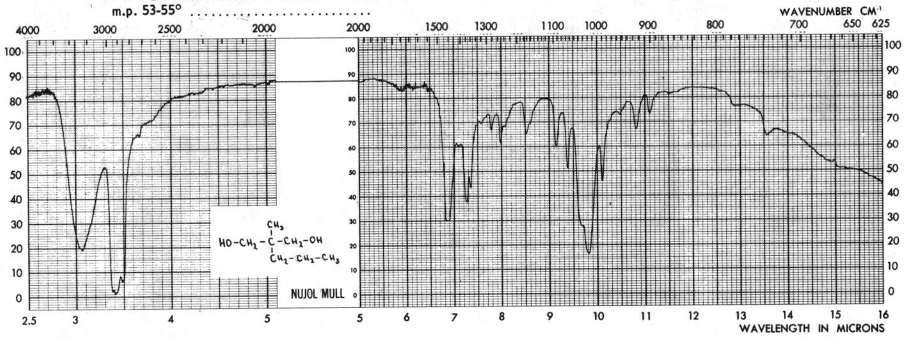

NUJOL MULL

H

14,247-6
2-*n*-Butyl-2-ethyl-1,3-propanediol
$HOCH_2C[(CH_2)_3CH_3](C_2H_5)CH_2OH$
M.W. 160.26 m.p. 41-44°

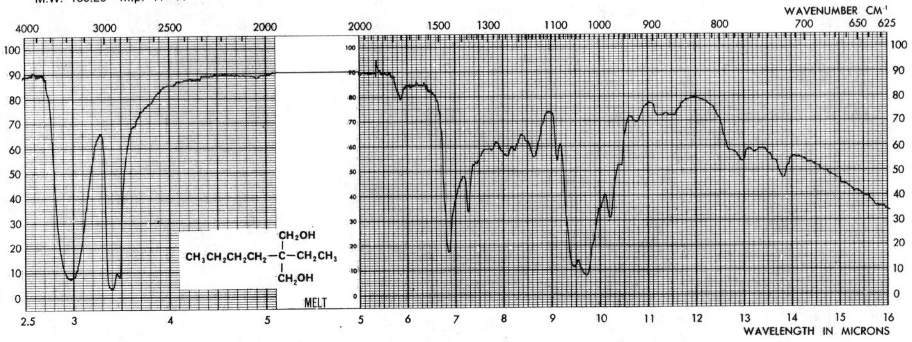

MELT

WAVENUMBER CM⁻¹ / WAVELENGTH IN MICRONS

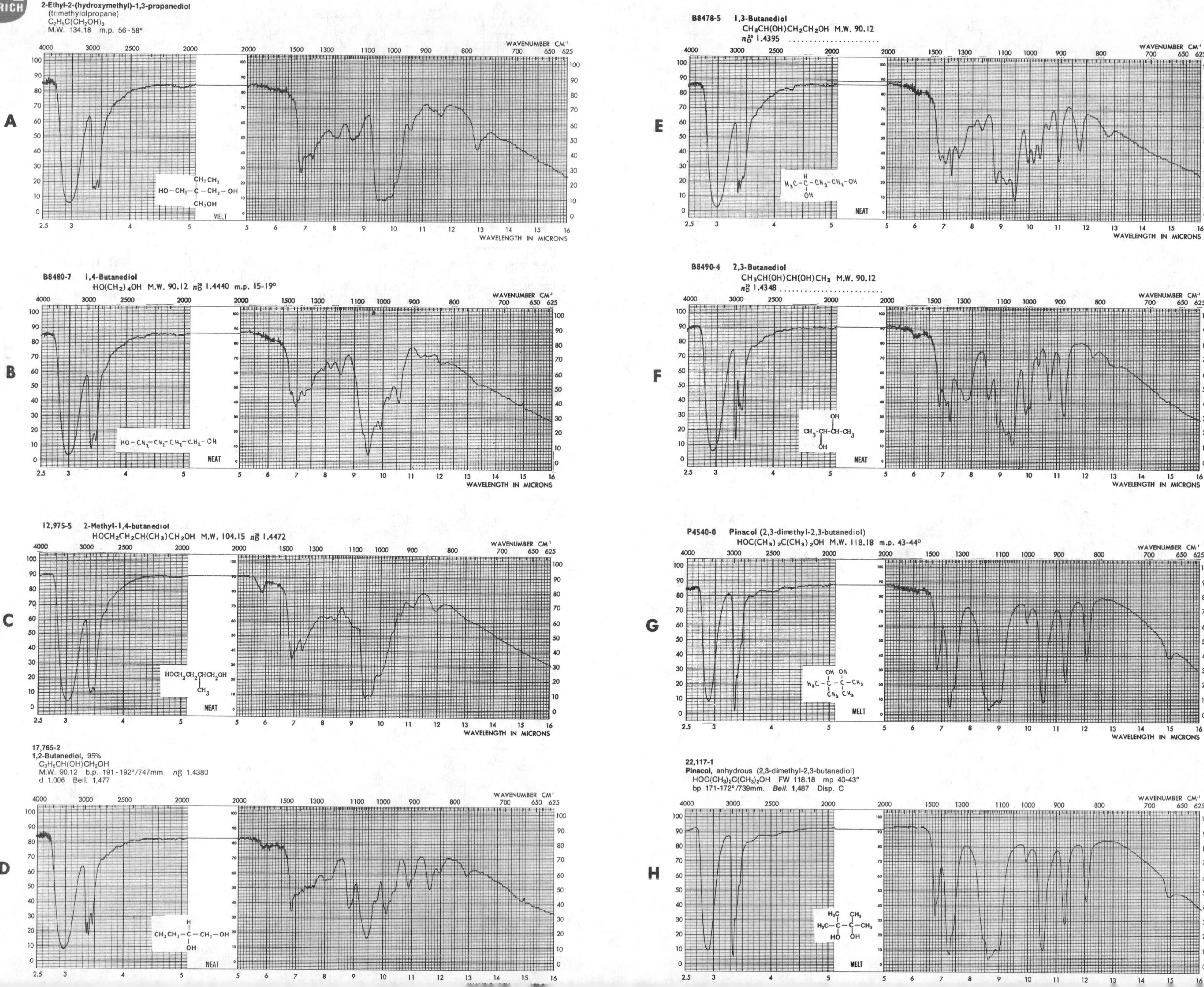
ALDRICH
14,808-3
2-Ethyl-2-(hydroxymethyl)-1,3-propanediol
(trimethylolpropane)
$C_2H_5C(CH_2OH)_3$
M.W. 134.18 m.p. 56-58°
A
MELT
B8480-7 1,4-Butanediol
$HO(CH_2)_4OH$ M.W. 90.12 n_D^{20} 1.4440 m.p. 15-19°
B
NEAT
12,975-5 2-Methyl-1,4-butanediol
$HOCH_2CH_2CH(CH_3)CH_2OH$ M.W. 104.15 n_D^{20} 1.4472
C
NEAT
17,765-2
1,2-Butanediol, 95%
$C_2H_5CH(OH)CH_2OH$
M.W. 90.12 b.p. 191-192°/747mm. n_D^{20} 1.4380
d 1.006 Beil. 1,477
D
NEAT
B8478-5 1,3-Butanediol
$CH_3CH(OH)CH_2CH_2OH$ M.W. 90.12
n_D^{20} 1.4395
E
NEAT
B8490-4 2,3-Butanediol
$CH_3CH(OH)CH(OH)CH_3$ M.W. 90.12
n_D^{20} 1.4348
F
NEAT
P4540-0 Pinacol (2,3-dimethyl-2,3-butanediol)
$HOC(CH_3)_2C(CH_3)_2OH$ M.W. 118.18 m.p. 43-44°
G
MELT
22,117-1
Pinacol, anhydrous (2,3-dimethyl-2,3-butanediol)
$HOC(CH_3)_2C(CH_3)_2OH$ FW 118.18 mp 40-43°
bp 171-172°/739mm. Beil. 1,487 Disp. C
H
MELT
WAVENUMBER CM⁻¹
WAVELENGTH IN MICRONS

P770-3 1,5-Pentanediol (pentamethylene glycol)
HO(CH₂)₅OH M.W. 104.15 n_D^{20} 1.4494
b.p. 137-138°/12 mm.

15,601-9
2,4-Pentanediol, 99%, mixture of isomers
CH₃CH(OH)CH₂CH(OH)CH₃
M.W. 104.15 b.p. 201-202° n_D^{20} 1.4355 d 0.95
Beil. 1,482

19,418-2
1,4-Pentanediol, 99%
CH₃CH(OH)(CH₂)₃OH FW 104.15
bp 72-73°/0mm. d 1.444 *Beil.* 1,480 Disp. C

21,369-1
DL-1,2-Hexanediol, 98+%
CH₃(CH₂)₃CH(OH)CH₂OH FW 118.18
bp 223-224° n_D^{20} 1.4425 d 0.951 *Beil.* 1(1),251
Disp. C

11,210-0 2-Methyl-2,4-pentanediol
CH₃CH(OH)CH₂C(CH₃)₂OH M.W. 118.18 n_D^{20} 1.4250
b.p. 197°

H1180-7 1,6-Hexanediol (hexamethylene glycol)
HO(CH₂)₆OH M.W. 118.18 m.p. 42°

19,818-8
1,5-Hexanediol, 99%
CH₃CH(OH)(CH₂)₄OH FW 118.18
bp 89-91°/0.500mm. n_D^{20} 1.4511 d 0.981
Beil. 1,484 Disp. C

H1190-4 2,5-Hexanediol
CH₃CH(OH)CH₂CH₂CH(OH)CH₃ M.W. 118.18
n_D^{20} 1.4426

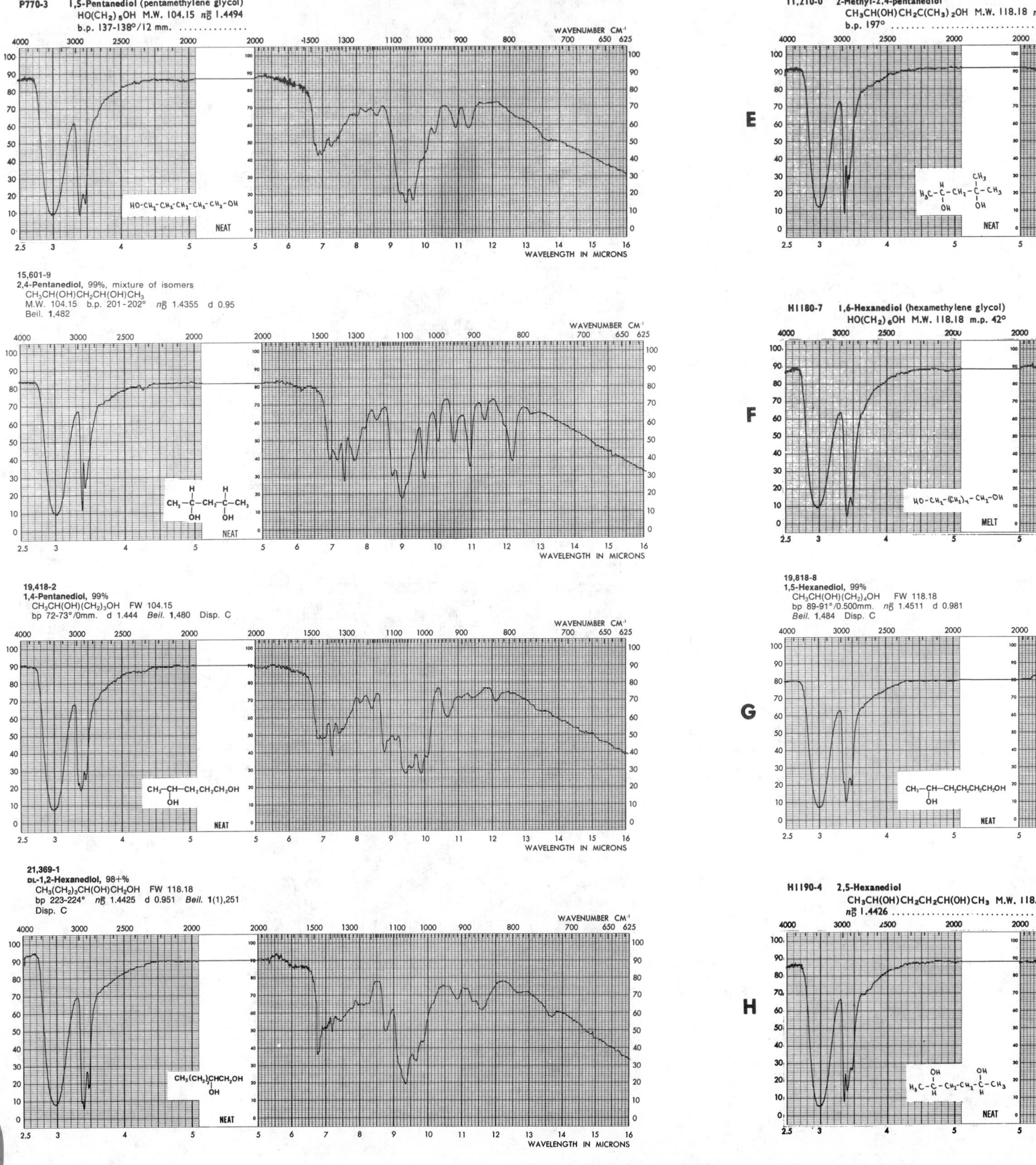

NON-AROMATIC ALCOHOLS

A

E2912-5 2-Ethyl-1,3-hexanediol
$CH_3CH_2CH_2CH(OH)CH(C_2H_5)CH_2OH$ M.W. 146.23
n_D^{20} 1.4497

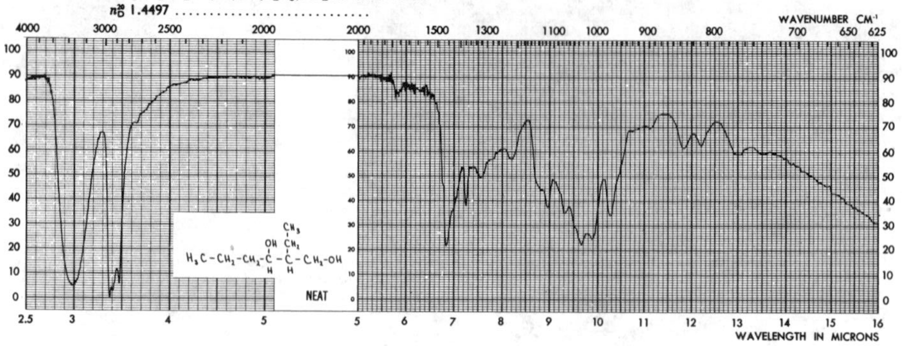

NEAT

B

14,361-8 2,5-Dimethyl-2,5-hexanediol
$(CH_3)_2C(OH)CH_2CH_2C(CH_3)_2OH$ M.W. 146.23
m.p. 86-90°

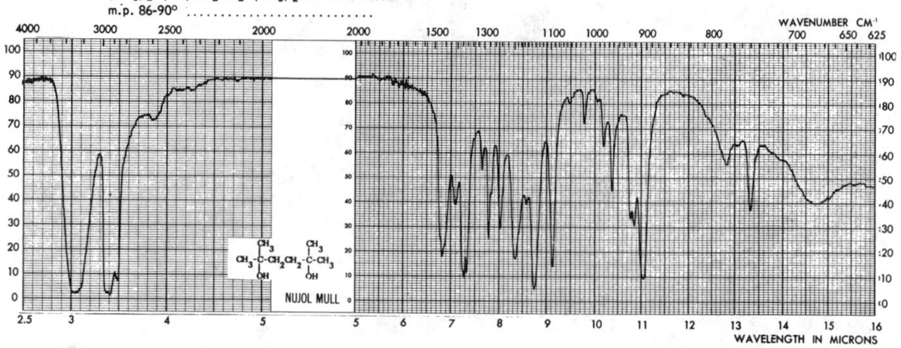

NUJOL MULL

C

H220-1 1,7-Heptanediol
$HO(CH_2)_7OH$ M.W. 132.21

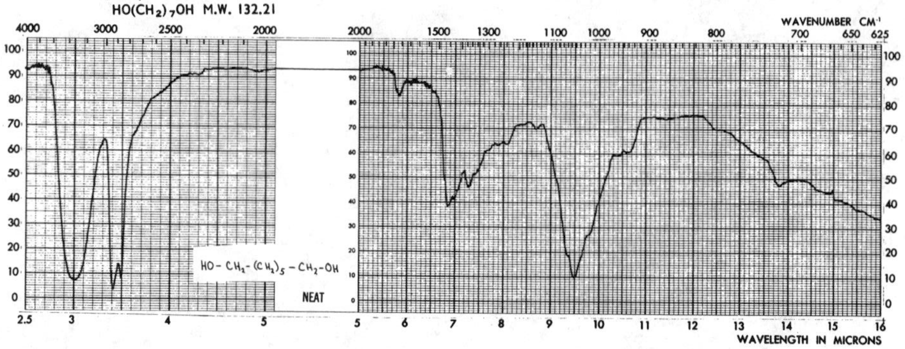

$HO-CH_2-(CH_2)_5-CH_2-OH$

NEAT

D

O-330-3 1,8-Octanediol (octamethylene glycol)
$HO(CH_2)_8OH$ M.W. 146.23
m.p. 61-62°

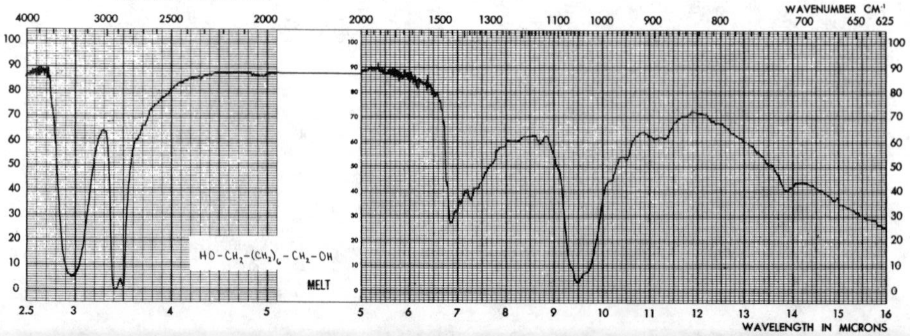

$HO-CH_2-(CH_2)_6-CH_2-OH$

MELT

E

21,370-5
1,2-Octanediol, 98+%
$CH_3(CH_2)_5CH(OH)CH_2OH$ FW 146.23 mp 36-38°
bp 131-132°/10mm. *Beil.* 1(3),2217 Disp. C

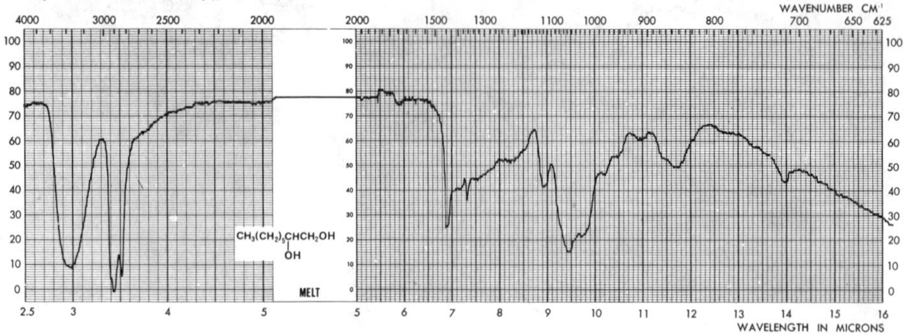

MELT

F

N2960-0 1,9-Nonanediol
$HO(CH_2)_9OH$ M.W. 160.26 m.p. 51.5-53°

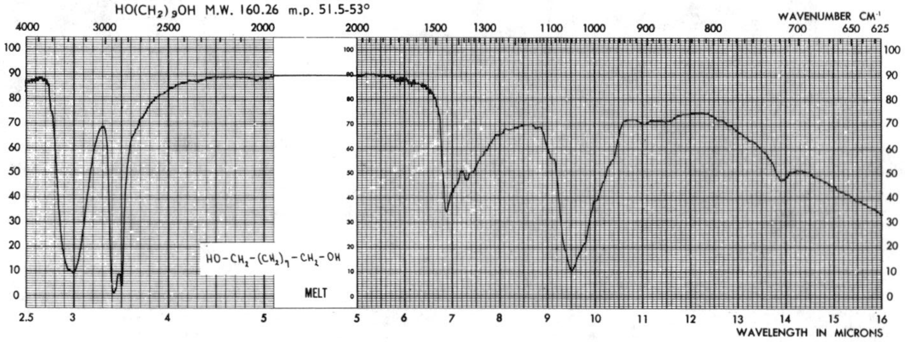

$HO-CH_2-(CH_2)_7-CH_2-OH$

MELT

G

D120-3 1,10-Decanediol (decamethylene glycol)
$HO(CH_2)_{10}OH$ M.W. 174.28 m.p. 72-75°

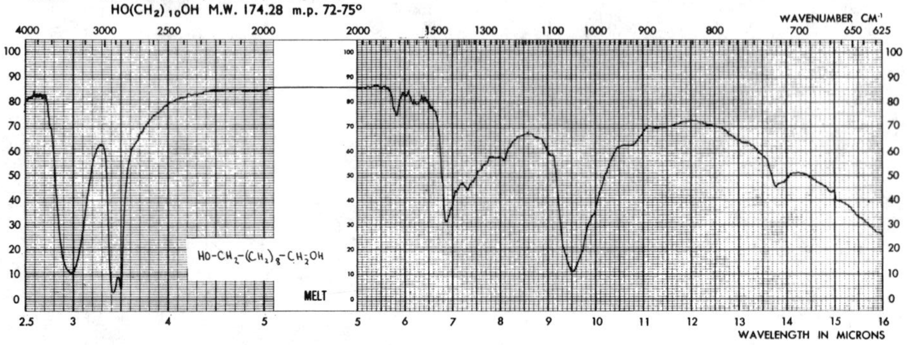

$HO-CH_2-(CH_2)_8-CH_2OH$

MELT

H

D22,130-9 1,12-Dodecanediol
$HO(CH_2)_{12}OH$ M.W. 202.33 m.p. 79.5-84°

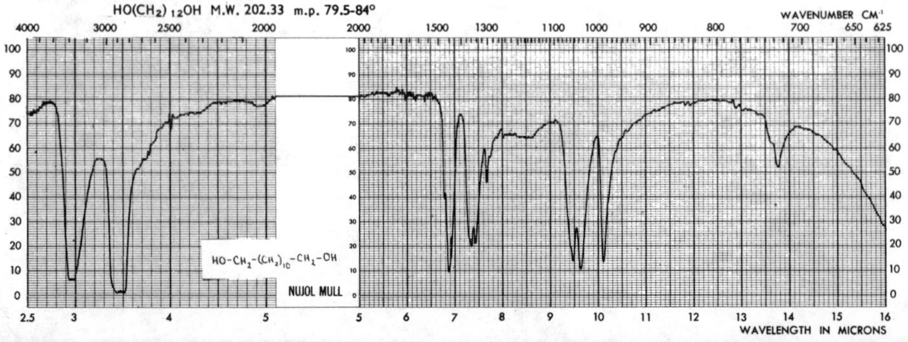

$HO-CH_2-(CH_2)_{10}-CH_2-OH$

NUJOL MULL

A

21,372-1
1,2-Dodecanediol, 98+%
$CH_3(CH_2)_9CH(OH)CH_2OH$ FW 202.34 mp 58-60°
Beil. 1(3),2237 Disp. C

$CH_3-(CH_2)_9-CH(OH)CH_2OH$ — MELT

B

17,748-2
1,16-Hexadecanediol, 98%
$HO(CH_2)_{16}OH$
M.W. 258.45 m.p. 92-93° b.p. 197-199°/3mm.

$HOCH_2(CH_2)_{14}CH_2OH$ — NUJOL MULL

C

21,374-8
1,2-Hexadecanediol, 98+%
$CH_3(CH_2)_{13}CH(OH)CH_2OH$ FW 258.45 mp 72-74°
Beil. 1(3),2244 Disp. C

$CH_3-(CH_2)_{13}-CH(OH)CH_2OH$ — NUJOL MULL

D

A2870-8 **Allyl alcohol (2-propen-1-ol)**
$H_2C{:}CHCH_2OH$ M.W. 58.08 n_D^{20} 1.4119
b.p. 97°

$H_2C=CH-CH_2-OH$ — NEAT

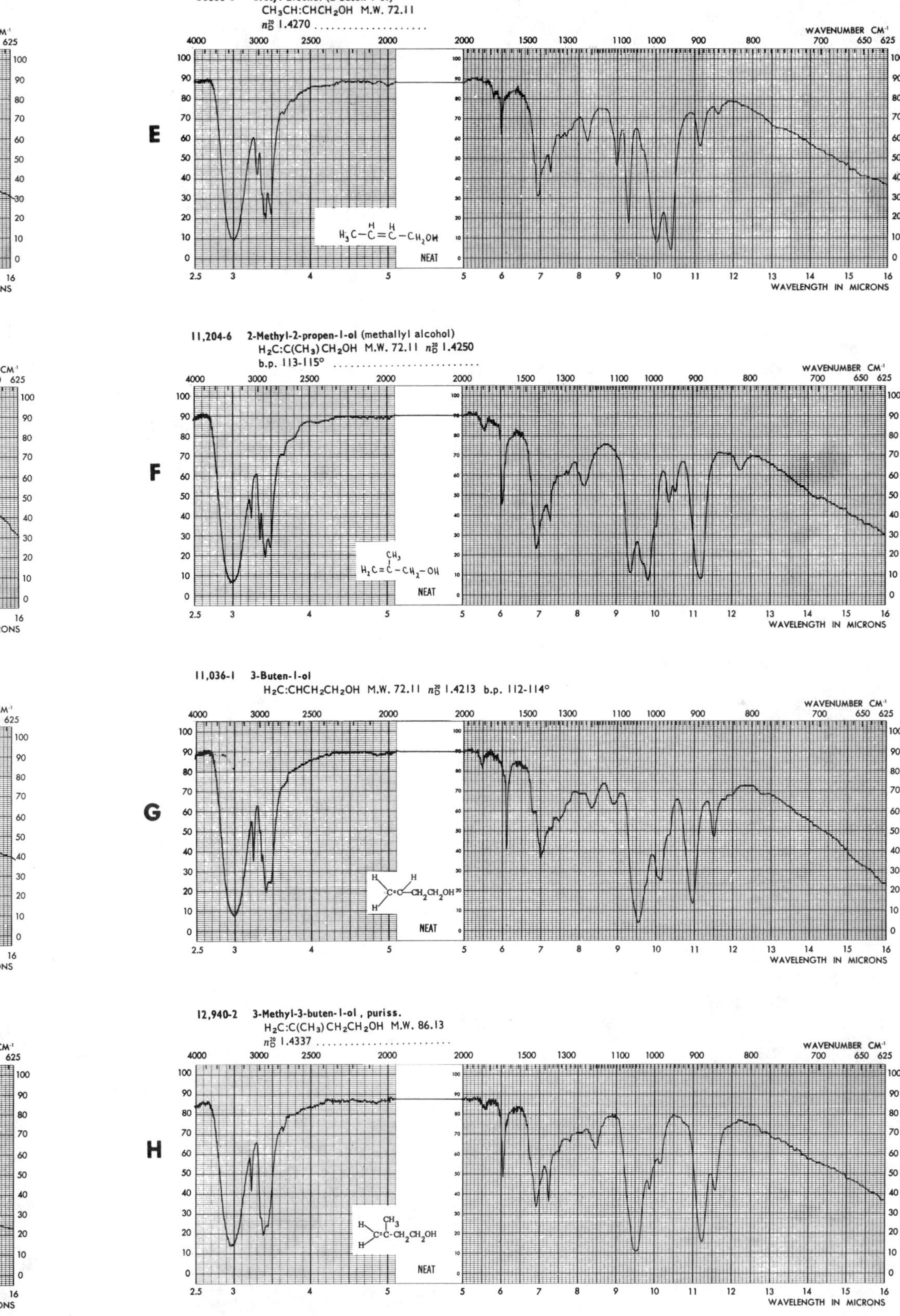

E

C8600-6 **Crotyl alcohol (2-buten-1-ol)**
$CH_3CH{:}CHCH_2OH$ M.W. 72.11
n_D^{20} 1.4270

F

11,204-6 **2-Methyl-2-propen-1-ol (methallyl alcohol)**
$H_2C{:}C(CH_3)CH_2OH$ M.W. 72.11 n_D^{20} 1.4250
b.p. 113-115°

G

11,036-1 **3-Buten-1-ol**
$H_2C{:}CHCH_2CH_2OH$ M.W. 72.11 n_D^{20} 1.4213 b.p. 112-114°

H

12,940-2 **3-Methyl-3-buten-1-ol, puriss.**
$H_2C{:}C(CH_3)CH_2CH_2OH$ M.W. 86.13
n_D^{20} 1.4337

ALDRICH®

A

16,235-3
3-Methyl-2-buten-1-ol, 96%
$(CH_3)_2C{=}CHCH_2OH$
M.W. 86.13 b.p. 140° n_D^{20} 1.4412 d 0.848
Beil. 1,444

NEAT

B

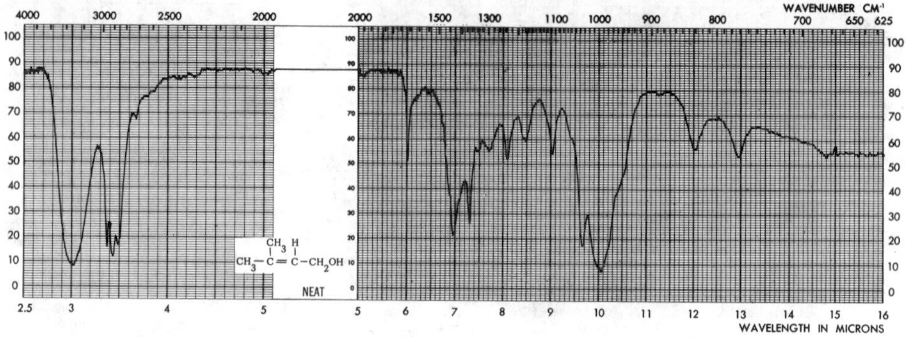

B8640-0 3-Buten-2-ol
$H_2C{:}CHCH(OH)CH_3$ M.W. 72.11 n_D^{20} 1.4140

NEAT

C

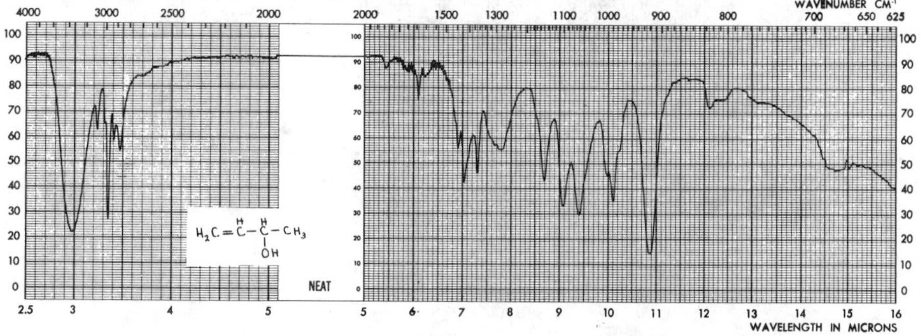

11,095-7 3-Methyl-3-buten-2-ol
$H_2C{:}C(CH_3)CH(OH)CH_3$ M.W. 86.13
n_D^{20} 1.4275

NEAT

D

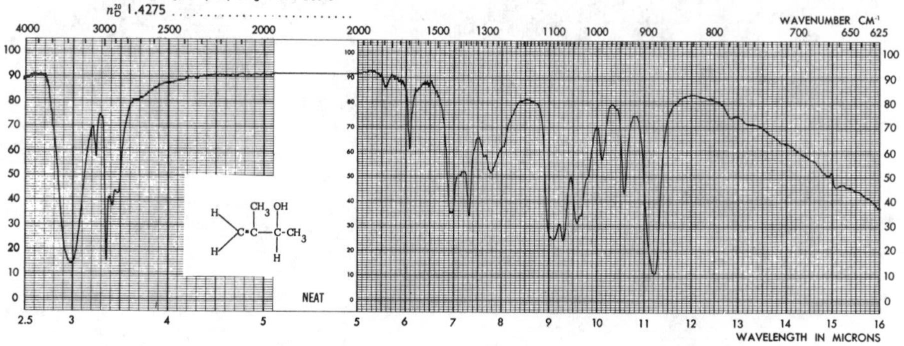

13,681-6 2-Methyl-3-buten-2-ol
$H_2C{:}CHC(CH_3)_2OH$ M.W. 86.13 n_D^{20} 1.4147 b.p. 98-99°

NEAT

E

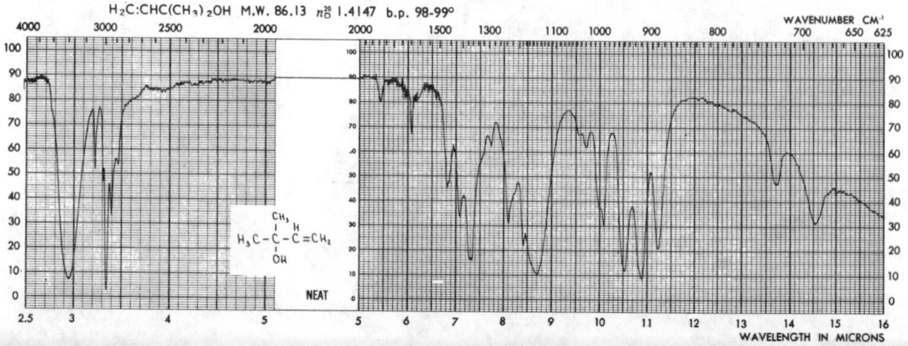

11,127-9 4-Penten-1-ol
$H_2C{:}CH(CH_2)_3OH$ M.W. 86.13 n_D^{20} 1.4289 b.p. 134-137°

NEAT

F

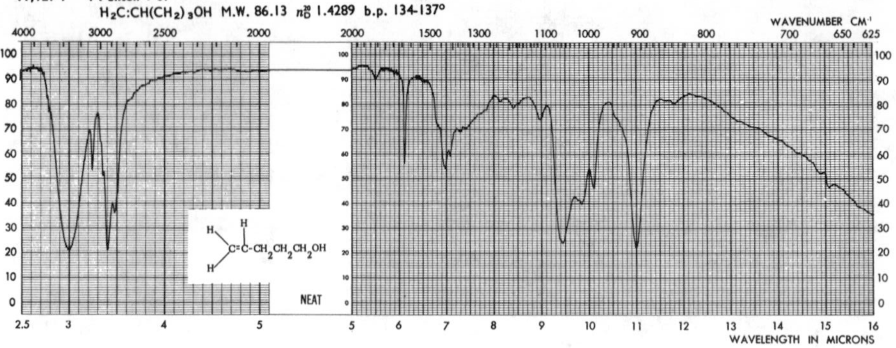

P880-7 4-Penten-2-ol
$H_2C{:}CHCH_2CH(OH)CH_3$ M.W. 86.13 n_D^{20} 1.4237
b.p. 139-142°

NEAT

G

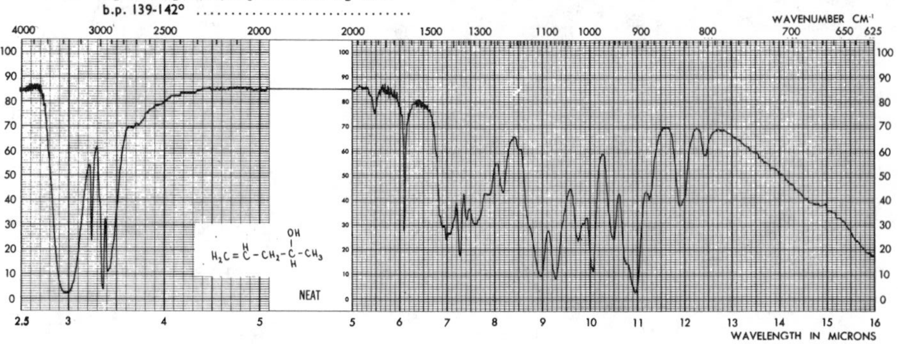

P860-2 1-Penten-3-ol
$C_2H_5CH(OH)CH{:}CH_2$ M.W. 86.13 n_D^{20} 1.4239
b.p. 37°/20 mm.

NEAT

H

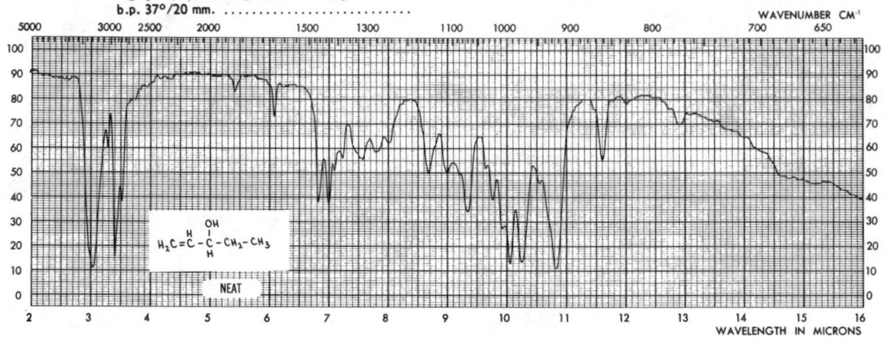

11,128-7 3-Penten-2-ol
$CH_3CH{:}CHCH(OH)CH_3$ M.W. 86.13 n_D^{20} 1.4271
b.p. 119-121°

NEAT

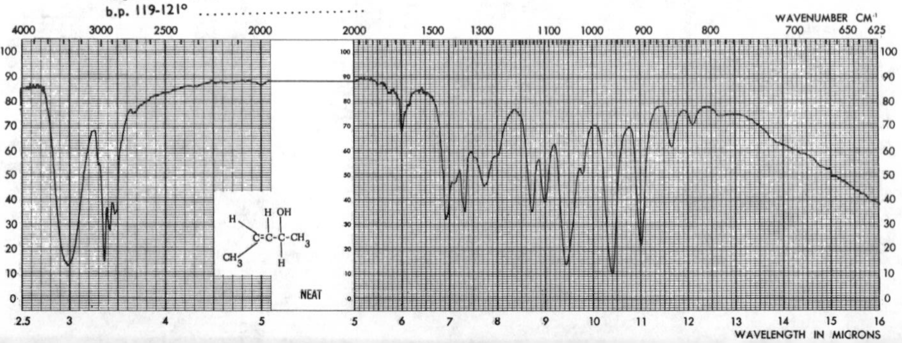

A

11,116-3 **4-Methyl-3-penten-2-ol**
$(CH_3)_2C{:}CHCH(OH)CH_3$ M.W. 100.16
n_D^{20} 1.4390

NEAT

B

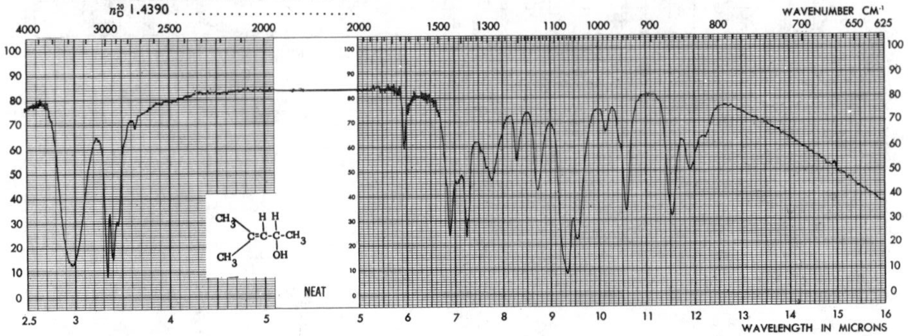

11,115-5 **4-Methyl-1-penten-3-ol**
$(CH_3)_2CHCH(OH)CH{:}CH_2$ M.W. 100.16 n_D^{20} 1.4273

NEAT

C

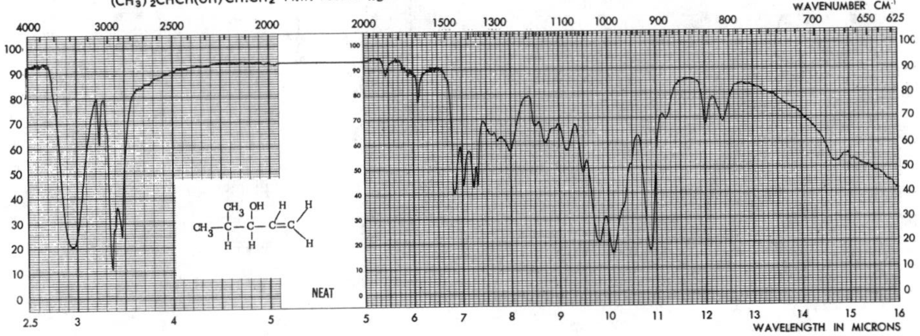

11,117-1 **2-Methyl-4-penten-2-ol**
$H_2C{:}CHCH_2C(CH_3)_2OH$ M.W. 100.16
n_D^{20} 1.4265

NEAT

D

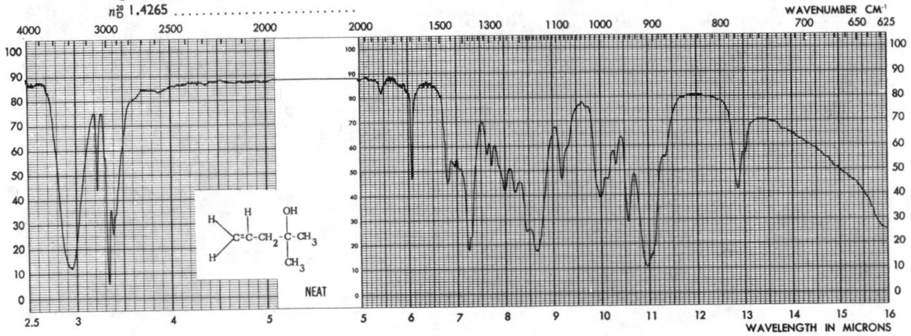

13,392-2 **2,3-Dimethyl-4-penten-2-ol**
$H_2C{:}CHCH(CH_3)C(CH_3)_2OH$ M.W. 114.19
n_D^{20} 1.4340

NEAT

E

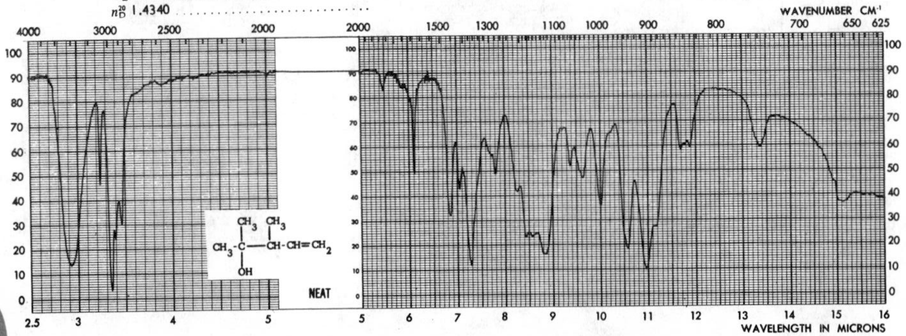

13,266-7 ***trans*-2-Hexen-1-ol**
$CH_3CH_2CH_2CH{:}CHCH_2OH$ M.W. 100.16
n_D^{20} 1.4343

NEAT

F

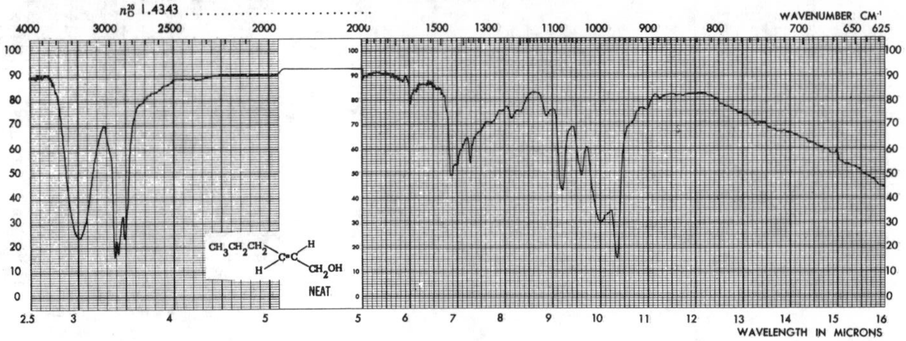

17,827-6
4,4-Dimethyl-2-methylene-1-pentanol, tech.
$(CH_3)_3CCH_2C(=CH_2)CH_2OH$
M.W. 128.22 n_D^{20} 1.4452 d 0.858

NEAT

G

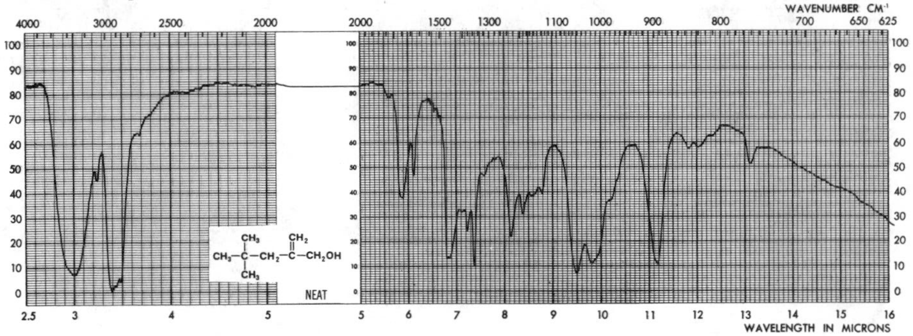

14,517-3 **2-Ethyl-2-hexen-1-ol, tech.**
$CH_3CH_2CH_2CH{:}C(C_2H_5)CH_2OH$ M.W. 128.22 n_D^{20} 1.4491
b.p. 80°/10 mm.

NEAT

H

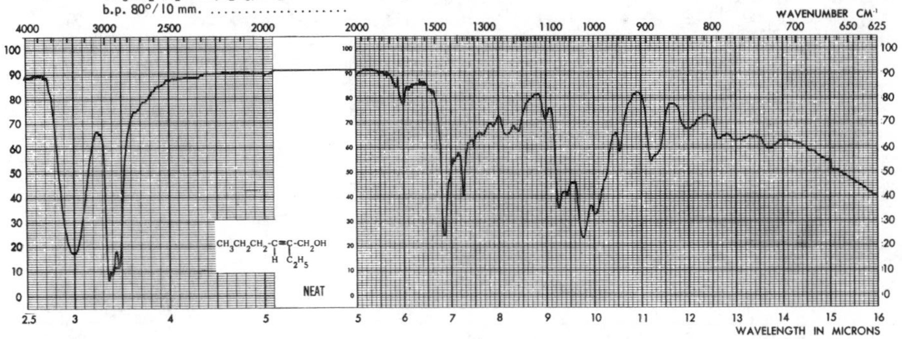

H1290-0 ***cis*-3-Hexen-1-ol**
$C_2H_5CH{:}CHCH_2CH_2OH$ M.W. 100.16 n_D^{20} 1.4395

NEAT

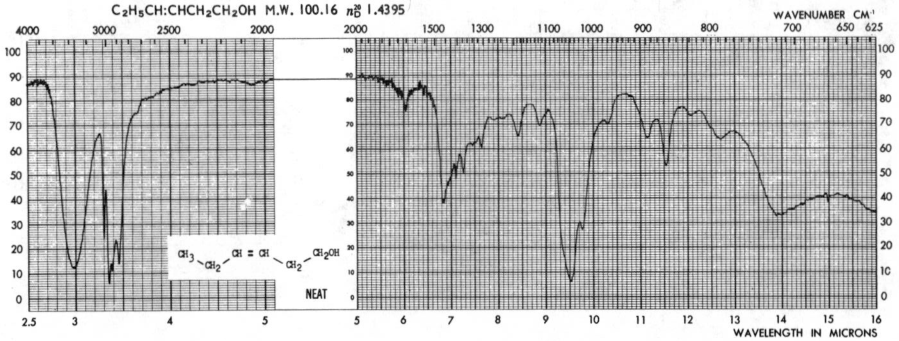

A

H1295-1 4-Hexen-3-ol
$CH_3CH{:}CHCH(OH)C_2H_5$ M.W. 100.16
n_D^{20} 1.4315
NEAT

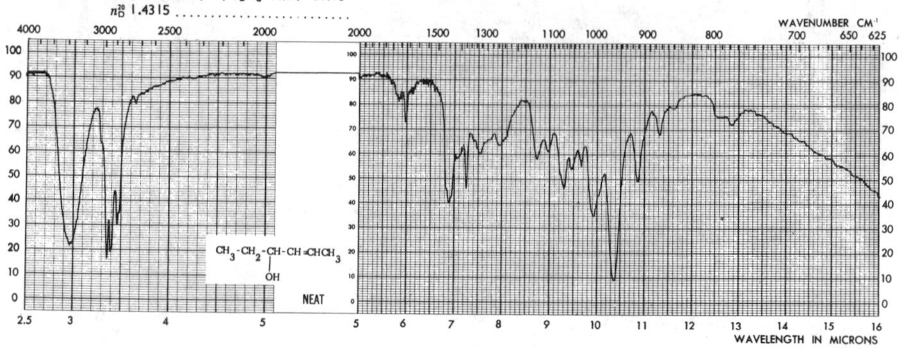

B

H1285-4 1-Hexen-3-ol
$CH_3CH_2CH_2CH(OH)CH{:}CH_2$ M.W. 100.16
n_D^{20} 1.4277
NEAT

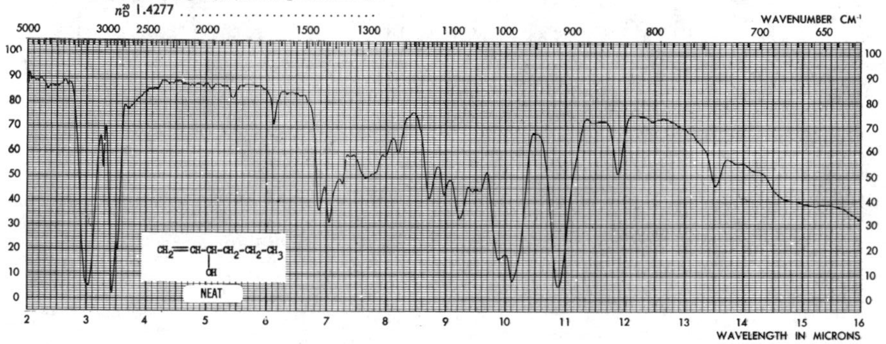

C

11,091-4 5-Hexen-3-ol
$H_2C{:}CHCH_2CH(OH)C_2H_5$ M.W. 100.16 n_D^{20} 1.4310
NEAT

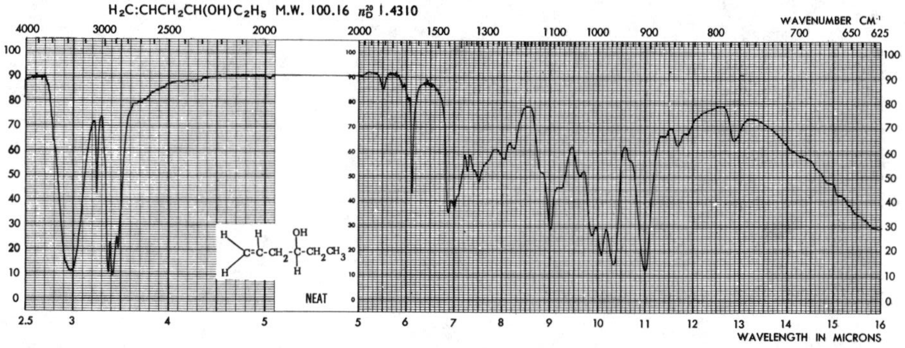

D

11,851-6 3-Ethyl-5-hexen-3-ol
$H_2C{:}CHCH_2C(OH)(C_2H_5)_2$ M.W. 128.22
n_D^{20} 1.4429
NEAT

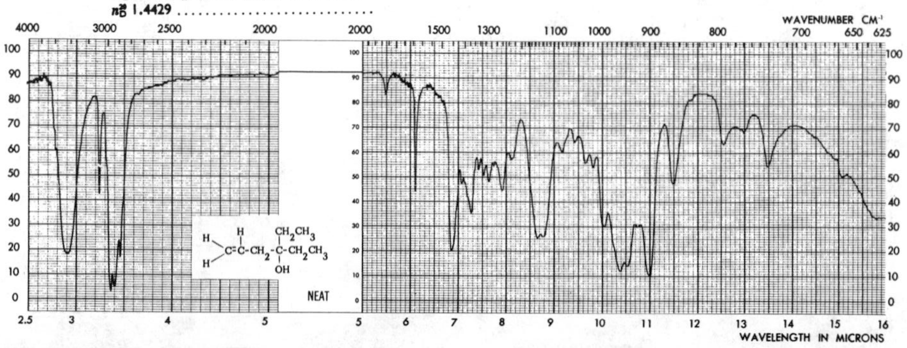

E

12,932-1 3,5-Dimethyl-5-hexen-3-ol
$H_2C{:}C(CH_3)CH_2C(CH_3)(OH)C_2H_5$ M.W. 128.22
n_D^{20} 1.4447
NEAT

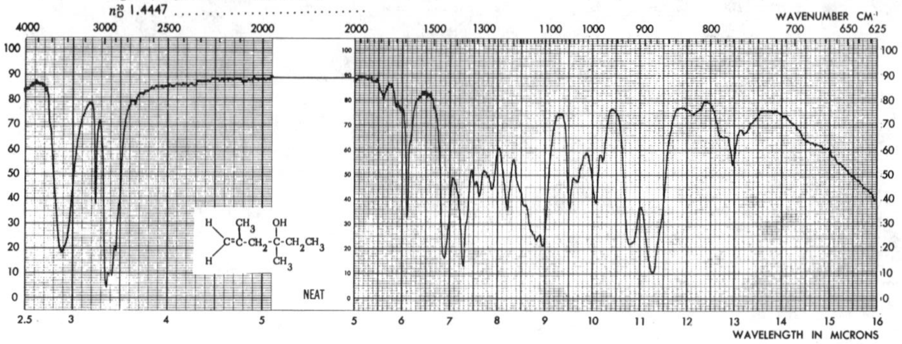

F

11,852-4 3-Hepten-1-ol
$CH_3CH_2CH_2CH{:}CHCH_2CH_2OH$ M.W. 114.19
n_D^{20} 1.4432
NEAT

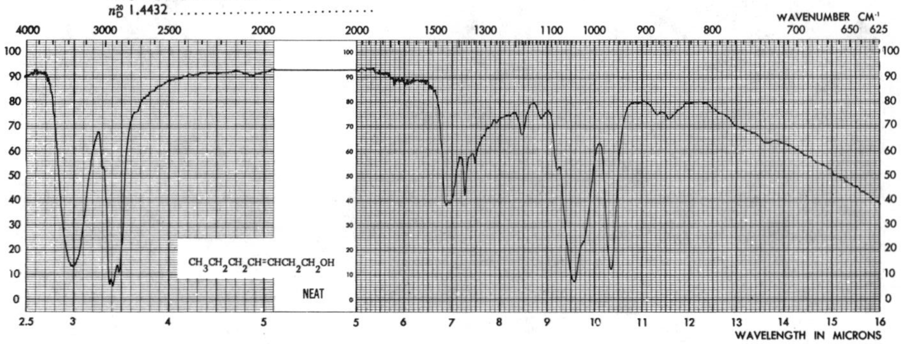

G

H375-5 1-Hepten-3-ol, puriss.
$CH_3(CH_2)_3CH(OH)CH{:}CH_2$ M.W. 114.19
n_D^{20} 1.4320
NEAT

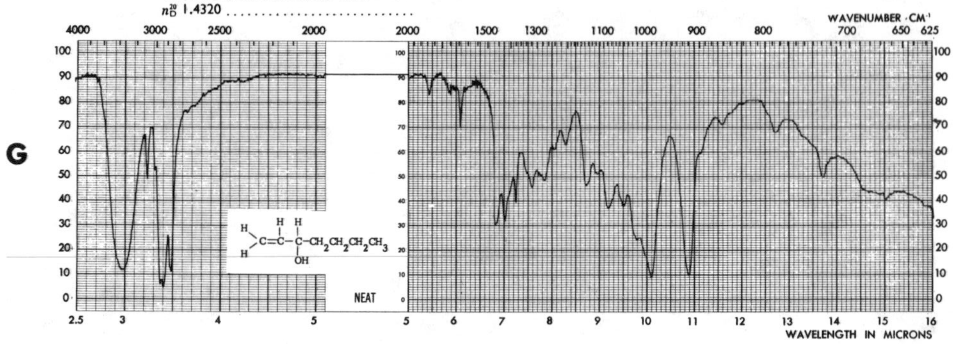

H

11,853-2 2-Hepten-4-ol
$CH_3CH_2CH_2CH(OH)CH{:}CHCH_3$ M.W. 114.19
n_D^{20} 1.4331
NEAT

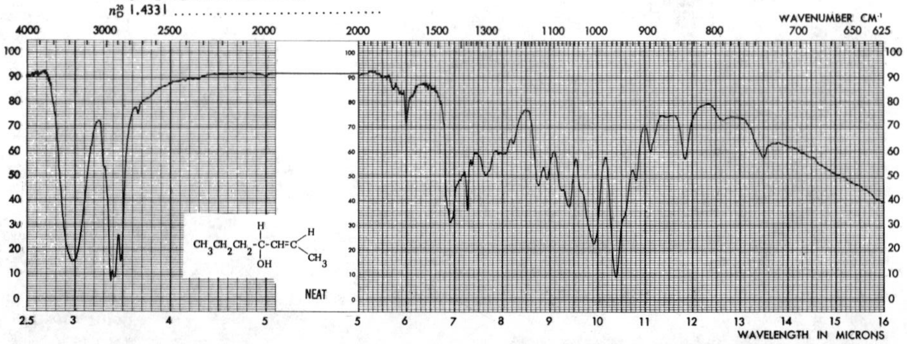

A

11,859-1 **2-Methyl-1-hepten-3-ol**
$CH_3(CH_2)_3CH(OH)C(CH_3){:}CH_2$ M.W. 128.22
n_D^{20} 1.4390

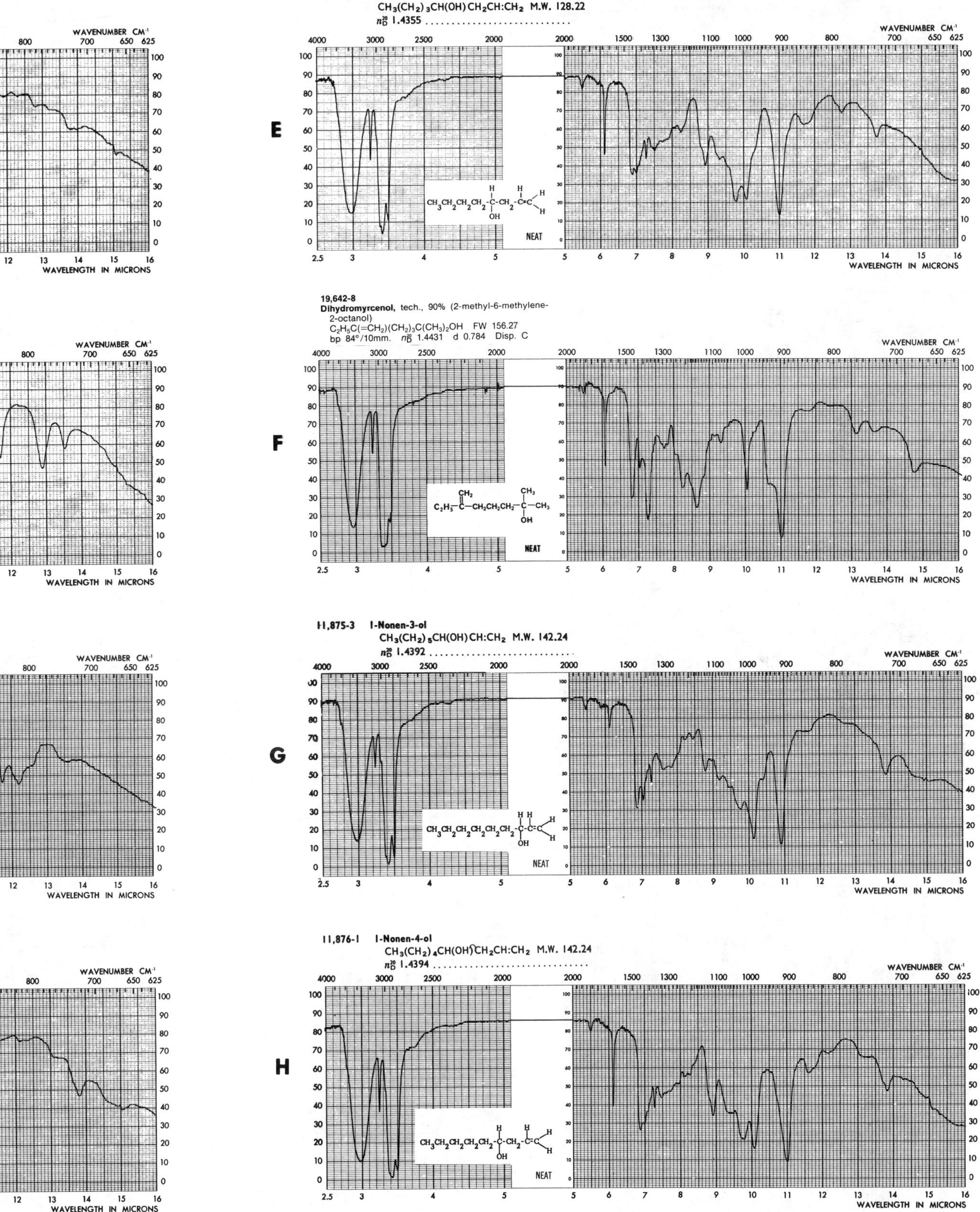

B

11,862-1 **4-Methyl-1-hepten-4-ol**
$CH_3CH_2CH_2C(CH_3)(OH)CH_2CH{:}CH_2$ M.W. 128.22
n_D^{20} 1.4358

C

19,587-1
6-Methyl-5-hepten-2-ol, 99%
$(CH_3)_2C{=}CHCH_2CH_2CH(OH)CH_3$ FW 128.22
bp 78°/14mm. n_D^{20} 1.4485 d 0.844
Beil. 1(4),2167 Disp. C

D

O-528-4 **1-Octen-3-ol, puriss.**
$CH_3(CH_2)_4CH(OH)CH{:}CH_2$ M.W. 128.22
n_D^{20} 1.4361

E

11,879-6 **1-Octen-4-ol**
$CH_3(CH_2)_3CH(OH)CH_2CH{:}CH_2$ M.W. 128.22
n_D^{20} 1.4355

F

19,642-8
Dihydromyrcenol, tech., 90% (2-methyl-6-methylene-2-octanol)
$C_2H_5C(=CH_2)(CH_2)_3C(CH_3)_2OH$ FW 156.27
bp 84°/10mm. n_D^{20} 1.4431 d 0.784 Disp. C

G

11,875-3 **1-Nonen-3-ol**
$CH_3(CH_2)_5CH(OH)CH{:}CH_2$ M.W. 142.24
n_D^{20} 1.4392

H

11,876-1 **1-Nonen-4-ol**
$CH_3(CH_2)_4CH(OH)CH_2CH{:}CH_2$ M.W. 142.24
n_D^{20} 1.4394

A 11,835-4 9-Decen-1-ol
$H_2C{:}CH(CH_2)_8OH$ M.W. 156.27
n_D^{20} 1.4460

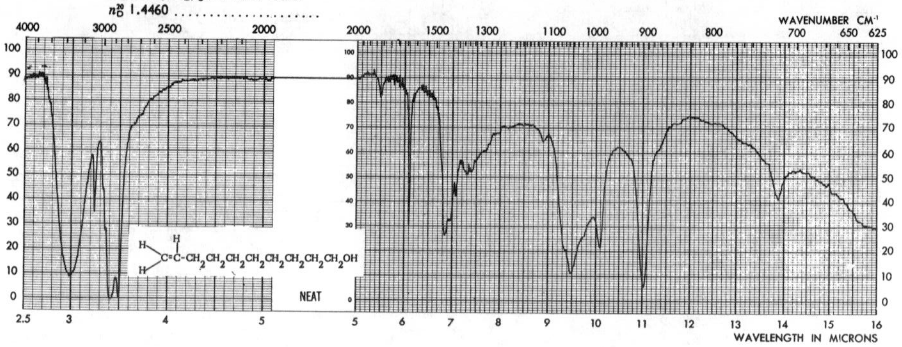

B C8320-1 Citronellol
$H_2C{:}C(CH_3)(CH_2)_3CH(CH_3)CH_2CH_2OH$ M.W. 156.27
n_D^{20} 1.4556

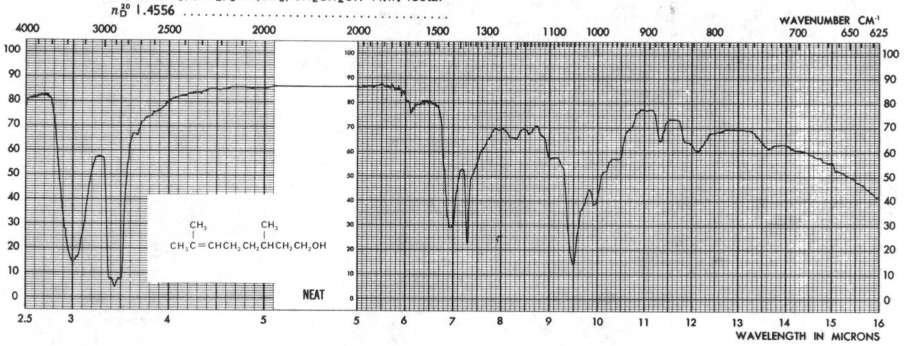

C U200-8 ω-Undecylenyl alcohol (10-undecen-1-ol)
$H_2C{:}CH(CH_2)_9OH$ M.W. 170.30 n_D^{20} 1.4500

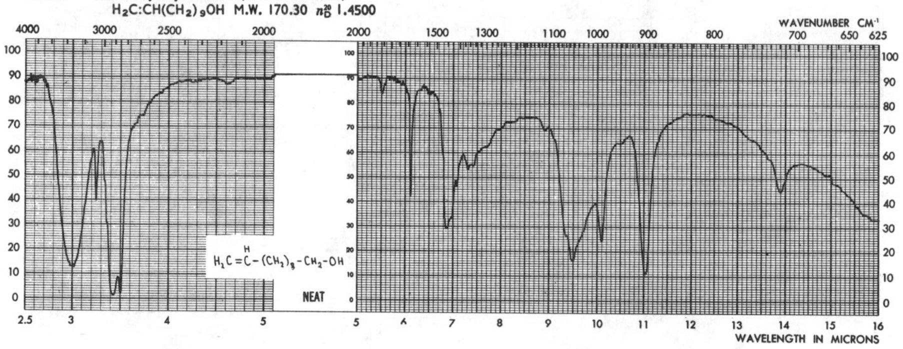

D O-760-0 Oleyl alcohol, tech.
$CH_3(CH_2)_7CH{:}CH(CH_2)_8OH$ M.W. 268.49 n_D^{20} 1.4603

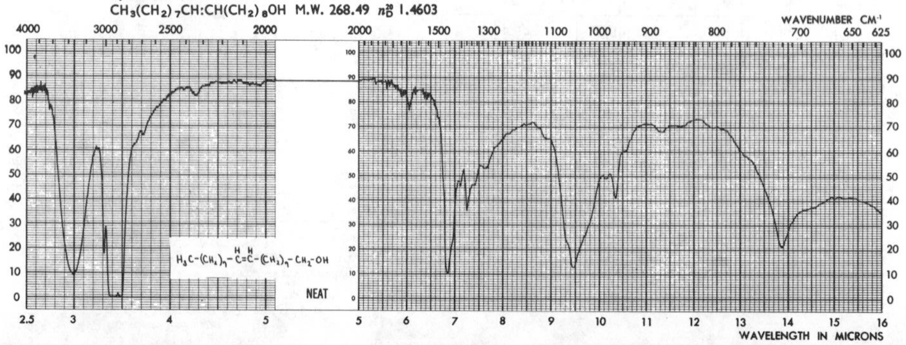

E 13,991-2 Phytol (3,7,11,15-tetramethyl-2-hexadecen-1-ol), tech.
$CH_3[CH(CH_3)(CH_2)_3]_3C(CH_3){:}CHCH_2OH$ M.W. 296.54
n_D^{20} 1.4701 b.p. 202-204°/10 mm.

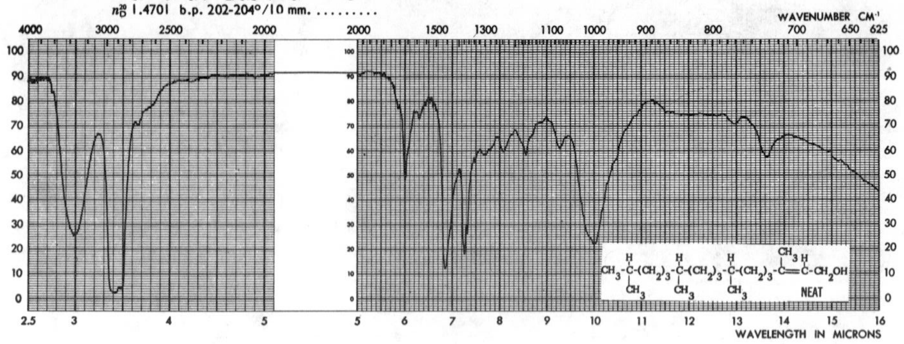

F B8620-6 2-Butene-1,4-diol
$HOCH_2CH{:}CHCH_2OH$ M.W. 88.11 n_D^{20} 1.4765

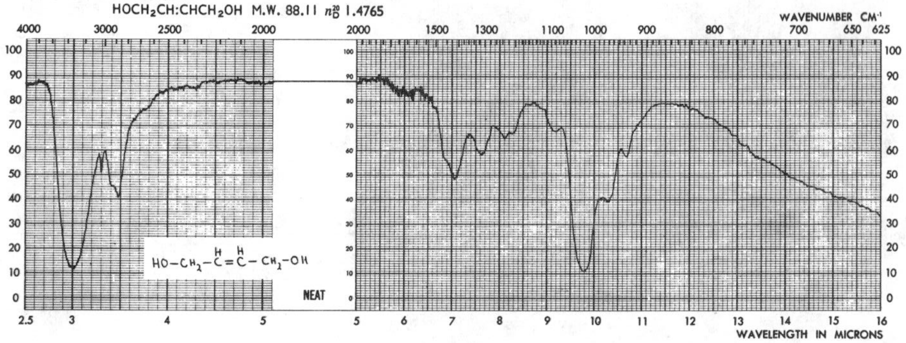

G H1280-3 3-Hexene-2,5-diol, tech., 70%; remainder 3-hexyne-2,5-diol
$CH_3CH(OH)CH{:}CHCH(OH)CH_3$ M.W. 116.16 n_D^{20} 1.4652

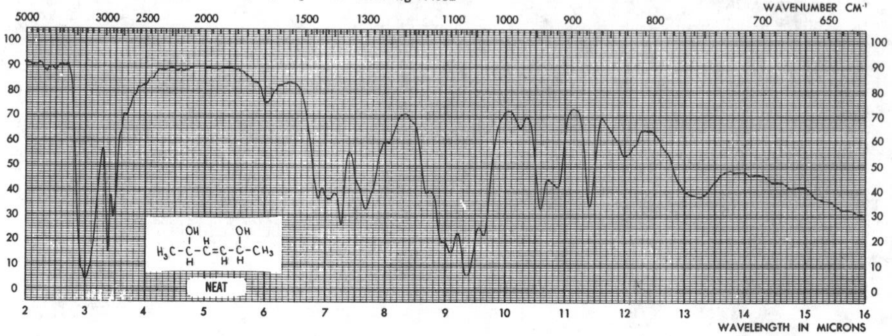

H H840-4 2,4-Hexadienol (sorbic alcohol), tech.
$CH_3CH{:}CHCH{:}CHCH_2OH$ M.W. 98.15
n_D^{20} 1.4981

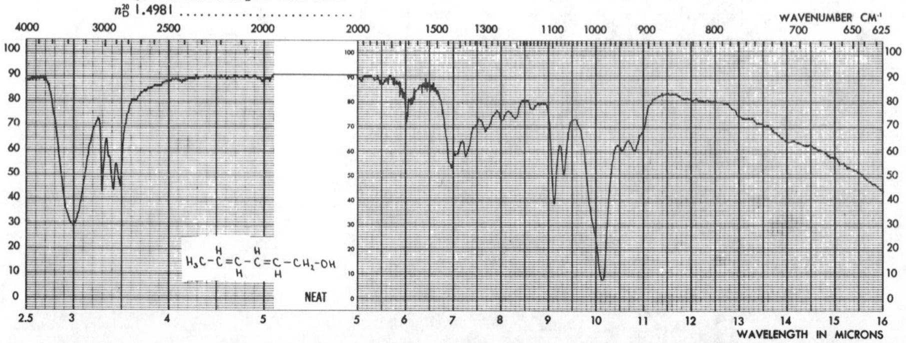

A

11,855-9 1,5-Hexadien-3-ol
$H_2C{:}CHCH_2CH(OH)CH{:}CH_2$ M.W. 98.15
n_D^{20} 1.4436

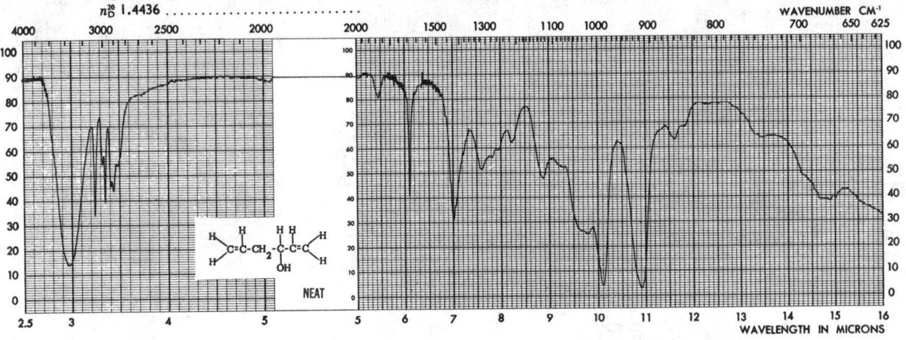

NEAT

B

12,930-5 2,5-Dimethyl-1,5-hexadien-3-ol
$H_2C{:}C(CH_3)CH_2CH(OH)C(CH_3){:}CH_2$ M.W. 126.20
n_D^{20} 1.4576

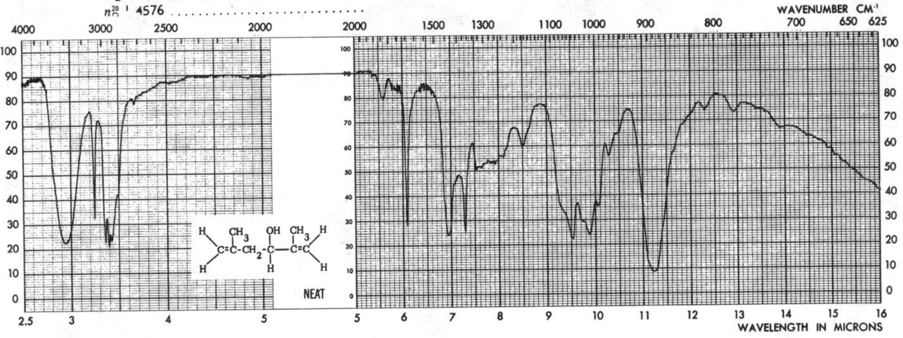

NEAT

C

11,158-9 1,6-Heptadien-4-ol
$H_2C{:}CHCH_2CH(OH)CH_2CH{:}CH_2$ M.W. 112.17 n_D^{20} 1.4489

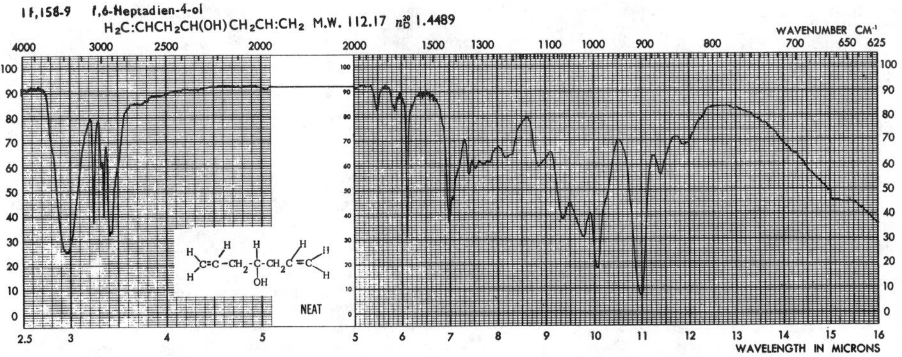

NEAT

D

11,858-3 4-Methyl-1,6-heptadien-4-ol
$H_2C{:}CHCH_2C(CH_3)(OH)CH_2CH{:}CH_2$ M.W. 126.20
n_D^{20} 1.4501

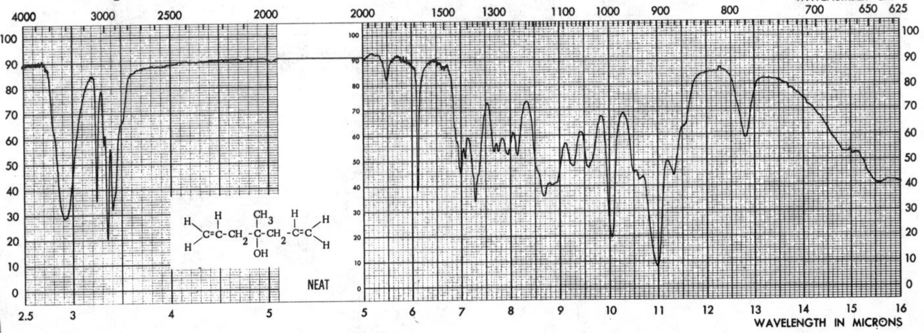

NEAT

E

L260-2 Linalool
$(CH_3)_2C{:}CHCH_2CH_2C(CH_3)(OH)CH{:}CH_2$ M.W. 154.25
n_D^{20} 1.4564 b.p. 80-82°/8 mm.

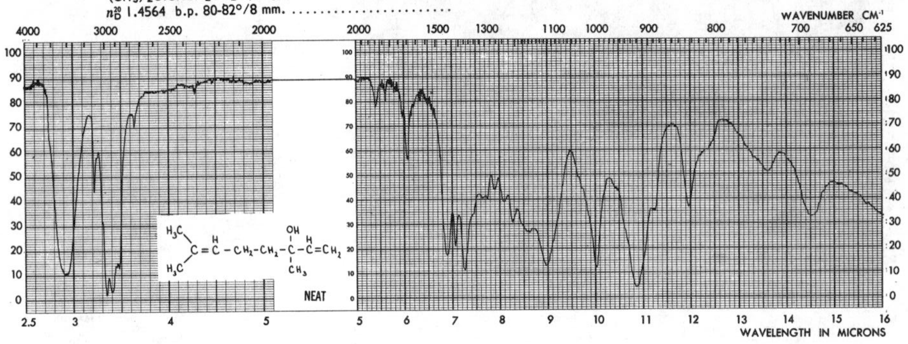

NEAT

F

16,333-3
Geraniol, 99+%, GOLD LABEL
$(CH_3)_2C{=}CHCH_2CH_2C(CH_3){=}CHCH_2OH$
M.W. 154.25 b.p. 229-230° n_D^{20} 1.4760 d 0.889
Beil. 1,457

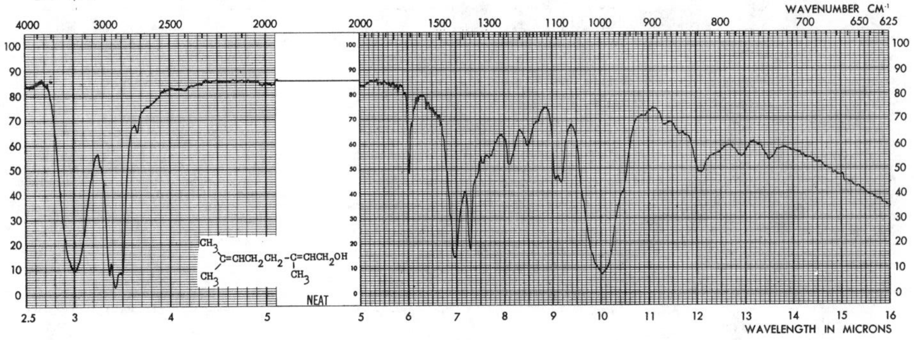

NEAT

G

H5960-5 3-Hydroxy-3,7,11-trimethyl-1,6,10-dodecatriene (nerolidol)
$(CH_3)_2C{:}CHCH_2CH_2C(CH_3){:}CHCH_2CH_2C(CH_3)(OH)CH{:}CH_2$
M.W. 222.37 n_D^{20} 1.4815 b.p. 114°/1.5mm.
$[\alpha]_D^{20}$ + 14.17° (in H_2O)

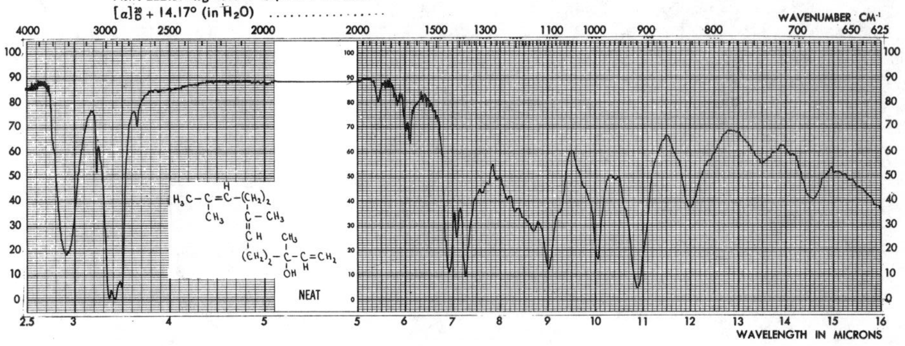

NEAT

H

F20-3 Farnesol
$(CH_3)_2C{:}CHCH_2CH_2C(CH_3){:}CHCH_2CH_2C(CH_3){:}CHCH_2OH$
M.W. 222.37 n_D^{20} 1.4889

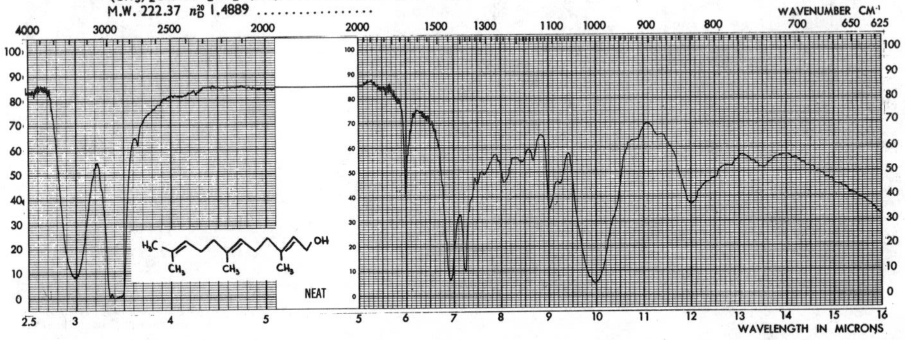

NEAT

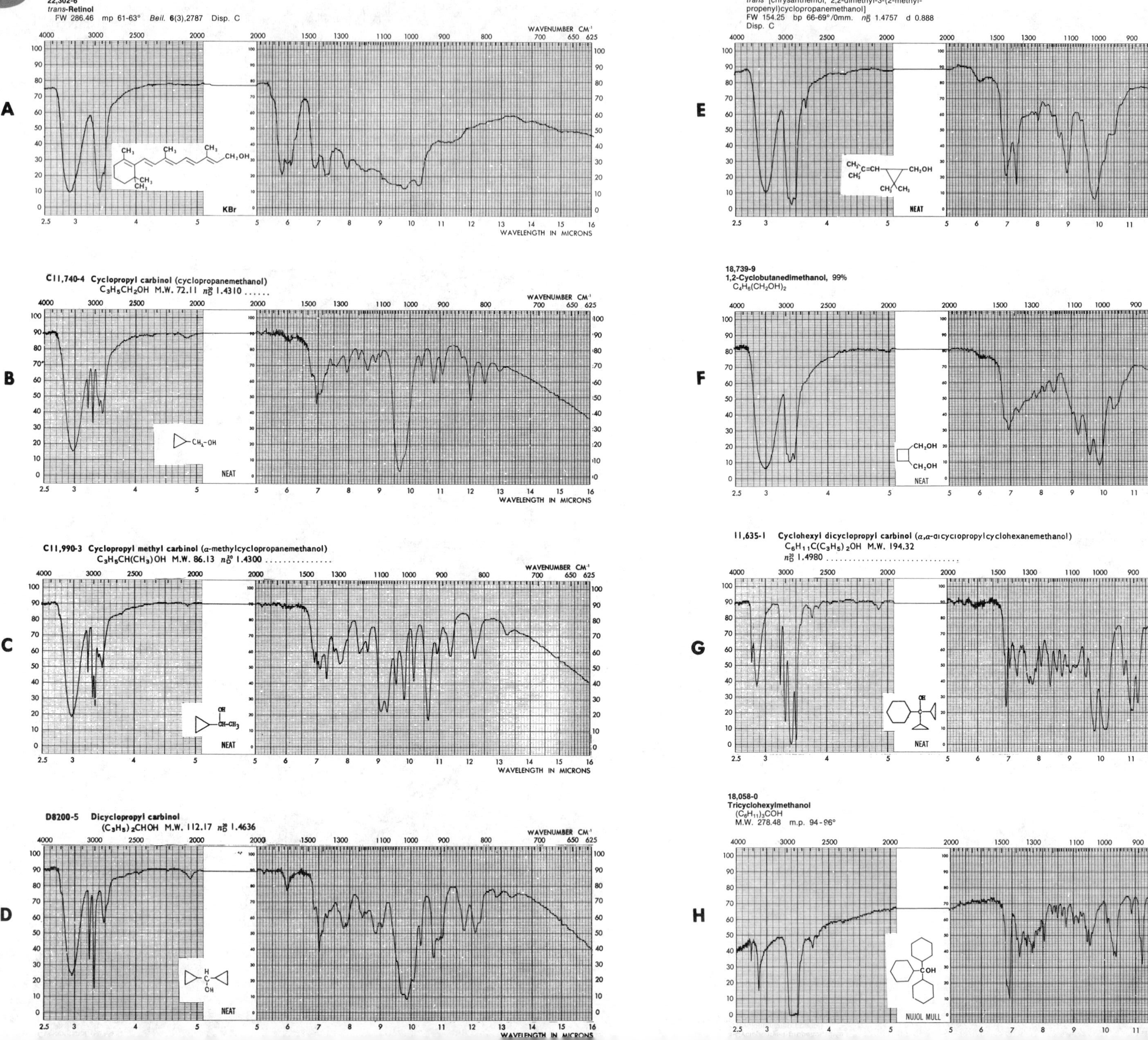
ALDRICH
A
22,302-6
trans-Retinol
FW 286.46 mp 61-63° Beil. 6(3),2787 Disp. C
KBr
B
C11,740-4 Cyclopropyl carbinol (cyclopropanemethanol)
C3H5CH2OH M.W. 72.11 n20D 1.4310
NEAT
C
C11,990-3 Cyclopropyl methyl carbinol (α-methylcyclopropanemethanol)
C3H5CH(CH3)OH M.W. 86.13 n20D 1.4300
NEAT
D
D8200-5 Dicyclopropyl carbinol
(C3H5)2CHOH M.W. 112.17 n20D 1.4636
NEAT
E
19,465-4
Chrysanthemyl alcohol, 98%, mixture of cis and trans [chrysanthemol, 2,2-dimethyl-3-(2-methylpropenyl)cyclopropanemethanol]
FW 154.25 bp 66-69°/0mm. n20D 1.4757 d 0.888
Disp. C
NEAT
F
18,739-9
1,2-Cyclobutanedimethanol, 99%
C4H6(CH2OH)2
NEAT
G
11,635-1 Cyclohexyl dicyclopropyl carbinol (α,α-dicyclopropylcyclohexanemethanol)
C6H11C(C3H5)2OH M.W. 194.32
n20D 1.4980
NEAT
H
18,058-0
Tricyclohexylmethanol
(C6H11)3COH
M.W. 278.48 m.p. 94-96°
NUJOL MULL
WAVENUMBER CM⁻¹
WAVELENGTH IN MICRONS

A

Cyclobutanol, 99+%
C_4H_7OH
M.W. 72.11 b.p. 123°/733mm. n_D^{20} 1.4371
d 0.921 Beil. **6**,4

NEAT

B

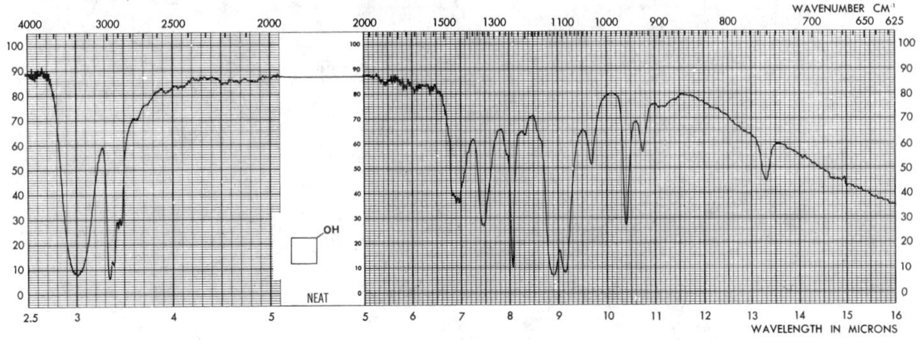

18,791-7
Cyclobutanemethanol, 99%
$C_4H_7CH_2OH$ FW 86.13 bp 143-144° n_D^{20} 1.4465
Disp. C

NEAT

C

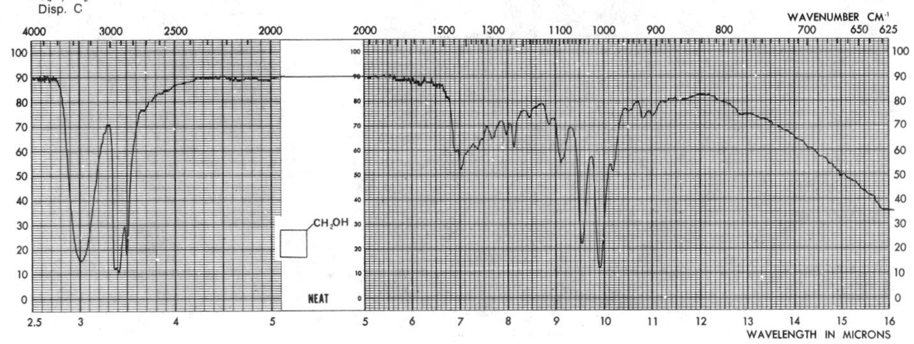

10,398-5 **Cyclopentanemethanol**
$C_5H_9CH_2OH$ M.W. 100.16 n_D^{20} 1.4534

NEAT

D

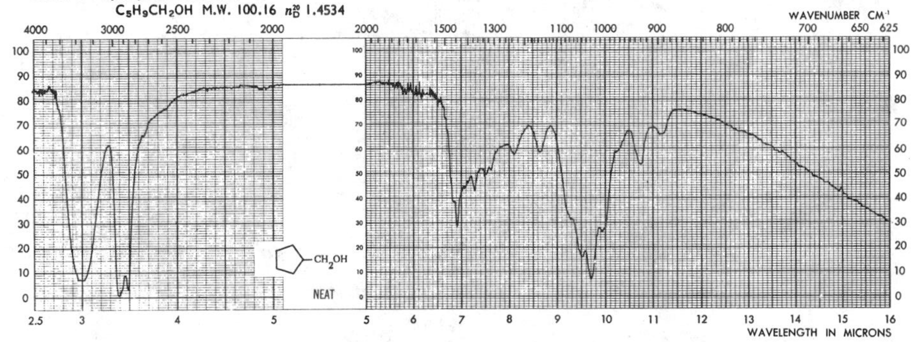

11,828-1 **2-Cyclopentylethanol** (cyclopentaneethanol)
$C_5H_9CH_2CH_2OH$ M.W. 114.19 n_D^{20} 1.4560 .

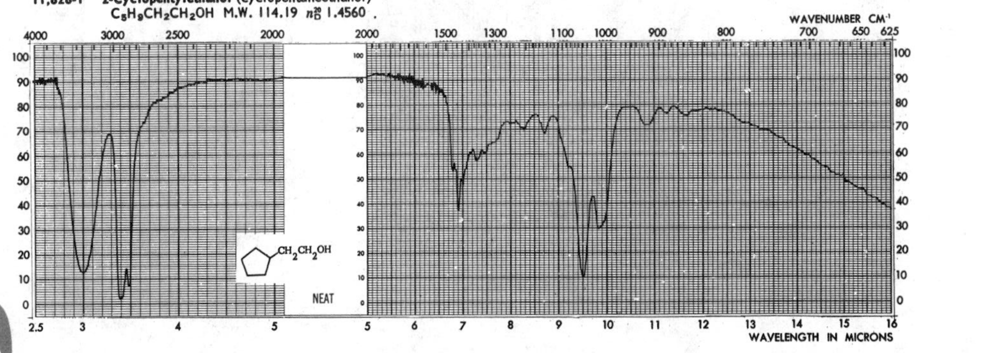

E

3-Cyclopentyl-1-propanol, 99%
(cyclopentanepropanol)
$C_5H_9(CH_2)_3OH$
M.W. 128.22 b.p. 93-95°/8mm. n_D^{20} 1.4595

NEAT

F

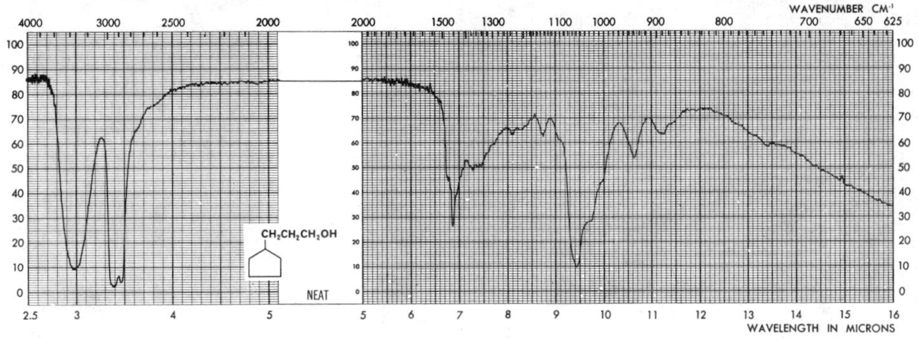

11,045-0
1-Cyclopentylethanol, 99%
(α-methylcyclopentanemethanol)
$CH_3CH(C_5H_9)OH$
M.W. 114.19 b.p. 167° n_D^{20} 1.4571 d 0.919
Beil. **6**(2),25

NEAT

G

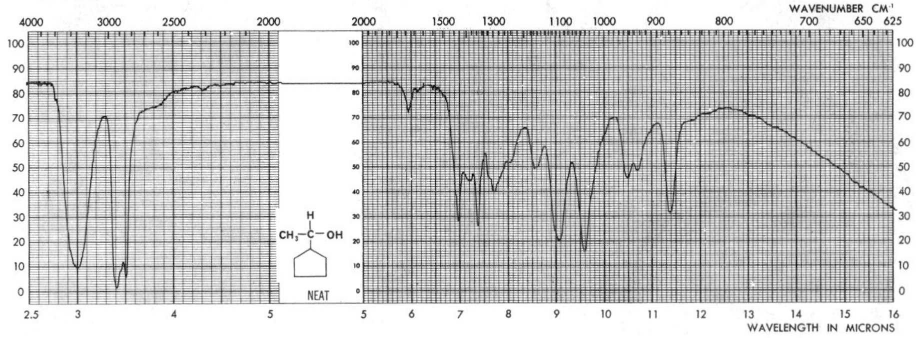

17,907-8
trans-**2-Methylcyclopentanol**, 97%
$CH_3C_5H_8OH$
M.W. 100.16 b.p. 150-151°/740mm. n_D^{20} 1.4500
d 0.92 Beil. **6**,8

NEAT

H

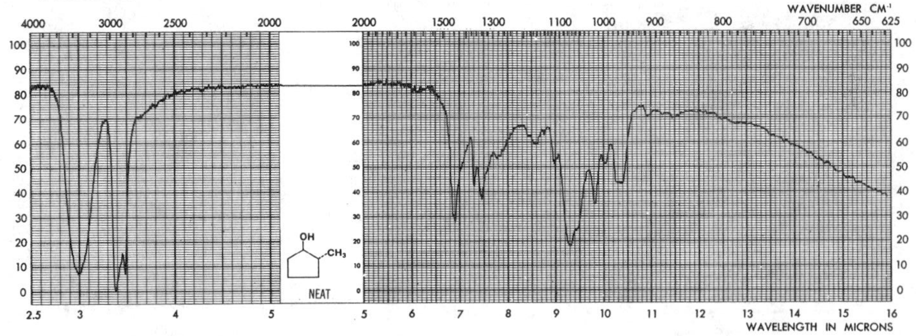

19,616-9
3-Methylcyclopentanol, 99%, mixture of isomers
$CH_3C_5H_8OH$ FW 100.16 bp 149-150° n_D^{20} 1.4465
d 0.910 *Beil.* **6**,9 Disp. C

NEAT

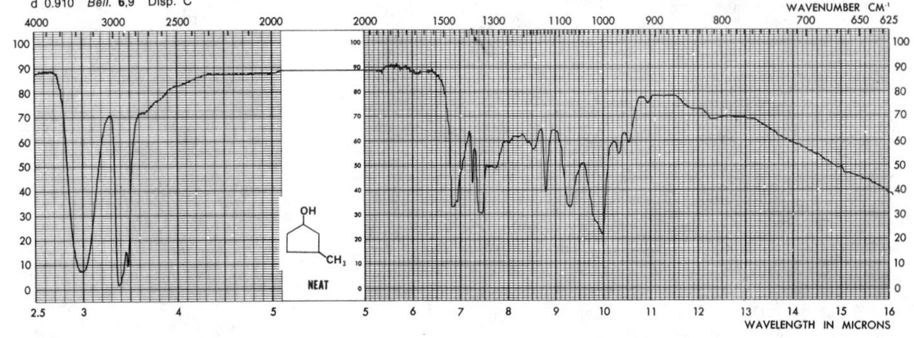

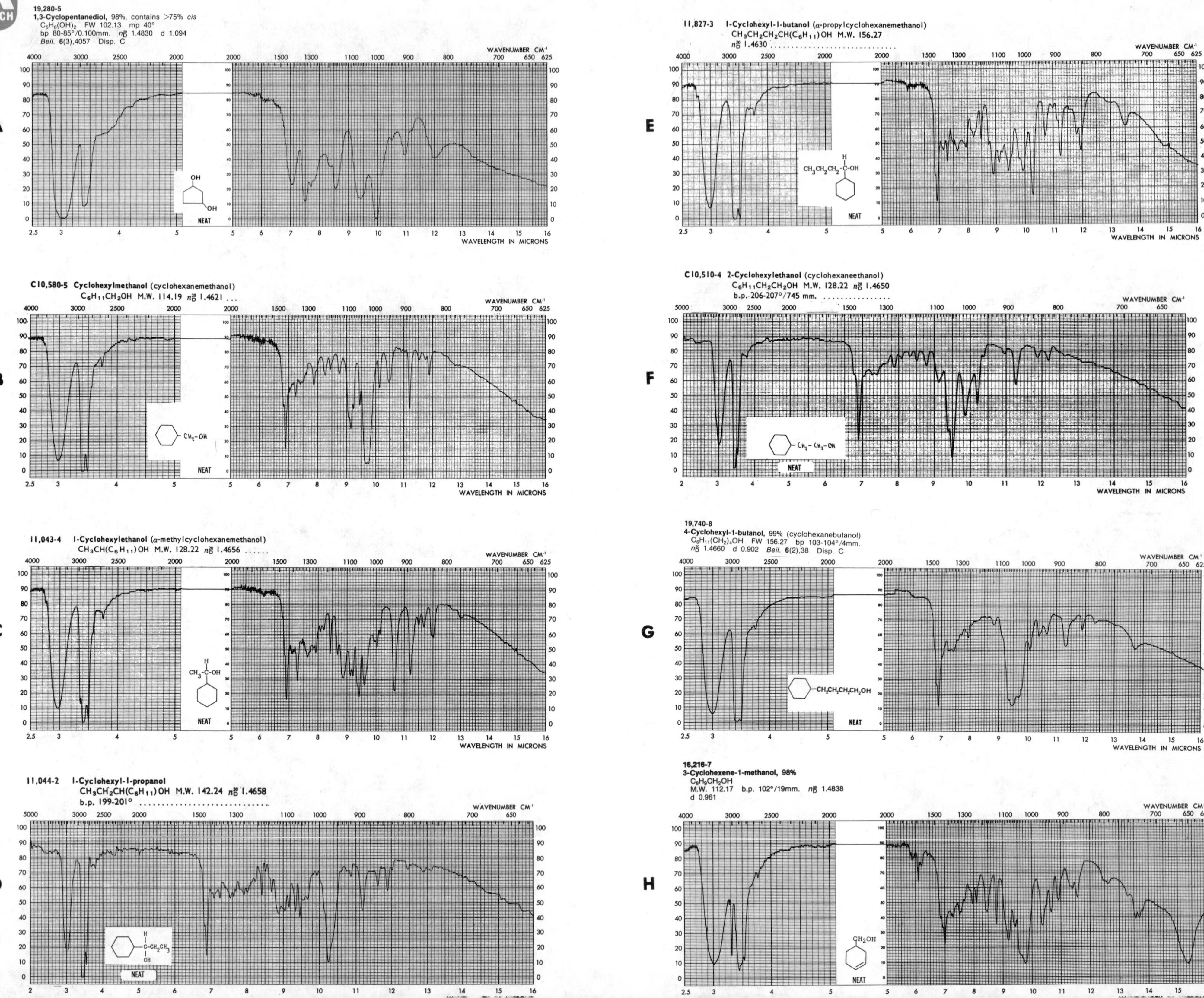
ALDRICH
A
19,280-5
1,3-Cyclopentanediol, 98%, contains >75% cis
$C_5H_8(OH)_2$ FW 102.13 mp 40°
bp 80-85°/0.100mm. n_D^{20} 1.4830 d 1.094
Beil. 6(3),4057 Disp. C
NEAT
B
C10,580-5 Cyclohexylmethanol (cyclohexanemethanol)
$C_6H_{11}CH_2OH$ M.W. 114.19 n_D^{20} 1.4621
NEAT
C
11,043-4 1-Cyclohexylethanol (α-methylcyclohexanemethanol)
$CH_3CH(C_6H_{11})OH$ M.W. 128.22 n_D^{20} 1.4656
NEAT
D
11,044-2 1-Cyclohexyl-1-propanol
$CH_3CH_2CH(C_6H_{11})OH$ M.W. 142.24 n_D^{20} 1.4658
b.p. 199-201°
NEAT
E
11,827-3 1-Cyclohexyl-1-butanol (α-propylcyclohexanemethanol)
$CH_3CH_2CH_2CH(C_6H_{11})OH$ M.W. 156.27
n_D^{20} 1.4630
NEAT
F
C10,510-4 2-Cyclohexylethanol (cyclohexaneethanol)
$C_6H_{11}CH_2CH_2OH$ M.W. 128.22 n_D^{20} 1.4650
b.p. 206-207°/745 mm.
NEAT
G
19,740-8
4-Cyclohexyl-1-butanol, 99% (cyclohexanebutanol)
$C_6H_{11}(CH_2)_4OH$ FW 156.27 bp 103-104°/4mm.
n_D^{20} 1.4660 d 0.902 Beil. 6(2),38 Disp. C
NEAT
H
16,216-7
3-Cyclohexene-1-methanol, 98%
$C_6H_9CH_2OH$
M.W. 112.17 b.p. 102°/19mm. n_D^{20} 1.4838
d 0.961
NEAT
WAVENUMBER CM⁻¹
WAVELENGTH IN MICRONS

A

18,380-6
3-Cyclohexene-1-ethanol, 98%
$C_6H_9CH_2CH_2OH$
M.W. 126.2 b.p. 94-95°/20mm. n_D^{20} 1.4840

NEAT

B

21,839-1
l-**Perillyl alcohol**, 85%
FW 152.24 bp 119-121°/11mm. n_D^{20} 1.4997
d 0.960 $[\alpha]^{22}$ -87° (c=1, CH_3OH) *Beil.* **6**(3),381
Disp. C

NEAT

C

21,841-3
(+)-Limonen-10-ol, 95%
FW 152.24 bp 109-112°/9mm. n_D^{20} 1.4990
d 0.961 $[\alpha]^{21}$ +105° (c=5, C_2H_5OH) *Beil.* **6**(3),376
Disp. C

NEAT

D

21,837-5
α-Terpineol, 98%
FW 154.25 bp 217-218° n_D^{20} 1.4813 d 0.933
$[\alpha]^{22}$ -40° (neat) *Beil.* **6**,57 Disp. C

NEAT

E

13,865-7 **Cycloheptanemethanol**
$C_7H_{13}CH_2OH$ M.W. 128.22 n_D^{20} 1.4731
b.p. 213°/714 mm.

NEAT

F

11,223-2 **Cyclooctanemethanol**
$C_8H_{15}CH_2OH$ M.W. 142.24 n_D^{20} 1.4825

NEAT

G

C12,144-4 **Cycloundecanemethanol**
$C_{11}H_{21}CH_2OH$ M.W. 184.32
n_D^{20} 1.4899

NEAT

H

11,224-0 **Cyclododecanemethanol**
$C_{12}H_{23}CH_2OH$ M.W. 198.35 m.p. 38-41°

MELT

ALDRICH

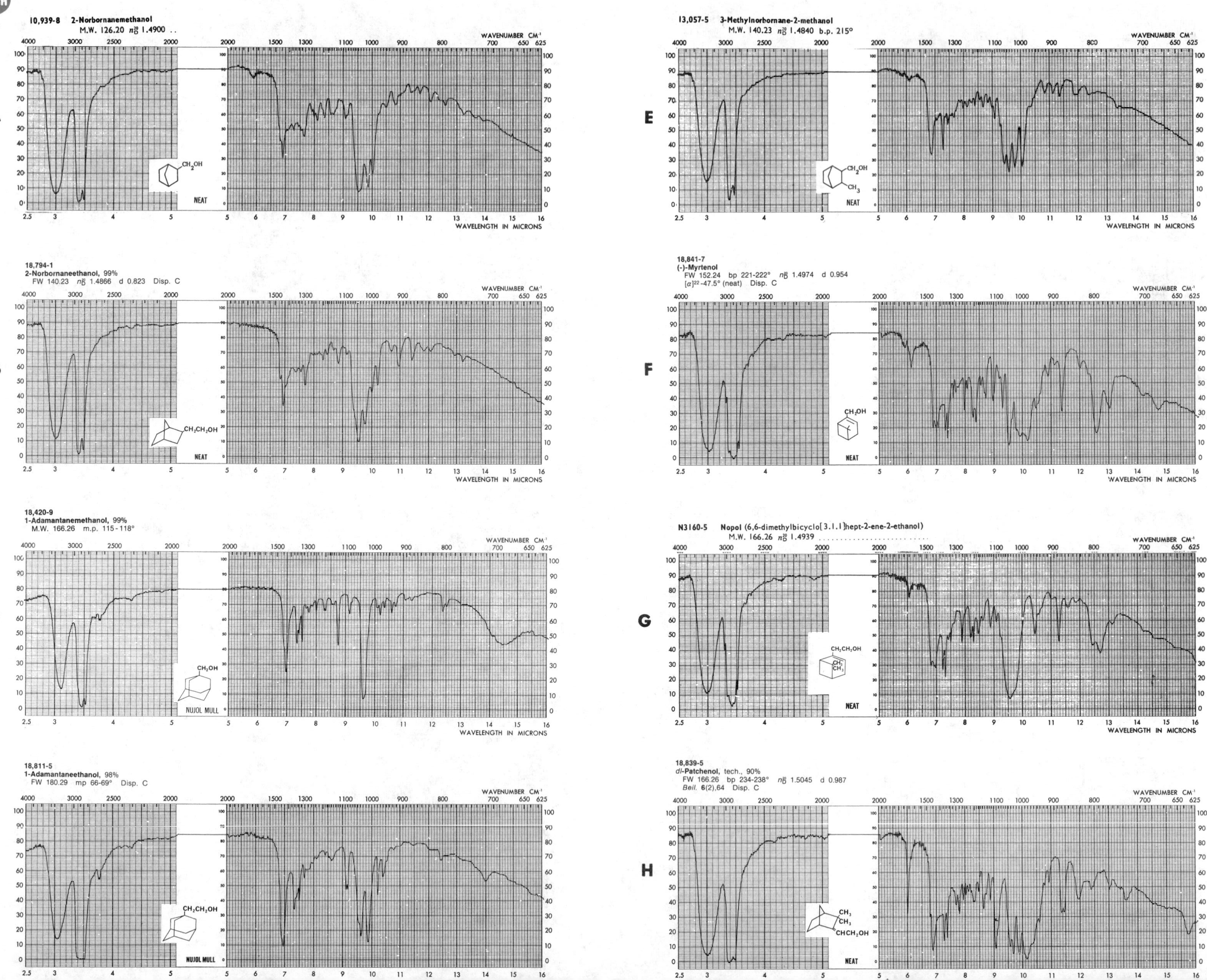
ALDRICH
A
10,939-8 2-Norbornanemethanol
M.W. 126.20 n_D^{20} 1.4900
NEAT
B
18,794-1
2-Norbornaneethanol, 99%
FW 140.23 n_D^{20} 1.4866 d 0.823 Disp. C
NEAT
C
18,420-9
1-Adamantanemethanol, 99%
M.W. 166.26 m.p. 115-118°
NUJOL MULL
D
18,811-5
1-Adamantaneethanol, 98%
FW 180.29 mp 66-69° Disp. C
NUJOL MULL
E
13,057-5 3-Methylnorbornane-2-methanol
M.W. 140.23 n_D^{20} 1.4840 b.p. 215°
NEAT
F
18,841-7
(-)-Myrtenol
FW 152.24 bp 221-222° n_D^{20} 1.4974 d 0.954
$[\alpha]^{22}$ -47.5° (neat) Disp. C
NEAT
G
N3160-5 Nopol (6,6-dimethylbicyclo[3.1.1]hept-2-ene-2-ethanol)
M.W. 166.26 n_D^{20} 1.4939
NEAT
H
18,839-5
dl-Patchenol, tech., 90%
FW 166.26 bp 234-238° n_D^{20} 1.5045 d 0.987
Beil. 6(2),64 Disp. C
NEAT
WAVENUMBER CM⁻¹
WAVELENGTH IN MICRONS

NON-AROMATIC ALCOHOLS

A

18,908-1
cis-**1,2-Cyclohexanedimethanol,** 98%
$C_6H_{10}(CH_2OH)_2$ FW 144.21 mp 43-45° Disp. C

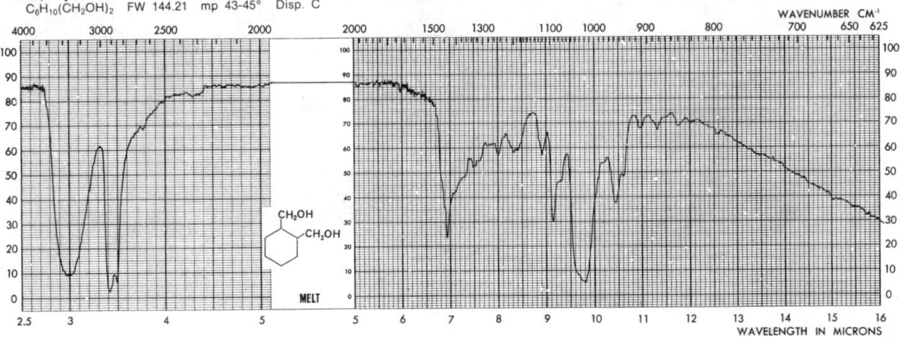

MELT

B

19,545-6
1,3-Cyclohexanedimethanol, 98%, mixture of isomers
$C_6H_{10}(CH_2OH)_2$ FW 144.21 bp 105-106°
n_D^{20} 1.4912 d 1.036 *Beil.* **6**(3),4100 Disp. C

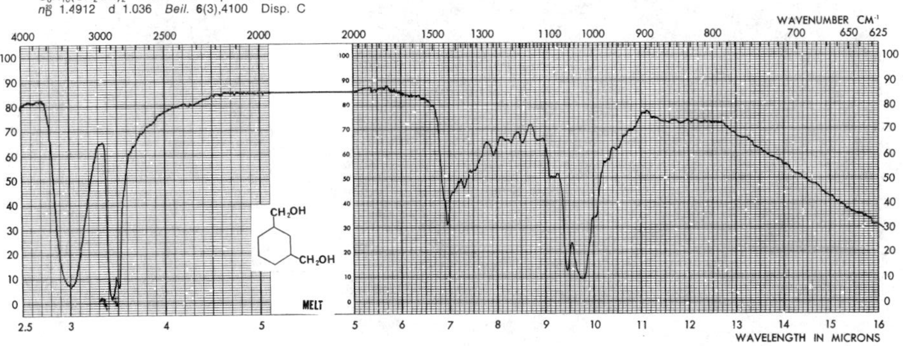

MELT

C

18,770-4
4-Methyl-1,2-cyclohexanedimethanol, 97%
$CH_3C_6H_9(CH_2OH)_2$ FW 158.24
bp 100-110°/0.100mm. n_D^{20} 1.4860 *NMR* **1**,111A
Disp. C

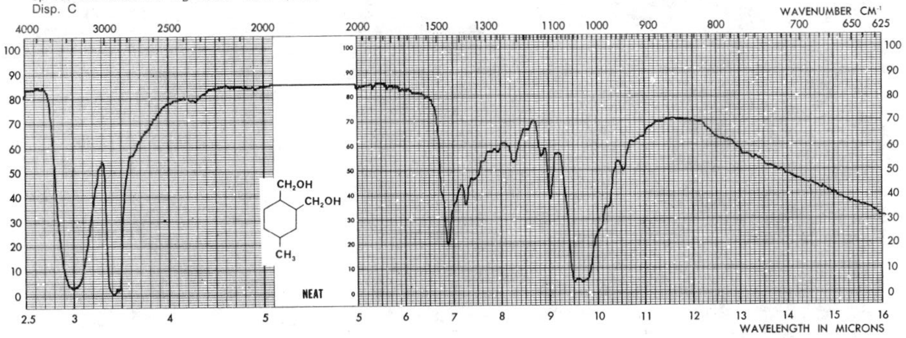

NEAT

D

12,559-8 **1,4-Cyclohexanedimethanol** (mixture of isomers)
$C_6H_{10}(CH_2OH)_2$ M.W. 144.21 ....

MELT

E

C10,091-9 *trans*-**1,4-Cyclohexanedimethanol**
$C_6H_{10}(CH_2OH)_2$ M.W. 144.21 m.p. 62.5-64.5°

MELT

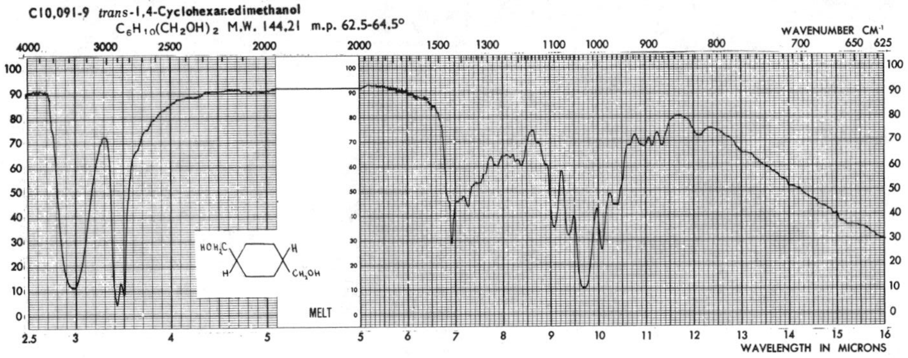

F

C10,091-9 *trans*-**1,4-Cyclohexanedimethanol**
$C_6H_{10}(CH_2OH)_2$ M.W. 144.21 m.p. 62.5-64.5°

NUJOL MULL

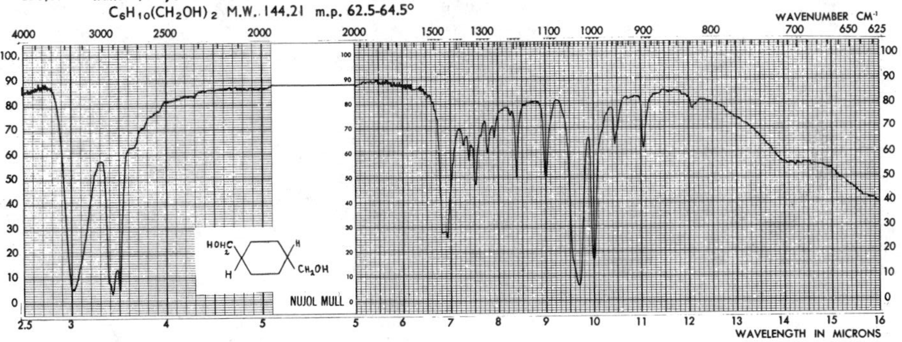

G

15,218-8 **5-Norbornene-2,2-dimethanol**
M.W. 154.21 m.p. 111-113.5°

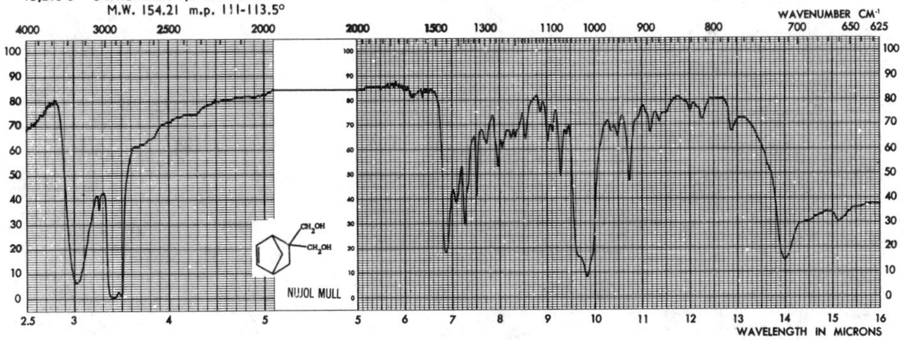

NUJOL MULL

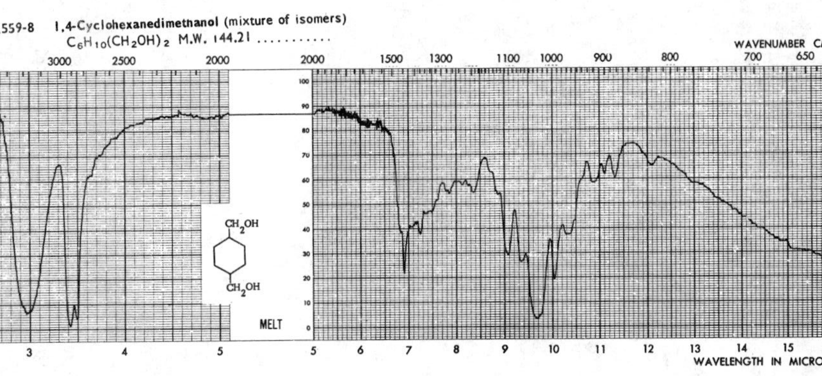

H

C11,220-8 **Cyclopentanol**
C_5H_9OH M.W. 86.13 n_D^{20} 1.4521

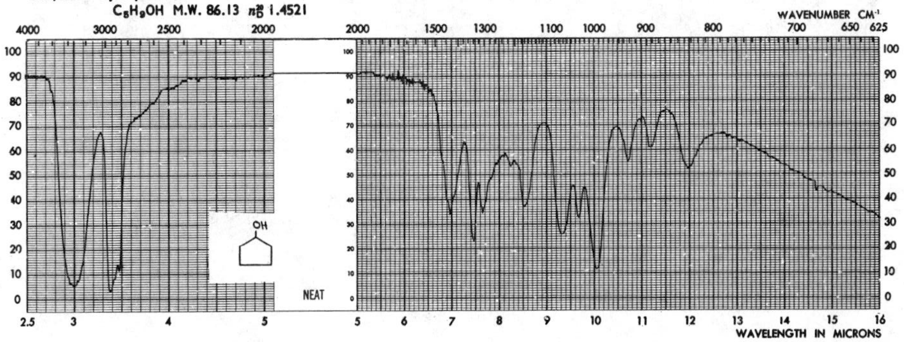

NEAT

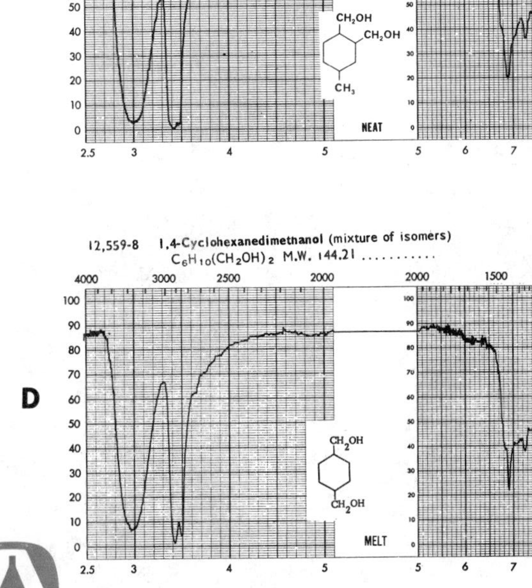

A

M3965-2 1-Methylcyclopentanol
$CH_3C_5H_8OH$ M.W. 100.16 m.p. 36-37°

MELT

B

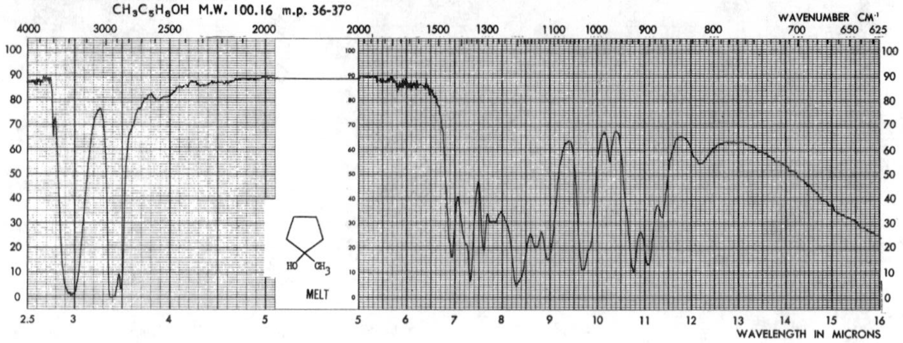

11,850-8 1-Ethylcyclopentanol
$C_2H_5C_5H_8OH$ M.W. 114.19 n_D^{20} 1.4520

NEAT

C

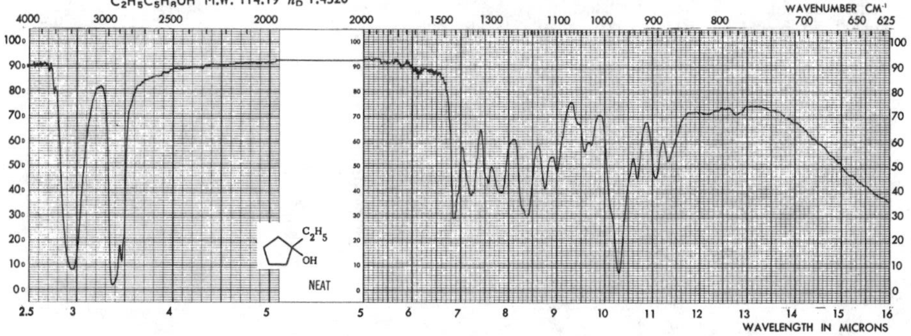

11,132-5 1-Propyl-1-cyclopentanol
$CH_3CH_2CH_2C_5H_8OH$ M.W. 128.22
n_D^{20} 1.4512

NEAT

D

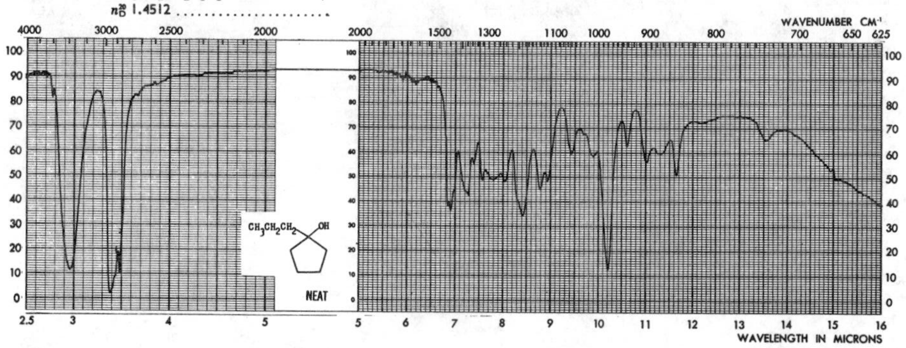

11,042-6 1-n-Butyl-1-cyclopentanol
$CH_3(CH_2)_3C_5H_8OH$ M.W. 142.24 n_D^{20} 1.4550

NEAT

E

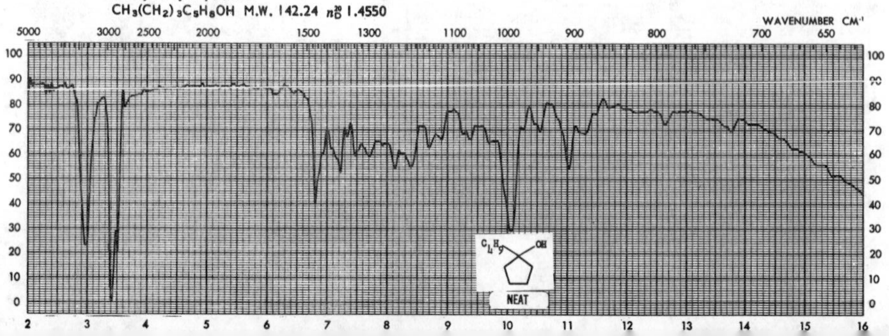

10,589-9 Cyclohexanol
$C_6H_{11}OH$ M.W. 100.16 n_D^{20} 1.4641
m.p. 20-22° b.p. 160-161°

NEAT

F

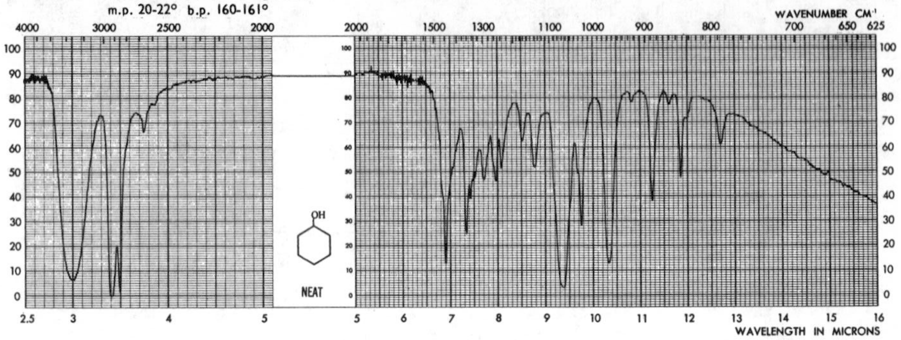

18,767-4
1-Cyclohexylcyclohexanol, 97%
$C_6H_{11}C_6H_{10}OH$ FW 182.31 mp 61-64°
bp 148°/20mm. *Beil.* **6**(1),56 Disp. C

MELT

G

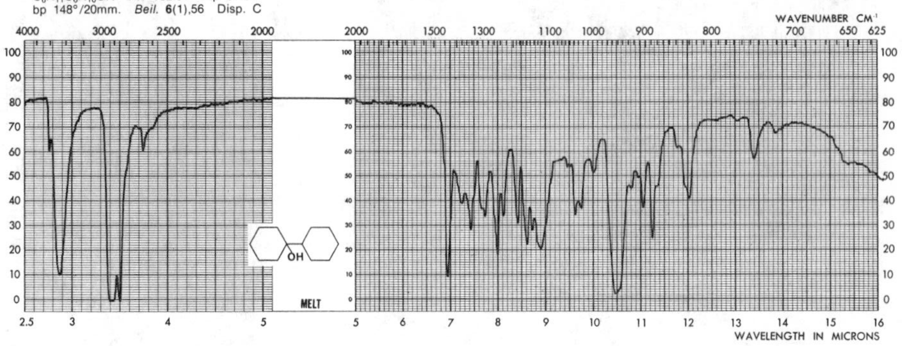

C10,265-2 2-Cyclohexen-1-ol
C_6H_9OH M.W. 98.15 n_D^{20} 1.4820

NEAT

H

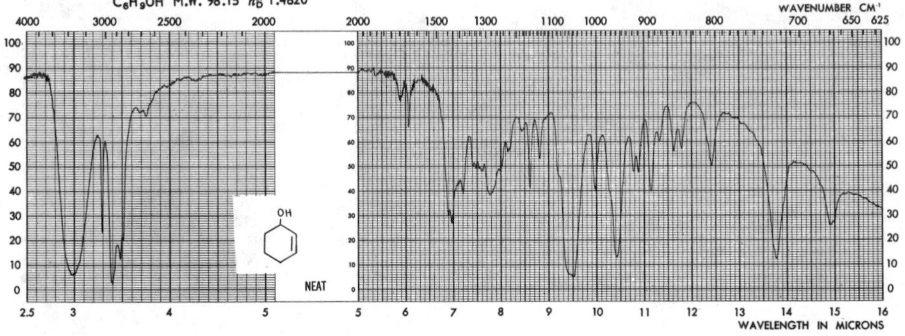

19,771-8
3-Methyl-2-cyclohexen-1-ol
$CH_3C_6H_8OH$ FW 112.17 bp 56°/1mm.
n_D^{20} 1.4860 d 0.946 Disp. C

NEAT

WAVENUMBER CM⁻¹ / WAVELENGTH IN MICRONS

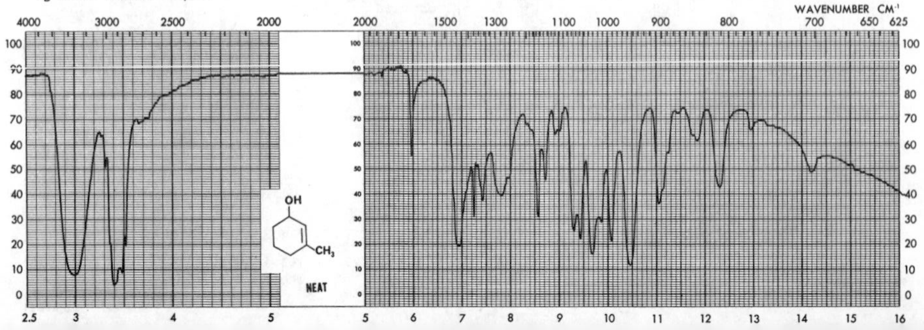

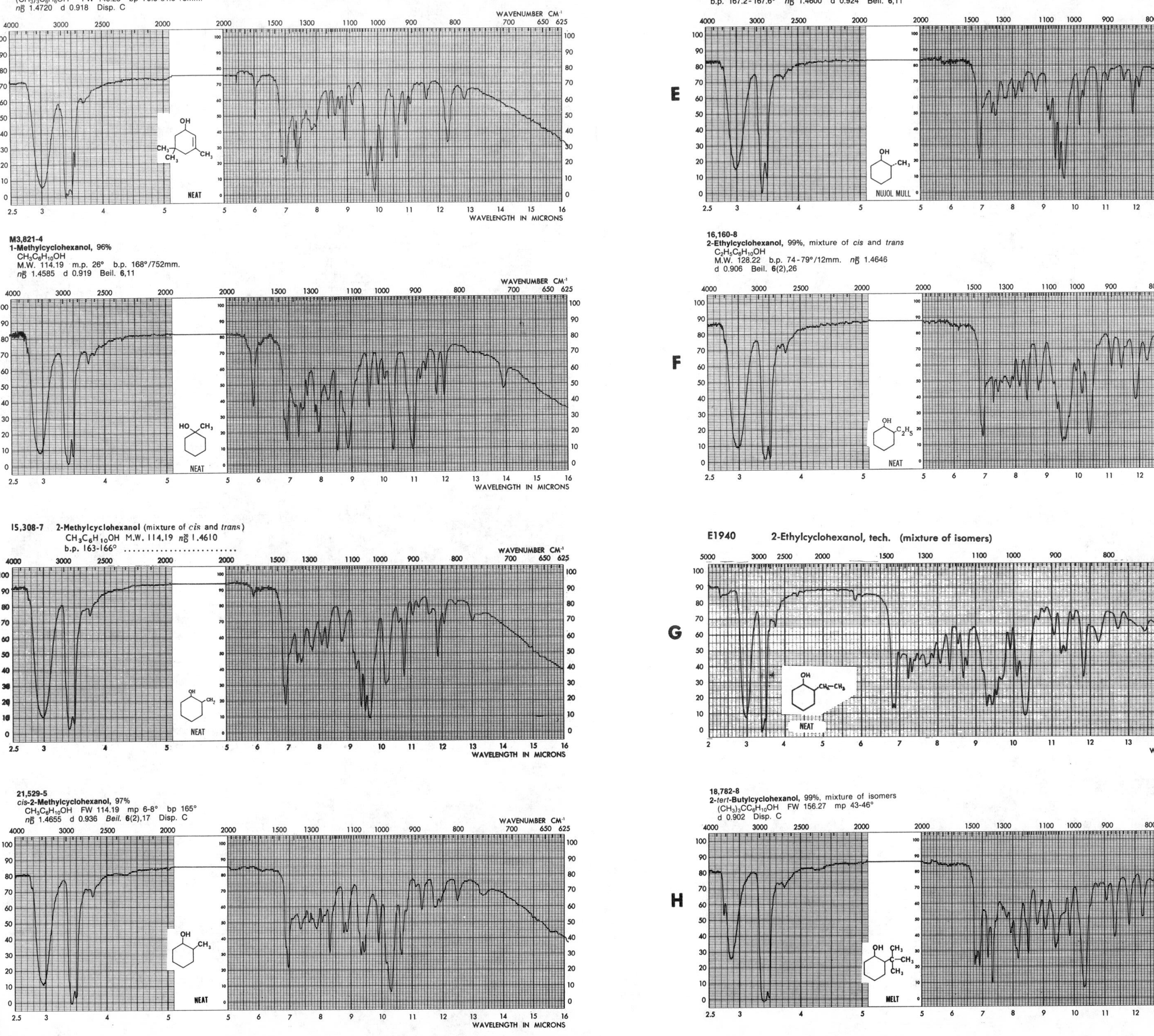
A
19,118-3
3,5,5-Trimethyl-2-cyclohexen-1-ol
$(CH_3)_3C_6H_6OH$ FW 140.23 bp 79.5-81.5°/8mm.
n_D^{20} 1.4720 d 0.918 Disp. C
NEAT
B
M3,821-4
1-Methylcyclohexanol, 96%
$CH_3C_6H_{10}OH$
M.W. 114.19 m.p. 26° b.p. 168°/752mm.
n_D^{20} 1.4585 d 0.919 Beil. 6,11
NEAT
C
15,308-7 2-Methylcyclohexanol (mixture of cis and trans)
$CH_3C_6H_{10}OH$ M.W. 114.19 n_D^{20} 1.4610
b.p. 163-166°
NEAT
D
21,529-5
cis-2-Methylcyclohexanol, 97%
$CH_3C_6H_{10}OH$ FW 114.19 mp 6-8° bp 165°
n_D^{20} 1.4655 d 0.936 Beil. 6(2),17 Disp. C
NEAT
E
17,882-9
trans-2-Methylcyclohexanol, 97%
$CH_3C_6H_{10}OH$
M.W. 114.19 m.p. -21.2 to -20.5°
b.p. 167.2-167.6° n_D^{20} 1.4600 d 0.924 Beil. 6,11
NUJOL MULL
F
16,160-8
2-Ethylcyclohexanol, 99%, mixture of cis and trans
$C_2H_5C_6H_{10}OH$
M.W. 128.22 b.p. 74-79°/12mm. n_D^{20} 1.4646
d 0.906 Beil. 6(2),26
NEAT
G
E1940 2-Ethylcyclohexanol, tech. (mixture of isomers)
NEAT
H
18,782-8
2-tert-Butylcyclohexanol, 99%, mixture of isomers
$(CH_3)_3CC_6H_{10}OH$ FW 156.27 mp 43-46°
d 0.902 Disp. C
MELT
WAVENUMBER CM⁻¹
WAVELENGTH IN MICRONS
ALDRICH

A

13,973-4 **3-Methylcyclohexanol** (mixture of *cis* and *trans*)
$CH_3C_6H_{10}OH$ M.W. 114.19 n_D^{20} 1.4572 ....

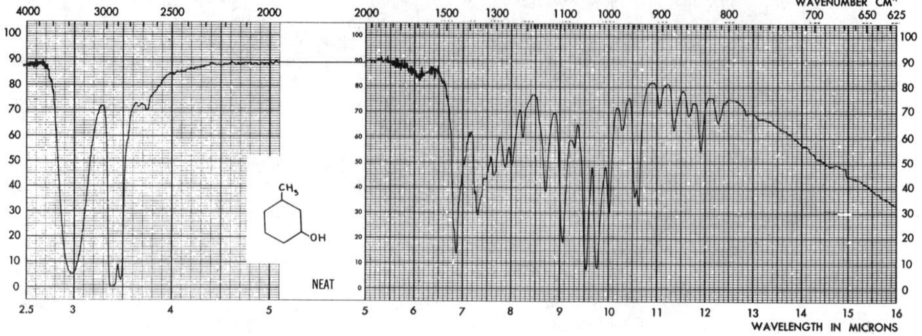

B

15,309-5 **4-Methylcyclohexanol** (mixture of *cis* and *trans*)
$CH_3C_6H_{10}OH$ M.W. 114.19 n_D^{20} 1.4559
b.p. 171-173° ....

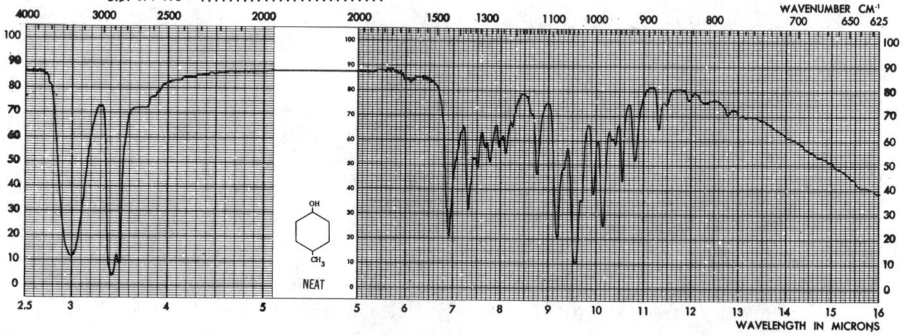

C

10,419-1 ***trans*-4-Methylcyclohexanol**
$CH_3C_6H_{10}OH$ M.W. 114.19 n_D^{20} 1.4554
b.p. 173-174° ....

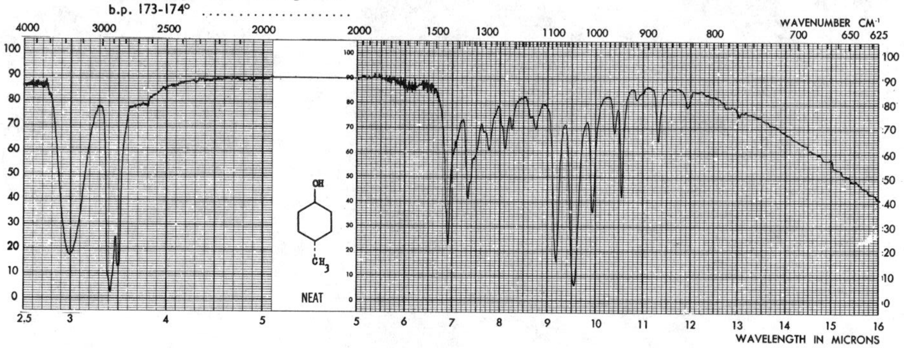

D

10,418-3 ***cis*-4-Methylcyclohexanol**
$CH_3C_6H_{10}OH$ M.W. 114.19 n_D^{20} 1.4617
b.p. 172-173° ....

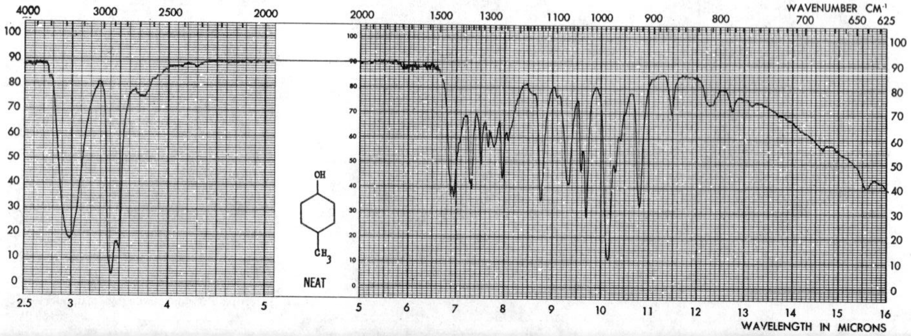

E

12,937-2 **4-Ethylcyclohexanol** (mixture of *cis* and *trans*), **puriss.**
$C_2H_5C_6H_{10}OH$ M.W. 128.22 n_D^{20} 1.4619 ..

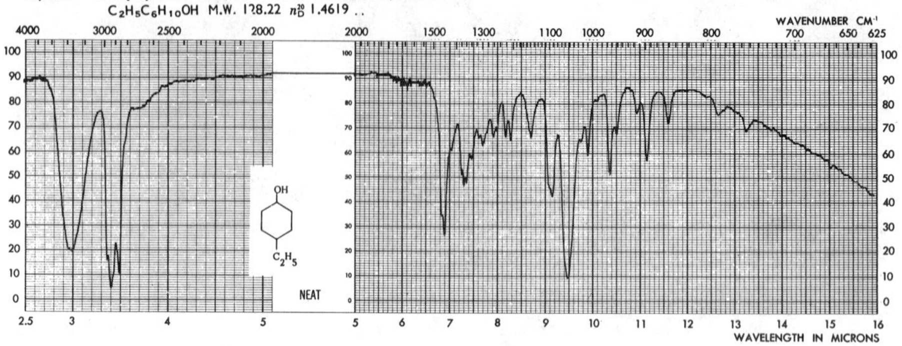

F

B9200-1 **4-tert.-Butylcyclohexanol** (mixture of isomers)
$(CH_3)_3CC_6H_{10}OH$ M.W. 156.27 m.p. 62-70°

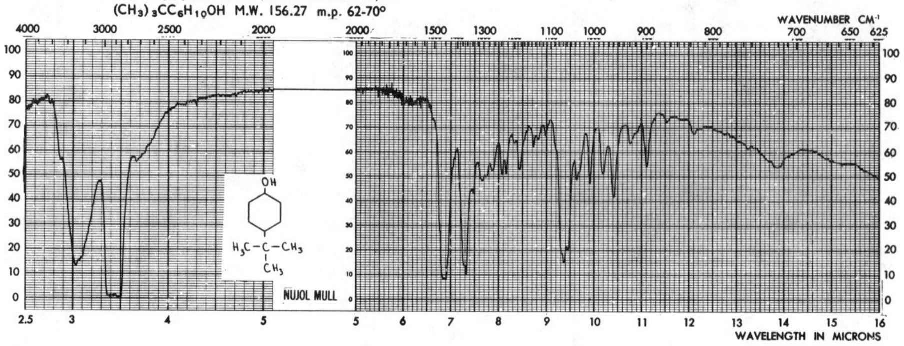

G

15,592-6
2,3-Dimethylcyclohexanol, 99%, mixture of isomers
$(CH_3)_2C_6H_9OH$
M.W. 128.22 n_D^{20} 1.4653

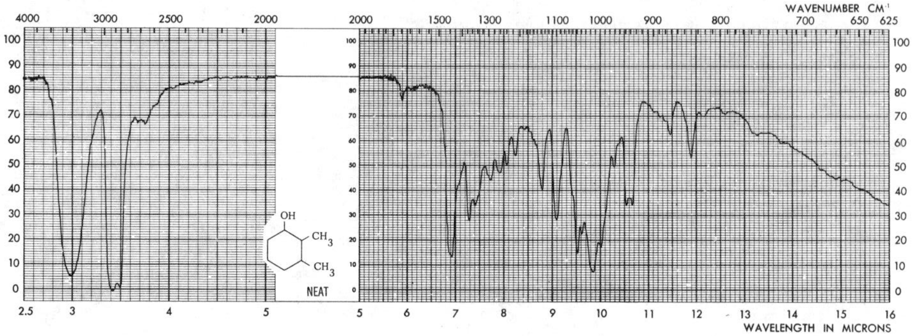

H

D15,340-0 **2,5-Dimethylcyclohexanol** (mixture of isomers)
$(CH_3)_2C_6H_9OH$ M.W. 128.22 n_D^{20} 1.4553 ....

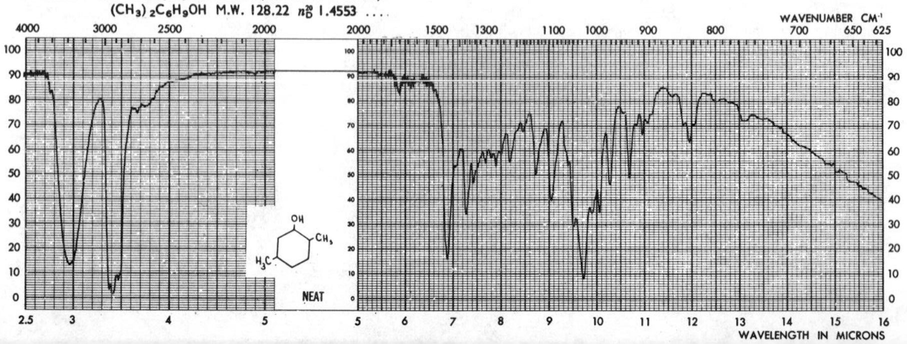

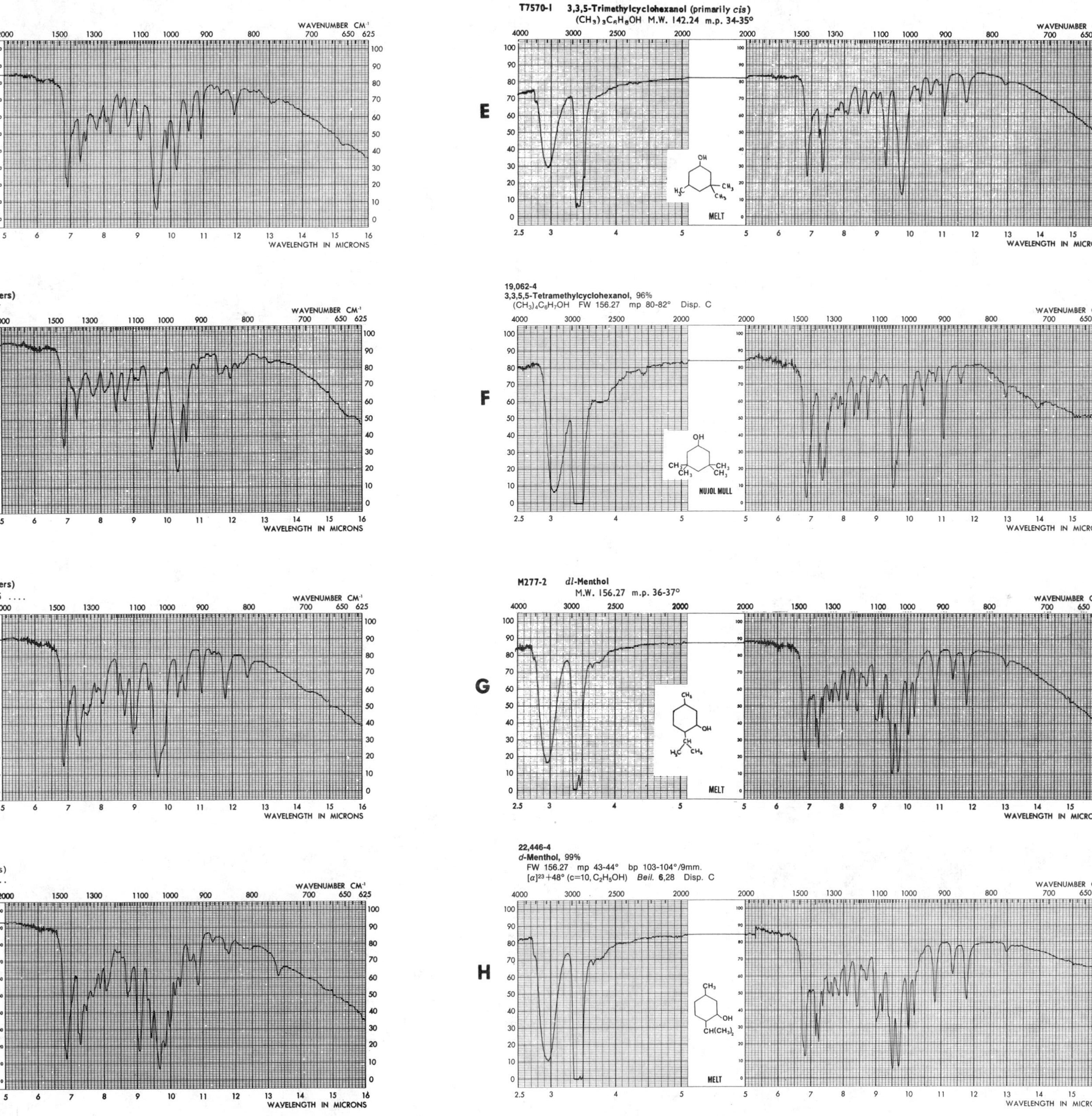

A
15,591-8
2,4-Dimethylcyclohexanol, 98%, mixture of isomers
$(CH_3)_2C_6H_9OH$
M.W. 128.22 b.p. 179° n_D^{20} 1.4580 d 0.923
Beil. 6,18
NEAT
B
11,053-1 **2,6-Dimethylcyclohexanol** (mixture of isomers)
$(CH_3)_2C_6H_9OH$ M.W. 128.22 n_D^{20} 1.4583
NEAT
C
12,644-6 **3,5-Dimethylcyclohexanol** (mixture of isomers)
$(CH_3)_2C_6H_9OH$ M.W. 128.22 n_D^{24} 1.4525
NEAT
D
15,593-4 **3,4-Dimethylcyclohexanol** (mixture of isomers)
$(CH_3)_2C_6H_9OH$ M.W. 128.22
NEAT
E
T7570-1 **3,3,5-Trimethylcyclohexanol** (primarily *cis*)
$(CH_3)_3C_6H_8OH$ M.W. 142.24 m.p. 34-35°
MELT
F
19,062-4
3,3,5,5-Tetramethylcyclohexanol, 96%
$(CH_3)_4C_6H_7OH$ FW 156.27 mp 80-82° Disp. C
NUJOL MULL
G
M277-2 *dl*-**Menthol**
M.W. 156.27 m.p. 36-37°
MELT
H
22,446-4
d-**Menthol,** 99%
FW 156.27 mp 43-44° bp 103-104°/9mm.
$[\alpha]^{23}$ +48° (c=10, C_2H_5OH) *Beil.* 6,28 Disp. C
MELT
WAVENUMBER CM⁻¹
WAVELENGTH IN MICRONS

ALDRICH

NON-AROMATIC ALCOHOLS

A

M278-0 *l*-**Menthol**
M.W. 156.27 m.p. 43-45°
$[\alpha]^{20}_{D}$ - 50° (c=10 in C_2H_5OH)
MELT

B

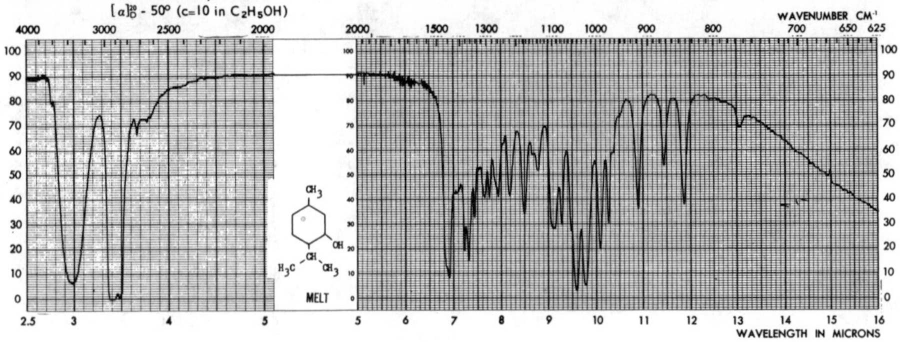

21,838-3
Terpinen-4-ol, 95%
FW 154.25 bp 88-90°C/6mmHg n^{20}_{D} 1.4775 d 0.933
Fp 175°F(79°C) *Beil.* **6**,55 Disp. C
NEAT

C

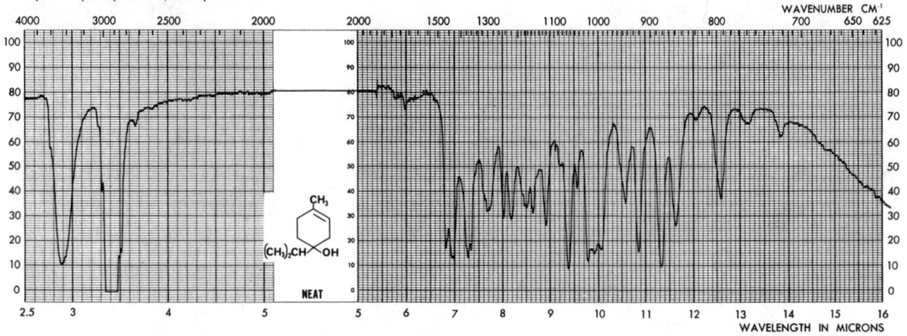

18,374-1
(+)-p-Menth-1-en-9-ol, 97%
M.W. 154.25 b.p. 115-116°/10mm. n^{20}_{D} 1.4860
$[\alpha]^{22}$ +94.5° (c=4.3, benzene)
NEAT

D

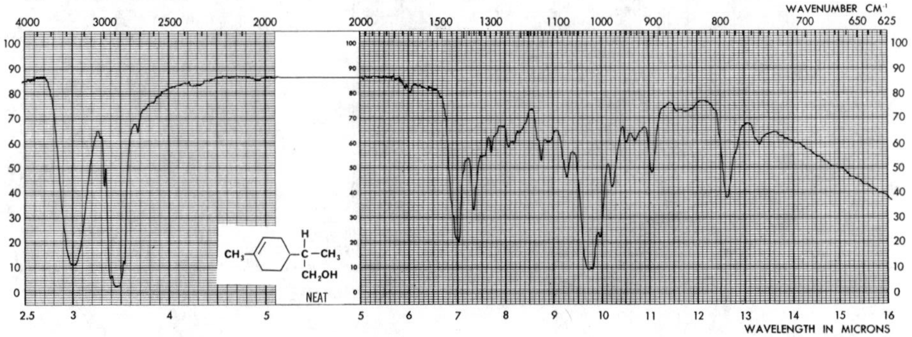

21,842-1
Dihydrocarveol, 95%, mixture of isomers
FW 154.25 bp 224-225° n^{20}_{D} 1.4779 d 0.926
$[\alpha]^{22}$ +21° (neat) *Beil.* **6**,63 Disp. C
NEAT

E

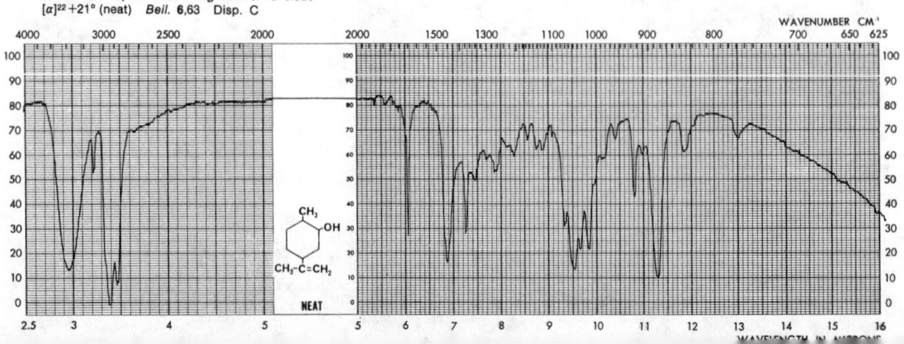

I—2,800-3
l-**Isopulegol**
M.W. 154.25 b.p. 91°/12mm. n^{20}_{D} 1.4725 d 0.911
Beil. 6,65
NEAT

F

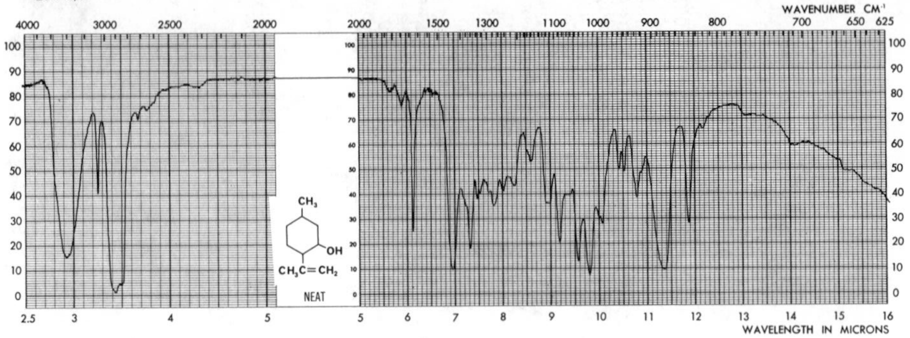

19,238-4
(-)-Carveol, 99%, mixture of isomers (*p*-mentha-6,8-dien-2-ol)
FW 152.24 bp 226-227°/751mm. n^{20}_{D} 1.4969
d 1.496 $[\alpha]^{22}$ -70.9° (neat) *Beil.* **6**(1),61 Disp. C
NEAT

G

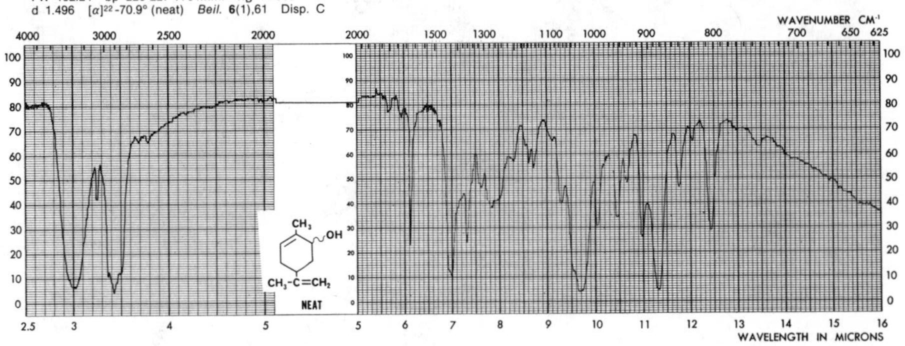

13,911-4 *l*-**Borneol**
M.W. 154.25 m.p. 207-208° $[\alpha]^{20}_{D}$ - 35.3°
(c=5.3, C_2H_5OH)
NUJOL MULL

H

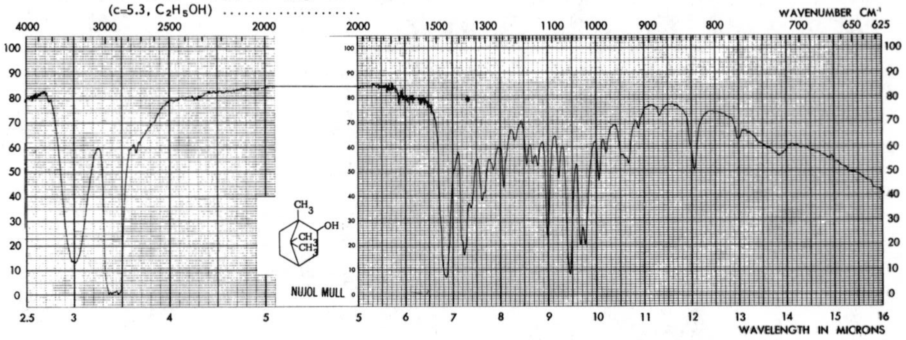

18,315-6
(-)-*cis*-Myrtanol
M.W. 154.25 b.p. 70-72°/1mm. n^{20}_{D} 1.4890
d 0.986 $[\alpha]^{23}$ -19.5° (neat)
NEAT

WAVENUMBER CM⁻¹: 4000 3000 2500 2000 1500 1300 1100 1000 900 800 700 650 625
WAVELENGTH IN MICRONS: 2.5 3 4 5 6 7 8 9 10 11 12 13 14 15 16

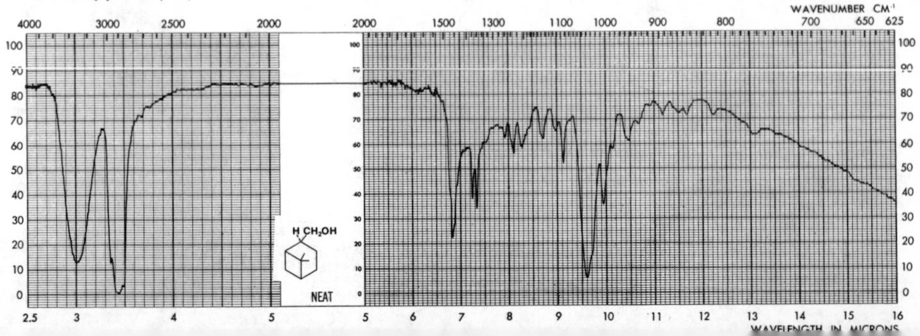

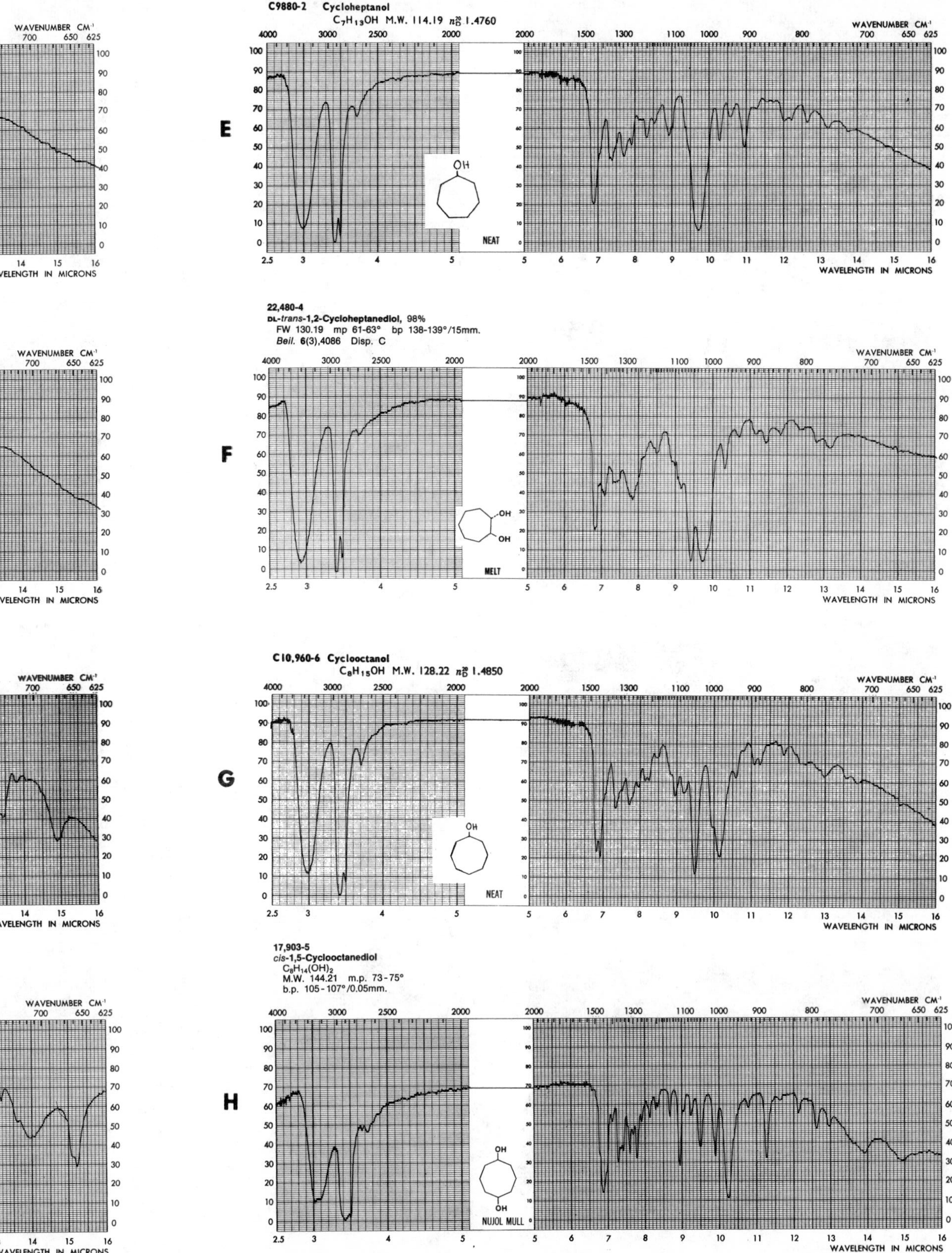

A 18,322-9
dl-**Isopinocampheol**, 98% (3-pinanol)
FW 154.25 mp 35-36° bp 217° *Beil.* **6**,67
Disp. C
MELT

B 22,190-2
(-)-**Isopinocampheol**, 98% (3-pinanol)
FW 154.25 mp 51-53° bp 219°
$[\alpha]^{22}$ -34° (c=20, C_2H_5OH) *Beil.* **6**(3),282 Disp. C
MELT

C 11,034-5 **1-Allyl-1-cyclohexanol**
$H_2C{:}CHCH_2C_6H_{10}OH$ M.W. 140.27 n_D^{20} 1.4787
b.p. 188-192°
NEAT

D 16,215-9
3-Cyclohexene-1,1-dimethanol, 98%
$C_6H_8(CH_2OH)_2$
M.W. 142.2 m.p. 88-90°
NUJOL MULL

E C9880-2 **Cycloheptanol**
$C_7H_{13}OH$ M.W. 114.19 n_D^{20} 1.4760
NEAT

F 22,480-4
DL-*trans*-**1,2-Cycloheptanediol**, 98%
FW 130.19 mp 61-63° bp 138-139°/15mm.
Beil. **6**(3),4086 Disp. C
MELT

G C10,960-6 **Cyclooctanol**
$C_8H_{15}OH$ M.W. 128.22 n_D^{20} 1.4850
NEAT

H 17,903-5
cis-**1,5-Cyclooctanediol**
$C_8H_{14}(OH)_2$
M.W. 144.21 m.p. 73-75°
b.p. 105-107°/0.05mm.
NUJOL MULL

A

11,857-5 **1-Methylcyclooctanol**
$CH_3C_8H_{14}OH$ M.W. 142.24 m.p. 33-36°
MELT

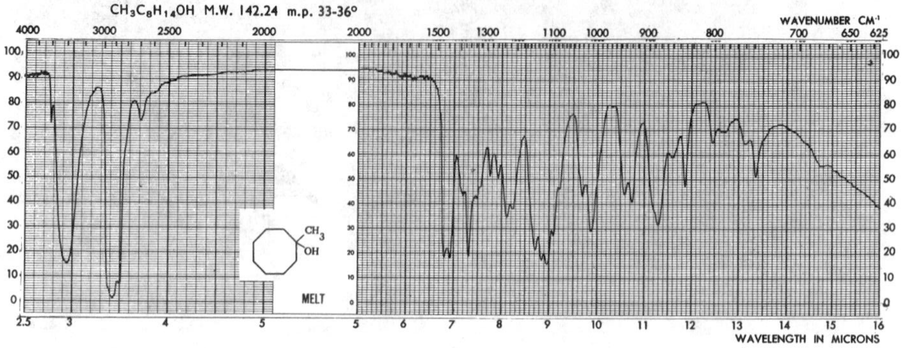

B

C9630-3 **Cyclodecanol**
$C_{10}H_{19}OH$ M.W. 156.27
MELT

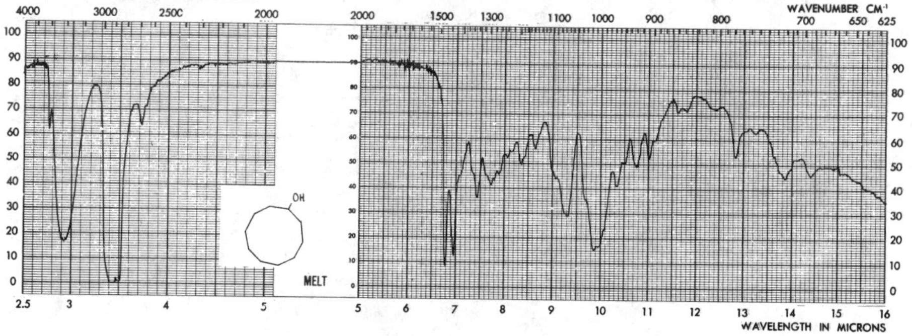

C

C9740-7 **Cyclododecanol**
$C_{12}H_{23}OH$ M.W. 184.32 m.p. 75-77°
NUJOL MULL

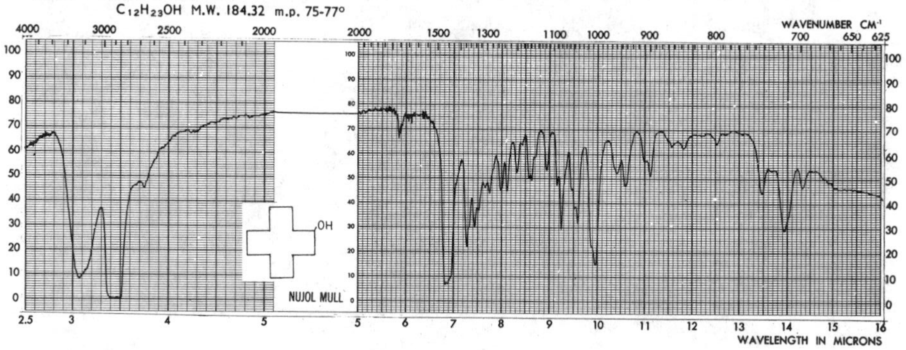

D

14,641-2 **Norborneol** (mixture of endo and exo)
M.W. 112.17 m.p. 122-128° ....
NUJOL MULL

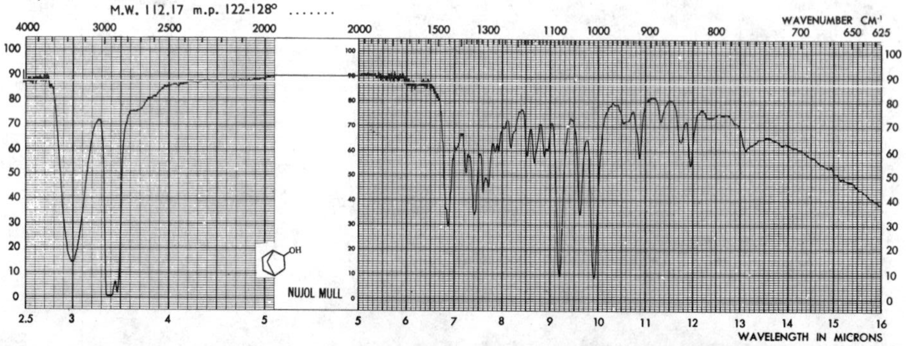

E

18,645-7
endo-**Norborneol**, 98%
M.W. 112.17
NUJOL MULL

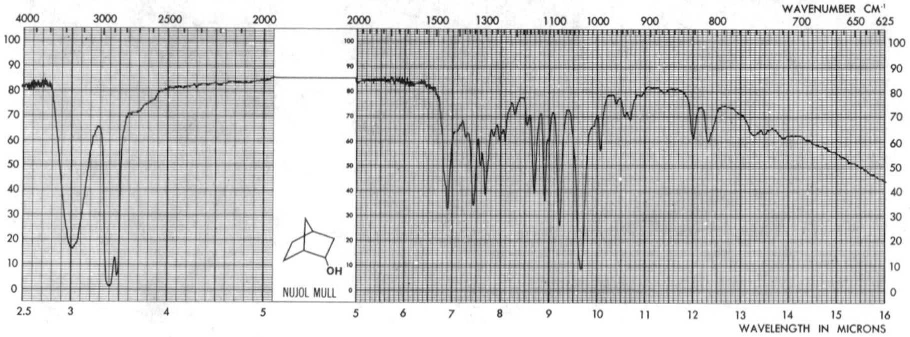

F

17,959-0
exo-**Norborneol**, 97%
M.W. 112.17 m.p. 117-119° b.p. 176-177°
NUJOL MULL

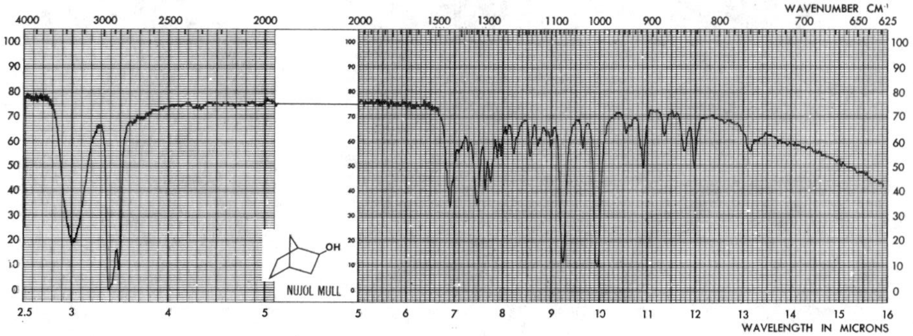

G

N3210-5 **5-Norbornen-2-ol** (mixture of endo and exo)
M.W. 110.16 m.p. 97-105° ....
NUJOL MULL

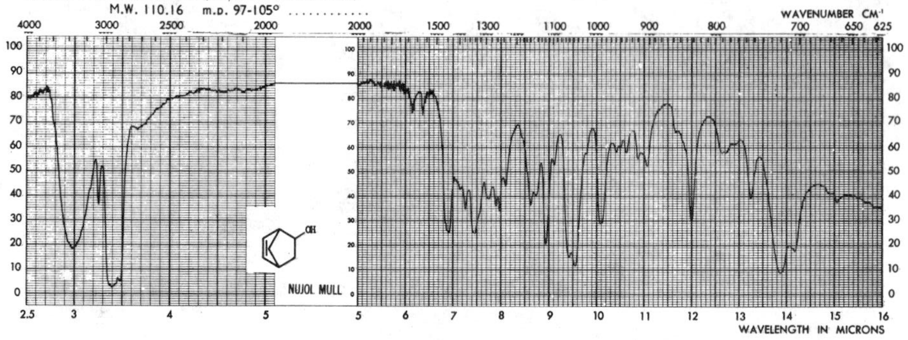

H

B5500-9 **Borneol, tech.**
M.W. 154.25 m.p. 202-208°
NUJOL MULL

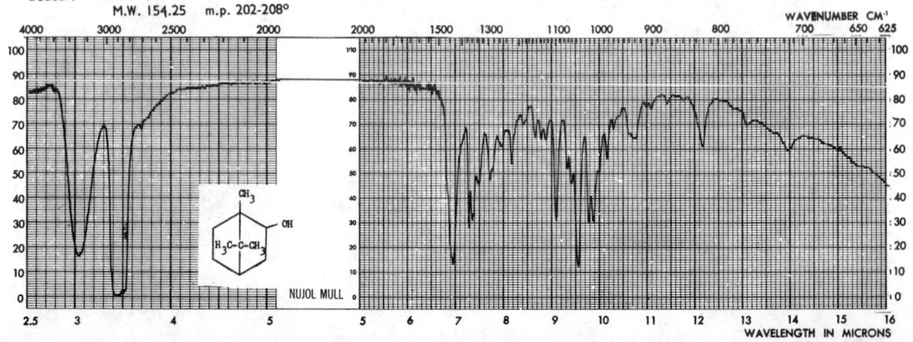

A

I-1390-1 **DL-Isoborneol**
M.W. 154.25 m.p. 210° (sublimes)
NUJOL MULL

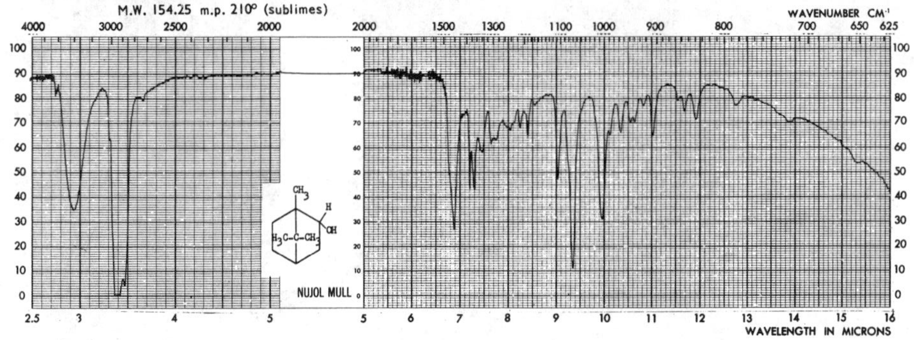

B

19,644-4
Fenchyl alcohol (1,3,3-trimethyl-2-norbornanol)
FW 154.25 mp 39-45°
$[\alpha]^{22}$ +22.9° (c=1.3, C_2H_5OH) Disp. C
MELT

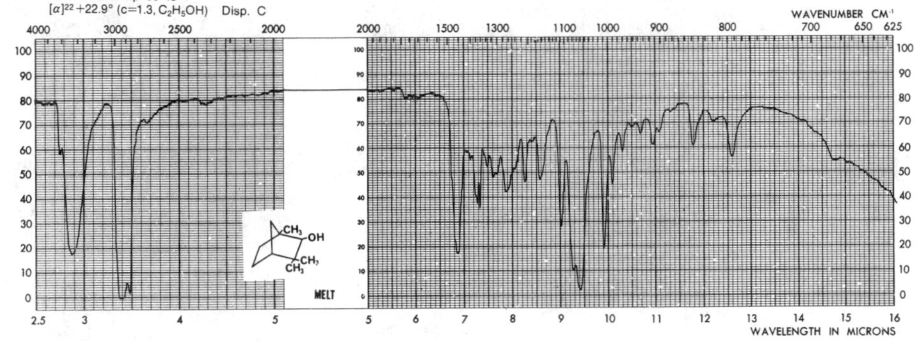

C

19,389-5
9-Ethylbicyclo[3.3.1]nonan-9-ol
FW 168.28 mp 60-63° Disp. C
MELT

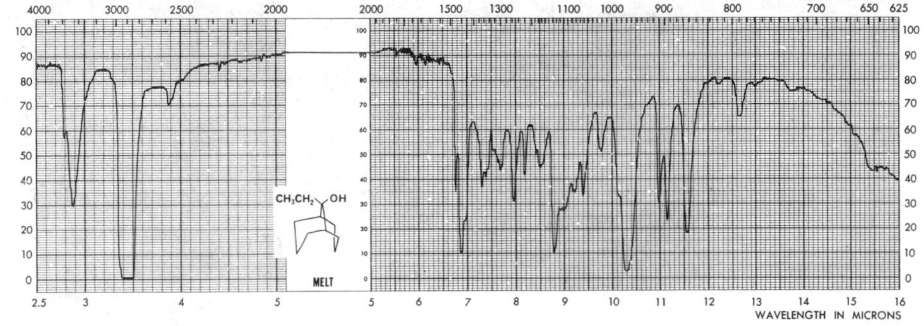

D

19,390-9
9-Cyclohexylbicyclo[3.3.1]nonan-9-ol
FW 222.37 mp 109-112° Disp. C
NUJOL MULL

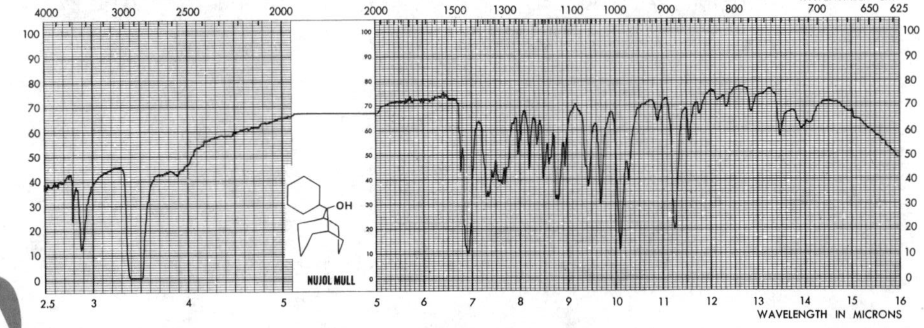

E

H5931-1 **8-Hydroxytricyclo[5.2.1.0^{2,6}]decane**
M.W. 152.24 n_D^{20} 1.5124 b.p. 239°
NEAT

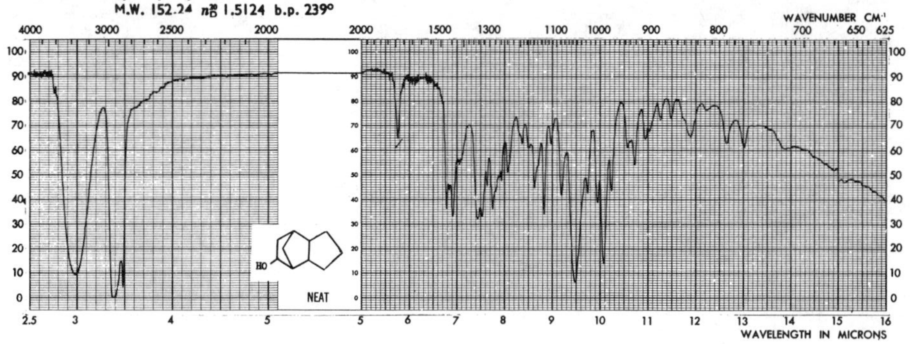

F

13,034-6 **1-Adamantanol** (1-hydroxyadamantane)
M.W. 152.24 m.p. > 300°
NUJOL MULL

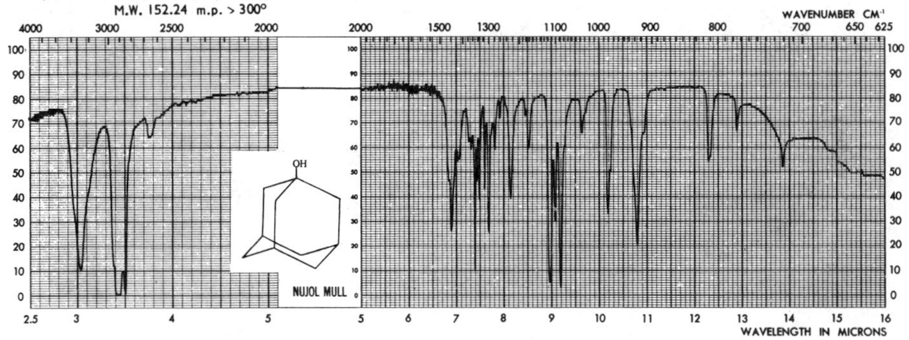

G

15,382-6 **2-Adamantanol** (2-hydroxyadamantane)
M.W. 152.24 m.p. 260-265° (sublimes)
NUJOL MULL

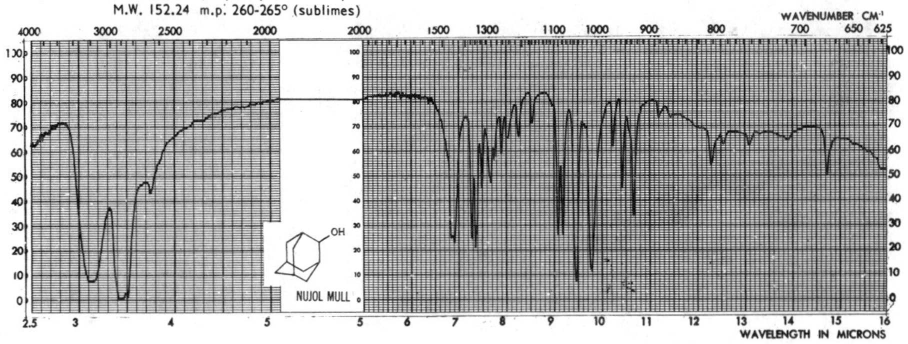

H

15,698-1
***cis*-Decahydro-1-naphthol**
$C_{10}H_{17}OH$
M.W. 154.25 m.p. 89-92° b.p. 238° Beil. 6,67
NUJOL MULL

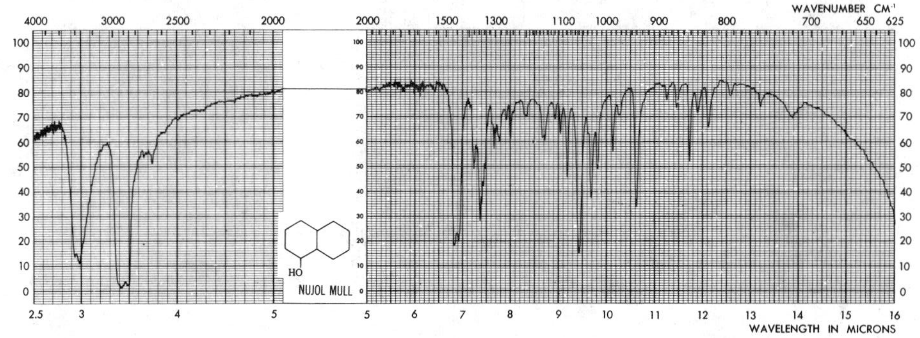

WAVENUMBER CM⁻¹ / WAVELENGTH IN MICRONS

A

D30-8 **Decahydro-2-naphthol** (mixture of *cis* and *trans*)
$C_{10}H_{17}OH$ M.W. 154.25 n_D^{20} 1.4992 ....

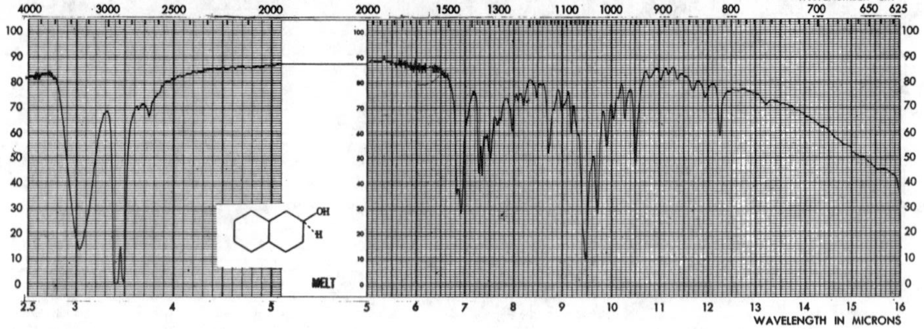

MELT

B

C1740-3 **Cedrol**
M.W. 222.37 m.p. 86.5-89°

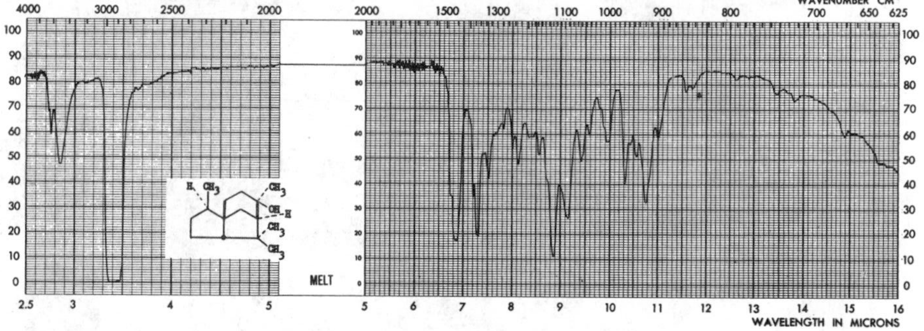

MELT

C

18,059-9
Tri-2-norbornylmethanol
M.W. 314.52 m.p. 134-137°

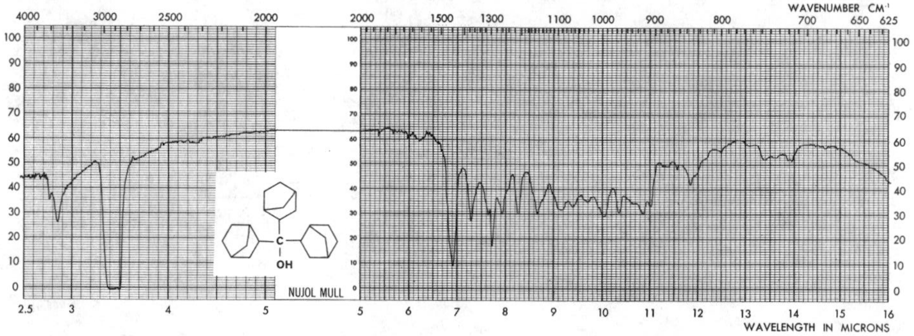

NUJOL MULL

D

13,194-6 **2,2,4,4-Tetramethyl-1,3-cyclobutanediol** (mixture of isomers)
$(CH_3)_4C_4H_2(OH)_2$ M.W. 144.21 m.p. 126-128° ....

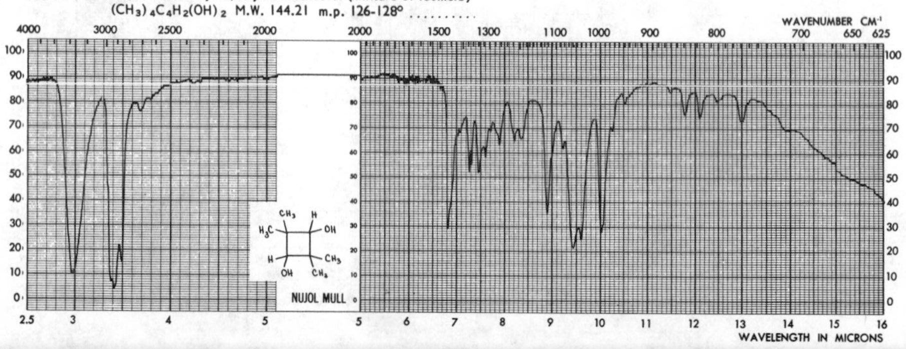

NUJOL MULL

E

C10,102-8 **1,2-Cyclohexanediol** (mixture of *cis* and *trans*)
$C_6H_{10}(OH)_2$ M.W. 116.16 m.p. 72.5-75°

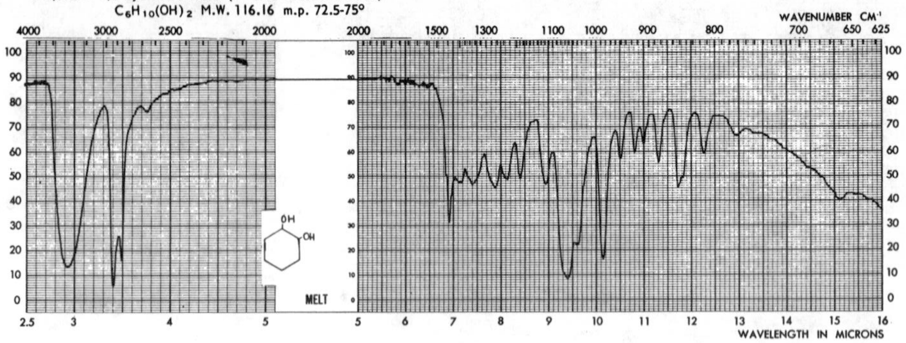

MELT

F

14,171-2 ***trans*-1,2-Cyclohexanediol**
$C_6H_{10}(OH)_2$ M.W. 116.16 m.p. 101-104° .

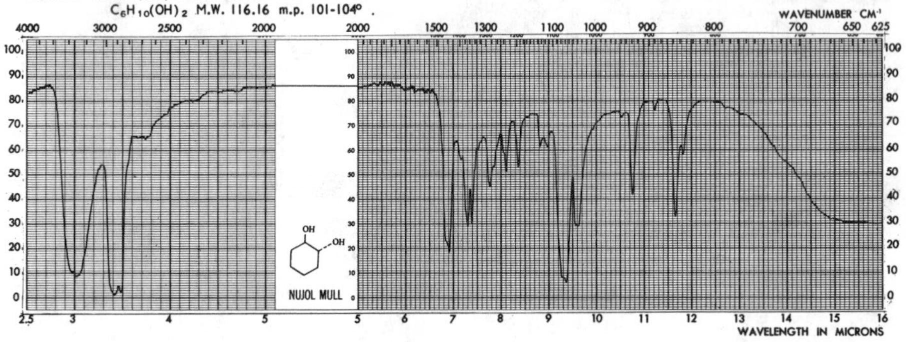

NUJOL MULL

G

C10,110-9 **1,3-Cyclohexanediol** (mixture of *cis* and *trans*)
$C_6H_{10}(OH)_2$ M.W. 116.16 n_D^{20} 1.4901 .....

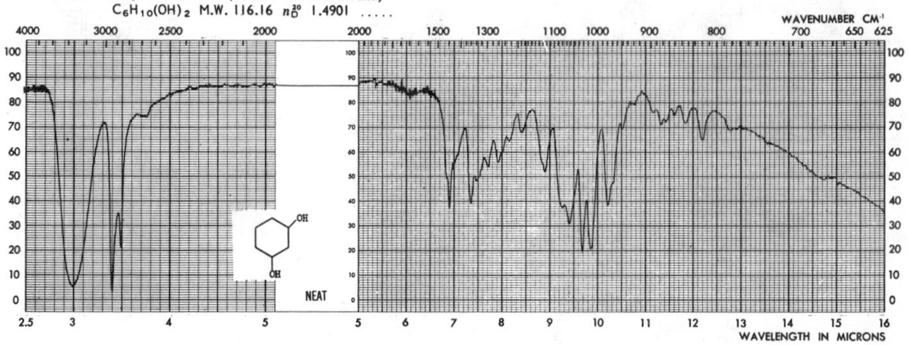

NEAT

H

C10,120-6 **1,4-Cyclohexanediol** (mixture of *cis* and *trans*)
$C_6H_{10}(OH)_2$ M.W. 116.16 ....

NUJOL MULL

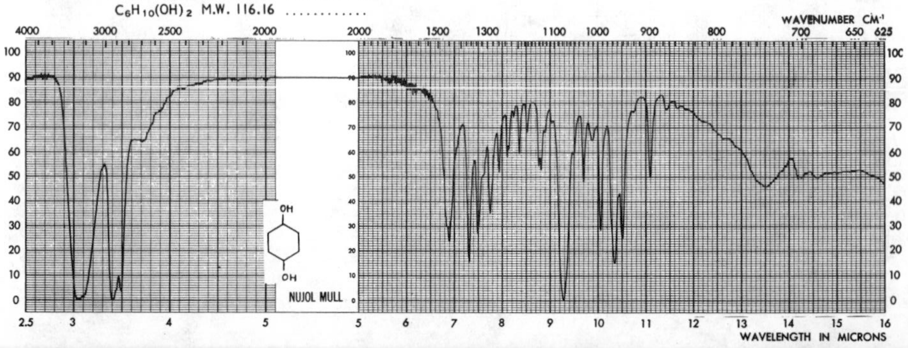

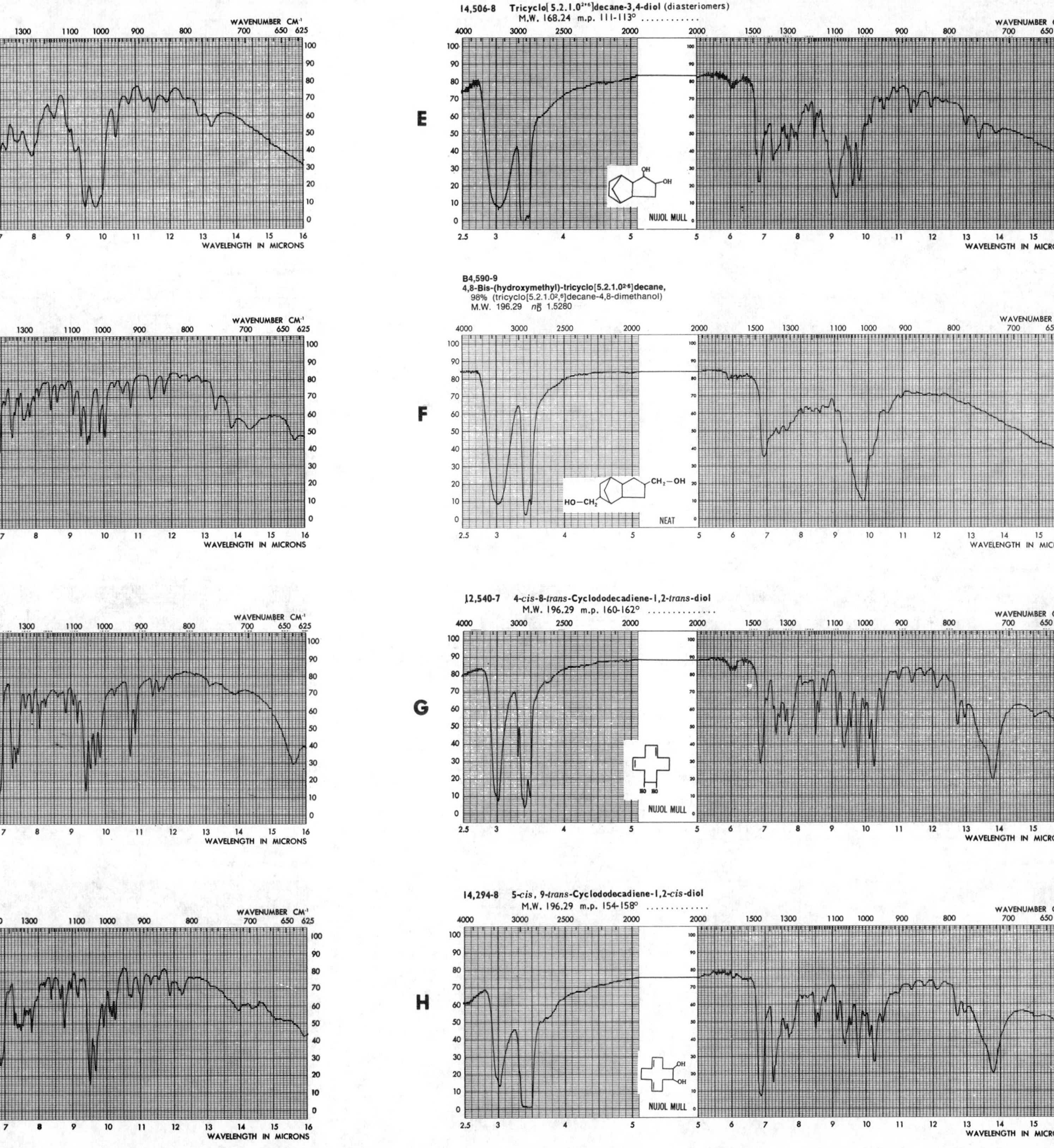

A
C9860-8 *trans*-1,2-Cycloheptanediol
$C_7H_{12}(OH)_2$ M.W. 130.19 m.p. 61-63°
MELT
B
14,642-0 *cis*-1,2-Cyclododecanediol
$C_{12}H_{22}(OH)_2$ M.W. 200.32 m.p. 154°
NUJOL MULL
C
14,509-2 *trans*-1,4-Decalindiol
M.W. 170.25 m.p. 156-157°
NUJOL MULL
D
15,027-4 1,5-Decalindiol (mixture of isomers)
M.W. 170.25 ....
NUJOL MULL
E
14,506-8 Tricyclo[5.2.1.0^{2,6}]decane-3,4-diol (diasteriomers)
M.W. 168.24 m.p. 111-113° ....
NUJOL MULL
F
B4,590-9
4,8-Bis-(hydroxymethyl)-tricyclo[5.2.1.0^{2,6}]decane,
98% (tricyclo[5.2.1.0^{2,6}]decane-4,8-dimethanol)
M.W. 196.29 n_D^{20} 1.5280
NEAT
G
12,540-7 4-*cis*-8-*trans*-Cyclododecadiene-1,2-*trans*-diol
M.W. 196.29 m.p. 160-162° ....
NUJOL MULL
H
14,294-8 5-*cis*, 9-*trans*-Cyclododecadiene-1,2-*cis*-diol
M.W. 196.29 m.p. 154-158° ....
NUJOL MULL
WAVENUMBER CM⁻¹
WAVELENGTH IN MICRONS
ALDRICH

A

1-665-2 **Inositol**
M.W. 180.16 m.p. 224-225°

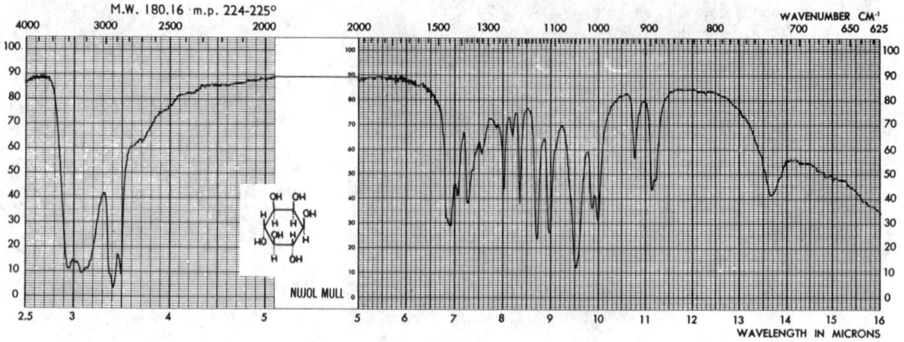

NUJOL MULL

B

C3990-3 **2-Chloroethanol** (ethylene chlorohydrin)
$ClCH_2CH_2OH$ M.W. 80.51 n_D^{20} 1.4412

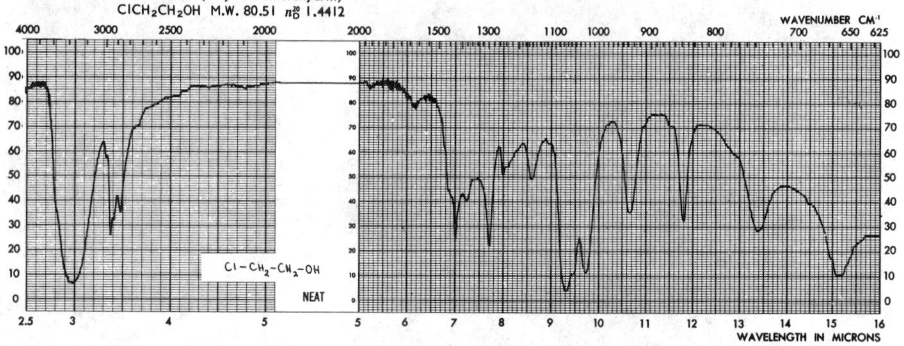

$Cl-CH_2-CH_2-OH$

NEAT

C

C4640-3 **1-Chloro-3-hydroxypropane** (trimethylene chlorohydrin, 3-chloro-1-propanol)
$Cl(CH_2)_3OH$ M.W. 94.54 n_D^{20} 1.4429 ....

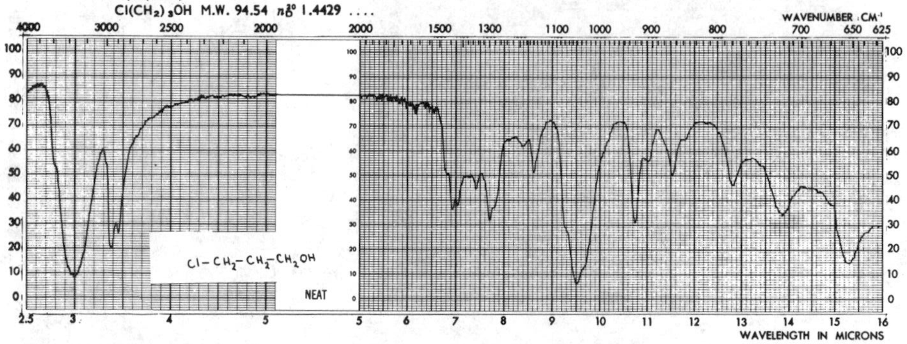

$Cl-CH_2-CH_2-CH_2OH$

NEAT

D

18,931-6
3-Chloro-2,2-dimethyl-1-propanol
$ClCH_2C(CH_3)_2CH_2OH$ FW 122.60 mp 35-37°
bp 87°/35mm. n_D^{20} 1.4504 Disp. C

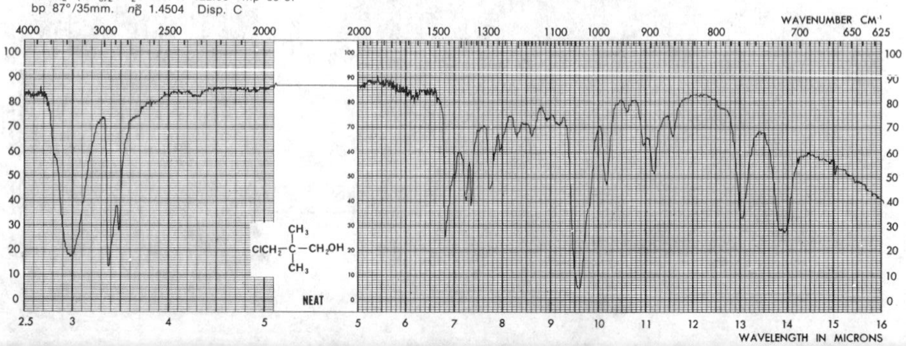

NEAT

E

20,769-1
2,2-Bis(chloromethyl)-1-propanol, 95%
$CH_3C(CH_2Cl)_2CH_2OH$ FW 157.04
bp 103-104°/12mm. n_D^{20} 1.4858 d 1.229 Disp. C

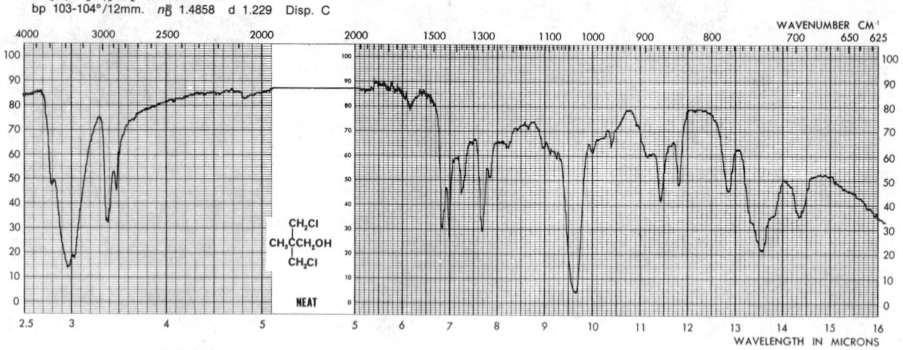

NEAT

F

C4500-8 **1-Chloro-6-hydroxyhexane** (hexamethylene chlorohydrin, 6-chloro-1-hexanol)
$Cl(CH_2)_6OH$ M.W. 136.62
n_D^{20} 1.4557 ....

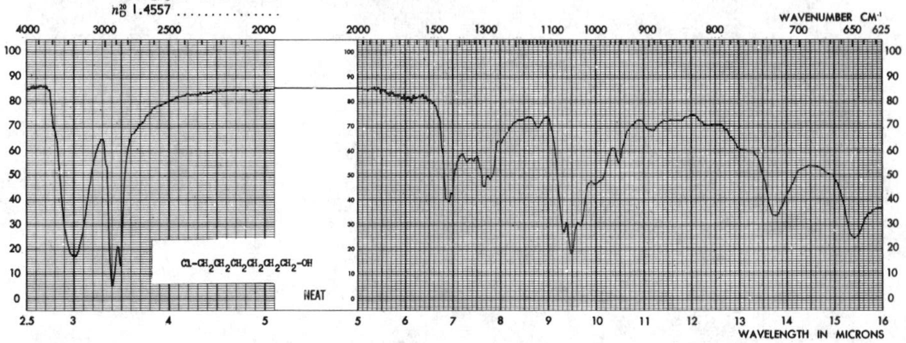

$Cl-CH_2CH_2CH_2CH_2CH_2CH_2-OH$

NEAT

G

18,648-1
6-Bromo-1-hexanol, 98%
$Br(CH_2)_6OH$
M.W. 181.08 b.p. 105-106°/5mm. n_D^{20} 1.4825
d 1.384 Beil. 1(4),1704

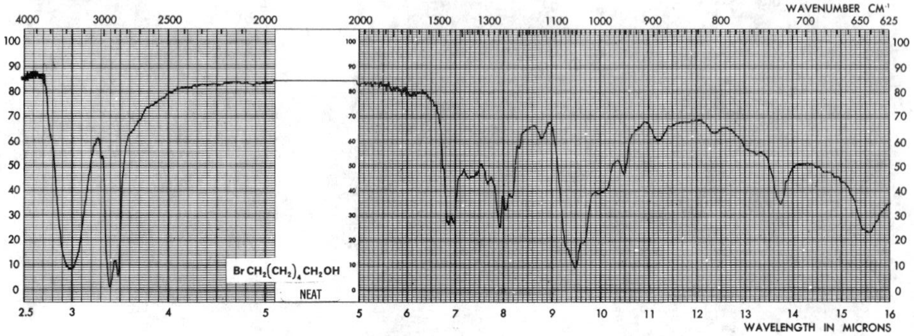

$BrCH_2(CH_2)_4CH_2OH$

NEAT

H

D6180-6 **2,2-Dichloroethanol**
Cl_2CHCH_2OH M.W. 114.96 n_D^{20} 1.4712

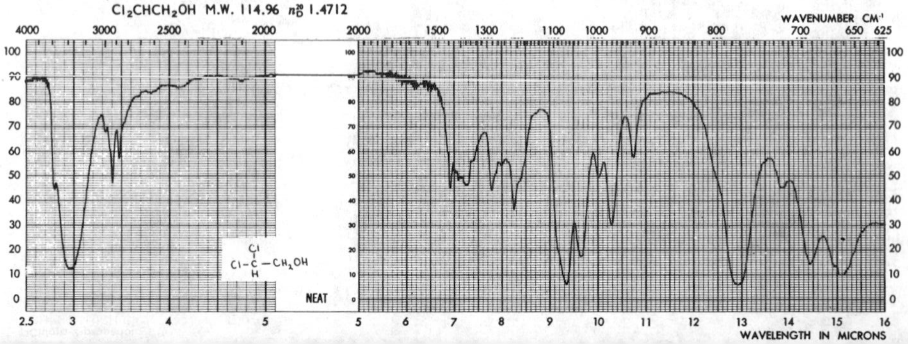

NEAT

A

T5480-1 **2,2,2-Trichloroethanol**
CCl_3CH_2OH M.W. 149.40 n_D^{20} 1.4861
b.p. 52-54°/10 mm.

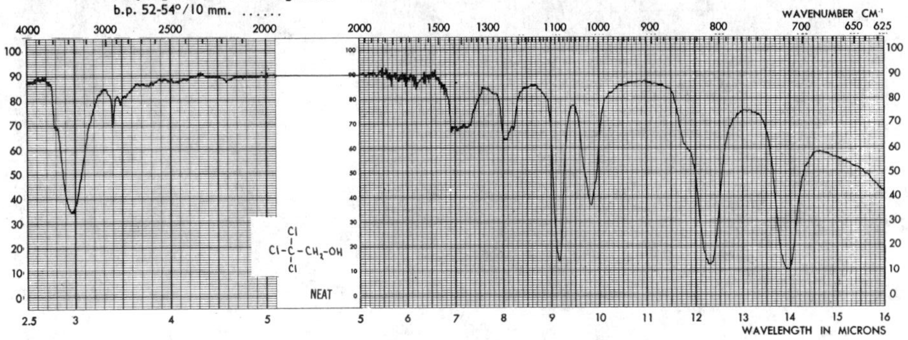

NEAT

B

T4,840-2
2,2,2-Tribromoethanol, 97%
CBr_3CH_2OH
M.W. 282.77 m.p. 80-81.5° b.p. 92-93°/10mm.
Beil. **1**(2),338

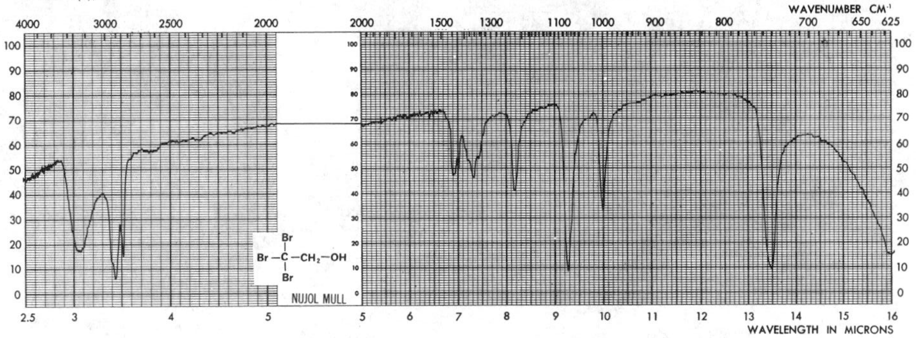

NUJOL MULL

C

13,740-5 **1,1,1-Trichloro-2-propanol** (1,1,1-trichloroisopropanol)
$CH_3CH(OH)CCl_3$ M.W. 163.43 m.p. 49-51°

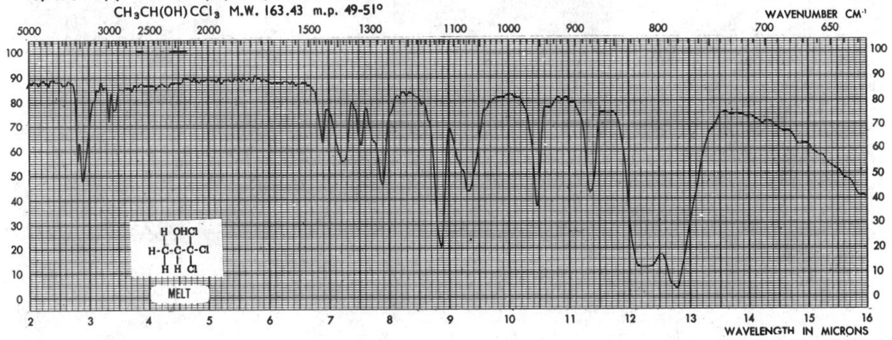

MELT

D

C1905-8 **Chloral hydrate** (2,2,2-trichloro-1,1-ethanediol)
$CCl_3CH(OH)_2$ M.W. 165.40 m.p. 57-63°

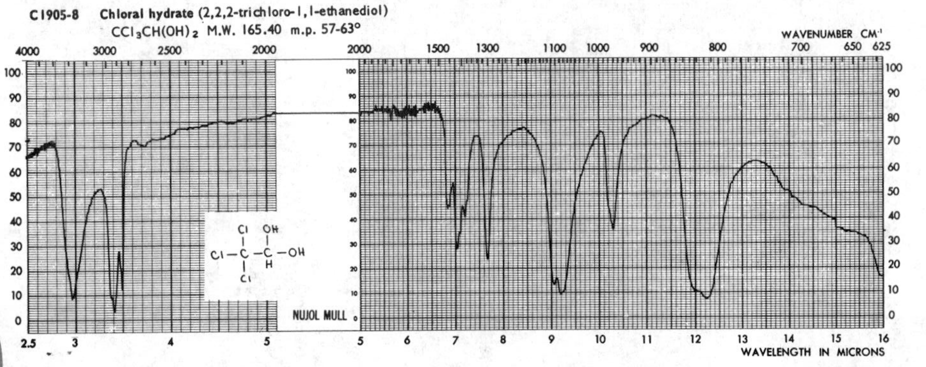

NUJOL MULL

E

1-Chloro-2-propanol, 97%
$CH_3CH(OH)CH_2Cl$
M.W. 94.54 b.p. 126-127° n_D^{20} 1.4375 d 1.115
Beil. **1**,363

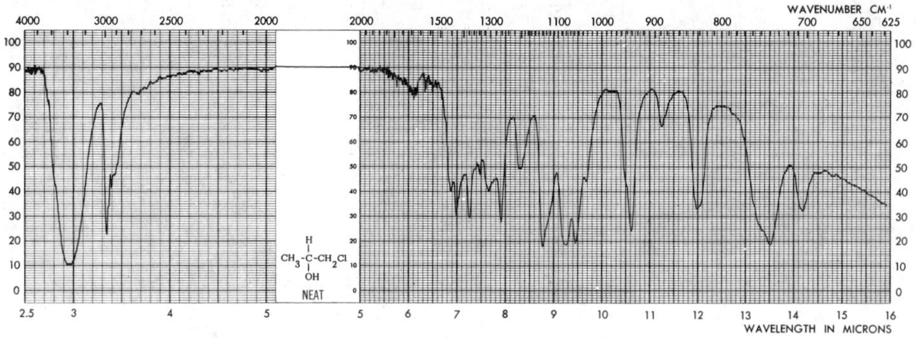

NEAT

F

10,727-1 **3-Chloro-1,2-propanediol**
$ClCH_2CH(OH)CH_2OH$ M.W. 110.54 n_D^{20} 1.4805
b.p. 215° (dec.)

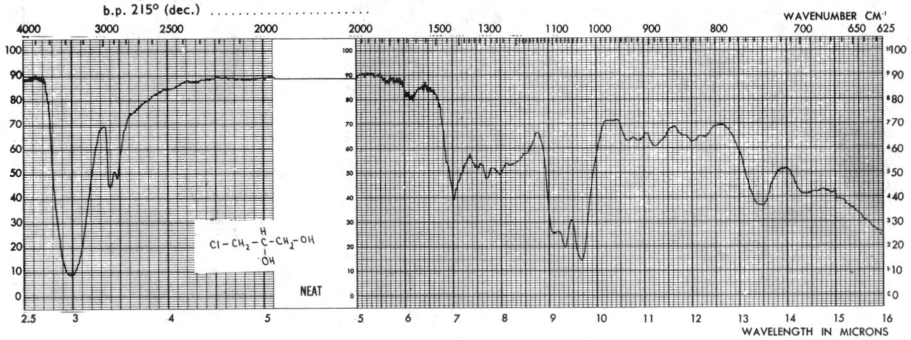

NEAT

G

18,448-9
1,3-Dichloro-2-propanol, 95%
$ClCH_2CH(OH)CH_2Cl$
M.W. 128.99 m.p. -4° b.p. 174.3° n_D^{20} 1.4835
d 1.351 Beil. **1**,364

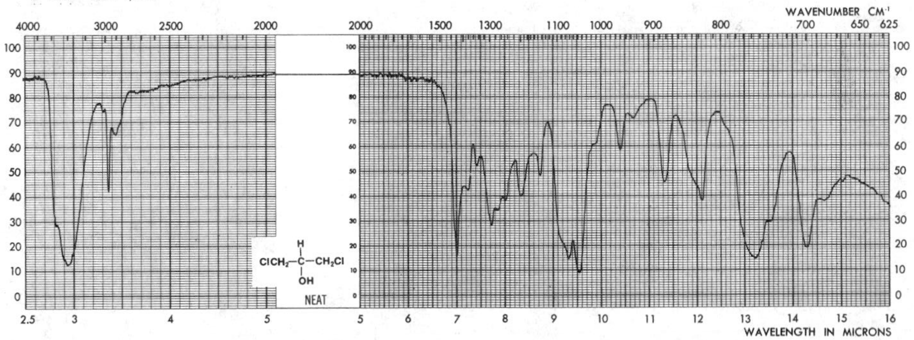

NEAT

H

11,205-4 **1,1,1-Trichloro-2-methyl-2-propanol hydrate**
$CCl_3C(CH_3)_2OH \cdot xH_2O$ M.W. 177.46 (anhydrous)
m.p. 80-82°

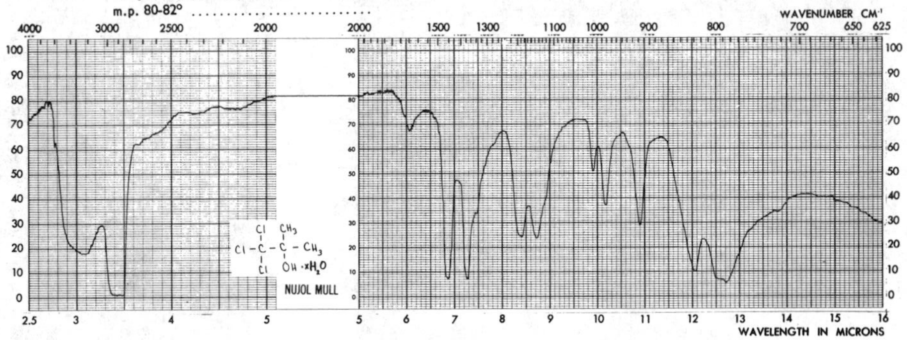

NUJOL MULL

A

C6888-1 **2-Chloro-2-propen-1-ol** (2-chloroallyl alcohol)
$H_2C:C(Cl)CH_2OH$ M.W. 92.53 n_D^{20} 1.4579

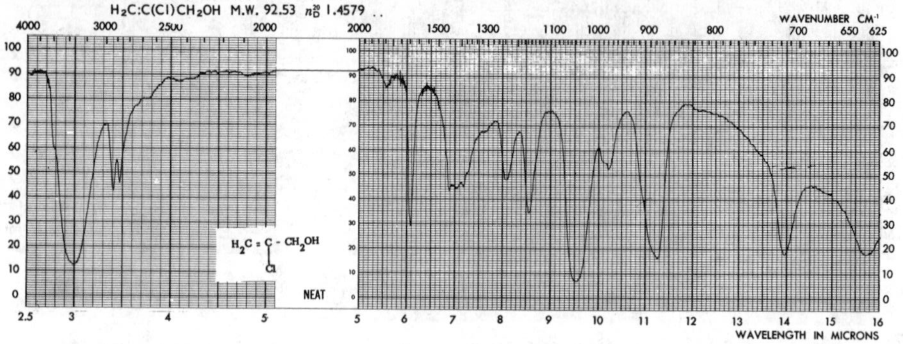

$H_2C=C(Cl)-CH_2OH$ NEAT

B

C3240-2 **2-Chlorocyclohexanol, tech.**
$ClC_6H_{10}OH$ M.W. 134.61 n_D^{20} 1.4881

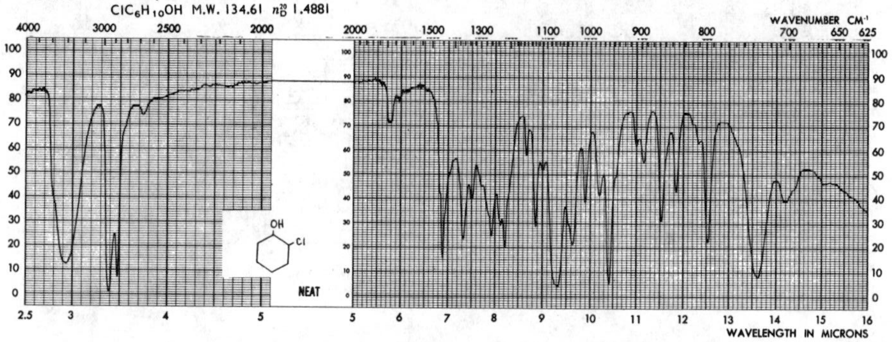

NEAT

C

13,321-3 **1-(Trichloromethyl)-cyclohexanol**
$CCl_3C_6H_{10}OH$ M.W. 217.52 m.p. 53-57°

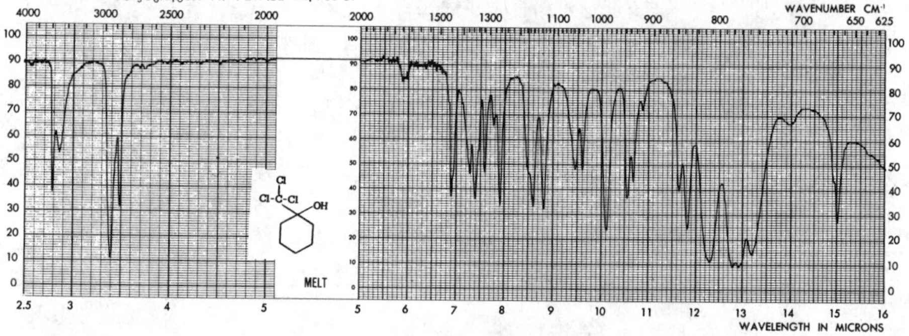

MELT

D

18,681-3
2,2,6,6-Tetrachlorocyclohexanol, 98%
$Cl_4C_6H_7OH$ FW 237.94 mp 56-59° Disp. C

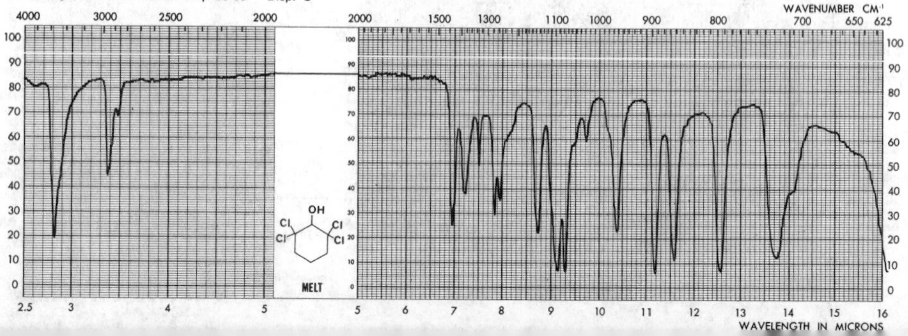

MELT

E

11,399-9 **1,4,5,6,7,7-Hexachloro-5-norbornene-2,3-dimethanol**
M.W. 360.88 m.p. 191.5-196°

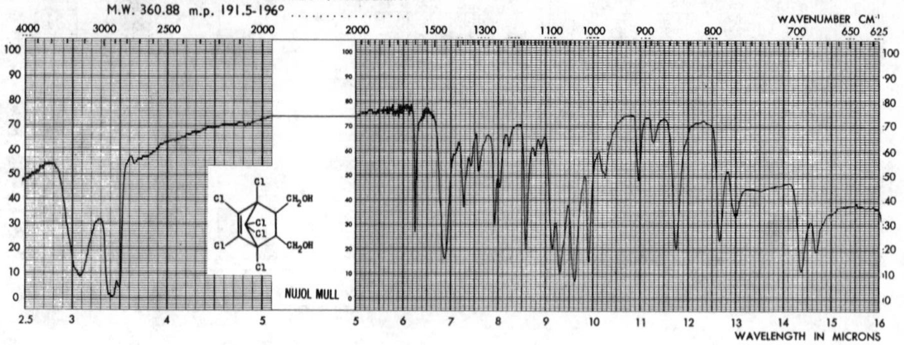

NUJOL MULL

F

16,034-2
2-Fluoroethanol
FCH_2CH_2OH
M.W. 64.06 m.p. 26.5° b.p. 103°/757mm.
n_D^{20} 1.3635 d 1.091 Beil. 1(1),170

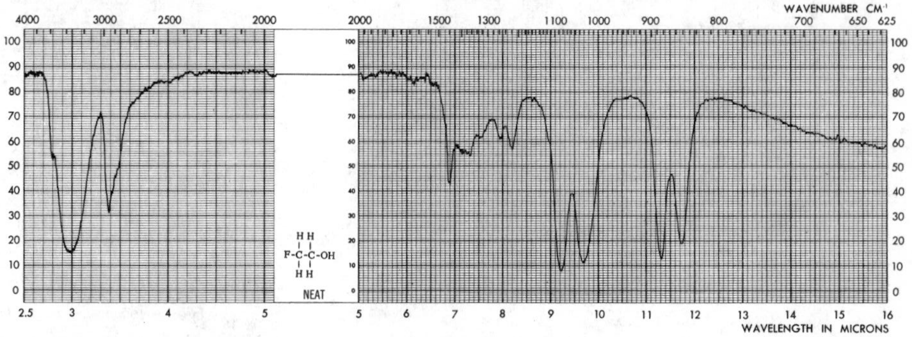

NEAT

G

T6300-2 **2,2,2-Trifluoroethanol, puriss.**
CF_3CH_2OH M.W. 100.04 n_D^{20} < 1.3000
b.p. 74-75°

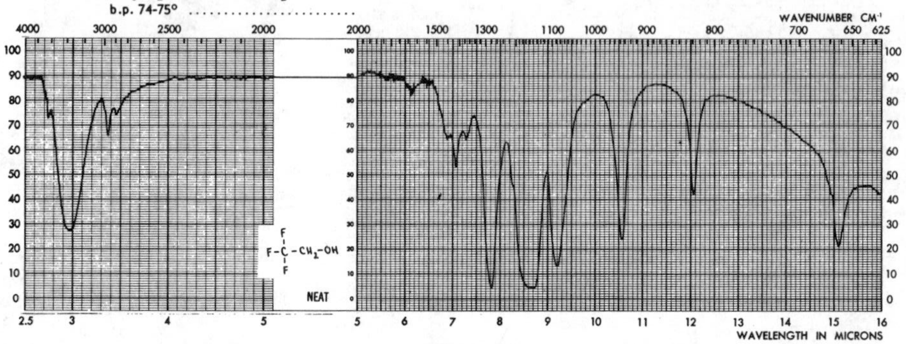

NEAT

H

T1180-0 **2,2,3,3-Tetrafluoro-1-propanol**
$F_2CHCF_2CH_2OH$ M.W. 132.06 n_D^{20} 1.3212 m.p. -20 to -15°
b.p. 109-110°

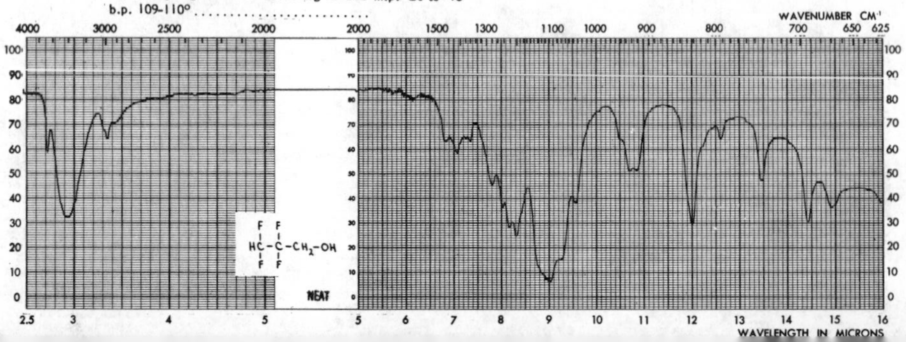

NEAT

A

M8225-6 **2-Methyl-3,3,4,4-tetrafluoro-2-butanol, tech.**
$F_2CHCF_2C(CH_3)_2OH$ M.W. 160.11
n_D^{20} 1.3524

$F_2CHCF_2C(CH_3)_2OH$ — NEAT

B

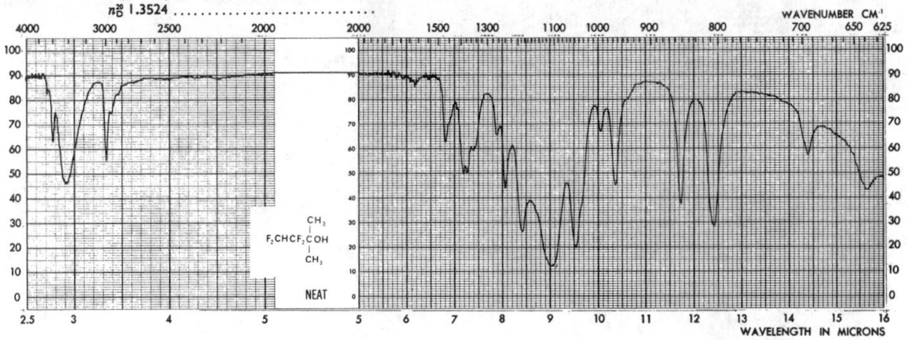

17,692-3
1,3-Difluoro-2-propanol, 99%
$FCH_2CH(OH)CH_2F$
M.W. 96.08 b.p. 54-55°/34mm. n_D^{20} 1.3725
d 1.24 *IRRITANT*

$FCH_2-CH(OH)-CH_2F$ — NEAT

C

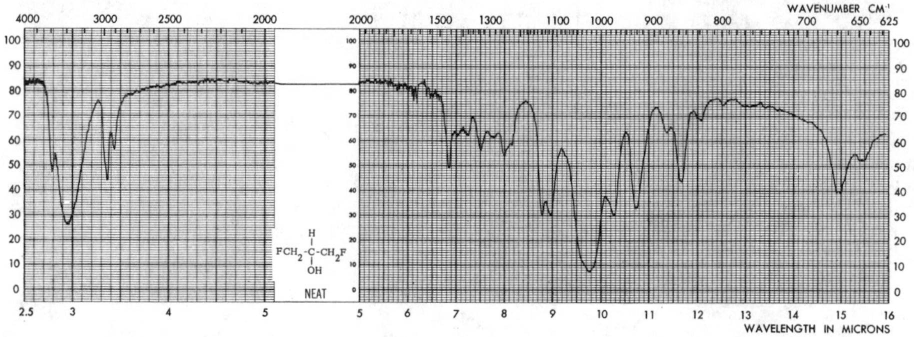

T6360-6 **1,1,1-Trifluoro-2-propanol, tech., 70%**
$CH_3CH(OH)CF_3$ M.W. 114.07

$CF_3-CH(OH)-CH_3$ — NEAT

D

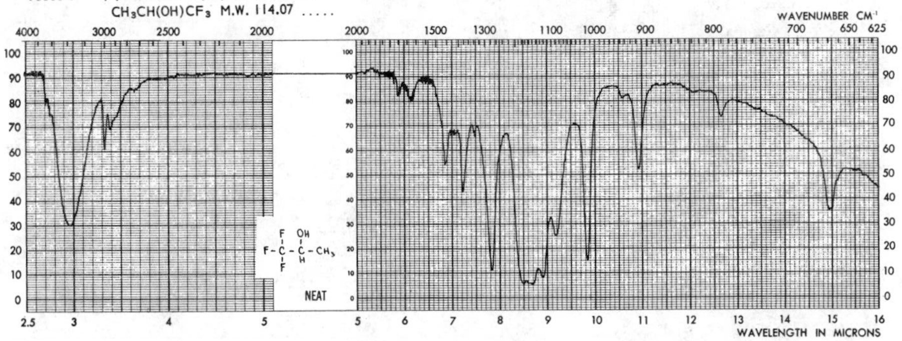

10,522-8 **1,1,1,3,3,3-Hexafluoro-2-propanol, puriss.**
$(CF_3)_2CHOH$ M.W. 168.04 n_D^{22} 1.2750 b.p. 59°

$CF_3-CH(OH)-CF_3$ — NEAT

E

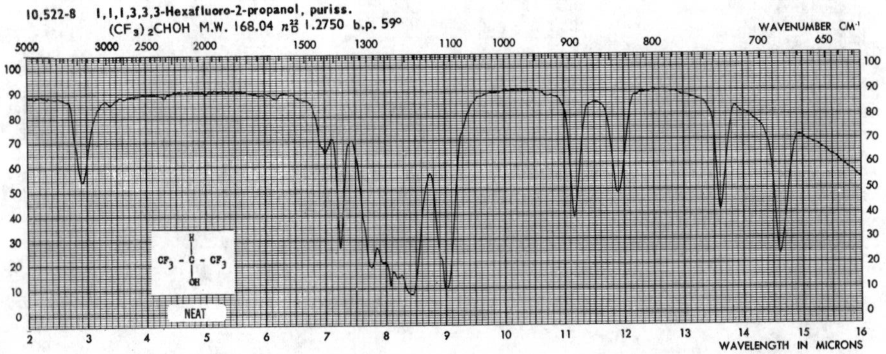

H160-4 **2,2,3,3,4,4,4-Heptafluoro-1-butanol, tech.**
$CF_3(CF_2)_2CH_2OH$ M.W. 200.05 n_D^{20} 1.3000

$CF_3-CF_2-CF_2-CH_2-OH$ — NEAT

F

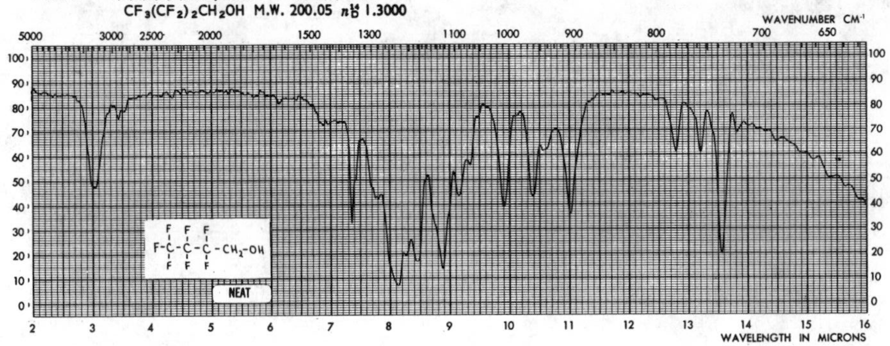

H880-3 **2,2,3,3,4,4-Hexafluoro-1,5-pentanediol**
$HOCH_2(CF_2)_3CH_2OH$ M.W. 212.09 m.p. 77-80°

$HO-CH_2-(CF_2)_3-CH_2OH$ — NUJOL MULL

G

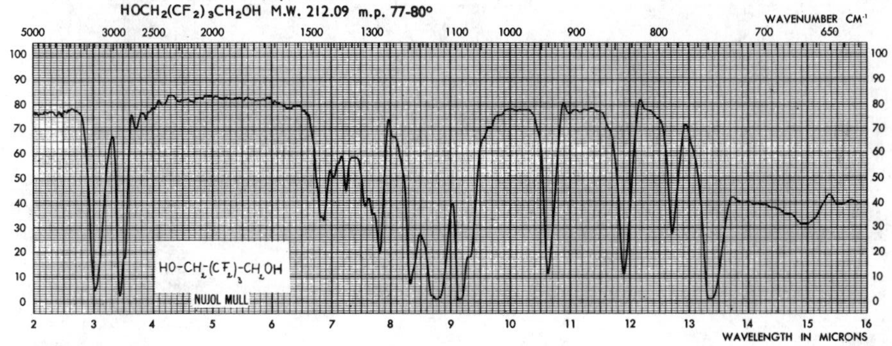

22,613-0
3-Bromo-1,2-propanediol, 99%
$BrCH_2CH(OH)CH_2OH$ FW 155.00
bp 72-75°/0.200mm. n_D^{20} 1.5187 d 1.771
Beil. 1(1),248 Disp. C

$BrCH_2CH(OH)-CH_2OH$ — NEAT

H

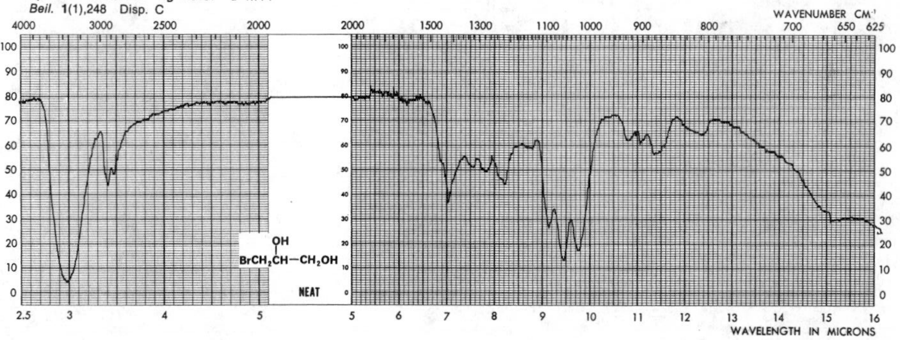

B6558-6 **2-Bromoethanol** (ethylene bromohydrin)
$BrCH_2CH_2OH$ M.W. 124.97 n_D^{20} 1.4922

$Br-CH_2-CH_2-OH$ — NEAT

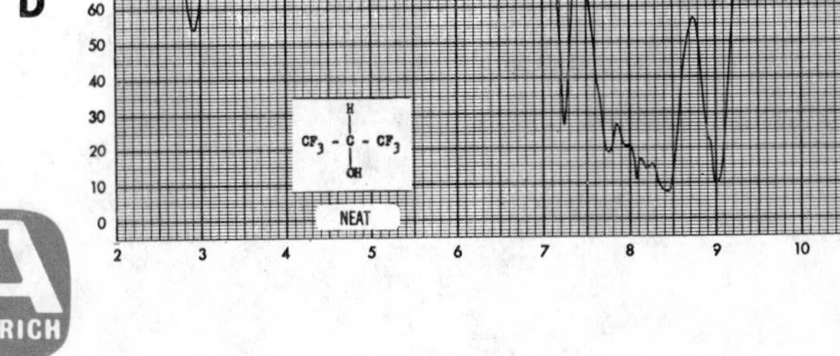

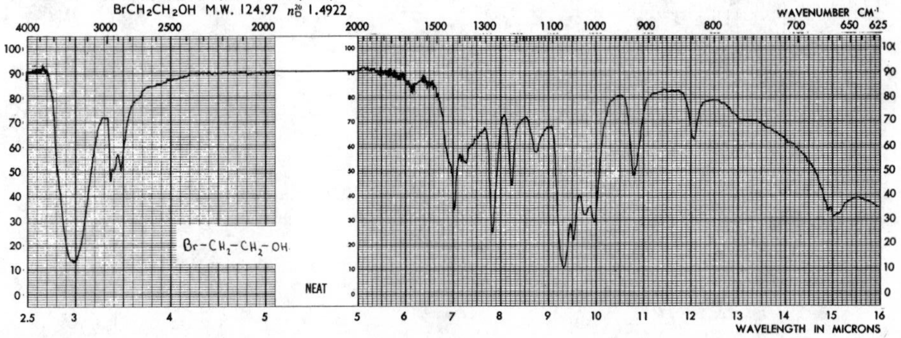

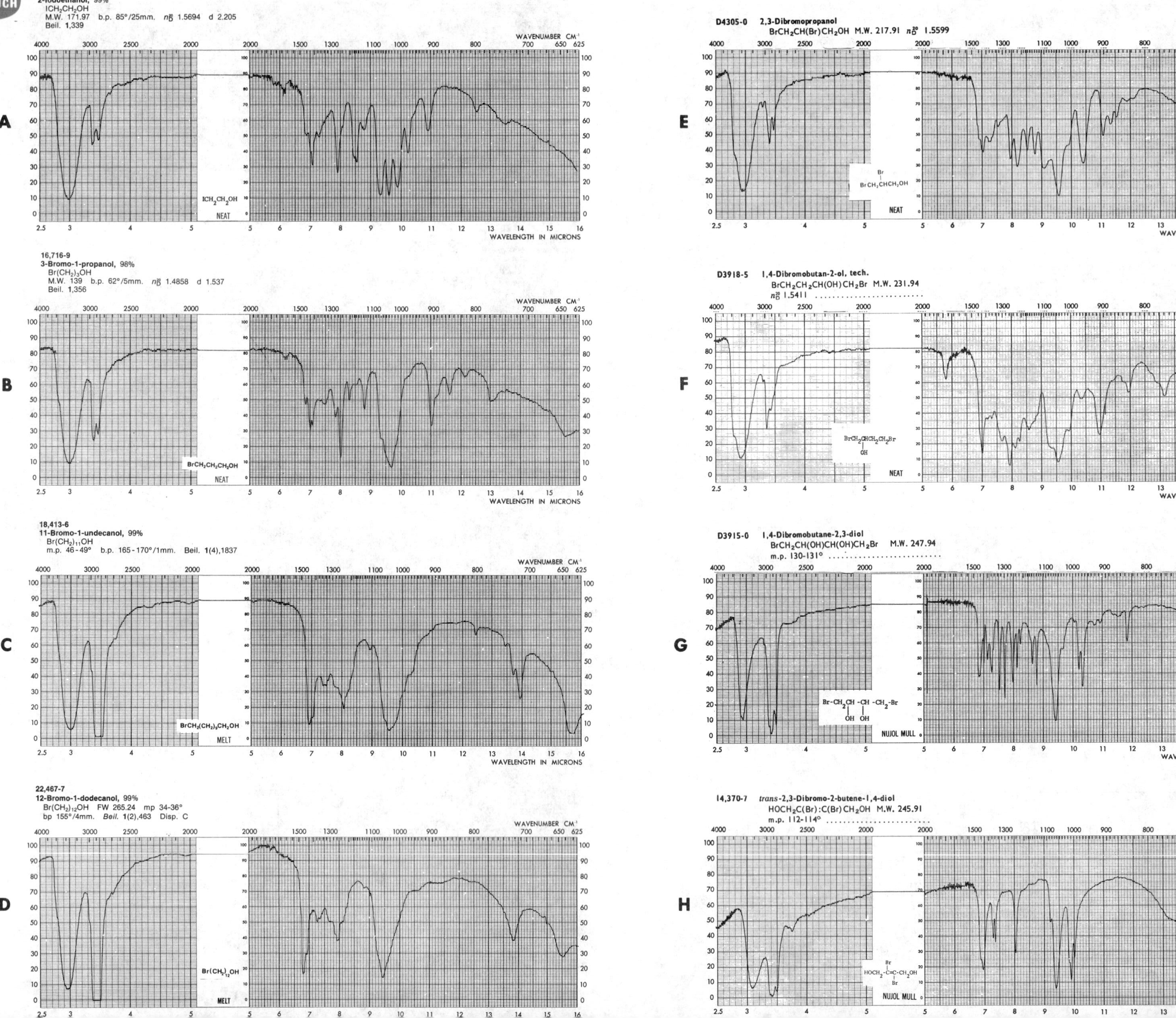

ALDRICH
A
17,685-0
2-Iodoethanol, 99%
ICH_2CH_2OH
M.W. 171.97 b.p. 85°/25mm. n_D^{20} 1.5694 d 2.205
Beil. 1,339
ICH_2CH_2OH
NEAT
B
16,716-9
3-Bromo-1-propanol, 98%
$Br(CH_2)_3OH$
M.W. 139 b.p. 62°/5mm. n_D^{20} 1.4858 d 1.537
Beil. 1,356
$BrCH_2CH_2CH_2OH$
NEAT
C
18,413-6
11-Bromo-1-undecanol, 99%
$Br(CH_2)_{11}OH$
m.p. 46-49° b.p. 165-170°/1mm. Beil. 1(4),1837
$BrCH_2(CH_2)_9CH_2OH$
MELT
D
22,467-7
12-Bromo-1-dodecanol, 99%
$Br(CH_2)_{12}OH$ FW 265.24 mp 34-36°
bp 155°/4mm. Beil. 1(2),463 Disp. C
$Br(CH_2)_{12}OH$
MELT
E
D4305-0 2,3-Dibromopropanol
$BrCH_2CH(Br)CH_2OH$ M.W. 217.91 n_D^{20} 1.5599
NEAT
F
D3918-5 1,4-Dibromobutan-2-ol, tech.
$BrCH_2CH_2CH(OH)CH_2Br$ M.W. 231.94
n_D^{20} 1.5411
NEAT
G
D3915-0 1,4-Dibromobutane-2,3-diol
$BrCH_2CH(OH)CH(OH)CH_2Br$ M.W. 247.94
m.p. 130-131°
NUJOL MULL
H
14,370-7 *trans*-2,3-Dibromo-2-butene-1,4-diol
$HOCH_2C(Br):C(Br)CH_2OH$ M.W. 245.91
m.p. 112-114°
NUJOL MULL
WAVENUMBER CM⁻¹
WAVELENGTH IN MICRONS

A

13,487-2 Glycerol, U.S.P.
$HOCH_2CH(OH)CH_2OH$ M.W. 92.10 n_D^{20} 1.4746 b.p. 182°/2 mm.
m.p. 17.8°

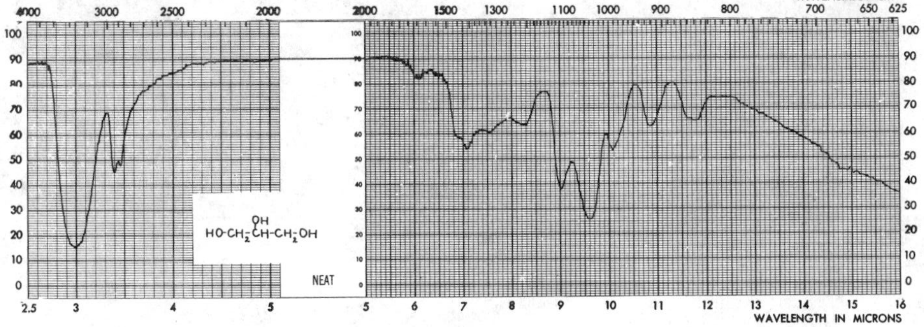

NEAT

B

T8780-7 1,1,1-Tris-(hydroxymethyl)-ethane [2-(hydroxymethyl)-2-methyl-1,3-propanediol], tech.
$CH_3C(CH_2OH)_3$ M.W. 120.15

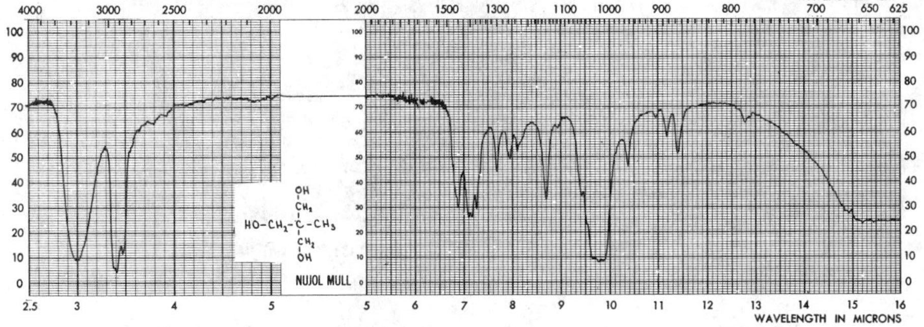

NUJOL MULL

C

10,763-8 2-Hydroxymethyl-2-propyl-1,3-propanediol
$CH_3(CH_2)_2C(CH_2OH)_3$ M.W. 148.20 m.p. 99-102°

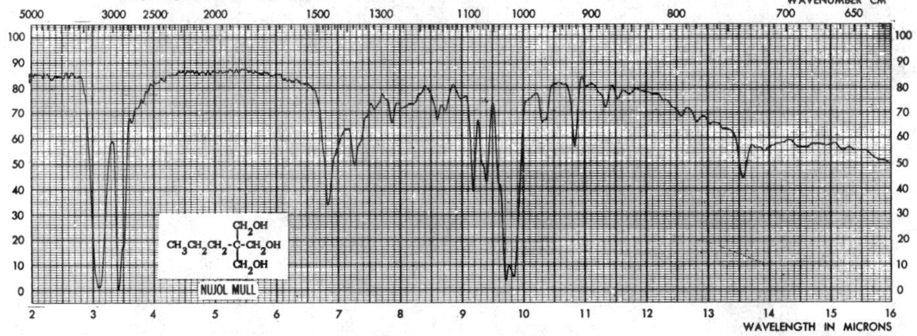

NUJOL MULL

D

T6620-6 1,2,6-Trihydroxyhexane (1,2,6-hexanetriol)
$HO(CH_2)_4CH(OH)CH_2OH$ M.W. 134.18 n_D^{20} 1.4813
b.p. 178°/5 mm.

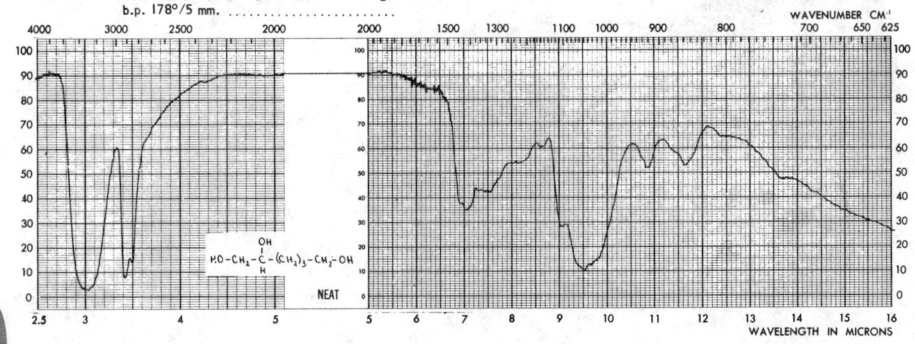

NEAT

E

12,648-9 2,5-Dimethyl-1,2,6-hexanetriol
$HOCH_2CH(CH_3)CH_2CH_2C(CH_3)(OH)CH_2OH$ M.W. 162.23
n_D^{20} 1.4800

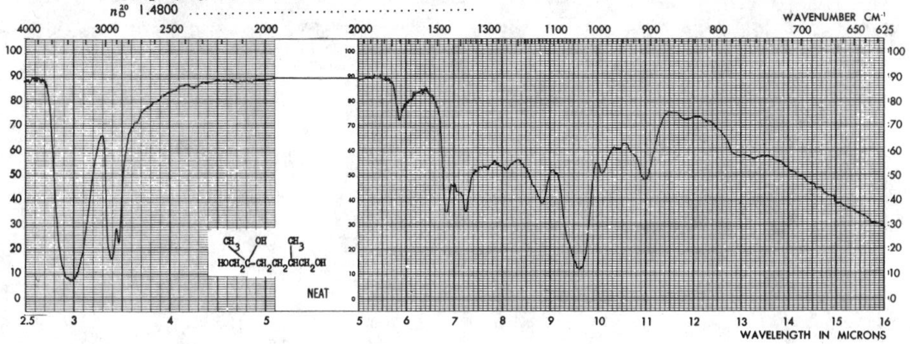

NEAT

F

P475-5 Pentaerythritol
$C(CH_2OH)_4$ M.W. 136.15 m.p. 255-260°

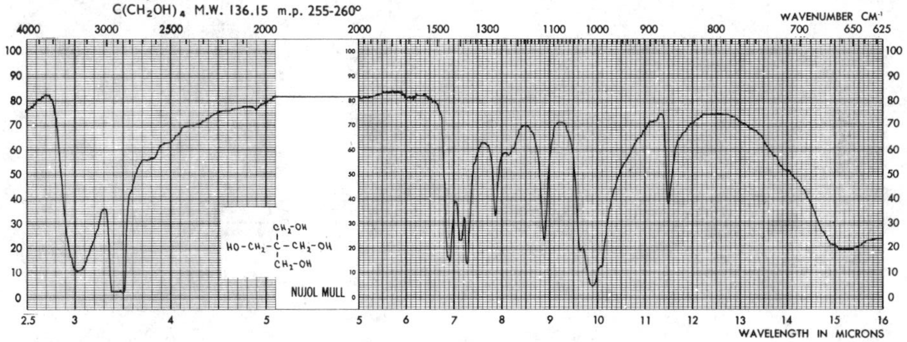

NUJOL MULL

G

E260-4 *meso*-Erythritol
$HOCH_2[CH(OH)]_2CH_2OH$ M.W. 122.12
m.p. 120-123°

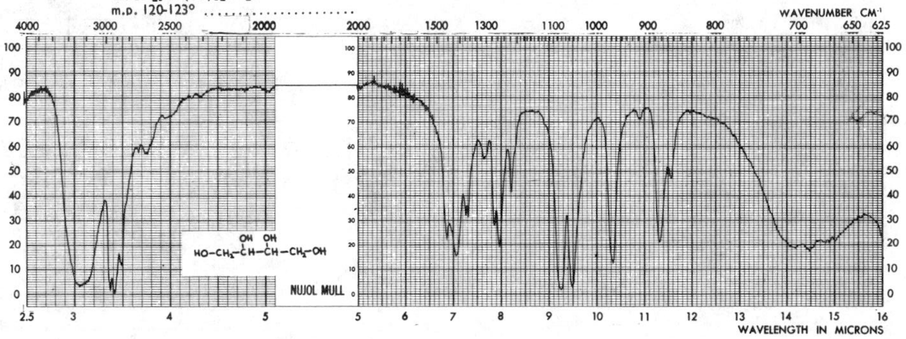

NUJOL MULL

H

15,337-0 Adonitol
$HOCH_2[CH(OH)]_3CH_2OH$ M.W. 152.15
m.p. 101-103.5°

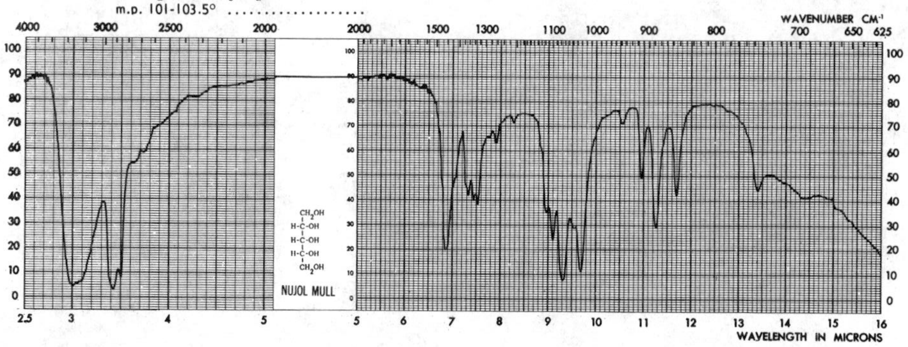

NUJOL MULL

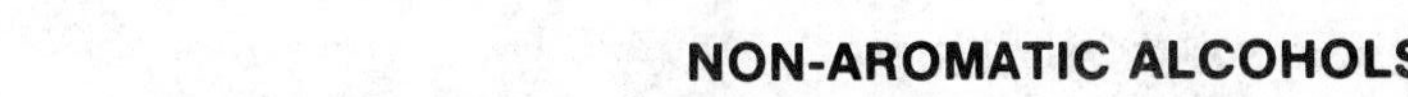

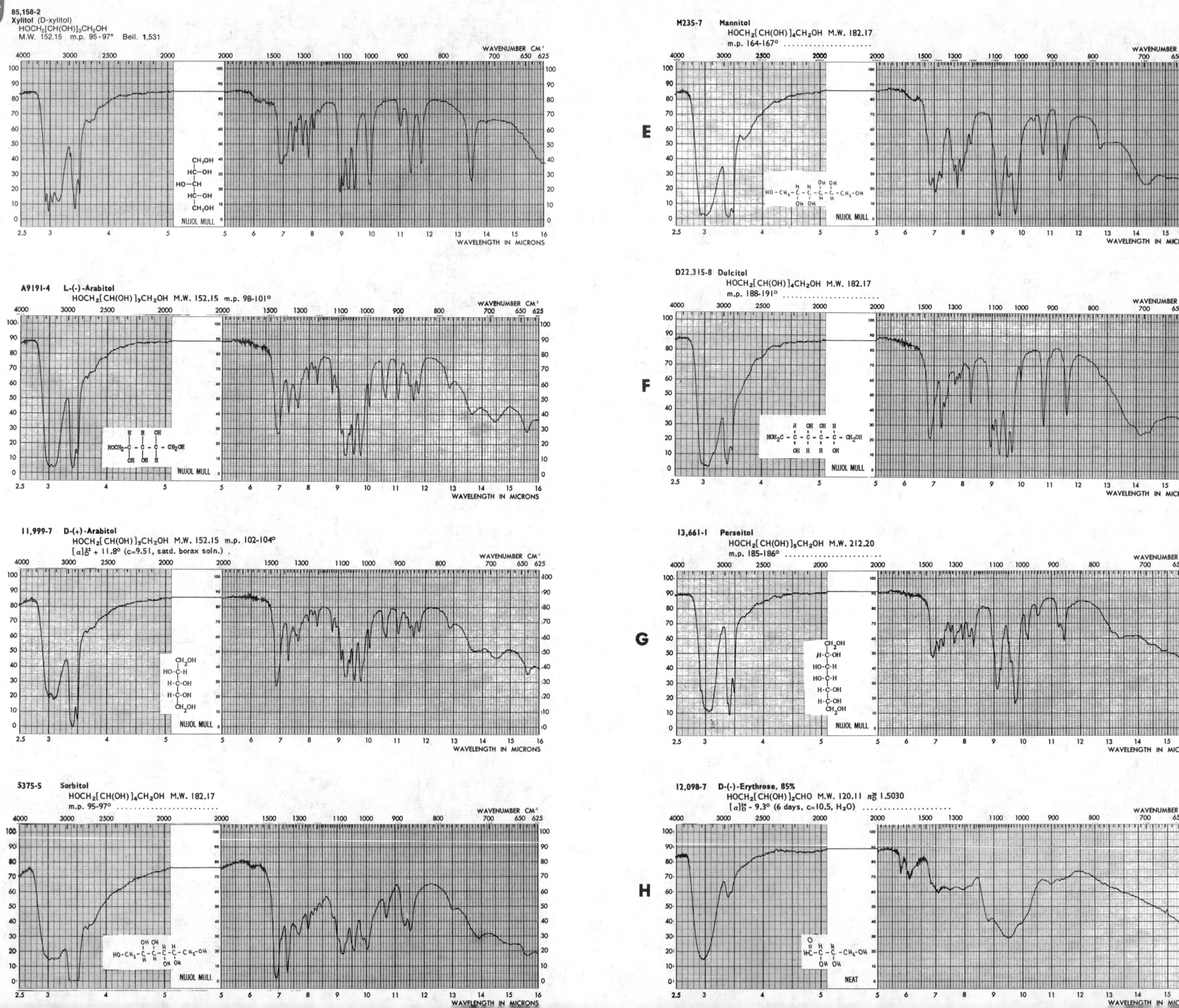
ALDRICH
A
85,158-2
Xylitol (D-xylitol)
HOCH2[CH(OH)]3CH2OH
M.W. 152.15 m.p. 95-97° Beil. 1,531
NUJOL MULL
B
A9191-4 L-(-)-Arabitol
HOCH2[CH(OH)]3CH2OH M.W. 152.15 m.p. 98-101°
NUJOL MULL
C
11,999-7 D-(+)-Arabitol
HOCH2[CH(OH)]3CH2OH M.W. 152.15 m.p. 102-104°
[α]D22 + 11.8° (c=9.51, satd. borax soln.)
NUJOL MULL
D
5375-5 Sorbitol
HOCH2[CH(OH)]4CH2OH M.W. 182.17
m.p. 95-97°
NUJOL MULL
E
M235-7 Mannitol
HOCH2[CH(OH)]4CH2OH M.W. 182.17
m.p. 164-167°
NUJOL MULL
F
D22,315-8 Dulcitol
HOCH2[CH(OH)]4CH2OH M.W. 182.17
m.p. 188-191°
NUJOL MULL
G
13,661-1 Perseitol
HOCH2[CH(OH)]5CH2OH M.W. 212.20
m.p. 185-186°
NUJOL MULL
H
12,098-7 D-(-)-Erythrose, 85%
HOCH2[CH(OH)]2CHO M.W. 120.11 nD20 1.5030
[α]D25 - 9.3° (6 days, c=10.5, H2O)
NEAT
WAVENUMBER CM-1
WAVELENGTH IN MICRONS

A

85,159-0
L-(-)-Xylose, 99+%, GOLD LABEL
M.W. 150.13 m.p. 150-152°
$[\alpha]^{24}$ -18.7° (c=4, H_2O, 24 hr.) Beil. **31**,55

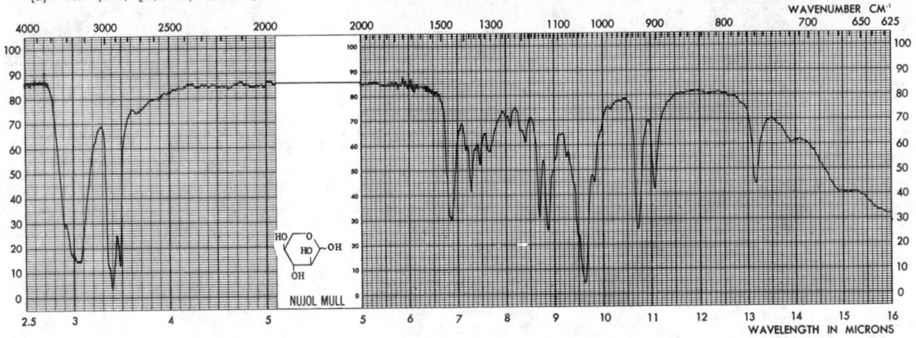

B

85,028-4
D-(+)-Fucose (rhodeose)
M.W. 164.16 m.p. 144-145° Beil. **31**,76

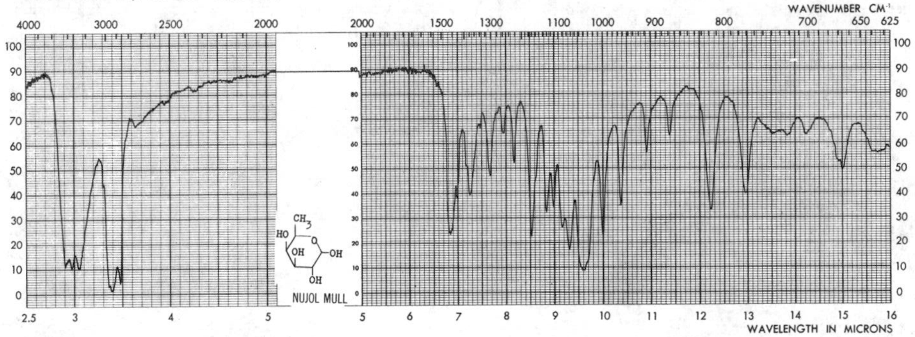

C

11,258-5 D-(+)-Mannose
$HOCH_2[CH(OH)]_4CHO$ M.W. 180.16 m.p. 133-135°
$[\alpha]_D$ + 14.2° ± 0.4° (in H_2O)

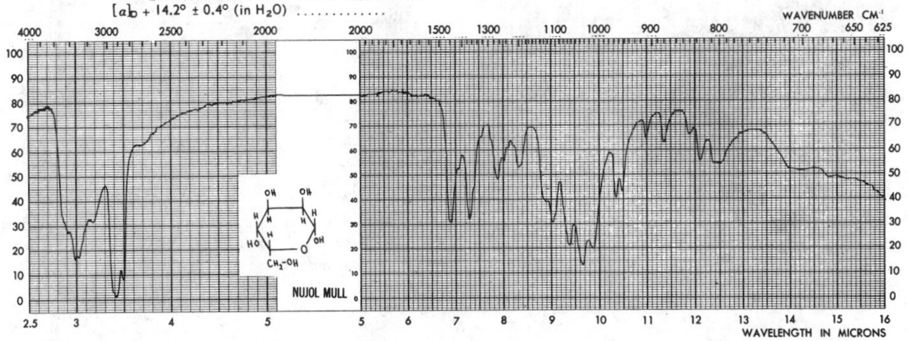

D

X107-5 D-(+)-Xylose, puriss.
M.W. 150.13 m.p. 146-147° $[\alpha]_D^{20}$ + 18.5° (c=10 in H_2O)

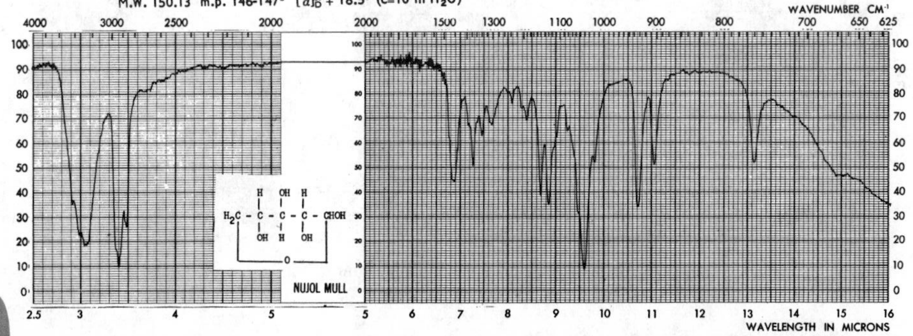

E

A9190-6 L-(+)-Arabinose, puriss.
M.W. 150.13 m.p. 157-160° $[\alpha]_D$ + 103° ± 1°
(c=1 in H_2O)

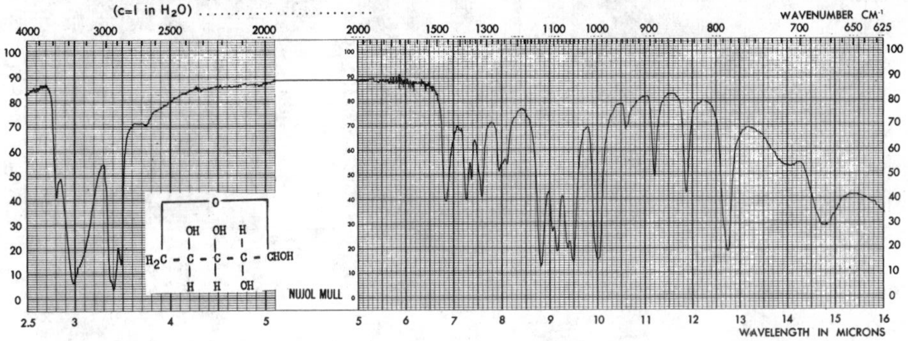

F

14,112-7 D-(-)-Arabinose, puriss.
M.W. 150.13 m.p. 162-164° $[\alpha]_D^{19.9}$ - 104.3°
(c=3, H_2O, 20 hrs.)

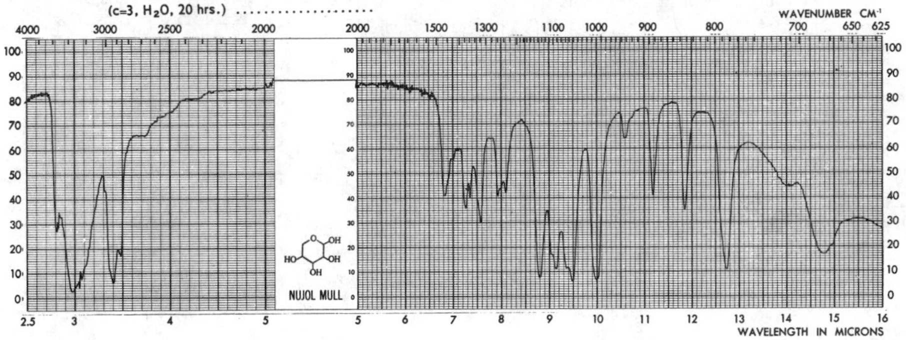

G

12,164-9 D-2-Deoxyribose
$HOCH_2[CH(OH)]_2CH_2CHO$ M.W. 134.13
$[\alpha]_D^{22}$ -59° (c=1, H_2O, 72 hrs.)

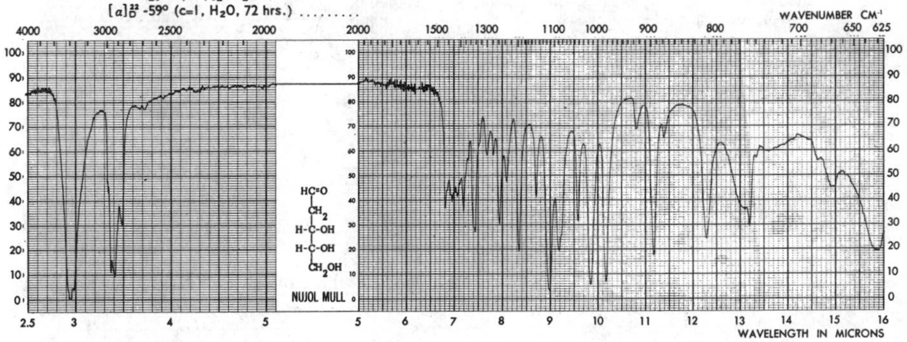

H

R175-7 D-(-)-Ribose
M.W. 150.13 m.p. 86-89°
$[\alpha]_D^{23}$ - 22.1° (c=1 in H_2O)

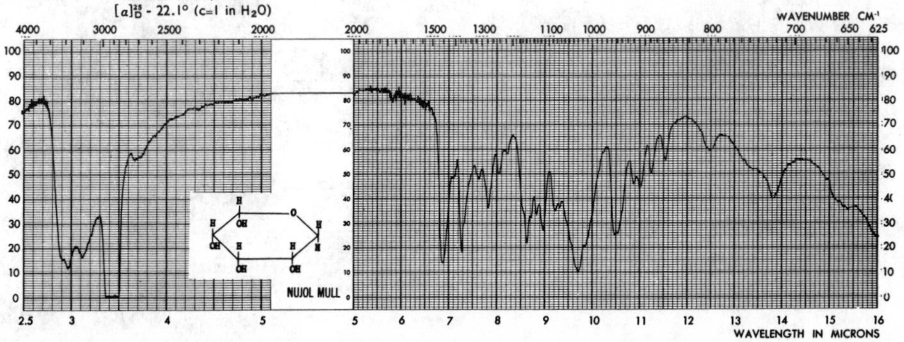

A

D10,350-0 **D-(+)-Digitoxose, puriss.**
$CH_3[CH(OH)]_3CH_2CHO$ M.W. 148.16
m.p. 122-124°

NUJOL MULL

B

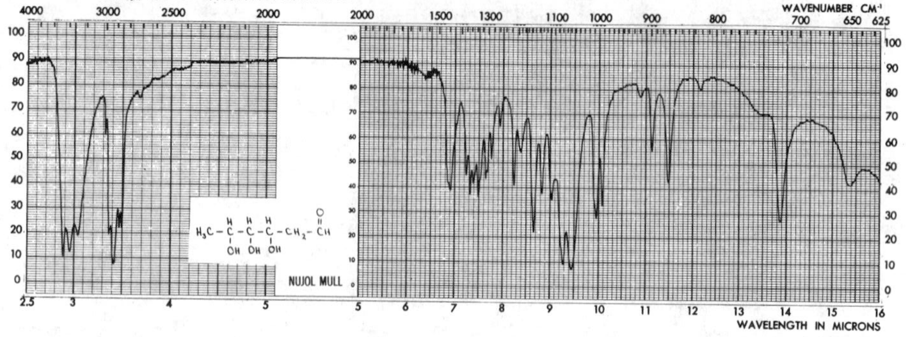

F1920 D-(+)-Fucose (6-desoxygalactose, rhodeose)

NUJOL MULL

C

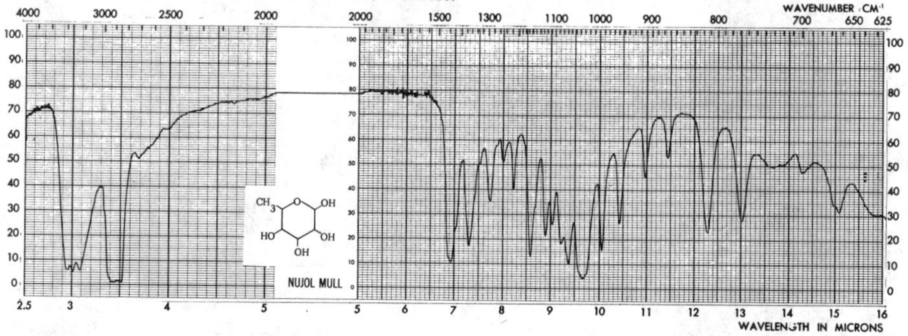

85,138-8
L-(-)-Fucose (6-deoxy-β-galactose)
M.W. 164.16 m.p. 133-137°
$[\alpha]^{24}$ -69° (c=9, H_2O, 24 hr.) Beil. **31**,78

NUJOL MULL

D

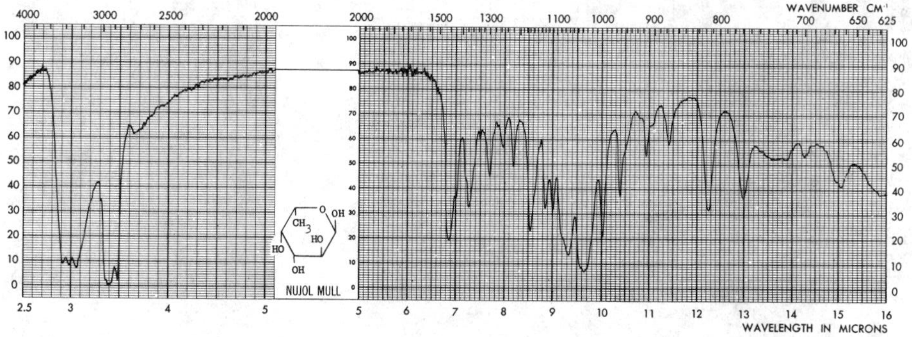

15,896-8
D-(+)-Glucose, anhydrous (dextrose)
M.W. 180.16 m.p. 156-158°
$[\alpha]^{23}$ +53° (c=10, H_2O) Beil. **31**,83

NUJOL MULL

E

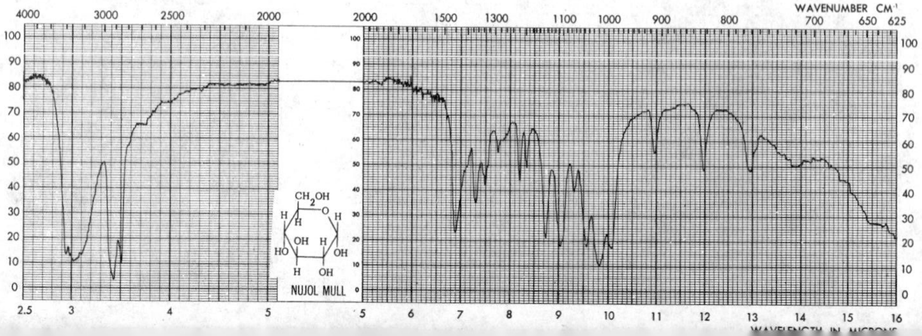

85,986-9
5-Thio-D-glucose, predominantly α-anomer
FW 196.22 mp 135-138°
$[\alpha]_D^{25}$ +188° (c=1, H_2O, 2hr.) Disp. L

NUJOL MULL

F

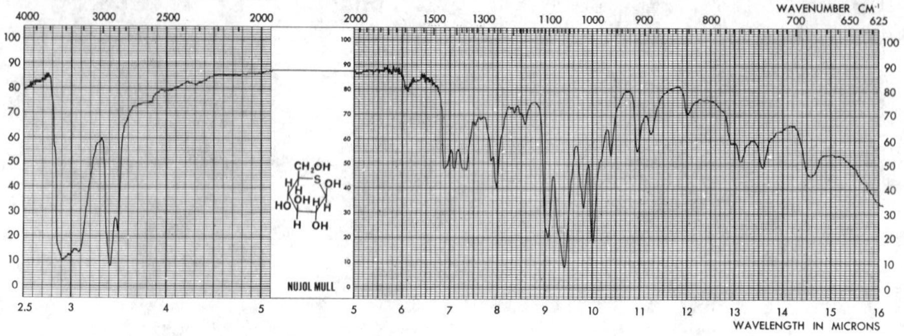

85,550-2
3-O-Methylglucose (3-O-methyl-α-D-glucopyranose)
M.W. 194.18 m.p. 167-169°

NUJOL MULL

G

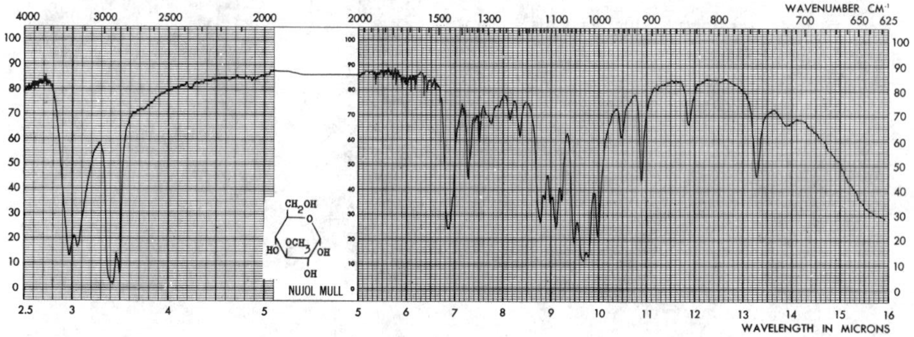

17,198-0
L-(+)-Rhamnose monohydrate (6-deoxy-L-mannose)
M.W. 182.17 m.p. 93-95° Beil. **31**,65

NUJOL MULL

H

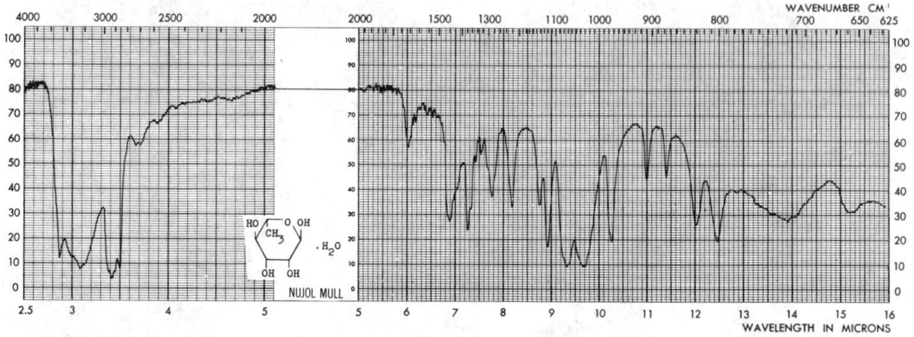

85,664-9
L-(-)-Mannose, 99+%, GOLD LABEL
M.W. 180.16 m.p. 129-131°
$[\alpha]^{24}$ -14.3° (c=4, H_2O, 1hr.)

NUJOL MULL

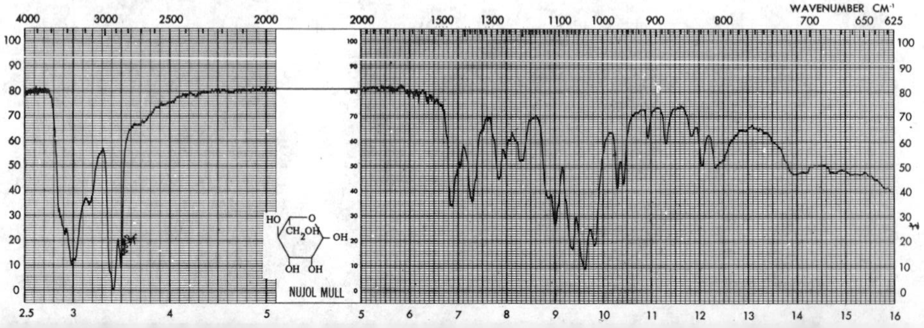

A 22,047-7
D-Lyxose, 99%, mixture of anomers
FW 150.13 mp 108-112° $[\alpha]^{25}$ -13.8° (c=4, H_2O)
Beil. **31**,56 Disp. L
NUJOL MULL

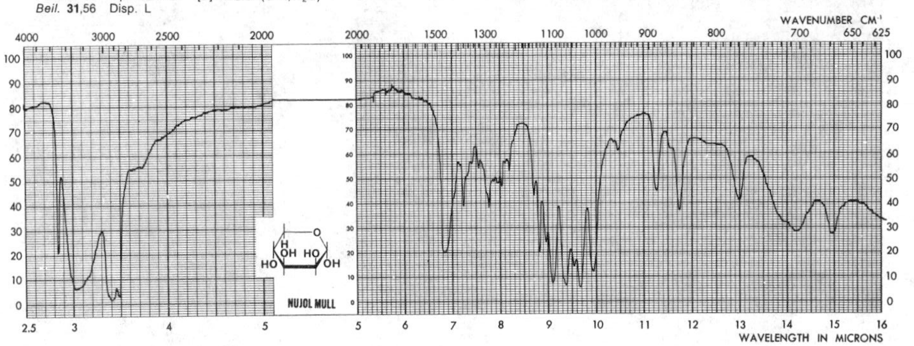

B 22,048-5
L-Lyxose, 99%, mixture of anomers
FW 150.13 mp 116-121° $[\alpha]^{25}$ +13.5° (c=1, H_2O)
Beil. **31**,57 Disp. L
NUJOL MULL

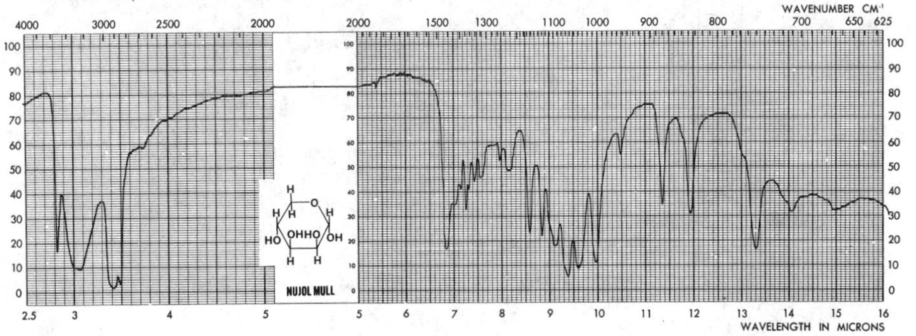

C 11,259-3 **D-(+)-Galactose**
$HOCH_2[CH(OH)]_4CHO$ M.W. 180.16
m.p. 167-169°
NUJOL MULL

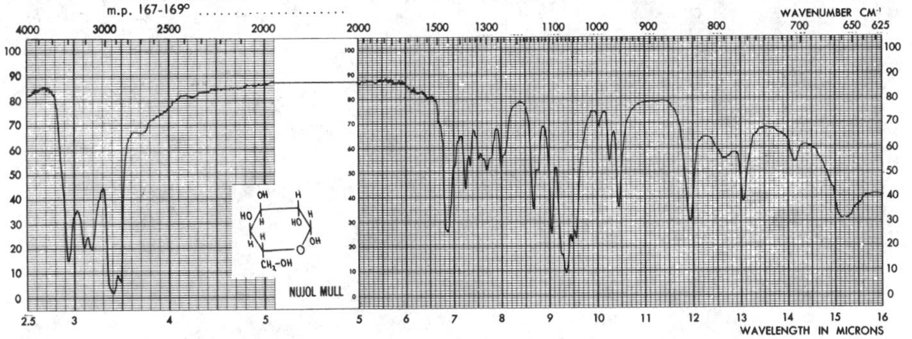

D 17,044-5
α-Methylglucoside, 99%
M.W. 194.18 m.p. 169-171° Beil. **31**,179
NUJOL MULL

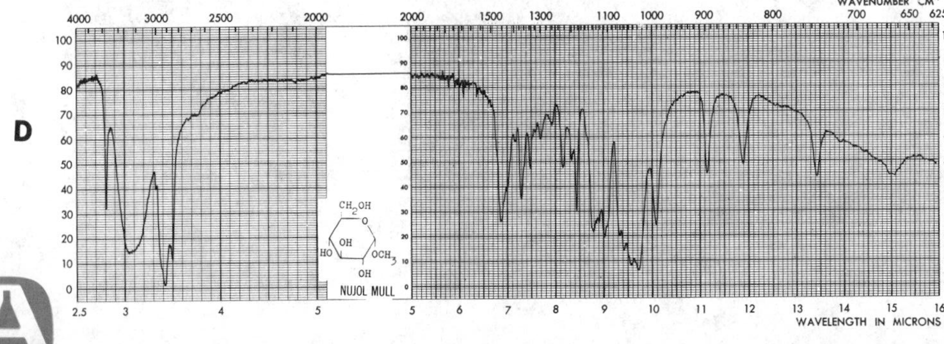

E D440-7 **2-Deoxy-D-galactose**
$HOCH_2[CH(OH)]_3CH_2CHO$ M.W. 164.16 m.p. 109-111°
NUJOL MULL

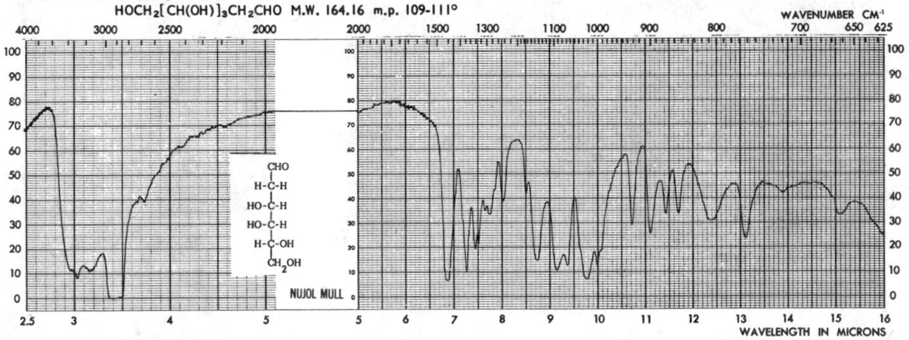

F D460-1 **2-Deoxy-D-glucose**
$HOCH_2[CH(OH)]_3CH_2CHO$ M.W. 164.16
m.p. 146-147°
NUJOL MULL

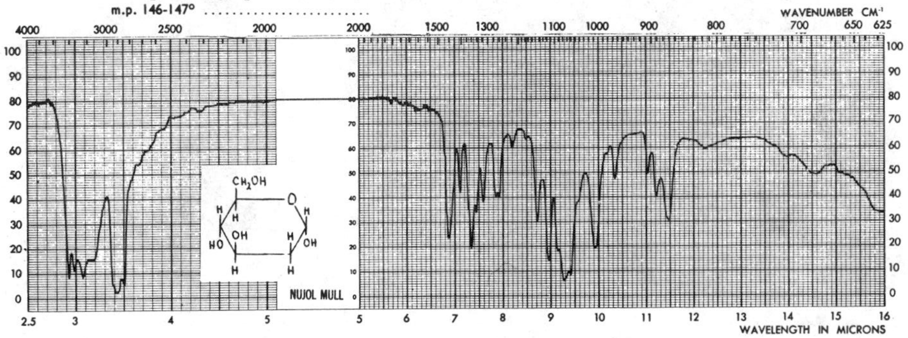

G M4710 **Methyl α-D-glucoside (methyl glucoside)**
M.W. 194.18 m.p. 166.5-170°
NUJOL MULL

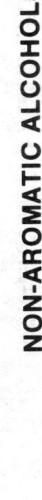

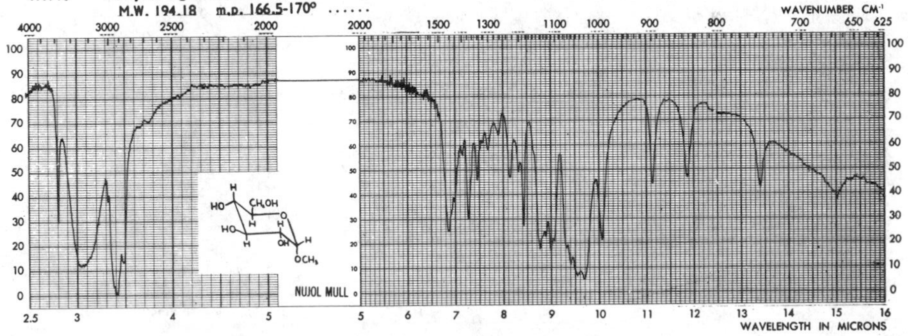

H 86,052-2
Methyl-β-D-arabinopyranoside
FW 164.16 Disp. L
NUJOL MULL

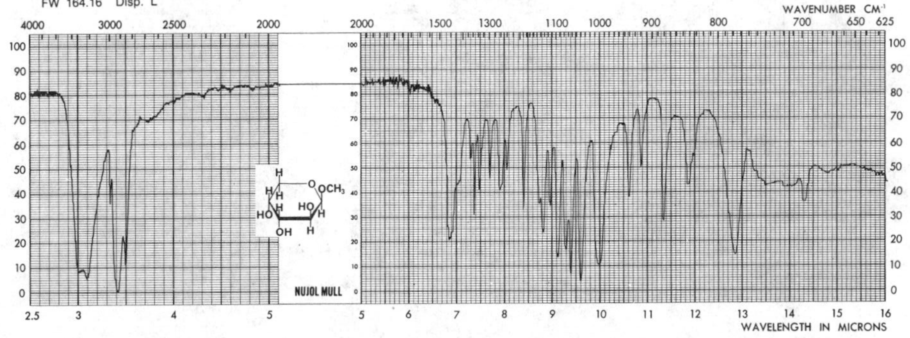

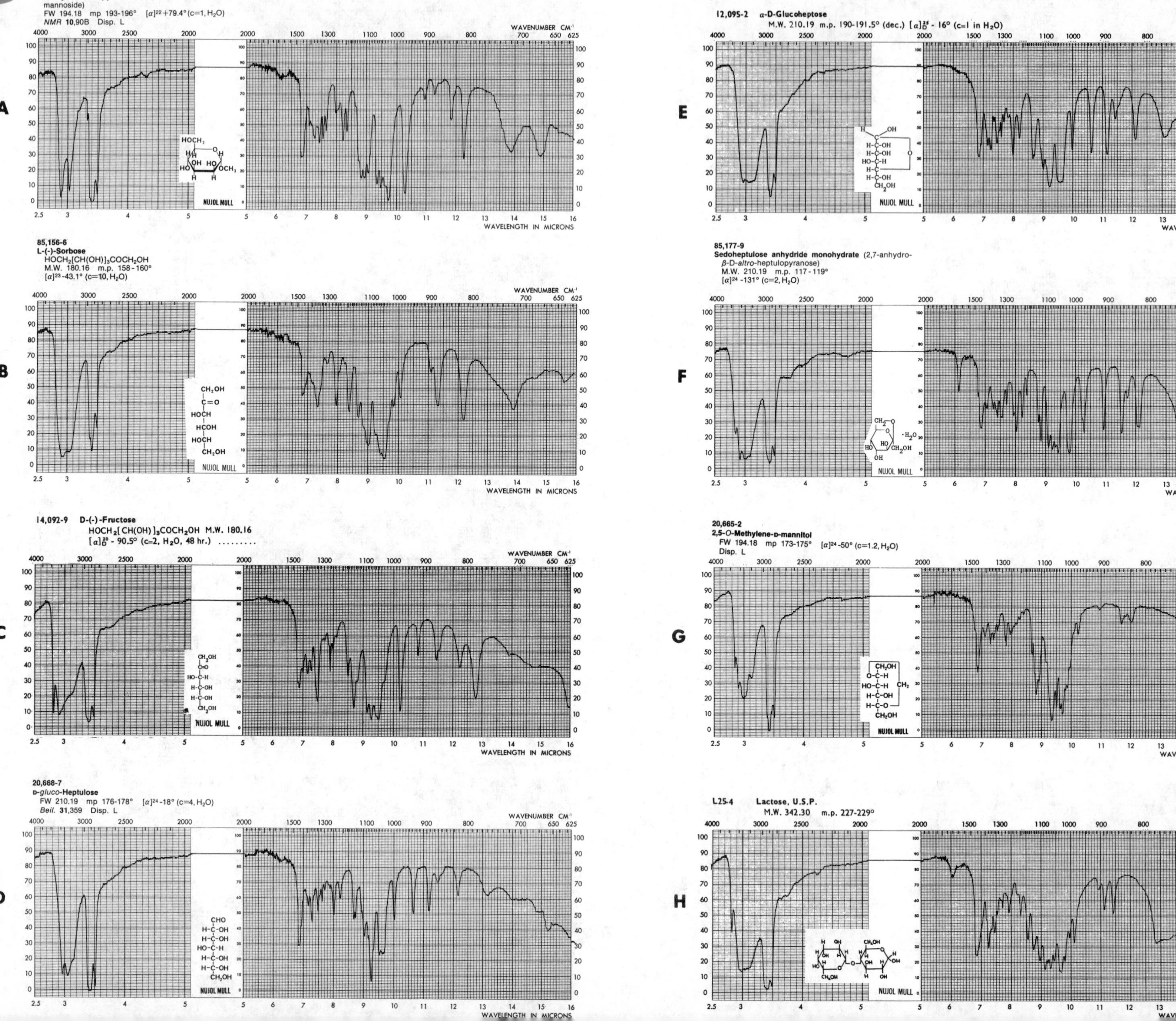
ALDRICH
A
86,026-3
α-Methyl-D-mannopyranoside, 99% (α-methyl-mannoside)
FW 194.18 mp 193-196° [α]22 +79.4° (c=1, H2O)
NMR 10,90B Disp. L
B
85,156-6
L-(-)-Sorbose
HOCH2[CH(OH)]3COCH2OH
M.W. 180.16 m.p. 158-160°
[α]23 -43.1° (c=10, H2O)
C
14,092-9 D-(-)-Fructose
HOCH2[CH(OH)]3COCH2OH M.W. 180.16
[α]20D - 90.5° (c=2, H2O, 48 hr.)
D
20,668-7
D-gluco-Heptulose
FW 210.19 mp 176-178° [α]24 -18° (c=4, H2O)
Beil. 31,359 Disp. L
E
12,095-2 α-D-Glucoheptose
M.W. 210.19 m.p. 190-191.5° (dec.) [α]25D - 16° (c=1 in H2O)
F
85,177-9
Sedoheptulose anhydride monohydrate (2,7-anhydro-β-D-altro-heptulopyranose)
M.W. 210.19 m.p. 117-119°
[α]24 -131° (c=2, H2O)
G
20,665-2
2,5-O-Methylene-D-mannitol
FW 194.18 mp 173-175° [α]24 -50° (c=1.2, H2O)
Disp. L
H
L25-4 Lactose, U.S.P.
M.W. 342.30 m.p. 227-229°
NUJOL MULL
WAVENUMBER CM-1
WAVELENGTH IN MICRONS

A

11,256-9 **D-(+)-Maltose**
M.W. 342.30 m.p. 130° (dec.

NUJOL MULL

B

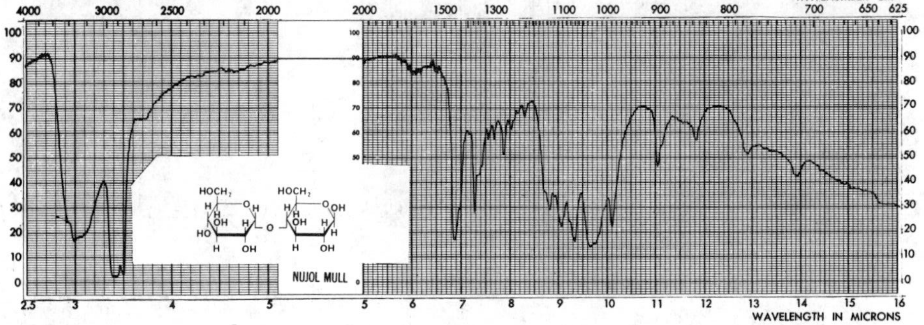

85,961-3
Maltitol, 70%, remainder moisture
M.W. 344.32 n_D^{20} 1.4722 $[\alpha]^{26}$ +77.3° (c=9.8, H_2O)

NEAT

C

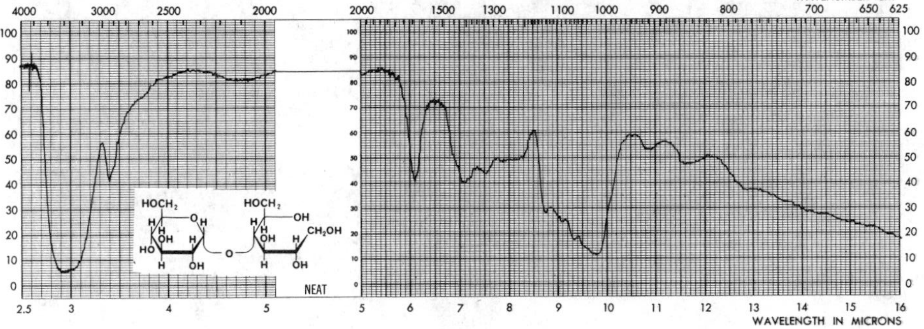

C1770-5 **D-Cellobiose (4-β-D-glucopyranosyl-D-glucopyranose)**
M.W. 342.30 m.p. 239° (dec.) $[\alpha]_D^{20}$ + 34° (c=1 in H_2O)

NUJOL MULL

D

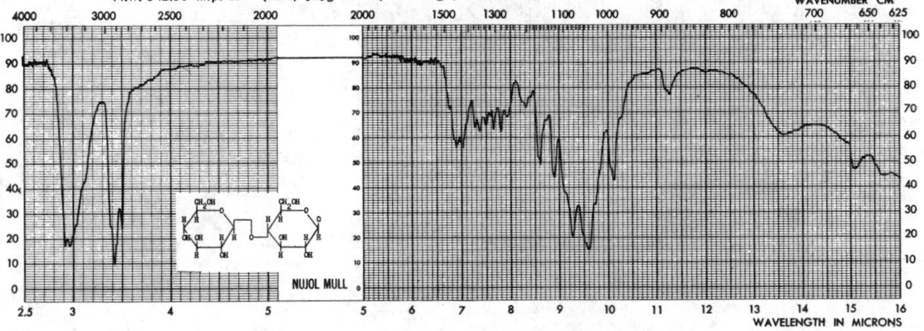

85,151-5
Palatinose (isomaltulose, 6-O-α-D-glucopyranosyl-D-fructofuranose)
M.W. 342.3 m.p. 125-128° $[\alpha]^{24}$ + 102° (c=2, H_2O)

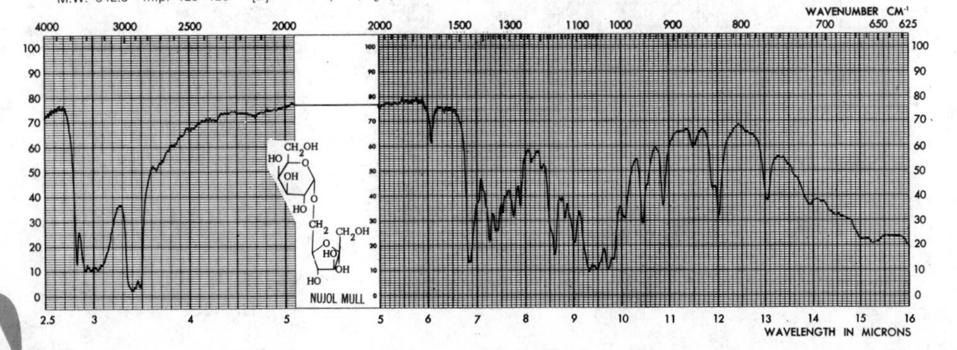

NUJOL MULL

E

85,148-5
α-Lactulose (4-O-β-D-galactopyranosyl-α-D-fructose)
M.W. 342.3 m.p. 173-178° (dec.)
$[\alpha]^{24}$ -48° (c=4, H_2O, 12 hr.)

NUJOL MULL

F

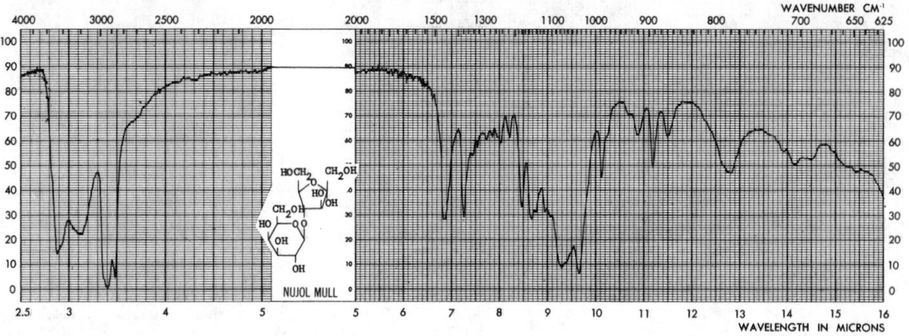

85,147-7
Isomaltose, 99% (6-O-α-D-glucopyranosyl-D-glucose)
M.W. 342.3 m.p. 92-94° $[\alpha]^{24}$ + 115° (c=3.8, H_2O)
Beil. **31**,405

NUJOL MULL

G

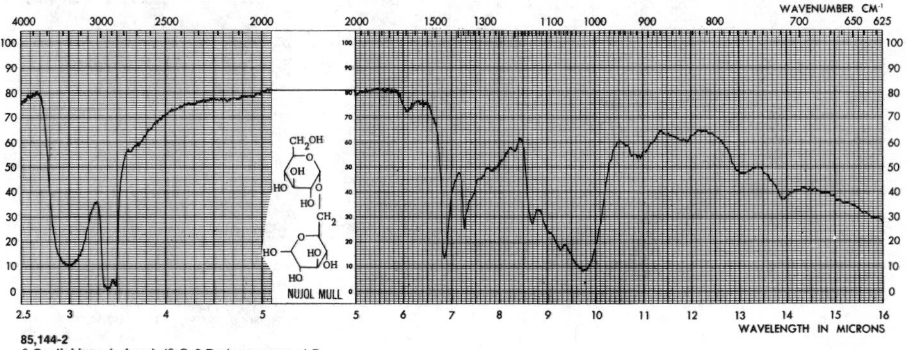

85,144-2
β-Gentiobiose (α-form) (6-O-β-D-glucopyranosyl-D-glucopyranose)
M.W. 342.3 m.p. 208-209° (dec.)
$[\alpha]^{24}$ + 11° (c=4, H_2O) Beil. **31**,397
HYGROSCOPIC

NUJOL MULL

H

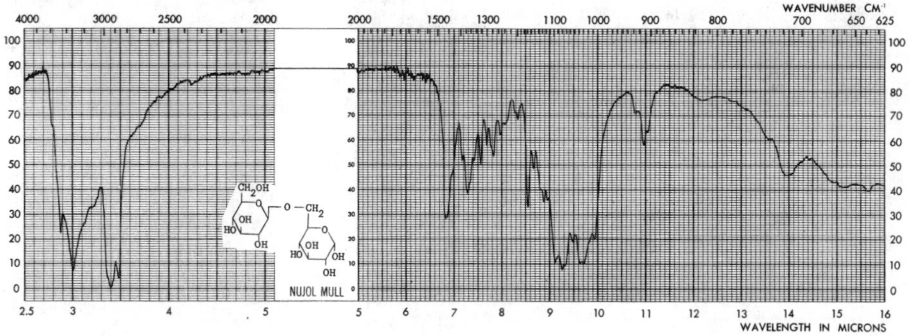

18,835-2
D-(+)-Trehalose dihydrate
FW 378.33 mp 210-211°
$[\alpha]^{22}$ +179.9° (c=7.5, H_2O) Disp. L

NUJOL MULL

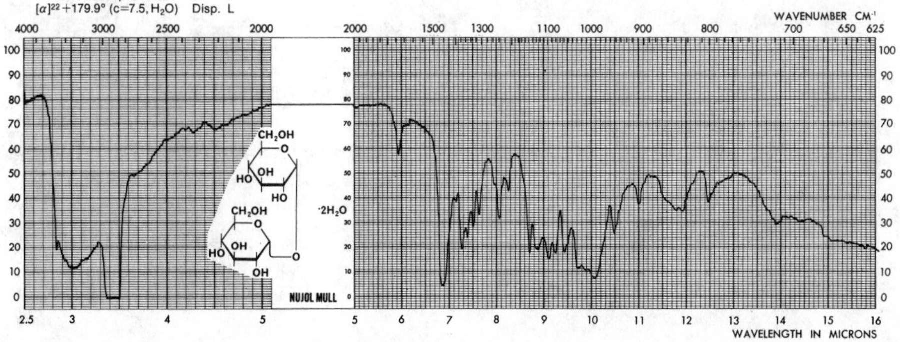

ALDRICH

A

17,994-9
Sucrose
M.W. 342.3 m.p. 190-192° (dec.) Beil. **31**,424

NUJOL MULL

B

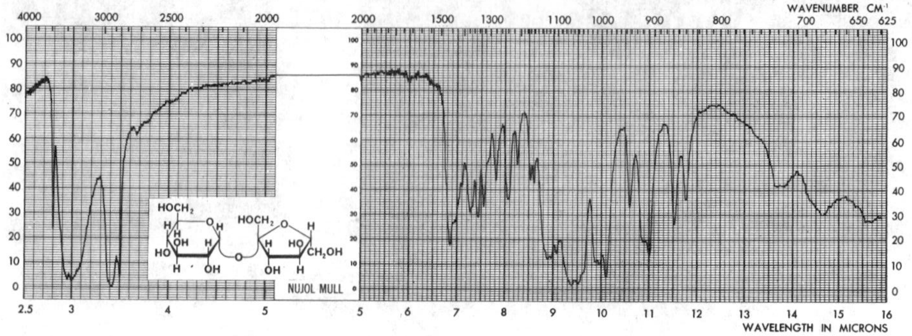

M269-1 **α-D-Melibiose** (6-α-D-galactopyranosyl-D-glucopyranose)
M.W. 342.30 m.p. 182° (dec.)

NUJOL MULL

C

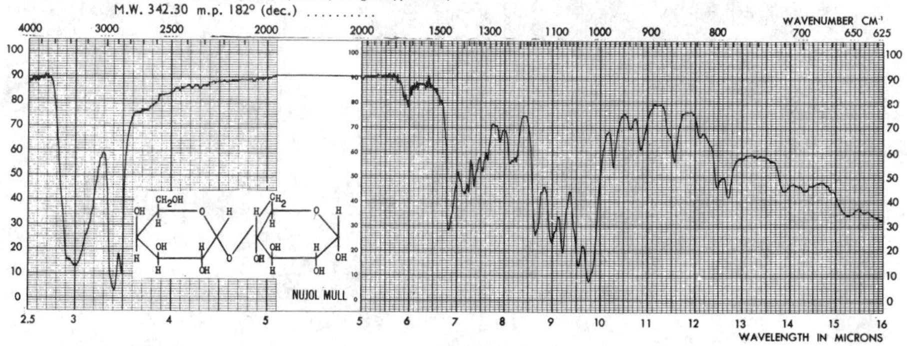

M268 **Melezitose dihydrate**
M.W. 540.47 m.p. 155° (dec.)

NUJOL MULL

D

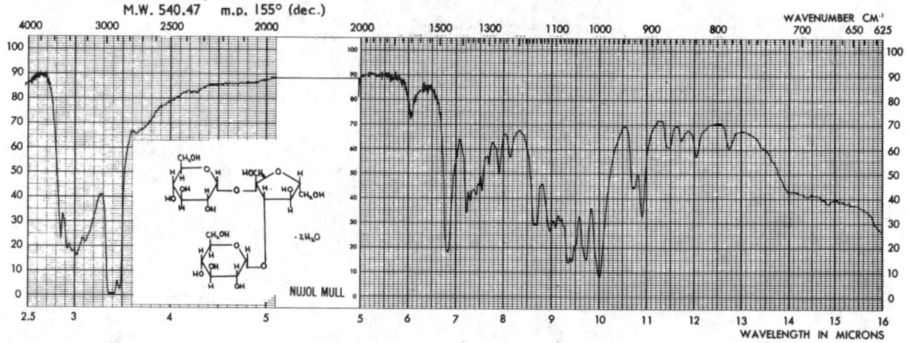

85,149-3
Maltotriose, 93% [O-α-D-glucopyranosyl-(1→4)-O-α-D-glucopyranosyl-(1→4)-O-α-D-glucose]
M.W. 504.44 m.p. 132-135°
[α]^24 +162° (c=2, H_2O)

NUJOL MULL

E

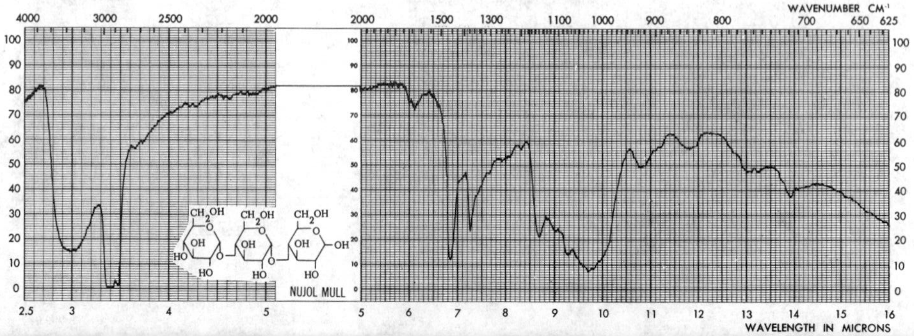

85,037-3
Melezitose dihydrate
M.W. 540.47 m.p. 160° (dec.)
[α]^23 +85.9° (c=4, H_2O) Beil. **31**,466

NUJOL MULL

F

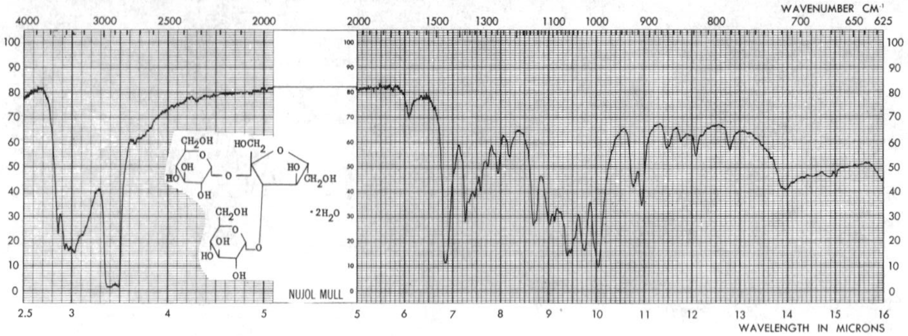

85,595-2
D-Raffinose pentahydrate
M.W. 594.52 m.p. 79-81° Beil. **31**,462

NUJOL MULL

G

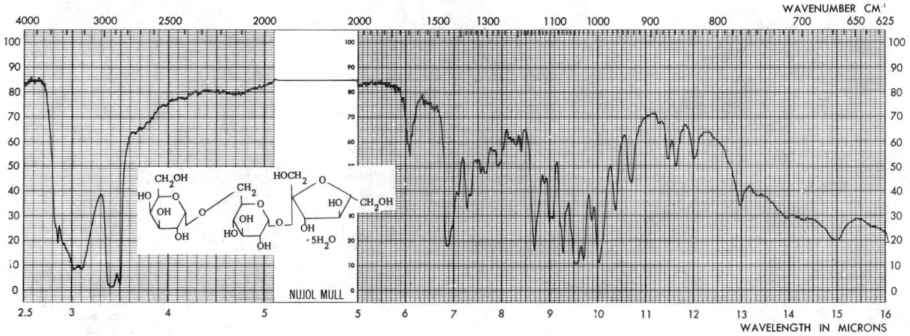

85,178-7
Stachyose tetrahydrate (α-D-galactosyl-α-D-galactosyl-α-D-glucosyl-β-D-fructose)
M.W. 738.64 m.p. 100-104°
[α]^24 +133° (c=4, H_2O)

NUJOL MULL

H

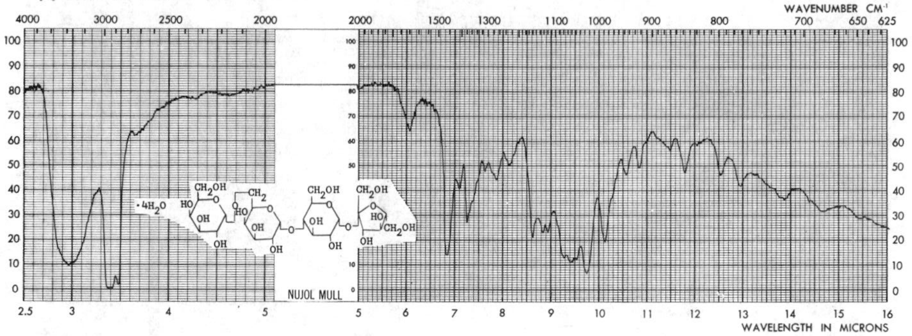

85,609-6
α-Cyclodextrin (cyclohexaamylose, α-Schardinger dextrin)
M.W. 1044.92 m.p. 278° (dec.)
[α]^25 +153° (c=1, H_2O)

NUJOL MULL

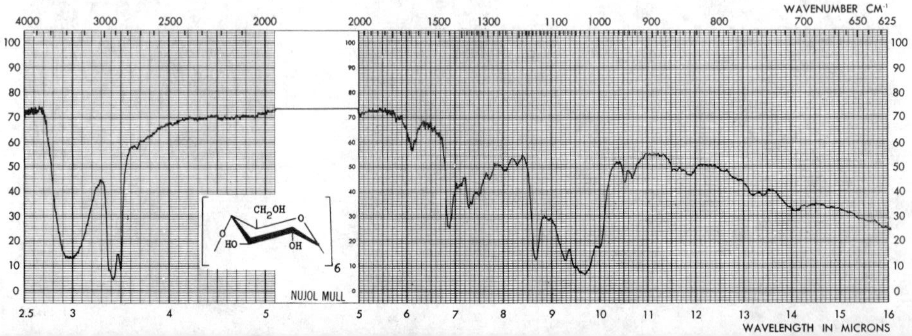

A

85,608-8
β-Cyclodextrin (cycloheptaamylose, β-Schardinger dextrin)
M.W. 1135.01 m.p. 298-300° (dec.)

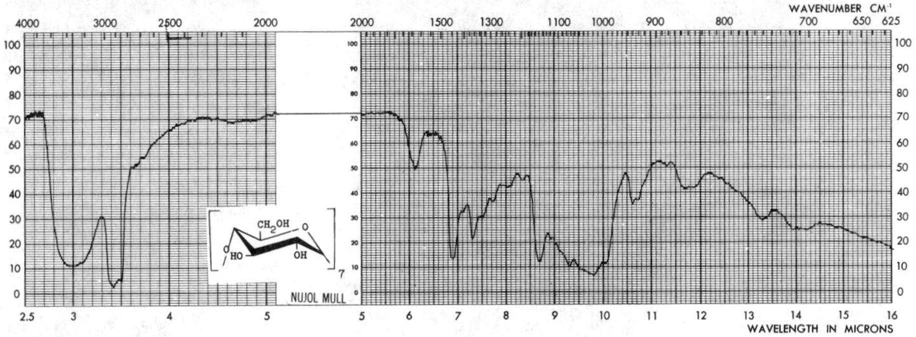

NUJOL MULL

B

86,141-3
γ-Cyclodextrin (cyclooctaamylose, γ-Schardinger dextrin)
FW 1297.15 mp 267° (dec.)
$[\alpha]_D^{}$ +17.6° (c=1, H_2O) Disp. C

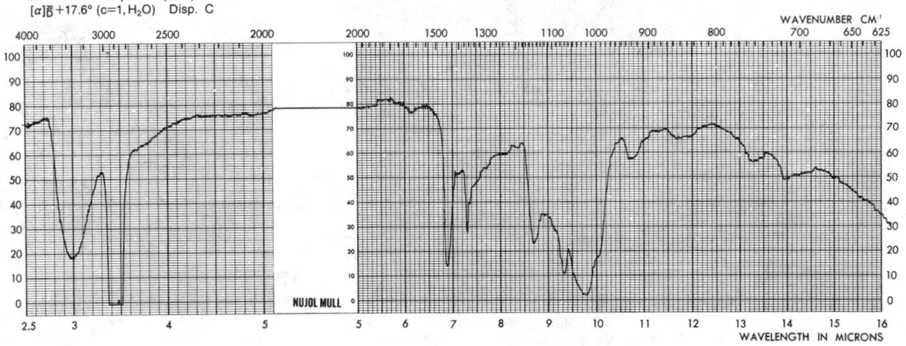

NUJOL MULL

C

85,139-6
Galactan, ex gum arabic (polygalactan)
m.p. 275° (dec.)

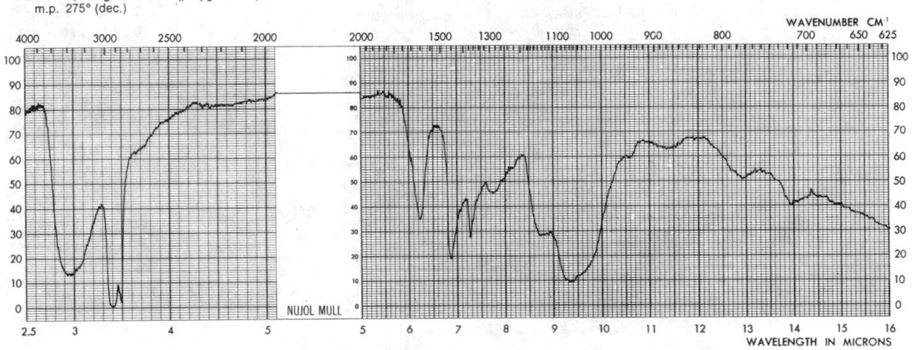

NUJOL MULL

D

85,136-1
Arabinogalactan (polyarabinogalactan)
m.p. >200° (dec.)

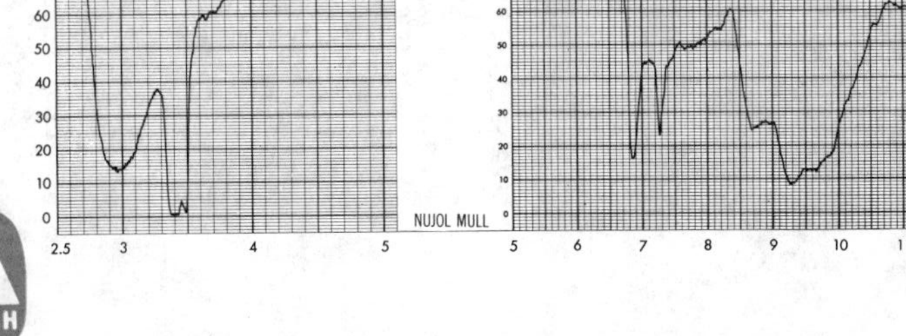

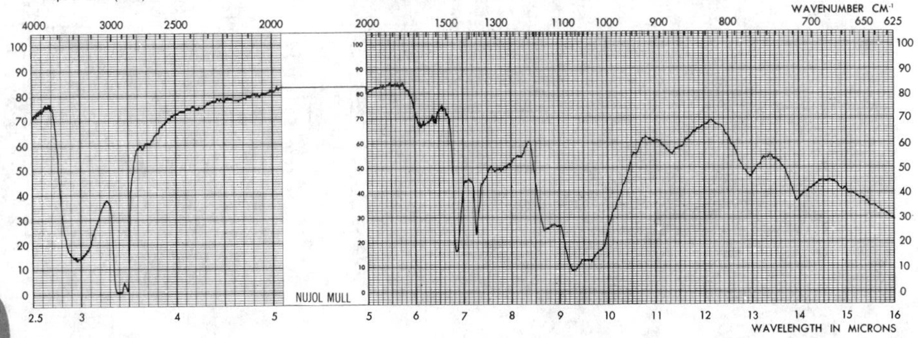

NUJOL MULL

E

85,157-4
Xylan, ex larch wood
m.p. >300°

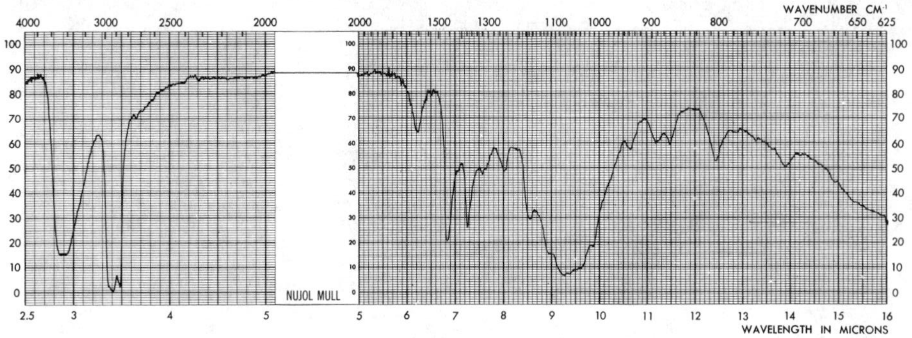

NUJOL MULL

F

85,143-4
D-Glycogen, ex mammalian liver
m.p. 255° (dec.) $[\alpha]^{24}$ +197.6° (c=0.1, H_2O)

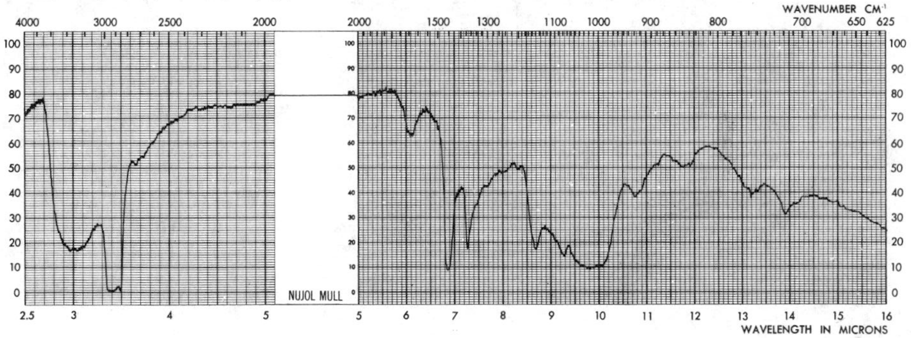

NUJOL MULL

G

17,993-0
Starch, soluble, A.C.S. reagent
m.p. 256-258° (dec.)

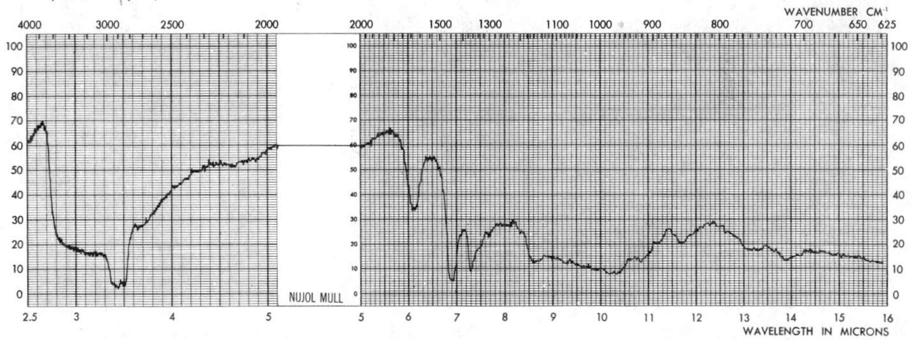

NUJOL MULL

H

D760-0 **Diacetone-D-glucose** (1,2,5,6-diisopropylidene-D-glucose)
M.W. 260.29 m.p. 105-108° $[\alpha]_D^{}$ - 18.5° (c=5 in H_2O)

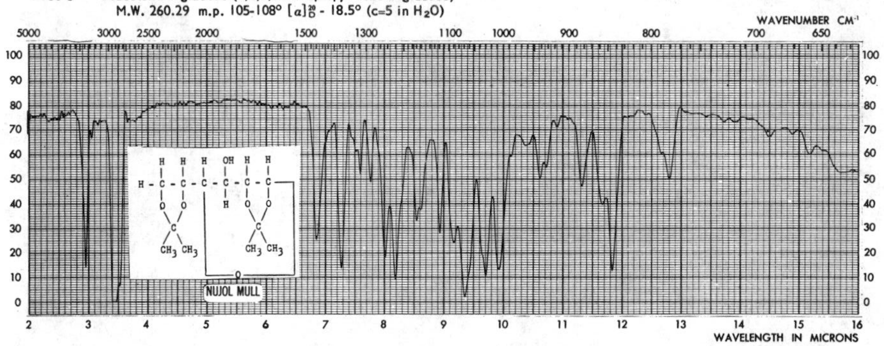

NUJOL MULL

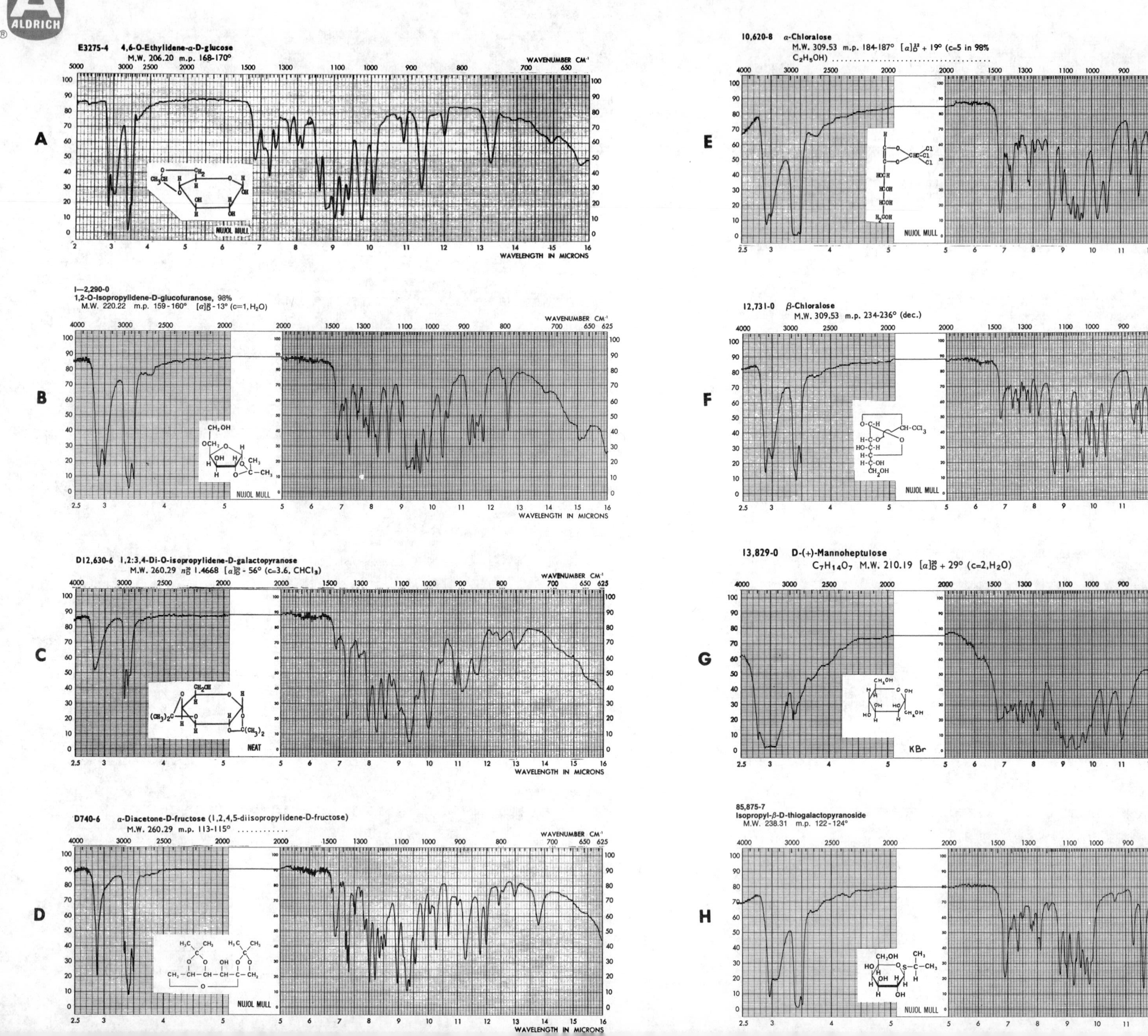
ALDRICH
A
E3275-4 4,6-O-Ethylidene-α-D-glucose
M.W. 206.20 m.p. 168-170°
NUJOL MULL
B
I—2,290-0
1,2-O-Isopropylidene-D-glucofuranose, 98%
M.W. 220.22 m.p. 159-160° [α]D - 13° (c=1, H2O)
NUJOL MULL
C
D12,630-6 1,2:3,4-Di-O-isopropylidene-D-galactopyranose
M.W. 260.29 nD 1.4668 [α]D - 56° (c=3.6, CHCl3)
NEAT
D
D740-6 α-Diacetone-D-fructose (1,2,4,5-diisopropylidene-D-fructose)
M.W. 260.29 m.p. 113-115°
NUJOL MULL
E
10,620-8 α-Chloralose
M.W. 309.53 m.p. 184-187° [α]D + 19° (c=5 in 98%
C2H5OH)
NUJOL MULL
F
12,731-0 β-Chloralose
M.W. 309.53 m.p. 234-236° (dec.)
NUJOL MULL
G
13,829-0 D-(+)-Mannoheptulose
C7H14O7 M.W. 210.19 [α]D + 29° (c=2,H2O)
KBr
H
85,875-7
Isopropyl-β-D-thiogalactopyranoside
M.W. 238.31 m.p. 122-124°
NUJOL MULL
WAVENUMBER CM⁻¹
WAVELENGTH IN MICRONS

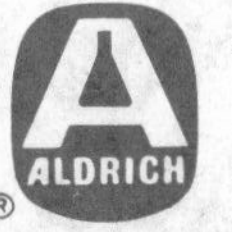

NON-AROMATIC ETHERS, ACETALS AND EPOXIDES

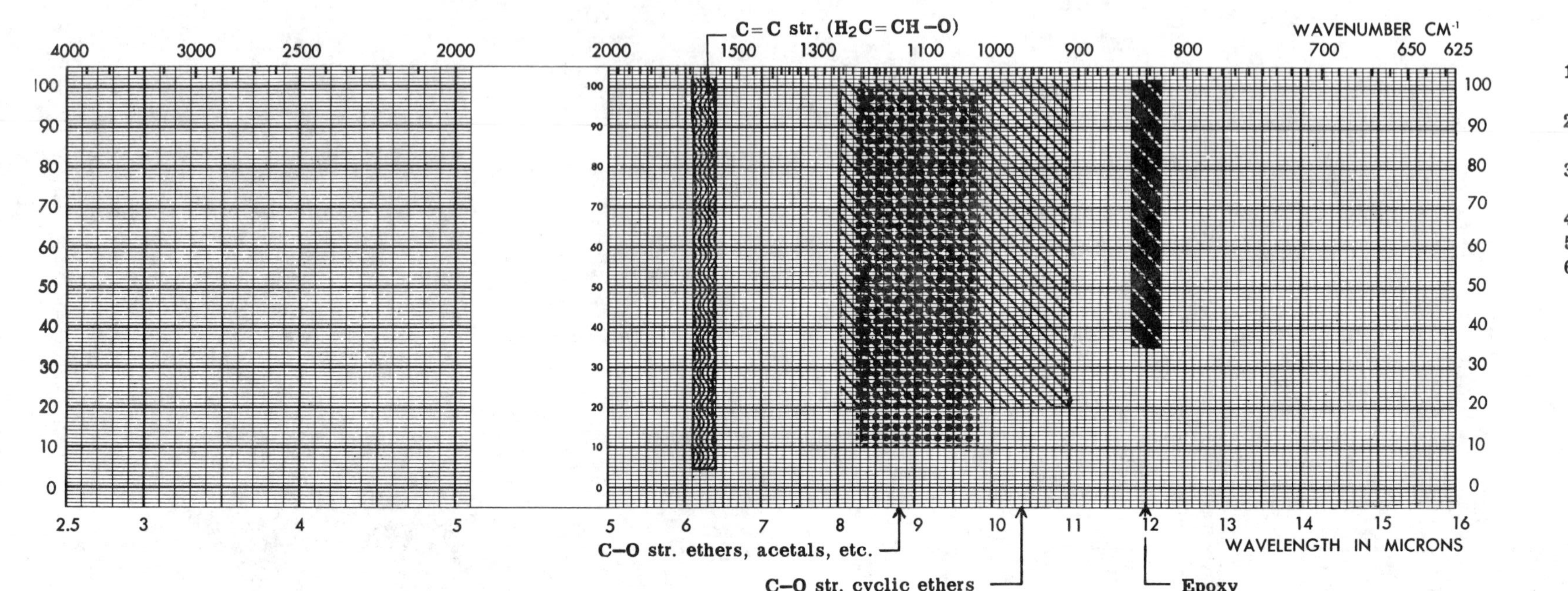

The aliphatic ethers display a strong C–O stretch absorption at 9 μ (1110 cm^{-1}), which varies only slightly from ether to ether. The absorption is quite broad and is the only characteristic absorption of the primary ether (RCH_2–O–CH_2R).

In spectra 128B-E, 129A-C see the effect of the ether oxygen attached to a vinyl group. The two absorptions of the vinyl group at 10 and 11 μ (1000 and 910 cm^{-1}) have now shifted to 10.4 μ and 12.2 μ (960 and 820 cm^{-1}) respectively. Also note that the strength of the C=C absorption at 6.2 μ (1615 cm^{-1}) approaches the intensity of a carbonyl band, and the strong ether absorption no longer appears at 9 μ (1110 cm^{-1}) but is instead shifted to 8.3 μ (1205 cm^{-1}).

The acetals and ketals absorb between 8.5 and 9.5 μ (1175 – 1055 cm^{-1}) with a much broader band displaying at least two maxima.

The C–O stretch of cyclic ethers also shows up as several bands but they are more widely separated and appear over a greater range, between 8 and 11 μ (1250 – 910 cm^{-1}), among the other skeletal vibrations of the ring. The three-membered epoxide ring C–O stretch vibration at 8 μ (1250 cm^{-1}) is weak and in a region of the spectrum where many other functional groups absorb, making it difficult to use for identification. Of more importance are the epoxy ring vibrations in the vicinity of 12 μ (835 cm^{-1}).

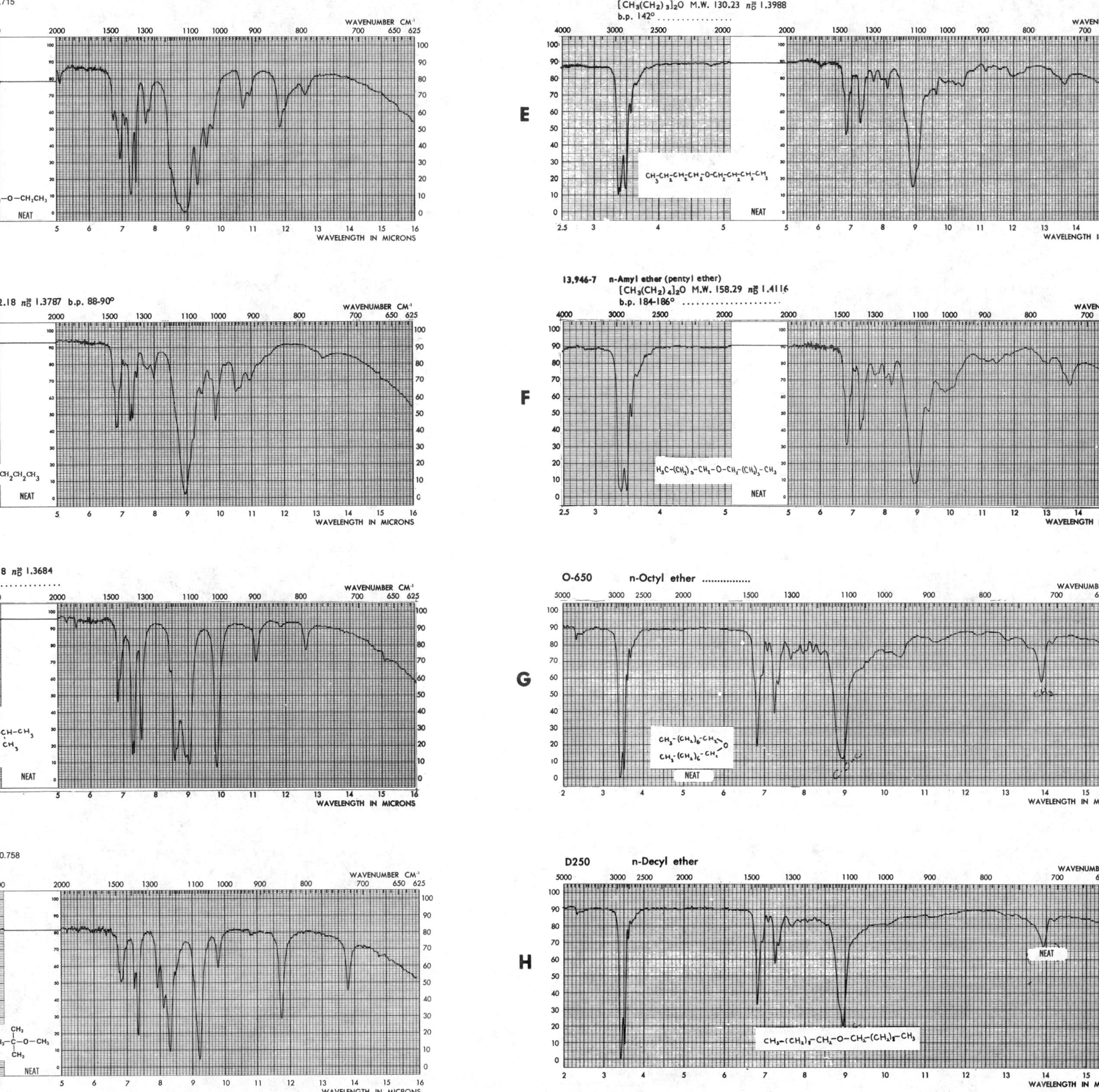
A
Ether, A.C.S. reagent, absolute (diethyl ether, ethyl ether)
$(C_2H_5)_2O$
M.W. 74.12 b.p. 34.6° n_D^{20} 1.3506 d 0.715
Beil. 1,314 IR 98A
$CH_3CH_2-O-CH_2CH_3$
NEAT
B
11,133-3 n-Propyl ether, puriss.
$(CH_3CH_2CH_2)_2O$ M.W. 102.18 n_D^{20} 1.3787 b.p. 88-90°
$CH_3CH_2CH_2-O-CH_2CH_2CH_3$
NEAT
C
13,496-1 Isopropyl ether
$[(CH_3)_2CH]_2O$ M.W. 102.18 n_D^{20} 1.3684
b.p. 68-69°
NEAT
D
17,978-7
tert.-Butyl methyl ether, 97%
$(CH_3)_3COCH_3$
M.W. 88.15 b.p. 53-56° n_D^{20} 1.3685 d 0.758
Beil. 1,381
NEAT
E
11,028-0 n-Butyl ether
$[CH_3(CH_2)_3]_2O$ M.W. 130.23 n_D^{20} 1.3988
b.p. 142°
NEAT
F
13,946-7 n-Amyl ether (pentyl ether)
$[CH_3(CH_2)_4]_2O$ M.W. 158.29 n_D^{20} 1.4116
b.p. 184-186°
NEAT
G
O-650 n-Octyl ether
NEAT
H
D250 n-Decyl ether
NEAT
WAVENUMBER CM⁻¹
WAVELENGTH IN MICRONS
ALDRICH

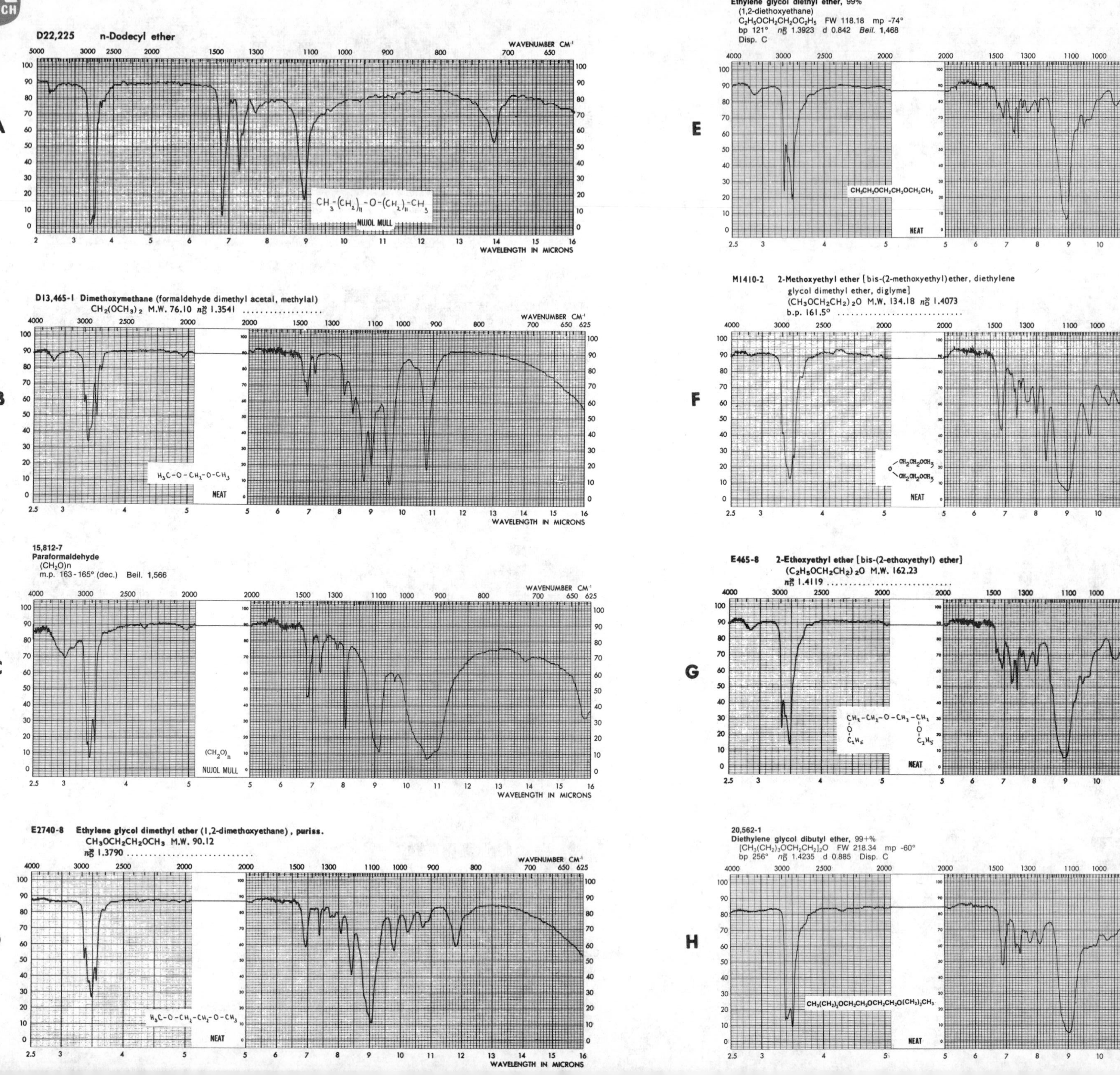
ALDRICH
A
D22,225 n-Dodecyl ether
$CH_3-(CH_2)_{11}-O-(CH_2)_{11}-CH_3$
NUJOL MULL
B
D13,465-1 Dimethoxymethane (formaldehyde dimethyl acetal, methylal)
$CH_2(OCH_3)_2$ M.W. 76.10 n_D^{20} 1.3541
$H_3C-O-CH_2-O-CH_3$
NEAT
C
15,812-7
Paraformaldehyde
$(CH_2O)n$
m.p. 163-165° (dec.) Beil. 1,566
$(CH_2O)_n$
NUJOL MULL
D
E2740-8 Ethylene glycol dimethyl ether (1,2-dimethoxyethane), puriss.
$CH_3OCH_2CH_2OCH_3$ M.W. 90.12
n_D^{20} 1.3790
$H_3C-O-CH_2-CH_2-O-CH_3$
NEAT
E
22,411-1
Ethylene glycol diethyl ether, 99%
(1,2-diethoxyethane)
$C_2H_5OCH_2CH_2OC_2H_5$ FW 118.18 mp -74°
bp 121° n_D^{20} 1.3923 d 0.842 Beil. 1,468
Disp. C
$CH_3CH_2OCH_2CH_2OCH_2CH_3$
NEAT
F
M1410-2 2-Methoxyethyl ether [bis-(2-methoxyethyl)ether, diethylene glycol dimethyl ether, diglyme]
$(CH_3OCH_2CH_2)_2O$ M.W. 134.18 n_D^{20} 1.4073
b.p. 161.5°
$O(CH_2CH_2OCH_3)_2$
NEAT
G
E465-8 2-Ethoxyethyl ether [bis-(2-ethoxyethyl) ether]
$(C_2H_5OCH_2CH_2)_2O$ M.W. 162.23
n_D^{20} 1.4119
$CH_2-CH_2-O-CH_2-CH_2$ / $O-C_2H_5$ / $O-C_2H_5$
NEAT
H
20,562-1
Diethylene glycol dibutyl ether, 99+%
$[CH_3(CH_2)_3OCH_2CH_2]_2O$ FW 218.34 mp -60°
bp 256° n_D^{20} 1.4235 d 0.885 Disp. C
$CH_3(CH_2)_3OCH_2CH_2OCH_2CH_2O(CH_2)_3CH_3$
NEAT
WAVENUMBER CM⁻¹
WAVELENGTH IN MICRONS

A

T5980-3 **Triethylene glycol dimethyl ether** [1,2-bis-(methoxyethoxy)-ethane]
$CH_3OCH_2CH_2OCH_2CH_2OCH_2CH_2OCH_3$ M.W. 178.23 n_D^{20} 1.4224
b.p. 216°

$CH_3-O-CH_2-CH_2-O-CH_2-CH_2-O-CH_2-CH_2-O-CH_3$
NEAT

B

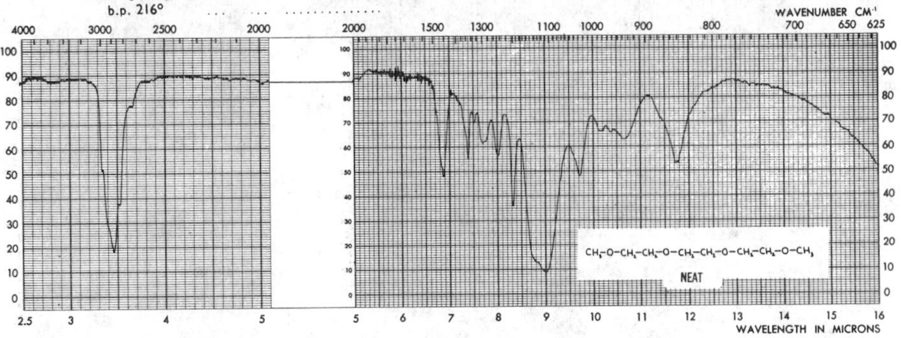

17,240-5
Tetraethylene glycol dimethyl ether, 99%
(2,5,8,11,14-pentaoxapentadecane, tetraglyme)
$CH_3(OCH_2CH_2)_4OCH_3$ FW 222.28 mp -30°
bp 275-276° n_D^{20} 1.4330 d 1.009 *Beil.* 1(3),2107
Disp. C

$CH_3OCH_2CH_2OCH_2CH_2OCH_2CH_2OCH_2CH_2OCH_3$
NEAT

C

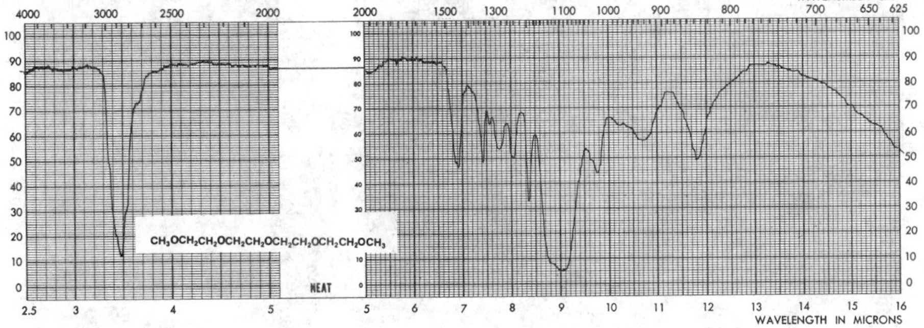

19,985-0
3,6,9,12-Tetraoxatridecanol, 95% (tetraethylene glycol monomethyl ether)
$CH_3O(CH_2CH_2O)_3CH_2CH_2OH$ FW 208.26
bp 163-166°/11mm. n_D^{20} 1.4453 d 0.987 Disp. C

$CH_3O(CH_2CH_2O)_3CH_2CH_2OH$
NEAT

D

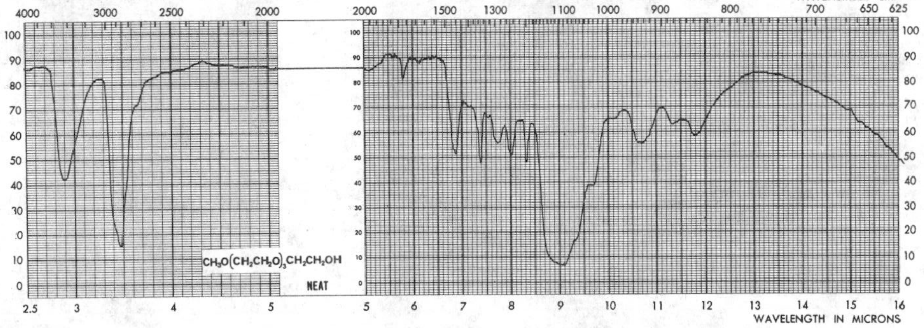

19,984-2
3,6,9,12,15-Pentaoxahexadecanol, 95+%
$CH_3O(CH_2CH_2O)_4CH_2CH_2OH$ FW 252.31
bp 130-133°/0mm. n_D^{20} 1.4500 d 0.933 Disp. C

$CH_3O(CH_2CH_2O)_4CH_2CH_2OH$
NEAT

E

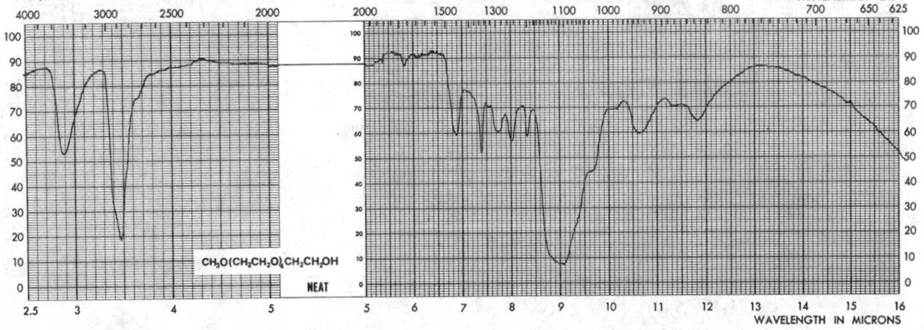

10,033-1 **Chloromethyl methyl ether**
$ClCH_2OCH_3$ M.W. 80.51 n_D^{20} 1.3961
b.p. 55-57°

$Cl-CH_2-O-CH_3$
NEAT

F

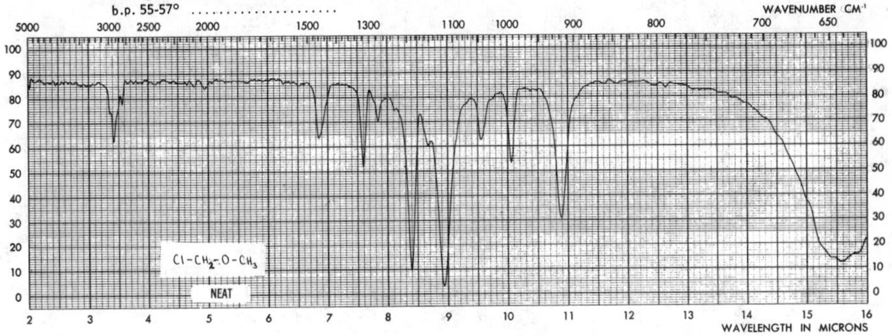

16,175-6
Bromomethyl methyl ether, tech.
$BrCH_2OCH_3$
M.W. 124.97 b.p. 87° n_D^{20} 1.4550 d 1.531
Beil. 1,582 *LACHRYMATOR*

$BrCH_2-O-CH_3$
NEAT

G

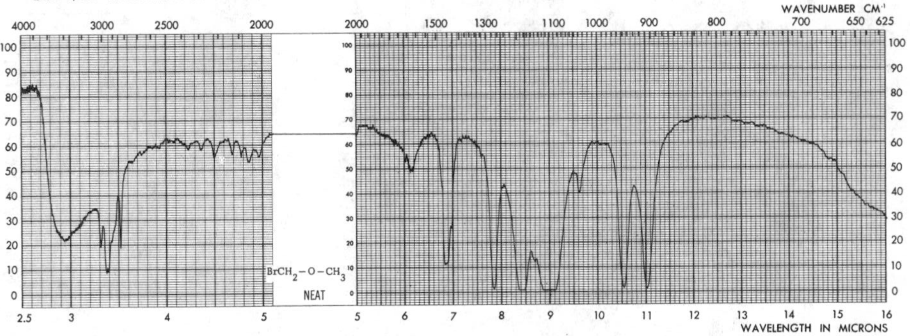

D6565-8 **α,α-Dichloromethyl methyl ether** (1,1-dichlorodimethyl ether)
Cl_2CHOCH_3 M.W. 114.96 n_D^{20} 1.4307

$H_3C-O-CH(Cl)-Cl$
NEAT

H

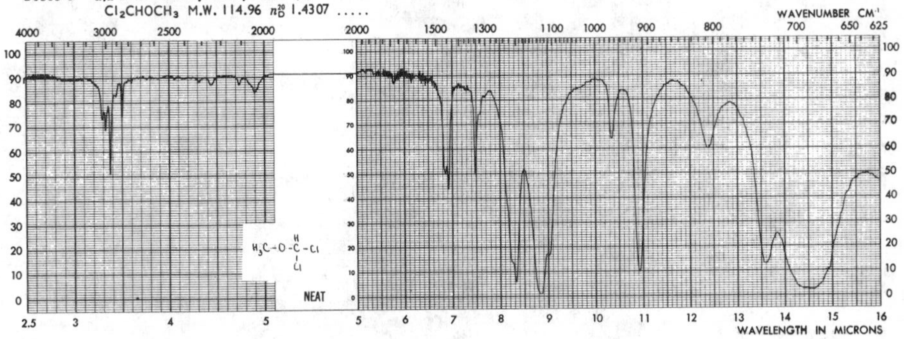

14,267-0 **Chloromethyl ethyl ether, tech.**
$C_2H_5OCH_2Cl$ M.W. 94.54 n_D^{20} 1.4030
b.p. 80-82°

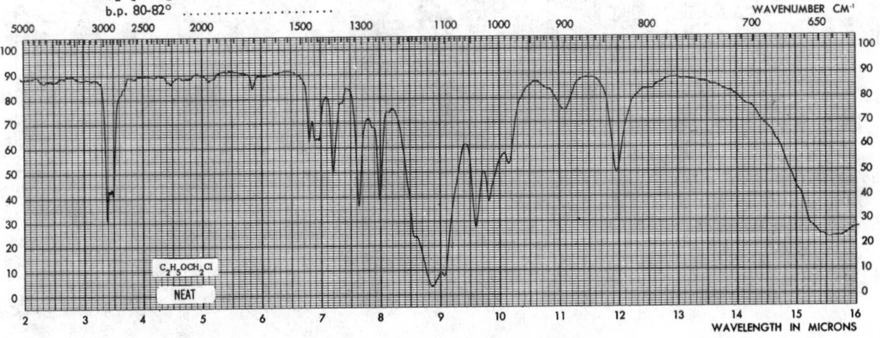

$C_2H_5OCH_2Cl$
NEAT

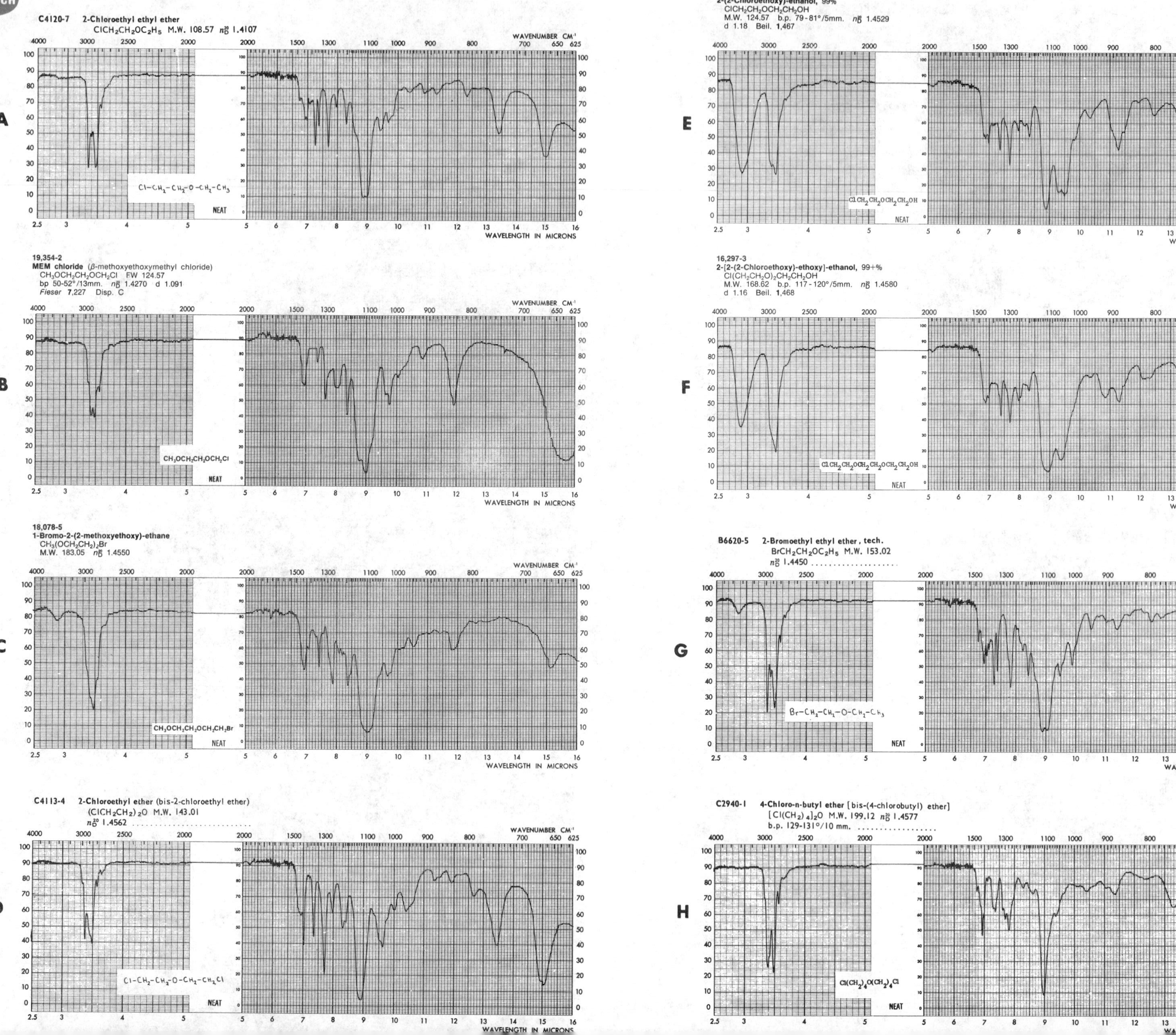

A

C4120-7 **2-Chloroethyl ethyl ether**
$ClCH_2CH_2OC_2H_5$ M.W. 108.57 n_D^{20} 1.4107

B

19,354-2
MEM chloride (β-methoxyethoxymethyl chloride)
$CH_3OCH_2CH_2OCH_2Cl$ FW 124.57
bp 50-52°/13mm. n_D^{20} 1.4270 d 1.091
Fieser **7**,227 Disp. C

C

18,078-5
1-Bromo-2-(2-methoxyethoxy)-ethane
$CH_3(OCH_2CH_2)_2Br$
M.W. 183.05 n_D^{20} 1.4550

D

C4113-4 **2-Chloroethyl ether** (bis-2-chloroethyl ether)
$(ClCH_2CH_2)_2O$ M.W. 143.01
n_D^{20} 1.4562

E

16,296-5
2-(2-Chloroethoxy)-ethanol, 99%
$ClCH_2CH_2OCH_2CH_2OH$
M.W. 124.57 b.p. 79-81°/5mm. n_D^{20} 1.4529
d 1.18 Beil. **1**,467

F

16,297-3
2-[2-(2-Chloroethoxy)-ethoxy]-ethanol, 99+%
$Cl(CH_2CH_2O)_2CH_2CH_2OH$
M.W. 168.62 b.p. 117-120°/5mm. n_D^{20} 1.4580
d 1.16 Beil. **1**,468

G

B6620-5 **2-Bromoethyl ethyl ether, tech.**
$BrCH_2CH_2OC_2H_5$ M.W. 153.02
n_D^{20} 1.4450

H

C2940-1 **4-Chloro-n-butyl ether** [bis-(4-chlorobutyl) ether]
$[Cl(CH_2)_4]_2O$ M.W. 199.12 n_D^{20} 1.4577
b.p. 129-131°/10 mm.

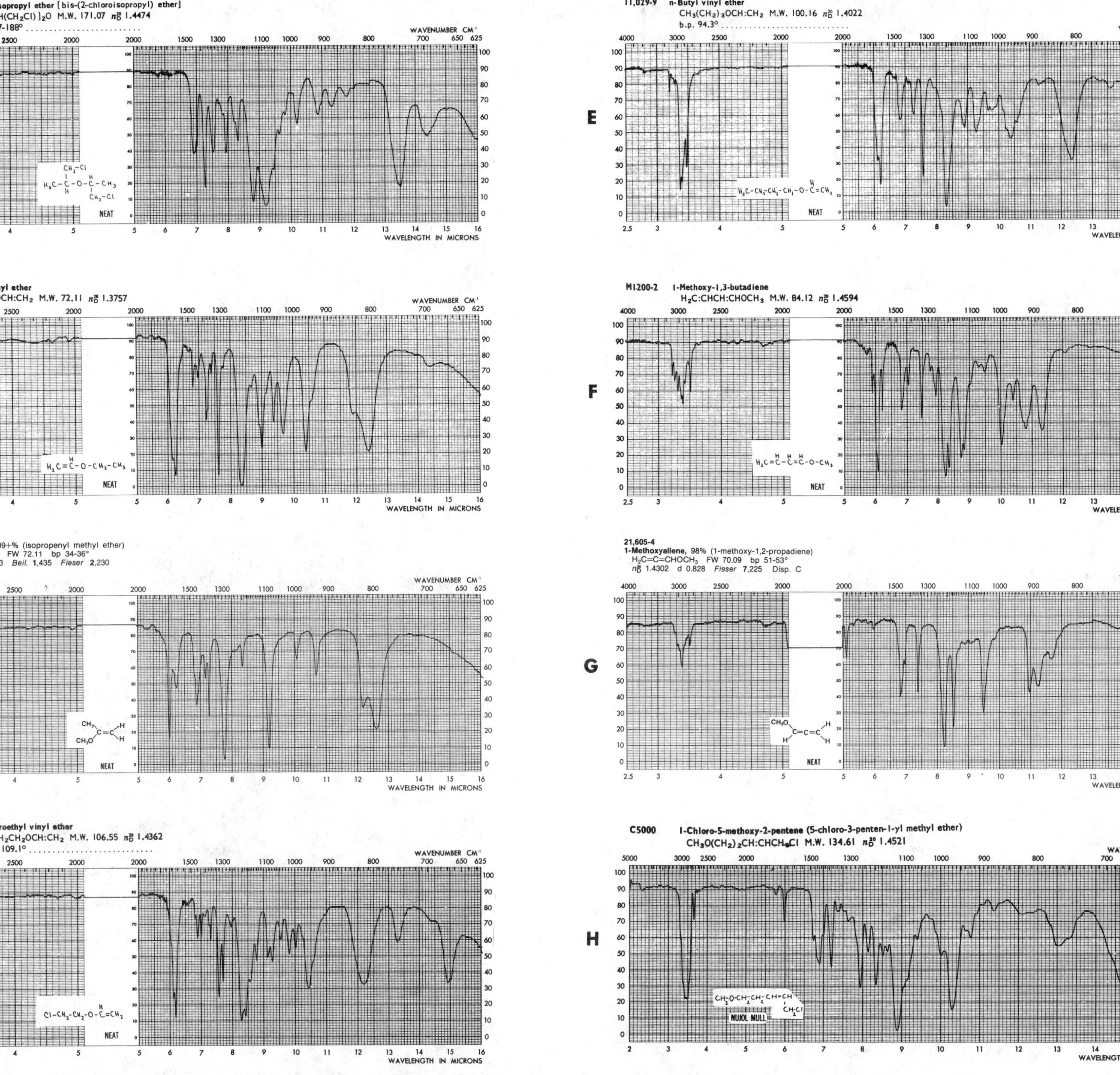
A
13,296-9 2-Chloroisopropyl ether [bis-(2-chloroisopropyl) ether]
$[CH_3CH(CH_2Cl)]_2O$ M.W. 171.07 n_D^{20} 1.4474
b.p. 187-188°
NEAT
B
E5125-2 Ethyl vinyl ether
$C_2H_5OCH{:}CH_2$ M.W. 72.11 n_D^{20} 1.3757
NEAT
C
17,464-5
2-Methoxypropene, 99+% (isopropenyl methyl ether)
$CH_3C(OCH_3){=}CH_2$ FW 72.11 bp 34-36°
n_D^{20} 1.3820 d 0.753 Beil. 1,435 Fieser 2,230
5,360 Disp. C
NEAT
D
10,998-3 2-Chloroethyl vinyl ether
$ClCH_2CH_2OCH{:}CH_2$ M.W. 106.55 n_D^{20} 1.4362
b.p. 109.1°
NEAT
E
11,029-9 n-Butyl vinyl ether
$CH_3(CH_2)_3OCH{:}CH_2$ M.W. 100.16 n_D^{20} 1.4022
b.p. 94.3°
NEAT
F
M1200-2 1-Methoxy-1,3-butadiene
$H_2C{:}CHCH{:}CHOCH_3$ M.W. 84.12 n_D^{20} 1.4594
NEAT
G
21,605-4
1-Methoxyallene, 98% (1-methoxy-1,2-propadiene)
$H_2C{=}C{=}CHOCH_3$ FW 70.09 bp 51-53°
n_D^{20} 1.4302 d 0.828 Fieser 7,225 Disp. C
NEAT
H
C5000 1-Chloro-5-methoxy-2-pentene (5-chloro-3-penten-1-yl methyl ether)
$CH_3O(CH_2)_2CH{:}CHCH_2Cl$ M.W. 134.61 n_D^{20} 1.4521
NUJOL MULL
WAVENUMBER CM⁻¹
WAVELENGTH IN MICRONS

ALDRICH

NON-AROMATIC ETHERS, ACETALS AND EPOXIDES

ALDRICH®

A 12,331-5 **1,4-Bis-(vinyloxy)-butane**
$H_2C{:}CHO(CH_2)_4OCH{:}CH_2$ M.W. 142.20 n_D^{20} 1.4406
b.p. 62-64°/10 mm.

B 13,954-8 **2-Vinyloxyethyl ether** (diethylene glycol divinyl ether)
$(H_2C{:}CHOCH_2CH_2)_2O$ M.W. 158.20 n_D^{20} 1.4464
b.p. 85°/12 mm.

C 15,646-9
3,6,9,12,15-Pentaoxa-1-heptadecene
$C_2H_5O(CH_2CH_2O)_4CH{=}CH_2$
M.W. 248.32 b.p. 296° n_D^{20} 1.4432

D 18,623-6
Acetaldehyde dimethyl acetal (dimethylacetal)
$CH_3CH(OCH_3)_2$
M.W. 90.12 d 0.826

E A90-2 **Acetal** (acetaldehyde diethyl acetal)
$CH_3CH(OC_2H_5)_2$ M.W. 118.17
n_D^{20} 1.3834

F 20,972-4
Glycolaldehyde diethyl acetal, 98%
(2,2-diethoxyethanol)
$HOCH_2CH(OC_2H_5)_2$ FW 134.18 bp 167°
n_D^{20} 1.4160 d 0.957 *Beil.* 1,818 Disp. C

G 16,403-8
Methoxyacetaldehyde dimethyl acetal
$CH_3OCH_2CH(OCH_3)_2$
M.W. 120.15 n_D^{20} 1.3920 d 0.932

H 14,930-6 **Methoxyacetaldehyde diethyl acetal, tech**
$CH_3OCH_2CH(OC_2H_5)_2$ M.W. 148.20
n_D^{20} 1.3990 b.p. 144-148°

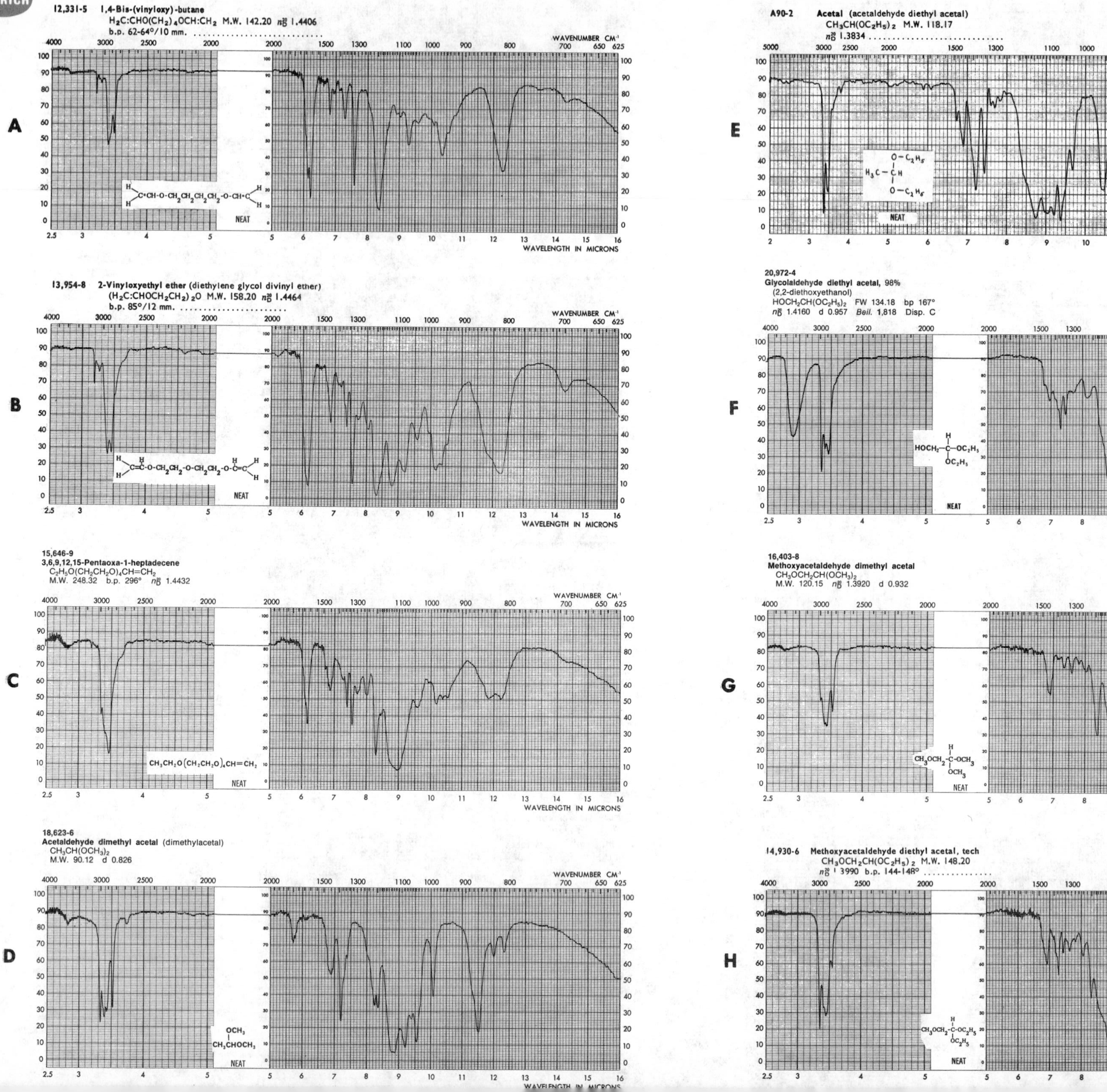

A 17,695-8
Propionaldehyde diethyl acetal, 99%
$C_2H_5CH(OC_2H_5)_2$
M.W. 132.2 b.p. 122.8° n_D^{20} 1.3884 d 0.815
Beil. 1,630

B E750-9 **3-Ethoxypropionaldehyde diethyl acetal (1,1,3-triethoxypropane)**
$C_2H_5OCH_2CH_2CH(OC_2H_5)_2$ M.W. 176.26
n_D^{20} 1.4060

C M1300-9 **3-Methoxybutyraldehyde dimethyl acetal (1,1,3-trimethoxybutane)**
$CH_3CH(OCH_3)CH_2CH(OCH_3)_2$ M.W. 148.20 n_D^{20} 1.4032
b.p. 157°

D 19,788-2
1,3,3-Trimethoxybutane, 98% (4-methoxy-2-butanone dimethyl acetal)
$CH_3C(OCH_3)_2CH_2CH_2OCH_3$ FW 148.20
bp 61-63°/20mm. n_D^{20} 1.4096 d 0.940
Beil. 1(3),3214 Disp. C

E 10,845-6 **Trimethyl orthoformate**
$CH(OCH_3)_3$ M.W. 106.12 n_D^{20} 1.3790
b.p. 99-102°

F 21,705-0
2-Methoxy-1,3-dioxolane, 99%
FW 104.11 bp 129-130° n_D^{20} 1.4091 d 1.092
Beil. 19(4),617 Disp. C

G T6045-3 **Triethyl orthoformate**
$CH(OC_2H_5)_3$ M.W. 148.20 n_D^{20} 1.3903
b.p. 146°

H 11,978-4 **Triallyl orthoformate**
$HC(OCH_2CH:CH_2)_3$ M.W. 184.24 n_D^{20} 1.4380
b.p. 192°

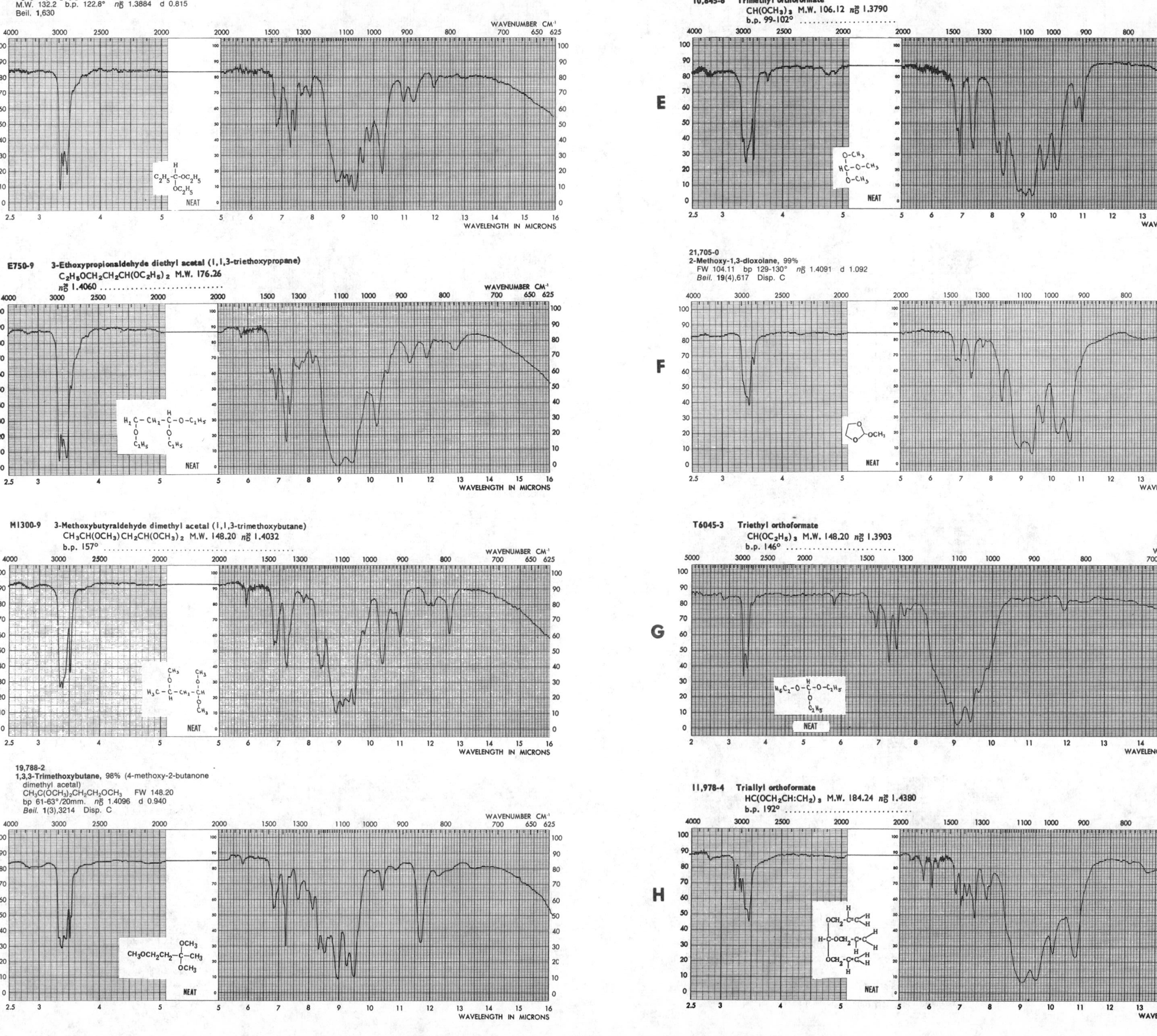

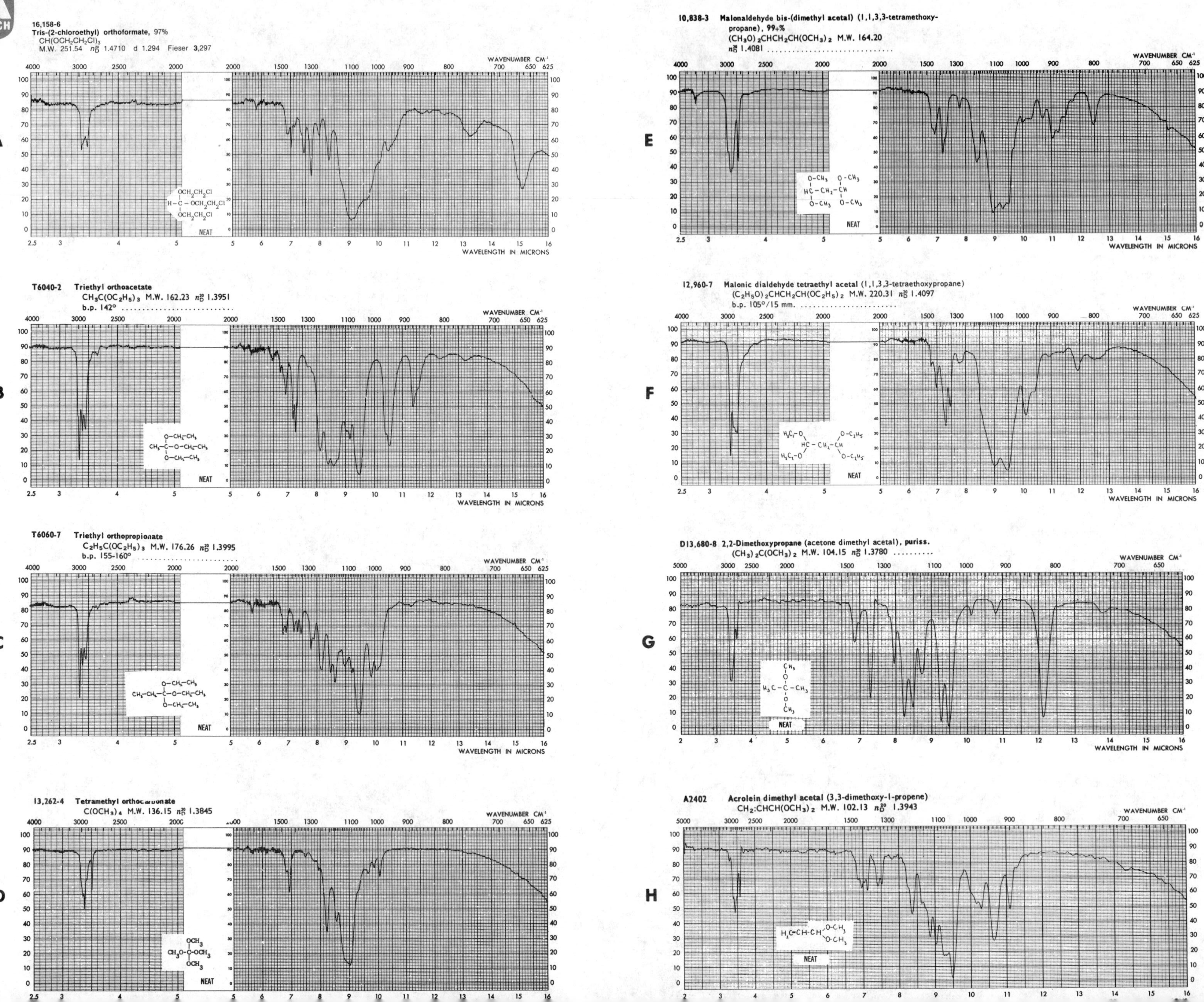
ALDRICH
A
16,158-6
Tris-(2-chloroethyl) orthoformate, 97%
$CH(OCH_2CH_2Cl)_3$
M.W. 251.54 n_D^{20} 1.4710 d 1.294 Fieser 3,297
NEAT
B
T6040-2 Triethyl orthoacetate
$CH_3C(OC_2H_5)_3$ M.W. 162.23 n_D^{20} 1.3951
b.p. 142°
NEAT
C
T6060-7 Triethyl orthopropionate
$C_2H_5C(OC_2H_5)_3$ M.W. 176.26 n_D^{20} 1.3995
b.p. 155-160°
NEAT
D
13,262-4 Tetramethyl orthocarbonate
$C(OCH_3)_4$ M.W. 136.15 n_D^{20} 1.3845
NEAT
E
10,838-3 Malonaldehyde bis-(dimethyl acetal) (1,1,3,3-tetramethoxypropane), 99+%
$(CH_3O)_2CHCH_2CH(OCH_3)_2$ M.W. 164.20
n_D^{20} 1.4081
NEAT
F
12,960-7 Malonic dialdehyde tetraethyl acetal (1,1,3,3-tetraethoxypropane)
$(C_2H_5O)_2CHCH_2CH(OC_2H_5)_2$ M.W. 220.31 n_D^{20} 1.4097
b.p. 105°/15 mm.
NEAT
G
D13,680-8 2,2-Dimethoxypropane (acetone dimethyl acetal), puriss.
$(CH_3)_2C(OCH_3)_2$ M.W. 104.15 n_D^{20} 1.3780
NEAT
H
A2402 Acrolein dimethyl acetal (3,3-dimethoxy-1-propene)
$CH_2:CHCH(OCH_3)_2$ M.W. 102.13 n_D^{20} 1.3943
NEAT
WAVENUMBER CM⁻¹
WAVELENGTH IN MICRONS

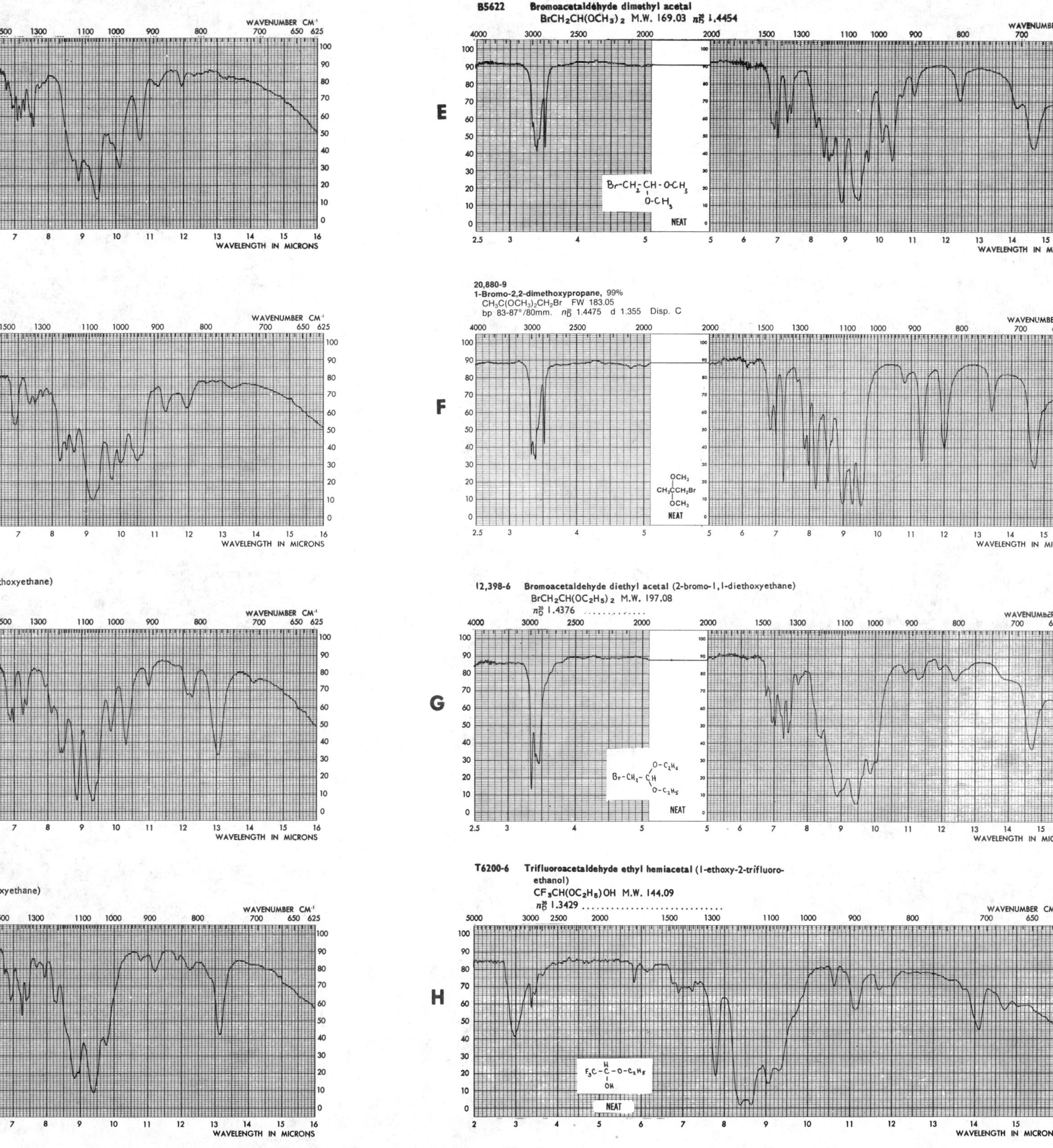

A2400-1 Acrolein diethyl acetal (3,3-diethoxy-1-propene)
$H_2C{:}CHCH(OC_2H_5)_2$ M.W. 130.19
n_D^{20} 1.4000
16,341-4
2,5-Dimethoxytetrahydro-2-furaldehyde dimethyl acetal, 98%
M.W. 206.24 n_D^{20} 1.4340
C1940-6 Chloroacetaldehyde dimethyl acetal (2-chloro-1,1-dimethoxyethane)
$ClCH_2CH(OCH_3)_2$ M.W. 124.57
n_D^{20} 1.4131
C1920-1 Chloroacetaldehyde diethyl acetal (2-chloro-1,1-diethoxyethane)
$ClCH_2CH(OC_2H_5)_2$ M.W. 152.62 n_D^{20} 1.4157
B5622 Bromoacetaldehyde dimethyl acetal
$BrCH_2CH(OCH_3)_2$ M.W. 169.03 n_D^{20} 1.4454
20,880-9
1-Bromo-2,2-dimethoxypropane, 99%
$CH_3C(OCH_3)_2CH_2Br$ FW 183.05
bp 83-87°/80mm. n_D^{20} 1.4475 d 1.355 Disp. C
12,398-6 Bromoacetaldehyde diethyl acetal (2-bromo-1,1-diethoxyethane)
$BrCH_2CH(OC_2H_5)_2$ M.W. 197.08
n_D^{20} 1.4376
T6200-6 Trifluoroacetaldehyde ethyl hemiacetal (1-ethoxy-2-trifluoro-ethanol)
$CF_3CH(OC_2H_5)OH$ M.W. 144.09
n_D^{20} 1.3429
A
B
C
D
E
F
G
H
NEAT
WAVENUMBER CM⁻¹
WAVELENGTH IN MICRONS
ALDRICH

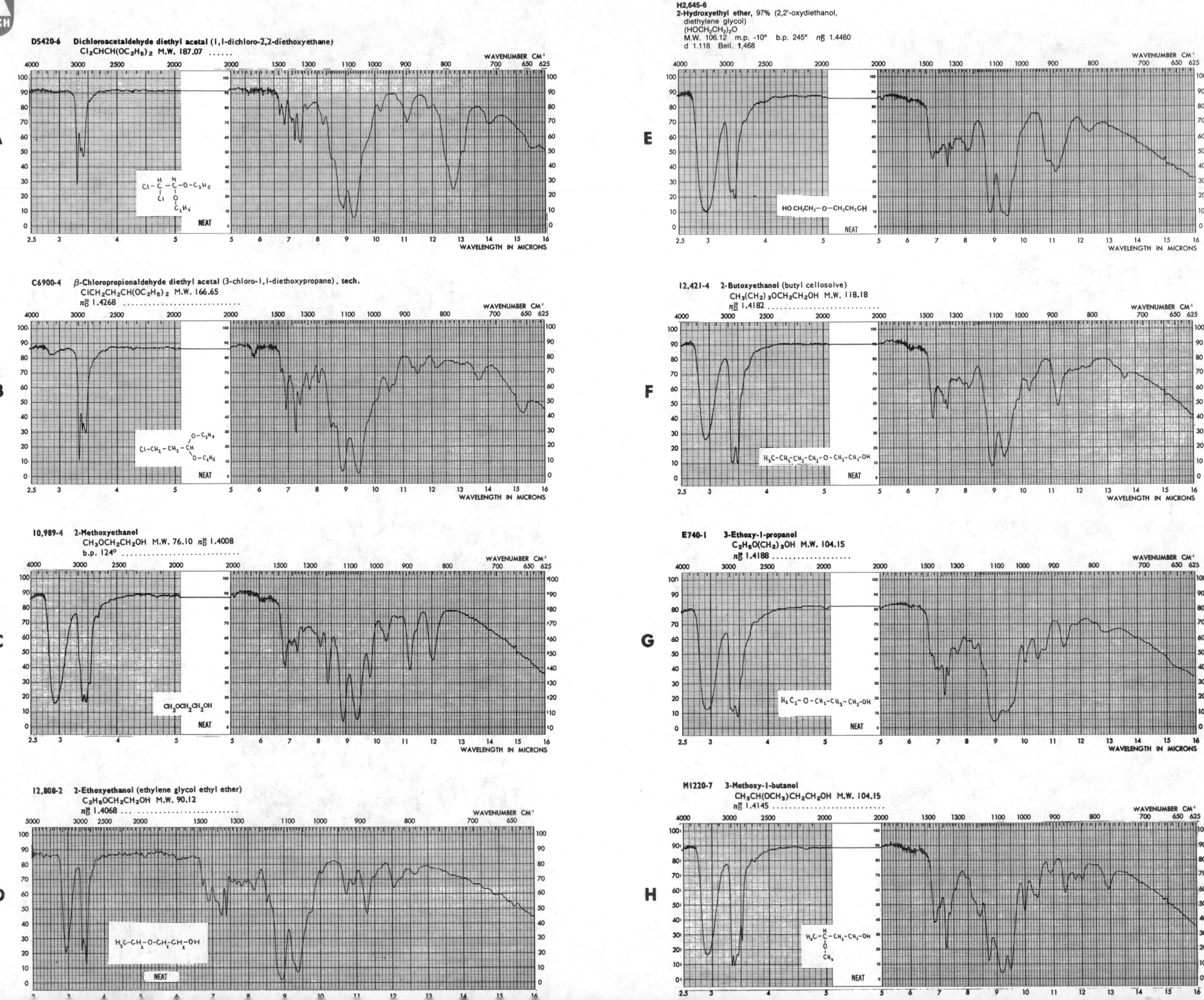
ALDRICH
A
D5420-6 Dichloroacetaldehyde diethyl acetal (1,1-dichloro-2,2-diethoxyethane)
$Cl_2CHCH(OC_2H_5)_2$ M.W. 187.07
Cl–C(H)(Cl)–C(H)–O–C₂H₅ / O–C₂H₅
NEAT
B
C6900-4 β-Chloropropionaldehyde diethyl acetal (3-chloro-1,1-diethoxypropane), tech.
$ClCH_2CH_2CH(OC_2H_5)_2$ M.W. 166.65
n_D^{20} 1.4268
Cl–CH₂–CH₂–CH(O–C₂H₅)(O–C₂H₅)
NEAT
C
10,989-4 2-Methoxyethanol
$CH_3OCH_2CH_2OH$ M.W. 76.10 n_D^{20} 1.4008
b.p. 124°
$CH_3OCH_2CH_2OH$
NEAT
D
12,808-2 2-Ethoxyethanol (ethylene glycol ethyl ether)
$C_2H_5OCH_2CH_2OH$ M.W. 90.12
n_D^{20} 1.4068
H₃C–CH₂–O–CH₂–CH₂–OH
NEAT
E
H2,645-6
2-Hydroxyethyl ether, 97% (2,2'-oxydiethanol, diethylene glycol)
$(HOCH_2CH_2)_2O$
M.W. 106.12 m.p. -10° b.p. 245° n_D^{20} 1.4460
d 1.118 Beil. 1,468
HOCH₂CH₂–O–CH₂CH₂OH
NEAT
F
12,421-4 2-Butoxyethanol (butyl cellosolve)
$CH_3(CH_2)_3OCH_2CH_2OH$ M.W. 118.18
n_D^{20} 1.4182
H₃C–CH₂–CH₂–CH₂–O–CH₂–CH₂–OH
NEAT
G
E740-1 3-Ethoxy-1-propanol
$C_2H_5O(CH_2)_3OH$ M.W. 104.15
n_D^{20} 1.4188
H₅C₂–O–CH₂–CH₂–CH₂–OH
NEAT
H
M1220-7 3-Methoxy-1-butanol
$CH_3CH(OCH_3)CH_2CH_2OH$ M.W. 104.15
n_D^{20} 1.4145
H₃C–C(H)(O–CH₃)–CH₂–CH₂–OH
NEAT
WAVENUMBER CM⁻¹
WAVELENGTH IN MICRONS

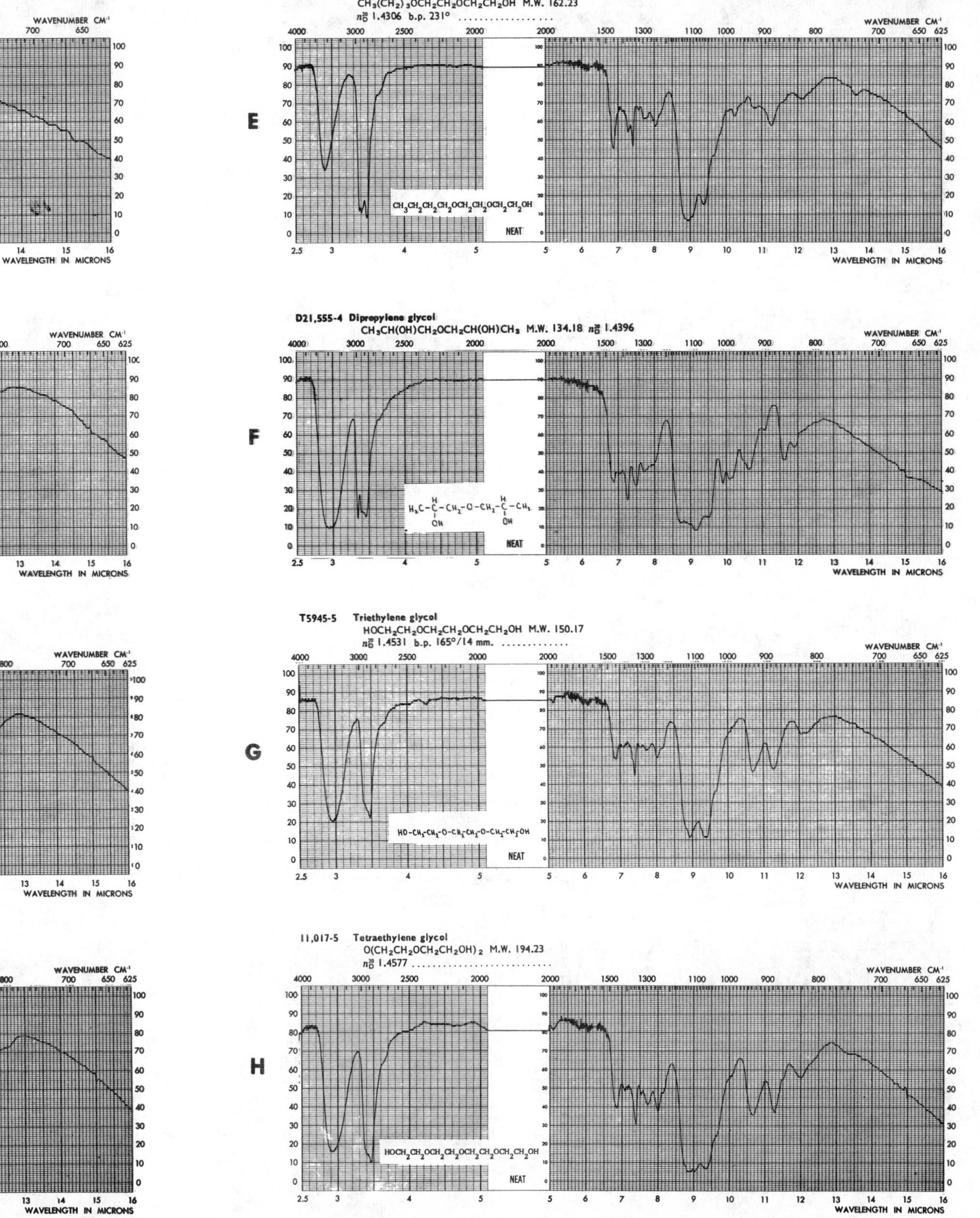

A 10,789-1 **2-Isopropoxyethanol**
$(CH_3)_2CHO(CH_2)_2OH$ M.W. 104.15 n_D^{20} 1.4099
b.p. 142°

B 13,102-4 **1,3-Diethoxy-2-propanol**
$C_2H_5OCH_2CH(OH)CH_2OC_2H_5$ M.W. 148.20 n_D^{20} 1.4212
b.p. 190-193°

C 10,990-8 **2-(2-Methoxyethoxy)-ethanol**
$CH_3OCH_2CH_2OCH_2CH_2OH$ M.W. 120.15 n_D^{20} 1.4233
b.p. 194°

D E455-0 **2-(2-Ethoxyethoxy)-ethanol (diethylene glycol monoethyl ether)**
$C_2H_5OCH_2CH_2OCH_2CH_2OH$ M.W. 134.18
n_D^{20} 1.4244

E 11,031-0 **2-(2-n-Butoxyethoxy)-ethanol**
$CH_3(CH_2)_3OCH_2CH_2OCH_2CH_2OH$ M.W. 162.23
n_D^{20} 1.4306 b.p. 231°

F D21,555-4 **Dipropylene glycol**
$CH_3CH(OH)CH_2OCH_2CH(OH)CH_3$ M.W. 134.18 n_D^{20} 1.4396

G T5945-5 **Triethylene glycol**
$HOCH_2CH_2OCH_2CH_2OCH_2CH_2OH$ M.W. 150.17
n_D^{20} 1.4531 b.p. 165°/14 mm.

H 11,017-5 **Tetraethylene glycol**
$O(CH_2CH_2OCH_2CH_2OH)_2$ M.W. 194.23
n_D^{20} 1.4577

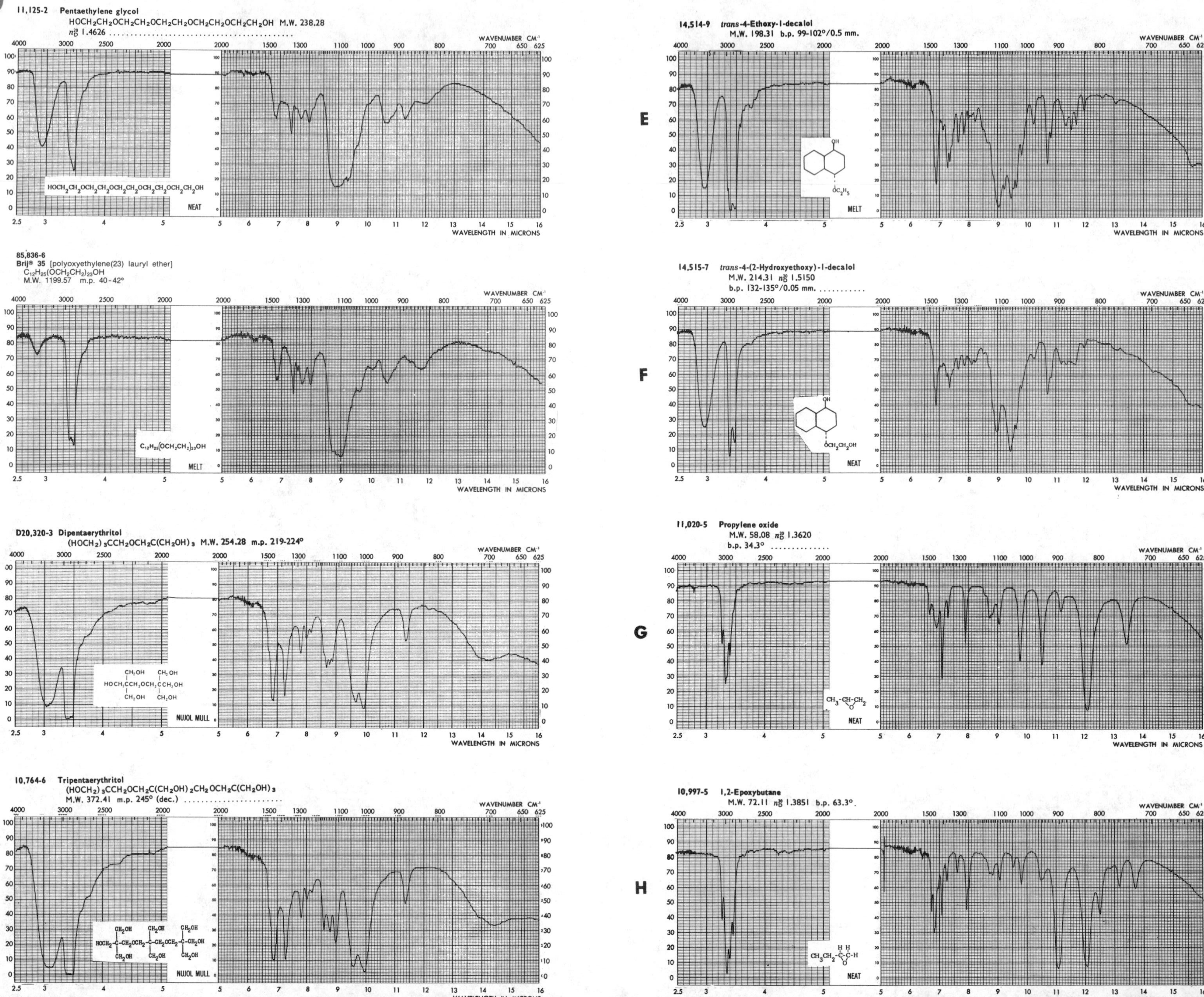
A
11,125-2 Pentaethylene glycol
HOCH₂CH₂OCH₂CH₂OCH₂CH₂OCH₂CH₂OCH₂CH₂OH M.W. 238.28
n20D 1.4626
NEAT
B
85,836-6
Brij® 35 [polyoxyethylene(23) lauryl ether]
C12H25(OCH2CH2)23OH
M.W. 1199.57 m.p. 40-42°
MELT
C
D20,320-3 Dipentaerythritol
(HOCH2)3CCH2OCH2C(CH2OH)3 M.W. 254.28 m.p. 219-224°
NUJOL MULL
D
10,764-6 Tripentaerythritol
(HOCH2)3CCH2OCH2C(CH2OH)2CH2OCH2C(CH2OH)3
M.W. 372.41 m.p. 245° (dec.)
NUJOL MULL
E
14,514-9 trans-4-Ethoxy-1-decalol
M.W. 198.31 b.p. 99-102°/0.5 mm.
MELT
F
14,515-7 trans-4-(2-Hydroxyethoxy)-1-decalol
M.W. 214.31 n20D 1.5150
b.p. 132-135°/0.05 mm.
NEAT
G
11,020-5 Propylene oxide
M.W. 58.08 n20D 1.3620
b.p. 34.3°
NEAT
H
10,997-5 1,2-Epoxybutane
M.W. 72.11 n20D 1.3851 b.p. 63.3°
NEAT
WAVENUMBER CM⁻¹
WAVELENGTH IN MICRONS

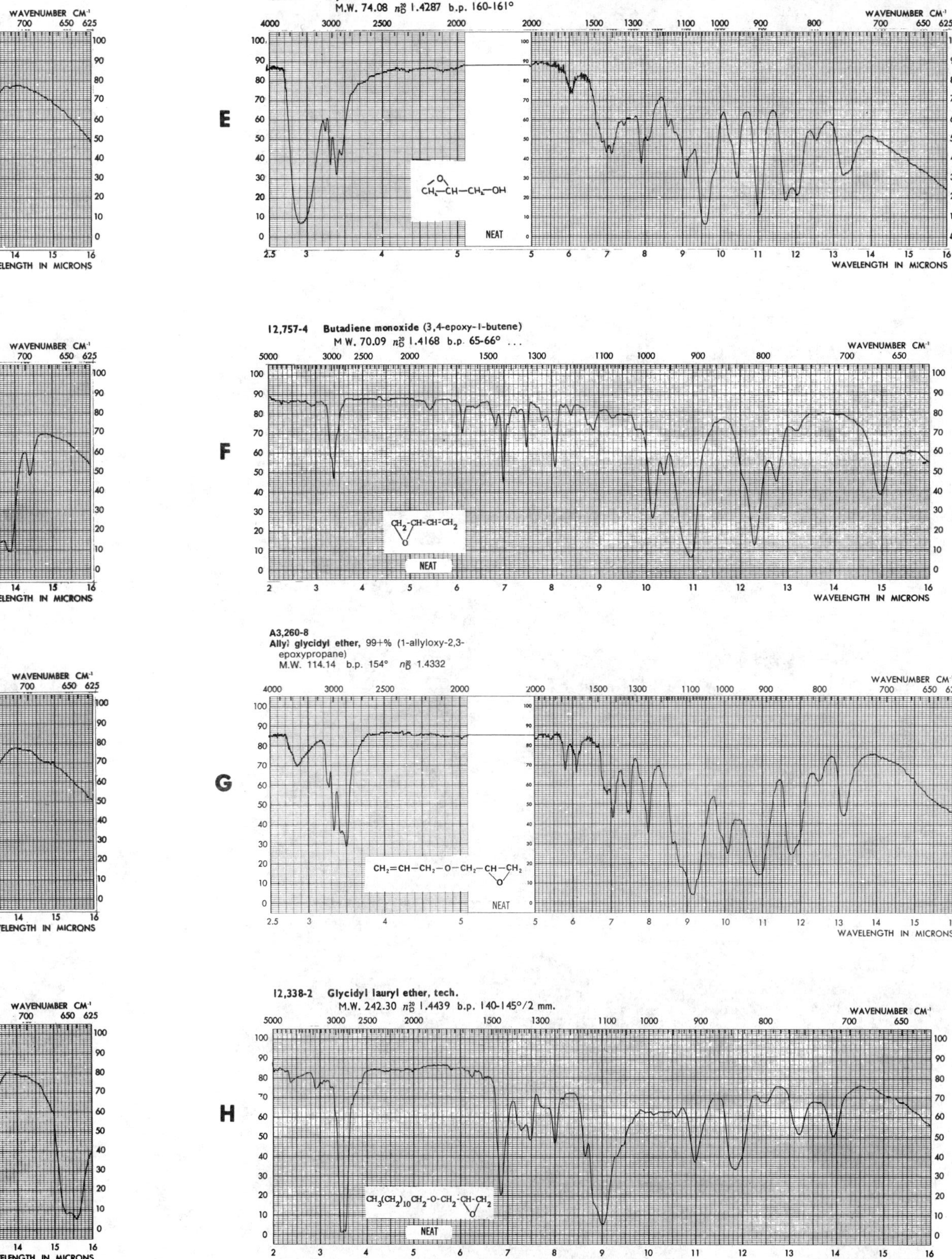
A
E110-1 Epifluorohydrin
M.W. 76.07 n_D^{20} 1.3703
NEAT
B
E105-5 Epichlorohydrin
M.W. 92.53 n_D^{20} 1.4361
NEAT
C
13,738-3 1,2-Epoxy-3,3,3-trichloropropane (3,3,3-trichloropropylene oxide)
M.W. 161.42 n_D^{20} 1.4778 b.p. 151°/745 mm.
NEAT
D
E101-2 Epibromohydrin
M.W. 136.99 n_D^{20} 1.4841
NEAT
E
G580-9 Glycidol
M.W. 74.08 n_D^{20} 1.4287 b.p. 160-161°
NEAT
F
12,757-4 Butadiene monoxide (3,4-epoxy-1-butene)
M.W. 70.09 n_D^{20} 1.4168 b.p. 65-66° ...
NEAT
G
A3,260-8
Allyl glycidyl ether, 99+% (1-allyloxy-2,3-epoxypropane)
M.W. 114.14 b.p. 154° n_D^{20} 1.4332
NEAT
H
12,338-2 Glycidyl lauryl ether, tech.
M.W. 242.30 n_D^{20} 1.4439 b.p. 140-145°/2 mm.
NEAT
WAVENUMBER CM⁻¹
WAVELENGTH IN MICRONS
ALDRICH

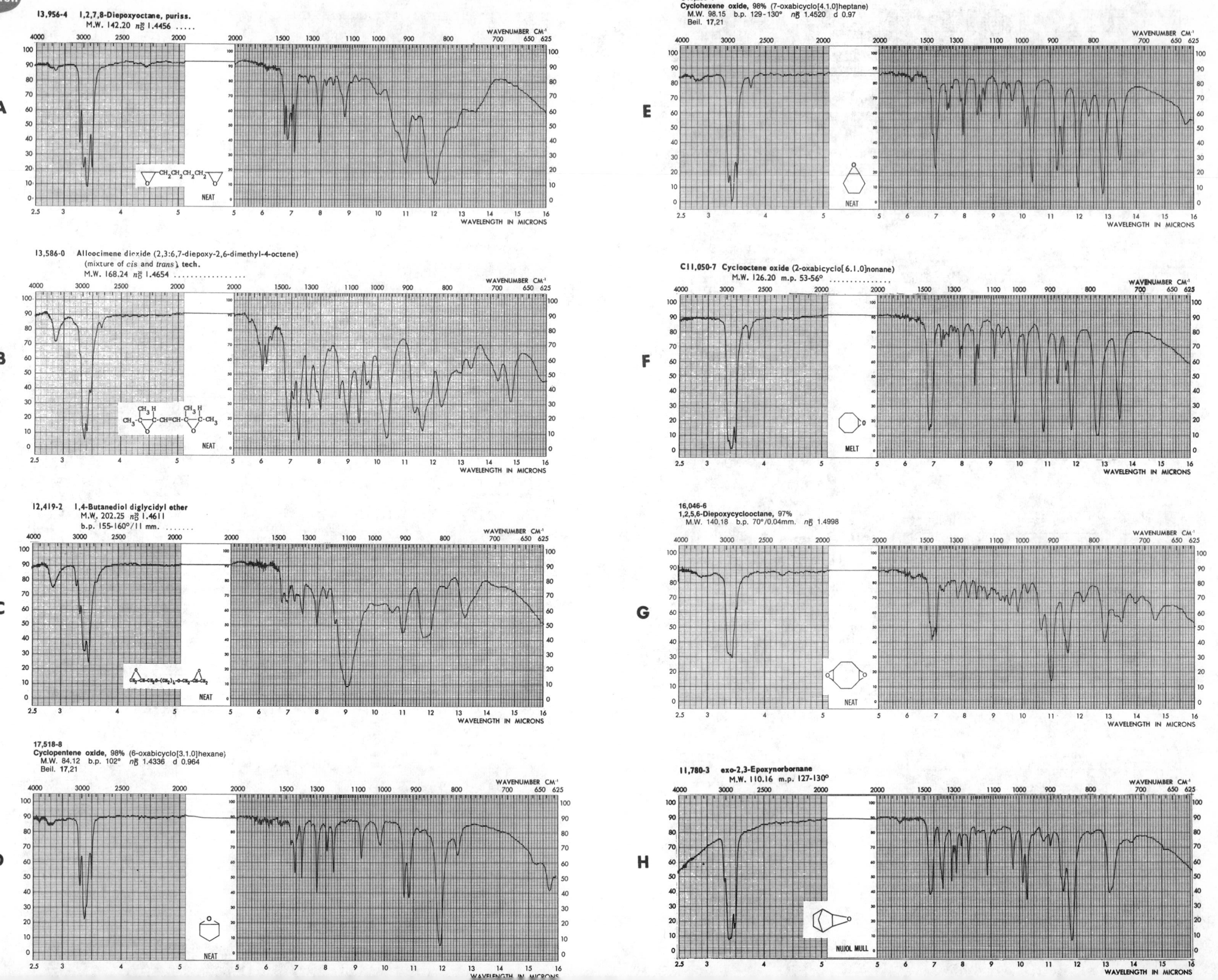
ALDRICH
A
13,956-4 1,2,7,8-Diepoxyoctane, puriss.
M.W. 142.20 n_D^{20} 1.4456
NEAT
B
13,586-0 Alloocimene dioxide (2,3:6,7-diepoxy-2,6-dimethyl-4-octene)
(mixture of *cis* and *trans*) tech.
M.W. 168.24 n_D^{20} 1.4654
NEAT
C
12,419-2 1,4-Butanediol diglycidyl ether
M.W. 202.25 n_D^{20} 1.4611
b.p. 155-160°/11 mm.
NEAT
D
17,518-8
Cyclopentene oxide, 98% (6-oxabicyclo[3.1.0]hexane)
M.W. 84.12 b.p. 102° n_D^{20} 1.4336 d 0.964
Beil. 17,21
NEAT
E
C10,250-4
Cyclohexene oxide, 98% (7-oxabicyclo[4.1.0]heptane)
M.W. 98.15 b.p. 129-130° n_D^{20} 1.4520 d 0.97
Beil. 17,21
NEAT
F
C11,050-7 Cyclooctene oxide (2-oxabicyclo[6.1.0]nonane)
M.W. 126.20 m.p. 53-56°
MELT
G
16,046-6
1,2,5,6-Diepoxycyclooctane, 97%
M.W. 140.18 b.p. 70°/0.04mm. n_D^{20} 1.4998
NEAT
H
11,780-3 exo-2,3-Epoxynorbornane
M.W. 110.16 m.p. 127-130°
NUJOL MULL
WAVENUMBER CM⁻¹
WAVELENGTH IN MICRONS

A 15,254-4 **3-Vinyl-7-oxabicyclo[4.1.0]heptane** (4-vinylcyclohexene monoxide)
M.W. 124.18 n_D^{20} 1.4687 b.p. 169° ....

B 21,832-4
(+)-Limonene oxide, 97%
FW 152.24 bp 113-114°/50mm. n_D^{20} 1.4661
d 0.929 $[\alpha]^{22}$ +69° (neat) *Beil.* 17,44 Disp. C

C 21,833-2
(-)-Limonene oxide, 90%, mixture of *cis* and *trans*
FW 152.24 bp 113-114°/50mm. n_D^{20} 1.4664
d 0.929 $[\alpha]^{24}$ -66° (neat) Disp. C

D C9720-2 **Cyclododecane epoxide** (1,2-epoxycyclododecane)
M.W. 182.31 n_D^{20} 1.4773 ....

E 14,932-2 **1,2-Epoxy-5,9-cyclododecadiene** (13-oxabicyclo[10.1.0]-trideca-4,8-diene)
M.W. 178.28 n_D^{20} 1.5057 ....

F D20,380-7 **Dipentene dioxide**
M.W. 168.24 n_D^{20} 1.4686

G 11,015-9 **Vinylcyclohexene dioxide**
M.W. 140.18 n_D^{20} 1.4782 b.p. 227°

H 21,830-8
α-Pinene oxide, 95%
FW 152.24 bp 102-103°/50mm. n_D^{20} 1.4690
d 0.964 $[\alpha]^{21}$ -64° (neat) *Beil.* 5,152 Disp. C

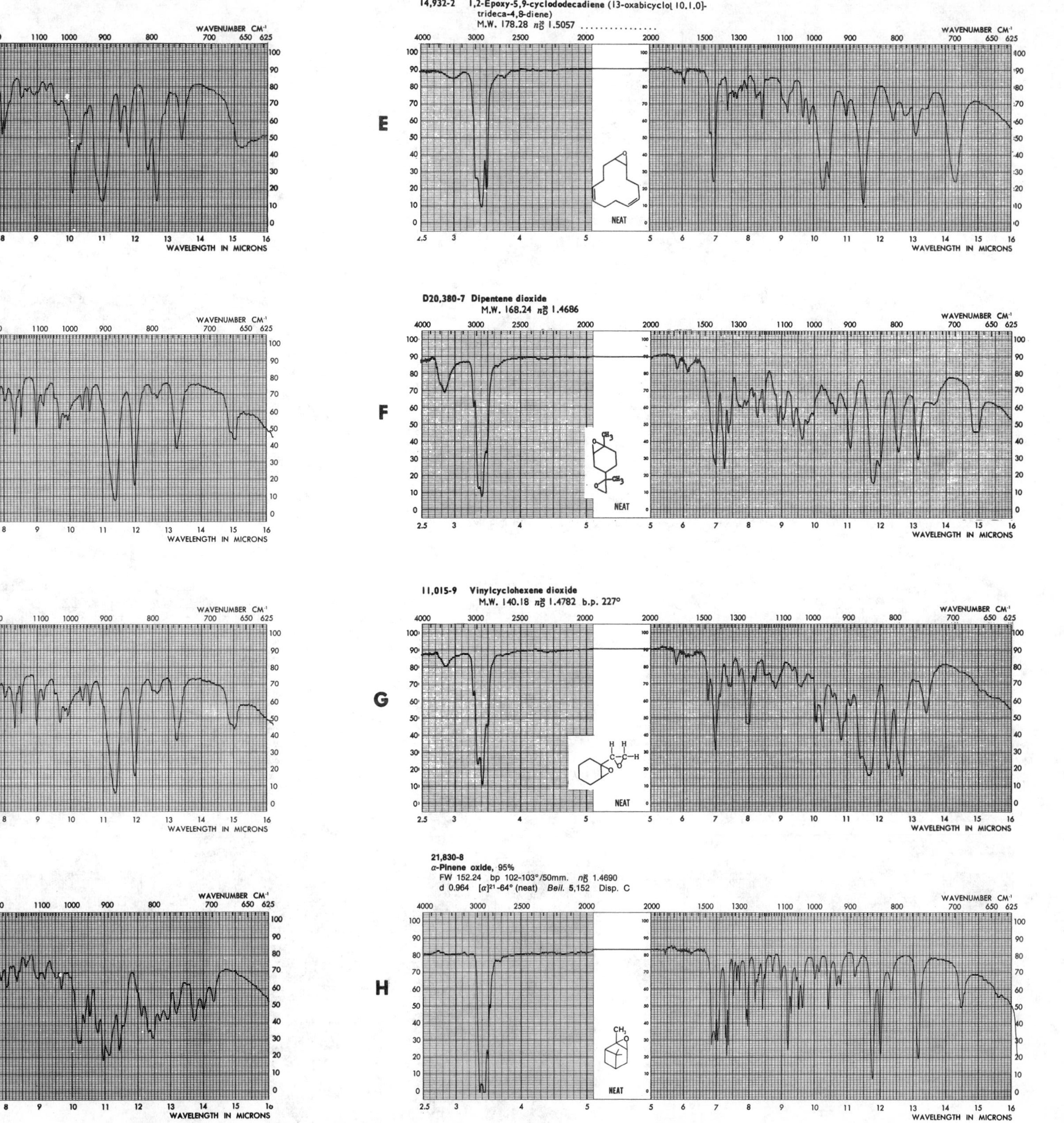

ALDRICH

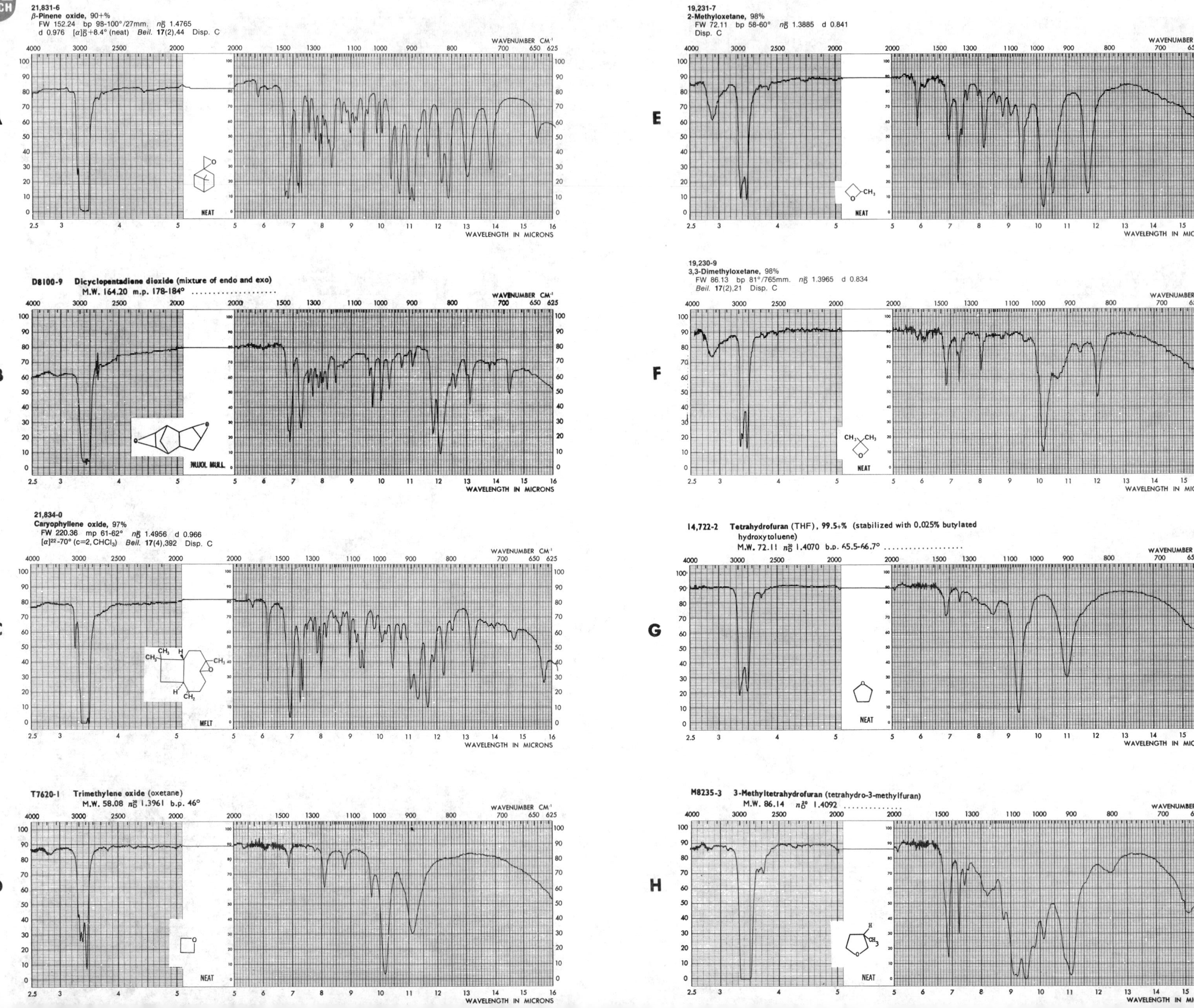
ALDRICH
A
21,831-6
β-Pinene oxide, 90+%
FW 152.24 bp 98-100°/27mm. n_D^{20} 1.4765
d 0.976 $[\alpha]_D^{20}$+8.4° (neat) Beil. 17(2),44 Disp. C
NEAT
B
D8100-9 Dicyclopentadiene dioxide (mixture of endo and exo)
M.W. 164.20 m.p. 178-184°
NUJOL MULL
C
21,834-0
Caryophyllene oxide, 97%
FW 220.36 mp 61-62° n_D^{20} 1.4956 d 0.966
$[\alpha]^{22}$-70° (c=2, $CHCl_3$) Beil. 17(4),392 Disp. C
MELT
D
T7620-1 Trimethylene oxide (oxetane)
M.W. 58.08 n_D^{20} 1.3961 b.p. 46°
NEAT
E
19,231-7
2-Methyloxetane, 98%
FW 72.11 bp 58-60° n_D^{20} 1.3885 d 0.841
Disp. C
NEAT
F
19,230-9
3,3-Dimethyloxetane, 98%
FW 86.13 bp 81°/765mm. n_D^{20} 1.3965 d 0.834
Beil. 17(2),21 Disp. C
NEAT
G
14,722-2 Tetrahydrofuran (THF), 99.5+% (stabilized with 0.025% butylated hydroxytoluene)
M.W. 72.11 n_D^{20} 1.4070 b.p. 65.5-66.7°
NEAT
H
M8235-3 3-Methyltetrahydrofuran (tetrahydro-3-methylfuran)
M.W. 86.14 n_D^{20} 1.4092
NEAT
WAVENUMBER CM⁻¹
WAVELENGTH IN MICRONS

A

D18,720-8 **2,5-Dimethyltetrahydrofuran, tech.**
M.W. 100.16 ....

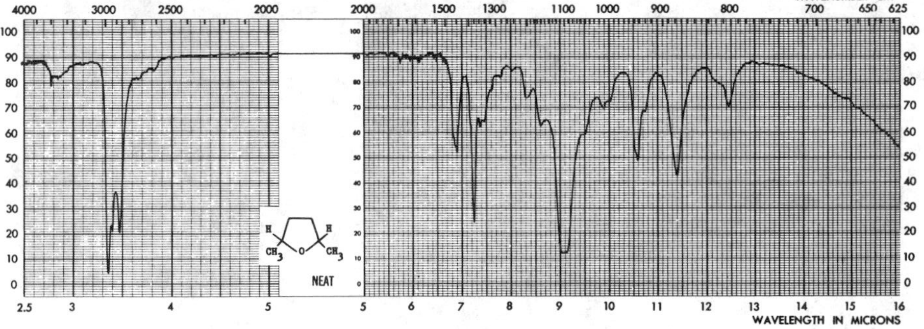

NEAT

B

22,370-0
2,2,5,5-Tetramethyltetrahydrofuran, 98% (tetrahydro-2,2,5,5-tetramethylfuran)
FW 128.22 bp 112° n_D^{20} 1.4050 d 0.811
Beil. **17**,16 Disp. T

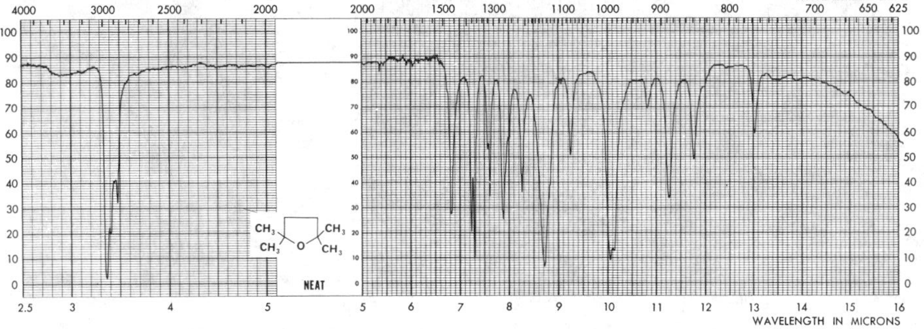

NEAT

C

13,420-1 **Methyl tetrahydrofurfuryl ether**
M.W. 116.16 n_D^{20} 1.4270 ....

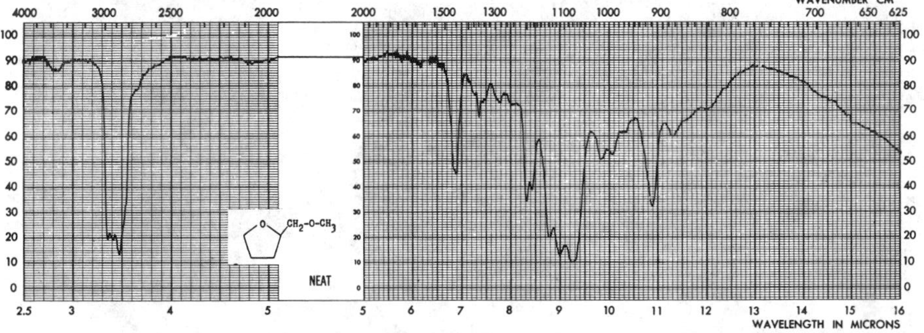

NEAT

D

20,991-0
2-Methoxytetrahydrofuran, 99%
FW 102.13 bp 105-107° n_D^{20} 1.4119 d 0.972
Beil. **17**(4),1019 Disp. C

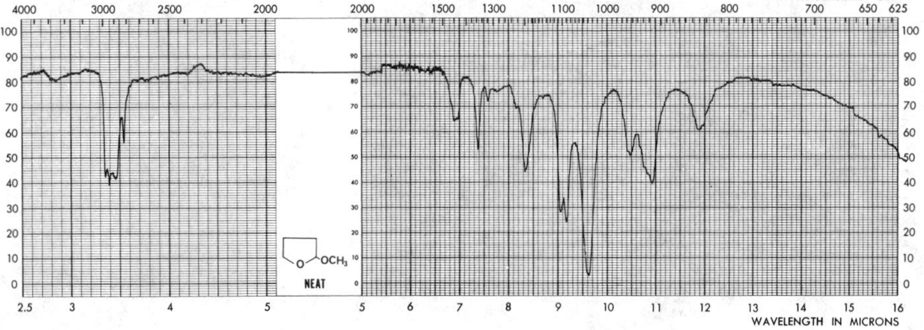

NEAT

E

20,992-9
2-Ethoxytetrahydrofuran, 99%
FW 116.16 bp 170-172° n_D^{20} 1.4140 d 0.908
Beil. **17**(4),1020 Disp. C

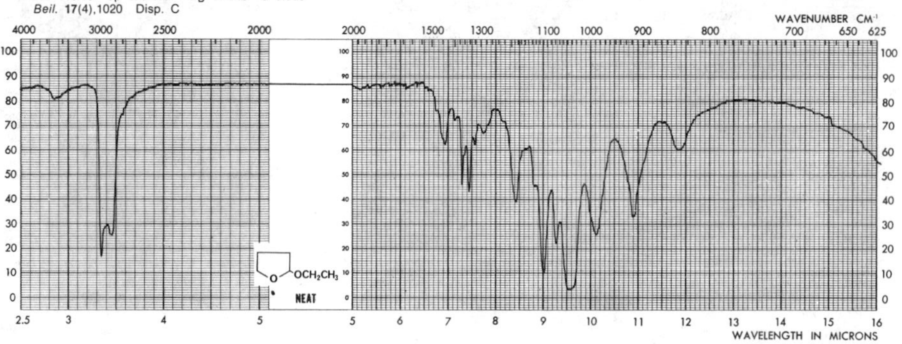

NEAT

F

D13,710-3 **2,5-Dimethoxytetrahydrofuran** (tetrahydro-2,5-dimethoxyfuran)
M.W. 132.16 n_D^{20} 1.4180 ....

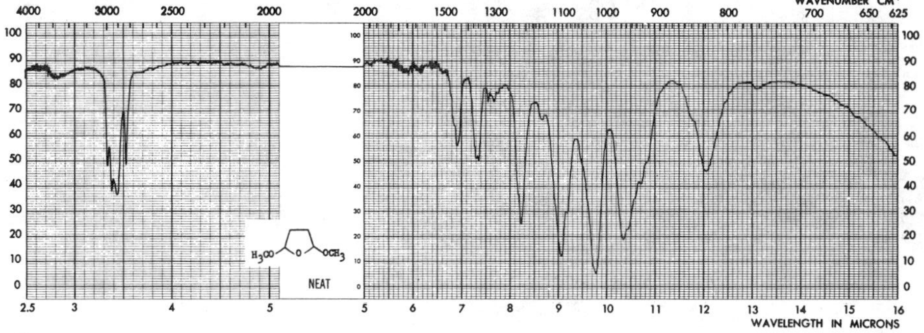

NEAT

G

H5910-9 **3-Hydroxytetrahydrofuran, 99%**
M.W. 88.11 n_D^{20} 1.4500 b.p. 181°

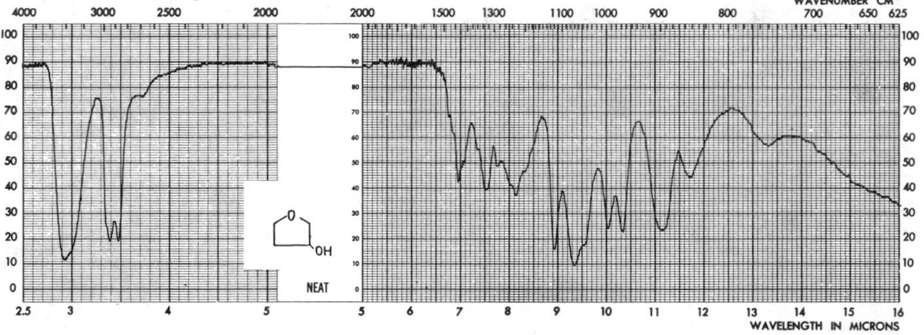

NEAT

H

T1265-3 **Tetrahydrofurfuryl alcohol, puriss.**
M.W. 102.13 n_D^{20} 1.4512 b.p. 178°

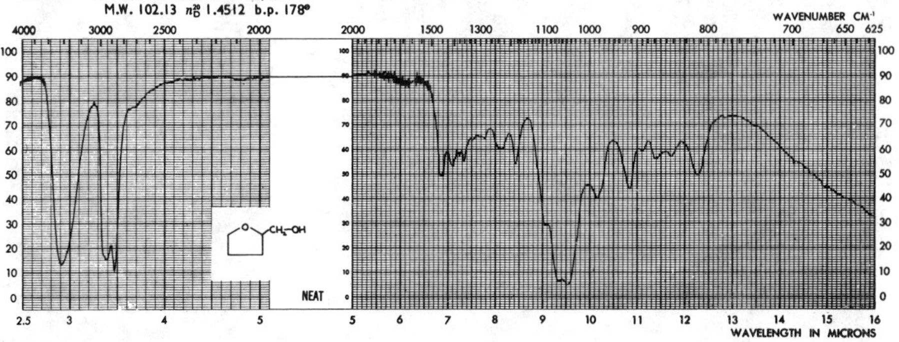

NEAT

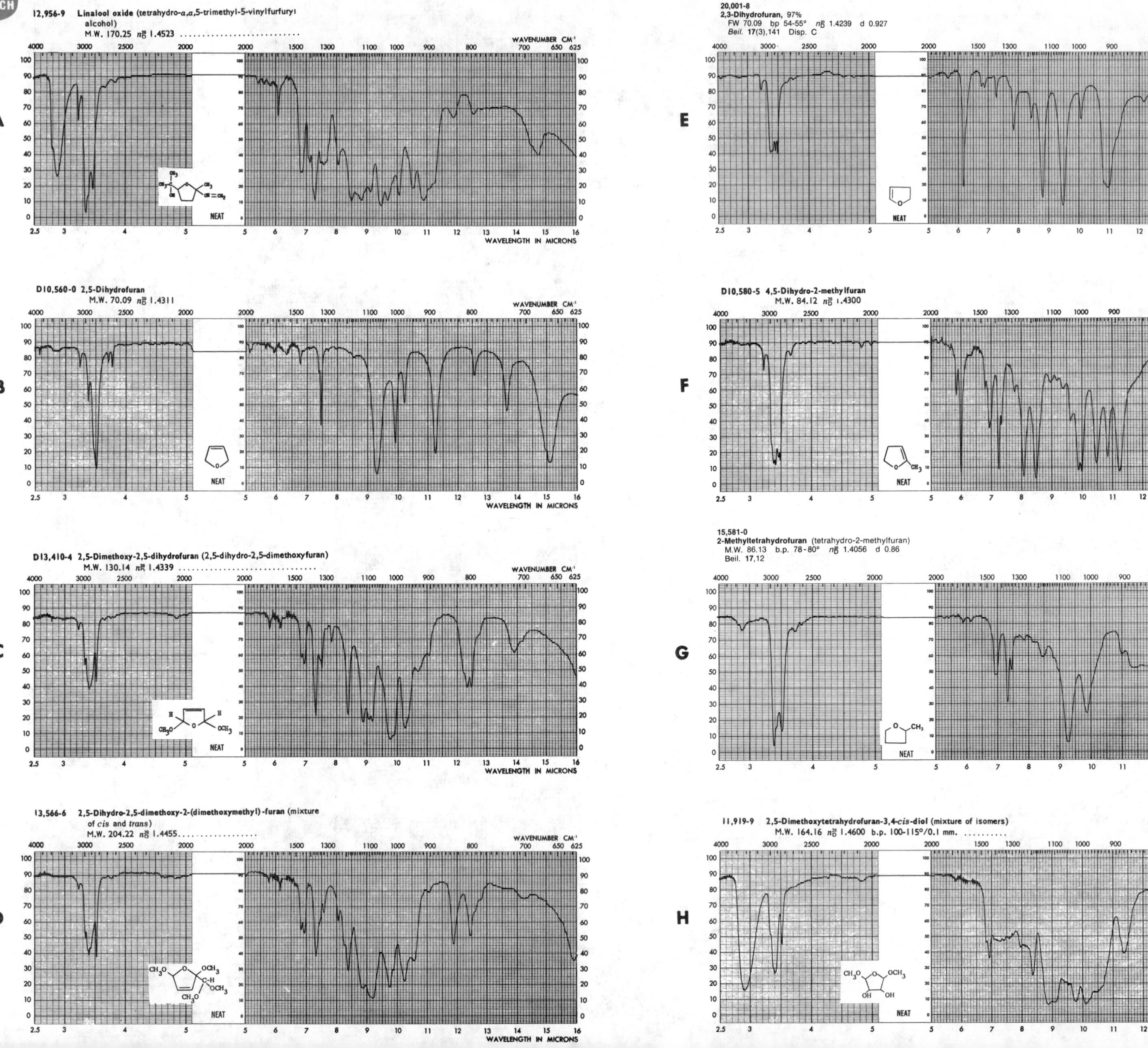
ALDRICH
A
12,956-9 Linalool oxide (tetrahydro-α,α,5-trimethyl-5-vinylfurfuryl alcohol)
M.W. 170.25 n_D^{20} 1.4523
B
D10,560-0 2,5-Dihydrofuran
M.W. 70.09 n_D^{20} 1.4311
C
D13,410-4 2,5-Dimethoxy-2,5-dihydrofuran (2,5-dihydro-2,5-dimethoxyfuran)
M.W. 130.14 n_D^{20} 1.4339
D
13,566-6 2,5-Dihydro-2,5-dimethoxy-2-(dimethoxymethyl)-furan (mixture of *cis* and *trans*)
M.W. 204.22 n_D^{20} 1.4455
E
20,001-8
2,3-Dihydrofuran, 97%
FW 70.09 bp 54-55° n_D^{20} 1.4239 d 0.927
Beil. 17(3),141 Disp. C
F
D10,580-5 4,5-Dihydro-2-methylfuran
M.W. 84.12 n_D^{20} 1.4300
G
15,581-0
2-Methyltetrahydrofuran (tetrahydro-2-methylfuran)
M.W. 86.13 b.p. 78-80° n_D^{20} 1.4056 d 0.86
Beil. 17,12
H
11,919-9 2,5-Dimethoxytetrahydrofuran-3,4-*cis*-diol (mixture of isomers)
M.W. 164.16 n_D^{20} 1.4600 b.p. 100-115°/0.1 mm.
NEAT
WAVENUMBER CM⁻¹
WAVELENGTH IN MICRONS

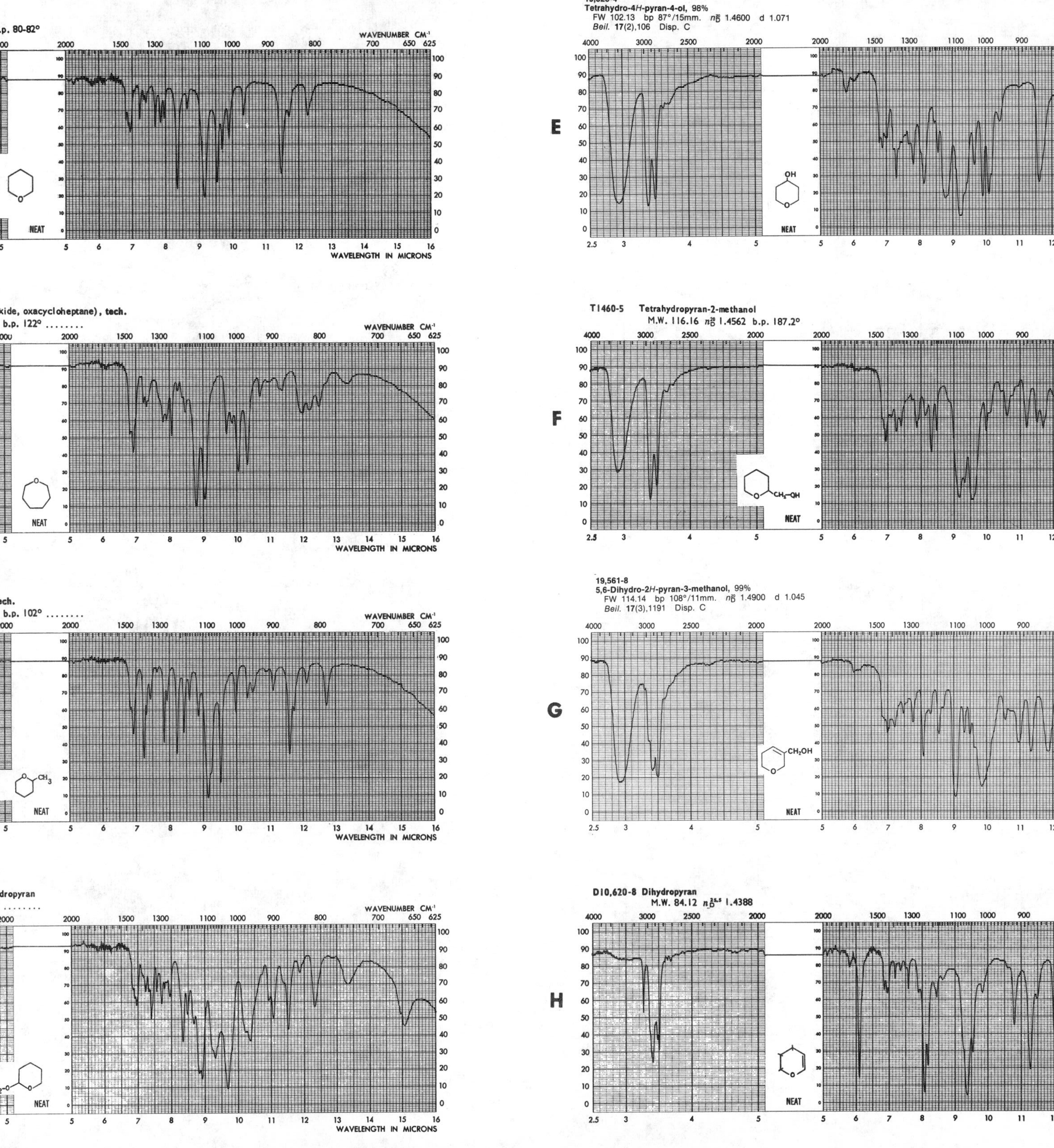
A
T1440-0 Tetrahydropyran
M.W. 86.13 n_D^{20} 1.4200 b.p. 80-82°
NEAT
B
13,927-0 Oxepane (hexamethylene oxide, oxacycloheptane), tech.
M.W. 100.16 n_D^{20} 1.4400 b.p. 122° ....
NEAT
C
13,928-9 2-Methyltetrahydropyran, tech.
M.W. 100.16 n_D^{20} 1.4180 b.p. 102° ....
NEAT
D
C4010-3 2-(2-Chloroethoxy)-tetrahydropyran
M.W. 164.64 n_D^{20} 1.4567 ....
Cl-CH$_2$-CH$_2$-O
NEAT
E
19,823-4
Tetrahydro-4H-pyran-4-ol, 98%
FW 102.13 bp 87°/15mm. n_D^{20} 1.4600 d 1.071
Beil. 17(2),106 Disp. C
OH
NEAT
F
T1460-5 Tetrahydropyran-2-methanol
M.W. 116.16 n_D^{20} 1.4562 b.p. 187.2°
CH$_2$-OH
NEAT
G
19,561-8
5,6-Dihydro-2H-pyran-3-methanol, 99%
FW 114.14 bp 108°/11mm. n_D^{20} 1.4900 d 1.045
Beil. 17(3),1191 Disp. C
CH$_2$OH
NEAT
H
D10,620-8 Dihydropyran
M.W. 84.12 $n_D^{26.5}$ 1.4388
NEAT
WAVENUMBER CM^{-1}
WAVELENGTH IN MICRONS
ALDRICH

ALDRICH®

A 19,397-6
5,6-Dihydro-4-methyl-2*H*-pyran, 97%
FW 98.15 bp 117-118° n_D^{20} 1.4495 d 0.912
Beil. **17**(3),160 Disp. C

B 18,917-0
5,6-Dihydro-4-methoxy-2*H*-pyran, 98%
FW 114.14 bp 59°/20mm. n_D^{20} 1.4627 d 1.022
Fieser **2**,271 **3**,197 **5**,438 **6**,367 Disp. C

C 18,073-4
3,4-Dihydro-2-methoxy-2H-pyran, 99%
M.W. 114.14 n_D^{20} 1.4425

D 15,974-3
3,4-Dihydro-2-ethoxy-2H-pyran
M.W. 128.17 b.p. 42°/16mm. n_D^{20} 1.4394
Fieser 1,362

E E605-7 **2-Ethoxy-4-methyl-3,4-dihydro-2H-pyran**
M.W. 142.20 n_D^{20} 1.4369

F 11,397-2 **3,4-Dihydro-2H-pyran-2,2-dimethanol**
M.W. 144.17 m.p. 46-48°

G O-870-4 **7-Oxabicyclo[2.2.1]heptane** (1,4-epoxycyclohexane)
M.W. 98.14 n_D^{20} 1.4480

H C8060-1 **Cineol** (eucalyptol)
M.W. 154.25 n_D^{20} 1.4562 m.p. -1 to +1°

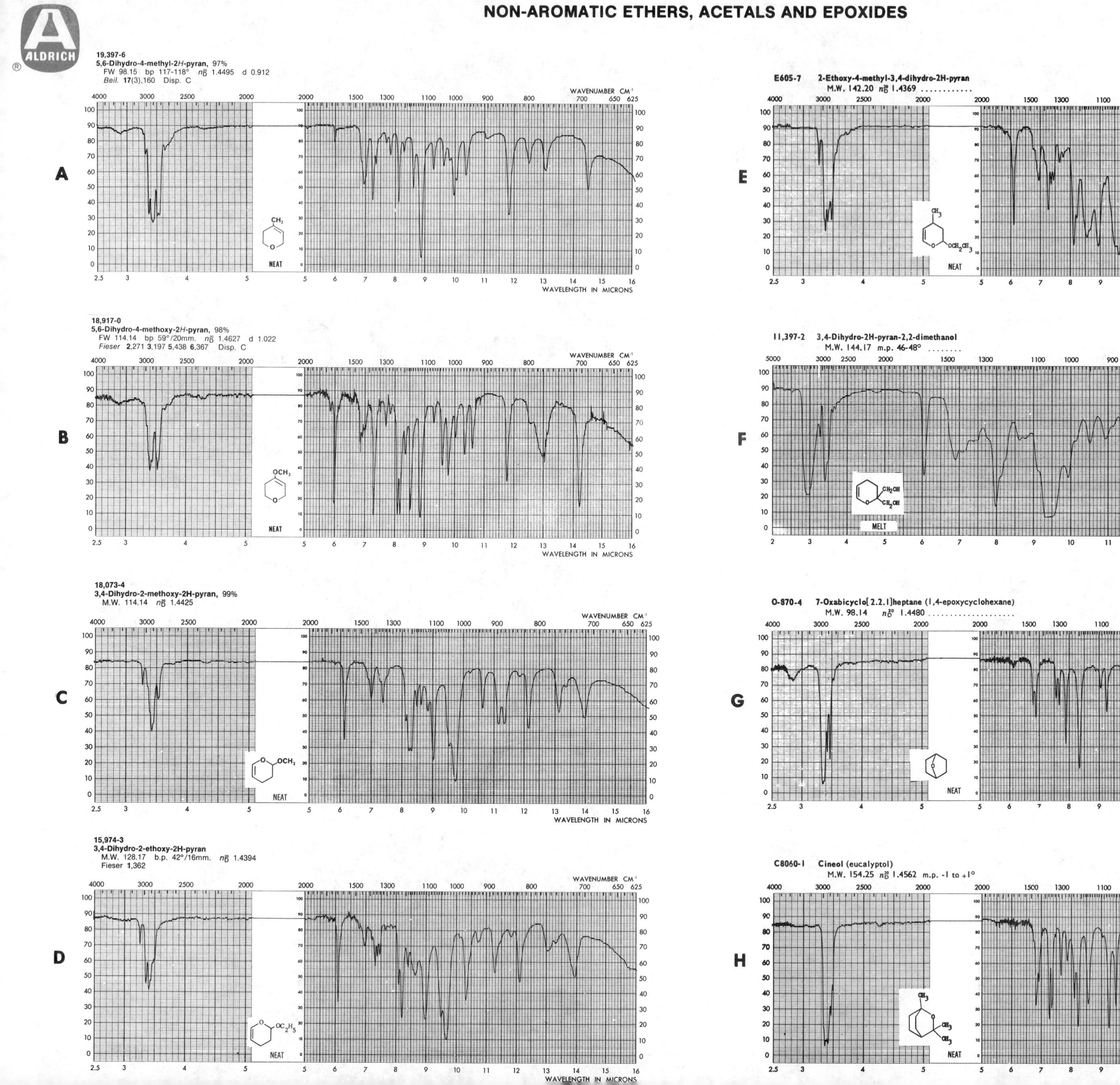

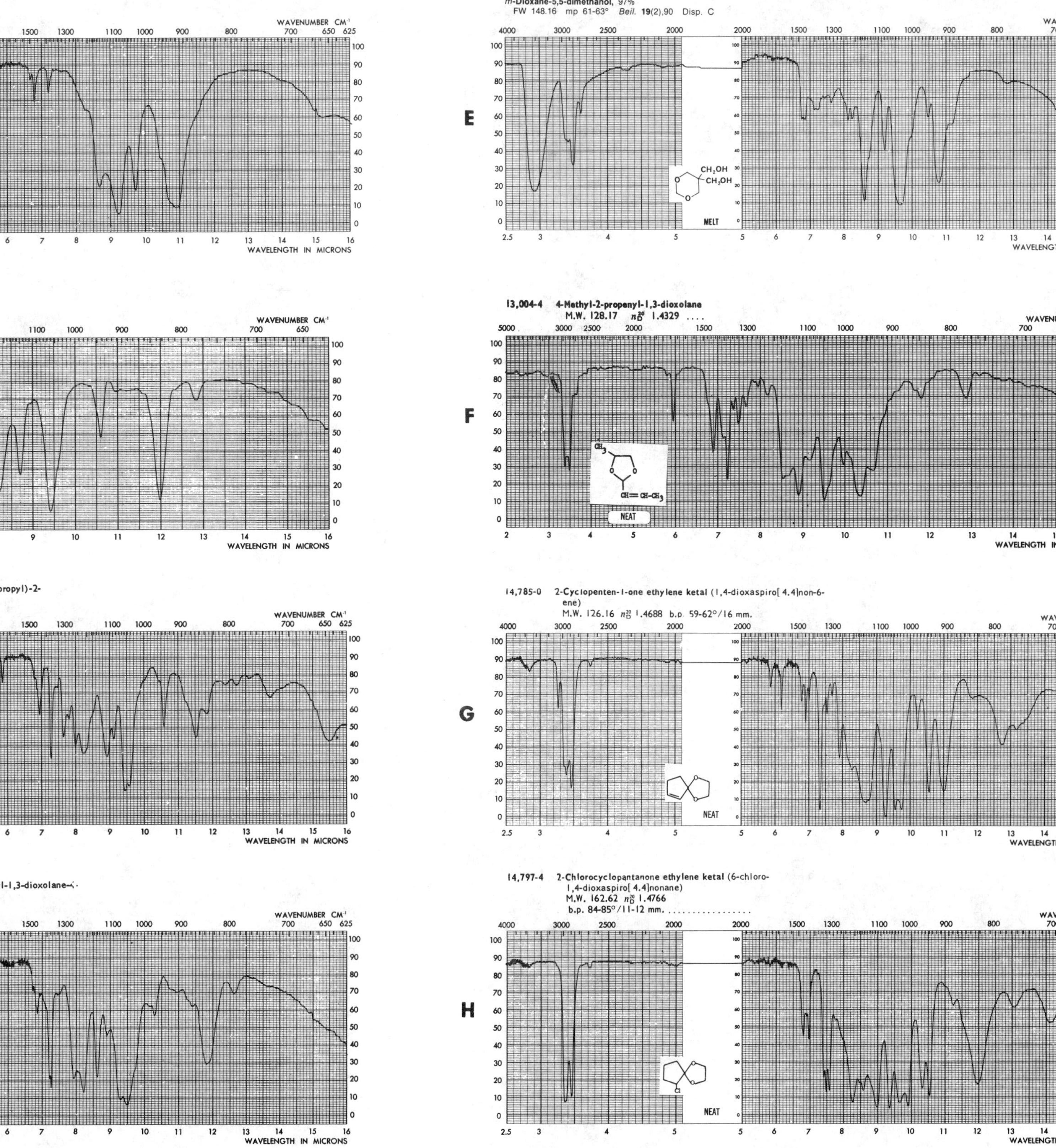

A 18,449-7
1,3-Dioxolane, 98%
M.W. 74.08 b.p. 74-75° n_D^{20} 1.4000
NEAT

B D15,562 **2,2-Dimethyl-1,3-dioxolane**
M.W. 102.14 n_D^{20} 1.3954
NEAT

C 15,155-6 **5-Chloro-2-pentanone ethylene ketal** [2-(3-chloropropyl)-2-methyl-1,3-dioxolane]
M.W. 164.63 n_D^{20} 1.4490 b.p. 73-76°/7 mm.
NEAT

D 12,269-6 **Solketal** (acetone ketal of glycerine, 2,2-dimethyl-1,3-dioxolane-4-methanol)
M.W. 132.16 n_D^{20} 1.4344
NEAT

E 22,062-0
m-**Dioxane-5,5-dimethanol**, 97%
FW 148.16 mp 61-63° *Beil.* **19**(2),90 Disp. C
MELT

F 13,004-4 **4-Methyl-2-propenyl-1,3-dioxolane**
M.W. 128.17 n_D^{20} 1.4329 ....
NEAT

G 14,785-0 **2-Cyclopenten-1-one ethylene ketal** (1,4-dioxaspiro[4.4]non-6-ene)
M.W. 126.16 n_D^{20} 1.4688 b.p. 59-62°/16 mm.
NEAT

H 14,797-4 **2-Chlorocyclopantanone ethylene ketal** (6-chloro-1,4-dioxaspiro[4.4]nonane)
M.W. 162.62 n_D^{20} 1.4766
b.p. 84-85°/11-12 mm. ....
NEAT

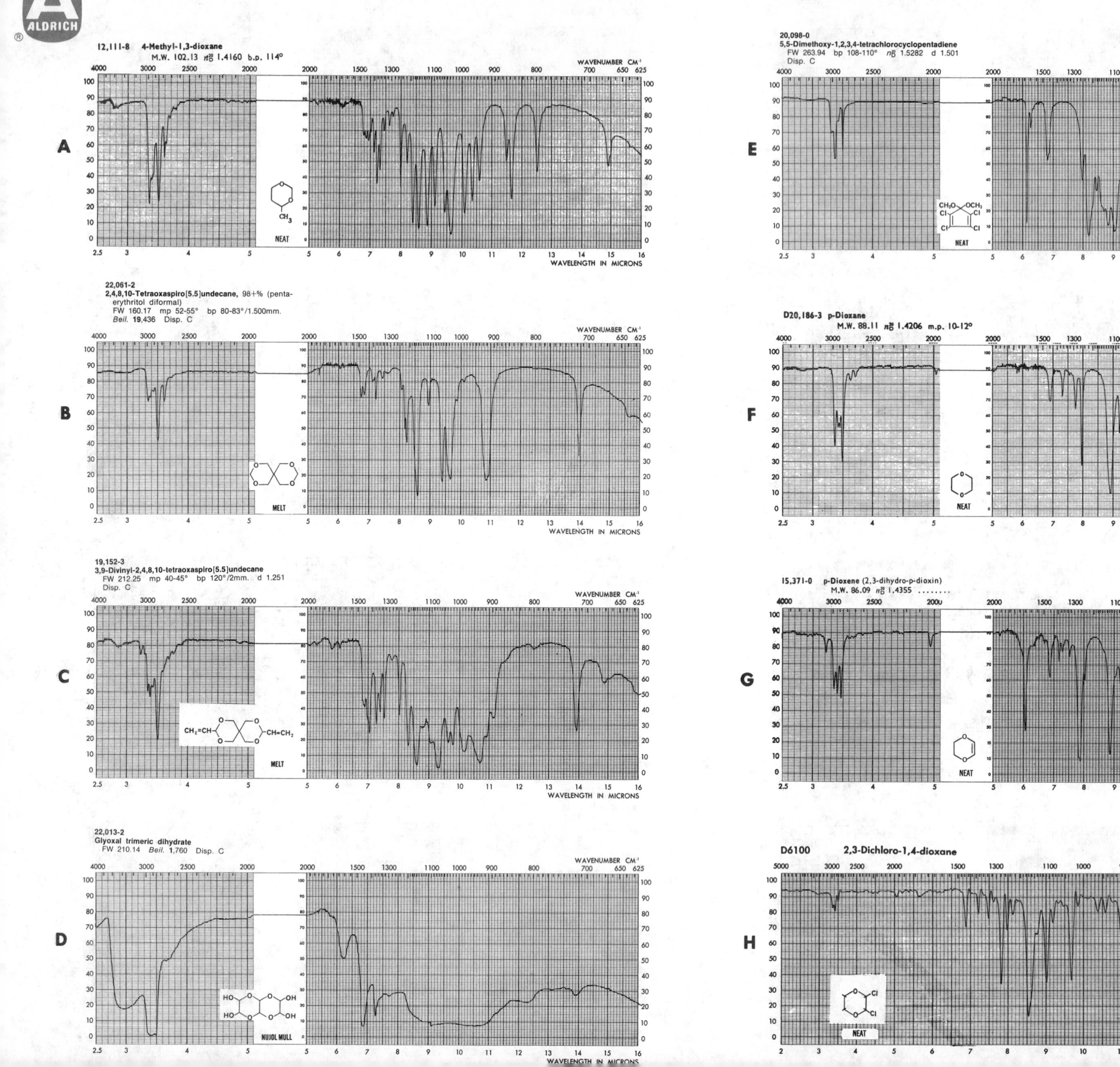
ALDRICH
A
12,111-8 4-Methyl-1,3-dioxane
M.W. 102.13 n_D^{20} 1.4160 b.p. 114°
NEAT
B
22,061-2
2,4,8,10-Tetraoxaspiro[5.5]undecane, 98+% (pentaerythritol diformal)
FW 160.17 mp 52-55° bp 80-83°/1.500mm.
Beil. 19,436 Disp. C
MELT
C
19,152-3
3,9-Divinyl-2,4,8,10-tetraoxaspiro[5.5]undecane
FW 212.25 mp 40-45° bp 120°/2mm. d 1.251
Disp. C
MELT
D
22,013-2
Glyoxal trimeric dihydrate
FW 210.14 Beil. 1,760 Disp. C
NUJOL MULL
E
20,098-0
5,5-Dimethoxy-1,2,3,4-tetrachlorocyclopentadiene
FW 263.94 bp 108-110° n_D^{20} 1.5282 d 1.501
Disp. C
NEAT
F
D20,186-3 p-Dioxane
M.W. 88.11 n_D^{20} 1.4206 m.p. 10-12°
NEAT
G
15,371-0 p-Dioxene (2,3-dihydro-p-dioxin)
M.W. 86.09 n_D^{20} 1.4355
NEAT
H
D6100 2,3-Dichloro-1,4-dioxane
NEAT
WAVENUMBER CM⁻¹
WAVELENGTH IN MICRONS

T8110-8 s-Trioxane
M.W. 90.08 m.p. 61-62.5°

10,994-0 Paraldehyde (2,4,6-trimethyl-s-trioxane), 99+%
M.W. 132.16 n_D^{20} 1.4045 m.p. 11-12°
b.p. 124°

15,840-2
Dicyclohexyl-18-crown-6, tech. (2,3,11,12-dicyclohexyl-1,4,7,10,13,16-hexaoxacyclooctadecane)
M.W. 372.5 *IRRITANT*

T1280-7 2-(Tetrahydrofurfuryloxy)-tetrahydropyran
M.W. 186.25 n_D^{20} 1.4606 b.p. 135°/25 mm.

14,869-5 2-Cyclopenten-1-yl ether
$(C_5H_7)_2O$ M.W. 150.22 n_D^{20} 1.4890.

21,716-6
1-Methoxy-1,3-cyclohexadiene, tech., 70%
(2,3-dihydroanisole)
FW 110.16 bp 40°/15mm. n_D^{20} 1.4885 d 0.929
Beil. **6**(3),367 Disp. C

21,615-1
1-Methoxy-1,4-cyclohexadiene, tech., 85%
(2,5-dihydroanisole)
FW 110.16 bp 148-150° n_D^{20} 1.4819 d 0.940
Beil. **6**(3),367 Disp. C

19,490-5
12-Crown-4, 99+% (1,4,7,10-tetraoxacyclododecane)
FW 176.21 mp 16° n_D^{20} 1.4621 d 1.089
Fieser **6**,133 Disp. C

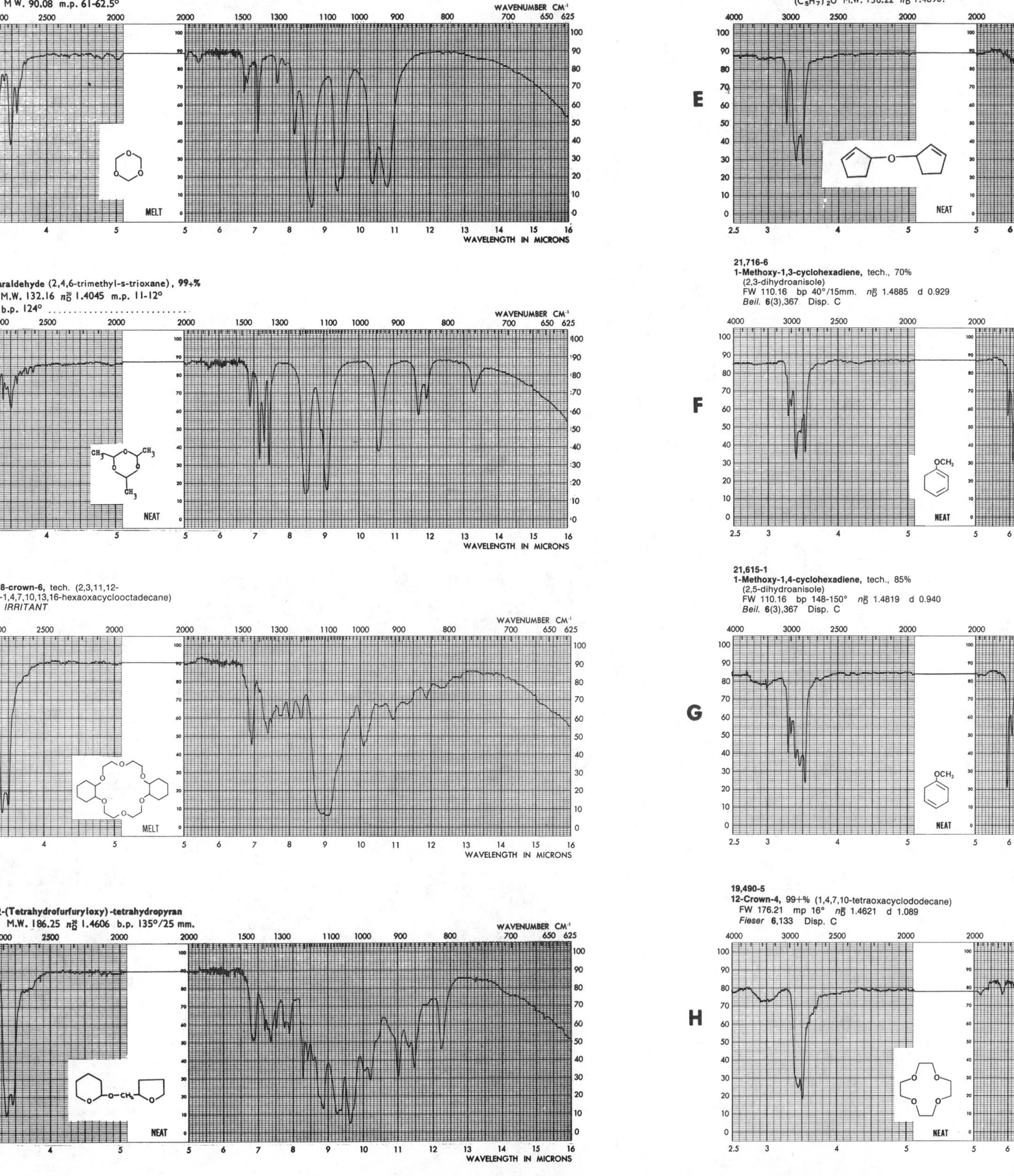

A

18,883-2
15-Crown-5 (1,4,7,10,13-pentaoxacyclopentadecane)
FW 220.27 bp 100-135°/0.200mm. n_D^{20} 1.4615
Fieser **6**,133 **7**,76 Disp. C

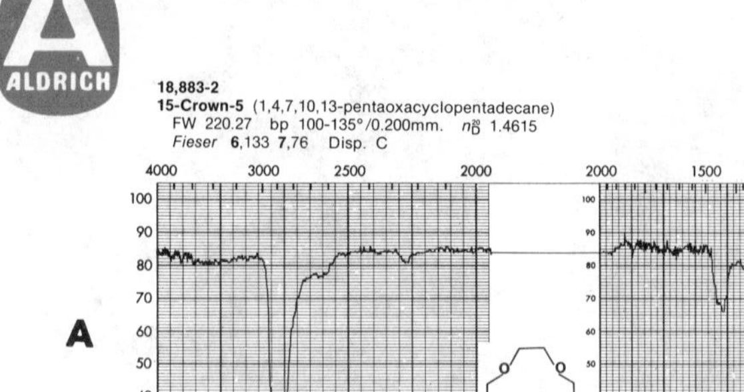

B

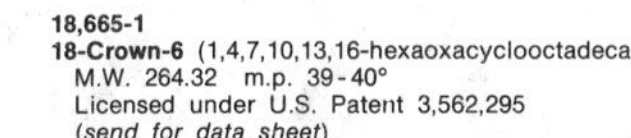

18,665-1
18-Crown-6 (1,4,7,10,13,16-hexaoxacyclooctadecane)
M.W. 264.32 m.p. 39-40°
Licensed under U.S. Patent 3,562,295
(*send for data sheet*)

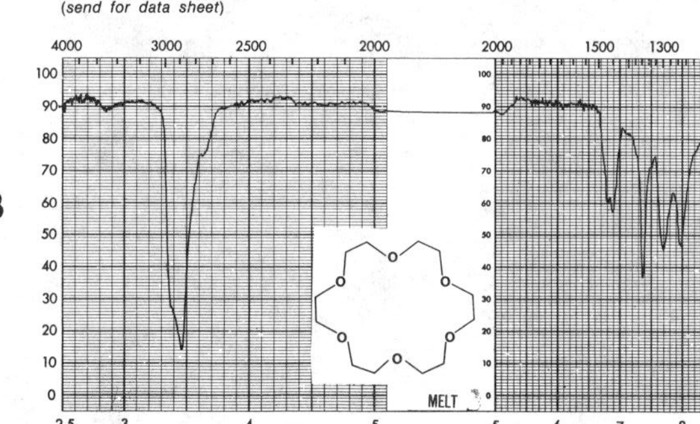

ALDRICH

NON-AROMATIC MERCAPTANS AND SULFIDES

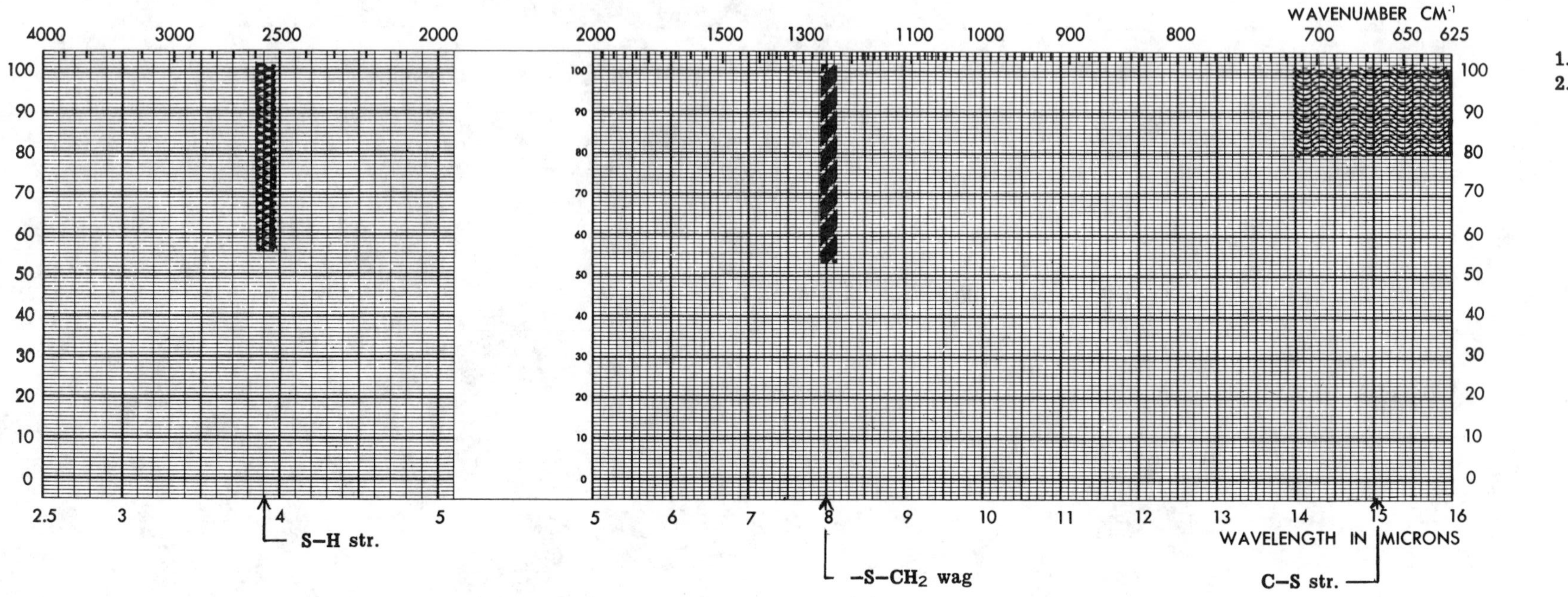

One of the weaker absorptions in the infrared spectrum is that of the S–H stretch. Fortunately its position at 3.9 μ (2565 cm^{-1}) allows it to be recognized in most instances. Notice, however, that in the long chain thiols from C_9 up, the overtone bands between 3.6 and 3.8 μ (2780 – 2630 cm^{-1}) are as strong or stronger than the S–H band. It is, therefore, very difficult to identify these compounds as mercaptans. The wag of the CH_2 group next to the sulfur shows up as a medium absorption at 8 μ (1250 cm^{-1}). It is the only absorption that can be associated with the presence of divalent sulfur because the carbon-sulfur stretch band is weak and ill-defined between 14 and 16 μ (715 – 625 cm^{-1}) and beyond. Of course this region is also occupied by bands from most other functional groups.

A E370-8 **Ethanethiol** (ethyl mercaptan)
C_2H_5SH M.W. 62.13

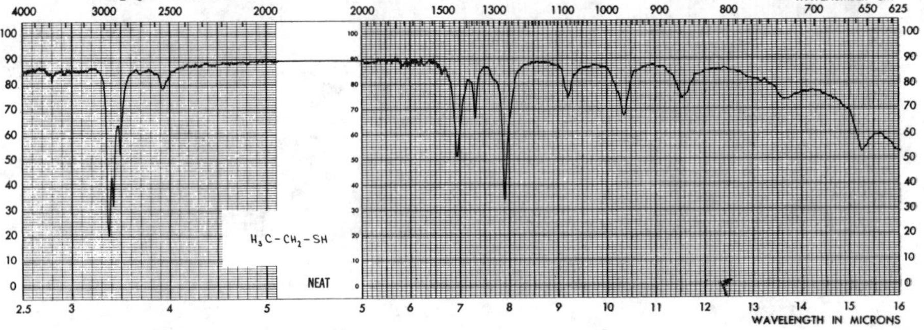

H_3C-CH_2-SH NEAT

B P5075-7 **1-Propanethiol** (n-propyl mercaptan)
$CH_3CH_2CH_2SH$ M.W. 76.16 n_D^{20} 1.4380
b.p. 66-70°

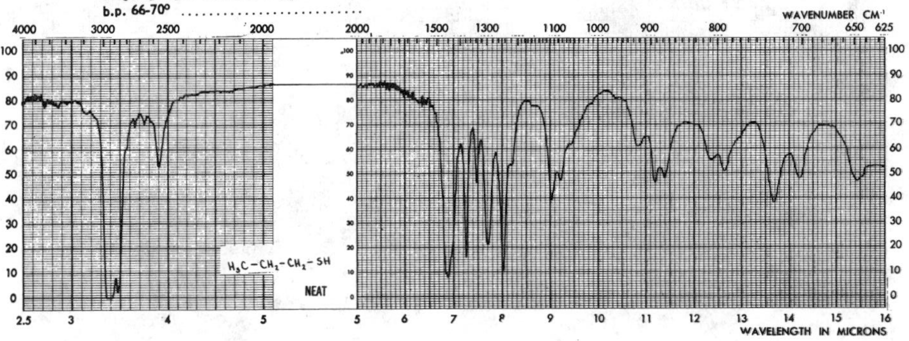

$H_3C-CH_2-CH_2-SH$ NEAT

C 11,292-5 **1-Butanethiol** (n-butyl mercaptan)
$CH_3(CH_2)_3SH$ M.W. 90.19 n_D^{20} 1.4410
b.p. 96-98°

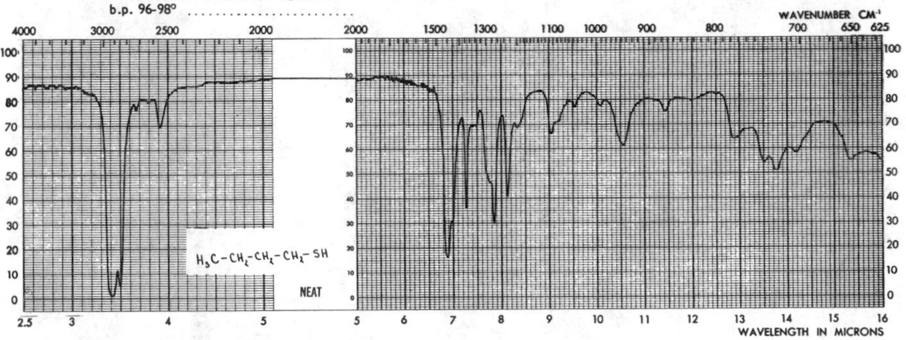

$H_3C-CH_2-CH_2-CH_2-SH$ NEAT

D P790-8 **1-Pentanethiol** (n-amyl mercaptan)
$CH_3(CH_2)_4SH$ M.W. 104.22 n_D^{20} 1.4468

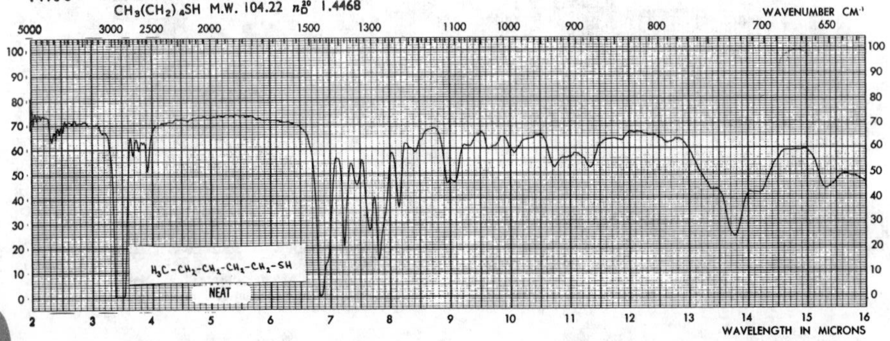

$H_3C-CH_2-CH_2-CH_2-CH_2-SH$ NEAT

E H450-6 **n-Heptyl mercaptan** (1-heptanethiol)
$CH_3(CH_2)_6SH$ M.W. 132.27 n_D^{20} 1.4520 b.p. 173-176°/765 mm.

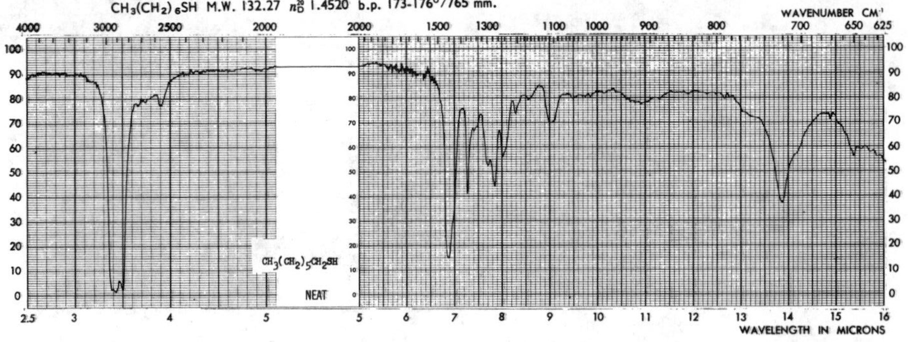

$CH_3(CH_2)_5CH_2SH$ NEAT

F 13,124-5 **1-Octanethiol**
$CH_3(CH_2)_7SH$ M.W. 146.30 n_D^{20} 1.4525

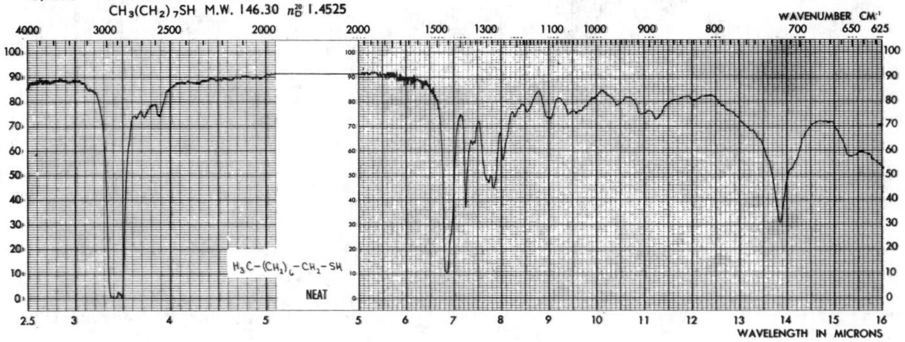

$H_3C-(CH_2)_6-CH_2-SH$ NEAT

G N3140-0 **n-Nonyl mercaptan** (1-nonanethiol), puriss.
$CH_3(CH_2)_8SH$ M.W. 160.32 n_D^{20} 1.4548

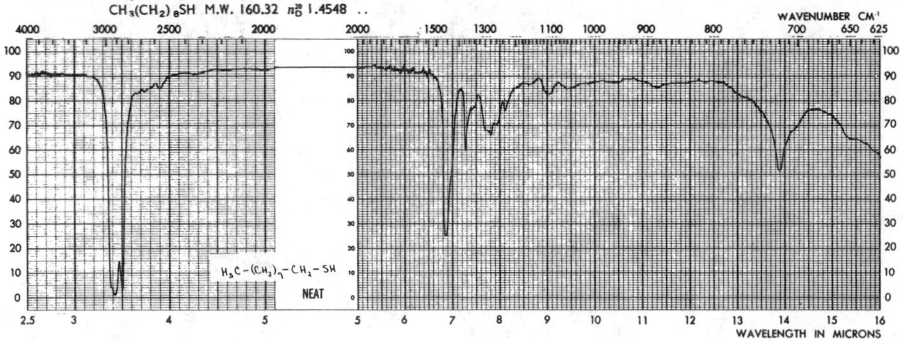

$H_3C-(CH_2)_7-CH_2-SH$ NEAT

H D160-2 **1-Decanethiol** (decyl mercaptan)
$CH_3(CH_2)_9SH$ M.W. 174.35 n_D^{20} 1.4549

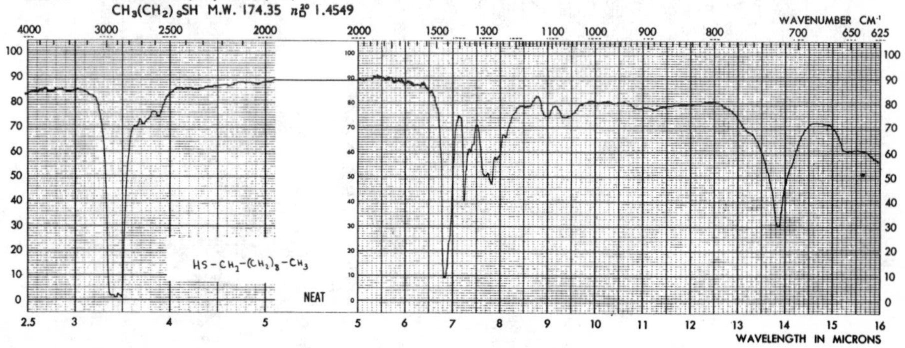

$HS-CH_2-(CH_2)_8-CH_3$ NEAT

A

U240-7 **n-Undecyl mercaptan** (undecanethiol)
$CH_3(CH_2)_{10}SH$ M.W. 188.38 n_D^{20} 1.4571

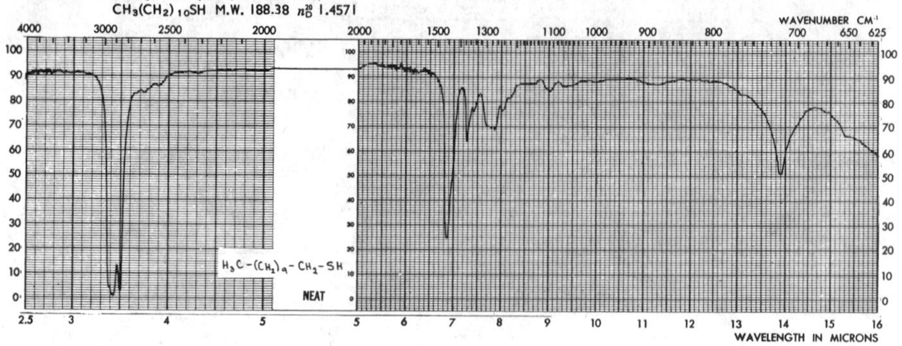

$H_3C-(CH_2)_9-CH_2-SH$ NEAT

B

D22,140-6 **1-Dodecanethiol** (lauryl mercaptan)
$CH_3(CH_2)_{11}SH$ M.W. 202.40 n_D^{20} 1.4587

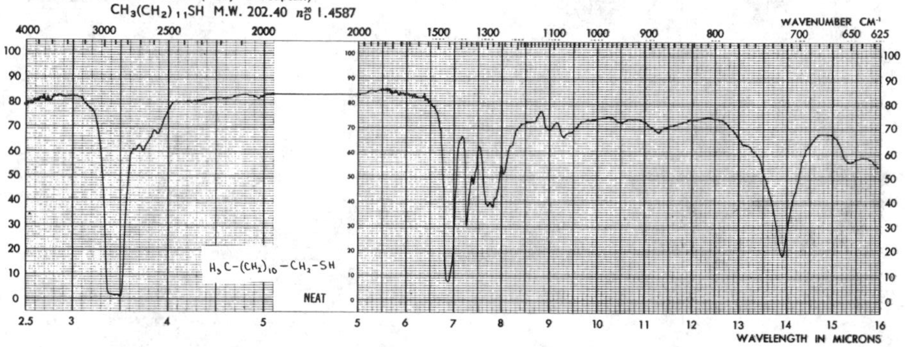

$H_3C-(CH_2)_{10}-CH_2-SH$ NEAT

C

T940-6 **Tetradecanethiol, tech.**
$CH_3(CH_2)_{13}SH$ M.W. 230.46 n_D^{20} 1.4597
b.p. 160-166°/3 mm.

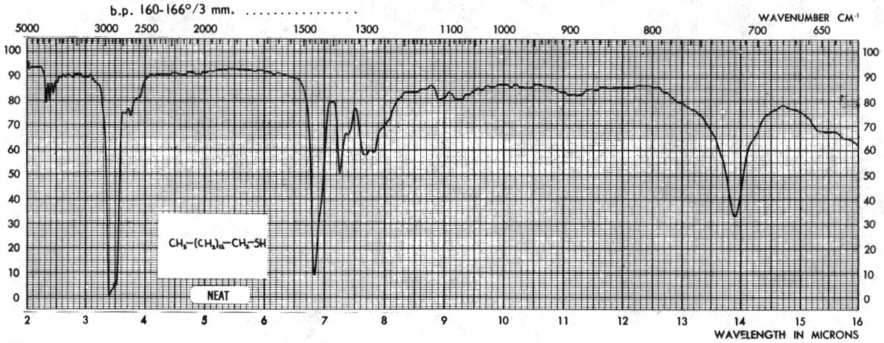

$CH_3-(CH_2)_{12}-CH_2-SH$ NEAT

D

H763-7 **n-Hexadecyl mercaptan** (hexadecanethiol)
$CH_3(CH_2)_{15}SH$ M.W. 258.51 m.p. 18-20°

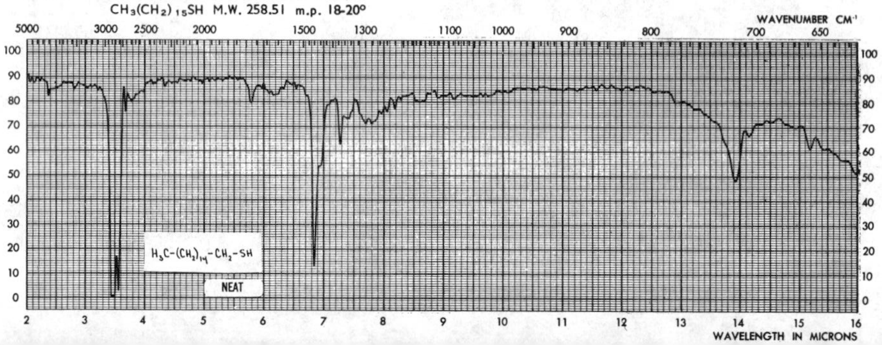

$H_3C-(CH_2)_{14}-CH_2-SH$ NEAT

E

O-185-8 **n-Octadecyl mercaptan** (octadecanethiol)
$CH_3(CH_2)_{17}SH$ M.W. 286.57 m.p. 29-31°

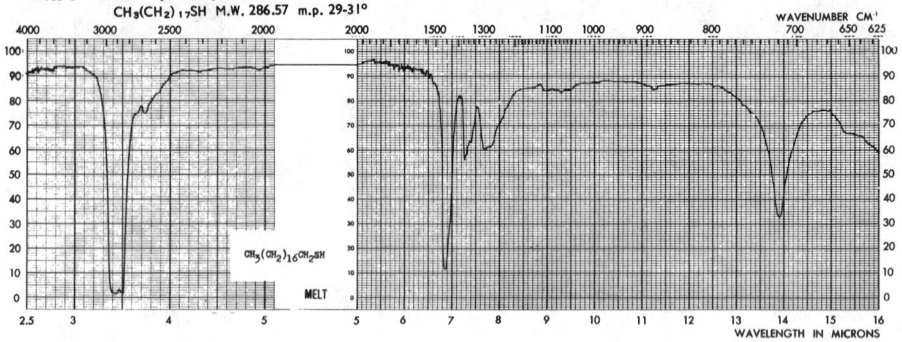

$CH_3(CH_2)_{16}CH_2SH$ MELT

F

P5077-3 **2-Propanethiol** (isopropyl mercaptan)
$(CH_3)_2CHSH$ M.W. 76.16 n_D^{20} 1.4241

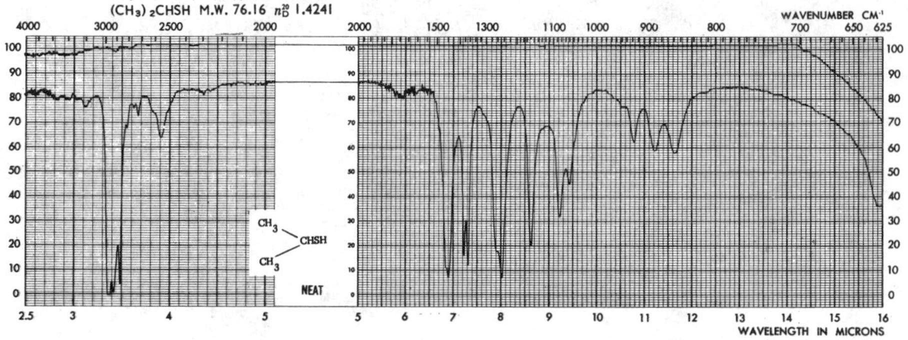

$(CH_3)_2CHSH$ NEAT

G

11,291-7 **2-Methyl-1-propanethiol** (isobutyl mercaptan)
$(CH_3)_2CHCH_2SH$ M.W. 90.19 n_D^{20} 1.4372
b.p. 87-89°

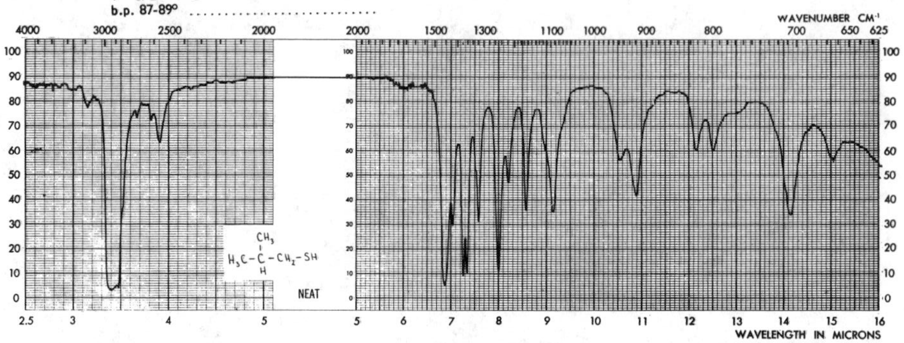

$H_3C-CH(CH_3)-CH_2-SH$ NEAT

H

10,291-1 **1-Methyl-1-propanethiol** (2-butanethiol, sec.-butyl mercaptan)
$C_2H_5CH(CH_3)SH$ M.W. 90.19
n_D^{20} 1.4360

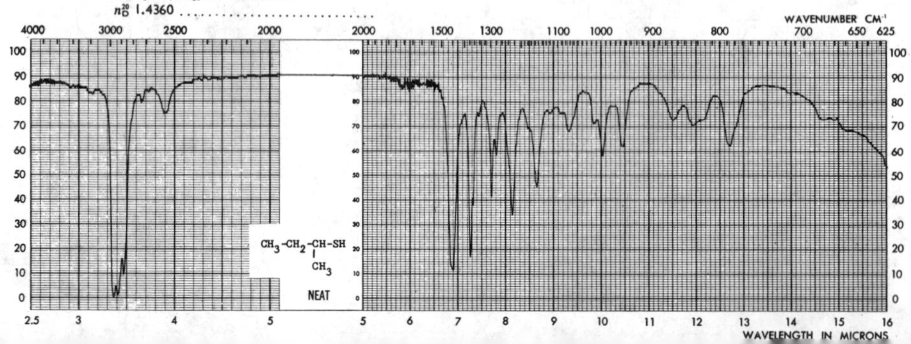

$CH_3-CH_2-CH(CH_3)-SH$ NEAT

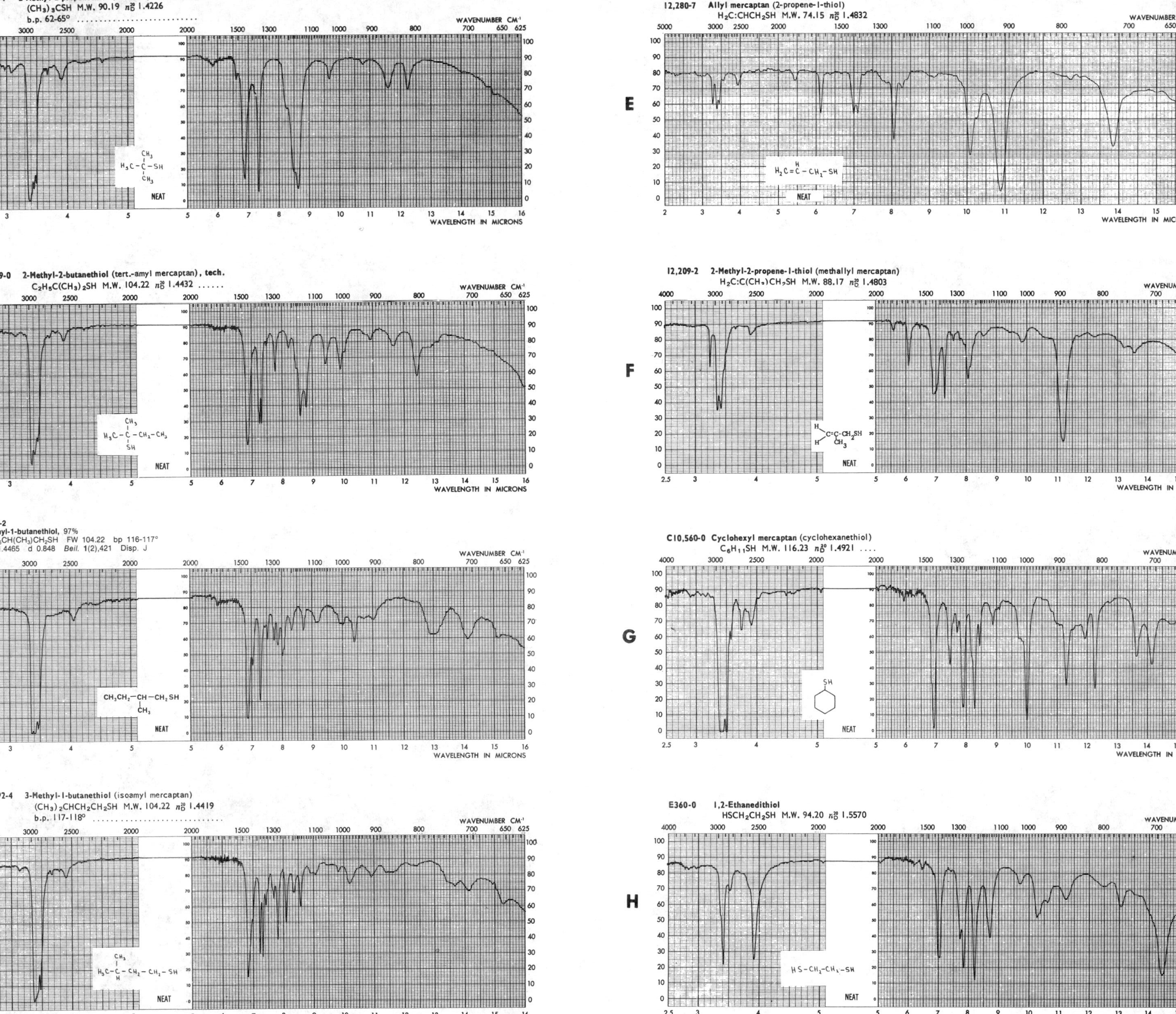
A
10,920-7 2-Methyl-2-propanethiol (tert.-butyl mercaptan)
$(CH_3)_3CSH$ M.W. 90.19 n_D^{20} 1.4226
b.p. 62-65°
NEAT
B
13,409-0 2-Methyl-2-butanethiol (tert.-amyl mercaptan), tech.
$C_2H_5C(CH_3)_2SH$ M.W. 104.22 n_D^{20} 1.4432
NEAT
C
19,113-2
2-Methyl-1-butanethiol, 97%
$C_2H_5CH(CH_3)CH_2SH$ FW 104.22 bp 116-117°
n_D^{20} 1.4465 d 0.848 Beil. 1(2),421 Disp. J
$CH_3CH_2-CH-CH_2SH$
NEAT
D
11,592-4 3-Methyl-1-butanethiol (isoamyl mercaptan)
$(CH_3)_2CHCH_2CH_2SH$ M.W. 104.22 n_D^{20} 1.4419
b.p. 117-118°
NEAT
E
12,280-7 Allyl mercaptan (2-propene-1-thiol)
$H_2C:CHCH_2SH$ M.W. 74.15 n_D^{20} 1.4832
NEAT
F
12,209-2 2-Methyl-2-propene-1-thiol (methallyl mercaptan)
$H_2C:C(CH_3)CH_2SH$ M.W. 88.17 n_D^{20} 1.4803
NEAT
G
C10,560-0 Cyclohexyl mercaptan (cyclohexanethiol)
$C_6H_{11}SH$ M.W. 116.23 n_D^{20} 1.4921
NEAT
H
E360-0 1,2-Ethanedithiol
$HSCH_2CH_2SH$ M.W. 94.20 n_D^{20} 1.5570
$HS-CH_2-CH_2-SH$
NEAT
WAVENUMBER CM⁻¹
WAVELENGTH IN MICRONS
ALDRICH

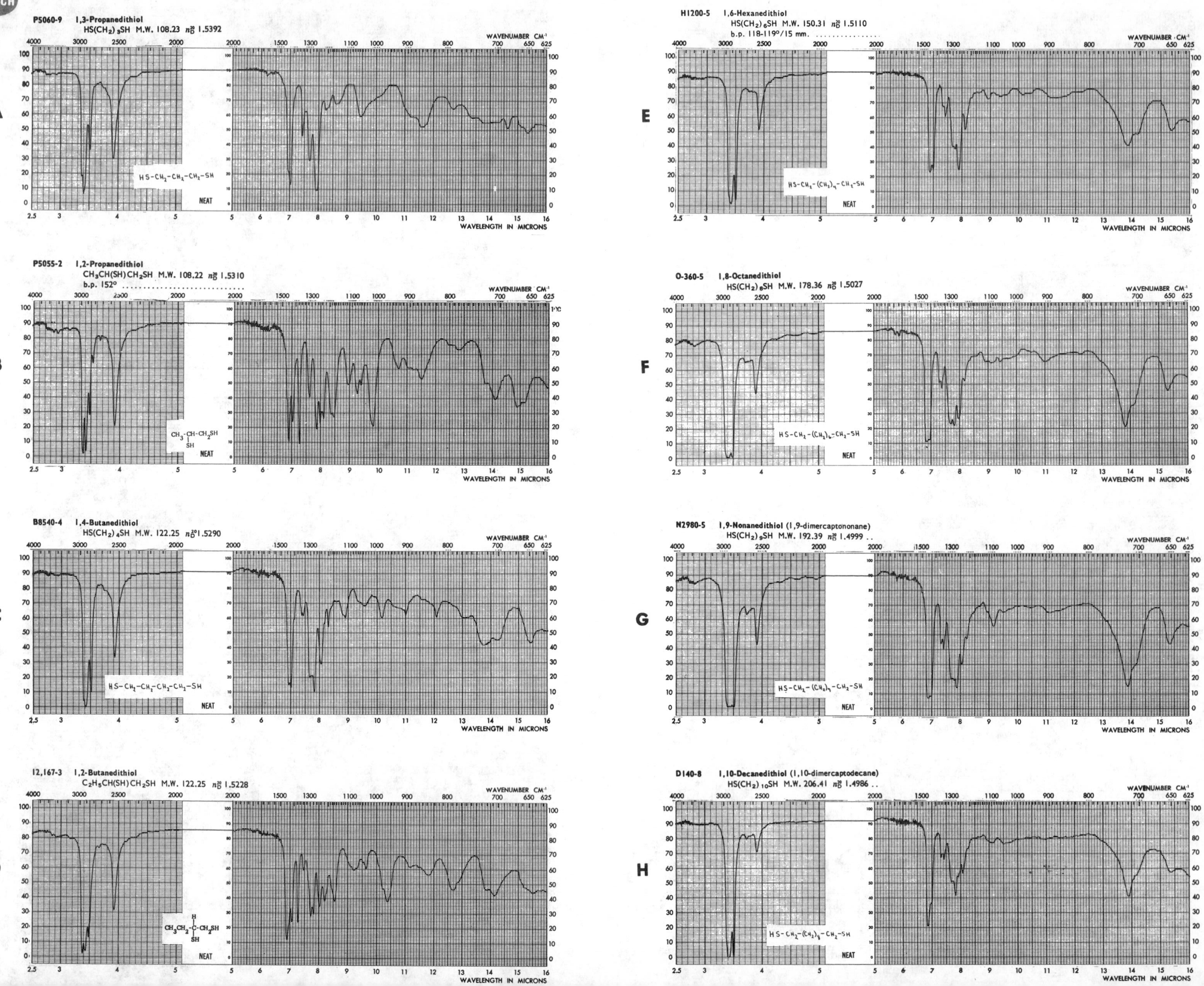
ALDRICH
A
P5060-9 1,3-Propanedithiol
HS(CH2)3SH M.W. 108.23 n20D 1.5392
HS-CH2-CH2-CH2-SH
NEAT
B
P5055-2 1,2-Propanedithiol
CH3CH(SH)CH2SH M.W. 108.22 n20D 1.5310
b.p. 152°
CH3-CH-CH2SH
SH
NEAT
C
B8540-4 1,4-Butanedithiol
HS(CH2)4SH M.W. 122.25 n20D 1.5290
HS-CH2-CH2-CH2-CH2-SH
NEAT
D
12,167-3 1,2-Butanedithiol
C2H5CH(SH)CH2SH M.W. 122.25 n20D 1.5228
CH3CH2-C(H)-CH2SH
SH
NEAT
E
H1200-5 1,6-Hexanedithiol
HS(CH2)6SH M.W. 150.31 n20D 1.5110
b.p. 118-119°/15 mm.
HS-CH2-(CH2)4-CH2-SH
NEAT
F
O-360-5 1,8-Octanedithiol
HS(CH2)8SH M.W. 178.36 n20D 1.5027
HS-CH2-(CH2)6-CH2-SH
NEAT
G
N2980-5 1,9-Nonanedithiol (1,9-dimercaptononane)
HS(CH2)9SH M.W. 192.39 n20D 1.4999
HS-CH2-(CH2)7-CH2-SH
NEAT
H
D140-8 1,10-Decanedithiol (1,10-dimercaptodecane)
HS(CH2)10SH M.W. 206.41 n20D 1.4986
HS-CH2-(CH2)8-CH2-SH
NEAT
WAVENUMBER CM-1
WAVELENGTH IN MICRONS

A

M400-7 **2-Mercaptoethyl sulfide** (2,2'-thiodiethanethiol)
$(HSCH_2CH_2)_2S$ M.W. 154.32 n_D^{20} 1.5982
b.p. 135-136°/10 mm.

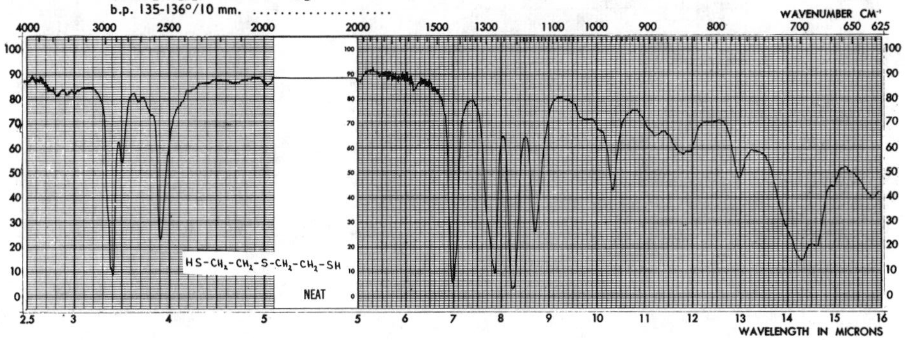

HS-CH₂-CH₂-S-CH₂-CH₂-SH — NEAT

B

M380-9 **2-Mercaptoethyl ether** (2,2'-oxydiethanethiol), **tech.**
$(HSCH_2CH_2)_2O$ M.W. 138.25 n_D^{20} 1.5276

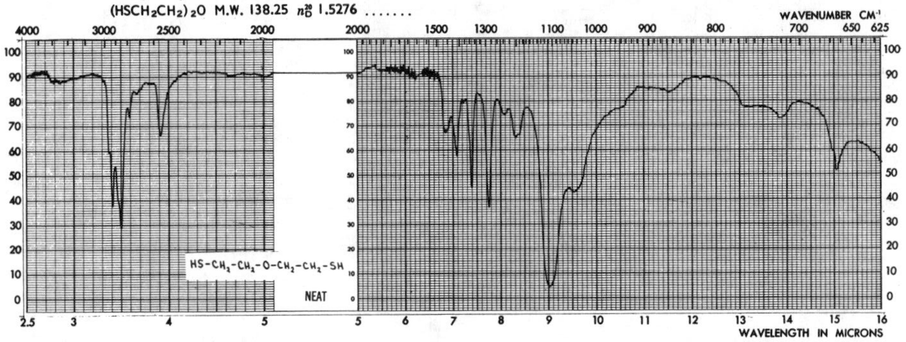

HS-CH₂-CH₂-O-CH₂-CH₂-SH — NEAT

C

M275-6 **2,9-p-Menthanedithiol** (dipentene dimercaptan)
M.W. 204.40 n_D^{20} 1.5317

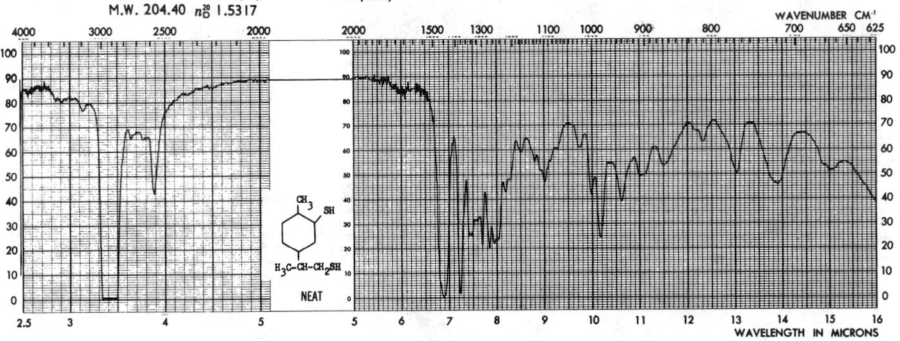

NEAT

D

C6860-1 **3-Chloropropanethiol**
$Cl(CH_2)_3SH$ M.W. 110.61 n_D^{20} 1.4919

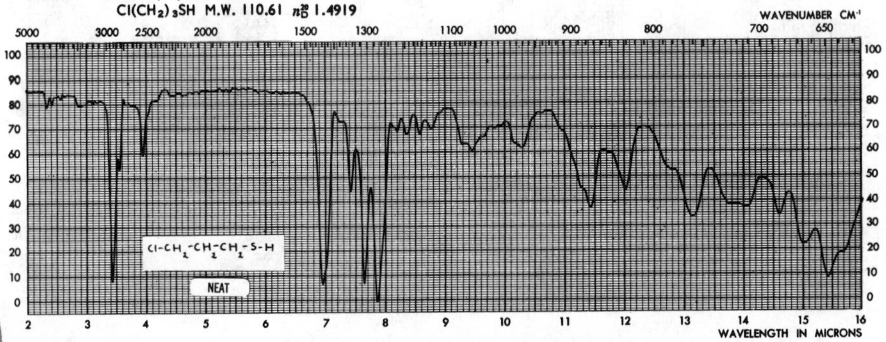

Cl-CH₂-CH₂-CH₂-S-H — NEAT

E

D6160-1 **2,2-Dichloro-1-ethanethiol**
Cl_2CHCH_2SH M.W. 131.02 n_D^{20} 1.5175

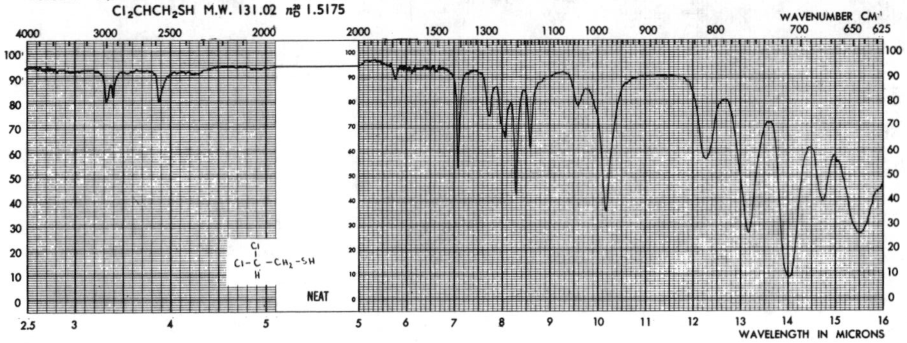

NEAT

F

M370-1 **2-Mercaptoethanol**
$HSCH_2CH_2OH$ M.W. 78.13 n_D^{20} 1.4964 b.p. 156.9°

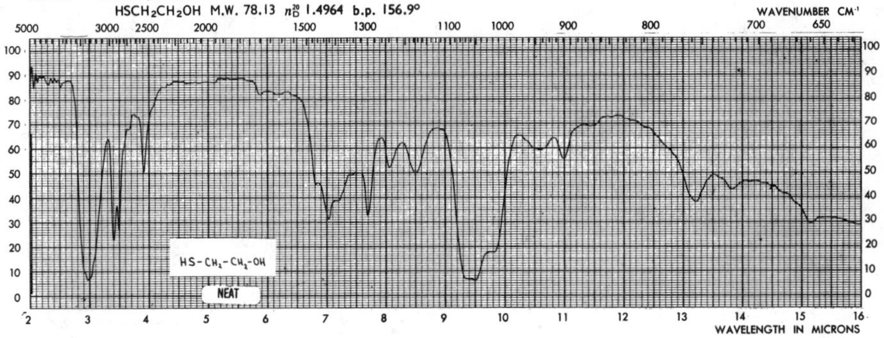

HS-CH₂-CH₂-OH — NEAT

G

21,009-9
1-Chloro-3-mercapto-2-propanol, 98%
$HSCH_2CH(OH)CH_2Cl$ FW 126.61
bp 57°/1.300mm. n_D^{20} 1.5276 d 1.277
Beil. 1(3),2156 Disp. J

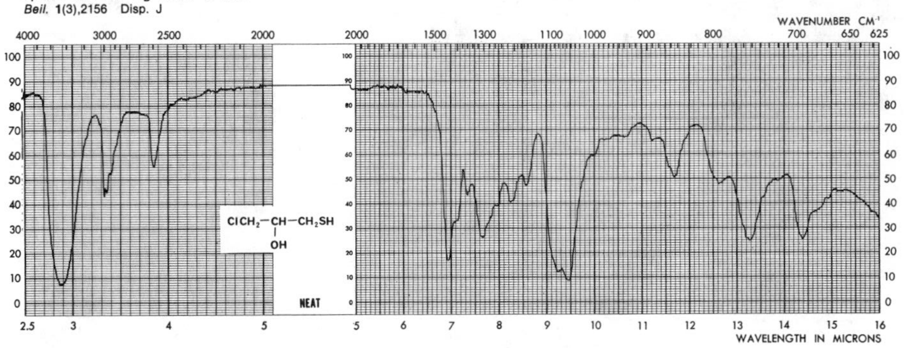

ClCH₂-CH(OH)-CH₂SH — NEAT

H

M560-7 **3-Mercapto-1,2-propanediol** (1-thioglycerol)
$HSCH_2CH(OH)CH_2OH$ M.W. 108.16 n_D^{20} 1.5243

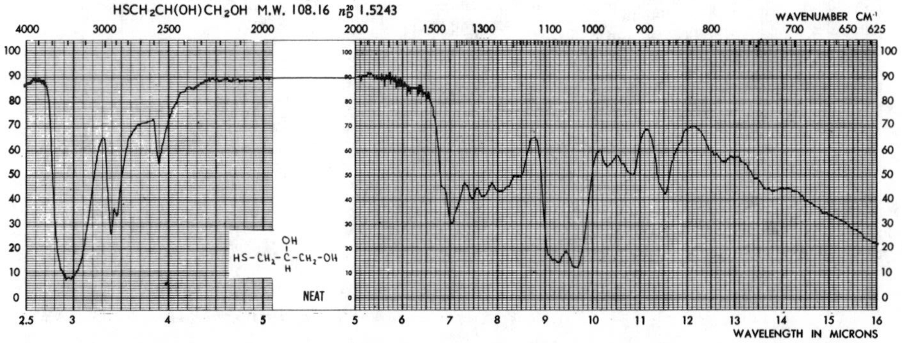

NEAT

ALDRICH ®

A 13,734-0 **1,3-Dimercapto-2-propanol, tech.**
$HSCH_2CH(OH)CH_2SH$ M.W. 124.22
n_D^{20} 1.5682

B D12,880-5 **2,3-Dimercapto-1-propanol (BAL)**
$HSCH_2CH(SH)CH_2OH$ M.W. 124.22 n_D^{20} 1.5731

C 22,229-1
3-Methylthio-1,2-propanediol, 99%
$CH_3SCH_2CH(OH)CH_2OH$ FW 122.19 n_D^{20} 1.5160
d 1.164 Disp. C

D 22,230-5
3-Ethylthio-1,2-propanediol, 97%
$C_2H_5SCH_2CH(OH)CH_2OH$ FW 136.21 n_D^{20} 1.5065
d 1.095 Disp. C

E 15,046-0 **Dithiothreitol** (Cleland's reagent, *threo*-1,4-dimercapto-2,3-butanediol, DTT)
$HSCH_2CH(OH)CH(OH)CH_2SH$ M.W. 154.25
m.p. 42-44°

F 16,176-4
Dithioerythritol, 99+%, GOLD LABEL (*erythro*-1,4-dimercapto-2,3-butanediol, DTE)
$HSCH_2CH(OH)CH(OH)CH_2SH$
M.W. 154.25 m.p. 82-84°

G 21,925-8
1,4-Dithio-L-threitol, 95% (optically active Cleland's reagent)
$HSCH_2CH(OH)CH(OH)CH_2SH$ FW 154.25
mp 49-51° $[\alpha]_D^{20}$ -14° (c=3, $CHCl_3$) Disp. J

H M8163-2 **Methyl sulfide**
$(CH_3)_2S$ M.W. 62.13 n_D^{20} 1.4351

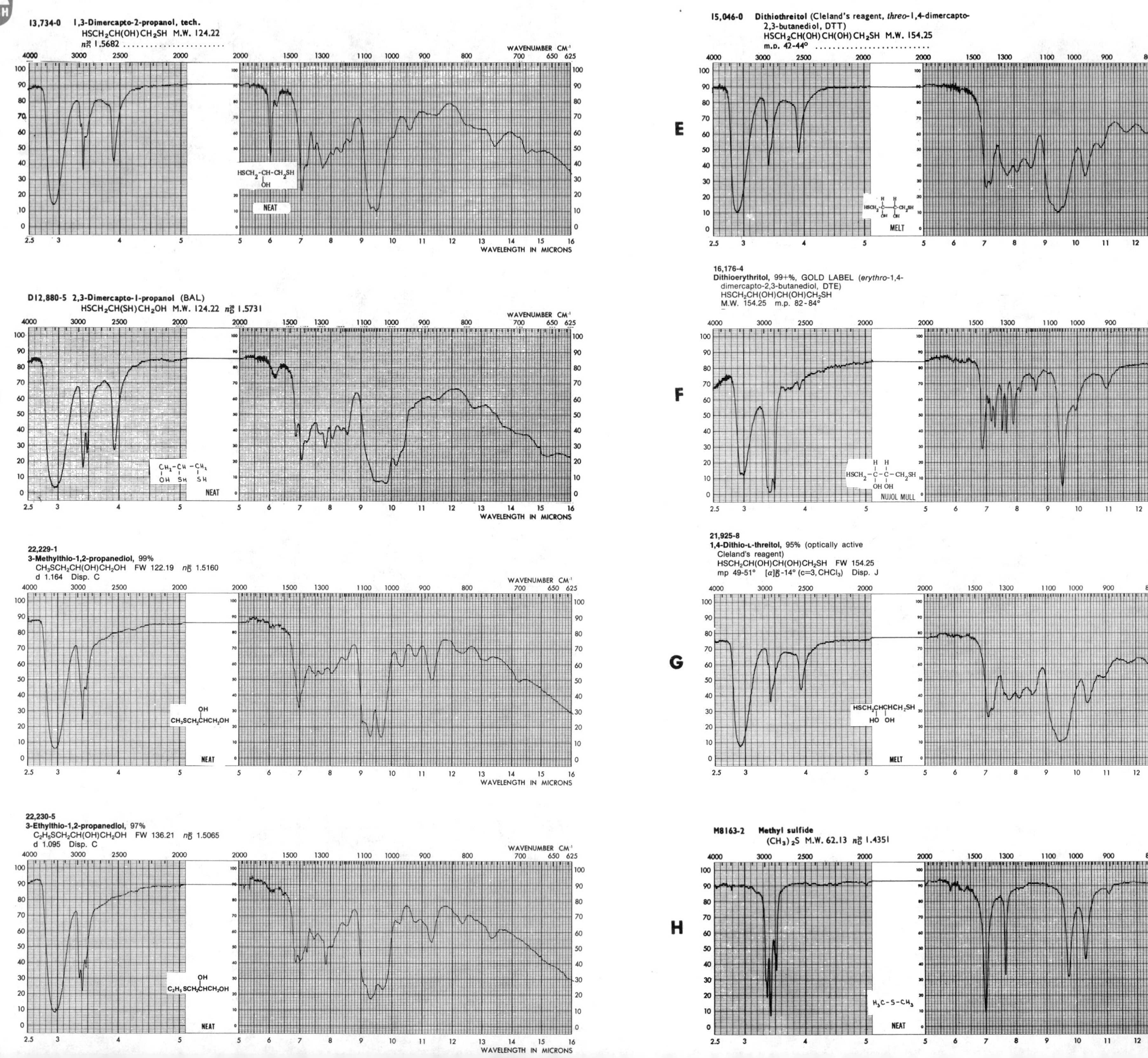

A 15,031-2 **Methyl disulfide (dimethyl disulfide)**
$(CH_3)_2S_2$ M.W. 94.20 n_D^{20} 1.5253
b.p. 110°

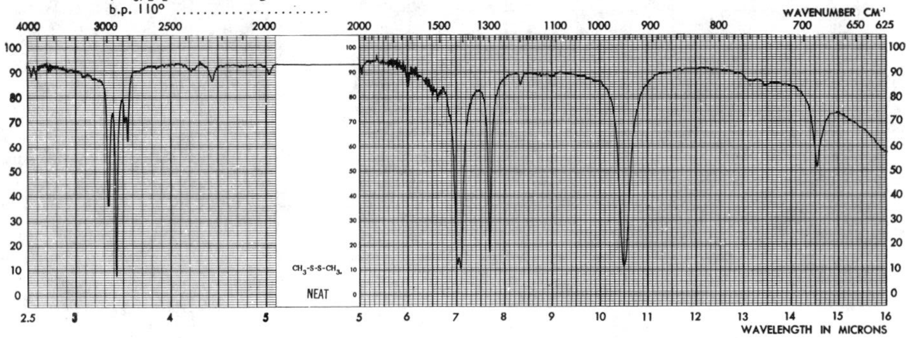

$CH_3-S-S-CH_3$
NEAT

WAVENUMBER CM⁻¹ — WAVELENGTH IN MICRONS

B 10,724-7 **Ethyl sulfide**
$(C_2H_5)_2S$ M.W. 90.19 n_D^{20} 1.4430 b.p. 92°

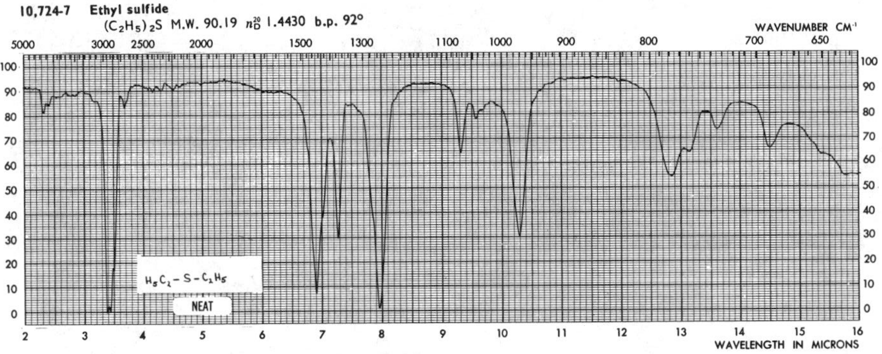

$H_5C_2-S-C_2H_5$
NEAT

WAVENUMBER CM⁻¹ — WAVELENGTH IN MICRONS

C E2622-3 **Ethyl disulfide**
$(C_2H_5)_2S_2$ M.W. 122.25 n_D^{20} 1.5060

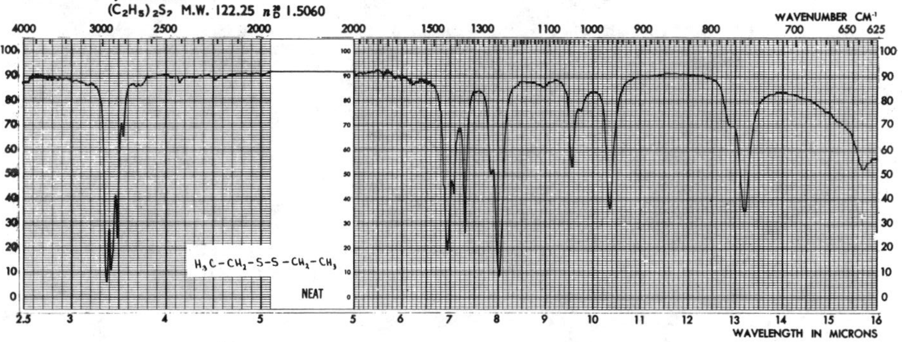

$H_3C-CH_2-S-S-CH_2-CH_3$
NEAT

WAVENUMBER CM⁻¹ — WAVELENGTH IN MICRONS

D D21,760 **2,5-Dithiahexane**
$CH_3S(CH_2)_2SCH_3$ M.W. 122.25 n_D^{20} 1.5275

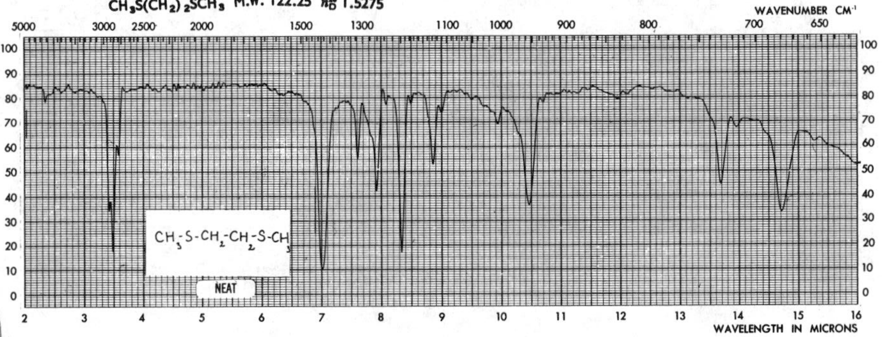

$CH_3-S-CH_2-CH_2-S-CH_3$
NEAT

WAVENUMBER CM⁻¹ — WAVELENGTH IN MICRONS

E M7540-3 **Methyl n-propyl sulfide**
$CH_3CH_2CH_2SCH_3$ M.W. 90.19 n_D^{20} 1.4438

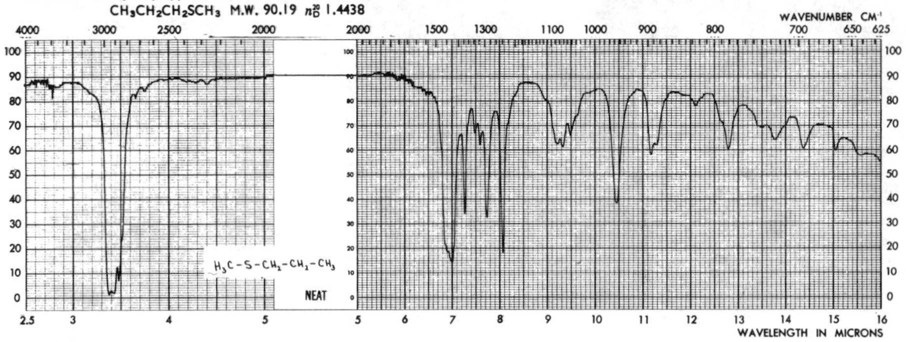

$H_3C-S-CH_2-CH_2-CH_3$
NEAT

WAVENUMBER CM⁻¹ — WAVELENGTH IN MICRONS

F P5428 **n-Propyl sulfide** ....

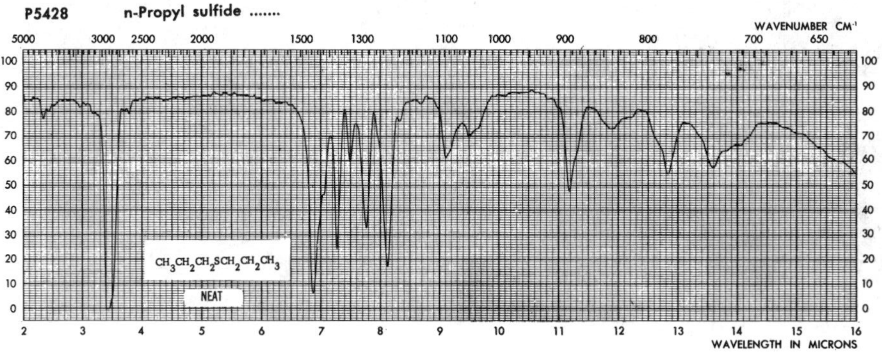

$CH_3CH_2CH_2SCH_2CH_2CH_3$
NEAT

WAVENUMBER CM⁻¹ — WAVELENGTH IN MICRONS

G 14,922-5 **Propyl disulfide, tech., 94%**
$(CH_3CH_2CH_2)_2S_2$ M.W. 150.31 n_D^{20} 1.4952
b.p. 192-197°

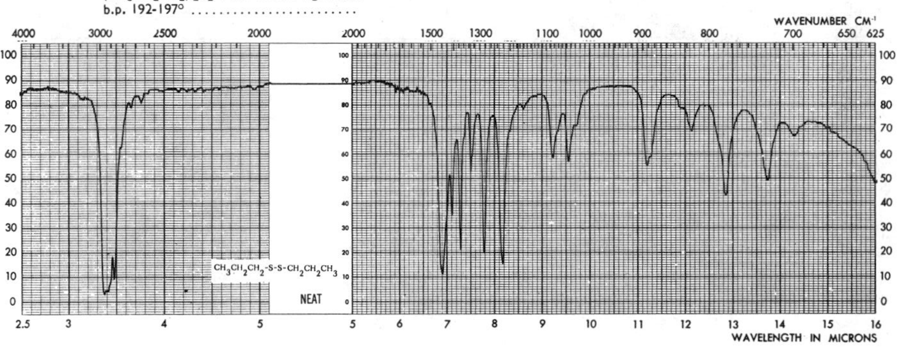

$CH_3CH_2CH_2-S-S-CH_2CH_2CH_3$
NEAT

WAVENUMBER CM⁻¹ — WAVELENGTH IN MICRONS

H 12,427-3 **n-Butyl methyl sulfide**
$CH_3(CH_2)_3SCH_3$ M.W. 104.22

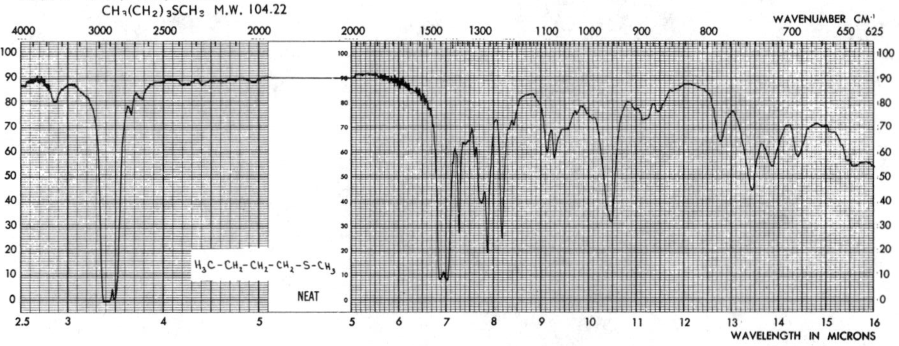

$H_3C-CH_2-CH_2-CH_2-S-CH_3$
NEAT

WAVENUMBER CM⁻¹ — WAVELENGTH IN MICRONS

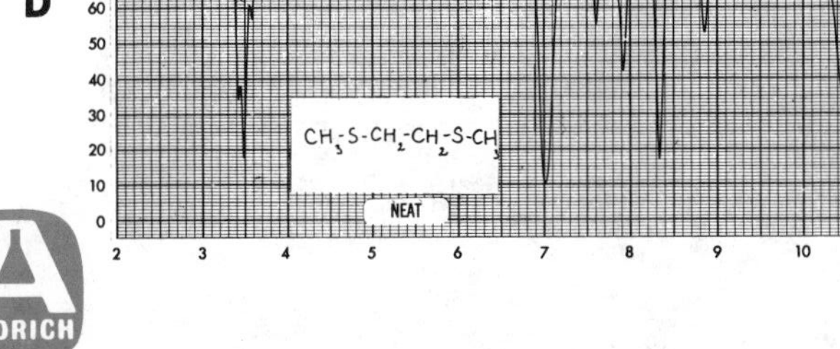

A

B10,179-6 n-Butyl sulfide (di-n-butyl sulfide)
$[CH_3(CH_2)_3]_2S$ M.W. 146.30 n_D^{20} 1.4530

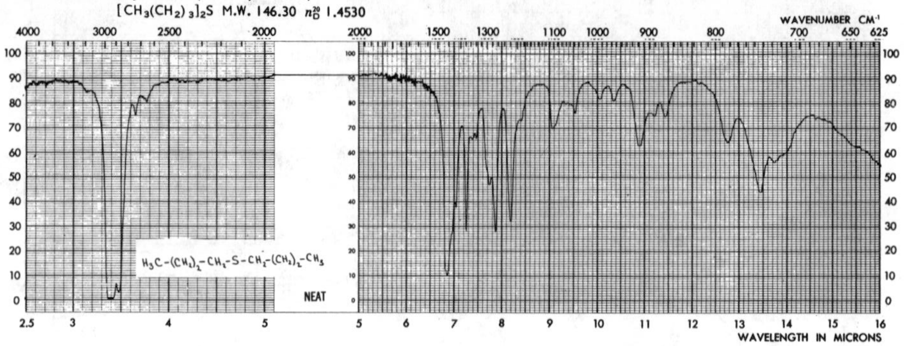

$H_3C-(CH_2)_2-CH_2-S-CH_2-(CH_2)_2-CH_3$

NEAT

B

B9398-9 n-Butyl disulfide
$[CH_3(CH_2)_3]_2S_2$ M.W. 178.36 n_D^{20} 1.4885

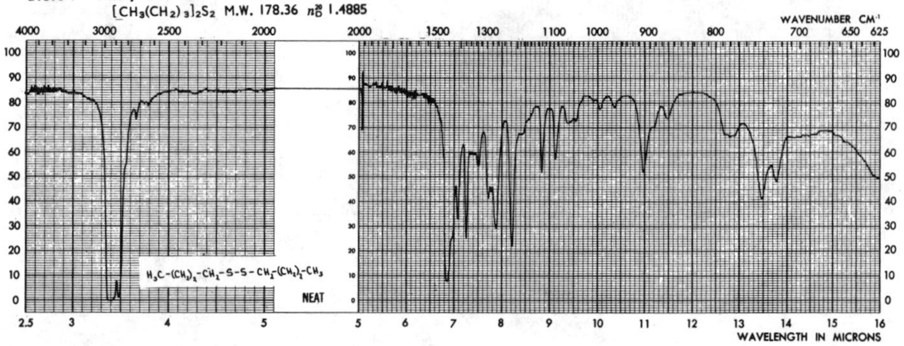

$H_3C-(CH_2)_2-CH_2-S-S-CH_2-(CH_2)_2-CH_3$

NEAT

C

H1460-1 n-Hexyl sulfide
$[CH_3(CH_2)_5]_2S$ M.W. 202.40 n_D^{20} 1.4587

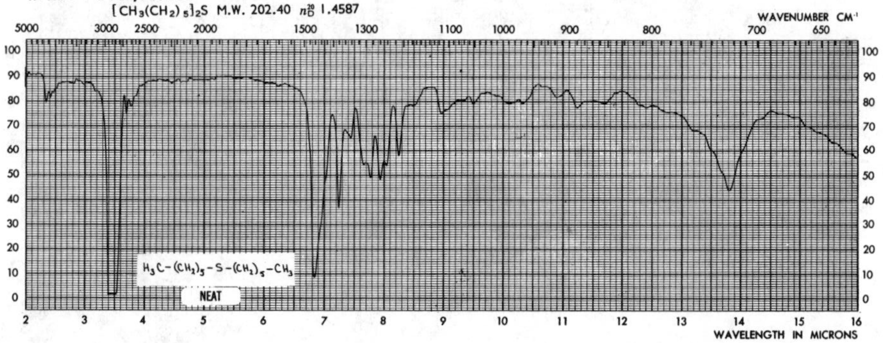

$H_3C-(CH_2)_5-S-(CH_2)_5-CH_3$

NEAT

D

O-700-7 n-Octyl sulfide
$[CH_3(CH_2)_7]_2S$ M.W. 258.51 n_D^{20} 1.4610
b.p. 180°/10 mm.

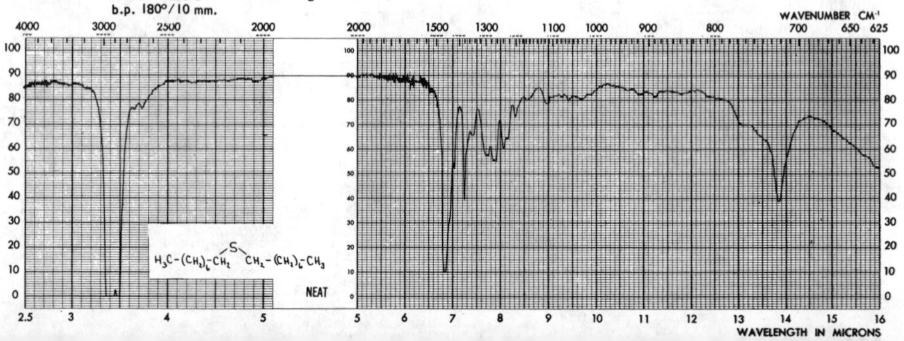

$H_3C-(CH_2)_6-CH_2-S-CH_2-(CH_2)_6-CH_3$

NEAT

E

D260 n-Decyl sulfide
$(C_{10}H_{21})_2S$ M.W. 314.62 n_D^{20} 1.4618

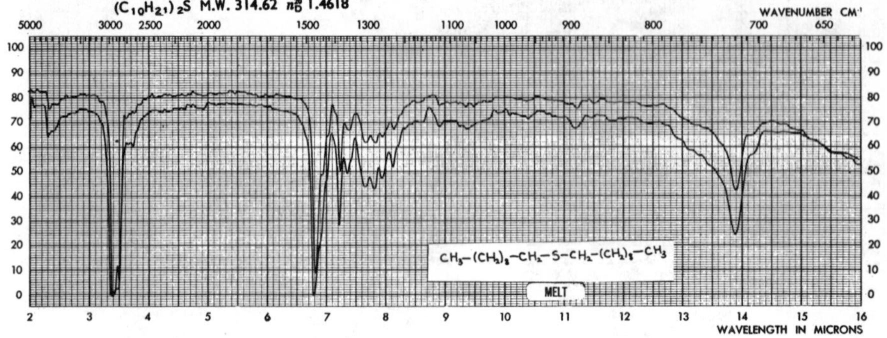

$CH_3-(CH_2)_8-CH_2-S-CH_2-(CH_2)_8-CH_3$

MELT

F

D22,280-1 n-Dodecyl sulfide
$[CH_3(CH_2)_{11}]_2S$ M.W. 370.73 m.p. 41.5-42°

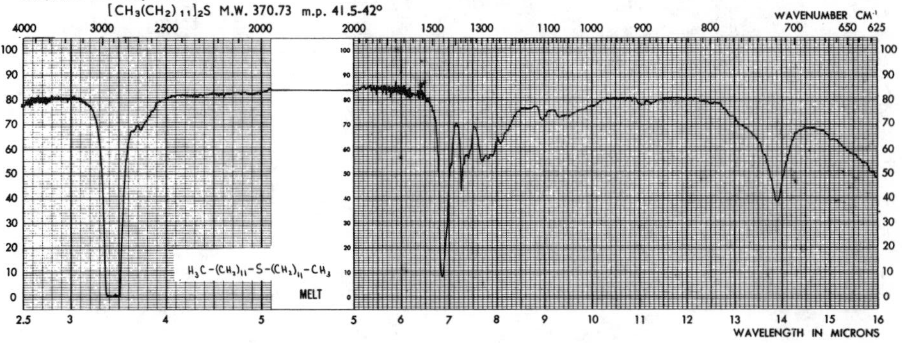

$H_3C-(CH_2)_{11}-S-(CH_2)_{11}-CH_3$

MELT

G

13,828-2 n-Octadecyl sulfide
$[CH_3(CH_2)_{17}]_2S$ M.W. 539.05 m.p. 66-68°

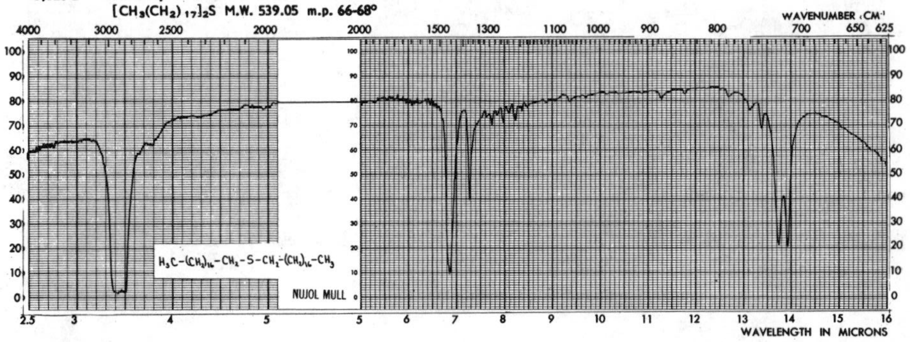

$H_3C-(CH_2)_{16}-CH_2-S-CH_2-(CH_2)_{16}-CH_3$

NUJOL MULL

H

I—2,680-9
Isopropyl sulfide, 98% (diisopropyl sulfide)
$[(CH_3)_2CH]_2S$
M.W. 118.24 b.p. 120°/763mm. n_D^{20} 1.4379
d 0.814 Beil. 1,367 *STENCH*

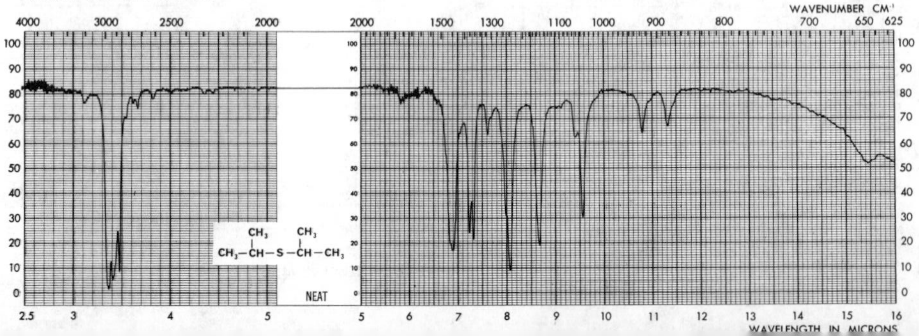

$CH_3-CH(CH_3)-S-CH(CH_3)-CH_3$

NEAT

A 1-2200-5 **Isopropyl disulfide, puriss.**
$[(CH_3)_2CH]_2S_2$ M.W. 150.31 n_D^{20} 1.4906
b.p. 175-177°

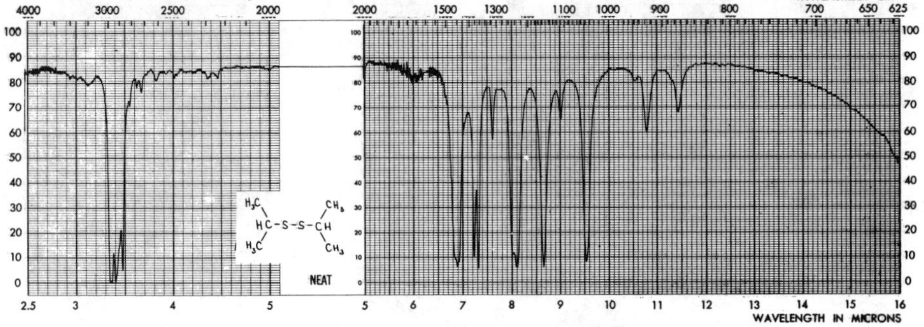

NEAT

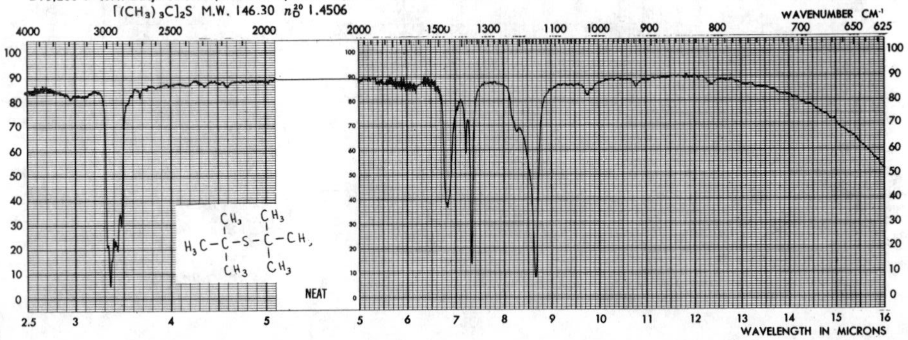

E 16,850-5
tert.-**Butyl disulfide**, tech., 88%, remainder trisulfide
$[(CH_3)_3C]_2S_2$
M.W. 178.36 b.p. 198-204° n_D^{20} 1.4930 d 0.909
STENCH

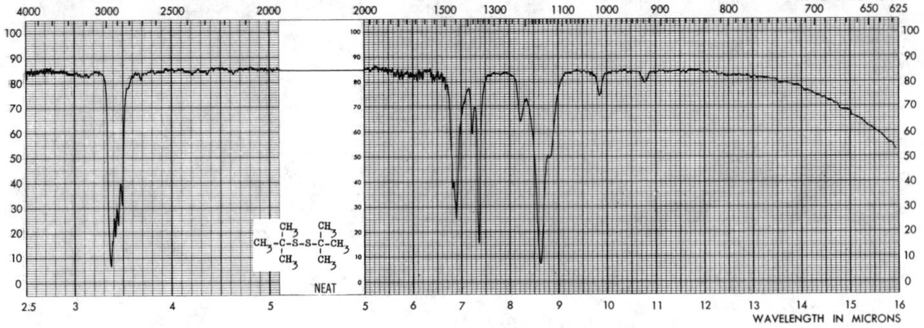

NEAT

B 12,431-1 **sec.-Butyl sulfide (di-sec.-butyl sulfide)**
$[C_2H_5CH(CH_3)]_2S$ M.W. 146.30

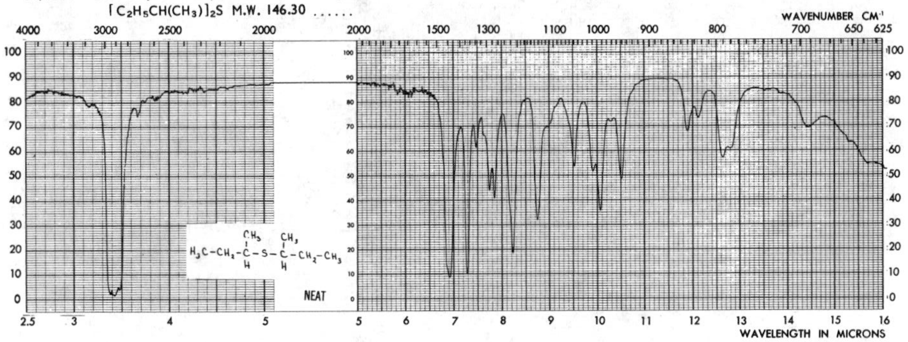

NEAT

F A3420-1 **Allyl methyl sulfide**
$H_2C{:}CHCH_2SCH_3$ M.W. 88.17 n_D^{20} 1.4714
b.p. 91-93°

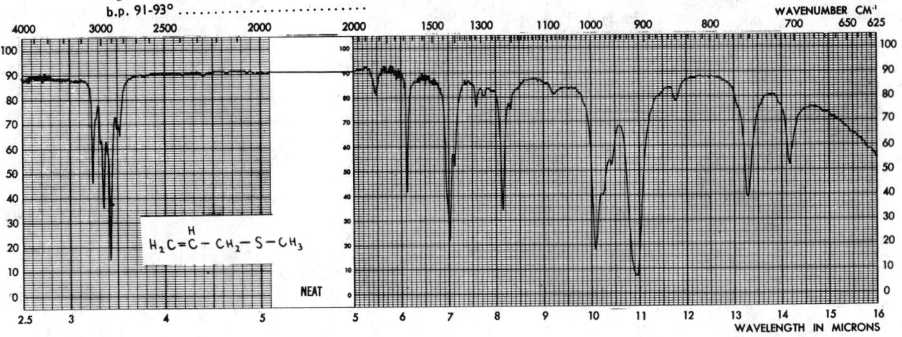

NEAT

C B9400-4 **sec.-Butyl disulfide**
$[C_2H_5CH(CH_3)]_2S_2$ M.W. 178.36

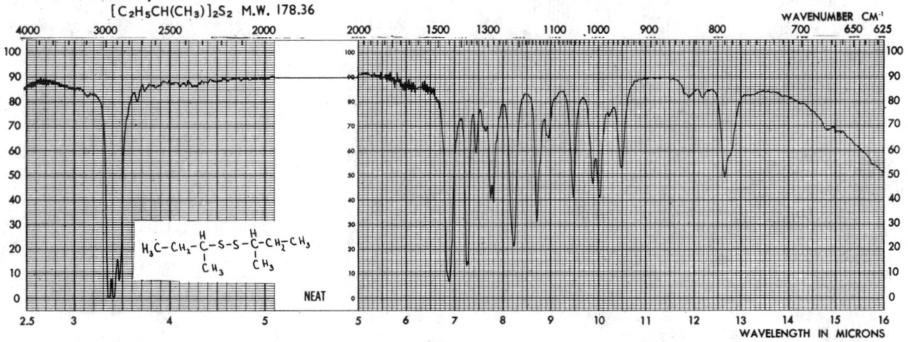

NEAT

G A3580-1 **Allyl sulfide**
$(H_2C{:}CHCH_2)_2S$ M.W. 114.21 n_D^{20} 1.4889

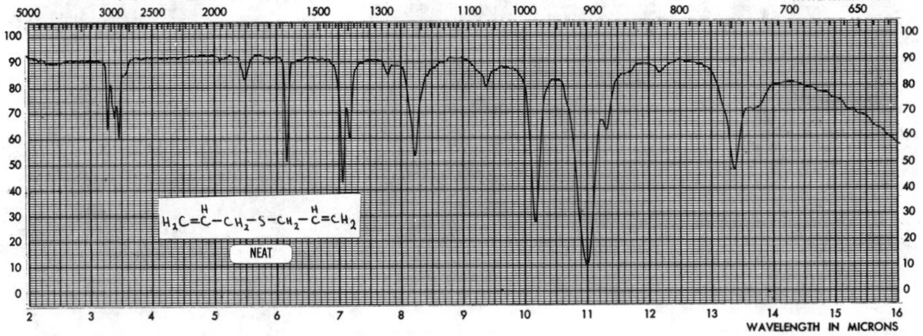

NEAT

D B10,200-8 **tert.-Butyl sulfide (di-tert.-butyl sulfide)**
$[(CH_3)_3C]_2S$ M.W. 146.30 n_D^{20} 1.4506

NEAT

H 12,210-6 **Methallyl sulfide**
$[H_2C{:}C(CH_3)CH_2]_2S$ M.W. 142.26
n_D^{20} 1.4835

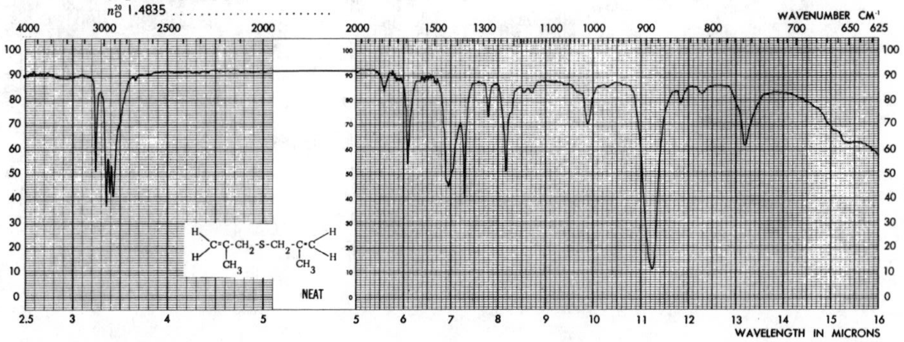

NEAT

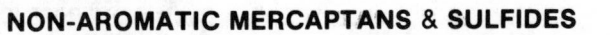

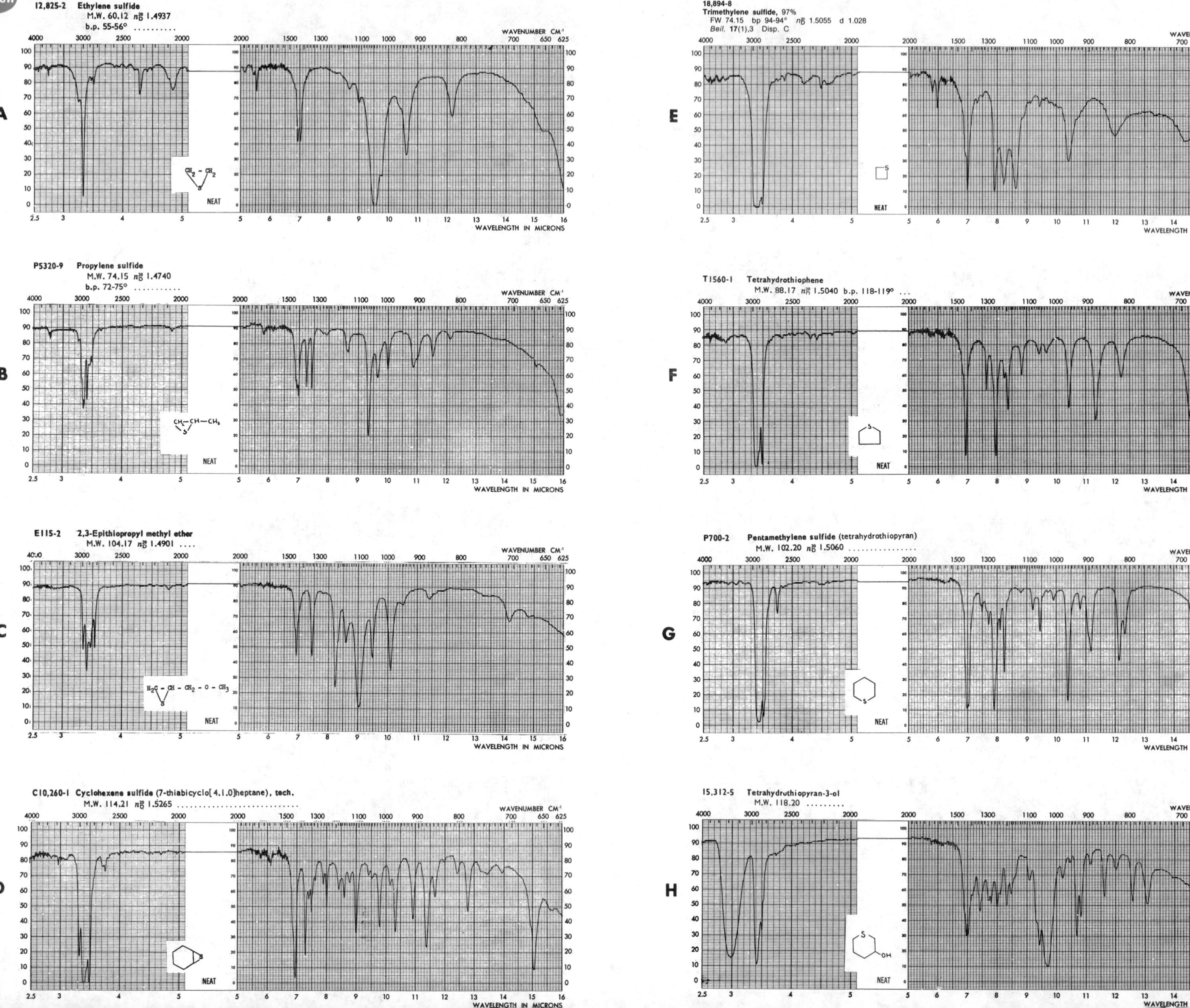
A
12,825-2 Ethylene sulfide
M.W. 60.12 n_D^{20} 1.4937
b.p. 55-56°
NEAT
B
P5320-9 Propylene sulfide
M.W. 74.15 n_D^{20} 1.4740
b.p. 72-75°
NEAT
C
E115-2 2,3-Epithiopropyl methyl ether
M.W. 104.17 n_D^{20} 1.4901
NEAT
D
C10,260-1 Cyclohexene sulfide (7-thiabicyclo[4.1.0]heptane), tech.
M.W. 114.21 n_D^{20} 1.5265
NEAT
E
18,894-8
Trimethylene sulfide, 97%
FW 74.15 bp 94-94° n_D^{20} 1.5055 d 1.028
Beil. 17(1),3 Disp. C
NEAT
F
T1560-1 Tetrahydrothiophene
M.W. 88.17 n_D^{20} 1.5040 b.p. 118-119°
NEAT
G
P700-2 Pentamethylene sulfide (tetrahydrothiopyran)
M.W. 102.20 n_D^{20} 1.5060
NEAT
H
15,312-5 Tetrahydrothiopyran-3-ol
M.W. 118.20
NEAT
WAVENUMBER CM⁻¹
WAVELENGTH IN MICRONS

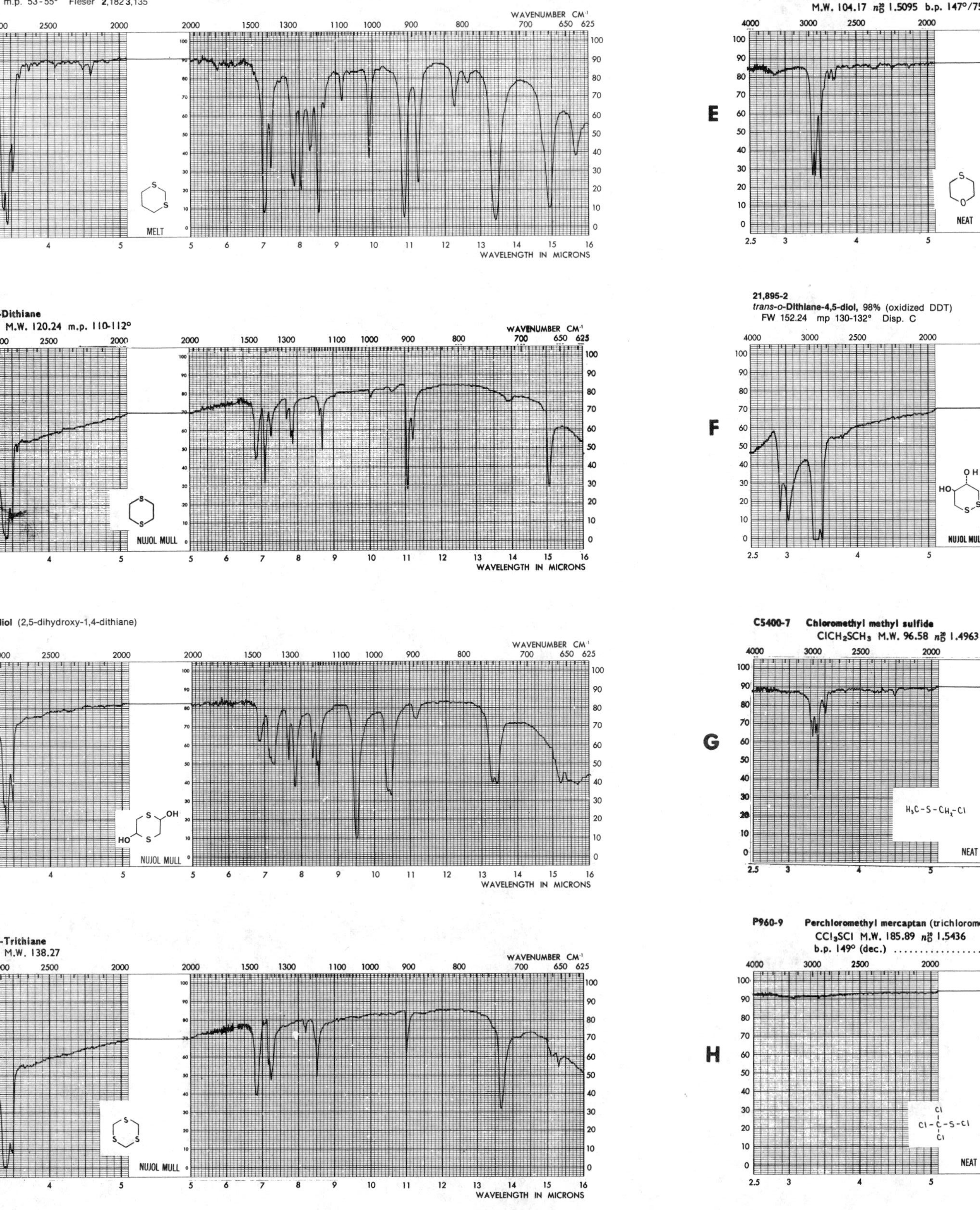
A
15,787-2
1,3-Dithiane, 97%
M.W. 120.24 m.p. 53-55° Fieser 2,182 3,135
MELT
B
D21,770-0 p-Dithiane
M.W. 120.24 m.p. 110-112°
NUJOL MULL
C
18,395-4
p-Dithiane-2,5-diol (2,5-dihydroxy-1,4-dithiane)
M.W. 152.24
NUJOL MULL
D
T8840-4 s-Trithiane
M.W. 138.27
NUJOL MULL
E
13,197-0 1,4-Thioxane (1,4-oxathiane)
M.W. 104.17 n_D^{20} 1.5095 b.p. 147°/755 mm.
NEAT
F
21,895-2
trans-o-Dithiane-4,5-diol, 98% (oxidized DDT)
FW 152.24 mp 130-132° Disp. C
NUJOL MULL
G
C5400-7 Chloromethyl methyl sulfide
$ClCH_2SCH_3$ M.W. 96.58 n_D^{20} 1.4963
$H_3C-S-CH_2-Cl$
NEAT
H
P960-9 Perchloromethyl mercaptan (trichloromethanesulfenyl chloride)
CCl_3SCl M.W. 185.89 n_D^{20} 1.5436
b.p. 149° (dec.)
NEAT
WAVENUMBER CM⁻¹
WAVELENGTH IN MICRONS
ALDRICH

A

T760-8 **1,2,2,2-Tetrachloroethyl-1-sulfenyl chloride**
$Cl_3CCH(Cl)SCl$ M.W. 234.36 n_D^{20} 1.5721 b.p. 57°/1 mm.

NEAT

B

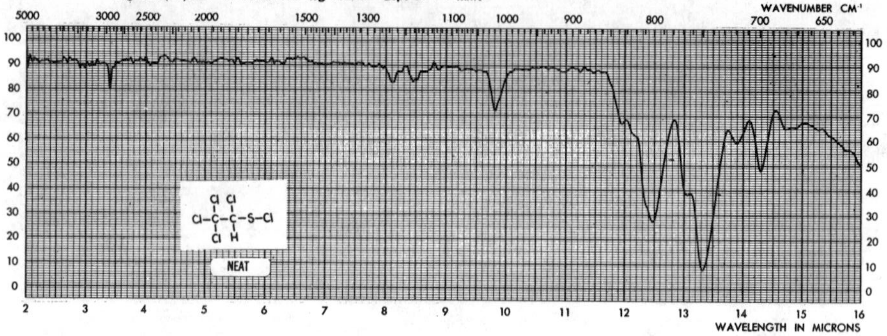

T8048-9 **Trimethylsulfonium iodide**
$(CH_3)_3SI$ M.W. 204.08 m.p. 213°

NUJOL MULL

C

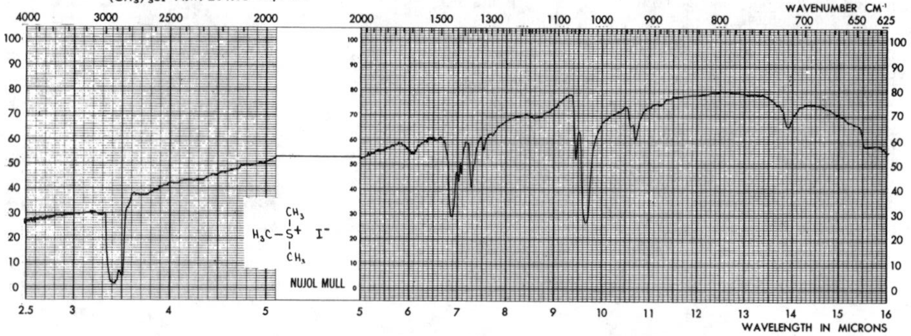

E3075-1 **Ethyl 2-hydroxyethyl sulfide [2-(ethylthio)-ethanol]**
$C_2H_5SCH_2CH_2OH$ M.W. 106.19 n_D^{20} 1.4869 ....

NEAT

D

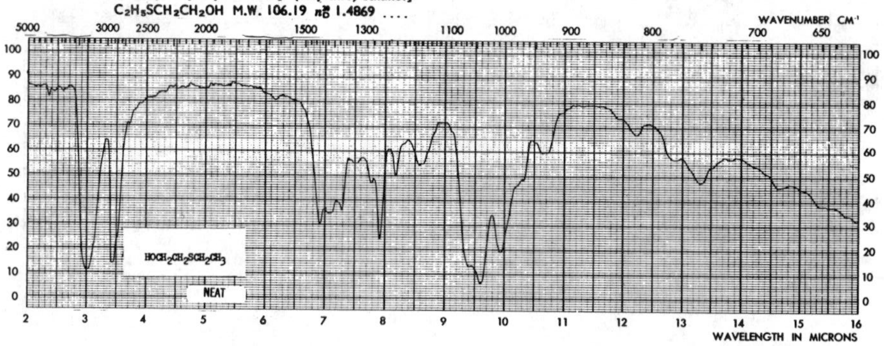

T2990-4 **2,2'-Thiodiethanol (thiodiglycol)**
$S(CH_2CH_2OH)_2$ M.W. 122.19 n_D^{20} 1.5164
b.p. 283° ....

NEAT

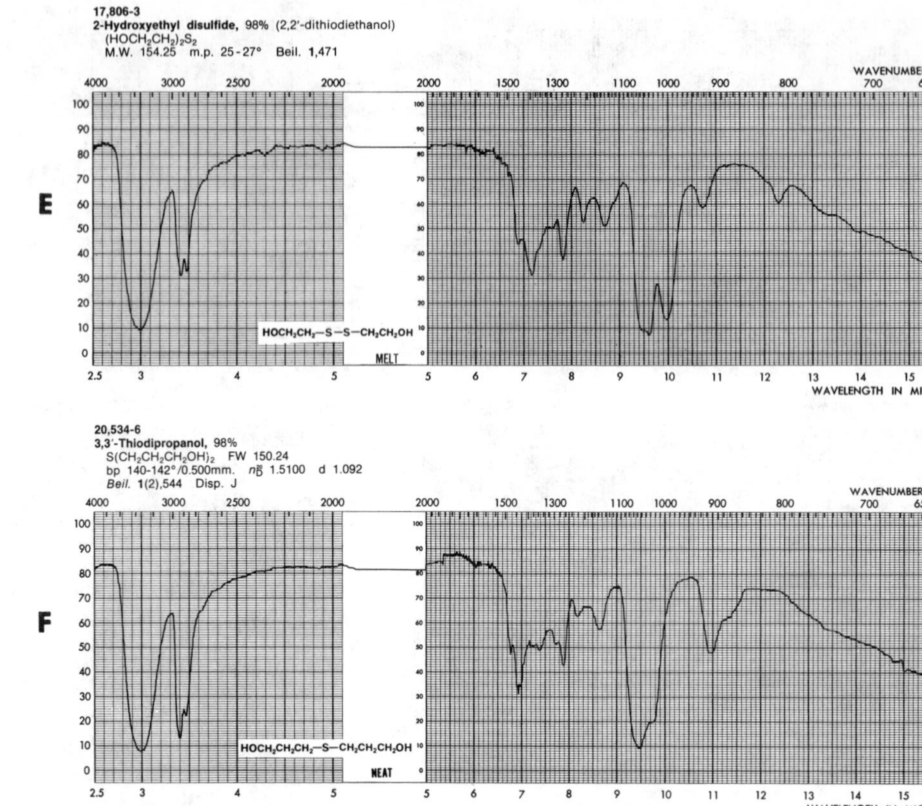

E

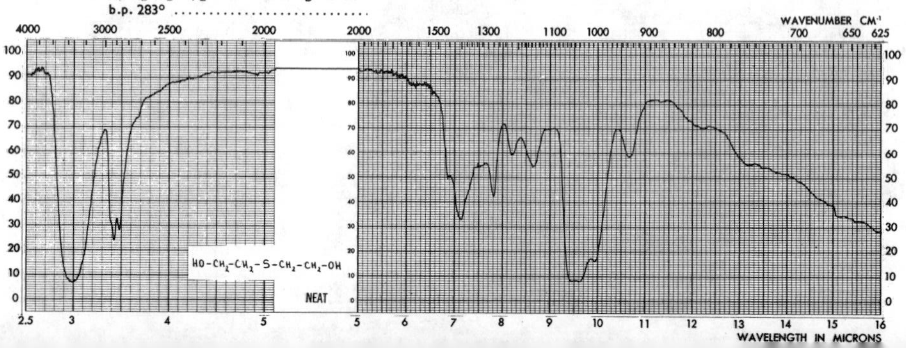

17,806-3
2-Hydroxyethyl disulfide, 98% (2,2'-dithiodiethanol)
$(HOCH_2CH_2)_2S_2$
M.W. 154.25 m.p. 25-27° Beil. 1,471

$HOCH_2CH_2-S-S-CH_2CH_2OH$

MELT

F

20,534-6
3,3'-Thiodipropanol, 98%
$S(CH_2CH_2CH_2OH)_2$ FW 150.24
bp 140-142°/0.500mm. n_D^{20} 1.5100 d 1.092
Beil. 1(2),544 Disp. J

$HOCH_2CH_2CH_2-S-CH_2CH_2CH_2OH$

NEAT

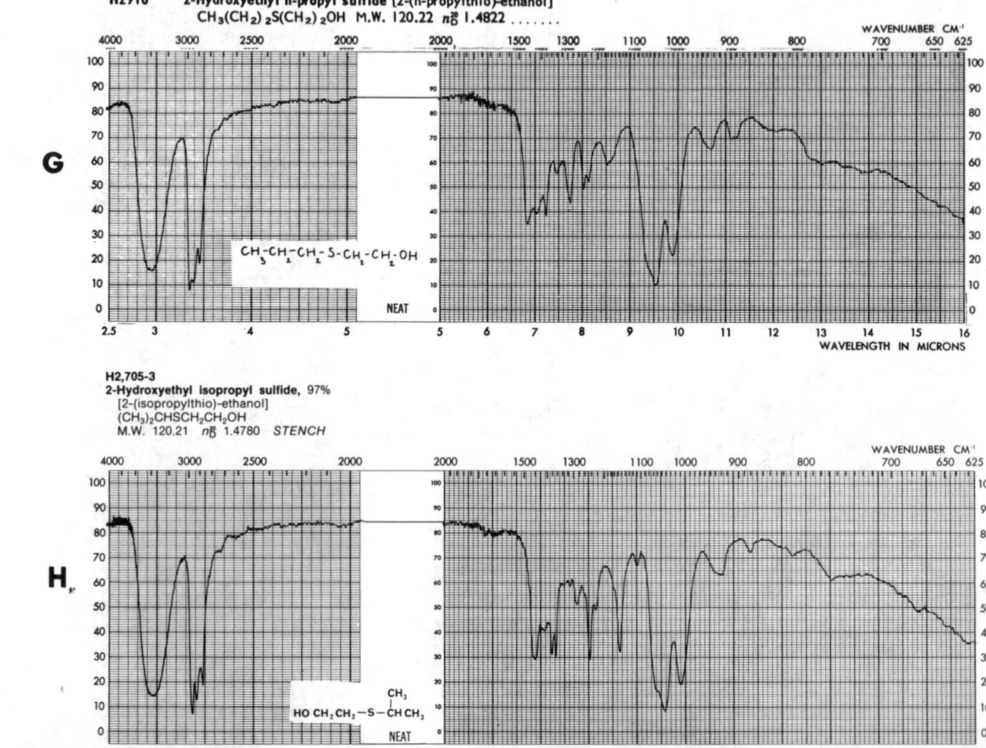

G

H2910 **2-Hydroxyethyl n-propyl sulfide [2-(n-propylthio)-ethanol]**
$CH_3(CH_2)_2S(CH_2)_2OH$ M.W. 120.22 n_D^{20} 1.4822 ....

NEAT

H

H2,705-3
2-Hydroxyethyl isopropyl sulfide, 97%
[2-(isopropylthio)-ethanol]
$(CH_3)_2CHSCH_2CH_2OH$
M.W. 120.21 n_D^{20} 1.4780 *STENCH*

NEAT

A

H1390 **n-Hexyl 2-hydroxyethyl sulfide [2-(hexylthio)-ethanol]**
$CH_3(CH_2)_5S(CH_2)_2OH$ M.W. 162.30 n_D^{20} 1.4759 . . . .

B

D22,228 **n-Dodecyl 2-hydroxyethyl sulfide [2-(dodecylthio)-ethanol]**
$HO(CH_2)_2S(CH_2)_{11}CH_3$ M.W. 246.46 n_D^{20} 1.4591

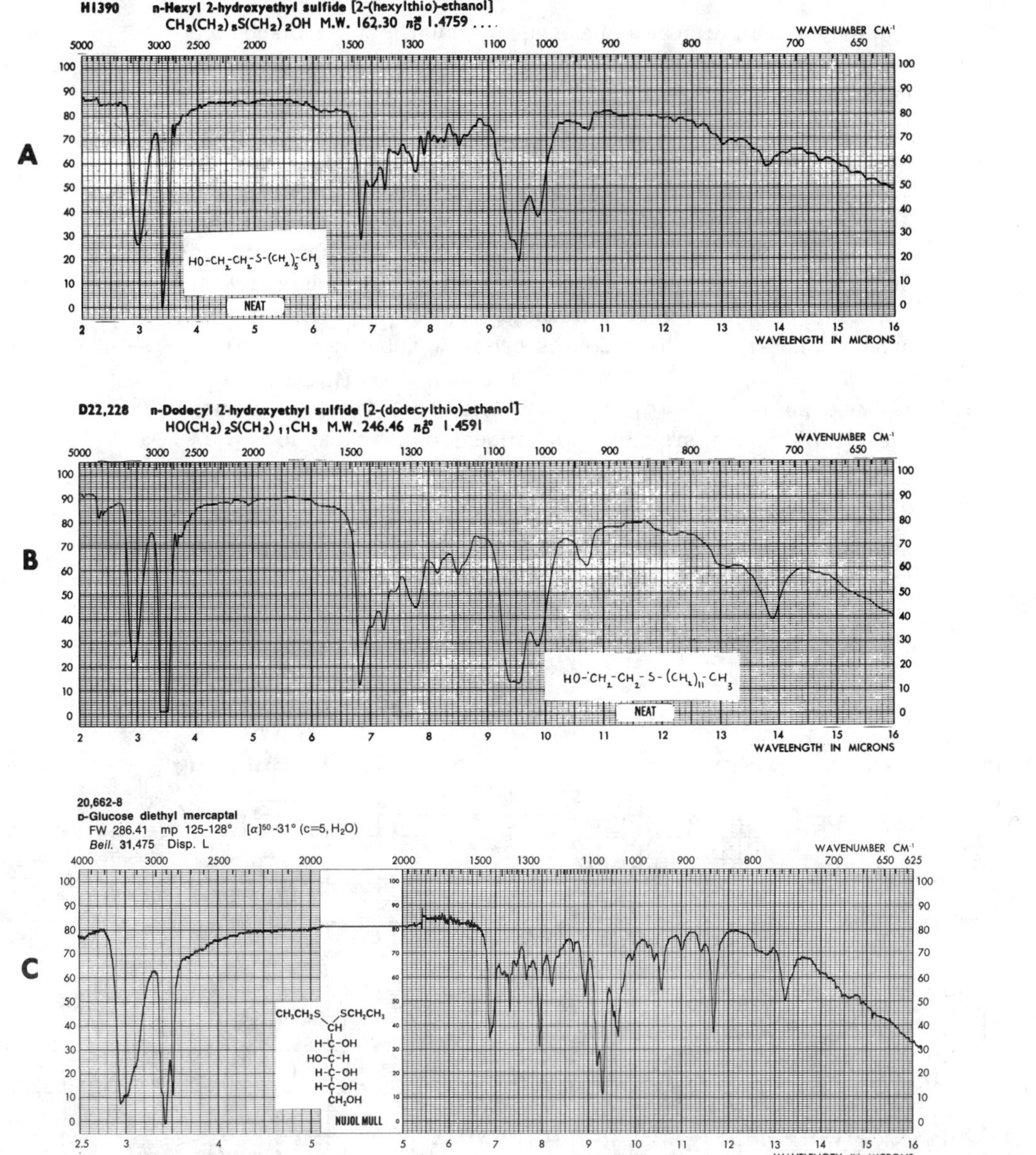

C

20,662-8
D-Glucose diethyl mercaptal
FW 286.41 mp 125-128° $[\alpha]^{20}$ -31° (c=5, H_2O)
Beil. 31,475 Disp. L

D

15,470-9 **Carbon disulfide, spectrophotometric grade, GOLD LABEL**
(meets A.C.S. specifications)
CS_2 M.W. 76.14 b.p. 46° . . .

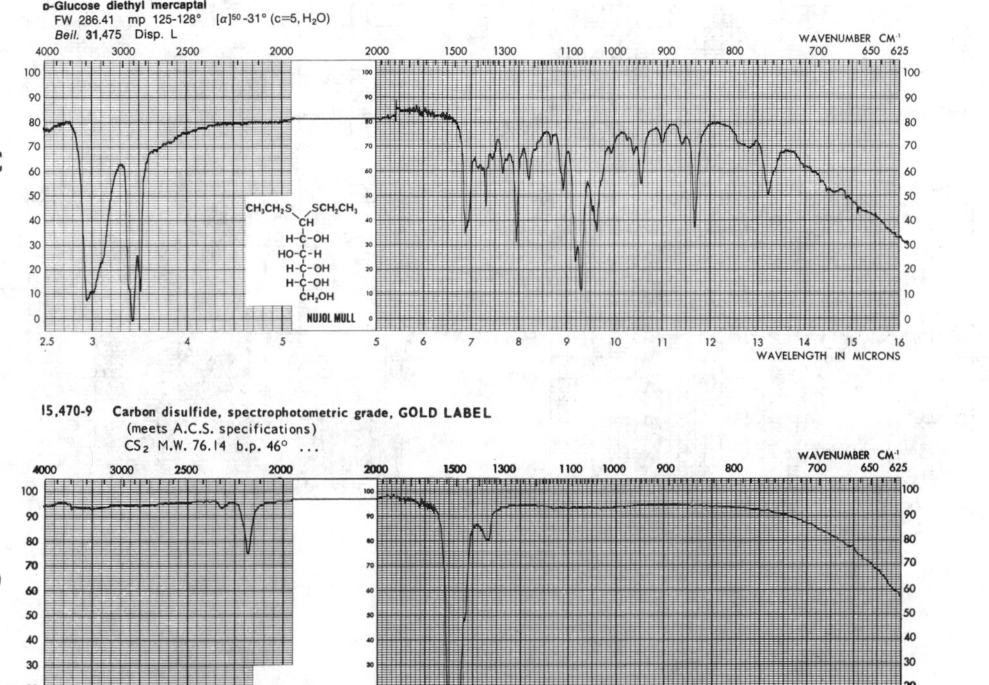

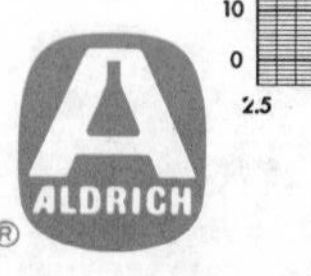

NON-AROMATIC AMINES

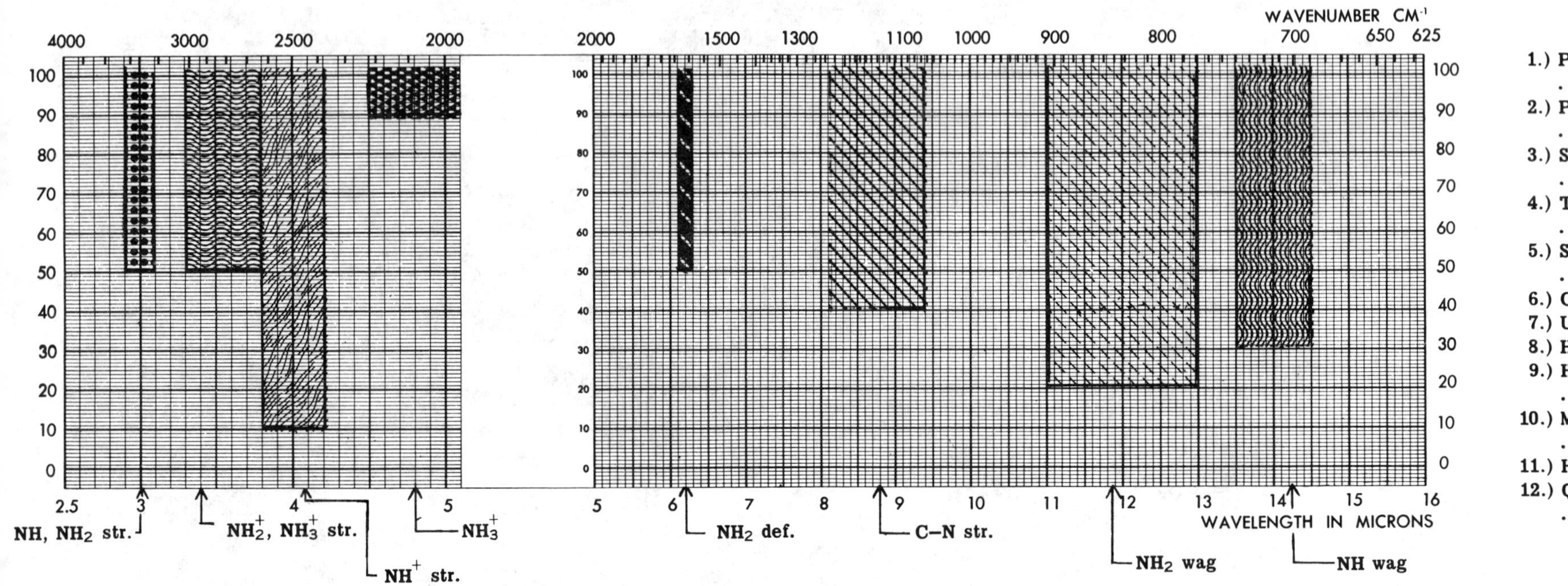

The spectra of the amine salts are not segregated in this section, but they have been dispersed among the free amines in an order of increasing complexity.

Primary Amines

The primary amine function displays its characteristic absorptions at 3 μ (3335 cm^{-1}), 6.2 μ (1615 cm^{-1}) and between 11 and 13 μ (910 – 770 cm^{-1}).

The NH_2 nitrogen-hydrogen stretch absorption is split around 3 μ (3335 cm^{-1}). The NH_2 deformation band at 6.2 μ (1615 cm^{-1}) is very similar in intensity to the 3 μ (3335 cm^{-1}) absorption and slightly increases in proportion to it as the length of the aliphatic chain increases. The presence of the strong and very broad absorption between 11 and 13 μ (910 – 770 cm^{-1}) makes the three absorptions unmistakable in identifying the primary amine.

On protonating the primary NH_2, the stretch absorptions at 3 μ (3335 cm^{-1}) shift to 3.3 to 3.8 μ (3030 – 2630 cm^{-1}) and are considerably different in shape and intensity from the original NH_2 bands. An additional weak to medium absorption between 4.5 and 5.5 μ (2220 – 1820 cm^{-1}) is very characteristic of the primary amine salt and will usually not be seen in secondary or tertiary amine salts (see spectra 165A and 181F).

Secondary Amines

The secondary amines usually display only a single band at 3 μ (3335 cm^{-1}). The 6.2 μ (1615 cm^{-1}) absorption is lost and the broad absorption between 11 and 13 μ (910 – 770 cm^{-1}) shifts to a higher wavelength position to close 14 μ (715 cm^{-1}). The heterocyclic members are an exception and their bands are shifted only slightly (see spectra 212F-213C). In the longer chain members of both the primary and secondary amine spectra, the sample must be prepared with a relatively thick path length in order to see the NH and NH_2 bands at 3 μ (3335 cm^{-1}). The secondary salts have bands similar to those of the primary amine salt around 3.3 – 3.8 μ (3030 – 2630 cm^{-1}) but in addition display one or more spikes between 4 and 4.5 μ (2500 – 2220 cm^{-1}).

Tertiary Amines

The tertiary amine no longer displays any of the bands at 3 μ (3335 cm^{-1}), 6.2 μ (1615 cm^{-1}) and 11 to 13 μ (910 – 770 cm^{-1}) but can be detected as the free amine by its effect on the CH_2 stretch absorption at 3.5 μ (2855 cm^{-1}). This absorption is shifted to a higher wavelength position of 3.6 μ (2780 cm^{-1}). The protonated tertiary amine absorbs strongly at 4 μ (2500 cm^{-1}) and is detached from the nujol C–H stretch absorption at 3.5 μ (2855 cm^{-1}). This band can be used to differentiate the tertiary amine salts and the primary and secondary salts (spectra 190F—191F).

Carbon-nitrogen Stretch Bands

The carbon-nitrogen stretch absorptions are very similar to those of carbon-oxygen stretch. The **primary carbon**-nitrogen ($R–CH_2–N$) absorbs 9.4 μ (1065 cm^{-1}) [except for the secondary amine which absorbs at 9 μ (1110 cm^{-1})]. This absorption shifts to 8.7 μ (1150 cm^{-1}) in the **secondary carbon**-nitrogen molecules ($R_2CH–N$) and finally to 8.1 μ (1235 cm^{-1}) in the **tertiary carbon**-nitrogen examples ($R_3C–N$). The intensities are not as great as those of the alcohol and ether series, as can be seen in the examples where both types of bonds are present.

The quaternary ammonium compounds (see spectra 228C—231H) do not display any outstanding bands. However, a band in the 10 to 10.5 μ (1000 – 950 cm^{-1}) region may be attributed to them.

A few points of caution in analyzing amines should be followed. When the spectrum is run in the solid phase, the above mentioned bands split and shift to a considerable extent and are quite deceptive. This can be observed more extensively in the aromatic section where more nujol mull curves are presented. Amines are generally hygroscopic and absorb carbon dioxide. The analyst should make certain that the absorptions at 3 and 6.2 μ (3335 and 1615 cm^{-1}) are those of the NH_2 group and not those of water. The solidification of an amine on running the infrared spectrum may be due to the formation of the amine carbonate.

NOTES

A

12,970-4 Methylamine hydrochloride
$CH_3NH_2 \cdot HCl$ M.W. 67.52 m.p. 233.5-235°
$CH_3NH_2 \cdot HCl$ — NUJOL MULL

B

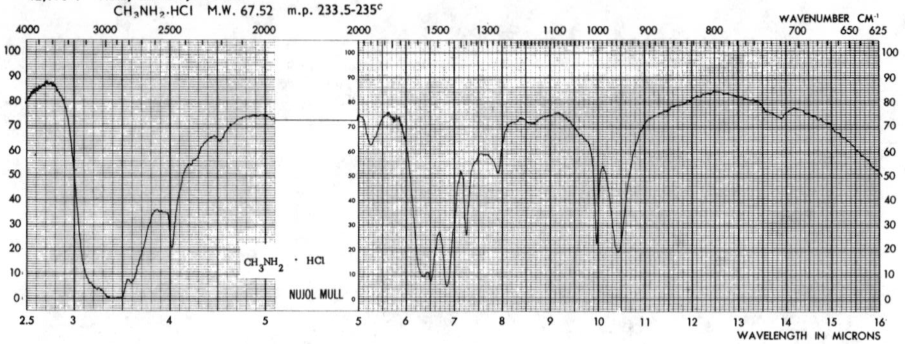

M5000-1 Methylhydrazine
CH_3NHNH_2 M.W. 46.07 n_D^{20} 1.4325
b.p. 87.5°
$H_3C-NH-NH_2$ — NEAT

C

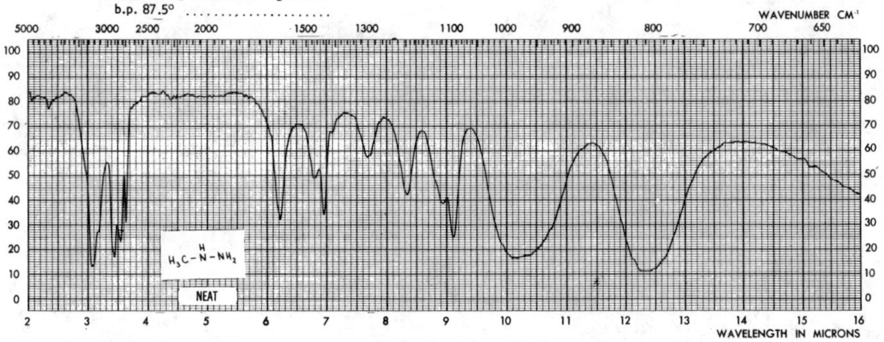

15,941-7
Hydroxylamine hydrochloride, 97%
$H_2NOH \cdot HCl$
M.W. 69.49 m.p. 155-157° (dec.)
Fieser **1**,478 **2**,217 *HYGROSCOPIC*
$H_2N-OH \cdot HCl$ — NUJOL MULL

D

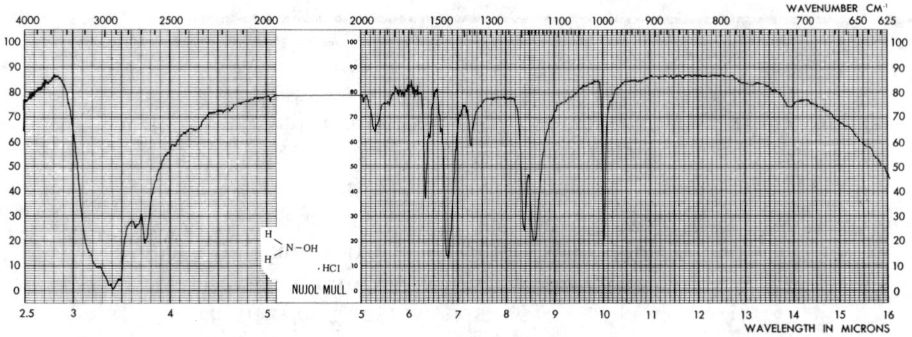

22,145-7
***N,N*-Dimethylhydroxylamine hydrochloride, 99%**
$HON(CH_3)_2 \cdot HCl$ FW 97.55 mp 107-109°
Beil. **4**(2),952 Disp. C
$HO-N(CH_3)_2 \cdot HCl$ — NUJOL MULL

E

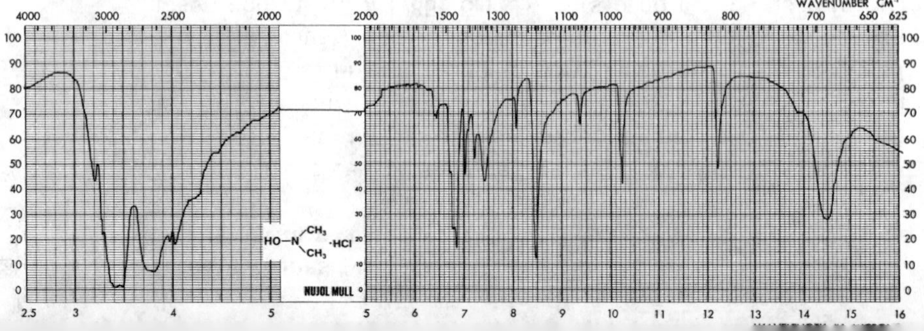

10,981-9 Propylamine
$CH_3CH_2CH_2NH_2$ M.W. 59.11 n_D^{20} 1.3902
b.p. 48.6°
$H_3C-CH_2-CH_2-NH_2$ — NEAT

F

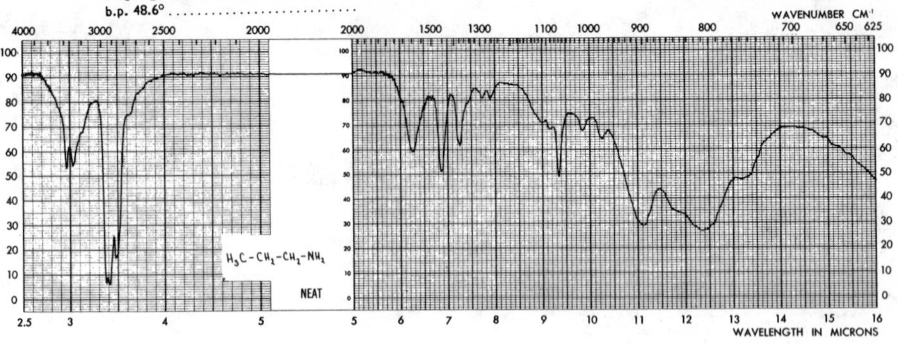

B8898-5 n-Butylamine
$CH_3(CH_2)_3NH_2$ M.W. 73.14 n_D^{20} 1.4015
$H_3C-CH_2-CH_2-CH_2-NH_2$ — NEAT

G

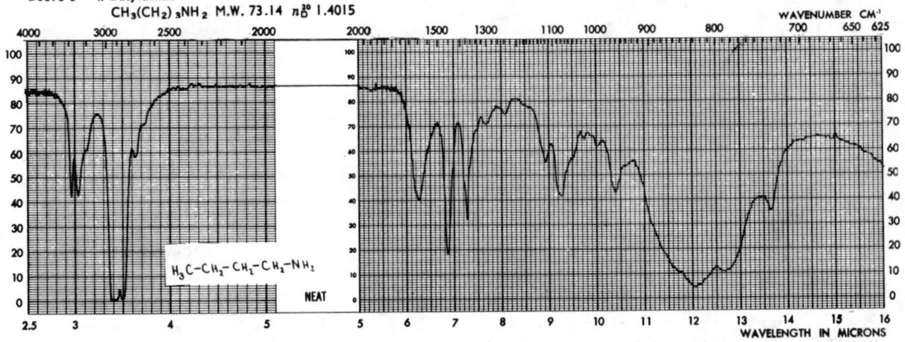

13,605-0 n-Amylamine
$CH_3(CH_2)_4NH_2$ M.W. 87.17 n_D^{20} 1.4110
b.p. 104°
$CH_3CH_2CH_2CH_2CH_2NH_2$ — NEAT

H

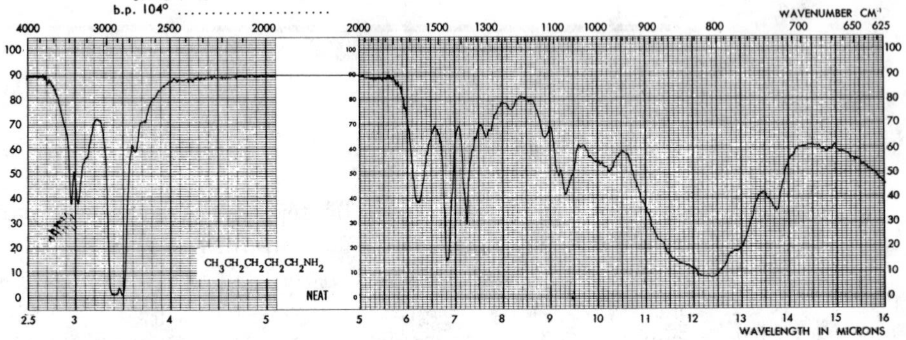

21,970-3
Hexylamine, 99%
$CH_3(CH_2)_5NH_2$ FW 101.19 mp -23°
bp 131-132° n_D^{20} 1.4180 d 0.766 *Beil.* **4**,188
Fieser **7**,170 Disp. C
$CH_3(CH_2)_5NH_2$ — NEAT

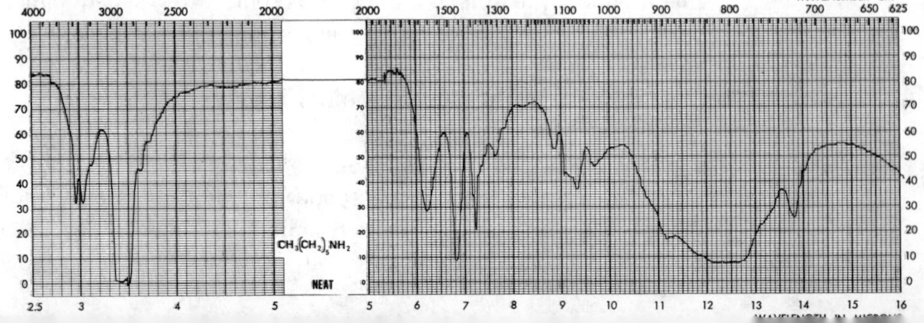

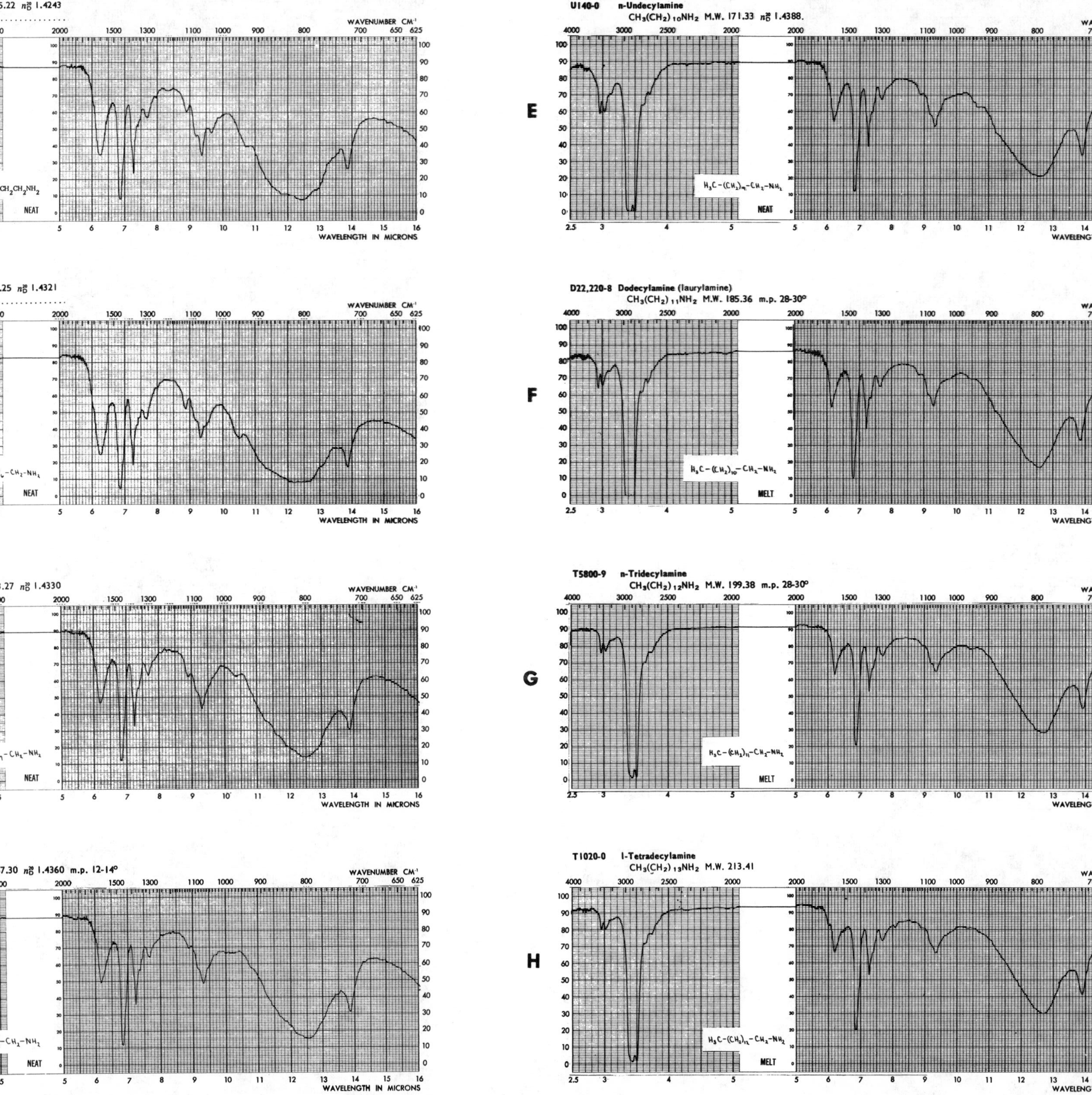

A
12,680-2 n-Heptylamine, puriss.
$CH_3(CH_2)_6NH_2$ M.W. 115.22 n_D^{20} 1.4243
b.p. 154-156°
$CH_3CH_2CH_2CH_2CH_2CH_2CH_2NH_2$
NEAT
B
O-580-2 n-Octylamine
$CH_3(CH_2)_7NH_2$ M.W. 129.25 n_D^{20} 1.4321
m.p. -5 to -1°
$H_3C-(CH_2)_6-CH_2-NH_2$
NEAT
C
N3100-1 n-Nonylamine
$CH_3(CH_2)_8NH_2$ M.W. 143.27 n_D^{20} 1.4330
$H_3C-(CH_2)_7-CH_2-NH_2$
NEAT
D
D240-4 n-Decylamine
$CH_3(CH_2)_9NH_2$ M.W. 157.30 n_D^{20} 1.4360 m.p. 12-14°
$H_3C-(CH_2)_8-CH_2-NH_2$
NEAT
E
U140-0 n-Undecylamine
$CH_3(CH_2)_{10}NH_2$ M.W. 171.33 n_D^{20} 1.4388.
$H_3C-(CH_2)_9-CH_2-NH_2$
NEAT
F
D22,220-8 Dodecylamine (laurylamine)
$CH_3(CH_2)_{11}NH_2$ M.W. 185.36 m.p. 28-30°
$H_3C-(CH_2)_{10}-CH_2-NH_2$
MELT
G
T5800-9 n-Tridecylamine
$CH_3(CH_2)_{12}NH_2$ M.W. 199.38 m.p. 28-30°
$H_3C-(CH_2)_{11}-CH_2-NH_2$
MELT
H
T1020-0 1-Tetradecylamine
$CH_3(CH_2)_{13}NH_2$ M.W. 213.41
$H_3C-(CH_2)_{12}-CH_2-NH_2$
MELT
WAVENUMBER CM⁻¹
WAVELENGTH IN MICRONS

ALDRICH ®

A P400-3 n-Pentadecylamine
$CH_3(CH_2)_{14}NH_2$ M.W. 227.44 m.p. 39-42°
$H_3C-(CH_2)_{13}-CH_2-NH_2$
MELT

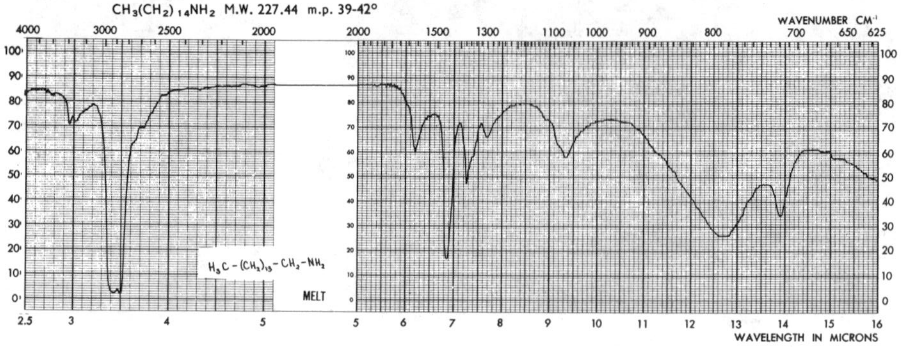

B H740-8 1-Hexadecylamine
$CH_3(CH_2)_{15}NH_2$ M.W. 241.46 m.p. 46-48°
$H_3C-(CH_2)_{14}-CH_2-NH_2$
MELT

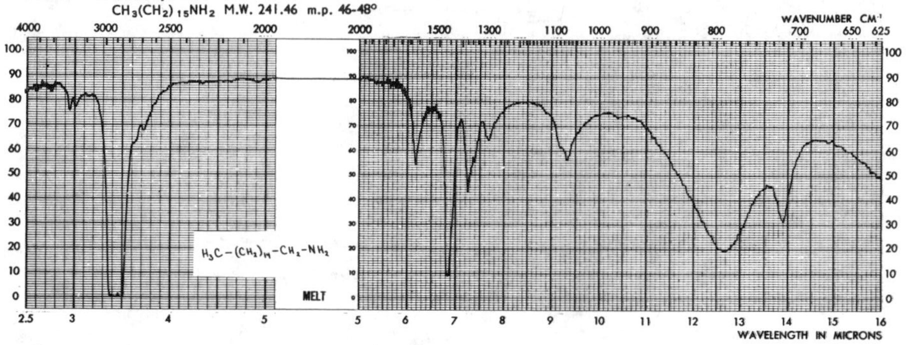

C H115-9 n-Heptadecylamine
$CH_3(CH_2)_{16}NH_2$ M.W. 255.49 m.p. 45-46°
$CH_3(CH_2)_{15}CH_2NH_2$
MELT

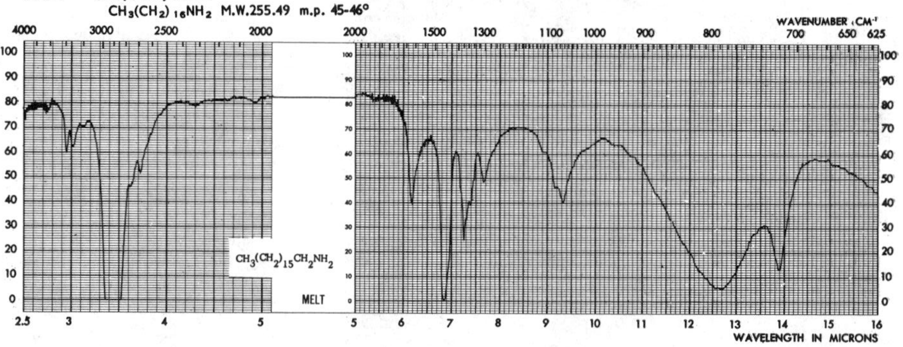

D O-140-8 Octadecylamine
$CH_3(CH_2)_{17}NH_2$ M.W. 269.52
m.p. 52-53°
$H_3C-(CH_2)_{16}-CH_2-NH_2$
MELT

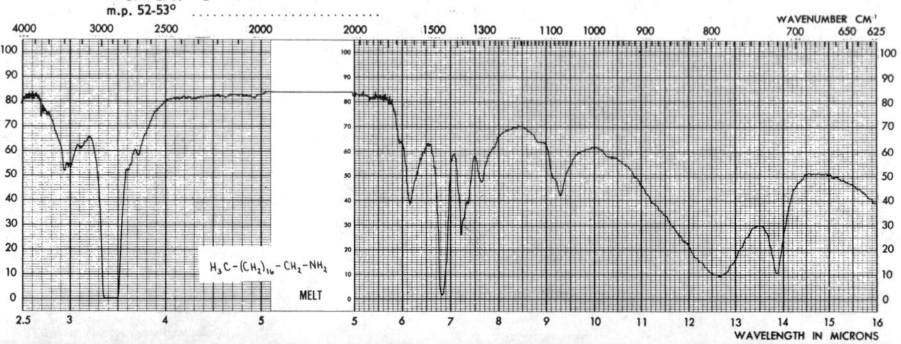

E 10,906-1 Isopropylamine
$(CH_3)_2CHNH_2$ M.W. 59.11 n_D^{20} 1.3746
b.p. 33°
$CH_3-CH(NH_2)-CH_3$
NEAT

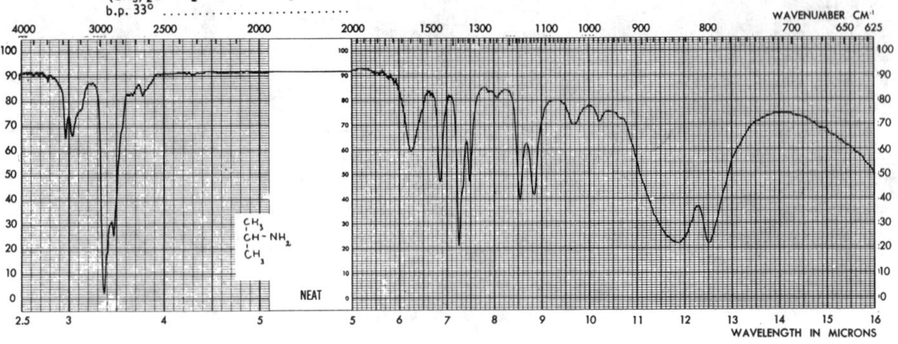

F B8900-0 sec.-Butylamine
$C_2H_5CH(NH_2)CH_3$ M.W. 73.14
n_D^{20} 1.3946
$CH_3CH_2CH(CH_3)-NH_2$
NEAT

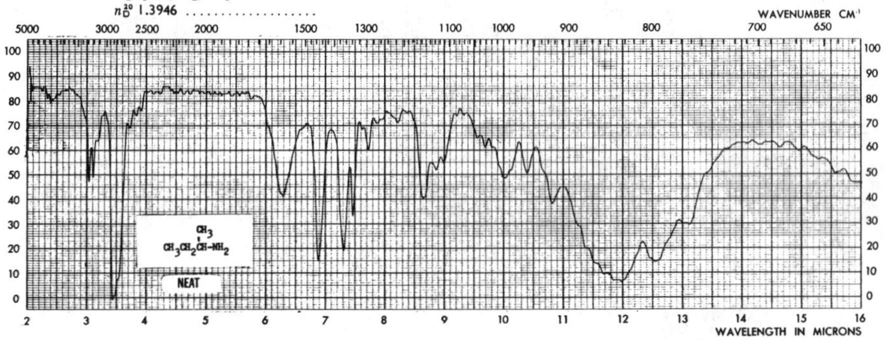

G 17,141-7
1-Methylbutylamine, 98%
$CH_3CH_2CH_2CH(CH_3)NH_2$
M.W. 87.17 b.p. 90.5-91.5° n_D^{20} 1.4029 d 0.736
Beil. 4,157
$CH_3CH_2CH_2CH(NH_2)CH_3$
NEAT

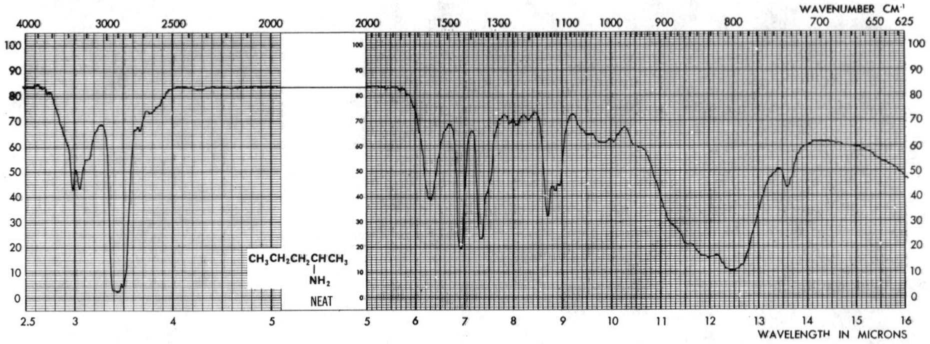

H I-1415-0 Isobutylamine
$(CH_3)_2CHCH_2NH_2$ M.W. 73.14 n_D^{20} 1.3951
b.p. 65-67°
$(H_3C)_2HC-CH_2-NH_2$
NEAT

(Each spectrum: WAVENUMBER CM⁻¹ 4000–625; WAVELENGTH IN MICRONS 2.5–16; transmittance 0–100)

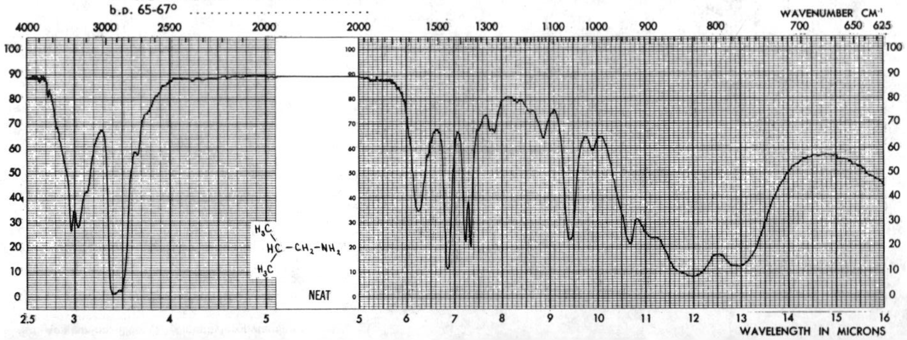

2,5-Dimethyl-2,5-hexanediamine, 97%
$H_2NC(CH_3)_2CH_2CH_2C(CH_3)_2NH_2$
M.W. 144.26 b.p. 63-64°/8mm. n_D^{20} 1.4459
d 0.832 *IRRITANT*

NEAT

B

B8920-5 tert.-Butylamine, puriss.
$(CH_3)_3CNH_2$ M.W. 73.14 n_D^{20} 1.3774

NEAT

C

19,497-2
***tert*-Butylhydrazine hydrochloride**, 95+%
$(CH_3)_3CNHNH_2 \cdot HCl$ FW 124.61 mp 191-194°
Beil. **4**(3),1734 *Fieser* **7**,30 Disp. C

NUJOL MULL

D

19,018-7
1,2-Dimethylpropylamine, 98+%
$(CH_3)_2CHCH(CH_3)NH_2$ FW 87.17 mp -50°
bp 84-87° n_D^{20} 1.4055 d 0.757 *Beil.* **4**,179
Disp. C

NEAT

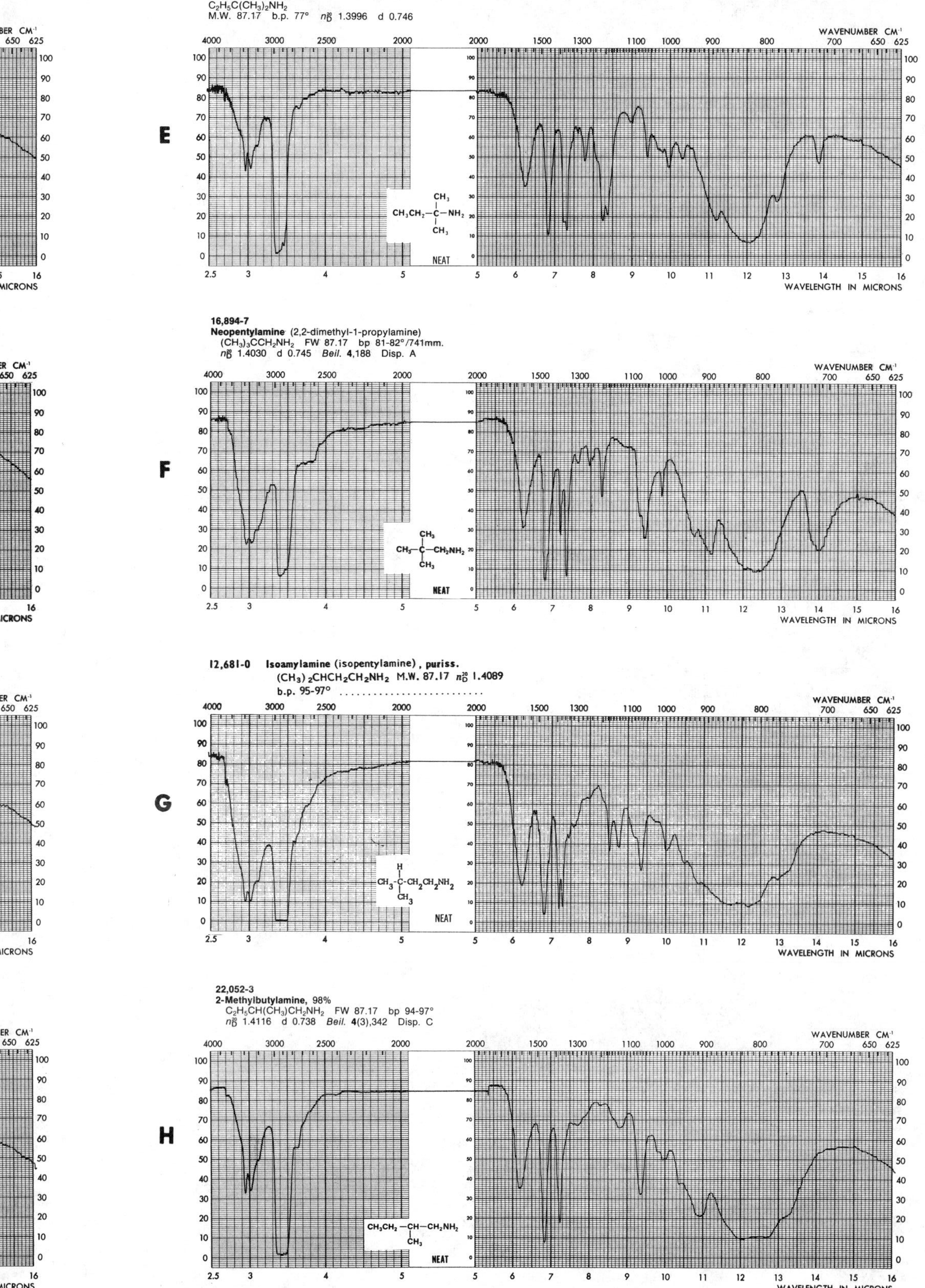

E

tert.**-Amylamine**, 98% (1,1-dimethylpropylamine, *tert*.-pentylamine)
$C_2H_5C(CH_3)_2NH_2$
M.W. 87.17 b.p. 77° n_D^{20} 1.3996 d 0.746

F

16,894-7
Neopentylamine (2,2-dimethyl-1-propylamine)
$(CH_3)_3CCH_2NH_2$ FW 87.17 bp 81-82°/741mm.
n_D^{20} 1.4030 d 0.745 *Beil.* **4**,188 Disp. A

G

12,681-0 Isoamylamine (isopentylamine), puriss.
$(CH_3)_2CHCH_2CH_2NH_2$ M.W. 87.17 n_D^{20} 1.4089
b.p. 95-97°

H

22,052-3
2-Methylbutylamine, 98%
$C_2H_5CH(CH_3)CH_2NH_2$ FW 87.17 bp 94-97°
n_D^{20} 1.4116 d 0.738 *Beil.* **4**(3),342 Disp. C

ALDRICH

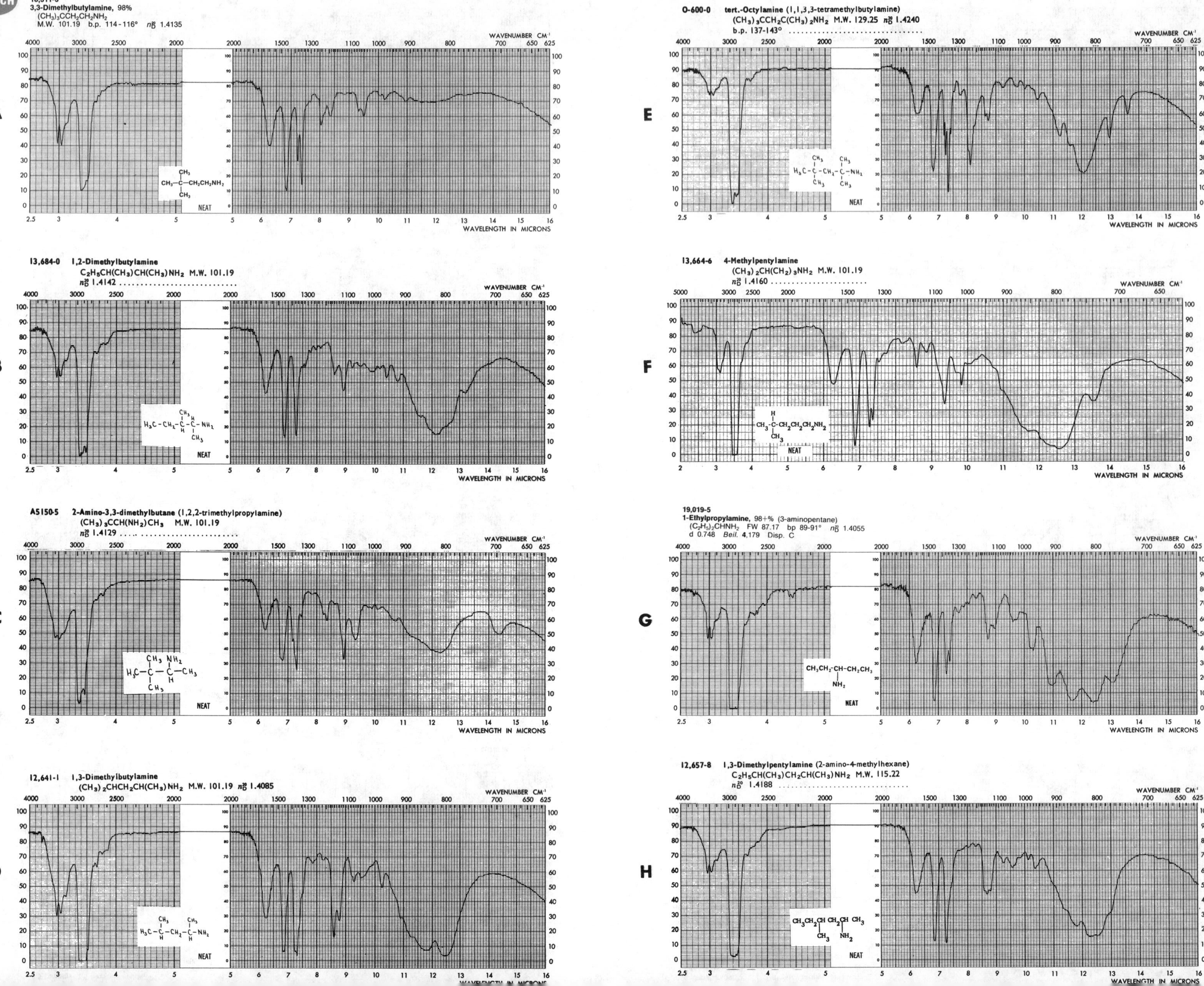
ALDRICH

A
18,311-3
3,3-Dimethylbutylamine, 98%
$(CH_3)_3CCH_2CH_2NH_2$
M.W. 101.19 b.p. 114-116° n_D^{20} 1.4135
NEAT

B
13,684-0 1,2-Dimethylbutylamine
$C_2H_5CH(CH_3)CH(CH_3)NH_2$ M.W. 101.19
n_D^{20} 1.4142
NEAT

C
A5150-5 2-Amino-3,3-dimethylbutane (1,2,2-trimethylpropylamine)
$(CH_3)_3CCH(NH_2)CH_3$ M.W. 101.19
n_D^{20} 1.4129
NEAT

D
12,641-1 1,3-Dimethylbutylamine
$(CH_3)_2CHCH_2CH(CH_3)NH_2$ M.W. 101.19 n_D^{20} 1.4085
NEAT

E
O-600-0 tert.-Octylamine (1,1,3,3-tetramethylbutylamine)
$(CH_3)_3CCH_2C(CH_3)_2NH_2$ M.W. 129.25 n_D^{20} 1.4240
b.p. 137-143°
NEAT

F
13,664-6 4-Methylpentylamine
$(CH_3)_2CH(CH_2)_3NH_2$ M.W. 101.19
n_D^{20} 1.4160
NEAT

G
19,019-5
1-Ethylpropylamine, 98+% (3-aminopentane)
$(C_2H_5)_2CHNH_2$ FW 87.17 bp 89-91° n_D^{20} 1.4055
d 0.748 Beil. 4,179 Disp. C
NEAT

H
12,657-8 1,3-Dimethylpentylamine (2-amino-4-methylhexane)
$C_2H_5CH(CH_3)CH_2CH(CH_3)NH_2$ M.W. 115.22
n_D^{20} 1.4188
NEAT

WAVENUMBER CM⁻¹
WAVELENGTH IN MICRONS

A

E2950-8 **2-Ethylhexylamine**
$CH_3(CH_2)_3CH(C_2H_5)CH_2NH_2$ M.W. 129.25
n_D^{20} 1.4300
NEAT

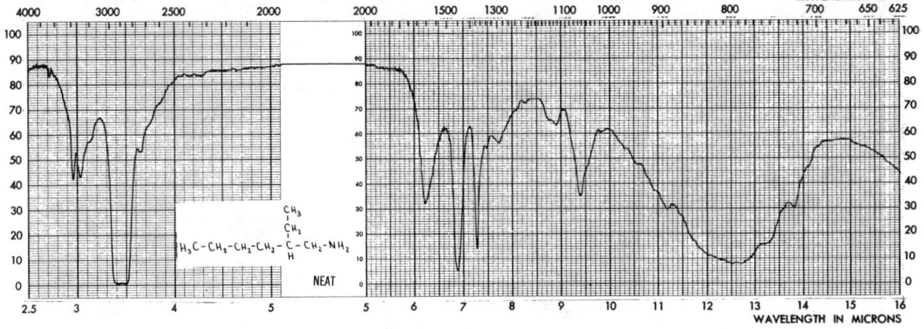

B

D16,129-2 **1,5-Dimethylhexylamine** (2-amino-6-methylheptane)
$(CH_3)_2CH(CH_2)_3CH(CH_3)NH_2$ M.W. 129.25
n_D^{20} 1.4209
NEAT

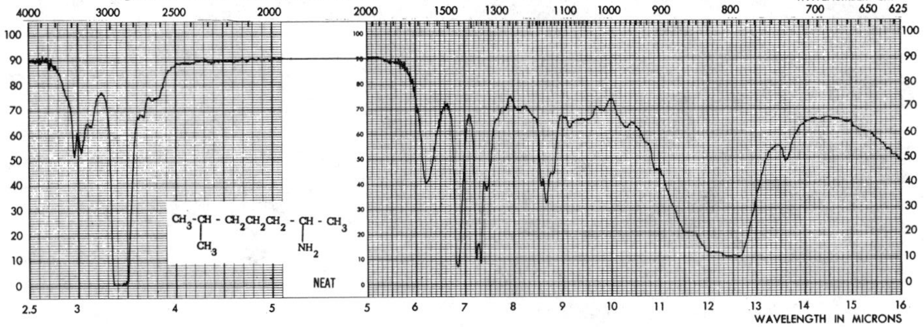

C

A5620-5 **2-Aminoheptane** (1-methylhexylamine)
$CH_3(CH_2)_4CH(NH_2)CH_3$ M.W. 115.22 n_D^{20} 1.4175
NEAT

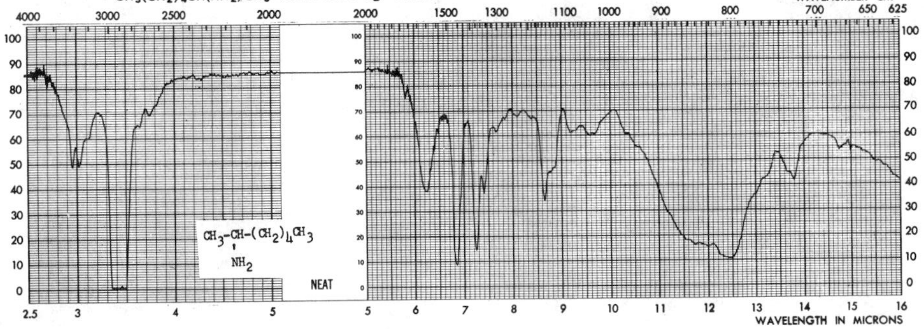

D

18,398-9
1-Methylheptylamine, 98%
$CH_3(CH_2)_5CH(CH_3)NH_2$
M.W. 129.25 b.p. 165° n_D^{20} 1.4235 d 0.771
Beil. 4,196
NEAT

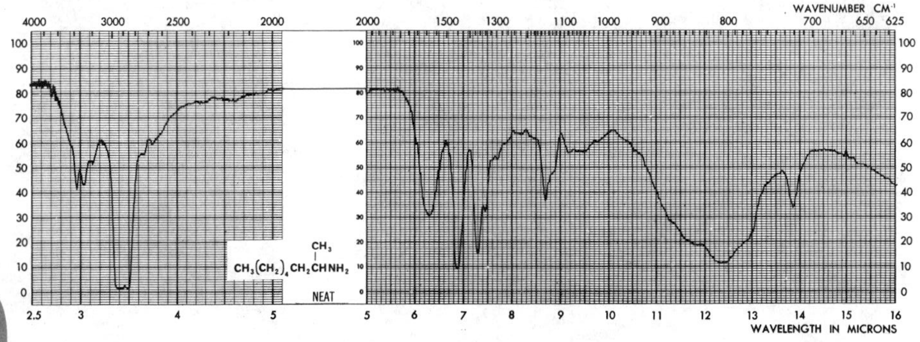

E

A7085-2 **2-Aminooctane** (1-methylheptylamine)
$CH_3(CH_2)_5CH(NH_2)CH_3$ M.W. 129.25
1.4214
NEAT

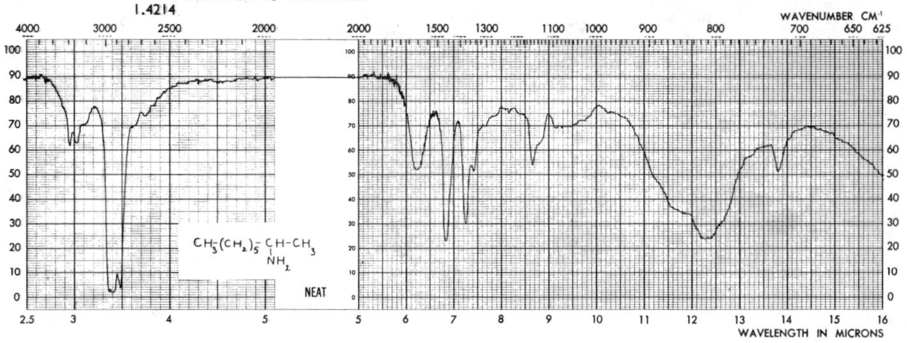

F

12,970-4 **Methylamine hydrochloride**
$CH_3NH_2{\cdot}HCl$ M.W. 67.52 m.p. 233.5-235°
NUJOL MULL

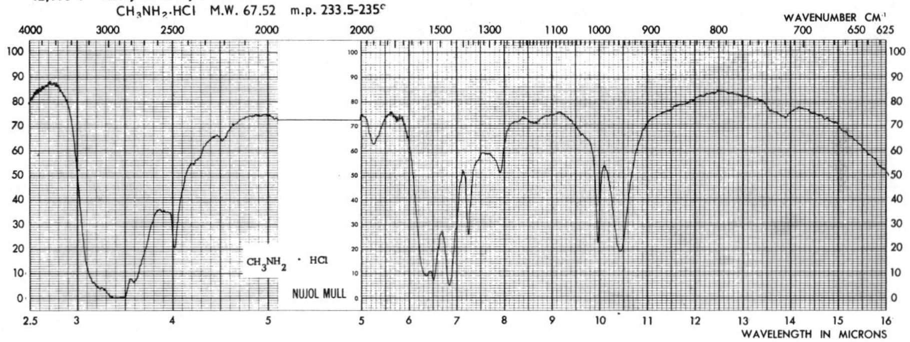

G

M5000-1 **Methylhydrazine**
CH_3NHNH_2 M.W. 46.07 n_D^{20} 1.4325
b.p. 87.5°
NEAT

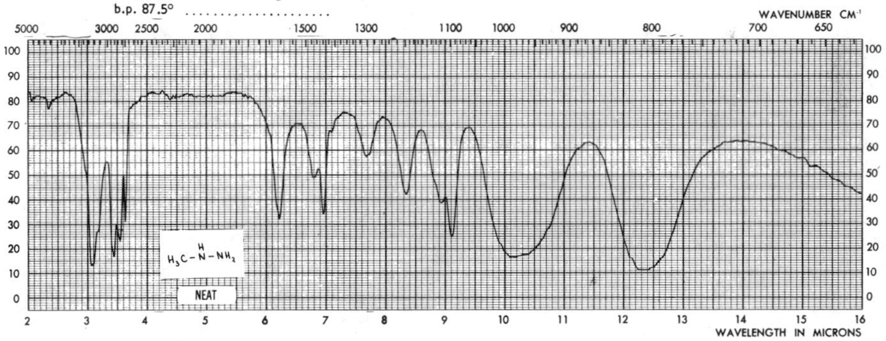

H

12,683-7 **Methanediamine dihydrochloride**
$CH_2(NH_2)_2{\cdot}2HCl$ M.W. 46.07
NUJOL MULL

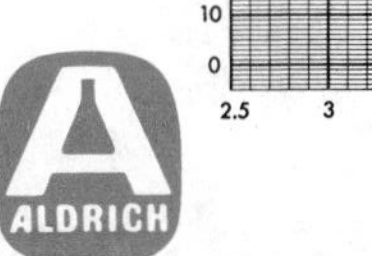

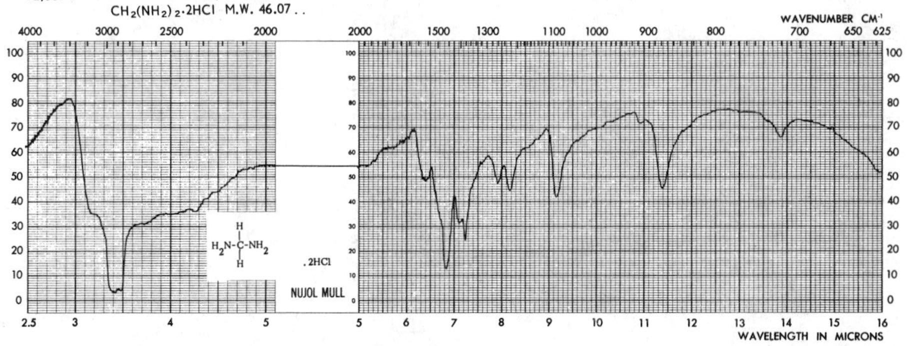

A

E2626-6 **Ethylenediamine**
$H_2NCH_2CH_2NH_2$ M.W. 60.10 n_D^{20} 1.4545

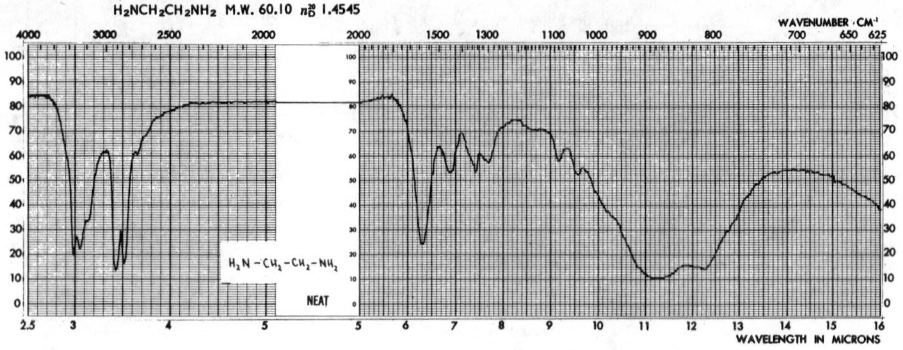

$H_2N-CH_2-CH_2-NH_2$ NEAT

B

19,580-4
Ethylenediamine dihydrochloride
$H_2NCH_2CH_2NH_2 \cdot 2HCl$ FW 133.02 mp >300°
Beil. 4,230 Disp. L

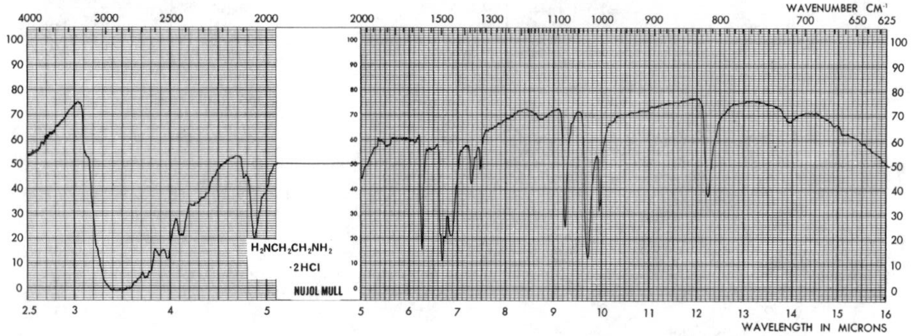

$H_2NCH_2CH_2NH_2 \cdot 2HCl$ NUJOL MULL

C

D2360-2 **1,3-Diaminopropane** (1,3-propanediamine)
$H_2N(CH_2)_3NH_2$ M.W. 74.13 n_D^{20} 1.4593

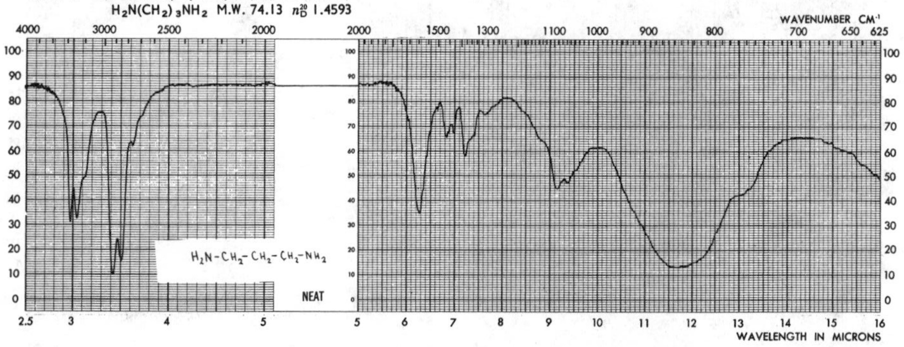

$H_2N-CH_2-CH_2-CH_2-NH_2$ NEAT

D

D2380-7 **1,3-Diaminopropane** (1,3-propanediamine) **dihydrochloride**
$H_2N(CH_2)_3NH_2 \cdot 2HCl$ M.W. 147.05 m.p. 246-250° ....

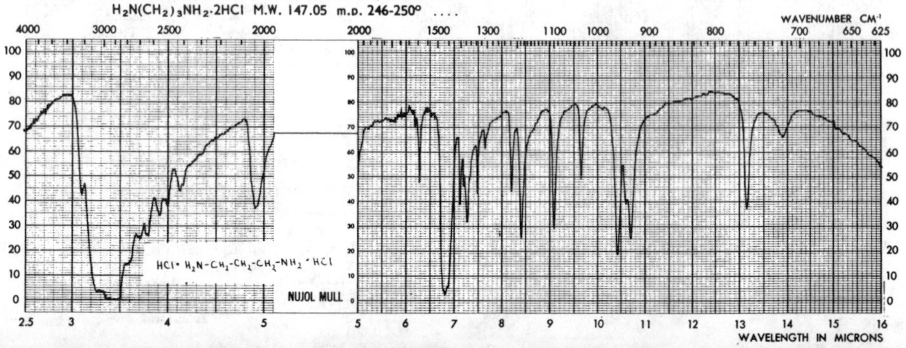

$HCl \cdot H_2N-CH_2-CH_2-CH_2-NH_2 \cdot HCl$ NUJOL MULL

E

11,749-8 **1,2-Diaminopropane** (1,2-propanediamine, propylenediamine)
$CH_3CH(NH_2)CH_2NH_2$ M.W. 74.13 n_D^{20} 1.4460
b.p. 117° ....

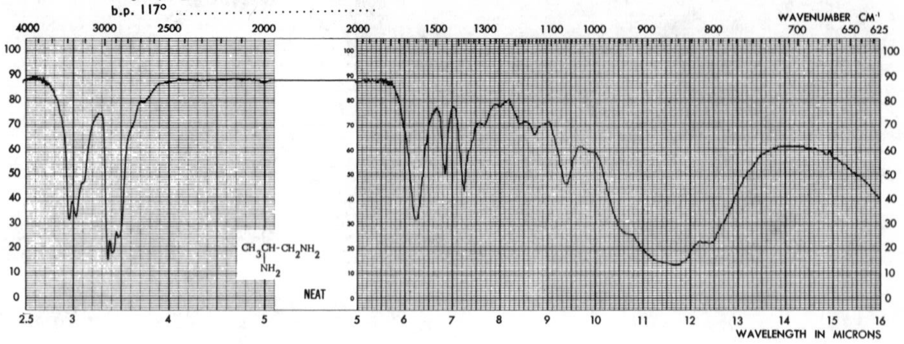

$CH_3CH(NH_2)-CH_2NH_2$ NEAT

F

D2080-8 **1,2-Diamino-2-methylpropane** (2-methyl-1,2-propanediamine)
$(CH_3)_2C(NH_2)CH_2NH_2$ M.W. 88.15 n_D^{20} 1.4410 ....

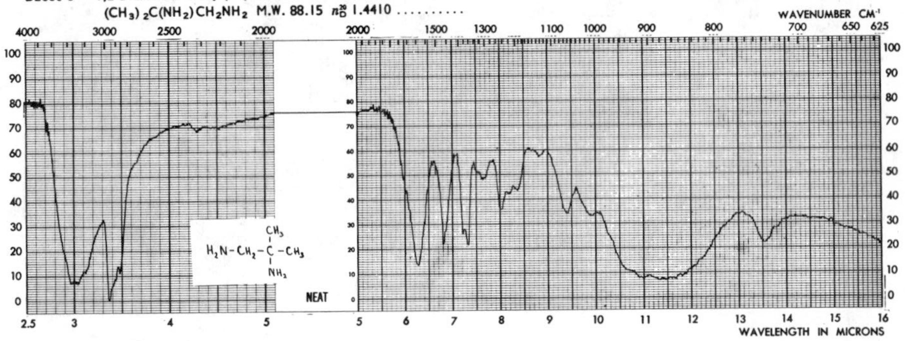

$H_2N-CH_2-C(CH_3)(NH_2)-CH_3$ NEAT

G

17,704-0
2,5-Dimethyl-2,5-hexanediamine, 97%
$H_2NC(CH_3)_2CH_2CH_2C(CH_3)_2NH_2$
M.W. 144.26 b.p. 63-64°/8mm. n_D^{20} 1.4459
d 0.832 *IRRITANT*

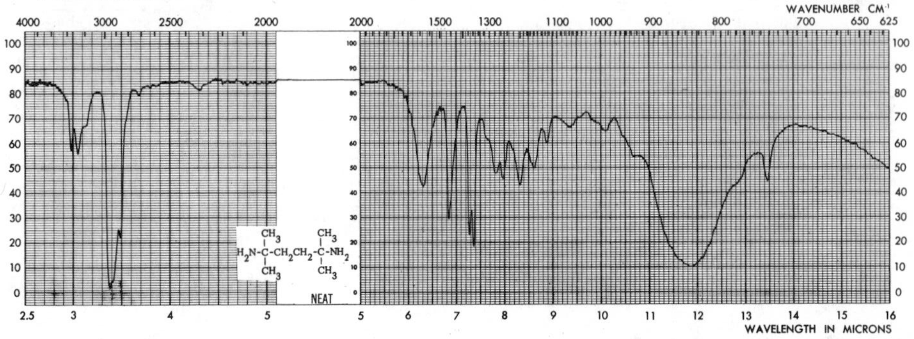

$H_2N-C(CH_3)_2-CH_2CH_2-C(CH_3)_2-NH_2$ NEAT

H

D1320-8 **1,4-Diaminobutane** (1,4-butanediamine, putrescine)
$H_2N(CH_2)_4NH_2$ M.W. 88.15
n_D^{20} 1.4569 ....

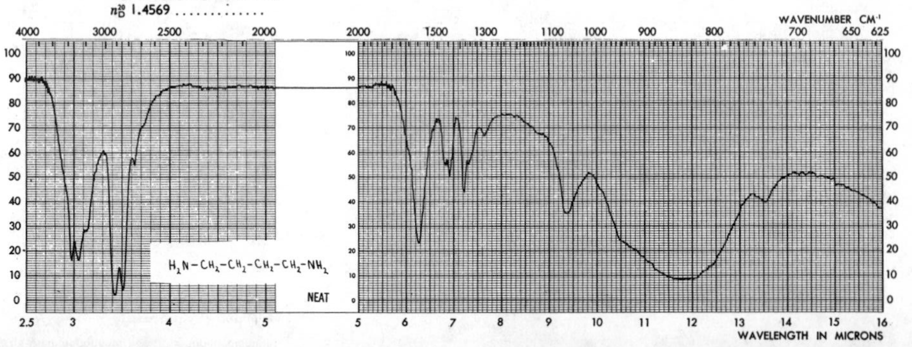

$H_2N-CH_2-CH_2-CH_2-CH_2-NH_2$ NEAT

(Each spectrum: WAVENUMBER CM⁻¹ 4000–625; WAVELENGTH IN MICRONS 2.5–16; transmittance 0–100.)

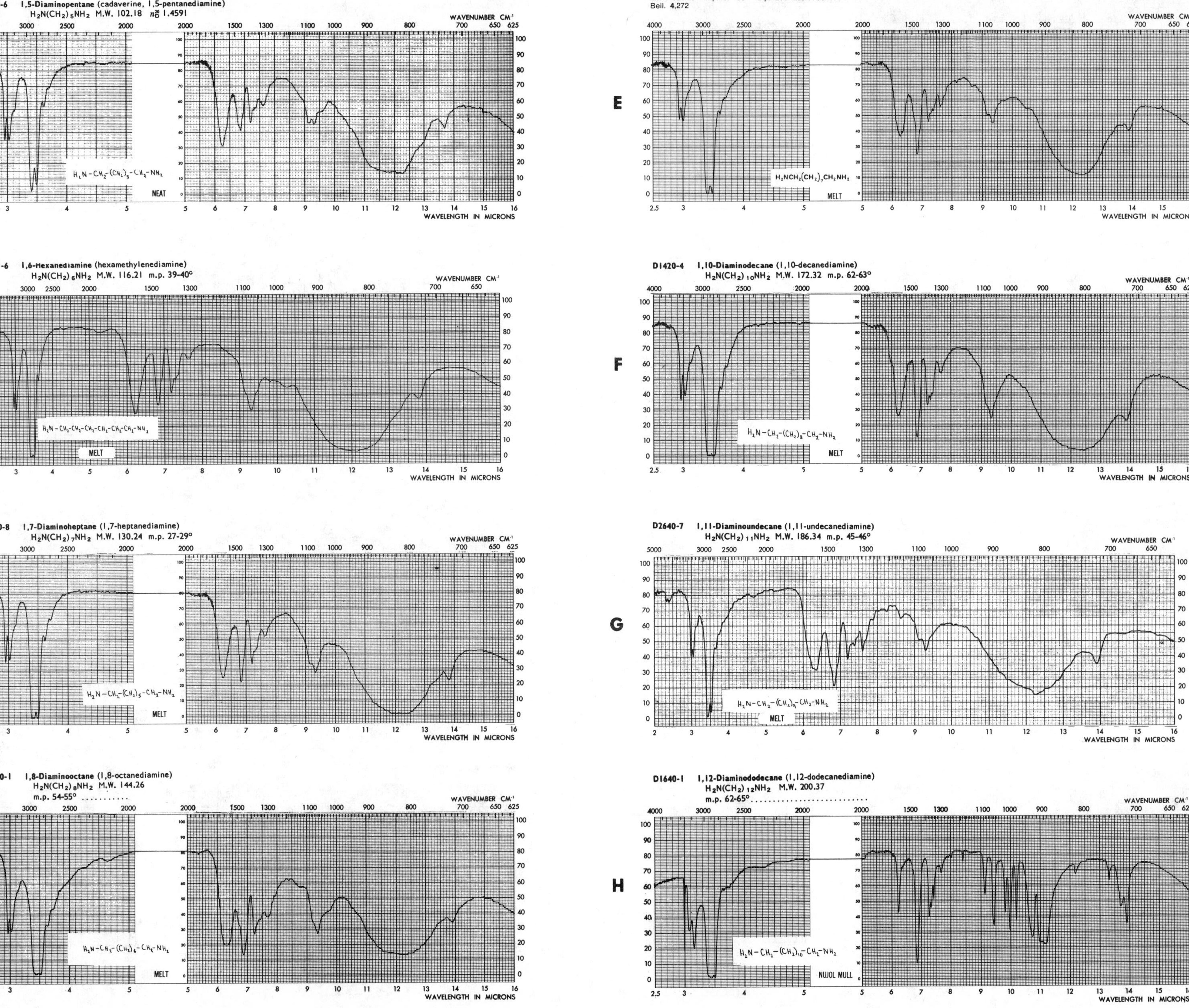
A
D2260-6 1,5-Diaminopentane (cadaverine, 1,5-pentanediamine)
$H_2N(CH_2)_5NH_2$ M.W. 102.18 n_D^{20} 1.4591
$H_2N-CH_2-(CH_2)_3-CH_2-NH_2$
NEAT
B
H1169-6 1,6-Hexanediamine (hexamethylenediamine)
$H_2N(CH_2)_6NH_2$ M.W. 116.21 m.p. 39-40°
$H_2N-CH_2-CH_2-CH_2-CH_2-CH_2-CH_2-NH_2$
MELT
C
D1740-8 1,7-Diaminoheptane (1,7-heptanediamine)
$H_2N(CH_2)_7NH_2$ M.W. 130.24 m.p. 27-29°
$H_2N-CH_2-(CH_2)_5-CH_2-NH_2$
MELT
D
D2240-1 1,8-Diaminooctane (1,8-octanediamine)
$H_2N(CH_2)_8NH_2$ M.W. 144.26
m.p. 54-55° ....
$H_2N-CH_2-(CH_2)_6-CH_2-NH_2$
MELT
E
1,9-Diaminononane, 98% (1,9-nonanediamine)
$H_2N(CH_2)_9NH_2$
M.W. 158.29 m.p. 37-38° b.p. 258-259°/756mm.
Beil. 4,272
$H_2NCH_2(CH_2)_7CH_2NH_2$
MELT
F
D1420-4 1,10-Diaminodecane (1,10-decanediamine)
$H_2N(CH_2)_{10}NH_2$ M.W. 172.32 m.p. 62-63°
$H_2N-CH_2-(CH_2)_8-CH_2-NH_2$
MELT
G
D2640-7 1,11-Diaminoundecane (1,11-undecanediamine)
$H_2N(CH_2)_{11}NH_2$ M.W. 186.34 m.p. 45-46°
$H_2N-CH_2-(CH_2)_9-CH_2-NH_2$
MELT
H
D1640-1 1,12-Diaminododecane (1,12-dodecanediamine)
$H_2N(CH_2)_{12}NH_2$ M.W. 200.37
m.p. 62-65° ....
$H_2N-CH_2-(CH_2)_{10}-CH_2-NH_2$
NUJOL MULL
WAVENUMBER CM⁻¹
WAVELENGTH IN MICRONS
ALDRICH

A

12,636-5 Dimethylamine hydrochloride
$(CH_3)_2NH{\cdot}HCl$ M.W. 81.55 m.p. 170-171°

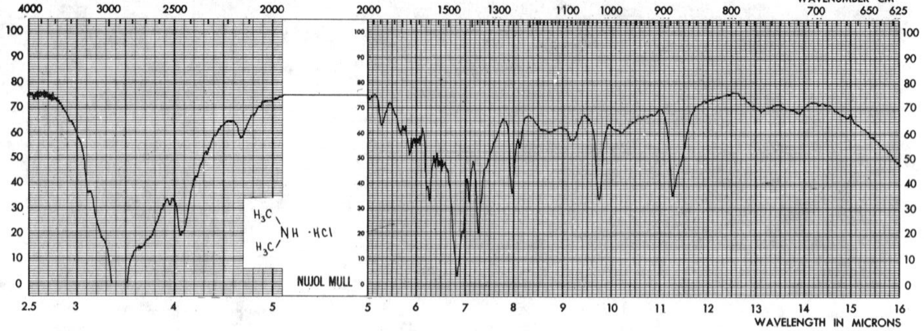

NUJOL MULL

B

D16,180-2 sym.-Dimethylhydrazine dihydrochloride
$CH_3NHNHCH_3{\cdot}2HCl$ M.W. 133.02 m.p. 167-169°

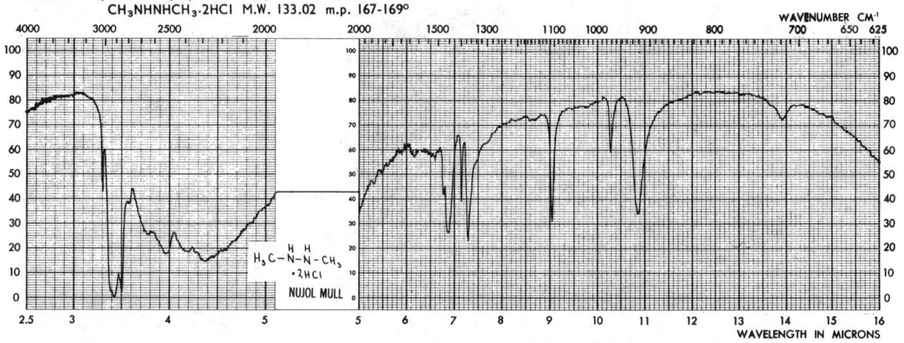

NUJOL MULL

C

D16,160-8 unsym.-Dimethylhydrazine
$(CH_3)_2NNH_2$ M.W. 60.10 n_D^{20} 1.4075

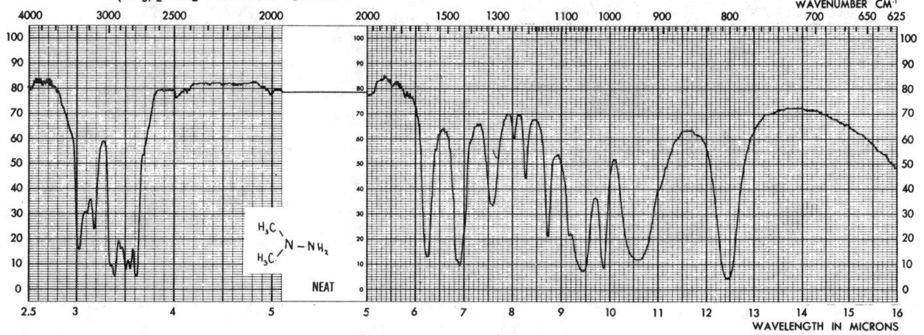

NEAT

D

11,000-0 Diethylamine
$(C_2H_5)_2NH$ M.W. 73.14 n_D^{20} 1.3861
b.p. 55.5°

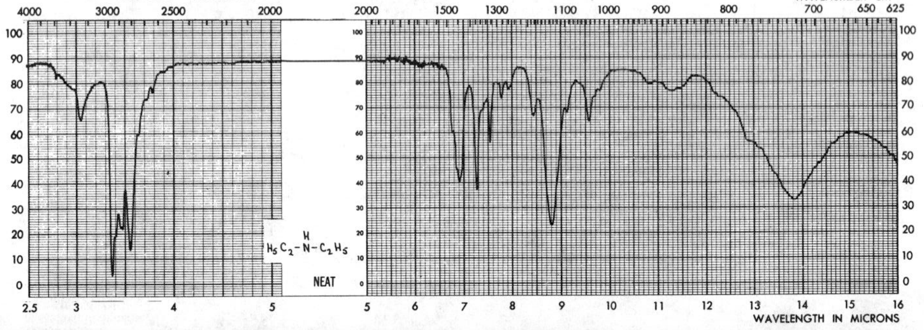

NEAT

E

12,774-4 Diethylamine hydrochloride
$(C_2H_5)_2NH{\cdot}HCl$ M.W. 109.60 m.p. 227-230°

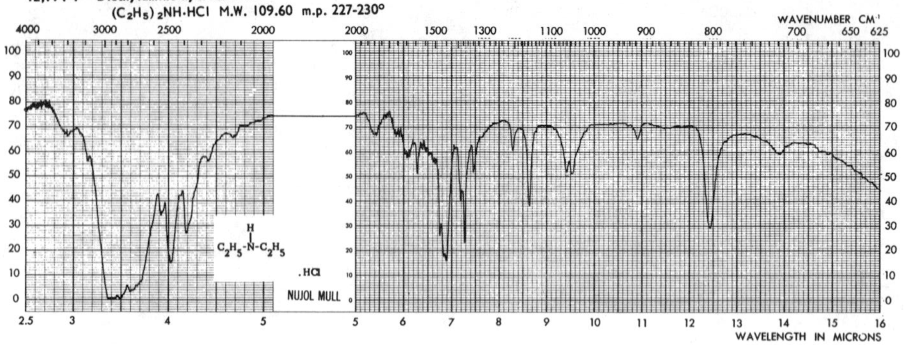

NUJOL MULL

F

14,115-1 Diethylamine phosphate
$(C_2H_5)_2NH{\cdot}H_3PO_4$ M.W. 171.14
m.p. 155-157°

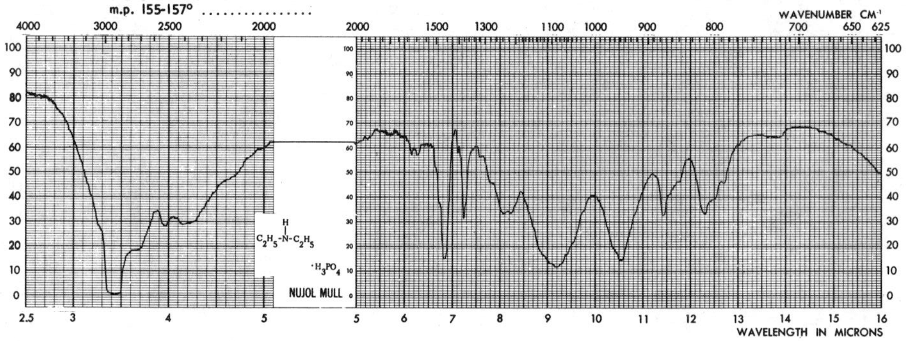

NUJOL MULL

G

D21,475-2 Dipropylamine
$(CH_3CH_2CH_2)_2NH$ M.W. 101.19 n_D^{20} 1.4049

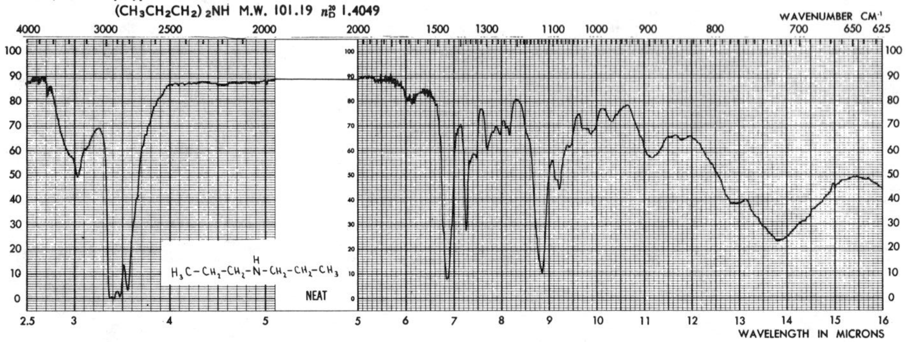

NEAT

H

11,001-9 Diisopropylamine
$[(CH_3)_2CH]_2NH$ M.W. 101.19 n_D^{20} 1.3897
b.p. 83.9°

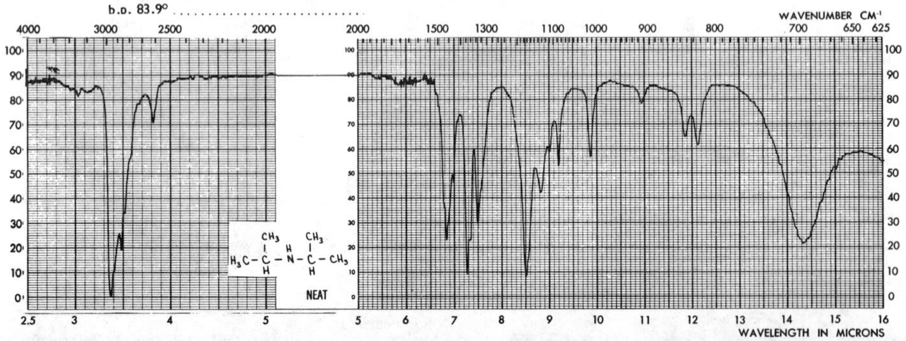

NEAT

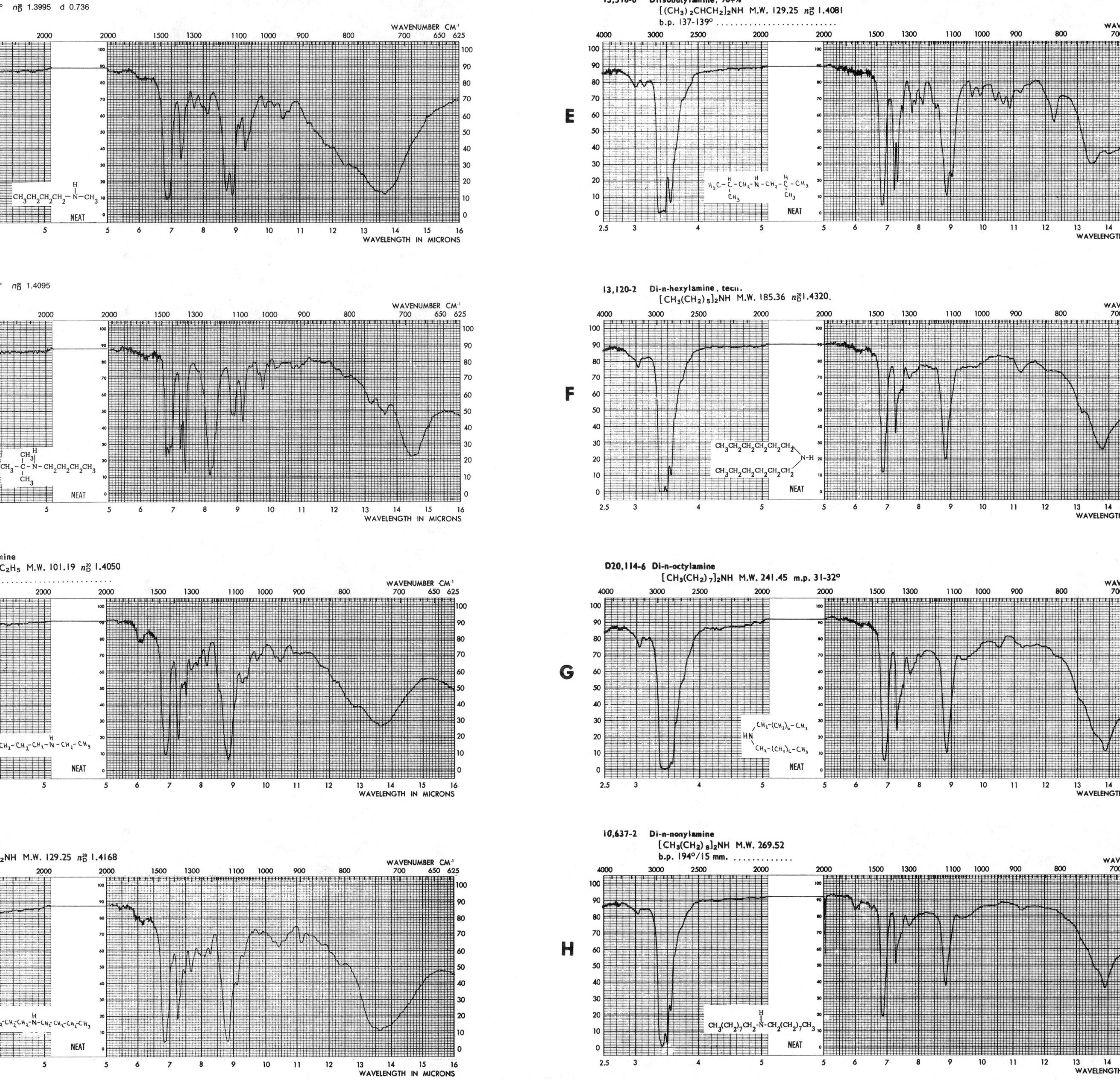
A
16,212-4
N-Methylbutylamine
$CH_3(CH_2)_3NHCH_3$
M.W. 87.17 b.p. 90.5-91.5° n_D^{20} 1.3995 d 0.736
Beil. 4,157 IRRITANT
NEAT
B
15,759-7
N-Butyl-tert.-butylamine, 98%
$(CH_3)_3CNH(CH_2)_3CH_3$
M.W. 129.25 b.p. 135-137° n_D^{20} 1.4095
IRRITANT
NEAT
C
13,300-0 N-Ethyl-n-butylamine
$CH_3(CH_2)_3NHC_2H_5$ M.W. 101.19 n_D^{20} 1.4050
b.p. 108°
NEAT
D
D4495-2 Di-n-butylamine
$[CH_3(CH_2)_3]_2NH$ M.W. 129.25 n_D^{20} 1.4168
NEAT
E
13,518-6 Diisobutylamine, 90+%
$[(CH_3)_2CHCH_2]_2NH$ M.W. 129.25 n_D^{20} 1.4081
b.p. 137-139°
NEAT
F
13,120-2 Di-n-hexylamine, tech.
$[CH_3(CH_2)_5]_2NH$ M.W. 185.36 n_D^{20} 1.4320.
NEAT
G
D20,114-6 Di-n-octylamine
$[CH_3(CH_2)_7]_2NH$ M.W. 241.45 m.p. 31-32°
NEAT
H
10,637-2 Di-n-nonylamine
$[CH_3(CH_2)_8]_2NH$ M.W. 269.52
b.p. 194°/15 mm.
NEAT
WAVENUMBER CM⁻¹
WAVELENGTH IN MICRONS
ALDRICH

A

M6500-9 **N-Methyl-n-octadecylamine**
$CH_3(CH_2)_{17}NHCH_3$ M.W. 283.54 m.p. 46°

MELT

B

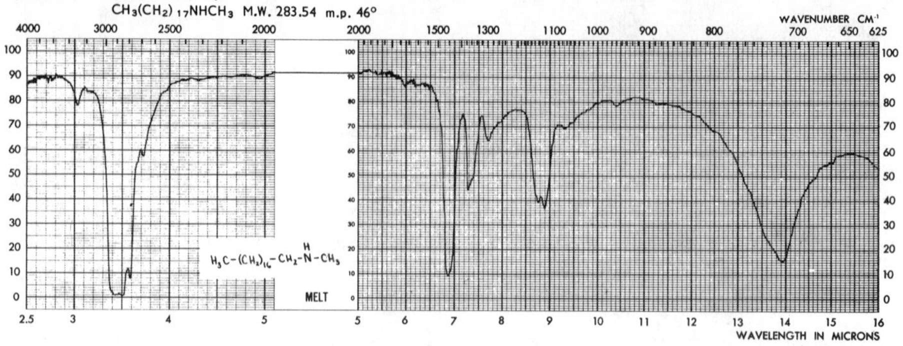

13,861-4 **Di-n-dodecylamine, tech.**
$[CH_3(CH_2)_{11}]_2NH$ M.W. 353.68 m.p. 45-48°

MELT

C

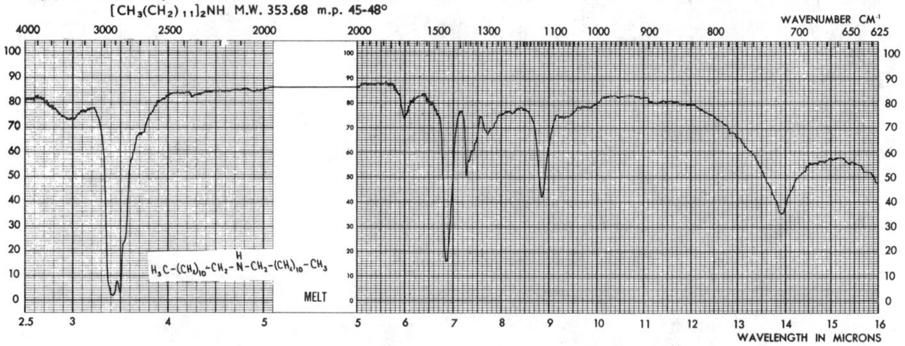

T7276-1 **Trimethylamine hydrochloride** (trimethylammonium chloride)
$(CH_3)_3N{\cdot}HCl$ M.W. 95.57
m.p. 278.5-280° (dec.)

NUJOL MULL

D

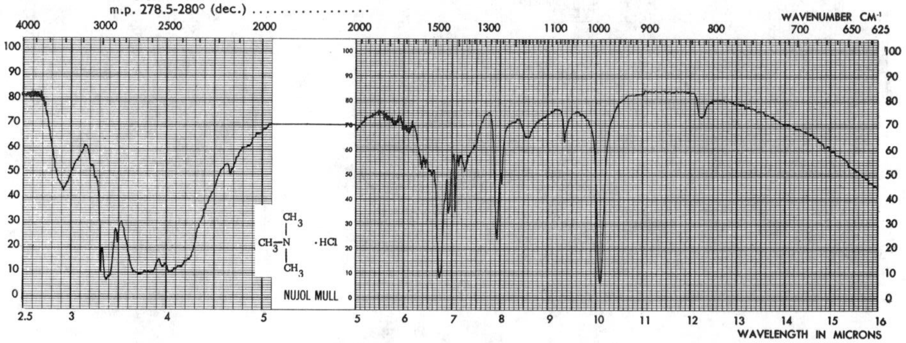

14,998-5 **Trimethylamine formate** (trimethylammonium formate)
$2(CH_3)_3N{\cdot}5HCO_2H$ M.W. 348.35 n_D^{20} 1.4095
b.p. 67 70°/4 mm.

NEAT

E

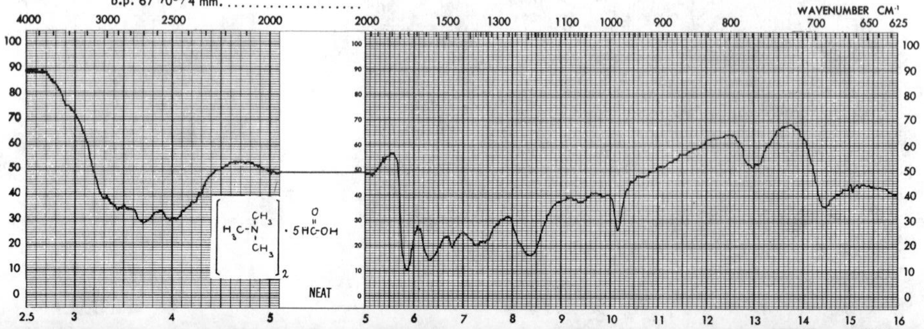

17,686-9
Trimethylamine-N-oxide dihydrate, 98%
$(CH_3)_3N(O){\cdot}2H_2O$
M.W. 111.14 m.p. 91-93°

NUJOL MULL

F

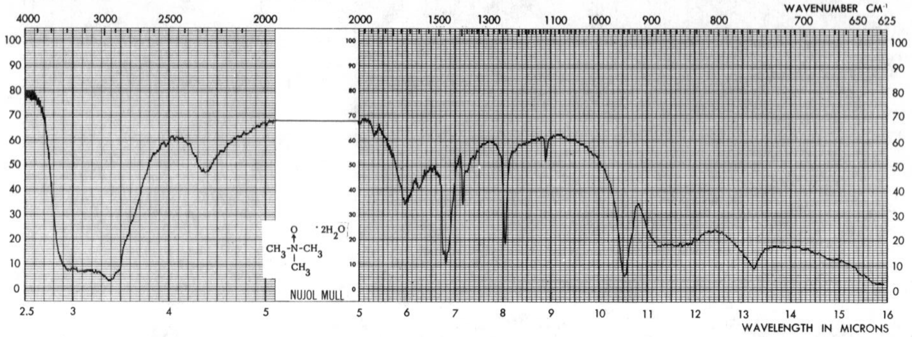

D9820-3 **Diethylmethylamine** (N-methyldiethylamine)
$(C_2H_5)_2NCH_3$ M.W. 87.17 n_D^{20} 1.3904

NEAT

G

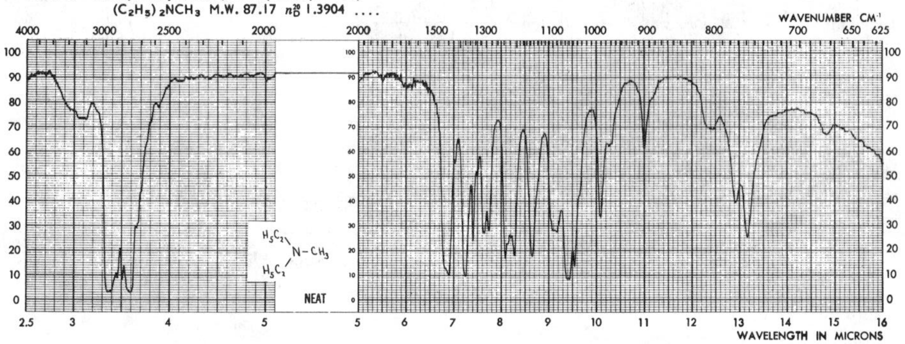

13,206-3 **Triethylamine**
$(C_2H_5)_3N$ M.W. 101.19 n_D^{20} 1.4000
b.p. 85-91°

NEAT

H

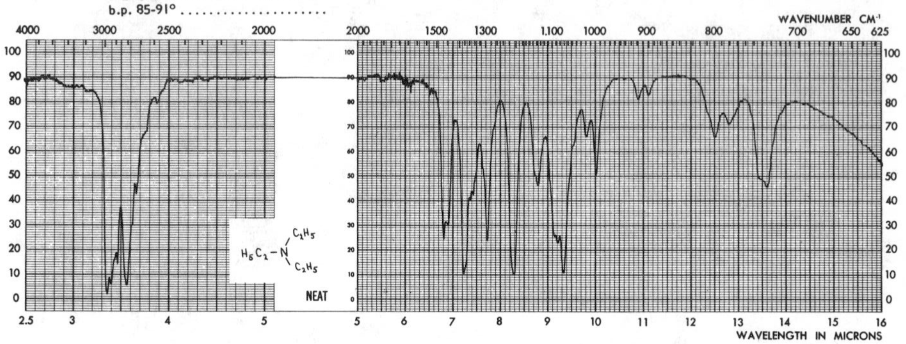

14,397-9 **Tripropylamine**
$(CH_3CH_2CH_2)_3N$ M.W. 143.27 n_D^{20} 1.4160
b.p. 155-158°

NEAT

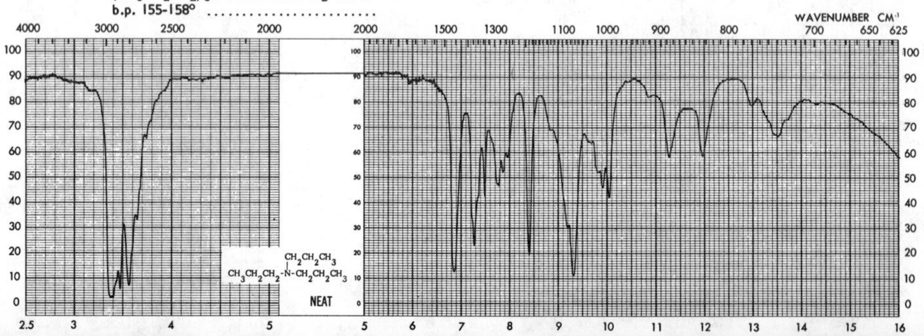

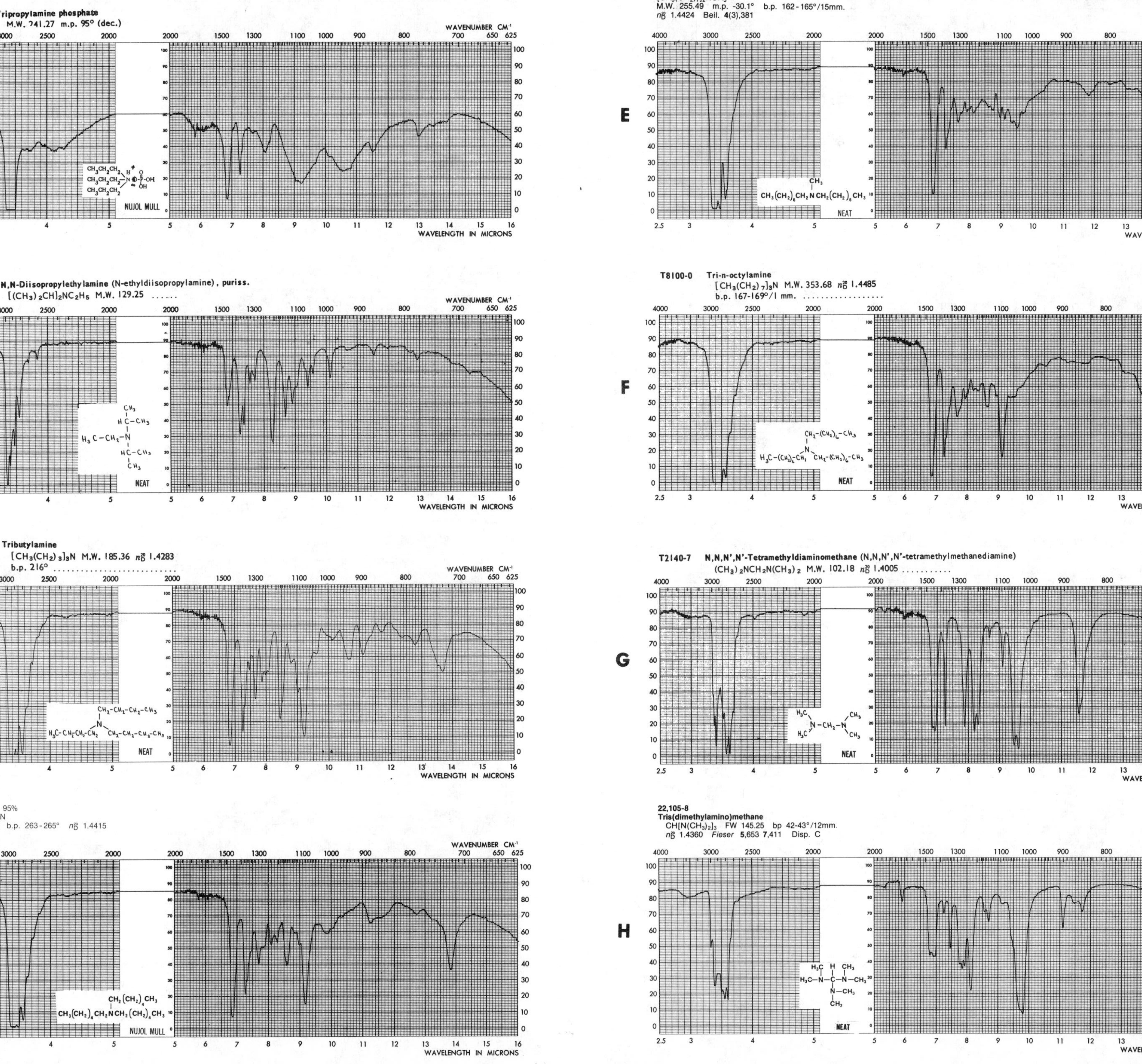

A
14,600-5 Tripropylamine phosphate
M.W. 241.27 m.p. 95° (dec.)
NUJOL MULL
B
D12,580-6 N,N-Diisopropylethylamine (N-ethyldiisopropylamine), puriss.
$[(CH_3)_2CH]_2NC_2H_5$ M.W. 129.25
NEAT
C
T4935-2 Tributylamine
$[CH_3(CH_2)_3]_3N$ M.W. 185.36 n_D^{20} 1.4283
b.p. 216°
NEAT
D
18,399-7
Trihexylamine, 95%
$[CH_3(CH_2)_5]_3N$
M.W. 269.52 b.p. 263-265° n_D^{20} 1.4415
Beil. 4,188
NUJOL MULL
E
18,377-6
N-Methyldioctylamine, 98%
$[CH_3(CH_2)_7]_2NCH_3$
M.W. 255.49 m.p. -30.1° b.p. 162-165°/15mm.
n_D^{20} 1.4424 Beil. 4(3),381
NEAT
F
T8100-0 Tri-n-octylamine
$[CH_3(CH_2)_7]_3N$ M.W. 353.68 n_D^{20} 1.4485
b.p. 167-169°/1 mm.
NEAT
G
T2140-7 N,N,N',N'-Tetramethyldiaminomethane (N,N,N',N'-tetramethylmethanediamine)
$(CH_3)_2NCH_2N(CH_3)_2$ M.W. 102.18 n_D^{20} 1.4005
NEAT
H
22,105-8
Tris(dimethylamino)methane
$CH[N(CH_3)_2]_3$ FW 145.25 bp 42-43°/12mm.
n_D^{20} 1.4360 Fieser 5,653 7,411 Disp. C
NEAT
WAVENUMBER CM⁻¹
WAVELENGTH IN MICRONS
ALDRICH

A

12,717-5 N,N,N',N'-Tetraethylmethanediamine
$(C_2H_5)_2NCH_2N(C_2H_5)_2$ M.W. 158.29 n_D^{20} 1.4255
b.p. 166-169°

NEAT

B

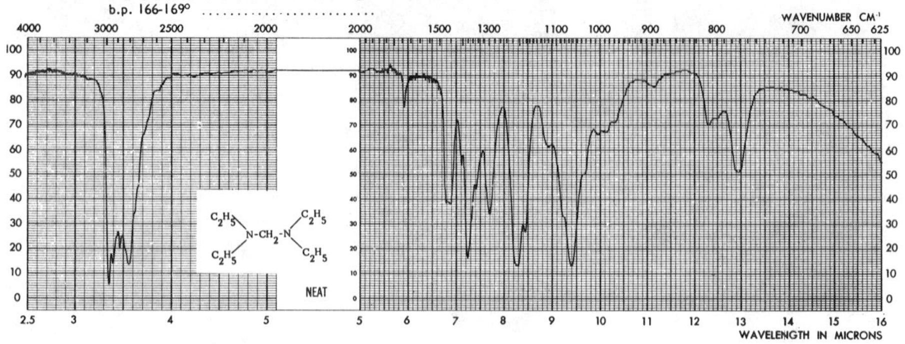

12,701-9 N-Methylethylenediamine
$CH_3NHCH_2CH_2NH_2$ M.W. 74.13 n_D^{20} 1.4395
b.p. 114-116°

NEAT

C

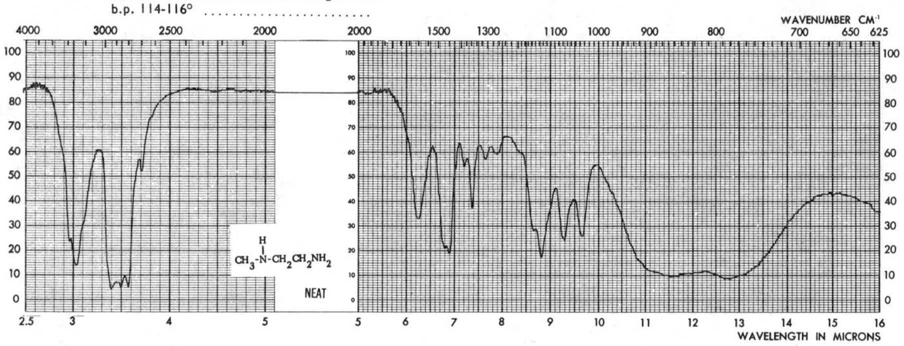

12,700-0 N-Ethylethylenediamine
$C_2H_5NHCH_2CH_2NH_2$ M.W. 88.15 n_D^{20} 1.4385
b.p. 128-130°

NEAT

D

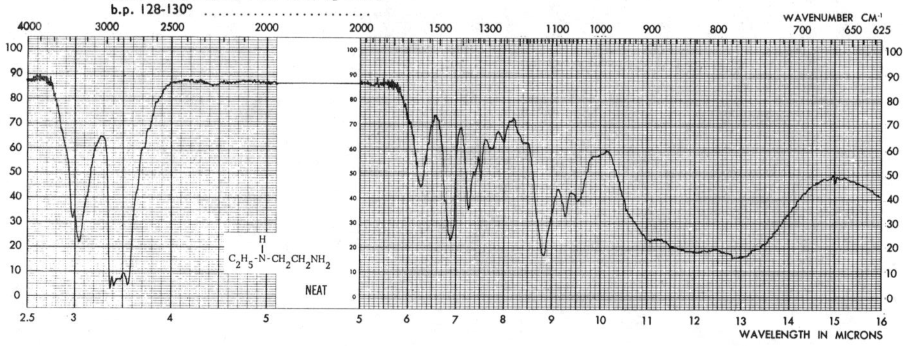

D15,780-5 sym.-Dimethylethylenediamine
$CH_3NHCH_2CH_2NHCH_3$ M.W. 88.15
n_D^{20} 1.4307

NEAT

E

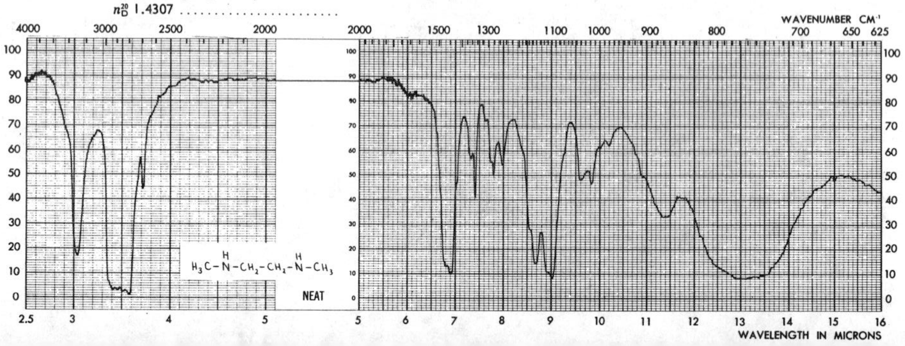

D15,800-3 unsym.-Dimethylethylenediamine
$(CH_3)_2NCH_2CH_2NH_2$ M.W. 88.15
n_D^{20} 1.4291

NEAT

F

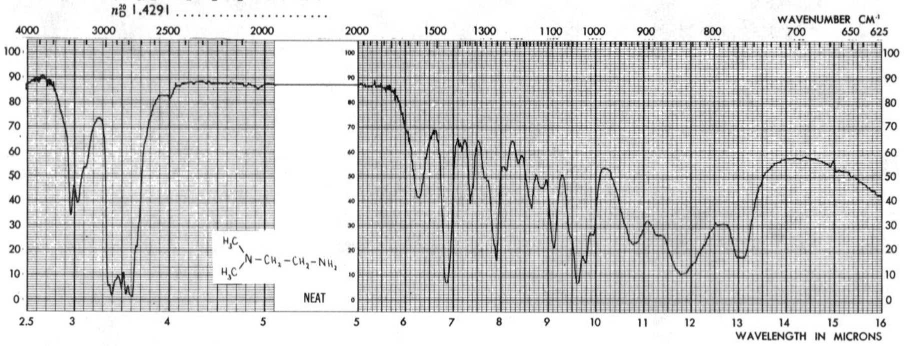

12,694-2 N,N'-Diethylethylenediamine
$C_2H_5NHCH_2CH_2NHC_2H_5$ M.W. 116.21 n_D^{20} 1.4326
b.p. 152-154°

NEAT

G

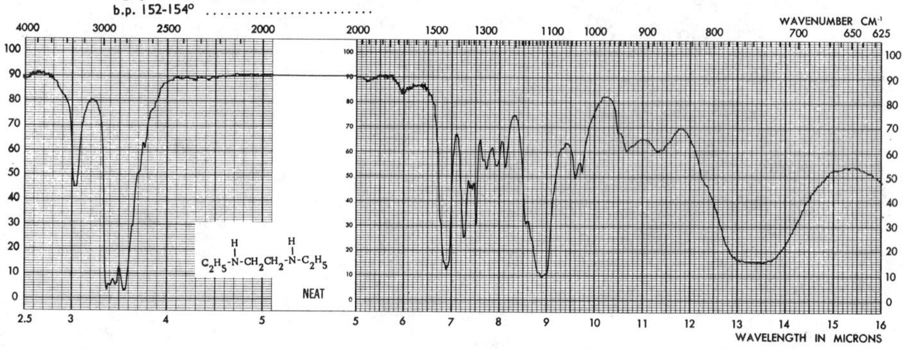

11,272-0 N,N-Diethylethylenediamine, 98+%
$(C_2H_5)_2NCH_2CH_2NH_2$ M.W. 116.21 n_D^{20} 1.4347
b.p. 145-147°

NEAT

H

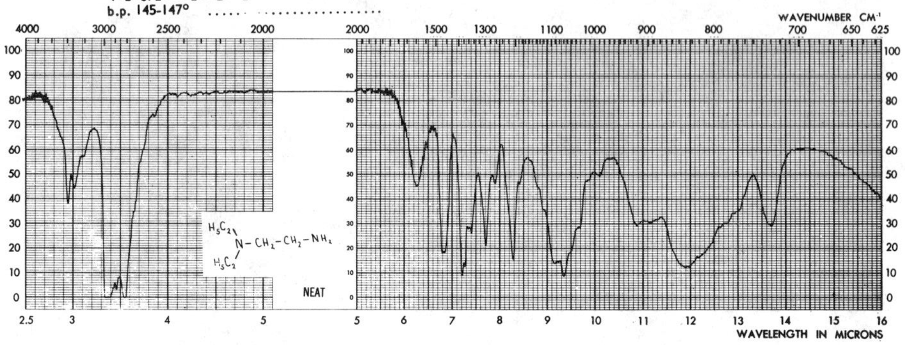

12,712-4 N,N,N'-Trimethylethylenediamine
$(CH_3)_2NCH_2CH_2NHCH_3$ M.W. 102.18 n_D^{20} 1.4196
b.p. 116-118°

NEAT

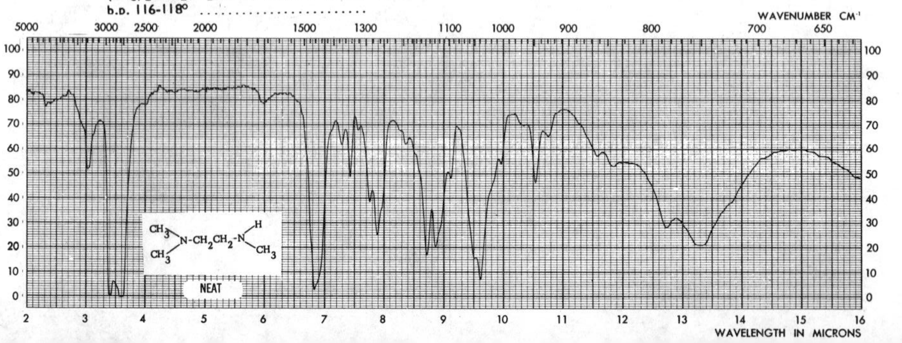

A — 12,711-6 **N,N,N'-Triethylethylenediamine, puriss.**
$(C_2H_5)_2NCH_2CH_2NHC_2H_5$ M.W. 144.26 n_D^{20} 1.4311
b.p. 169-170°

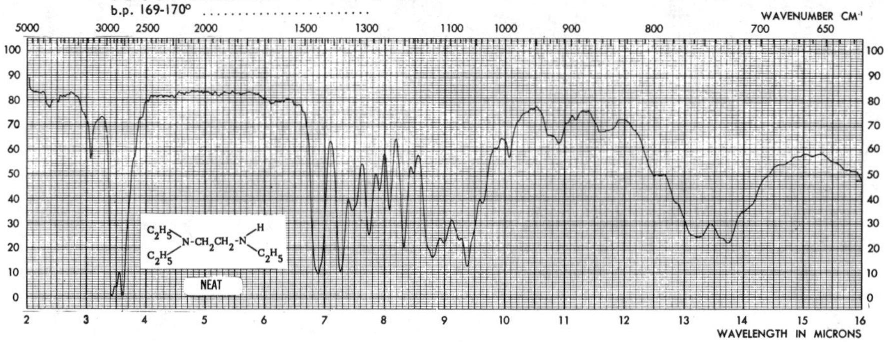

NEAT

B — T2250-0 **N,N,N',N'-Tetramethylethylenediamine**
$(CH_3)_2NCH_2CH_2N(CH_3)_2$ M.W. 116.21 n_D^{20} 1.4179
b.p. 120-122°

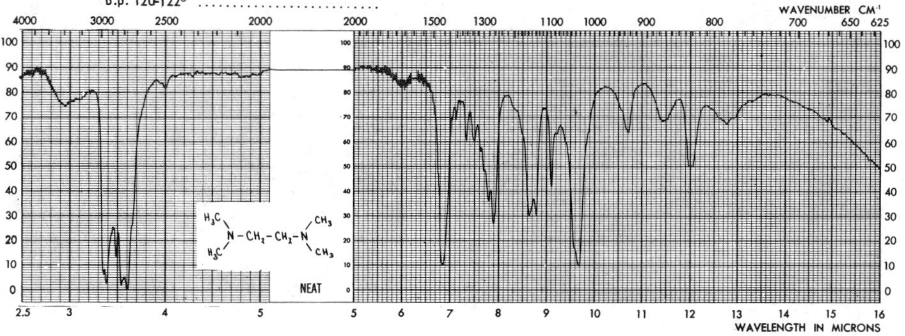

NEAT

C — 12,707-8 **N,N,N',N'-Tetraethylethylenediamine, puriss.**
$(C_2H_5)_2NCH_2CH_2N(C_2H_5)_2$ M.W. 172.32 n_D^{20} 1.4343
b.p. 189-192°

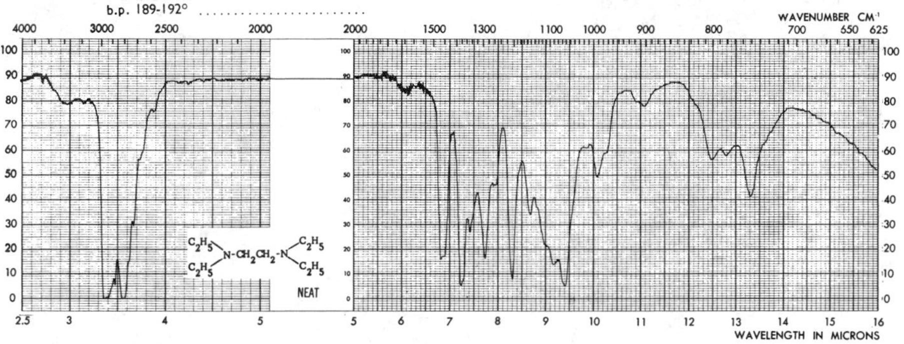

NEAT

D — I-2210-2 **N-Isopropylethylenediamine**
$(CH_3)_2CHNHCH_2CH_2NH_2$ M.W. 102.18 n_D^{20} 1.4369

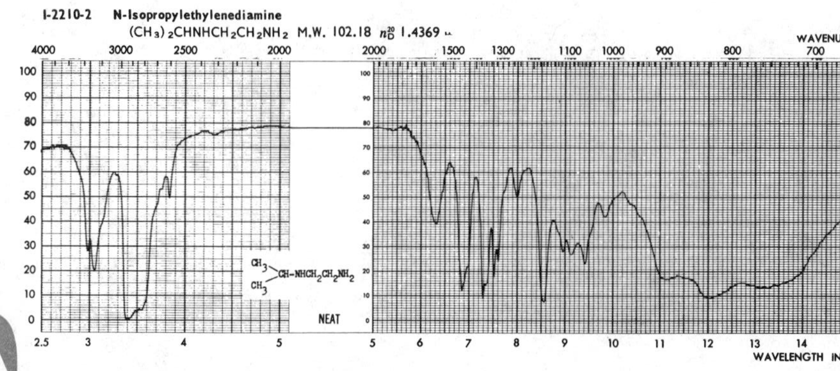

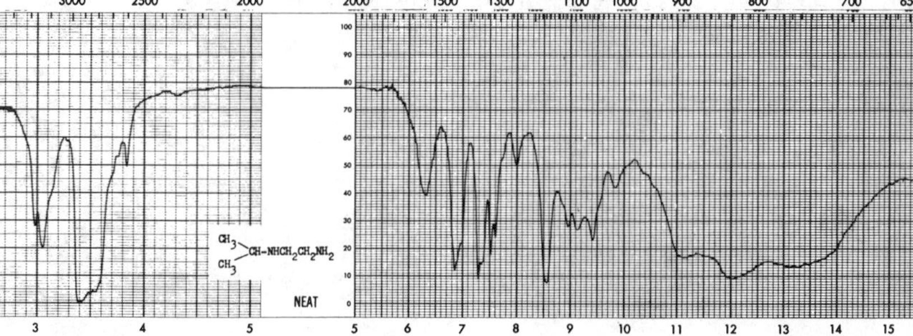

NEAT

E — 12,702-7 **N-Methyl-1,3-propanediamine**
$CH_3NH(CH_2)_3NH_2$ M.W. 88.15 n_D^{20} 1.4468
b.p. 150°

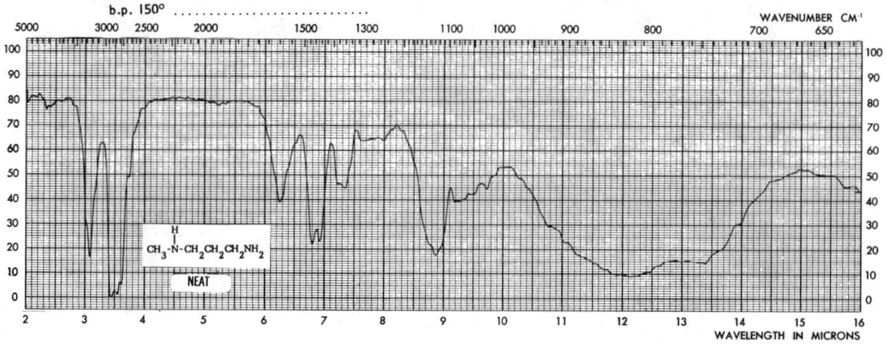

NEAT

F — D14,500-9 **3-Dimethylaminopropylamine** (N,N-dimethyl-1,3-propanediamine)
$(CH_3)_2N(CH_2)_3NH_2$ M.W. 102.18
n_D^{20} 1.4350

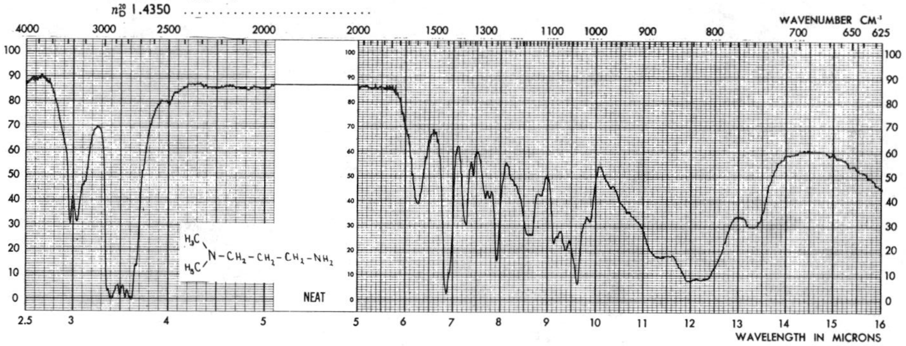

NEAT

G — D8920-4 **3-Diethylaminopropylamine (N,N-diethyl-1,3-propanediamine), puriss.**
$(C_2H_5)_2N(CH_2)_3NH_2$ M.W. 130.24
n_D^{20} 1.4416

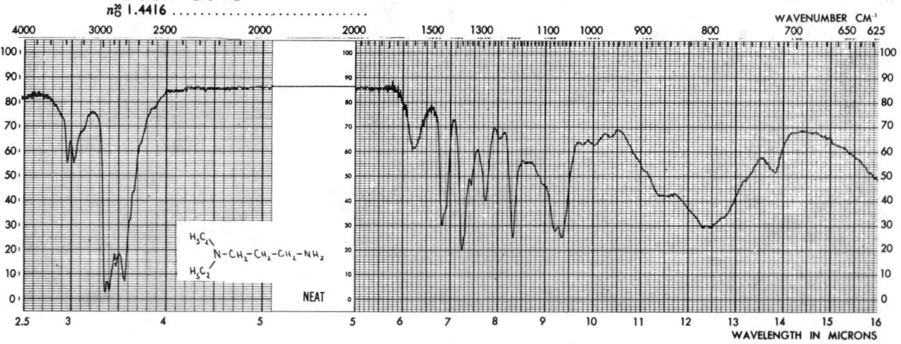

NEAT

H — 13,842-8 **N,N'-Diethyl-1,3-propanediamine**
$C_2H_5NH(CH_2)_3NHC_2H_5$ M.W. 130.24
n_D^{20} 1.4374

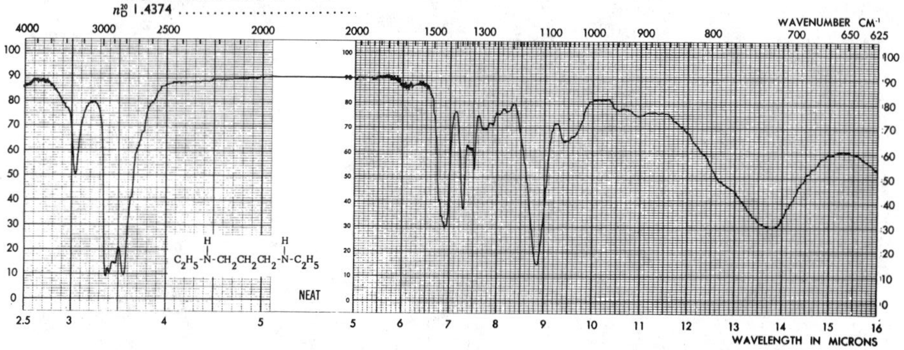

NEAT

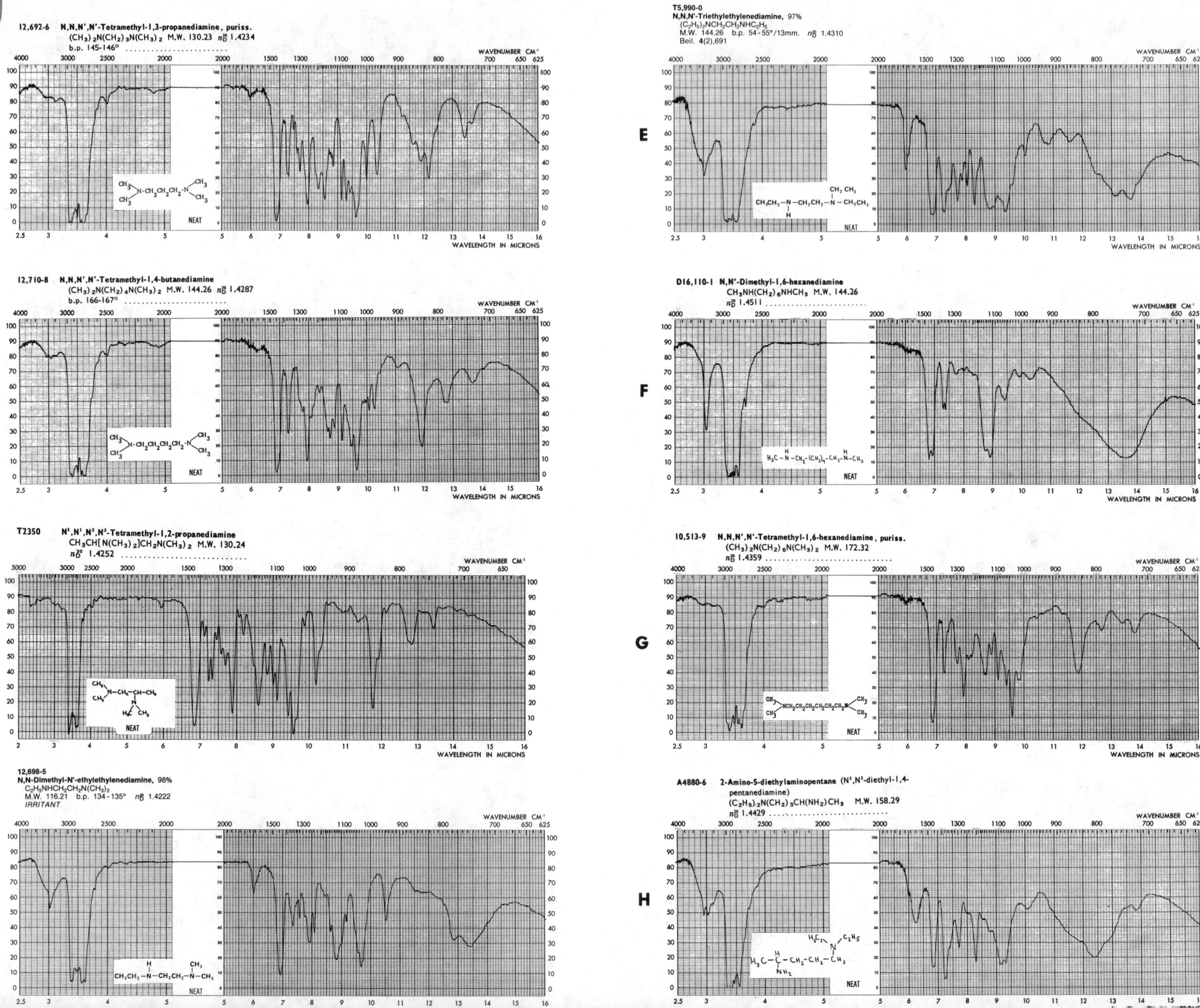
ALDRICH
A
12,692-6 N,N,N',N'-Tetramethyl-1,3-propanediamine, puriss.
(CH3)2N(CH2)3N(CH3)2 M.W. 130.23 n20D 1.4234
b.p. 145-146°
NEAT
B
12,710-8 N,N,N',N'-Tetramethyl-1,4-butanediamine
(CH3)2N(CH2)4N(CH3)2 M.W. 144.26 n20D 1.4287
b.p. 166-167°
NEAT
C
T2350 N1,N1,N2,N2-Tetramethyl-1,2-propanediamine
CH3CH[N(CH3)2]CH2N(CH3)2 M.W. 130.24
n20D 1.4252
NEAT
D
12,698-5
N,N-Dimethyl-N'-ethylethylenediamine, 98%
C2H5NHCH2CH2N(CH3)2
M.W. 116.21 b.p. 134-135° n20D 1.4222
IRRITANT
NEAT
E
T5,990-0
N,N,N'-Triethylethylenediamine, 97%
(C2H5)2NCH2CH2NHC2H5
M.W. 144.26 b.p. 54-55°/13mm. n20D 1.4310
Beil. 4(2),691
NEAT
F
D16,110-1 N,N'-Dimethyl-1,6-hexanediamine
CH3NH(CH2)6NHCH3 M.W. 144.26
n20D 1.4511
NEAT
G
10,513-9 N,N,N',N'-Tetramethyl-1,6-hexanediamine, puriss.
(CH3)2N(CH2)6N(CH3)2 M.W. 172.32
n20D 1.4359
NEAT
H
A4880-6 2-Amino-5-diethylaminopentane (N1,N1-diethyl-1,4-pentanediamine)
(C2H5)2N(CH2)3CH(NH2)CH3 M.W. 158.29
n20D 1.4429
NEAT
WAVENUMBER CM-1
WAVELENGTH IN MICRONS

A

D4560-6 3-(Di-n-butylamino)-propylamine (N,N-dibutyl-1,3-propanediamine)
$[CH_3(CH_2)_3]_2N(CH_2)_3NH_2$ M.W. 186.34
n_D^{20} 1.4463

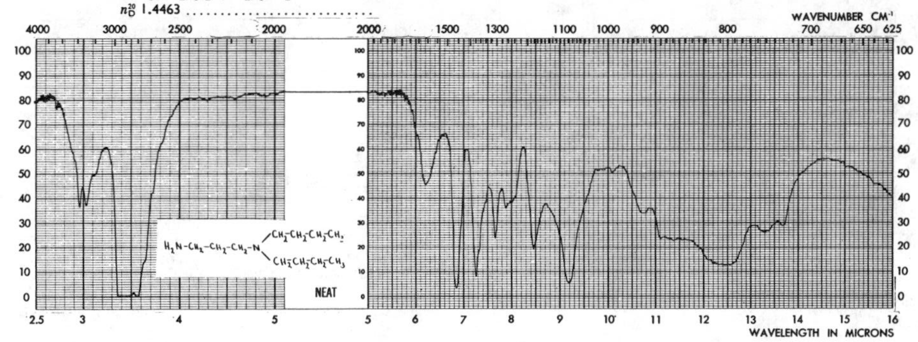

NEAT

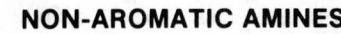

B

D9385-6 Diethylenetriamine
$H_2NCH_2CH_2NHCH_2CH_2NH_2$ M.W. 103.17
n_D^{20} 1.4826

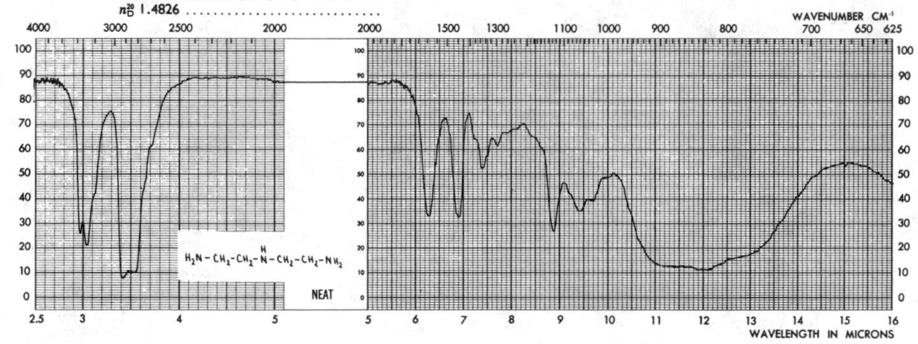

NEAT

C

12,715-9 N-(2-Aminoethyl)-1,3-propanediamine
$H_2N(CH_2)_3NHCH_2CH_2NH_2$ M.W. 117.19
n_D^{20} 1.4824

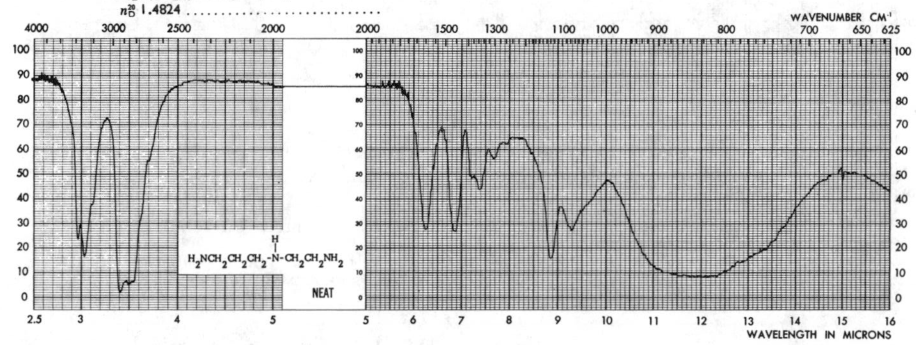

NEAT

D

18,844-1
3,3'-Diamino-*N*-methyldipropylamine
$CH_3N(CH_2CH_2CH_2NH_2)_2$ FW 145.25 Disp. A

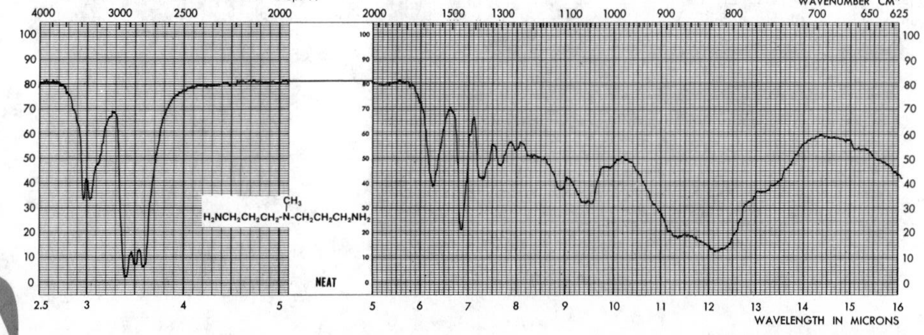

NEAT

E

12,714-0 N-(2-Aminoethyl)-1,4-butanediamine
$H_2N(CH_2)_4NHCH_2CH_2NH_2$ M.W. 131.22
n_D^{20} 1.4799

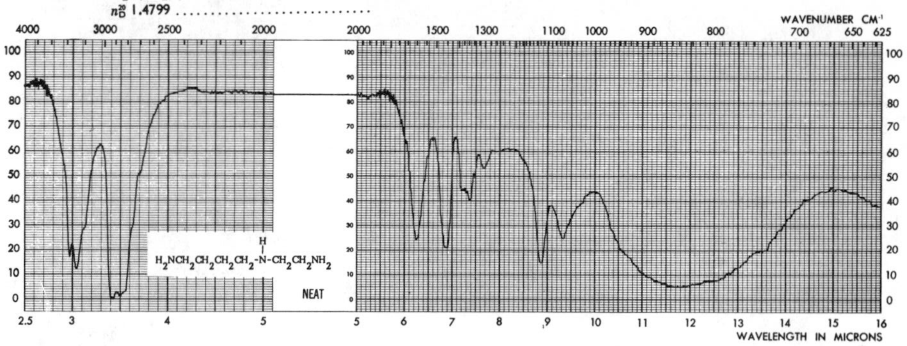

NEAT

F

S382-8 Spermidine
$H_2N(CH_2)_4NH(CH_2)_3NH_2$ M.W. 145.25 n_D^{20} 1.4790

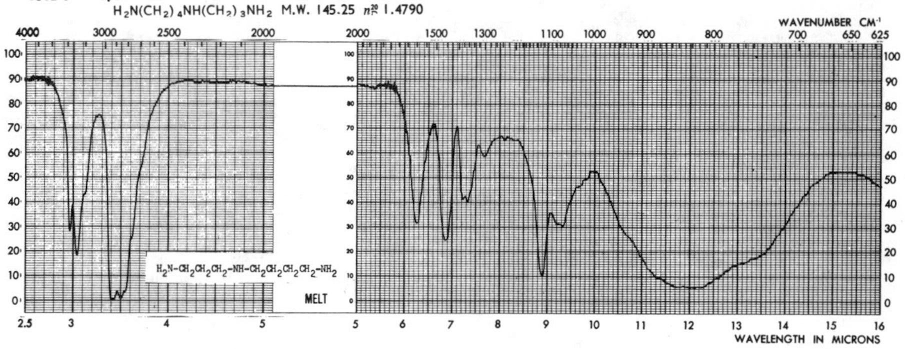

MELT

G

I-100-6 3,3'-Iminobispropylamine (3,3'-diaminodipropylamine)
$HN[(CH_2)_3NH_2]_2$ M.W. 131.22 n_D^{20} 1.4806
b.p. 151° (dec.)/50 mm.

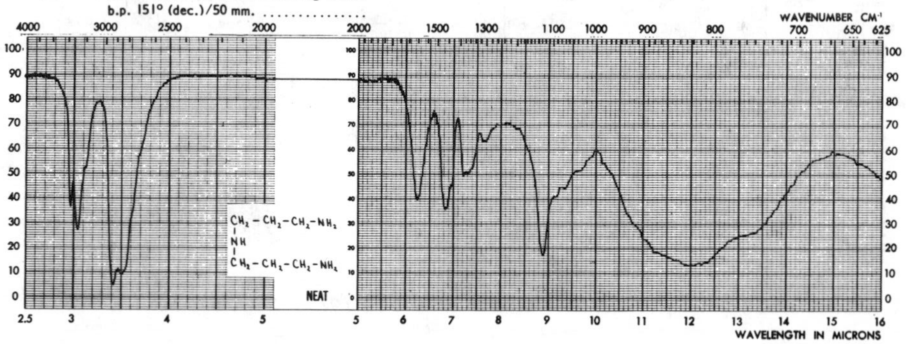

NEAT

H

B3680-2 Bis-(2-aminopropyl)-amine (dipropylenetriamine, 2,6-dimethyl-diethylenetriamine)
$[CH_3CH(NH_2)CH_2]_2NH$ M.W. 131.22 n_D^{20} 1.4689

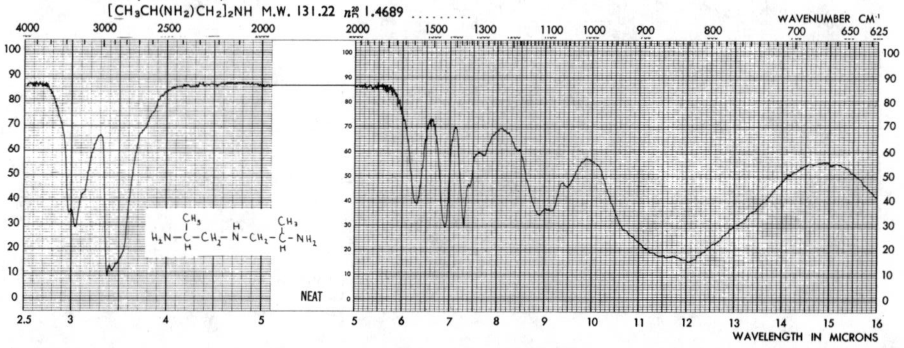

NEAT

A

I—2,480-6
N¹-Isopropyl-2-methyl-1,2-propanediamine, 98%
$(CH_3)_2CHNHCH_2C(CH_3)_2NH_2$
M.W. 130.24 b.p. 147-149° n_D^{20} 1.4269

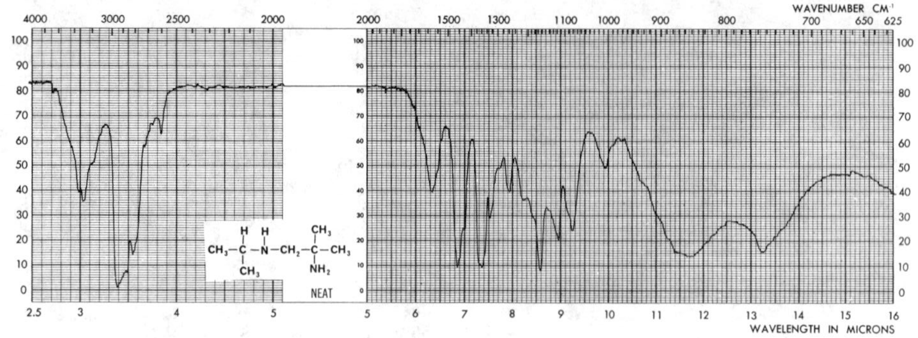

NEAT

B

13,209-8 **Triethylenetetramine, tech.**
$H_2NCH_2CH_2NHCH_2CH_2NHCH_2CH_2NH_2$ M.W. 146.24
n_D^{20} 1.4971 b.p. 266-267°

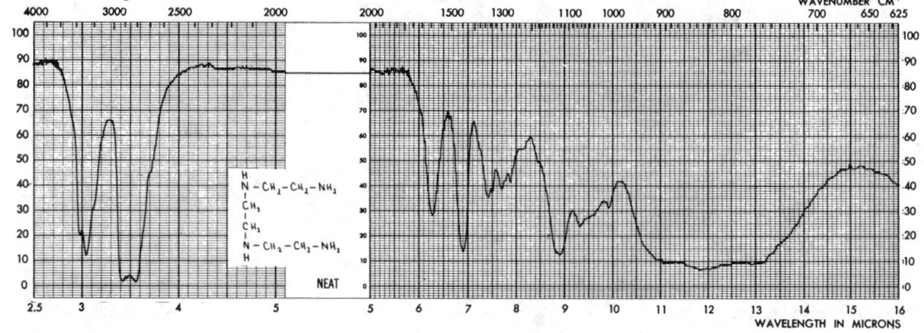

NEAT

C

16,196-9
Triethylenetetramine tetrahydrochloride, recrystallized
$H_2NCH_2CH_2NHCH_2CH_2NHCH_2CH_2NH_2 \cdot 4HCl$
M.W. 292.08 m.p. 269-270°

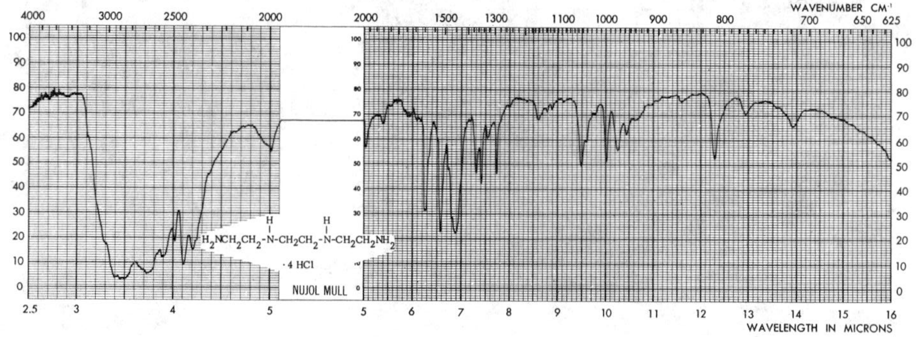

NUJOL MULL

D

T1150-9 **Tetraethylenepentamine, tech.**
$HN(CH_2CH_2NHCH_2CH_2NH_2)_2$ M.W. 189.31 n_D^{20} 1.5042
b.p. 340.3°

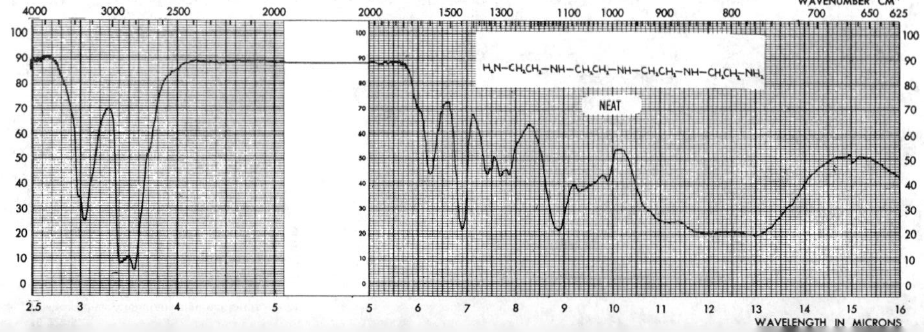

NEAT

E

S383-6 **Spermine**
$H_2N(CH_2)_3NH(CH_2)_4NH(CH_2)_3NH_2$ M.W. 202.35
m.p. 29-30.5°

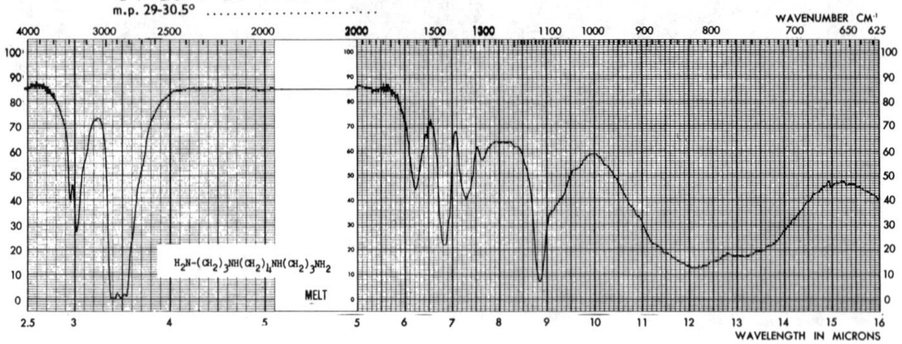

MELT

F

A6380-5 **Aminomethylcyclopropane (cyclopropanemethylamine) hydrochloride**
$C_3H_5CH_2NH_2 \cdot HCl$ M.W. 107.58
m.p. 206-209°

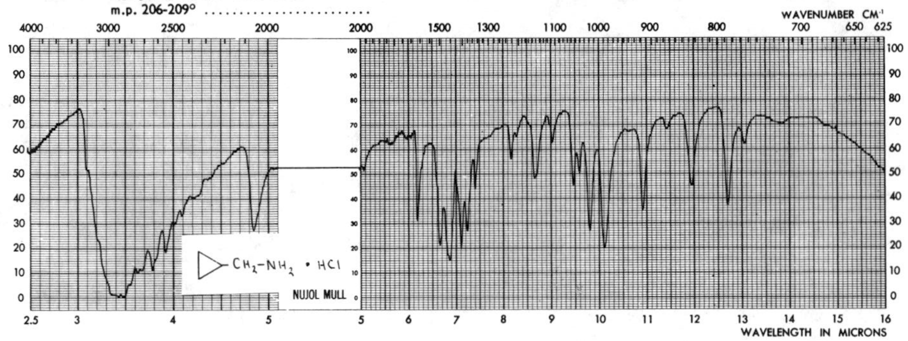

NUJOL MULL

G

12,550-4 **Cyclopropylamine**
$C_3H_5NH_2$ M.W. 57.10
n_D^{20} 1.4206

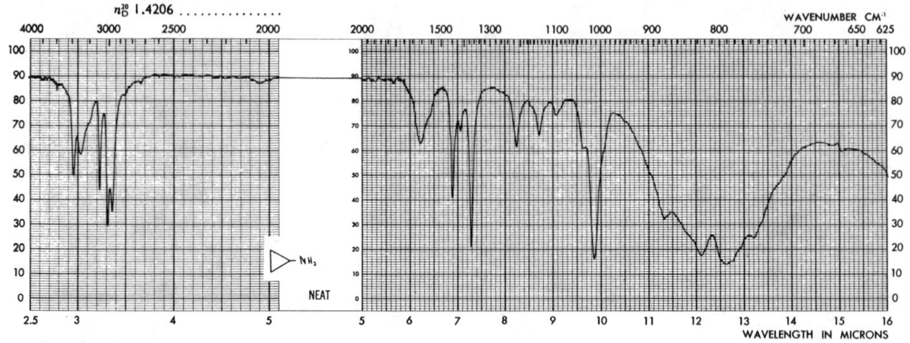

NEAT

H

15,927-1
Cyclobutylamine hydrochloride, 98%
$C_4H_7NH_2 \cdot HCl$
M.W. 107.58 m.p. 182-184° Beil. 12,4

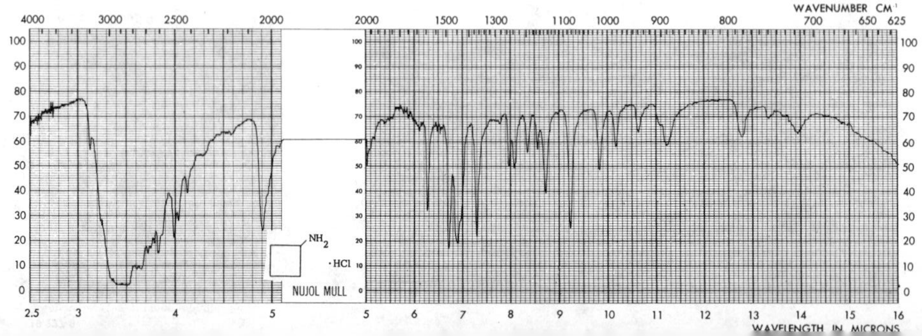

NUJOL MULL

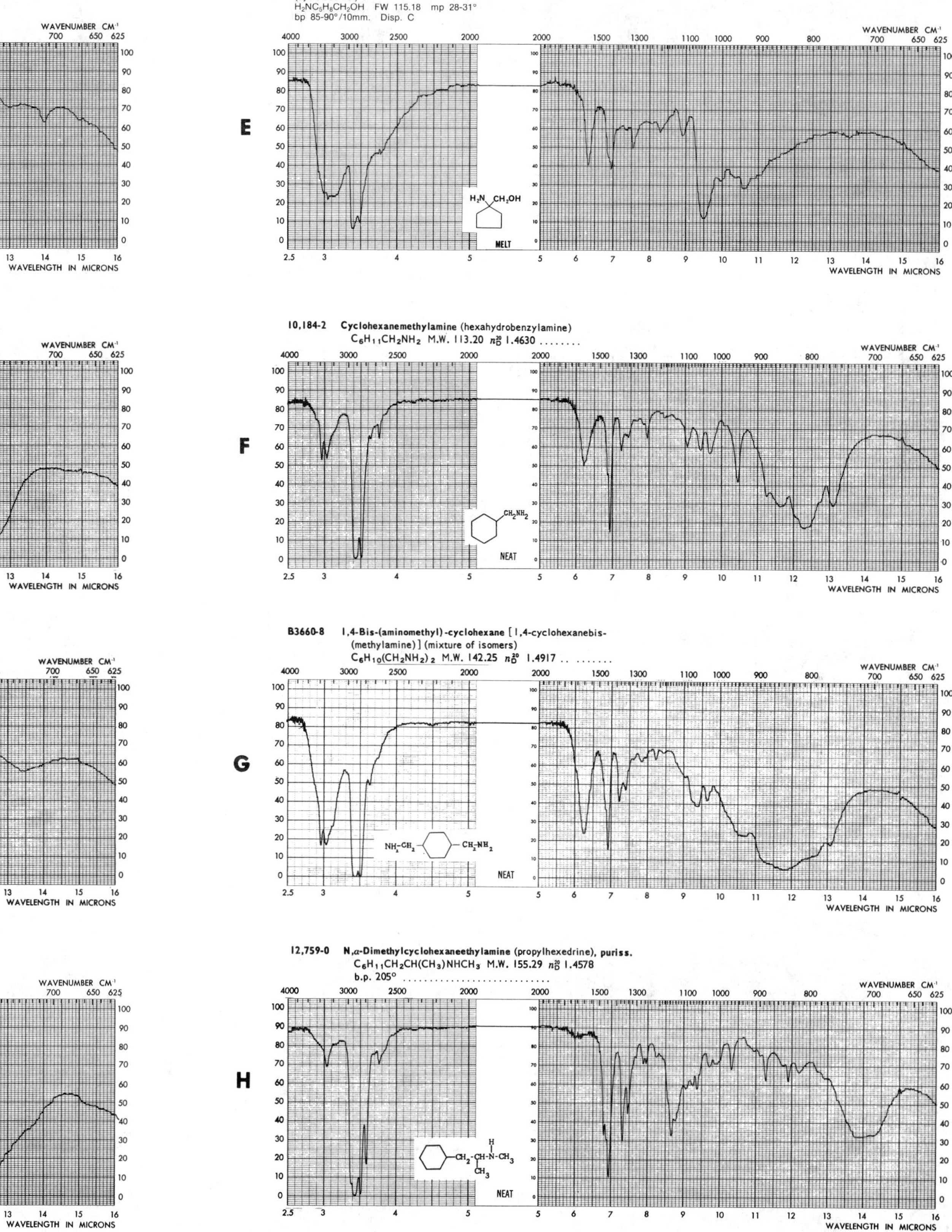

A 19,229-5
Aminomethylcyclobutane hydrochloride, 97%
(cyclobutanemethylamine)
$C_4H_7CH_2NH_2 \cdot HCl$ FW 121.61 mp 241° (dec.)
Beil. **12**,5 Disp. C
NUJOL MULL

B C11,500-2 **Cyclopentylamine**
$C_5H_9NH_2$ M.W. 85.15 n_D^{20} 1.4482
NEAT

C M4000-6 **N-Methylcyclopentylamine**
$C_5H_9NHCH_3$ M.W. 99.18 n_D^{20} 1.4451 b.p. 115°/
NEAT

D 19,478-6
5-Amino-2,2,4-trimethyl-1-cyclopentanemethylamine,
99%, mixture of isomers
$H_2NC_5H_5(CH_3)_3CH_2NH_2$ FW 156.27 bp 221°
n_D^{20} 1.4733 d 0.901 Disp. C
NEAT

E 19,227-9
1-Amino-1-cyclopentanemethanol, 98%
(cycloleucinol)
$H_2NC_5H_8CH_2OH$ FW 115.18 mp 28-31°
bp 85-90°/10mm. Disp. C
MELT

F 10,184-2 **Cyclohexanemethylamine** (hexahydrobenzylamine)
$C_6H_{11}CH_2NH_2$ M.W. 113.20 n_D^{20} 1.4630
NEAT

G B3660-8 **1,4-Bis-(aminomethyl)-cyclohexane** [1,4-cyclohexanebis-(methylamine)] (mixture of isomers)
$C_6H_{10}(CH_2NH_2)_2$ M.W. 142.25 n_D^{20} 1.4917
NEAT

H 12,759-0 **N,α-Dimethylcyclohexaneethylamine** (propylhexedrine), **puriss.**
$C_6H_{11}CH_2CH(CH_3)NHCH_3$ M.W. 155.29 n_D^{20} 1.4578
b.p. 205°
NEAT

A

12,166-5 **Cyclohexanebutylamine**
$C_6H_{11}(CH_2)_4NH_2$ M.W. 155.29 n_D^{20} 1.4650
NEAT

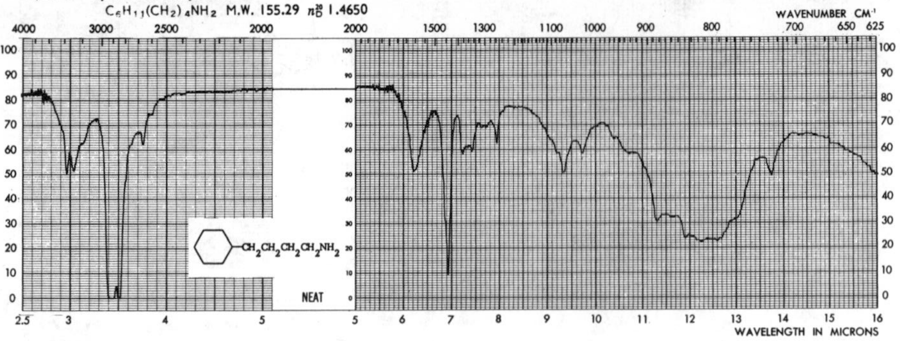

B

C10,465-5 **Cyclohexylamine**
$C_6H_{11}NH_2$ M.W. 99.18 n_D^{20} 1.4580
NEAT

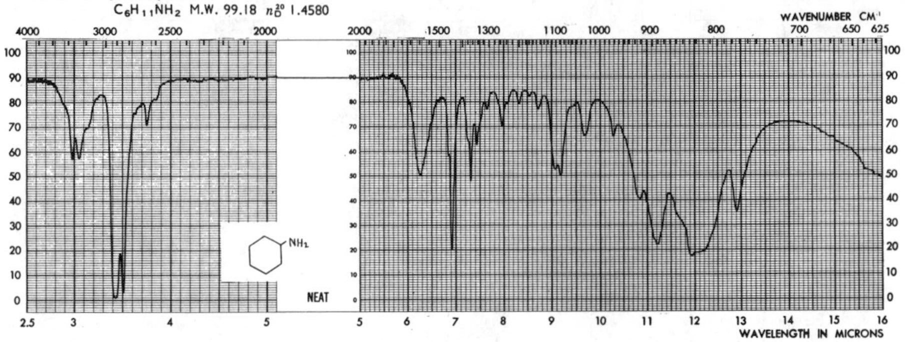

C

18,646-5
N-Cyclohexylhydroxylamine hydrochloride
$C_6H_{11}NHOH \cdot HCl$
M.W. 151.64 m.p. 137-140° (dec.)
NUJOL MULL

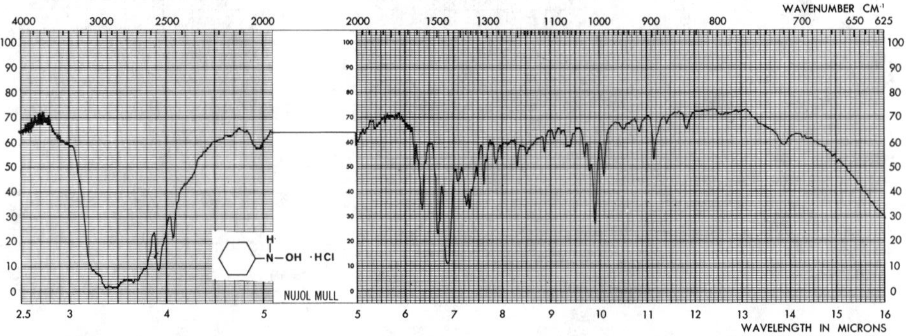

D

10,332-2 **N-Methylcyclohexylamine**
$C_6H_{11}NHCH_3$ M.W. 113.20 n_D^{20} 1.4560 b.p. 149°
NEAT

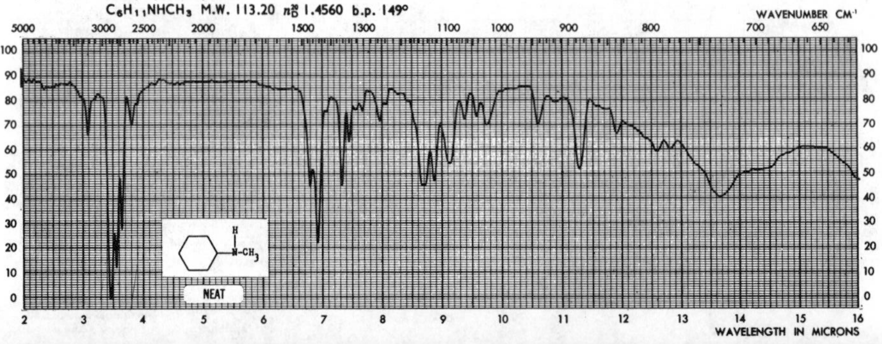

E

D7950-0 **Dicyclohexylamine**
$(C_6H_{11})_2NH$ M.W. 181.32 n_D^{20} 1.4842
m.p. -2 to -1° ....
NEAT

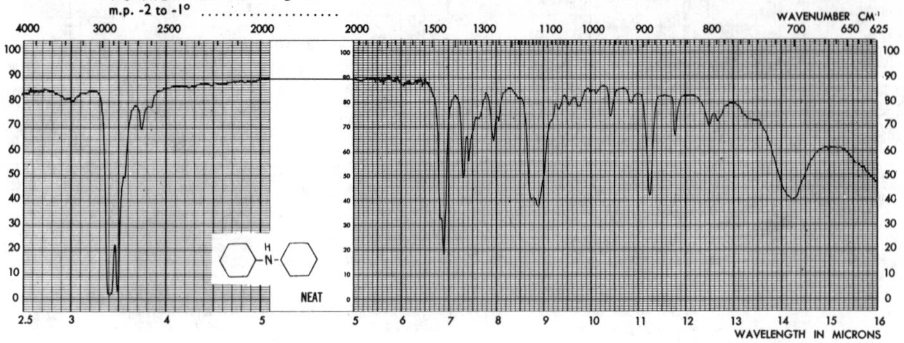

F

13,585-2 **4,4'-Methylenebis-(cyclohexylamine)**
$CH_2(C_6H_{10}NH_2)_2$ M.W. 210.36 m.p. 48-51°
MELT

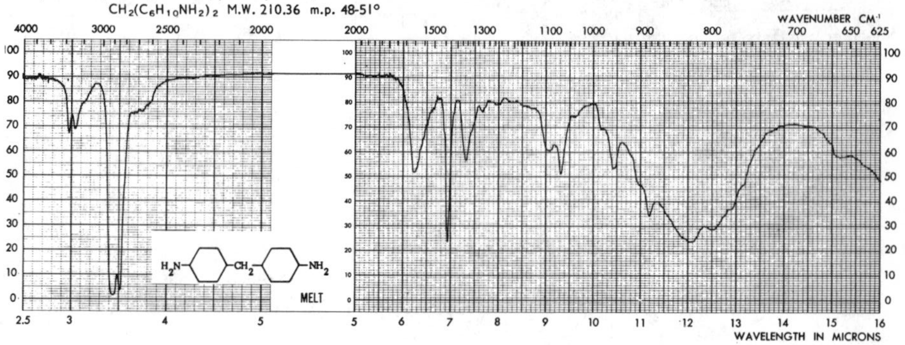

G

13,255-1 **1,2-Diaminocyclohexane** (predominantly *trans*)
$C_6H_{10}(NH_2)_2$ M.W. 114.19 n_D^{20} 1.4805 ....
NEAT

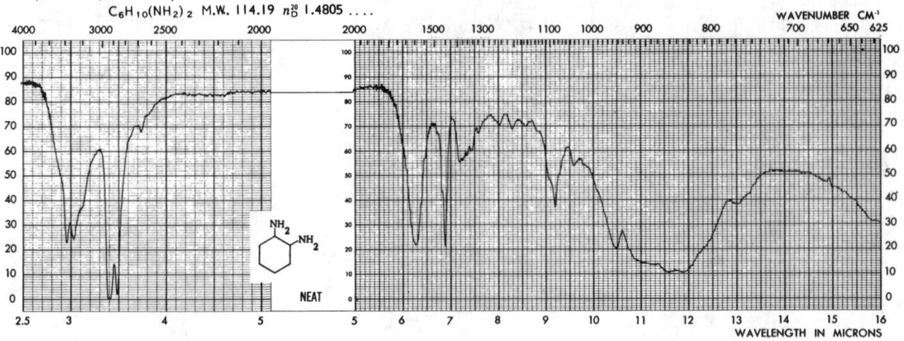

H

22,257-7
2-Aminocyclohexanol hydrochloride, 97%, mixture of *cis* and *trans*
$H_2NC_6H_{10}OH \cdot HCl$ FW 151.64 mp 172-175°
Beil. 13(3),708 Disp. C
NUJOL MULL

WAVENUMBER CM⁻¹ / WAVELENGTH IN MICRONS

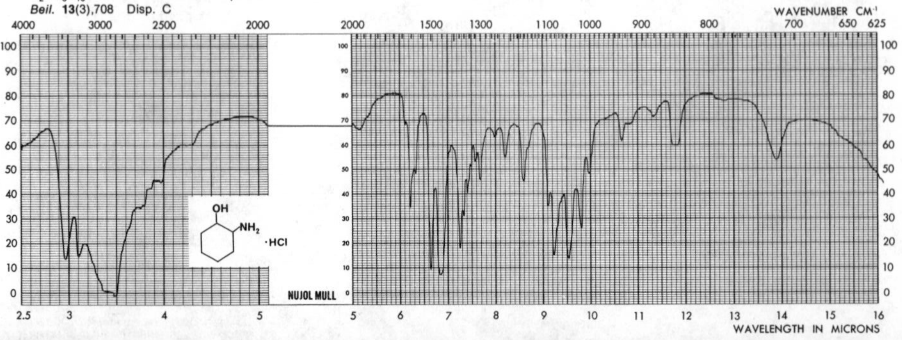

A 10,210-5 **N,N-Diethylcyclohexylamine**
$C_6H_{11}N(C_2H_5)_2$ M.W. 155.29 n_D^{20} 1.4571 b.p. 194-195°

B 16,197-7
N-Isopropylcyclohexylamine, 99%
$C_6H_{11}NHCH(CH_3)_2$
M.W. 141.26 b.p. 60-65°/12mm. n_D^{20} 1.4480
IRRITANT

C C10,805 **N-Cyclohexyl-1,3-propanediamine**
$C_6H_{11}NH(CH_2)_3NH_2$ M.W. 156.27
n_D^{20} 1.4814

D 19,343-7
2-Methylcyclohexylamine, 98%, mixture of *cis* and *trans*
$CH_3C_6H_{10}NH_2$ FW 113.20 bp 149-150°
n_D^{20} 1.4565 d 0.856 *Beil.* **12**,9 Disp. C

E **3-Methylcyclohexylamine**, 98%, mixture of *cis* and *trans*
$CH_3C_6H_{10}NH_2$ FW 113.20 bp 150°/730mm.
n_D^{20} 1.4525 d 0.855 *Beil.* **12**,10 Disp. C

F 19,735-1
2,3-Dimethylcyclohexylamine, 99+%, mixture of isomers
$(CH_3)_2C_6H_9NH_2$ FW 127.23 bp 158-160°
n_D^{20} 1.4595 d 0.835 Disp. C

G 17,746-6
4-Methylcyclohexylamine, 97%, mixture of *cis* and *trans*
$CH_3C_6H_{10}NH_2$
M.W. 113.2 b.p. 151-154° n_D^{20} 1.4531 d 0.855
Beil. **12**,12

H 14,356-1 **4-tert.-Butylcyclohexylamine** (mixture of *cis* and *trans*)
$(CH_3)_3CC_6H_{10}NH_2$ M.W. 155.29 n_D^{20} 1.4650
b.p. 81-82°/8 mm.

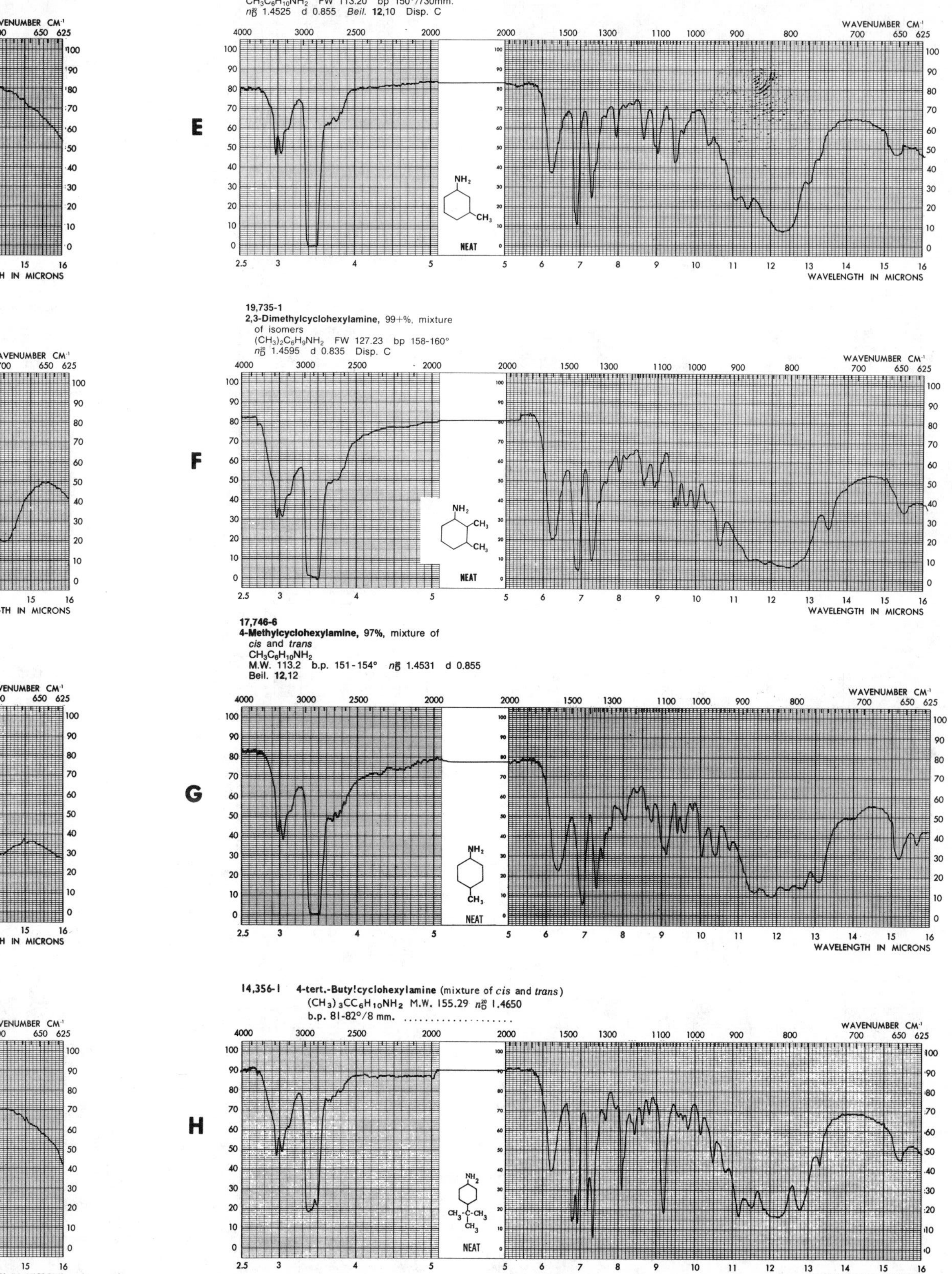

A

18,046-7
1,3-Cyclohexanebis(methylamine), 99% [1,3-bis(aminomethyl)cyclohexane]
$C_6H_{10}(CH_2NH_2)_2$
M.W. 142.25

NEAT

B

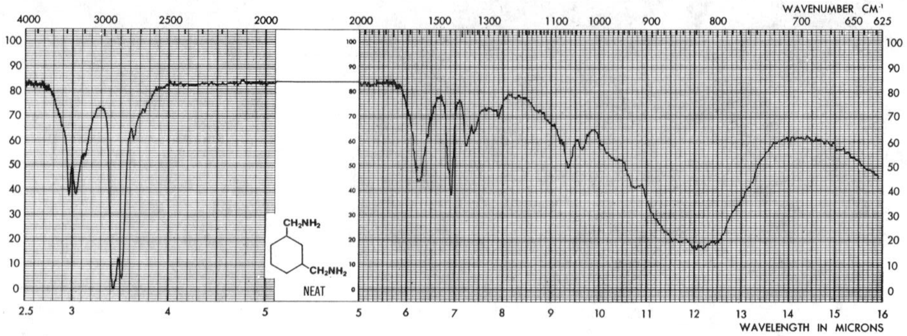

22,257-7
2-Aminocyclohexanol hydrochloride, 97%, mixture of *cis* and *trans*
$H_2NC_6H_{10}OH \cdot HCl$ FW 151.64 mp 172-175°
Beil. **13**(3),708 Disp. C

NUJOL MULL

C

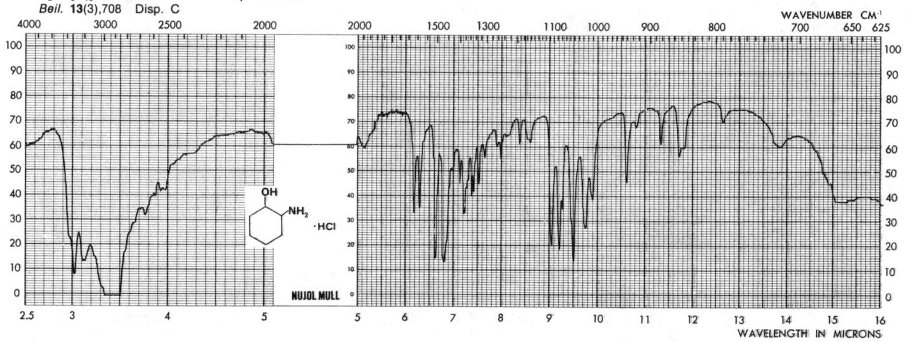

19,141-8
1-Aminomethyl-1-cyclohexanol hydrochloride, 98%
$H_2NCH_2C_6H_{10}OH \cdot HCl$ FW 165.67 mp 217-219°
Disp. C

NUJOL MULL

D

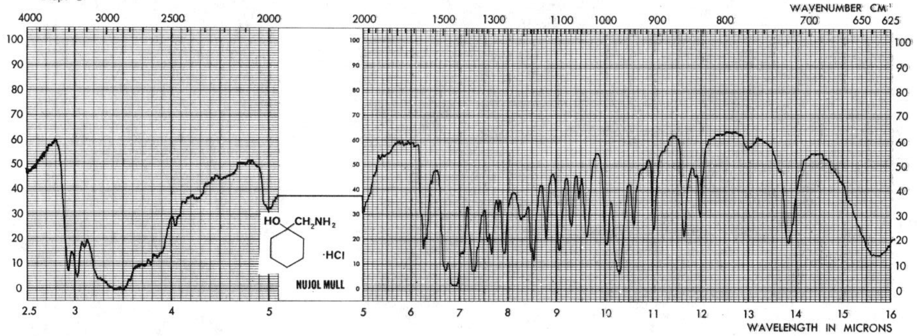

A3,100-8
Allylcyclohexylamine, 98%
$C_6H_{11}NHCH_2CH{=}CH_2$
M.W. 139.24 b.p. 65-66°/12mm. n_D^{20} 1.4664
IRRITANT

NEAT

E

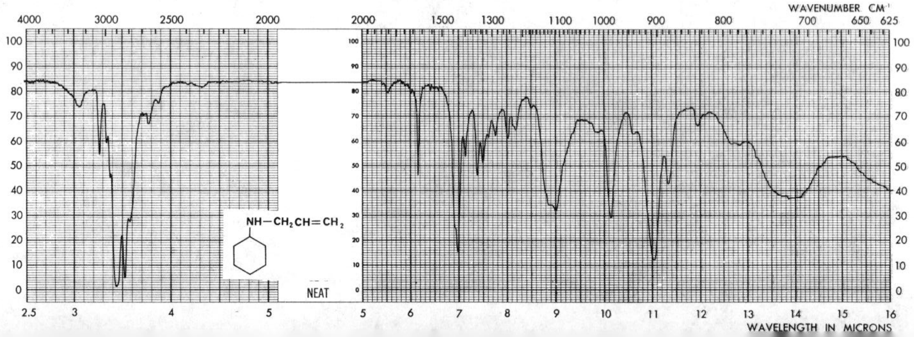

11,818-4 **5-Amino-1,3,3-trimethylcyclohexanemethylamine**
$H_2NC_6H_7(CH_3)_3CH_2NH_2$ M.W. 170.30 n_D^{20} 1.4887
b.p. 247°

NEAT

F

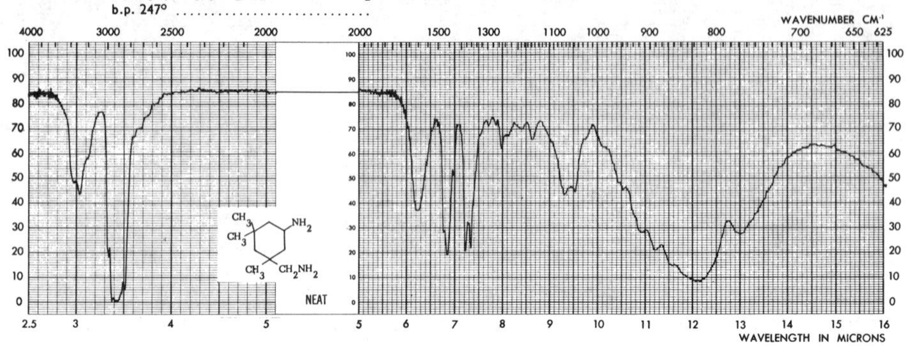

D1960-5 **1,8-Diamino-p-menthane** (1,8-p-menthanediamine), **tech.**
M.W. 170.30 n_D^{20} 1.4805

NEAT

G

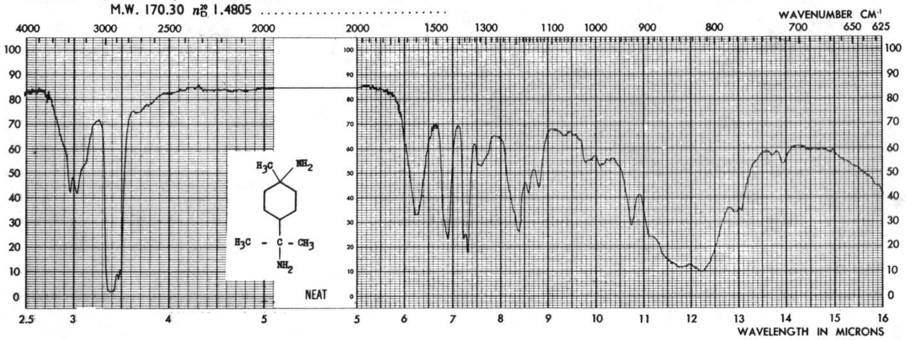

19,479-4
3-Aminomethyl-3,5,5-trimethylcyclohexanol, 99%, mixture of *cis* and *trans*
$H_2NCH_2C_6H_7(CH_3)_3OH$ FW 171.29 mp 43-48°
bp 265° n_D^{20} 1.4904 d 0.969 Disp. C

MELT

H

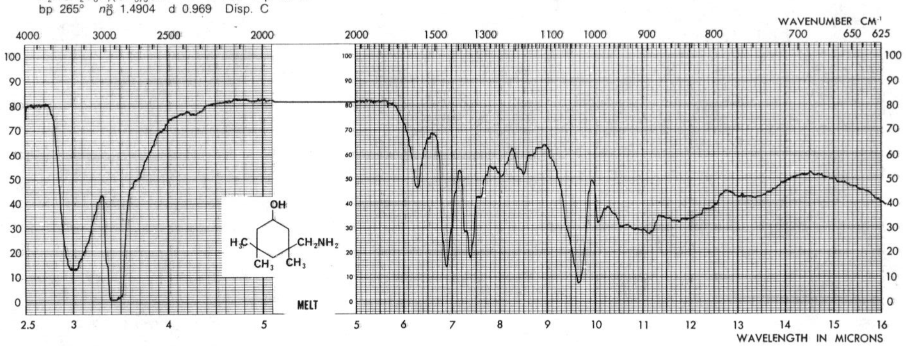

14,801-6 **Cycloheptanemethylamine** (aminomethylcycloheptane)
$C_7H_{13}CH_2NH_2$ M.W. 127.22 n_D^{20} 1.4722

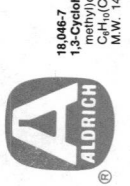

NEAT

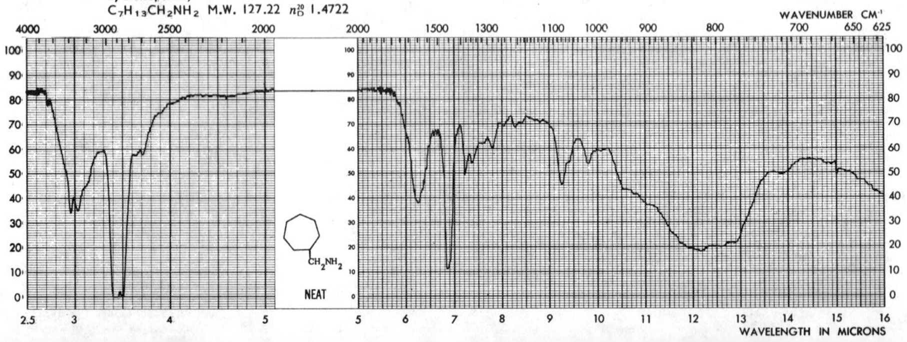

A

C9960-4 Cycloheptylamine
$C_7H_{13}NH_2$ M.W. 113.20 n_D^{20} 1.4724

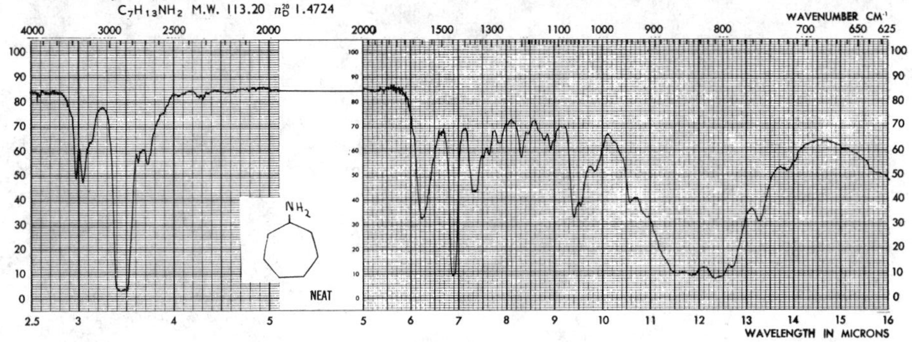

NEAT

B

C11,060-4 Cyclooctylamine
$C_8H_{15}NH_2$ M.W. 127.23 n_D^{20} 1.4824

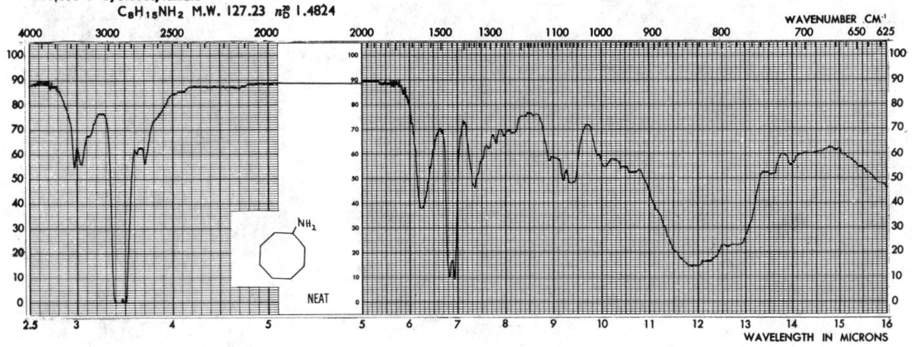

NEAT

C

M3920-2 N-Methylcyclooctylamine
$C_8H_{15}NHCH_3$ M.W. 141.26 n_D^{20} 1.4761

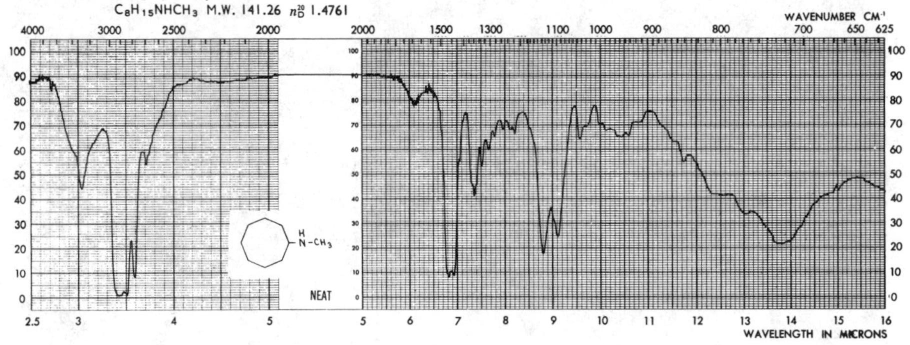

NEAT

D

12,979-8 N-Methylcyclodecylamine
$C_{10}H_{19}NHCH_3$ M.W. 169.31 n_D^{20} 1.4832

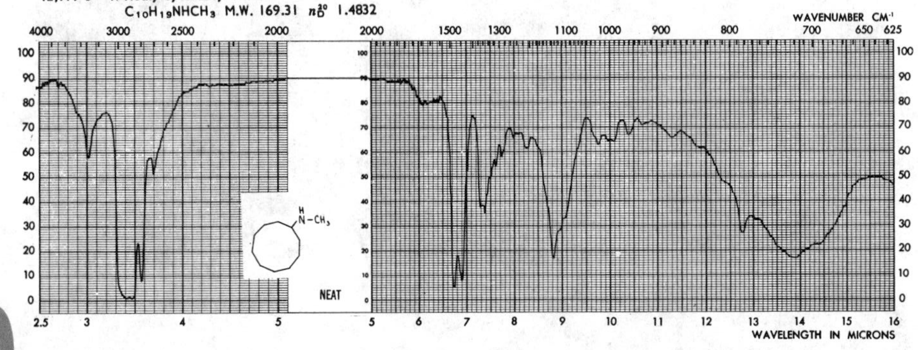

NEAT

E

C9780-6 Cyclododecylamine
$C_{12}H_{23}NH_2$ M.W. 183.34
m.p. 28-30°

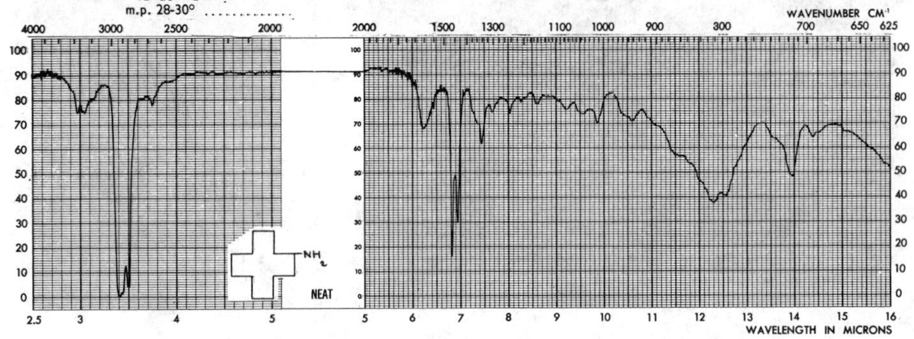

NEAT

F

M3770-6 N-Methylcyclododecylamine
$C_{12}H_{23}NHCH_3$ M.W. 197.35 n_D^{20} 1.4851

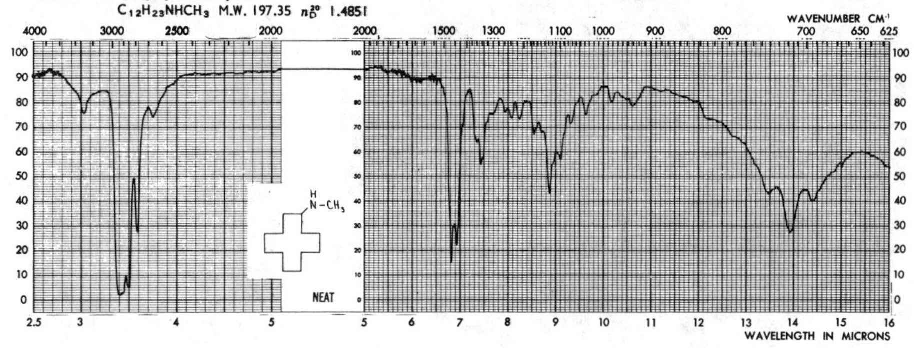

NEAT

G

17,960-4
***exo*-2-Aminonorbornane** (*exo*-2-norbornanamine)
M.W. 111.19 b.p. 49°/10mm. n_D^{20} 1.4807

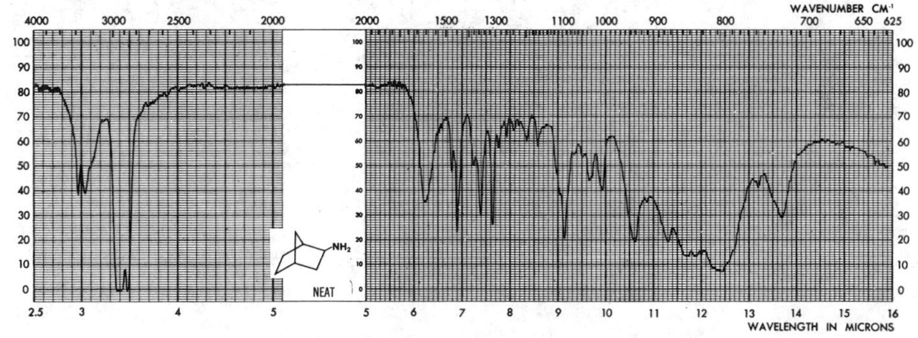

NEAT

H

13,351-5 2-Aminonorbornane (2-norbornanamine) **hydrochloride**
M.W. 147.65 m.p. 301.5-302.5° (dec.)

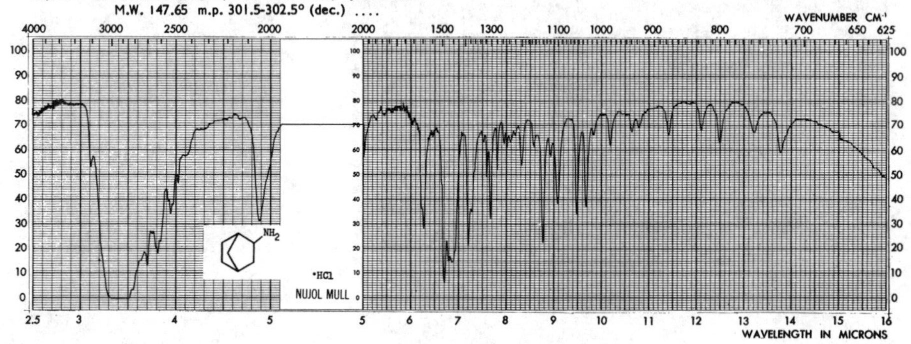

•HCl
NUJOL MULL

A A6345 **endo-2-Aminomethylbicyclo[2.2.1]heptane hydrochloride**
M.W. 161.68 m.p. > 330°
NUJOL MULL

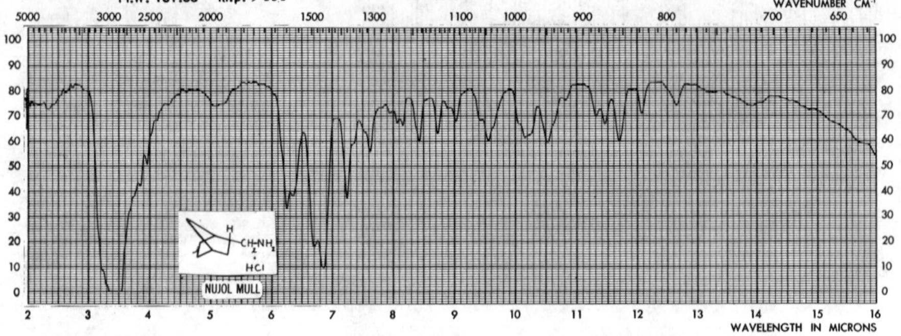

B 19,558-8
Nopinylamine
FW 139.24 mp 30-33° bp 74-78°/15mm.
$[\alpha]^{22}$ -19° (c=1.3, CH_3OH) *Beil.* **12**,38 Disp. C
MELT

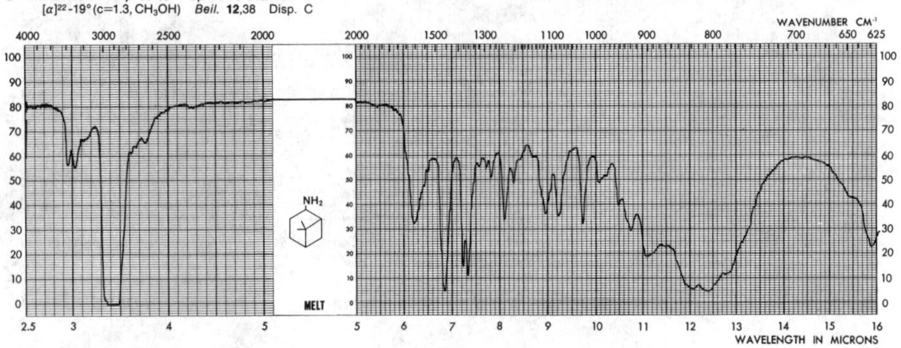

C 18,080-7
(-)-*cis*-Myrtanylamine, 98%
M.W. 153.27 b.p. 94-99°/27mm. n_D^{20} 1.4877
d 0.915 $[\alpha]^{22}$ -30.5° (neat)
NEAT

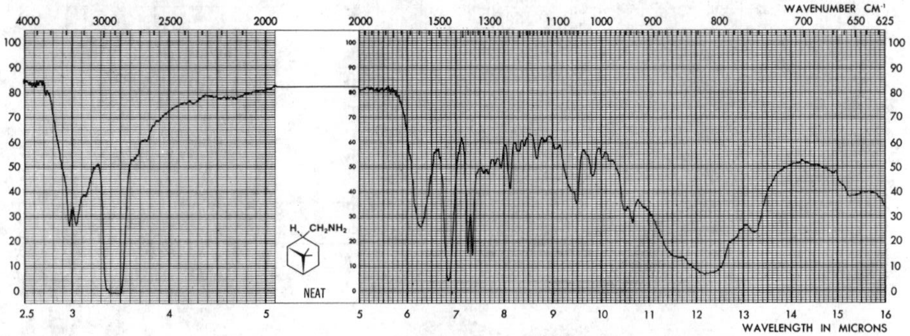

D 19,338-0
(+)-3-Pinanemethylamine hydrochloride
FW 203.76 mp >300° $[\alpha]^{24}$ +39.6° (c=5, H_2O)
Disp. C
NUJOL MULL

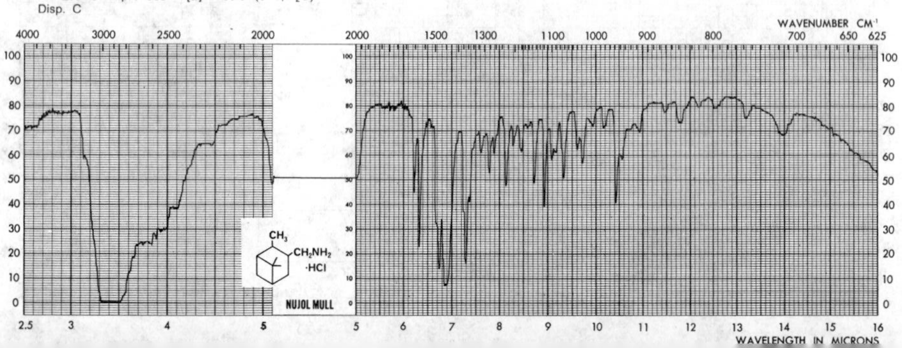

E 19,339-9
(-)-3-Pinanemethylamine hydrochloride
FW 203.76 mp >300° $[\alpha]^{24}$ -40.1° (c=5, H_2O)
Disp. C
NUJOL MULL

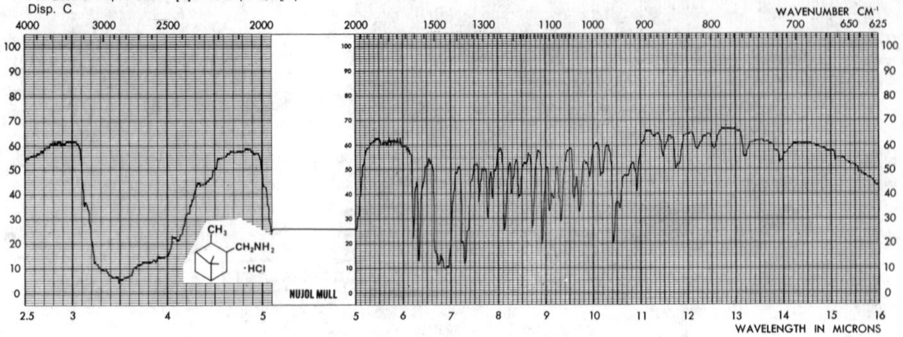

F 13,857-6 **1-Adamantanamine** (1-aminoadamantane)
M.W. 151.25 m.p. 108-109°
NUJOL MULL

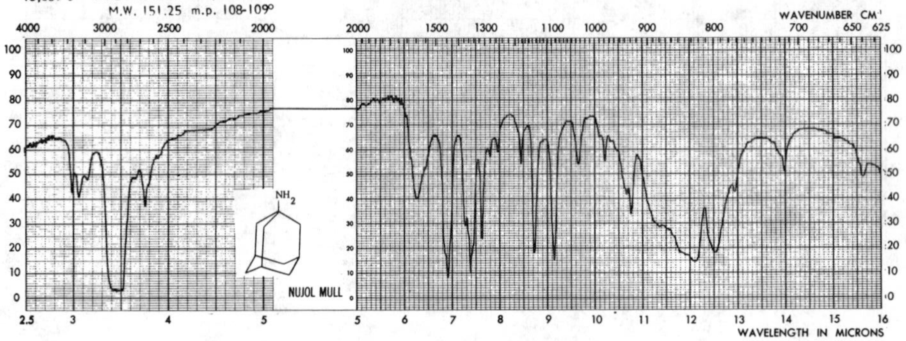

G 11,519-3 **1-Adamantanamine** (1-aminoadamantane) **hydrochloride, puriss.**
(send for data sheet)
M.W. 187.71 m.p. > 300°
NUJOL MULL

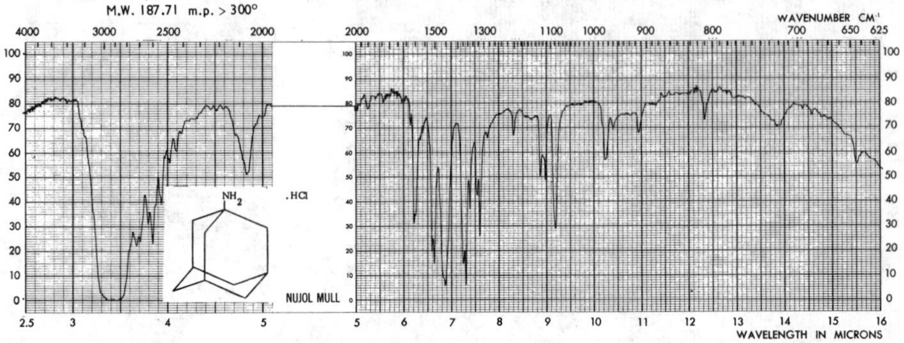

H 15,381-8 **2-Adamantanamine** (2-aminoadamantane) **hydrochloride**
M.W. 187.71 m.p. > 300°
NUJOL MULL

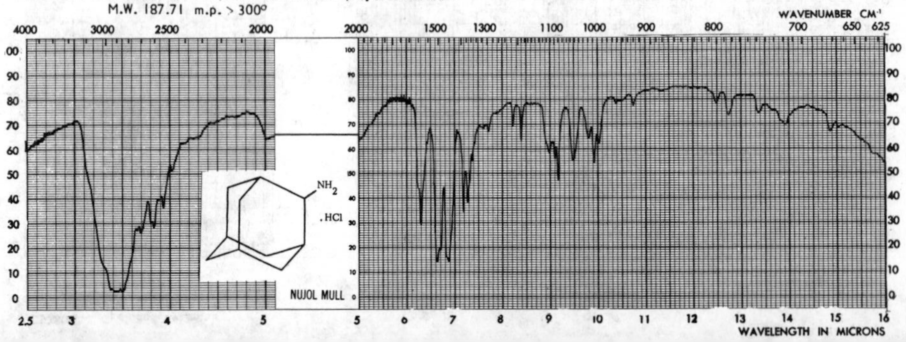

A 13,962-9 **1-Adamantanamine (1-aminoadamantane) sulfate**
M.W. 400.59 m.p. > 300°

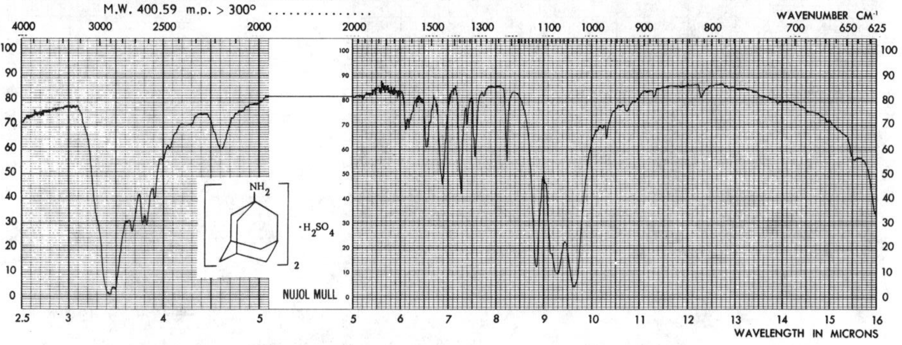

NUJOL MULL

B 13,963-7 1-Adamantanamine (1-aminoadamantane) fumarate
M.W. 418.58 m.p. 264° (dec.)

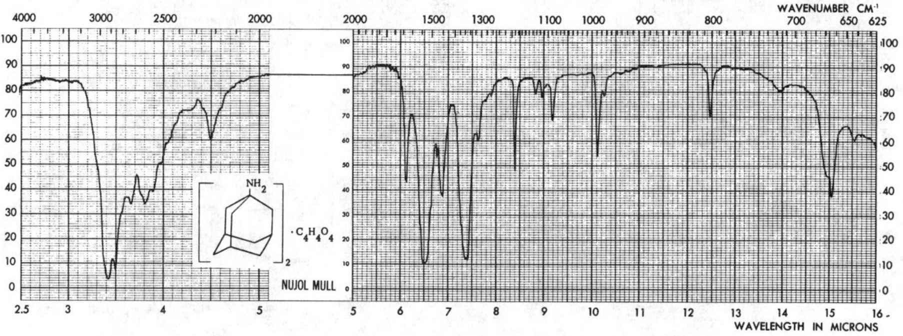

NUJOL MULL

C 13,964-5 **1-Adamantanamine (1-aminoadamantane) citrate monohydrate**
M.W. 361.40 m.p. 136° (dec.)

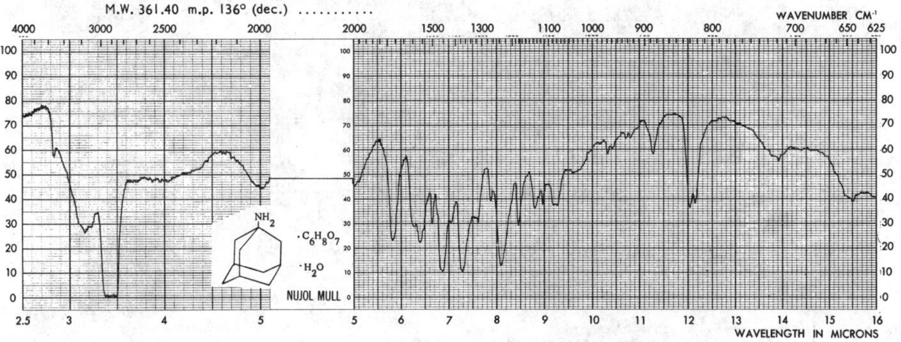

NUJOL MULL

D 18,037-8
1-Adamantanemethylamine, 99% [1-(aminomethyl)-adamantane]
M.W. 165.28 b.p. 83-85°/0.3mm. n_D^{20} 1.5137

NEAT

E 14,583-1 **Allylamine**
$H_2C{:}CHCH_2NH_2$ M.W. 57.10 n_D^{20} 1.4203
b.p. 53°

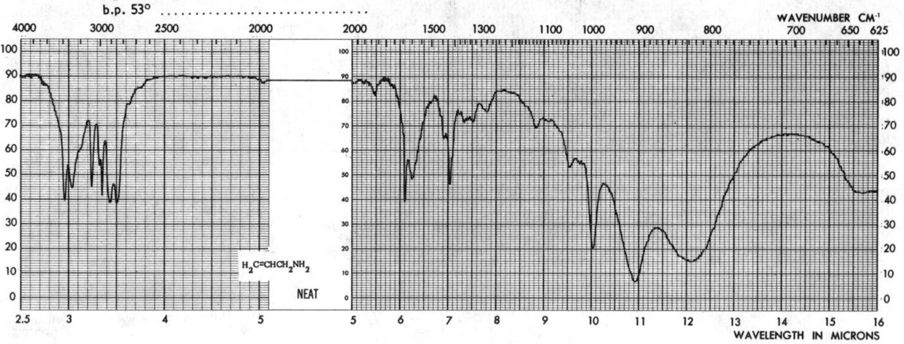

NEAT

F D960-3 **Diallylamine**
$(H_2C{:}CHCH_2)_2NH$ M.W. 97.16 n_D^{20} 1.4387

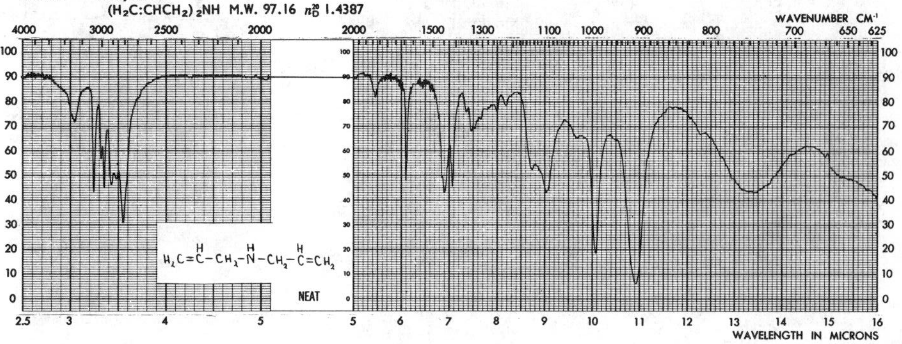

NEAT

G 16,224-8
2-Methylallylamine, 98+%
$H_2C{=}C(CH_3)CH_2NH_2$
M.W. 71.12 b.p. 79° n_D^{20} 1.4315 d 0.783
IRRITANT

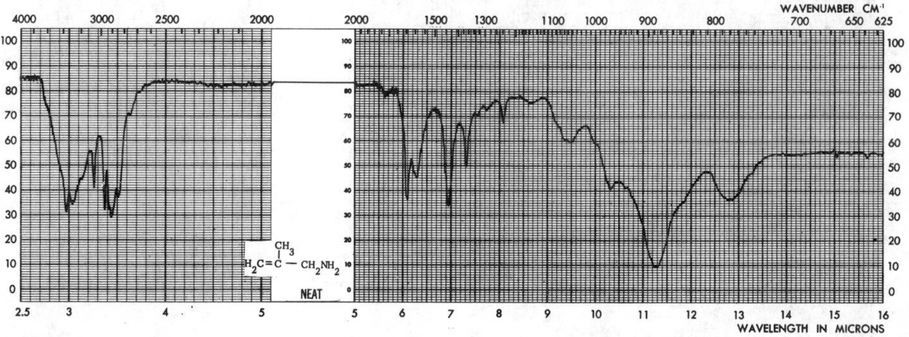

NEAT

H 16,225-6
Bis-(2-methylallyl)-amine
$[H_2C{=}C(CH_3)CH_2]_2NH$
M.W. 125.22 b.p. 149° n_D^{20} 1.4495 d 0.8
IRRITANT

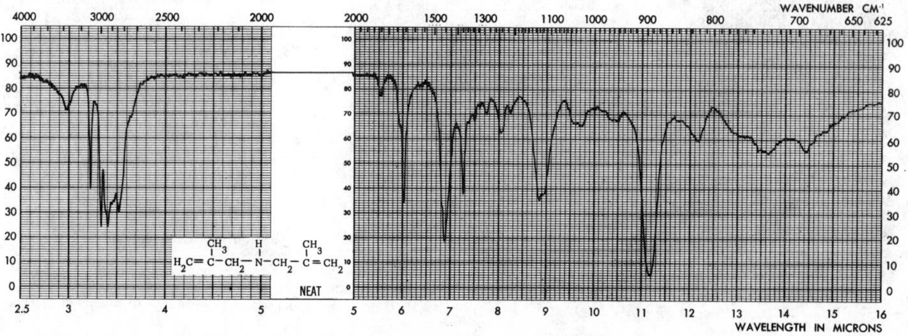

NEAT

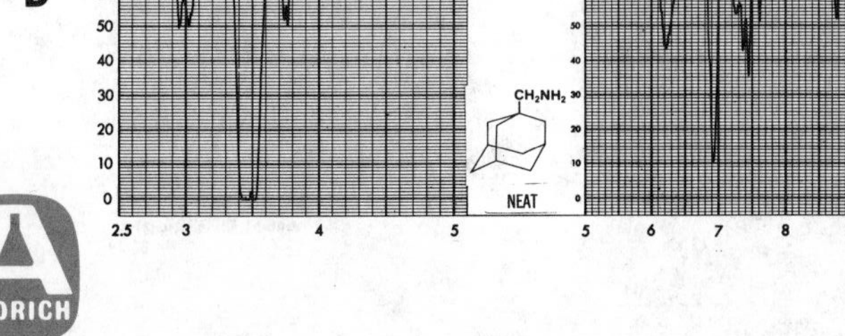

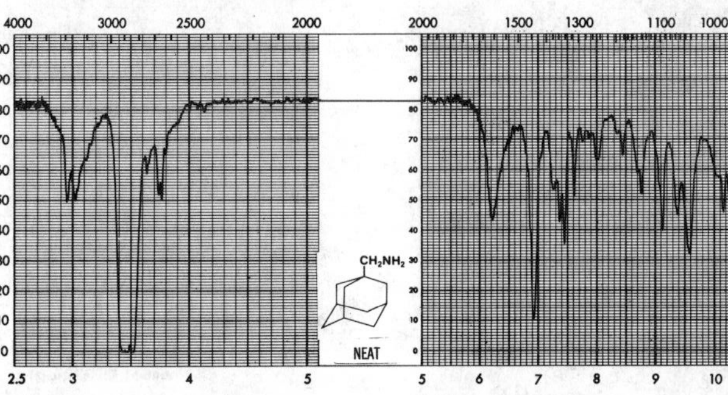

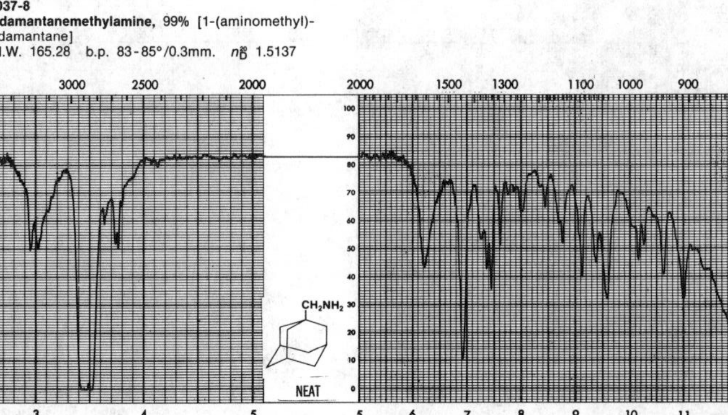

ALDRICH

A

16,226-4
Tris-(2-methylallyl)-amine, 99%
$[H_2C{=}C(CH_3)CH_2]_3N$
M.W. 179.31 n_D^{20} 1.4575 d 0.794

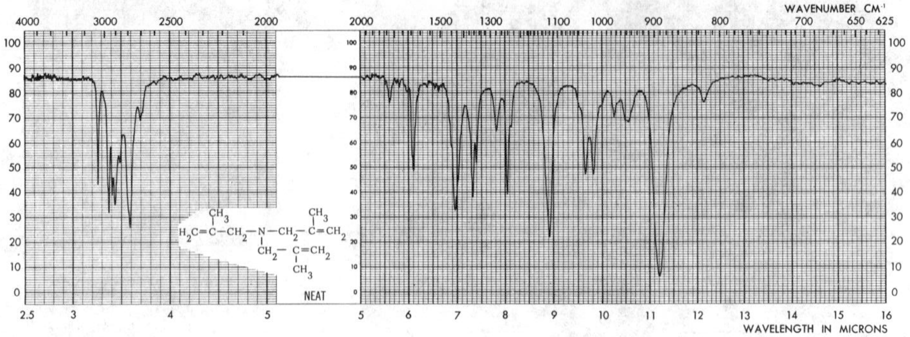

NEAT

B

T4500-4 Triallylamine
$(H_2C{:}CHCH_2)_3N$ M.W. 137.23 n_D^{20} 1.4501
b.p. 150-151°

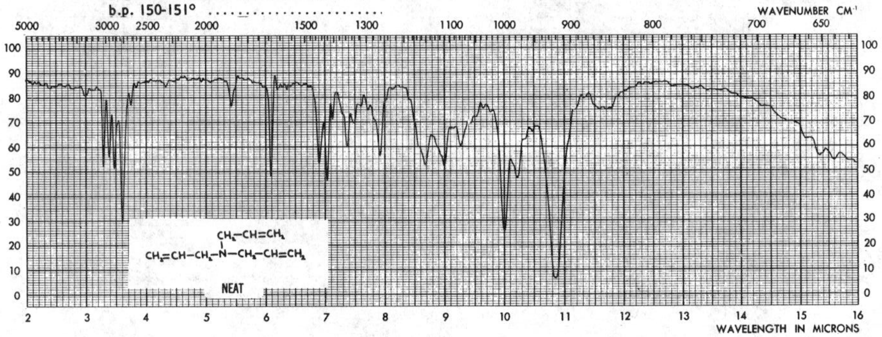

NEAT

C

12,684-5 N,N'-Diethyl-2-butene-1,4-diamine
$C_2H_5NHCH_2CH{:}CHCH_2NHC_2H_5$ M.W. 142.25 n_D^{20} 1.4587
b.p. 80-83°/8 mm.

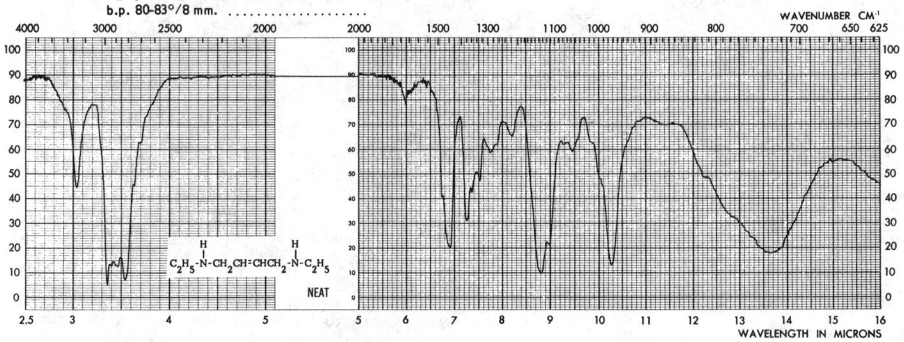

NEAT

D

12,709-4 N,N,N',N'-Tetramethyl-2-butene-1,4-diamine
$(CH_3)_2NCH_2CH{:}CHCH_2N(CH_3)_2$ M.W. 142.25
n_D^{20} 1.4416 b.p. 65-66°/17 mm.

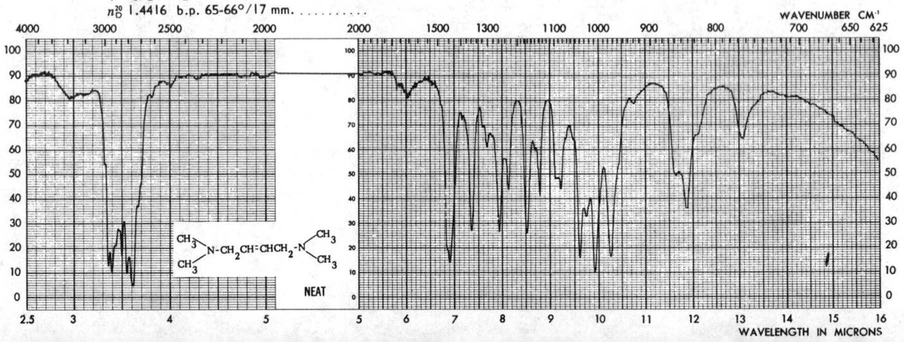

NEAT

E

12,705-1 N,N,N',N'-Tetraethyl-2-butene-1,4-diamine
$(C_2H_5)_2NCH_2CH{:}CHCH_2N(C_2H_5)_2$ M.W. 198.35
n_D^{20} 1.4521 b.p. 98-101°/8 mm.

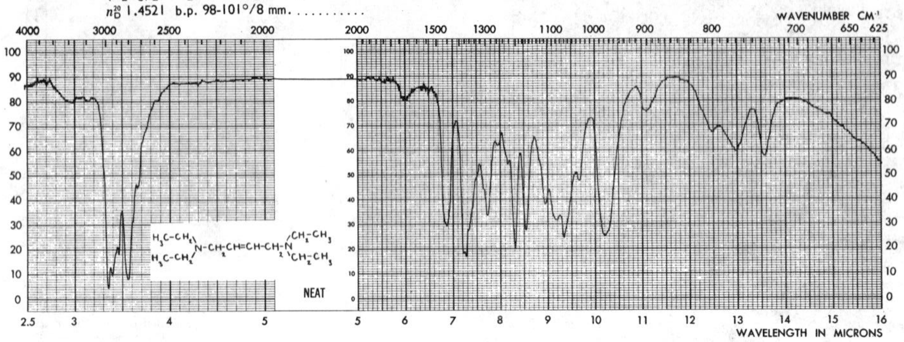

NEAT

F

O-780-5 Oleylamine
$CH_3(CH_2)_7CH{:}CH(CH_2)_8NH_2$ M.W. 267.50 n_D^{20} 1.4578

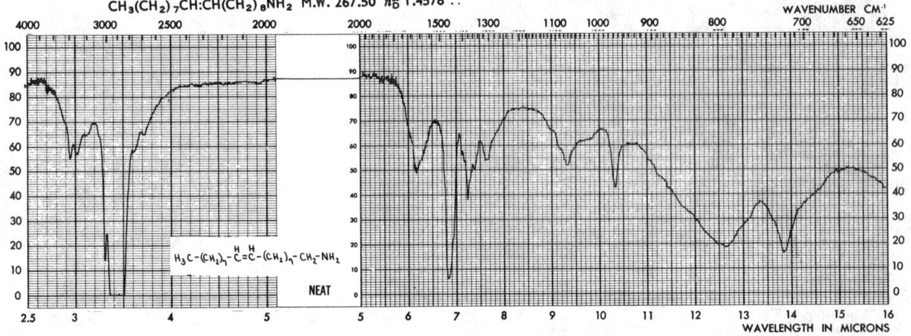

NEAT

G

17,974-4
2-Fluoroethylamine hydrochloride, 95%
$FCH_2CH_2NH_2 \cdot HCl$
M.W. 99.54 m.p. 90-92°

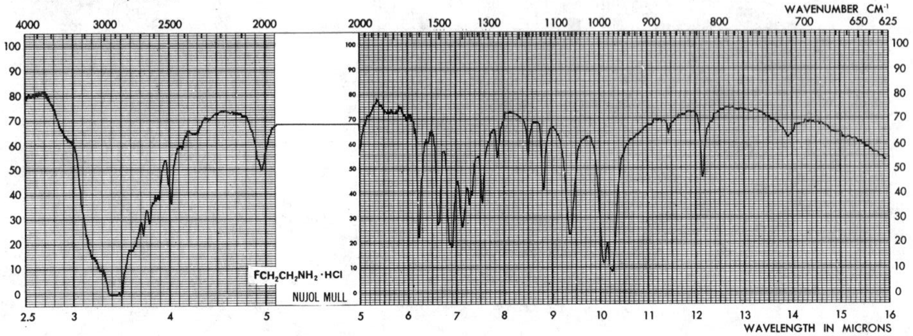

NUJOL MULL

H

18,038-6
2,2,2-Trifluoroethylamine hydrochloride
$CF_3CH_2NH_2 \cdot HCl$
M.W. 135.52 m.p. 220-222° (sublimes)

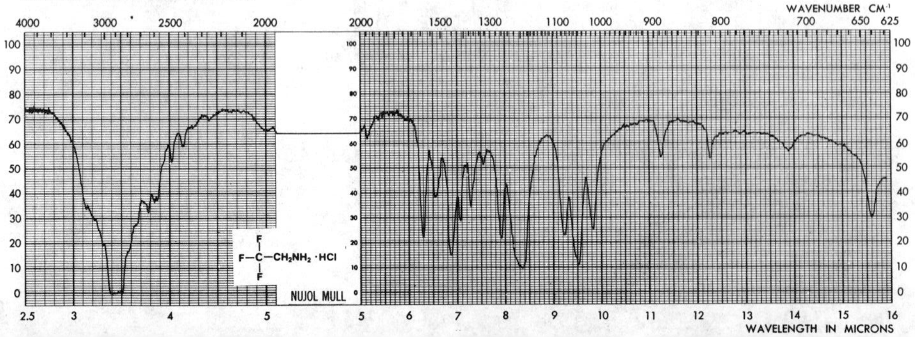

NUJOL MULL

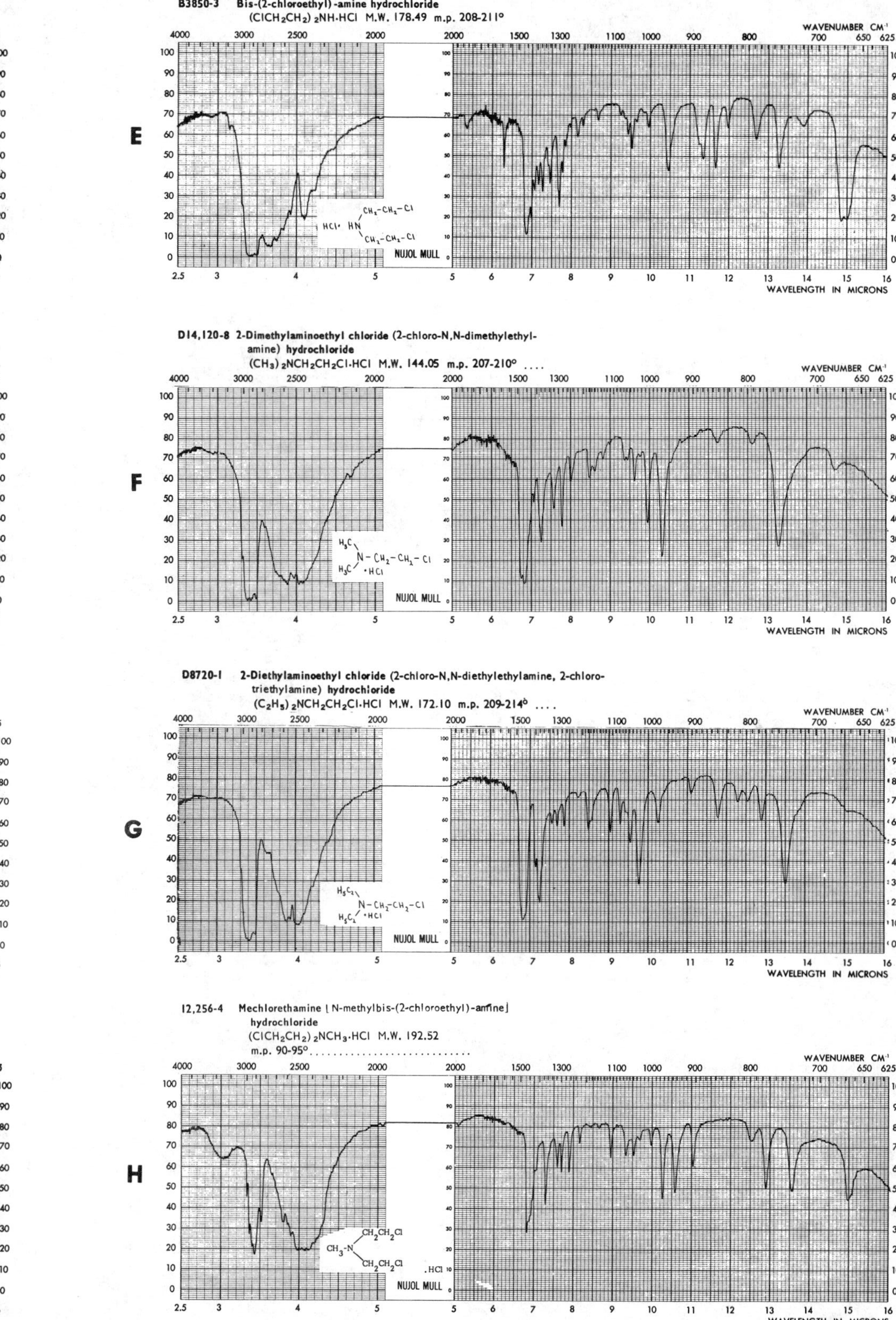

A C4020-0 **2-Chloroethylamine hydrochloride**
$ClCH_2CH_2NH_2 \cdot HCl$ M.W. 115.99
m.p. 143-146°

B B6570-5 **2-Bromoethylamine hydrobromide**
$BrCH_2CH_2NH_2 \cdot HBr$ M.W. 204.90
m.p. 175-177°

C 14,254-9 **3-Chloropropylamine hydrochloride**
$Cl(CH_2)_3NH_2 \cdot HCl$ M.W. 130.02
m.p. 148-150°

D B7980-3 **3-Bromopropylamine hydrobromide**
$Br(CH_2)_3NH_2 \cdot HBr$ M.W. 218.93
m.p. 173-174°

E B3850-3 **Bis-(2-chloroethyl)-amine hydrochloride**
$(ClCH_2CH_2)_2NH \cdot HCl$ M.W. 178.49 m.p. 208-211°

F D14,120-8 **2-Dimethylaminoethyl chloride (2-chloro-N,N-dimethylethylamine) hydrochloride**
$(CH_3)_2NCH_2CH_2Cl \cdot HCl$ M.W. 144.05 m.p. 207-210°

G D8720-1 **2-Diethylaminoethyl chloride (2-chloro-N,N-diethylethylamine, 2-chlorotriethylamine) hydrochloride**
$(C_2H_5)_2NCH_2CH_2Cl \cdot HCl$ M.W. 172.10 m.p. 209-214°

H 12,256-4 Mechlorethamine [N-methylbis-(2-chloroethyl)-amine] hydrochloride
$(ClCH_2CH_2)_2NCH_3 \cdot HCl$ M.W. 192.52
m.p. 90-95°

NUJOL MULL

A D14,520-3 **3-Dimethylaminopropyl chloride** (3-chloro-N,N-dimethylpropylamine) **hydrochloride**
$(CH_3)_2N(CH_2)_3Cl \cdot HCl$ M.W. 158.07 m.p. 141-144°

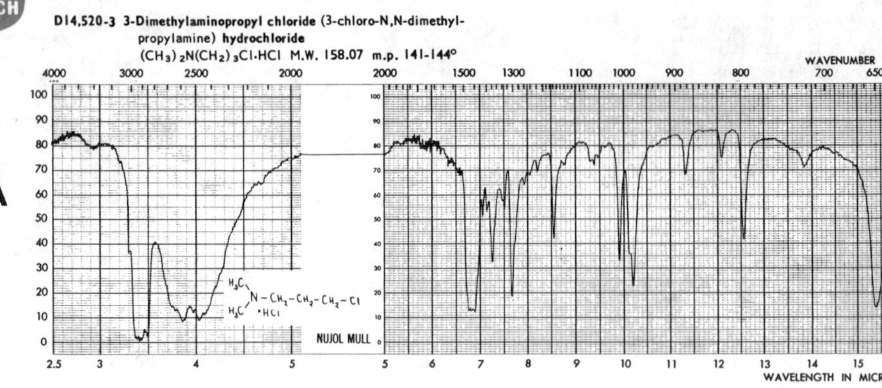

B D14,240-9 **2-Dimethylaminoisopropyl chloride** (2-chloro-N,N-dimethylpropylamine) **hydrochloride**
$CH_3CH(Cl)CH_2N(CH_3)_2 \cdot HCl$ M.W. 158.07
m.p. 194-195° ....

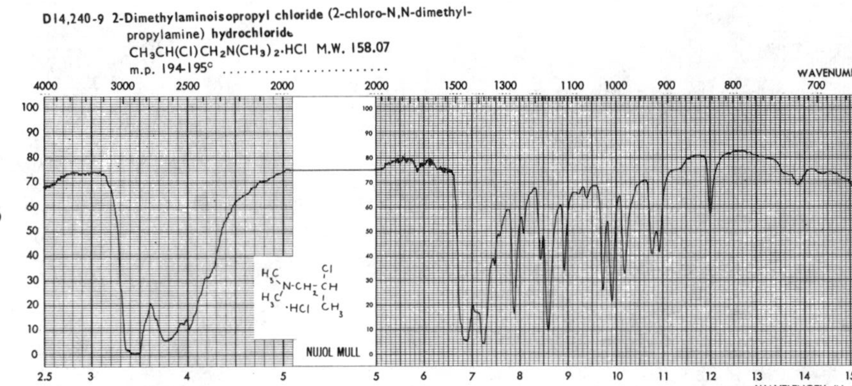

C 15,289-7 **3-Dimethylamino-2-methylpropyl chloride** (3-chloro-N,N,2-trimethylpropylamine) **hydrochloride**
$(CH_3)_2NCH_2CH(CH_3)CH_2Cl \cdot HCl$ M.W. 172.10
m.p. 167-170° ....

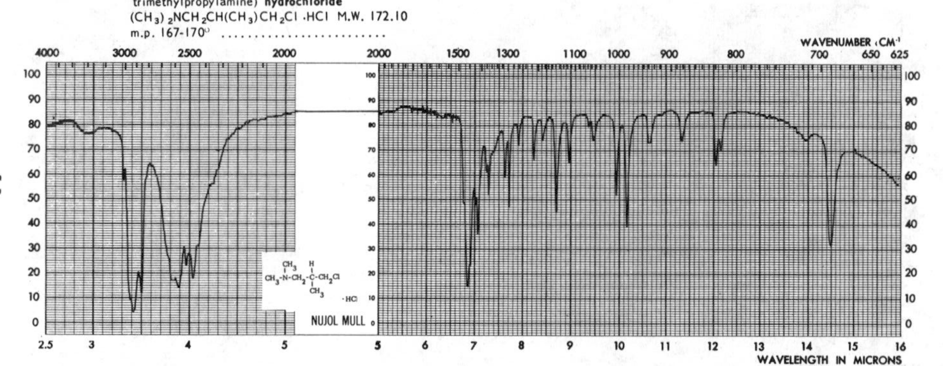

D D12,520-2 **2-Diisopropylaminoethyl chloride** [2-chloro-N,N-diisopropylethylamine, N-(2-chloroethyl)-diisopropylamine] **hydrochloride**
$[(CH_3)_2CH]_2NCH_2CH_2Cl \cdot HCl$ M.W. 200.15 m.p. 133-135°

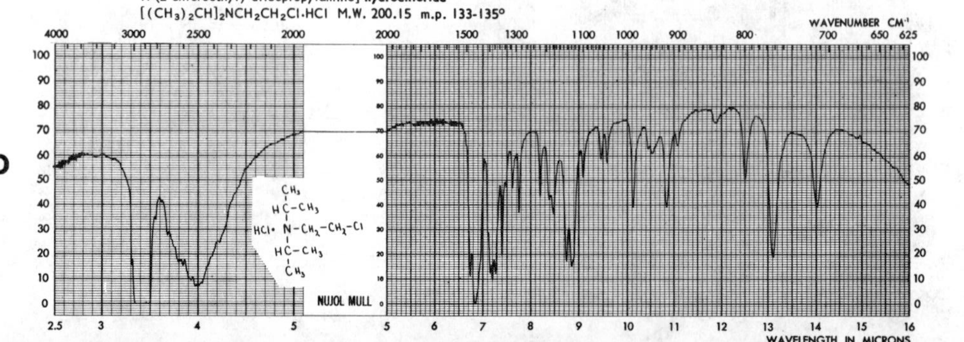

E T8530-8 **Tris-(2-chloroethyl)-amine hydrochloride**
$(ClCH_2CH_2)_3N \cdot HCl$ M.W. 240.99 m.p. 119-124°

F 17,799-7
3-Diethylaminopropyl chloride hydrochloride, 99%
(3-chloro-N,N-diethylpropylamine)
$(C_2H_5)_2N(CH_2)_3Cl \cdot HCl$
M.W. 186.13 m.p. 86-88°

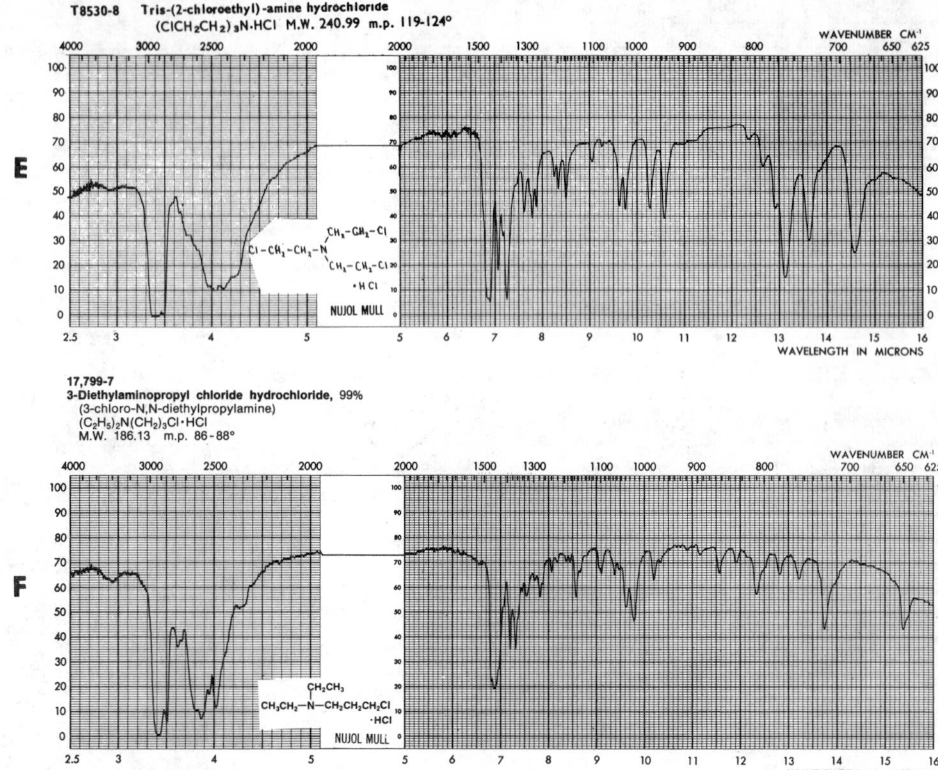

G 11,967-9 **2-Chloro-N,N,N',N'-tetraethyl-1,3-propanediamine**
$C_{11}H_{25}ClN_2$ M.W. 220.79 n_D^{20} 1.4520

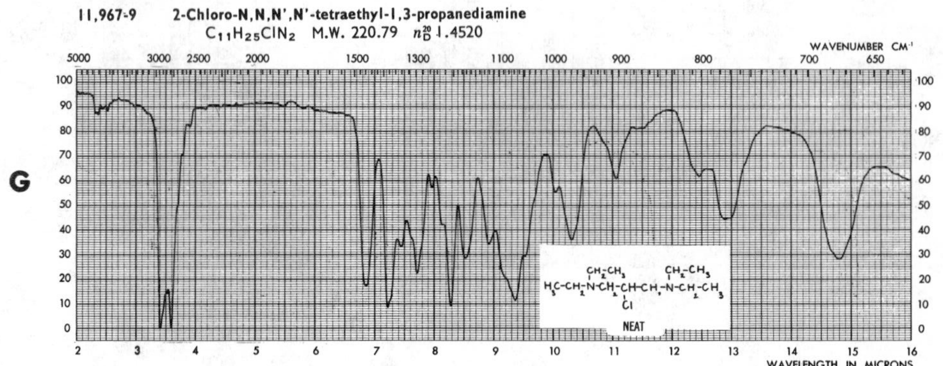

H 13,895-9 **1,1,1,3,3,3-Hexafluoro-2,2-propanediamine, puriss.**
$CF_3C(NH_2)_2CF_3$ M.W. 182.07 n_D^{20} 1.3256 ......

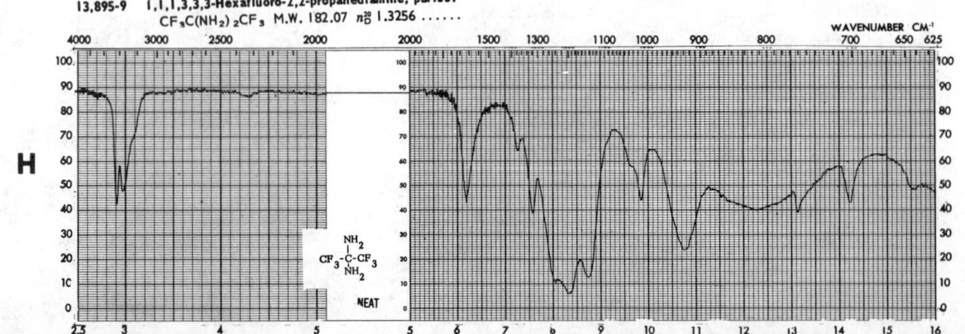

A 14,369-3 **2-Methoxyethylamine**
$CH_3OCH_2CH_2NH_2$ M.W. 75.11 n_D^{20} 1.4054
b.p. 95°

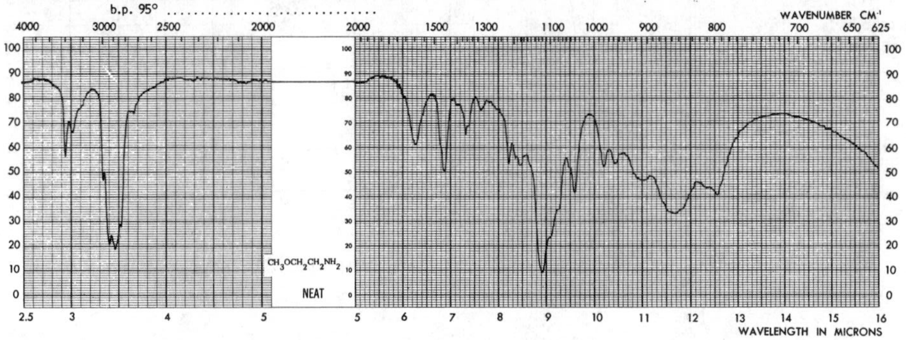

$CH_3OCH_2CH_2NH_2$ NEAT

B E460-7 **2-Ethoxyethylamine**
$C_2H_5OCH_2CH_2NH_2$ M.W. 89.14
n_D^{20} 1.4098

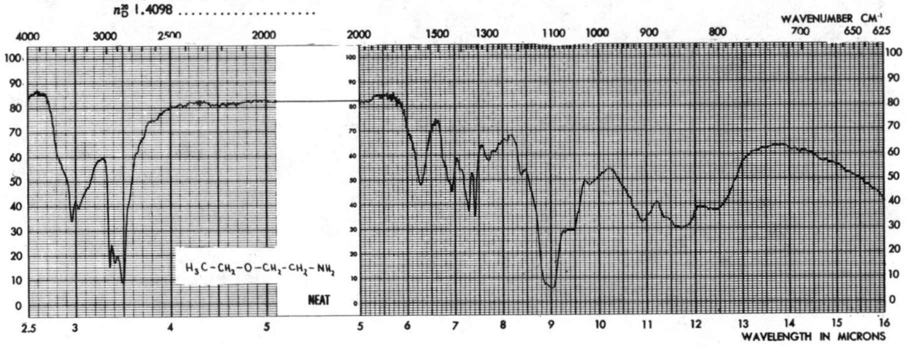

$H_3C-CH_2-O-CH_2-CH_2-NH_2$ NEAT

C M2500-7 **3-Methoxypropylamine**
$CH_3O(CH_2)_3NH_2$ M.W. 89.14 n_D^{20} 1.4179
b.p. 116°

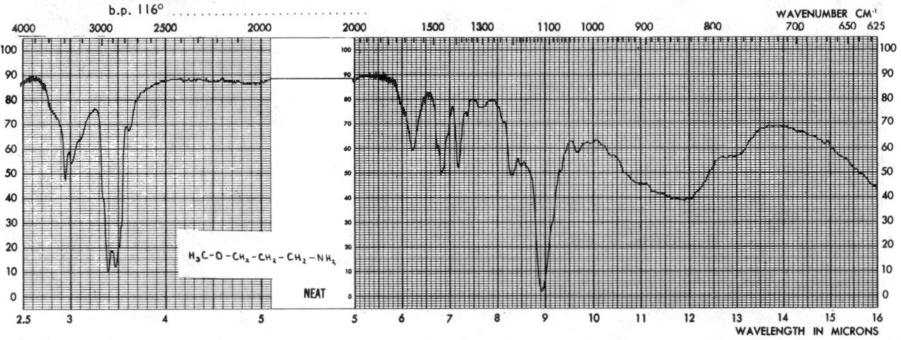

$H_3C-O-CH_2-CH_2-CH_2-NH_2$ NEAT

D A6100-4 **2-Amino-1-methoxypropane** (β-methoxyisopropylamine)
$CH_3CH(NH_2)CH_2OCH_3$ M.W. 89.14
n_D^{20} 1.4041

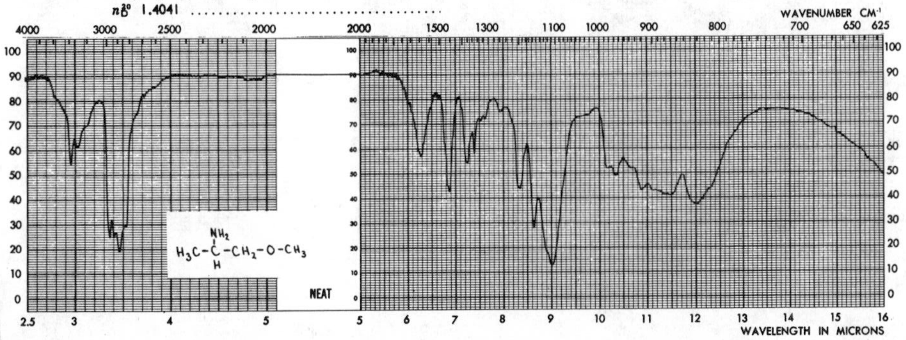

$H_3C-CH(NH_2)-CH_2-O-CH_3$ NEAT

E 12,353-6 **3-Isopropoxypropylamine**
$(CH_3)_2CHO(CH_2)_3NH_2$ M.W. 117.19 n_D^{20} 1.4192
b.p. 43°/12 mm.

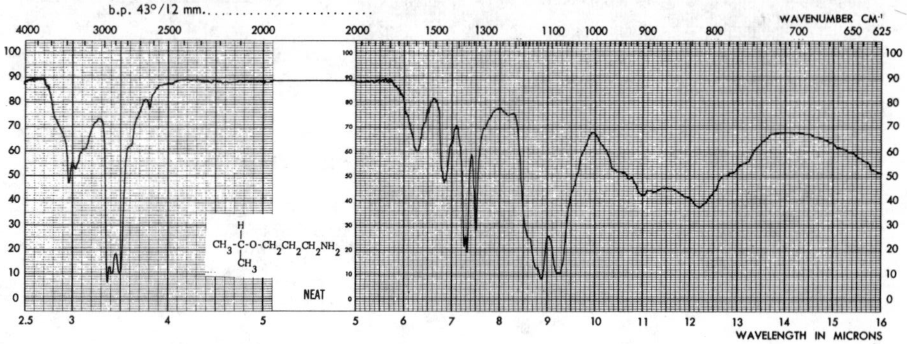

$CH_3-CH(CH_3)-O-CH_2CH_2CH_2NH_2$ NEAT

F 11,651-3 **3-(2-Methoxyethoxy)-propylamine**
$CH_3OCH_2CH_2O(CH_2)_3NH_2$ M.W. 133.19 n_D^{20} 1.4310
b.p. 75-80°/12 mm.

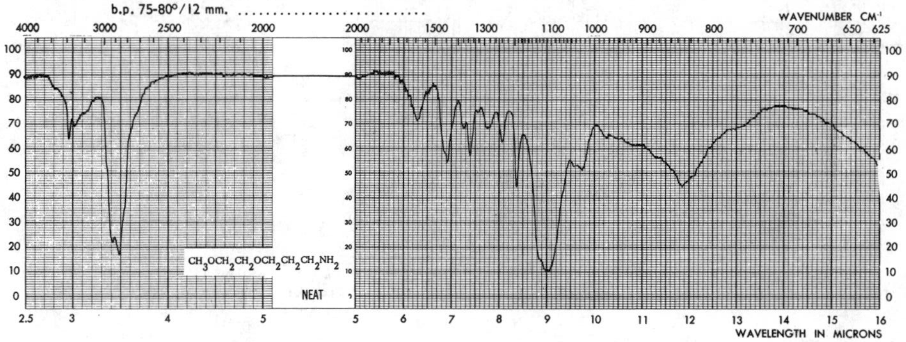

$CH_3OCH_2CH_2OCH_2CH_2CH_2NH_2$ NEAT

G E795 **N-(3-Ethoxypropyl)-ethylamine**
$C_2H_5O(CH_2)_3NHC_2H_5$ M.W. 131.21 n_D^{20} 1.4168

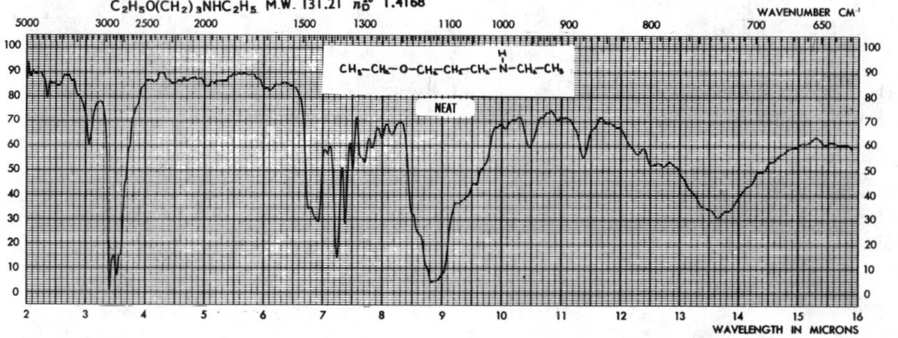

$CH_3-CH_2-O-CH_2-CH_2-CH_2-NH-CH_2-CH_3$ NEAT

H 13,652-2 **N-(Methoxymethyl)-diethylamine**
$CH_3OCH_2N(C_2H_5)_2$ M.W. 117.19 n_D^{20} 1.4080
b.p. 114-121°

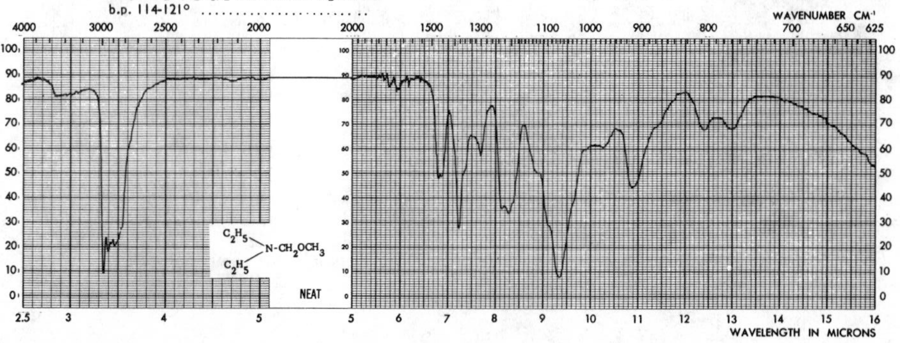

$(C_2H_5)_2N-CH_2OCH_3$ NEAT

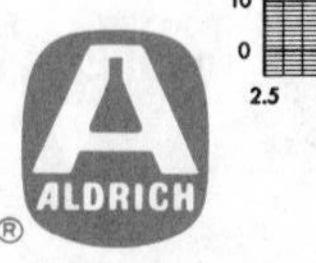

ALDRICH®

A

19,548-0
(*S,S*)-(+)-2,3-Dimethoxy-1,4-bis(dimethylamino)butane
(DDB, 2,3-dimethoxy-*N,N,N',N'*-tetramethyl-1,4-butanediamine)
$[(CH_3)_2NCH_2CH(OCH_3)-]_2$ FW 204.32
bp 62-64°/3mm. n_D^{20} 1.4343 d 0.896
$[\alpha]^{22}$ +14.5° (neat) Disp. C

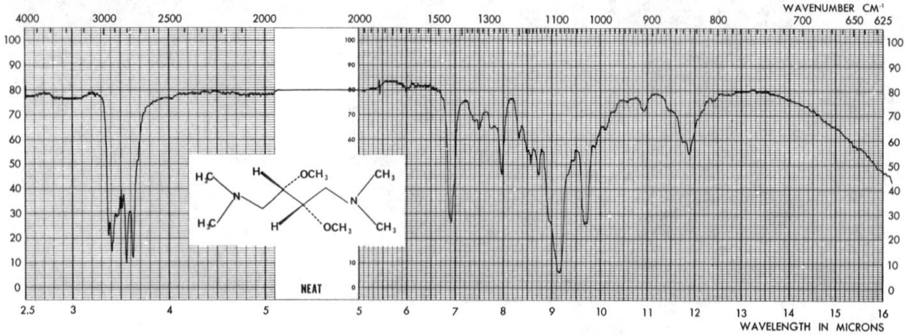

NEAT

B

B4400-7 **Bis-(2-ethoxyethyl)-amine**
$(C_2H_5OCH_2CH_2)_2NH$ M.W. 161.25 n_D^{20} 1.4213

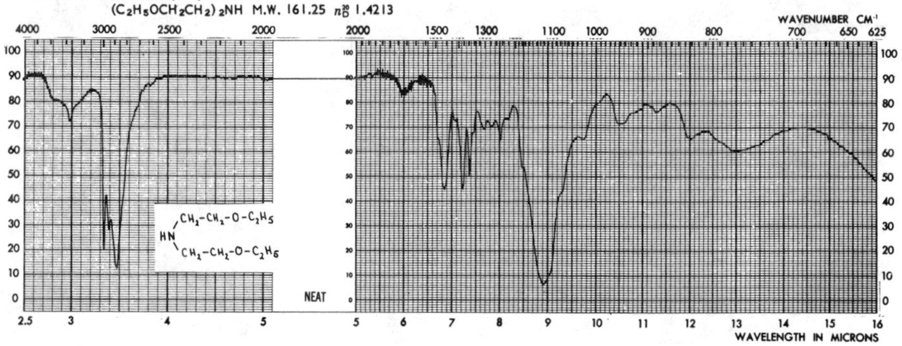

NEAT

C

13,654-9 **2,2'-Oxybis-(N,N-dimethylethylamine)** [2-(dimethylamino)-ethyl ether]
$O[CH_2CH_2N(CH_3)_2]_2$ M.W. 160.26
n_D^{20} 1.4302

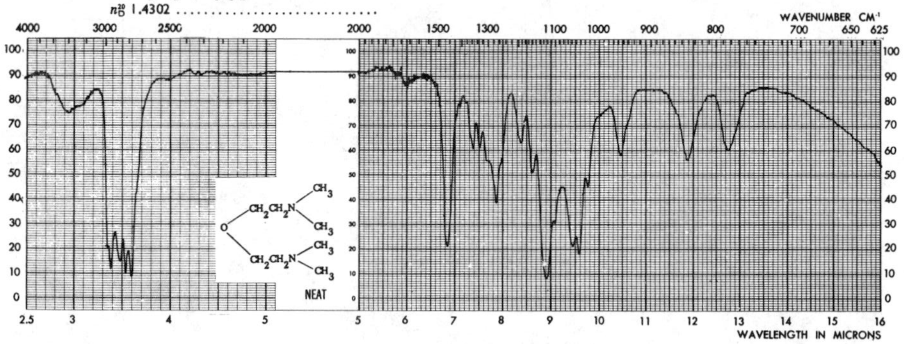

NEAT

D

13,191-1 **Tetrahydrofurfurylamine**
M.W. 101.15 n_D^{20} 1.4560 b.p. 153-154°/744 mm.

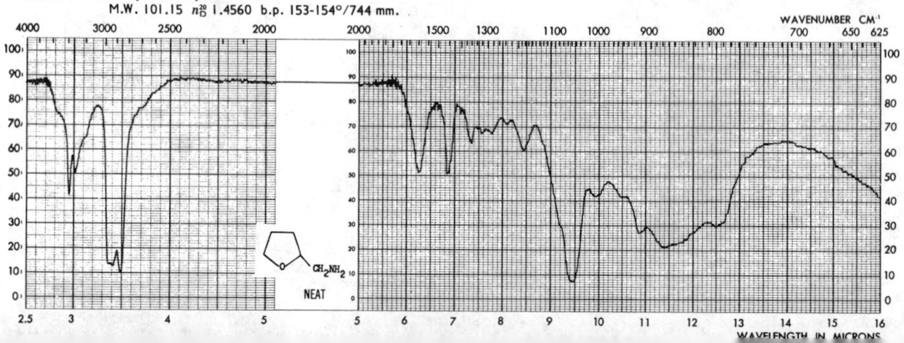

NEAT

E

M8239-6 **N-Methyltetrahydrofurfurylamine**
M.W. 115.18 n_D^{20} 1.4473 b.p. 157-158°/748 mm.

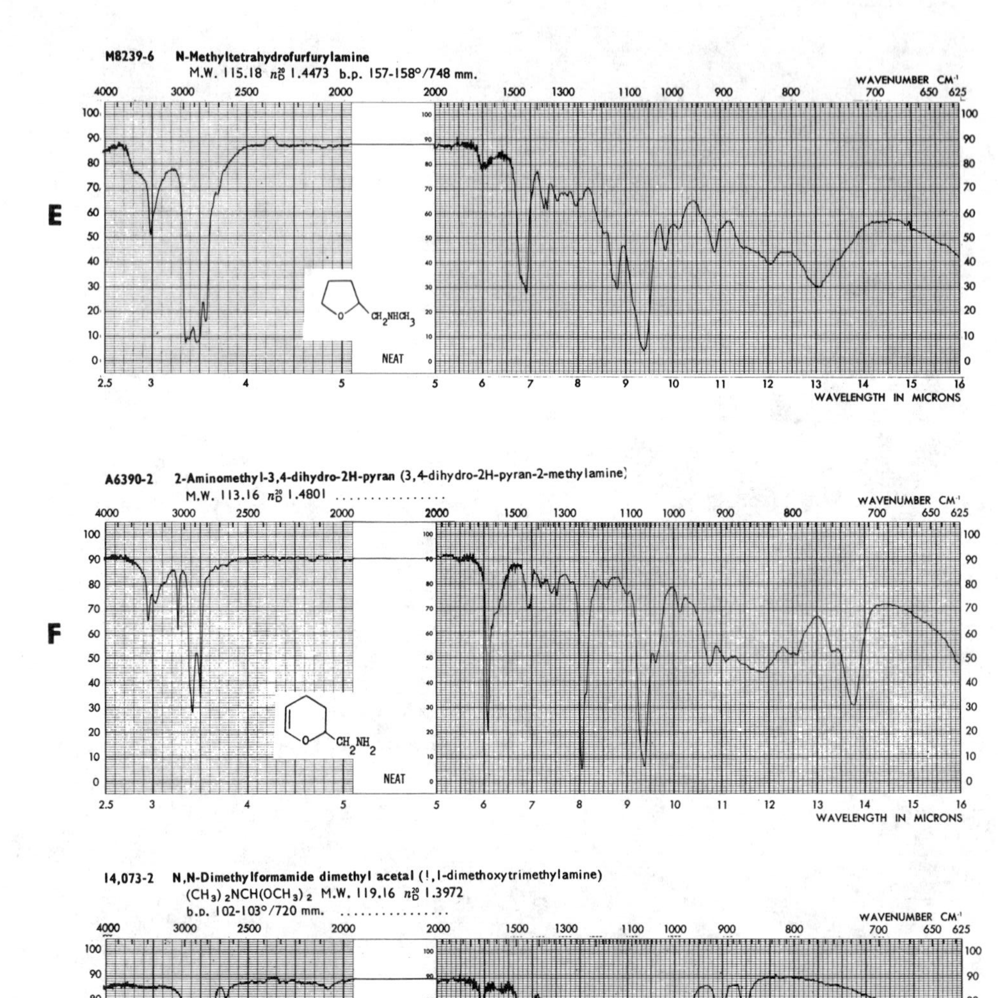

NEAT

F

A6390-2 **2-Aminomethyl-3,4-dihydro-2H-pyran** (3,4-dihydro-2H-pyran-2-methylamine)
M.W. 113.16 n_D^{20} 1.4801

NEAT

G

14,073-2 **N,N-Dimethylformamide dimethyl acetal** (1,1-dimethoxytrimethylamine)
$(CH_3)_2NCH(OCH_3)_2$ M.W. 119.16 n_D^{20} 1.3972
b.p. 102-103°/720 mm.

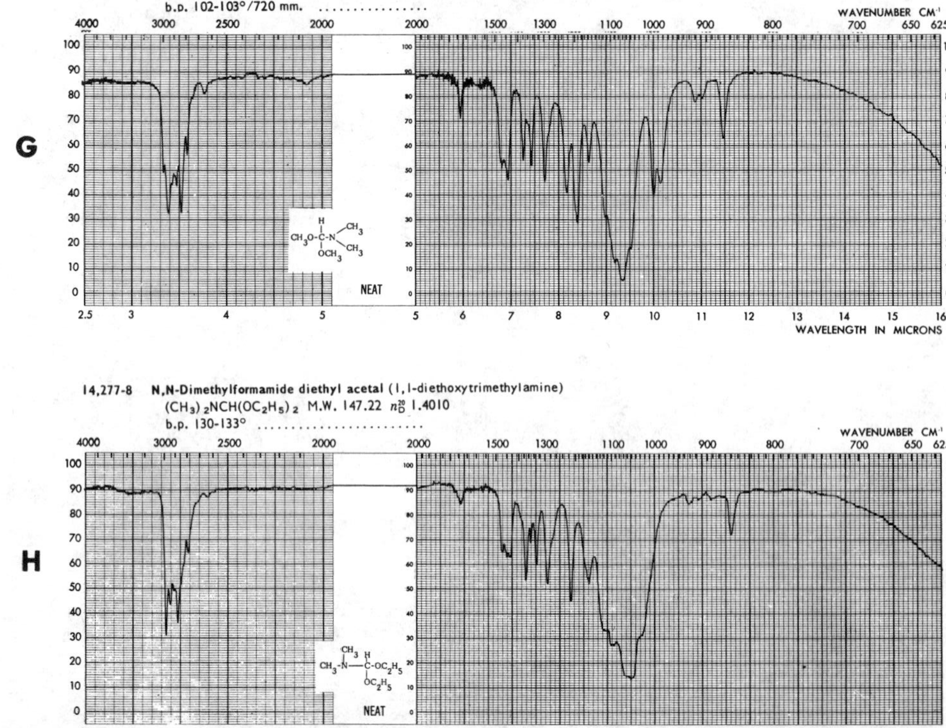

NEAT

H

14,277-8 **N,N-Dimethylformamide diethyl acetal** (1,1-diethoxytrimethylamine)
$(CH_3)_2NCH(OC_2H_5)_2$ M.W. 147.22 n_D^{20} 1.4010
b.p. 130-133°

NEAT

A 17,852-7 **N,N-Dimethylformamide dipropyl acetal** (1,1-dipropoxytrimethylamine)
$(CH_3)_2NCH(OCH_2CH_2CH_3)_2$
M.W. 175.27 b.p. 67-68°/14mm. n_D^{20} 1.4088
d 0.854

B 17,854-3 **N,N-Dimethylformamide dibutyl acetal** (1,1-dibutoxytrimethylamine)
$(CH_3)_2NCH[O(CH_2)_3CH_3]_2$
M.W. 203.33 b.p. 87-88°/12mm. n_D^{20} 1.4196
d 0.852

C 17,853-5 **N,N-Dimethylformamide diisopropyl acetal** (1,1-diisopropoxytrimethylamine)
$(CH_3)_2NCH[OCH(CH_3)_2]_2$
M.W. 175.27 b.p. 79-80°/60mm. n_D^{20} 1.4000
d 0.838

D 14,024-4 **N,N-Dimethylformamide dineopentyl acetal** (1,1-dineopentyloxytrimethylamine), puriss.
$(CH_3)_2NCH[OCH_2C(CH_3)_3]_2$ M.W. 231.38 n_D^{20} 1.4117
b.p. 85-87°/10 mm.

E 14,278-6 **N,N-Dimethylformamide dicyclohexyl acetal** (1,1-dicyclohexyloxytrimethylamine)
$(CH_3)_2NCH(OC_6H_{11})_2$ M.W. 255.40 n_D^{20} 1.4678
b.p. 115-116°/0.75 mm.

F 12,196-7 **Aminoacetaldehyde dimethyl acetal** (2,2-dimethoxyethylamine)
$H_2NCH_2CH(OCH_3)_2$ M.W. 105.14 n_D^{20} 1.4171 b.p. 135-139°/95 mm.

G A3720-0 **Aminoacetaldehyde diethyl acetal** (2,2-diethoxyethylamine)
$H_2NCH_2CH(OC_2H_5)_2$ M.W. 133.19
n_D^{20} 1.4170

H M2800-6 **Methylaminoacetaldehyde dimethyl acetal**
$CH_3NHCH_2CH(OCH_3)_2$ M.W. 119.16 n_D^{20} 1.4098

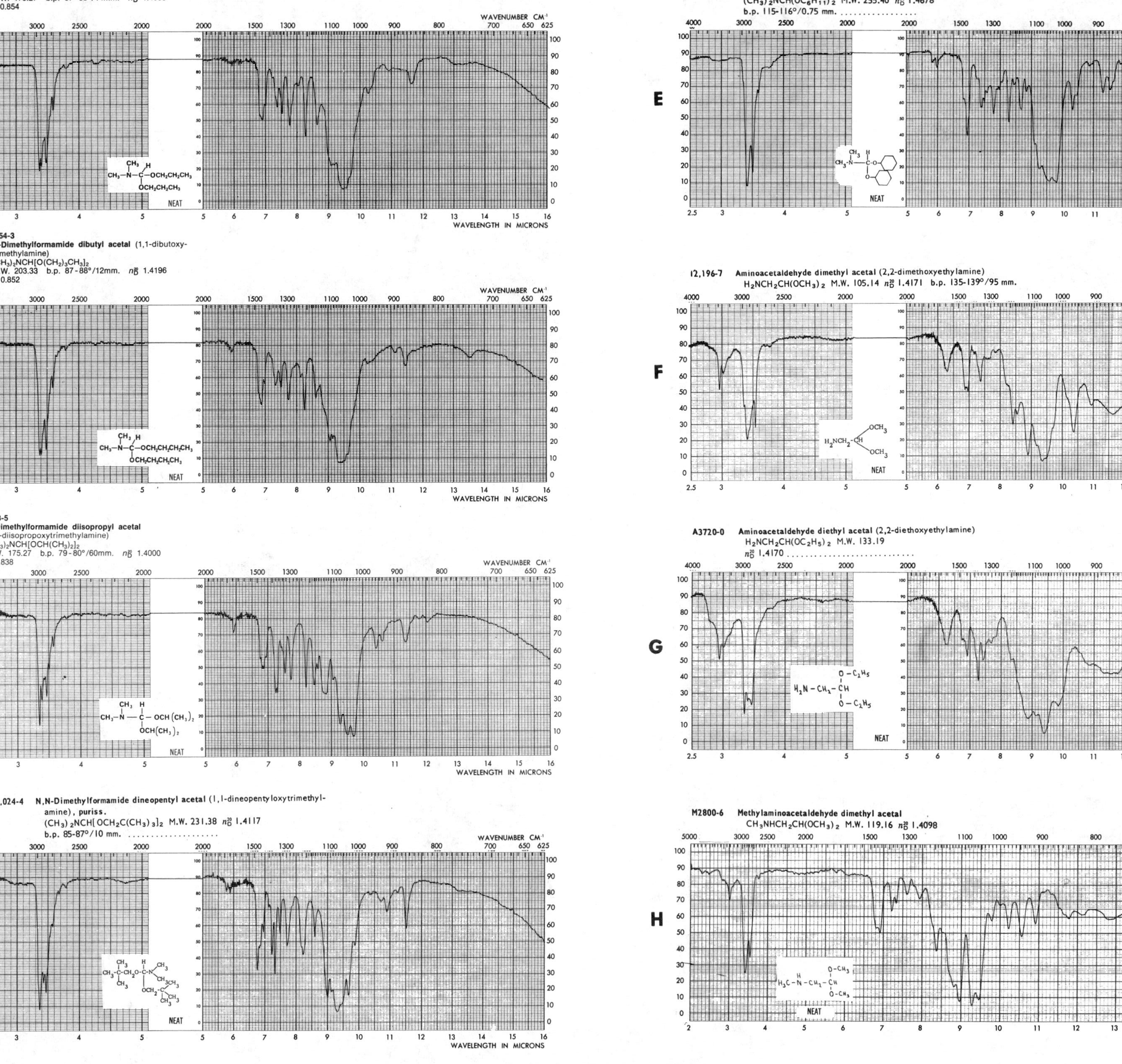

A

M2780-8 **Methylaminoacetaldehyde diethyl acetal**
$CH_3NHCH_2CH(OC_2H_5)_2$ M.W. 147.22
n_D^{20} 1.4126

NEAT

B

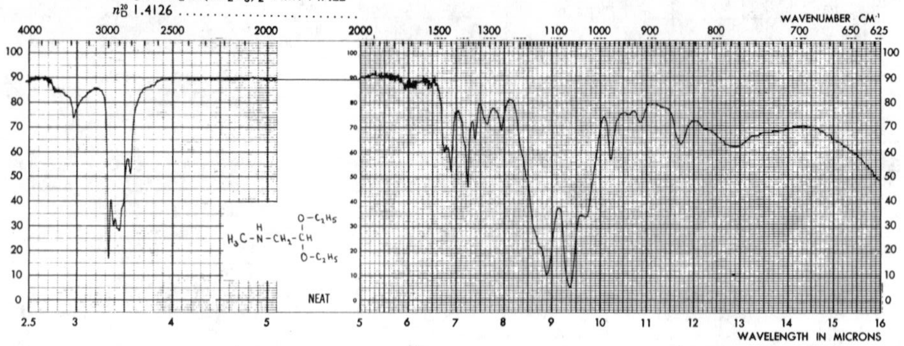

11,476-6 **N,N-Bis-(2,2-diethoxyethyl)-amine** [2,2'-iminobis-(acetaldehyde diethyl acetal)]
$[(C_2H_5O)_2CHCH_2]_2NH$ M.W. 249.35 n_D^{20} 1.4247
b.p. 260-262°/745 mm.

NEAT

C

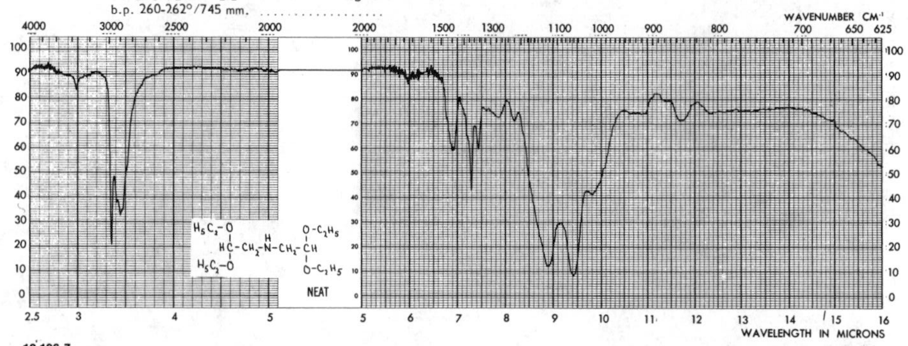

12,196-7
Aminoacetaldehyde dimethyl acetal, 98%
(2,2-dimethoxyethylamine)
$H_2NCH_2CH(OCH_3)_2$
M.W. 105.14 b.p. 135-139°/95mm. n_D^{20} 1.4170
Beil. **4**(2),758

NEAT

D

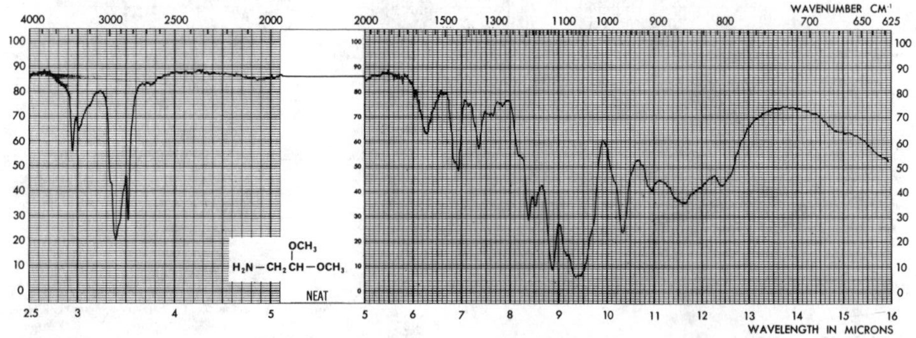

D13,880-0 **Dimethylaminoacetaldehyde diethyl acetal** (2,2-diethoxy-N,N-dimethylethylamine)
$(CH_3)_2NCH_2CH(OC_2H_5)_2$ M.W. 161.25
n_D^{20} 1.4129

NEAT

E

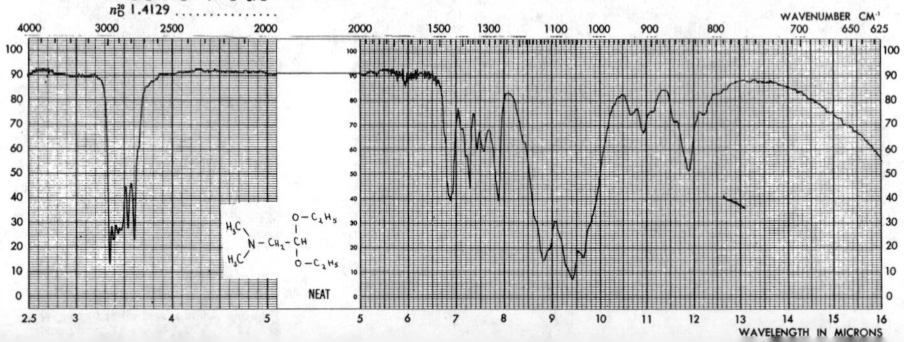

D8580-2 **Diethylaminoacetaldehyde diethyl acetal** (2,2-diethoxytriethylamine)
$(C_2H_5)_2NCH_2CH(OC_2H_5)_2$ M.W. 189.30
n_D^{20} 1.4189

NEAT

F

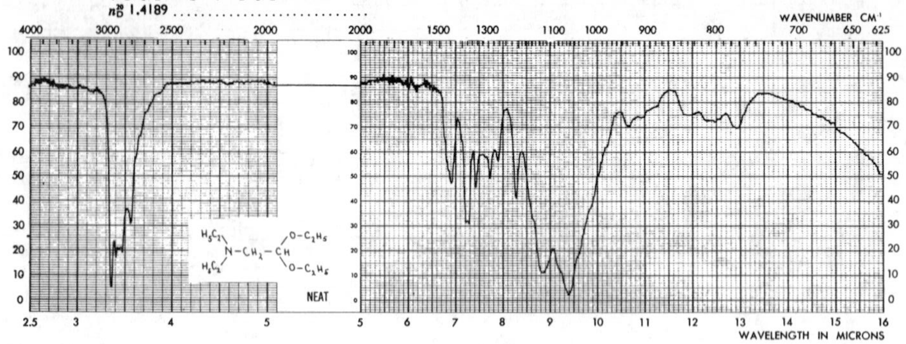

A4415-0 **4-Aminobutyraldehyde diethyl acetal** (4,4-diethoxybutylamine)
$H_2N(CH_2)_3CH(OC_2H_5)_2$ M.W. 161.25
n_D^{20} 1.4275

NEAT

G

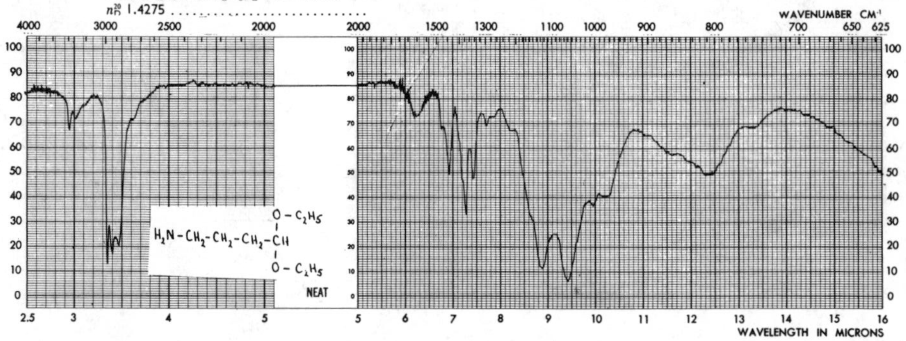

11,582-7 **N,N-Bis-(2,2-diethoxyethyl)-methylamine** [2,2'-methyliminobis-(acetaldehyde diethyl acetal)]
$[(C_2H_5O)_2CHCH_2]_2NCH_3$ M.W. 263.38
n_D^{20} 1.4259

NEAT

H

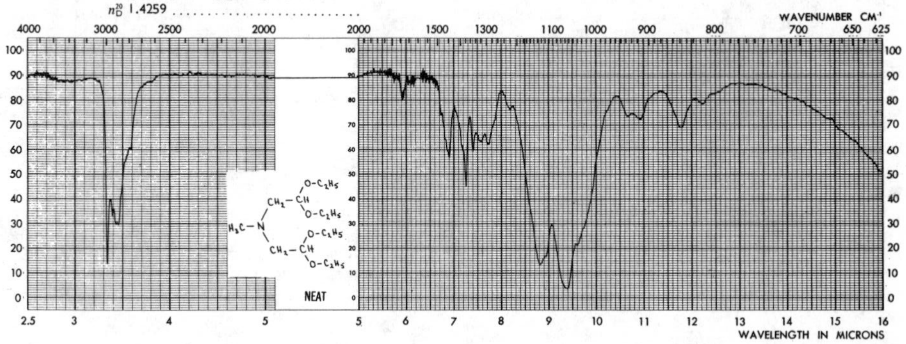

14,274-3 **1-Aza-4,6-dioxabicyclo[3.3.0]octane**
M.W. 115.13 n_D^{20} 1.4668 b.p. 101-101.5°/28 mm.

NEAT

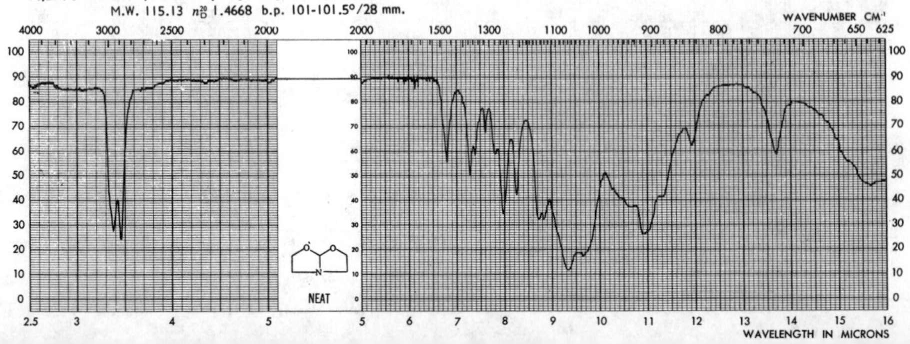

A

14,512-2 **1-Aza-4,6-dioxa-5-methylbicyclo[3.3.0]octane**
M.W. 129.16 n_D^{20} 1.4556 b.p. 60°/11 mm. . .

NEAT

B

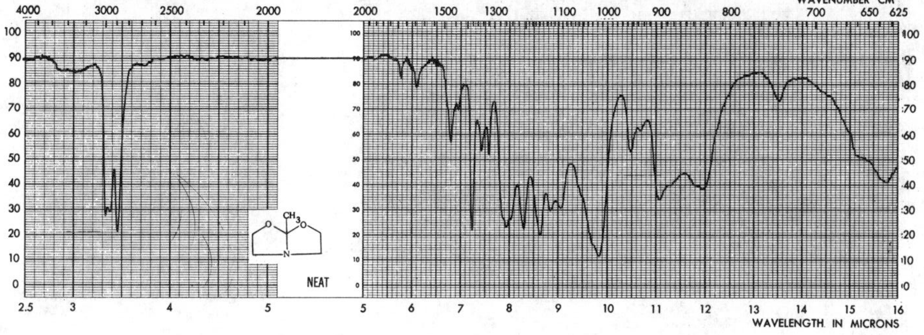

14,261-1 **N,N,5,5-Tetramethyl-1,3-dioxan-2-amine**
M.W. 159.23 n_D^{20} 1.4367
b.p. 87.5-90.5°/16 mm. . . . .

NEAT

C

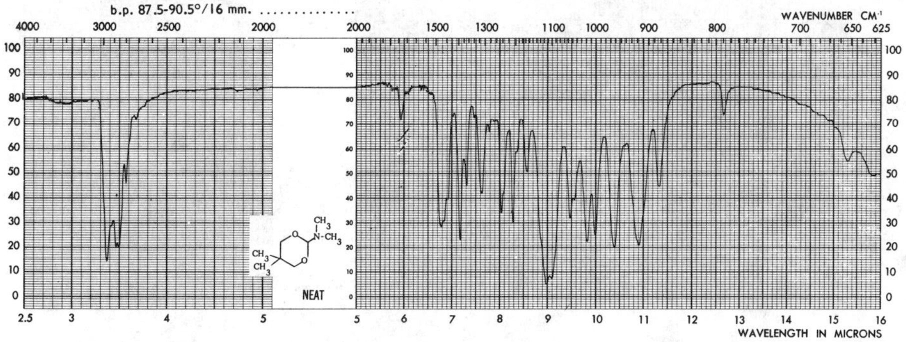

14,521-1 **1-Aza-3,5-dimethyl-4,6-dioxabicyclo[3.3.0]octane**
M.W. 143.19 n_D^{20} 1.4470 b.p. 67-68°/10 mm.

NEAT

D

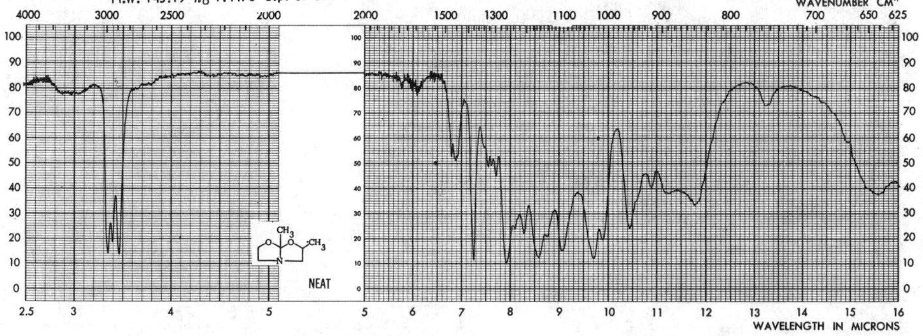

M5040-0 **N-Methylhydroxylamine hydrochloride**
$CH_3NHOH{\cdot}HCl$ M.W. 83.52
m.p. 83-84° . . . .

NUJOL MULL

E

D16,370-8 **O,N-Dimethylhydroxylamine hydrochloride**
$CH_3ONHCH_3{\cdot}HCl$ M.W. 97.55
m.p. 112-115° . . . .

NUJOL MULL

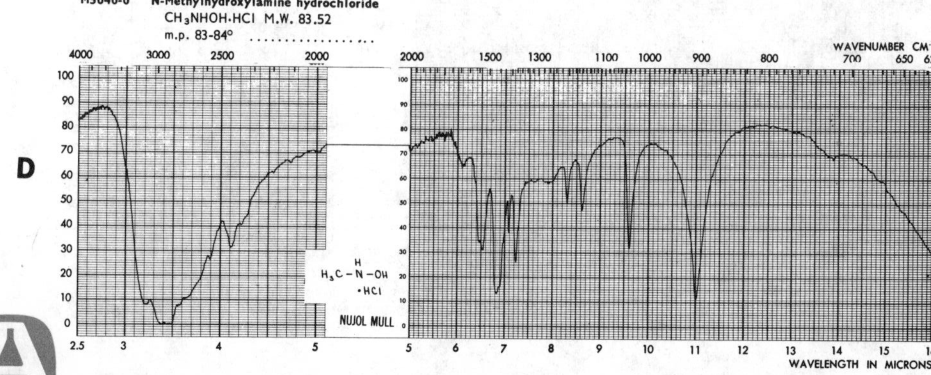

F

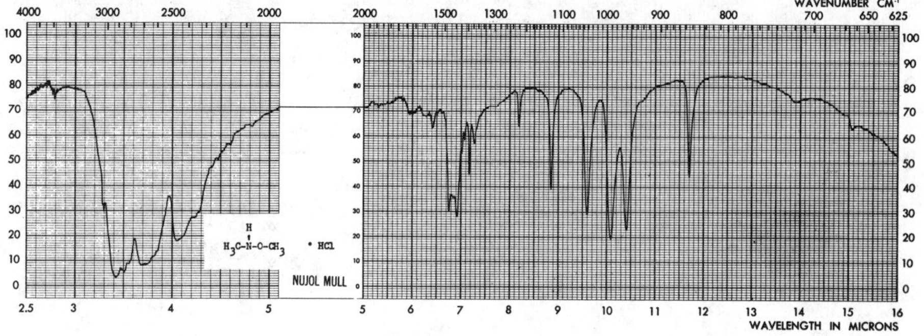

D9720-7 **N,N-Diethylhydroxylamine**
$(C_2H_5)_2NOH$ M.W. 89.14 n_D^{20} 1.4238

NEAT

G

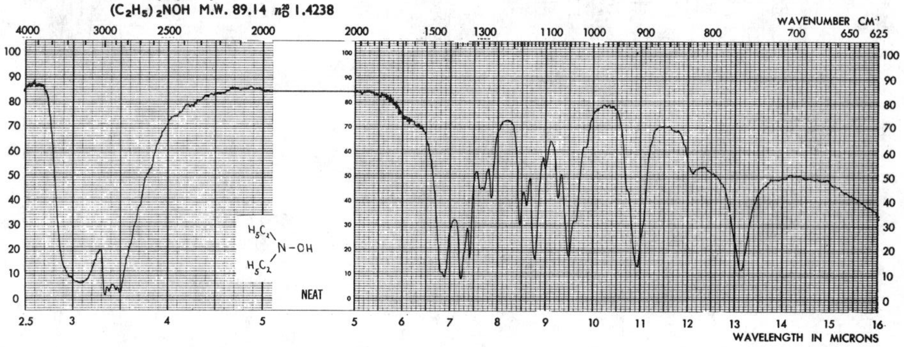

19,475-1
N-(*tert*-**Butyl)hydroxylamine hydrochloride,** 98+%
$(CH_3)_3CNHOH{\cdot}HCl$ FW 125.60 mp 176-180°
Disp. L

NUJOL MULL

H

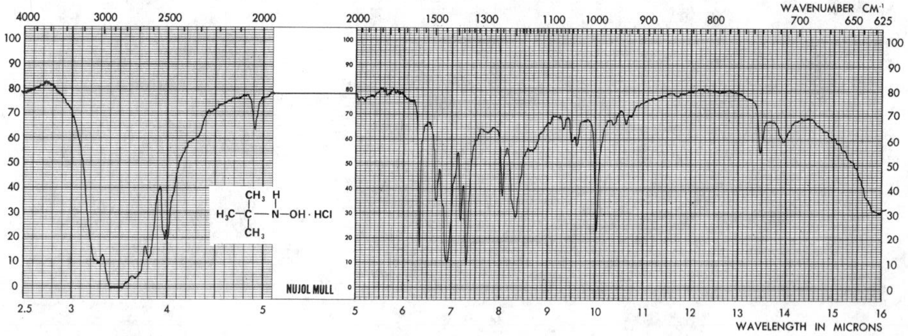

12,886-4 **N-Hydroxypiperidine**
M.W. 101.15 m.p. 37-40°

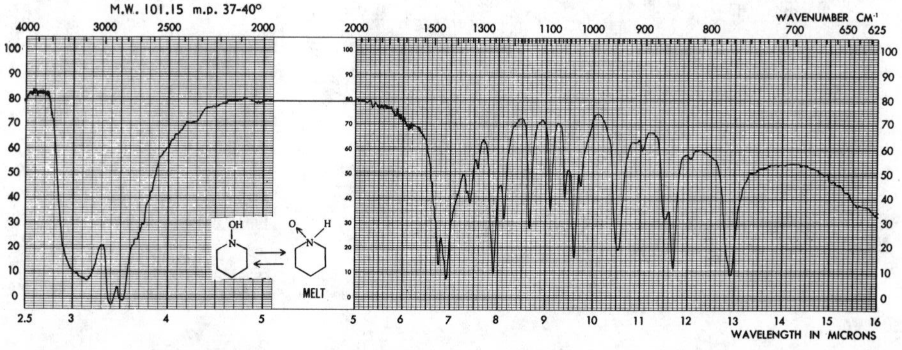

MELT

A

10,820-0 **Acetaldehyde ammonia** (1-aminoethanol)
$CH_3CH(OH)NH_2$ M.W. 61.08 m.p. 100-102°

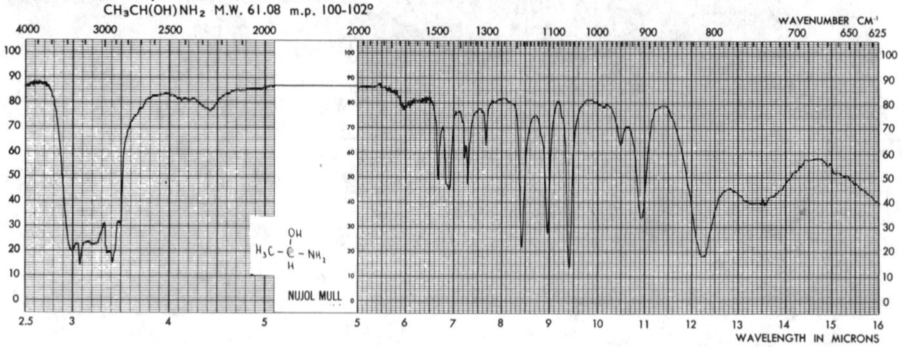

B

11,016-7 **Ethanolamine** (2-aminoethanol)
$H_2NCH_2CH_2OH$ M.W. 61.08 n_D^{20} 1.4524
b.p. 170° ....

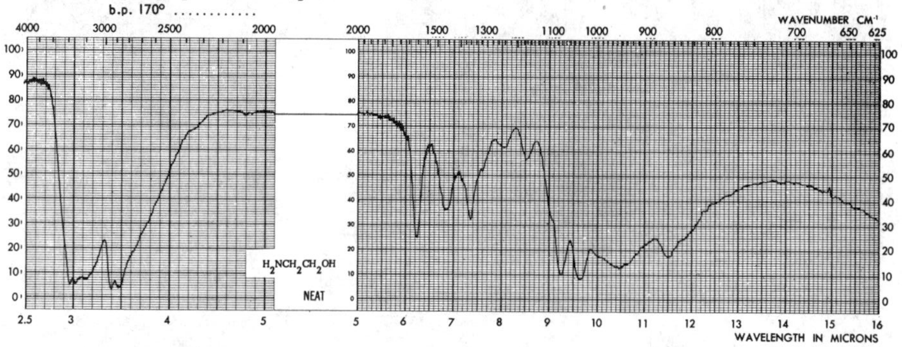

C

18,674-0
Ethanolamine hydrochloride, 98+% (2-aminoethanol)
$H_2NCH_2CH_2OH \cdot HCl$ FW 97.55 mp 78-85°
Disp. L

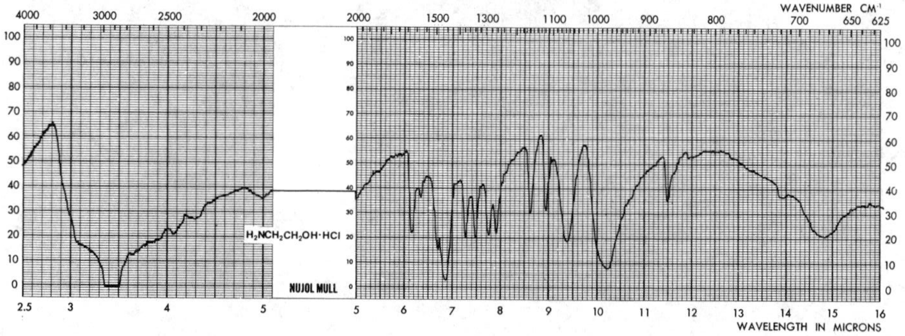

D

18,340-7
2-(Aminomethyl)-2-propanol hydrochloride
(2-hydroxyisobutylamine)
$H_2NCH_2C(CH_3)_2OH \cdot HCl$
M.W. 125.6

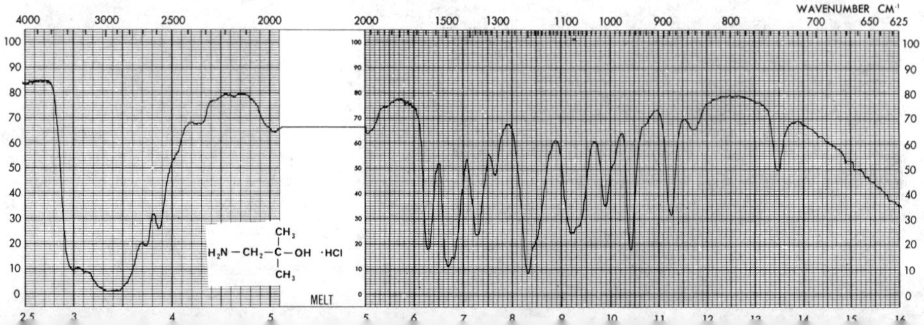

E

12,862-7 **2-Hydroxyethylhydrazine** (2-hydrazinoethanol)
$HOCH_2CH_2NHNH_2$ M.W. 76.10 n_D^{20} 1.4922
b.p. 218-220°/754 mm. ....

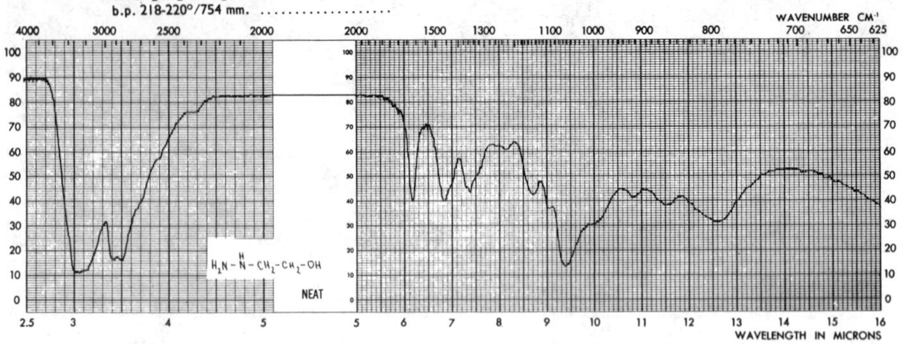

F

A7640-0 **3-Amino-1-propanol**
$H_2N(CH_2)_3OH$ M.W. 75.11 n_D^{20} 1.4598 m.p. 10-12° .....

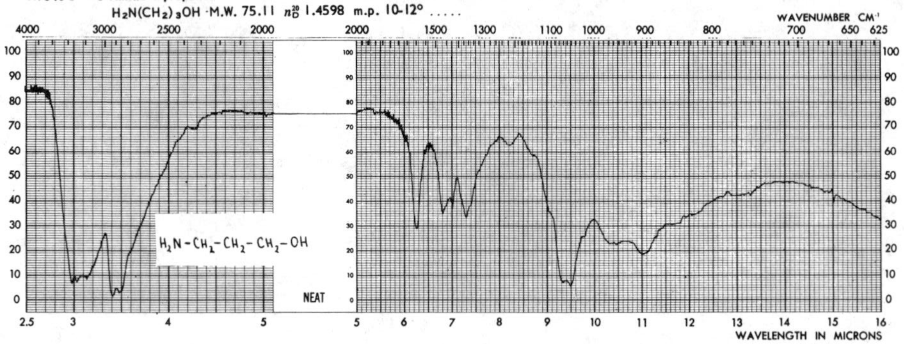

G

12,720-5 **2-Amino-1-propanol hydrochloride**
$CH_3CH(NH_2)CH_2OH \cdot HCl$ M.W. 111.57

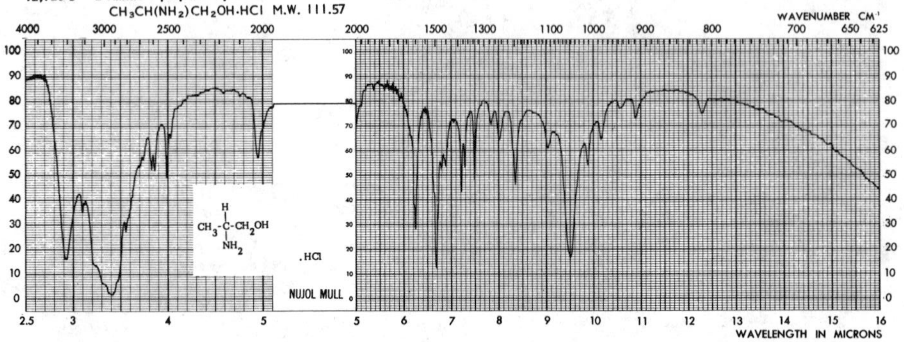

H

19,217-1
DL-2-Amino-1-propanol, 98% (DL-alaninol)
$CH_3CH(NH_2)CH_2OH$ FW 75.11 bp 173-176°
n_D^{20} 1.4495 d 0.943 *Beil.* **4**(1),432 Disp. L

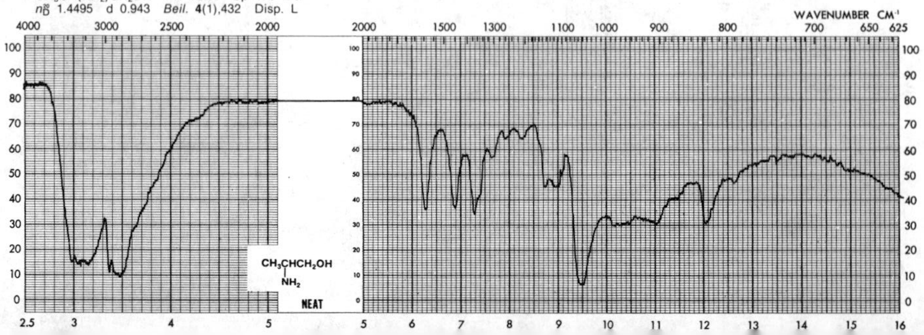

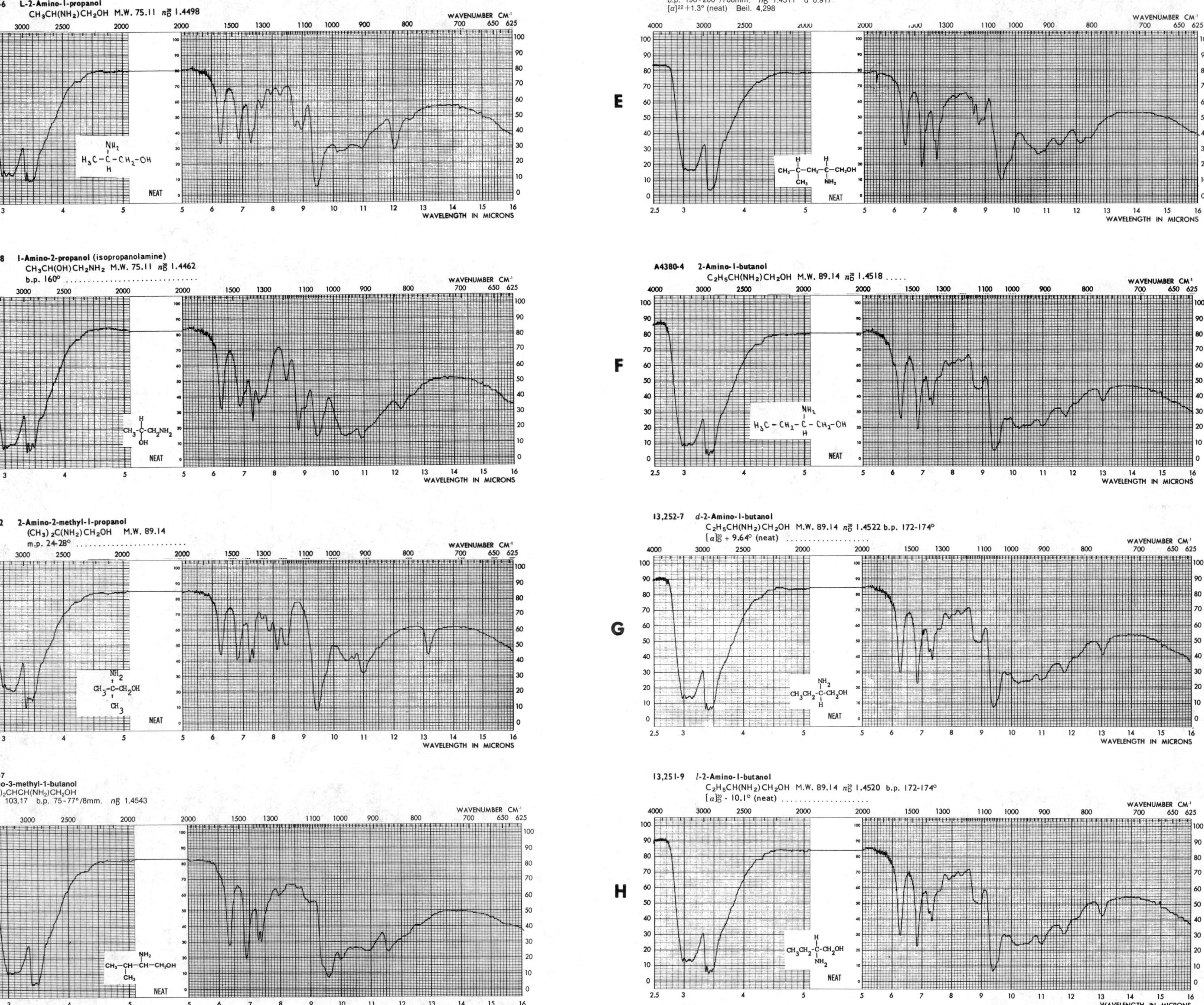
A
A7620-6 L-2-Amino-1-propanol
$CH_3CH(NH_2)CH_2OH$ M.W. 75.11 n_D^{20} 1.4498
NEAT
B
11,024-8 1-Amino-2-propanol (isopropanolamine)
$CH_3CH(OH)CH_2NH_2$ M.W. 75.11 n_D^{20} 1.4462
b.p. 160°
NEAT
C
A6518-2 2-Amino-2-methyl-1-propanol
$(CH_3)_2C(NH_2)CH_2OH$ M.W. 89.14
m.p. 24-28°
NEAT
D
18,483-7
2-Amino-3-methyl-1-butanol
$(CH_3)_2CHCH(NH_2)CH_2OH$
M.W. 103.17 b.p. 75-77°/8mm. n_D^{20} 1.4543
NEAT
E
18,404-7
L-Leucinol, 98% (2-amino-4-methyl-1-pentanol)
$(CH_3)_2CHCH_2CH(NH_2)CH_2OH$
b.p. 198-200°/768mm. n_D^{20} 1.4511 d 0.917
$[\alpha]^{22}$ +1.3° (neat) Beil. 4,298
NEAT
F
A4380-4 2-Amino-1-butanol
$C_2H_5CH(NH_2)CH_2OH$ M.W. 89.14 n_D^{20} 1.4518
NEAT
G
13,252-7 d-2-Amino-1-butanol
$C_2H_5CH(NH_2)CH_2OH$ M.W. 89.14 n_D^{20} 1.4522 b.p. 172-174°
$[\alpha]_D^{20}$ + 9.64° (neat)
NEAT
H
13,251-9 l-2-Amino-1-butanol
$C_2H_5CH(NH_2)CH_2OH$ M.W. 89.14 n_D^{20} 1.4520 b.p. 172-174°
$[\alpha]_D^{20}$ - 10.1° (neat)
NEAT
WAVENUMBER CM⁻¹
WAVELENGTH IN MICRONS

ALDRICH

ALDRICH ®

A 18,670-8
L-2-Amino-3-methyl-1-butanol, 96% (L-valinol)
$(CH_3)_2CHCH(NH_2)CH_2OH$
M.W. 103.17 b.p. 81°/8mm. n_D^{20} 1.4548
$[\alpha]^{22}$ +14.6° (neat)

B 17,703-2
3-Amino-3-methyl-1-butanol, 97%
$H_2NC(CH_3)_2CH_2CH_2OH$
M.W. 103.17 b.p. 85-87°/18mm. n_D^{20} 1.4515
d 0.92

C 17,833-0 **4-Amino-1-butanol,** 98%
$H_2N(CH_2)_4OH$ M.W. 89.14 b.p. 206° n_D^{20} 1.4610
d 0.967 *Beil.* 4,291 Disp. A

D 12,304-8 **5-Amino-1-pentanol**
$H_2N(CH_2)_5OH$ M.W. 103.17 m.p. > 30°

E A5635-3 **6-Amino-1-hexanol**
$H_2N(CH_2)_6OH$ M.W. 117.19 m.p. 52-54°

F 14,508-4 **4-(Aminomethyl)-cyclohexanemethanol** (diasteriomers)
$H_2NCH_2C_6H_{10}CH_2OH$ M.W. 143.23
n_D^{20} 1.4936

G A5405 **2-(2-Aminoethoxy)-ethanol**
$H_2N(CH_2)_2O(CH_2)_2OH$ M.W. 105.14 n_D^{20} 1.4600

H 13,304-3 **2-(Methylamino)-ethanol** (N-methylethanolamine)
$CH_3NHCH_2CH_2OH$ M.W. 75.11 n_D^{20} 1.4387
b.p. 159.6°

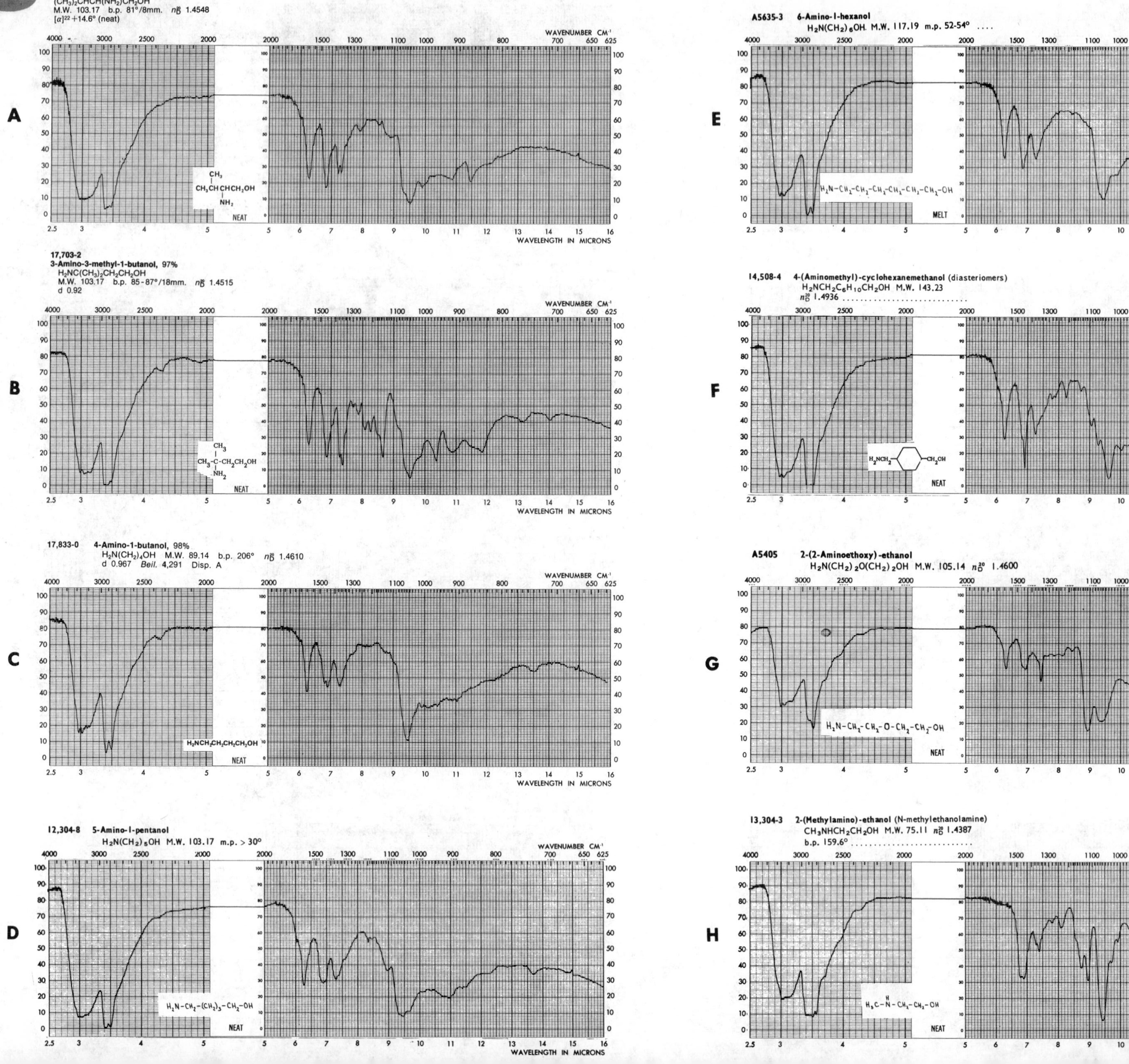

A

15,641-8
2-(Ethylamino)-ethanol, 98%
$C_2H_5NHCH_2CH_2OH$
M.W. 89.14 b.p. 169-170° n_D^{20} 1.4402 d 0.914
Beil. 4,282

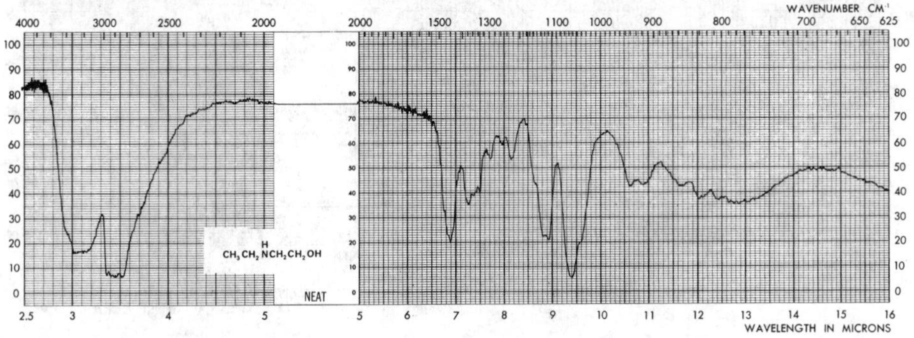

B

22,276-3
2-(Propylamino)ethanol, 97%
$CH_3CH_2CH_2NHCH_2CH_2OH$ FW 103.17
bp 182°/746mm. n_D^{20} 1.4415 d 0.900 *Beil.* 4,282
Disp. C

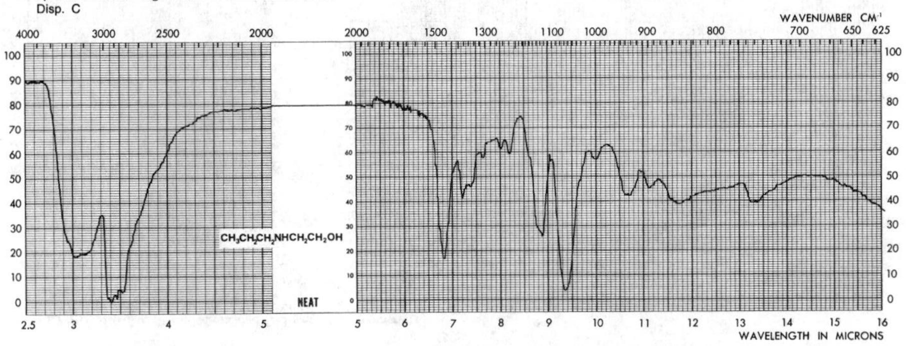

C

10,921-5 **2-(n-Butylamino)-ethanol (N-n-butylethanolamine)**
$CH_3(CH_2)_3NHCH_2CH_2OH$ M.W. 117.19 n_D^{20} 1.4450
b.p. 215°

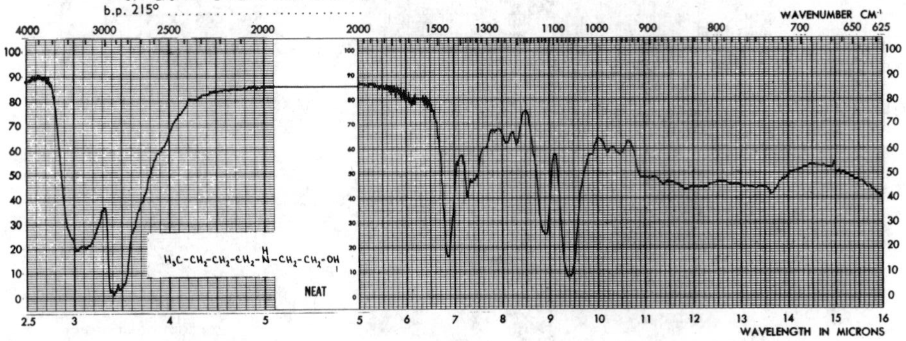

D

B8960-4 **2-(tert.-Butylamino)-ethanol**
$(CH_3)_3CNHCH_2CH_2OH$ M.W. 117.19
m.p. 39-44°

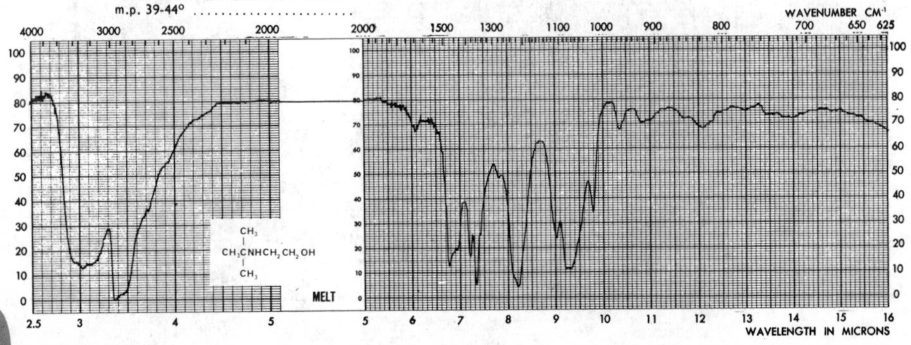

E

12,546-6 **2-Cyclohexylaminoethanol**
$C_6H_{11}NHCH_2CH_2OH$ M.W. 143.23 m.p. 34-37°

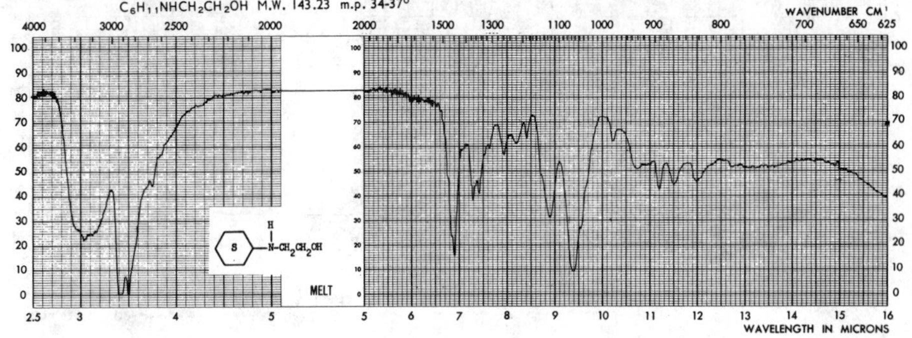

F

D8330-3 **Diethanolamine (2,2'-iminodiethanol)**
$(HOCH_2CH_2)_2NH$ M.W. 105.14
n_D^{20} 1.4744 m.p. 28°

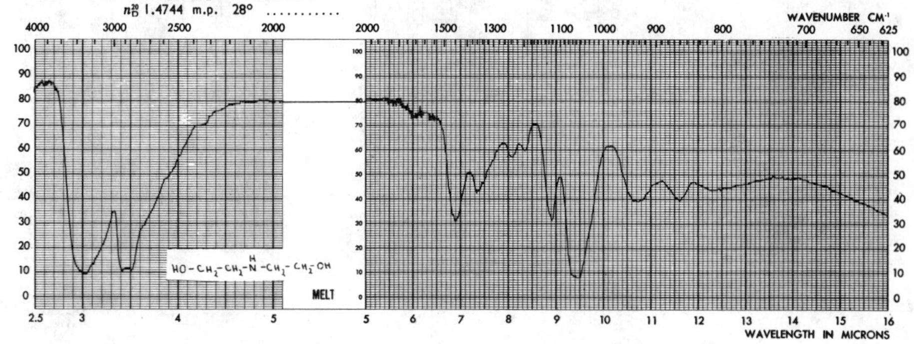

G

20,928-7
Diethanolamine hydrochloride, 98% (2,2'-imino-diethanol)
$(HOCH_2CH_2)_2NH \cdot HCl$ FW 141.60 n_D^{20} 1.5150
d 1.261 Disp. L,C

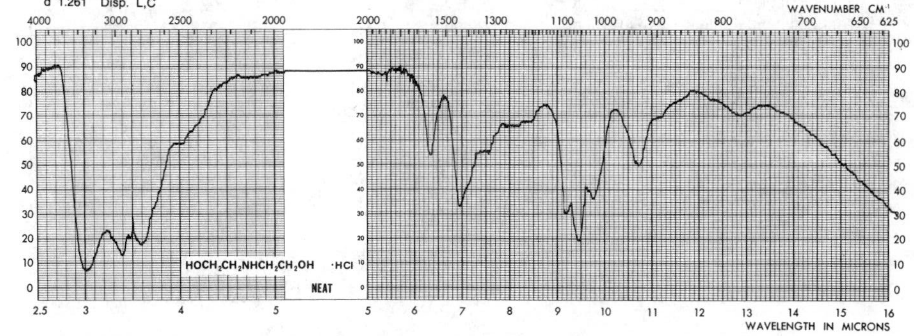

H

17,609-5
2,2'-Oxybis(ethylamine) dihydrochloride
$O(CH_2CH_2NH_2)_2 \cdot 2HCl$ FW 177.07 mp 232-235°
NMR 2,39A Disp. C

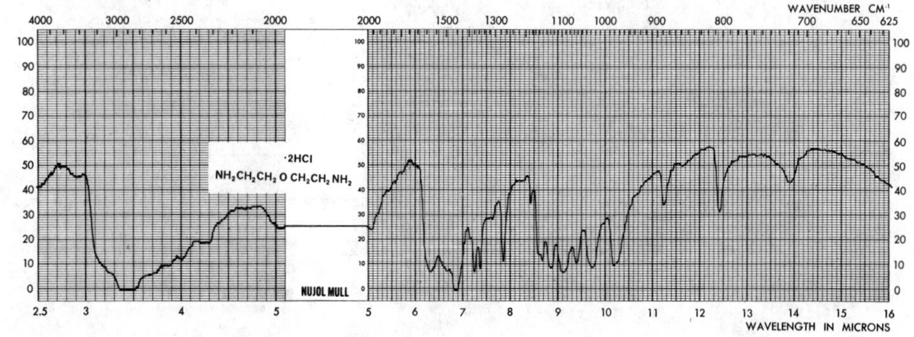

Axes (all spectra): WAVENUMBER CM⁻¹ 4000 3000 2500 2000 1500 1300 1100 1000 900 800 700 650 625; WAVELENGTH IN MICRONS 2.5–16; transmittance 0–100

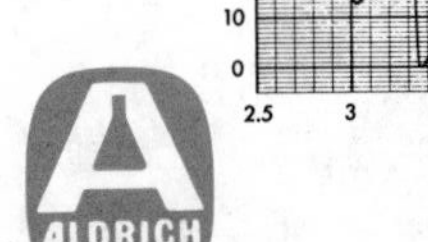

A

13,301-9 1,1'-Iminodi-2-propanol (diisopropanolamine)
$HN[CH_2CH(OH)CH_3]_2$ M.W. 133.19 .....

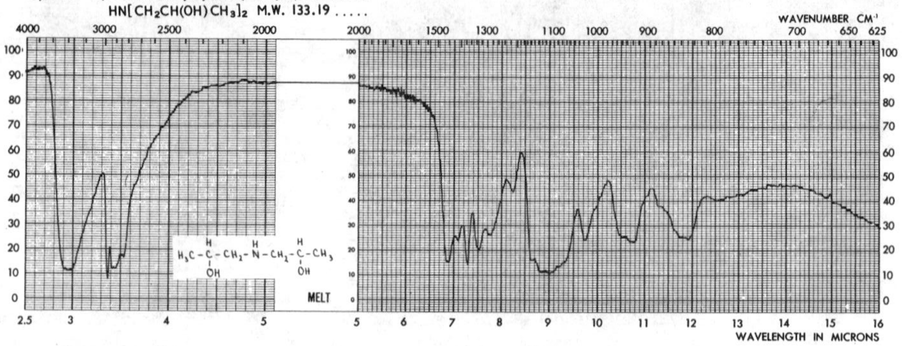

MELT

B

16,872-6
2-(Diisopropylamino)-ethanol, 99%
$[(CH_3)_2CH]_2NCH_2CH_2OH$
M.W. 145.25 b.p. 187-192° n_D^{20} 1.4417 d 0.826
Beil. 4(1),430

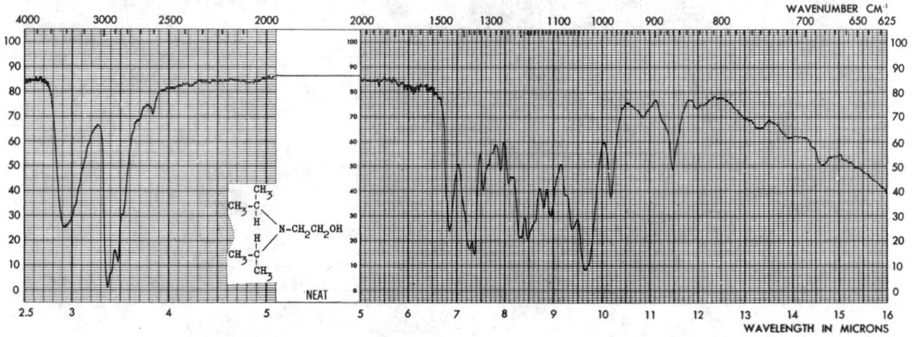

NEAT

C

D15,740-6 N,N-Dimethylethanolamine (2-dimethylaminoethanol)
$HOCH_2CH_2N(CH_3)_2$ M.W. 89.14
n_D^{20} 1.4294 ....

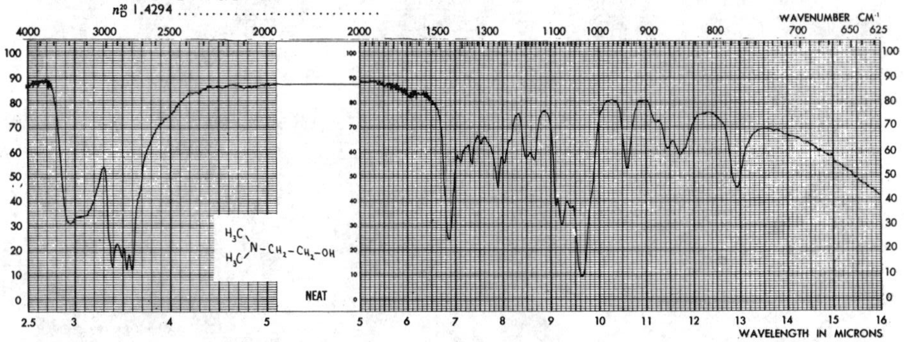

NEAT

D

D9400-3 N,N-Diethylethanolamine (2-diethylaminoethanol), puriss.
$HOCH_2CH_2N(C_2H_5)_2$ M.W. 117.19
n_D^{20} 1.4414 ....

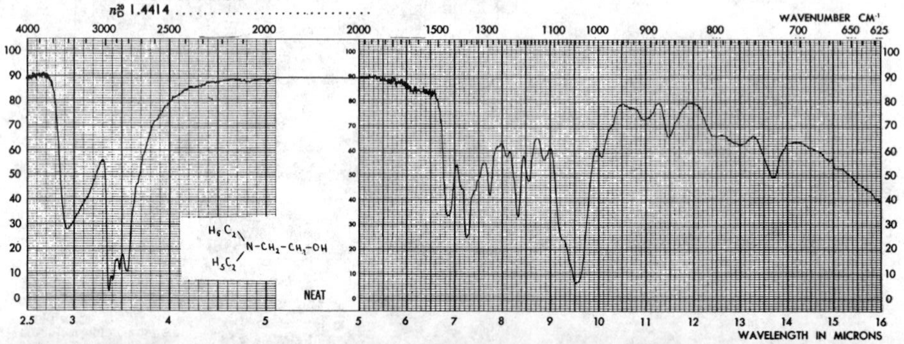

NEAT

E

D14,440-1 3-Dimethylamino-1-propanol
$(CH_3)_2N(CH_2)_3OH$ M.W. 103.17
n_D^{20} 1.4350 ....

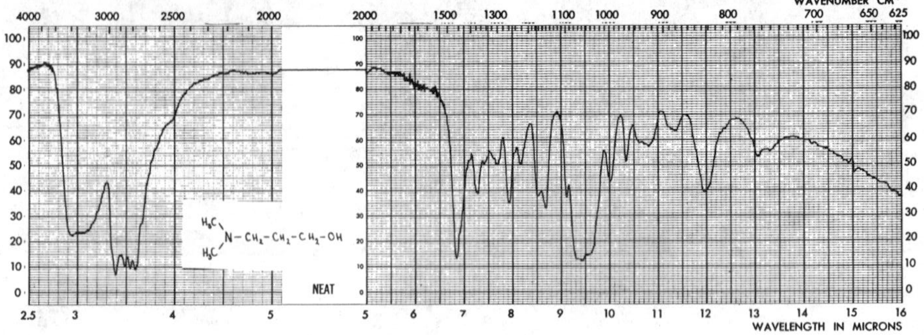

NEAT

F

14,999-3 3-Diethylamino-1-propanol
$(C_2H_5)_2N(CH_2)_3OH$ M.W. 131.22
n_D^{20} 1.4435 b.p. 81-83°/15 mm.

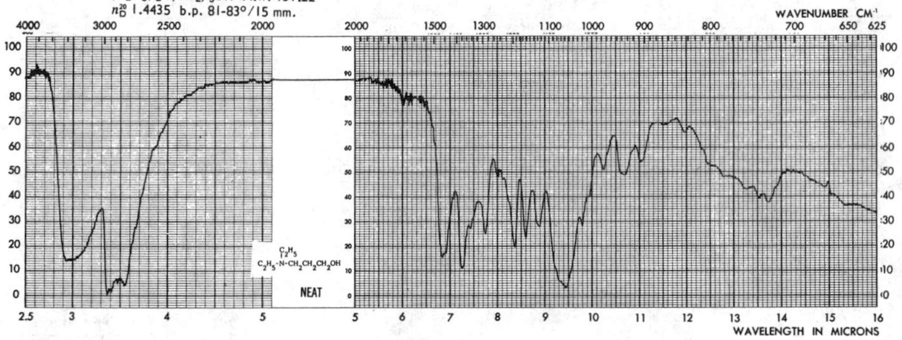

NEAT

G

19,055-1
5-Diethylamino-2-pentanol
$(C_2H_5)_2N(CH_2)_3CH(OH)CH_3$ FW 159.27 d 0.866
Disp. C

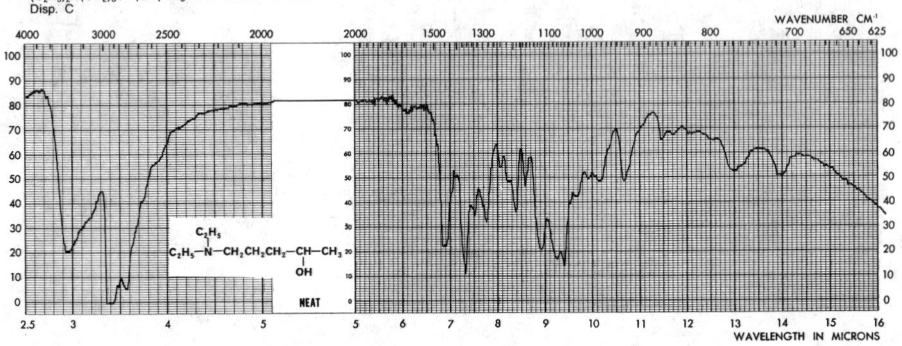

NEAT

H

D14,420-7 1-Dimethylamino-2-propanol
$(CH_3)_2NCH_2CH(OH)CH_3$ M.W. 103.17
n_D^{20} 1.4193 ....

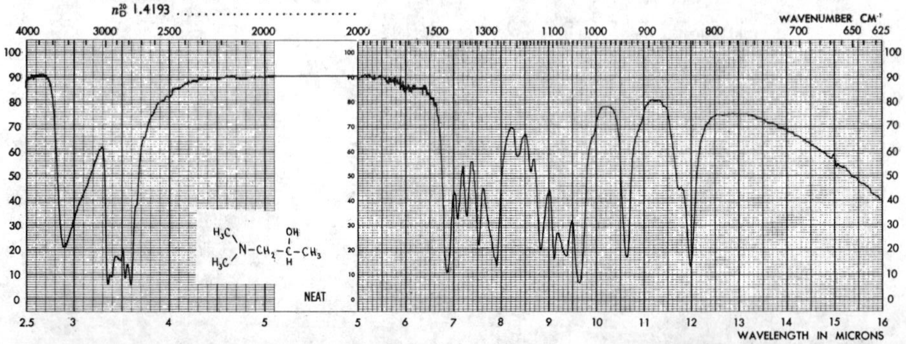

NEAT

A

D8848-8 1-Diethylamino-2-propanol
$(C_2H_5)_2NCH_2CH(OH)CH_3$ M.W. 131.22 n_D^{20} 1.4255

NEAT

B

D14,300 2-Dimethylamino-2-methyl-1-propanol
$CH_3C(CH_3)[N(CH_3)_2]CH_2OH$ M.W. 117.19 n_D^{20} 1.4474

NEAT

C

11,206-2 N-Ethyldiethanolamine (2,2'-ethyliminodiethanol)
$(HOCH_2CH_2)_2NC_2H_5$ M.W. 133.19 n_D^{20} 1.4665
b.p. 127-129°/9 mm.

NEAT

D

12,425-7 N-n-Butyldiethanolamine [2,2'-(butylimino)-diethanol]
$CH_3(CH_2)_3N(CH_2CH_2OH)_2$ M.W. 161.25 n_D^{20} 1.4625

NEAT

E

T5830-0 Triethanolamine (2,2',2''-nitrilotriethanol), 99%
$(HOCH_2CH_2)_3N$ M.W. 149.19 n_D^{20} 1.4821 m.p. 20-22°
b.p. 360°

NEAT

F

15,891-7
Triethanolamine hydrochloride, 99+% (2,2',2''-nitrilotriethanol)
$(HOCH_2CH_2)_3N \cdot HCl$
M.W. 185.65 m.p. 177-179° Beil. 4,285

NUJOL MULL

G

14,609-9 2,2-Bis(hydroxymethyl)-2,2',2''-nitrilotriethanol [bis(2-hydroxyethyl)iminotris(hydroxymethyl)methane, "bis-tris"]
$(HOCH_2CH_2)_2NC(CH_2OH)_3$ M.W. 209.25
m.p. 102-103°

NUJOL MULL

H

A7600-1 3-Amino-1,2-propanediol
$H_2NCH_2CH(OH)CH_2OH$ M.W. 91.11
n_D^{20} 1.4920

NEAT

A

21,021-8
3-(Dimethylamino)-1,2-propanediol, 98%
$(CH_3)_2NCH_2CH(OH)CH_2OH$ FW 119.16
bp 216-217° n_D^{20} 1.4609 d 1.004 *Beil.* 4,302
Disp. C

B

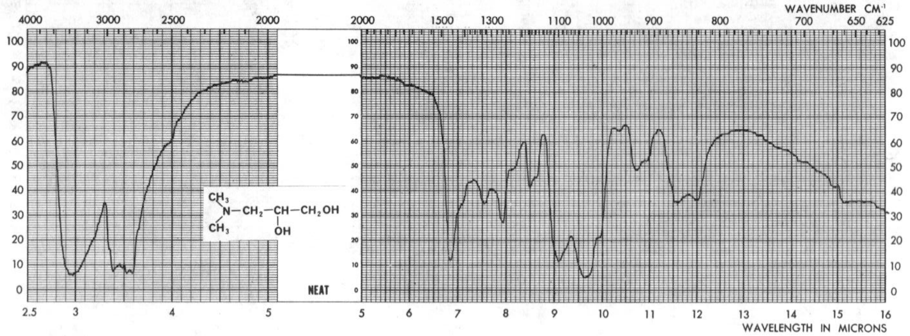

21,022-6
3-(Diethylamino)-1,2-propanediol, 98%
$(C_2H_5)_2NCH_2CH(OH)CH_2OH$ FW 147.22
bp 233-235° n_D^{20} 1.4602 d 0.965 *Beil.* 4,302
Disp. C

C

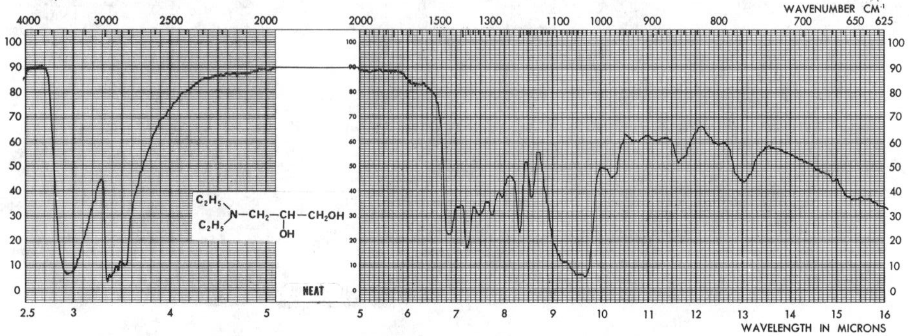

22,065-5
3-(*tert*-Butylamino)-1,2-propanediol, 97%
$(CH_3)_3CNHCH_2CH(OH)CH_2OH$ FW 147.22
mp 68-70° bp 90-92°/1mm. Disp. C

D

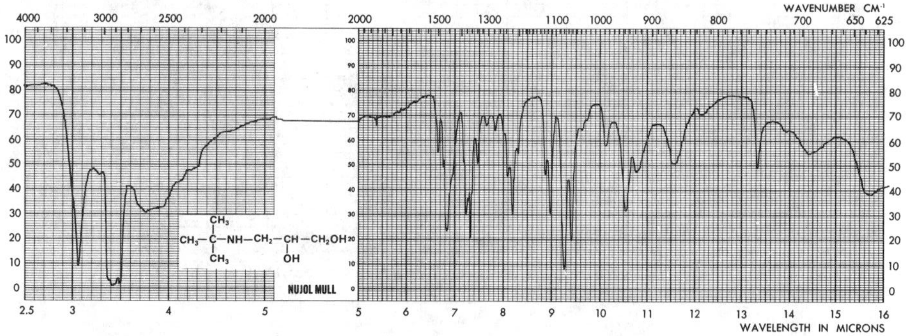

M4220-3 **N-Methyldiethanolamine** (2,2'-methyliminodiethanol)
$(HOCH_2CH_2)_2NCH_3$ M.W. 119.16 n_D^{20} 1.4678
b.p. 246-248°

E

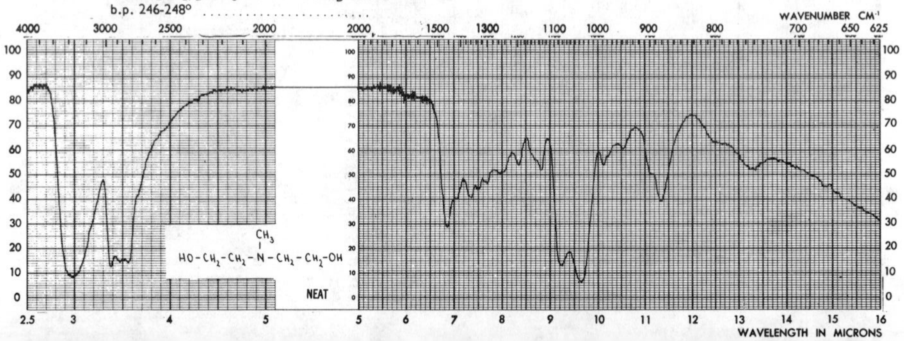

A6517-4 **2-Amino-2-methyl-1,3-propanediol**
$HOCH_2C(CH_3)(NH_2)CH_2OH$ M.W. 105.14
m.p. 111-112.5°

F

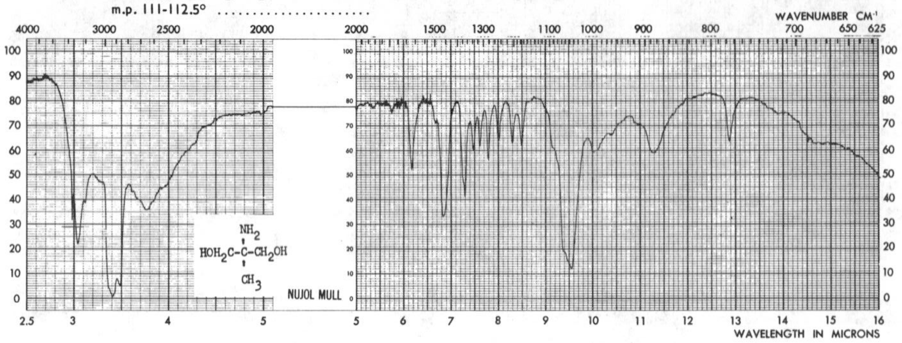

A4940- **2-Amino-1,3-dihydroxy-2-ethylpropane**
$HOCH_2C(NH_2)(C_2H_5)CH_2OH$ M.W. 119.16
m.p. 38-42°

G

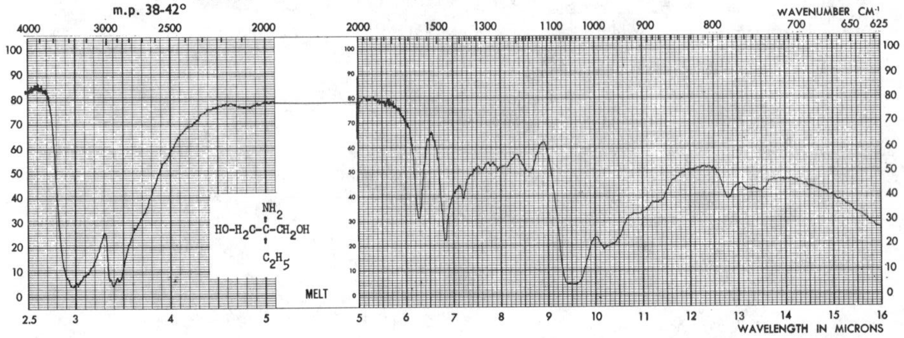

15,456-3 **Tris-(hydroxymethyl)-aminomethane** [2-amino-2-(hydroxymethyl)-1,3-propanediol, TRIS, tromethamine],
99.9+%, ultrapure grade, GOLD LABEL
$(HOCH_2)_3CNH_2$ M.W. 121.14 m.p. 171.2-172.3°

H

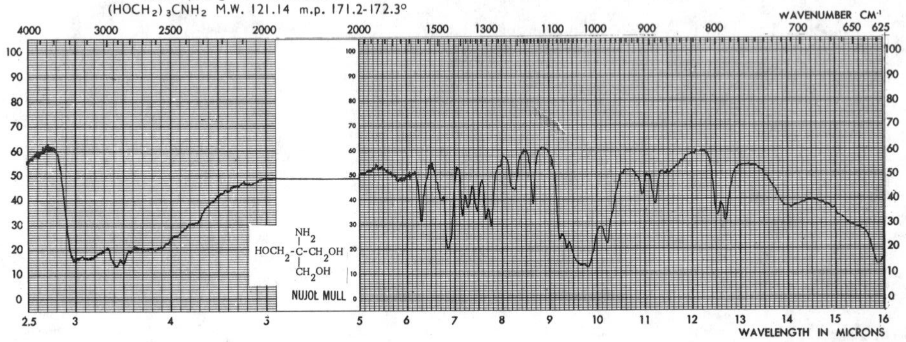

T8760-2 **Tris-(hydroxymethyl)-aminomethane** [2-amino-2-(hydroxymethyl)-1,3-propanediol], **puriss.**
$(HOCH_2)_3CNH_2$ M.W. 121.14 m.p. 168-171°

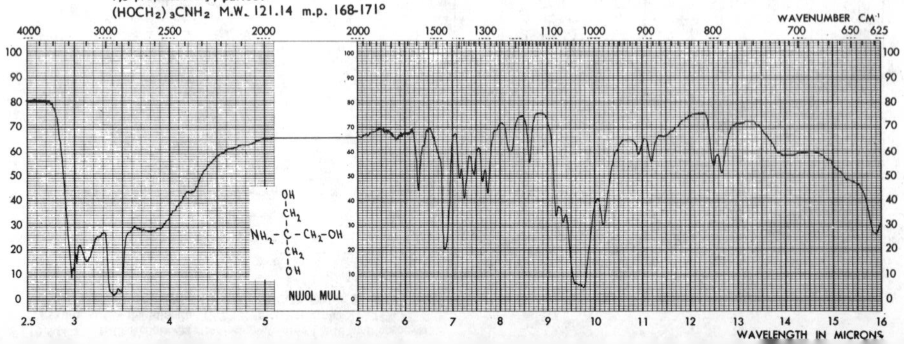

A

12,758-2 **2-(2-Aminoethylamino)-ethanol**
$H_2NCH_2CH_2NHCH_2CH_2OH$ M.W. 104.15 n_D^{20} 1.4861
b.p. 238-240°/752 mm.

NEAT

B

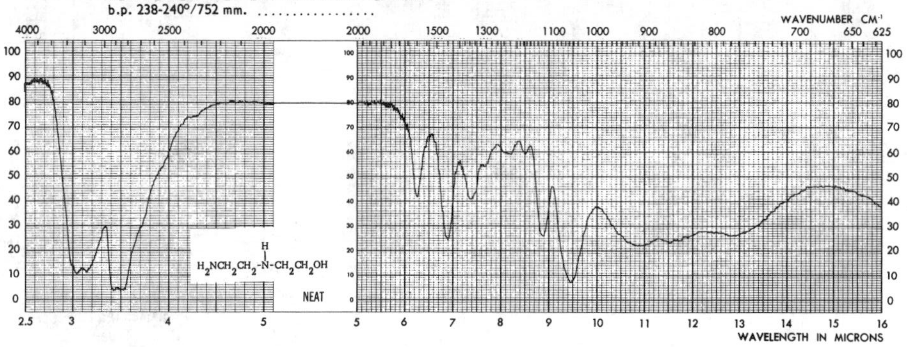

17,857-8
2-[(2-Aminoethyl)-thio]-ethanol, 97%
$H_2NCH_2CH_2SCH_2CH_2OH$
M.W. 121.2 b.p. 105-108°/0.15mm. n_D^{20} 1.5325
d 1.12

NEAT

C

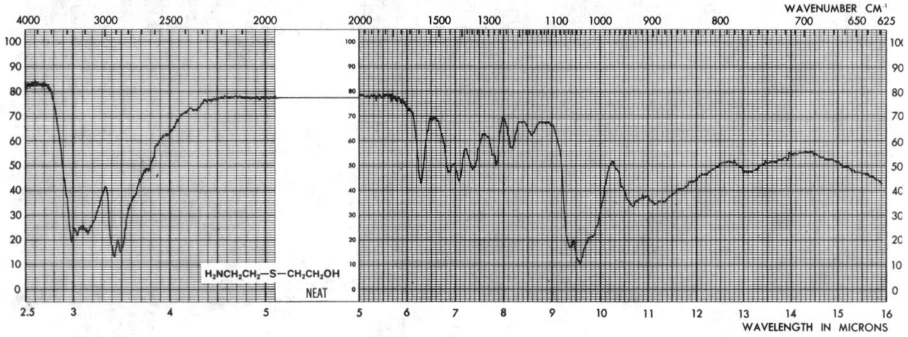

D1760-2 **1,3-Diamino-N-(β-hydroxyethyl)-propane [2-(3-aminopropylamino)-ethanol]**
$HOCH_2CH_2NH(CH_2)_3NH_2$ M.W. 118.18 n_D^{20} 1.4831

NEAT

D

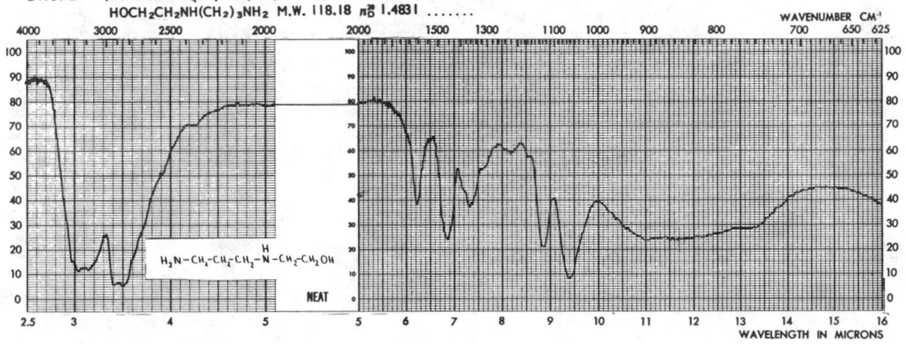

14,346-4 **1-(2-Aminoethylamino)-2-propanol**
$H_2NCH_2CH_2NHCH_2CH(OH)CH_3$ M.W. 118.18 n_D^{20} 1.4743
b.p. 177°

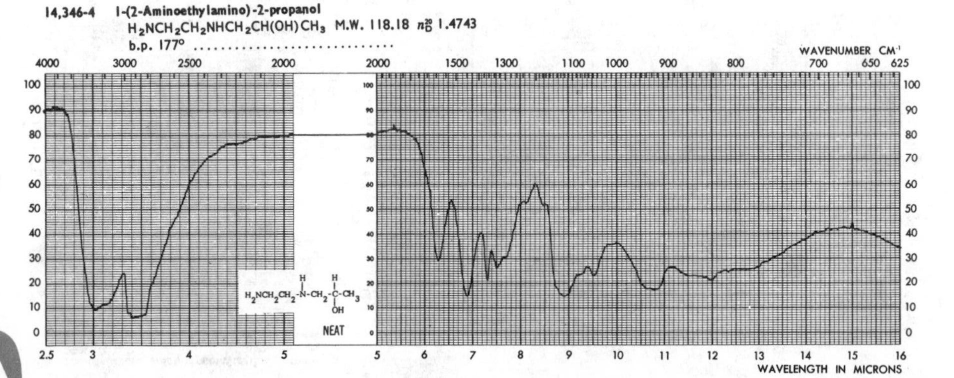

NEAT

E

10,944-4 **N-(3-Aminopropyl)-diethanolamine [N-(3-aminopropyl)-iminodiethanol]**
$H_2N(CH_2)_3N(CH_2CH_2OH)_2$ M.W. 162.23 n_D^{20} 1.5020
b.p. 165-170°/2 mm.

NEAT

F

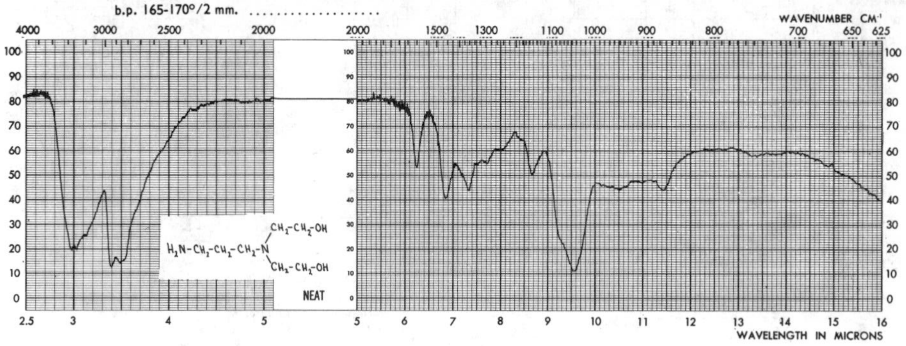

85,575-8
2-Amino-2-ethyl-1,3-propanediol, 99%
$HOCH_2C(C_2H_5)(NH_2)CH_2OH$
M.W. 119.16 m.p. 35-37°

MELT

G

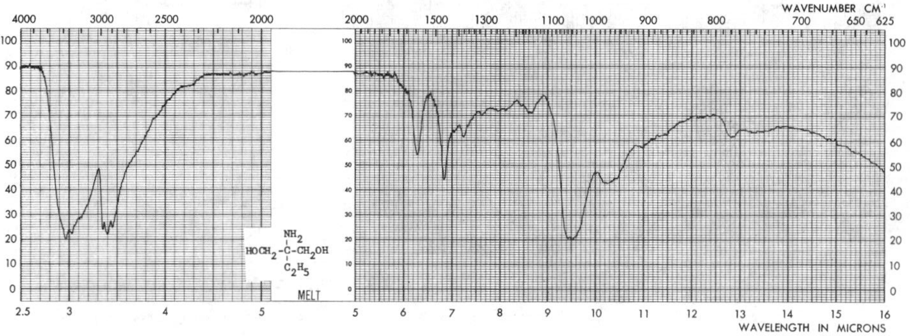

85,764-5
Tris-(hydroxymethyl)-aminomethane hydrochloride,
99+%, GOLD LABEL (TRIS)
$(HOCH_2)_3CNH_2 \cdot HCl$
M.W. 157.6 m.p. 150-152° (dec.)

NUJOL MULL

H

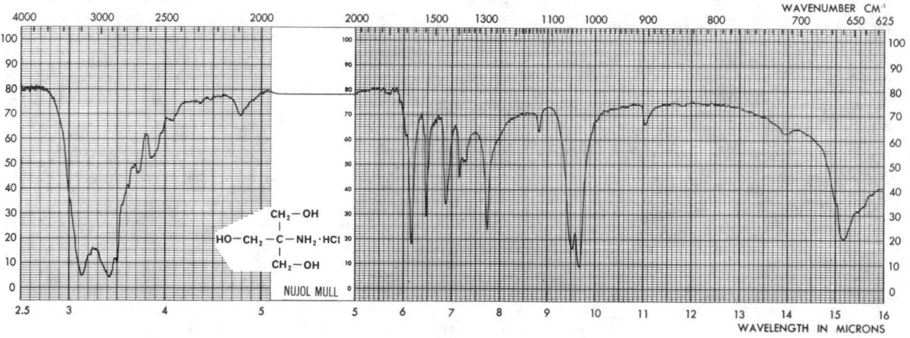

15,666-3
2,2-Bis-(hydroxymethyl)-2,2',2''-nitrilotriethanol, 99+%,
GOLD LABEL ("bis-tris")
$(HOCH_2CH_2)_2NC(CH_2OH)_3$
M.W. 209.24 m.p. 104°

NUJOL MULL

ALDRICH ®

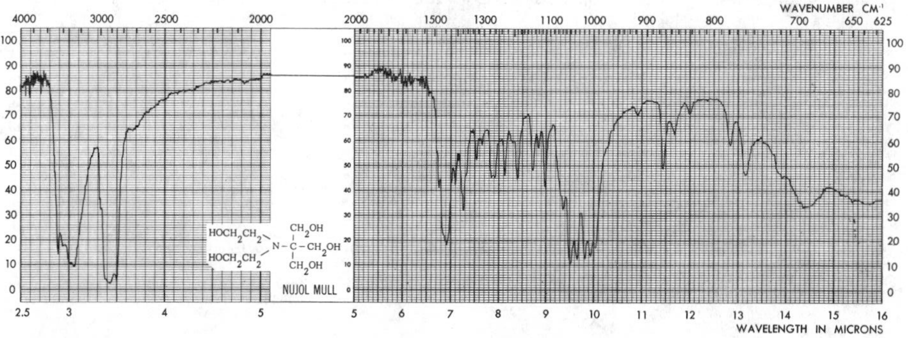

A

21,701-8
1,3-Bis[tris(hydroxymethyl)methylamino]propane,
99+%, GOLD LABEL
$CH_2[CH_2NHC(CH_2OH)_3]_2$ FW 282.34
mp 168-170° *Beil.* 4(3),859 Disp. D

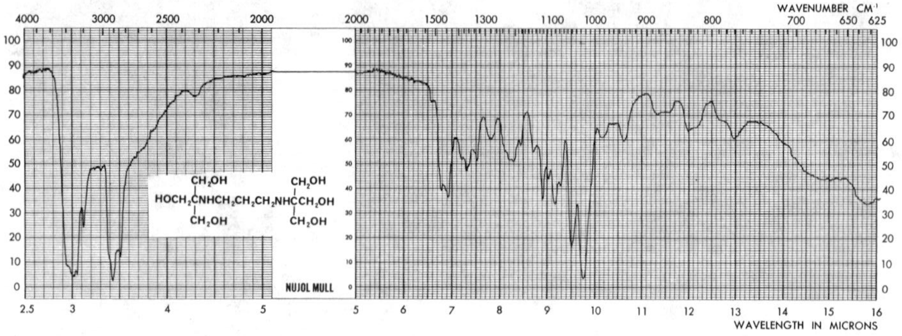

NUJOL MULL

B

D1860-9 **1,3-Diamino-2-hydroxypropane** (1,3-diamino-2-propanol)
$H_2NCH_2CH(OH)CH_2NH_2$ M.W. 90.13
m.p. 40-45°

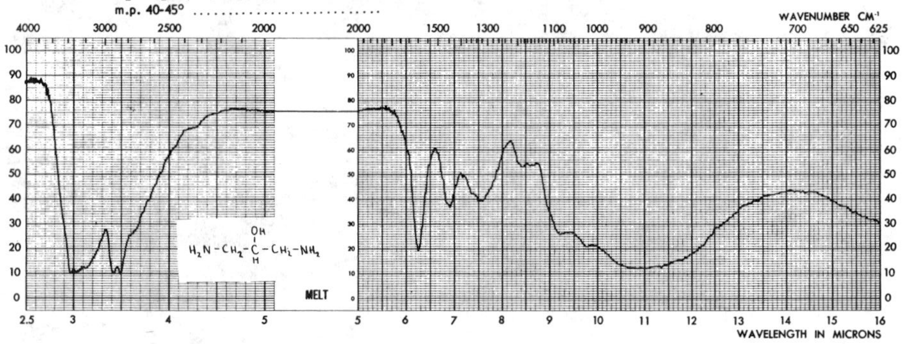

MELT

C

14,248-4 **1-Amino-3-diethylamino-2-propanol**
$(C_2H_5)_2NCH_2CH(OH)CH_2NH_2$ M.W. 146.23
n_D^{20} 1.4642

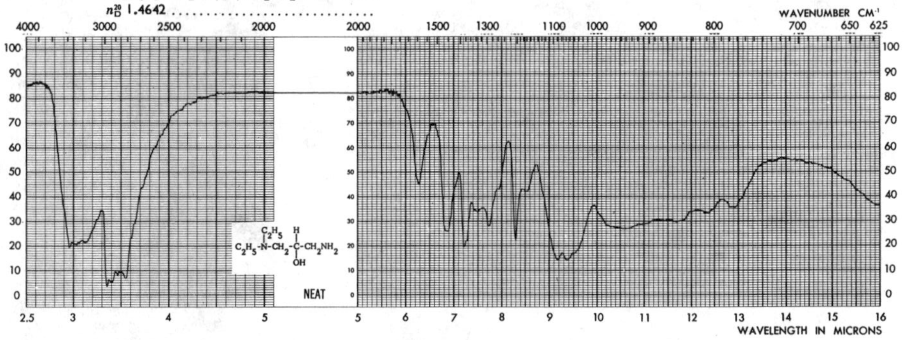

NEAT

D

M4700-0 **N-Methylglucamine**
$HOCH_2[CH(OH)]_4CH_2NHCH_3$ M.W. 195.22
m.p. 129-131.5°

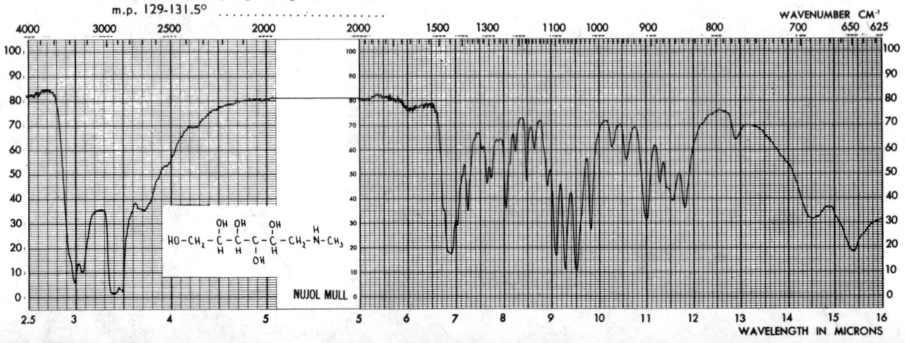

NUJOL MULL

E

13,849-5 **D-(+)-Galactosamine hydrochloride**
$HOCH_2[CH(OH)]_3CH(NH_2)CHO \cdot HCl$ M.W. 215.64
m.p. > 320°

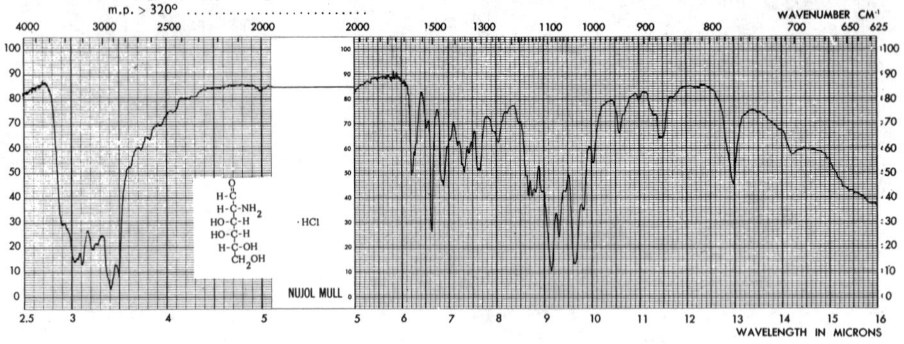

NUJOL MULL

F

G220-6 **Glucosamine hydrochloride**
$HOCH_2[CH(OH)]_3CH(NH_2)CHO \cdot HCl$ M.W. 215.64

NUJOL MULL

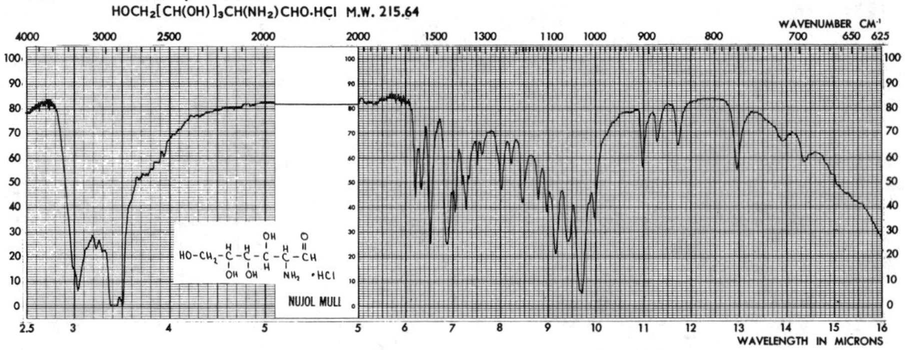

G

B4298-5 **1,3-Bis-(dimethylamino)-2-propanol** (N,N,N',N'-tetramethyl-1,3-diamino-2-propanol)
$(CH_3)_2NCH_2CH(OH)CH_2N(CH_3)_2$ M.W. 146.23
n_D^{20} 1.4400

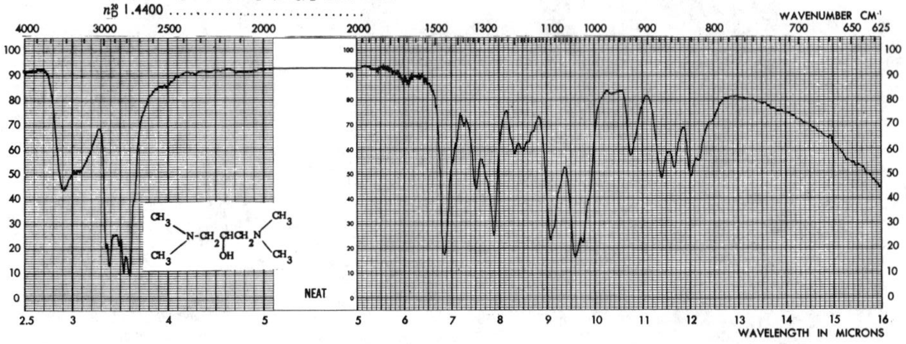

NEAT

H

12,292-0 **2-Aminoethanethiol (cysteamine) hydrochloride**
$H_2NCH_2CH_2SH \cdot HCl$ M.W. 113.61
m.p. 68-70°

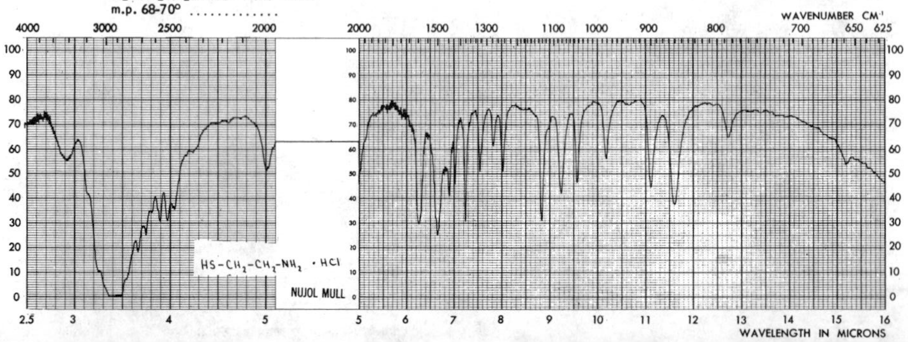

$HS-CH_2-CH_2-NH_2 \cdot HCl$

NUJOL MULL

A

14,677-3 **2-Aminoethanethiol** (cysteamine) **bitartrate**
$H_2NCH_2CH_2SH \cdot C_4H_6O_6$ M.W. 227.24
m.p. 112-115°

$H_2NCH_2CH_2SH$ · CO_2H–CH(OH)–CH(OH)–CO_2H

NUJOL MULL

B

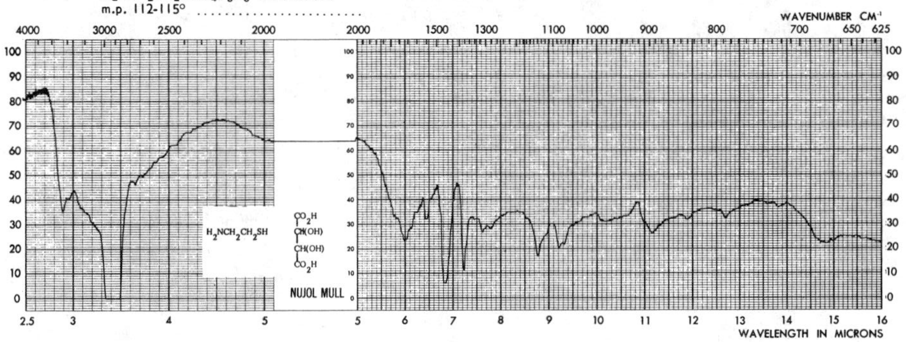

12,042-1 **2-(Ethylthio)-ethylamine hydrochloride**
$C_2H_5SCH_2CH_2NH_2 \cdot HCl$ M.W. 141.66 m.p. 142-145°

CH_3CH_2-S-$CH_2CH_2NH_2$ .HCl

NUJOL MULL

C

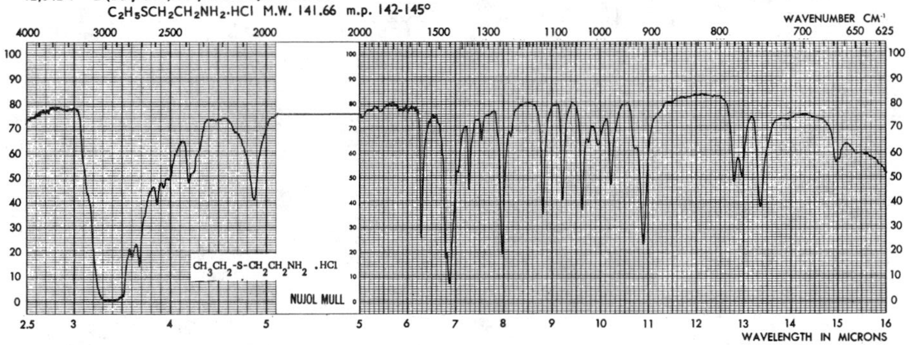

17,857-8
2-[(2-Aminoethyl)-thio]-ethanol, 97%
$H_2NCH_2CH_2SCH_2CH_2OH$
M.W. 121.2 b.p. 105-108°/0.15mm. n_D^{20} 1.5325
d 1.12

$H_2NCH_2CH_2$—S—CH_2CH_2OH

NEAT

D

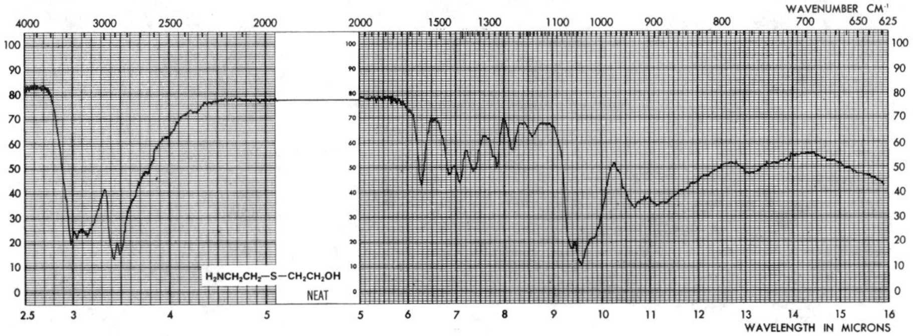

86,023-9
L-Methioninol (L-2-amino-4-methylthio-1-butanol)
$CH_3SCH_2CH_2CH(NH_2)CH_2OH$ FW 135.23
n_D^{20} 1.5216 $[\alpha]^{21}$ -12.7° (c=1.4, C_2H_5OH) Disp. A

$CH_3SCH_2CH_2CH(NH_2)CH_2OH$

MELT

E

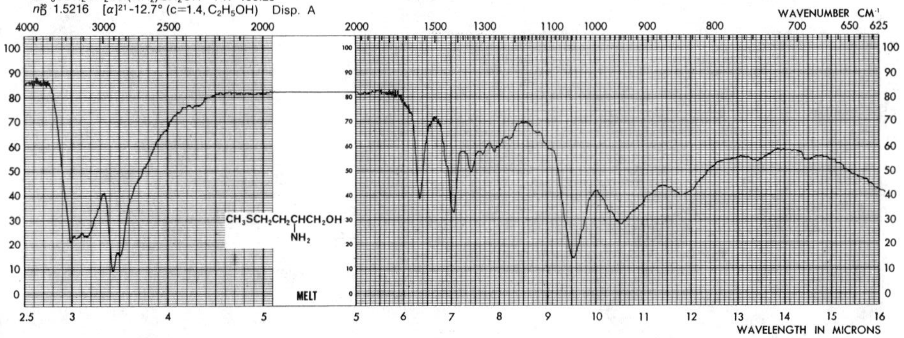

C12,150-9 **Cystamine dihydrochloride**
$S_2(CH_2CH_2NH_2)_2 \cdot 2HCl$ M.W. 225.20
m.p. 217-220° (dec.)

H_2N-CH_2CH_2-S-S-CH_2CH_2-NH_2 · 2HCl

NUJOL MULL

F

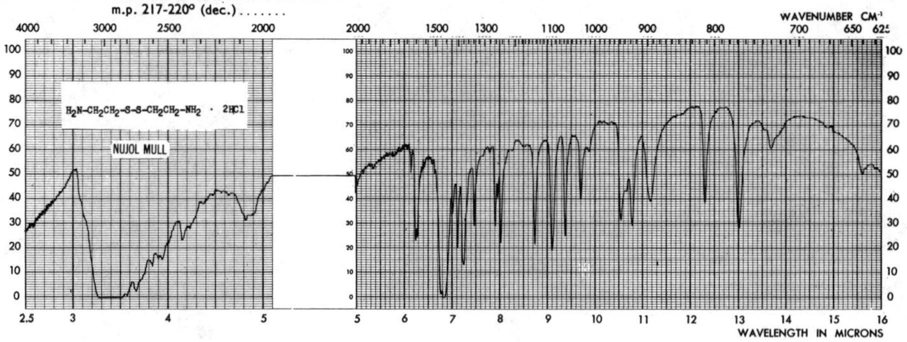

D14,100-3 **2-Dimethylaminoethanethiol hydrochloride**
$(CH_3)_2NCH_2CH_2SH \cdot HCl$ M.W. 141.67
m.p. 158-160°

$(H_3C)_2N$-CH_2-CH_2-SH ·HCl

NUJOL MULL

G

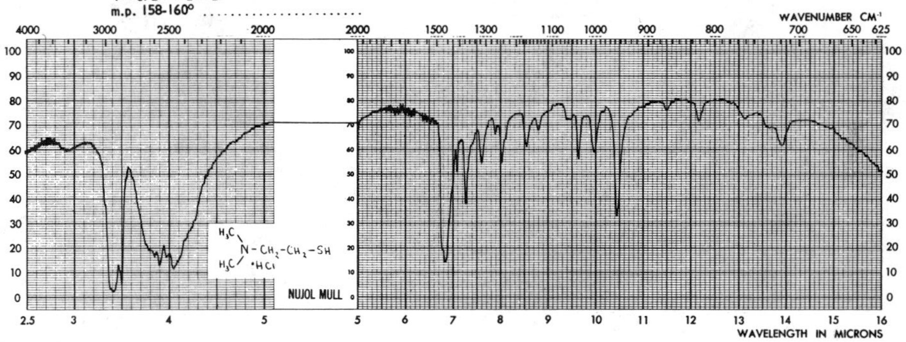

D8660-4 **2-Diethylaminoethanethiol hydrochloride**
$(C_2H_5)_2NCH_2CH_2SH \cdot HCl$ M.W. 169.72
m.p. 171-173°

$(H_5C_2)_2N$-CH_2-CH_2-SH ·HCl

NUJOL MULL

H

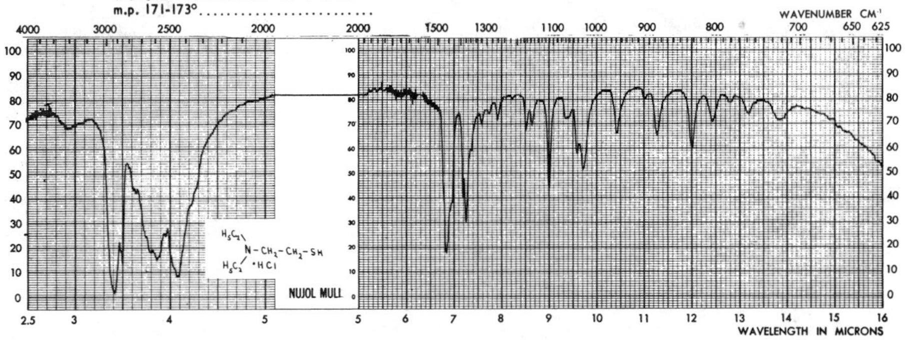

15,826-7
2-(Diisopropylamino)-ethanethiol hydrochloride,
$[(CH_3)_2CH]_2NCH_2CH_2SH \cdot HCl$
M.W. 197.77 m.p. 127-130°

$[(CH_3)_2CH]_2N$-CH_2CH_2SH ·HCl

NUJOL MULL

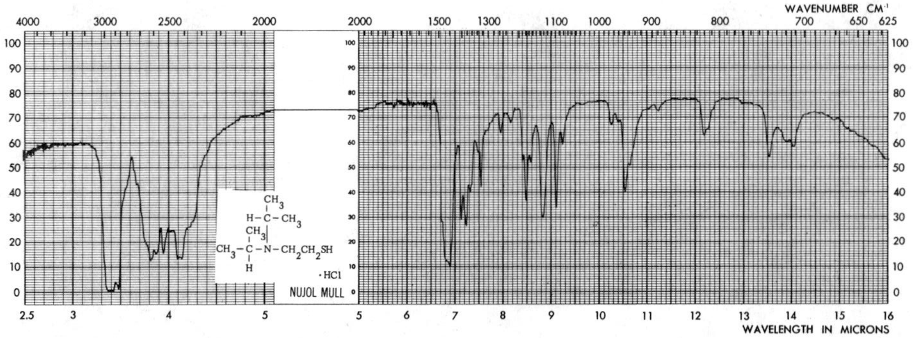

A

B8950-7 **2-n-Butylaminoethanethiol**
$CH_3(CH_2)_3NHCH_2CH_2SH$ M.W. 133.26 n_D^{20} 1.4711

$CH_3CH_2CH_2CH_2NHCH_2CH_2SH$

NEAT

B

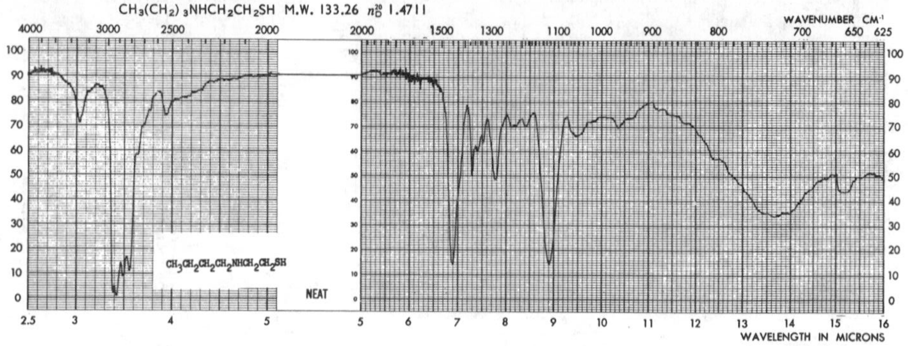

D245-5 **2-n-Decylaminoethanethiol**
$CH_3(CH_2)_9NHCH_2CH_2SH$ M.W. 217.42 n_D^{20} 1.4701

$CH_3(CH_2)_8CH_2NHCH_2CH_2SH$

NEAT

C

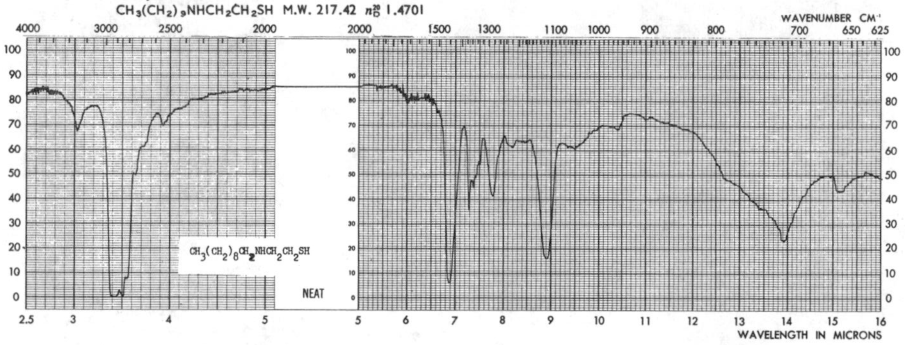

C10,467-1 **2-Cyclohexylaminoethanethiol**
$C_6H_{11}NHCH_2CH_2SH$ M.W. 159.30 n_D^{20} 1.5064

NEAT

D

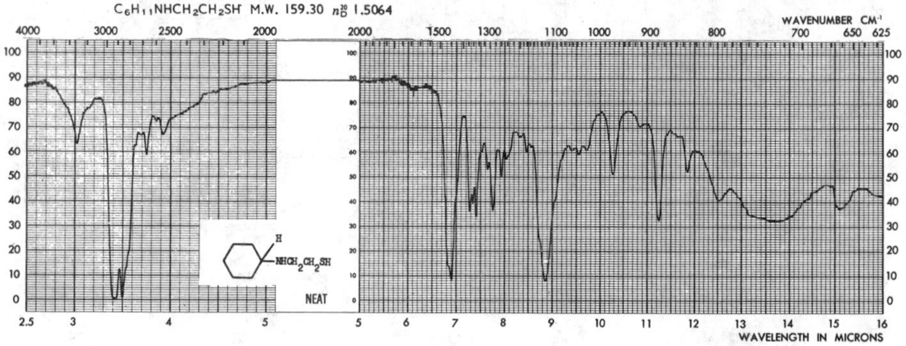

D8930-1 **2-(3-Diethylaminopropylamino)-ethanethiol**
$(C_2H_5)_2N(CH_2)_3NHCH_2CH_2SH$ M.W. 190.35
n_D^{20} 1.4824 . . . .

$(C_2H_5)_2NCH_2CH_2CH_2NHCH_2CH_2SH$

NEAT

E

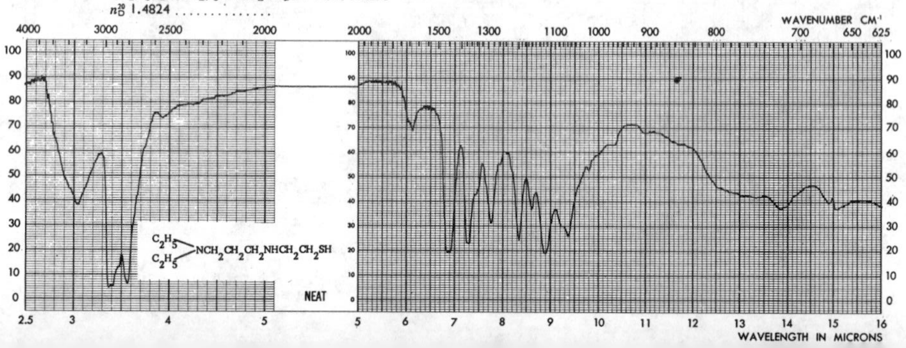

14,969-1 **Thiazolidine**
M.W. 89.16 n_D^{20} 1.5508

NEAT

F

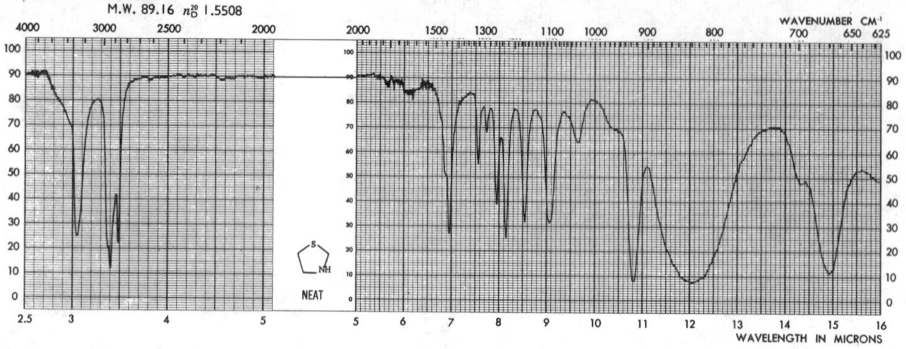

19,627-4
Thiomorpholine (tetrahydro-4*H*-1,4-thiazine, thiamorpholine)
FW 103.19 bp 169° n_D^{20} 1.5384 d 1.026
Beil. 27,9 Disp. C

NEAT

G

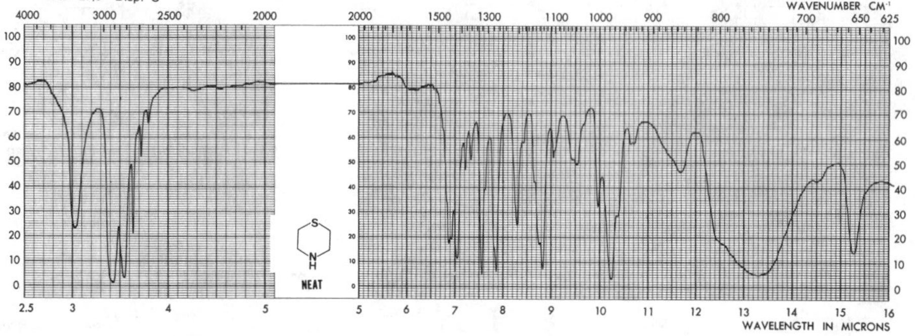

10,690-9
1-Aziridineethanol, 94% [N-(2-hydroxyethyl)-ethylenimine]
M.W. 87.12 b.p. 168° n_D^{20} 1.4550

CH_2CH_2OH

NEAT

H

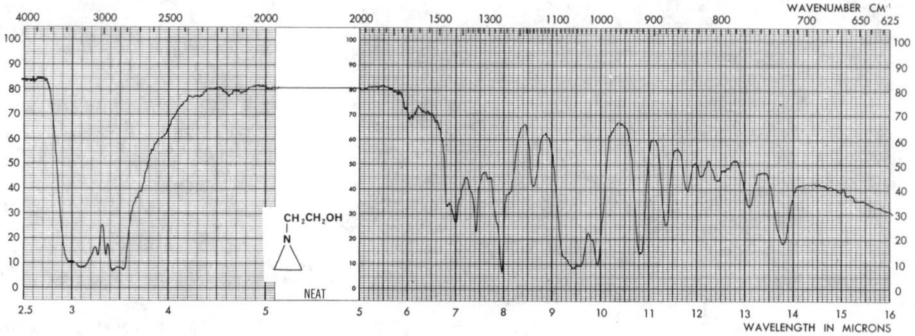

P7380-3 **Pyrrolidine**
M.W. 71.12 n_D^{20} 1.4431 b.p. 87.5-88.5° . . . . .

NEAT

WAVENUMBER CM^{-1} — WAVELENGTH IN MICRONS

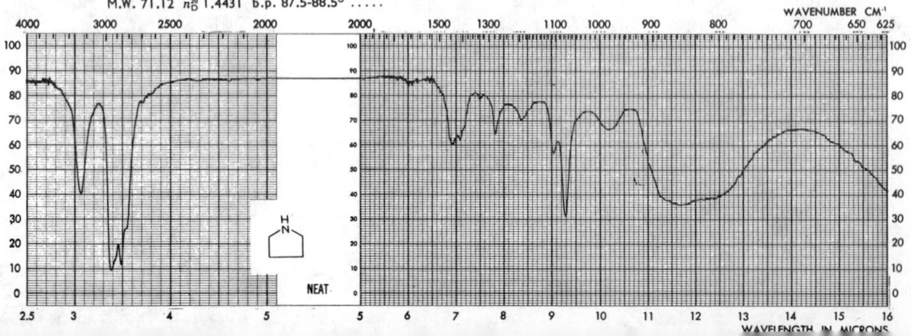

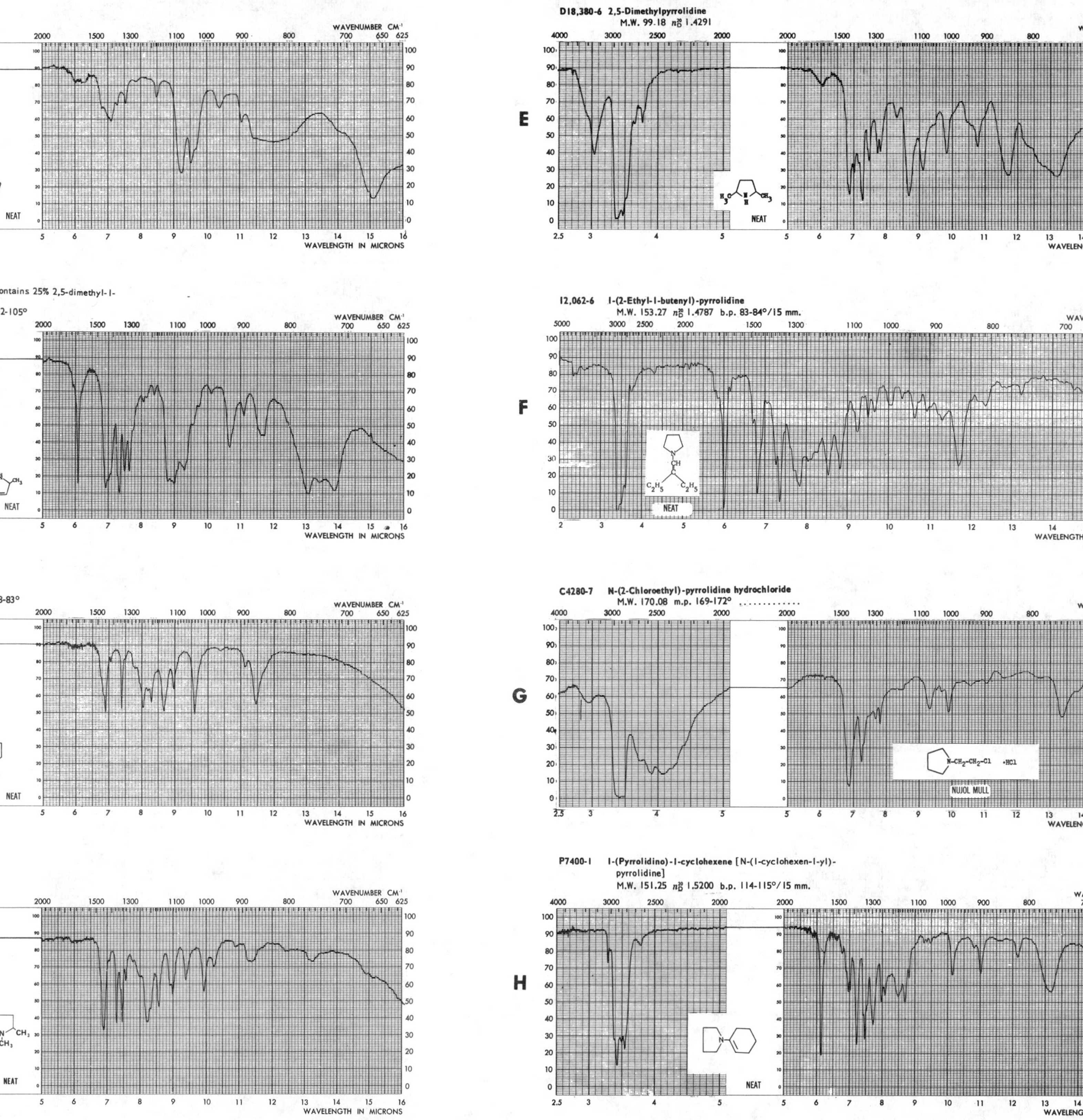

A
P7590-3 3-Pyrroline
M.W. 69.11 n_D^{20} 1.4676
b.p. 90-91°/748 mm.
NEAT
B
15,132-7 2,5-Dimethyl-3-pyrroline, 75% (contains 25% 2,5-dimethyl-1-pyrroline)
M.W. 97.16 n_D^{20} 1.4404 b.p. 102-105°
NEAT
C
M7920-4 N-Methylpyrrolidine
M.W. 85.15 n_D^{20} 1.4247 b.p. 78-83°
NEAT
D
19,144-2
1,2-Dimethylpyrrolidine, 97%
FW 99.18 bp 96-97° n_D^{20} 1.4250 d 0.797
Beil. 20,92 Disp. C
NEAT
E
D18,380-6 2,5-Dimethylpyrrolidine
M.W. 99.18 n_D^{20} 1.4291
NEAT
F
12,062-6 1-(2-Ethyl-1-butenyl)-pyrrolidine
M.W. 153.27 n_D^{20} 1.4787 b.p. 83-84°/15 mm.
NEAT
G
C4280-7 N-(2-Chloroethyl)-pyrrolidine hydrochloride
M.W. 170.08 m.p. 169-172°
NUJOL MULL
H
P7400-1 1-(Pyrrolidino)-1-cyclohexene [N-(1-cyclohexen-1-yl)-pyrrolidine]
M.W. 151.25 n_D^{20} 1.5200 b.p. 114-115°/15 mm.
NEAT
WAVENUMBER CM⁻¹
WAVELENGTH IN MICRONS

ALDRICH

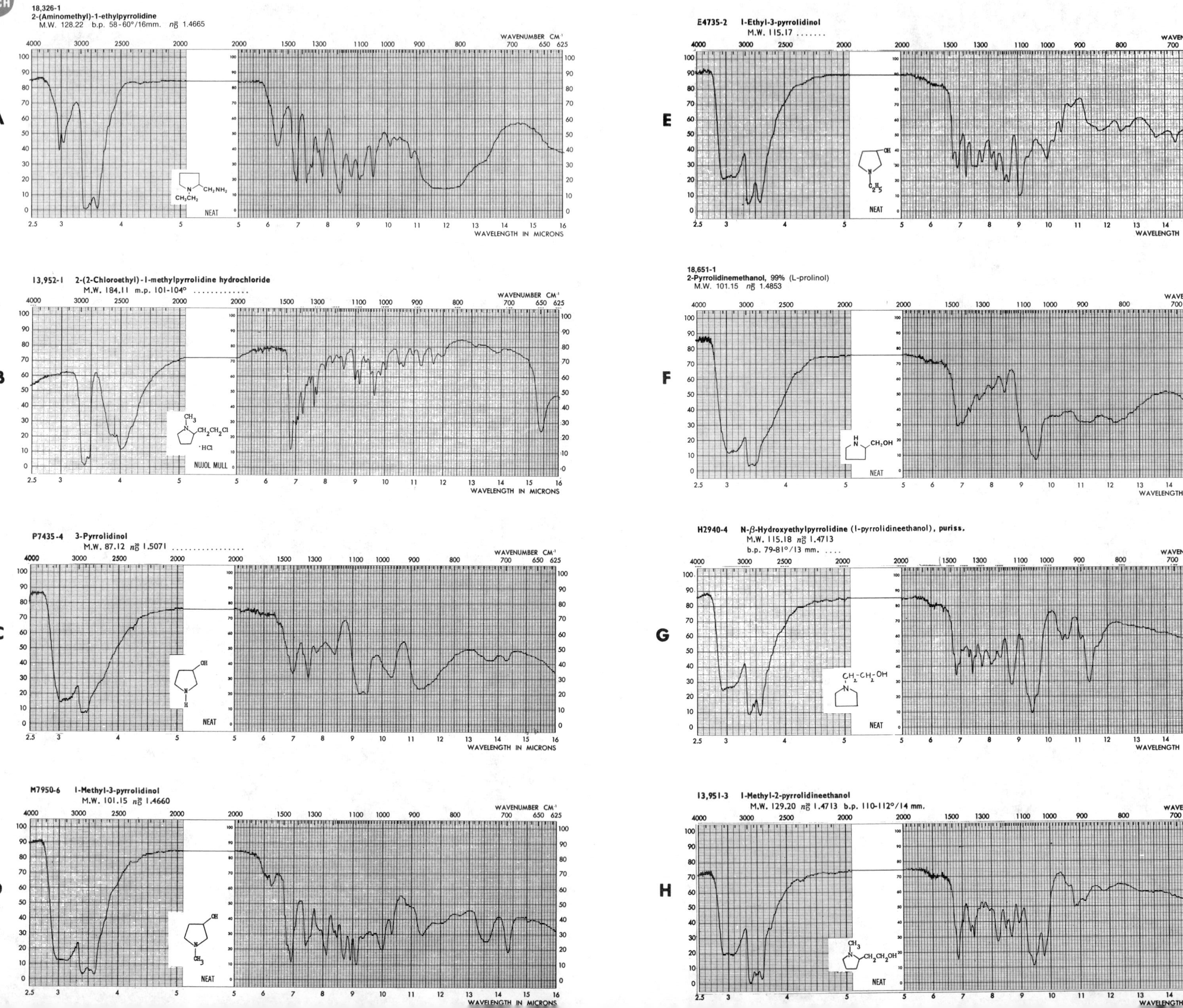
A
18,326-1
2-(Aminomethyl)-1-ethylpyrrolidine
M.W. 128.22 b.p. 58-60°/16mm. n_D^{20} 1.4665
NEAT
B
13,952-1 2-(2-Chloroethyl)-1-methylpyrrolidine hydrochloride
M.W. 184.11 m.p. 101-104°
NUJOL MULL
C
P7435-4 3-Pyrrolidinol
M.W. 87.12 n_D^{20} 1.5071
NEAT
D
M7950-6 1-Methyl-3-pyrrolidinol
M.W. 101.15 n_D^{20} 1.4660
NEAT
E
E4735-2 1-Ethyl-3-pyrrolidinol
M.W. 115.17
NEAT
F
18,651-1
2-Pyrrolidinemethanol, 99% (L-prolinol)
M.W. 101.15 n_D^{20} 1.4853
NEAT
G
H2940-4 N-β-Hydroxyethylpyrrolidine (1-pyrrolidineethanol), puriss.
M.W. 115.18 n_D^{20} 1.4713
b.p. 79-81°/13 mm.
NEAT
H
13,951-3 1-Methyl-2-pyrrolidineethanol
M.W. 129.20 n_D^{20} 1.4713 b.p. 110-112°/14 mm.
NEAT
WAVENUMBER CM⁻¹
WAVELENGTH IN MICRONS

A E4733-6 **1-Ethyl-2-pyrrolidinemethanol**
M.W. 129.20 n_D^{20} 1.4693 . . .
NEAT

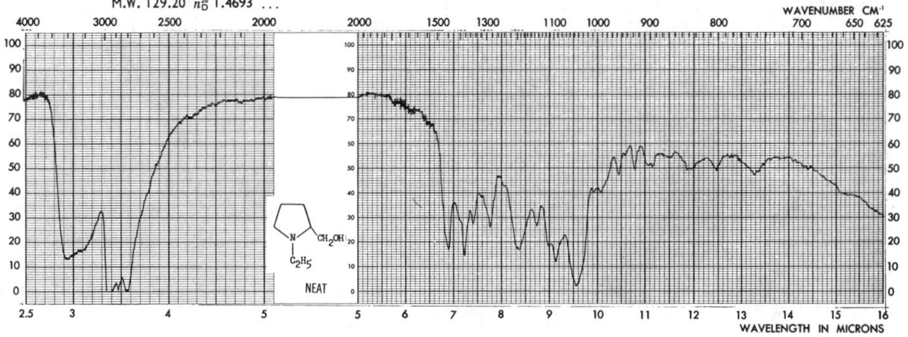

B 21,851-0
3-Pyrrolidino-1,2-propanediol, 96%
FW 145.20 mp 46-48° bp 158°/30mm.
Beil. **20**(1),4 Disp. C
MELT

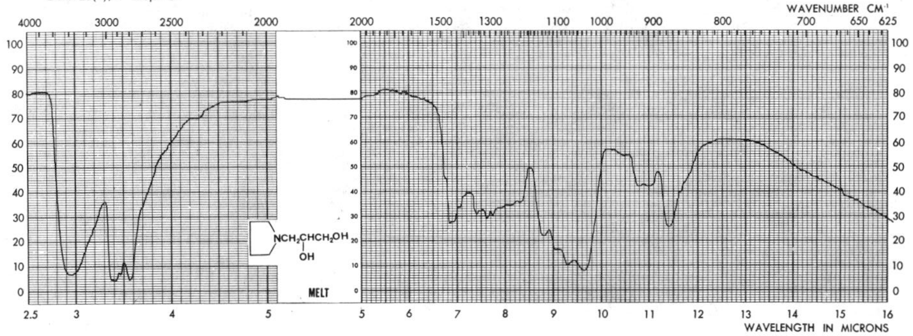

C 10,949-5 **2-Methylcyclopenta[b]pyrrolidin-6-ol** (8-hydroxy-3-methyl-2-azabicyclo[3.3.0]octane)
M.W. 141.21 m.p. 72-75° . . . .
NUJOL MULL

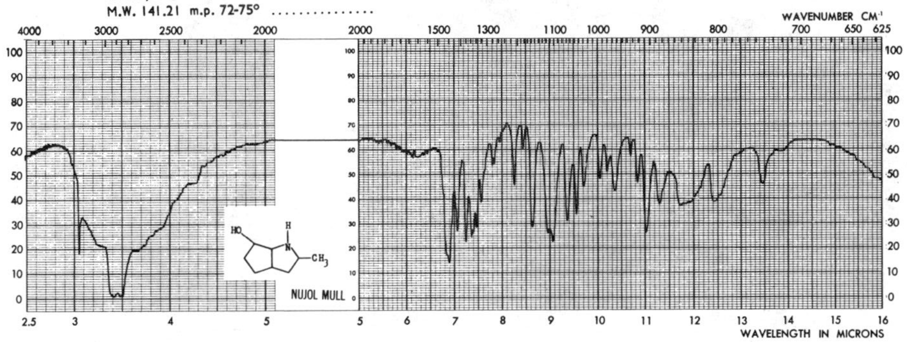

D 12,310-2 **N-Aminopyrrolidine hydrochloride**
M.W. 122.60 m.p. 109-110° . . . .
NUJOL MULL

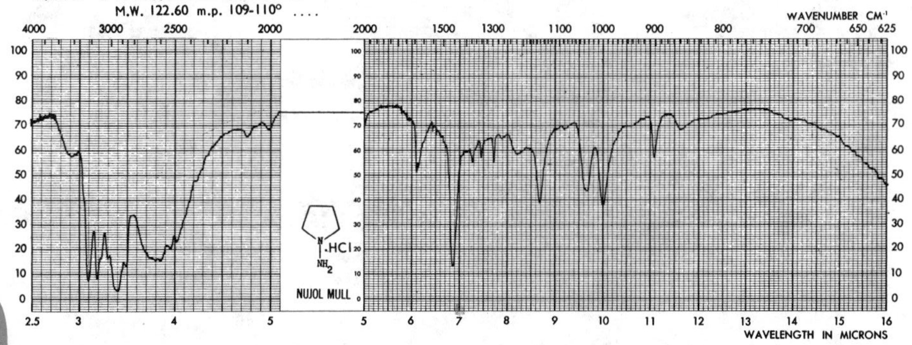

E A5535-7 **N-(2-Aminoethyl)-pyrrolidine**
M.W. 114.19 n_D^{20} 1.4687 . . .
NEAT

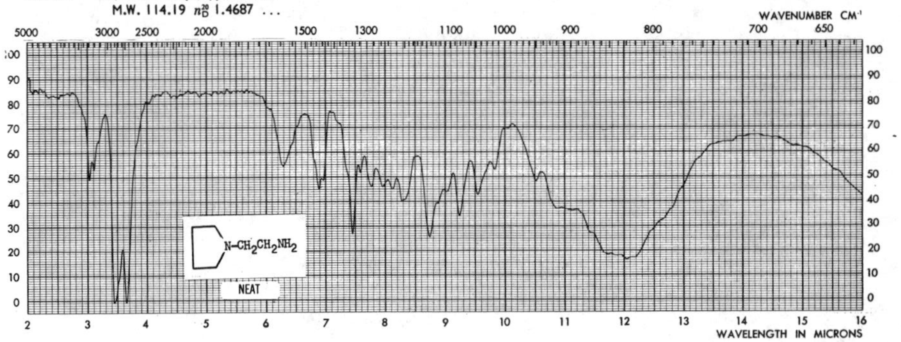

F 14,944-6
1-Pyrrolidino-1-cyclopentene [N-(1-cyclopenten-1-yl)-pyrrolidine]
M.W. 137.23 b.p. 100-110°/15mm. n_D^{20} 1.5155
NEAT

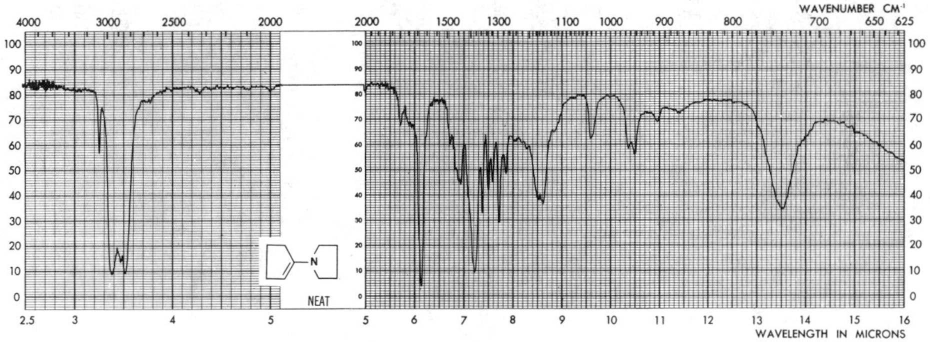

G 10,409-4 **Piperidine**
M.W. 85.15 n_D^{20} 1.4525 b.p. 106.5°
NEAT

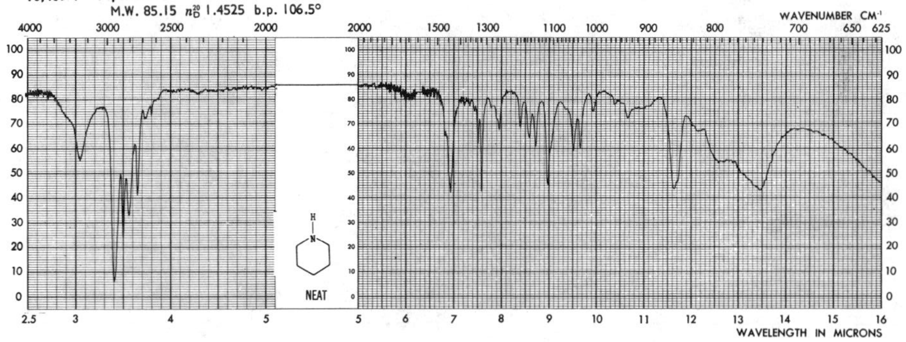

H P4610-5 **Piperidine hydrochloride**
M.W. 121.61 m.p. 245-248°
NUJOL MULL

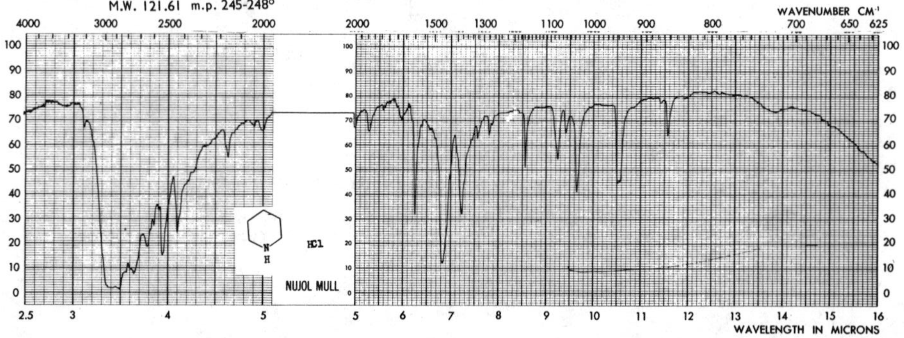

A

11,965-2 **3-Azaspiro[5.5]undecane hydrochloride**
$C_{10}H_{19}N$ M.W. 189.73 m.p. 235-237°

NUJOL MULL

B

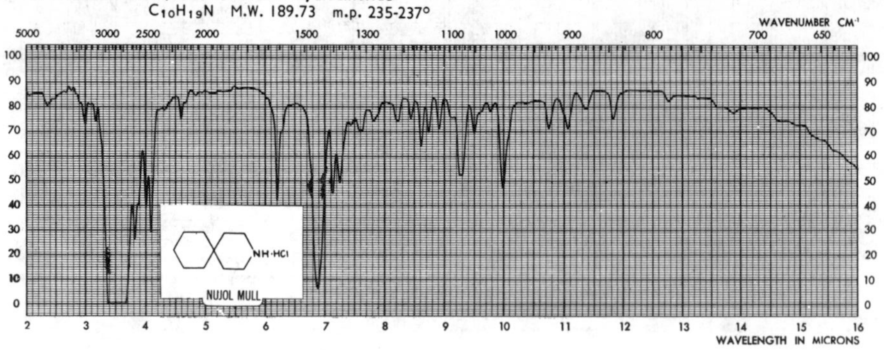

15,005-3
4-Piperidinopiperidine, tech., 95% (1,4'-bipiperidine)
M.W. 168.28 m.p. 64-66°

MELT

C

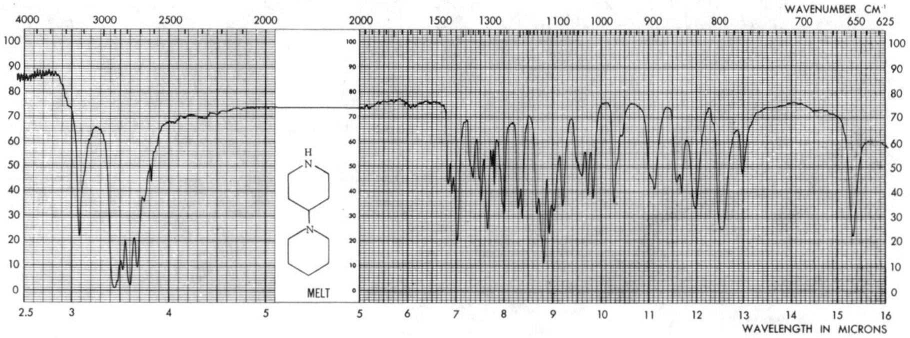

18,074-2
4,4'-Bipiperidine dihydrochloride, 97%
M.W. 241.21 m.p. >300° Beil. **23**,38

NUJOL MULL

D

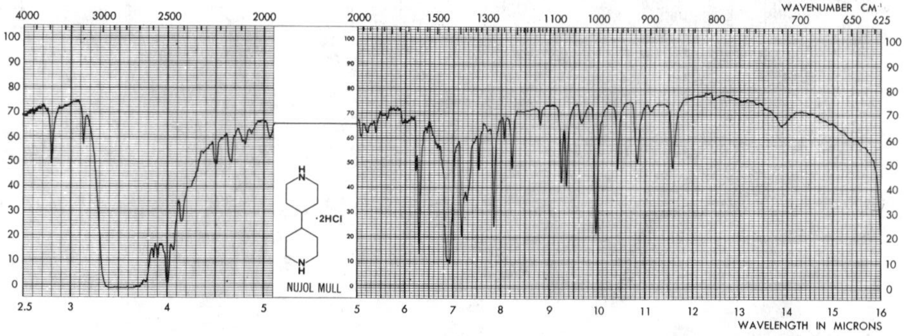

13,475-9 **1,2,3,6-Tetrahydropyridine**
M.W. 83.13 n_D^{20} 1.4800 ...

NEAT

E

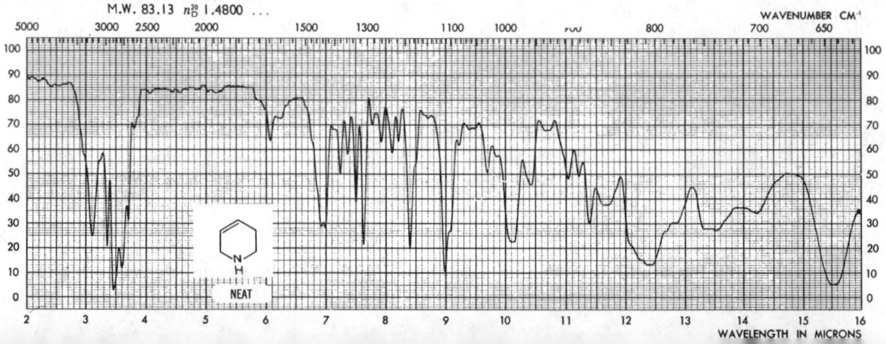

M7280-3 **2-Methylpiperidine** (2-pipecoline)
M.W. 99.18 n_D^{20} 1.4459
b.p. 118-119°/753 mm. ......

NEAT

F

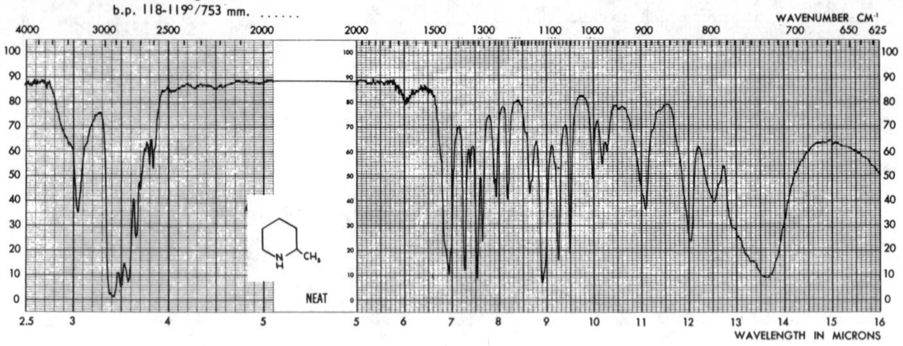

18,723-2
Dipiperidinomethane, tech., 95% (1,1'-methylene-dipiperidine)
M.W. 182.31 b.p. 235° n_D^{20} 1.4825 d 0.915

NEAT

G

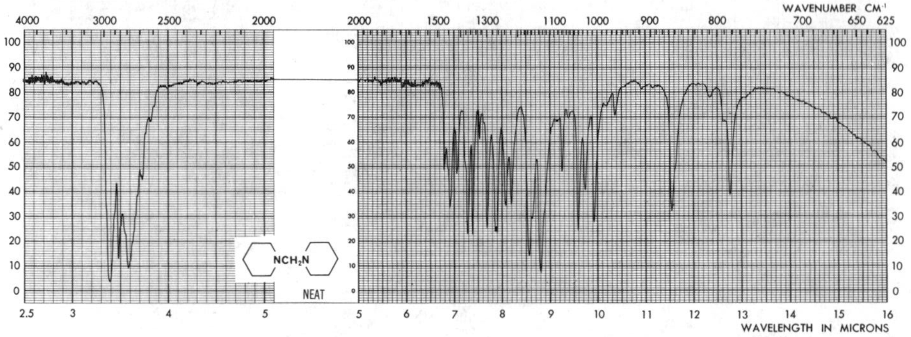

E4570-8 **1-Ethylpiperidine**
M.W. 113.20 n_D^{20} 1.4480

NEAT

H

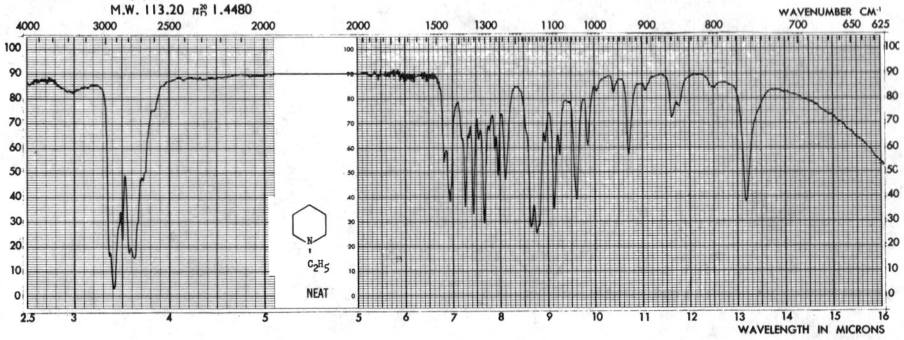

12,064-2 **1-(2-Ethyl-1-butenyl)-piperidine**
M.W. 167.30 n_D^{20} 1.4701 b.p. 90°/15 mm.

NEAT

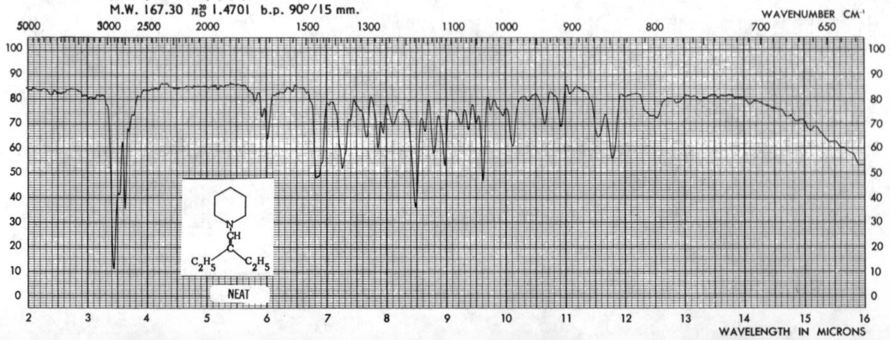

A

M7260-9 **N-Methylpiperidine**
M.W. 99.18 n_D^{20} 1.4378
NEAT

B

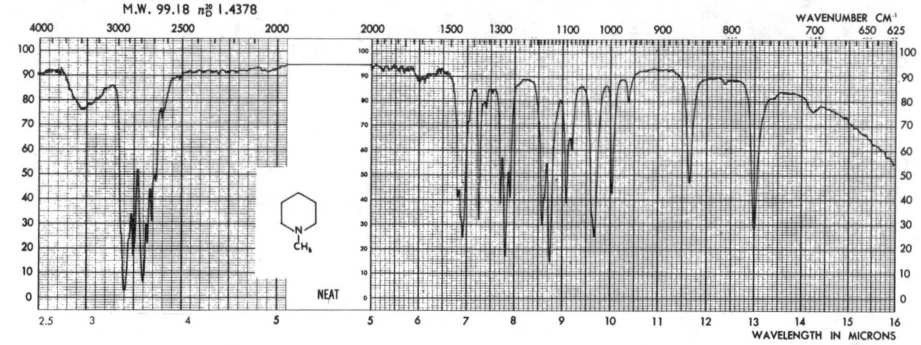

19,746-7
1,2-Dimethylpiperidine, 98%
FW 113.20 bp 125-126° n_D^{20} 1.4405 d 0.721
Disp. C
NEAT

C

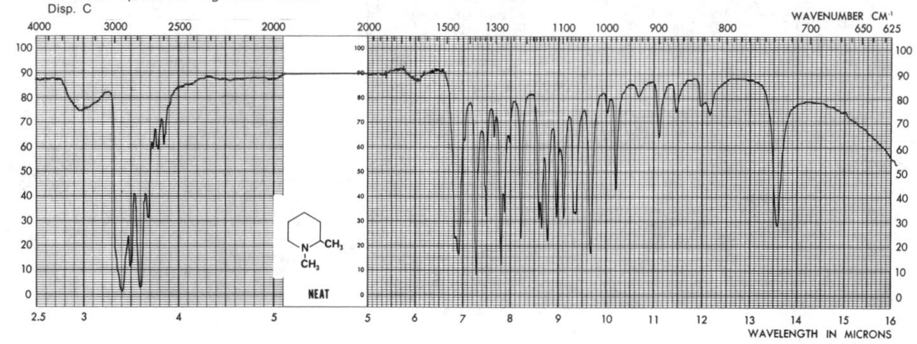

D18,030-0
2,6-Dimethylpiperidine, 99% (2,6-lupetidine)
M.W. 113.2 b.p. 127-128°/768mm. n_D^{20} 1.4394
d 0.84 Beil. **20**,108 Fieser **2**,156
NEAT

D

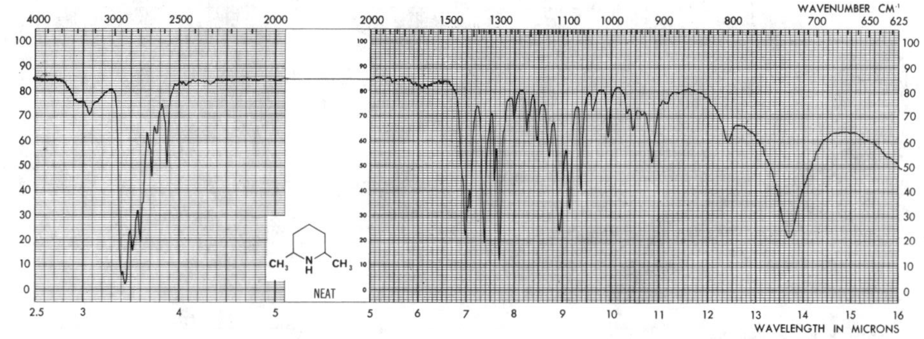

18,610-4
3,5-Dimethylpiperidine, 96% (3,5-lupetidine)
FW 113.20 bp 144° n_D^{20} 1.4454 d 0.853
Disp. C
NEAT

E

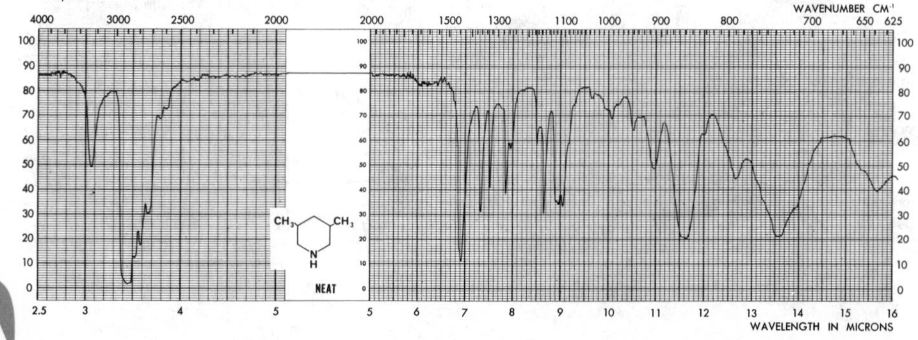

11,575-4 **2,2,6,6-Tetramethylpiperidine; puriss.**
M.W. 141.26 n_D^{20} 1.4449 b.p. 152° ...
NEAT

F

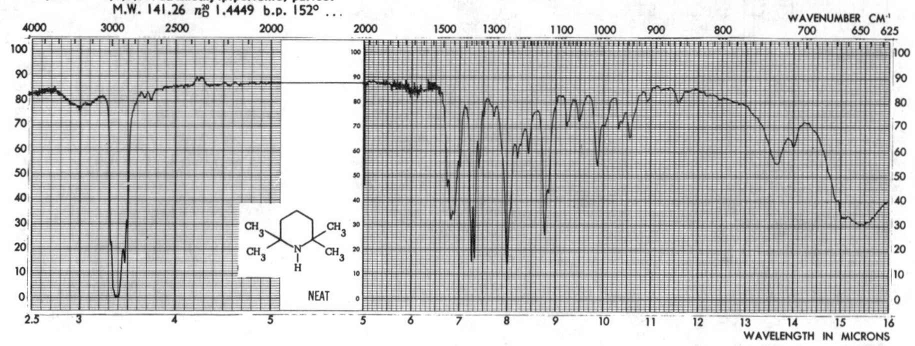

E4580-5 **2-Ethylpiperidine**
M.W. 113.20 n_D^{21} 1.4494
NEAT

G

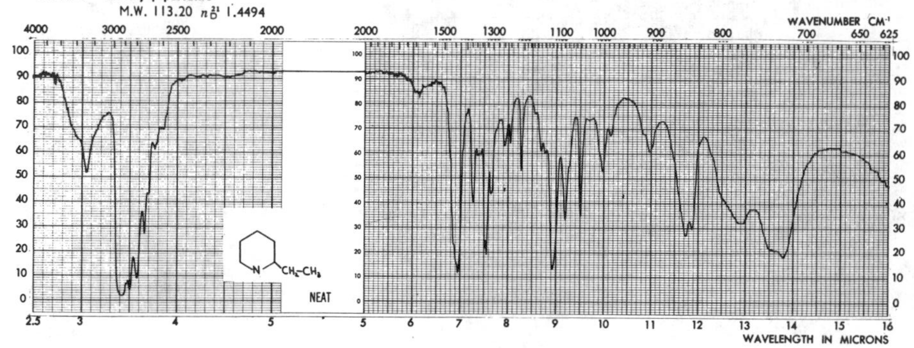

P5410-8 **2-n-Propylpiperidine**
M.W. 127.22 n_D^{20} 1.4306
NEAT

H

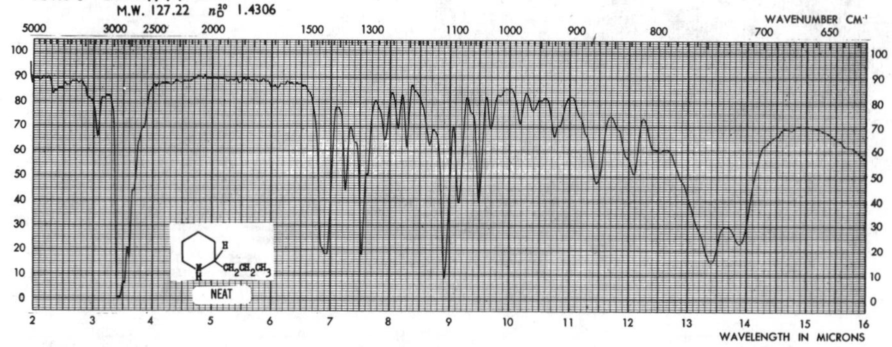

85,515-4
Coniine hydrobromide (2-propylpiperidine)
M.W. 208.15 m.p. 198-200° Beil. **20**,110
SEVERE POISON
NUJOL MULL

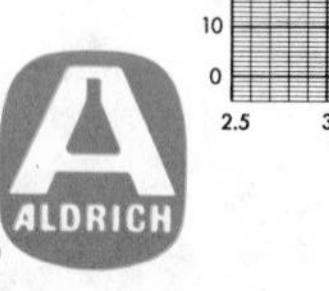

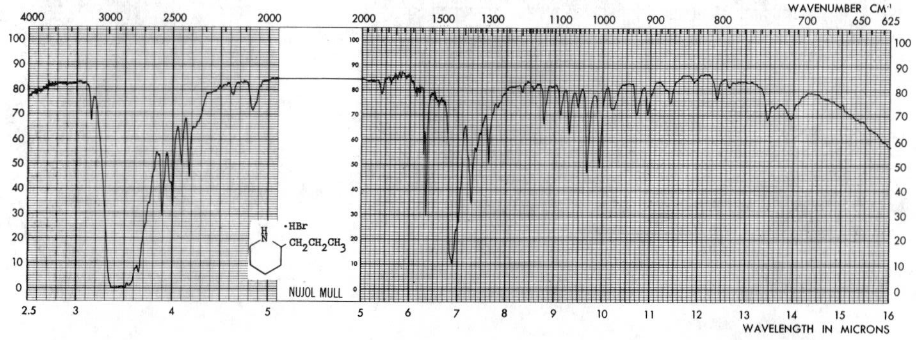

A

M7300-1 **3-Methylpiperidine** (3-pipecoline)
M.W. 99.18 n_D^{20} 1.4470 m.p. 0-5° b.p. 125-126°

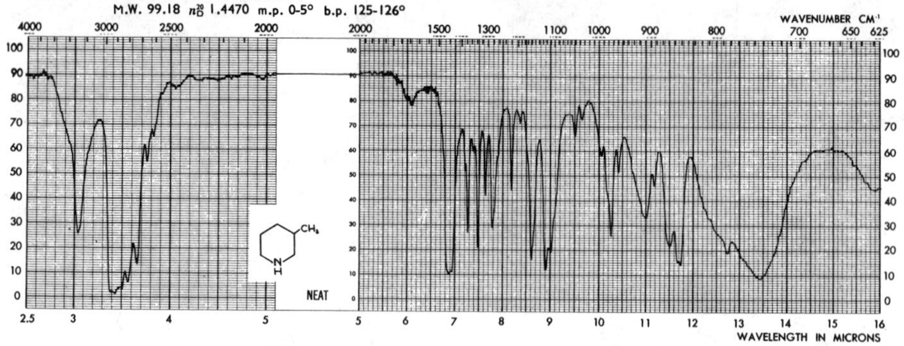

NEAT

B

M7320-6 **4-Methylpiperidine** (4-pipecoline)
M.W. 99.18 n_D^{20} 1.4458 ....

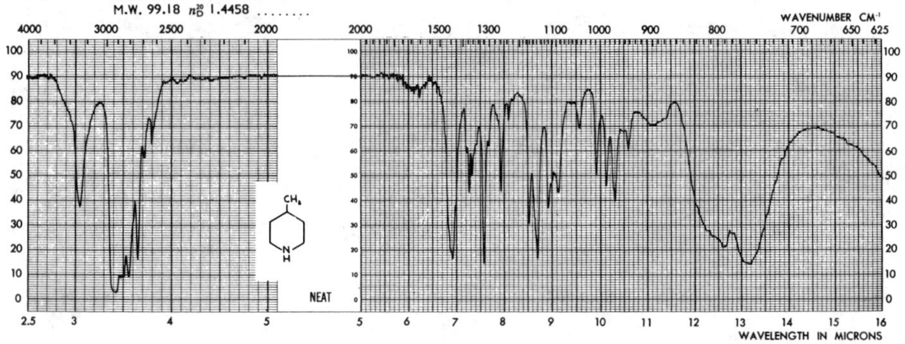

NEAT

C

P5412 **4-n-Propylpiperidine**
M.W. 127.22 n_D^{20} 1.4545

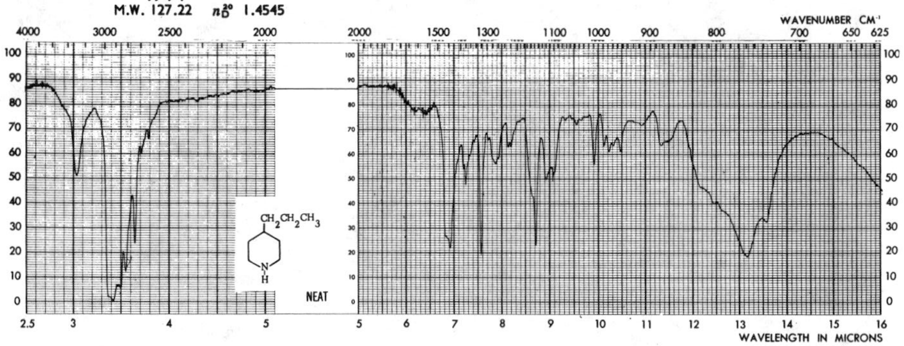

NEAT

D

21,414-0
4,4'-Ethylenedipiperidine dihydrochloride, tech.
FW 269.26 mp >300° Disp. C

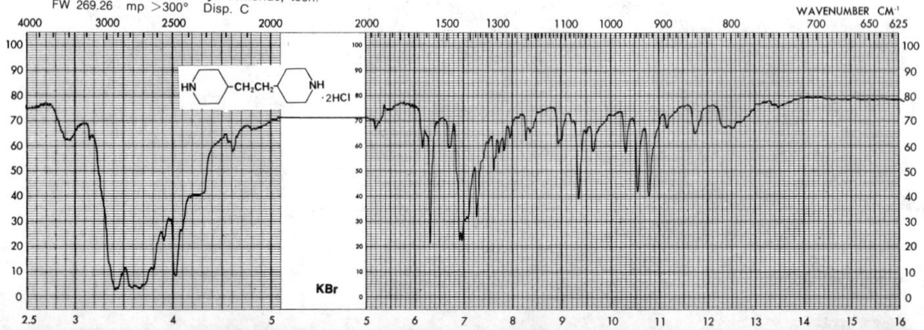

·2HCl

KBr

E

19,226-0
4,4'-Trimethylenebis(1-methylpiperidine), 98+%
FW 238.42 mp 13° bp 215°/50mm. n_D^{20} 1.4820
d 0.896 Disp. C

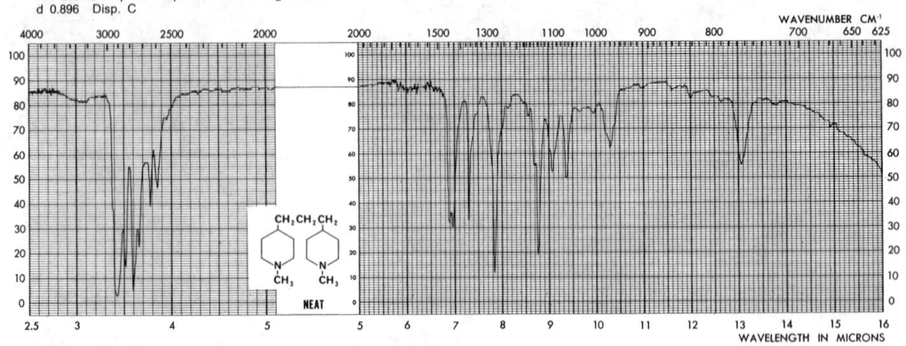

NEAT

F

12,120-7 **4,4'-Trimethylenedipiperidine**
M.W. 210.36 m.p. 67-68.5°

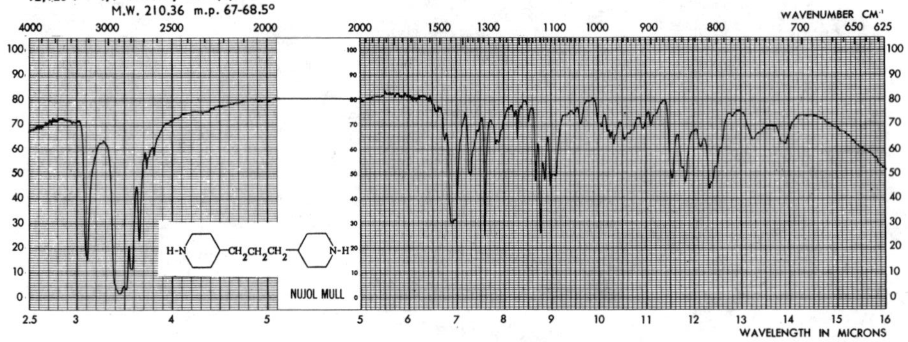

NUJOL MULL

G

19,225-2
1,1'-Methylenebis(3-methylpiperidine), 98+%
FW 210.37 bp 160°/50mm. n_D^{20} 1.4734 d 0.887
Disp. C

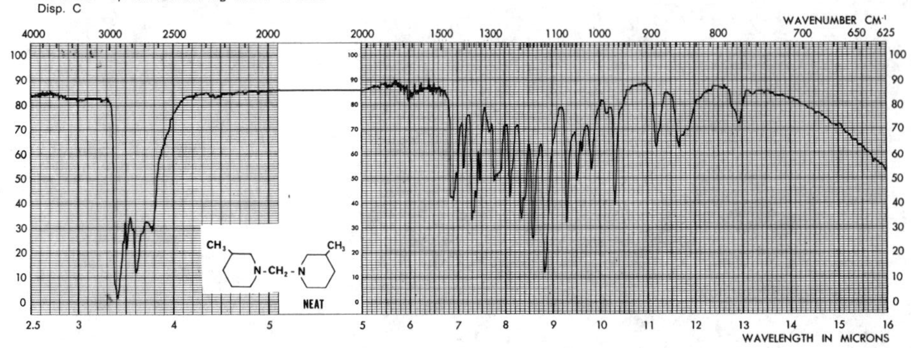

NEAT

H

19,223-6
1,2-Dipiperidinoethane, 98% [1,1'-(1,2-ethanediyl)bis-piperidine]
FW 196.34 mp -0.50° bp 265° n_D^{20} 1.4876
d 0.916 *Beil.* **20**(1),19 Disp. C

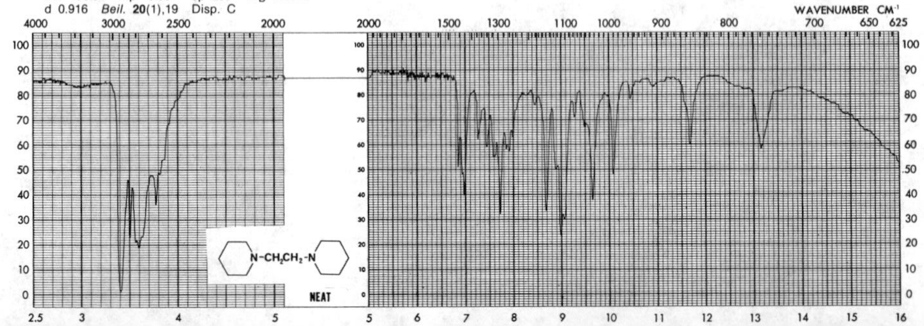

NEAT

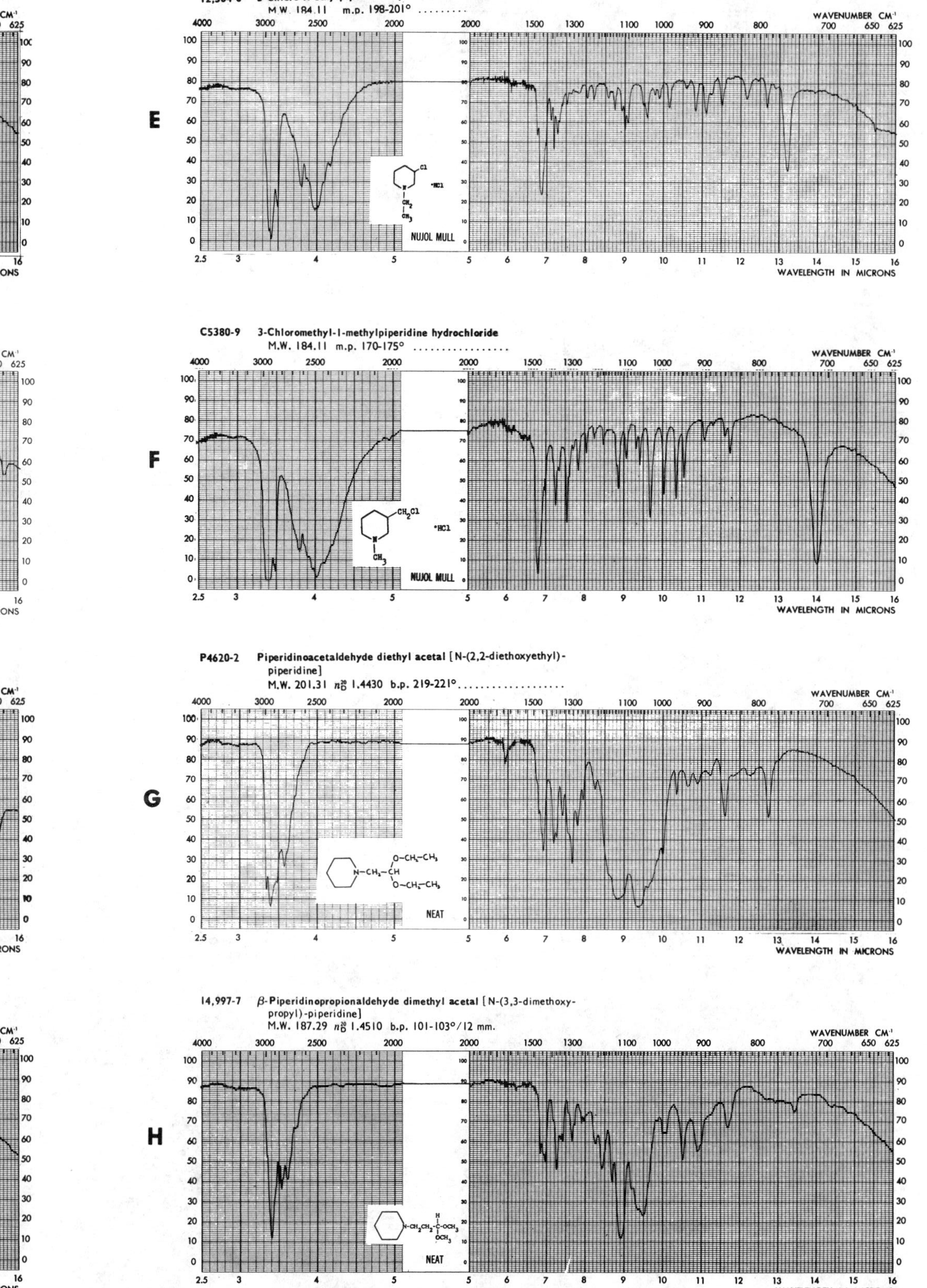

A C4260-2 **N-(2-Chloroethyl)-piperidine hydrochloride**
M.W. 184.11 m.p. 233-236° ....
NUJOL MULL

B 18,075-0
1,1'-Bis(2-chloroethyl)-4,4'-bipiperidine dihydrochloride, 97% (BPM)
FW 366.20 mp >300° *NMR* 2,65C Disp. C
NUJOL MULL

C 15,291-9 N-(3-Chloropropyl)-piperidine hydrochloride
M.W. 198.14 m.p. 218-220° ....
NUJOL MULL

D C5630-1 **4-Chloro-N-methylpiperidine hydrochloride**
M.W. 170.08 m.p. 164-167°
NUJOL MULL

E 12,504-0 **3-Chloro-N-ethylpiperidine hydrochloride**
M.W. 184.11 m.p. 198-201° ....
NUJOL MULL

F C5380-9 **3-Chloromethyl-1-methylpiperidine hydrochloride**
M.W. 184.11 m.p. 170-175° ....
NUJOL MULL

G P4620-2 **Piperidinoacetaldehyde diethyl acetal** [N-(2,2-diethoxyethyl)-piperidine]
M.W. 201.31 n_D^{20} 1.4430 b.p. 219-221°..................
NEAT

H 14,997-7 **β-Piperidinopropionaldehyde dimethyl acetal** [N-(3,3-dimethoxypropyl)-piperidine]
M.W. 187.29 n_D^{20} 1.4510 b.p. 101-103°/12 mm.
NEAT

A

15,294-3 **α-Methyl-1-piperidineethanol** [N-(2-hydroxypropyl)-piperidine]
M.W. 143.23 n_D^{20} 1.4608

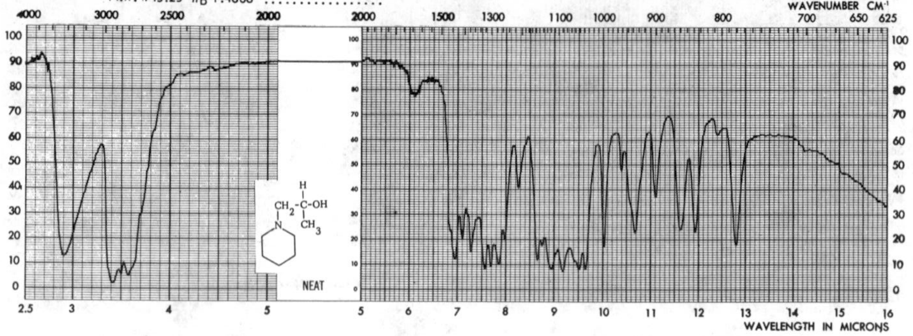

NEAT

B

15,293-5 **1-Piperidinepropanol** [N-(3-hydroxypropyl)-piperidine]
M.W. 143.23 n_D^{20} 1.4766
b.p. 93.5-95°/9 mm.

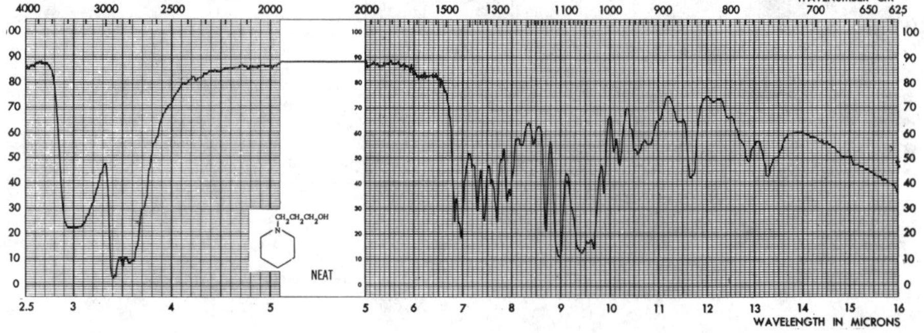

NEAT

C

15,319-2 **3-Piperidino-1,2-propanediol**
M.W. 159.23 m.p. 76-79°

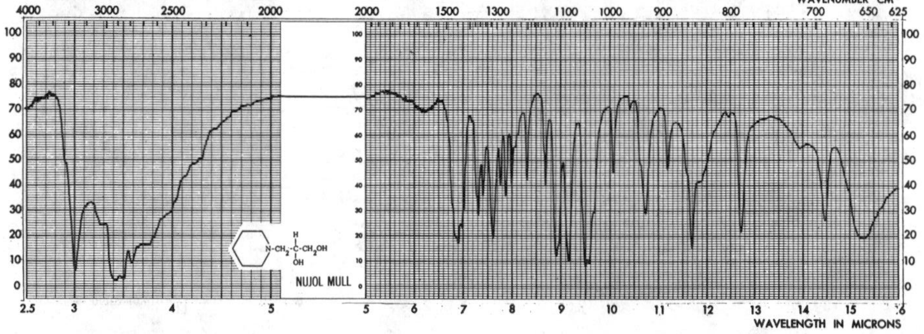

NUJOL MULL

D

15,522-5 **2-Piperidinemethanol** [2-(hydroxymethyl)-piperidine],
tech., 93%
M.W. 115.18 m.p. 68-70°

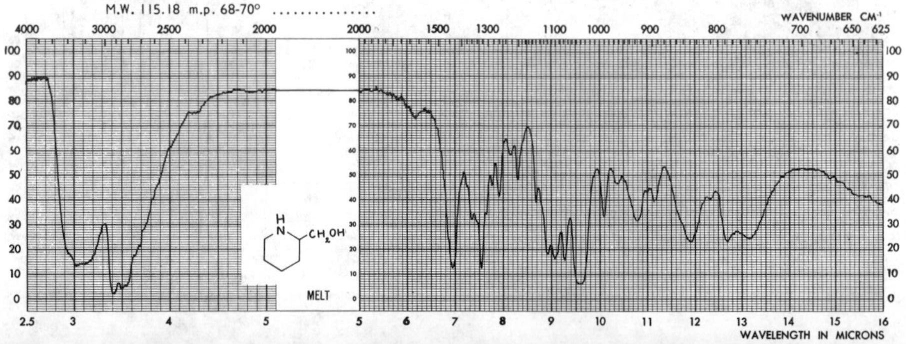

MELT

E

13,152-0 **2-Piperidineethanol** [2-(2-hydroxyethyl)-piperidine]
M.W. 129.20 m.p. 32-34°

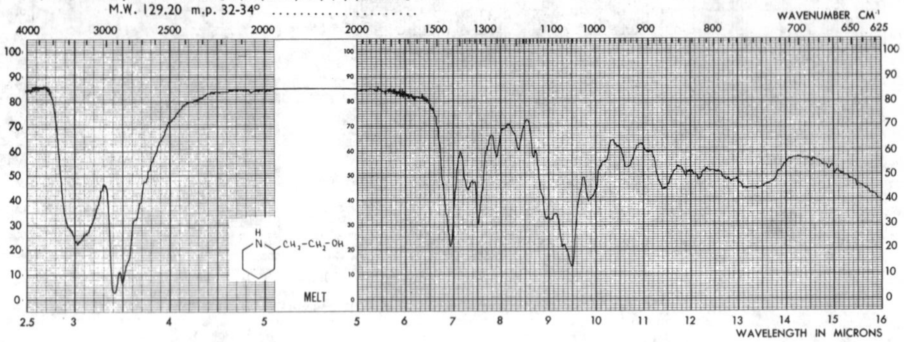

MELT

F

15,523-3
3-Piperidinemethanol [3-(hydroxymethyl)-piperidine]
M.W. 115.18 b.p. 106-107°/3.5mm. d 1.026
Beil. **21**(2),8

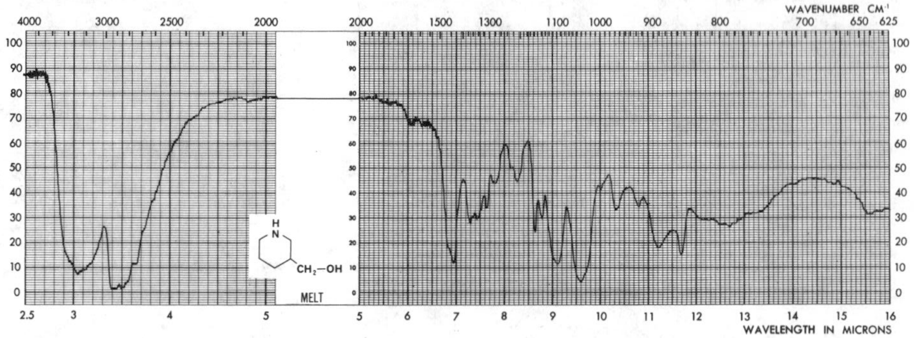

MELT

G

15,524-1 **1-Methyl-2-piperidinemethanol**
M.W. 129.20 n_D^{20} 1.4823 b.p. 79-80°/7 mm.

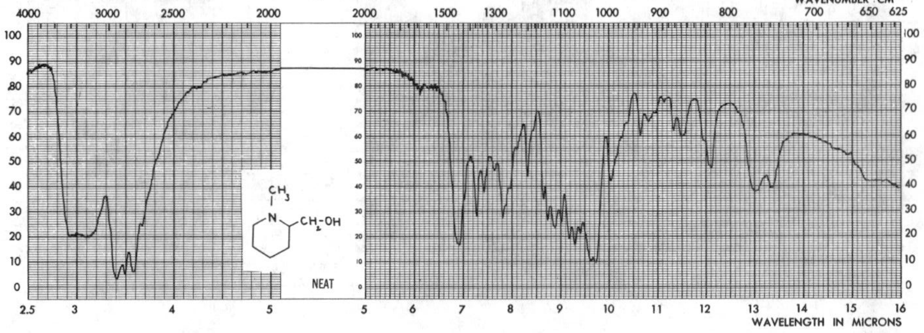

NEAT

H

H5380-1 **3-Hydroxypiperidine** (3-piperidinol)
M.W. 101.15

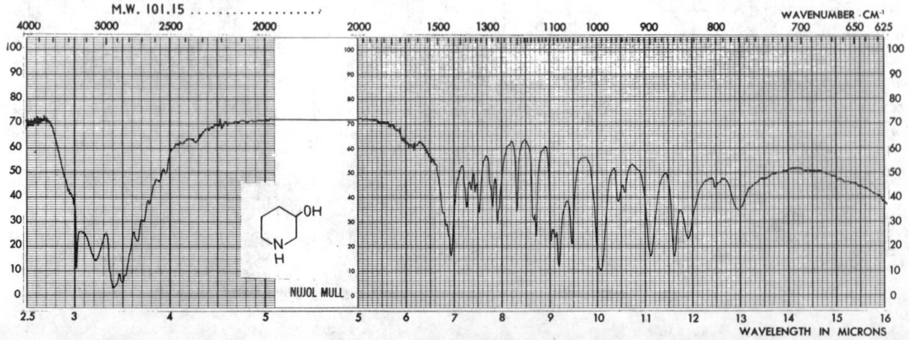

NUJOL MULL

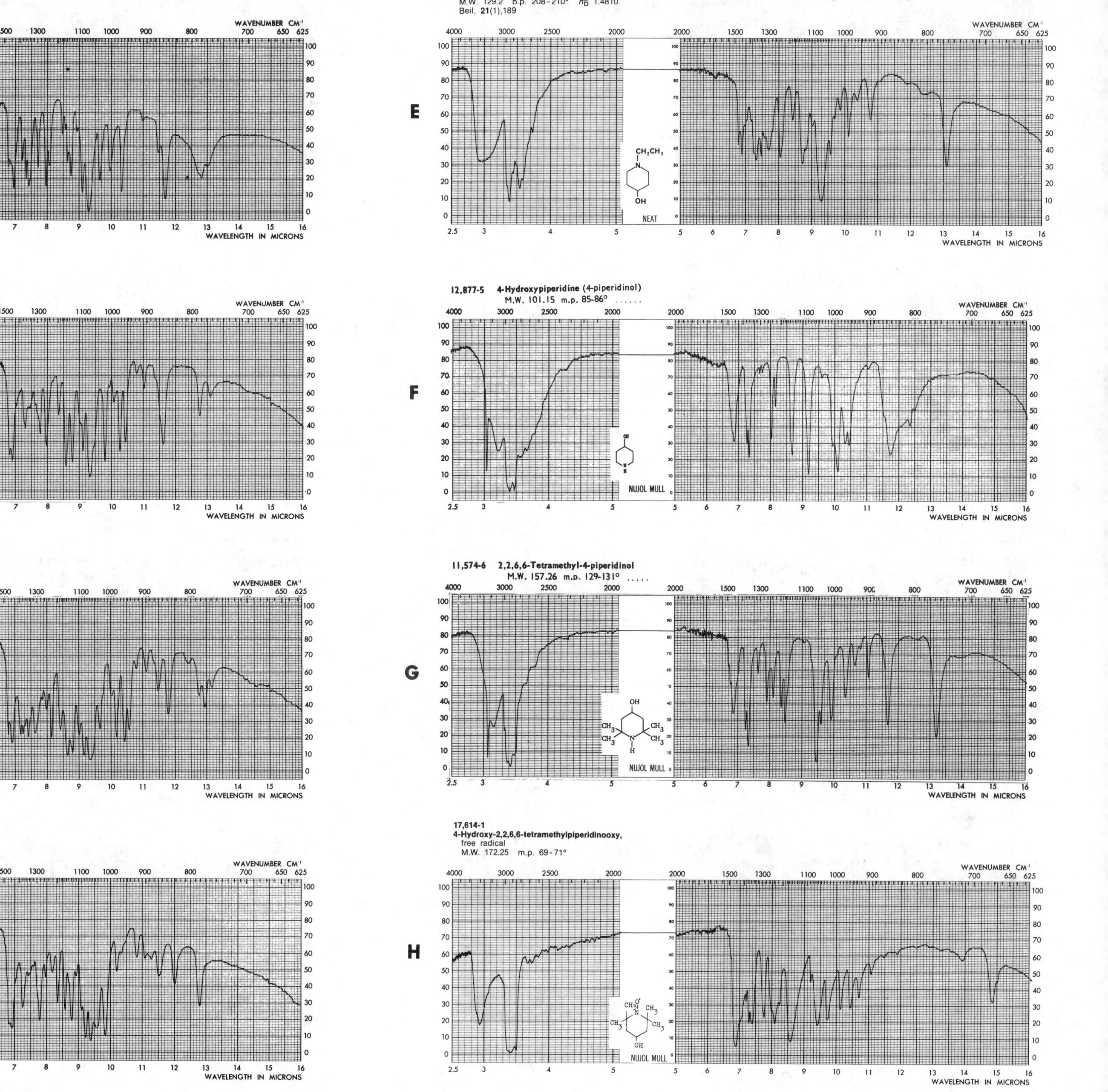
A
A5870-4 N-Amino-3-hydroxypiperidine (1-amino-3-piperidinol)
M.W. 116.16 m.p. 84-86° ....
NUJOL MULL
B
H4200-1 3-Hydroxy-N-methylpiperidine (1-methyl-3-piperidinol)
M.W. 115.18 n_D^{20} 1.4747 ....
NEAT
C
E3220-7 N-Ethyl-3-hydroxypiperidine (1-ethyl-3-piperidinol)
M.W. 129.20 n_D^{20} 1.4761 ....
NEAT
D
14,614-5 1-Methyl-3-piperidinemethanol
M.W. 129.20 n_D^{20} 1.4772 ..
NEAT
E
15,175-0
N-Ethyl-4-hydroxypiperidine (1-ethyl-4-piperidinol)
M.W. 129.2 b.p. 208-210° n_D^{20} 1.4810
Beil. 21(1),189
NEAT
F
12,877-5 4-Hydroxypiperidine (4-piperidinol)
M.W. 101.15 m.p. 85-86° .....
NUJOL MULL
G
11,574-6 2,2,6,6-Tetramethyl-4-piperidinol
M.W. 157.26 m.p. 129-131° .....
NUJOL MULL
H
17,614-1
4-Hydroxy-2,2,6,6-tetramethylpiperidinooxy,
free radical
M.W. 172.25 m.p. 69-71°
NUJOL MULL
WAVENUMBER CM⁻¹
WAVELENGTH IN MICRONS

ALDRICH ®

NON-AROMATIC AMINES

A

16,394-5
4-Amino-2,2,6,6-tetramethylpiperidinooxy, free radical, 97%
M.W. 171.26

MELT

B

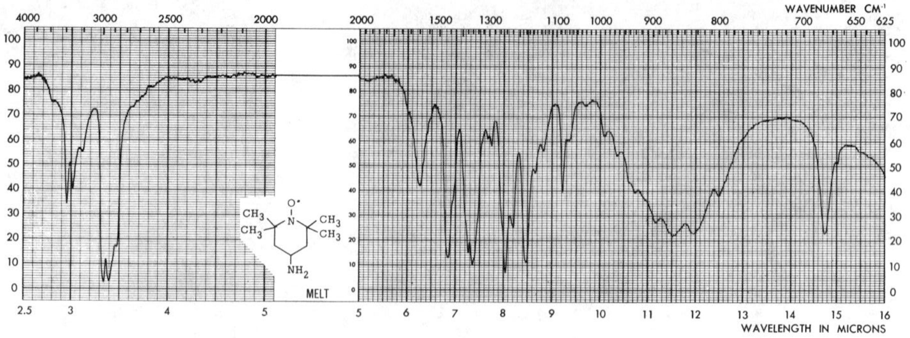

H4220-6 **4-Hydroxy-N-methylpiperidine (1-methyl-4-piperidinol)**
M.W. 115.18 m.p. 29-31°

MELT

C

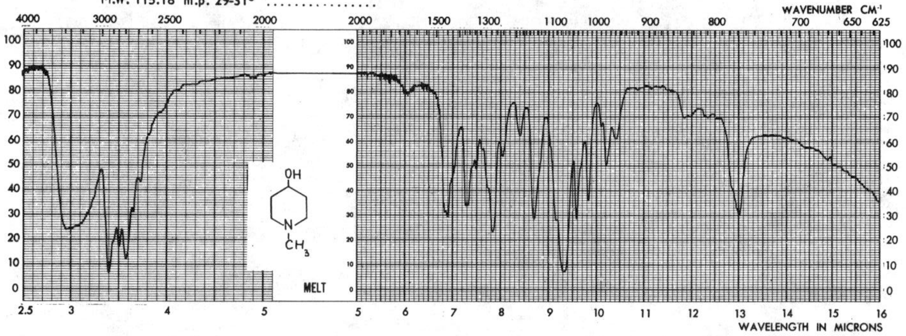

22,463-4
***N*-Ethyl-4-hydroxypiperidine,** 99% (1-ethyl-4-piperidinol)
FW 129.20 bp 108-109°/15mm. n_D^{20} 1.4816
d 0.969 *Beil.* **21**(1),189 *IR* **2**,194E Disp. C

NEAT

D

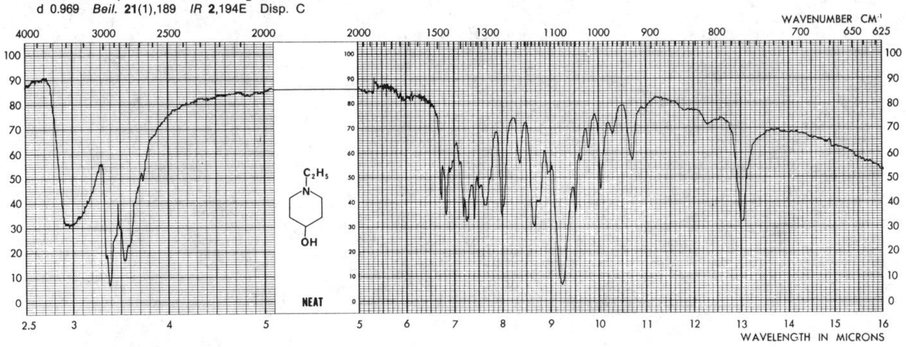

17,836-5
1,4-Dioxa-8-azaspiro[4.5]decane, 98% (4-piperidone ethylene ketal)
M.W. 143.19 b.p. 108-110°/26mm. n_D^{20} 1.4819
d 1.117

NEAT

E

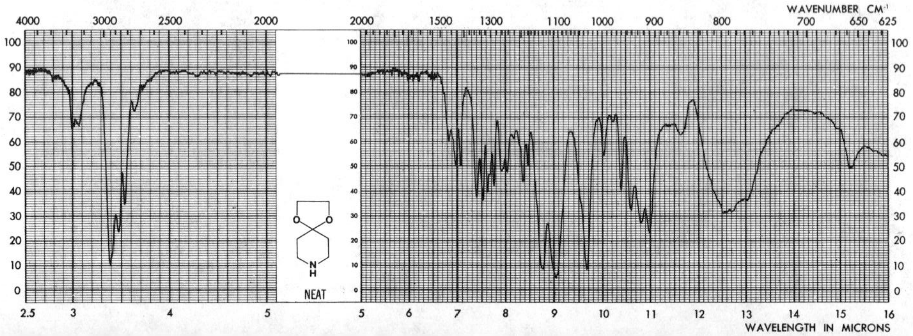

17,690-7
1-Methyl-1,2,3,6-tetrahydropyridine, 99%
M.W. 97.16 b.p. 113-114° n_D^{20} 1.4570 d 0.837

NEAT

F

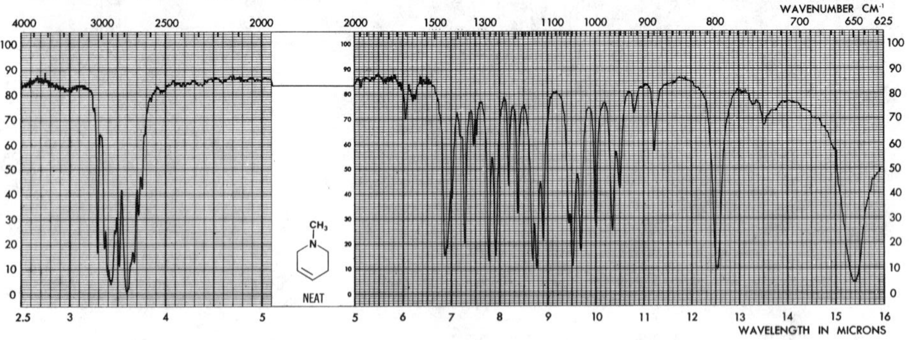

14,873-3 **1-Methyl-1,2,3,6-tetrahydro-4-pyridinemethanol**
M.W. 127.19 n_D^{20} 1.4980
b.p. 80°/0.25 mm.

MELT

G

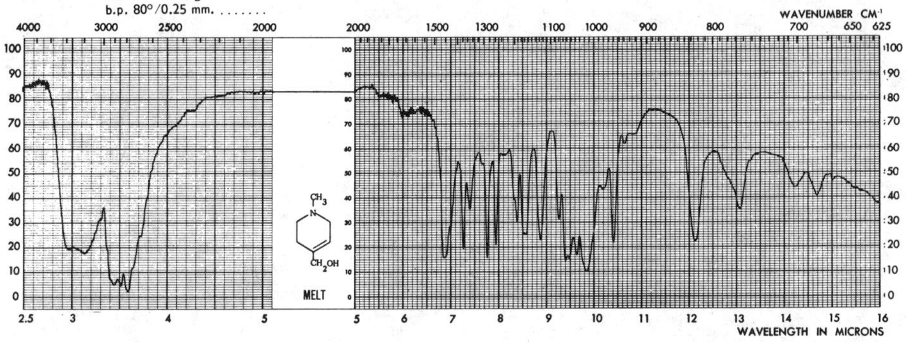

12,121-5 **4-[3-(4-Piperidyl)-propyl]-N-piperidineethanol**
M.W. 254.42 m.p. 84.5-87°

NUJOL MULL

H

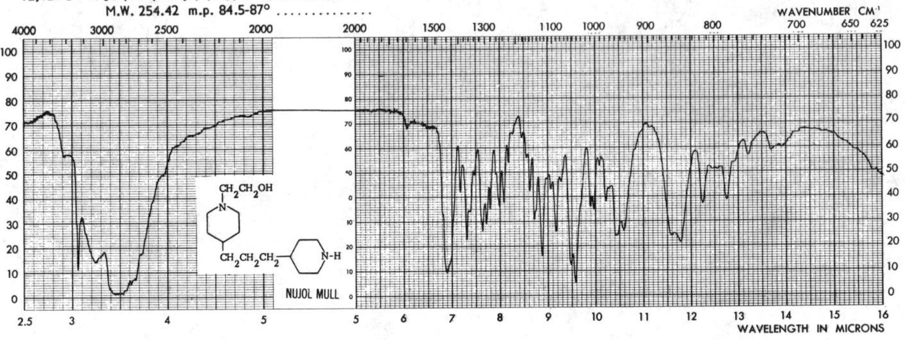

12,122-3 **4,4'-Trimethylenebis-(N-piperidineethanol)**
M.W. 298.47 m.p. 94-96°

NUJOL MULL

(Each spectrum: WAVENUMBER CM⁻¹ 4000–625; WAVELENGTH IN MICRONS 2.5–16; transmittance 0–100.)

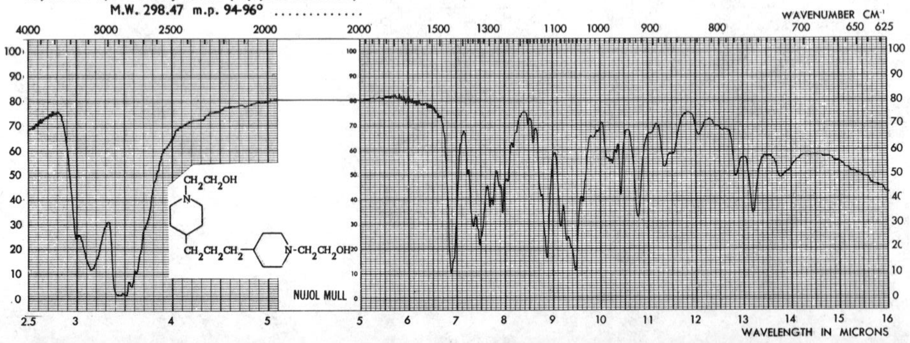

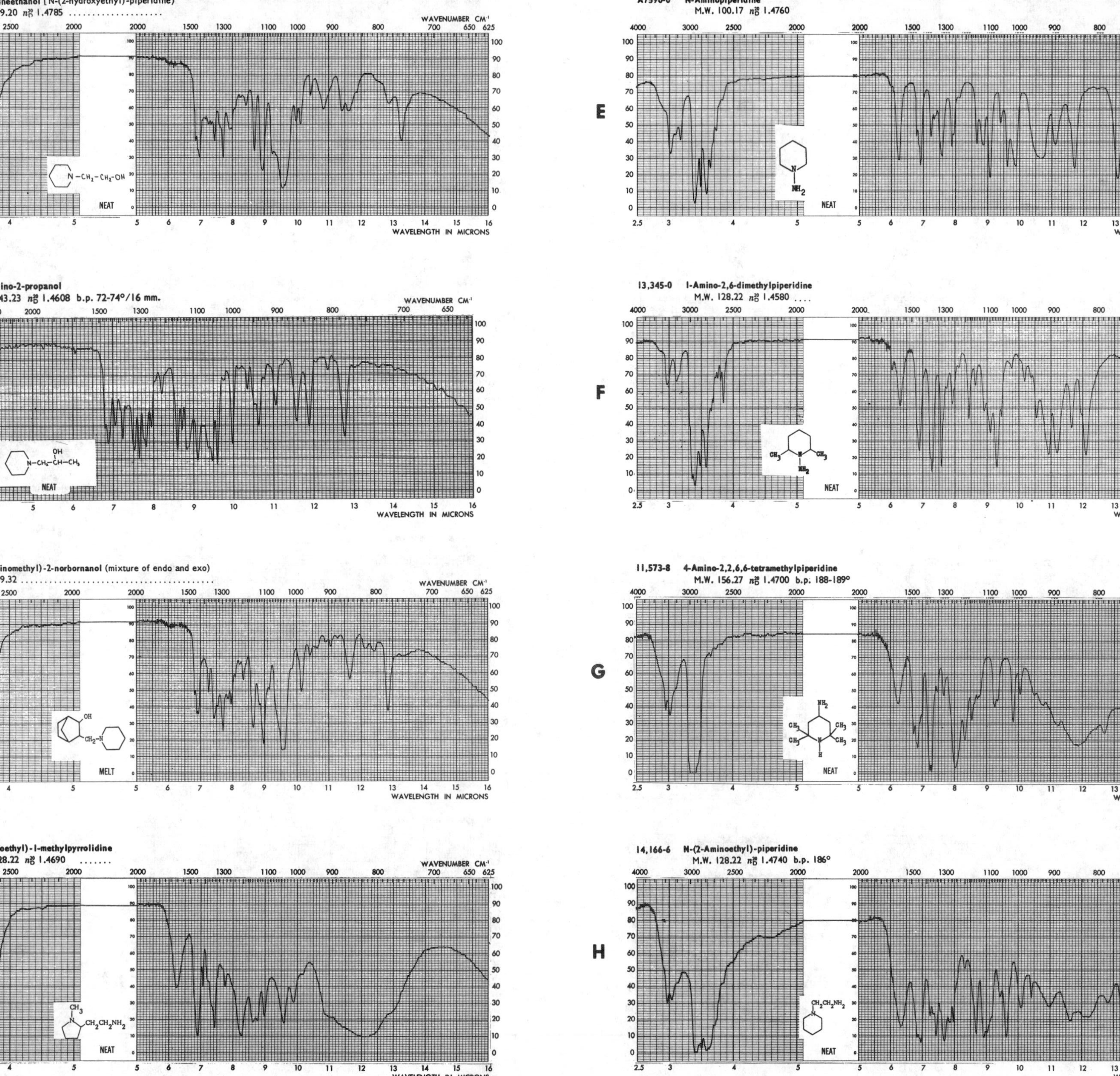

A
11,606-8 N-Piperidineethanol [N-(2-hydroxyethyl)-piperidine]
M.W. 129.20 n_D^{20} 1.4785
NEAT
B
P4780-2 1-Piperidino-2-propanol
M.W. 143.23 n_D^{20} 1.4608 b.p. 72-74°/16 mm.
NEAT
C
13,153-9 3-(Piperidinomethyl)-2-norbornanol (mixture of endo and exo)
M.W. 209.32
MELT
D
13,950-5 2-(2-Aminoethyl)-1-methylpyrrolidine
M.W. 128.22 n_D^{20} 1.4690
NEAT
E
A7590-0 N-Aminopiperidine
M.W. 100.17 n_D^{20} 1.4760
NEAT
F
13,345-0 1-Amino-2,6-dimethylpiperidine
M.W. 128.22 n_D^{20} 1.4580
NEAT
G
11,573-8 4-Amino-2,2,6,6-tetramethylpiperidine
M.W. 156.27 n_D^{20} 1.4700 b.p. 188-189°
NEAT
H
14,166-6 N-(2-Aminoethyl)-piperidine
M.W. 128.22 n_D^{20} 1.4740 b.p. 186°
NEAT
WAVENUMBER CM⁻¹
WAVELENGTH IN MICRONS
ALDRICH

A

P4860-4 **3-Piperidino-1-propylamine** [N-(3-aminopropyl)-piperidine]
M.W. 142.25 n_D^{20} 1.4740 ....
NEAT

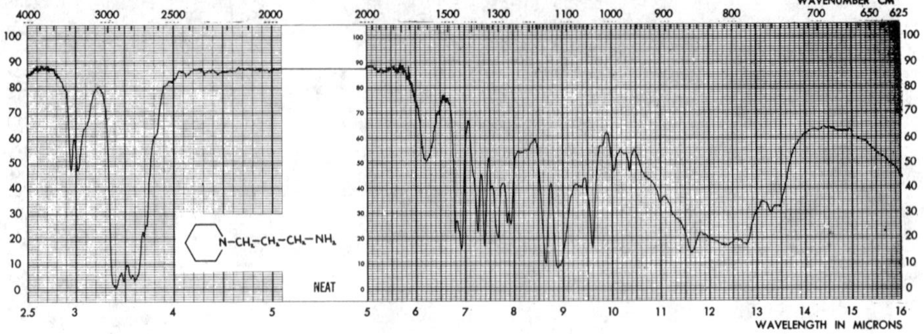

B

18,611-2
1-(3-Aminopropyl)-2-pipecoline, 96%
FW 156.27 bp 96-97°/15mm. d 1.476 Disp. C
NEAT

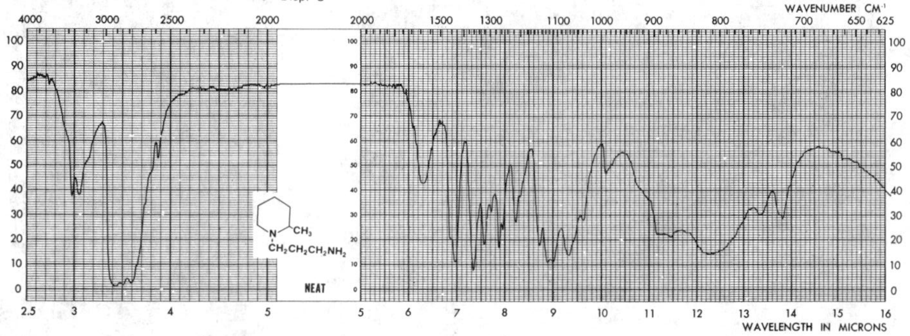

C

A6515-8 **4-(Aminomethyl)-piperidine, puriss.**
M.W. 114.19 n_D^{20} 1.4990 ....
NEAT

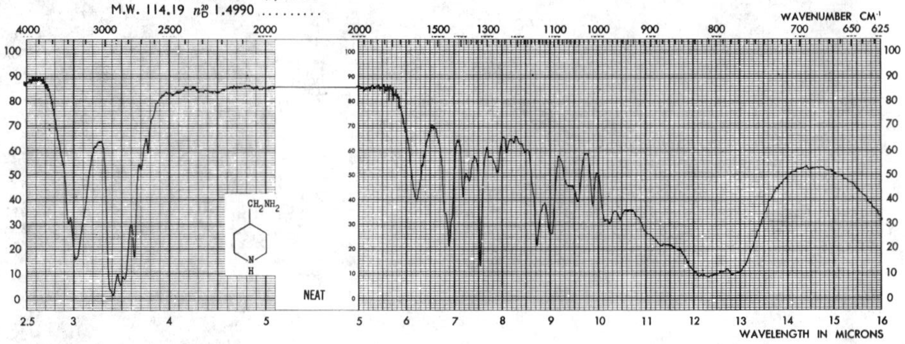

D

22,140-6
1-Methyl-4-(methylamino)piperidine, tech., 90%
FW 128.22 n_D^{20} 1.4672 d 0.882 Disp. C
NEAT

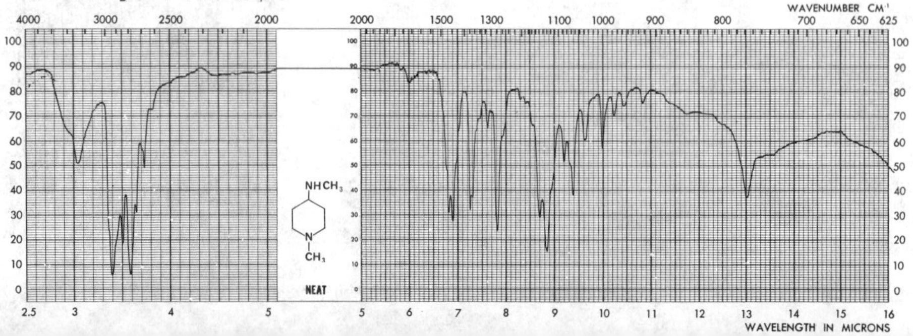

E

12,293-9 **3-Amino-N-ethylpiperidine**
M.W. 128.22 ....
NEAT

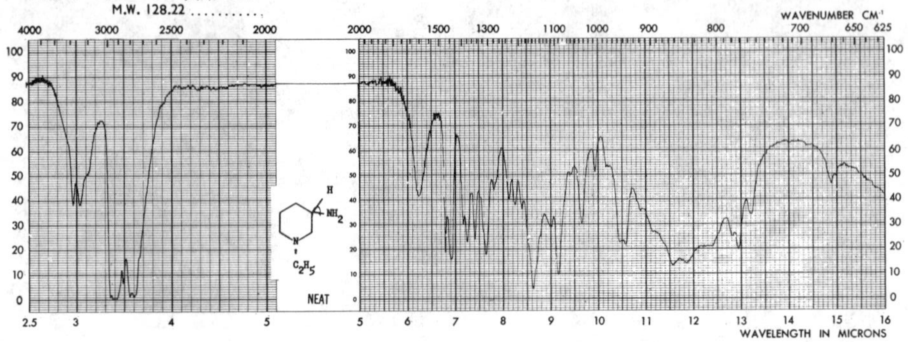

F

15,299-4 **3-Ethyl-3-methyldiaziridine**
M.W. 86.14 n_D^{20} 1.4390 b.p. 32° 17 mm. . .
NEAT

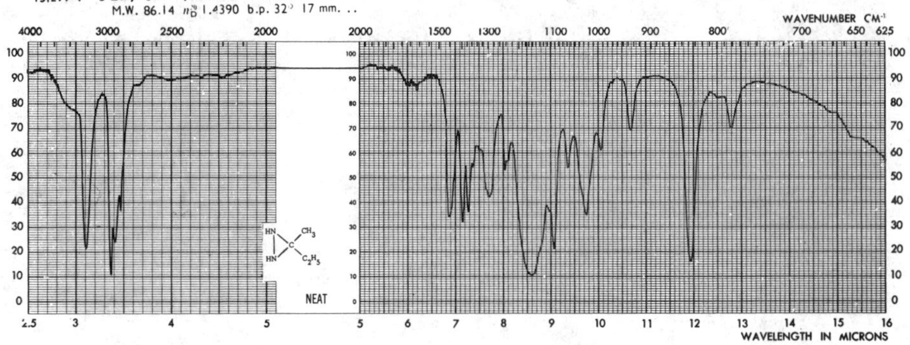

G

P4590-7 **Piperazine, anhydrous**
M.W. 86.14 m.p. 109-112°
NUJOL MULL

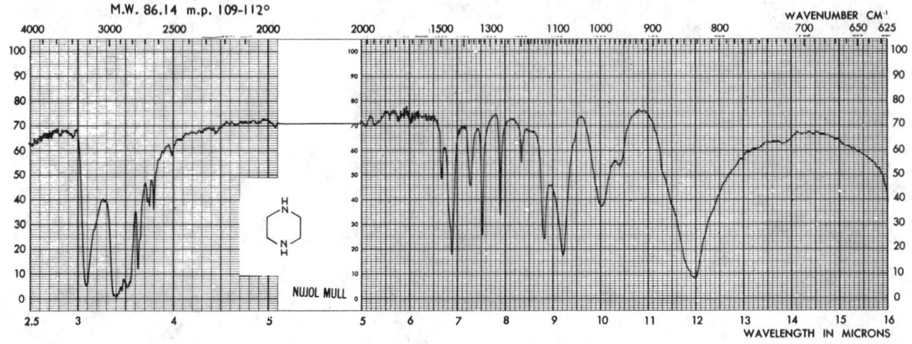

H

P4,591-5
Piperazine hexahydrate, 98%
M.W. 194.23 m.p. 44-45° b.p. 145-156°
Beil. **23**,4
NUJOL MULL

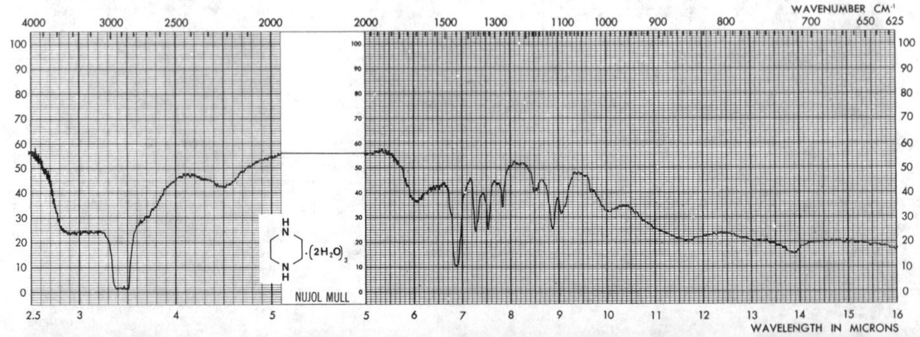

A 13,000-1 N-Methylpiperazine
M.W. 100.17 n_D^{20} 1.4646 b.p. 138°
NEAT

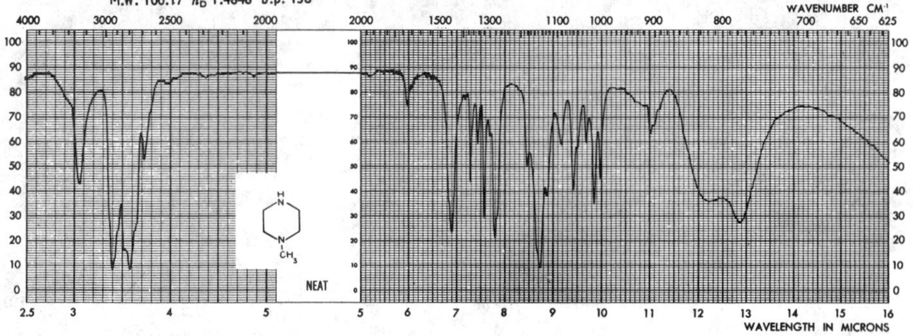

B 14,167-4 1-n-Propylpiperazine dihydrobromide
M.W. 290.05 m.p. 252-257° (dec.)
NUJOL MULL

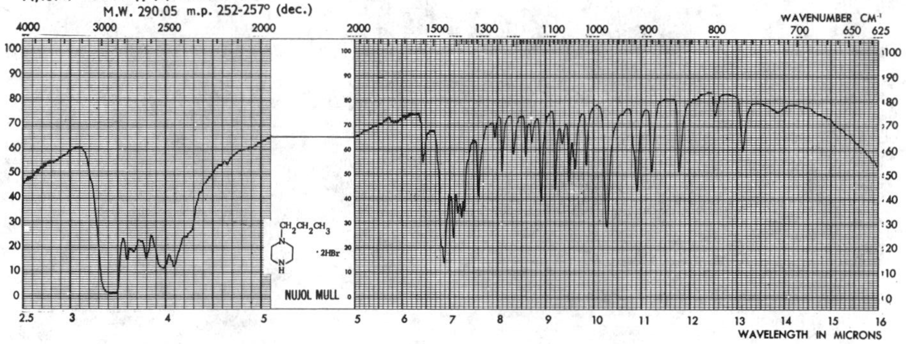

C D17,930-2 N,N'-Dimethylpiperazine
M.W. 114.19 n_D^{20} 1.4463
NEAT

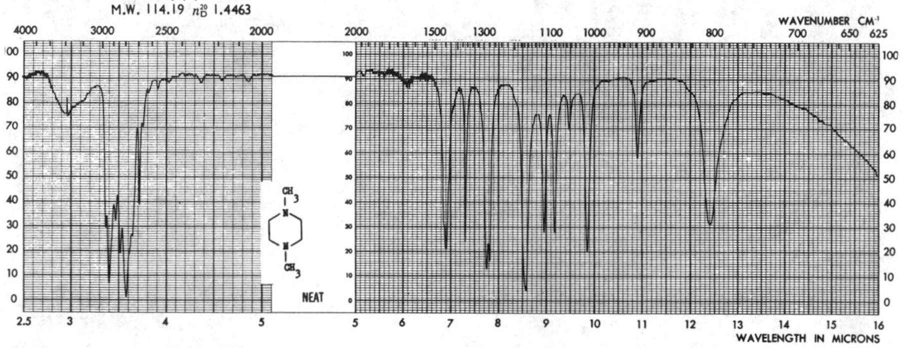

D M7240-4 2-Methylpiperazine
M.W. 100.17 ....
MELT

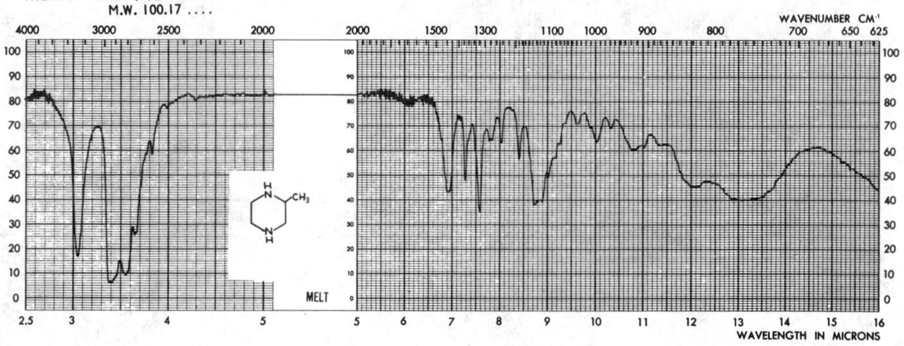

E D17,980-9
2,6-Dimethylpiperazine
M.W. 114.19 m.p. 111-113° b.p. 162°
Beil. **23**(1),8
NUJOL MULL

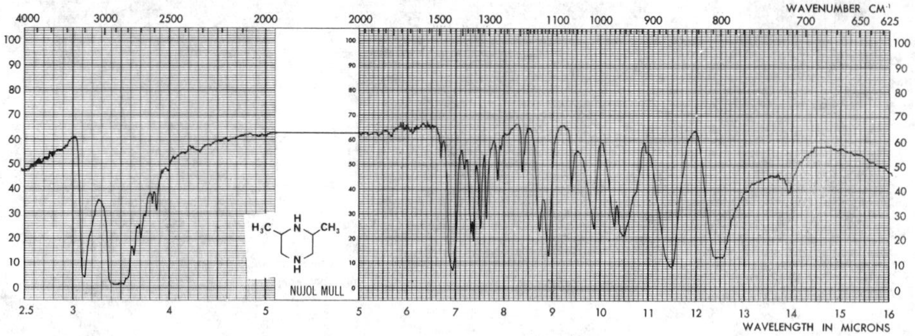

F 12,805-8 2,5-Dimethylpiperazine (88% *cis*, 12% *trans*)
M.W. 114.19 n_D^{20} 1.4720 ....
NEAT

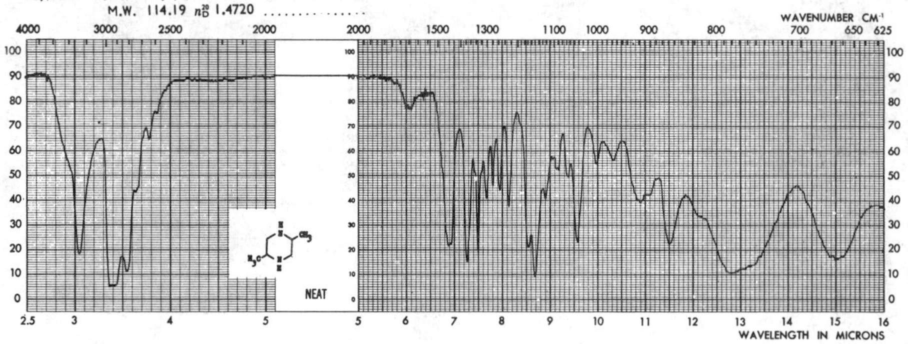

G D17,960-4
2,5-Dimethylpiperazine, 75% *trans*, 25% *cis*
M.W. 114.19 b.p. 162-165° Beil. **23**,19
NUJOL MULL

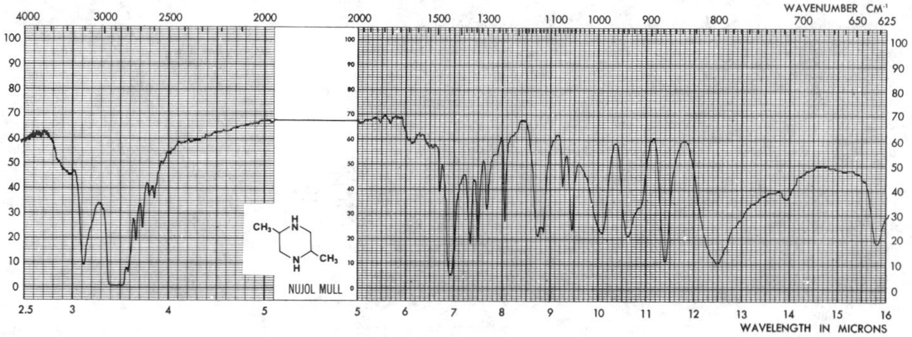

H T8000-4 2,4,6-Trimethylpiperidine
M.W. 127.23 n_D^{20} 1.4412
NEAT

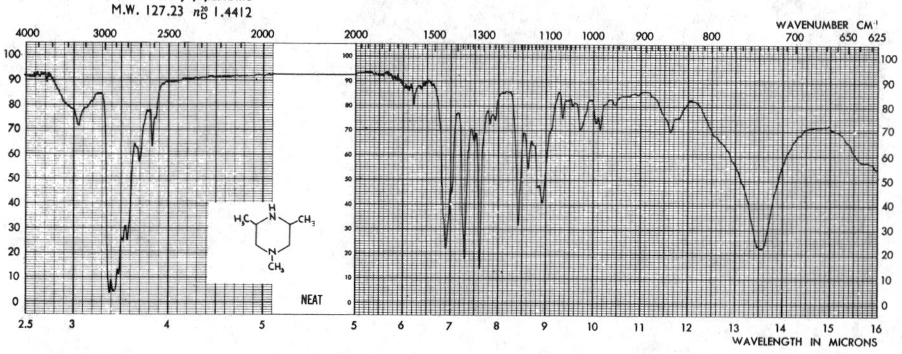

ALDRICH

A H2880-7 **N-β-Hydroxyethylpiperazine** (1-piperazineethanol)
M.W. 130.19 n_D^{20} 1.5014 b.p. 246.3°/760 mm. ...

B 19,359-3
1-Piperazinepropanol
FW 144.22 mp 49-53° bp 128-132°/5mm.
Disp. C

C B4,540-2
N,N'-Bis-(2-hydroxyethyl)-piperazine, 99%
(N,N'-piperazinediethanol)
M.W. 174.24 m.p. 133.5-136°
b.p. 215-220°/50mm. Beil. **23**,10

D 19,360-7
1-(3-Chloropropyl)piperazine dihydrochloride hemihydrate
FW 244.60 mp 217° (dec.) Disp. C

E 21,023-4
3-(1-Piperazinyl)-1,2-propanediol, 98%
FW 160.22 mp 73-77° bp 128-130°/0.100mm.
Disp. C

F 14,075-9 **N,N'-Bis-(2-hydroxyethyl)-2,5-dimethylpiperazine** (2,5-dimethyl-1,4-piperazinediethanol)
M.W. 202.30

G 14,076-7 **N,N'-Bis-(2-hydroxypropyl)-2,5-dimethylpiperazine** (2,5-dimethyl-1,4-piperazinedi-2-propanol)
M.W. 230.35

H 13,002-8 **3-(4-Methylpiperazinomethyl)-2-norbornanol dihydrochloride**
M.W. 370.19 m.p. 290° (dec.)

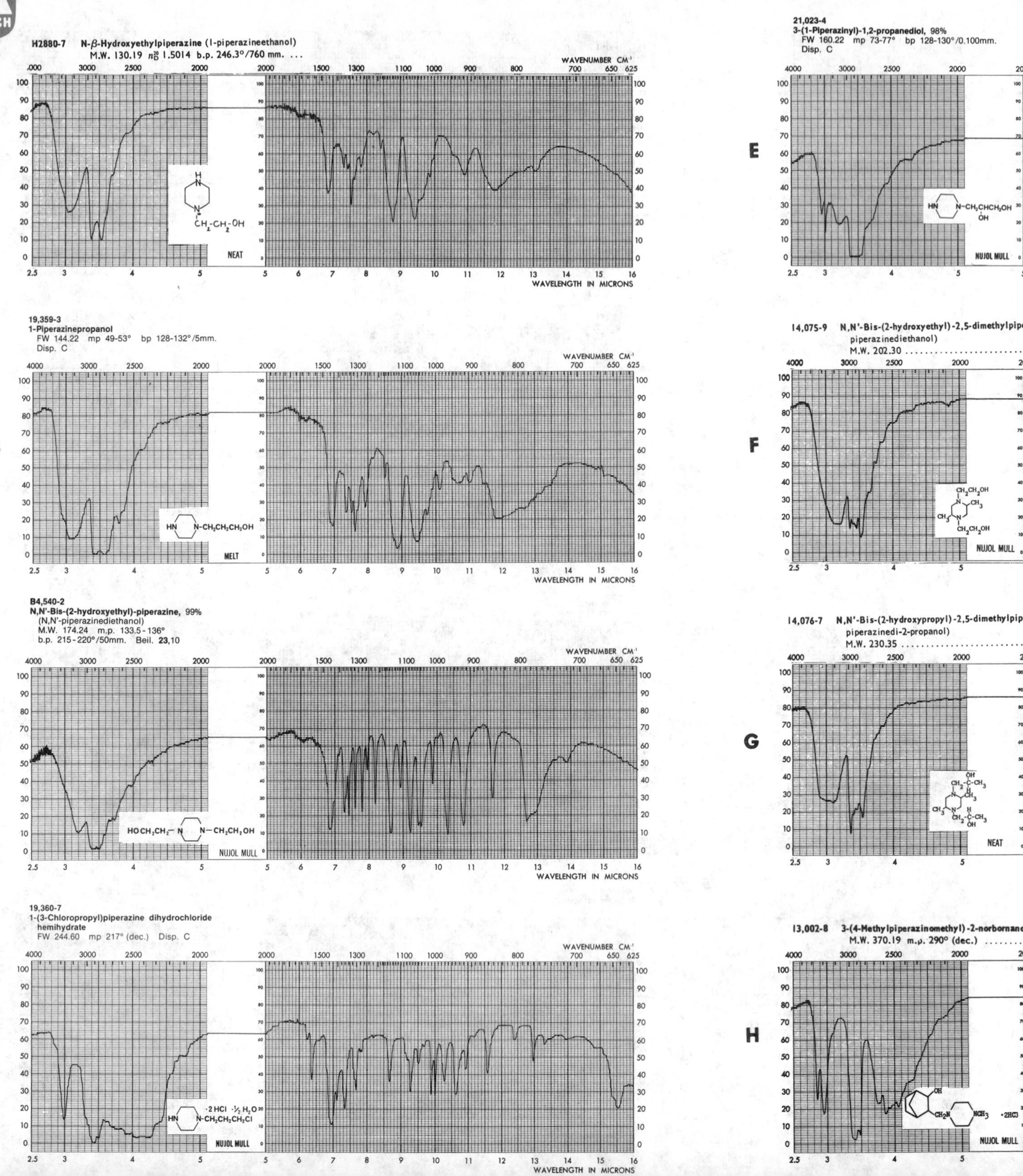

A 12,296-3 **1-Amino-4-(β-hydroxyethyl)-piperazine (4-amino-1-piperazineethanol)**
M.W. 145.21 m.p. 106-108° ....

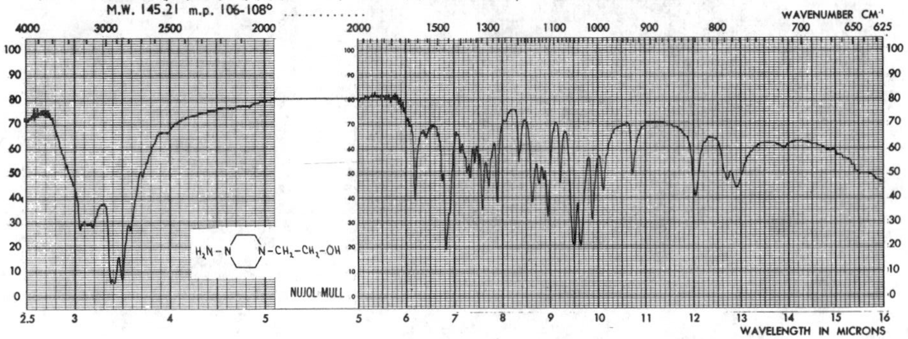

NUJOL MULL

B A6513-1 **1-Amino-4-methylpiperazine hydrochloride**
M.W. 151.64 m.p. 229-233° (dec.) .....

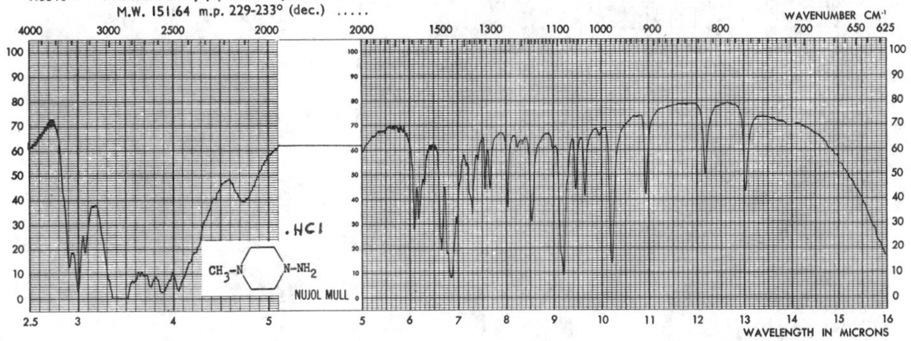

NUJOL MULL

C 10,142-7 **1,4-Diaminopiperazine dihydrate**
M.W. 152.20 m.p. 79-81° ....

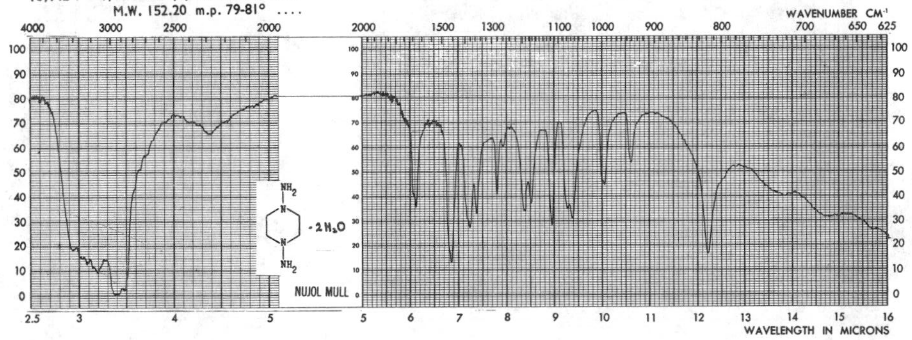

NUJOL MULL

D A5520-9 **N-(2-Aminoethyl)-piperazine**
M.W. 129.21 n_D^{20} 1.4983 ...

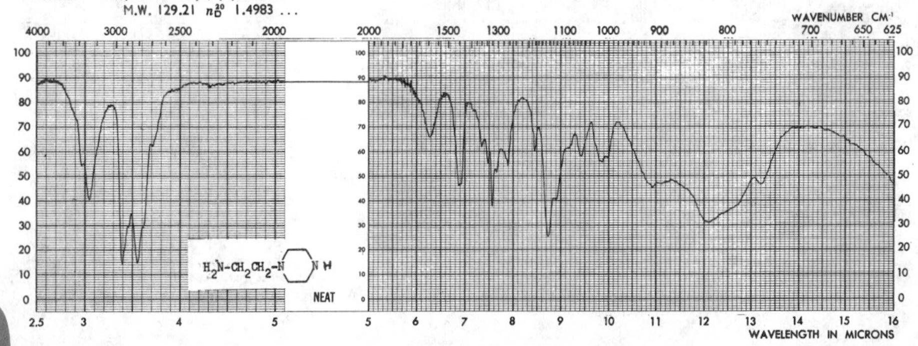

NEAT

E A7660-5 **N-(γ-Aminopropyl)-N'-methylpiperazine**
M.W. 157.26 n_D^{20} 1.4806 ....

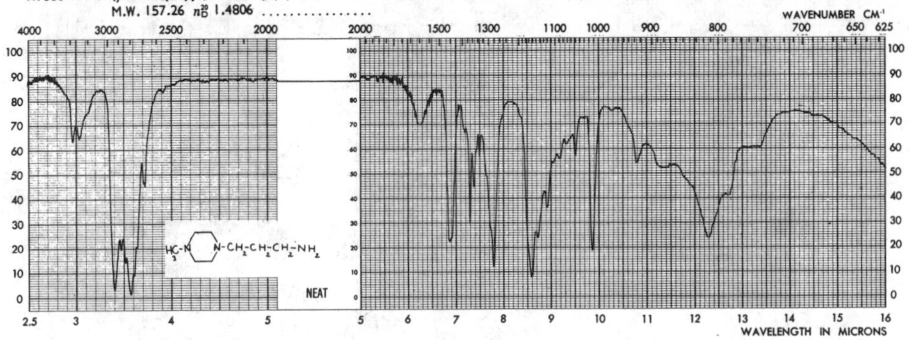

NEAT

F 10,943-6 **N,N'-Bis-(3-aminopropyl)-piperazine**
M.W. 200.33 n_D^{20} 1.4972 b.p. 150-152°/2 mm.

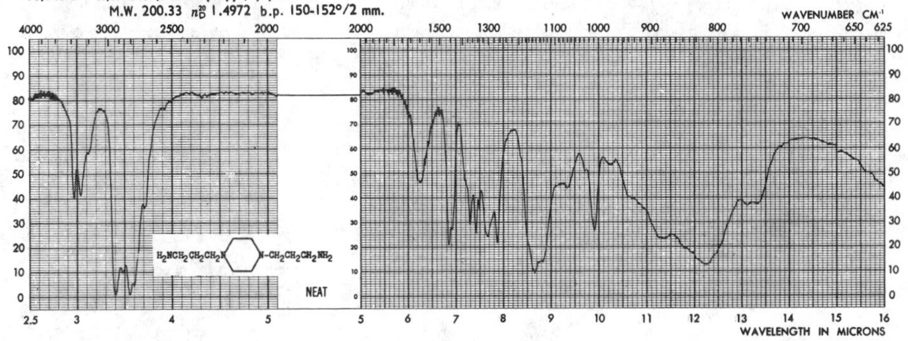

NEAT

G H1040-1 **Hexamethyleneimine** (homopiperidine)
M.W. 99.18 n_D^{20} 1.4631
b.p. 138°/749 mm. .....

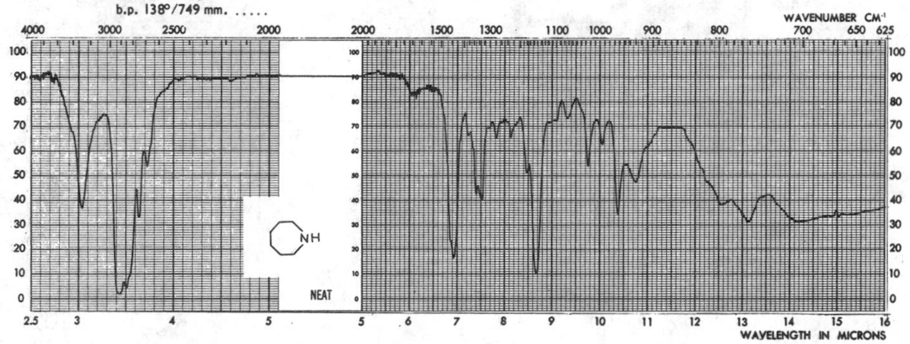

NEAT

H 19,480-8
3,3,5-Trimethylhexahydroazepine, 98%, mixture of isomers (3,3,5-trimethyl-1-azacycloheptane)
FW 141.26 bp 180° n_D^{20} 1.4563 d 0.852
Disp. C

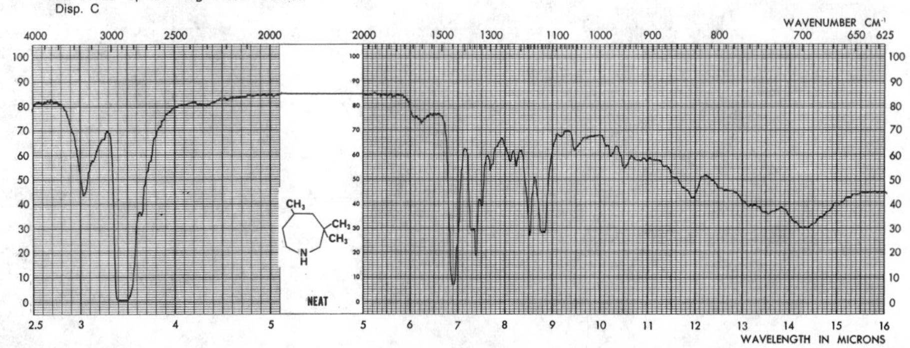

NEAT

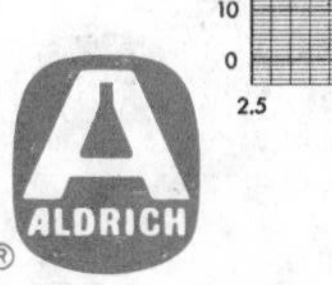

A

H1065-7 **2-(Hexamethyleneimino)-ethyl chloride (N-2-chloroethyl-hexamethyleneimine) hydrochloride**
M.W. 198.14 m.p. 208-210°

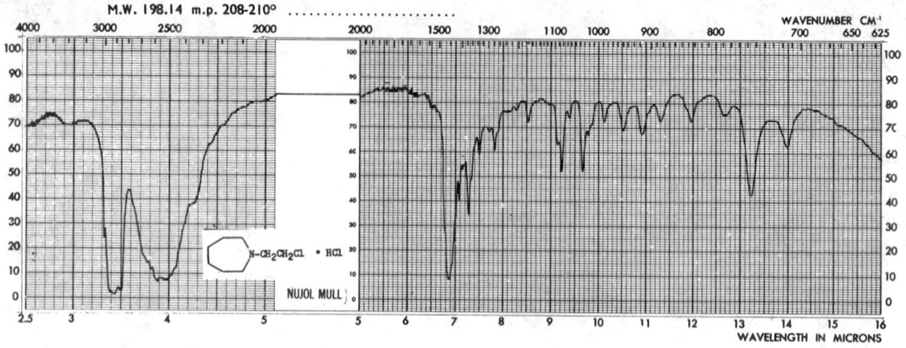

NUJOL MULL

B

H215-5 **Heptamethyleneimine**
M.W. 113.20 n_D^{20} 1.4720

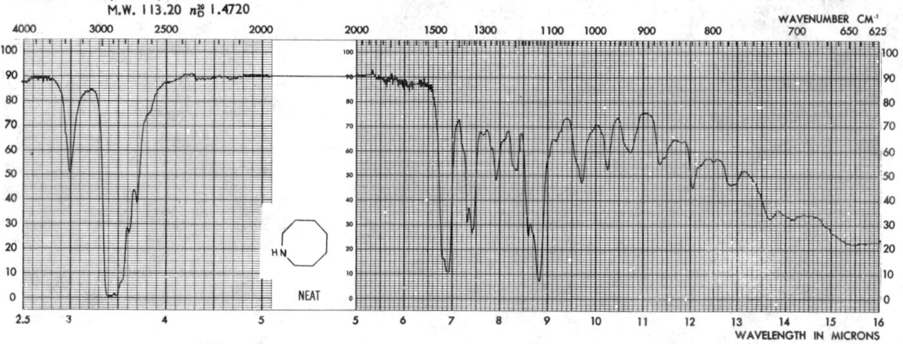

NEAT

C

A5645-0 **N-Aminohomopiperidine** (N-aminohexamethyleneimine)
M.W. 114.20 n_D^{20} 1.4831

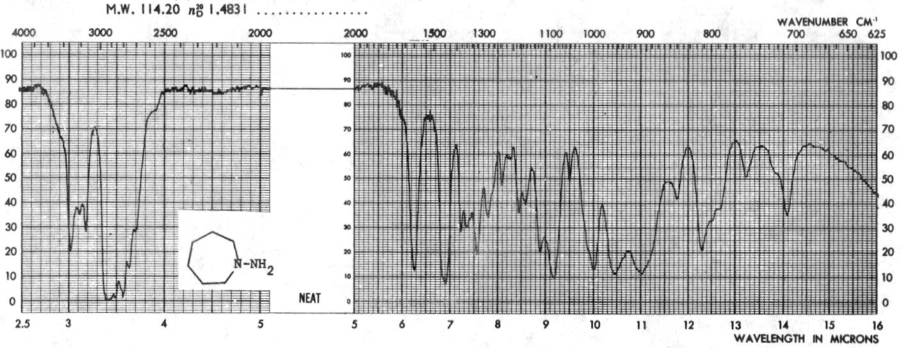

NEAT

D

H1120-3 **3-Hexamethyleneimino-1-propylamine**
M.W. 156.27 n_D^{20} 1.4798

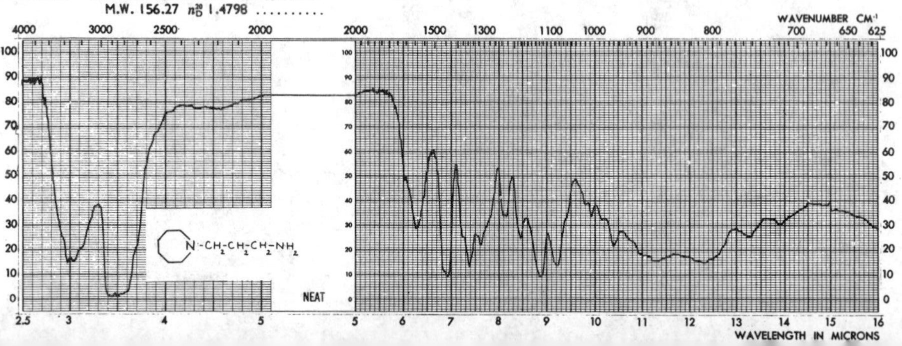

NEAT

E

O-310-9 **Octamethyleneimine**
M.W. 127.23 n_D^{20} 1.4760

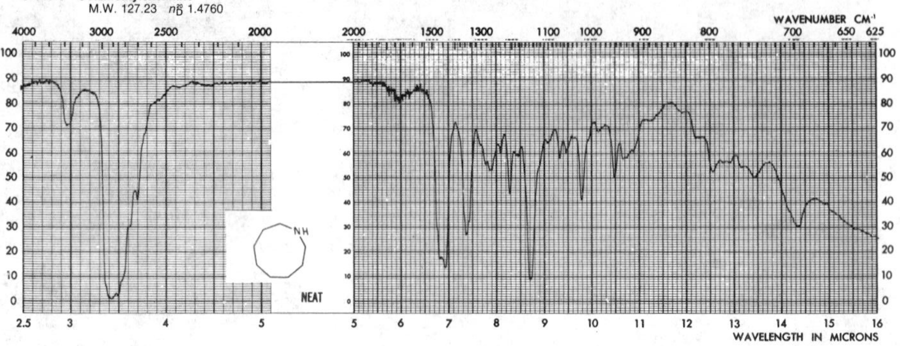

NEAT

F

18,030-0
Dodecamethyleneimine (azacyclotridecane)
M.W. 183.34 b.p. 156°/25mm. n_D^{20} 1.4797
d 0.891

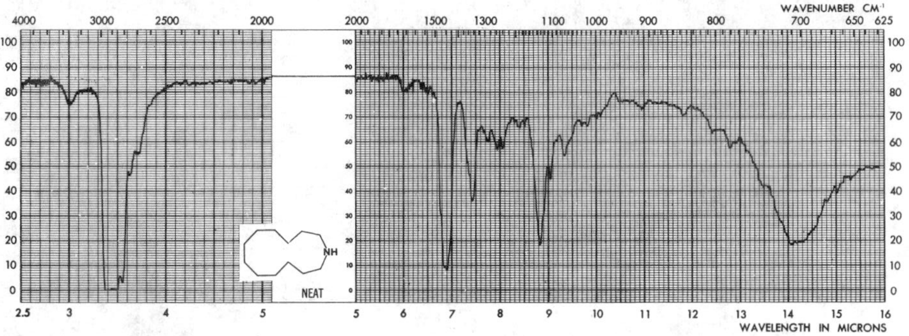

NEAT

G

H1660-4 **Homopiperazine**
M.W. 100.17 n_D^{20} 1.4853 b.p. 169.1°

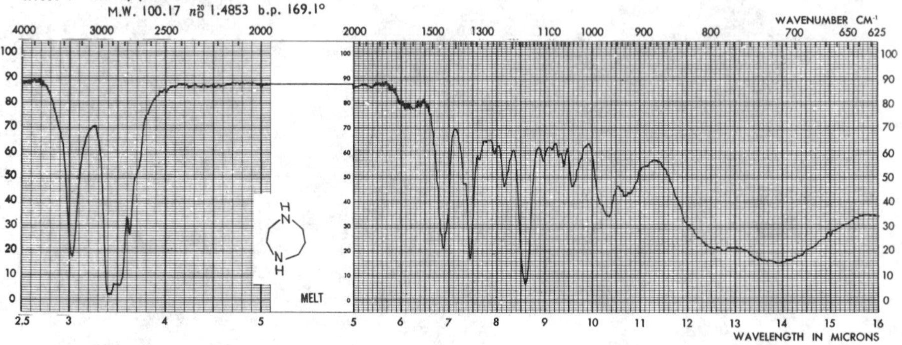

MELT

H

19,393-3
Hexacyclen trisulfate, 98% (1,4,7,10,13,16-hexaazacyclooctadecane)
FW 552.65 mp 280° (dec.) Disp. C

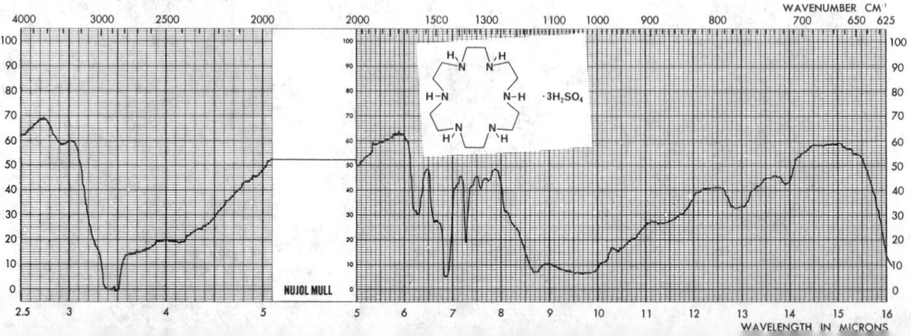

NUJOL MULL

A

18,609-0
1-Methylhomopiperazine, 99% (hexahydro-1-methyl-1*H*-1,4-diazepine)
FW 114.19 n_D^{20} 1.4768 Disp. C

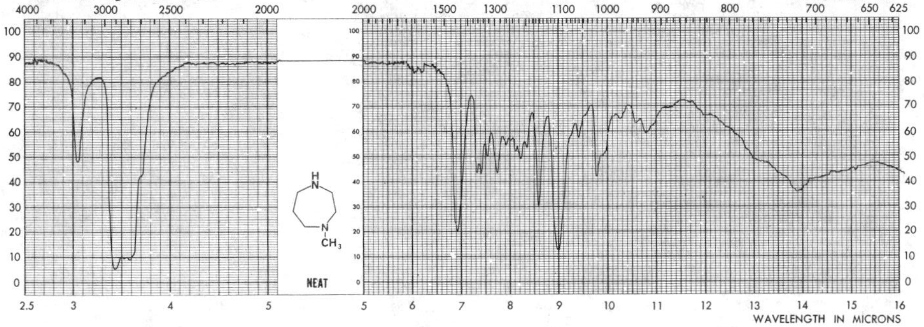

NEAT

B

22,143-0
1,3,5-Triethylhexahydro-*s*-triazine, 97%
FW 171.29 bp 207-208° n_D^{20} 1.4595 d 0.894
Beil. **26**,2 Disp. C

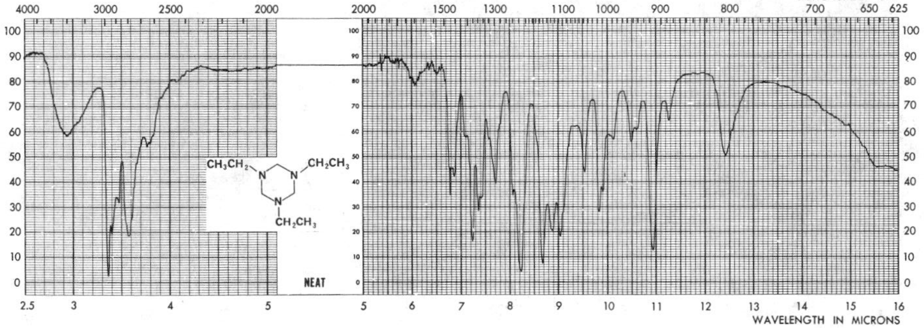

NEAT

C

22,144-9
1,3,5-Tricyclohexylhexahydro-*s*-triazine, 99%
FW 333.57 mp 74-75° bp 97°/6mm. Disp. C

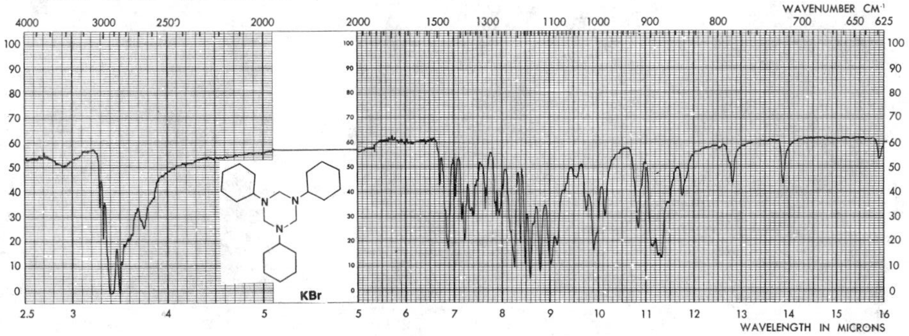

KBr

D

H1130-0 **Hexamethylenetetramine** (methenamine)
M.W. 140.19 m.p. 285-295° (sublimes)

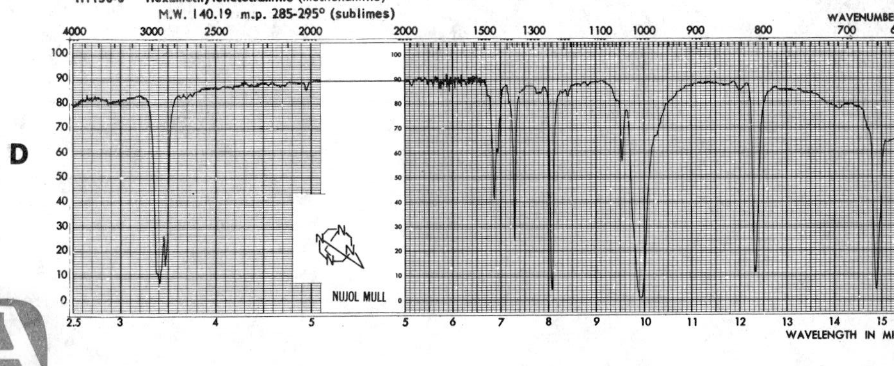

E

19,760-2
Quinuclidine
FW 111.19 mp 159° (sublimes) *Beil.* **20**,144
Disp. C

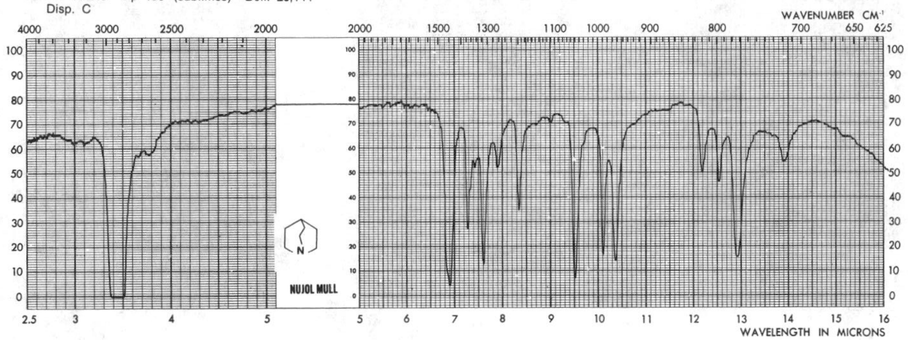

NUJOL MULL

F

13,591-7 **Quinuclidine hydrochloride**
M.W. 147.65 m.p. > 310°

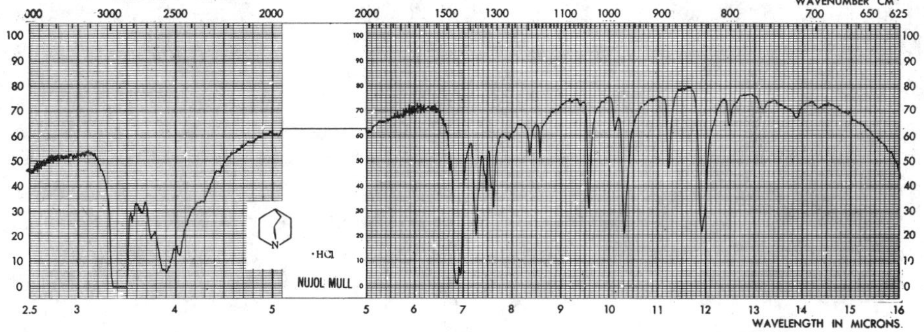

NUJOL MULL

G

12,521-0 **3-Chloroquinuclidine hydrochloride**
M.W. 182.09 m.p. 230-235°

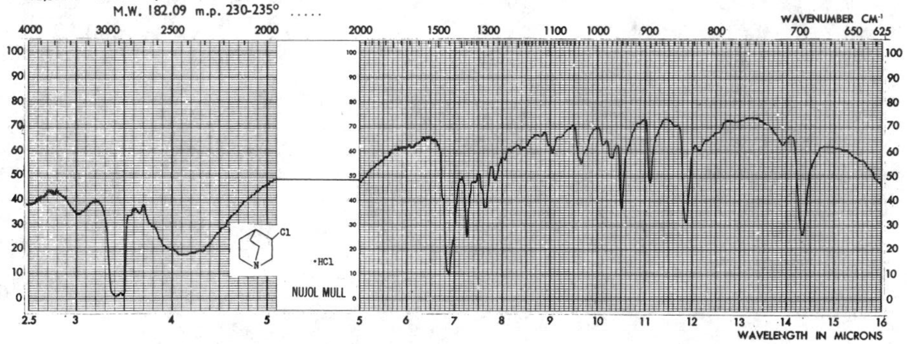

NUJOL MULL

H

Q187-5 **3-Quinuclidinol**
M.W. 127.19 m.p. 223-225°

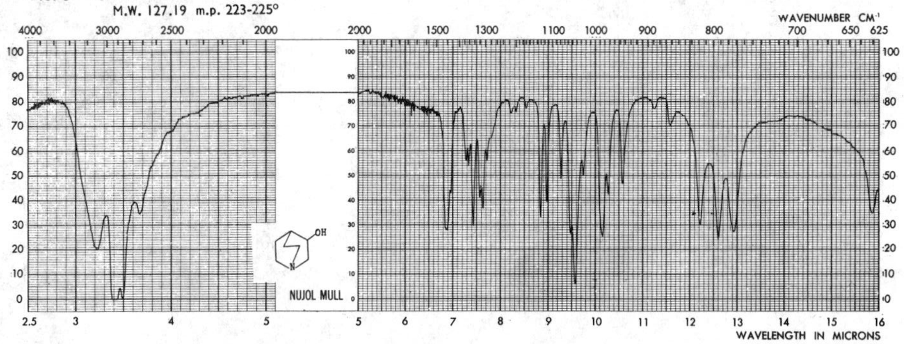

NUJOL MULL

ALDRICH

A

Q188-3 **3-Quinuclidinol hydrochloride**
M.W. 163.65 m.p. > 330° . . .

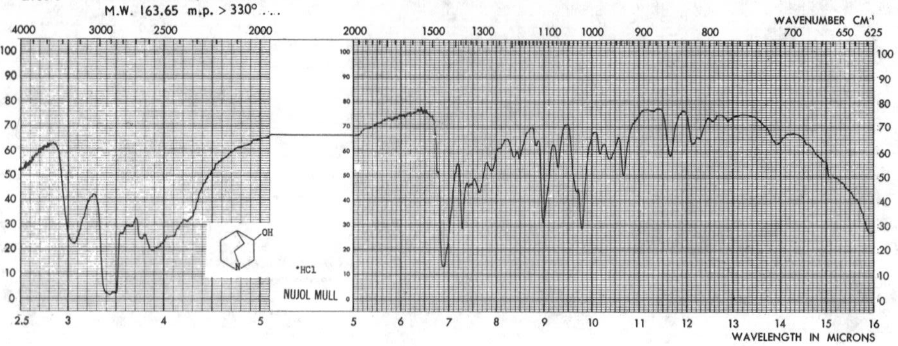

NUJOL MULL

B

10,035-8 **3-Aminoquinuclidine dihydrochloride**
M.W. 199.14 m.p. 321-323° . . . . .

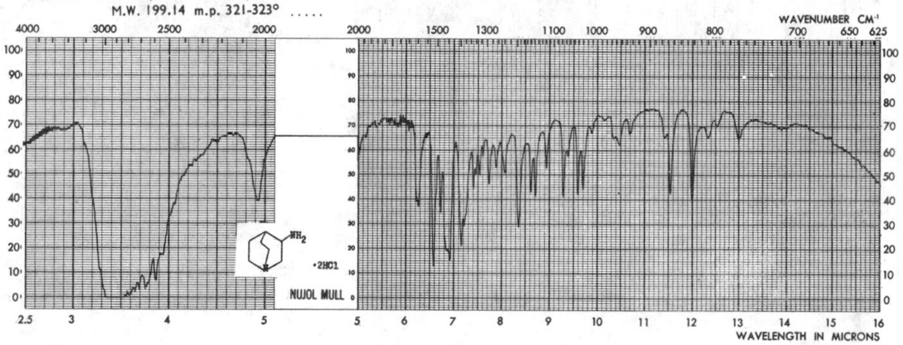

NUJOL MULL

C

D2780-2 **1,4-Diazabicyclo[2.2.2]octane** (TED, triethylenediamine)
M.W. 112.18 m.p. 158-160° . . . .

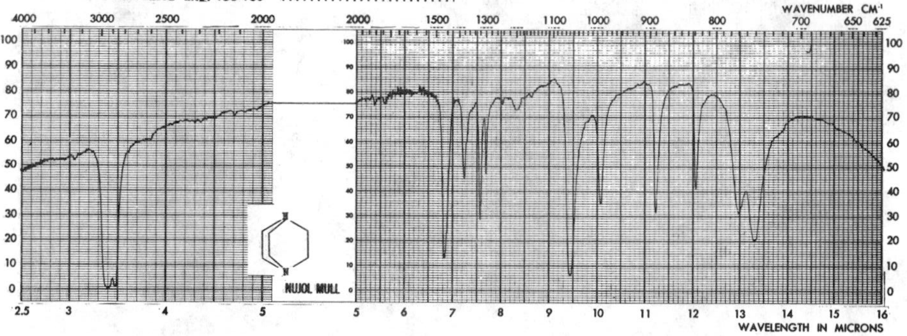

NUJOL MULL

D

A9380-1 **3-Azabicyclo[3.2.2]nonane**
M.W. 125.22 . . . .

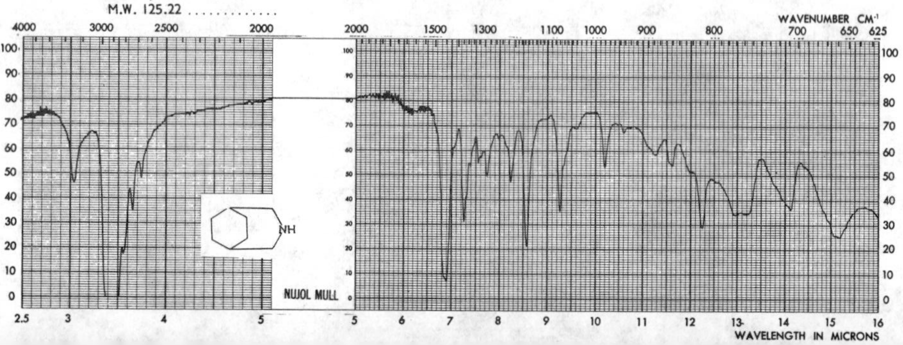

NUJOL MULL

E

T8940-0 **Tropine (3-tropanol), tech.**
M.W. 141.21 . . . .

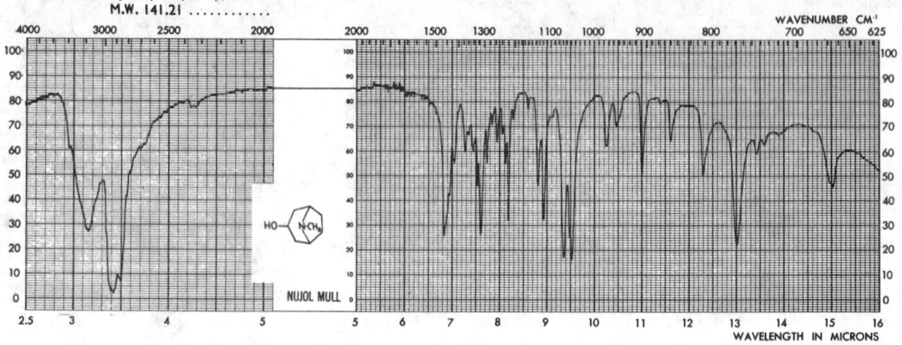

NUJOL MULL

F

14,289-1 **Tropine-N-oxide monohydrate**
M.W. 175.23 m.p. 249° (dec.)

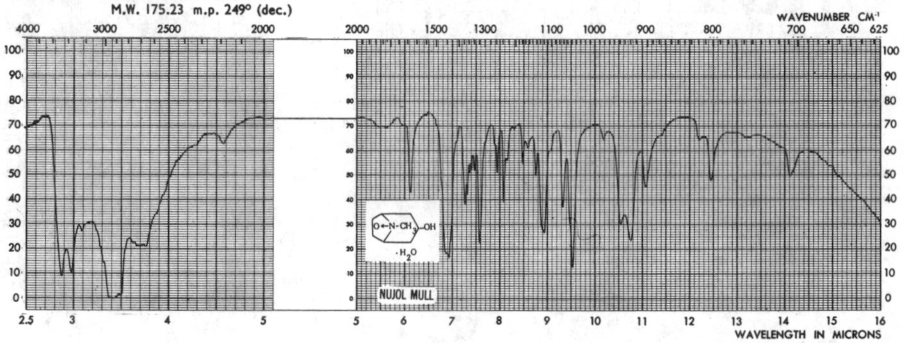

NUJOL MULL

G

19,481-6
1,3,3-Trimethyl-6-azabicyclo[3.2.1]octane, 97%
FW 153.27 bp 194° n_D^{20} 1.4716 d 0.902
Disp. C

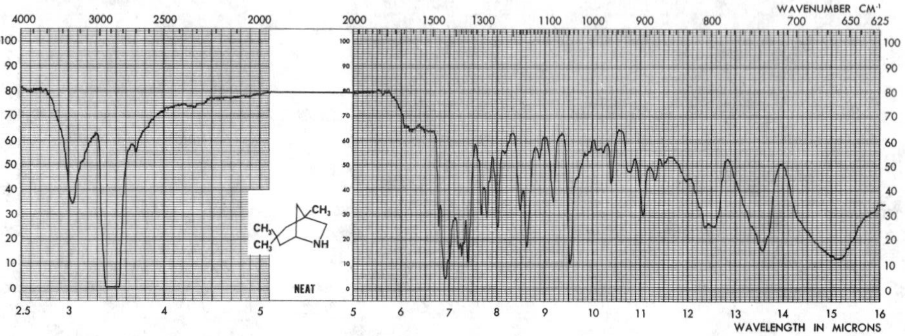

NEAT

H

13,423-6 **Morpholine, puriss.**
M.W. 87.12 n_D^{20} 1.4541 m.p. -7 to -5°
b.p. 128° . . . .

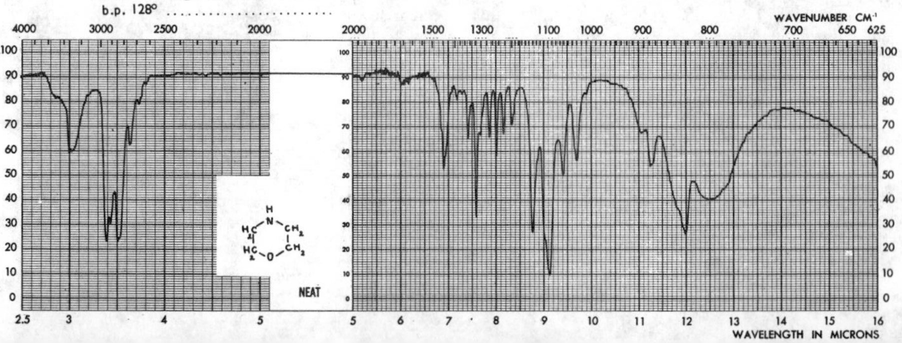

NEAT

A

12,652-7 **2,6-Dimethylmorpholine**
M.W. 115.18 n_D^{20} 1.4470
NEAT

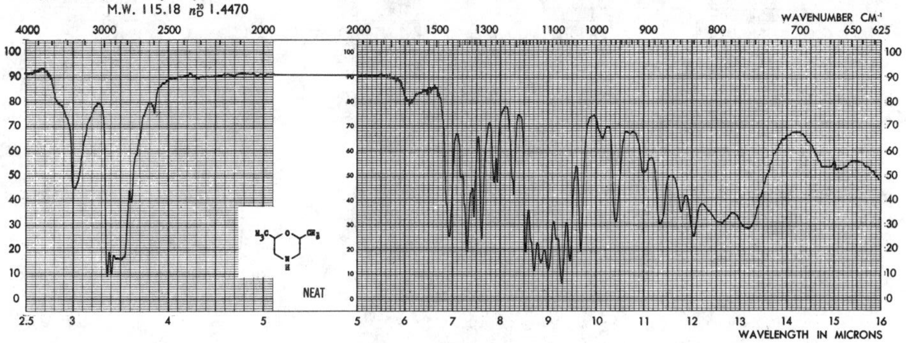

B

M5655-7 **N-Methylmorpholine**
M.W. 101.15 n_D^{20} 1.4349 b.p. 115-116°/750 mm.
NEAT

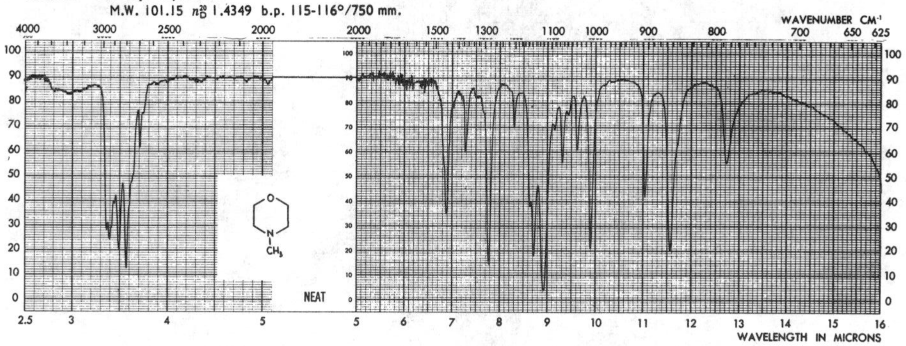

C

10,993-2 **N-Ethylmorpholine**
M.W. 115.18 n_D^{20} 1.4401 b.p. 139°
NEAT

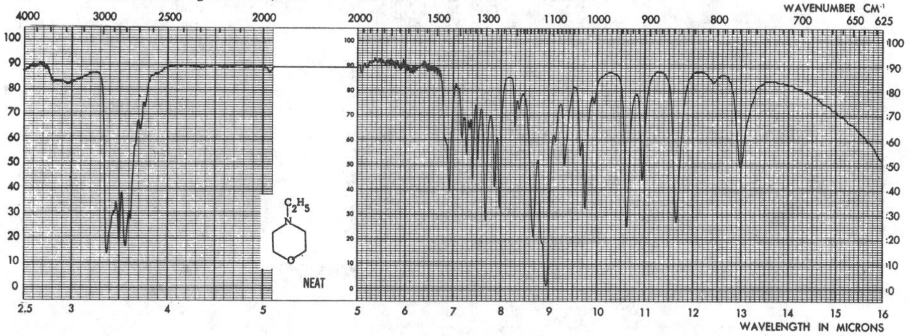

D

12,063-4 **4-(2-Ethyl-1-butenyl)-morpholine**
M.W. 169.27 n_D^{20} 1.4683 b.p. 95°/17 mm. . .
NEAT

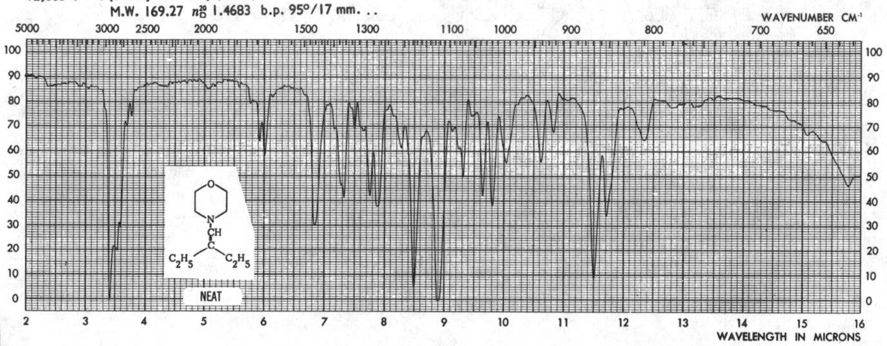

E

12,066-9 **4-(2-Ethyl-1-hexenyl)-morpholine**
M.W. 197.32 n_D^{20} 1.4681 b.p. 114-115°/14 mm.
NEAT

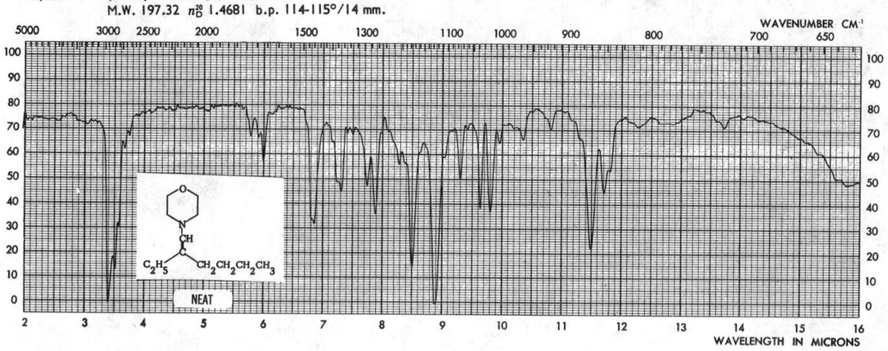

F

C11,490-1
N-(1-Cyclopenten-1-yl)-morpholine, 98%
(1-morpholinocyclopentene)
M.W. 153.23 b.p. 105-106°/12mm. n_D^{20} 1.5105
NEAT

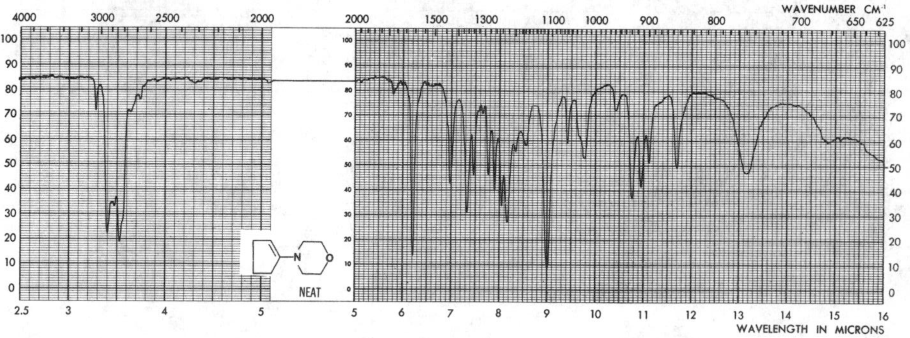

G

M8780-0 **N-Morpholino-1-cyclohexene** [N-(1-cyclohexen-1-yl)-morpholine]
M.W. 167.25 n_D^{20} 1.5128 . . . .
NEAT

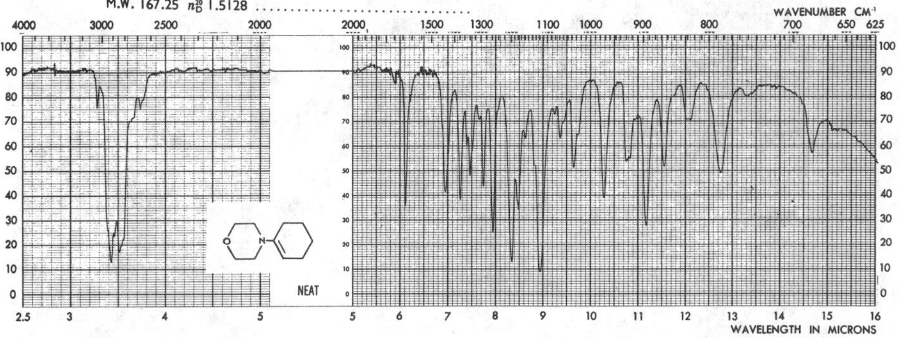

H

C4220-3 **N-(2-Chloroethyl)-morpholine hydrochloride**
M.W. 186.08 m.p. 184-186° . . . .
NUJOL MULL

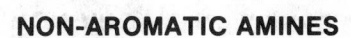

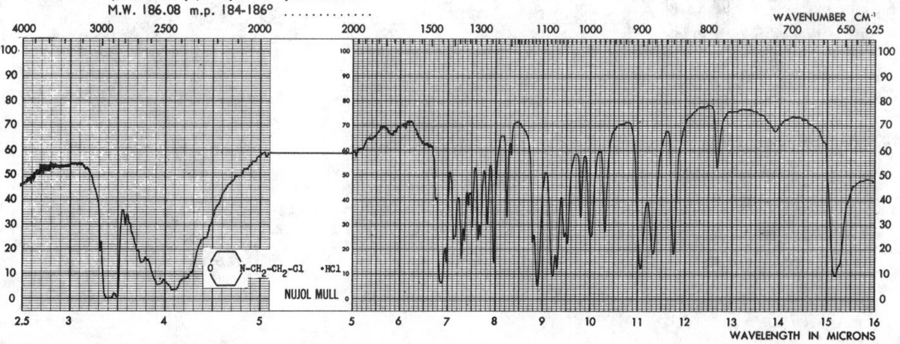

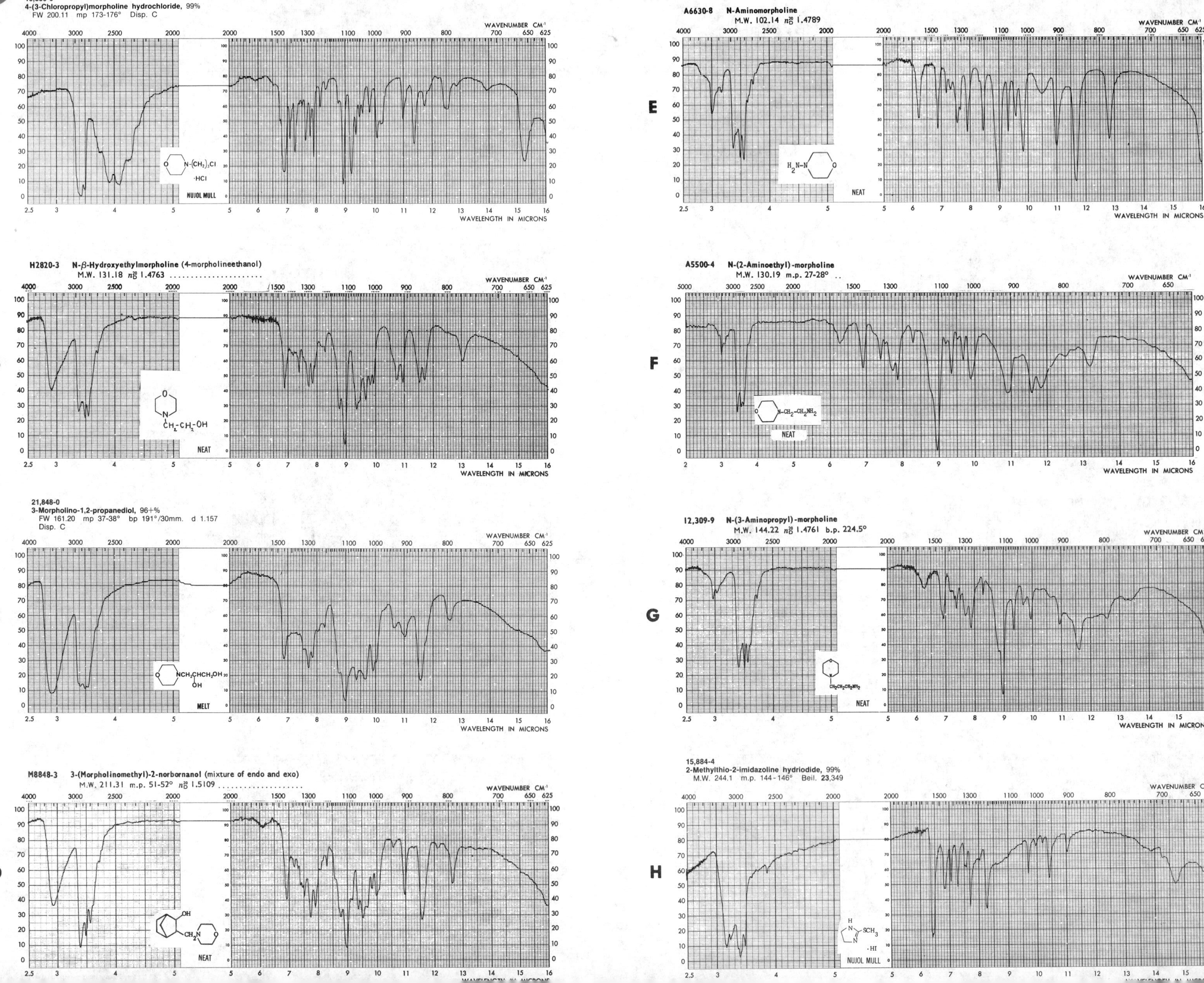
ALDRICH

A
19,356-9
4-(3-Chloropropyl)morpholine hydrochloride, 99%
FW 200.11 mp 173-176° Disp. C
NUJOL MULL

B
H2820-3 N-β-Hydroxyethylmorpholine (4-morpholineethanol)
M.W. 131.18 n_D^{20} 1.4763
NEAT

C
21,848-0
3-Morpholino-1,2-propanediol, 96+%
FW 161.20 mp 37-38° bp 191°/30mm. d 1.157
Disp. C
MELT

D
M8848-3 3-(Morpholinomethyl)-2-norbornanol (mixture of endo and exo)
M.W. 211.31 m.p. 51-52° n_D^{20} 1.5109
NEAT

E
A6630-8 N-Aminomorpholine
M.W. 102.14 n_D^{20} 1.4789
NEAT

F
A5500-4 N-(2-Aminoethyl)-morpholine
M.W. 130.19 m.p. 27-28°
NEAT

G
12,309-9 N-(3-Aminopropyl)-morpholine
M.W. 144.22 n_D^{20} 1.4761 b.p. 224.5°
NEAT

H
15,884-4
2-Methylthio-2-imidazoline hydriodide, 99%
M.W. 244.1 m.p. 144-146° Beil. 23,349
NUJOL MULL

WAVENUMBER CM⁻¹
WAVELENGTH IN MICRONS

A

2,4,4-Trimethyl-2-oxazoline, 99%
M.W. 113.16 b.p. 112-113° n_D^{20} 1.4213 d 0.887
Reagent for the preparation of aliphatic carboxylic acids and esters. *J. Amer. Chem. Soc.*, **92**, 6644 (1970).

B

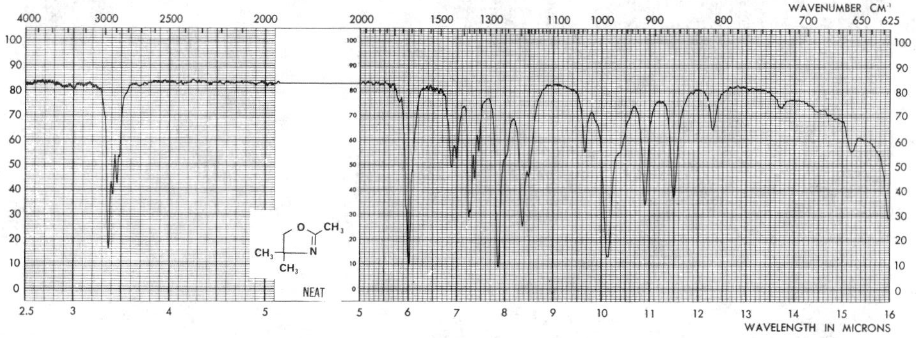

17,815-2
2,2,4,4,6-Pentamethyl-2,3,4,5-tetrahydropyrimidine, tech.
M.W. 154.26 n_D^{20} 1.4680 d 0.873

C

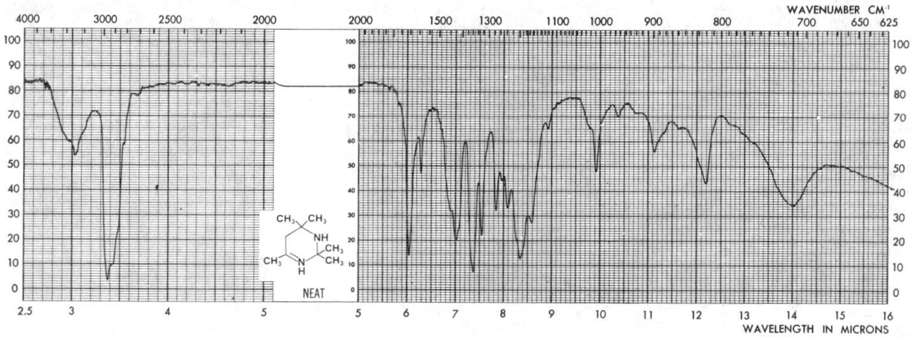

T1955-0 Tetramethylammonium tetrafluoroborate
$(CH_3)_4NBF_4$ M.W. 160.95 m.p. > 330° ...

D

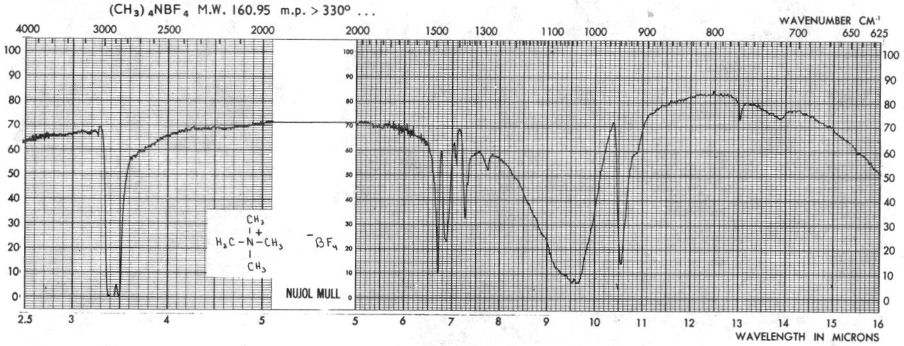

B8970 mono-n-Butylammonium tetrafluoroborate
$C_4H_9NH_3BF_4$

E

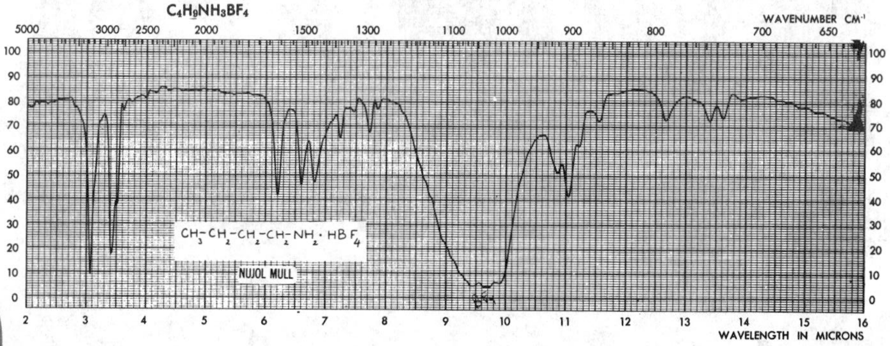

T1953-4 Tetramethylammonium hexafluorophosphate
$(CH_3)_4NPF_6$ M.W. 219.11 m.p. > 300° ...

F

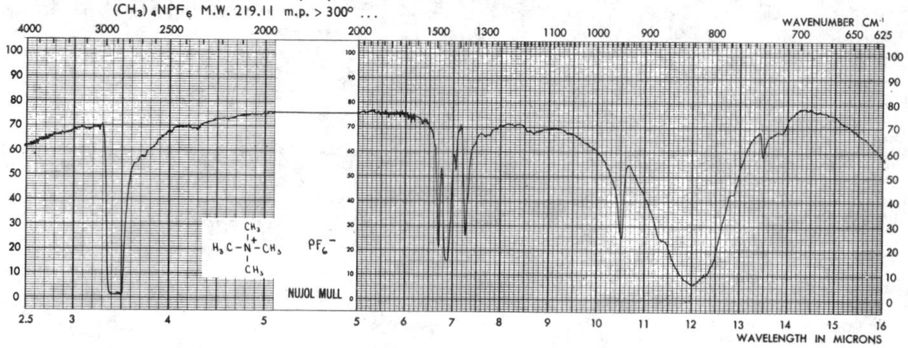

19,575-8
Tetramethylammonium bromide, 98%
$(CH_3)_4NBr$ FW 154.06 mp >300° Disp. C

G

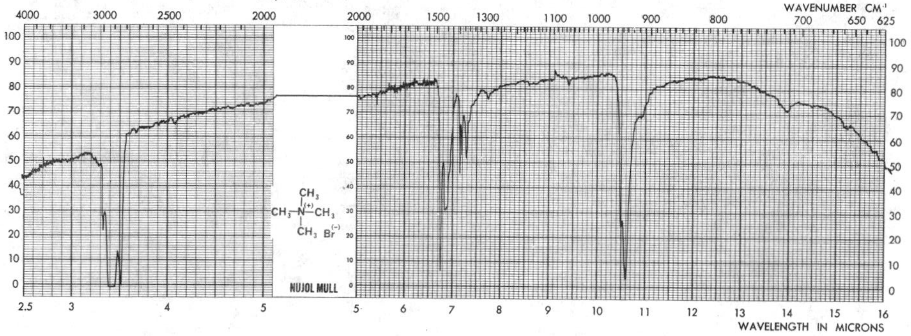

T1952-6 Tetramethylammonium chloride
$(CH_3)_4NCl$ M.W. 109.60 m.p. > 320°

H

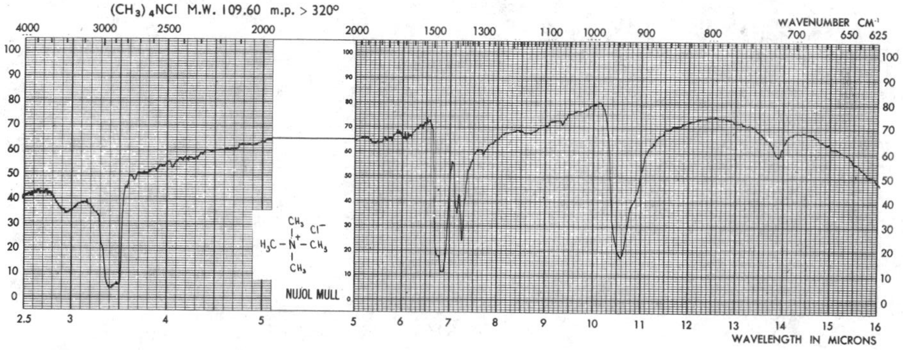

22,321-2
Tetramethylammonium hydroxide pentahydrate, 99%
$(CH_3)_4NOH \cdot 5H_2O$ FW 181.23 mp 65-68°
Beil. 4,50 Disp. H

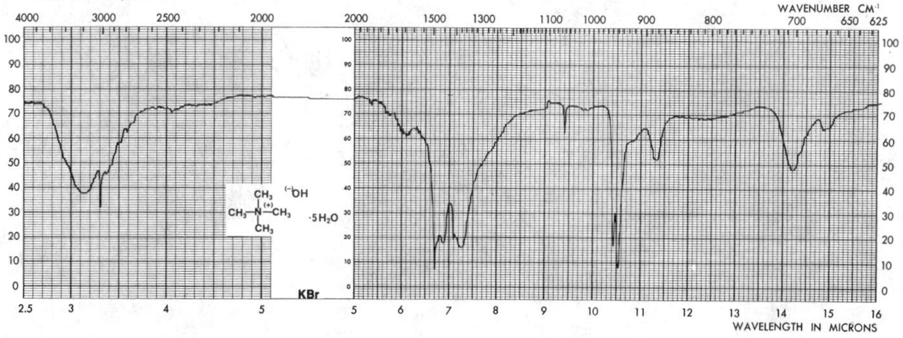

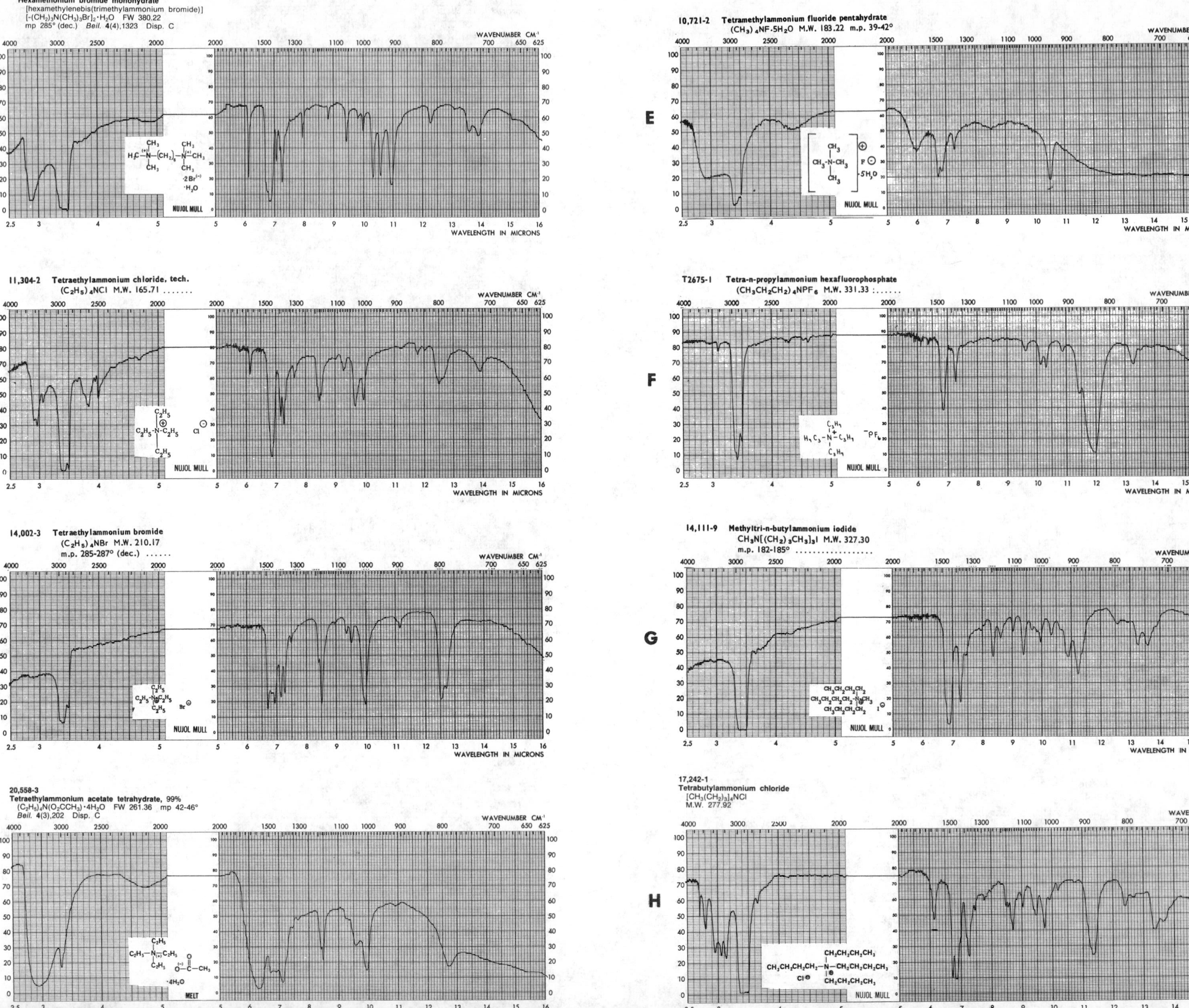
ALDRICH

A
21,967-3
Hexamethonium bromide monohydrate
[hexamethylenebis(trimethylammonium bromide)]
$[-(CH_2)_3N(CH_3)_3Br]_2 \cdot H_2O$ FW 380.22
mp 285° (dec.) Beil. 4(4),1323 Disp. C
NUJOL MULL

B
11,304-2 Tetraethylammonium chloride, tech.
$(C_2H_5)_4NCl$ M.W. 165.71
NUJOL MULL

C
14,002-3 Tetraethylammonium bromide
$(C_2H_5)_4NBr$ M.W. 210.17
m.p. 285-287° (dec.)
NUJOL MULL

D
20,558-3
Tetraethylammonium acetate tetrahydrate, 99%
$(C_2H_5)_4N(O_2CCH_3) \cdot 4H_2O$ FW 261.36 mp 42-46°
Beil. 4(3),202 Disp. C
MELT

E
10,721-2 Tetramethylammonium fluoride pentahydrate
$(CH_3)_4NF \cdot 5H_2O$ M.W. 183.22 m.p. 39-42°
NUJOL MULL

F
T2675-1 Tetra-n-propylammonium hexafluorophosphate
$(CH_3CH_2CH_2)_4NPF_6$ M.W. 331.33
NUJOL MULL

G
14,111-9 Methyltri-n-butylammonium iodide
$CH_3N[(CH_2)_3CH_3]_3I$ M.W. 327.30
m.p. 182-185°
NUJOL MULL

H
17,242-1
Tetrabutylammonium chloride
$[CH_3(CH_2)_3]_4NCl$
M.W. 277.92

WAVENUMBER CM⁻¹
WAVELENGTH IN MICRONS

A

19,311-9
Tetrabutylammonium bromide, 99%
$[CH_3(CH_2)_3]_4NBr$ FW 322.38 mp 103-104°
Fieser 4,477 5,644 7,353 Disp. L

NUJOL MULL

B

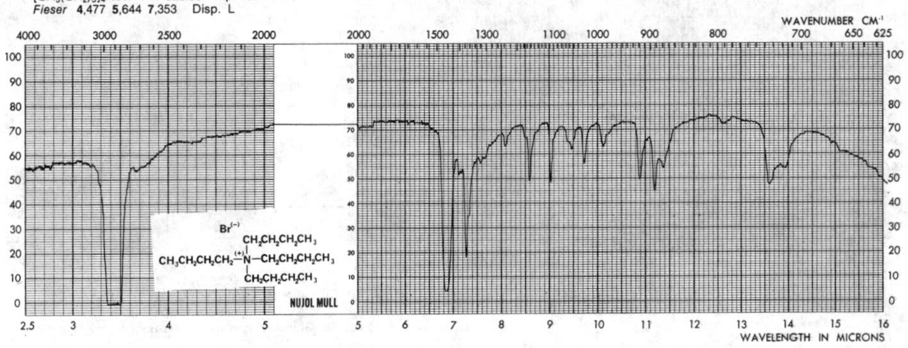

14,077-5 **Tetrabutylammonium iodide**
$[CH_3(CH_2)_3]_4NI$ M.W. 369.38
m.p. 145-148°

NUJOL MULL

C

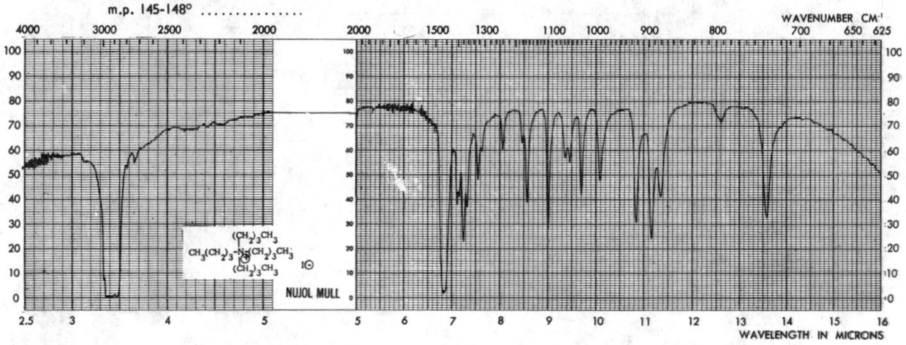

15,583-7 **Tetrabutylammonium hydrogen sulfate**
$[CH_3(CH_2)_3]_4NHSO_4$ M.W. 339.54

NUJOL MULL

D

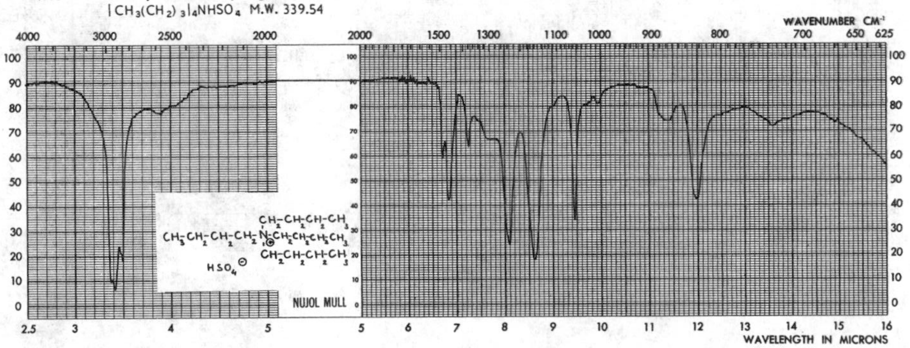

86,042-5
Myristyltrimethylammonium bromide, 99+%
$CH_3(CH_2)_{13}N(CH_3)_3Br$ FW 336.41 mp 245-250°
Disp. L

NUJOL MULL

E

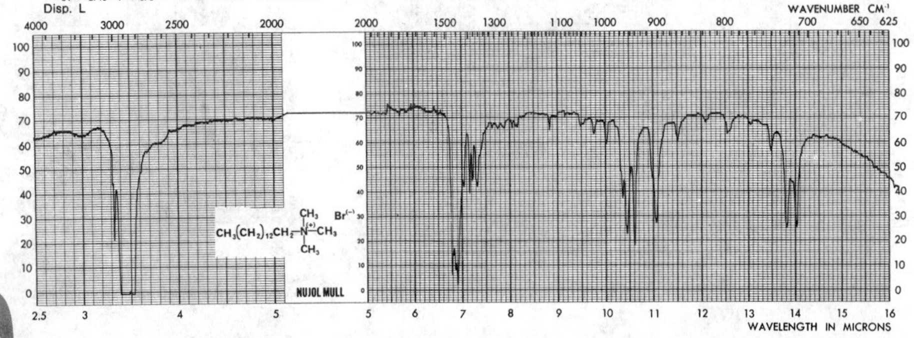

22,396-4
Bis(tetrabutylammonium) dichromate, 99%
$[(CH_3[CH_2]_3)_4N]_2Cr_2O_7$ FW 700.93 mp 139-143°
Fieser 7,194 Disp. V

NUJOL MULL

F

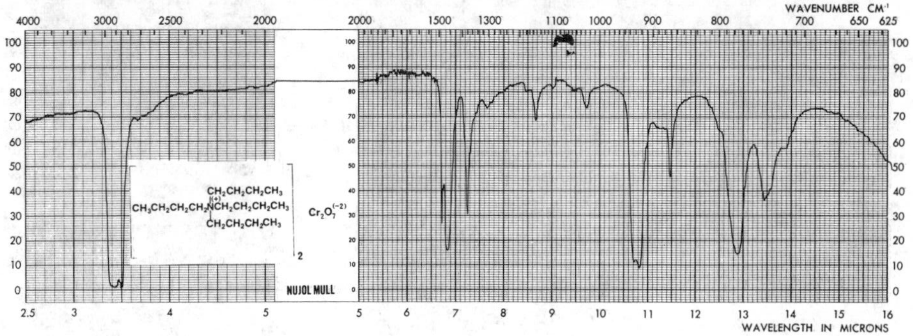

20,561-3
Aliquat® 336 (tricaprylylmethylammonium chloride)
$CH_3N[(CH_2)_7CH_3]_3Cl$ FW 404.17 n_D^{20} 1.4665
d 0.884 *Fieser* 5,460 6,404 7,380 Disp. L

NEAT

G

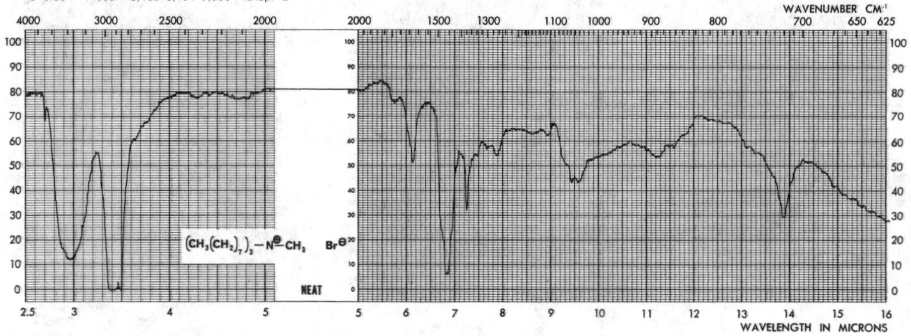

85,657-6
Adogen 464 [methyltrialkyl(C_8-C_{10})ammonium chloride]
n_D^{20} 1.4665

NEAT

H

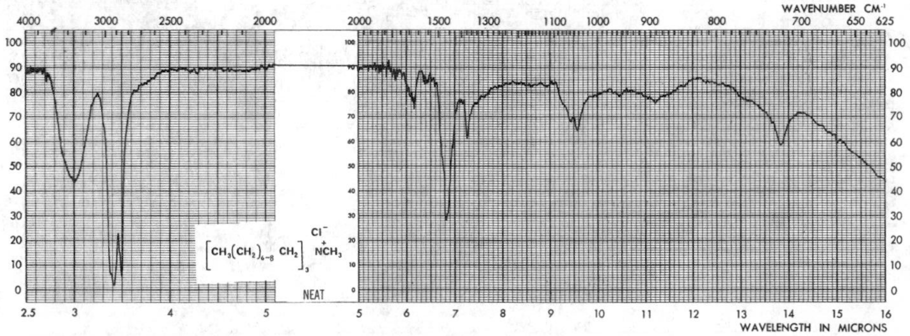

85,582-0
Cetyltrimethylammonium bromide
(cetrimonium bromide)
$CH_3(CH_2)_{15}N(CH_3)_3Br$
M.W. 364.46 m.p. >230° (dec.)

NUJOL MULL

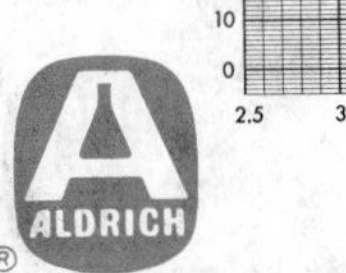

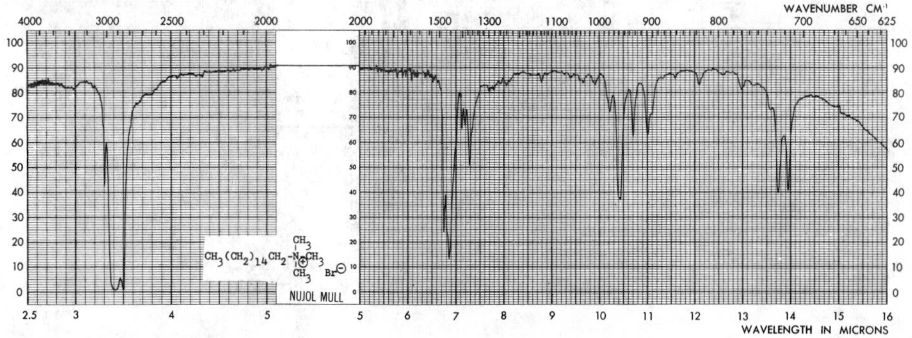

A

14,633-1 **Allyltrimethylammonium bromide**
$H_2C{:}CHCH_2N(CH_3)_3Br$ M.W. 180.10
m.p. 145-152°

NUJOL MULL

B

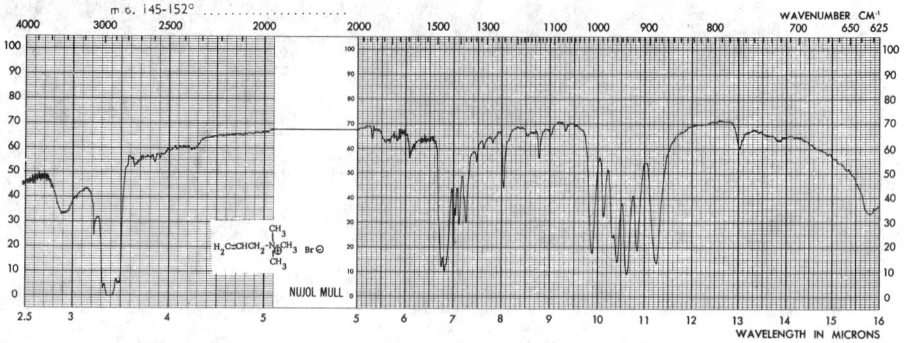

14,632-3 **Allyltriethylammonium bromide**
$H_2C{:}CHCH_2N(C_2H_5)_3Br$ M.W. 222.18
m.p. 236-238° (dec.)

NUJOL MULL

C

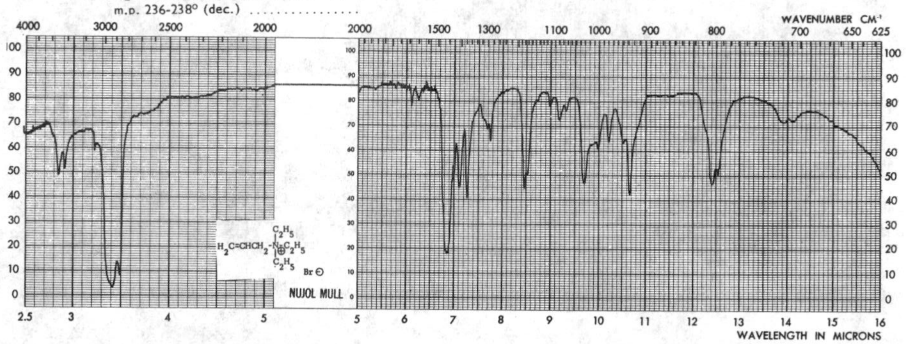

11,719-6 **(2-Bromoethyl)-trimethylammonium bromide**
$BrCH_2CH_2N(CH_3)_3Br$ M.W. 246.99
m.p. 246° (dec.)

NUJOL MULL

D

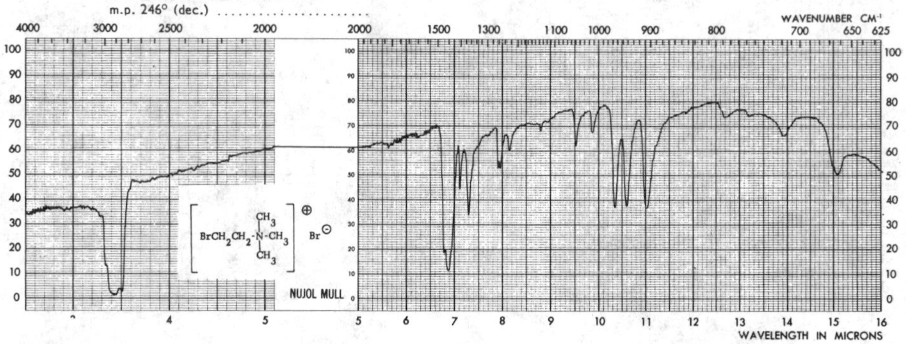

D8370-2 **2,2-Diethoxyethyltrimethylammonium iodide (betaine-aldehyde diethylacetal iodide)**
$(C_2H_5O)_2CHCH_2N(CH_3)_3I$ M.W. 303.18
m.p. 118-119° (low) m.p. 129-131° (high)

NUJOL MULL

E

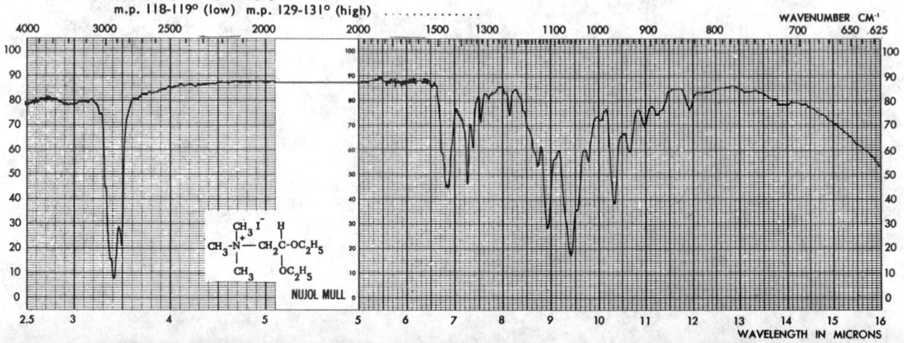

C7970-0 **Choline chloride** [(2-hydroxyethyl)-trimethylammonium chloride]
$HOCH_2CH_2N(CH_3)_3Cl$ M.W. 139.63 m.p. 303-305° (dec.)

NUJOL MULL

F

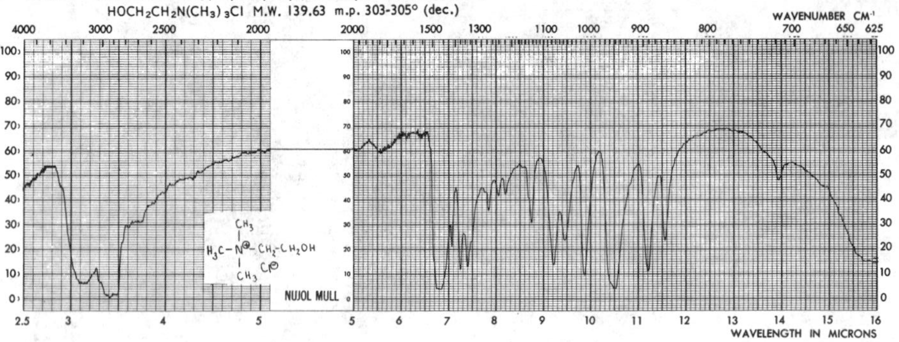

C7971-9 **Choline iodide** [(2-hydroxyethyl)-trimethylammonium iodide]
$HOCH_2CH_2N(CH_3)_3I$ M.W. 230.08 m.p. 263-264°

NUJOL MULL

G

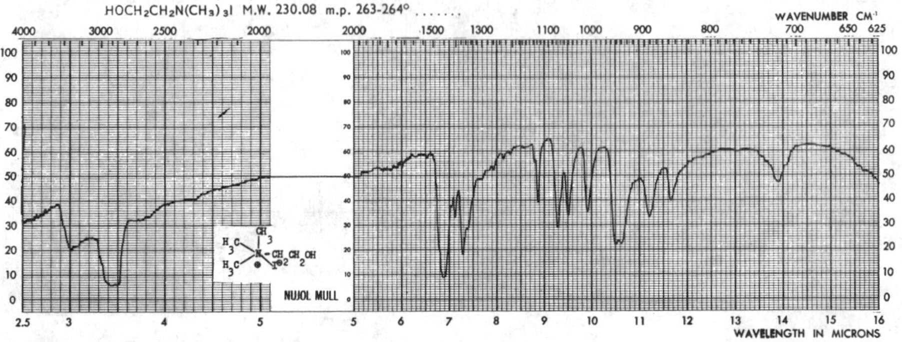

H3,055-0
(2-Hydroxyethyl)-triethylammonium iodide, 99%
$HOCH_2CH_2N(C_2H_5)_3I$
M.W. 273.16 m.p. 290° (dec.)

NUJOL MULL

H

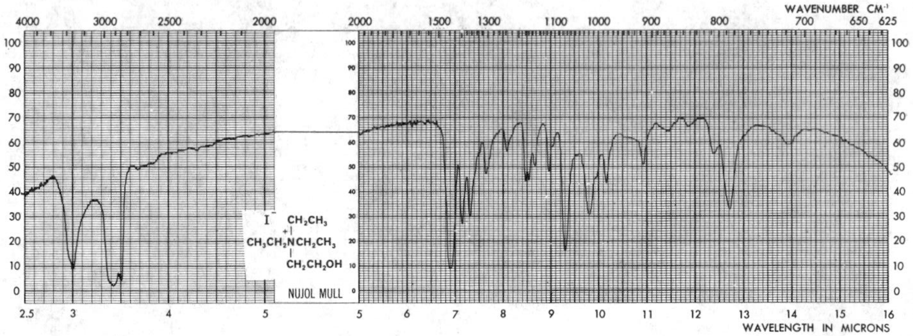

86,146-4
Pentolinium tartrate, 99% [1,1'-pentamethylenebis(1-methylpyrrolidinium hydrogen tartrate)]
FW 538.60 mp 213° (dec.) Disp. C

NUJOL MULL

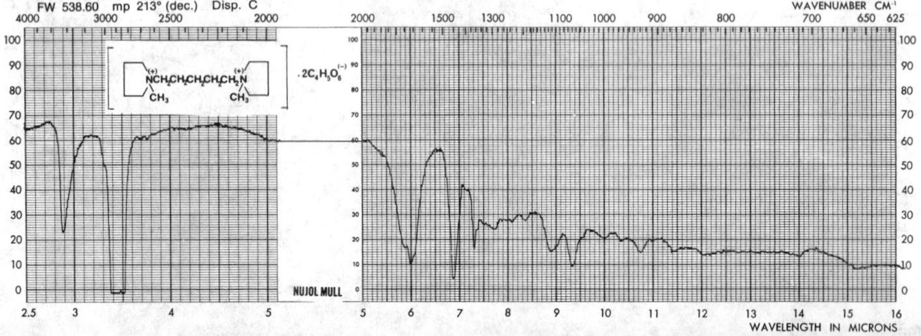

22,556-8
Tetrapropylammonium bromide, 98%
$(CH_3CH_2CH_2)_4NBr$ FW 266.27 mp 270° (dec.)
Beil. 4(1),364 Disp. C

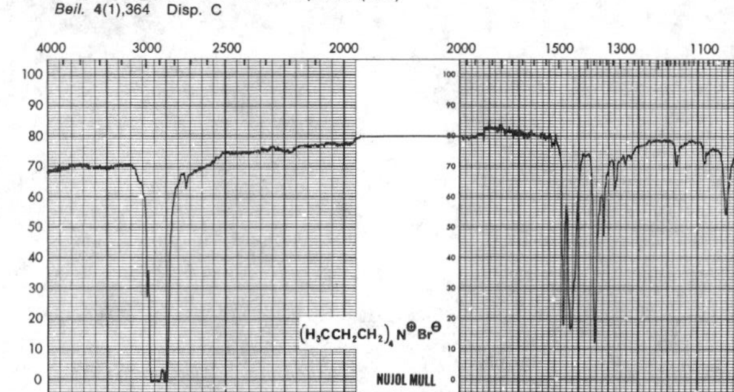

NON-AROMATIC NITRO AND NITROSO COMPOUNDS

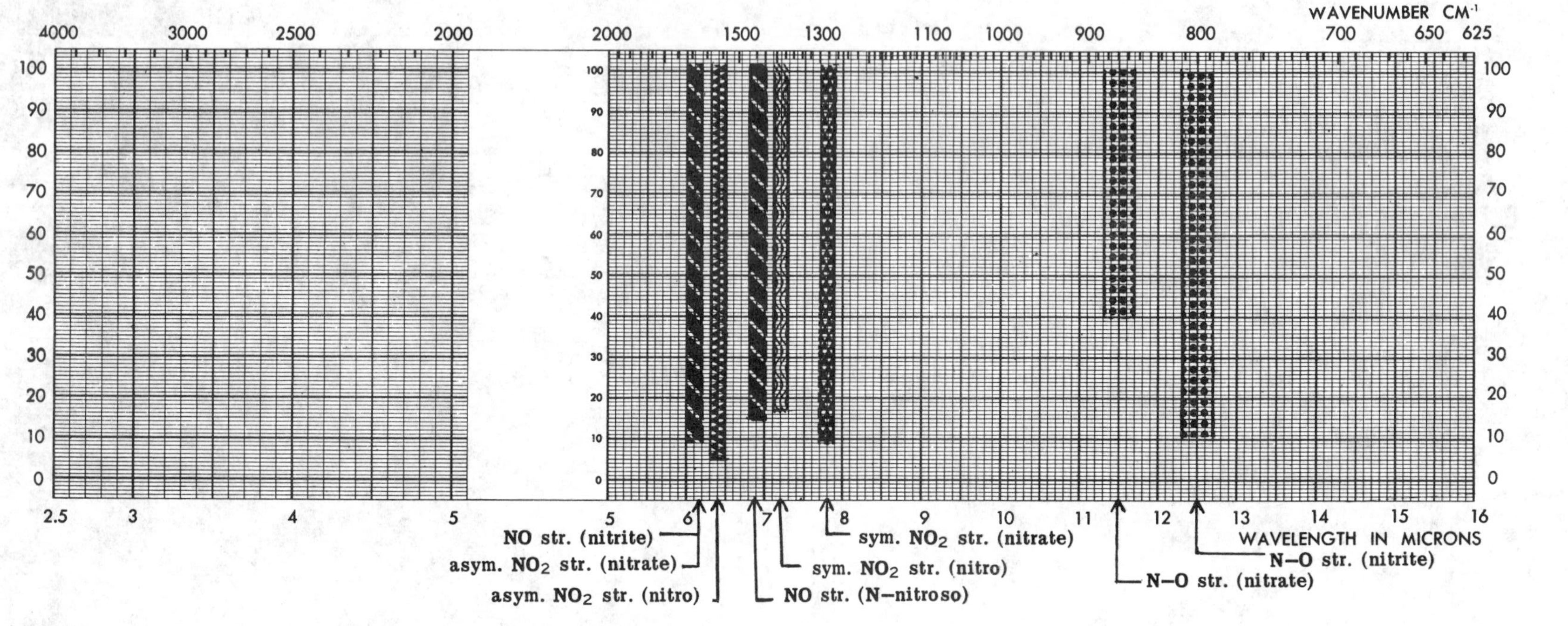

1.) Nitrite 234A-B
2.) Nitrate 234C
3.) Nitroso 234D-G
4.) Nitro 234H-237F

Although this collection is not as extensive as others, it does contain members of the organic nitrite, (C–O–N=O), organic nitrate, (C–O–NO_2), N-nitroso (N–N=O) and the nitro (C–NO_2) groups.

The nitrite has two absorptions around 6.1 μ (1640 cm^{-1}). The higher wavelength absorption is the less intense. These two absorptions are accompanied by a very strong nitrogen-oxygen stretch absorption around 12.5 μ (800 cm^{-1}).

The organic nitrate has three principal absorptions:

1.) the asymmetric NO_2 stretch absorption around 6.1 μ (1640 cm^{-1});

2.) the symmetric NO_2 stretch absorption around 7.8 μ (1280 cm^{-1});

3.) the nitrogen-oxygen stretch vibrations appearing at 11.5 μ (870 cm^{-1}).

The N-nitroso group has its N=O stretch absorption very close to 6.9 μ (1450 cm^{-1}), which is masked when the compound is mulled in mineral oil.

The nitro group attached to a carbon atom has its primary absorptions at 6.4 μ and 7.2 μ (1565 and 1390 cm^{-1}), with the 6.4 μ (1565 cm^{-1}) band the stronger of the two.

A

15,048-7 **Amyl nitrite** (pentyl nitrite)
$CH_3(CH_2)_4ONO$ M.W. 117.15 n_D^{20} 1.3881
b.p. 105°

$CH_3CH_2CH_2CH_2CH_2ONO$ — NEAT

B

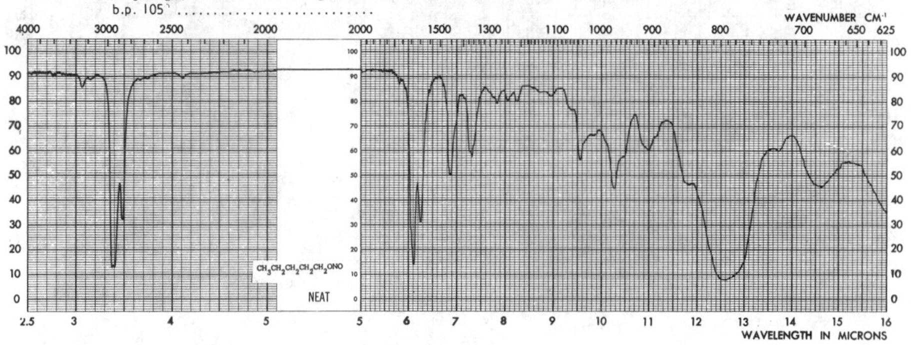

15,049-5 **Isoamyl nitrite** (isopentyl nitrite)
$(CH_3)_2CHCH_2CH_2ONO$ M.W. 117.15 n_D^{20} 1.3860
b.p. 99°

NEAT

C

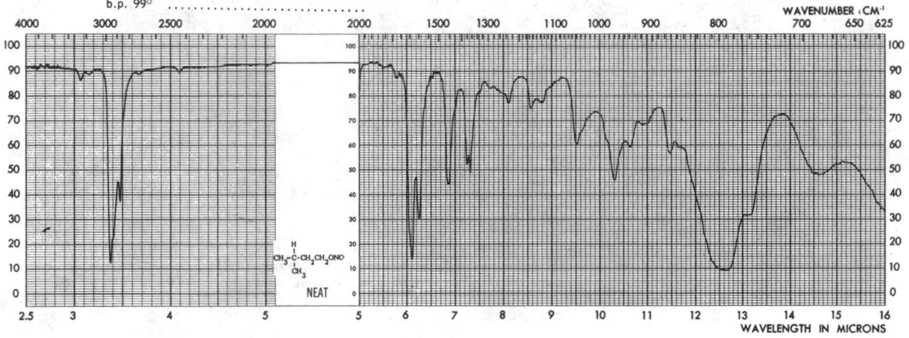

10,909-6 **n-Propyl nitrate**
$CH_3CH_2CH_2ONO_2$ M.W. 105.09 n_D^{20} 1.3976
b.p. 110°

$H_3C-CH_2-CH_2-O-NO_2$ — NEAT

D

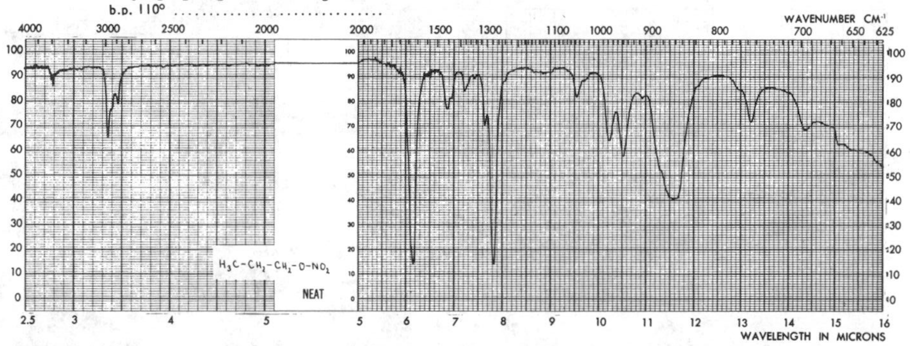

18,026-2
2-Methyl-2-nitrosopropane (nitroso-*tert.*-butane)
$(CH_3)_3CNO$
M.W. 87.12 m.p. 81-83° Beil. 1,129

NUJOL MULL

E

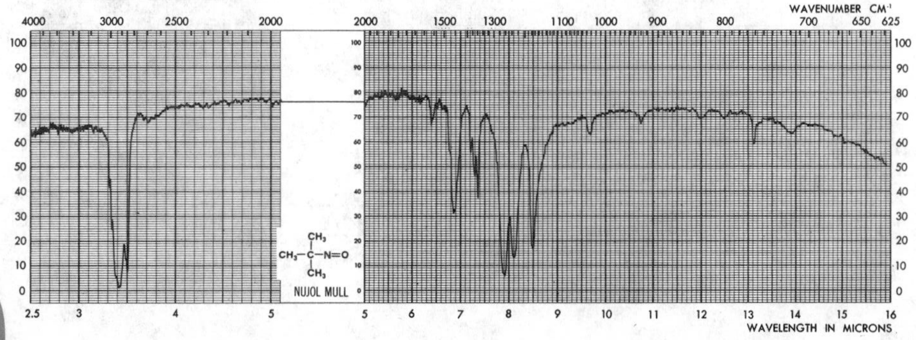

N2500-1 **N-Nitrosodimethylamine, puriss.**
$(CH_3)_2NNO$ M.W. 74.08 n_D^{20} 1.4368
b.p. 150-152°

$O=N-N(CH_3)_2$ — NEAT

F

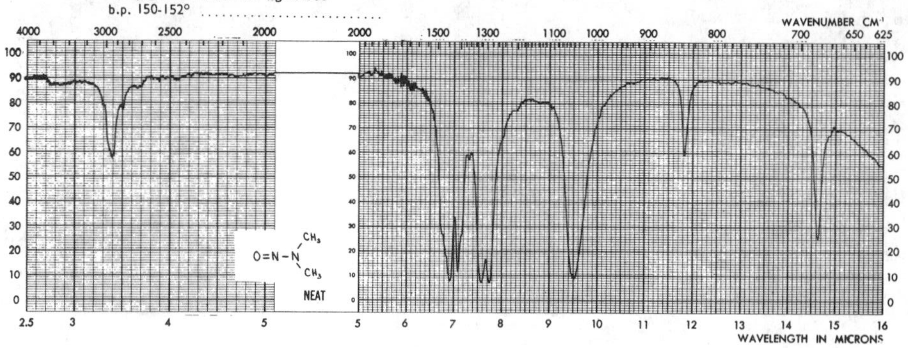

15,824-0
1-Nitrosopyrrolidine
M.W. 100.12 b.p. 214° n_D^{20} 1.4896 Beil. **20**,6
CARCINOGEN

NEAT

G

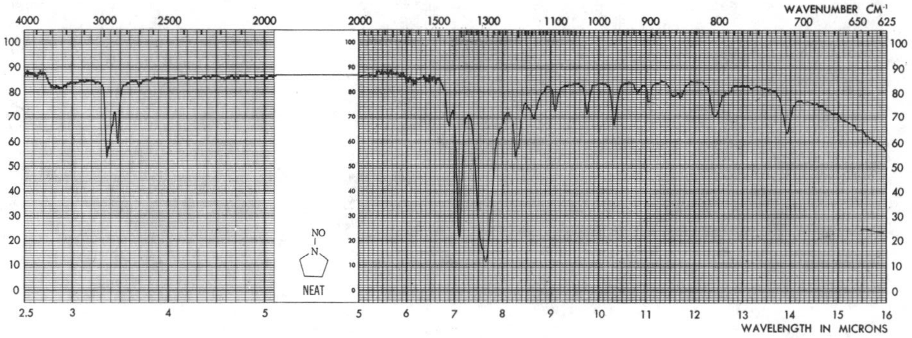

14,373-1 **N-Nitrosodicyclohexylamine**
$(C_6H_{11})_2NNO$ M.W. 210.32 m.p. 105-108°

NUJOL MULL

H

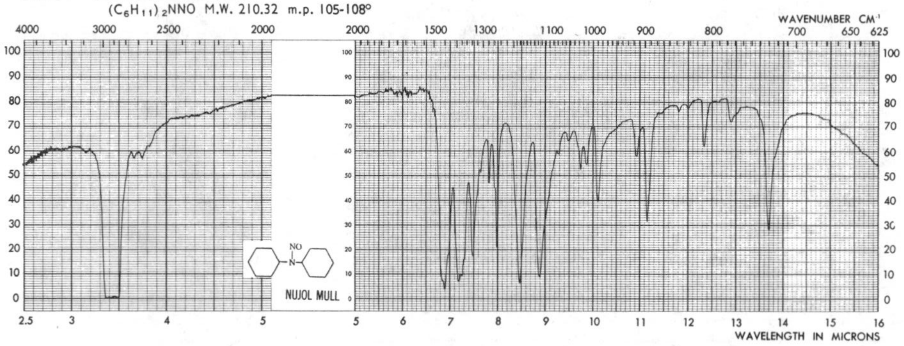

10,817-0 **Nitromethane**
CH_3NO_2 M.W. 61.04 n_D^{20} 1.3806
b.p. 100-102°

$H-C(H)(H)-NO_2$ — NEAT

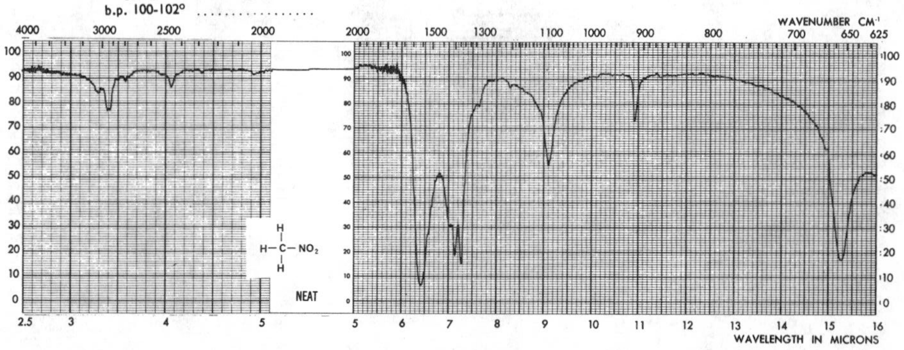

A

T2500-3 **Tetranitromethane**
$C(NO_2)_4$ M.W. 196.03 n_D^{20} 1.4354 b.p. 126°
MELT

B

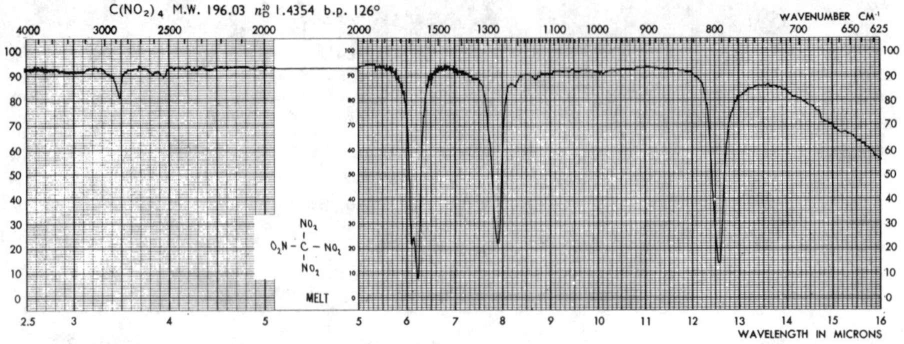

13,020-6 **Nitroethane**
$C_2H_5NO_2$ M.W. 75.07 n_D^{20} 1.3900
b.p. 112-114°
NEAT

C

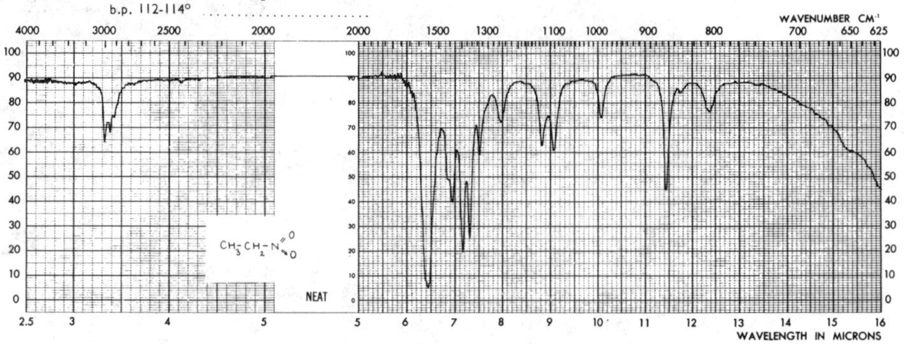

12,116-9 **1,1-Dinitroethane (30% solution in ethylene chloride)**
$CH_3CH(NO_2)_2$ M.W. 120.06 (dry)
NEAT

D

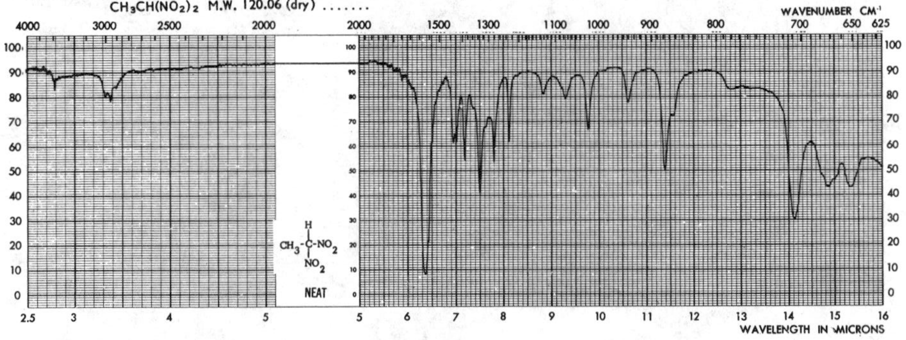

N2285-1 **1-Nitropropane**
$CH_3CH_2CH_2NO_2$ M.W. 89.09 n_D^{20} 1.4002
NEAT

E

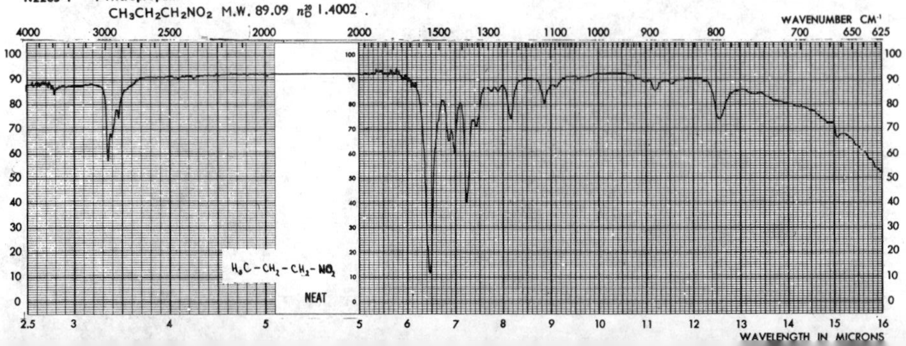

13,026-5
2-Nitropropane, 98%
$(CH_3)_2CHNO_2$
M.W. 89.09 m.p. -93° b.p. 120° n_D^{20} 1.3945
d 0.992 Beil. 1,116
NEAT

F

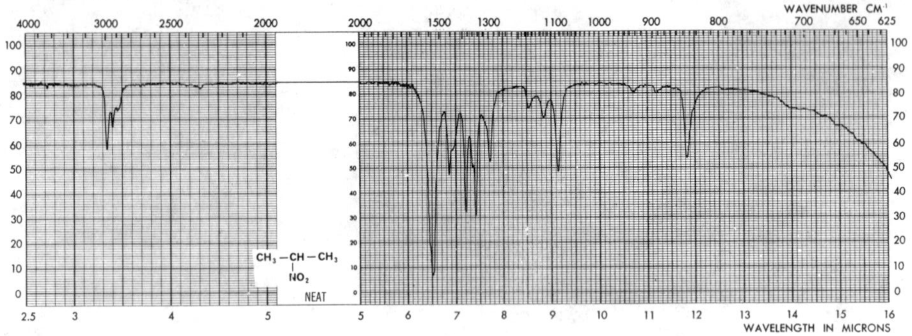

18,902-2
2-Methyl-2-nitropropane
FW 103.12 bp 126-127° n_D^{20} 1.4036 d 0.950
Beil. 1,129 Disp. T
NEAT

G

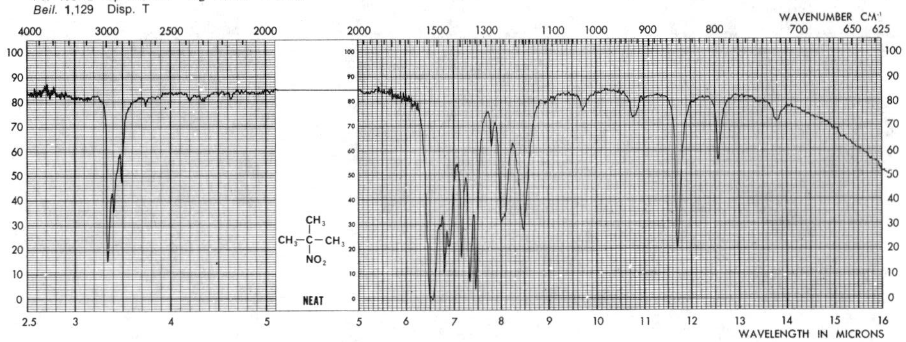

N1660-6 **Nitrocyclohexane**
$C_6H_{11}NO_2$ M.W. 129.16 n_D^{20} 1.4606 b.p. 205.5-206°/768 mm.
NEAT

H

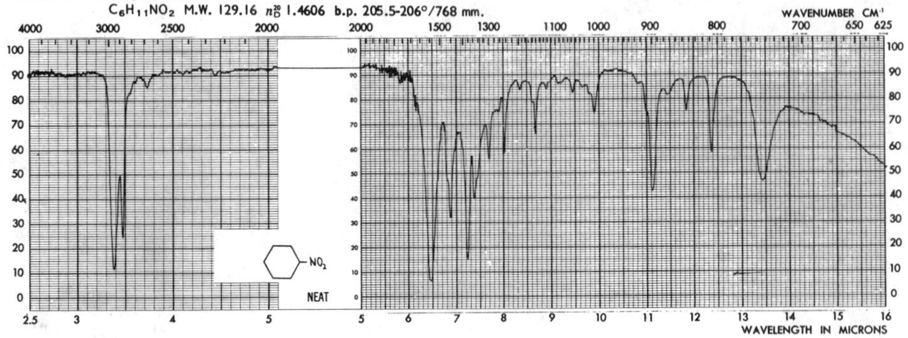

21,953-3
1-Nitro-1-cyclohexene, 99%
FW 127.15 bp 66-68°/1.500mm. n_D^{20} 1.5049
d 1.127 *Beil.* 5(2),41 Disp. C
NEAT

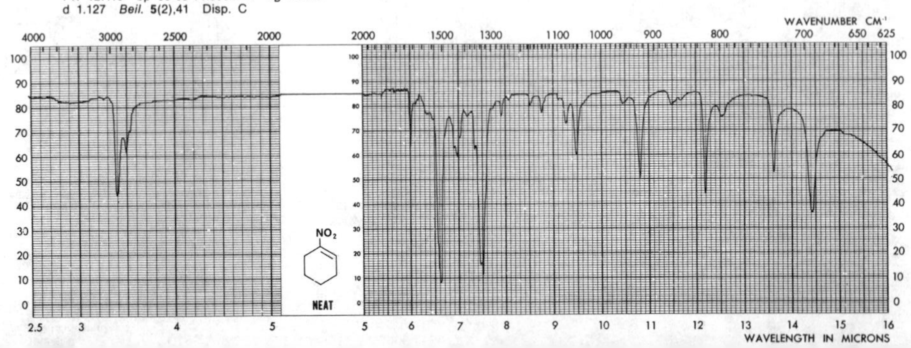

A 14,663-3 **2-Nitroethanol**
$HOC_2H_4NO_2$ M.W. 91.07 n_D^{20} 1.4420
b.p. 60°/0.5 mm.
$O_2NCH_2CH_2OH$ NEAT

B 14,759-1 **2-Nitro-1-propanol**
$CH_3CH(NO_2)CH_2OH$ M.W. 105.09 n_D^{20} 1.4390
b.p. 72-74°/1-2 mm.
NEAT

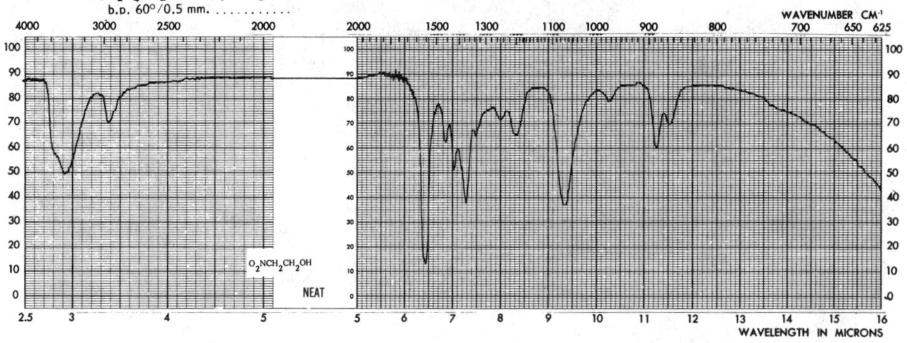

C 12,438-9 **2-Nitro-1-butanol**
$C_2H_5CH(NO_2)CH_2OH$ M.W. 119.12 n_D^{20} 1.4412
b.p. 105°/10 mm.
NEAT

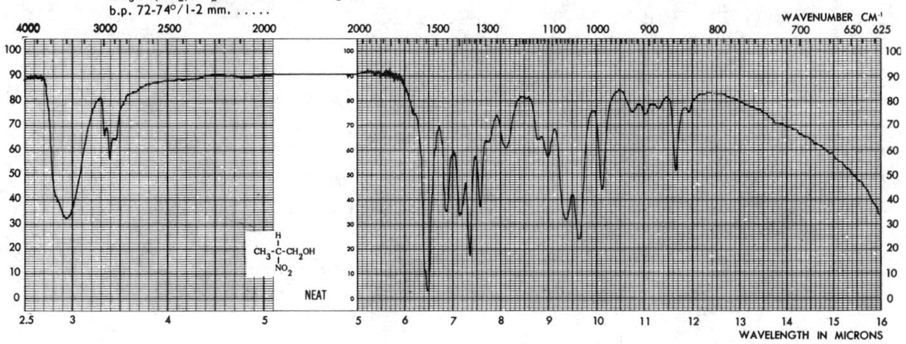

D 14,664-1 **3-Nitro-2-butanol**
$CH_3CH(NO_2)CH(OH)CH_3$ M.W. 119.12 n_D^{20} 1.4414
b.p. 55°/0.5 mm.
NEAT

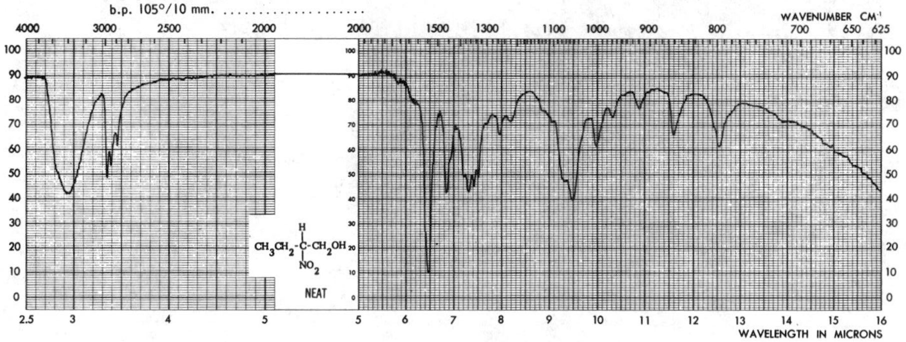

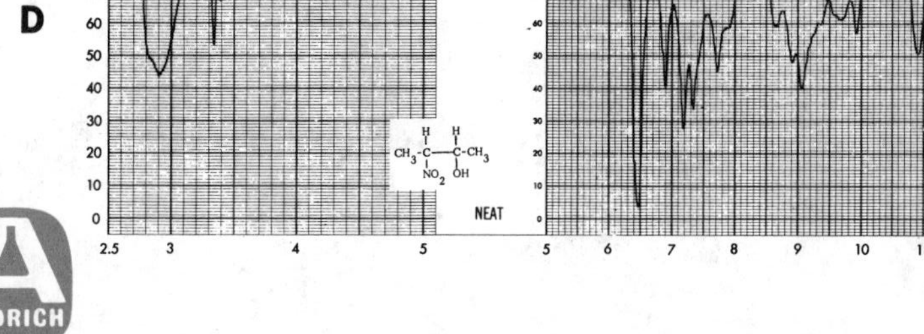

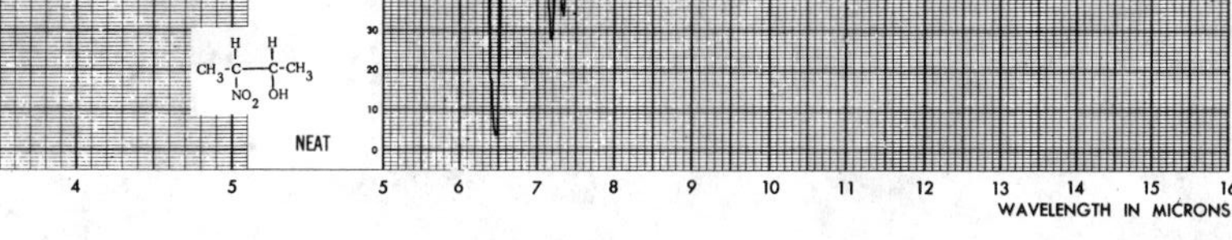

E 15,970-0 **3-Nitro-2-pentanol, 99%**
$C_2H_5CH(NO_2)CH(OH)CH_3$
M.W. 133.15 b.p. 60°/0.5mm. n_D^{20} 1.4430
d 1.075 Beil. 1,385
NEAT

F 15,634-5 **2,3-Dimethyl-2,3-dinitrobutane**
$(CH_3)_2C(NO_2)C(CH_3)_2NO_2$
M.W. 176.17 m.p. 214-215° (dec.) Beil. 1,153
NUJOL MULL

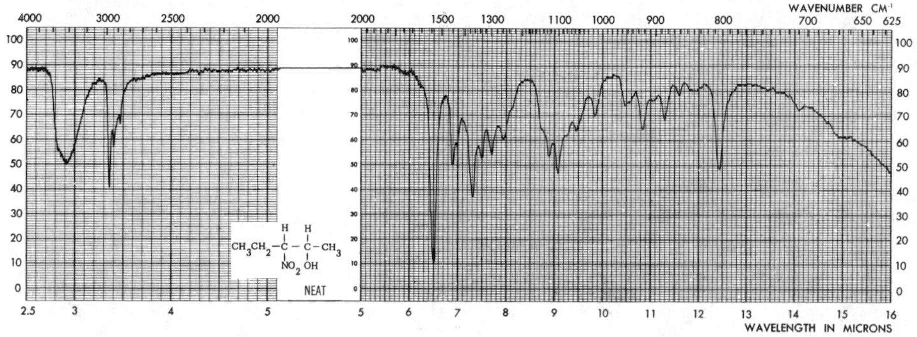

G 12,439-7 **2-Methyl-2-nitro-1-propanol**
$(CH_3)_2C(NO_2)CH_2OH$ M.W. 119.12
m.p. 90-91.5°
NUJOL MULL

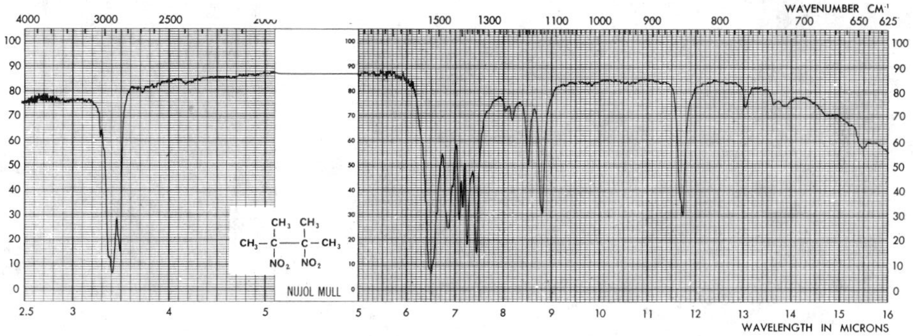

H 12,117-7 **2,2-Dinitropropanol** (30% solution in ethylene chloride)
$CH_3C(NO_2)_2CH_2OH$ M.W. 150.09 (dry)
n_D^{20} 1.4495
NEAT

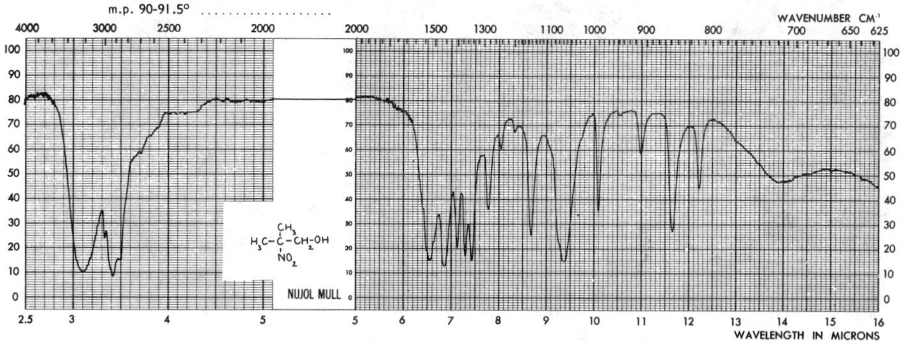

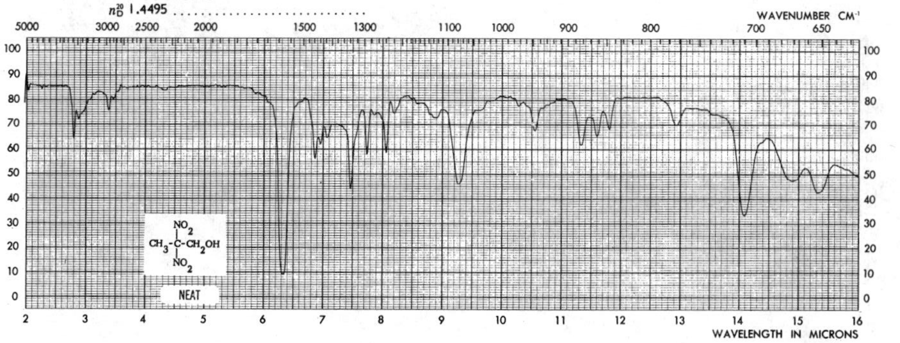

A

10,816-2 **2-Methyl-2-nitro-1,3-propanediol**
$HOCH_2C(CH_3)(NO_2)CH_2OH$ M.W. 135.12
m.p. 154-156°

B

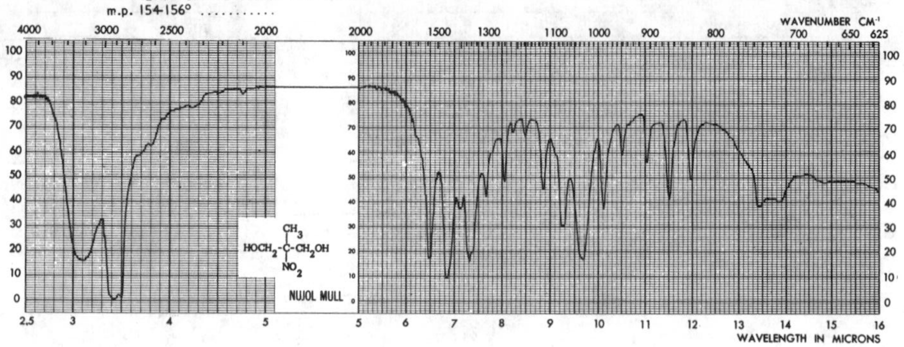

10,818-9 **2-(Hydroxymethyl)-2-nitro-1,3-propanediol**
$O_2NC(CH_2OH)_3$ M.W. 151.12
m.p. 174° (dec.)

C

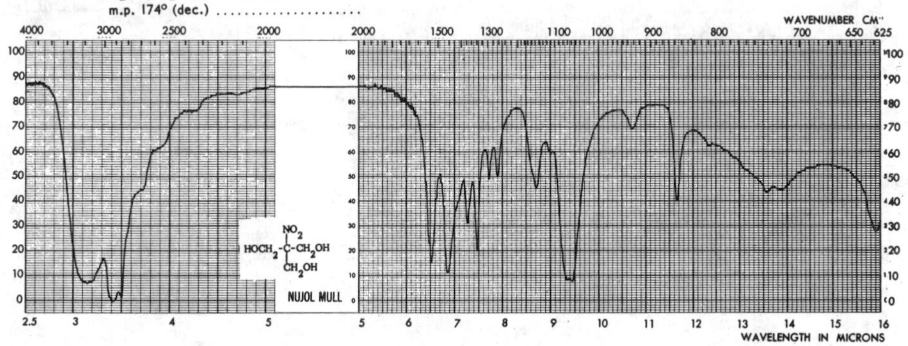

12,115-0 **1-Chloro-1-nitroethane**
$CH_3CH(Cl)NO_2$ M.W. 109.51 n_D^{20} 1.4286
b.p. 125.2°

D

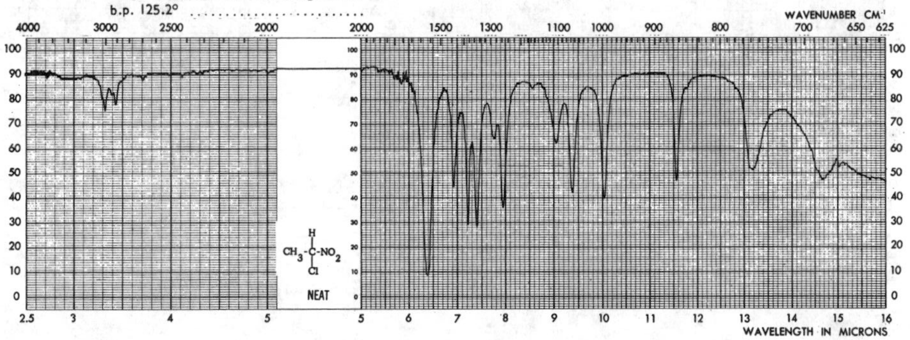

B7430 **2-Bromo-2-nitropropane**
$(CH_3)_2C(Br)NO_2$ M.W. 168.00 n_D^{20} 1.4641

E

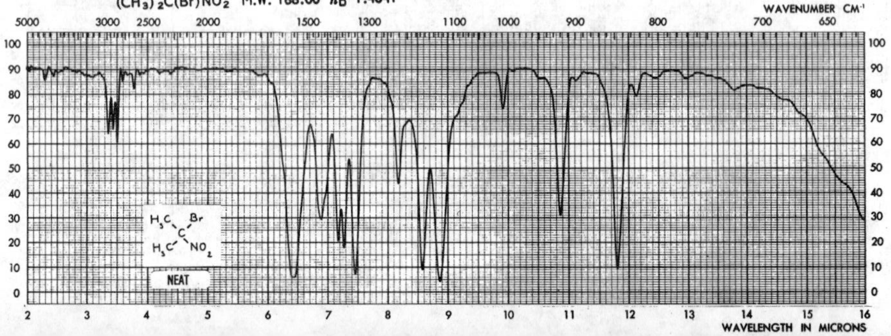

13,470-8 **2-Bromo-2-nitro-1,3-propanediol (bronopol)**
$HOCH_2C(Br)(NO_2)CH_2OH$ M.W. 200.00
m.p. 130-133°

F

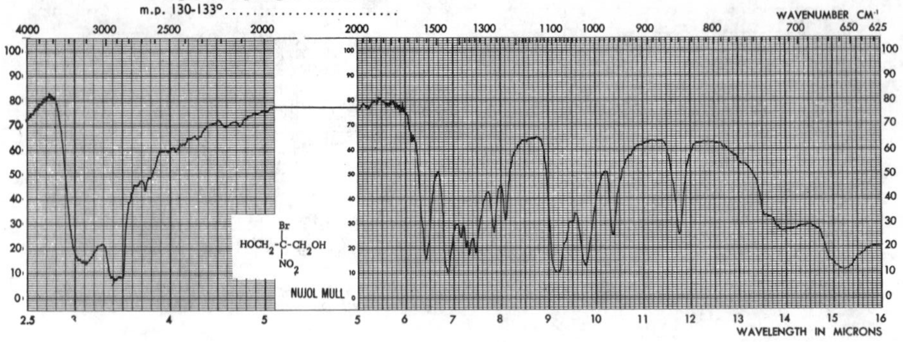

19,233-3
Ethyl nitroacetate, 98%
$O_2NCH_2CO_2C_2H_5$ FW 133.10 bp 105-107°/25mm.
n_D^{20} 1.4237 d 1.199 *Beil.* **2**,225 Disp. C

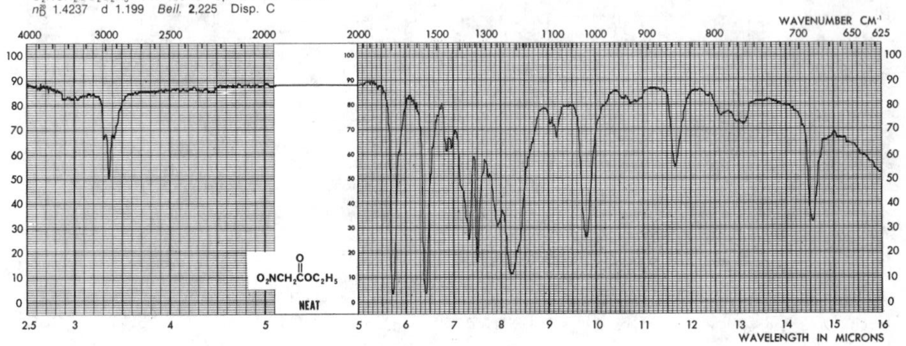

NON-AROMATIC KETONES

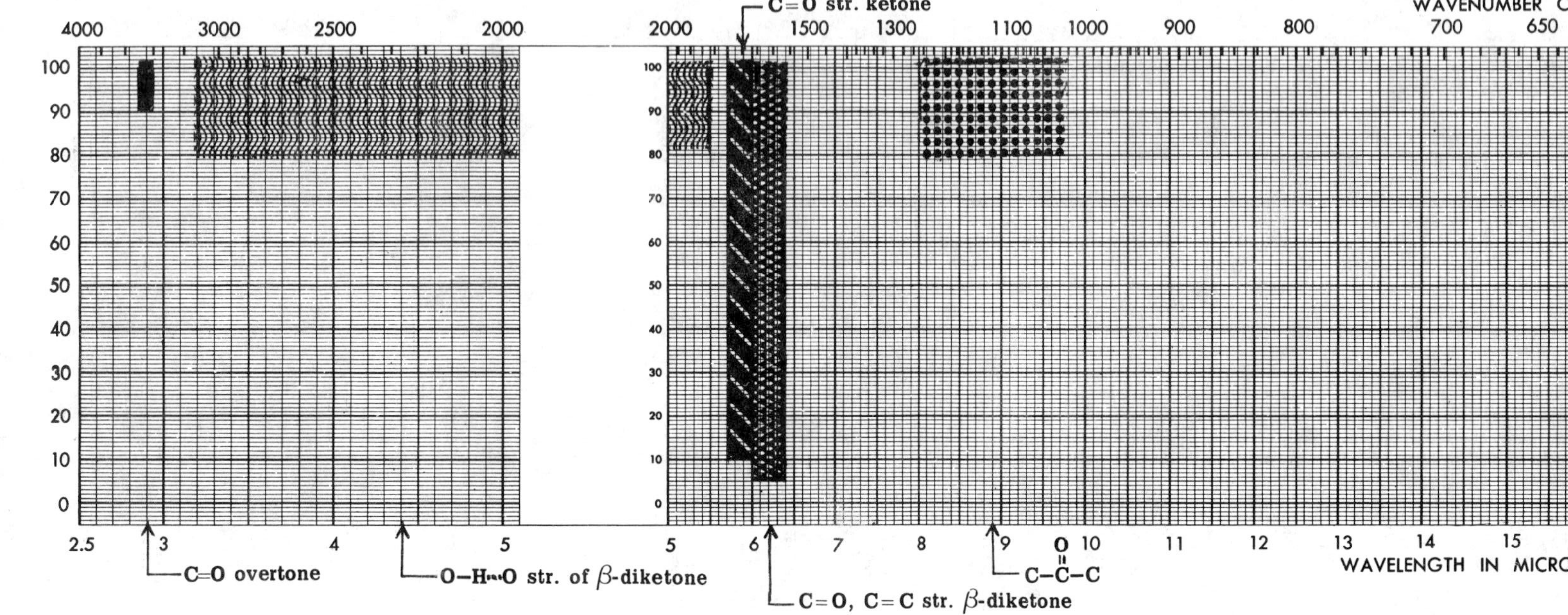

1.) Saturated	240A-246C
2.) Unsaturated	246D-247E
3.) Halogenated......	247F-249F
4.) Hydroxy	249G-250H
5.) Acetal	251A-251D
6.) Diketones	251E-254C
7.) Cyclic	252G-271C
8.) Amino	271D-274E
9.) Heterocyclic	272F-274F

In this and the following eight sections, you will see the influence of various groups on the intensity, shape and position of the carbonyl absorption which in general absorbs within the extremes of 5 and 6.7 μ (2000 – 1495 cm^{-1}). The position of the band within this range provides a considerable amount of information concerning the carbonyl and its adjacent groups. The additional absorptions of attached groups help in pinpointing the nature of the carbonyl.

The ketone function presents us with one of the simplest forms of the carbonyl. Of all the carbonyls, the ketone is outstanding in its lack of additional characteristic absorptions. Aside from the C=O stretch band near 5.85 μ (1710 cm^{-1}), those that are associated with the ketone function between 8 and 9.7 μ (1250 – 1030 cm^{-1}) are relatively weak, variable in position and found in a region where bands from many other functional groups appear. The sharp but weak peak around 2.9 μ (3450 cm^{-1}) is the overtone absorption of the carbonyl stretch band and is often mistaken for an alcohol impurity. In some of the spectra in this collection, the broad absorption at a slightly lower wavelength than the overtone is attributable to traces of moisture.

The shift of the carbonyl absorption to a higher wavelength due to the conjugation of the carbonyl with the C=C can be noted in spectra 246 D — 247 E. A shift to a lower wavelength can be observed in both the cyclic ketones of less than six members and the ketones which are halogen substituted on the alpha carbon. (See spectra 248B—249F).

Except for the β-diketones, the members of the diketone collection absorb very close to the normal 5.85 μ (1710 cm^{-1}) region. The enol-keto tautomers of the β-diketone display a very unique set of absorptions of high intensity in the carbonyl region. The keto-tautomer displays a doublet between 5.7 and 5.9 μ (1755 – 1695 cm^{-1}), while the enolic tautomer displays its carbonyl around 6.3 μ (1585 cm^{-1}). The associated hydrogen-oxygen bond appears as a very broad absorption between 3.2 and 5.5 μ (3125 – 1820 cm^{-1}). The cyclic β-diketones of this series appear to be entirely in the enolic form while the noncyclic are a mixture of the enol and keto forms.

A

15,459-8 **Acetone, spectrophotometric grade, GOLD LABEL**
(meets A.C.S. spectrophotometric requirements)
CH_3COCH_3 M.W. 58.08 b.p. 56°

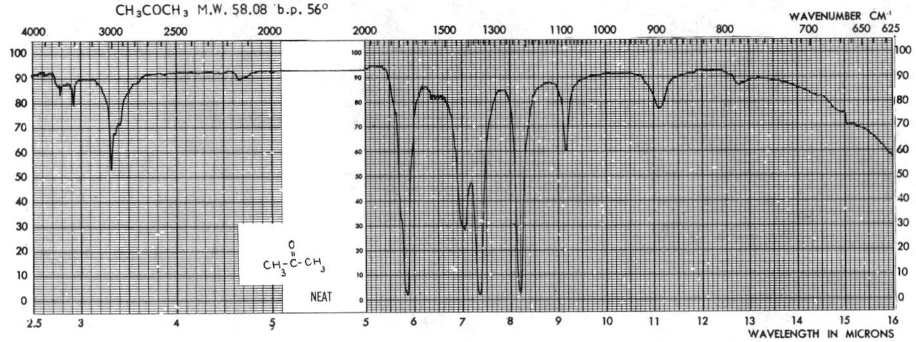

B

11,026-4 **2-Butanone** (methyl ethyl ketone), 99+%
$C_2H_5COCH_3$ M.W. 72.11 n_D^{20} 1.3770
b.p. 79.6°

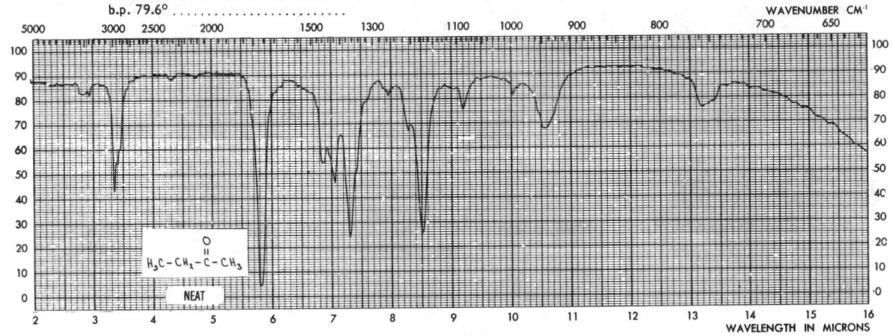

C

P4560-5 **Pinacolone** (tert.-butyl methyl ketone, 3,3-dimethyl-2-butanone)
$(CH_3)_3CCOCH_3$ M.W. 100.16 n_D^{20} 1.3964
b.p. 104-107°

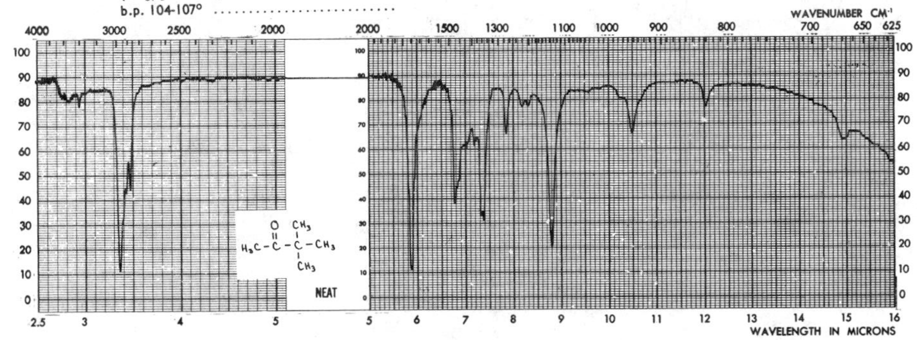

D

P810-6 **2-Pentanone** (methyl propyl ketone)
$CH_3CH_2CH_2COCH_3$ M.W. 86.13 n_D^{20} 1.3897
b.p. 100.5-101.5°

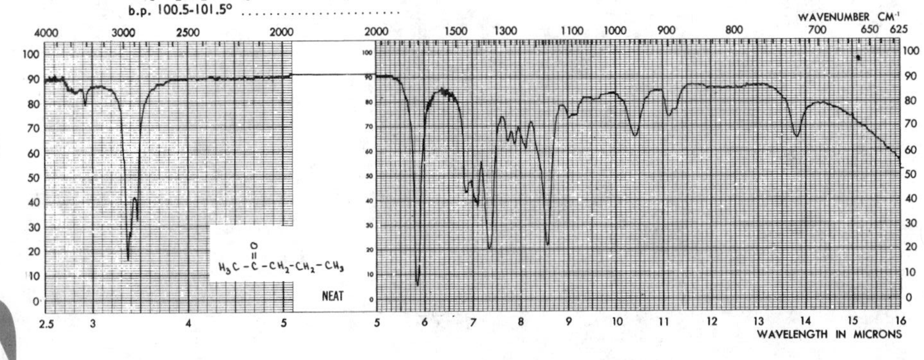

E

12,760-4 **3-Pentanone** (diethyl ketone)
$C_2H_5COC_2H_5$ M.W. 86.13 n_D^{20} 1.3920
b.p. 102°

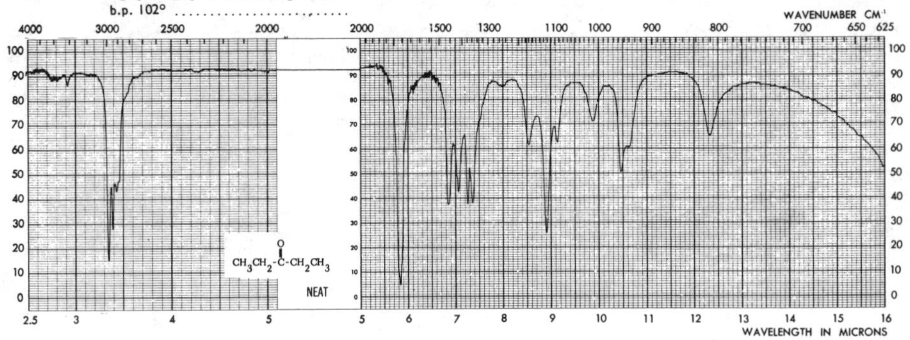

F

M6700-1 **3-Methyl-2-pentanone** (sec.-butyl methyl ketone)
$C_2H_5CH(CH_3)COCH_3$ M.W. 100.16 n_D^{20} 1.4002
b.p. 118°/758 mm.

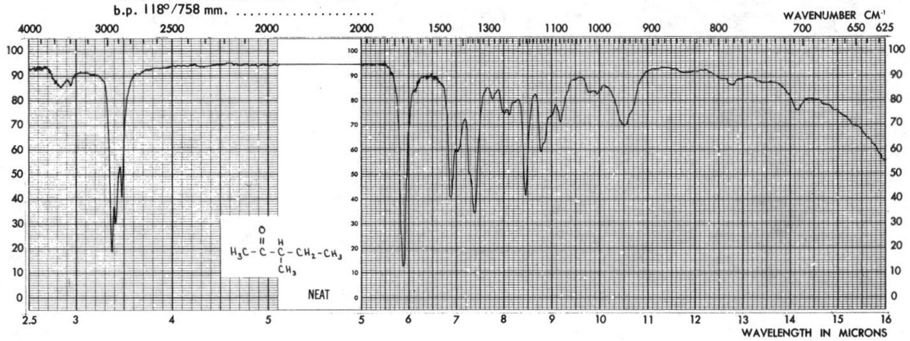

G

10,299-7 **3-Ethyl-2-pentanone**
$(C_2H_5)_2CHCOCH_3$ M.W. 114.19 n_D^{20} 1.4090
b.p. 137-138°

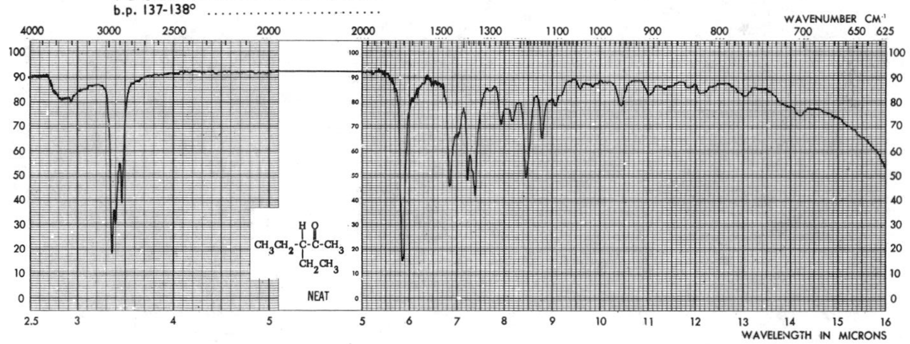

H

M6710-9 **4-Methyl-2-pentanone** (isobutyl methyl ketone)
$(CH_3)_2CHCH_2COCH_3$ M.W. 100.16 n_D^{20} 1.3962
b.p. 114-116°

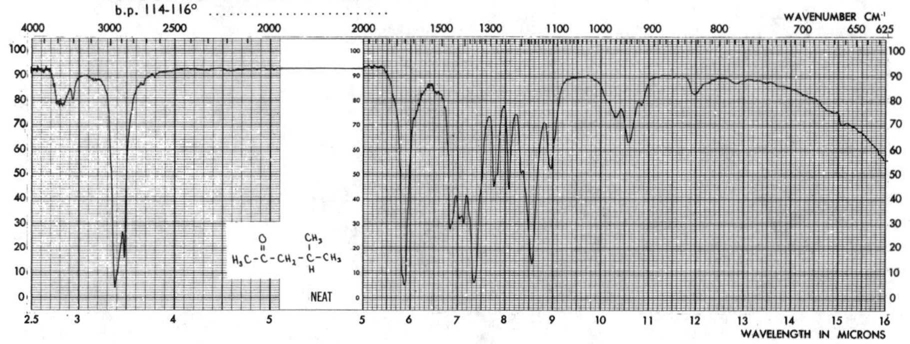

A

10,870-7 **2-Methyl-3-pentanone, puriss.**
$C_2H_5COCH(CH_3)_2$ M.W. 100.16 n_D^{20} 1.3983
b.p. 114-115°

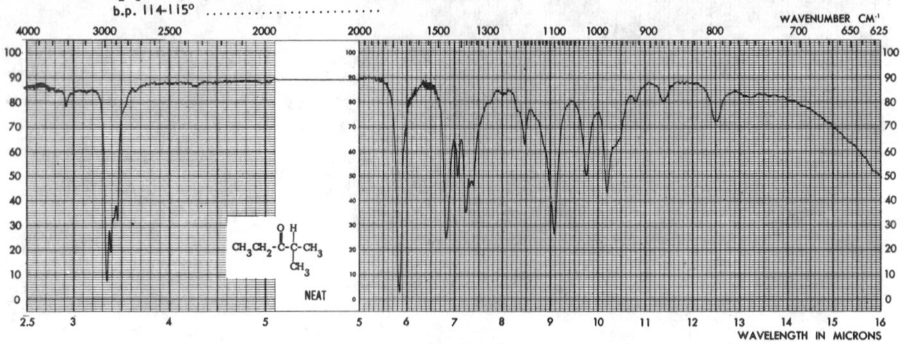

CH_3CH_2-CO-CH(CH_3)-CH_3 — NEAT

B

13,686-7 **2,4-Dimethyl-3-pentanone** (diisopropyl ketone)
$(CH_3)_2CHCOCH(CH_3)_2$ M.W. 114.19
n_D^{20} 1.3986

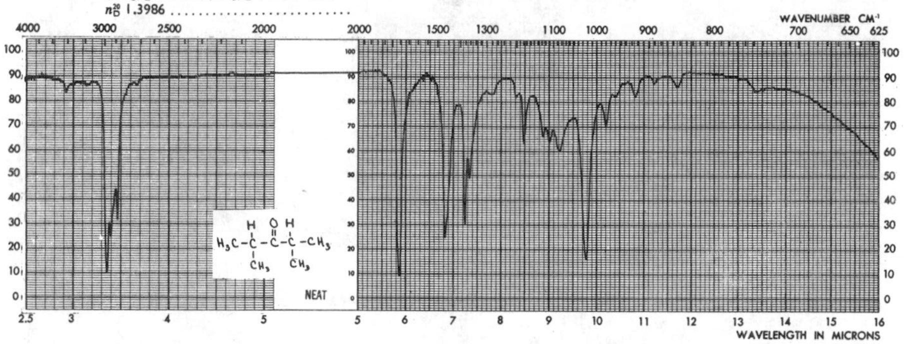

H_3C-CH(CH_3)-CO-CH(CH_3)-CH_3 — NEAT

C

13,687-5 **4,4-Dimethyl-2-pentanone** (methyl neopentyl ketone)
$(CH_3)_3CCH_2COCH_3$ M.W. 114.19 n_D^{20} 1.3999
b.p. 125-130°

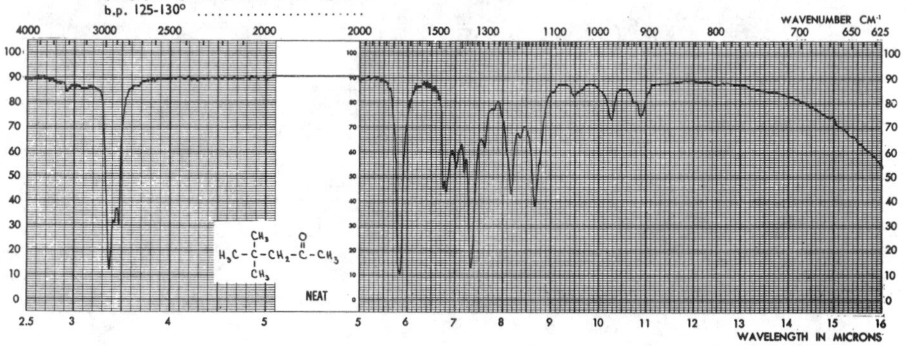

H_3C-C(CH_3)$_2$-CH_2-CO-CH_3 — NEAT

D

10,281-4 **2,2-Dimethyl-3-pentanone, puriss.**
$C_2H_5COC(CH_3)_3$ M.W. 114.19 n_D^{20} 1.4065

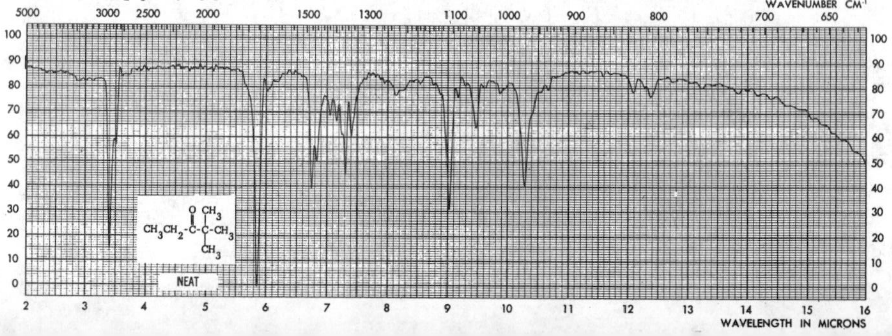

CH_3CH_2-CO-C(CH_3)$_2$-CH_3 — NEAT

E

10,300-4 **2-Hexanone, puriss.**
$CH_3(CH_2)_3COCH_3$ M.W. 100.16 n_D^{20} 1.4022
b.p. 127°

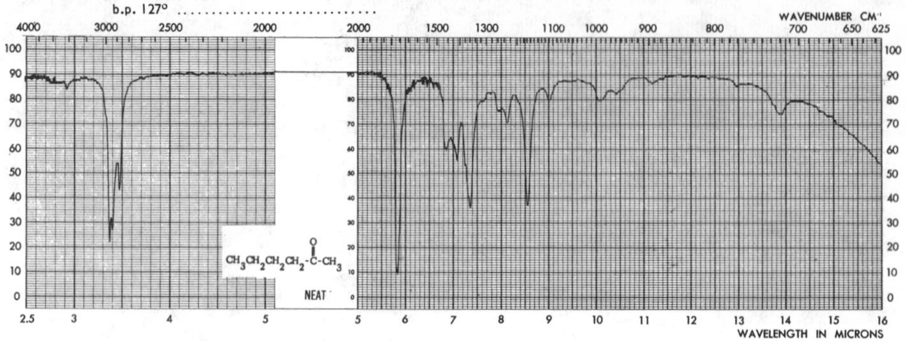

$CH_3CH_2CH_2CH_2$-CO-CH_3 — NEAT

F

10,302-0 **3-Hexanone, puriss.**
$CH_3CH_2CH_2COC_2H_5$ M.W. 100.16 n_D^{20} 1.4002
b.p. 123°

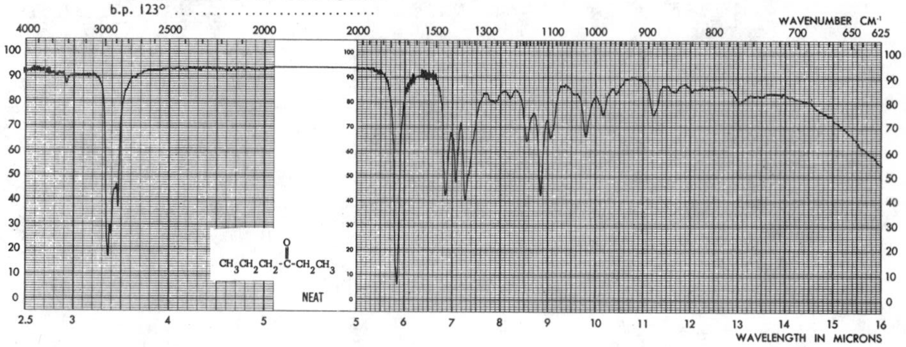

$CH_3CH_2CH_2$-CO-CH_2CH_3 — NEAT

G

10,792-1 **3-Methyl-2-hexanone, puriss.**
$CH_3CH_2CH_2CH(CH_3)COCH_3$ M.W. 114.19
n_D^{20} 1.4095

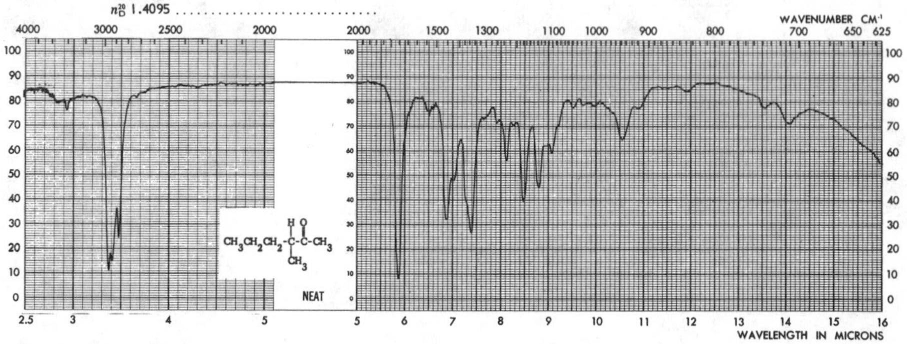

$CH_3CH_2CH_2$-CH(CH_3)-CO-CH_3 — NEAT

H

10,794-8 **2-Methyl-3-hexanone, puriss.**
$CH_3CH_2CH_2COCH(CH_3)_2$ M.W. 114.19 n_D^{20} 1.4064
b.p. 131-132°

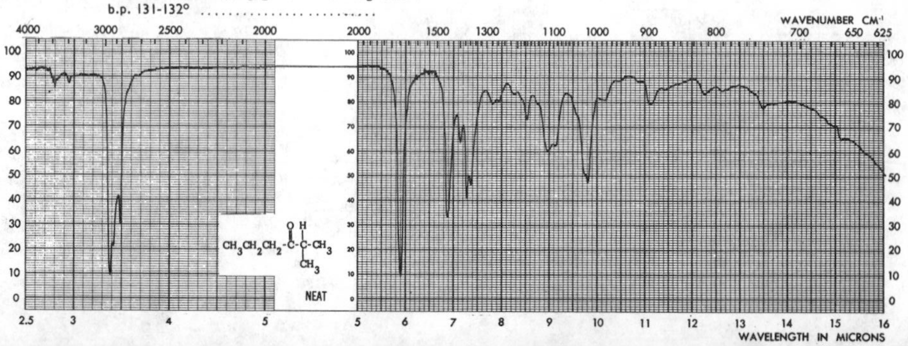

$CH_3CH_2CH_2$-CO-CH(CH_3)-CH_3 — NEAT

A

10,795-6 4-Methyl-3-hexanone, puriss.
$C_2H_5CH(CH_3)COC_2H_5$ M.W. 114.19
n_D^{20} 1.4086

NEAT

B

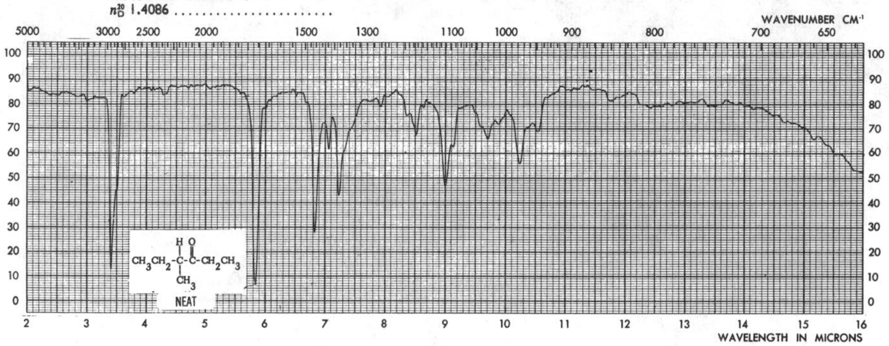

11,025-6 5-Methyl-2-hexanone
$(CH_3)_2CHCH_2CH_2COCH_3$ M.W. 114.19 n_D^{20} 1.4062
b.p. 145°

NEAT

C

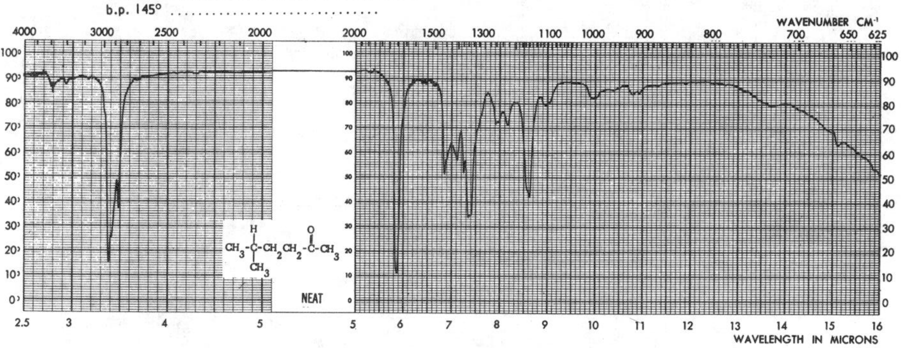

10,862-6 5-Methyl-3-hexanone, puriss.
$(CH_3)_2CHCH_2COC_2H_5$ M.W. 114.19
n_D^{20} 1.4047

NEAT

D

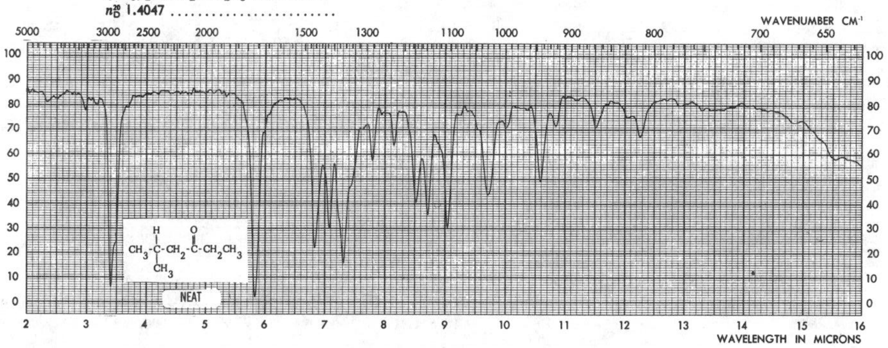

10,298-9 4-Ethyl-3-hexanone, puriss.
$(C_2H_5)_2CHCOC_2H_5$ M.W. 128.22
n_D^{20} 1.4160

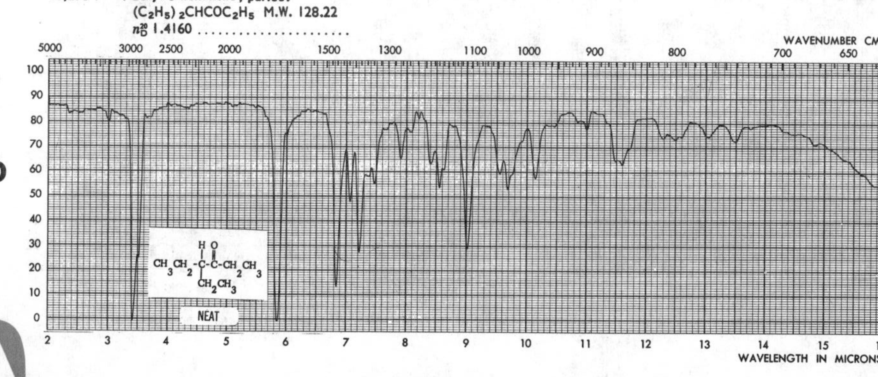

E

10,237-7 3,4-Dimethyl-2-hexanone, puriss.
$C_2H_5CH(CH_3)CH(CH_3)COCH_3$ M.W. 128.22
n_D^{20} 1.4193

NEAT

F

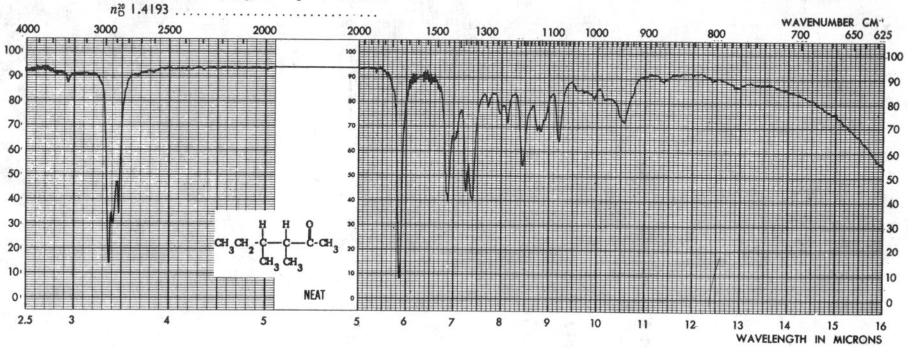

10,262-8 2,2-Dimethyl-3-hexanone
$CH_3CH_2CH_2COC(CH_3)_3$ M.W. 128.22
n_D^{20} 1.4119

NEAT

G

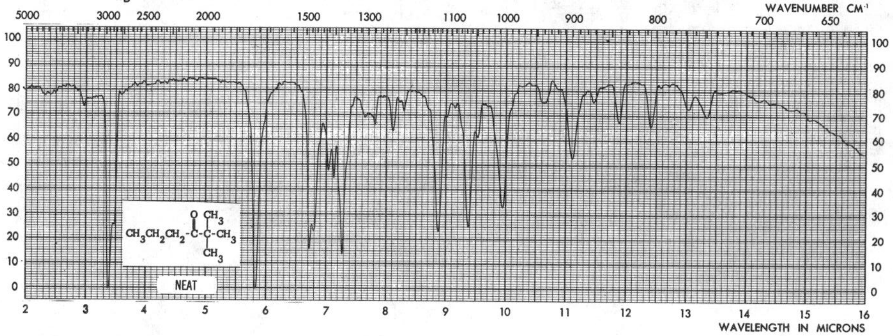

10,279-2 2,4-Dimethyl-3-hexanone, puriss.
$C_2H_5CH(CH_3)COCH(CH_3)_2$ M.W. 128.22
n_D^{20} 1.4100

NEAT

H

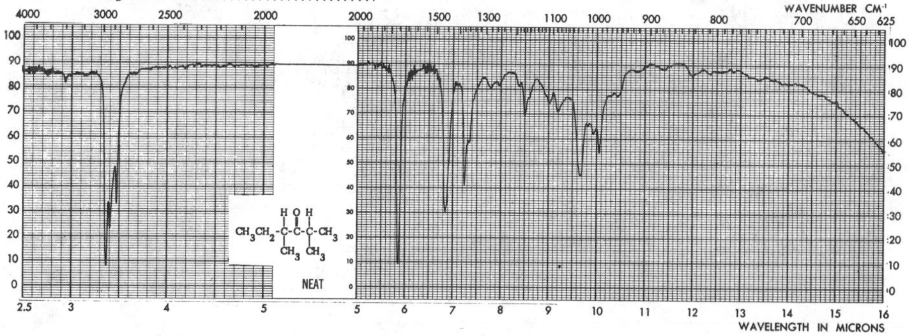

12,336-6 2-Heptanone
$CH_3(CH_2)_4COCH_3$ M.W. 114.19 n_D^{20} 1.4098
b.p. 145-147°

NEAT

ALDRICH

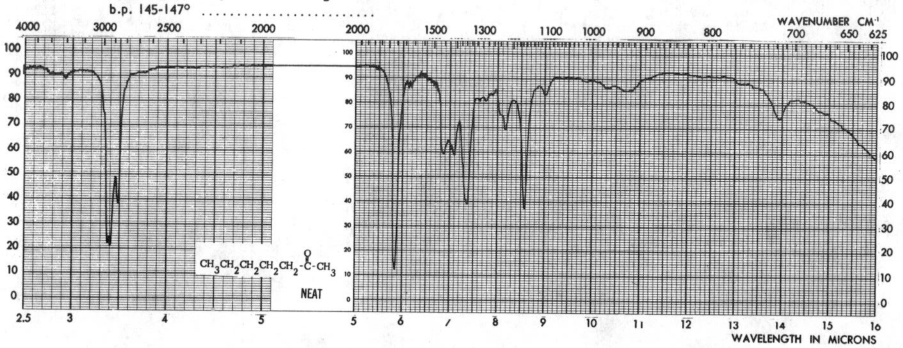

A

H315-1 **3-Heptanone (butyl ethyl ketone)**
$CH_3(CH_2)_3COC_2H_5$ M.W. 114.19 n_D^{20} 1.4057
b.p. 146-149°

NEAT

B

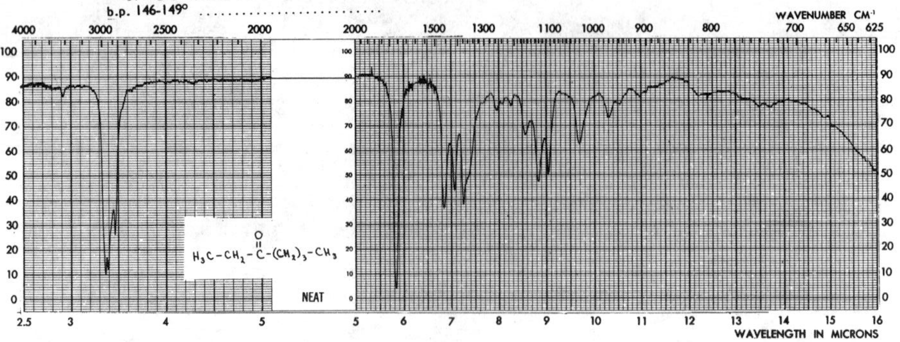

10,174-5 **4-Heptanone**, 98% (di-*n*-propyl ketone)
$CH_3CH_2CH_2COCH_2CH_2CH_3$ M.W. 114.19
b.p. 145° n_D^{20} 1.4070 d 0.817 *Beil.* 1,699
Merck Index 8,391

NEAT

C

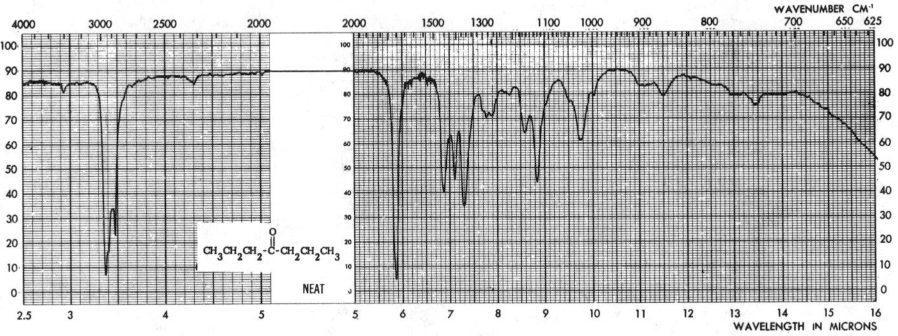

12,337-4 **3-Methyl-2-heptanone**
$CH_3(CH_2)_3CH(CH_3)COCH_3$ M.W. 128.22 n_D^{20} 1.4148
b.p. 162°

NEAT

D

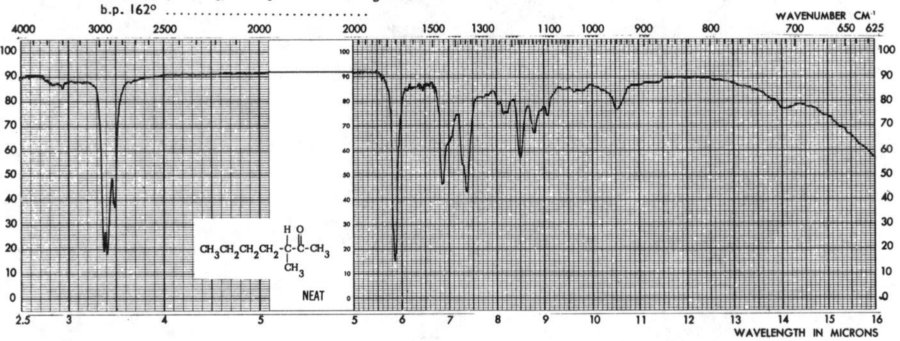

10,312-8 **2-Methyl-3-heptanone, puriss.**
$CH_3(CH_2)_3COCH(CH_3)_2$ M.W. 128.22
n_D^{20} 1.4131

NEAT

E

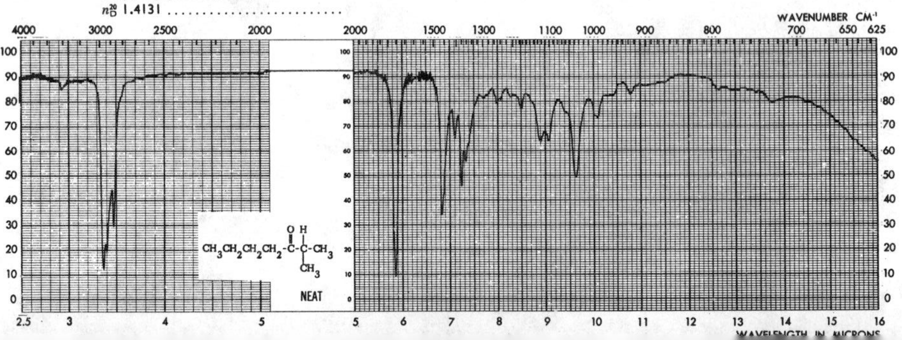

10,609-7 **4-Methyl-3-heptanone, puriss.**
$CH_3CH_2CH_2CH(CH_3)COC_2H_5$ M.W. 128.22
n_D^{20} 1.4161

NEAT

F

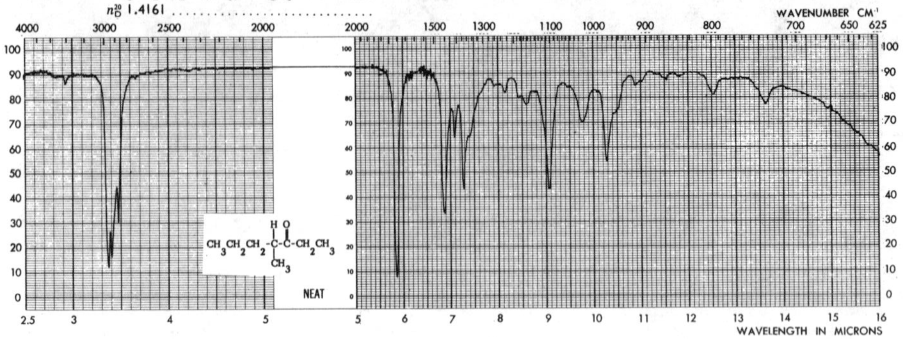

10,940-1 **5-Methyl-3-heptanone**
$C_2H_5CH(CH_3)CH_2COC_2H_5$ M.W. 128.22
n_D^{20} 1.4142

NEAT

G

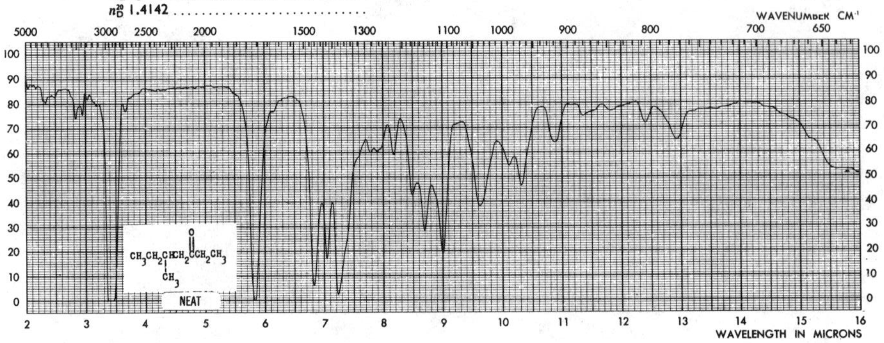

12,927-5 **2,2-Dimethyl-3-heptanone, puriss.**
$CH_3(CH_2)_3COC(CH_3)_3$ M.W. 142.24
n_D^{20} 1.4166

NEAT

H

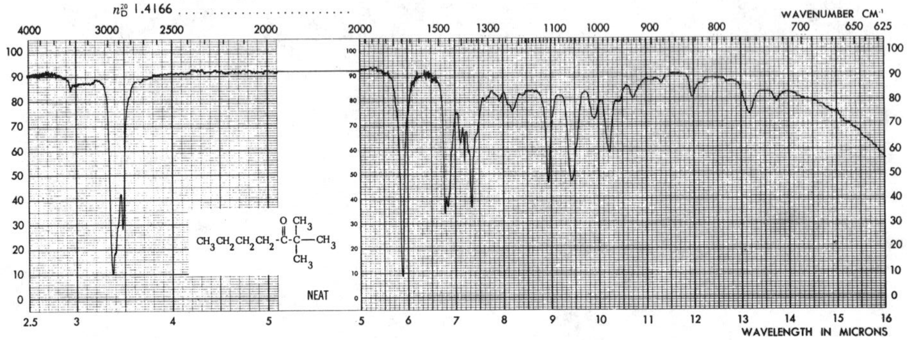

12,928-3 **2,4-Dimethyl-3-heptanone, puriss.**
$CH_3CH_2CH_2CH(CH_3)COCH(CH_3)_2$ M.W. 142.24
n_D^{20} 1.4142

NEAT

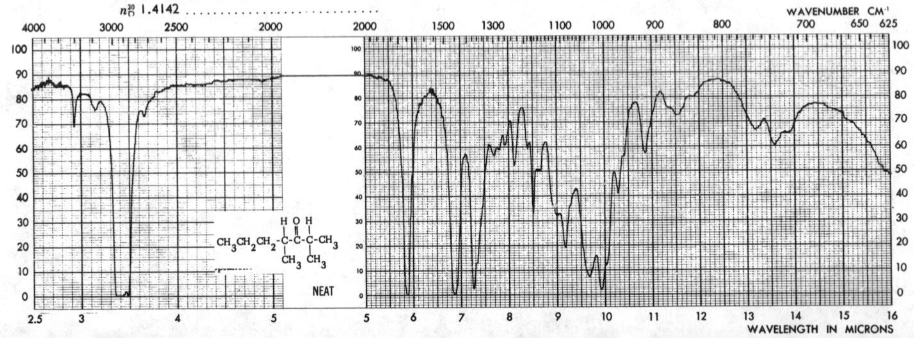

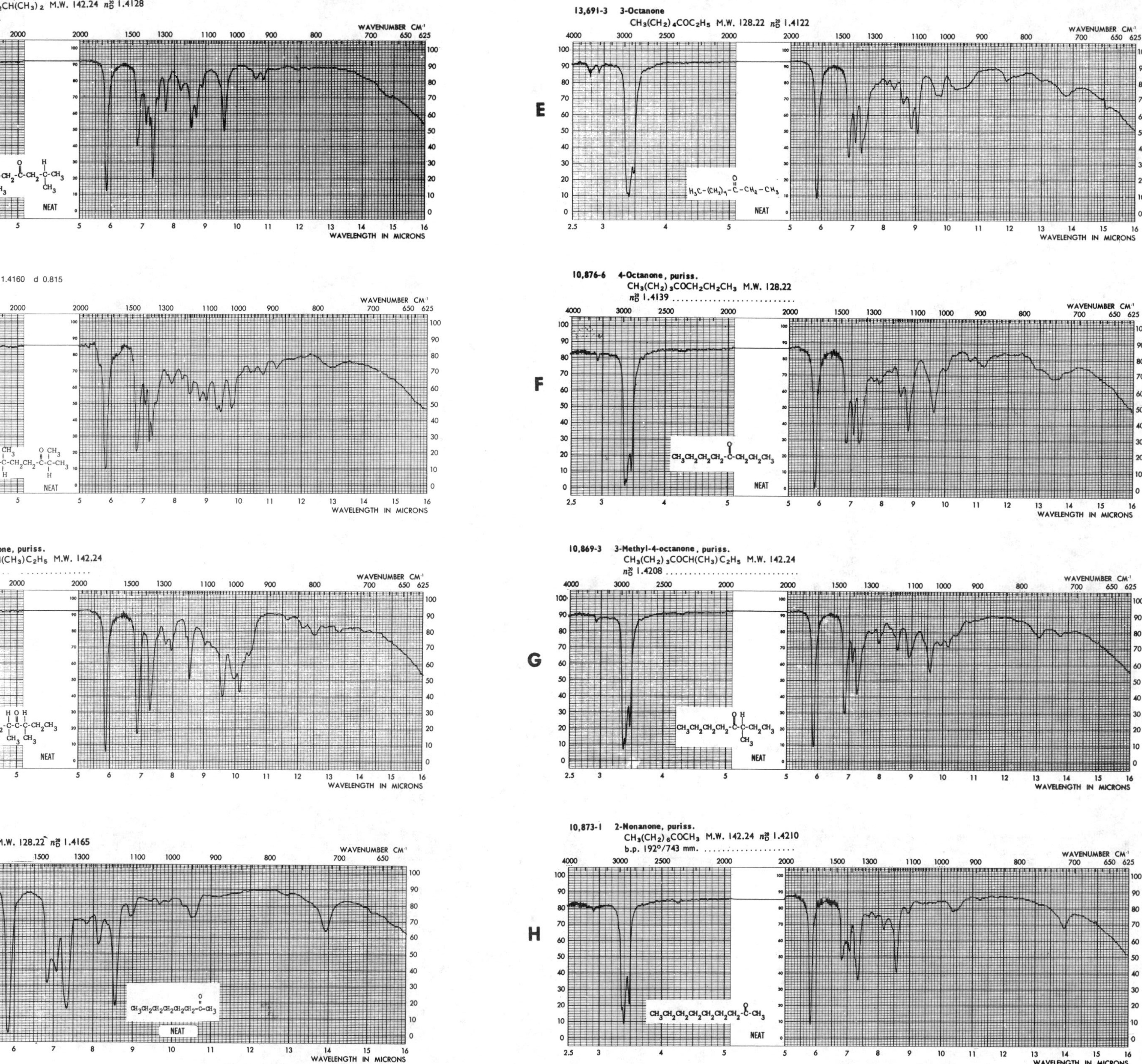
A
10,999-1 2,6-Dimethyl-4-heptanone (diisobutyl ketone), tech., 80%
(CH3)2CHCH2COCH2CH(CH3)2 M.W. 142.24 nD 1.4128
b.p. 169°
NEAT
B
16,180-2
2,6-Dimethyl-3-heptanone, tech.
(CH3)2CHCH2CH2COCH(CH3)2
M.W. 142.24 b.p. 171-172° nD 1.4160 d 0.815
Beil. 1,710
NEAT
C
12,929-1 3,5-Dimethyl-4-heptanone, puriss.
C2H5CH(CH3)COCH(CH3)C2H5 M.W. 142.24
nD 1.4164
NEAT
D
O-470-9 2-Octanone
CH3(CH2)5COCH3 M.W. 128.22 nD 1.4165
NEAT
E
13,691-3 3-Octanone
CH3(CH2)4COC2H5 M.W. 128.22 nD 1.4122
NEAT
F
10,876-6 4-Octanone, puriss.
CH3(CH2)3COCH2CH2CH3 M.W. 128.22
nD 1.4139
NEAT
G
10,869-3 3-Methyl-4-octanone, puriss.
CH3(CH2)3COCH(CH3)C2H5 M.W. 142.24
nD 1.4208
NEAT
H
10,873-1 2-Nonanone, puriss.
CH3(CH2)6COCH3 M.W. 142.24 nD 1.4210
b.p. 192°/743 mm.
NEAT
WAVENUMBER CM⁻¹
WAVELENGTH IN MICRONS
ALDRICH

ALDRICH

NON-AROMATIC KETONES

A

13,694-8 **5-Nonanone** (di-n-butyl ketone)
$CH_3(CH_2)_3CO(CH_2)_3CH_3$ M.W. 142.24
n_D^{20} 1.4161

$H_3C-(CH_2)_3-C(=O)-(CH_2)_3-CH_3$ NEAT

B

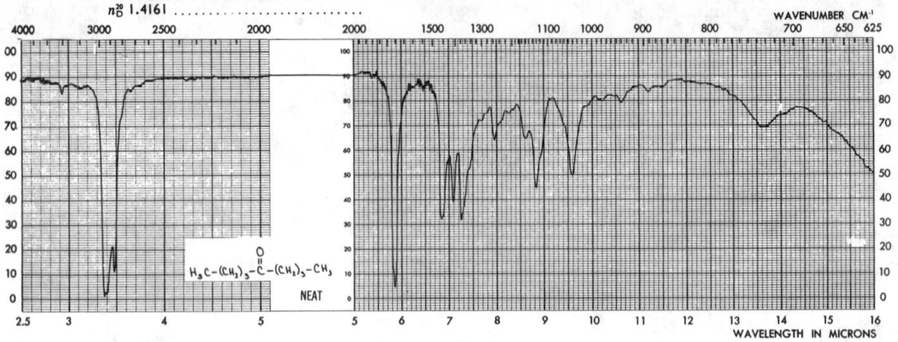

10,868-5 **3-Methyl-4-nonanone, puriss.**
$CH_3(CH_2)_4COCH(CH_3)C_2H_5$ M.W. 156.27
n_D^{20} 1.4229

$CH_3CH_2CH_2CH_2CH_2-C(=O)-CH(CH_3)-CH_2CH_3$ NEAT

C

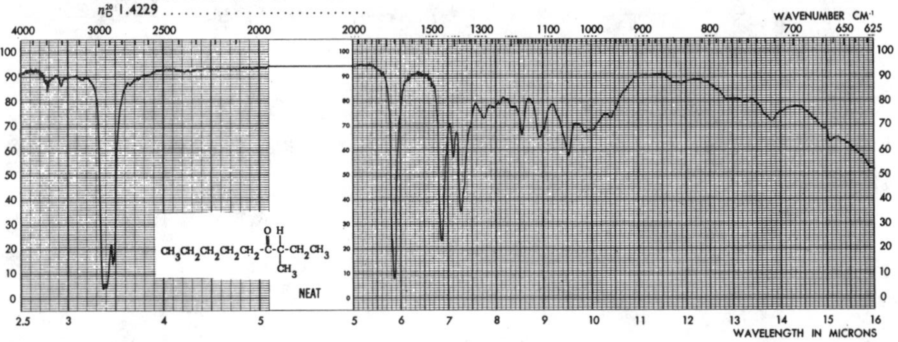

19,620-7
2-Decanone, 95%
$CH_3(CH_2)_7COCH_3$ FW 156.27 mp 3.50°
bp 211° n_D^{20} 1.4249 d 0.825 *Beil.* 1,711
Disp. C

$CH_3(CH_2)_6CH_2-C(=O)-CH_3$ NEAT

D

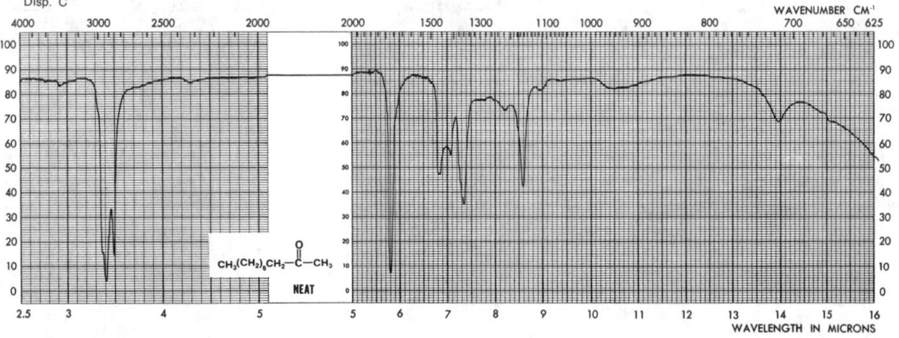

19,467-0
4-Decanone, 98% (hexyl propyl ketone)
$CH_3(CH_2)_5COCH_2CH_2CH_3$ FW 156.27
bp 206-207° n_D^{20} 1.4237 d 0.824 *Beil.* 1,711
Disp. C

$CH_3CH_2CH_2CH_2CH_2CH_2-C(=O)-CH_2CH_2CH_3$ NEAT

E

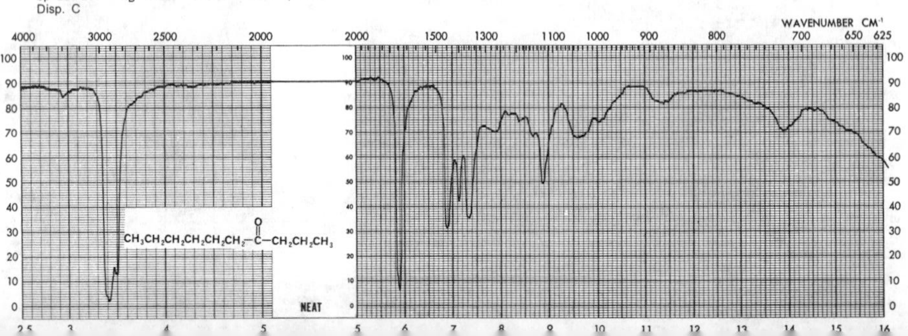

U130-3 **2-Undecanone** (methyl nonyl ketone)
$CH_3(CH_2)_8COCH_3$ M.W. 170.30 n_D^{20} 1.4272 m.p. 11-13°
b.p. 231.5-232.5°

$H_3C-(CH_2)_8-C(=O)-CH_3$ NEAT

F

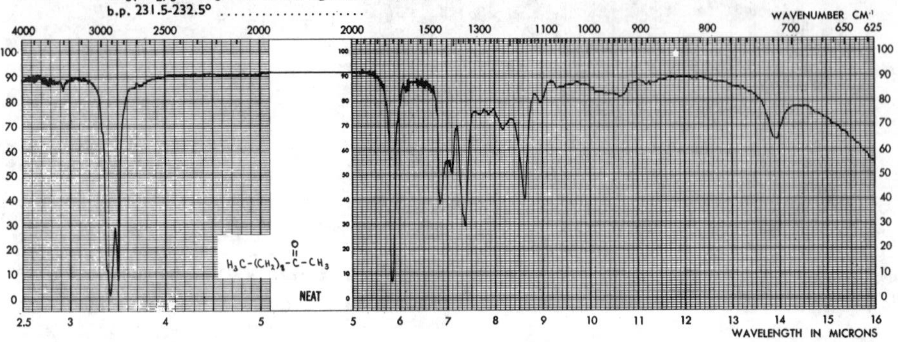

13,699-9 **6-Undecanone** (di-n-amyl ketone)
$CH_3(CH_2)_4CO(CH_2)_4CH_3$ M.W. 170.30
n_D^{20} 1.4270

$H_3C-(CH_2)_4-C(=O)-(CH_2)_4-CH_3$ NEAT

G

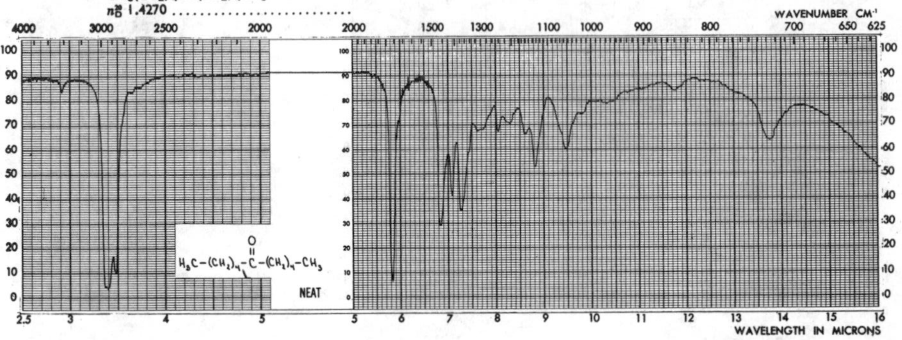

D10,420-5 **Di-n-hexyl ketone (7-tridecanone)**
$CH_3(CH_2)_5CO(CH_2)_5CH_3$ M.W. 198.35
m.p. 30-32.5°

$H_3C-(CH_2)_5-C(=O)-(CH_2)_5-CH_3$ MELT

H

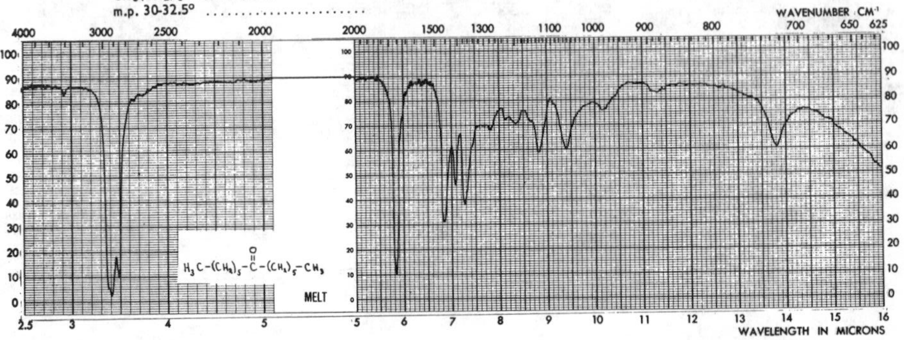

15,838-0
8-Pentadecanone
$CH_3(CH_2)_6CO(CH_2)_6CH_3$
M.W. 226.4 m.p. 41-43° b.p. 178° Beil. 1,717

$CH_3(CH_2)_5CH_2-C(=O)-CH_2(CH_2)_5CH_3$ MELT

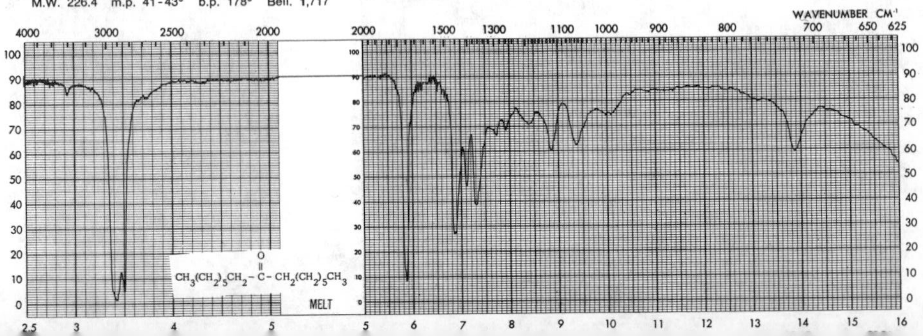

A

15,990-5
9-Heptadecanone, 98%
$CH_3(CH_2)_7CO(CH_2)_7CH_3$
M.W. 254.46 m.p. 51-53°

MELT

B

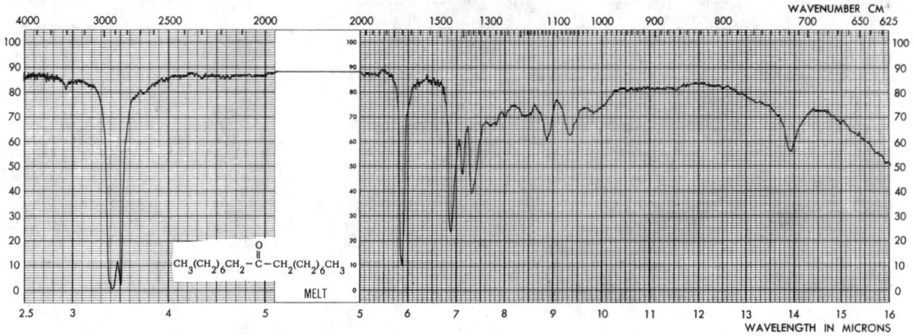

10,366-7 **10-Nonadecanone** (di-n-nonyl ketone)
$CH_3(CH_2)_8CO(CH_2)_8CH_3$ M.W. 282.51 m.p. 55-57°

MELT

C

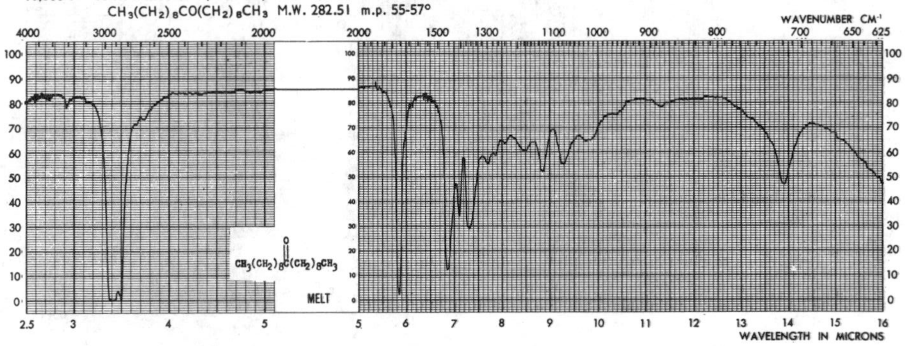

10,023-4 **11-Heneicosanone** (di-n-decyl ketone)
$CH_3(CH_2)_9CO(CH_2)_9CH_3$ M.W. 310.57 m.p. 59-61°

MELT

D

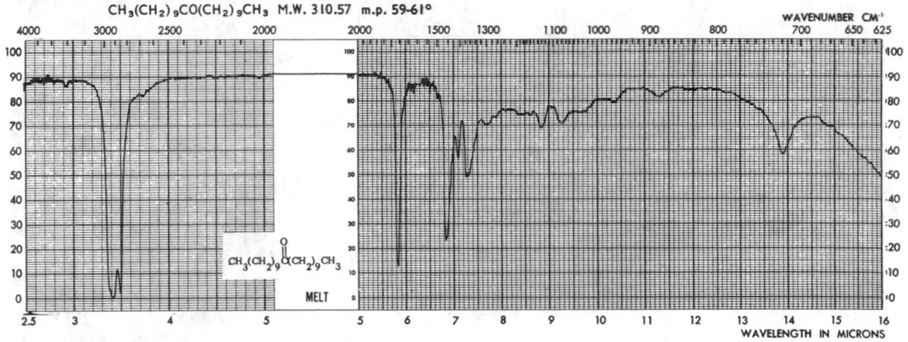

M8750-9 **Methyl vinyl ketone** (3-buten-2-one)
(stabilized with 1% hydroquinone)
$H_2C{:}CHCOCH_3$ M.W. 70.09 n_D^{20} 1.4117 b.p. 34°/120 mm.

NEAT

E

E5130-9 **Ethyl vinyl ketone** (1-penten-3-one)
$C_2H_5COCH{:}CH_2$ M.W. 84.12 n_D^{20} 1.4200

NEAT

F

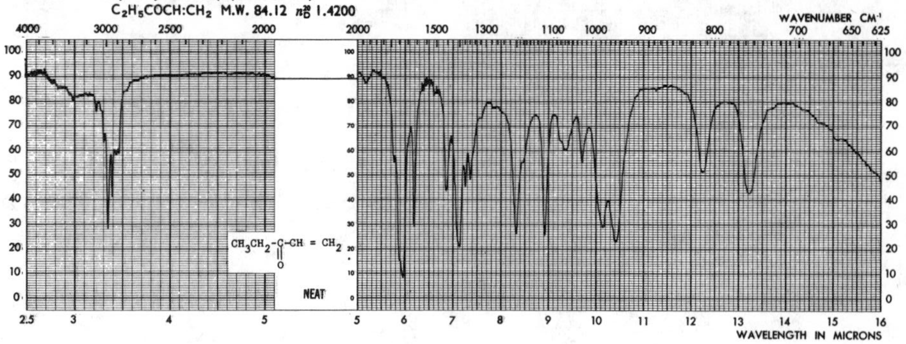

14,501-7 **3-Penten-2-one**
$CH_3CH{:}CHCOCH_3$ M.W. 84.12 n_D^{20} 1.4370
b.p. 121-124°

NEAT

G

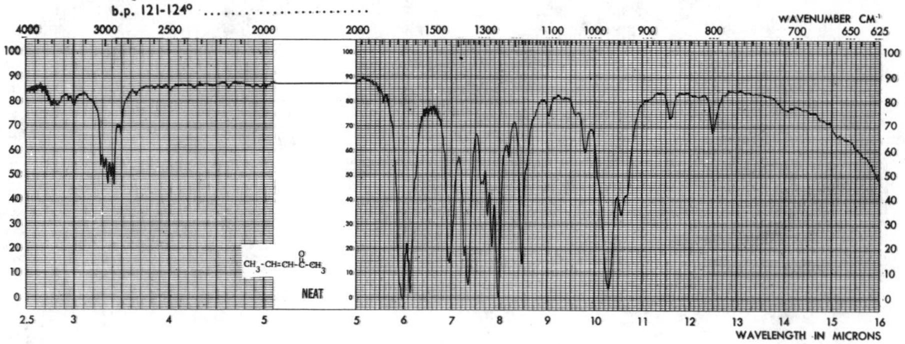

12,206-8 **4-Methoxy-3-buten-2-one**
$CH_3OCH{:}CHCOCH_3$ M.W. 100.11
n_D^{20} 1.4660

NEAT

H

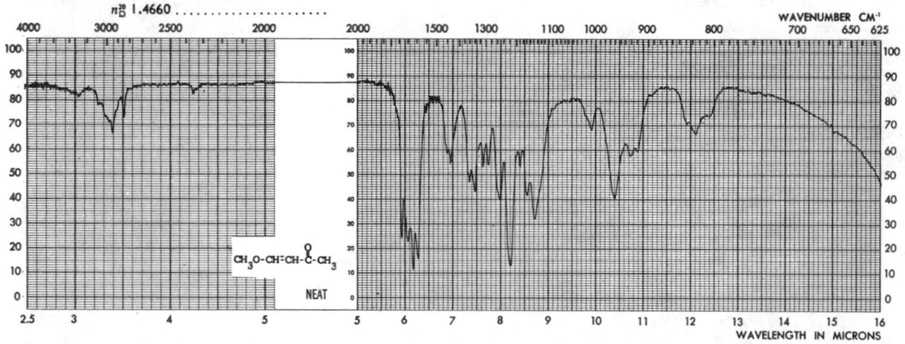

M785-5 **Mesityl oxide** (4-methyl-3-penten-2-one)
$(CH_3)_2C{:}CHCOCH_3$ M.W. 98.15 n_D^{20} 1.4419 b.p. 128°

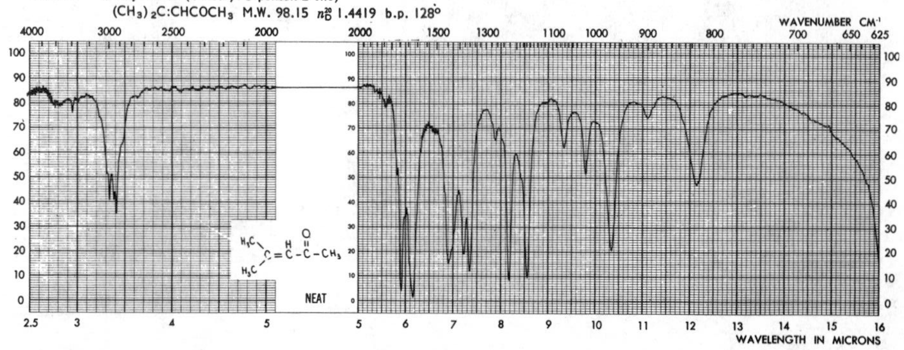

NEAT

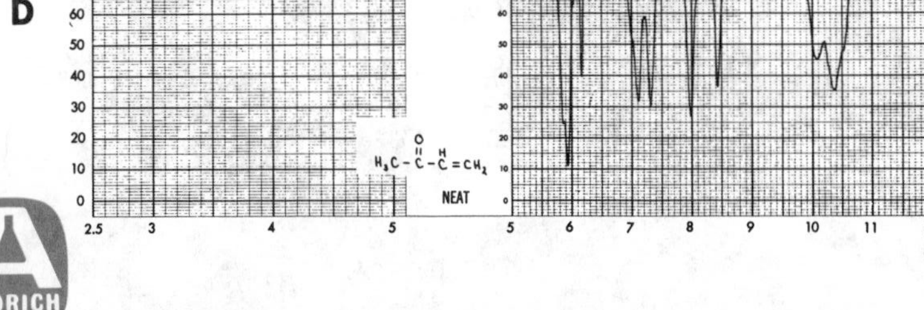

NON-AROMATIC KETONES

A

M6790-7 **3-Methyl-3-penten-2-one**
$CH_3CH{:}C(CH_3)COCH_3$ M.W. 98.15 n_D^{20} 1.4515

NEAT

B

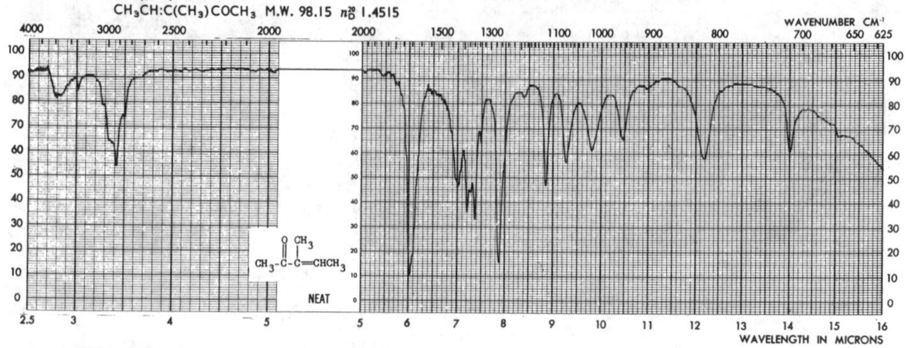

18,760-7
5-Methyl-3-hexen-2-one, tech., 80%
$(CH_3)_2CHCH{=}CHCOCH_3$ FW 112.17 n_D^{20} 1.4400
Disp. C

NEAT

C

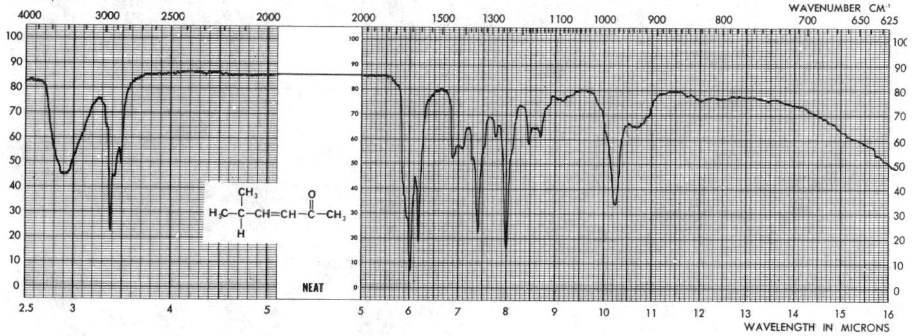

H1300-1 **5-Hexen-2-one (allylacetone)**
$H_2C{:}CHCH_2CH_2COCH_3$ M.W. 98.15 n_D^{20} 1.4197
b.p. 128-129°

NEAT

D

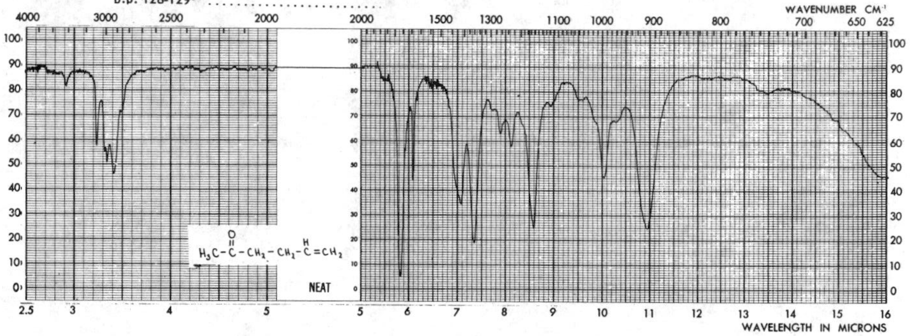

M4880-5 **6-Methyl-5-hepten-2-one**
$(CH_3)_2C{:}CHCH_2CH_2COCH_3$ M.W. 126.20 n_D^{20} 1.4391

NEAT

E

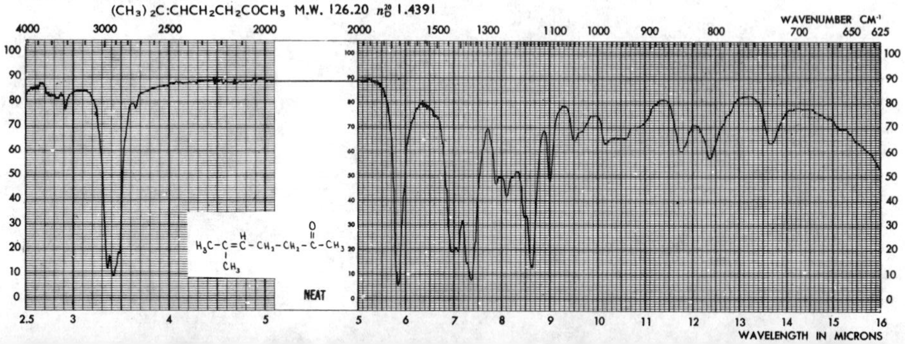

14,923-3 **Phorone** (2,6-dimethyl-2,5-heptadien-4-one)
$(CH_3)_2C{:}CHCOCH{:}C(CH_3)_2$ M.W. 138.21
m.p. 27°

MELT

F

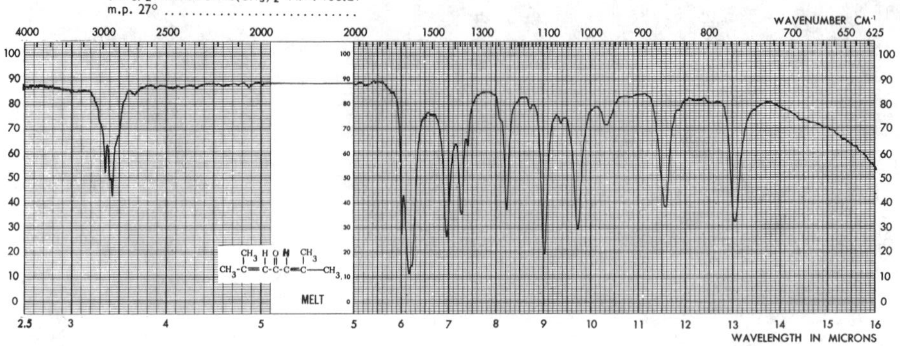

16,747-9
Chloroacetone (chloro-2-propanone), tech.
$ClCH_2COCH_3$
M.W. 92.53 m.p. -44.5° b.p. 119.7° n_D^{20} 1.4330
d 1.13 Beil. 1,653

NEAT

G

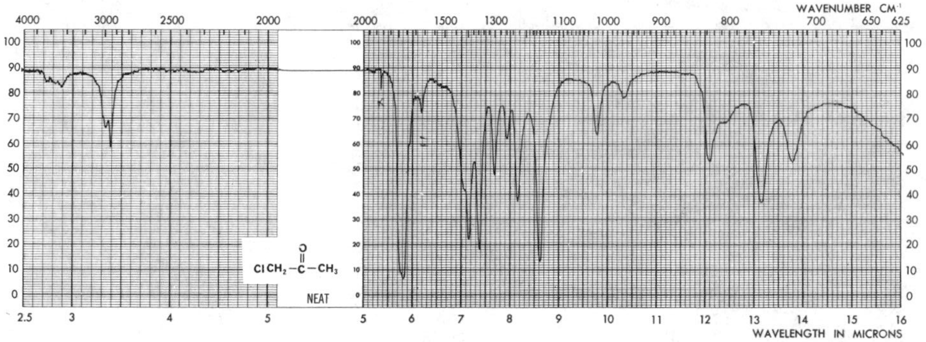

16,854-8
1,3-Dichloroacetone, 99%
$ClCH_2COCH_2Cl$
M.W. 126.97 m.p. 40-42° b.p. 173° d 1.383
Beil. 1,655 *LACHRYMATOR*

MELT

H

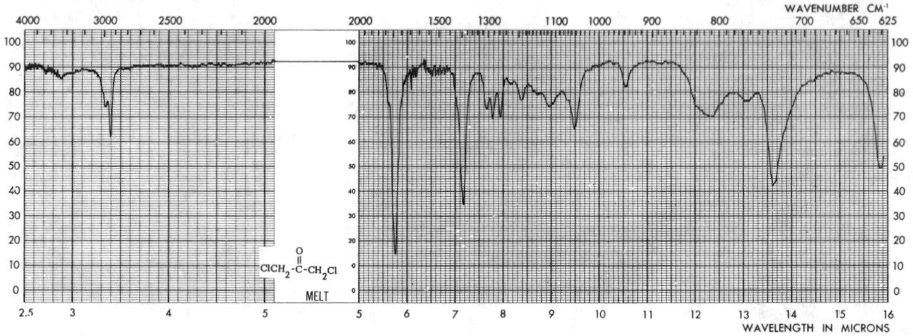

C6250-6 **1-Chloro-3-pentanone, tech.**
$ClCH_2CH_2COC_2H_5$ M.W. 120.58
n_D^{20} 1.4340

NEAT

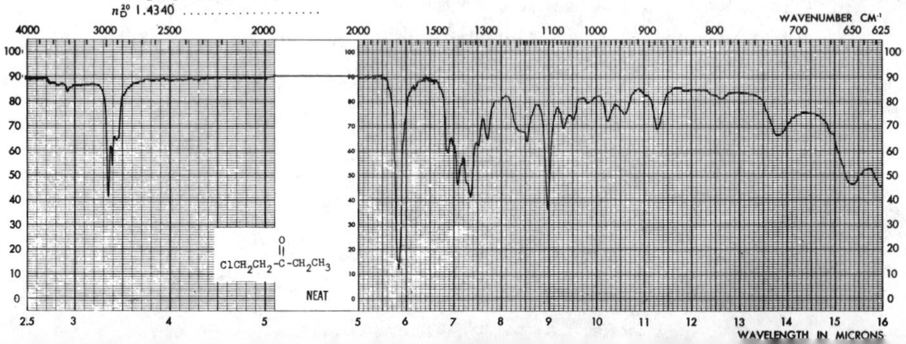

A C6260-3 5-Chloro-2-pentanone
$Cl(CH_2)_3COCH_3$ M.W. 120.58
n_D^{20} 1.4375
NEAT

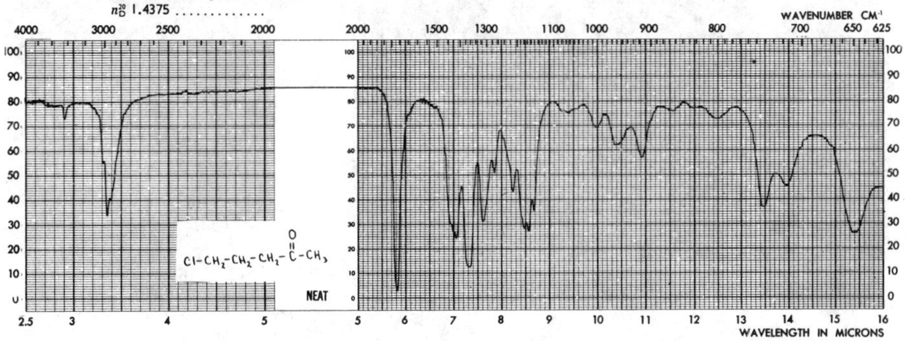

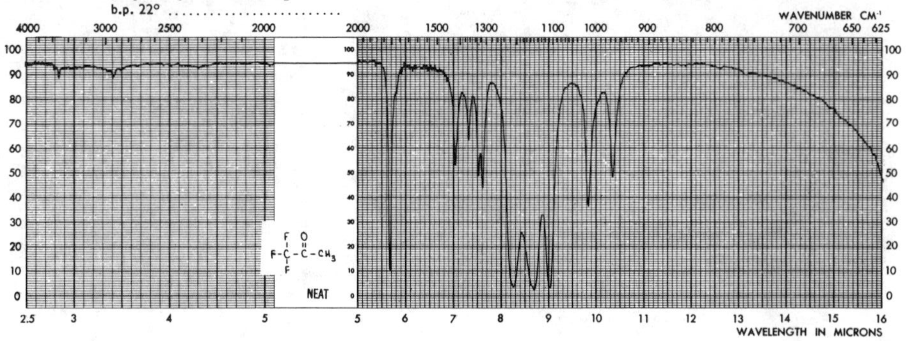

B H530-8 Hexachloroacetone (hexachloro-2-propanone)
CCl_3COCCl_3 M.W. 264.75 n_D^{20} 1.5112 b.p. 66-70°/6 mm.
NEAT

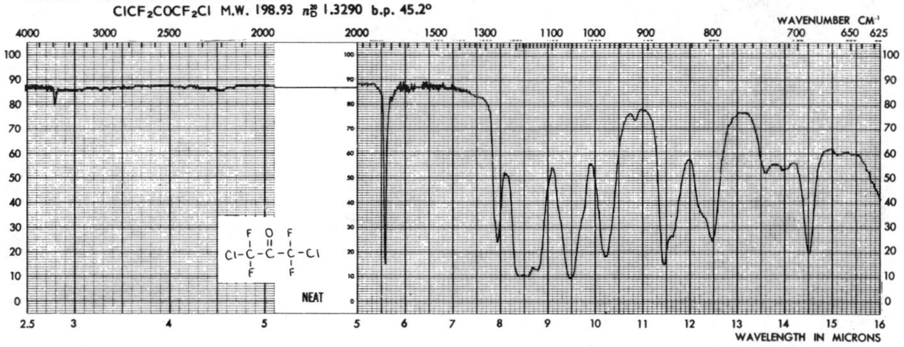

C 11,546-0 Fluoroacetone
CH_3COCH_2F M.W. 76.07 n_D^{20} 1.3700
b.p. 75°
NEAT

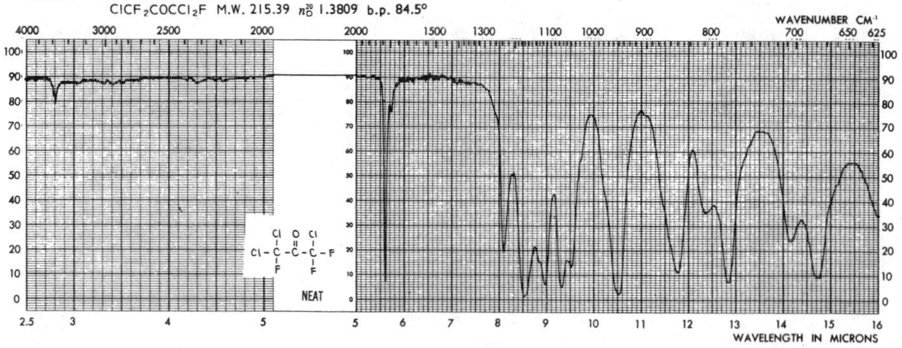

D D10,130-3 1,3-Difluoroacetone
FCH_2COCH_2F M.W. 94.06 n_D^{20} 1.3735
NEAT

E T6280-4 1,1,1-Trifluoroacetone
CF_3COCH_3 M.W. 112.05 n_D^{15} 1.2900
b.p. 22°
NEAT

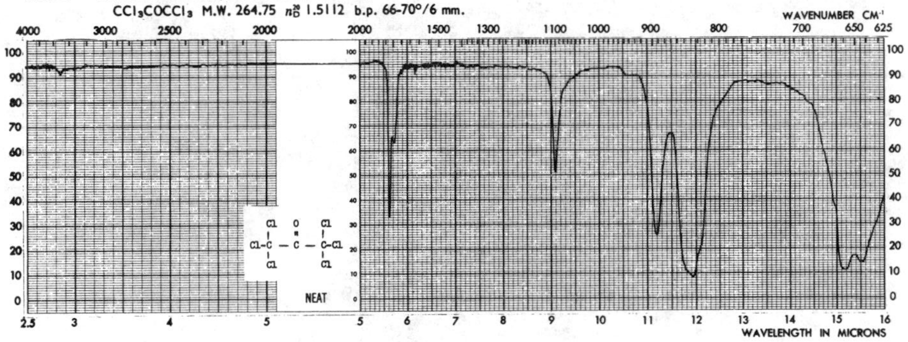

F D7540-8 1,3-Dichloro-1,1,3,3-tetrafluoroacetone
$ClCF_2COCF_2Cl$ M.W. 198.93 n_D^{20} 1.3290 b.p. 45.2°
NEAT

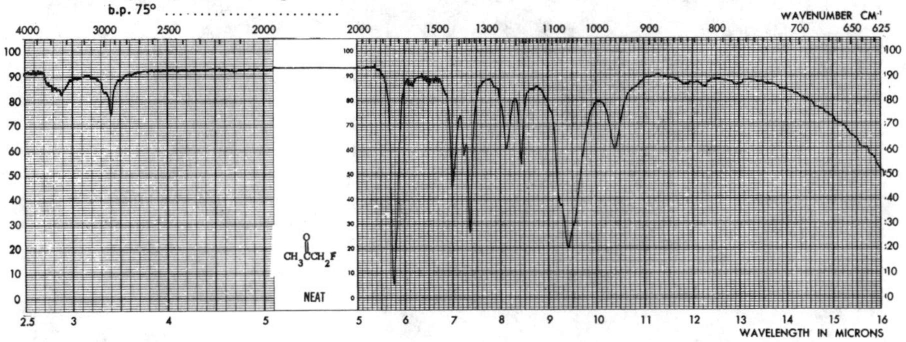

G T5640-5 1,1,3-Trichlorotrifluoroacetone
$ClCF_2COCCl_2F$ M.W. 215.39 n_D^{20} 1.3809 b.p. 84.5°
NEAT

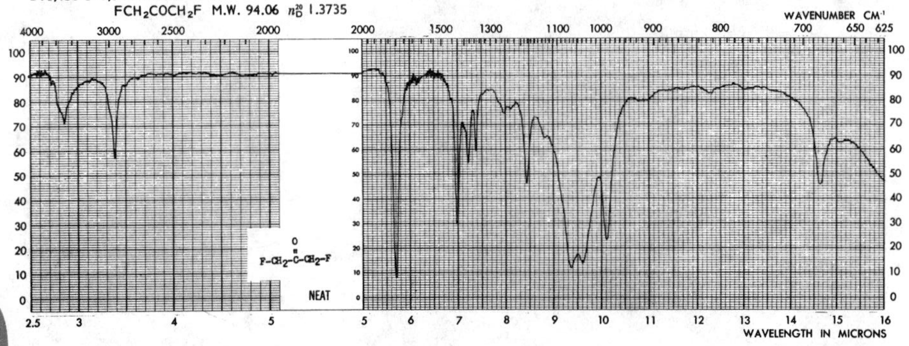

H 13,923-8 Hexafluoroacetone (hexafluoro-2-propanone) sesquihydrate
$CF_3COCF_3 \cdot 1\frac{1}{2}H_2O$ M.W. 193.04 n_D^{20} 1.3079
$\cdot 1\,1/2H_2O$
NEAT

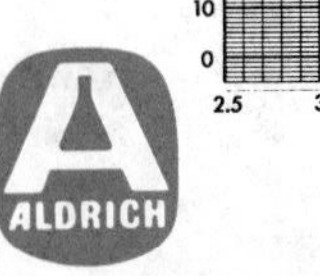

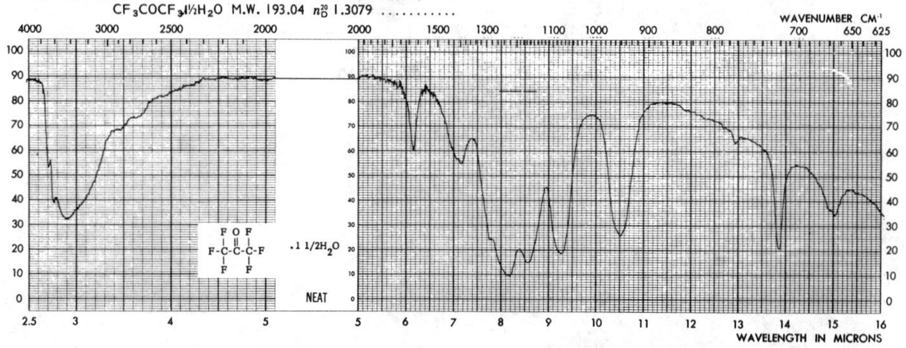

A 17,516-1
2,2-Dimethyl-6,6,7,7,8,8,8-heptafluoro-3,5-octanedione, 98%
$CF_3CF_2CF_2COCH_2COC(CH_3)_3$
M.W. 296.19 n_D^{20} 1.3766
NEAT

B 13,739-1 **1,1,1-Trichloroacetone**
CH_3COCCl_3 M.W. 161.42 n_D^{20} 1.4622
b.p. 135°/745 mm.
NEAT

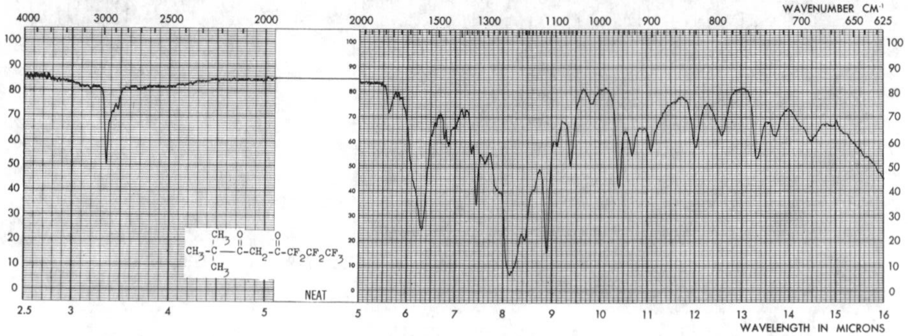

C 13,736-7 **1,1,3,3-Tetrachloroacetone**
$Cl_2CHCOCHCl_2$ M.W. 195.86 n_D^{20} 1.4944
b.p. 182°/745 mm.
NEAT

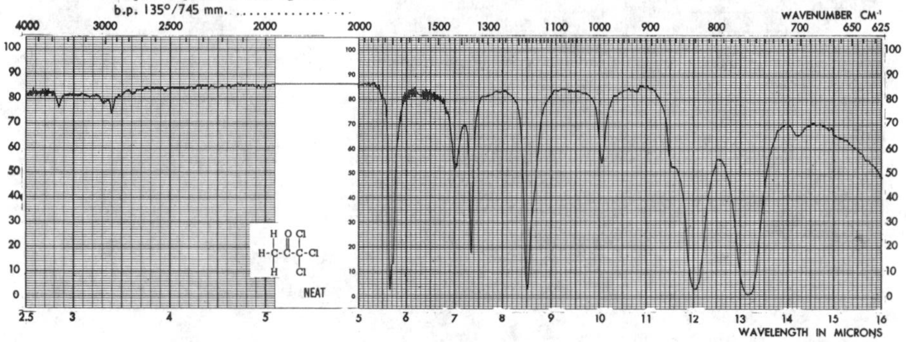

D 13,860-6 **Pentachloroacetone, tech.**
$Cl_2CHCOCCl_3$ M.W. 230.31 n_D^{20} 1.4967
NEAT

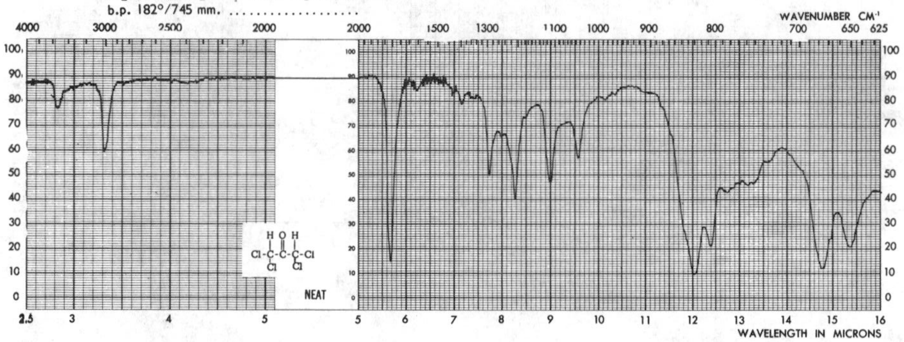

E 16,760-6
3-Chloro-2-butanone, tech., 95%
$CH_3CH(Cl)COCH_3$ FW 106.55 bp 114-117°
n_D^{20} 1.4172 d 1.055 *Beil.* 1,669 Disp. C
NEAT

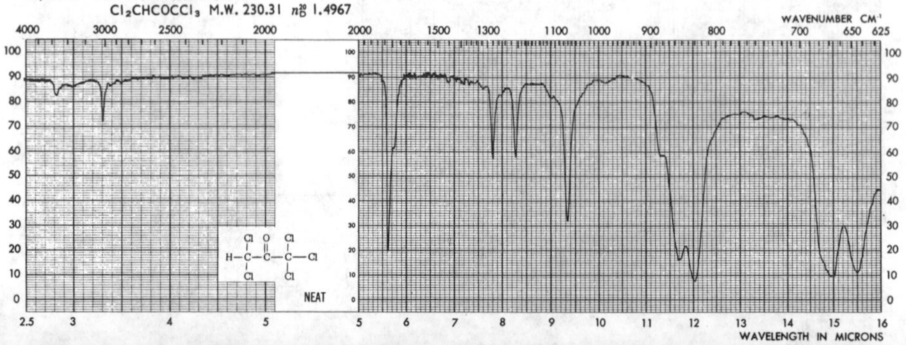

F 15,952-2
3-Bromo-2-butanone, 96%
$CH_3CH(Br)COCH_3$
M.W. 151.01 b.p. 33-36°/11mm. n_D^{20} 1.4585
LACHRYMATOR
NEAT

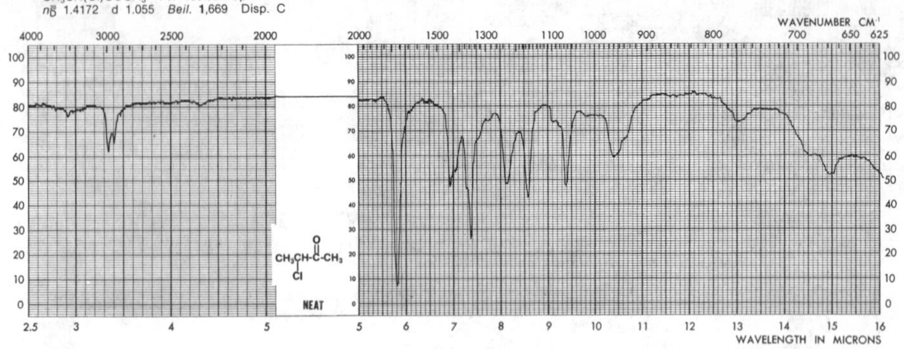

G 13,818-5 **Acetol** (hydroxyacetone)
CH_3COCH_2OH M.W. 74.08 n_D^{20} 1.4252
b.p. 57-58°/30 mm.
NEAT

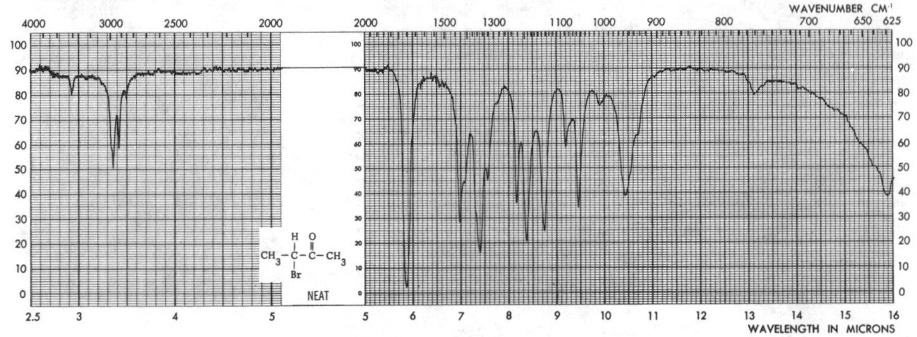

H D10,720-4 **1,3-Dihydroxyacetone** (1,3-dihydroxy-2-propanone)
$HOCH_2COCH_2OH$ M.W. 90.08
m.p. 89-91.5°
NUJOL MULL

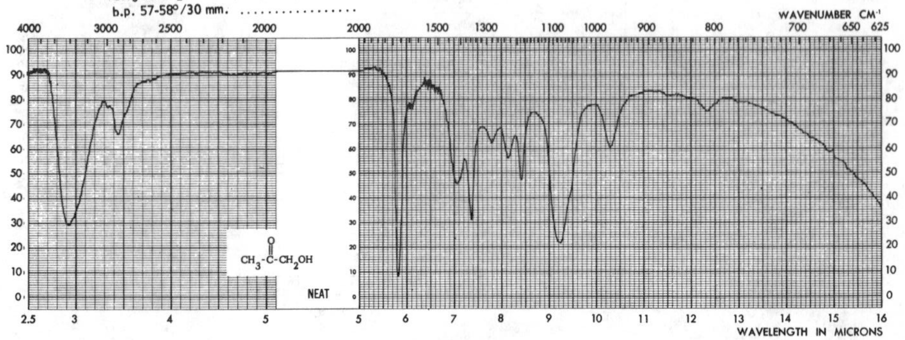

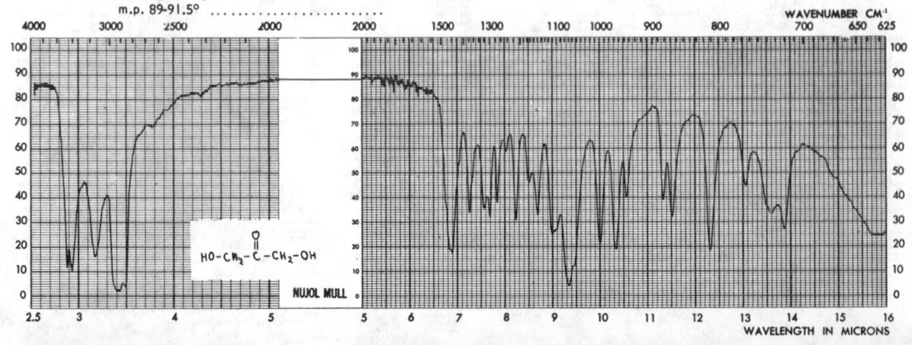

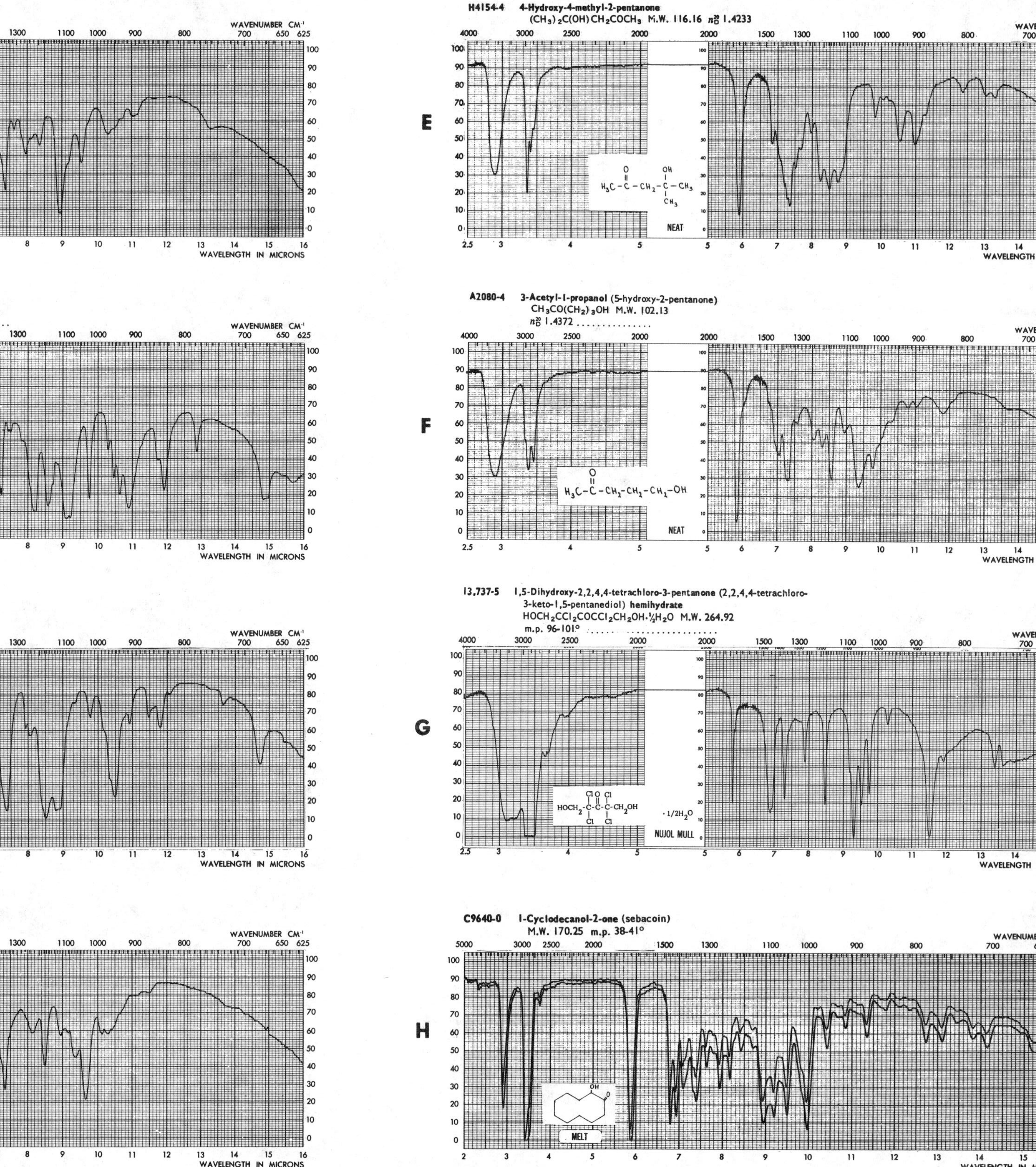

A 10,897-9 **3-Hydroxy-2-butanone (acetoin) (85% aqueous solution)**
$CH_3CH(OH)COCH_3$ M.W. 88.11 (dry basis)
n_D^{20} 1.4171 . . . .
NEAT

B A1795-1 **Acetyl methyl carbinol, crystalline dimer (acetoin dimer)**
$[CH_3COCH(OH)CH_3]_2$ M.W. 176.21 m.p. 101-113° . . . . .
NUJOL MULL

C H3960-4 **3-Hydroxy-3-methyl-2-butanone**
$(CH_3)_2C(OH)COCH_3$ M.W. 102.13 n_D^{20} 1.4146
b.p. 140-141° . . . .
NEAT

D 12,871-6 **4-Hydroxy-3-methyl-2-butanone**
$HOCH_2CH(CH_3)COCH_3$ M.W. 102.13 n_D^{20} 1.4379
b.p. 90-95°/15 mm. . . . .
NEAT

E H4154-4 **4-Hydroxy-4-methyl-2-pentanone**
$(CH_3)_2C(OH)CH_2COCH_3$ M.W. 116.16 n_D^{20} 1.4233
NEAT

F A2080-4 **3-Acetyl-1-propanol (5-hydroxy-2-pentanone)**
$CH_3CO(CH_2)_3OH$ M.W. 102.13
n_D^{20} 1.4372 . . . .
NEAT

G 13,737-5 **1,5-Dihydroxy-2,2,4,4-tetrachloro-3-pentanone (2,2,4,4-tetrachloro-3-keto-1,5-pentanediol) hemihydrate**
$HOCH_2CCl_2COCCl_2CH_2OH \cdot \frac{1}{2}H_2O$ M.W. 264.92
m.p. 96-101° . . . .
NUJOL MULL

H C9640-0 **1-Cyclodecanol-2-one (sebacoin)**
M.W. 170.25 m.p. 38-41°
MELT

NON-AROMATIC KETONES

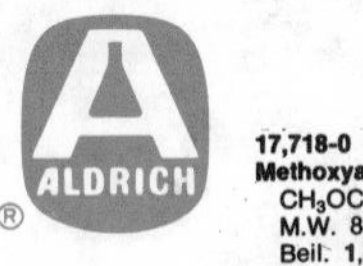

A

17,718-0
Methoxyacetone, 99% (methoxy-2-propanone)
$CH_3OCH_2COCH_3$
M.W. 88.11 b.p. 118° n_D^{20} 1.3970 d 0.957
Beil. 1,822

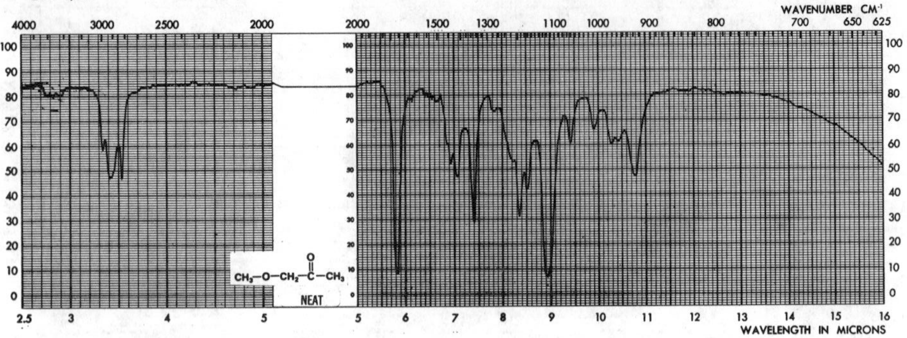

CH_3—O—CH_2—C(=O)—CH_3 NEAT

B

17,021-6
Pyruvaldehyde dimethyl acetal, 99%
$CH_3COCH(OCH_3)_2$
M.W. 118.13 b.p. 143-147° n_D^{20} 1.3978 d 0.976
Beil. 1(1),395

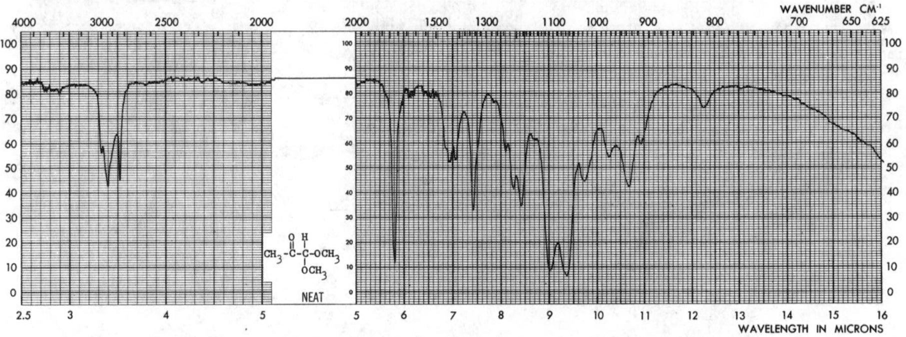

NEAT

C

17,547-1
1-Methoxymethyl-5-norbornen-2-one, tech., 90%
M.W. 152.19 n_D^{20} 1.4795

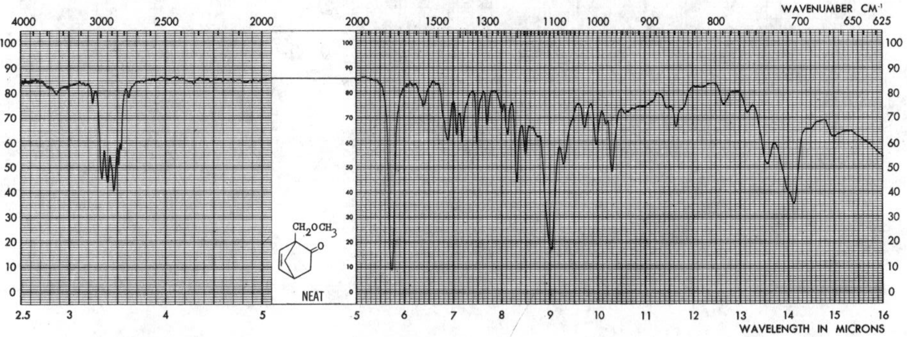

NEAT

D

A1220-8 **Acetylacetaldehyde dimethyl acetal** (3-ketobutyraldehyde dimethyl acetal)
$CH_3COCH_2CH(OCH_3)_2$ M.W. 132.16
n_D^{22} 1.4132

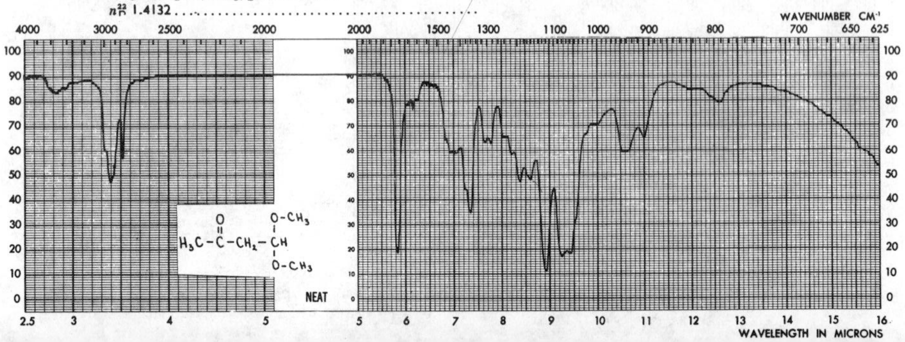

NEAT

E

B8530-7 **2,3-Butanedione** (diacetyl)
$CH_3COCOCH_3$ M.W. 86.09 n_D^{20} 1.3951 m.p. -5.5 to -3.5°

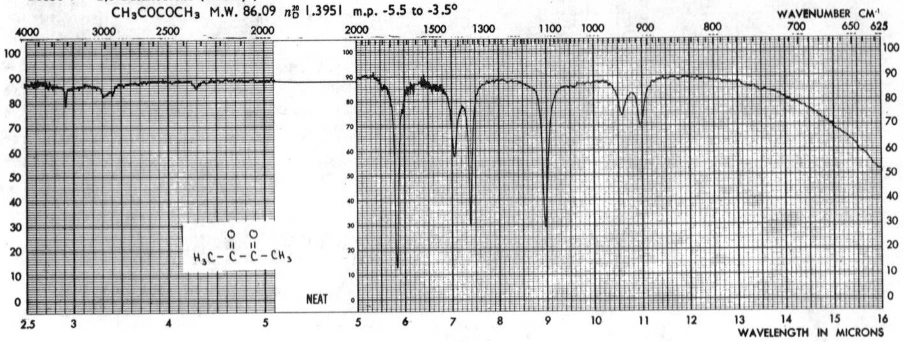

NEAT

F

D3916-9 **1,4-Dibromo-2,3-butanedione** (sym.-dibromodiacetyl)
$BrCH_2COCOCH_2Br$ M.W. 243.91
m.p. 116-118°

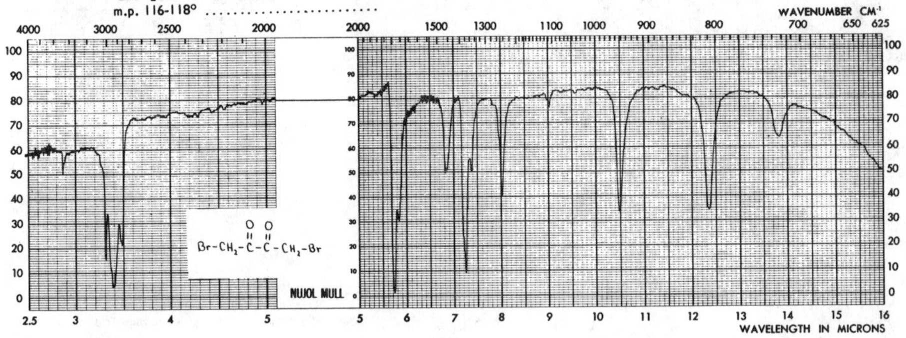

NUJOL MULL

G

14,416-9 **2,3-Hexanedione**
$CH_3CH_2CH_2COCOCH_3$ M.W. 114.14 n_D^{20} 1.4150
b.p. 128°

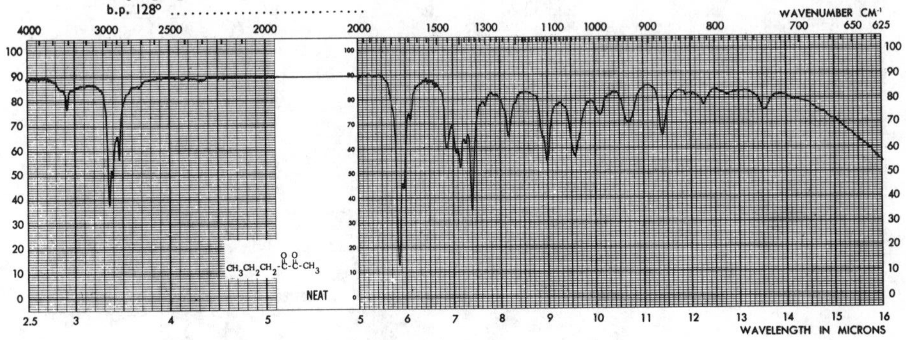

NEAT

H

H240-6 **2,3-Heptanedione**
$CH_3(CH_2)_3COCOCH_3$ M.W. 128.17 n_D^{20} 1.4109

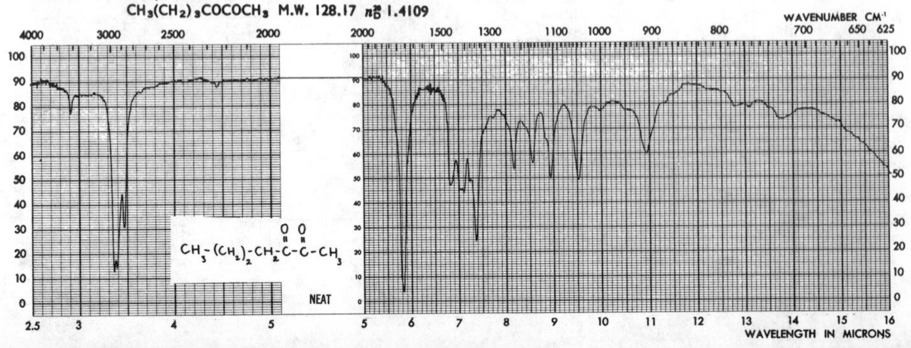

NEAT

A A1060-4 **Acetonylacetone** (2,5-hexanedione)
$CH_3COCH_2CH_2COCH_3$ M.W. 114.14
n_D^{20} 1.4260 m.p. -6.5 to -5.5°

NEAT

B O-340 **2,7-Octanedione**

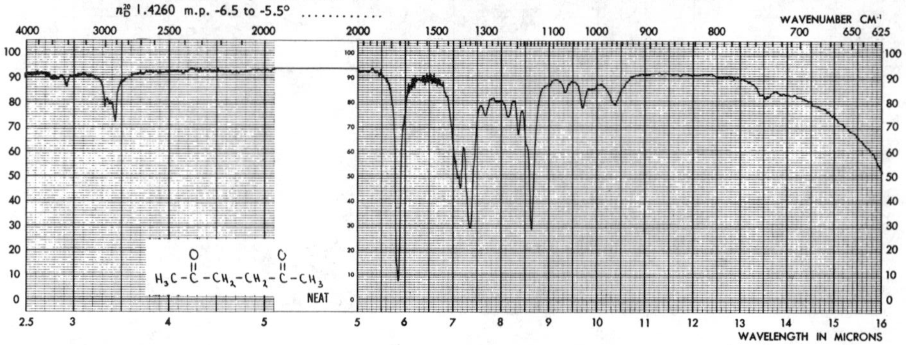

MELT

C P775-4 **2,4-Pentanedione** (acetylacetone), **puriss.**
$CH_3COCH_2COCH_3$ M.W. 100.12 n_D^{20} 1.4494
b.p. 133-135°

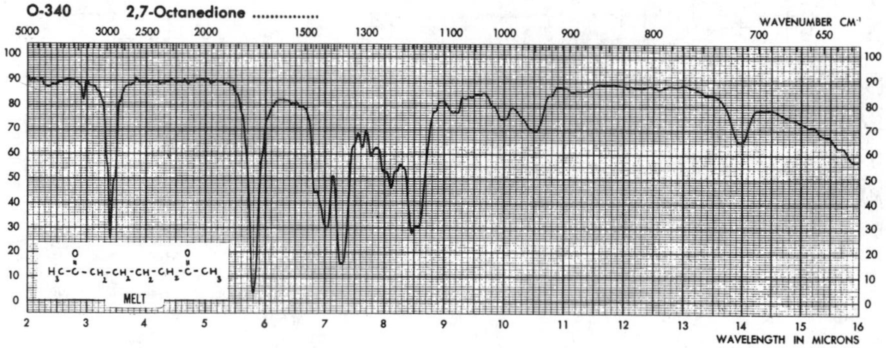

NEAT

D 15,575-6 **2,2,6,6-Tetramethyl-3,5-heptanedione** (dipivaloylmethane)
$(CH_3)_3CCOCH_2COC(CH_3)_3$ M.W. 184.28 n_D^{20} 1.4589
b.p. 72-73°/6 mm.

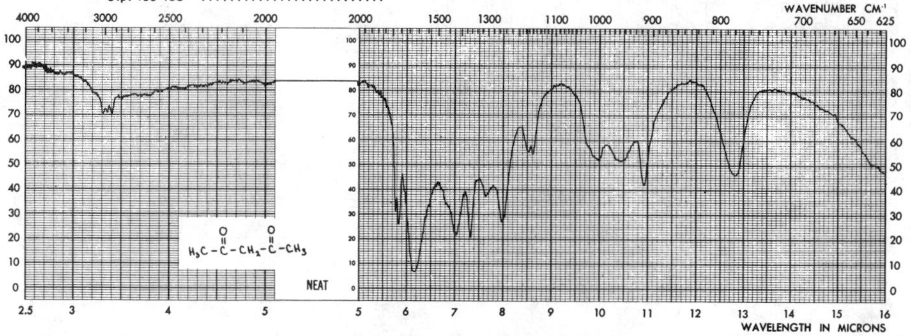

NEAT

E A1650 **3-Acetyl-2-hexanone**
$(CH_3CO)_2CH(CH_2)_2CH_3$ M.W. 142.20 n_D^{20} 1.4430

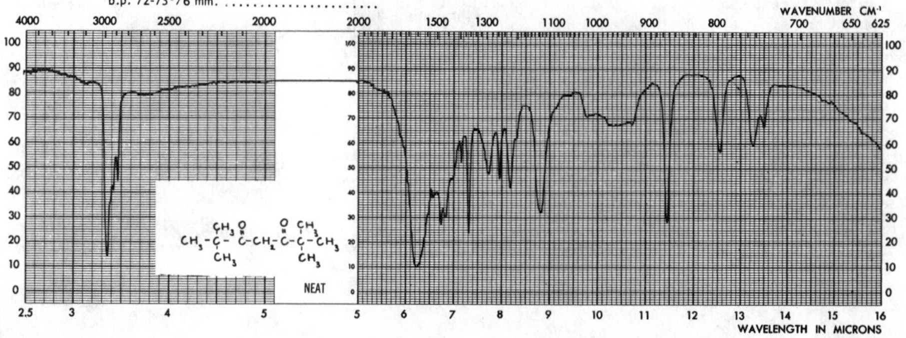

NEAT

F A1645 **3-Acetyl-2-heptanone**
$(CH_3CO)_2CH(CH_2)_3CH_3$ M.W. 156.23 n_D^{20} 1.4443

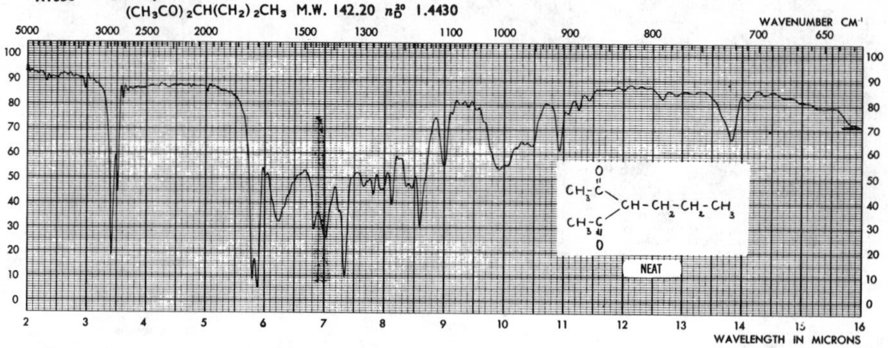

NEAT

G 17,716-4
1,3-Cyclopentanedione, 99%
$C_5H_6(=O)_2$
M.W. 98.1 m.p. 151-153°

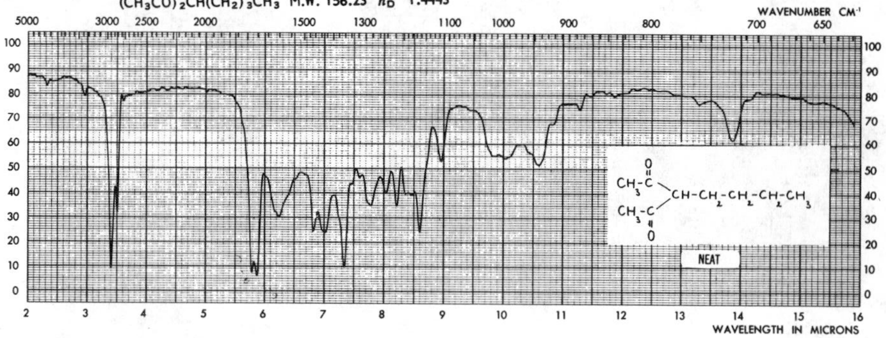

NUJOL MULL

H 11,702-1 **2-Methyl-1,3-cyclopentanedione**
M.W. 112.13 m.p. 208-210°

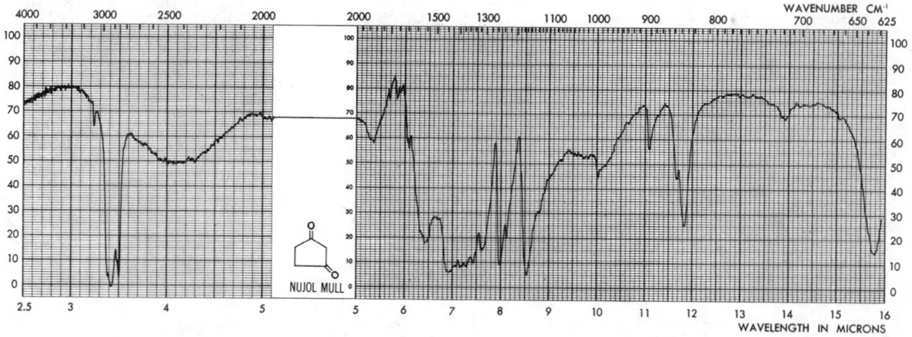

NUJOL MULL

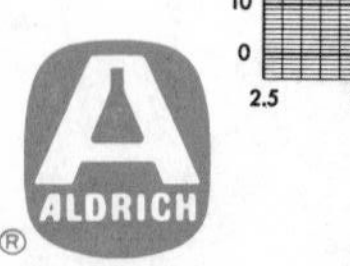

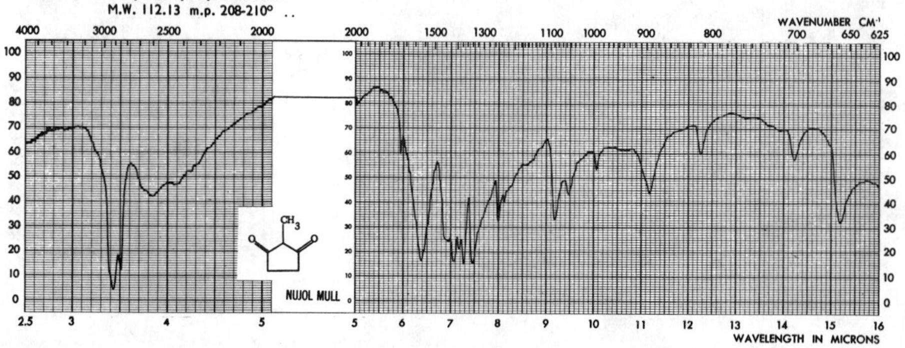

A

19,456-5
2-Ethyl-1,3-cyclopentanedione, 99%
FW 126.16 mp 174-175° Disp. C

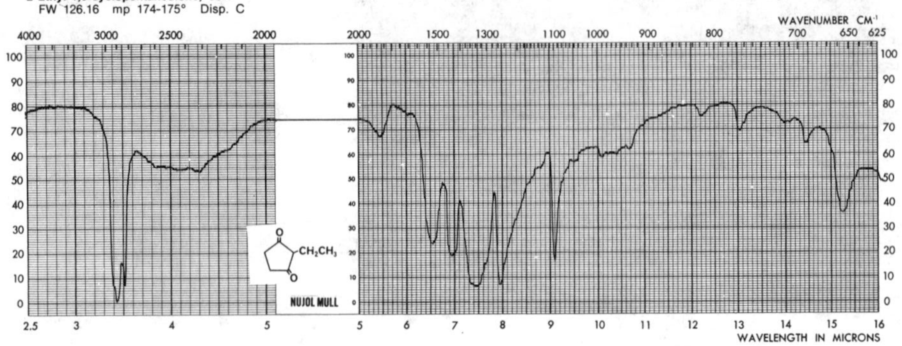

NUJOL MULL

B

16,168-3
4-Cyclopentene-1,3-dione, 98%
$C_5H_4(=O)_2$
M.W. 96.09 m.p. 30-31°

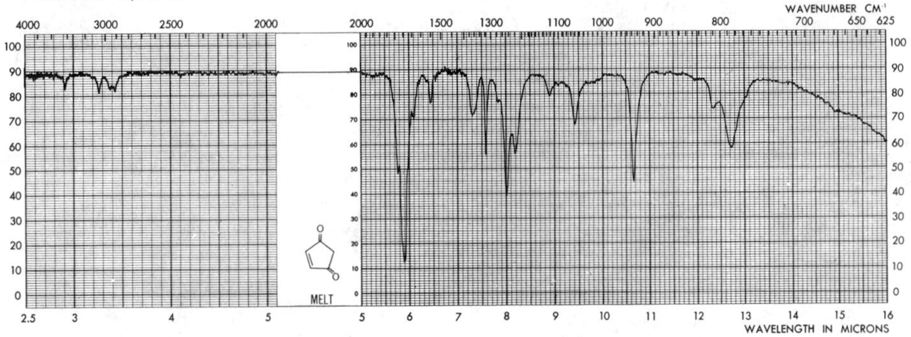

MELT

C

C12,000-6 Cyclopropyl methyl ketone
$C_3H_5COCH_3$ M.W. 84.12 n_D^{20} 1.4241

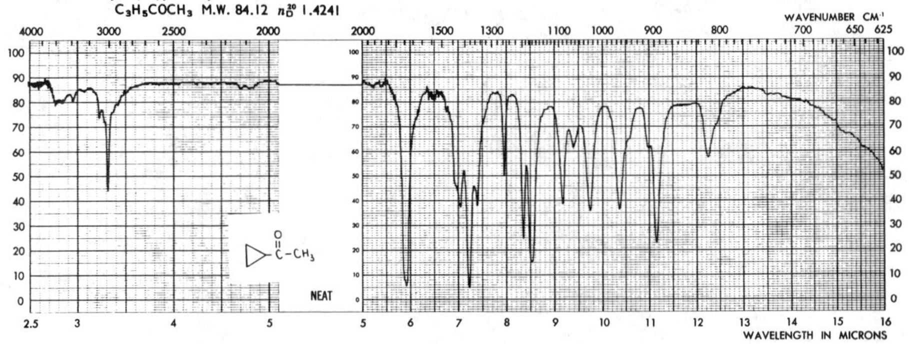

NEAT

D

C10,160-5 1,3-Cyclohexanedione (dihydroresorcinol)
$C_6H_8(:O)_2$ M.W. 112.13

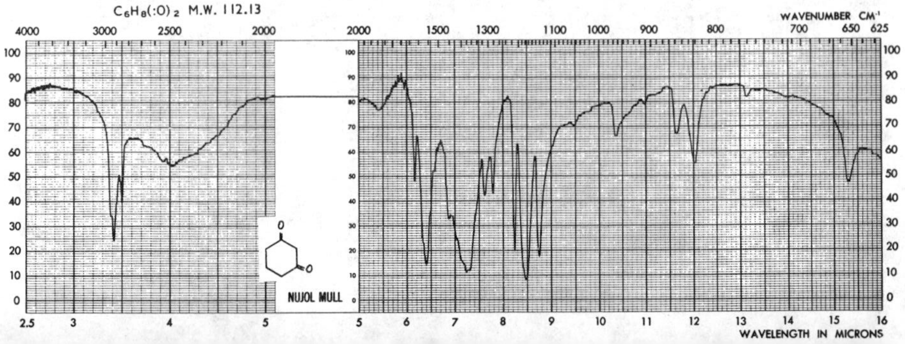

NUJOL MULL

E

M3793-5 2-Methyl-1,3-cyclohexanedione
$CH_3C_6H_7(:O)_2$ M.W. 126.16
m.p. 205-207° ....

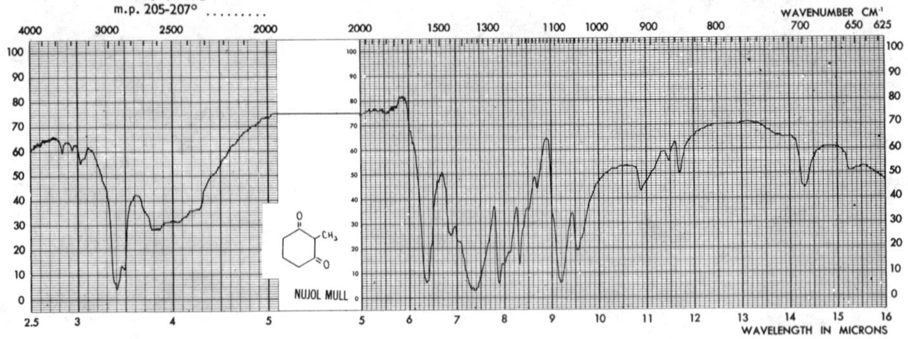

NUJOL MULL

F

D15,330-3 5,5-Dimethyl-1,3-cyclohexanedione (dimedone, methone)
$(CH_3)_2C_6H_6(:O)_2$ M.W. 140.18 m.p. 150° ....

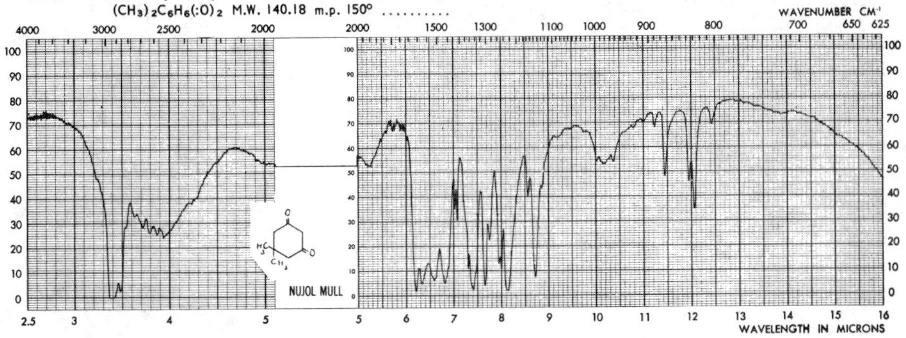

NUJOL MULL

G

17,976-0
2-Acetylcyclohexanone, 99%
$CH_3COC_6H_9(=O)$
M.W. 140.18 b.p. 111-112°/18mm. n_D^{20} 1.5090
d 1.078 Beil. 7,559

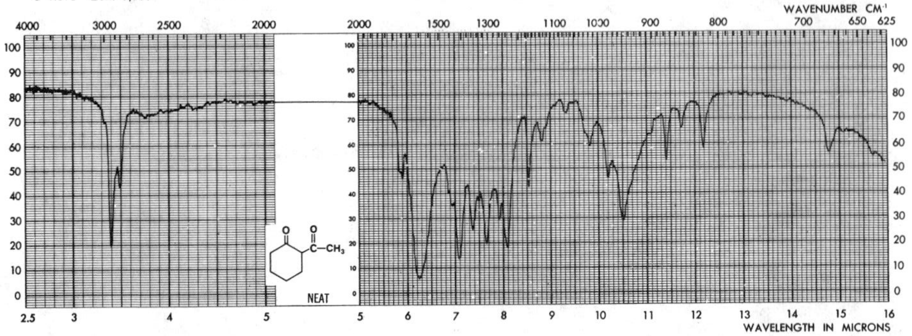

NEAT

H

17,977-9
2-Acetylcyclopentanone, 99%
$CH_3COC_5H_7(=O)$
M.W. 126.16 b.p. 72-75°/80mm. n_D^{20} 1.4905
d 1.043 Beil. 7,558

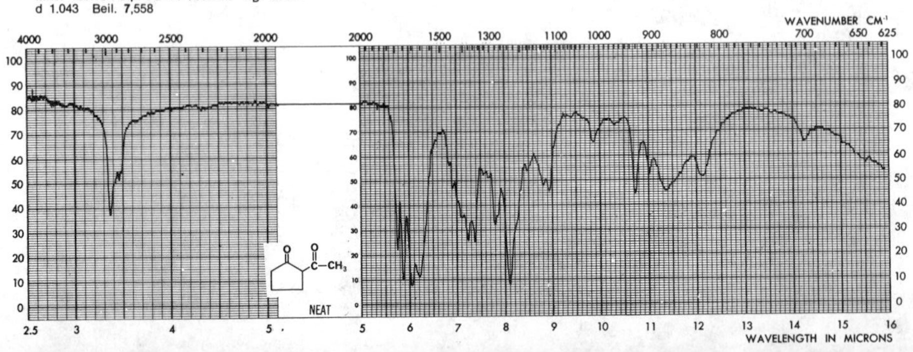

NEAT

A — 14,996-9 Ethyl β-(1-adamantyl)-β-oxopropionate
M.W. 250.34 n_D^{20} 1.4990
b.p. 108-110°/0.06 mm.

B — 14,738-9 Triacetylmethane [3-(α-hydroxyethylidene)-2,4-pentanedione]
$CH_3COC[:C(CH_3)OH]COCH_3$ M.W. 142.15
n_D^{20} 1.4780

C — 15,649-3
2-Acetyl-1,3-cyclohexanedione, 99+%, GOLD LABEL
$CH_3COC_6H_7(=O)_2$
M.W. 154.17

D — 10,563-5 Methyl 1-methylcyclopropyl ketone
$CH_3C_3H_4COCH_3$ M.W. 98.15 n_D^{20} 1.4331 b.p. 125-128°

E — 12,604-7 Dicyclopropyl ketone
$(C_3H_5)_2CO$ M.W. 110.16 n_D^{20} 1.4648

F — C10,460-4 Cyclohexylacetone
$C_6H_{11}CH_2COCH_3$ M.W. 140.23 n_D^{20} 1.4520
b.p. 195-196°

G — D8040 Dicyclohexyl ketone

H — 14,823-7 1-Adamantyl methyl ketone
M.W. 178.28 m.p. 53-55°

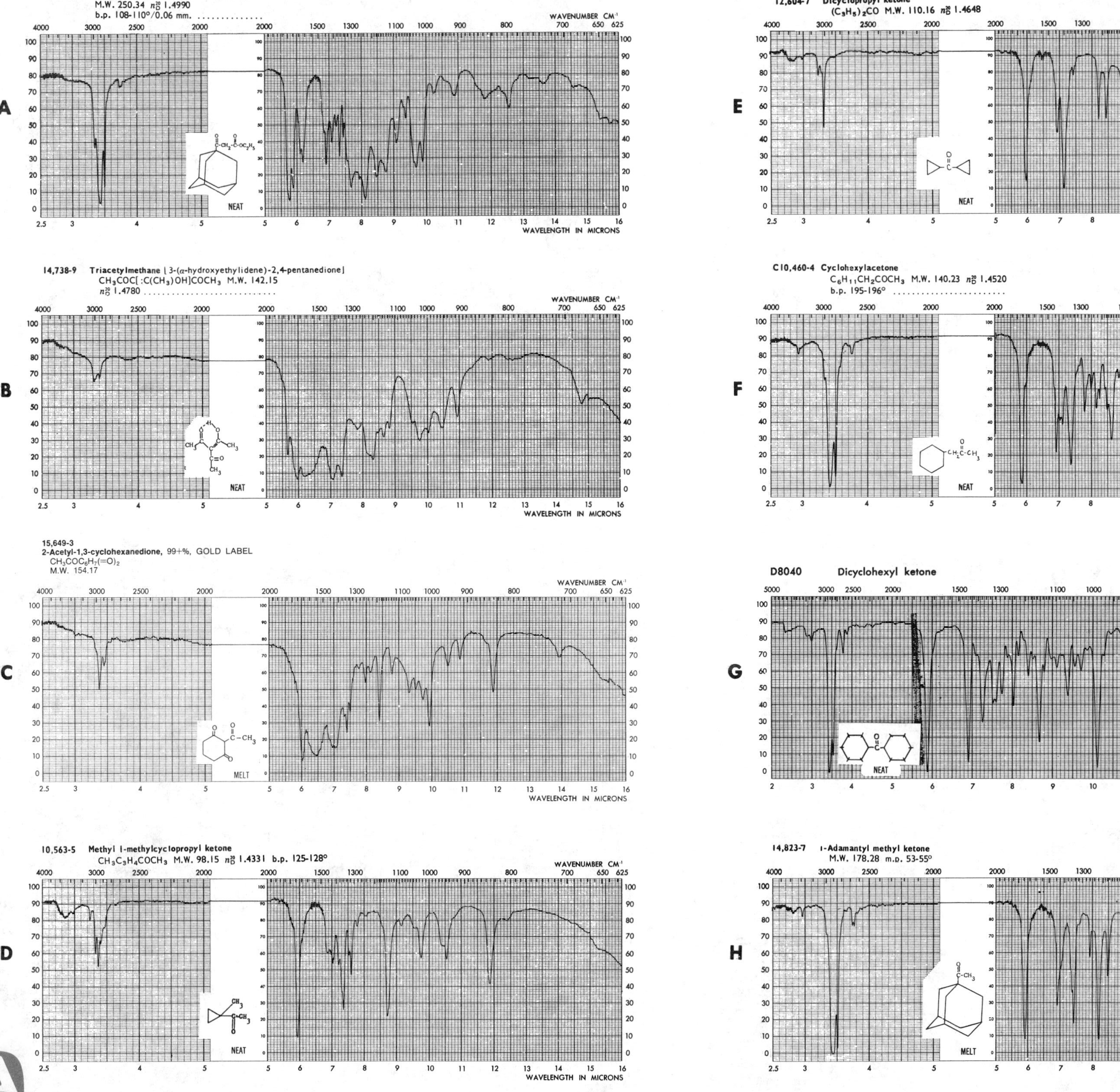

A

14,929-2 1-Adamantyl bromomethyl ketone
M.W. 257.18 m.p. 76-79° .....
NUJOL MULL

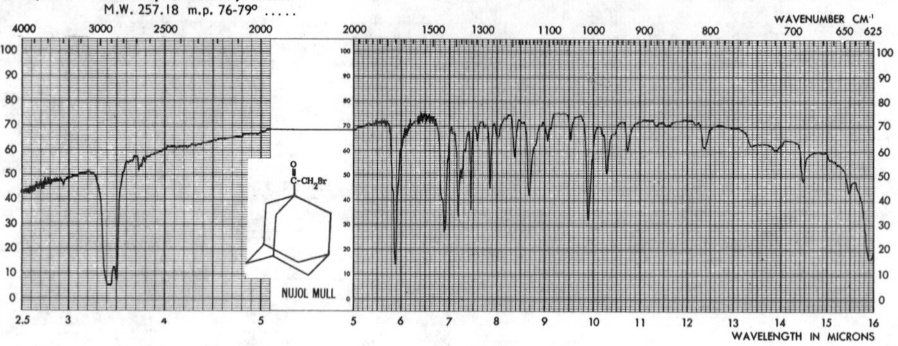

B

C9600-1 Cyclobutanone
$C_4H_6(:O)$ M.W. 70.09 n_D^{20} 1.4195
NEAT

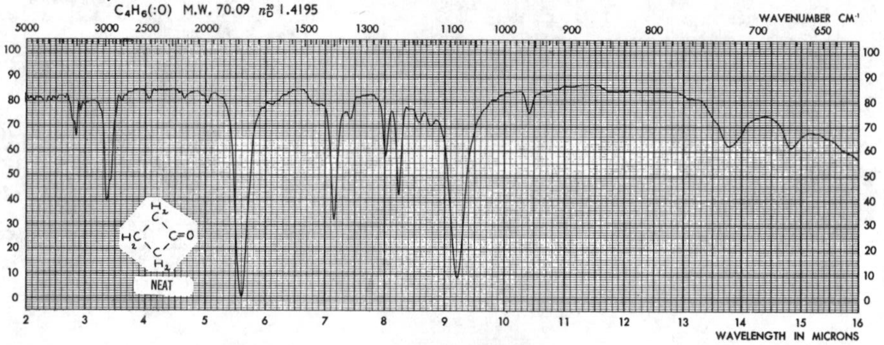

C

C11,240-2 Cyclopentanone, puriss.
$C_5H_8(:O)$ M.W. 84.12 n_D^{20} 1.4359
NEAT

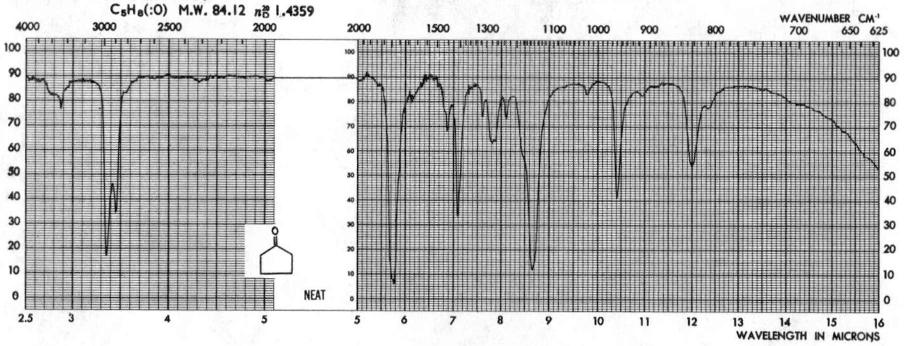

D

19,210-4
cis-Bicyclo[3.3.0]octane-3,7-dione, 99%
FW 138.17 mp 83-86° *Beil.* 7(3),3280 Disp. C
NUJOL MULL

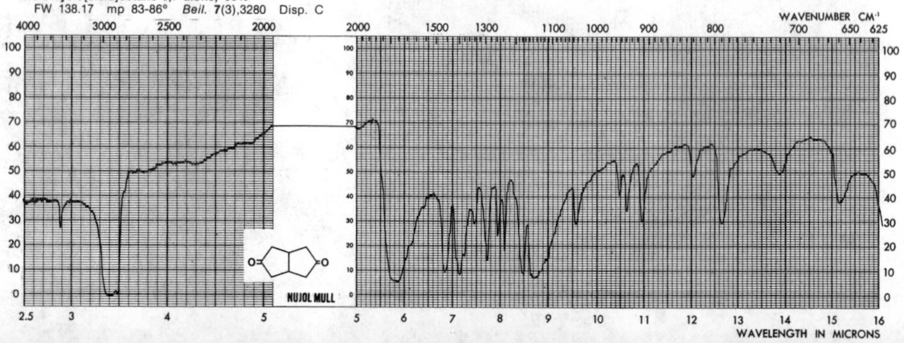

E

22,084-1
cis-1,5-Dimethylbicyclo[3.3.0]octane-3,7-dione, 98+%
FW 166.22 mp 219-221° Disp. C
NUJOL MULL

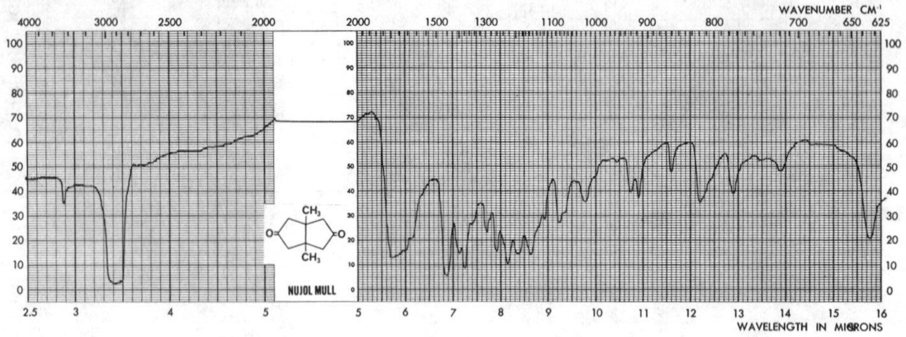

F

15,764-3
dl-3-Methylcyclopentanone, 99%
$CH_3C_5H_7(=O)$
M.W. 98.15 b.p. 145° n_D^{20} 1.4341 d 0.913
Beil. 7,11
NEAT

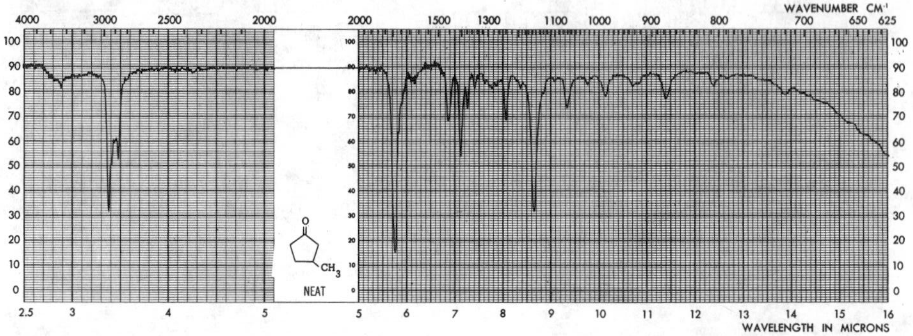

G

M3970-9 (+)-3-Methylcyclopentanone
$CH_3C_5H_7(:O)$ M.W. 98.15 n_D^{20} 1.4337 b.p. 143-143.5°
$[\alpha]_D^{24}$ + 143.7° (neat) ....
NEAT

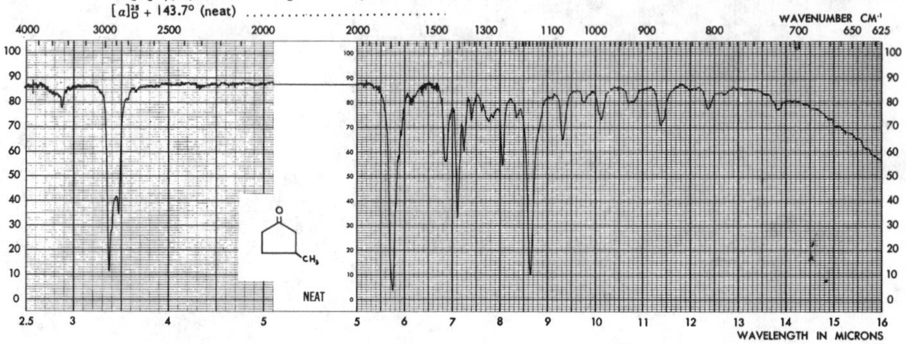

H

12,645-4 2,5-Dimethylcyclopentanone (mixture of *cis* and *trans*)
$(CH_3)_2C_5H_6(:O)$ M.W. 112.17 n_D^{20} 1.4310 .
NEAT

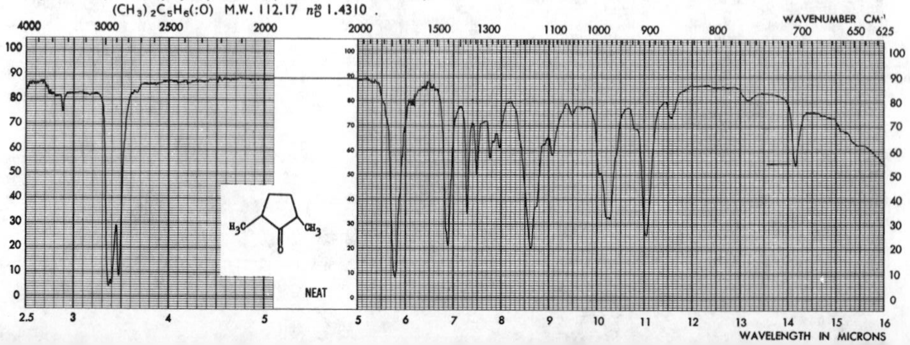

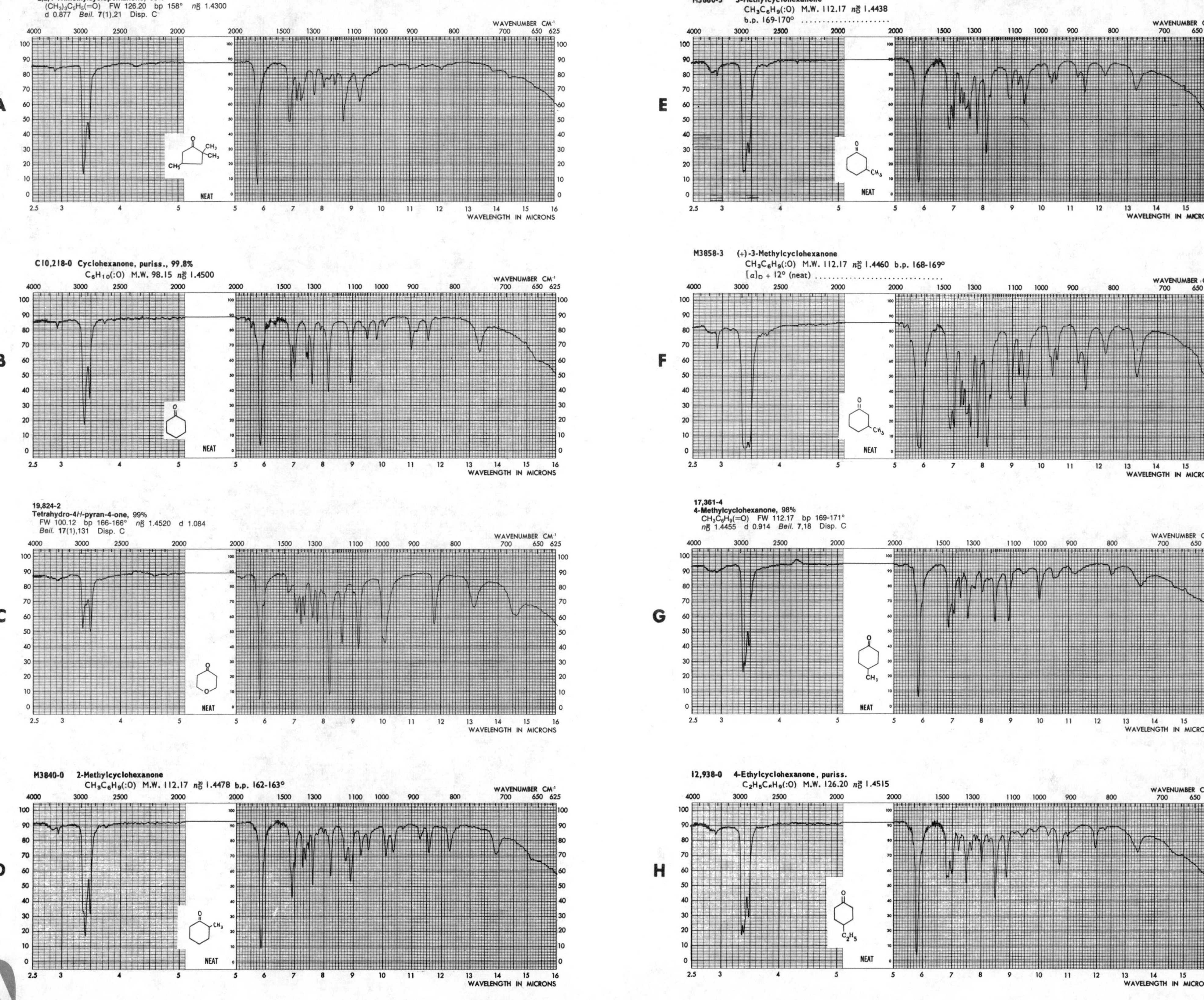
A
19,477-8
2,2,4-Trimethylcyclopentanone, 99%
(CH3)3C5H5(=O) FW 126.20 bp 158° nD 1.4300
d 0.877 Beil. 7(1),21 Disp. C
B
C10,218-0 Cyclohexanone, puriss., 99.8%
C6H10(:O) M.W. 98.15 nD 1.4500
C
19,824-2
Tetrahydro-4H-pyran-4-one, 99%
FW 100.12 bp 166-166° nD 1.4520 d 1.084
Beil. 17(1),131 Disp. C
D
M3840-0 2-Methylcyclohexanone
CH3C6H9(:O) M.W. 112.17 nD 1.4478 b.p. 162-163°
E
M3860-5 3-Methylcyclohexanone
CH3C6H9(:O) M.W. 112.17 nD 1.4438
b.p. 169-170°
F
M3858-3 (+)-3-Methylcyclohexanone
CH3C6H9(:O) M.W. 112.17 nD 1.4460 b.p. 168-169°
[α]D + 12° (neat)
G
17,361-4
4-Methylcyclohexanone, 98%
CH3C6H9(=O) FW 112.17 bp 169-171°
nD 1.4455 d 0.914 Beil. 7,18 Disp. C
H
12,938-0 4-Ethylcyclohexanone, puriss.
C2H5C6H9(:O) M.W. 126.20 nD 1.4515
WAVENUMBER CM-1
WAVELENGTH IN MICRONS
NEAT
ALDRICH

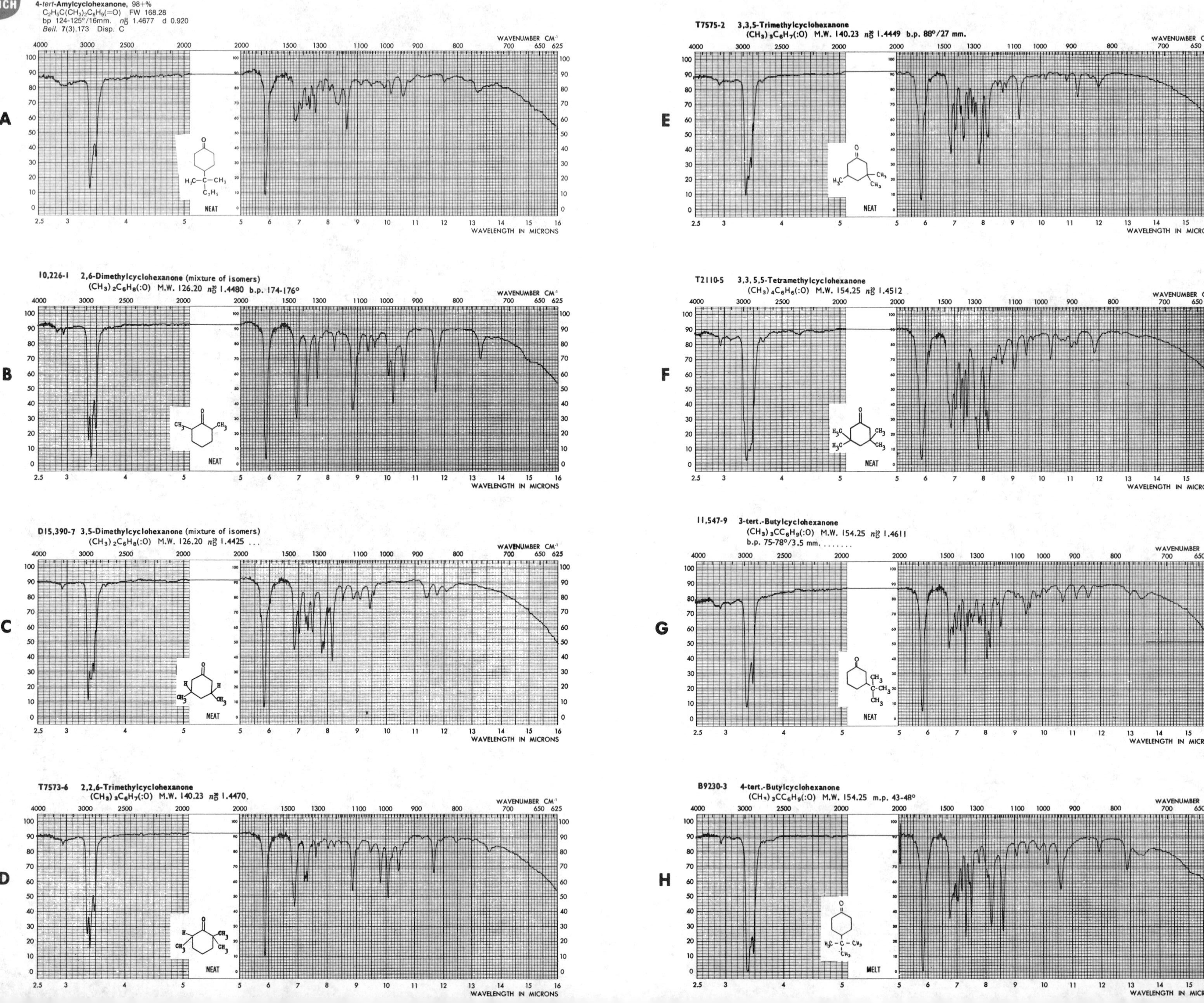
ALDRICH
A
19,326-7
4-*tert*-Amylcyclohexanone, 98+%
$C_2H_5C(CH_3)_2C_6H_9(=O)$ FW 168.28
bp 124-125°/16mm. n_D^{20} 1.4677 d 0.920
Beil. 7(3),173 Disp. C
NEAT
B
10,226-1 2,6-Dimethylcyclohexanone (mixture of isomers)
$(CH_3)_2C_6H_8(:O)$ M.W. 126.20 n_D^{20} 1.4480 b.p. 174-176°
NEAT
C
D15,390-7 3,5-Dimethylcyclohexanone (mixture of isomers)
$(CH_3)_2C_6H_8(:O)$ M.W. 126.20 n_D^{20} 1.4425 . . .
NEAT
D
T7573-6 2,2,6-Trimethylcyclohexanone
$(CH_3)_3C_6H_7(:O)$ M.W. 140.23 n_D^{20} 1.4470.
NEAT
E
T7575-2 3,3,5-Trimethylcyclohexanone
$(CH_3)_3C_6H_7(:O)$ M.W. 140.23 n_D^{20} 1.4449 b.p. 88°/27 mm.
NEAT
F
T2110-5 3,3,5,5-Tetramethylcyclohexanone
$(CH_3)_4C_6H_6(:O)$ M.W. 154.25 n_D^{20} 1.4512
NEAT
G
11,547-9 3-tert.-Butylcyclohexanone
$(CH_3)_3CC_6H_9(:O)$ M.W. 154.25 n_D^{20} 1.4611
b.p. 75-78°/3.5 mm. . . . .
NEAT
H
B9230-3 4-tert.-Butylcyclohexanone
$(CH_3)_3CC_6H_9(:O)$ M.W. 154.25 m.p. 43-48°
MELT
WAVENUMBER CM⁻¹
WAVELENGTH IN MICRONS

A

M280-2 **Menthone** (mixture of *dl*-menthone and *dl*-isomenthone)
M.W. 154.25 n_D^{20} 1.4510 ....

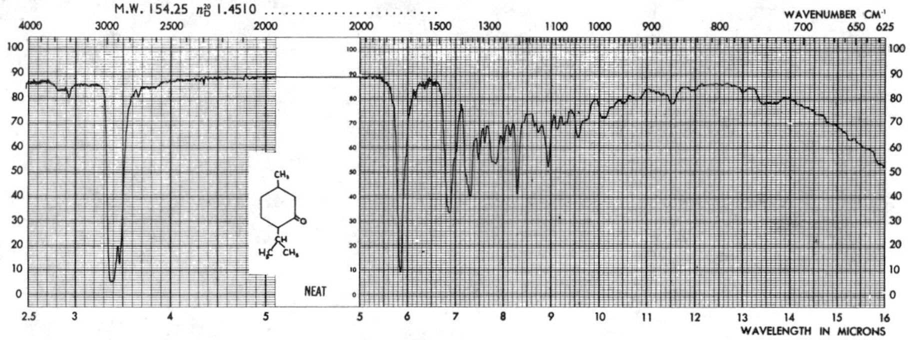

NEAT

B

21,823-5
***l*-Menthone**, 85%
FW 154.25 bp 207-210° n_D^{20} 1.4502 d 0.893
$[\alpha]_D^{20}$ -15° (neat) *Beil.* **7**,38 Disp. C

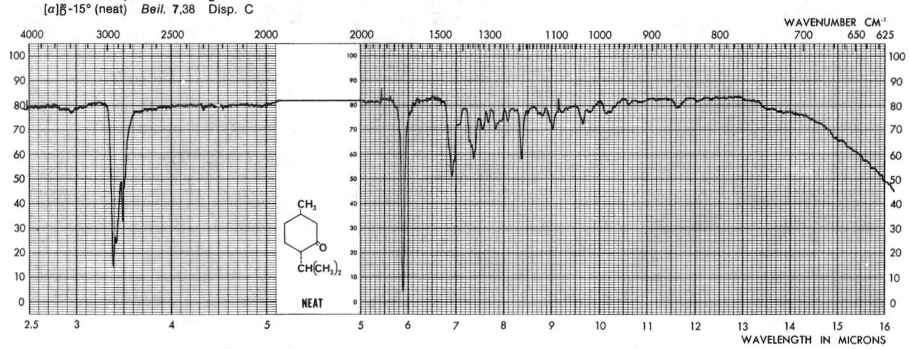

NEAT

C

C3260-7 **2-Chlorocyclohexanone**
$ClC_6H_9(:O)$ M.W. 132.59 n_D^{20} 1.4835

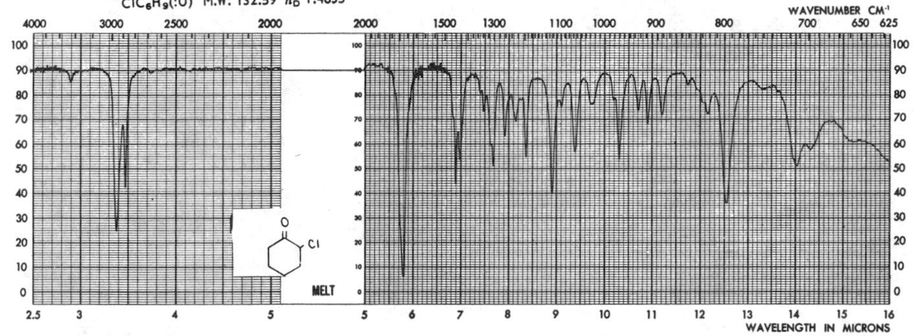

MELT

D

H2,440-2
2-Hydroxycyclohexanone (adipoin)
$HOC_6H_9(=O)$
M.W. 114.14

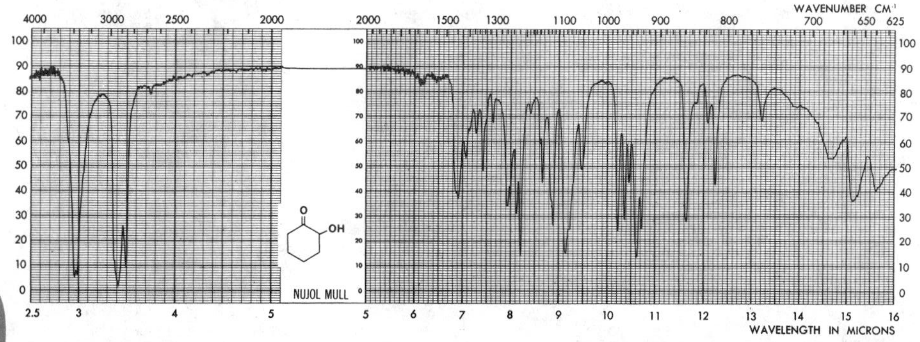

NUJOL MULL

E

D14,060-0
2-Dimethylaminocyclohexanone, 98%
$(CH_3)_2NC_6H_9(=O)$
M.W. 141.21 n_D^{20} 1.4663

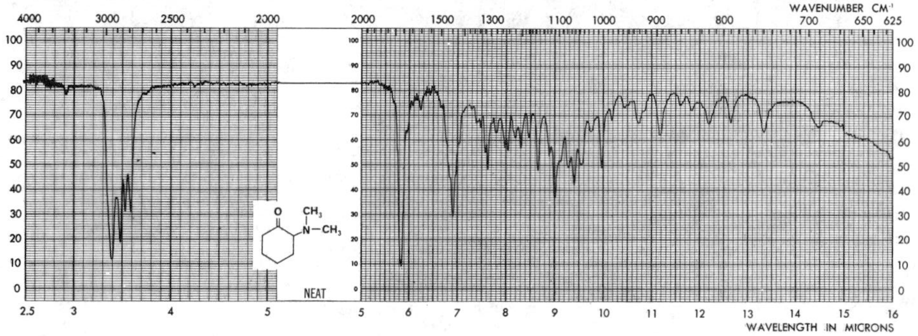

NEAT

F

18,665-6
3,3-Dichloro-2,2-dihydroxycyclohexanone
$Cl_2C_6H_6(OH)_2(=O)$ FW 199.04 mp 120-124°
Disp. C

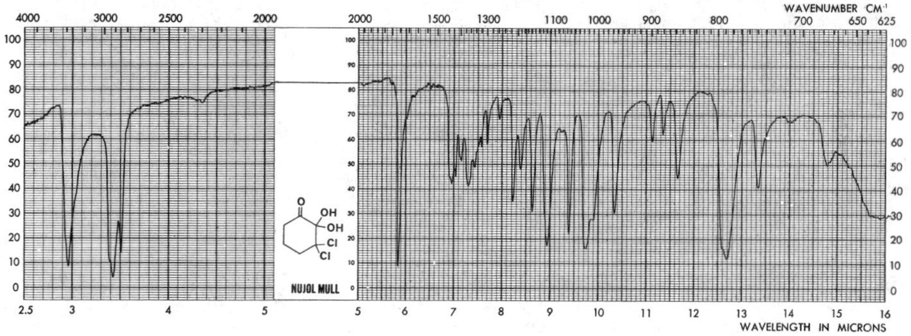

NUJOL MULL

G

C9900-0 **Cycloheptanone**
$C_7H_{12}(:O)$ M.W. 112.17 n_D^{20} 1.4611

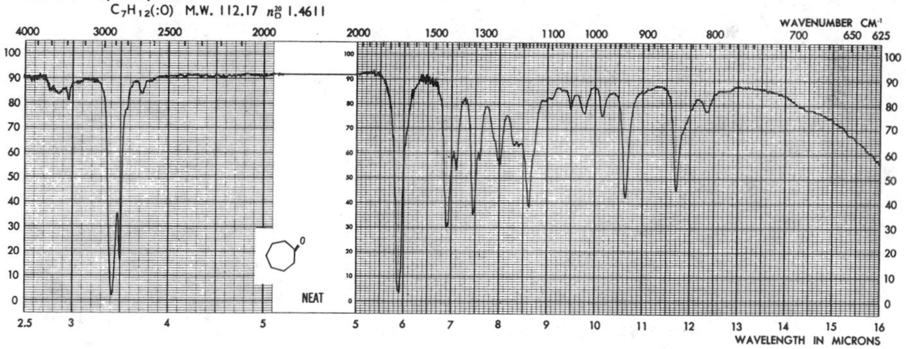

NEAT

H

C10,980-0 **Cyclooctanone**
$C_8H_{14}(:O)$ M.W. 126.20
m.p. 38-40° ....

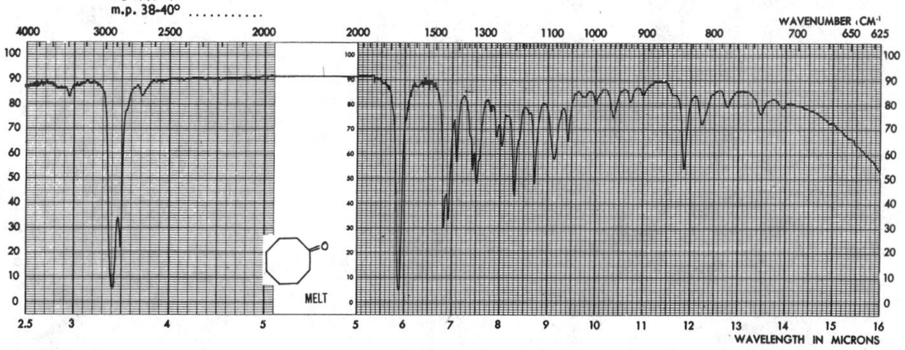

MELT

WAVENUMBER CM⁻¹ — WAVELENGTH IN MICRONS

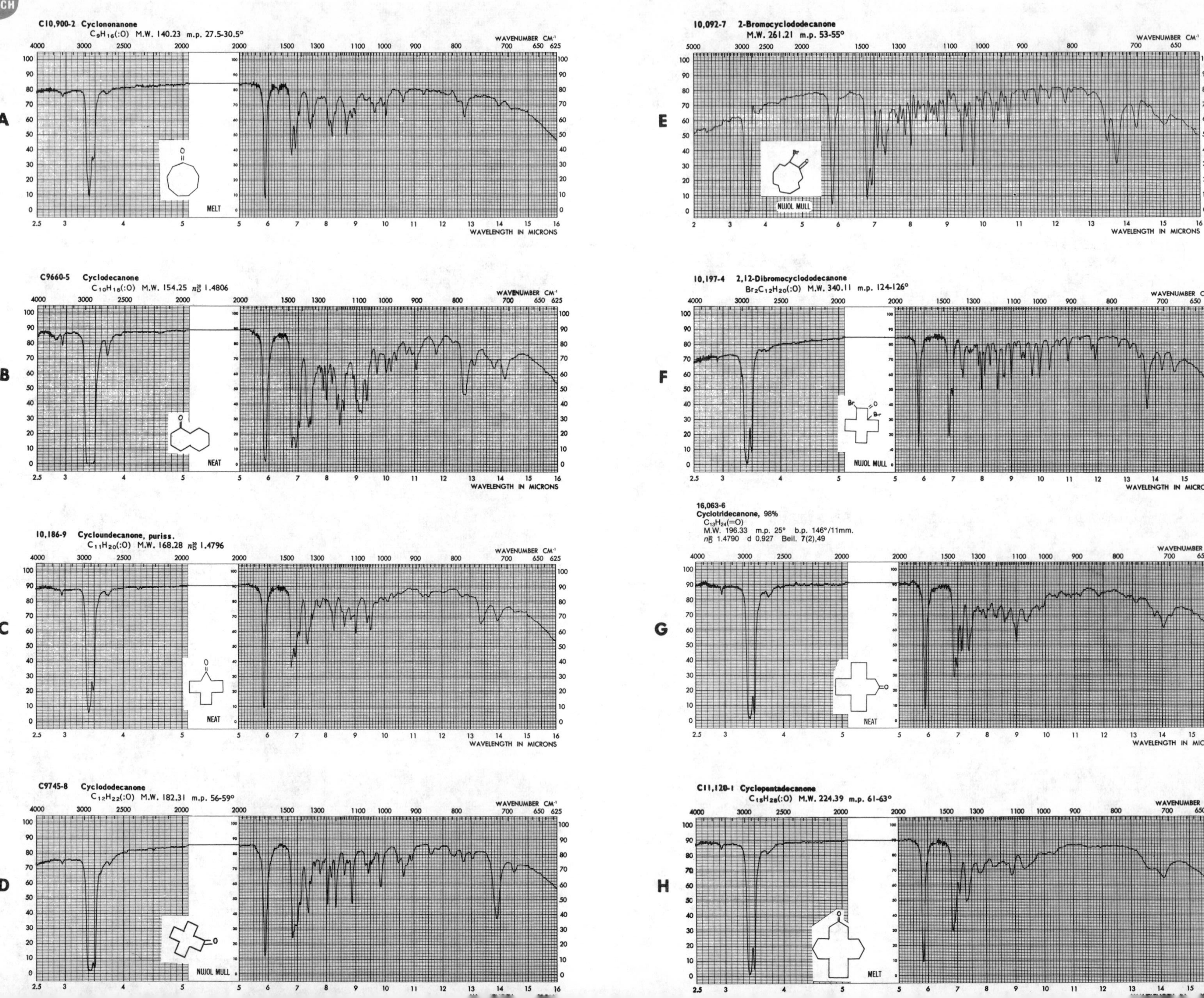
ALDRICH
A
C10,900-2 Cyclononanone
$C_9H_{16}(:O)$ M.W. 140.23 m.p. 27.5-30.5°
MELT
B
C9660-5 Cyclodecanone
$C_{10}H_{18}(:O)$ M.W. 154.25 n_D^{20} 1.4806
NEAT
C
10,186-9 Cycloundecanone, puriss.
$C_{11}H_{20}(:O)$ M.W. 168.28 n_D^{20} 1.4796
NEAT
D
C9745-8 Cyclododecanone
$C_{12}H_{22}(:O)$ M.W. 182.31 m.p. 56-59°
NUJOL MULL
E
10,092-7 2-Bromocyclododecanone
M.W. 261.21 m.p. 53-55°
NUJOL MULL
F
10,197-4 2,12-Dibromocyclododecanone
$Br_2C_{12}H_{20}(:O)$ M.W. 340.11 m.p. 124-126°
NUJOL MULL
G
16,063-6
Cyclotridecanone, 98%
$C_{13}H_{24}(=O)$
M.W. 196.33 m.p. 25° b.p. 146°/11mm.
n_D^{20} 1.4790 d 0.927 Beil. 7(2),49
NEAT
H
C11,120-1 Cyclopentadecanone
$C_{15}H_{28}(:O)$ M.W. 224.39 m.p. 61-63°
MELT
WAVENUMBER CM⁻¹
WAVELENGTH IN MICRONS

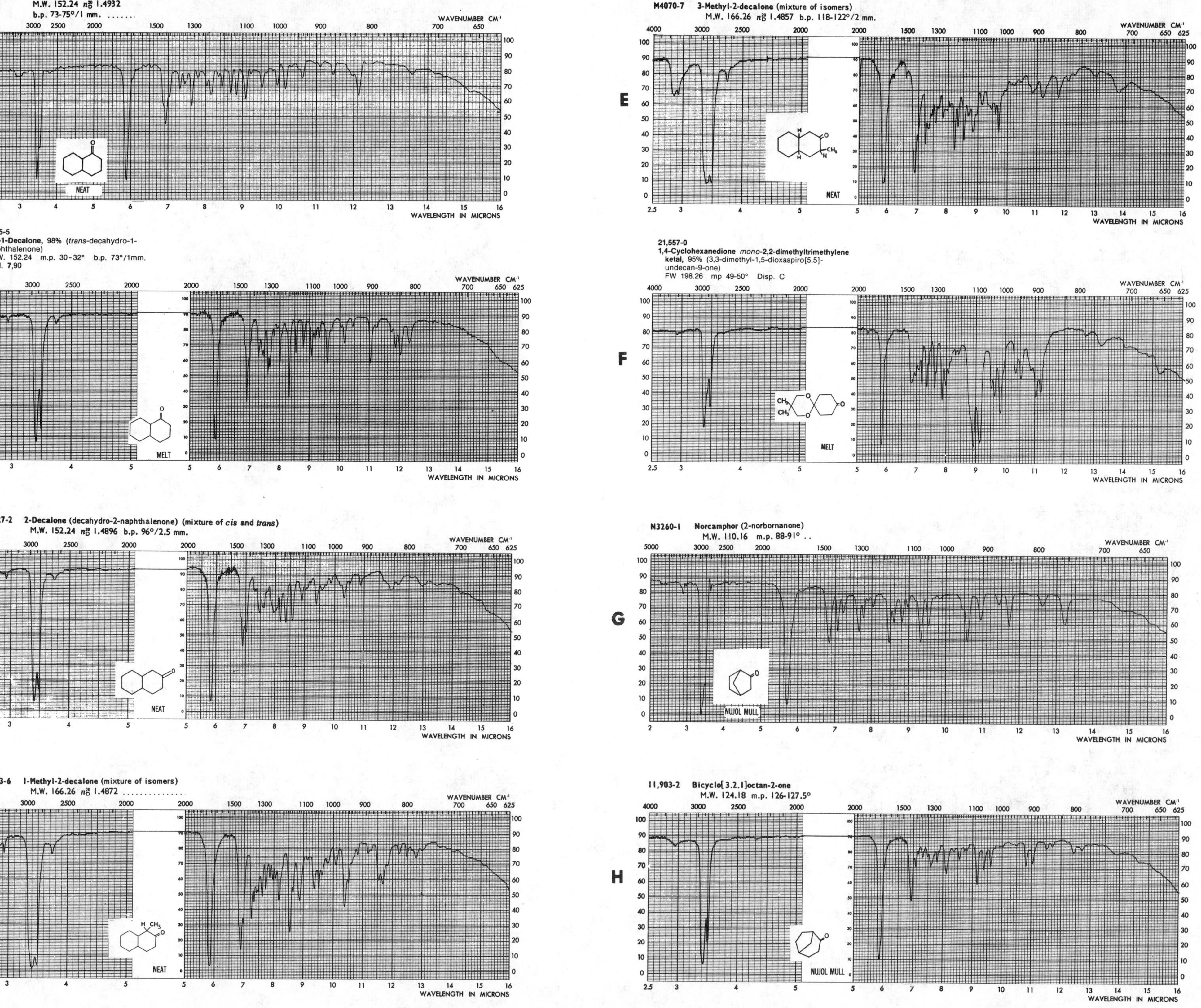
A
12,772-8 1-Decalone (decahydro-1-naphthalenone) (mixture of *cis* and *trans*).
M.W. 152.24 n_D^{20} 1.4932
b.p. 73-75°/1 mm.
NEAT
B
15,665-5
trans-1-Decalone, 98% (*trans*-decahydro-1-naphthalenone)
M.W. 152.24 m.p. 30-32° b.p. 73°/1mm.
Beil. 7,90
MELT
C
11,027-2 2-Decalone (decahydro-2-naphthalenone) (mixture of *cis* and *trans*)
M.W. 152.24 n_D^{20} 1.4896 b.p. 96°/2.5 mm.
NEAT
D
12,983-6 1-Methyl-2-decalone (mixture of isomers)
M.W. 166.26 n_D^{20} 1.4872
NEAT
E
M4070-7 3-Methyl-2-decalone (mixture of isomers)
M.W. 166.26 n_D^{20} 1.4857 b.p. 118-122°/2 mm.
NEAT
F
21,557-0
1,4-Cyclohexanedione *mono*-2,2-dimethyltrimethylene ketal, 95% (3,3-dimethyl-1,5-dioxaspiro[5.5]-undecan-9-one)
FW 198.26 mp 49-50° Disp. C
MELT
G
N3260-1 Norcamphor (2-norbornanone)
M.W. 110.16 m.p. 88-91°
NUJOL MULL
H
11,903-2 Bicyclo[3.2.1]octan-2-one
M.W. 124.18 m.p. 126-127.5°
NUJOL MULL
WAVENUMBER CM⁻¹
WAVELENGTH IN MICRONS
ALDRICH

NON-AROMATIC KETONES

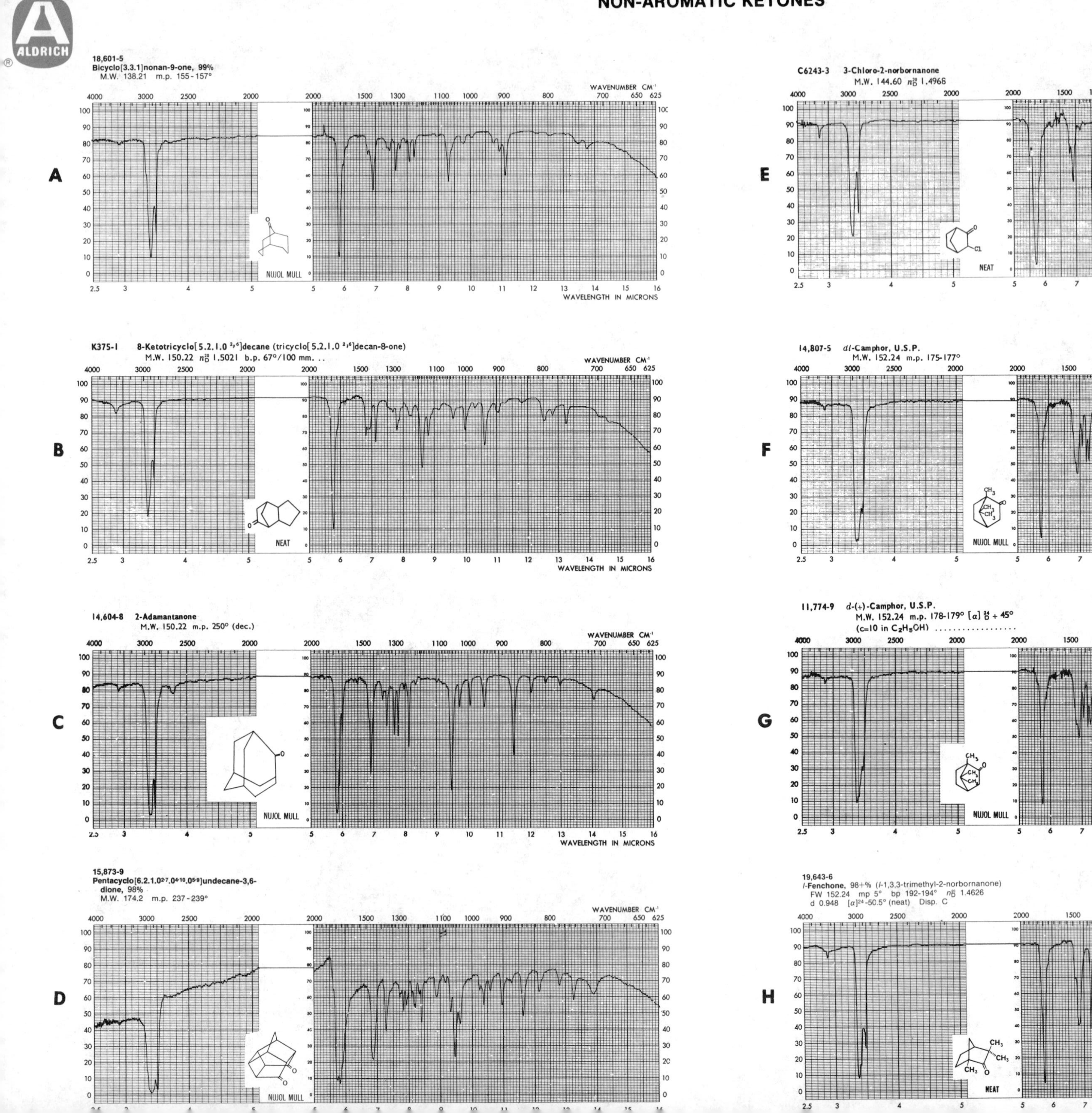
ALDRICH

A
18,601-5
Bicyclo[3.3.1]nonan-9-one, 99%
M.W. 138.21 m.p. 155-157°
NUJOL MULL

B
K375-1 8-Ketotricyclo[5.2.1.0 ²,⁶]decane (tricyclo[5.2.1.0 ²,⁶]decan-8-one)
M.W. 150.22 n_D^{20} 1.5021 b.p. 67°/100 mm. . .
NEAT

C
14,604-8 2-Adamantanone
M.W. 150.22 m.p. 250° (dec.)
NUJOL MULL

D
15,873-9
Pentacyclo[6.2.1.0²,⁷.0⁴,¹⁰.0⁵,⁹]undecane-3,6-dione, 98%
M.W. 174.2 m.p. 237-239°
NUJOL MULL

E
C6243-3 3-Chloro-2-norbornanone
M.W. 144.60 n_D^{20} 1.4968
NEAT

F
14,807-5 dl-Camphor, U.S.P.
M.W. 152.24 m.p. 175-177°
NUJOL MULL

G
11,774-9 d-(+)-Camphor, U.S.P.
M.W. 152.24 m.p. 178-179° $[\alpha]_D^{25}$ + 45°
(c=10 in C_2H_5OH) . . . .
NUJOL MULL

H
19,643-6
l-Fenchone, 98+% (l-1,3,3-trimethyl-2-norbornanone)
FW 152.24 mp 5° bp 192-194° n_D^{20} 1.4626
d 0.948 $[\alpha]^{24}$ -50.5° (neat) Disp. C
NEAT

WAVENUMBER CM⁻¹
WAVELENGTH IN MICRONS

A

C35-2 *l*-(-)-Camphor
M.W. 152.24 m.p. 174-176° $[\alpha]_D^{20}$ - 38.1°
(c=11.84 in CH_3OH)

NUJOL MULL

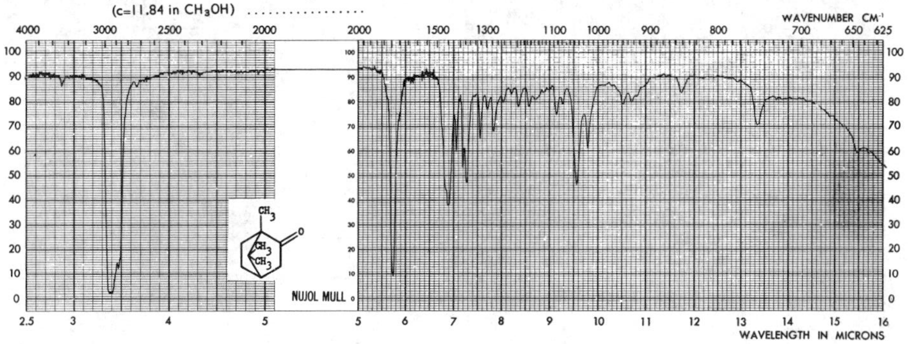

B

15,081-9 *dl*-Camphor, zone refined, 99.9 %, GOLD LABEL
M.W. 152.24 m.p. 176.30°

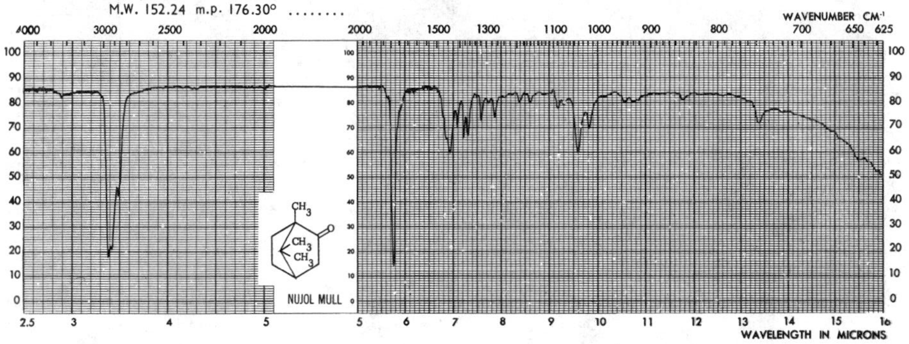

NUJOL MULL

C

14,716-8 *d*-3-Bromocamphor
M.W. 231.14 m.p. 75-78° $[\alpha]_D^{20}$ + 132°
(c=5.3, CH_3OH)

NUJOL MULL

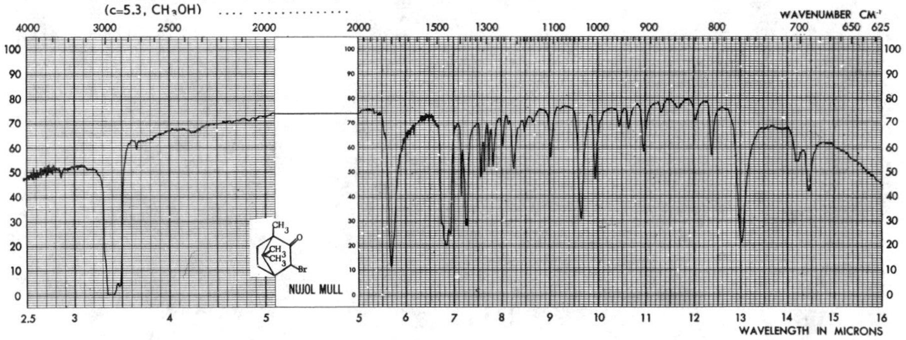

D

19,593-6
3-Heptafluorobutyryl-*d*-camphor, 99%
FW 348.26 bp 60-70°/0.200mm. n_D^{20} 1.4215
d 1.218 $[\alpha]^{22}$+125° (c=2.6, CCl_4) Disp. C

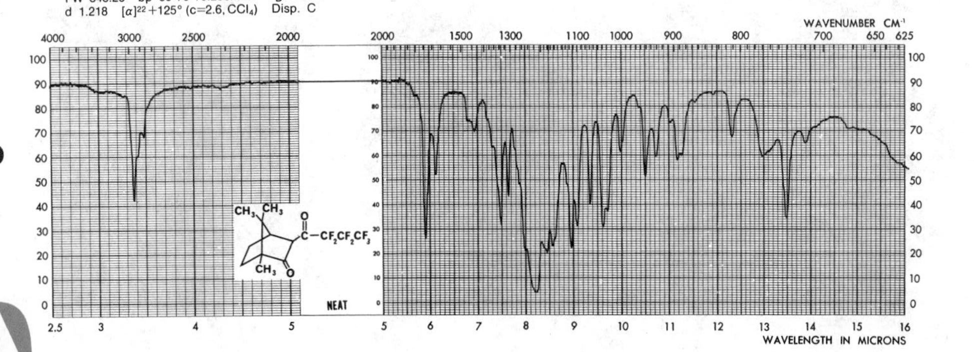

E

18,900-6
3-(Trifluoroacetyl)-*d*-camphor
FW 248.25 bp 100-101°/16mm. n_D^{20} 1.4515
$[\alpha]^{22}$+146.6° (c=2.3, CCl_4) Disp. C

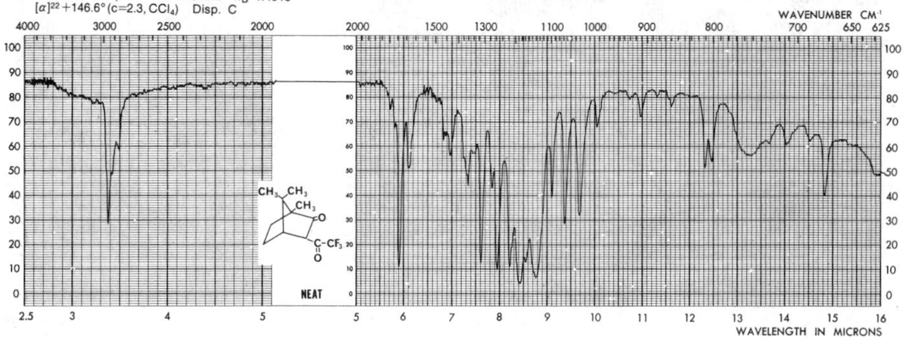

NEAT

F

21,761-1
1-Methoxybicyclo[2.2.2]oct-5-en-2-yl methyl ketone, 98%
FW 180.25 bp 120-125°/13mm. n_D^{20} 1.4947
d 1.044 Disp. C

NEAT

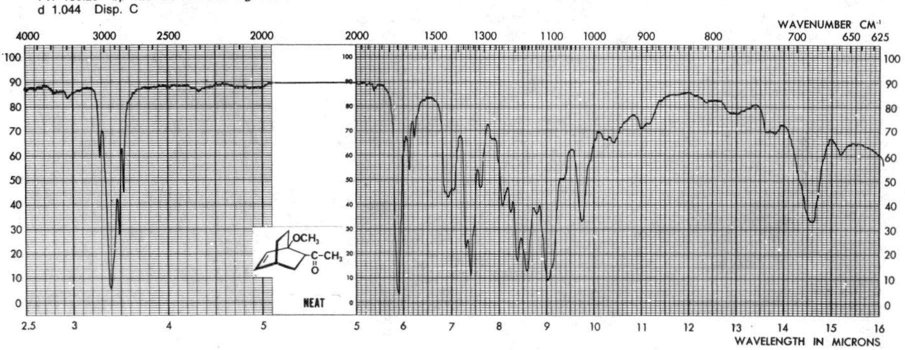

G

16,200-0
7-*syn*-Methoxymethyl-5-norbornen-2-one, tech., 90%
M.W. 152.19 n_D^{20} 1.4820

NEAT

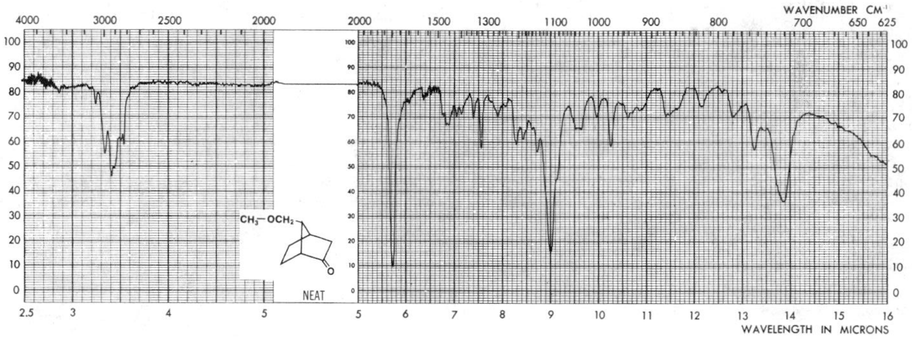

H

N1551-0 *α*-*d*-Nitrocamphor, sodium salt
M.W. 219.21 m.p. > 320° $[\alpha]_D^{23}$ + 279° (c=4 in H_2O)

NUJOL MULL

ALDRICH

NON-AROMATIC KETONES

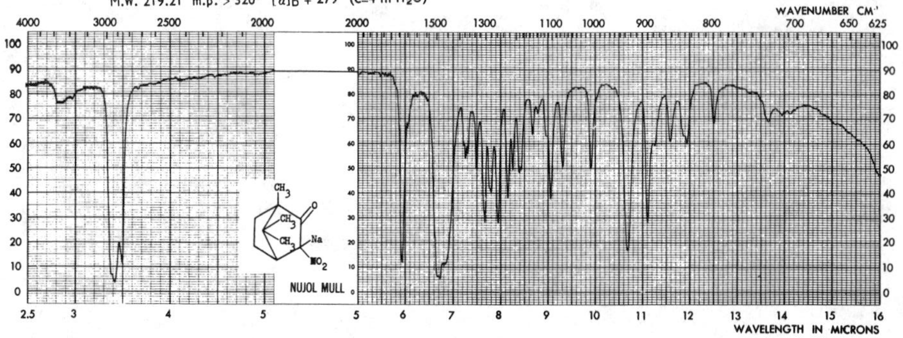

A

21,825-1
l-Verbenone, 94%
FW 150.22 bp 227-228° n_D^{20} 1.4955 d 0.974
$[\alpha]^{19}$-193° (c=10, C_2H_5OH) *Beil.* 7,161 Disp. C

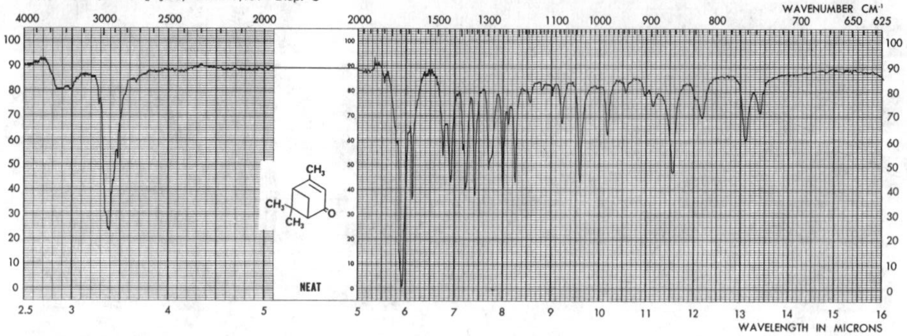

NEAT

B

A1440-5 1-Acetyl-1-cyclohexene
$C_6H_9COCH_3$ M.W. 124.18 n_D^{20} 1.4900

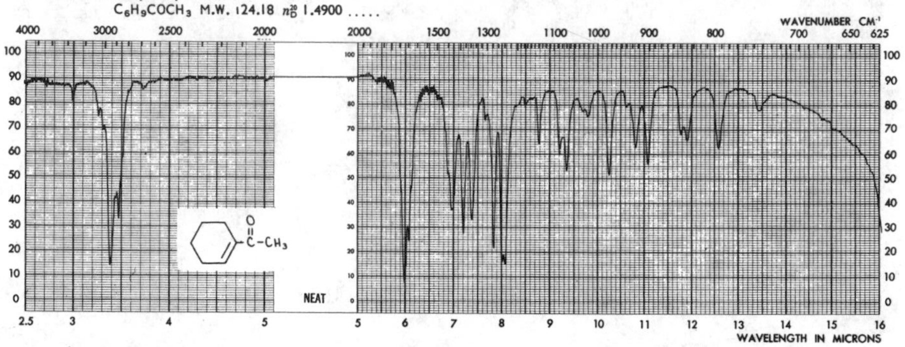

NEAT

C

10,293-8 2-Acetyl-5-norbornene (methyl 5-norbornen-2-yl ketone), mixture of endo and exo, tech.
M.W. 136.19 n_D^{20} 1.4845
b.p. 84-86°/18 mm.

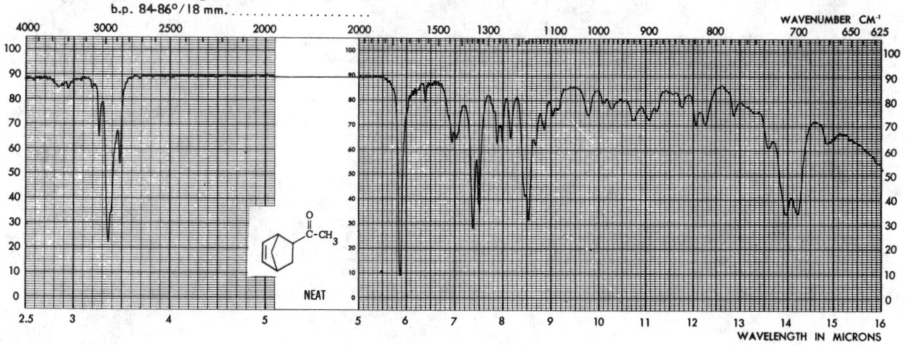

NEAT

D

C10,320-9 1-Cyclohexenylacetone, tech.
$C_6H_9CH_2COCH_3$ M.W. 138.21 n_D^{20} 1.4732

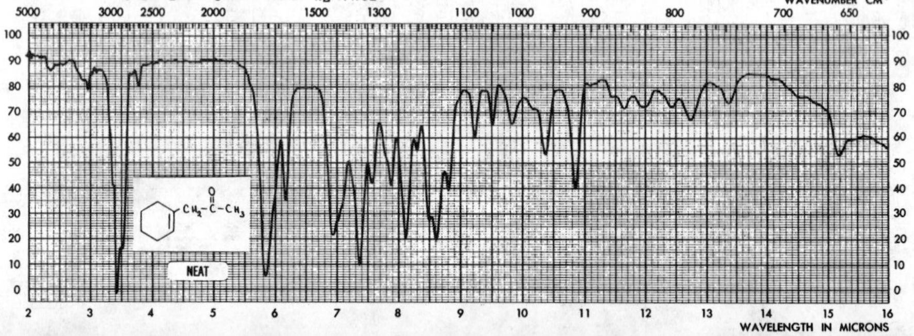

NEAT

E

1-1260-3 β-Ionone
M.W. 192.30 n_D^{20} 1.5180 b.p. 126-128/12mm.

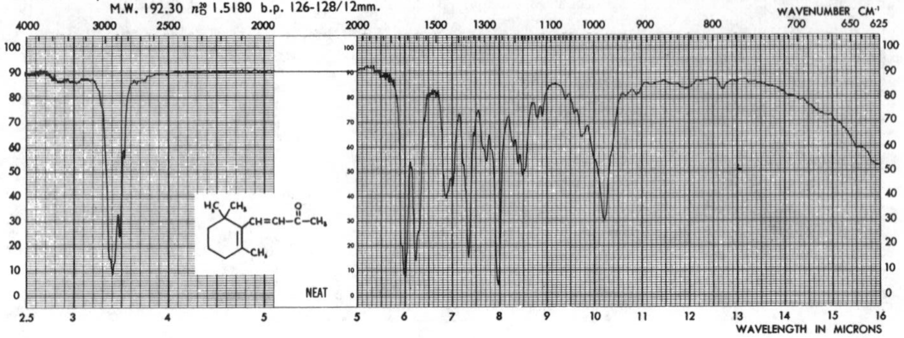

NEAT

F

21,828-6
(+)-Dihydrocarvone, 98%, mixture of isomers
FW 152.24 bp 87-88°/6mm. n_D^{20} 1.4707 d 0.929
$[\alpha]^{22}$+17° (neat) *Beil.* 7(3),337 Disp. C

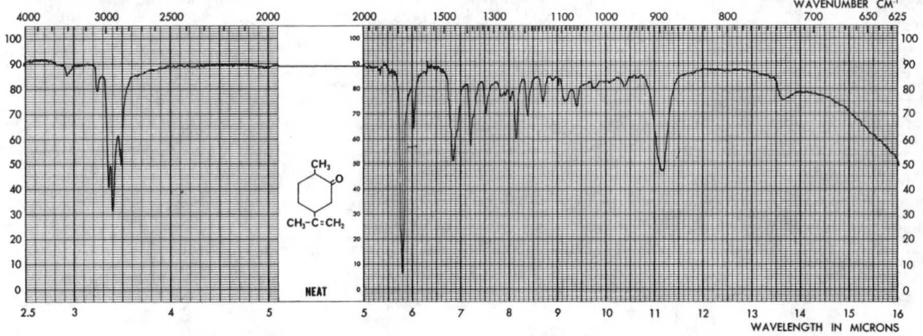

NEAT

G

1-1240-9 α-Ionone, tech., 77%
M.W. 192.30 n_D^{20} 1.5016

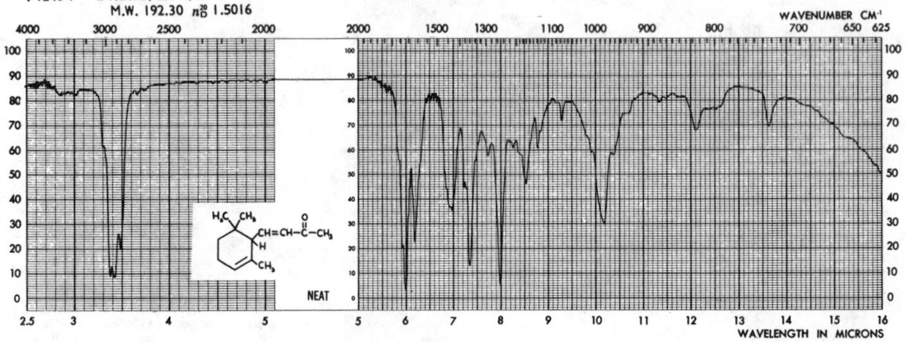

NEAT

H

12,343-9 Perchloro-2-cyclobuten-1-one
M.W. 205.86 n_D^{20} 1.5295 b.p. 176°

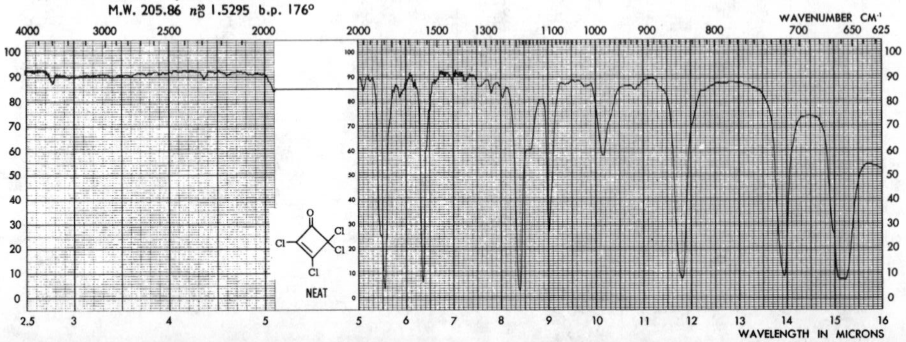

NEAT

A

C11,290-9 **2-Cyclopentenone**
$C_5H_6(:O)$ M.W. 82.10 n_D^{20} 1.4822
NEAT

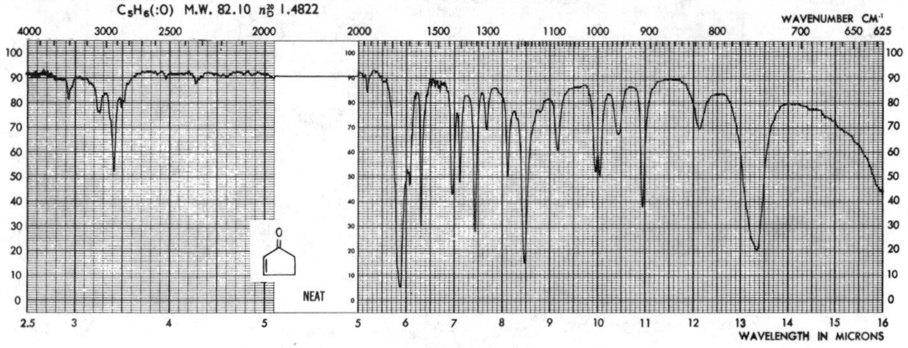

B

14,577-7 **3-Methyl-2-cyclopenten-1-one, tech. (stabilized with hydroquinone)**
$CH_3C_5H_5(:O)$ M.W. 96.13 n_D^{20} 1.4792
b.p. 74°/15 mm.
NEAT

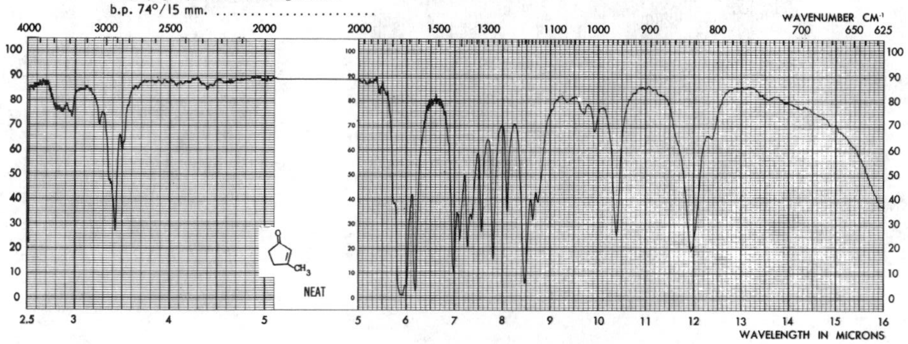

C

C3280-1 **2-Chlorocyclopentanone**
$ClC_5H_7(:O)$ M.W. 118.56 n_D^{20} 1.4770
NEAT

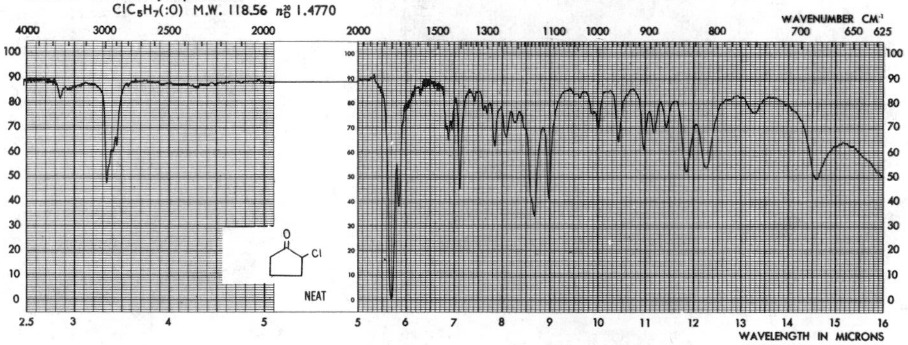

D

17,850-0
3-Methyl-1,2-cyclopentanedione, 99% (2-hydroxy-3-methyl-2-cyclopenten-1-one)
M.W. 112.13 m.p. 105-107° Beil. 7(1),310
NUJOL MULL

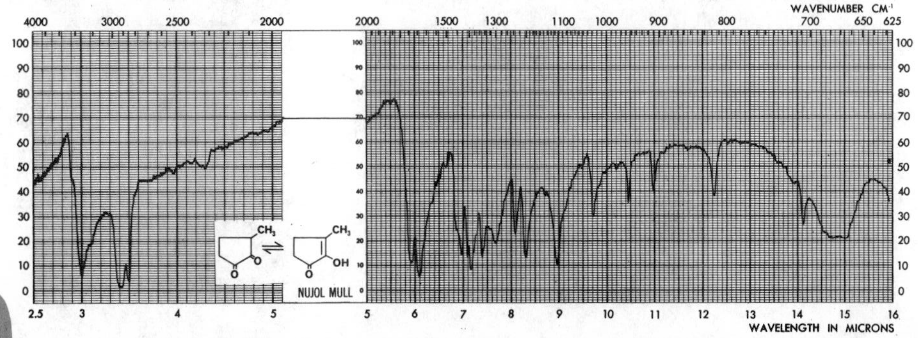

E

C10,281-4 **2-Cyclohexen-1-one**
$C_6H_8(:O)$ M.W. 96.13 n_D^{20} 1.4829
NEAT

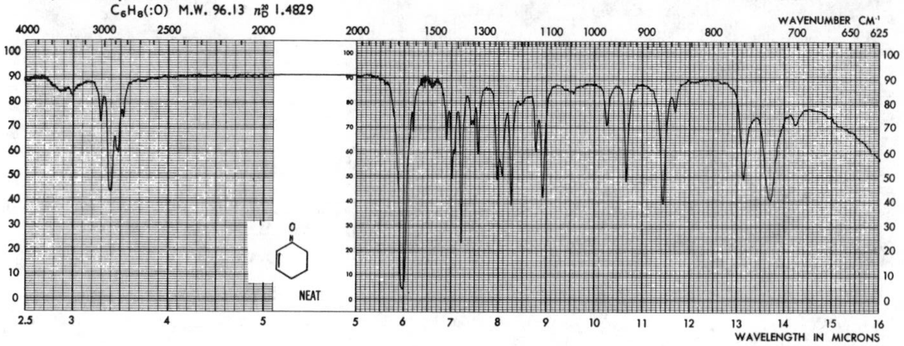

F

16,068-7
2-Cyclohepten-1-one, 96%
$C_7H_{10}(=O)$
M.W. 110.16 n_D^{20} 1.4950
NEAT

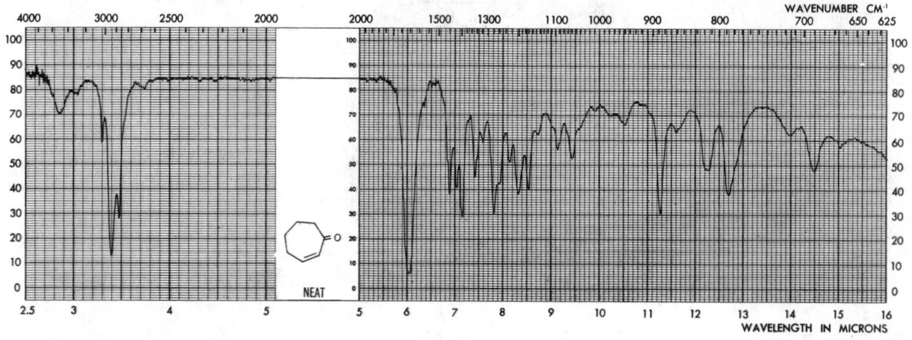

G

M3910-5 **3-Methyl-2-cyclohexen-1-one**
$CH_3C_6H_7(:O)$ M.W. 110.16 n_D^{20} 1.4945 b.p. 199-200° ...
NEAT

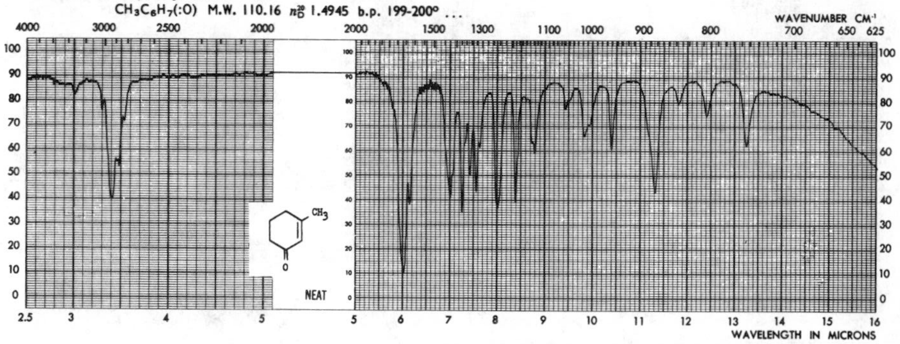

H

E445-3 **3-Ethoxy-2-cyclohexen-1-one**
$C_2H_5OC_6H_7(:O)$ M.W. 140.18 n_D^{20} 1.4989. 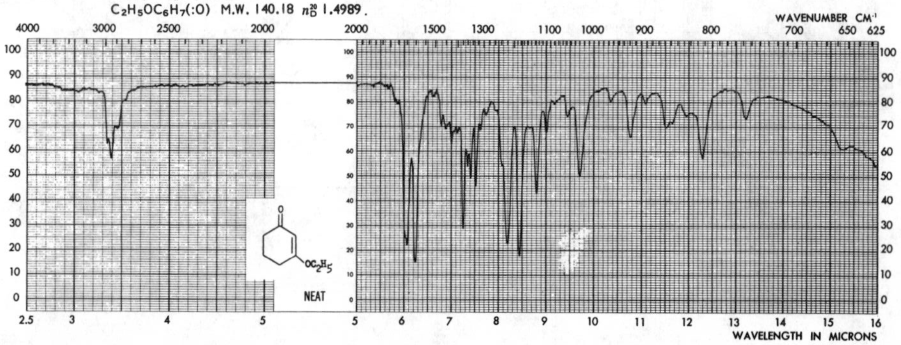
NEAT

(Each spectrum: WAVENUMBER CM⁻¹ 4000–625; WAVELENGTH IN MICRONS 2.5–16; % transmittance 0–100)

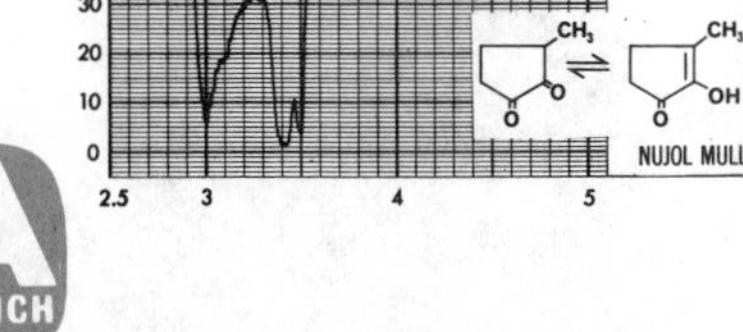

ALDRICH

A

D15,400-8 3,5-Dimethyl-2-cyclohexen-1-one
$(CH_3)_2C_6H_6(:O)$ M.W. 124.18 n_D^{20} 1.4812

NEAT

B

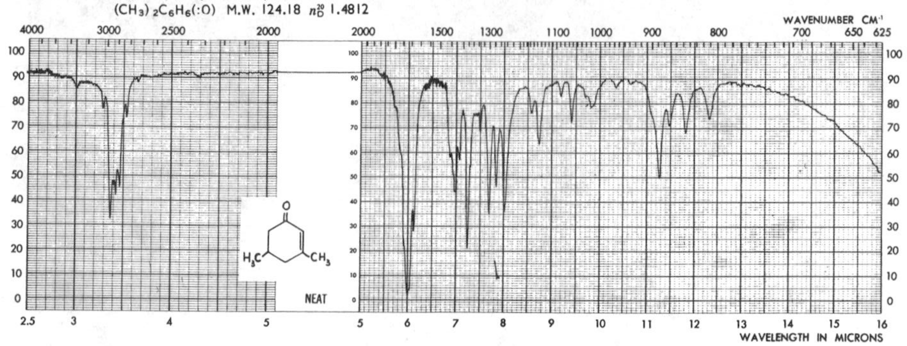

I-1870-9 Isophorone
M.W. 138.21 n_D^{20} 1.4759 b.p. 213-214°

NEAT

C

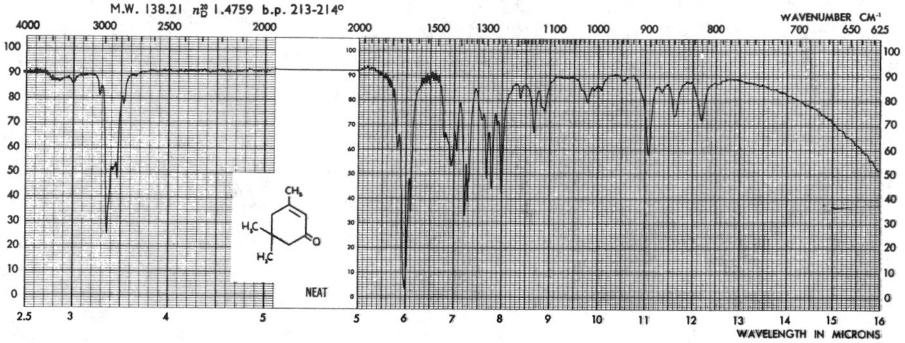

19,466-2
2-Cyclopentylidenecyclopentanone, 97+%
FW 150.22 bp 139-142°/20mm. n_D^{20} 1.5231
d 1.001 Disp. C

NEAT

D

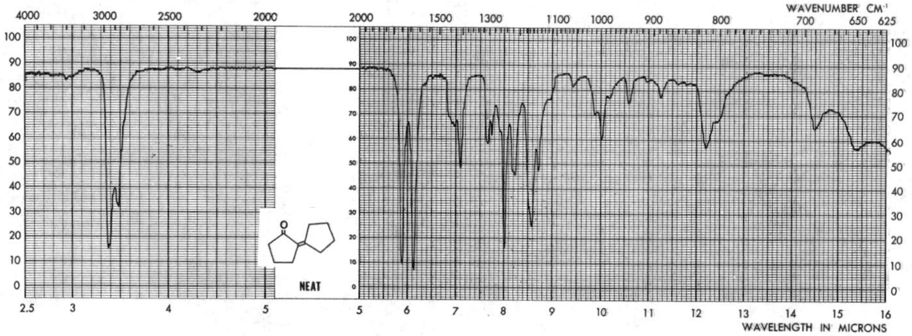

12,817-1 2-(β-Ethylbutylidene)-1-cyclohexanone
$(C_2H_5)_2CHCH:C_6H_8(:O)$ M.W. 180.29 n_D^{20} 1.4830

NEAT

E

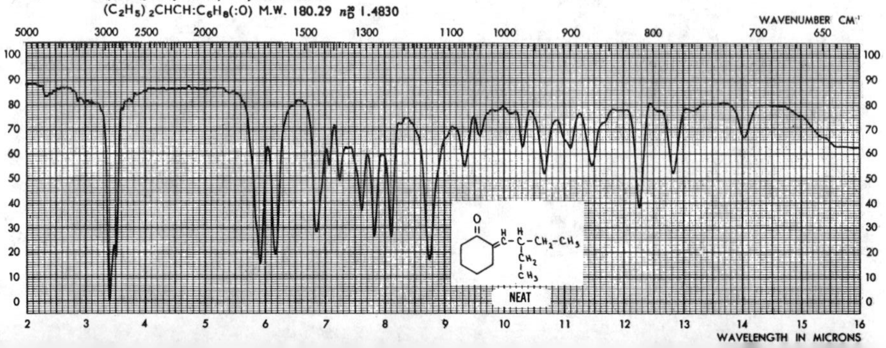

P5570-8 (+)-Pulegone, tech.
M.W. 152.24 n_D^{20} 1.4850 b.p. 224°
$[\alpha]_D^{20}$ + 22° (neat)

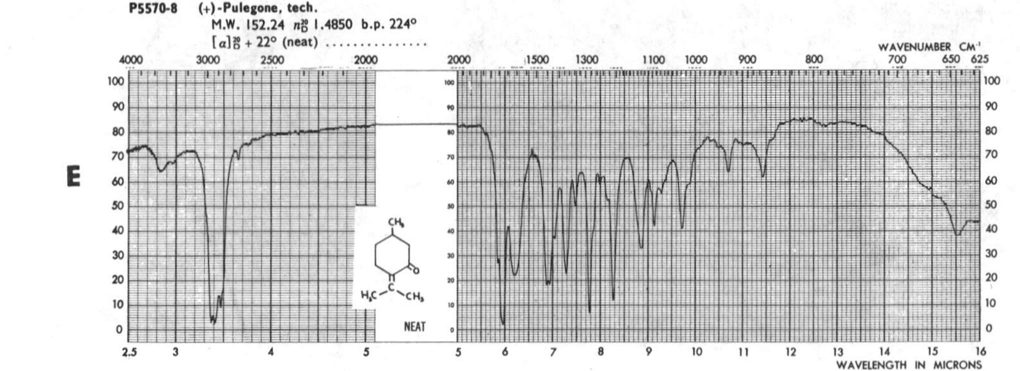

F

11,269-0 *d*-**Carvone** (p-mentha-6,8-dien-2-one)
M.W. 150.22 n_D^{20} 1.4968 b.p. 98-100°/10 mm.
$[\alpha]_D$ + 58° ± 2° (neat)

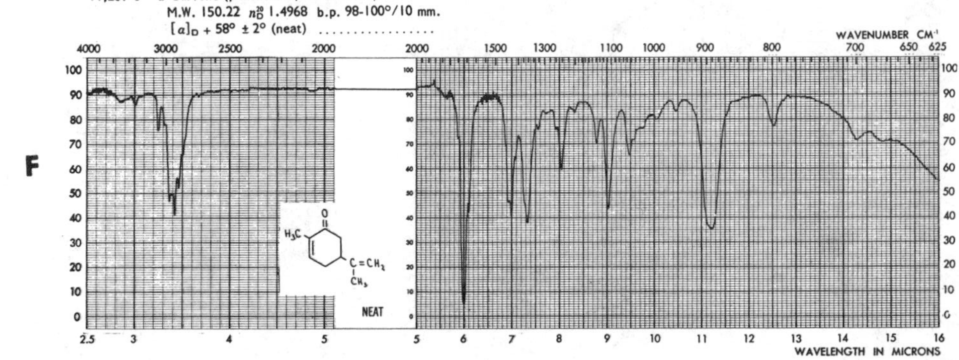

G

12,493-1 *l*-**Carvone**, 98% (p-mentha-6,8-dien-2-one)
M.W. 150.22 b.p. 227 - 230° n_D^{20} 1.4985 d 0.959
$[\alpha]_D^{20}$ -58° ± 2° (neat) *Beil.* 7,157
Merck Index 8,214 *IR* 205C Disp. C

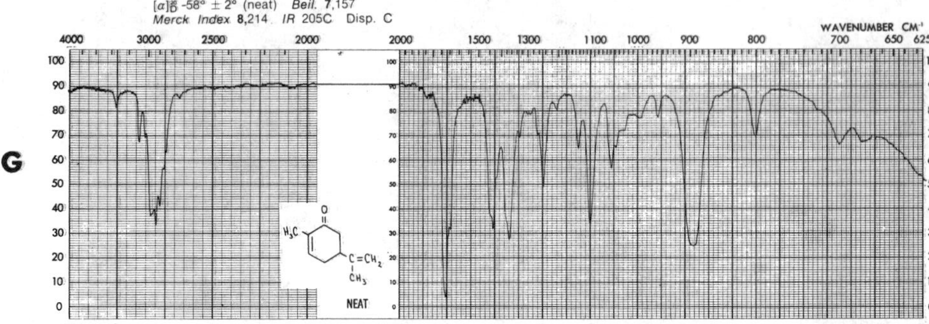

H

M4605-5 3-Methylene-2-norbornanone
M.W. 122.17 n_D^{20} 1.4891

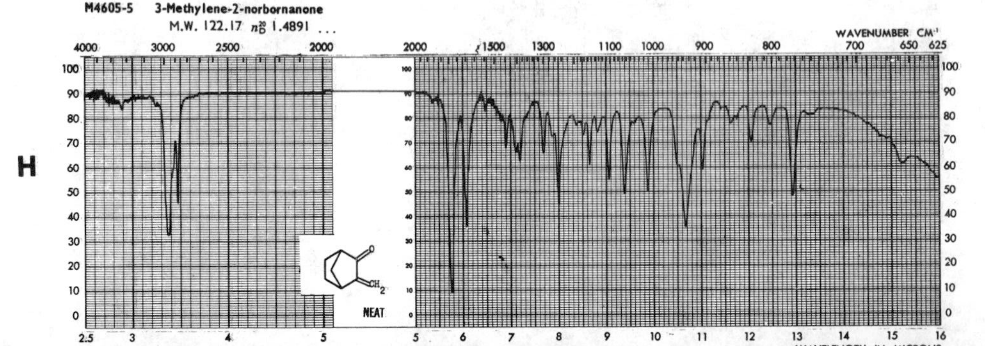

A M6520-3 Δ^{1,9},1-Methyl-2-octalone
M.W. 164.25 n_D^{20} 1.5237 b.p. 116-120°/2 mm.
NEAT

B M6540-8 Δ^{1,9},3-Methyl-2-octalone
M.W. 164.25 n_D^{20} 1.5102 b.p. 116-120°/2 mm.
NEAT

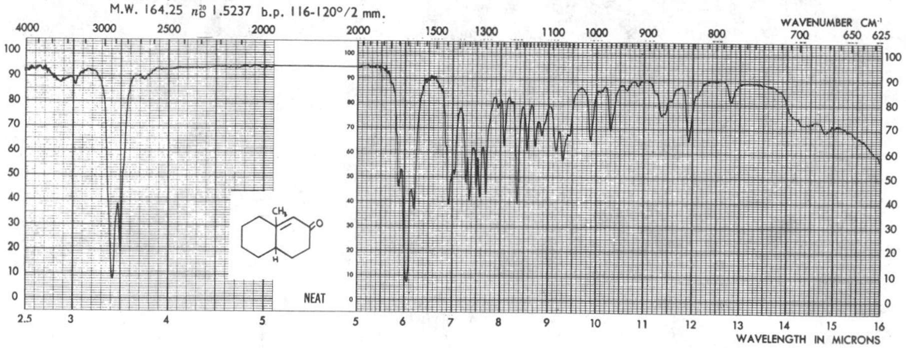

C 15,166-1 7a-Methyl-5,6,7,7a-tetrahydro-1,5-indandione
M.W. 164.20 m.p. 72-73.5°
NUJOL MULL

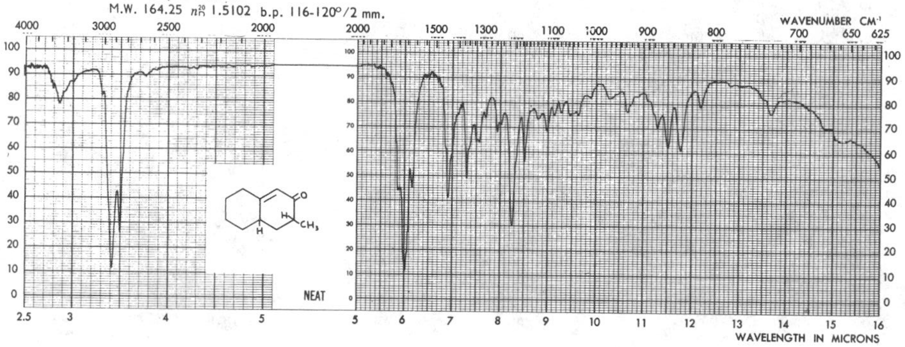

D M6515-7 9-Methyl-Δ$^{5(10)}$-octalin-1,6-dione [3,4,8,8a-tetrahydro-8a-methyl-1,6(2H,7H)-naphthalenedione]
M.W. 178.23 m.p. 51-53°
MELT

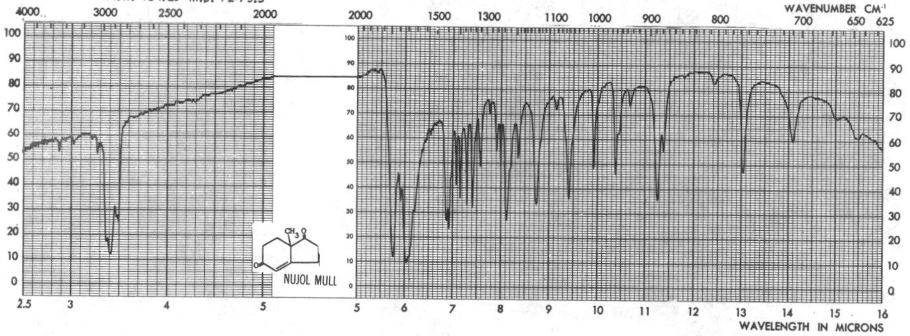

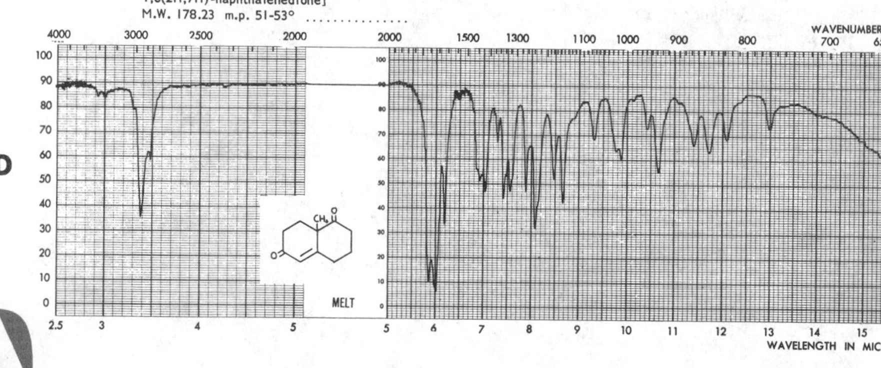

E 10,234-2 5,8a-Dimethyl-3,4,8,8a-tetrahydro-1,6(2H,7H)-naphthalenedione
M.W. 192.26 m.p. 40-45°
MELT

F T2100-8 Tetramethyl-1,3-cyclobutanedione
M.W. 140.18 m.p. 114-116°
NUJOL MULL

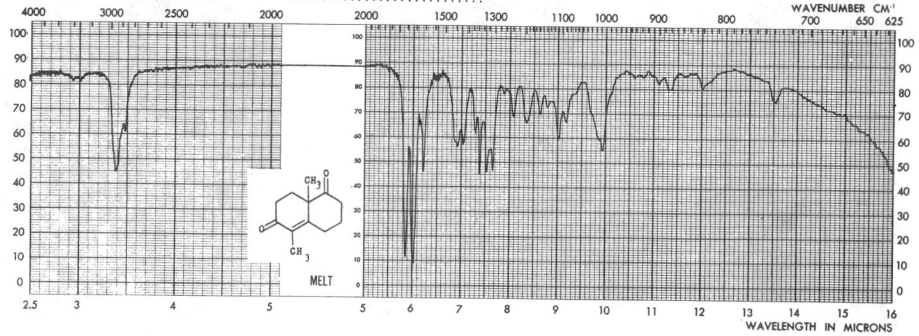

G C10,140-0 1,2-Cyclohexanedione
$C_6H_8(:O)_2$ M.W. 112.13 m.p. 35-38°
MELT

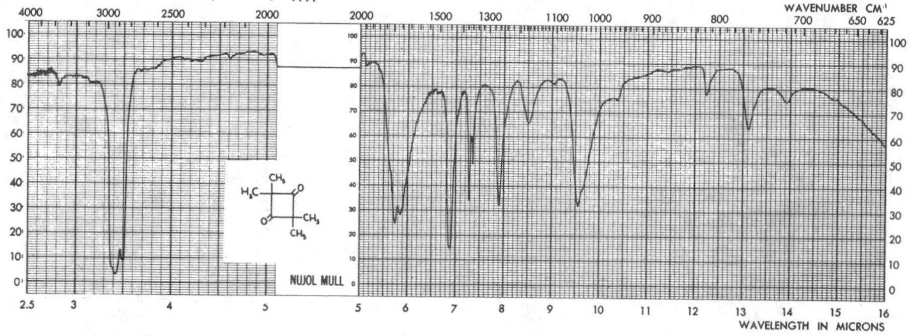

H 12,542-3 1,4-Cyclohexanedione
$C_6H_8(:O)_2$ M.W. 112.13 m.p. 77-78.5°
MELT

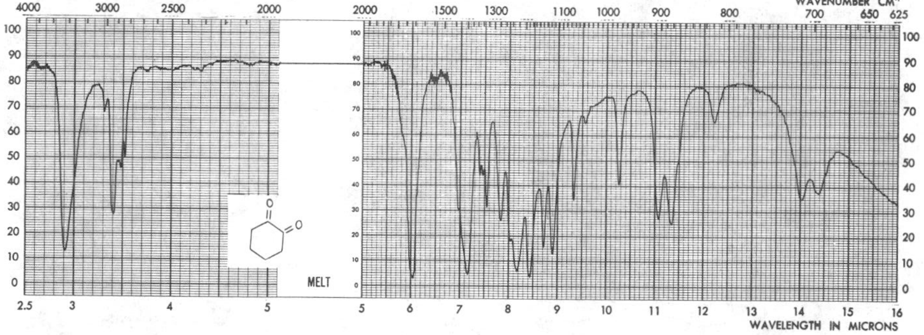

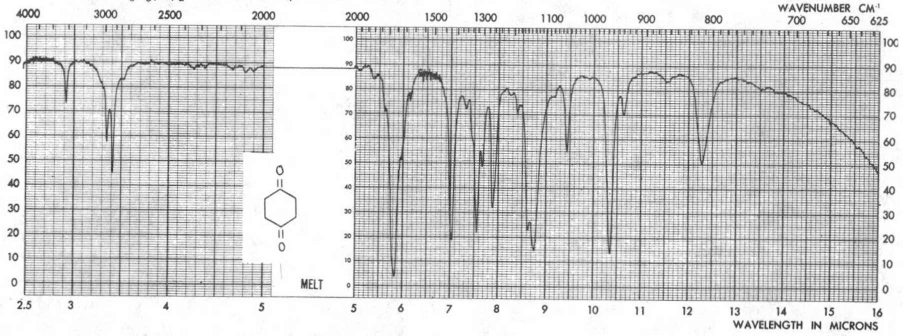

ALDRICH

A C9620-6 1,2-Cyclodecanedione
$C_{10}H_{16}(:O)_2$ M.W. 168.24 m.p. 42.5-45°
MELT

B 12,489-3 *dl*-Camphoroquinone (2,3-bornanedione)
M.W. 166.22 m.p. 197.5-199° . . . . . .
NUJOL MULL

C 19,546-4
2,5-Dihydroxy-*p*-benzoquinone, 98%
$(HO)_2C_6H_2(=O)_2$ FW 140.10 mp 220° (sublimes)
Beil. 8,377 Disp. C
NUJOL MULL

D 12,856-2 Hexaketocyclohexane octahydrate
M.W. 312.18 m.p. 99° (dec.) . . .
NUJOL MULL

E 13,173-3 Rhodizonic acid dihydrate
M.W. 206.11 m.p. 300° (dec.)
NUJOL MULL

F R140-4 Rhodizonic acid, dipotassium salt
M.W. 246.26 m.p. > 310° . .
NUJOL MULL

G R160-9 Rhodizonic acid, disodium salt
M.W. 214.04 m.p. > 300° . . . .
NUJOL MULL

H 11,472-3 Rhodizonic acid, barium salt
M.W. 305.40 m.p. > 300° .
NUJOL MULL

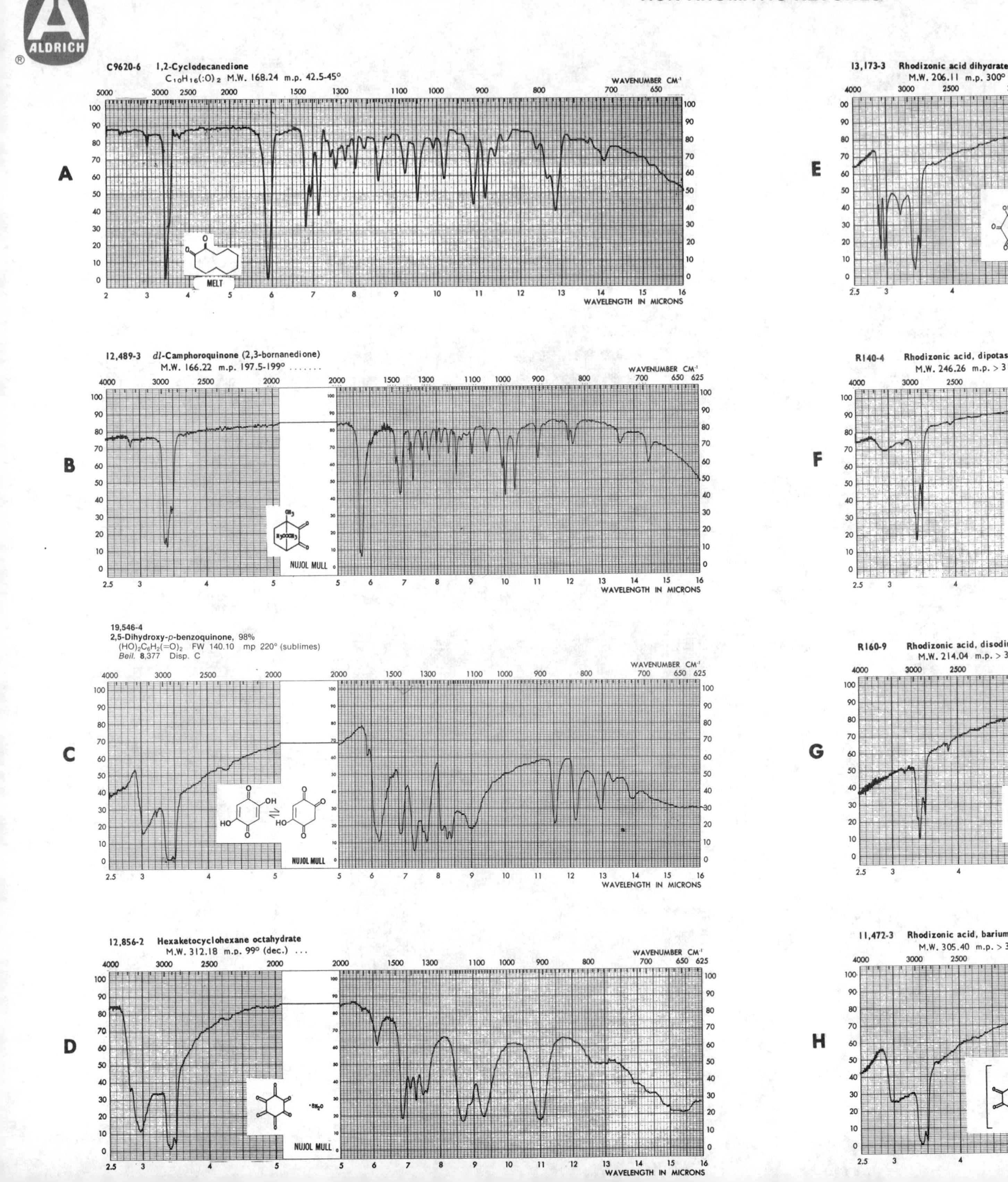

A

B1035-8 **p-Benzoquinone**
$C_6H_4(:O)_2$ M.W. 108.10 m.p. 113-115°

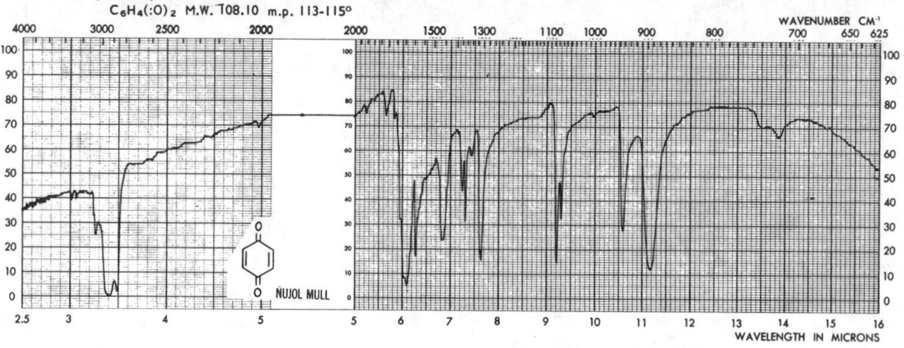

NUJOL MULL

B

21,131-1
Methyl-*p*-benzoquinone, 98+% (*p*-toluquinone)
$CH_3C_6H_3(=O)_2$ FW 122.12 mp 67-70°
Beil. 7,645 Disp. C

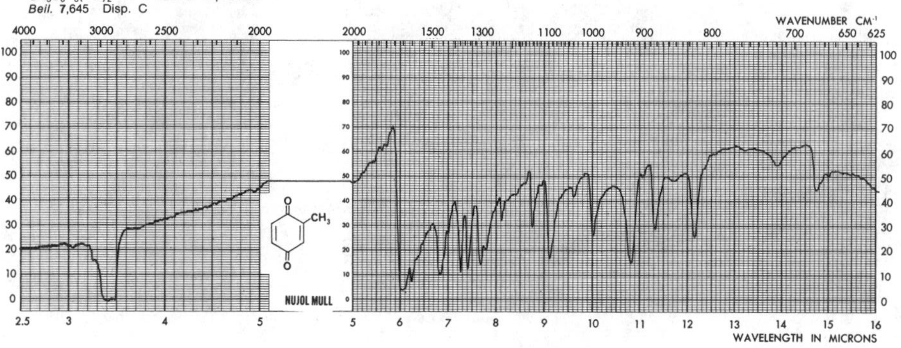

NUJOL MULL

C

D14,970-5 **2,6-Dimethylbenzoquinone**
$(CH_3)_2C_6H_2$-1,4-$(:O)_2$ M.W. 136.15 m.p. 68-71°

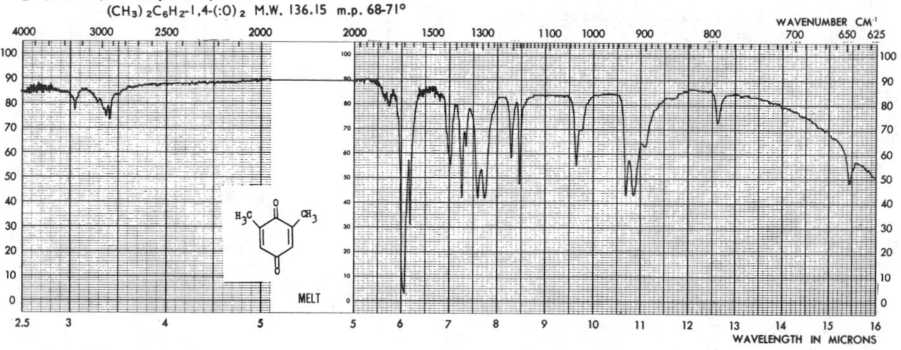

MELT

D

15,393-1
2,6-Di-*tert*.-butyl-p-benzoquinone, 98%
$[(CH_3)_3C]_2C_6H_2(=O)_2$
M.W. 220.31 m.p. 65-67°

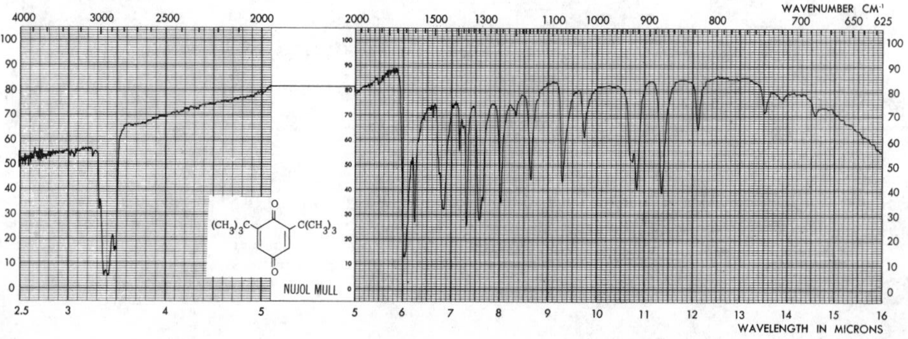

NUJOL MULL

E

D22,320-4 **Duroquinone** (tetramethyl-p-benzoquinone)
M.W. 164.20 m.p. 108-111°

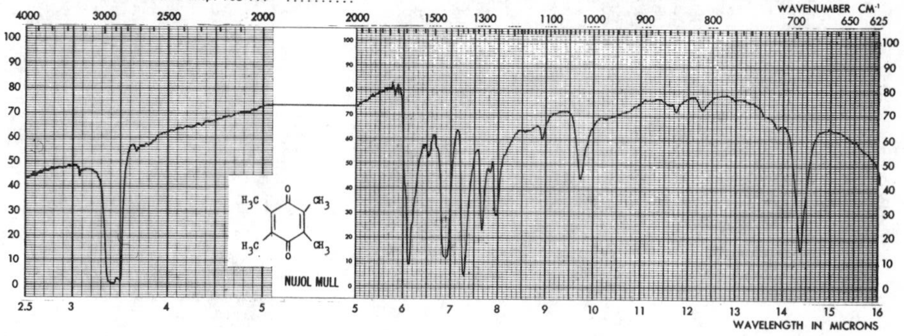

NUJOL MULL

F

10,435-3 **Tetrafluoro-1,4-benzoquinone**
$C_6F_4(:O)_2$ M.W. 180.06 m.p. 185-187°

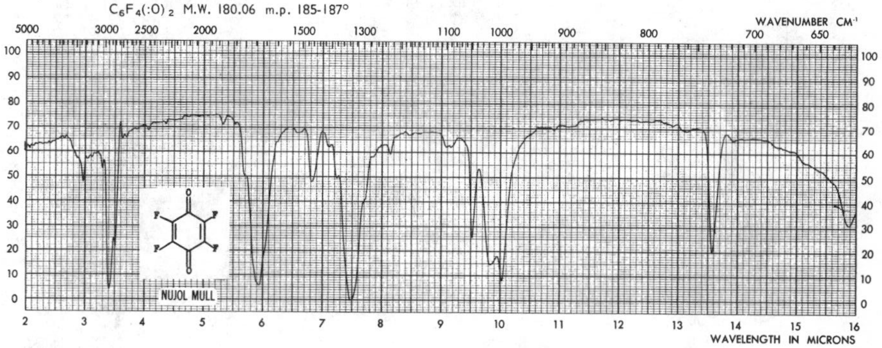

NUJOL MULL

G

15,745-7
3,5-Di-*tert*.-butyl-o-benzoquinone, 98%
$[(CH_3)_3C]_2C_6H_2(=O)_2$
M.W. 220.31 m.p. 111-113° Fieser 3,78

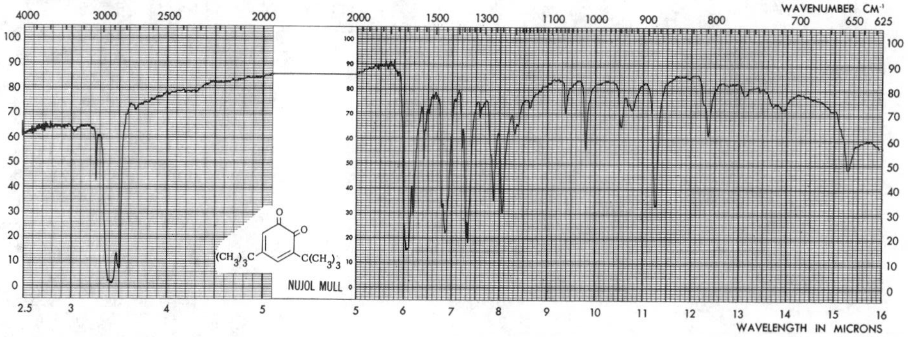

NUJOL MULL

H

T660-1 **Tetrachloro-o-benzoquinone** (o-chloranil)
$C_6Cl_4(:O)_2$ M.W. 245.88 m.p. 127-129°

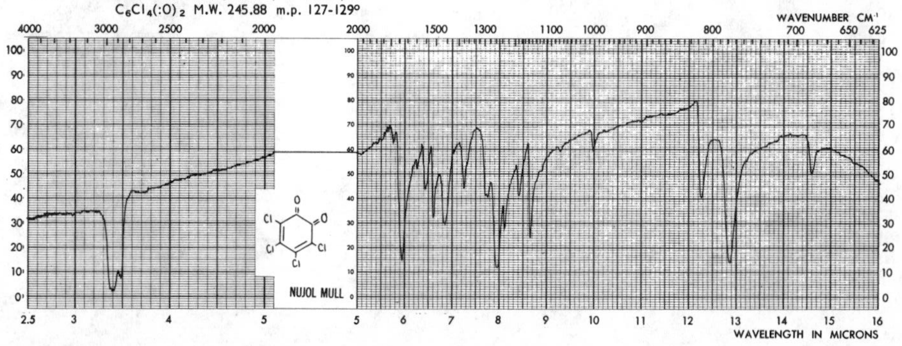

NUJOL MULL

A

15,147-5 **Tetrabromo-o-benzoquinone** (o-bromanil)
$C_6Br_4(:O)_2$ M.W. 423.70 m.p. 148-151°

NUJOL MULL

B

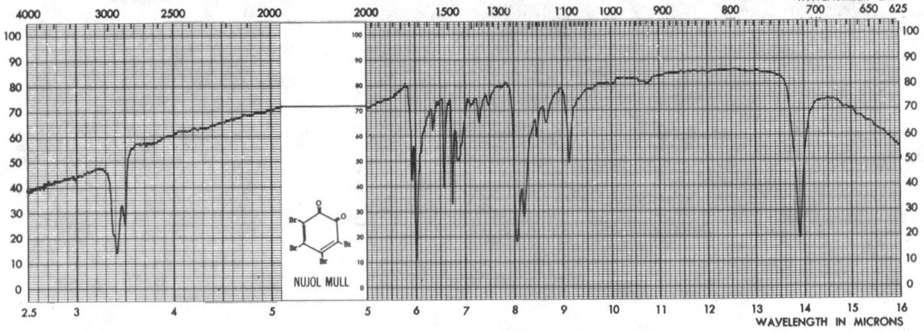

H580-4 **Hexachloro-2,4-cyclohexadienone**
M.W. 300.78 m.p. 47-50° ......

NUJOL MULL

C

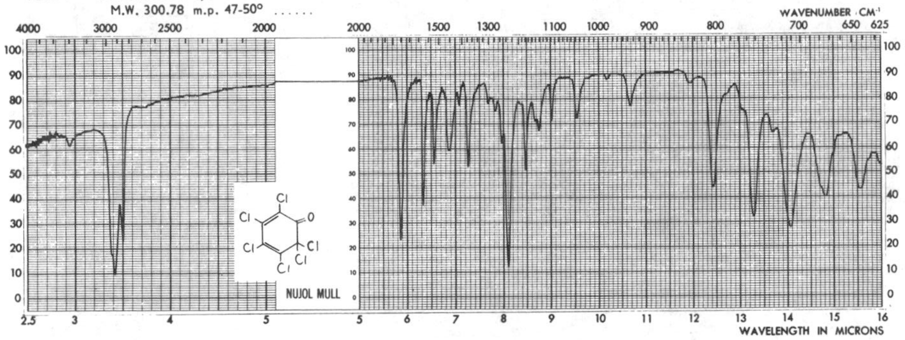

12,603-9 **2,6-Dichloroquinone-4-chloroimide** (N,2,6-trichloro-p-benzoquinone-imine)
M.W. 210.45 m.p. 65-67° ....

MELT

D

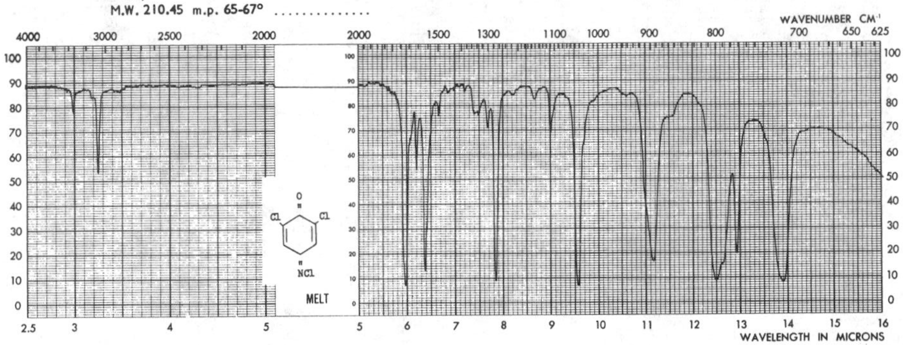

D4340-9 **2,6-Dibromoquinone-4-chloroimide** (2,6-dibromo-N-chloro-p-benzoquinoneimine)
M.W. 299.36 m.p. 80° ....

NUJOL MULL

E

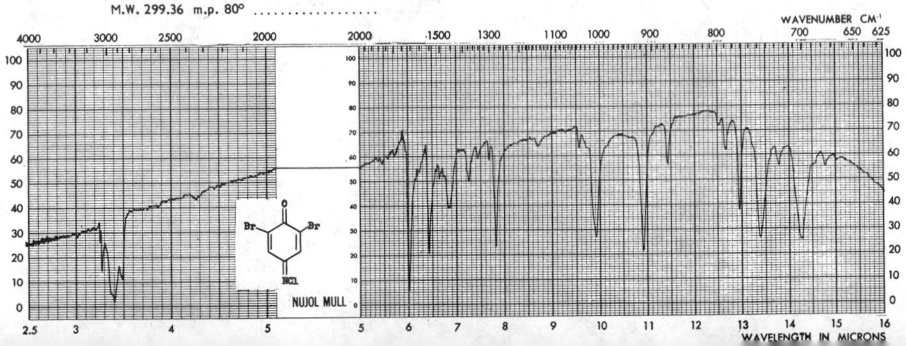

C1910-4 **Chloranilic acid** (2,5-dichloro-3,6-dihydroxy-p-benzoquinone)
M.W. 208.98 m.p. 305° (dec.) ....

NUJOL MULL

F

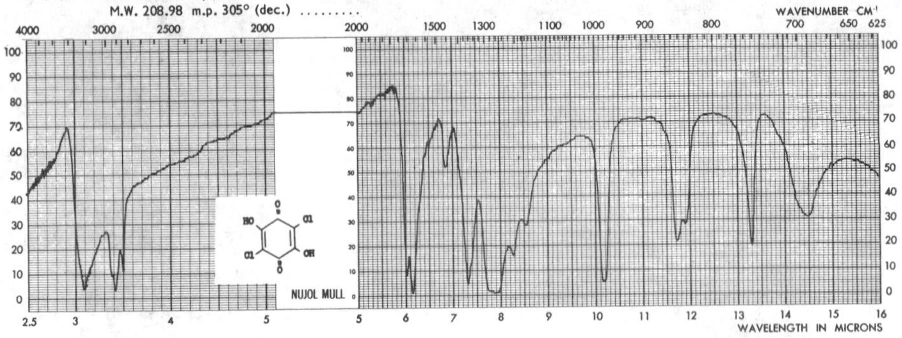

15,061-4 **Chloranilic acid** (2,5-dichloro-3,6-dihydroxy-p-benzoquinone)
disodium salt dihydrate
M.W. 288.98 m.p. >300° ....

NUJOL MULL

G

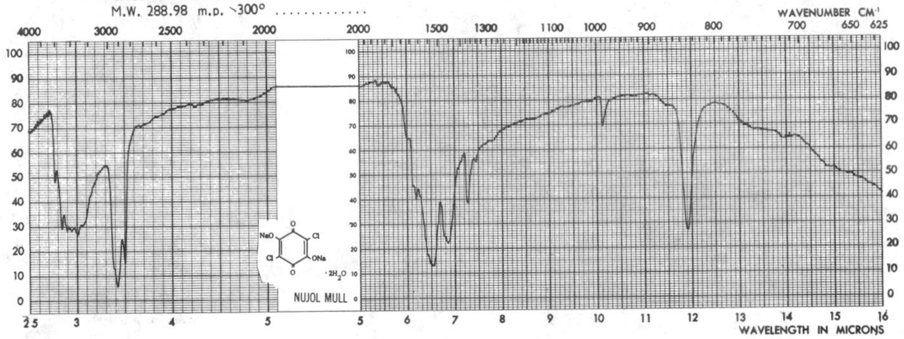

10,797-2 **Chloranilic acid** (2,5-dichloro-3,6-dihydroxy-p-benzoquinone),
barium salt
M.W. 344.31 m.p. > 300°

NUJOL MULL

H

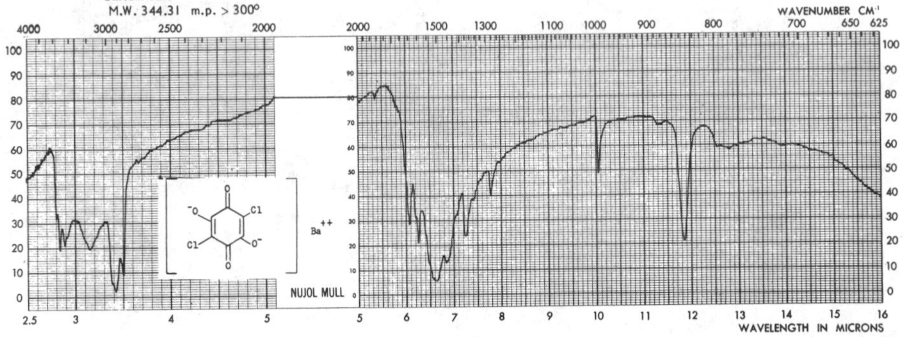

10,743-3
Chloranilic acid, mercury salt (2,5-dichloro-3,6-dihydroxy-p-benzoquinone)
M.W. 407.56 m.p. >300° Beil. 8,379

NUJOL MULL

WAVENUMBER CM⁻¹ / WAVELENGTH IN MICRONS

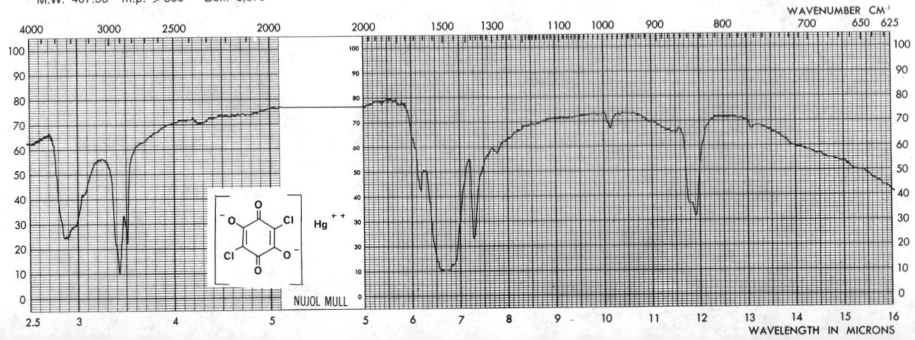

A

10,796-4 **Chloranilic acid** (2,5-dichloro-3,6-dihydroxy-p-benzoquinone), **lanthanum salt**
M.W. 898.72 m.p. > 300°

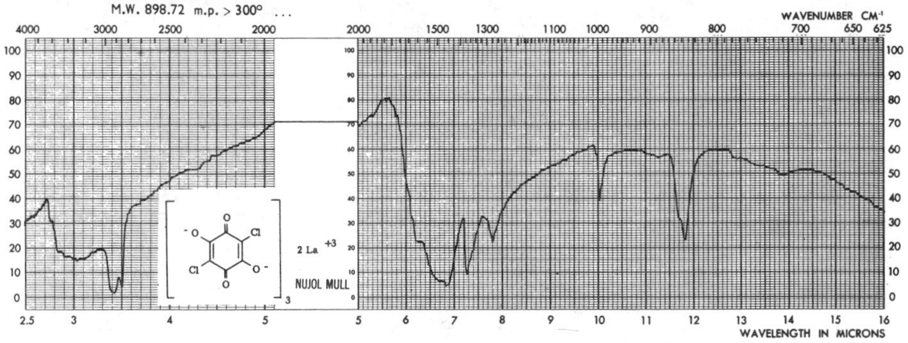

NUJOL MULL

B

T1700-0 **Tetrahydroxy-1,4-quinone** (tetrahydroxy-p-benzoquinone) **dihydrate**
M.W. 208.12 m.p. > 300°

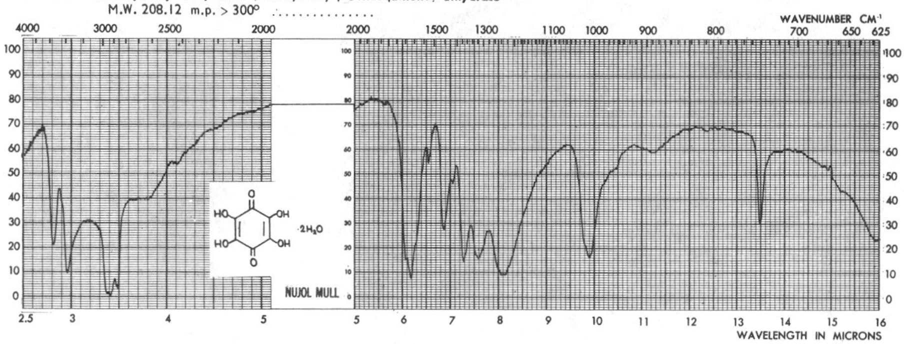

NUJOL MULL

C

17,722-9
4H-Pyran-4-one, 99%
M.W. 96.09 m.p. 32.5° b.p. 210-215°
Beil. 17,271

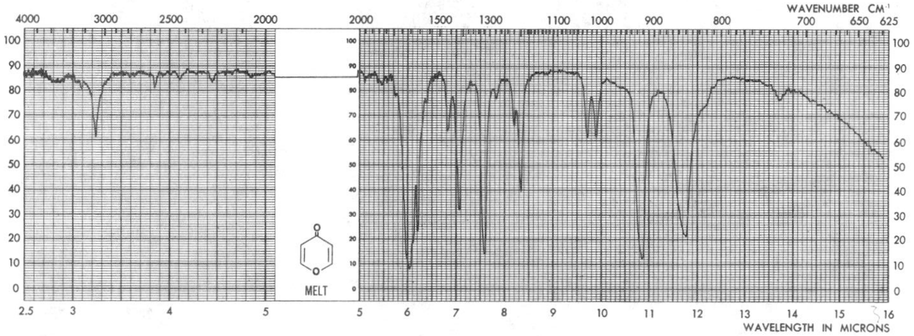

MELT

D

D18,340-7 **2,6-Dimethyl-γ-pyrone** (2,6-dimethyl-4H-pyran-4-one)
M.W. 124.14 m.p. 133-137°

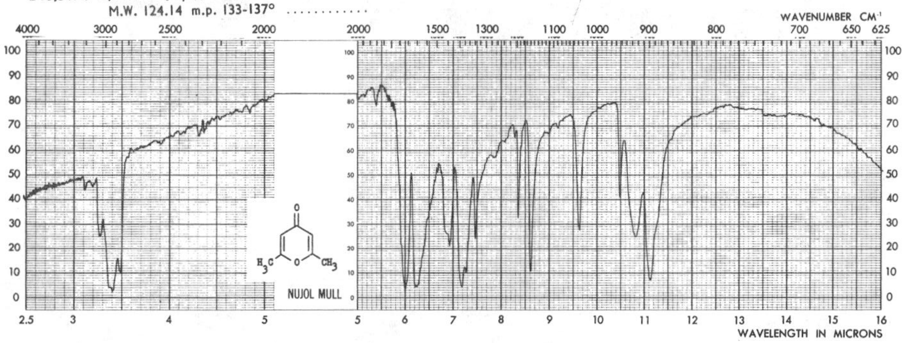

NUJOL MULL

E

H4340-7 **3-Hydroxy-2-methyl-4-pyrone**
M.W. 126.11 m.p. 160-162°

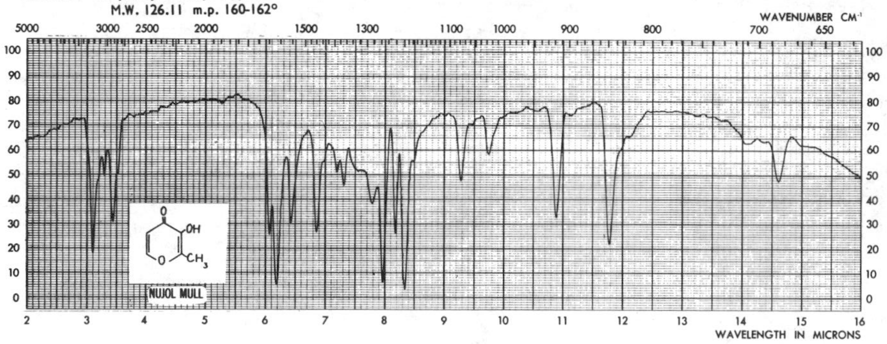

NUJOL MULL

F

C4860-0 **Chlorokojic acid** (2-chloromethyl-5-hydroxy-4H-pyran-4-one)
M.W. 160.56 m.p. 164-167°

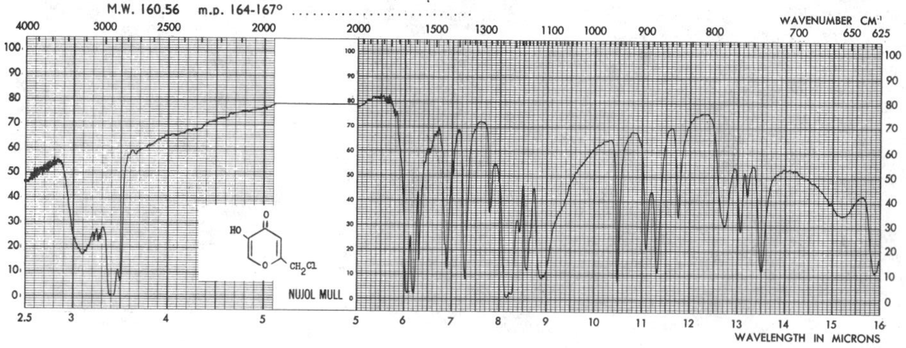

NUJOL MULL

G

K380-8 **Kojic acid** [5-hydroxy-2-(hydroxymethyl)-4H-pyran-4-one]
M.W. 142.11 m.p. 153-155°

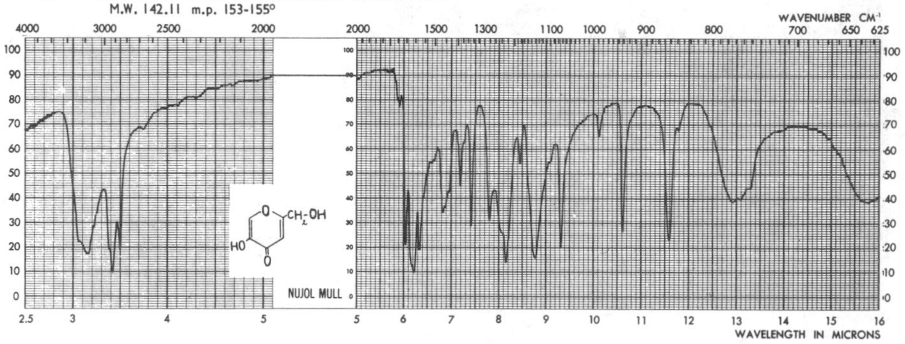

NUJOL MULL

H

85,061-6
6-(Diethylaminomethyl)-kojic acid hydrochloride
M.W. 263.72 m.p. 150-152°

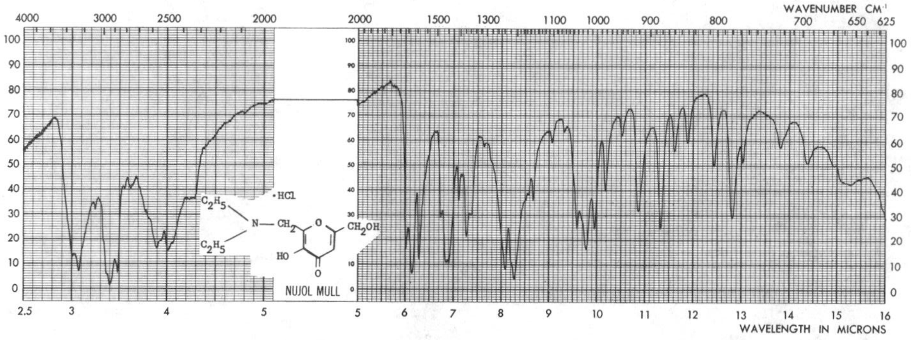

NUJOL MULL

A 12,344-7 **3,4-Dihydroxy-3-cyclobutene-1,2-dione** (squaric acid)
M.W. 114.06 m.p. >300°
NUJOL MULL

B T8970-2 **Tropolone** (2-hydroxy-2,4,6-cycloheptatrienone)
M.W. 122.12 m.p. 51-54°
MELT

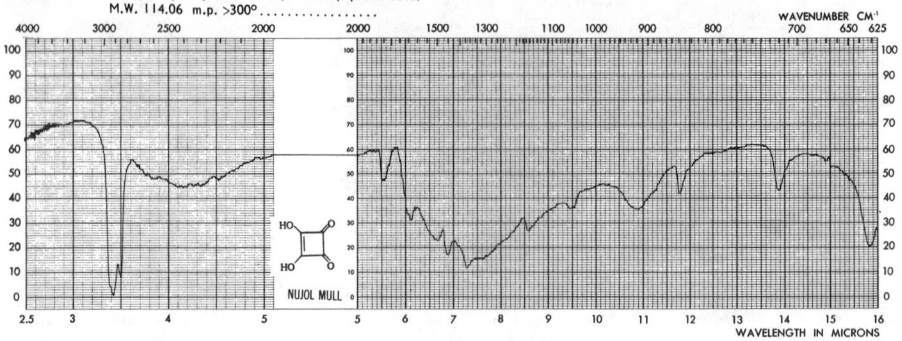

C T3440-1 **β-Thujaplicin** (hinokitiol)
M.W. 164.20 m.p. 49-53°
MELT

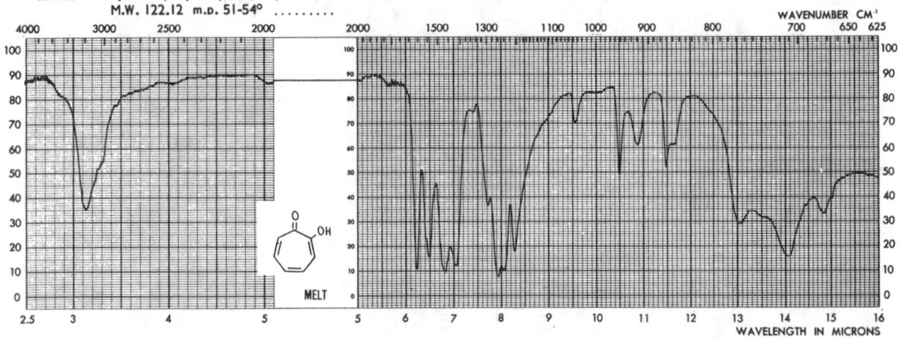

D 19,933-8
1,4-Diamino-2-butanone dihydrochloride, 99%
$H_2NCH_2CH_2COCH_2NH_2 \cdot 2HCl$ FW 175.06
mp 221° (dec.) Disp. C
KBr

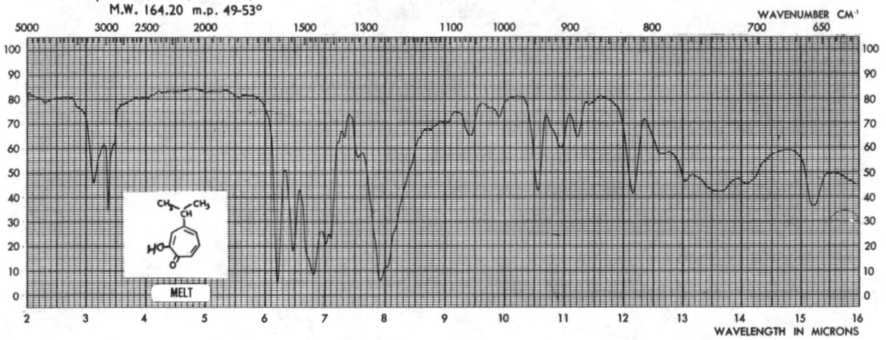

E 10,769-7 **(Dimethylamino)-acetone** [1-(dimethylamino)-2-propanone]
$(CH_3)_2NCH_2COCH_3$ M.W. 101.15 n_D^{20} 1.4200 b.p. 119-120°
NEAT

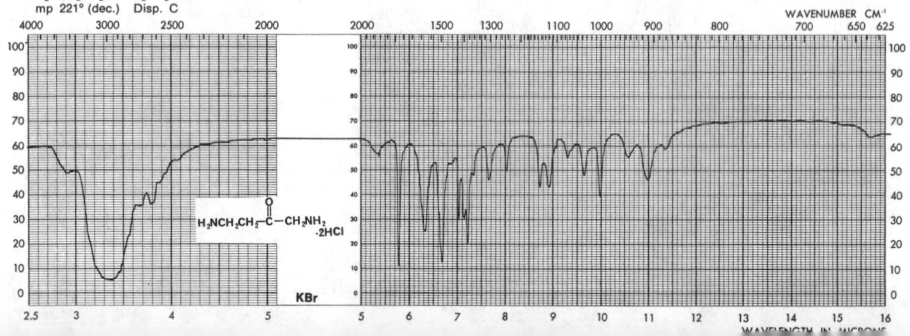

F D8600-0 **Diethylaminoacetone**
$(C_2H_5)_2NCH_2COCH_3$ M.W. 129.20
n_D^{20} 1.4208
NEAT

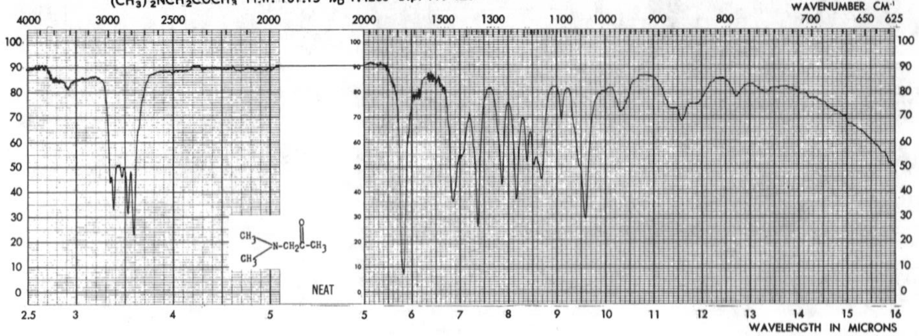

G 16,183-7
1-Dipropylamino-2-propanone, 97%
$(CH_3CH_2CH_2)_2NCH_2COCH_3$
M.W. 157.26 b.p. 188° n_D^{20} 1.4297 d 0.848
Beil. 4,316
NEAT

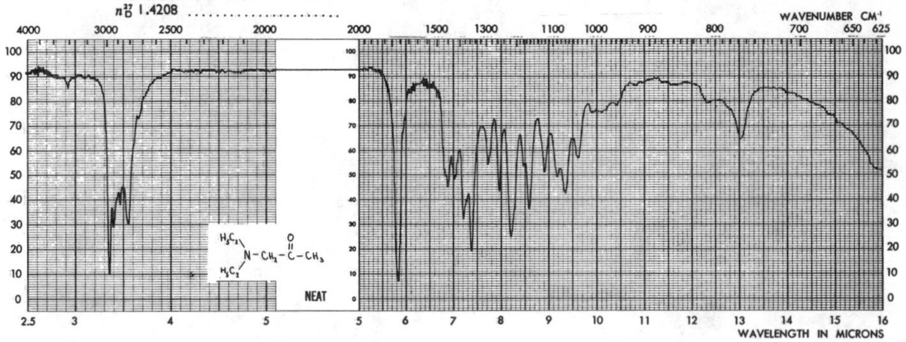

H 12,606-3 **1-Diethylamino-3-butanone** (4-diethylamino-2-butanone)
$(C_2H_5)_2NCH_2CH_2COCH_3$ M.W. 143.23
n_D^{20} 1.4308
NEAT

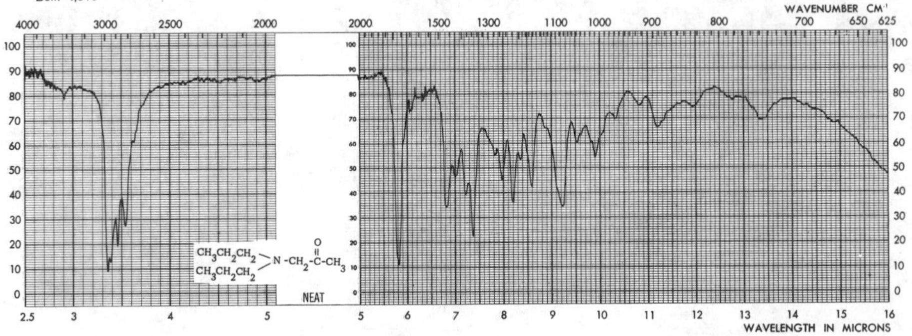

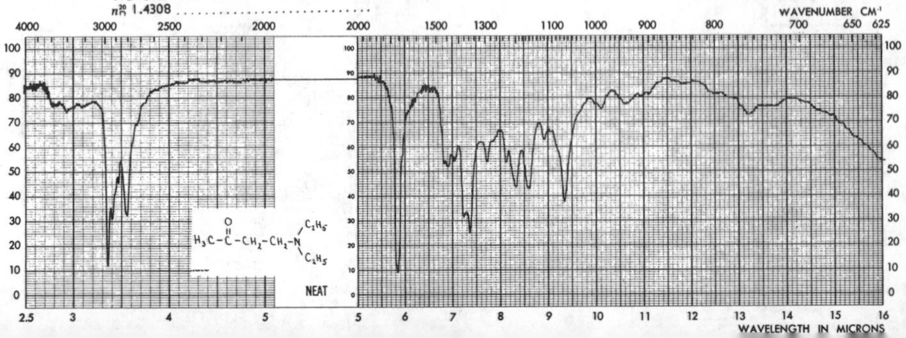

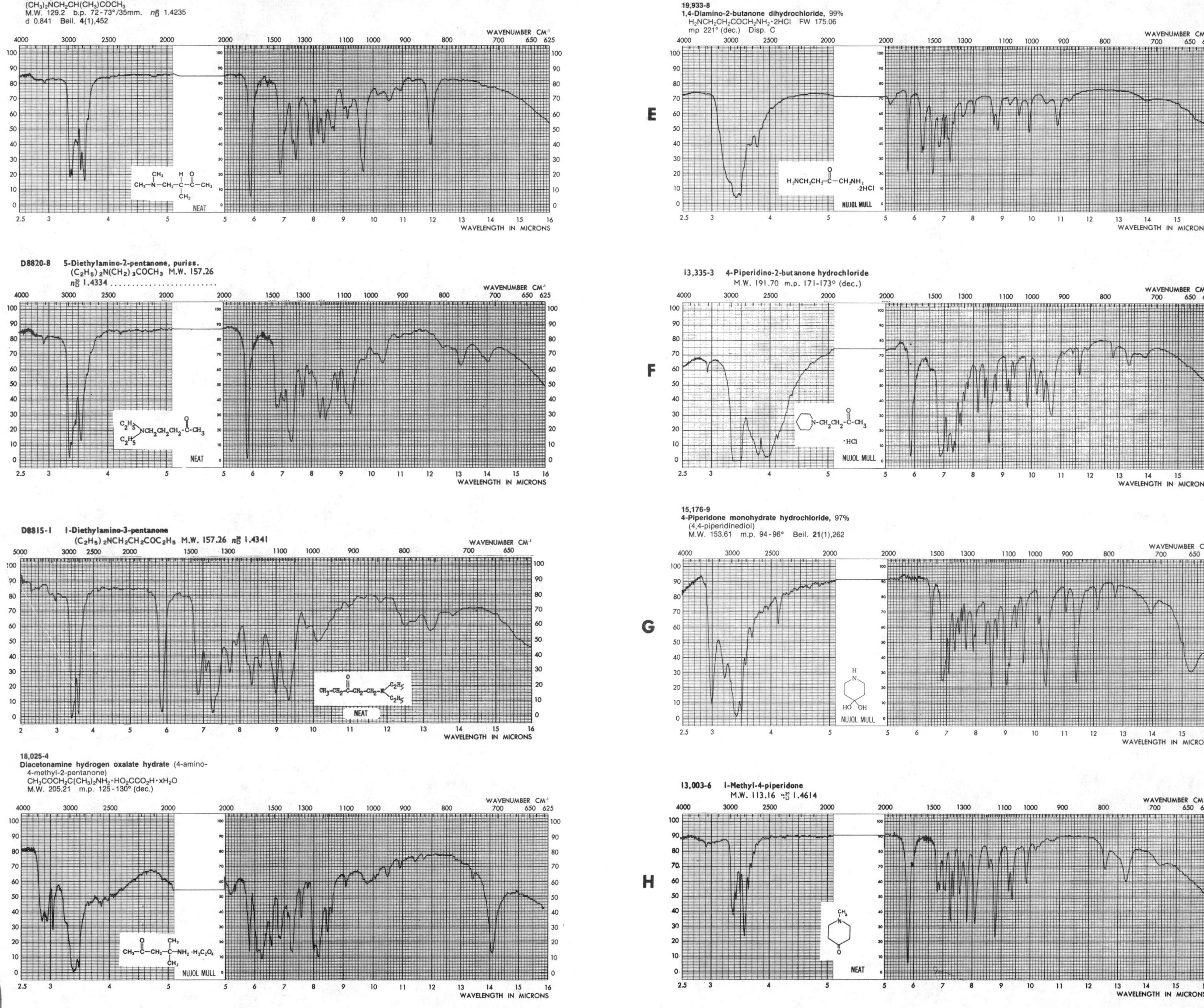
A
17,708-3
4-Dimethylamino-3-methyl-2-butanone, 97%
$(CH_3)_2NCH_2CH(CH_3)COCH_3$
M.W. 129.2 b.p. 72-73°/35mm. n_D^{20} 1.4235
d 0.841 Beil. 4(1),452
NEAT
B
D8820-8 5-Diethylamino-2-pentanone, puriss.
$(C_2H_5)_2N(CH_2)_3COCH_3$ M.W. 157.26
n_D^{20} 1.4334
NEAT
C
D8815-1 1-Diethylamino-3-pentanone
$(C_2H_5)_2NCH_2CH_2COC_2H_5$ M.W. 157.26 n_D^{20} 1.4341
NEAT
D
18,025-4
Diacetonamine hydrogen oxalate hydrate (4-amino-4-methyl-2-pentanone)
$CH_3COCH_2C(CH_3)_2NH_2 \cdot HO_2CCO_2H \cdot xH_2O$
M.W. 205.21 m.p. 125-130° (dec.)
NUJOL MULL
E
19,933-8
1,4-Diamino-2-butanone dihydrochloride, 99%
$H_2NCH_2CH_2COCH_2NH_2 \cdot 2HCl$ FW 175.06
mp 221° (dec.) Disp. C
NUJOL MULL
F
13,335-3 4-Piperidino-2-butanone hydrochloride
M.W. 191.70 m.p. 171-173° (dec.)
NUJOL MULL
G
15,176-9
4-Piperidone monohydrate hydrochloride, 97%
(4,4-piperidinediol)
M.W. 153.61 m.p. 94-96° Beil. 21(1),262
NUJOL MULL
H
13,003-6 1-Methyl-4-piperidone
M.W. 113.16 n_D^{20} 1.4614
NEAT
WAVENUMBER CM⁻¹
WAVELENGTH IN MICRONS
ALDRICH

A

15,174-2 1-Butyl-4-piperidone
M.W. 155.24 n_D^{20} 1.4599

NEAT

B

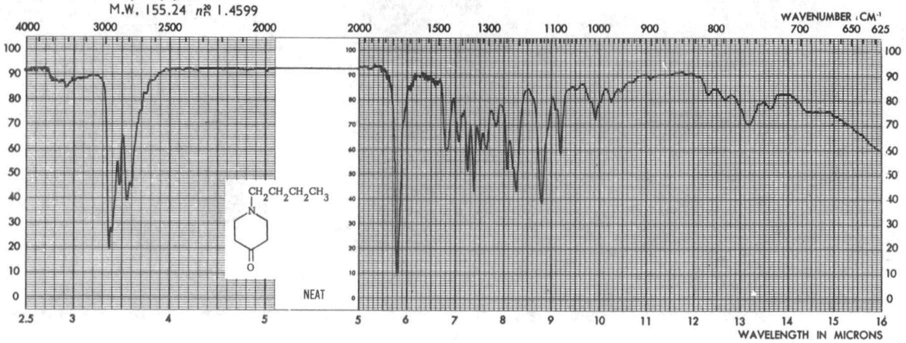

13,048-6 1-Ethyl-3-piperidone hydrochloride
M.W. 163.65 m.p. 178.5-181°

NUJOL MULL

C

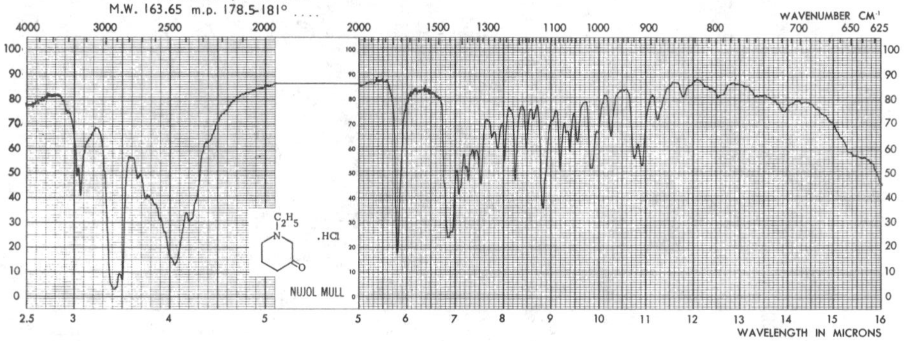

11,576-2 2,2,6,6-Tetramethyl-4-piperidone hydrochloride
M.W. 191.70 m.p. 190-194° (dec.)

NUJOL MULL

D

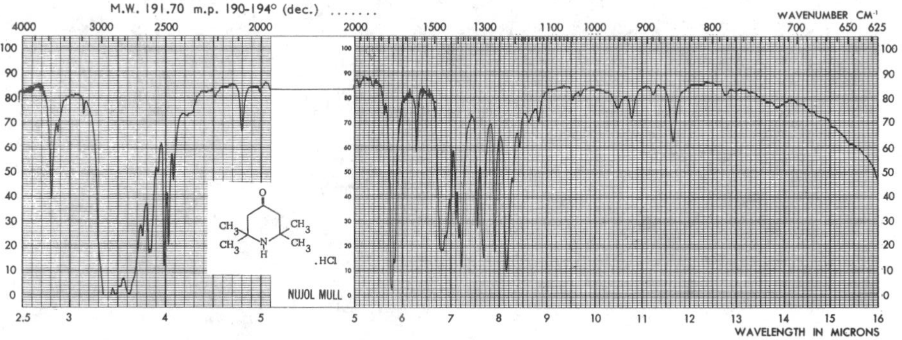

17,948-5
4-Oxo-2,2,6,6-tetramethylpiperidinooxy, free radical
M.W. 170.23

MELT

E

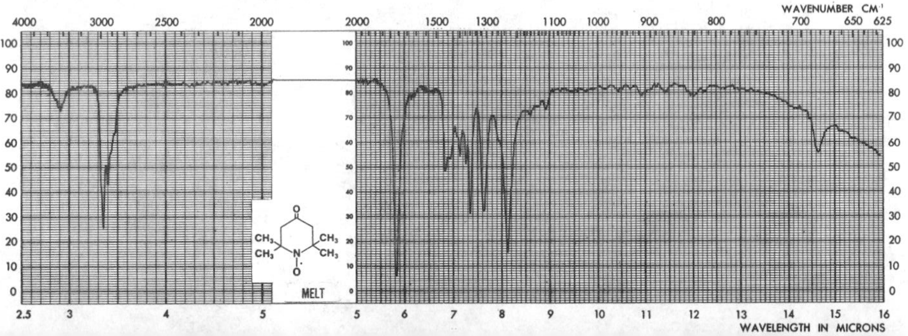

D14,275-1 3-(N,N-Dimethylaminomethyl)-2-norbornanone
M.W. 167.25 n_D^{20} 1.4794

NEAT

F

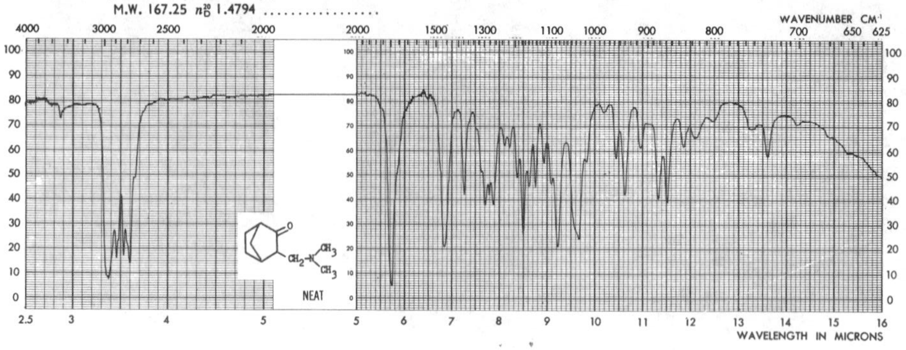

Q190-5 3-Quinuclidinone hydrochloride
M.W. 161.63
m.p. 313° (dec.)

NUJOL MULL

G

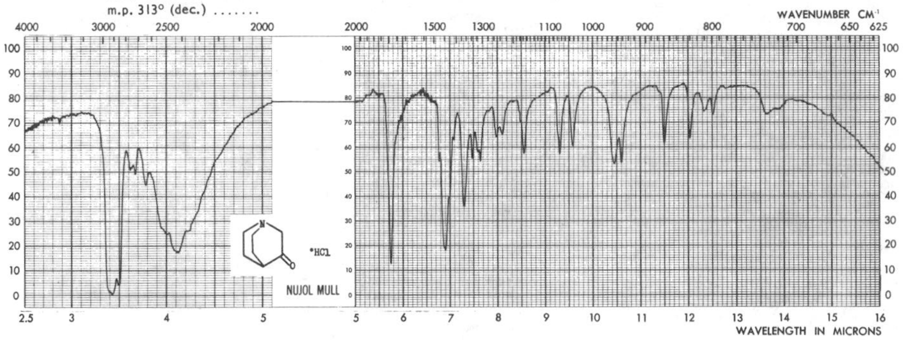

M4612-8 2-Methylene-3-quinuclidinone dihydrate (3,3-dihydroxy-2-quinuclidinemethanol) hydrochloride
M.W. 209.68 m.p. 272-273°

NUJOL MULL

H

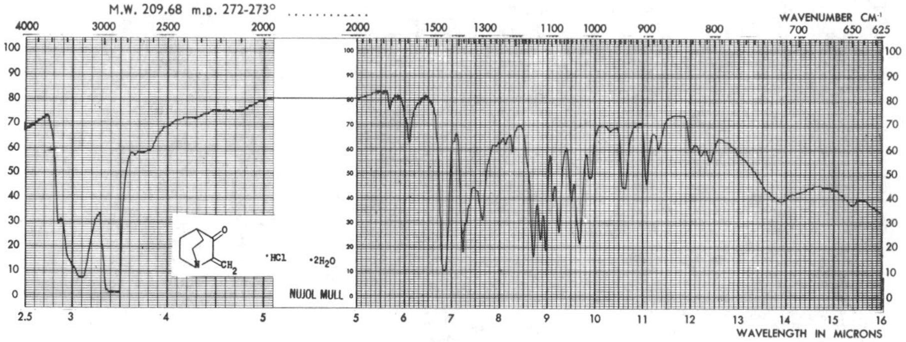

M7250-1 3-(4-Methylpiperazinomethyl)-2-norbornanone
M.W. 222.34 m.p. 39-40°

MELT

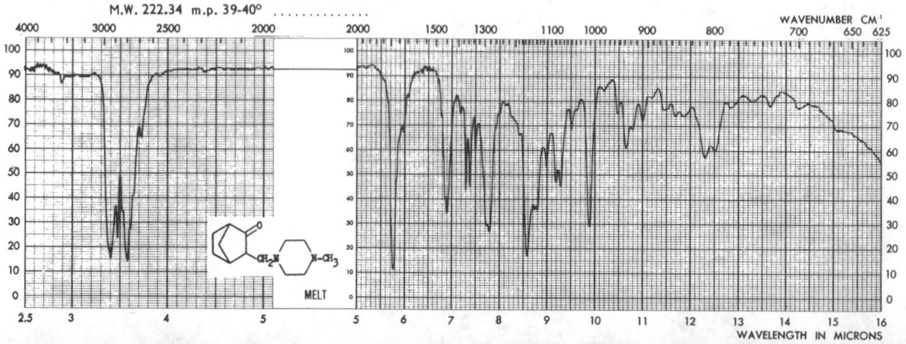

A T8960-5 **Tropinone**
M.W. 139.30 m.p. 41-44°
MELT

B T8965-6 **Tropinone hydrobromide**
M.W. 220.22 m.p. 208° (dec.)
NUJOL MULL

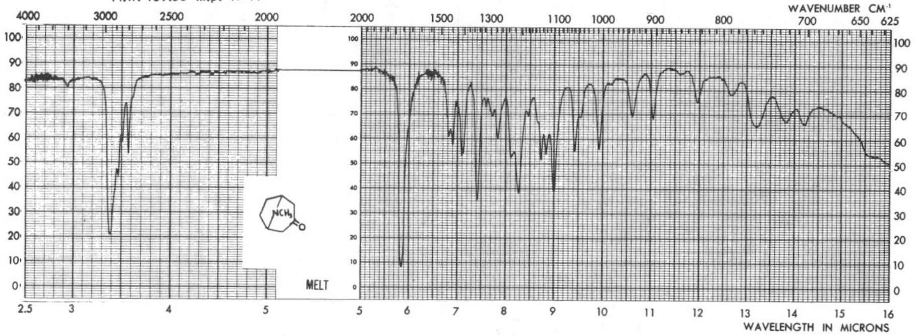

C 14,700-1 **1-Methyl-1-(8-oxo-2-bicyclo[3.2.1]octyl) pyrrolidinium iodide**
M.W. 335.23 m.p. 230-233°
NUJOL MULL

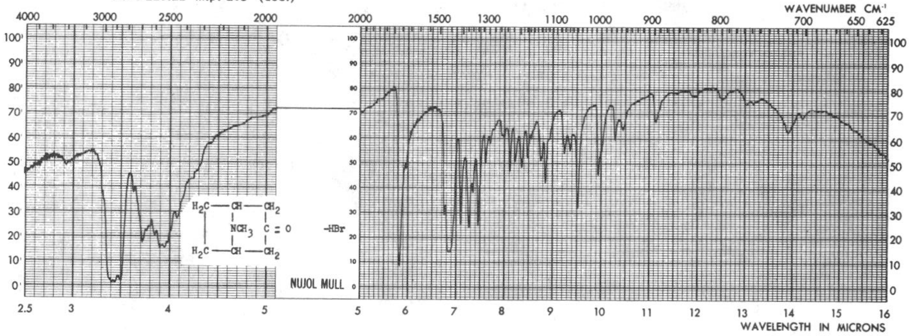

D 11,914-8 **6-Hydroxytropinone**
M.W. 155.20 m.p. 121-123°
NUJOL MULL

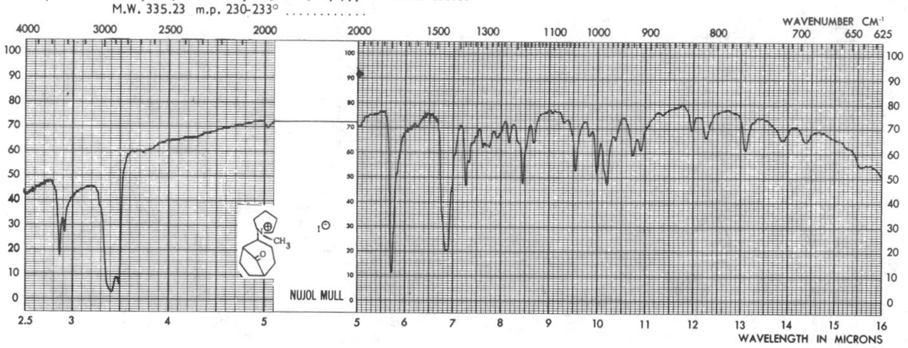

E 11,915-6 **Teloidinone** (6,7-dihydroxytropinone)
M.W. 171.20 m.p. 190-192°
NUJOL MULL

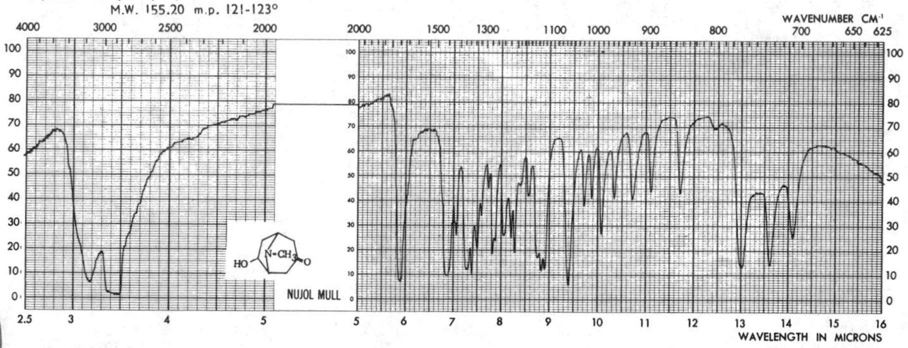

F 15,516-0
Tetrahydrothiopyran-4-one
M.W. 116.18 m.p. 59-61° Beil. **17**(2),287
MELT

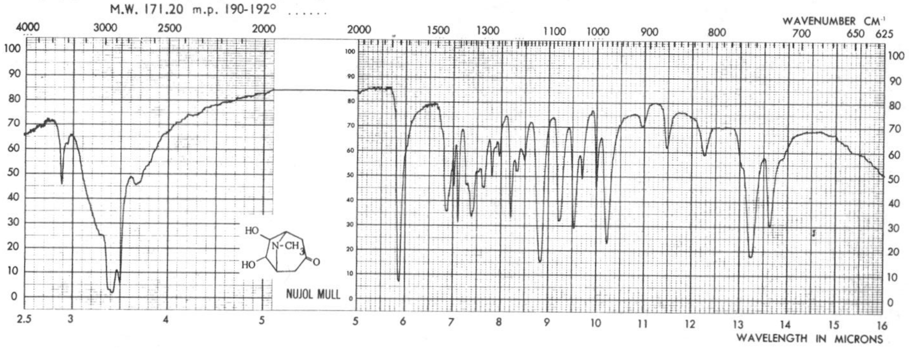

G 22,448-0
2-Nitrocyclohexanone, 99%
$O_2NC_6H_9(=O)$ FW 143.14 mp 39-43°
Beil. **7**(2),12 Disp. C
MELT

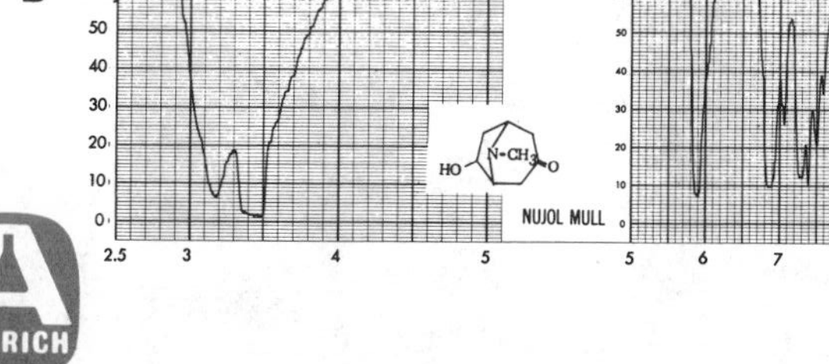

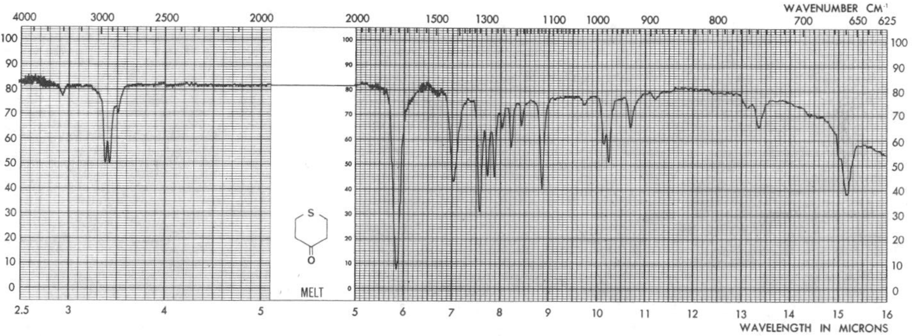

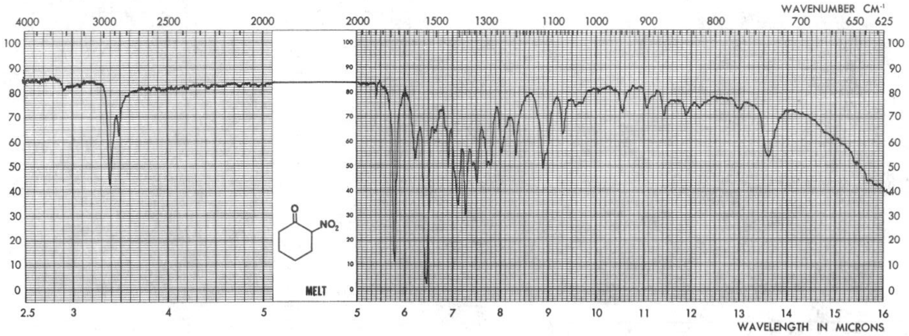

NON-AROMATIC ALDEHYDES

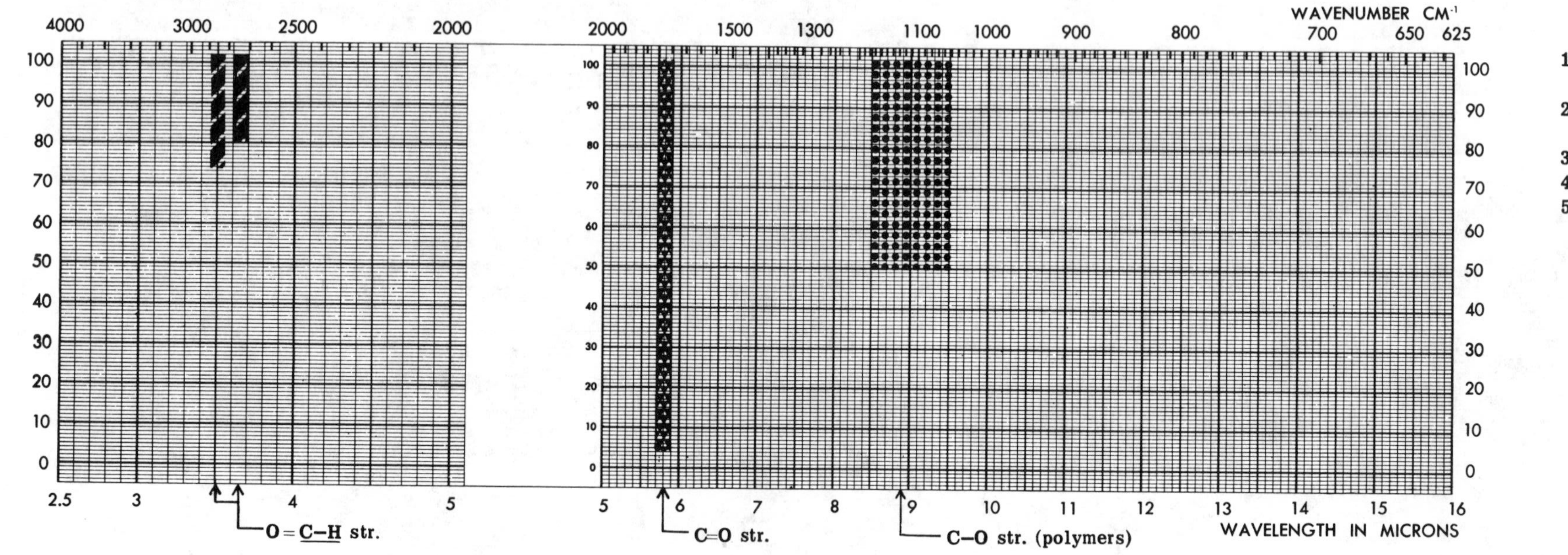

The aliphatic aldehyde carbonyl absorbs around 5.8 μ (1725 cm^{-1}). The effect of conjugation on this absorption is very similar to that on the ketones and shifts it to the 5.9 – 6 μ (1695 – 1665 cm^{-1}) region as can be seen in spectra 279 A - D, 279 F - 280 B. An opposite shift to 5.7 μ (1755 cm^{-1}) or lower occurs by the addition of a halogen atom on the α-carbon.

The lone hydrogen attached directly to the carbonyl appears at 3.65 μ and 3.5 μ (2740 and 2855 cm^{-1}) with the 3.65 μ (2740 cm^{-1}) band distinctly separate from other aliphatic C-H bands. Its intensity is medium to weak.

The last spectra of the aldehyde collection do not display the aldehyde absorption because of inter- and intramolecular hemiacetal formation. For example in spectrum 282B

$HO{-}CH_2{-}CH_2{-}CH_2{-}CH_2{-}\overset{O}{\overset{\|}{C}}H$ exists as (2-hydroxytetrahydropyran: six-membered ring with O and OH)

Aldehydes often form trimers and other polymers which show a strong and broad ether band in the vicinity of 9 μ (1110 cm^{-1}). The presence of this band in the spectrum overlaps other weak absorptions so that a small amount of polymer may be difficult to detect.

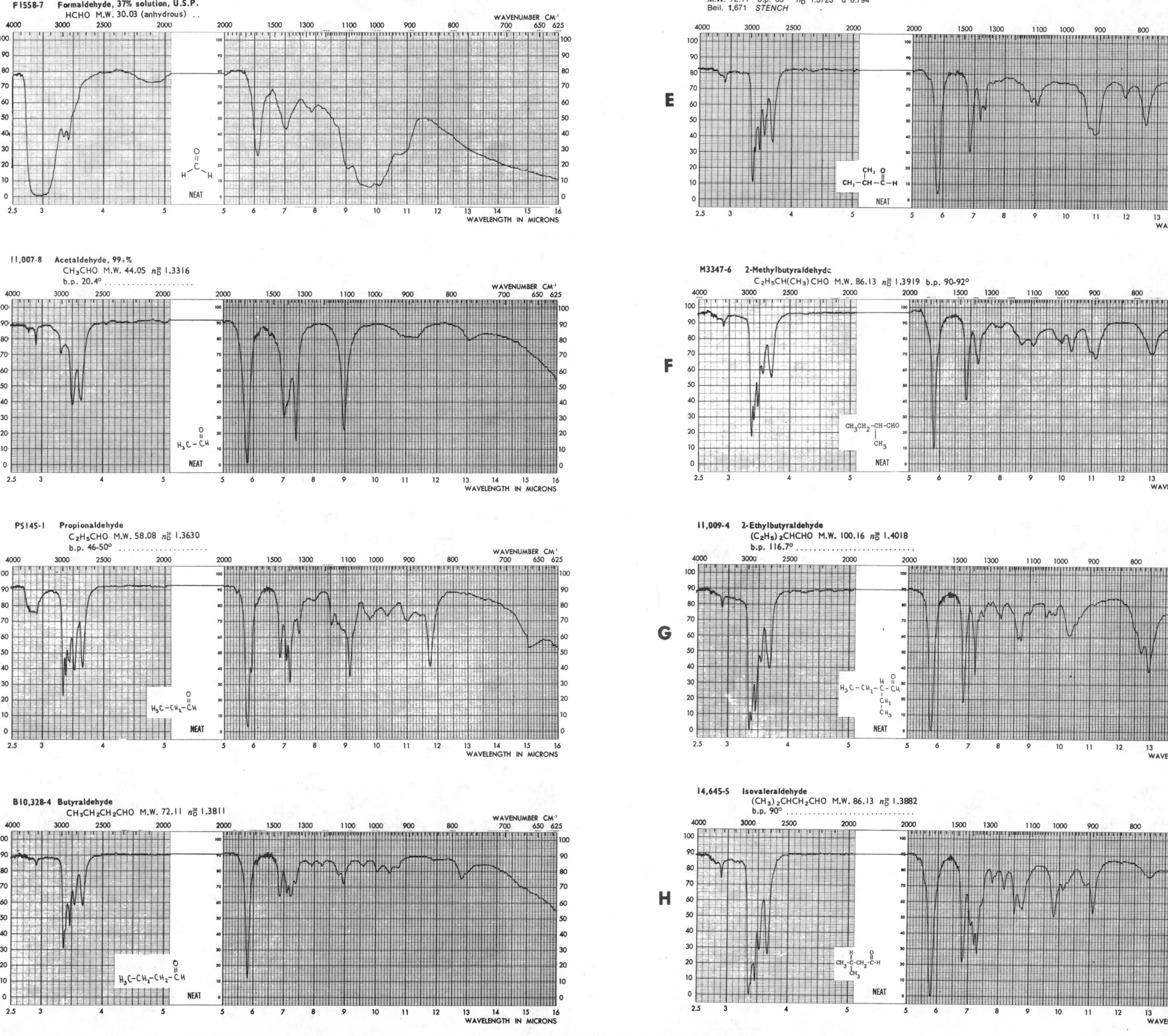
A
F1558-7 Formaldehyde, 37% solution, U.S.P.
HCHO M.W. 30.03 (anhydrous)
NEAT
B
11,007-8 Acetaldehyde, 99+%
CH_3CHO M.W. 44.05 n_D^{20} 1.3316
b.p. 20.4°
H_3C-CH (=O)
NEAT
C
P5145-1 Propionaldehyde
C_2H_5CHO M.W. 58.08 n_D^{20} 1.3630
b.p. 46-50°
H_3C-CH_2-CH (=O)
NEAT
D
B10,328-4 Butyraldehyde
$CH_3CH_2CH_2CHO$ M.W. 72.11 n_D^{20} 1.3811
$H_3C-CH_2-CH_2-CH$ (=O)
NEAT
E
I—1,550-5
Isobutyraldehyde, 98% (2-methylpropionaldehyde)
$(CH_3)_2CHCHO$
M.W. 72.11 b.p. 63° n_D^{20} 1.3723 d 0.794
Beil. 1,671 STENCH
NEAT
F
M3347-6 2-Methylbutyraldehyde
$C_2H_5CH(CH_3)CHO$ M.W. 86.13 n_D^{20} 1.3919 b.p. 90-92°
$CH_3CH_2-CH-CHO$ (CH_3)
NEAT
G
11,009-4 2-Ethylbutyraldehyde
$(C_2H_5)_2CHCHO$ M.W. 100.16 n_D^{20} 1.4018
b.p. 116.7°
NEAT
H
14,645-5 Isovaleraldehyde
$(CH_3)_2CHCH_2CHO$ M.W. 86.13 n_D^{20} 1.3882
b.p. 90°
NEAT
WAVENUMBER CM⁻¹
WAVELENGTH IN MICRONS

ALDRICH

NON-AROMATIC ALDEHYDES

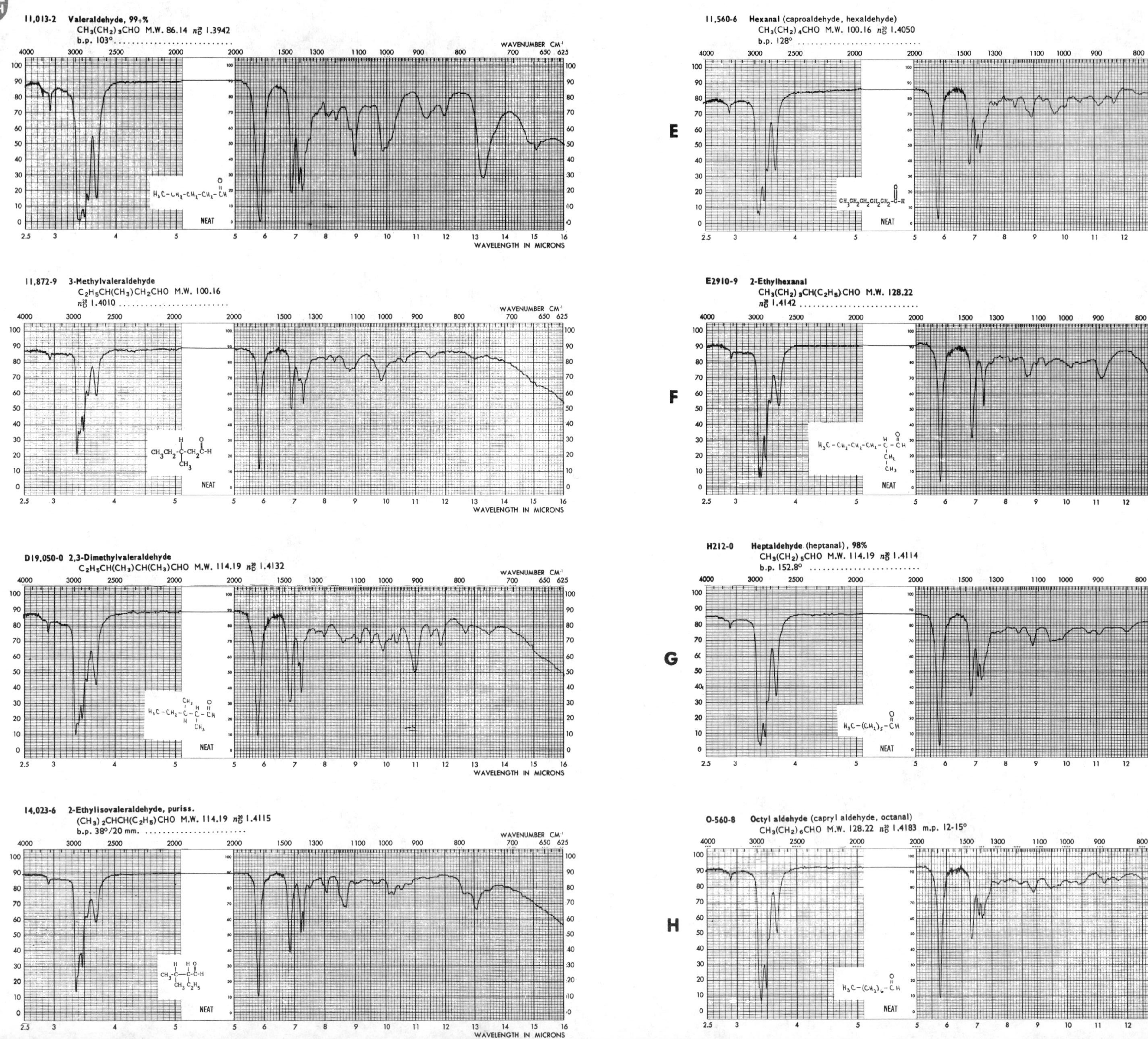
A
11,013-2 Valeraldehyde, 99+%
CH3(CH2)3CHO M.W. 86.14 n20D 1.3942
b.p. 103°
NEAT
B
11,872-9 3-Methylvaleraldehyde
C2H5CH(CH3)CH2CHO M.W. 100.16
n20D 1.4010
NEAT
C
D19,050-0 2,3-Dimethylvaleraldehyde
C2H5CH(CH3)CH(CH3)CHO M.W. 114.19 n20D 1.4132
NEAT
D
14,023-6 2-Ethylisovaleraldehyde, puriss.
(CH3)2CHCH(C2H5)CHO M.W. 114.19 n20D 1.4115
b.p. 38°/20 mm.
NEAT
E
11,560-6 Hexanal (caproaldehyde, hexaldehyde)
CH3(CH2)4CHO M.W. 100.16 n20D 1.4050
b.p. 128°
NEAT
F
E2910-9 2-Ethylhexanal
CH3(CH2)3CH(C2H5)CHO M.W. 128.22
n20D 1.4142
NEAT
G
H212-0 Heptaldehyde (heptanal), 98%
CH3(CH2)5CHO M.W. 114.19 n20D 1.4114
b.p. 152.8°
NEAT
H
O-560-8 Octyl aldehyde (capryl aldehyde, octanal)
CH3(CH2)6CHO M.W. 128.22 n20D 1.4183 m.p. 12-15°
NEAT
WAVENUMBER CM⁻¹
WAVELENGTH IN MICRONS

A

N3080-3 **Nonyl aldehyde** (1-nonanal, pelargonaldehyde)
$CH_3(CH_2)_7CHO$ M.W. 142.24 n_D^{20} 1.4217 b.p. 93.5°/23 mm.

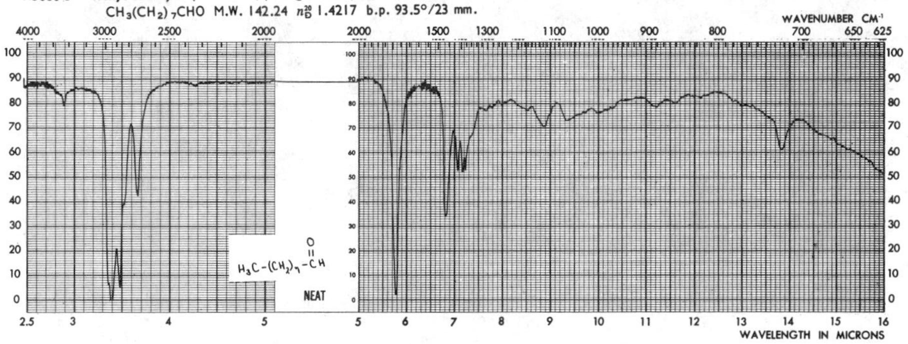

NEAT

B

12,577-6 **Decyl aldehyde** (decanal)
$CH_3(CH_2)_8CHO$ M.W. 156.27 n_D^{20} 1.4390

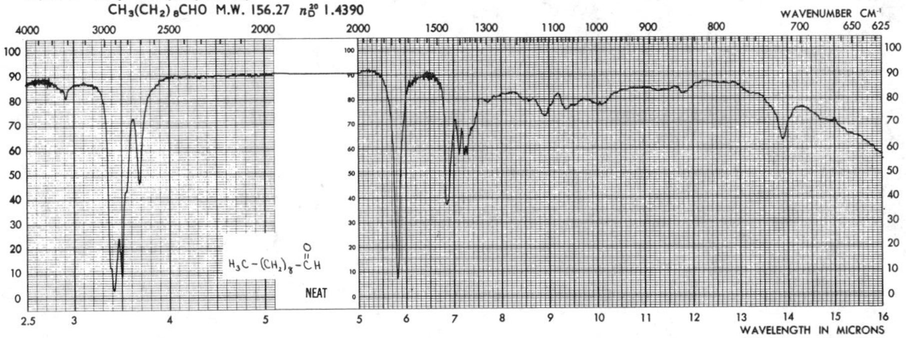

NEAT

C

U220-2 **Undecylic aldehyde** (undecanal)
$CH_3(CH_2)_9CHO$ M.W. 170.30 n_D^{23} 1.4322
b.p. 109-115°/5 mm.

NEAT

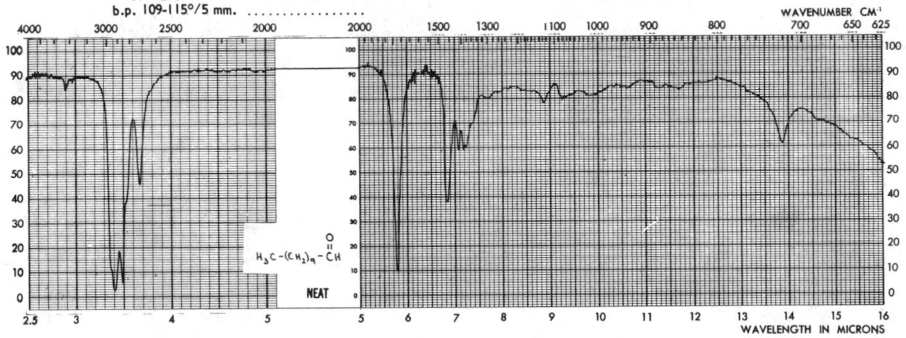

D

M8675-8 **2-Methylundecanal**
$CH_3(CH_2)_8CH(CH_3)CHO$ M.W. 184.32 n_D^{20} 1.4321

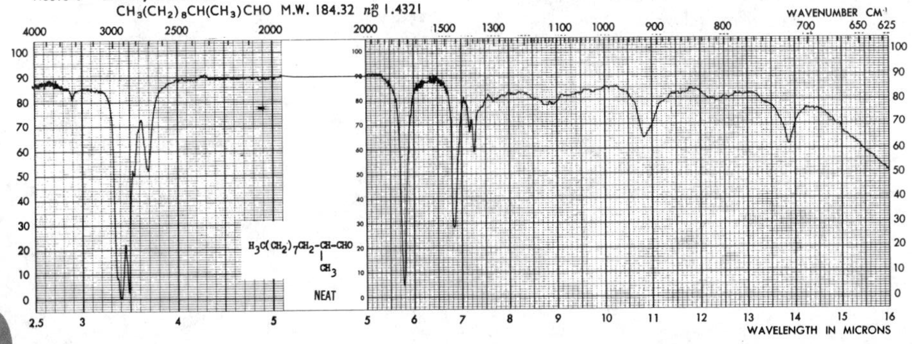

NEAT

E

D22,200-3 **Dodecyl aldehyde** (lauraldehyde)
$CH_3(CH_2)_{10}CHO$ M.W. 184.32 n_D^{20} 1.4344

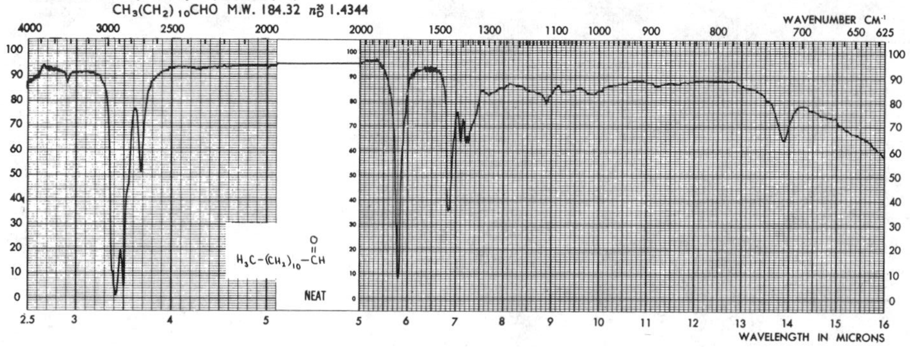

NEAT

F

T1000-6 **Tetradecyl aldehyde** (myristyl aldehyde)
$CH_3(CH_2)_{12}CHO$ M.W. 212.38
b.p. 166°/12 mm.

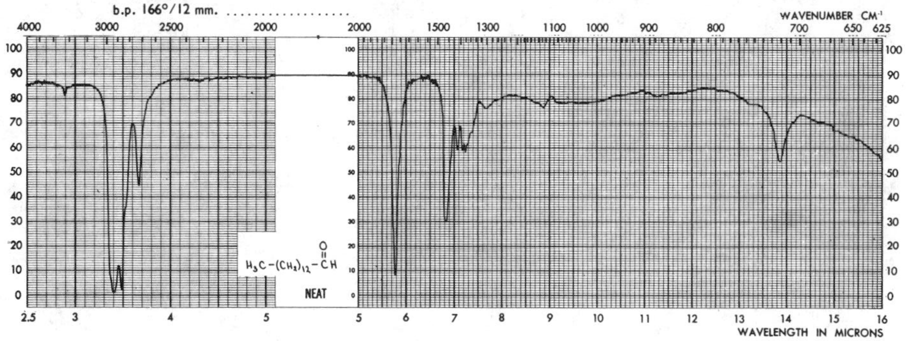

NEAT

G

O-100-9 **Octadecyl aldehyde** (stearaldehyde)
$[CH_3(CH_2)_{16}CHO]$. M.W. 268.49 (monomer)

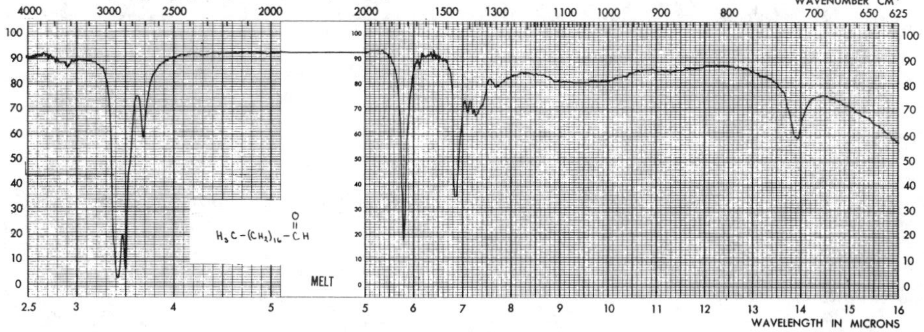

MELT

H

21,877-4
7-Methoxy-3,7-dimethyloctanal, 98%
$CH_3OC(CH_3)_2(CH_2)_3CH(CH_3)CH_2CHO$ FW 186.30
bp 60°/0.450mm. n_D^{20} 1.4374 d 0.877 Disp. C

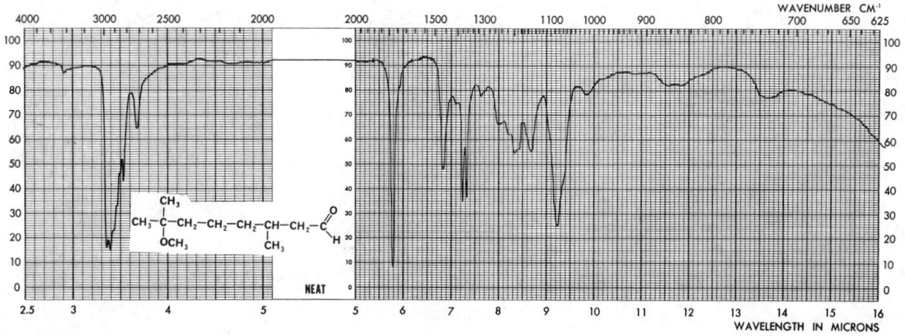

NEAT

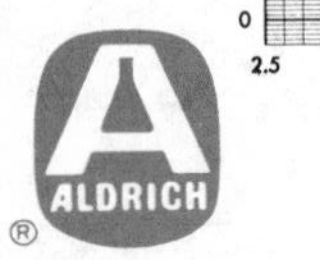

A

11,022-1 **Acrolein (acrylaldehyde)**
$H_2C{:}CHCHO$ M.W. 56.06 n_D^{20} 1.4065
b.p. 53°

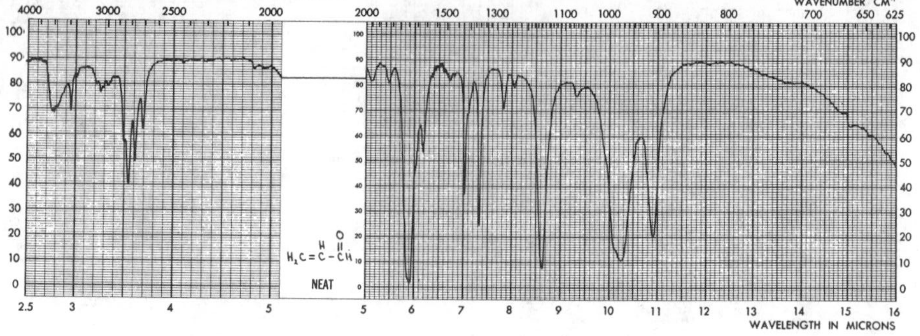

NEAT

B

13,298-5 **Crotonaldehyde, anhydrous, 99%**
$CH_3CH{:}CHCHO$ M.W. 70.09 n_D^{20} 1.4370
b.p. 104-105°

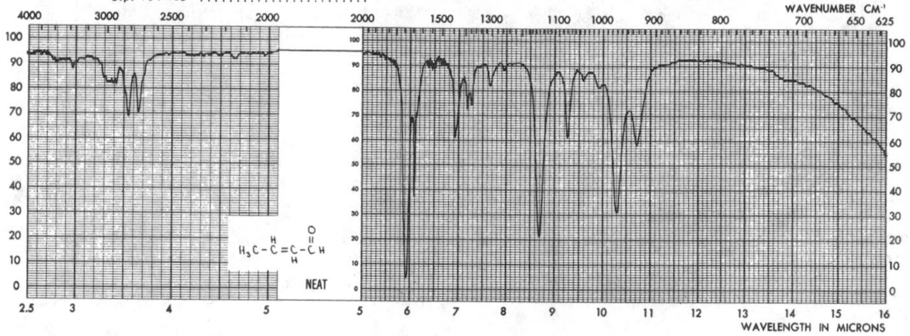

NEAT

C

19,261-9
Tiglic aldehyde, 98+% (*trans*-2-methyl-2-butenal)
$CH_3CH{=}C(CH_3)CHO$ FW 84.12 bp 115-119°
n_D^{20} 1.4475 d 0.871 *Beil.* 1,733 Disp. B

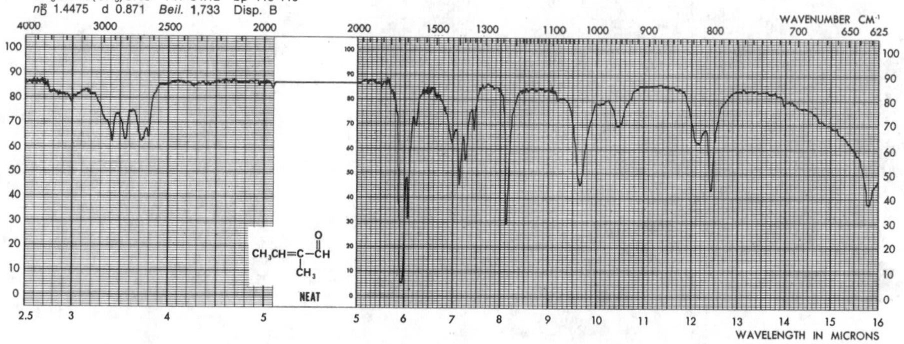

NEAT

D

13,265-9 ***trans*-2-Hexenal**
$CH_3CH_2CH_2CH{:}CHCHO$ M.W. 98.15 n_D^{20} 1.4455
b.p. 47°/17 mm.

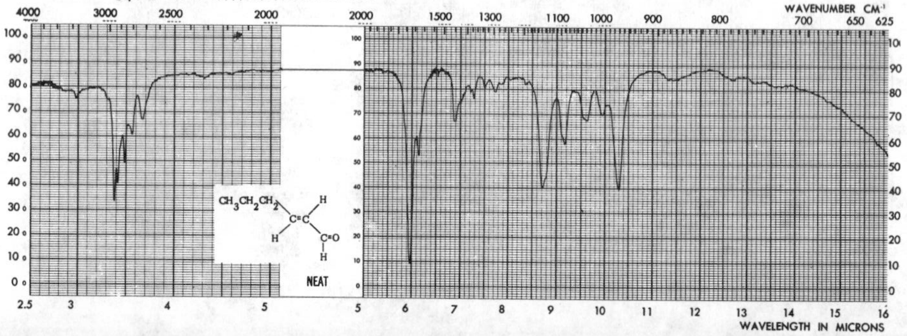

NEAT

E

13,227-6 **Undecylenic aldehyde (10-undecenal)**
$H_2C{:}CH(CH_2)_8CHO$ M.W. 168.28 n_D^{20} 1.4427

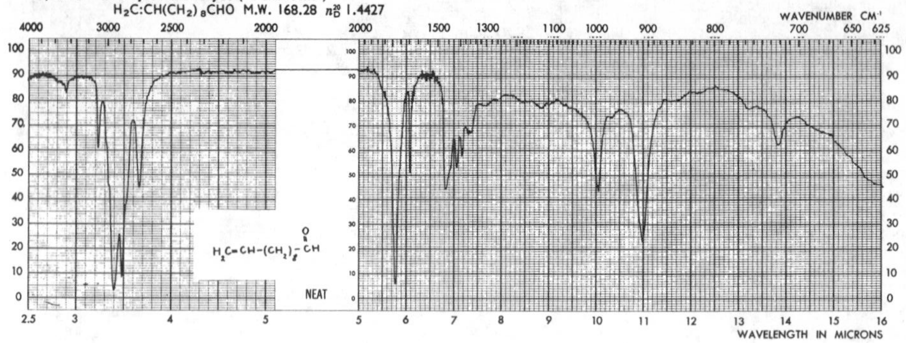

NEAT

F

H800-5 **2,4-Hexadienal (sorbic aldehyde), tech.**
$CH_3CH{:}CHCH{:}CHCHO$ M.W. 96.13 n_D^{20} 1.5421

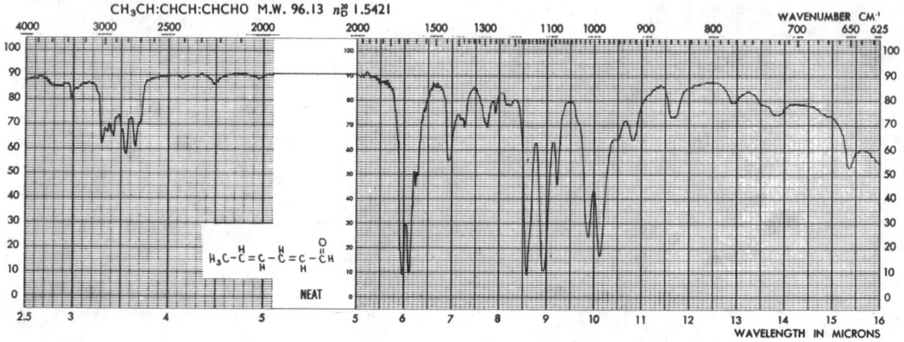

NEAT

G

18,054-8
***trans,trans*-2,4-Heptadienal**
$C_2H_5CH{=}CHCH{=}CHCHO$
M.W. 110.16 b.p. 84-84.5° n_D^{20} 1.5315 d 0.881

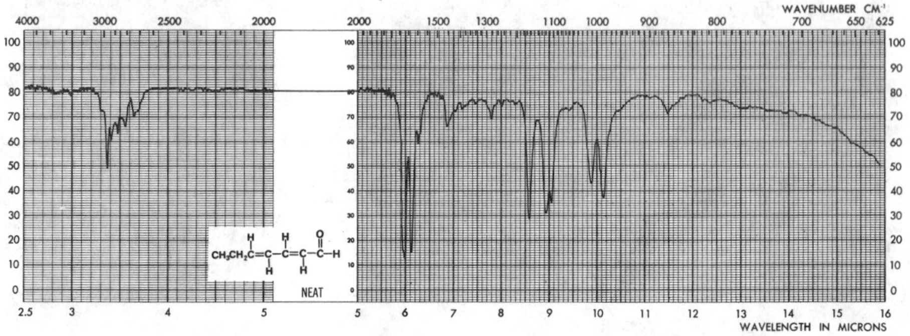

NEAT

H

18,056-4
***trans,trans*-2,4-Octadienal,** tech.
$CH_3CH_2CH_2CH{=}CHCH{=}CHCHO$
M.W. 124.18 n_D^{20} 1.5224

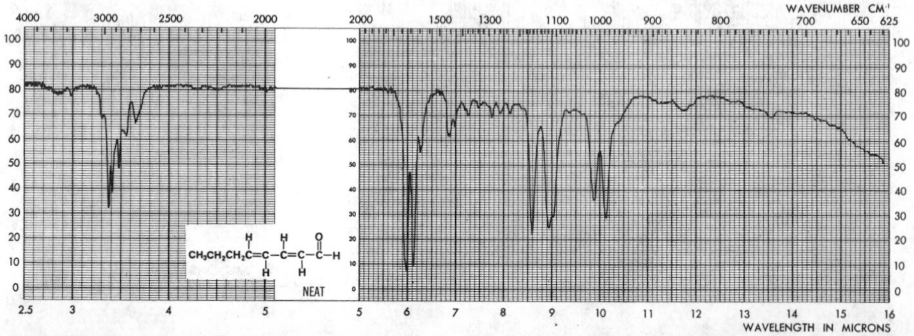

NEAT

WAVENUMBER CM⁻¹
WAVELENGTH IN MICRONS

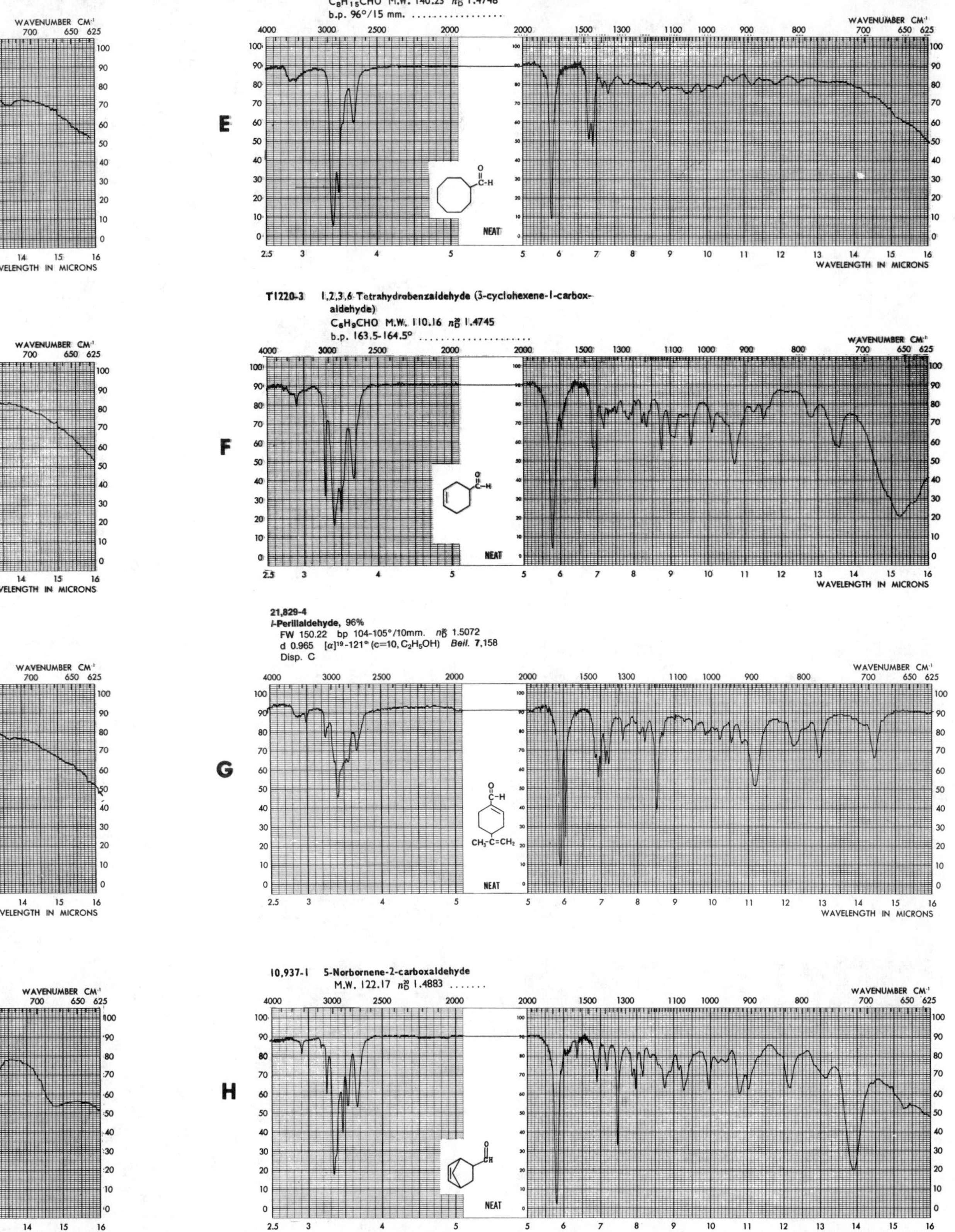

A

18,055-6
trans,trans-**2,4-Nonadienal**
$CH_3(CH_2)_3CH=CHCH=CHCHO$
M.W. 138.21 b.p. 97-98°/10mm. n_D^{20} 1.5207
d 0.862
NEAT

B

C8300-7 **Citral** (3,7-dimethyl-2,6-octadienal)
$(CH_3)_2C{:}CHCH_2CH_2C(CH_3){:}CHCHO$ M.W. 152.24
n_D^{20} 1.4876
NEAT

C

21,827-8
l-**Citronellal**, 99%
$(CH_3)_2C=CHCH_2CH_2CH(CH_3)CH_2CHO$ FW 154.25
bp 205-206° n_D^{20} 1.4469 d 0.851
$[\alpha]^{21}$-11° (neat) *Beil.* **1**,747 Disp. C
NEAT

D

10,846-4 **Cyclohexanecarboxaldehyde** (hexahydrobenzaldehyde)
$C_6H_{11}CHO$ M.W. 112.17 n_D^{20} 1.4500
b.p. 77-78°/20 mm.
NEAT

E

10,933-9 **Cyclooctanecarboxaldehyde, tech.**
$C_8H_{15}CHO$ M.W. 140.23 n_D^{20} 1.4748
b.p. 96°/15 mm.
NEAT

F

T1220-3 **1,2,3,6-Tetrahydrobenzaldehyde** (3-cyclohexene-1-carboxaldehyde)
C_6H_9CHO M.W. 110.16 n_D^{20} 1.4745
b.p. 163.5-164.5°
NEAT

G

21,829-4
l-**Perillaldehyde**, 96%
FW 150.22 bp 104-105°/10mm. n_D^{20} 1.5072
d 0.965 $[\alpha]^{19}$-121° (c=10, C_2H_5OH) *Beil.* **7**,158
Disp. C
NEAT

H

10,937-1 **5-Norbornene-2-carboxaldehyde**
M.W. 122.17 n_D^{20} 1.4883
NEAT

ALDRICH

NON-AROMATIC ALDEHYDES

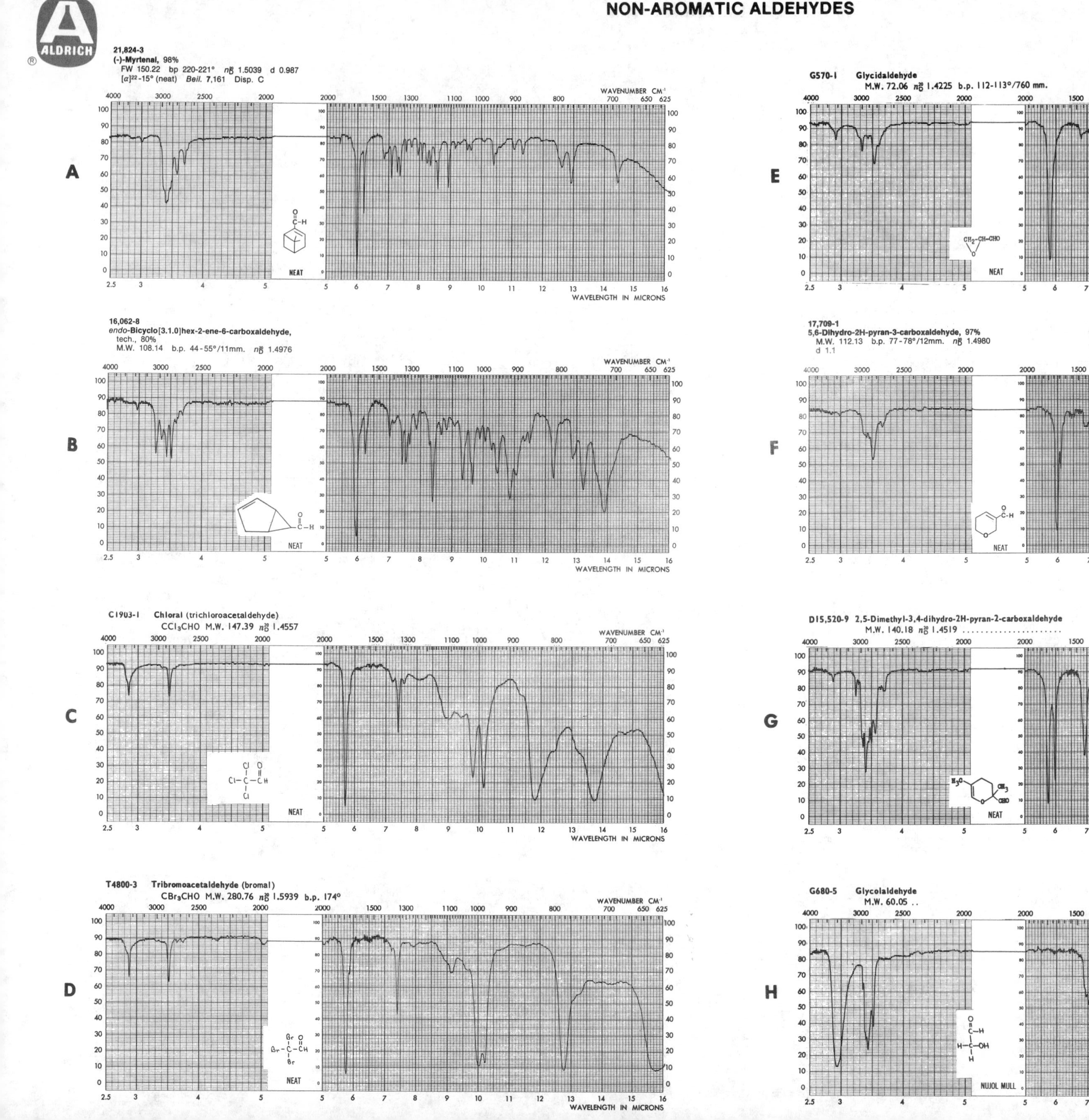

A — 21,824-3
(-)-Myrtenal, 98%
FW 150.22 bp 220-221° n_D^{20} 1.5039 d 0.987
$[\alpha]^{22}$ -15° (neat) *Beil.* 7,161 Disp. C
NEAT

B — 16,062-8
endo-Bicyclo[3.1.0]hex-2-ene-6-carboxaldehyde,
tech., 80%
M.W. 108.14 b.p. 44-55°/11mm. n_D^{20} 1.4976
NEAT

C — C1903-1 Chloral (trichloroacetaldehyde)
CCl_3CHO M.W. 147.39 n_D^{20} 1.4557
NEAT

D — T4800-3 Tribromoacetaldehyde (bromal)
CBr_3CHO M.W. 280.76 n_D^{20} 1.5939 b.p. 174°
NEAT

E — G570-1 Glycidaldehyde
M.W. 72.06 n_D^{20} 1.4225 b.p. 112-113°/760 mm.
NEAT

F — 17,709-1
5,6-Dihydro-2H-pyran-3-carboxaldehyde, 97%
M.W. 112.13 b.p. 77-78°/12mm. n_D^{20} 1.4980
d 1.1
NEAT

G — D15,520-9 2,5-Dimethyl-3,4-dihydro-2H-pyran-2-carboxaldehyde
M.W. 140.18 n_D^{20} 1.4519
NEAT

H — G680-5 Glycolaldehyde
M.W. 60.05
NUJOL MULL

A2810-4 **Aldol (acetaldol), tech.**
$CH_3CH(OH)CH_2CHO$ M.W. 88.11 n_D^{20} 1.4497
b.p. 83° (dec.)

12,876-7 **5-Hydroxypentanal** (5-hydroxyvaleraldehyde)
$HO(CH_2)_4CHO$ M.W. 102.13 $n_D^{20.5}$ 1.4517
b.p. 115-120°/15 mm.

G480-2 **DL-Glyceraldehyde**
$HOCH_2CH(OH)CHO$ M.W. 90.08

G478-0 **D-Glyceraldehyde**
$HOCH_2CH(OH)CHO$ M.W. 90.08 n_D^{20} 1.5022

85,146-9
L-(-)-Glyceraldehyde, 90%
$HOCH_2CH(OH)CHO$
M.W. 90.08 n_D^{20} 1.4840 $[\alpha]^{24}$ -8.6° (c=2, H_2O)

17,733-4
Pyruvic aldehyde, 40% aqueous solution
CH_3COCHO
M.W. 72.06 n_D^{20} 1.4209 Beil. 1,762

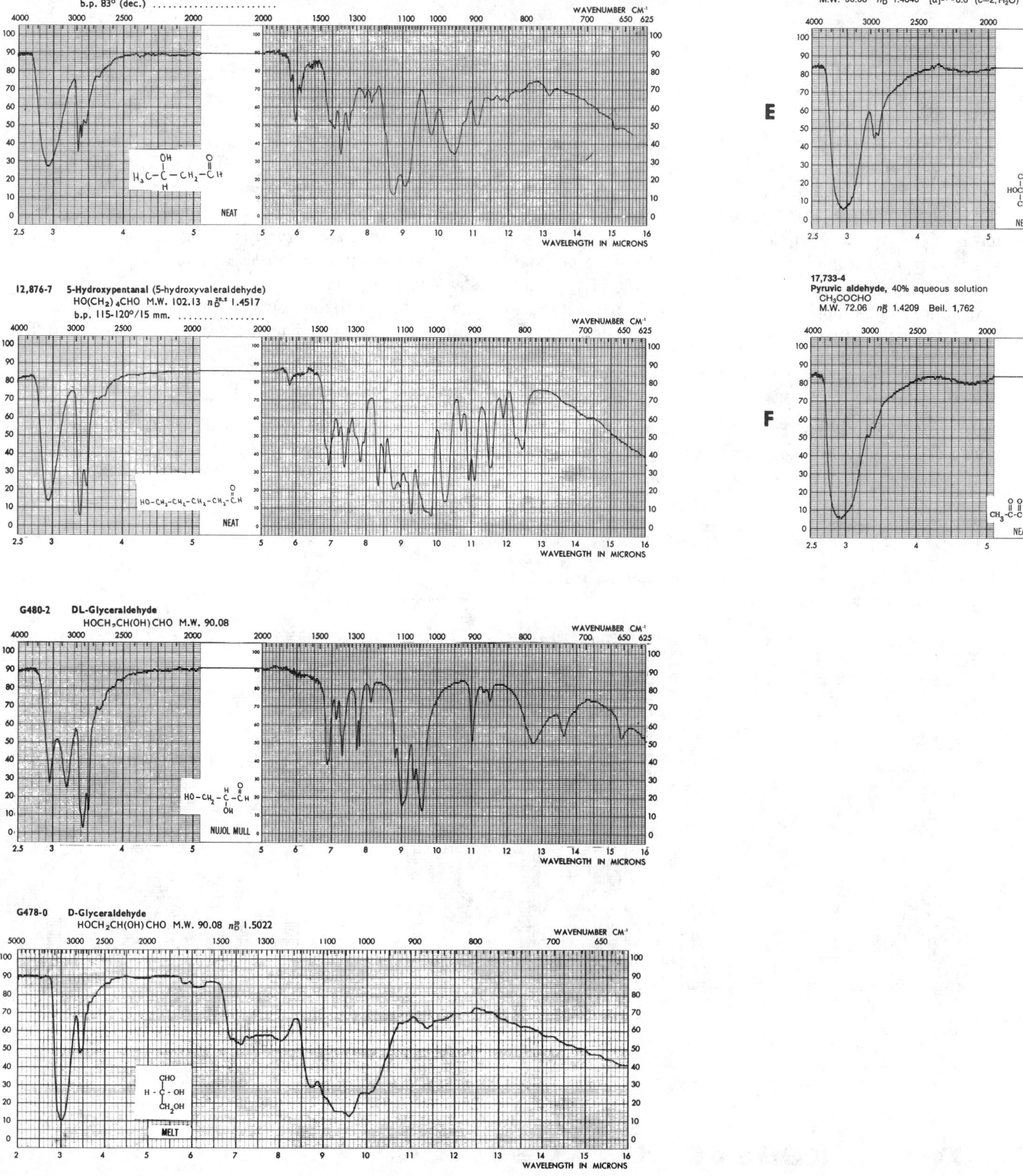

ALDRICH

NON-AROMATIC CARBOXYLIC ACIDS

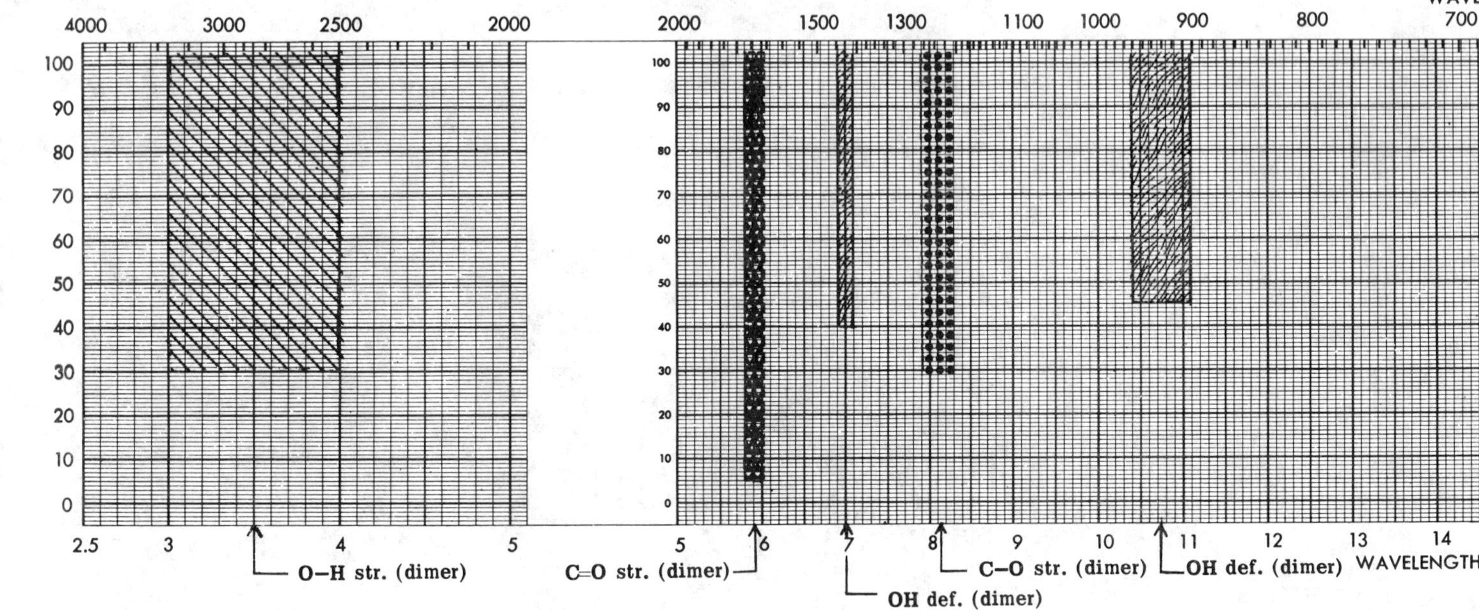

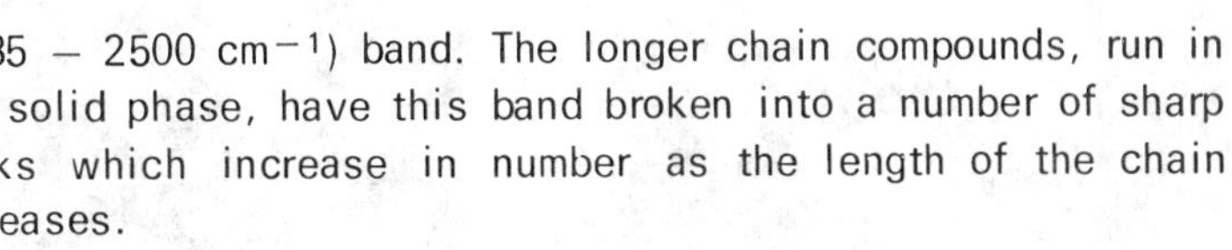

Carboxylic acids usually exist as dimers and display their carbonyl bands between 5.8 and 5.9 μ (1725 – 1695 cm^{-1}). The effect of α,β-unsaturation on this absorption is less than that observed in the ketones and aldehydes and shifts the carbonyl absorption to a slightly higher wavelength.

There are four other outstanding characteristic absorptions of the carboxylic acid function. The first is the oxygen-hydrogen stretch band between 3 and 4 μ (3335 – 2500 cm^{-1}). Its position, shape and intensity is consistent throughout this series and is due to the strong hydrogen bonding of the acid dimer. It is interesting to see the CH stretch band around 3.4 μ (2940 cm^{-1}) increase in intensity relative to the OH stretch absorption as the chain length increases in spectra 284A—285D.

The second is the carbon-oxygen stretch vibration which appears around 8 μ (1250 cm^{-1}) and is as intense as the 3 to 4 μ (3335 – 2500 cm^{-1}) band. The longer chain compounds, run in the solid phase, have this band broken into a number of sharp peaks which increase in number as the length of the chain increases.

The third is a broad and medium intensity OH deformation band between 10.5 and 11 μ (950 – 910 cm^{-1}).

A fourth absorption (OH deformation) near 7 μ (1430 cm^{-1}) appears within the CH_2 bending bands.

In nujol mulls the long-chain acids (C_{16} or higher) display a split in the CH_2 wag absorption around 13.8 μ (725 cm^{-1}).

The α-hydroxycarboxylic acids have their carbonyl stretch absorption shifted from the usual 5.8 μ (1725 cm^{-1}) region to a lower wavelength. This α-hydroxyl group has its very sharp OH stretch band at 2.8 μ (3570 cm^{-1}). (See spectra 303G—305A).

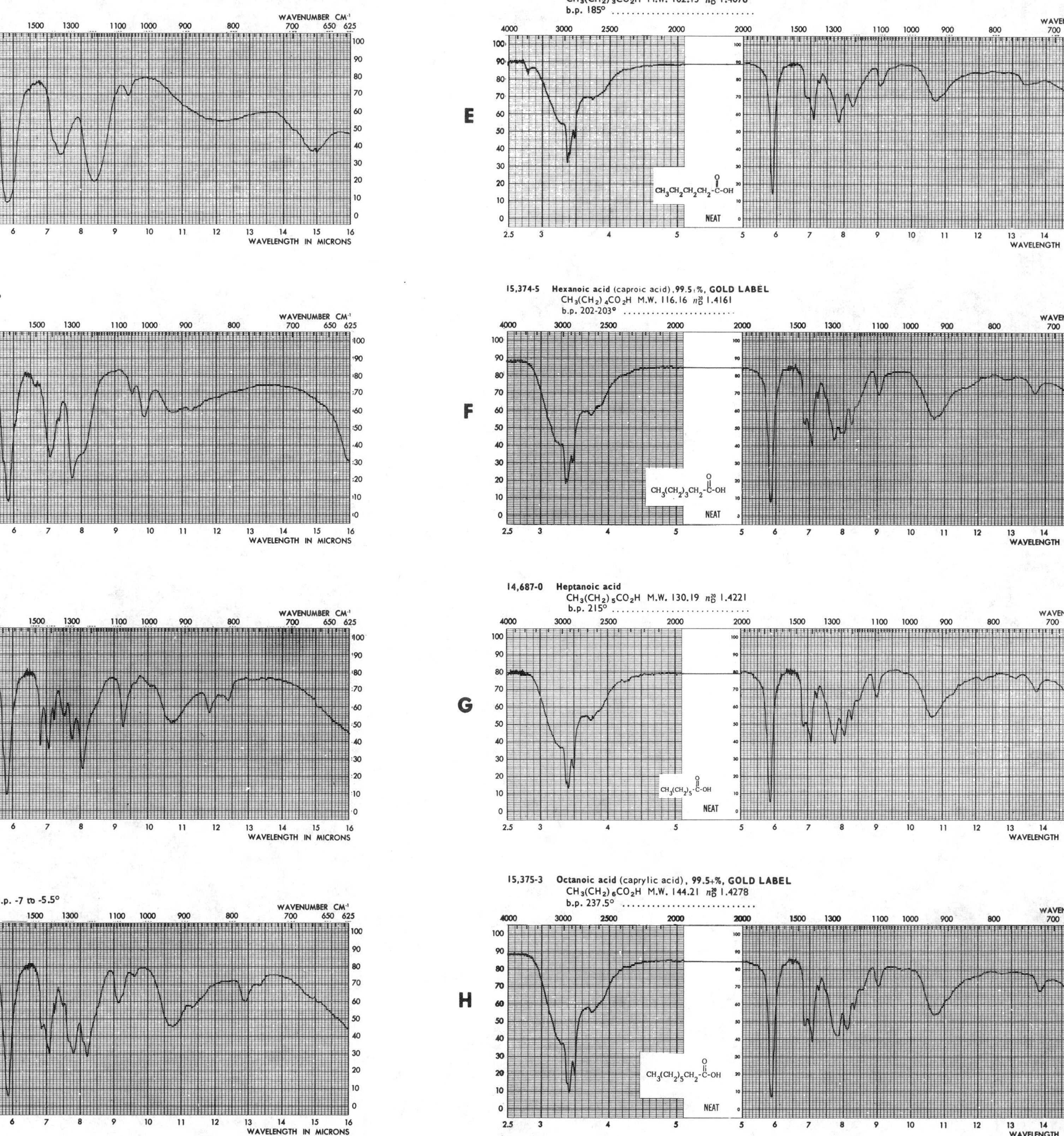
A
10,652-6 Formic acid, 97+%
HCO_2H M.W. 46.03 n_D^{20} 1.3721 m.p. 5-8°
H-C(=O)-OH
NEAT
B
10,908-8 Acetic acid, glacial, 99.8%
CH_3CO_2H M.W. 60.05 n_D^{20} 1.3737 m.p. 16.2°
b.p. 118°
$H_3C-C(=O)-OH$
NEAT
C
10,979-7 Propionic acid, puriss.
$C_2H_5CO_2H$ M.W. 74.08 n_D^{20} 1.3860
b.p. 141°
$C_2H_5-C(=O)-OH$
NEAT
D
B10,350-0 n-Butyric acid, puriss.
$CH_3CH_2CH_2CO_2H$ M.W. 88.11 n_D^{20} 1.3969 m.p. -7 to -5.5°
$H_3C-CH_2-CH_2-C(=O)-OH$
NEAT
E
11,014-0 Valeric acid, 99+%
$CH_3(CH_2)_3CO_2H$ M.W. 102.13 n_D^{20} 1.4076
b.p. 185°
$CH_3CH_2CH_2CH_2-C(=O)-OH$
NEAT
F
15,374-5 Hexanoic acid (caproic acid), 99.5+%, GOLD LABEL
$CH_3(CH_2)_4CO_2H$ M.W. 116.16 n_D^{20} 1.4161
b.p. 202-203°
$CH_3(CH_2)_3CH_2-C(=O)-OH$
NEAT
G
14,687-0 Heptanoic acid
$CH_3(CH_2)_5CO_2H$ M.W. 130.19 n_D^{20} 1.4221
b.p. 215°
$CH_3(CH_2)_5-C(=O)-OH$
NEAT
H
15,375-3 Octanoic acid (caprylic acid), 99.5+%, GOLD LABEL
$CH_3(CH_2)_6CO_2H$ M.W. 144.21 n_D^{20} 1.4278
b.p. 237.5°
$CH_3(CH_2)_5CH_2-C(=O)-OH$
NEAT
WAVENUMBER CM⁻¹
WAVELENGTH IN MICRONS
ALDRICH

ALDRICH

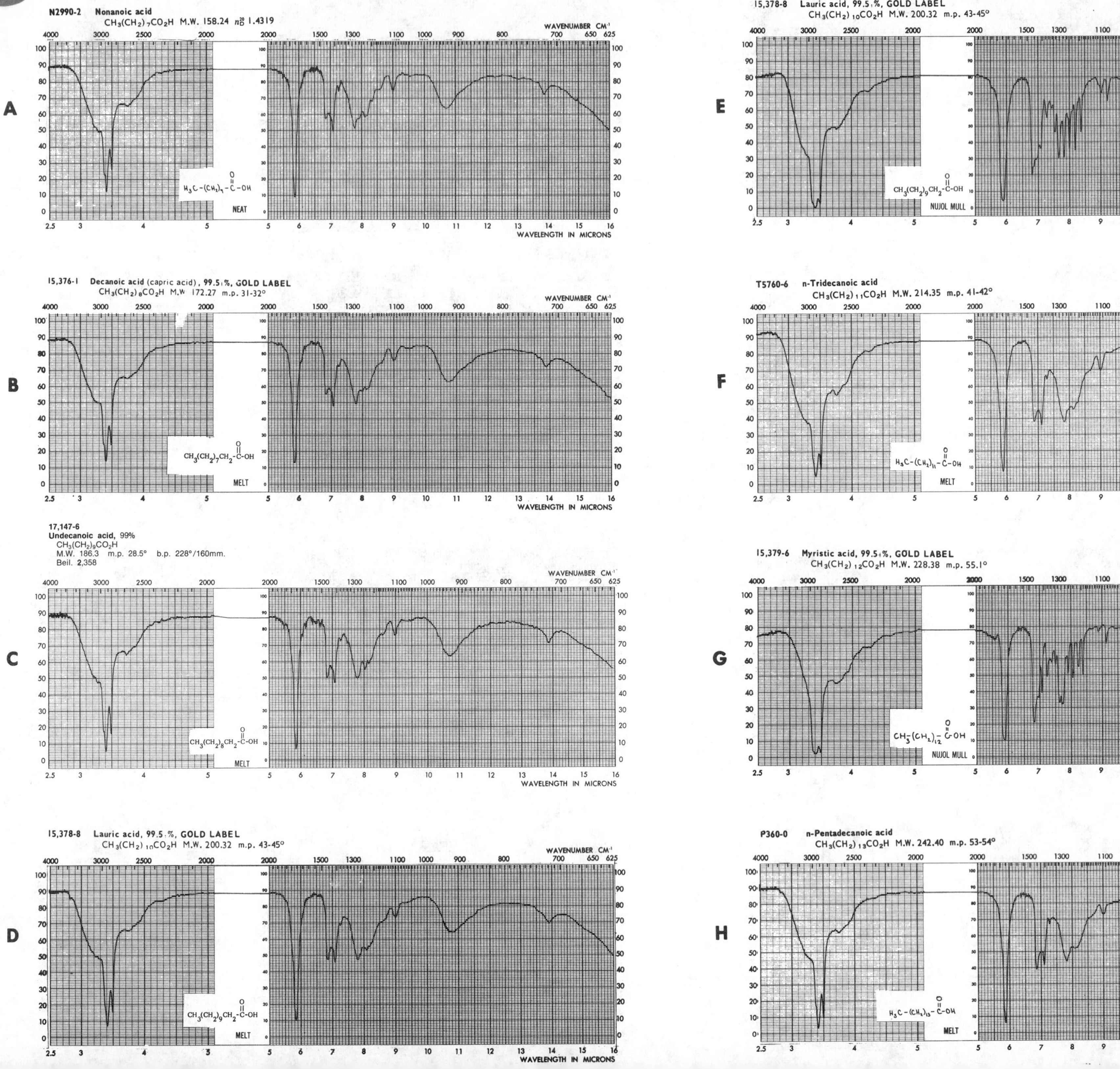
A
N2990-2 Nonanoic acid
$CH_3(CH_2)_7CO_2H$ M.W. 158.24 n_D^{20} 1.4319
NEAT
B
15,376-1 Decanoic acid (capric acid), 99.5+%, GOLD LABEL
$CH_3(CH_2)_8CO_2H$ M.W. 172.27 m.p. 31-32°
MELT
C
17,147-6
Undecanoic acid, 99%
$CH_3(CH_2)_9CO_2H$
M.W. 186.3 m.p. 28.5° b.p. 228°/160mm.
Beil. 2,358
MELT
D
15,378-8 Lauric acid, 99.5+%, GOLD LABEL
$CH_3(CH_2)_{10}CO_2H$ M.W. 200.32 m.p. 43-45°
MELT
E
15,378-8 Lauric acid, 99.5+%, GOLD LABEL
$CH_3(CH_2)_{10}CO_2H$ M.W. 200.32 m.p. 43-45°
NUJOL MULL
F
T5760-6 n-Tridecanoic acid
$CH_3(CH_2)_{11}CO_2H$ M.W. 214.35 m.p. 41-42°
MELT
G
15,379-6 Myristic acid, 99.5+%, GOLD LABEL
$CH_3(CH_2)_{12}CO_2H$ M.W. 228.38 m.p. 55.1°
NUJOL MULL
H
P360-0 n-Pentadecanoic acid
$CH_3(CH_2)_{13}CO_2H$ M.W. 242.40 m.p. 53-54°
MELT
WAVENUMBER CM⁻¹
WAVELENGTH IN MICRONS

A

P5-1 **Palmitic acid, 90%**
$CH_3(CH_2)_{14}CO_2H$ M.W. 256.43
m.p. 61-62.5°

B

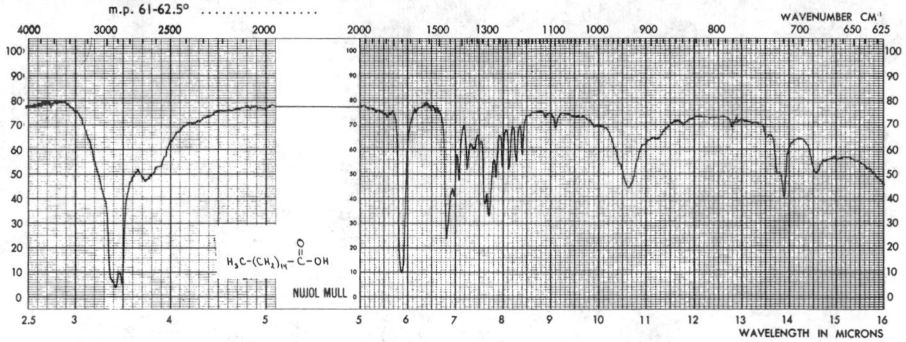

H100-0 **n-Heptadecanoic acid (margaric acid)**
$CH_3(CH_2)_{15}CO_2H$ M.W. 270.46 m.p. 62-64°

C

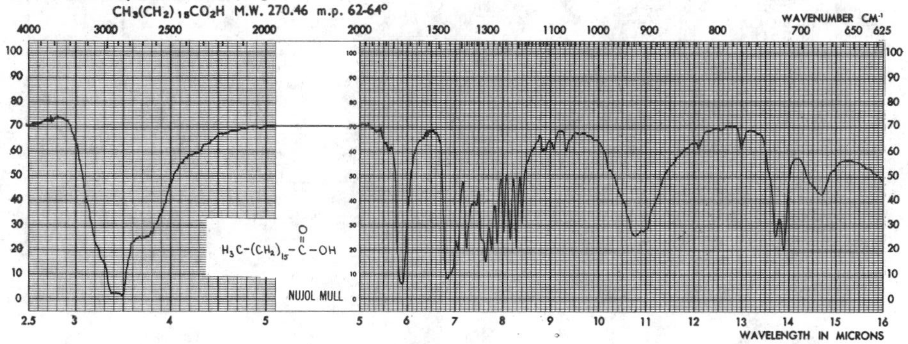

17,536-6
Stearic acid, 95%
$CH_3(CH_2)_{16}CO_2H$
M.W. 284.48 m.p. 67-69° b.p. 361° d 0.845
Beil. **2**,377

D

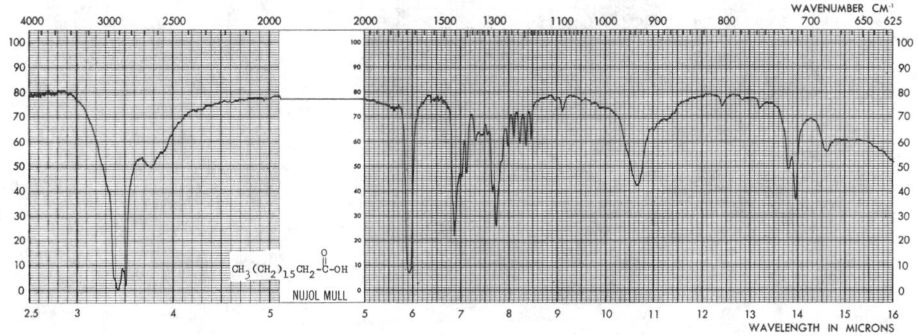

N2900-7 **n-Nonadecanoic acid**
$CH_3(CH_2)_{17}CO_2H$ M.W. 298.51 m.p. 68-69°

E

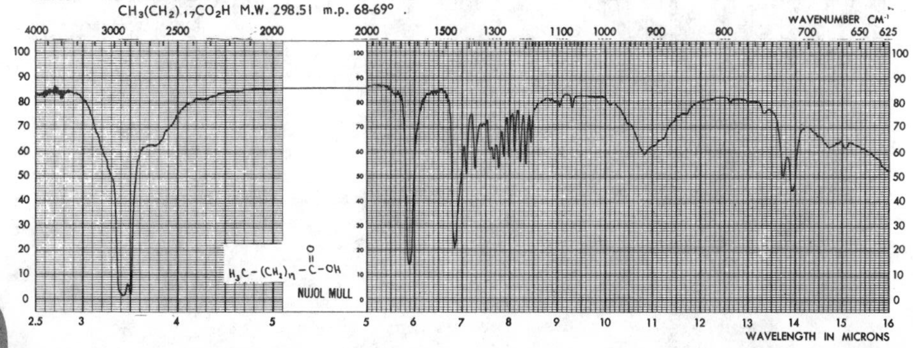

E23-1 **Eicosanoic acid (arachidic acid)**
$CH_3(CH_2)_{18}CO_2H$ M.W. 312.54 m.p. 76-78°

F

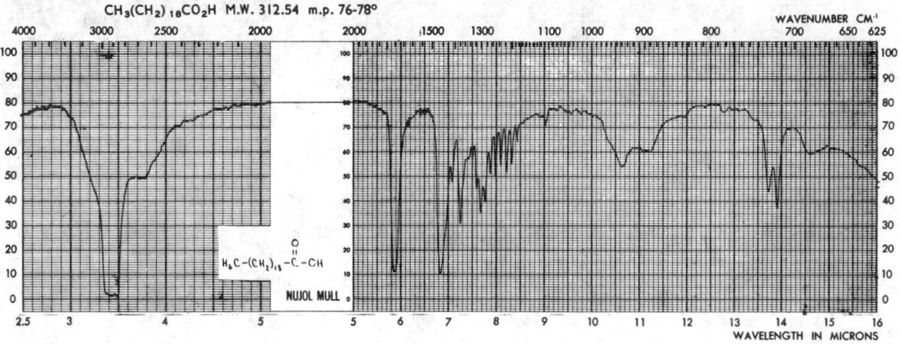

21,966-5
Heneicosanoic acid, 99%
$CH_3(CH_2)_{19}CO_2H$ FW 326.57 mp 74-75°
Beil. **2**(1),179 Disp. I

G

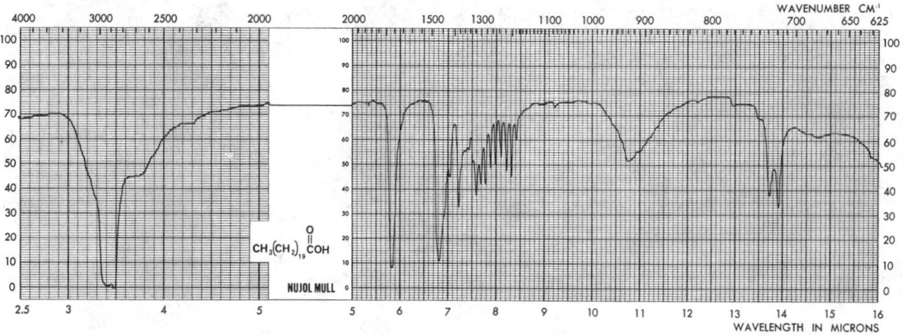

21,694-1
Docosanoic acid, 97% (behenic acid)
$CH_3(CH_2)_{20}CO_2H$ FW 340.60 mp 80-82°
Beil. **2**,391 Disp. C

H

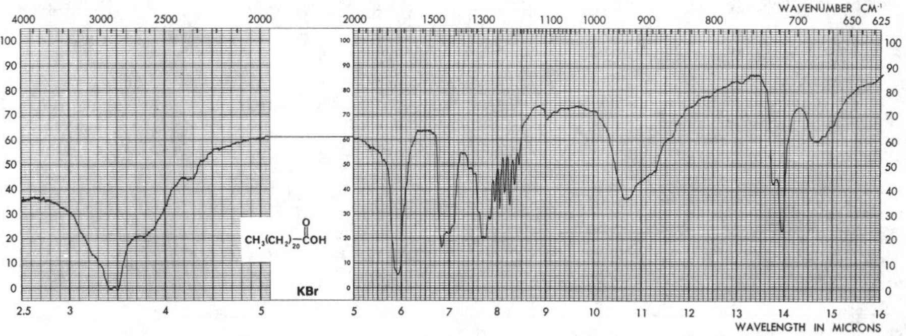

21,859-6
Tricosanoic acid, 99%
$CH_3(CH_2)_{21}CO_2H$ FW 354.62 mp 79-80°
Beil. **2**(2),378 Disp. I

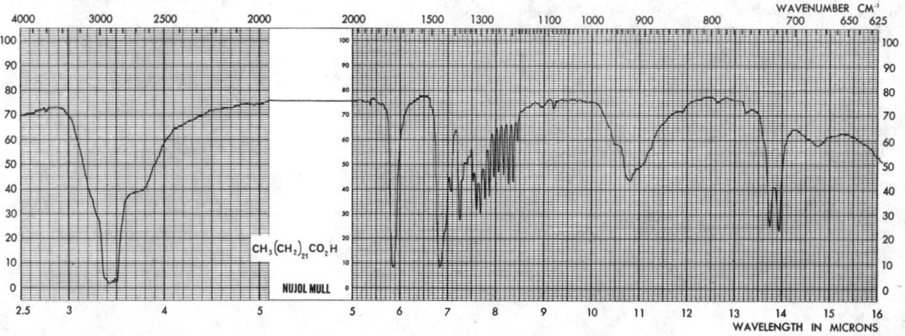

A 13,480-5 **Triacontanoic acid**
$CH_3(CH_2)_{28}CO_2H$ M.W. 452.81
m.p. 93.5-95.5°

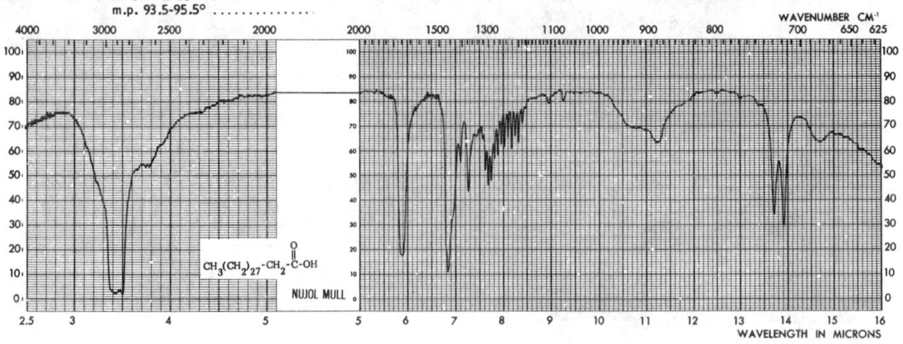

$CH_3(CH_2)_{27}$-CH_2-C(=O)-OH — NUJOL MULL

B I-1555-6 **Isobutyric acid, puriss.**
$(CH_3)_2CHCO_2H$ M.W. 88.11 n_D^{20} 1.3919
b.p. 153-154°

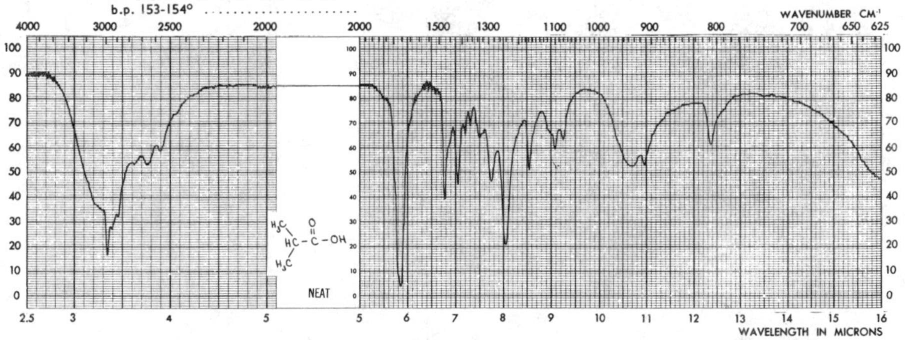

NEAT

C T7180-3 **Trimethylacetic acid** (pivalic acid), 99+%
$(CH_3)_3CCO_2H$ M.W. 102.13 m.p. 35-39°

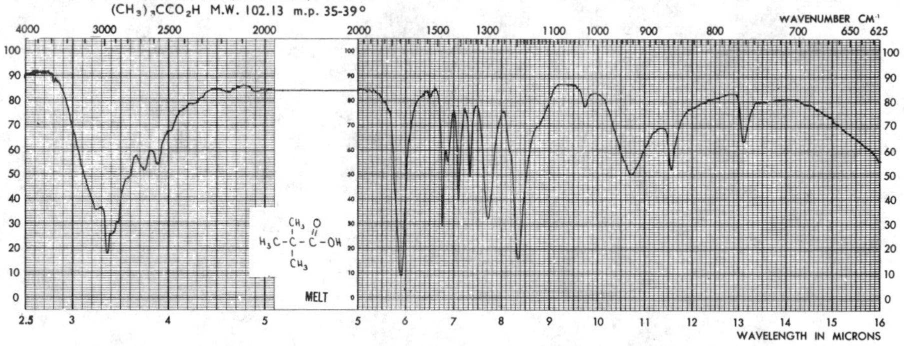

MELT

D 12,954-2 **Isovaleric acid, puriss.**
$(CH_3)_2CHCH_2CO_2H$ M.W. 102.13 n_D^{20} 1.4042
b.p. 175-177°

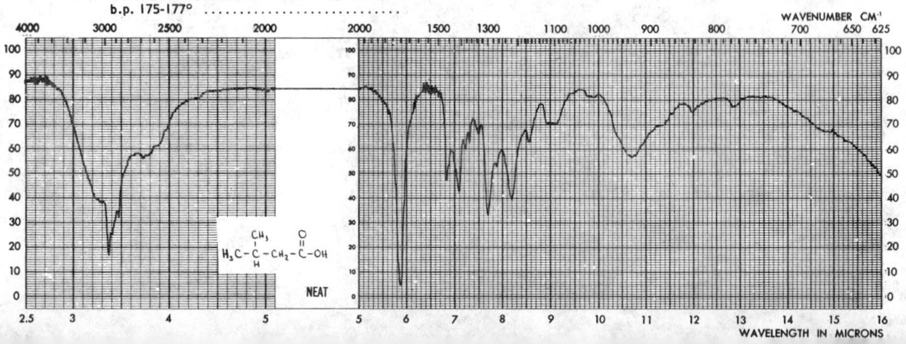

NEAT

E 19,307-0
2-Methylbutyric acid, 98%
$C_2H_5CH(CH_3)CO_2H$ FW 102.13 bp 176.5°
n_D^{20} 1.4055 d 0.936 *Beil.* **2**(4),888 Disp. I

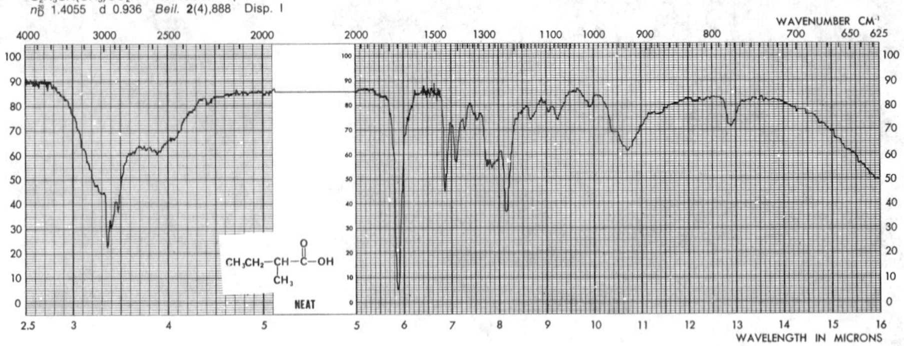

NEAT

F D15,260 **2,2-Dimethylbutyric acid**
$CH_3CH_2C(CH_3)_2CO_2H$ M.W. 116.16 n_D^{20} 1.4139

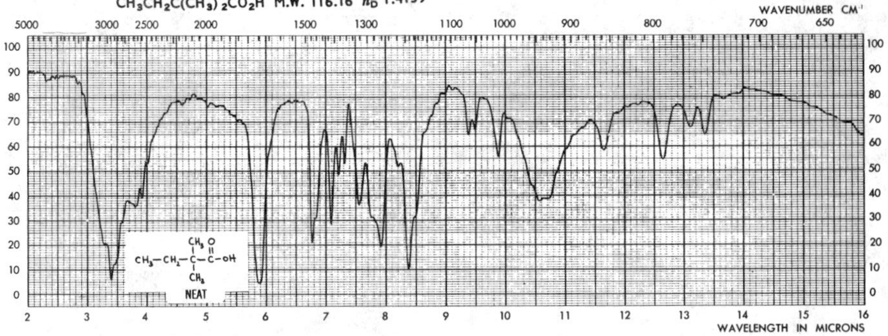

NEAT

G B8840-3 **tert.-Butylacetic acid** (3,3-dimethylbutyric acid)
$(CH_3)_3CCH_2CO_2H$ M.W. 116.16
n_D^{20} 1.4080

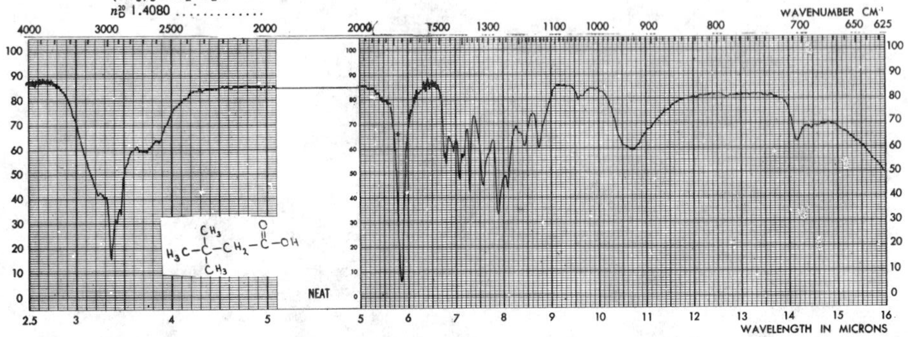

NEAT

H 10,995-9 **2-Ethylbutyric acid, puriss.**
$(C_2H_5)_2CHCO_2H$ M.W. 116.16 n_D^{20} 1.4124
b.p. 194°

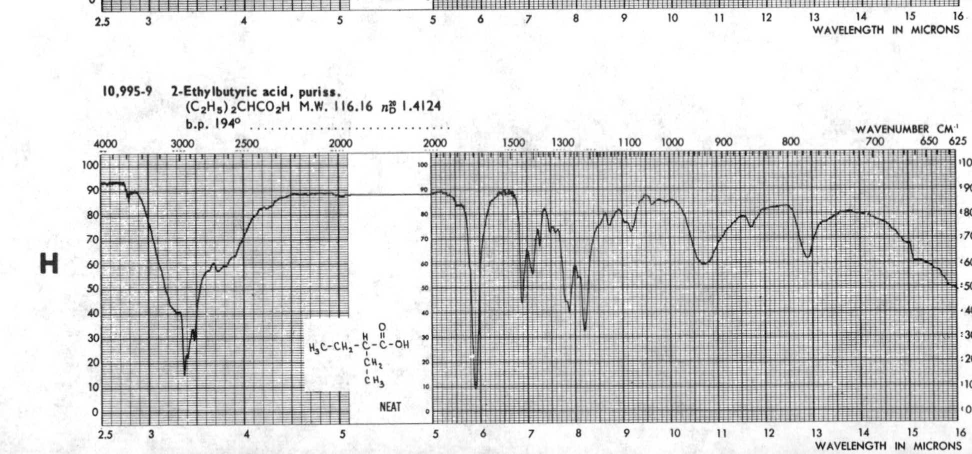

A 10,987-8 2-Methylvaleric acid
$CH_3CH_2CH_2CH(CH_3)CO_2H$ M.W. 116.16 n_D^{20} 1.4131
b.p. 186°
NEAT

B 22,245-3
3-Methylvaleric acid, 97%
$C_2H_5CH(CH_3)CH_2CO_2H$ FW 116.16 bp 196-198°
n_D^{20} 1.4159 d 0.930 *Beil.* 2,331 Disp. C
NEAT

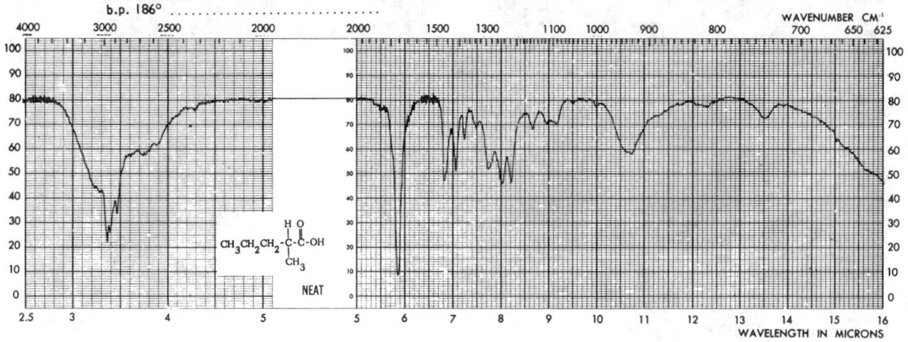

C D19,060-8 2,2-Dimethylvaleric acid
$CH_3CH_2CH_2C(CH_3)_2CO_2H$ M.W. 130.19
n_D^{20} 1.4204
NEAT

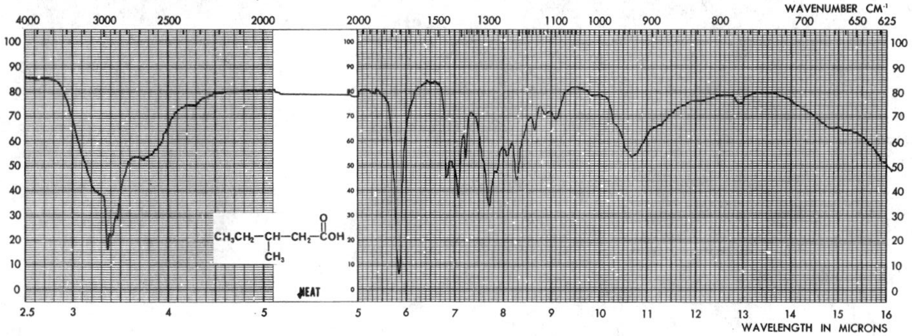

D P5470-1 2-Propylvaleric acid (di-n-propylacetic acid)
$(CH_3CH_2CH_2)_2CHCO_2H$ M.W. 144.21 n_D^{20} 1.4225
NEAT

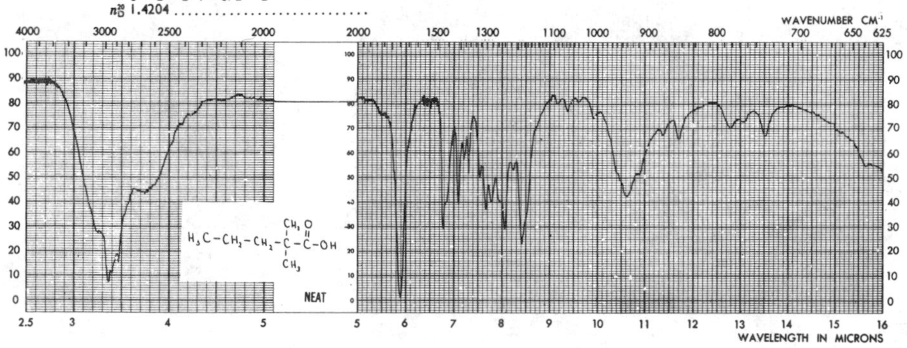

E E2914-1 2-Ethylhexanoic acid
$CH_3(CH_2)_3CH(C_2H_5)CO_2H$ M.W. 144.21
n_D^{20} 1.4241
NEAT

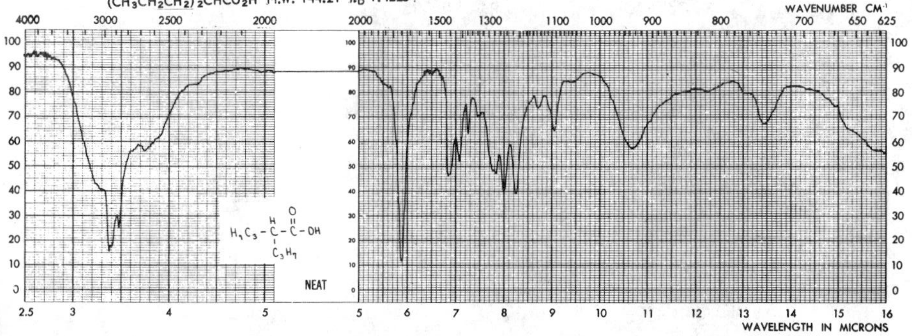

F O-875-5 Oxalic acid
NUJOL MULL

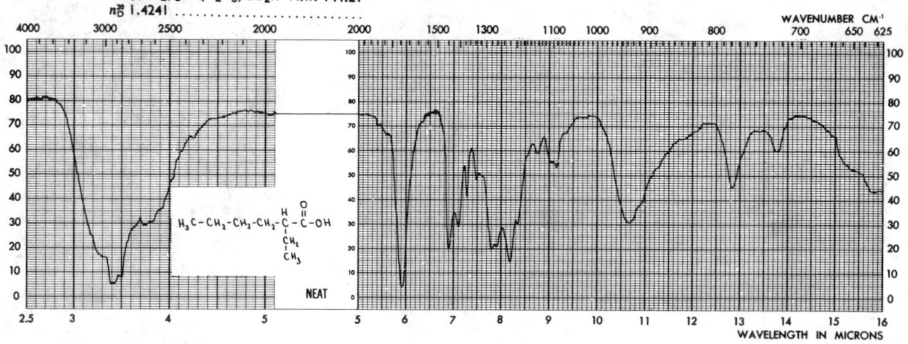

G O-875 Oxalic acid dihydrate
$HO_2CCO_2H{\cdot}2H_2O$ M.W. 126.07
m.p. 101-102°
NUJOL MULL

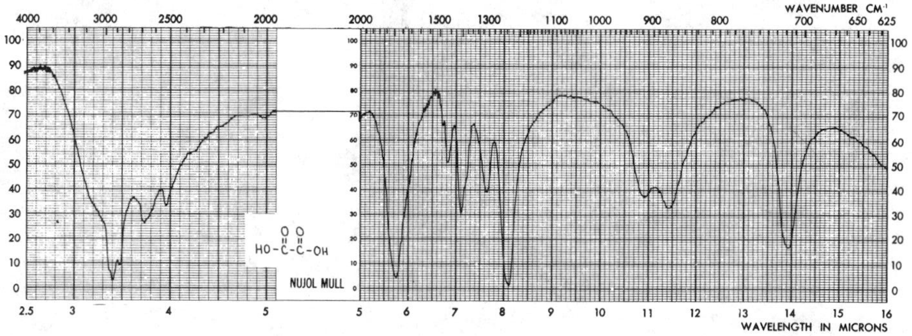

H M129-6 Malonic acid
$HO_2CCH_2CO_2H$ M.W. 104.06 m.p. 135-137°
NUJOL MULL

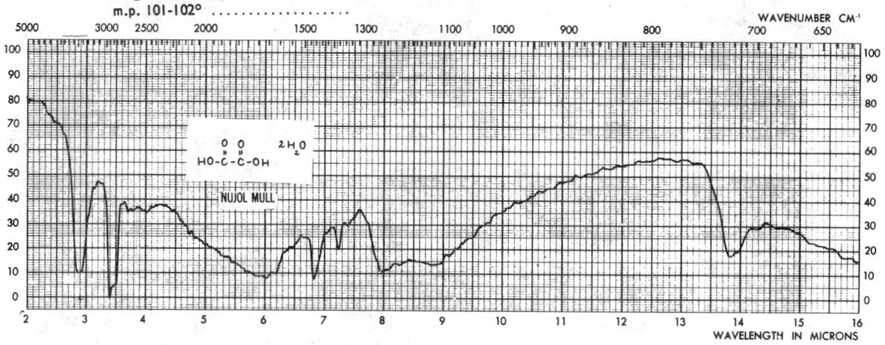

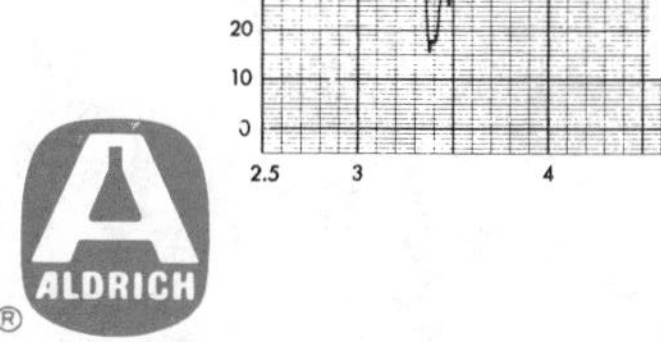

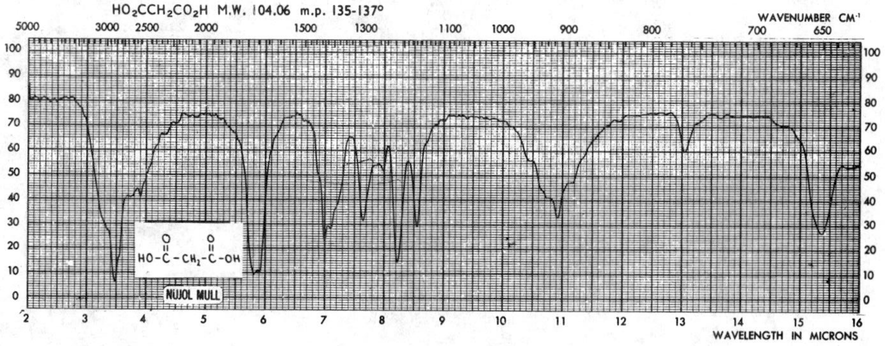

A M5405-8 Methylmalonic acid
$HO_2CCH(CH_3)CO_2H$ M.W. 118.09 m.p. 129-130°
NUJOL MULL

B D16,800-9 Dimethylmalonic acid
$HO_2CC(CH_3)_2CO_2H$ M.W. 132.12
m.p. 192° (dec.)
NUJOL MULL

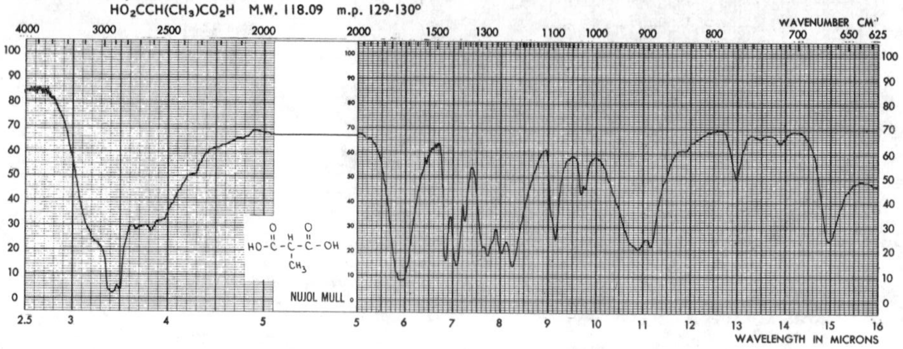

C 10,268-7 Ethylmalonic acid
$HO_2CCH(C_2H_5)CO_2H$ M.W. 132.12 m.p. 108-111.5°
NUJOL MULL

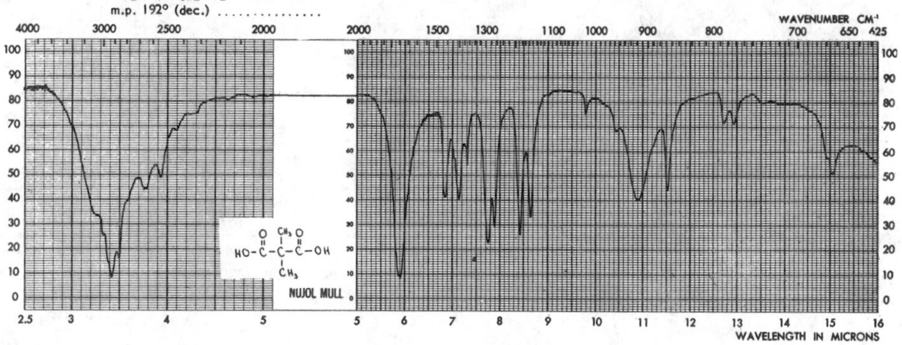

D 12,027-8 Diethylmalonic acid
$HO_2CC(C_2H_5)_2CO_2H$ M.W. 160.17 m.p. 121.5-124.5°
NUJOL MULL

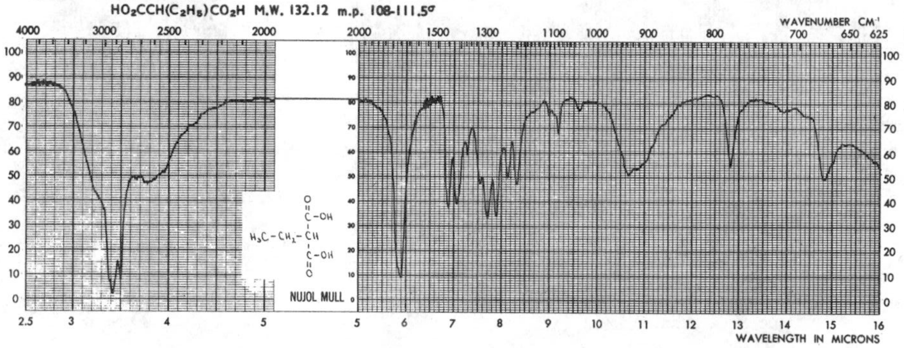

E 13,438-4 Succinic acid
$HO_2CCH_2CH_2CO_2H$ M.W. 118.09
m.p. 185-190°
NUJOL MULL

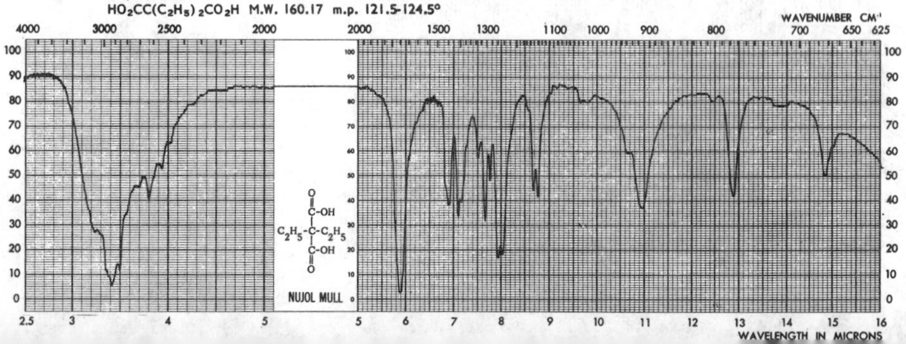

F M8120-9 Methylsuccinic acid
$HO_2CCH_2CH(CH_3)CO_2H$ M.W. 132.12
NUJOL MULL

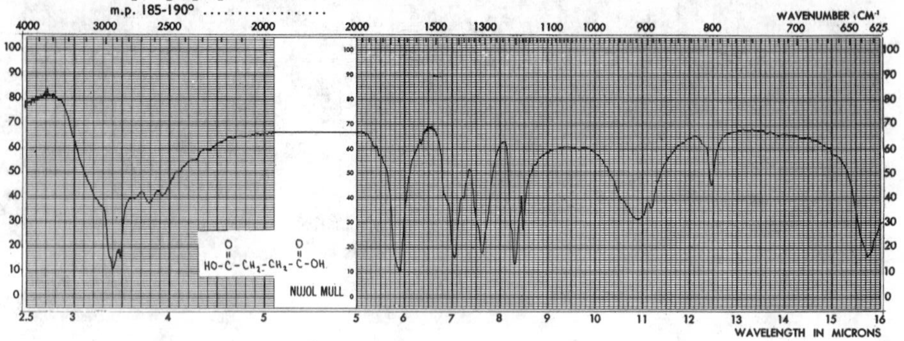

G D18,600-7 2,2-Dimethylsuccinic acid
$HO_2CCH_2C(CH_3)_2CO_2H$ M.W. 146.14
m.p. 139-142°
NUJOL MULL

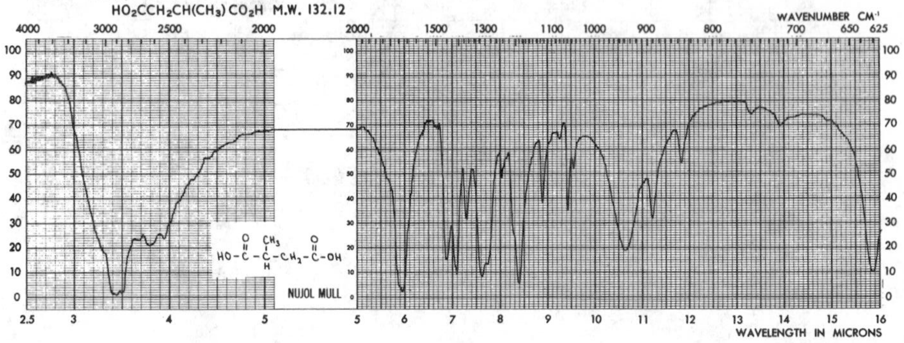

H 15,121-1 2-Ethyl-2-methylsuccinic acid
$HO_2CCH_2C(CH_3)(C_2H_5)CO_2H$ M.W. 160.17
m.p. 104-107°
NUJOL MULL

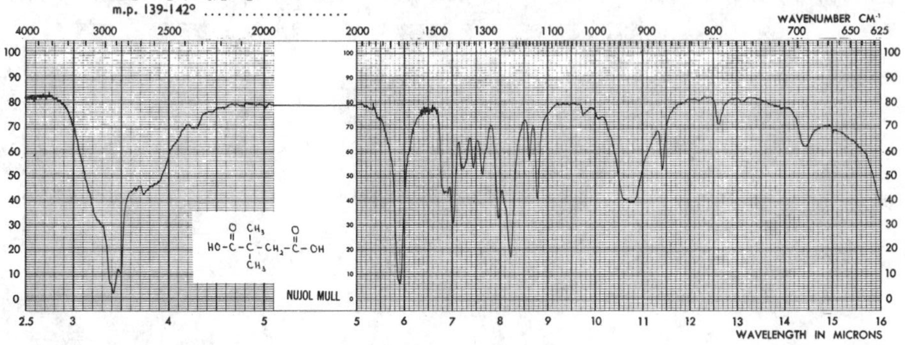

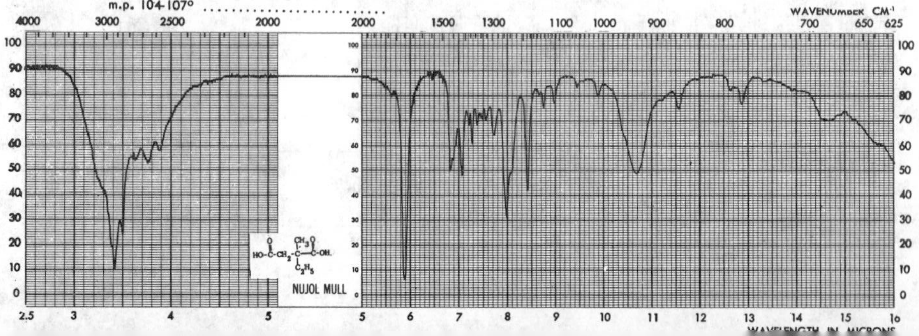

A

16,801-7
meso-2,3-Dimethylsuccinic acid
$HO_2CCH(CH_3)CH(CH_3)CO_2H$ FW 146.14
mp 200° (dec.) *Beil.* 2,665 Disp. I

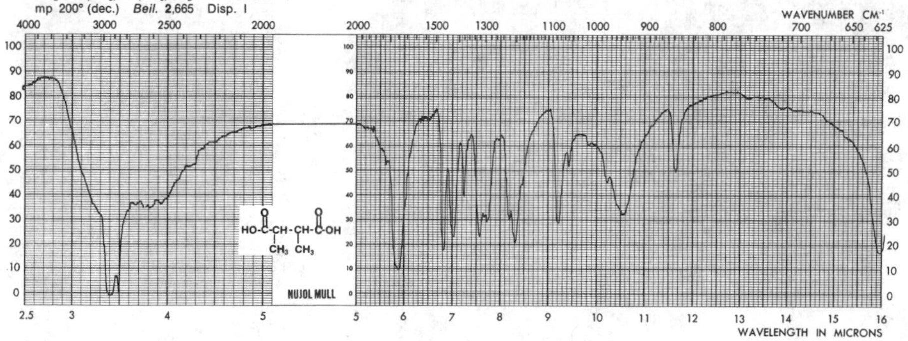

NUJOL MULL

B

D18,620-1 2,3-Dimethylsuccinic acid (mixture of DL and *meso*)
$HO_2CCH(CH_3)CH(CH_3)CO_2H$ M.W. 146.14 ....

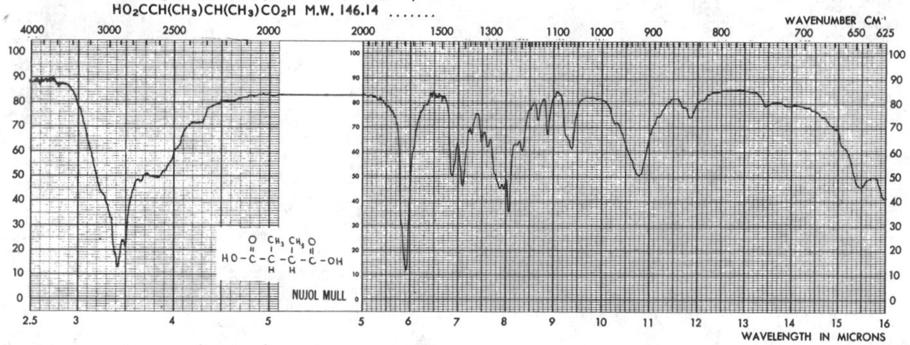

NUJOL MULL

C

G340-7 Glutaric acid
$HO_2C(CH_2)_3CO_2H$ M.W. 132.12 m.p. 95-98°

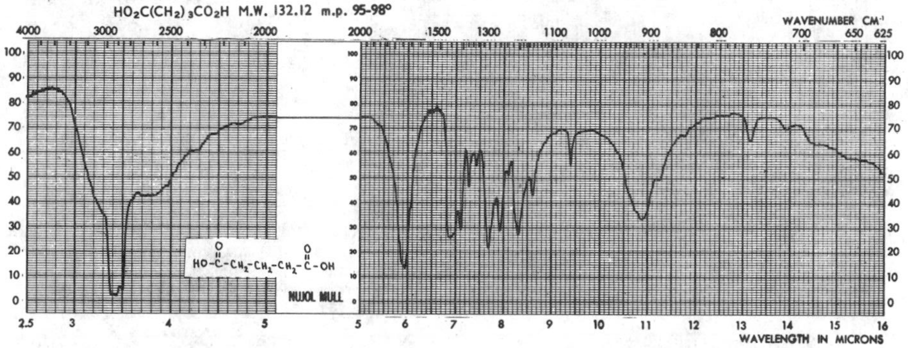

NUJOL MULL

D

12,986-0 2-Methylglutaric acid
$HO_2CCH_2CH_2CH(CH_3)CO_2H$ M.W. 146.14 m.p. 78-80°

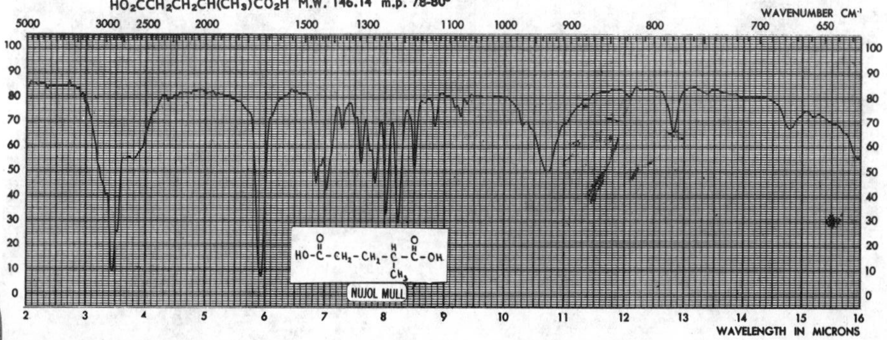

NUJOL MULL

E

20,526-5
2,2-Dimethylglutaric acid, 98+%
$HO_2CCH_2CH_2C(CH_3)_2CO_2H$ FW 160.17
mp 83-85° *Beil.* 2,676 Disp. I

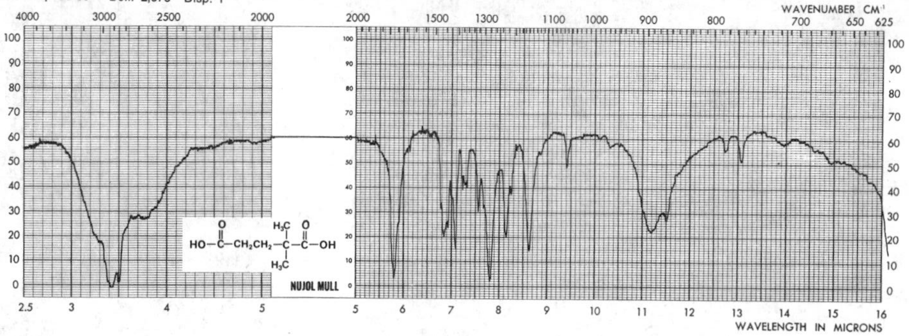

NUJOL MULL

F

M4760-4 3-Methylglutaric acid
$HO_2CCH_2CH(CH_3)CH_2CO_2H$ M.W. 146.14
m.p. 85-87° ....

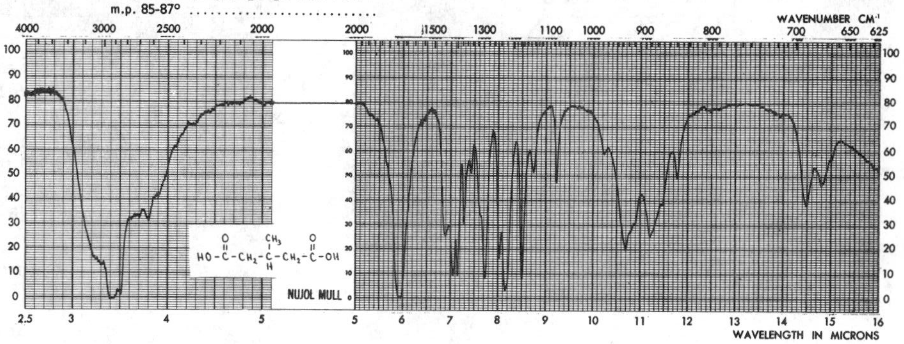

NUJOL MULL

G

D15,940-9 3,3-Dimethylglutaric acid
$HO_2CCH_2C(CH_3)_2CH_2CO_2H$ M.W. 160.17
m.p. 100-105° ....

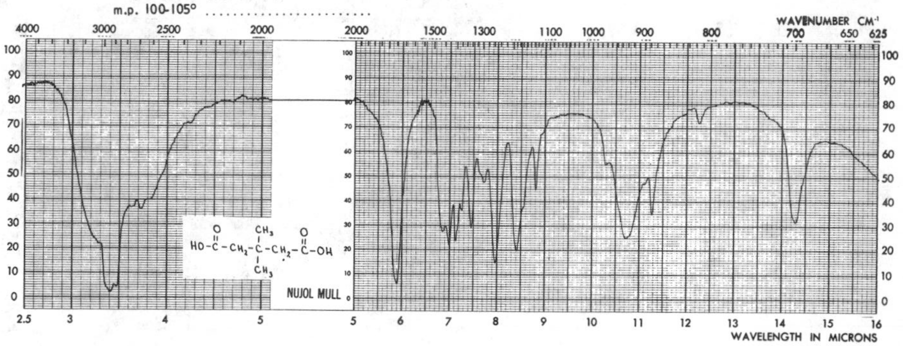

NUJOL MULL

H

A2635-7 Adipic acid (hexanedioic acid)
$HO_2C(CH_2)_4CO_2H$ M.W. 146.14
m.p. 152-153° ....

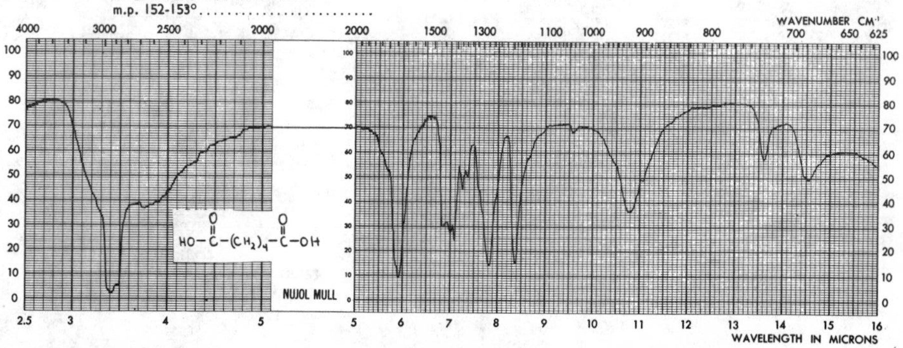

NUJOL MULL

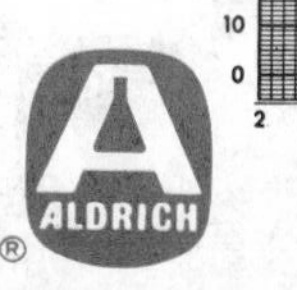

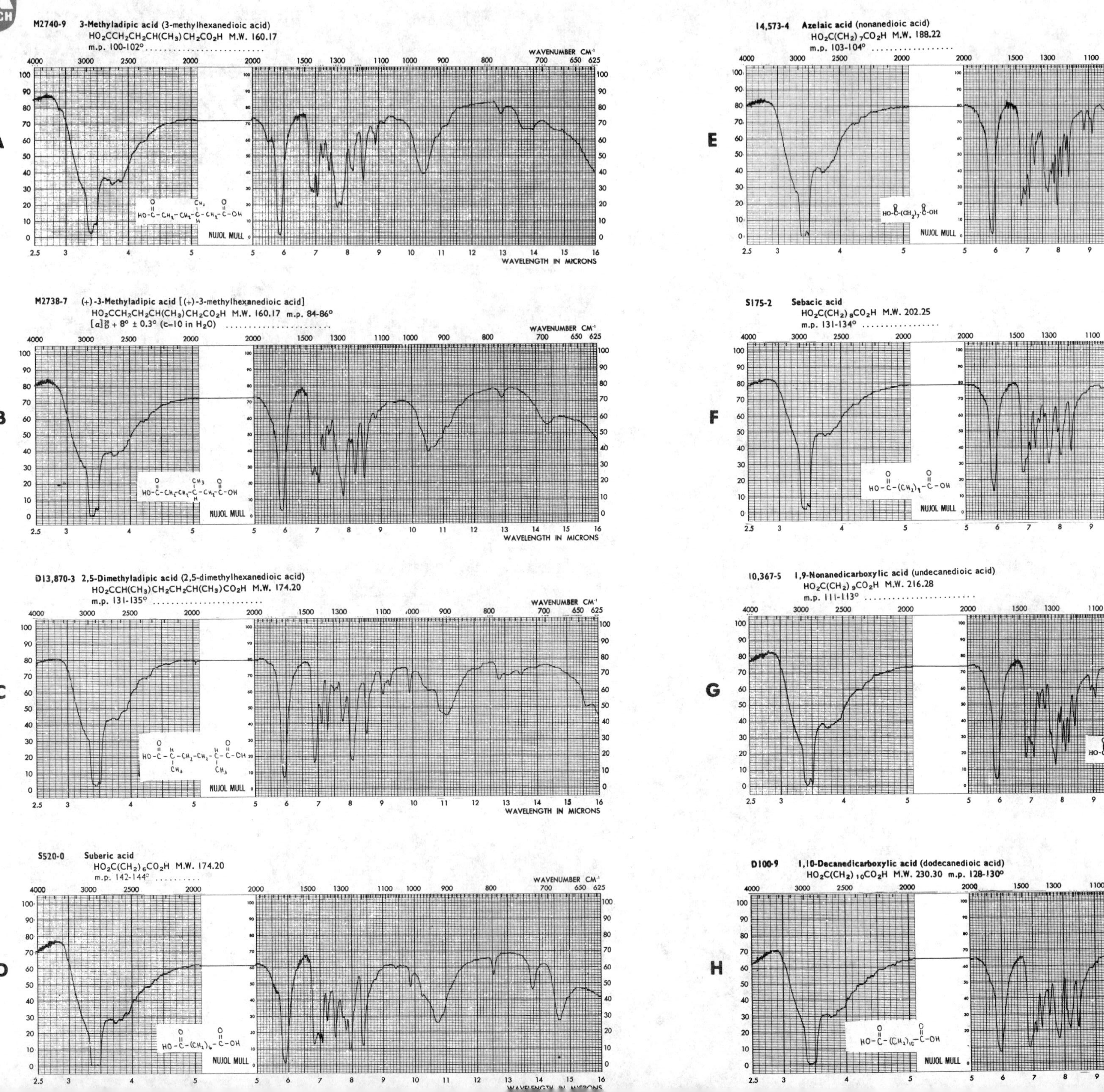
ALDRICH
A
M2740-9 3-Methyladipic acid (3-methylhexanedioic acid)
HO2CCH2CH2CH(CH3)CH2CO2H M.W. 160.17
m.p. 100-102°
NUJOL MULL
B
M2738-7 (+)-3-Methyladipic acid [(+)-3-methylhexanedioic acid]
HO2CCH2CH2CH(CH3)CH2CO2H M.W. 160.17 m.p. 84-86°
[α]D + 8° ± 0.3° (c=10 in H2O)
NUJOL MULL
C
D13,870-3 2,5-Dimethyladipic acid (2,5-dimethylhexanedioic acid)
HO2CCH(CH3)CH2CH2CH(CH3)CO2H M.W. 174.20
m.p. 131-135°
NUJOL MULL
D
S520-0 Suberic acid
HO2C(CH2)6CO2H M.W. 174.20
m.p. 142-144°
NUJOL MULL
E
14,573-4 Azelaic acid (nonanedioic acid)
HO2C(CH2)7CO2H M.W. 188.22
m.p. 103-104°
NUJOL MULL
F
S175-2 Sebacic acid
HO2C(CH2)8CO2H M.W. 202.25
m.p. 131-134°
NUJOL MULL
G
10,367-5 1,9-Nonanedicarboxylic acid (undecanedioic acid)
HO2C(CH2)9CO2H M.W. 216.28
m.p. 111-113°
NUJOL MULL
H
D100-9 1,10-Decanedicarboxylic acid (dodecanedioic acid)
HO2C(CH2)10CO2H M.W. 230.30 m.p. 128-130°
NUJOL MULL
WAVENUMBER CM-1
WAVELENGTH IN MICRONS

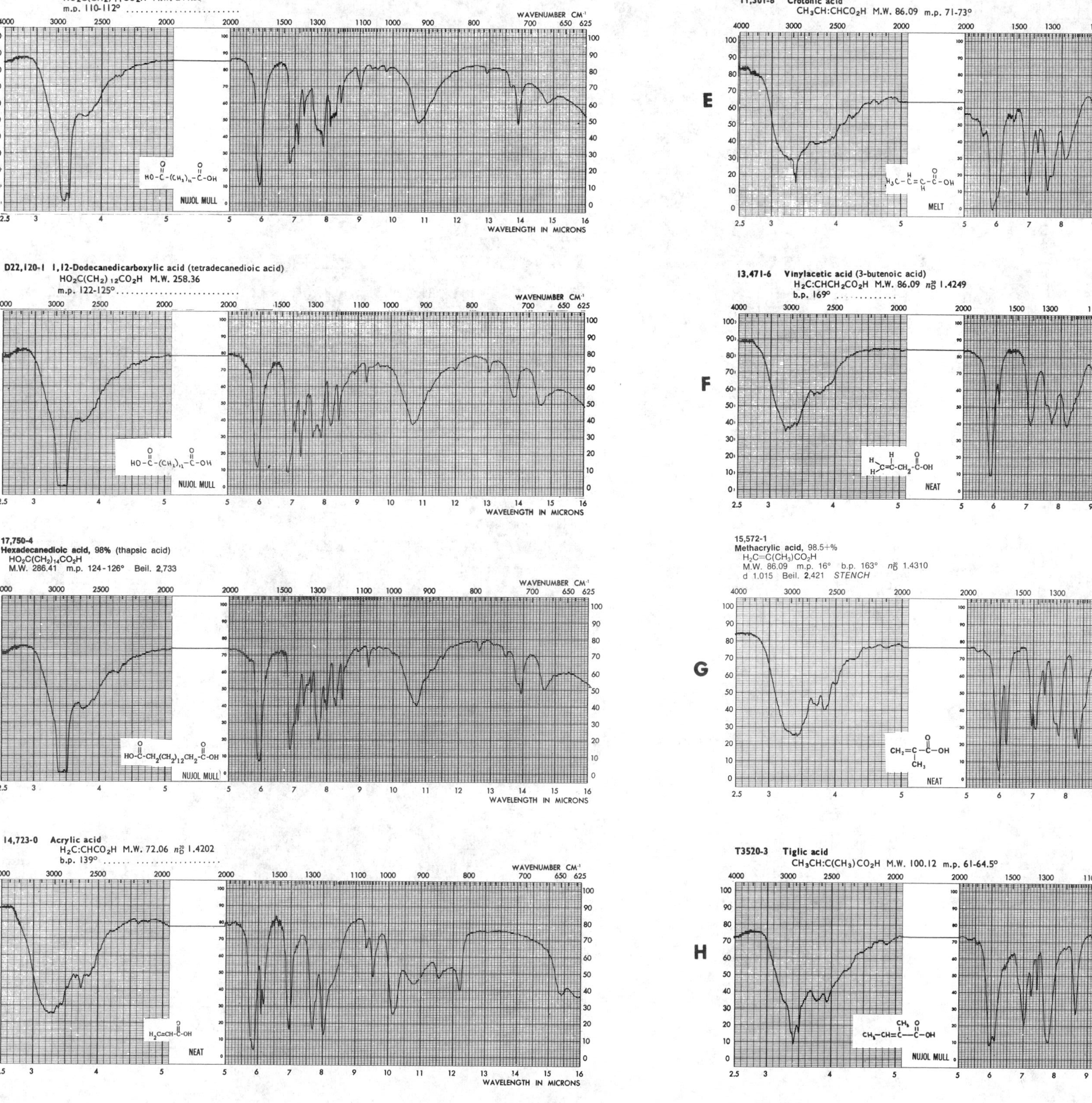

A
U60-1 1,11-Undecanedicarboxylic acid (brassylic acid, tridecanedioic acid)
HO2C(CH2)11CO2H M.W. 244.33
m.p. 110-112°
NUJOL MULL
B
D22,120-1 1,12-Dodecanedicarboxylic acid (tetradecanedioic acid)
HO2C(CH2)12CO2H M.W. 258.36
m.p. 122-125°
NUJOL MULL
C
17,750-4
Hexadecanedioic acid, 98% (thapsic acid)
HO2C(CH2)14CO2H
M.W. 286.41 m.p. 124-126° Beil. 2,733
NUJOL MULL
D
14,723-0 Acrylic acid
H2C:CHCO2H M.W. 72.06 n20D 1.4202
b.p. 139°
NEAT
E
11,301-8 Crotonic acid
CH3CH:CHCO2H M.W. 86.09 m.p. 71-73°
MELT
F
13,471-6 Vinylacetic acid (3-butenoic acid)
H2C:CHCH2CO2H M.W. 86.09 n20D 1.4249
b.p. 169°
NEAT
G
15,572-1
Methacrylic acid, 98.5+%
H2C=C(CH3)CO2H
M.W. 86.09 m.p. 16° b.p. 163° n20D 1.4310
d 1.015 Beil. 2,421 STENCH
NEAT
H
T3520-3 Tiglic acid
CH3CH:C(CH3)CO2H M.W. 100.12 m.p. 61-64.5°
NUJOL MULL
WAVENUMBER CM-1
WAVELENGTH IN MICRONS
ALDRICH

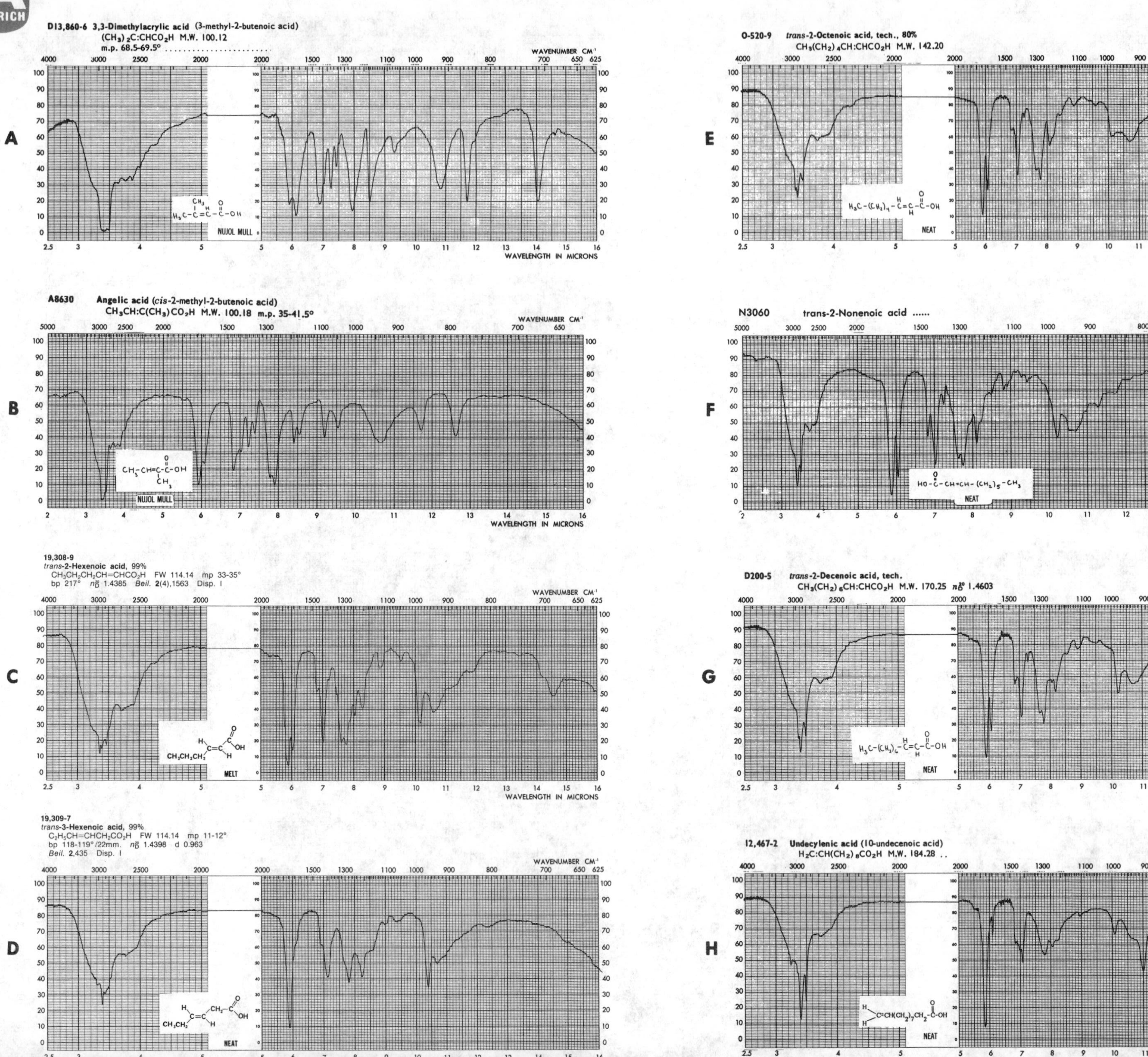
ALDRICH
A
D13,860-6 3,3-Dimethylacrylic acid (3-methyl-2-butenoic acid)
$(CH_3)_2C{:}CHCO_2H$ M.W. 100.12
m.p. 68.5-69.5°
NUJOL MULL
B
A8630 Angelic acid (*cis*-2-methyl-2-butenoic acid)
$CH_3CH{:}C(CH_3)CO_2H$ M.W. 100.18 m.p. 35-41.5°
NUJOL MULL
C
19,308-9
trans-2-Hexenoic acid, 99%
$CH_3CH_2CH_2CH{=}CHCO_2H$ FW 114.14 mp 33-35°
bp 217° n_D^{20} 1.4385 *Beil.* 2(4),1563 Disp. I
MELT
D
19,309-7
trans-3-Hexenoic acid, 99%
$C_2H_5CH{=}CHCH_2CO_2H$ FW 114.14 mp 11-12°
bp 118-119°/22mm. n_D^{20} 1.4398 d 0.963
Beil. 2,435 Disp. I
NEAT
E
O-520-9 *trans*-2-Octenoic acid, tech., 80%
$CH_3(CH_2)_4CH{:}CHCO_2H$ M.W. 142.20
NEAT
F
N3060 trans-2-Nonenoic acid
NEAT
G
D200-5 *trans*-2-Decenoic acid, tech.
$CH_3(CH_2)_6CH{:}CHCO_2H$ M.W. 170.25 n_D^{20} 1.4603
NEAT
H
12,467-2 Undecylenic acid (10-undecenoic acid)
$H_2C{:}CH(CH_2)_8CO_2H$ M.W. 184.28
NEAT
WAVENUMBER CM⁻¹
WAVELENGTH IN MICRONS

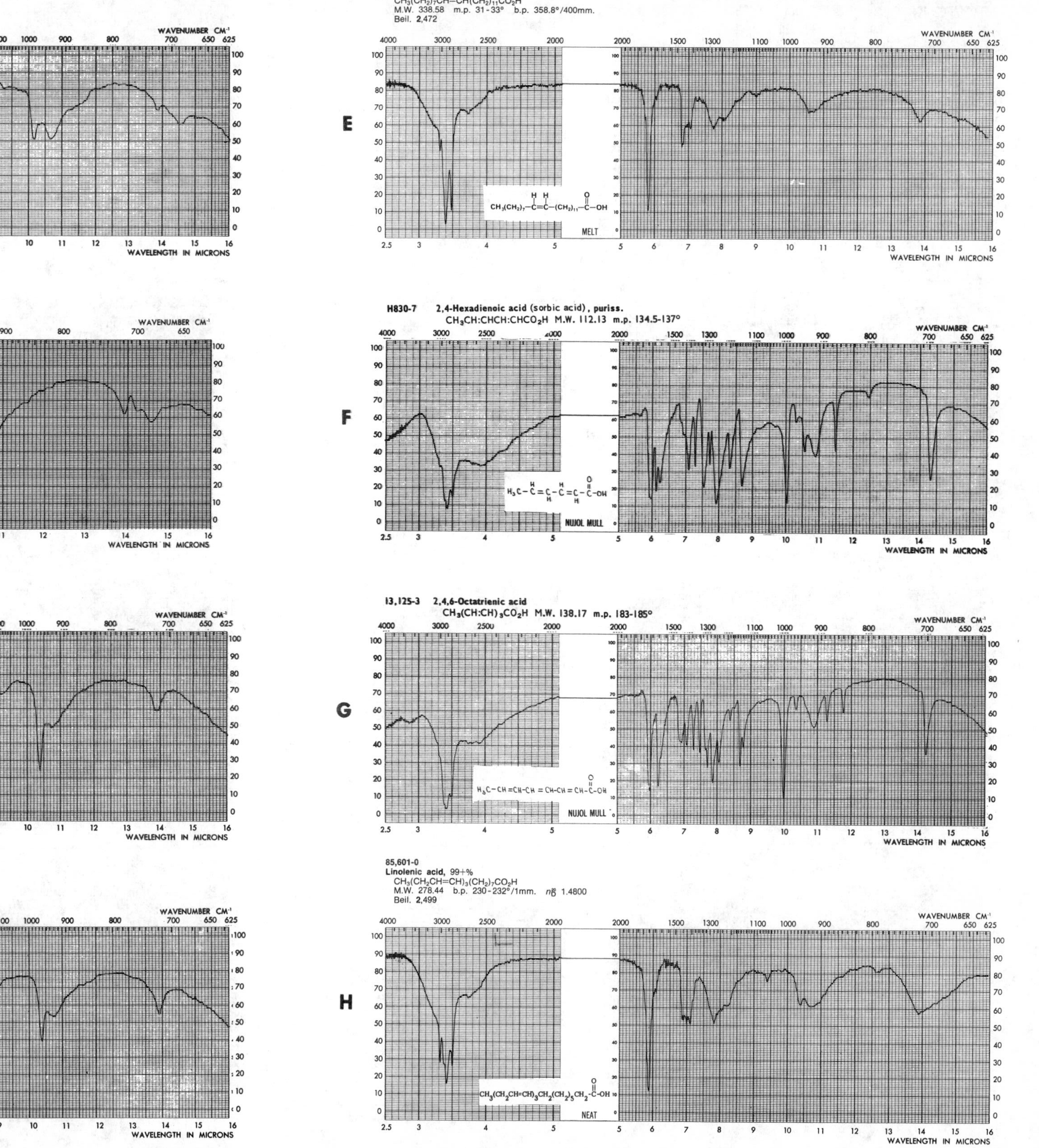
A
D22,180-5 2-Dodecenoic acid, tech.
$CH_3(CH_2)_8CH{:}CHCO_2H$ M.W. 198.31
n_D^{20} 1.4623
NEAT
B
T5780 trans-2-Tridecenoic acid
NEAT
C
E30-4 Elaidic acid, puriss.
$CH_3(CH_2)_7CH{:}CH(CH_2)_7CO_2H$ M.W. 282.47
m.p. 43-45°
MELT
D
B5560-2 Brassidic acid (13-docosenoic acid), tech.
$CH_3(CH_2)_7CH{:}CH(CH_2)_{11}CO_2H$ M.W. 338.58 m.p. 51-52°
MELT
E
85,843-9
Erucic acid, 99% (cis-13-docosenoic acid)
$CH_3(CH_2)_7CH{=}CH(CH_2)_{11}CO_2H$
M.W. 338.58 m.p. 31-33° b.p. 358.8°/400mm.
Beil. 2,472
MELT
F
H830-7 2,4-Hexadienoic acid (sorbic acid), puriss.
$CH_3CH{:}CHCH{:}CHCO_2H$ M.W. 112.13 m.p. 134.5-137°
NUJOL MULL
G
13,125-3 2,4,6-Octatrienic acid
$CH_3(CH{:}CH)_3CO_2H$ M.W. 138.17 m.p. 183-185°
NUJOL MULL
H
85,601-0
Linolenic acid, 99+%
$CH_3(CH_2CH{=}CH)_3(CH_2)_7CO_2H$
M.W. 278.44 b.p. 230-232°/1mm. n_D^{20} 1.4800
Beil. 2,499
NEAT
WAVENUMBER CM⁻¹
WAVELENGTH IN MICRONS
ALDRICH

NON-AROMATIC CARBOXYLIC ACIDS

A3355-8 **(Allyl)-methallylacetic acid** (2-allyl-4-methyl-4-pentenoic acid)
$H_2C:C(CH_3)CH_2CH(CH_2CH:CH_2)CO_2H$
M.W. 154.21 n_D^{20} 1.4541

F1935-3 **Fumaric acid**
$HO_2CCH:CHCO_2H$ M.W. 116.07
m.p. 299-300°

M15-3 **Maleic acid**
$HO_2CCH:CHCO_2H$ M.W. 116.07
m.p. 130-131°

13,104-0 **Mesaconic acid**
$HO_2CCH:C(CH_3)CO_2H$ M.W. 130.10
m.p. 200-202°

C8260-4 **Citraconic acid**
$CH_3C(CO_2H):CHCO_2H$ M.W. 130.10
m.p. 90-92°

G260-5 **Glutaconic acid**
$HO_2CCH_2CH:CHCO_2H$ M.W. 130.10 m.p. 127-132°

17,724-5
Traumatic acid, 97% (2-dodecenedioic acid)
$HO_2C(CH_2)_8CH=CHCO_2H$
M.W. 228.29 m.p. 165-167°

I-2920-4 **Itaconic acid** (methylenesuccinic acid), **puriss.**
$HO_2CCH_2C(:CH_2)CO_2H$ M.W. 130.10
m.p. 162.5-164.5°

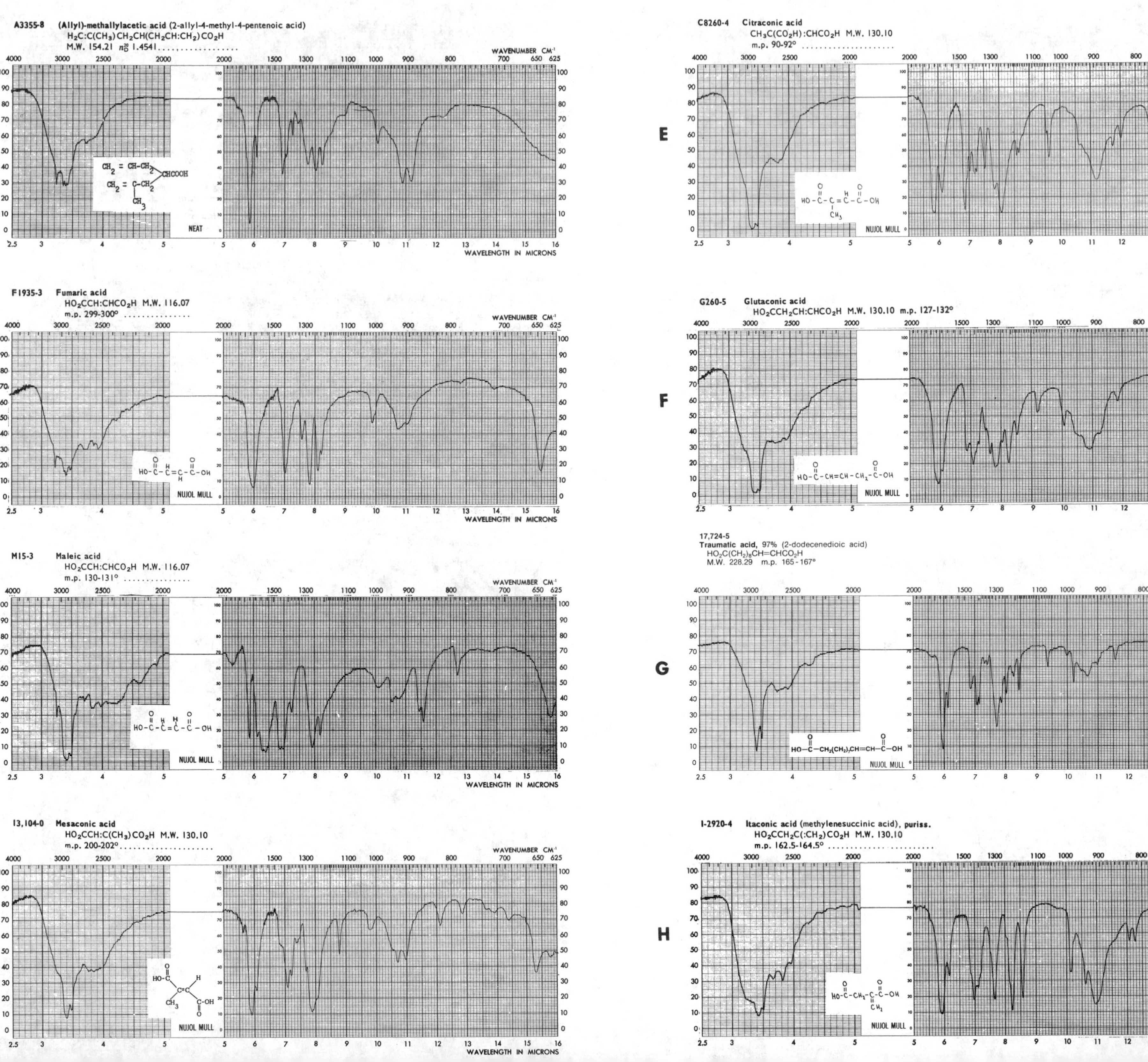

A 0-88-1 1-Octadecenylsuccinic acid
$HO_2CCH[CH:CH(CH_2)_{15}CH_3]CH_2CO_2H$ M.W. 368.56
m.p. 77-78.5°

B H1785-6 *trans*-β-Hydromuconic acid (*trans*-3-hexenedioic acid, *trans*-Δβ-dihydromuconic acid)
$HO_2CCH_2CH:CHCH_2CO_2H$ M.W. 144.12
m.p. 195-196°

C M9000-3 *trans, trans*-Muconic acid (*trans, trans*-1,3-butadiene-1,4-dicarboxylic acid)
$HO_2CCH:CHCH:CHCO_2H$ M.W. 142.11 m.p. 289-290° (dec.)

D 14,334-0 *cis,cis*-α,α'-Dimethylmuconic acid (*cis,cis*-2,5-dimethyl-2,4-hexadienedioic acid)
$HO_2CC(CH_3):CHCH:C(CH_3)CO_2H$ M.W. 170.17
m.p. 220-222.5°

E 22,301-8 *trans*-Retinoic acid
FW 300.45 mp 180-181° *Beil.* 9(3),3118
Disp. C

F T5350-3 Tricarballylic acid (1,2,3-propanetricarboxylic acid)
$HO_2CCH_2CH(CO_2H)CH_2CO_2H$ M.W. 176.12 m.p. 158-160°

G M8520-4 β-Methyltricarballylic acid
$HO_2CCH_2C(CH_3)(CO_2H)CH_2CO_2H$ M.W. 190.15
m.p. 160-162° (dec.)

H 13,859-2 1,3,5-Pentanetricarboxylic acid
$HO_2CCH_2CH_2CH(CO_2H)CH_2CH_2CO_2H$ M.W. 204.18
m.p. 111-115°

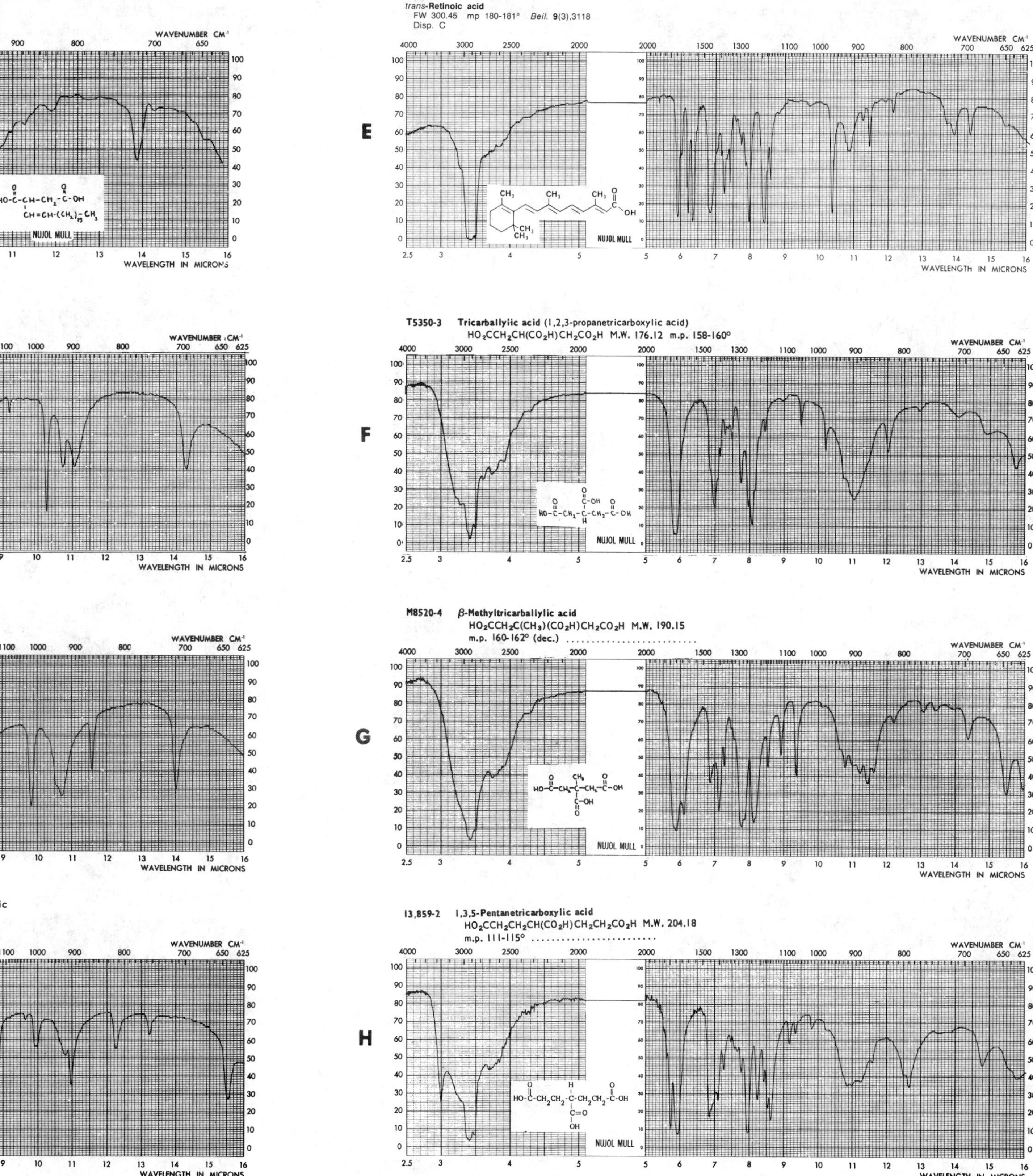

ALDRICH

NON-AROMATIC CARBOXYLIC ACIDS

ALDRICH

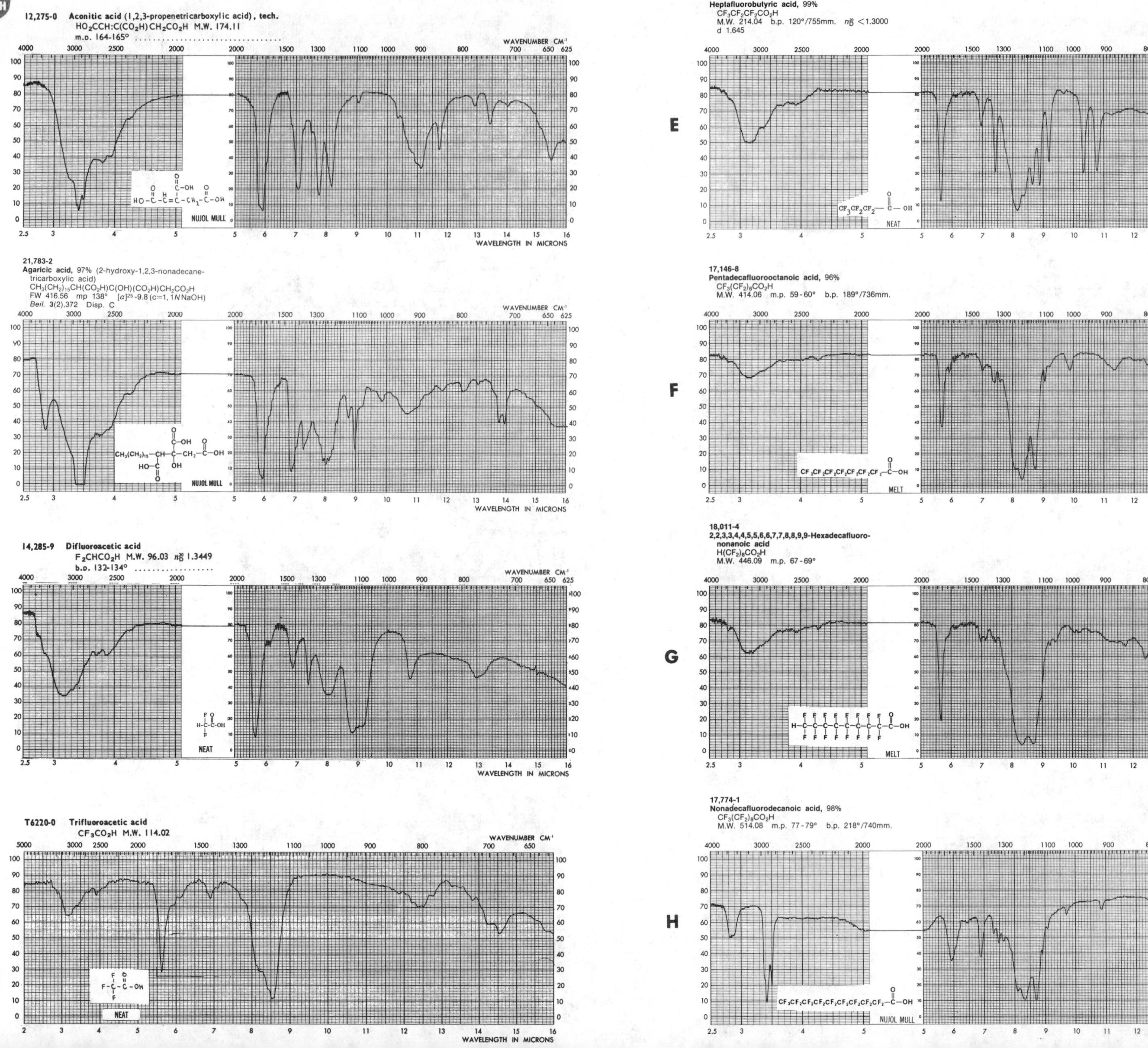
A
12,275-0 Aconitic acid (1,2,3-propenetricarboxylic acid), tech.
$HO_2CCH{:}C(CO_2H)CH_2CO_2H$ M.W. 174.11
m.p. 164-165°
NUJOL MULL
B
21,783-2
Agaricic acid, 97% (2-hydroxy-1,2,3-nonadecanetricarboxylic acid)
$CH_3(CH_2)_{15}CH(CO_2H)C(OH)(CO_2H)CH_2CO_2H$
FW 416.56 mp 138° $[\alpha]^{25}$ -9.8 (c=1, 1N NaOH)
Beil. 3(2),372 Disp. C
NUJOL MULL
C
14,285-9 Difluoroacetic acid
F_2CHCO_2H M.W. 96.03 n_D^{20} 1.3449
b.p. 132-134°
NEAT
D
T6220-0 Trifluoroacetic acid
CF_3CO_2H M.W. 114.02
NEAT
E
16,419-4
Heptafluorobutyric acid, 99%
$CF_3CF_2CF_2CO_2H$
M.W. 214.04 b.p. 120°/755mm. n_D^{20} <1.3000
d 1.645
NEAT
F
17,146-8
Pentadecafluorooctanoic acid, 96%
$CF_3(CF_2)_6CO_2H$
M.W. 414.06 m.p. 59-60° b.p. 189°/736mm.
MELT
G
18,011-4
2,2,3,3,4,4,5,5,6,6,7,7,8,8,9,9-Hexadecafluorononanoic acid
$H(CF_2)_8CO_2H$
M.W. 446.09 m.p. 67-69°
MELT
H
17,774-1
Nonadecafluorodecanoic acid, 98%
$CF_3(CF_2)_8CO_2H$
M.W. 514.08 m.p. 77-79° b.p. 218°/740mm.
NUJOL MULL
WAVENUMBER CM⁻¹
WAVELENGTH IN MICRONS

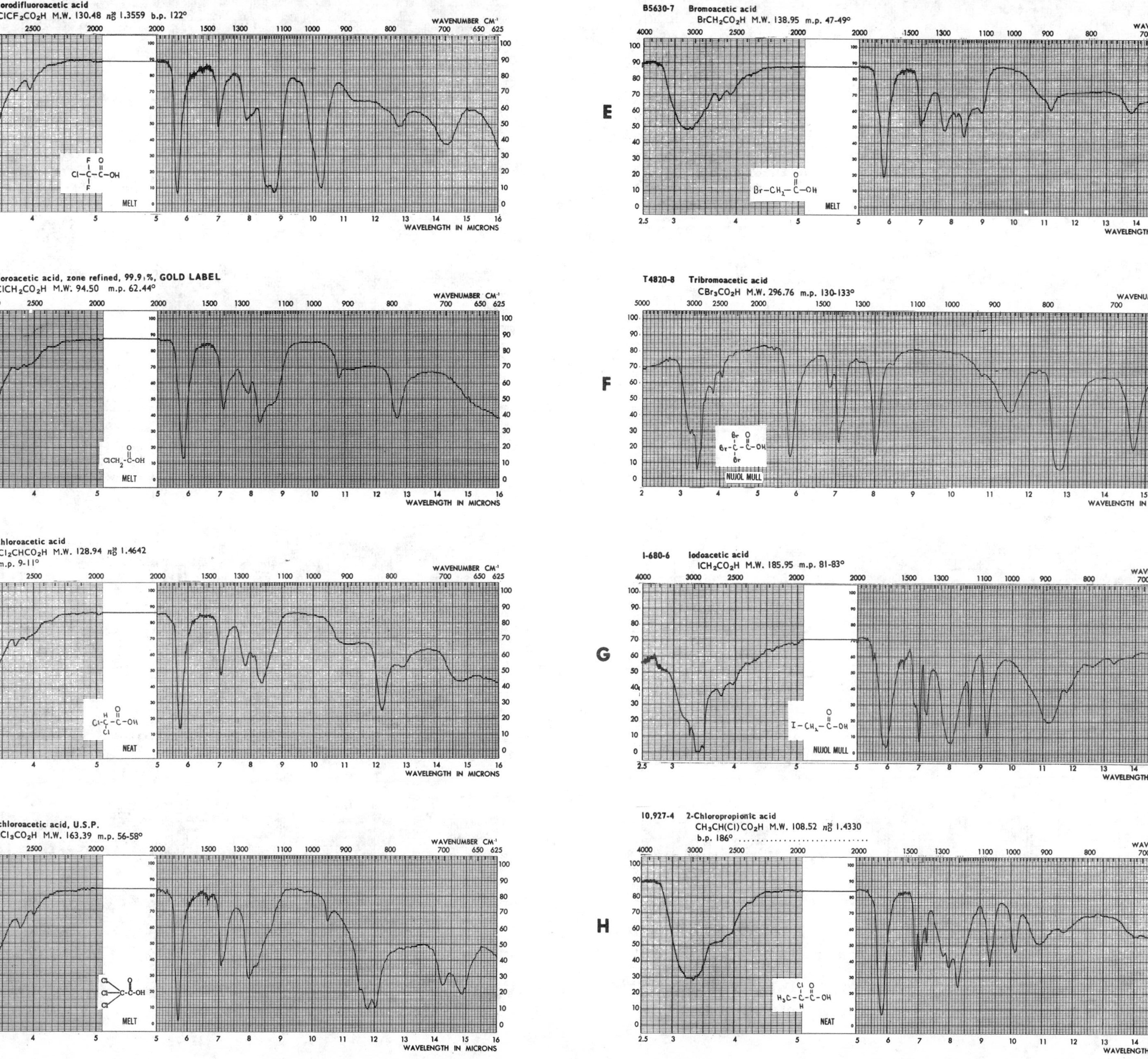
A
C3420-0 Chlorodifluoroacetic acid
$ClCF_2CO_2H$ M.W. 130.48 n_D^{20} 1.3559 b.p. 122°
MELT
B
15.093-2 Chloroacetic acid, zone refined, 99.9+%, GOLD LABEL
$ClCH_2CO_2H$ M.W. 94.50 m.p. 62.44°
MELT
C
D5470-2 Dichloroacetic acid
Cl_2CHCO_2H M.W. 128.94 n_D^{20} 1.4642
m.p. 9-11°
NEAT
D
11,611-4 Trichloroacetic acid, U.S.P.
CCl_3CO_2H M.W. 163.39 m.p. 56-58°
MELT
E
B5630-7 Bromoacetic acid
$BrCH_2CO_2H$ M.W. 138.95 m.p. 47-49°
MELT
F
T4820-8 Tribromoacetic acid
CBr_3CO_2H M.W. 296.76 m.p. 130-133°
NUJOL MULL
G
I-680-6 Iodoacetic acid
ICH_2CO_2H M.W. 185.95 m.p. 81-83°
NUJOL MULL
H
10,927-4 2-Chloropropionic acid
$CH_3CH(Cl)CO_2H$ M.W. 108.52 n_D^{20} 1.4330
b.p. 186°
NEAT
WAVENUMBER CM⁻¹
WAVELENGTH IN MICRONS
ALDRICH

A

13,269-1 **3-Chloropropionic acid**
$ClCH_2CH_2CO_2H$ M.W. 108.52
m.p. 38-41°

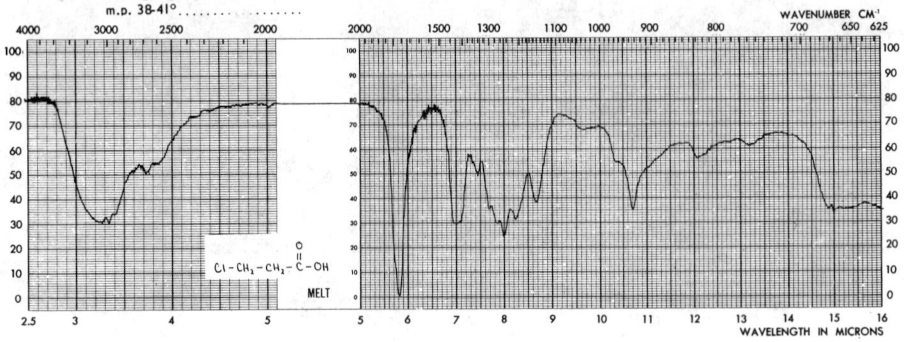

Cl-CH₂-CH₂-C(=O)-OH — MELT

B

B7830-0 **2-Bromopropionic acid, tech.**
$CH_3CH(Br)CO_2H$ M.W. 152.98 n_D^{20} 1.4725

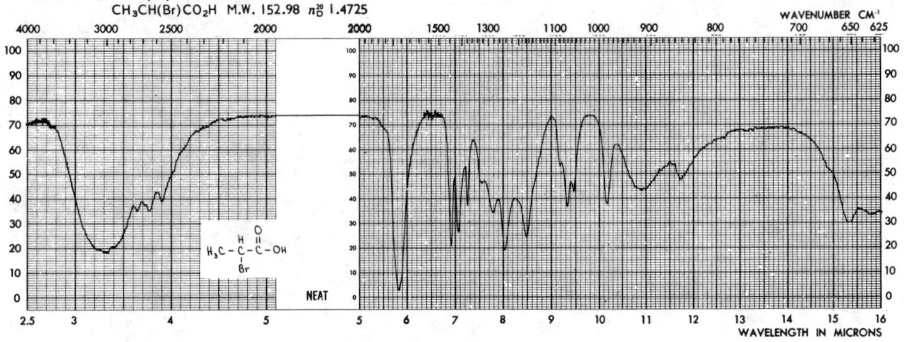

$H_3C-CH(Br)-C(=O)-OH$ — NEAT

C

10,128-1 **3-Bromopropionic acid**
$BrCH_2CH_2CO_2H$ M.W. 152.98
m.p. 59-60°

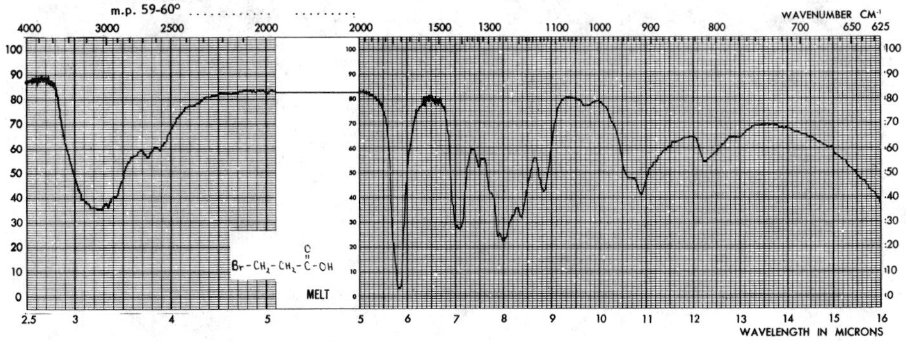

Br-CH₂-CH₂-C(=O)-OH — MELT

D

I-1045-7 **3-Iodopropionic acid, puriss.**
$ICH_2CH_2CO_2H$ M.W. 199.98 m.p. 78°

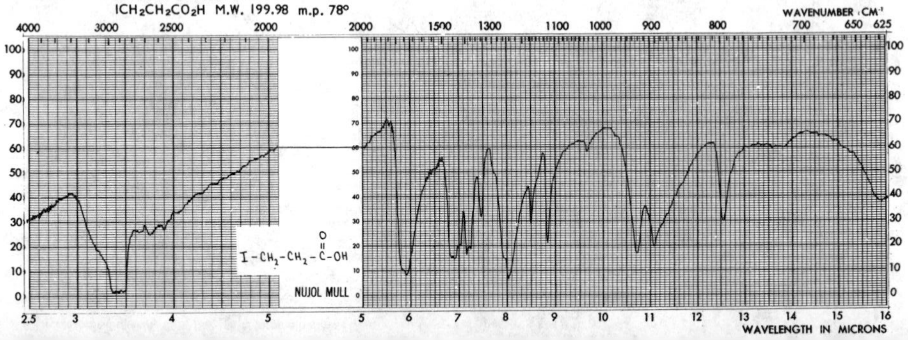

I-CH₂-CH₂-C(=O)-OH — NUJOL MULL

E

D7280-8 **2,3-Dichloropropionic acid, tech.**
$ClCH_2CH(Cl)CO_2H$ M.W. 142.97 n_D^{20} 1.4650

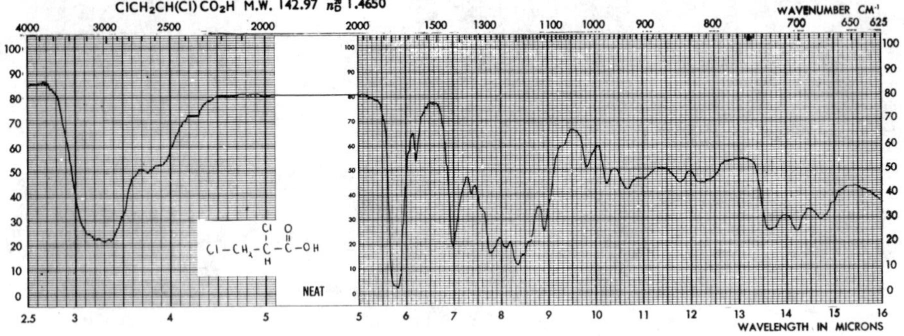

Cl-CH₂-CH(Cl)-C(=O)-OH — NEAT

F

13,994-7 **2,3-Dibromopropionic acid**
$BrCH_2CH(Br)CO_2H$ M.W. 231.88
m.p. 64-66°

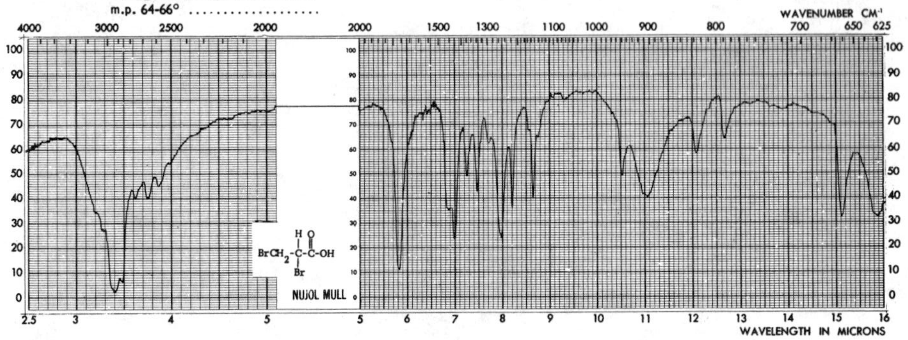

$BrCH_2-CH(Br)-C(=O)-OH$ — NUJOL MULL

G

C6853-9 **β-Chloropivalic acid** (3-chloro-2,2-dimethylpropionic acid)
$ClCH_2C(CH_3)_2CO_2H$ M.W. 136.58 m.p. 36-42°

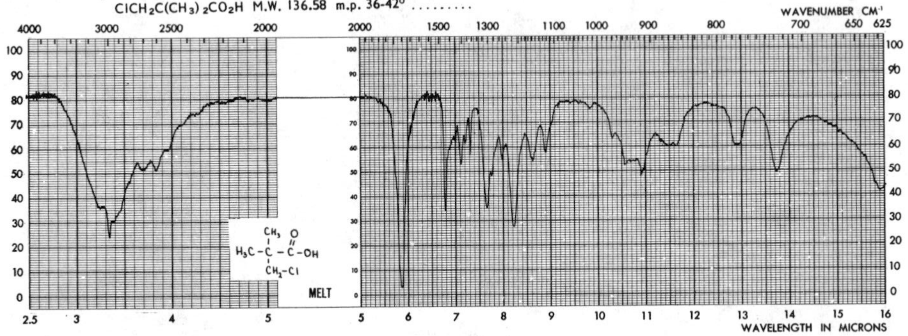

$H_3C-C(CH_3)(CH_2-Cl)-C(=O)-OH$ — MELT

H

18,513-2
β,β-Dichloropivalic acid, 99% (3,3-dichloro-2,2-dimethylpropionic acid)
$Cl_2CHC(CH_3)_2CO_2H$
M.W. 171.02 m.p. 74-76°

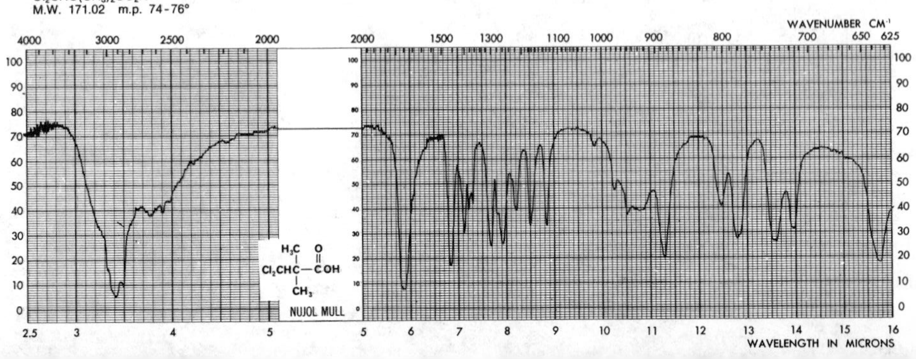

$Cl_2CHC(CH_3)_2-C(=O)OH$ — NUJOL MULL

WAVENUMBER CM⁻¹ — WAVELENGTH IN MICRONS

A [illegible]
β,β'-Dichloropivalic acid, 99% [2,2-bis(chloromethyl)-propionic acid]
$CH_3C(CH_2Cl)_2CO_2H$
M.W. 171.02 m.p. 64-66°
MELT

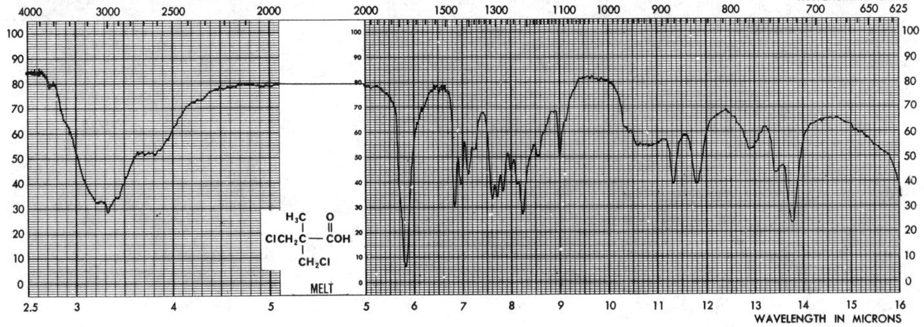

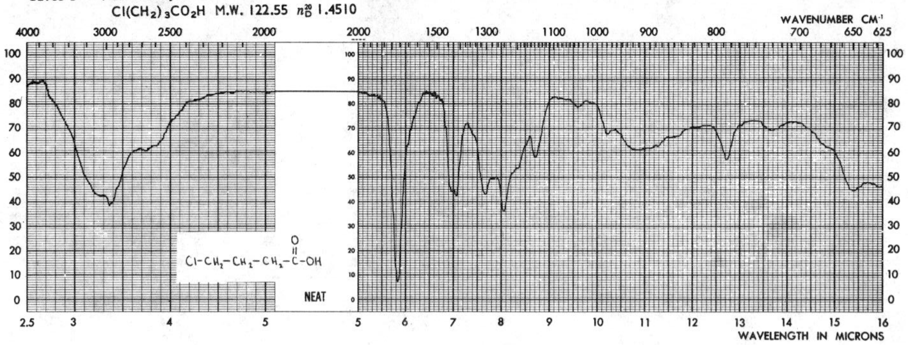

B T8555-3 **Tris-(chloromethyl)-acetic acid**
$(ClCH_2)_3CCO_2H$ M.W. 205.48 m.p. 108-110°
NUJOL MULL

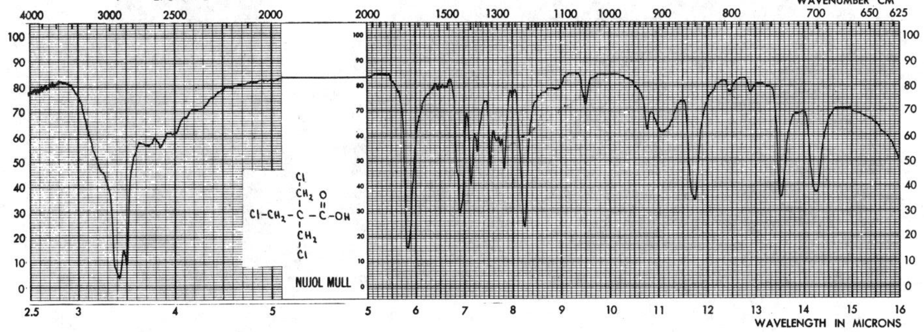

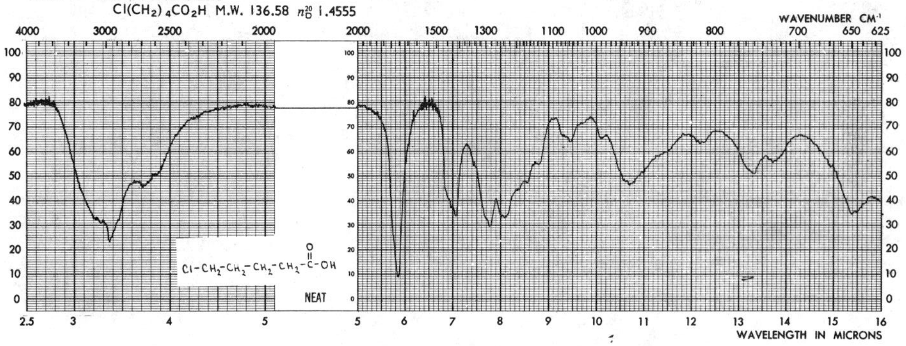

C 14,787-7 **2-Bromobutyric acid**
$C_2H_5CH(Br)CO_2H$ M.W. 167.02 n_D^{20} 1.4720
b.p. 99-103°/10 mm.
NEAT

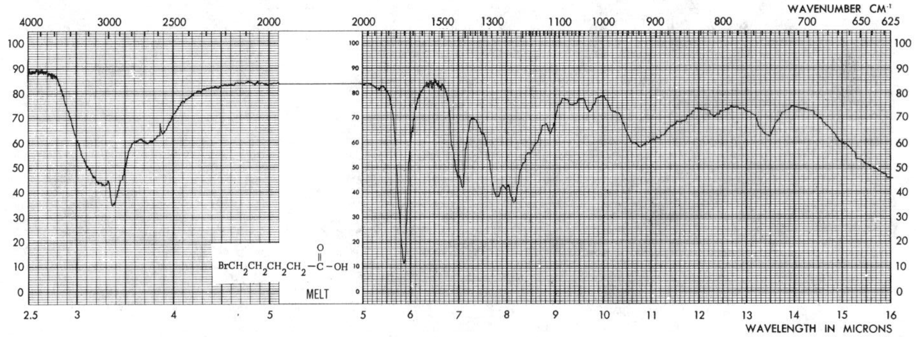

D C2980-0 **3-Chlorobutyric acid**
$CH_3CH(Cl)CH_2CO_2H$ M.W. 122.55
n_D^{20} 1.4408
NEAT

E C2983-5 **4-Chlorobutyric acid**
$Cl(CH_2)_3CO_2H$ M.W. 122.55 n_D^{20} 1.4510
NEAT

F C7290-0 **5-Chlorovaleric acid**
$Cl(CH_2)_4CO_2H$ M.W. 136.58 n_D^{20} 1.4555
NEAT

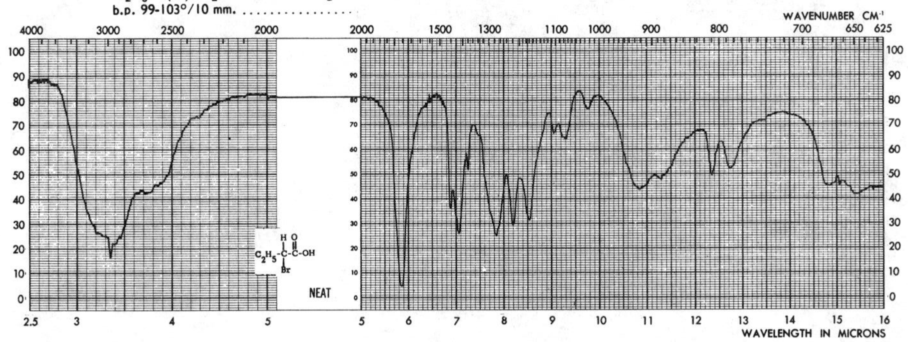

G 15,841-0
5-Bromovaleric acid, 99+%
$Br(CH_2)_4CO_2H$
M.W. 181.03 m.p. 38-40° Beil. 2,303
MELT

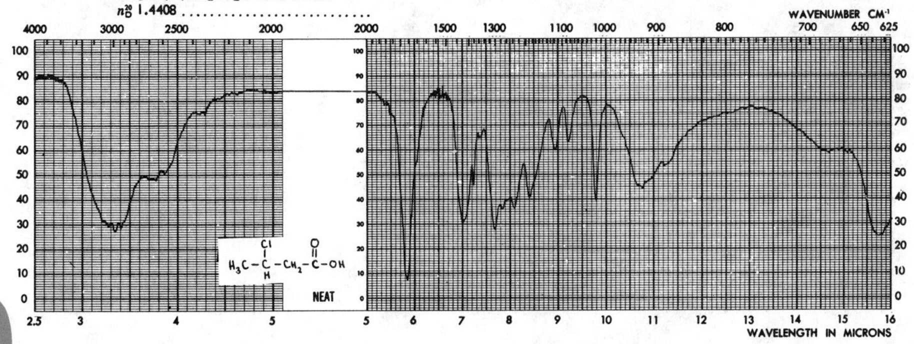

H 15,045-2 **6-Bromohexanoic acid**
$Br(CH_2)_5CO_2H$ M.W. 195.06 m.p. 31-33°
MELT

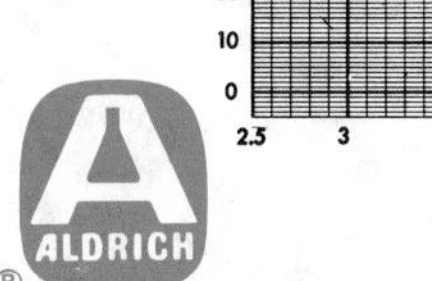

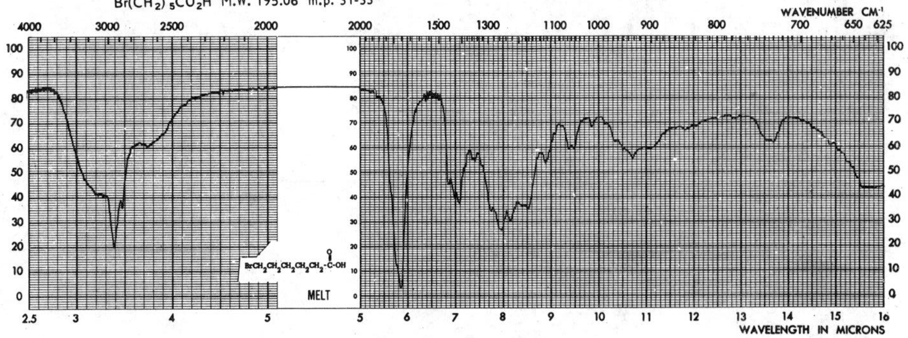

A

B8280-4 11-Bromoundecanoic acid, puriss.
$Br(CH_2)_{10}CO_2H$ M.W. 265.20 m.p. 48-51°

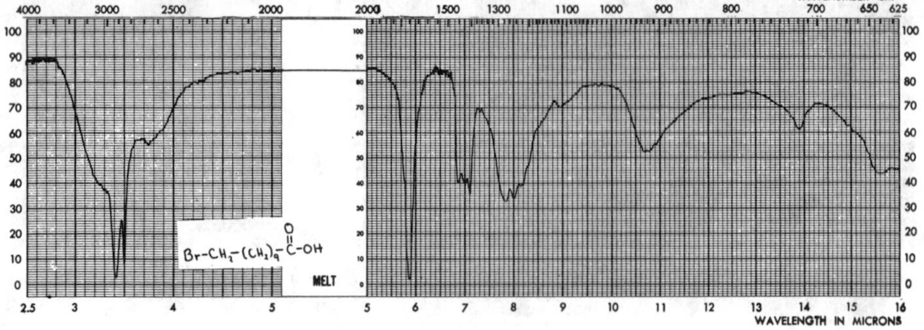

MELT

B

20,099-9
12-Bromododecanoic acid, 97%
$Br(CH_2)_{11}CO_2H$ FW 279.22 mp 52-55°
Beil. **2**(2),321 Disp. C

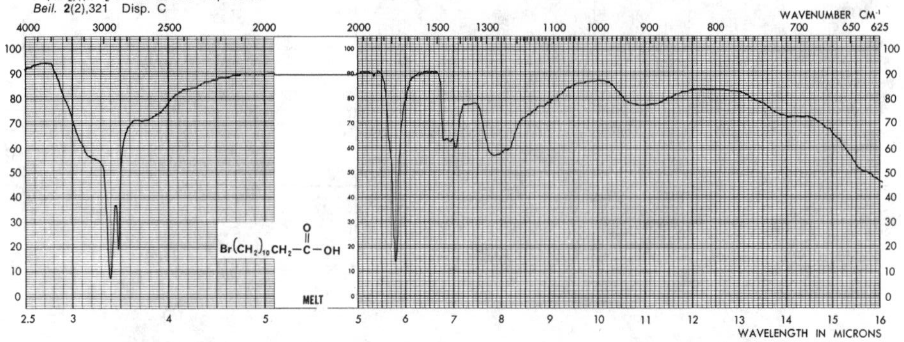

MELT

C

B7110-1 2-Bromolauric acid (2-bromododecanoic acid)
$CH_3(CH_2)_9CH(Br)CO_2H$ M.W. 279.22 m.p. 31-35°

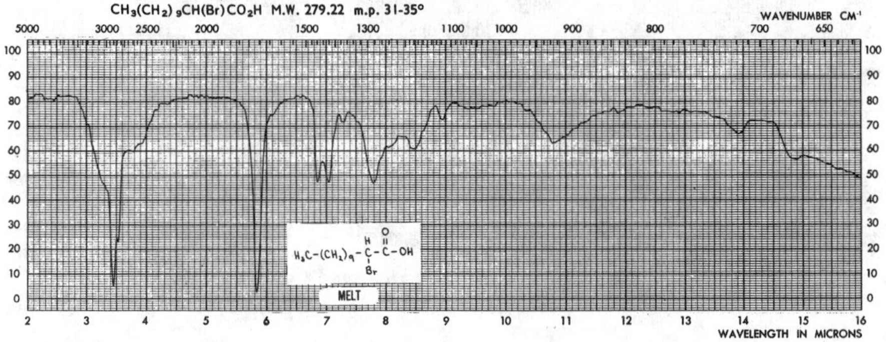

MELT

D

B8080-1 2-Bromostearic acid (2-bromooctadecanoic acid), tech.
$CH_3(CH_2)_{15}CH(Br)CO_2H$ M.W. 363.39

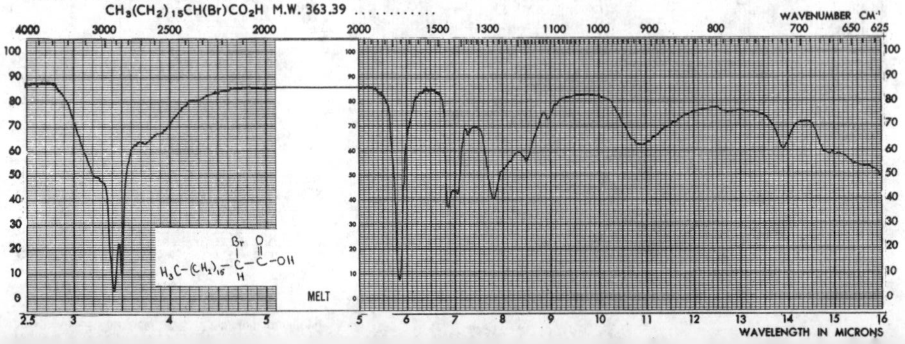

MELT

E

B8120-4 Bromosuccinic acid
$HO_2CCH_2CH(Br)CO_2H$ M.W. 196.99
m.p. 165° (dec.)

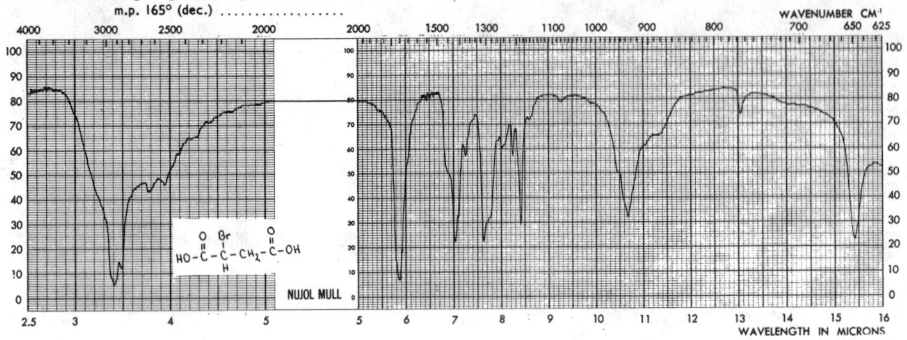

NUJOL MULL

F

10,547-3 2,3-Dibromosuccinic acid
$HO_2CCH(Br)CH(Br)CO_2H$ M.W. 275.89
m.p. 275°

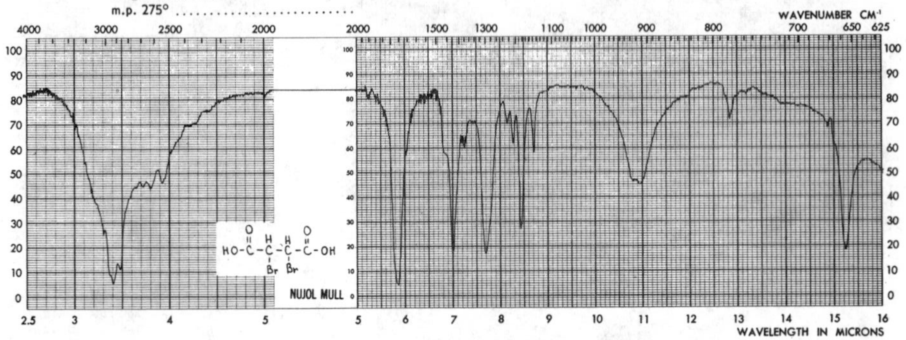

NUJOL MULL

G

17,740-7
cis-3-Chloroacrylic acid, 98%
$ClCH{=}CHCO_2H$
M.W. 106.51 m.p. 61-62° Beil. 2,400

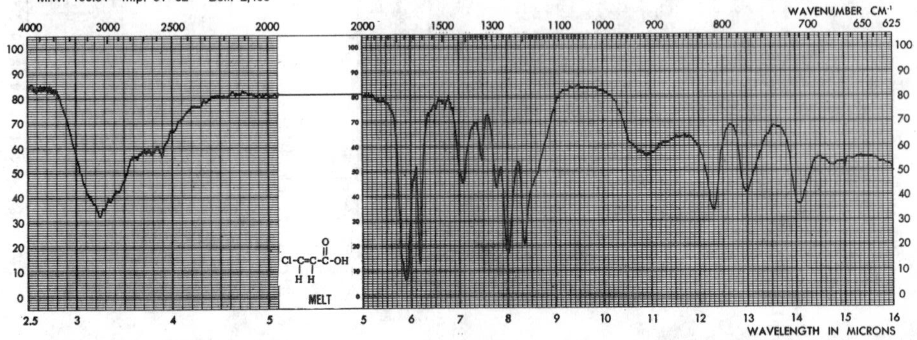

MELT

H

C2235-0 *trans*-3-Chloroacrylic acid
$ClCH{:}CHCO_2H$ M.W. 106.51 m.p. 81-83°

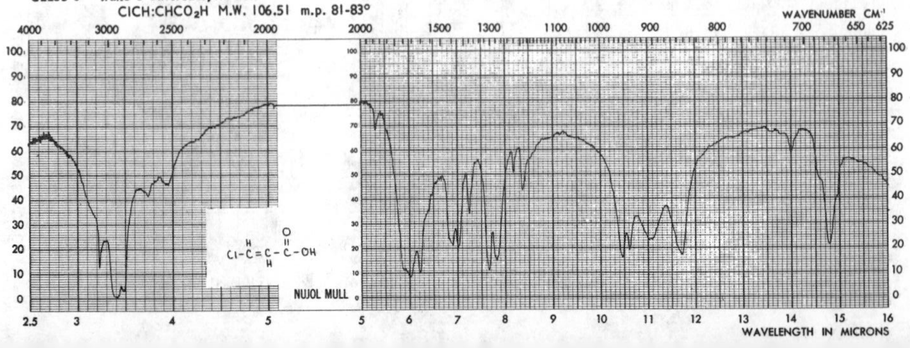

NUJOL MULL

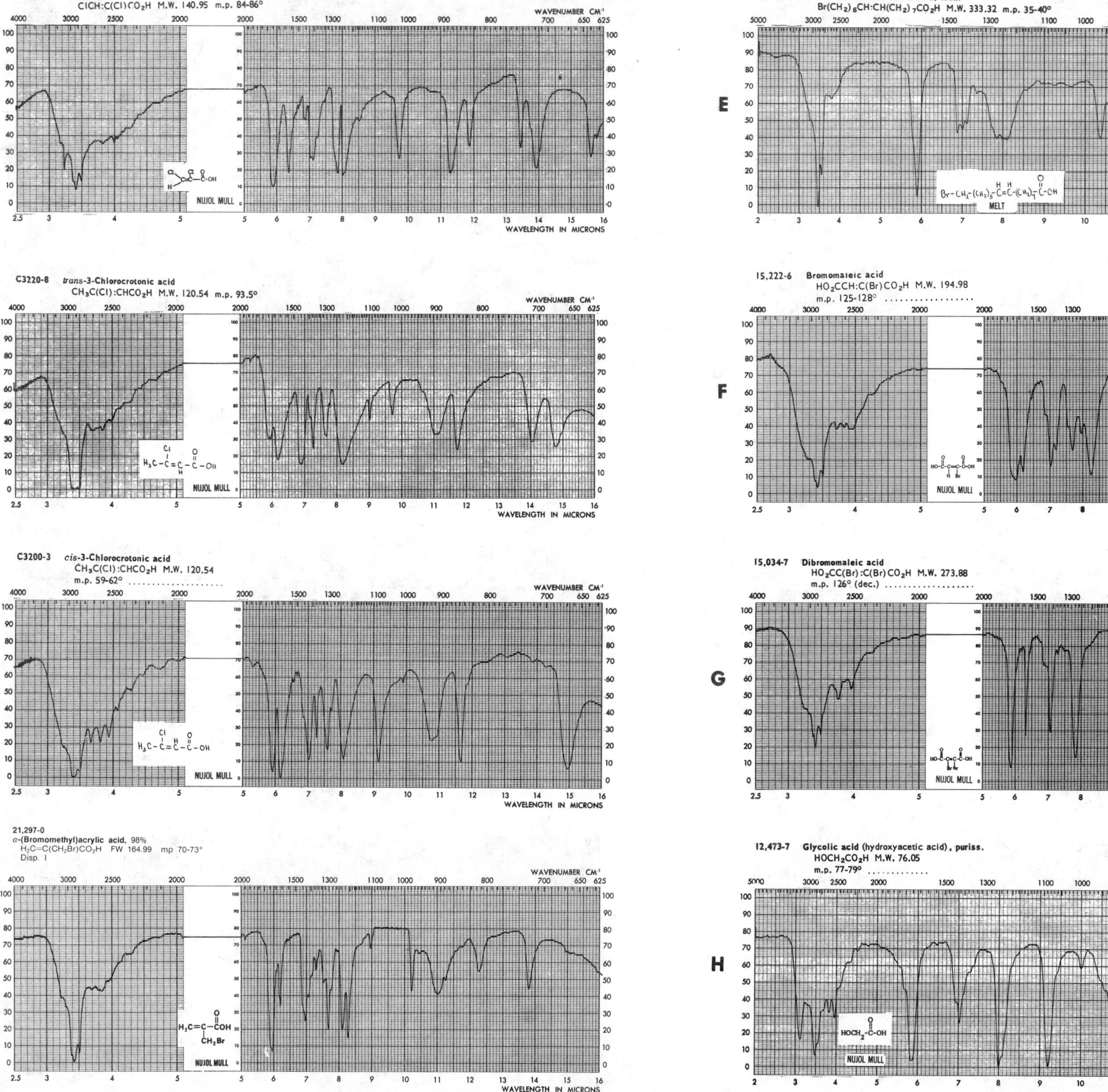

A
14,566-1 2,3-Dichloroacrylic acid
ClCH:C(Cl)CO₂H M.W. 140.95 m.p. 84-86°
NUJOL MULL
B
C3220-8 trans-3-Chlorocrotonic acid
CH₃C(Cl):CHCO₂H M.W. 120.54 m.p. 93.5°
NUJOL MULL
C
C3200-3 cis-3-Chlorocrotonic acid
CH₃C(Cl):CHCO₂H M.W. 120.54
m.p. 59-62°
NUJOL MULL
D
21,297-0
α-(Bromomethyl)acrylic acid, 98%
H₂C=C(CH₂Br)CO₂H FW 164.99 mp 70-73°
Disp. I
NUJOL MULL
E
B6820-8 16-Bromo-9-hexadecenoic acid, tech.
Br(CH₂)₆CH:CH(CH₂)₇CO₂H M.W. 333.32 m.p. 35-40°
MELT
F
15,222-6 Bromomaleic acid
HO₂CCH:C(Br)CO₂H M.W. 194.98
m.p. 125-128°
NUJOL MULL
G
15,034-7 Dibromomaleic acid
HO₂CC(Br):C(Br)CO₂H M.W. 273.88
m.p. 126° (dec.)
NUJOL MULL
H
12,473-7 Glycolic acid (hydroxyacetic acid), puriss.
HOCH₂CO₂H M.W. 76.05
m.p. 77-79°
NUJOL MULL
WAVENUMBER CM⁻¹
WAVELENGTH IN MICRONS
ALDRICH

NON-AROMATIC CARBOXYLIC ACIDS

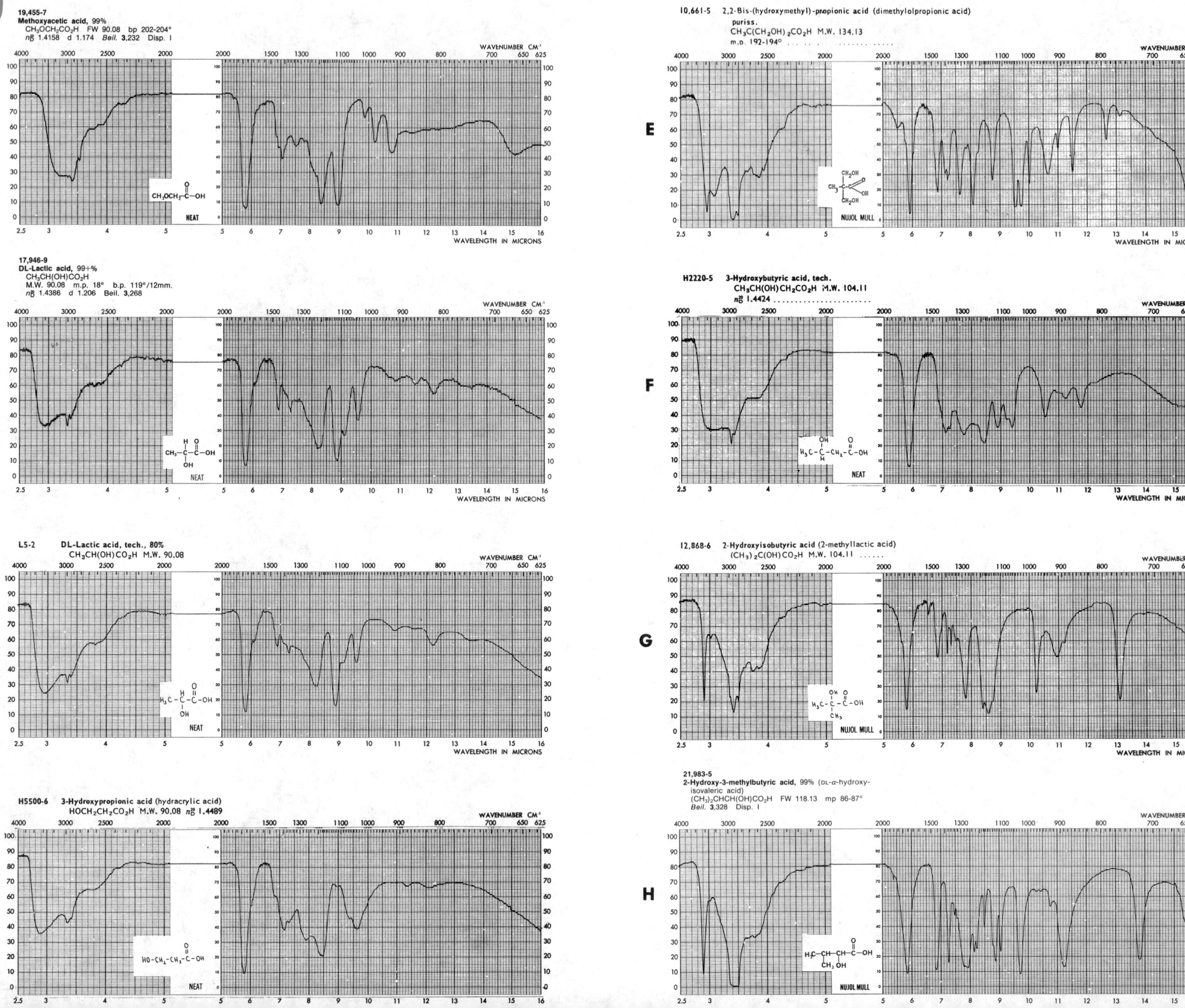
A
19,455-7
Methoxyacetic acid, 99%
$CH_3OCH_2CO_2H$ FW 90.08 bp 202-204°
n_D^{20} 1.4158 d 1.174 Beil. 3,232 Disp. I
NEAT

B
17,946-9
DL-Lactic acid, 99+%
$CH_3CH(OH)CO_2H$
M.W. 90.08 m.p. 18° b.p. 119°/12mm.
n_D^{20} 1.4386 d 1.206 Beil. 3,268
NEAT

C
L5-2 DL-Lactic acid, tech., 80%
$CH_3CH(OH)CO_2H$ M.W. 90.08
NEAT

D
H5500-6 3-Hydroxypropionic acid (hydracrylic acid)
$HOCH_2CH_2CO_2H$ M.W. 90.08 n_D^{20} 1.4489
NEAT

E
10,661-5 2,2-Bis-(hydroxymethyl)-propionic acid (dimethylolpropionic acid)
puriss.
$CH_3C(CH_2OH)_2CO_2H$ M.W. 134.13
m.p. 192-194°
NUJOL MULL

F
H2220-5 3-Hydroxybutyric acid, tech.
$CH_3CH(OH)CH_2CO_2H$ M.W. 104.11
n_D^{20} 1.4424
NEAT

G
12,868-6 2-Hydroxyisobutyric acid (2-methyllactic acid)
$(CH_3)_2C(OH)CO_2H$ M.W. 104.11
NUJOL MULL

H
21,983-5
2-Hydroxy-3-methylbutyric acid, 99% (DL-α-hydroxy-isovaleric acid)
$(CH_3)_2CHCH(OH)CO_2H$ FW 118.13 mp 86-87°
Beil. 3,328 Disp. I
NUJOL MULL

WAVENUMBER CM⁻¹
WAVELENGTH IN MICRONS

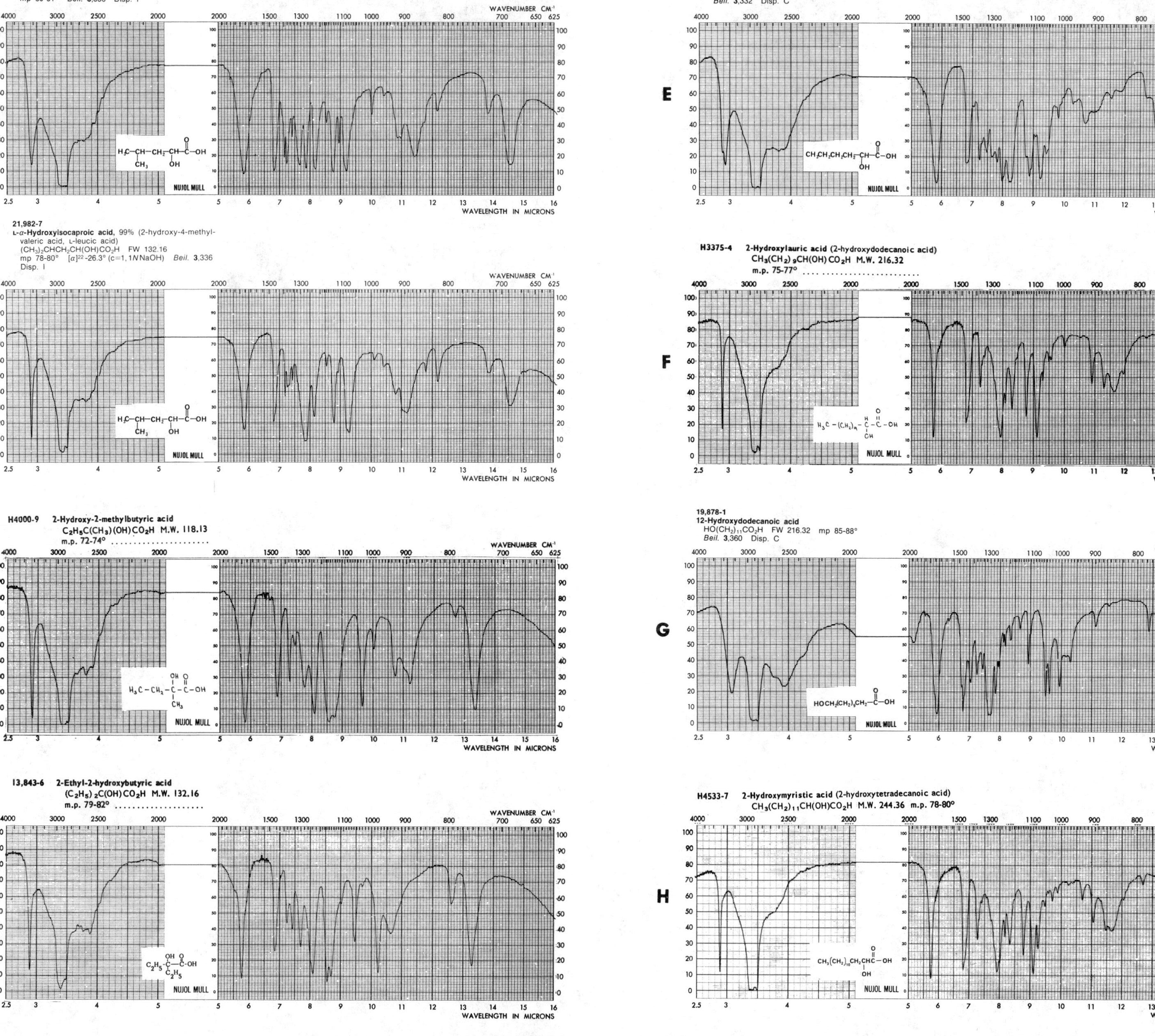

A 21,981-9
DL-α-Hydroxyisocaproic acid, 99% (2-hydroxy-4-methylvaleric acid, DL-leucic acid)
$(CH_3)_2CHCH_2CH(OH)CO_2H$ FW 132.16
mp 60-61° *Beil.* **3**,336 Disp. I

B 21,982-7
L-α-Hydroxyisocaproic acid, 99% (2-hydroxy-4-methylvaleric acid, L-leucic acid)
$(CH_3)_2CHCH_2CH(OH)CO_2H$ FW 132.16
mp 78-80° $[\alpha]^{22}$ -26.3° (c=1, 1*N* NaOH) *Beil.* **3**,336
Disp. I

C H4000-9 **2-Hydroxy-2-methylbutyric acid**
$C_2H_5C(CH_3)(OH)CO_2H$ M.W. 118.13
m.p. 72-74°

D 13,843-6 **2-Ethyl-2-hydroxybutyric acid**
$(C_2H_5)_2C(OH)CO_2H$ M.W. 132.16
m.p. 79-82°

E 21,980-0
DL-α-Hydroxycaproic acid, 98% (2-hydroxyhexanoic acid)
$CH_3(CH_2)_3CH(OH)CO_2H$ FW 132.16 mp 55-58°
Beil. **3**,332 Disp. C

F H3375-4 **2-Hydroxylauric acid (2-hydroxydodecanoic acid)**
$CH_3(CH_2)_9CH(OH)CO_2H$ M.W. 216.32
m.p. 75-77°

G 19,878-1
12-Hydroxydodecanoic acid
$HO(CH_2)_{11}CO_2H$ FW 216.32 mp 85-88°
Beil. **3**,360 Disp. C

H H4533-7 **2-Hydroxymyristic acid (2-hydroxytetradecanoic acid)**
$CH_3(CH_2)_{11}CH(OH)CO_2H$ M.W. 244.36 m.p. 78-80°

A

H4950-2 **2-Hydroxypalmitic acid** (2-hydroxyhexadecanoic acid)
$CH_3(CH_2)_{13}CH(OH)CO_2H$ M.W. 272.43 m.p. 83-86°

NUJOL MULL

B

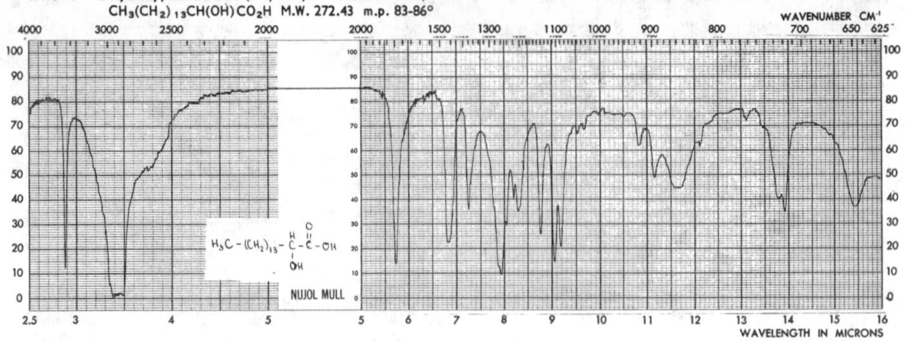

17,749-0
16-Hydroxyhexadecanoic acid, 95% (juniperic acid)
$HO(CH_2)_{15}CO_2H$
M.W. 272.43 m.p. 97-99° Beil. 3,362

NUJOL MULL

C

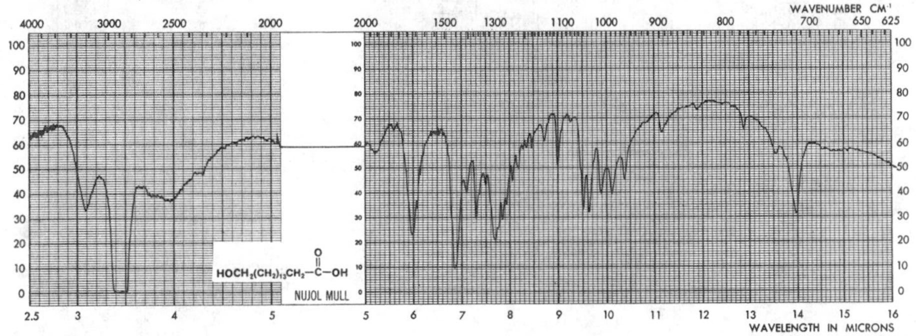

21,996-7
DL-**12-Hydroxystearic acid**, 99%
$CH_3(CH_2)_5CH(OH)(CH_2)_{10}CO_2H$ FW 300.49
mp 80-81° *Beil.* 3(2),250 Disp. C

NUJOL MULL

D

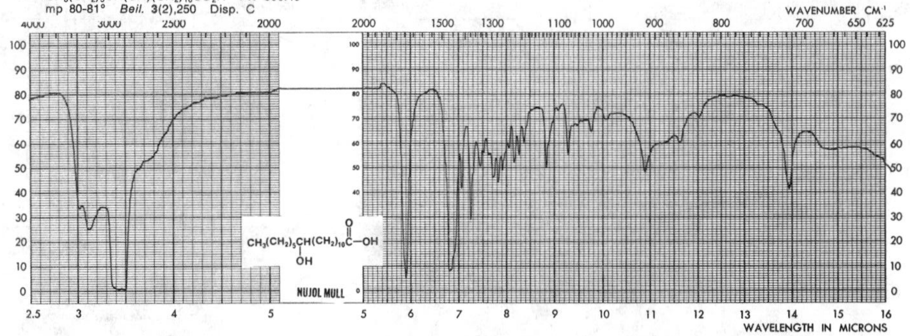

A2820-1 **Aleuritic acid** (DL-*erythro*-9,10,16-trihydroxyhexadecanoic acid), tech.
$HO(CH_2)_6[CH(OH)]_2(CH_2)_7CO_2H$ M.W. 304.43
m.p. 100-105°

NUJOL MULL

E

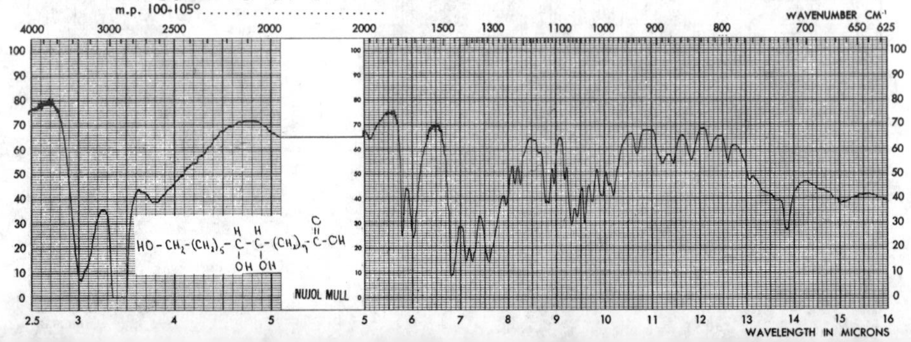

13,180-6 **Tartronic acid** (hydroxymalonic acid)
$HO_2CCH(OH)CO_2H$ M.W. 120.06
m.p. 154° (dec.)

NUJOL MULL

F

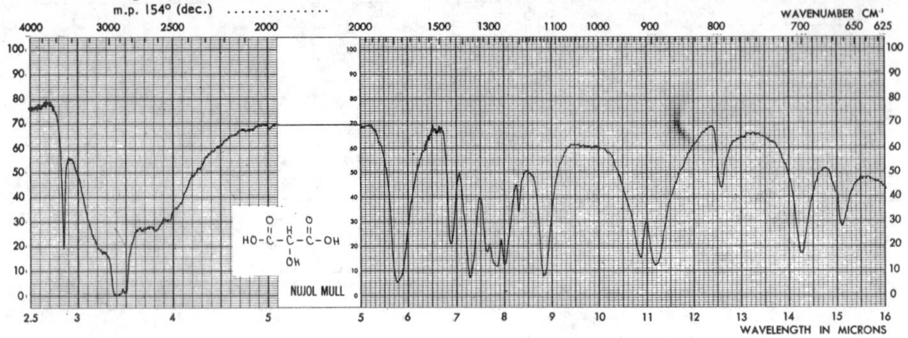

16,343-0
Ketomalonic acid monohydrate, 99% (dihydroxymalonic acid, mesoxalic acid)
$HO_2CC(OH)_2CO_2H$
M.W. 136.06 m.p. 118-120° (dec.) Beil. 3,766

NUJOL MULL

G

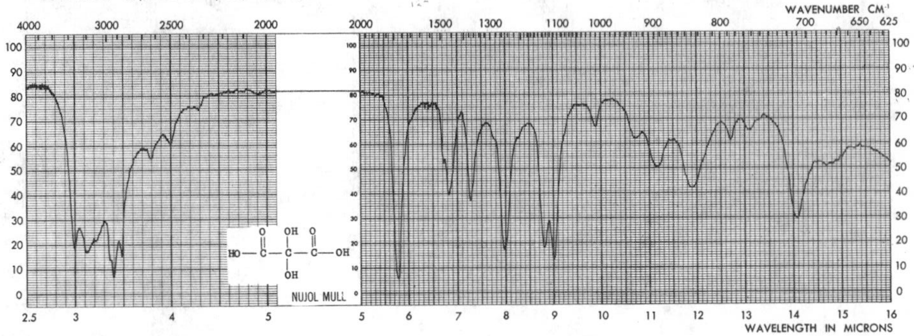

M121-0 **DL-Malic acid** (DL-hydroxysuccinic acid)
$HO_2CCH_2CH(OH)CO_2H$ M.W. 134.09
m.p. 128-132°

NUJOL MULL

H

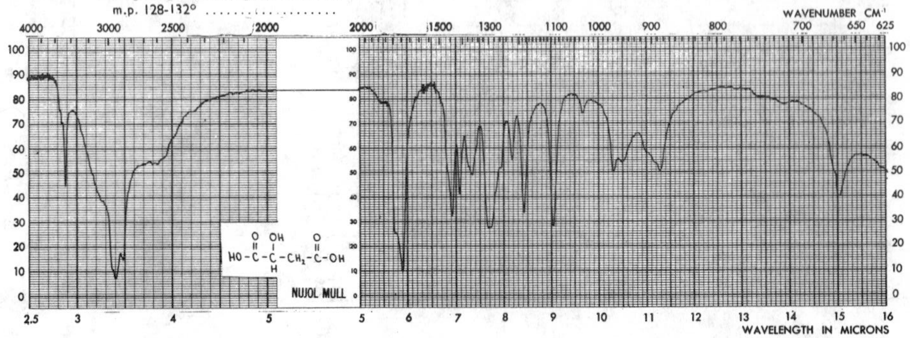

12,241-6 ***d*-Malic acid** (*d*-hydroxysuccinic acid)
$HO_2CCH_2CH(OH)CO_2H$ M.W. 134.09 m.p. 95-100°
$[\alpha]^{23}_{D}$ + 24.9° (c=5.6, pyridine)

NUJOL MULL

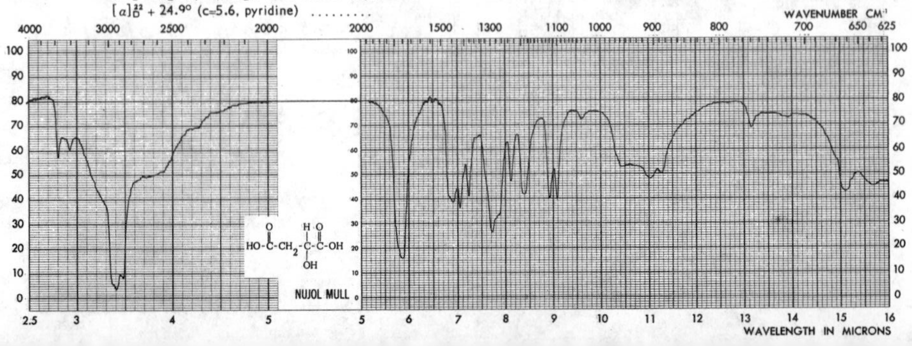

A 11,257-7 *l*-Malic acid (*l*-hydroxysuccinic acid)
$HO_2CCH_2CH(OH)CO_2H$ M.W. 134.09
m.p. 101-103° $[\alpha]^{20}_{D}$ - 28.6° (c=5.5 in pyridine)
NUJOL MULL

B C8310-4 DL-Citramalic acid (DL-α-methylmalic acid)
$HO_2CCH_2C(CH_3)(OH)CO_2H$ M.W. 148.11
m.p. 114-116°
NUJOL MULL

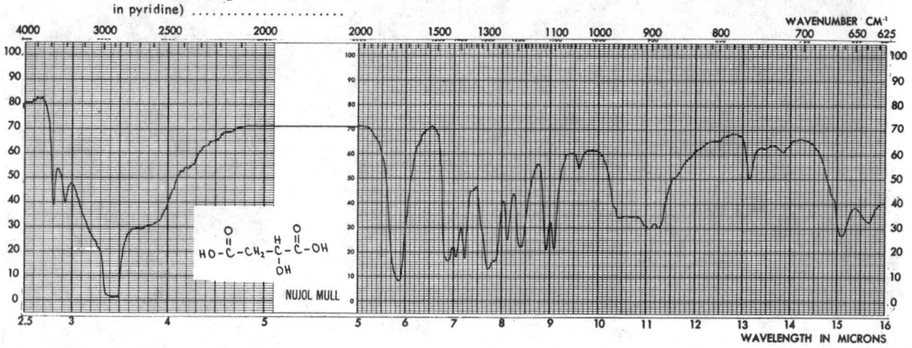

C 21,985-1
3-Hydroxy-3-methylglutaric acid, 97%
$HOC(CH_3)(CH_2CO_2H)_2$ FW 162.14 mp 99-102°
Beil. 3,450 Disp. I
NUJOL MULL

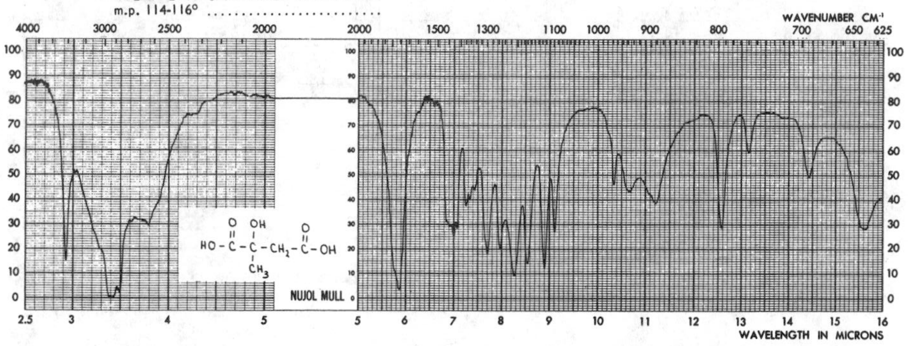

D T40-0 DL-Tartaric acid hydrate
$HO_2CCH(OH)CH(OH)CO_2H{\cdot}xH_2O$ M.W. 150.09 (anhydrous)
m.p. 210° (dec.)
NUJOL MULL

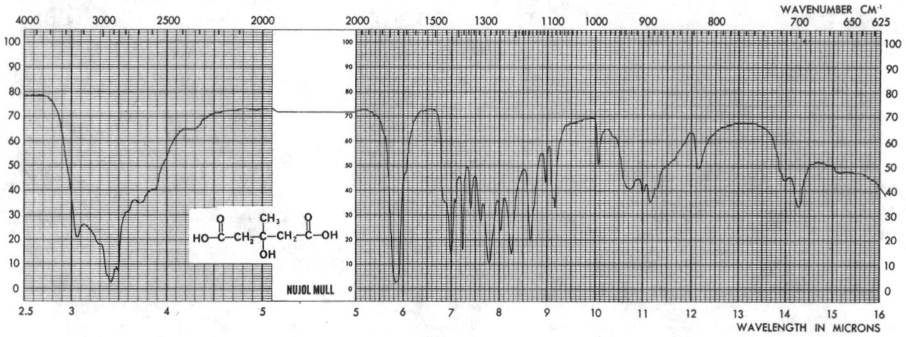

E T60-5 *meso*-Tartaric acid hydrate
$HO_2CCH(OH)CH(OH)CO_2H{\cdot}H_2O$ M.W. 168.10
m.p. 73-75° (loses water); melts at 146-148°
NUJOL MULL

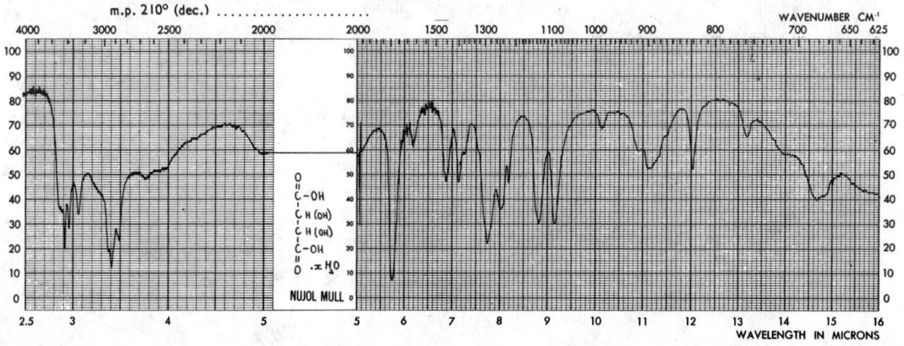

F T10-9 *d*-Tartaric acid, puriss.
$HO_2CCH(OH)CH(OH)CO_2H$ M.W. 150.09 m.p. 171-174°
$[\alpha]^{20}_{D}$ + 12.7° (c=17.4 in H_2O)
NUJOL MULL

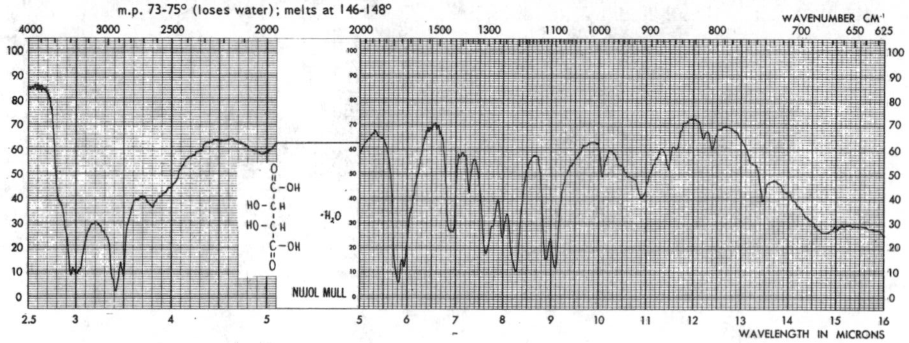

G T20-6 *l*-Tartaric acid (unnatural tartaric acid)
$HO_2CCH(OH)CH(OH)CO_2H$ M.W. 150.09 m.p. 168-173°
$[\alpha]^{20}_{D}$ - 12.35° (c=20.4 in H_2O)
NUJOL MULL

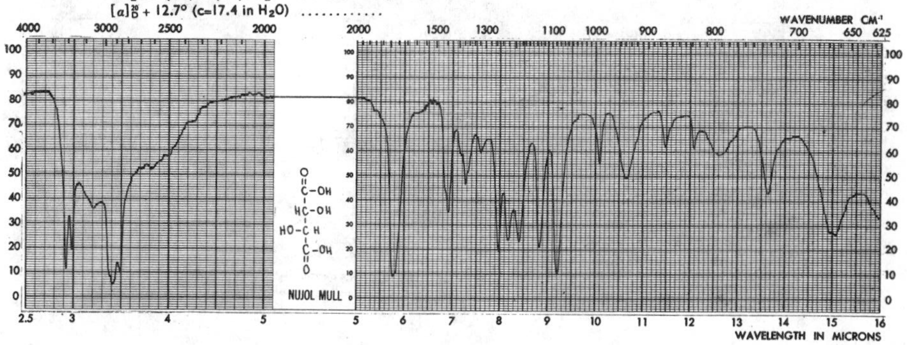

H D12,140-1 Dihydroxytartaric acid
$HO_2CC(OH)_2C(OH)_2CO_2H$ M.W. 182.08
m.p. 104-107° (dec.)
NUJOL MULL

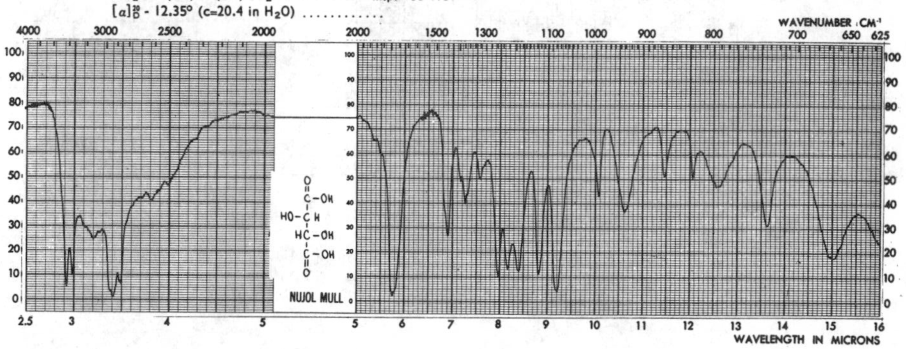

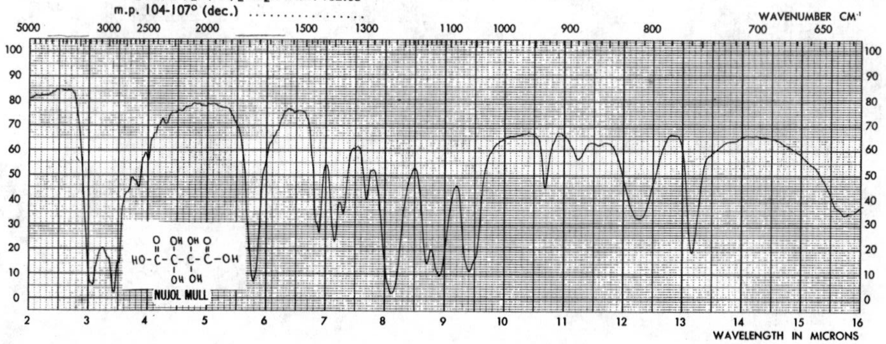

A

M8961-7 **Mucic acid**
$HO_2C[CH(OH)]_4CO_2H$ M.W. 210.14
m.p. 204.5° (dec.)

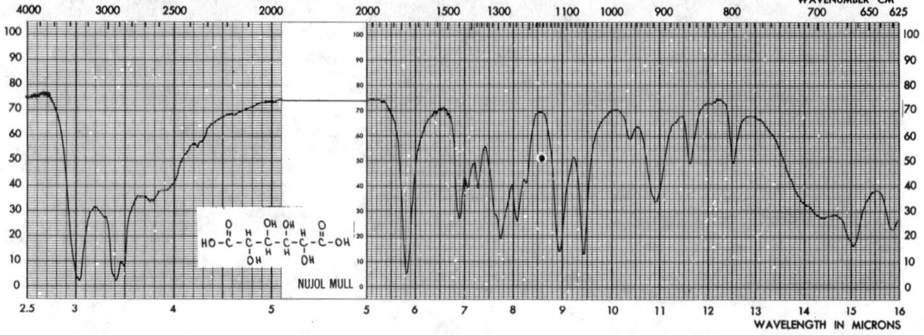

NUJOL MULL

B

C8315-5 **Citric acid, anhydrous, U.S.P.**
$HO_2CCH_2C(OH)(CO_2H)CH_2CO_2H$ M.W. 192.12
m.p. 153-154.5°

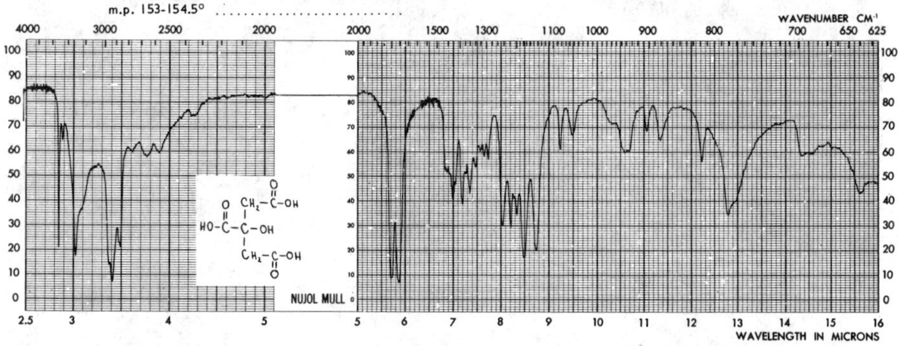

NUJOL MULL

C

D11,320-4 **Dihydroxymaleic acid** (dihydroxyfumaric acid), see J. Am. Chem. Soc. 75, 6244 (1953)
$HO_2CC(OH):C(OH)CO_2H$ M.W. 148.07
m.p. 156° (dec.)

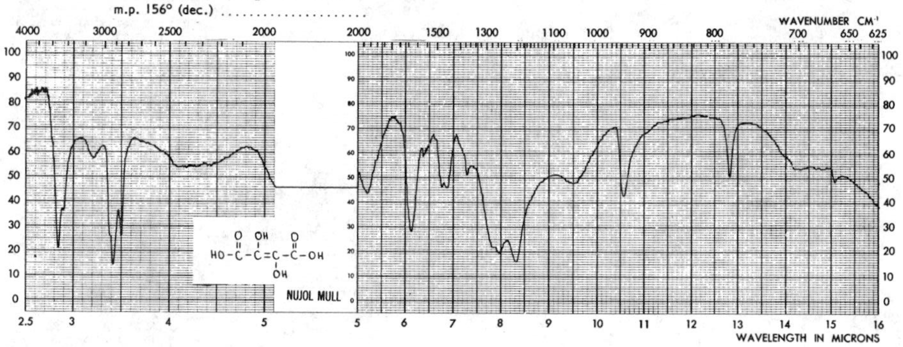

NUJOL MULL

D

10,858-8 **2,2-Dihydroxy-3,3,3-trichloropropionic acid** (trichloropyruvic acid hydrate)
$CCl_3C(OH)_2CO_2H$ M.W. 209.41 m.p. 95-96°

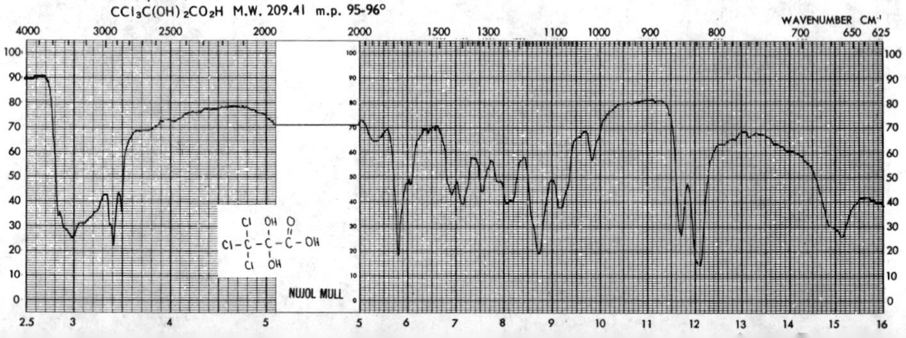

NUJOL MULL

E

14,876-8 *dl*-**Pinolic acid** [*dl*-2,2-dimethyl-3-(1-hydroxyethyl)-1-cyclobutaneacetic acid]
$CH_3CH(OH)C_4H_4(CH_3)_2CH_2CO_2H$ M.W. 186.25
m.p. 97-99°

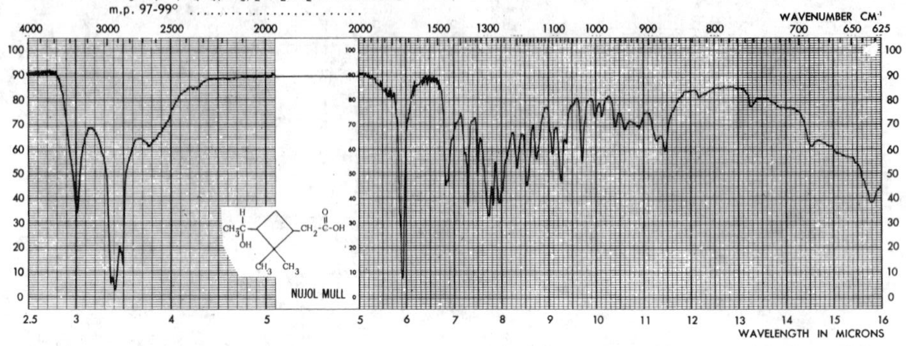

NUJOL MULL

F

10,148-6 **1-Hydroxycyclopentanecarboxylic acid**
$HOC_5H_8CO_2H$ M.W. 130.14 m.p. 105-107°

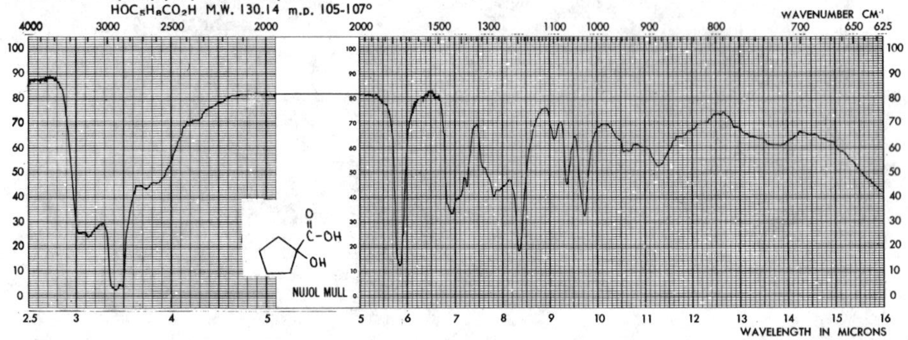

NUJOL MULL

G

13,862-2 **Quinic acid** (1,3,4,5-tetrahydroxycyclohexanecarboxylic acid)
$(HO)_4C_6H_7CO_2H$ M.W. 192.17 m.p. 159-162° (dec.)
$[\alpha]_D^{25}$ - 43.9° (c=11.2, H_2O)

NUJOL MULL

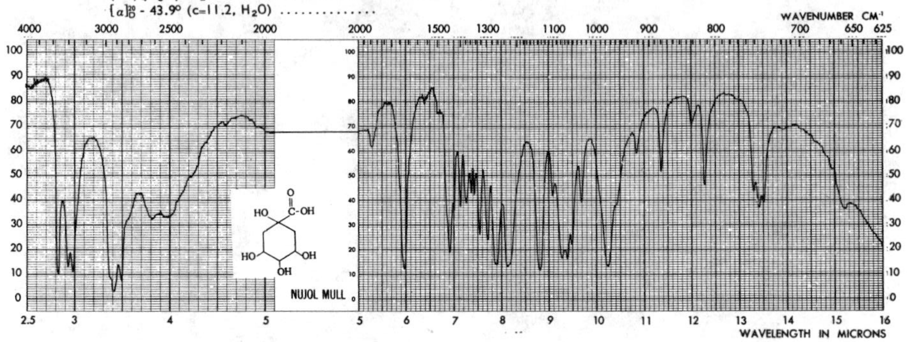

H

S320-8 **Shikimic acid** (3,4,5-trihydroxy-1-cyclohexene-1-carboxylic acid)
M.W. 174.15 m.p. 188-190°

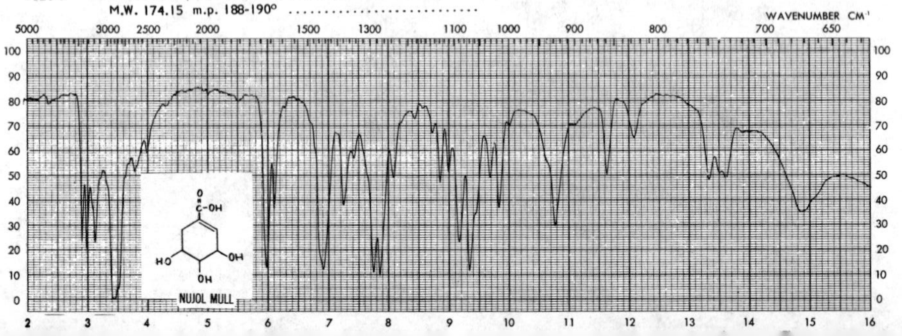

NUJOL MULL

WAVENUMBER CM^{-1} — WAVELENGTH IN MICRONS

A

85,728-9
D-(+)-Galacturonic acid monohydrate
M.W. 212.16 m.p. 164-165° (dec.)
$[\alpha]^{23}$ +51.7° (c=10, H_2O, 5hr.)

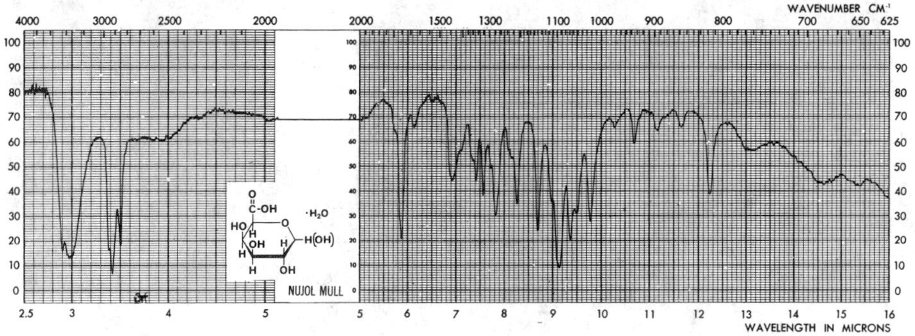

NUJOL MULL

B

15,351-6 Lactobionic acid
M.W. 358.30 m.p. 113-118° $[\alpha]^{12}_{D}$ +23.3°
(c 10.04, H_2O, 24 hr.)

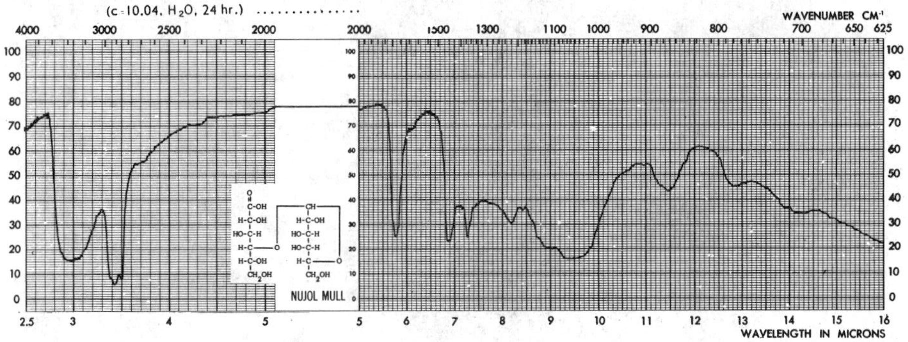

NUJOL MULL

C

A2830-9 Alginic acid
m.p. 180° (dec.)

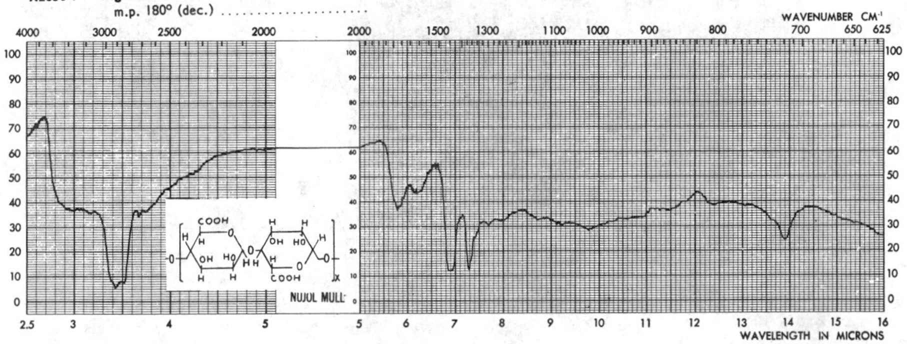

NUJOL MULL

D

13,711-1 Ethoxyacetic acid
$C_2H_5OCH_2CO_2H$ M.W. 104.11 n^{20}_{D} 1.4190
b.p. 97-100°/11 mm.

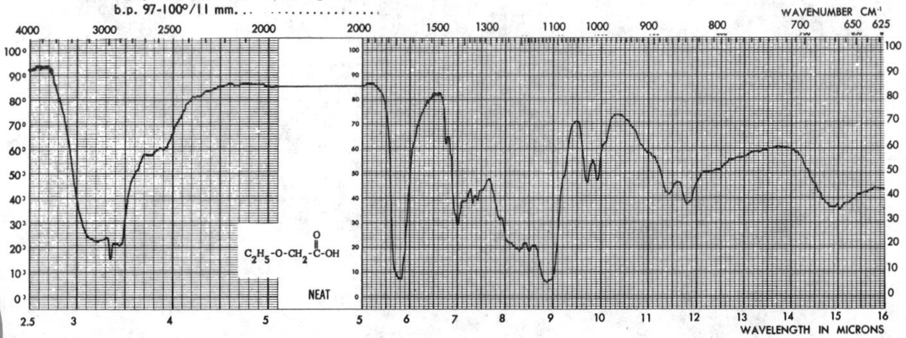

NEAT

E

E760-6 3-Ethoxypropionic acid
$C_2H_5OCH_2CH_2CO_2H$ M.W. 118.13
n^{20}_{D} 1.4228

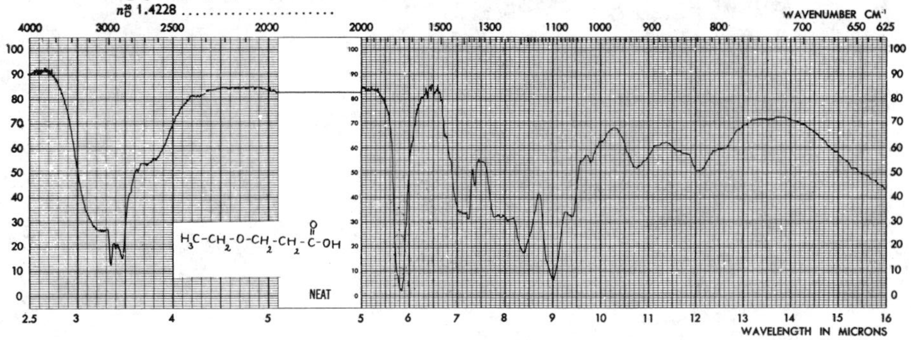

NEAT

F

19,983-4
3,6,9,12,15-Pentaoxahexadecanoic acid, 95+%
$CH_3O(CH_2CH_2O)_4CH_2CO_2H$ FW 266.29
n^{20}_{D} 1.4545 d 1.058 Disp. C

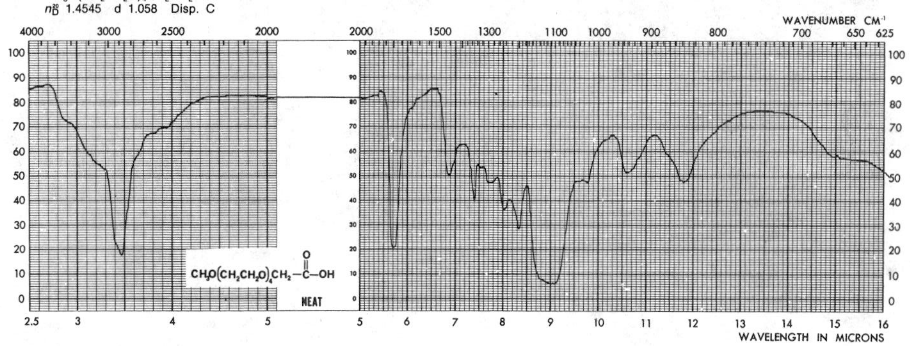

NEAT

G

14,307-3 Diglycolic acid (2,2'-oxydiacetic acid)
$O(CH_2CO_2H)_2$ M.W. 134.09 m.p. 142-145°

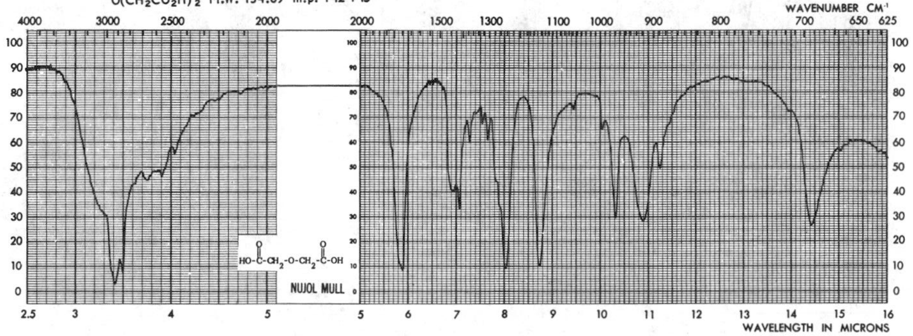

NUJOL MULL

H

M300-0 *l*-Menthoxyacetic acid
M.W. 214.31 n^{20}_{D} 1.4672 (supercooled) m.p. 52-55°
$[\alpha]^{20}_{D}$ - 88° (c=4.1, CH_3OH)

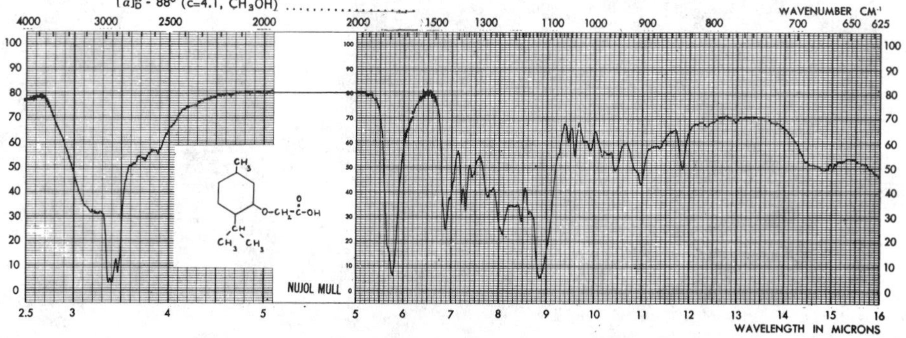

NUJOL MULL

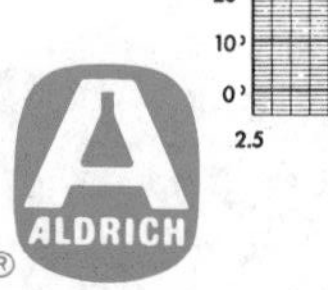

A

12,301-3 2-Tetrahydrofuranacetic acid
M.W. 130.14 n_D^{20} 1.4546

NEAT

B

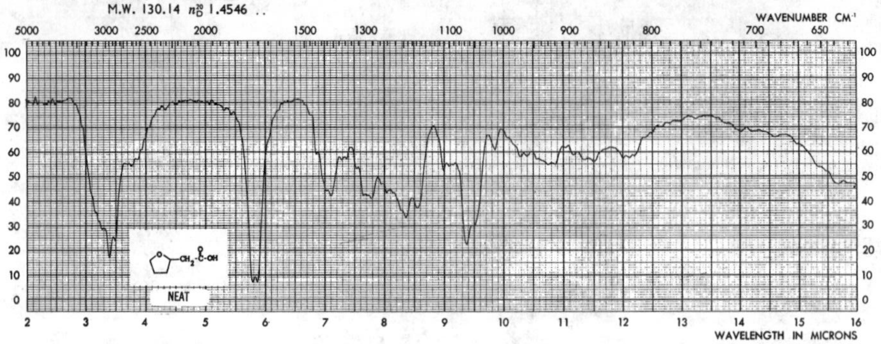

14,483-5 Tetrahydrofuran-2,3,4,5-tetracarboxylic acid (diasteriomers)
M.W. 248.15 m.p. 205° (dec.)

NUJOL MULL

C

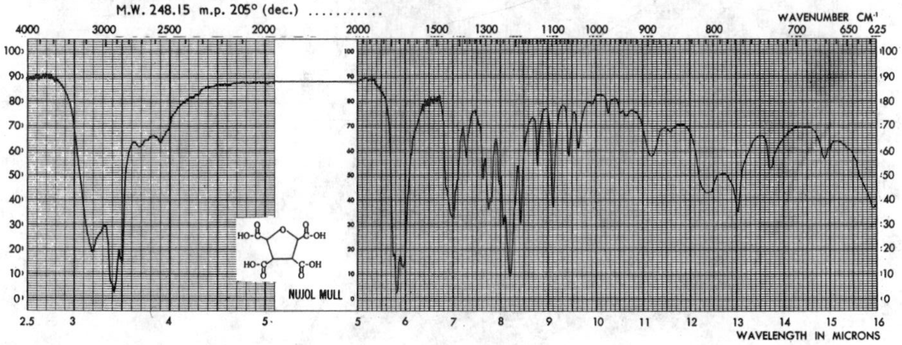

M310-8 Mercaptoacetic acid (thioglycolic acid)
$HSCH_2CO_2H$ M.W. 92.12 n_D^{20} 1.5030 b.p. 96°/5 mm.

HS-CH₂-C(=O)-OH

NEAT

D

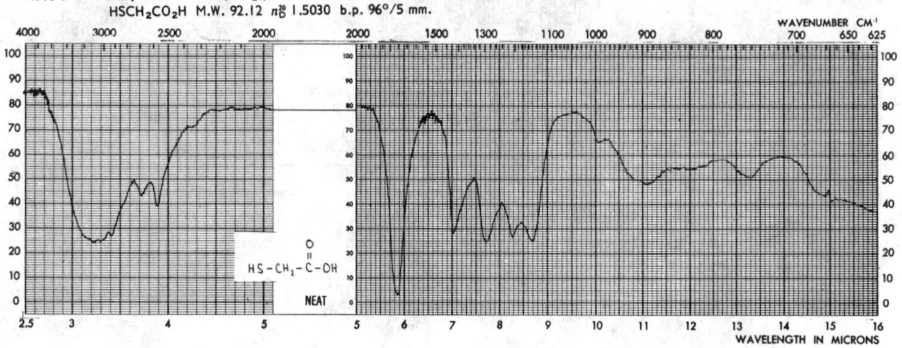

T3100-3 Thiolactic acid (2-mercaptopropionic acid)
$CH_3CH(SH)CO_2H$ M.W. 106.14 n_D^{20} 1.4809 m.p. 10-14°
b.p. 94-96°/10 mm.

NEAT

E

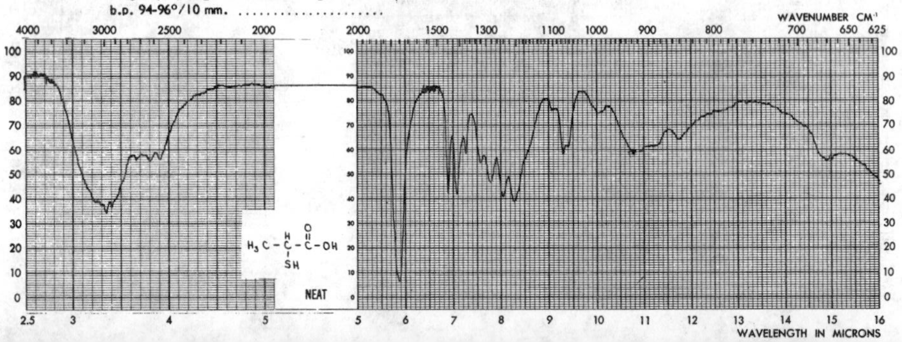

M580-1 3-Mercaptopropionic acid, puriss.
$HSCH_2CH_2CO_2H$ M.W. 106.14 n_D^{20} 1.4911 m.p. 17-19°
b.p. 110.5-111.5°/15 mm.

NEAT

F

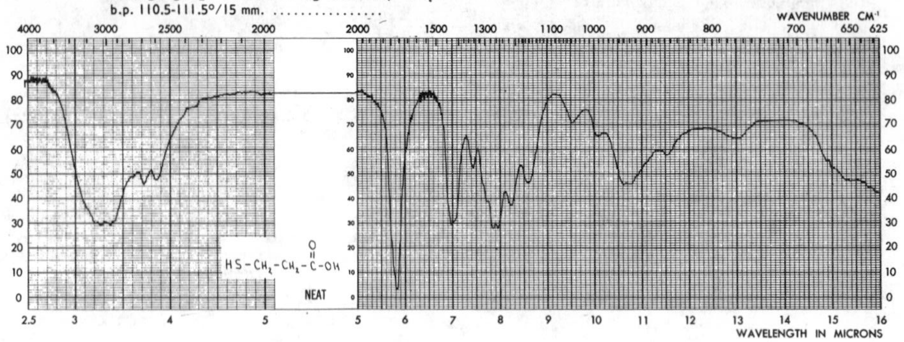

T3080-5 Thiolacetic acid (thioacetic acid)
CH_3COSH M.W. 76.12 n_D^{20} 1.4630
b.p. 85-87°

NEAT

G

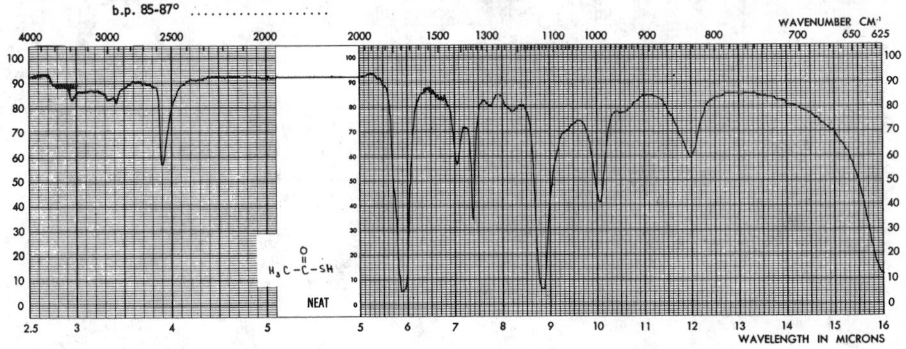

T3140-2 Thiolpropionic acid (thiopropionic acid)
C_2H_5COSH M.W. 90.14 n_D^{20} 1.4668
b.p. 108-110°

NEAT

H

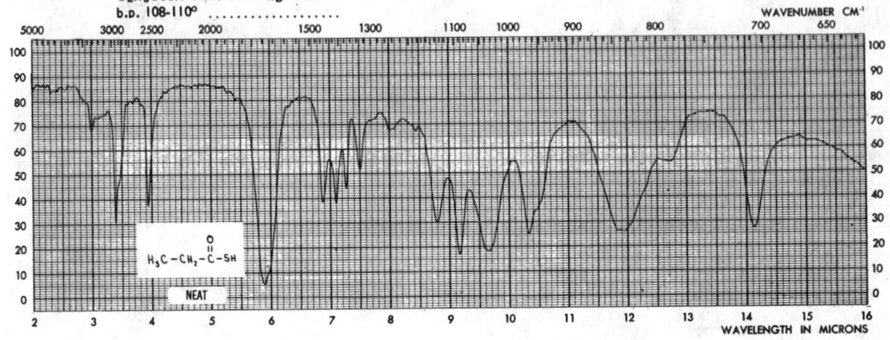

M618-2 Mercaptosuccinic acid (thiomalic acid)
$HO_2CCH_2CH(SH)CO_2H$ M.W. 150.15
m.p. 152-154°

NUJOL MULL

WAVENUMBER CM⁻¹ / WAVELENGTH IN MICRONS

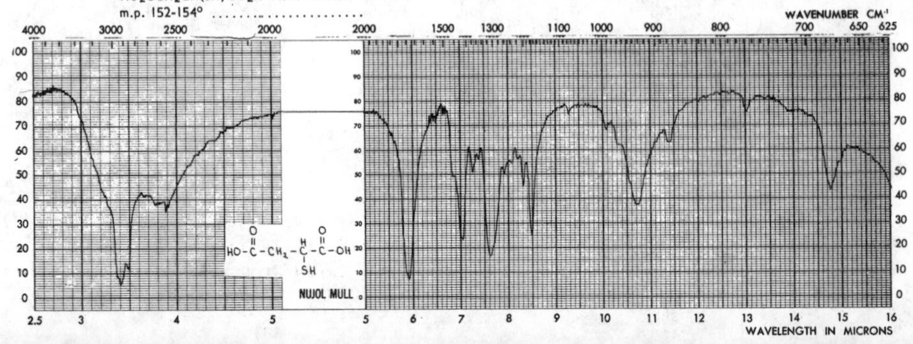

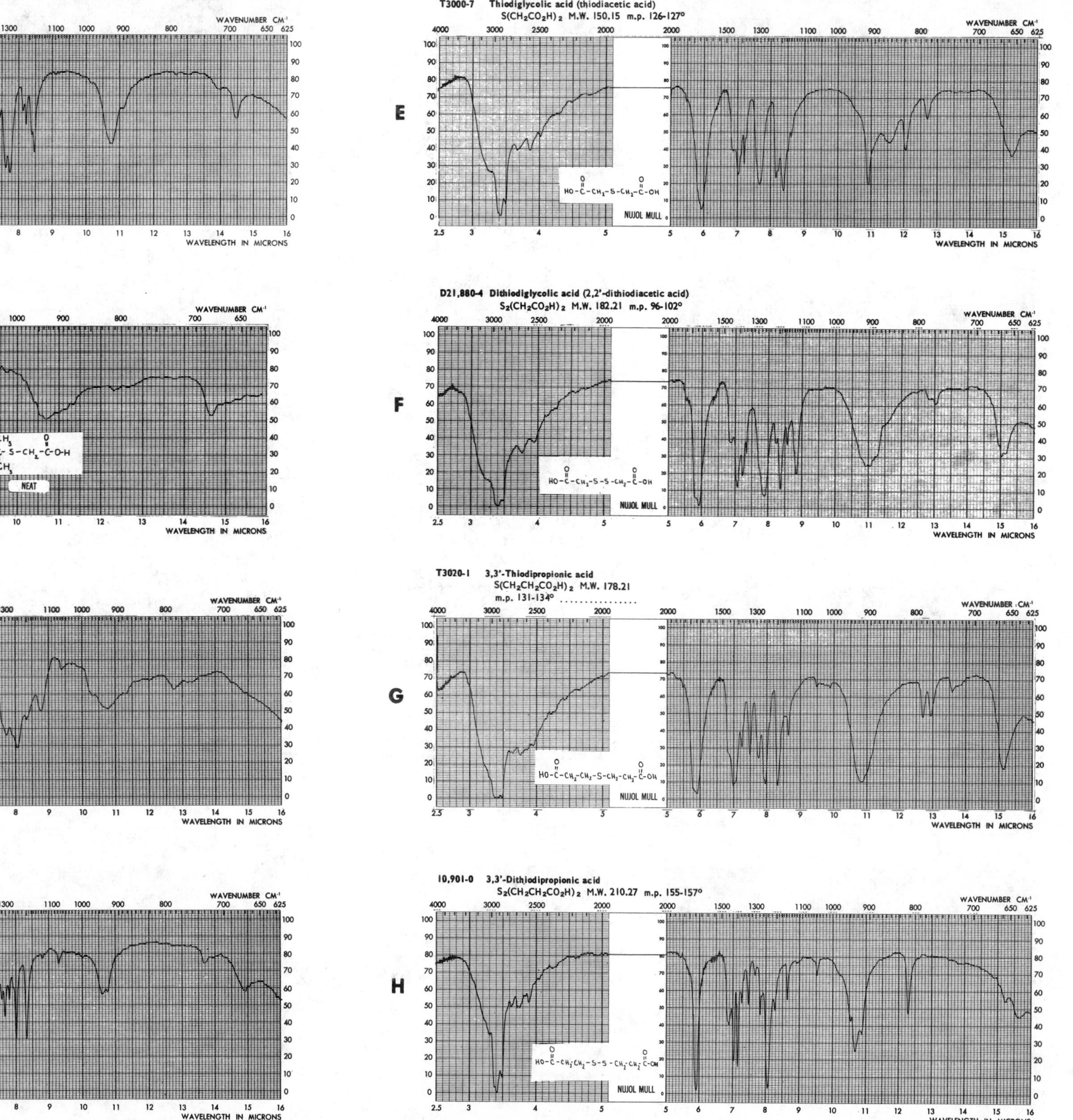

A — 85,298-8 2,3-Dimercaptosuccinic acid, 98%
$HO_2CCH(SH)CH(SH)CO_2H$
M.W. 182.22 m.p. 196-198° (dec.)
NUJOL MULL

B — B10,245 S-tert.-Butylthioglycolic acid
$(CH_3)_3CSCH_2CO_2H$ M.W. 148.22 n_D^{20} 1.4789
NEAT

C — E4875 4-(Ethylthio)-butyric acid
$C_2H_5S(CH_2)_3CO_2H$ M.W. 148.23 n_D^{20}
NEAT

D — T2860-6 DL-Thioctic acid (DL-6,8-dithiooctanoic acid)
M.W. 206.33 m.p. 62-65°
NUJOL MULL

E — T3000-7 Thiodiglycolic acid (thiodiacetic acid)
$S(CH_2CO_2H)_2$ M.W. 150.15 m.p. 126-127°
NUJOL MULL

F — D21,880-4 Dithiodiglycolic acid (2,2'-dithiodiacetic acid)
$S_2(CH_2CO_2H)_2$ M.W. 182.21 m.p. 96-102°
NUJOL MULL

G — T3020-1 3,3'-Thiodipropionic acid
$S(CH_2CH_2CO_2H)_2$ M.W. 178.21
m.p. 131-134°
NUJOL MULL

H — 10,901-0 3,3'-Dithiodipropionic acid
$S_2(CH_2CH_2CO_2H)_2$ M.W. 210.27 m.p. 155-157°
NUJOL MULL

A
C1560-5 **3-Carboxypropyl disulfide** (4,4'-dithiodibutyric acid)
$[-S(CH_2)_3CO_2H]_2$ M.W. 238.32
m.p. 108-110°

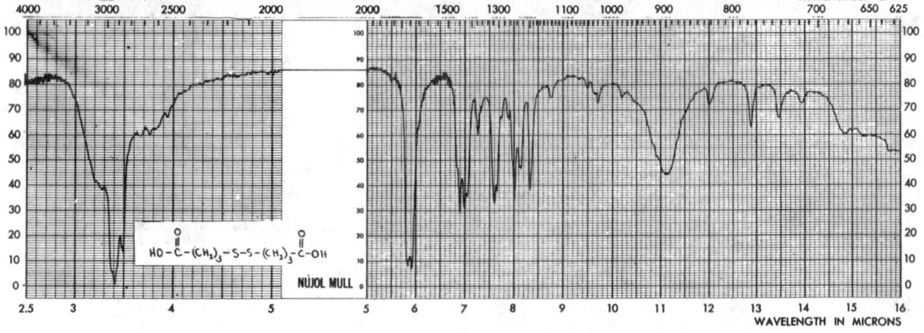

B
G1060-1 **Glyoxylic acid hydrate**
$HCOCO_2H{\cdot}xH_2O$ M.W. 74.04 (anhydrous)
m.p. 50-52°

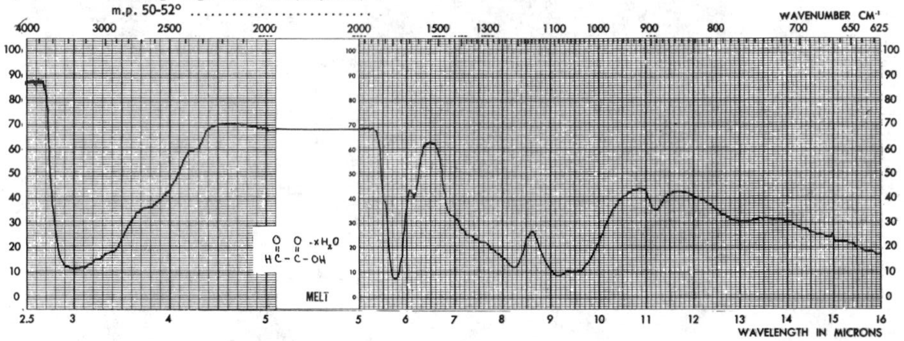

C
P7620-9 **Pyruvic acid, 95%**
CH_3COCO_2H M.W. 88.06 n_D^{20} 1.4335

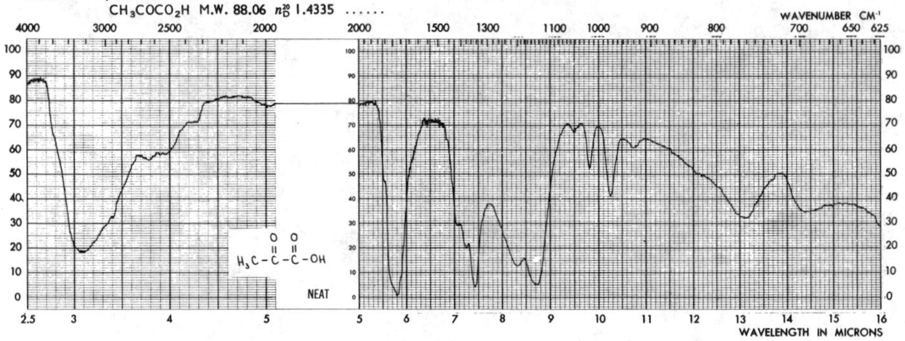

D
K40-1 **2-Ketobutyric acid**
$C_2H_5COCO_2H$ M.W. 102.09 m.p. 33-36°

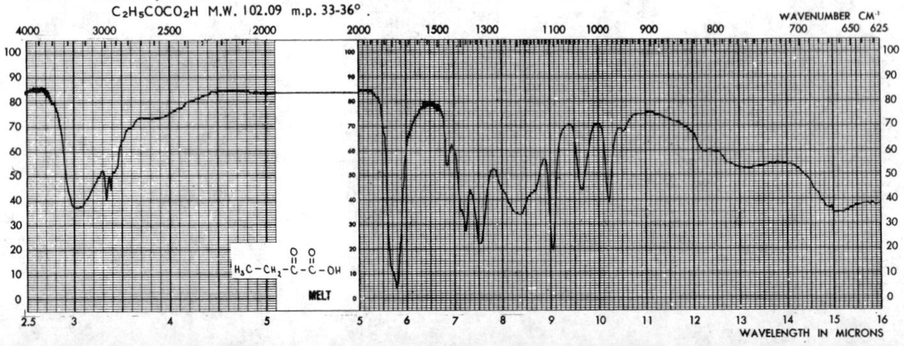

E
K120-1 **2-Ketodecanoic acid**
$CH_3(CH_2)_7COCO_2H$ M.W. 186.25 m.p. 45-48°

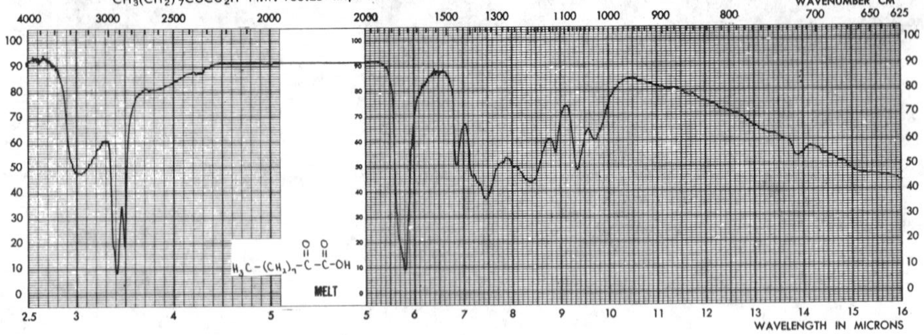

F
L200-9 **Levulinic acid**
$CH_3COCH_2CH_2CO_2H$ M.W. 116.12 n_D^{20} 1.4396
b.p. 245-246°

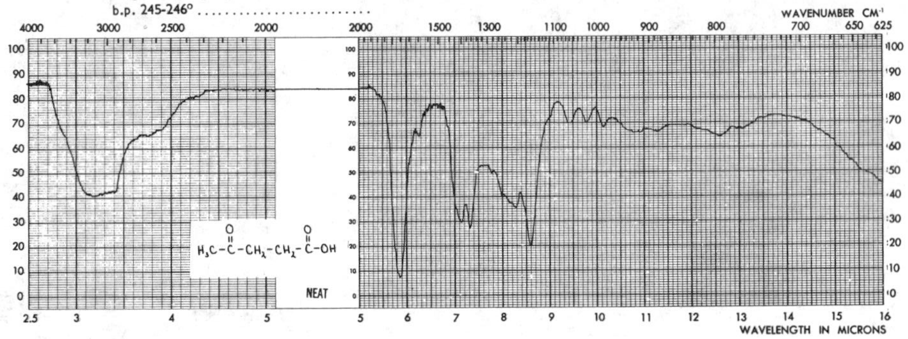

G
19,015-2
2-Methyllevulinic acid, 95%
$CH_3COCH_2CH(CH_3)CO_2H$ FW 130.14
bp 165°/40mm. n_D^{20} 1.4431 d 1.110 *Beil.* 3,689
Disp. C

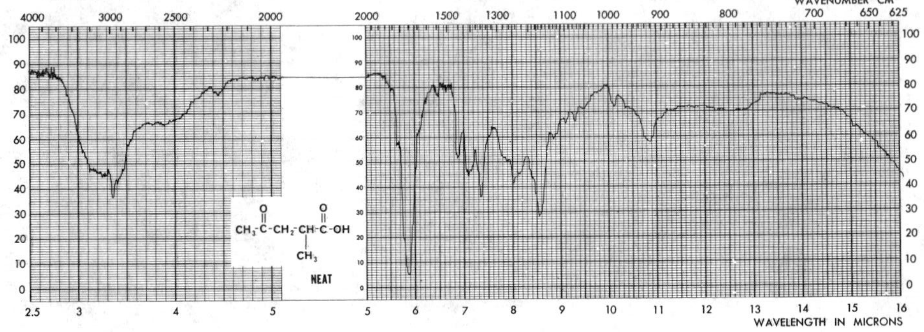

H
A1320-4 **4-Acetylbutyric acid** (5-ketohexanoic acid)
$CH_3CO(CH_2)_3CO_2H$ M.W. 130.14
n_D^{20} 1.4451

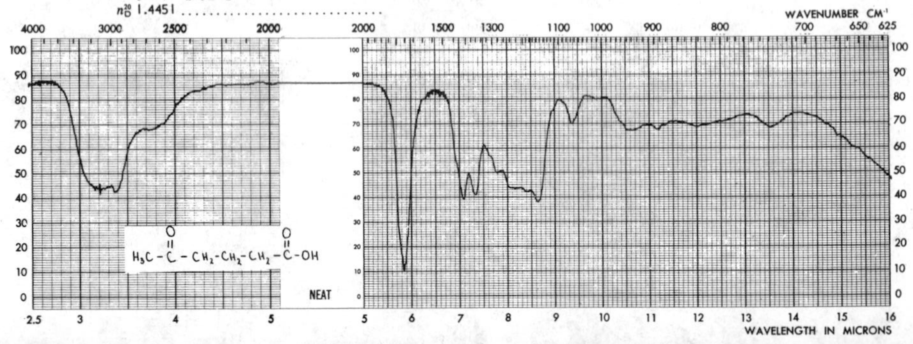

A

17,125-5
Oxalacetic acid
$HO_2CCH_2COCO_2H$
M.W. 132.07 m.p. 161° (dec.) Beil. 3,777

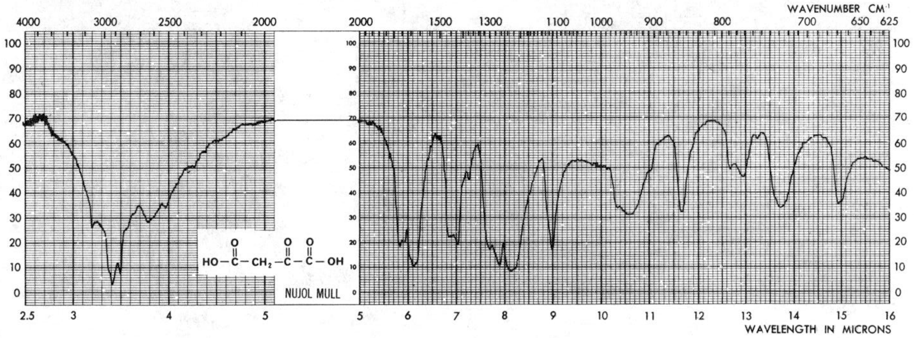

NUJOL MULL

B

K160-0 **2-Ketoglutaric acid**
$HO_2CCH_2CH_2COCO_2H$ M.W. 146.10
m.p. 113-115°

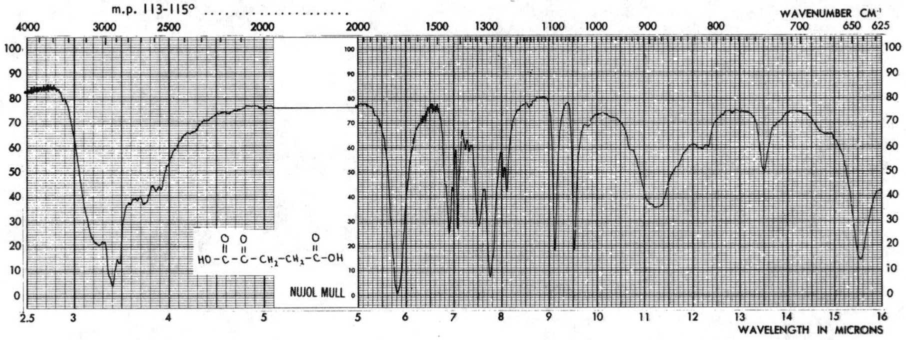

NUJOL MULL

C

16,511-5
1,3-Acetonedicarboxylic acid (3-oxoglutaric acid)
$HO_2CCH_2COCH_2CO_2H$
M.W. 146.1 m.p. 133° (dec.) Beil. 3,789

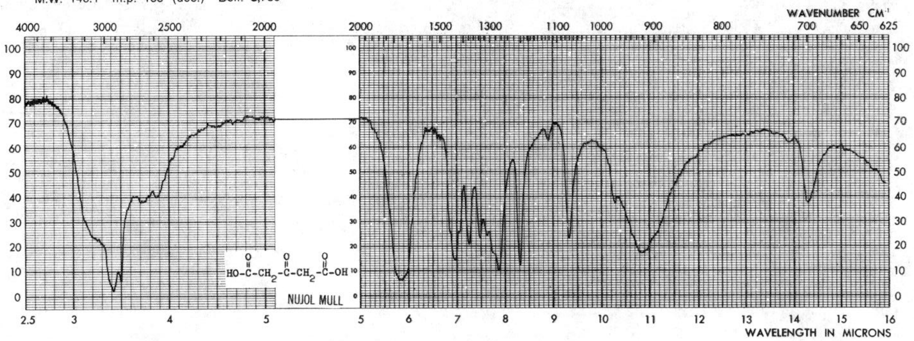

NUJOL MULL

D

K350-6 **4-Ketopimelic acid**
$HO_2CCH_2CH_2COCH_2CH_2CO_2H$ M.W. 174.15
m.p. 140-141°

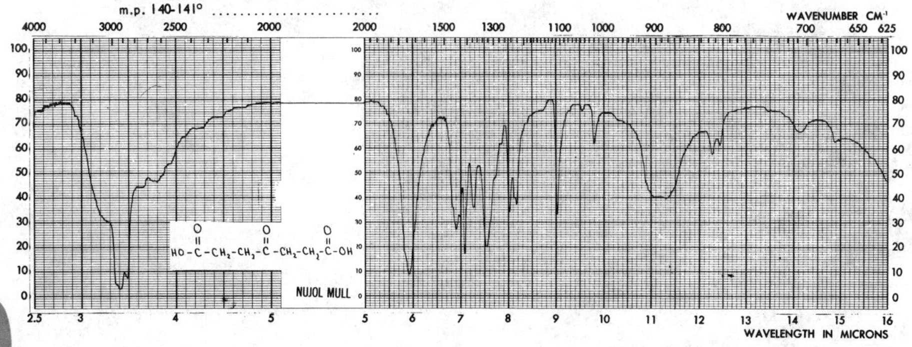

NUJOL MULL

E

11,010-8 **Pinonic acid** (3-acetyl-2,2-dimethylcyclobutaneacetic acid)
$CH_3COC_4H_4(CH_3)_2CH_2CO_2H$ M.W. 184.24 m.p. 104-107°

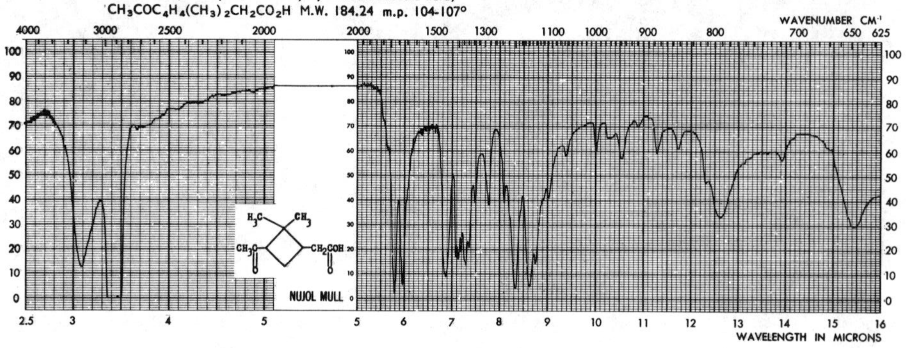

NUJOL MULL

F

18,692-9
1-Chloro-2-oxo-1-cyclopentanecarboxylic acid
(2-chlorocyclopentanone-2-carboxylic acid)
$ClC_5H_6(=O)CO_2H$ FW 162.57 mp 109-113° (dec.)
Disp. C

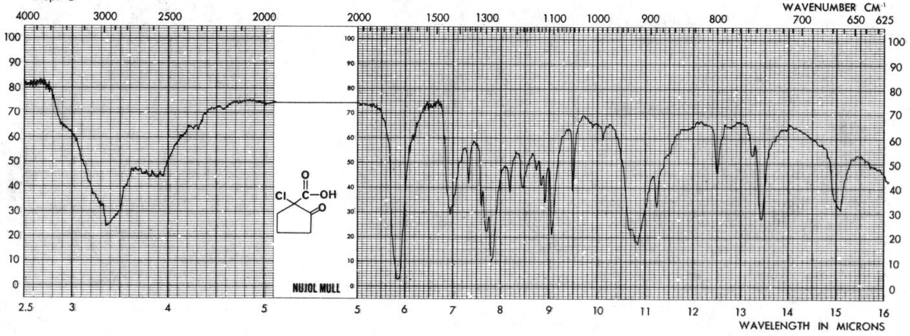

NUJOL MULL

G

19,572-3
3,4-Dihydro-2,2-dimethyl-4-oxo-2*H*-pyran-6-carboxylic acid
FW 170.16 mp 170° (dec.) *Beil.* 3,764 Disp. C

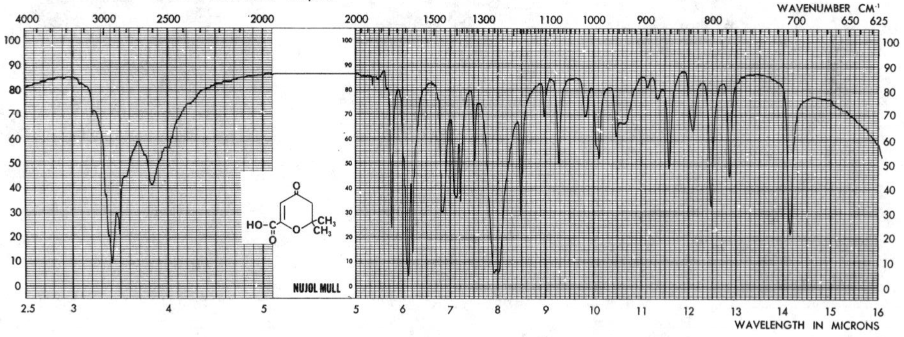

NUJOL MULL

H

12,495-8 **Chelidonic acid** (4-oxo-4H-pyran-2,6-dicarboxylic acid) **monohydrate**
M.W. 184.10 m.p. 265° (dec.)

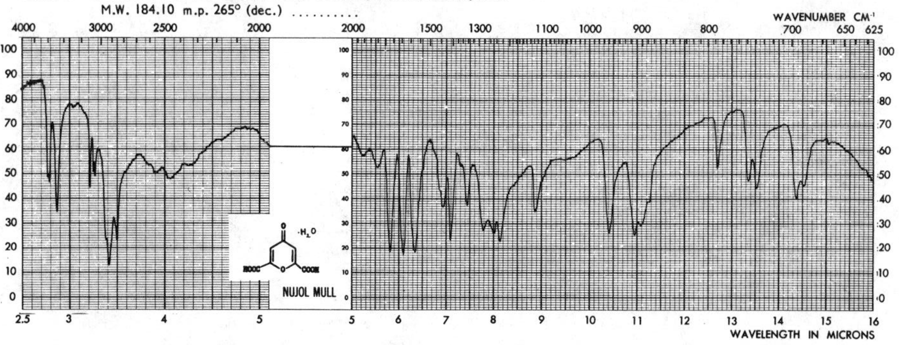

NUJOL MULL

15,259-5 2-Oxo-1,1,3,3-cyclohexanetetrapropionic acid (cyclohexanone-2,2,6,6-tetrapropionic acid)
(O:)$C_6H_6(CH_2CH_2CO_2H)_4$ M.W. 386.40
m.p. 179-180°

C11,660-2 Cyclopropanecarboxylic acid, puriss.
$C_3H_5CO_2H$ M.W. 86.09 n_D^{20} 1.4380
m.p. 17-19°

20,560-5
1-Methylcyclopropanecarboxylic acid, 98%
$CH_3C_3H_4CO_2H$ FW 100.12 mp 34-36°
bp 183-185° *Beil.* 9(2),5 Disp. I

20,975-9
2-Methylcyclopropanecarboxylic acid, 98%
$CH_3C_3H_4CO_2H$ FW 100.12 bp 190-191°/745mm.
n_D^{20} 1.4395 d 1.027 *Beil.* 9,6 Disp. C,I

20,976-7
2,2-Dichloro-1-methylcyclopropanecarboxylic acid, 98%
$Cl_2C_3H_2(CH_3)CO_2H$ FW 169.01 mp 60-65°
bp 85°/8mm. Disp. C

22,053-1
3-Methylenecyclopropane-*trans*-1,2-dicarboxylic acid
FW 142.11 mp 193-196° *Beil.* 9(4),3935
Disp. C

C9560-9 Cyclobutanecarboxylic acid
$C_4H_7CO_2H$ M.W. 100.12
n_D^{20} 1.4433

C11,200-3 Cyclopentanecarboxylic acid
$C_5H_9CO_2H$ M.W. 114.14 n_D^{20} 1.4527

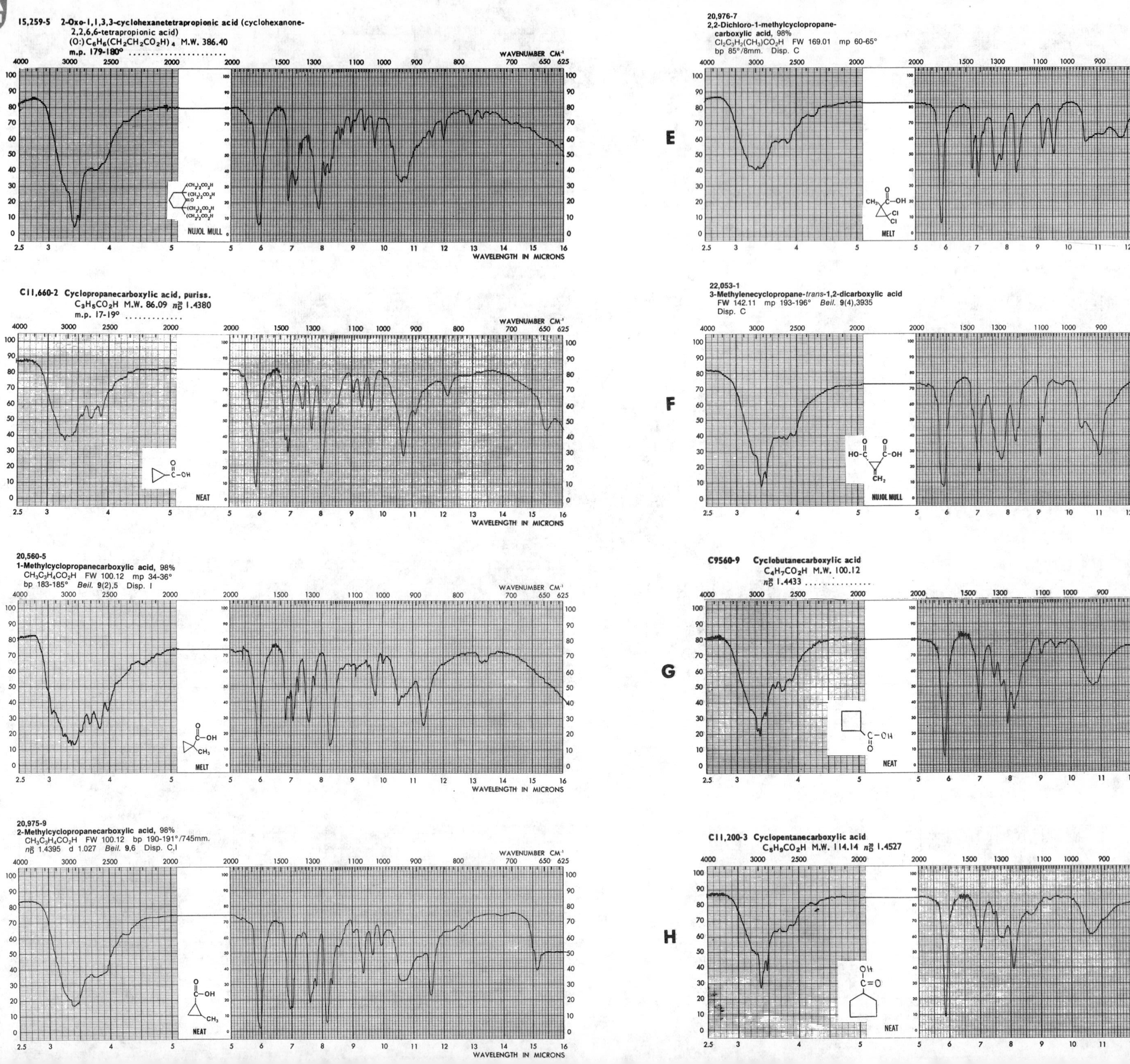

A 12,549-0 **Cyclopentylacetic acid** (cyclopentaneacetic acid)
$C_5H_9CH_2CO_2H$ M.W. 128.17 n_D^{20} 1.4502

B C11,590-8
3-Cyclopentylpropionic acid
cyclopentanepropionic acid
$C_5H_9CH_2CH_2CO_2H$
M.W. 142.2 b.p. 130-132°/12mm. n_D^{20} 1.4570
IR 246G

C C11,540-1 **2-Cyclopentyl-n-hexanoic acid** (α-butylcyclopentaneacetic acid)
$CH_3(CH_2)_3CH(C_5H_9)CO_2H$ M.W. 184.28 n_D^{20} 1.4579

D 13,588-7 **(2-Cyclopenten-1-yl)malonic acid**
$HO_2CCH(C_5H_7)CO_2H$ M.W. 170.17
m.p. 146-148°

E C11,285-2 **2-Cyclopentene-1-acetic acid**
$C_5H_7CH_2CO_2H$ M.W. 126.16 n_D^{20} 1.4657

F 10,183-4 **Cyclohexanecarboxylic acid** (hexahydrobenzoic acid)
$C_6H_{11}CO_2H$ M.W. 128.17 m.p. 31-32°

G 14,282-4 **1-Methyl-1-cyclohexanecarboxylic acid**
$CH_3C_6H_{10}CO_2H$ M.W. 142.20 m.p. 36-39°

H C10,450-7 **Cyclohexylacetic acid** (cyclohexaneacetic acid)
$C_6H_{11}CH_2CO_2H$ M.W. 142.20 m.p. 33°

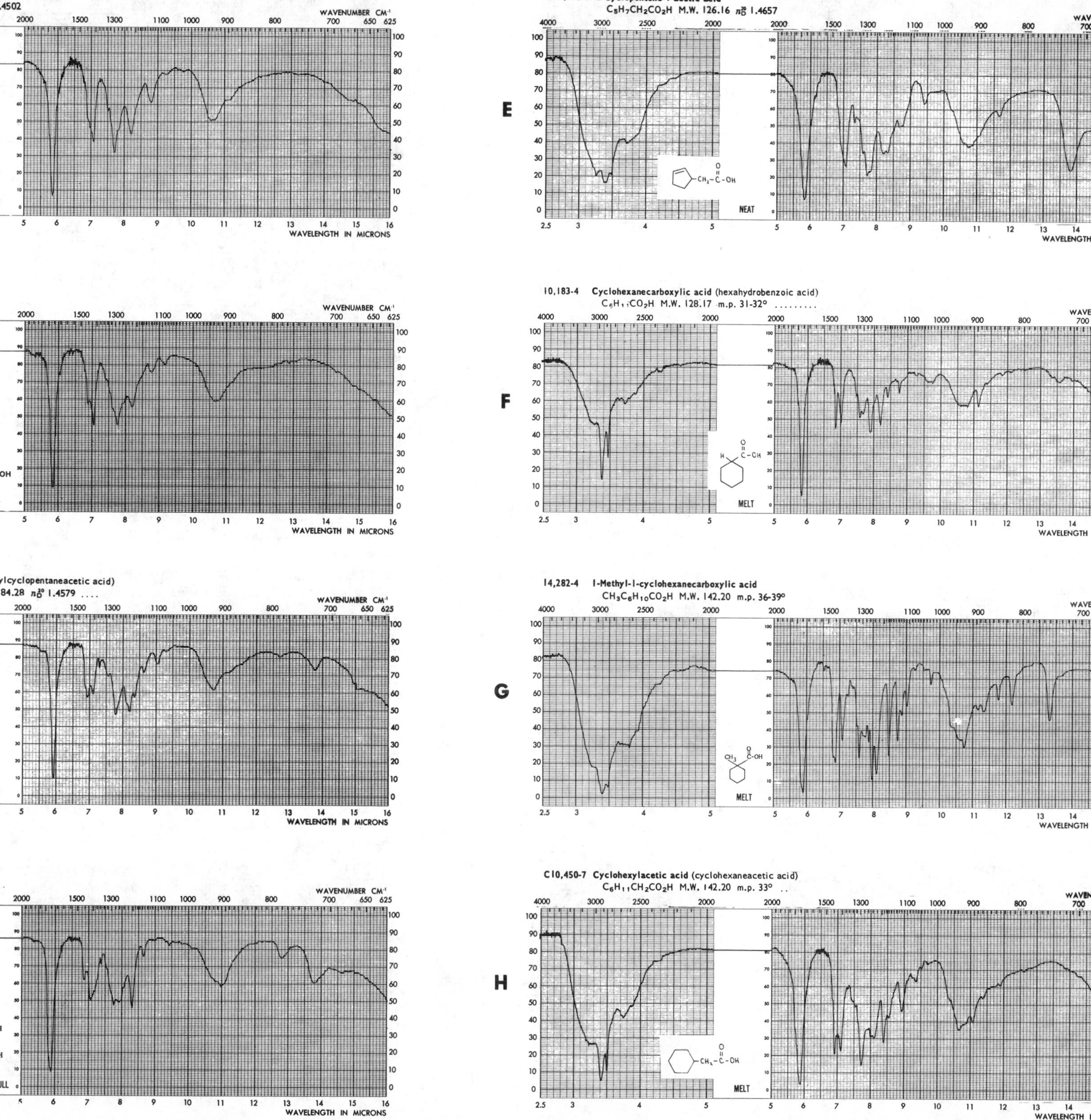

A 17,134-4
1,1-Cyclohexanediacetic acid, 99%
$C_6H_{10}(CH_2CO_2H)_2$
M.W. 200.23 m.p. 181-185°

B **C10,813-8 3-Cyclohexylpropionic acid** (cyclohexanepropionic acid)
$C_6H_{11}CH_2CH_2CO_2H$ M.W. 156.22 n_D^{20} 1.4634
b.p. 143°/11 mm.

C 12,761-2 **Cyclohexanebutyric acid** (4-cyclohexylbutyric acid)
$C_6H_{11}(CH_2)_3CO_2H$ M.W. 170.25
m.p. 30-32°

D **C10,501-5 2-Cyclohexylbutyric acid** [α-(ethyl)-cyclohexaneacetic acid], tech.
$C_2H_5CH(C_6H_{11})CO_2H$ M.W. 170.25
m.p. 53-59°

E **C9850-0 Cycloheptanecarboxylic acid**
$C_7H_{13}CO_2H$ M.W. 142.20 n_D^{20} 1.4704

F **10,153-2**
1-Hydroxycycloheptanecarboxylic acid, 97%
$HOC_7H_{12}CO_2H$
M.W. 158.2 m.p. 74-77° Beil. 10,7

G **C12,143-6 Cycloundecanecarboxylic acid**
$C_{11}H_{21}CO_2H$ M.W. 198.31 n_D^{20} 1.4911

H **12,726-4 2-Norbornaneacetic acid, puriss.**
M.W. 154.21 n_D^{20} 1.4822 b.p. 107-108°/3 mm.

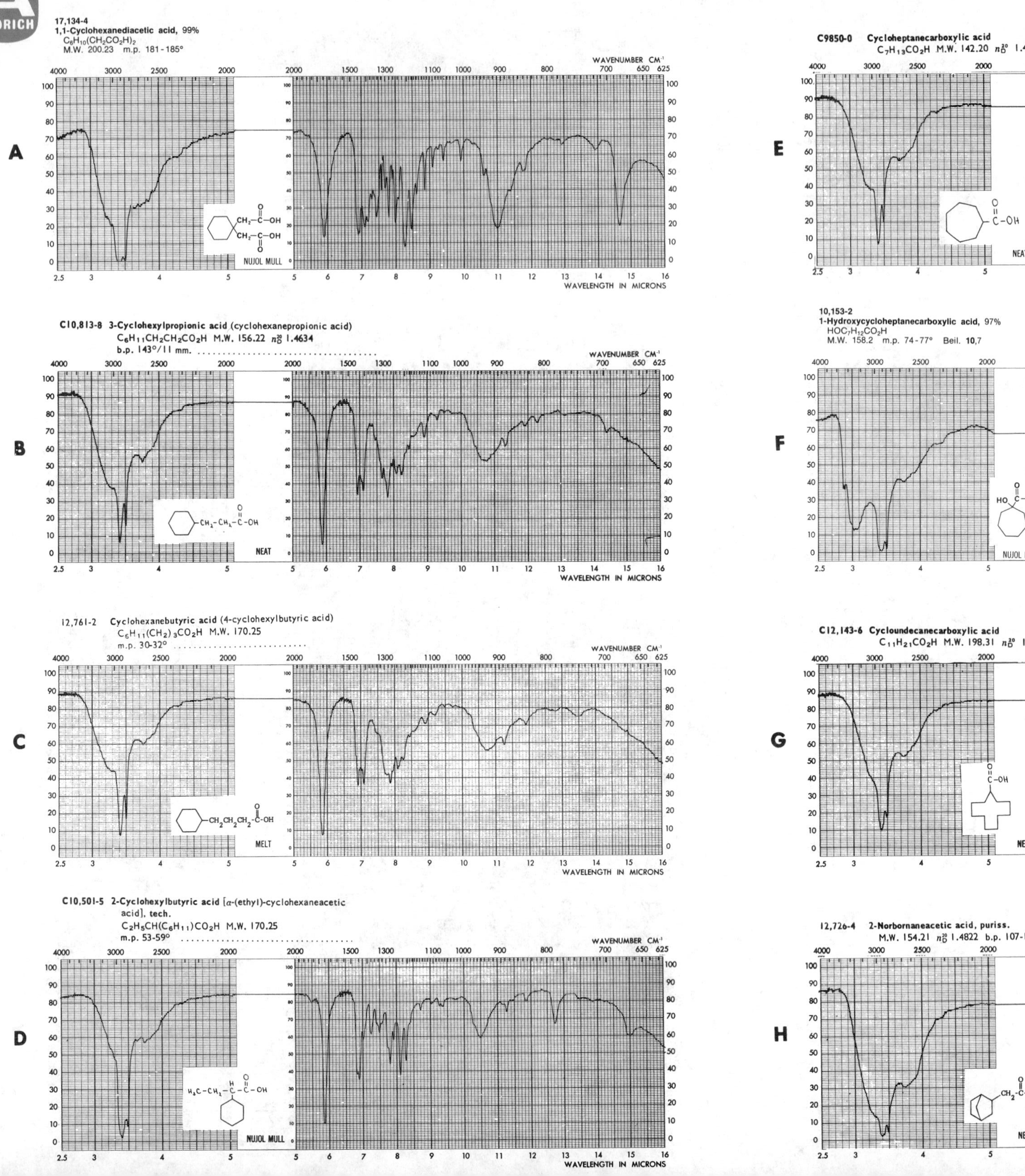

A 14,757-5 exo-α-Chloro-2-norbornaneacetic acid
M.W. 188.66 m.p. 44-46° ....
MELT

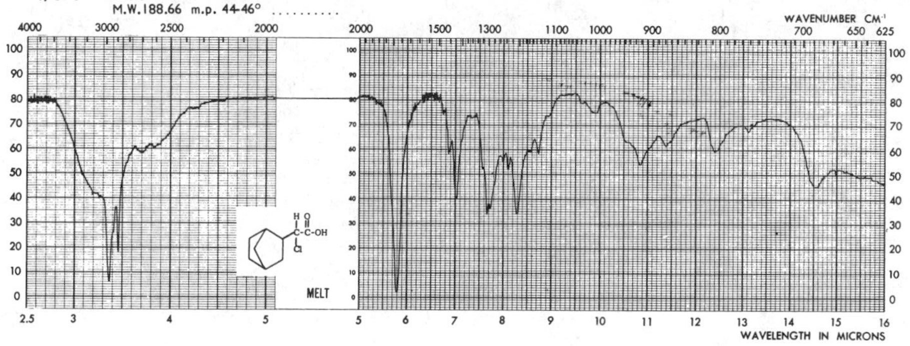

B 19,340-2
(+)-3-Pinanecarboxylic acid, 97%
FW 182.27 mp 52-56° $[\alpha]^{23}+29.6°$ (c=5, $CHCl_3$)
Disp. C
NUJOL MULL

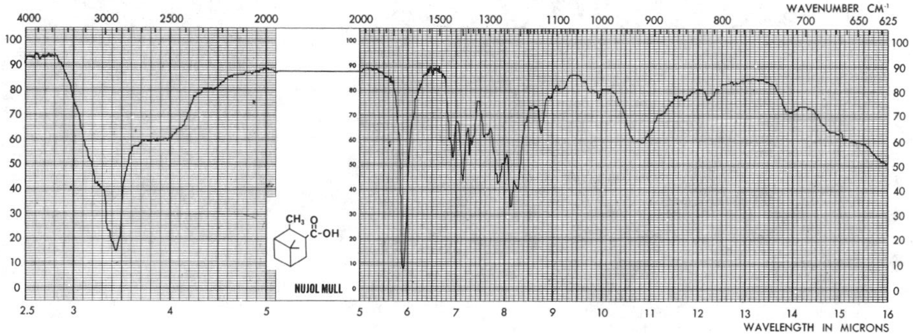

C 19,341-0
(-)-3-Pinanecarboxylic acid, 97%
FW 182.27 mp 56-59° $[\alpha]^{23}-31.2°$ (c=5, $CHCl_3$)
Disp. C
MELT

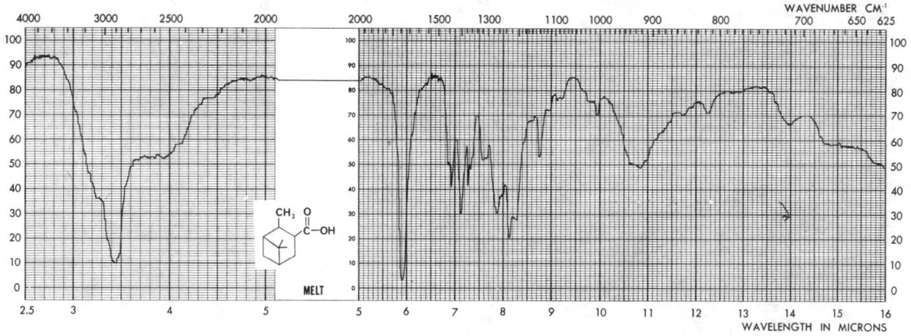

D T5725-8 Tricyclo[5.2.1.0^{2,6}]decane-4-carboxylic acid
M.W. 180.24 n_D^{20} 1.5095 ....
MELT

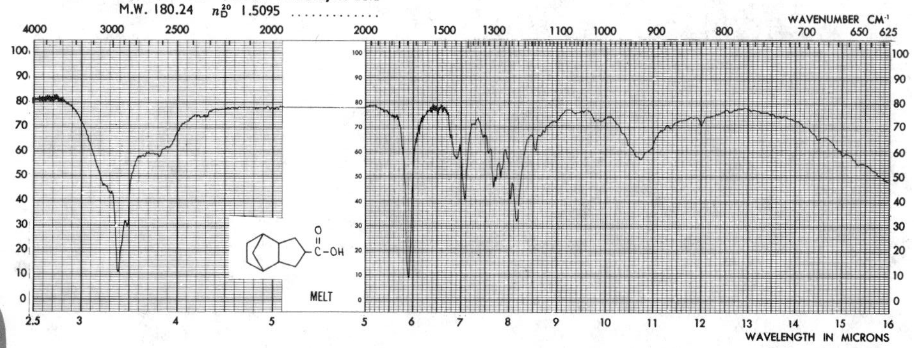

E 10,639-9 1-Adamantanecarboxylic acid
M.W. 180.25 m.p. 174-175°
NUJOL MULL

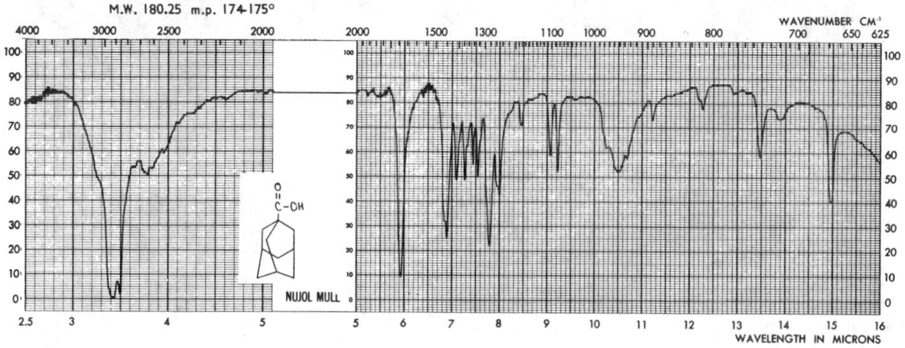

F 18,748-8
3-Methyl-1-adamantaneacetic acid, 99%
FW 208.30 mp 102-104° Disp. C
NUJOL MULL

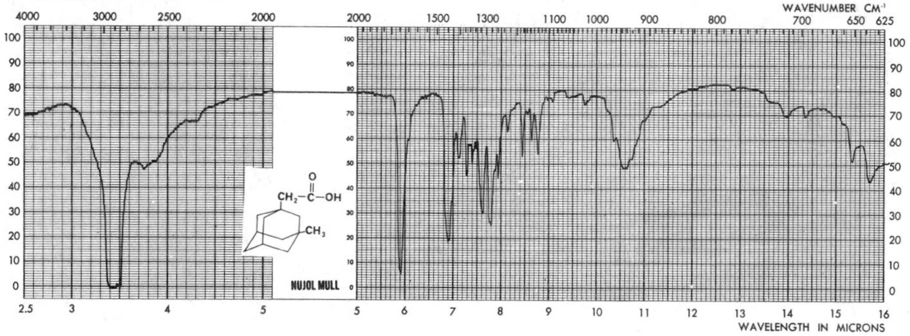

G C10,235-0 3-Cyclohexene-1-carboxylic acid (1,2,3,6-tetrahydrobenzoic acid)
$C_6H_9CO_2H$ M.W. 126.16 n_D^{20} 1.4802 ......
NEAT

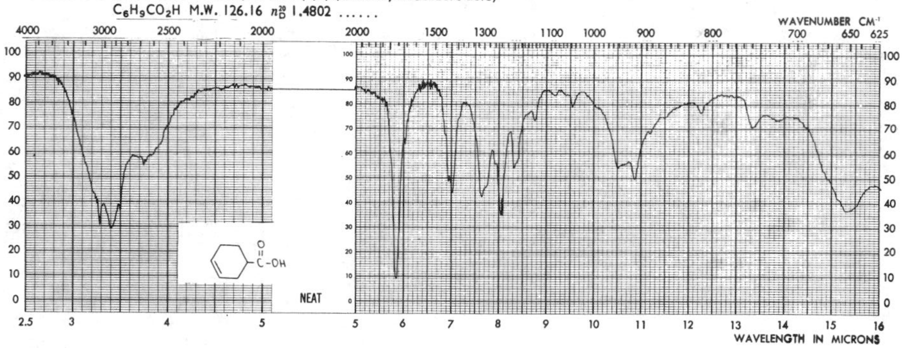

H C10,380 α-(1-Cyclohexenyl)-butyric acid
$CH_3CH_2CH(C_6H_9)CO_2H$ M.W. 168.24 n_D^{20} 1.4807
NEAT

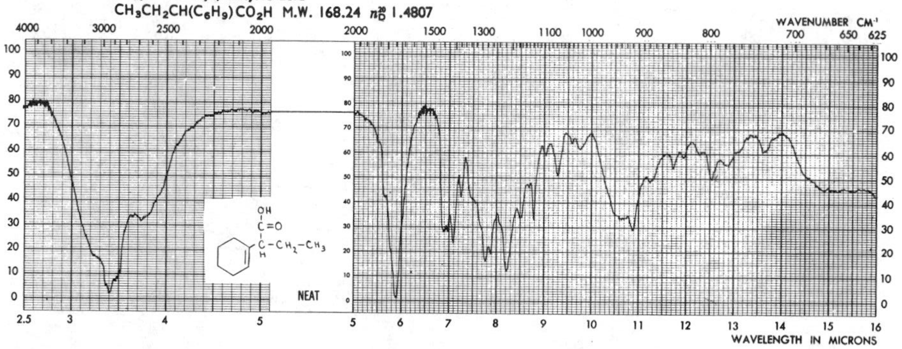

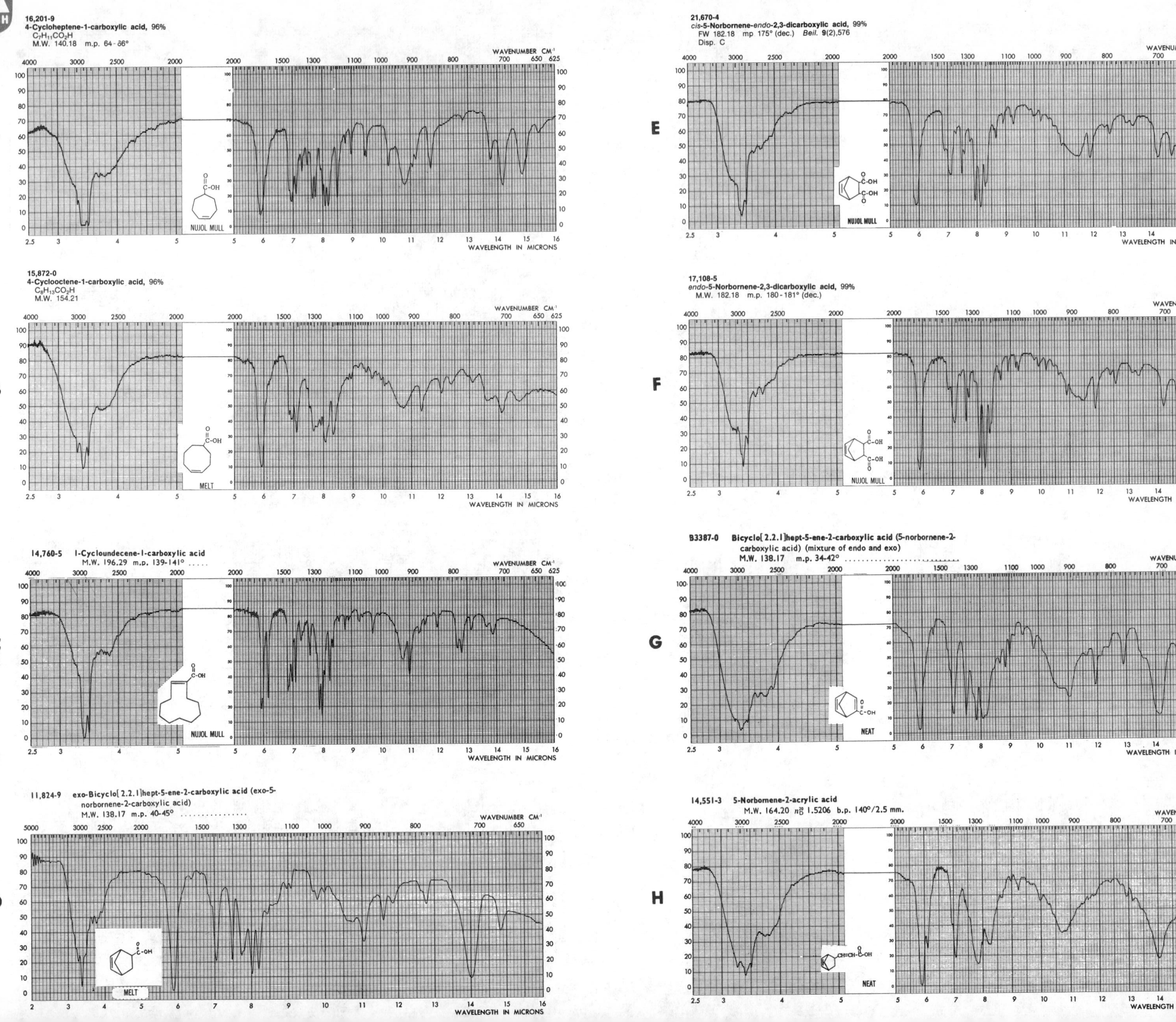
ALDRICH
A
16,201-9
4-Cycloheptene-1-carboxylic acid, 96%
$C_7H_{11}CO_2H$
M.W. 140.18 m.p. 64-66°
NUJOL MULL
B
15,872-0
4-Cyclooctene-1-carboxylic acid, 96%
$C_8H_{13}CO_2H$
M.W. 154.21
MELT
C
14,760-5 1-Cycloundecene-1-carboxylic acid
M.W. 196.29 m.p. 139-141°
NUJOL MULL
D
11,824-9 exo-Bicyclo[2.2.1]hept-5-ene-2-carboxylic acid (exo-5-norbornene-2-carboxylic acid)
M.W. 138.17 m.p. 40-45°
MELT
E
21,670-4
cis-5-Norbornene-endo-2,3-dicarboxylic acid, 99%
FW 182.18 mp 175° (dec.) Beil. 9(2),576
Disp. C
NUJOL MULL
F
17,108-5
endo-5-Norbornene-2,3-dicarboxylic acid, 99%
M.W. 182.18 m.p. 180-181° (dec.)
NUJOL MULL
G
B3387-0 Bicyclo[2.2.1]hept-5-ene-2-carboxylic acid (5-norbornene-2-carboxylic acid) (mixture of endo and exo)
M.W. 138.17 m.p. 34-42°
NEAT
H
14,551-3 5-Norbornene-2-acrylic acid
M.W. 164.20 n_D^{20} 1.5206 b.p. 140°/2.5 mm.
NEAT
WAVENUMBER CM⁻¹
WAVELENGTH IN MICRONS

A

21,835-9
l-Perillic acid, 95%
FW 166.22 mp 129-131° $[\alpha]^{21}$ -102° (c=2, CH_3OH)
Beil. 9,85 Disp. C

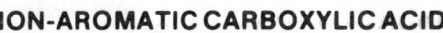

NUJOL MULL

B

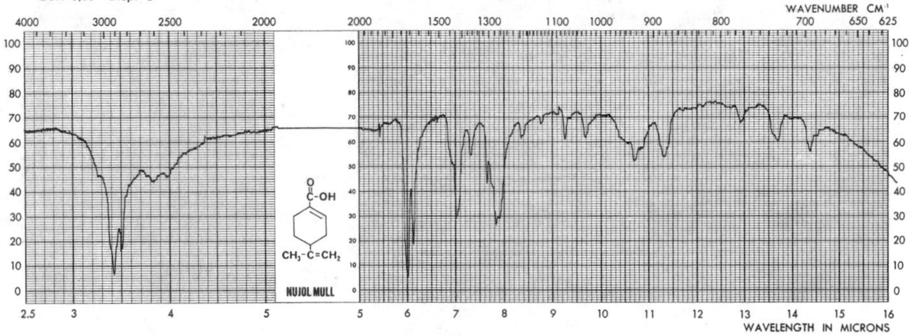

C9580-3 1,1-Cyclobutanedicarboxylic acid
$C_4H_6(CO_2H)_2$ M.W. 144.13
m.p. 159-163° ....

NUJOL MULL

C

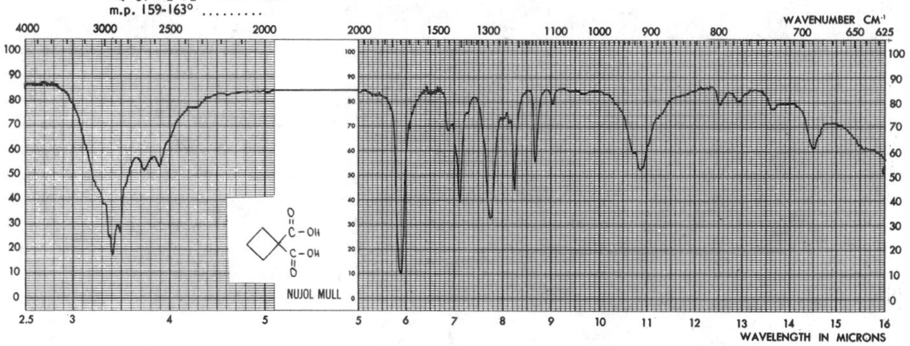

14,531-9 *trans*-1,2-Cyclobutanedicarboxylic acid
$C_4H_6(CO_2H)_2$ M.W. 144.13 m.p. 127-129°

NUJOL MULL

D

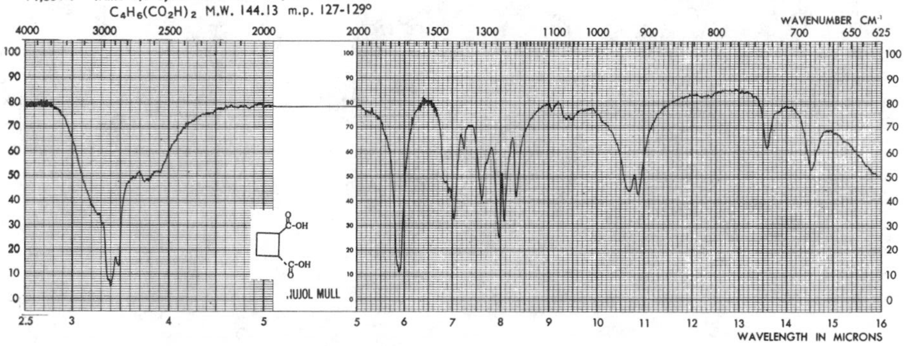

T2190-3 3,3-Tetramethyleneglutaric acid (1,1-cyclopentanediacetic acid)
$C_5H_8(CH_2CO_2H)_2$ M.W. 186.21
m.p. 175-176° ....

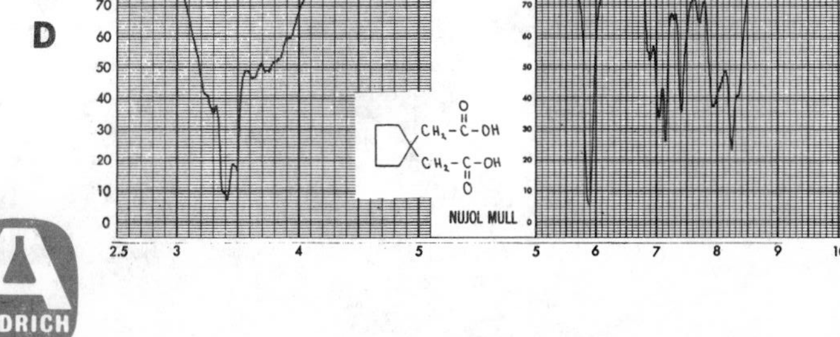

NUJOL MULL

E

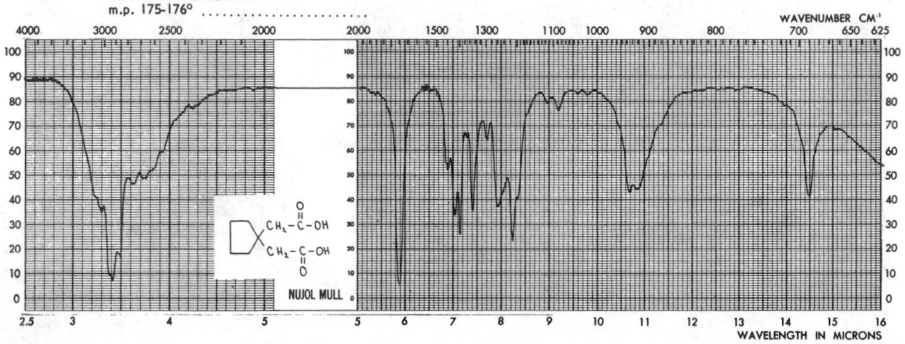

C40-9 *d*-Camphoric acid
M.W. 200.23
$[\alpha]^{25}_D$ = + 46.5° (c=10 in C_2H_5OH)

NUJOL MULL

F

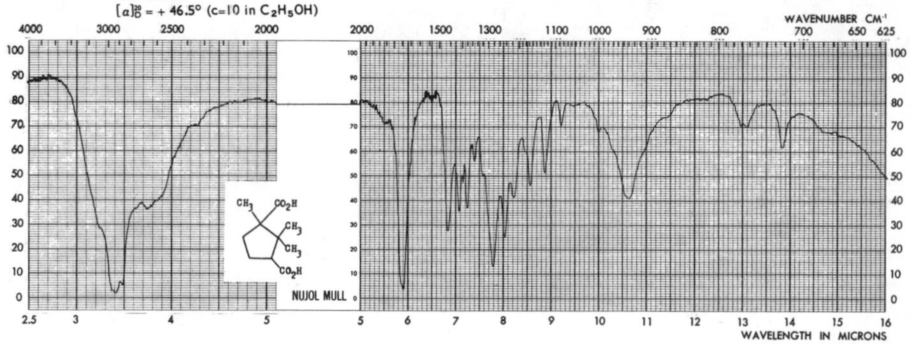

14,751-6 *trans*-1,2-Cyclohexanedicarboxylic acid (*trans*-hexahydrophthalic acid)
$C_6H_{10}(CO_2H)_2$ M.W. 172.18 m.p. 228-230°

NUJOL MULL

G

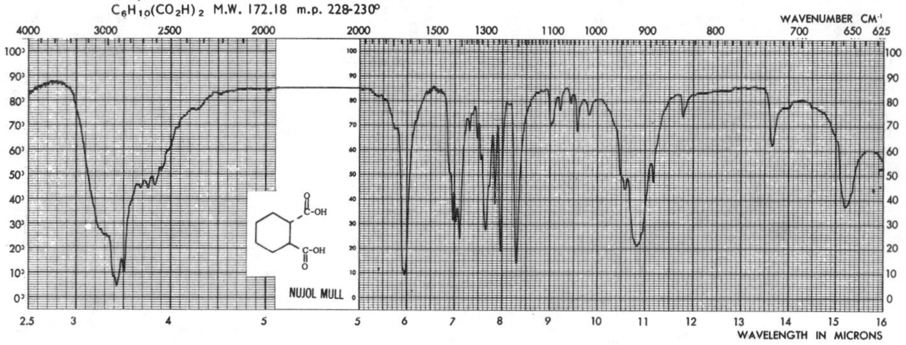

12,345-5 *cis*-1,2-Cyclohexanedicarboxylic acid (*cis*-hexahydrophthalic acid)
$C_6H_{10}(CO_2H)_2$ M.W. 172.18
m.p. 193-195° (dec.) ....

NUJOL MULL

H

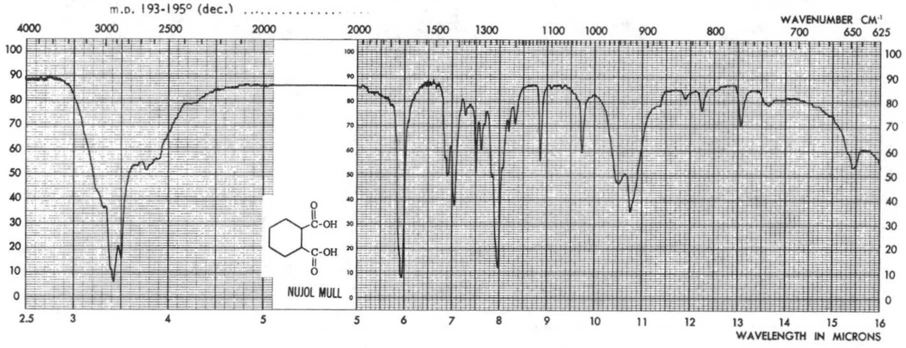

C10,075-7 *trans*-1,4-Cyclohexanedicarboxylic acid
$C_6H_{10}(CO_2H)_2$ M.W. 172.18 ....

NUJOL MULL

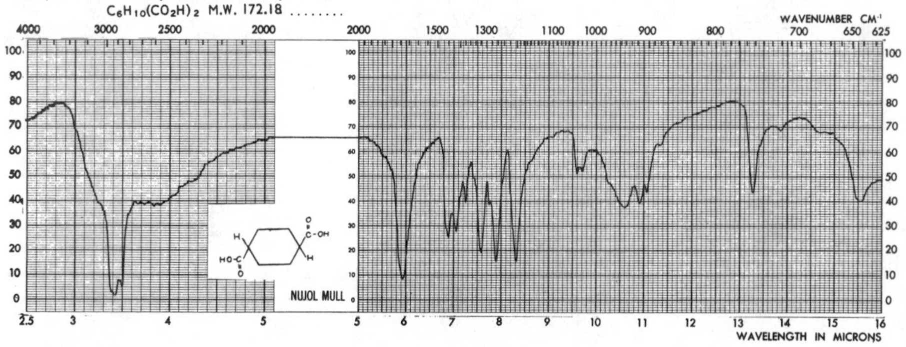

A

15,044-4 **Hexahydro-4-methylphthalic acid** (4-methyl-1,2-cyclohexane-dicarboxylic acid)
$CH_3C_6H_9(CO_2H)_2$ M.W. 186.21
m.p. 162-165°

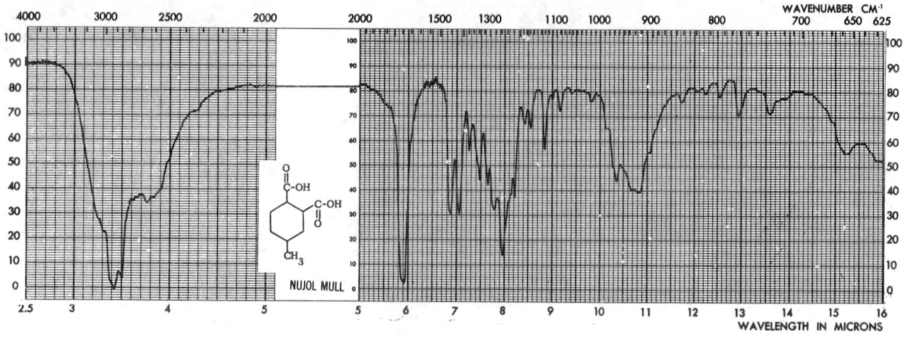

NUJOL MULL

B

14,717-6 **5-Norbornene-2,3-dicarboxylic acid** (mixture of endo and exo)
M.W. 182.18 m.p. 184° (dec.)

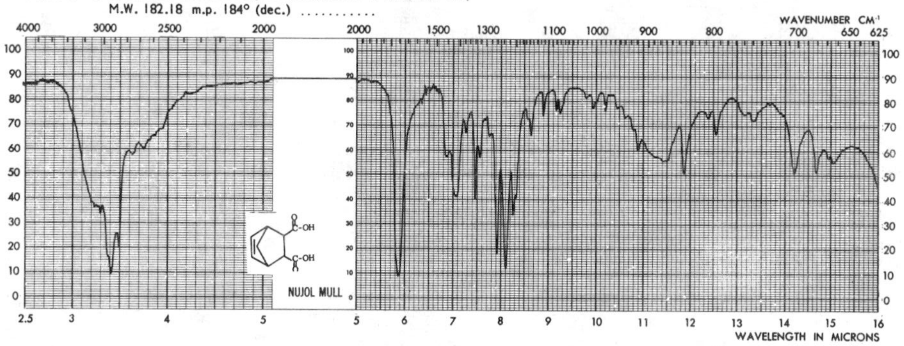

NUJOL MULL

C

C11,210-0 *cis, cis, cis, cis*-**1,2,3,4-Cyclopentanetetracarboxylic acid**
$C_5H_6(CO_2H)_4$ M.W. 246.17 m.p. 192-195° (dec.)

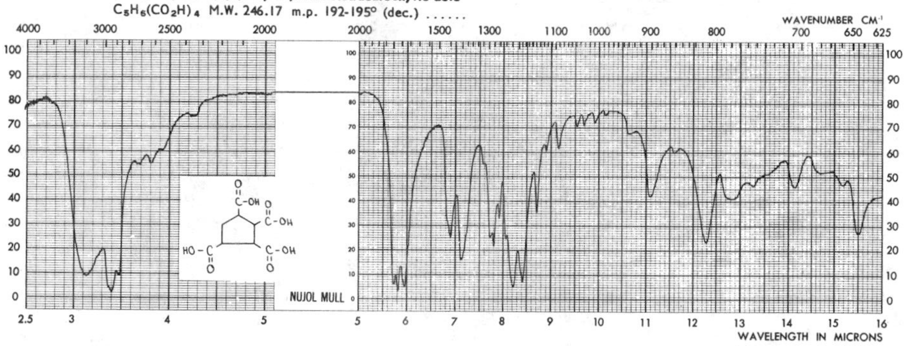

NUJOL MULL

D

14,622-6 **1,3-Adamantanediacetic acid**
M.W. 252.31 m.p. 234-237°

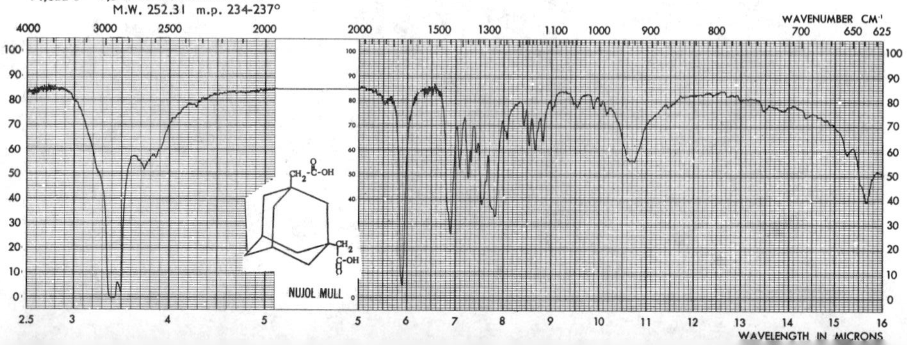

NUJOL MULL

E

14,516-5 **α-Chloro-3,5,7-trimethyl-1-adamantaneacetic acid**
M.W. 270.80 m.p. 169-171°

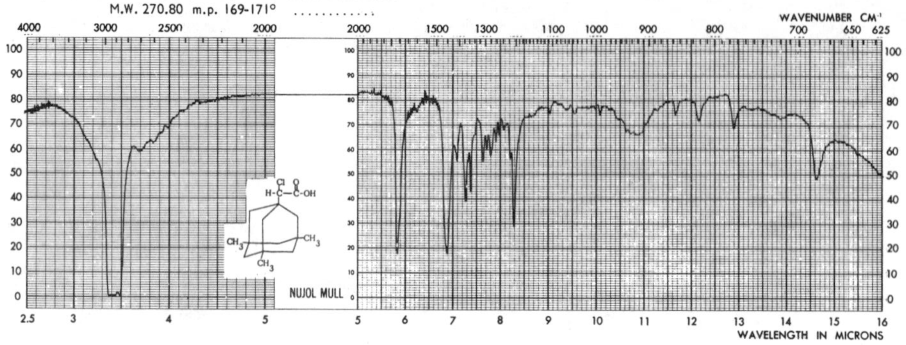

NUJOL MULL

F

12,727-2 **1-Adamantaneacetic acid, puriss.**
M.W. 194.28 m.p. 131-132°

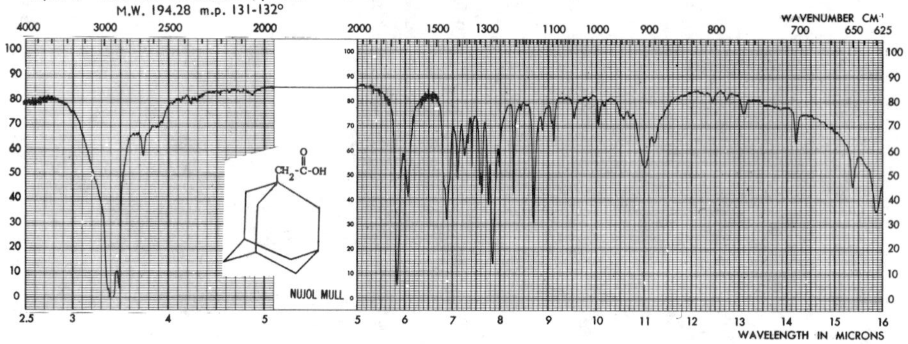

NUJOL MULL

G

17,776-8
dl-**3-Camphorcarboxylic acid**, 98%
M.W. 196.25 m.p. 133-135° (dec.) Beil. **10**(1),309

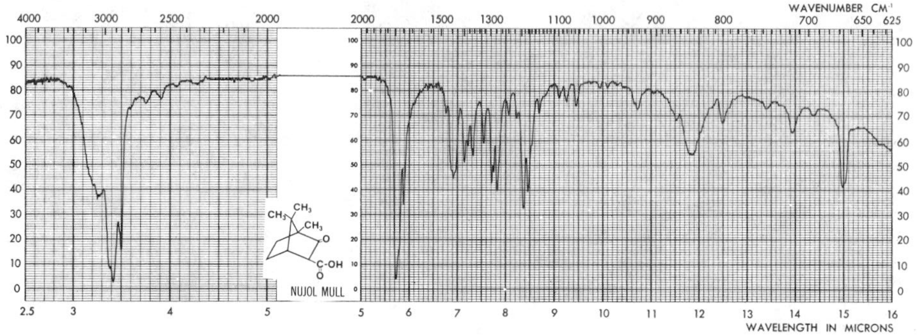

NUJOL MULL

H

D8860-7 **3-(Diethylamino)-propionic acid hydrochloride**
$(C_2H_5)_2NCH_2CH_2CO_2H{\cdot}HCl$ M.W. 181.66
m.p. 138-142°

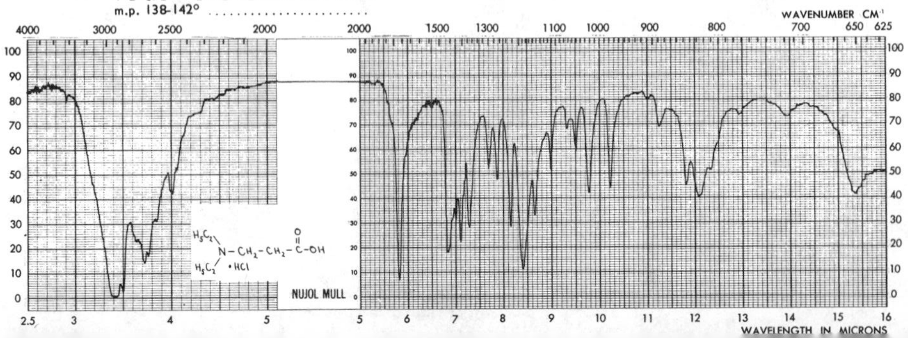

NUJOL MULL

A

C1600-8 DL-Carnitine hydrochloride
$HO_2CCH_2CH(OH)CH_2N(CH_3)_3Cl$ M.W. 197.66
m.p. 196-197° (dec.)

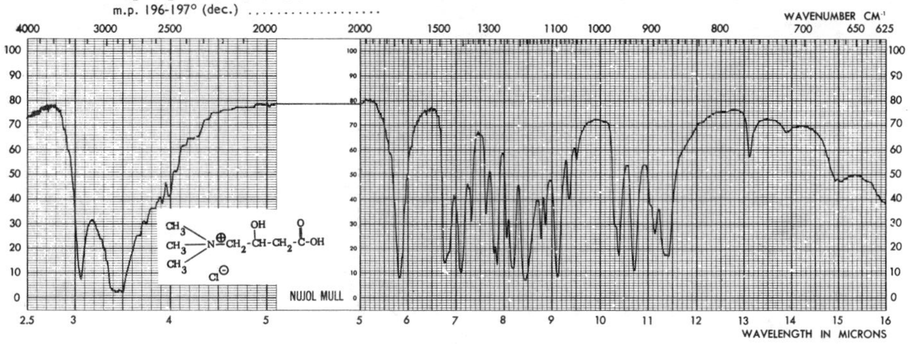

NUJOL MULL

B

A140-1 2-Acetamidoacrylic acid, puriss.
$H_2C{:}C(NHCOCH_3)CO_2H$ M.W. 129.12
m.p. 185-186° (dec.)

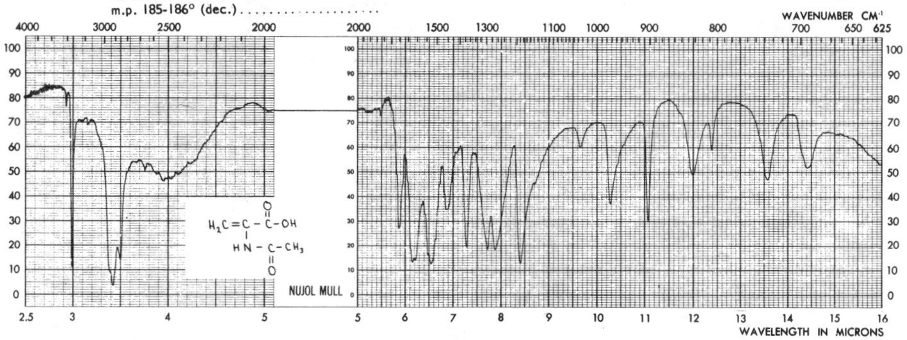

NUJOL MULL

C

85,765-3
trans-4-(Aminomethyl)-cyclohexanecarboxylic acid
(tranexamic acid)
$H_2NCH_2C_6H_{10}CO_2H$
M.W. 157.21 m.p. >300°

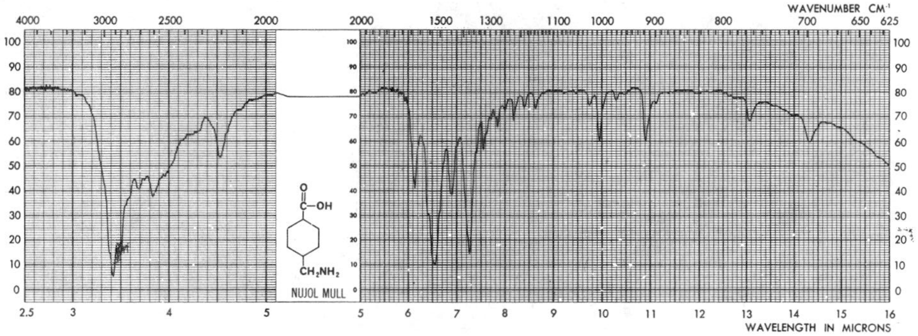

NUJOL MULL

D

I-1800-8 Isonipecotic acid (hexahydroisonicotinic acid)
M.W. 129.16 m.p. > 300°

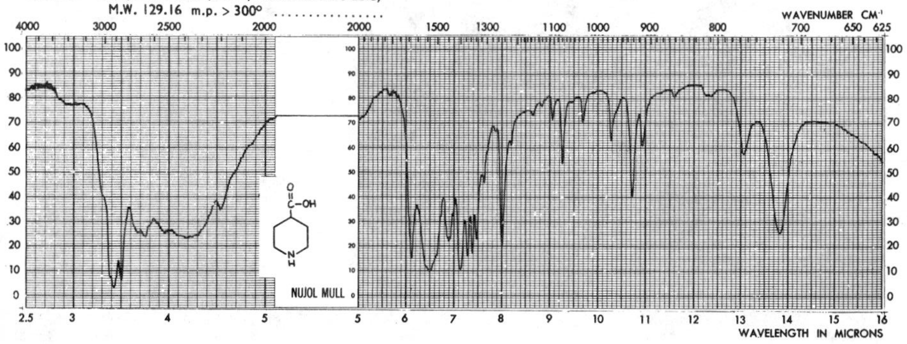

NUJOL MULL

E

D9390-2 Diethylenetriaminepentaacetic acid [(carboxymethylimino) bis(ethylene-dinitrilo)-tetraacetic acid]
$(HO_2CCH_2)_2NCH_2CH_2N(CH_2CO_2H)CH_2CH_2N(CH_2CO_2H)_2$
M.W. 393.35 m.p. 220° (dec.)

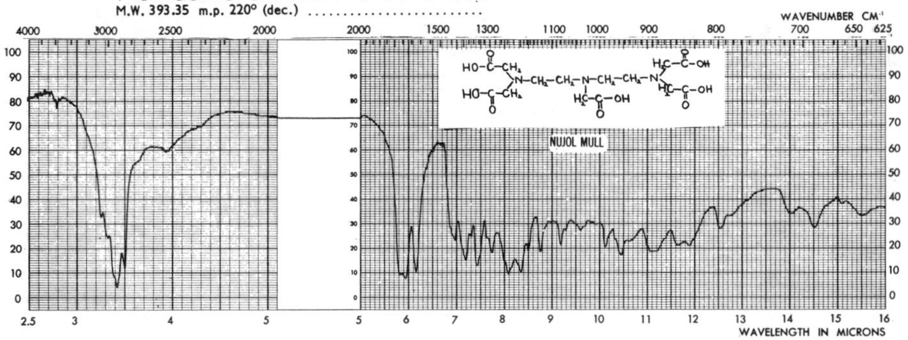

NUJOL MULL

F

N2290-8 3-Nitropropionic acid
$O_2NCH_2CH_2CO_2H$ M.W. 119.08 m.p. 60-62°

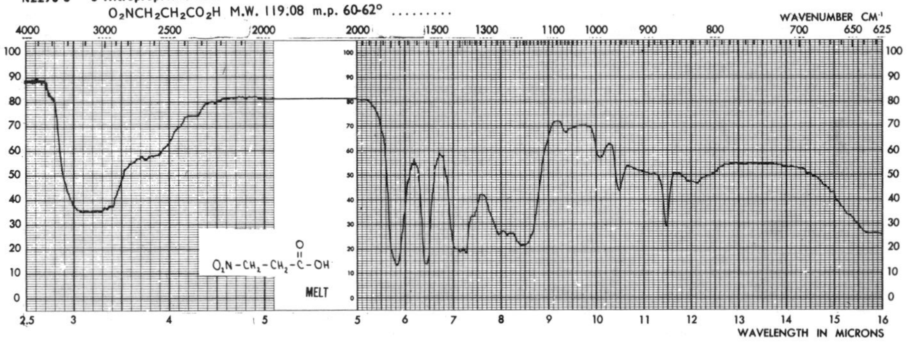

MELT

G

C1860-4 Chelidonic acid (4-oxo-4H-pyran-2,6-dicarboxylic acid), monosodium salt dihydrate, tech.
M.W. 242.12 m.p. > 325°

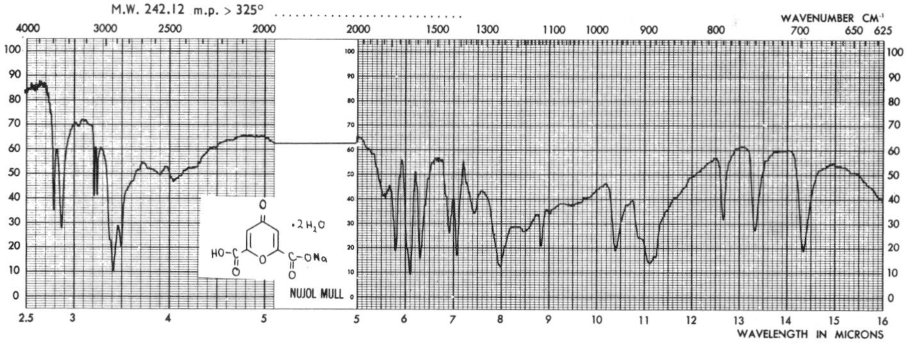

NUJOL MULL

H

17,969-8
2,3,4,6-Di-O-isopropylidene-2-keto-L-gulonic acid monohydrate, 99+%, GOLD LABEL
M.W. 292.29 m.p. 106-108°
$[\alpha]^{23}$ -15.9° (c=2, $CHCl_3$)

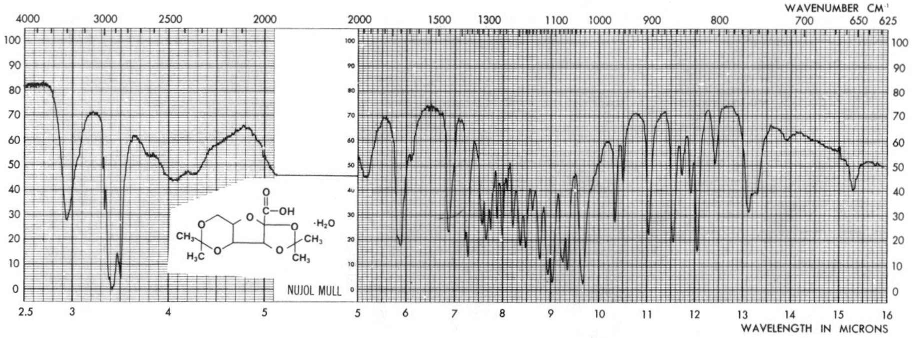

NUJOL MULL

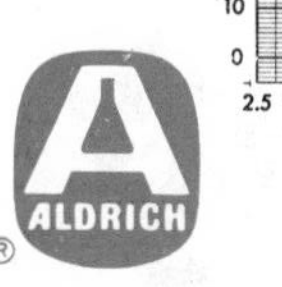

A

16,502-6
Abietic acid, tech., 85%
FW 302.46 mp 130-132° *Beil.* **9**(2),424 Disp. C

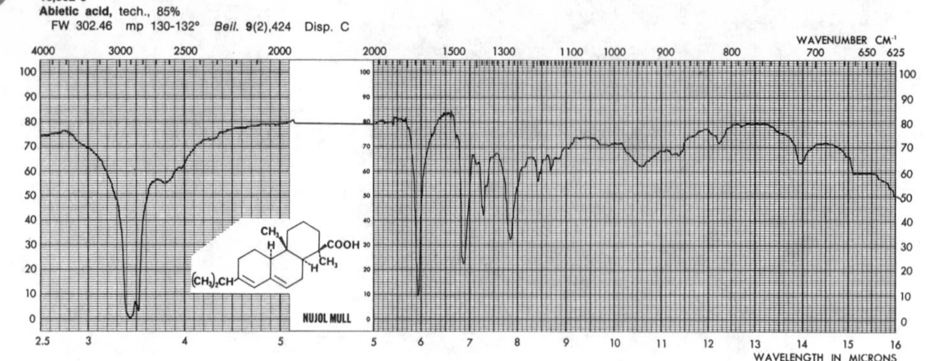

B

86,085-9
Citrinin (4,6-dihydro-8-hydroxy-3,4,5-trimethyl-6-oxo-3*H*-2-benzopyran-7-carboxylic acid)
FW 250.25 $[\alpha]^{23}$ -30.3° (c=1, C_2H_5OH) Disp. C

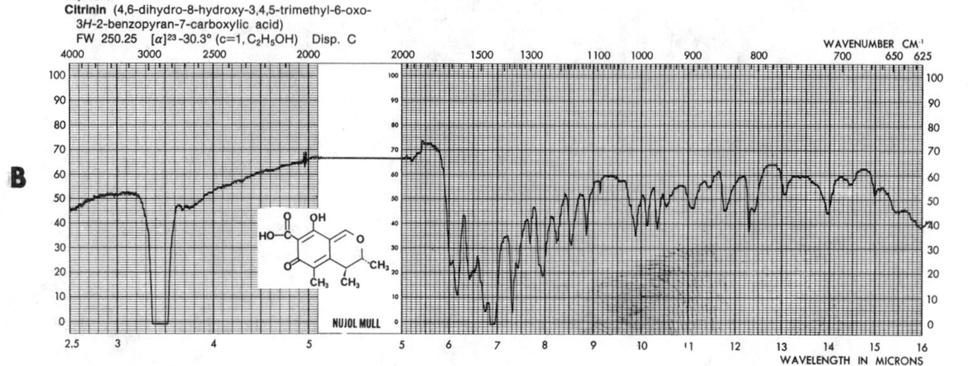

C

21,671-2
Tannic acid
FW 1701.23 mp 218° Disp. C

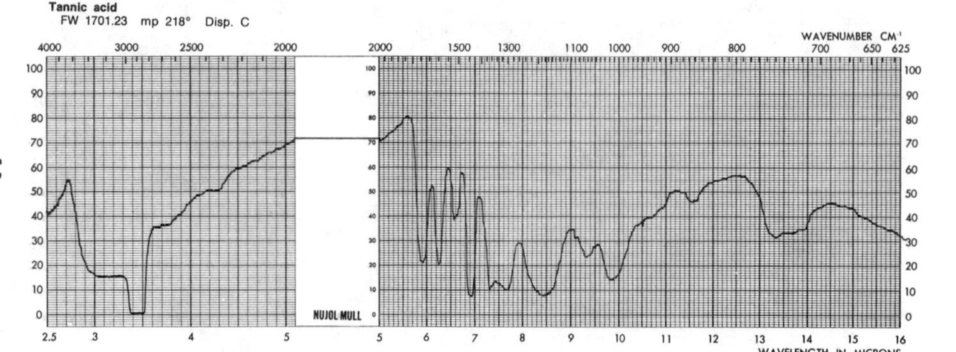

NON-AROMATIC ACID SALTS

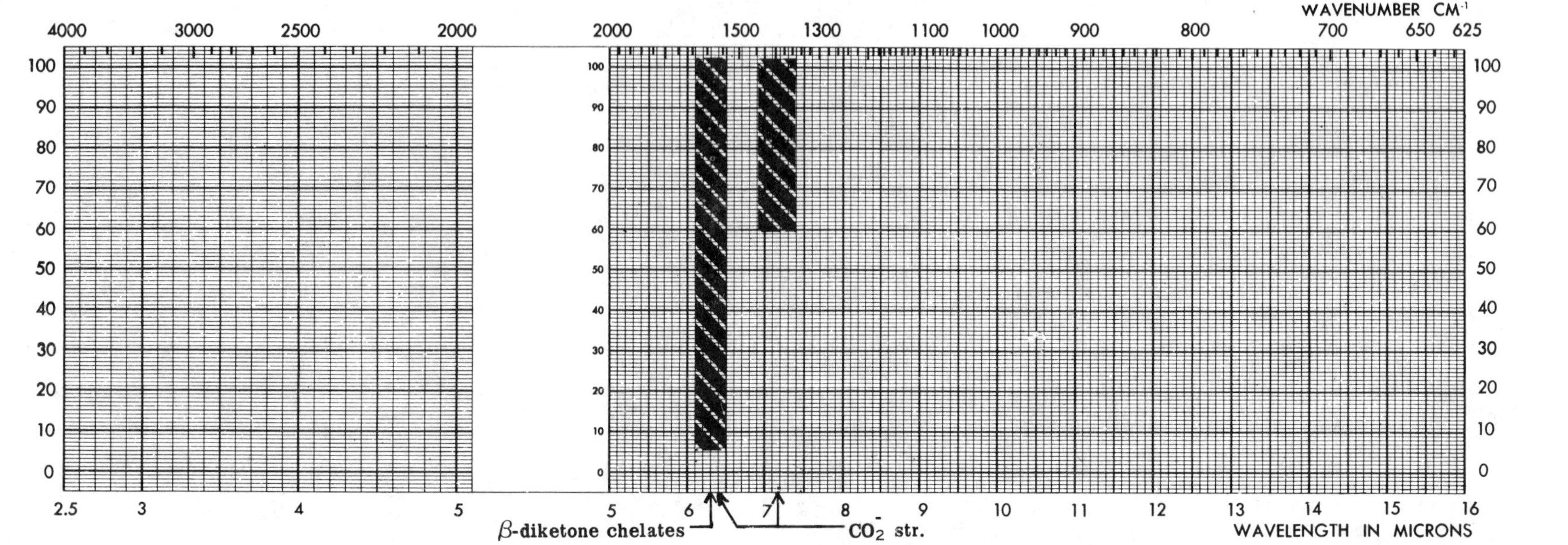

Substitution of the acidic proton in the carboxylic acid function with a different cation causes the characteristic absorptions of the carboxylic acid to vanish. The acid carbonyl absorption around 5.8 μ (1725 cm^{-1}) is replaced by a strong band between 6.2 and 6.5 μ (1615 – 1540 cm^{-1}). [The influence of an adjacent CF_3 group shifts this band to 5.9 – 6.1 μ (1695 – 1640 cm^{-1}), see spectra 327F—328A.

The metal chelated acetylacetonates of this section show a pair of very strong absorptions between 6.2 and 6.6 μ (1615 – 1515 cm^{-1}). In the case of the tin and vanadium members, these two absorptions are fused into a single strong absorption at 6.5 μ (1540 cm^{-1}). In spectra 333E to 334G, the absorptions are shifted to a lower wavelength again due to the influence of the CF_3 group.

A 10,760-3 **Formic acid, sodium salt** (sodium formate)
HCO_2Na M.W. 68.01 m.p. 261° (dec.)
NUJOL MULL

B 10,761-1 **Formic acid, calcium salt** (calcium formate)
$(HCO_2)_2Ca$ M.W. 130.11 m.p. >300°
NUJOL MULL

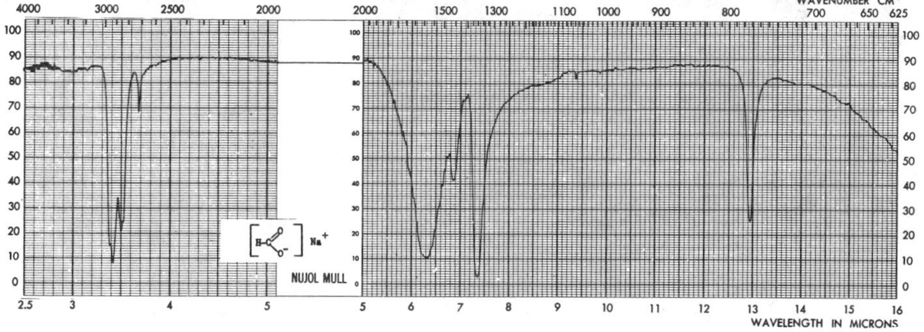

C 15,626-4
Ammonium formate, 97%
HCO_2NH_4 FW 63.06 mp 119-121° *Beil.* 2,8
Fieser 1,38 Disp. D
NUJOL MULL

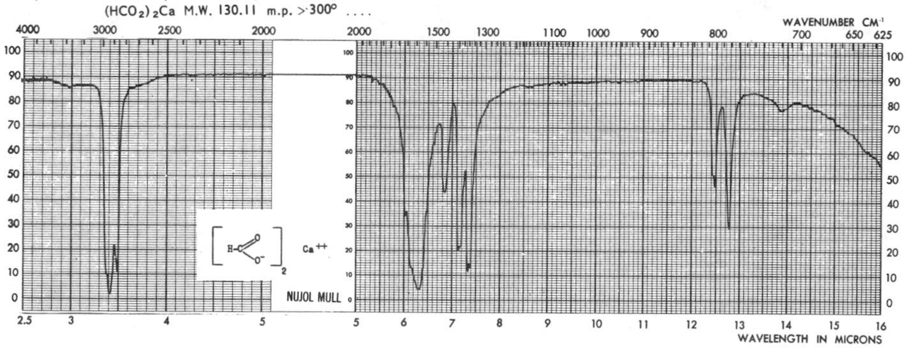

D 15,852-6
Ammonium acetate, 98%
$CH_3CO_2NH_4$
M.W. 77.08 m.p. 112-114° Beil. 2,96
Fieser 1,38 *HYGROSCOPIC*
NUJOL MULL

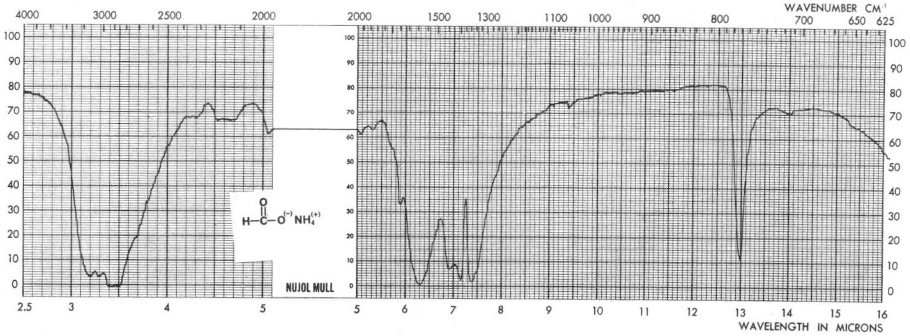

E 21,319-5
Lithium acetate dihydrate, 98% (acetic acid, lithium salt)
$CH_3CO_2Li \cdot 2H_2O$ FW 102.02 mp 53-56°
Beil. 2,107 Disp. L
MELT

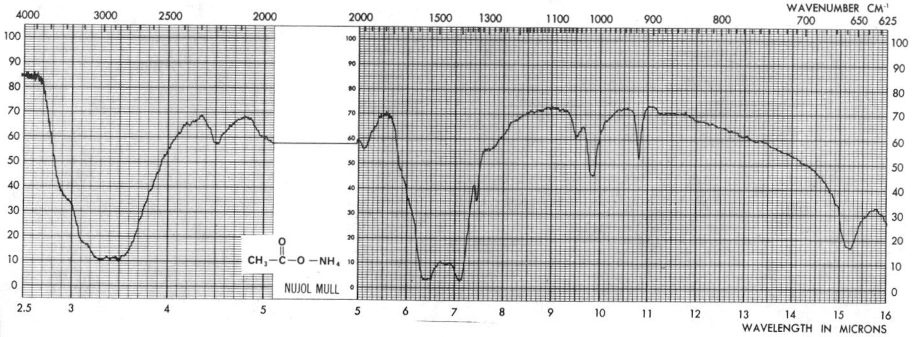

F 11,019-1 **Acetic acid, sodium salt** (sodium acetate), **anhydrous**
CH_3CO_2Na M.W. 82.03 m.p. > 300°
NUJOL MULL

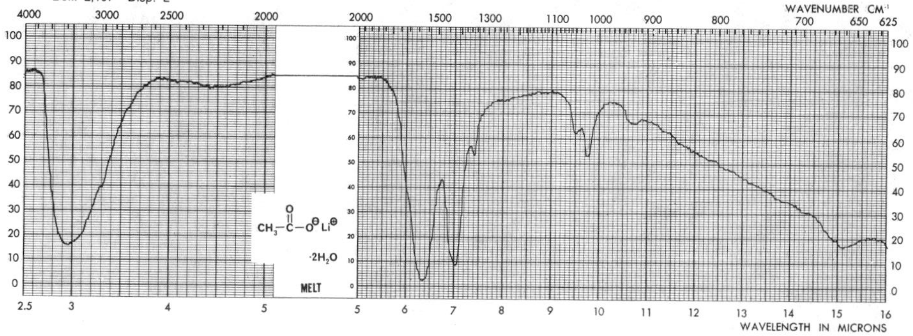

G 11,018-3 **Acetic acid, potassium salt** (potassium acetate), **anhydrous**
CH_3CO_2K M.W. 98.15 m.p. 300-302°
NUJOL MULL

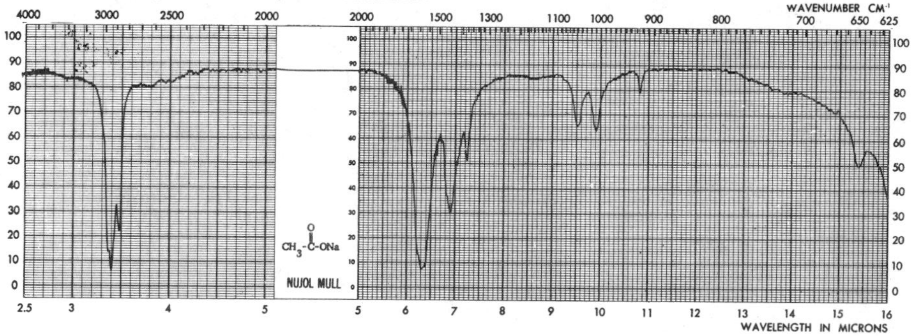

H 22,335-2
Zinc acetate dihydrate, 98+%
$(CH_3CO_2)_2Zn$ FW 219.50 d 1.840 Disp. L
NUJOL MULL

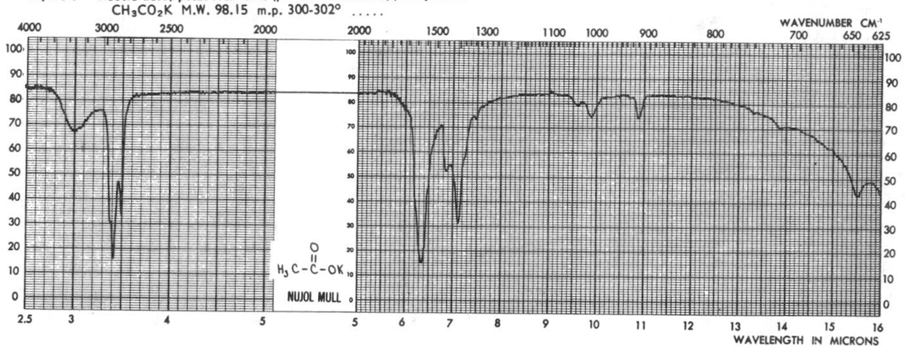

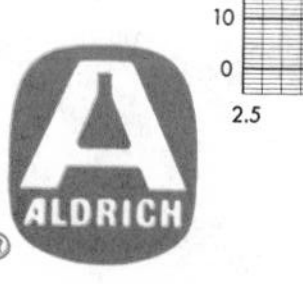

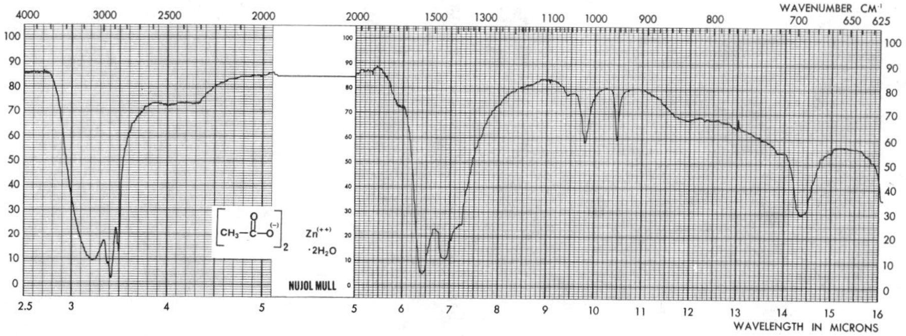

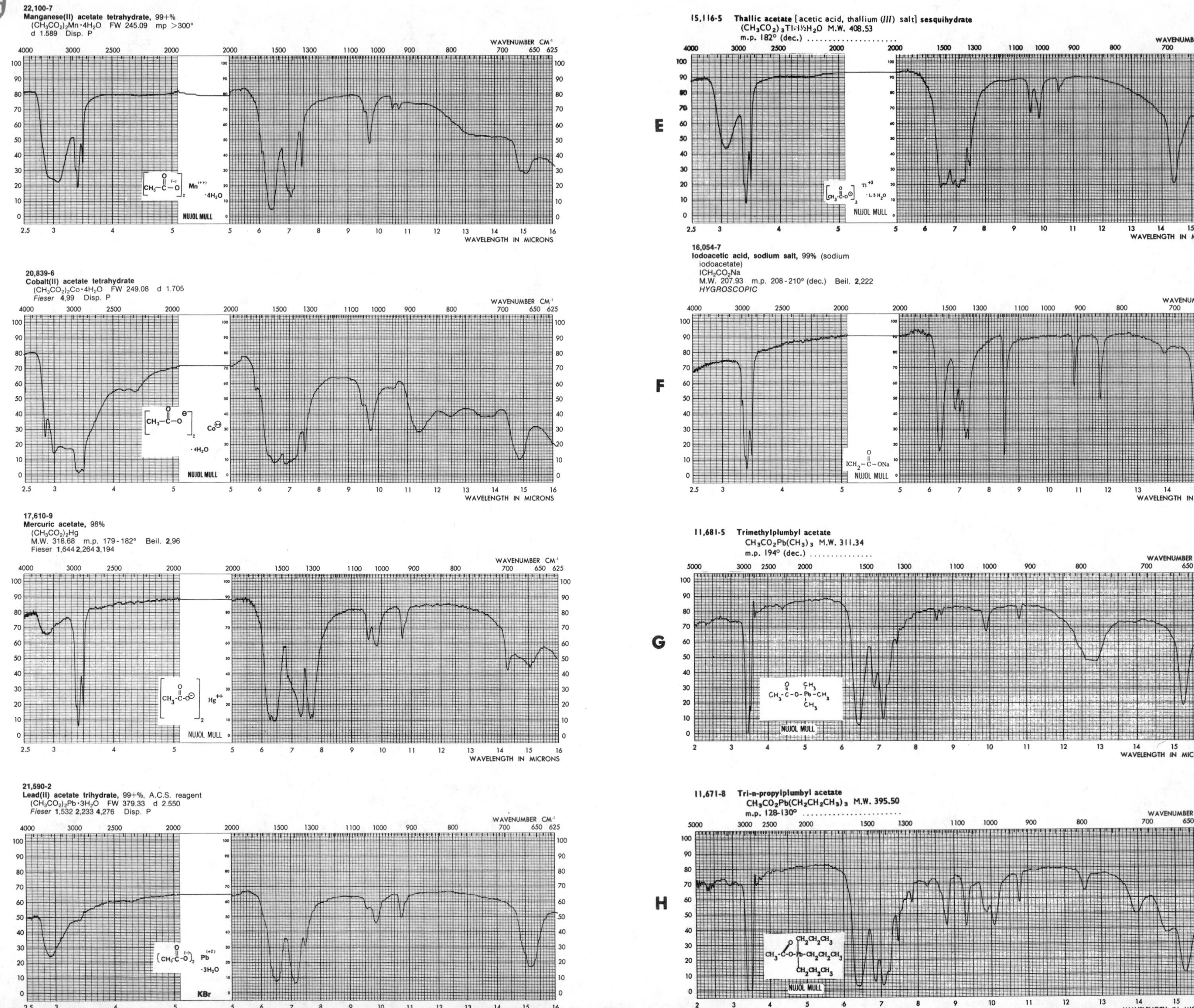

A 22,100-7
Manganese(II) acetate tetrahydrate, 99+%
$(CH_3CO_2)_2Mn \cdot 4H_2O$ FW 245.09 mp >300°
d 1.589 Disp. P
NUJOL MULL

B 20,839-6
Cobalt(II) acetate tetrahydrate
$(CH_3CO_2)_2Co \cdot 4H_2O$ FW 249.08 d 1.705
Fieser 4,99 Disp. P
NUJOL MULL

C 17,610-9
Mercuric acetate, 98%
$(CH_3CO_2)_2Hg$
M.W. 318.68 m.p. 179-182° Beil. 2,96
Fieser 1,644 2,264 3,194
NUJOL MULL

D 21,590-2
Lead(II) acetate trihydrate, 99+%, A.C.S. reagent
$(CH_3CO_2)_2Pb \cdot 3H_2O$ FW 379.33 d 2.550
Fieser 1,532 2,233 4,276 Disp. P
KBr

E 15,116-5 **Thallic acetate** [acetic acid, thallium (*III*) salt] **sesquihydrate**
$(CH_3CO_2)_3Tl \cdot 1\frac{1}{2}H_2O$ M.W. 408.53
m.p. 182° (dec.)
NUJOL MULL

F 16,054-7
Iodoacetic acid, sodium salt, 99% (sodium iodoacetate)
ICH_2CO_2Na
M.W. 207.93 m.p. 208-210° (dec.) Beil. 2,222
HYGROSCOPIC
NUJOL MULL

G 11,681-5 **Trimethylplumbyl acetate**
$CH_3CO_2Pb(CH_3)_3$ M.W. 311.34
m.p. 194° (dec.)
NUJOL MULL

H 11,671-8 **Tri-n-propylplumbyl acetate**
$CH_3CO_2Pb(CH_2CH_2CH_3)_3$ M.W. 395.50
m.p. 128-130°
NUJOL MULL

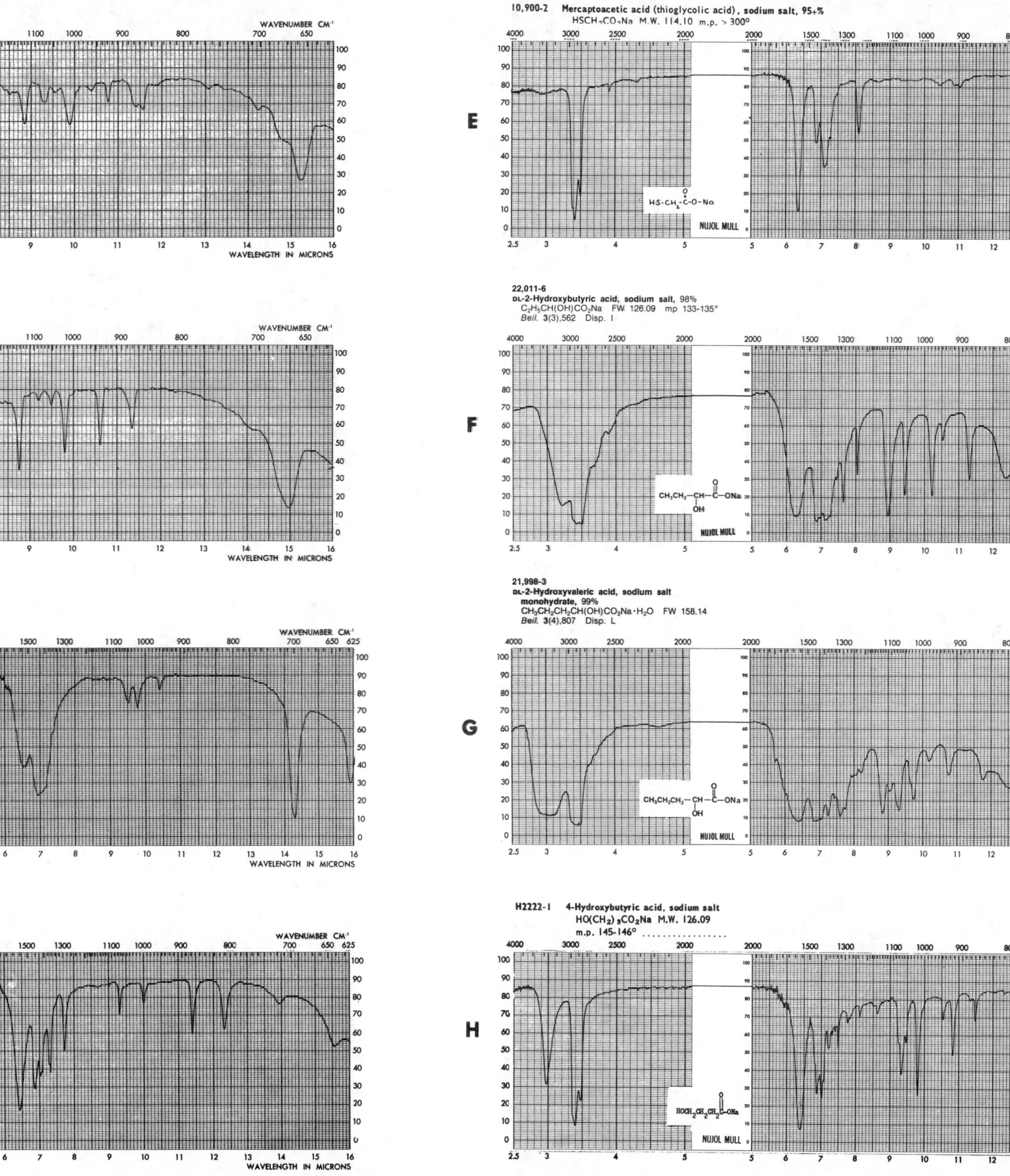

A 11,672-6 Tri-n-butylplumbyl acetate
$CH_3CO_2Pb[(CH_2)_3CH_3]_3$ M.W. 437.58
m.p. 85-87°

B 11,673-4 Di-n-butylplumbylene diacetate
$(CH_3CO_2)_2Pb[(CH_2)_3CH_3]_2$ M.W. 439.51
m.p. 55-59°

C 18,519-1
Lead tetraacetate
$(CH_3CO_2)_4Pb$

D 10,919-3 Propionic acid, sodium salt
$C_2H_5CO_2Na$ M.W. 96.06 m.p. 285-286°

E 10,900-2 Mercaptoacetic acid (thioglycolic acid), sodium salt, 95+%
$HSCH_2CO_2Na$ M.W. 114.10 m.p. > 300°

F 22,011-6
DL-2-Hydroxybutyric acid, sodium salt, 98%
$C_2H_5CH(OH)CO_2Na$ FW 126.09 mp 133-135°
Beil. 3(3),562 Disp. I

G 21,998-3
DL-2-Hydroxyvaleric acid, sodium salt monohydrate, 99%
$CH_3CH_2CH_2CH(OH)CO_2Na \cdot H_2O$ FW 158.14
Beil. 3(4),807 Disp. L

H H2222-1 4-Hydroxybutyric acid, sodium salt
$HO(CH_2)_3CO_2Na$ M.W. 126.09
m.p. 145-146°

A

22,171-6
Ammonium oxalate monohydrate, 99%
$(-CO_2NH_4)_2 \cdot H_2O$ FW 142.11 d 1.500 Disp. L

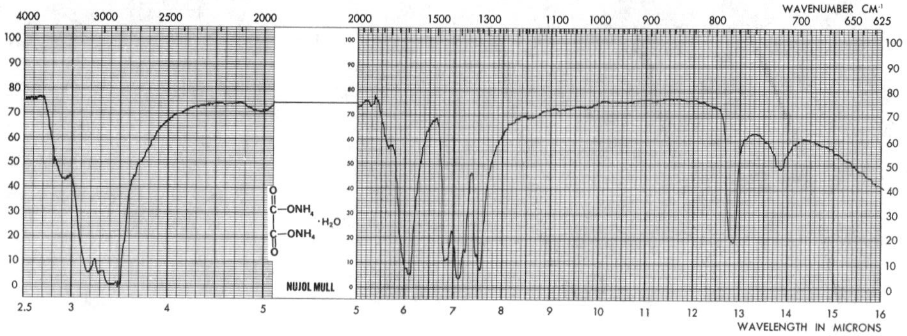

NUJOL MULL

B

22,343-3
Sodium oxalate, 99+%, A.C.S. reagent
NaO_2CCO_2Na FW 134.00 d 2.340 Disp. L

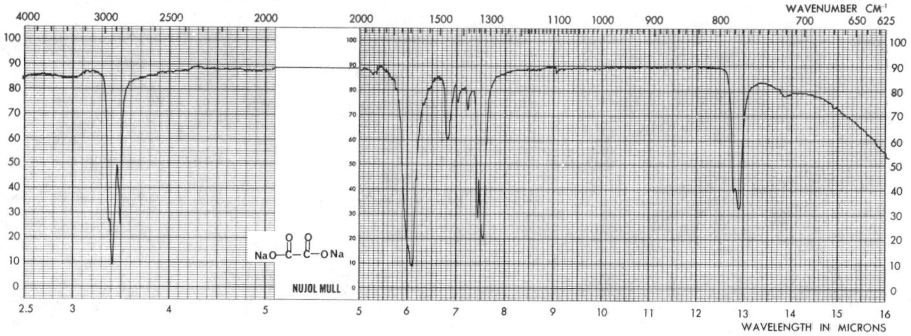

NUJOL MULL

C

22,342-5
Potassium oxalate monohydrate, 99%,
A.C.S. reagent
$KO_2CCO_2K \cdot H_2O$ FW 184.24 d 2.127 Disp. L

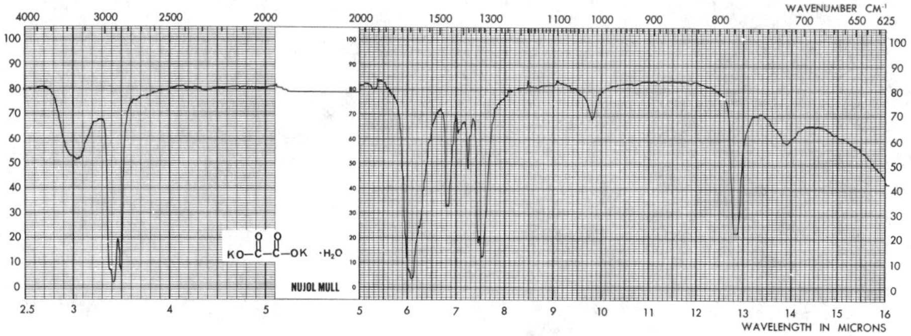

NUJOL MULL

D

13,440-6 **Succinic acid, disodium salt hexanydrate**
$NaO_2CCH_2CH_2CO_2Na \cdot 6H_2O$ M.W. 270.14

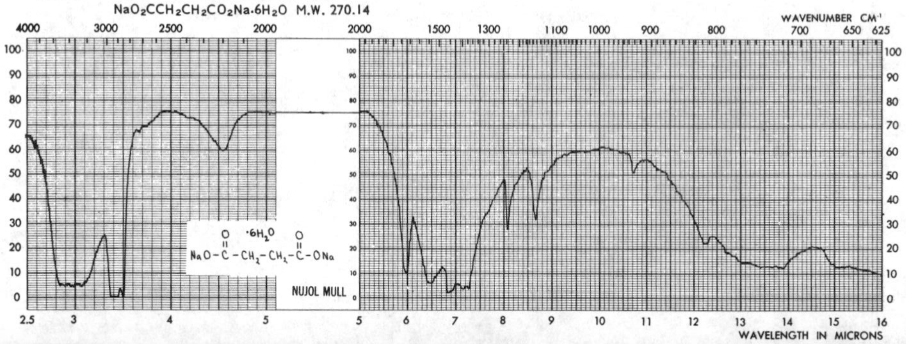

NUJOL MULL

E

13,439-2 **Succinic acid, diammonium salt**
$H_4NO_2CCH_2CH_2CO_2NH_4$ M.W. 152.15 m.p. 172-174° (dec.)

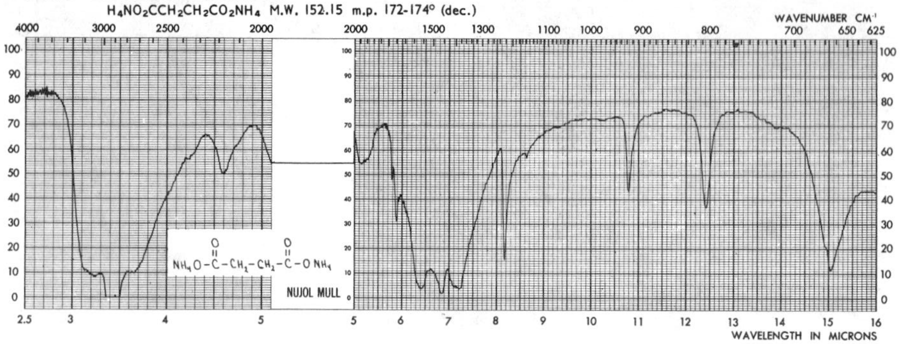

NUJOL MULL

F

13,210-1 **Trifluoroacetic acid, sodium salt**
CF_3CO_2Na M.W. 136.00 m.p. 207° (dec.)

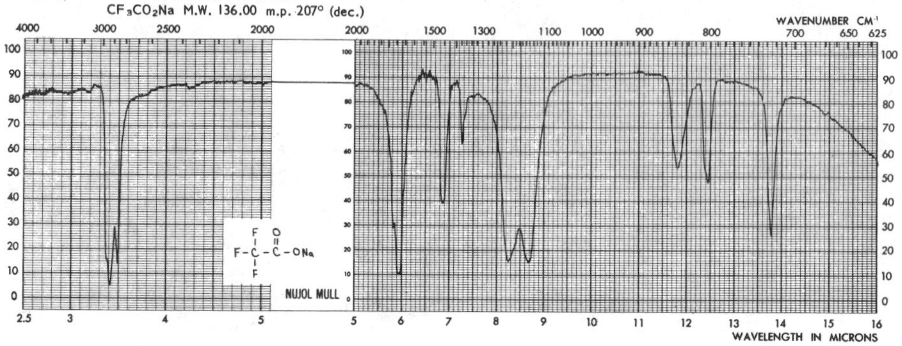

NUJOL MULL

G

T6240-5 **Trifluoroacetic acid, silver salt** (silver trifluoroacetate)
CF_3CO_2Ag M.W. 220.88 m.p. 155° (dec.)

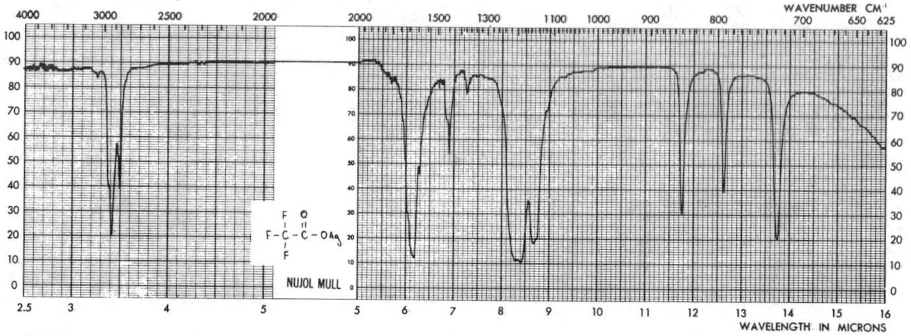

NUJOL MULL

H

15,648-5
Mercuric trifluoroacetate [trifluoroacetic acid, mercury(II) salt]
$(CF_3CO_2)_2Hg$
M.W. 426.62 Beil. **2**(2),186 Fieser **1**,659
HYGROSCOPIC

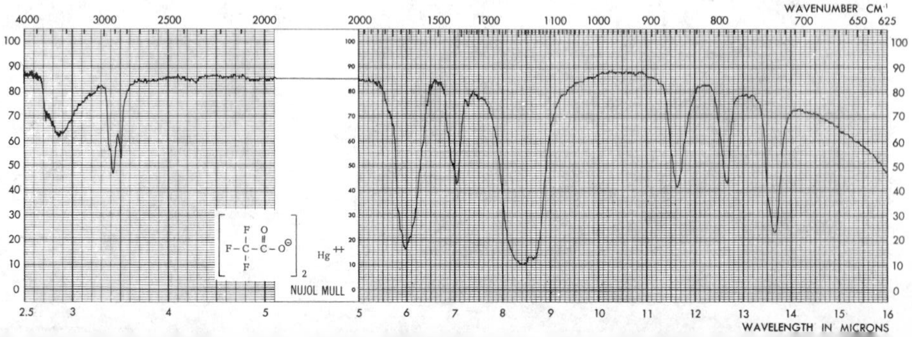

NUJOL MULL

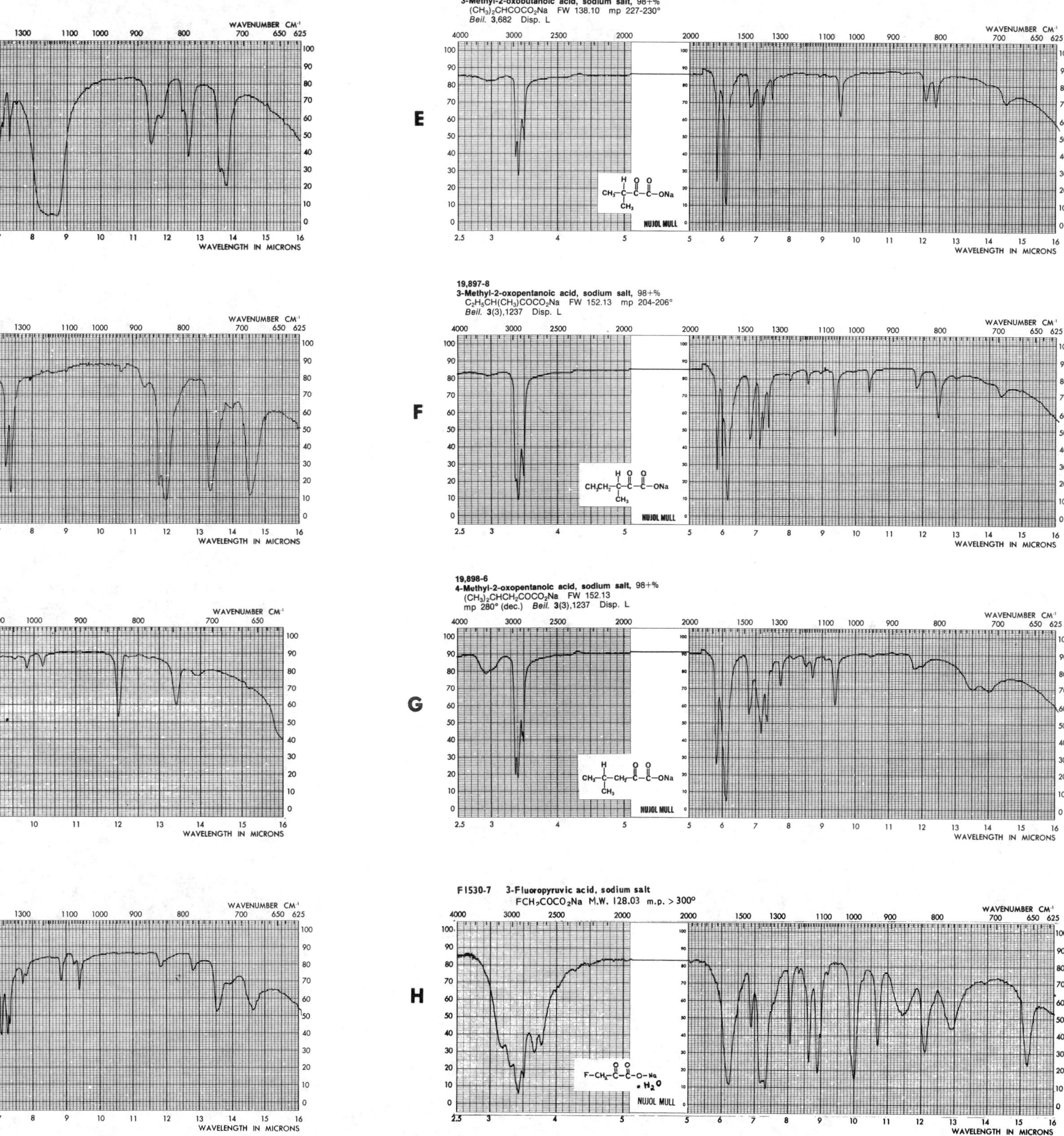

A 15,053-3 **Thallic trifluoroacetate** [trifluoroacetic acid, thallium (III) salt]
$(CF_3CO_2)_3Tl$ M.W. 543.42
m.p. 168-170° (dec.)

B 19,078-0
Trichloroacetic acid, sodium salt, tech., 90%
(sodium trichloroacetate)
CCl_3CO_2Na FW 185.37 mp >300°
Fieser 1,1107 2,388 6,553 7,341 Disp. D

C P7622-5 **Pyruvic acid, sodium salt**
CH_3COCO_2Na M.W. 110.04
m.p. 300° (dec.)

D 21,276-8
2-Oxopentanoic acid, sodium salt, 98% (2-keto-valeric acid, 2-oxovaleric acid)
$CH_3CH_2CH_2COCO_2Na$ FW 138.10 mp 236° (dec.)
Disp. L

E 19,899-4
3-Methyl-2-oxobutanoic acid, sodium salt, 98+%
$(CH_3)_2CHCOCO_2Na$ FW 138.10 mp 227-230°
Beil. 3,682 Disp. L

F 19,897-8
3-Methyl-2-oxopentanoic acid, sodium salt, 98+%
$C_2H_5CH(CH_3)COCO_2Na$ FW 152.13 mp 204-206°
Beil. 3(3),1237 Disp. L

G 19,898-6
4-Methyl-2-oxopentanoic acid, sodium salt, 98+%
$(CH_3)_2CHCH_2COCO_2Na$ FW 152.13
mp 280° (dec.) *Beil.* 3(3),1237 Disp. L

H F1530-7 **3-Fluoropyruvic acid, sodium salt**
FCH_2COCO_2Na M.W. 128.03 m.p. > 300°

A

G500-0 **Glyceric acid, calcium salt, dihydrate**
$[HOCH_2CH(OH)CO_2]_2Ca \cdot 2H_2O$ M.W. 286.25
m.p. 139-140° (dec.)

$[HO-CH_2-CH(OH)-C(=O)-O]_2 Ca \cdot 2H_2O$ — NUJOL MULL

B

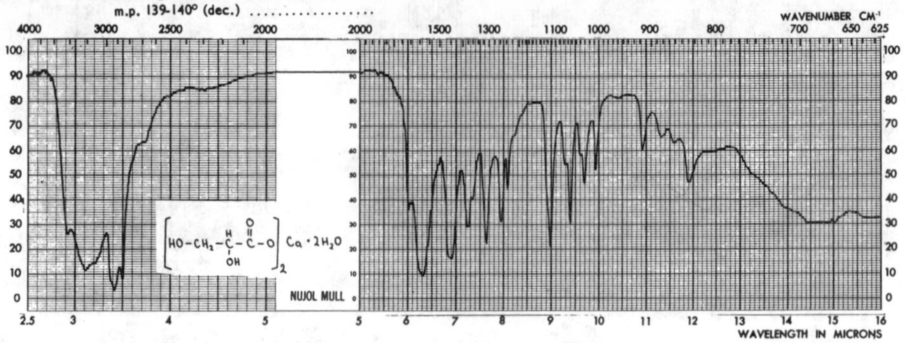

86,037-9
Gluconic acid, potassium salt, 99% (potassium gluconate)
$HOCH_2[CH(OH)]_4CO_2K$ FW 234.25
mp 183-185° (dec.) $[\alpha]^{21}$ +14.1° (c=1.2, H_2O)
Disp. L

NUJOL MULL

C

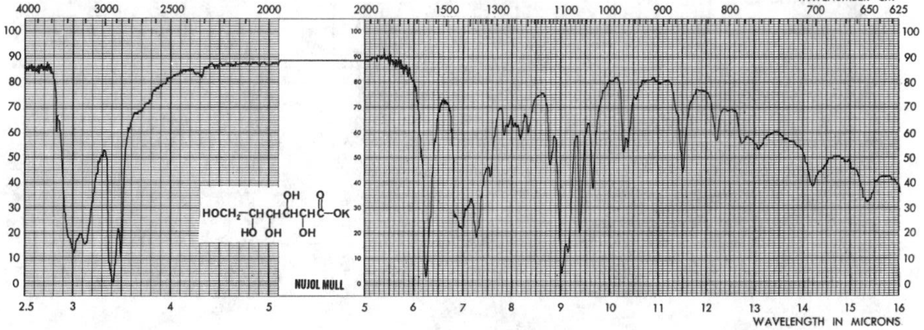

18,633-3
Gluconic acid, sodium salt, 97%
$HOCH_2[CH(OH)]_4CO_2Na$ FW 218.14
mp 206-209° (dec.) $[\alpha]^{23}$ +12.1° (c=1.75, H_2O)
Beil. 3(1),188 Disp. L

NUJOL MULL

D

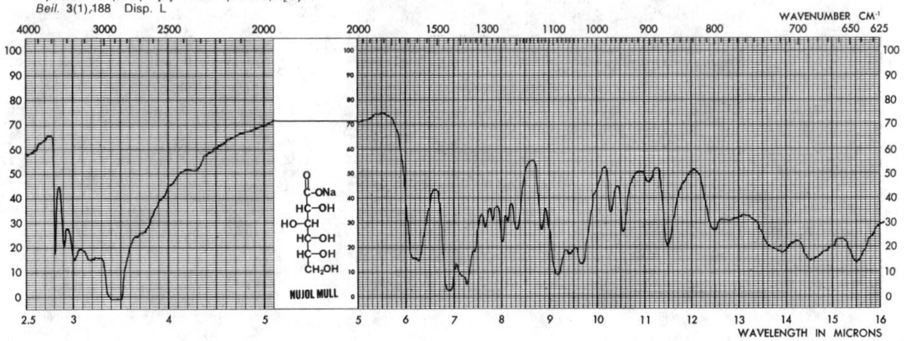

22,292-5
D-Saccharic acid, monopotassium salt, 98%
(D-glucaric acid, D-glucosaccharic acid)
$HO_2C[CH(OH)]_4CO_2K$ FW 248.24 mp 188° (dec.)
$[\alpha]^{21}$ +5° (c=1, H_2O) *Beil.* 3,579 Disp. L

NUJOL MULL

E

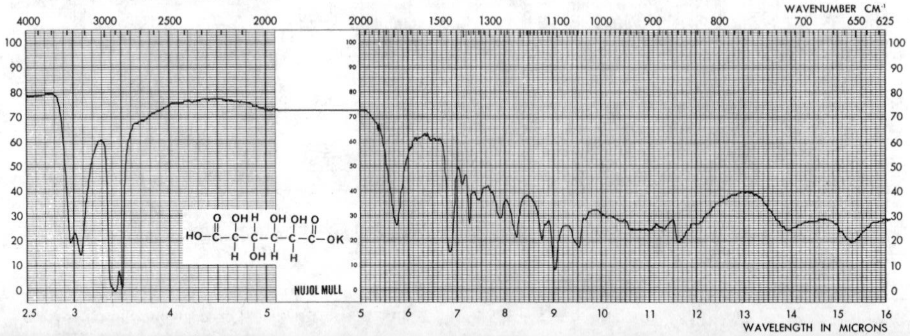

K220-8 **Ketomalonic acid monohydrate (dihydroxymalonic acid), disodium salt, tech.**
$NaO_2CC(OH)_2CO_2Na$ M.W. 180.03 m.p. > 300°

NUJOL MULL

F

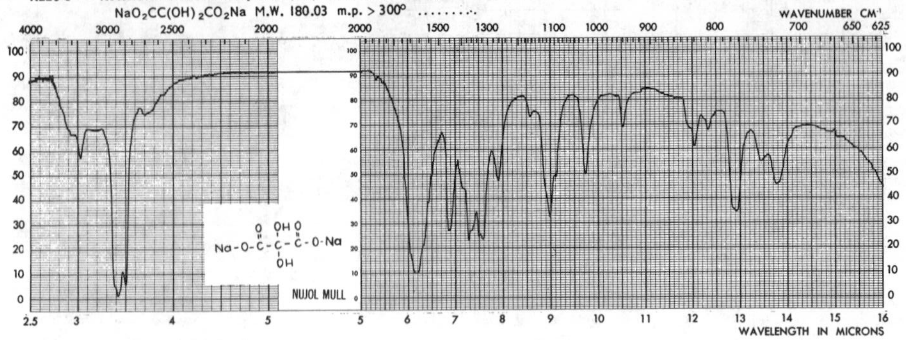

16,342-2
Dihydroxytartaric acid, disodium salt dihydrate, tech., 94%
$NaO_2CC(OH)_2C(OH)_2CO_2Na \cdot 2H_2O$
M.W. 262.08 m.p. 285-288° (dec.) Beil. 3,830

$\cdot 2H_2O$ — NUJOL MULL

G

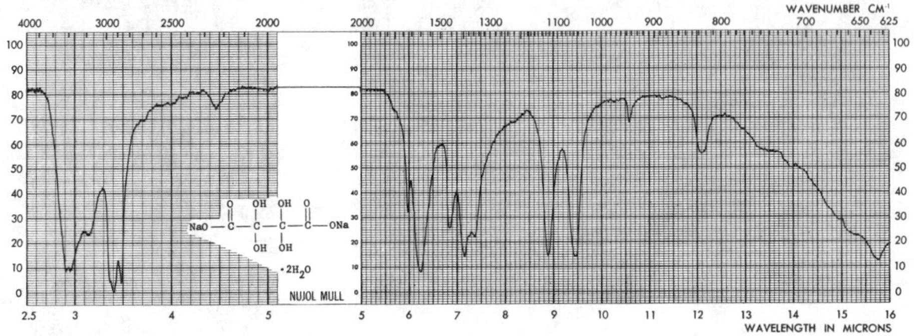

21,725-5
Potassium sodium tartrate tetrahydrate, A.C.S. reagent (Rochelle salt)
$KO_2CCH(OH)CH(OH)CO_2Na \cdot 4H_2O$ FW 282.23
Beil. 3,525 Disp. S

$\cdot 4H_2O$ — KBr

H

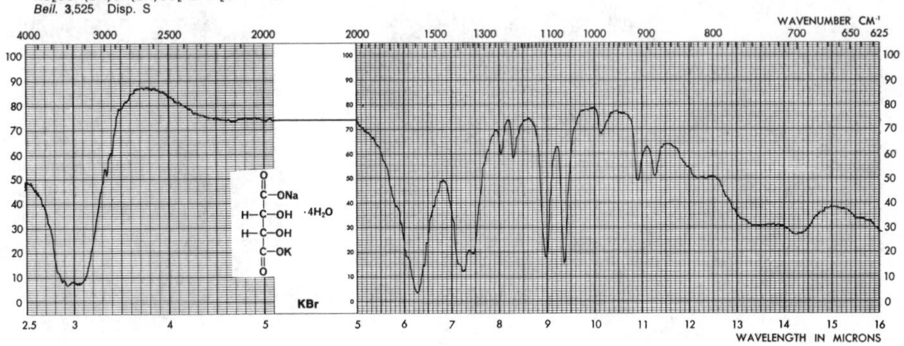

21,949-5
D-Glucuronic acid, sodium salt, 99%
FW 216.12 mp 138° (dec.) $[\alpha]^{21}$ +21.5° (c=1, H_2O)
Beil. 3,886 Disp. L

NUJOL MULL

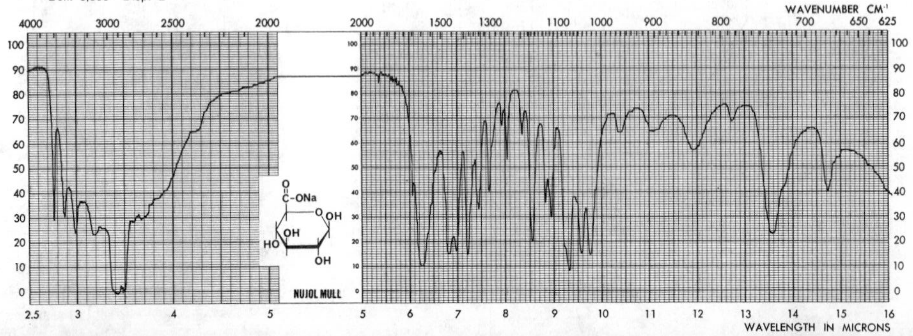

A

(lithium citrate)
$LiO_2CCH_2C(OH)(CO_2Li)CH_2CO_2Li \cdot 4H_2O$
FW 281.98 mp 112° (dec.) *Beil.* **3**(1),196
Disp. L

NUJOL MULL

B

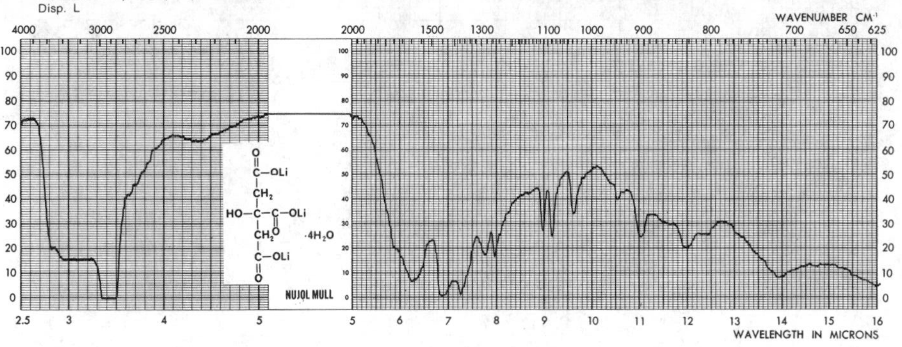

85,578-2
Citric acid, trisodium salt dihydrate (sodium citrate)
$NaO_2CCH_2C(OH)(CO_2Na)CH_2CO_2Na \cdot 2H_2O$
M.W. 294.1 m.p. >300°

NUJOL MULL

C

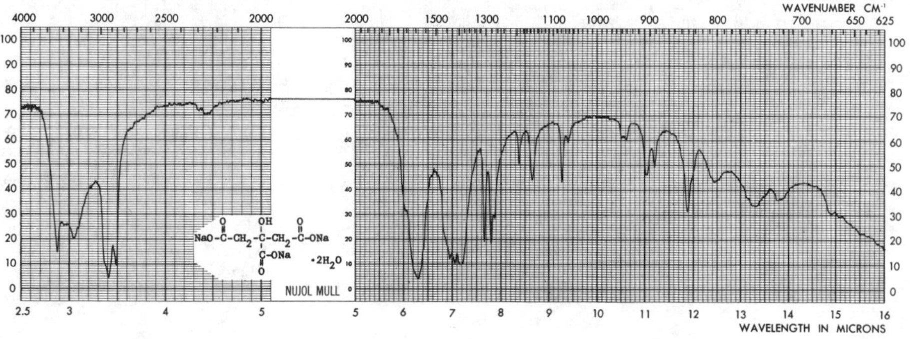

22,008-6
DL-Isocitric acid, trisodium salt hydrate
$NaO_2CCH_2CH(CO_2Na)CH(OH)CO_2Na \cdot xH_2O$
FW 258.07 *Beil.* **3**,555 Disp. D

NUJOL MULL

D

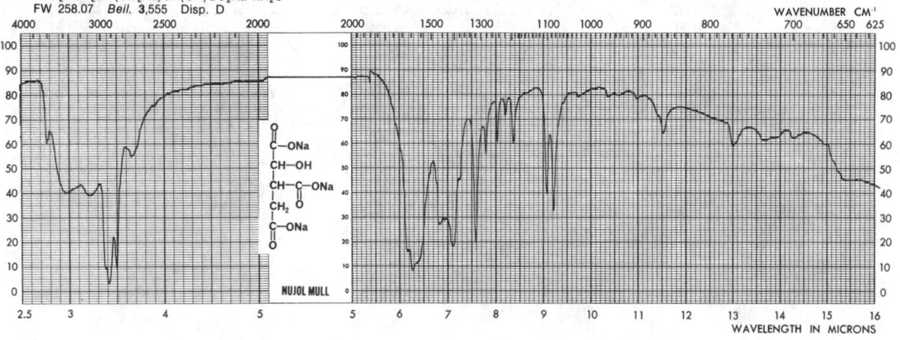

T5000 **Tri-n-butyltin bismaleate**

MELT

E

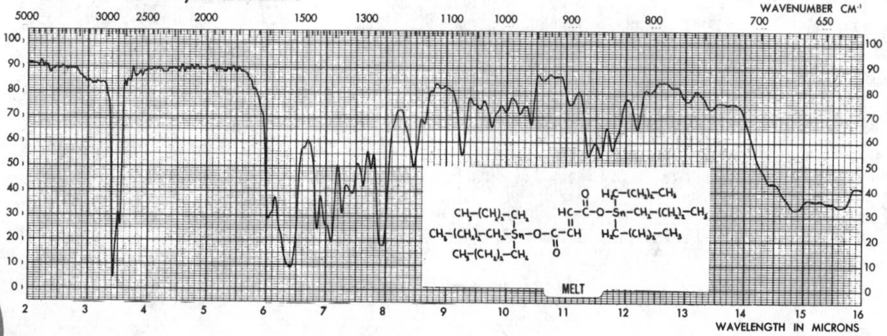

15,388-5 **2,4-Pentanedione (acetylacetone), thallium(I) salt**
$CH_3COCH{:}C(CH_3)OTl$ M.W. 303.48
m.p. 154-156° (dec.)

NUJOL MULL

F

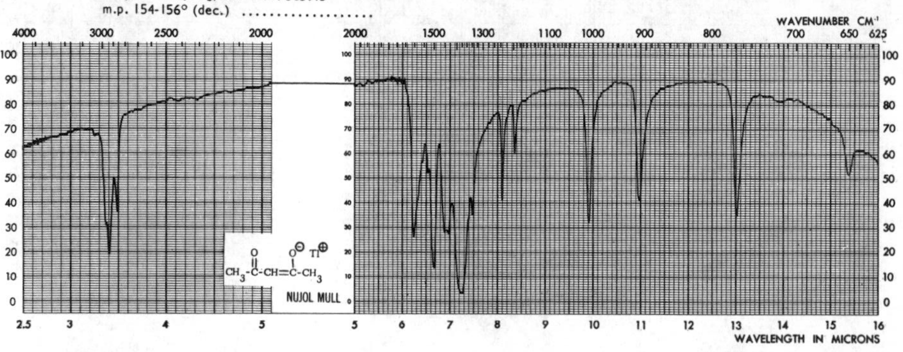

15,385-0 **Ethyl acetoacetate, thallium(I) salt**
$CH_3COCH{:}C(OC_2H_5)OTl$ M.W. 333.51
m.p. 90-91°

NUJOL MULL

G

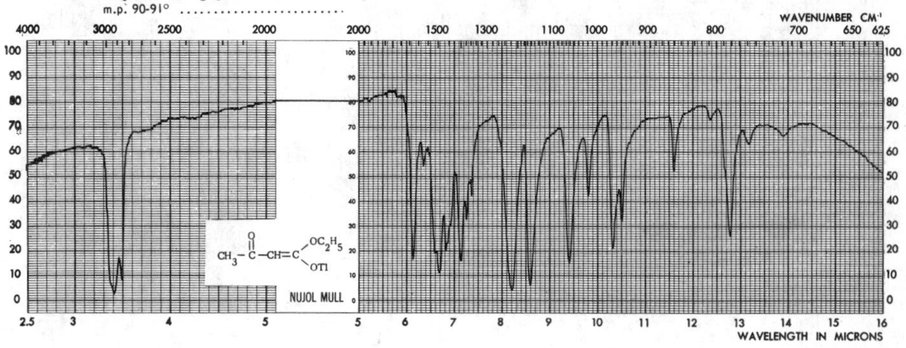

16,410-0
Ethyl acetoacetate, sodium salt
$CH_3C(ONa){=}CHCO_2C_2H_5$
M.W. 152.13 m.p. 168-171° (dec.)

NUJOL MULL

H

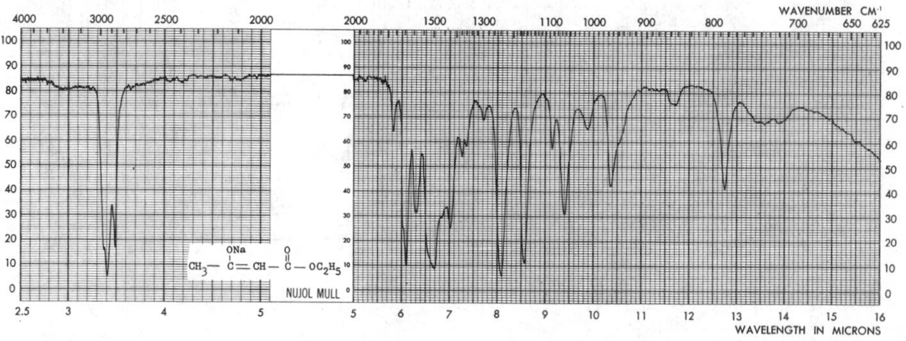

12,957-7 **Magnesium acetylacetonate** (2,4-pentanedione, magnesium derivative) **hydrate**
M.W. 240.55 m.p. 295-296° (dec.)

NUJOL MULL

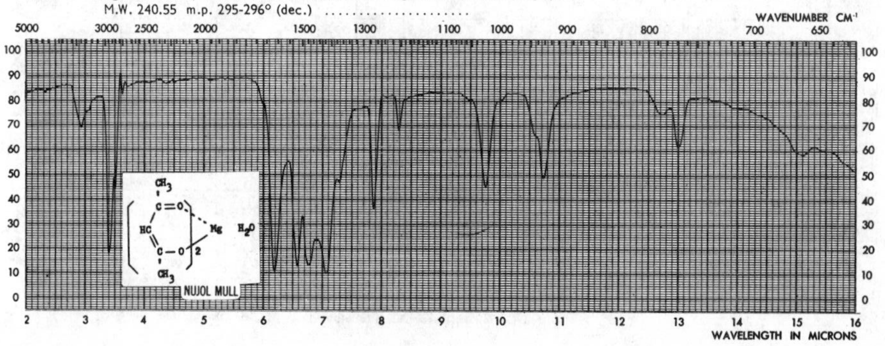

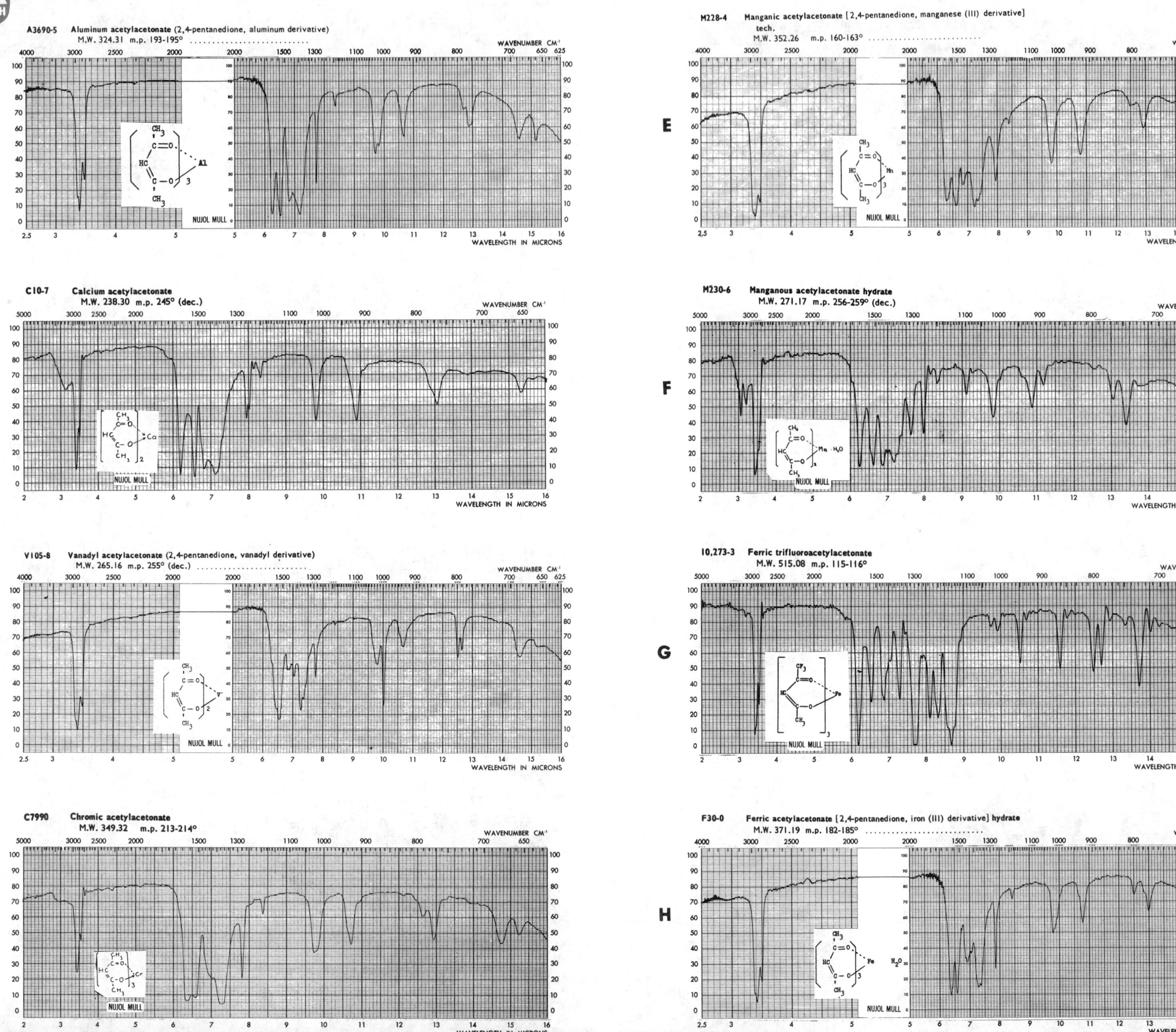
ALDRICH
A
A3690-5 Aluminum acetylacetonate (2,4-pentanedione, aluminum derivative)
M.W. 324.31 m.p. 193-195°
NUJOL MULL
B
C10-7 Calcium acetylacetonate
M.W. 238.30 m.p. 245° (dec.)
NUJOL MULL
C
V105-8 Vanadyl acetylacetonate (2,4-pentanedione, vanadyl derivative)
M.W. 265.16 m.p. 255° (dec.)
NUJOL MULL
D
C7990 Chromic acetylacetonate
M.W. 349.32 m.p. 213-214°
NUJOL MULL
E
M228-4 Manganic acetylacetonate [2,4-pentanedione, manganese (III) derivative]
tech.
M.W. 352.26 m.p. 160-163°
NUJOL MULL
F
M230-6 Manganous acetylacetonate hydrate
M.W. 271.17 m.p. 256-259° (dec.)
NUJOL MULL
G
10,273-3 Ferric trifluoroacetylacetonate
M.W. 515.08 m.p. 115-116°
NUJOL MULL
H
F30-0 Ferric acetylacetonate [2,4-pentanedione, iron (III) derivative] hydrate
M.W. 371.19 m.p. 182-185°
NUJOL MULL
WAVENUMBER CM⁻¹
WAVELENGTH IN MICRONS

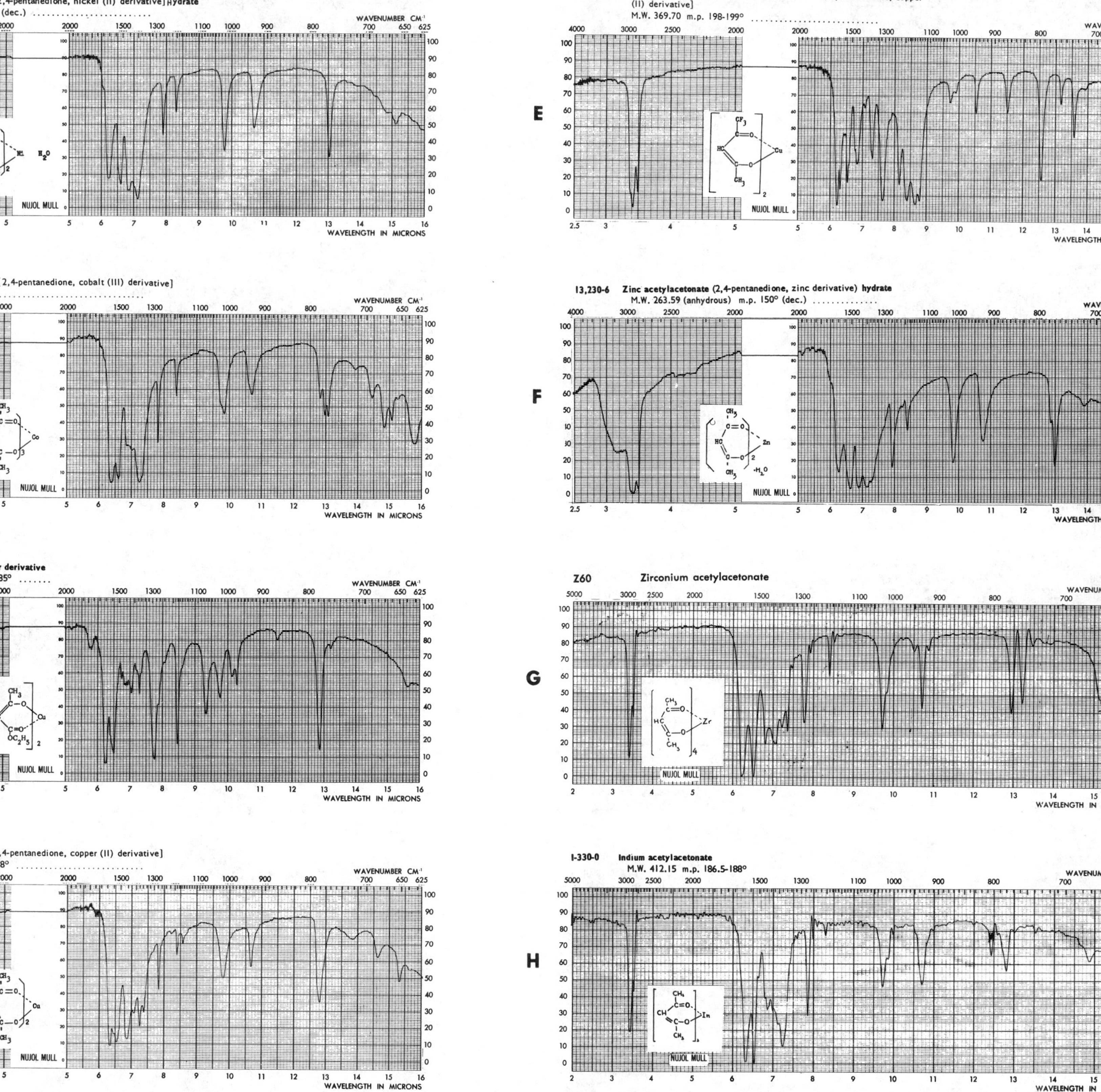
A
N750-8 Nickel acetylacetonate [2,4-pentanedione, nickel (II) derivative] Hydrate
M.W. 274.94 m.p. 300° (dec.)
B
C8390-2 Cobaltic acetylacetonate [2,4-pentanedione, cobalt (III) derivative]
M.W. 356.26
C
13,537-2 Ethyl acetoacetate, copper derivative
M.W. 321.81 m.p. 182-185°
D
C8785-1 Cupric acetylacetonate [2,4-pentanedione, copper (II) derivative]
M.W. 261.76 m.p. 284-288°
E
10,182-6 Cupric trifluoroacetylacetonate [1,1,1-trifluoro-2,4-pentanedione, copper (II) derivative]
M.W. 369.70 m.p. 198-199°
F
13,230-6 Zinc acetylacetonate (2,4-pentanedione, zinc derivative) hydrate
M.W. 263.59 (anhydrous) m.p. 150° (dec.)
G
Z60 Zirconium acetylacetonate
H
I-330-0 Indium acetylacetonate
M.W. 412.15 m.p. 186.5-188°
NUJOL MULL
WAVENUMBER CM⁻¹
WAVELENGTH IN MICRONS
ALDRICH

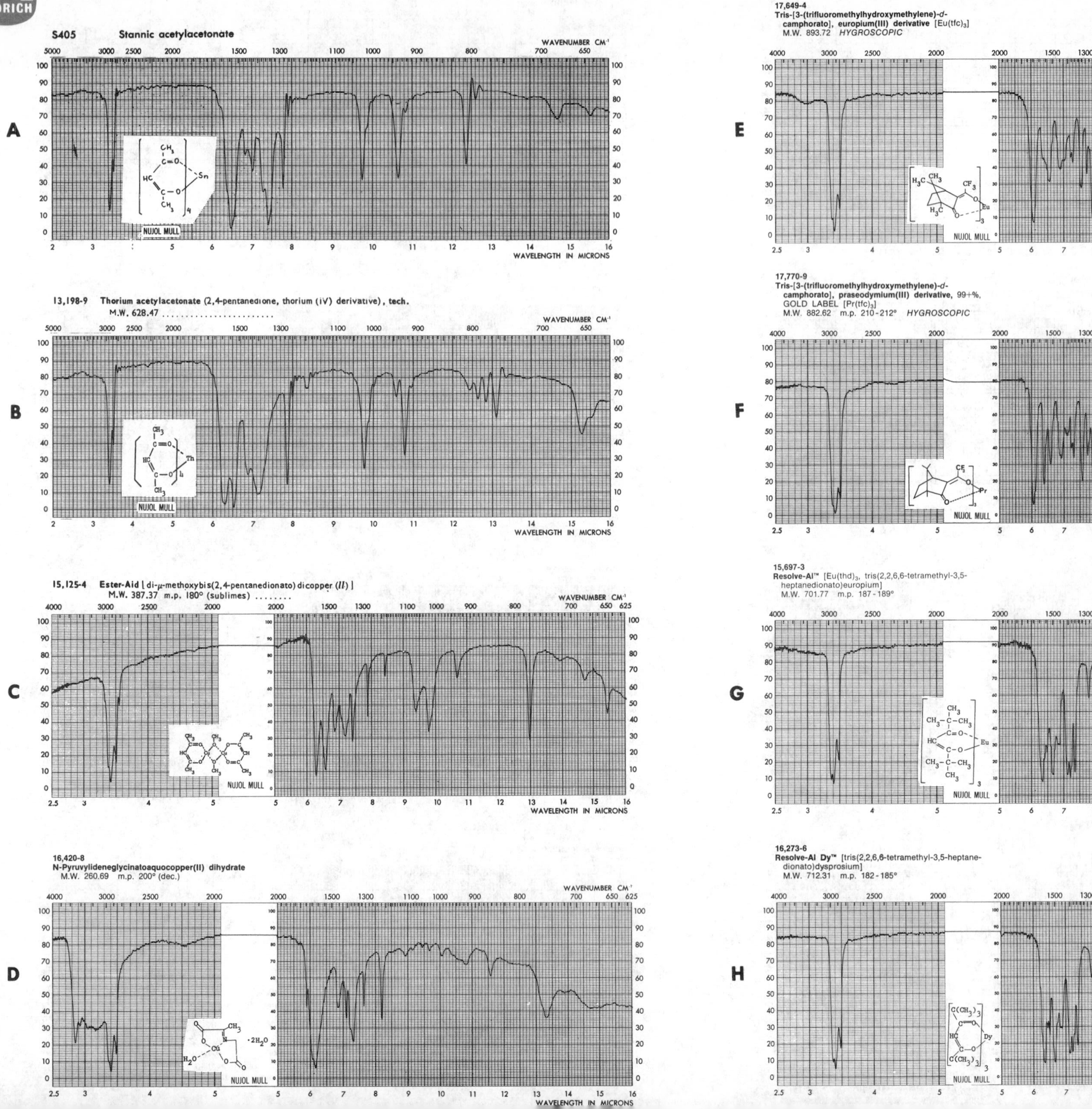
ALDRICH
A
S405 Stannic acetylacetonate
NUJOL MULL
B
13,198-9 Thorium acetylacetonate (2,4-pentanedione, thorium (IV) derivative), tech.
M.W. 628.47
NUJOL MULL
C
15,125-4 Ester-Aid [di-μ-methoxybis(2,4-pentanedionato)dicopper (II)]
M.W. 387.37 m.p. 180° (sublimes)
NUJOL MULL
D
16,420-8
N-Pyruvylideneglycinatoaquocopper(II) dihydrate
M.W. 260.69 m.p. 200° (dec.)
NUJOL MULL
E
17,649-4
Tris-[3-(trifluoromethylhydroxymethylene)-d-camphorato], europium(III) derivative [Eu(tfc)3]
M.W. 893.72 HYGROSCOPIC
NUJOL MULL
F
17,770-9
Tris-[3-(trifluoromethylhydroxymethylene)-d-camphorato], praseodymium(III) derivative, 99+%, GOLD LABEL [Pr(tfc)3]
M.W. 882.62 m.p. 210-212° HYGROSCOPIC
NUJOL MULL
G
15,697-3
Resolve-Al™ [Eu(thd)3, tris(2,2,6,6-tetramethyl-3,5-heptanedionato)europium]
M.W. 701.77 m.p. 187-189°
NUJOL MULL
H
16,273-6
Resolve-Al Dy™ [tris(2,2,6,6-tetramethyl-3,5-heptanedionato)dysprosium]
M.W. 712.31 m.p. 182-185°
NUJOL MULL
WAVENUMBER CM⁻¹
WAVELENGTH IN MICRONS

A

16,274-4
Resolve-Al Ho™, 99+%, GOLD LABEL [tris(2,2,6,6-tetramethyl-3,5-heptanedionato)holmium]
M.W. 714.74 m.p. 180-183°

B

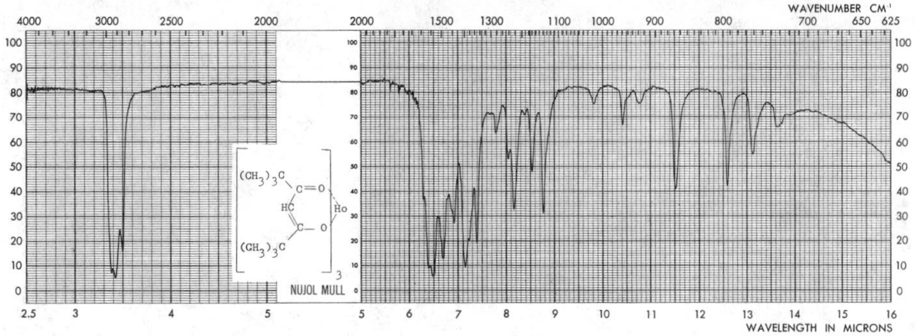

16,275-2
Resolve-Al Yb™, 99+%, GOLD LABEL [tris(2,2,6,6-tetramethyl-3,5-heptanedionato)ytterbium]
M.W. 722.85 m.p. 165-168° *HYGROSCOPIC*

C

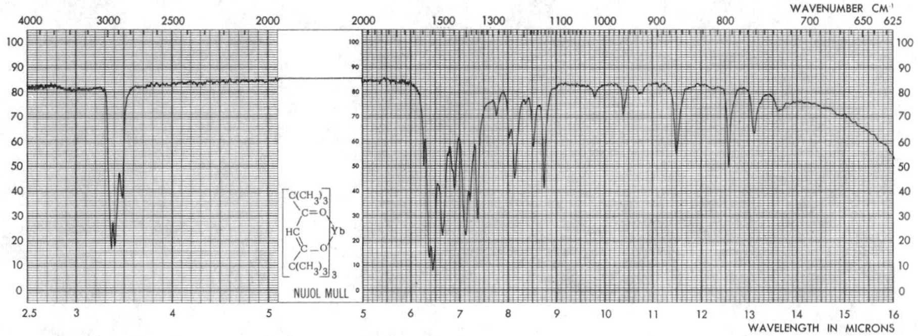

16,088-1
Resolve-Al Pr™, 99+%, GOLD LABEL [Pr(thd)$_3$, tris(2,2,6,6-tetramethyl-3,5-heptanedionato)-praseodymium]
M.W. 690.72 m.p. 219-221°

D

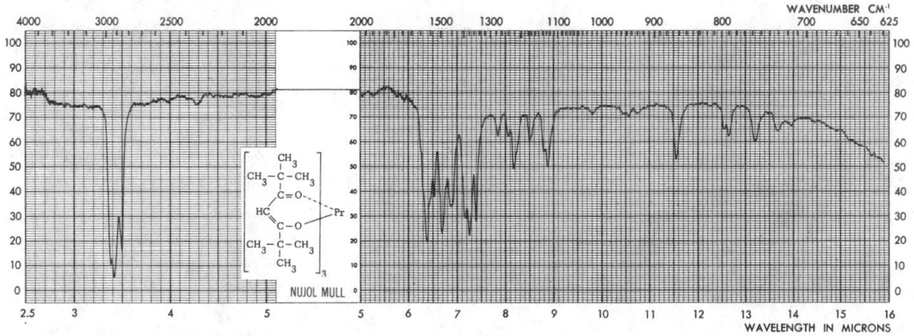

16,474-7
Tris-[3-(heptafluoropropylhydroxymethylene)-*d*-camphorato], europium(III) derivative, 99+%, GOLD LABEL [Eu(hfc)$_3$]
M.W. 1193.73 m.p. 156-158°

E

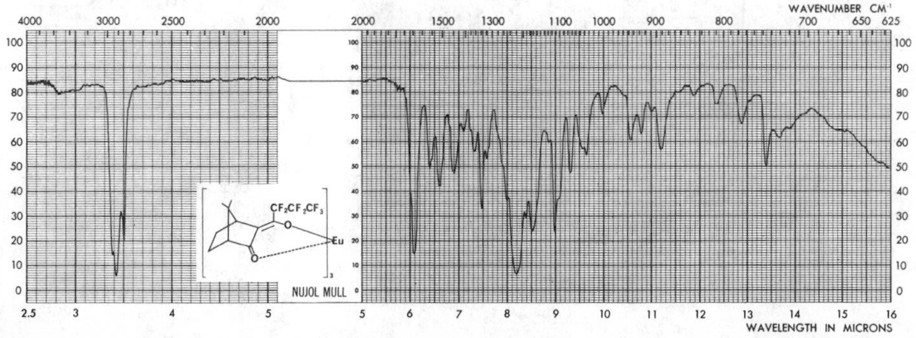

Resolve-Al AgFOD™, 99+%, GOLD LABEL [(6,6,7,7,8,8,8-Heptafluoro-2,2-dimethyl-3,5-octanedionato)silver]
FW 403.05 mp 160° (dec.) *Fieser* **7**,290
Disp. D

F

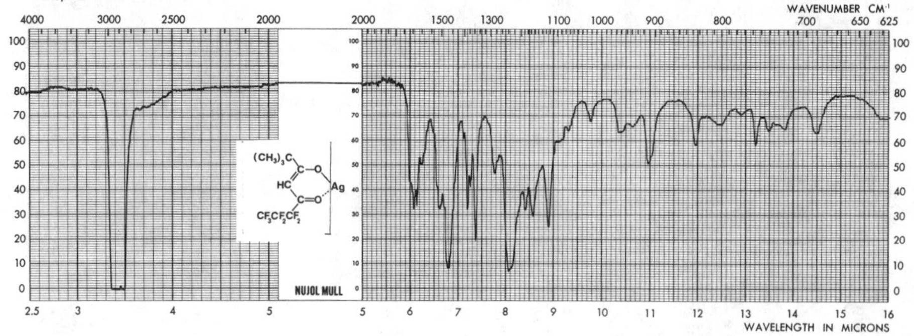

16,093-8
Resolve-Al EuFOD™, 99+%, GOLD LABEL [Eu(fod)$_3$, Sievers' Reagent, tris(6,6,7,7,8,8,8-heptafluoro-2,2-dimethyl-3,5-octanedionato)europium]
M.W. 1037.5 m.p. 203-207°

G

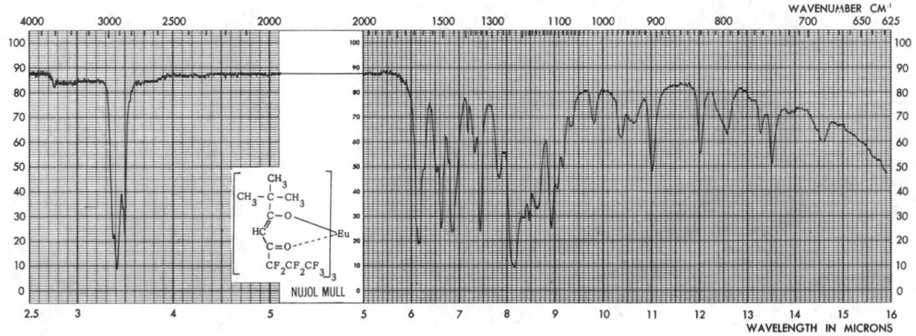

16,135-7
Resolve-Al PrFOD™, 99+%, GOLD LABEL [Pr(fod)$_3$, Rondeau's Reagent, tris(6,6,7,7,8,8,8-heptafluoro-2,2-dimethyl-3,5-octanedionato)praseodymium]
M.W. 1026.45 m.p. 215-219° *HYGROSCOPIC*

H

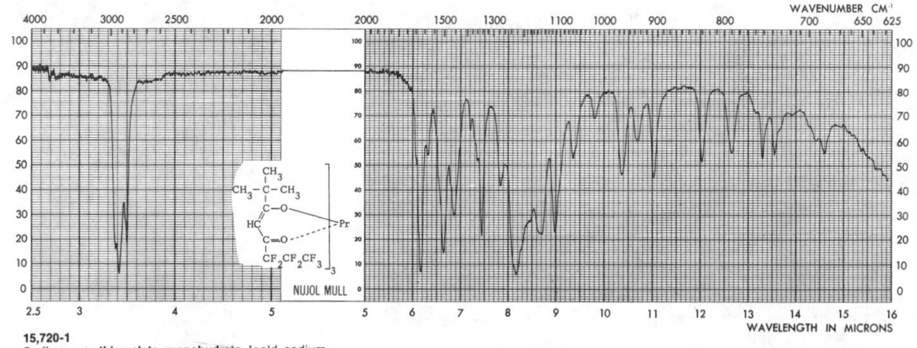

15,720-1
Sodium aurothiomalate monohydrate [gold sodium thiomalate, (1,2-dicarboxyethylthio)gold, disodium salt]
$NaO_2CCH_2CH(SAu)CO_2Na \cdot H_2O$
M.W. 408.1 m.p. >300°

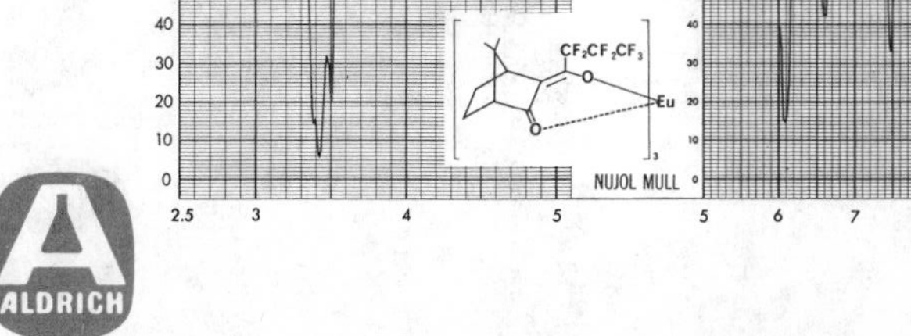

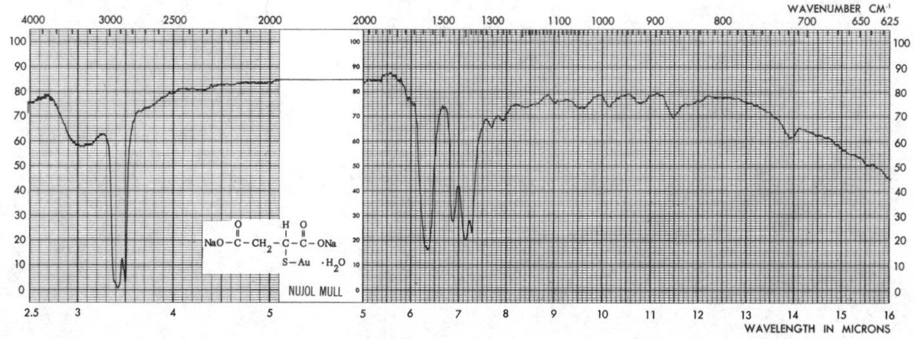

A

17,817-9
3,4-Dihydro-2H-pyran-2-carboxylic acid, sodium salt, 97%
M.W. 150.11 m.p. 242-244°

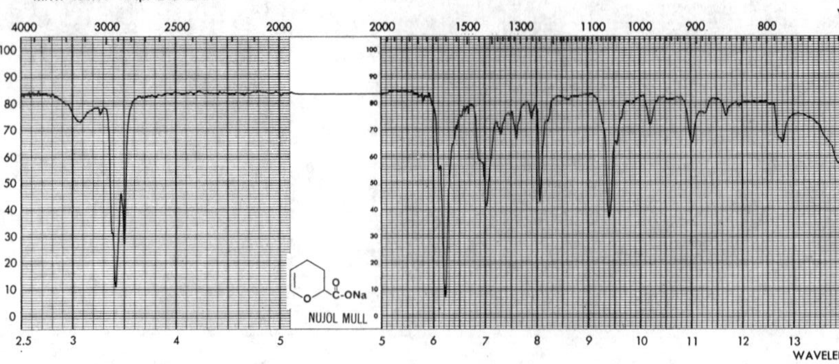

NON-AROMATIC AMINO ACIDS

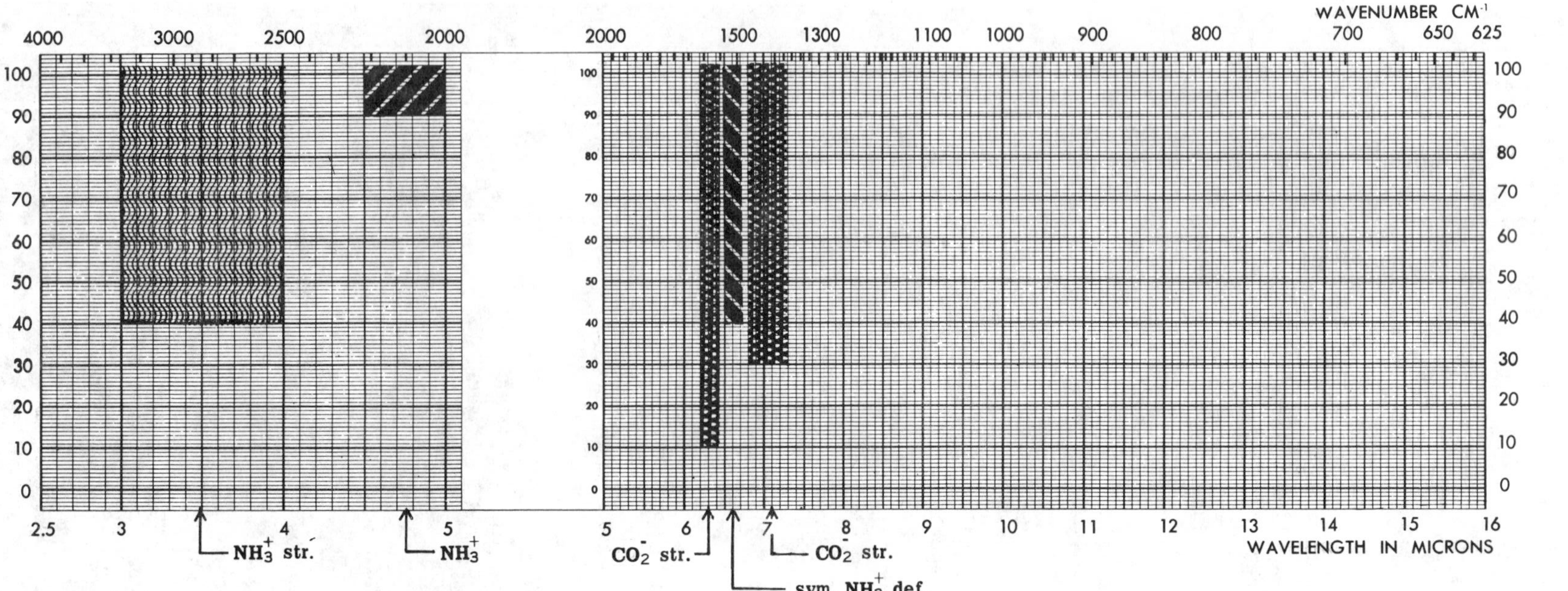

The amino acid zwitter ion displays a combination of absorptions from both entities of the zwitter ion pair, the protonated amino cation and the carboxylate anion. The NH_3^+ nitrogen-hydrogen stretch vibration absorbs between 3 and 4 μ (3335 – 2500 cm^{-1}) in combination with the highly characteristic medium to weak absorption between 4.5 and 5 μ (2220 – 2000 cm^{-1}). The carbonyl stretch band of the carboxylate anion appears around 6.3 μ (1585 cm^{-1}) and 6.8 to 7.3 μ (1470 – 1370 cm^{-1}).

Replacing the carboxyl H^+ with a metal cation results in the NH_2 stretch bands again appearing around 3 μ (3335 cm^{-1}). (See spectra 338F and 351F). In a similar manner, protonating the NH_2 function with a stronger mineral acid yields the free carboxylic acid group. (See spectra 351E, 352C, G, 353A, etc.). The carbonyl stretch absorption is shifted, however, to 5.75 μ (1740 cm^{-1}) rather than to the normal 5.8 – 5.9 μ (1725 – 1695 cm^{-1}) region due to the influence of the NH_3^+ function in the α-position.

Because of the similarity of all the amino acids between 3 and 8 μ (3335 – 1250 cm^{-1}), the medium absorptions at the higher wavelength frequencies should be used for specific amino acid identification and gross purity checks. Absorption patterns in this region vary considerably from acid to acid.

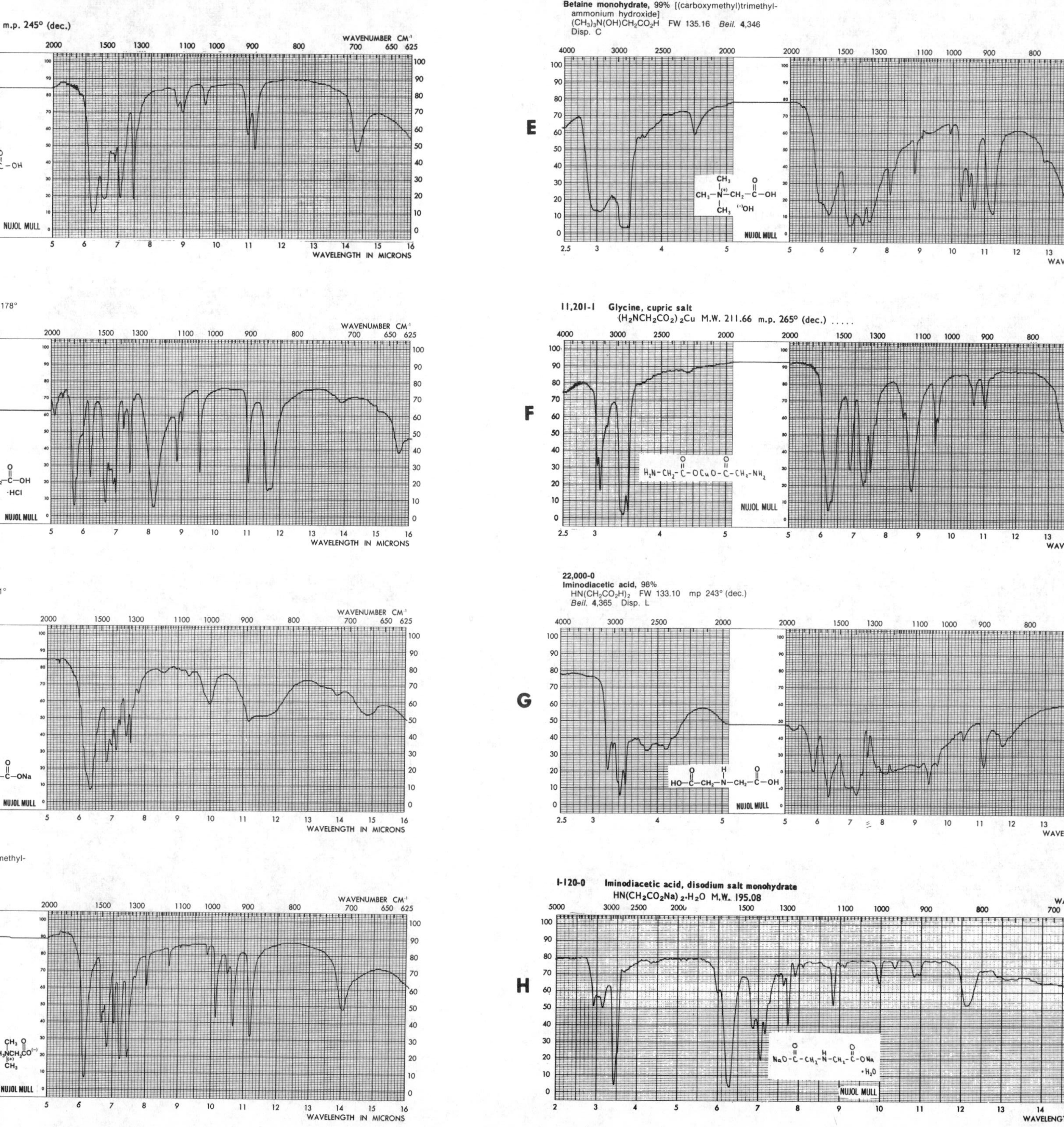

A G620-1 **Glycine**
$H_2NCH_2CO_2H$ M.W. 75.07 m.p. 245° (dec.)

B 21,950-9
Glycine hydrochloride, 98%
$H_2NCH_2CO_2H\cdot HCl$ FW 111.53 mp 175-178°
Beil. **4**,340 Disp. I

C 21,951-7
Glycine, sodium salt, 99%
$H_2NCH_2CO_2Na$ FW 97.05 mp 197-201°
Beil. **4**(1),465 Disp. L

D 21,906-1
Betaine, anhydrous, 98% [(carboxymethyl)trimethylammonium hydroxide inner salt]
$(CH_3)_3NCH_2CO_2$ FW 117.15 mp >300°
Beil. **4**,347 Disp. C

E 21,913-4
Betaine monohydrate, 99% [(carboxymethyl)trimethylammonium hydroxide]
$(CH_3)_3N(OH)CH_2CO_2H$ FW 135.16 *Beil.* **4**,346
Disp. C

F 11,201-1 **Glycine, cupric salt**
$(H_2NCH_2CO_2)_2Cu$ M.W. 211.66 m.p. 265° (dec.)

G 22,000-0
Iminodiacetic acid, 98%
$HN(CH_2CO_2H)_2$ FW 133.10 mp 243° (dec.)
Beil. **4**,365 Disp. L

H I-120-0 **Iminodiacetic acid, disodium salt monohydrate**
$HN(CH_2CO_2Na)_2\cdot H_2O$ M.W. 195.08

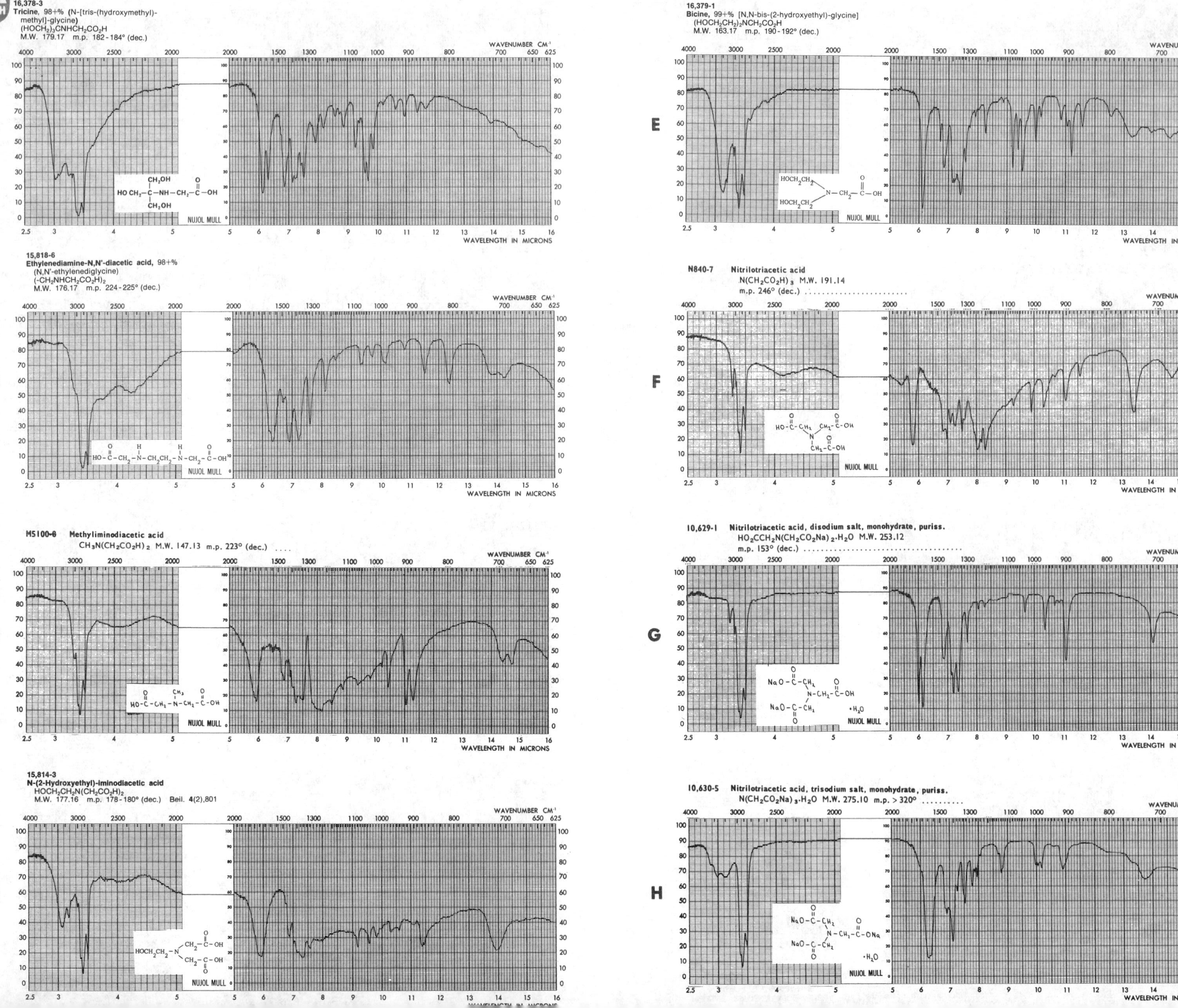
ALDRICH
A
16,378-3
Tricine, 98+% (N-[tris-(hydroxymethyl)-methyl]-glycine)
$(HOCH_2)_3CNHCH_2CO_2H$
M.W. 179.17 m.p. 182-184° (dec.)
B
15,818-6
Ethylenediamine-N,N'-diacetic acid, 98+%
(N,N'-ethylenediglycine)
$(-CH_2NHCH_2CO_2H)_2$
M.W. 176.17 m.p. 224-225° (dec.)
C
M5100-6 Methyliminodiacetic acid
$CH_3N(CH_2CO_2H)_2$ M.W. 147.13 m.p. 223° (dec.)
D
15,814-3
N-(2-Hydroxyethyl)-iminodiacetic acid
$HOCH_2CH_2N(CH_2CO_2H)_2$
M.W. 177.16 m.p. 178-180° (dec.) Beil. 4(2),801
E
16,379-1
Bicine, 99+% [N,N-bis-(2-hydroxyethyl)-glycine]
$(HOCH_2CH_2)_2NCH_2CO_2H$
M.W. 163.17 m.p. 190-192° (dec.)
F
N840-7 Nitrilotriacetic acid
$N(CH_2CO_2H)_3$ M.W. 191.14
m.p. 246° (dec.)
G
10,629-1 Nitrilotriacetic acid, disodium salt, monohydrate, puriss.
$HO_2CCH_2N(CH_2CO_2Na)_2 \cdot H_2O$ M.W. 253.12
m.p. 153° (dec.)
H
10,630-5 Nitrilotriacetic acid, trisodium salt, monohydrate, puriss.
$N(CH_2CO_2Na)_3 \cdot H_2O$ M.W. 275.10 m.p. > 320°
NUJOL MULL
WAVENUMBER CM⁻¹
WAVELENGTH IN MICRONS

A

15,815-1
3,3',3''-Nitrilotripropionic acid
$N(CH_2CH_2CO_2H)_3$
M.W. 233.22 m.p. 186-188° (dec.)

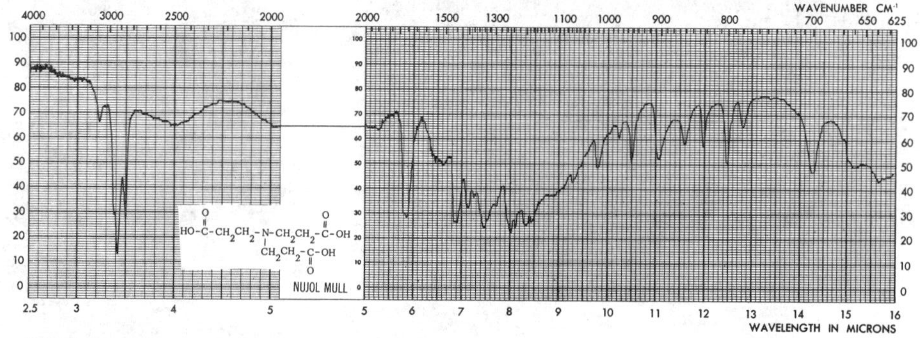

NUJOL MULL

B

H2,650-2
N-(2-Hydroxyethyl)-ethylenediaminetriacetic acid,
99% [N-carboxymethyl-N'-(2-hydroxyethyl)-N,N'-ethylenediglycine]
$HOCH_2CH_2N(CH_2CO_2H)CH_2CH_2N(CH_2CO_2H)_2$
M.W. 278.26 m.p. 212-214° (dec.)
Chelating agent for ferric ion.

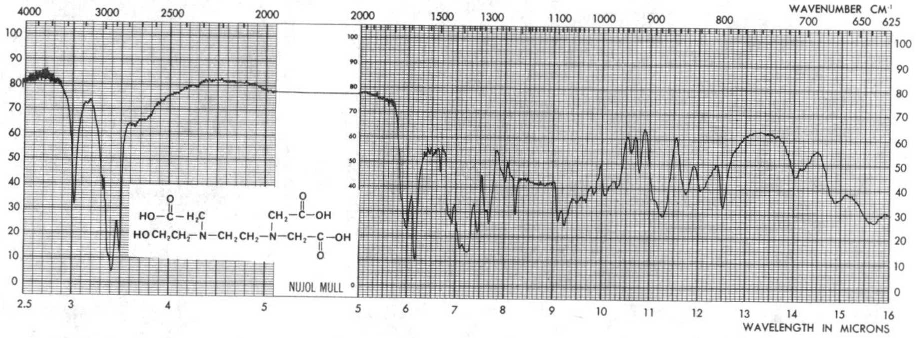

NUJOL MULL

C

E2628-2 **Ethylenediaminetetraacetic acid [(ethylenedinitrilo)-tetraacetic acid, EDTA]**
$(HO_2CCH_2)_2NCH_2CH_2N(CH_2CO_2H)_2$ M.W. 292.24

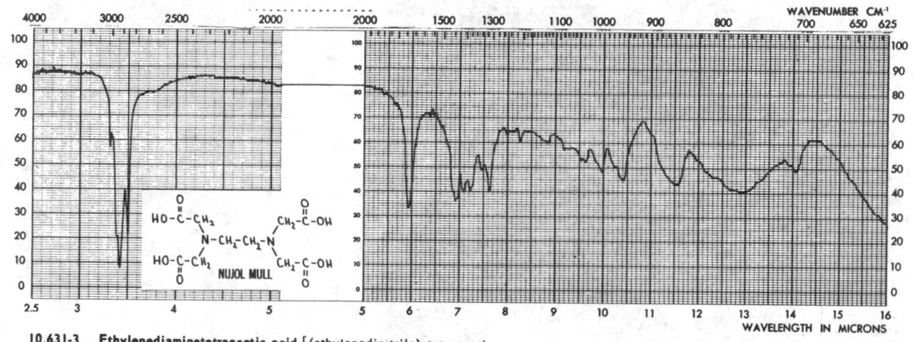

NUJOL MULL

D

10,631-3 **Ethylenediaminetetraacetic acid [(ethylenedinitrilo)-tetraacetic acid, EDTA], disodium salt, dihydrate, puriss.**
$NaO_2CCH_2N(CH_2CO_2H)CH_2CH_2N(CH_2CO_2Na)CH_2CO_2H \cdot 2H_2O$ M.W. 372.24 m.p. 252° (dec.)

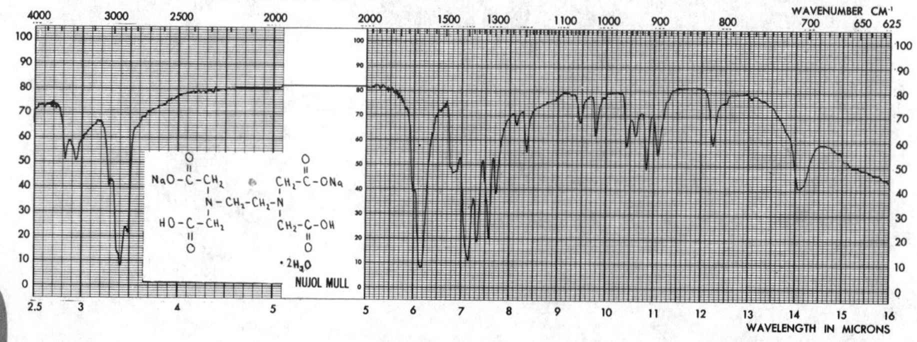

NUJOL MULL

E

10,632-1 **Ethylenediaminetetraacetic acid [(ethylenedinitrilo)-tetraacetic acid, EDTA], trisodium salt, monohydrate**
$(NaO_2CCH_2)_2NCH_2CH_2N(CH_2CO_2Na)CH_2CO_2H \cdot H_2O$
M.W. 376.21 m.p. 245° (dec.)

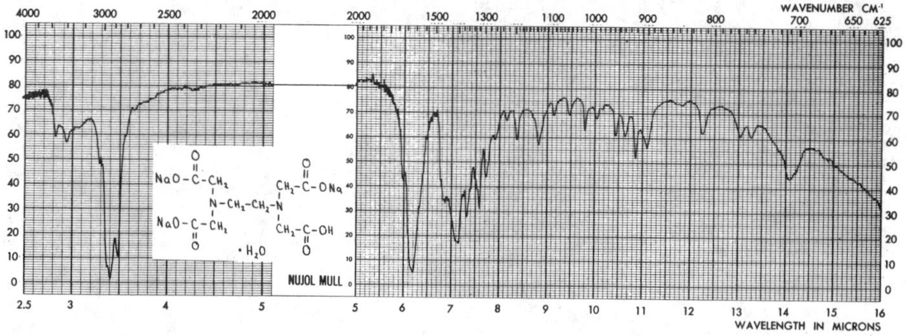

NUJOL MULL

F

E2629-0 **Ethylenediaminetetraacetic acid [(ethylenedinitrilo)-tetraacetic acid, EDTA], tetrasodium salt, tetrahydrate**
$(NaO_2CCH_2)_2NCH_2CH_2N(CH_2CO_2Na)_2 \cdot 4H_2O$ M.W. 452.23
m.p. > 320°

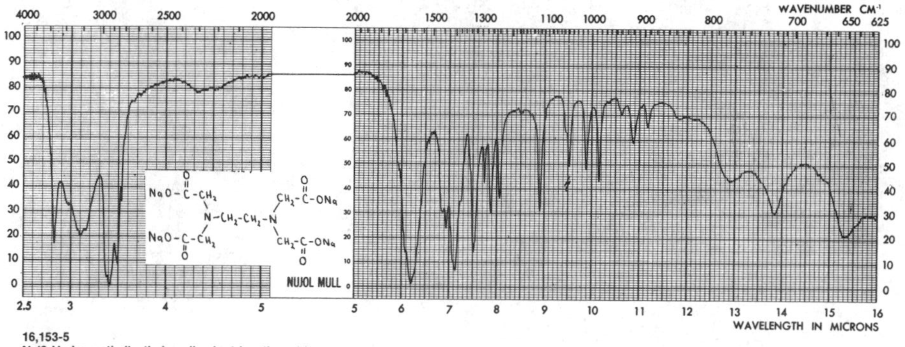

NUJOL MULL

G

16,153-5
N-(2-Hydroxyethyl)-ethylenediaminetriacetic acid, trisodium salt dihydrate, 99+%, GOLD LABEL
$HOCH_2CH_2N(CH_2CO_2Na)CH_2CH_2N(CH_2CO_2Na)_2 \cdot 2H_2O$
M.W. 380.24 m.p. 288-290° (dec.)

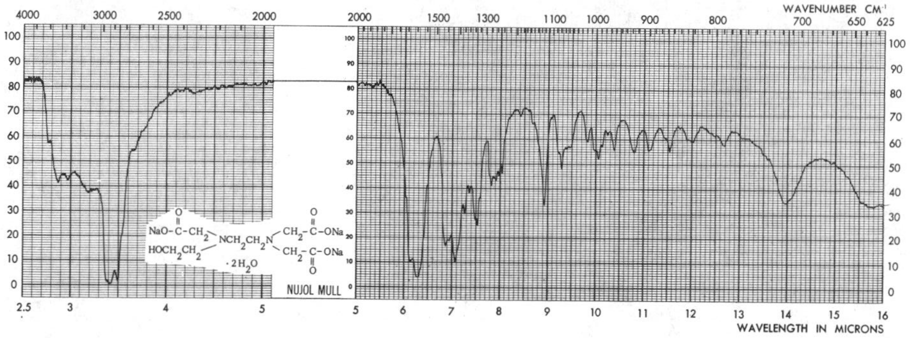

NUJOL MULL

H

12,581-4 *trans*-1,2-Diaminocyclohexane-N,N,N',N'-tetraacetic acid
(CDTA, 1,2-cyclohexylenedinitrilotetraacetic acid) monohydrate
$C_6H_{10}[N(CH_2CO_2H)_2]_2 \cdot H_2O$ M.W. 364.36
m.p. 210-220° (dec.)

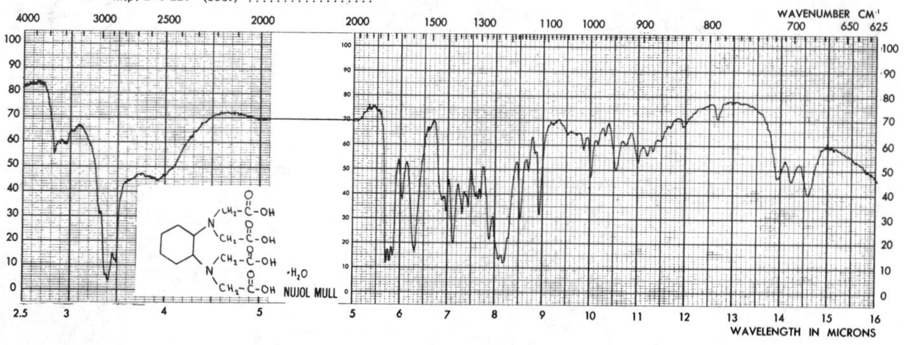

NUJOL MULL

A

15,813-5
1,2-Diaminopropane-N,N,N',N'-tetraacetic acid, 98+%
[(propylenedinitrilo)tetraacetic acid]
$(HO_2CCH_2)_2NCH(CH_3)CH_2N(CH_2CO_2H)_2$
M.W. 306.27 m.p. 241-243° (dec.)

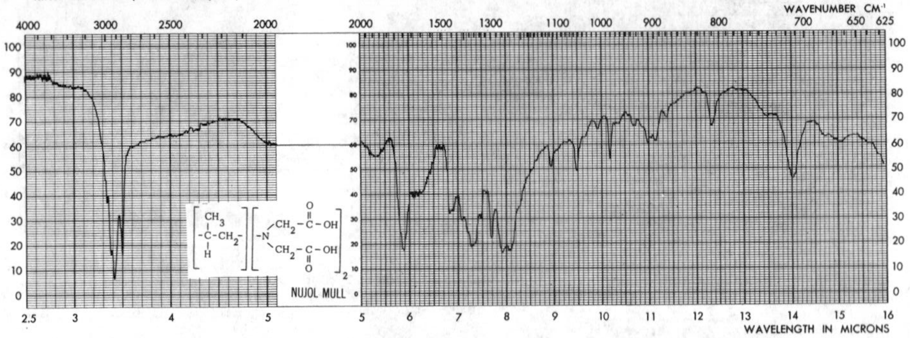

NUJOL MULL

B

15,817-8
1,3-Diamino-2-hydroxypropane-N,N,N',N'-tetraacetic acid
$HOCH[CH_2N(CH_2CO_2H)_2]_2$
M.W. 322.27 m.p. 193-195° (dec.)

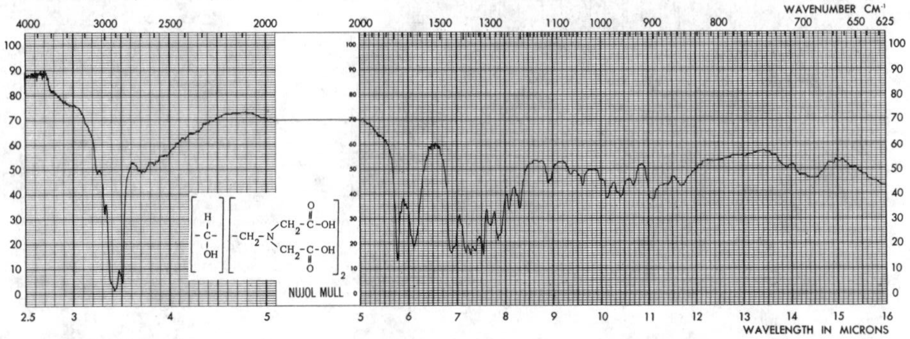

NUJOL MULL

C

13,177-6 **Sarcosine**
$CH_3NHCH_2CO_2H$ M.W. 89.09 m.p. 208° (dec.) ....

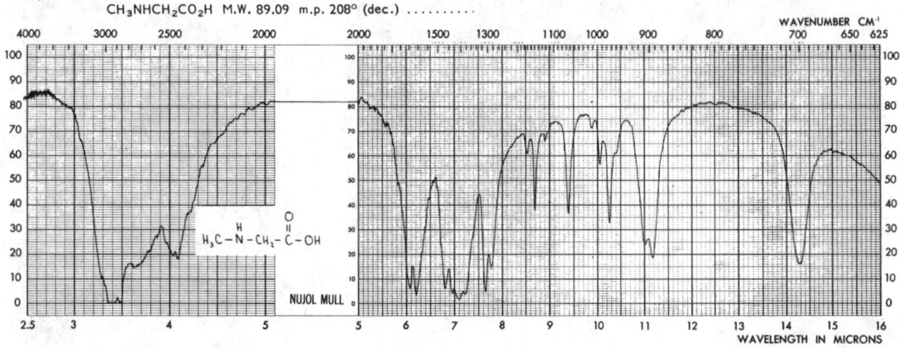

NUJOL MULL

D

22,310-7
Sarcosine hydrochloride, 99%
$CH_3NHCH_2CO_2H \cdot HCl$ FW 125.56 mp 173-175°
Beil. 4,345 Disp. L

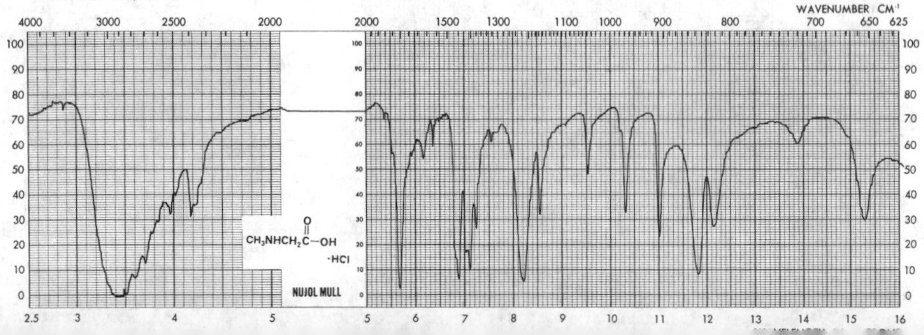

NUJOL MULL

E

21,960-6
***N,N*-Dimethylglycine hydrochloride**, 99%
$(CH_3)_2NCH_2CO_2H \cdot HCl$ FW 139.58 mp 189-194°
Beil. 4(1),469 Disp. L

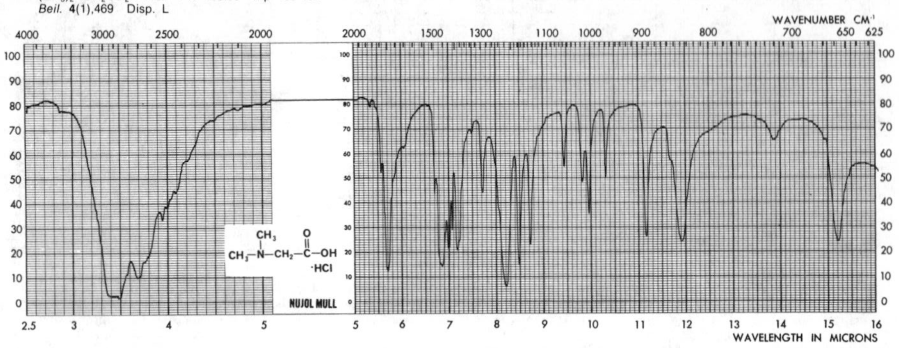

NUJOL MULL

F

13,522-4 **DL-Alanine**
$CH_3CH(NH_2)CO_2H$ M.W. 89.09
m.p. 289° (dec.) ....

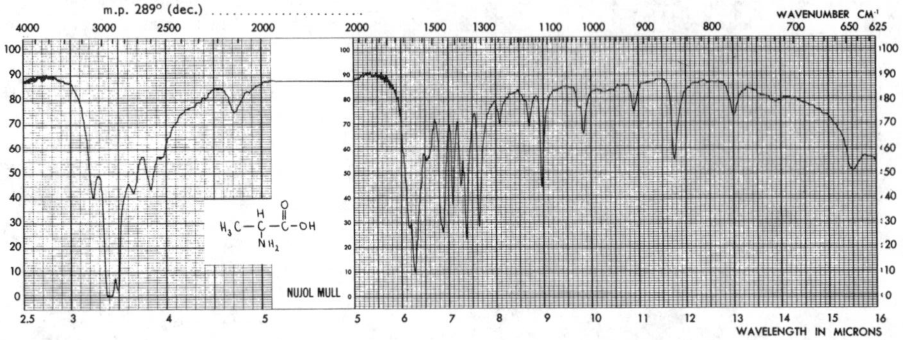

NUJOL MULL

G

16,265-5
D-Alanine, 99+%, GOLD LABEL
$CH_3CH(NH_2)CO_2H$
M.W. 89.09 m.p. 291-293° (dec.)
$[\alpha]^{25}$-14° (c=10, 6N HCl) Beil. 4,385

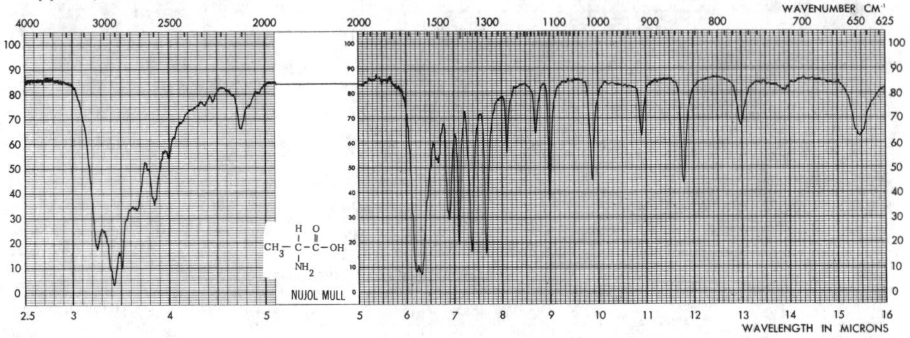

NUJOL MULL

H

A2680-2 **L-Alanine**
$CH_3CH(NH_2)CO_2H$ M.W. 89.09
m.p. 314.5-315.5° (dec.) ....

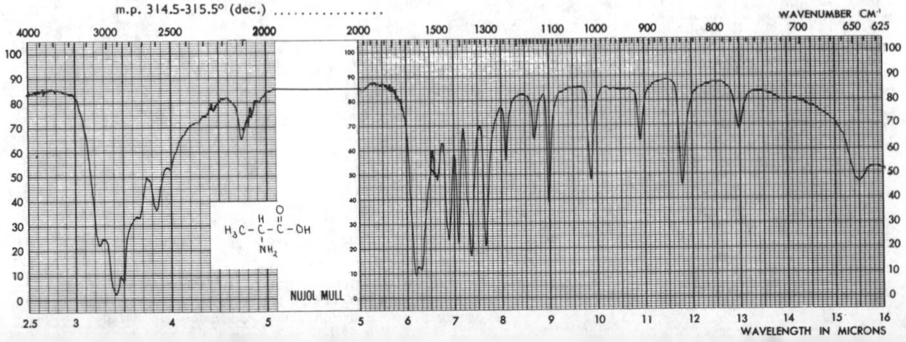

NUJOL MULL

WAVENUMBER CM⁻¹ — WAVELENGTH IN MICRONS

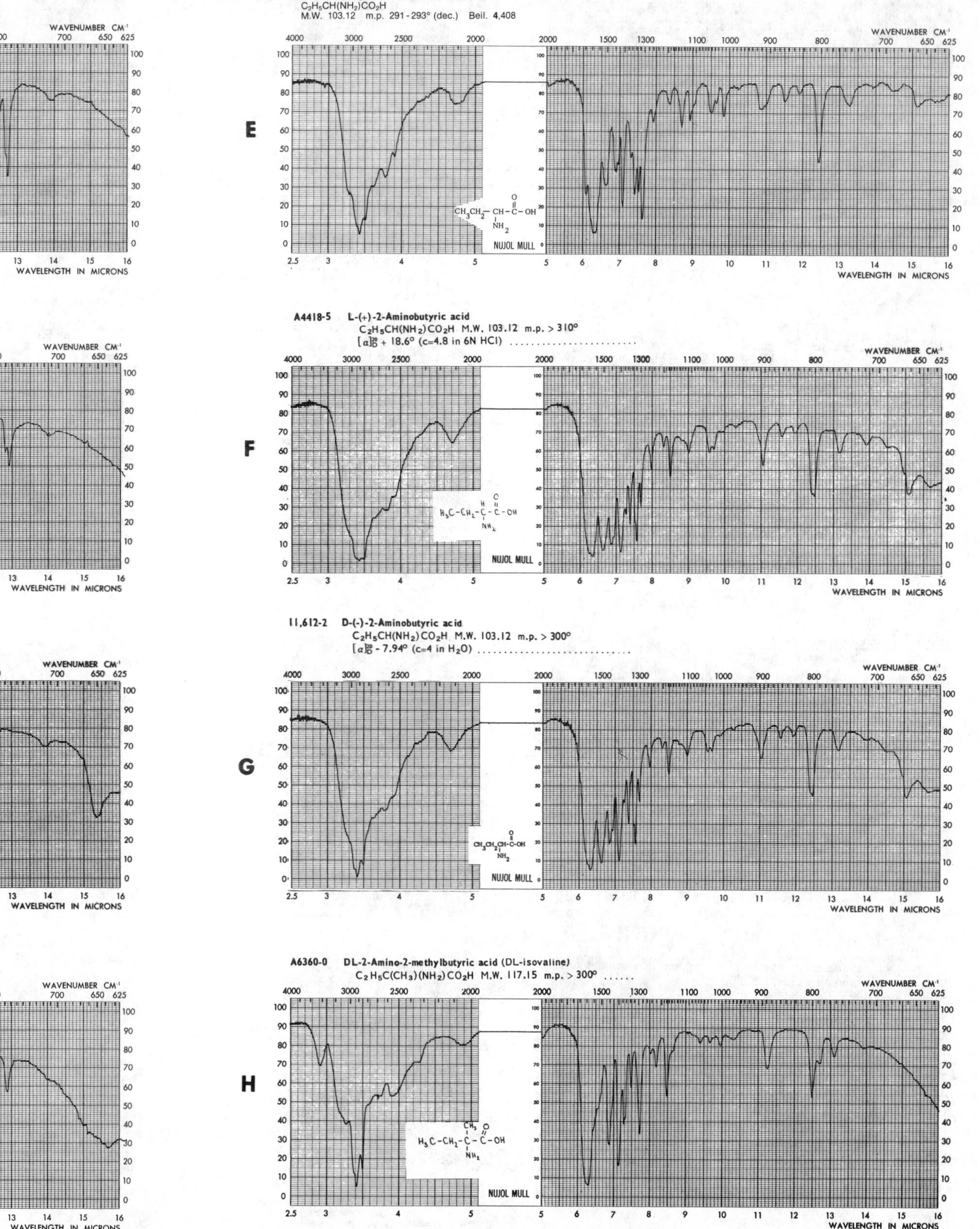

A

85,099-3
α-**Aminoisobutyric acid** (2-methylalanine)
$(CH_3)_2C(NH_2)CO_2H$
M.W. 103.12 m.p. >300° Beil. 4,414

B

86,022-0
α-**(Methylamino)isobutyric acid**
$CH_3NHC(CH_3)_2CO_2H$ FW 117.15 mp >300°
Disp. L

C

14,606-4 *β*-**Alanine**
$H_2NCH_2CH_2CO_2H$ M.W. 89.09
m.p. 196° (dec.)

D

21,779-4
DL-*β*-**Aminoisobutyric acid hydrate, 99%**
$H_2NCH_2CH(CH_3)CO_2H \cdot xH_2O$ FW 103.12
mp 179-182° *Beil.* 4(3),1330 Disp. D

E

16,266-3
DL-2-Aminobutyric acid, 99+%, GOLD LABEL
$C_2H_5CH(NH_2)CO_2H$
M.W. 103.12 m.p. 291-293° (dec.) Beil. 4,408

F

A4418-5 **L-(+)-2-Aminobutyric acid**
$C_2H_5CH(NH_2)CO_2H$ M.W. 103.12 m.p. > 310°
$[\alpha]_D^{25}$ + 18.6° (c=4.8 in 6N HCl)

G

11,612-2 **D-(-)-2-Aminobutyric acid**
$C_2H_5CH(NH_2)CO_2H$ M.W. 103.12 m.p. > 300°
$[\alpha]_D^{25}$ - 7.94° (c=4 in H_2O)

H

A6360-0 **DL-2-Amino-2-methylbutyric acid (DL-isovaline)**
$C_2H_5C(CH_3)(NH_2)CO_2H$ M.W. 117.15 m.p. > 300°

ALDRICH ®

NON-AROMATIC AMINO ACIDS

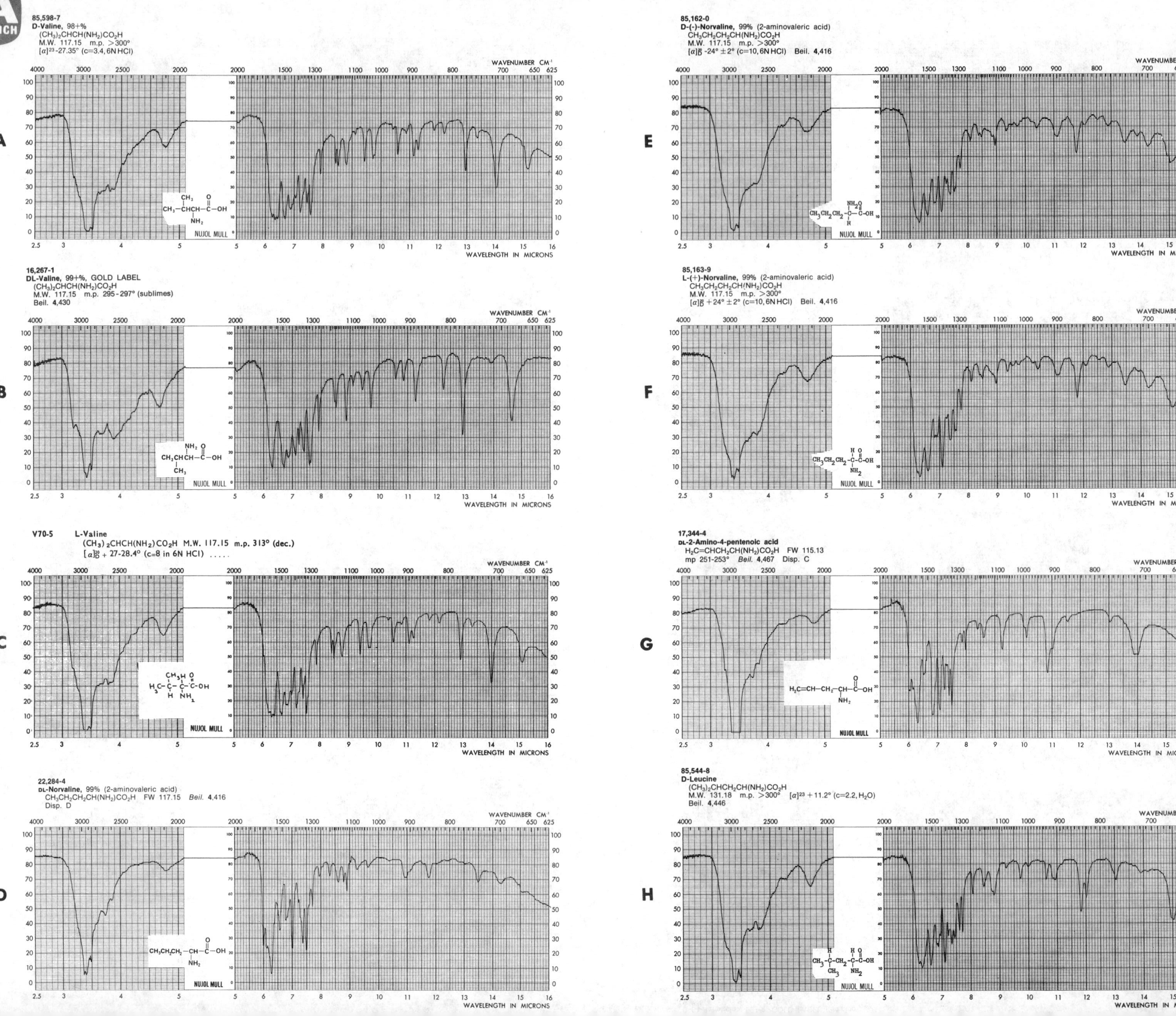
ALDRICH
A
85,598-7
D-Valine, 98+%
(CH3)2CHCH(NH2)CO2H
M.W. 117.15 m.p. >300°
[α]23 -27.35° (c=3.4, 6N HCl)
NUJOL MULL
B
16,267-1
DL-Valine, 99+%, GOLD LABEL
(CH3)2CHCH(NH2)CO2H
M.W. 117.15 m.p. 295-297° (sublimes)
Beil. 4,430
NUJOL MULL
C
V70-5 L-Valine
(CH3)2CHCH(NH2)CO2H M.W. 117.15 m.p. 313° (dec.)
[α]20D + 27-28.4° (c=8 in 6N HCl)
NUJOL MULL
D
22,284-4
DL-Norvaline, 99% (2-aminovaleric acid)
CH3CH2CH2CH(NH2)CO2H FW 117.15 Beil. 4,416
Disp. D
NUJOL MULL
E
85,162-0
D-(-)-Norvaline, 99% (2-aminovaleric acid)
CH3CH2CH2CH(NH2)CO2H
M.W. 117.15 m.p. >300°
[α]20D -24° ± 2° (c=10, 6N HCl) Beil. 4,416
NUJOL MULL
F
85,163-9
L-(+)-Norvaline, 99% (2-aminovaleric acid)
CH3CH2CH2CH(NH2)CO2H
M.W. 117.15 m.p. >300°
[α]20D +24° ± 2° (c=10, 6N HCl) Beil. 4,416
NUJOL MULL
G
17,344-4
DL-2-Amino-4-pentenoic acid
H2C=CHCH2CH(NH2)CO2H FW 115.13
mp 251-253° Beil. 4,467 Disp. C
NUJOL MULL
H
85,544-8
D-Leucine
(CH3)2CHCH2CH(NH2)CO2H
M.W. 131.18 m.p. >300° [α]23 +11.2° (c=2.2, H2O)
Beil. 4,446
NUJOL MULL
WAVENUMBER CM-1
WAVELENGTH IN MICRONS

A

L60-2 **L-Leucine**
$(CH_3)_2CHCH_2CH(NH_2)CO_2H$ M.W. 131.18
m.p. 300° (dec.)

NUJOL MULL

B

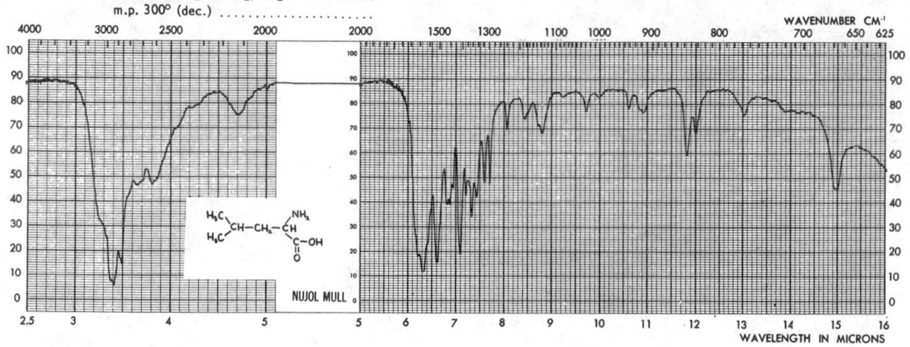

16,272-8
DL-Leucine, 99+%, GOLD LABEL
$(CH_3)_2CHCH_2CH(NH_2)CO_2H$
M.W. 131.18 m.p. 293-296° (sublimes)
Beil. 4,447

NUJOL MULL

C

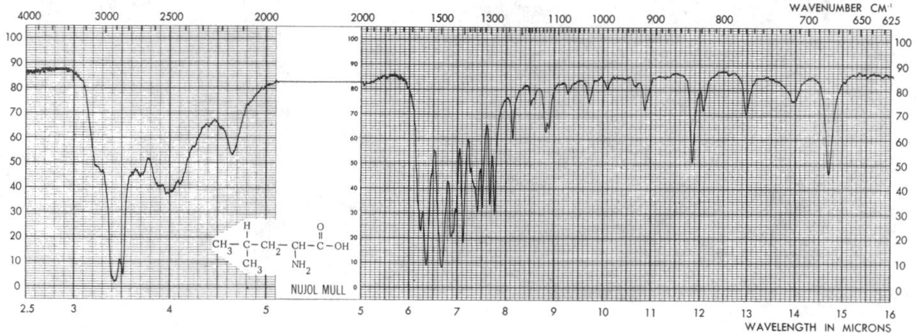

15,171-8 **L-Isoleucine**
$C_2H_5CH(CH_3)CH(NH_2)CO_2H$ M.W. 131.18 m.p. 288° (dec.)

NUJOL MULL

D

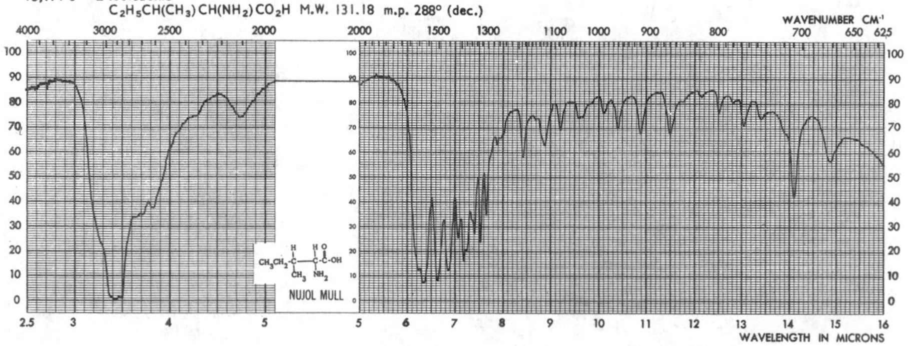

17,109-3
DL-Norleucine, 98% (2-aminohexanoic acid)
$CH_3(CH_2)_3CH(NH_2)CO_2H$
M.W. 131.18 m.p. >300° Beil. 4,433

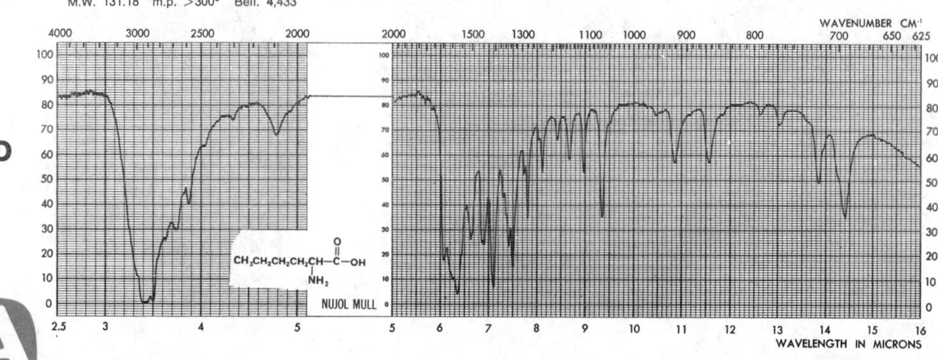

E

D-(-)-Norleucine, 99+%, GOLD LABEL (2-amino-hexanoic acid)
$CH_3(CH_2)_3CH(NH_2)CO_2H$
M.W. 131.18 m.p. >300°
$[\alpha]^{24}$ -23.1° (c=4.7, 6N HCl) Beil. 4,433

NUJOL MULL

F

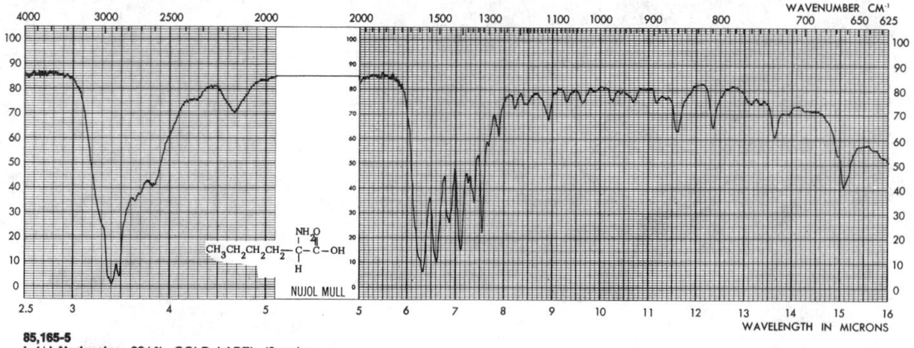

85,165-5
L-(+)-Norleucine, 99+%, GOLD LABEL (2-amino-hexanoic acid)
$CH_3(CH_2)_3CH(NH_2)CO_2H$
M.W. 131.18 m.p. >300°
$[\alpha]^{24}$ +23.3° (c=4.2, 5N HCl) Beil. 4,432

NUJOL MULL

G

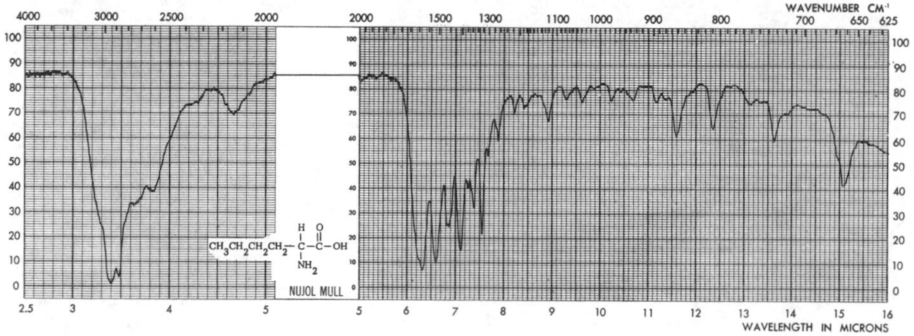

21,770-0
DL-α-Aminocaprylic acid, 99%
(DL-aminooctanoic acid)
$CH_3(CH_2)_5CH(NH_2)CO_2H$ FW 159.23
mp 260° (dec.) *Beil.* 4,461 Disp. D

NUJOL MULL

H

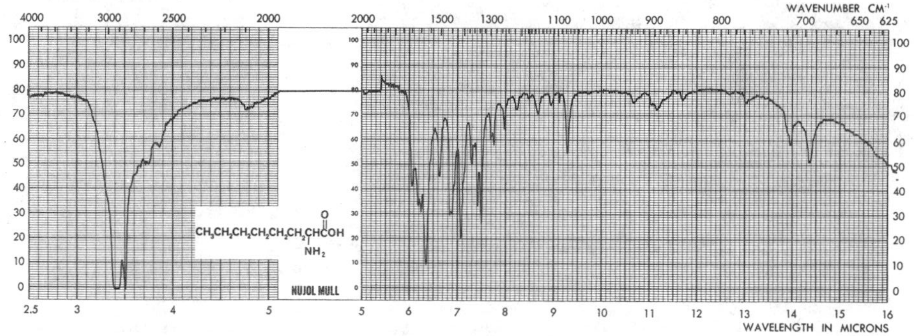

A5988 **α-Aminolauric acid, puriss.**
$CH_3(CH_2)_9CH(NH_2)CO_2H$ M.W. 215.34 m.p. 248° (dec.)

NUJOL MULL

ALDRICH ®

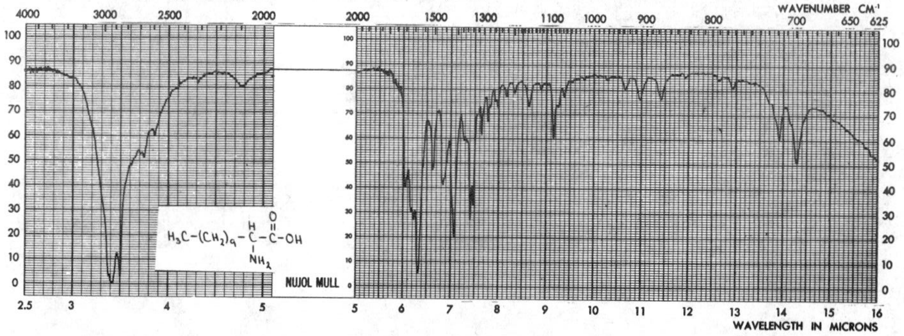

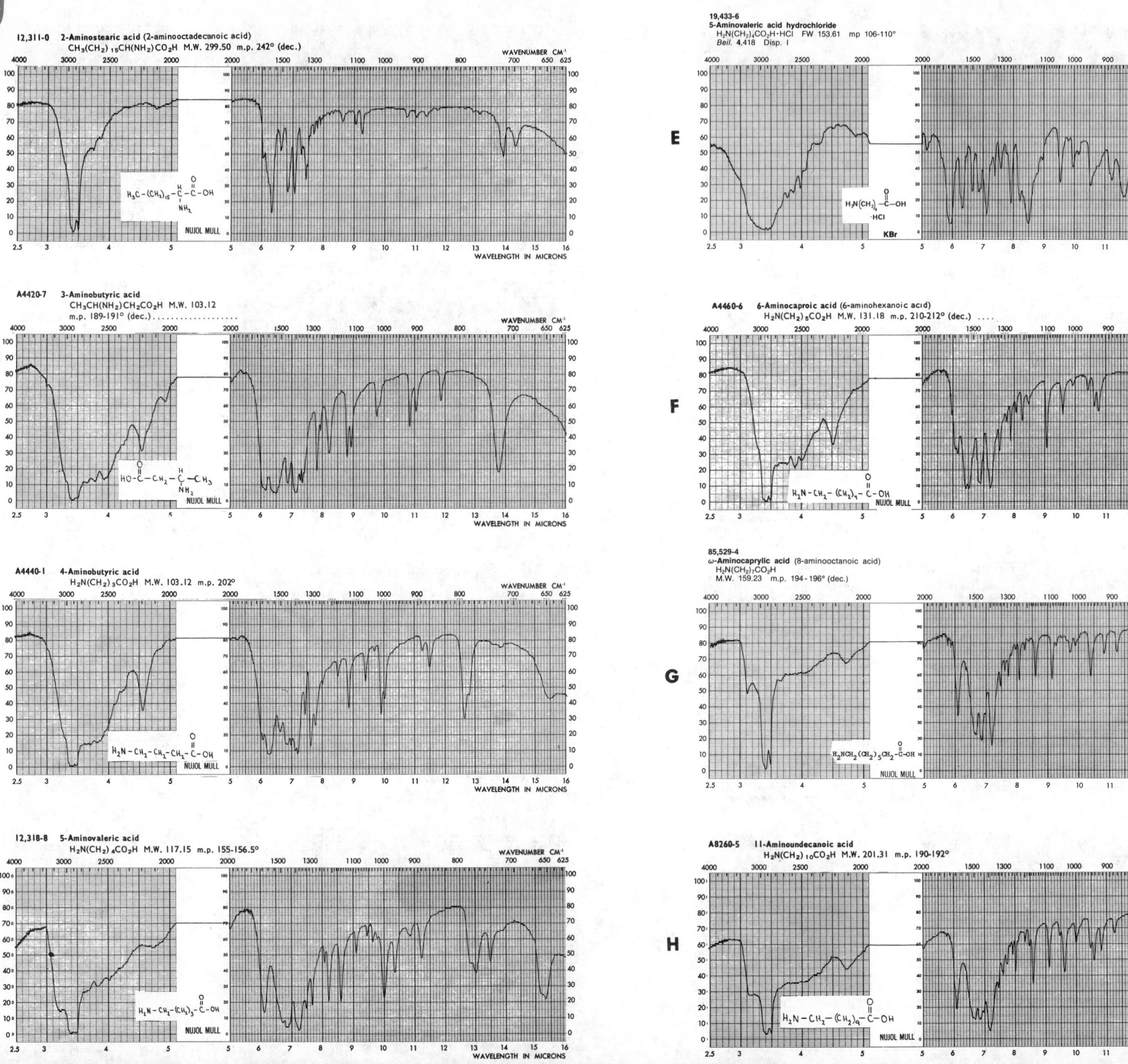
ALDRICH
A
12,311-0 2-Aminostearic acid (2-aminooctadecanoic acid)
$CH_3(CH_2)_{15}CH(NH_2)CO_2H$ M.W. 299.50 m.p. 242° (dec.)
NUJOL MULL
B
A4420-7 3-Aminobutyric acid
$CH_3CH(NH_2)CH_2CO_2H$ M.W. 103.12
m.p. 189-191° (dec.)
NUJOL MULL
C
A4440-1 4-Aminobutyric acid
$H_2N(CH_2)_3CO_2H$ M.W. 103.12 m.p. 202°
NUJOL MULL
D
12,318-8 5-Aminovaleric acid
$H_2N(CH_2)_4CO_2H$ M.W. 117.15 m.p. 155-156.5°
NUJOL MULL
E
19,433-6
5-Aminovaleric acid hydrochloride
$H_2N(CH_2)_4CO_2H \cdot HCl$ FW 153.61 mp 106-110°
Beil. 4,418 Disp. I
KBr
F
A4460-6 6-Aminocaproic acid (6-aminohexanoic acid)
$H_2N(CH_2)_5CO_2H$ M.W. 131.18 m.p. 210-212° (dec.)
NUJOL MULL
G
85,529-4
ω-Aminocaprylic acid (8-aminooctanoic acid)
$H_2N(CH_2)_7CO_2H$
M.W. 159.23 m.p. 194-196° (dec.)
NUJOL MULL
H
A8260-5 11-Aminoundecanoic acid
$H_2N(CH_2)_{10}CO_2H$ M.W. 201.31 m.p. 190-192°
NUJOL MULL
WAVENUMBER CM⁻¹
WAVELENGTH IN MICRONS

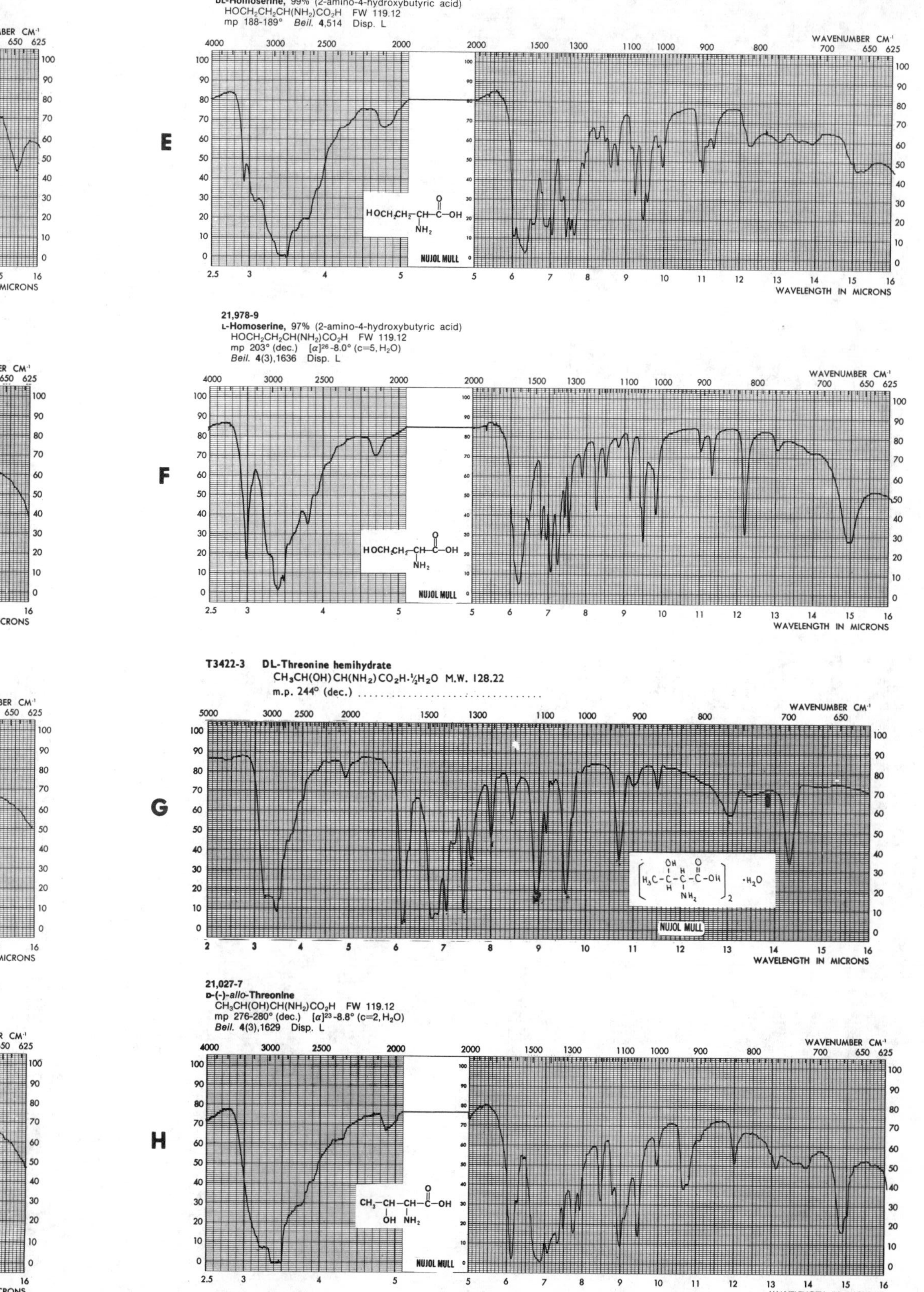

A

15,924-7
12-Aminododecanoic acid, 95%
$H_2N(CH_2)_{11}CO_2H$
M.W. 215.34 m.p. 185-187°

B

S259-7 **DL-Serine**
$HOCH_2CH(NH_2)CO_2H$ M.W. 105.09
m.p. 240° (dec.)

C

85,569-3
D-Serine
$HOCH_2CH(NH_2)CO_2H$
M.W. 105.09 m.p. 220° (dec.) Beil. 4,505

D

S260-0 **L-Serine**
$HOCH_2CH(NH_2)CO_2H$ M.W. 105.09 $[\alpha]_D^{20}$ + 13.7° to + 14.7°
(c=10 in IN HCl)

E

21,977-0
DL-Homoserine, 99% (2-amino-4-hydroxybutyric acid)
$HOCH_2CH_2CH(NH_2)CO_2H$ FW 119.12
mp 188-189° *Beil.* 4,514 Disp. L

F

21,978-9
L-Homoserine, 97% (2-amino-4-hydroxybutyric acid)
$HOCH_2CH_2CH(NH_2)CO_2H$ FW 119.12
mp 203° (dec.) $[\alpha]^{26}$ -8.0° (c=5, H_2O)
Beil. 4(3),1636 Disp. L

G

T3422-3 **DL-Threonine hemihydrate**
$CH_3CH(OH)CH(NH_2)CO_2H \cdot \frac{1}{2}H_2O$ M.W. 128.22
m.p. 244° (dec.)

H

21,027-7
D-(-)-*allo*-Threonine
$CH_3CH(OH)CH(NH_2)CO_2H$ FW 119.12
mp 276-280° (dec.) $[\alpha]^{23}$ -8.8° (c=2, H_2O)
Beil. 4(3),1629 Disp. L

A
21,026-9
L-(+)-*allo*-Threonine
$CH_3CH(OH)CH(NH_2)CO_2H$ FW 119.12
mp 272-276° (dec.) $[\alpha]^{23}$ +9.0° (c=2, H_2O)
Beil. 4(3),1629 Disp. L

B
A5,665-5
DL-4-Amino-3-hydroxybutyric acid, 98%
$H_2NCH_2CH(OH)CH_2CO_2H$
M.W. 119.12 m.p. 202° (dec.) Beil. **4**(2),938
Antispasmodic. Reduces uptake of iodine by the thyroid glands in animals. *Biochem. Pharmacol.*, 17, 1120 (1968).

C
T3420-7 L-Threonine
$CH_3CH(OH)CH(NH_2)CO_2H$ M.W. 119.12
m.p. 270° (dec.) ....

D
85,937-0
5-Hydroxy-DL-lysine hydrochloride
$H_2NCH_2CH(OH)CH_2CH_2CH(NH_2)CO_2H \cdot HCl$
M.W. 198.65 m.p. 225-227° (dec.)

E
M2905-3 Methylaminomethyltartronic acid
$CH_3NHCH_2C(OH)(CO_2H)_2$ M.W. 163.13 m.p. 163° (dec.)

F
A5990-5 5-Aminolevulinic acid hydrochloride
$H_2NCH_2COCH_2CH_2CO_2H \cdot HCl$ M.W. 167.59

G
A9630-4 L-2-Azetidinecarboxylic acid
M.W. 110.11 $[\alpha]^{20}_D$ - 108° (in H_2O)

H
17,182-4
DL-Proline, 95%
M.W. 115.13 m.p. 208-210° (dec.) Beil. **22**,4

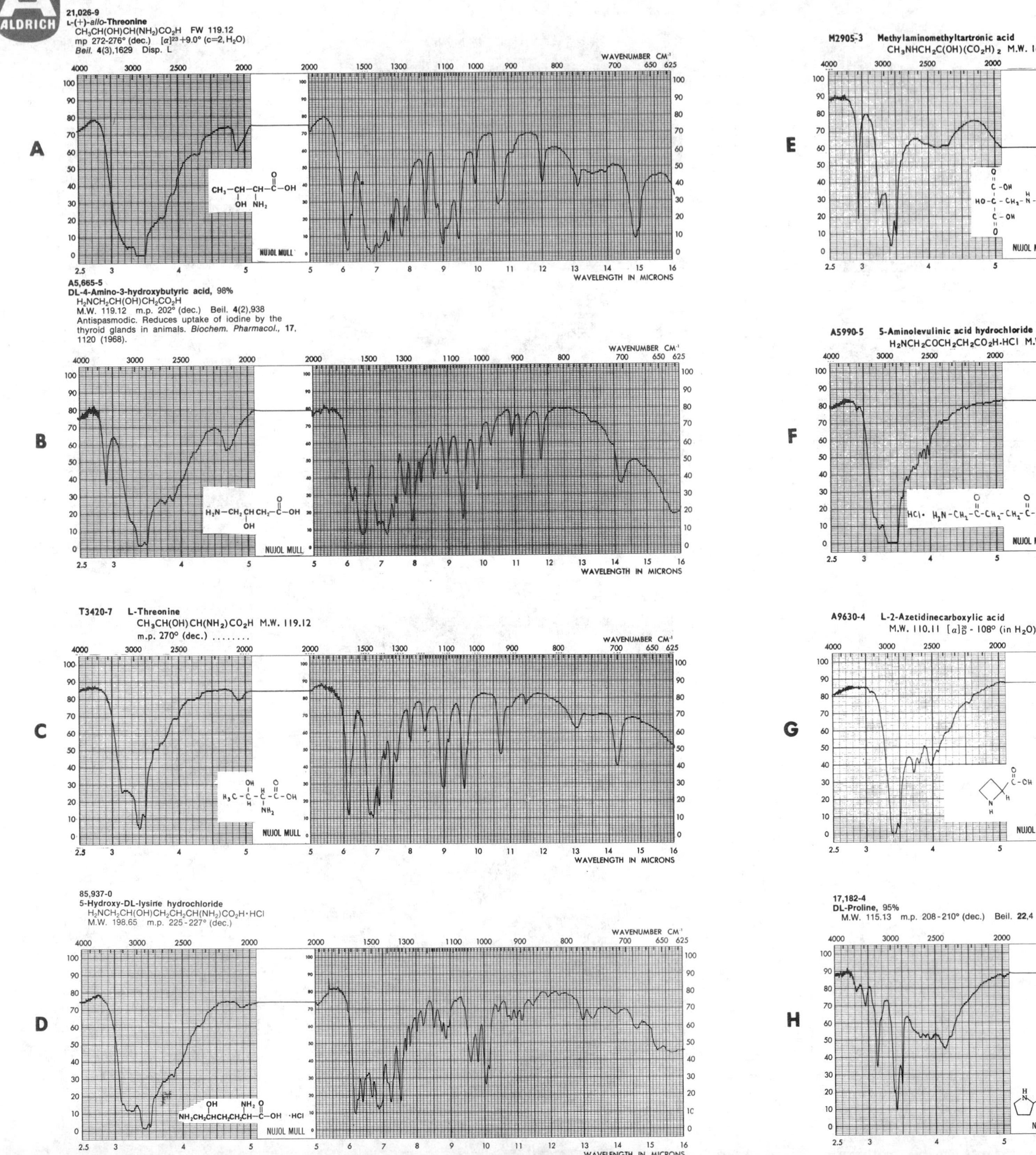

A

85,891-9
D-(+)-Proline, 99+%, GOLD LABEL
FW 115.13 mp 223° (dec.) $[\alpha]^{22}$ +85.0° (c=4, H_2O)
Beil. **22**,2 *Fieser* **7**,307 Disp. L

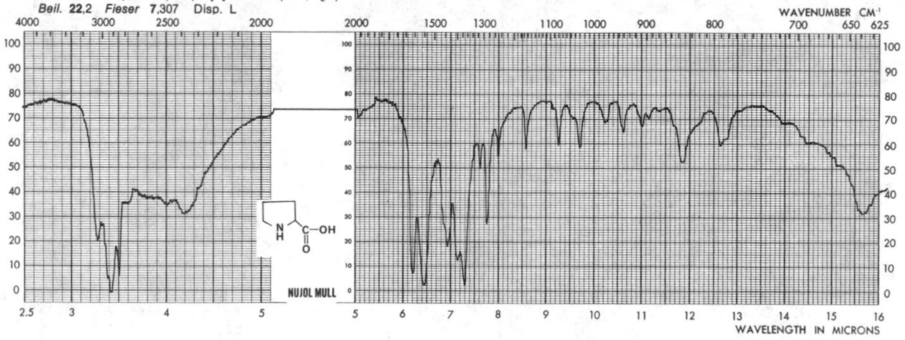

NUJOL MULL

E

21,995-9
cis-**4-Hydroxy-L-proline**, 99%

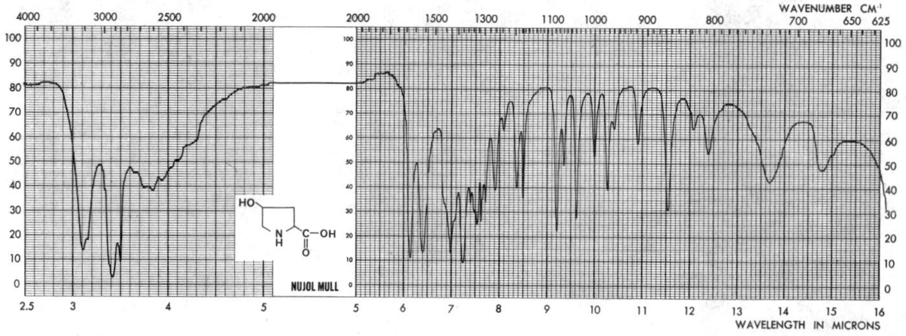

NUJOL MULL

B

13,154-7 **L-(-)-Proline, puriss.**
M.W. 115.14 m.p. 220-227° $[\alpha]^{20}_{D}$ - 84.5°

NUJOL MULL

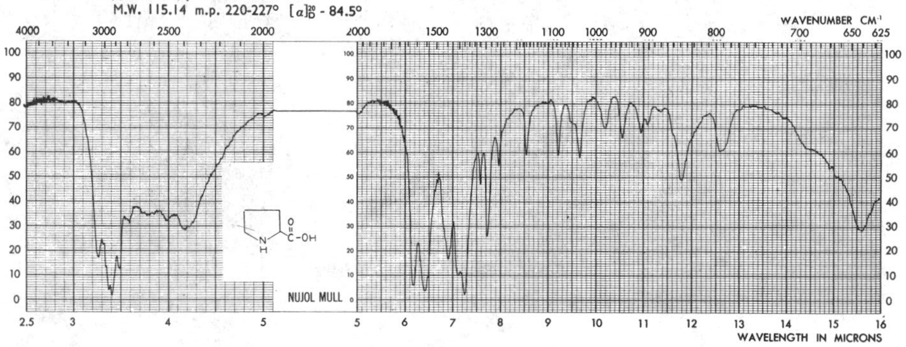

F

A4810-5 **1-Amino-1-cyclopentanecarboxylic acid**
$H_2NC_5H_8CO_2H$ M.W. 129.16 m.p. 320-322°(dec.) ....

NUJOL MULL

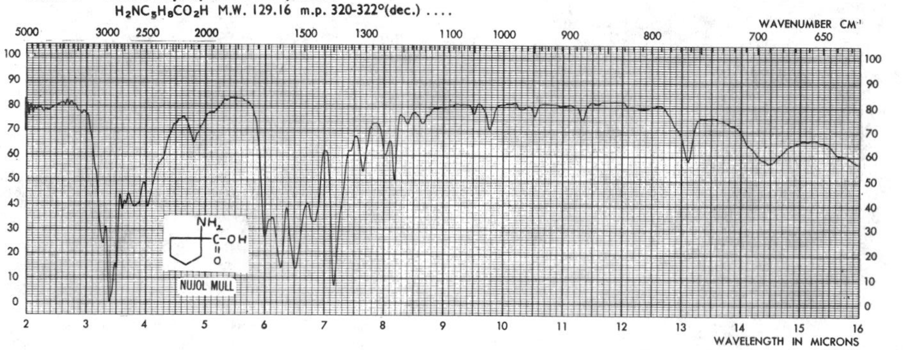

C

H5440-9 **4-Hydroxy-L-proline, puriss.**
M.W. 131.13 m.p. 273-275° (dec.)

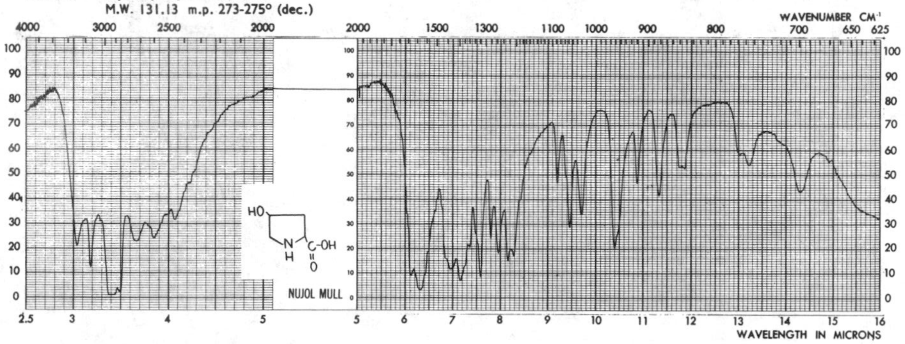

NUJOL MULL

G

A4810-5 **1-Amino-1-cyclopentanecarboxylic acid**
$H_2NC_5H_8CO_2H$ M.W. 129.16 m.p. 320-322°(dec.) ....

NUJOL MULL

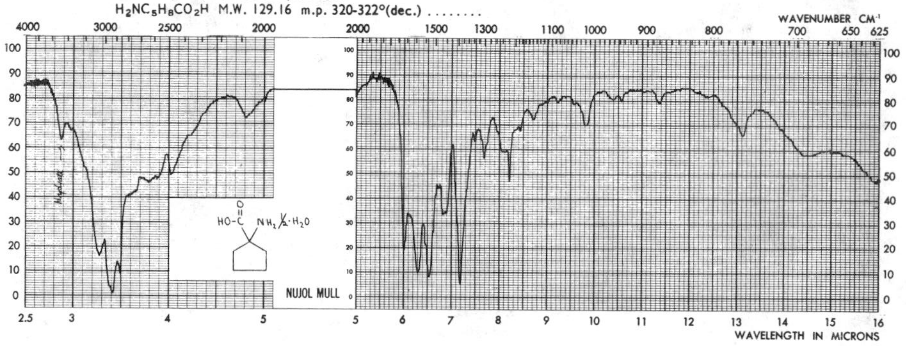

D

21,994-0
cis-**4-Hydroxy-D-proline**, 99%
$[\alpha]^{20}_{D}$ +58° (c=2, H_2O)

NUJOL MULL

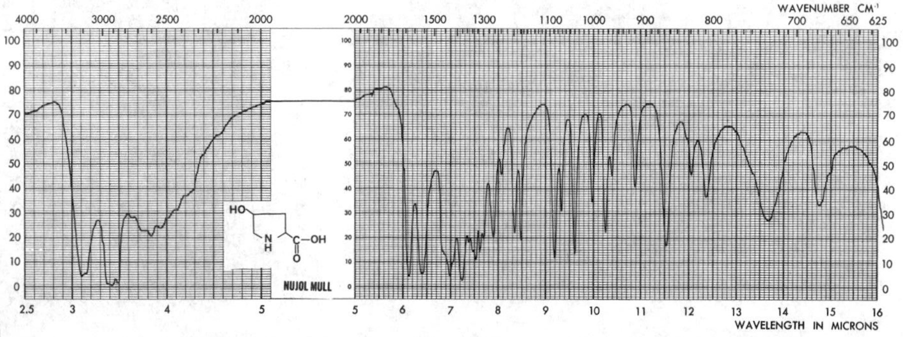

H

21,869-3
1-Amino-1-cyclohexanecarboxylic acid, 98%
$H_2NC_6H_{10}CO_2H$ FW 143.19 mp >300°
Beil. **14**,299 Disp. L

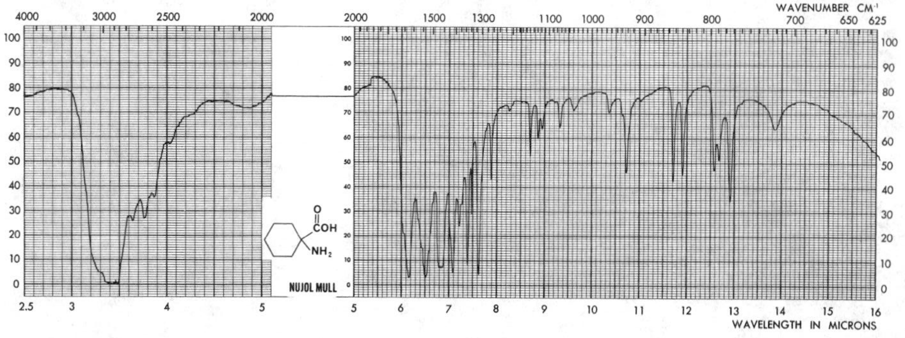

NUJOL MULL

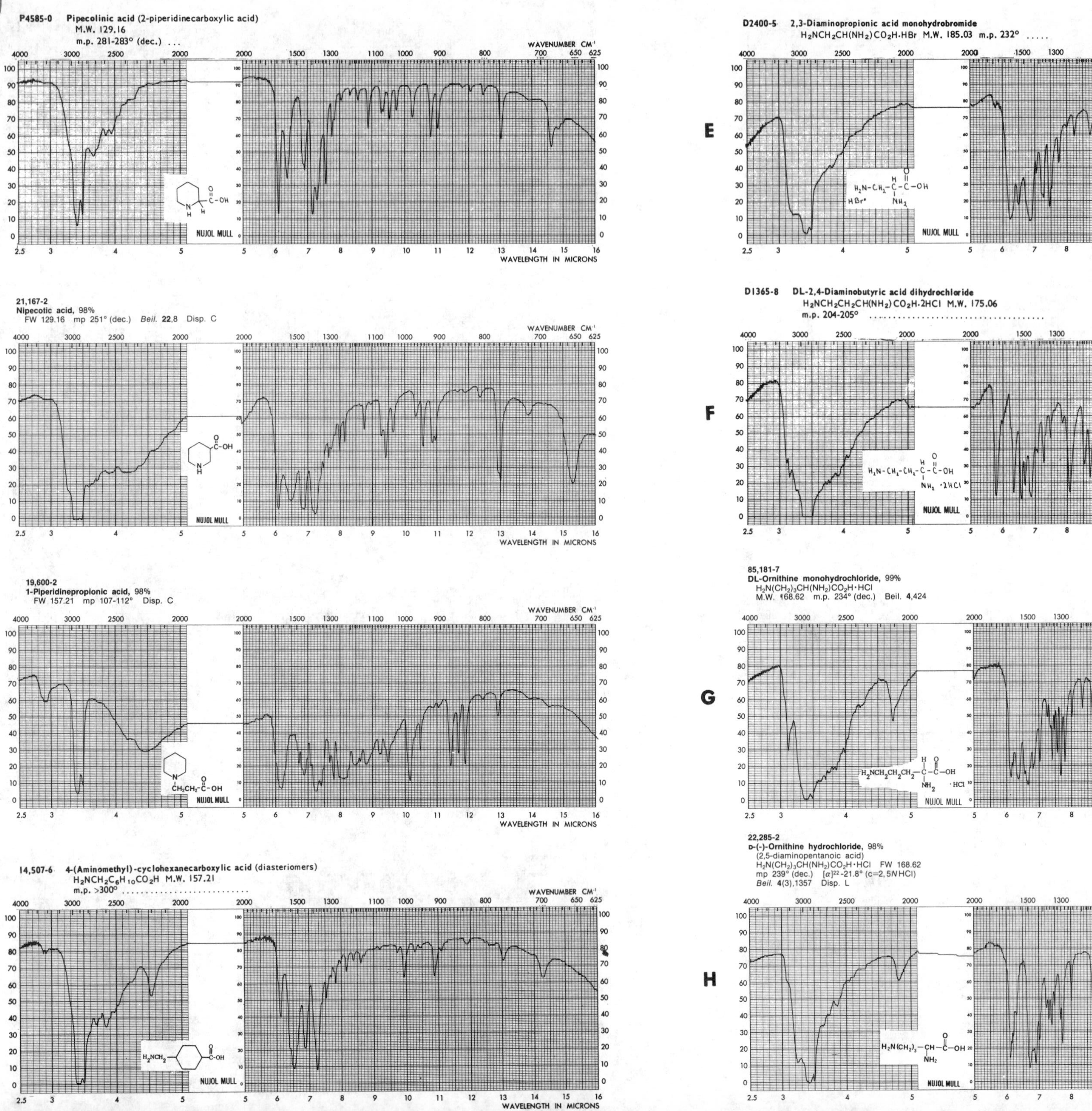
ALDRICH
A
P4585-0 Pipecolinic acid (2-piperidinecarboxylic acid)
M.W. 129.16
m.p. 281-283° (dec.)
B
21,167-2
Nipecotic acid, 98%
FW 129.16 mp 251° (dec.) Beil. 22,8 Disp. C
C
19,600-2
1-Piperidinepropionic acid, 98%
FW 157.21 mp 107-112° Disp. C
D
14,507-6 4-(Aminomethyl)-cyclohexanecarboxylic acid (diasteriomers)
H2NCH2C6H10CO2H M.W. 157.21
m.p. >300°
E
D2400-5 2,3-Diaminopropionic acid monohydrobromide
H2NCH2CH(NH2)CO2H·HBr M.W. 185.03 m.p. 232°
F
D1365-8 DL-2,4-Diaminobutyric acid dihydrochloride
H2NCH2CH2CH(NH2)CO2H·2HCl M.W. 175.06
m.p. 204-205°
G
85,181-7
DL-Ornithine monohydrochloride, 99%
H2N(CH2)3CH(NH2)CO2H·HCl
M.W. 168.62 m.p. 234° (dec.) Beil. 4,424
H
22,285-2
D-(-)-Ornithine hydrochloride, 98%
(2,5-diaminopentanoic acid)
H2N(CH2)3CH(NH2)CO2H·HCl FW 168.62
mp 239° (dec.) [α]22 -21.8° (c=2.5N HCl)
Beil. 4(3),1357 Disp. L
NUJOL MULL
WAVENUMBER CM⁻¹
WAVELENGTH IN MICRONS

A

O-830-5 **L-(+)-Ornithine** (L-(+)-2,5-diaminopentanoic acid) **hydrochloride**
$H_2N(CH_2)_3CH(NH_2)CO_2H \cdot HCl$ M.W. 168.62
m.p. 228° (dec.) $[\alpha]^{25}_{D}$ + 11° (c=5.5) .....

NUJOL MULL

B

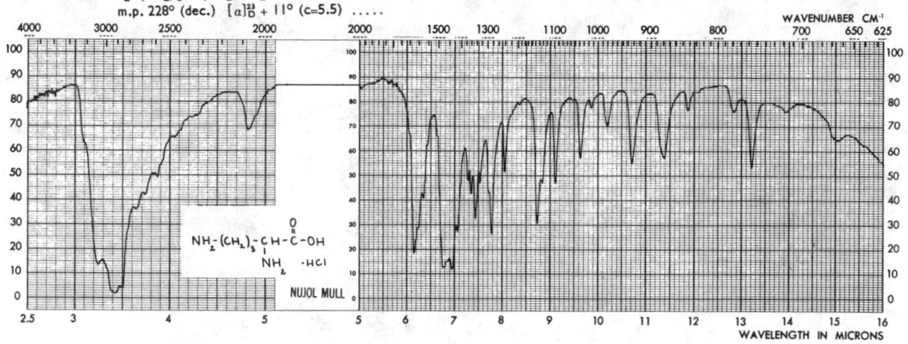

16,971-4
L-(+)-Lysine
$H_2N(CH_2)_4CH(NH_2)CO_2H$
M.W. 146.19 m.p. 212-214° (dec.)
$[\alpha]^{25}_{D}$ +25.2 (c=2, 6NHCl) Beil. 4,435

NUJOL MULL

C

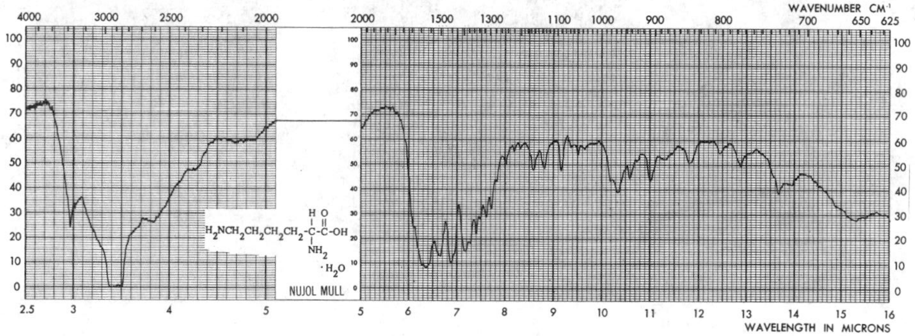

85,895-1
Nε-Methyl-L-lysine hydrochloride, 98%
$CH_3NH(CH_2)_4CH(NH_2)CO_2H \cdot HCl$
M.W. 196.68 m.p. 250-254° (dec.) Beil. 4(3),1406

NUJOL MULL

D

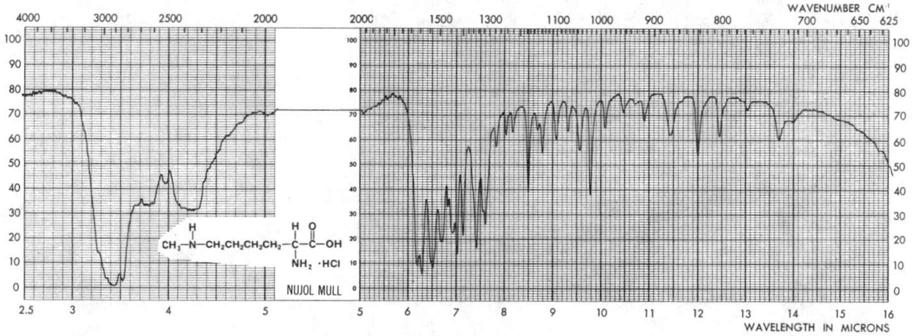

L460-5 **L-Lysine monohydrochloride, puriss.**
$H_2N(CH_2)_4CH(NH_2)CO_2H \cdot HCl$ M.W. 182.65 m.p. 263-264°

NUJOL MULL

E

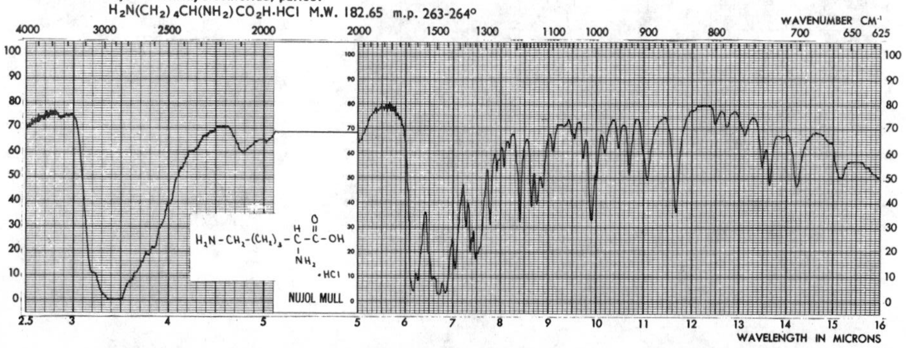

14,793-1 **Betaine hydrochloride**
$(CH_3)_3N(Cl)CH_2CO_2H$ M.W. 153.62
m.p. 241-242° (dec.) ....

NUJOL MULL

F

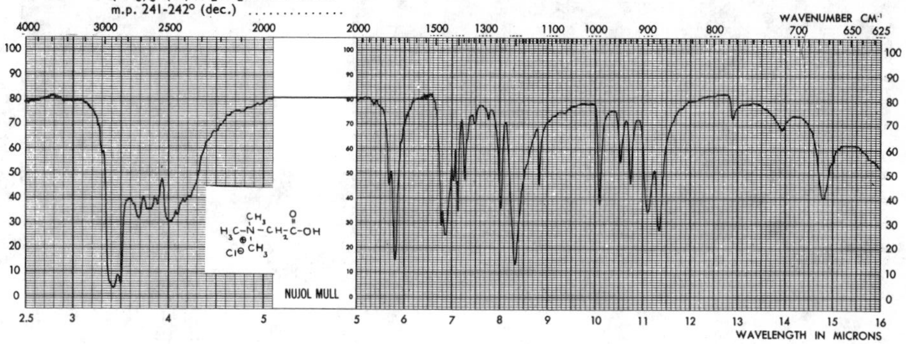

A9309-7 **DL-Aspartic acid** (DL-aminosuccinic acid)
$HO_2CCH_2CH(NH_2)CO_2H$ M.W. 133.10 m.p. 275° (dec.)

NUJOL MULL

G

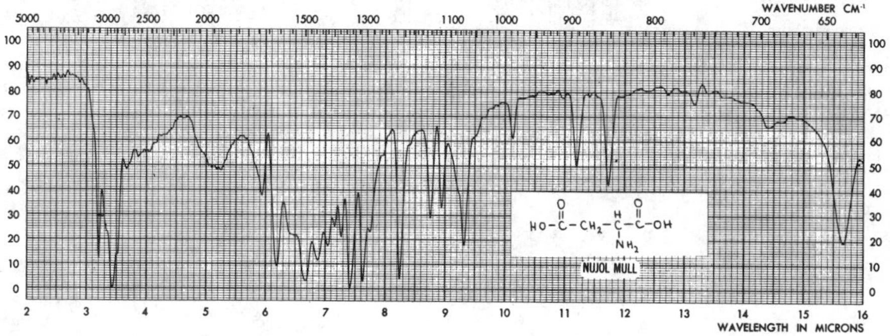

21,909-6
D-Aspartic acid, 99+% (D-aminosuccinic acid)
$HO_2CCH_2CH(NH_2)CO_2H$ FW 133.10 mp >300°
$[\alpha]^{20}_{D}$ -24° (c=2.3, 6N HCl) *Beil.* **4**,471 Disp. L

NUJOL MULL

H

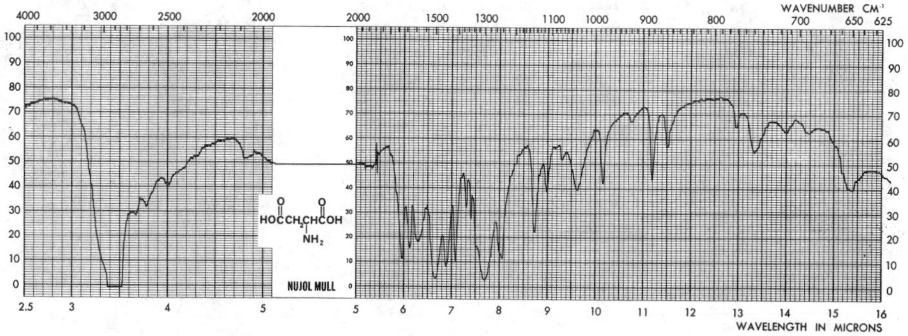

A9310-0 **L-Aspartic acid** (L-aminosuccinic acid)
$HO_2CCH_2CH(NH_2)CO_2H$ M.W. 133.10 m.p. 324° (dec.)
$[\alpha]^{24}_{D}$ + 24.6° (c=2 in 6N HCl) ....

NUJOL MULL

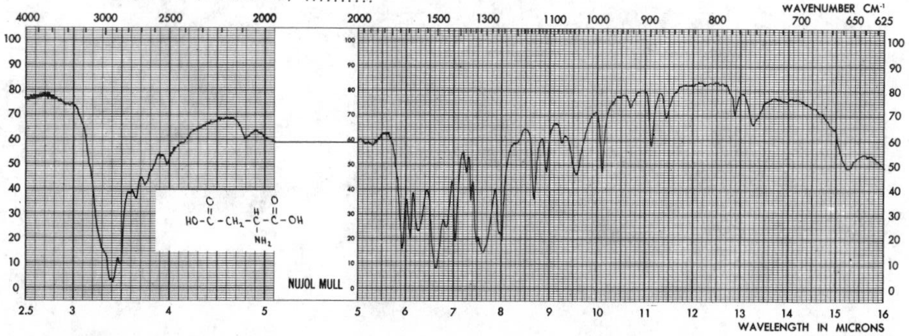

A

G279-6 **DL-Glutamic acid**
$HO_2CCH_2CH_2CH(NH_2)CO_2H$ M.W. 147.13
m.p. 202° (dec.)

NUJOL MULL

B

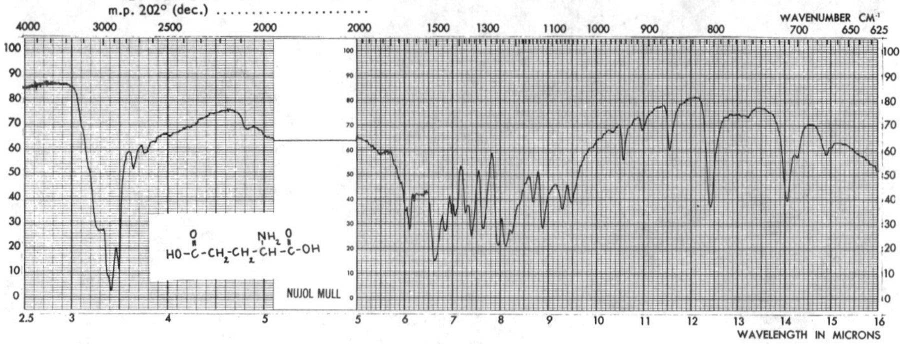

G279-6 **DL-Glutamic acid hydrate**
$HO_2CCH_2CH_2CH(NH_2)CO_2H$ M.W. 147.13
m.p. 202° (dec.)

NUJOL MULL

C

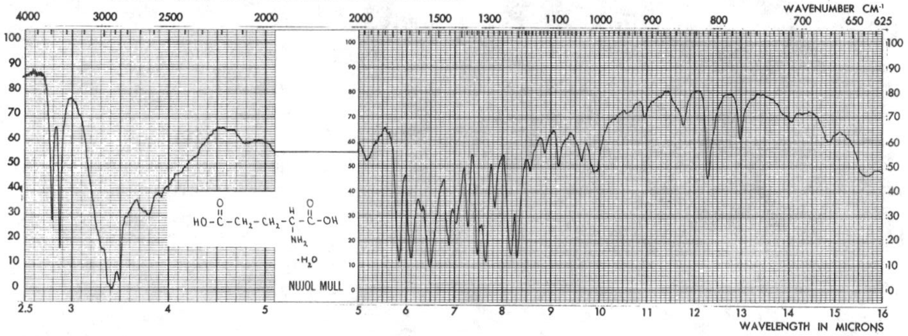

85,735-1
D-Glutamic acid, 99+%, GOLD LABEL
$HO_2CCH_2CH_2CH(NH_2)CO_2H$
M.W. 147.13 m.p. 200-202° (sublimes)
$[\alpha]^{23}$ -31.2° (c=5, 5N HCl)

NUJOL MULL

D

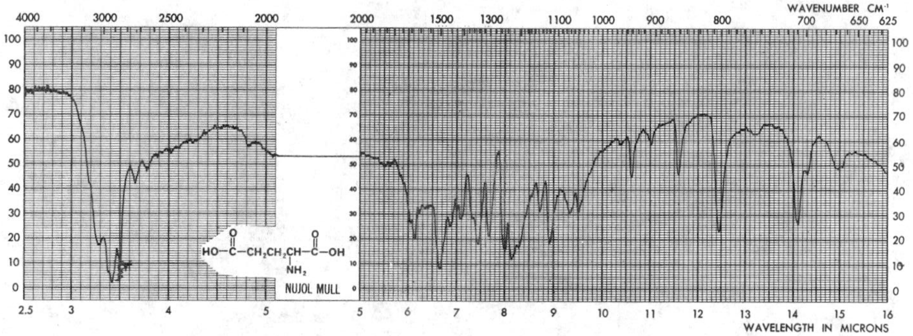

12,843-0 **L-Glutamic acid**
$HO_2CCH_2CH_2CH(NH_2)CO_2H$ M.W. 147.13 m.p. 205° (dec.)

NUJOL MULL

E

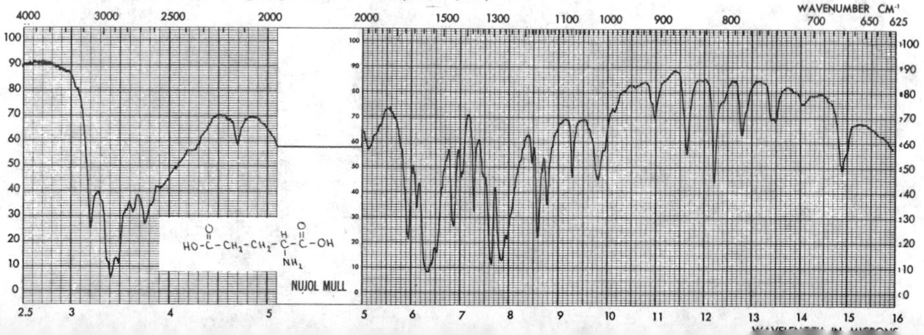

14,941-1 **L-(+)-Glutamic acid hydrochloride**
$HO_2CCH_2CH_2CH(NH_2)CO_2H{\cdot}HCl$ M.W. 183.59
$[\alpha]^{19}_{D}$ +24.91° (c=5.54, H_2O)

NUJOL MULL

F

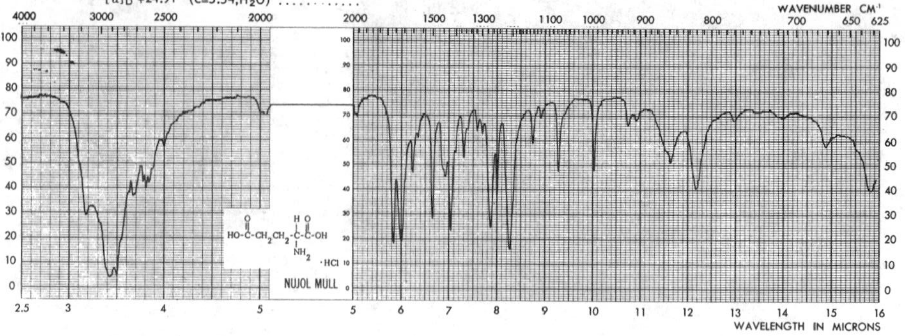

G283-4 **L-Glutamic acid, sodium salt**
$NaO_2CCH_2CH_2CH(NH_2)CO_2Na$ M.W. 191.10
m.p. 232°

NUJOL MULL

G

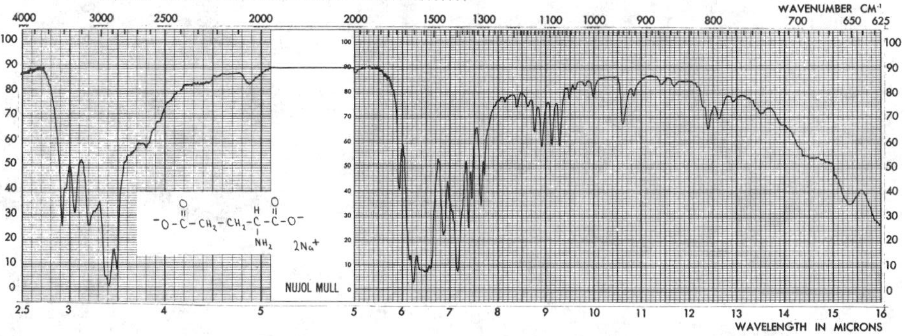

14,894-6 **DL-2-Methylglutamic acid hemihydrate**
$HO_2CCH_2CH_2C(CH_3)(NH_2)CO_2H{\cdot}\frac{1}{2}H_2O$ M.W. 170.17
m.p. 160° (dec.)

NUJOL MULL

H

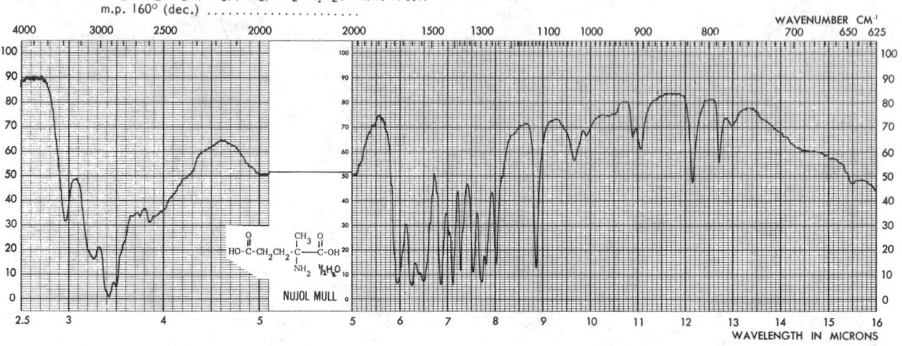

12,471-0 **DL-2-Aminoadipic acid**
$HO_2C(CH_2)_3CH(NH_2)CO_2H$ M.W. 161.16
m.p. 196-198°

NUJOL MULL

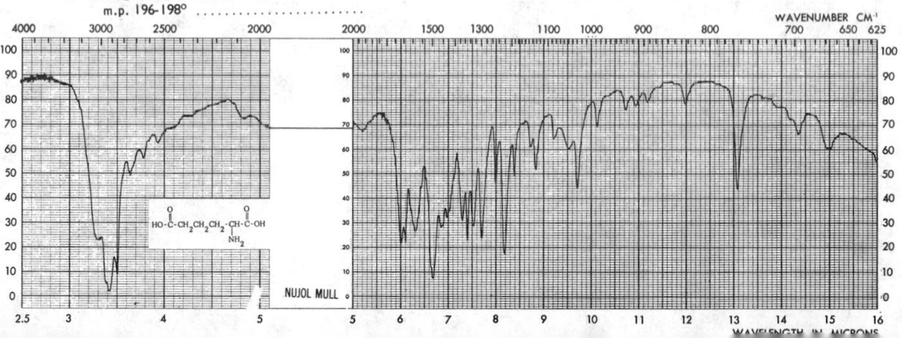

A

C1340-8 **Carboxymethoxylamine [(aminooxy)-acetic acid] hemihydrochloride**
$(H_2NOCH_2CO_2H)_2 \cdot HCl$ M.W. 218.59 m.p. 156° (dec.)

B

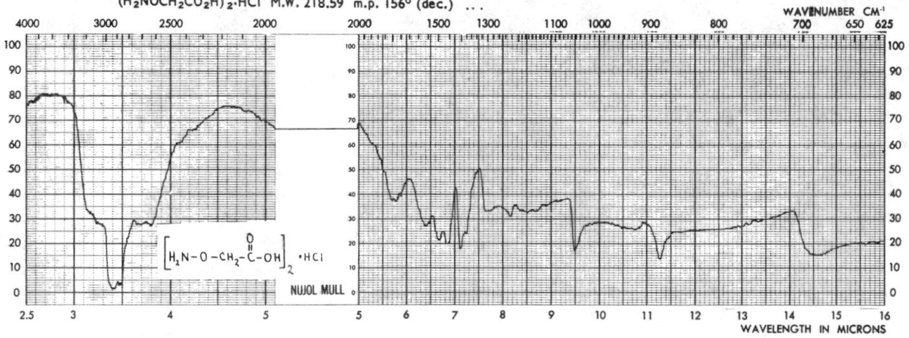

16,814-9
L-(+)-Cysteine, 97%
$HSCH_2CH(NH_2)CO_2H$ FW 121.16 mp 220° (dec.)
$[\alpha]^{23}$ +8.7° (c=10, 1*N* HCl) *Beil.* **4**,506 Disp. L

C

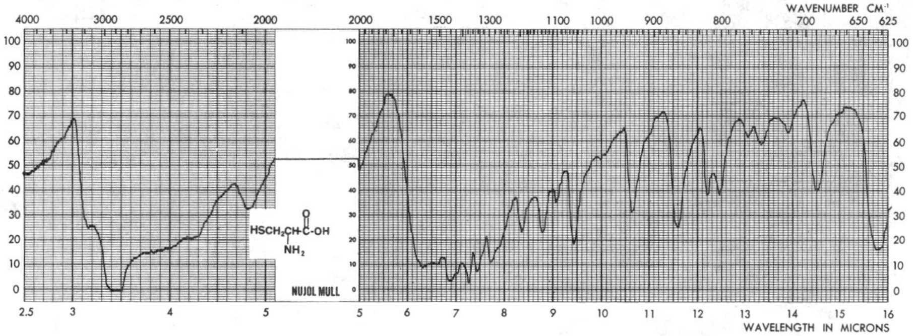

C12,180-0 **L-Cysteine hydrochloride hydrate**
$HSCH_2CH(NH_2)CO_2H \cdot HCl \cdot H_2O$ M.W. 175.63

D

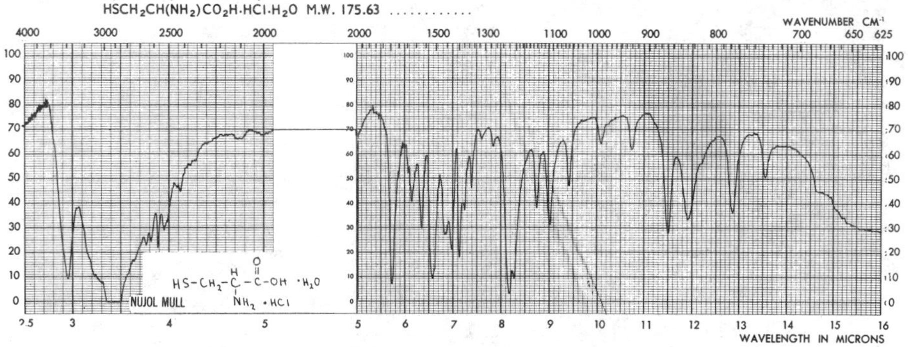

P60-8 **DL-Penicillamine, puriss.**
$(CH_3)_2C(SH)CH(NH_2)CO_2H$ M.W. 149.21 m.p. 204-205° (dec.)

E

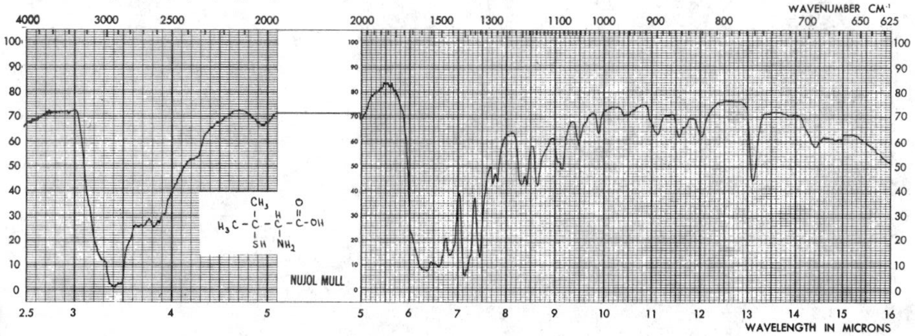

P40-3 **D-(-)-Penicillamine, puriss.**
$(CH_3)_2C(SH)CH(NH_2)CO_2H$ M.W. 149.21 m.p. 212° (dec.)
$[\alpha]^{26}_D$ - 61.3° (c=2.5 in 1N NaOH)

F

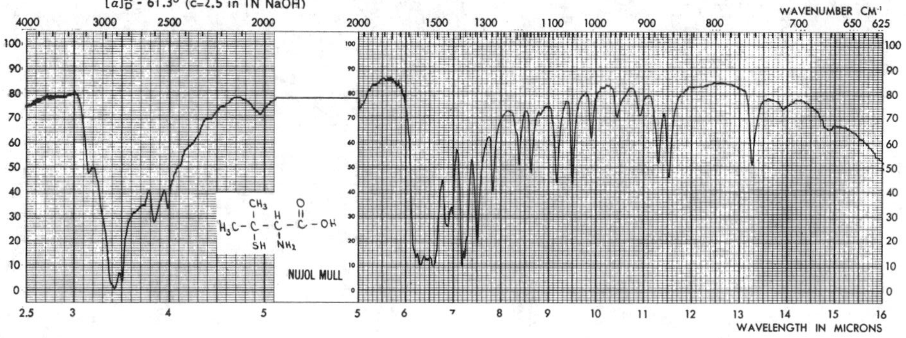

P40-3 **D-(-)-Penicillamine, puriss.**
$(CH_3)_2C(SH)CH(NH_2)CO_2H$ M.W. 149.21 m.p. 212°
$[\alpha]^{26}_D$ -61.3° (c=2.5 in 1N NaOH)

G

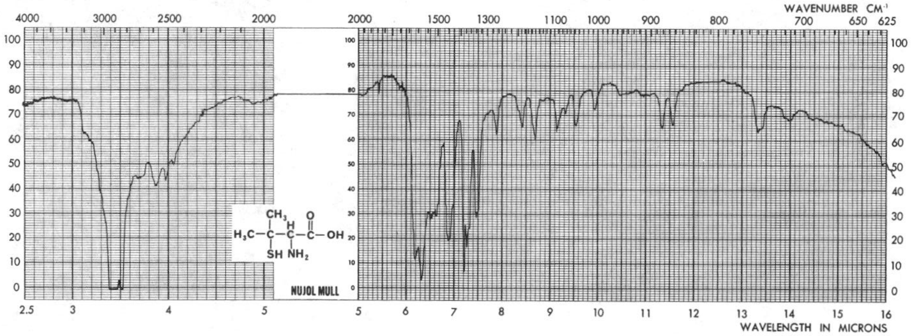

P61-6 **L-(+)-Penicillamine hydrochloride**
$(CH_3)_2C(SH)CH(NH_2)CO_2H \cdot HCl$ M.W. 185.67
m.p. 175-178° (dried) $[\alpha]^{20}_D$ + 39.7°

H

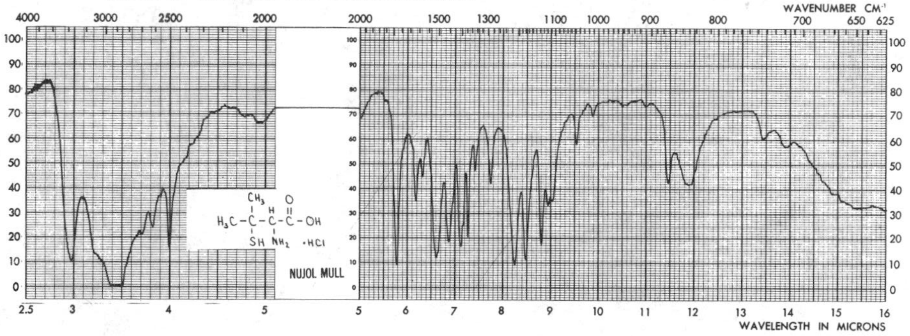

19,631-2
L-(+)-Penicillamine, 99+%, GOLD LABEL
$(CH_3)_2C(SH)CH(NH_2)CO_2H$ FW 149.21
mp 206° (dec.) $[\alpha]^{24}$ +61.9° (c=0.5, 1*N* NaOH)
Beil. **4**(3),1662 Disp. C

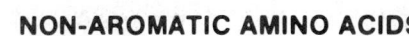

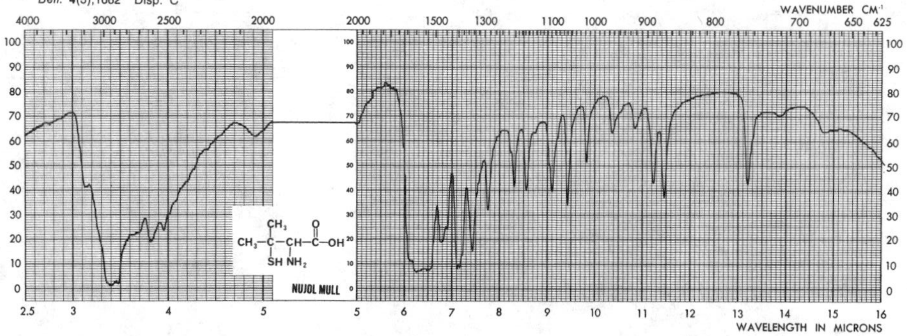

A

C12,160-6 **Cysteamine-N-acetic acid [N-(β-mercaptoethyl)-glycine] hydrochloride**
$HSCH_2CH_2NHCH_2CO_2H \cdot HCl$ M.W. 171.65 m.p. 163-165°

NUJOL MULL

B

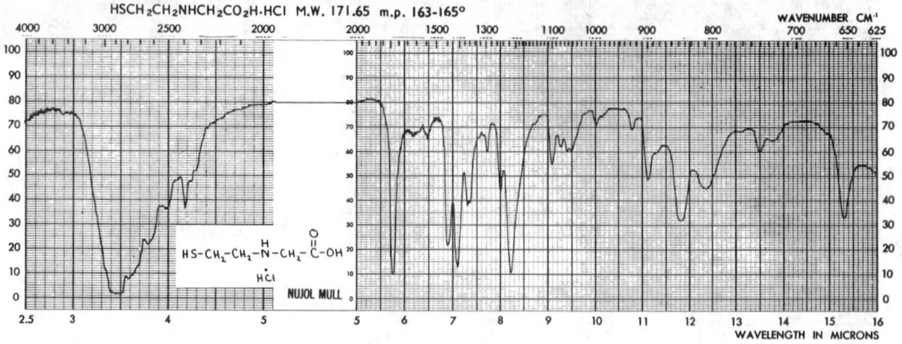

M4045-6 **S-Methyl-L-cysteine [2-amino-3-(methylthio)-propionic acid]**
$CH_3SCH_2CH(NH_2)CO_2H$ M.W. 135.19 m.p. 238° (dec.)
$[\alpha]^{25}_{D}$ - 31.2° (in H_2O)

NUJOL MULL

C

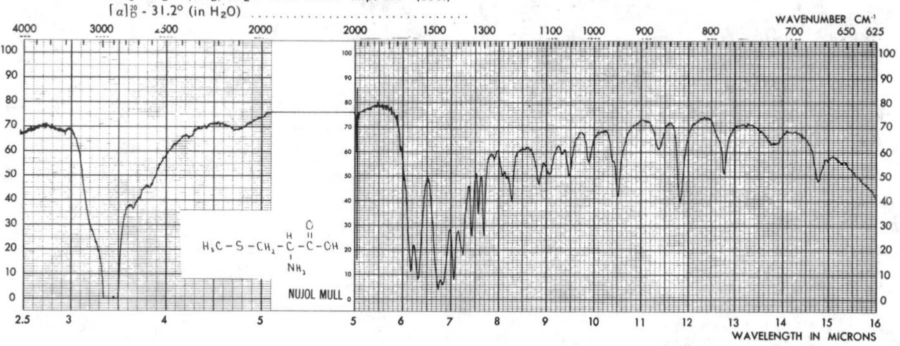

M885-1 **DL-Methionine**
$CH_3SCH_2CH_2CH(NH_2)CO_2H$ M.W. 149.21
m.p. 276-277°

NUJOL MULL

D

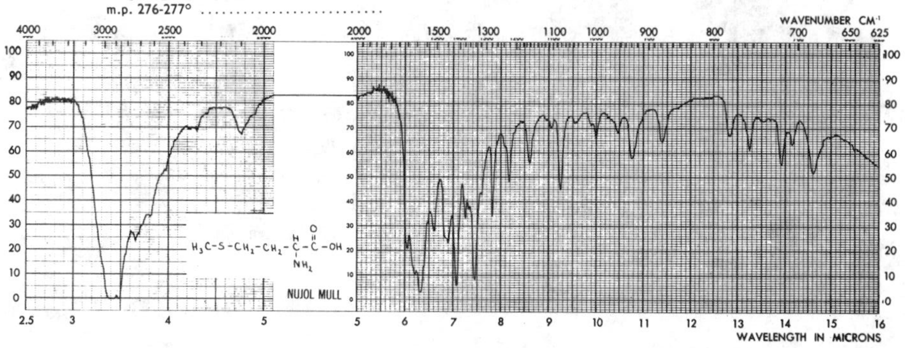

85,571-5
DL-Cysteine hydrochloride monohydrate
$HSCH_2CH(NH_2)CO_2H \cdot HCl \cdot H_2O$
M.W. 175.63 m.p. 109-112° Beil. 4,513

NUJOL MULL

E

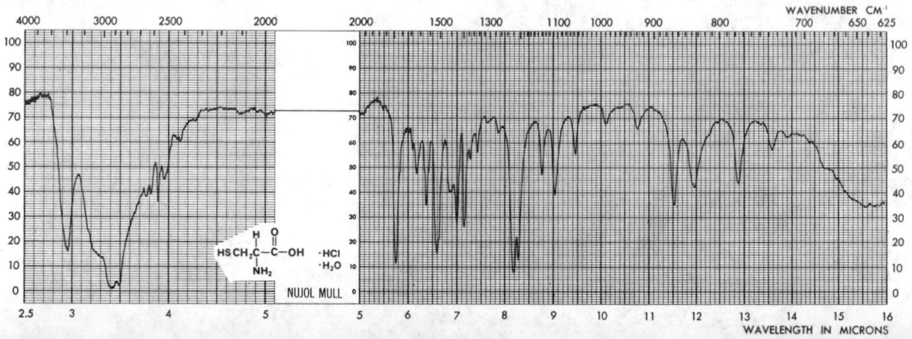

85,547-2
S-Methyl-L-cysteine
$CH_3SCH_2CH(NH_2)CO_2H$
M.W. 135.19 m.p. 228-232° (dec.)

NUJOL MULL

F

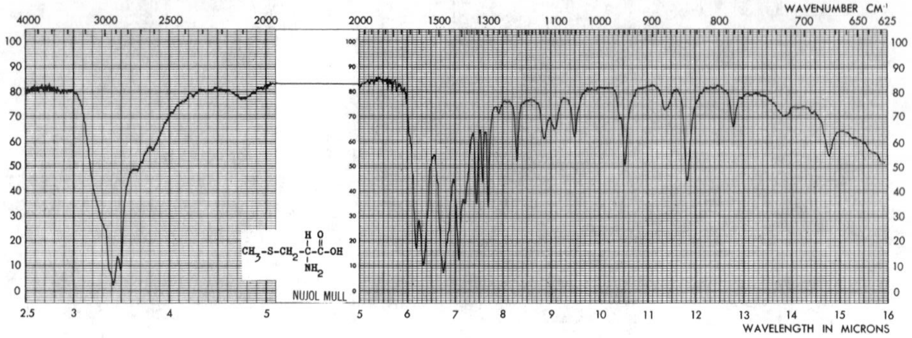

19,314-3
DL-Homocysteine (2-amino-4-mercaptobutyric acid)
$HSCH_2CH_2CH(NH_2)CO_2H$ FW 135.19
mp 220° (dec.) *Beil.* 4(3),1647 Disp. L

NUJOL MULL

G

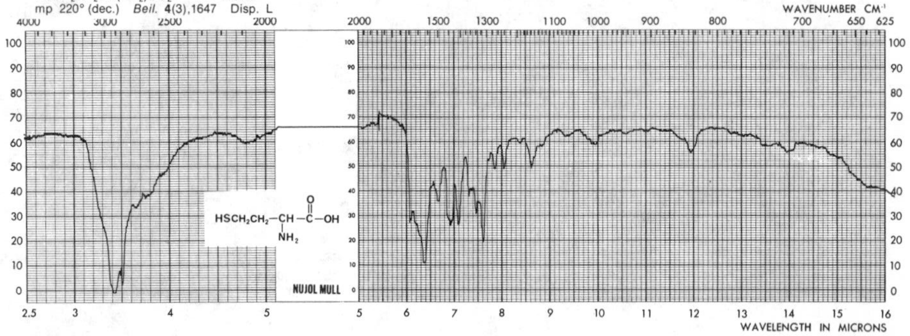

85,590-1
D-Methionine, 99+%, GOLD LABEL
$CH_3SCH_2CH_2CH(NH_2)CO_2H$
M.W. 149.21 m.p. 273-275° (dec.)
$[\alpha]^{23}$ -21.3° (c=0.8, 0.2N HCl)

NUJOL MULL

H

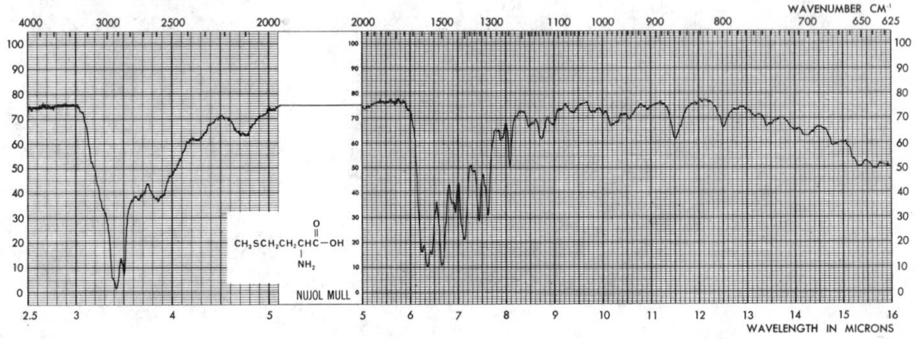

15,169-6 **L-Methionine**
$CH_3SCH_2CH_2CH(NH_2)CO_2H$ M.W. 149.21 m.p. 284° (dec.)
$[\alpha]^{25}_{D}$ +24.3° (c=8, 6N HCl)

NUJOL MULL

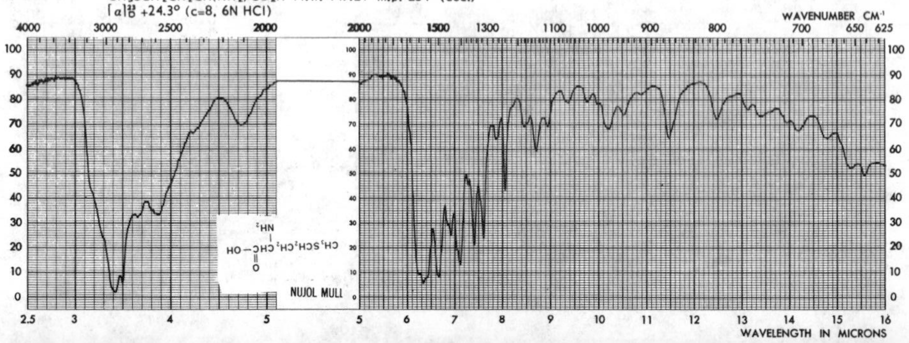

A 85,121-3
S-Carboxymethyl-L-cysteine (3-carboxymethylthio-L-alanine)
$HO_2CCH_2SCH_2CH(NH_2)CO_2H$
M.W. 179.19 m.p. 205-207°

B 10,040-4 **DL-Ethionine** [DL-2-amino-4-(ethylthio)-butyric acid]
$C_2H_5SCH_2CH_2CH(NH_2)CO_2H$ M.W. 163.24
m.p. 269-273° (dec.)

C 21,932-0
D-Ethionine, 98% [D-2-amino-4-(ethylthio)-butyric acid]
$C_2H_5SCH_2CH_2CH(NH_2)CO_2H$ FW 163.24
mp 278° (dec.) $[\alpha]^{22}$ -21° (c=1, 1N HCl)
Beil. 4(3),1646 Disp. C

D 21,933-9
L-Ethionine, 99% [L-2-amino-4-(ethylthio)butyric acid]
$C_2H_5SCH_2CH_2CH(NH_2)CO_2H$ FW 163.24
mp 280° (dec.) $[\alpha]^{22}$ +21.7° (c=1, 1N HCl)
Beil. 4(3),1643 Disp. C

E L50-5 **DL-Lanthionine**
$S[CH_2CH(NH_2)CO_2H]_2$ M.W. 208.24 m.p. 304° (dec.)

F 15,056-8 Glutathione, oxidized (GSSG) hydrate
$[HO_2CCH(NH_2)CH_2CH_2CONHCH(CONHCH_2CO_2H)\text{-}CH_2S\text{-}]_2 \cdot xH_2O$ M.W. 612.64 (anhydrous)
m.p. 178-182° (dec.)

G C12,200-9 **L-Cystine**
$S_2[CH_2CH(NH_2)CO_2H]_2$ M.W. 240.30

H D22,078-7 **Djenkolic acid**
$HO_2CCH(NH_2)CH_2SCH_2SCH_2CH(NH_2)CO_2H$ M.W. 254.33
m.p. 275° (dec.) $[\alpha]_D^{20}$ -65° (in 1N HCl)

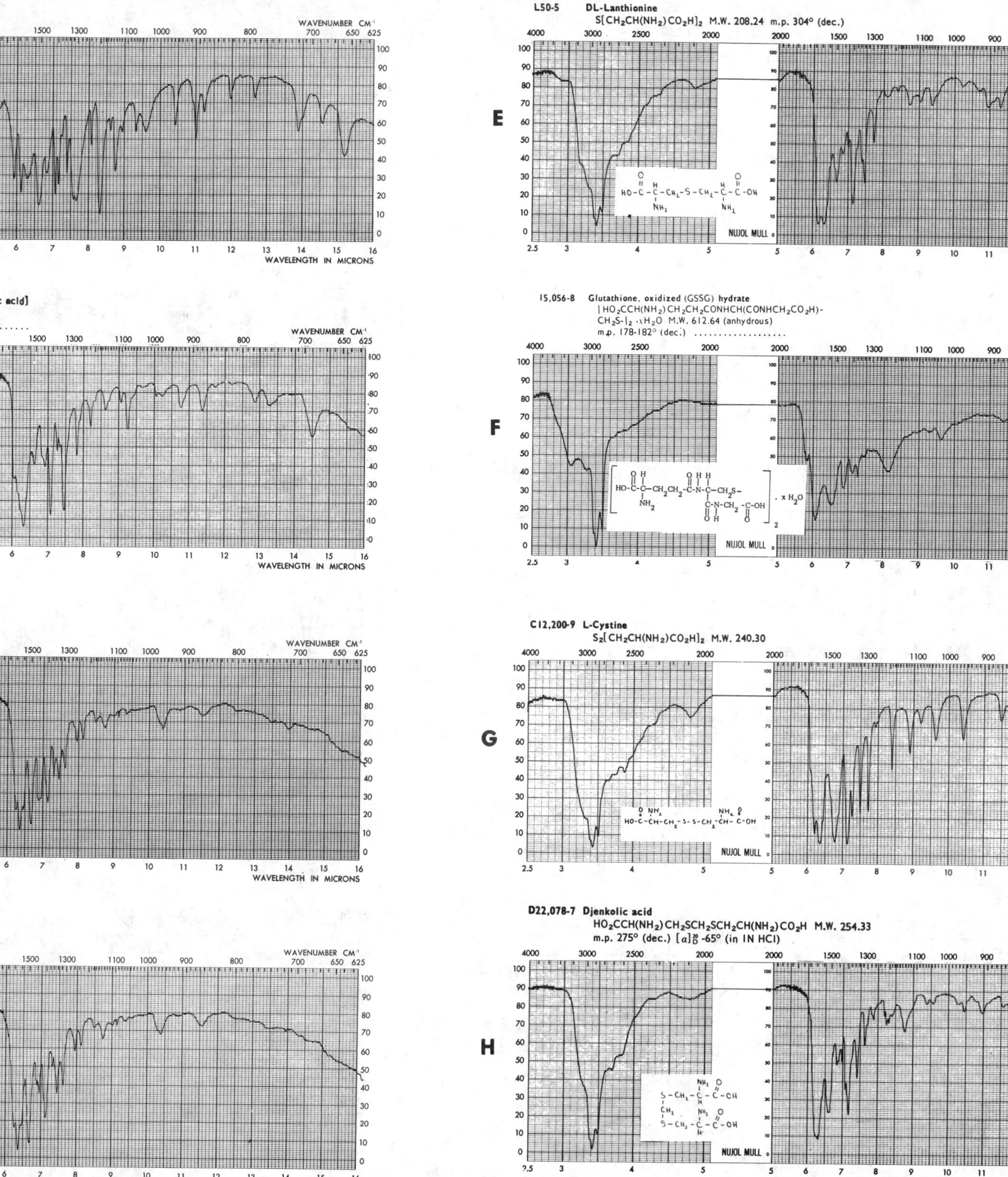

A

P110-1 **D-Penicillamine disulfide** [3,3'-dithiobis-(2-amino-3-methylbutyric acid)]
$[-SC(CH_3)_2CH(NH_2)CO_2H]_2$ M.W. 296.41 m.p. 204° (dec.)

NUJOL MULL

B

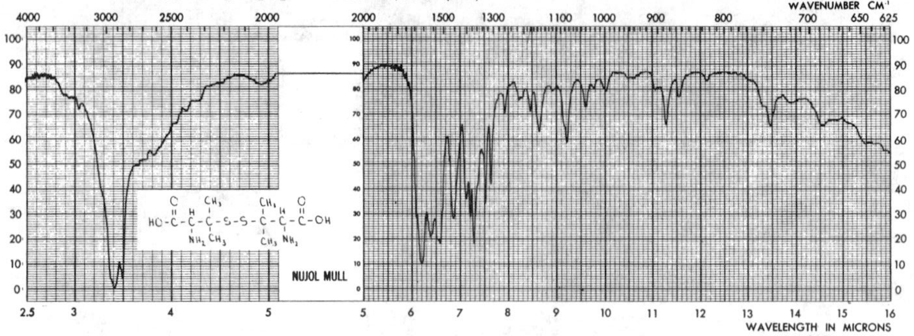

T2750-2 **L-Thiazolidine-4-carboxylic acid**
M.W. 133.17 m.p. 203° (dec.)
$[\alpha]_D^{25}$ - 141° (c=1.3, H_2O)

NUJOL MULL

C

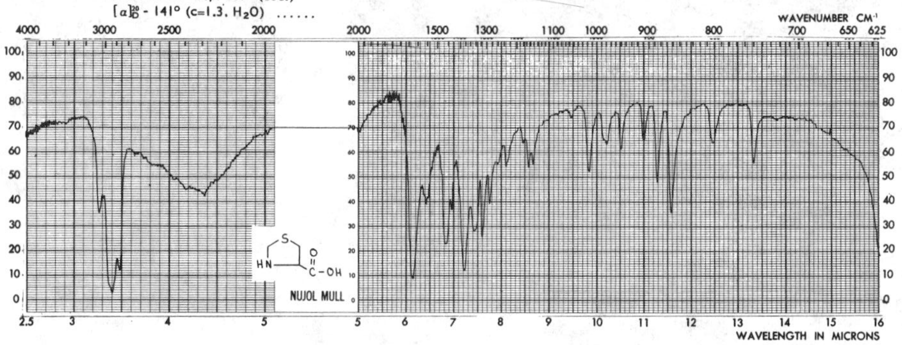

P100-4 **DL-Penicillamine acetone adduct** (2,2,5,5-tetramethyl-4-thiazolidinecarboxylic acid) **hydrochloride**
M.W. 225.74 m.p. 200-201° (dec.)

NUJOL MULL

D

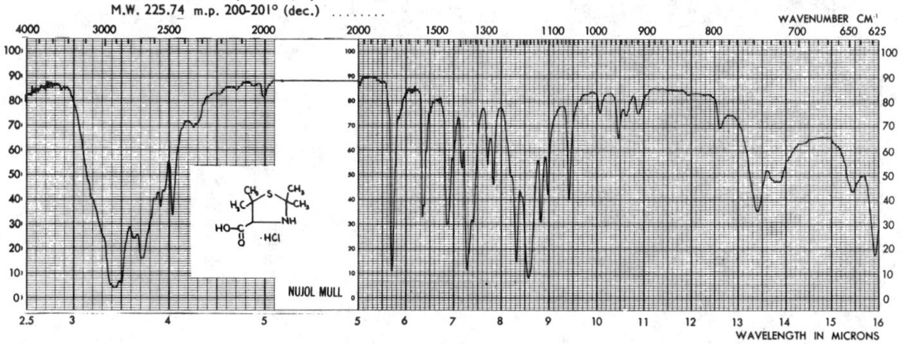

17,043-7
Muramic acid
FW 251.24 mp 148° (dec.) Disp. D

NUJOL MULL

E

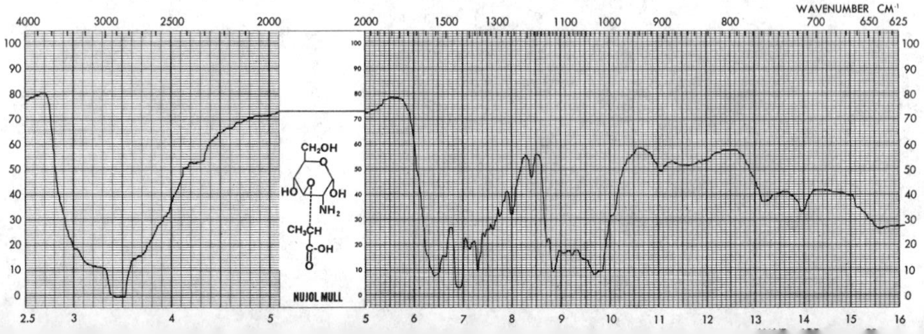

D12,380-3 **3,5-Diiodo-4-pyridone-N-acetic acid** (1,4-dihydro-3,5-diiodo-4-oxo-1-pyridineacetic acid), **puriss.**
M.W. 404.93 m.p. 244° (dec.)

NUJOL MULL

F

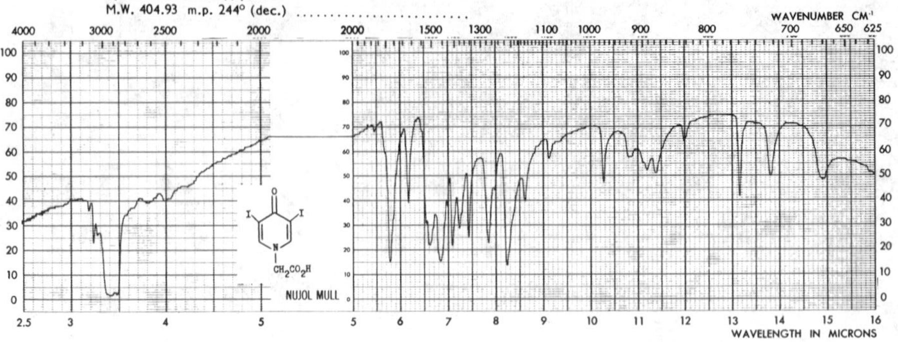

M8761-4 **Mimosine** (leucenol, optically active)
M.W. 198.18 m.p. 228-229°
$[\alpha]_D^{22}$ -21° (in H_2O)

NUJOL MULL

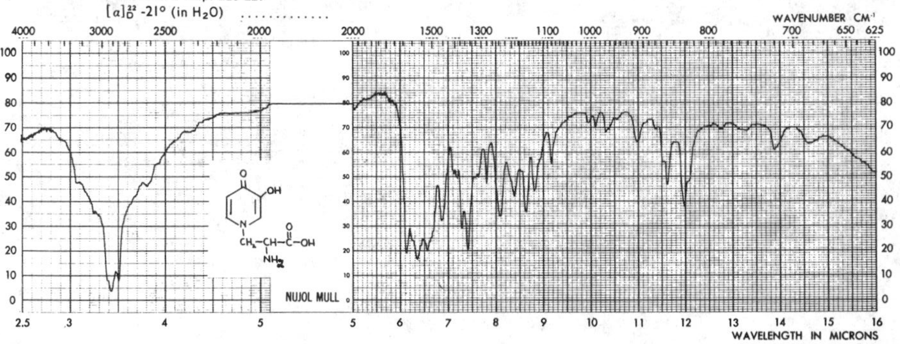

ALDRICH

NON-AROMATIC ESTERS AND LACTONES

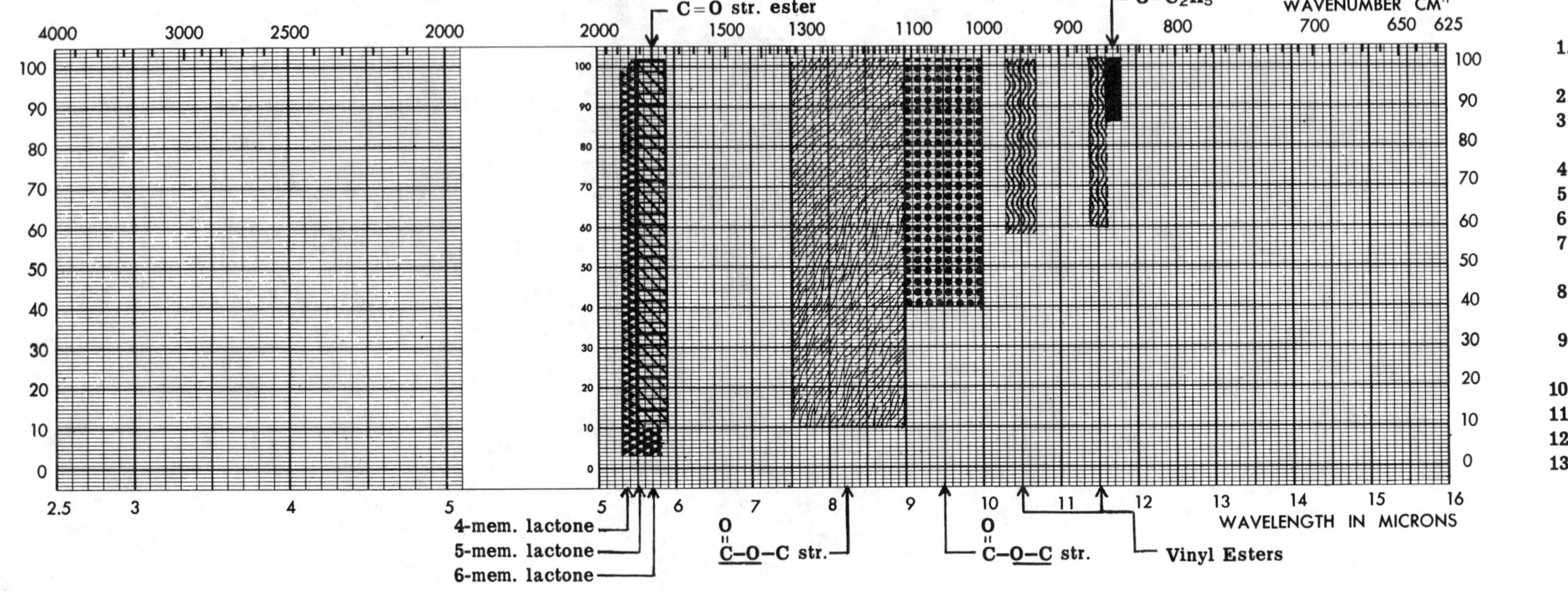

The carbonyl stretch band of the unconjugated ester lies very close to 5.75 μ (1740 cm^{-1}). It is accompanied by the stretch bands of the carbon-oxygen single bond $(-\overset{O}{\overset{\|}{C}}-O-R)$ between 8 and 10 μ (1250 – 1000 cm^{-1}).

Generally, the spectra of the smaller molecules in a series differ from those of the higher members. Here also, the formates do not show the O–CH_2 stretch as clearly as other esters. Furthermore, the acetate carbonyl-oxygen stretch vibration appears very close to 8 μ (1250 cm^{-1}) whereas other esters absorb near 8.5 μ (1175 cm^{-1}). In this case, the vibration is very useful in identifying the acetate group.

The carbon-oxygen stretch band of the ethyl and higher esters is at 9.7 μ (1030 cm^{-1}), whereas the methyl esters absorb at slightly higher wavelengths close to 9.85 μ (1015 cm^{-1}). The ethyl esters display a weak but characteristic absorption at 11.7 μ (855 cm^{-1}).

The 10 μ and 11 μ (1000 and 910 cm^{-1}) vinyl bands appearing when the vinyl group is attached to a carbon atom are shifted to 10.5 μ and 11.5 μ (950 and 870 cm^{-1}) in the spectra of the vinyl esters (see spectra 376C—378C).

Diesters such as those of spectra 366C—369H are quite similar to the monoesters except the malonates where the $\overset{O}{\overset{\|}{C}}-O-C$ stretch absorption appears as a very broad band between 7.5 and 9 μ (1335 – 1110 cm^{-1}).

The β-keto esters display bands in the carbonyl region reflecting their enol-keto tautomerism as previously seen in the β-diketones of the non-aromatic ketone section (spectra 401H—405B). The enol content of the compounds ranges from an estimated 10 – 15% in spectra 401H—402E to nearly 100% in spectrum 404G.

The final spectra of this section are of internal esters or lactones. Their $\overset{O}{\overset{\|}{C}}-O-C$ stretch absorptions lie in close proximity to those observed in the normal esters. However, the carbonyl stretch vibration appears between 5.3 and 5.5 μ (1885 – 1820 cm^{-1}) for the four-membered lactones and shifts to higher wavelength with increase in ring size, or when the carbonyl is conjugated to a double bond. The saturated five-membered lactone carbonyl absorbs at 5.65 – 5.70 μ, and the six-membered lactones are indistinguishable from the corresponding esters. The size of the lactone ring can therefore be determined by the carbonyl band position.

The thio-lactones (spectra 408E, 409A) have their carbonyl band shifted from the normal lactone position to near 5.9 μ (1695 cm^{-1}). With replacement of the $\overset{O}{\overset{\|}{C}}-O-C$ structure by $\overset{O}{\overset{\|}{C}}-S-C$, the strong bands between 7.5 and 10 μ (1335 – 1000 cm^{-1}) disappear.

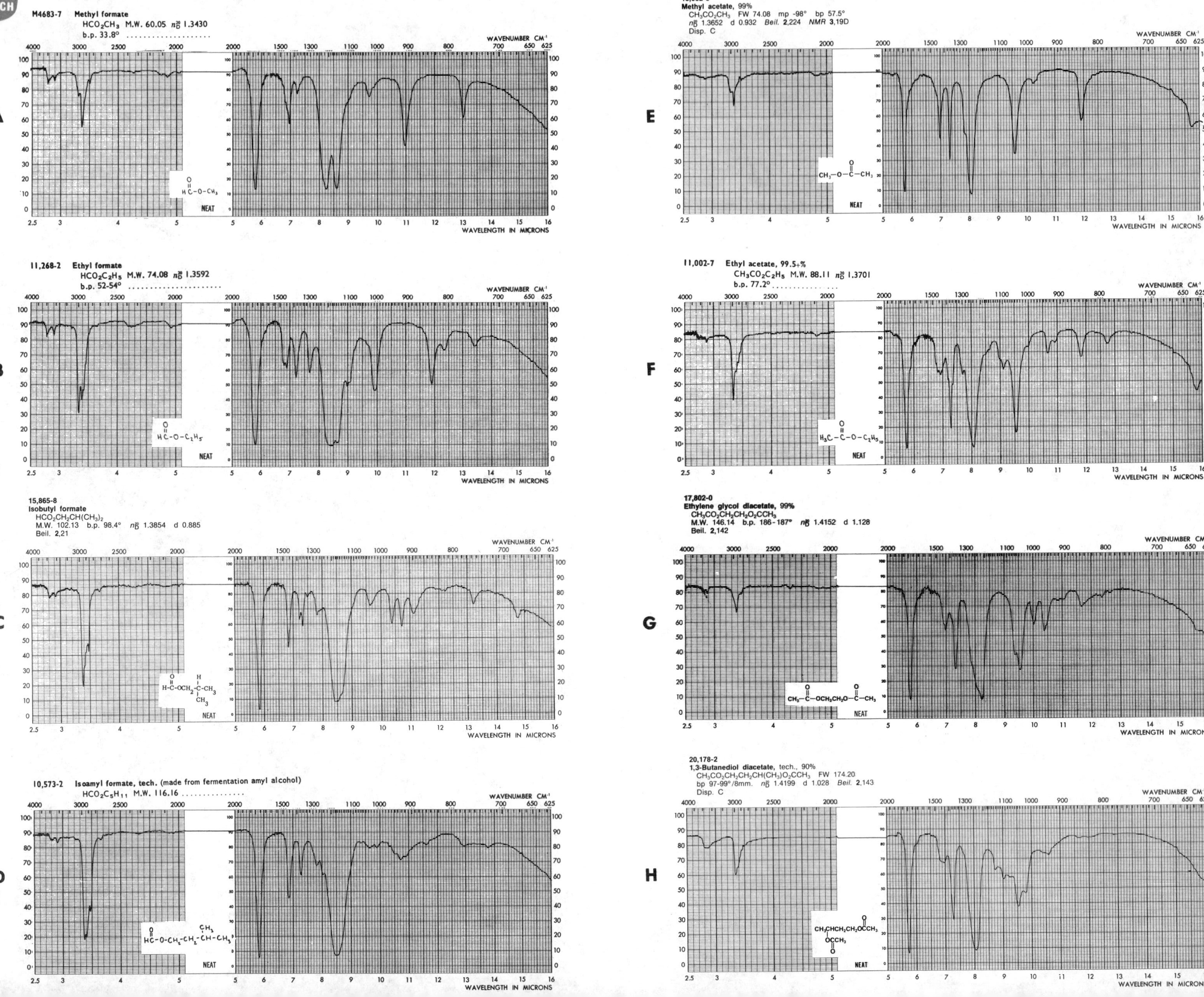
ALDRICH
A
M4683-7 Methyl formate
HCO_2CH_3 M.W. 60.05 n_D^{20} 1.3430
b.p. 33.8°
$HC(=O)-O-CH_3$
NEAT
B
11,268-2 Ethyl formate
$HCO_2C_2H_5$ M.W. 74.08 n_D^{20} 1.3592
b.p. 52-54°
$HC(=O)-O-C_2H_5$
NEAT
C
15,865-8
Isobutyl formate
$HCO_2CH_2CH(CH_3)_2$
M.W. 102.13 b.p. 98.4° n_D^{20} 1.3854 d 0.885
Beil. 2,21
NEAT
D
10,573-2 Isoamyl formate, tech. (made from fermentation amyl alcohol)
$HCO_2C_5H_{11}$ M.W. 116.16
NEAT
E
18,632-5
Methyl acetate, 99%
$CH_3CO_2CH_3$ FW 74.08 mp -98° bp 57.5°
n_D^{20} 1.3652 d 0.932 Beil. 2,224 NMR 3,19D
Disp. C
$CH_3-O-C(=O)-CH_3$
NEAT
F
11,002-7 Ethyl acetate, 99.5+%
$CH_3CO_2C_2H_5$ M.W. 88.11 n_D^{20} 1.3701
b.p. 77.2°
$H_3C-C(=O)-O-C_2H_5$
NEAT
G
17,802-0
Ethylene glycol diacetate, 99%
$CH_3CO_2CH_2CH_2O_2CCH_3$
M.W. 146.14 b.p. 186-187° n_D^{20} 1.4152 d 1.128
Beil. 2,142
NEAT
H
20,178-2
1,3-Butanediol diacetate, tech., 90%
$CH_3CO_2CH_2CH_2CH(CH_3)O_2CCH_3$ FW 174.20
bp 97-99°/8mm. n_D^{20} 1.4199 d 1.028 Beil. 2,143
Disp. C
NEAT
WAVENUMBER CM⁻¹
WAVELENGTH IN MICRONS

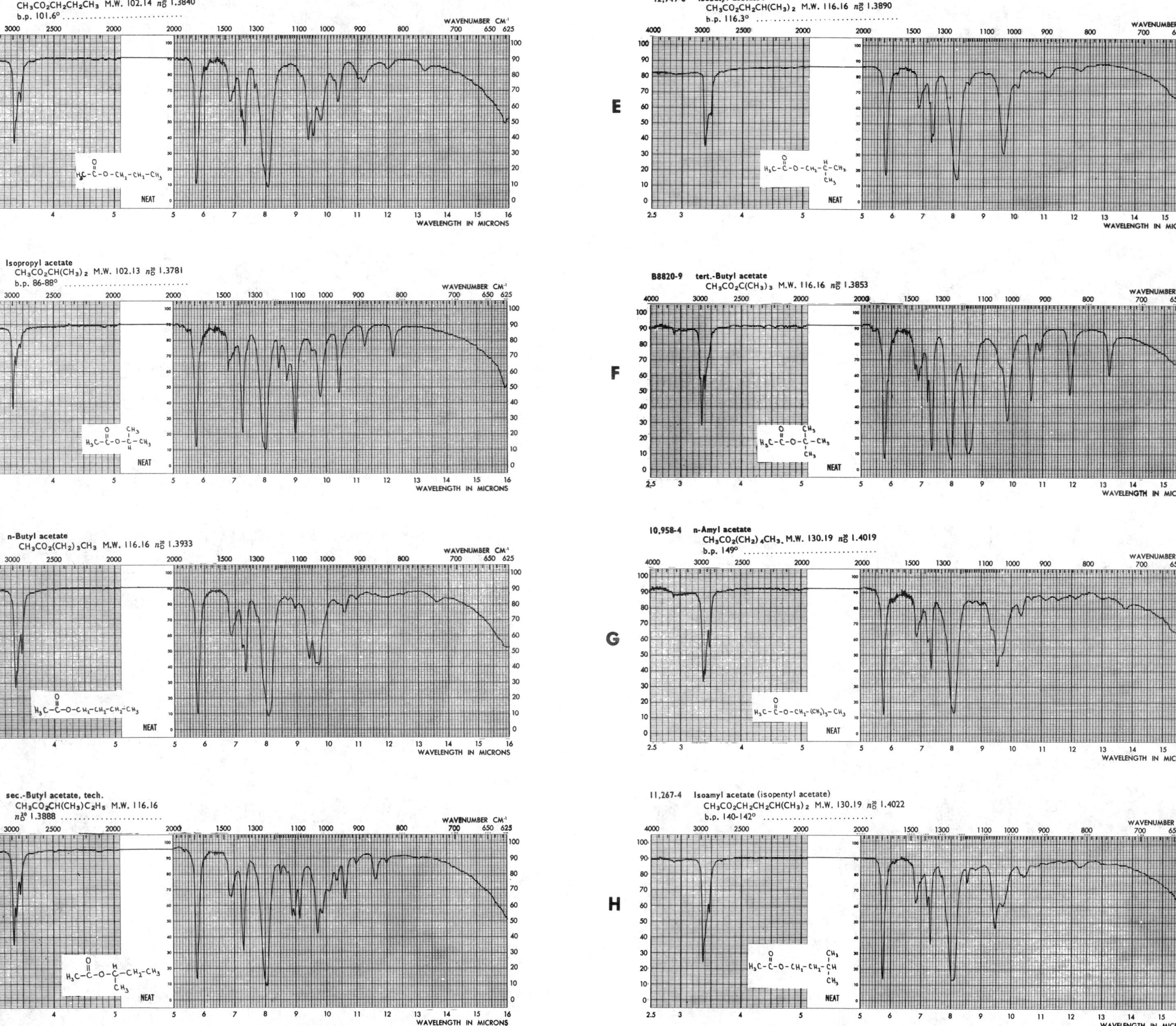

A
13,310-8 n-Propyl acetate, 99+%
$CH_3CO_2CH_2CH_2CH_3$ M.W. 102.14 n_D^{20} 1.3840
b.p. 101.6°
NEAT
B
11,299-2 Isopropyl acetate
$CH_3CO_2CH(CH_3)_2$ M.W. 102.13 n_D^{20} 1.3781
b.p. 86-88°
NEAT
C
B8818-7 n-Butyl acetate
$CH_3CO_2(CH_2)_3CH_3$ M.W. 116.16 n_D^{20} 1.3933
NEAT
D
B8819-5 sec.-Butyl acetate, tech.
$CH_3CO_2CH(CH_3)C_2H_5$ M.W. 116.16
n_D^{20} 1.3888
NEAT
E
12,949-6 Isobutyl acetate, 90+%
$CH_3CO_2CH_2CH(CH_3)_2$ M.W. 116.16 n_D^{20} 1.3890
b.p. 116.3°
NEAT
F
B8820-9 tert.-Butyl acetate
$CH_3CO_2C(CH_3)_3$ M.W. 116.16 n_D^{20} 1.3853
NEAT
G
10,958-4 n-Amyl acetate
$CH_3CO_2(CH_2)_4CH_3$ M.W. 130.19 n_D^{20} 1.4019
b.p. 149°
NEAT
H
11,267-4 Isoamyl acetate (isopentyl acetate)
$CH_3CO_2CH_2CH_2CH(CH_3)_2$ M.W. 130.19 n_D^{20} 1.4022
b.p. 140-142°
NEAT
WAVENUMBER CM⁻¹
WAVELENGTH IN MICRONS
ALDRICH

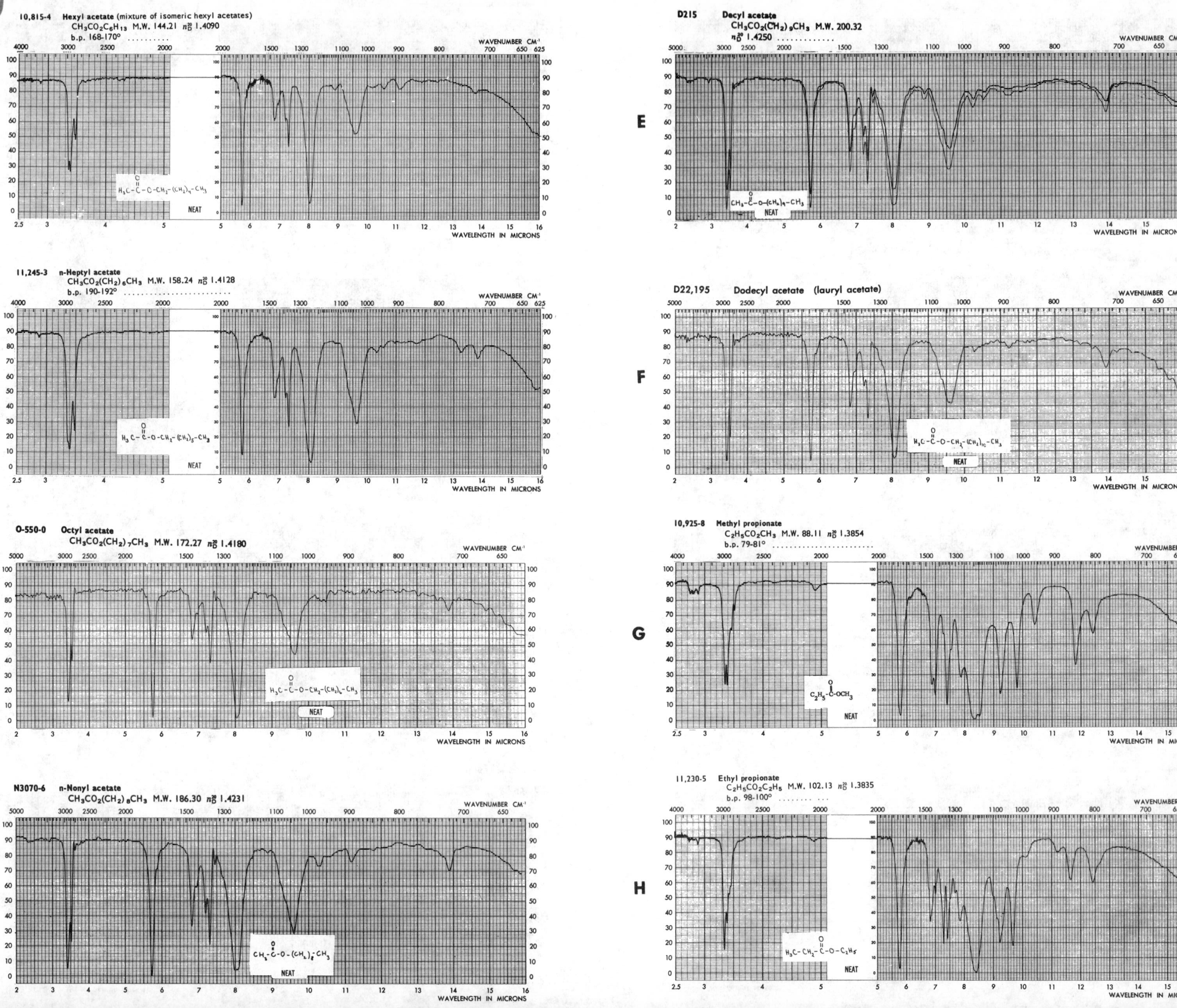
ALDRICH
A
10,815-4 Hexyl acetate (mixture of isomeric hexyl acetates)
$CH_3CO_2C_6H_{13}$ M.W. 144.21 n_D^{20} 1.4090
b.p. 168-170°
NEAT
B
11,245-3 n-Heptyl acetate
$CH_3CO_2(CH_2)_6CH_3$ M.W. 158.24 n_D^{20} 1.4128
b.p. 190-192°
NEAT
C
O-550-0 Octyl acetate
$CH_3CO_2(CH_2)_7CH_3$ M.W. 172.27 n_D^{20} 1.4180
NEAT
D
N3070-6 n-Nonyl acetate
$CH_3CO_2(CH_2)_8CH_3$ M.W. 186.30 n_D^{20} 1.4231
NEAT
E
D215 Decyl acetate
$CH_3CO_2(CH_2)_9CH_3$ M.W. 200.32
n_D^{20} 1.4250
NEAT
F
D22,195 Dodecyl acetate (lauryl acetate)
NEAT
G
10,925-8 Methyl propionate
$C_2H_5CO_2CH_3$ M.W. 88.11 n_D^{20} 1.3854
b.p. 79-81°
NEAT
H
11,230-5 Ethyl propionate
$C_2H_5CO_2C_2H_5$ M.W. 102.13 n_D^{20} 1.3835
b.p. 98-100°
NEAT
WAVENUMBER CM⁻¹
WAVELENGTH IN MICRONS

A 11,226-7 **n-Propyl propionate**
$C_2H_5CO_2CH_2CH_2CH_3$ M.W. 116.16 n_D^{20} 1.6015
b.p. 122°

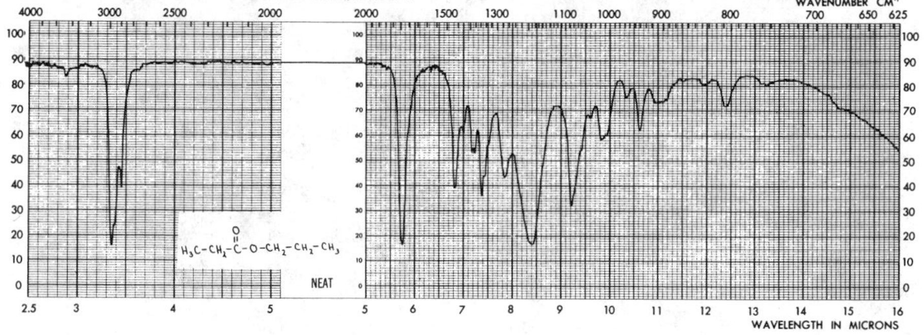

$H_3C-CH_2-C(=O)-O-CH_2-CH_2-CH_3$ NEAT

B E1570-1 **Ethyl butyrate**
$CH_3CH_2CH_2CO_2C_2H_5$ M.W. 116.16
n_D^{20} 1.3920

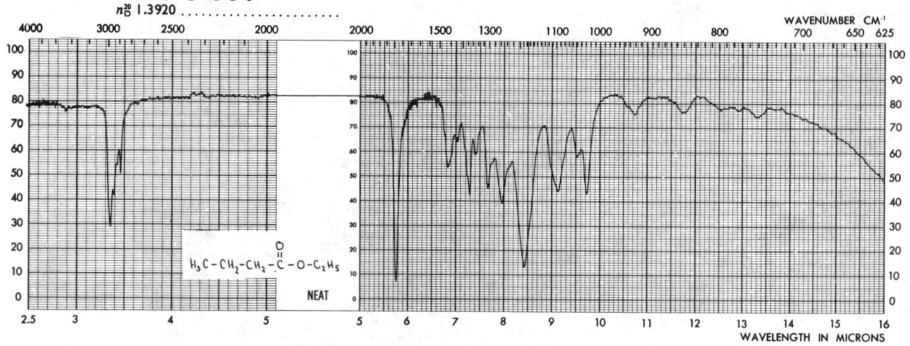

$H_3C-CH_2-CH_2-C(=O)-O-C_2H_5$ NEAT

C 14,800-8 **Methyl isobutyrate**
$(CH_3)_2CHCO_2CH_3$ M.W. 102.14 n_D^{20} 1.3821
b.p. 90°

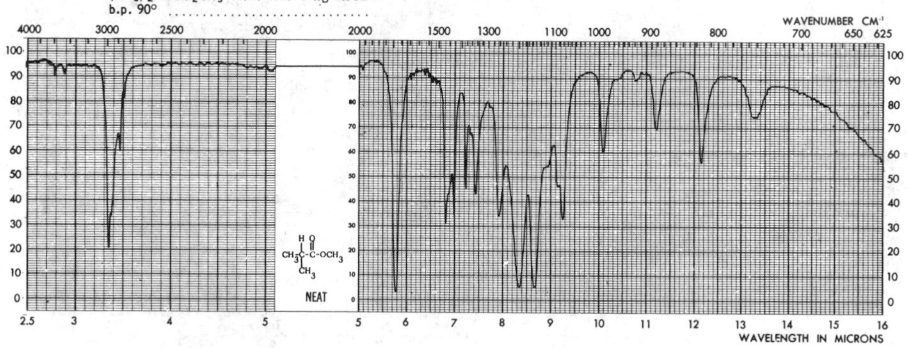

$CH_3CH(CH_3)-C(=O)-OCH_3$ NEAT

D 14,899-7 **Methyl valerate**
$CH_3(CH_2)_3CO_2CH_3$ M.W. 116.16 n_D^{20} 1.3962
b.p. 128°

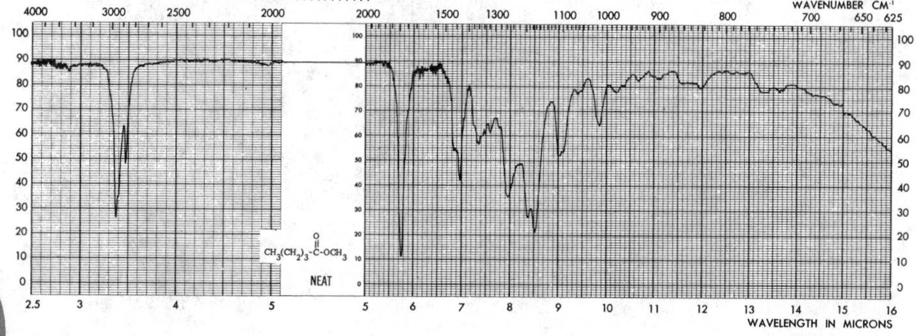

$CH_3(CH_2)_3-C(=O)-OCH_3$ NEAT

E 11,228-3 **Ethyl isovalerate**
$(CH_3)_2CHCH_2CO_2C_2H_5$ M.W. 130.19 n_D^{20} 1.3950
b.p. 131-133°

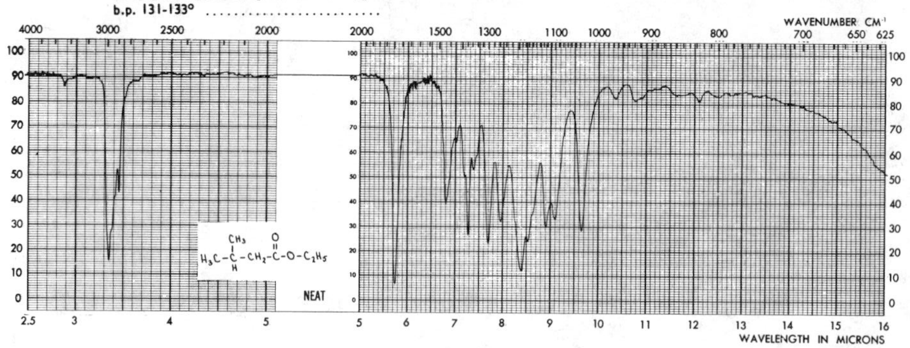

$H_3C-CH(CH_3)-CH_2-C(=O)-O-C_2H_5$ NEAT

F M8650-2 **Methyl trimethylacetate** (methyl pivalate)
$(CH_3)_3CCO_2CH_3$ M.W. 116.16 n_D^{20} 1.3886

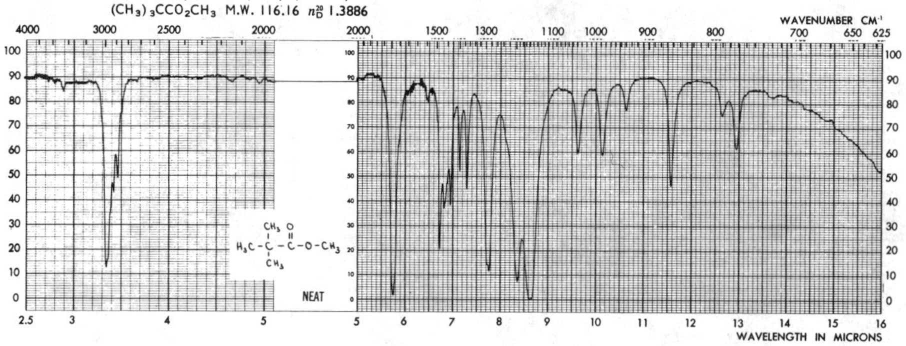

$H_3C-C(CH_3)_2-C(=O)-O-CH_3$ NEAT

G 14,896-2 **Ethyl caproate** (ethyl hexanoate), **puriss.**
$CH_3(CH_2)_4CO_2C_2H_5$ M.W. 144.21
n_D^{20} 1.4065 b.p. 168°

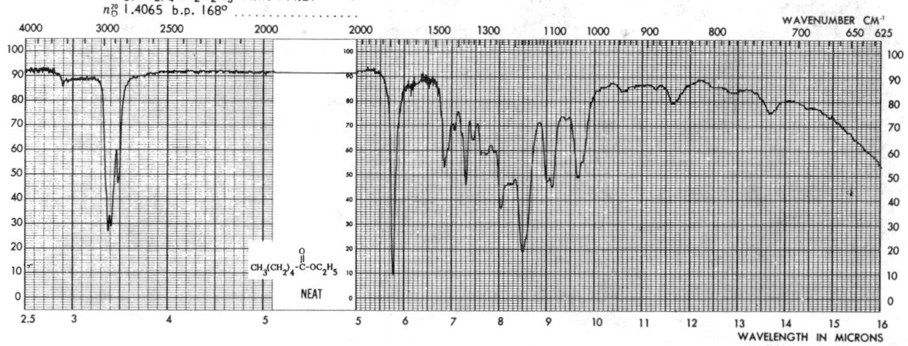

$CH_3(CH_2)_4-C(=O)-OC_2H_5$ NEAT

H 11,236-4 **Ethyl heptanoate**
$CH_3(CH_2)_5CO_2C_2H_5$ M.W. 158.24 n_D^{20} 1.4102
b.p. 189°

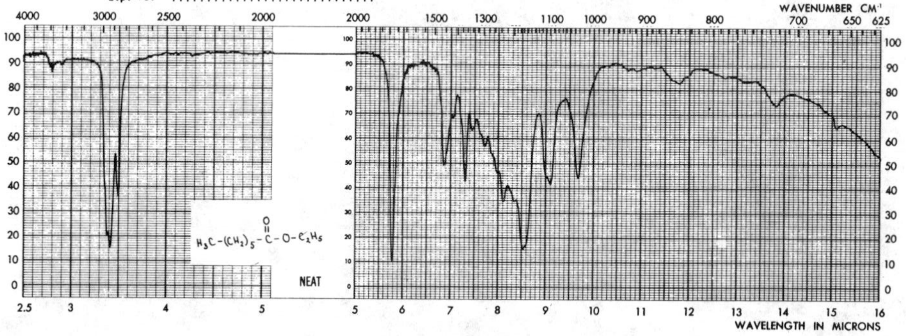

$H_3C-(CH_2)_5-C(=O)-O-C_2H_5$ NEAT

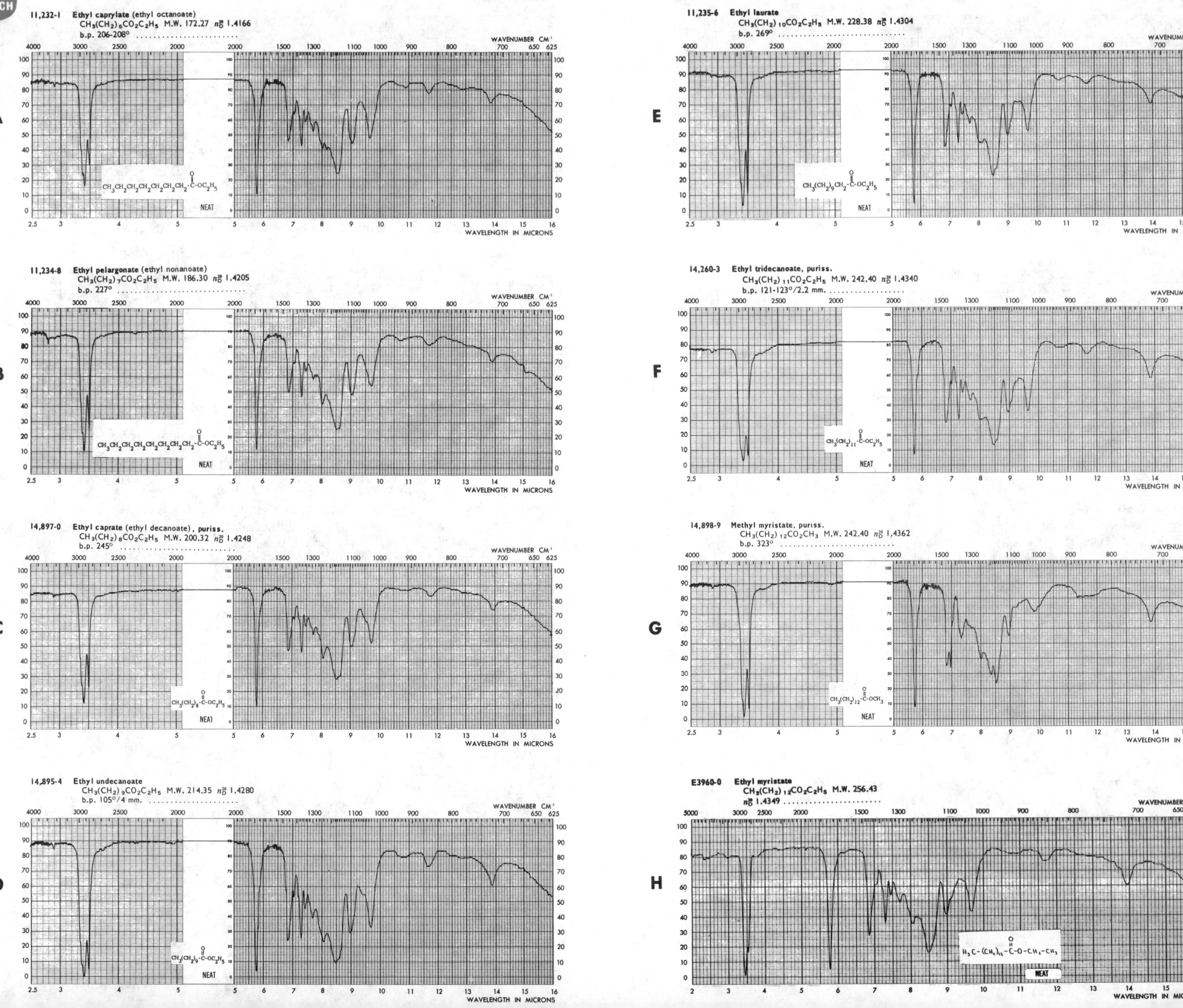
ALDRICH
A
11,232-1 Ethyl caprylate (ethyl octanoate)
$CH_3(CH_2)_6CO_2C_2H_5$ M.W. 172.27 n_D^{20} 1.4166
b.p. 206-208°
$CH_3CH_2CH_2CH_2CH_2CH_2CH_2\text{-}\overset{O}{\overset{\|}{C}}\text{-}OC_2H_5$
NEAT
B
11,234-8 Ethyl pelargonate (ethyl nonanoate)
$CH_3(CH_2)_7CO_2C_2H_5$ M.W. 186.30 n_D^{20} 1.4205
b.p. 227°
$CH_3CH_2CH_2CH_2CH_2CH_2CH_2CH_2\text{-}\overset{O}{\overset{\|}{C}}\text{-}OC_2H_5$
NEAT
C
14,897-0 Ethyl caprate (ethyl decanoate), puriss.
$CH_3(CH_2)_8CO_2C_2H_5$ M.W. 200.32 n_D^{20} 1.4248
b.p. 245°
$CH_3(CH_2)_8\text{-}\overset{O}{\overset{\|}{C}}\text{-}OC_2H_5$
NEAT
D
14,895-4 Ethyl undecanoate
$CH_3(CH_2)_9CO_2C_2H_5$ M.W. 214.35 n_D^{20} 1.4280
b.p. 105°/4 mm.
$CH_3(CH_2)_9\text{-}\overset{O}{\overset{\|}{C}}\text{-}OC_2H_5$
NEAT
E
11,235-6 Ethyl laurate
$CH_3(CH_2)_{10}CO_2C_2H_5$ M.W. 228.38 n_D^{20} 1.4304
b.p. 269°
$CH_3(CH_2)_9CH_2\text{-}\overset{O}{\overset{\|}{C}}\text{-}OC_2H_5$
NEAT
F
14,260-3 Ethyl tridecanoate, puriss.
$CH_3(CH_2)_{11}CO_2C_2H_5$ M.W. 242.40 n_D^{20} 1.4340
b.p. 121-123°/2.2 mm.
$CH_3(CH_2)_{11}\text{-}\overset{O}{\overset{\|}{C}}\text{-}OC_2H_5$
NEAT
G
14,898-9 Methyl myristate, puriss.
$CH_3(CH_2)_{12}CO_2CH_3$ M.W. 242.40 n_D^{20} 1.4362
b.p. 323°
$CH_3(CH_2)_{12}\text{-}\overset{O}{\overset{\|}{C}}\text{-}OCH_3$
NEAT
H
E3960-0 Ethyl myristate
$CH_3(CH_2)_{12}CO_2C_2H_5$ M.W. 256.43
n_D^{20} 1.4349
$H_3C\text{-}(CH_2)_{12}\text{-}\overset{O}{\overset{\|}{C}}\text{-}O\text{-}CH_2\text{-}CH_3$
NEAT
WAVENUMBER CM⁻¹
WAVELENGTH IN MICRONS

A

13,761-8 **Ethyl pentadecanoate**
$CH_3(CH_2)_{13}CO_2C_2H_5$ M.W. 270.46
n_D^{20} 1.4385

$CH_3(CH_2)_{12}CH_2-\overset{O}{\overset{\|}{C}}-OC_2H_5$ NEAT

B

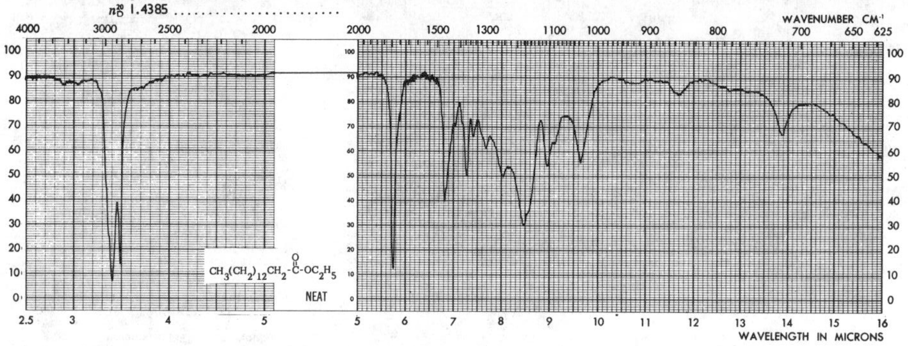

13,755-3 **Ethyl heptadecanoate**
$CH_3(CH_2)_{15}CO_2C_2H_5$ M.W. 298.51 m.p. 27°

$CH_3(CH_2)_{14}CH_2-\overset{O}{\overset{\|}{C}}-OC_2H_5$ MELT

C

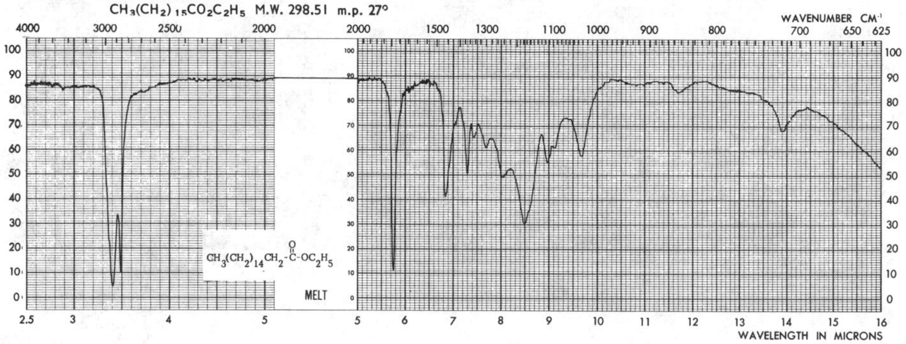

M8070-9 **Methyl stearate**
$CH_3(CH_2)_{16}CO_2CH_3$ M.W. 298.51
m.p. 39-41°

$H_3C-(CH_2)_{16}-\overset{O}{\overset{\|}{C}}-O-CH_3$ MELT

D

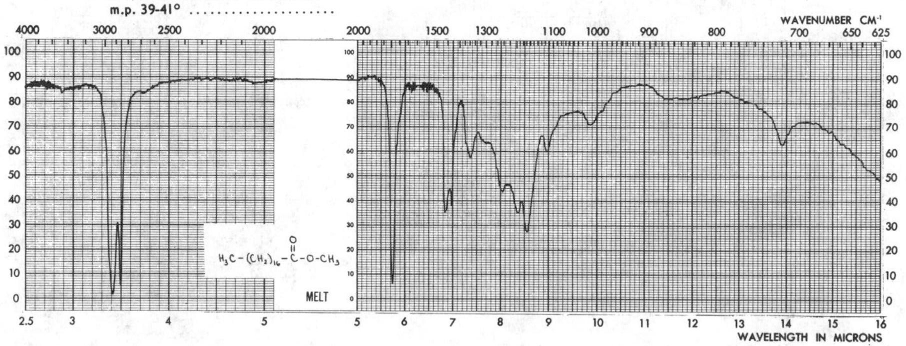

22,317-4
Ethyl stearate, 99%
$CH_3(CH_2)_{16}CO_2C_2H_5$ FW 312.54 mp 33-35°
bp 213-215°/15mm. *Beil.* 2,379 Disp. C

$CH_3(CH_2)_{15}CH_2-\overset{O}{\overset{\|}{C}}-OCH_2CH_3$ MELT

E

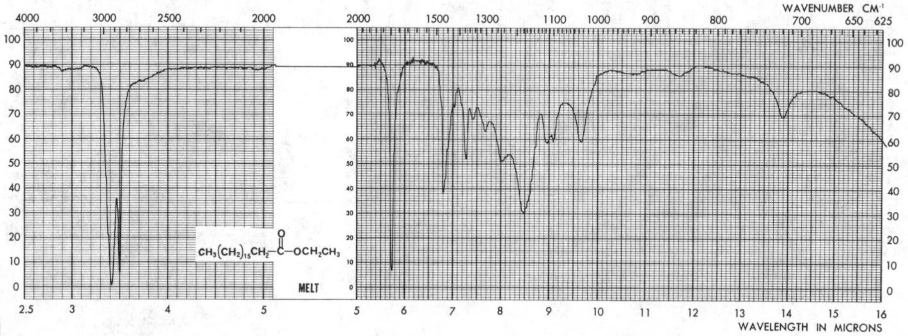

13,758-8 **Ethyl nonadecanoate**
$CH_3(CH_2)_{17}CO_2C_2H_5$ M.W. 326.57
m.p. 37-39°

$CH_3(CH_2)_{16}CH_2-\overset{O}{\overset{\|}{C}}-OC_2H_5$ MELT

F

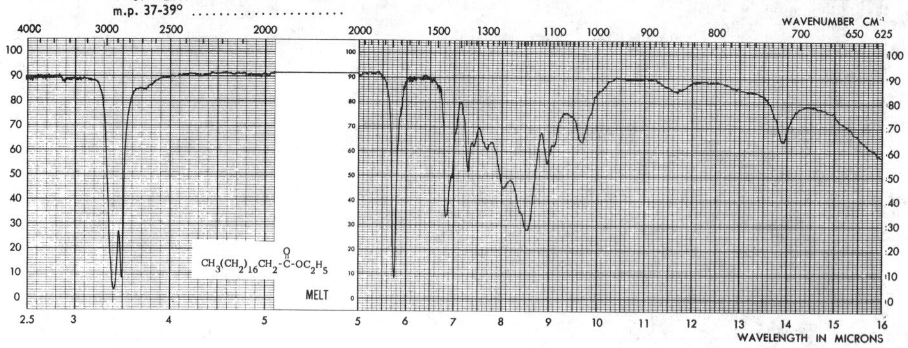

85,527-8
Methyl docosanoate, 98+% (methyl behenate)
$CH_3(CH_2)_{20}CO_2CH_3$
M.W. 354.62 m.p. 54-56°

$CH_3(CH_2)_{19}CH_2-\overset{O}{\overset{\|}{C}}-OCH_3$ NUJOL MULL

G

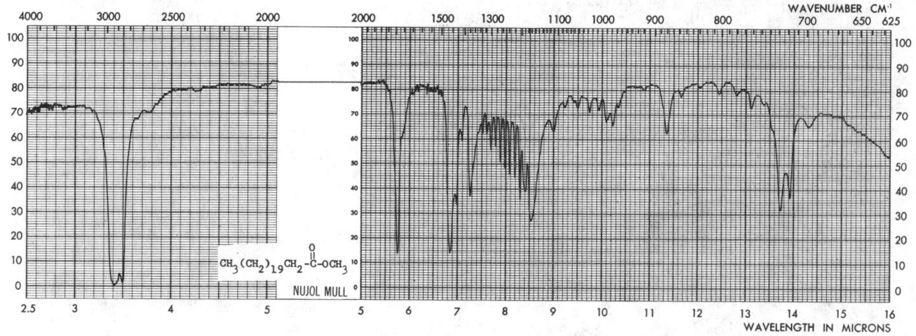

B10,170-2 **Butyl stearate, tech., 70%**
$CH_3(CH_2)_{16}CO_2(CH_2)_3CH_3$ M.W. 340.59
m.p. 25-27°

$H_3C-(CH_2)_{16}-\overset{O}{\overset{\|}{C}}-O-CH_2-CH_2-CH_2-CH_3$ NEAT

H

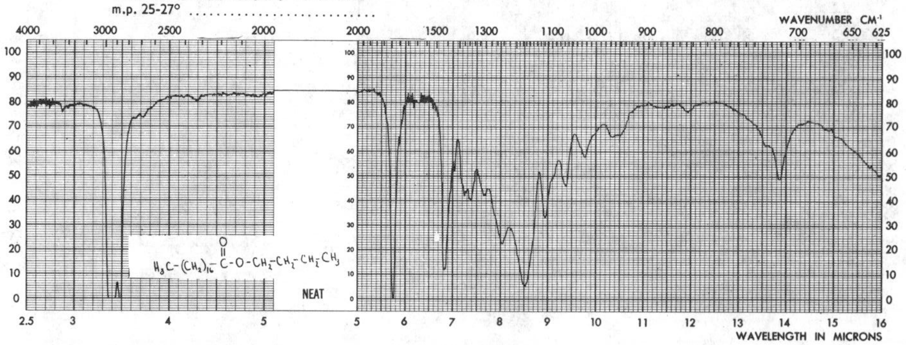

14,900-4 **Methyl enanthate** (methyl heptanoate)
$CH_3(CH_2)_5CO_2CH_3$ M.W. 144.21 n_D^{20} 1.4108
b.p. 164-166°

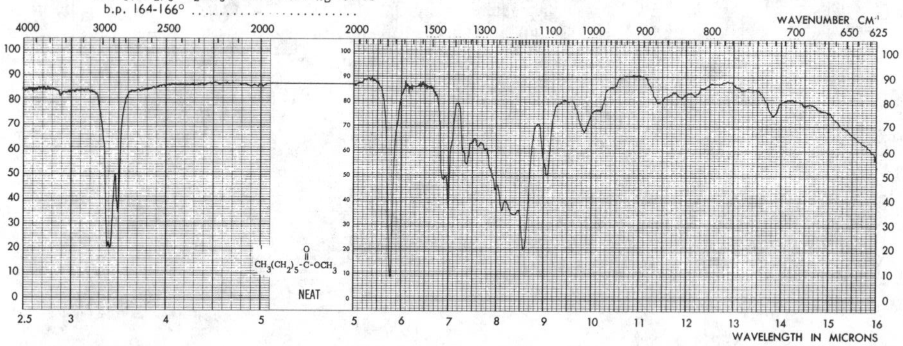

$CH_3(CH_2)_5-\overset{O}{\overset{\|}{C}}-OCH_3$ NEAT

(Each spectrum axes: WAVENUMBER CM⁻¹ 4000–625; WAVELENGTH IN MICRONS 2.5–16; transmittance 0–100)

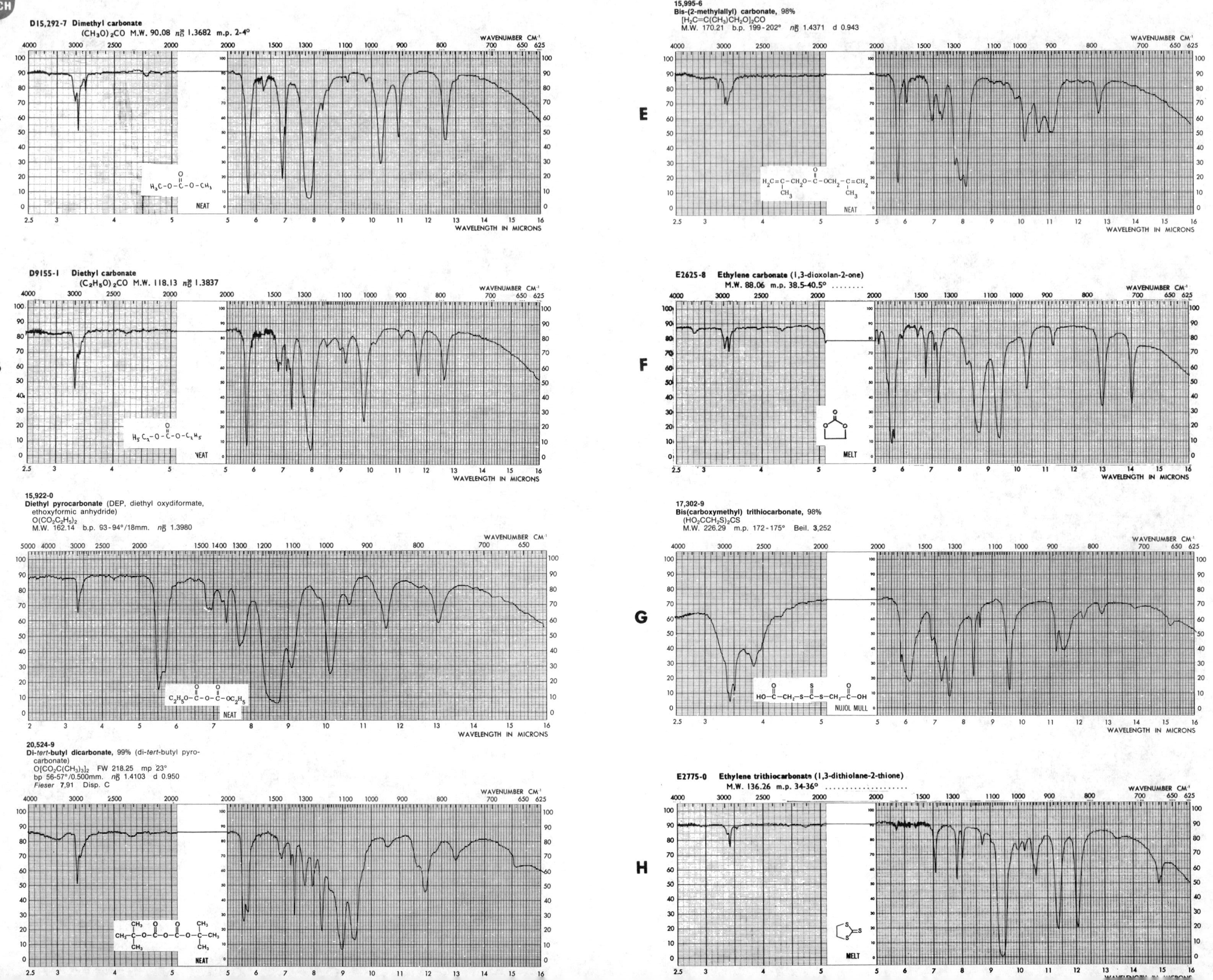
ALDRICH
A
D15,292-7 Dimethyl carbonate
$(CH_3O)_2CO$ M.W. 90.08 n_D^{20} 1.3682 m.p. 2-4°
NEAT
B
D9155-1 Diethyl carbonate
$(C_2H_5O)_2CO$ M.W. 118.13 n_D^{20} 1.3837
NEAT
C
15,922-0
Diethyl pyrocarbonate (DEP, diethyl oxydiformate, ethoxyformic anhydride)
$O(CO_2C_2H_5)_2$
M.W. 162.14 b.p. 93-94°/18mm. n_D^{20} 1.3980
NEAT
D
20,524-9
Di-tert-butyl dicarbonate, 99% (di-tert-butyl pyrocarbonate)
$O[CO_2C(CH_3)_3]_2$ FW 218.25 mp 23°
bp 56-57°/0.500mm. n_D^{20} 1.4103 d 0.950
Fieser 7,91 Disp. C
NEAT
E
15,995-6
Bis-(2-methylallyl) carbonate, 98%
$[H_2C{=}C(CH_3)CH_2O]_2CO$
M.W. 170.21 b.p. 199-202° n_D^{20} 1.4371 d 0.943
NEAT
F
E2625-8 Ethylene carbonate (1,3-dioxolan-2-one)
M.W. 88.06 m.p. 38.5-40.5°
MELT
G
17,302-9
Bis(carboxymethyl) trithiocarbonate, 98%
$(HO_2CCH_2S)_2CS$
M.W. 226.29 m.p. 172-175° Beil. 3,252
NUJOL MULL
H
E2775-0 Ethylene trithiocarbonate (1,3-dithiolane-2-thione)
M.W. 136.26 m.p. 34-36°
MELT
WAVENUMBER CM⁻¹
WAVELENGTH IN MICRONS

A P5265-2 **Propylene carbonate (1,2-propanediol cyclic carbonate)**
M.W. 102.09 n_D^{20} 1.4189
NEAT

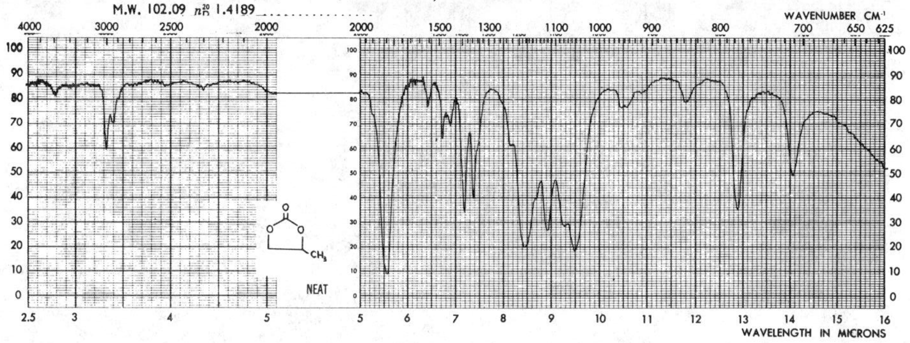

B D6250 **1,2-Dichloroethylene carbonate (4,5-dichloro-1,3-dioxolan-2-one)**
M.W. 156.95 n_D^{20} 1.4620
NEAT

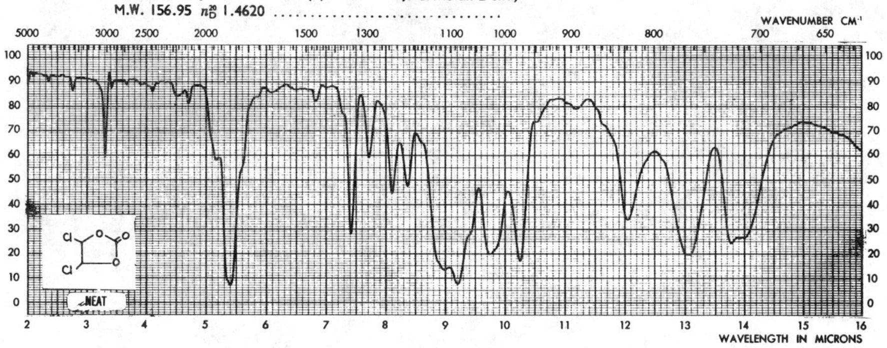

C 13,562-3 **Dimethyl oxalate**
$CH_3O_2CCO_2CH_3$ M.W. 118.09 m.p. 50-54°
$CH_3O-\overset{O}{\overset{\|}{C}}-\overset{O}{\overset{\|}{C}}-OCH_3$
NUJOL MULL

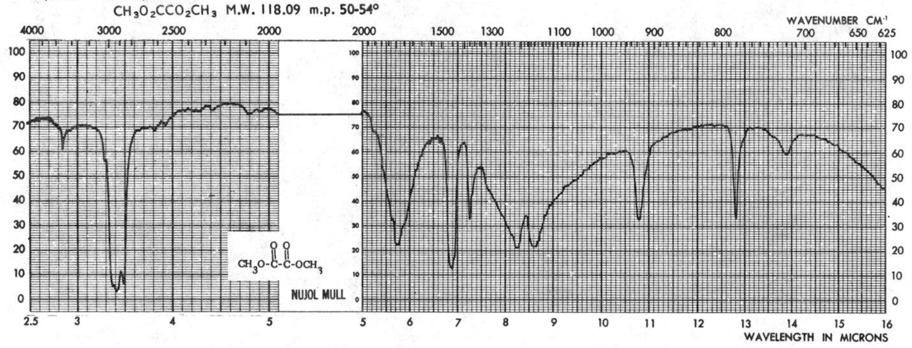

D 13,536-4 **Diethyl oxalate**
$C_2H_5O_2CCO_2C_2H_5$ M.W. 146.14 n_D^{20} 1.4096
b.p. 185°
$H_5C_2-O-\overset{O}{\overset{\|}{C}}-\overset{O}{\overset{\|}{C}}-O-C_2H_5$
NEAT

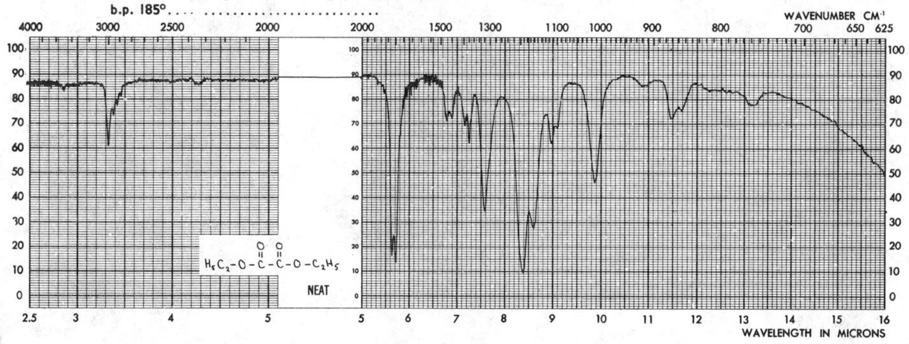

E 13,644-1 **Dimethyl malonate**
$CH_3O_2CCH_2CO_2CH_3$ M.W. 132.12 n_D^{20} 1.4135
b.p. 76-78°/15 mm.
$CH_3O-\overset{O}{\overset{\|}{C}}-CH_2-\overset{O}{\overset{\|}{C}}-OCH_3$
NEAT

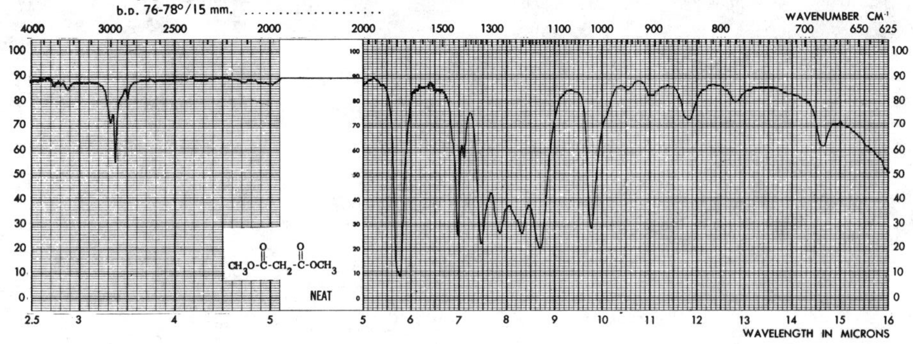

F D9775-4 **Diethyl malonate**
$C_2H_5O_2CCH_2CO_2C_2H_5$ M.W. 160.17
n_D^{20} 1.4135
$H_5C_2-O-\overset{O}{\overset{\|}{C}}-CH_2-\overset{O}{\overset{\|}{C}}-O-C_2H_5$
NEAT

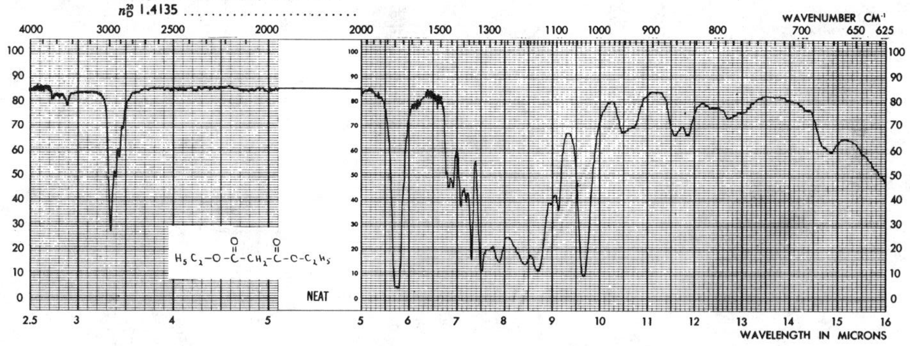

G 12,613-6 **Diethyl methylmalonate**
$C_2H_5O_2CCH(CH_3)CO_2C_2H_5$ M.W. 174.20
n_D^{20} 1.4123
NEAT

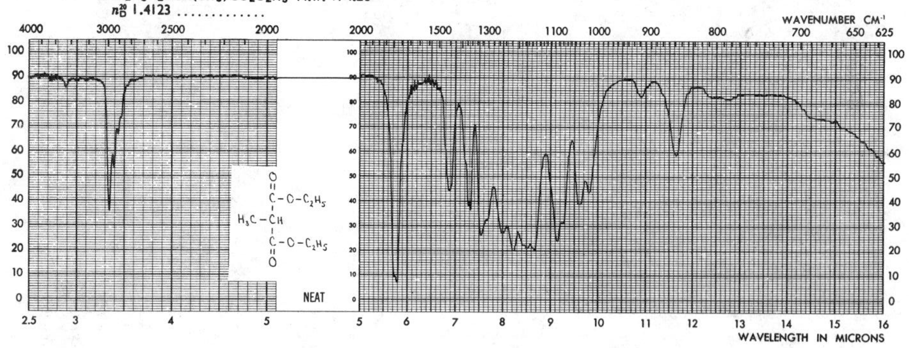

H D9520-4 **Diethyl ethylmalonate**
$C_2H_5O_2CCH(C_2H_5)CO_2C_2H_5$ M.W. 188.22
n_D^{20} 1.4158
NEAT

WAVENUMBER CM⁻¹ — WAVELENGTH IN MICRONS

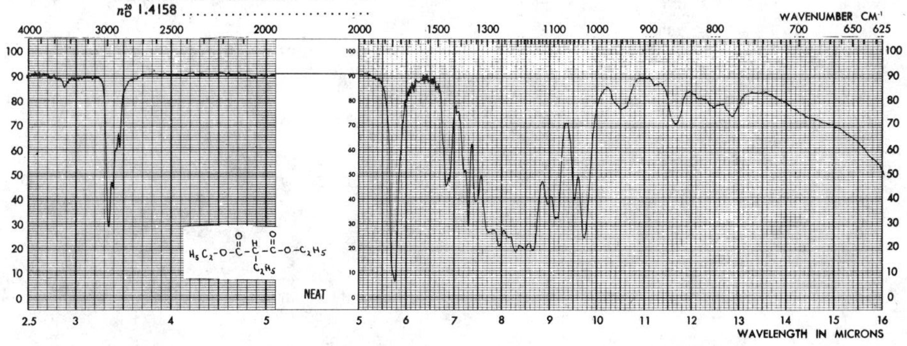

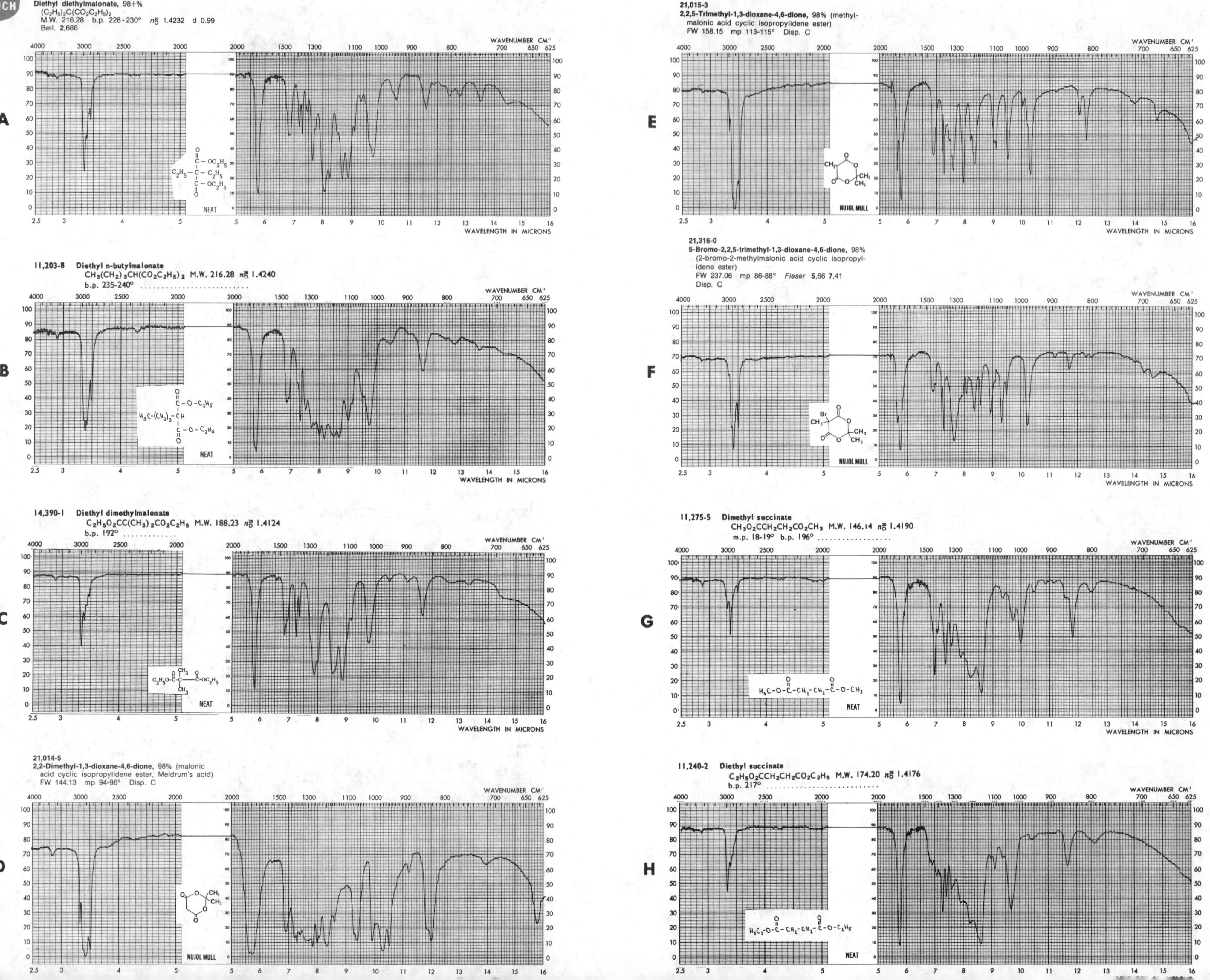
ALDRICH
A
15,681-7
Diethyl diethylmalonate, 98+%
$(C_2H_5)_2C(CO_2C_2H_5)_2$
M.W. 216.28 b.p. 228-230° n_D^{20} 1.4232 d 0.99
Beil. 2,686
NEAT
B
11,203-8 Diethyl n-butylmalonate
$CH_3(CH_2)_3CH(CO_2C_2H_5)_2$ M.W. 216.28 n_D^{20} 1.4240
b.p. 235-240°
NEAT
C
14,390-1 Diethyl dimethylmalonate
$C_2H_5O_2CC(CH_3)_2CO_2C_2H_5$ M.W. 188.23 n_D^{20} 1.4124
b.p. 192°
NEAT
D
21,014-5
2,2-Dimethyl-1,3-dioxane-4,6-dione, 98% (malonic acid cyclic isopropylidene ester, Meldrum's acid)
FW 144.13 mp 94-96° Disp. C
NUJOL MULL
E
21,015-3
2,2,5-Trimethyl-1,3-dioxane-4,6-dione, 98% (methylmalonic acid cyclic isopropylidene ester)
FW 158.15 mp 113-115° Disp. C
NUJOL MULL
F
21,316-0
5-Bromo-2,2,5-trimethyl-1,3-dioxane-4,6-dione, 98% (2-bromo-2-methylmalonic acid cyclic isopropylidene ester)
FW 237.06 mp 86-88° Fieser 5,66 7,41
Disp. C
NUJOL MULL
G
11,275-5 Dimethyl succinate
$CH_3O_2CCH_2CH_2CO_2CH_3$ M.W. 146.14 n_D^{20} 1.4190
m.p. 18-19° b.p. 196°
NEAT
H
11,240-2 Diethyl succinate
$C_2H_5O_2CCH_2CH_2CO_2C_2H_5$ M.W. 174.20 n_D^{20} 1.4176
b.p. 217°
NEAT
WAVENUMBER CM⁻¹
WAVELENGTH IN MICRONS

A

19,016-0
Diethyl methylsuccinate, 97+%
$C_2H_5O_2CCH_2CH(CH_3)CO_2C_2H_5$ FW 188.22
bp 217-218° n_D^{20} 1.4199 d 1.012 *Beil.* **2**,639
Disp. C

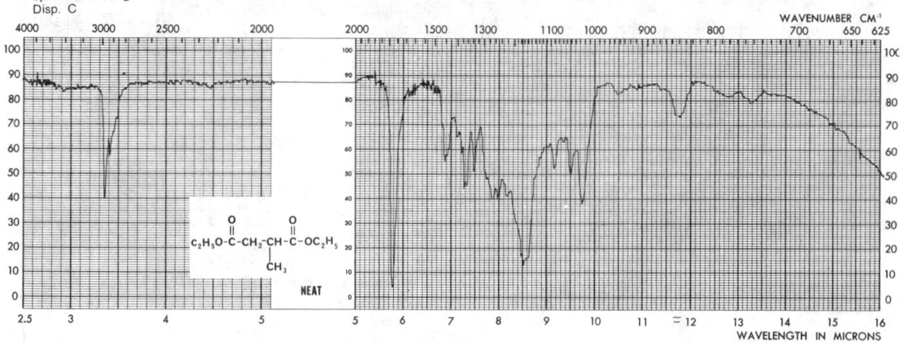

NEAT

B

D15,880-1 **Dimethyl glutarate**
$CH_3O_2C(CH_2)_3CO_2CH_3$ M.W. 160.17
n_D^{20} 1.4246

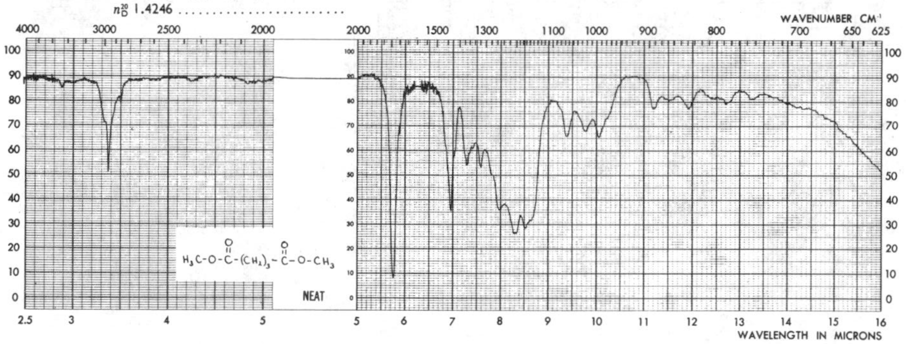

NEAT

C

D9600-6 **Diethyl glutarate, puriss.**
$C_2H_5O_2C(CH_2)_3CO_2C_2H_5$ M.W. 188.22
n_D^{20} 1.4240

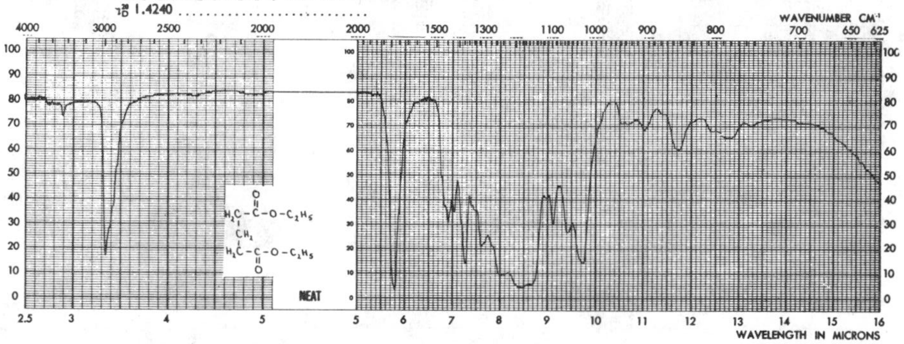

NEAT

D

D9310 **Diethyl 2,4-dimethylglutarate** (mixture of isomers)
$CH_2[CH(CH_3)CO_2C_2H_5]_2$ M.W. 216.28 n_D^{20} 1.4220

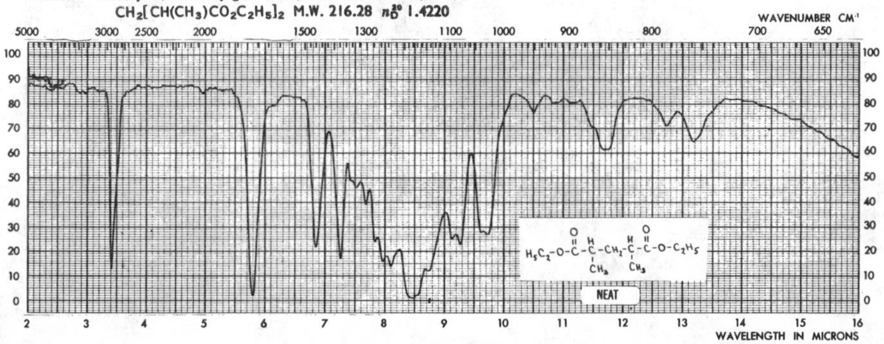

NEAT

E

18,625-2
Dimethyl adipate
$CH_3O_2C(CH_2)_4CO_2CH_3$
M.W. 174.2 d 1.05

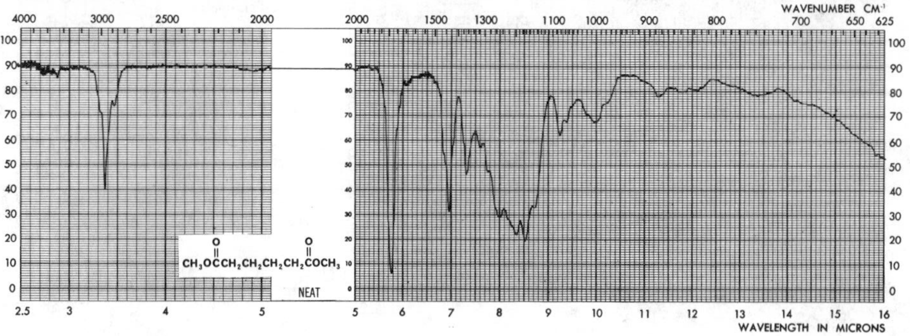

NEAT

F

11,148-1 **Dimethyl 2-methyladipate**
$CH_3O_2C(CH_2)_3CH(CH_3)CO_2CH_3$ M.W. 188.22
n_D^{20} 1.4287

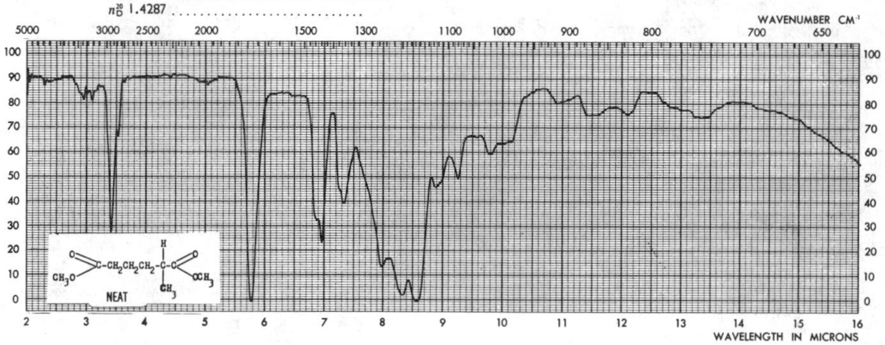

NEAT

G

11,142-2 **Dimethyl 2,5-dimethyladipate** (dimethyl 2,5-dimethylhexanedioate)
$CH_3O_2CCH(CH_3)CH_2CH_2CH(CH_3)CO_2CH_3$ M.W. 202.25
n_D^{20} 1.4292

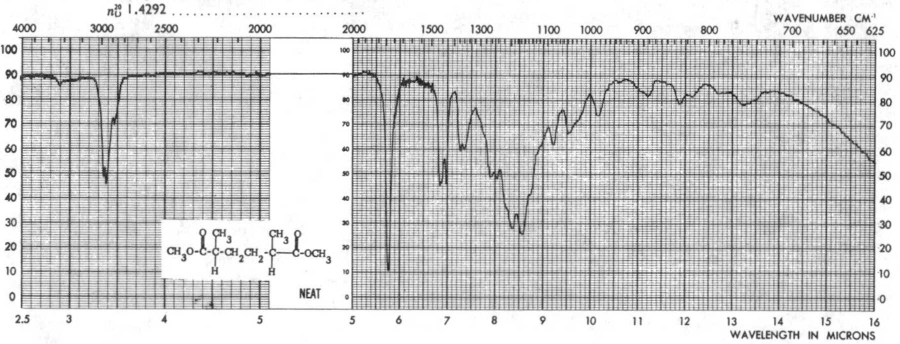

NEAT

H

18,006-8
Dimethyl pimelate, 99%
$CH_3O_2C(CH_2)_5CO_2CH_3$
M.W. 188.22 b.p. 121-122°/11mm. n_D^{20} 1.4314
d 1.041 Beil. **2**(1),281

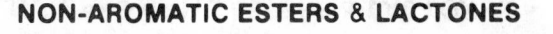

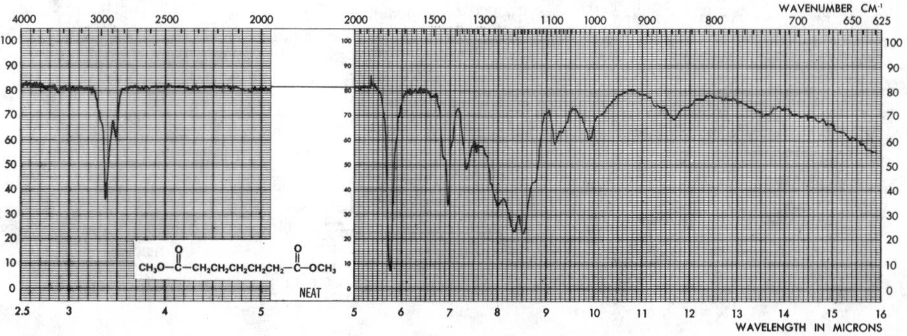

NEAT

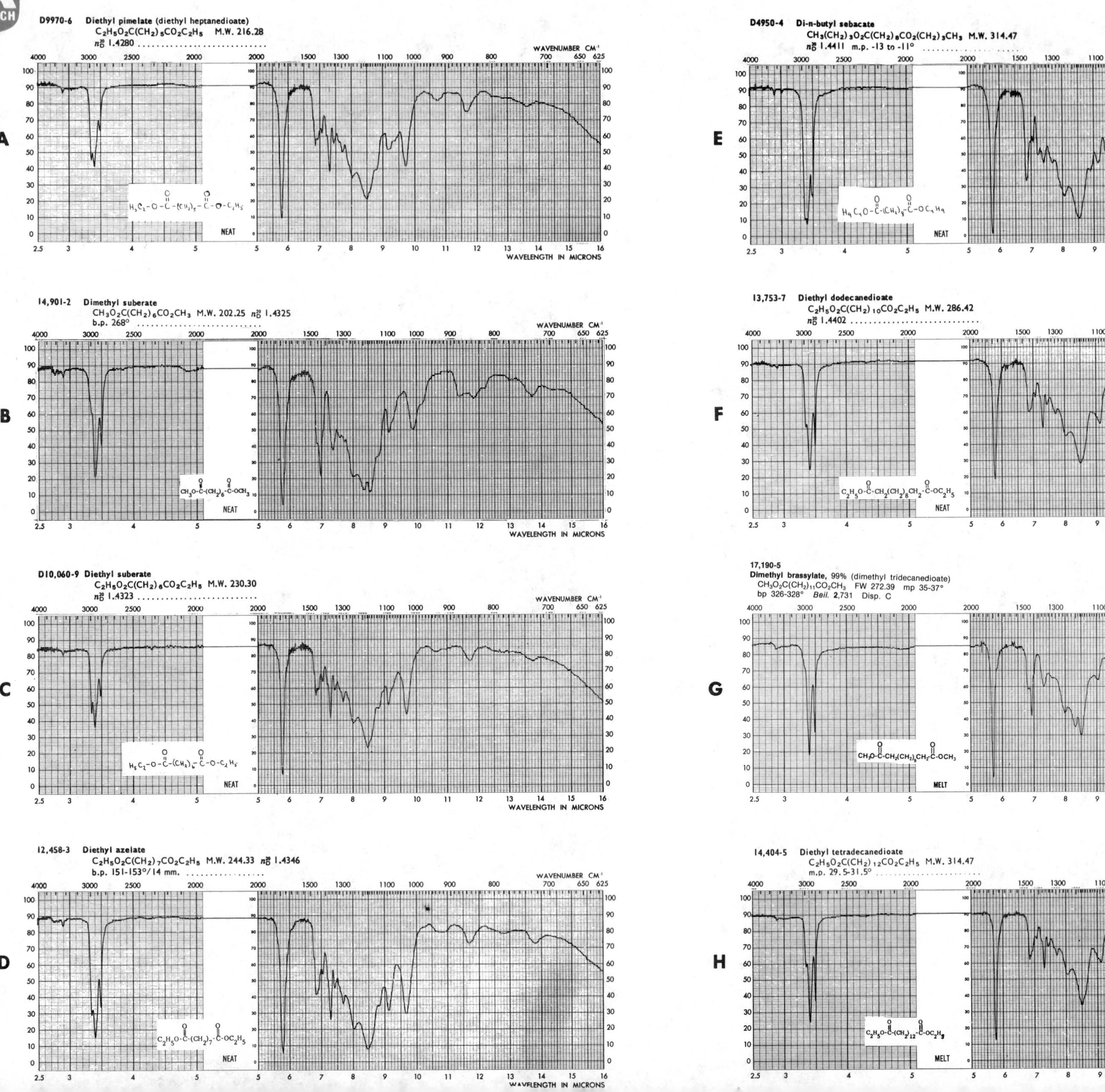

ALDRICH
A
D9970-6 Diethyl pimelate (diethyl heptanedioate)
$C_2H_5O_2C(CH_2)_5CO_2C_2H_5$ M.W. 216.28
n_D^{20} 1.4280
NEAT
B
14,901-2 Dimethyl suberate
$CH_3O_2C(CH_2)_6CO_2CH_3$ M.W. 202.25 n_D^{20} 1.4325
b.p. 268°
NEAT
C
D10,060-9 Diethyl suberate
$C_2H_5O_2C(CH_2)_6CO_2C_2H_5$ M.W. 230.30
n_D^{20} 1.4323
NEAT
D
12,458-3 Diethyl azelate
$C_2H_5O_2C(CH_2)_7CO_2C_2H_5$ M.W. 244.33 n_D^{20} 1.4346
b.p. 151-153°/14 mm.
NEAT
E
D4950-4 Di-n-butyl sebacate
$CH_3(CH_2)_3O_2C(CH_2)_8CO_2(CH_2)_3CH_3$ M.W. 314.47
n_D^{20} 1.4411 m.p. -13 to -11°
NEAT
F
13,753-7 Diethyl dodecanedioate
$C_2H_5O_2C(CH_2)_{10}CO_2C_2H_5$ M.W. 286.42
n_D^{20} 1.4402
NEAT
G
17,190-5
Dimethyl brassylate, 99% (dimethyl tridecanedioate)
$CH_3O_2C(CH_2)_{11}CO_2CH_3$ FW 272.39 mp 35-37°
bp 326-328° Beil. 2,731 Disp. C
MELT
H
14,404-5 Diethyl tetradecanedioate
$C_2H_5O_2C(CH_2)_{12}CO_2C_2H_5$ M.W. 314.47
m.p. 29.5-31.5°
MELT
WAVENUMBER CM⁻¹
WAVELENGTH IN MICRONS

A — T4370-2 **Triacetin**
$(CH_3CO_2CH_2)_2CH(O_2CCH_3)$ M.W. 218.21
n_D^{20} 1.4302 b.p. 258-259°
NEAT

B — 11,302-6 **Tributyrin (glyceryl tributyrate), puriss.**
$(CH_3CH_2CH_2CO_2CH_2)_2CH(O_2CCH_2CH_2CH_3)$ M.W. 302.37
n_D^{20} 1.4352 b.p. 318°
NEAT

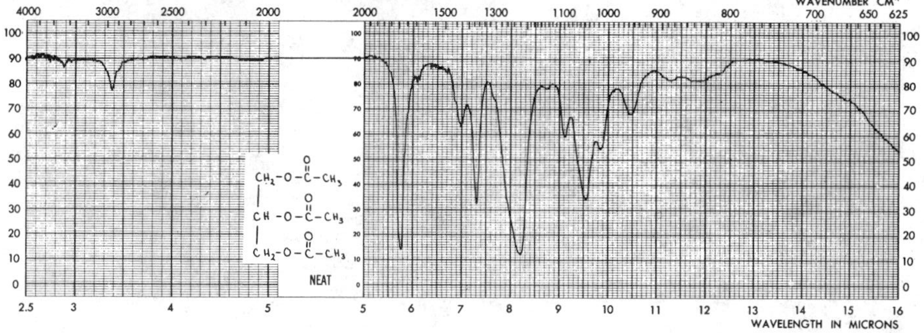

C — 17,991-4
Cottonseed oil
n_D^{20} 1.4725 d 0.918
NEAT

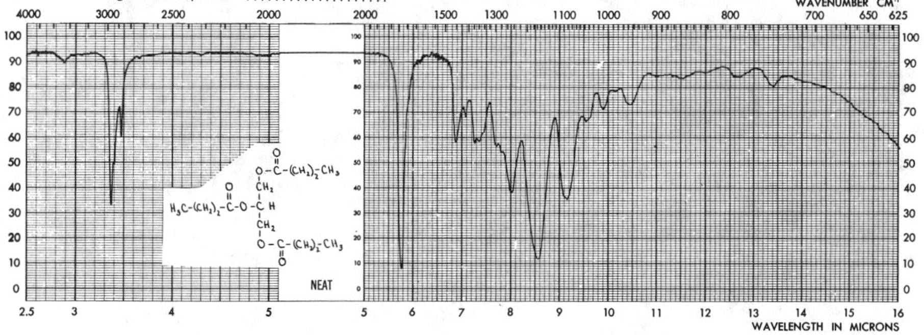

D — T6020-8 **Triethyl methanetricarboxylate**
$CH(CO_2C_2H_5)_3$ M.W. 232.23 n_D^{20} 1.4243
b.p. 253°
MELT

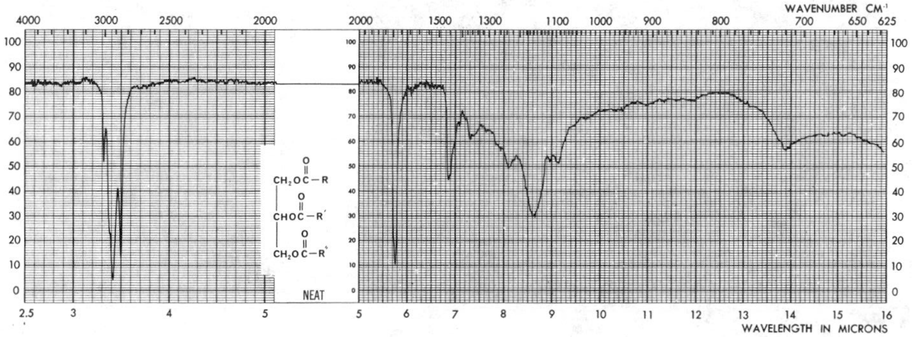

E — 10,758-1 **2,2-Bis-(acetoxymethyl)-propyl acetate**
$(CH_3CO_2CH_2)_3CCH_3$ M.W. 246.26 n_D^{20} 1.4359
NEAT

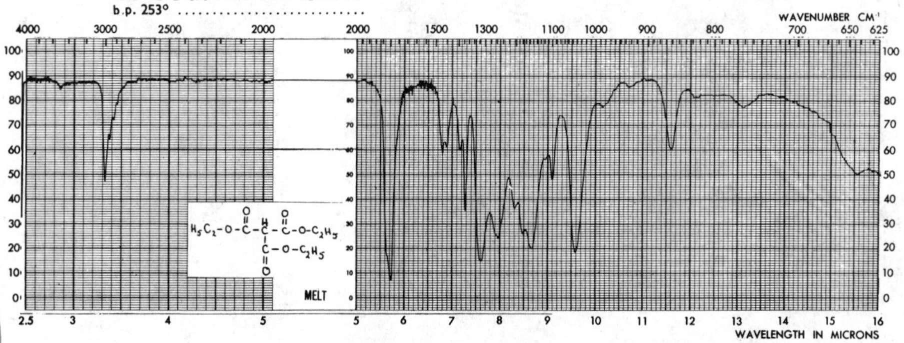

F — T5985-4 **Triethyl 1,1,2-ethanetricarboxylate**
$C_2H_5O_2CCH_2CH(CO_2C_2H_5)_2$ M.W. 246.26 n_D^{20} 1.4290
b.p. 99°/0.5 mm.
NEAT

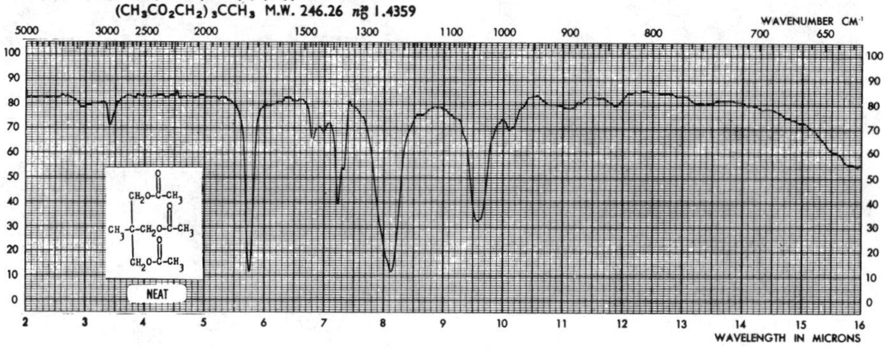

G — 20,948-1
1,1,2-Triacetoxyethane, 98%
$(CH_3CO_2)_2CHCH_2O_2CCH_3$ FW 204.18 mp 49-51°
bp 125-130°/11mm. *Beil.* **2**(2),168 Disp. C
MELT

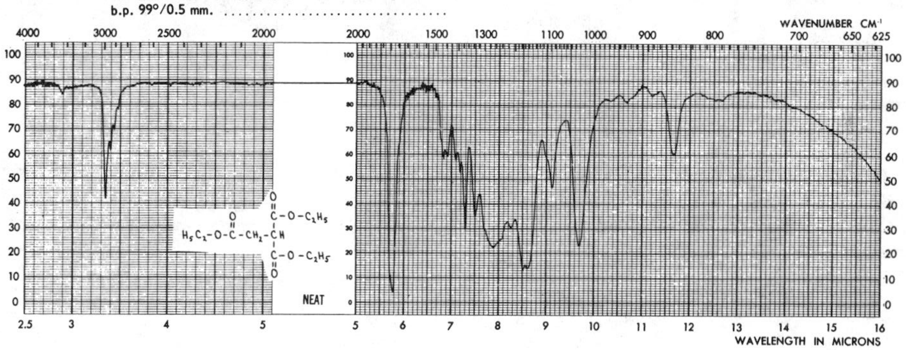

H — 22,039-6
Ethyl 2-acetoxy-2-methylacetoacetate, 98% (ethyl 2-acetyllactate acetate)
$CH_3COC(O_2CCH_3)(CH_3)CO_2C_2H_5$ FW 202.21
bp 80-84°/1mm. n_D^{20} 1.4285 d 1.079
Beil. **3**(4),1942 Disp. C
NEAT

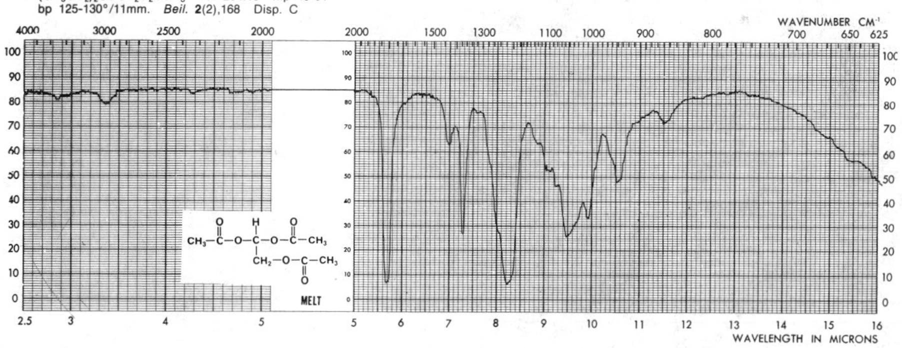

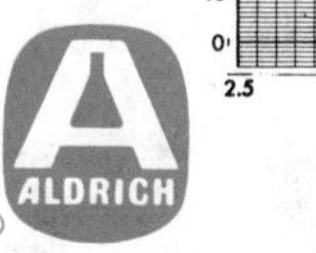

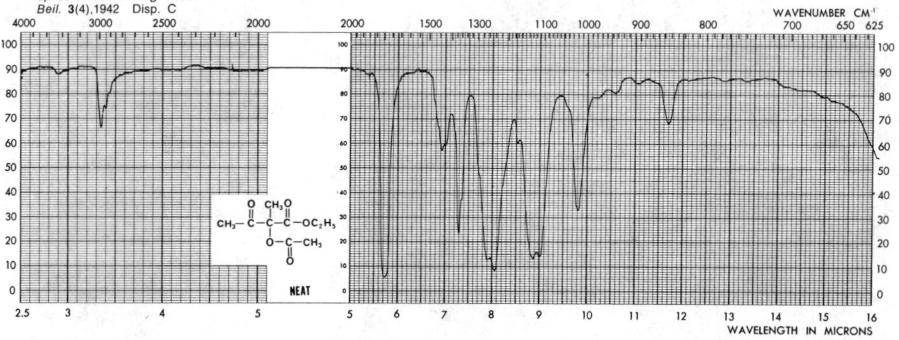

A 10,607-0 Diethyl 2-[2-(carbomethoxy)-propyl]-malonate
$CH_3CH(CO_2CH_3)CH_2CH(CO_2C_2H_5)_2$ M.W. 260.29
n_D^{20} 1.4328 b.p. 157°/15 mm.

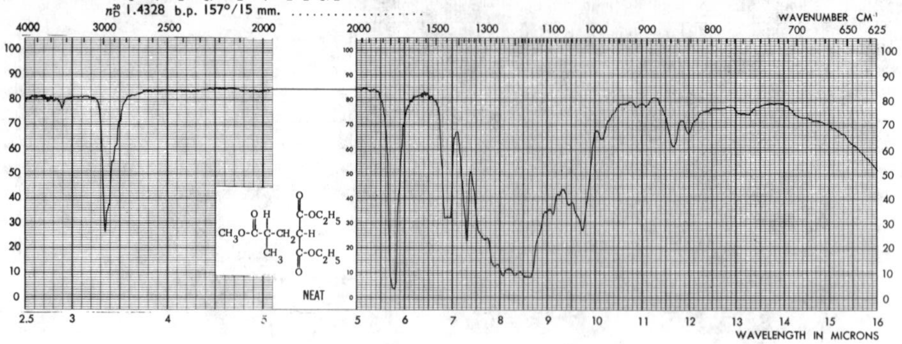

NEAT

B T6090-9 Triethyl 1,3,5-pentanetricarboxylate (triethyl 4-carboxypimelate)
$C_2H_5O_2CCH_2CH_2CH(CO_2C_2H_5)CH_2CH_2CO_2C_2H_5$
M.W. 288.34 n_D^{20} 1.4390 b.p. 162-164°/0.5 mm.

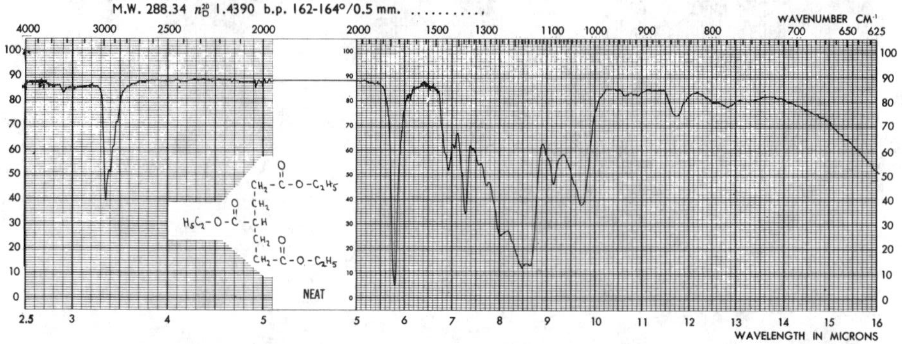

NEAT

C 13,188-1 Tetraethyl 1,1,2,2-ethanetetracarboxylate
$(C_2H_5O_2C)_2CHCH(CO_2C_2H_5)_2$ M.W. 318.32 m.p. 72-73°

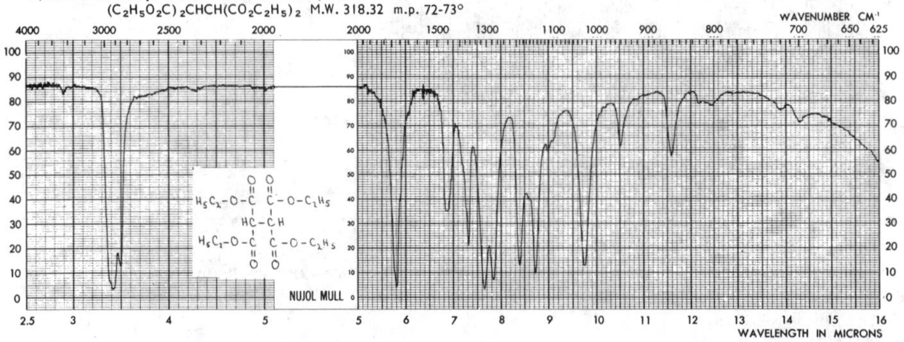

NUJOL MULL

D 14,608-0 Sorbitol hexaacetate
$CH_3CO_2CH_2[CH(O_2CCH_3)]_4CH_2O_2CCH_3$ M.W. 434.40
m.p. 100-104°

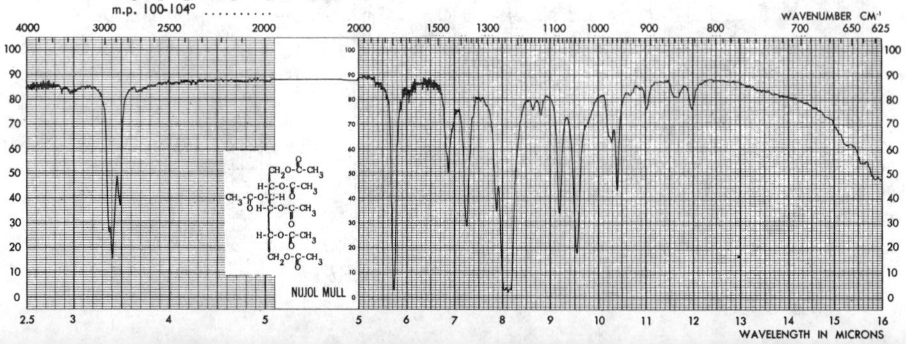

NUJOL MULL

E 15,902-6
β-D-Ribofuranose 1,2,3,5-tetraacetate
M.W. 318.28 m.p. 79-81°
$[\alpha]^{26}$ - 11.4° (c=10, $CHCl_3$)

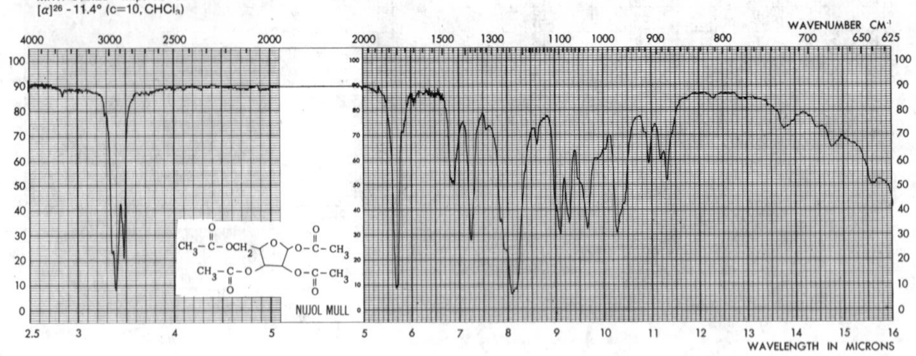

NUJOL MULL

F 85,824-2
Methyl-α-D-galactopyranoside 2,3,4,6-tetraacetate
$[\alpha]_D^{25}$ +132° (c=1, $CHCl_3$)
M.W. 362.33 m.p. 85-87°

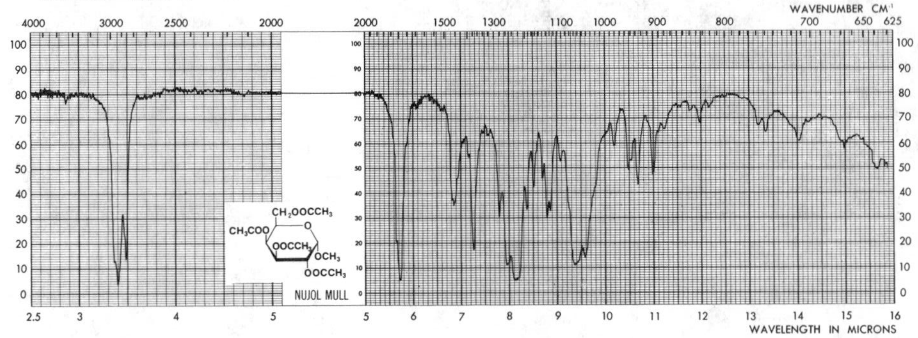

NUJOL MULL

G G235-4 α-D-Glucose pentaacetate
M.W. 390.34 m.p. 109-111°

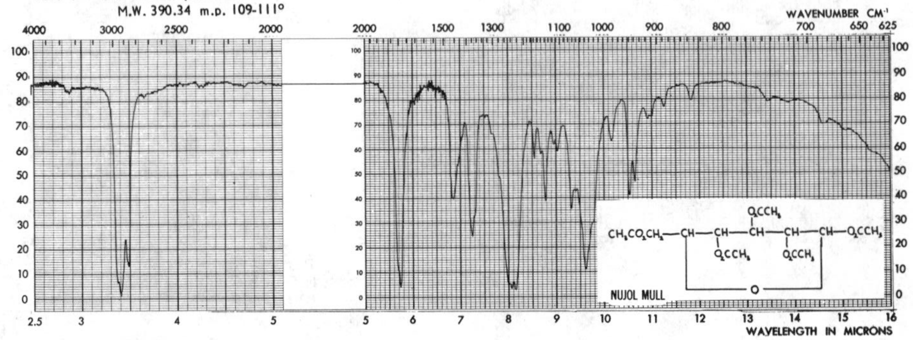

NUJOL MULL

H G5 α-D-Galactose pentaacetate
M.W. 390.34 m.p. 92.5-96.5°

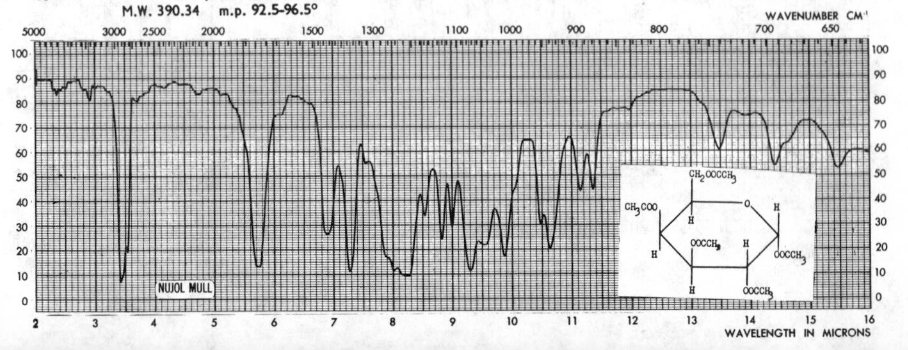

NUJOL MULL

WAVENUMBER CM⁻¹ — WAVELENGTH IN MICRONS

A

13,403-1 β-D-Galactose pentaacetate
M.W. 390.34 m.p. 143-144°

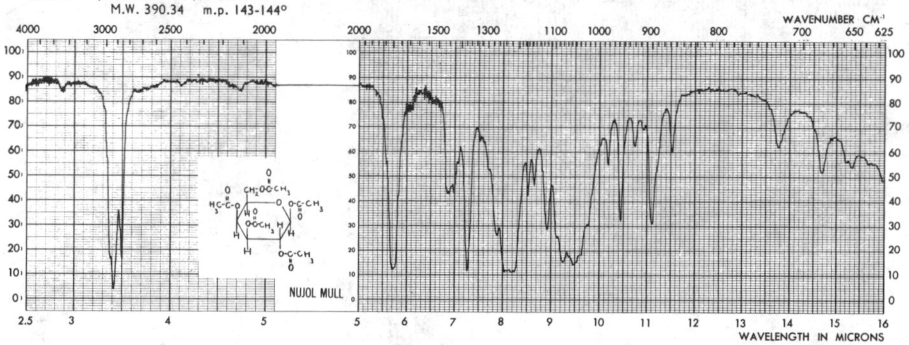

NUJOL MULL

B

85,503-0
1,2,3,4-Tetra-O-acetyl-β-D-ribopyranose, 99%
M.W. 318.28 m.p. 109-111°

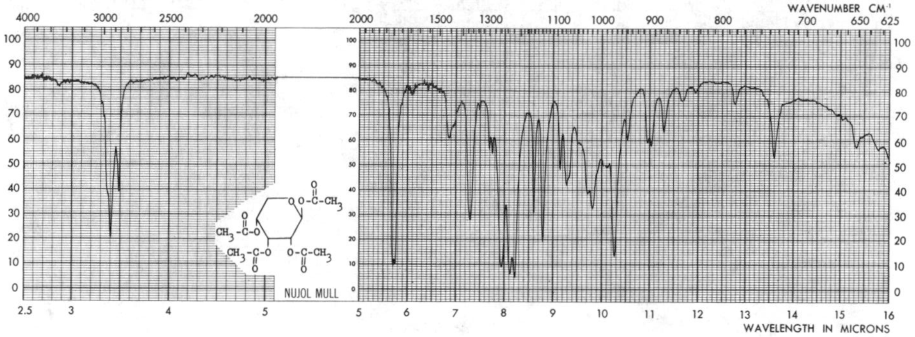

NUJOL MULL

C

T4440-7 Triacetylglucal
M.W. 272.25 m.p. 51-53°

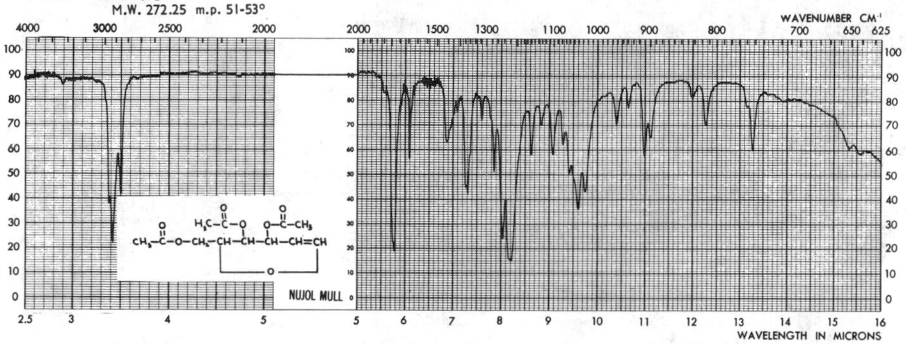

NUJOL MULL

D

10,447-7 β-d-Thioglucose tetraacetate
M.W. 364.37 m.p. 116-118° $[\alpha]_D^{20}$ + 5.8° (in c=2.2, $CHCl_3$)

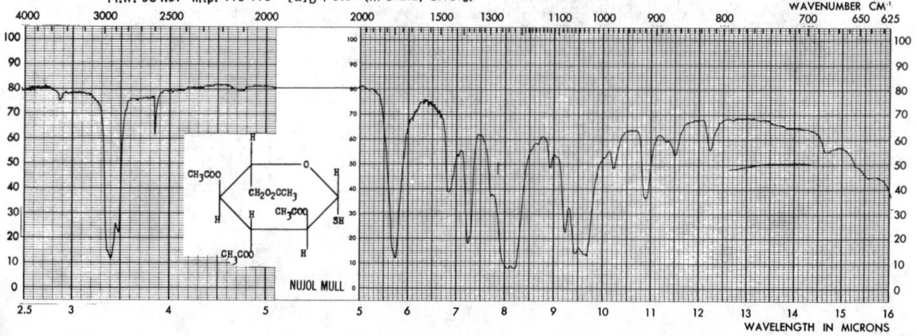

NUJOL MULL

E

13,131-8 Pectin (citrus)
m.p. 150-230° (dec.)

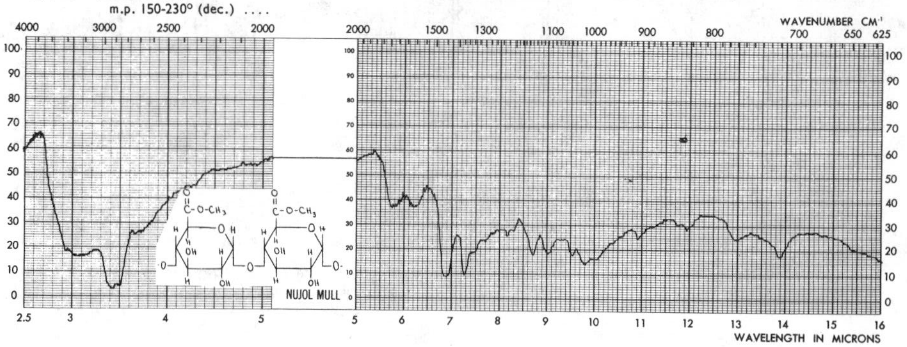

NUJOL MULL

F

10,157-5
α-D-Cellobiose octaacetate
M.W. 678.59 m.p. 224-226°
$[\alpha]_D^{20}$ + 40° (c=6, $CHCl_3$)

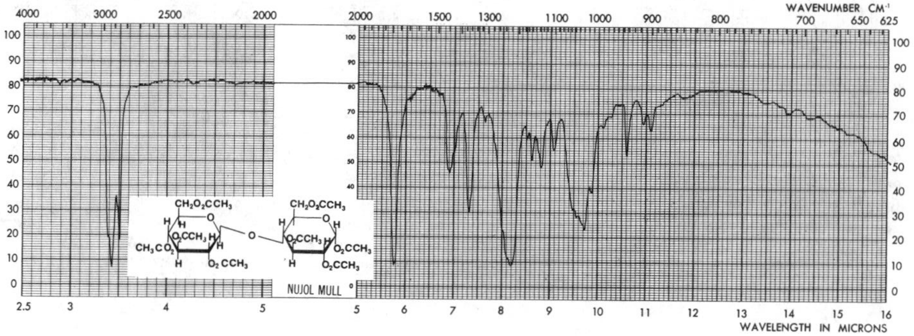

NUJOL MULL

G

M4040-5 Methyl cyclopropanecarboxylate
$C_3H_5CO_2CH_3$ M.W. 100.12 n_D^{20} 1.4181
b.p. 119°

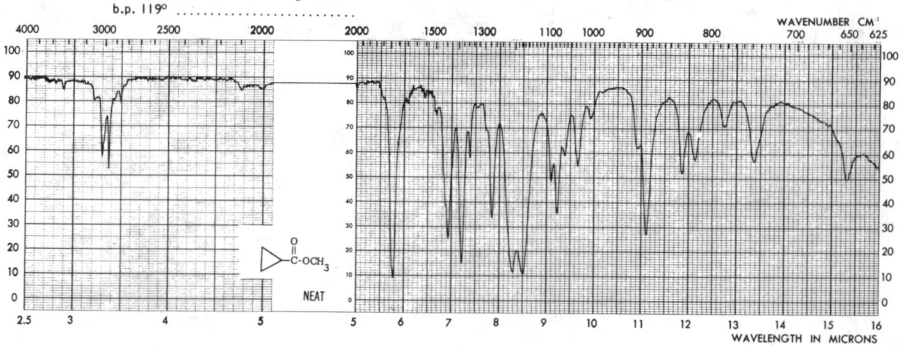

NEAT

H

E2160-4 Ethyl cyclopropanecarboxylate
$C_3H_5CO_2C_2H_5$ M.W. 114.14 n_D^{20} 1.4197

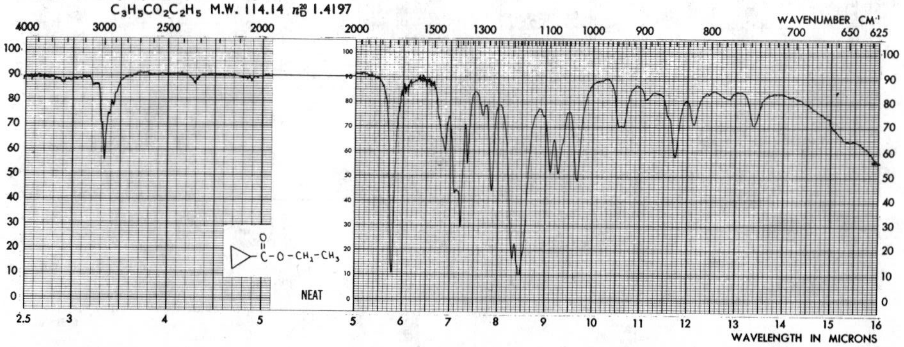

NEAT

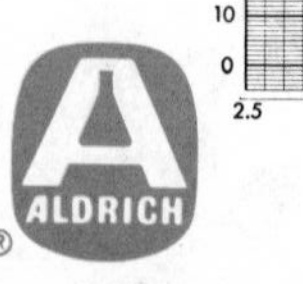

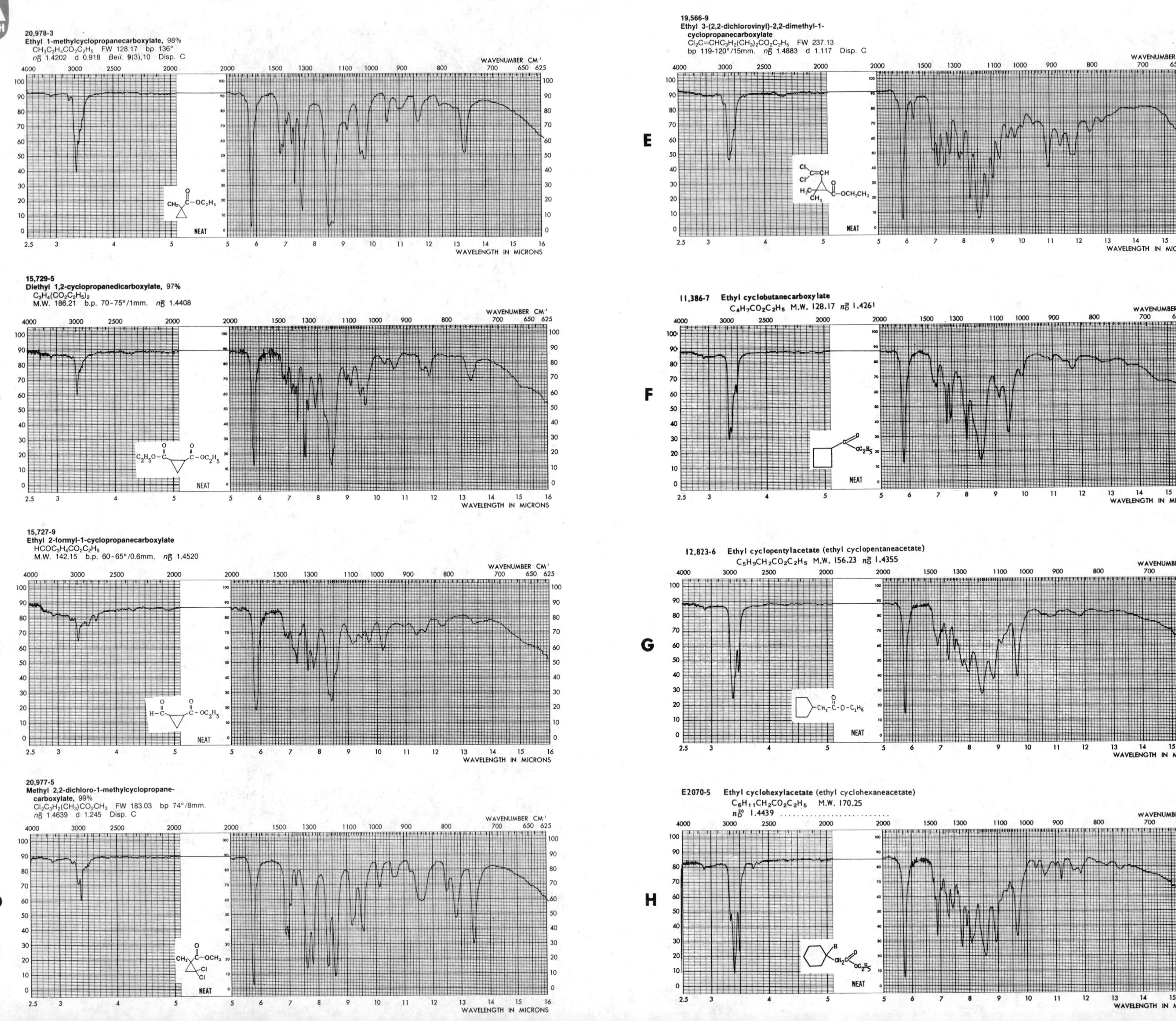
ALDRICH
A
20,978-3
Ethyl 1-methylcyclopropanecarboxylate, 98%
$CH_3C_3H_4CO_2C_2H_5$ FW 128.17 bp 136°
n_D^{20} 1.4202 d 0.918 Beil. 9(3),10 Disp. C
NEAT
B
15,729-5
Diethyl 1,2-cyclopropanedicarboxylate, 97%
$C_3H_4(CO_2C_2H_5)_2$
M.W. 186.21 b.p. 70-75°/1mm. n_D^{20} 1.4408
NEAT
C
15,727-9
Ethyl 2-formyl-1-cyclopropanecarboxylate
$HCOC_3H_4CO_2C_2H_5$
M.W. 142.15 b.p. 60-65°/0.6mm. n_D^{20} 1.4520
NEAT
D
20,977-5
Methyl 2,2-dichloro-1-methylcyclopropanecarboxylate, 99%
$Cl_2C_3H_2(CH_3)CO_2CH_3$ FW 183.03 bp 74°/8mm.
n_D^{20} 1.4639 d 1.245 Disp. C
NEAT
E
19,566-9
Ethyl 3-(2,2-dichlorovinyl)-2,2-dimethyl-1-cyclopropanecarboxylate
$Cl_2C{=}CHC_3H_2(CH_3)_2CO_2C_2H_5$ FW 237.13
bp 119-120°/15mm. n_D^{20} 1.4883 d 1.117 Disp. C
NEAT
F
11,386-7 Ethyl cyclobutanecarboxylate
$C_4H_7CO_2C_2H_5$ M.W. 128.17 n_D^{20} 1.4261
NEAT
G
12,823-6 Ethyl cyclopentylacetate (ethyl cyclopentaneacetate)
$C_5H_9CH_2CO_2C_2H_5$ M.W. 156.23 n_D^{20} 1.4355
NEAT
H
E2070-5 Ethyl cyclohexylacetate (ethyl cyclohexaneacetate)
$C_6H_{11}CH_2CO_2C_2H_5$ M.W. 170.25
n_D^{20} 1.4439
NEAT
WAVENUMBER CM⁻¹
WAVELENGTH IN MICRONS

A

14,771-0 **Diethyl 1,1-cyclopropanedicarboxylate**
$C_3H_4(CO_2C_2H_5)_2$ M.W. 186.21 n_D^{20} 1.4330
b.p. 94-96°/10 mm. . . . . . .

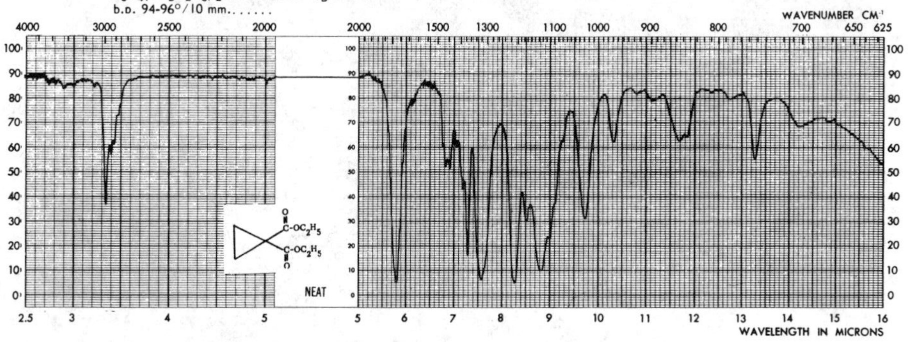

NEAT

B

D9180-2 **Diethyl 1,1-cyclobutanedicarboxylate** (diethyl 2,2-trimethylenemalonate)
$C_4H_6(CO_2C_2H_5)_2$ M.W. 200.23 n_D^{20} 1.4344 . . . .

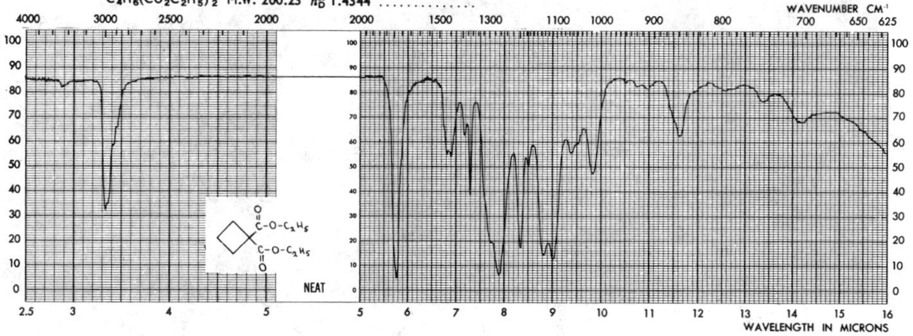

NEAT

C

14,828-8 **Dimethyl pinate** (methyl 2,2-dimethyl-3-methoxycarbonyl-1-cyclobutaneacetate)
$CH_3O_2CC_4H_4(CH_3)_2CH_2CO_2CH_3$ M.W. 214.26 n_D^{20} 1.4473
b.p. 90-93°/1 mm. . . . .

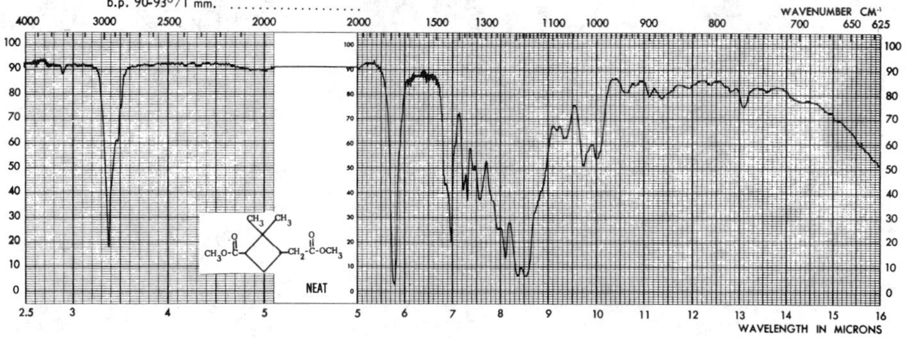

NEAT

D

19,742-4
Methyl cyclohexanecarboxylate, 98%
$C_6H_{11}CO_2CH_3$ FW 142.20 bp 183° n_D^{20} 1.4445
d 0.995 Disp. C

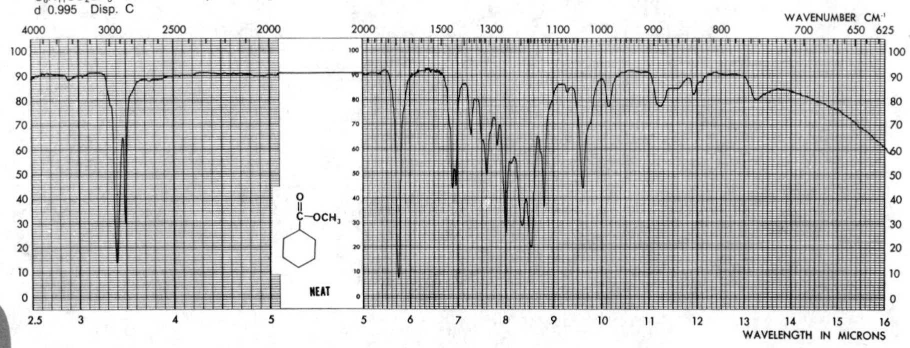

NEAT

E

20,960-0
Methyl cyclohexylacetate, 99% (methyl cyclohexaneacetate)
$C_6H_{11}CH_2CO_2CH_3$ FW 156.23 bp 201°
n_D^{20} 1.4456 d 0.951 Disp. C

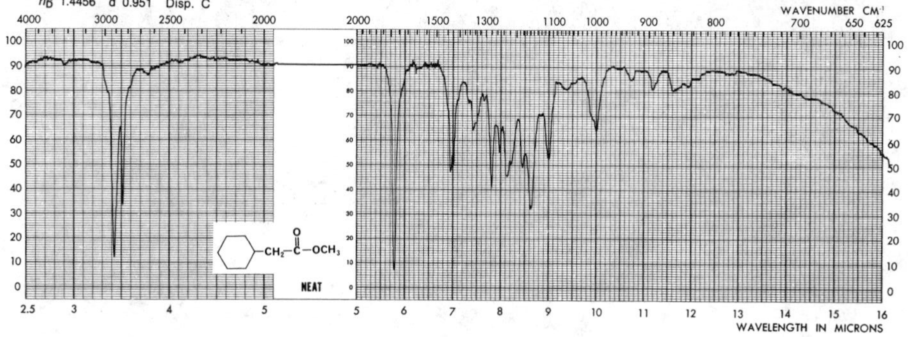

NEAT

F

20,959-7
Ethyl cyclohexanepropionate, 99%
$C_6H_{11}CH_2CH_2CO_2C_2H_5$ FW 184.28 n_D^{20} 1.4484
d 0.848 Disp. C

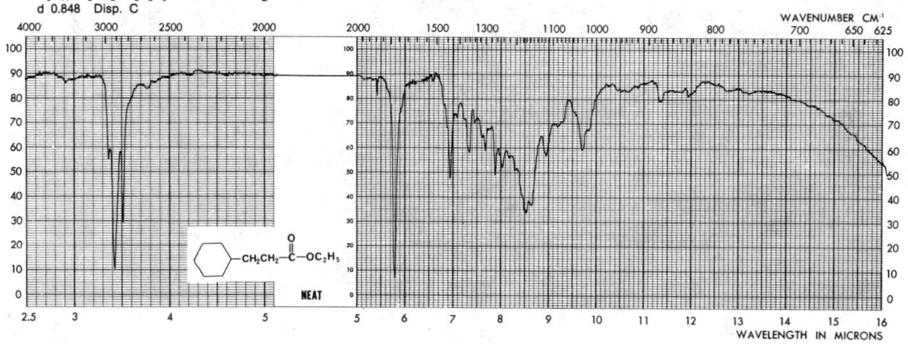

NEAT

G

19,331-3
2-Cyclohexylethyl acetate, 99+% (cyclohexane-ethyl acetate)
$CH_3CO_2CH_2CH_2C_6H_{11}$ FW 170.25
bp 97-98°/15mm. n_D^{20} 1.4461 d 0.949 Disp. C

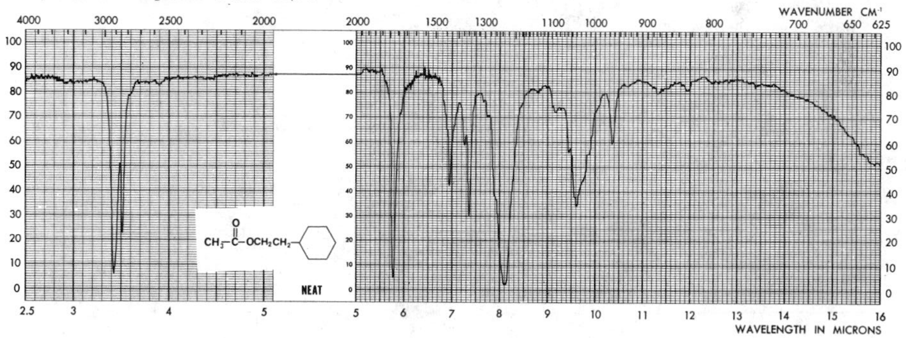

NEAT

H

D15,320-6 **Dimethyl 1,4-cyclohexanedicarboxylate** (mixture of isomers)
$C_6H_{10}(CO_2CH_3)_2$ M.W. 200.23 n_D^{20} 1.4570 . . . .

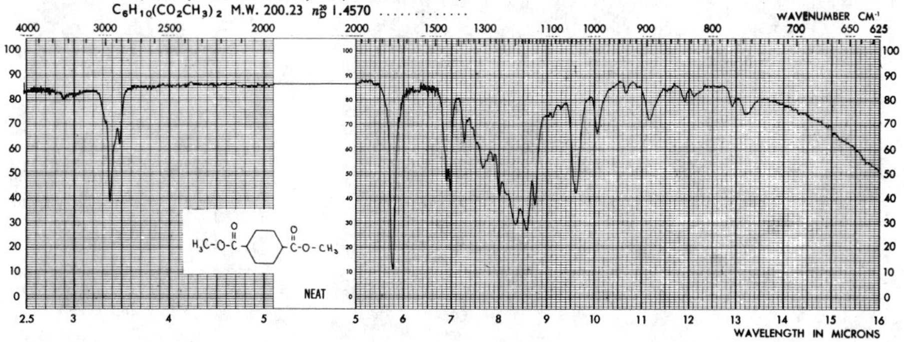

NEAT

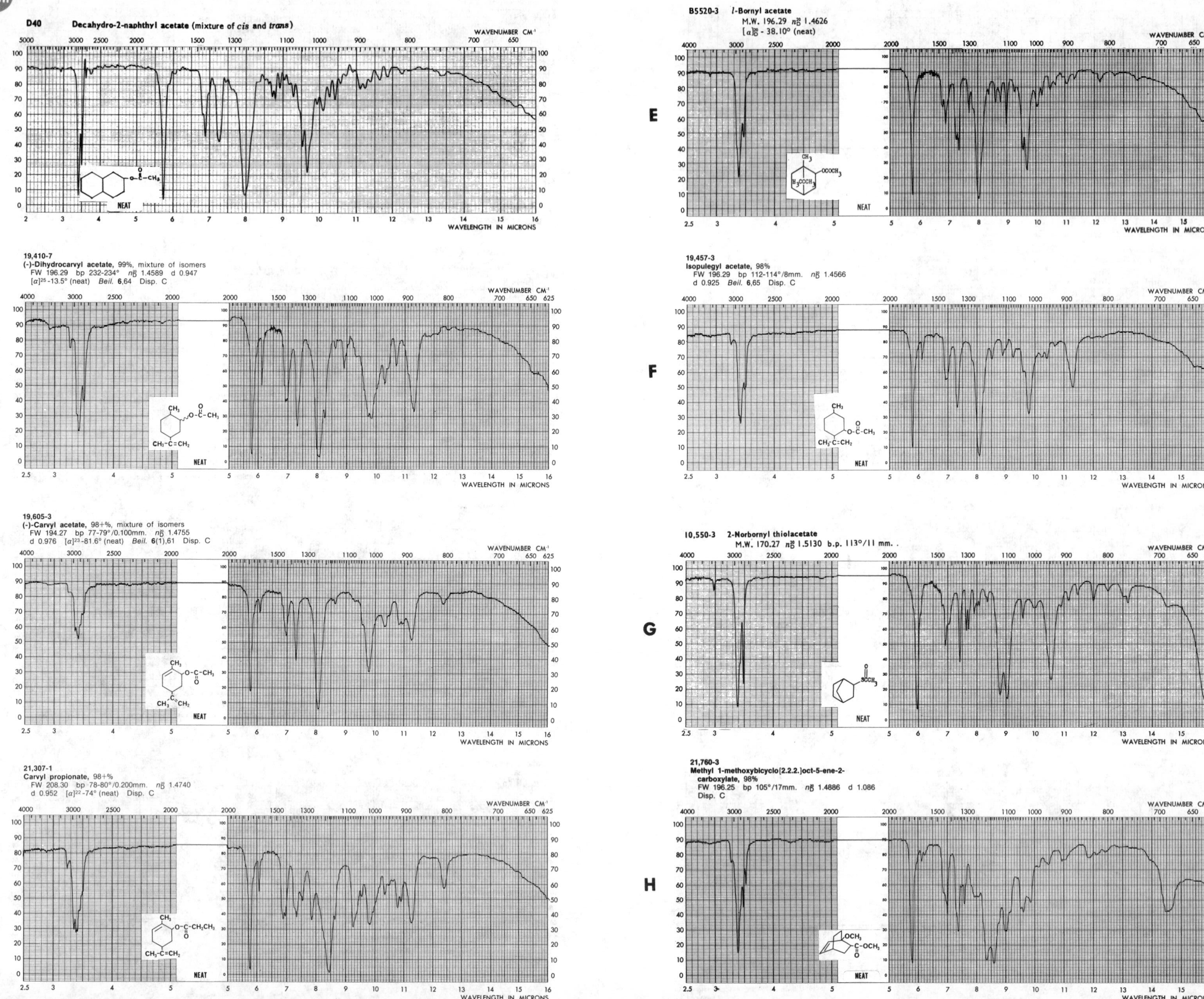
ALDRICH
A
D40 Decahydro-2-naphthyl acetate (mixture of *cis* and *trans*)
B
19,410-7
(-)-Dihydrocarvyl acetate, 99%, mixture of isomers
FW 196.29 bp 232-234° n_D^{20} 1.4589 d 0.947
$[\alpha]^{25}$ -13.5° (neat) *Beil.* 6,64 Disp. C
C
19,605-3
(-)-Carvyl acetate, 98+%, mixture of isomers
FW 194.27 bp 77-79°/0.100mm. n_D^{20} 1.4755
d 0.976 $[\alpha]^{23}$-81.6° (neat) *Beil.* 6(1),61 Disp. C
D
21,307-1
Carvyl propionate, 98+%
FW 208.30 bp 78-80°/0.200mm. n_D^{20} 1.4740
d 0.952 $[\alpha]^{22}$-74° (neat) Disp. C
E
B5520-3 *l*-Bornyl acetate
M.W. 196.29 n_D^{20} 1.4626
$[\alpha]_D^{20}$ - 38.10° (neat)
F
19,457-3
Isopulegyl acetate, 98%
FW 196.29 bp 112-114°/8mm. n_D^{20} 1.4566
d 0.925 *Beil.* 6,65 Disp. C
G
10,550-3 2-Norbornyl thiolacetate
M.W. 170.27 n_D^{20} 1.5130 b.p. 113°/11 mm.
H
21,760-3
Methyl 1-methoxybicyclo[2.2.2.]oct-5-ene-2-carboxylate, 98%
FW 196.25 bp 105°/17mm. n_D^{20} 1.4886 d 1.086
Disp. C
WAVENUMBER CM⁻¹
WAVELENGTH IN MICRONS

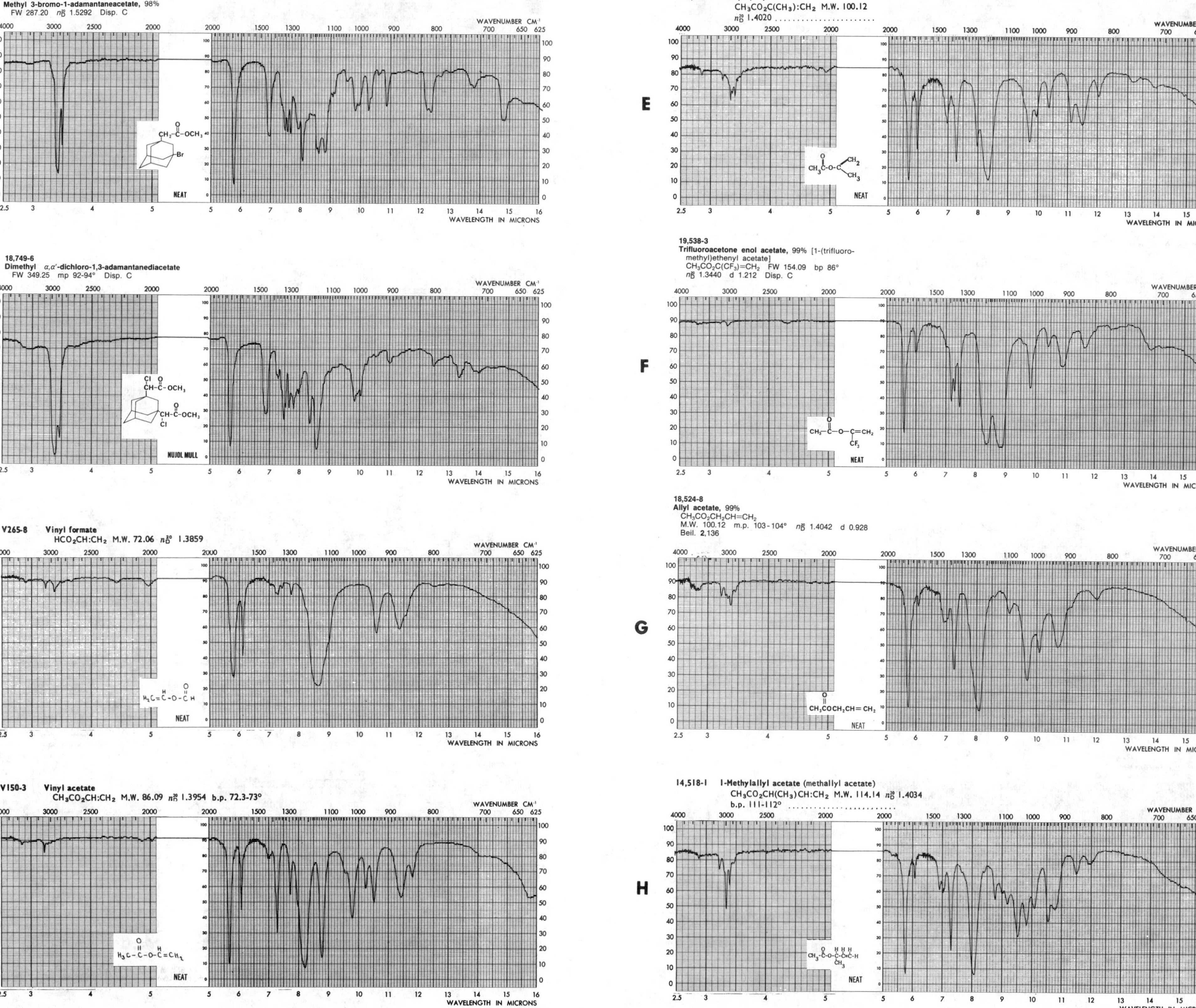

A 18,746-1
Methyl 3-bromo-1-adamantaneacetate, 98%
FW 287.20 n_D^{20} 1.5292 Disp. C
NEAT

B 18,749-6
Dimethyl *α,α'*-**dichloro-1,3-adamantanediacetate**
FW 349.25 mp 92-94° Disp. C
NUJOL MULL

C V265-8 **Vinyl formate**
$HCO_2CH{:}CH_2$ M.W. 72.06 n_D^{20} 1.3859
NEAT

D V150-3 **Vinyl acetate**
$CH_3CO_2CH{:}CH_2$ M.W. 86.09 n_D^{20} 1.3954 b.p. 72.3-73°
NEAT

E 11,778-1 **Isopropenyl acetate**
$CH_3CO_2C(CH_3){:}CH_2$ M.W. 100.12
n_D^{20} 1.4020
NEAT

F 19,538-3
Trifluoroacetone enol acetate, 99% [1-(trifluoromethyl)ethenyl acetate]
$CH_3CO_2C(CF_3){=}CH_2$ FW 154.09 bp 86°
n_D^{20} 1.3440 d 1.212 Disp. C
NEAT

G 18,524-8
Allyl acetate, 99%
$CH_3CO_2CH_2CH{=}CH_2$
M.W. 100.12 m.p. 103-104° n_D^{20} 1.4042 d 0.928
Beil. **2**,136
NEAT

H 14,518-1 **1-Methylallyl acetate** (methallyl acetate)
$CH_3CO_2CH(CH_3)CH{:}CH_2$ M.W. 114.14 n_D^{20} 1.4034
b.p. 111-112°
NEAT

A 11,032-9 **4-Penten-1-yl acetate (5-acetoxy-1-pentene)**
$CH_3CO_2(CH_2)_3CH:CH_2$ M.W. 128.17 n_D^{20} 1.4192

B 22,086-8
1-Acetoxy-1,3-butadiene, 99%
(1,3-butadienyl acetate)
$CH_3CO_2CH=CHCH=CH_2$ FW 112.13
bp 60-61°/40mm. n_D^{20} 1.4690 d 0.945
Beil. **2**(3),295 *Fieser* 1,7 Disp. C

C G80-3 **Geranyl acetate**
$CH_3CO_2CH_2CH:C(CH_3)CH_2CH_2CH:C(CH_3)_2$ M.W. 196.29
n_D^{20} 1.4622 b.p. 242-245° (dec.)

D L280-7 **Linalyl acetate**
$CH_3CO_2C(CH:CH_2)(CH_3)CH_2CH_2CH:C(CH_3)_2$ M.W. 196.29
n_D^{20} 1.4513

E 18,390-3
4-Hydroxy-3-penten-2-one acetate, tech.
$CH_3C(O_2CCH_3)=CHCOCH_3$
M.W. 142.15 b.p. 195° n_D^{20} 1.4525

F 12,440-0 **Vinyl pivalate**
$(CH_3)_3CCO_2CH:CH_2$ M.W. 128.17
n_D^{20} 1.4064

G 13,764-2 **Vinyl tert.-butylacetate**
$(CH_3)_3CCH_2CO_2CH:CH_2$ M.W. 142.20
n_D^{20} 1.4162

H 13,606-9 **Vinyl 2-ethylhexanoate** (stabilized with 35 ppm hydroquinone)
$CH_3(CH_2)_3CH(C_2H_5)CO_2CH:CH_2$ M.W. 170.25
n_D^{20} 1.4267

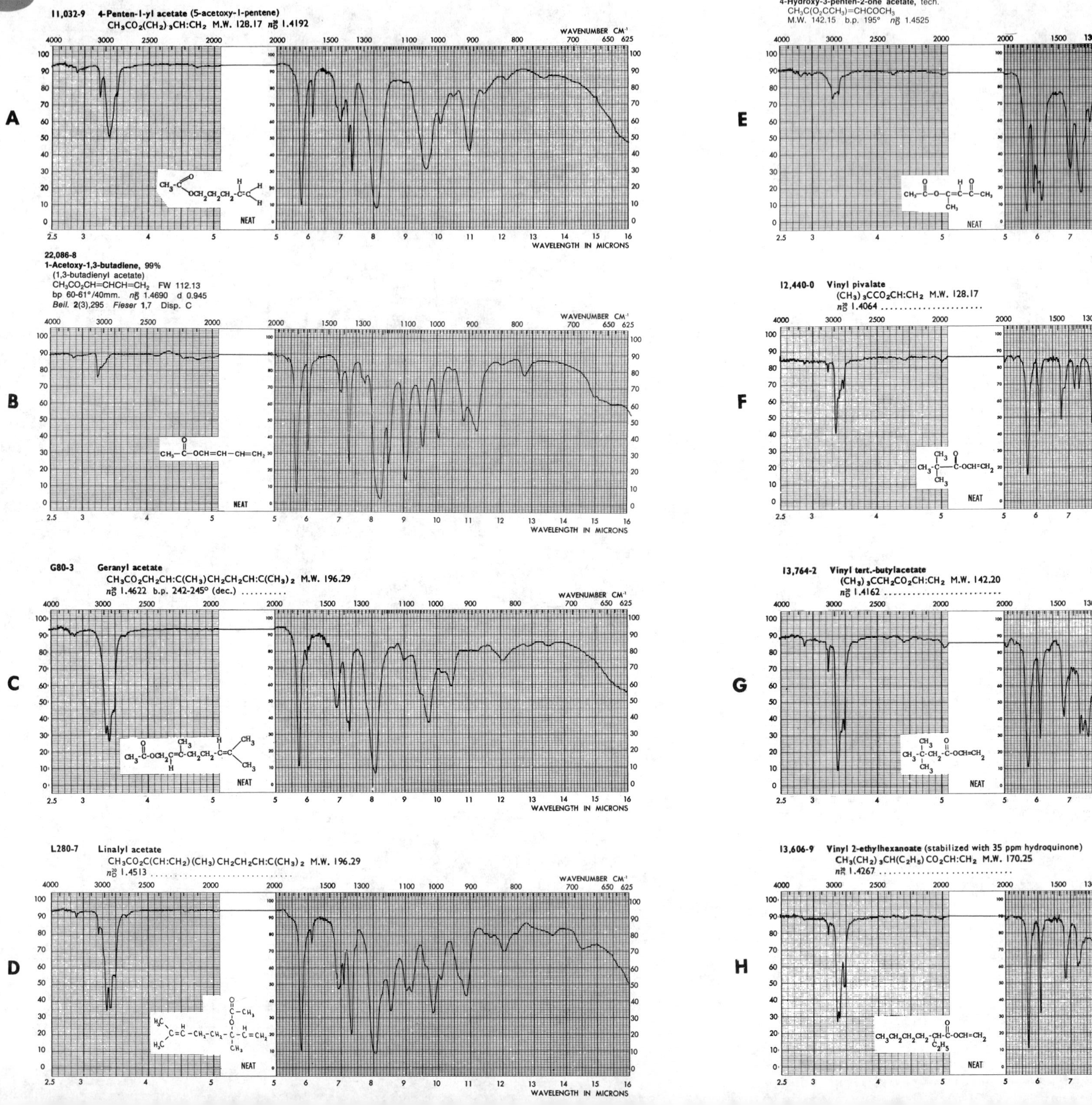

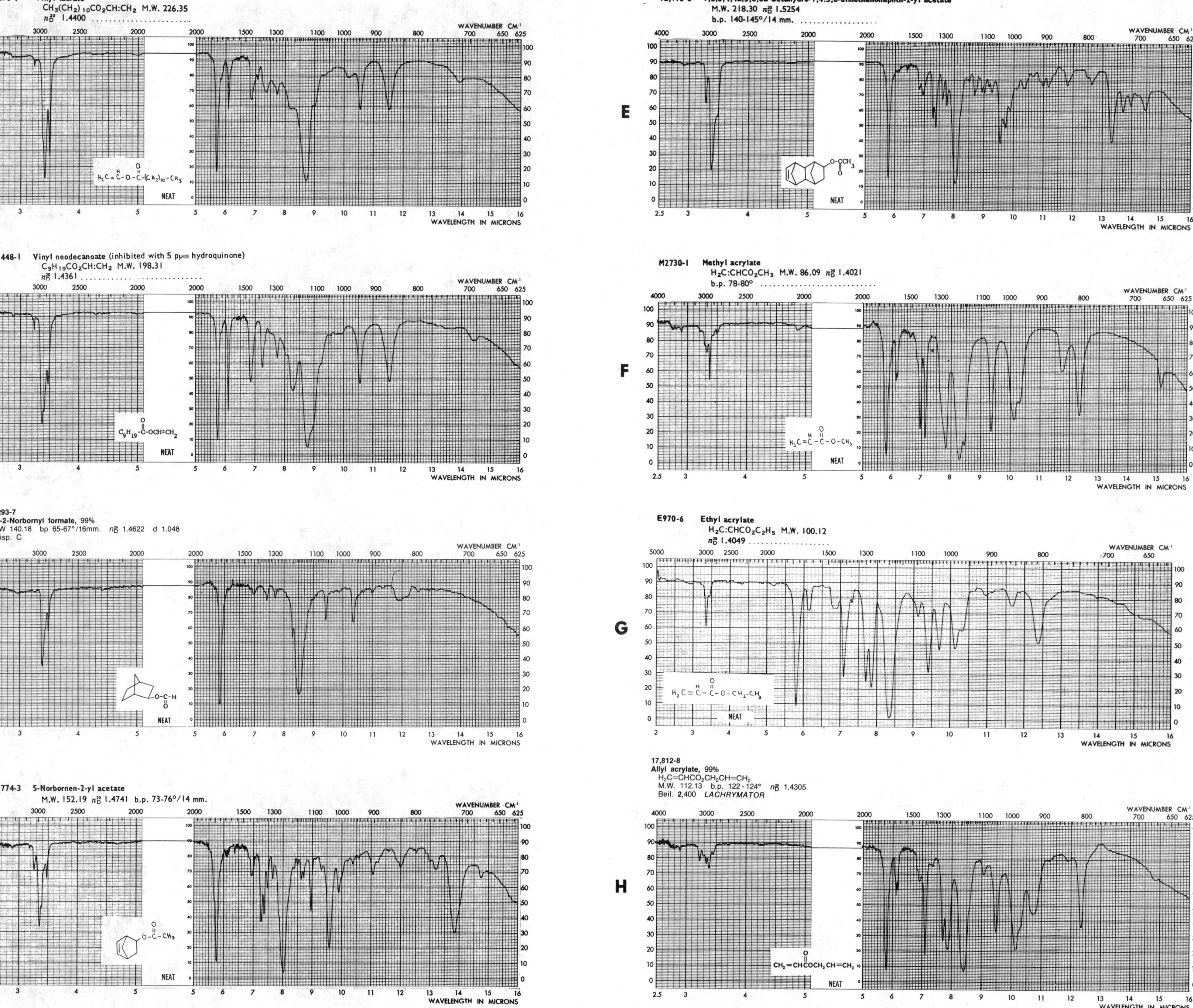
A
V270-4 Vinyl laurate
$CH_3(CH_2)_{10}CO_2CH:CH_2$ M.W. 226.35
n_D^{20} 1.4400
NEAT
B
13,448-1 Vinyl neodecanoate (inhibited with 5 ppm hydroquinone)
$C_9H_{19}CO_2CH:CH_2$ M.W. 198.31
n_D^{20} 1.4361
NEAT
C
19,293-7
exo-2-Norbornyl formate, 99%
FW 140.18 bp 65-67°/16mm. n_D^{20} 1.4622 d 1.048
Disp. C
NEAT
D
10,774-3 5-Norbornen-2-yl acetate
M.W. 152.19 n_D^{20} 1.4741 b.p. 73-76°/14 mm.
NEAT
E
12,173-8 1,2,3,4,4a,5,8,8a-Octahydro-1,4:5,8-dimethanonaphth-2-yl acetate
M.W. 218.30 n_D^{20} 1.5254
b.p. 140-145°/14 mm.
NEAT
F
M2730-1 Methyl acrylate
$H_2C:CHCO_2CH_3$ M.W. 86.09 n_D^{20} 1.4021
b.p. 78-80°
NEAT
G
E970-6 Ethyl acrylate
$H_2C:CHCO_2C_2H_5$ M.W. 100.12
n_D^{20} 1.4049
NEAT
H
17,812-8
Allyl acrylate, 99%
$H_2C{=}CHCO_2CH_2CH{=}CH_2$
M.W. 112.13 b.p. 122-124° n_D^{20} 1.4305
Beil. 2,400 LACHRYMATOR
NEAT
WAVENUMBER CM⁻¹
WAVELENGTH IN MICRONS
ALDRICH

A

M5590-9 **Methyl methacrylate**
$H_2C:C(CH_3)CO_2CH_3$ M.W. 100.12 n_D^{20} 1.4140
b.p. 100°

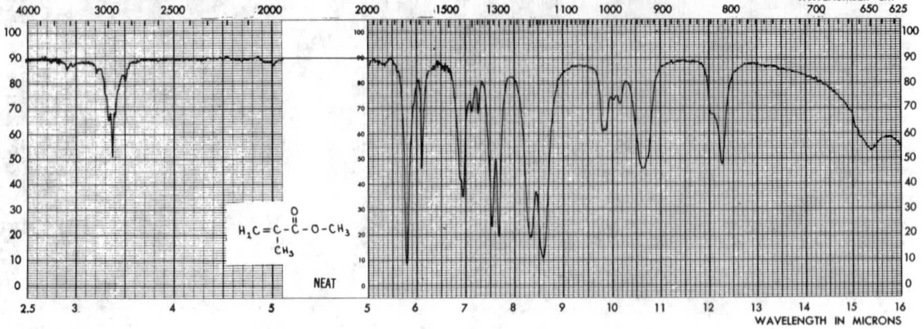

NEAT

B

13,945-9 **Methyl crotonate**
$CH_3CH:CHCO_2CH_3$ M.W. 100.12 n_D^{20} 1.4233
b.p. 118-120°

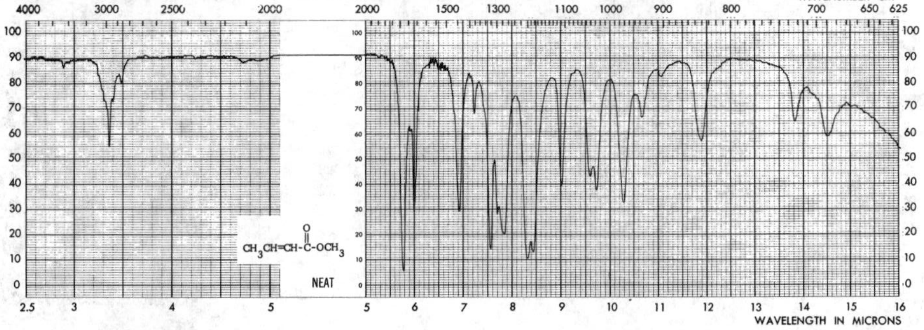

NEAT

C

14,099-6
Ethyl crotonate, 96%
$CH_3CH{=}CHCO_2C_2H_5$ FW 114.14 bp 142-143°
n_D^{20} 1.4248 d 0.918 *Beil.* **2**,411 *NMR* **3**,38A
Disp. C

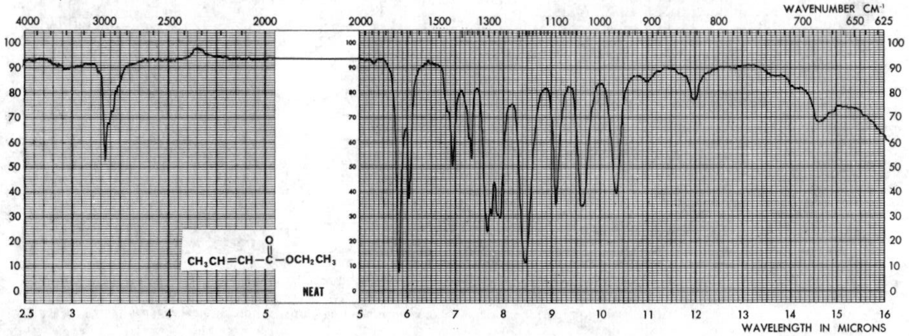

NEAT

D

19,432-8
Ethyl 3,3-dimethylacrylate, 98% (ethyl 3-methylcrotonate)
$(CH_3)_2C{=}CHCO_2C_2H_5$ FW 128.17 bp 154-155°
n_D^{20} 1.4365 d 0.922 *Beil.* **2**,433 Disp. C

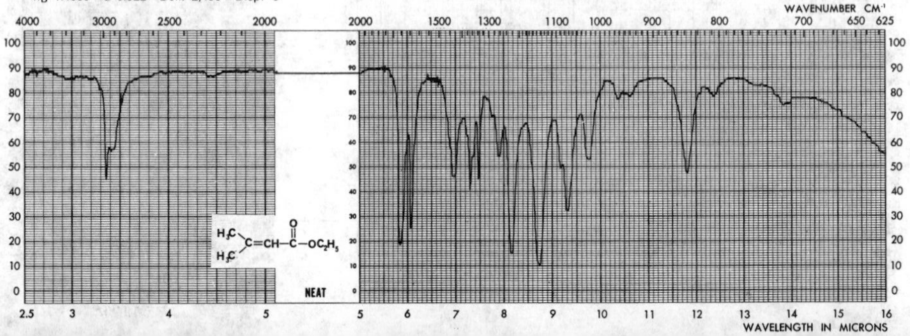

NEAT

E

E2650 **Ethylene dimethacrylate**
$H_2C:C(CH_3)CO_2(CH_2)_2O_2CC(CH_3):CH_2$ M.W. 198.22
n_D^{20} 1.4549

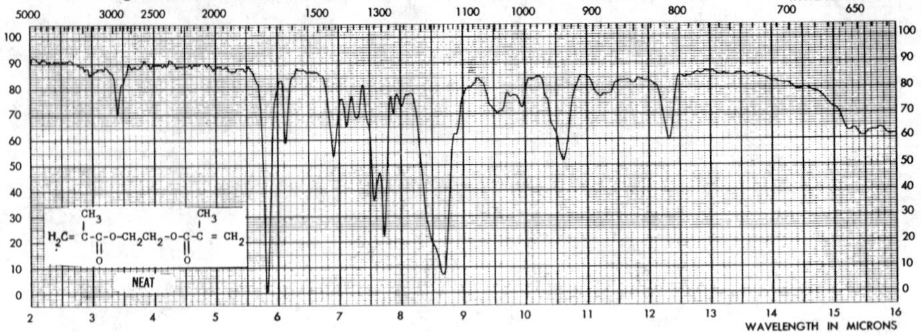

NEAT

F

11,512-6 **Methyl 10-undecenoate** (methyl undecylenate)
$H_2C:CH(CH_2)_8CO_2CH_3$ M.W. 198.31 n_D^{20} 1.4400
b.p. 248°

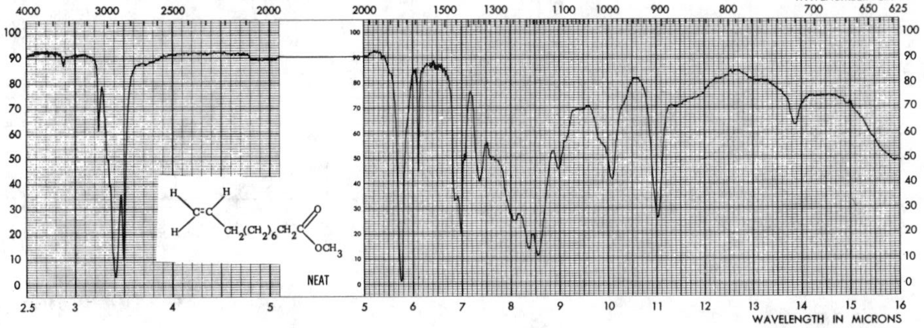

NEAT

G

M6575-0 **Methyl oleate, tech.**
$CH_3(CH_2)_7CH:CH(CH_2)_7CO_2CH_3$ M.W. 296.50
n_D^{20} 1.4520

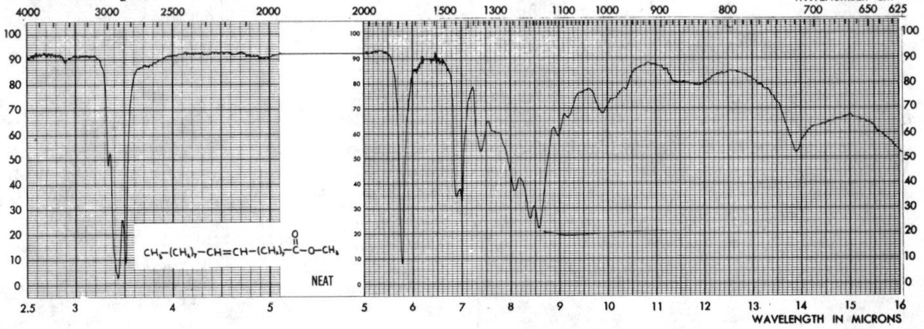

NEAT

H

10,335-7 **Methyl linoleate, tech.**
$CH_3(CH_2)_4CH:CHCH_2CH:CH(CH_2)_7CO_2CH_3$ M.W. 294.48
n_D^{20} 1.4619 b.p. 192°/4 mm.

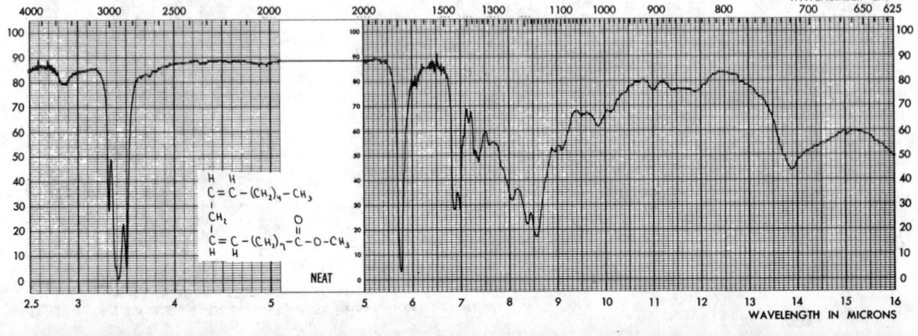

NEAT

A

Ethyl sorbate, 99%
$CH_3CH{=}CHCH{=}CHCO_2C_2H_5$
M.W. 140.18 b.p. 195.5° n_D^{20} 1.4942 d 0.956
Beil. 2,484

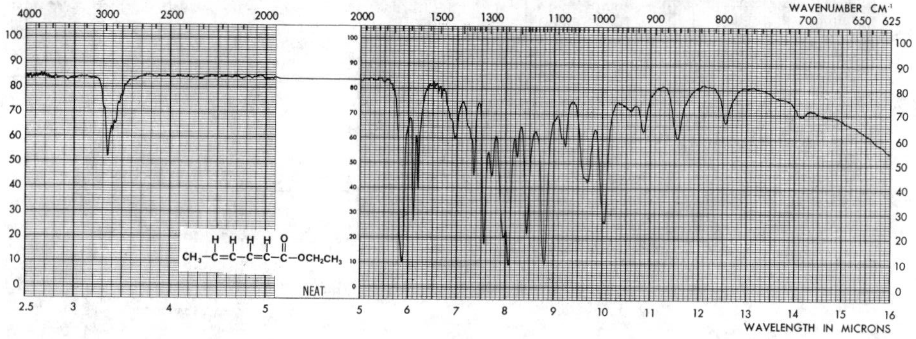

NEAT

B

85,776-9
Linoleic acid ethyl ester, 98% (ethyl linoleate)
$CH_3(CH_2)_4CH{=}CHCH_2CH{=}CH(CH_2)_7CO_2C_2H_5$
M.W. 308.51 n_D^{20} 1.4600

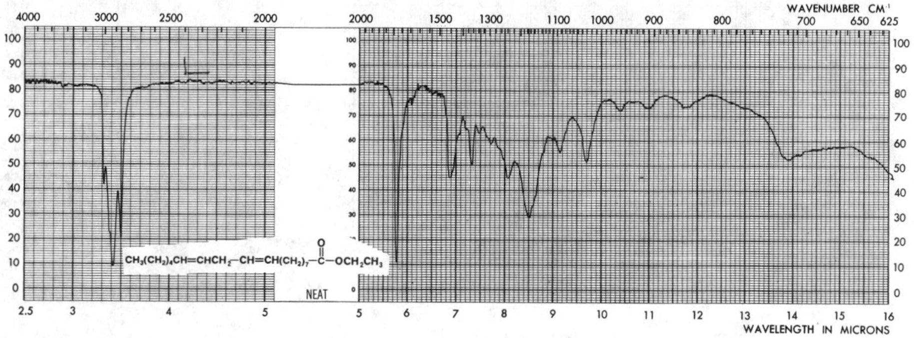

NEAT

C

10,267-9 Ethyl linoleate, tech.
$CH_3(CH_2)_4CH{:}CHCH_2CH{:}CH(CH_2)_7CO_2C_2H_5$ M.W. 308.51
n_D^{20} 1.4590 b.p. 193°/6 mm.

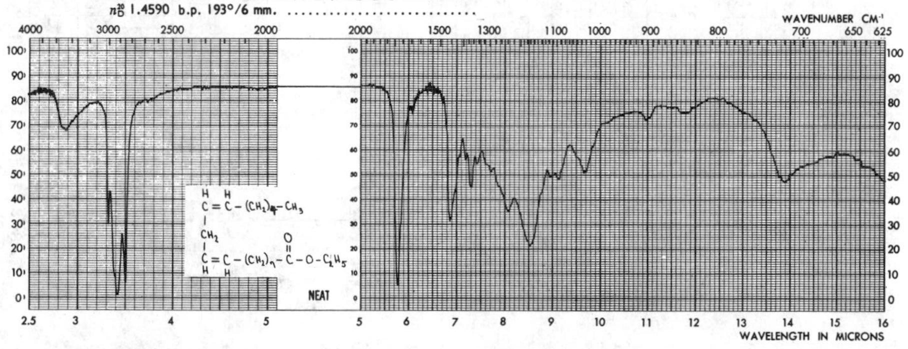

NEAT

D

V260-7 Vinylene carbonate, puriss.
M.W. 86.05 n_D^{20} 1.4212 (supercooled)
m.p. 22°

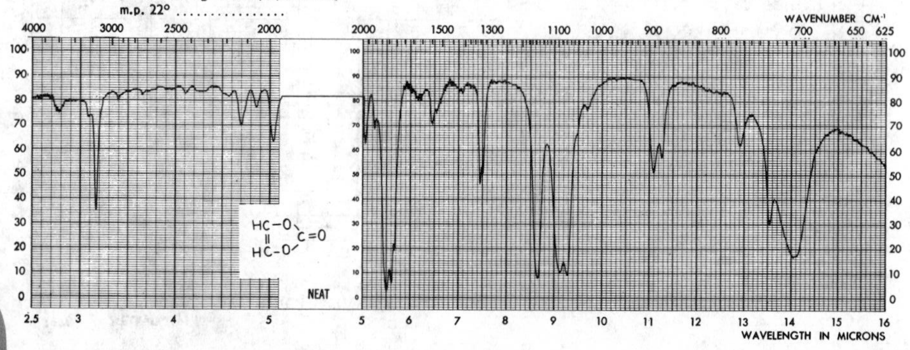

NEAT

E

D9770-3 Diethyl maleate
$C_2H_5O_2CCH{:}CHCO_2C_2H_5$ M.W. 172.18
n_D^{20} 1.4390

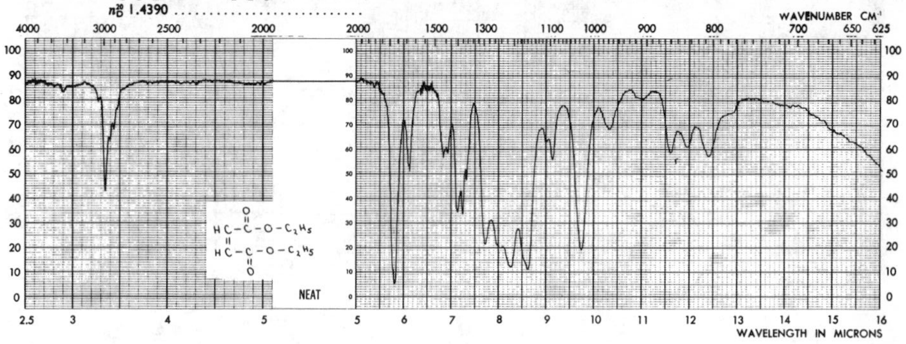

NEAT

F

D4710 Di-n-butyl maleate
$C_4H_9O_2CCH{:}CHCO_2C_4H_9$ M.W. 228.29
n_D^{20} 1.4439

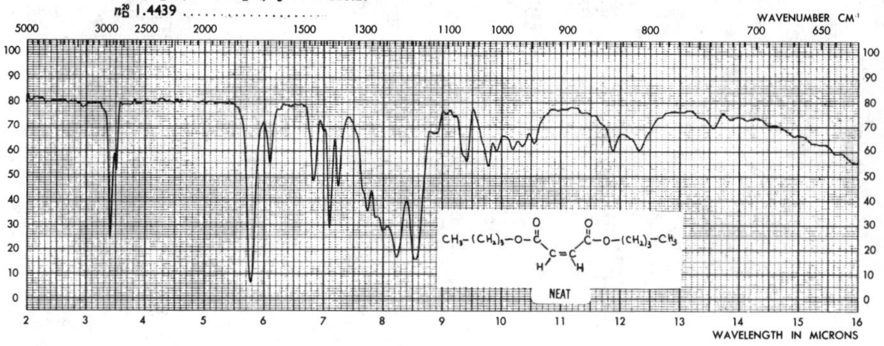

NEAT

G

D9565-4 Diethyl fumarate, puriss.
$C_2H_5O_2CCH{:}CHCO_2C_2H_5$ M.W. 172.18 n_D^{20} 1.4406 m.p. 1-2°

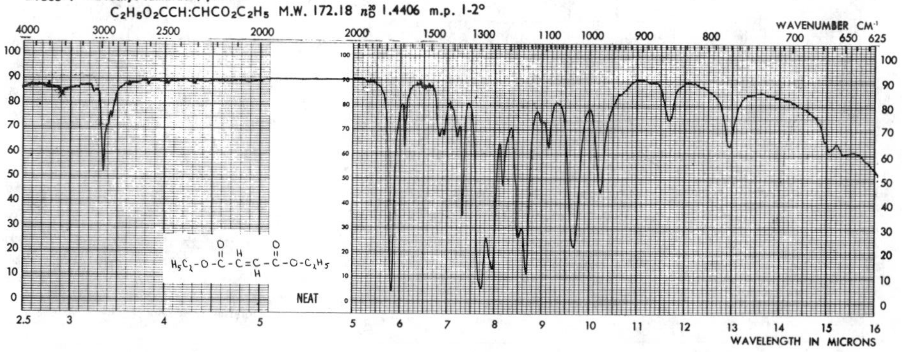

NEAT

H

D4695 Dibutyl fumarate
$C_4H_9O_2CCH{:}CHCO_2C_4H_9$ M.W. 228.29 n_D^{20} 1.4459

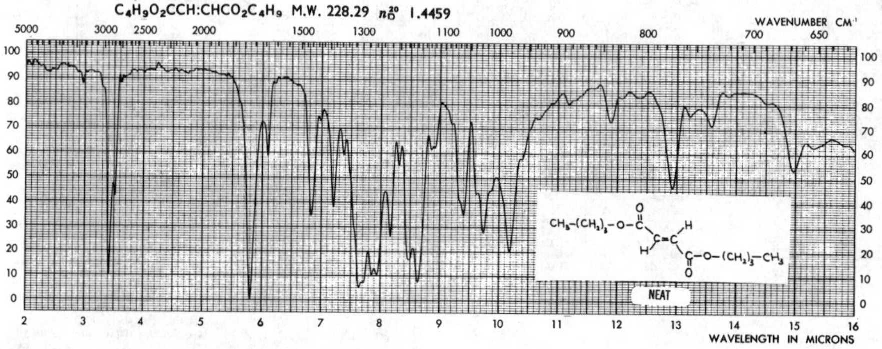

NEAT

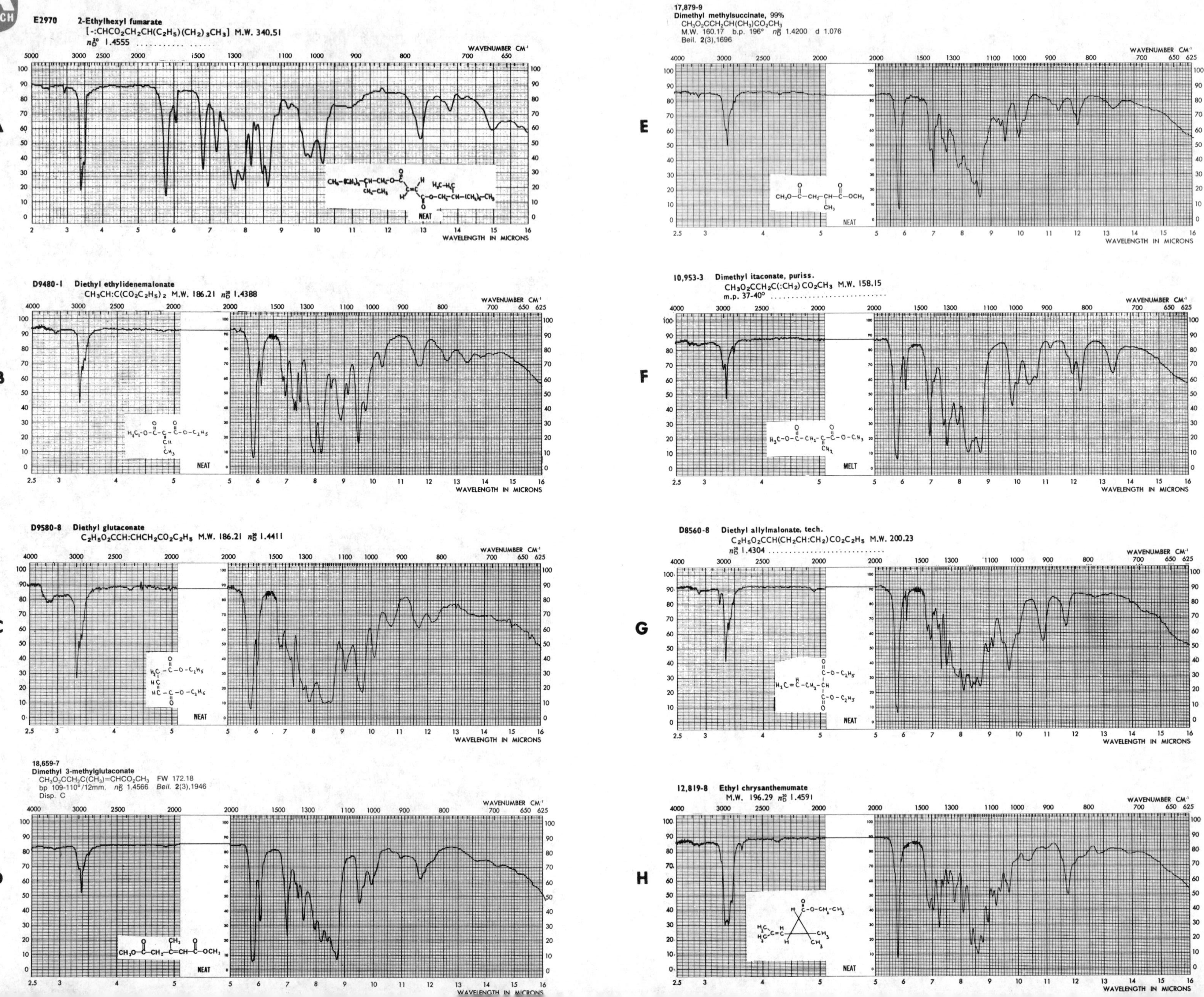
ALDRICH
A
E2970 2-Ethylhexyl fumarate
[-:CHCO$_2$CH$_2$CH(C$_2$H$_5$)(CH$_2$)$_3$CH$_3$] M.W. 340.51
n_D^{20} 1.4555
NEAT
B
D9480-1 Diethyl ethylidenemalonate
CH$_3$CH:C(CO$_2$C$_2$H$_5$)$_2$ M.W. 186.21 n_D^{20} 1.4388
NEAT
C
D9580-8 Diethyl glutaconate
C$_2$H$_5$O$_2$CCH:CHCH$_2$CO$_2$C$_2$H$_5$ M.W. 186.21 n_D^{20} 1.4411
NEAT
D
18,659-7
Dimethyl 3-methylglutaconate
CH$_3$O$_2$CCH$_2$C(CH$_3$)=CHCO$_2$CH$_3$ FW 172.18
bp 109-110°/12mm. n_D^{20} 1.4566 Beil. 2(3),1946
Disp. C
NEAT
E
17,879-9
Dimethyl methylsuccinate, 99%
CH$_3$O$_2$CCH$_2$CH(CH$_3$)CO$_2$CH$_3$
M.W. 160.17 b.p. 196° n_D^{20} 1.4200 d 1.076
Beil. 2(3),1696
NEAT
F
10,953-3 Dimethyl itaconate, puriss.
CH$_3$O$_2$CCH$_2$C(:CH$_2$)CO$_2$CH$_3$ M.W. 158.15
m.p. 37-40°
MELT
G
D8560-8 Diethyl allylmalonate, tech.
C$_2$H$_5$O$_2$CCH(CH$_2$CH:CH$_2$)CO$_2$C$_2$H$_5$ M.W. 200.23
n_D^{20} 1.4304
NEAT
H
12,819-8 Ethyl chrysanthemumate
M.W. 196.29 n_D^{20} 1.4591
NEAT
WAVENUMBER CM⁻¹
WAVELENGTH IN MICRONS

A 10,531-7 Methyl 3-cyclohexenecarboxylate
$C_6H_9CO_2CH_3$ M.W. 140.18 n_D^{20} 1.4610 b.p. 70°/10 mm.
NEAT

B M6477-0 Methyl 5-norbornene-2-carboxylate
M.W. 152.19 n_D^{20} 1.4739 b.p. 63-64°/5 mm.
NEAT

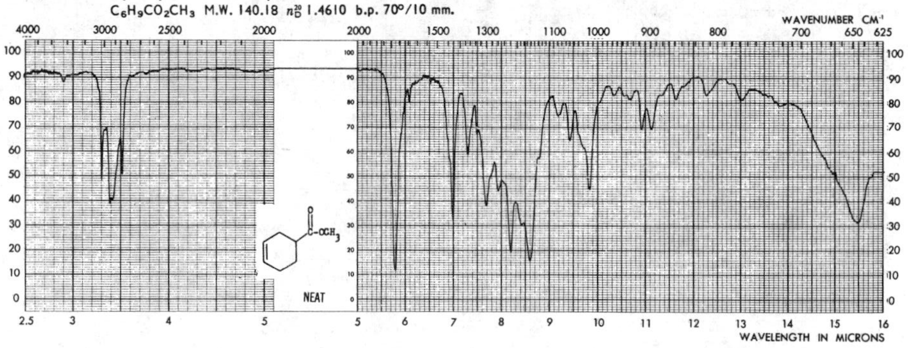

C 15,219-6 Ethyl 5-norbornene-2-carboxylate (mixture of endo and exo)
M.W. 166.22 n_D^{20} 1.4675 b.p. 86°/10 mm.
NEAT

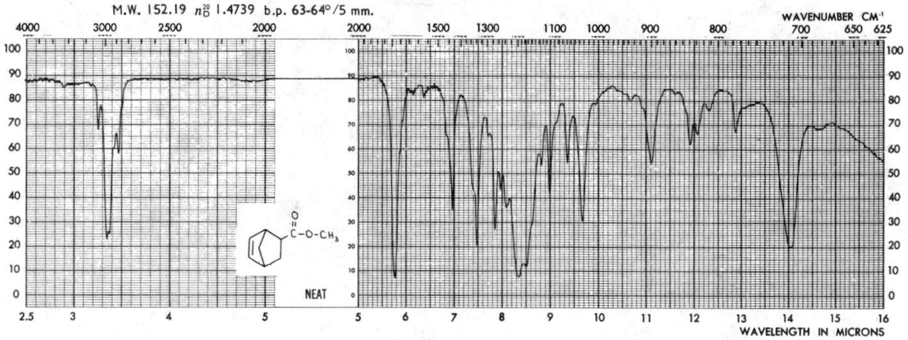

D 15,679-5
Methallylidene diacetate
$(CH_3CO_2)_2CHC(CH_3)=CH_2$
M.W. 172.18 m.p. -15 to 0° b.p. 191° n_D^{20} 1.4245
d 1.051
NEAT

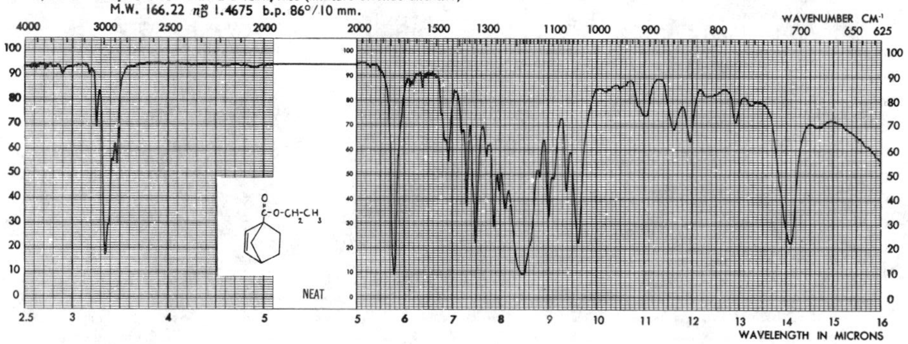

E T7770 1,1,1-Trimethylolpropane trimethacrylate
NEAT

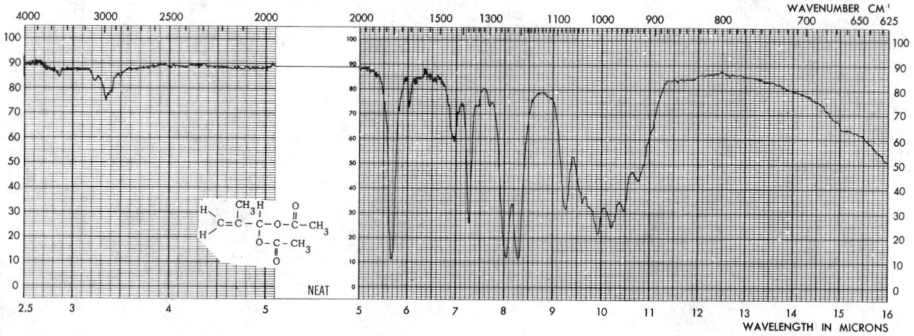

F C4140-1 2-Chloroethyl formate
$HCO_2(CH_2)_2Cl$ M.W. 108.52 n_D^{20} 1.4263 b.p. 128-132°
NEAT

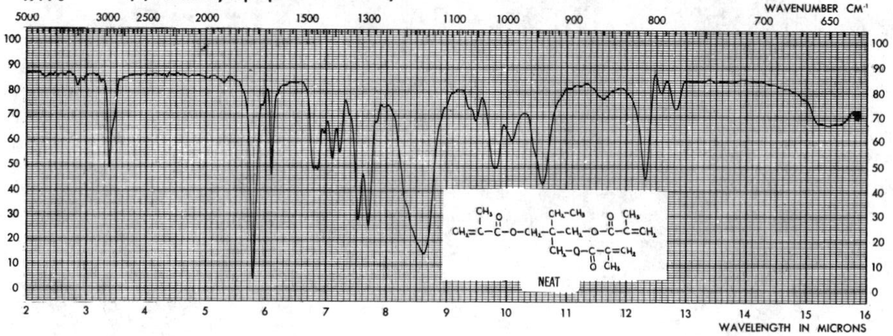

G C4015-4 2-Chloroethyl acetate
$CH_3CO_2CH_2CH_2Cl$ M.W. 122.55 n_D^{20} 1.4215
NEAT

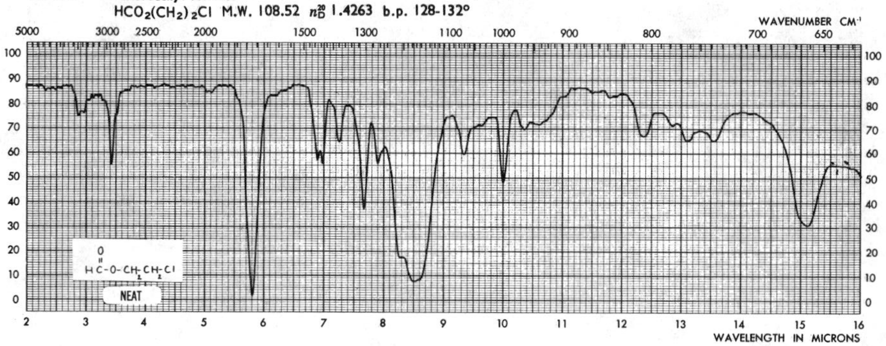

H 13,768-5 2-Bromoethyl acetate
$CH_3CO_2CH_2CH_2Br$ M.W. 167.02 n_D^{20} 1.4547
b.p. 159°
NEAT

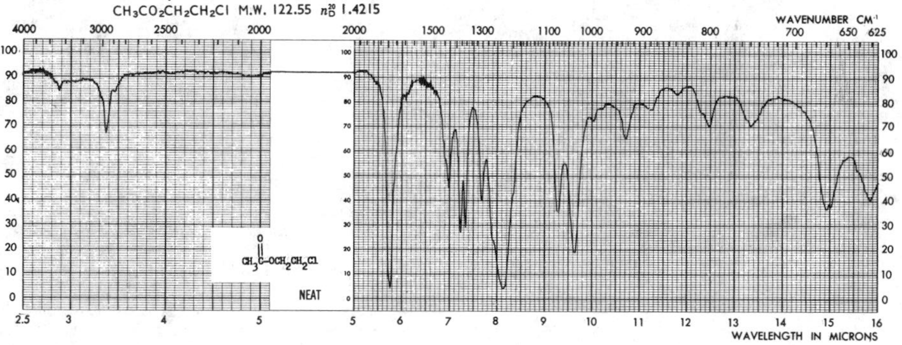

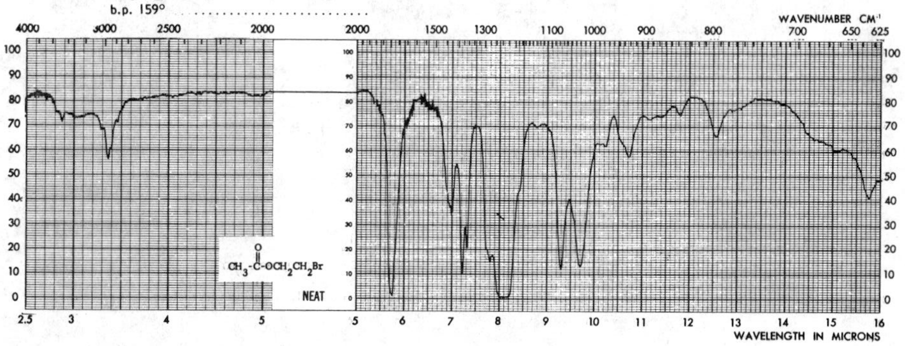

A C2920-7 **4-Chlorobutyl acetate**
$CH_3CO_2(CH_2)_4Cl$ M.W. 150.61 n_D^{20} 1.4347
NEAT

B 14,118-6 **Chloromethyl pivalate** (pivaloyloxymethyl chloride, POM)
$(CH_3)_3CCO_2CH_2Cl$ M.W. 150.61
n_D^{20} 1.4170
NEAT

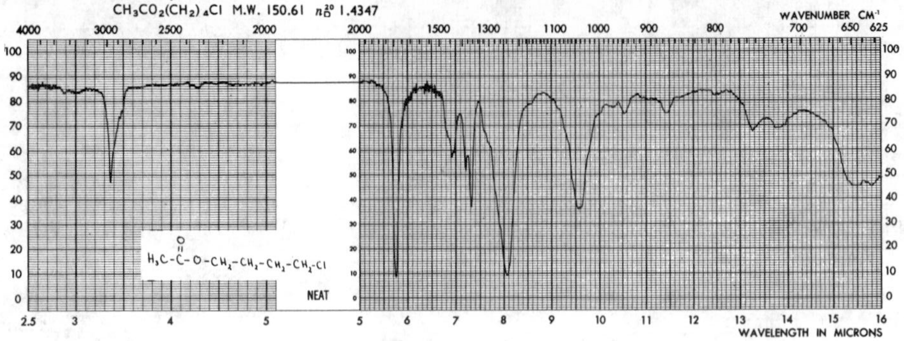

C M3210-0 **Methyl 4-bromocrotonate**
$BrCH_2CH{:}CHCO_2CH_3$ M.W. 179.02 n_D^{20} 1.4980
b.p. 83-85°/13 mm.
NEAT

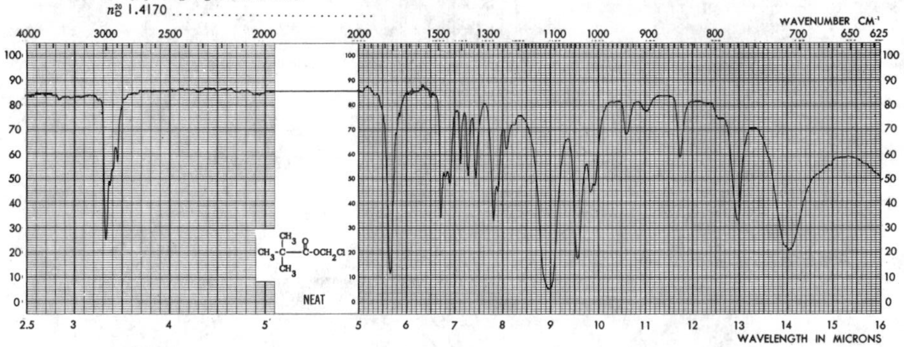

D E1383-0 **Ethyl 4-bromocrotonate**
$BrCH_2CH{:}CHCO_2C_2H_5$ M.W. 193.05 n_D^{20} 1.4899
b.p. 66-67°/0.3 mm.
NEAT

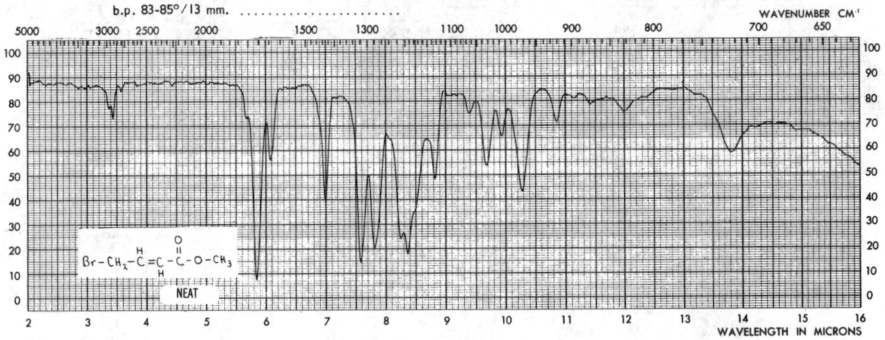

E C5270-5 **Chloromethylethylene carbonate** (4-chloromethyl-1,3-dioxolan-2-one)
M.W. 136.53 n_D^{25} 1.4662
NEAT

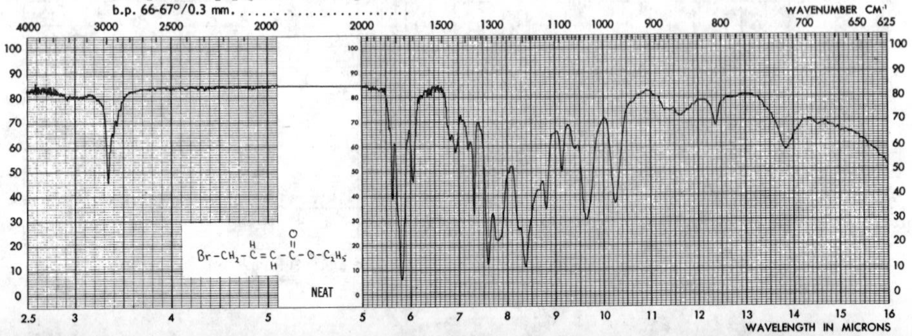

F 18,391-1
Methyl 2-chloroacetoacetate, 95%
$CH_3COCH(Cl)CO_2CH_3$
M.W. 150.56 m.p. -32.7° b.p. 0-131° n_D^{20} 1.4465
d 1.236
NEAT

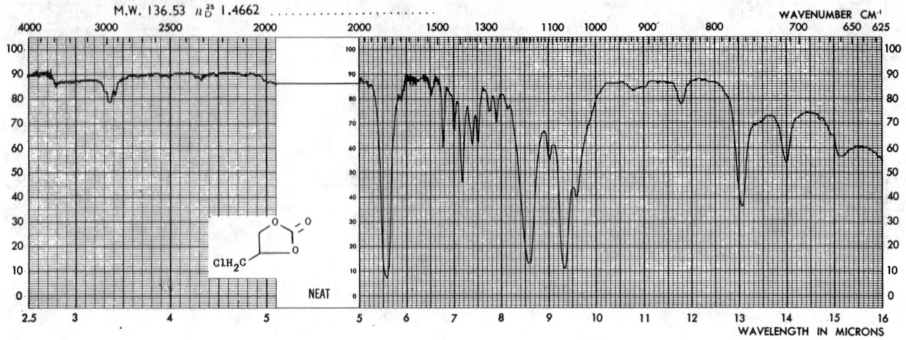

G D9160-8 **Diethyl chloromalonate**
$C_2H_5O_2CCH(Cl)CO_2C_2H_5$ M.W. 194.61 n_D^{20} 1.4310
NEAT

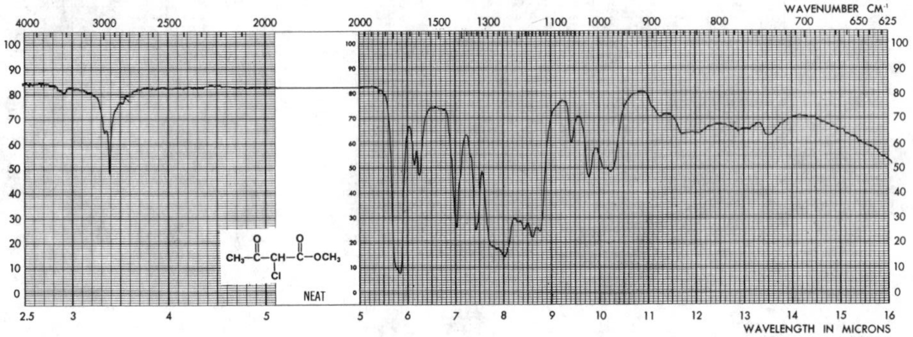

H D9120-9 **Diethyl bromomalonate**
$C_2H_5O_2CCH(Br)CO_2C_2H_5$ M.W. 239.07
n_D^{20} 1.4522
NEAT

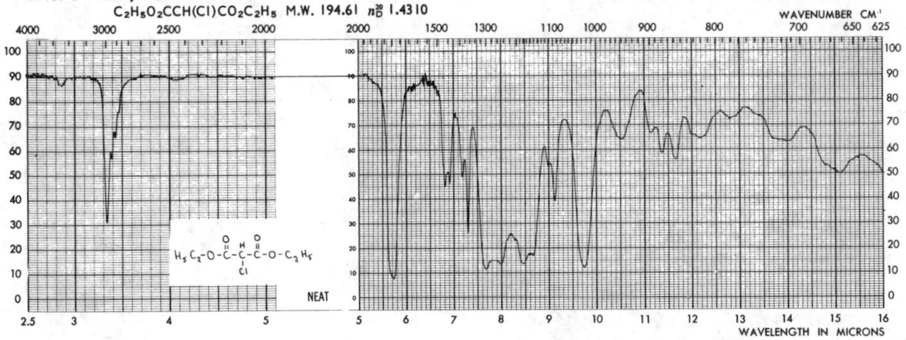

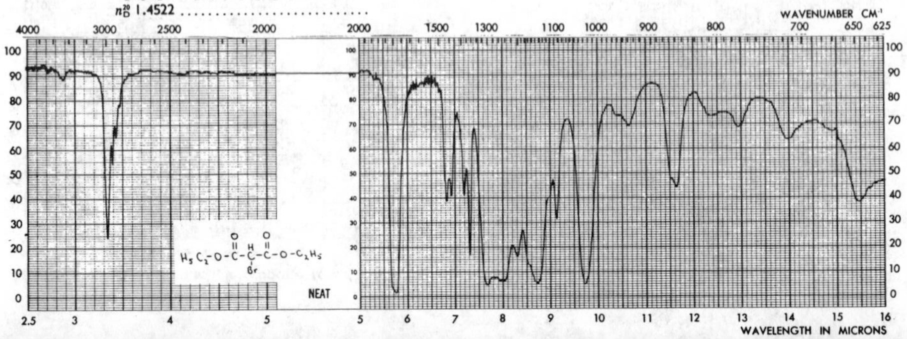

A 13,944-0 **Diethyl 2-bromo-2-methylmalonate**
$C_2H_5O_2CC(Br)(CH_3)CO_2C_2H_5$ M.W. 253.10
n_D^{20} 1.4490
NEAT

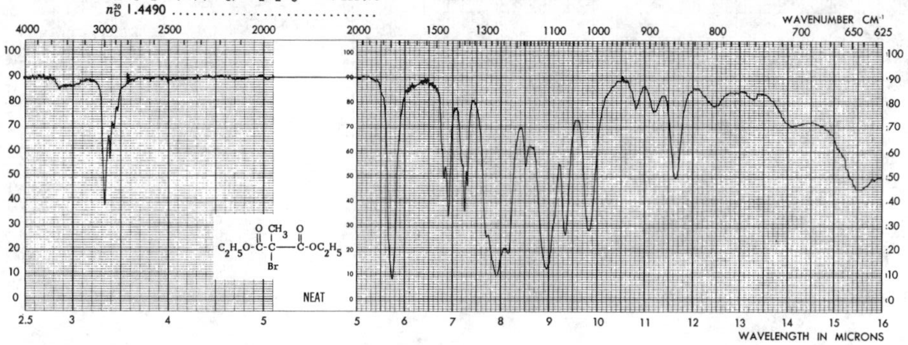

B 13,244-6 **Diethyl 3-chloropropylmalonate**
$Cl(CH_2)_3CH(CO_2C_2H_5)_2$ M.W. 236.70
n_D^{20} 1.4432
NEAT

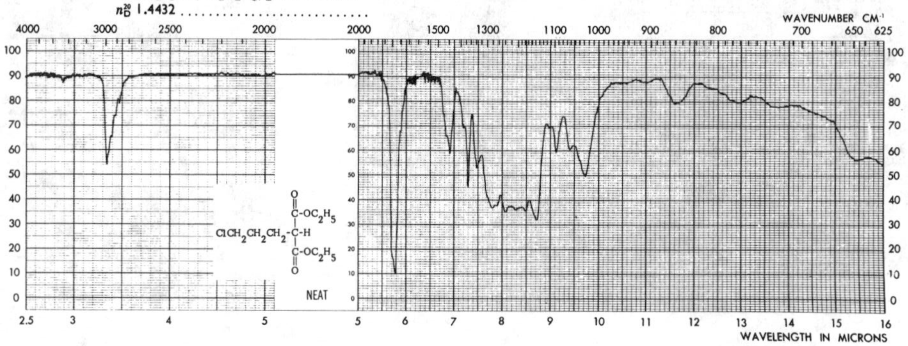

C 15,216-1 **Diethyl ethyl(1-methyl-3-oxobutyl)malonate**
$CH_3COCH_2CH(CH_3)C(C_2H_5)(CO_2C_2H_5)_2$
M.W. 272.34 n_D^{20} 1.4428 b.p. 102-103°/0.5 mm.
NEAT

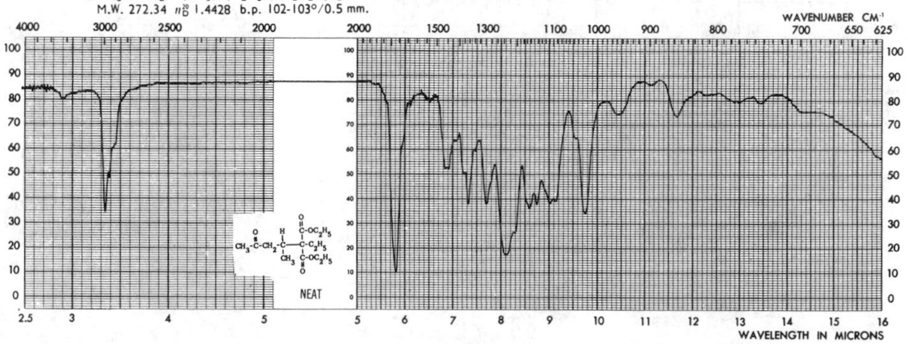

D 17,514-5
Ethyl heptafluorobutyrate, 97%
$CF_3CF_2CF_2CO_2C_2H_5$
M.W. 242.09 n_D^{20} 1.3020
NEAT

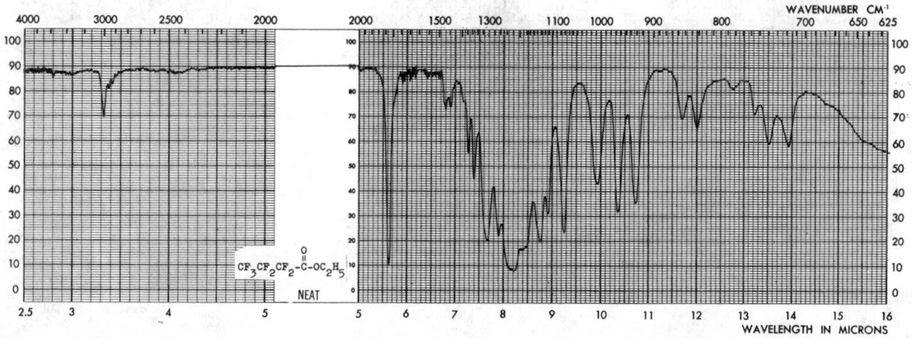

E E4380 **Ethyl perfluoroglutarate (diethyl hexafluoroglutarate)**
$C_2H_5O_2C(CF_2)_3CO_2C_2H_5$ M.W. 296.16
n_D^{20} 1.3599
NEAT

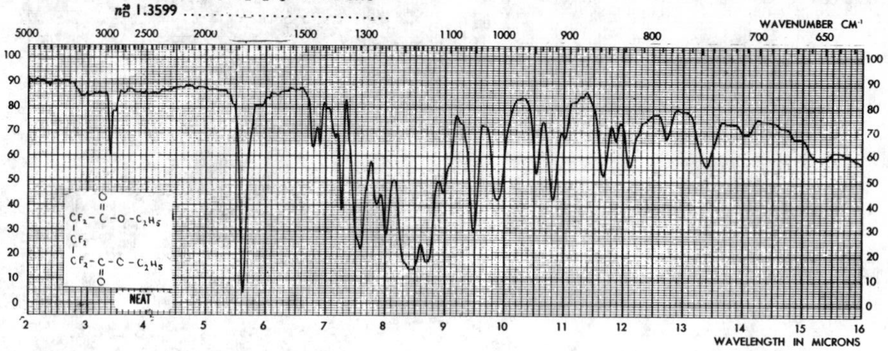

F 16,381-3
Ethyl fluoroacetate
$FCH_2CO_2C_2H_5$
M.W. 106.1 b.p. 119.3°/753mm. n_D^{20} 1.3755
d 1.098 Beil. 2,193
NEAT

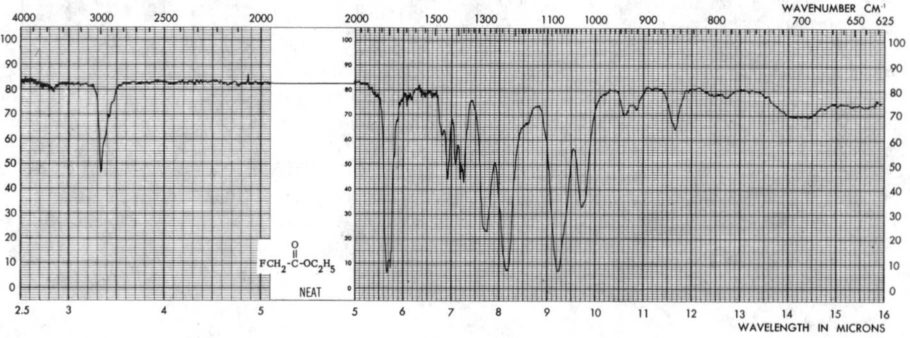

G 10,841-3 **Methyl chloroacetate, 99+%**
$ClCH_2CO_2CH_3$ M.W. 108.52 n_D^{20} 1.4220
b.p. 130° /740 mm.
NEAT

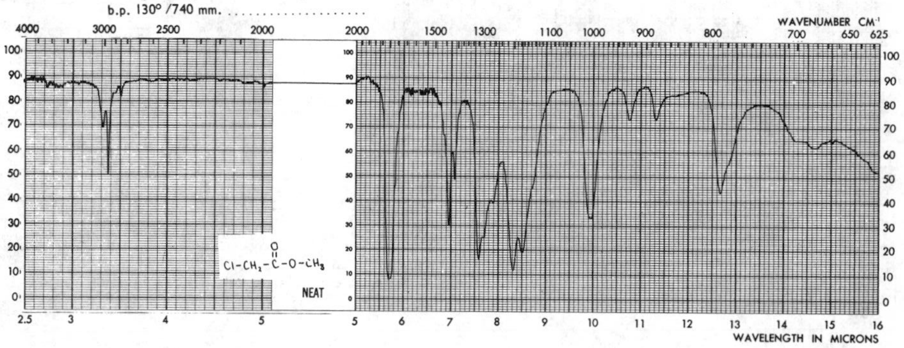

H E1685-6 **Ethyl chloroacetate**
$ClCH_2CO_2C_2H_5$ M.W. 122.55 n_D^{20} 1.4205
NEAT

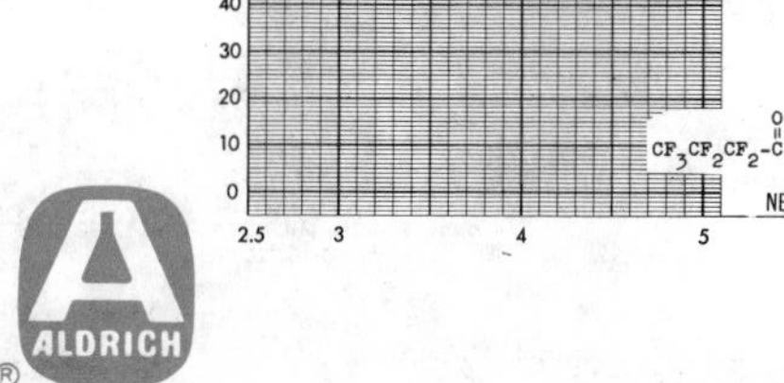

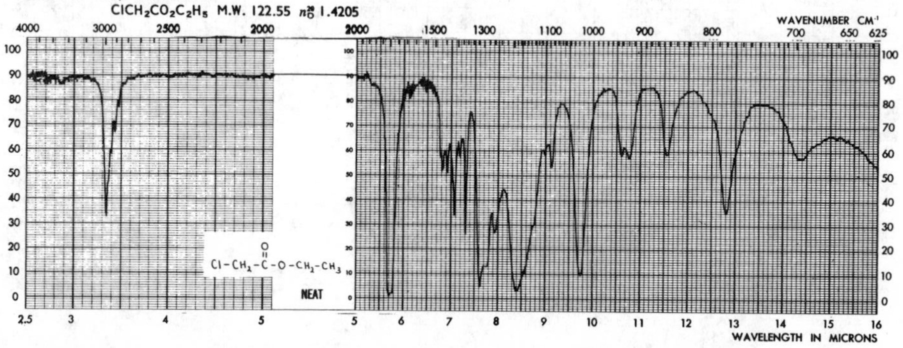

A

15,791-0
Methyl bromoacetate
$BrCH_2CO_2CH_3$
M.W. 152.98 b.p. 51-52°/15mm. n_D^{20} 1.4586
Beil. 2,213 *LACHRYMATOR*

$BrCH_2-C(=O)-OCH_3$ NEAT

B

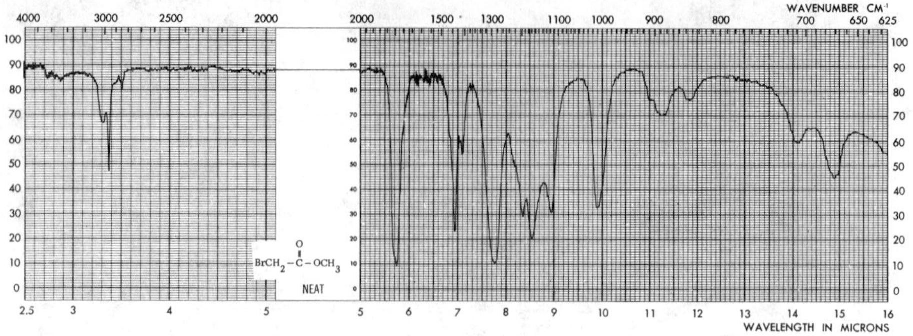

13,397-3 **Ethyl bromoacetate**
$BrCH_2CO_2C_2H_5$
M.W. 167.02

$Br-CH_2-C(=O)-O-C_2H_5$ NEAT

C

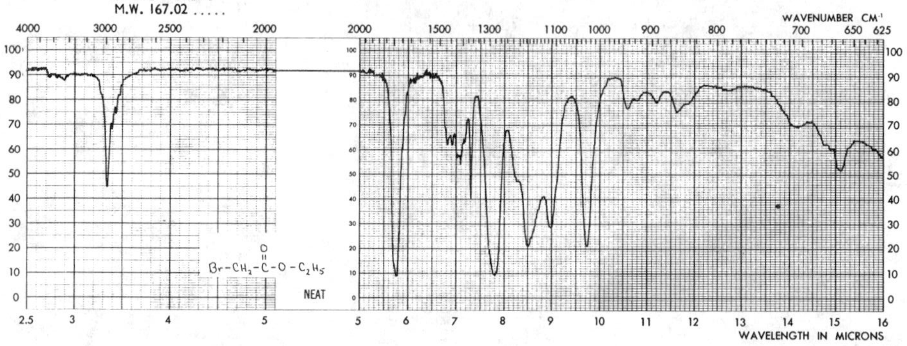

10,864-2 **n-Propyl chloroacetate**
$ClCH_2CO_2CH_2CH_2CH_3$ M.W. 136.58 n_D^{20} 1.4250

$Cl-CH_2-C(=O)-O-CH_2-CH_2-CH_3$ NEAT

D

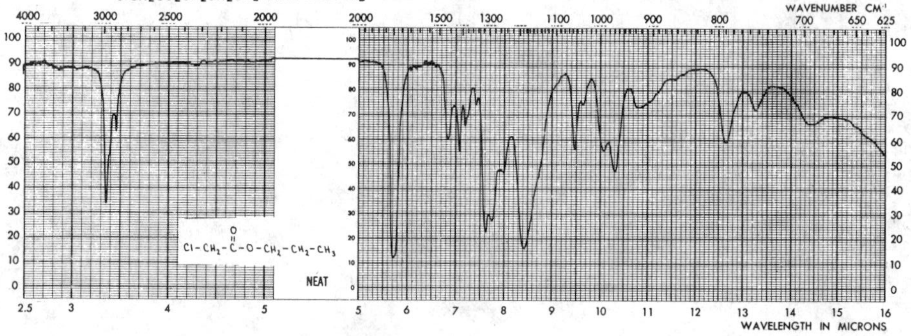

10,867-7 **n-Butyl chloroacetate**
$ClCH_2CO_2(CH_2)_3CH_3$ M.W. 150.61 n_D^{20} 1.4287
b.p. 175°

$Cl-CH_2-C(=O)-O-CH_2-CH_2-CH_2-CH_3$ NEAT

E

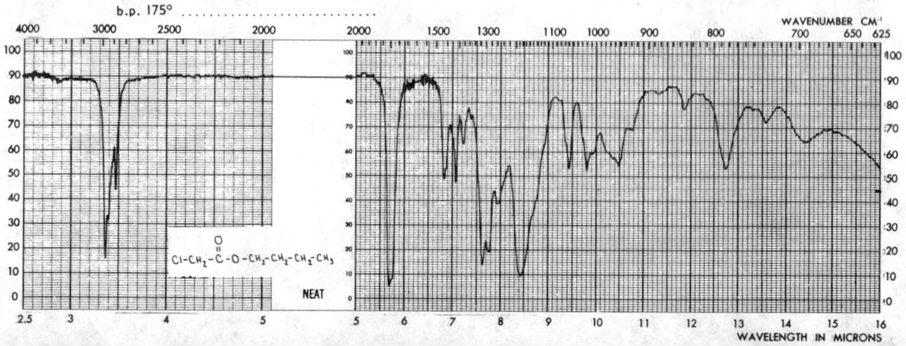

12,423-0 **tert.-Butyl bromoacetate**
$BrCH_2CO_2C(CH_3)_3$ M.W. 195.06 n_D^{20} 1.4430

$BrCH_2C(=O)-O-C(CH_3)_3$ NEAT

F

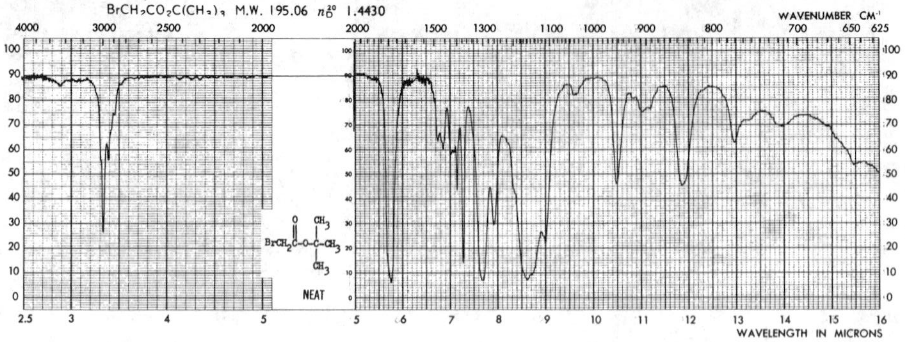

10,871-5 **Isoamyl chloroacetate** (isopentyl chloroacetate)
$ClCH_2CO_2CH_2CH_2CH(CH_3)_2$ M.W. 164.63 n_D^{20} 1.4316

$Cl-CH_2-C(=O)-O-CH_2-CH_2-CH(CH_3)-CH_3$ NEAT

G

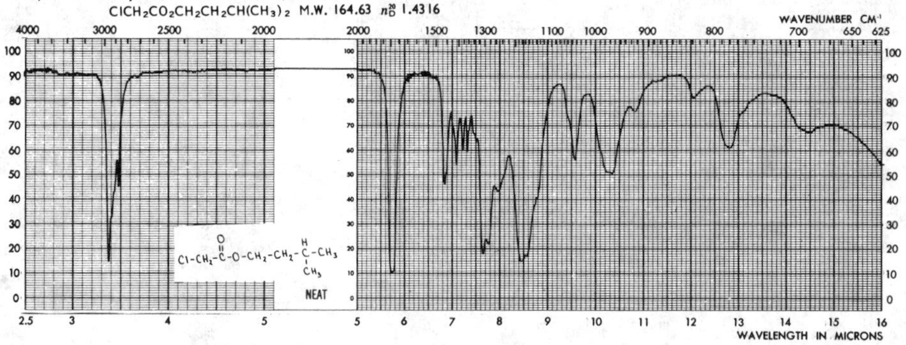

10,840-5 **Methyl dichloroacetate, 99+%**
$Cl_2CHCO_2CH_3$ M.W. 142.97 n_D^{20} 1.4421
b.p. 143°

$Cl-CH(Cl)-C(=O)-O-CH_3$ NEAT

H

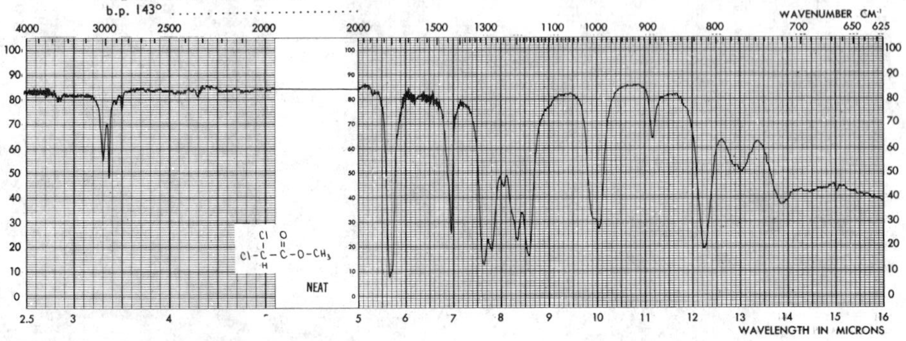

16,315-5
Ethyl trichloroacetate, 99%
$CCl_3CO_2C_2H_5$
M.W. 191.44 b.p. 168° n_D^{20} 1.4447 d 1.378
Beil. 2(2),200 Fieser 1,386 3,143

$Cl-C(Cl)(Cl)-C(=O)-OC_2H_5$ NEAT

(Each spectrum: WAVENUMBER CM⁻¹ 4000–625; WAVELENGTH IN MICRONS 2.5–16; transmittance 0–100)

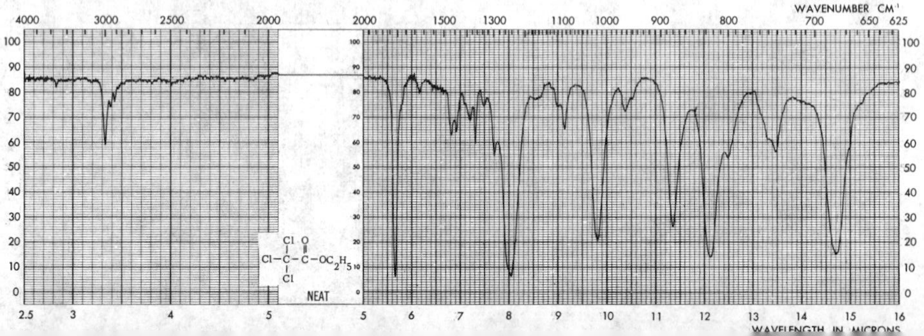

A

E5000-0 **Ethyl trifluoroacetate**
$CF_3CO_2C_2H_5$ M.W. 142.08 n_D^{20} 1.3068

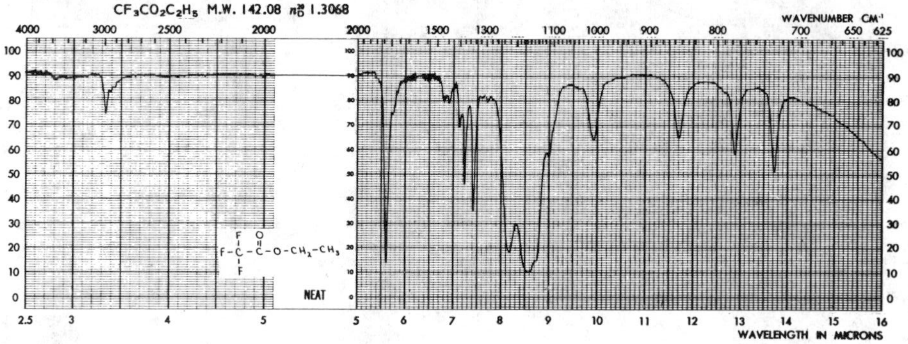

NEAT

B

17,747-4
S-Ethyl trifluorothioacetate, 99%
$CF_3COSC_2H_5$
M.W. 158.14 b.p. 90.5° n_D^{20} 1.3772 d 1.234

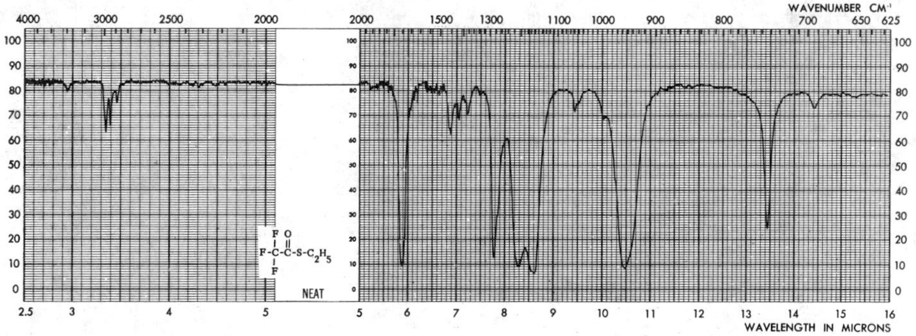

NEAT

C

10,703-4
Ethyl 2-fluoropropionate, 96%
$CH_3CH(F)CO_2C_2H_5$
M.W. 120.12 b.p. 122-123° n_D^{20} 1.3800

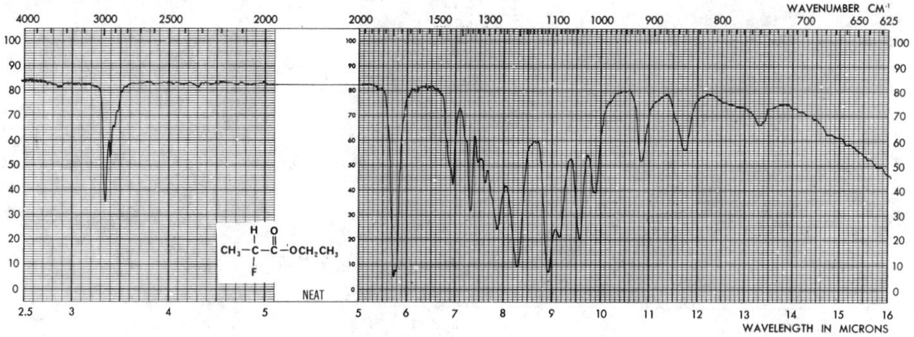

NEAT

D

13,913-0 **Methyl 2-chloropropionate**
$CH_3CH(Cl)CO_2CH_3$ M.W. 122.55
n_D^{20} 1.4193 ....

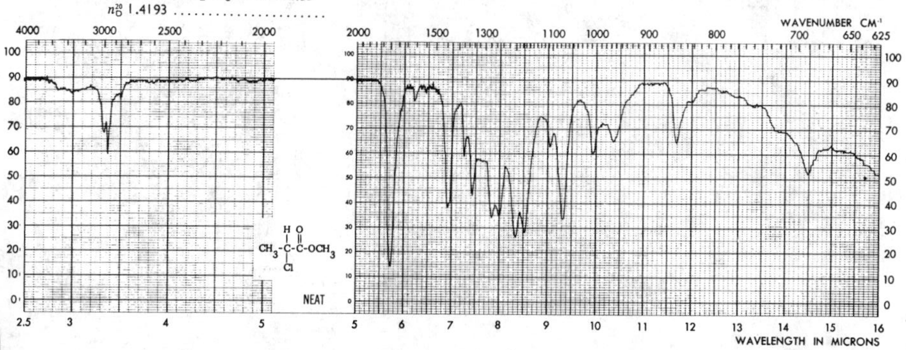

NEAT

E

19,241-4
Ethyl 2-chloropropionate
$CH_3CH(Cl)CO_2C_2H_5$ FW 136.58 bp 146-149°
n_D^{20} 1.4170 d 1.072 *Beil.* 2,248 Disp. C

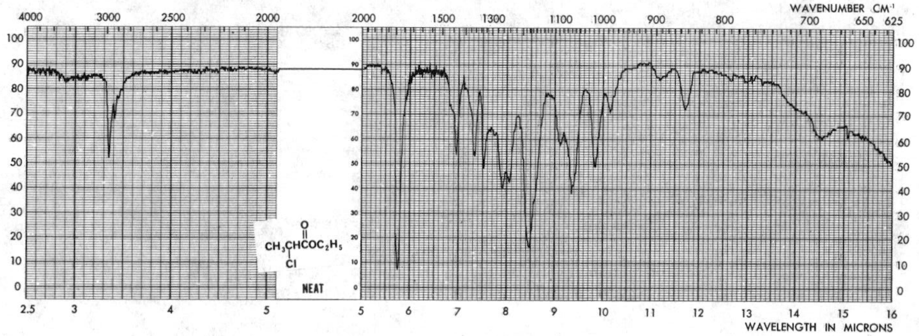

NEAT

F

E1455-1 **Ethyl 2-bromopropionate**
$CH_3CH(Br)CO_2C_2H_5$ M.W. 181.04 n_D^{20} 1.4429

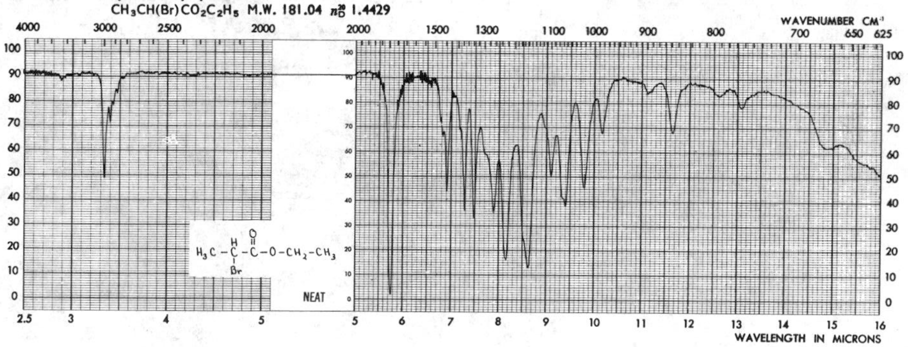

NEAT

G

E1785-2 **Ethyl 3-chloropropionate**
$ClCH_2CH_2CO_2C_2H_5$ M.W. 136.58
n_D^{20} 1.4231 ....

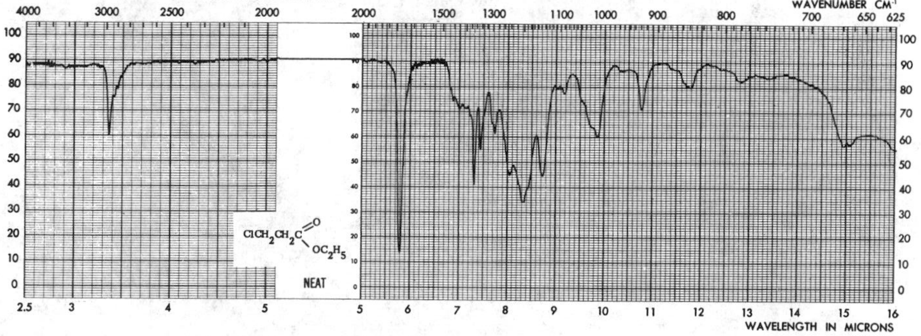

NEAT

H

12,816-3 **Ethyl 3-bromopropionate**
$BrCH_2CH_2CO_2C_2H_5$ M.W. 181.04 n_D^{20} 1.4516 ....

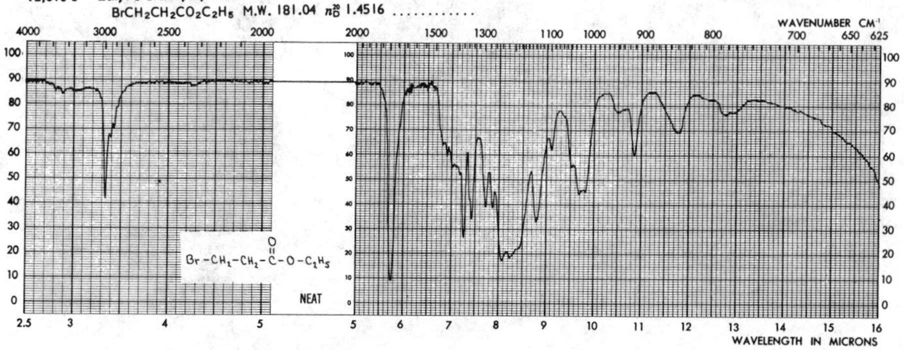

NEAT

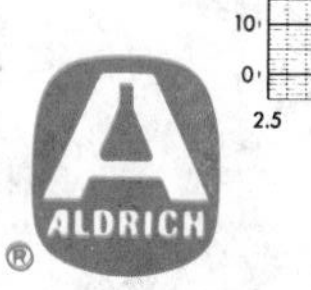

A

20,013-1
Methyl 2,3-dichloropropionate, tech., 70%
$ClCH_2CH(Cl)CO_2CH_3$ FW 157.00 bp 92°/50mm.
n_D^{20} 1.4447 d 1.328 *Beil.* **2**(1),111 Disp. C

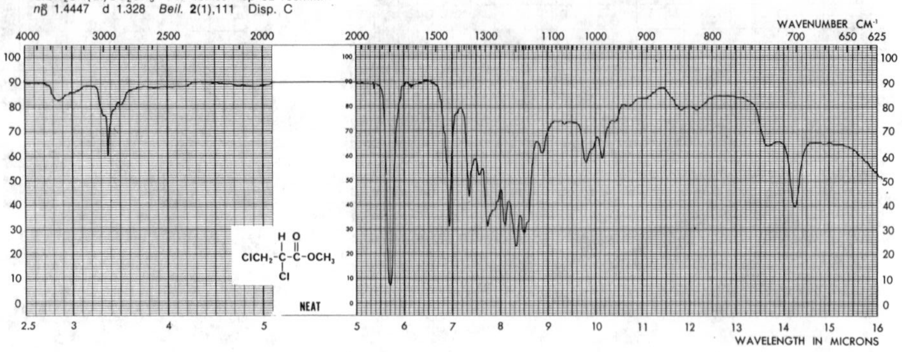

$ClCH_2-\overset{H}{C}(Cl)-\overset{O}{C}-OCH_3$

NEAT

WAVENUMBER CM⁻¹ — WAVELENGTH IN MICRONS

B

E2280-5 **Ethyl 2,3-dibromopropionate**
$BrCH_2CH(Br)CO_2C_2H_5$ M.W. 259.94 n_D^{20} 1.4986

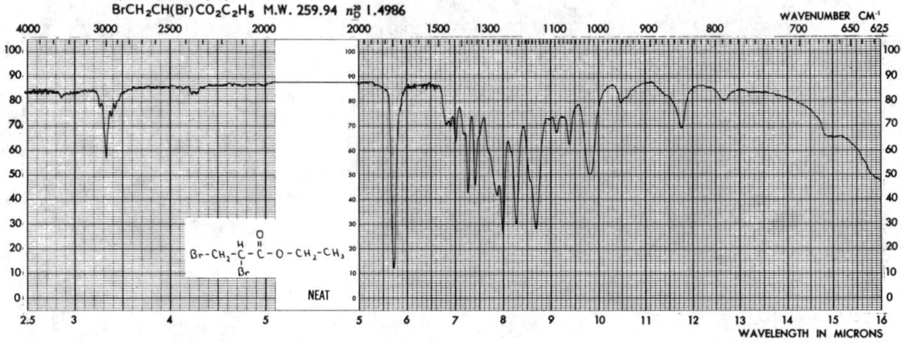

$Br-CH_2-\overset{H}{C}(Br)-\overset{O}{C}-O-CH_2-CH_3$

NEAT

WAVENUMBER CM⁻¹ — WAVELENGTH IN MICRONS

C

E1381-4 **Ethyl 2-bromobutyrate**
$C_2H_5CH(Br)CO_2C_2H_5$ M.W. 195.06
n_D^{20} 1.4460

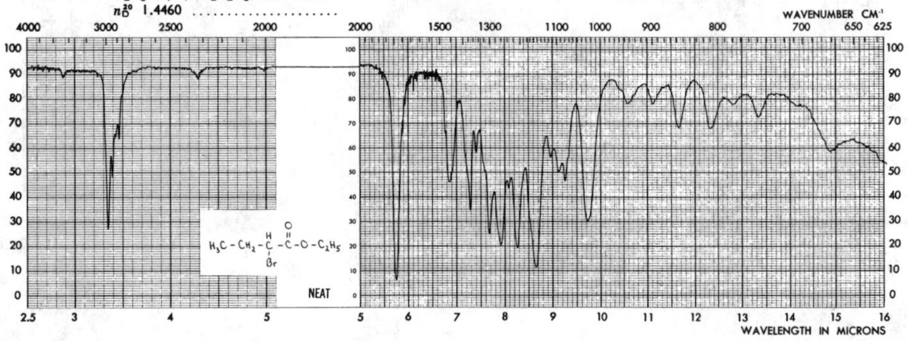

$H_3C-CH_2-\overset{H}{C}(Br)-\overset{O}{C}-O-C_2H_5$

NEAT

WAVENUMBER CM⁻¹ — WAVELENGTH IN MICRONS

D

M3480-4 **Methyl 4-chlorobutyrate, puriss.**
$Cl(CH_2)_3CO_2CH_3$ M.W. 136.58 n_D^{20} 1.4321 b.p. 55°/4 mm.

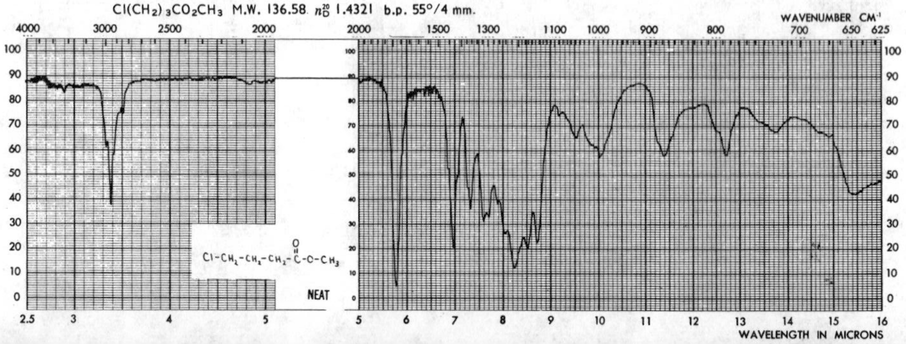

$Cl-CH_2-CH_2-CH_2-\overset{O}{C}-O-CH_3$

NEAT

WAVENUMBER CM⁻¹ — WAVELENGTH IN MICRONS

E

E1695-3 **Ethyl 4-chlorobutyrate**
$Cl(CH_2)_3CO_2C_2H_5$ M.W. 150.61 n_D^{20} 1.4306

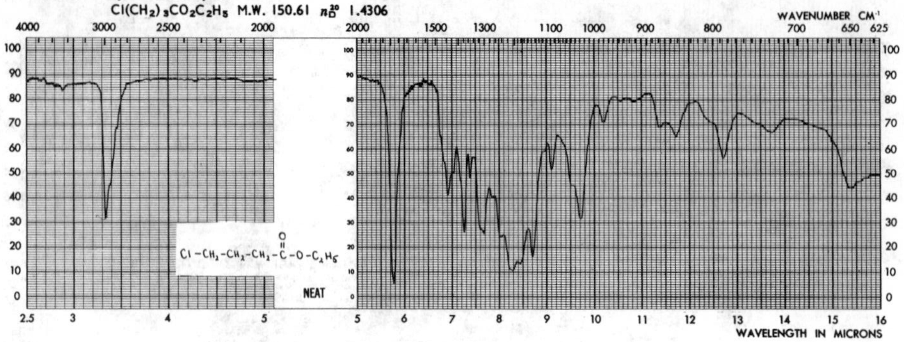

$Cl-CH_2-CH_2-CH_2-\overset{O}{C}-O-C_2H_5$

NEAT

WAVENUMBER CM⁻¹ — WAVELENGTH IN MICRONS

F

E1440-3 **Ethyl 2-bromoisobutyrate (ethyl 2-bromo-2-methylpropionate)**
$(CH_3)_2C(Br)CO_2C_2H_5$ M.W. 195.06
n_D^{20} 1.4446

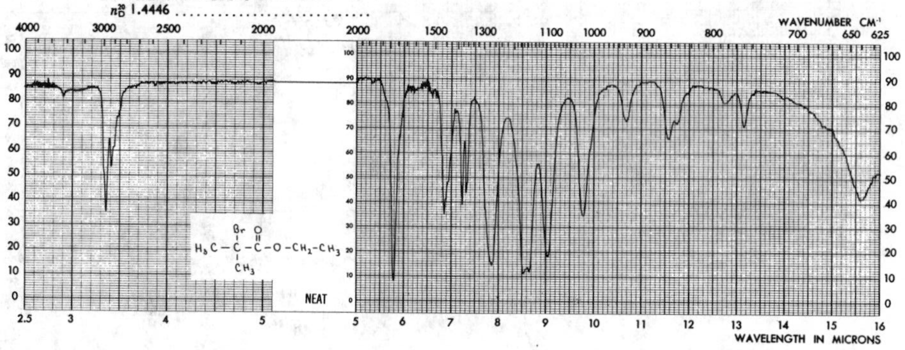

$H_3C-\overset{Br}{C}(CH_3)-\overset{O}{C}-O-CH_2-CH_3$

NEAT

WAVENUMBER CM⁻¹ — WAVELENGTH IN MICRONS

G

E1460-8 **Ethyl 2-bromovalerate**
$CH_3CH_2CH_2CH(Br)CO_2C_2H_5$ M.W. 209.09
n_D^{20} 1.4467

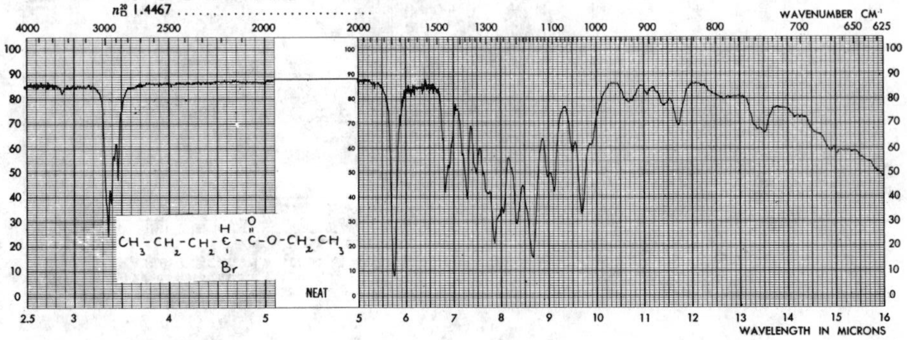

$CH_3-CH_2-CH_2-\overset{H}{C}(Br)-\overset{O}{C}-O-CH_2-CH_3$

NEAT

WAVENUMBER CM⁻¹ — WAVELENGTH IN MICRONS

H

16,711-8
Ethyl 4-bromobutyrate
$Br(CH_2)_3CO_2C_2H_5$
M.W. 195.06 b.p. 196-197° n_D^{20} 1.4559 d 1.363
Beil. **2**,283

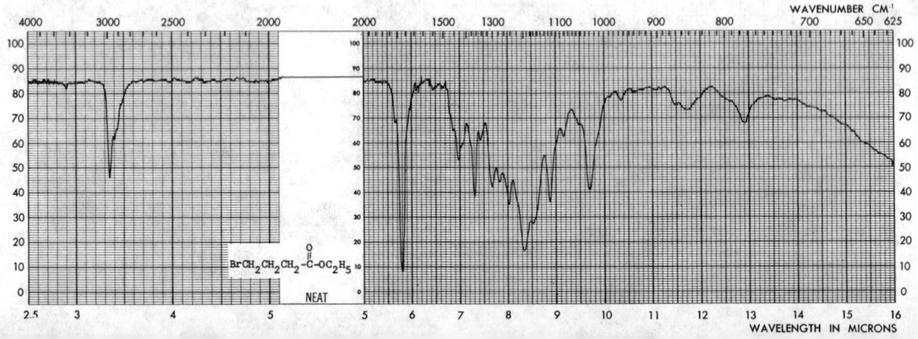

$BrCH_2CH_2CH_2-\overset{O}{C}-OC_2H_5$

NEAT

WAVENUMBER CM⁻¹ — WAVELENGTH IN MICRONS

A

19,729-7
Ethyl α-bromocyclobutanecarboxylate, 99%
$BrC_4H_6CO_2C_2H_5$ FW 207.07 bp 85-88°/12mm.
n_D^{20} 1.4709 d 1.279 Disp. C

NEAT

B

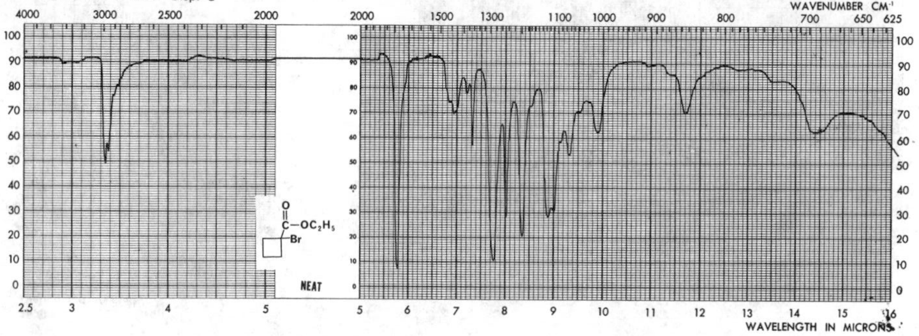

13,598-4 **Methyl 5-chlorovalerate**
$Cl(CH_2)_4CO_2CH_3$ M.W. 150.61 n_D^{20} 1.4372
b.p. 90-91°/15 mm.

NEAT

C

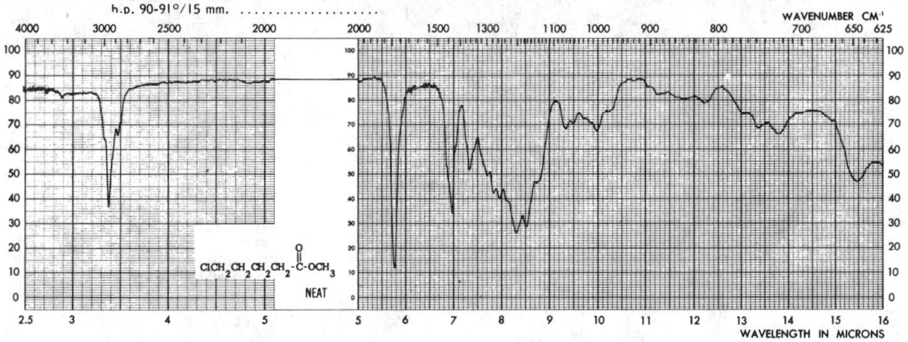

M3260-7 **Methyl 5-bromovalerate**
$Br(CH_2)_4CO_2CH_3$ M.W. 195.06
n_D^{20} 1.4639

NEAT

D

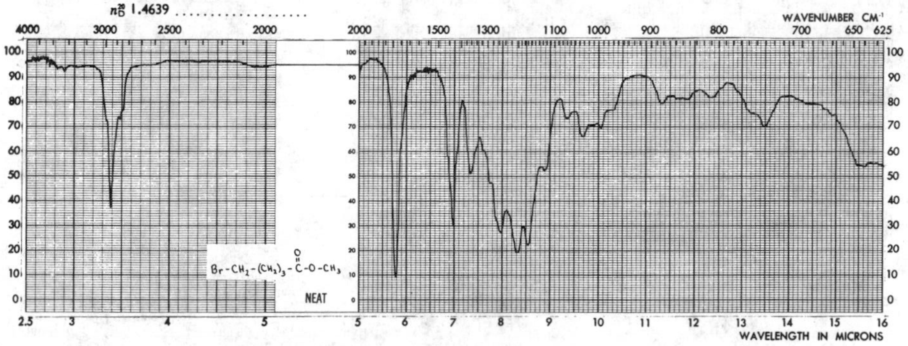

12,910-0 **Ethyl 5-bromovalerate**
$Br(CH_2)_4CO_2C_2H_5$ M.W. 209.09 n_D^{20} 1.4580
b.p. 104-109°/12 mm.

NEAT

E

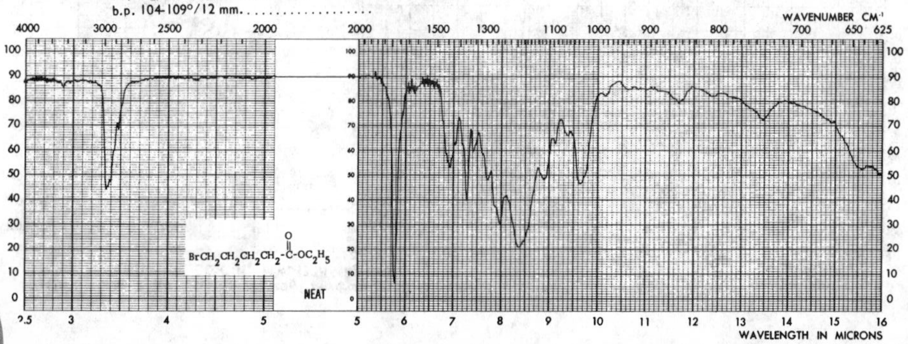

13,597-6 **Ethyl 5-chlorovalerate**
$Cl(CH_2)_4CO_2C_2H_5$ M.W. 164.63 n_D^{20} 1.4358
b.p. 105°/17 mm.

NEAT

F

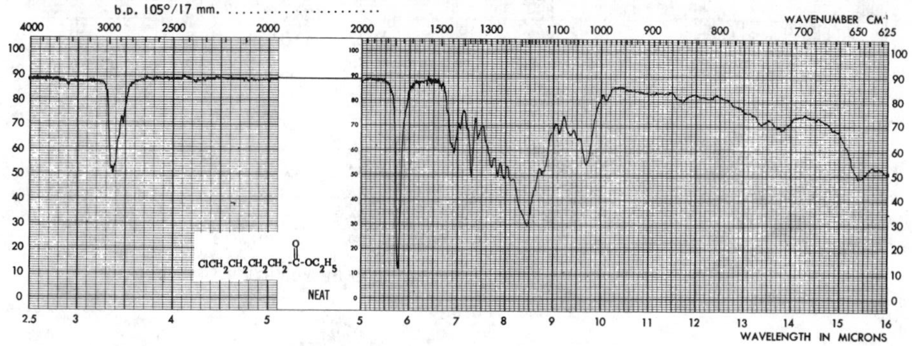

E3410-2 **Ethyl lactate**
$CH_3CH(OH)CO_2C_2H_5$ M.W. 118.13
n_D^{20} 1.4101

NEAT

G

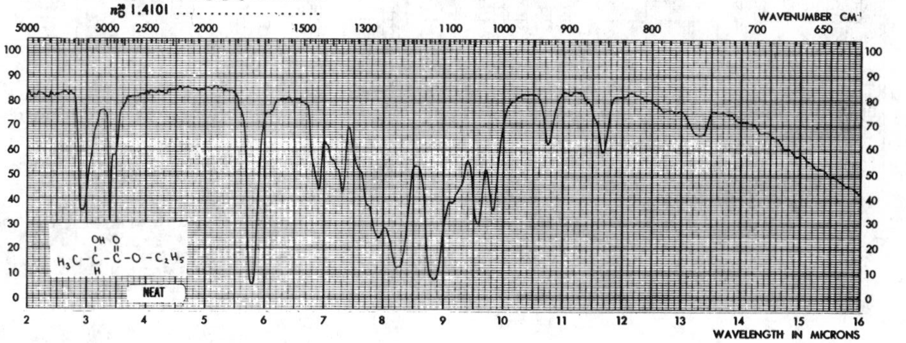

E3060-3 **Ethyl 3-hydroxybutyrate**
$CH_3CH(OH)CH_2CO_2C_2H_5$ M.W. 132.16
n_D^{20} 1.4180

NEAT

H

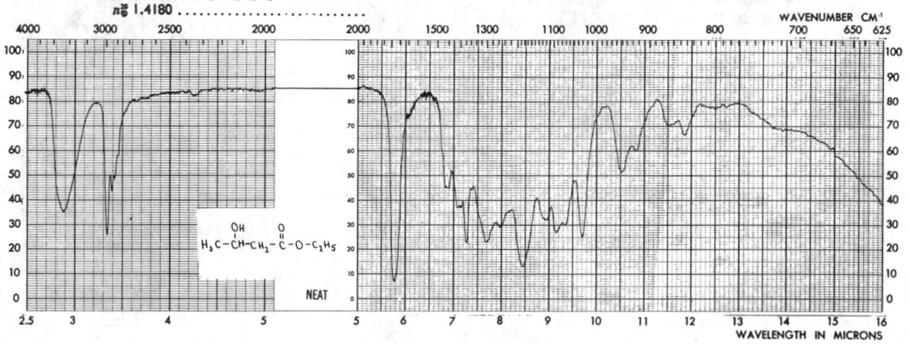

M5020-6 **Methyl 2-hydroxyisobutyrate (methyl 2-methyllactate)**
$(CH_3)_2C(OH)CO_2CH_3$ M.W. 118.13

NEAT

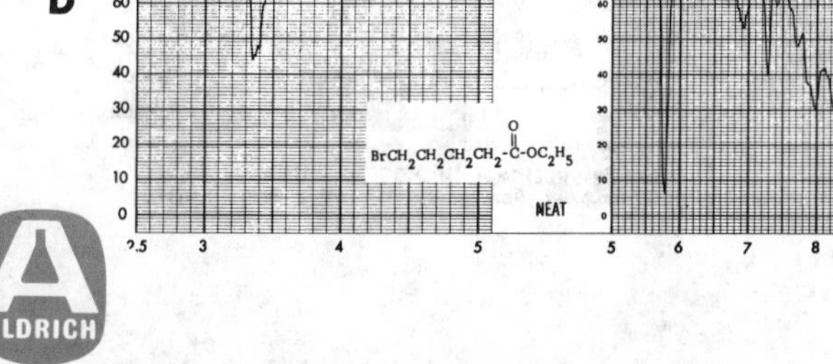

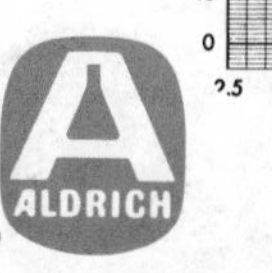

NON-AROMATIC ESTERS & LACTONES

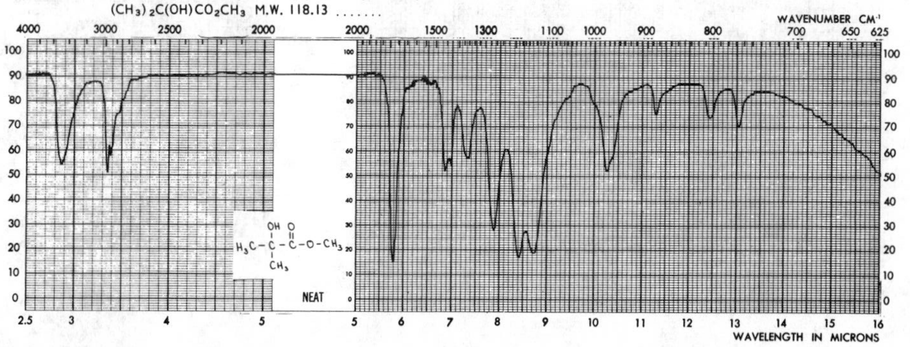

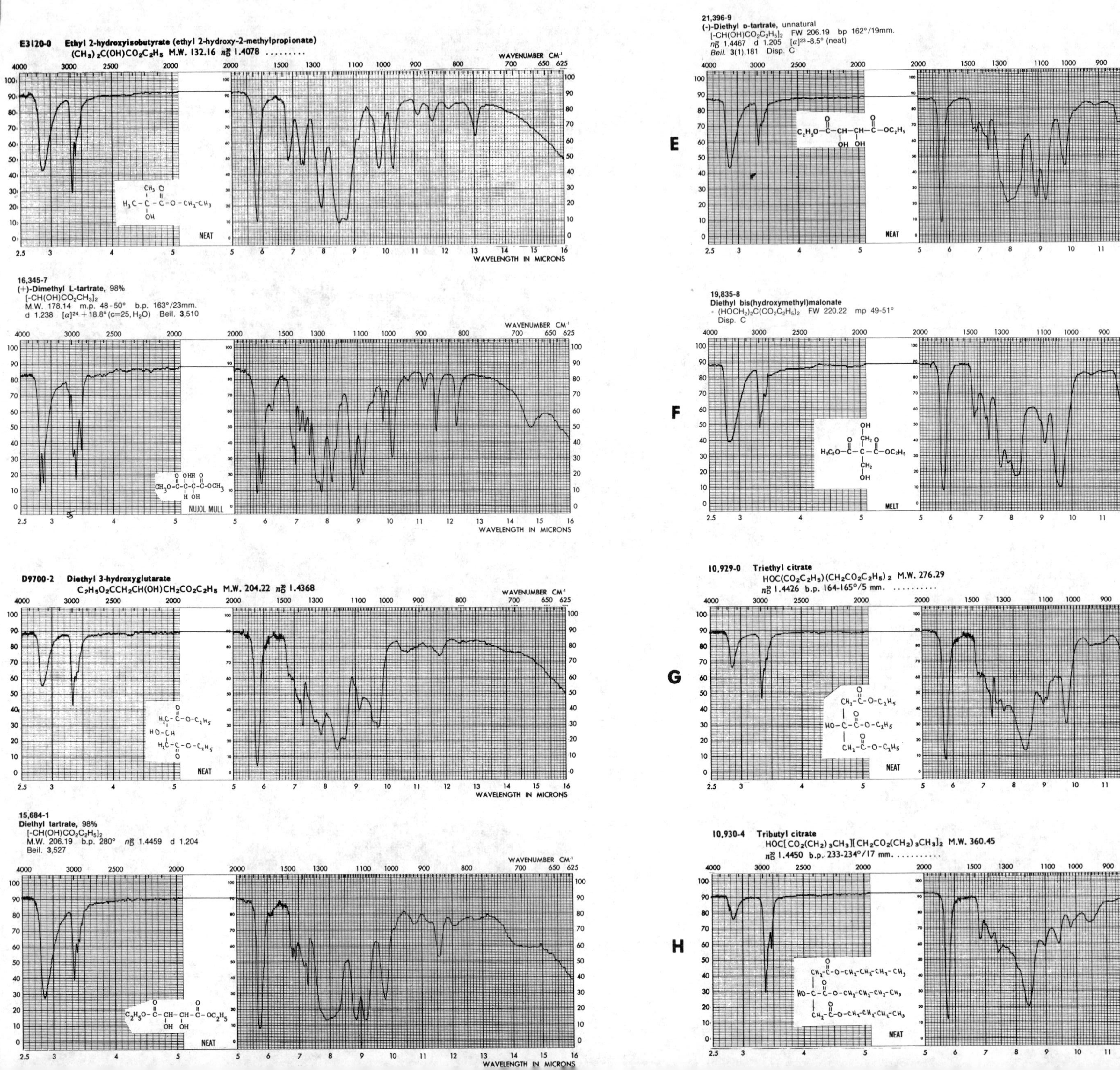

A — E3120-0 **Ethyl 2-hydroxyisobutyrate (ethyl 2-hydroxy-2-methylpropionate)**
$(CH_3)_2C(OH)CO_2C_2H_5$ M.W. 132.16 n_D^{20} 1.4078 .... NEAT

B — 16,345-7
(+)-Dimethyl L-tartrate, 98%
$[-CH(OH)CO_2CH_3]_2$
M.W. 178.14 m.p. 48-50° b.p. 163°/23mm.
d 1.238 $[\alpha]^{24}$ +18.8° (c=25, H_2O) Beil. 3,510
NUJOL MULL

C — D9700-2 **Diethyl 3-hydroxyglutarate**
$C_2H_5O_2CCH_2CH(OH)CH_2CO_2C_2H_5$ M.W. 204.22 n_D^{20} 1.4368
NEAT

D — 15,684-1
Diethyl tartrate, 98%
$[-CH(OH)CO_2C_2H_5]_2$
M.W. 206.19 b.p. 280° n_D^{20} 1.4459 d 1.204
Beil. 3,527
NEAT

E — 21,396-9
(-)-Diethyl D-tartrate, unnatural
$[-CH(OH)CO_2C_2H_5]_2$ FW 206.19 bp 162°/19mm.
n_D^{20} 1.4467 d 1.205 $[\alpha]^{23}$ -8.5° (neat)
Beil. 3(1),181 Disp. C
NEAT

F — 19,835-8
Diethyl bis(hydroxymethyl)malonate
$(HOCH_2)_2C(CO_2C_2H_5)_2$ FW 220.22 mp 49-51°
Disp. C
MELT

G — 10,929-0 **Triethyl citrate**
$HOC(CO_2C_2H_5)(CH_2CO_2C_2H_5)_2$ M.W. 276.29
n_D^{20} 1.4426 b.p. 164-165°/5 mm. ....
NEAT

H — 10,930-4 **Tributyl citrate**
$HOC[CO_2(CH_2)_3CH_3][CH_2CO_2(CH_2)_3CH_3]_2$ M.W. 360.45
n_D^{20} 1.4450 b.p. 233-234°/17 mm. ....
NEAT

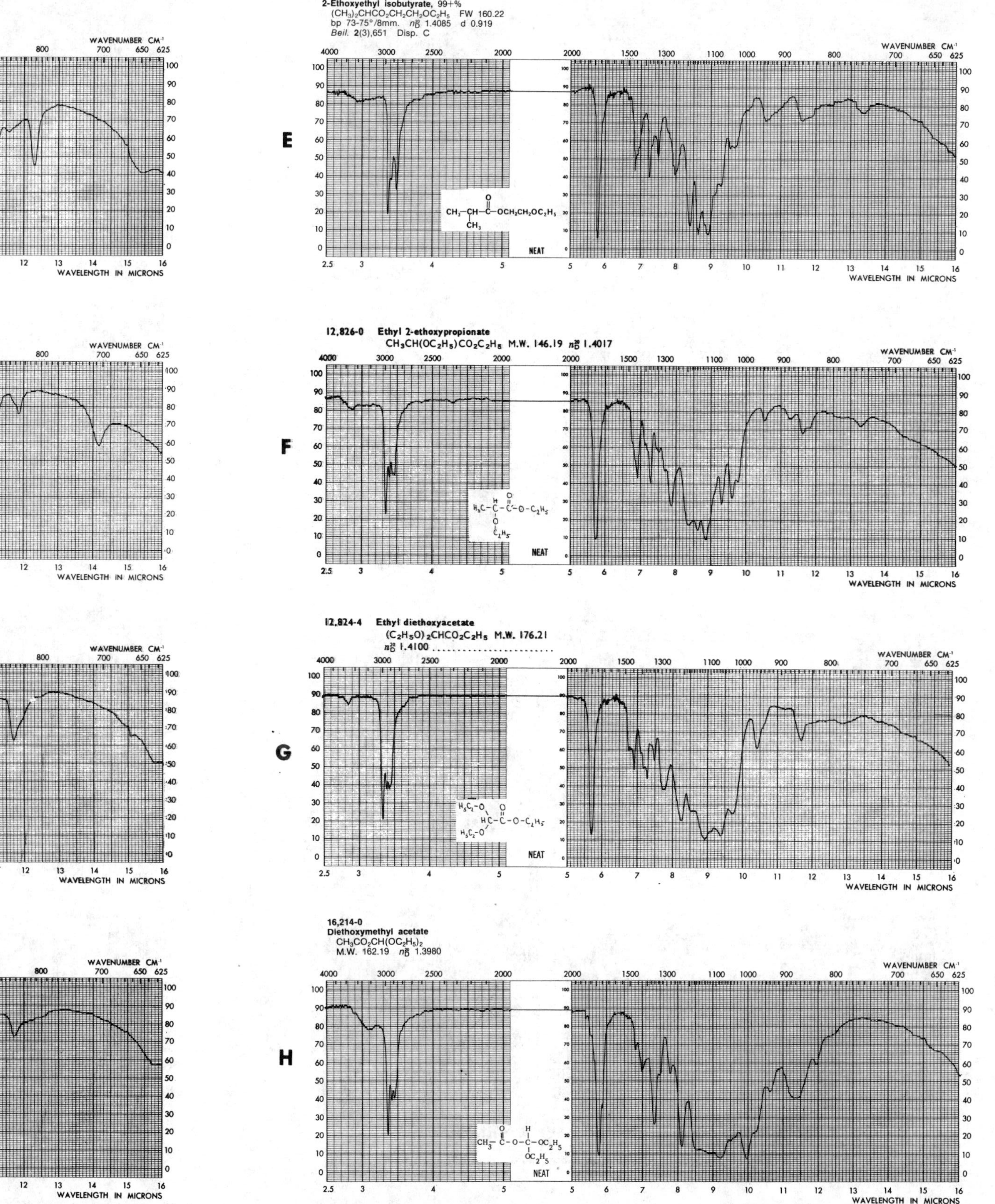

A 12,863-5 **2-Hydroxyethyl methacrylate (glycol methacrylate)**
$H_2C{:}C(CH_3)CO_2CH_2CH_2OH$ M.W. 130.14 n_D^{20} 1.4504
b.p. 67°/3.5 mm.

B 14,920-9 **Methyl methoxyacetate**
$CH_3OCH_2CO_2CH_3$ M.W. 104.10 n_D^{20} 1.3964
b.p. 128-130°

C 10,988-6 **2-Methoxyethyl acetate**
$CH_3CO_2CH_2CH_2OCH_3$ M.W. 118.13 n_D^{20} 1.4004
b.p. 145°

D 10,996-7 **2-Ethoxyethyl acetate**
$CH_3CO_2CH_2CH_2OC_2H_5$ M.W. 132.16 n_D^{20} 1.4040
b.p. 156°

E 19,346-1
2-Ethoxyethyl isobutyrate, 99+%
$(CH_3)_2CHCO_2CH_2CH_2OC_2H_5$ FW 160.22
bp 73-75°/8mm. n_D^{20} 1.4085 d 0.919
Beil. 2(3),651 Disp. C

F 12,826-0 **Ethyl 2-ethoxypropionate**
$CH_3CH(OC_2H_5)CO_2C_2H_5$ M.W. 146.19 n_D^{20} 1.4017

G 12,824-4 **Ethyl diethoxyacetate**
$(C_2H_5O)_2CHCO_2C_2H_5$ M.W. 176.21
n_D^{20} 1.4100

H 16,214-0
Diethoxymethyl acetate
$CH_3CO_2CH(OC_2H_5)_2$
M.W. 162.19 n_D^{20} 1.3980

ALDRICH

A

E2780-7 **Ethyl 2,3-epoxybutyrate**
M.W. 130.14 ....

NEAT

B

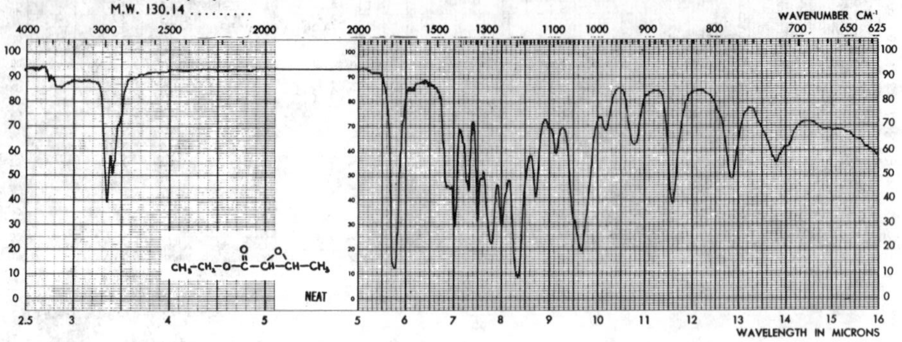

10,516-3 **Methyl 10,11-epoxyundecanoate**
M.W. 214.31 n_D^{20} 1.4450 b.p. 110-120°/0.25-0.5 mm.

NEAT

C

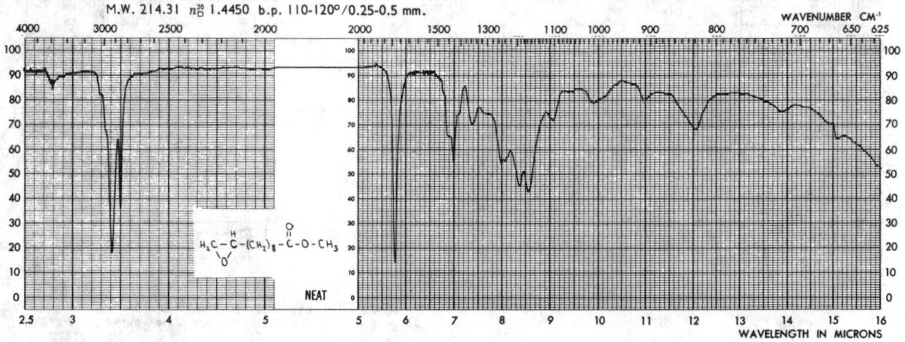

D9420-8 **Diethyl ethoxymethylenemalonate**
$C_2H_5OCH{:}C(CO_2C_2H_5)_2$ M.W. 216.23
n_D^{20} 1.4620 ....

NEAT

D

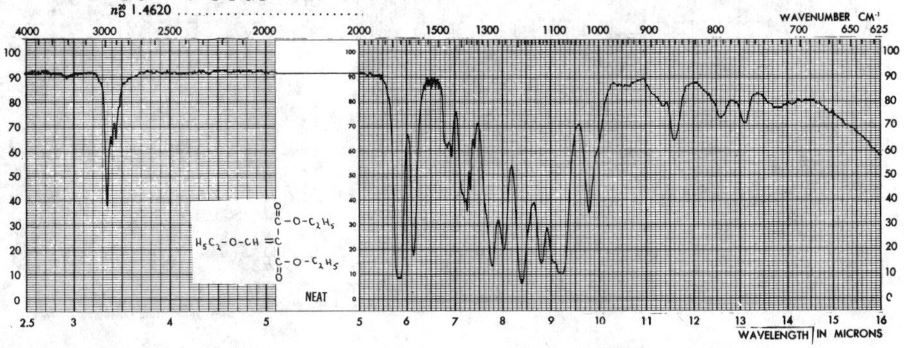

15,644-2
Ethylenebis-(2-oxyethyl acetate), 98+% (triethylene glycol diacetate)
$(CH_3CO_2CH_2CH_2OCH_2-)_2$
M.W. 234.25 b.p. 286° n_D^{20} 1.4380 Beil. **2**,141

NEAT

E

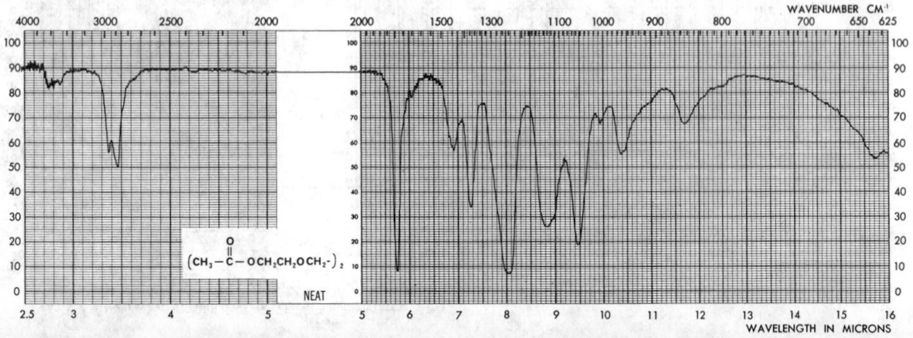

T5950 **Triethyleneglycol dimethacrylate** ....

NEAT

F

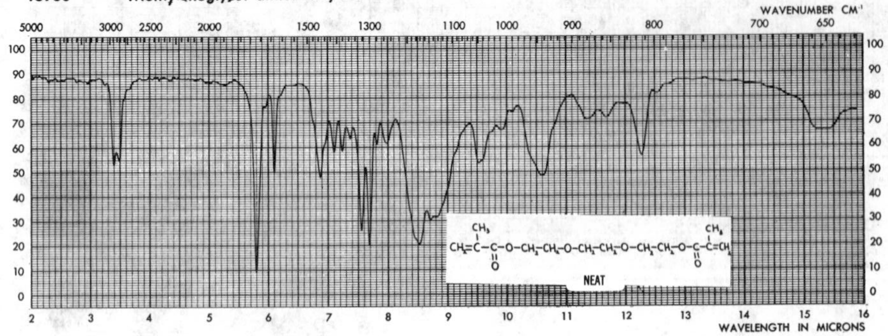

T1105 **Tetraethyleneglycol dimethacrylate**

NEAT

G

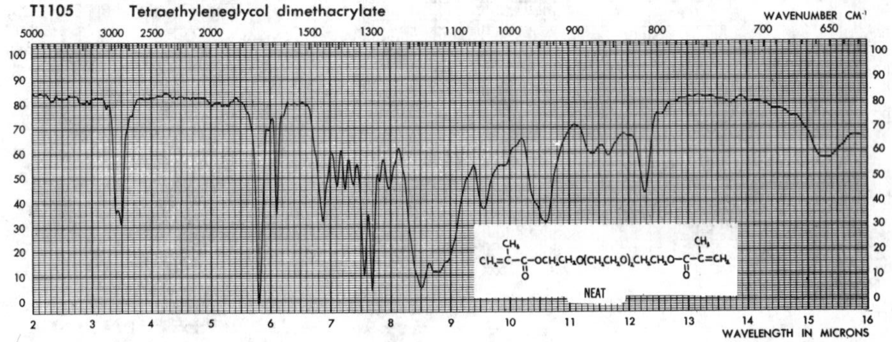

15,123-8 **Glycidyl methacrylate** (2,3-epoxypropyl methacrylate)
tech., 92%
M.W. 142.15 n_D^{20} 1.4494 b.p. 189° ....

NEAT

H

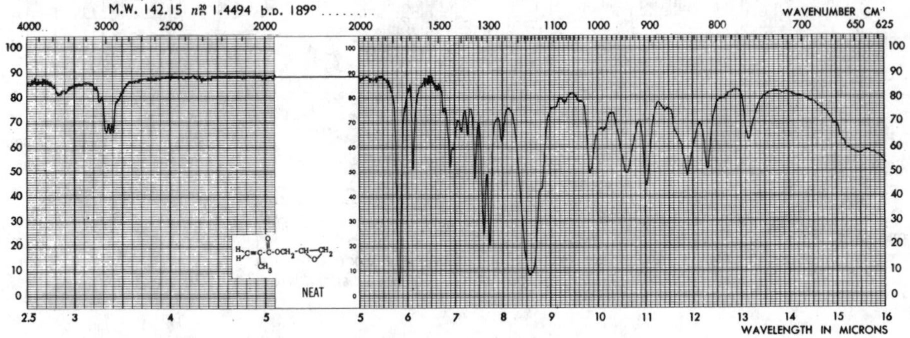

15,611-6 **Tetrahydrofurfuryl acetate**
M.W. 144.17 n_D^{20} 1.4373 b.p. 84-86°/17 mm.

NEAT

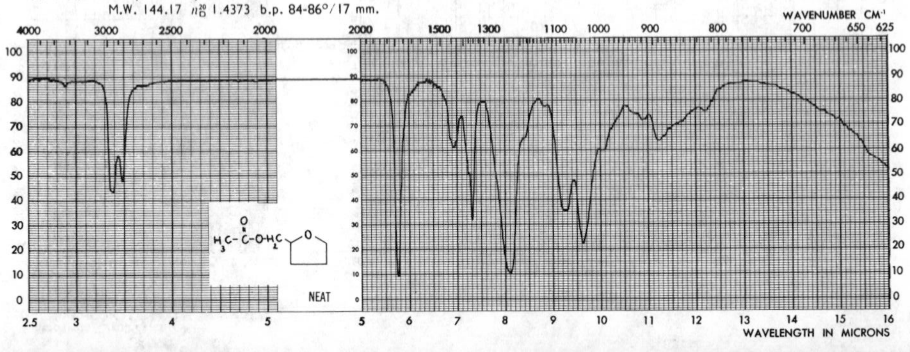

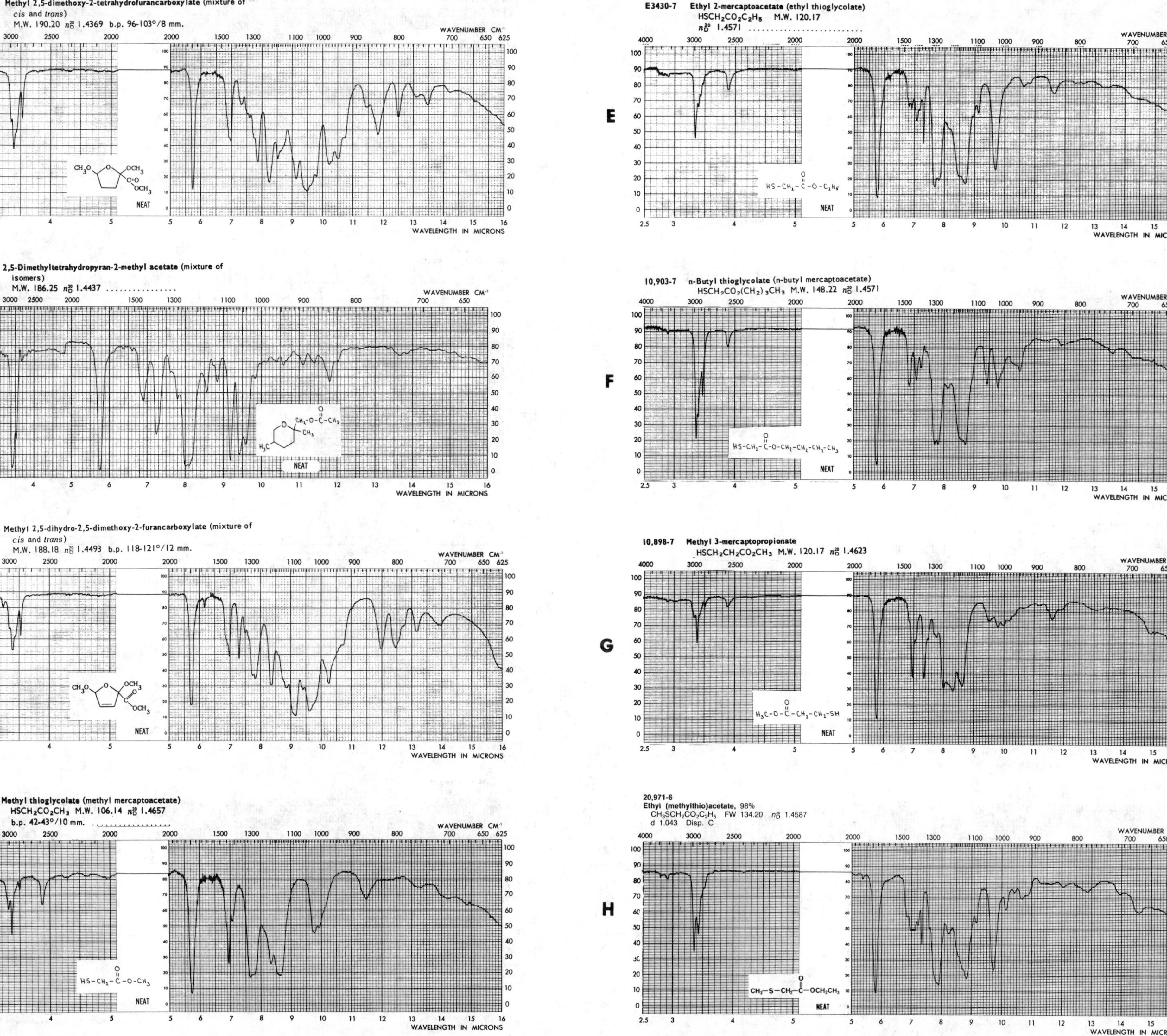
A
11,917-2 Methyl 2,5-dimethoxy-2-tetrahydrofurancarboxylate (mixture of cis and trans)
M.W. 190.20 n_D^{20} 1.4369 b.p. 96-103°/8 mm.
NEAT
B
12,660-8 2,5-Dimethyltetrahydropyran-2-methyl acetate (mixture of isomers)
M.W. 186.25 n_D^{20} 1.4437
NEAT
C
11,918-0 Methyl 2,5-dihydro-2,5-dimethoxy-2-furancarboxylate (mixture of cis and trans)
M.W. 188.18 n_D^{20} 1.4493 b.p. 118-121°/12 mm.
NEAT
D
10,899-5 Methyl thioglycolate (methyl mercaptoacetate)
$HSCH_2CO_2CH_3$ M.W. 106.14 n_D^{20} 1.4657
b.p. 42-43°/10 mm.
NEAT
E
E3430-7 Ethyl 2-mercaptoacetate (ethyl thioglycolate)
$HSCH_2CO_2C_2H_5$ M.W. 120.17
n_D^{20} 1.4571
NEAT
F
10,903-7 n-Butyl thioglycolate (n-butyl mercaptoacetate)
$HSCH_2CO_2(CH_2)_3CH_3$ M.W. 148.22 n_D^{20} 1.4571
NEAT
G
10,898-7 Methyl 3-mercaptopropionate
$HSCH_2CH_2CO_2CH_3$ M.W. 120.17 n_D^{20} 1.4623
NEAT
H
20,971-6
Ethyl (methylthio)acetate, 98%
$CH_3SCH_2CO_2C_2H_5$ FW 134.20 n_D^{20} 1.4587
d 1.043 Disp. C
NEAT
WAVENUMBER CM⁻¹
WAVELENGTH IN MICRONS
ALDRICH

A

10,337-3
Methyl 3-(methylthio)-propionate, 98%
$CH_3SCH_2CH_2CO_2CH_3$
M.W. 134.2 b.p. 74-75°/13mm. n_D^{20} 1.4650
STENCH

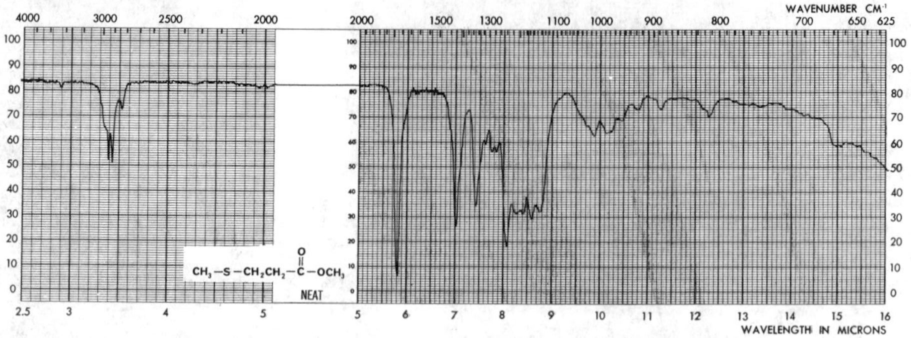

B

M375 **2-Mercaptoethyl acetate**
$CH_3CO_2(CH_2)_2SH$ M.W. 120.17 n_D^{20} 1.4593

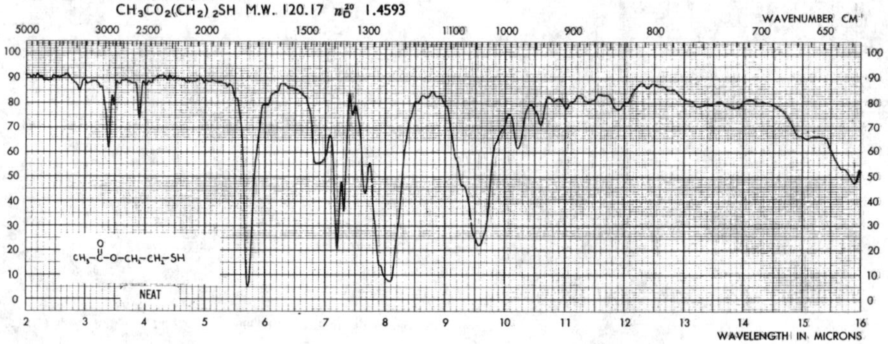

C

D18,830-1 **Dimethyl 3,3'-thiodipropionate**
$S(CH_2CH_2CO_2CH_3)_2$ M.W. 206.26 n_D^{20} 1.4740

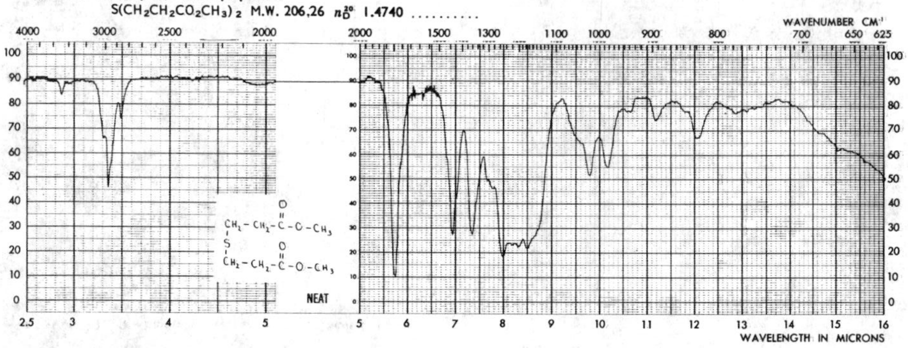

D

19,298-8
3-Chloropropyl thiolacetate, tech., 90+%
$CH_3COS(CH_2)_3Cl$ FW 152.64 bp 83-84°/10mm.
n_D^{20} 1.4946 d 1.159 *Beil.* **2**(3),493 Disp. C

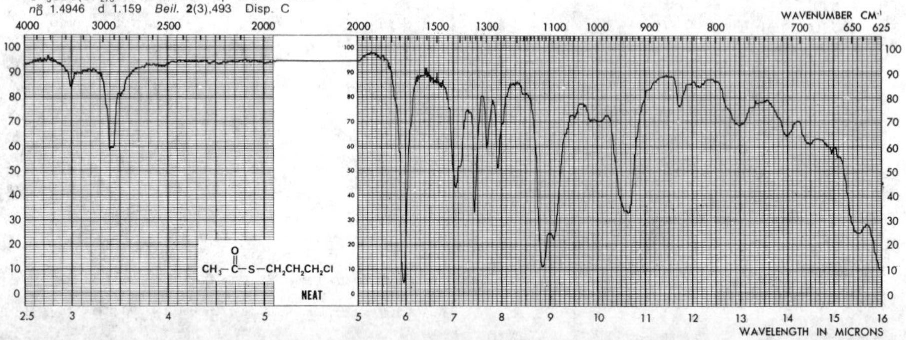

E

14,526-2 **(Carbethoxymethyl)dimethylsulfonium bromide**
$C_2H_5O_2CCH_2S(CH_3)_2Br$ M.W. 229.14
m.p. 90° (dec.)

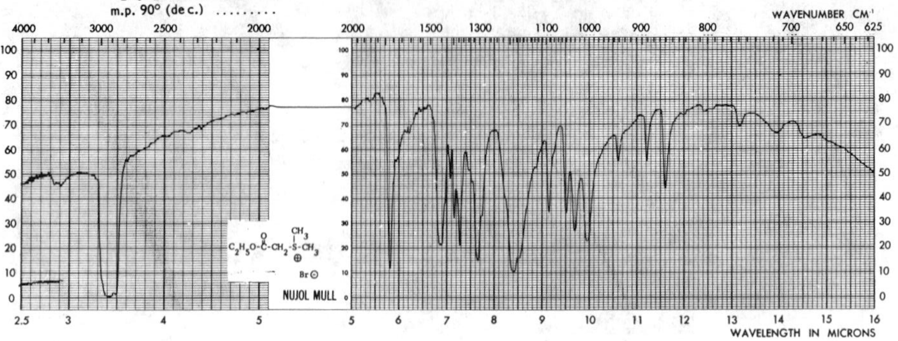

F

G660-0 **Glycine methyl ester hydrochloride**
$H_2NCH_2CO_2CH_3 \cdot HCl$ M.W. 125.56 m.p. 165-168° (dec.)

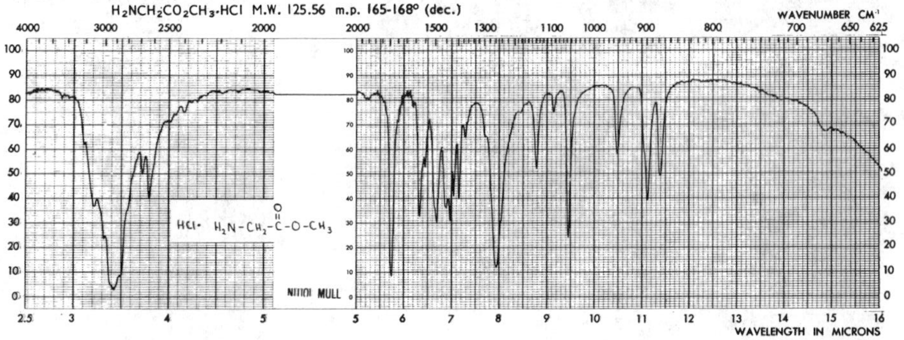

G

G650-3 **Glycine ethyl ester hydrochloride**
$H_2NCH_2CO_2C_2H_5 \cdot HCl$ M.W. 139.58 m.p. 145-146.5°

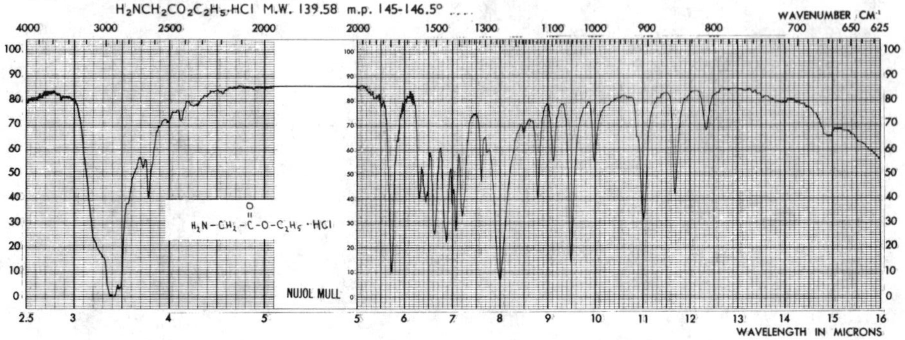

H

85,566-9
L-Alanine ethyl ester hydrochloride
$CH_3CH(NH_2)CO_2C_2H_5 \cdot HCl$
M.W. 153.61 m.p. 62° (dec.) Beil. **4**,382

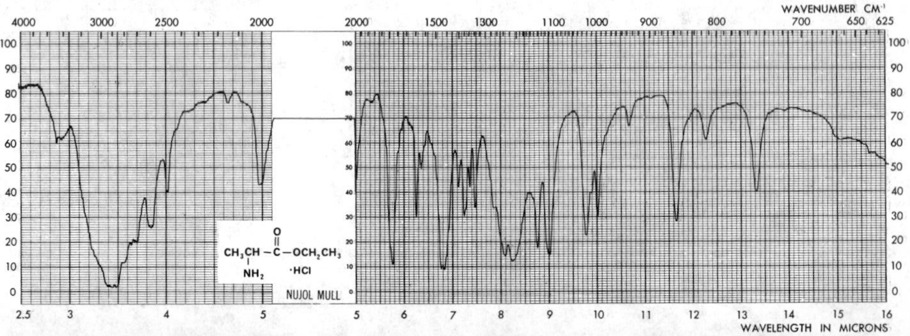

A 12,827-9 Ethyl hydrazinoacetate hydrochloride
$H_2NNHCH_2CO_2C_2H_5 \cdot HCl$ M.W. 154.60
m.p. 147-149°
NUJOL MULL

B E1055-6 Ethyl 3-aminobutyrate
$CH_3CH(NH_2)CH_2CO_2C_2H_5$ M.W. 131.18
n_D^{25} 1.4241
NEAT

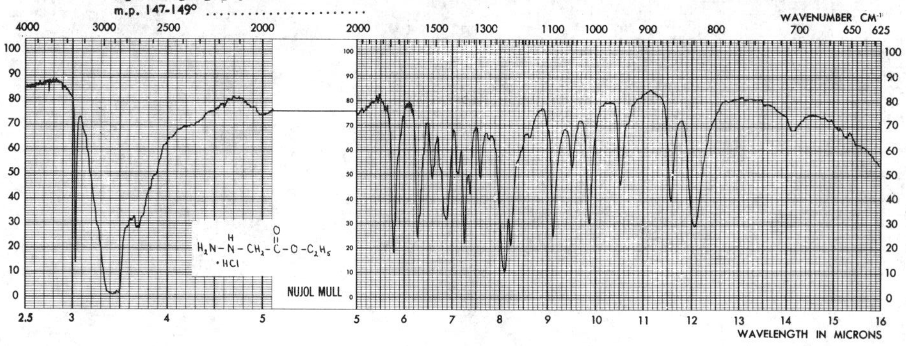

C 18,999-5
Ethyl 3-(diethylamino)propionate
$(C_2H_5)_2NCH_2CH_2CO_2C_2H_5$ FW 173.26
bp 83-84°/12mm. n_D^{20} 1.4253 d 0.881 *Beil.* 4,404
Disp. C
NEAT

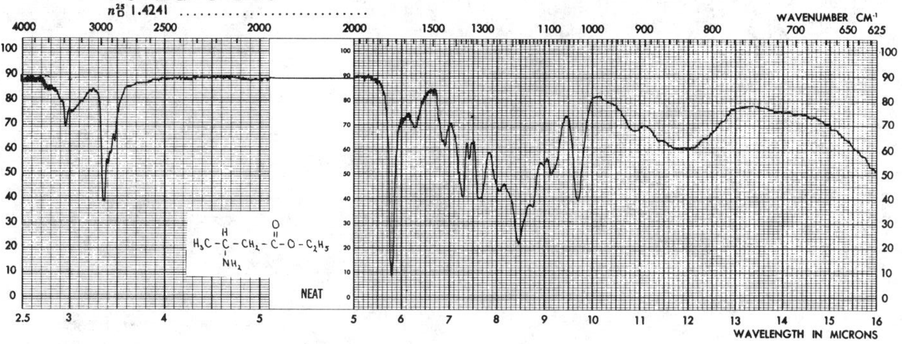

D 85,676-2
L-Alanine *tert.*-butyl ester hydrochloride
$CH_3CH(NH_2)CO_2C(CH_3)_3 \cdot HCl$
M.W. 181.66 m.p. 163-164° (dec.)
NUJOL MULL

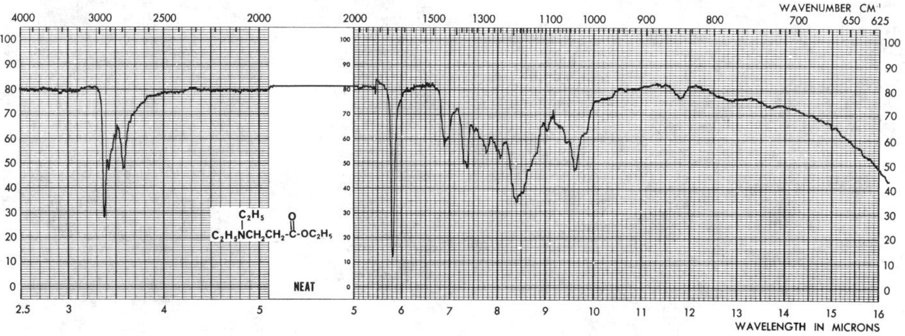

E 86,027-1
L-Valine methyl ester hydrochloride, 99%
$(CH_3)_2CHCH(NH_2)CO_2CH_3 \cdot HCl$ FW 167.64
mp 171-173° Disp. L
NUJOL MULL

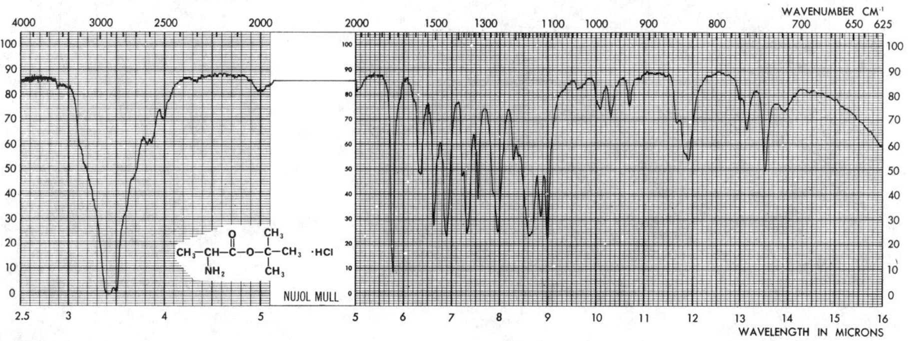

F 22,089-8
L-Valine ethyl ester hydrochloride, 99%
$(CH_3)_2CHCH(NH_2)CO_2C_2H_5 \cdot HCl$ FW 181.66
mp 102-105° $[\alpha]_D^{20}$ +6.7° (c=2, H_2O) Disp. L
NUJOL MULL

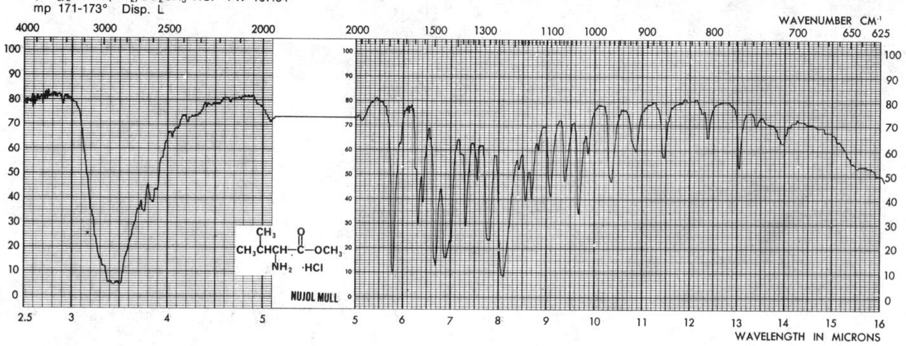

G L100-2 L-Leucine methyl ester hydrochloride
$(CH_3)_2CHCH_2CH(NH_2)CO_2CH_3 \cdot HCl$ M.W. 181.66
m.p. 146-147°
NUJOL MULL

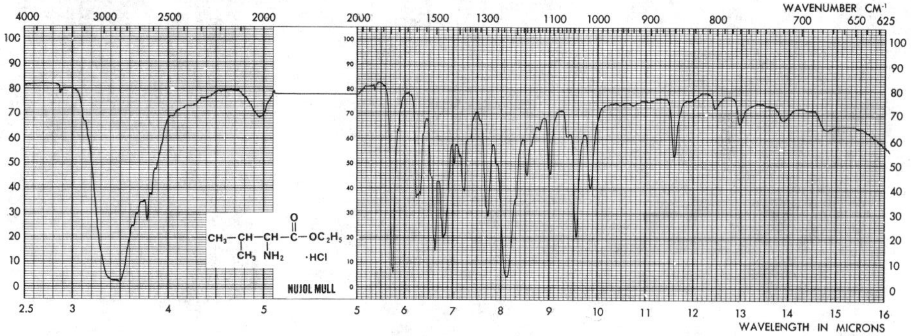

H E1060-2 Ethyl 4-aminobutyrate hydrochloride
$H_2N(CH_2)_3CO_2C_2H_5 \cdot HCl$ M.W. 167.64 m.p. 53-73°
MELT

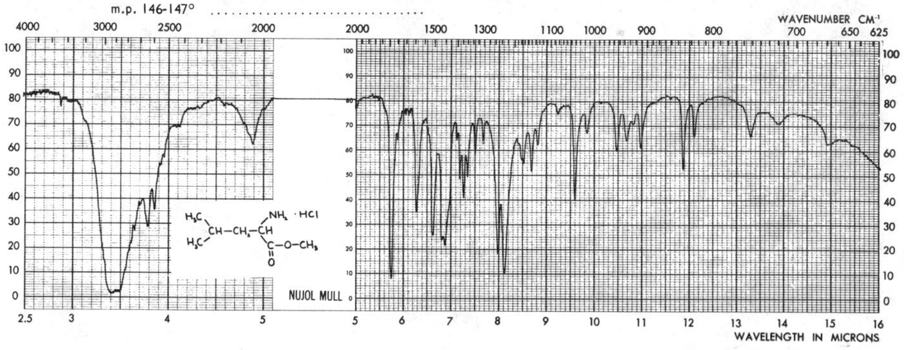

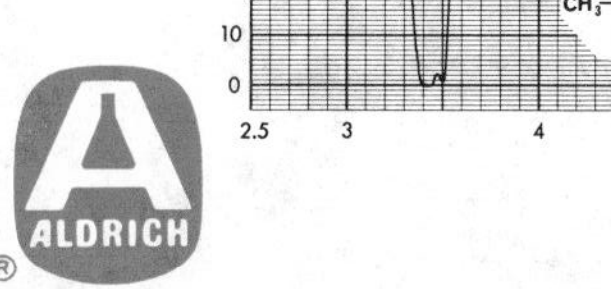

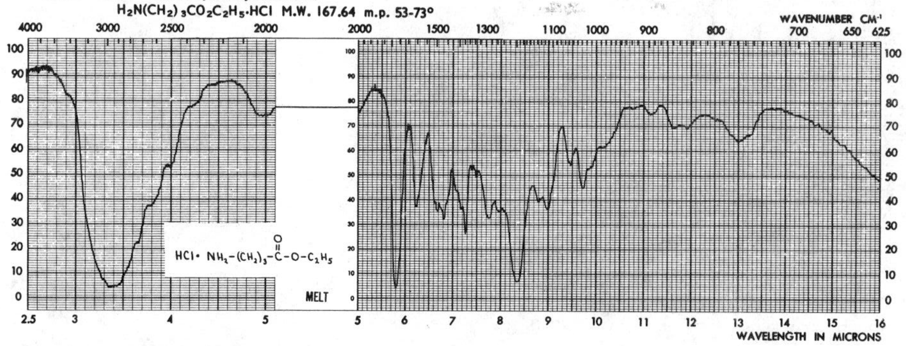

A

12,971-2 Methyl 3-aminocrotonate
$CH_3C(NH_2):CHCO_2CH_3$ M.W. 115.13 m.p. 79-82°

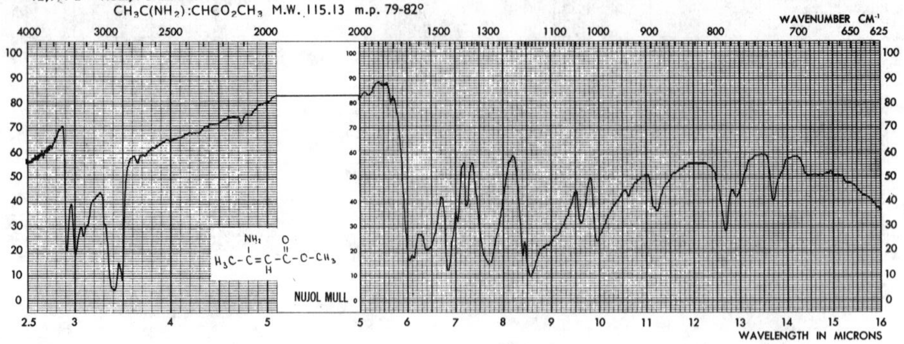

NUJOL MULL

B

E1080-7 Ethyl 3-aminocrotonate
$CH_3C(NH_2):CHCO_2C_2H_5$ M.W. 129.16
n_D^{20} 1.4890

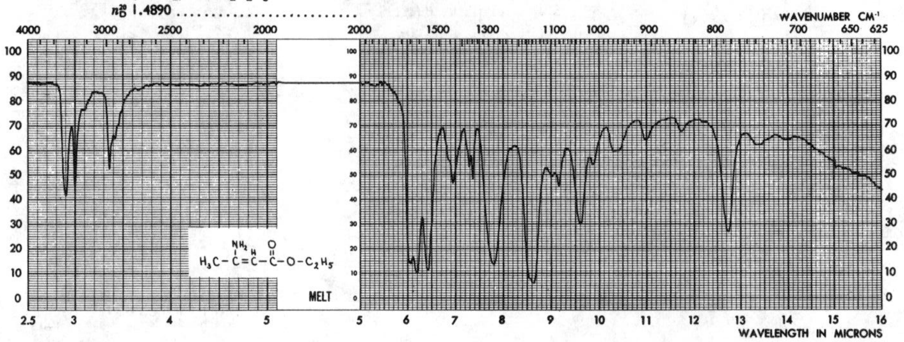

MELT

C

C12,190-8 L-Cysteine ethyl ester hydrochloride
$HSCH_2CH(NH_2)CO_2C_2H_5 \cdot HCl$ M.W. 185.67
m.p. 123-125°

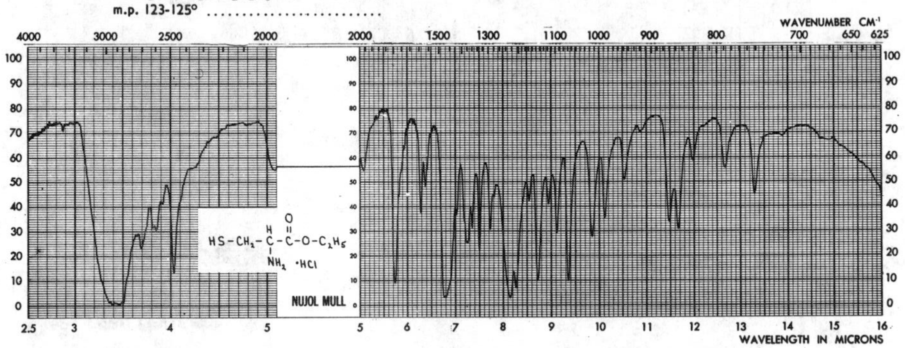

NUJOL MULL

D

85,732-7
L-Cystine dimethyl ester dihydrochloride
$[-SCH_2CH(NH_2)CO_2CH_3]_2 \cdot 2HCl$
M.W. 341.28 m.p. 182-183° (dec.)

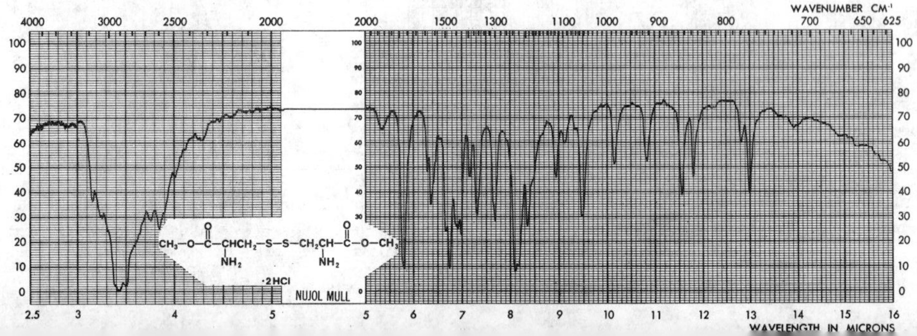

NUJOL MULL

E

86,040-9
L-Methionine methyl ester hydrochloride, 99+%
$CH_3SCH_2CH_2CH(NH_2)CO_2CH_3 \cdot HCl$ FW 199.70
mp 151-153° $[\alpha]^{22}$ +25.9° (c=1, H_2O) Disp. L

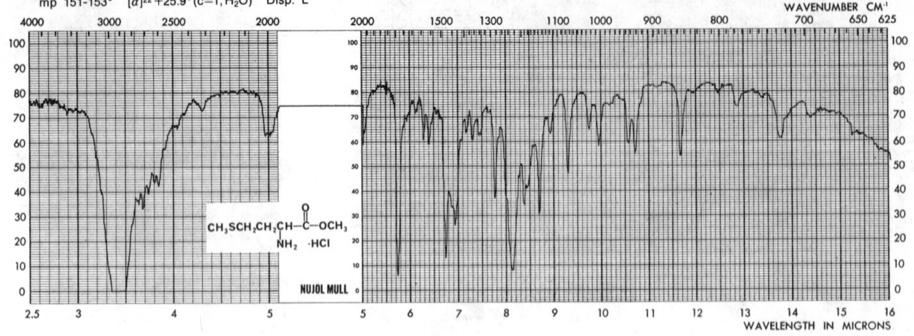

NUJOL MULL

F

22,067-1
L-Methionine ethyl ester hydrochloride, 99%
$CH_3SCH_2CH_2CH(NH_2)CO_2C_2H_5 \cdot HCl$ FW 213.73
mp 90-92° $[\alpha]^{21}$ +17.7° (c=2, C_2H_5OH) Disp. L

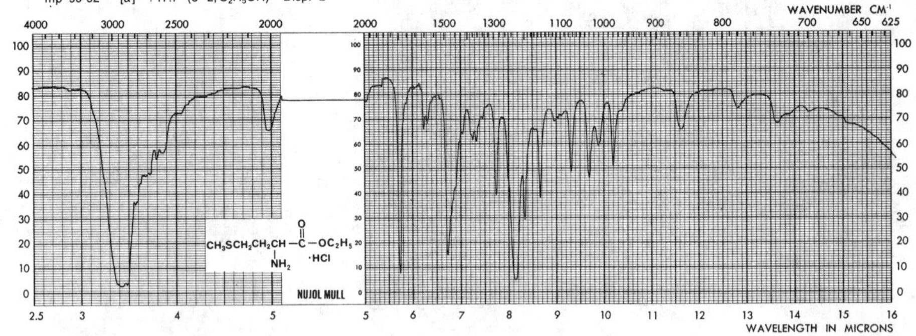

NUJOL MULL

G

22,313-1
DL-Serine methyl ester hydrochloride, 99%
$HOCH_2CH(NH_2)CO_2CH_3 \cdot HCl$ FW 155.58
mp 134-136° *Beil.* 4,512 Disp. L

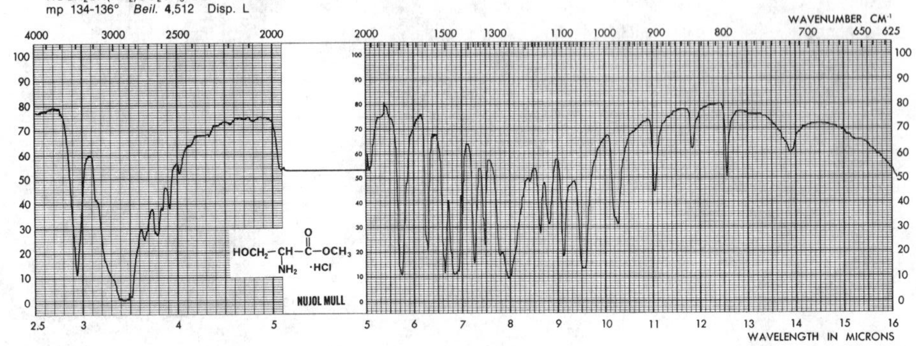

NUJOL MULL

H

S265-1 L-Serine methyl ester hydrochloride
$HOCH_2CH(NH_2)CO_2CH_3 \cdot HCl$ M.W. 155.58
m.p. 163° (dec.)

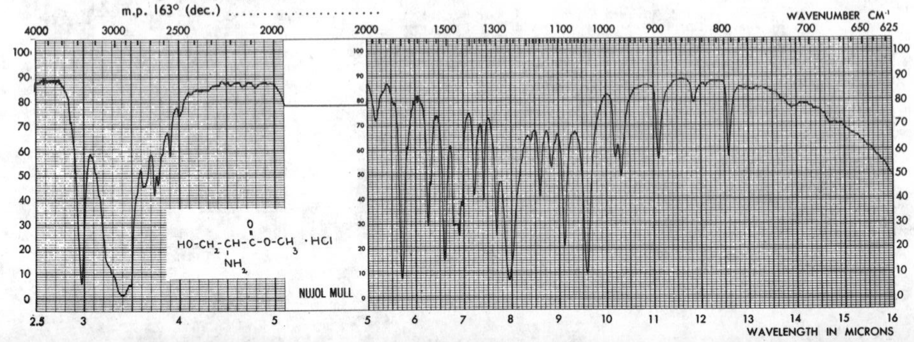

NUJOL MULL

A

22,312-3
L-Serine ethyl ester hydrochloride, 99%
$HOCH_2CH(NH_2)CO_2C_2H_5 \cdot HCl$ FW 169.61
mp 130-132° $[\alpha]_D^{25}$ -4.4° (c=2, H_2O) Disp. L

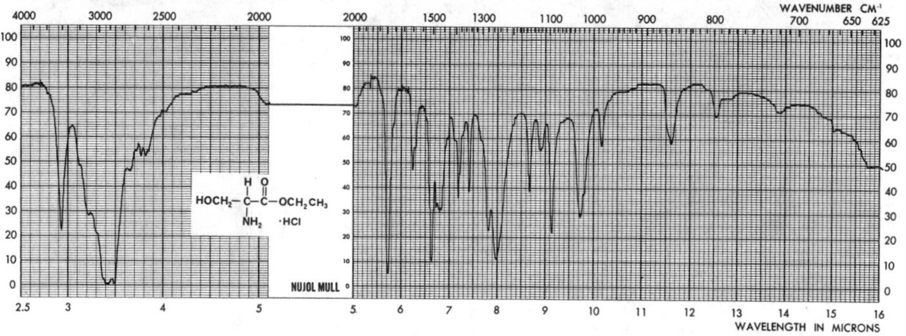

NUJOL MULL

B

D8758-9 **Diethyl aminomalonate hydrochloride**
$C_2H_5O_2CCH(NH_2)CO_2C_2H_5 \cdot HCl$ M.W. 211.65
m.p. 166° (dec.)

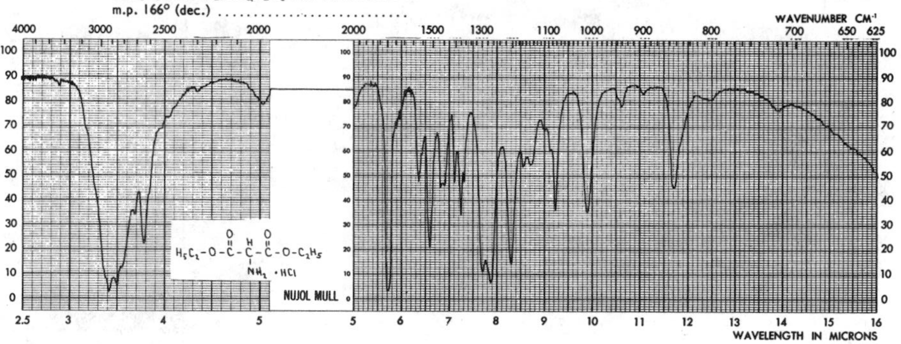

NUJOL MULL

C

85,826-9
L-Glutamic acid 5-methyl ester, 99%
$CH_3O_2CCH_2CH_2CH(NH_2)CO_2H$
M.W. 161.16 m.p. 182° (dec.)
$[\alpha]_D^{25}$ +29° (c=2, 6N HCl)

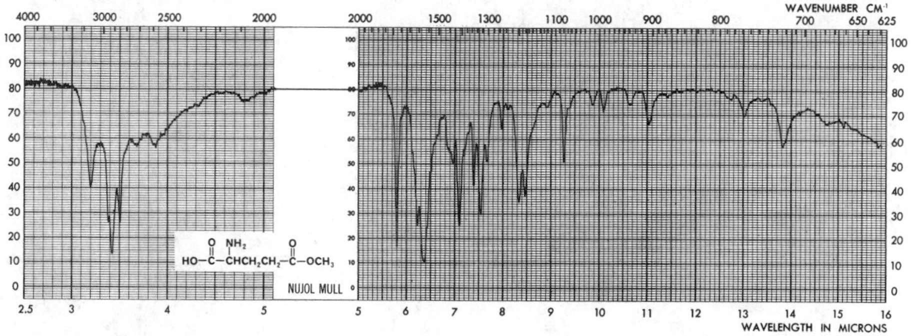

NUJOL MULL

D

85,708-4
L-Aspartic acid di-*tert*.-butyl ester hydrochloride
$(CH_3)_3CO_2CCH_2CH(NH_2)CO_2C(CH_3)_3 \cdot HCl$
M.W. 281.78 m.p. 151-153° (dec.)

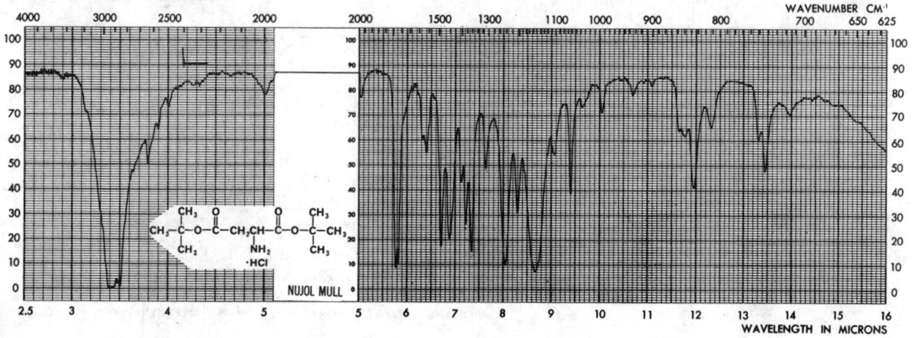

NUJOL MULL

E

13,535-6 **Acetylcholine chloride**
$CH_3CO_2CH_2CH_2N(CH_3)_3Cl$ M.W. 181.66

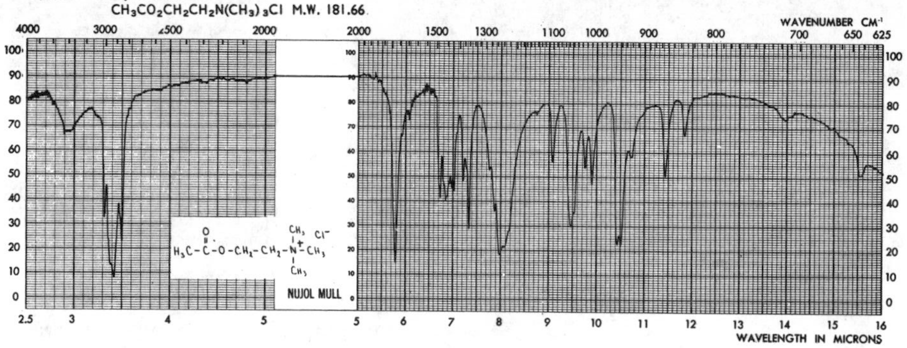

NUJOL MULL

F

10,043-9 **Acetylcholine iodide**
$CH_3CO_2CH_2CH_2N(CH_3)_3I$ M.W. 273.12
m.p. 159-161°

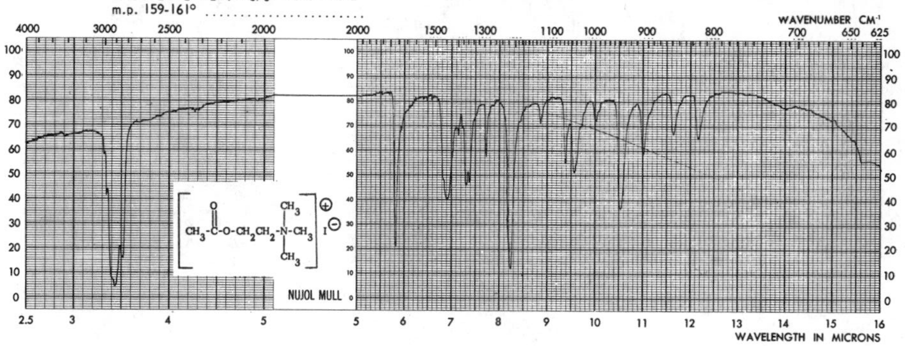

NUJOL MULL

G

85,968-0
Acetylcholine bromide, 98%
$CH_3CO_2CH_2CH_2N(CH_3)_3Br$
M.W. 226.12 m.p. 144-146°

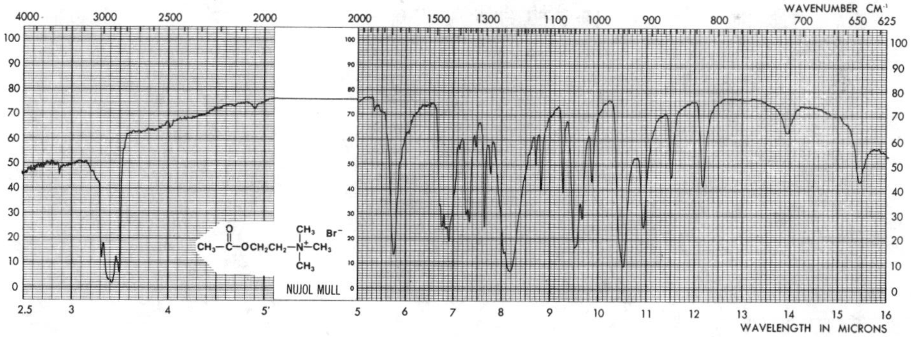

NUJOL MULL

H

85,533-2
S-Acetylthiocholine bromide [(2-mercaptoethyl)-trimethylammonium bromide acetate]
$CH_3COSCH_2CH_2N(CH_3)_3Br$
M.W. 242.18 m.p. 158-160° (dec.)

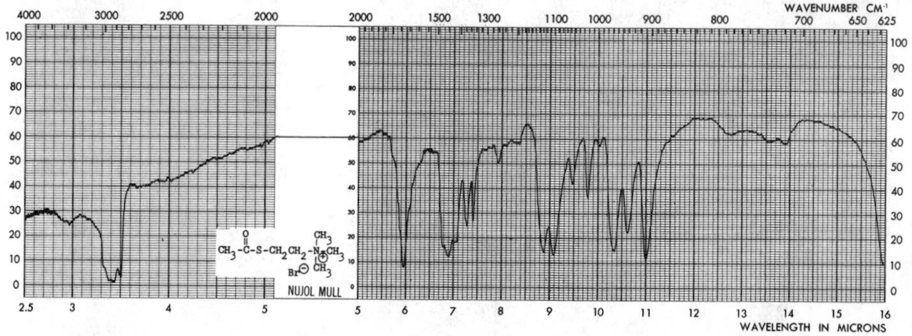

NUJOL MULL

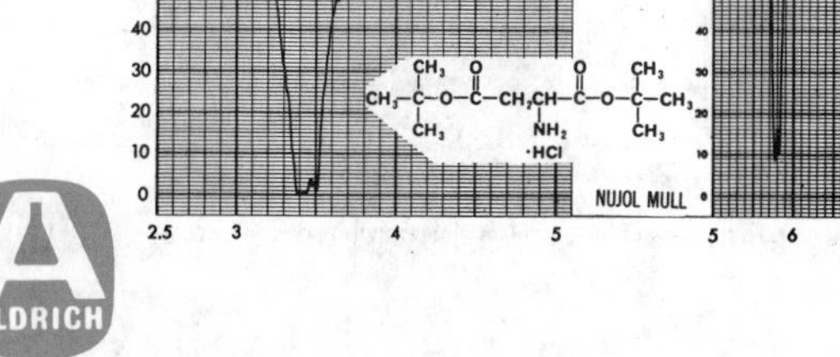

ALDRICH

A — A2230-0 **S-Acetylthiocholine iodide** [(2-mercaptoethyl)-trimethylammonium iodide acetate]
$CH_3COSCH_2CH_2N(CH_3)_3I$ M.W. 289.18
m.p. 205-208.5°

B — A1800-1 **Acetyl-β-methylcholine chloride**
$CH_3CO_2CH(CH_3)CH_2N(CH_3)_3Cl$ M.W. 195.69
m.p. 171-173°

C — 85,554-5 **Acetyl-β-methylcholine bromide**
(methacholine bromide)
$CH_3CO_2CH(CH_3)CH_2N(CH_3)_3Br$
M.W. 240.15 m.p. 136-137°

D — 10,411-6 **Propionylcholine iodide**
$C_2H_5CO_2CH_2CH_2N(CH_3)_3I$ M.W. 287.14 m.p. 126-128°

E — 10,412-4 **S-Propionylthiocholine iodide** [(2-mercaptoethyl)trimethylammonium iodide propionate]
$C_2H_5COSCH_2CH_2N(CH_3)_3I$ M.W. 303.21 m.p. 195-198°

F — 85,537-5 **Butyrylcholine chloride** [(2-hydroxyethyl)-trimethylammonium chloride butyrate]
$CH_3CH_2CH_2CO_2CH_2CH_2N(CH_3)_3Cl$
M.W. 209.72 m.p. 116-118°

G — 10,116-8 **Butyrylcholine iodide** [(2-hydroxyethyl)-trimethylammonium iodide butyrate]
$CH_3CH_2CH_2CO_2CH_2CH_2N(CH_3)_3I$ M.W. 301.17 m.p. 87-90°

H — B10,425-6 **S-Butyrylthiocholine iodide** [(2-mercaptoethyl)-trimethylammonium iodide butyrate]
$CH_3CH_2CH_2COSCH_2CH_2N(CH_3)_3I$ M.W. 317.23
m.p. 172-174.5°

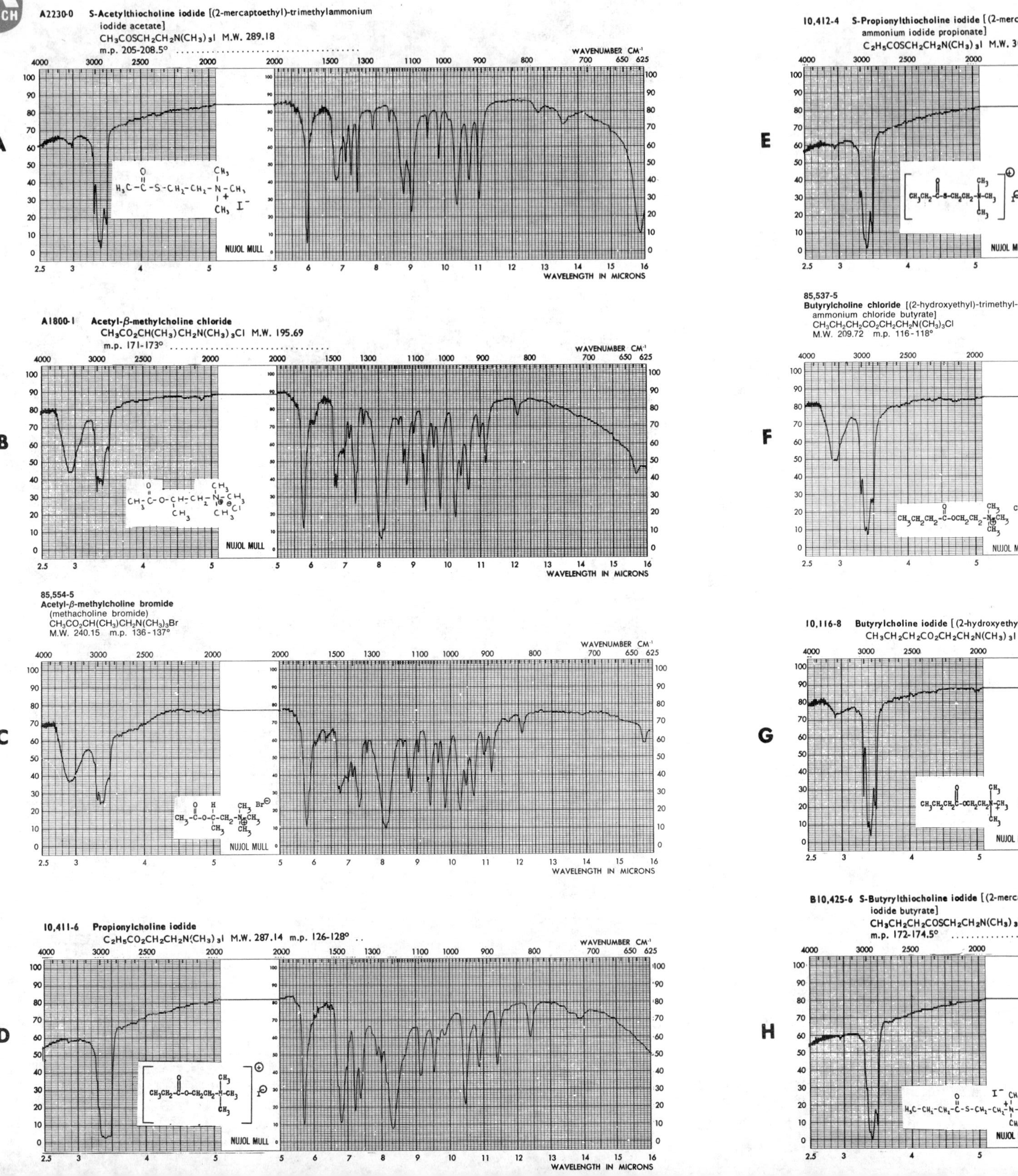

A 14,322-7 **Diethyl (dimethylaminomethylene)-malonate**
$(CH_3)_2NCH{:}C(CO_2C_2H_5)_2$ M.W. 215.25 n_D^{20} 1.5097
b.p. 134-136°/0.6 mm.
NUJOL MULL

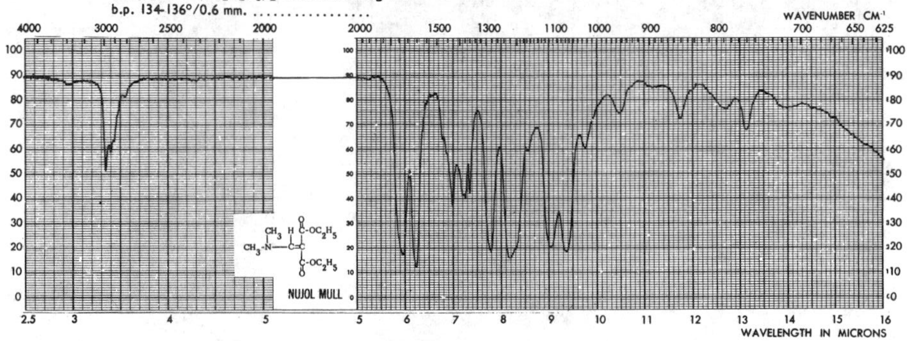

B 12,023-5 **Diethyl (2-dimethylaminoethyl)-malonate**
$C_2H_5O_2CCH[CH_2CH_2N(CH_3)_2]CO_2C_2H_5$ M.W. 231.29
n_D^{20} 1.4346 b.p. 126-133°/13 mm.
NEAT

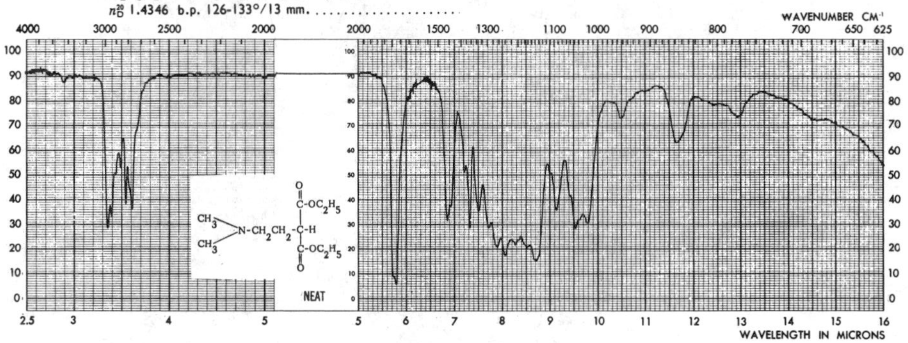

C 12,020-0 **Diethyl (2-diethylaminoethyl)-malonate**
$C_2H_5O_2CCH[CH_2CH_2N(C_2H_5)_2]CO_2C_2H_5$ M.W. 259.35
n_D^{20} 1.4390 b.p. 141-148°/13 mm.
NEAT

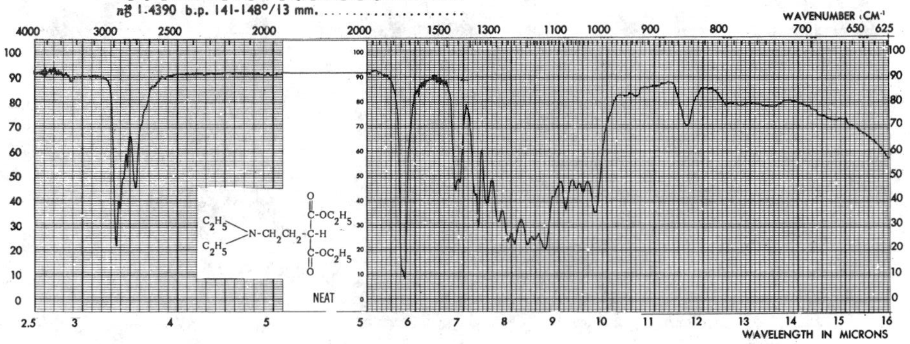

D 12,024-3 **Diethyl (3-dimethylaminopropyl)-malonate**
$C_2H_5O_2CCH[(CH_2)_3N(CH_3)_2]CO_2C_2H_5$ M.W. 245.32
n_D^{20} 1.4386 b.p. 144-149°/13 mm.
NEAT

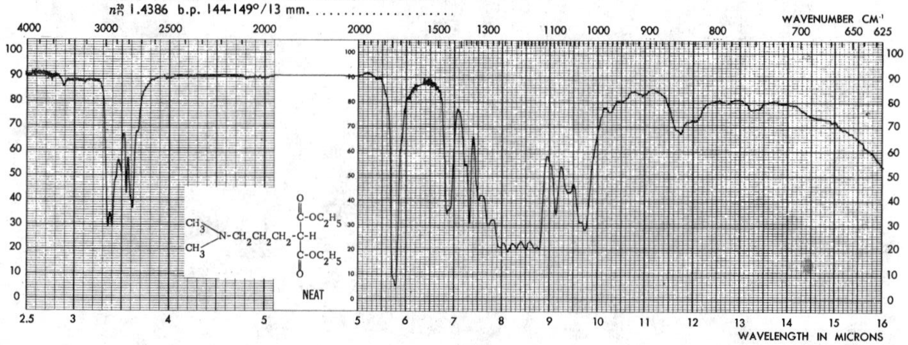

E 12,021-9 **Diethyl (3-diethylaminopropyl)-malonate**
$C_2H_5O_2CCH[(CH_2)_3N(C_2H_5)_2]CO_2C_2H_5$ M.W. 273.37
n_D^{20} 1.4419 b.p. 157-165°/15 mm.
NEAT

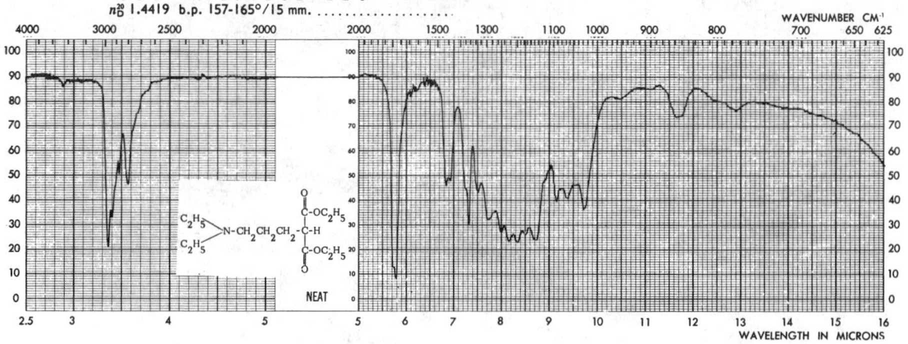

F T6030-5 **Triethyl nitrilotricarboxylate (triethyl N-tricarboxylate)**
$N(CO_2C_2H_5)_3$ M.W. 233.22 n_D^{20} 1.4282
b.p. 143-144°/13 mm.
NEAT

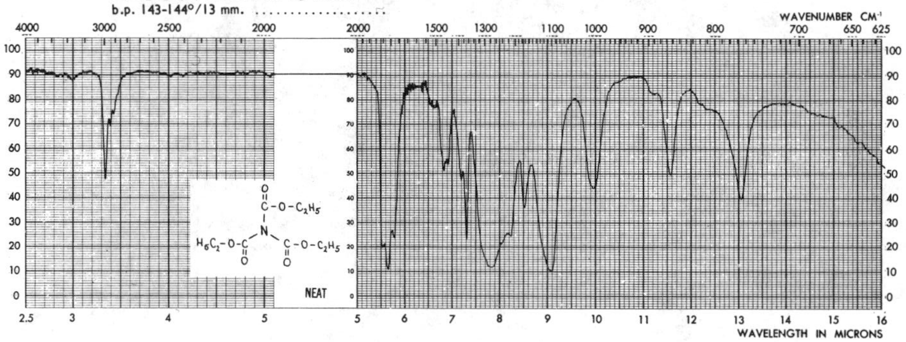

G 10,514-7 **Tetraethyl ethylenediaminetetraacetate** (EDTA tetraethyl ester)
$(C_2H_5O_2CCH_2)_2NCH_2CH_2N(CH_2CO_2C_2H_5)_2$ M.W. 404.46
m.p. 34-36°
MELT

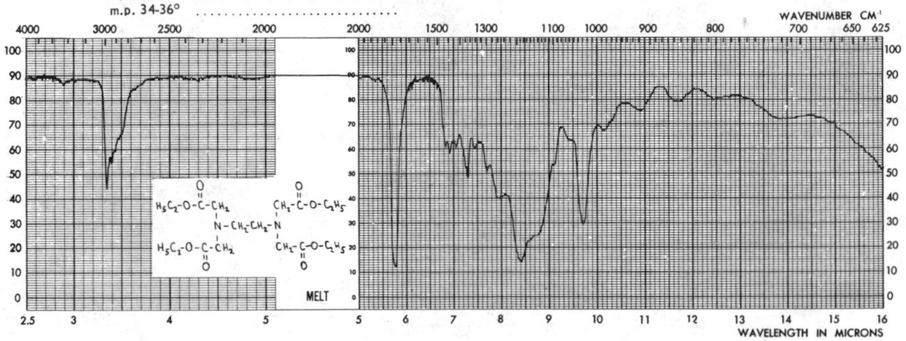

H 13,155-5 **Propyl 3,5-diiodo-4-oxo-1(4H)-pyridineacetate**
M.W. 447.01 m.p. 185-187°
NUJOL MULL

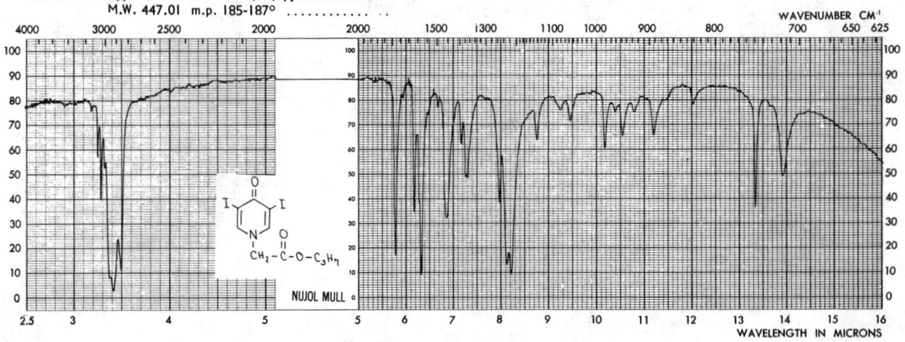

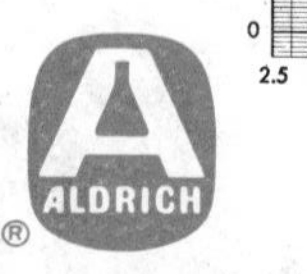

NON-AROMATIC ESTERS & LACTONES

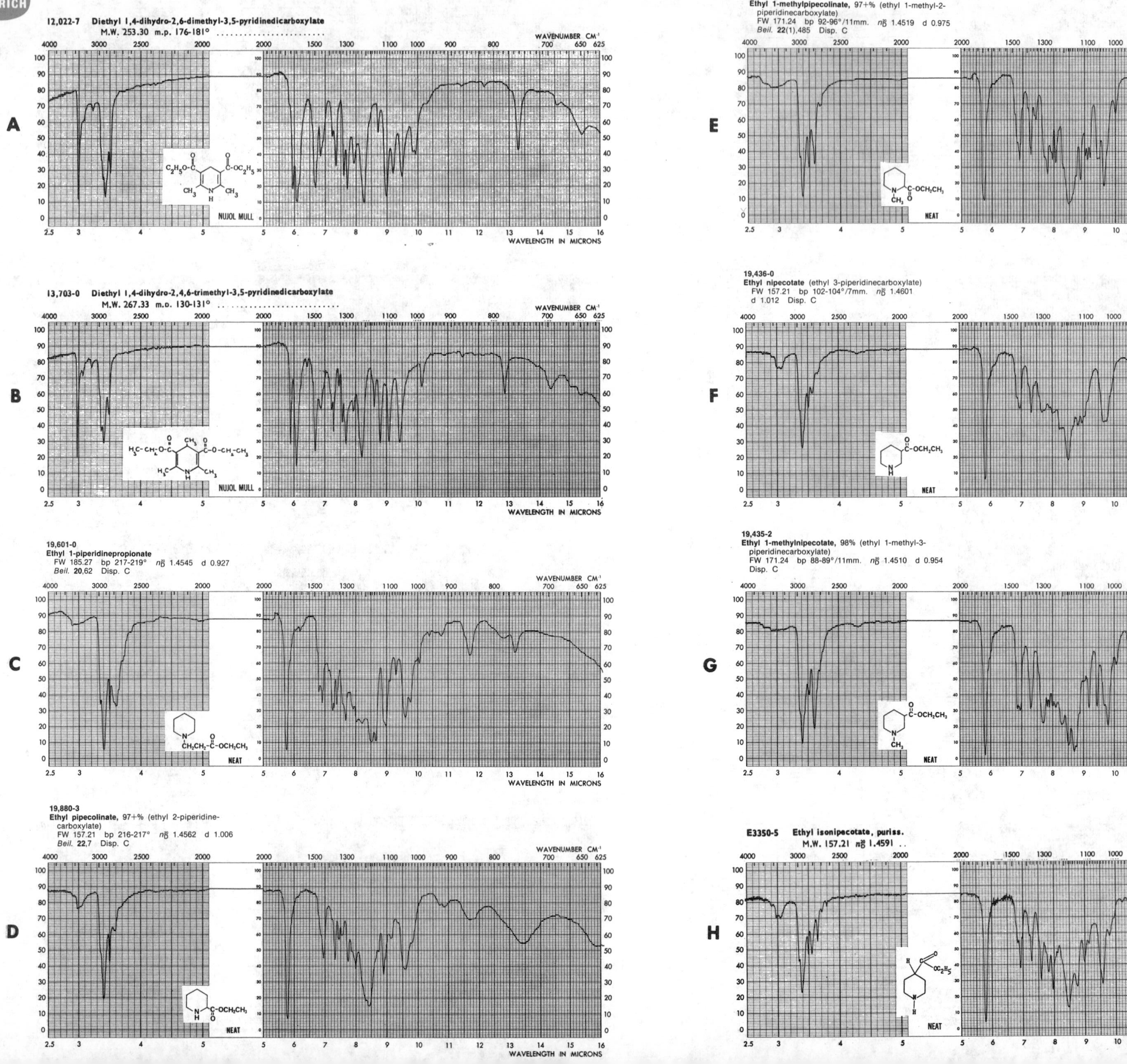

A 12,022-7 **Diethyl 1,4-dihydro-2,6-dimethyl-3,5-pyridinedicarboxylate**
M.W. 253.30 m.p. 176-181° NUJOL MULL

B 13,703-0 **Diethyl 1,4-dihydro-2,4,6-trimethyl-3,5-pyridinedicarboxylate**
M.W. 267.33 m.p. 130-131° NUJOL MULL

C 19,601-0
Ethyl 1-piperidinepropionate
FW 185.27 bp 217-219° n_D^{20} 1.4545 d 0.927
Beil. **20**,62 Disp. C NEAT

D 19,880-3
Ethyl pipecolinate, 97+% (ethyl 2-piperidinecarboxylate)
FW 157.21 bp 216-217° n_D^{20} 1.4562 d 1.006
Beil. **22**,7 Disp. C NEAT

E 19,881-1
Ethyl 1-methylpipecolinate, 97+% (ethyl 1-methyl-2-piperidinecarboxylate)
FW 171.24 bp 92-96°/11mm. n_D^{20} 1.4519 d 0.975
Beil. **22**(1),485 Disp. C NEAT

F 19,436-0
Ethyl nipecotate (ethyl 3-piperidinecarboxylate)
FW 157.21 bp 102-104°/7mm. n_D^{20} 1.4601
d 1.012 Disp. C NEAT

G 19,435-2
Ethyl 1-methylnipecotate, 98% (ethyl 1-methyl-3-piperidinecarboxylate)
FW 171.24 bp 88-89°/11mm. n_D^{20} 1.4510 d 0.954
Disp. C NEAT

H E3350-5 **Ethyl isonipecotate, puriss.**
M.W. 157.21 n_D^{20} 1.4591 NEAT

A

11,757-9 **Ethyl 4-carbethoxy-1-piperidineacetate**
M.W. 243.31 n_D^{20} 1.4598

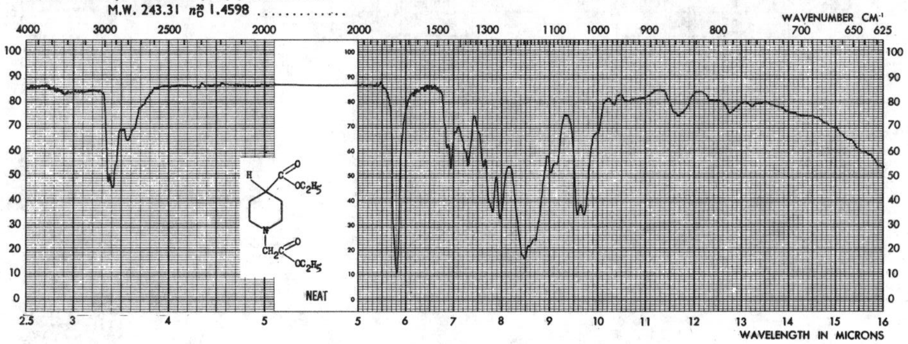

NEAT

B

19,151-5
Methyl 4-oxo-3-piperidinecarboxylate hydrochloride
FW 193.63 mp 177° (dec.) Disp. C

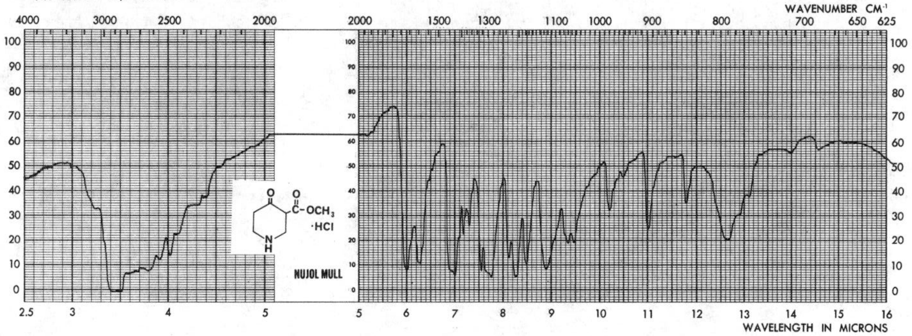

NUJOL MULL

C

M7980-8 **Methyl pyruvate**
$CH_3COCO_2CH_3$ M.W. 102.09 n_D^{20} 1.4065
b.p. 134-137°

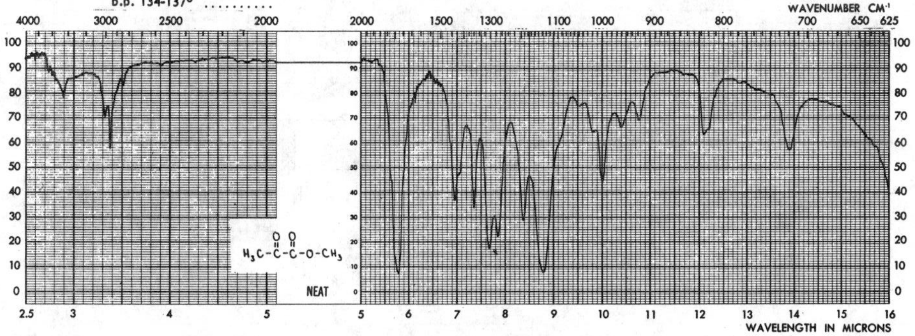

NEAT

D

E4780-8 **Ethyl pyruvate**
$CH_3COCO_2C_2H_5$ M.W. 116.12 n_D^{20} 1.4056

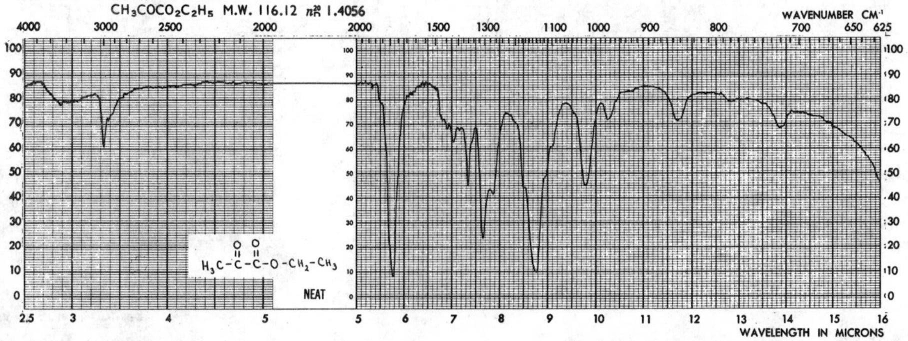

NEAT

E

21,845-6
Ethyl 3-methyl-2-oxobutyrate (ketovaline ethyl ester)
$(CH_3)_2CHCOCO_2C_2H_5$ FW 144.17 bp 62°/11mm.
n_D^{20} 1.4115 d 0.989 *Beil.* 3,683 Disp. C

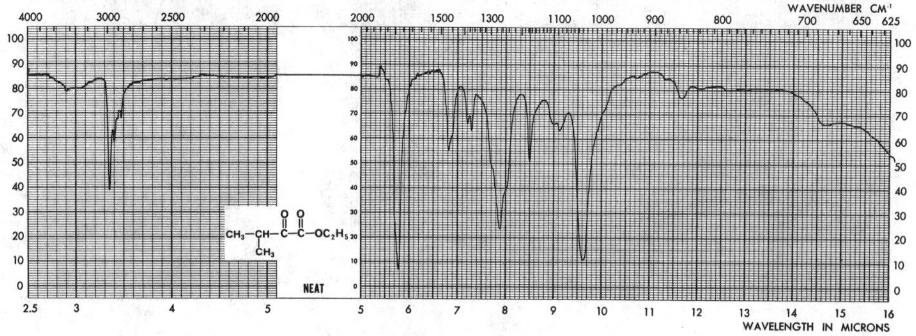

NEAT

F

21,846-4
Ethyl 4-methyl-2-oxovalerate, 99% (ketoleucine ethyl ester)
$(CH_3)_2CHCH_2COCO_2C_2H_5$ FW 158.20
bp 74°/11mm. n_D^{20} 1.4185 d 0.970 *Beil.* 3,690
Disp. C

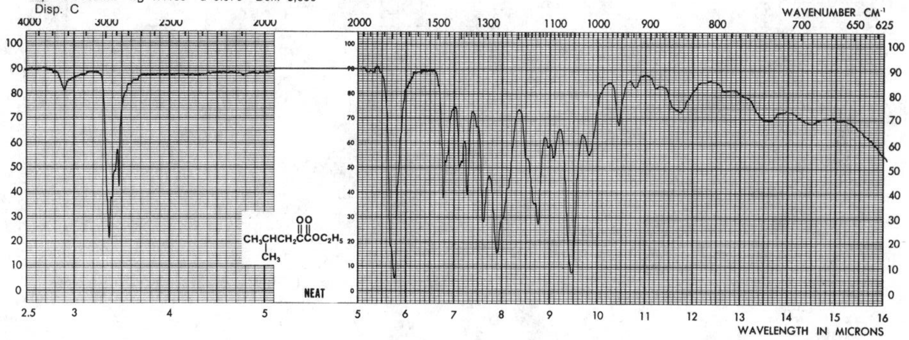

NEAT

G

E1457-8 **Ethyl bromopyruvate**
$BrCH_2COCO_2C_2H_5$ M.W. 195.03
n_D^{20} 1.4713

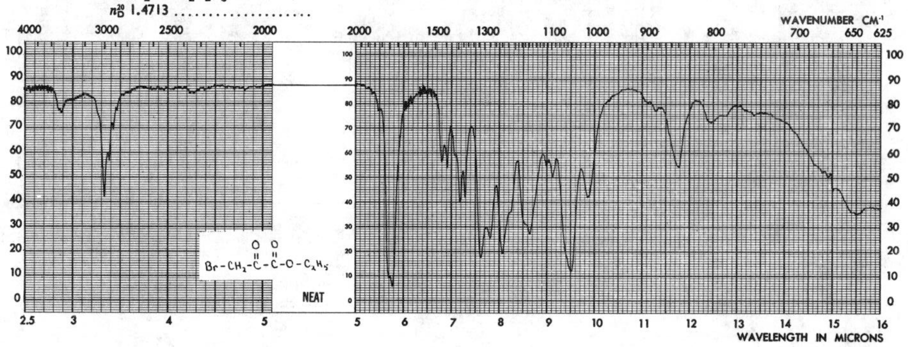

NEAT

H

12,262-9 **Ethyl levulinate**
$CH_3COCH_2CH_2CO_2C_2H_5$ M.W. 144.17 n_D^{20} 1.4222
b.p. 93-94°/18 mm.

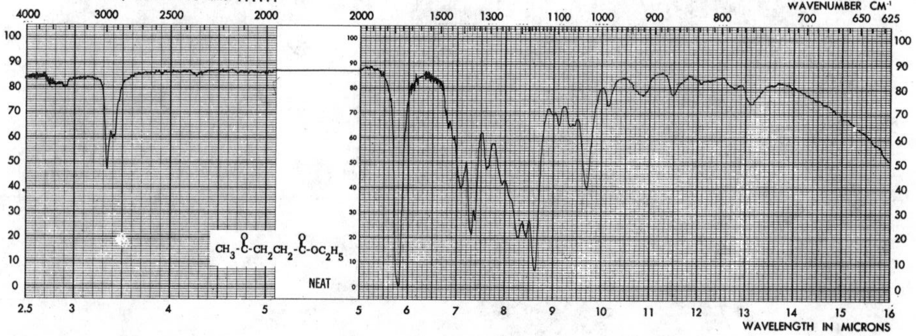

NEAT

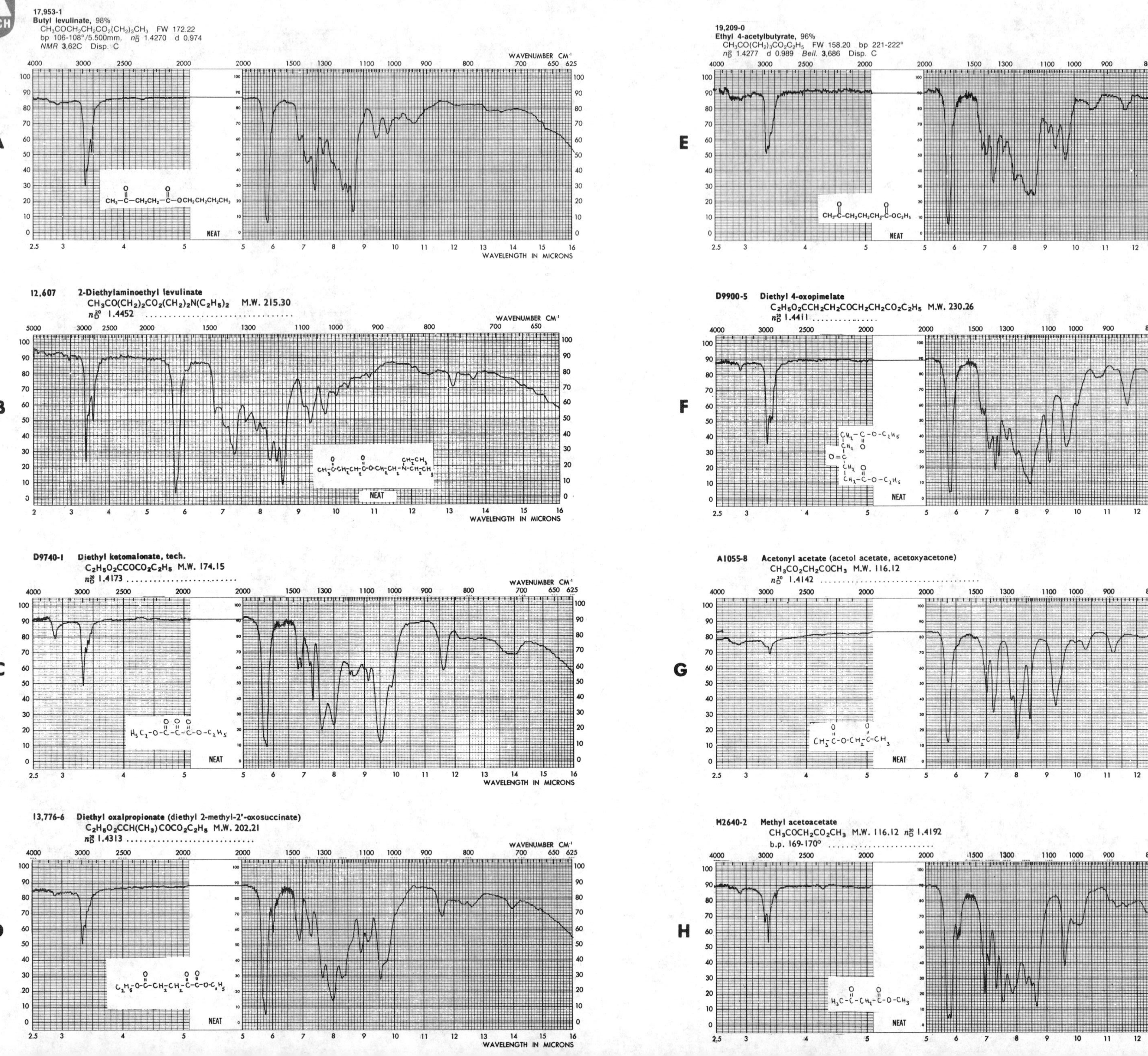
ALDRICH
A
17,953-1
Butyl levulinate, 98%
CH3COCH2CH2CO2(CH2)3CH3 FW 172.22
bp 106-108°/5.500mm. n20D 1.4270 d 0.974
NMR 3,62C Disp. C
NEAT
B
12,607 2-Diethylaminoethyl levulinate
CH3CO(CH2)2CO2(CH2)2N(C2H5)2 M.W. 215.30
n20D 1.4452
NEAT
C
D9740-1 Diethyl ketomalonate, tech.
C2H5O2CCOCO2C2H5 M.W. 174.15
n20D 1.4173
NEAT
D
13,776-6 Diethyl oxalpropionate (diethyl 2-methyl-2'-oxosuccinate)
C2H5O2CCH(CH3)COCO2C2H5 M.W. 202.21
n20D 1.4313
NEAT
E
19,209-0
Ethyl 4-acetylbutyrate, 96%
CH3CO(CH2)3CO2C2H5 FW 158.20 bp 221-222°
n20D 1.4277 d 0.989 Beil. 3,686 Disp. C
NEAT
F
D9900-5 Diethyl 4-oxopimelate
C2H5O2CCH2CH2COCH2CH2CO2C2H5 M.W. 230.26
n20D 1.4411
NEAT
G
A1055-8 Acetonyl acetate (acetol acetate, acetoxyacetone)
CH3CO2CH2COCH3 M.W. 116.12
n20D 1.4142
NEAT
H
M2640-2 Methyl acetoacetate
CH3COCH2CO2CH3 M.W. 116.12 n20D 1.4192
b.p. 169-170°
NEAT
WAVENUMBER CM-1
WAVELENGTH IN MICRONS

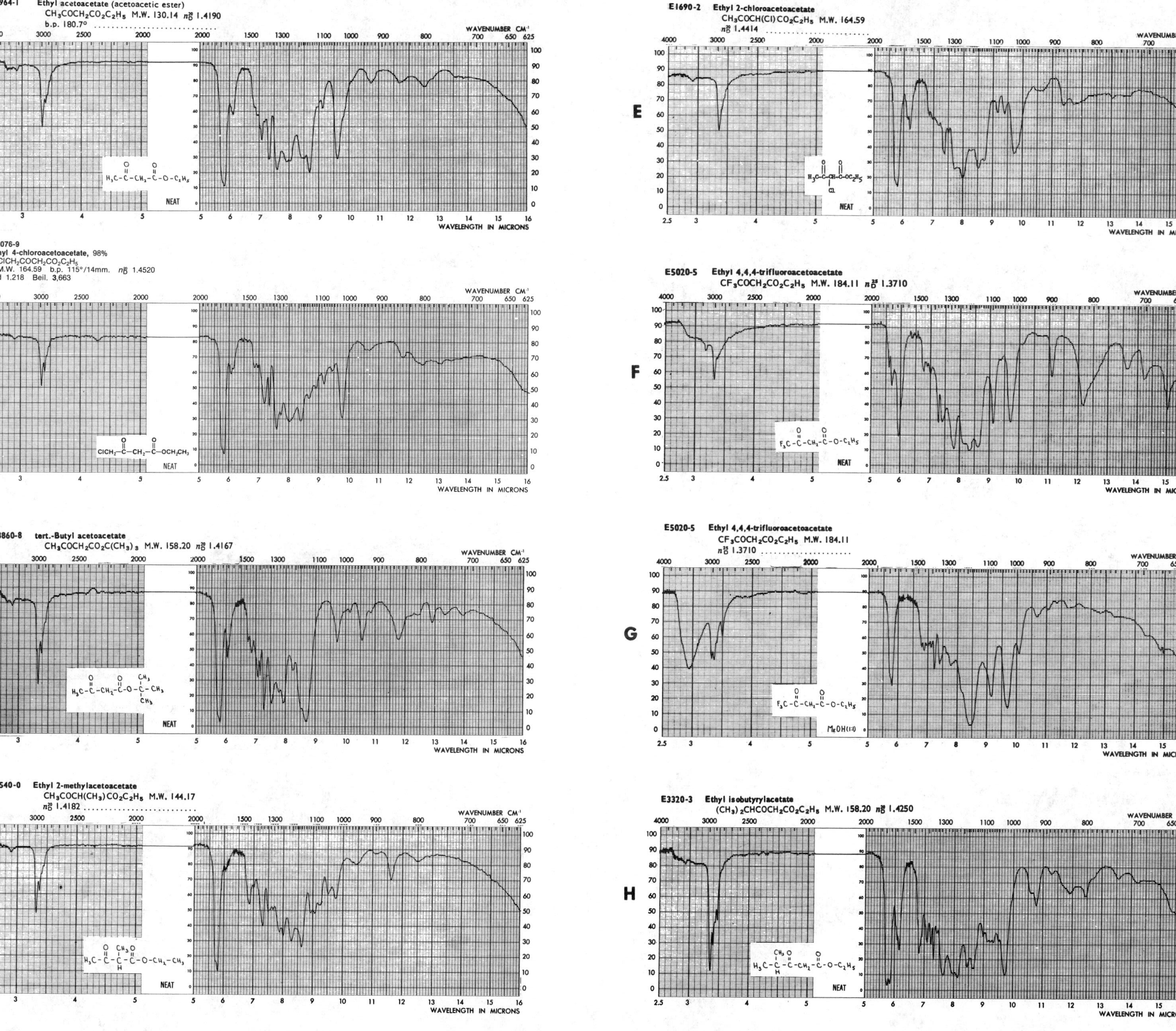

A
E964-1 Ethyl acetoacetate (acetoacetic ester)
CH3COCH2CO2C2H5 M.W. 130.14 n20D 1.4190
b.p. 180.7°
NEAT
B
18,076-9
Ethyl 4-chloroacetoacetate, 98%
ClCH2COCH2CO2C2H5
M.W. 164.59 b.p. 115°/14mm. n20D 1.4520
d 1.218 Beil. 3,663
NEAT
C
B8860-8 tert.-Butyl acetoacetate
CH3COCH2CO2C(CH3)3 M.W. 158.20 n20D 1.4167
NEAT
D
E3540-0 Ethyl 2-methylacetoacetate
CH3COCH(CH3)CO2C2H5 M.W. 144.17
n20D 1.4182
NEAT
E
E1690-2 Ethyl 2-chloroacetoacetate
CH3COCH(Cl)CO2C2H5 M.W. 164.59
n20D 1.4414
NEAT
F
E5020-5 Ethyl 4,4,4-trifluoroacetoacetate
CF3COCH2CO2C2H5 M.W. 184.11 n20D 1.3710
NEAT
G
E5020-5 Ethyl 4,4,4-trifluoroacetoacetate
CF3COCH2CO2C2H5 M.W. 184.11
n20D 1.3710
MeOH(1:1)
H
E3320-3 Ethyl isobutyrylacetate
(CH3)2CHCOCH2CO2C2H5 M.W. 158.20 n20D 1.4250
NEAT
WAVENUMBER CM⁻¹
WAVELENGTH IN MICRONS
ALDRICH

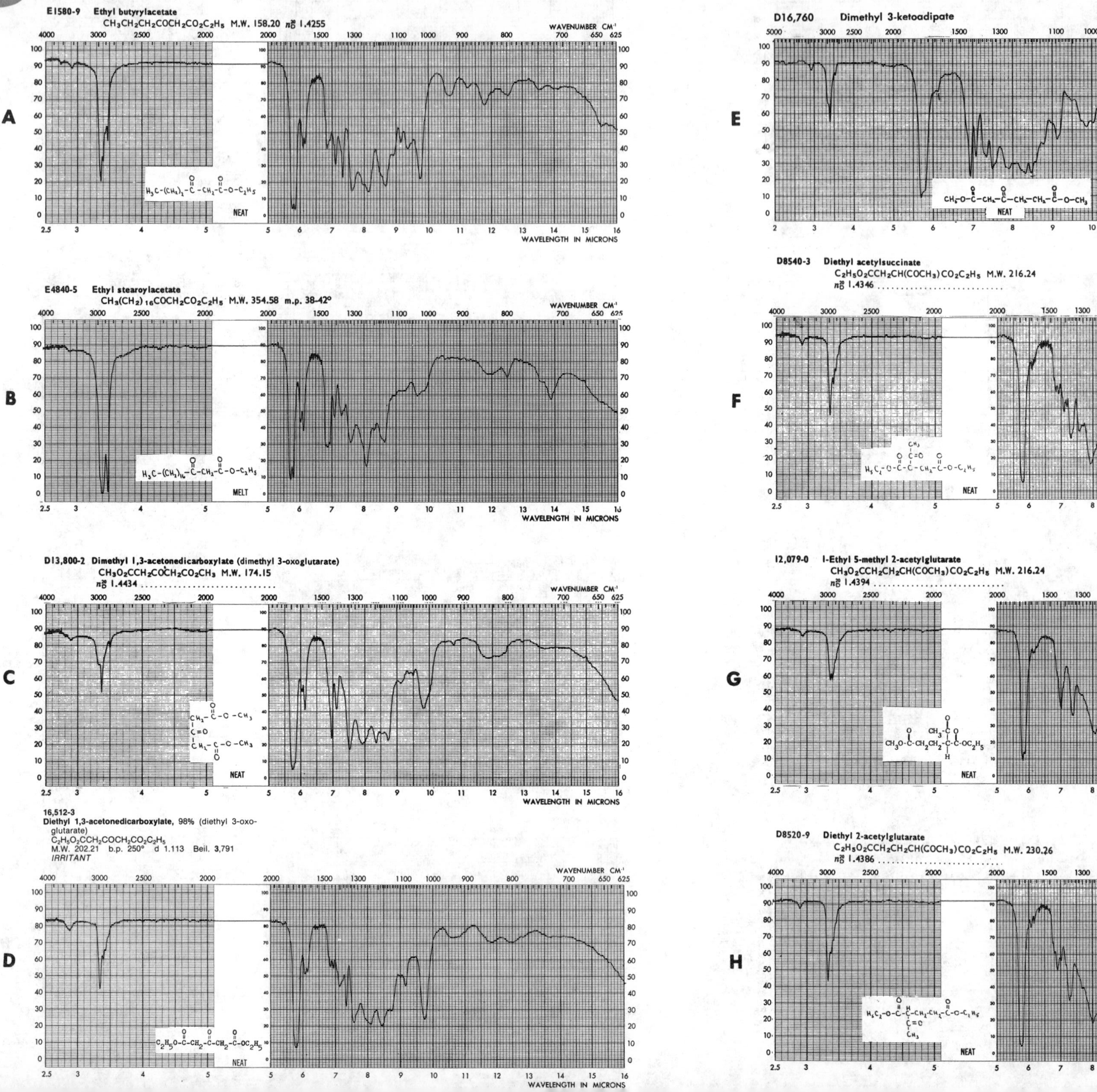
A
E1580-9 Ethyl butyrylacetate
$CH_3CH_2CH_2COCH_2CO_2C_2H_5$ M.W. 158.20 n_D^{20} 1.4255
NEAT
B
E4840-5 Ethyl stearoylacetate
$CH_3(CH_2)_{16}COCH_2CO_2C_2H_5$ M.W. 354.58 m.p. 38-42°
MELT
C
D13,800-2 Dimethyl 1,3-acetonedicarboxylate (dimethyl 3-oxoglutarate)
$CH_3O_2CCH_2COCH_2CO_2CH_3$ M.W. 174.15
n_D^{20} 1.4434
NEAT
D
16,512-3
Diethyl 1,3-acetonedicarboxylate, 98% (diethyl 3-oxoglutarate)
$C_2H_5O_2CCH_2COCH_2CO_2C_2H_5$
M.W. 202.21 b.p. 250° d 1.113 Beil. 3,791
IRRITANT
NEAT
E
D16,760 Dimethyl 3-ketoadipate
NEAT
F
D8540-3 Diethyl acetylsuccinate
$C_2H_5O_2CCH_2CH(COCH_3)CO_2C_2H_5$ M.W. 216.24
n_D^{20} 1.4346
NEAT
G
12,079-0 1-Ethyl 5-methyl 2-acetylglutarate
$CH_3O_2CCH_2CH_2CH(COCH_3)CO_2C_2H_5$ M.W. 216.24
n_D^{20} 1.4394
NEAT
H
D8520-9 Diethyl 2-acetylglutarate
$C_2H_5O_2CCH_2CH_2CH(COCH_3)CO_2C_2H_5$ M.W. 230.26
n_D^{20} 1.4386
NEAT
WAVENUMBER CM⁻¹
WAVELENGTH IN MICRONS

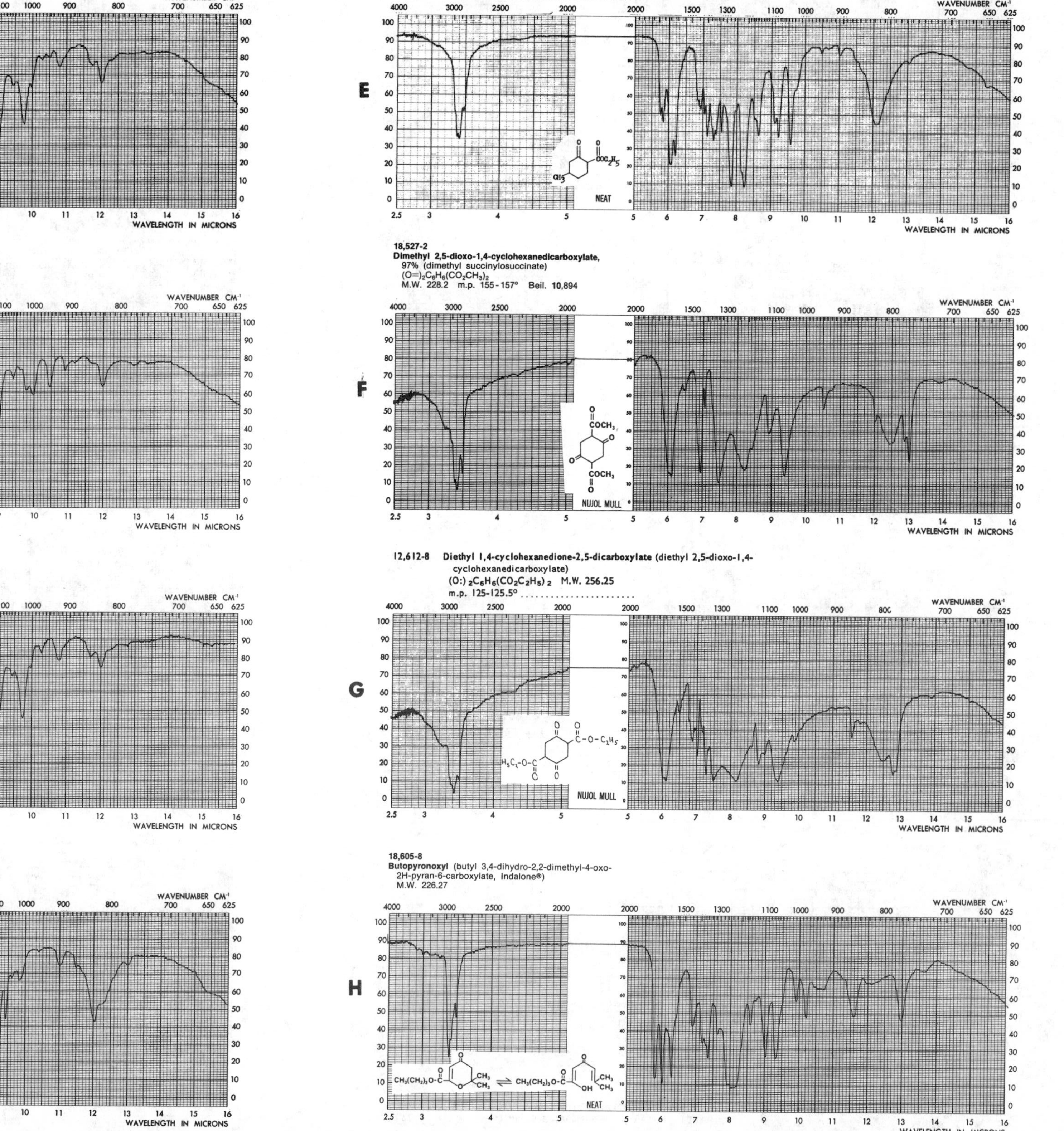

A 11,912-1 **2-Cyclopentanonecarboxylic acid ester** (mixture of 50% ethyl and 50% methyl)
n_D^{20} 1.4538
NEAT

B 16,810-6
Methyl 2-oxocyclopentanecarboxylate
(O=)$C_5H_7CO_2CH_3$
M.W. 142.15 b.p. 105°/19mm. n_D^{20} 1.4560
d 1.145 Beil. **10**,597
NEAT

C 16,809-2
Ethyl 2-oxocyclopentanecarboxylate, 97%
(O=)$C_5H_7CO_2C_2H_5$
M.W. 156.18 b.p. 218°/704mm. n_D^{20} 1.4485
d 1.054 Beil. **10**,597
NEAT

D E2000-4 **Ethyl 2-cyclohexanonecarboxylate** (contains approximately 40% of corresponding methyl ester)
(O:)$C_6H_9CO_2C_2H_5$ n_D^{20} 1.4799
NEAT

E E3570-2 **Ethyl 4-methyl-2-cyclohexanone-1-carboxylate** (ethyl 4-methyl-2-oxo-1-cyclohexanecarboxylate)
$CH_3C_6H_8(:O)CO_2C_2H_5$ M.W. 184.24
n_D^{20} 1.4730
NEAT

F 18,527-2
Dimethyl 2,5-dioxo-1,4-cyclohexanedicarboxylate,
97% (dimethyl succinylosuccinate)
$(O=)_2C_6H_6(CO_2CH_3)_2$
M.W. 228.2 m.p. 155-157° Beil. **10**,894
NUJOL MULL

G 12,612-8 **Diethyl 1,4-cyclohexanedione-2,5-dicarboxylate** (diethyl 2,5-dioxo-1,4-cyclohexanedicarboxylate)
$(O:)_2C_6H_6(CO_2C_2H_5)_2$ M.W. 256.25
m.p. 125-125.5°
NUJOL MULL

H 18,605-8
Butopyronoxyl (butyl 3,4-dihydro-2,2-dimethyl-4-oxo-2H-pyran-6-carboxylate, Indalone®)
M.W. 226.27
NEAT

NON-AROMATIC ESTERS & LACTONES

ALDRICH

A C555-6 **3-Carbethoxy-4-piperidone** (ethyl 4-oxo-3-piperidinecarboxylate) hydrochloride
M.W. 207.66 m.p. 175.5°

B 12,831-7 **Ethyl 3-quinuclidinone-2-carboxylate** (ethyl 3-oxo-2-quinuclidinecarboxylate) hydrochloride
M.W. 197.23 m.p. 184-186°

C E1980-4 **Ethyl 2-cyclohexanoneacetate** (ethyl 2-oxocyclohexaneacetate)
(O:)$C_6H_9CH_2CO_2C_2H_5$ M.W. 184.24 n_D^{20} 1.4580

D C500-9 **4-Carbethoxy-3-methyl-2-cyclohexen-1-one** (ethyl 2-methyl-4-oxo-2-cyclohexene-1-carboxylate, Hagemann's ester)
M.W. 182.22 n_D^{20} 1.4848

E 12,724-8 **4-Carbethoxy-2-ethyl-3-methyl-2-cyclohexen-1-one** (ethyl 3-ethyl-2-methyl-4-oxo-2-cyclohexene-1-carboxylate, 2-ethyl-Hagemann's ester), tech.
M.W. 210.27

F 14,098-8 **Verbenalin** (verbenaloside)
M.W. 388.38 m.p. 181-183°

G 16,718-5
Methyl 2-bromopropionate, 99%
$CH_3CH(Br)CO_2CH_3$ FW 167.01 bp 51°/19mm.
n_D^{20} 1.4520 d 1.497 *Beil.* 2,253 Disp. C

H 10,586-4 **Ethyl 3-formylcyclohexanecarboxylate**
$HCOC_6H_{10}CO_2C_2H_5$ M.W. 184.24 n_D^{20} 1.4592

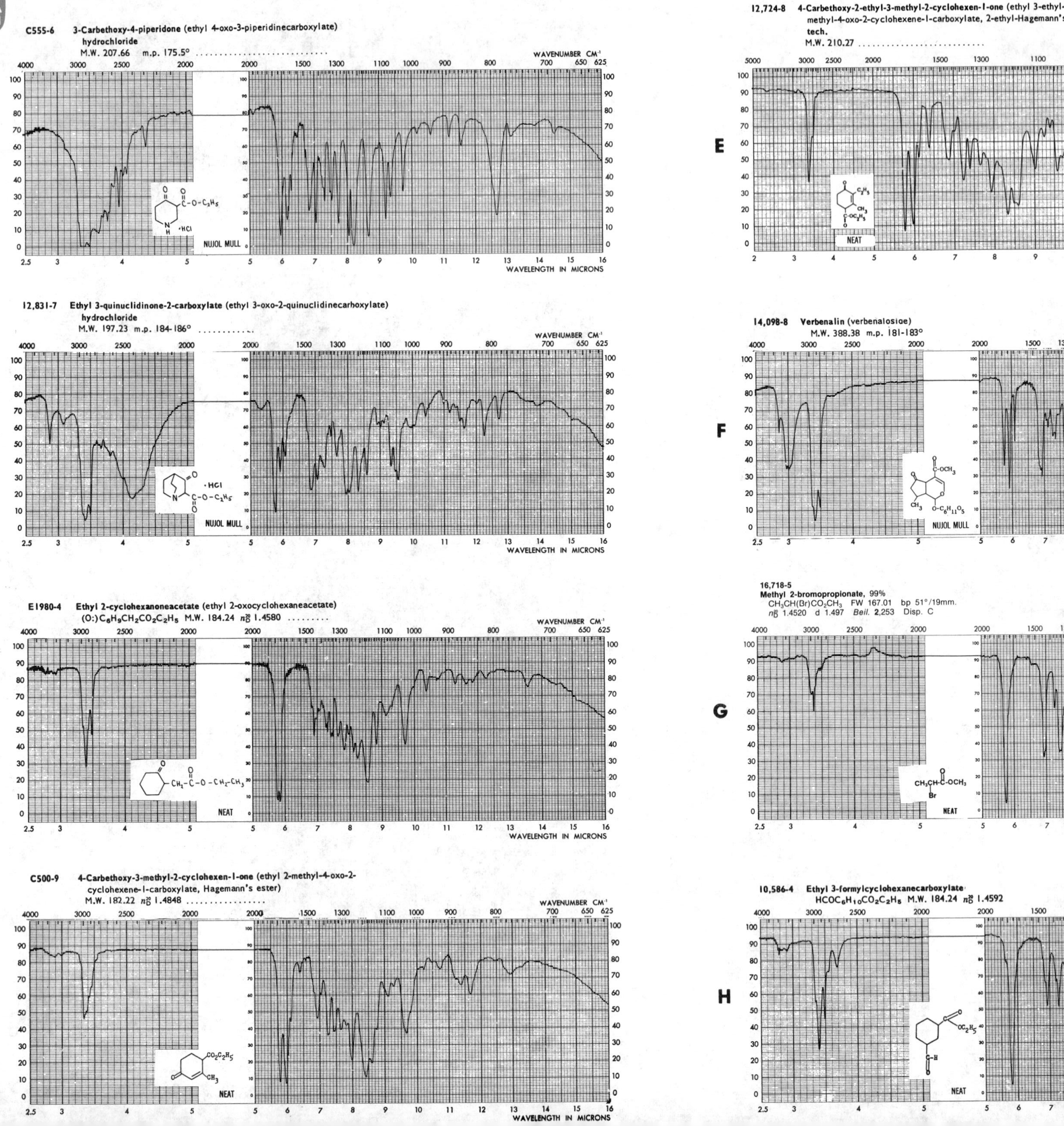

A 12,842-2 **Fumaric acid monoethyl ester** (mono-ethyl fumarate)
$HO_2CCH{:}CHCO_2C_2H_5$ M.W. 144.13 m.p. 61-63°

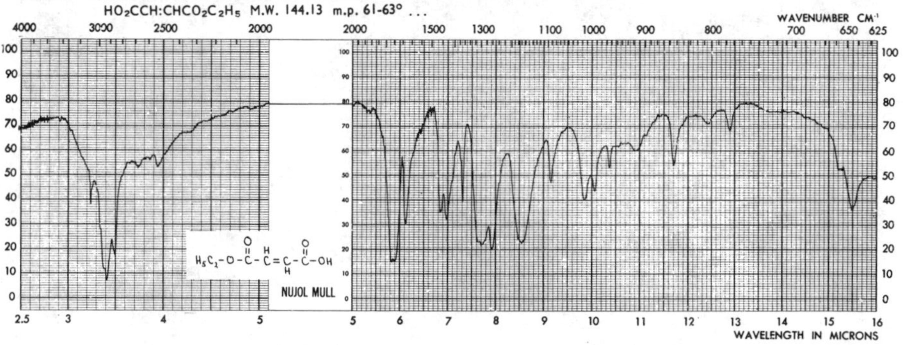

NUJOL MULL

B M8110-1 **mono-Methyl succinate**
$HO_2CCH_2CH_2CO_2CH_3$ M.W. 132.12
m.p. 58.5-62°

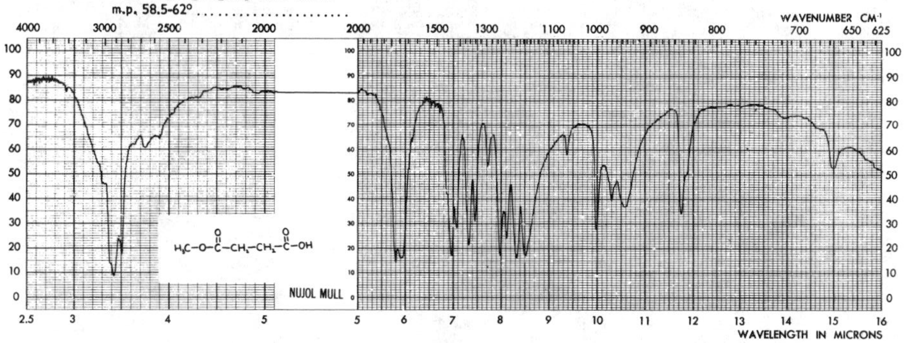

NUJOL MULL

C M8110-1 **mono-Methyl succinate**
$HO_2CCH_2CH_2CO_2CH_3$ M.W. 132.12
m.p. 56-59°

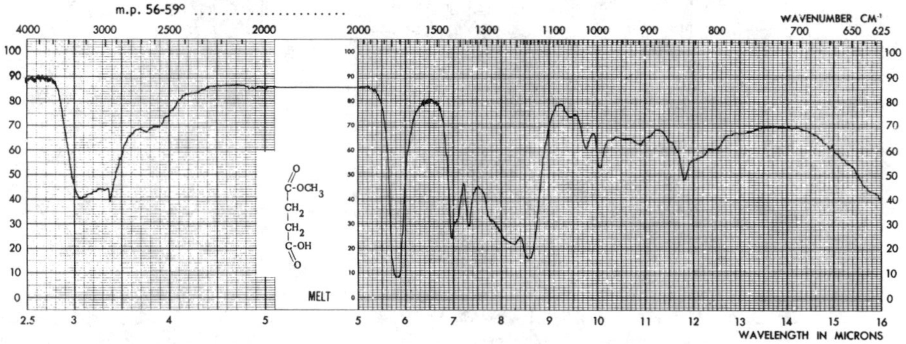

MELT

D A1205-4 ***d*-5-Acetoxy-4-methylpentanoic acid**
$CH_3CO_2CH_2CH(CH_3)CH_2CH_2CO_2H$ M.W. 174.20 n_D^{20} 1.4392
$[\alpha]_D^{20}$ + 4° (15% in ethanol)

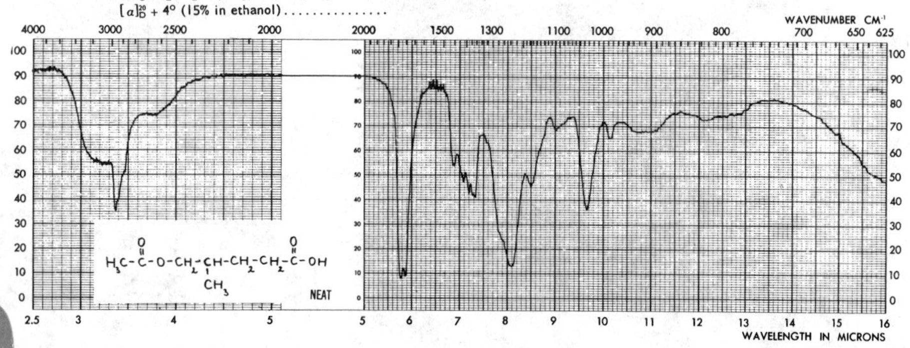

NEAT

E M4735-3 **mono-Methyl glutarate**
$HO_2C(CH_2)_3CO_2CH_3$ M.W. 146.14
n_D^{20} 1.4381

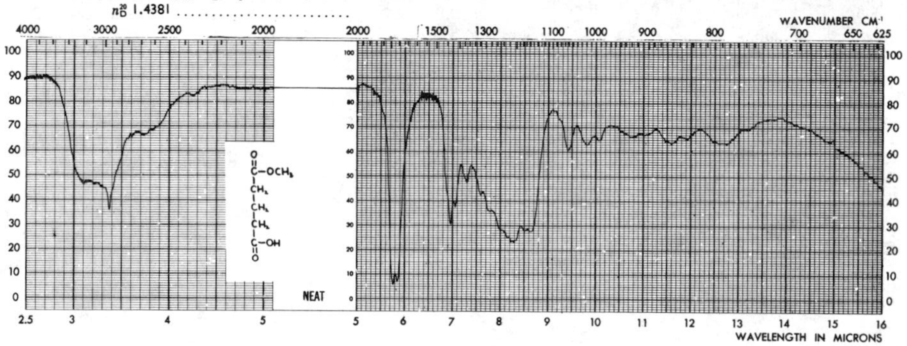

NEAT

F A2640-3 **Adipic acid monomethyl ester** (mono-methyl adipate)
$HO_2C(CH_2)_4CO_2CH_3$ M.W. 160.17 n_D^{20} 1.4401
m.p. 8-9°

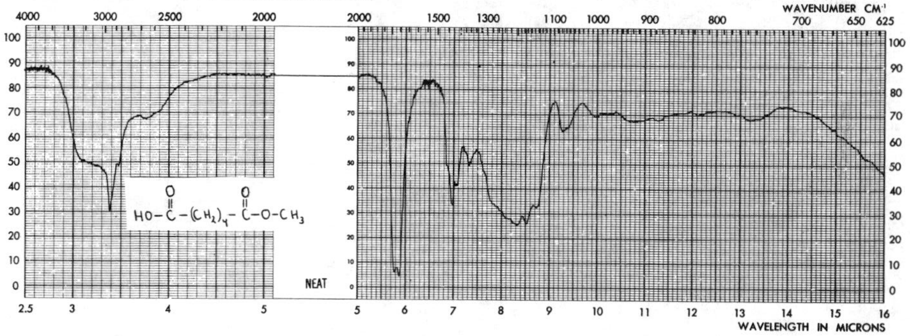

NEAT

G 12,276-9 **Adipic acid monoethyl ester** (mono-ethyl adipate)
$HO_2C(CH_2)_4CO_2C_2H_5$ M.W. 174.20
n_D^{20} 1.4387

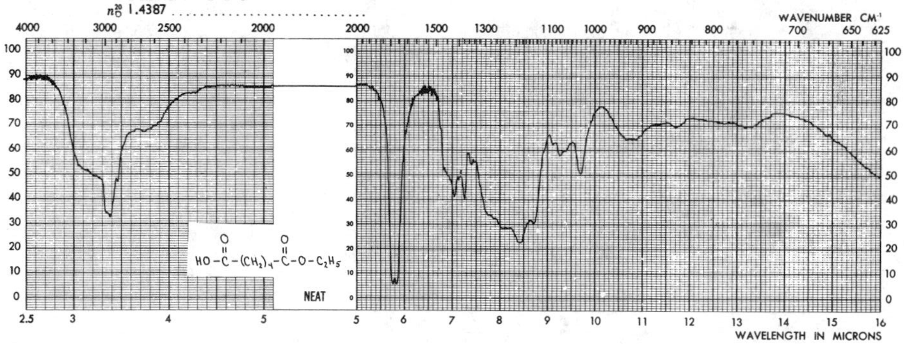

NEAT

H A9620-7 **Azelaic acid monomethyl ester** (mono-methyl azelate)
$HO_2C(CH_2)_7CO_2CH_3$ M.W. 202.25
n_D^{20} 1.4474

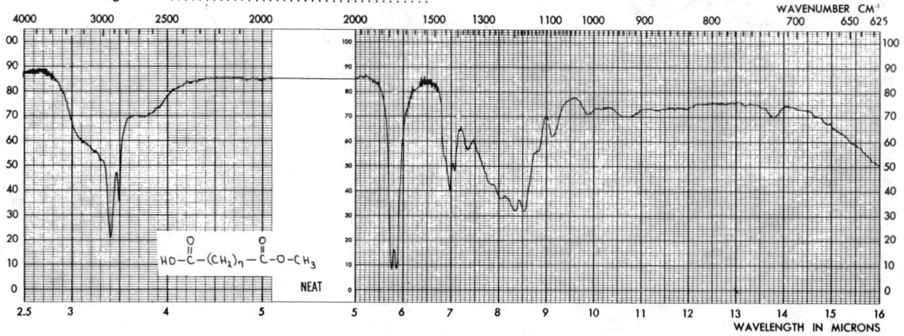

NEAT

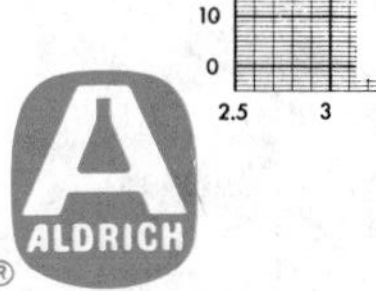

A

A1090-6 **Acetoxyacetic acid**
$CH_3CO_2CH_2CO_2H$ M.W. 118.09 m.p. 67-70° ....

MELT

B

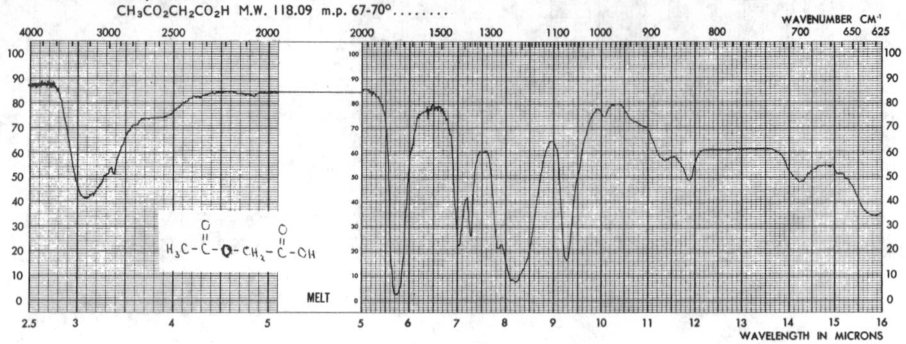

P5135-4 **β-Propiolactone** (hydracrylic acid β-lactone)
M.W. 72.06 n_D^{20} 1.4131 b.p. 162° (dec.) ...

NEAT

C

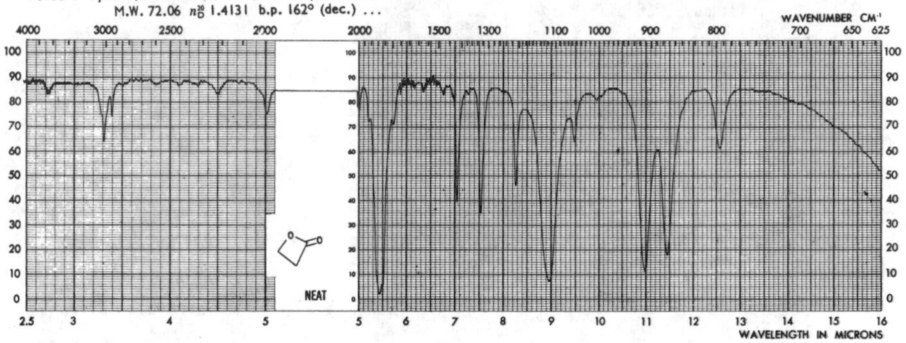

12,445-1 **β-Butyrolactone** (3-hydroxybutyric acid β-lactone)
M.W. 86.09 n_D^{20} 1.4110 ....

NEAT

D

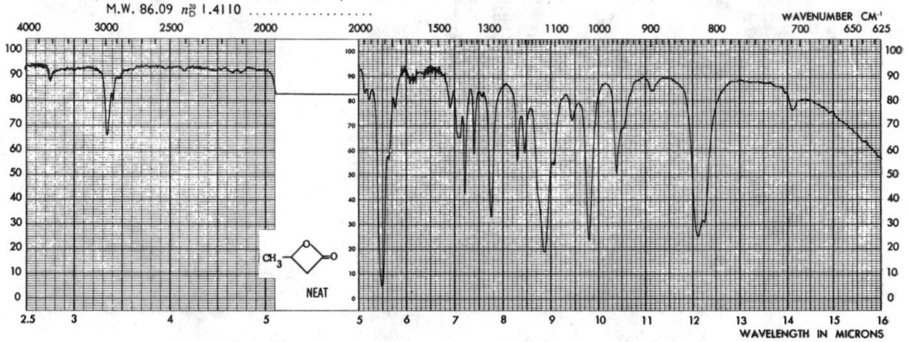

D12,720-5 **Diketene, tech.**
M.W. 84.07 n_D^{20} 1.4330

NEAT

E

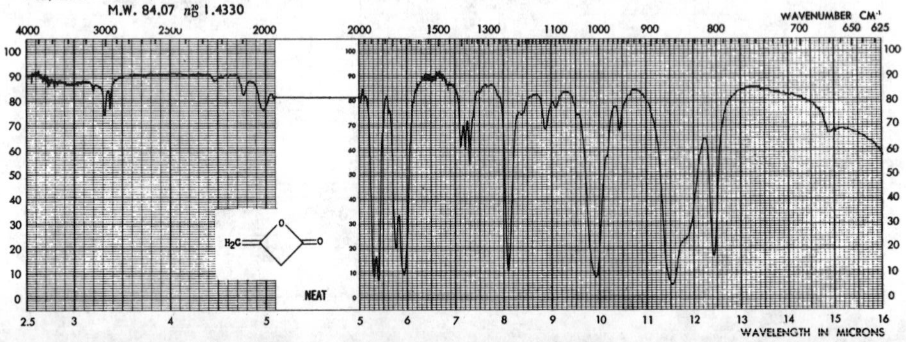

H5990-7 **3-Hydroxy-2,2,4-trimethyl-3-pentenoic acid β-lactone**
M.W. 140.18 n_D^{17} 1.4391 ....

NEAT

F

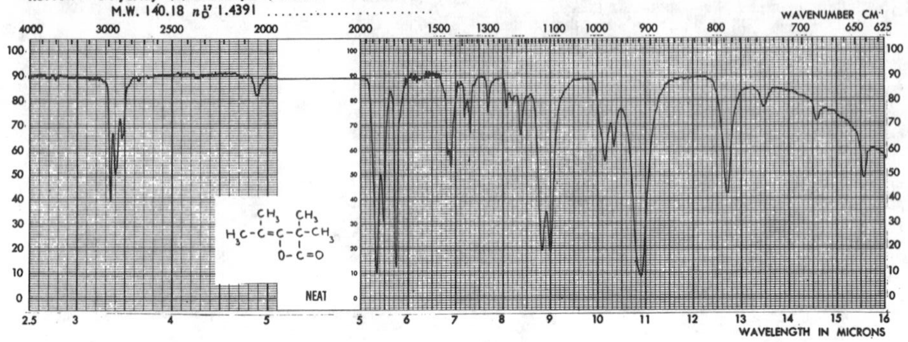

B10,360-8 **γ-Butyrolactone** (4-hydroxybutyric acid γ-lactone), **puriss.**
M.W. 86.09 n_D^{20} 1.4365 ....

NEAT

G

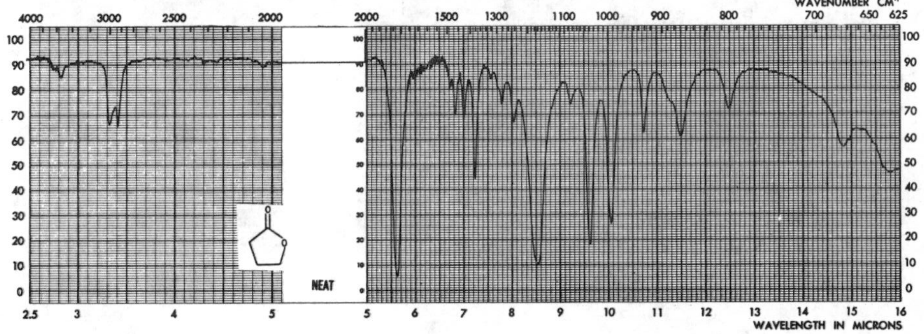

V40-3 **γ-Valerolactone**
M.W. 100.12 n_D^{20} 1.4322 b.p. 207-208°

NEAT

H

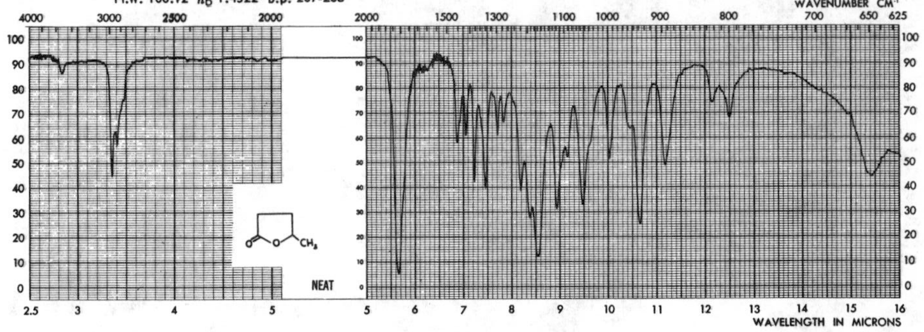

11,775-7 **α-Methyl-γ-butyrolactone**
M.W. 100.12 n_D^{20} 1.4317 b.p. 78-81°/10 mm.

NEAT

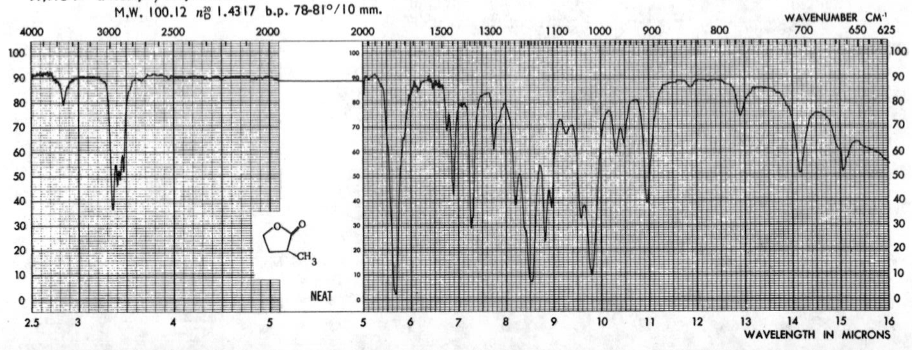

A O-400-8 γ-Octanoic lactone
M.W. 142.20 n_D^{20} 1.4444
NEAT

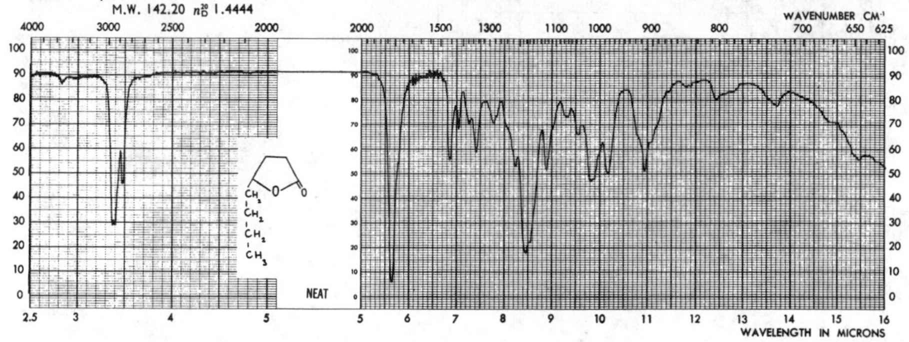

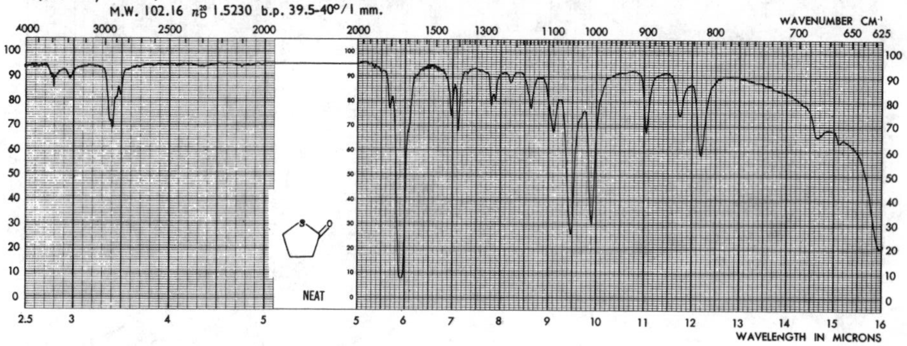

B D80-4 γ-Decalactone (4-hydroxydecanoic acid γ-lactone)
M.W. 170.25 n_D^{20} 1.4488
NEAT

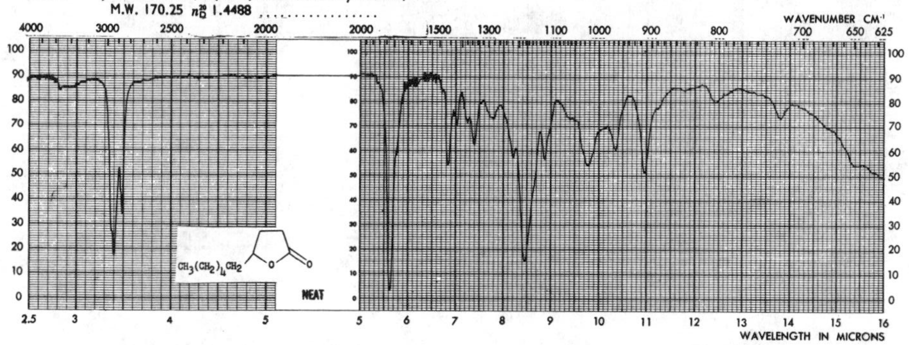

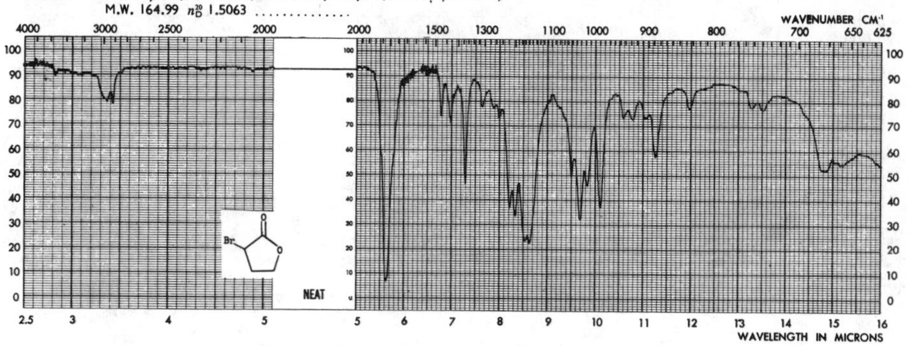

C U80 γ-Undecanoic lactone
$CH_3-(CH_2)_6-CH-CH_2-CH_2-C{=}O$ (–O–)
NEAT

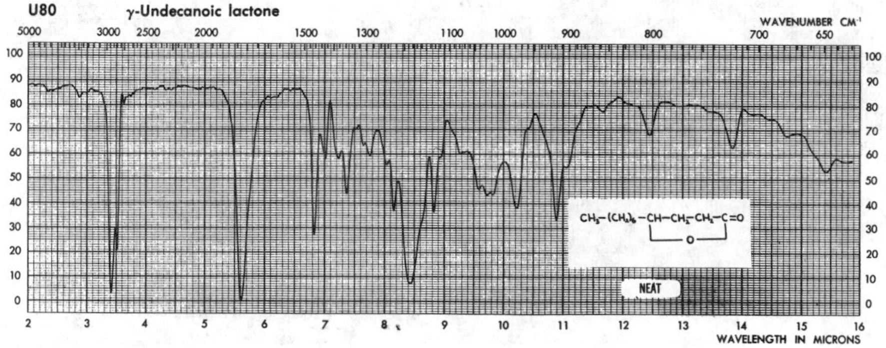

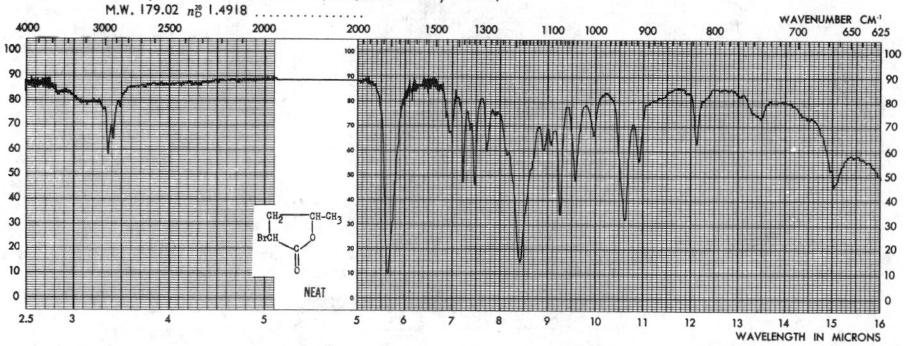

D 16,736-3
ε-Caprolactone (6-hexanolactone)
M.W. 114.14 b.p. 96.5-97.5°/15mm. d 1.03
Beil. 17(2),290
NEAT

E 10,544-9 γ-Thiobutyrolactone (4-butyrothiolactone)
M.W. 102.16 n_D^{20} 1.5230 b.p. 39.5-40°/1 mm.
NEAT

F B5960-8 α-Bromo-γ-butyrolactone (2-bromo-4-hydroxybutyric acid γ-lactone)
M.W. 164.99 n_D^{20} 1.5063
NEAT

G 12,418-4 α-Bromo-γ-valerolactone (2-bromo-4-hydroxyvaleric acid γ-lactone)
M.W. 179.02 n_D^{20} 1.4918
NEAT

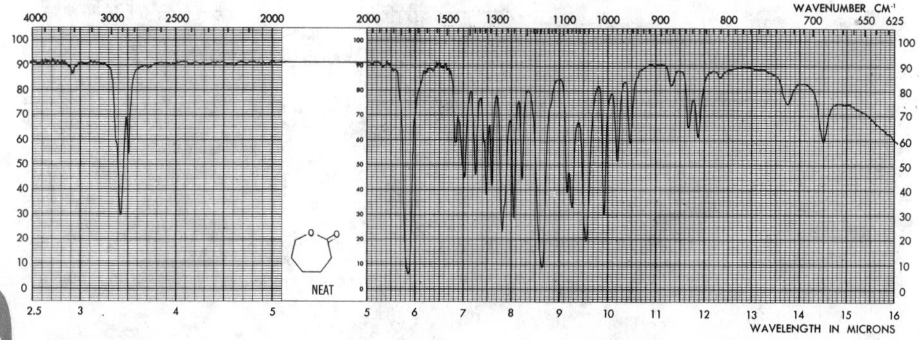

H A4450-9 α-Amino-γ-butyrolactone hydrobromide
M.W. 182.02 m.p. 221° (dec.)
NUJOL MULL

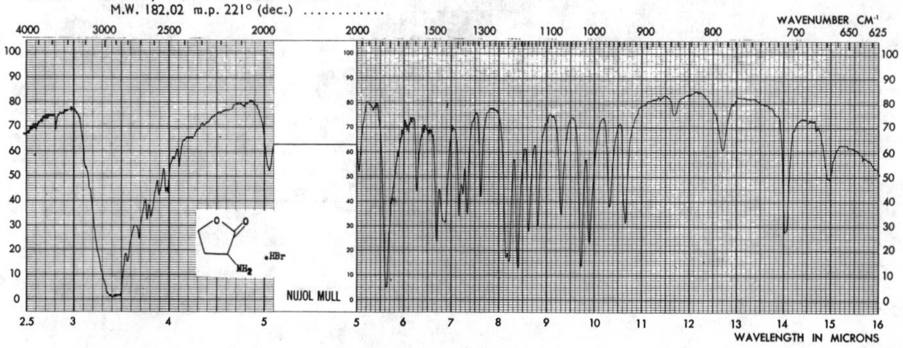

(Spectra axes: WAVENUMBER CM⁻¹; WAVELENGTH IN MICRONS)

A — H1580-2 **DL-Homocysteine thiolactone hydrochloride**
M.W. 153.63 m.p. 207° (dec.) NUJOL MULL

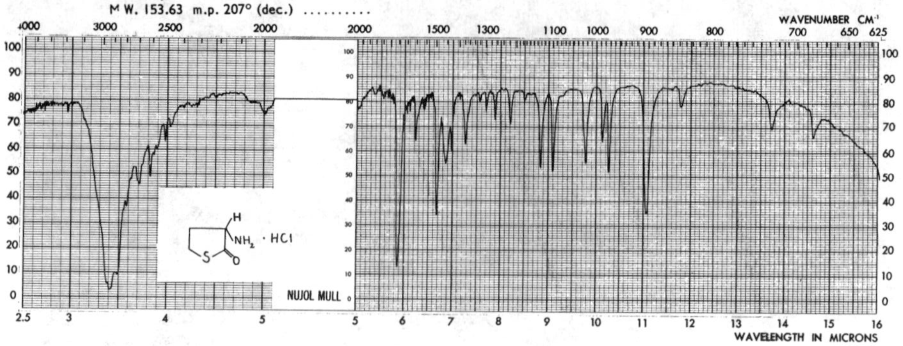

B — H5911-7 **6-Hydroxytetrahydropyran-2-carboxylic acid lactone**
(6,8-dioxabicyclo[3.2.1]octan-7-one)
M.W. 128.13 n_D^{20} 1.4593 NEAT

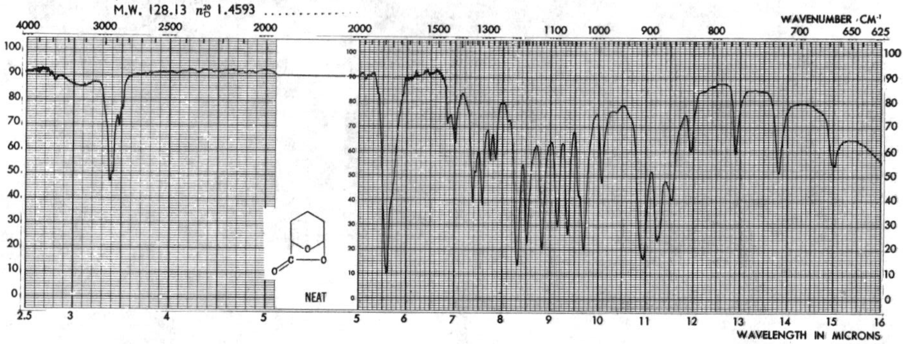

C — S125-6 **Santonin**
M.W. 246.29 m.p. 172.5-173° NUJOL MULL

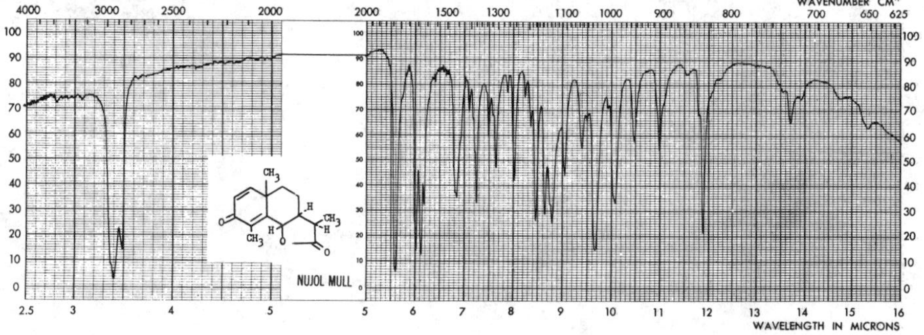

D — P4,470-6 **Picrotoxin**
M.W. 602.59 m.p. 200-202°
$[\alpha]_D^{20}$ -30° (c=2, C_2H_5OH) NUJOL MULL
·PICROTIN

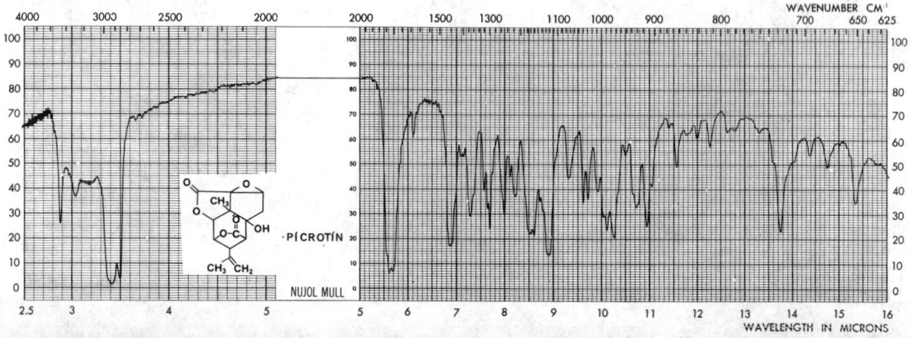

E — A8640-6 **α-Angelicalactone** (4-hydroxy-3-pentenoic acid γ-lactone)
M.W. 98.10 n_D^{20} 1.4460 NEAT

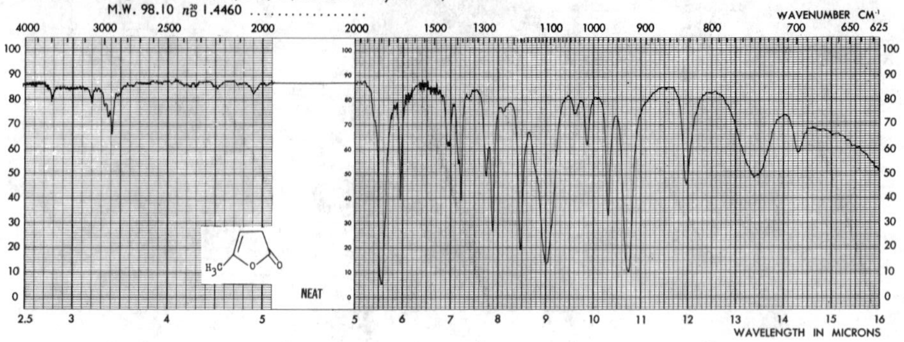

F — M8980-3 **Mucochloric acid**
$ClC(CHO){:}C(Cl)CO_2H$ M.W. 168.96 m.p. 128-131° NUJOL MULL

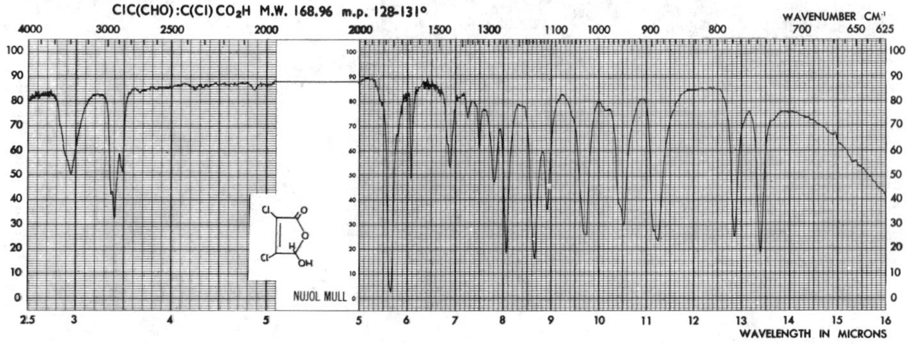

G — M8962-5 **Mucobromic acid**
$BrC(CHO){:}C(Br)CO_2H$ M.W. 257.88
m.p. 121-122° NUJOL MULL

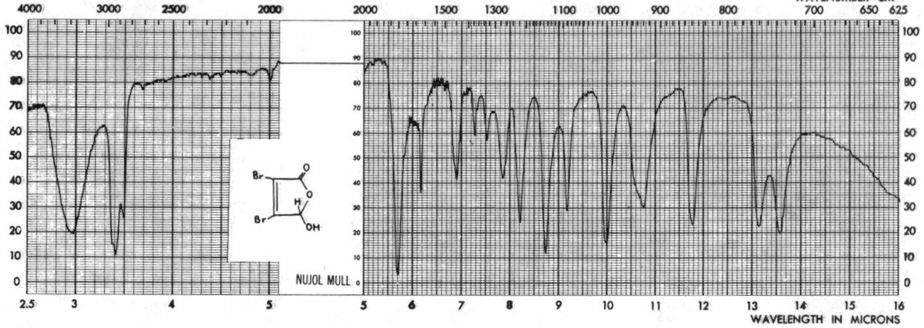

H — A9290-2 **L-Ascorbic acid** (Vitamin C)
M.W. 176.13 m.p. 190-192° (dec.) NUJOL MULL

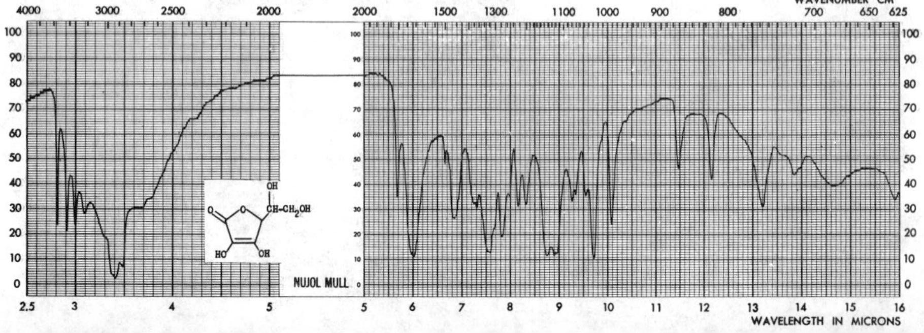

A

11,325-5 D-(+)-Arabonic acid γ-lactone
M.W. 148.12 m.p. 99-100°

NUJOL MULL

B

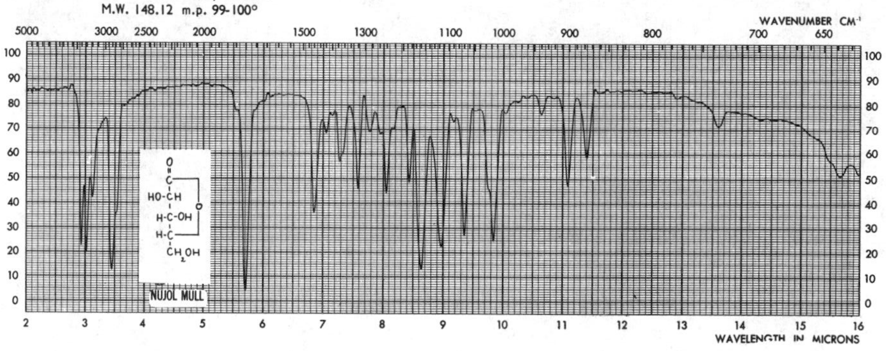

11,742-0 D-(+)-Ribonic acid γ-lactone
M.W. 148.11 n_D^{20} 1.4752 $[\alpha]_D^{22}$ + 19.5°
(c=1.08, acetone)

NEAT

C

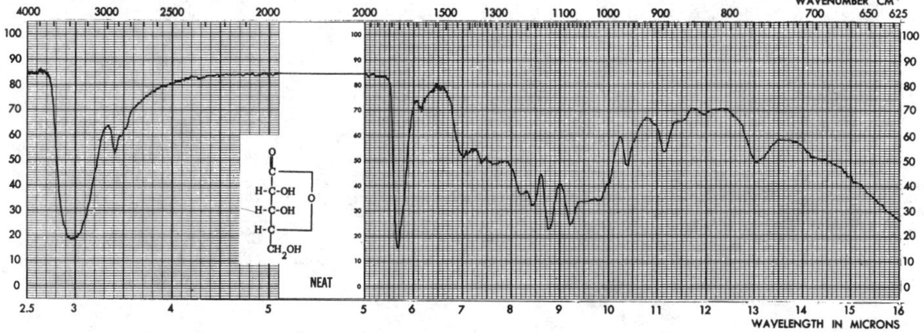

12,564-4 α-D-Glucoheptonic acid γ-lactone
M.W. 208.17 m.p. 152-153°

NUJOL MULL

D

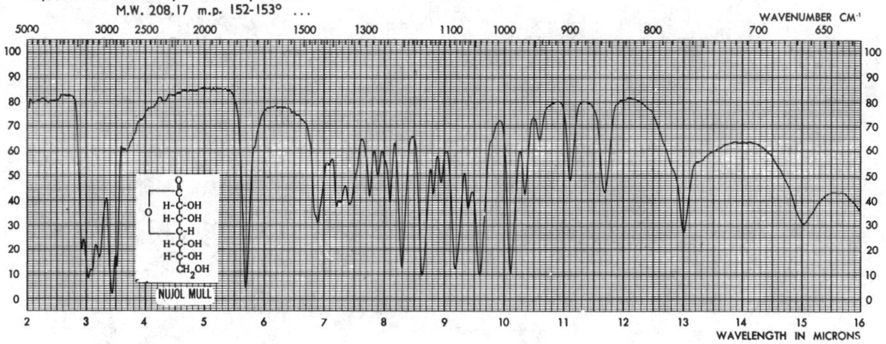

G85-4 Gibberellic acid
M.W. 346.38 m.p. 231.5-233°

NUJOL MULL

E

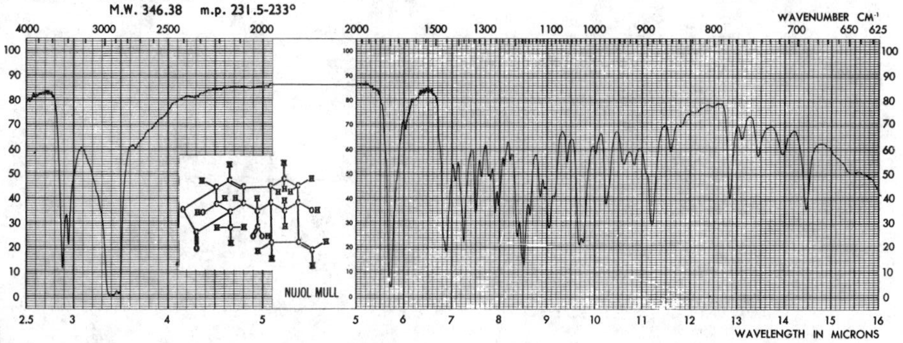

85,619-3
Erythromycin
M.W. 733.95 m.p. 138-140°

NUJOL MULL

F

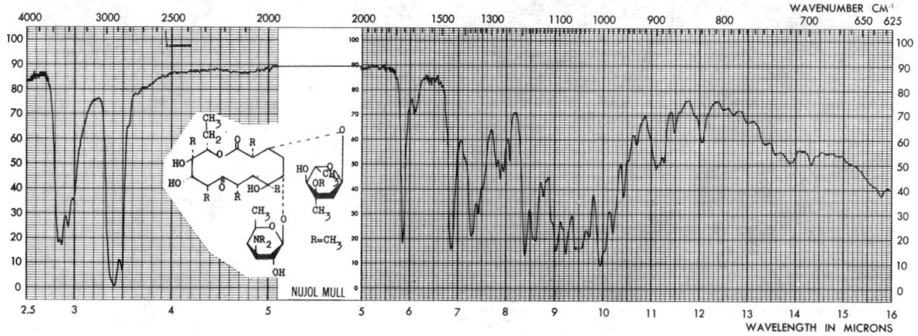

A1340-9 2-Acetylbutyrolactone
M.W. 128.13 n_D^{20} 1.4585

NEAT

G

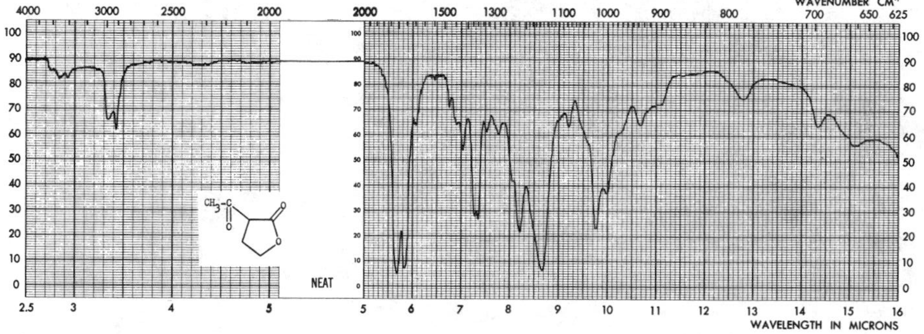

11,634-3 α-Acetyl-α-methyl-γ-butyrolactone
M.W. 142.15 n_D^{20} 1.4544

NEAT

H

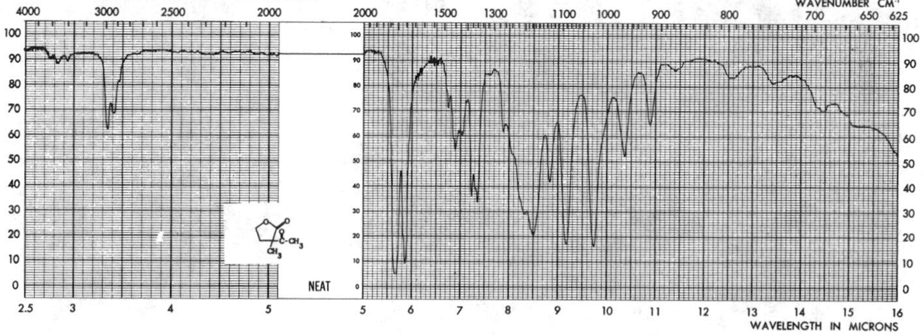

14,995-0 4-Hydroxy-4-methyl-3-(3-oxobutyl)-valeric acid γ-lactone
(homoterpenyl methyl ketone)
M.W. 184.24 m.p. 59-60°

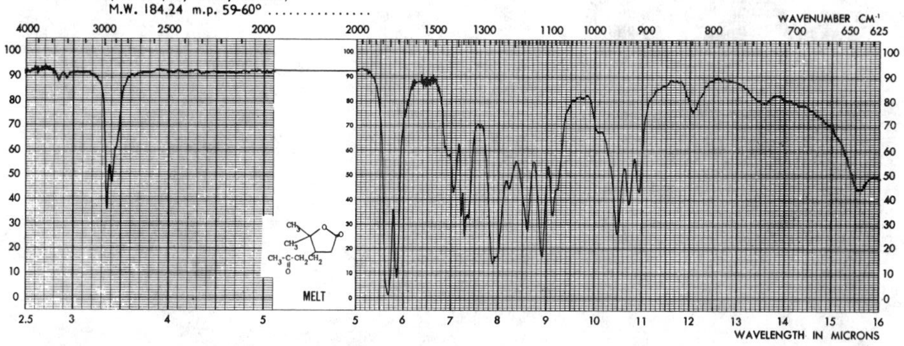

MELT

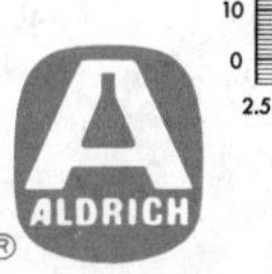

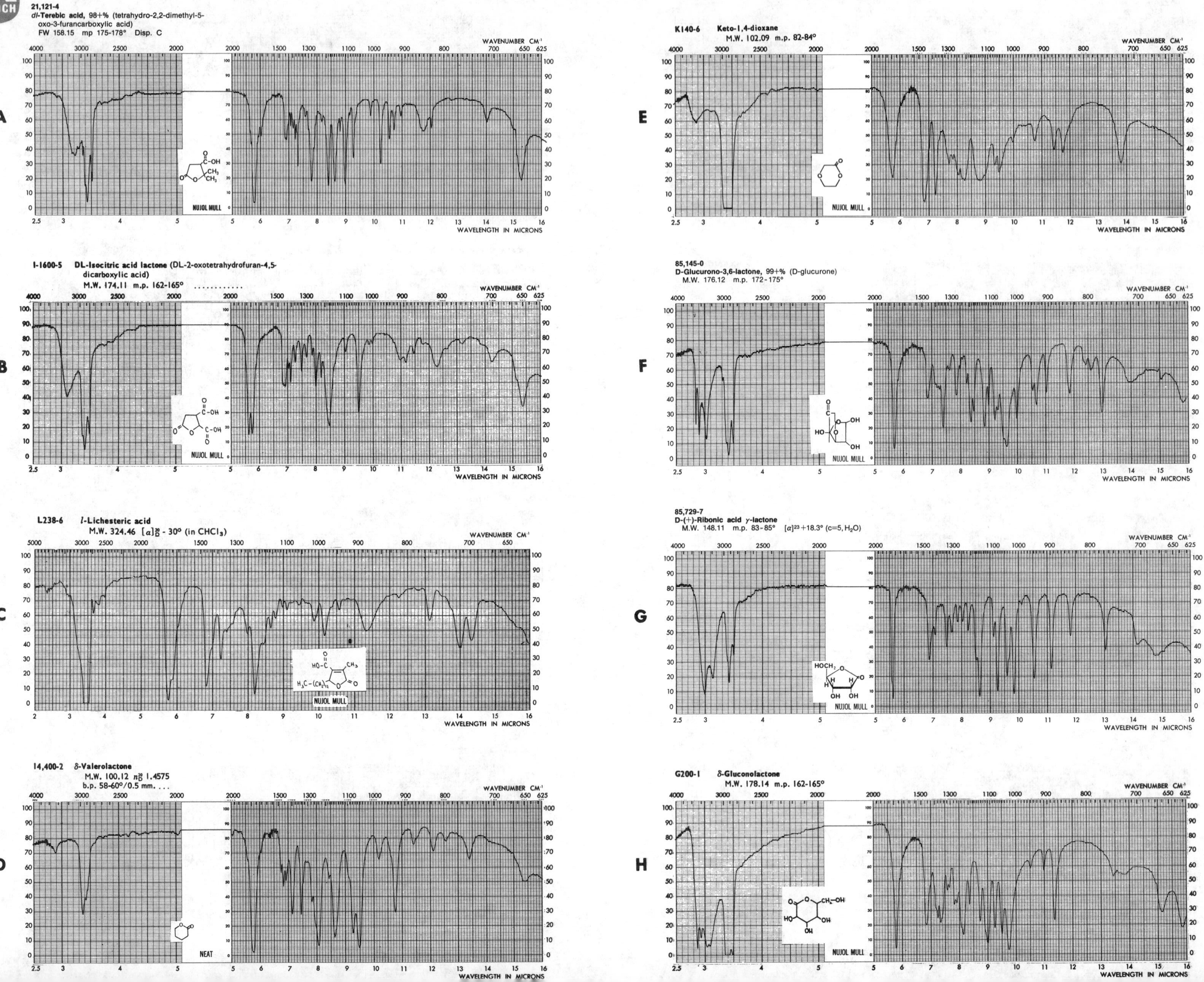
ALDRICH
A
21,121-4
dl-Terebic acid, 98+% (tetrahydro-2,2-dimethyl-5-oxo-3-furancarboxylic acid)
FW 158.15 mp 175-178° Disp. C
NUJOL MULL
B
I-1600-5 DL-Isocitric acid lactone (DL-2-oxotetrahydrofuran-4,5-dicarboxylic acid)
M.W. 174.11 m.p. 162-165°
NUJOL MULL
C
L238-6 l-Lichesteric acid
M.W. 324.46 $[\alpha]_D^{25}$ - 30° (in $CHCl_3$)
NUJOL MULL
D
14,400-2 δ-Valerolactone
M.W. 100.12 n_D^{20} 1.4575
b.p. 58-60°/0.5 mm. . . .
NEAT
E
K140-6 Keto-1,4-dioxane
M.W. 102.09 m.p. 82-84°
NUJOL MULL
F
85,145-0
D-Glucurono-3,6-lactone, 99+% (D-glucurone)
M.W. 176.12 m.p. 172-175°
NUJOL MULL
G
85,729-7
D-(+)-Ribonic acid γ-lactone
M.W. 148.11 m.p. 83-85° $[\alpha]^{23}$ +18.3° (c=5, H_2O)
NUJOL MULL
H
G200-1 δ-Gluconolactone
M.W. 178.14 m.p. 162-165°
NUJOL MULL
WAVENUMBER CM⁻¹
WAVELENGTH IN MICRONS

A

21,935-5
D-Gulonic acid γ-lactone, 99%
FW 178.14 mp 182-188° $[\alpha]_D^{25}$ -55° (c=4, H_2O)
Beil. 18,204 Disp. L

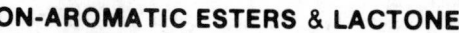

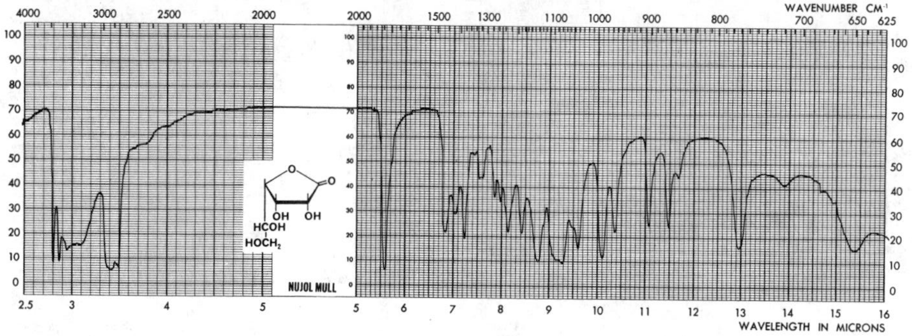

NUJOL MULL

B

22,293-3
D-Saccharic acid 1,4-lactone monohydrate
FW 210.13 mp 91-93° $[\alpha]^{25}$ +32° (c=1.2, H_2O)
Beil. 18,550 Disp. C

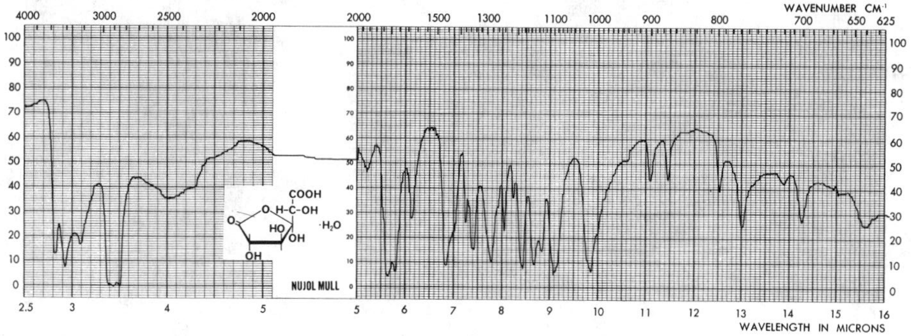

NUJOL MULL

C

20,664-4
α,β-Glucooctanoic acid lactone
FW 238.20 mp 188° (dec.) $[\alpha]^{24}$ +26° (c=3, H_2O)
Beil. 18,255 Disp. L

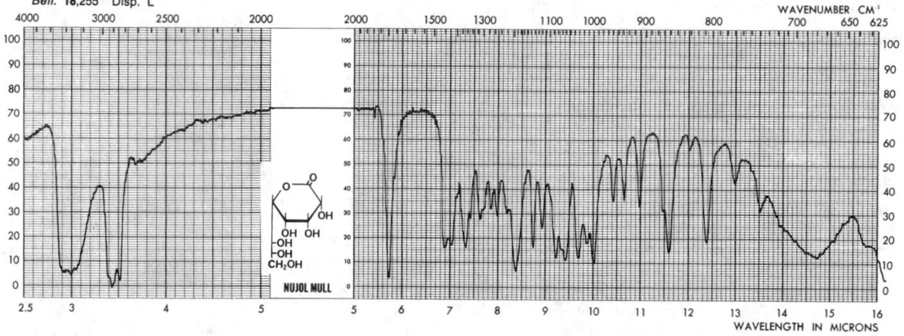

NUJOL MULL

D

85,606-1
Isoascorbic acid (D-araboascorbic acid)
M.W. 176.12 m.p. 169-172° (dec.)

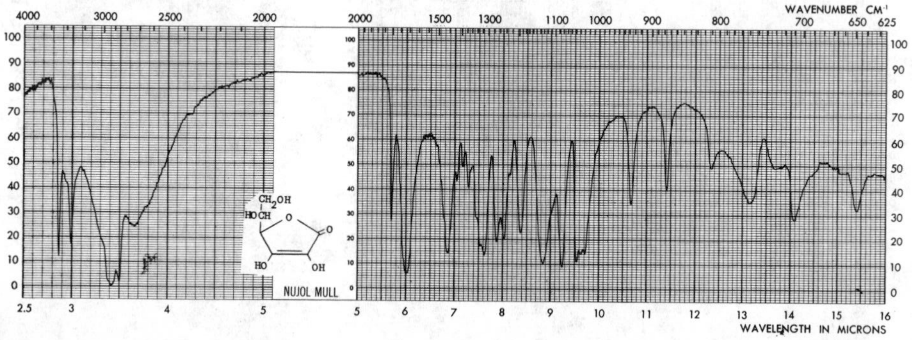

NUJOL MULL

E

20,666-0
D-*glycero*-L-*manno*-Heptonic acid γ-lactone
FW 208.17 mp 149-151° $[\alpha]^{24}$ -50° (c=10, H_2O)
Beil. 18,236 Disp. L

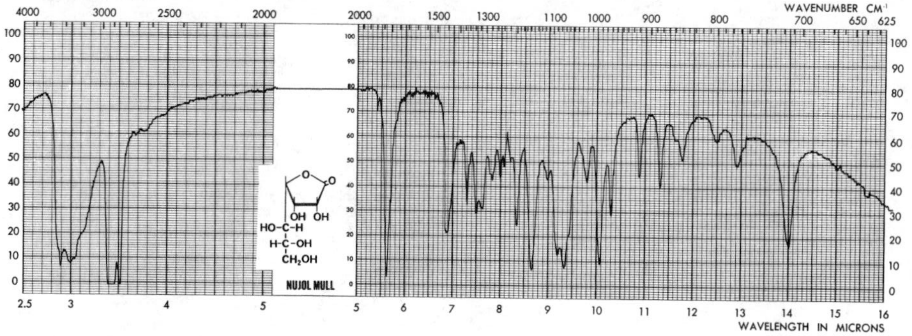

NUJOL MULL

F

H4341-5 4-Hydroxy-6-methyl-2-pyrone (3,5-dihydroxysorbic acid δ-lactone)
M.W. 126.11 m.p. 192-194

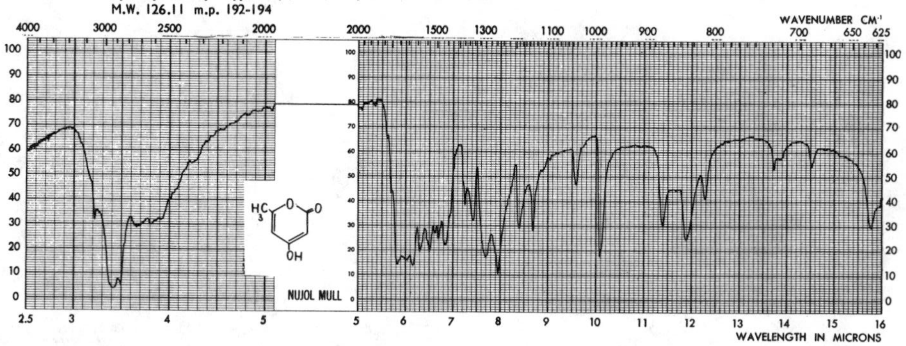

NUJOL MULL

G

15,428-8 4-Methoxy-6-methyl-2H-pyran-2-one
M.W. 140.14 m.p. 83-86°

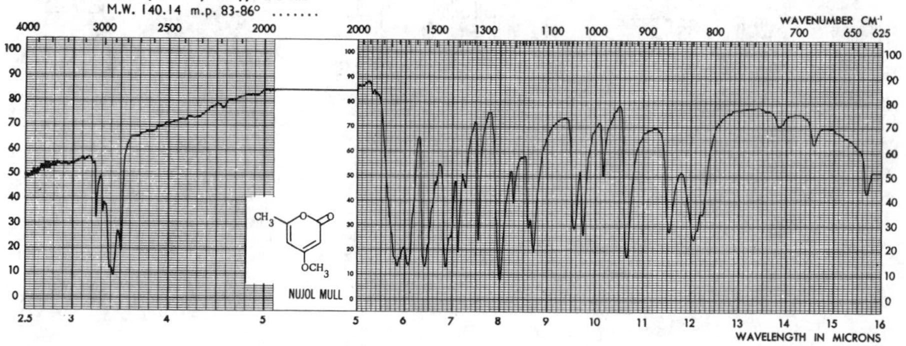

NUJOL MULL

H

C8540-9 Coumalic acid monohydrate
M.W. 158.11 m.p. 203-205°

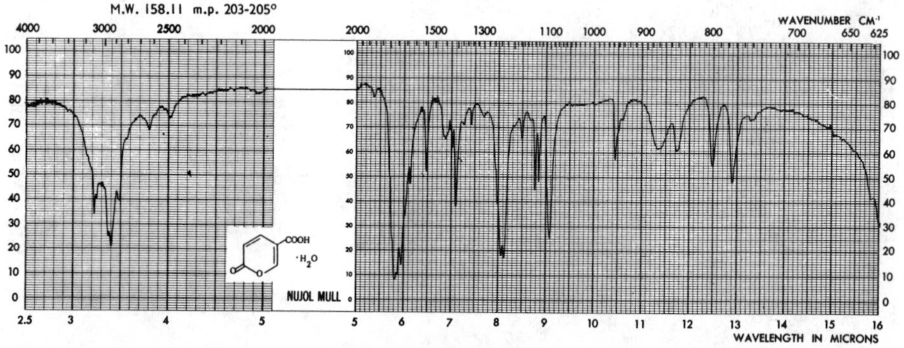

NUJOL MULL

A

I-1640-4 Isodehydracetic acid
M.W. 168.15 m.p. 151-154°

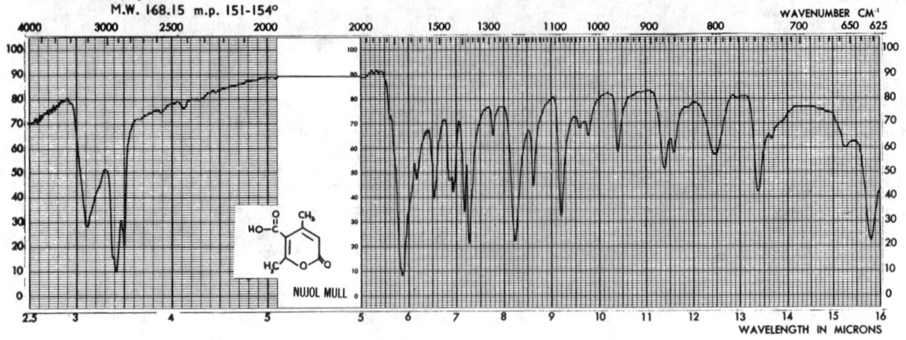

NUJOL MULL

B

A1180-5 4-Acetoxy-6-hydroxy-2-pyrone
M.W. 170.12 m.p. 89-93°

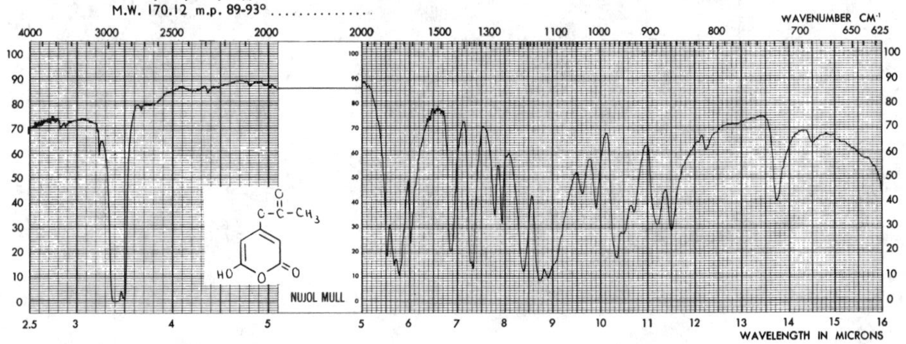

NUJOL MULL

C

19,034-9
Methyl isodehydracetate, 97% (methyl 4,6-dimethyl-2-oxo-2*H*-pyran-5-carboxylate)
FW 182.18 mp 60-63° bp 167°/14mm.
Beil. 18,410 Disp. C

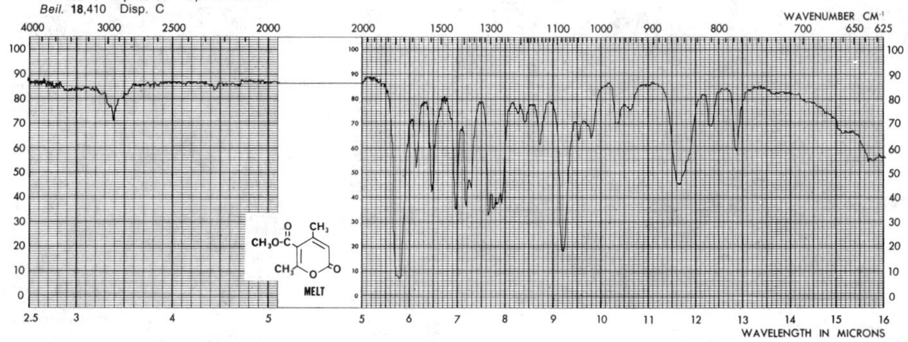

MELT

D

E3340-8 Ethyl isodehydracetate (ethyl 4,6-dimethyl-2-oxo-2H-pyran-5-carboxylate)
M.W. 196.20 n_D^{20} 1.5157

NEAT

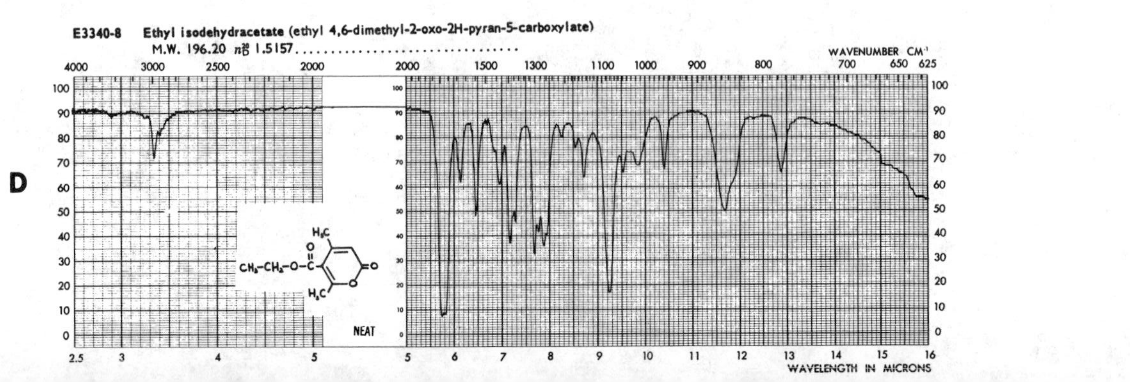

E

D290-0 Dehydroacetic acid
M.W. 168.15 m.p. 111-113°

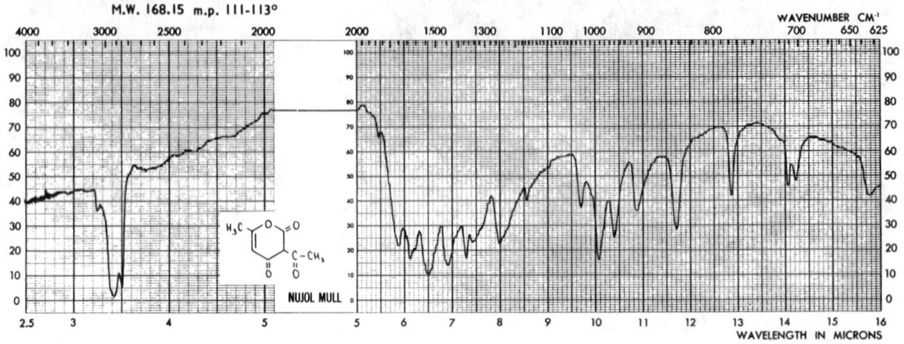

NUJOL MULL

F

22,308-5
Santonin, 99%
FW 246.29 mp 172-173° $[\alpha]^{21}$ -174° (c=2, CH_3OH)
Beil. 17,499 *IR* 2,362E Disp. C

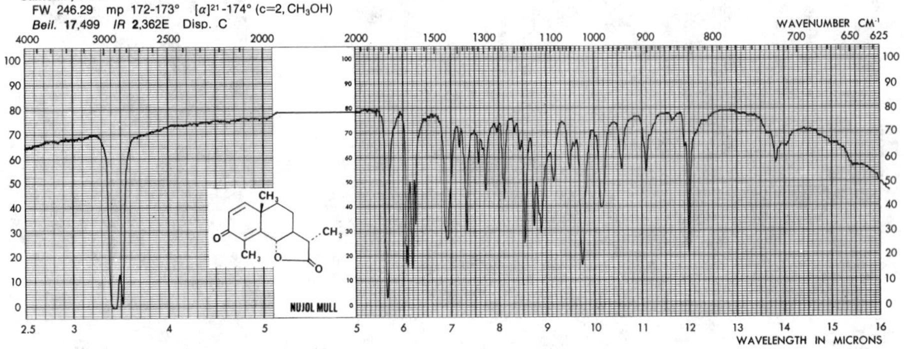

NUJOL MULL

NON-AROMATIC ANHYDRIDES

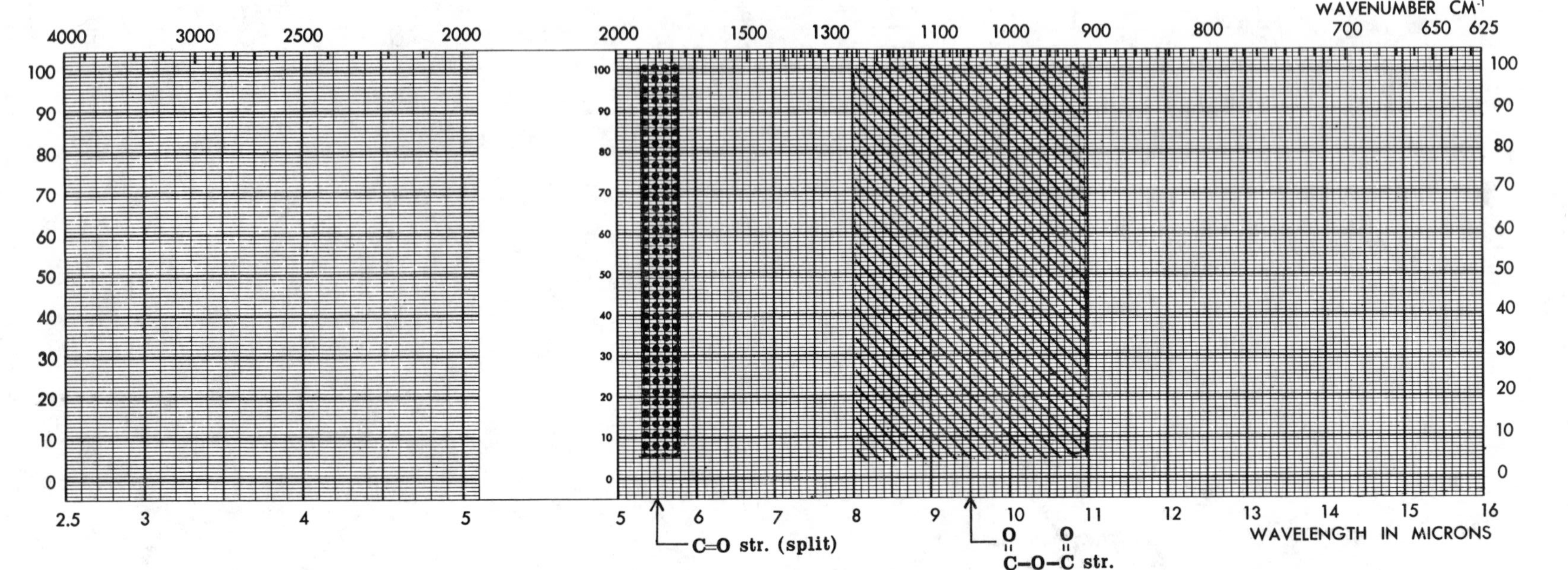

1.) Open Chain 416A-417F
2.) Cyclic 417G-421G

The carbonyl stretch bands of the anhydrides are the most distinctive of the carbonyl family. There are two strong bands between 5.3 and 5.8 μ (1885 – 1725 cm^{-1}), separated by approximately 0.2 μ (65 cm^{-1}). The lower wavelength band is the stronger of the two. In spectrum number 416B the sulfur junction causes the opposite effect. A halogen on the α-carbon in spectra 417D and E, shifts the bands to lower wavelengths.

In the cyclic anhydrides, a split is also observed with the higher wavelength absorption being the stronger of the two. The six-membered cyclic anhydrides do not have their carbonyl bands split quite as much as the five-membered or linear anhydrides. Their absorptions are also at higher wavelengths than those observed for the five-membered anhydrides.

Accompanying the carbonyl absorptions are those associated with the C(=O)–O–C(=O) stretch vibrations between 8 and 10 μ (1250 – 1000 cm^{-1}). The five-membered cyclic anhydrides have this region extended to 11 μ (910 cm^{-1}) where an additional very strong absorption appears.

A

11,004-3 **Acetic anhydride, 99+%**
$(CH_3CO)_2O$ M.W. 102.09 n_D^{20} 1.3880 b.p. 140°

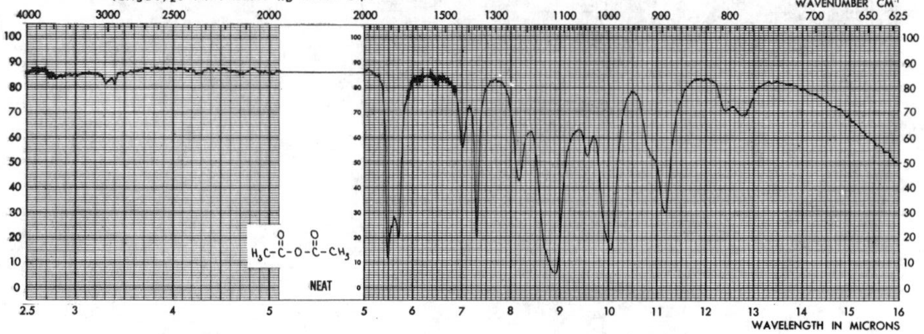

NEAT

B

A2220-3 **Acetyl sulfide**
$(CH_3CO)_2S$ M.W. 118.15
n_D^{20} 1.4748

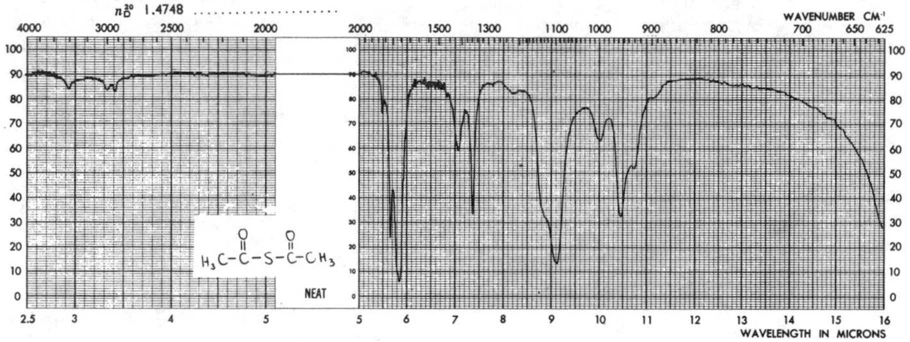

NEAT

C

P5147-8 **Propionic anhydride**
$C_2H_5CO_2COC_2H_5$ M.W. 130.15
n_D^{20} 1.4021

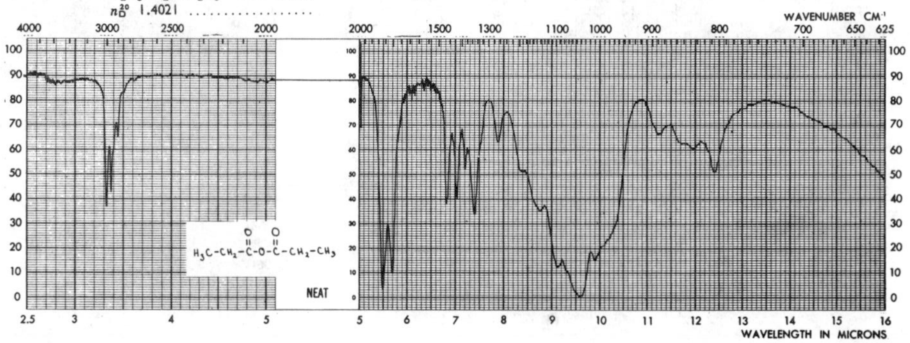

NEAT

D

B10,355-1 **n-Butyric anhydride** •
$(CH_3CH_2CH_2CO)_2O$ M.W. 158.20
n_D^{20} 1.4128

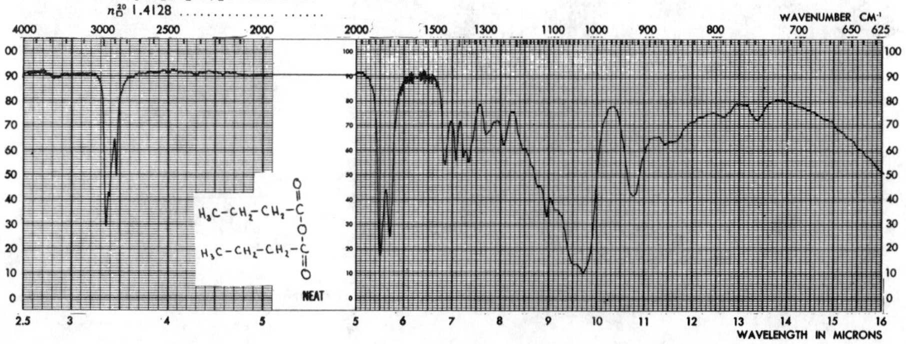

NEAT

E

19,453-0
Hexanoic anhydride, 99% (caproic anhydride)
$[CH_3(CH_2)_4CO]_2O$ FW 214.31 bp 246-248°
n_D^{20} 1.4280 d 0.926 *Beil.* **2**,324 Disp. I

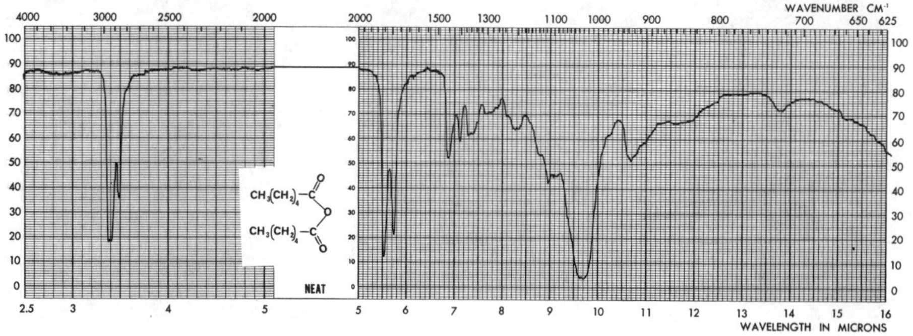

NEAT

F

19,454-9
Heptanoic anhydride
$[CH_3(CH_2)_5CO]_2O$ FW 242.36 mp -12.40°
bp 268° n_D^{20} 1.4332 d 0.923 *Beil.* **2**,340 Disp. I

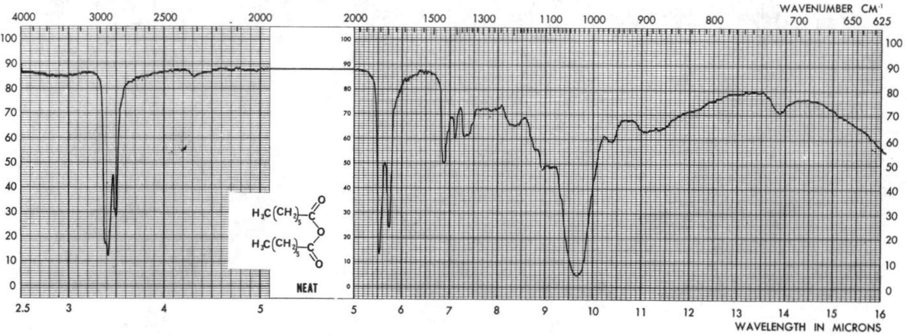

NEAT

G

13,097-4 **Crotonic anhydride**
$(CH_3CH{:}CHCO)_2O$ M.W. 154.17 n_D^{20} 1.4742
b.p. 248°

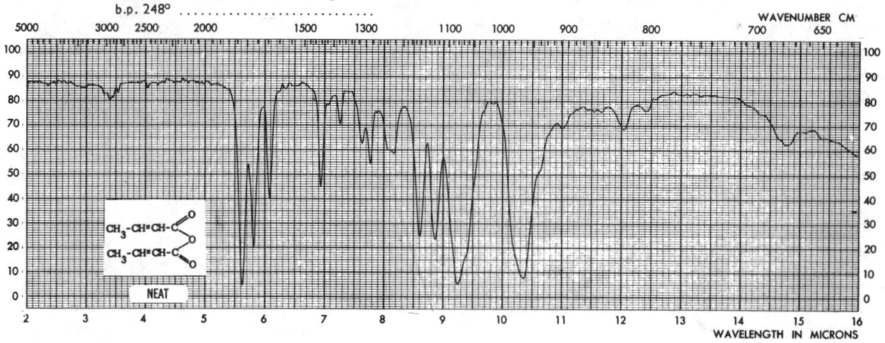

NEAT

H

10,853-7 **Cyclobutanecarboxylic acid anhydride**
$(C_4H_7CO)_2O$ M.W. 182.22 n_D^{20} 1.4619

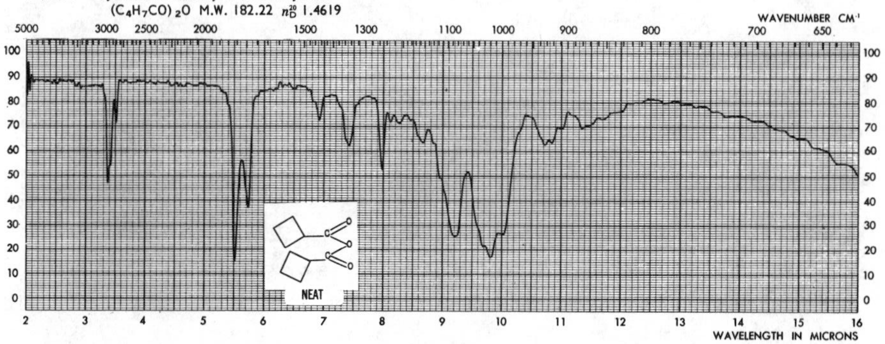

NEAT

ALDRICH

A

14,350-2 Trimethylacetic anhydride (pivalic anhydride)
$[(CH_3)_3CCO]_2O$ M.W. 186.25 n_D^{20} 1.4092
b.p. 193°

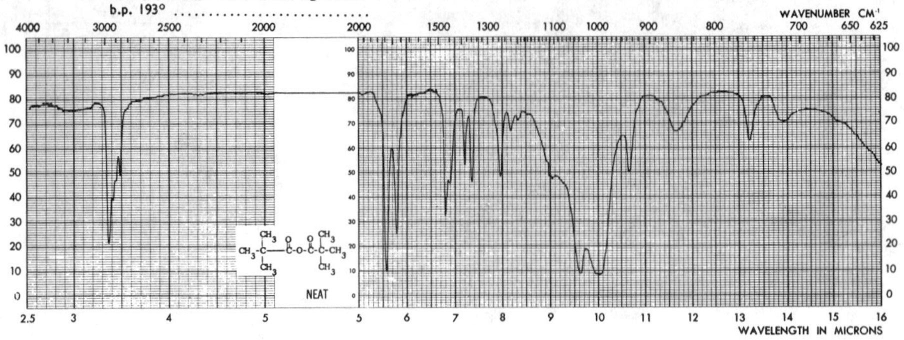

NEAT

B

13,481-3 Methoxalic acid anhydride
$(CH_3O_2CCO)_2O$ M.W. 190.11 m.p. 48-52°

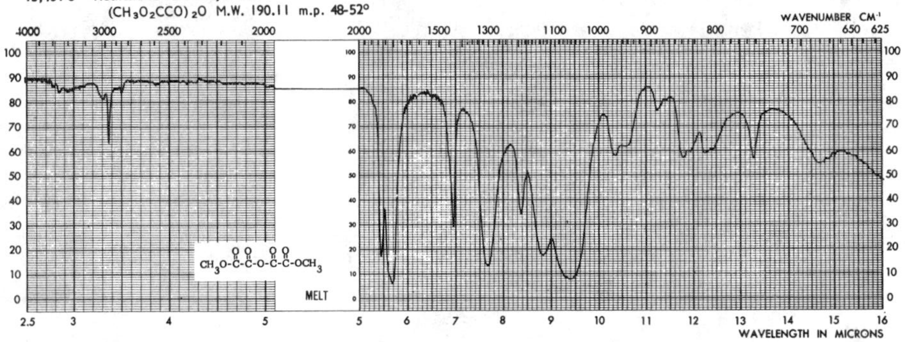

MELT

C

21,516-3
Chloroacetic anhydride
$(ClCH_2CO)_2O$ FW 170.98 mp 56-59°
bp 120-123°/20mm. *Beil.* **2**,199 *Fieser* **1**,129
Disp. I

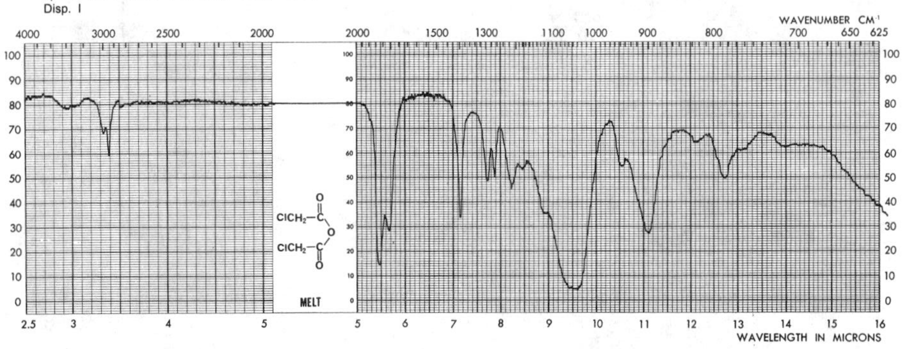

MELT

D

14,926-8 Dichloroacetic anhydride, puriss.
$(Cl_2CHCO)_2O$ M.W. 239.87 m.p. ca. 29°

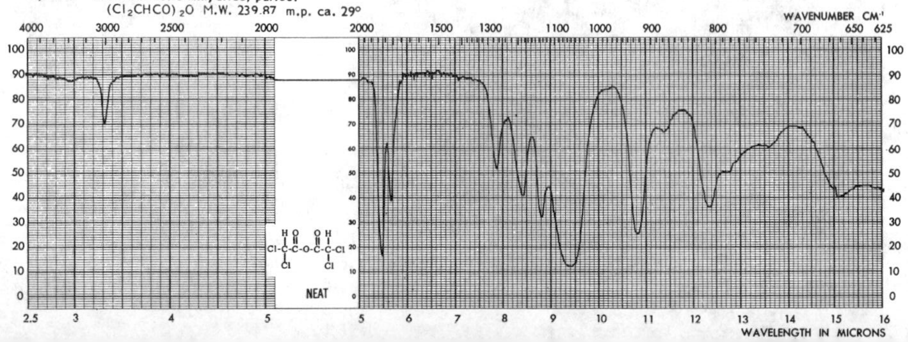

NEAT

E

10,623-2 Trifluoroacetic anhydride
$(CF_3CO)_2O$ M.W. 210.03 b.p. 40-43°

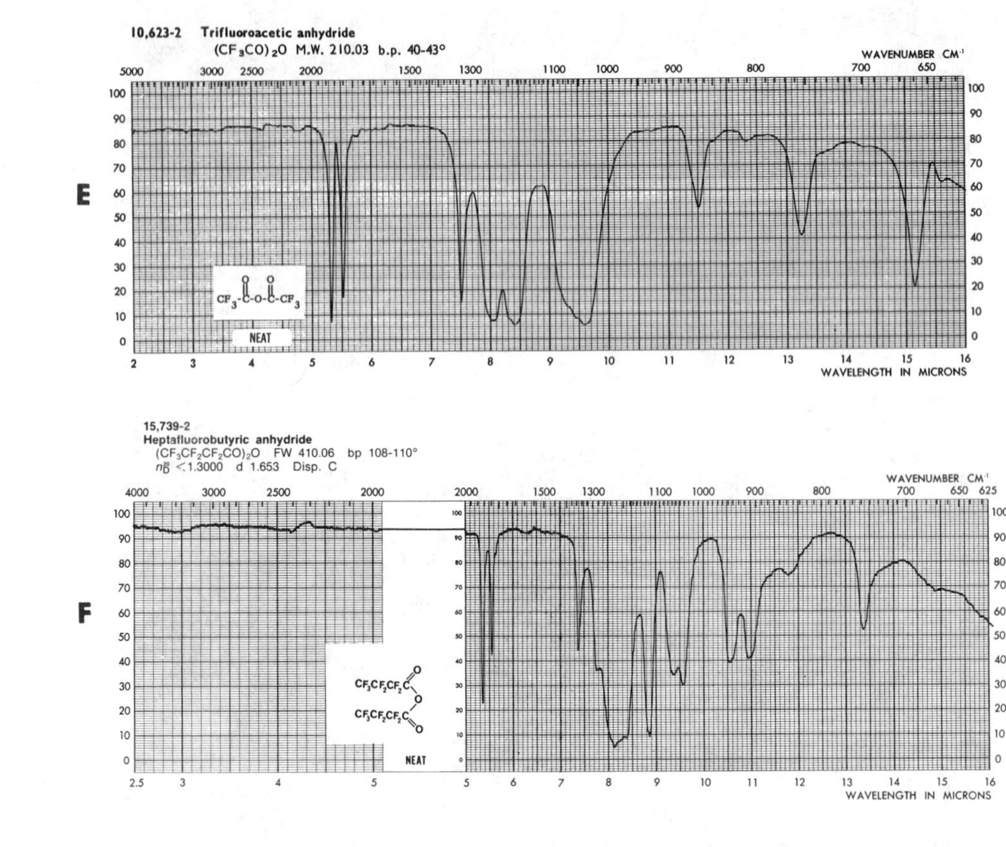

F

15,739-2
Heptafluorobutyric anhydride
$(CF_3CF_2CF_2CO)_2O$ FW 410.06 bp 108-110°
n_D^{20} <1.3000 d 1.653 Disp. C

NEAT

G

13,441-4 Succinic anhydride
M.W. 100.07 m.p. 119-120°

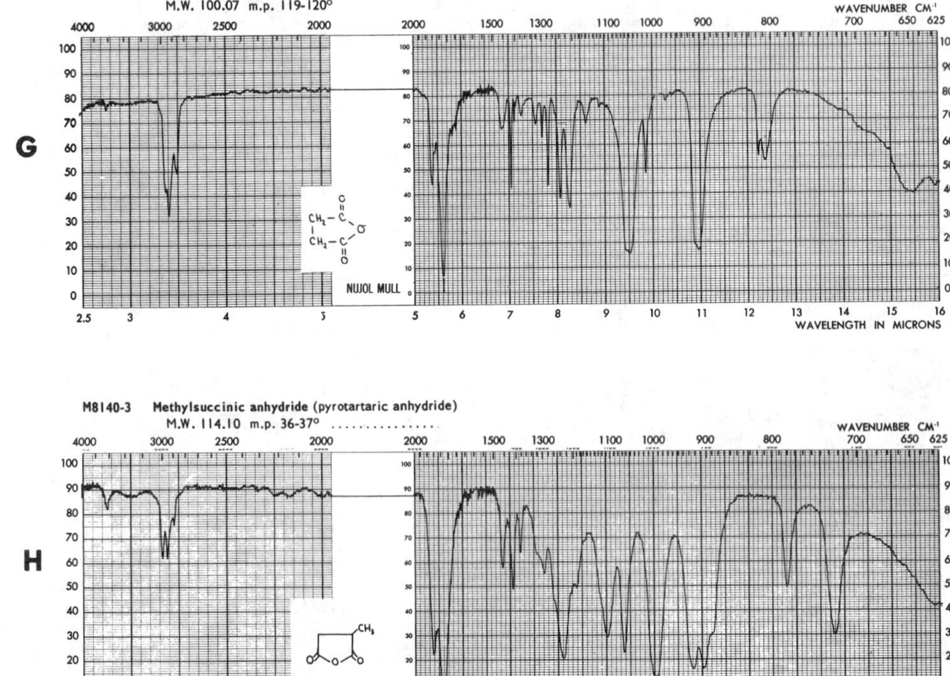

H

M8140-3 Methylsuccinic anhydride (pyrotartaric anhydride)
M.W. 114.10 m.p. 36-37°

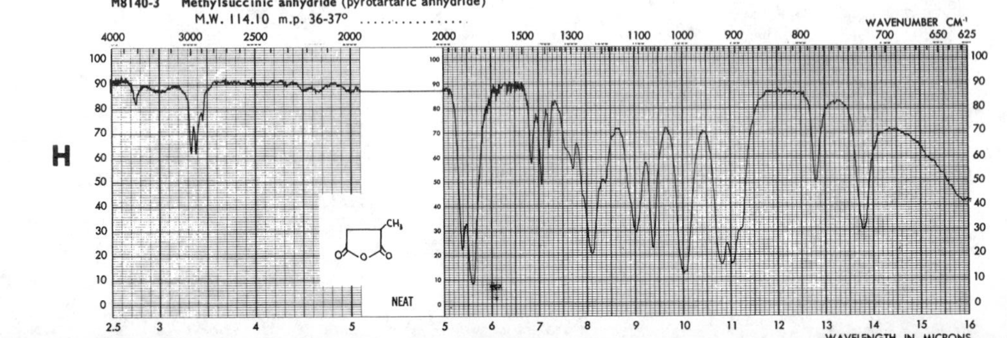

A

19,732-7
S-Acetylmercaptosuccinic anhydride [2-(acetylthio)-succinic anhydride]
FW 174.18 mp 76-79° Disp. C

B

14,543-2 *cis*-1,2-Cyclobutanedicarboxylic anhydride
M.W. 126.11 m.p. 75-78° ....

C

12,346-3 *cis*-1,2-Cyclohexanedicarboxylic anhydride (*cis*-hexahydrophthalic anhydride)
M.W. 154.17 m.p. 31.5-33° ....

D

14,484-3 Tetrahydrofuran-2,3,4,5-tetracarboxylic dianhydride (diasteriomers)
M.W. 212.12 m.p. 222-225° ....

E

14,829-6 *trans*-1,2-Cyclohexanedicarboxylic anhydride (*trans*-hexahydrophthalic anhydride)
M.W. 154.17 m.p. 145-147° ....

F

14,993-4 Hexahydro-4-methylphthalic anhydride (4-methyl-1,2-cyclohexanedicarboxylic anhydride)
M.W. 168.19 n_D^{20} 1.4774 ....

G

16,133-0
1,2,3,4-Cyclobutanetetracarboxylic dianhydride, tech.
70%, remainder corres. acid
M.W. 196.11 m.p. >300° *HYGROSCOPIC*

H

C11,215-1 *cis, cis, cis, cis*-1,2,3,4-Cyclopentanetetracarboxylic dianhydride
M.W. 210.15 m.p. 225-229° (dec.) ....

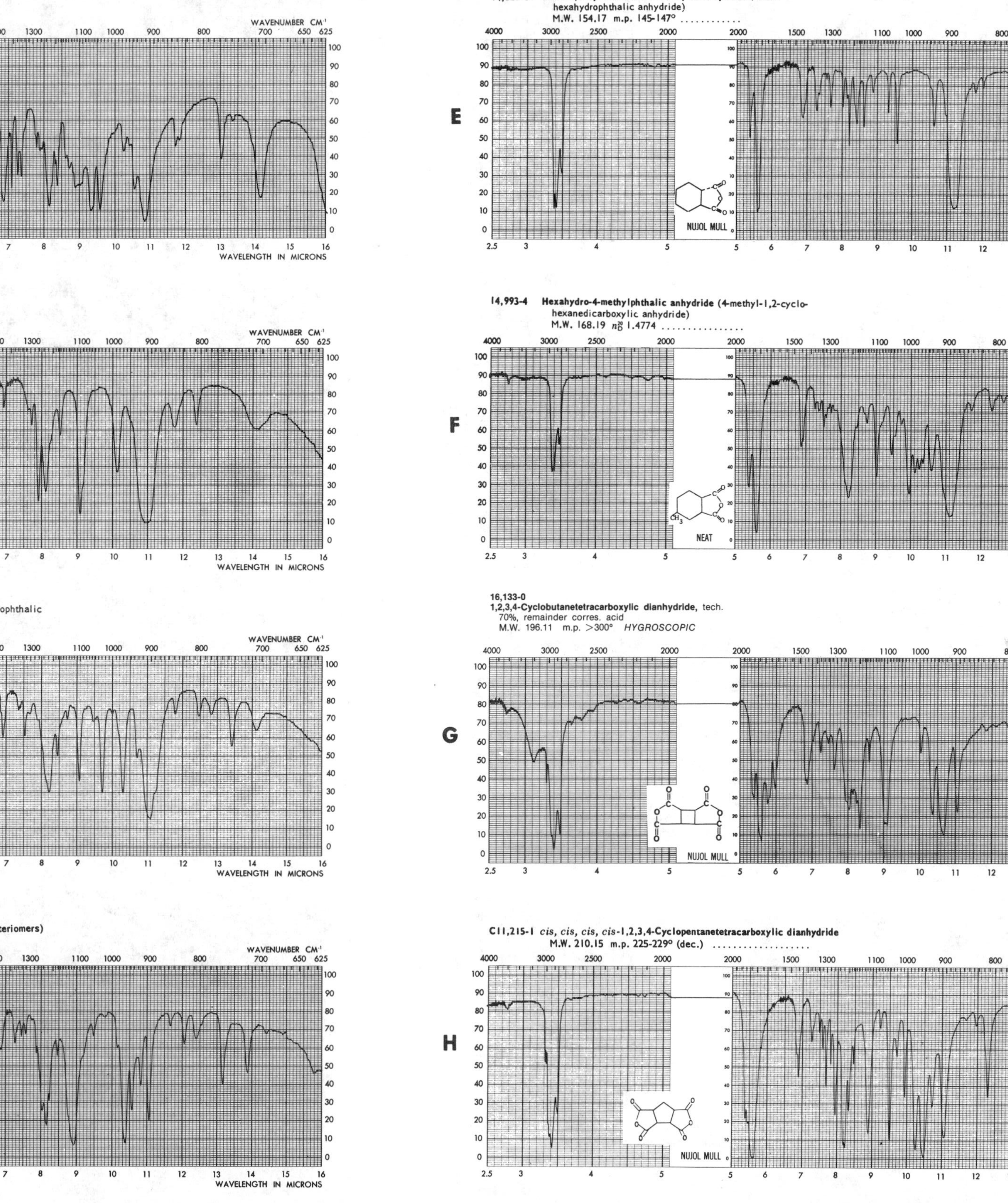

A 17,858-6
Bicyclo[2.2.2]oct-7-ene-2,3,5,6-tetracarboxylic-2,3,5,6-dianhydride
M.W. 248.19 m.p. >300°
NUJOL MULL

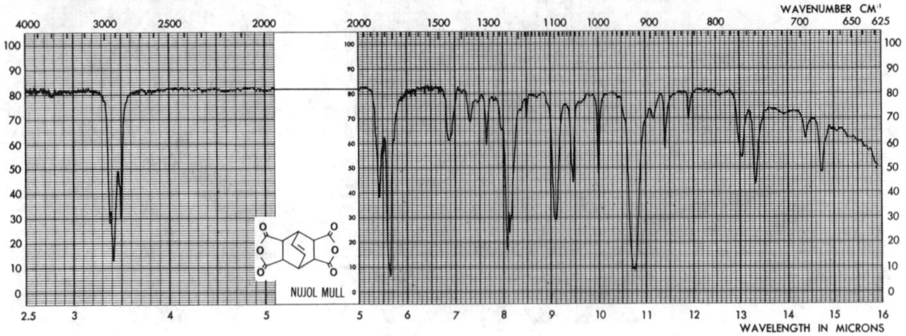

B D210-2 1-Decenylsuccinic anhydride
M.W. 238.33 n_D^{20} 1.4691
$CH_3(CH_2)_7CH = CH$
NEAT

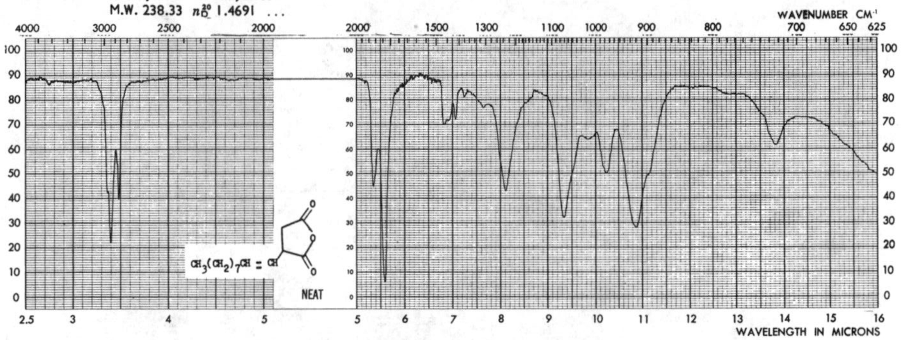

C D22,190-2 1-Dodecenylsuccinic anhydride, tech.
M.W. 266.38 m.p. 38-40°
MELT

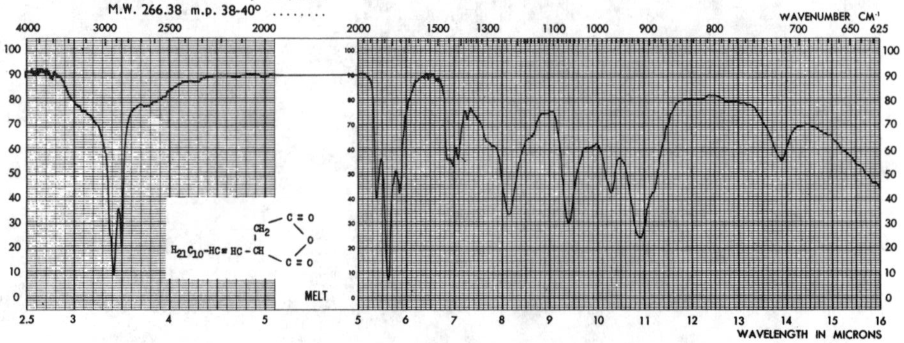

D 13,689-1 *cis*-1,2,3,6-Tetrahydrophthalic anhydride (*cis*-4-cyclohexene-1,2-dicarboxylic anhydride)
M.W. 152.15 m.p. 101-101.5°
NUJOL MULL

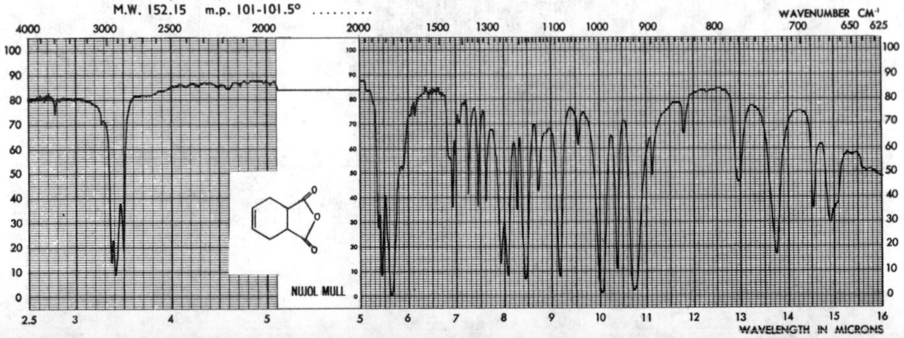

E 10,904-5 3,6-Endomethylene-1,2,3,6-tetrahydrophthalic anhydride
M.W. 164.16 m.p. 155-157°
NUJOL MULL

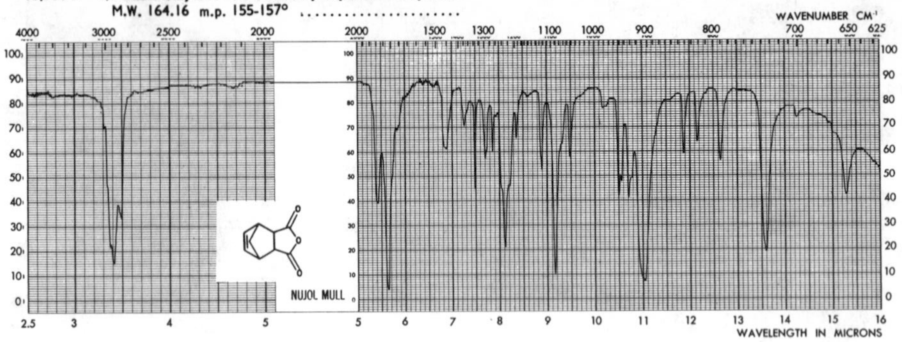

F 10,914-2 endo-Bicyclo[2.2.2]octa-5-ene-2,3-dicarboxylic anhydride
M.W. 178.19 m.p. 140-141°
NUJOL MULL

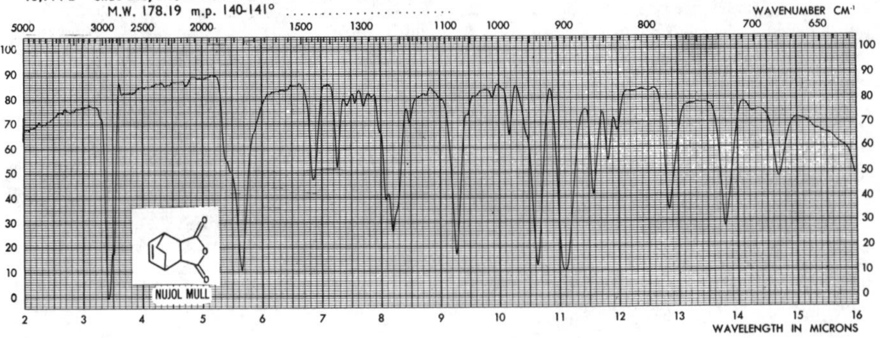

G E100-4 3,6-Endoxo-1,2,3,6-tetrahydrophthalic anhydride (7-oxabicyclo[2.2.1]-hept-5-ene-2,3-dicarboxylic anhydride)
M.W. 166.13 m.p. 115-118°
NUJOL MULL

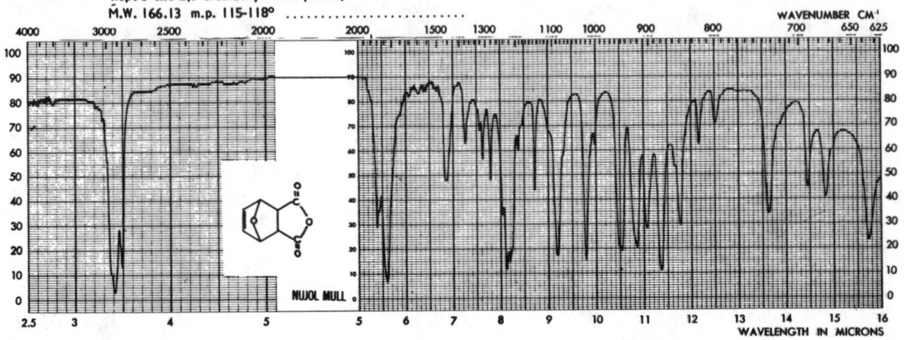

H M18-8 Maleic anhydride
M.W. 98.06 m.p. 54-56°
MELT

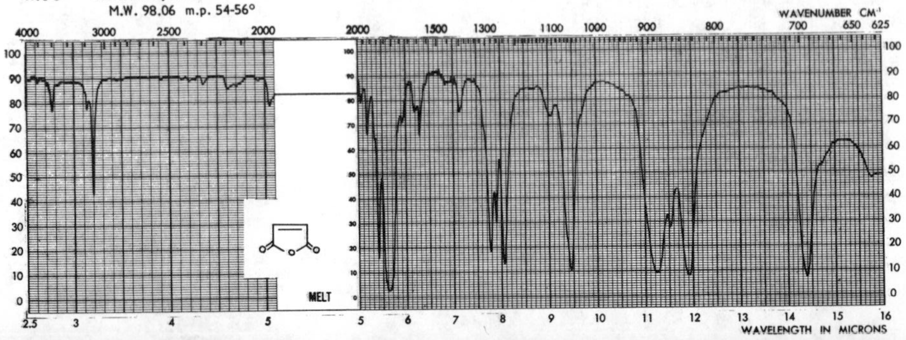

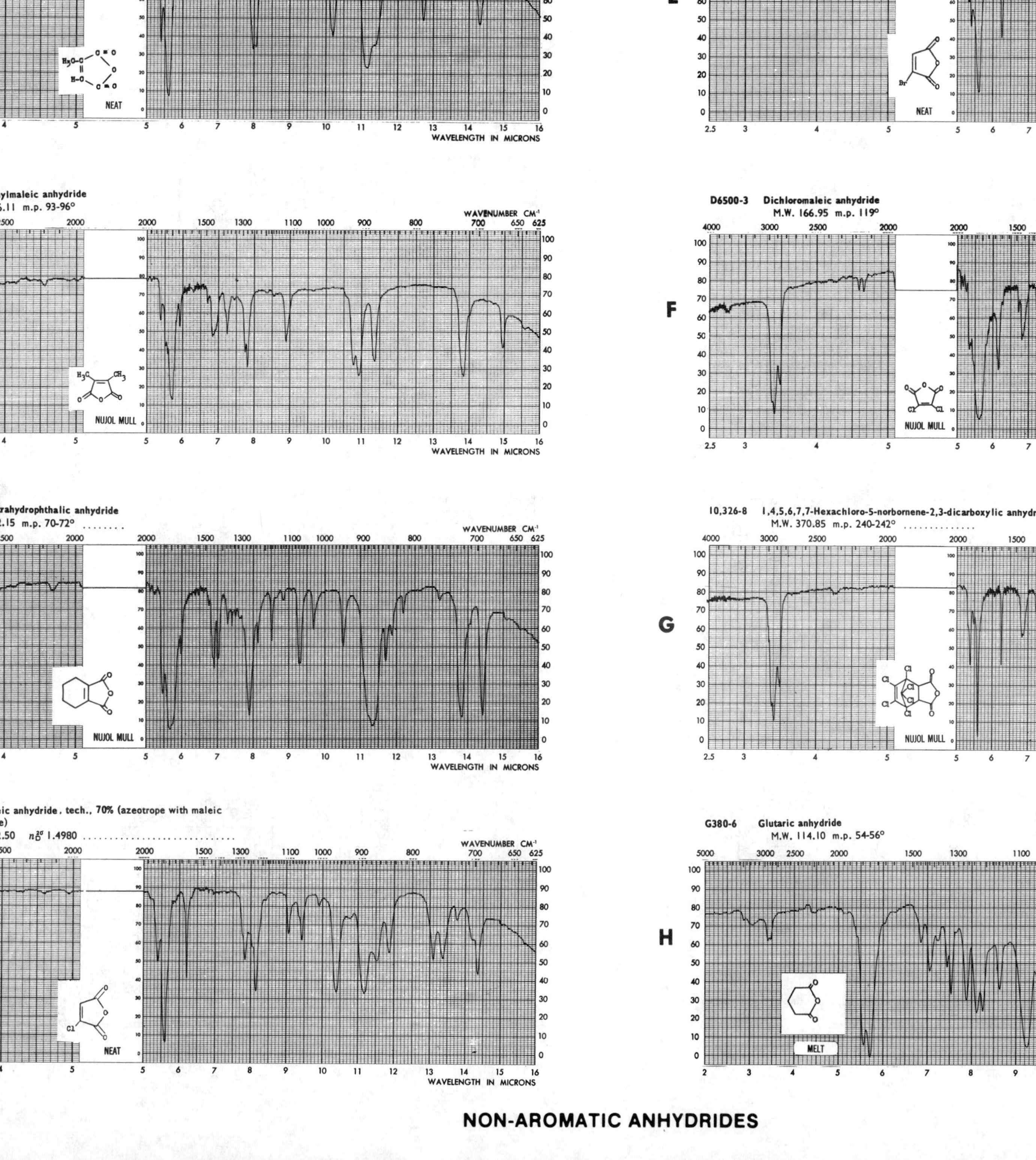
A
12,531-8 Citraconic anhydride
M.W. 112.08 n_D^{20} 1.4712
NEAT
E
10,502-3 Bromomaleic anhydride
M.W. 176.96 n_D^{20} 1.5400
NEAT
B
D16,780-0 2,3-Dimethylmaleic anhydride
M.W. 126.11 m.p. 93-96°
NUJOL MULL
F
D6500-3 Dichloromaleic anhydride
M.W. 166.95 m.p. 119°
NUJOL MULL
C
T1400-1 3,4,5,6-Tetrahydrophthalic anhydride
M.W. 152.15 m.p. 70-72°
NUJOL MULL
G
10,326-8 1,4,5,6,7,7-Hexachloro-5-norbornene-2,3-dicarboxylic anhydride
M.W. 370.85 m.p. 240-242°
NUJOL MULL
D
C4900-3 Chloromaleic anhydride, tech., 70% (azeotrope with maleic anhydride)
M.W. 132.50 n_D^{20} 1.4980
NEAT
H
G380-6 Glutaric anhydride
M.W. 114.10 m.p. 54-56°
MELT
WAVENUMBER CM⁻¹
WAVELENGTH IN MICRONS
ALDRICH

NON-AROMATIC ANHYDRIDES

A

M4780-9 3-Methylglutaric anhydride
M.W. 128.13 b.p. 282-284°

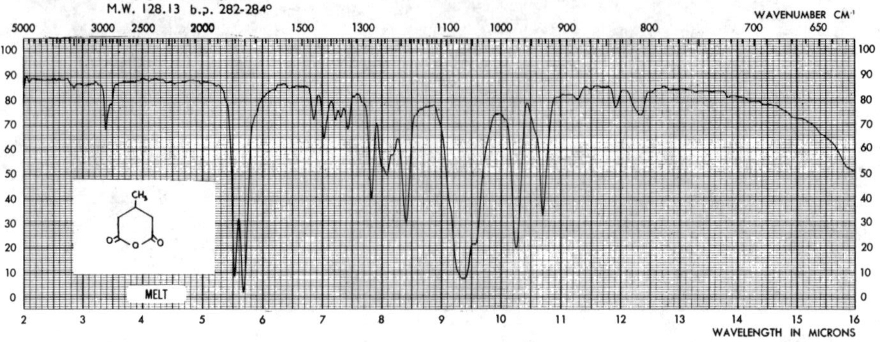

MELT

B

D15,960-3 2,2-Dimethylglutaric anhydride
M.W. 142.15 m.p. 34-38° ...

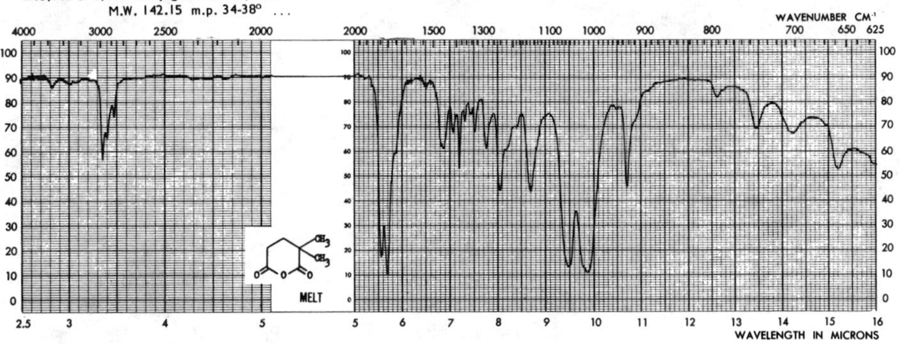

MELT

C

D15,980-8 3,3-Dimethylglutaric anhydride
M.W. 142.15 ....

NUJOL MULL

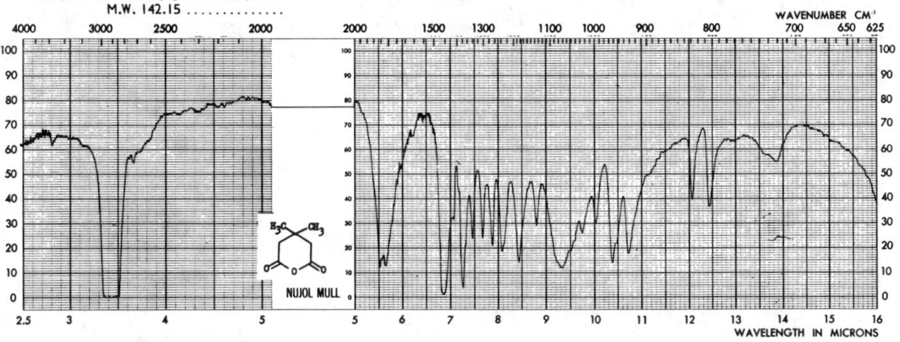

D

19,259-7
3-Ethyl-3-methylglutaric anhydride
FW 156.18 bp 185°/20mm. d 1.058
Beil. **17**(1),231 Disp. C

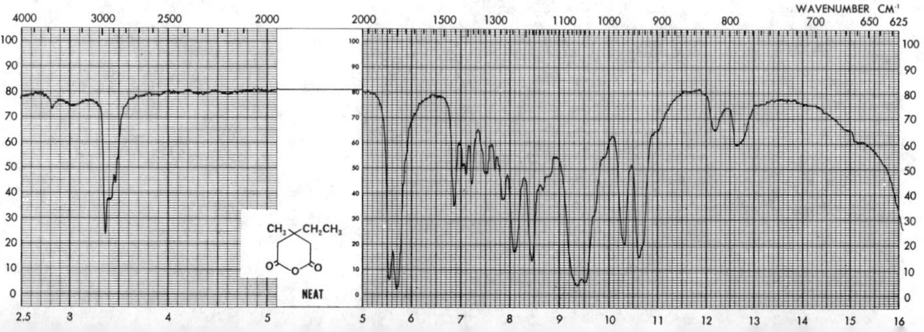

NEAT

E

T2195-4 3,3-Tetramethyleneglutaric anhydride
M.W. 168.19 m.p. 66-68° ....

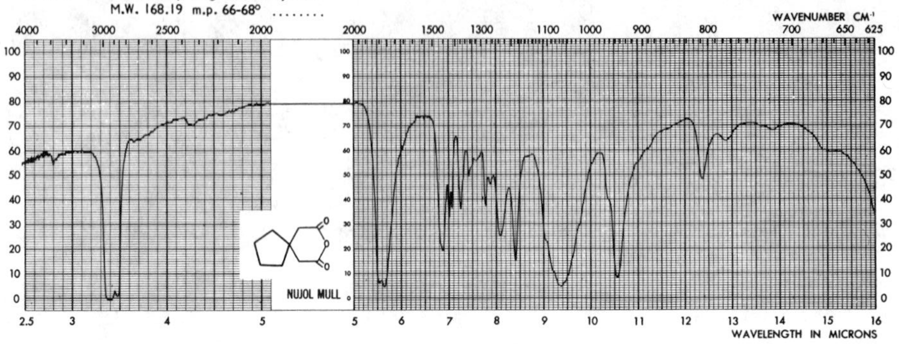

NUJOL MULL

F

C80-8 *dl*-Camphoric anhydride
M.W. 182.22 m.p. 222-225°

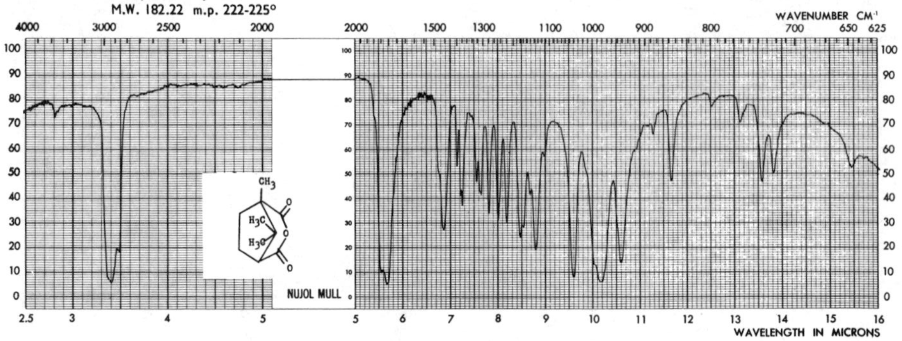

NUJOL MULL

G

D10,370-5 Diglycolic anhydride
M.W. 116.08 m.p. 92-93°

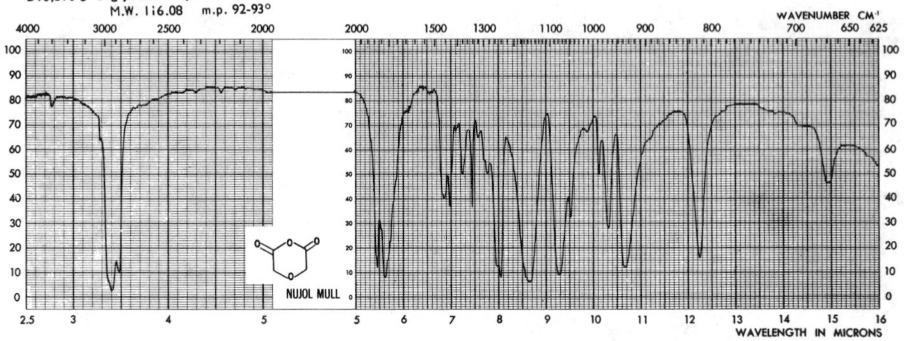

NUJOL MULL

NON-AROMATIC ACID HALIDES

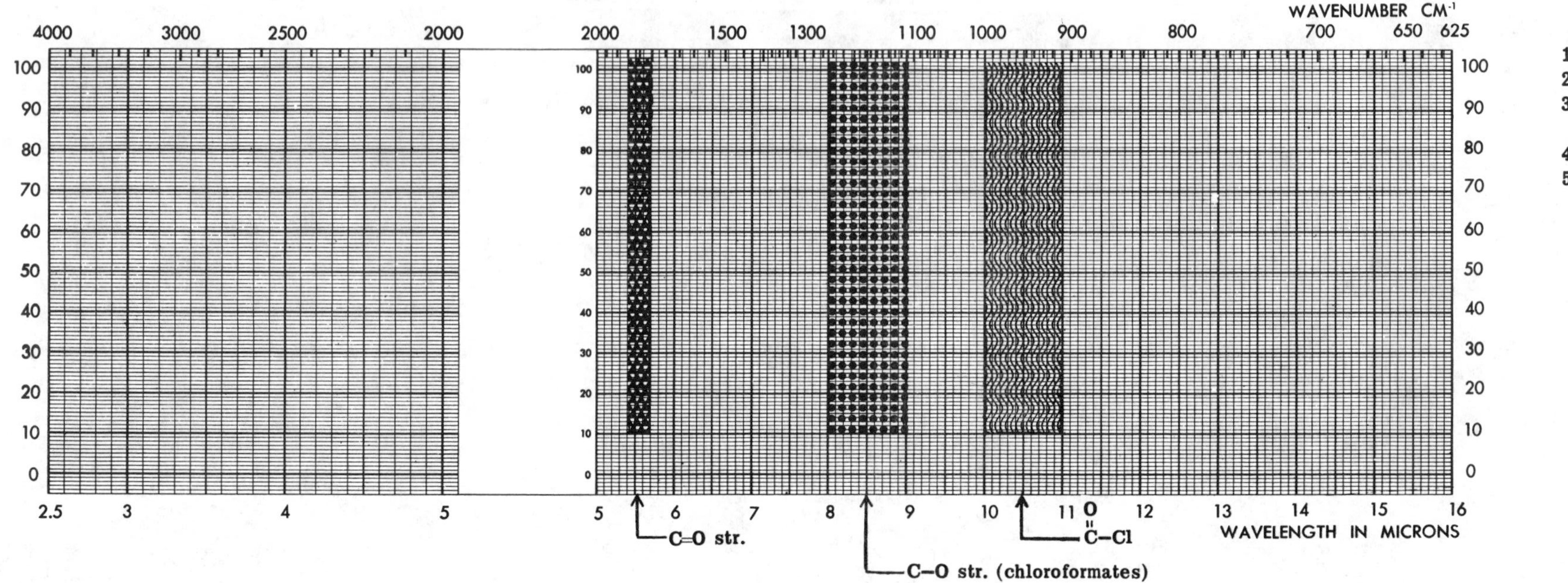

The influence of a halogen attached directly to the carbonyl causes the C=O stretch absorption to appear around 5.5 μ (1820 cm^{-1}). This absorption may be split, especially when there is α-carbon substitution, such as in spectra 425B, C and H. Conjugation of the carbonyl shifts the absorption in the usual manner to a slightly higher wavelength position. A band also associated with the acid halide is found in the vicinity of 10 to 11 μ (1000 – 910 cm^{-1}) and in general is quite broad. There are no distinctive differences between monoacid and diacid halides.

The heavier bromine attached to the carbonyl sometimes shifts the absorption to a slightly higher wavelength. (See spectra 424B, 430C and G).

The chloroformates absorb close to 5.6 μ (1785 cm^{-1}) and have the additional C–O stretch bands between 8 and 9 μ (1250 – 1110 cm^{-1}).

The effect of nitrogen attached directly to the acid chloride carbonyl as in carbamyl chlorides shifts the carbonyl to a somewhat higher wavelength than that of the chloroformates.

Caution must be exercised in running the infrared spectra of the acid chlorides, because of their extreme reactivity with moisture. It is often quite difficult to ascertain whether a sample was contaminated with the corresponding acid before analysis or while being prepared for analysis.

A 11,418-9 **Acetyl chloride**
CH_3COCl M.W. 78.50 n_D^{20} 1.3886
b.p. 50-52°

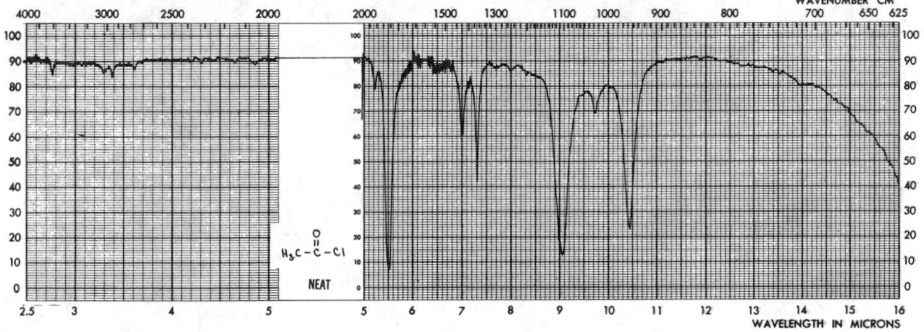

NEAT

B 13,596-8 **Acetyl bromide**
CH_3COBr M.W. 122.95 n_D^{20} 1.4486
b.p. 75-77°

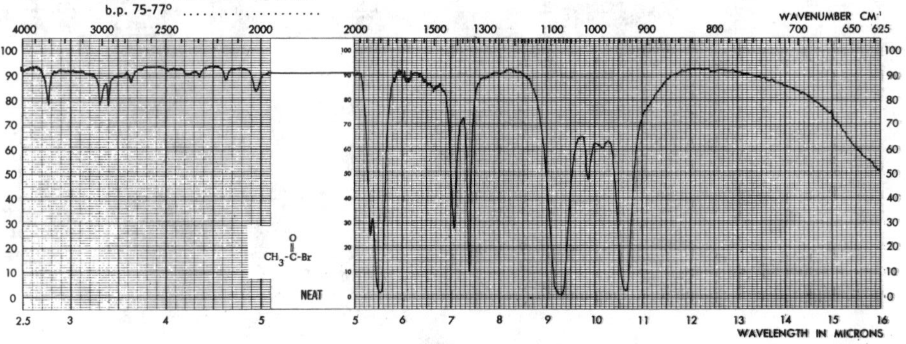

NEAT

C 10,449-3 **Chloroacetyl chloride**
$ClCH_2COCl$ M.W. 112.94 n_D^{20} 1.4530
b.p. 105.5-106.5°

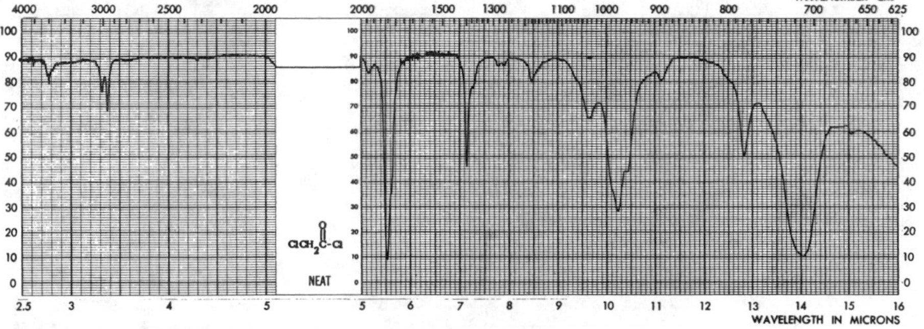

NEAT

D 20,955-4
Bromoacetyl chloride, 98%
$BrCH_2COCl$ FW 157.40 bp 127-128° n_D^{20} 1.4960
d 1.908 *Beil.* **2**,215 Disp. I

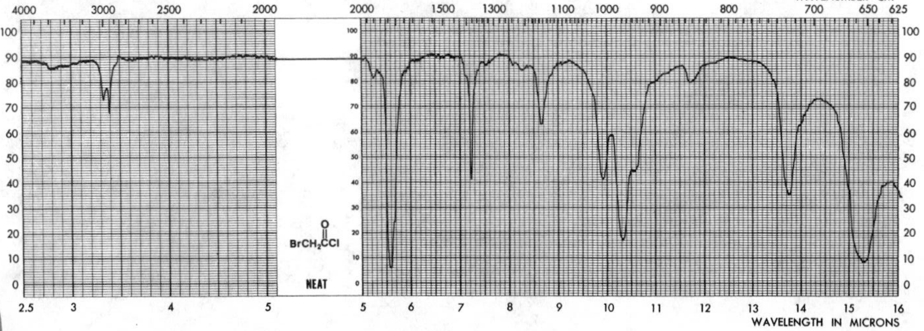

NEAT

E B5641-2 **Bromoacetyl bromide**
$BrCH_2COBr$ M.W. 201.87 n_D^{20} 1.5449

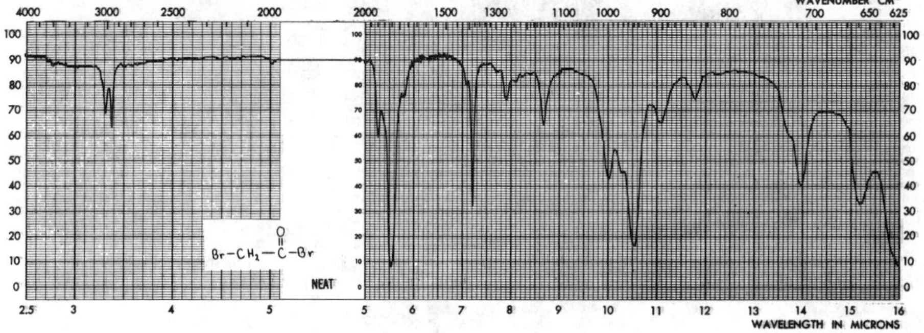

NEAT

F D5500-8 **Dichloroacetyl chloride**
$Cl_2CHCOCl$ M.W. 147.39 n_D^{20} 1.4603

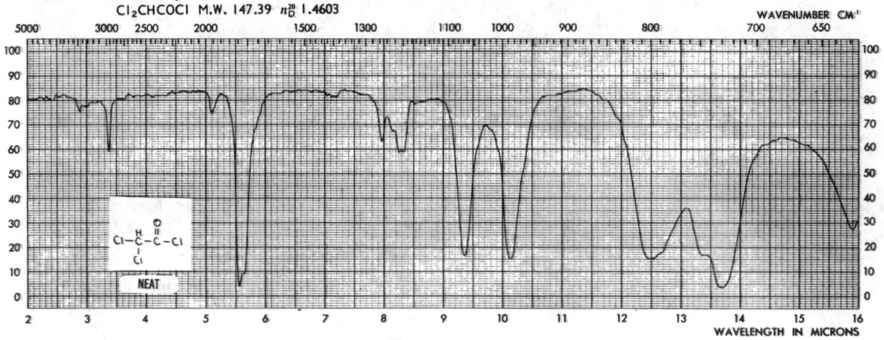

NEAT

G 15,159-9 **Trichloroacetyl chloride**
CCl_3COCl M.W. 181.83 n_D^{20} 1.4689
b.p. 114-116°

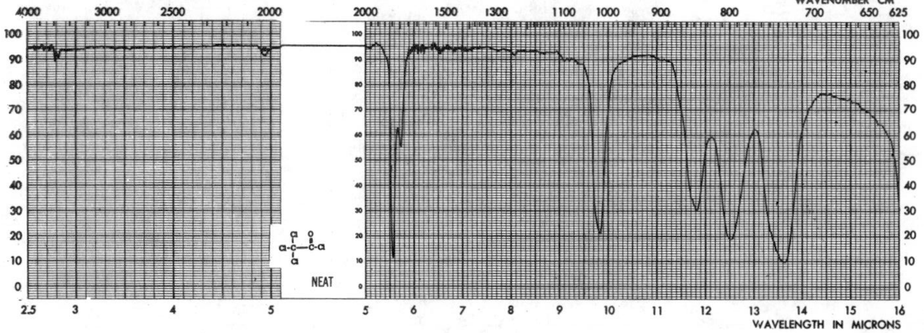

NEAT

H P5155-9 **Propionyl chloride**
C_2H_5COCl M.W. 92.53 n_D^{20} 1.4032 b.p. 77-79°

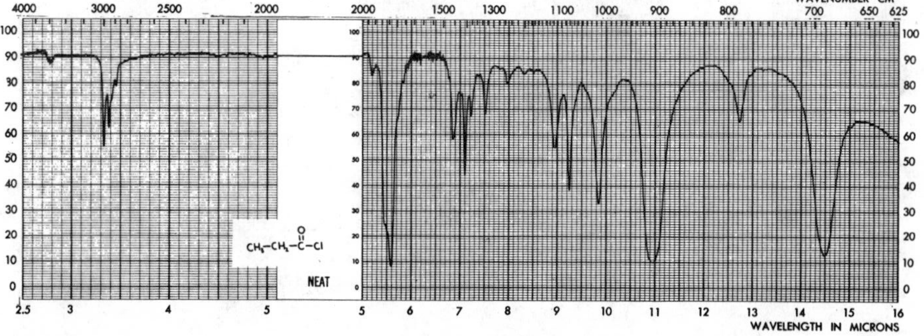

NEAT

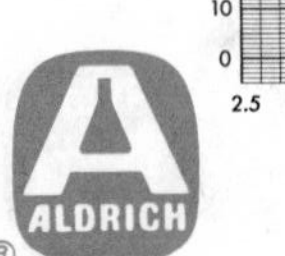

NON-AROMATIC ACID HALIDES

A

C6912-8 **3-Chloropropionyl chloride**
$ClCH_2CH_2COCl$ M.W. 126.97
n_D^{20} 1.4549

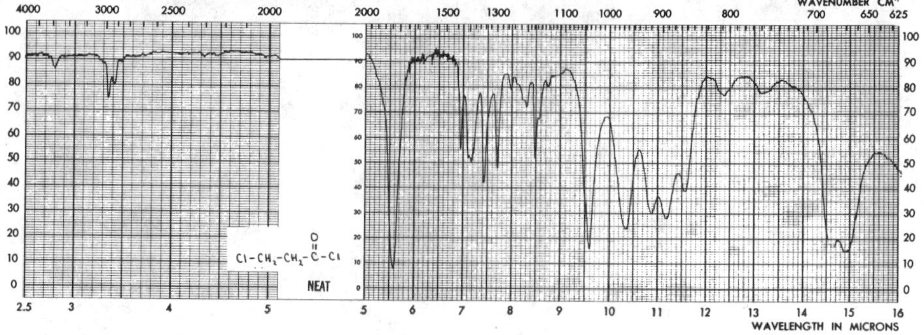

$Cl-CH_2-CH_2-C(=O)-Cl$ NEAT

B

15,713-9
2-Chloropropionyl chloride
$CH_3CH(Cl)COCl$
M.W. 126.97 b.p. 109-111° n_D^{20} 1.4400
Beil. 2,248 *LACHRYMATOR*

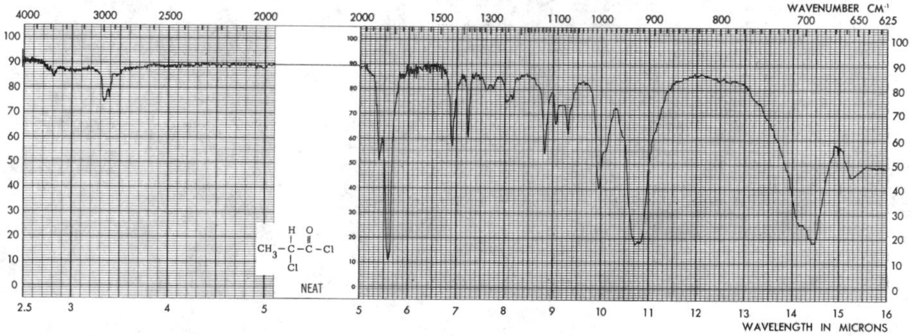

$CH_3-CH(Cl)-C(=O)-Cl$ NEAT

C

14,580-7 **2-Bromopropionyl chloride, tech.**
$CH_3CH(Br)COCl$ M.W. 171.43 n_D^{20} 1.4800

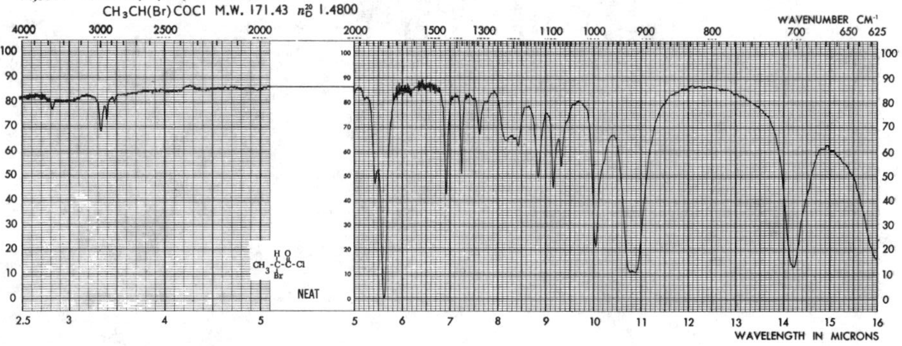

$CH_3-CH(Br)-C(=O)-Cl$ NEAT

D

14,251-4 **3-Bromopropionyl chloride**
$BrCH_2CH_2COCl$ M.W. 171.43 n_D^{20} 1.4968
b.p. 55-57°/17 mm.

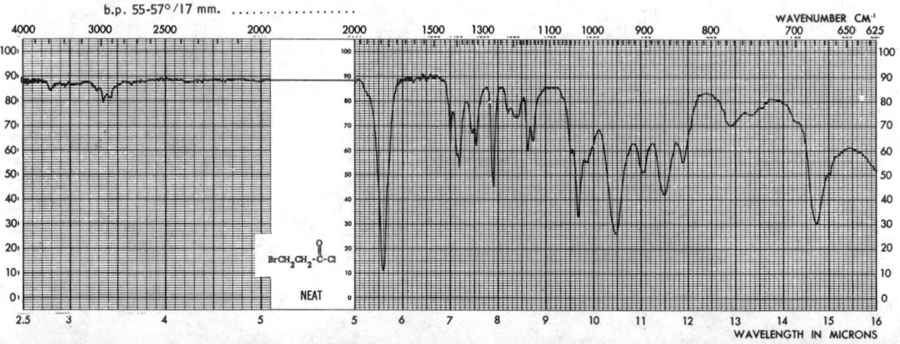

$BrCH_2CH_2-C(=O)-Cl$ NEAT

E

10,961-4 **Butyryl chloride**
$CH_3CH_2CH_2COCl$ M.W. 106.55 n_D^{20} 1.4122
b.p. 100-102°

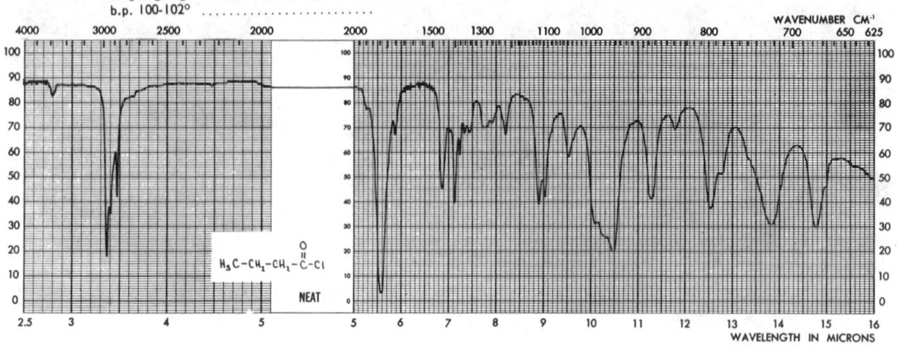

$H_3C-CH_2-CH_2-C(=O)-Cl$ NEAT

F

13,912-2 **Isobutyryl chloride**
$(CH_3)_2CHCOCl$ M.W. 106.55 n_D^{20} 1.4073
b.p. 91-93°

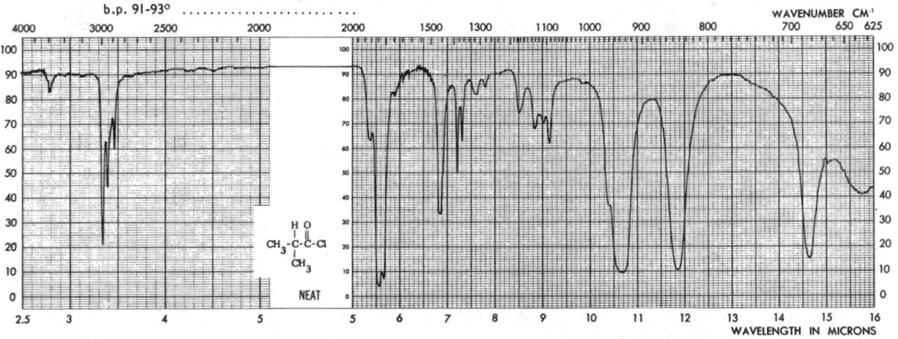

$CH_3-CH(CH_3)-C(=O)-Cl$ NEAT

G

15,742-2
Isovaleryl chloride, 98%
$(CH_3)_2CHCH_2COCl$
M.W. 120.58 b.p. 115-117° n_D^{20} 1.4161 d 0.989
Beil. 2,315 *CORROSIVE*

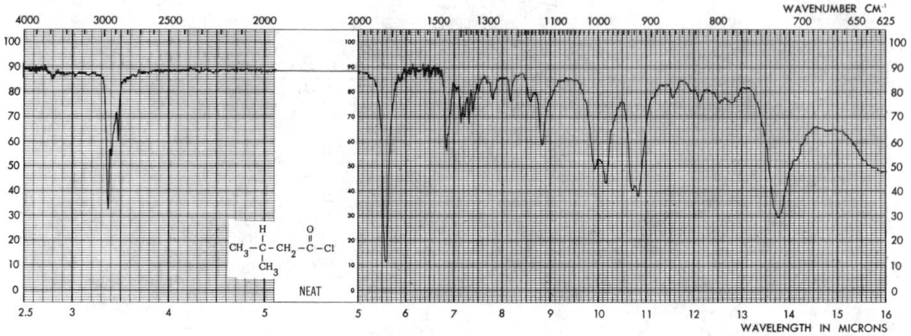

$CH_3-CH(CH_3)-CH_2-C(=O)-Cl$ NEAT

H

T7260-5 **Trimethylacetyl chloride (pivaloyl chloride)**
$(CH_3)_3CCOCl$ M.W. 120.58 n_D^{20} 1.4139 b.p. 105-106°

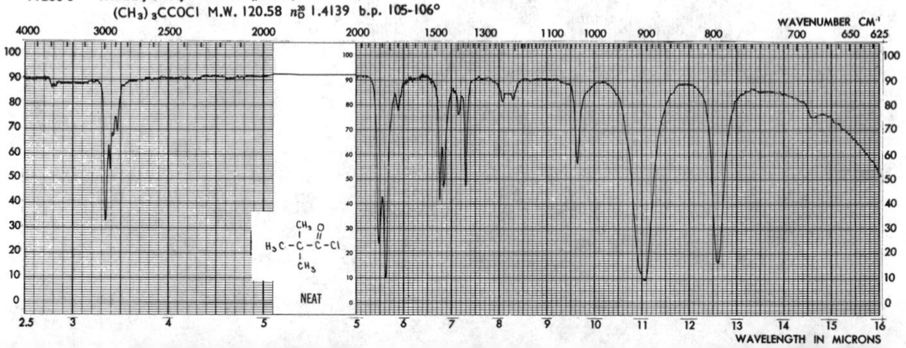

$H_3C-C(CH_3)_2-C(=O)-Cl$ NEAT

Axes (each spectrum): WAVENUMBER CM^{-1} 4000, 3000, 2500, 2000, 1500, 1300, 1100, 1000, 900, 800, 700, 650, 625; WAVELENGTH IN MICRONS 2.5–16; transmittance 0–100

A

B8880-2 **tert.-Butylacetyl chloride** (3,3-dimethylbutyryl chloride)
$(CH_3)_3CCH_2COCl$ M.W. 134.61
n_D^{20} 1.3852 . . . .

$H_3C-C(CH_3)_2-CH_2-C(=O)-Cl$

NEAT

B

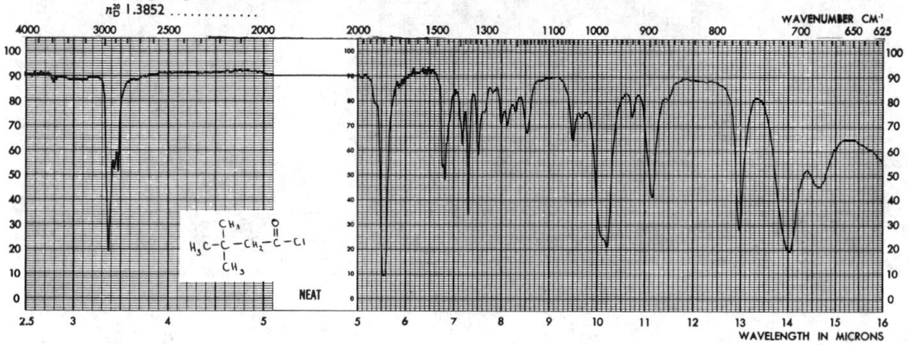

15,743-0
2-Ethylbutyryl chloride, 98%
$(C_2H_5)_2CHCOCl$
M.W. 134.61 b.p. 137-139° n_D^{20} 1.4245 d 0.982
Beil. **2**,334 *CORROSIVE*

$C_2H_5-CH(C_2H_5)-C(=O)-Cl$

NEAT

C

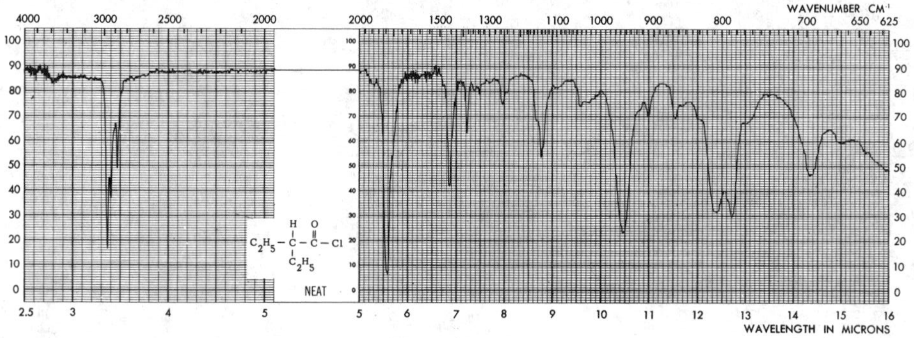

C3060-4 **4-Chlorobutyryl chloride**
$Cl(CH_2)_3COCl$ M.W. 141.00
n_D^{20} 1.4609 . . . .

$Cl-CH_2-CH_2-CH_2-C(=O)-Cl$

NEAT

D

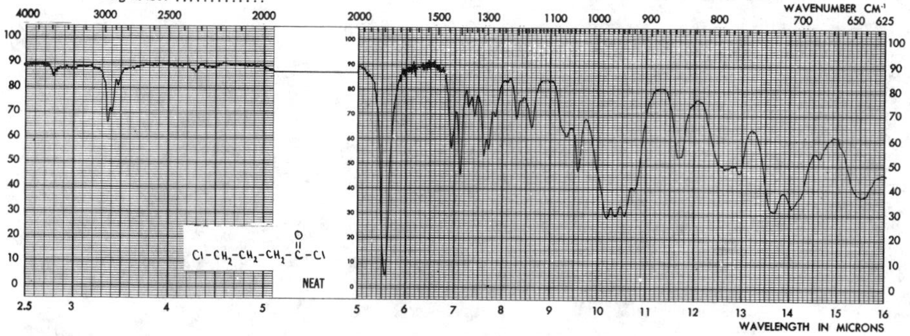

15,714-7
Valeryl chloride, 98%
$CH_3(CH_2)_3COCl$
M.W. 120.58 b.p. 125-127° n_D^{20} 1.4216 d 1.016
Beil. **2**,301 *CORROSIVE*

$CH_3CH_2CH_2CH_2-C(=O)-Cl$

NEAT

E

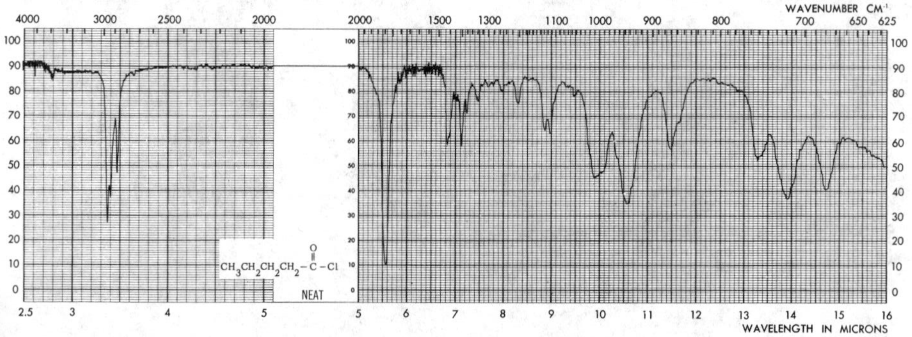

12,524-5 **5-Chlorovaleryl chloride**
$Cl(CH_2)_4COCl$ M.W. 155.03 n_D^{20} 1.4639

$Cl-CH_2-CH_2-CH_2-CH_2-C(=O)-Cl$

NEAT

F

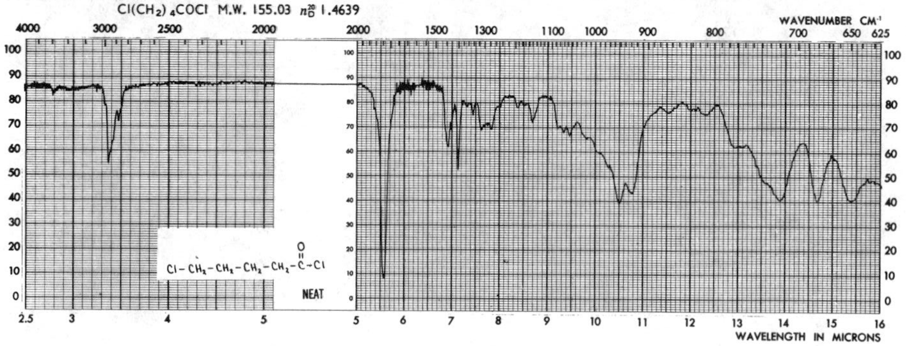

15,741-4
2-Methylvaleryl chloride, 97%
$CH_3CH_2CH_2CH(CH_3)COCl$
M.W. 134.61 b.p. 140-144° n_D^{20} 1.4263 d 0.978
Beil. **2**(2),288 *CORROSIVE*

$CH_3CH_2CH_2-CH(CH_3)-C(=O)-Cl$

NEAT

G

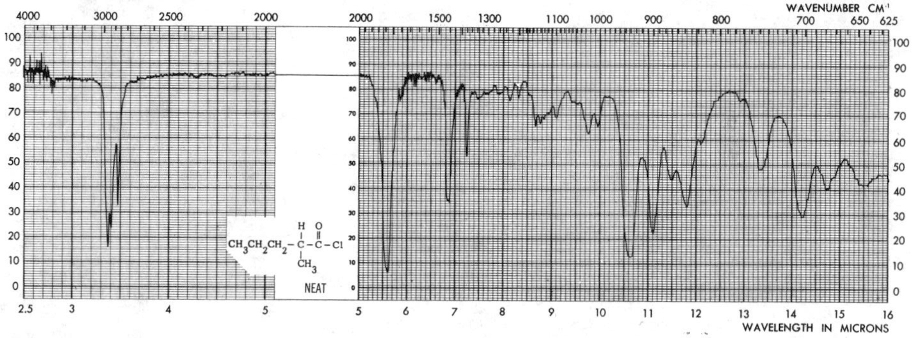

15,695-7
Hexanoyl chloride, 97% (caproyl chloride)
$CH_3(CH_2)_4COCl$
M.W. 134.61 b.p. 47-49°/15mm. n_D^{20} 1.4263
d 0.959 Beil. **2**,324 *CORROSIVE*

$CH_3CH_2CH_2CH_2CH_2-C(=O)-Cl$

NEAT

H

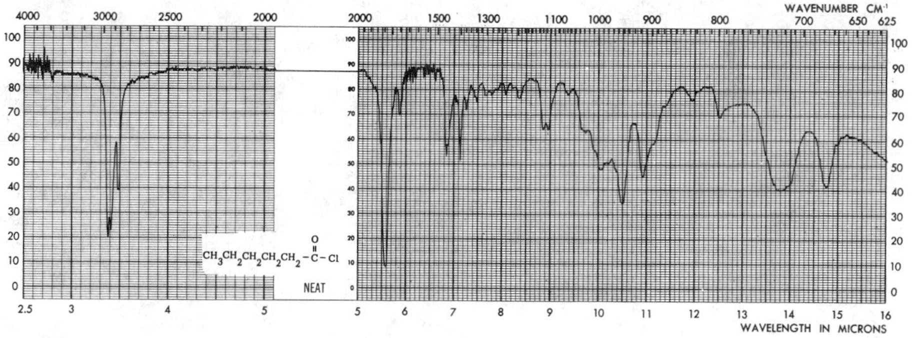

15,740-6
2-Ethylhexanoyl chloride, 98%
$CH_3(CH_2)_3CH(C_2H_5)COCl$
M.W. 162.66 b.p. 67-68°/11mm. n_D^{20} 1.4335
Beil. **2**(2),304 *CORROSIVE*

$CH_3CH_2CH_2CH_2-CH(C_2H_5)-C(=O)-Cl$

NEAT

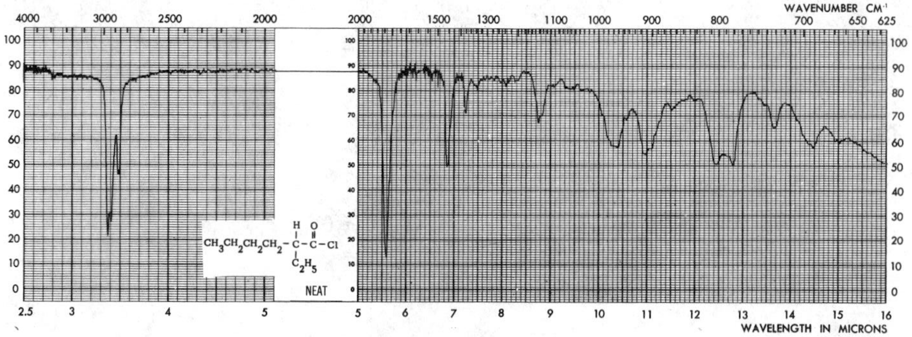

A 14,724-9 **Heptanoyl chloride**
$CH_3(CH_2)_5COCl$ M.W. 148.63 n_D^{20} 1.4300
b.p. 173°

B O-473-3 **Octanoyl chloride (capryloyl chloride)**
$CH_3(CH_2)_6COCl$ M.W. 162.66 n_D^{20} 1.4335

C 15,683-3
Nonanoyl chloride, 98%
$CH_3(CH_2)_7COCl$
M.W. 176.69 b.p. 108-110°/22mm. n_D^{20} 1.4377
d 0.98 Beil. **2**,353 *CORROSIVE*

D 14,029-5 **Decanoyl chloride**
$CH_3(CH_2)_8COCl$ M.W. 190.72 n_D^{20} 1.4410
b.p. 94-96°/5 mm.

E 15,693-0
Lauroyl chloride, 98%
$CH_3(CH_2)_{10}COCl$
M.W. 218.77 b.p. 134-137°/11mm. n_D^{20} 1.4459
d 0.946 Beil. **2**,363 *CORROSIVE*

F 18,520-5
Myristoyl chloride, 97% (tetradecanoyl chloride)
$CH_3(CH_2)_{12}COCl$
M.W. 246.82 m.p. -1° Beil. **2**,368

G P7-8 **Palmitoyl chloride**
$CH_3(CH_2)_{14}COCl$ M.W. 274.88
n_D^{20} 1.4514 m.p. 11-12°

H A2410-9 **Acryloyl chloride**
$H_2C{:}CHCOCl$ M.W. 90.51 n_D^{20} 1.4350
b.p. 72-76°

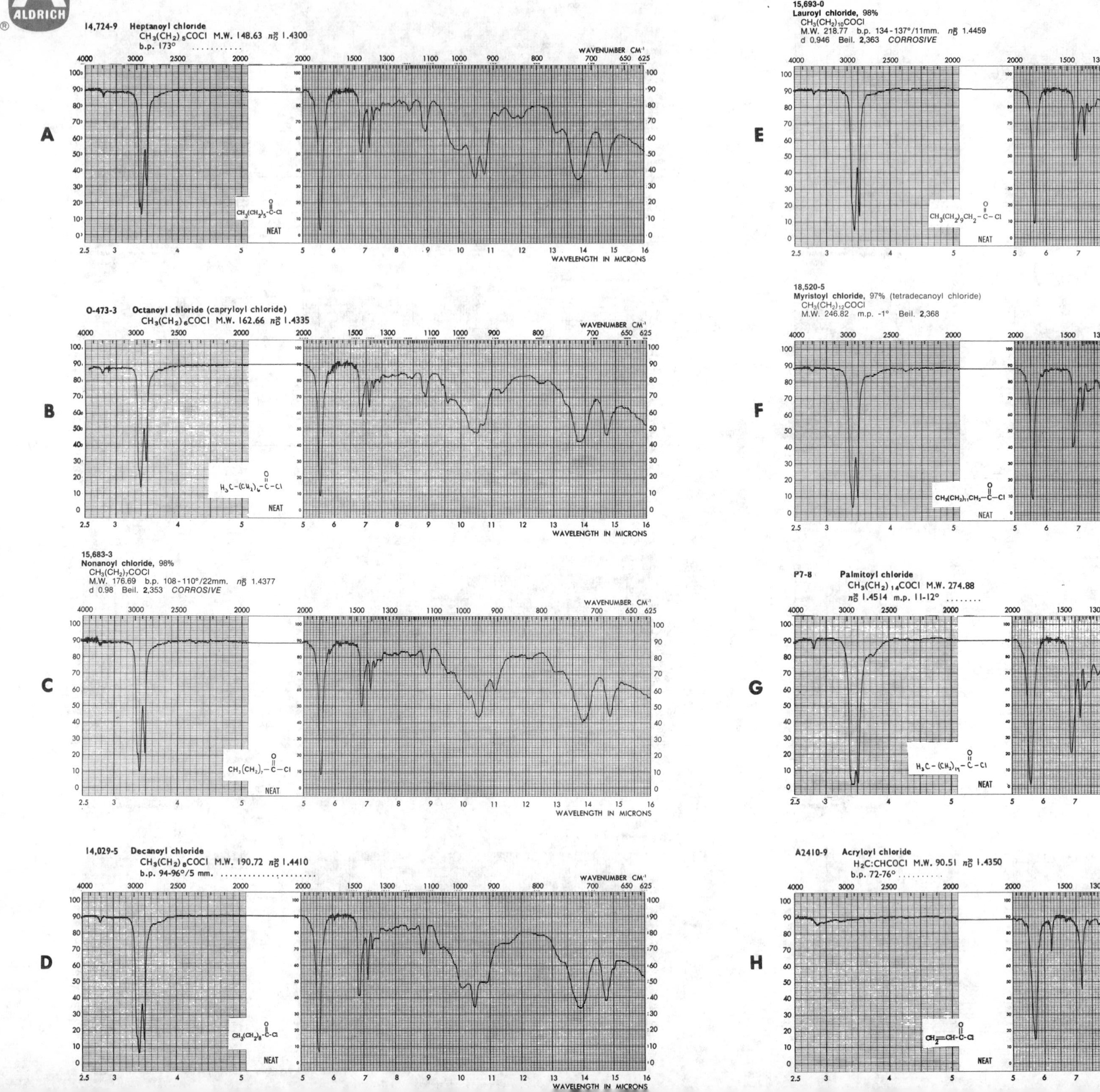

A

16,278-7
Vinylacetic acid chloride (3-butenoyl chloride)
$H_2C{=}CHCH_2COCl$
M.W. 104.54 b.p. 75-76° n_D^{20} 1.4322 d 1.14
Beil. 2,400 *CORROSIVE*

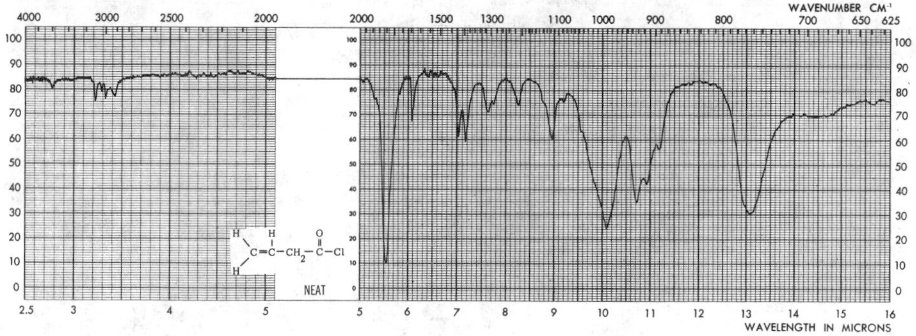

NEAT

B

12,778-7 **Crotonyl chloride**
$CH_3CH{:}CHCOCl$ M.W. 104.54 n_D^{20} 1.4595
b.p. 120-123° . . . .

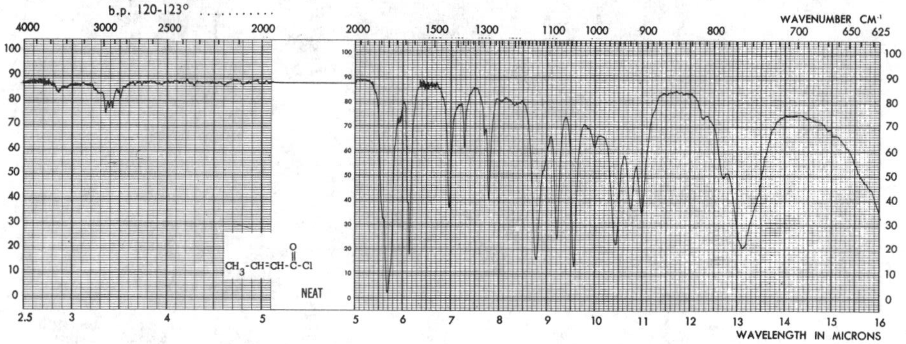

NEAT

C

15,631-0
Methacryloyl chloride, tech., 90%
$H_2C{=}C(CH_3)COCl$ FW 104.54 bp 95-96°
n_D^{20} 1.4447 d 1.070 *Beil.* 2(2),394 Disp. I,C

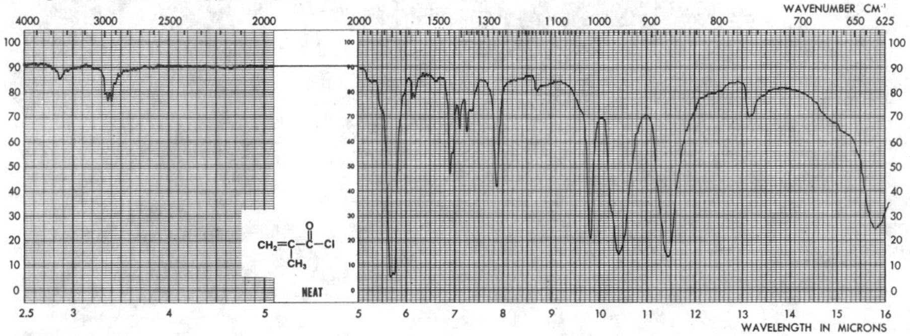

NEAT

D

18,366-0
3,3-Dimethylacryloyl chloride, 97% (3-methyl-crotonoyl chloride)
$(CH_3)_2C{=}CHCOCl$
M.W. 118.56 b.p. 145-147° n_D^{20} 1.4770 d 1.065
Beil. 2,433

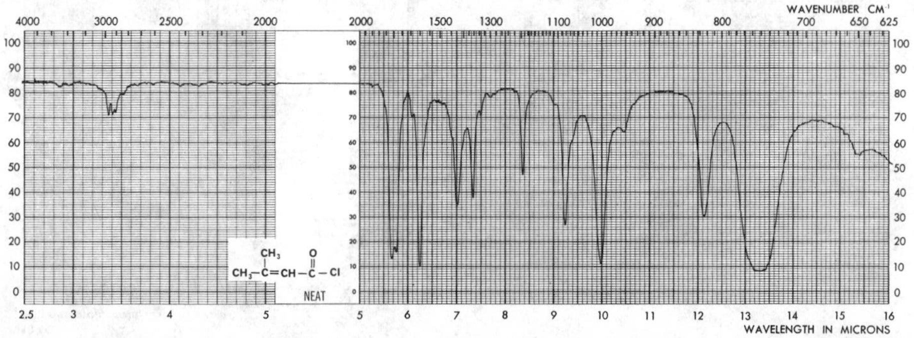

NEAT

E

14,786-9 **2,3-Dichloroacryloyl chloride**
$ClCH{:}C(Cl)COCl$ M.W. 159.40 n_D^{20} 1.5170
b.p. 80°/70 mm. . . . .

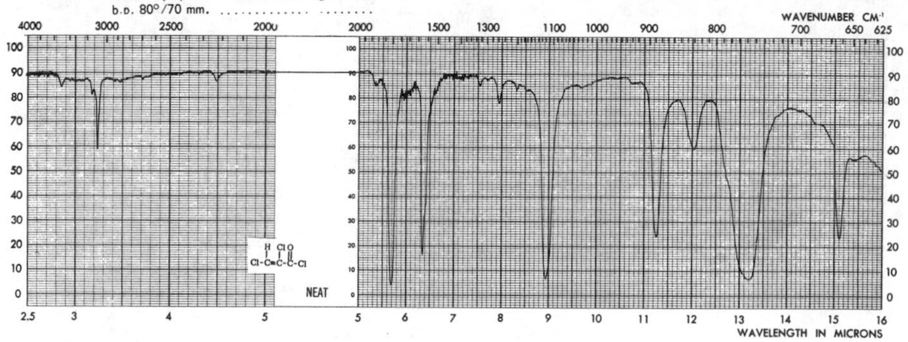

NEAT

F

16,166-7
10-Undecenoyl chloride, 98%
$H_2C{=}CH(CH_2)_8COCl$
M.W. 202.73 b.p. 120-122°/10mm. n_D^{20} 1.4532
d 0.944 Beil. 2,459 *CORROSIVE*

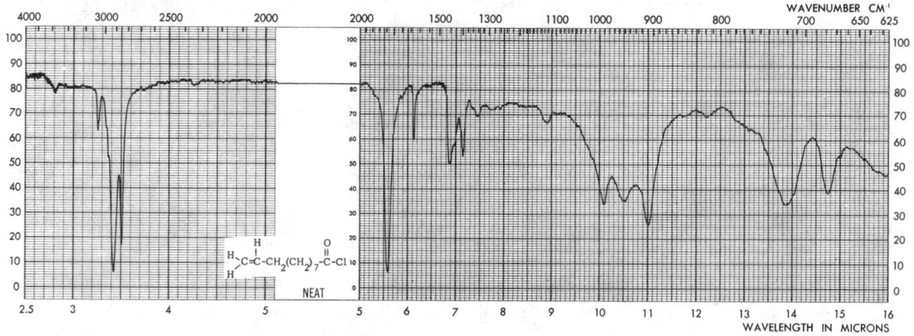

NEAT

G

M3530-4 **Methyl chloroformate**
$ClCO_2CH_3$ M.W. 94.50 n_D^{20} 1.3865 b.p. 70-72°

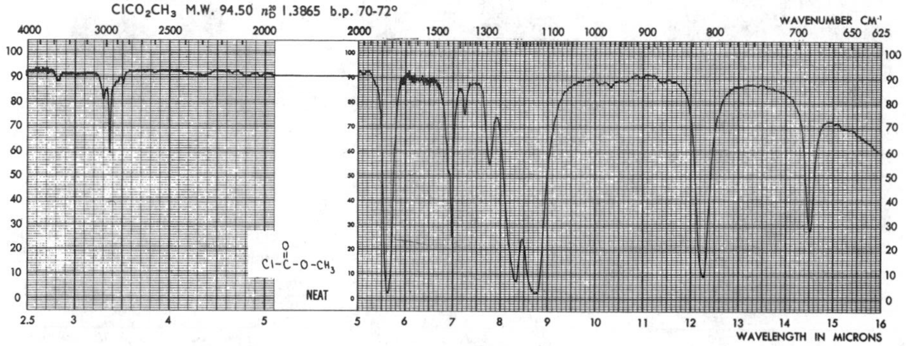

NEAT

H

E1710-0 **Ethyl chloroformate**
$ClCO_2C_2H_5$ M.W. 108.52 n_D^{20} 1.3941

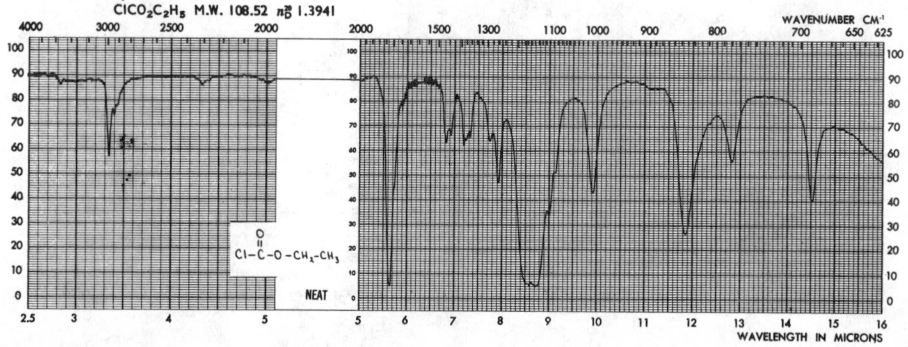

NEAT

A

18,446-2
Butyl chloroformate, 98%
$ClCO_2(CH_2)_3CH_3$
M.W. 136.58 b.p. 142° n_D^{20} 1.4114 d 1.074
Beil. 3(2),11

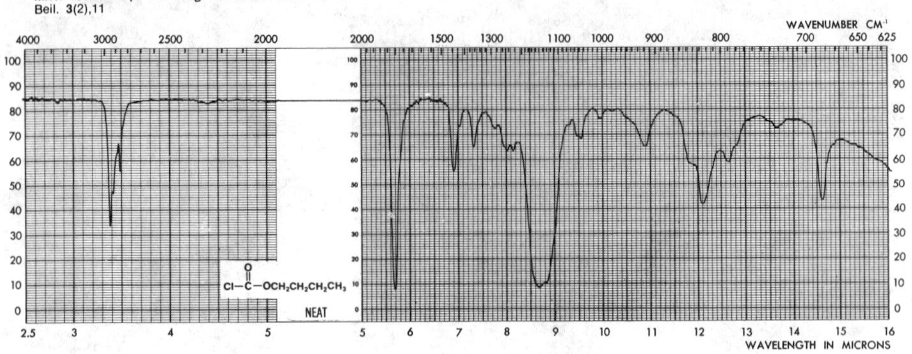

Cl—C(=O)—OCH₂CH₂CH₂CH₃ NEAT

B

17,798-9
Isobutyl chloroformate, 99%
$ClCO_2CH_2CH(CH_3)_2$
M.W. 136.58 b.p. 128.8° n_D^{20} 1.4070 d 1.053
Beil. 3,12 *CORROSIVE*

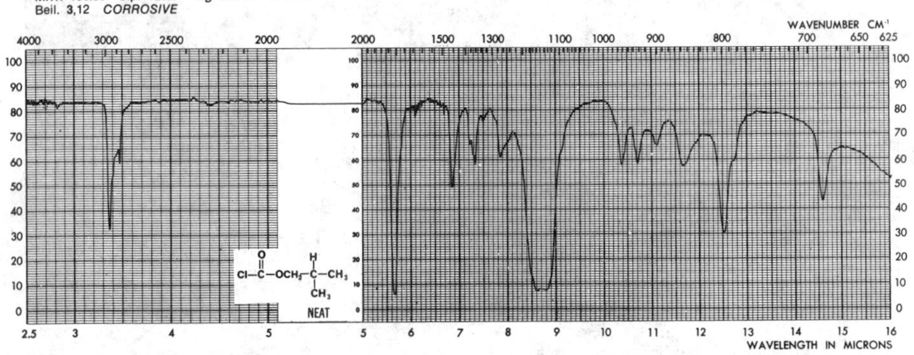

Cl—C(=O)—OCH₂—CH(CH₃)—CH₃ NEAT

C

14,207-7
2,2,2-Trichloroethyl chloroformate, 96%
(β,β,β-trichloroethoxycarbonyl chloride)
$ClCO_2CH_2CCl_3$
M.W. 211.86 b.p. 171-172° n_D^{20} 1.4703
Fieser 2,426 3,296 *LACHRYMATOR*

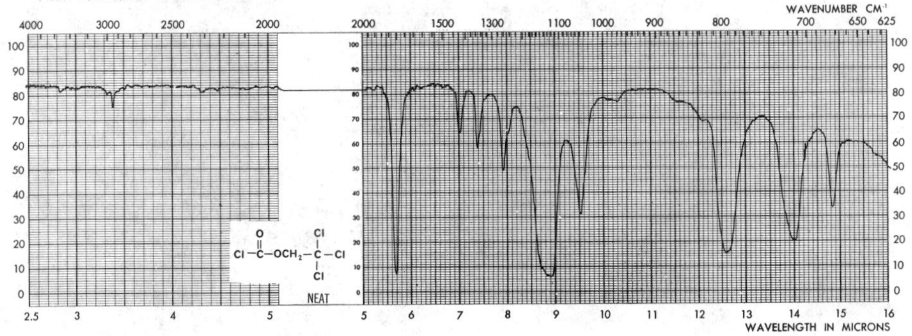

Cl—C(=O)—OCH₂—CCl₃ NEAT

D

15,144-0 **Methyl oxalyl chloride** (methyl chloroglyoxylate)
$ClCOCO_2CH_3$ M.W. 122.51 n_D^{20} 1.4189
b.p. 118-120°

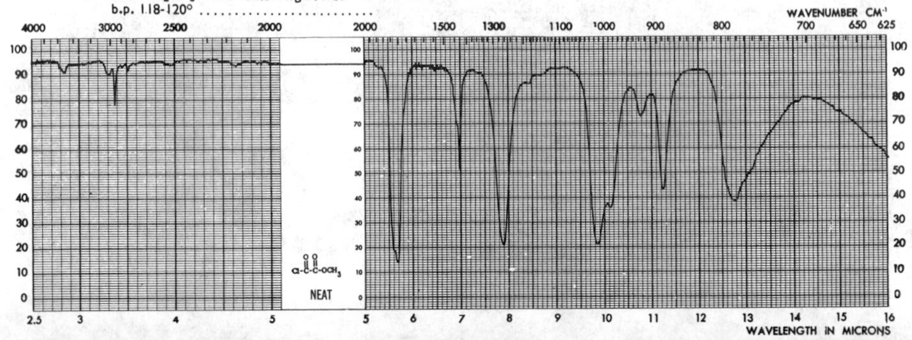

Cl-C(=O)-C(=O)-OCH₃ NEAT

E

E4310-1 **Ethyl oxalyl chloride (ethyl chloroglyoxylate)**
$ClCOCO_2C_2H_5$ M.W. 136.53 n_D^{20} 1.4164

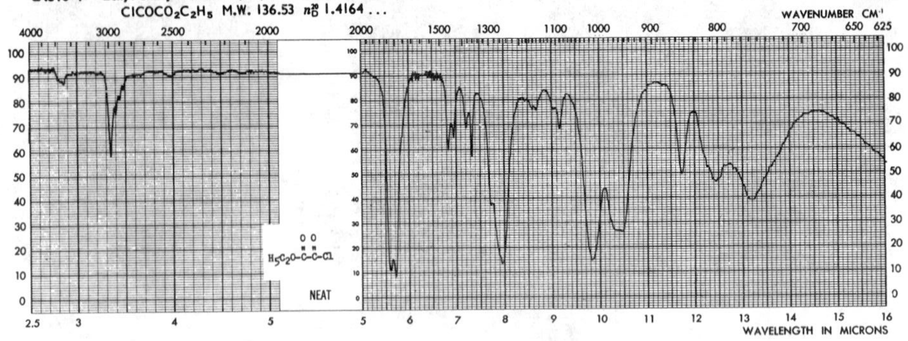

H₅C₂O-C(=O)-C(=O)-Cl NEAT

F

Ethyl malonyl chloride [ethyl (chloroformyl)-acetate]
$ClCOCH_2CO_2C_2H_5$
M.W. 150.56 b.p. 79-80°/25mm. n_D^{20} 1.4290
Beil. 2,582 *CORROSIVE*

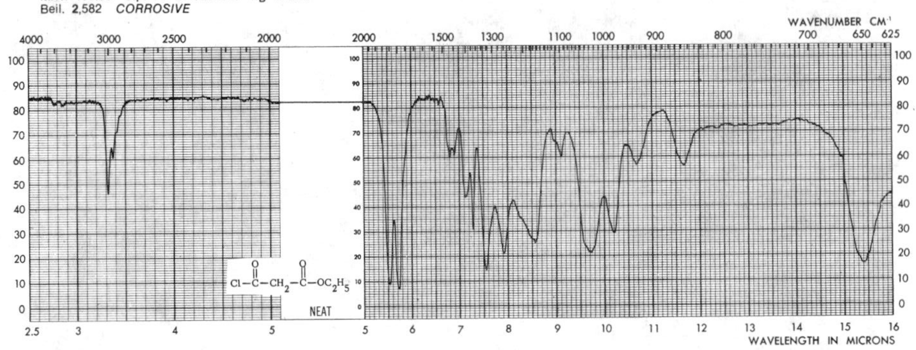

Cl—C(=O)—CH₂—C(=O)—OC₂H₅ NEAT

G

C1104-9 **3-Carbomethoxypropionyl chloride** [3-(chloroformyl) methyl propionate, methyl 3-(chloroformyl)-propionate]
$CH_3O_2CCH_2CH_2COCl$ M.W. 150.56
n_D^{20} 1.4404

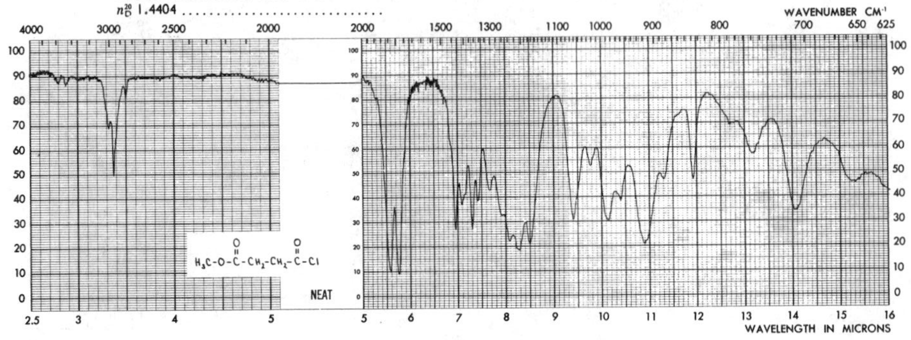

H₃C-O-C(=O)-CH₂-CH₂-C(=O)-Cl NEAT

H

M3535-5 **Methyl 4-(chloroformyl)-butyrate**
$ClCO(CH_2)_3CO_2CH_3$ M.W. 164.59 n_D^{20} 1.4460

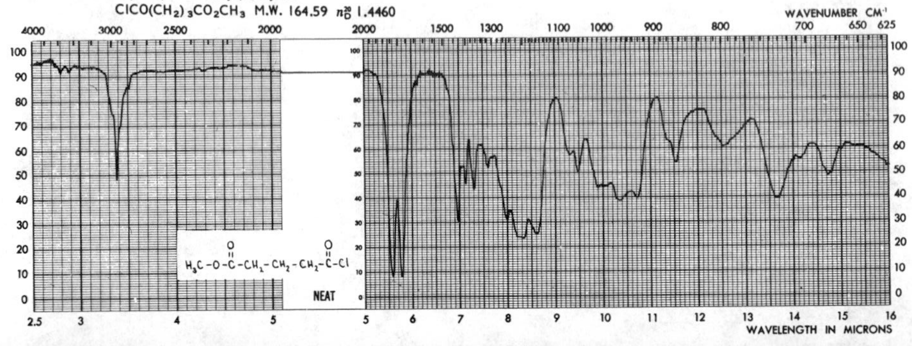

H₃C-O-C(=O)-CH₂-CH₂-CH₂-C(=O)-Cl NEAT

A 11,515-0 **Thiophosgene**
ClCSCl M.W. 114.98
b.p. 73.5°

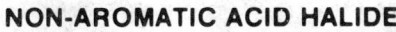

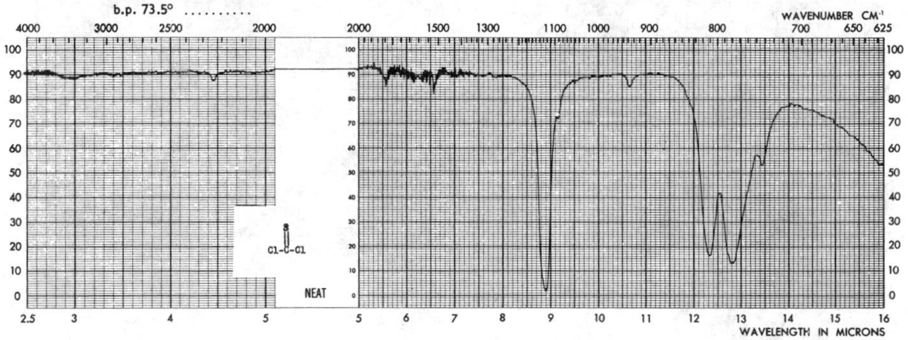

Structure: Cl–C(=S)–Cl. NEAT

B O-880-1 **Oxalyl chloride**
ClCOCOCl M.W. 126.93 n_D^{20} 1.4288 m.p. -10 to -8°
b.p. 63.5-64°/763 mm.

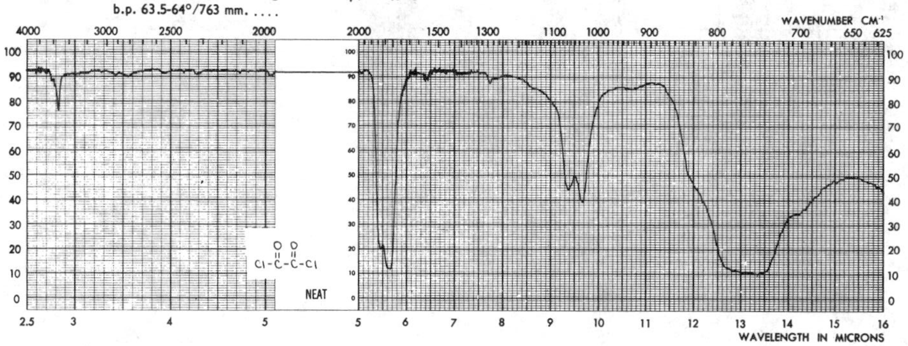

Structure: Cl–C(=O)–C(=O)–Cl. NEAT

C 11,303-4 **Oxalyl bromide**
BrCOCOBr M.W. 215.84
n_D^{20} 1.5200

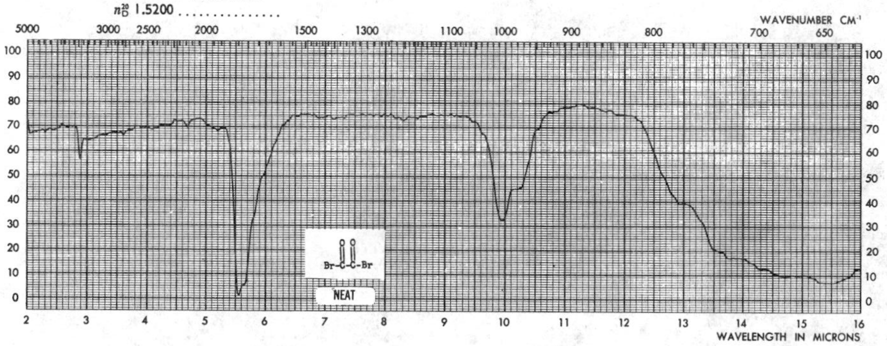

Structure: Br–C(=O)–C(=O)–Br. NEAT

D M160-1 **Malonyl dichloride (malonyl chloride)**
$ClCOCH_2COCl$ M.W. 140.95 n_D^{20} 1.4600
b.p. 58°/27 mm.

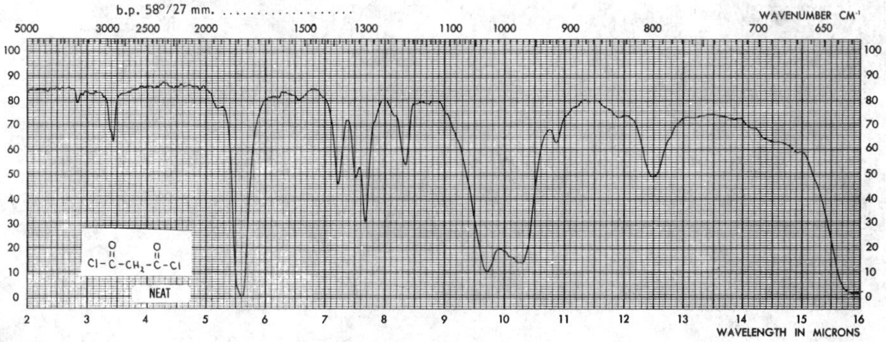

Structure: Cl–C(=O)–CH_2–C(=O)–Cl. NEAT

E S645-2 **Succinyl chloride (succinic acid dichloride)**
$ClCOCH_2CH_2COCl$ M.W. 154.98 n_D^{20} 1.4691 m.p. 16-17°

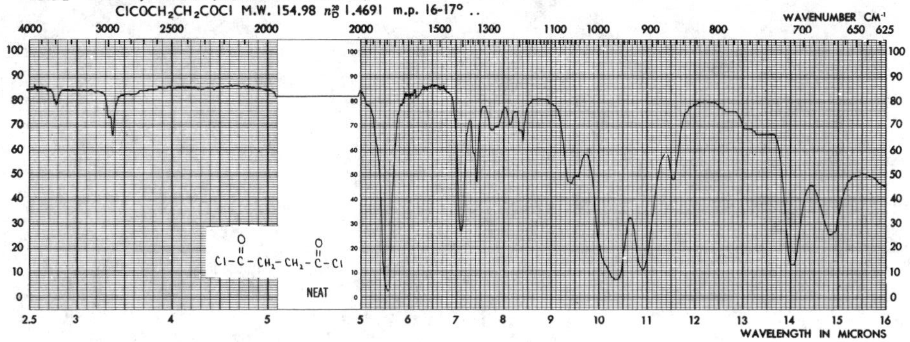

Structure: Cl–C(=O)–CH_2–CH_2–C(=O)–Cl. NEAT

F G460-8 **Glutaryl dichloride (glutaryl chloride)**
$ClCO(CH_2)_3COCl$ M.W. 169.01 n_D^{20} 1.4720
b.p. 216-218°

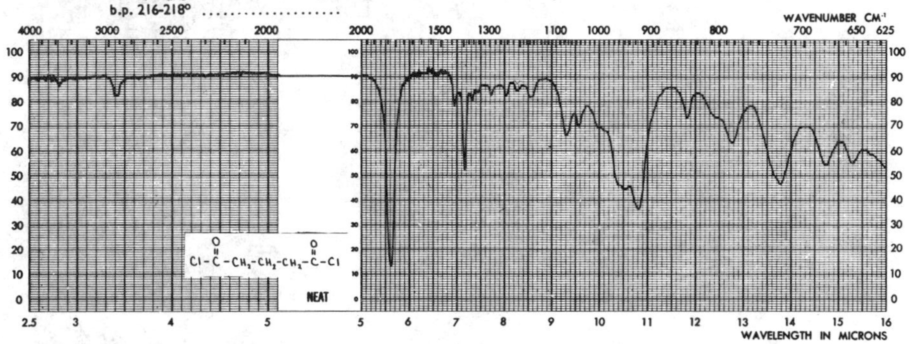

Structure: Cl–C(=O)–CH_2–CH_2–CH_2–C(=O)–Cl. NEAT

G 14,087-2 **Glutaryl bromide**
$BrCO(CH_2)_3COBr$ M.W. 257.92 n_D^{20} 1.5340
b.p. 220°

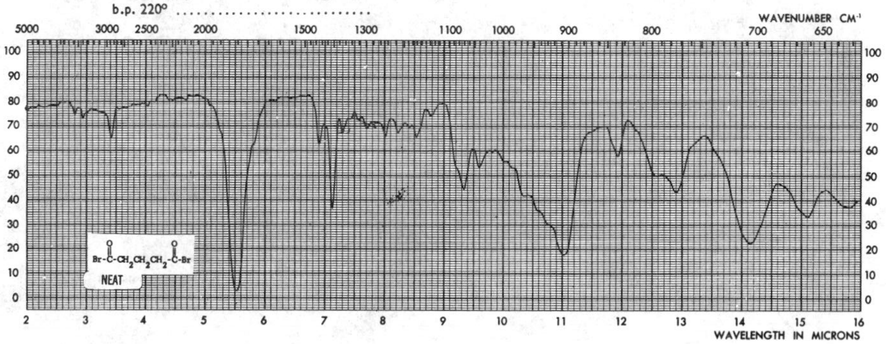

Structure: Br–C(=O)–$CH_2CH_2CH_2$–C(=O)–Br. NEAT

H 16,521-2
Adipoyl chloride, 98%
$ClCO(CH_2)_4COCl$
M.W. 183.03 b.p. 102-104°/5mm. n_D^{20} 1.4706
d 1.259 Beil. 2,653

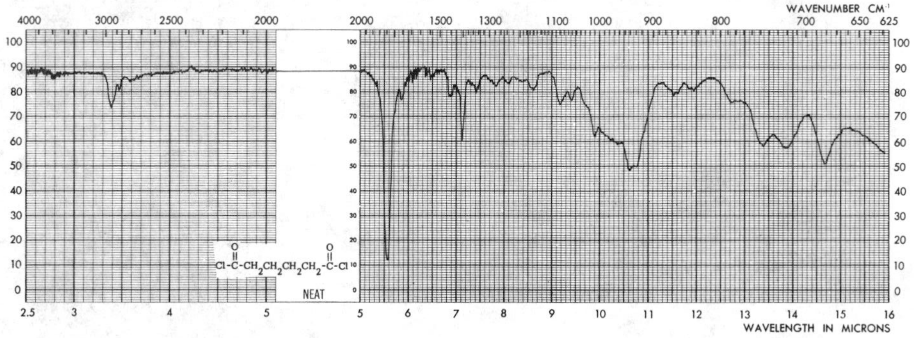

Structure: Cl–C(=O)–$CH_2CH_2CH_2CH_2$–C(=O)–Cl. NEAT

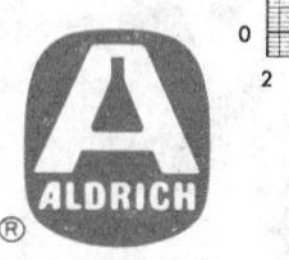

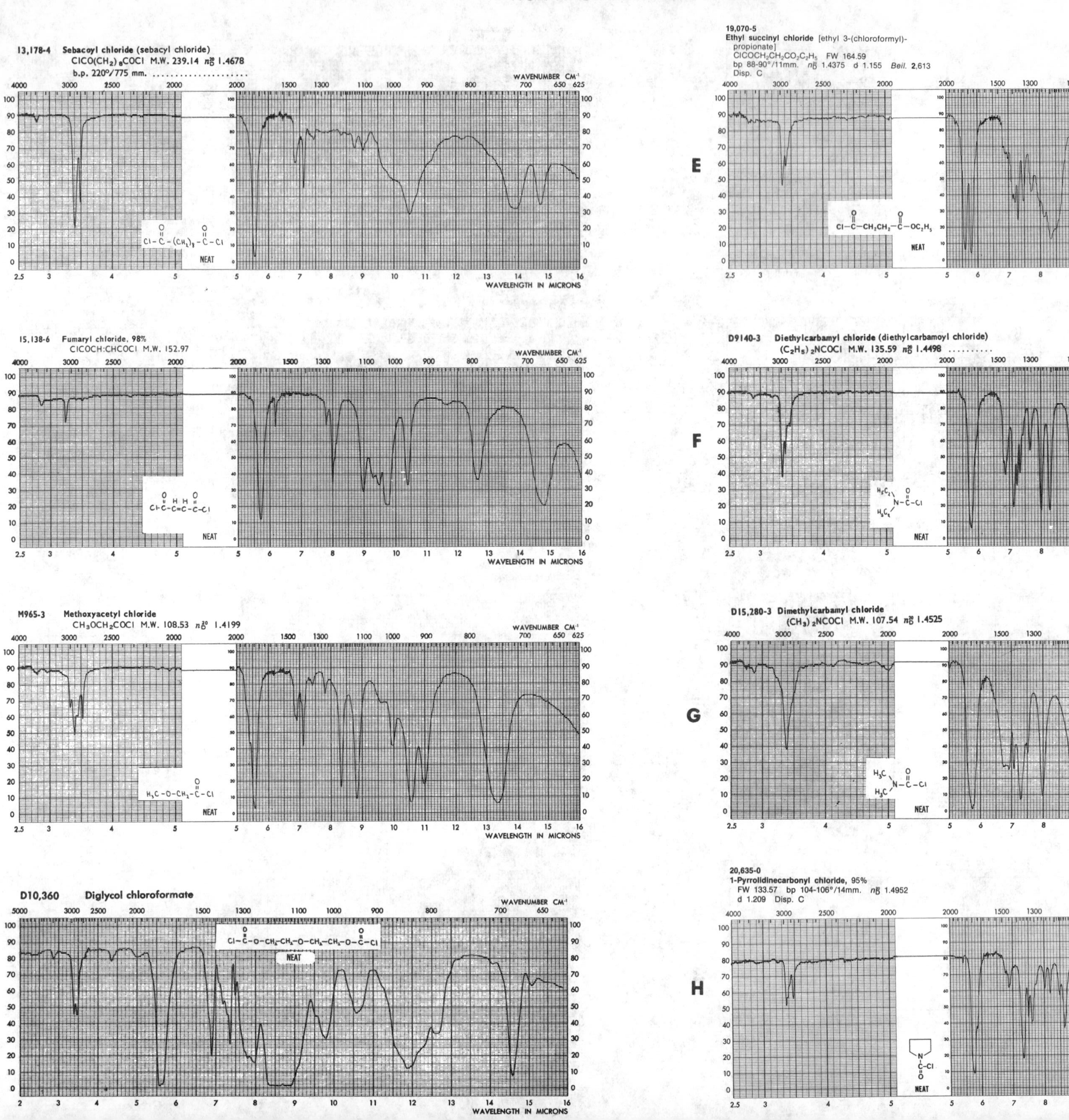
ALDRICH
A 13,178-4 Sebacoyl chloride (sebacyl chloride)
ClCO(CH2)8COCl M.W. 239.14 n20D 1.4678
b.p. 220°/775 mm.
B 15,138-6 Fumaryl chloride, 98%
ClCOCH:CHCOCl M.W. 152.97
C M965-3 Methoxyacetyl chloride
CH3OCH2COCl M.W. 108.53 n20D 1.4199
D D10,360 Diglycol chloroformate
E 19,070-5
Ethyl succinyl chloride [ethyl 3-(chloroformyl)-propionate]
ClCOCH2CH2CO2C2H5 FW 164.59
bp 88-90°/11mm. n20D 1.4375 d 1.155 Beil. 2,613
Disp. C
F D9140-3 Diethylcarbamyl chloride (diethylcarbamoyl chloride)
(C2H5)2NCOCl M.W. 135.59 n20D 1.4498
G D15,280-3 Dimethylcarbamyl chloride
(CH3)2NCOCl M.W. 107.54 n20D 1.4525
H 20,635-0
1-Pyrrolidinecarbonyl chloride, 95%
FW 133.57 bp 104-106°/14mm. n20D 1.4952
d 1.209 Disp. C
NEAT
WAVENUMBER CM-1
WAVELENGTH IN MICRONS

A

13,589-5 **Dimethylthiocarbamoyl chloride**
$(CH_3)_2NCSCl$ M.W. 123.60
m.p. 42-44° ....

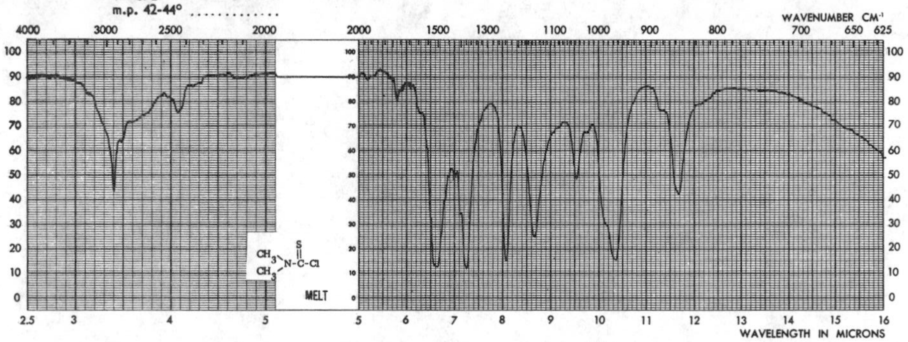

MELT

B

E1790-9 **Ethyl chlorothiolformate**
$ClCOSC_2H_5$ M.W. 124.59

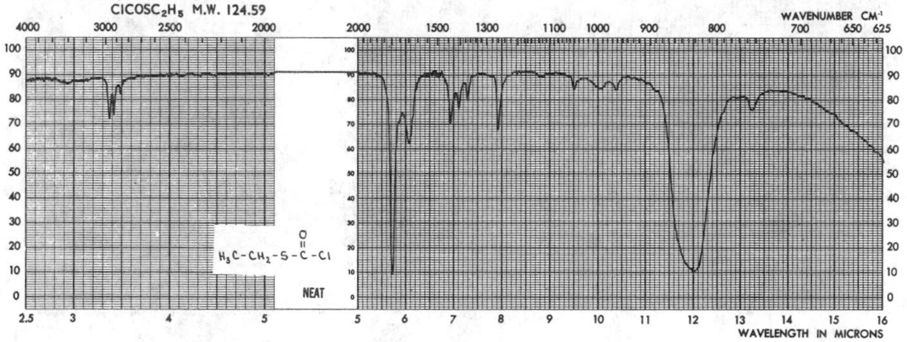

NEAT

C

I-2930-1 **Itaconyl chloride** (methylenesuccinic acid chloride)
$ClCOCH_2C(:CH_2)COCl$ M.W. 166.99 n_D^{20} 1.4910

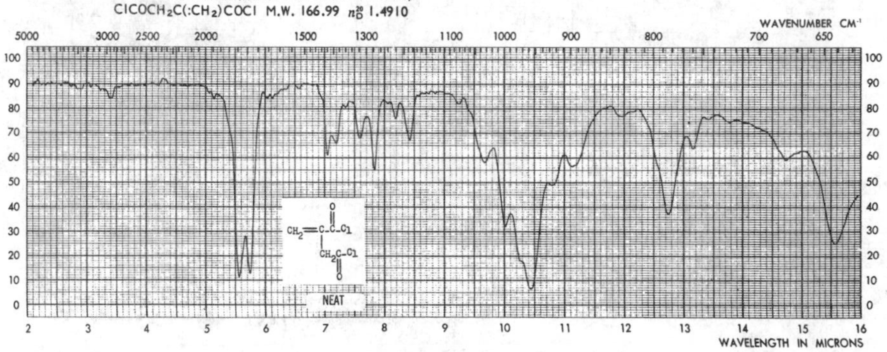

NEAT

D

C11,680-7 **Cyclopropanecarboxylic acid chloride**
C_3H_5COCl M.W. 104.54 n_D^{20} 1.4522

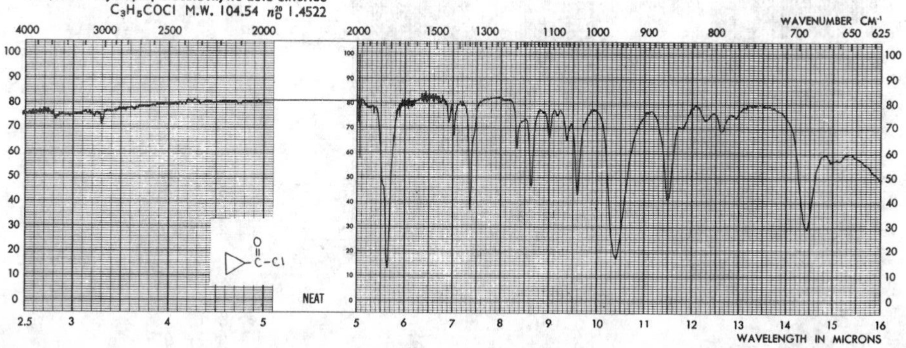

NEAT

E

C9,570-6
Cyclobutanecarboxylic acid chloride
C_4H_7COCl

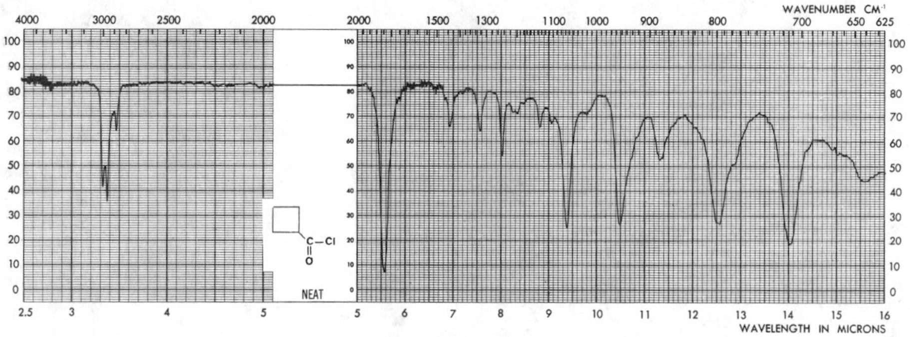

NEAT

F

14,556-4 ***trans*-1,2-Cyclobutanedicarboxylic acid chloride**
$C_4H_6(COCl)_2$ M.W. 181.02
n_D^{20} 1.4892 ....

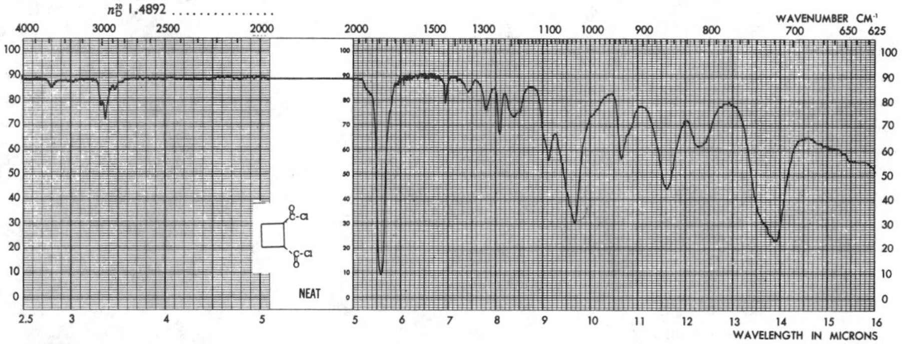

NEAT

G

15,696-5
Cyclohexanecarboxylic acid chloride, 98%
(cyclohexanecarbonyl chloride)
$C_6H_{11}COCl$
M.W. 146.62 b.p. 184° n_D^{20} 1.4700 d 1.096
Beil. 9,9 *LACHRYMATOR*

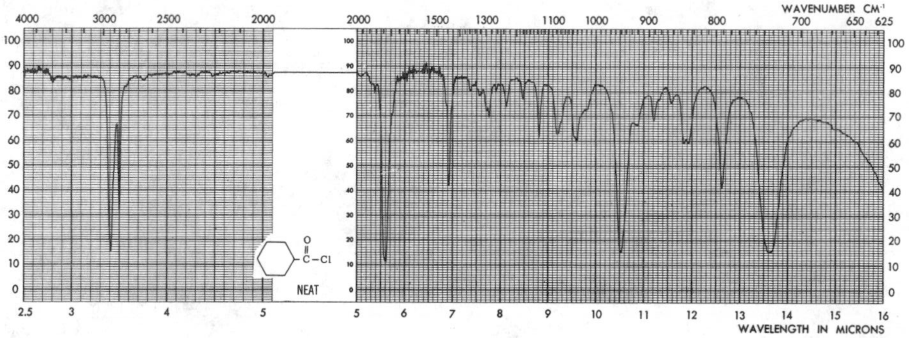

NEAT

H

11,772-2 **1-Adamantanecarboxylic acid chloride** (1-adamantanecarbonyl chloride)
M.W. 198.70 m.p. 51-53° ...

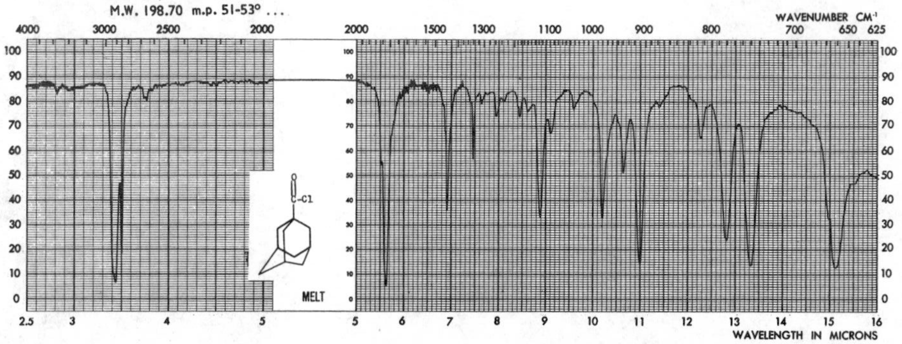

MELT

A

N3207-5 **5-Norbornene-2-carbonyl chloride**
M.W. 156.61 n_D^{20} 1.4979

B

11,415-4 ***trans*-3,6-Endomethylene-1,2,3,6-tetrahydrophthaloyl chloride**
(*trans*-5-norbornene-2,3-dicarbonyl chloride)
M.W. 219.07 n_D^{20} 1.5165
b.p. 114-118°/11 mm.

C

22,570-3
β-Chloropivaloyl chloride, 98% (3-chloro-2,2-dimethylpropionyl chloride)
$ClCH_2C(CH_3)_2COCl$ FW 155.02 bp 85-86°/60mm.
n_D^{20} 1.4531 d 1.199 *Beil.* **2**(3),714 Disp. I,C

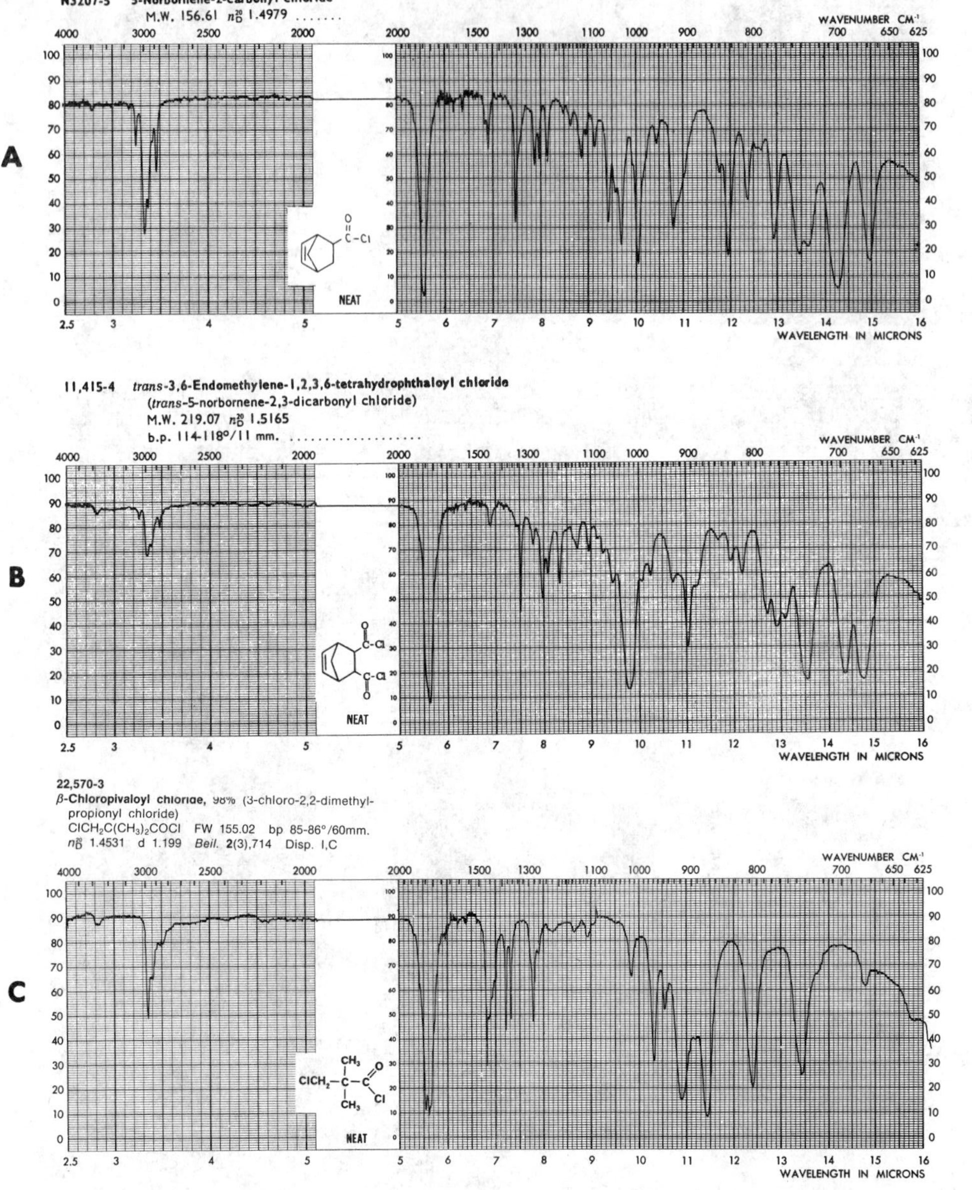

ALDRICH

NON-AROMATIC AMIDES

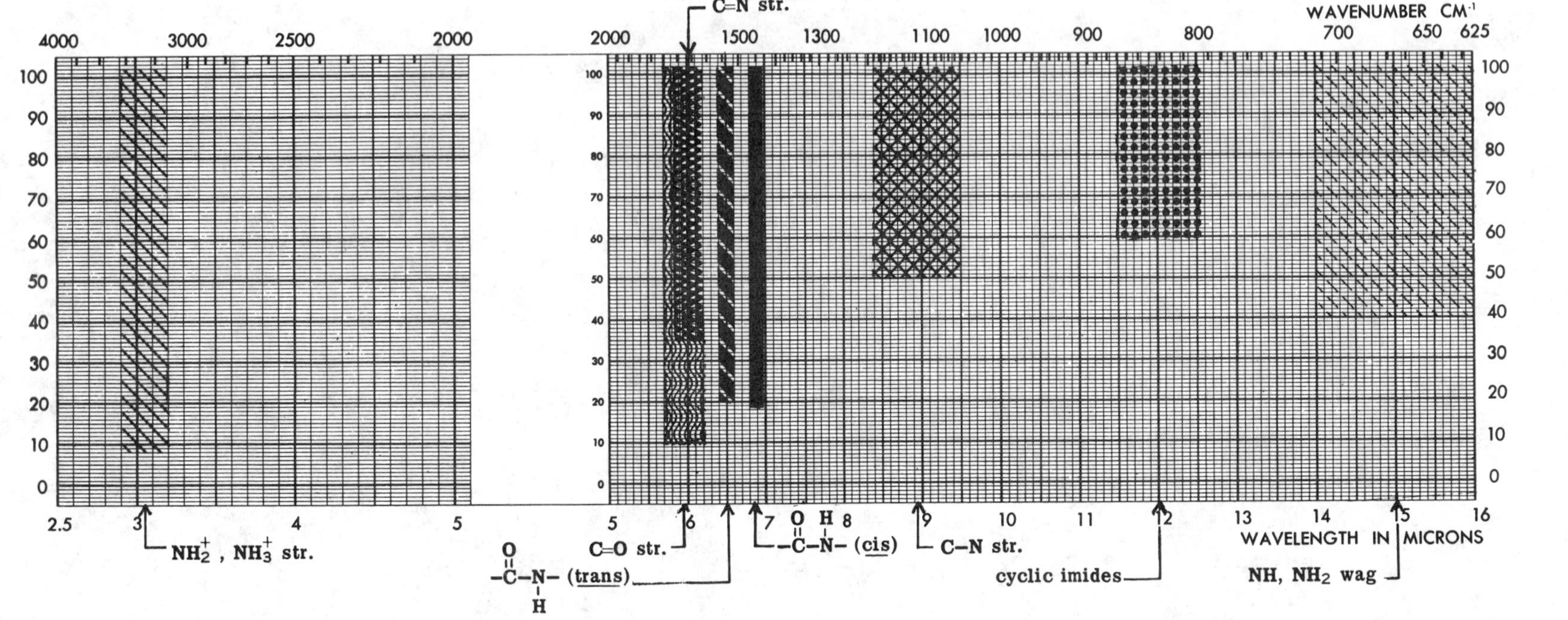

The shape of the amide carbonyl stretch absorption is one of the broadest of the carbonyl family and is positioned between 5.9 and 6.2 μ (1695 – 1615 cm^{-1}).

The primary amide $\overset{O}{\overset{\|}{C}}NH_2$ has, in addition to the carbonyl absorption at 6.1 μ (1640 cm^{-1}), the stretch bands of the NH_2 at 2.9 and 3.1 μ (3450 and 3225 cm^{-1}) which are similar in shape to the primary amine. The NH_2 deformation band is fused to the C=O stretch absorption around 6.2 μ (1615 cm^{-1}) and contributes to its broadness. The NH_2 wag vibration appears as a broad sloping band beginning at 13 μ (770 cm^{-1}) with the maximum occurring beyond the 16 μ (625 cm^{-1}) region.

In the secondary amide, the single NH stretch absorption appears very close to 3 μ (3335 cm^{-1}) with a secondary absorption at 3.25 μ (3075 cm^{-1}) being that of the 6.5 u (1540 cm^{-1}) NH overtone. The 3 μ (3335 cm^{-1}) absorption becomes very sharp and relatively strong when the NH group is sterically hindered as in spectrum 441H. The strong band at 6.5 μ (1540 cm^{-1}) is due to the hydrogen in the *trans* position to the carbonyl. However, when the hydrogen is forced into the *cis* position as in lactams, the absorption is shifted to near 7 μ (1430 cm^{-1}). When the lactam is larger than 8 members, the hydrogen again assumes the *trans* position (see spectra 470G—470H). The carbonyl of the five-membered lactam absorbs strongly at 5.9 μ (1695 cm^{-1}) while in larger rings, it absorbs near 6.1 μ (1640 cm^{-1}).

For tertiary amides, only the carbonyl stretch band remains at 6 to 6.1 μ (1665 – 1640 cm^{-1}). It is sharper than the primary or secondary amide carbonyl bands.

The carbon-nitrogen stretch bands appear in similar positions to those seen in the amine section; namely, in the vicinity of 8.5 to 9.5 μ (1175 – 1055 cm^{-1}).

The hydrazides are similar to their amide counterparts and display absorptions near 3, 6.1 and 6.5 μ (3335, 1640 and 1540 cm^{-1}).

The carbamate bands are a combination of the amide and ester absorptions. The carbonyl stretch band shifts to 5.9 μ (1695 cm^{-1}), a position between that of the normal ester and amide. The NH and NH_2 stretch bands at 3 μ (3335 cm^{-1}) and the bands at 6.2 μ and 6.5 μ (1615 and 1540 cm^{-1}) remain essentially unaltered as in corresponding amides. Absorptions between 8 and 10 μ (1250 – 1000 cm^{-1}) are a result of the $\overset{O}{\overset{\|}{C}}-O-C$ stretch vibrations of the ester portion of the carbamate.

The cyclic imides have their main carbonyl stretch absorption close to 5.9 μ (1695 cm^{-1}). It is broad and often accompanied by a lower wavelength shoulder near 5.7 μ (1755 cm^{-1}). The NH of the imide absorbs near 3.1 to 3.2 μ (3225 – 3125 cm^{-1}). A medium to strong absorption between 11.5 and 12.5 μ (870 – 800 cm^{-1}) also characterizes the cyclic *imide.*

Cyclic *amides* such as those seen in spectra 478E—483H have bands very similar to the open-chain amides. The N-halogenated members have their carbonyl band shifted to near 5.7 μ (1755 cm^{-1}). (See spectrum 478G).

The imine group (C=N) absorbs between 5.9 and 6.3 μ (1695 – 1585 cm^{-1}) and is somewhat weaker than the amide carbonyl.

In spectra 488C—489D, the N-nitro group can be seen absorbing very strongly at 8 μ (1250 cm^{-1}), while the N-nitroso group displays its N=O stretch band at 6.6 μ (1515 cm^{-1}) and its N–O stretch band near 10.1 μ (990 cm^{-1}).

The C=S of the thioamides does not have any outstanding characteristic bands. However, its presence in the amide molecules (spectra 491D—497H) allows for the NH and NH_2 absorptions to be seen in the 6 to 6.5 μ (1665 – 1540 cm^{-1}) region without carbonyl stretch interference.

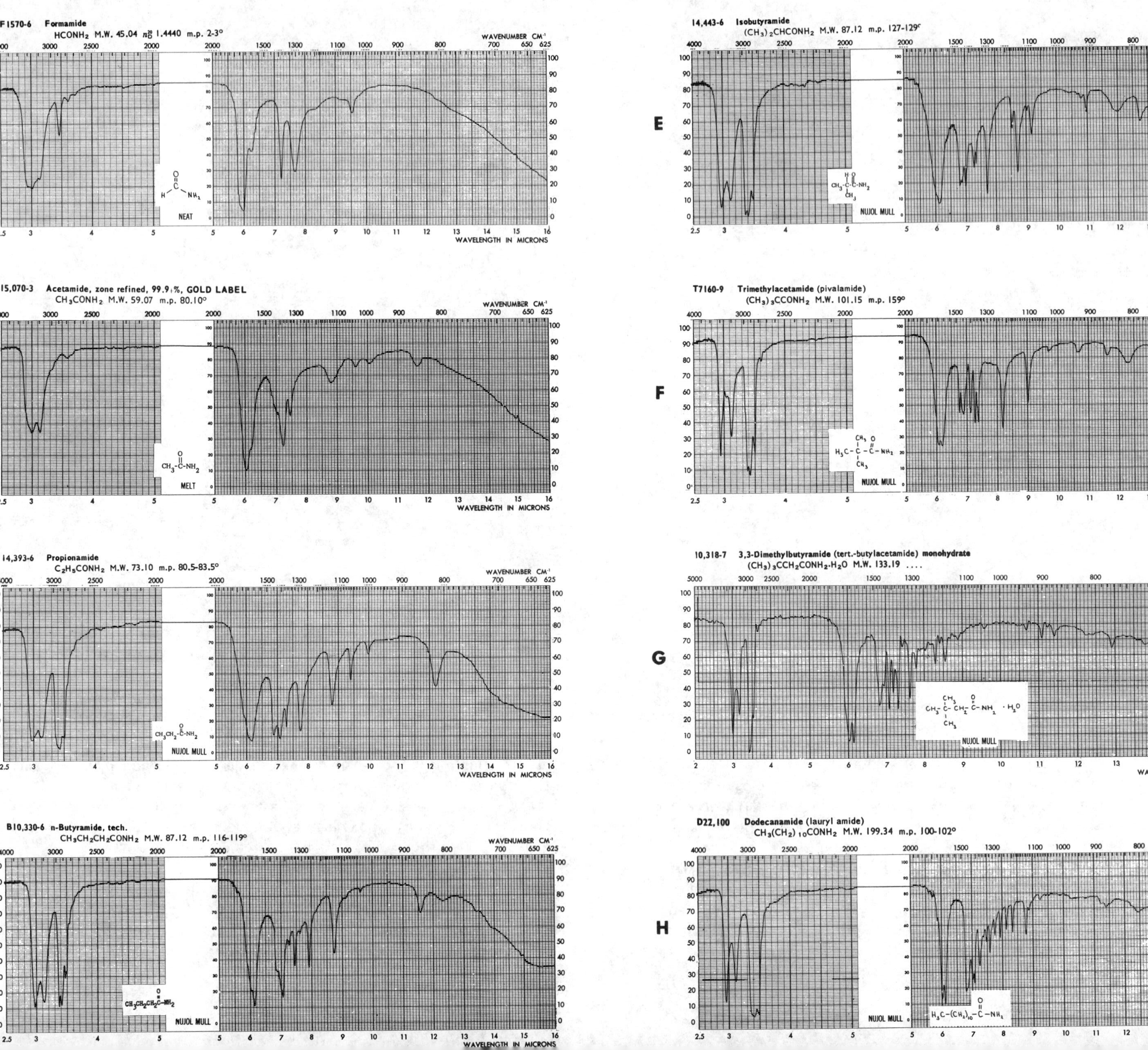
ALDRICH
A
F1570-6 Formamide
HCONH2 M.W. 45.04 n20D 1.4440 m.p. 2-3°
NEAT
B
15,070-3 Acetamide, zone refined, 99.9+%, GOLD LABEL
CH3CONH2 M.W. 59.07 m.p. 80.10°
MELT
C
14,393-6 Propionamide
C2H5CONH2 M.W. 73.10 m.p. 80.5-83.5°
NUJOL MULL
D
B10,330-6 n-Butyramide, tech.
CH3CH2CH2CONH2 M.W. 87.12 m.p. 116-119°
NUJOL MULL
E
14,443-6 Isobutyramide
(CH3)2CHCONH2 M.W. 87.12 m.p. 127-129°
NUJOL MULL
F
T7160-9 Trimethylacetamide (pivalamide)
(CH3)3CCONH2 M.W. 101.15 m.p. 159°
NUJOL MULL
G
10,318-7 3,3-Dimethylbutyramide (tert.-butylacetamide) monohydrate
(CH3)3CCH2CONH2·H2O M.W. 133.19
NUJOL MULL
H
D22,100 Dodecanamide (lauryl amide)
CH3(CH2)10CONH2 M.W. 199.34 m.p. 100-102°
NUJOL MULL
WAVENUMBER CM-1
WAVELENGTH IN MICRONS

A

H660 **Hexadecanamide (palmitamide)**

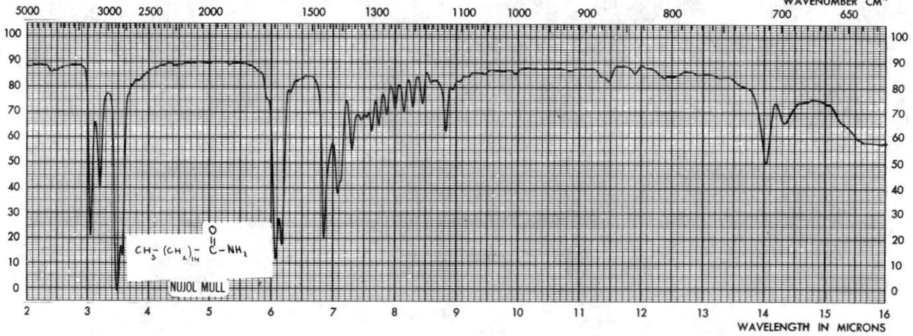

NUJOL MULL

B

0-60-1 **Octadecanamide (stearamide)**
$CH_3(CH_2)_{16}CONH_2$ M.W. 283.50 m.p. 98-100° ....

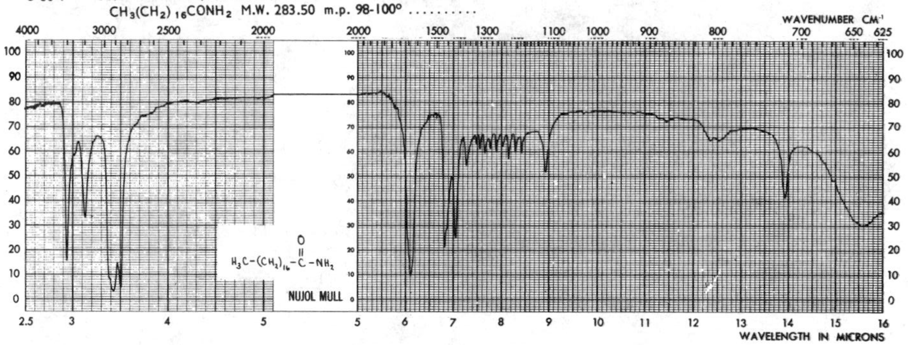

NUJOL MULL

C

85,760-2
ADA [N-(2-acetamido)-iminodiacetic acid, N-(carbamoylmethyl)-iminodiacetic acid]
$H_2NCOCH_2N(CH_2CO_2H)_2$
M.W. 190.16 m.p. 219° (dec.)

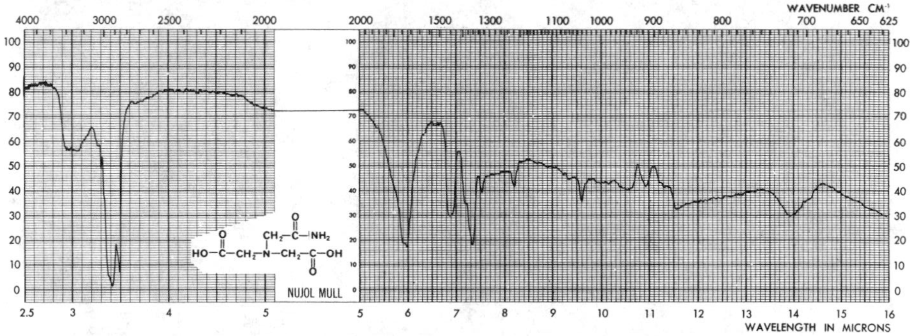

NUJOL MULL

D

14,866-0 **Acrylamide, puriss., electrophoresis grade**
$H_2C{:}CHCONH_2$ M.W. 71.08 m.p. 83-85°

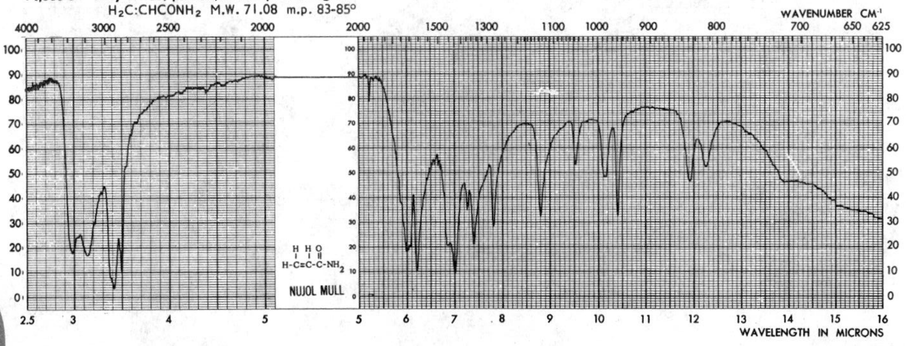

NUJOL MULL

E

10,960-6 **Methacrylamide**
$H_2C{:}C(CH_3)CONH_2$ M.W. 85.11
m.p. 109-111° ....

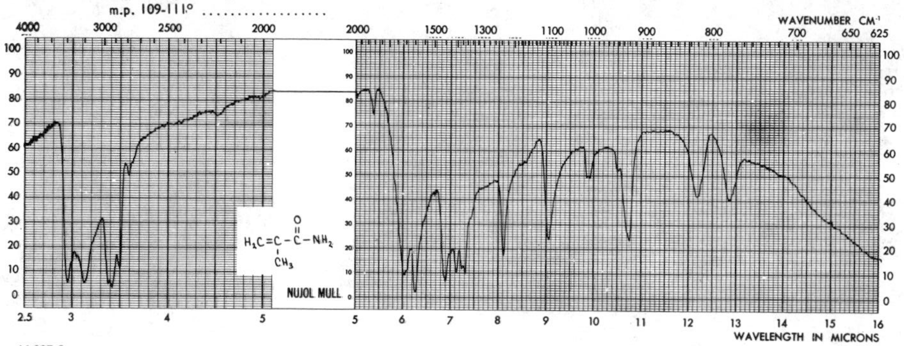

NUJOL MULL

F

14,607-2
N,N'-Methylenebisacrylamide
$(H_2C{=}CHCONH)_2CH_2$
M.W. 154.17 m.p. 300°
Cross linking agent for preparation of polyacrylamides.

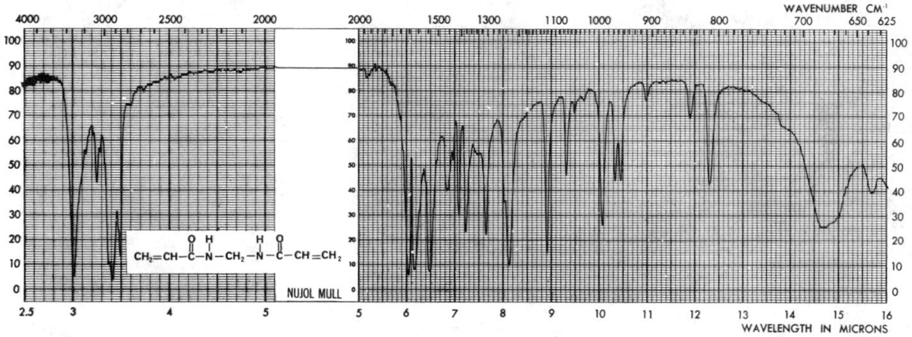

NUJOL MULL

G

15,686-8
N,N'-Diallyltartardiamide, 99+%, GOLD LABEL
(N,N'-diallyltartramide)
$[-CH(OH)CONHCH_2CH{=}CH_2]_2$
M.W. 228.25 m.p. 186-188° Beil. **4**,218

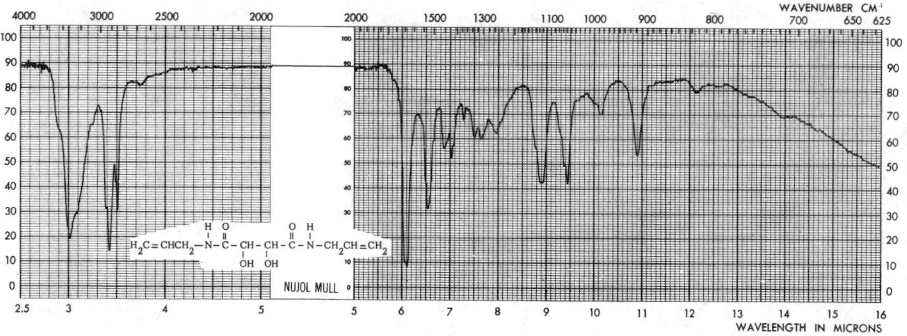

NUJOL MULL

H

22,234-8
Diacetone acrylamide, 99% [N-(1,1-dimethyl-3-oxobutyl)acrylamide]
$H_2C{=}CHCONHC(CH_3)_2CH_2COCH_3$ FW 169.23
mp 54-56° Disp. C

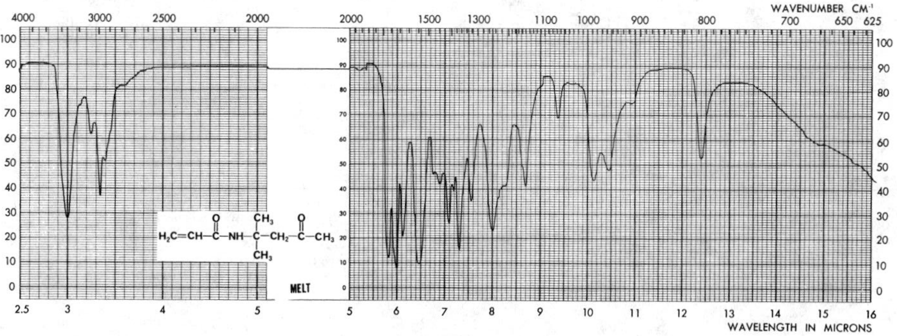

MELT

ALDRICH

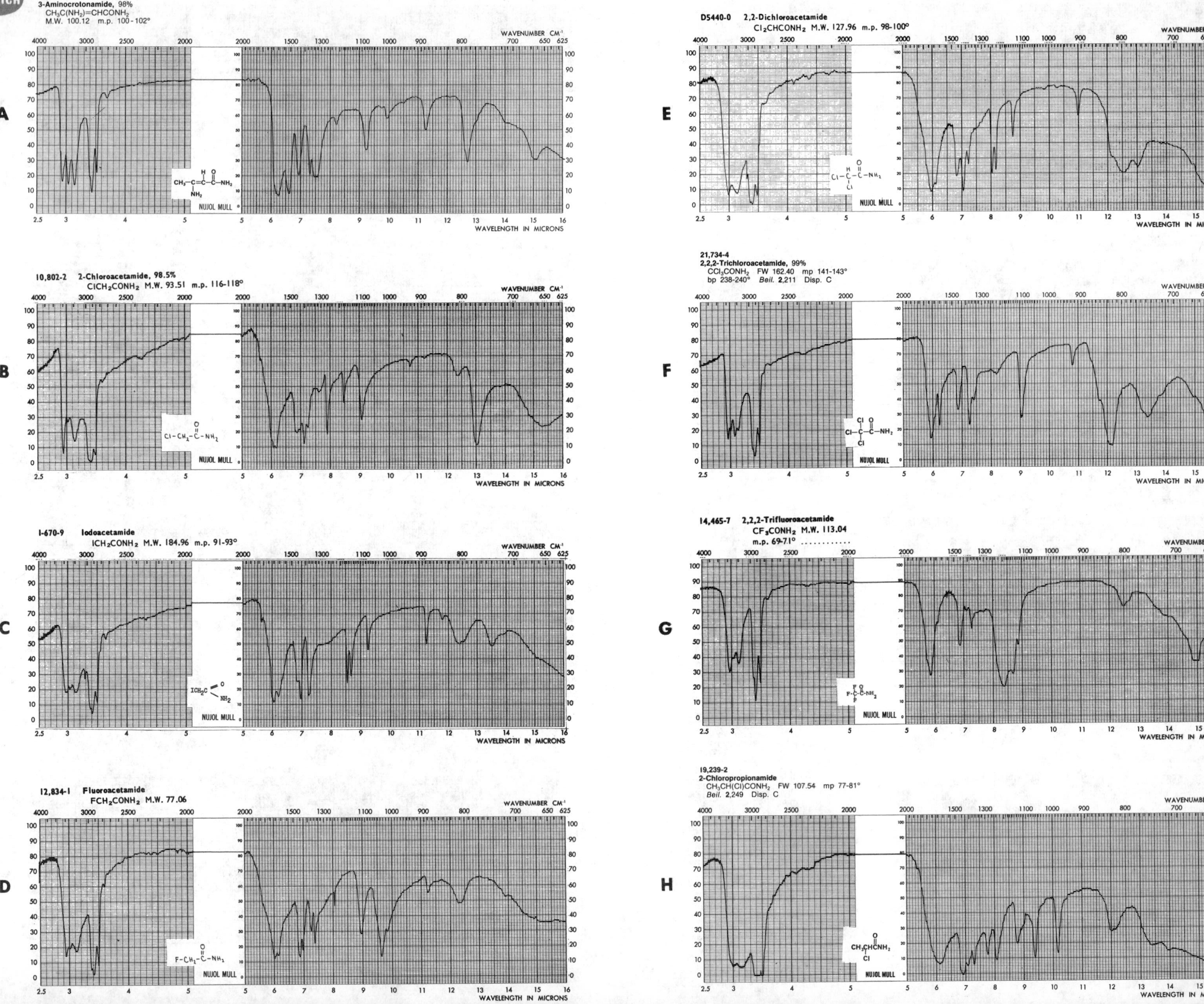
ALDRICH
A
18,386-5
3-Aminocrotonamide, 98%
$CH_3C(NH_2)=CHCONH_2$
M.W. 100.12 m.p. 100-102°
NUJOL MULL
B
10,802-2 2-Chloroacetamide, 98.5%
$ClCH_2CONH_2$ M.W. 93.51 m.p. 116-118°
NUJOL MULL
C
I-670-9 Iodoacetamide
ICH_2CONH_2 M.W. 184.96 m.p. 91-93°
NUJOL MULL
D
12,834-1 Fluoroacetamide
FCH_2CONH_2 M.W. 77.06
NUJOL MULL
E
D5440-0 2,2-Dichloroacetamide
$Cl_2CHCONH_2$ M.W. 127.96 m.p. 98-100°
NUJOL MULL
F
21,734-4
2,2,2-Trichloroacetamide, 99%
CCl_3CONH_2 FW 162.40 mp 141-143°
bp 238-240° Beil. 2,211 Disp. C
NUJOL MULL
G
14,465-7 2,2,2-Trifluoroacetamide
CF_3CONH_2 M.W. 113.04
m.p. 69-71°
NUJOL MULL
H
19,239-2
2-Chloropropionamide
$CH_3CH(Cl)CONH_2$ FW 107.54 mp 77-81°
Beil. 2,249 Disp. C
NUJOL MULL
WAVENUMBER CM⁻¹
WAVELENGTH IN MICRONS

A 12,520-2 3-Chloropropionamide
$ClCH_2CH_2CONH_2$ M.W. 107.55 m.p. 96-100°
NUJOL MULL

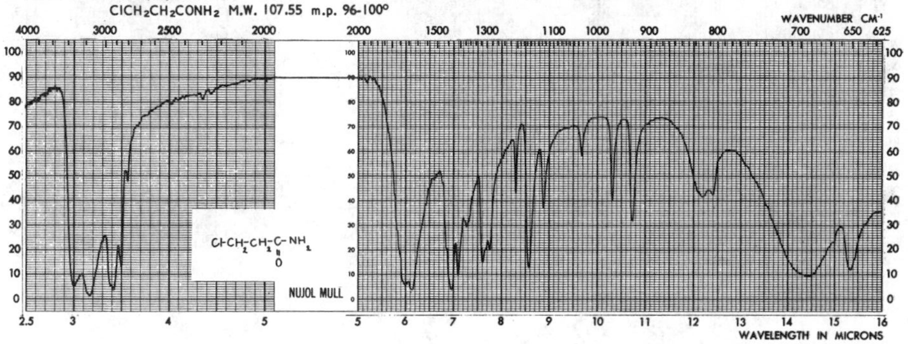

B 14,750-8 Fertilysin [N,N'-bis-(dichloroacetyl)-1,8-octamethylenediamine, N,N'-octamethylenebis-(dichloroacetamide)]
$Cl_2CHCONH(CH_2)_8NHCOCHCl_2$ M.W. 366.12
NUJOL MULL

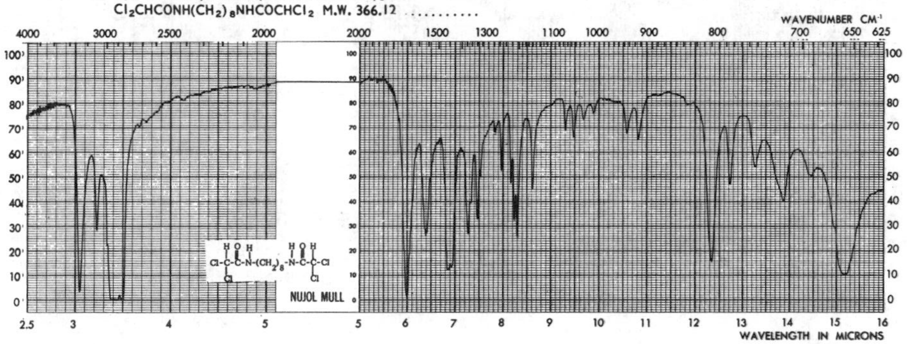

C 12,911-9 5-Hydroxyvaleramide
$HO(CH_2)_4CONH_2$ M.W. 117.15
m.p. 108.5-110.5°
NUJOL MULL

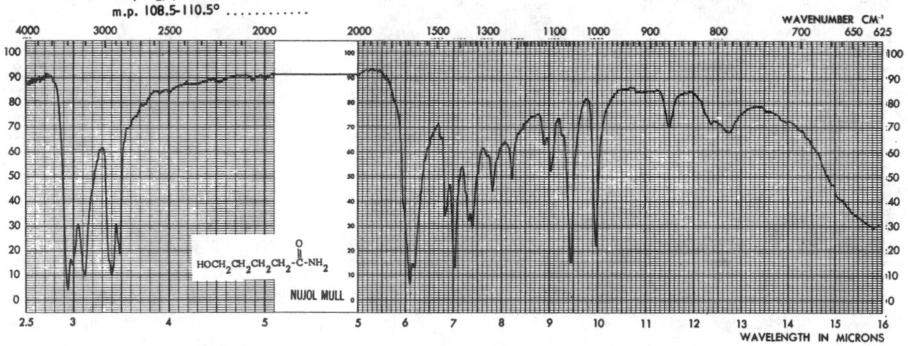

D 10,654-2 O-(2-Hydroxyethyl)-glycolamide [(2-hydroxyethoxy)-acetamide]
$HOCH_2CH_2OCH_2CONH_2$ M.W. 119.12 m.p. 91-93°
NUJOL MULL

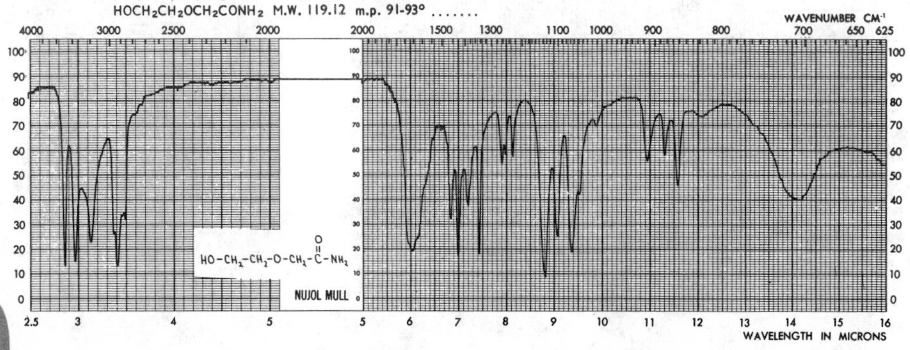

E T2880-0 DL-6-Thioctic amide (DL-α-lipoamide)
M.W. 205.34 m.p. 127-128°
NUJOL MULL

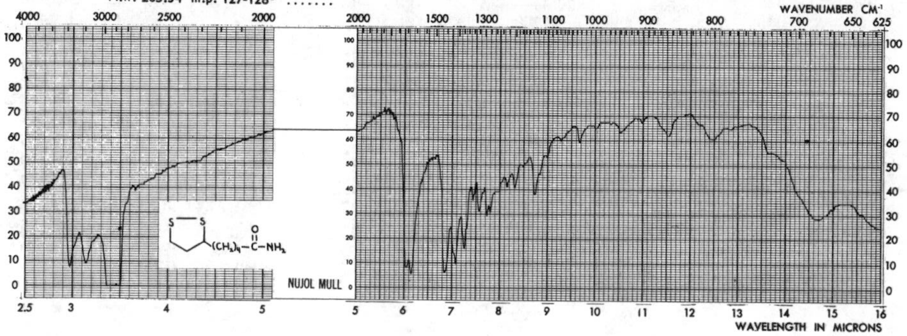

F G610-4 Glycinamide hydrochloride
$H_2NCH_2CONH_2 \cdot HCl$ M.W. 110.54
m.p. 191-195°
NUJOL MULL

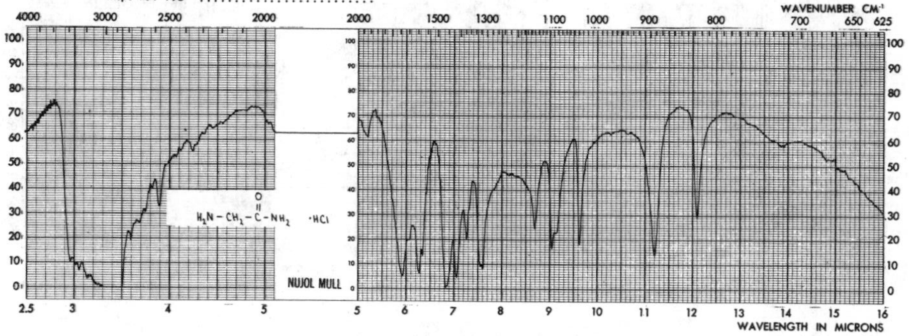

G M4670-5 N-Methylformamide
$HCONHCH_3$ M.W. 59.07 n_D^{20} 1.4302 b.p. 180-185°
NEAT

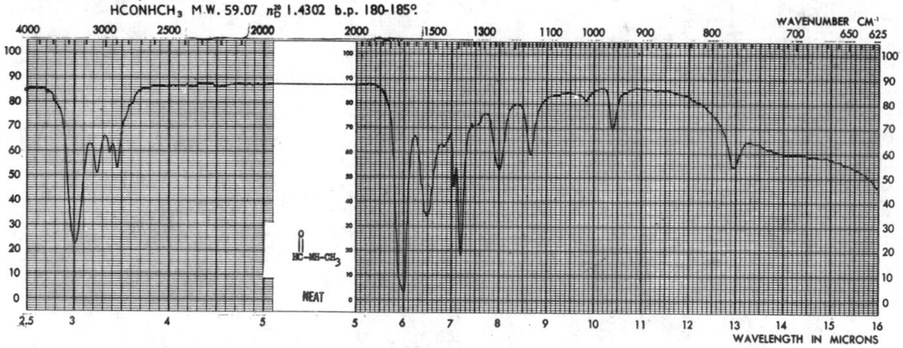

H 11,747-1 tert.-Butylformamide
$HCONHC(CH_3)_3$ M.W. 101.15 n_D^{20} 1.4312
NEAT

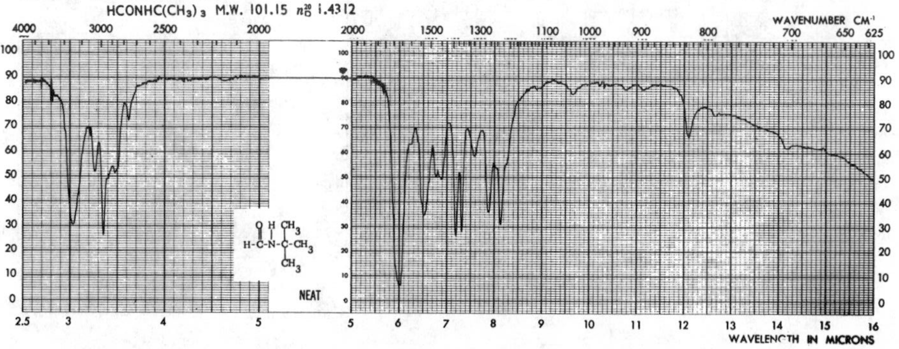

A

12,068-5 N-Cyclohexylformamide
$HCONHC_6H_{11}$ M.W. 117.19 m.p. 33-36°
b.p. 113°/0.7 mm.

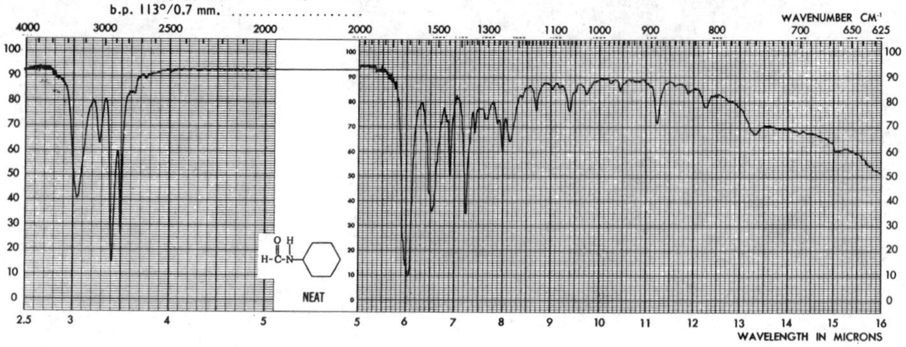

NEAT

B

15,973-5
N,N',N''-Methylidynetrisformamide, 97%
$(HCONH)_3CH$
M.W. 145.12 m.p. 170-172° (dec.) Fieser 1,1251

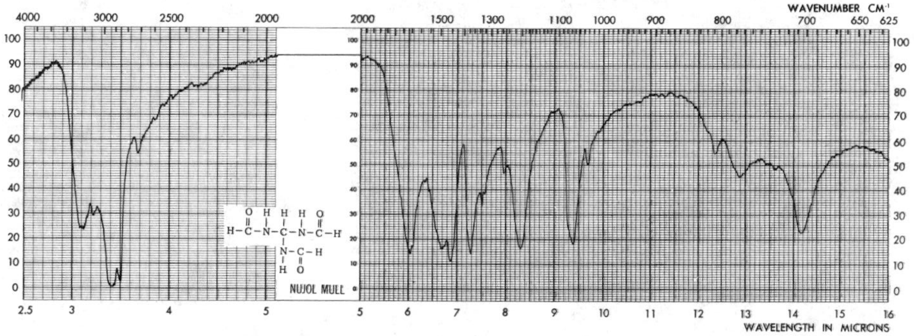

NUJOL MULL

C

M2630-5 N-Methylacetamide, puriss.
$CH_3CONHCH_3$ M.W. 73.10 m.p. 28°

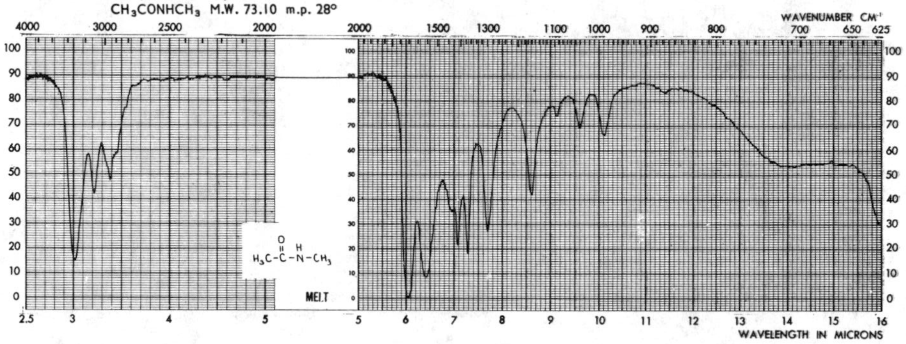

MELT

D

14,740-0 N-Ethylacetamide
$CH_3CONHC_2H_5$ M.W. 87.12 n_D^{20} 1.4319
b.p. 90-92°/8 mm.

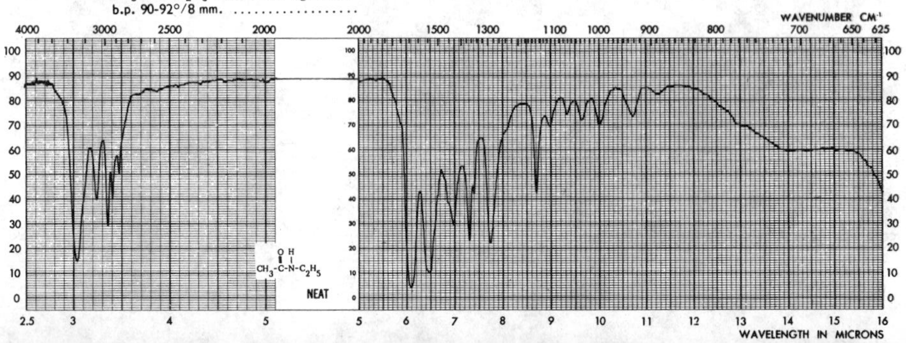

NEAT

E

22,423-5
***N,N'*-Hexamethylenebisacetamide**, 98% (*N,N'*-diacetyl-1,6-hexanediamine)
$CH_3CONH(CH_2)_6NHCOCH_3$ FW 200.28
mp 128-129° *Beil.* 4,269 Disp. C

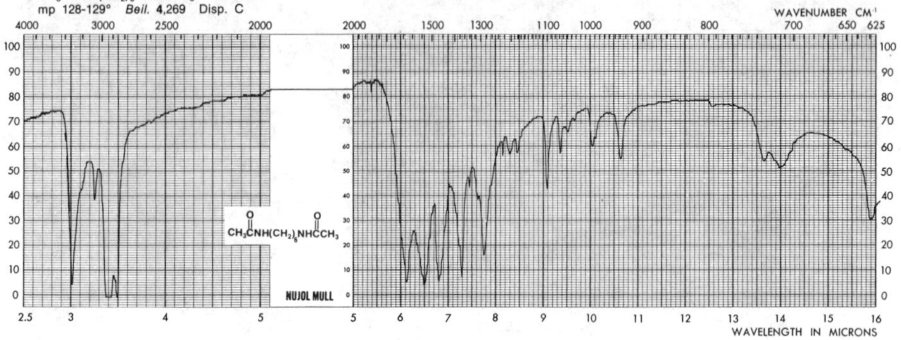

NUJOL MULL

F

13,513-5 N-Bromoacetamide (NBA)
$CH_3CONHBr$ M.W. 137.97 m.p. 108-109°

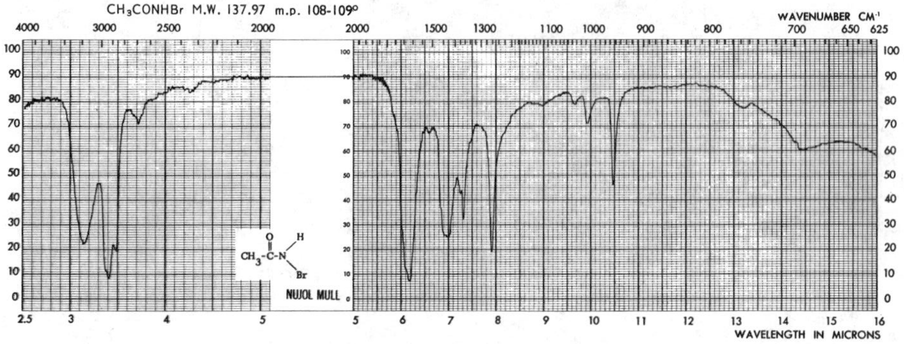

NUJOL MULL

G

D595-0 Diacetamide
$(CH_3CO)_2NH$ M.W. 101.11 m.p. 75.5-76.5°

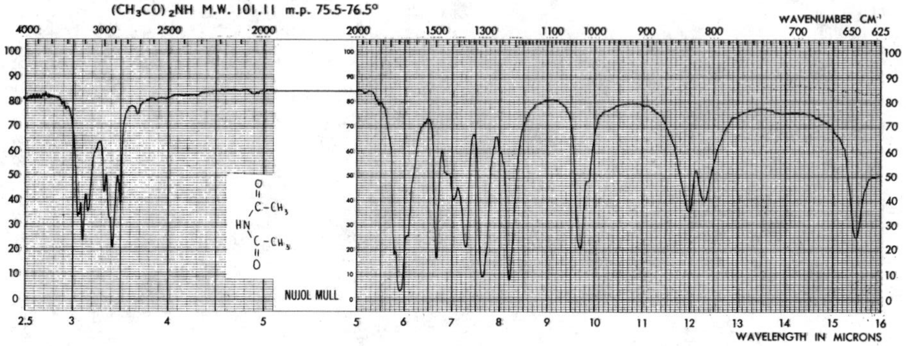

NUJOL MULL

H

13,710-3 N-(1-Adamantyl)-acetamide
M.W. 193.29 m.p. 148-149°

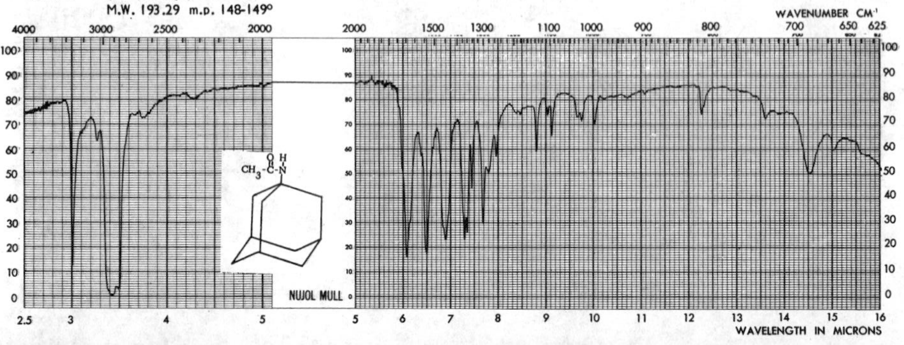

NUJOL MULL

WAVENUMBER CM⁻¹

WAVELENGTH IN MICRONS

A

10,045-5 N-Acetylethanolamine (N-2-hydroxyethylacetamide)
$CH_3CONHCH_2CH_2OH$ M.W. 103.12 n_D^{20} 1.4674 . .

NEAT

B

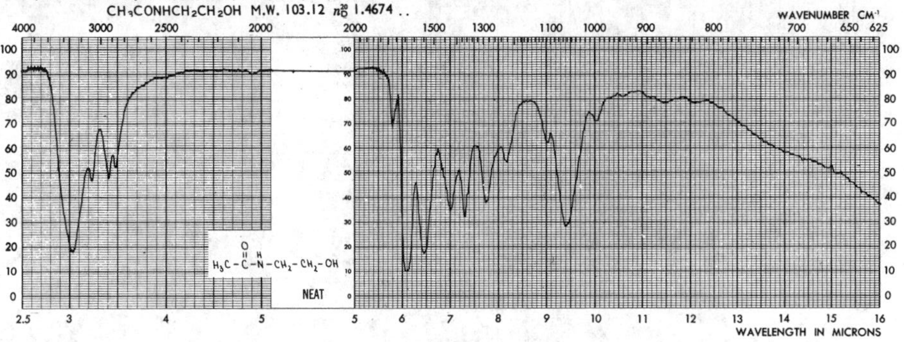

19,131-0
N-(2-Chloroethyl)acetamide
$CH_3CONHCH_2CH_2Cl$ FW 121.57 n_D^{20} 1.4805
d 1.204 Disp. C

NEAT

C

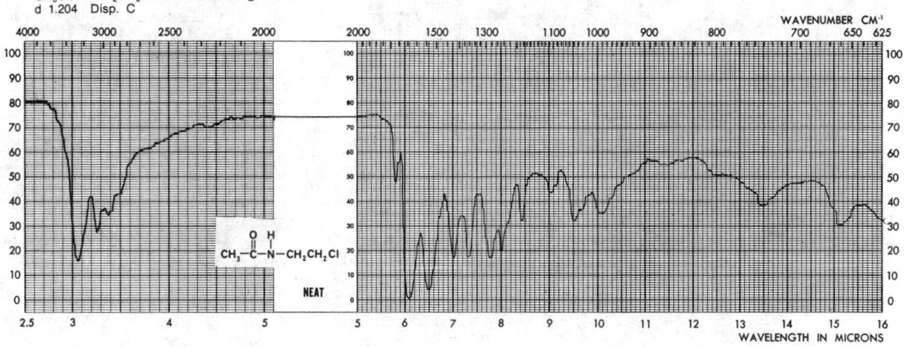

A280-7 2-Acetamido-3-butanone, tech.
$CH_3CH(NHCOCH_3)COCH_3$ M.W. 129.16
n_D^{20} 1.4606 . . . .

NEAT

D

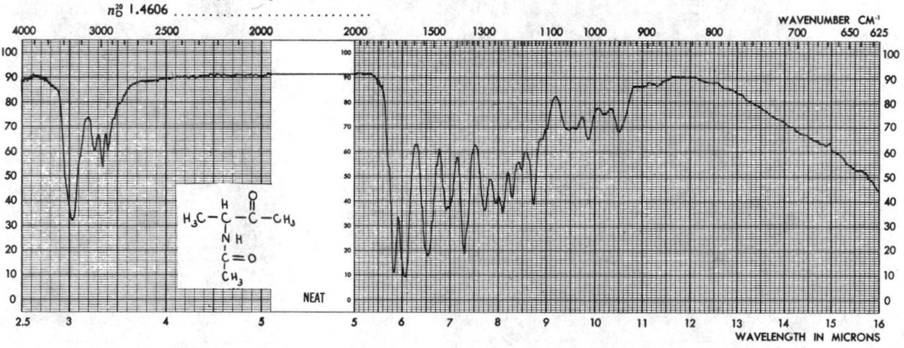

17,830-6
N,S-Diacetylcysteamine, 99%
$CH_3CONHCH_2CH_2SCOCH_3$
M.W. 161.22 m.p. 30-32°

MELT

E

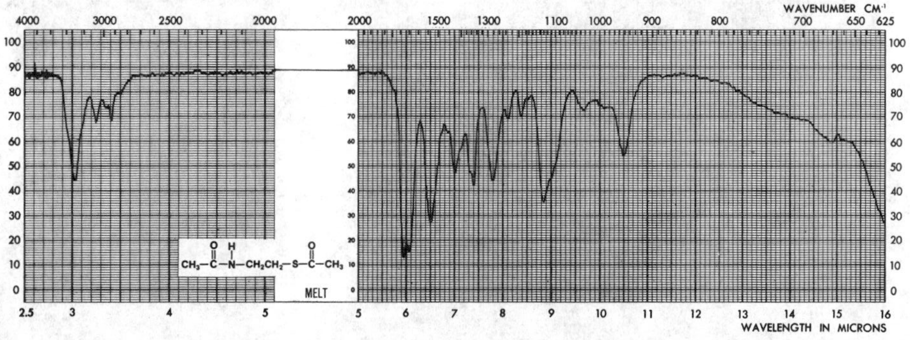

19,430-1
6-Acetamidohexanoic acid, 99%
$CH_3CONH(CH_2)_5CO_2H$ FW 173.21 mp 102-104°
Beil. **4**(3),1396 Disp. I

NUJOL MULL

F

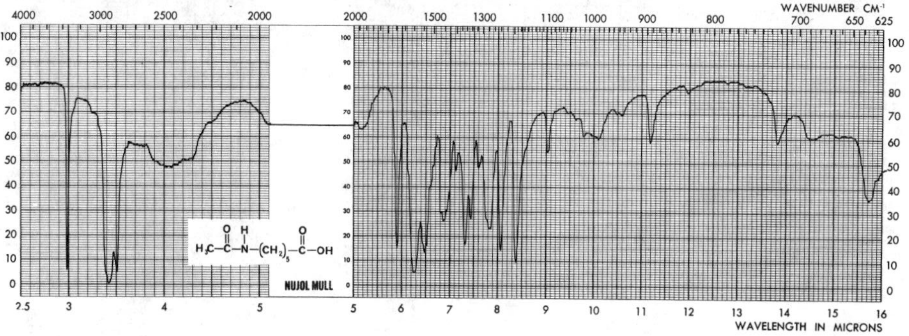

21,948-7
Glucuronamide, 99%
FW 193.16 mp 166-167° *Beil.* **3**(4),2009 Disp. L

NUJOL MULL

G

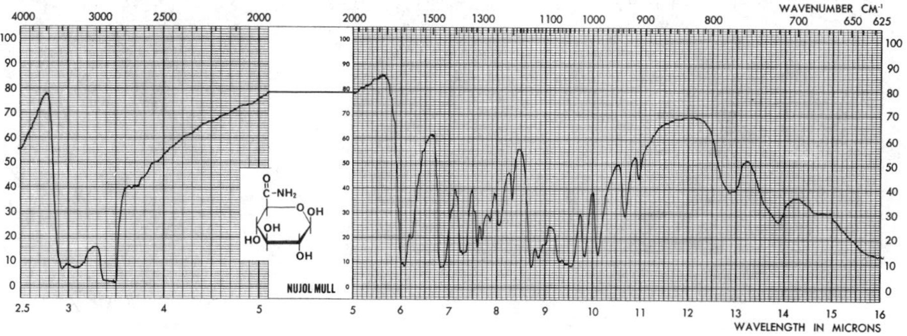

85,134-5
N-Acetyl-D-galactosamine (2-acetamido-2-deoxy-D-galactopyranose)
M.W. 221.21 m.p. 160-161° $[\alpha]^{24}$ + 85° (c=2, H_2O)

NUJOL MULL

H

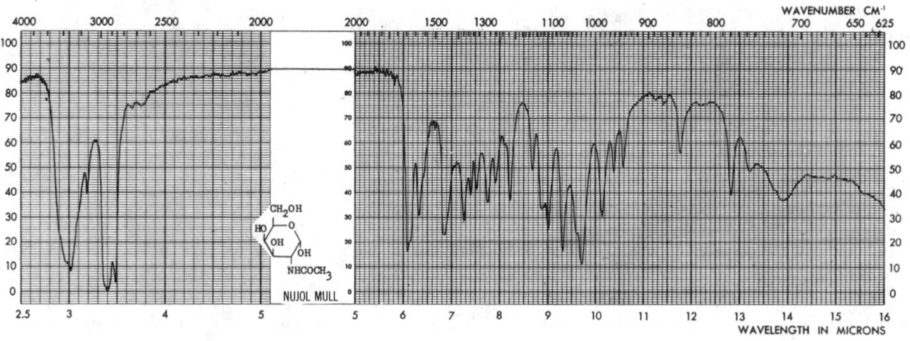

A1628-9 N-Acetyl-α-D-glucosamine (2-acetamido-2-deoxy-α-D-glucopyranose)
M.W. 221.21 m.p. 211° (dec.) . . . .

NUJOL MULL

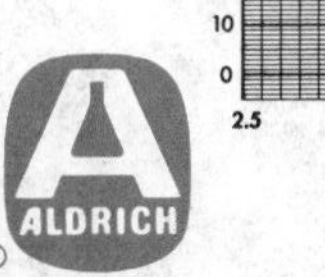

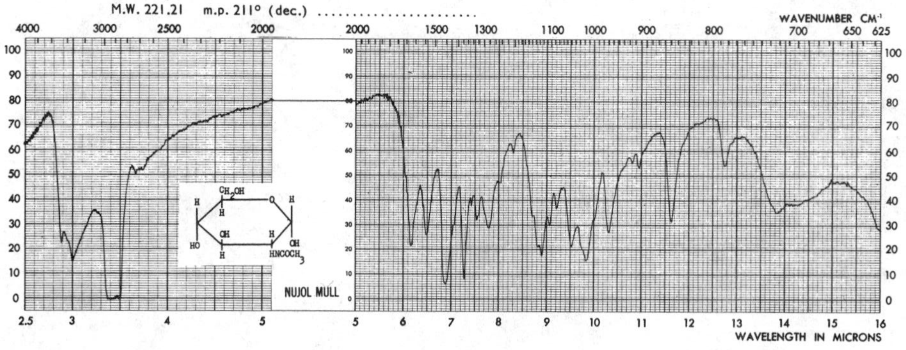

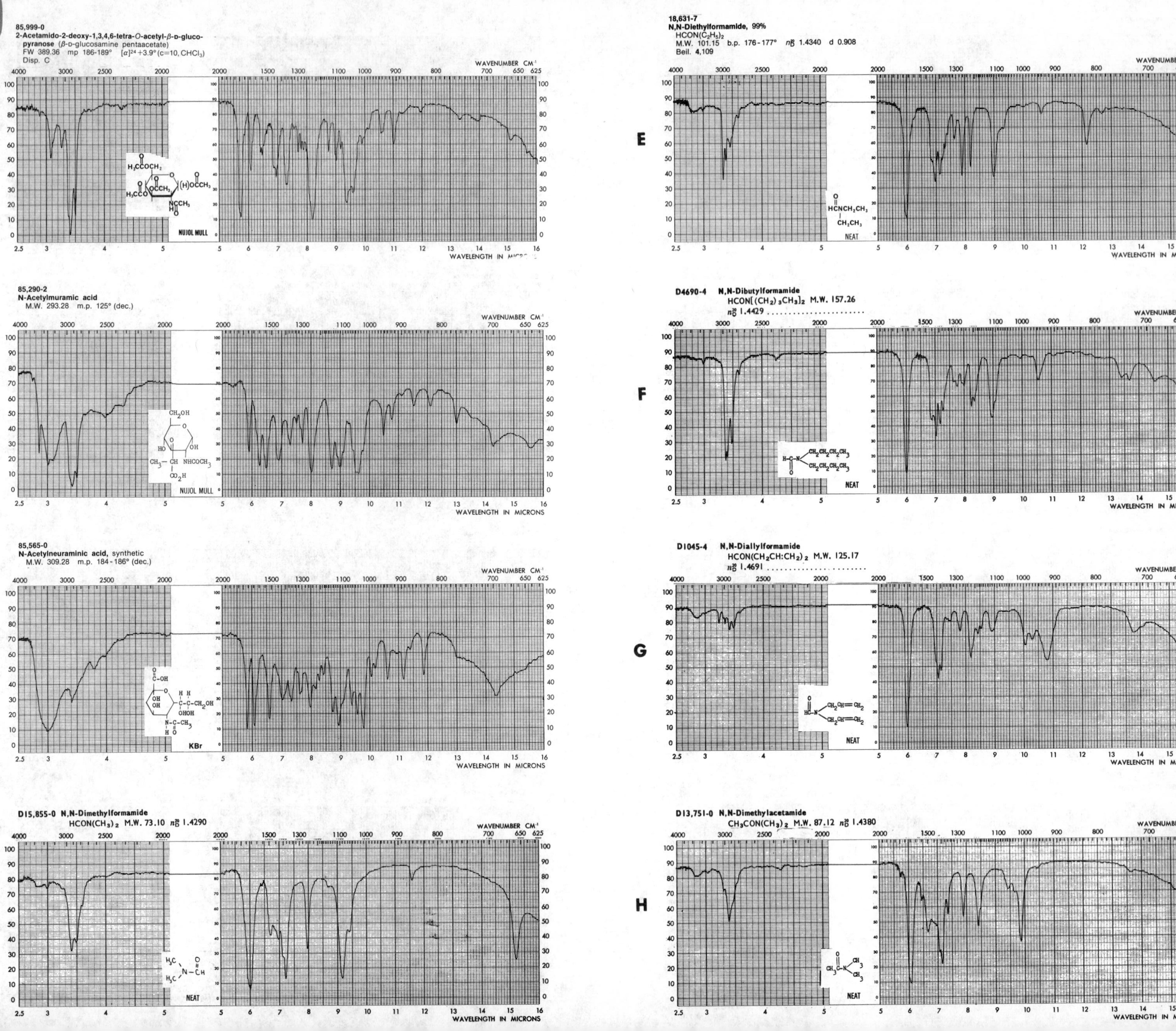
ALDRICH
A
85,999-0
2-Acetamido-2-deoxy-1,3,4,6-tetra-O-acetyl-β-D-glucopyranose (β-D-glucosamine pentaacetate)
FW 389.36 mp 186-189° [α]²⁴ +3.9° (c=10, CHCl₃)
Disp. C
NUJOL MULL
B
85,290-2
N-Acetylmuramic acid
M.W. 293.28 m.p. 125° (dec.)
NUJOL MULL
C
85,565-0
N-Acetylneuraminic acid, synthetic
M.W. 309.28 m.p. 184-186° (dec.)
KBr
D
D15,855-0 N,N-Dimethylformamide
HCON(CH₃)₂ M.W. 73.10 n²⁰D 1.4290
NEAT
E
18,631-7
N,N-Diethylformamide, 99%
HCON(C₂H₅)₂
M.W. 101.15 b.p. 176-177° n²⁰D 1.4340 d 0.908
Beil. 4,109
NEAT
F
D4690-4 N,N-Dibutylformamide
HCON[(CH₂)₃CH₃]₂ M.W. 157.26
n²⁰D 1.4429
NEAT
G
D1045-4 N,N-Diallylformamide
HCON(CH₂CH:CH₂)₂ M.W. 125.17
n²⁰D 1.4691
NEAT
H
D13,751-0 N,N-Dimethylacetamide
CH₃CON(CH₃)₂ M.W. 87.12 n²⁰D 1.4380
NEAT
WAVENUMBER CM⁻¹
WAVELENGTH IN MICRONS

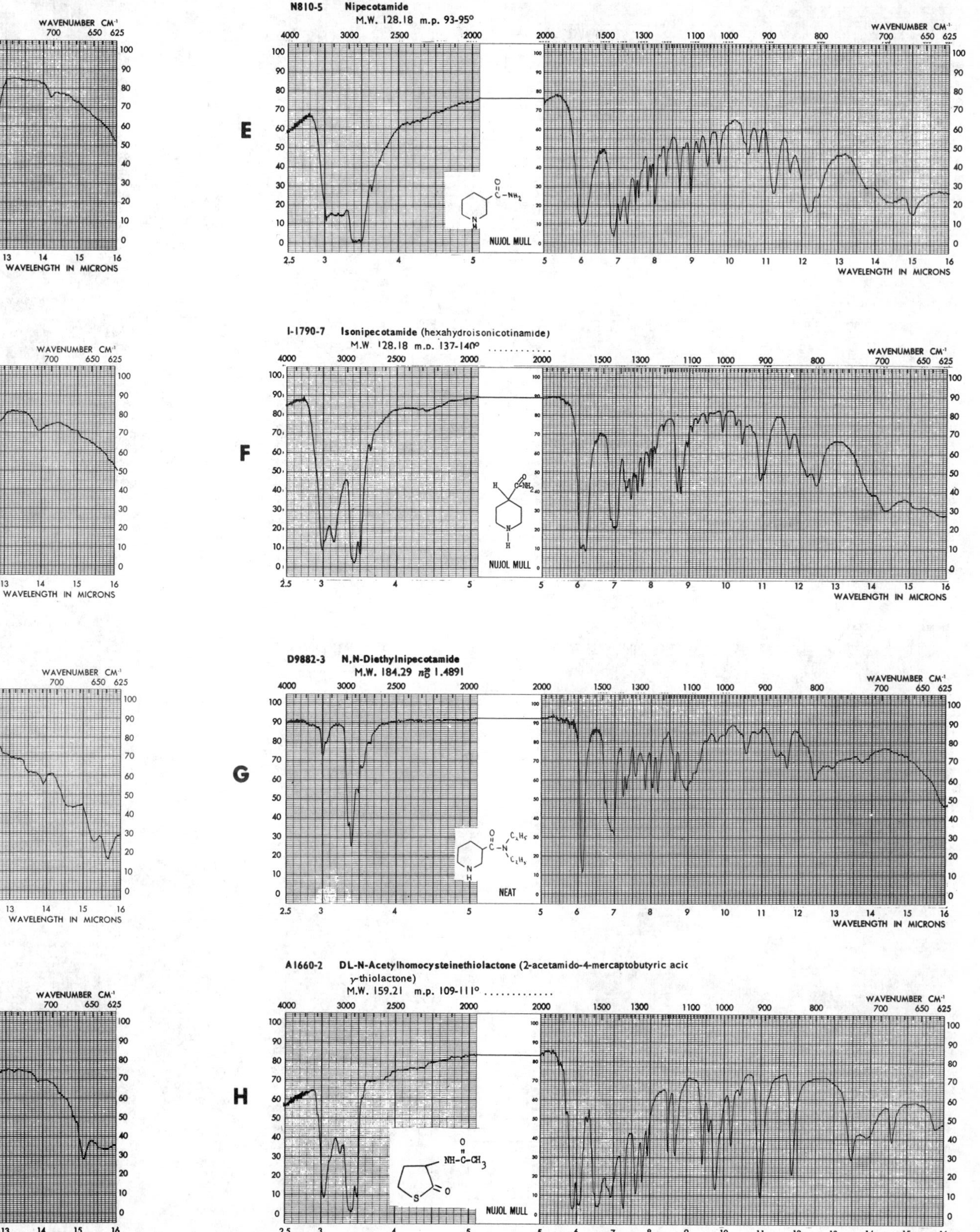

A 13,752-9 N,N-Diethylacetamide
$CH_3CON(C_2H_5)_2$ M.W. 115.18 n_D^{20} 1.4401
b.p. 65-66°/10 mm. NEAT

B 19,419-0
N,N-Diethyldodecanamide, 98+%
$CH_3(CH_2)_{10}CON(C_2H_5)_2$ FW 255.45
bp 166-167°/2mm. n_D^{20} 1.4545 d 0.847 Disp. C
NEAT

C 16,391-0
3-Carbamoyl-2,2,5,5-tetramethylpyrrolidin-1-yloxy, free radical, 97%
M.W. 185.25 m.p. 173-175°
NUJOL MULL

D 15,568-3 3-Carbamoyl-2,2,5,5-tetramethyl-3-pyrrolin-1-yloxy, free radical
M.W. 183.23 m.p. 198-200°
NUJOL MULL

E N810-5 Nipecotamide
M.W. 128.18 m.p. 93-95°
NUJOL MULL

F I-1790-7 Isonipecotamide (hexahydroisonicotinamide)
M.W. 128.18 m.p. 137-140°
NUJOL MULL

G D9882-3 N,N-Diethylnipecotamide
M.W. 184.29 n_D^{20} 1.4891
NEAT

H A1660-2 DL-N-Acetylhomocysteinethiolactone (2-acetamido-4-mercaptobutyric acid γ-thiolactone)
M.W. 159.21 m.p. 109-111°
NUJOL MULL

ALDRICH

A

B10,405 **1-n-Butyrylaziridine**
M.W. 113.16 n_D^{20} 1.4380
NEAT

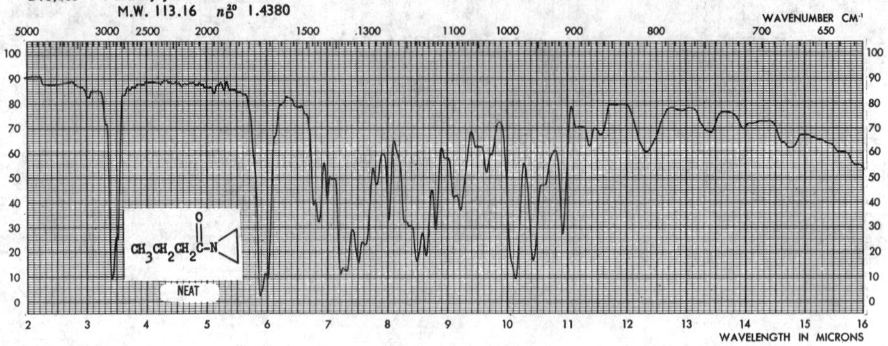

B

12,434-6 **1-Isobutyrylaziridine, tech.**
M.W. 113.16 n_D^{20} 1.4390
NEAT

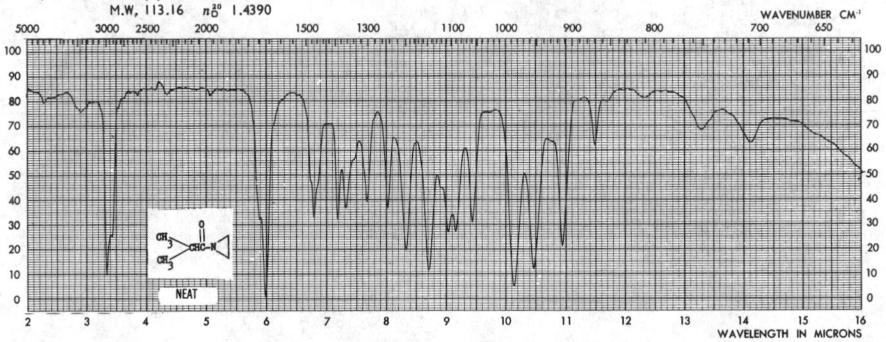

C

20,088-3
1-(3-Methylbutyryl)pyrrolidine, 98% (isovaleryl-pyrrolidide)
FW 155.24 n_D^{20} 1.4710 d 0.938 Disp. C
NEAT

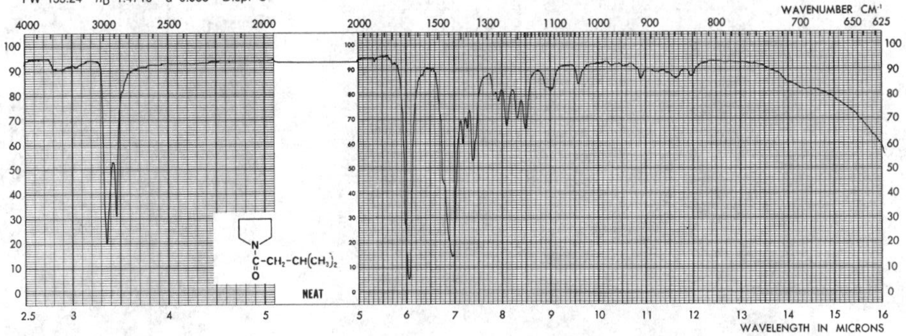

D

19,783-1
1-(Pyrrolidinocarbonylmethyl)piperazine, 95+%
FW 197.28 mp 79-81° Disp. C
NUJOL MULL

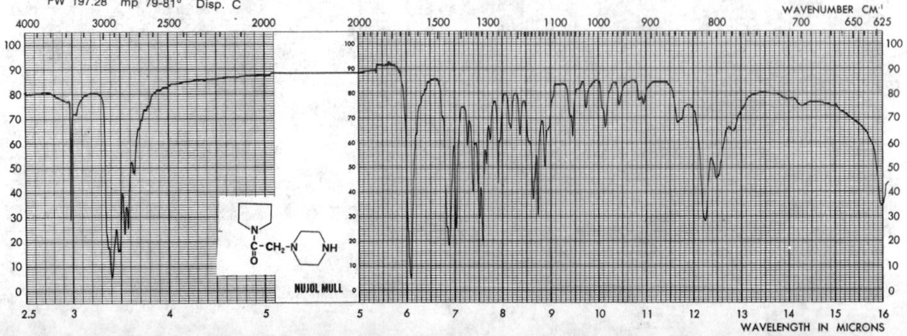

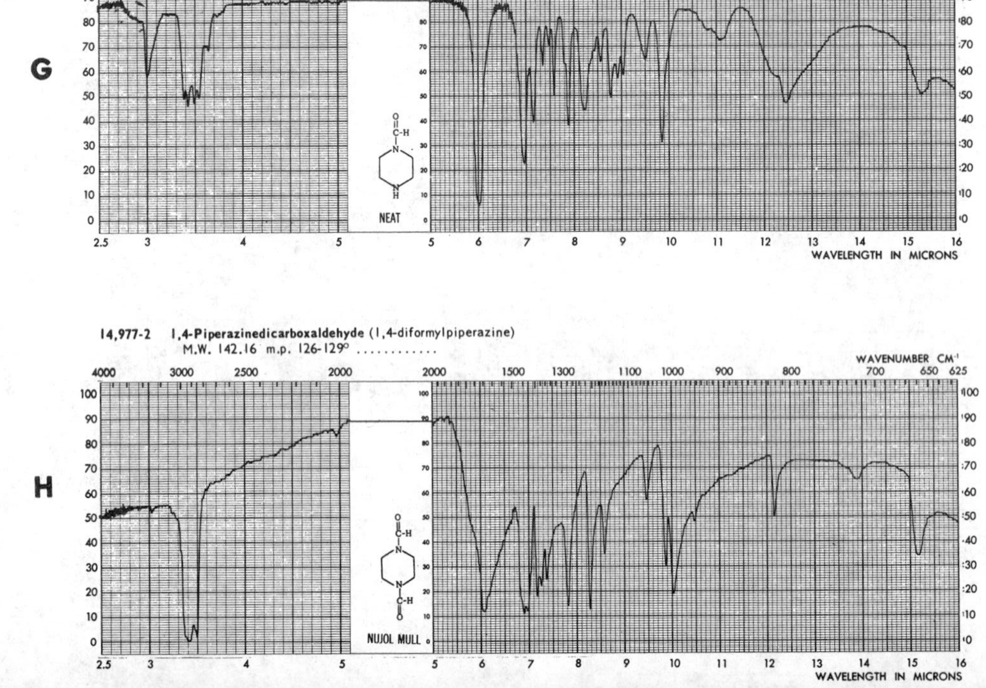

E

F1740-7 **N-Formylpiperidine**
M.W. 113.16 n_D^{20} 1.4700 b.p. 222°
NEAT

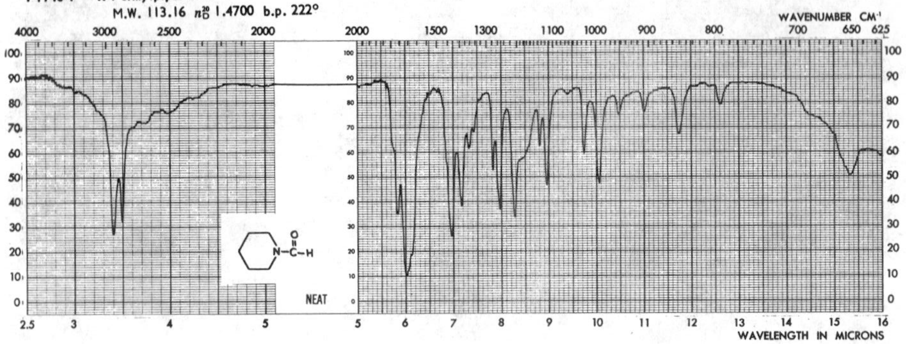

F

F1655-9 **N-Formylhexamethyleneimine** (N,N-hexamethyleneformamide)
M.W. 127.19 n_D^{20} 1.4865
NEAT

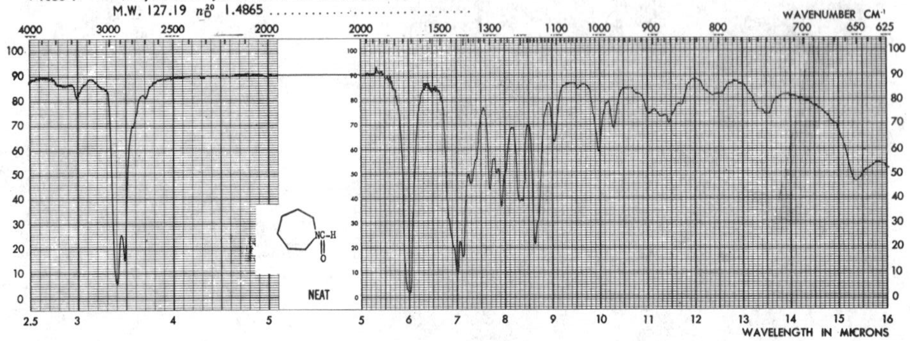

G

14,931-4 **1-Piperazinecarboxaldehyde** (1-formylpiperazine)
M.W. 114.15 n_D^{20} 1.5094 b.p. 94-97°/0.5 mm.
NEAT

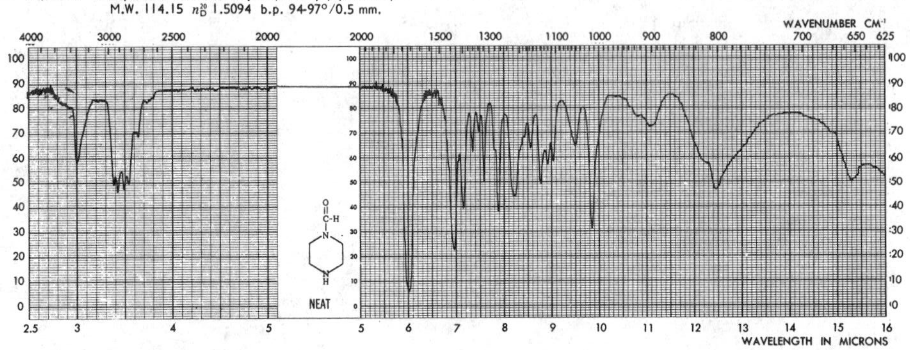

H

14,977-2 **1,4-Piperazinedicarboxaldehyde** (1,4-diformylpiperazine)
M.W. 142.16 m.p. 126-129°
NUJOL MULL

A

22,092-2
N-Isopropyl-1-piperazineacetamide, 95+%
FW 185.27 mp 86-89° Disp. C

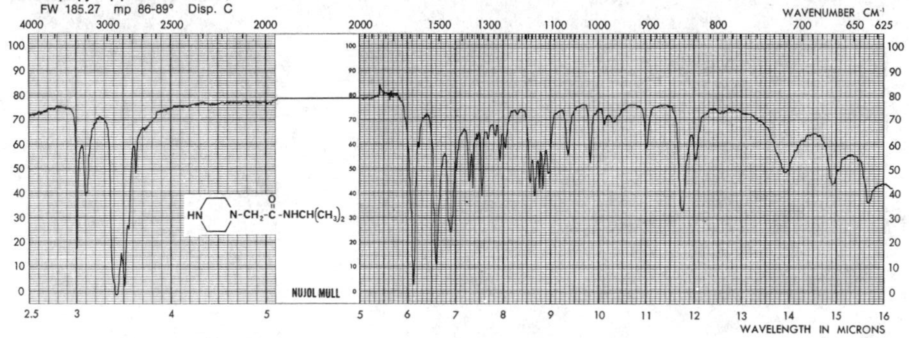

NUJOL MULL

B

13,105-9 2-Methylpiperazine-N,N'-dicarboxaldehyde
M.W. 156.19

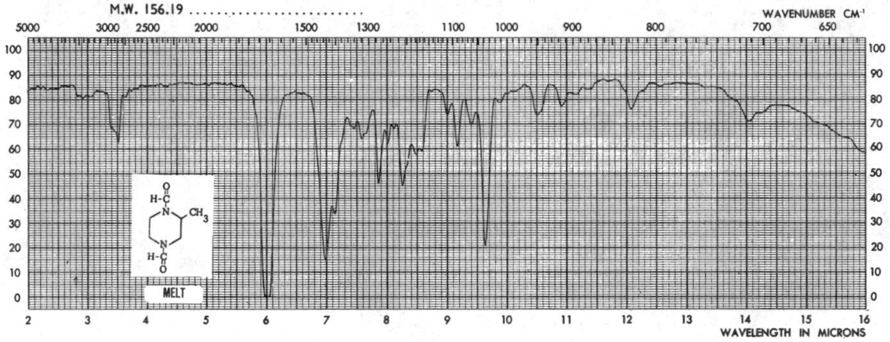

MELT

C

19,780-7
1-(Morpholinocarbonylmethyl)piperazine, 96%
FW 213.28 mp 64-66° Disp. C

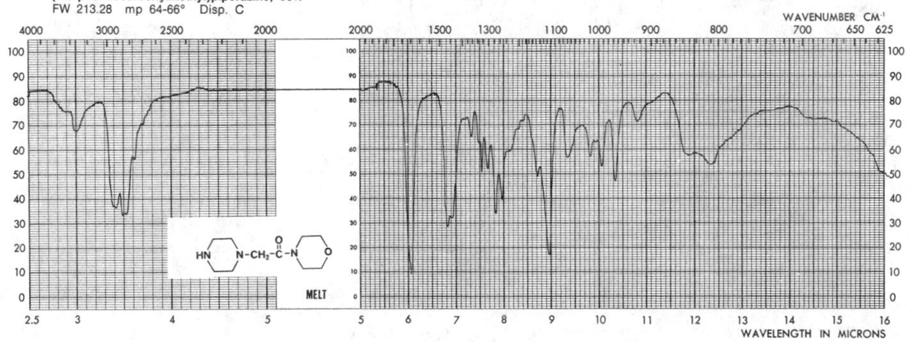

MELT

D

F1670-2 N-Formylmorpholine (morpholinocarboxaldehyde)
M.W. 115.13 n_D^{20} 1.4849 b.p. 120°/15 mm.

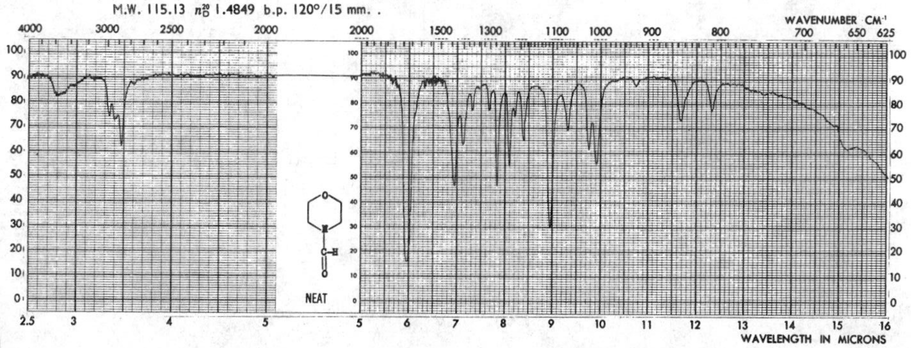

NEAT

E

A1883-4 N-Acetylmorpholine
M.W. 129.16 n_D^{20} 1.4827

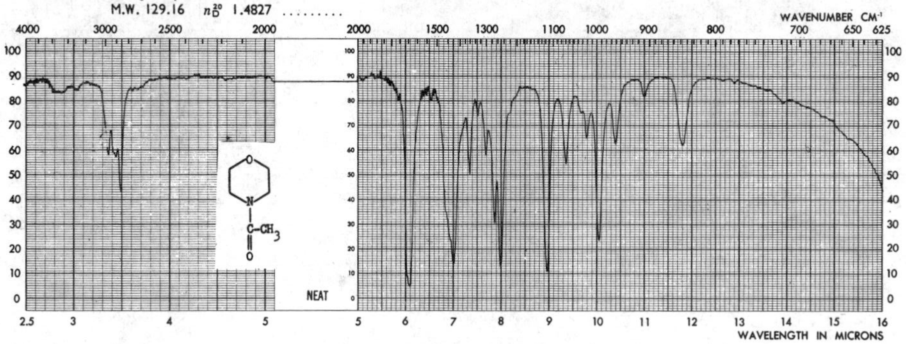

NEAT

F

10,537-6 N,N'-Malonyldimorpholine
M.W. 242.28 m.p. 137-140°

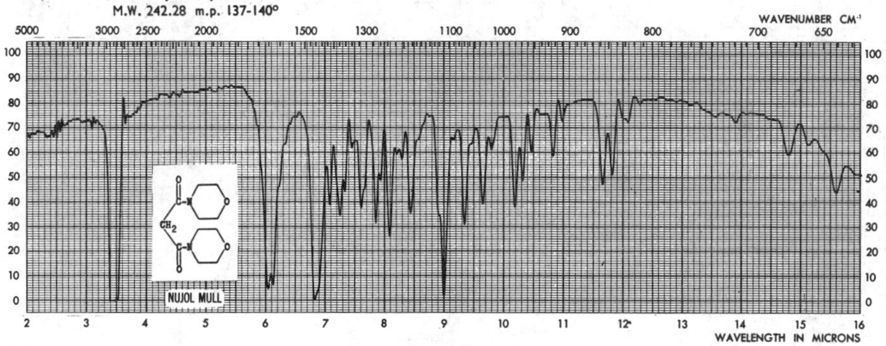

NUJOL MULL

G

19,806-4
Ethyl 4-amino-1-piperidinecarboxylate, 95%
FW 172.23 n_D^{20} 1.4825 d 1.004 Disp. C

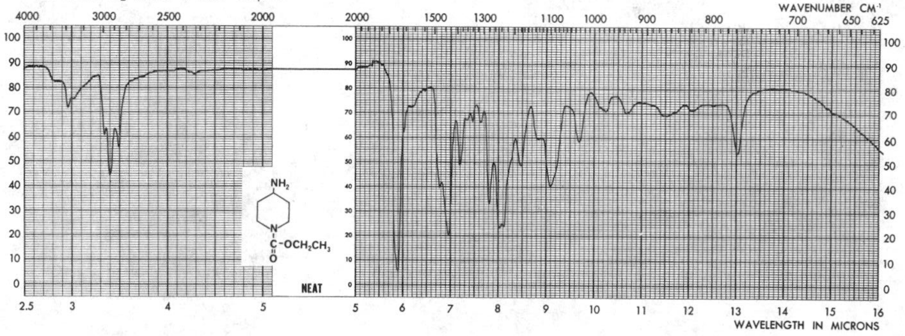

NEAT

H

15,297-8
N-Acetyl-4-piperidone, 99%
M.W. 141.17 b.p. 218° n_D^{20} 1.5026
HYGROSCOPIC

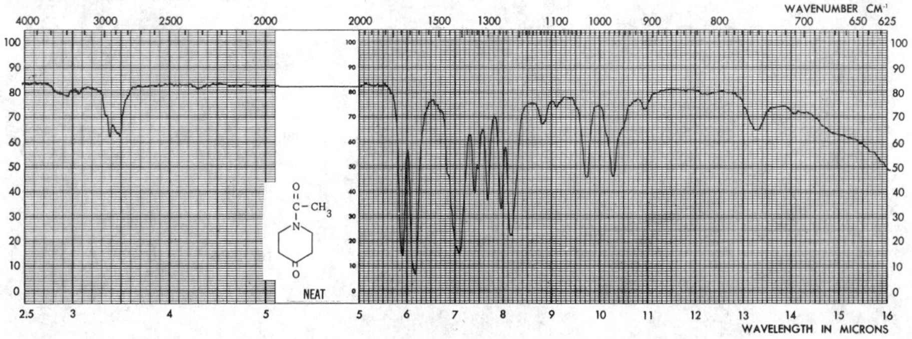

NEAT

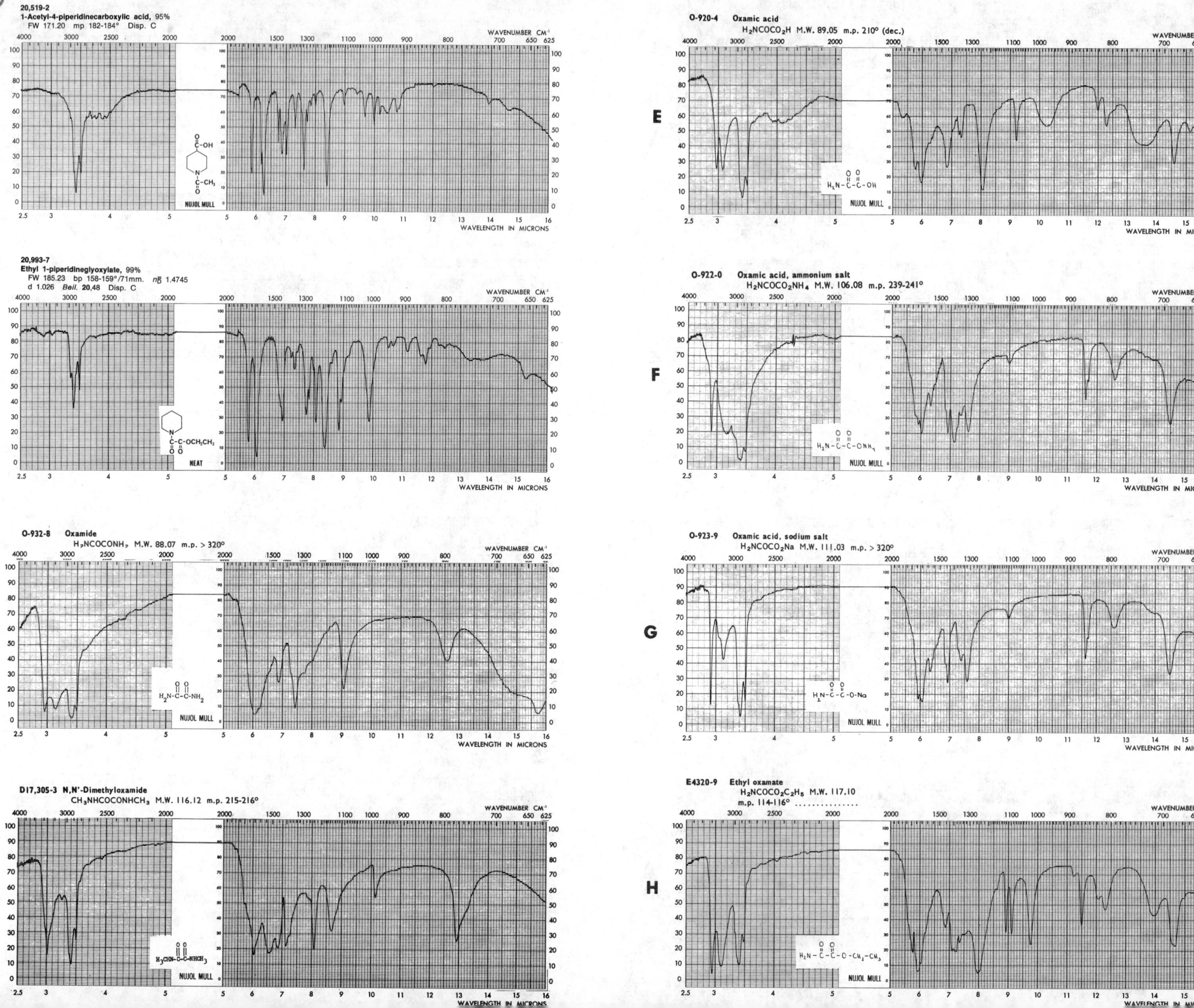
ALDRICH
A
20,519-2
1-Acetyl-4-piperidinecarboxylic acid, 95%
FW 171.20 mp 182-184° Disp. C
NUJOL MULL
B
20,993-7
Ethyl 1-piperidineglyoxylate, 99%
FW 185.23 bp 158-159°/71mm. n_D^{20} 1.4745
d 1.026 Beil. 20,48 Disp. C
NEAT
C
O-932-8 Oxamide
$H_2NCOCONH_2$ M.W. 88.07 m.p. > 320°
NUJOL MULL
D
D17,305-3 N,N'-Dimethyloxamide
$CH_3NHCOCONHCH_3$ M.W. 116.12 m.p. 215-216°
NUJOL MULL
E
O-920-4 Oxamic acid
H_2NCOCO_2H M.W. 89.05 m.p. 210° (dec.)
NUJOL MULL
F
O-922-0 Oxamic acid, ammonium salt
$H_2NCOCO_2NH_4$ M.W. 106.08 m.p. 239-241°
NUJOL MULL
G
O-923-9 Oxamic acid, sodium salt
H_2NCOCO_2Na M.W. 111.03 m.p. > 320°
NUJOL MULL
H
E4320-9 Ethyl oxamate
$H_2NCOCO_2C_2H_5$ M.W. 117.10
m.p. 114-116°
NUJOL MULL
WAVENUMBER CM⁻¹
WAVELENGTH IN MICRONS

A 12,959-3 **Malonamide** (malonodiamide)
$H_2NCOCH_2CONH_2$ M.W. 102.09
m.p. 168-170°
NUJOL MULL

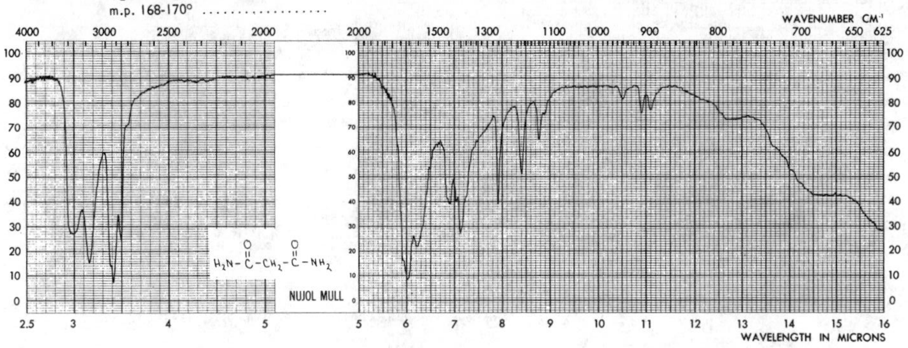

B M5400-7 **2-Methylmalonamide**
$H_2NCOCH(CH_3)CONH_2$ M.W. 116.12 m.p. 214-216°
NUJOL MULL

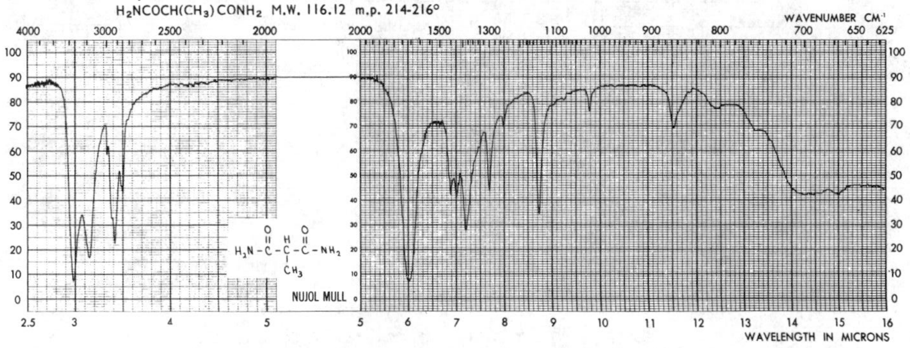

C 13,437-6 **Succinamic acid**
$H_2NCOCH_2CH_2CO_2H$ M.W. 117.10 m.p. 153-156°
NUJOL MULL

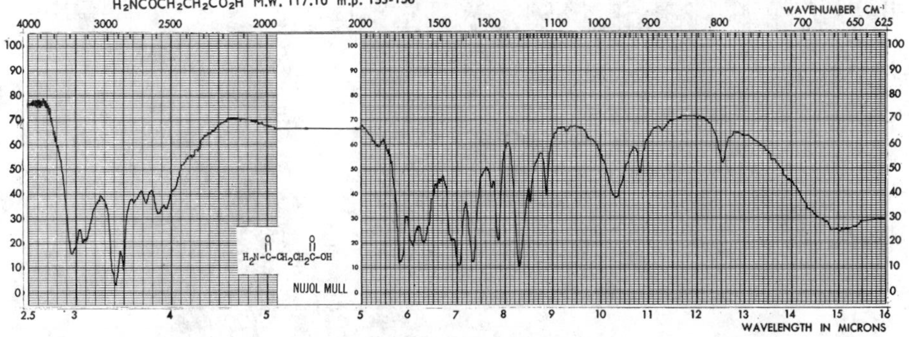

D 12,475-3 **Succinamide** (succinic diamide)
$H_2NCOCH_2CH_2CONH_2$ M.W. 116.12
m.p. 260° (dec.)
NUJOL MULL

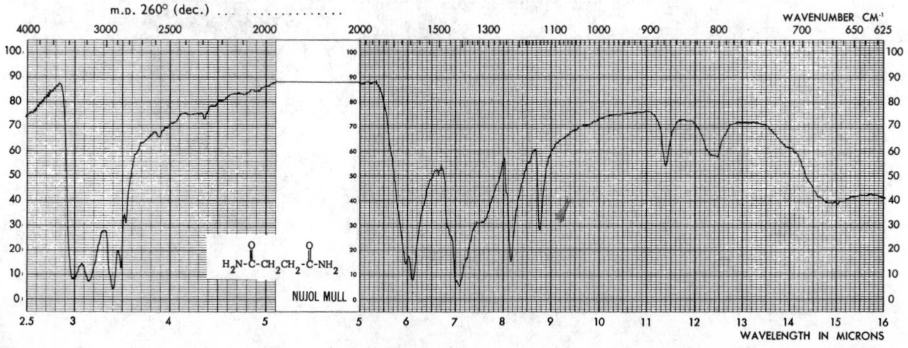

E 14,832-6 **N,N'-Methylenebisacrylamide, puriss., electrophoresis grade**
$(H_2C{:}CHCONH)_2CH_2$ M.W. 154.17
m.p. >300°
NUJOL MULL

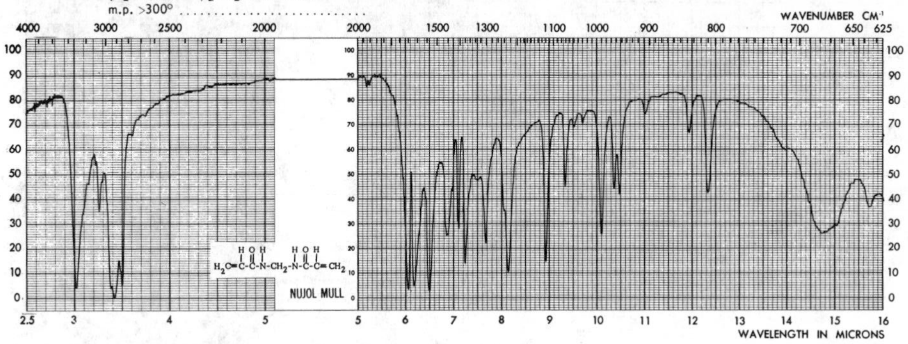

F T2823 **2,2'-Thiobisacetamide**
$S(-CH_2CONH_2)_2$ M.W. 148.19 m.p. 171-173°
NUJOL MULL

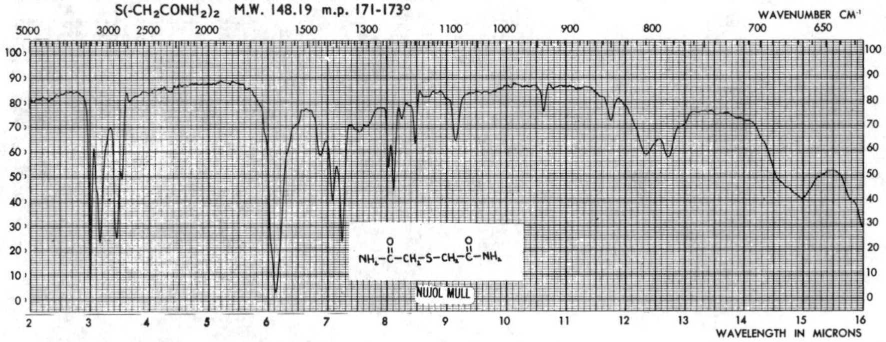

G 16,637-5
Formic acid hydrazide (formylhydrazine)
$HCONHNH_2$
M.W. 60.06 m.p. 58-60° Beil. 2,93
MELT

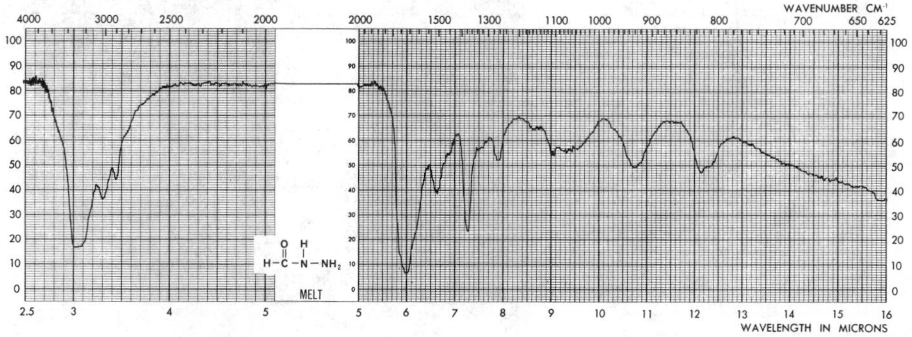

H A830-9 **Acethydrazide** (acetic acid hydrazide)
$CH_3CONHNH_2$ M.W. 74.08 m.p. 62-67°
MELT

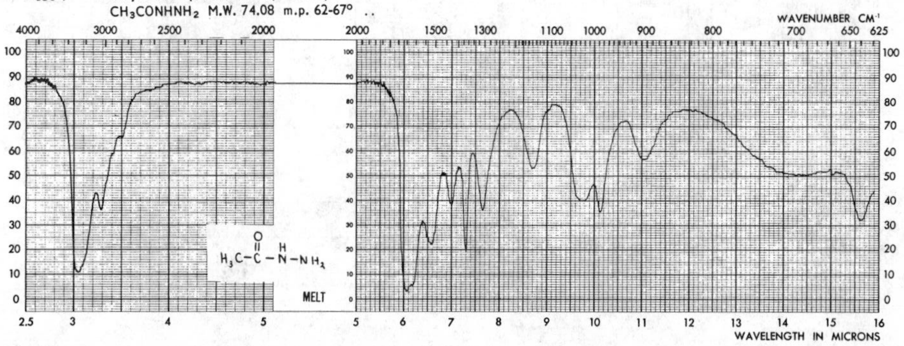

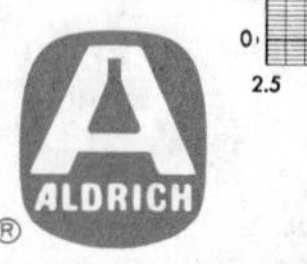

A

16,031-8
Chloroacetic acid hydrazide hydrochloride, 97%
$ClCH_2CONHNH_2 \cdot HCl$
M.W. 144.99 m.p. 161-163° (dec.)

NUJOL MULL

B

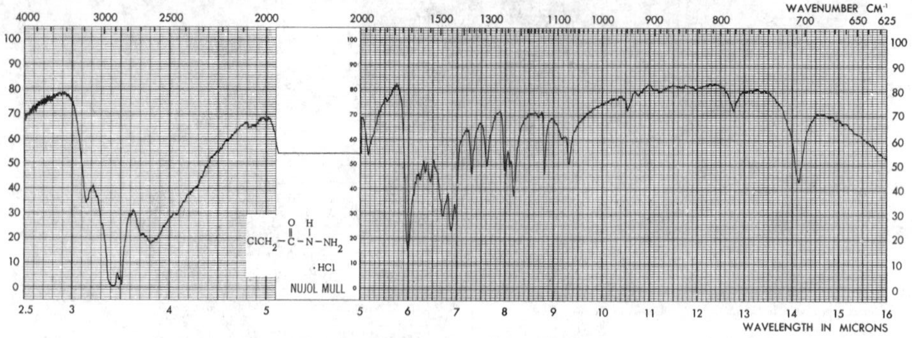

10,508-2 **Butyric acid hydrazide**
$CH_3CH_2CH_2CONHNH_2$ M.W. 102.14 m.p. 43-44°

MELT

C

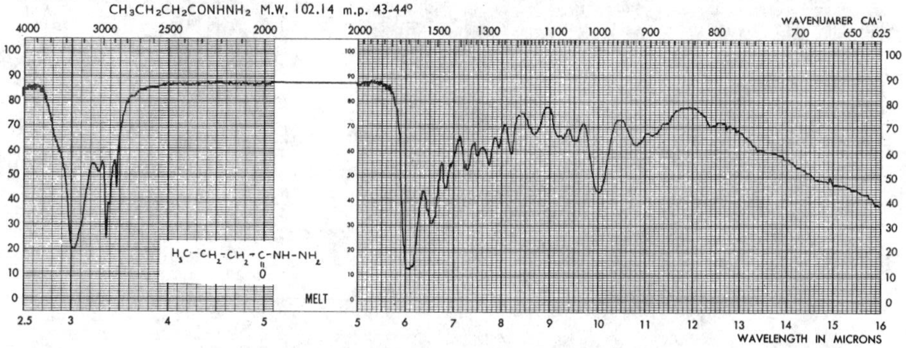

C11,700-5 **Cyclopropanecarboxylic acid hydrazide**
$C_3H_5CONHNH_2$ M.W. 100.12 m.p. 95-98°

NUJOL MULL

D

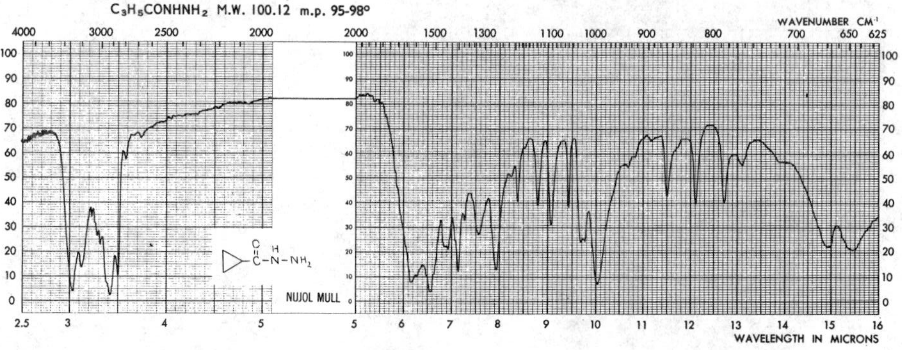

G90-0 **Girard's Reagent T** [(carboxymethyl)-trimethylammonium chloride hydrazide]
$H_2NNHCOCH_2N(CH_3)_3Cl$ M.W. 167.64
m.p. 188-192°

NUJOL MULL

E

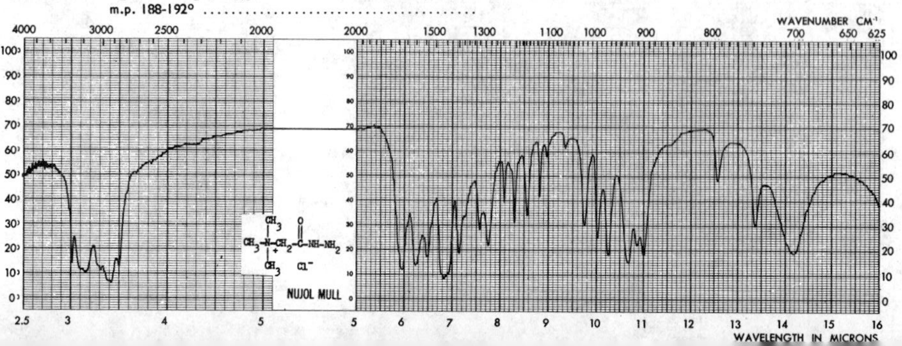

D10,300-4 **sym.-Diformylhydrazine** (1,2-diformylhydrazine)
HCONHNHCHO M.W. 88.07 m.p. 155-157°

NUJOL MULL

F

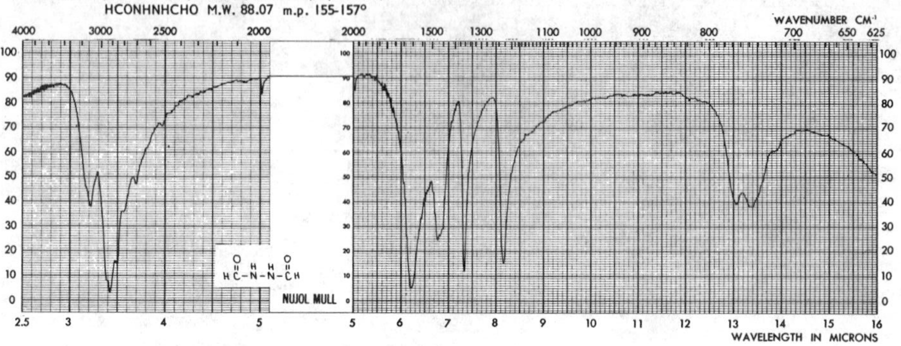

D840-2 **sym.-Diacetylhydrazine**
$CH_3CONHNHCOCH_3$ M.W. 116.12 m.p. 137-140°

NUJOL MULL

G

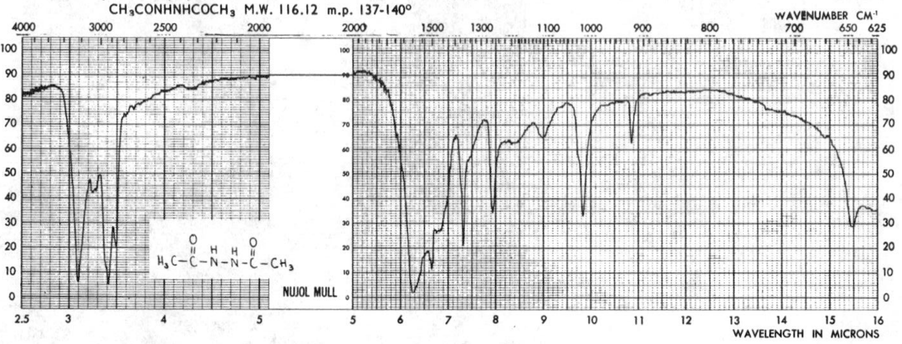

O-930-1 **Oxamic hydrazide** (semioxamazide)
$H_2NCOCONHNH_2$ M.W. 103.08
m.p. 218-219° (dec.)

NUJOL MULL

H

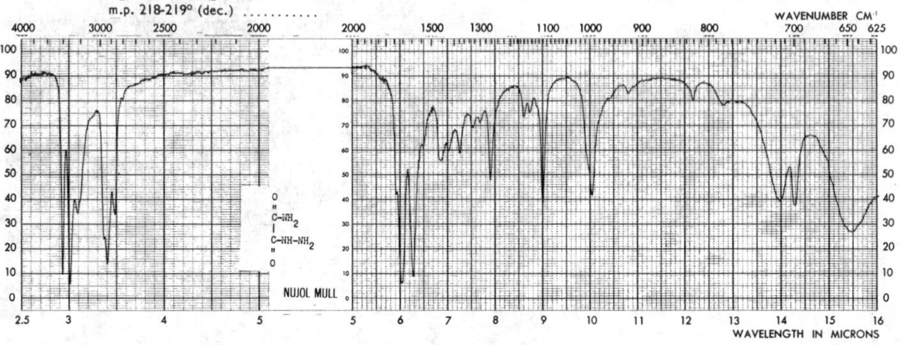

12,442-7 **Oxalic acid bis-(cyclohexylidenehydrazide)** (cuprizon I)
M.W. 278.36 m.p. 208-212°

NUJOL MULL

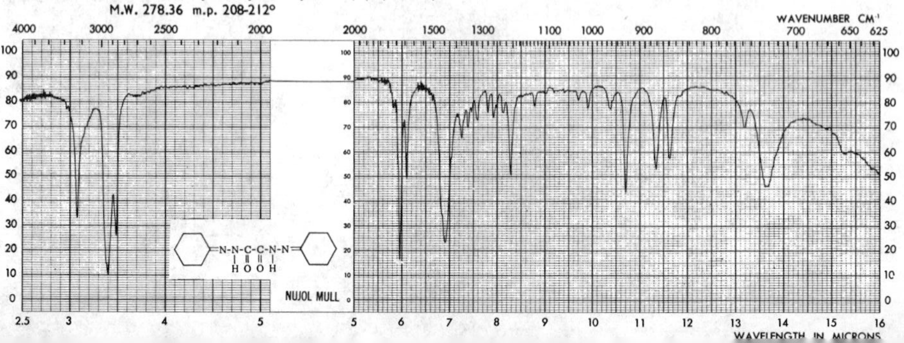

A 13,129-6 **Oxalyl dihydrazide**
$H_2NNHCOCONHNH_2$ M.W. 118.10
m.p. 244-245° (dec.)
NUJOL MULL

B S550-2 **Succinic acid dihydrazide**
$H_2NNHCOCH_2CH_2CONHNH_2$ M.W. 146.15 m.p. 166-168°
NUJOL MULL

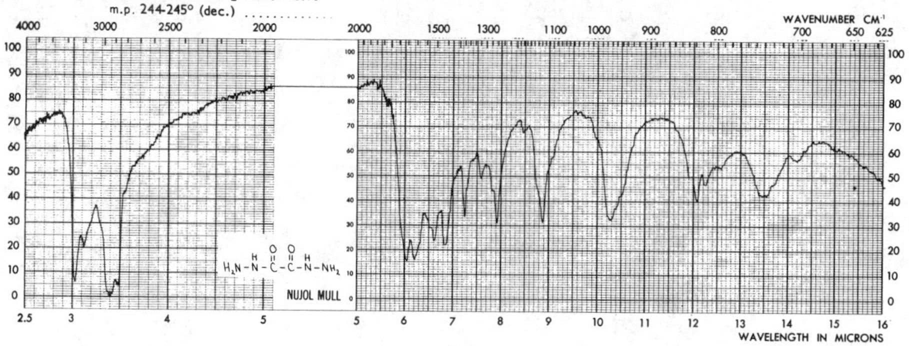

C G420-9 **Glutaric dihydrazide**
$H_2NNHCO(CH_2)_3CONHNH_2$ M.W. 160.18
m.p. 175-177°
NUJOL MULL

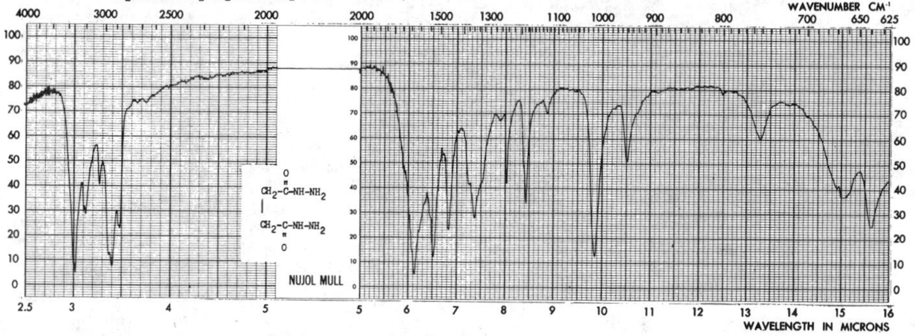

D 21,782-4
Adipic dihydrazide, 98%
$H_2NNHCO(CH_2)_4CONHNH_2$ FW 174.20
mp 180-182° *Beil.* **2**(1),277 Disp. C
NUJOL MULL

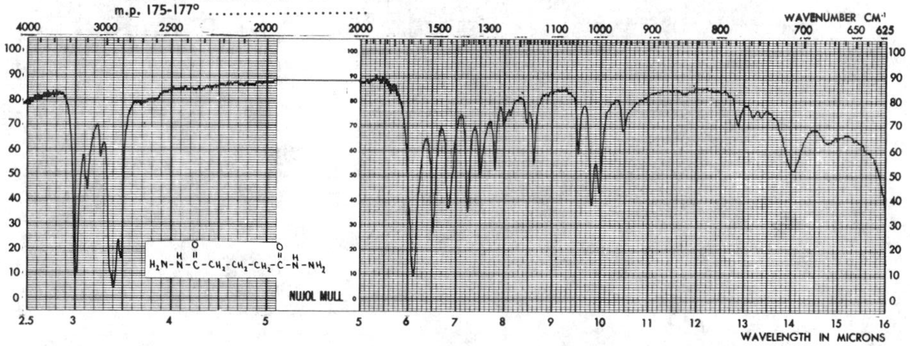

E 18,673-2
4-(Acethydrazino)-1-methylpiperidine, 98% [acetic acid 2-(1-methyl-4-piperidyl)hydrazide]
M.W. 171.24 m.p. 99-102°
NUJOL MULL

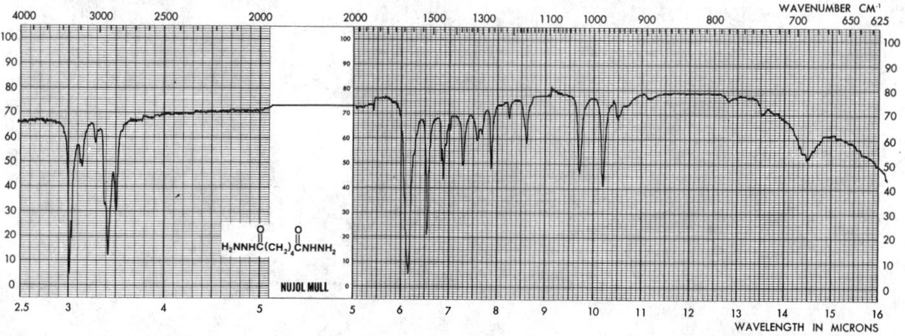

F I-1265-4 **Iproniazid phosphate** (isonicotinic acid 2-isopropylhydrazide phosphate)
M.W. 277.21 m.p. 180-182°
NUJOL MULL

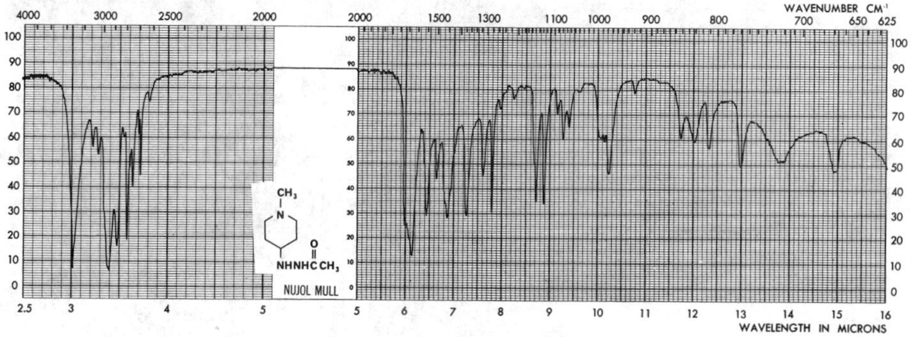

G 17,794-6
Succinic acid 2,2-dimethylhydrazide, 99%
$HO_2CCH_2CH_2CONHN(CH_3)_2$
M.W. 160.17 m.p. 162-164°
NUJOL MULL

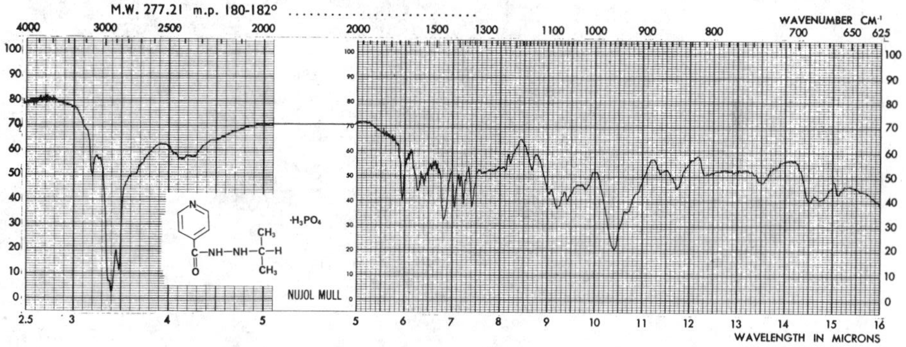

H 13,259-4 **2,5-Dimethoxytetrahydro-2-furoic acid hydrazide** (mixture of *cis* and *trans*)
M.W. 190.20 m.p. 58-62°
MELT

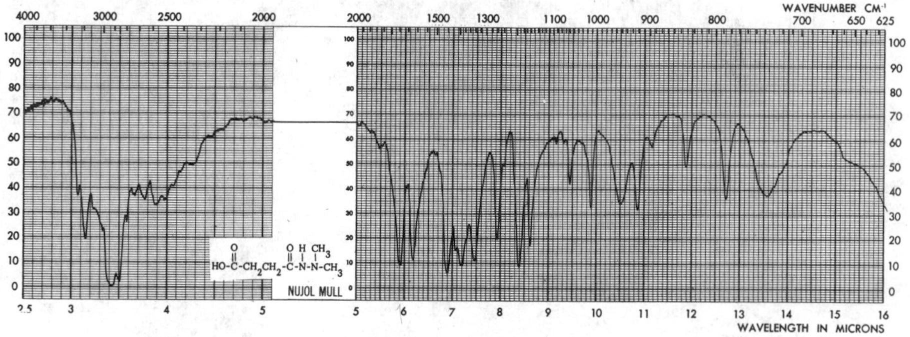

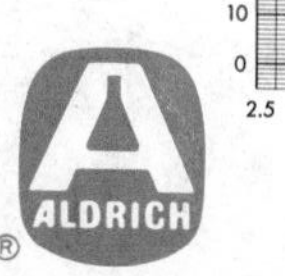

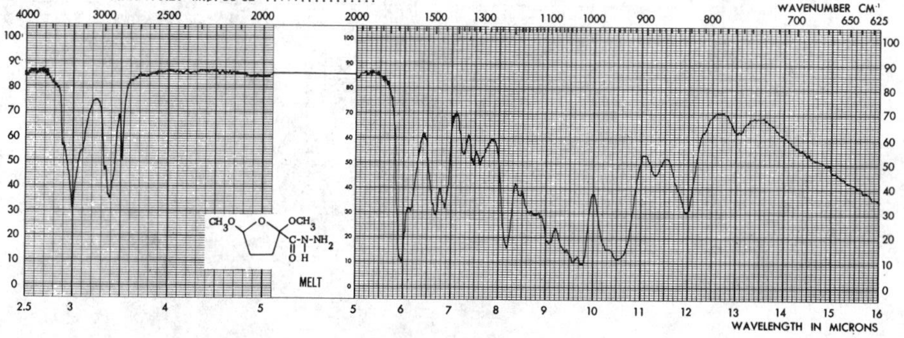

A 13,259-4 **2,5-Dimethoxytetrahydro-2-furoic acid hydrazide** (mixture of *cis* and *trans*)
M.W. 190.20 m.p. 58-62° .... NUJOL MULL

B U285-7 **Urethane** (ethyl carbamate)
$H_2NCO_2C_2H_5$ M.W. 89.09 m.p. 48.5-50° MELT

C 14,209-3 **N,N-Dichlorourethan (DCU)**
(send for data sheet)
$Cl_2NCO_2C_2H_5$ M.W 157.99 n_D^{20} 1.4595
b.p. 55-56°/15 mm.

D 11,947-4 **N-Hydroxyurethane**
$HONHCO_2C_2H_5$ M.W. 105.09 NEAT

E E5122-8 **N-Ethylurethane** (ethyl N-ethylcarbamate)
$C_2H_5NHCO_2C_2H_5$ M.W. 117.15 n_D^{20} 1.4234 NEAT

F 16,056-3
N,N'-Methylenebis-(ethyl carbamate), 99%
$CH_2(NHCO_2C_2H_5)_2$
M.W. 190.2 m.p. 130-131° Beil. 3,24
Fieser 1,677
NUJOL MULL

G A2300 **Acetylurethan**
$CH_3CONHCO_2C_2H_5$ M.W. 131.13 NUJOL MULL

H 16,739-8
tert.-**Butyl carbamate**, 98%
$H_2NCO_2C(CH_3)_3$
M.W. 117.15 m.p. 105-108° Beil. 3(2),26
NUJOL MULL

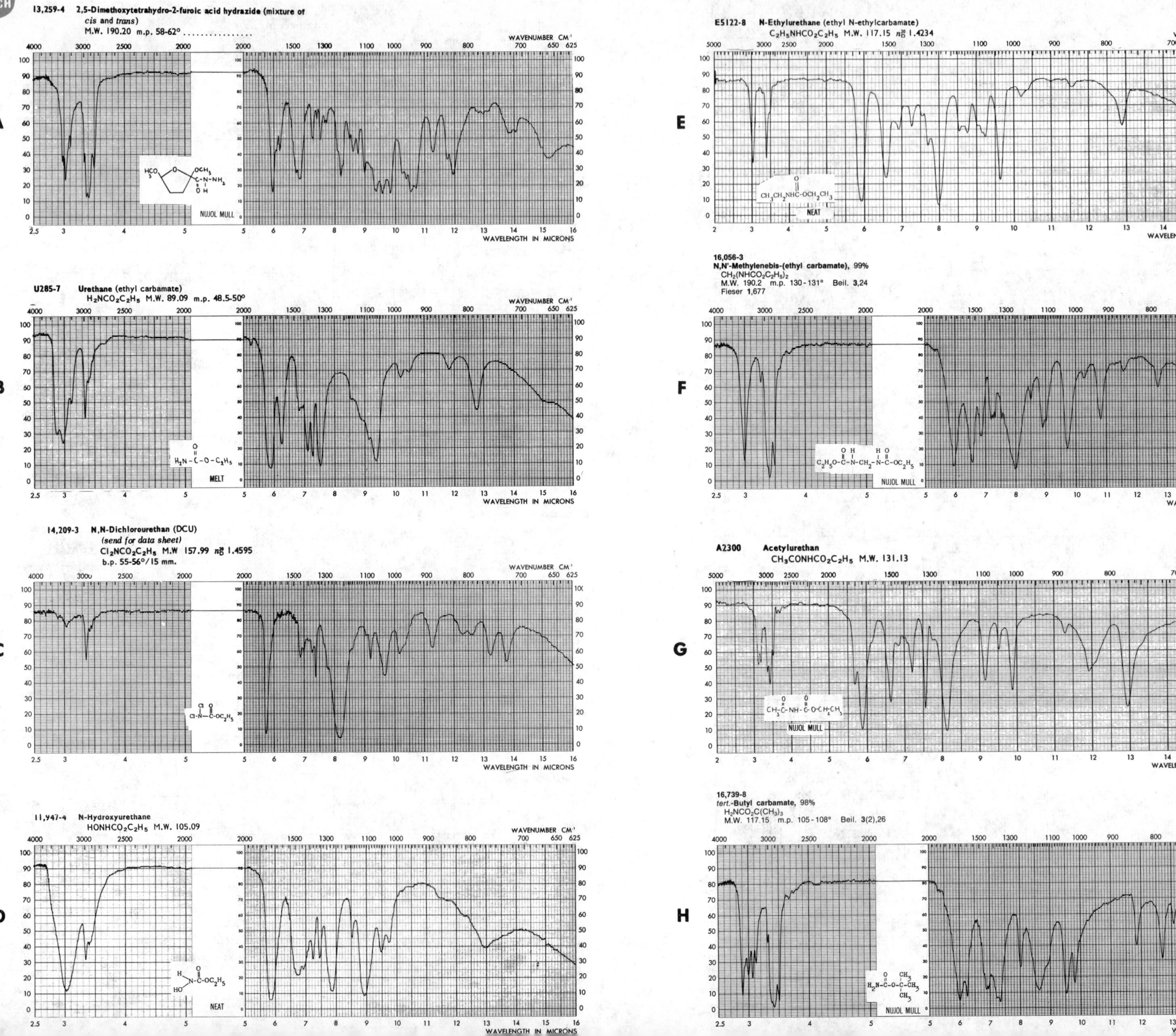

A 15,238-2 1-Methyl-2,2,3,3-tetrafluoropropyl carbamate
$H_2NCO_2CH(CH_3)CF_2CHF_2$ M.W. 189.11
m.p. 59-61°
NUJOL MULL

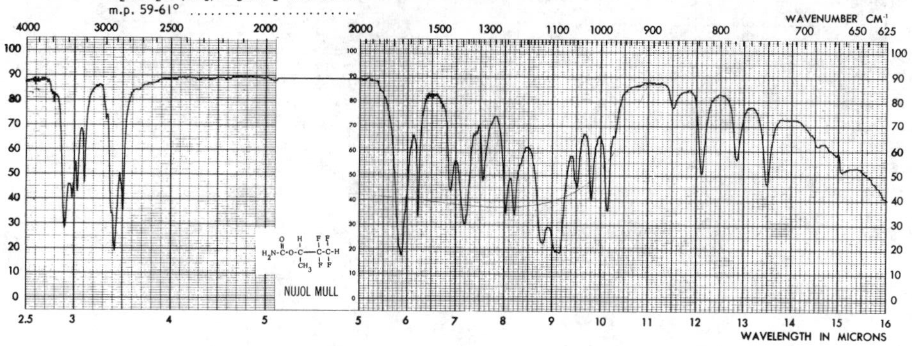

B C240-9 Carbamylcholine chloride [carbachol, (2-hydroxyethyl)-trimethylammonium chloride carbamate]
$H_2NCO_2CH_2CH_2N(CH_3)_3Cl$ M.W. 182.65
m.p. 211-214° (dec.)
NUJOL MULL

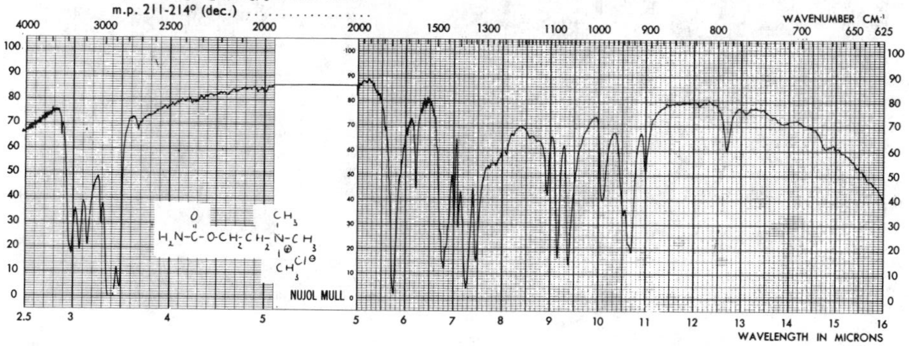

C O-940-9 2-Oxazolidone
M.W. 87.08 m.p. 86-89°
NUJOL MULL

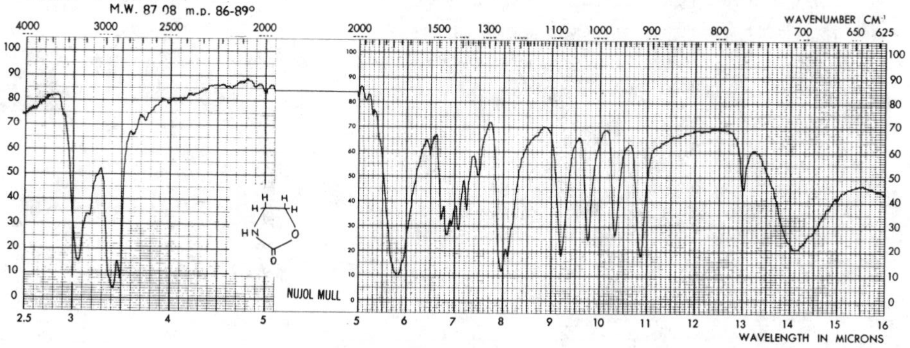

D 13,565-8 5-Chloromethyl-2-oxazolidinone
M.W. 135.55 m.p. 104-105°
NUJOL MULL

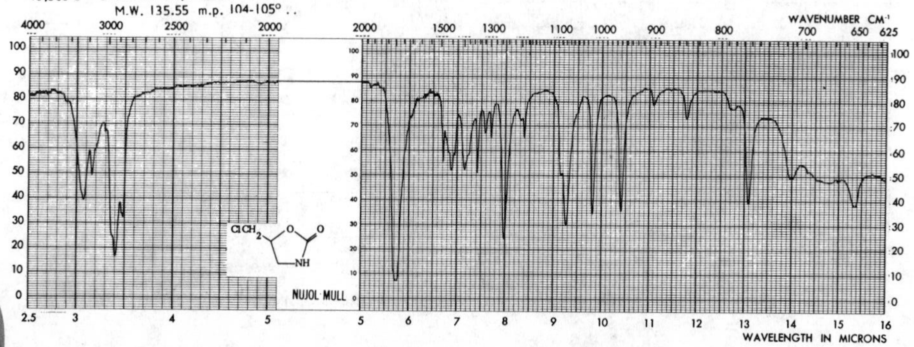

E 11,509-6 3-Amino-2-oxazolidinone
M.W. 102.09 m.p. 62-66°
NUJOL MULL

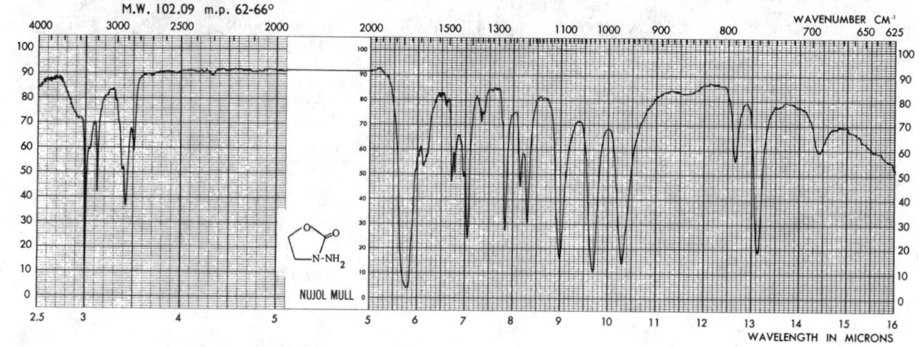

F 20,086-7
3-Amino-2-oxazolidinone sulfate, 97+%
FW 200.17 mp 165-167° Disp. C
NUJOL MULL

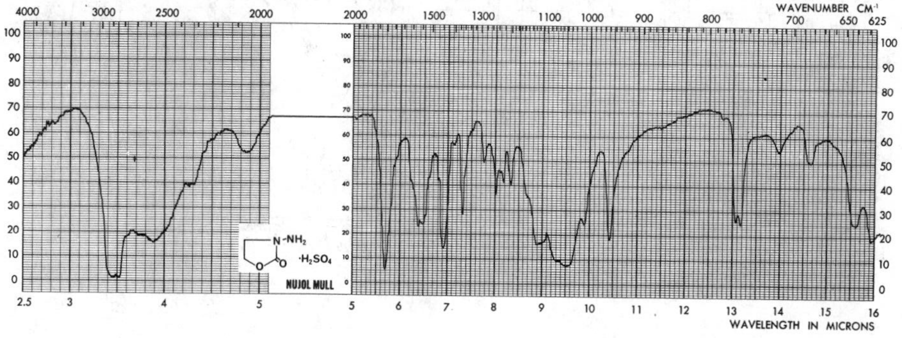

G 21,900-2
5,5-Dimethyloxazolidine-2,4-dione, 99%
(dimethadione)
FW 129.12 mp 77-80° *Beil.* 27,252 Disp. C
NUJOL MULL

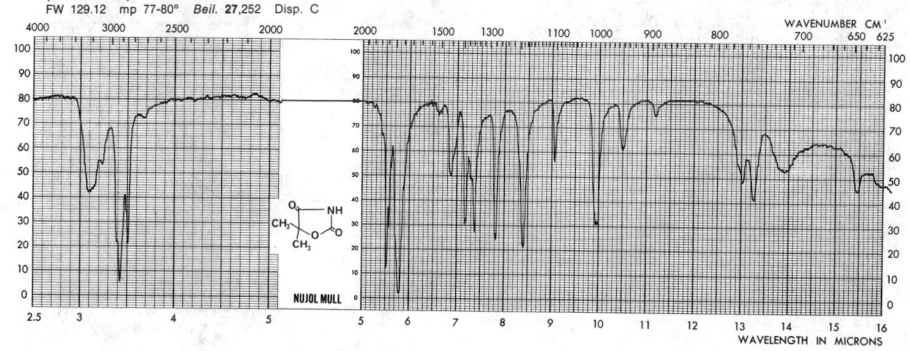

H 11,823-0 Ethyl 2-norbornylcarbamate
M.W. 183.25 m.p. 42-43°
MELT

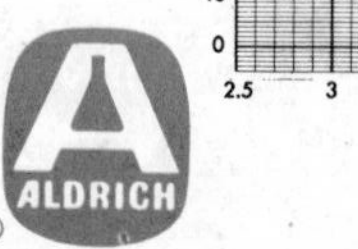

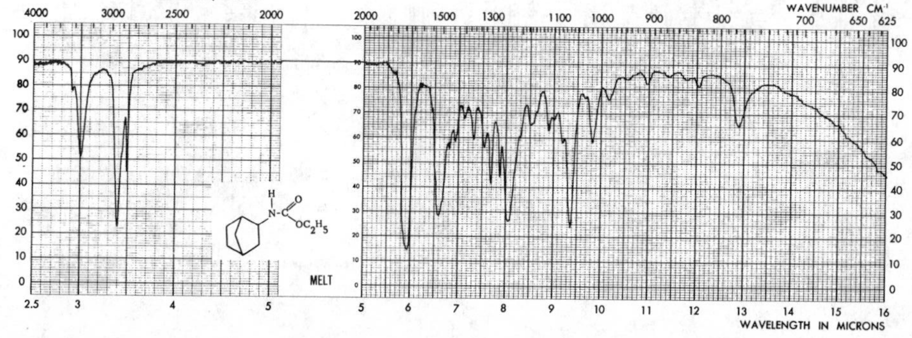

ALDRICH

A 11,811-7 **Ethyl 3-nortricyclylcarbamate** (ethyl tricyclo[2.2.1.0^{2,6}]heptane-3-carbamate)
M.W. 181.24 m.p. 54-56° MELT

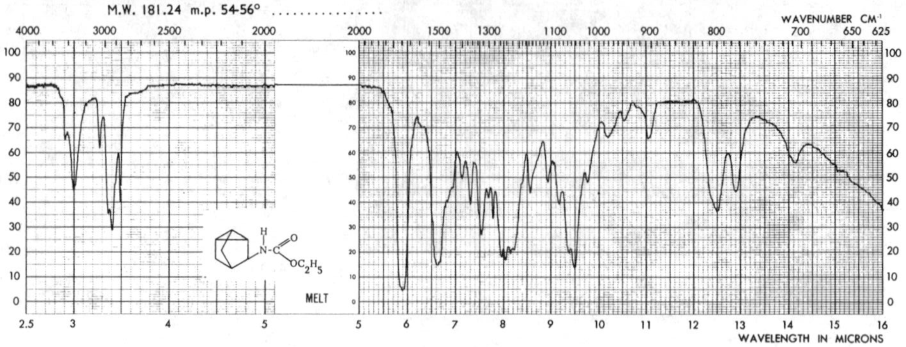

B 20,639-3 **Ethyl 1-pyrrolidinecarboxylate**
FW 143.19 bp 98-99°/20mm. n_D^{20} 1.4545 d 1.022
Disp. C NEAT

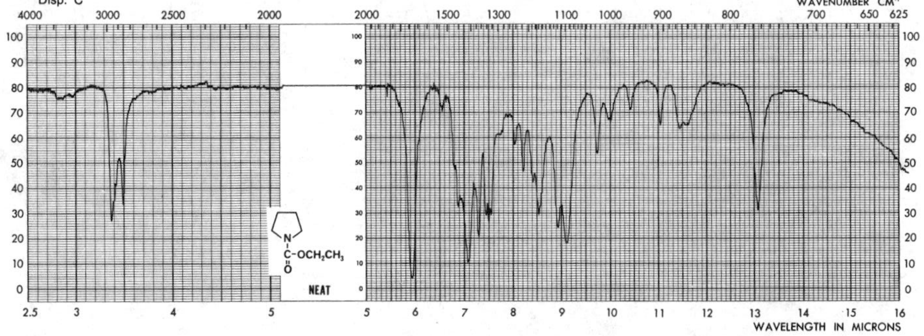

C 15,373-7 **N-Carbethoxy-4-piperidone** (ethyl 4-oxo-1-piperidinecarboxylate)
M.W. 171.20 n_D^{20} 1.4752 NEAT

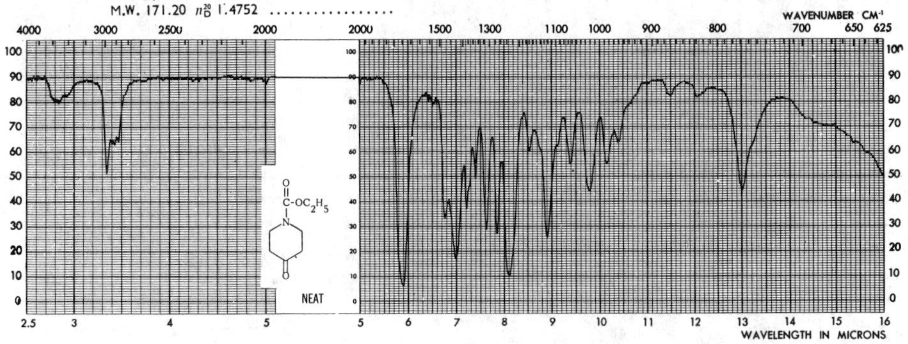

D E4560-0 **Ethyl N-piperazinocarboxylate**
M.W. 158.20 n_D^{20} 1.4765 NEAT

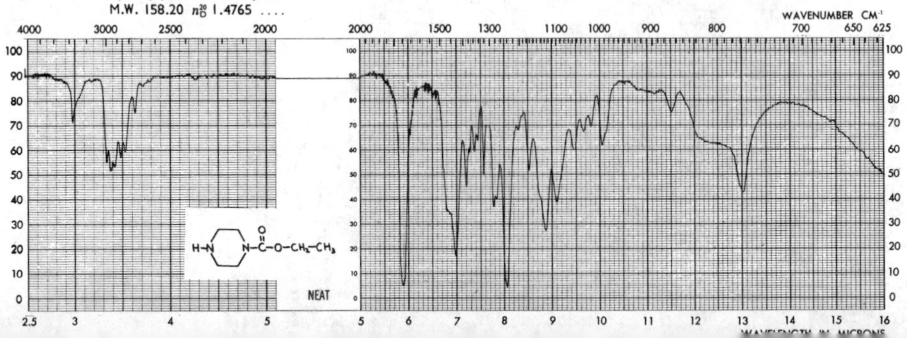

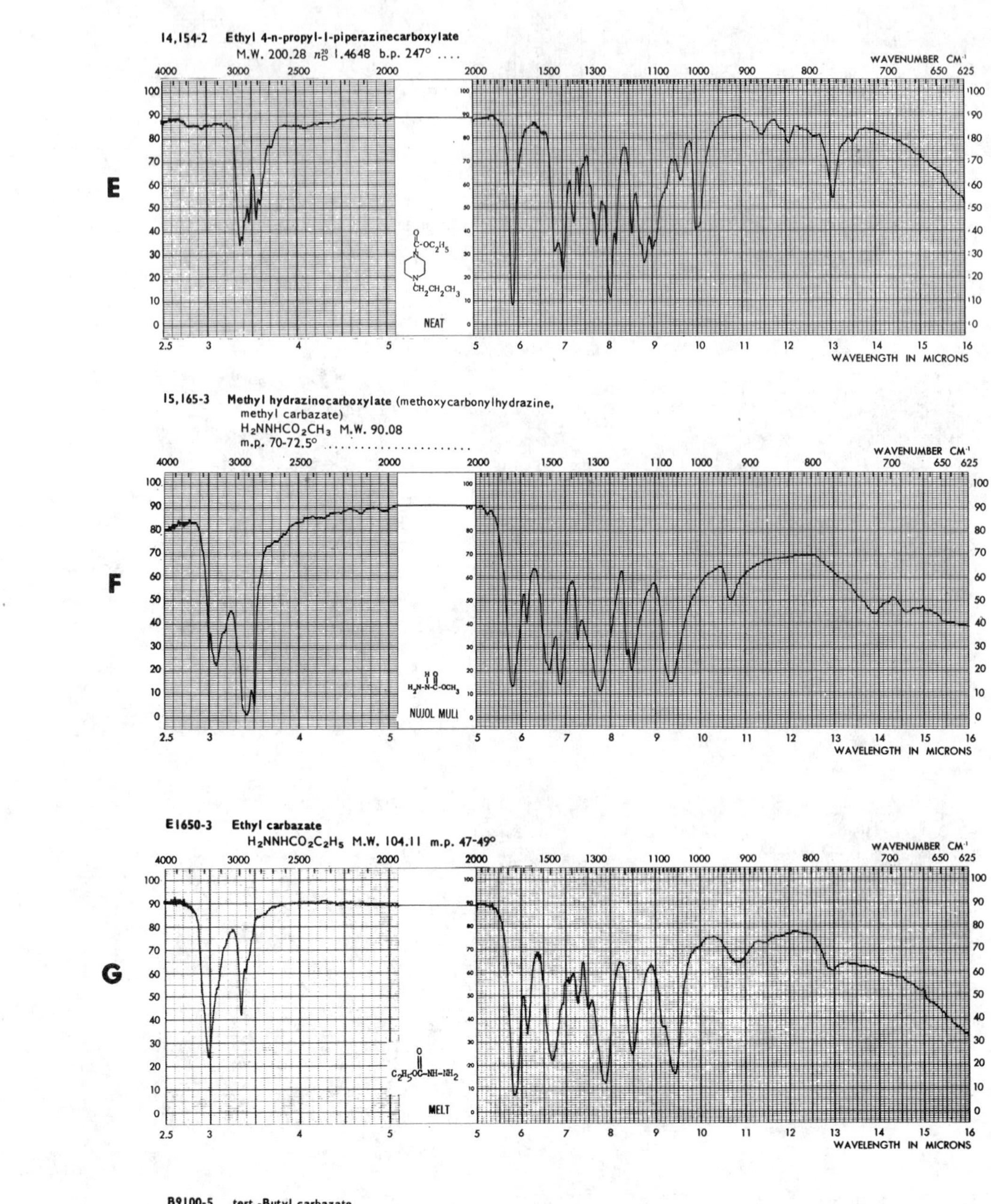

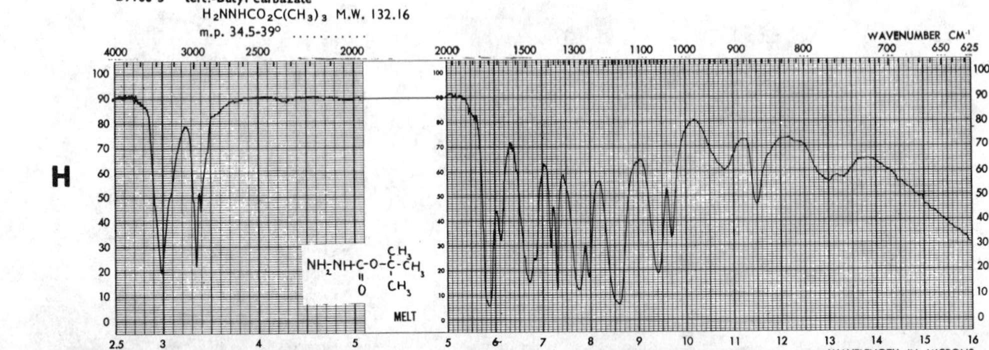

E 14,154-2 **Ethyl 4-n-propyl-1-piperazinecarboxylate**
M.W. 200.28 n_D^{20} 1.4648 b.p. 247° NEAT

F 15,165-3 **Methyl hydrazinocarboxylate** (methoxycarbonylhydrazine, methyl carbazate)
$H_2NNHCO_2CH_3$ M.W. 90.08
m.p. 70-72.5° NUJOL MULL

G E1650-3 **Ethyl carbazate**
$H_2NNHCO_2C_2H_5$ M.W. 104.11 m.p. 47-49° MELT

H B9100-5 **tert.-Butyl carbazate**
$H_2NNHCO_2C(CH_3)_3$ M.W. 132.16
m.p. 34.5-39° MELT

A D5140-1 sym.-Dicarbethoxyhydrazine
$C_2H_5O_2CNHNHCO_2C_2H_5$ M.W. 176.17
m.p. 130-132°
NUJOL MULL

B 14,046-5 Di-tert.-butyl hydrazodiformate (tert.-butyl hydrazodiformate)
$[-NHCO_2C(CH_3)_3]_2$ M.W. 232.28
m.p. 123-126°
NUJOL MULL

C D14,695-1 Dimethyl azodicarboxylate, tech. *
$CH_3O_2CN:NCO_2CH_3$ M.W. 146.11
n_D^{20} 1.4306
NEAT

D D9000-8 Diethyl azodicarboxylate
$C_2H_5O_2CN:NCO_2C_2H_5$ M.W. 174.16
n_D^{20} 1.4240
NEAT

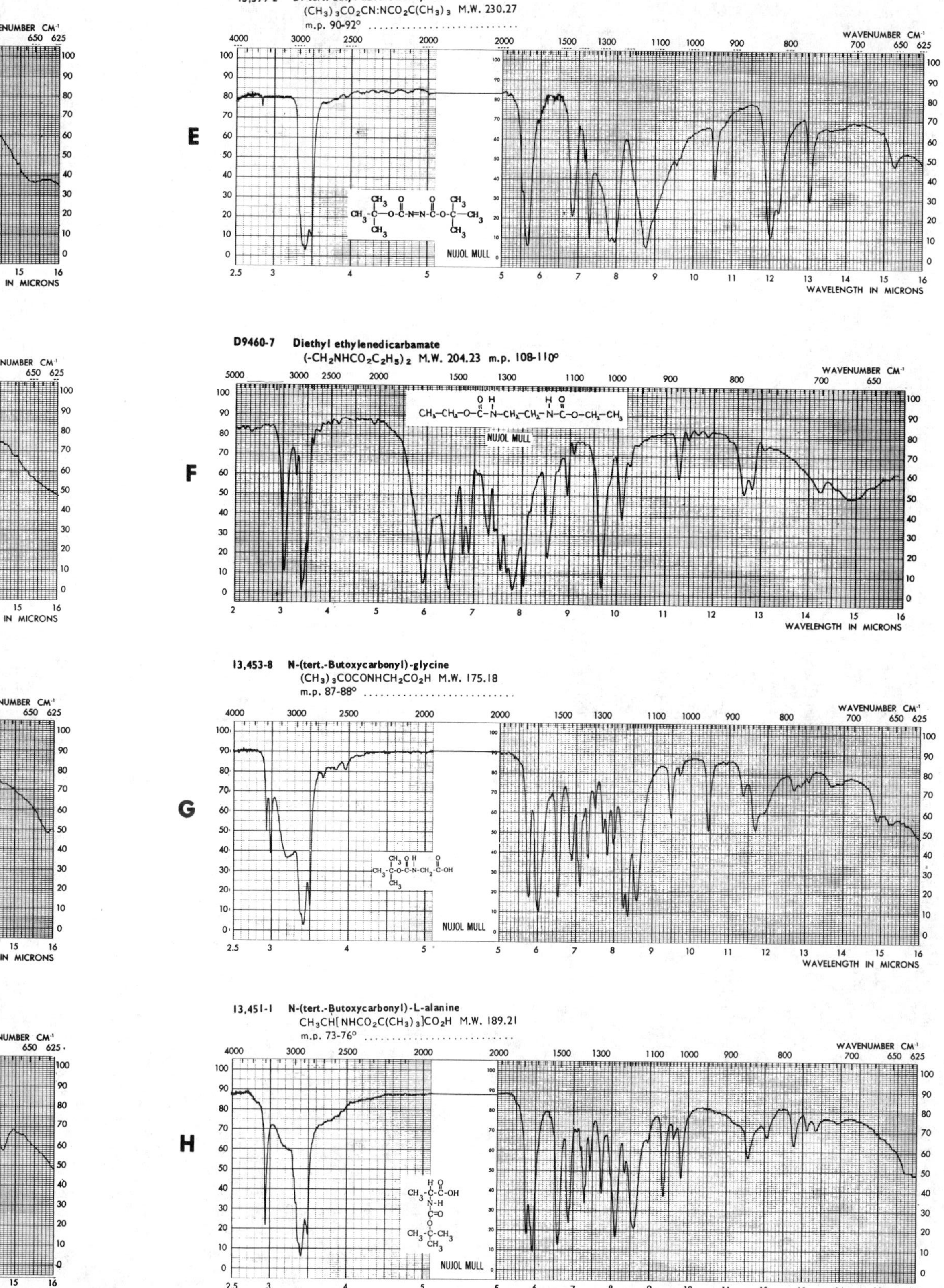

E 13,599-2 Di-tert.-butyl azodicarboxylate
$(CH_3)_3CO_2CN:NCO_2C(CH_3)_3$ M.W. 230.27
m.p. 90-92°
NUJOL MULL

F D9460-7 Diethyl ethylenedicarbamate
$(-CH_2NHCO_2C_2H_5)_2$ M.W. 204.23 m.p. 108-110°
NUJOL MULL

G 13,453-8 N-(tert.-Butoxycarbonyl)-glycine
$(CH_3)_3COCONHCH_2CO_2H$ M.W. 175.18
m.p. 87-88°
NUJOL MULL

H 13,451-1 N-(tert.-Butoxycarbonyl)-L-alanine
$CH_3CH[NHCO_2C(CH_3)_3]CO_2H$ M.W. 189.21
m.p. 73-76°
NUJOL MULL

A

13,450-3 **N-(tert.-Butoxycarbonyl)-DL-alanine**
$CH_3CH[NHCO_2C(CH_3)_3]CO_2H$ M.W. 189.21
m.p. 109-110°

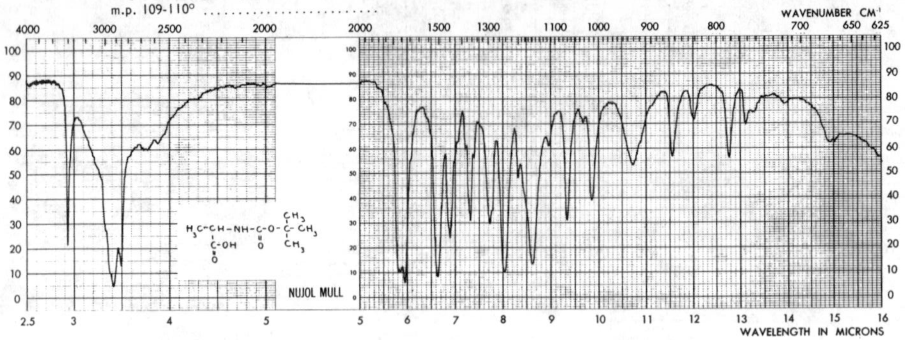

NUJOL MULL

B

13,454-6 **N-(tert.-Butoxycarbonyl)-L-leucine monohydrate**
$(CH_3)_2CHCH_2CH[NHCO_2C(CH_3)_3]CO_2H \cdot H_2O$
M.W. 249.31 m.p. 80-85°

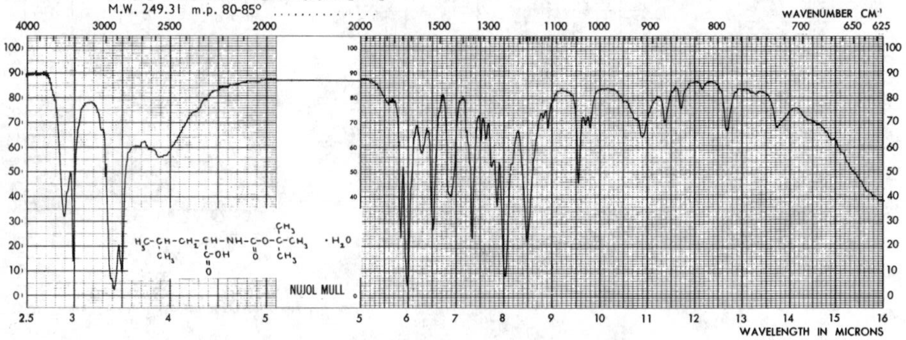

NUJOL MULL

C

13,457-0 **N-(tert.-Butoxycarbonyl)-L-proline**
M.W. 215.25 m.p. 132-134°

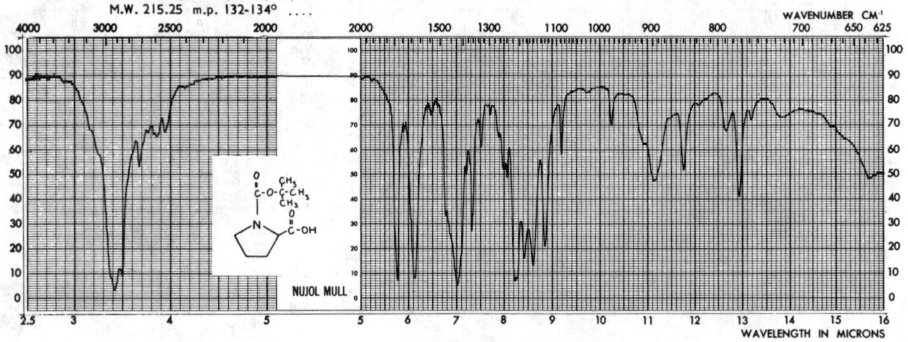

NUJOL MULL

D

85,930-3
Glycyl-L-hydroxyproline
M.W. 188.18 m.p. 218-219° (dec.) Beil. **22**(2),144

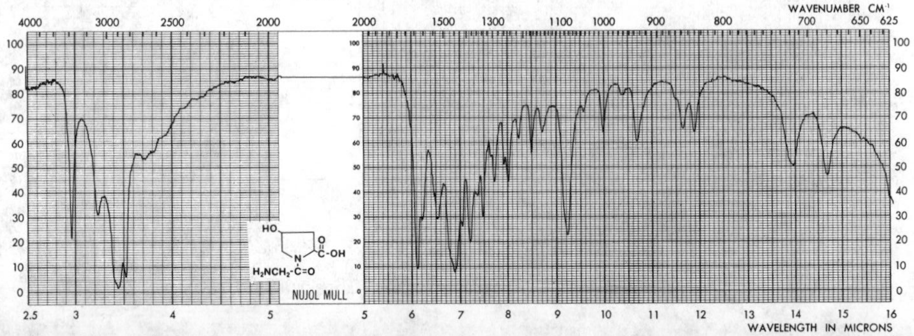

NUJOL MULL

E

A1630-0 **N-Acetylglycine** (acetamidoacetic acid, aceturic acid)
$CH_3CONHCH_2CO_2H$ M.W. 117.10 m.p. 207°

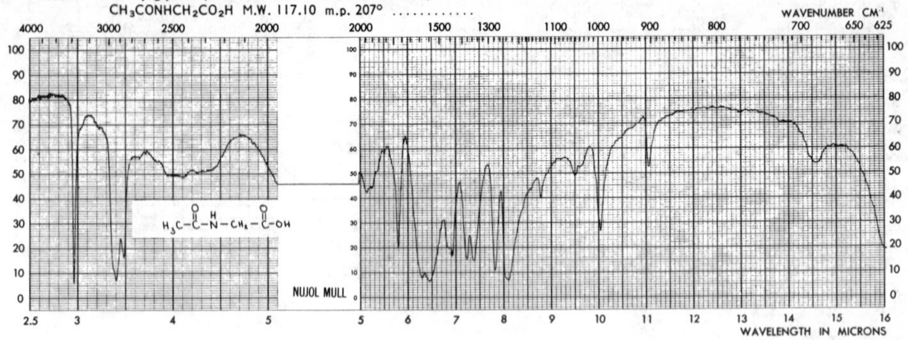

NUJOL MULL

F

16,157-8
2-Aminomalonamide, 97%
$H_2NCH(CONH_2)_2$
M.W. 117.11 m.p. 188.5° (dec.) Beil. **4**,470

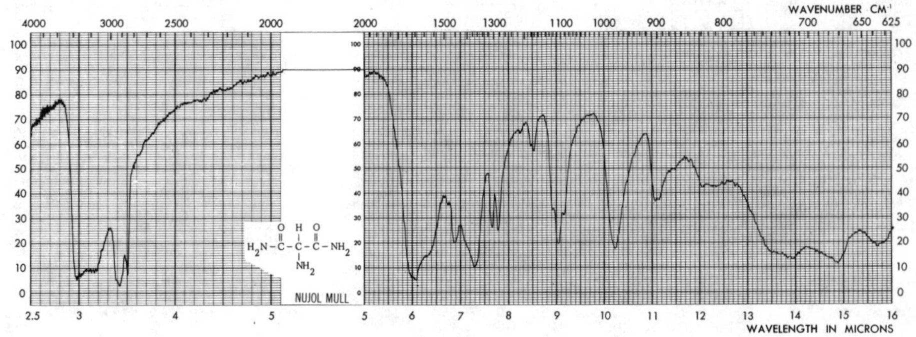

NUJOL MULL

G

H1680-9 **Hydantoic acid**
$H_2NCONHCH_2CO_2H$ M.W. 118.09 m.p. 176° (dec.)

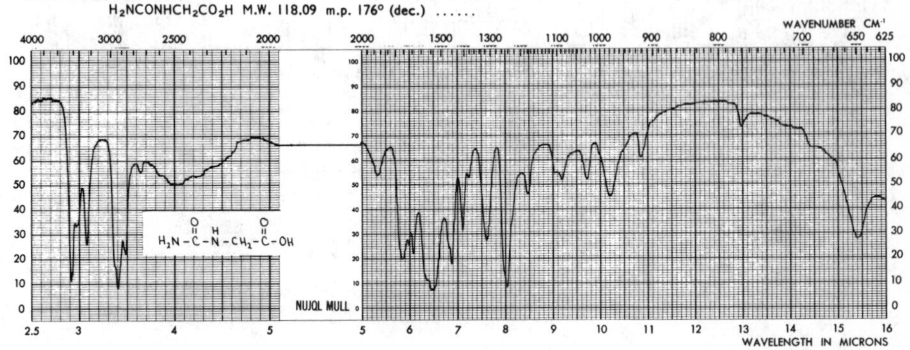

NUJOL MULL

H

G780-1 **Glycylglycine**
$H_2NCH_2CONHCH_2CO_2H$ M.W. 132.12
m.p. 215° (dec.)

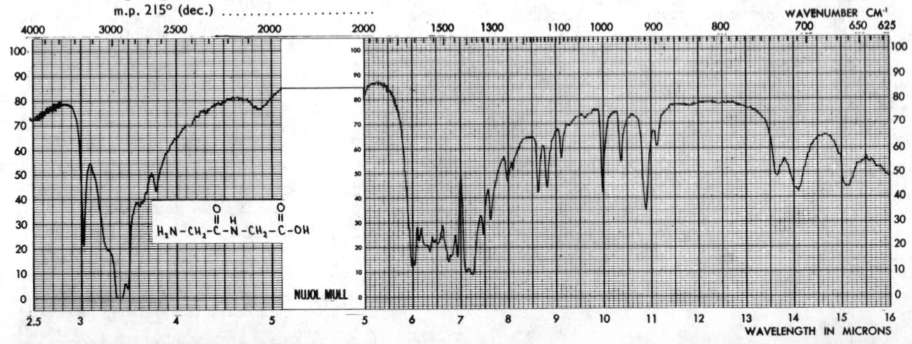

NUJOL MULL

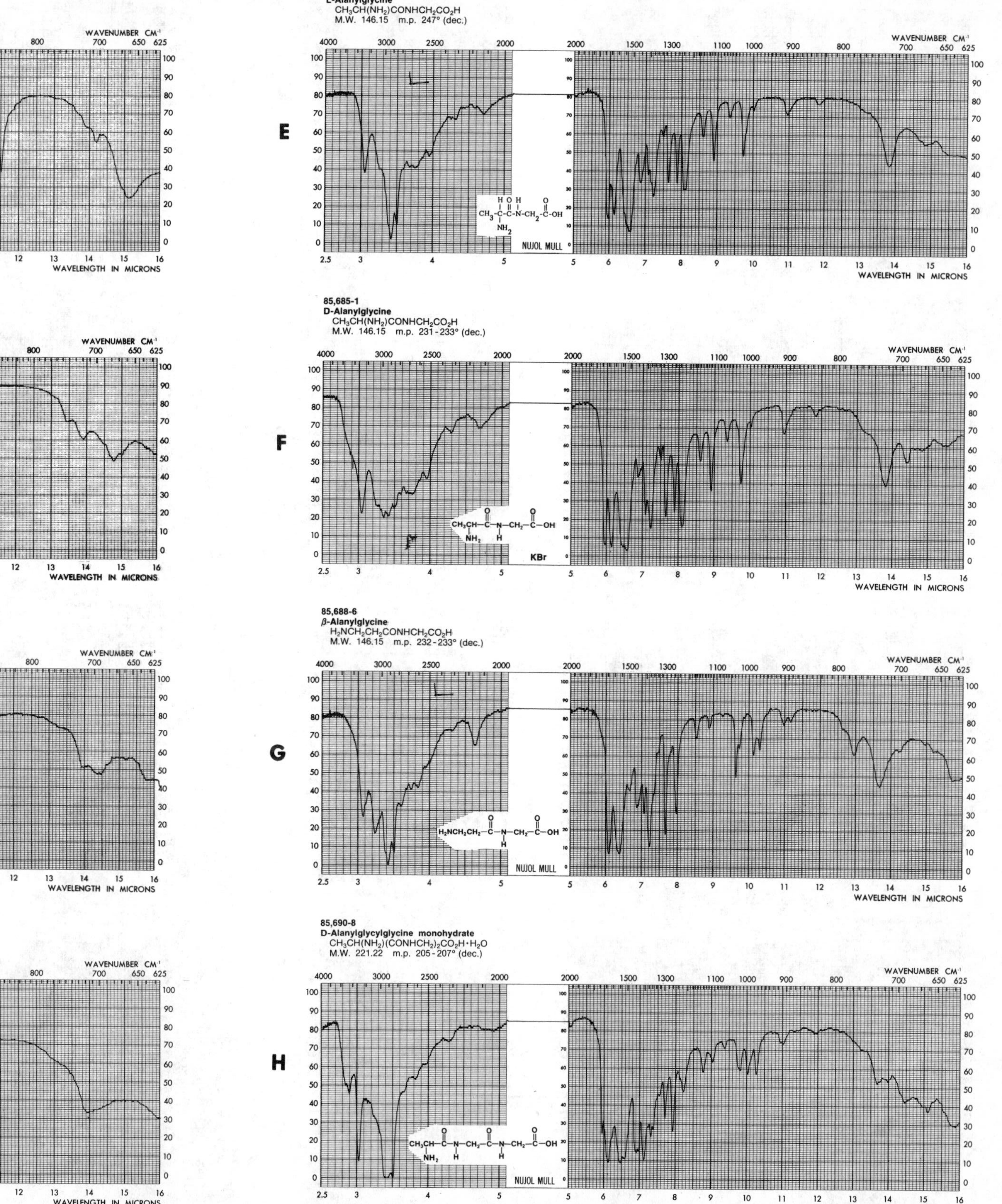

A 12,845-7 **Glycylglycine hydrochloride monohydrate**
$H_2NCH_2CONHCH_2CO_2H{\cdot}HCl{\cdot}H_2O$ M.W. 186.60
m.p. 142° (dec.)
NUJOL MULL

B G820-4 **Glycylglycylglycine**
$H_2NCH_2CONHCH_2CONHCH_2CO_2H$ M.W. 189.17
m.p. 245° (dec.)
NUJOL MULL

C 86,008-5
Glycylglycylglycylglycine, 97% (tetraglycine)
$H_2NCH_2(CONHCH_2)_3CO_2H$ FW 246.23 mp >300°
Disp. L
NUJOL MULL

D 85,943-5
Polyglycine
m.p. >300° Beil. **4**(2),771
NUJOL MULL

E 85,687-8
L-Alanylglycine
$CH_3CH(NH_2)CONHCH_2CO_2H$
M.W. 146.15 m.p. 247° (dec.)
NUJOL MULL

F 85,685-1
D-Alanylglycine
$CH_3CH(NH_2)CONHCH_2CO_2H$
M.W. 146.15 m.p. 231-233° (dec.)
KBr

G 85,688-6
β-Alanylglycine
$H_2NCH_2CH_2CONHCH_2CO_2H$
M.W. 146.15 m.p. 232-233° (dec.)
NUJOL MULL

H 85,690-8
D-Alanylglycylglycine monohydrate
$CH_3CH(NH_2)(CONHCH_2)_2CO_2H{\cdot}H_2O$
M.W. 221.22 m.p. 205-207° (dec.)
NUJOL MULL

ALDRICH

ALDRICH

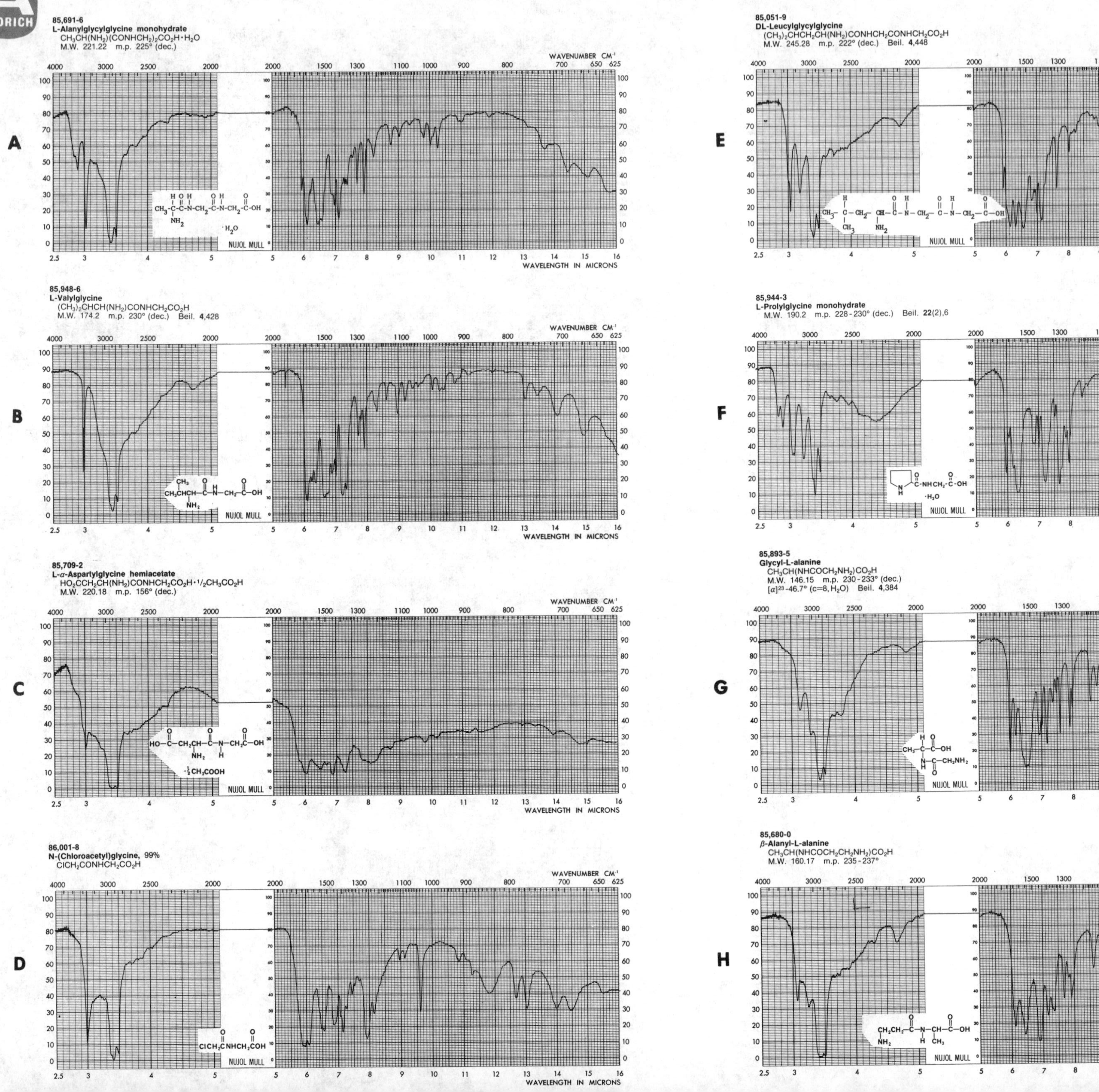
A
85,691-6
L-Alanylglycylglycine monohydrate
$CH_3CH(NH_2)(CONHCH_2)_2CO_2H \cdot H_2O$
M.W. 221.22 m.p. 225° (dec.)
NUJOL MULL
B
85,948-6
L-Valylglycine
$(CH_3)_2CHCH(NH_2)CONHCH_2CO_2H$
M.W. 174.2 m.p. 230° (dec.) Beil. 4,428
NUJOL MULL
C
85,709-2
L-α-Aspartylglycine hemiacetate
$HO_2CCH_2CH(NH_2)CONHCH_2CO_2H \cdot 1/2CH_3CO_2H$
M.W. 220.18 m.p. 156° (dec.)
NUJOL MULL
D
86,001-8
N-(Chloroacetyl)glycine, 99%
$ClCH_2CONHCH_2CO_2H$
NUJOL MULL
E
85,051-9
DL-Leucylglycylglycine
$(CH_3)_2CHCH_2CH(NH_2)CONHCH_2CONHCH_2CO_2H$
M.W. 245.28 m.p. 222° (dec.) Beil. 4,448
NUJOL MULL
F
85,944-3
L-Prolylglycine monohydrate
M.W. 190.2 m.p. 228-230° (dec.) Beil. 22(2),6
NUJOL MULL
G
85,893-5
Glycyl-L-alanine
$CH_3CH(NHCOCH_2NH_2)CO_2H$
M.W. 146.15 m.p. 230-233° (dec.)
$[\alpha]^{23}$ -46.7° (c=8, H_2O) Beil. 4,384
NUJOL MULL
H
85,680-0
β-Alanyl-L-alanine
$CH_3CH(NHCOCH_2CH_2NH_2)CO_2H$
M.W. 160.17 m.p. 235-237°
NUJOL MULL
WAVENUMBER CM⁻¹
WAVELENGTH IN MICRONS

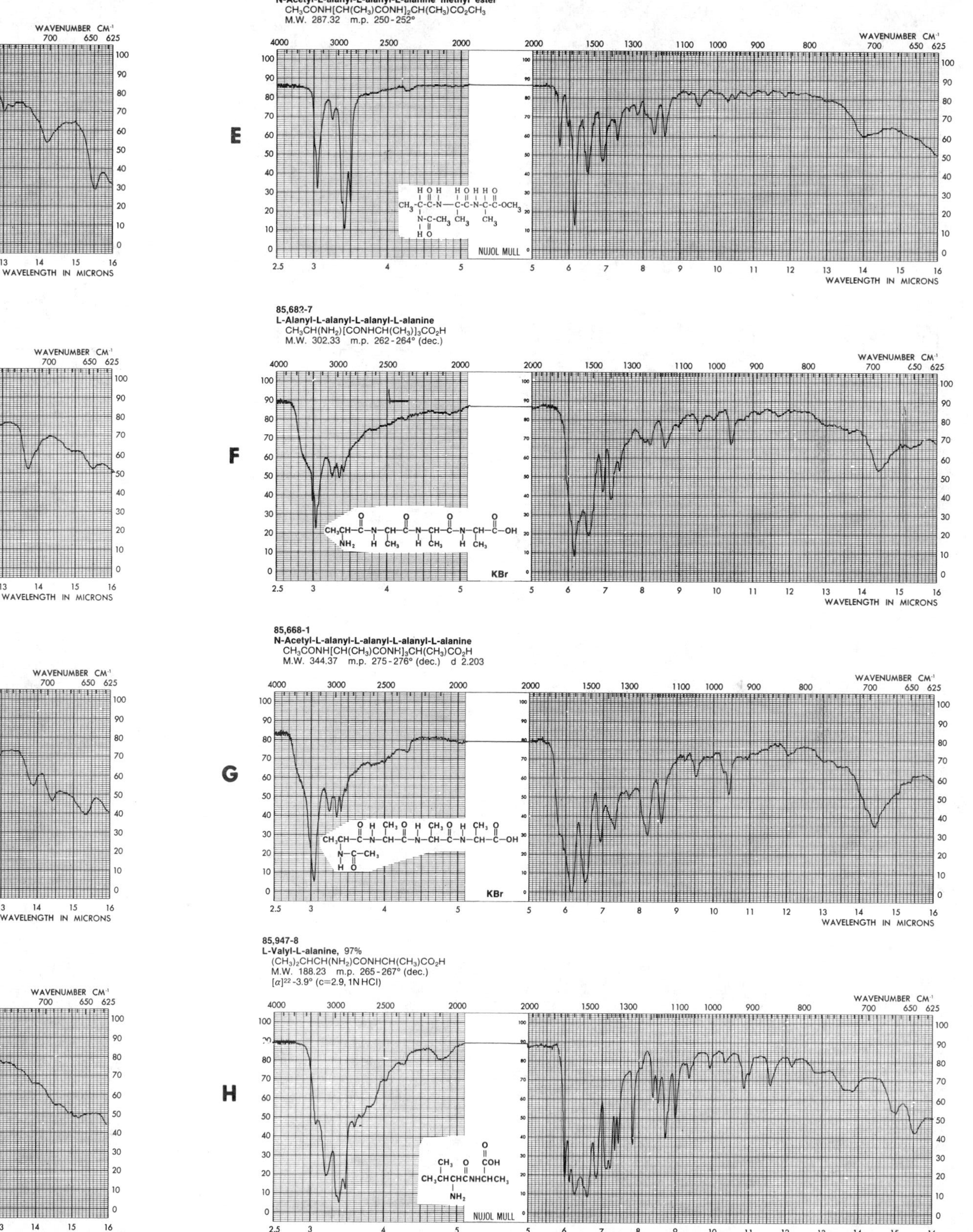

A 85,094-2
DL-Alanyl-DL-alanine
$CH_3CH[NHCOCH(NH_2)CH_3]CO_2H$
M.W. 160.17 m.p. 268-270° Beil. 4,385
NUJOL MULL

B 85,679-7
L-Alanyl-L-alanine
$CH_3CH[NHCOCH(NH_2)CH_3]CO_2H$
M.W. 160.17 m.p. 286-288° (dec.)
NUJOL MULL

C 85,681-9
L-Alanyl-L-alanyl-L-alanine
$CH_3CH(NH_2)[CONHCH(CH_3)]_2CO_2H$
M.W. 231.25 m.p. 224° (dec.)
NUJOL MULL

D 85,666-5
N-Acetyl-L-alanyl-L-alanyl-L-alanine
$CH_3CONH[CH(CH_3)CONH]_2CH(CH_3)CO_2H$
M.W. 273.29 m.p. 248° (dec.)
NUJOL MULL

E 85,667-3
N-Acetyl-L-alanyl-L-alanyl-L-alanine methyl ester
$CH_3CONH[CH(CH_3)CONH]_2CH(CH_3)CO_2CH_3$
M.W. 287.32 m.p. 250-252°
NUJOL MULL

F 85,682-7
L-Alanyl-L-alanyl-L-alanyl-L-alanine
$CH_3CH(NH_2)[CONHCH(CH_3)]_3CO_2H$
M.W. 302.33 m.p. 262-264° (dec.)
KBr

G 85,668-1
N-Acetyl-L-alanyl-L-alanyl-L-alanyl-L-alanine
$CH_3CONH[CH(CH_3)CONH]_3CH(CH_3)CO_2H$
M.W. 344.37 m.p. 275-276° (dec.) d 2.203
KBr

H 85,947-8
L-Valyl-L-alanine, 97%
$(CH_3)_2CHCH(NH_2)CONHCH(CH_3)CO_2H$
M.W. 188.23 m.p. 265-267° (dec.)
$[\alpha]^{22}$ -3.9° (c=2.9, 1N HCl)
NUJOL MULL

WAVENUMBER CM⁻¹ / WAVELENGTH IN MICRONS

ALDRICH

NON-AROMATIC AMIDES

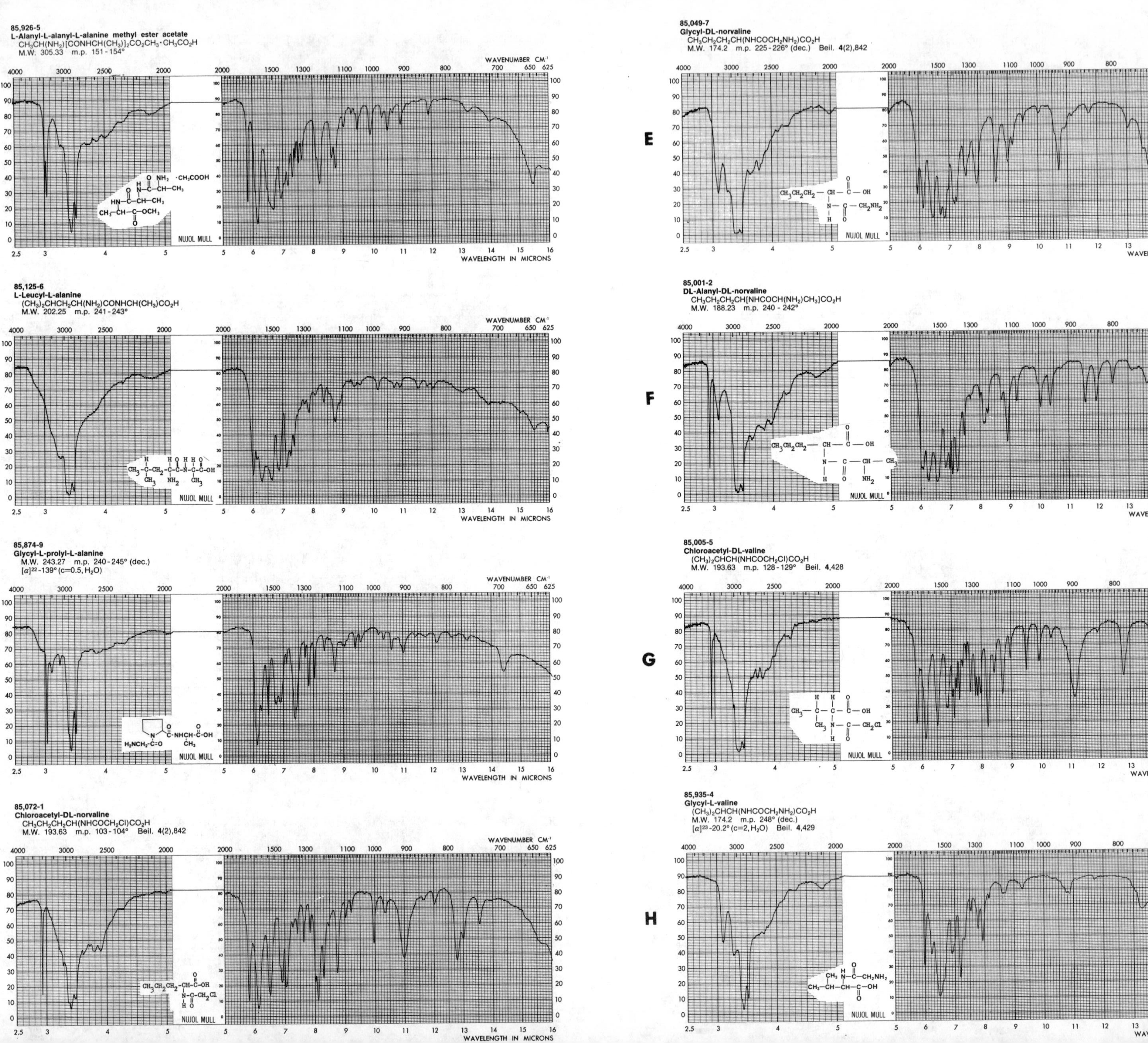

A 85,926-5
L-Alanyl-L-alanyl-L-alanine methyl ester acetate
$CH_3CH(NH_2)[CONHCH(CH_3)]_2CO_2CH_3 \cdot CH_3CO_2H$
M.W. 305.33 m.p. 151-154°

B 85,125-6
L-Leucyl-L-alanine
$(CH_3)_2CHCH_2CH(NH_2)CONHCH(CH_3)CO_2H$
M.W. 202.25 m.p. 241-243°

C 85,874-9
Glycyl-L-prolyl-L-alanine
M.W. 243.27 m.p. 240-245° (dec.)
$[\alpha]^{22}$ -139° (c=0.5, H_2O)

D 85,072-1
Chloroacetyl-DL-norvaline
$CH_3CH_2CH_2CH(NHCOCH_2Cl)CO_2H$
M.W. 193.63 m.p. 103-104° Beil. 4(2),842

E 85,049-7
Glycyl-DL-norvaline
$CH_3CH_2CH_2CH(NHCOCH_2NH_2)CO_2H$
M.W. 174.2 m.p. 225-226° (dec.) Beil. 4(2),842

F 85,001-2
DL-Alanyl-DL-norvaline
$CH_3CH_2CH_2CH[NHCOCH(NH_2)CH_3]CO_2H$
M.W. 188.23 m.p. 240-242°

G 85,005-5
Chloroacetyl-DL-valine
$(CH_3)_2CHCH(NHCOCH_2Cl)CO_2H$
M.W. 193.63 m.p. 128-129° Beil. 4,428

H 85,935-4
Glycyl-L-valine
$(CH_3)_2CHCH(NHCOCH_2NH_2)CO_2H$
M.W. 174.2 m.p. 248° (dec.)
$[\alpha]^{23}$ -20.2° (c=2, H_2O) Beil. 4,429

A

85,706-8
L-Alanyl-L-valine
$(CH_3)_2CHCH[NHCOCH(NH_2)CH_3]CO_2H$
M.W. 188.23 m.p. 258-260°

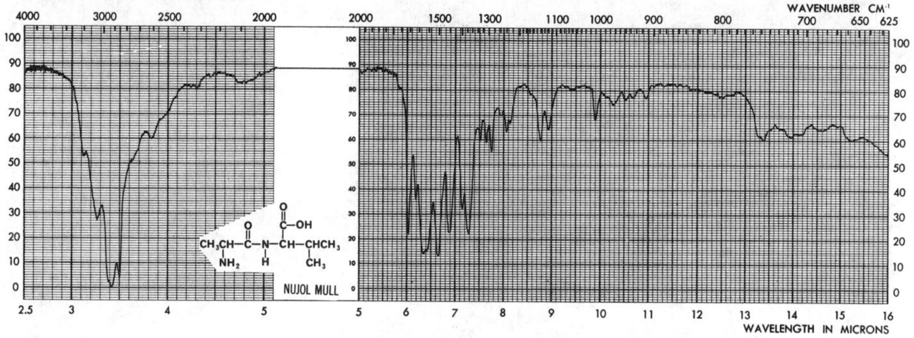

B

85,949-4
L-Valyl-L-valine
$(CH_3)_2CHCH(NH_2)CONHCH[CH(CH_3)_2]CO_2H$
M.W. 216.28 m.p. 250° (dec.) Beil. 4,429

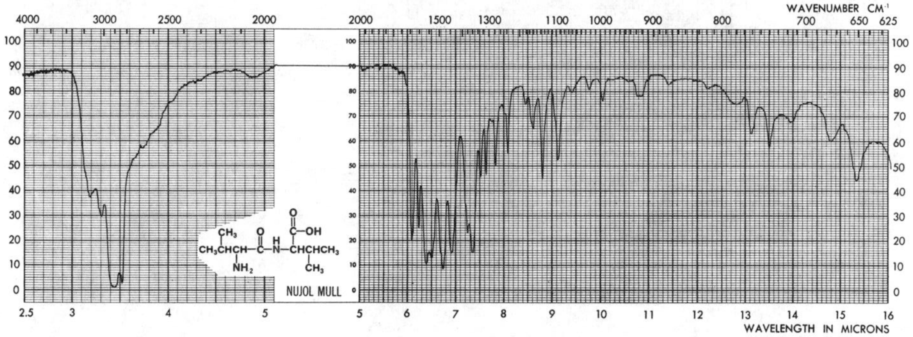

C

85,693-2
L-Alanyl-L-isoleucine
$C_2H_5CH(CH_3)CH[NHCOCH(NH_2)CH_3]CO_2H$
M.W. 202.25 m.p. 230-232° (dec.)

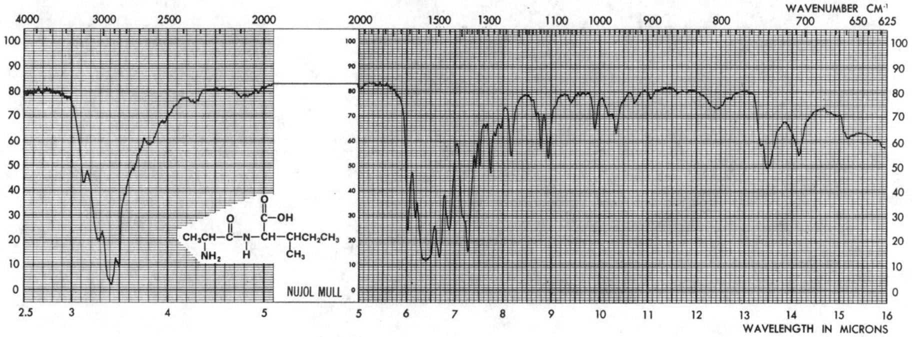

D

85,823-4
N-Acetyl-DL-leucine, 98%
$(CH_3)_2CHCH_2CH(NHCOCH_3)CO_2H$
M.W. 173.21 m.p. 158-160° Beil. 4,451

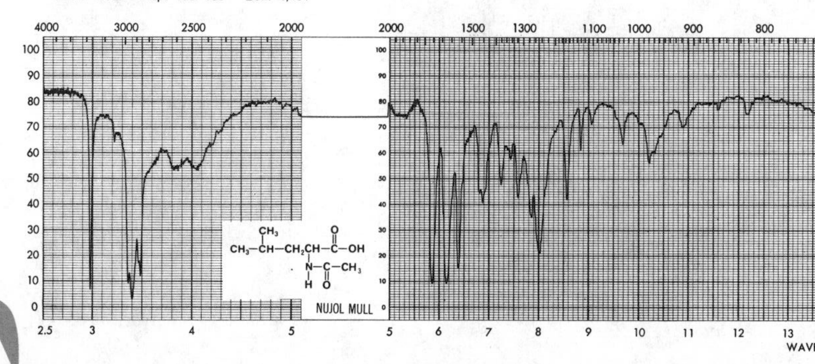

E

85,067-5
Glycyl-DL-leucine
$(CH_3)_2CHCH_2CH(NHCOCH_2NH_2)CO_2H$
M.W. 188.23 m.p. 238-239° (dec.) Beil. 4,453

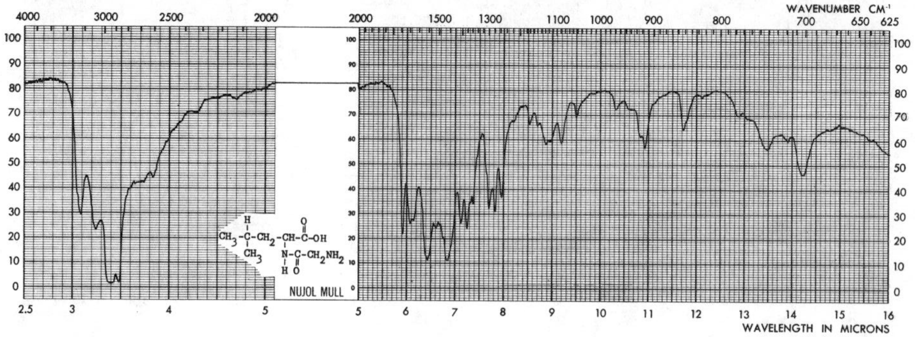

F

85,007-1
Glycyl-L-leucine
$(CH_3)_2CHCH_2CH(NHCOCH_2NH_2)CO_2H$
M.W. 188.23 m.p. 233-235°
$[\alpha]^{22}$ -34.5° (c=2, H_2O) Beil. 4,453

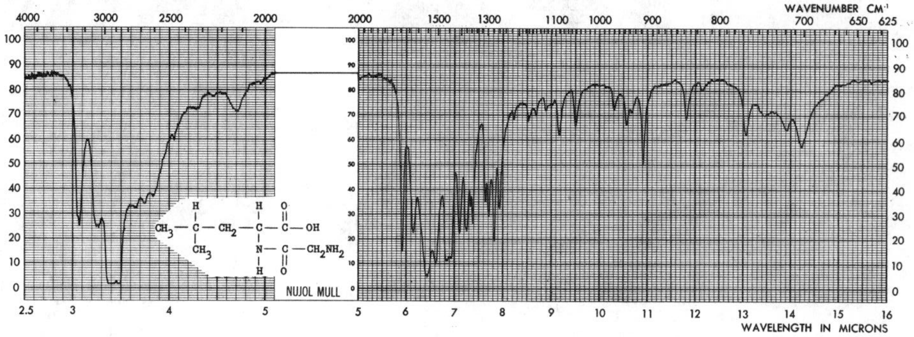

G

85,694-0
DL-Alanyl-DL-leucine
$(CH_3)_2CHCH_2CH[NHCOCH(NH_2)CH_3]CO_2H$
M.W. 202.25 m.p. 226-228° Beil. 4,453

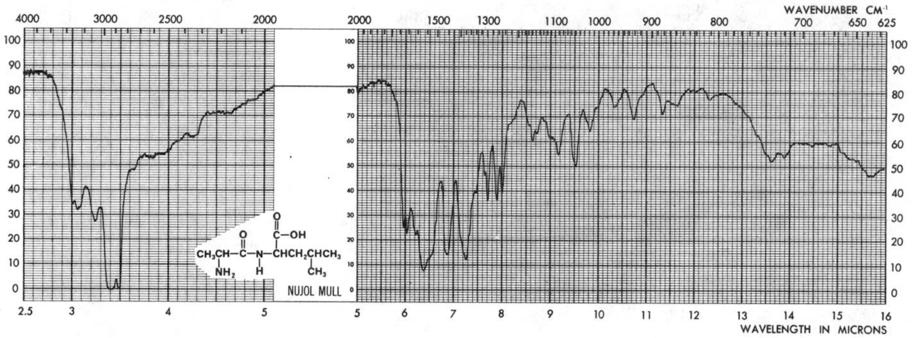

H

85,695-9
L-Alanyl-L-leucine
$(CH_3)_2CHCH_2CH[NHCOCH(NH_2)CH_3]CO_2H$
M.W. 202.25 m.p. 248-250°

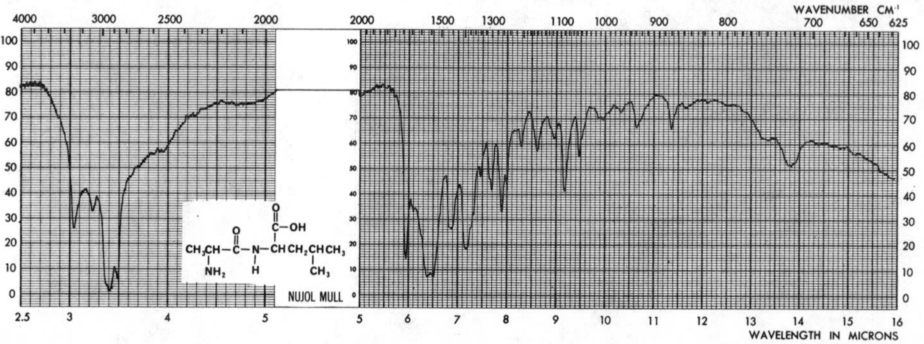

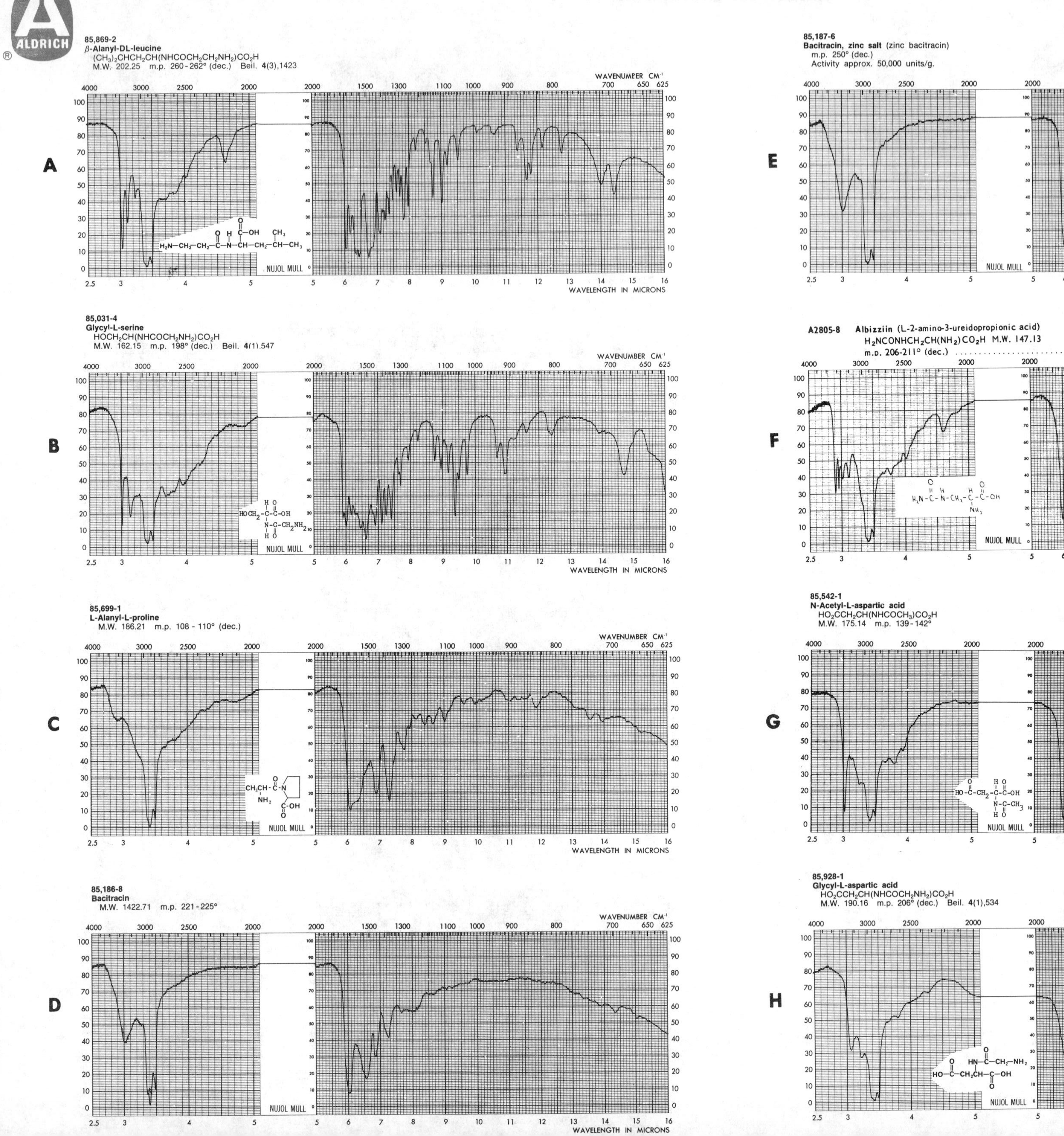

A 85,869-2
β-Alanyl-DL-leucine
$(CH_3)_2CHCH_2CH(NHCOCH_2CH_2NH_2)CO_2H$
M.W. 202.25 m.p. 260-262° (dec.) Beil. **4**(3),1423

B 85,031-4
Glycyl-L-serine
$HOCH_2CH(NHCOCH_2NH_2)CO_2H$
M.W. 162.15 m.p. 198° (dec.) Beil. **4**(1),547

C 85,699-1
L-Alanyl-L-proline
M.W. 186.21 m.p. 108 - 110° (dec.)

D 85,186-8
Bacitracin
M.W. 1422.71 m.p. 221-225°

E 85,187-6
Bacitracin, zinc salt (zinc bacitracin)
m.p. 250° (dec.)
Activity approx. 50,000 units/g.

F A2805-8 Albizziin (L-2-amino-3-ureidopropionic acid)
$H_2NCONHCH_2CH(NH_2)CO_2H$ M.W. 147.13
m.p. 206-211° (dec.)

G 85,542-1
N-Acetyl-L-aspartic acid
$HO_2CCH_2CH(NHCOCH_3)CO_2H$
M.W. 175.14 m.p. 139-142°

H 85,928-1
Glycyl-L-aspartic acid
$HO_2CCH_2CH(NHCOCH_2NH_2)CO_2H$
M.W. 190.16 m.p. 206° (dec.) Beil. **4**(1),534

85,700-9
L-Alanyl-L-serine
$HOCH_2CH[NHCOCH(NH_2)CH_3]CO_2H$
M.W. 176.17 m.p. 221° (dec.)

85,564-2
N-Acetyl-L-glutamic acid
$HO_2CCH_2CH_2CH(NHCOCH_3)CO_2H$
M.W. 189.17 m.p. 199-201° Beil. 4(2),908

85,683-5
L-Alanyl-L-aspartic acid
$HO_2CCH_2CH[NHCOCH(NH_2)CH_3]CO_2H$
M.W. 204.18 m.p. 212-214° (dec.)

85,707-6
L-Arginyl-L-aspartic acid
$HO_2CCH_2CH[NHCOCH(NH_2)(CH_2)_3NH$-
$C(=NH)NH_2]CO_2H$
M.W. 289.29 m.p. 181-183° (dec.)

15,357-5 DL-Asparagine (DL-2-aminosuccinamic acid) **monohydrate**
$H_2NCOCH_2CH(NH_2)CO_2H \cdot H_2O$
M.W. 150.14

21,911-8
D-Asparagine monohydrate, 99% (D-2-amino-succinamic acid)
$H_2NCOCH_2CH(NH_2)CO_2H \cdot H_2O$ FW 150.14
mp 275° (dec.) $[\alpha]^{25}$ -31° (c=2.2, 3.4*N* HCl)
Beil. 4,471 Disp. L

A9300-3 L-Asparagine (L-2-aminosuccinamic acid) **anhydrous**
$H_2NCOCH_2CH(NH_2)CO_2H$ M.W. 132.12
m.p. 236° (dec.)

17,653-2
L-(+)-Asparagine monohydrate, 99% (L-2-amino-succinamic acid)
$H_2NCOCH_2CH(NH_2)CO_2H \cdot H_2O$ FW 150.14
mp 233-235° $[\alpha]_D^{20}$ +31° (c=10, 3*N* HCl)
NMR 3,10A Disp. L

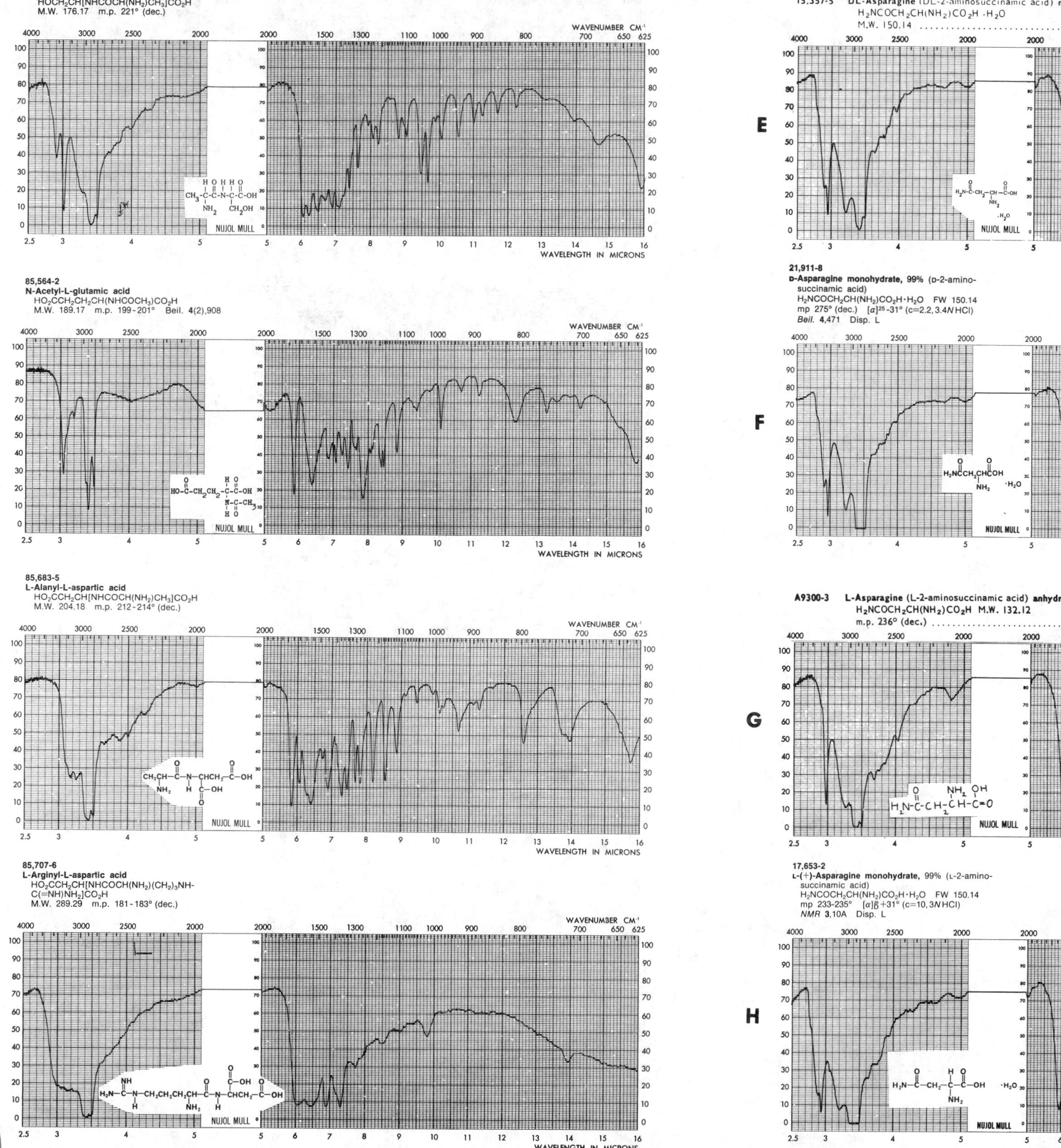

A

85,029-2
Glycyl-DL-asparagine
$H_2NCOCH_2CH(NHCOCH_2NH_2)CO_2H$
M.W. 189.17 m.p. 207° (dec.) Beil. 4,482

NUJOL MULL

B

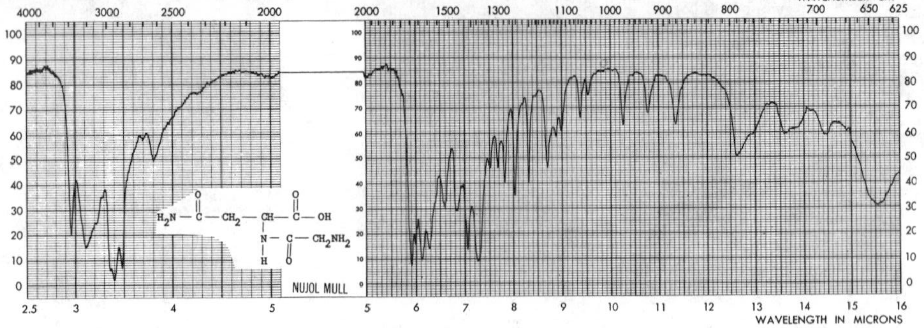

85,854-4
D-(-)-Glutamine, 99%
$H_2NCOCH_2CH_2CH(NH_2)CO_2H$
M.W. 146.15 m.p. 184-186° (dec.)
$[\alpha]^{23}$ -6.5° (c=4, H_2O) Beil. 4,491

NUJOL MULL

C

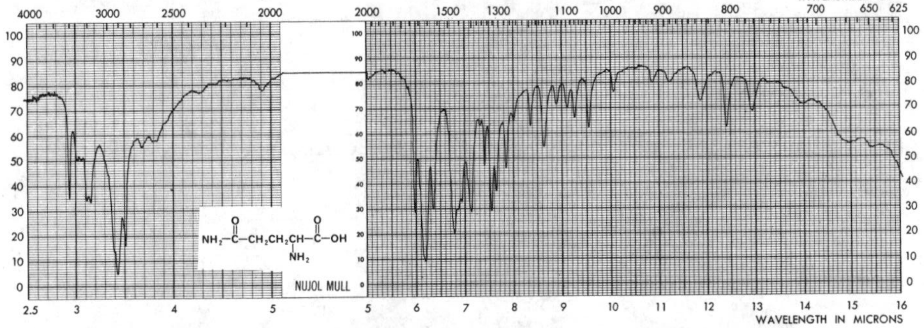

85,701-7
L-Alanyl-L-threonine
$CH_3CH(OH)CH[NHCOCH(NH_2)CH_3]CO_2H$
M.W. 190.2 m.p. 223° (dec.)

NUJOL MULL

D

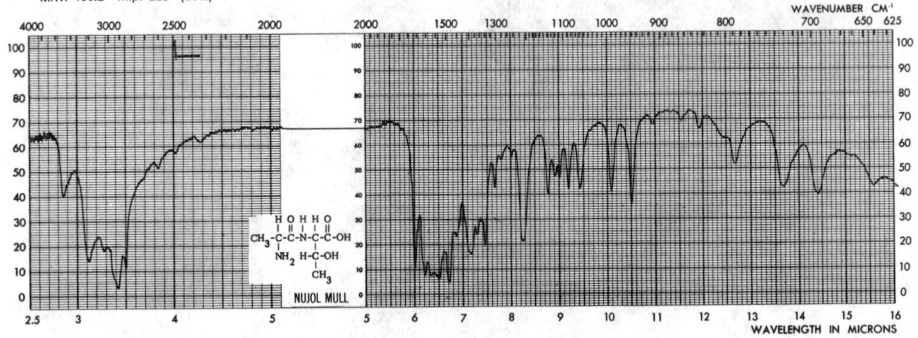

G320-2 **L-(+)-Glutamine**
$H_2NCOCH_2CH_2CH(NH_2)CO_2H$ M.W. 146.15 m.p. 180° (dec.)
$[\alpha]^{23}_D$ + 6.5° (in H_2O)

NUJOL MULL

E

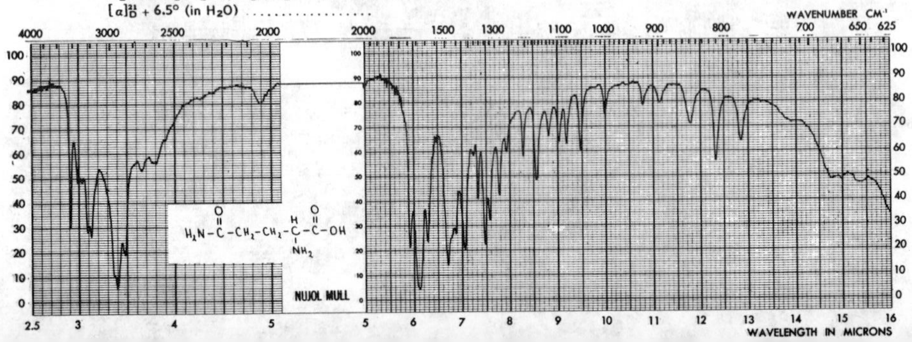

85,539-1
N-Acetyl-L-glutamine, 99%
$H_2NCOCH_2CH_2CH(NHCOCH_3)CO_2H$
M.W. 188.18 m.p. 201-203°

NUJOL MULL

F

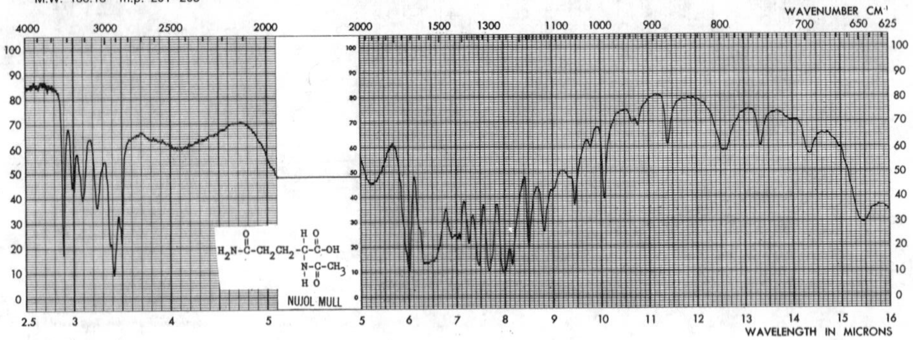

85,670-3
Nα-Acetyl-L-lysine
$H_2N(CH_2)_4CH(NHCOCH_3)CO_2H$
M.W. 188.23 m.p. 256-258° (dec.)

NUJOL MULL

G

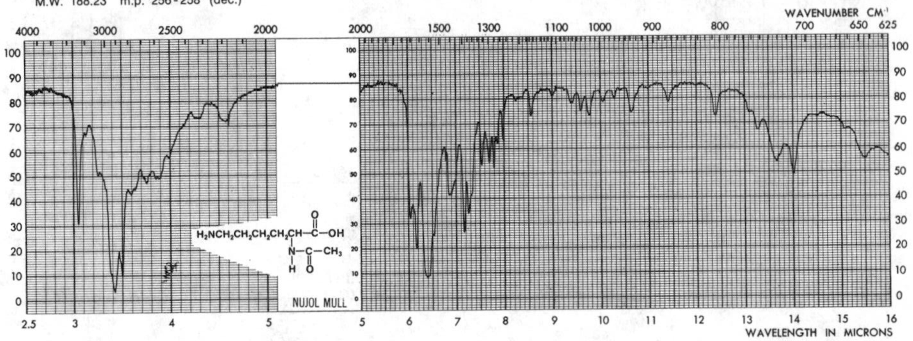

85,925-7
Nα-Acetyl-L-lysine-N-methylamide monohydrate
$H_2N(CH_2)_4CH(NHCOCH_3)CONHCH_3 \cdot H_2O$
M.W. 219.29 m.p. 174-176°

NUJOL MULL

H

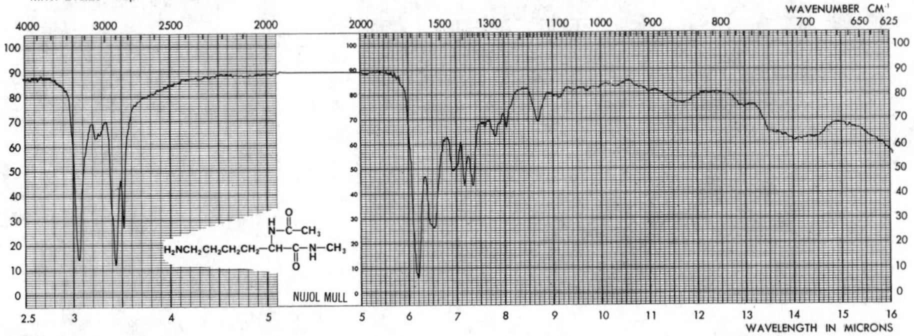

11,579-7 **Nε-Acetyl-L-lysine**
$CH_3CONH(CH_2)_4CH(NH_2)CO_2H$ M.W. 188.23
m.p. 243-245° (dec.) $[\alpha]^{23}_D$ + 22.5°
(c=2 in 5N HCl)

NUJOL MULL

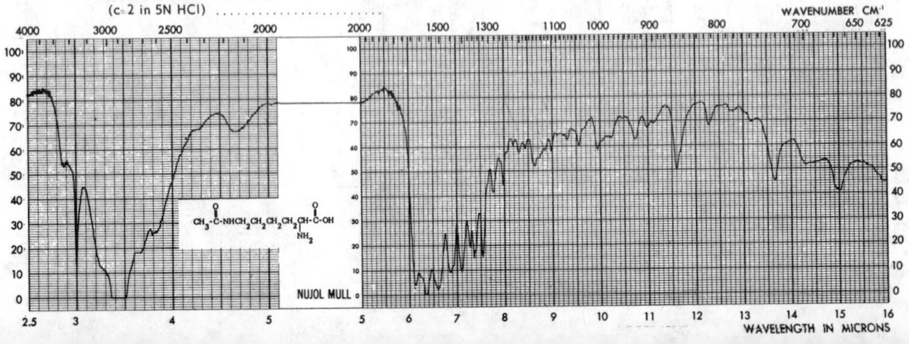

A

85,671-1
Nα-Acetyl-L-ornithine
$H_2N(CH_2)_3CH(NHCOCH_3)CO_2H$
M.W. 174.2 m.p. 213-215° (dec.)

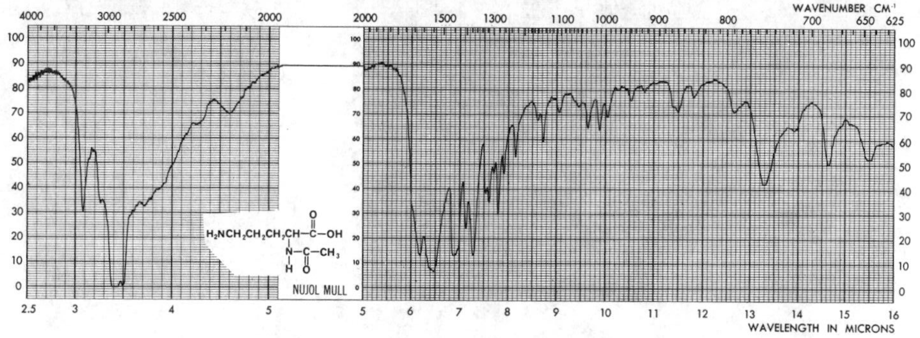

NUJOL MULL

B

85,572-3
DL-Citrulline, 97% (DL-2-amino-5-ureidovaleric acid)
$H_2NCONH(CH_2)_3CH(NH_2)CO_2H$
M.W. 175.19

NUJOL MULL

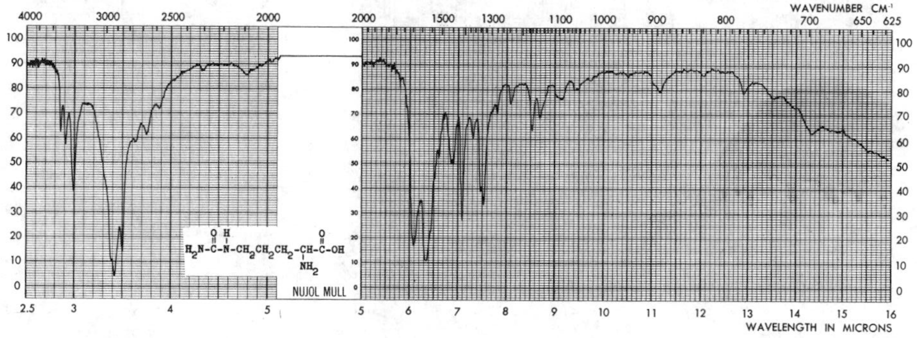

C

85,909-5
Nα-Acetyl-L-lysine methyl ester hydrochloride
$H_2N(CH_2)_4CH(NHCOCH_3)CO_2CH_3 \cdot HCl$
M.W. 238.72 m.p. 108-114°
$[\alpha]^{22}$ -18° (c=10, 6N HCl)

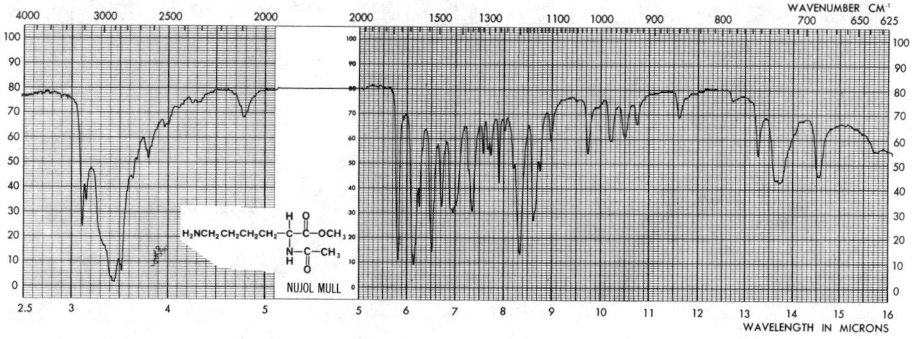

NUJOL MULL

D

C8370-8 L-(+)-Citrulline [L-(+)-2-amino-5-ureidovaleric acid]
$H_2NCONH(CH_2)_3CH(NH_2)CO_2H$ M.W. 175.19
m.p. 220° (dec.) $[\alpha]^{20}_{D}$ + 3.7° (c=2 in H_2O)

NUJOL MULL

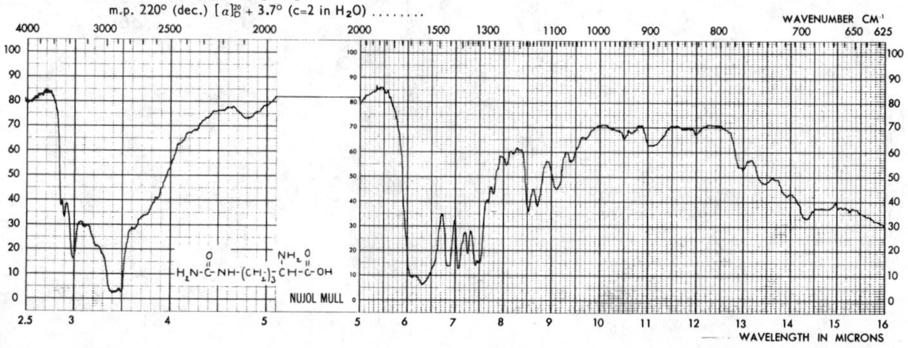

E

A290-4 4-Acetamidobutyric acid, puriss.
$CH_3CONH(CH_2)_3CO_2H$ M.W. 145.16
m.p. 130-130.5°

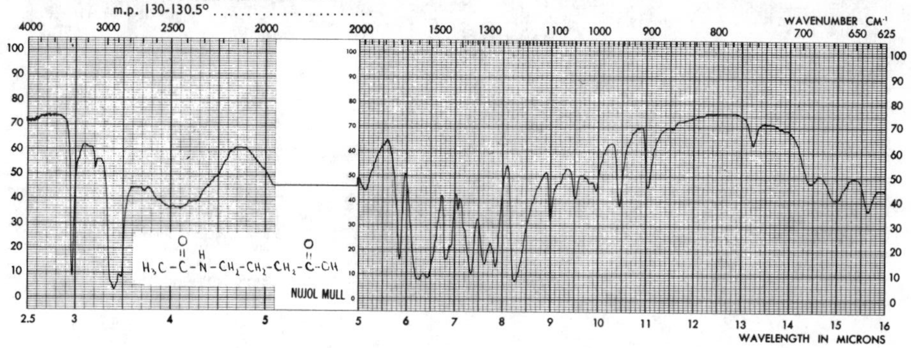

NUJOL MULL

F

M888 L-Methionylglycine
$CH_3S(CH_2)_2CH(NH_2)CONHCH_2CO_2H$ M.W. 206.26
m.p. 182-185°

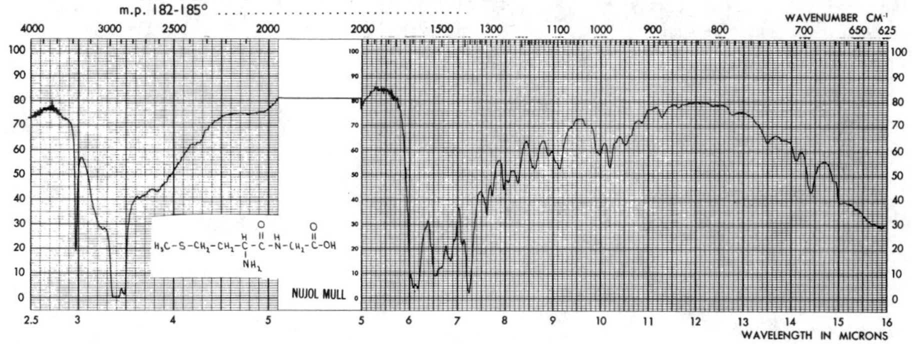

NUJOL MULL

G

85,534-0
N-Acetyl-L-methionine, 98+%
$CH_3SCH_2CH_2CH(NHCOCH_3)CO_2H$
M.W. 191.25 m.p. 104-107°

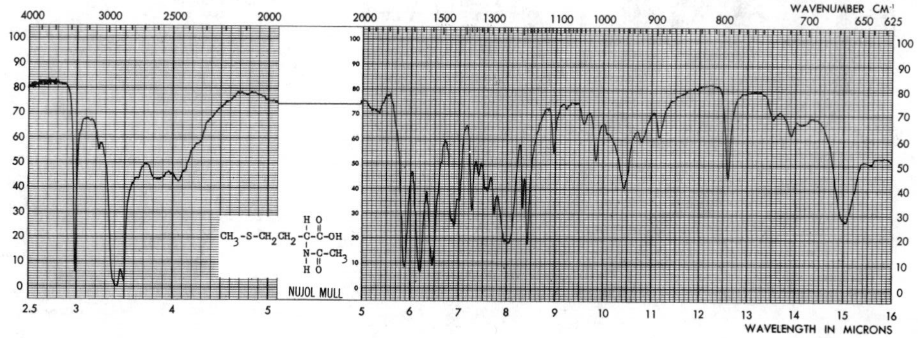

NUJOL MULL

H

G890-5 Glycyl-DL-methionine
$CH_3SCH_2CH_2CH(NHCOCH_2NH_2)CO_2H$ M.W. 206.26
m.p. 215° (dec.)

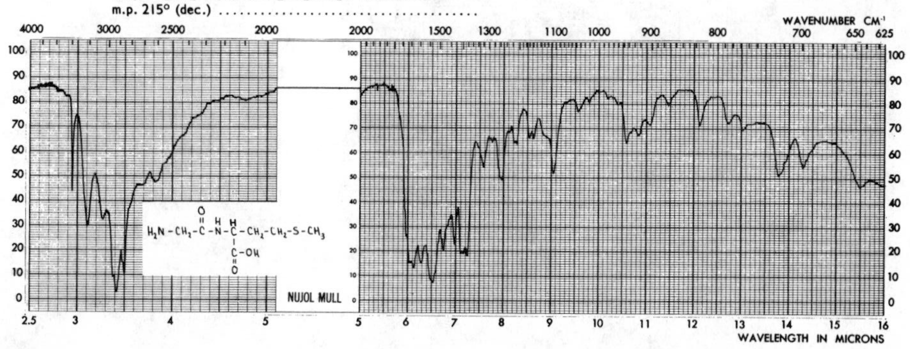

NUJOL MULL

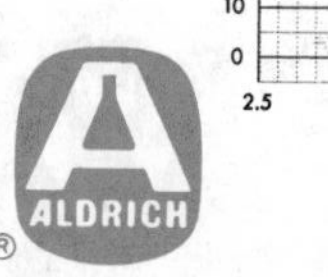

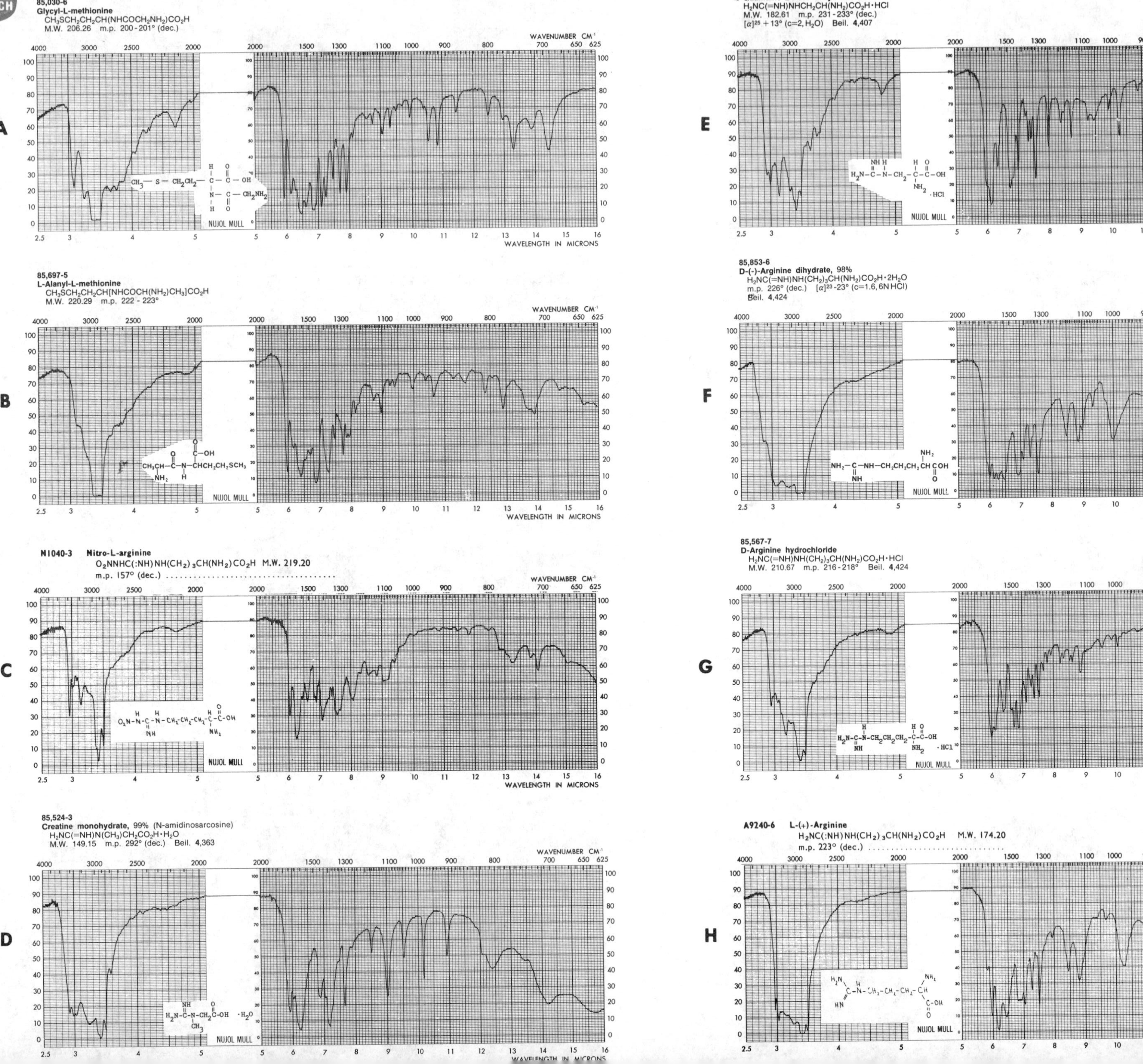
ALDRICH
A
85,030-6
Glycyl-L-methionine
$CH_3SCH_2CH_2CH(NHCOCH_2NH_2)CO_2H$
M.W. 206.26 m.p. 200-201° (dec.)
B
85,697-5
L-Alanyl-L-methionine
$CH_3SCH_2CH_2CH[NHCOCH(NH_2)CH_3]CO_2H$
M.W. 220.29 m.p. 222-223°
C
N1040-3 Nitro-L-arginine
$O_2NNHC(:NH)NH(CH_2)_3CH(NH_2)CO_2H$ M.W. 219.20
m.p. 157° (dec.)
D
85,524-3
Creatine monohydrate, 99% (N-amidinosarcosine)
$H_2NC(=NH)N(CH_3)CH_2CO_2H \cdot H_2O$
M.W. 149.15 m.p. 292° (dec.) Beil. 4,363
E
15,700-7
3-Guanidino-L-alanine hydrochloride
$H_2NC(=NH)NHCH_2CH(NH_2)CO_2H \cdot HCl$
M.W. 182.61 m.p. 231-233° (dec.)
$[\alpha]^{25}$ + 13° (c=2, H_2O) Beil. 4,407
F
85,853-6
D-(-)-Arginine dihydrate, 98%
$H_2NC(=NH)NH(CH_2)_3CH(NH_2)CO_2H \cdot 2H_2O$
m.p. 226° (dec.) $[\alpha]^{23}$ -23° (c=1.6, 6N HCl)
Beil. 4,424
G
85,567-7
D-Arginine hydrochloride
$H_2NC(=NH)NH(CH_2)_3CH(NH_2)CO_2H \cdot HCl$
M.W. 210.67 m.p. 216-218° Beil. 4,424
H
A9240-6 L-(+)-Arginine
$H_2NC(:NH)NH(CH_2)_3CH(NH_2)CO_2H$ M.W. 174.20
m.p. 223° (dec.)
NUJOL MULL
WAVENUMBER CM⁻¹
WAVELENGTH IN MICRONS

A

13,846-0 **DL-Arginine monohydrochloride**
$H_2NC(:NH)NH(CH_2)_3CH(NH_2)CO_2H \cdot HCl$ M.W. 210.67
m.p. 220-223° (dec.)

NUJOL MULL

B

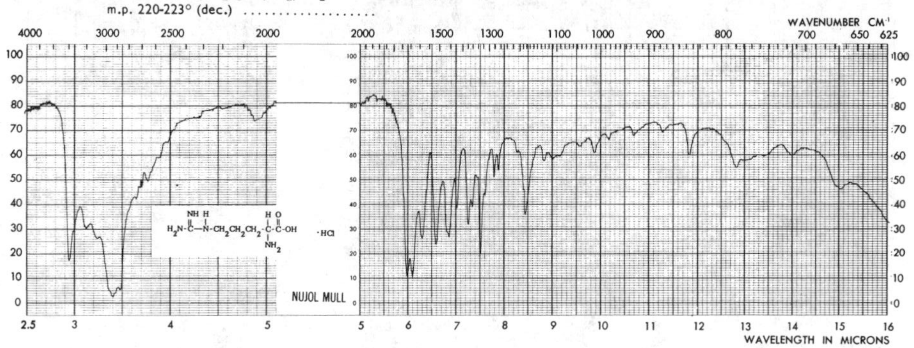

A9260-0 **L-Arginine hydrochloride**
$H_2NC(:NH)NH(CH_2)_3CH(NH_2)CO_2H \cdot HCl$ M.W. 210.67
m.p. 226°

NUJOL MULL

C

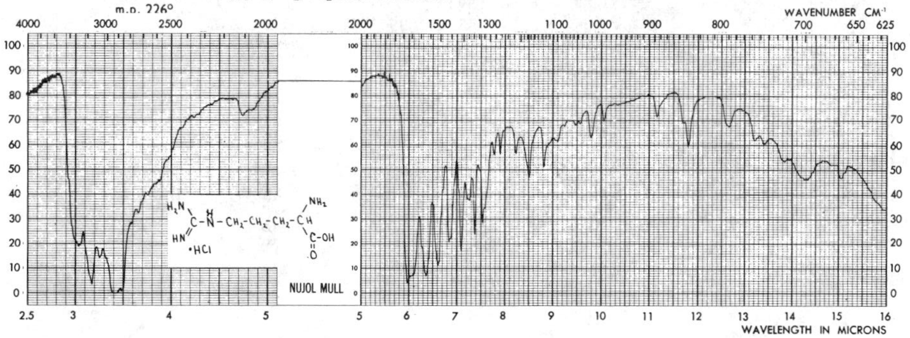

15,711-2
L-(+)-Homoarginine hydrochloride, 99+%,
GOLD LABEL
$H_2NC(=NH)NH(CH_2)_4CH(NH_2)CO_2H \cdot HCl$
M.W. 224.69 m.p. 213-215°
$[\alpha]^{26}$ +21° (c=1, 1N HCl)

NUJOL MULL

D

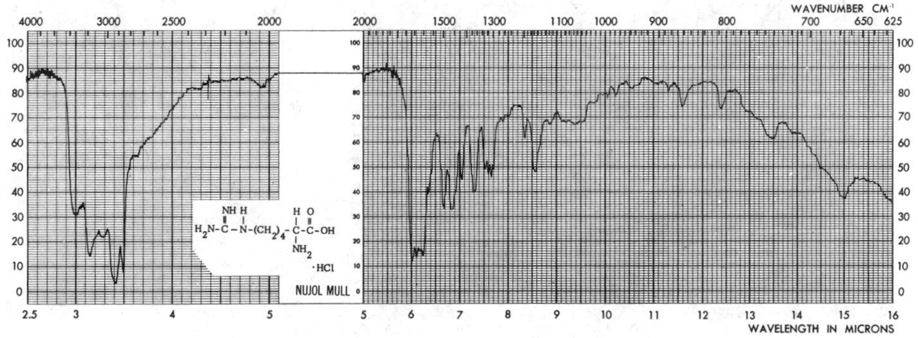

13,806-1 **N-Acetyl-L-cysteine**
$HSCH_2CH(NHCOCH_3)CO_2H$ M.W. 163.20
m.p. 109-111°

NUJOL MULL

E

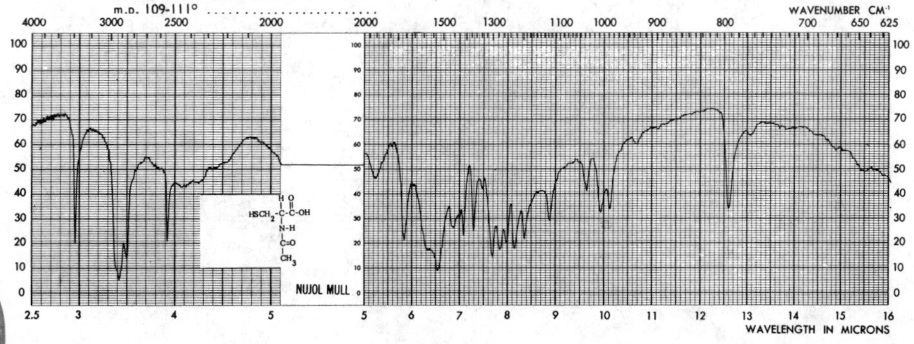

85,907-9
S-(Ethylcarbamoyl)-L-cysteine, 99%
$C_2H_5NHCOSCH_2CH(NH_2)CO_2H$
M.W. 192.24 m.p. 183-185° (dec.)
$[\alpha]^{20}_{D}$ -87° (c=0.8, CH_3CO_2H)

NUJOL MULL

F

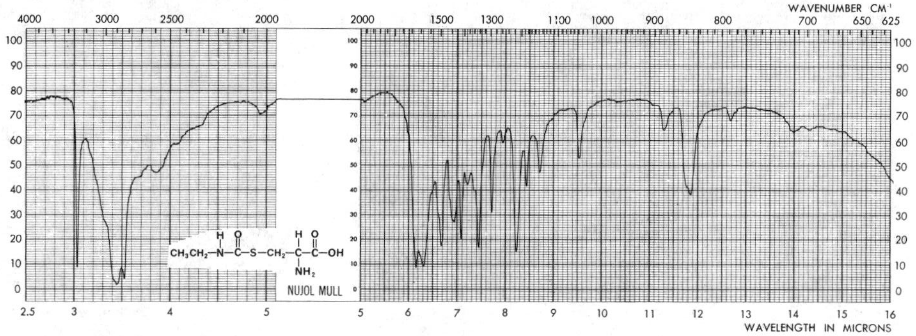

A1900-8 **N-Acetyl-DL-penicillamine**
$(CH_3)_2C(SH)CH(NHCOCH_3)CO_2H$ M.W. 191.25
m.p. 176-178° (dec.)

NUJOL MULL

G

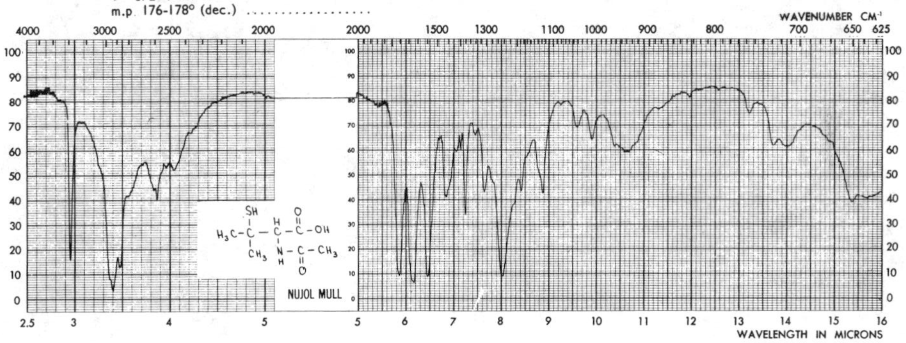

A1780 **DL-N-Acetyl-β-mercaptoisoleucine**
$C_2H_5C(SH)(CH_3)CH(NHCOCH_3)CO_2H$ M.W. 205.28
m.p. 154.5-156°

NUJOL MULL

H

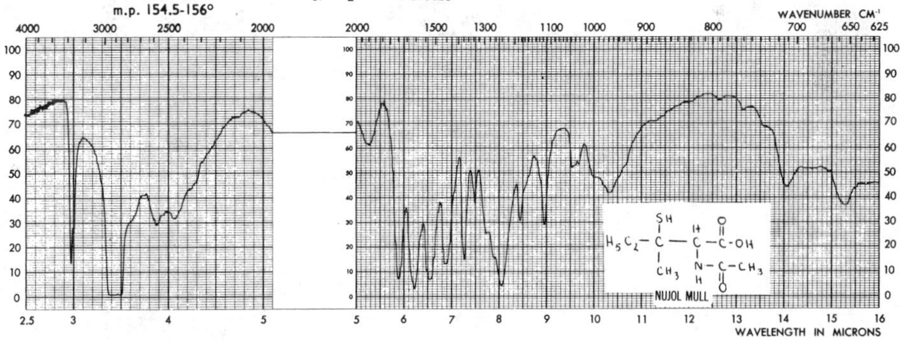

11,578-9 **S-Carbamyl-L-cysteine hydrate**
$H_2NCOSCH_2CH(NH_2)CO_2H \cdot H_2O$ M.W. 182.20
m.p. 148-150° (dec.)

NUJOL MULL

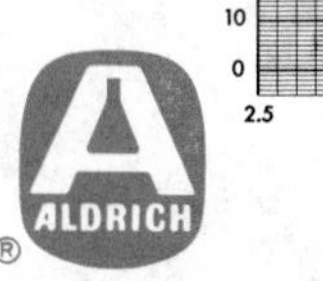

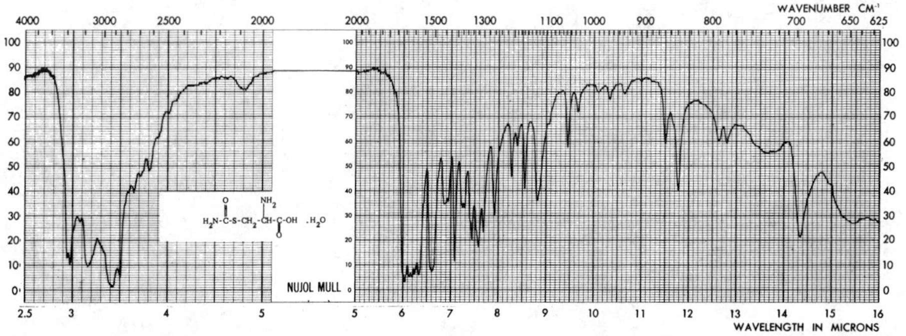

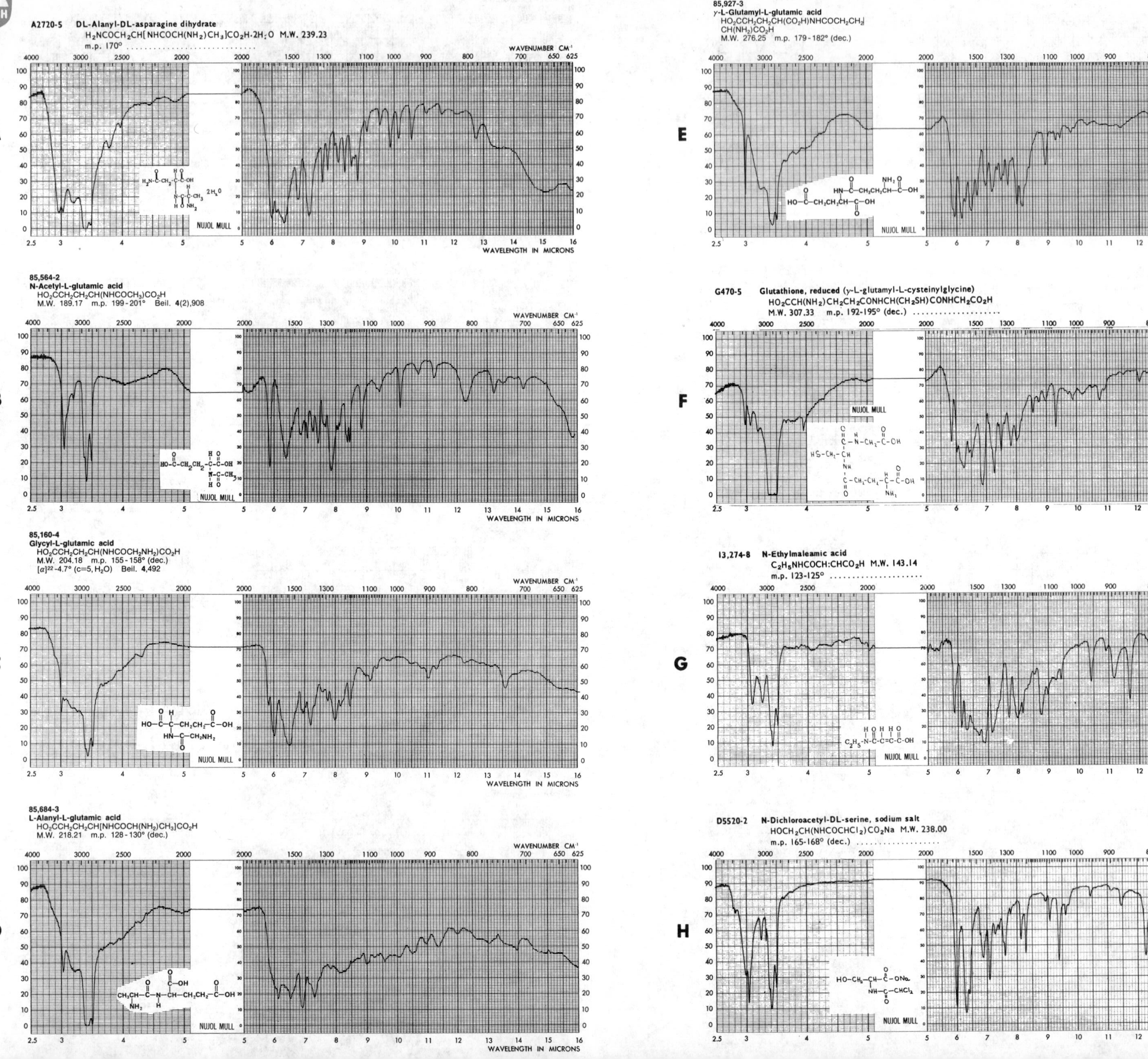

ALDRICH
A
A2720-5 DL-Alanyl-DL-asparagine dihydrate
$H_2NCOCH_2CH[NHCOCH(NH_2)CH_3]CO_2H \cdot 2H_2O$ M.W. 239.23
m.p. 170°
B
85,564-2
N-Acetyl-L-glutamic acid
$HO_2CCH_2CH_2CH(NHCOCH_3)CO_2H$
M.W. 189.17 m.p. 199-201° Beil. 4(2),908
C
85,160-4
Glycyl-L-glutamic acid
$HO_2CCH_2CH_2CH(NHCOCH_2NH_2)CO_2H$
M.W. 204.18 m.p. 155-158° (dec.)
$[\alpha]^{22}$ -4.7° (c=5, H_2O) Beil. 4,492
D
85,684-3
L-Alanyl-L-glutamic acid
$HO_2CCH_2CH_2CH[NHCOCH(NH_2)CH_3]CO_2H$
M.W. 218.21 m.p. 128-130° (dec.)
E
85,927-3
γ-L-Glutamyl-L-glutamic acid
$HO_2CCH_2CH_2CH(CO_2H)NHCOCH_2CH_2CH(NH_2)CO_2H$
M.W. 276.25 m.p. 179-182° (dec.)
F
G470-5 Glutathione, reduced (γ-L-glutamyl-L-cysteinylglycine)
$HO_2CCH(NH_2)CH_2CH_2CONHCH(CH_2SH)CONHCH_2CO_2H$
M.W. 307.33 m.p. 192-195° (dec.)
G
13,274-8 N-Ethylmaleamic acid
$C_2H_5NHCOCH{:}CHCO_2H$ M.W. 143.14
m.p. 123-125°
H
D5520-2 N-Dichloroacetyl-DL-serine, sodium salt
$HOCH_2CH(NHCOCHCl_2)CO_2Na$ M.W. 238.00
m.p. 165-168° (dec.)
NUJOL MULL
WAVENUMBER CM⁻¹
WAVELENGTH IN MICRONS

A

E940-4 **Ethyl acetamidoacetate**
$CH_3CONHCH_2CO_2C_2H_5$ M.W. 145.16
m.p. 43-46° ....

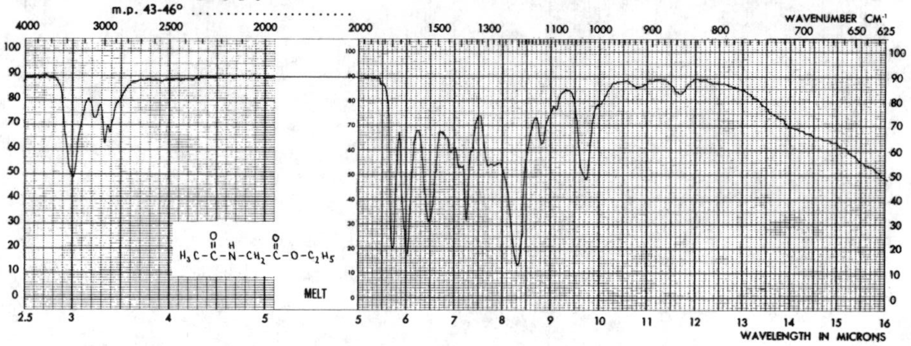

MELT

B

D9560-3 **Diethyl formamidomalonate**
$C_2H_5O_2CCH(NHCHO)CO_2C_2H_5$ M.W. 203.19 m.p. 51-54°

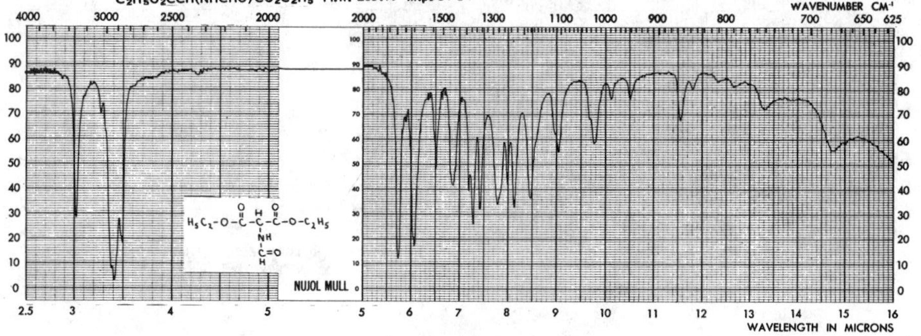

NUJOL MULL

C

D8460-1 **Diethyl acetamidomalonate**
$C_2H_5O_2CCH(NHCOCH_3)CO_2C_2H_5$ M.W. 217.22
m.p. 96.5-98° ....

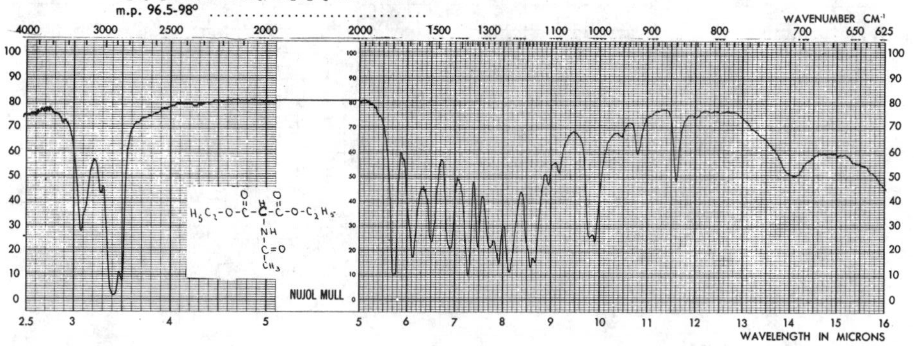

NUJOL MULL

D

P7437-0 **2-Pyrrolidinone (2-pyrrolidone)**
M.W. 85.11 m.p. 23-25° ....

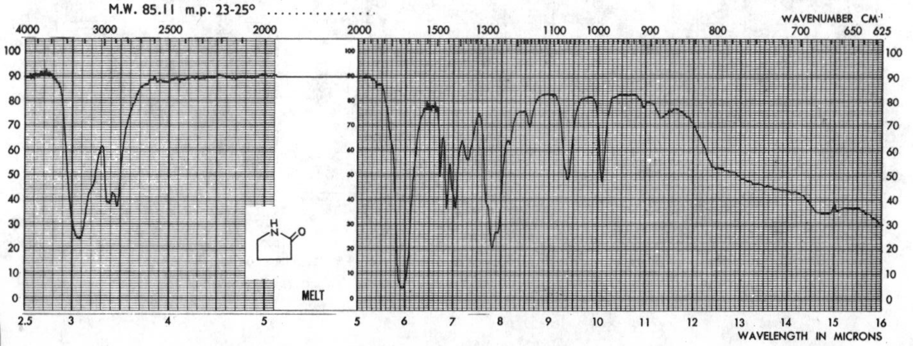

MELT

E

M7970-0 **5-Methyl-2-pyrrolidinone**
M.W. 99.13 m.p. 41-43°

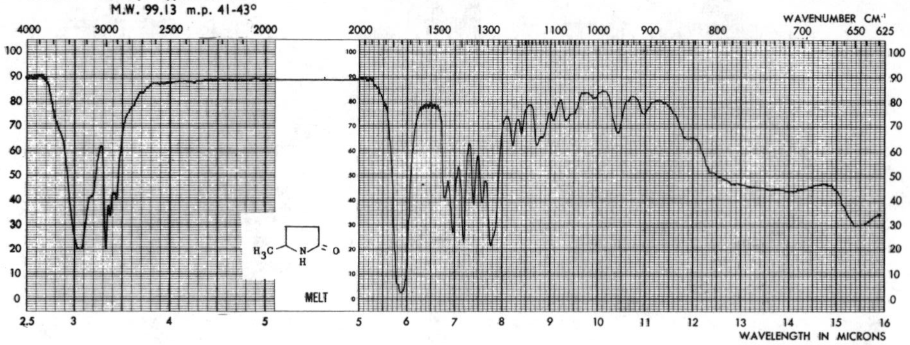

MELT

F

M7960-3 **1-Methyl-2-pyrrolidinone**
M.W. 99.13 n_D^{20} 1.4684 b.p. 202°

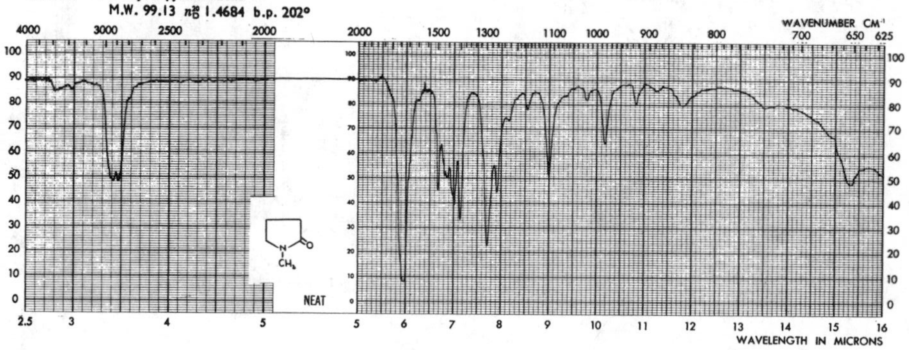

NEAT

G

D18,410-1 **1,5-Dimethyl-2-pyrrolidinone**
M.W. 113.16 n_D^{20} 1.4650 ...

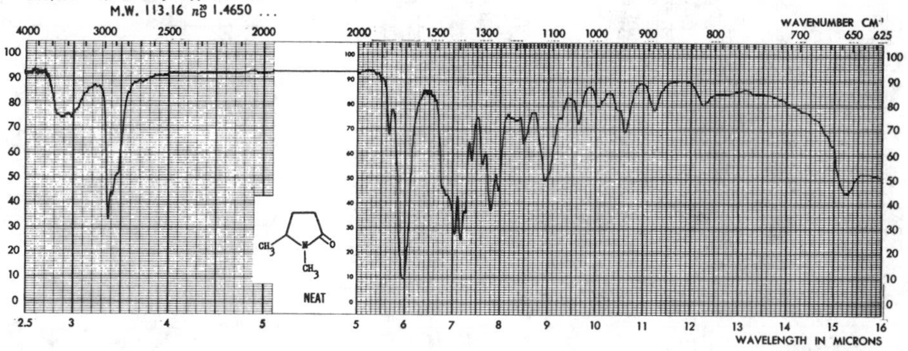

NEAT

H

14,635-8 **1-Ethyl-2-pyrrolidinone**
M.W. 113.16 n_D^{20} 1.4652 b.p. 97°/20 mm.

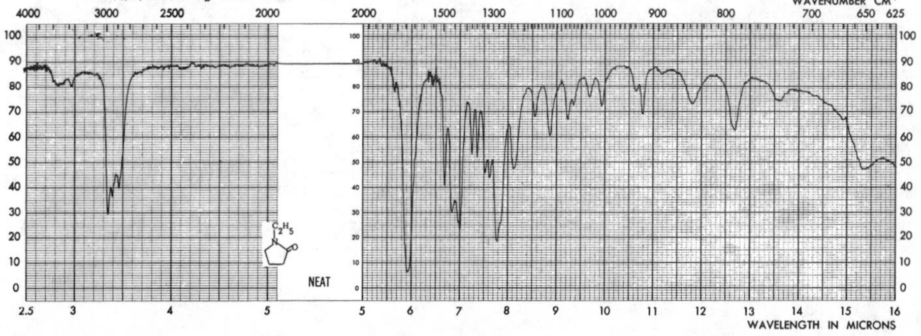

NEAT

A

14,636-6 **1-Butyl-2-pyrrolidinone**
M.W. 141.21 n_D^{20} 1.4640 b.p. 121°/16 mm.

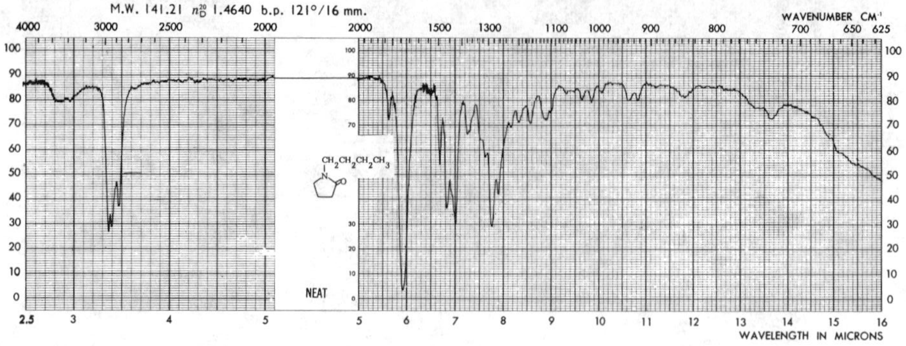

NEAT

B

V340-9 **N-Vinyl-2-pyrrolidinone**
M.W. 111.14 n_D^{20} 1.5133

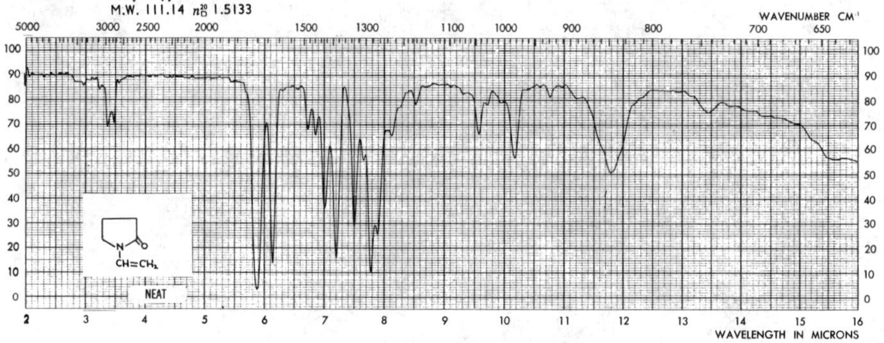

NEAT

C

13,656-5 **N-(3-Aminopropyl)-2-pyrrolidinone**
M.W. 142.20 n_D^{20} 1.4977 b.p. 120-123°/0.2 mm.

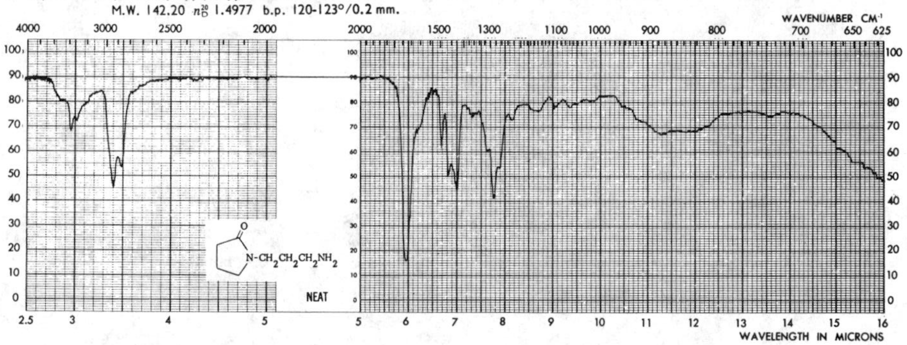

NEAT

D

P7520-2 **L-2-Pyrrolidone-5-carboxylic acid** (L-pyroglutamic acid)
M.W. 129.12 m.p. 154-157°
$[\alpha]_D^{25}$ - 10° (in H_2O)

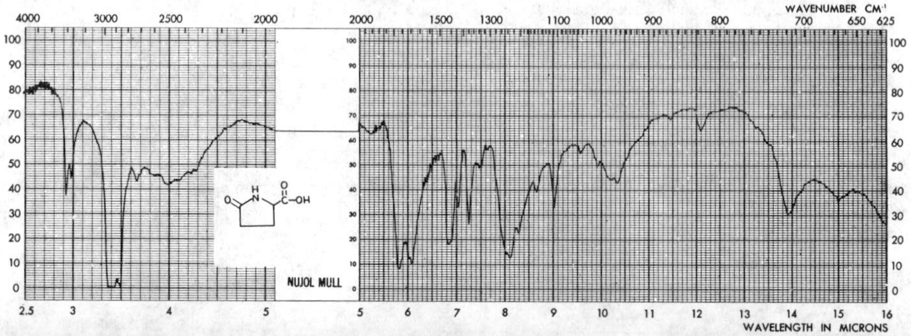

NUJOL MULL

E

19,633-9
Methyl 2-oxo-1-pyrrolidineacetate, 95%
FW 157.17 n_D^{20} 1.4719 d 1.131 Disp. C

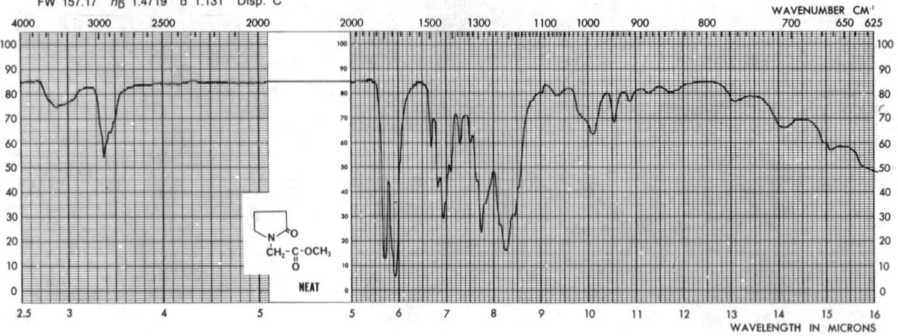

NEAT

F

12,049-9 **1-Methyl-5-oxo-3-pyrrolidinecarboxylic acid**
M.W. 143.14 m.p. 155-157°

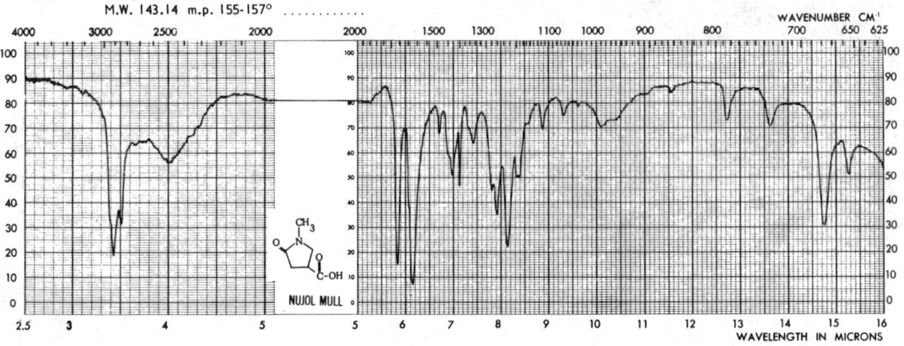

NUJOL MULL

G

13,111-3 **DL-Cycloserine** (DL-4-amino-3-isoxazolidinone)
M.W. 102.09 m.p. 147.5° (dec.)

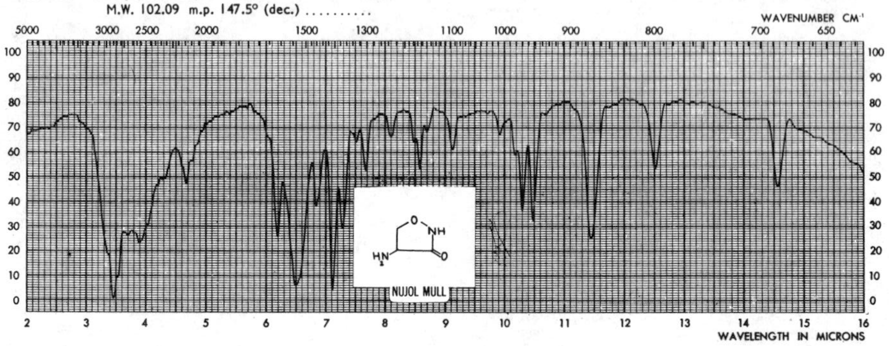

NUJOL MULL

H

A7090-9 **6-Aminopenicillanic acid**
M.W. 216.26 m.p. 198-204° (dec.)

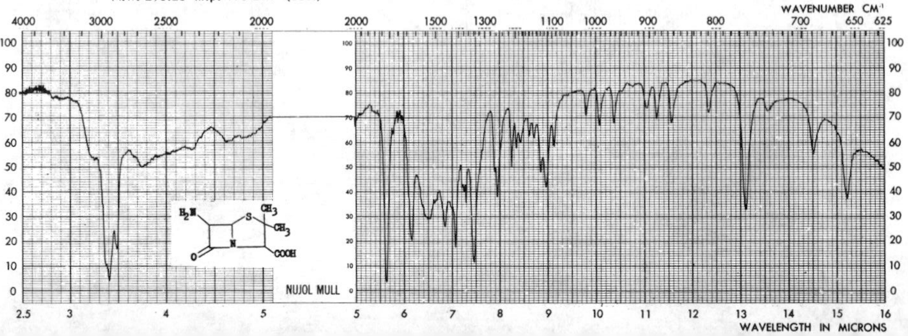

NUJOL MULL

A V20-9 δ-Valerolactam (2-piperidone)
M.W. 99.13 m.p. 37°

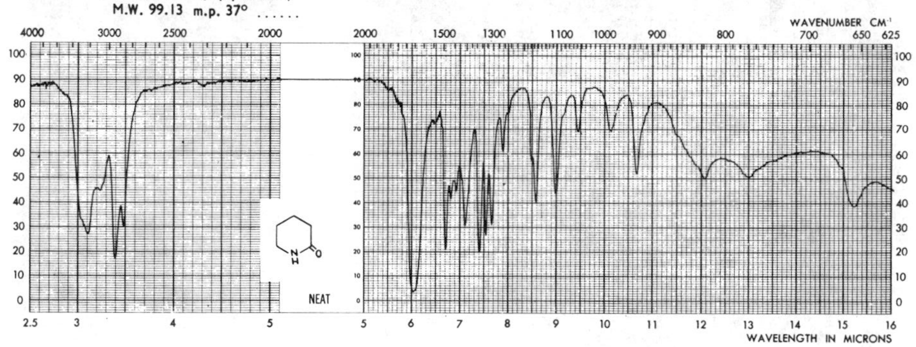

NEAT

B M7378-8 1-Methyl-2-piperidone
M.W. 113.16 n_D^{20} 1.4832
b.p. 105-106°/12 mm.

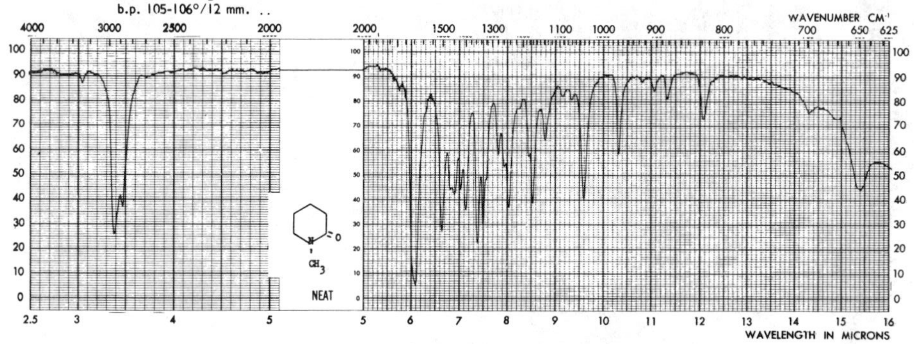

NEAT

C K280-1 3-Ketomorpholine (3-morpholinone)
M.W. 101.11 m.p. 96-98°

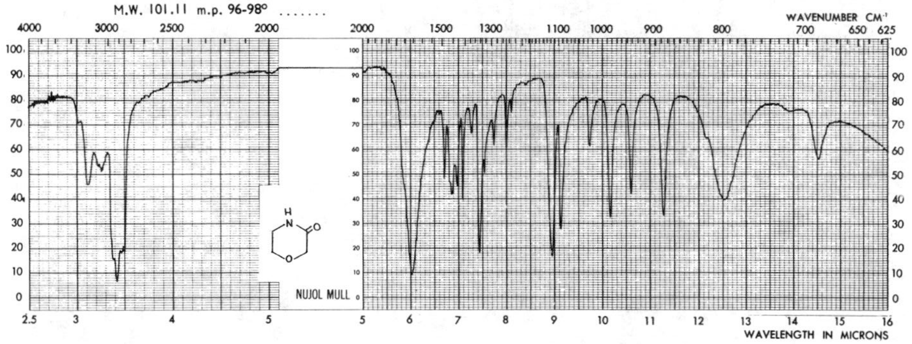

NUJOL MULL

D 15,082-7 ε-Caprolactam (2-oxohexamethyleneimine), zone refined, 99.9+%, GOLD LABEL
M.W. 113.16 m.p. 68.92°

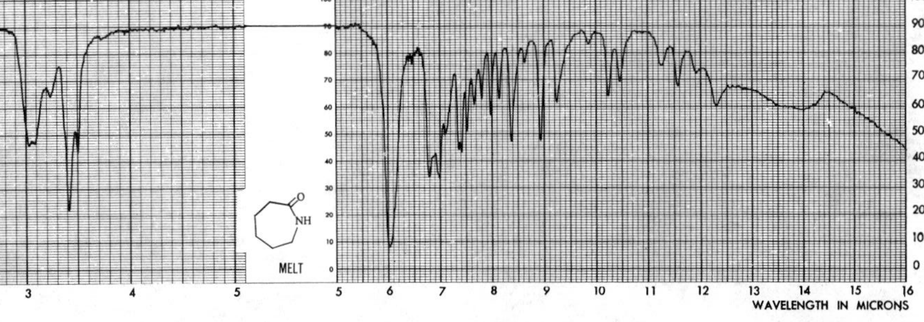

MELT

E C220-4 ε-Caprolactam (2-oxohexamethyleneimine), puriss.
M.W. 113.16 m.p. 69-72°

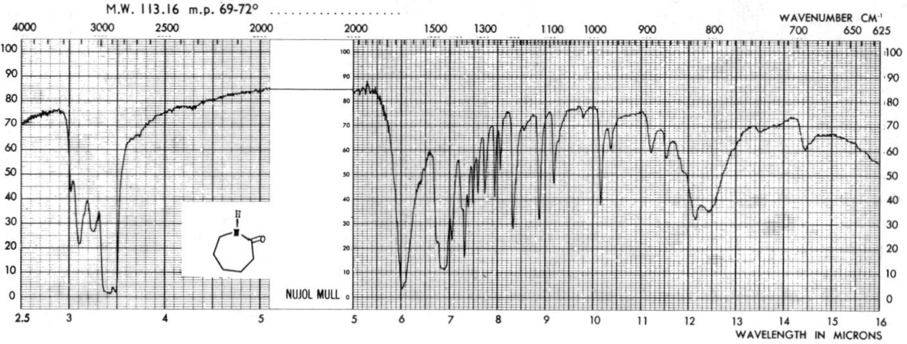

NUJOL MULL

F A9463-8 2-Azacyclooctanone (cycloheptanone isooxime)
M.W. 127.19 m.p. 35-38°

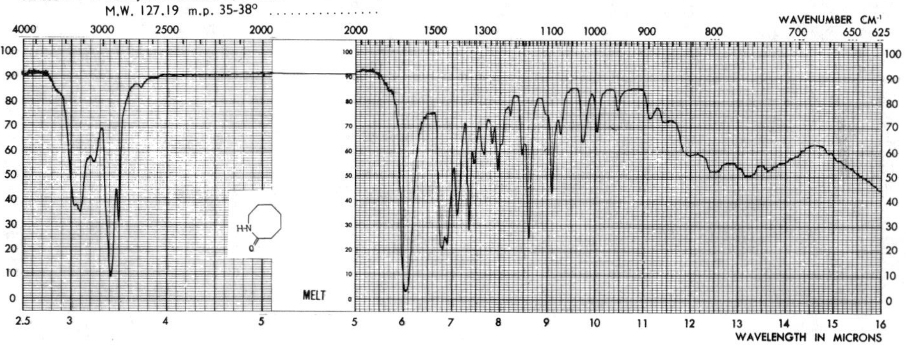

MELT

G 12,327-7 2-Azacyclononanone (cyclooctanone isooxime)
M.W. 141.22 m.p. 77.5-79.5°

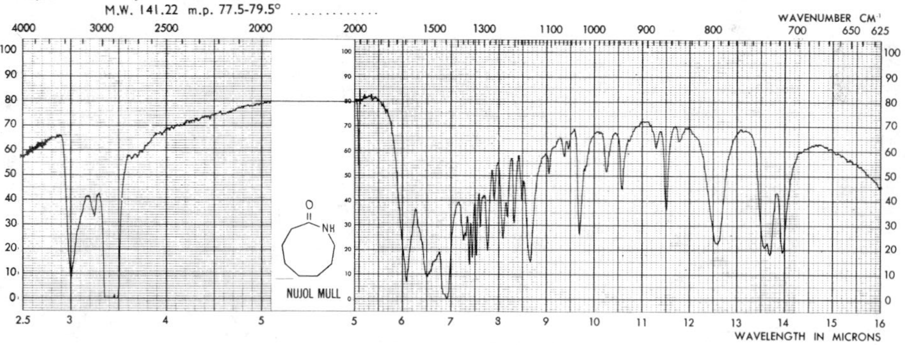

NUJOL MULL

H A9465-4 2-Azacyclotridecanone (cyclododecanone isooxime)
M.W. 197.32 m.p. 150-153°

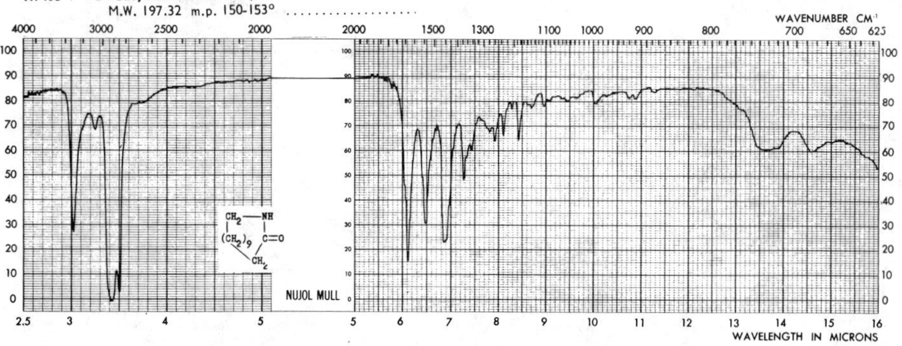

NUJOL MULL

A

G640-6 **Glycine anhydride** (2,5-piperazinedione)
M.W. 114.10 m.p. 318-320° (dec.)

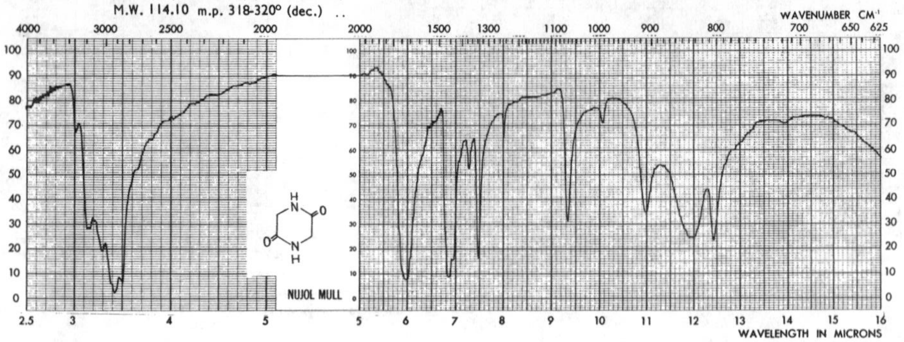

NUJOL MULL

B

22,309-3
Sarcosine anhydride, 99% (1,4-dimethyl-2,5-piperazinedione)
FW 142.16 mp 145-147° *Beil.* **24**,265 Disp. C

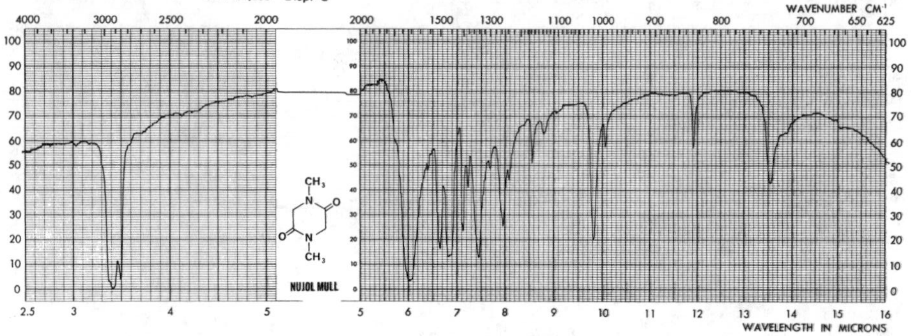

NUJOL MULL

C

11,618-1 **3-Hydroxy-2-piperidone**
M.W. 115.13 m.p. 134-137°

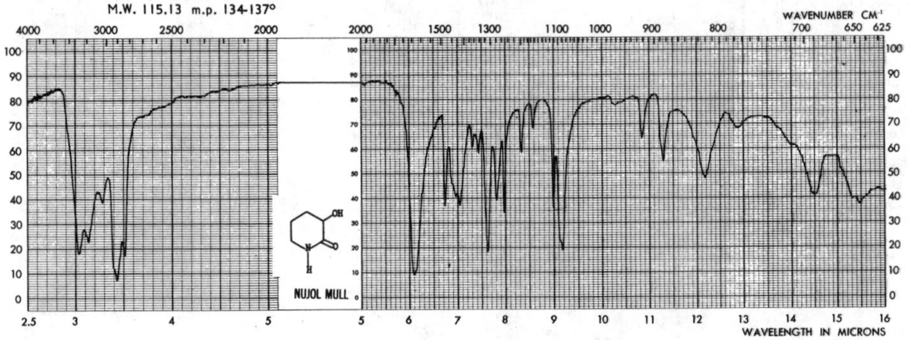

NUJOL MULL

D

T3162-3 **3-Thiomorpholinone**
M.W. 117.17 m.p. 89-93°

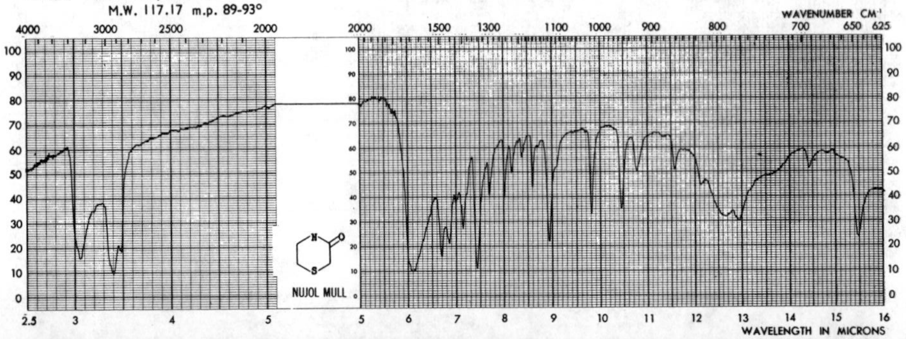

NUJOL MULL

E

21,010-2
Pyrithyldione, 98% [3,3-diethyl-2,4(1*H*,3*H*)-pyridinedione]
FW 167.21 bp 187-189°/14mm. Disp. C

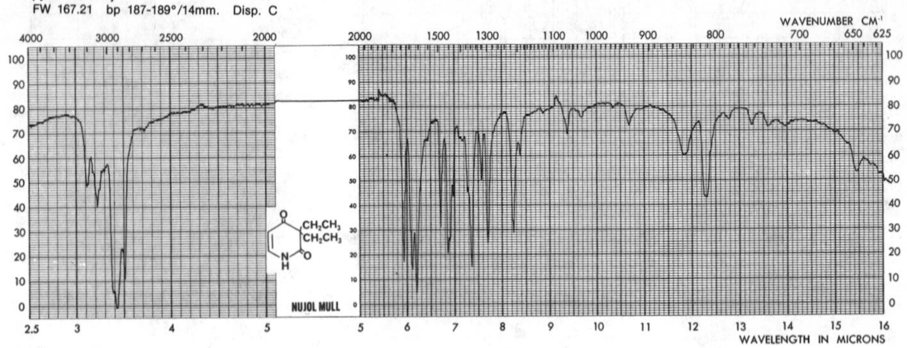

NUJOL MULL

F

C550-5 **3-Carbethoxy-2-piperidone** (ethyl 2-oxo-3-piperidinecarboxylate)
M.W. 171.20 m.p. 80-82°

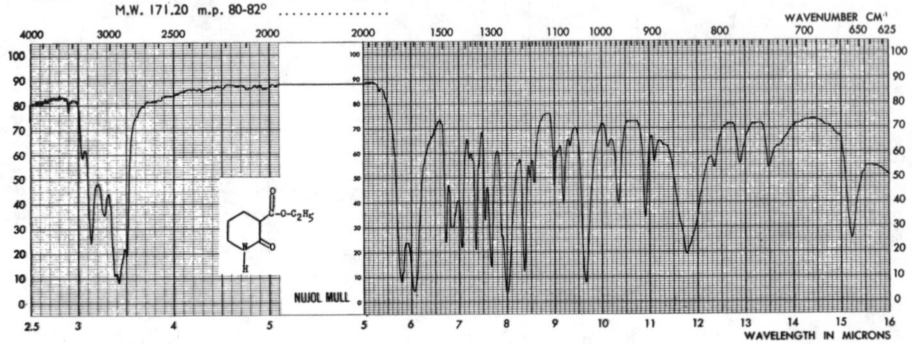

NUJOL MULL

G

S555-3 **Succinimide**
M.W. 99.09 m.p. 124-125°

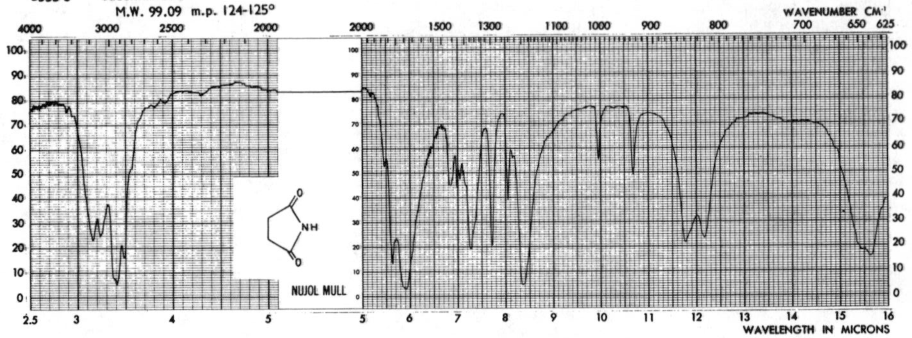

NUJOL MULL

H

16,350-3
α,α-Dimethyl-β-methylsuccinimide, 99+%, GOLD LABEL (2,2,3-trimethylsuccinimide)
M.W. 141.17 m.p. 119-121° Beil. **21**,394

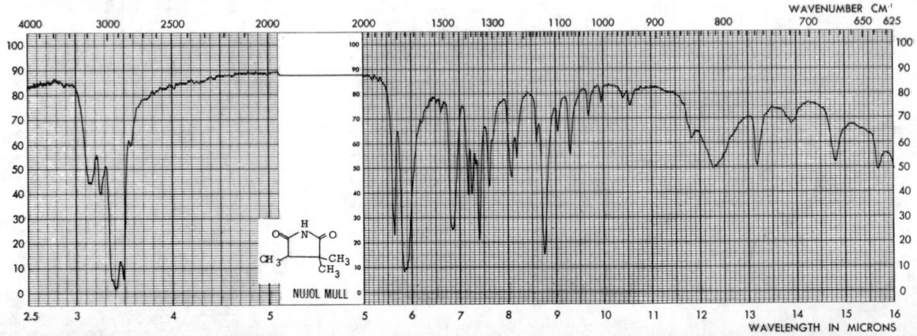

NUJOL MULL

A 19,495-6
α-Methyl-α-propylsuccinimide, 99+%, GOLD LABEL
FW 155.20 mp 76-77° Disp. C

B 13,067-2 N-Hydroxysuccinimide
M.W. 115.09 m.p. 96-98.5°

C 10,968-1 N-Chlorosuccinimide, 98+%
M.W. 133.53 m.p. 144-146°

D 22,005-1
N-Iodosuccinimide
FW 224.99 *Fieser* 1,510 Disp. C

E 10,414-0 N-Vinylsuccinimide, tech.
M.W. 125.13 m.p. 47-51°.

F 12,347-1 *cis*-1,2-Cyclohexanedicarboximide (*cis*-hexahydrophthalimide)
M.W. 153.18 m.p. 133-138°

G T1420-6 *cis*-Δ4-Tetrahydrophthalimide (*cis*-4-cyclohexene-1,2-dicarboximide)
M.W. 151.17 m.p. 140-142°

H 11,508-8 N-Hydroxy-5-norbornene-2,3-dicarboximide
M.W. 179.18 m.p. 165-167°

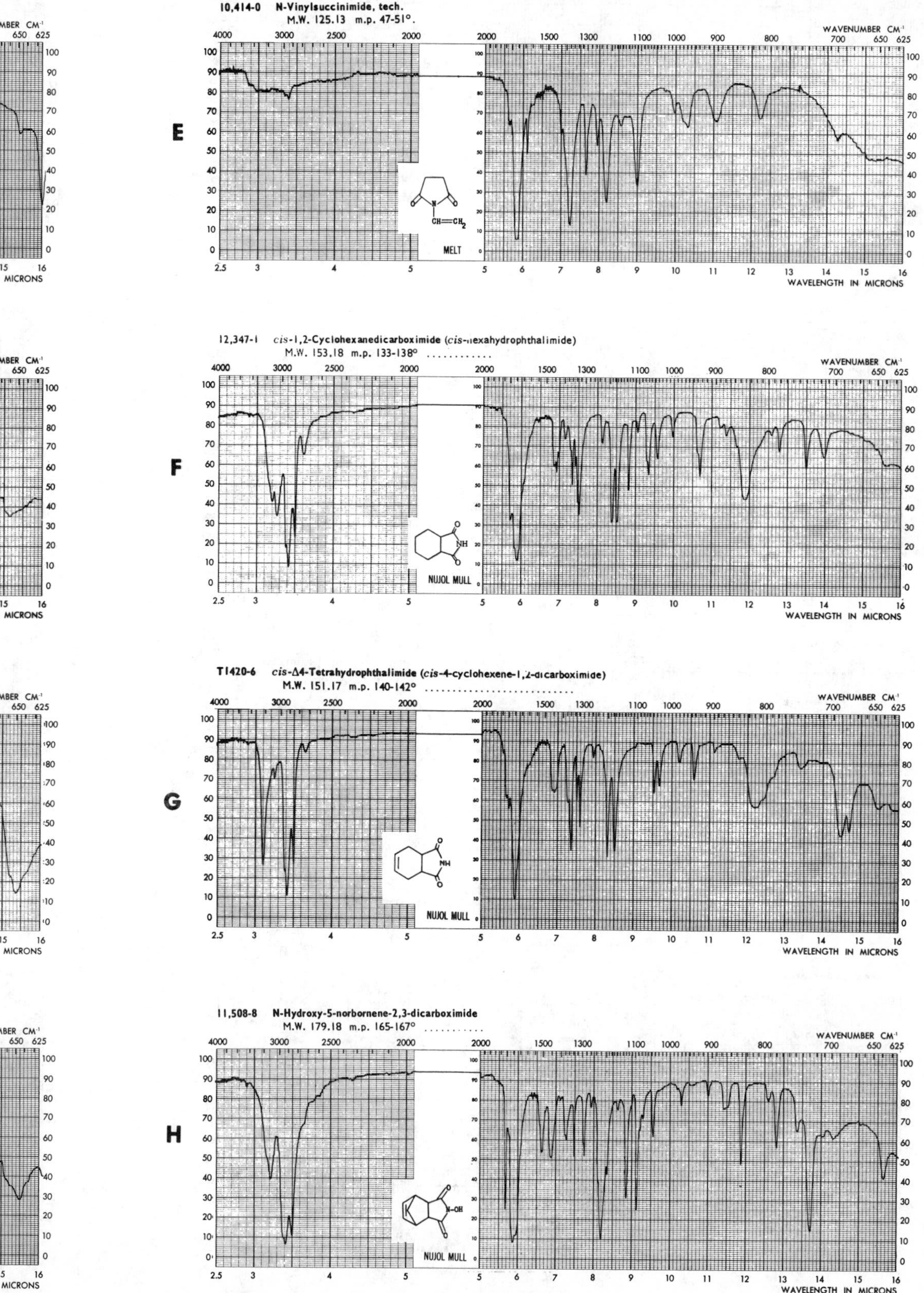

A 12,958-5 Maleimide
M.W. 97.07 m.p. 92-95°
NUJOL MULL

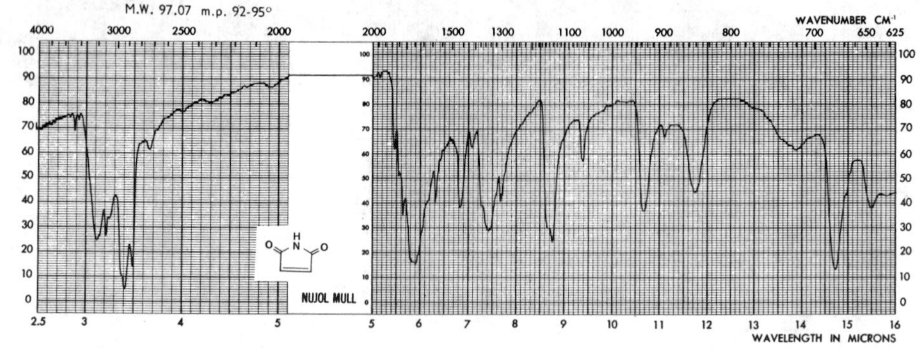

B M5375-2 N-Methylmaleimide
M.W. 111.10 m.p. 92-94°
NUJOL MULL

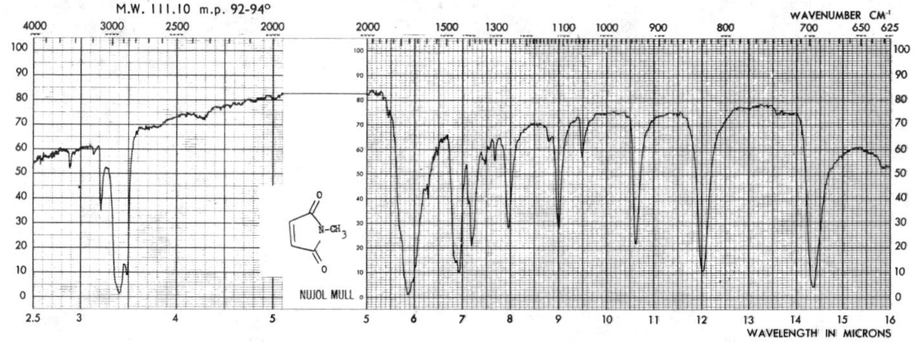

C 12,828-7 N-Ethylmaleimide (NEM), puriss.
M.W. 125.13 m.p. 46-48° ......
MELT

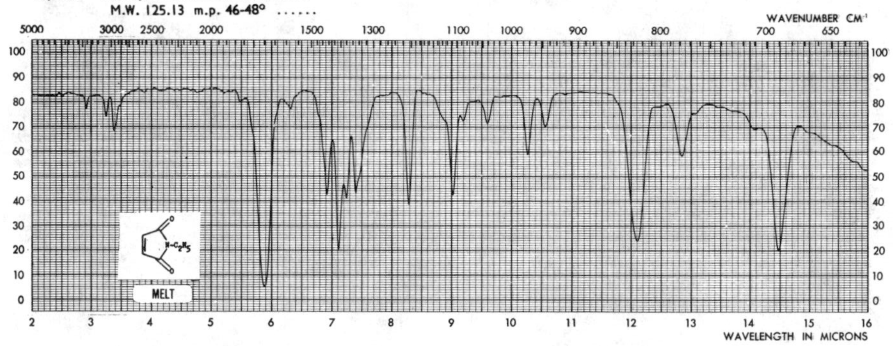

D B8125-5 N-Bromosuccinimide (NBS)
M.W. 177.99 m.p. 182-186.5°
NUJOL MULL

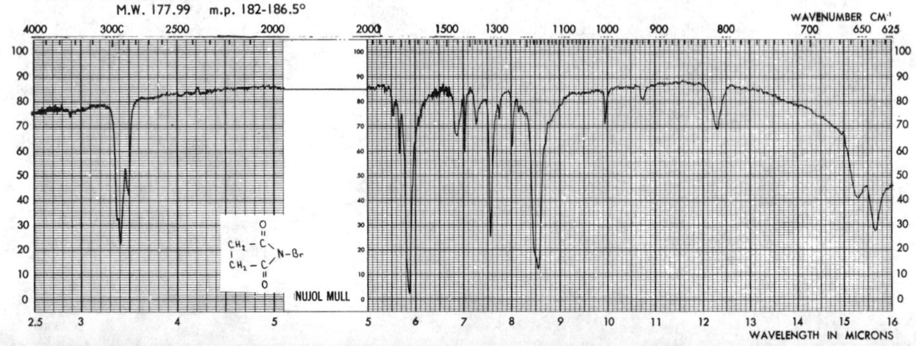

E 12,033-2 2,5-Dioxo-3-pyrroline-1-carboxamide
M.W. 140.10 m.p. 145-150° ......
NUJOL MULL

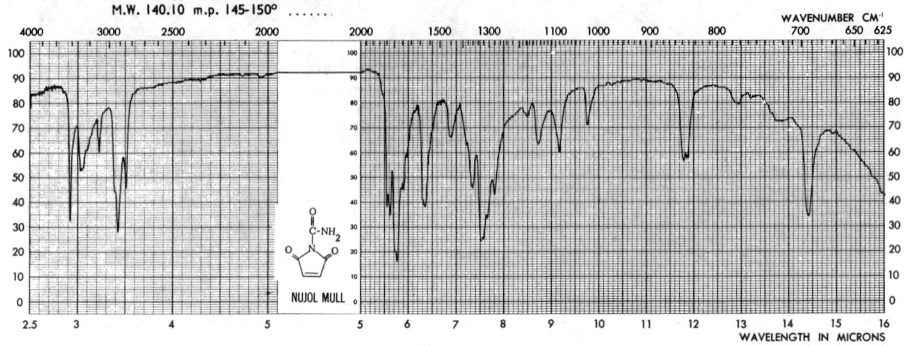

F C10,445-0 Cycloheximide
M.W. 281.34 m.p. 110-111°
NUJOL MULL

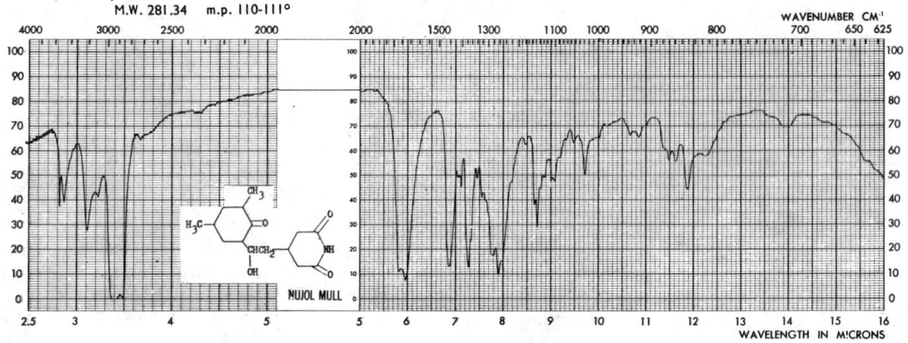

G 17,809-8
Glutarimide, 98%
M.W. 113.12 m.p. 155-157° Beil. 21,382
NUJOL MULL

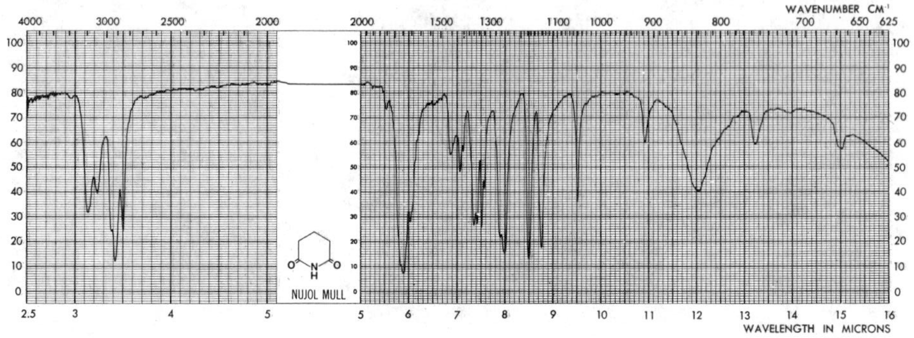

H D16,000-8 3,3-Dimethylglutarimide
M.W. 141.17 m.p. 144-146°
NUJOL MULL

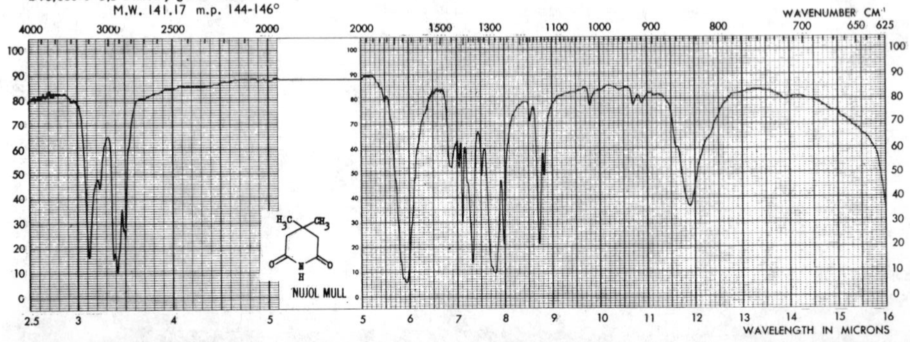

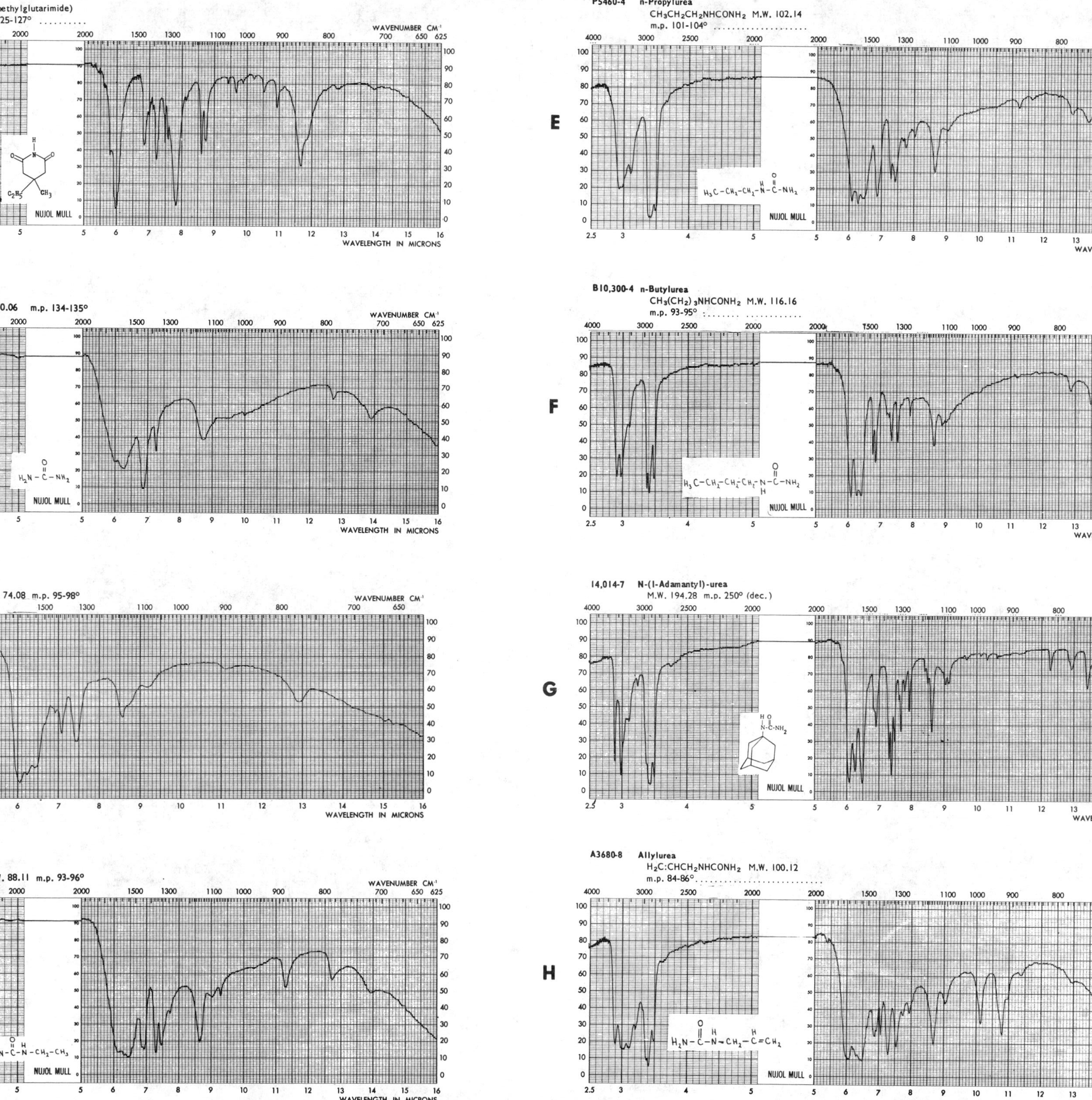

A
11,189-9 Bemegride (3-ethyl-3-methylglutarimide)
M.W. 155.20 m.p. 125-127°
NUJOL MULL
B
U270-9 Urea, reagent crystals
H_2NCONH_2 M.W. 60.06 m.p. 134-135°
NUJOL MULL
C
M8680-4 Methylurea
$CH_3NHCONH_2$ M.W. 74.08 m.p. 95-98°
MELT
D
E5100-7 Ethylurea
$C_2H_5NHCONH_2$ M.W. 88.11 m.p. 93-96°
NUJOL MULL
E
P5460-4 n-Propylurea
$CH_3CH_2CH_2NHCONH_2$ M.W. 102.14
m.p. 101-104°
NUJOL MULL
F
B10,300-4 n-Butylurea
$CH_3(CH_2)_3NHCONH_2$ M.W. 116.16
m.p. 93-95°
NUJOL MULL
G
14,014-7 N-(1-Adamantyl)-urea
M.W. 194.28 m.p. 250° (dec.)
NUJOL MULL
H
A3680-8 Allylurea
$H_2C{:}CHCH_2NHCONH_2$ M.W. 100.12
m.p. 84-86°
NUJOL MULL
WAVENUMBER CM⁻¹
WAVELENGTH IN MICRONS
ALDRICH

NON-AROMATIC AMIDES

ALDRICH

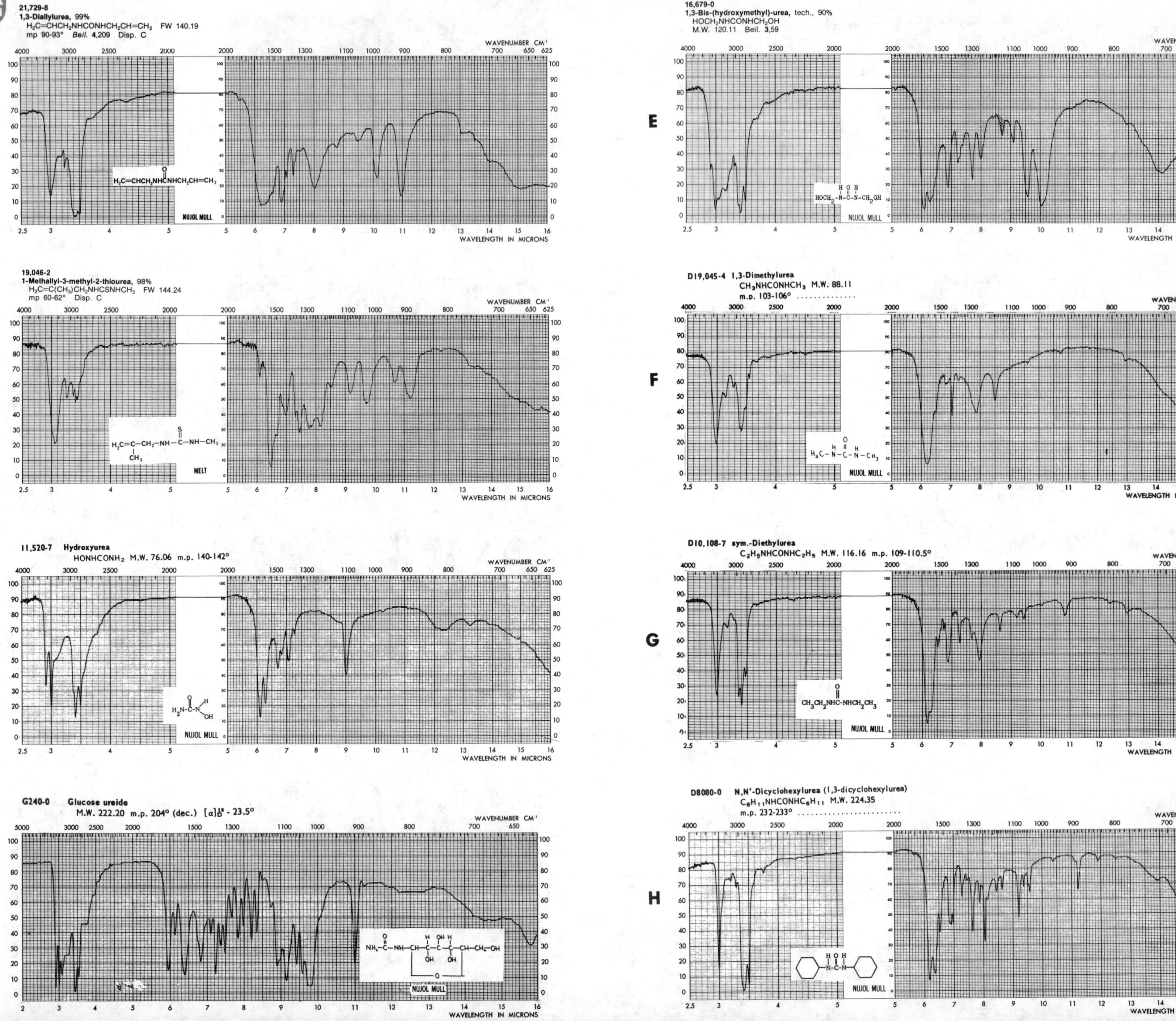
A
21,729-8
1,3-Diallylurea, 99%
$H_2C{=}CHCH_2NHCONHCH_2CH{=}CH_2$ FW 140.19
mp 90-93° Beil. 4,209 Disp. C
NUJOL MULL
B
19,046-2
1-Methallyl-3-methyl-2-thiourea, 98%
$H_2C{=}C(CH_3)CH_2NHCSNHCH_3$ FW 144.24
mp 60-62° Disp. C
MELT
C
11,520-7 Hydroxyurea
$HONHCONH_2$ M.W. 76.06 m.p. 140-142°
NUJOL MULL
D
G240-0 Glucose ureide
M.W. 222.20 m.p. 204° (dec.) $[\alpha]_D^{18}$ - 23.5°
NUJOL MULL
E
16,679-0
1,3-Bis-(hydroxymethyl)-urea, tech., 90%
$HOCH_2NHCONHCH_2OH$
M.W. 120.11 Beil. 3,59
NUJOL MULL
F
D19,045-4 1,3-Dimethylurea
$CH_3NHCONHCH_3$ M.W. 88.11
m.p. 103-106°
NUJOL MULL
G
D10,108-7 sym.-Diethylurea
$C_2H_5NHCONHC_2H_5$ M.W. 116.16 m.p. 109-110.5°
NUJOL MULL
H
D8080-0 N,N'-Dicyclohexylurea (1,3-dicyclohexylurea)
$C_6H_{11}NHCONHC_6H_{11}$ M.W. 224.35
m.p. 232-233°
NUJOL MULL
WAVENUMBER CM⁻¹
WAVELENGTH IN MICRONS

A 1-60-1 **2-Imidazolidone (ethyleneurea)**
M.W. 86.09 m.p. 131-133°
NUJOL MULL

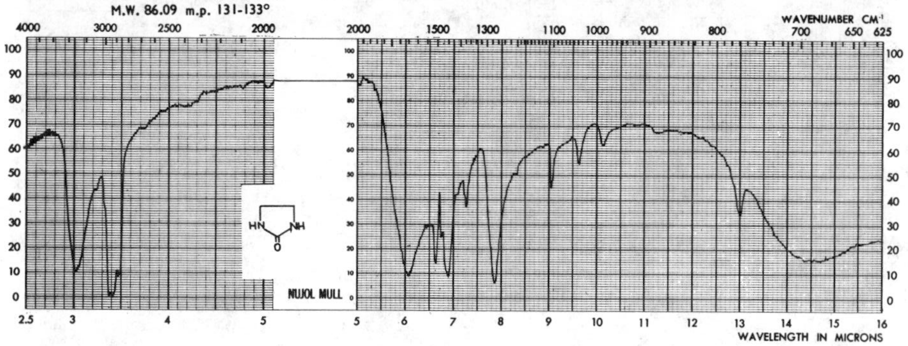

B 14,504-1 **4-Methyl-2-imidazolidinone**
M.W. 100.12 m.p. 115-120°
NUJOL MULL

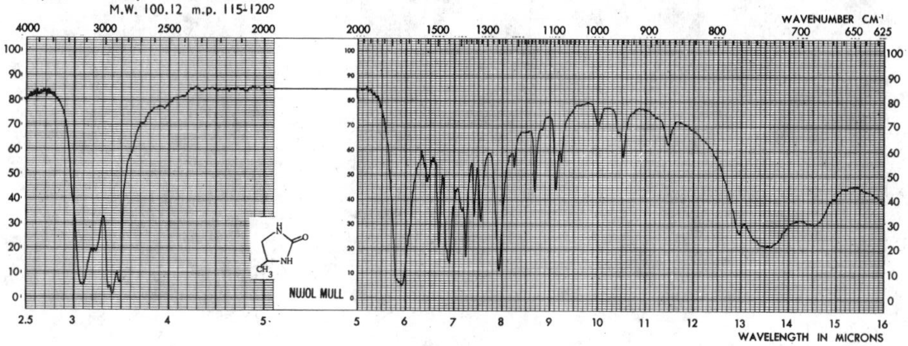

C 19,345-3
1,3-Dimethyl-2-imidazolidinone, 98%
FW 114.15 bp 106-108°/17mm. n_D^{20} 1.4720
d 1.044 Disp. C
NEAT

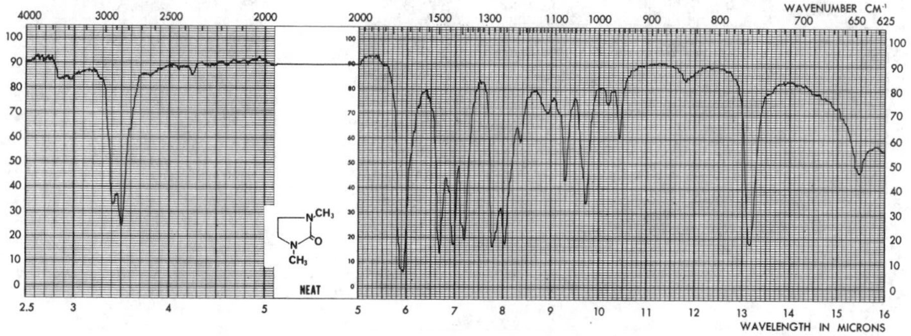

D 86,016-6
2-Imidazolidone-4-carboxylic acid (2-oxo-4-imidazolidinecarboxylic acid)
FW 130.10 mp 184-186° (dec.) Disp. C
NUJOL MULL

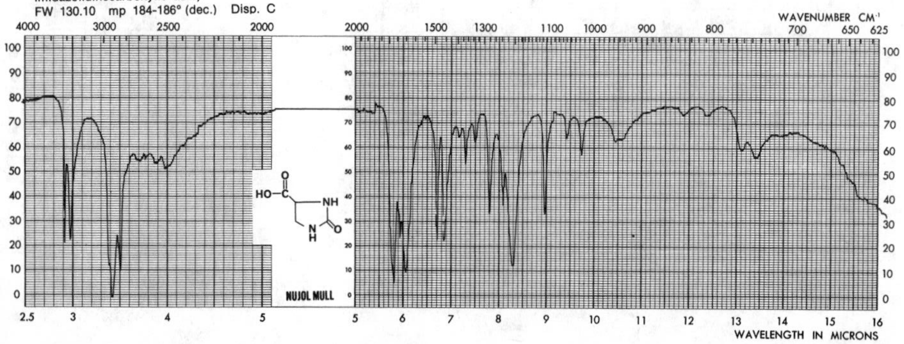

E T1520-2 **Tetrahydro-2-pyrimidone**
M.W. 100.12 m.p. 263-265°
NUJOL MULL

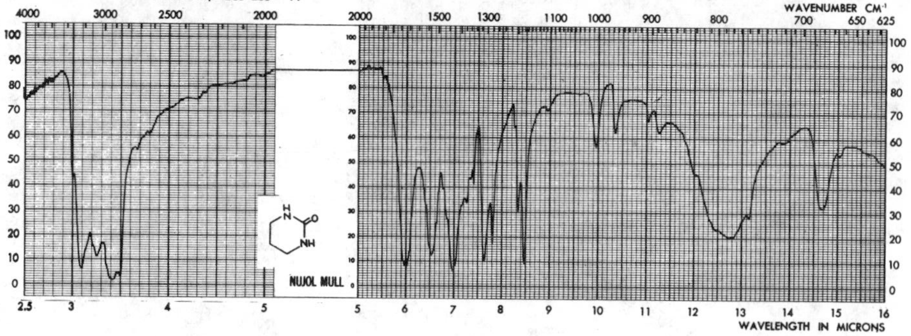

F T2450-3 **1,1,3,3-Tetramethylurea**
$(CH_3)_2NCON(CH_3)_2$ M.W. 116.16
n_D^{20} 1.4506
NEAT

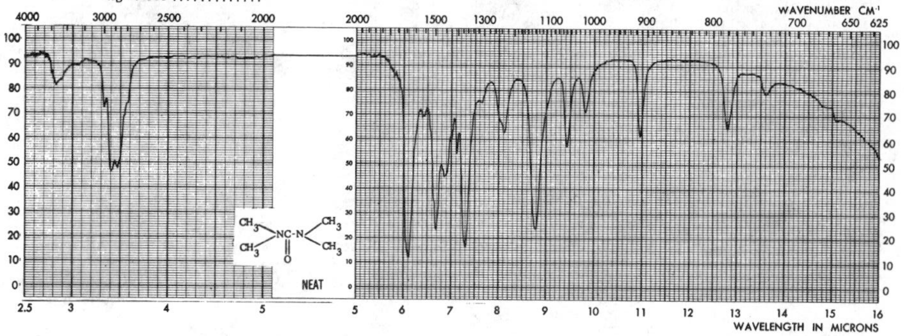

G B5045-7 **Bis-(pentamethylene)-urea** (1,1'-carbonyldipiperidine)
M.W. 196.30 m.p. 44-47°
MELT

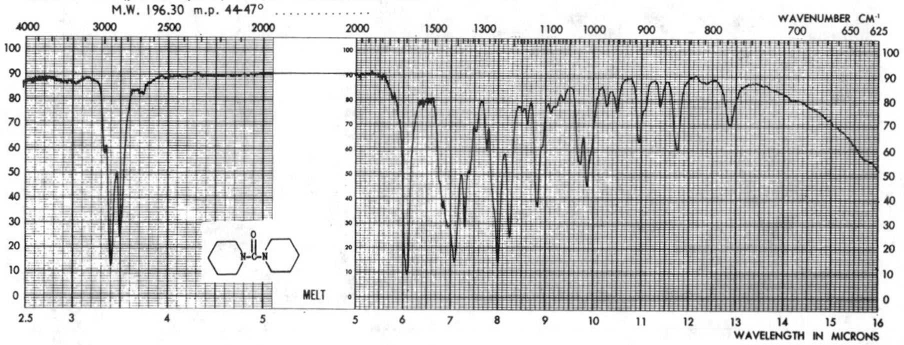

H 19,781-5
***N*-Isopropyl-4-methyl-1-piperazinecarboxamide**, 95+%
FW 185.27 mp 86-89° Disp. C
NUJOL MULL

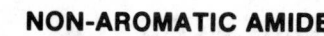

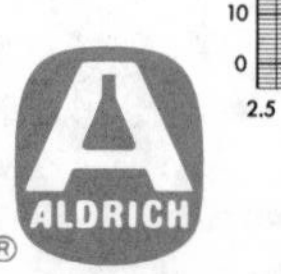

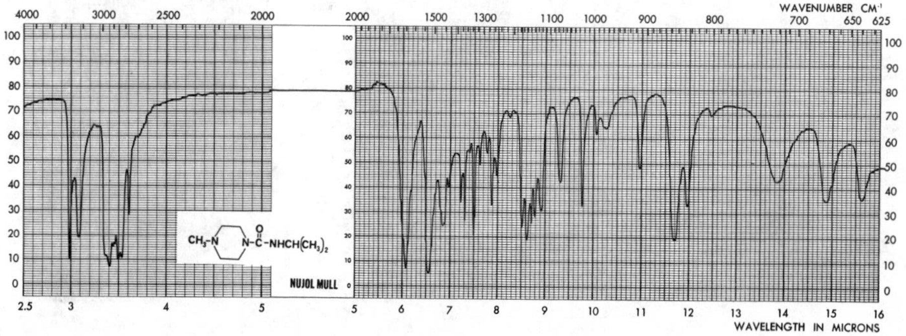

A

S220-1 **Semicarbazide hydrochloride, puriss.**
$H_2NCONHNH_2 \cdot HCl$ M.W. 111.53
m.p. 175-177° (dec.)

NUJOL MULL

B

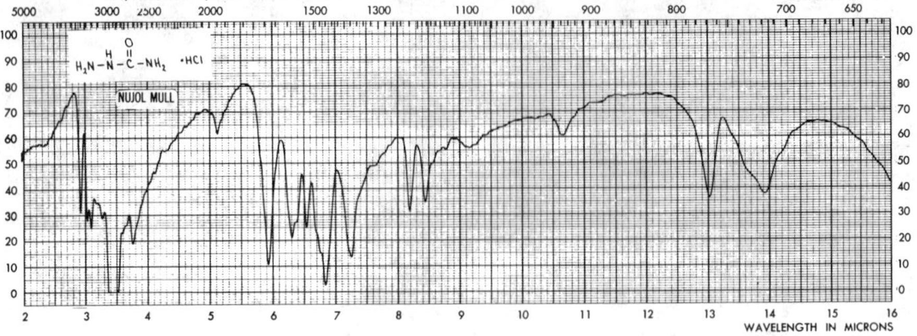

10,571-6 **Acetone semicarbazone**
$(CH_3)_2C{:}NNHCONH_2$ M.W. 115.13
m.p. 184-187°

NUJOL MULL

C

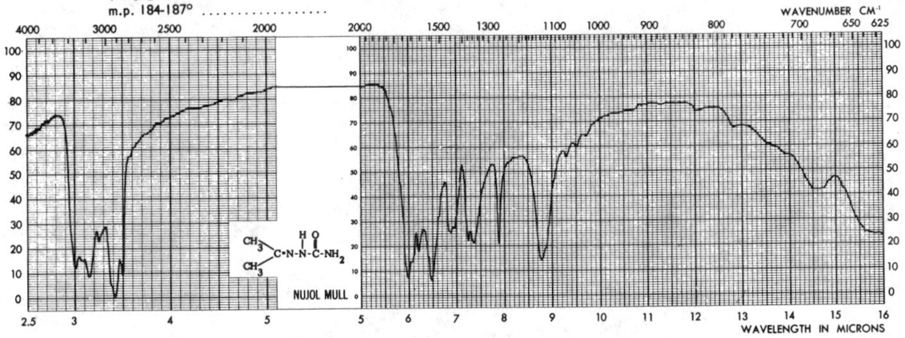

15,547-0 **Ethyl allophanate**
$H_2NCONHCO_2C_2H_5$ M.W. 132.12

NUJOL MULL

D

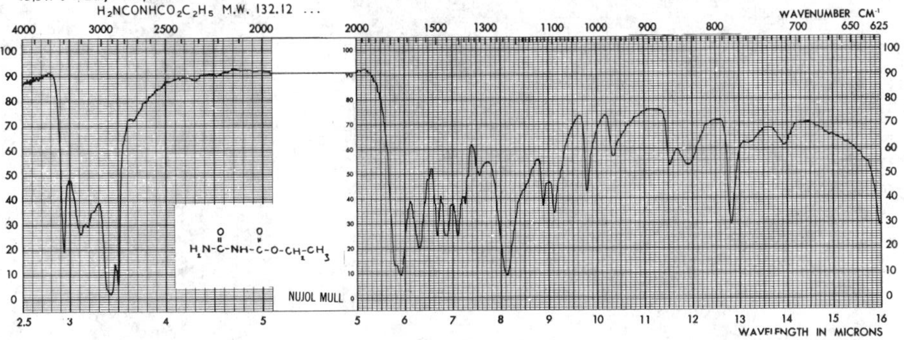

C1100-6 **Carbohydrazide**
$H_2NNHCONHNH_2$ M.W. 90.09 m.p. 157-158°

NUJOL MULL

E

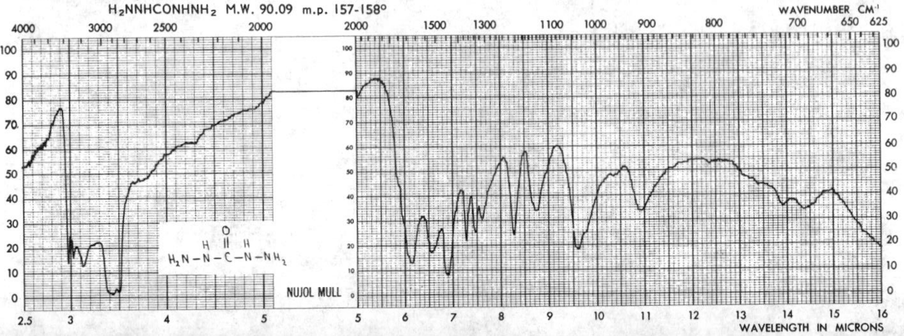

22,322-0
Thiocarbohydrazide, 98%
$H_2NNHCSNHNH_2$ FW 106.15 mp 171° (dec.)
Beil. 3,197 Disp. C

NUJOL MULL

F

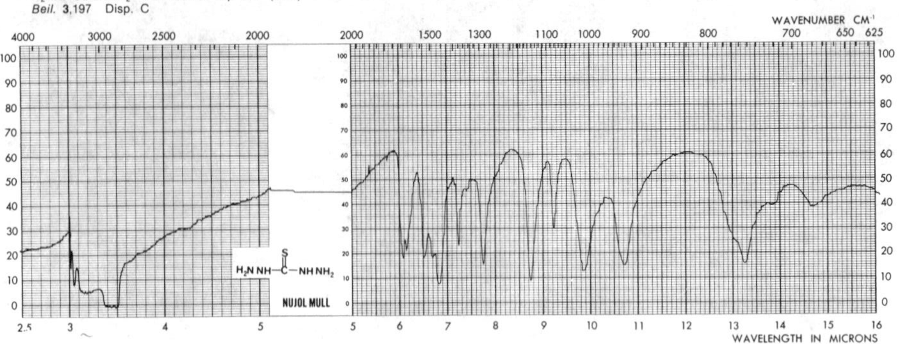

B5420-7 **Biuret**
$H_2NCONHCONH_2$ M.W. 103.08
m.p. 188-190° (dec.)

NUJOL MULL

G

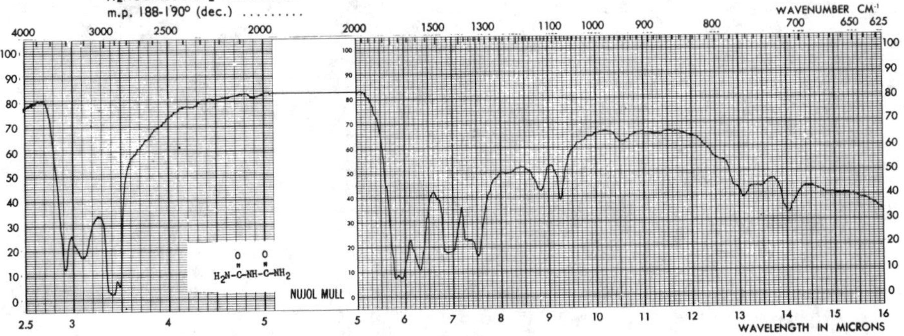

10,946-0 **1-Acetyl-3-methylurea**
$CH_3CONHCONHCH_3$ M.W. 116.12
m.p. 181-184°

NUJOL MULL

H

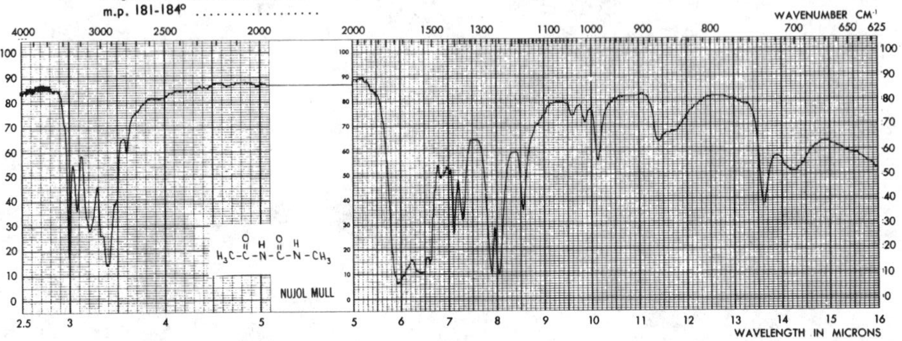

N1530-8 **Nitrobiuret, tech.**
$O_2NNHCONHCONH_2$ M.W. 148.08
m.p. 150° (dec.)

NUJOL MULL

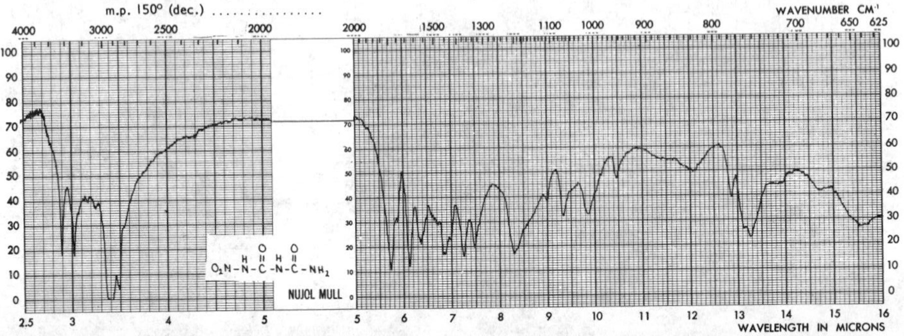

A

B5415 **Biurea** (sym.-dicarbamylhydrazine)
$(H_2NCONH-)_2$ M.W. 118.10 m.p. 274° (dec.)

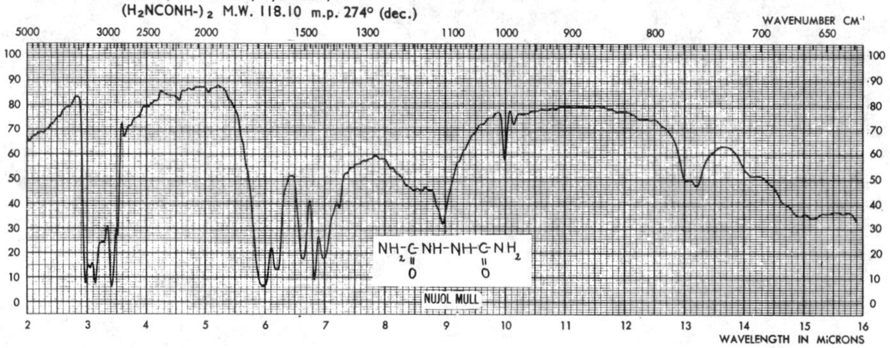

NUJOL MULL

B

21,784-0
Allantoic acid hemihydrate, 97%
(diureidoacetic acid)
$(H_2NCONH)_2CHCO_2H \cdot {}^1/_2H_2O$ FW 185.14
mp 180° (dec.) *Beil.* **3**,599 Disp. L

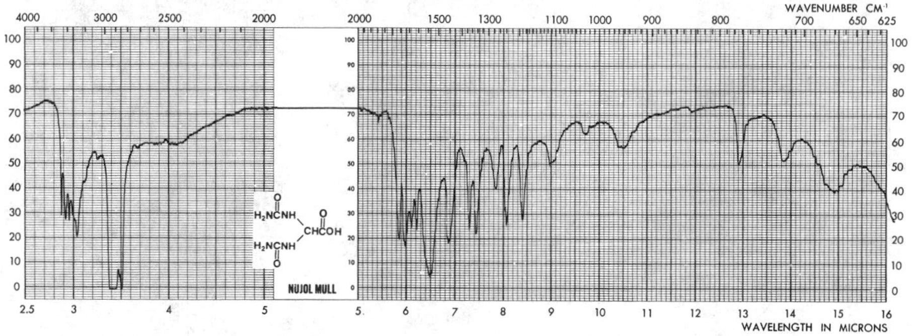

NUJOL MULL

C

A9660-6 **Azodicarbonamide**
$H_2NCON{:}NCONH_2$ M.W. 116.08 m.p. 225°

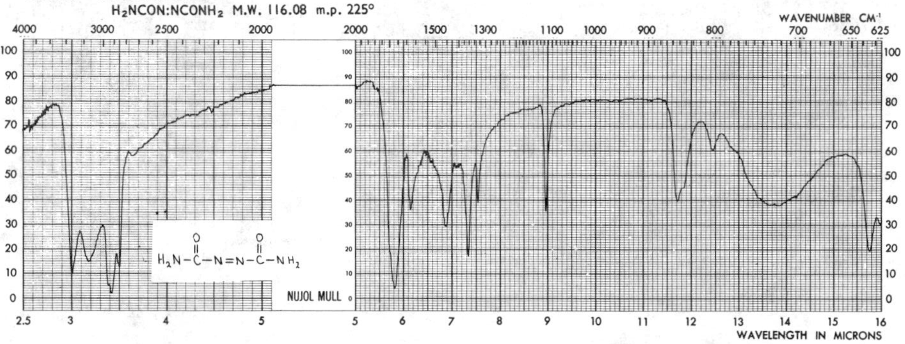

NUJOL MULL

D

19,315-1
1,1'-Azobis(*N,N*-dimethylformamide), 98% [azo-dicarboxylic acid bis(dimethylamide), diamide]
$(CH_3)_2NCON{=}NCON(CH_3)_2$ FW 172.19
mp 113-115° *Beil.* **4**(1),354 Disp. C

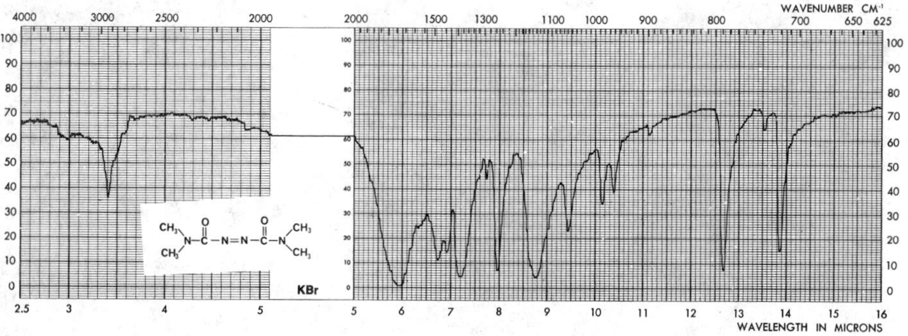

KBr

E

A5450-4 **1-(β-Aminoethyl)-2-imidazolidone, tech.**
M.W. 129.16

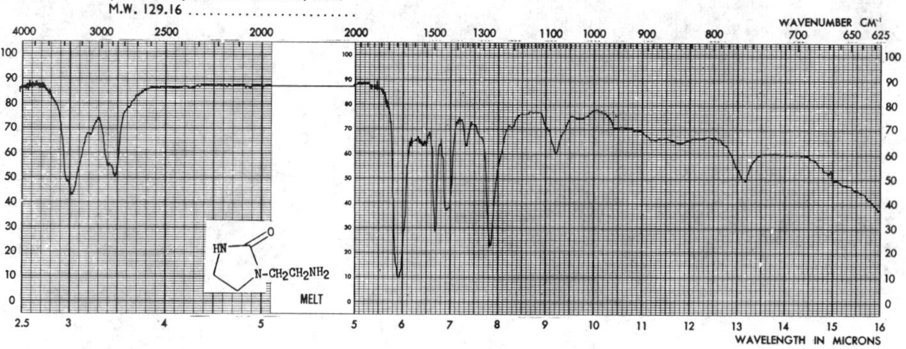

MELT

F

G730-5 **Glycoluril (acetyleneurea)**
M.W. 142.12 m.p. > 320°

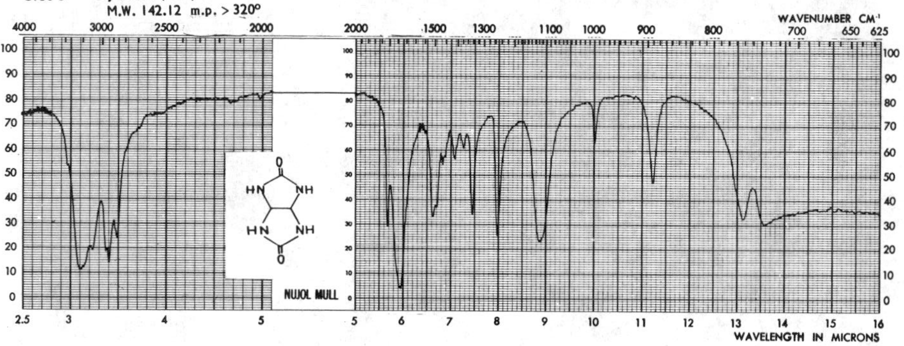

NUJOL MULL

G

11,407-3 **N,N',N'',N'''-Tetrachloroglycoluril**
M.W. 279.90 m.p. 208° (dec.)

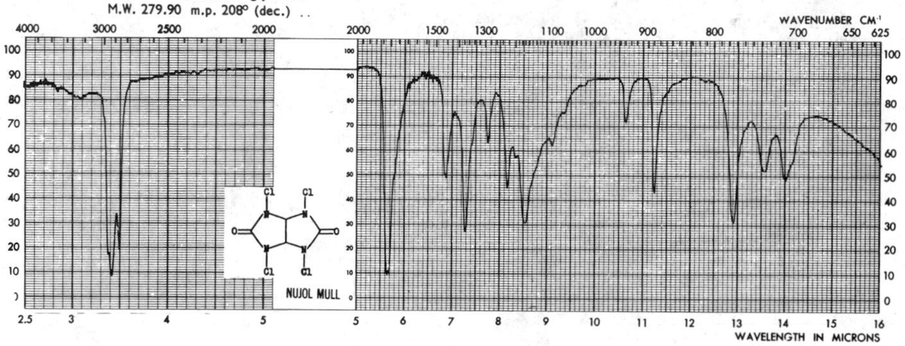

NUJOL MULL

H

19,037-3
***N,N',N'',N'''*-Tetraacetylglycoluril,** 98+%
FW 310.27 mp 229-232° *Beil.* **26**,443
Fieser **1**,563 Disp. C

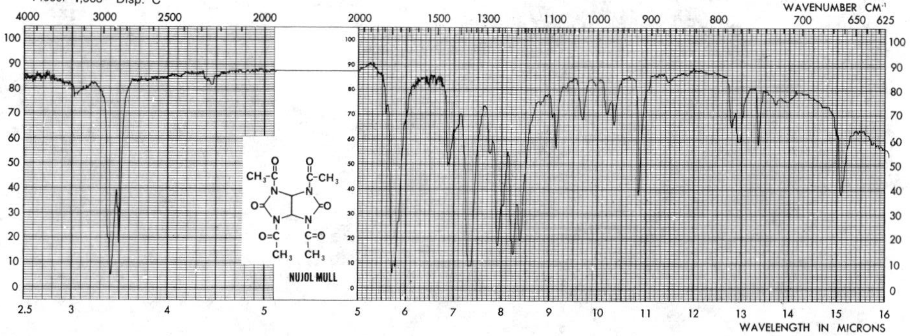

NUJOL MULL

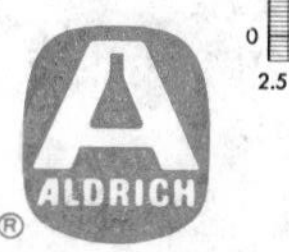

ALDRICH

A

15,636-1
Hydantoin, 99%
M.W. 100.08 m.p. 221-223° Beil. **24**,242

NUJOL MULL

B

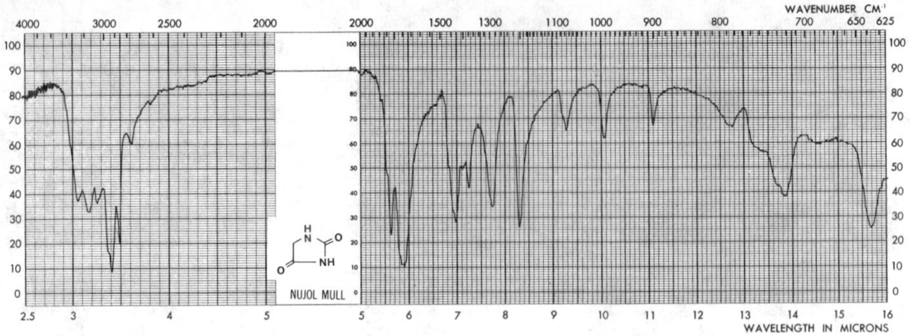

M4988-7 **1-Methylhydantoin**
M.W. 114.11 m.p. 156-157°

NUJOL MULL

C

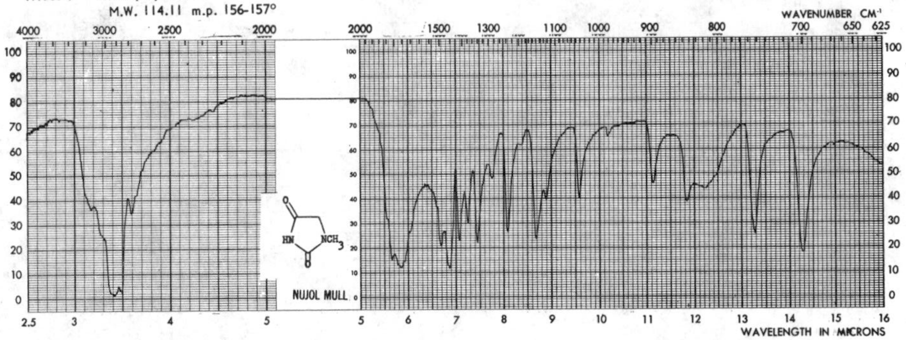

D16,140-3 **5,5-Dimethylhydantoin**
M.W. 128.13 m.p. 176-178°

NUJOL MULL

D

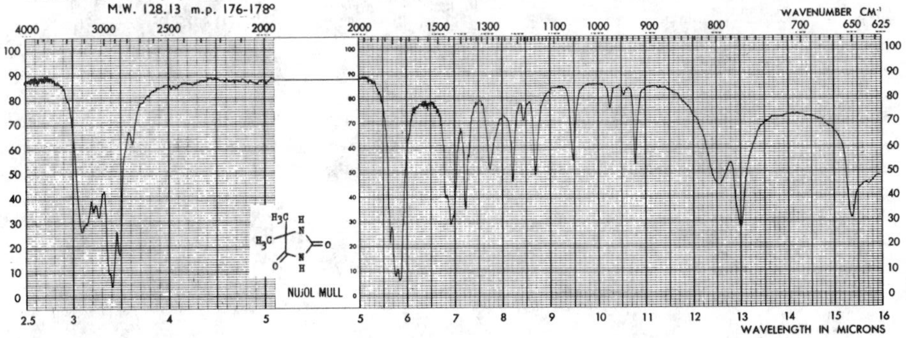

15,790-2
1,3-Dibromo-5,5-dimethylhydantoin, 98%
M.W. 285.93 m.p. 197-199° (dec.)
Fieser 1,208 2,108 *IRRITANT*

NUJOL MULL

E

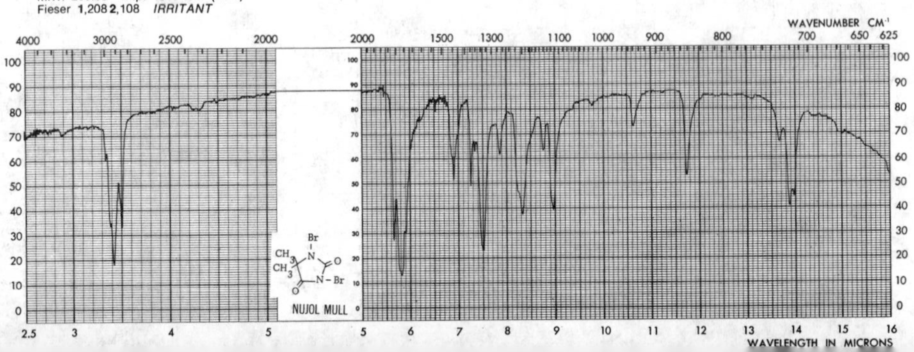

85,062-4
5-Hydantoinacetic acid
M.W. 158.11 m.p. 214-215° (dec.) Beil. **24**(2),136

NUJOL MULL

F

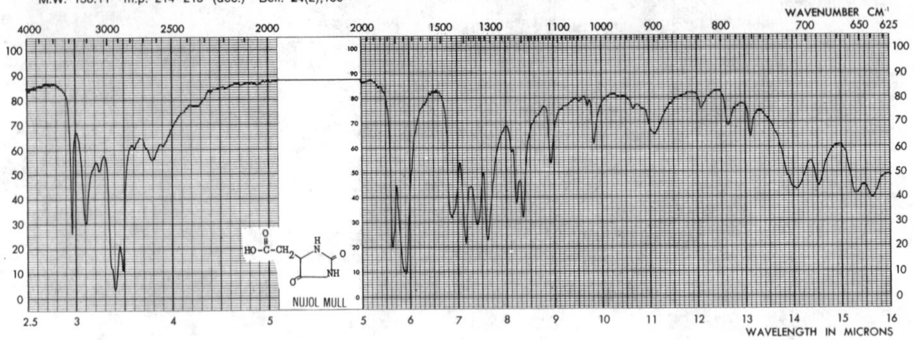

A2839-2 **Allantoin (5-ureidohydantoin)**
M.W. 158.12 m.p. 240° (dec.)

NUJOL MULL

G

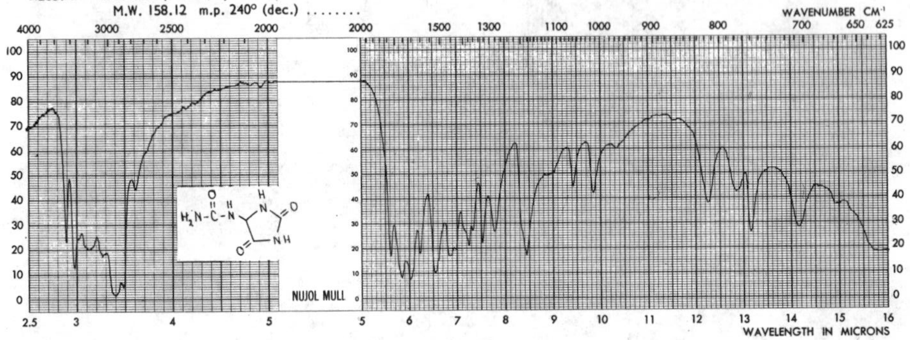

19,417-4
7-Aminodesacetoxycephalosporanic acid,
98% (7-ADCA)
FW 214.24 mp 234° (dec.)
$[\alpha]^{22}$ -30.1° (c=1, 1*N* NaOH) Disp. C

NUJOL MULL

H

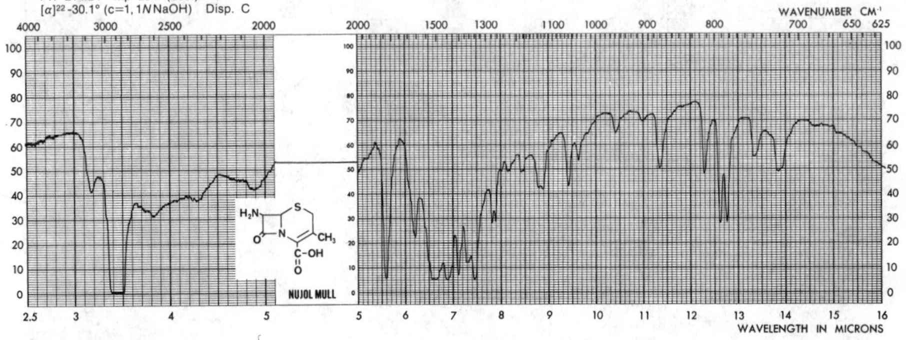

19,114-0
7-Aminocephalosporanic acid, 99% (7-ACA)
FW 272.28 mp >300° Disp. C

NUJOL MULL

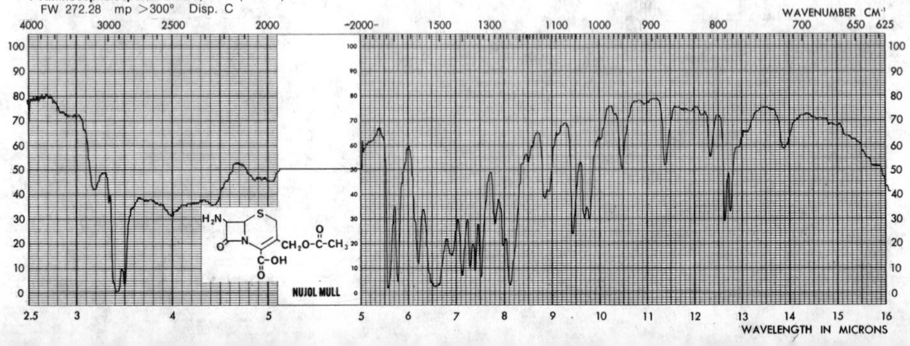

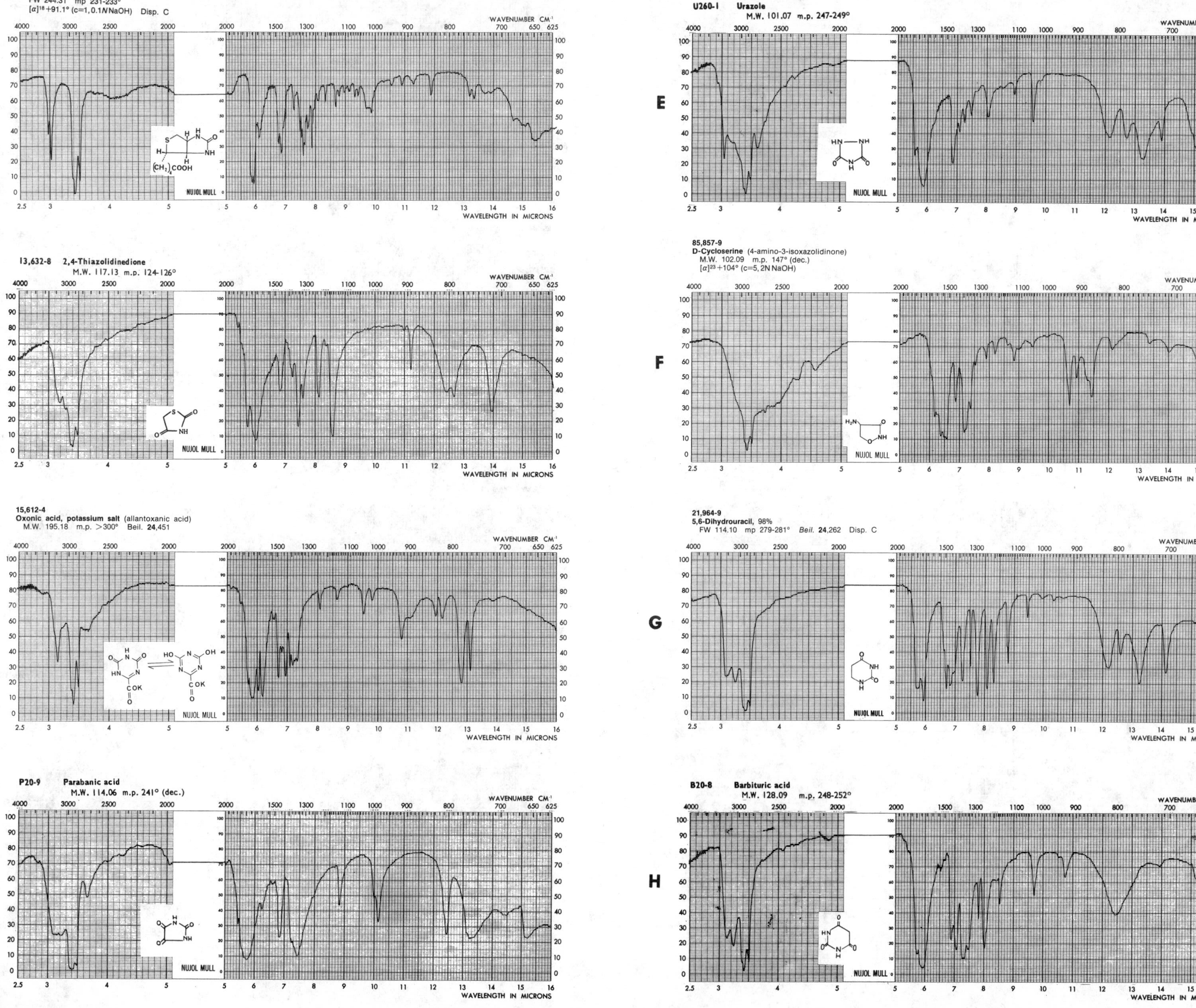
A
86,164-2
d-Biotin, 99% (Vitamin H)
FW 244.31 mp 231-233°
[α]18 +91.1° (c=1,0.1N NaOH) Disp. C
B
13,632-8 2,4-Thiazolidinedione
M.W. 117.13 m.p. 124-126°
C
15,612-4
Oxonic acid, potassium salt (allantoxanic acid)
M.W. 195.18 m.p. >300° Beil. 24,451
D
P20-9 Parabanic acid
M.W. 114.06 m.p. 241° (dec.)
E
U260-1 Urazole
M.W. 101.07 m.p. 247-249°
F
85,857-9
D-Cycloserine (4-amino-3-isoxazolidinone)
M.W. 102.09 m.p. 147° (dec.)
[α]23 +104° (c=5, 2N NaOH)
G
21,964-9
5,6-Dihydrouracil, 98%
FW 114.10 mp 279-281° Beil. 24,262 Disp. C
H
B20-8 Barbituric acid
M.W. 128.09 m.p. 248-252°
NUJOL MULL
WAVENUMBER CM⁻¹
WAVELENGTH IN MICRONS

ALDRICH

NON-AROMATIC AMIDES

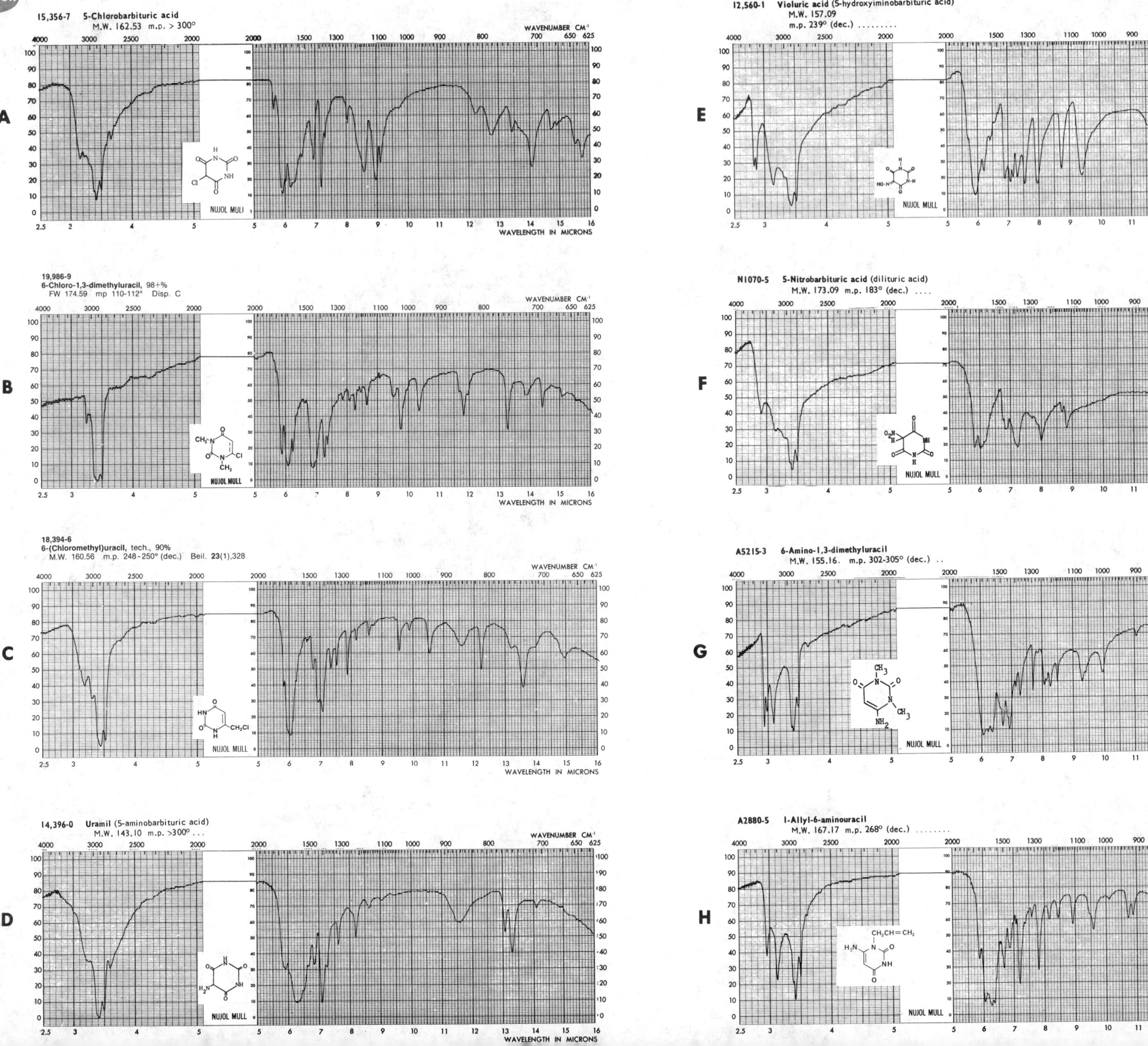
ALDRICH
A
15,356-7 5-Chlorobarbituric acid
M.W. 162.53 m.p. > 300°
NUJOL MULL
B
19,986-9
6-Chloro-1,3-dimethyluracil, 98+%
FW 174.59 mp 110-112° Disp. C
NUJOL MULL
C
18,394-6
6-(Chloromethyl)uracil, tech., 90%
M.W. 160.56 m.p. 248-250° (dec.) Beil. 23(1),328
NUJOL MULL
D
14,396-0 Uramil (5-aminobarbituric acid)
M.W. 143.10 m.p. >300° ...
NUJOL MULL
E
12,560-1 Violuric acid (5-hydroxyiminobarbituric acid)
M.W. 157.09
m.p. 239° (dec.) ....
NUJOL MULL
F
N1070-5 5-Nitrobarbituric acid (dilituric acid)
M.W. 173.09 m.p. 183° (dec.) ....
NUJOL MULL
G
A5215-3 6-Amino-1,3-dimethyluracil
M.W. 155.16. m.p. 302-305° (dec.) ..
NUJOL MULL
H
A2880-5 1-Allyl-6-aminouracil
M.W. 167.17 m.p. 268° (dec.) ....
NUJOL MULL
WAVENUMBER CM⁻¹
WAVELENGTH IN MICRONS

A

21,820-0
1,3-Diallyl-6-aminouracil monohydrate, 97%
FW 225.24 mp 79-82° Disp. C

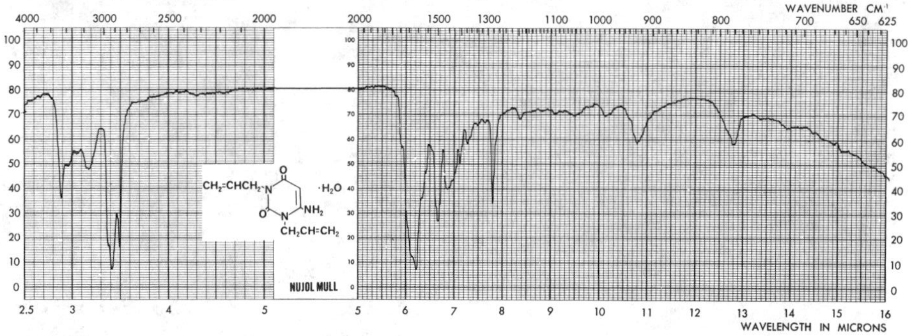

NUJOL MULL

B

D1590-1 **5,6-Diamino-1,3-dimethyluracil hydrate**
M.W. 170.17 (anhydrous) m.p. 210-214° (dec.)

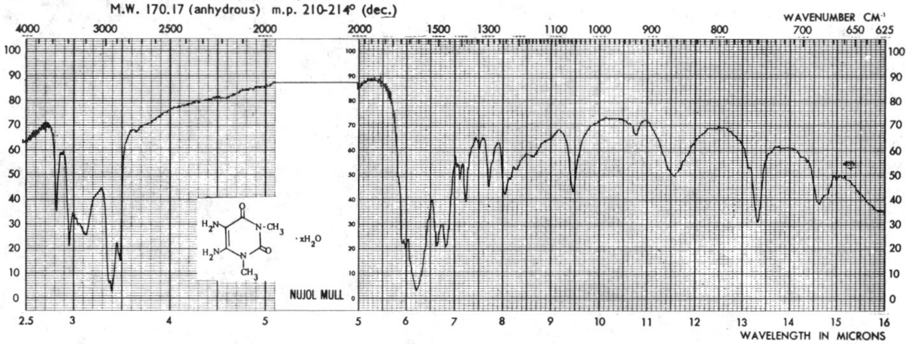

NUJOL MULL

C

14,610-2 **5-Ethyl-5-(3-hydroxy-1-methylbutyl)-barbituric acid**
M.W. 242.28 m.p. 188-191°

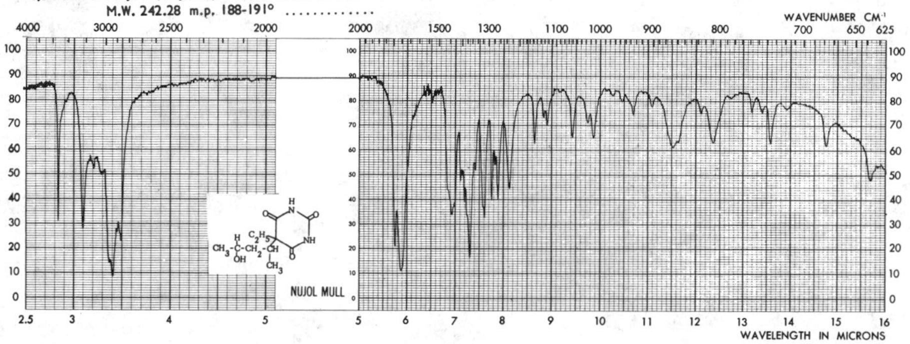

NUJOL MULL

D

11,419-7 **1,3-Dimethyl-5-nitrouracil**

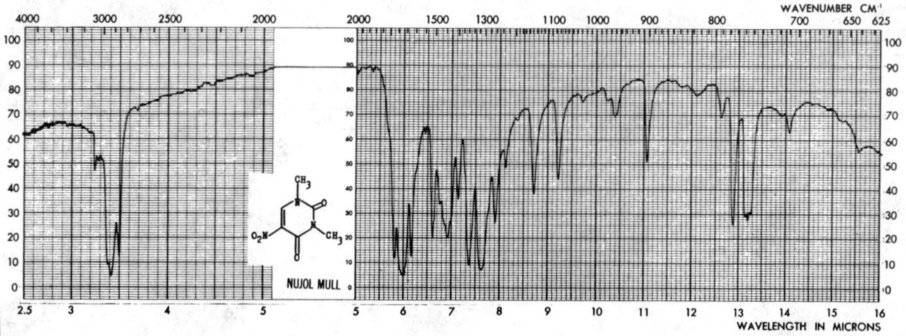

NUJOL MULL

E

14,660-9 **(Hexahydro-2,4,6-trioxo-5-pyrimidinyl)-iminodiacetic acid**
(uramil-N,N-diacetic acid) **monohydrate**
M.W. 277.19 m.p. 245° (dec.)

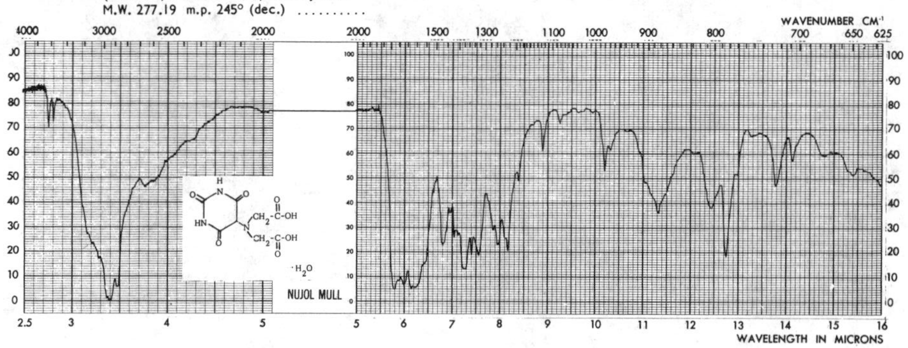

NUJOL MULL

F

11,423-5 **Triallyl-s-triazine-2,4,6(1H,3H,5H)-trione**
M.W. 249.27 n_D^{20} 1.5129 b.p. 149-152°/4 mm.

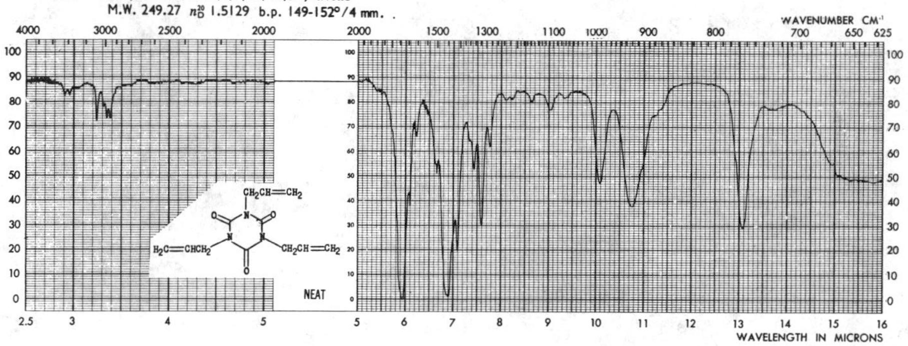

NEAT

G

21,892-8
Dichloroisocyanuric acid, sodium salt, 98%
FW 219.95 Disp. C

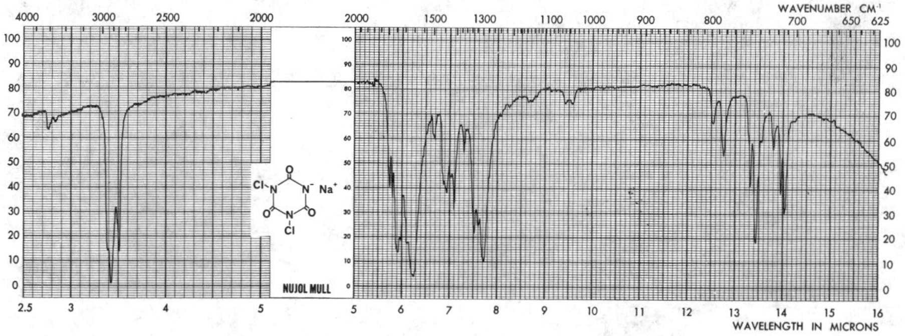

NUJOL MULL

H

17,612-5
Trichloroisocyanuric acid, 97%
M.W. 232.41 m.p. 249-251° Beil. **26**,256
IRRITANT

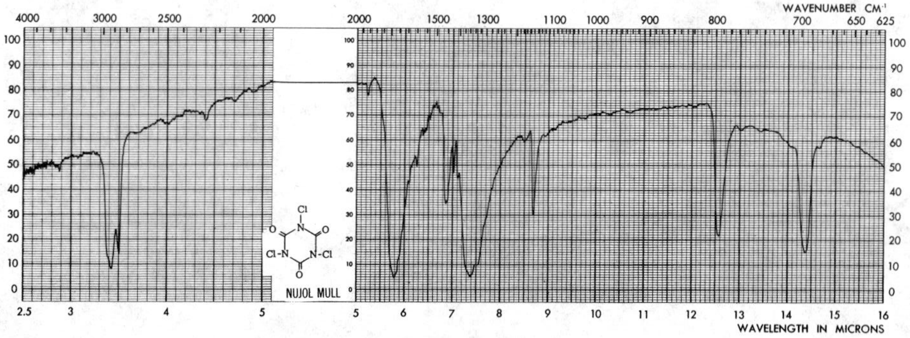

NUJOL MULL

ALDRICH

NON-AROMATIC AMIDES

A

M9020-8 **Murexide**
M.W. 302.20 m.p. > 300°

NUJOL MULL

B

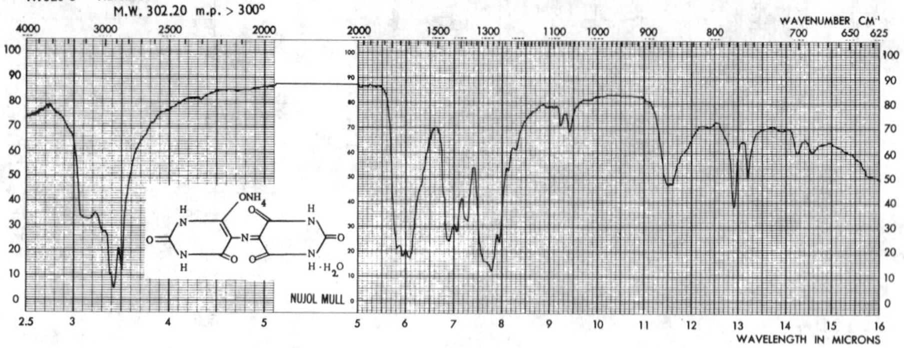

11,998-9 **Alloxantin** (uroxin)
M.W. 322.19 m.p. 197° (dec.)

NUJOL MULL

C

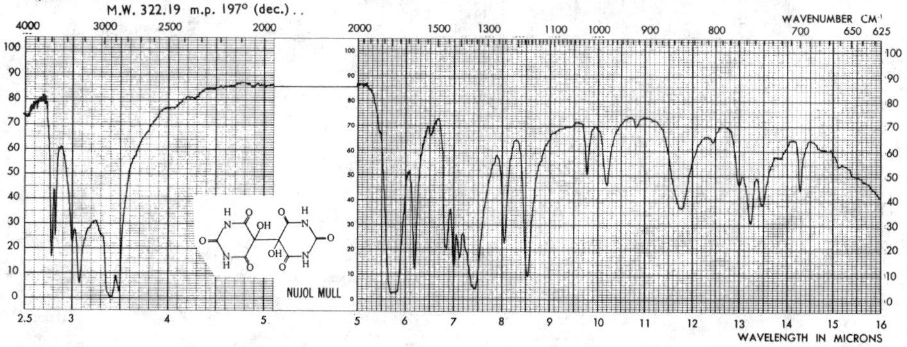

P470-4 **5,5'-(1,3-Pentadien-1-yl-5-ylidene)-dibarbituric acid hydrate, reagent for magnesium**
M.W. 318.25 (anhydrous) m.p. 300° (dec.)

NUJOL MULL

D

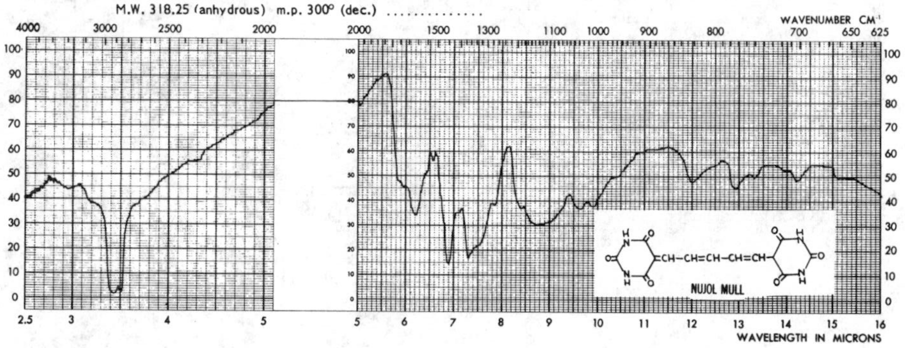

11,517-7
6-Azauridine [2-β-D-ribofuranosyl-as-triazine-3,5(2H,4H)-dione]
M.W. 245.19 m.p. 157-159° **IR** 992F

NUJOL MULL

E

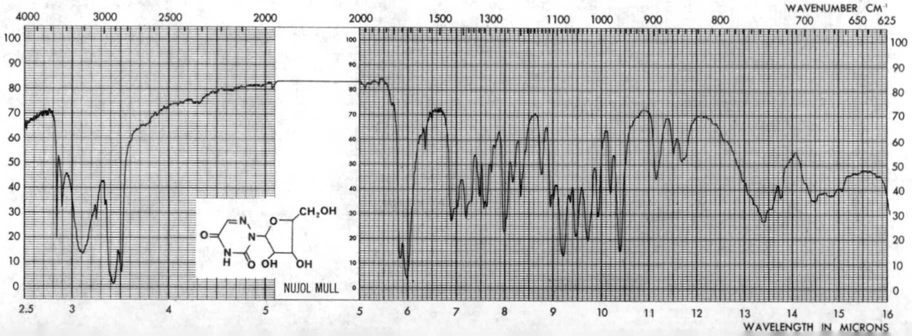

T2720-0 **Theophylline-7-acetic acid**
M.W. 238.20 m.p. 267-268°

NUJOL MULL

F

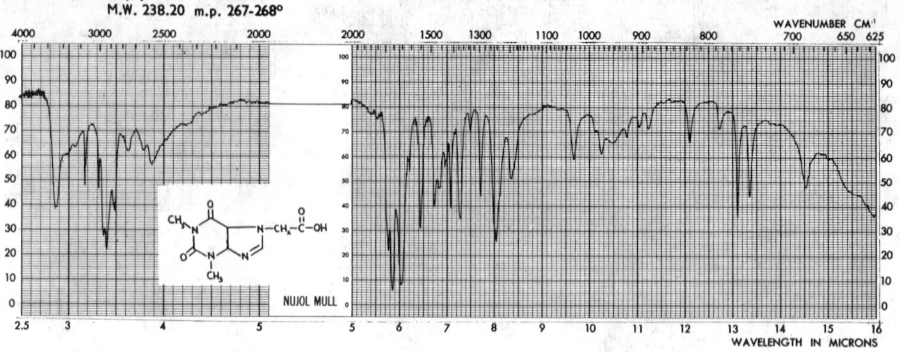

M7825-9 **1-Methyl-2-pyridone, puriss.**
M.W. 109.13 n_D^{20} 1.5690 b.p. 250°/740 mm.

NEAT

G

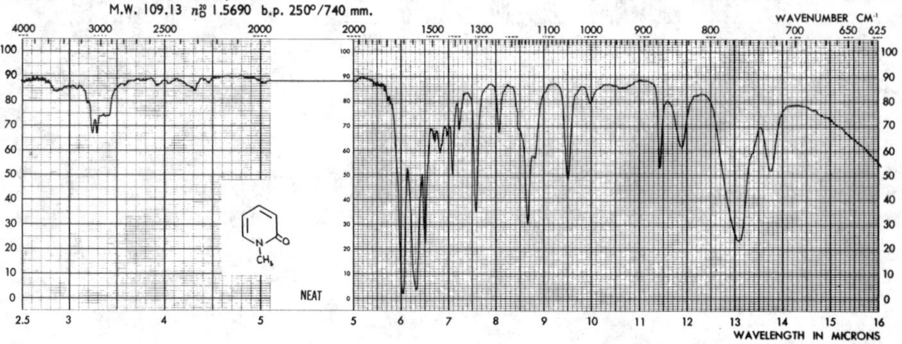

85,522-7
Thermopsine
M.W. 244.34 m.p. 205-207°

NUJOL MULL

H

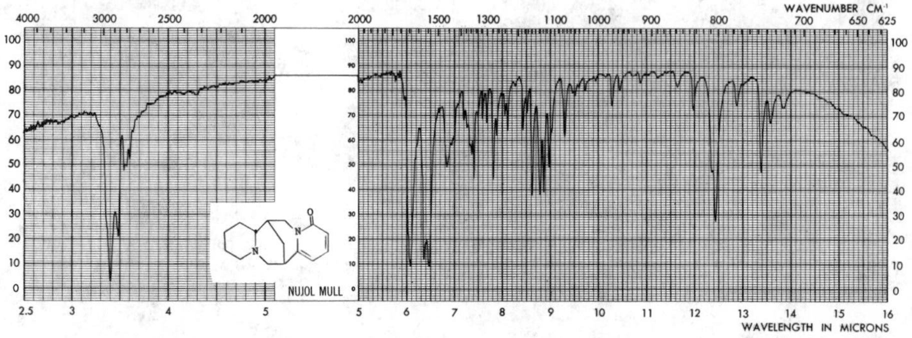

14,283-2 **3-Methoxycarbonylmethoxy-1-methoxycarbonylmethyl-2(1H)-pyridone**
M.W. 255.23 m.p. 101-102°

NUJOL MULL

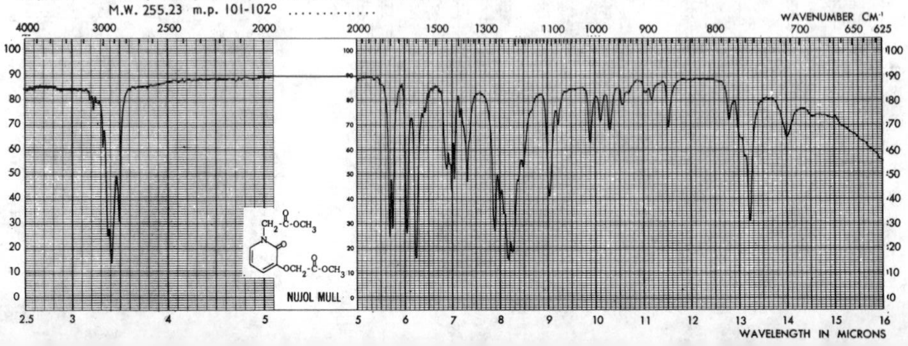

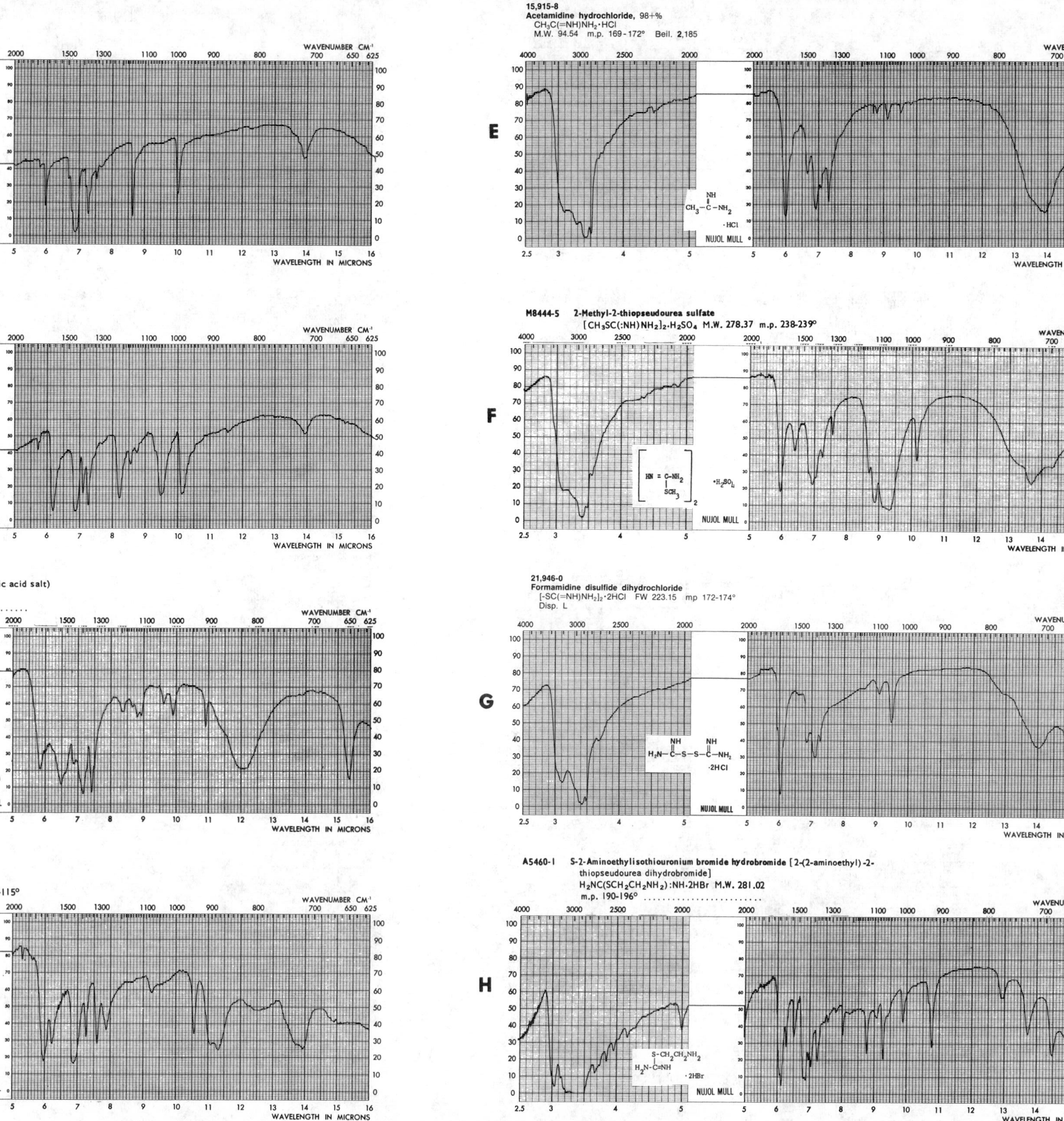

A — 21,491-4 **Eschenmoser's salt** (*N,N*-dimethylmethyleneammonium iodide)
$H_2C{=}N(CH_3)_2I$ FW 185.01 mp 219° (dec.)
Beil. **4**(4),153 Disp. C,B

B — 16,287-6 **Phosgene iminium chloride**, tech. [(dichloromethylene)dimethylammonium chloride]
$Cl_2C{=}N(CH_3)_2Cl$ FW 162.45 mp 183-187° (dec.)
Fieser **4**,135 **5**,195 Disp. S

C — F1580-3 **Formamidine acetate** (formamidine acetic acid salt)
$HC(:NH)NH_2{\cdot}CH_3CO_2H$ M.W. 104.11
m.p. 158-160° (dec.)

D — 14,019-8 **Formamidoxime**
$HC(:NOH)NH_2$ M.W. 60.06 m.p. 112-115°

E — 15,915-8 **Acetamidine hydrochloride**, 98+%
$CH_3C(=NH)NH_2{\cdot}HCl$
M.W. 94.54 m.p. 169-172° Beil. **2**,185

F — M8444-5 **2-Methyl-2-thiopseudourea sulfate**
$[CH_3SC(:NH)NH_2]_2{\cdot}H_2SO_4$ M.W. 278.37 m.p. 238-239°

G — 21,946-0 **Formamidine disulfide dihydrochloride**
$[-SC(=NH)NH_2]_2{\cdot}2HCl$ FW 223.15 mp 172-174°
Disp. L

H — A5460-1 **S-2-Aminoethylisothiouronium bromide hydrobromide** [2-(2-aminoethyl)-2-thiopseudourea dihydrobromide]
$H_2NC(SCH_2CH_2NH_2):NH{\cdot}2HBr$ M.W. 281.02
m.p. 190-196°

ALDRICH

NON-AROMATIC AMIDES

A

M5370-1 **O-Methylisourea hydrogen sulfate** (2-methylpseudourea sulfate)
$CH_3OC(:NH)NH_2 \cdot H_2SO_4$ M.W. 172.16 m.p. 118-120° .....

NUJOL MULL

B

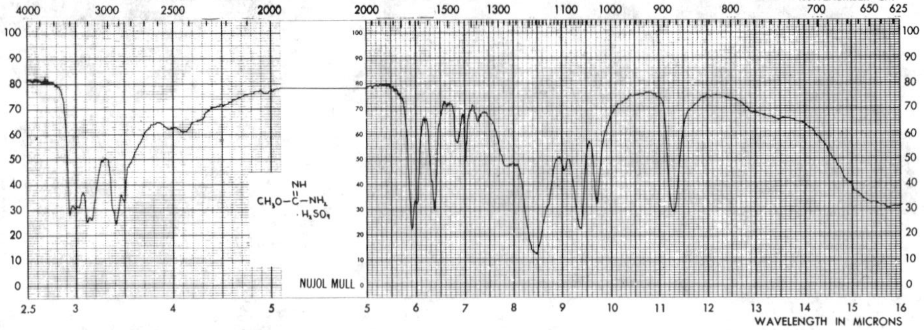

18,884-0
Ethyl acetimidate hydrochloride
$CH_3C(=NH)OC_2H_5 \cdot HCl$ FW 123.58 mp 112-114°
Beil. **2**,182 Disp. C

NUJOL MULL

C

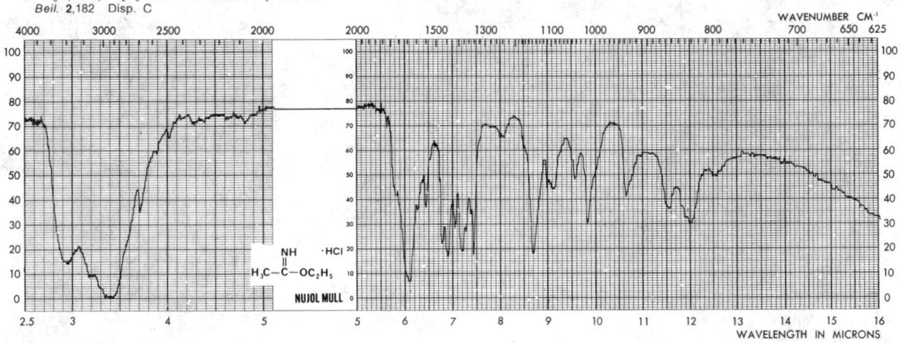

17,952-3
Dimethyl suberimidate dihydrochloride
$CH_3OC(=NH)(CH_2)_6C(=NH)OCH_3 \cdot 2HCl$
M.W. 273.2 m.p. 213-214°

NUJOL MULL

D

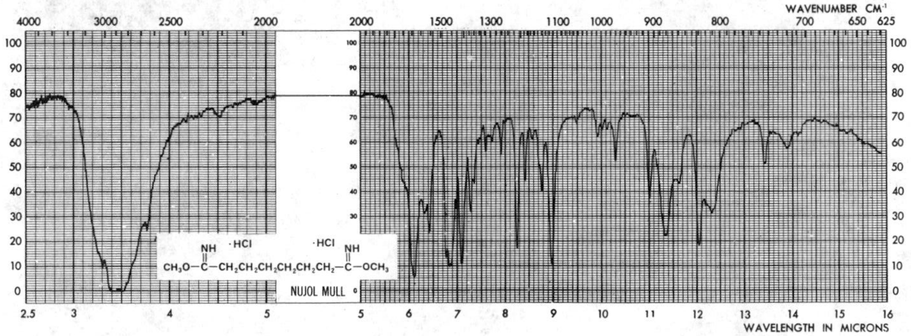

G1170-5 **Guanidine hydrochloride, tech.**
$H_2NC(:NH)NH_2 \cdot HCl$ M.W. 95.53
m.p. 175-180°

NUJOL MULL

E

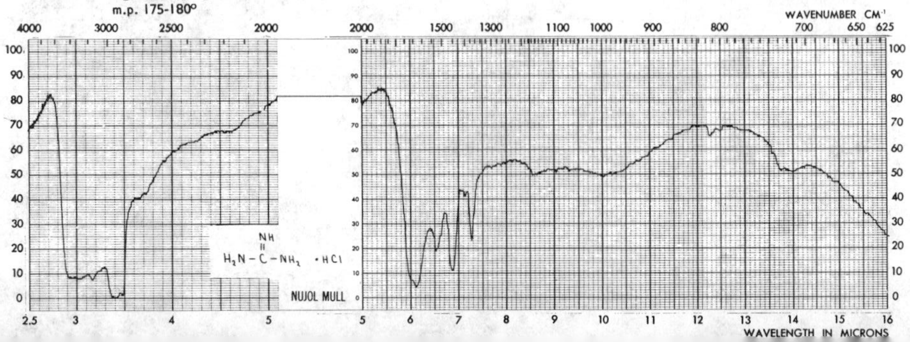

G1165-9 **Guanidine carbonate**
$[H_2NC(:NH)NH_2]_2 \cdot H_2CO_3$ M.W. 180.17
m.p. 198° ....

NUJOL MULL

F

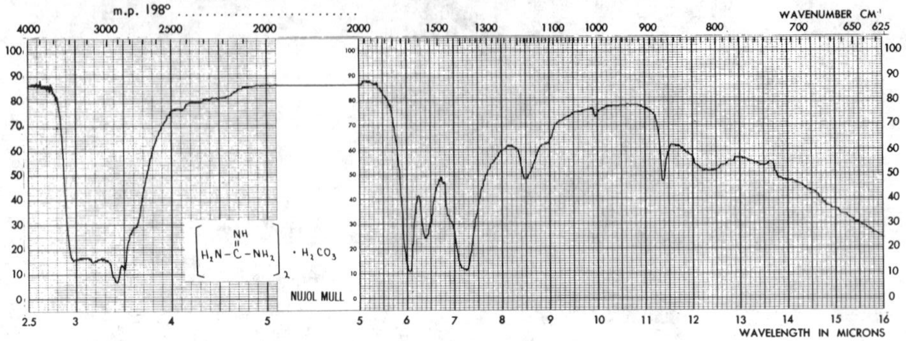

22,240-2
Methylguanidine hydrochloride, 99%
$CH_3NHC(=NH)NH_2 \cdot HCl$ FW 109.56
Beil. **4**(2),571 Disp. D

NUJOL MULL

G

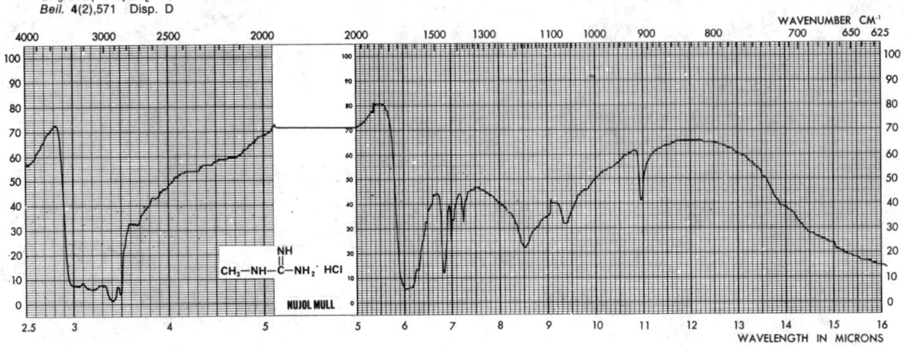

17,793-8
1,1-Dimethylguanidine hydrochloride, 98%
$(CH_3)_2NC(=NH)NH_2 \cdot HCl$
M.W. 123.59 m.p. 103-106° Beil. **4**,75

NUJOL MULL

H

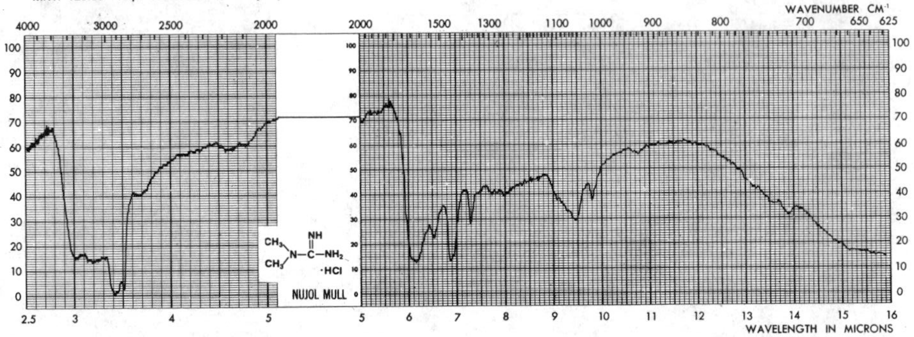

17,791-1
1,1-Diethylguanidine hydrochloride, 99%
$(C_2H_5)_2NC(=NH)NH_2 \cdot HCl$
M.W. 151.64 m.p. 145-147° Beil. 4,121

NUJOL MULL

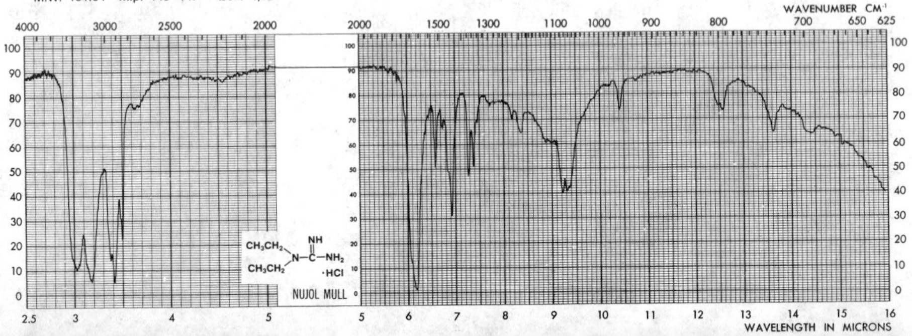

A 19,717-3
2-Hydrazino-2-imidazoline hydrobromide, 98%
FW 181.04 mp 185-187° Disp. C

B 19,790-4
1-(2,2-Diethoxyethyl)guanidine sulfate, 99%
$[(C_2H_5O)_2CHCH_2NHC(=NH)NH_2]_2 \cdot H_2SO_4$
FW 448.54 mp 162-165° Disp. C

C G15 Galegine sulfate
$(CH_3)_2C:CHCH_2N:C(NH_2)_2\ H_2SO_4$ M.W. 225.27
m.p. 221-225°

D 85,040-3
Galegine sulfate
$(CH_3)_2C{=}CHCH_2NHC(=NH)NH_2 \cdot 1/2 H_2SO_4$
M.W. 176.23 m.p. 223-225° Beil. **4**(2),672

E 10,926-6 Aminoguanidine bicarbonate
$H_2NNHC(:NH)NH_2 \cdot H_2CO_3$ M.W. 136.11
m.p. 173° (dec.)

F A5610-8 Aminoguanidine nitrate dihydrate
$H_2NNHC(:NH)NH_2 \cdot HNO_3 \cdot 2H_2O$ M.W. 173.17
m.p. 145-147° (anhydrous)

G 14,341-3 N,N'-Diaminoguanidine monohydrochloride, tech.
$H_2NNHC(:NH)NHNH_2 \cdot HCl$ M.W. 125.56
m.p. 180-182° (dec.)

H 16,424-0
Triaminoguanidine hydrochloride
$H_2NNHC(=NNH_2)NHNH_2 \cdot HCl$
M.W. 140.57 m.p. 228-231° (dec.) Beil. **3**,122

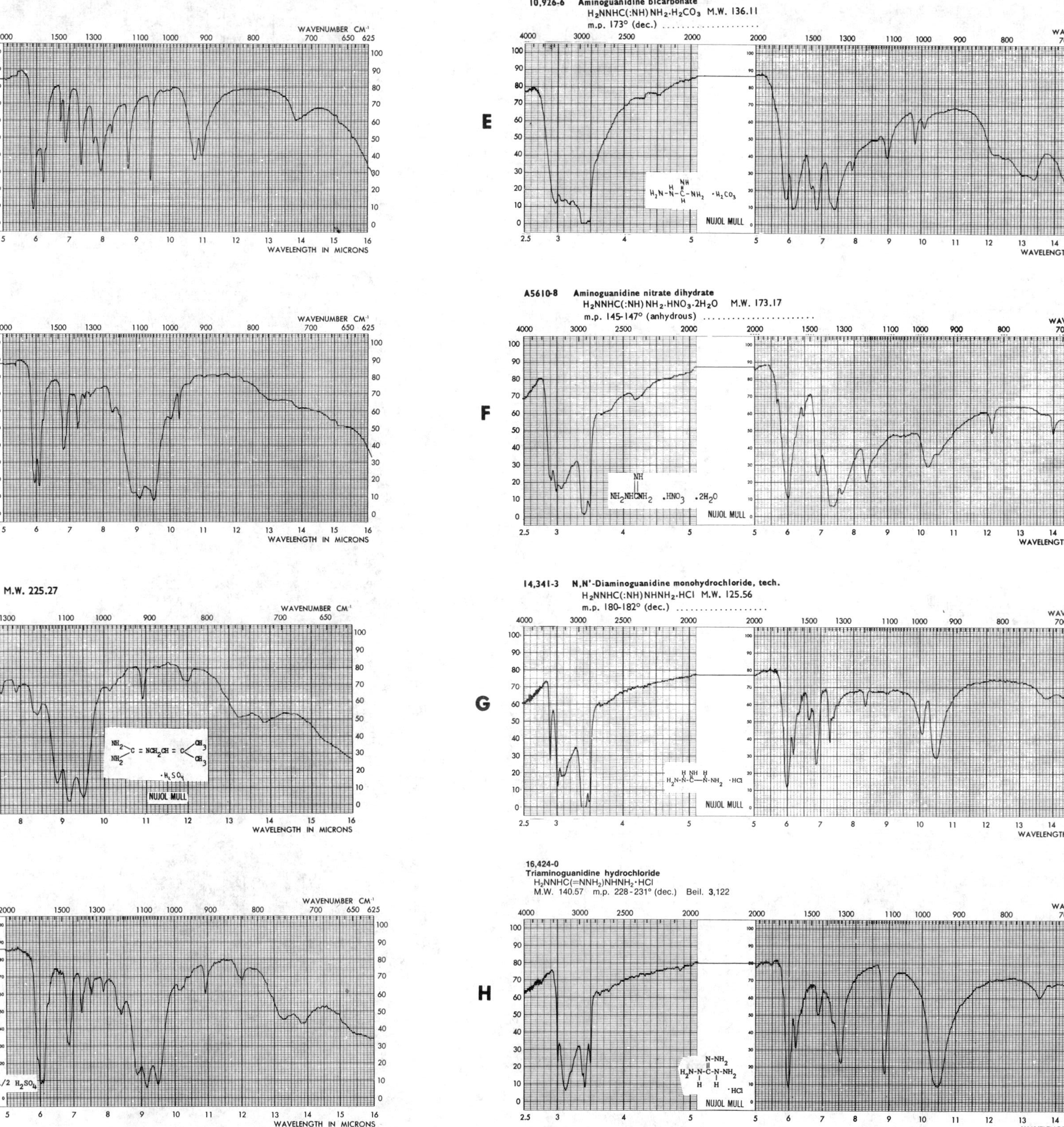

A

G1160-8 **Guanidineacetic acid (glycocyamine)**
$H_2NC(:NH)NHCH_2CO_2H$ M.W. 117.11

NUJOL MULL

B

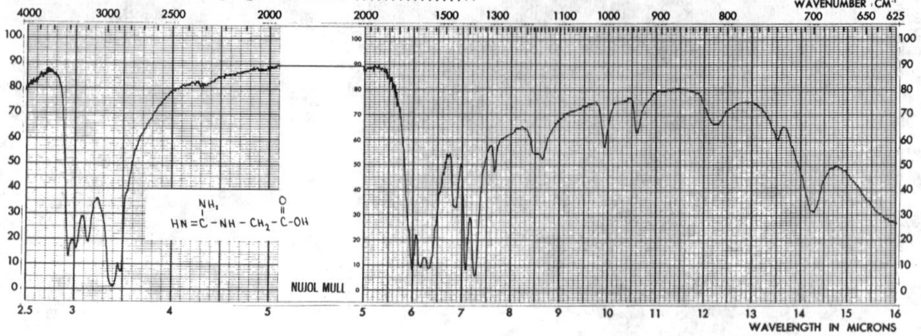

17,651-6
Malonamamidine hydrochloride, 99%
$H_2NC(=NH)CH_2CONH_2 \cdot HCl$
M.W. 137.57 m.p. 174-176° Beil. 2,590

NUJOL MULL

C

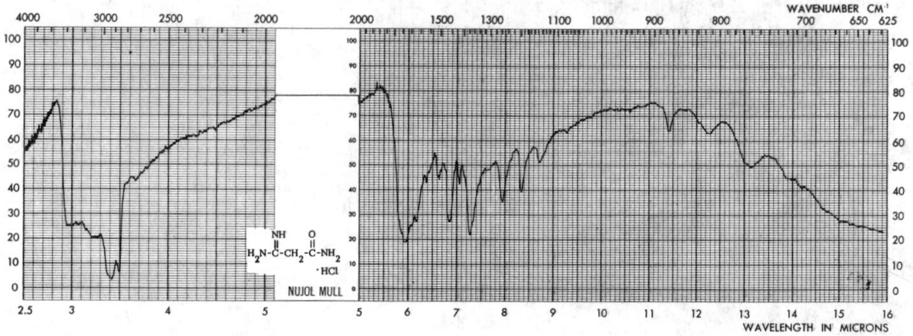

10,144-3 **Agmatine [(4-aminobutyl)-guanidine] sulfate**
$H_2N(CH_2)_4NHC(:NH)NH_2 \cdot H_2SO_4$ M.W. 228.27
m.p. 282° (dec.)

NUJOL MULL

D

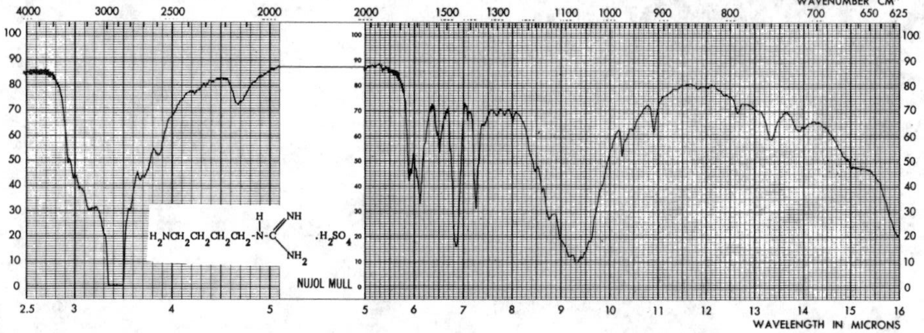

11,942-3 **Hyrudonine (1,10-diamidinospermidine) sesquisulfate monohydrate**
$H_2NC(:NH)NH(CH_2)_4NH(CH_2)_3NHC(:NH)NH_2 \cdot 1\frac{1}{2}H_2SO_4 \cdot H_2O$
M.W. 394.46 m.p. 129-133°

NUJOL MULL

E

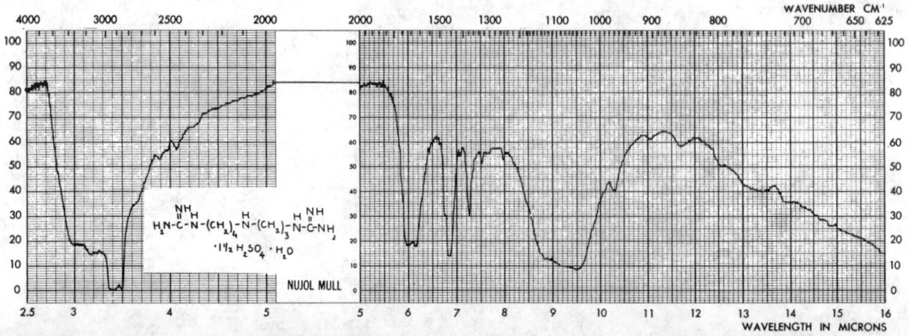

B3400-1 **Biguanide**
$H_2NC(:NH)NHC(:NH)NH_2$ M.W. 101.11 m.p. 134° (dec.)

NUJOL MULL

F

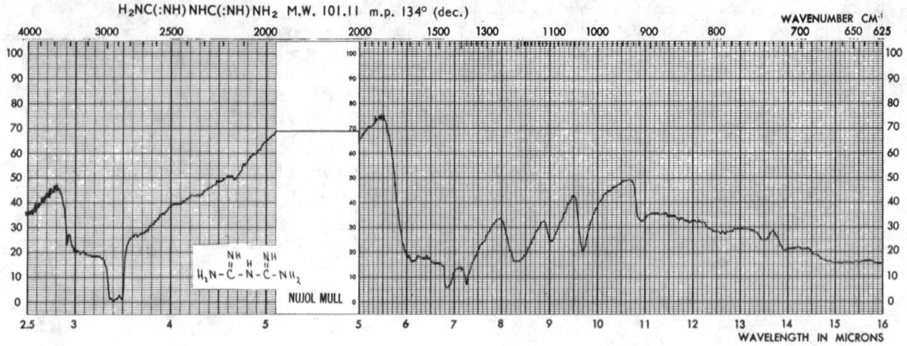

B3420-6 **Biguanide sulfate monohydrate**
$[H_2NC(:NH)NHC(:NH)NH_2]_2 \cdot H_2SO_4 \cdot H_2O$ M.W. 318.32
m.p. 250° (dec.)

NUJOL MULL

G

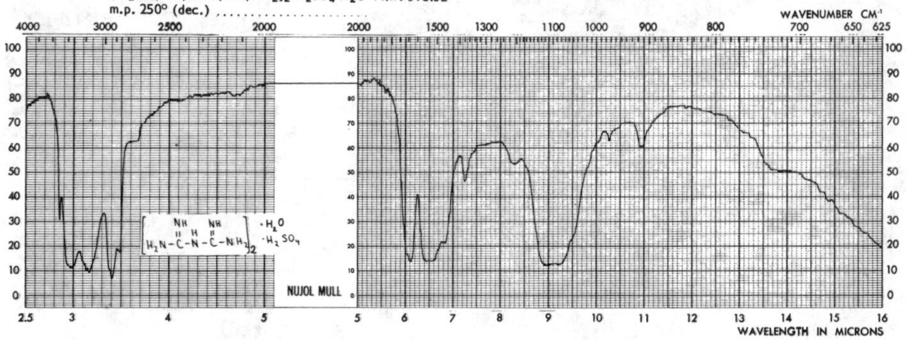

D15,095 **1,1-Dimethylbiguanide hydrochloride**
$(CH_3)_2NC(:NH)NHC(:NH)NH_2 \cdot HCl$ M.W. 165.63
m.p. 223-226°

NUJOL MULL

H

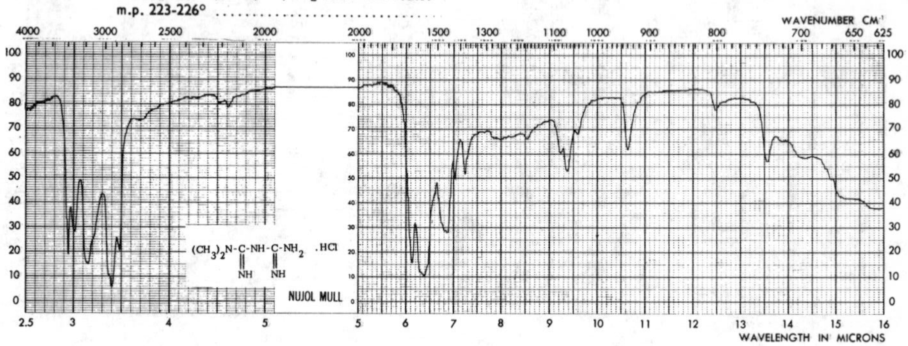

10,757-3 **N-Cyclohexylbiguanide hydrochloride**
$C_6H_{11}NHC(:NH)NHC(:NH)NH_2 \cdot HCl$ M.W. 219.72
m.p. 226-228°

NUJOL MULL

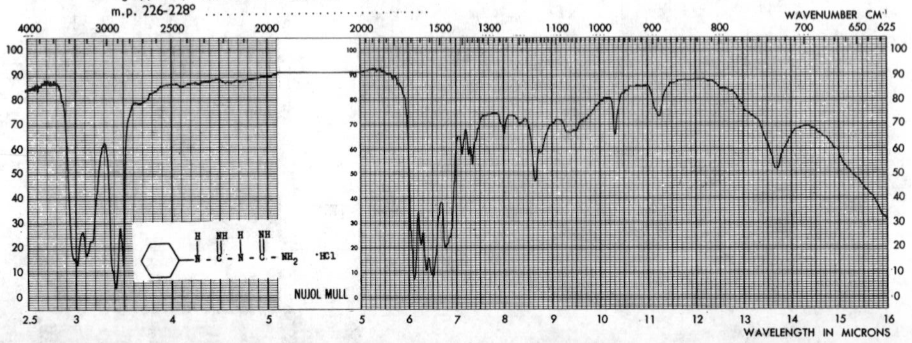

A 12,847-3 **Guanylurea sulfate**
$[H_2NC(:NH)NHCONH_2]_2 \cdot H_2SO_4$ M.W. 302.27
m.p. 200° (dec.)

B 13,949-1 **Methylglyoxal bis-(guanylhydrazone) dihydrochloride monohydrate**
$CH_3C[:NNHC(:NH)NH_2]CH[:NNHC(:NH)NH_2] \cdot 2HCl \cdot H_2O$
M.W. 275.14 m.p. 255° (dec.)

C N1735-1 **Nitroguanidine**
$O_2NNHC(:NH)NH_2$ M.W. 104.07 m.p. 239° (dec.)

D 12,994-1 **N-Methyl-N'-nitro-N-nitrosoguanidine**
(send for data sheet)
$CH_3N(NO)C(:NH)NHNO_2$ M.W. 147.09
m.p. 110-111° (dec.)

E E4160-5 **N-Ethyl-N'-nitro-N-nitrosoguanidine**
(send for data sheet)
$C_2H_5N(NO)C(:NH)NHNO_2$ M.W. 161.12
m.p. 108° (dec.)

F 14,319-7 **N'-Nitro-N-nitroso-N-propylguanidine**
(send for data sheet)
$CH_3CH_2CH_2N(NO)C(:NH)NHNO_2$ M.W. 175.15
m.p. 111° (dec.)

G 14,223-9 **N-Butyl-N'-nitro-N-nitrosoguanidine**
(send for data sheet)
$CH_3(CH_2)_3N(NO)C(:NH)NHNO_2$ M.W. 189.18
m.p. 125° (dec.)

H 14,316-2 **N-Isobutyl-N'-nitro-N-nitrosoguanidine**
(send for data sheet)
$(CH_3)_2CHCH_2N(NO)C(:NH)NHNO_2$ M.W. 189.18
m.p. 95° (dec.)

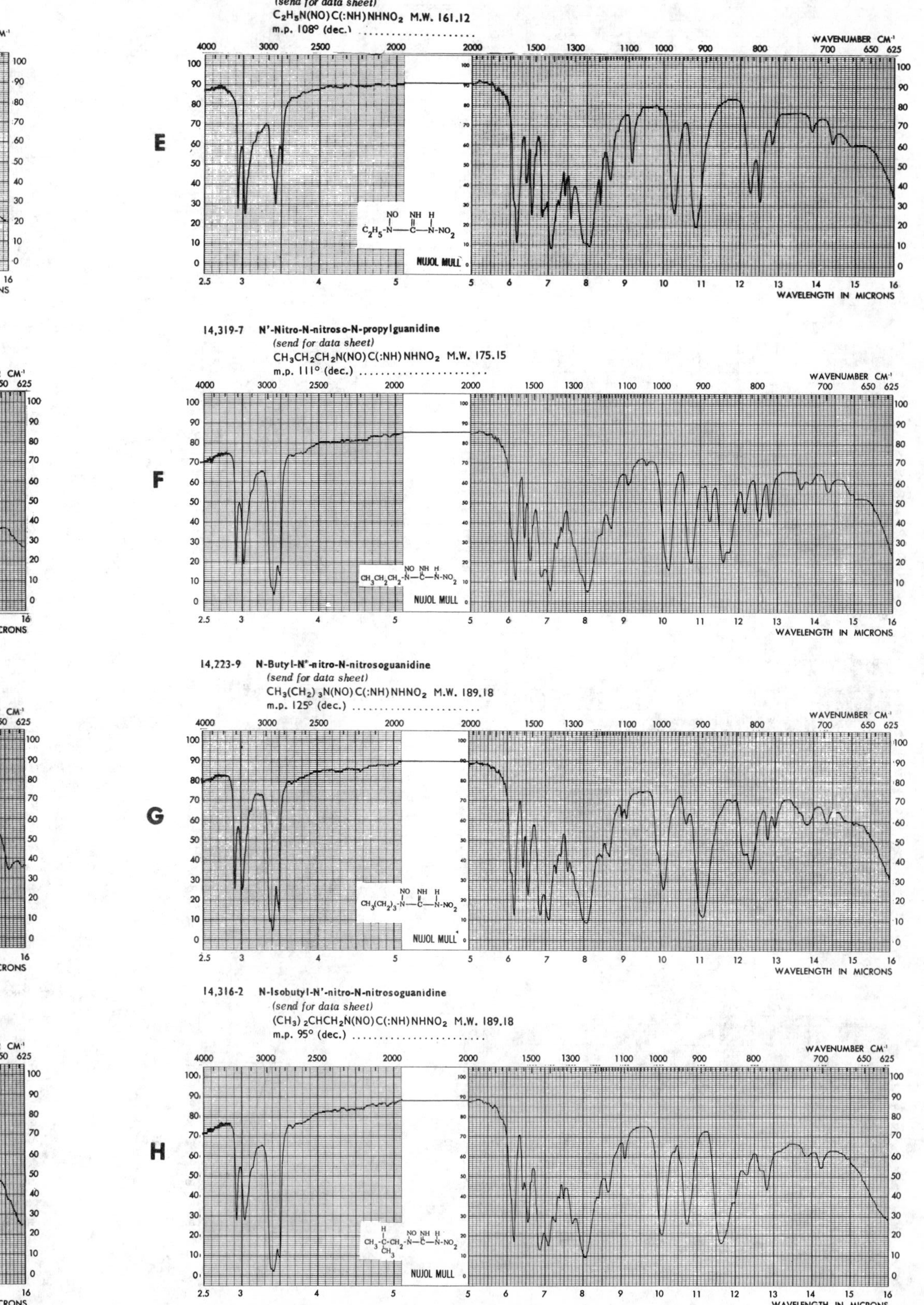

A

14,310-3 N-Amyl-N'-nitro-N-nitrosoguanidine
(send for data sheet)
$CH_3(CH_2)_4N(NO)C(:NH)NHNO_2$ M.W. 203.20
m.p. 112° (dec.)
NUJOL MULL

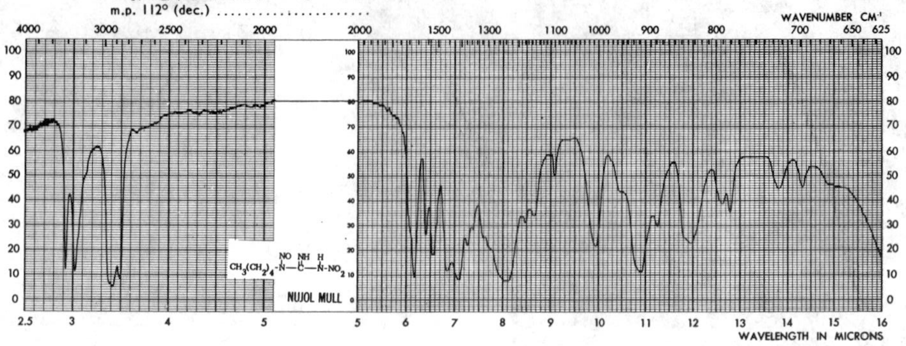

B

14,315-4 N-Isoamyl-N'-nitro-N-nitrosoguanidine
(send for data sheet)
$(CH_3)_2CHCH_2CH_2N(NO)C(:NH)NHNO_2$ M.W. 203.20
m.p. 110° (dec.)
NUJOL MULL

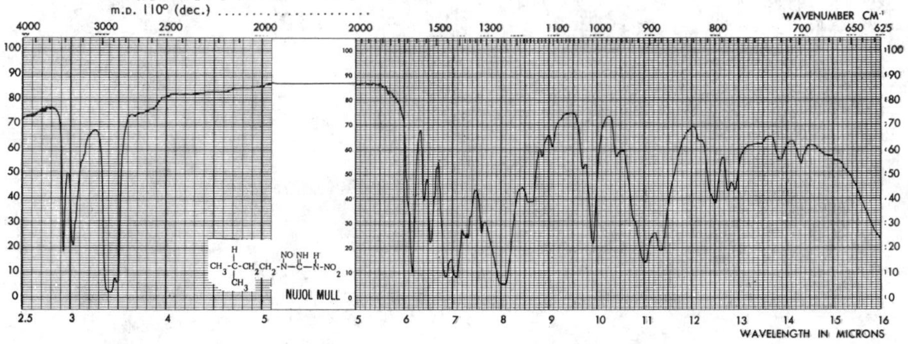

C

14,313-8 N-Hexyl-N'-nitro-N-nitrosoguanidine
$C_7H_{15}N_5O_3$ M.W. 217.23 m.p. 100° (dec.)
NUJOL MULL

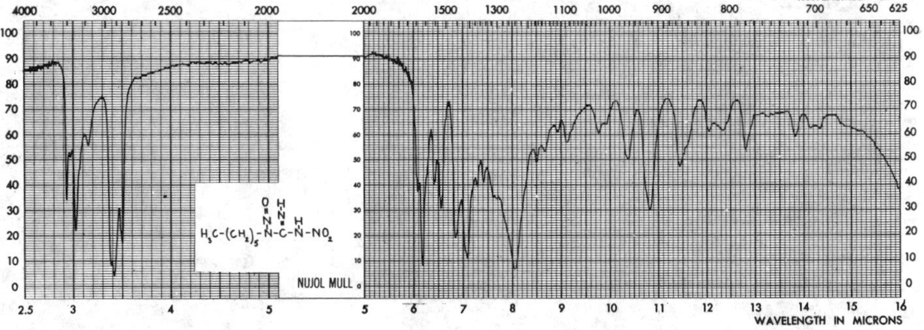

D

14,317-0 N'-Nitro-N-nitroso-N-octylguanidine
$C_9H_{19}N_5O_3$ M.W. 245.28 m.p. 105° (dec.)
NUJOL MULL

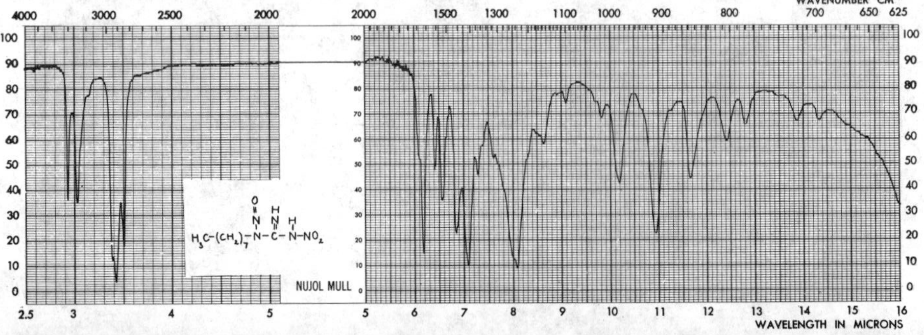

E

13,744-8 2-Methyl-2-oxazoline
M.W. 85.11 n_D^{20} 1.4340
NEAT

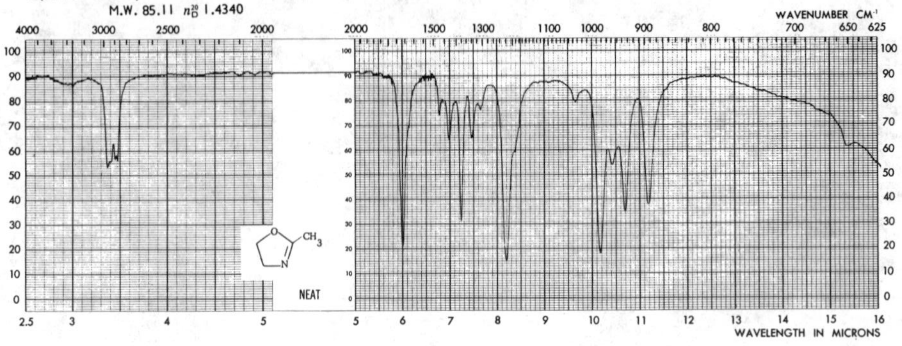

F

13,745-6 2-Ethyl-2-oxazoline
M.W. 99.13 n_D^{20} 1.4370
NEAT

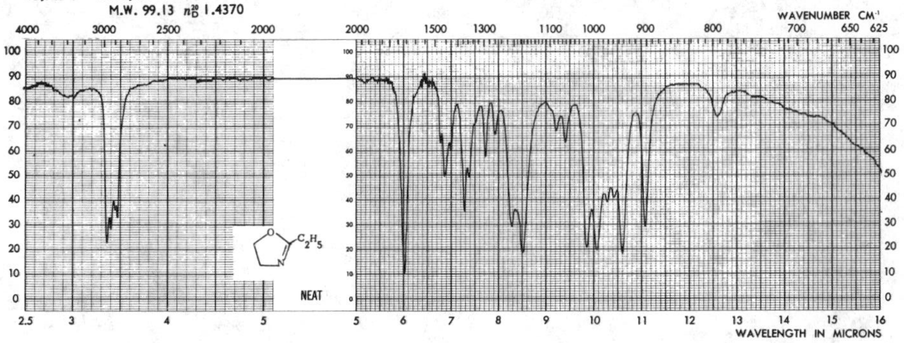

G

M8340-6 2-Methylthiazoline
M.W. 101.17 n_D^{20} 1.5173
NEAT

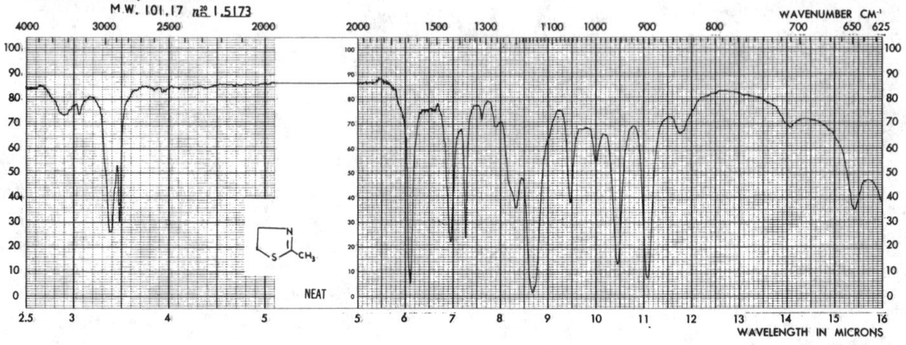

H

A8,080-7
2-Amino-2-thiazoline, 97%
M.W. 102.16 m.p. 79-80.5° Beil. **27**,136
Respiratory analeptic.
NUJOL MULL

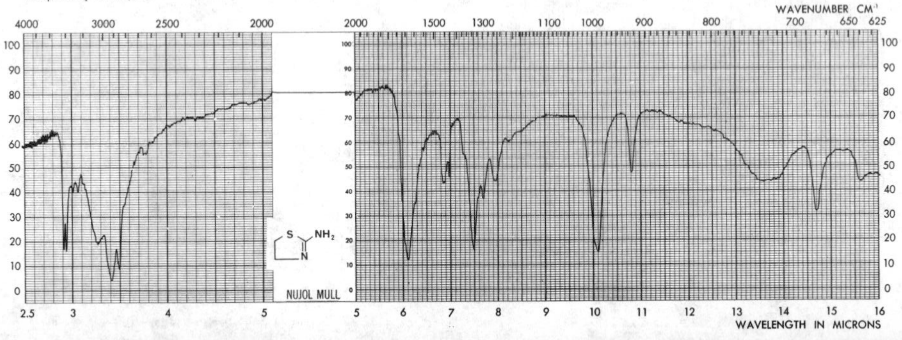

A 15,244-7 5-Chloromethyl-2-iminooxazolidine
M.W. 134.57 m.p. 137.5-140° ...
NUJOL MULL

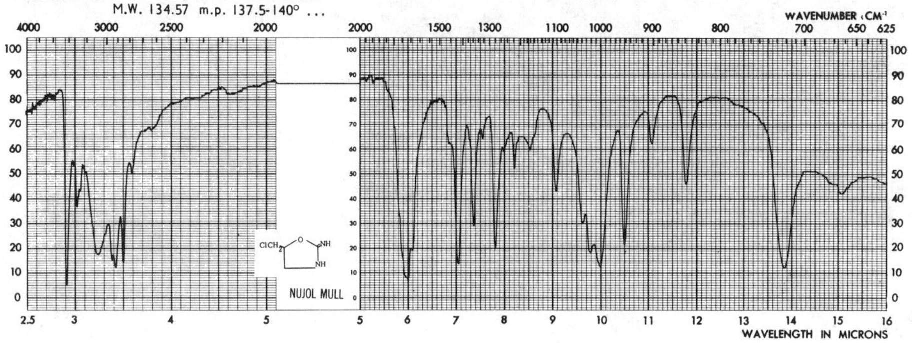

B 10,648-8 2-Amino-2-thiazoline hydrochloride
M.W. 138.62 m.p. 203-205° ..
NUJOL MULL

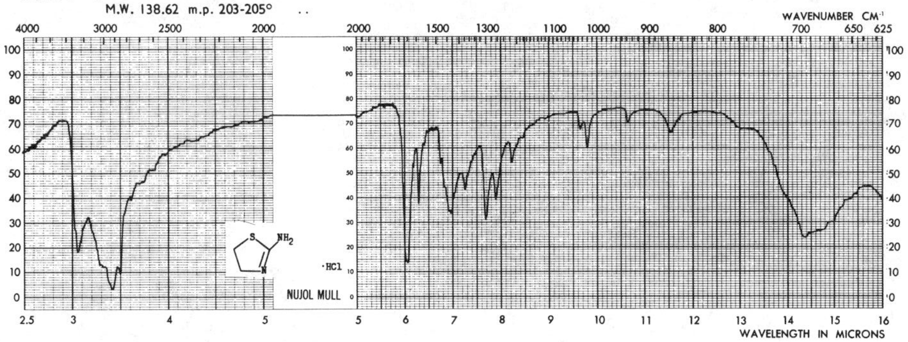

C P5560-0 Pseudothiohydantoin
M.W. 116.14 m.p. 249° (dec.)
NUJOL MULL

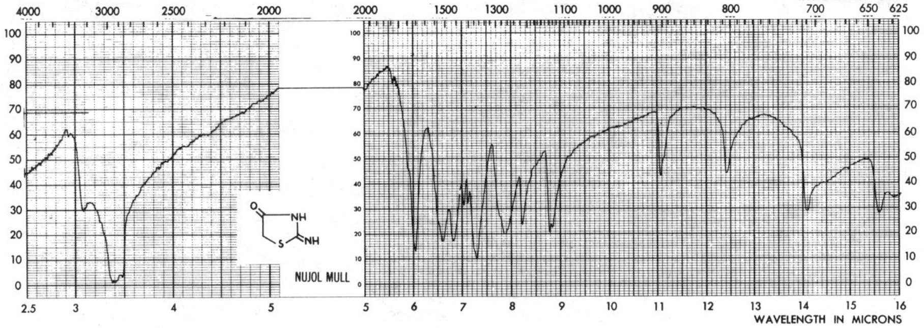

D 14,152-6 3-Amino-3-pyrazoline dihydrochloride
M.W. 158.03 m.p. 180° (dec.) ....
NUJOL MULL

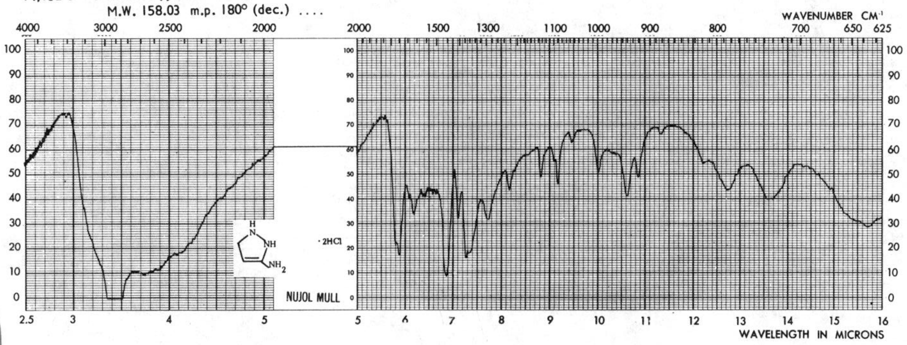

E 13,318-3 2-Amino-4-imino-2-thiazoline hydrochloride
M.W. 151.62 m.p. > 230° (dec.) ....
NUJOL MULL

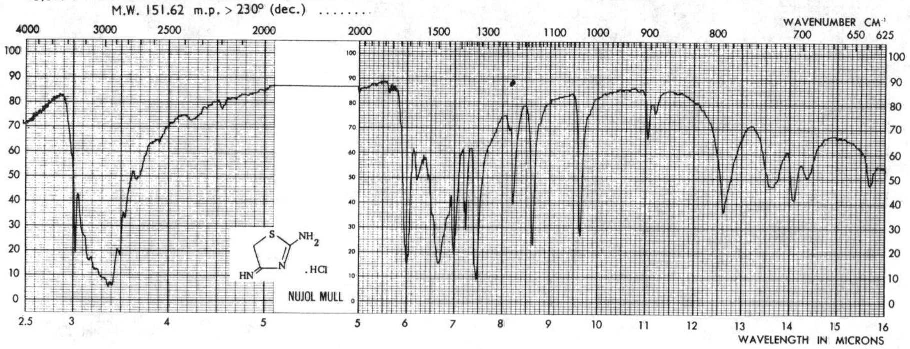

F 17,963-9
5,6-Dihydro-2,4,4,6-tetramethyl-4H-1,3-oxazine
M.W. 141.21 b.p. 47-49°/17mm. n_D^{20} 1.4410
d 0.886
NEAT

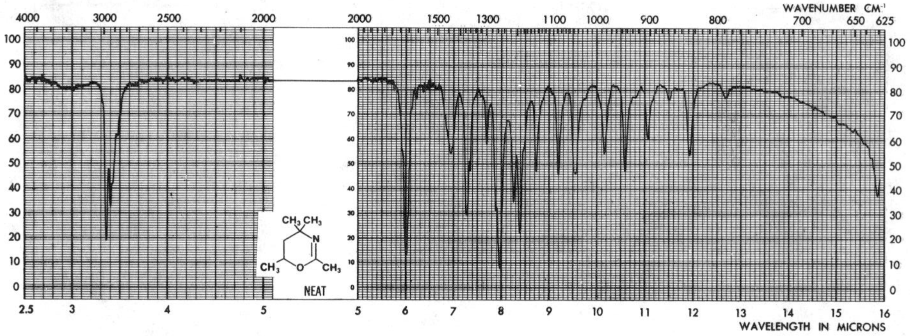

G 13,117-2 2-Iminopiperidine hydrochloride
M.W. 134.61 m.p. 151.5-153°
NUJOL MULL

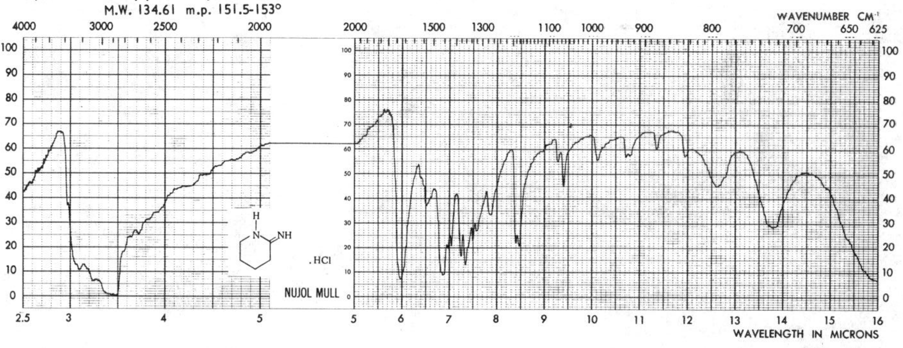

H A9580-4 1-Aza-2-methoxy-1-cycloheptene (O-methylcaprolactim)
M.W. 127.19 n_D^{20} 1.4630 ....
NEAT

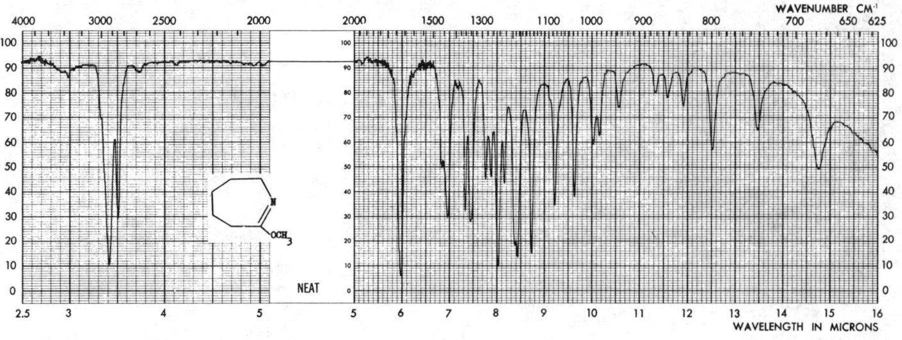

A

13,658-1 **1,5-Diazabicyclo[4.3.0]non-5-ene (DBN)**
(send for data sheet)
M.W. 124.19 n_D^{20} 1.5190 b.p. 95-98°/7.5 mm.
NEAT

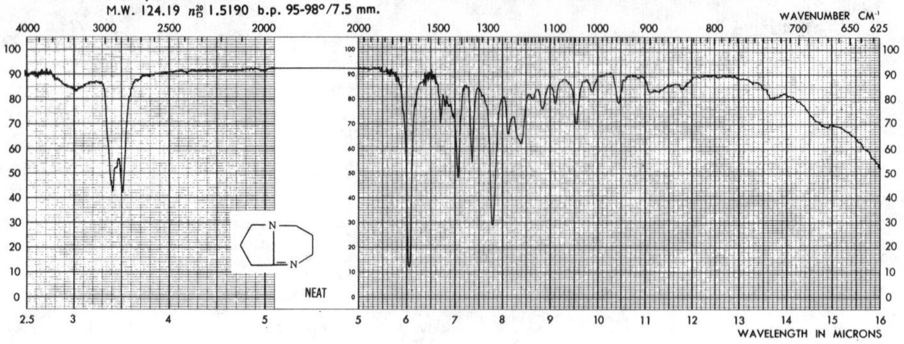

B

13,900-9 **1,5-Diazabicyclo[5.4.0]undec-5-ene** (DBU, 2,3,4,6,7,8,9,10-octahydro-pyrimido[1,2-a]azepine)
(send for data sheet)
M.W. 152.24 n_D^{20} 1.5219 b.p. 80-83°/0.6 mm.
NEAT

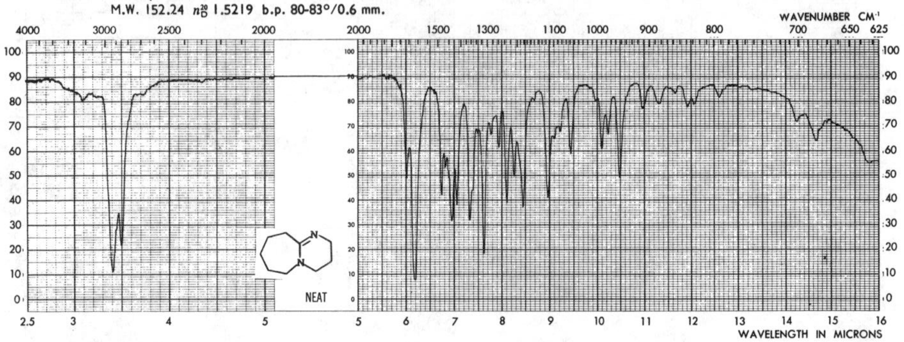

C

16,320-1
N,N'-Dicyclohexyl-4-morpholinecarboxamidine
M.W. 293.46 m.p. 105-107°
NUJOL MULL

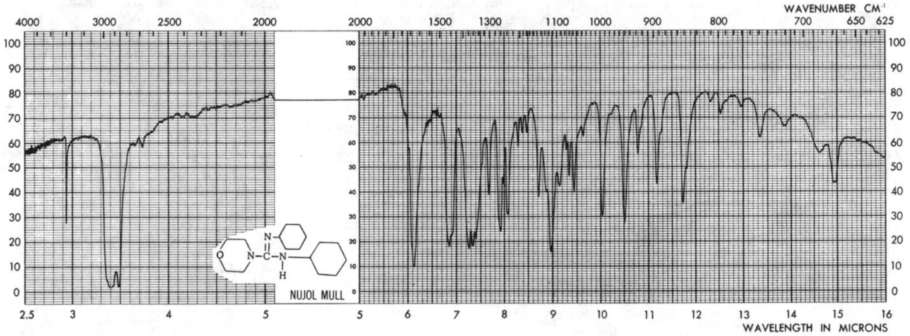

D

16,364-3
N,N-Dimethylthioformamide, 99%
$HCSN(CH_3)_2$
M.W. 89.16 b.p. 58-60°/1mm. n_D^{20} 1.5757
d 1.047 Beil. **4**,70 Fieser **3**,128 *STENCH*
NEAT

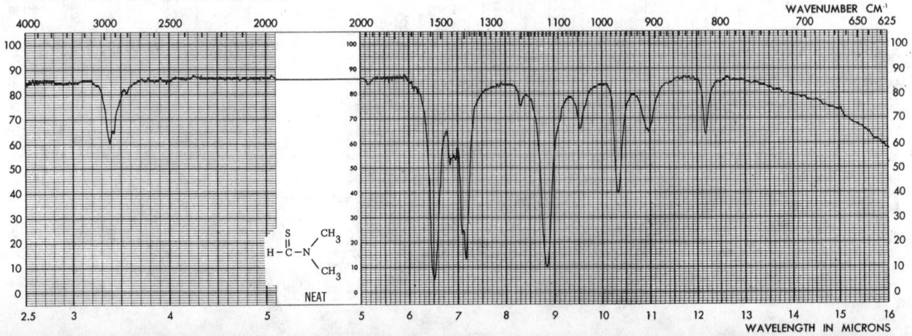

E

T3355-3 **Thiourea, puriss.**
H_2NCSNH_2 M.W. 76.12 m.p. 180-181°
NUJOL MULL

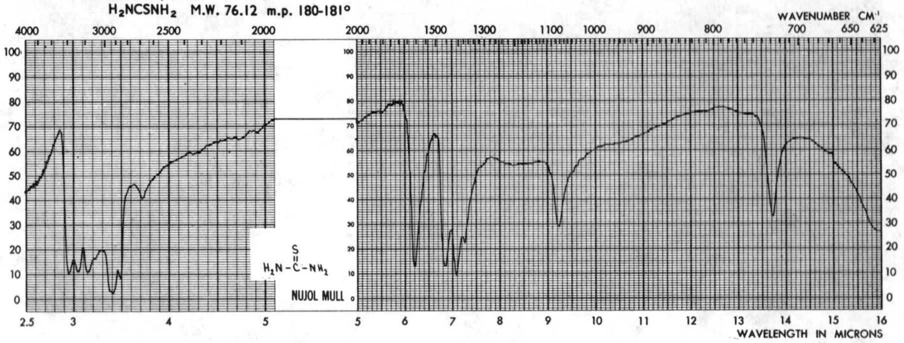

F

16,367-8
Thioacetamide, A.C.S. reagent, 99%
CH_3CSNH_2
M.W. 75.13 m.p. 112-114° Beil. **2**,232
NUJOL MULL

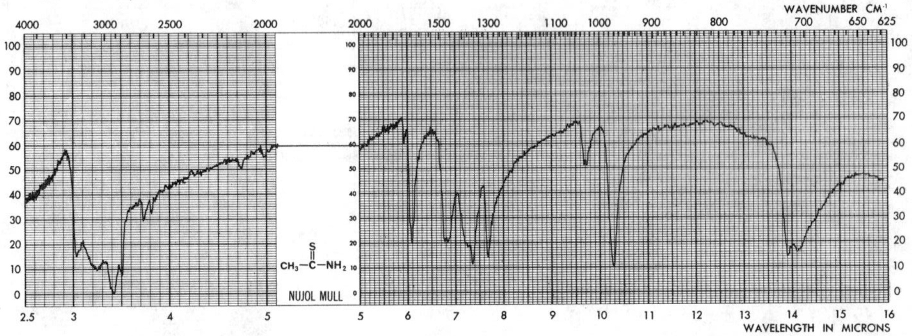

G

M8460-7 **N-Methylthiourea**
$CH_3NHCSNH_2$ M.W. 90.15 m.p. 118-119°
NUJOL MULL

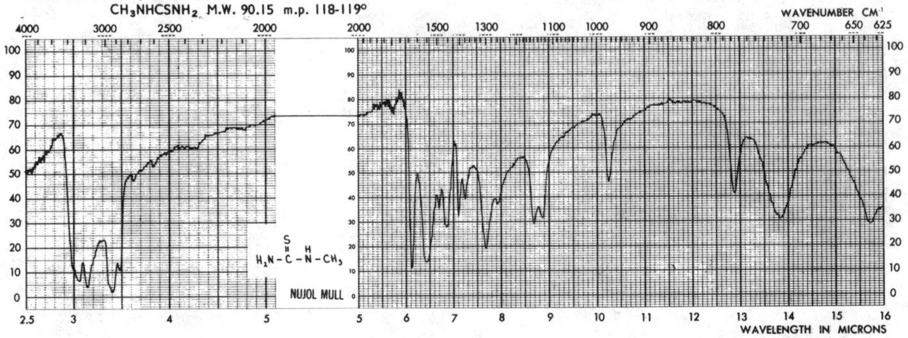

H

16,368-6
1,1,3,3-Tetraethyl-2-thiourea
$(C_2H_5)_2NCSN(C_2H_5)_2$
M.W. 188.34 b.p. 126-128°/10mm. n_D^{20} 1.5226
d 0.966 Beil. **4**(1),356
NEAT

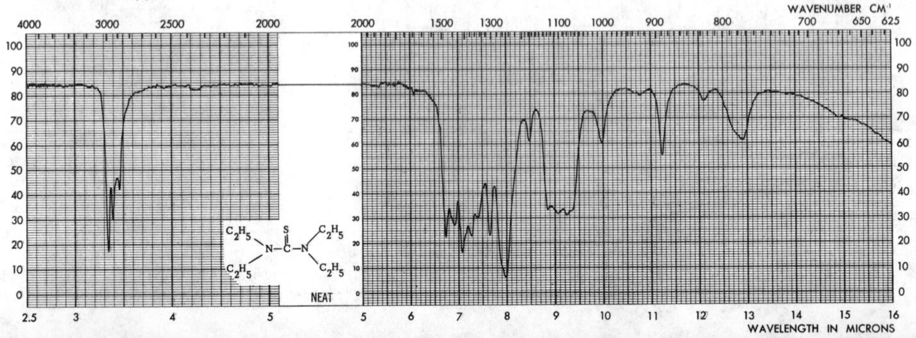

A T3340-5 **Thiosemicarbazide**
$H_2NCSNHNH_2$ M.W. 91.14
m.p. 180-181° (dec.) ......
NUJOL MULL

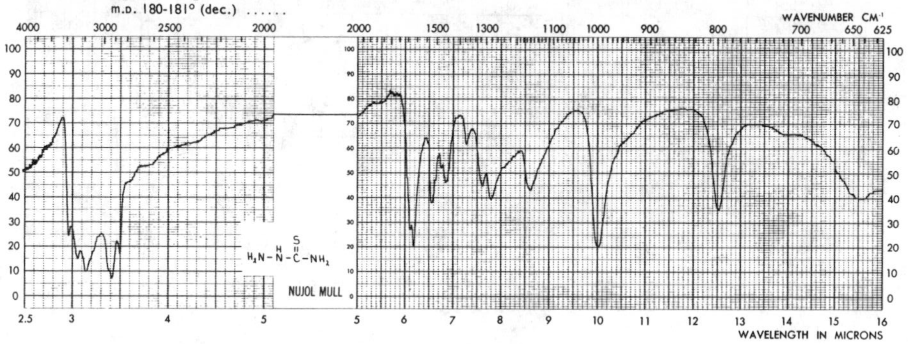

B 13,006-0 **4-Methylthiosemicarbazide**
$CH_3NHCSNHNH_2$ M.W. 105.16 m.p. 135-138°
NUJOL MULL

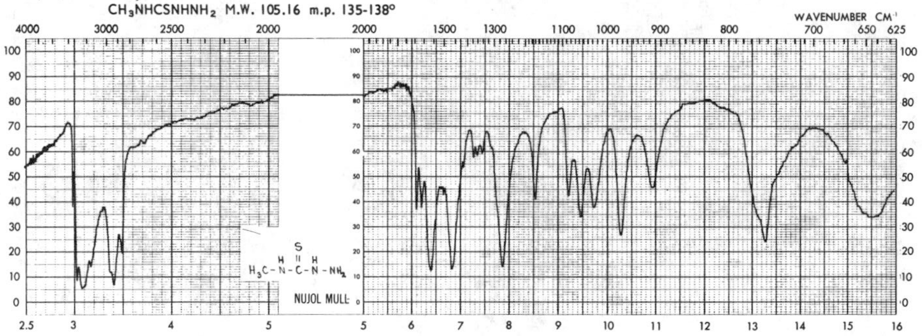

C E4930-4 **4-Ethyl-3-thiosemicarbazide**
$C_2H_5NHCSNHNH_2$ M.W. 119.20 m.p. 82-84°
NUJOL MULL

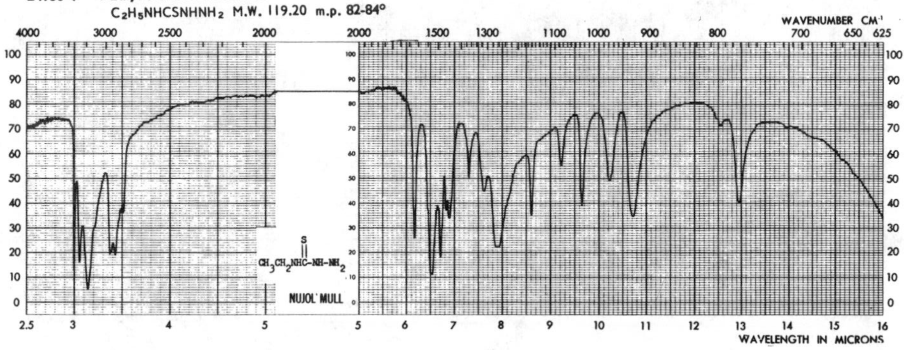

D 10,880-4 **Allylthiourea** (thiosinamine)
$H_2C{:}CHCH_2NHCSNH_2$ M.W. 116.19
m.p. 73-75° ....
NUJOL MULL

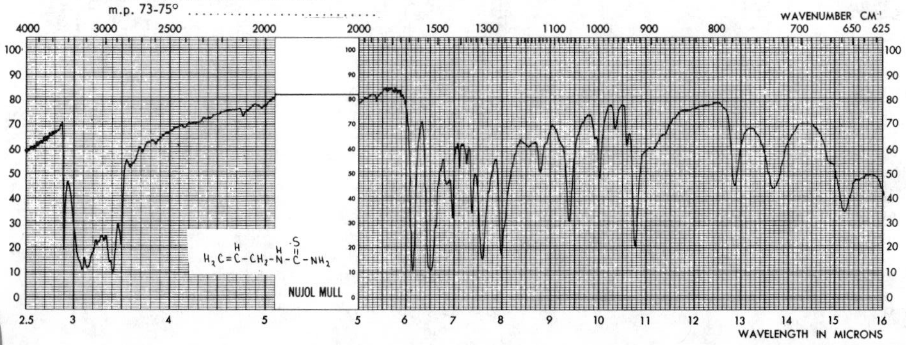

E A3590-9 **4-Allylthiosemicarbazide**
$H_2C{:}CHCH_2NHCSNHNH_2$ M.W. 131.20 m.p. 93-96° ......
NUJOL MULL

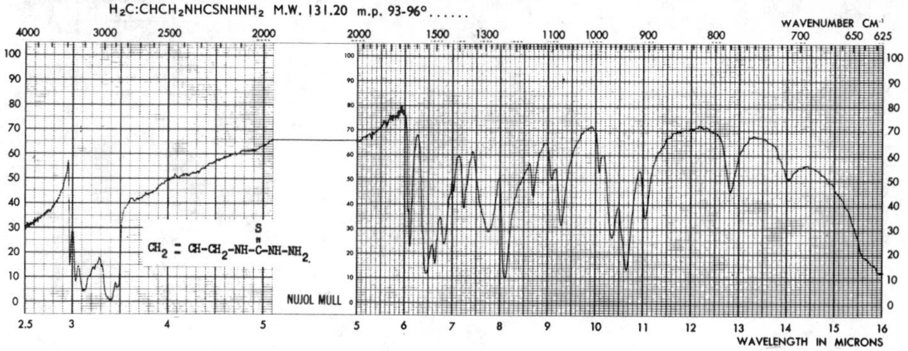

F A1052-3 **Acetone thiosemicarbazone**
$(CH_3)_2C{:}NNHCSNH_2$ M.W. 131.20 m.p. 176-178° (dec.)
NUJOL MULL

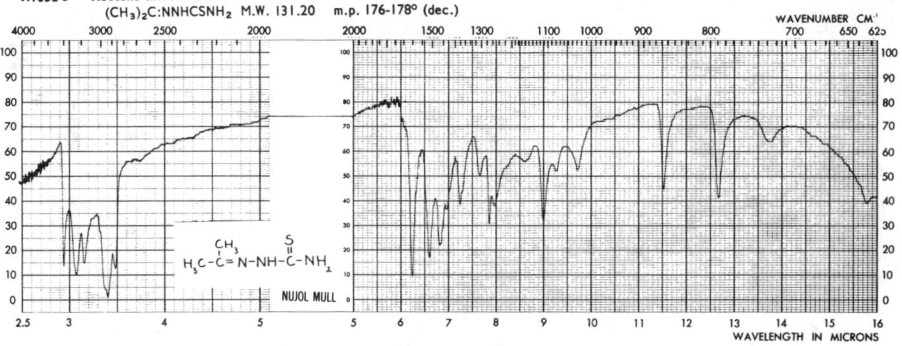

G D18,870-0 **N,N'-Dimethylthiourea**
$CH_3NHCSNHCH_3$ M.W. 104.18 ....
MELT

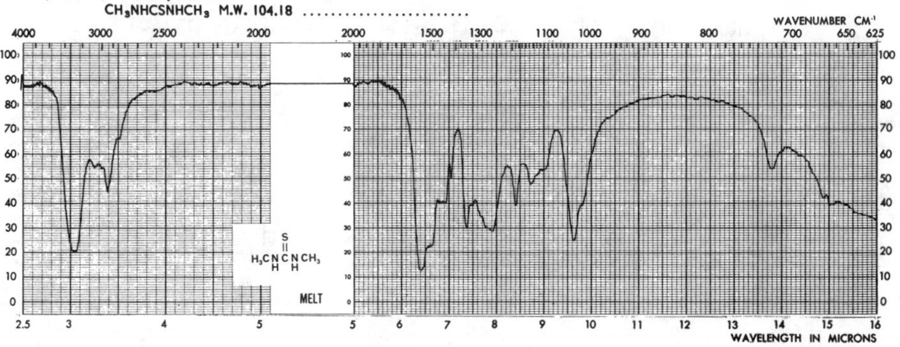

H D10,090 **N,N'-Diethylthiourea**
$C_2H_5NHCSNHC_2H_5$ M.W. 132.23 m.p. 76-77°
NUJOL MULL

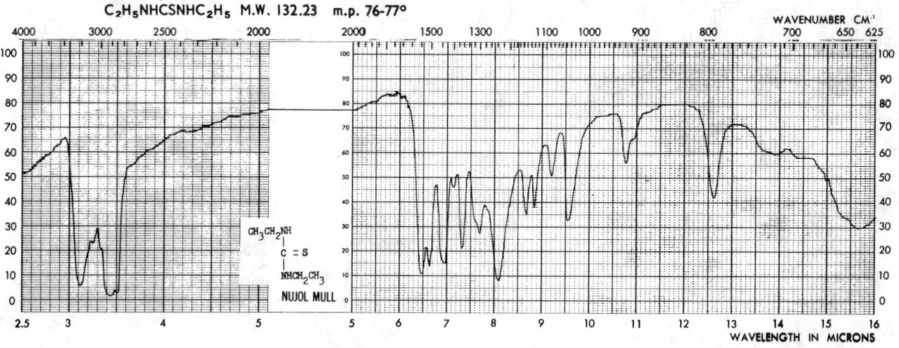

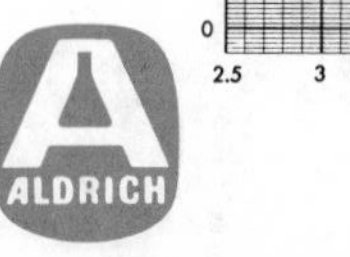

A

D12,680-2 sym.-Diisopropylthiourea, puriss.
$(CH_3)_2CHNHCSNHCH(CH_3)_2$ M.W. 160.28 m.p. 143-145°

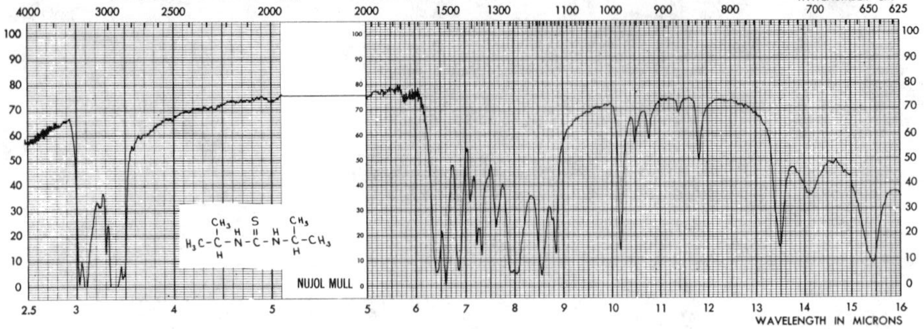

NUJOL MULL

B

D4959-8 N,N'-Di-n-butylthiourea
$CH_3(CH_2)_3NHCSNH(CH_2)_3CH_3$ M.W. 188.34
m.p. 63-65°

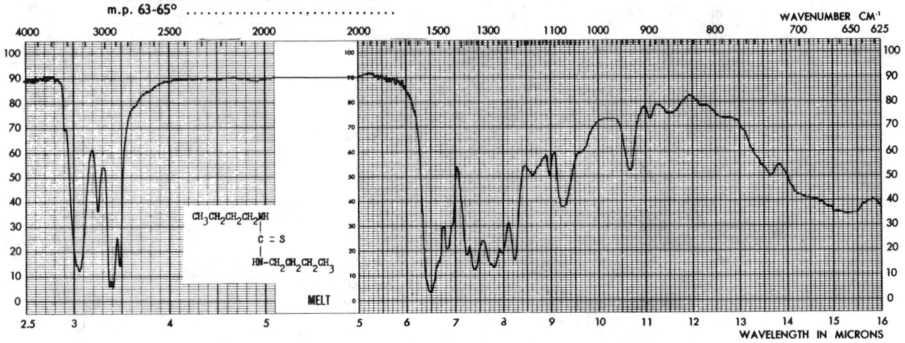

MELT

C

D4960-1 N,N'-Di-tert.-butylthiourea
$(CH_3)_3CNHCSNHC(CH_3)_3$ M.W. 188.34 m.p. 168-171° (dec.)

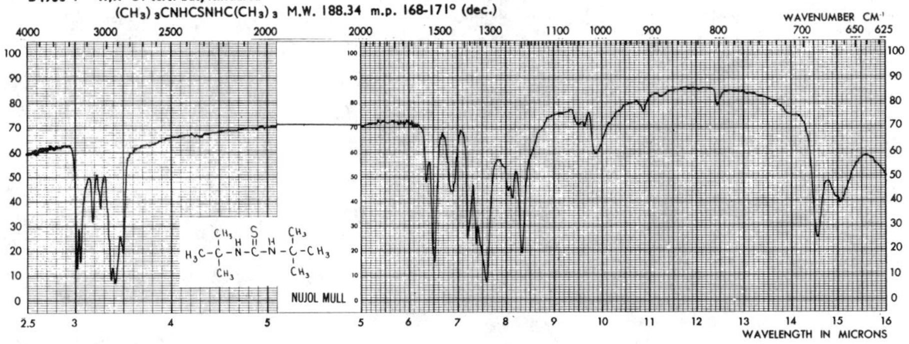

NUJOL MULL

D

10,791-3 sym.-Diallylthiourea, tech.
$H_2C{:}CHCH_2NHCSNHCH_2CH{:}CH_2$ M.W. 156.25 m.p. 41-43°

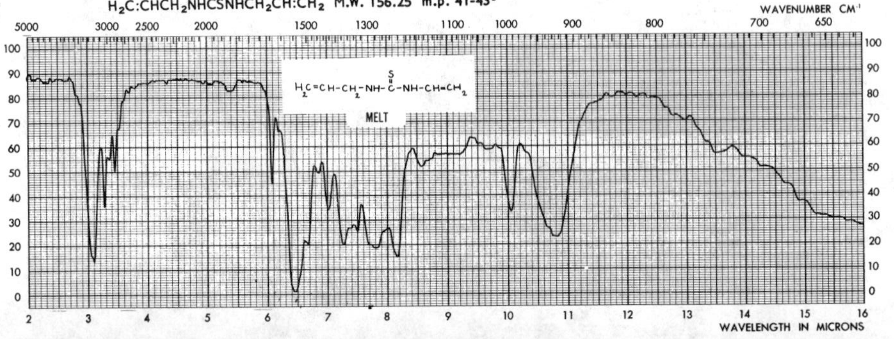

MELT

E

C10,660-7 1-Cyclohexyl-3-(2-morpholinoethyl)-thiourea
M.W. 271.43 m.p. 127-129°

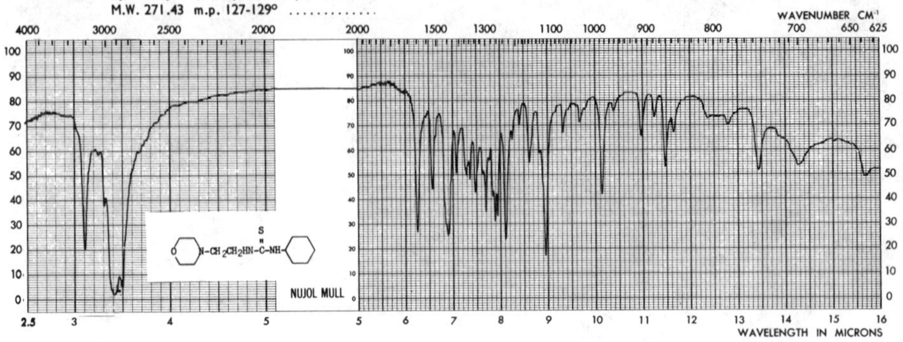

NUJOL MULL

F

1-50-4 2-Imidazolidinethione (ethylenethiourea)
M.W. 102.16 m.p. 199-203°

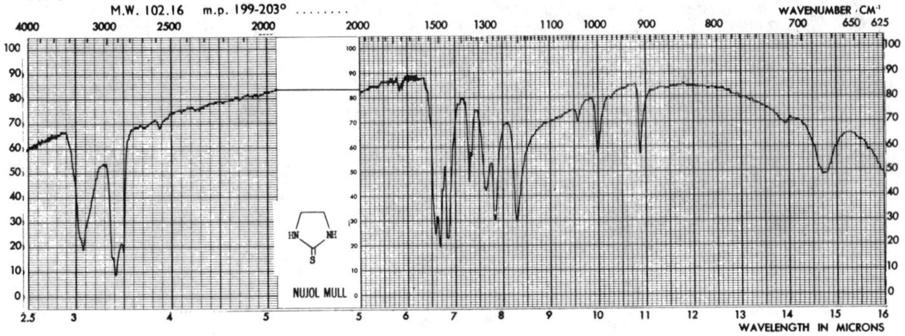

NUJOL MULL

G

M620-4 2-Mercaptothiazoline (2-thiazoline-2-thiol)
M.W. 119.21 m.p. 105-107°

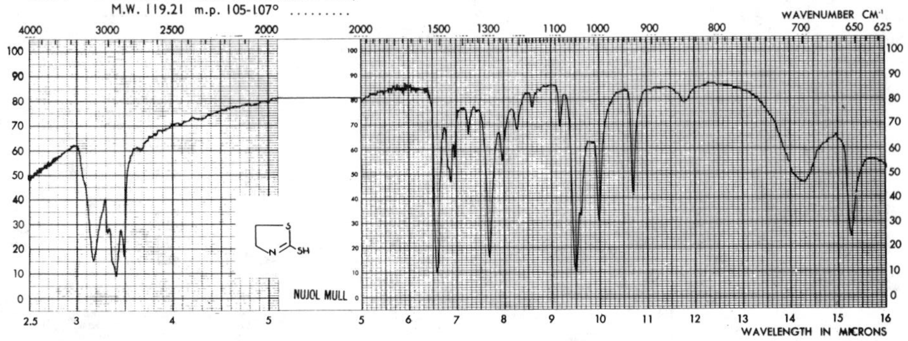

NUJOL MULL

H

11,516-9 Tetramethylthiourea
$(CH_3)_2NCSN(CH_3)_2$ M.W. 132.23

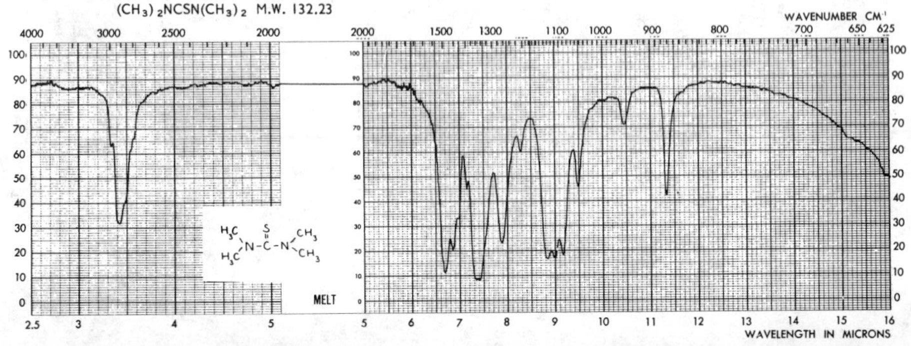

MELT

A 11,516-9 1,1,3,3-Tetramethyl-2-thiourea
$(CH_3)_2NCSN(CH_3)_2$ M.W. 132.23
m.p. 76-78°
NUJOL MULL

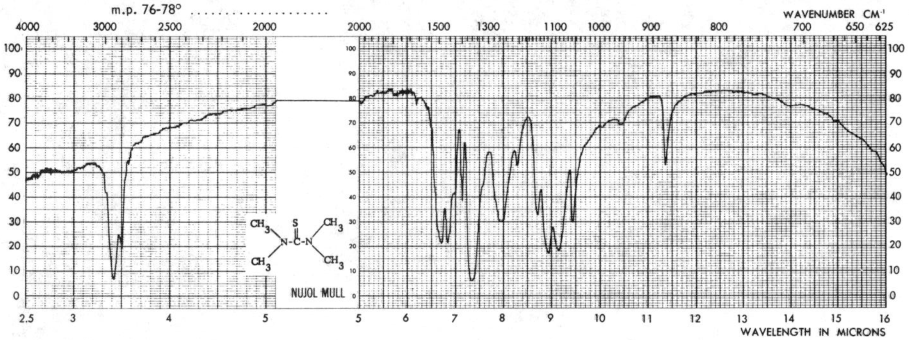

B T1515-6 3,4,5,6-Tetrahydro-2-pyrimidinethiol
M.W. 116.19 m.p. 210-212°
NUJOL MULL

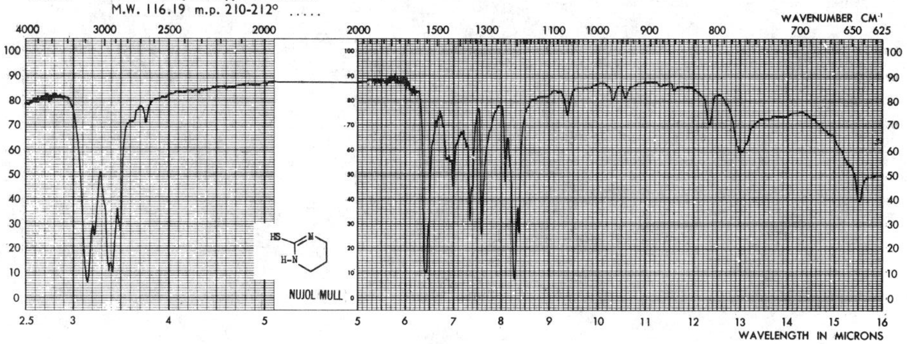

C F1790-3 1-Formylthiosemicarbazide
$H_2NCSNHNHCHO$ M.W. 119.15 m.p. 161-163°
NUJOL MULL

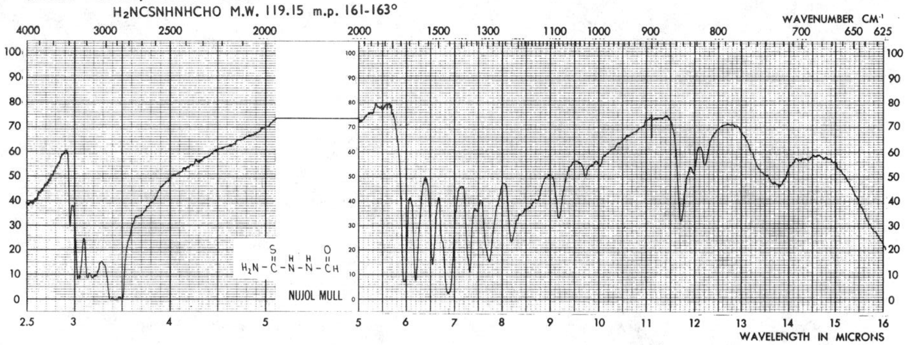

D A2285-8 N-Acetylthiourea
$CH_3CONHCSNH_2$ M.W. 118.16
m.p. 165-169°
NUJOL MULL

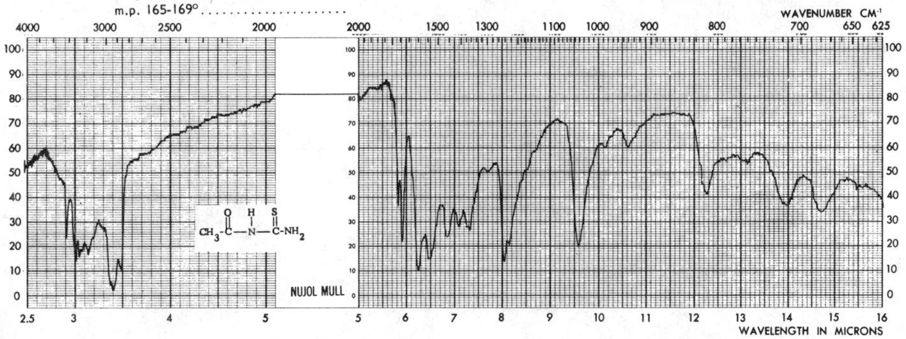

E A2280-7 1-Acetylthiosemicarbazide
$CH_3CONHNHCSNH_2$ M.W. 133.17
m.p. 165-168°
NUJOL MULL

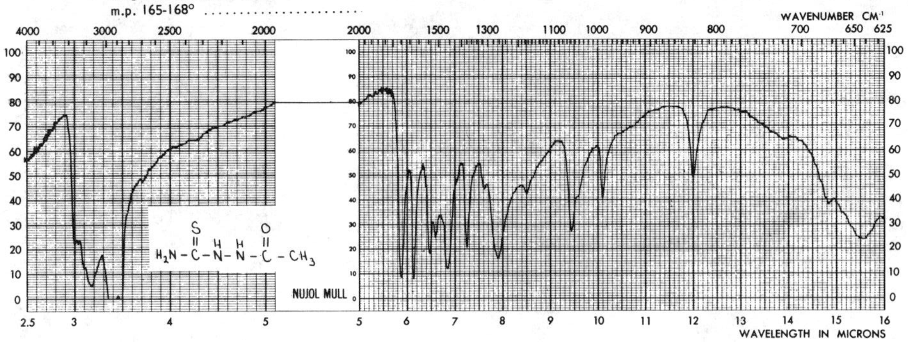

F D21,920-7 Dithiooxamide
$H_2NCSCSNH_2$ M.W. 120.20 m.p. 142° (dec.)
NUJOL MULL

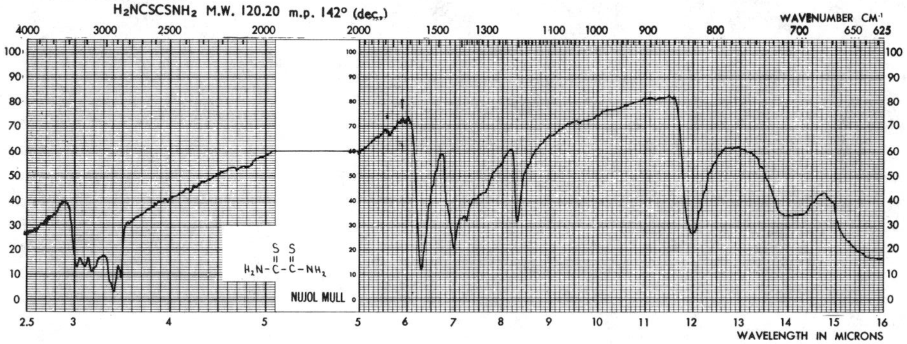

G D8020-7 N,N'-Dicyclohexyldithiooxamide
$C_6H_{11}NHCSCSNHC_6H_{11}$ M.W. 284.49 m.p. 147-150°
NUJOL MULL

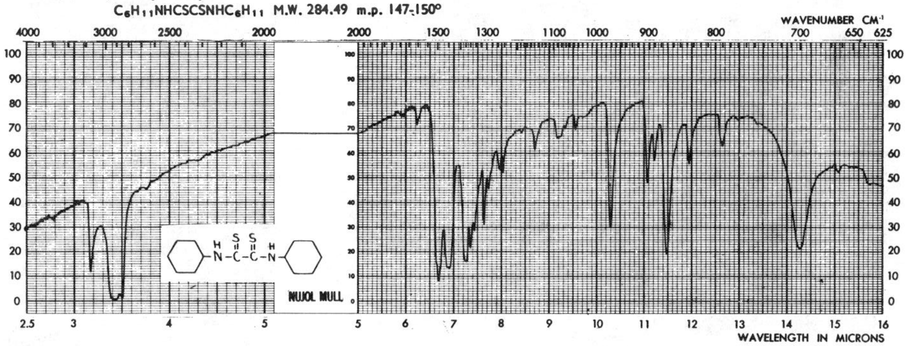

H 85,778-5
Dicyclopentamethylenethiuram disulfide
[bis-(piperidinothiocarbonyl) disulfide]
M.W. 320.56
NUJOL MULL

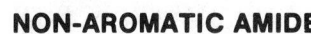

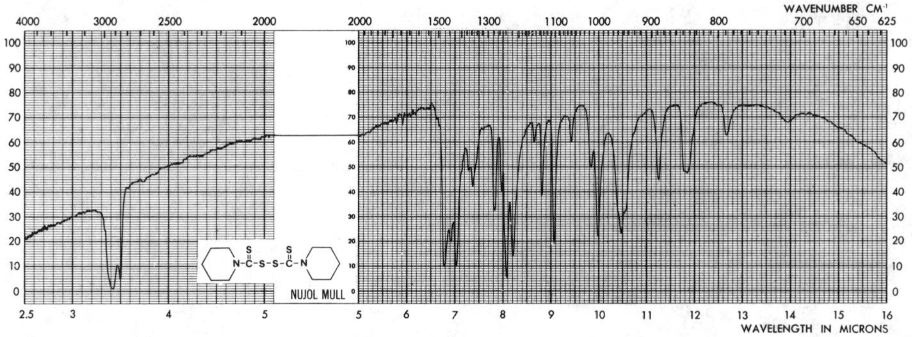

A

T2420-1 **Tetramethylthiuram disulfide** [bis-(dimethylthiocarbamyl) disulfide]
$(CH_3)_2NCS_2CS_2N(CH_3)_2$ M.W. 240.43
m.p. 146-148°

NUJOL MULL

B

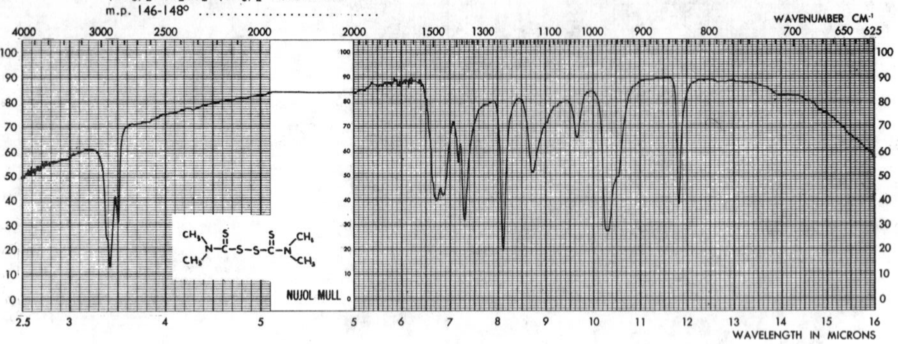

T1160-6 **Tetraethylthiuram disulfide**
$(C_2H_5)_2NCS_2CS_2N(C_2H_5)_2$ M.W. 296.54 m.p. 71-72°

NUJOL MULL

C

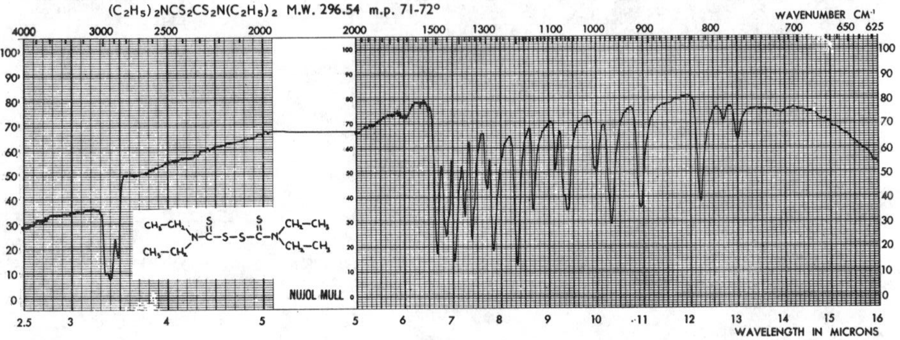

85,662-2
Bis-(4-methyl-1-homopiperazinylthiocarbonyl) disulfide
M.W. 378.65 m.p. 86-88°

NUJOL MULL

D

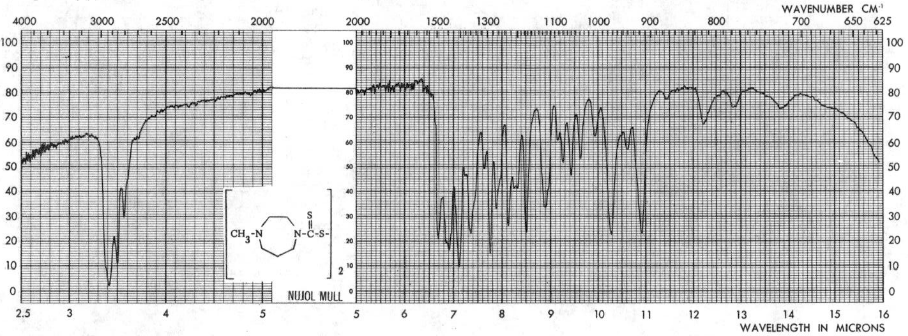

D15,660-4 **Dimethyldithiocarbamic acid, sodium salt dihydrate**
$(CH_3)_2NCS_2Na{\cdot}2H_2O$ M.W. 179.24

NUJOL MULL

E

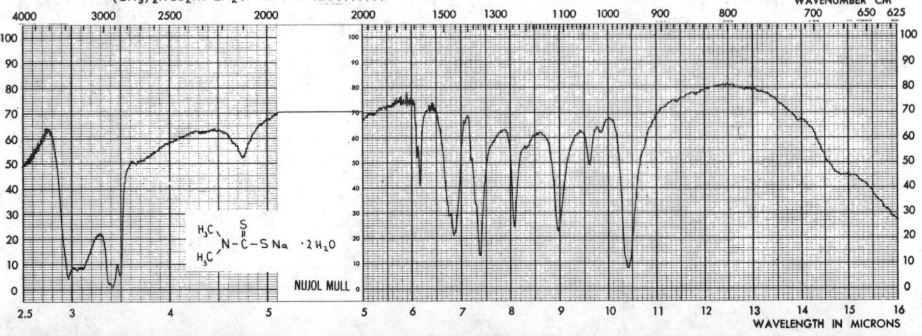

13,264-0 **Diethyldithiocarbamic acid, lead salt**
$[(C_2H_5)_2NCS_2]_2Pb$ M.W. 503.73 (dry)
m.p. 204-206°

NUJOL MULL

F

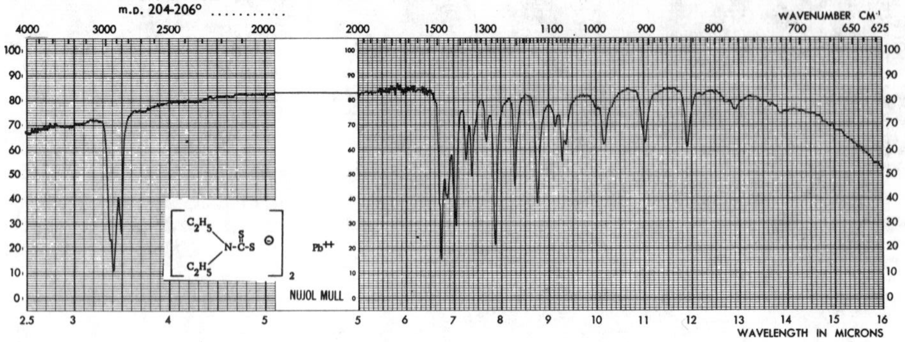

D9350-3 **Diethyldithiocarbamic acid, silver salt**
$(C_2H_5)_2NCS_2Ag$ M.W. 256.14 m.p. 170-175°

NUJOL MULL

G

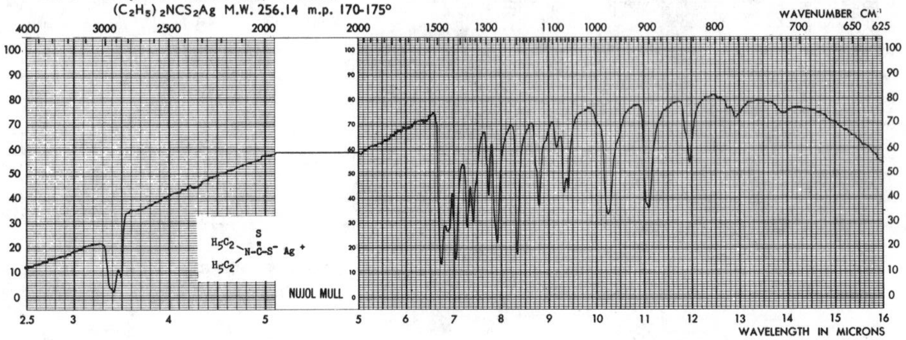

14,269-7 **1-Pyrrolidinecarbodithioic acid, ammonium salt**
M.W. 164.29 m.p. 142-144°

NUJOL MULL

H

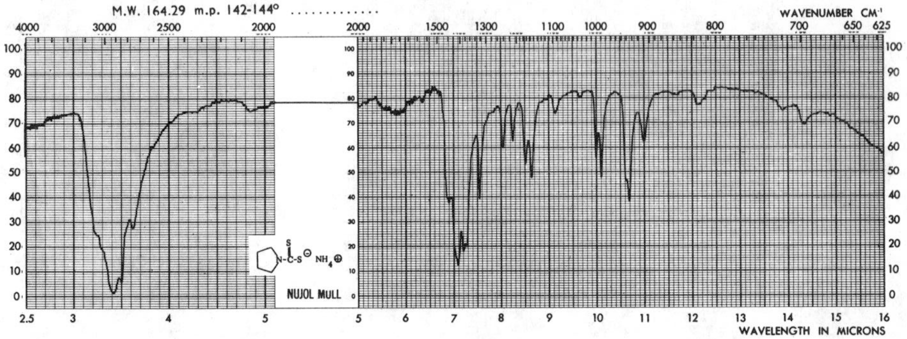

T2828-2 **ω-Thiocaprolactam** (2-thioxohexamethyleneimine)
M.W. 129.23 m.p. 97-102°

NUJOL MULL

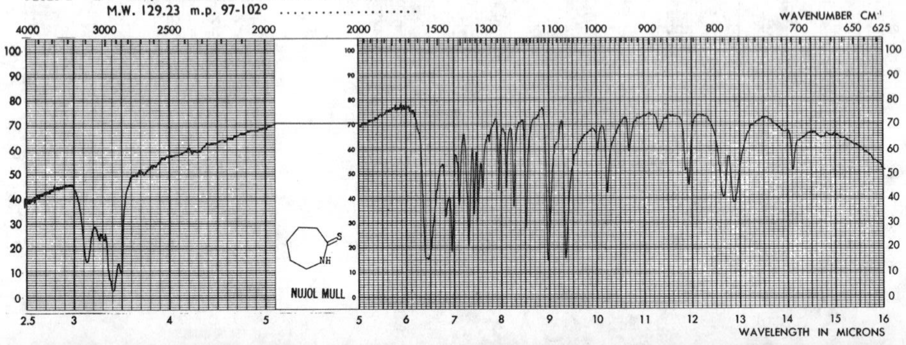

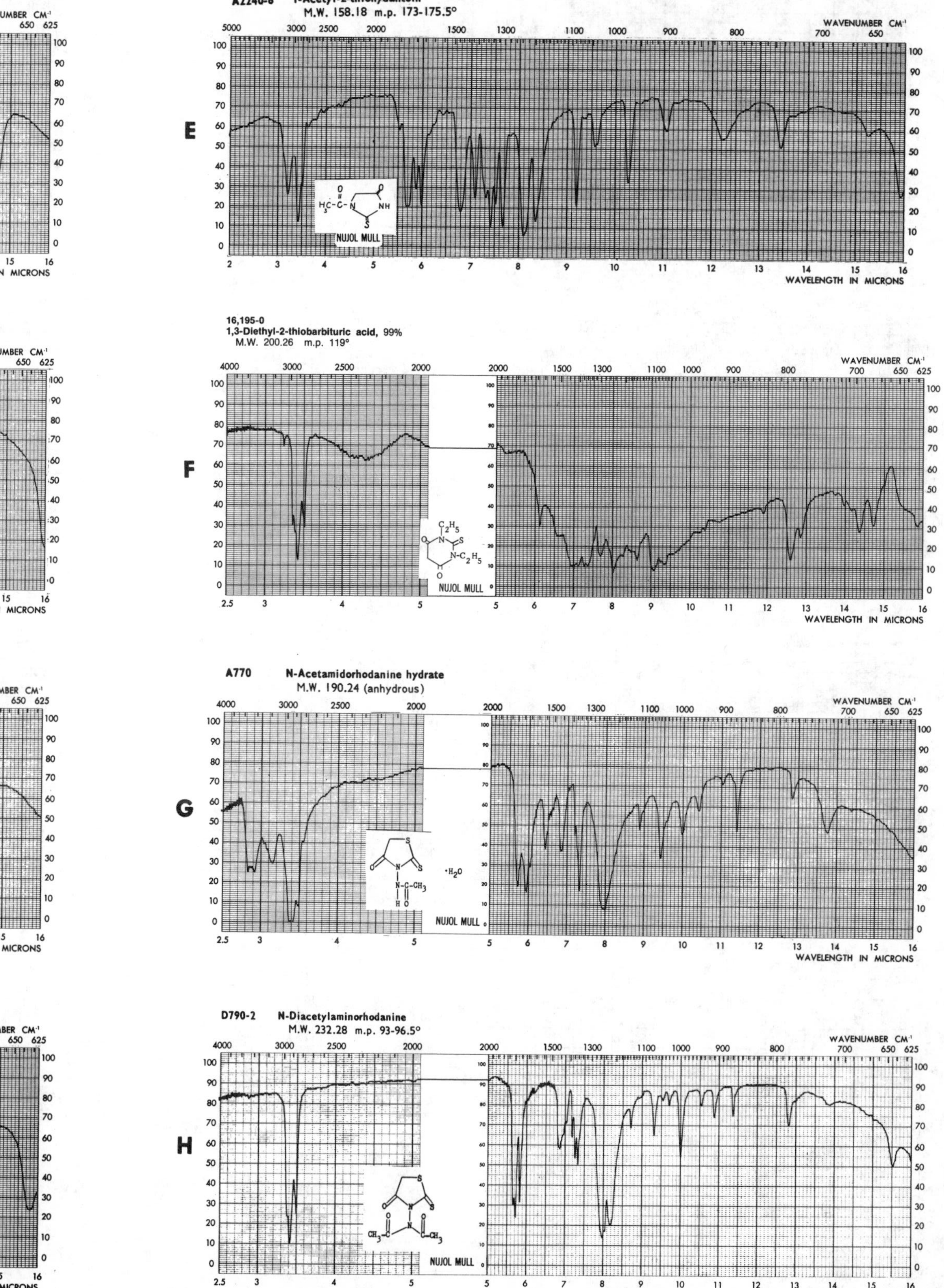

A — 11,819-2 Rhodanine (2-thioxo-4-thiazolidinone)
M.W. 133.19 m.p. 165-168°

B — M8045-8 N-Methylrhodanine
M.W. 147.22 m.p. 69-71°

C — A3560-7 N-Allylrhodanine
M.W. 173.26 n_D^{20} 1.5858

D — A7950-7 N-Aminorhodanine
M.W. 148.21 m.p. 100-103.5°

E — A2240-8 1-Acetyl-2-thiohydantoin
M.W. 158.18 m.p. 173-175.5°

F — 16,195-0 1,3-Diethyl-2-thiobarbituric acid, 99%
M.W. 200.26 m.p. 119°

G — A770 N-Acetamidorhodanine hydrate
M.W. 190.24 (anhydrous)

H — D790-2 N-Diacetylaminorhodanine
M.W. 232.28 m.p. 93-96.5°

A

E4830 Ethyl N-rhodanineacetate
M.W. 219.28 m.p. 63-64°

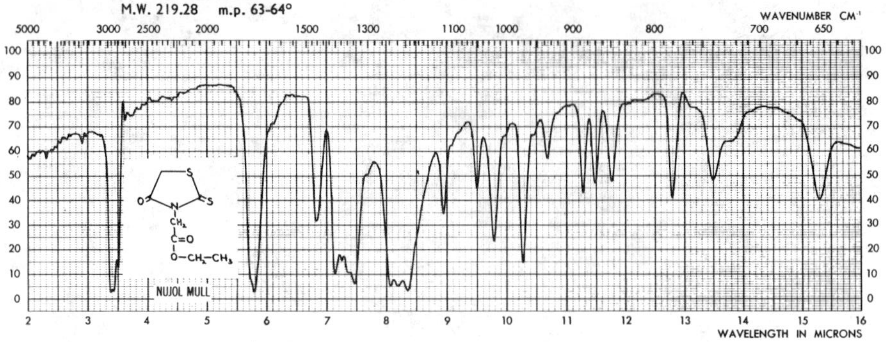

NUJOL MULL

B

13,386-8 Diethyl 5,5'-birhodanine-N,N'-diacetate
M.W. 436.55 m.p. 173-176°

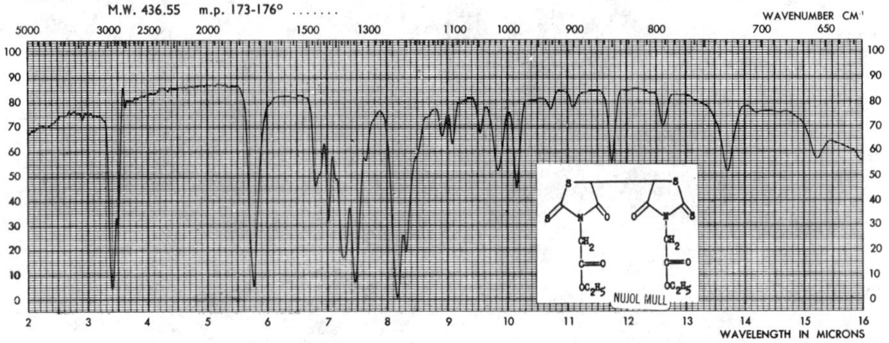

NUJOL MULL

C

R110-2 Rhodanine-N-acetic acid
M.W. 191.23 m.p. 145-148°

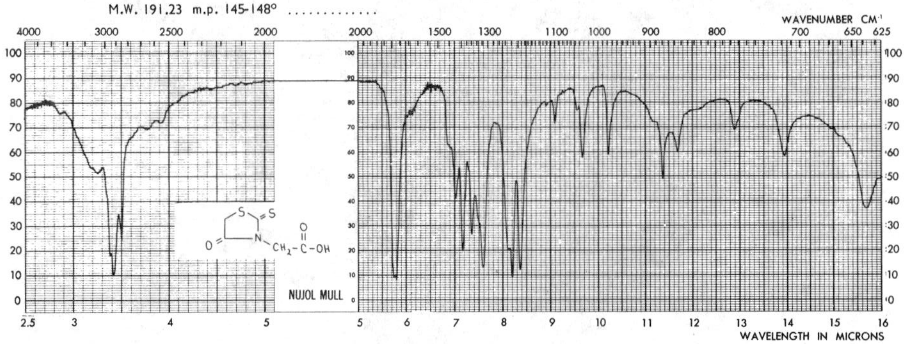

NUJOL MULL

D

R115 N-3-Rhodaninepropionic acid
M.W. 205.25 m.p. 158-161°

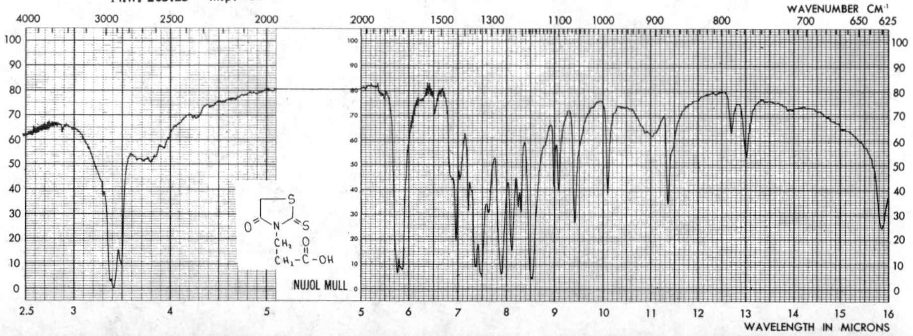

NUJOL MULL

E

D991 N,N'-Diallyl-Δ5,5'-birhodanine
M.W. 342.48 m.p. 186-189°

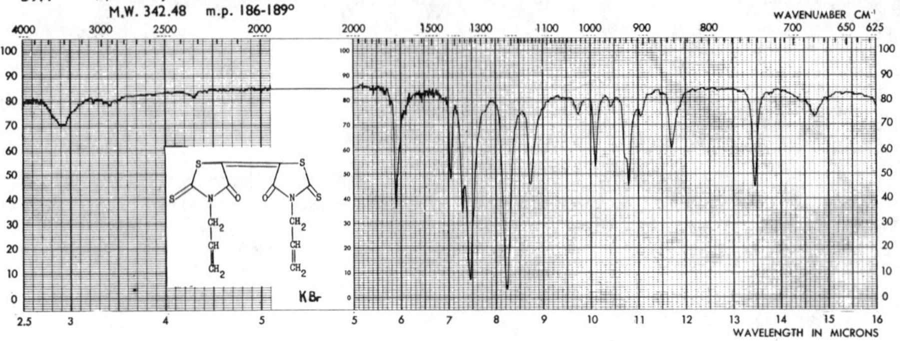

KBr

F

T3040-6 2-Thiohydantoin
M.W. 116.14 m.p. 229-231° (dec.)

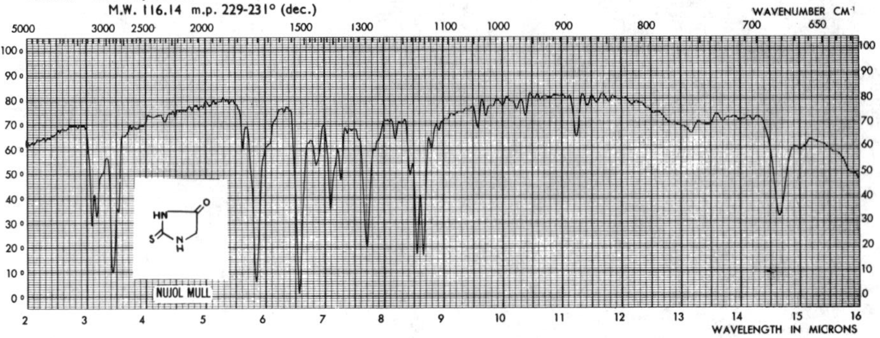

NUJOL MULL

G

12,202-5 3-Ethyl-2-thioxo-4-oxazolidinone
M.W. 145.18 m.p. 40-41.5°

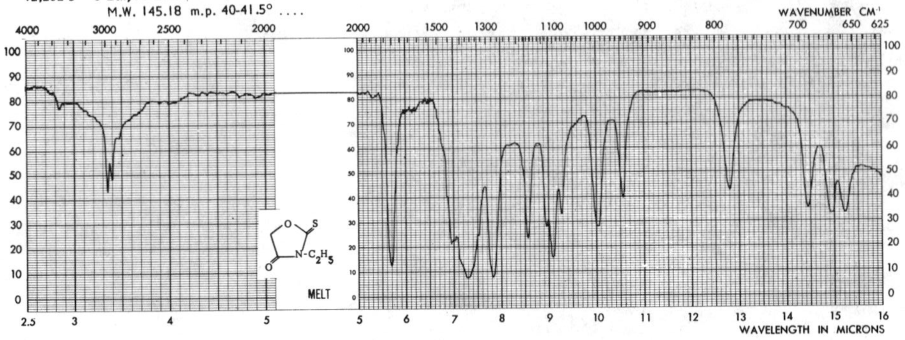

MELT

H

D16,540 5,5-Dimethyl-4-imino-2-thiohydantoin (5,5-dimethyl-4-iminoimidazolidine-2-thione)

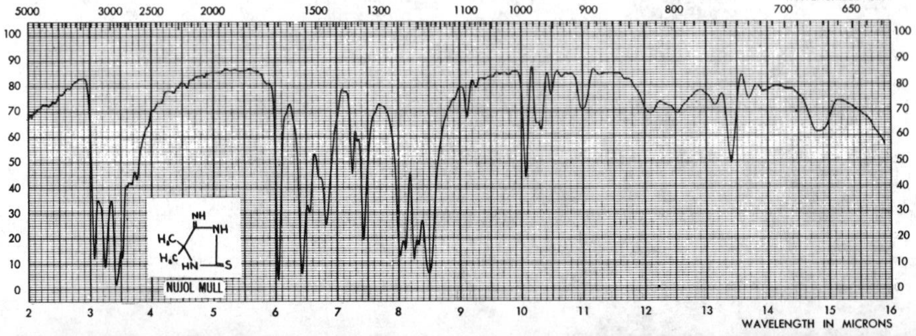

NUJOL MULL

A

13,966-1 **Methyl 2,2,2-trichloroacetimidate**
$CCl_3C(:NH)OCH_3$ M.W. 176.44 n_D^{20} 1.4780
b.p. 45°/15 mm. ....

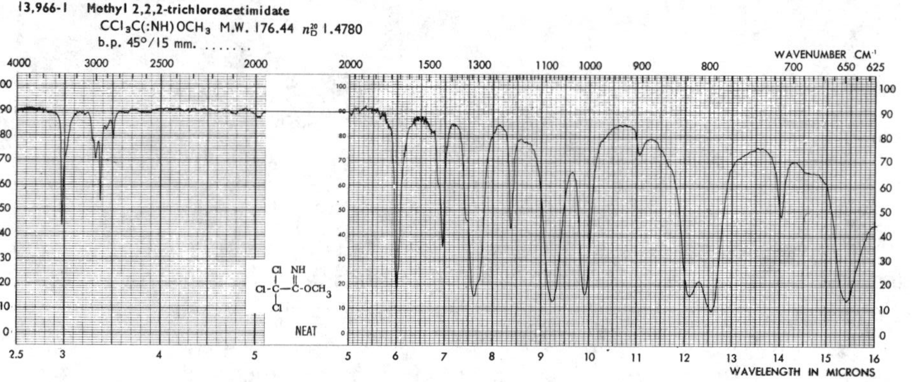

B

22,635-1
***N*-Hydroxymaleimide,** 98+%
FW 113.07 mp 133-135° Disp. C

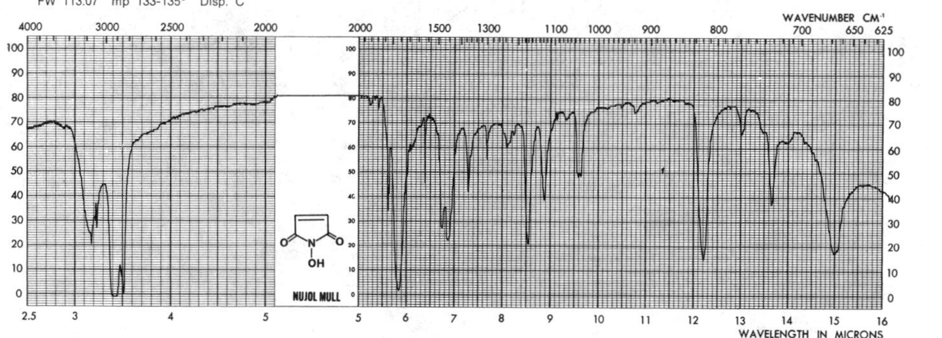

NON-AROMATIC NITRILES AND CUMULATED DOUBLE BONDS

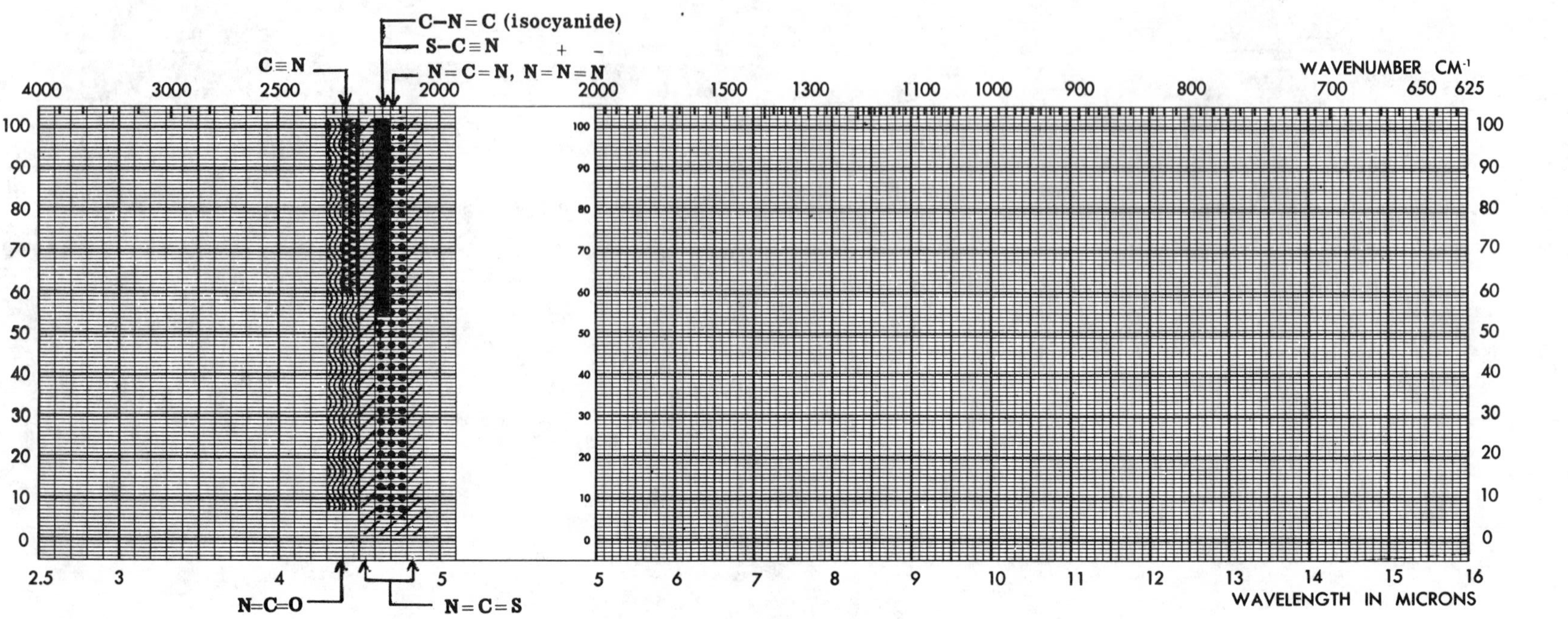

Due to the lack of bands of other functional groups, the region between 4.4 and 5 μ (2275 – 2000 cm^{-1}) is very useful in observing the triple and cumulated double bond absorptions. This section excludes two series, alkynes and allenes. The alkynes are discussed separately while allenes appear in the non-aromatic hydrocarbon section. (See spectra 506D, E, G, 508D).

The nitrile absorption occurs between 4.4 and 4.5 μ (2275 – 2220 cm^{-1}) and is weak to strong in intensity depending on the surrounding atoms. The absorption is considerably weaker when electronegative groups are substituted on the α-carbon as can be seen in spectra 506D,E, G, 508D. In fact, in spectrum 508D the absorption is lost entirely. When the cyanide group is placed directly on nitrogen such as in spectra 509G—510D, the intensity and broadness of the absorption are greatly increased.

The single isocyanide of this collection absorbs between 4.6 and 4.7 μ (2175 – 2130 cm^{-1}) (500D, G and 506A).

The isocyanate absorbs very strongly near 4.4 μ (2275 cm^{-1}).

The thiocyanate has an absorption similar in intensity to the nitrile but is shifted to between 4.6 and 4.7 μ (2175 – 2130 cm^{-1}).

The isothiocyanate absorbs very strongly with a broad band appearing between 4.5 and 4.9 μ (2220 – 2040 cm^{-1}). It is usually split and has a number of shoulders appearing on either side of the main absorption.

The carbodiimide absorbs at 4.7 μ (2130 cm^{-1}) as does the azide. The bands are of similar intensities and can be split as seen in spectra 524B—524G. The ionic cyanides in general absorb between 4.6 and 5 μ (2175 – 2000 cm^{-1}). (See spectra 524H—525F).

The relative band intensity of each of the groups mentioned above should be noted when compared to other functional group absorptions of the same molecule.

Compounds with spectra appearing in this section are sensitive to hydrolysis and care should be taken by the spectroscopist to avoid exposing them to atmospheric moisture. The resulting product of hydrolysis is the amide as shown by its band at 6 μ (1665 cm^{-1}).

A

11,008-6 **Acetonitrile, 99%**
CH_3CN M.W. 41.05 n_D^{20} 1.3440 b.p. 81.6°

$H_3C-C\equiv N$
NEAT

B

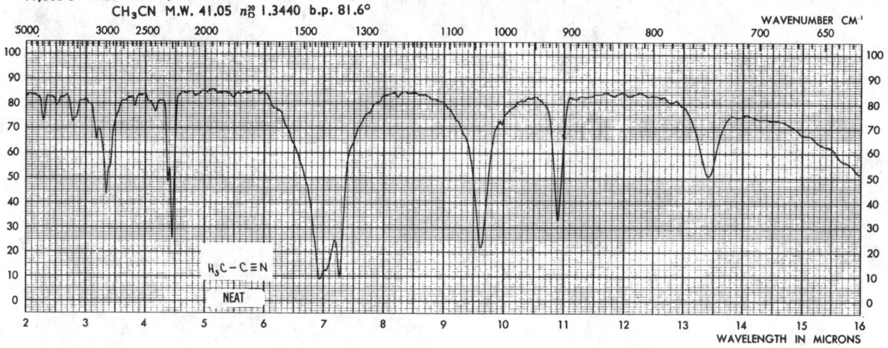

14,204-2
Propionitrile
C_2H_5CN
M.W. 55.08 m.p. -93° b.p. 97° n_D^{20} 1.3660
d 0.772 Beil. **2**,245 *SEVERE POISON*

$CH_3CH_2-C\equiv N$
NEAT

C

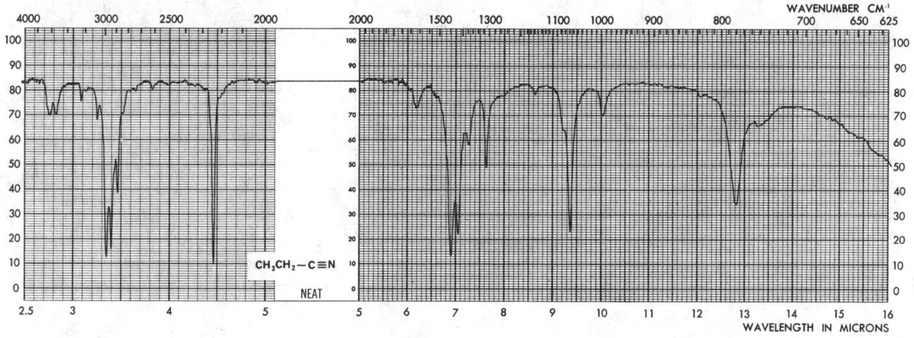

B10,380-2 **n-Butyronitrile**
$CH_3CH_2CH_2CN$ M.W. 69.11 n_D^{20} 1.3842

$CH_3CH_2CH_2CN$
NEAT

D

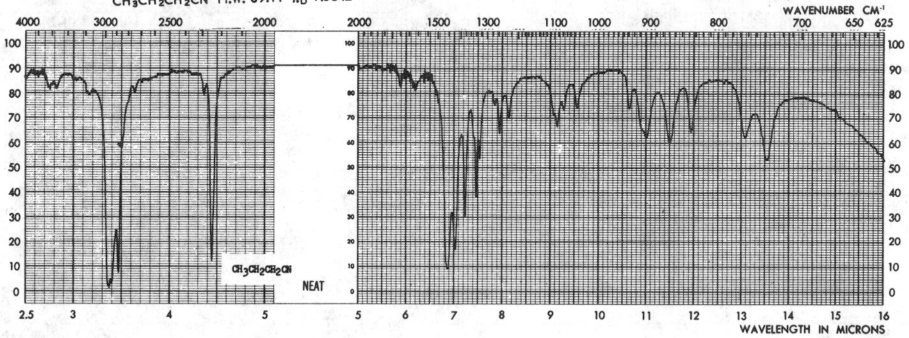

13,328-0 **n-Butyl isocyanide** (n-butyl isonitrile)
$CH_3(CH_2)_3NC$ M.W. 83.13 ....

$CH_3CH_2CH_2CH_2N{=}C$
NEAT

E

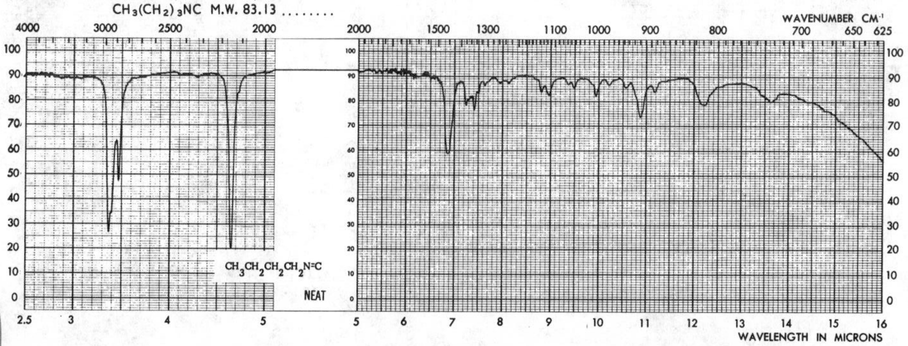

I-1560-2 **Isobutyronitrile** (isopropyl cyanide)
$(CH_3)_2CHCN$ M.W. 69.11 n_D^{20} 1.3720

$(H_3C)_2HC-C\equiv N$
NEAT

F

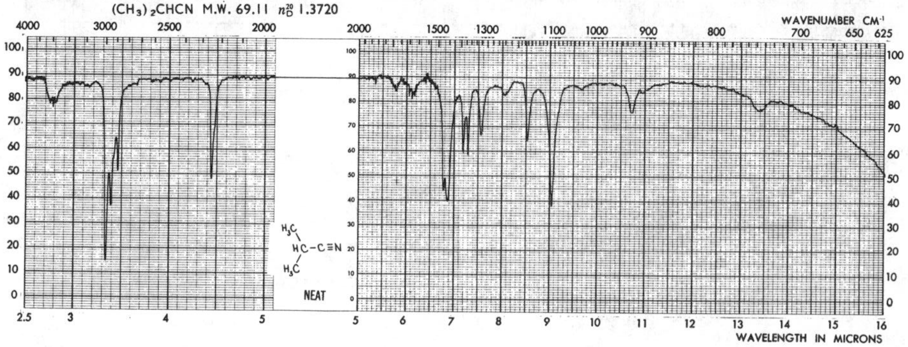

16,665-0
Hexanenitrile, 99%
$CH_3(CH_2)_4CN$
M.W. 97.16 b.p. 161-164° n_D^{20} 1.4061 d 0.809
Beil. **2**,324

$CH_3CH_2CH_2CH_2CH_2CN$
NEAT

G

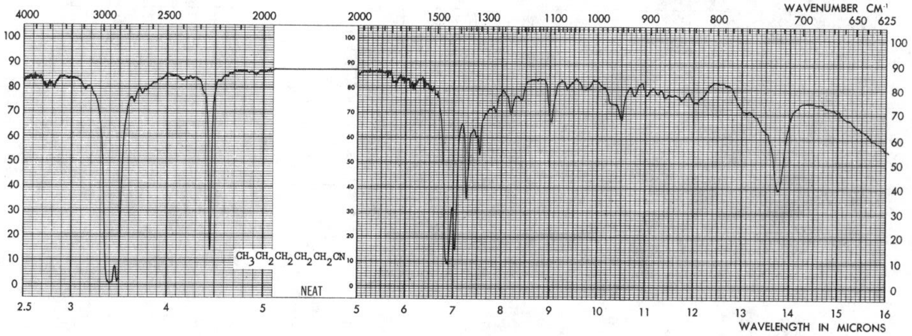

17,732-6
Hexyl isocyanide, 98%
$CH_3(CH_2)_5NC$
M.W. 111.19 b.p. 168-169° n_D^{20} 1.4131 *STENCH*

$CH_3CH_2CH_2CH_2CH_2CH_2NC$
NEAT

H

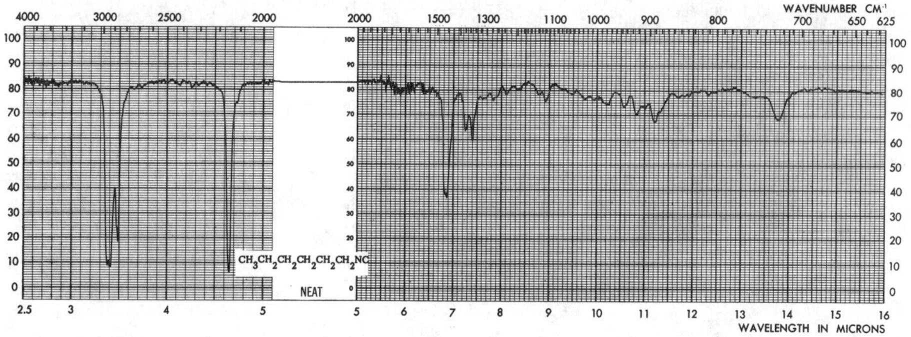

12,853-8 **n-Heptyl cyanide** (caprylonitrile, octanenitrile)
$CH_3(CH_2)_6CN$ M.W. 125.22 n_D^{20} 1.4203
b.p. 198-200° ....

$H_3C-(CH_2)_6-C\equiv N$
NEAT

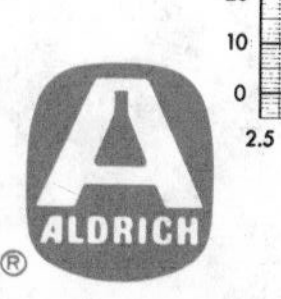

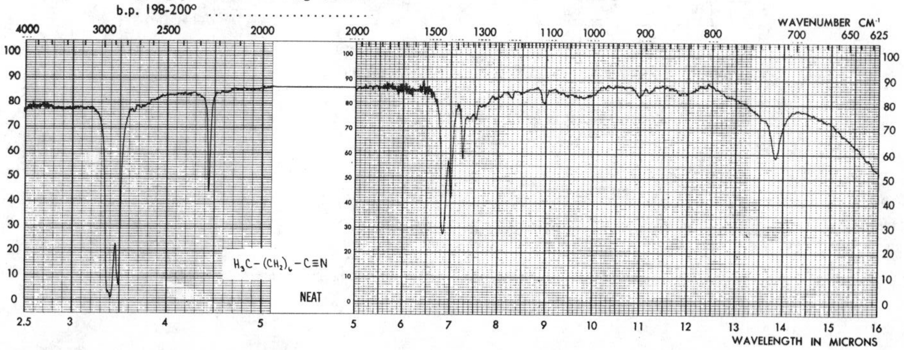

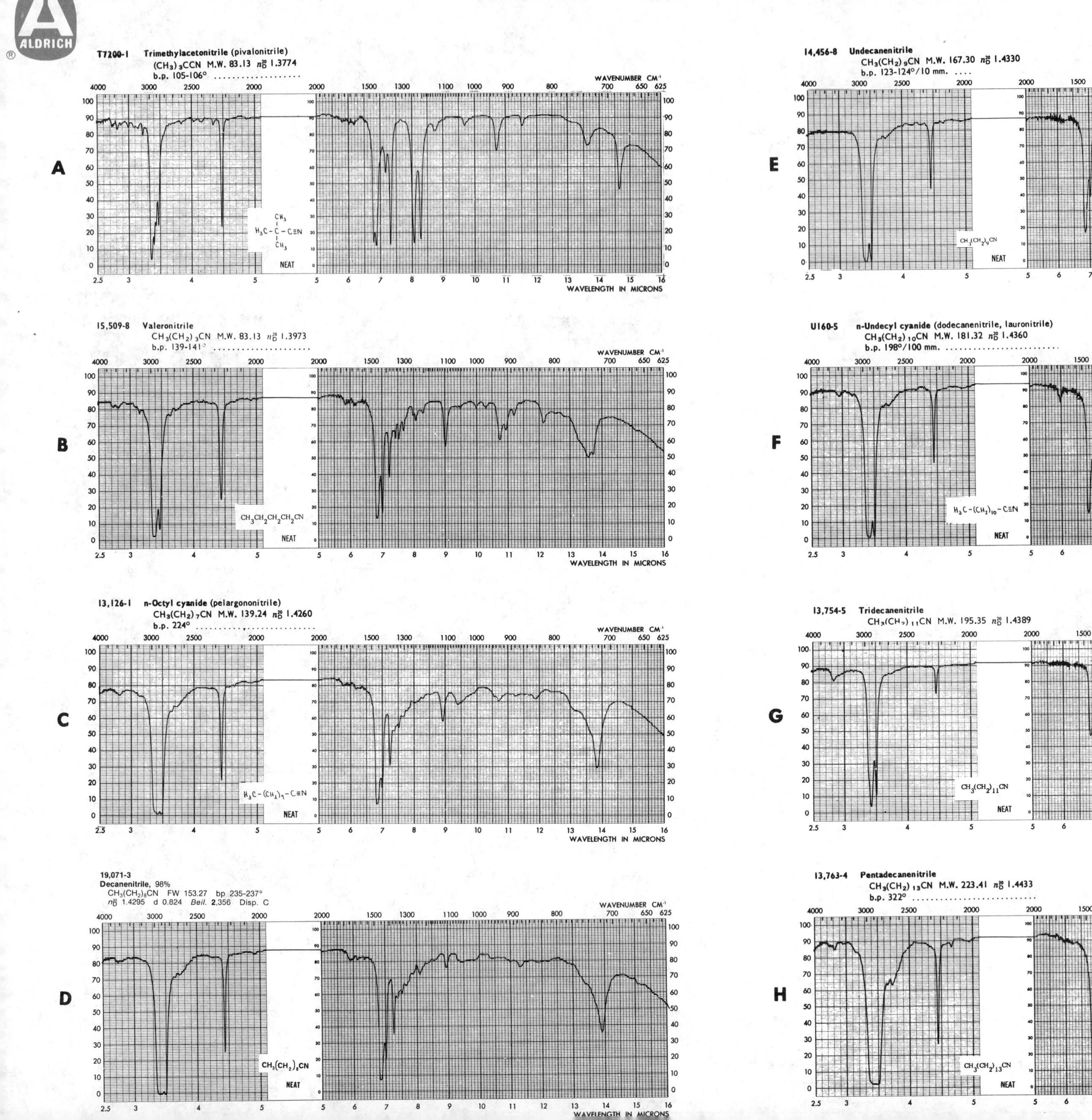
ALDRICH
A
T7200-1 Trimethylacetonitrile (pivalonitrile)
$(CH_3)_3CCN$ M.W. 83.13 n_D^{20} 1.3774
b.p. 105-106°
$H_3C-C(CH_3)_2-C≡N$
NEAT
B
15,509-8 Valeronitrile
$CH_3(CH_2)_3CN$ M.W. 83.13 n_D^{20} 1.3973
b.p. 139-141°
$CH_3CH_2CH_2CH_2CN$
NEAT
C
13,126-1 n-Octyl cyanide (pelargononitrile)
$CH_3(CH_2)_7CN$ M.W. 139.24 n_D^{20} 1.4260
b.p. 224°
$H_3C-(CH_2)_7-C≡N$
NEAT
D
19,071-3
Decanenitrile, 98%
$CH_3(CH_2)_8CN$ FW 153.27 bp 235-237°
n_D^{20} 1.4295 d 0.824 Beil. 2,356 Disp. C
$CH_3(CH_2)_8CN$
NEAT
E
14,456-8 Undecanenitrile
$CH_3(CH_2)_9CN$ M.W. 167.30 n_D^{20} 1.4330
b.p. 123-124°/10 mm.
$CH_3(CH_2)_9CN$
NEAT
F
U160-5 n-Undecyl cyanide (dodecanenitrile, lauronitrile)
$CH_3(CH_2)_{10}CN$ M.W. 181.32 n_D^{20} 1.4360
b.p. 198°/100 mm.
$H_3C-(CH_2)_{10}-C≡N$
NEAT
G
13,754-5 Tridecanenitrile
$CH_3(CH_2)_{11}CN$ M.W. 195.35 n_D^{20} 1.4389
$CH_3(CH_2)_{11}CN$
NEAT
H
13,763-4 Pentadecanenitrile
$CH_3(CH_2)_{13}CN$ M.W. 223.41 n_D^{20} 1.4433
b.p. 322°
$CH_3(CH_2)_{13}CN$
NEAT
WAVENUMBER CM⁻¹
WAVELENGTH IN MICRONS

A

13,405-8 **n-Hexadecyl cyanide** (heptadecanenitrile, margaronitrile)
$CH_3(CH_2)_{15}CN$ M.W. 251.44 m.p. 31.5-32.5° ......

$CH_3(CH_2)_{15}CN$ MELT

B

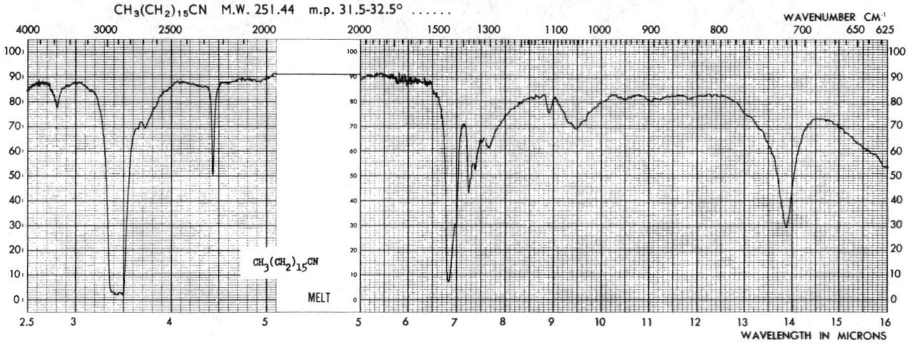

12,258-0 **Stearonitrile** (heptadecyl cyanide)
$CH_3(CH_2)_{16}CN$ M.W. 265.49 m.p. 38-40°

$CH_3(CH_2)_{15}CH_2CN$ MELT

C

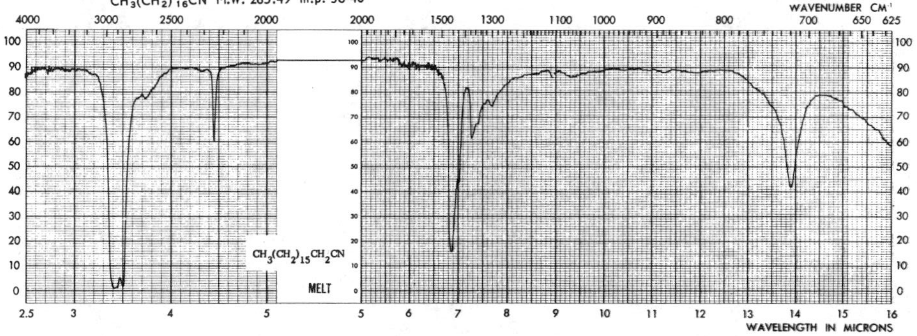

13,759-6 **Nonadecanenitrile**
$CH_3(CH_2)_{17}CN$ M.W. 279.51 m.p. 40-42°

$CH_3(CH_2)_{17}CN$ MELT

D

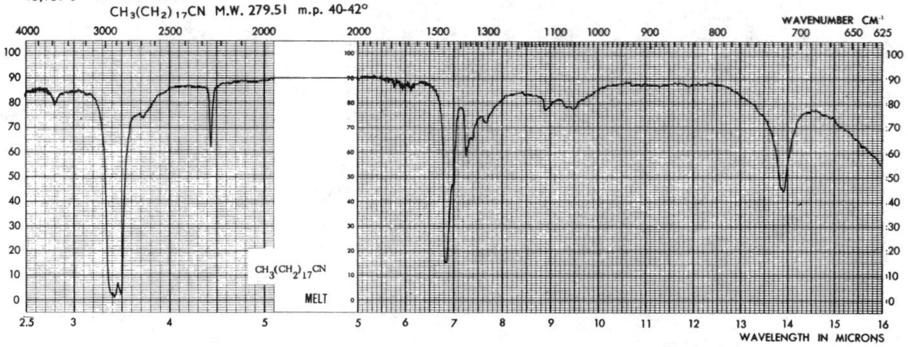

M140-7 **Malononitrile**
$NCCH_2CN$ M.W. 66.06 m.p. 32-34°

N≡C−CH₂−C≡N MELT

E

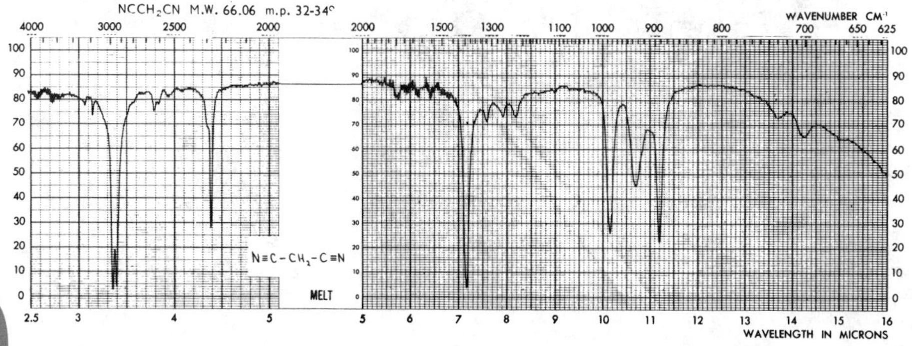

16,096-2
Succinonitrile
$NCCH_2CH_2CN$
M.W. 80.09 m.p. 46-48° b.p. 265-267° d 0.985
Beil. 2,615

$NCCH_2CH_2CN$ MELT

F

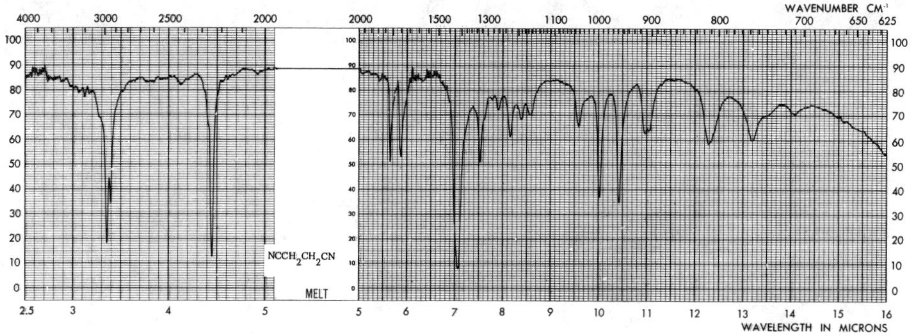

13,062-1 **Glutaronitrile**
$NC(CH_2)_3CN$ M.W. 94.12 n_D^{20} 1.4370
b.p. 122-124°/5 mm. ....

$NCCH_2CH_2CH_2CN$ NEAT

G

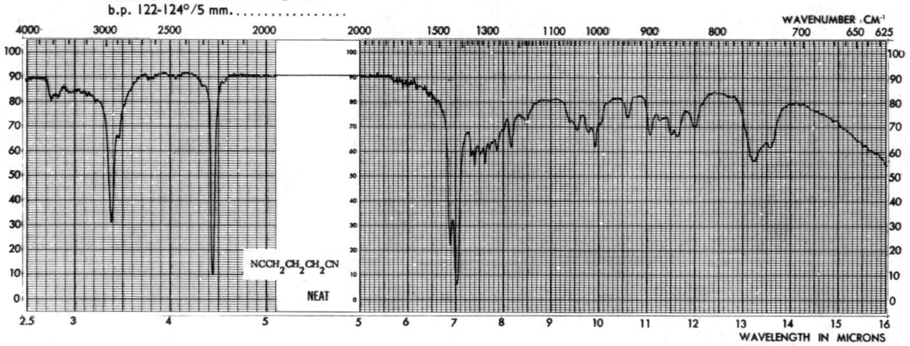

21,139-7
dl-**2-Methylglutaronitrile**, tech., 85%
$NCCH_2CH_2CH(CH_3)CN$ FW 108.14
bp 125-130°/10mm. d 0.950 *Beil.* 2,656 Disp. C

NC−CH₂CH₂−CH(CH₃)−CN NEAT

H

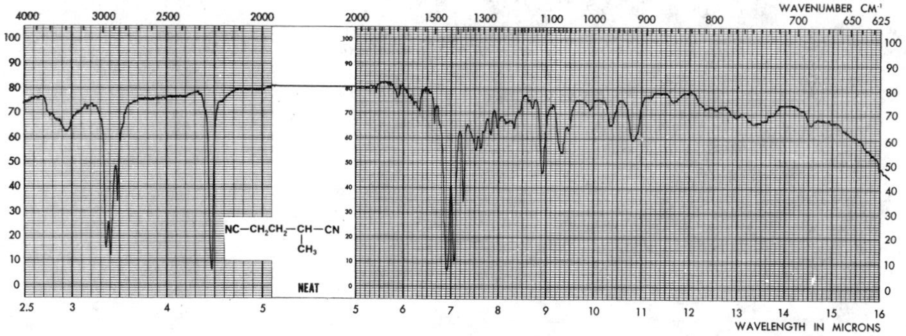

D7700-1 **1,4-Dicyanobutane** (adiponitrile)
$NC(CH_2)_4CN$ M.W. 108.14 n_D^{20} 1.4369
m.p. 1-3° ....

N≡C−CH₂−CH₂−CH₂−CH₂−C≡N NEAT

(All spectra: WAVENUMBER CM⁻¹ 4000–625; WAVELENGTH IN MICRONS 2.5–16; % transmittance 0–100)

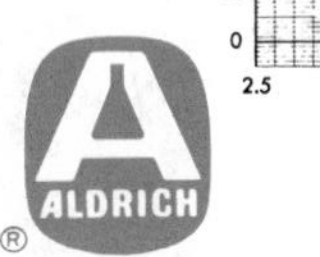

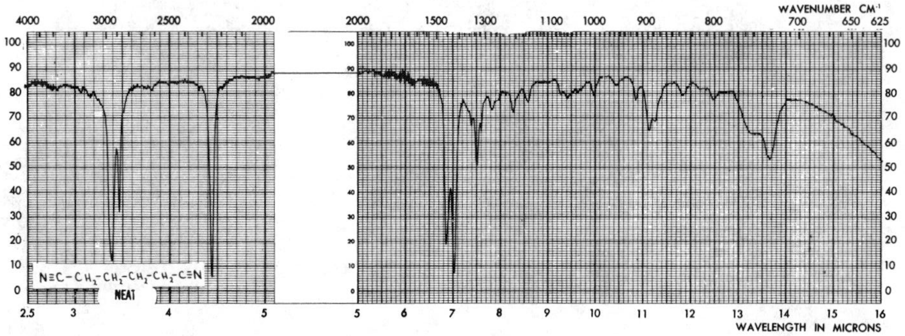

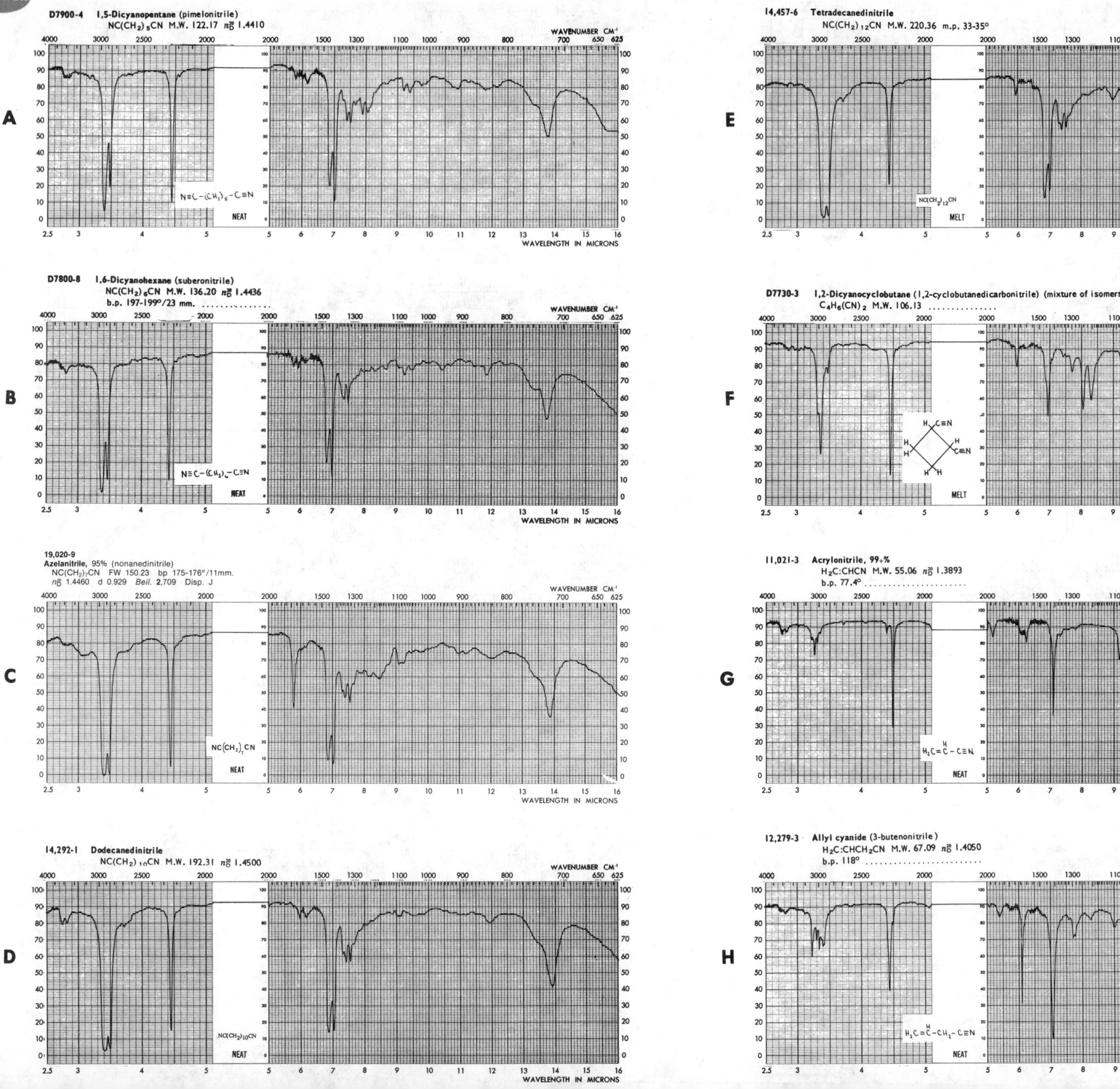
ALDRICH
A
D7900-4 1,5-Dicyanopentane (pimelonitrile)
NC(CH2)5CN M.W. 122.17 n20D 1.4410
N≡C–(CH2)5–C≡N
NEAT
B
D7800-8 1,6-Dicyanohexane (suberonitrile)
NC(CH2)6CN M.W. 136.20 n20D 1.4436
b.p. 197-199°/23 mm.
N≡C–(CH2)6–C≡N
NEAT
C
19,020-9
Azelanitrile, 95% (nonanedinitrile)
NC(CH2)7CN FW 150.23 bp 175-176°/11mm.
n20D 1.4460 d 0.929 Beil. 2,709 Disp. J
NC(CH2)7CN
NEAT
D
14,292-1 Dodecanedinitrile
NC(CH2)10CN M.W. 192.31 n20D 1.4500
NC(CH2)10CN
NEAT
E
14,457-6 Tetradecanedinitrile
NC(CH2)12CN M.W. 220.36 m.p. 33-35°
NC(CH2)12CN
MELT
F
D7730-3 1,2-Dicyanocyclobutane (1,2-cyclobutanedicarbonitrile) (mixture of isomers)
C4H6(CN)2 M.W. 106.13
MELT
G
11,021-3 Acrylonitrile, 99+%
H2C:CHCN M.W. 55.06 n20D 1.3893
b.p. 77.4°
H2C=CH–C≡N
NEAT
H
12,279-3 Allyl cyanide (3-butenonitrile)
H2C:CHCH2CN M.W. 67.09 n20D 1.4050
b.p. 118°
H2C=CH–CH2–C≡N
NEAT
WAVENUMBER CM-1
WAVELENGTH IN MICRONS

A C8580 Crotononitrile
$CH_3CH{:}CHCN$ M.W. 67.09 n_D^{23} 1.4220

B 19,541-3
Methacrylonitrile
$H_2C{=}C(CH_3)CN$ FW 67.09 mp -35.80°
bp 90-92° n_D^{20} 1.4002 d 0.800 *Beil.* 2,423
Disp. J,C

C 13,101-6
Fumaronitrile, 98%
NCCH=CHCN FW 78.07 mp 95-97° bp 186°
Beil. 2(1),302 *NMR* 3,159A Disp. J

D D7720-6 1,4-Dicyano-2-butene (dihydromucononitrile)
$NCCH_2CH{:}CHCH_2CN$ M.W. 106.13

E 15,767-8
3,7-Dimethyl-2,6-octadienenitrile, 97%, mixture of isomers
$(CH_3)_2C{=}CHCH_2CH_2C(CH_3){=}CHCN$
M.W. 149.24 n_D^{20} 1.4753

F 12,554-7 2-Methyleneglutaronitrile
$NCCH_2CH_2C({:}CH_2)CN$ M.W. 106.13 n_D^{20} 1.4561
b.p. 103°/5 mm.

G T880-9 Tetracyanoethylene
$(NC)_2C{:}C(CN)_2$ M.W. 128.08 m.p. 197-199°

H 15,763-5
7,7,8,8-Tetracyanoquinodimethane, 98% (2,5-cyclohexadiene-Δ1α,4α'-dimalononitrile)
M.W. 204.19 m.p. 287-289° (dec.) Fieser 1,1136

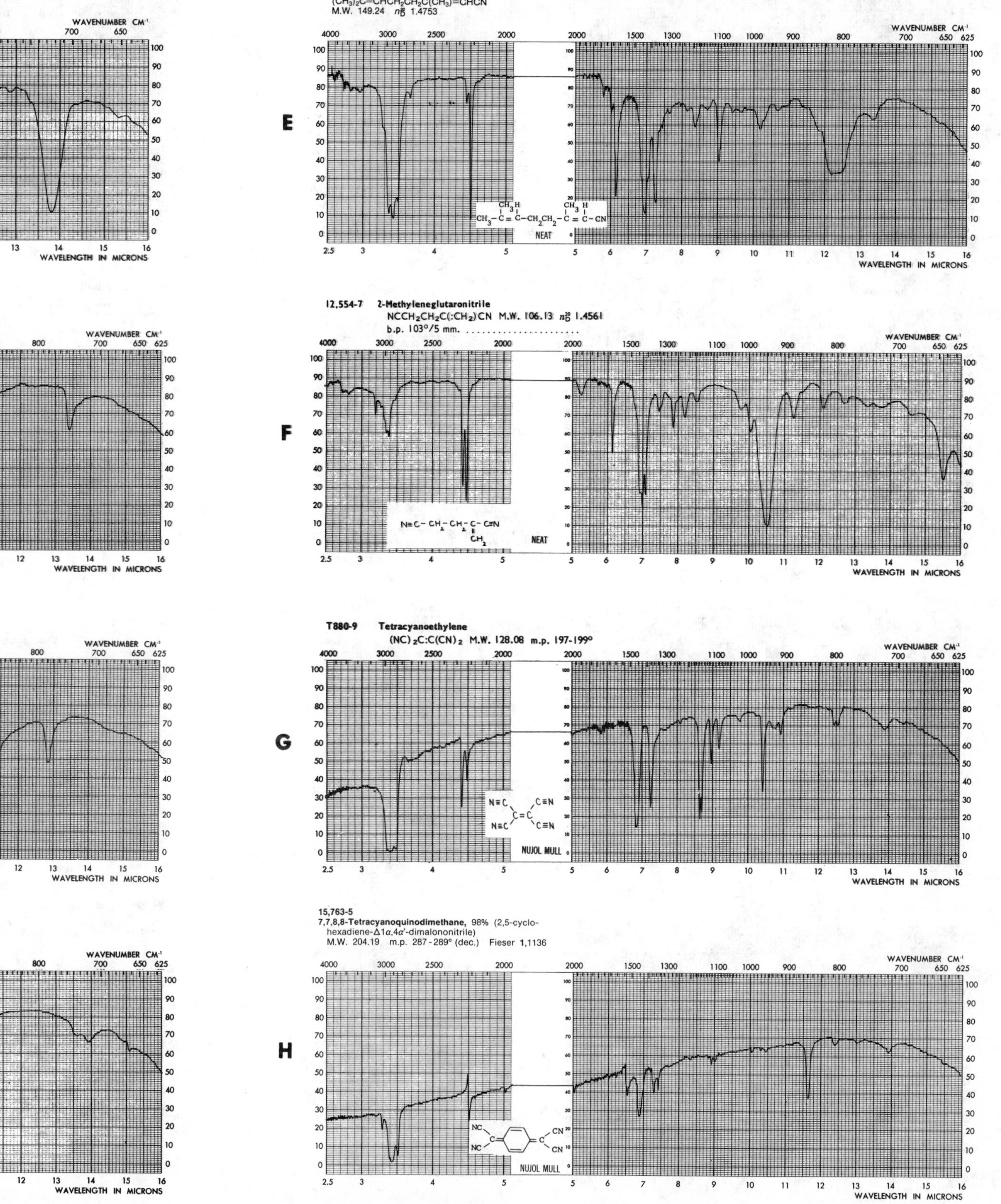

ALDRICH

A

C11,760-9 Cyclopropyl cyanide (cyclopropanecarbonitrile)
C_3H_5CN M.W. 67.09 n_D^{20} 1.4207

NEAT

B

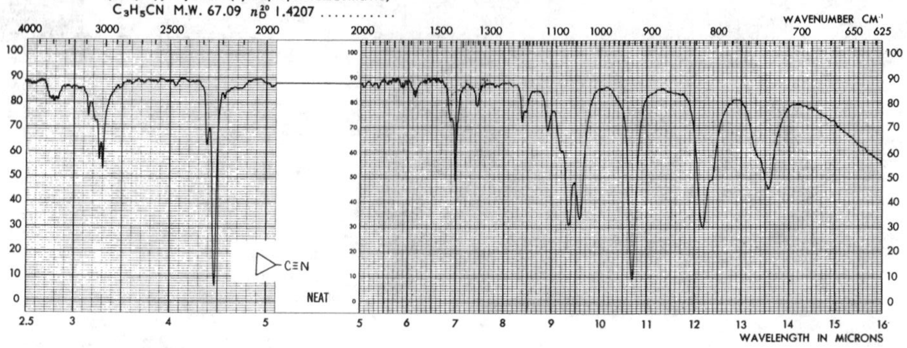

12,165-7 Cyclohexanebutyronitrile
$C_6H_{11}(CH_2)_3CN$ M.W. 151.25
n_D^{20} 1.4598

NEAT

C

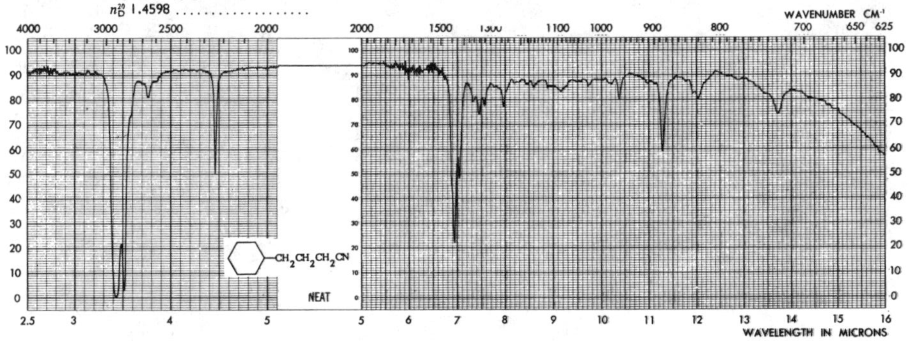

C9975-2 Cycloheptyl cyanide (cycloheptanecarbonitrile)
$C_7H_{13}CN$ M.W. 123.20 n_D^{20} 1.4644

NEAT

D

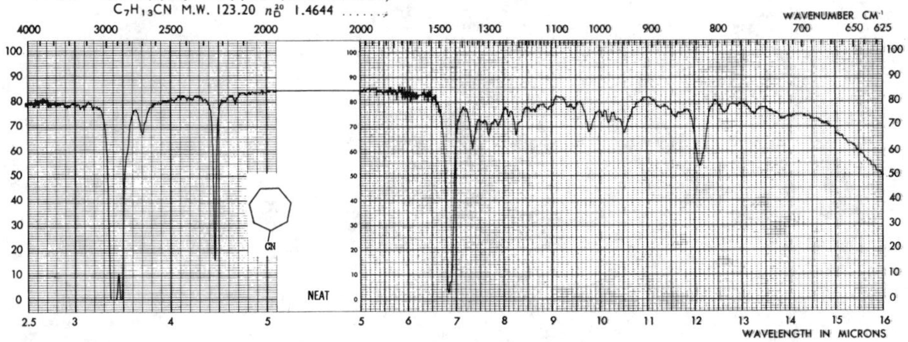

N3205-9 2-Norbornanecarbonitrile
M.W. 121.18 m.p. 43-45°

MELT

E

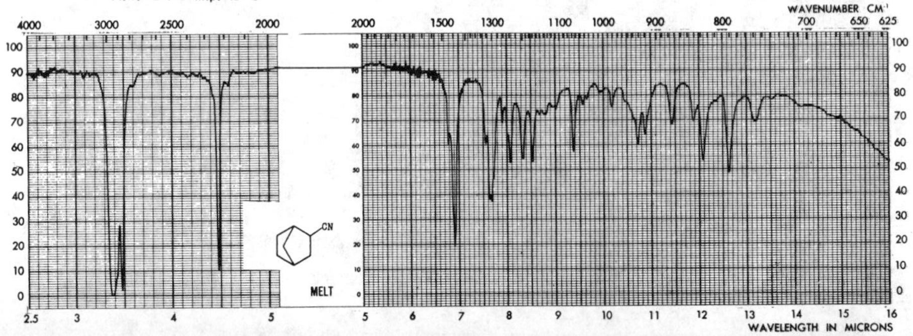

13,805-3 1-Adamantanecarbonitrile (1-cyanoadamantane)
M.W. 161.25 m.p. 185-190°

NUJOL MULL

F

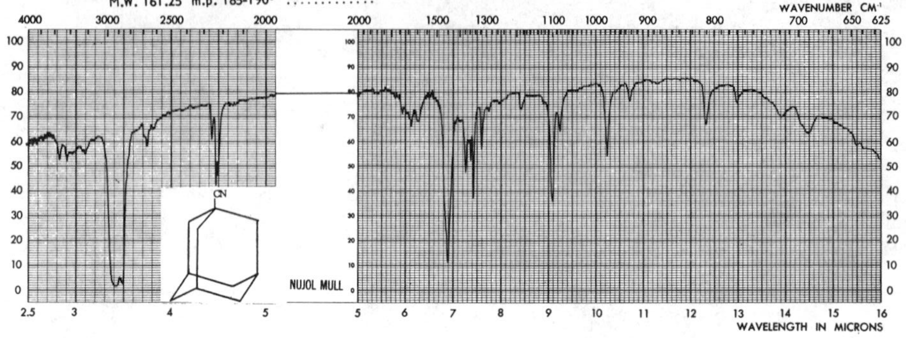

12,163-0 1-Cyclopenteneacetonitrile
$C_5H_7CH_2CN$ M.W. 107.16 n_D^{20} 1.4652

NEAT

G

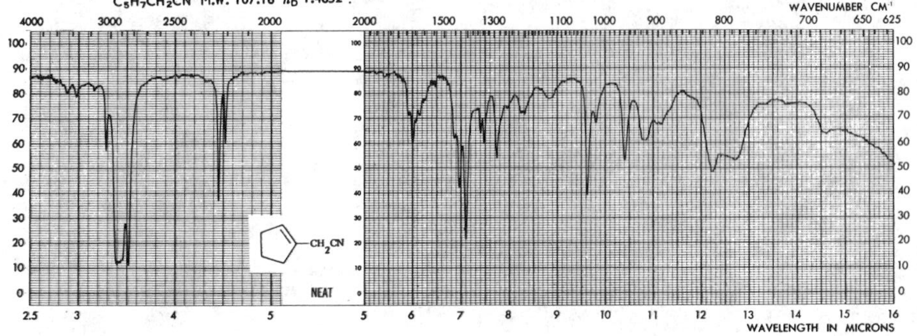

C10,232-6 3-Cyclohexene-1-carbonitrile
C_6H_9CN M.W. 107.16 n_D^{20} 1.4716

NEAT

H

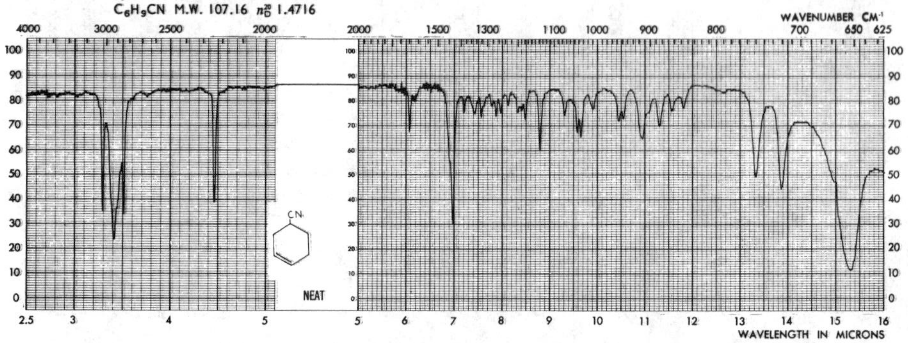

C10,340-3 1-Cyclohexenylacetonitrile (1-cyclohexene-1-acetonitrile)
$C_6H_9CH_2CN$ M.W. 121.18

NEAT

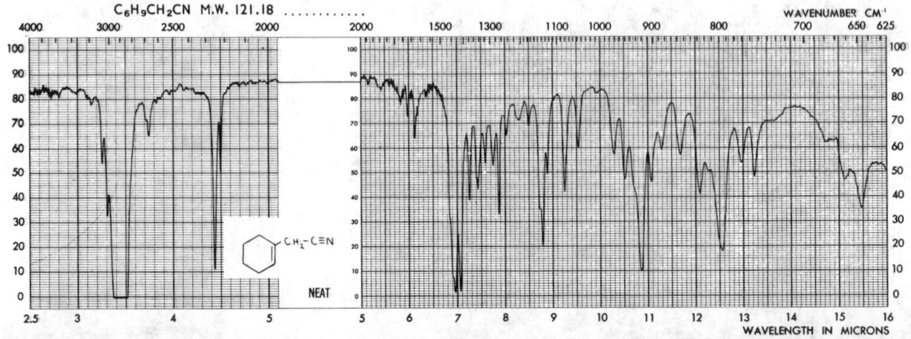

A

13,330-2
Cyclohexyl isocyanide
$C_6H_{11}NC$
M.W. 109.17 n_D^{20} 1.4502 *SEVERE POISON*

NEAT

B

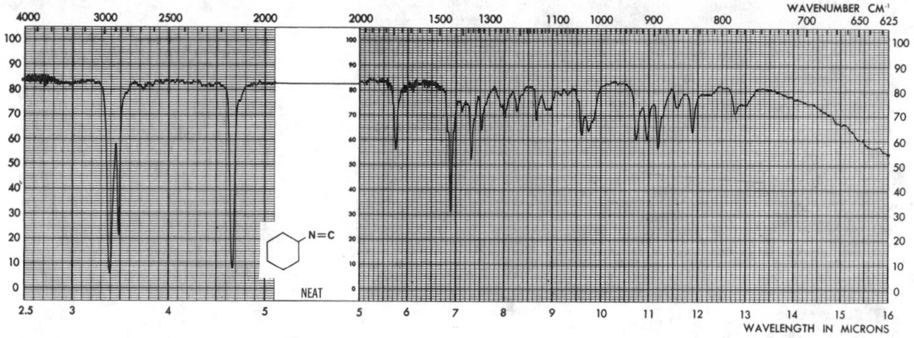

16,185-3
α-Ethyl-1-cycloheptene-1-acetonitrile, tech., 90%
[α-(1-cyclohepten-1-yl)-butyronitrile]
$C_7H_{11}CH(C_2H_5)CN$
M.W. 163.26 n_D^{20} 1.4962 d 0.934 *IRRITANT*

NEAT

C

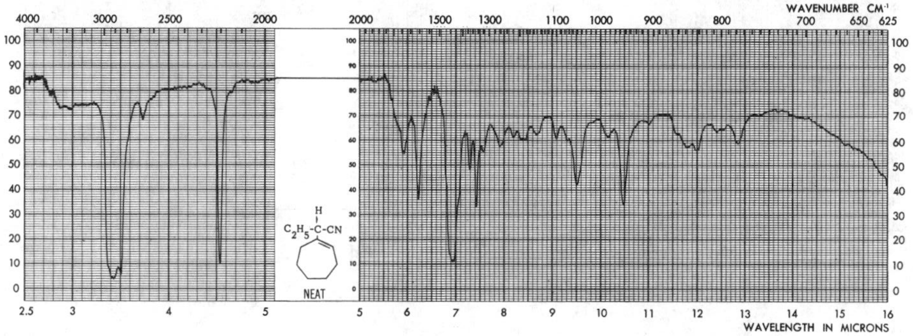

15,057-6 **5-Norbornene-2-carbonitrile**
M.W. 119.17 n_D^{20} 1.4883
b.p. 82-86°/10 mm. .....

NEAT

D

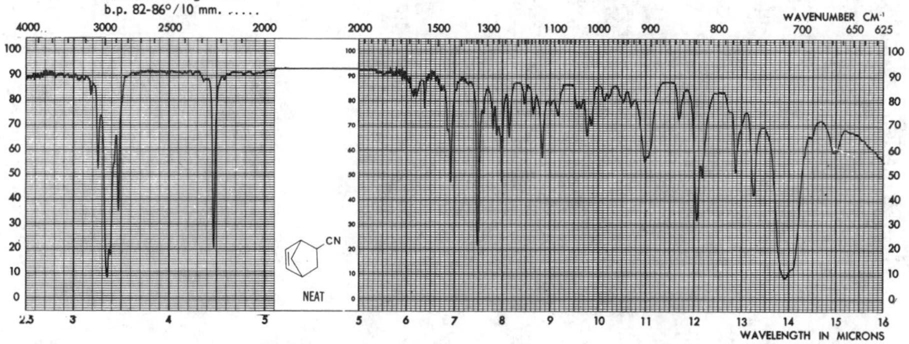

C1965-1 **Chloroacetonitrile**
$ClCH_2CN$ M.W. 75.50 n_D^{20} 1.4225

NEAT

E

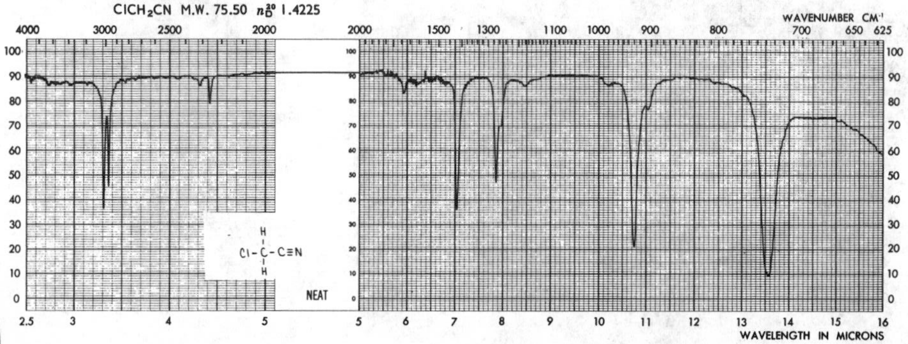

T5380-5 **Trichloroacetonitrile**
CCl_3CN M.W. 144.39 b.p. 83-84°

NEAT

F

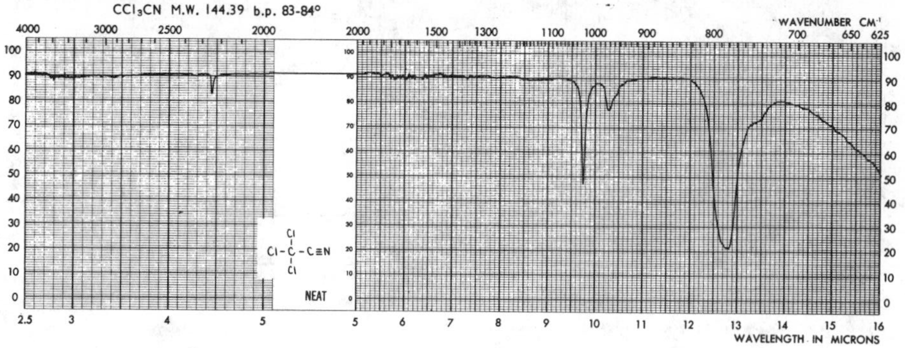

I-690-3 **Iodoacetonitrile**
ICH_2CN M.W. 166.95 n_D^{20} 1.5730

NEAT

G

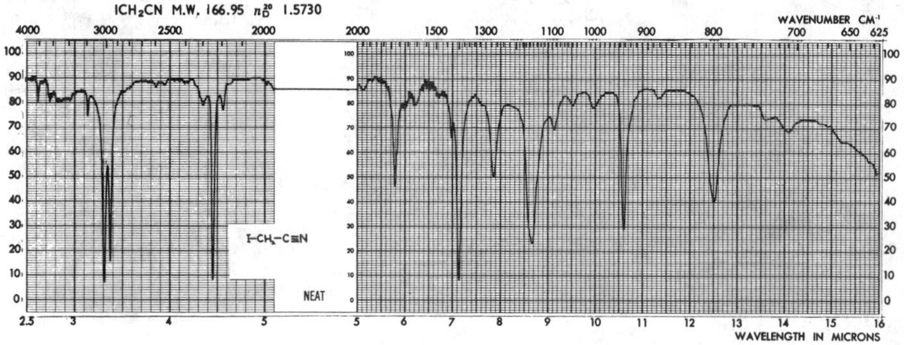

D3820-0 **Dibromoacetonitrile**
Br_2CHCN M.W. 198.86 n_D^{20} 1.5393

NEAT

H

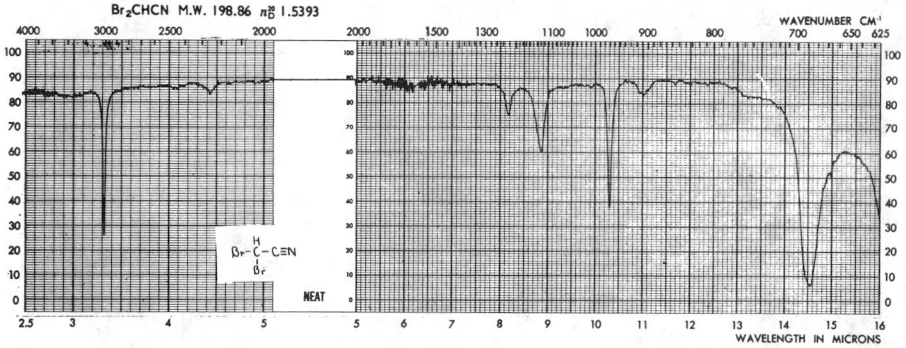

C6910-1 **3-Chloropropionitrile**
$ClCH_2CH_2CN$ M.W. 89.53
n_D^{20} 1.4379 ....

NEAT

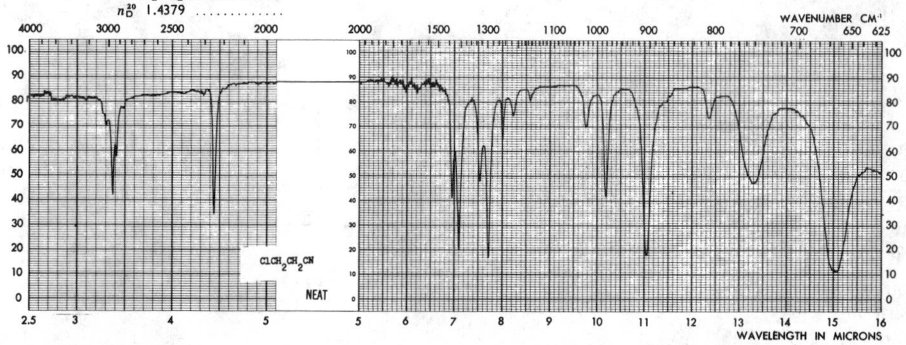

A

19,240-6
2-Chloropropionitrile
$CH_3CH(Cl)CN$ FW 89.53 bp 120-122°
n_D^{20} 1.4127 d 1.012 *Beil.* **2**,249 Disp. J

B

15,042-8
3-Chloro-2-methylpropionitrile, tech., 85+%
$ClCH_2CH(CH_3)CN$
M.W. 103.55 b.p. 60°/15mm. n_D^{20} 1.4344
LACHRYMATOR

C

10,923-1 **3-Bromopropionitrile**
$BrCH_2CH_2CN$ M.W. 133.98 n_D^{20} 1.4800
b.p. 76-78°/10 mm.

D

C3000-0 **4-Chlorobutyronitrile**
$Cl(CH_2)_3CN$ M.W. 103.55 n_D^{20} 1.4413

E

B5980-2 **4-Bromobutyronitrile**
$Br(CH_2)_3CN$ M.W. 148.01 n_D^{20} 1.4759

F

C7300-1 **5-Chlorovaleronitrile**
$Cl(CH_2)_4CN$ M.W. 117.58 n_D^{20} 1.4462

G

B8320-7 **5-Bromovaleronitrile**
$Br(CH_2)_4CN$ M.W. 162.04 n_D^{20} 1.4758

H

D6505-4 **Dichloromalononitrile**
$NCCCl_2CN$ M.W. 134.95 n_D^{23} 1.4312

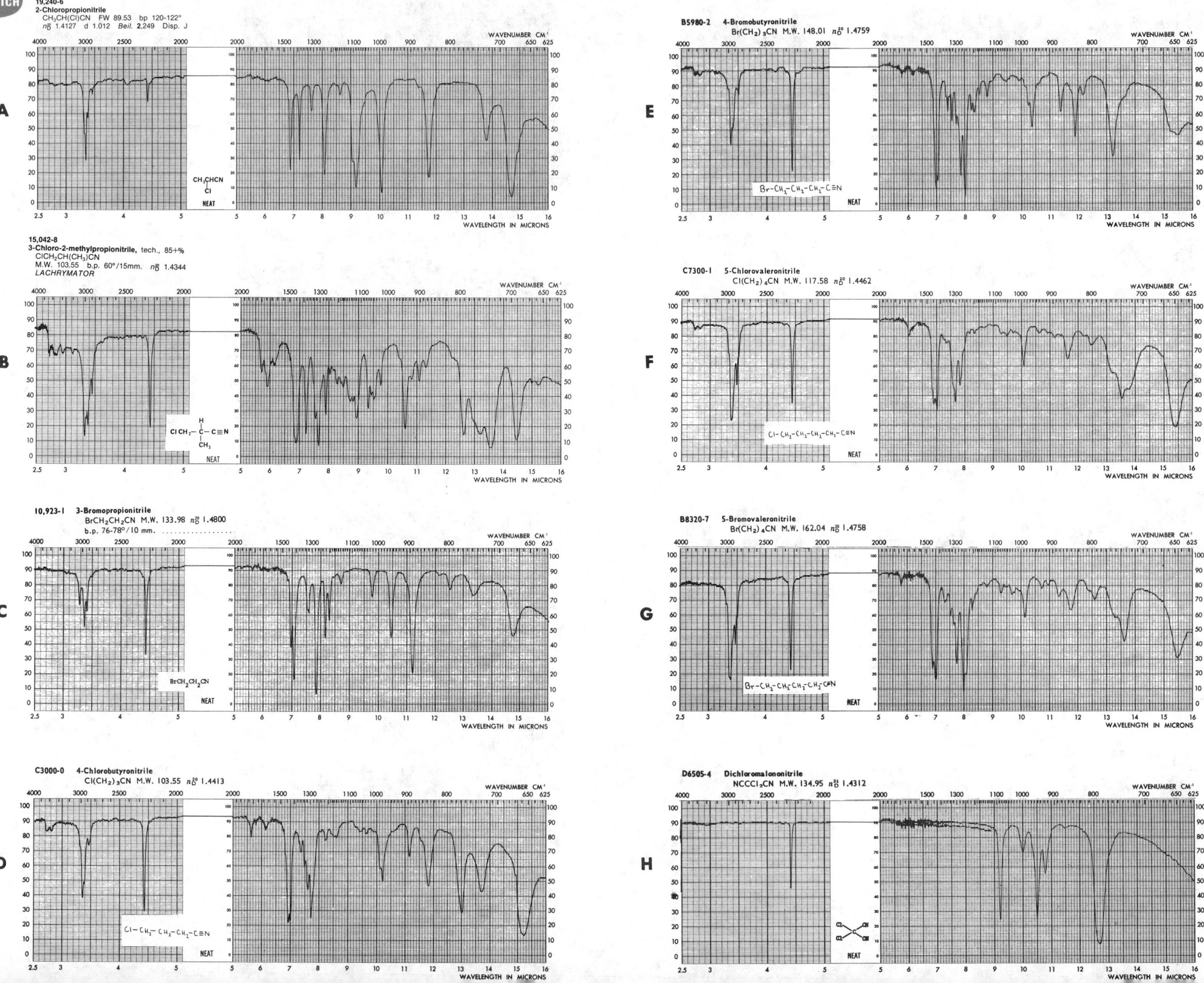

A C2236-9 2-Chloroacrylonitrile
$H_2C{:}C(Cl)CN$ M.W. 87.51 n_D^{20} 1.4323
$CH_2=C(Cl)-CN$
NUJOL MULL

B 10,992-4 3-Hydroxypropionitrile (hydracrylonitrile)
$HOCH_2CH_2CN$ M.W. 71.08 n_D^{20} 1.4240
b.p. 230°
$HOCH_2CH_2CN$
NEAT

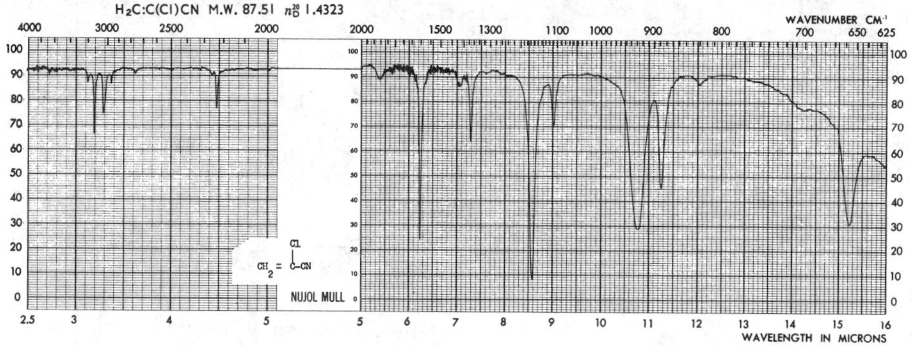

C A1000-0 Acetone cyanohydrin (2-hydroxyisobutyronitrile)
$(CH_3)_2C(OH)CN$ M.W. 85.11
n_D^{20} 1.3992
$H_3C-C(OH)(C{\equiv}N)-CH_3$
NEAT

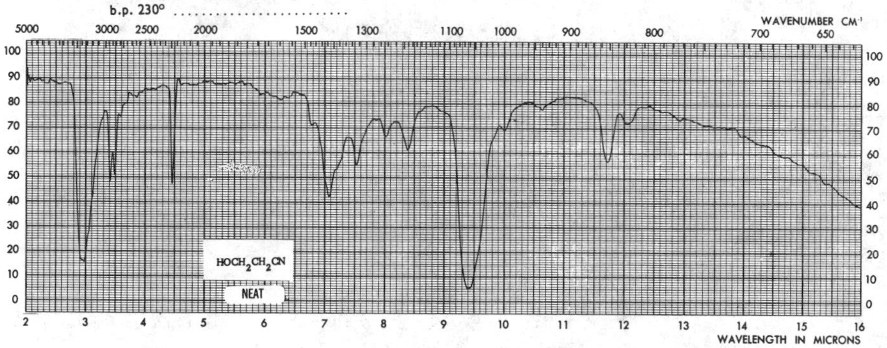

D M900-9 Methoxyacetonitrile
CH_3OCH_2CN M.W. 71.08 n_D^{20} 1.3798
b.p. 118-119°/731 mm.
$H_3C-O-CH_2-C{\equiv}N$
NEAT

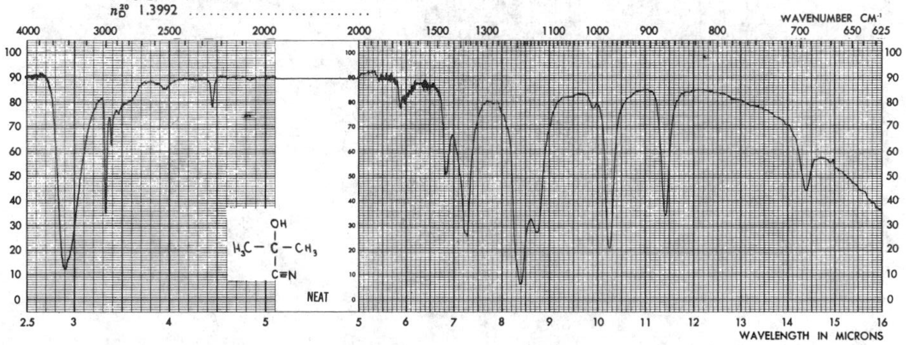

E 16,082-2
(Methylthio)-acetonitrile, 99%
CH_3SCH_2CN
M.W. 87.14 b.p. 61-63°/15mm. n_D^{20} 1.4826
d 1.039 *IRRITANT*
$CH_3-S-CH_2-C{\equiv}N$
NEAT

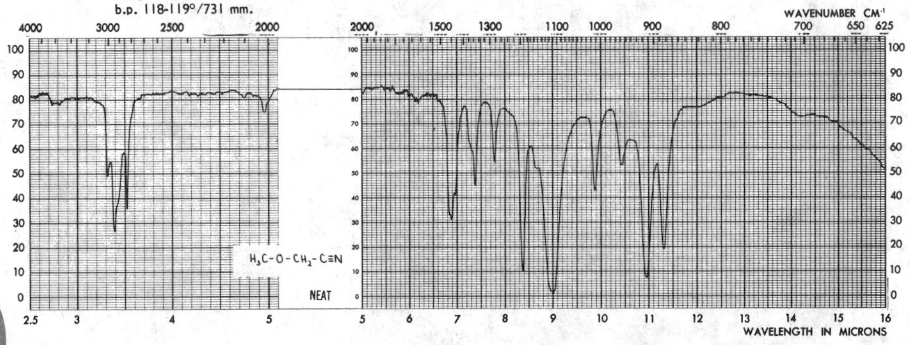

F 11,762-5 3-Methoxypropionitrile, puriss.
$CH_3OCH_2CH_2CN$ M.W. 85.11 n_D^{20} 1.4046
b.p. 164-165°
$CH_3OCH_2CH_2CN$
NEAT

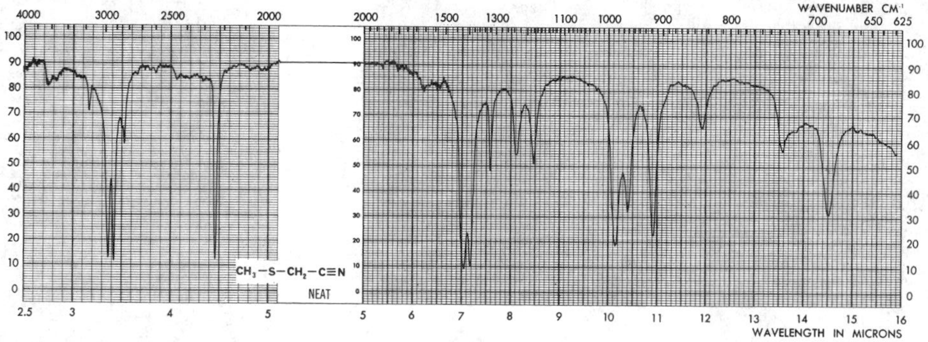

G E780-0 3-Ethoxypropionitrile
$C_2H_5OCH_2CH_2CN$ M.W. 99.13 n_D^{20} 1.4070
$H_5C_2-O-CH_2-CH_2-C{\equiv}N$
NEAT

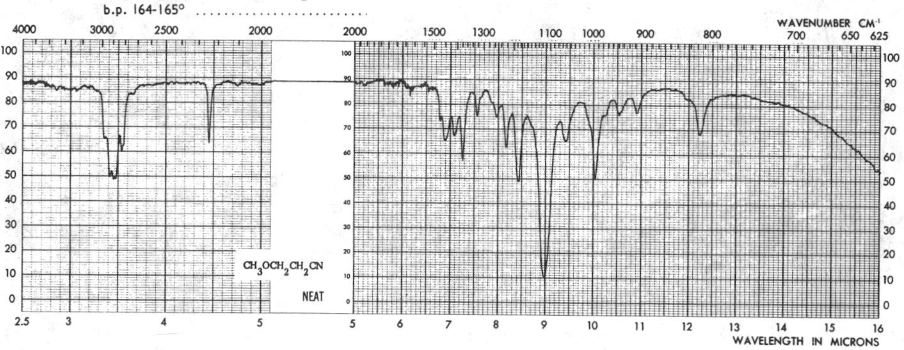

H C9120-4 2-Cyanoethyl ether (3,3'-oxydipropionitrile), tech.
$(NCCH_2CH_2)_2O$ M.W. 124.14
n_D^{20} 1.4461
$N{\equiv}C-CH_2-CH_2-O-CH_2-CH_2-C{\equiv}N$
NEAT

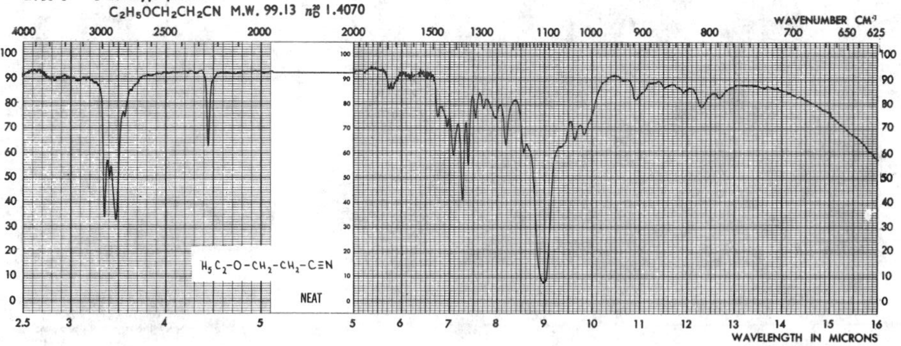

ALDRICH

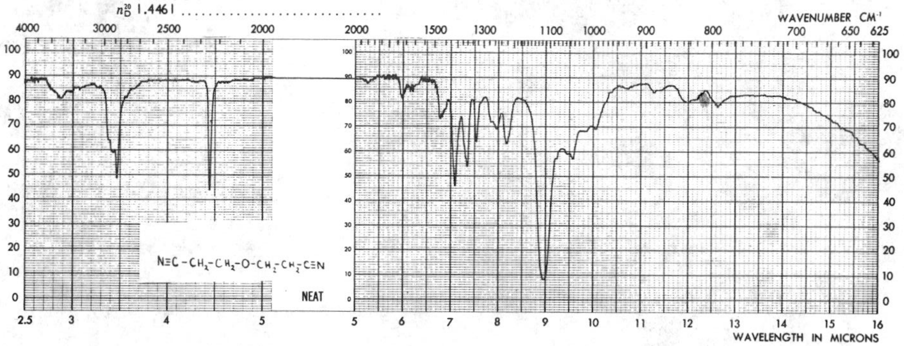

ALDRICH ®

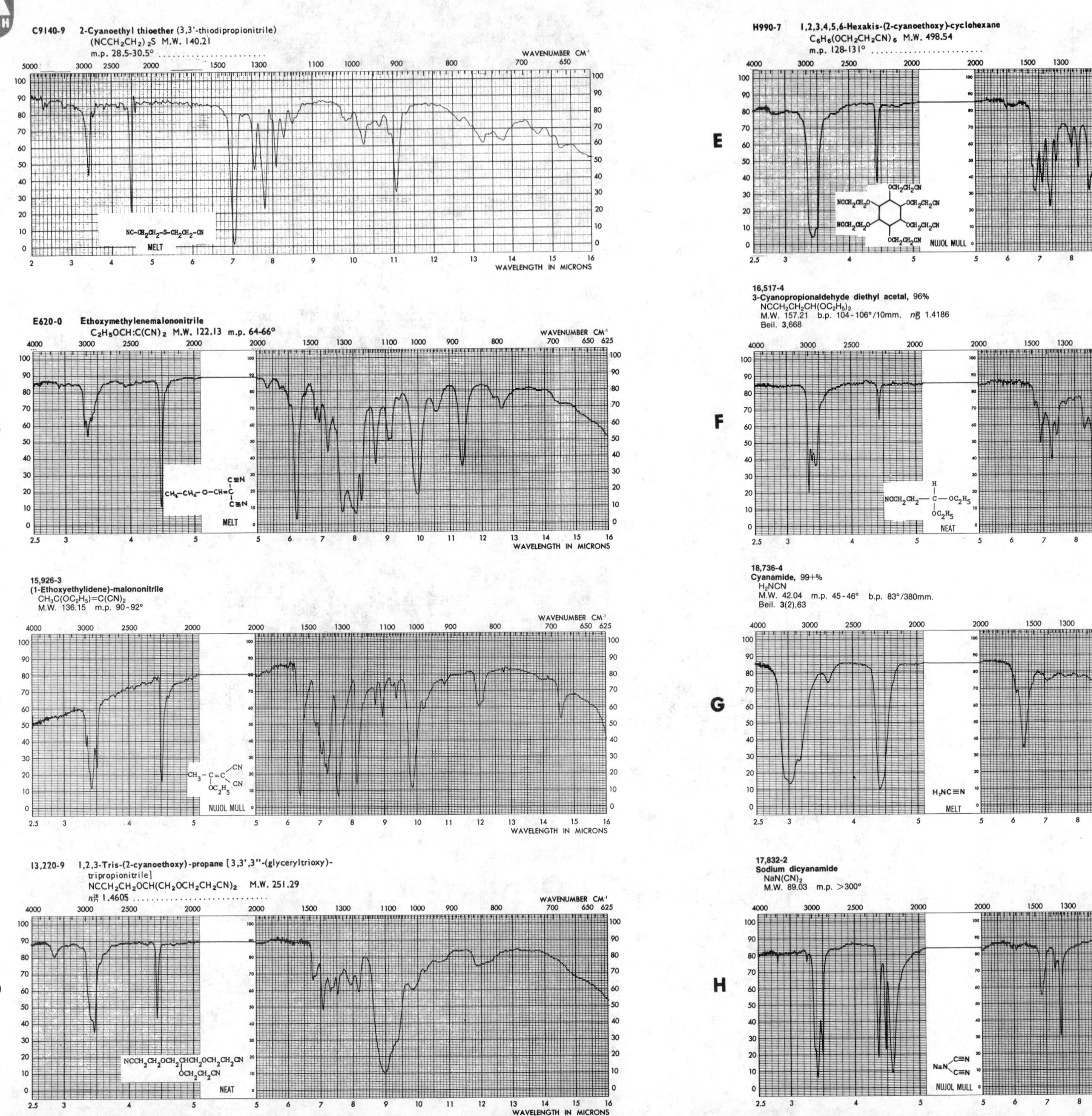

A — C9140-9 2-Cyanoethyl thioether (3,3'-thiodipropionitrile)
$(NCCH_2CH_2)_2S$ M.W. 140.21
m.p. 28.5-30.5°
MELT

B — E620-0 Ethoxymethylenemalononitrile
$C_2H_5OCH{:}C(CN)_2$ M.W. 122.13 m.p. 64-66°
MELT

C — 15,926-3
(1-Ethoxyethylidene)-malononitrile
$CH_3C(OC_2H_5){=}C(CN)_2$
M.W. 136.15 m.p. 90-92°
NUJOL MULL

D — 13,220-9 1,2,3-Tris-(2-cyanoethoxy)-propane [3,3',3''-(glyceryltrioxy)-tripropionitrile]
$NCCH_2CH_2OCH(CH_2OCH_2CH_2CN)_2$ M.W. 251.29
n_D^{20} 1.4605
NEAT

E — H990-7 1,2,3,4,5,6-Hexakis-(2-cyanoethoxy)-cyclohexane
$C_6H_6(OCH_2CH_2CN)_6$ M.W. 498.54
m.p. 128-131°
NUJOL MULL

F — 16,517-4
3-Cyanopropionaldehyde diethyl acetal, 96%
$NCCH_2CH_2CH(OC_2H_5)_2$
M.W. 157.21 b.p. 104-106°/10mm. n_D^{20} 1.4186
Beil. 3,668
NEAT

G — 18,736-4
Cyanamide, 99+%
H_2NCN
M.W. 42.04 m.p. 45-46° b.p. 83°/380mm.
Beil. 3(2),63
MELT

H — 17,832-2
Sodium dicyanamide
$NaN(CN)_2$
M.W. 89.03 m.p. >300°
NUJOL MULL

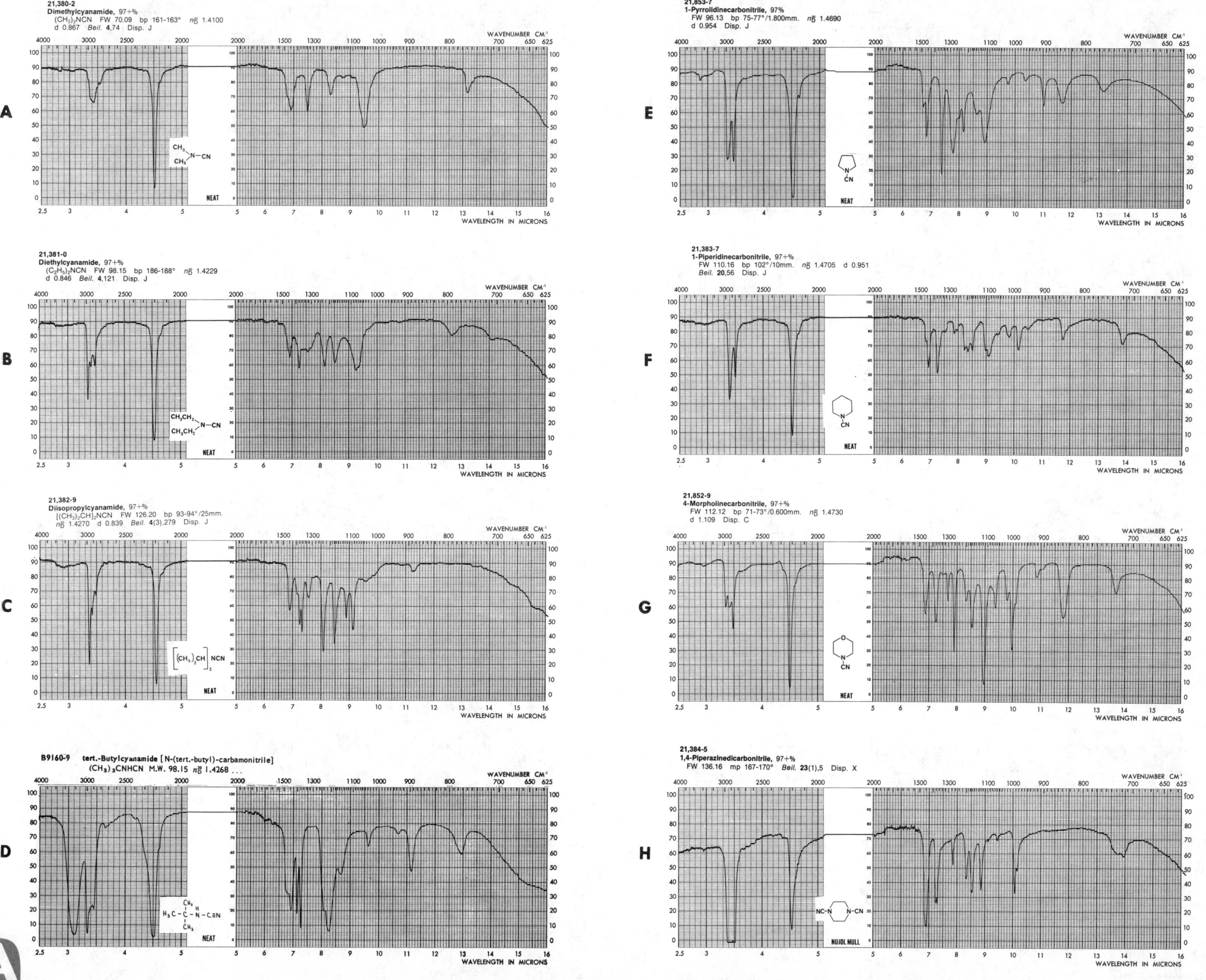
A
21,380-2
Dimethylcyanamide, 97+%
$(CH_3)_2NCN$ FW 70.09 bp 161-163° n_D^{20} 1.4100
d 0.867 Beil. 4,74 Disp. J
NEAT
B
21,381-0
Diethylcyanamide, 97+%
$(C_2H_5)_2NCN$ FW 98.15 bp 186-188° n_D^{20} 1.4229
d 0.846 Beil. 4,121 Disp. J
NEAT
C
21,382-9
Diisopropylcyanamide, 97+%
$[(CH_3)_2CH]_2NCN$ FW 126.20 bp 93-94°/25mm.
n_D^{20} 1.4270 d 0.839 Beil. 4(3),279 Disp. J
NEAT
D
B9160-9 tert.-Butylcyanamide [N-(tert.-butyl)-carbamonitrile]
$(CH_3)_3CNHCN$ M.W. 98.15 n_D^{20} 1.4268 . . .
NEAT
E
21,853-7
1-Pyrrolidinecarbonitrile, 97%
FW 96.13 bp 75-77°/1.800mm. n_D^{20} 1.4690
d 0.954 Disp. J
NEAT
F
21,383-7
1-Piperidinecarbonitrile, 97+%
FW 110.16 bp 102°/10mm. n_D^{20} 1.4705 d 0.951
Beil. 20,56 Disp. J
NEAT
G
21,852-9
4-Morpholinecarbonitrile, 97+%
FW 112.12 bp 71-73°/0.600mm. n_D^{20} 1.4730
d 1.109 Disp. C
NEAT
H
21,384-5
1,4-Piperazinedicarbonitrile, 97+%
FW 136.16 mp 167-170° Beil. 23(1),5 Disp. X
NUJOL MULL
WAVENUMBER CM⁻¹
WAVELENGTH IN MICRONS
ALDRICH

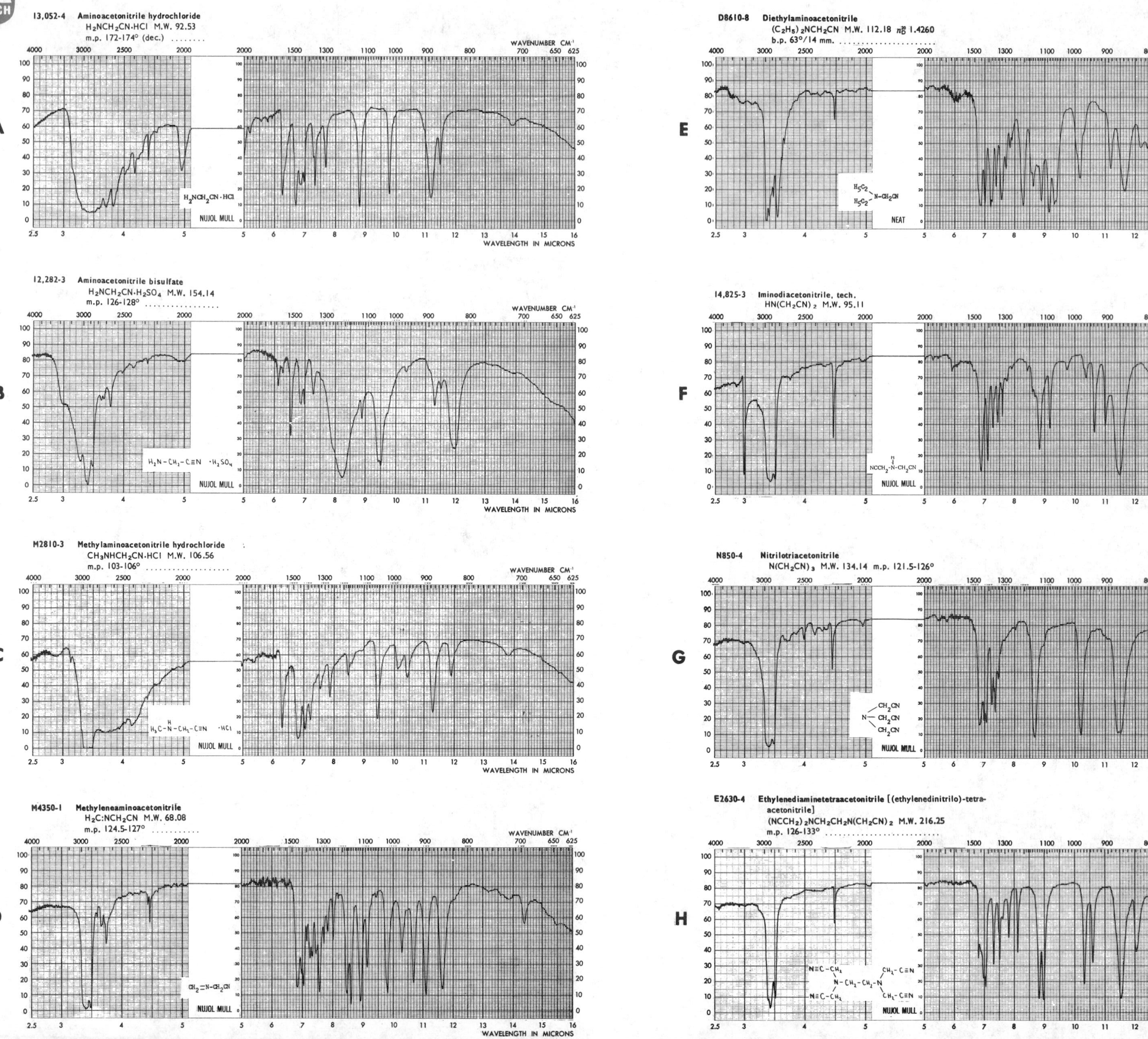
ALDRICH
A
13,052-4 Aminoacetonitrile hydrochloride
H2NCH2CN·HCl M.W. 92.53
m.p. 172-174° (dec.)
NUJOL MULL
B
12,282-3 Aminoacetonitrile bisulfate
H2NCH2CN·H2SO4 M.W. 154.14
m.p. 126-128°
NUJOL MULL
C
M2810-3 Methylaminoacetonitrile hydrochloride
CH3NHCH2CN·HCl M.W. 106.56
m.p. 103-106°
NUJOL MULL
D
M4350-1 Methyleneaminoacetonitrile
H2C:NCH2CN M.W. 68.08
m.p. 124.5-127°
NUJOL MULL
E
D8610-8 Diethylaminoacetonitrile
(C2H5)2NCH2CN M.W. 112.18 n20D 1.4260
b.p. 63°/14 mm.
NEAT
F
14,825-3 Iminodiacetonitrile, tech.
HN(CH2CN)2 M.W. 95.11
NUJOL MULL
G
N850-4 Nitrilotriacetonitrile
N(CH2CN)3 M.W. 134.14 m.p. 121.5-126°
NUJOL MULL
H
E2630-4 Ethylenediaminetetraacetonitrile [(ethylenedinitrilo)-tetra-acetonitrile]
(NCCH2)2NCH2CH2N(CH2CN)2 M.W. 216.25
m.p. 126-133°
NUJOL MULL
WAVENUMBER CM-1
WAVELENGTH IN MICRONS

A — A7642-7 3-Aminopropionitrile fumarate, puriss.
$H_2NCH_2CH_2CN \cdot \frac{1}{2}HO_2CCH{:}CHCO_2H$ M.W. 128.13
m.p. 172-173° ....

$(H_2N-CH_2-CH_2-C\equiv N)_2 \cdot HO-\overset{O}{\overset{\|}{C}}-\overset{H}{C}=\underset{H}{C}-\overset{O}{\overset{\|}{C}}-OH$ — NUJOL MULL

B — P4625-3 Piperidinoacetonitrile
M.W. 124.19 m.p. 27-29°

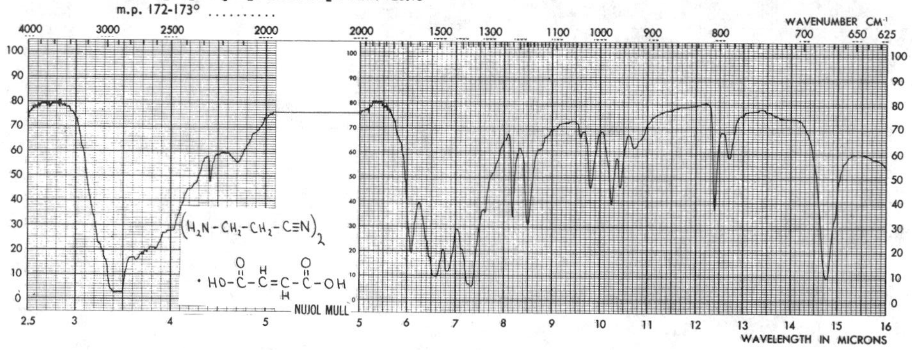

(piperidine)N-CH_2-CN — NEAT

C — 19,602-9
1-Piperidinepropionitrile, 99%
FW 138.21 bp 110-111°/16mm. n_D^{20} 1.4695
d 0.933 Disp. C

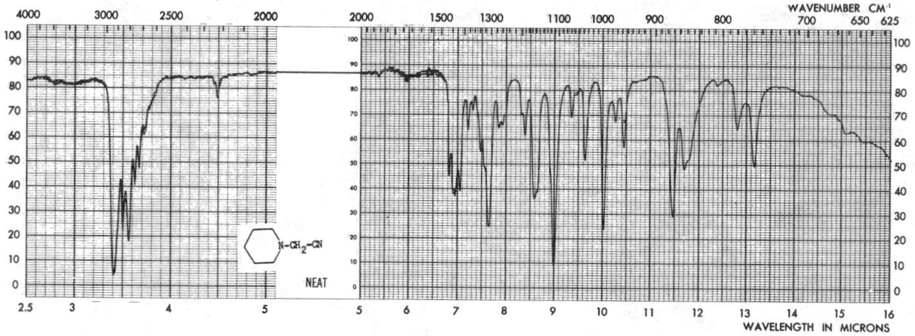

(piperidine)N-CH_2CH_2CN — NEAT

D — H1045-2 (Hexamethyleneimino)-acetonitrile
M.W. 138.21 n_D^{20} 1.4730 ....

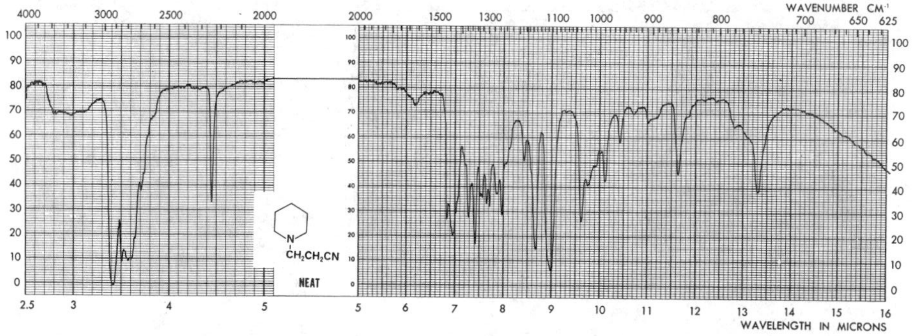

(azepane)N-CH_2-C≡N — NEAT

E — 12,186-0 (n-Butylamino)-acetonitrile
$CH_3(CH_2)_3NHCH_2CN$ M.W. 112.18 n_D^{20} 1.4337
b.p. 85°/9 mm. ....

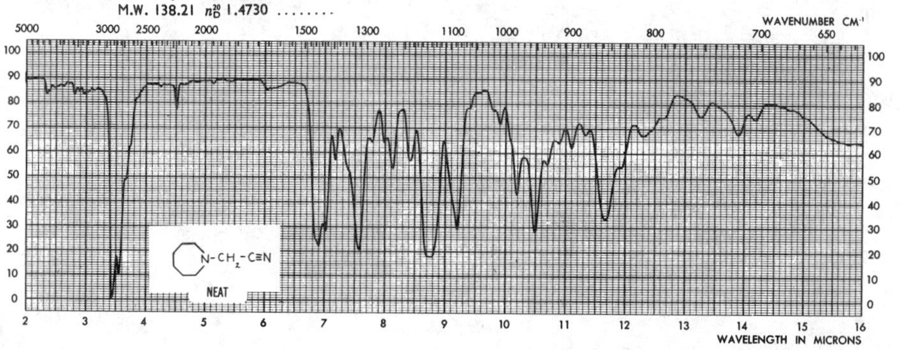

$CH_3CH_2CH_2CH_2-\overset{H}{N}-CH_2CN$ — NEAT

F — M2760-3 N-Methyl-β-alaninenitrile (3-methylaminopropionitrile)
$CH_3NHCH_2CH_2CN$ M.W. 84.12 n_D^{20} 1.4307 ....

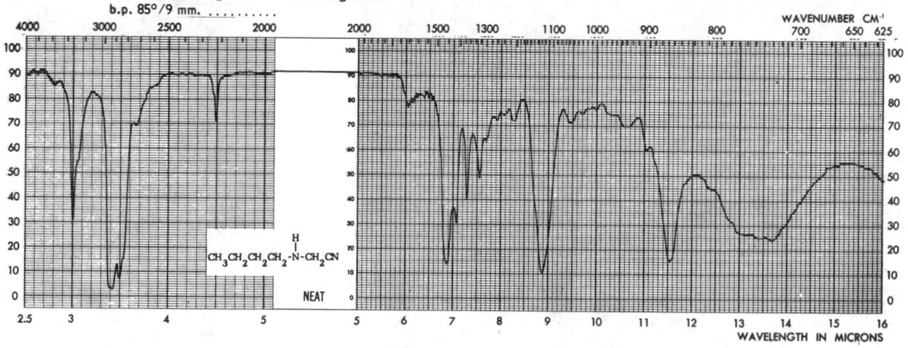

$H_3C-\overset{H}{N}-CH_2-CH_2-C\equiv N$ — NEAT

G — 13,916-5 3-(Cyclohexylamino)-propionitrile [N-(2-cyanoethyl)cyclohexylamine]
$C_6H_{11}NHCH_2CH_2CN$ M.W. 152.24 n_D^{20} 1.4749 ....

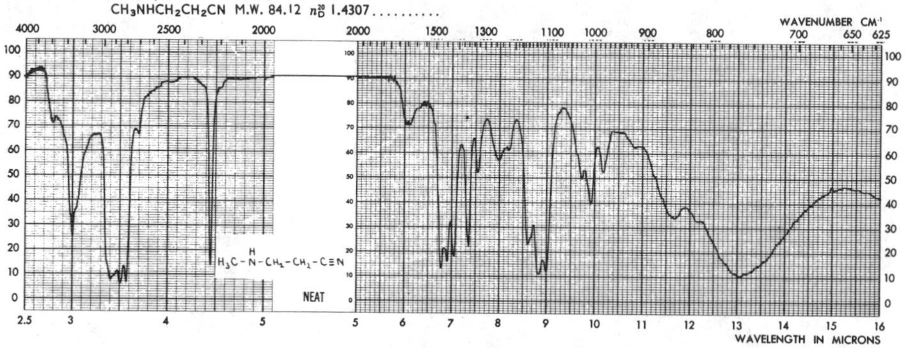

(cyclohexyl)$-\overset{H}{N}-CH_2CH_2CN$ — NEAT

H — D8880-1 3-Diethylaminopropionitrile
$(C_2H_5)_2NCH_2CH_2CN$ M.W. 126.20 n_D^{20} 1.4350

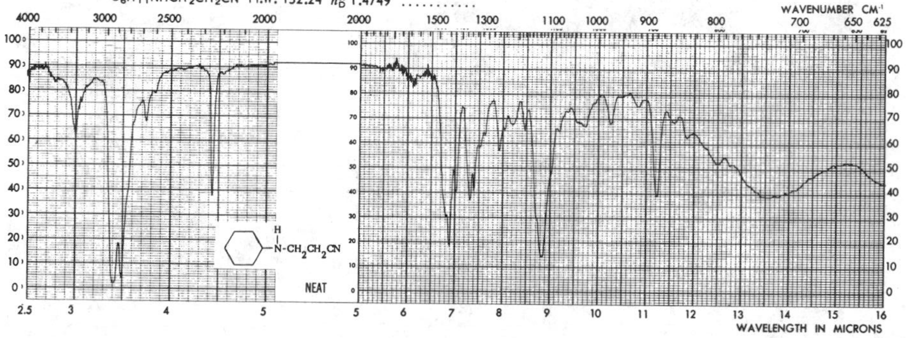

$(H_5C_2)_2N-CH_2-CH_2-C\equiv N$ — NEAT

WAVENUMBER CM⁻¹ / WAVELENGTH IN MICRONS

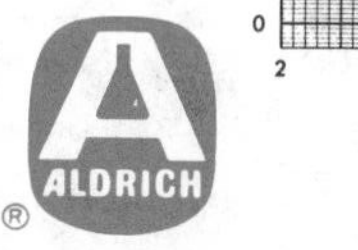

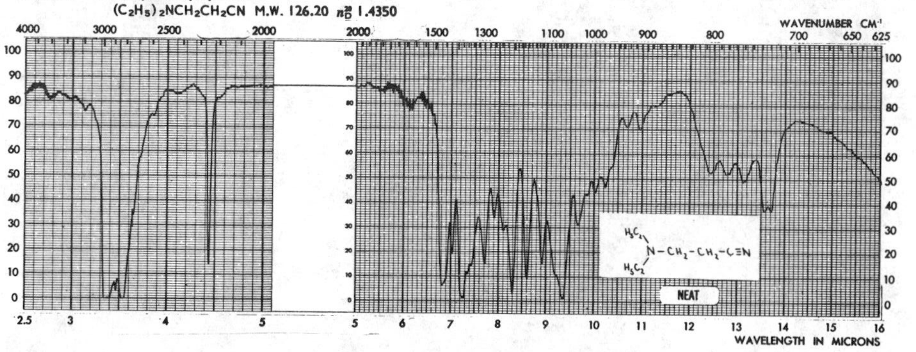

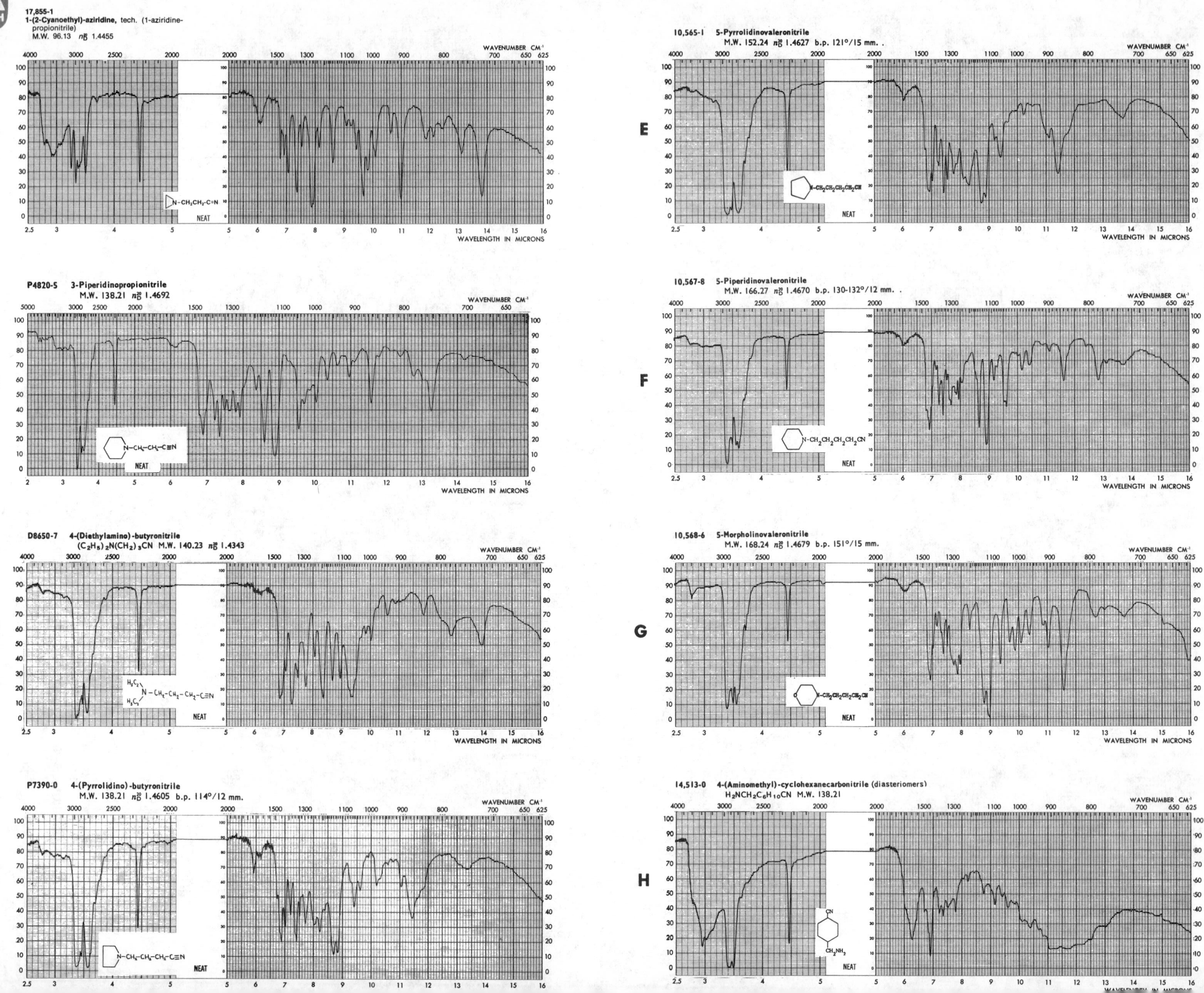
ALDRICH
A
17,855-1
1-(2-Cyanoethyl)-aziridine, tech. (1-aziridinepropionitrile)
M.W. 96.13 n 1.4455
B
P4820-5 3-Piperidinopropionitrile
M.W. 138.21 n 1.4692
C
D8650-7 4-(Diethylamino)-butyronitrile
(C2H5)2N(CH2)3CN M.W. 140.23 n 1.4343
D
P7390-0 4-(Pyrrolidino)-butyronitrile
M.W. 138.21 n 1.4605 b.p. 114°/12 mm.
E
10,565-1 5-Pyrrolidinovaleronitrile
M.W. 152.24 n 1.4627 b.p. 121°/15 mm.
F
10,567-8 5-Piperidinovaleronitrile
M.W. 166.27 n 1.4670 b.p. 130-132°/12 mm.
G
10,568-6 5-Morpholinovaleronitrile
M.W. 168.24 n 1.4679 b.p. 151°/15 mm.
H
14,513-0 4-(Aminomethyl)-cyclohexanecarbonitrile (diasteriomers)
H2NCH2C6H10CN M.W. 138.21
NEAT
WAVENUMBER CM⁻¹
WAVELENGTH IN MICRONS

A

21,717-4
1-Methoxybicyclo[2.2.2]oct-5-ene-2-carbonitrile
FW 163.22 n_D^{20} 1.4996 d 1.058 Disp. X,C

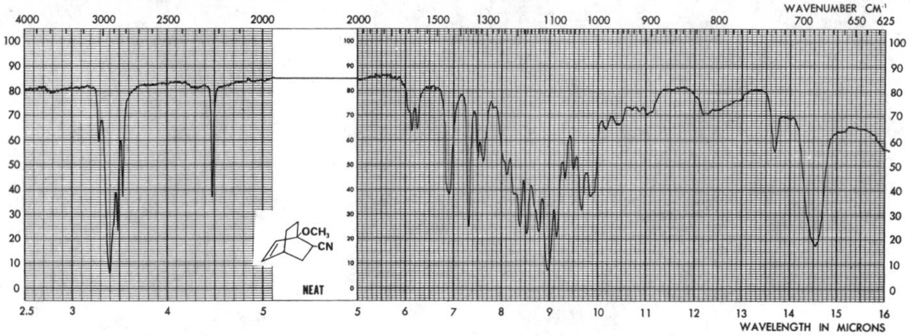

NEAT

B

14,770-2 **3-Dimethylaminoacrylonitrile**
$(CH_3)_2NCH{:}CHCN$ M.W. 96.13 n_D^{20} 1.5330
b.p. 76-80°/0.3 mm.

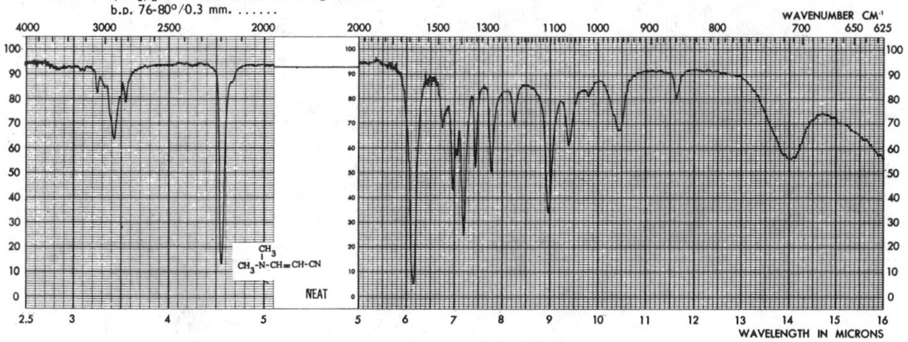

NEAT

C

14,444-4 **(Dimethylaminomethylene)malononitrile**
$(CH_3)_2NCH{:}C(CN)_2$ M.W. 121.14 m.p. 84-85°

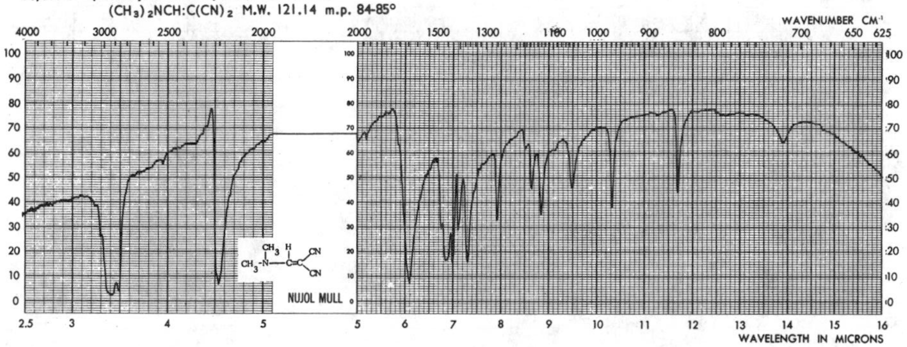

NUJOL MULL

D

11,764-1 **3-Aminocrotononitrile** (diacetonitrile)
$CH_3C(NH_2){:}CHCN$ M.W. 82.11 m.p. 49-52°

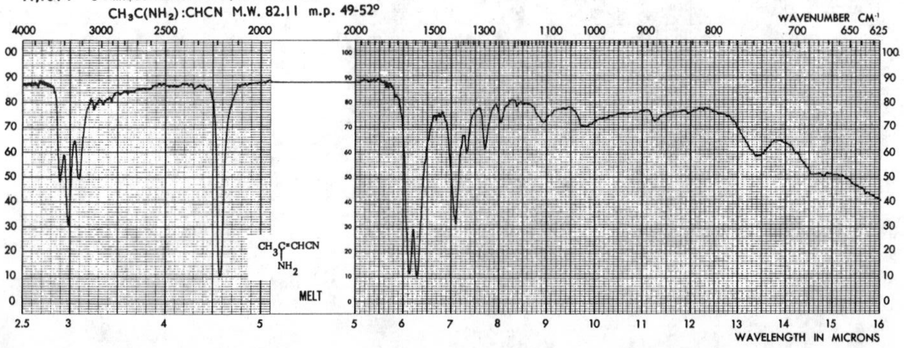

MELT

E

16,388-0
Diaminomaleonitrile, 98% (DAMN)
$NCC(NH_2){=}C(NH_2)CN$
M.W. 108.1 m.p. 178-179° Beil. 4(2),949
SEVERE POISON

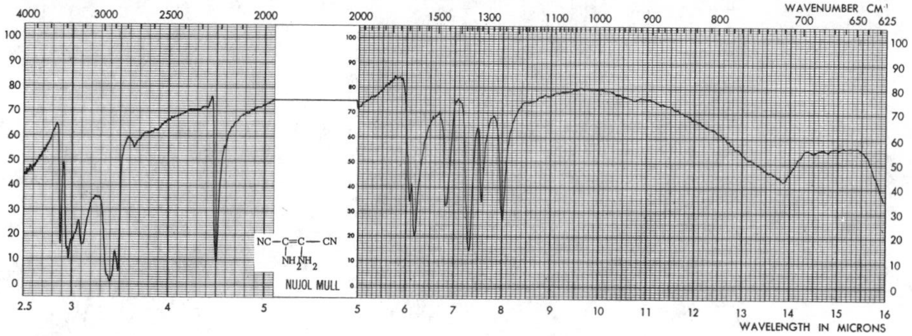

NUJOL MULL

F

16,396-1
Diiminosuccinonitrile (DISN)
$NCC({=}NH)C({=}NH)CN$
M.W. 106.09 m.p. >300° *SEVERE POISON*

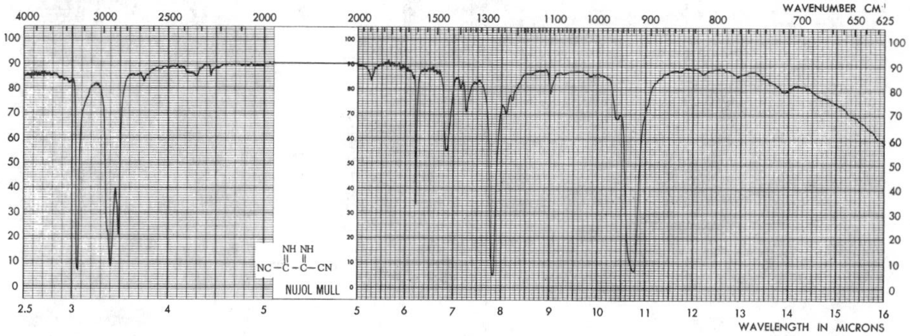

NUJOL MULL

G

10,741-7
2-Amino-1-propene-1,1,3-tricarbonitrile, 97%
(2-amino-1,1,3-tricyanopropene, malononitrile dimer)
$NCCH_2C(NH_2){=}C(CN)_2$
M.W. 132.13 m.p. 171-173°

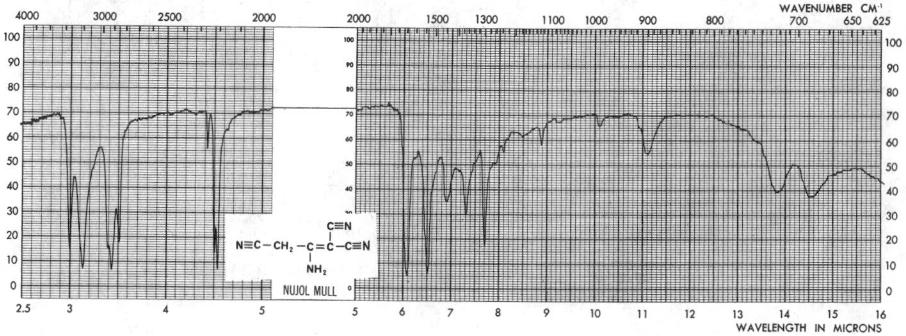

NUJOL MULL

H

A9640-1 **2,2'-Azobis-(2-methylpropionitrile)**
$(CH_3)_2C(CN)N{:}NC(CH_3)_2CN$ M.W. 164.21
m.p. 101.5°

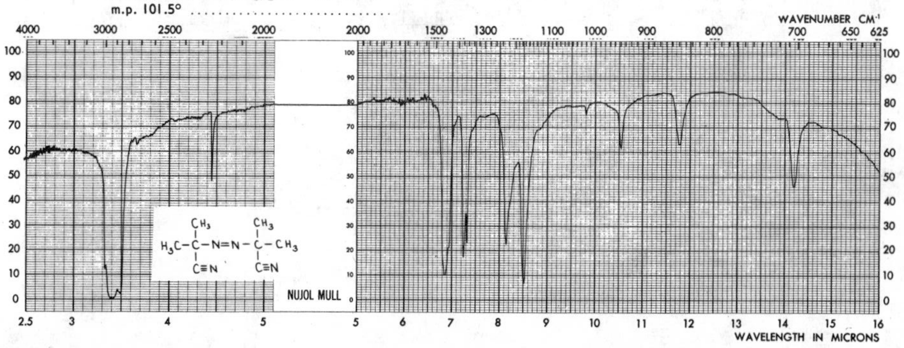

NUJOL MULL

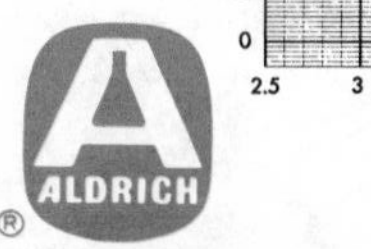

ALDRICH

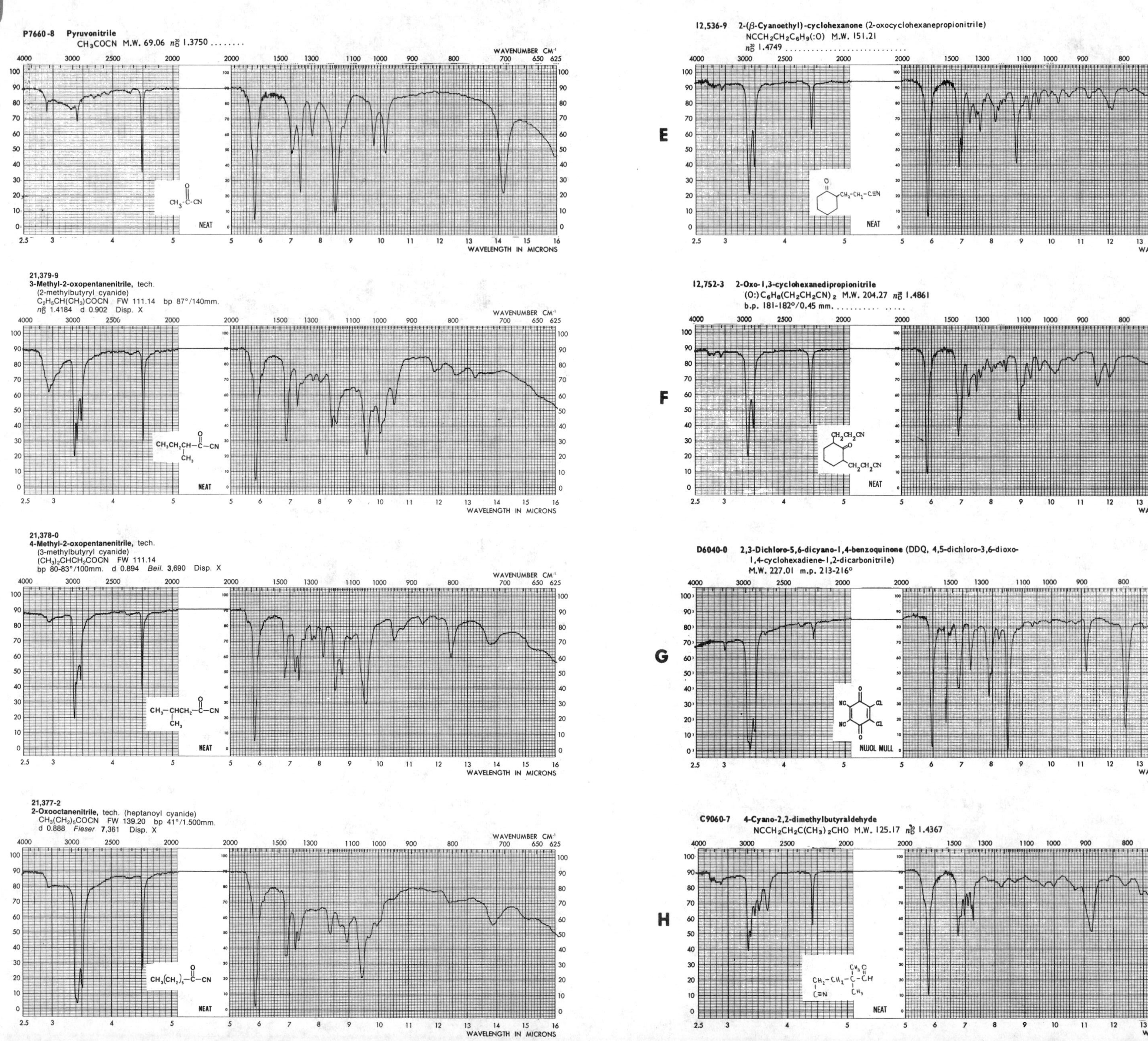

A P7660-8 **Pyruvonitrile**
CH_3COCN M.W. 69.06 n_D^{20} 1.3750 ....
NEAT

B 21,379-9
3-Methyl-2-oxopentanenitrile, tech.
(2-methylbutyryl cyanide)
$C_2H_5CH(CH_3)COCN$ FW 111.14 bp 87°/140mm.
n_D^{20} 1.4184 d 0.902 Disp. X
NEAT

C 21,378-0
4-Methyl-2-oxopentanenitrile, tech.
(3-methylbutyryl cyanide)
$(CH_3)_2CHCH_2COCN$ FW 111.14
bp 80-83°/100mm. d 0.894 *Beil.* 3,690 Disp. X
NEAT

D 21,377-2
2-Oxooctanenitrile, tech. (heptanoyl cyanide)
$CH_3(CH_2)_5COCN$ FW 139.20 bp 41°/1.500mm.
d 0.888 *Fieser* 7,361 Disp. X
NEAT

E 12,536-9 **2-(β-Cyanoethyl)-cyclohexanone** (2-oxocyclohexanepropionitrile)
$NCCH_2CH_2C_6H_9(:O)$ M.W. 151.21
n_D^{20} 1.4749 ....
NEAT

F 12,752-3 **2-Oxo-1,3-cyclohexanedipropionitrile**
$(O:)C_6H_8(CH_2CH_2CN)_2$ M.W. 204.27 n_D^{20} 1.4861
b.p. 181-182°/0.45 mm. ....
NEAT

G D6040-0 **2,3-Dichloro-5,6-dicyano-1,4-benzoquinone** (DDQ, 4,5-dichloro-3,6-dioxo-1,4-cyclohexadiene-1,2-dicarbonitrile)
M.W. 227.01 m.p. 213-216°
NUJOL MULL

H C9060-7 **4-Cyano-2,2-dimethylbutyraldehyde**
$NCCH_2CH_2C(CH_3)_2CHO$ M.W. 125.17 n_D^{20} 1.4367
NEAT

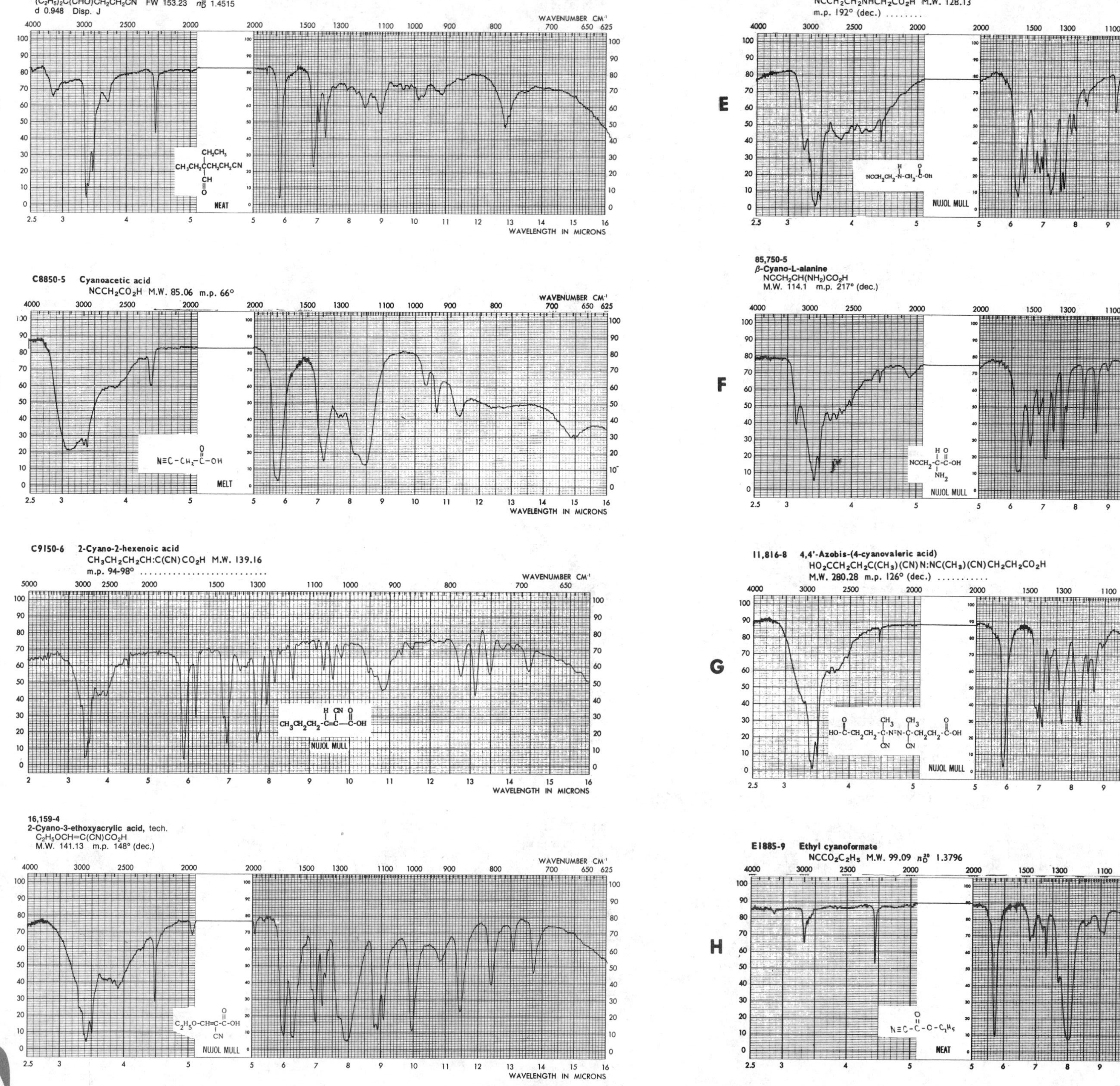

A — 20,637-7
4-Ethyl-4-formylhexanenitrile, 95%
$(C_2H_5)_2C(CHO)CH_2CH_2CN$ FW 153.23 n_D^{20} 1.4515
d 0.948 Disp. J
NEAT

B — C8850-5 **Cyanoacetic acid**
$NCCH_2CO_2H$ M.W. 85.06 m.p. 66°
MELT

C — C9150-6 **2-Cyano-2-hexenoic acid**
$CH_3CH_2CH_2CH{:}C(CN)CO_2H$ M.W. 139.16
m.p. 94-98°
NUJOL MULL

D — 16,159-4
2-Cyano-3-ethoxyacrylic acid, tech.
$C_2H_5OCH{=}C(CN)CO_2H$
M.W. 141.13 m.p. 148° (dec.)
NUJOL MULL

E — 12,555-5 **N-(2-Cyanoethyl)-glycine**
$NCCH_2CH_2NHCH_2CO_2H$ M.W. 128.13
m.p. 192° (dec.)
NUJOL MULL

F — 85,750-5
β-Cyano-L-alanine
$NCCH_2CH(NH_2)CO_2H$
M.W. 114.1 m.p. 217° (dec.)
NUJOL MULL

G — 11,816-8 **4,4'-Azobis-(4-cyanovaleric acid)**
$HO_2CCH_2CH_2C(CH_3)(CN)N{:}NC(CH_3)(CN)CH_2CH_2CO_2H$
M.W. 280.28 m.p. 126° (dec.)
NUJOL MULL

H — E1885-9 **Ethyl cyanoformate**
$NCCO_2C_2H_5$ M.W. 99.09 n_D^{20} 1.3796
NEAT

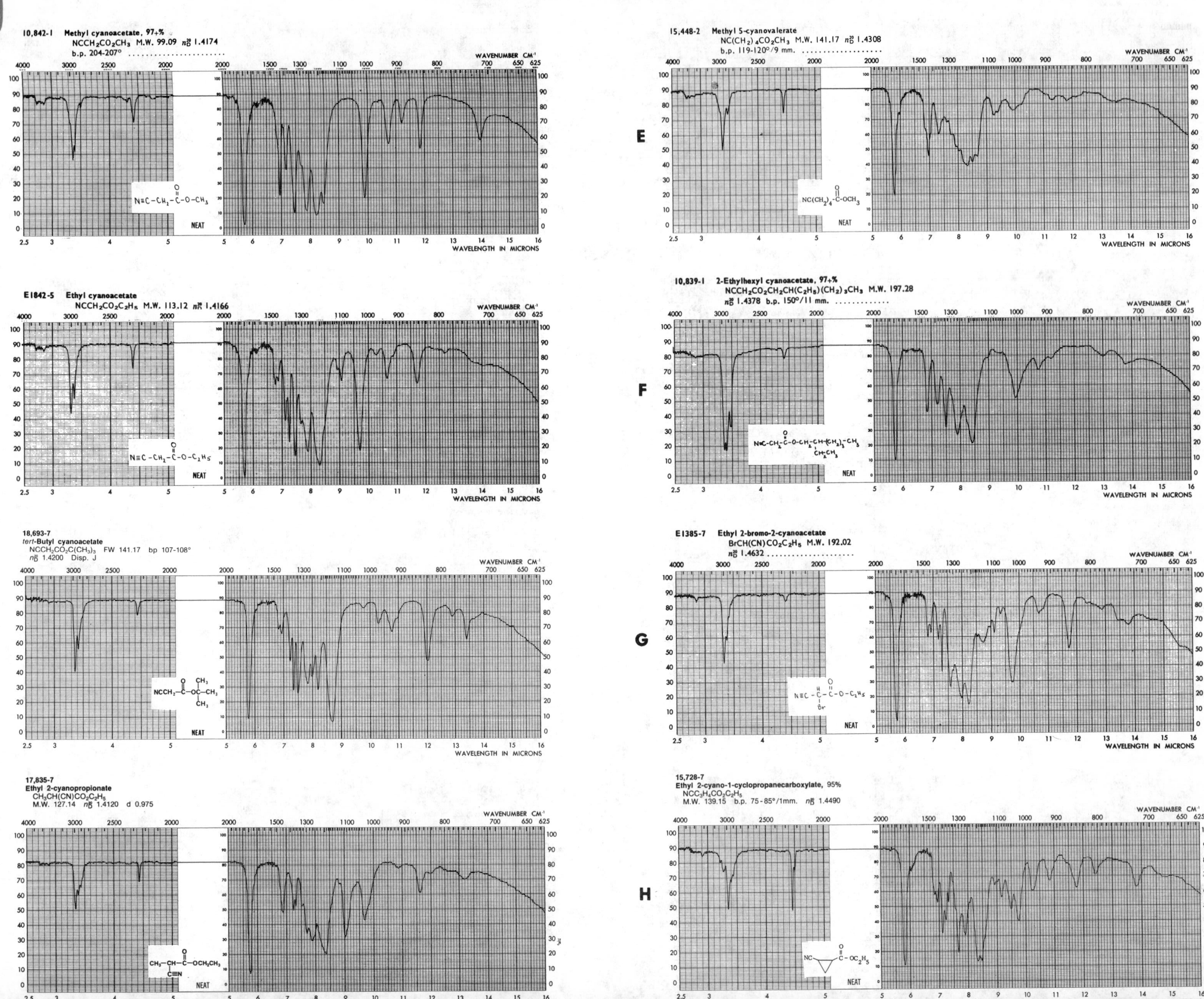
ALDRICH
A
10,842-1 Methyl cyanoacetate, 97+%
$NCCH_2CO_2CH_3$ M.W. 99.09 n_D^{20} 1.4174
b.p. 204-207°
N≡C–CH₂–C(=O)–O–CH₃
NEAT
B
E1842-5 Ethyl cyanoacetate
$NCCH_2CO_2C_2H_5$ M.W. 113.12 n_D^{20} 1.4166
N≡C–CH₂–C(=O)–O–C₂H₅
NEAT
C
18,693-7
tert-Butyl cyanoacetate
$NCCH_2CO_2C(CH_3)_3$ FW 141.17 bp 107-108°
n_D^{20} 1.4200 Disp. J
NCCH₂–C(=O)–OC(CH₃)₃
NEAT
D
17,835-7
Ethyl 2-cyanopropionate
$CH_3CH(CN)CO_2C_2H_5$
M.W. 127.14 n_D^{20} 1.4120 d 0.975
CH₃–CH(C≡N)–C(=O)–OCH₂CH₃
NEAT
E
15,448-2 Methyl 5-cyanovalerate
$NC(CH_2)_4CO_2CH_3$ M.W. 141.17 n_D^{20} 1.4308
b.p. 119-120°/9 mm.
NC(CH₂)₄–C(=O)–OCH₃
NEAT
F
10,839-1 2-Ethylhexyl cyanoacetate, 97+%
$NCCH_2CO_2CH_2CH(C_2H_5)(CH_2)_3CH_3$ M.W. 197.28
n_D^{20} 1.4378 b.p. 150°/11 mm.
N≡C–CH₂–C(=O)–O–CH₂–CH(CH₂CH₃)–(CH₂)₃–CH₃
NEAT
G
E1385-7 Ethyl 2-bromo-2-cyanoacetate
$BrCH(CN)CO_2C_2H_5$ M.W. 192.02
n_D^{20} 1.4632
N≡C–CH(Br)–C(=O)–O–C₂H₅
NEAT
H
15,728-7
Ethyl 2-cyano-1-cyclopropanecarboxylate, 95%
$NCC_3H_4CO_2C_2H_5$
M.W. 139.15 b.p. 75-85°/1mm. n_D^{20} 1.4490
NEAT
WAVENUMBER CM⁻¹
WAVELENGTH IN MICRONS

A 10,147-8 **1-Cyanocyclopentyl acetate**
$CH_3CO_2C_5H_8CN$ M.W. 153.18 n_D^{20} 1.4470
NEAT

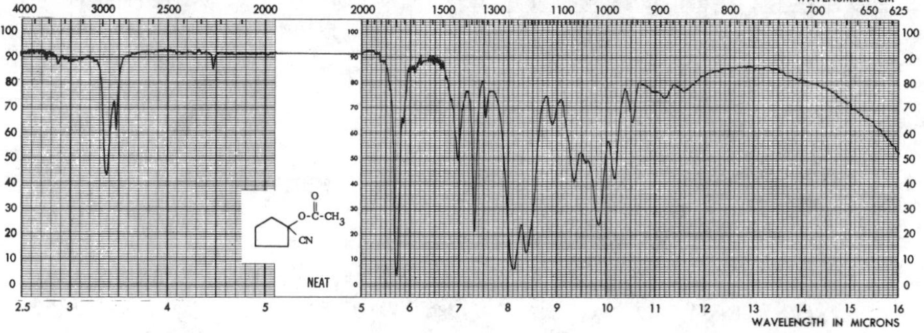

B 10,149-4 **1-Cyanocyclohexyl acetate**
$CH_3CO_2C_6H_{10}CN$ M.W. 167.21 m.p. 43-44°
MELT

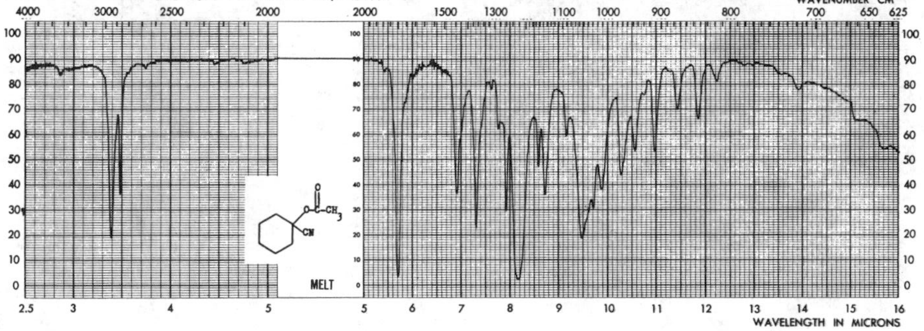

C 19,146-9
Cyclohexanone cyanohydrin, tech. (1-hydroxy-1-cyclohexanecarbonitrile)
$HOC_6H_{10}CN$ FW 125.17 mp 29° n_D^{20} 1.4576
d 1.031 *Beil.* **10**,5 Disp. C
NEAT

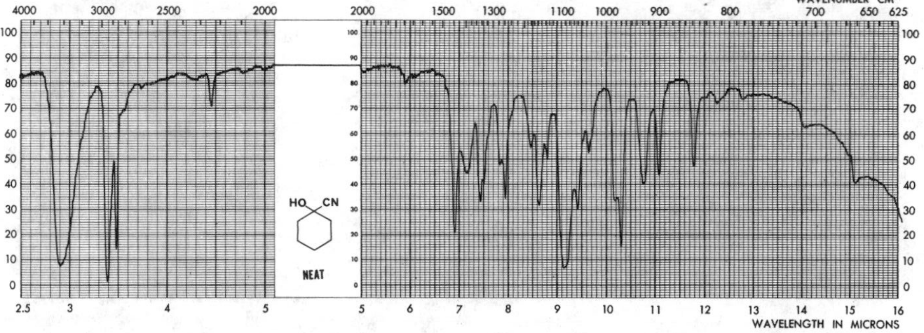

D 10,315-2 **1-Ethyl 5-methyl 2-acetyl-2-(2-cyanoethyl)-glutarate**
$CH_3O_2CCH_2CH_2C(COCH_3)(CH_2CH_2CN)CO_2C_2H_5$ M.W. 269.30
n_D^{20} 1.4620 b.p. 152-153°/0.2 mm.
NEAT

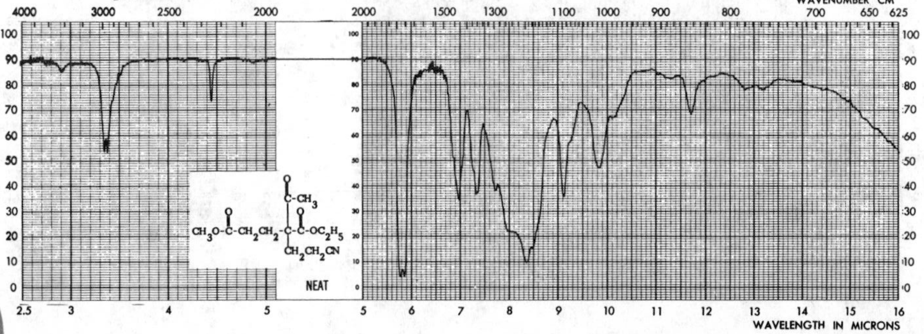

E 15,951-4
Diethyl bis-(2-cyanoethyl)-malonate, 97%
$(NCCH_2CH_2)_2C(CO_2C_2H_5)_2$
M.W. 266.3 m.p. 61-63° Beil. **2**,818
MELT

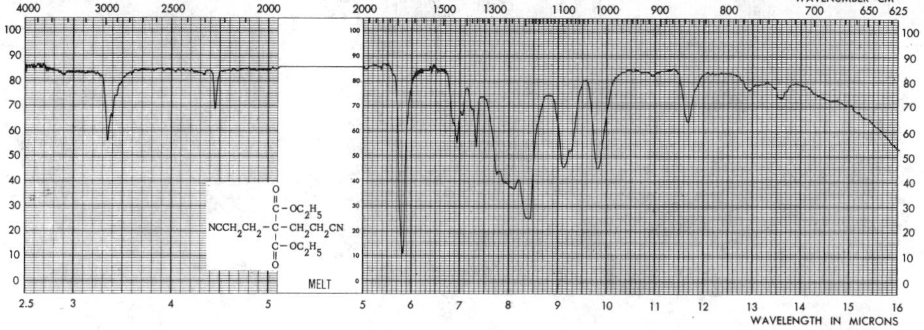

F 15,956-5
Diethyl 2-(2-cyanoethyl)-malonate, 98%
$NCCH_2CH_2CH(CO_2C_2H_5)_2$
M.W. 213.23 b.p. 115-118°/2mm. n_D^{20} 1.4368
NEAT

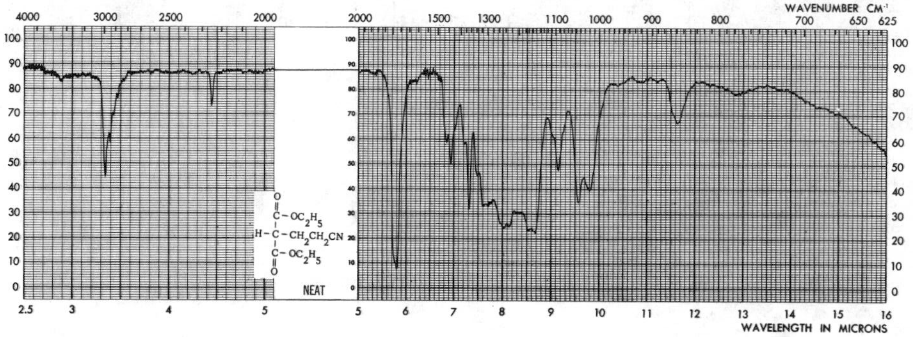

G 19,247-3
Ethyl 2-cyano-2-(hydrazinomethylene)acetate, 99%
(ethyl 2-cyano-3-hydrazinoacrylate)
$H_2NNHCH{=}C(CN)CO_2C_2H_5$ FW 155.16
mp 96-99° Disp. J
NUJOL MULL

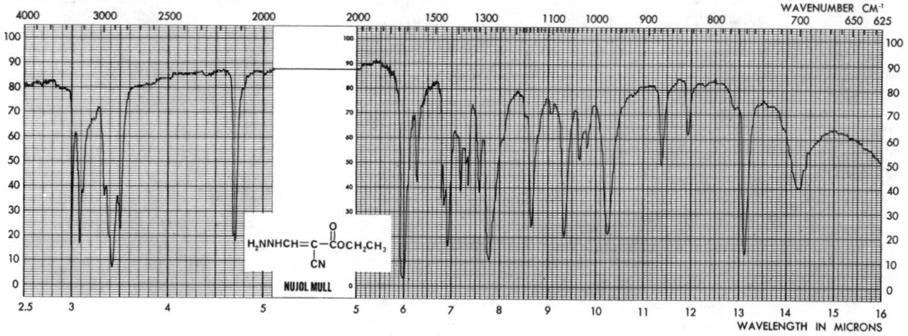

H 14,401-0 **Ethyl 2-cyano-3-dimethylaminoacrylate**
$(CH_3)_2NCH{:}C(CN)CO_2C_2H_5$ M.W. 168.20
m.p. 78-80°
NUJOL MULL

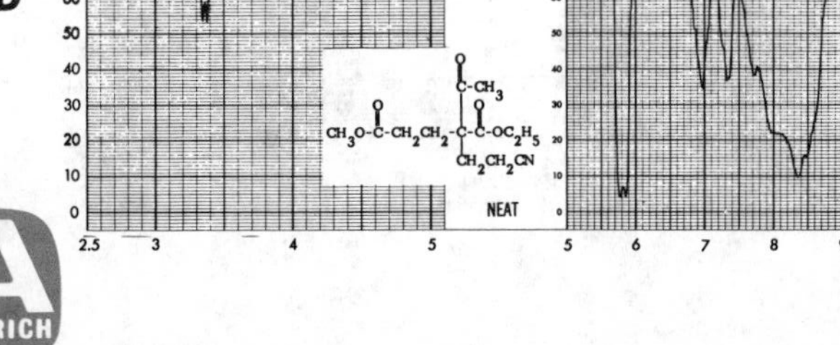

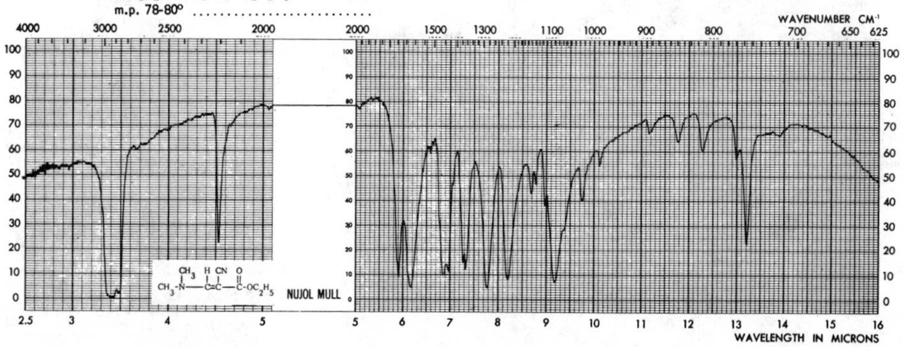

A E2800-5 **Ethyl (ethoxymethylene)-cyanoacetate** (ethyl 2-cyano-3-ethoxyacrylate)
$C_2H_5OCH{:}C(CN)CO_2C_2H_5$ M.W. 169.18 m.p. 51-53° (MELT)

B E960-9 **Ethyl acetamidocyanoacetate** (N-acetyl-2-cyanoglycine ethyl ester)
$CH_3CONHCH(CN)CO_2C_2H_5$ M.W. 170.17 m.p. 129-131° (NUJOL MULL)

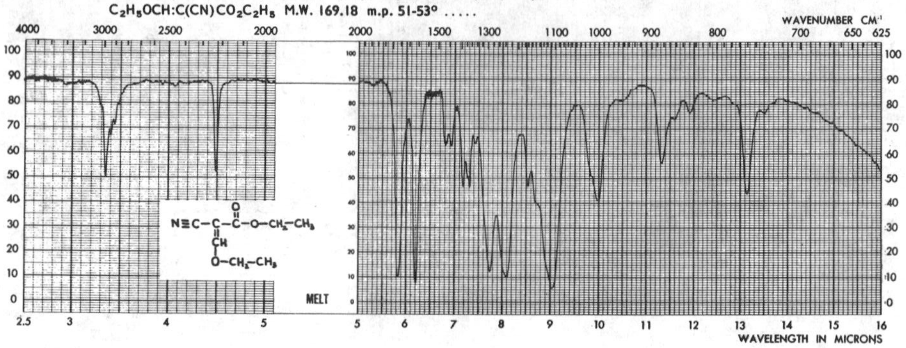

C 10,844-8 **2-Cyanoacetamide, 99%**
$NCCH_2CONH_2$ M.W. 84.08 m.p. 121-122° (NUJOL MULL)

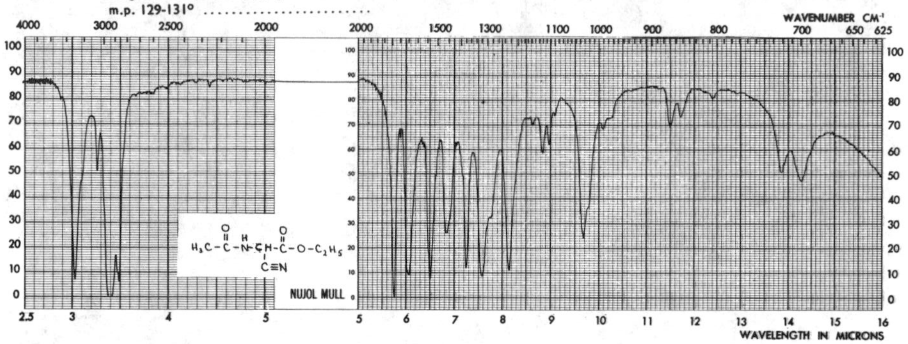

D C8860-2 **Cyanoacetohydrazide** (cyanoacetic acid hydrazide)
$NCCH_2CONHNH_2$ M.W. 99.09 m.p. 108-110° (NUJOL MULL)

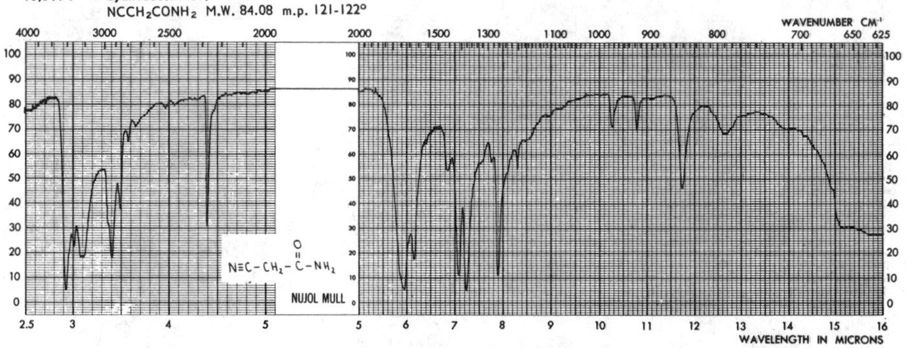

E C8880-7 **Cyanoacetylurea**
$NCCH_2CONHCONH_2$ M.W. 127.10 m.p. 214° (dec.) (NUJOL MULL)

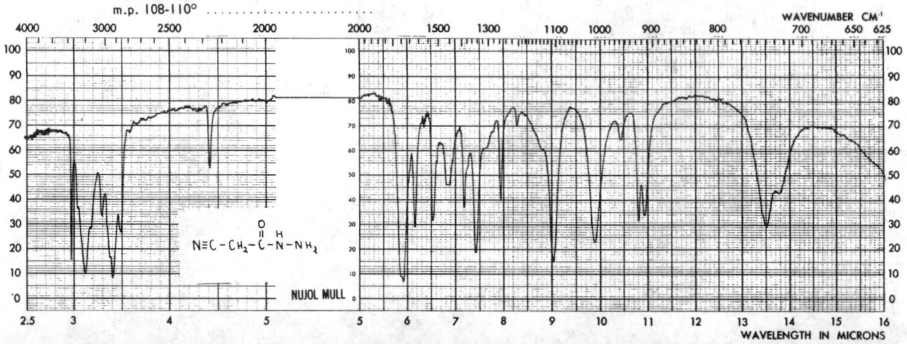

F 11,513-4 **1-Cyanoacetylpyrrolidine**
M.W. 138.17 m.p. 72-76° (MELT)

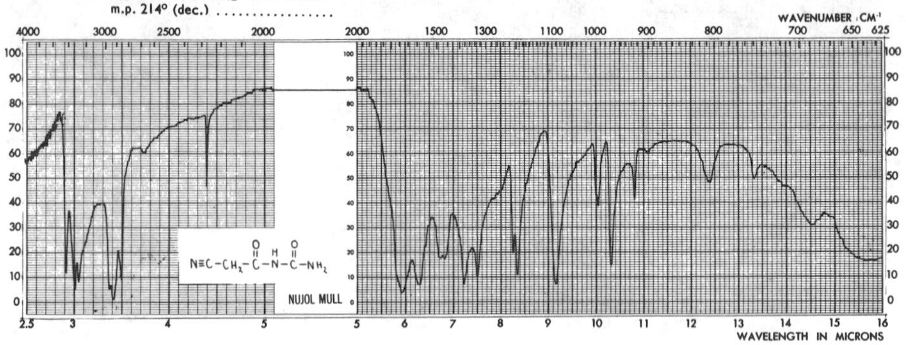

G 13,655-7 **2-Oxo-1-pyrrolidinepropionitrile**
M.W. 138.17 n_D^{20} 1.4873 b.p. 138-140°/0.3 mm. (NEAT)

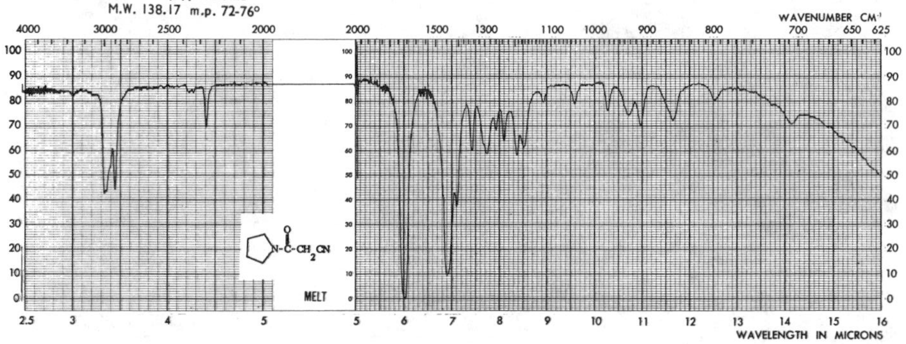

H 10,218-0 **1-Cyanoacetylpiperidine**
M.W. 152.20 m.p. 88-91° (NUJOL MULL)

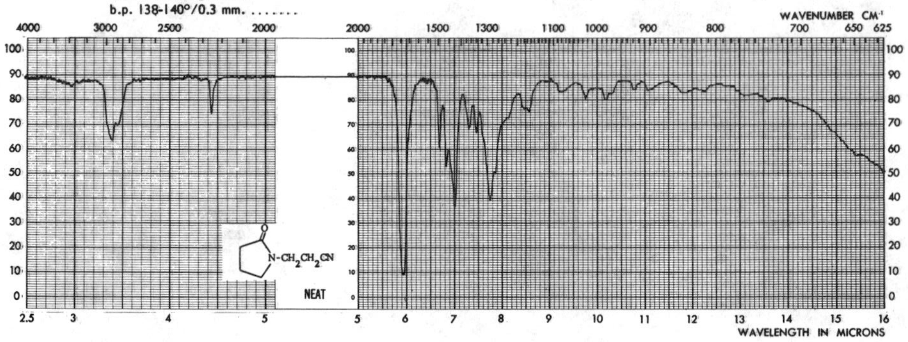

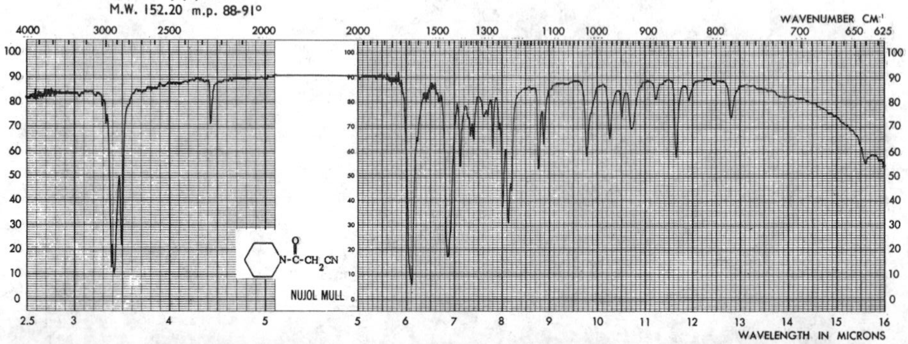

A 11,514-2 **4-Cyanoacetylmorpholine**
M.W. 154.17 m.p. 80-85°
NUJOL MULL

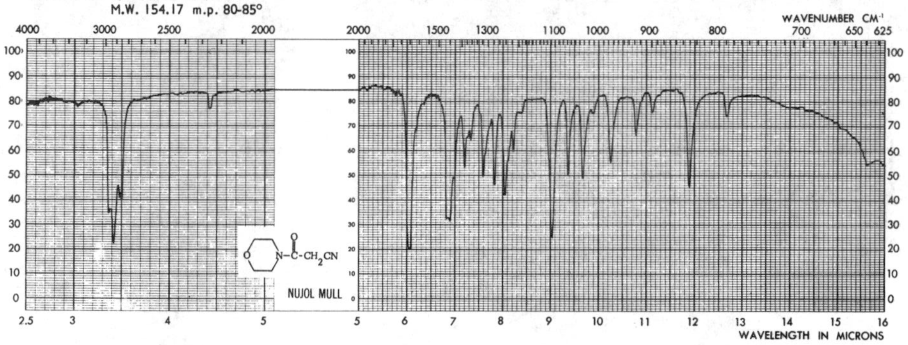

B 14,676-5 **N-(Cyanomethyl)-acetamide**
$CH_3CONHCH_2CN$ M.W. 98.11 m.p. 79-81°
NUJOL MULL

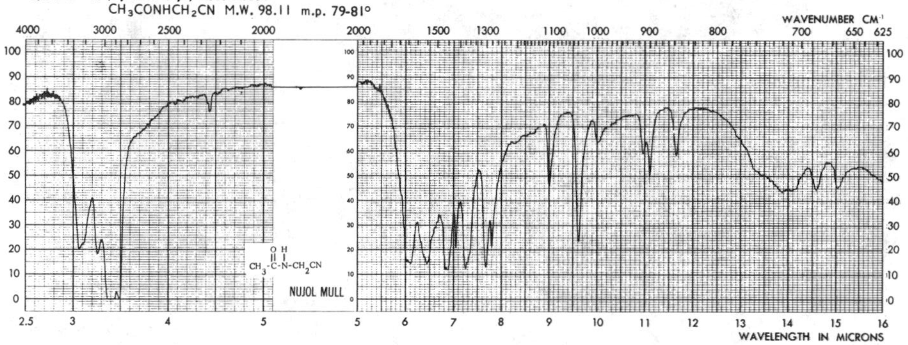

C D7660-9 **Dicyandiamide (cyanoguanidine)**
NCNHC(:NH)NH_2 M.W. 84.08
m.p. 211-212°
NUJOL MULL

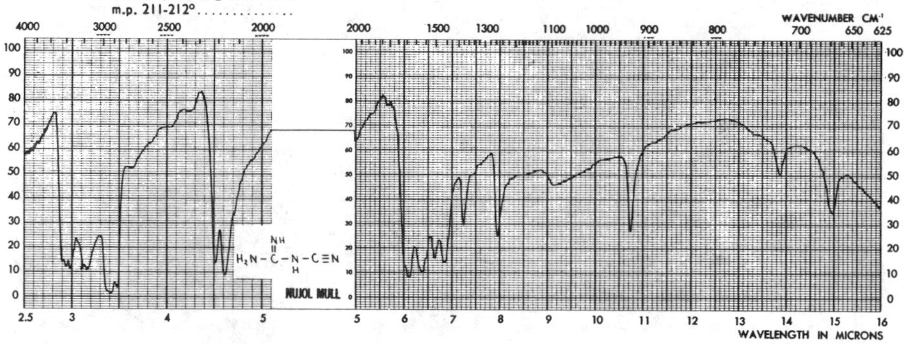

D C8900-5 **N-Cyanoacetylurethane** (ethyl cyanoacetylcarbamate)
$NCCH_2CONHCO_2C_2H_5$ M.W. 156.14
m.p. 167-169°
NUJOL MULL

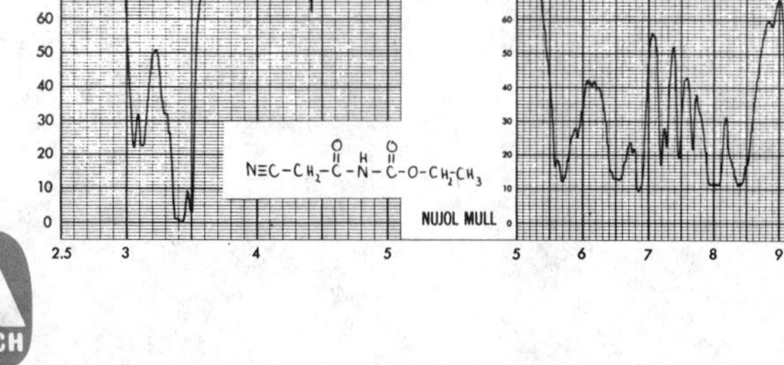

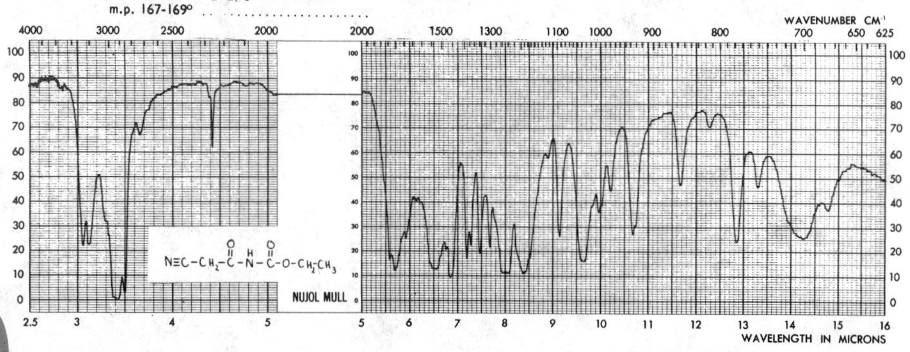

E 19,291-0
2,4-Dicyano-3-methylglutaramide, 99%
$CH_3CH[CH(CN)CONH_2]_2$ FW 194.19
mp 159-160° *Beil.* **2**(2),704 Disp. J
NUJOL MULL

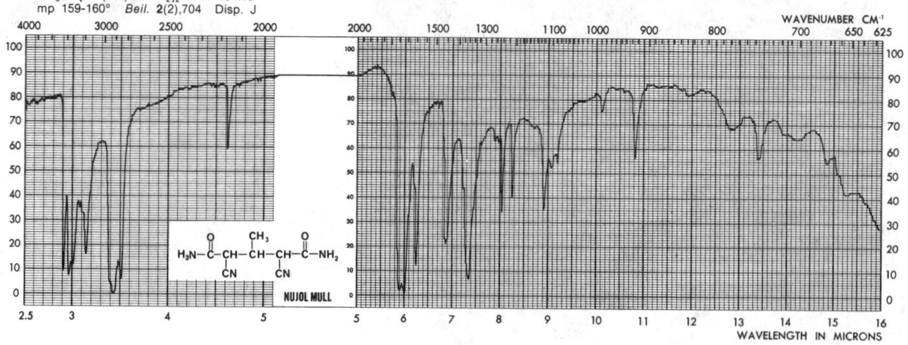

F 11,368-9 **1,2-Dihydro-3,6-dioxo-1-pyridazinepropionitrile**
M.W. 165.15 m.p. 213-215°
NUJOL MULL

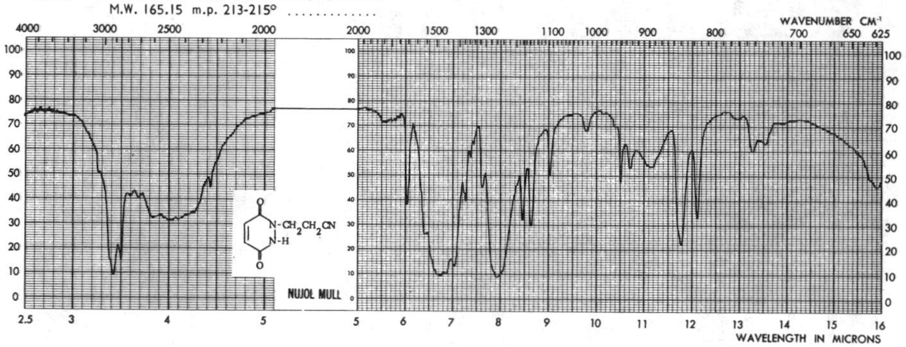

G 21,388-8
1-Cyano-3-methylisothiourea, sodium salt, 94+%
$CH_3NHC(SNa)$=NCN FW 137.14 mp 290° (dec.)
Beil. **4**,71 Disp. J
NUJOL MULL

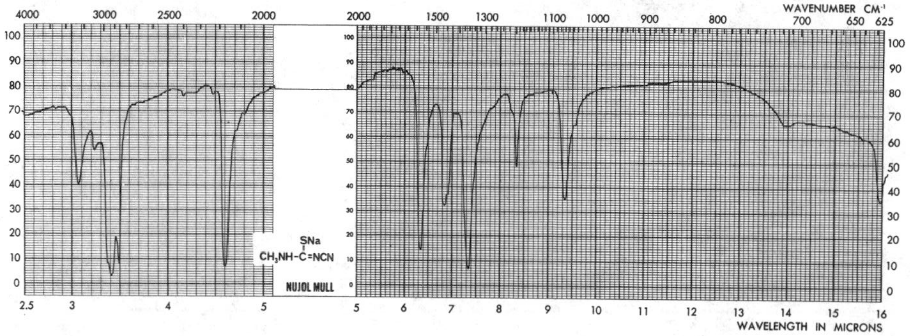

H 17,022-4
Methyl isocyanate
CH_3NCO
M.W. 57.05 b.p. 37-39° n_D^{20} 1.3695 d 0.967
Beil. 7,77
NUJOL MULL

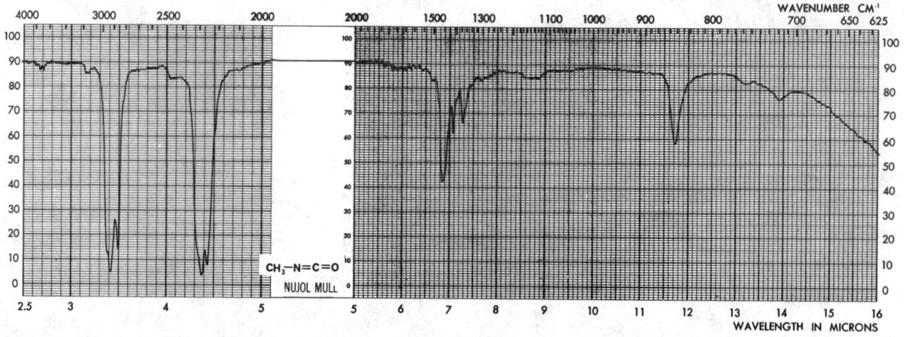

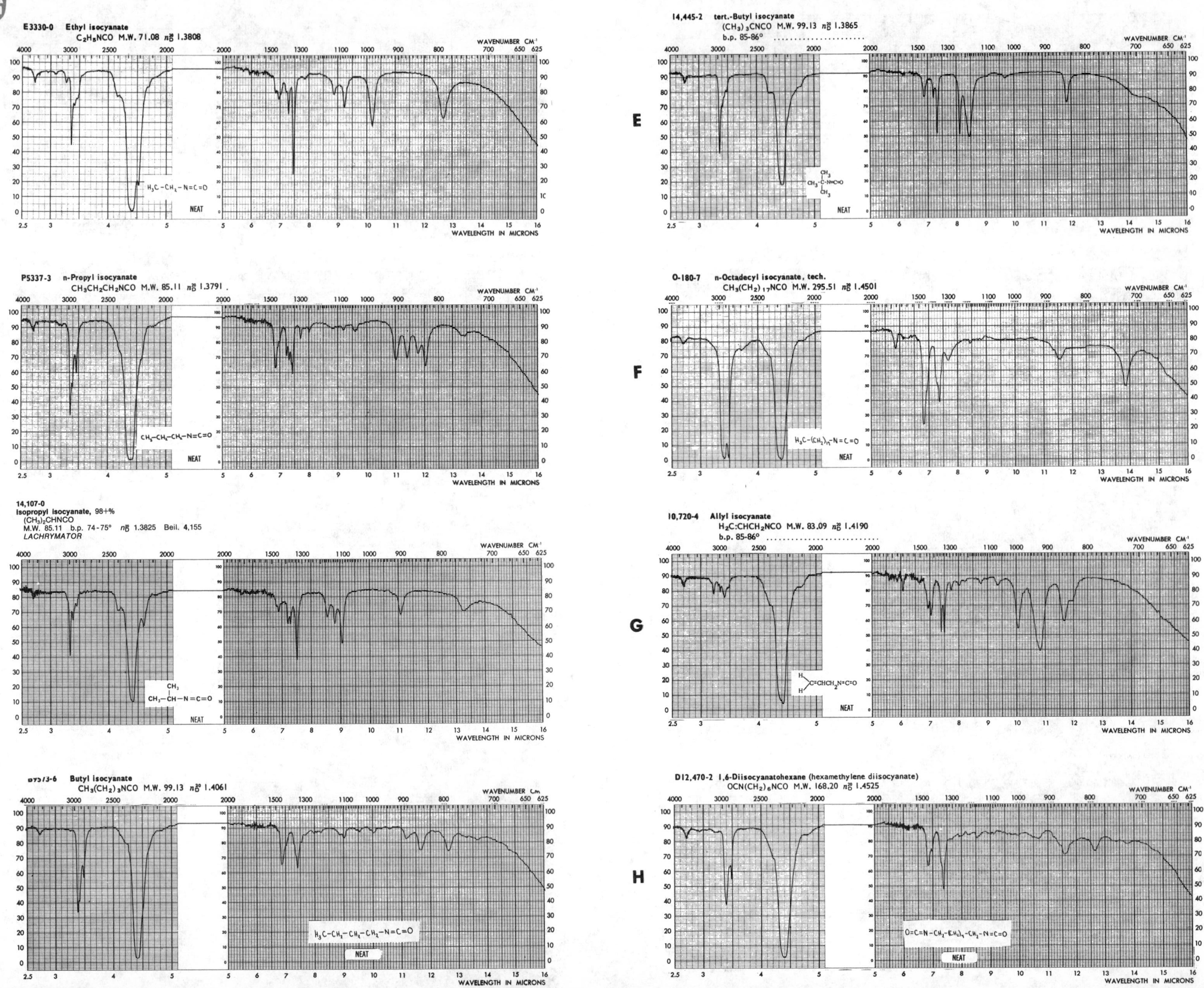
ALDRICH
A
E3330-0 Ethyl isocyanate
C_2H_5NCO M.W. 71.08 n_D^{20} 1.3808
$H_3C-CH_2-N=C=O$
NEAT
B
P5337-3 n-Propyl isocyanate
$CH_3CH_2CH_2NCO$ M.W. 85.11 n_D^{20} 1.3791
$CH_3-CH_2-CH_2-N=C=O$
NEAT
C
14,107-0
Isopropyl isocyanate, 98+%
$(CH_3)_2CHNCO$
M.W. 85.11 b.p. 74-75° n_D^{20} 1.3825 Beil. 4,155
LACHRYMATOR
NEAT
D
Butyl isocyanate
$CH_3(CH_2)_3NCO$ M.W. 99.13 n_D^{20} 1.4061
$H_3C-CH_2-CH_2-CH_2-N=C=O$
NEAT
E
14,445-2 tert.-Butyl isocyanate
$(CH_3)_3CNCO$ M.W. 99.13 n_D^{20} 1.3865
b.p. 85-86°
NEAT
F
O-180-7 n-Octadecyl isocyanate, tech.
$CH_3(CH_2)_{17}NCO$ M.W. 295.51 n_D^{20} 1.4501
$H_3C-(CH_2)_{17}-N=C=O$
NEAT
G
10,720-4 Allyl isocyanate
$H_2C{:}CHCH_2NCO$ M.W. 83.09 n_D^{20} 1.4190
b.p. 85-86°
NEAT
H
D12,470-2 1,6-Diisocyanatohexane (hexamethylene diisocyanate)
$OCN(CH_2)_6NCO$ M.W. 168.20 n_D^{20} 1.4525
$O=C=N-CH_2-(CH_2)_4-CH_2-N=C=O$
NEAT
WAVENUMBER CM⁻¹
WAVELENGTH IN MICRONS

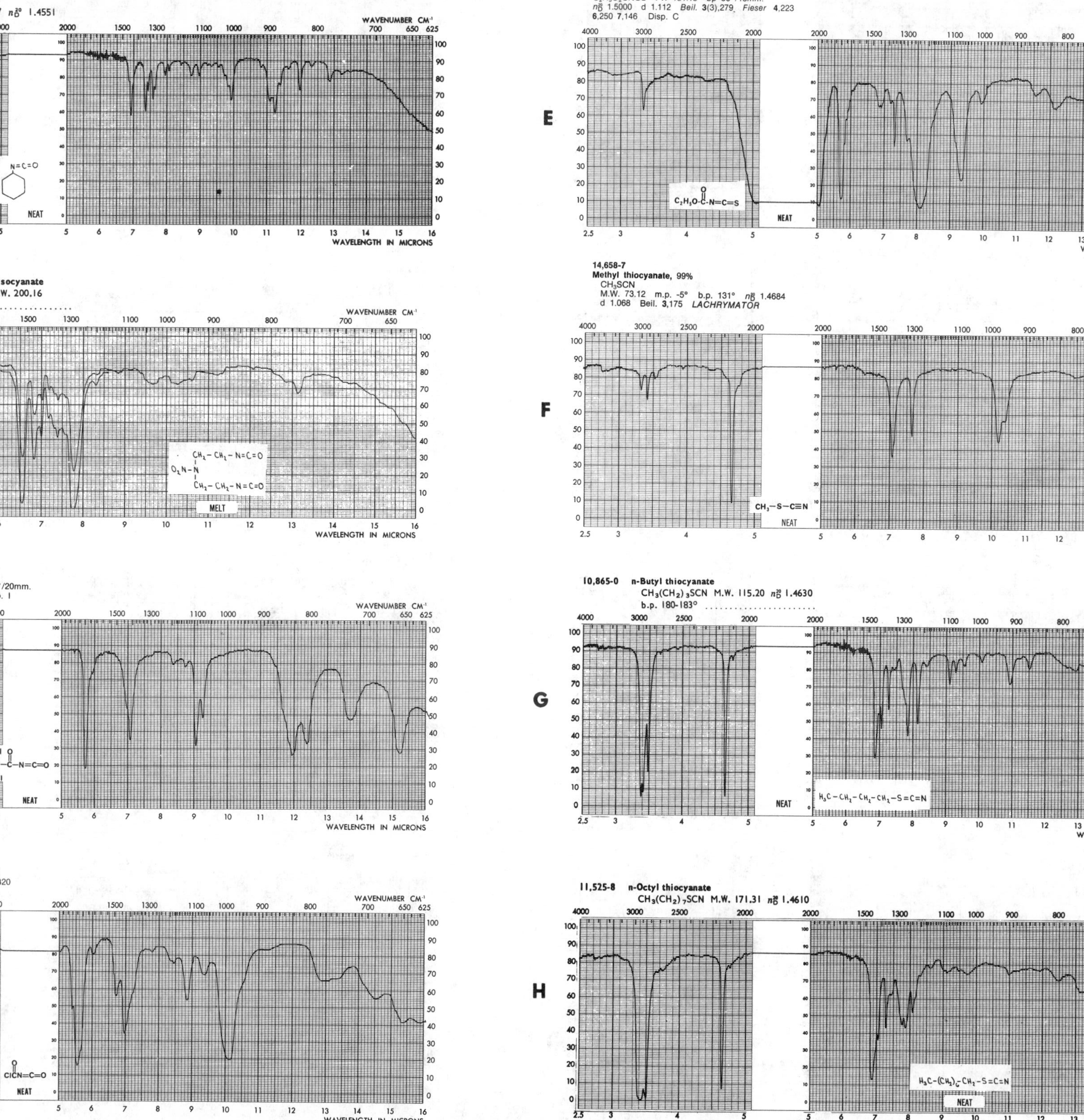

A C10,519-8 **Cyclohexyl isocyanate**
$C_6H_{11}NCO$ M.W. 125.17 n_D^{20} 1.4551
NEAT

B 12,118-5 **3-Nitro-3-azapentane-1,5-diisocyanate**
$O_2NN(CH_2CH_2NCO)_2$ M.W. 200.16
m.p. 36.5-38°
MELT

C 21,732-8
Trichloroacetyl isocyanate
CCl_3CONCO FW 188.40 bp 80-85°/20mm.
n_D^{20} 1.4809 *Fieser* 2,425 7,382 Disp. I
NEAT

D 20,100-6
N-**(Chlorocarbonyl) isocyanate**, 97%
ClCONCO FW 105.48 bp 63° n_D^{20} 1.4320
d 1.310 *Fieser* 5,109 Disp. I
NEAT

E **Ethoxycarbonyl isothiocyanate**, 99% (ethyl isothiocyanatoformate)
$C_2H_5O_2CNCS$ FW 131.15 bp 56°/18mm.
n_D^{20} 1.5000 d 1.112 *Beil.* 3(3),279 *Fieser* 4,223
6,250 7,146 Disp. C
NEAT

F 14,658-7
Methyl thiocyanate, 99%
CH_3SCN
M.W. 73.12 m.p. -5° b.p. 131° n_D^{20} 1.4684
d 1.068 Beil. 3,175 *LACHRYMATOR*
NEAT

G 10,865-0 **n-Butyl thiocyanate**
$CH_3(CH_2)_3SCN$ M.W. 115.20 n_D^{20} 1.4630
b.p. 180-183°
NEAT

H 11,525-8 **n-Octyl thiocyanate**
$CH_3(CH_2)_7SCN$ M.W. 171.31 n_D^{20} 1.4610
NEAT

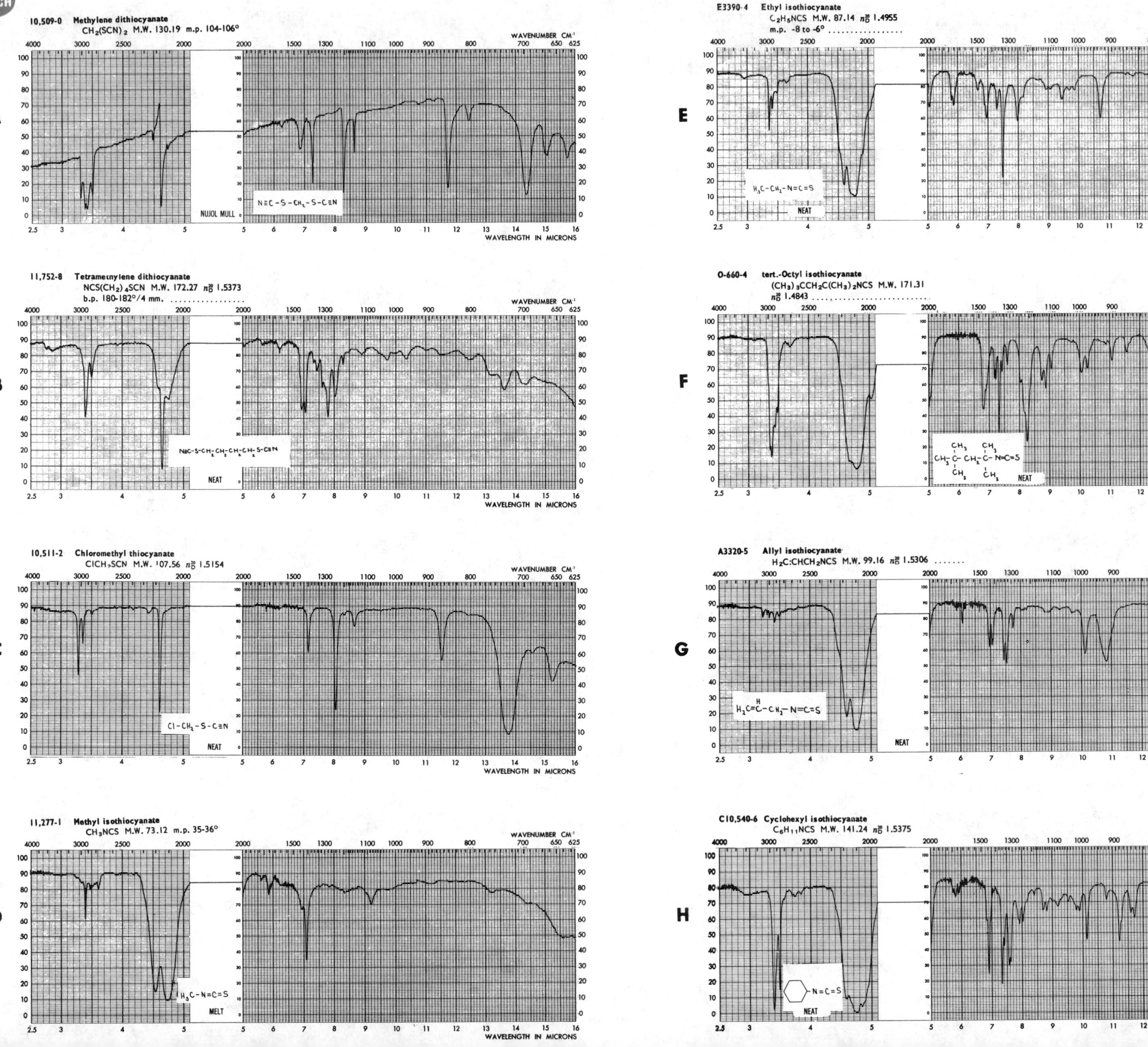
ALDRICH
A
10,509-0 Methylene dithiocyanate
$CH_2(SCN)_2$ M.W. 130.19 m.p. 104-106°
N≡C-S-CH₂-S-C≡N
NUJOL MULL
B
11,752-8 Tetramethylene dithiocyanate
$NCS(CH_2)_4SCN$ M.W. 172.27 n_D^{20} 1.5373
b.p. 180-182°/4 mm.
N≡C-S-CH₂-CH₂-CH₂-CH₂-S-C≡N
NEAT
C
10,511-2 Chloromethyl thiocyanate
$ClCH_2SCN$ M.W. 107.56 n_D^{20} 1.5154
Cl-CH₂-S-C≡N
NEAT
D
11,277-1 Methyl isothiocyanate
CH_3NCS M.W. 73.12 m.p. 35-36°
H₃C-N=C=S
MELT
E
E3390-4 Ethyl isothiocyanate
C_2H_5NCS M.W. 87.14 n_D^{20} 1.4955
m.p. -8 to -6°
H₃C-CH₂-N=C=S
NEAT
F
O-660-4 tert.-Octyl isothiocyanate
$(CH_3)_3CCH_2C(CH_3)_2NCS$ M.W. 171.31
n_D^{20} 1.4843
NEAT
G
A3320-5 Allyl isothiocyanate
$H_2C:CHCH_2NCS$ M.W. 99.16 n_D^{20} 1.5306
H₂C=CH-CH₂-N=C=S
NEAT
H
C10,540-6 Cyclohexyl isothiocyanate
$C_6H_{11}NCS$ M.W. 141.24 n_D^{20} 1.5375
N=C=S
NEAT
WAVENUMBER CM⁻¹
WAVELENGTH IN MICRONS

A 14,336-7 1-Adamantyl isothiocyanate
M.W. 193.31 m.p. 166.5-168°

B D12,540-7 N,N'-Diisopropylcarbodiimide
$(CH_3)_2CHN{:}C{:}NCH(CH_3)_2$ M.W. 126.20 n_D^{20} 1.4356

C D8000-2 N,N'-Dicyclohexylcarbodiimide
$C_6H_{11}N{:}C{:}NC_6H_{11}$ M.W. 206.33 m.p. 34-35°

D C10,640-2 1-Cyclohexyl-3-(2-morpholinoethyl)-carbodiimide metho-p-toluenesulfonate (CMC metho-p-toluenesulfonate, morpho CDI)
M.W. 423.58 m.p. 113-115° (dec.)

E 16,146-2
1-(3-Dimethylaminopropyl)-3-ethylcarbodiimide hydrochloride, 98+%
M.W. 191.71 m.p. 111-113°

F E2220-1 Ethyl diazoacetate *
$N_2CHCO_2C_2H_5$ M.W. 114.10 n_D^{20} 1.4620
b.p. 140-141°/720 mm.

G B8690-7 tert.-Butoxycarbonyl azide (tert.-butyl azidoformate)
(send for data sheet)
$N_3CO_2C(CH_3)_3$ M.W. 143.15 n_D^{20} 1.4230
b.p. 73-76°/70 mm.

H 16,055-5
Cyanourea, sodium salt, 98%
$NCN{=}C(ONa)NH_2$
M.W. 107.05 m.p. >300° Beil. 3,82

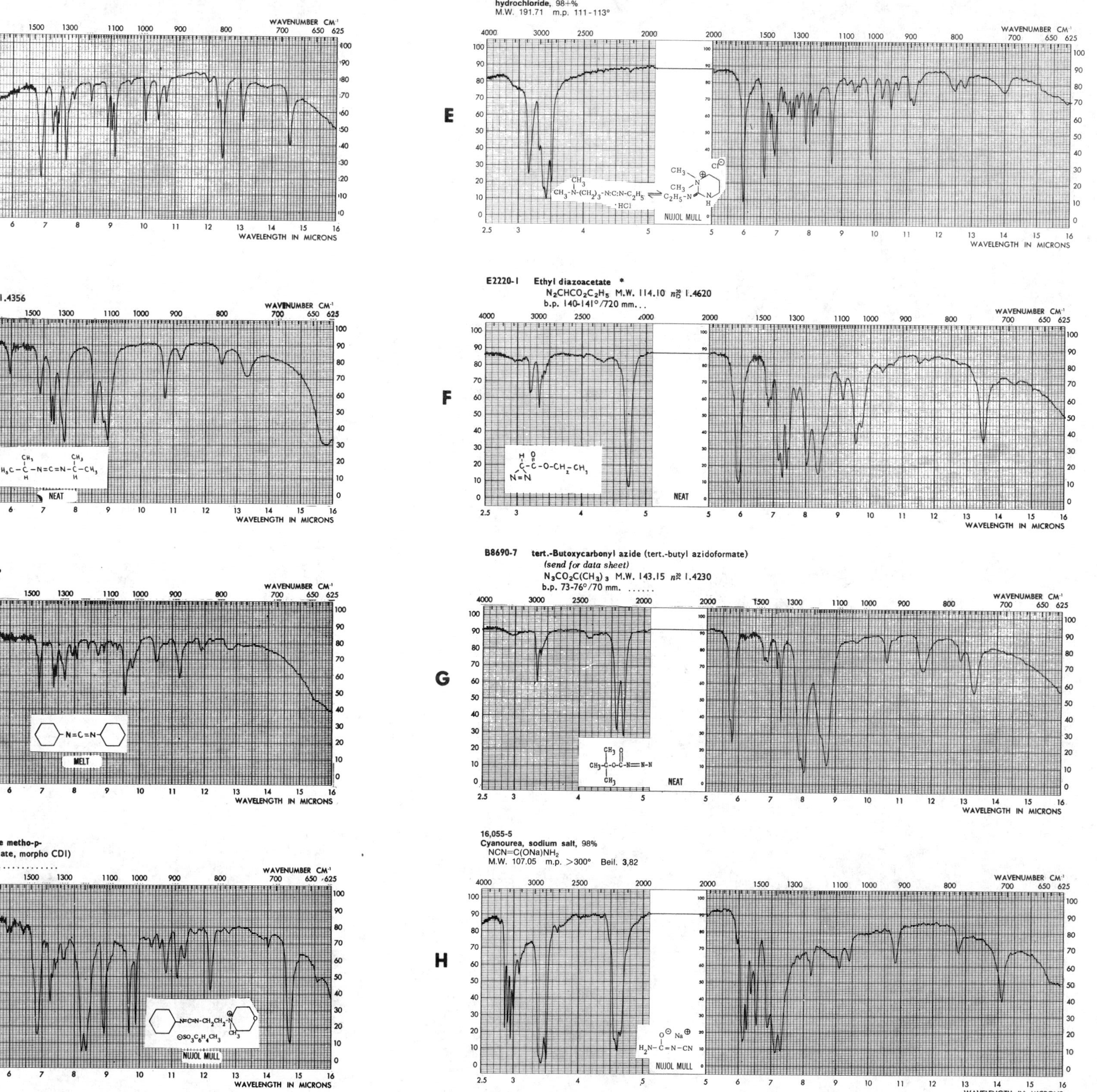

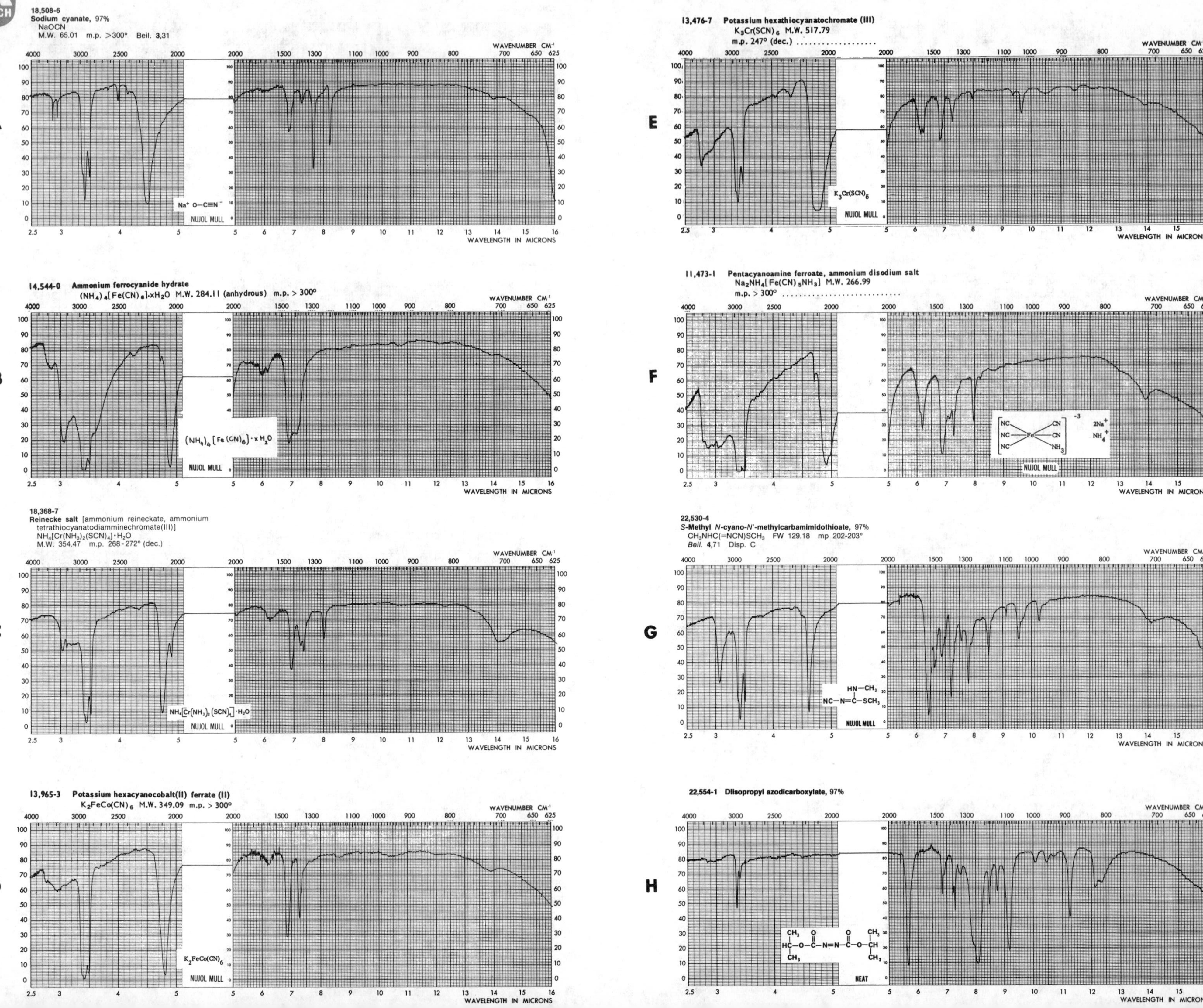
ALDRICH
A
18,508-6
Sodium cyanate, 97%
NaOCN
M.W. 65.01 m.p. >300° Beil. 3,31
Na+ O—C≡N−
NUJOL MULL
B
14,544-0 Ammonium ferrocyanide hydrate
(NH4)4[Fe(CN)6]·xH2O M.W. 284.11 (anhydrous) m.p. > 300°
(NH4)4[Fe(CN)6]·x H2O
NUJOL MULL
C
18,368-7
Reinecke salt [ammonium reineckate, ammonium tetrathiocyanatodiamminechromate(III)]
NH4[Cr(NH3)2(SCN)4]·H2O
M.W. 354.47 m.p. 268-272° (dec.)
NH4[Cr(NH3)2(SCN)4]·H2O
NUJOL MULL
D
13,965-3 Potassium hexacyanocobalt(II) ferrate (II)
K2FeCo(CN)6 M.W. 349.09 m.p. > 300°
K2FeCo(CN)6
NUJOL MULL
E
13,476-7 Potassium hexathiocyanatochromate (III)
K3Cr(SCN)6 M.W. 517.79
m.p. 247° (dec.)
K3Cr(SCN)6
NUJOL MULL
F
11,473-1 Pentacyanoamine ferroate, ammonium disodium salt
Na2NH4[Fe(CN)5NH3] M.W. 266.99
m.p. > 300°
NUJOL MULL
G
22,530-4
S-Methyl N-cyano-N'-methylcarbamimidothioate, 97%
CH3NHC(=NCN)SCH3 FW 129.18 mp 202-203°
Beil. 4,71 Disp. C
HN—CH3
NC—N=C—SCH3
NUJOL MULL
H
22,554-1 Diisopropyl azodicarboxylate, 97%
NEAT
WAVENUMBER CM-1
WAVELENGTH IN MICRONS

NON-AROMATIC SULFUR-OXYGEN COMPOUNDS

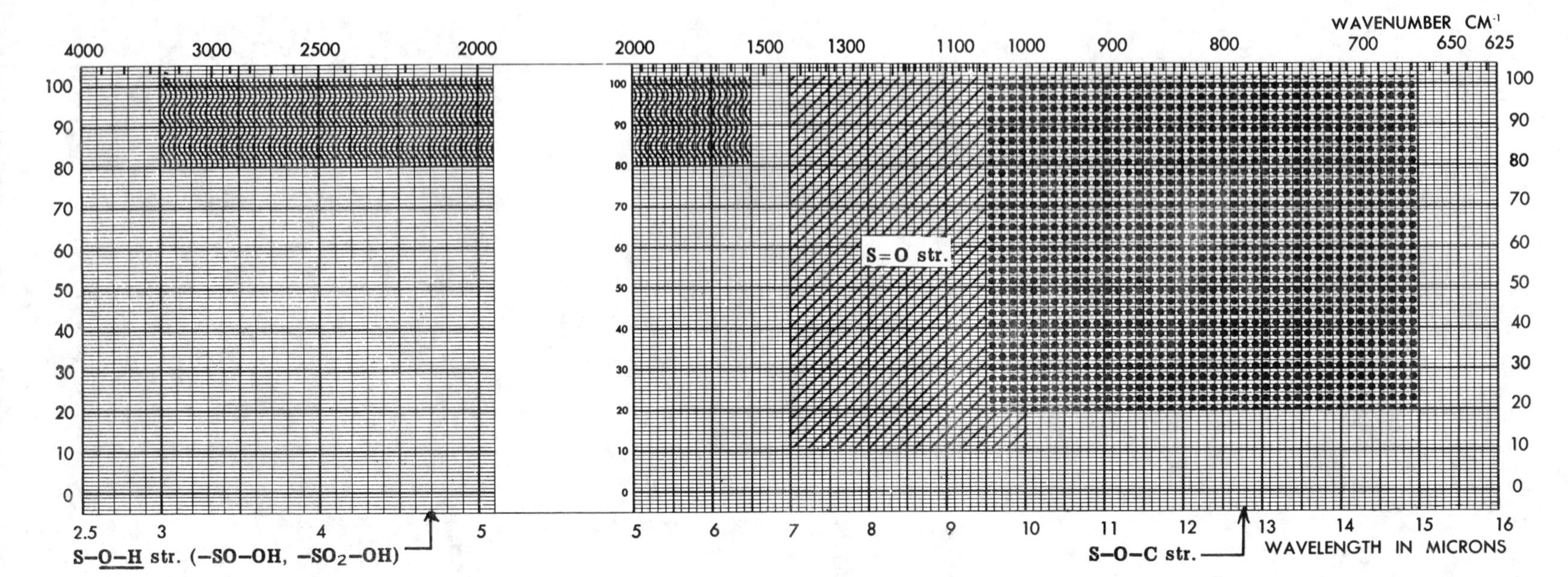

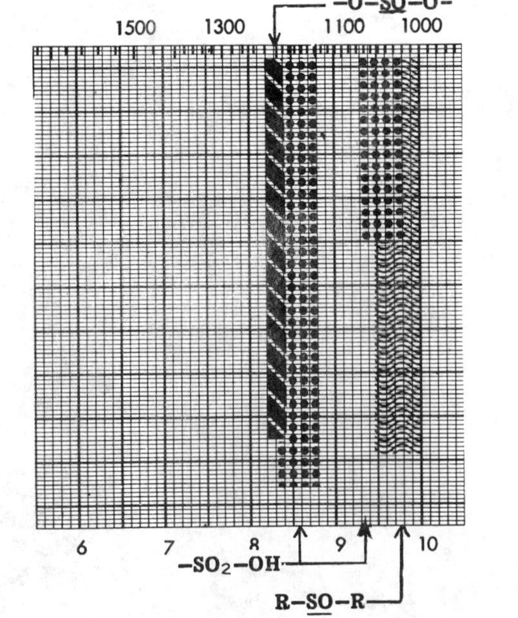

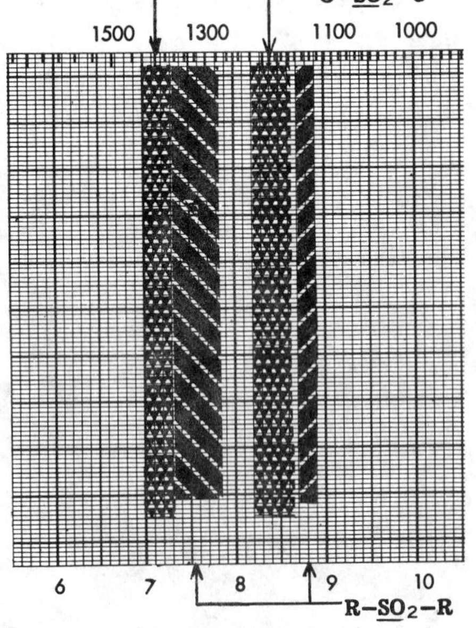

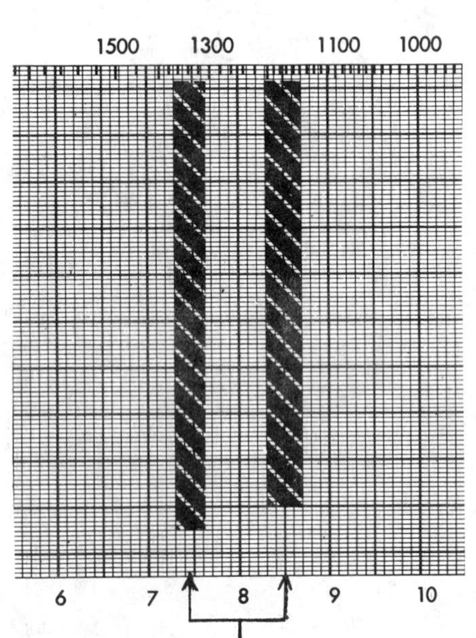

The stretch vibrations of the S=O absorb between 7 and 10 μ (1430 – 1000 cm^{-1}) depending on the groups attached. The sulfoxide has one strong and broad absorption in the vicinity of 9.5 to 10 μ (1055 – 1000 cm^{-1}). The sulfone O=S=O has two strong bands near 7.7 μ (1300 cm^{-1}), asymmetric stretch, and 8.8 μ (1135 cm^{-1}), symmetric stretch.

The S=O vibration of the sulfite absorbs near 8.3 μ (1205 cm^{-1}). The S–O–C group displays two bands in the vicinity of 10 and 11 μ (1000 – 910 cm^{-1}) with the exception of dimethyl sulfite (spectrum 532D) which has one wide band between 10 and 10.5 μ (1000 – 950 cm^{-1}). Another pair of bands varying in separation occurs between 13 and 15 μ (770 – 665 cm^{-1}).

Sulfonic acid salts absorb very strongly near 8.5 μ (1175 cm^{-1}) and have a medium intensity absorption near 9.5 μ (1055 cm^{-1}). These bands are also present in the hydrated form of the free sulfonic acid (spectra 532H—533C) along with very broad OH bands between 3 and 6.5 μ (3335 – 1540 cm^{-1}).

The sulfonate esters, sulfonyl chlorides and sulfonamides display their SO_2 stretch bands around 7.5 and 8.5 μ (1335 and 1175 cm^{-1}). These two absorptions are accompanied by several strong S–O–C stretch absorptions between 10 and 13 μ (1000 – 770 cm^{-1}) in the sulfonate esters, while the sulfonamides display the usual nitrogen-hydrogen absorptions around 3 and 6.2 μ (3335 and 1615 cm^{-1}). These NH_2 and NH bands are analogous to the corresponding primary amine, primary amide, and the secondary amine, secondary amide absorptions.

The SO_2 stretch vibrations of the organic sulfates absorb near 7.2 and 8.3 μ (1390 and 1205 cm^{-1}) and show their S–O–C absorptions between 9.5 and 13 μ (1055 – 770 cm^{-1}).

Due to the hygroscopic nature of many of the compounds included in this section, water bands near 2.9 and 6.1 μ (3450 and 1640 cm^{-1}) may be observed.

ALDRICH

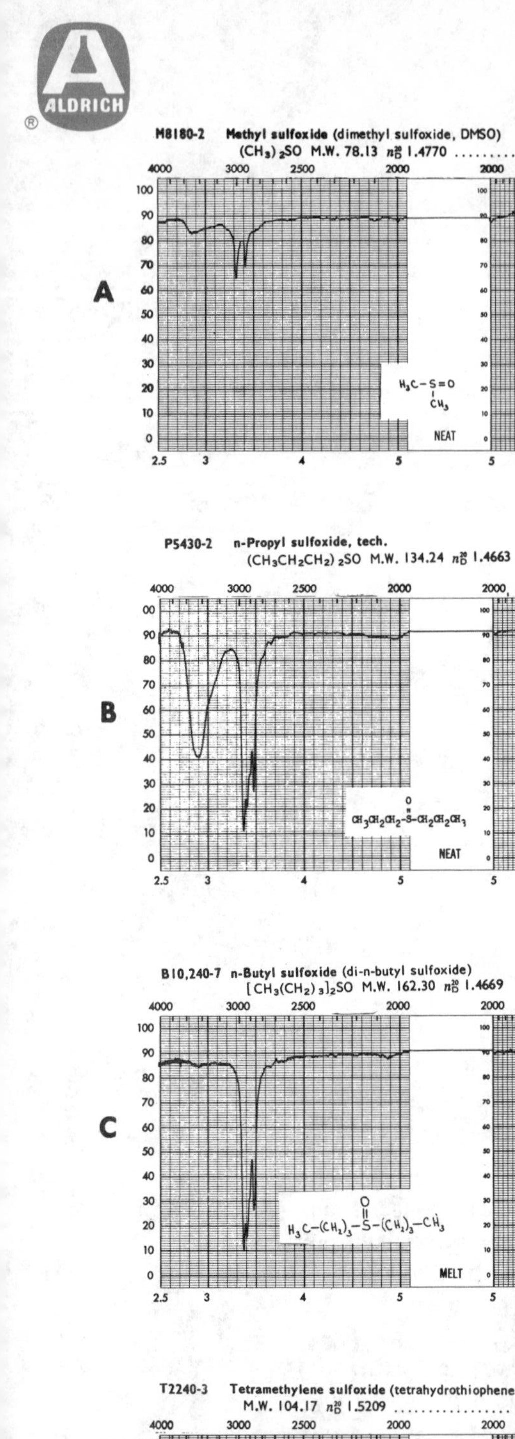

A

M8180-2 **Methyl sulfoxide** (dimethyl sulfoxide, DMSO)
$(CH_3)_2SO$ M.W. 78.13 n_D^{20} 1.4770

B

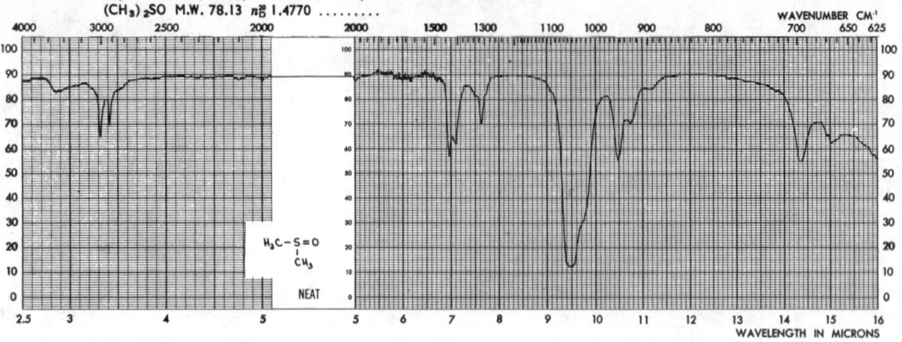

P5430-2 **n-Propyl sulfoxide, tech.**
$(CH_3CH_2CH_2)_2SO$ M.W. 134.24 n_D^{20} 1.4663

C

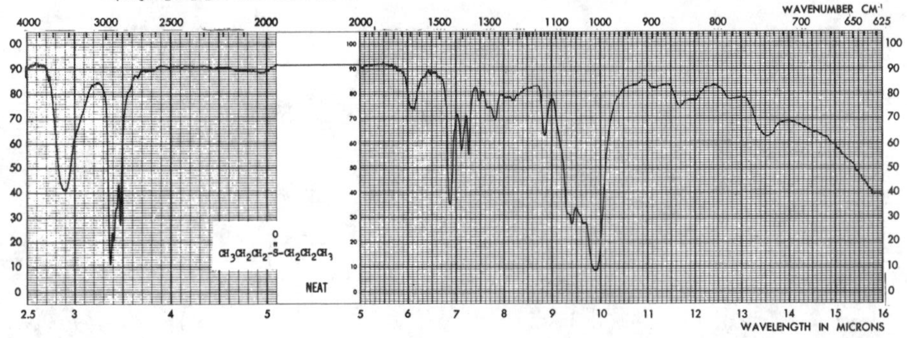

B10,240-7 **n-Butyl sulfoxide** (di-n-butyl sulfoxide)
$[CH_3(CH_2)_3]_2SO$ M.W. 162.30 n_D^{20} 1.4669

D

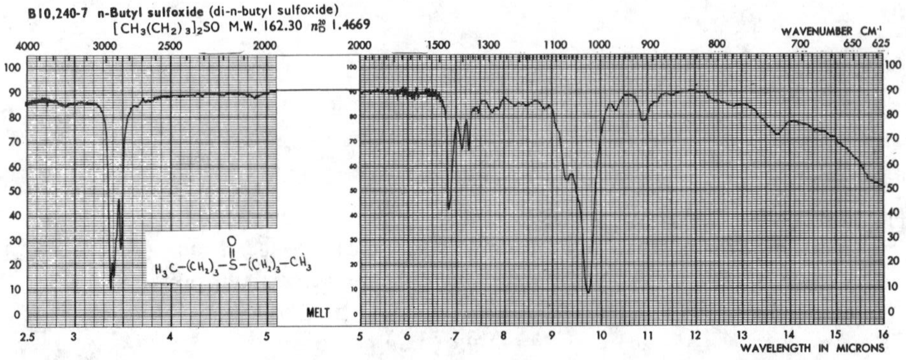

T2240-3 **Tetramethylene sulfoxide** (tetrahydrothiophene oxide)
M.W. 104.17 n_D^{20} 1.5209

E

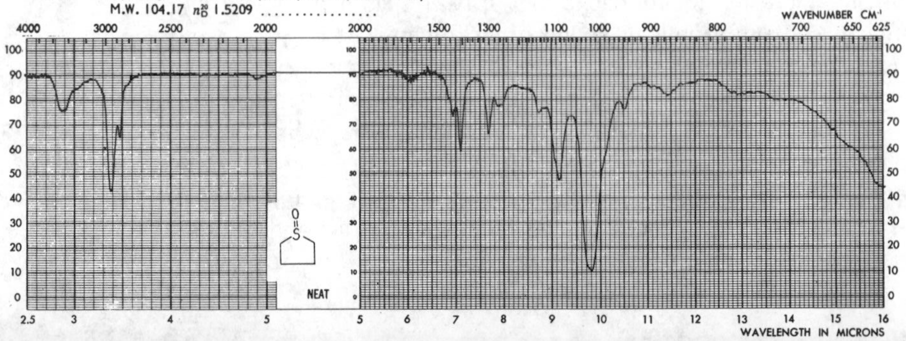

12,178-9 **2,2'-Sulfinyldiethanol**
$OS(CH_2CH_2OH)_2$ M.W. 138.19 m.p. 109-110°

F

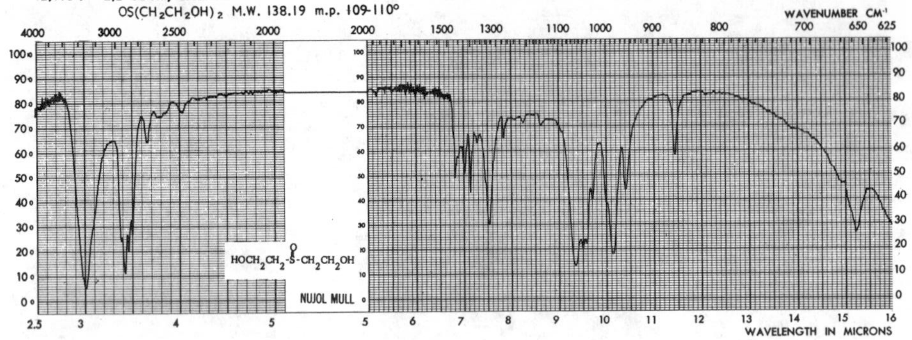

16,387-2
Ethyl malonyl chloride, tech.[ethyl (chloroformyl) acetate]
$ClCOCH_2CO_2C_2H_5$ FW 150.56 bp 79-80°/25mm.
n_D^{20} 1.4290 d 1.176 Fp 154°F(67°C) Beil. **2**,582
NMR **3**,95D *IR* **2**,381D Disp. I *CORROSIVE*

G

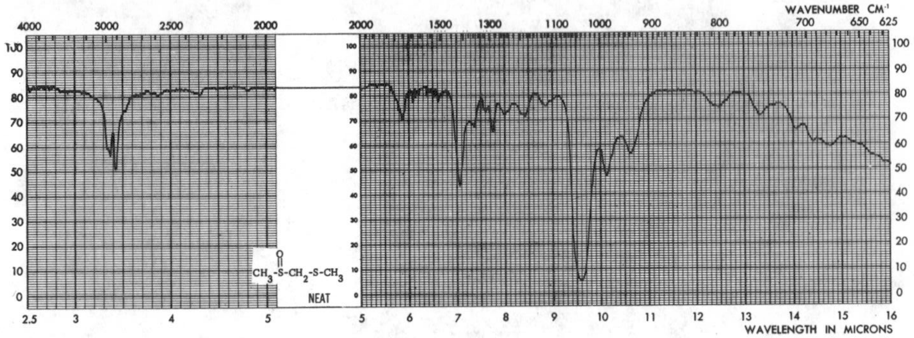

85,126-4
DL-Methionine sulfoxide
$CH_3SOCH_2CH_2CH(NH_2)CO_2H$
M.W. 165.21 m.p. 232-234° (dec.)

H

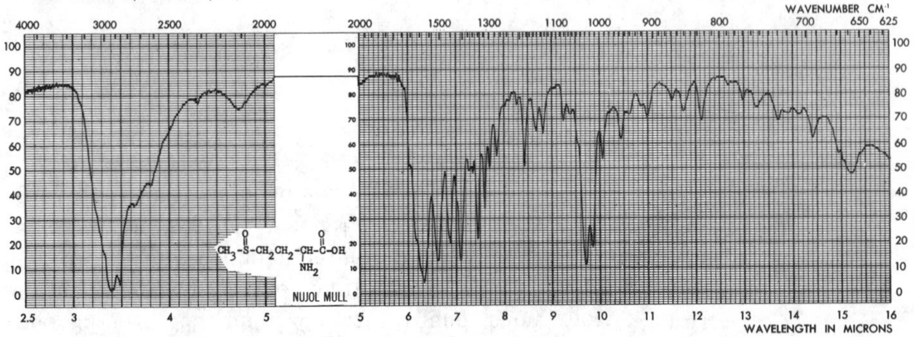

T8050-0 **Trimethylsulfoxonium iodide**
$(CH_3)_3S(O)I$ M.W. 220.08

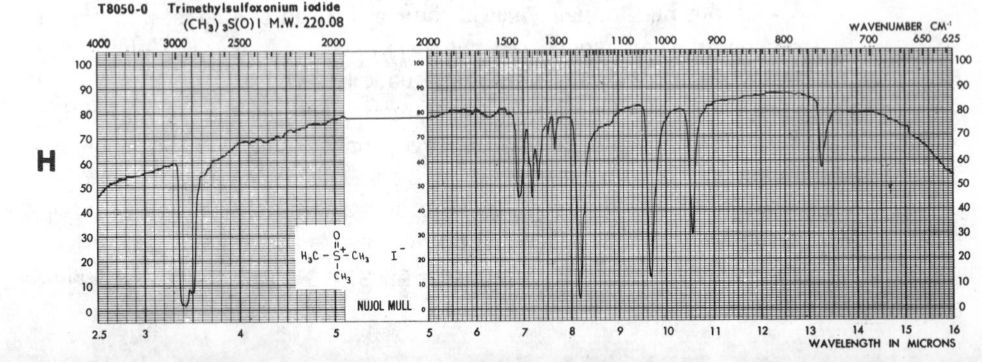

A

M8170-5 **Methyl sulfone** (dimethyl sulfone)
$(CH_3)_2SO_2$ M.W. 94.13 m.p. 108-110° ....

NUJOL MULL

B

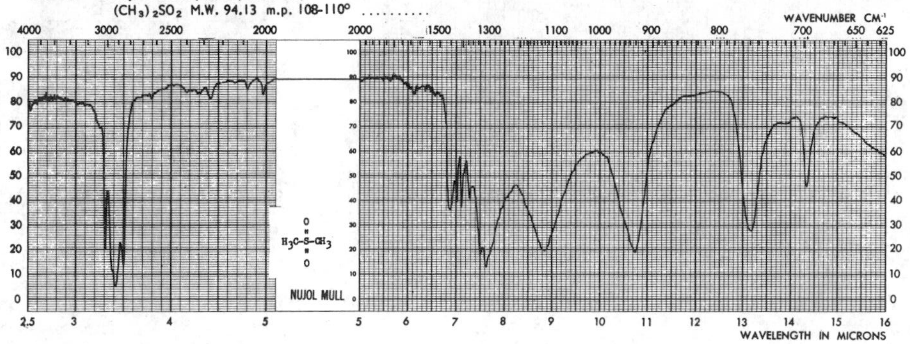

20,879-5
Methyl methanethiolsulfonate (*S*-methyl thiomethane-sulfonate)
$CH_3SO_2SCH_3$ FW 126.20 bp 69-71°/0.400mm.
n_D^{20} 1.5175 d 1.227 *Fieser* 5,454 7,243
Disp. C

NEAT

C

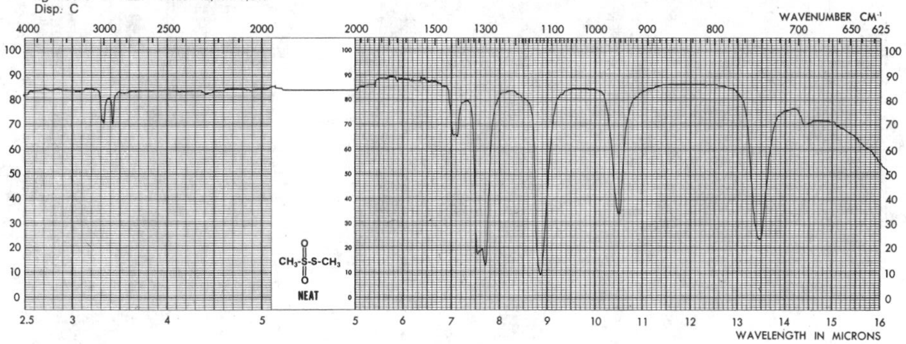

P5429-9 **n-Propyl sulfone**
$(CH_3CH_2CH_2)_2SO_2$ M.W. 150.24 m.p. 28-30°

MELT

D

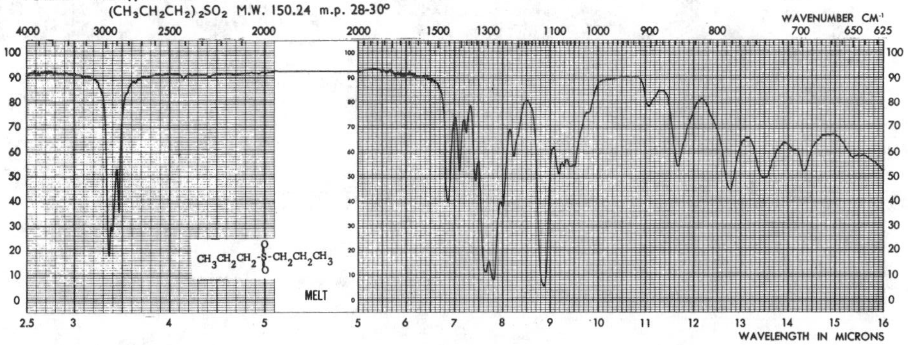

B10,220-2 **n-Butyl sulfone** (di-n-butyl sulfone)
$[CH_3(CH_2)_3]_2SO_2$ M.W. 178.29 m.p. 43-45°

MELT

E

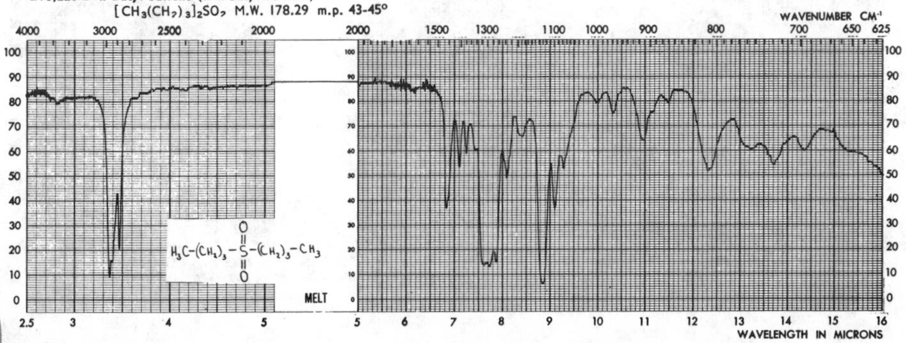

V370-0 **Vinyl sulfone** (divinyl sulfone)
$(H_2C{:}CH)_2SO_2$ M.W. 118.15 n_D^{20} 1.4765
b.p. 102-105°/10 mm. ....

NEAT

F

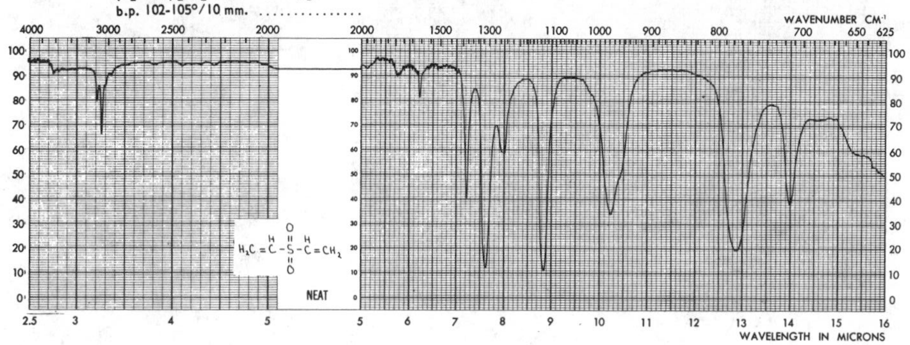

18,008-4
2,2'-Sulfonyldiethanol, 65% solution in water
(2-hydroxyethyl sulfone)
$O_2S(CH_2CH_2OH)_2$
M.W. 154.18 n_D^{20} 1.4335

NEAT

G

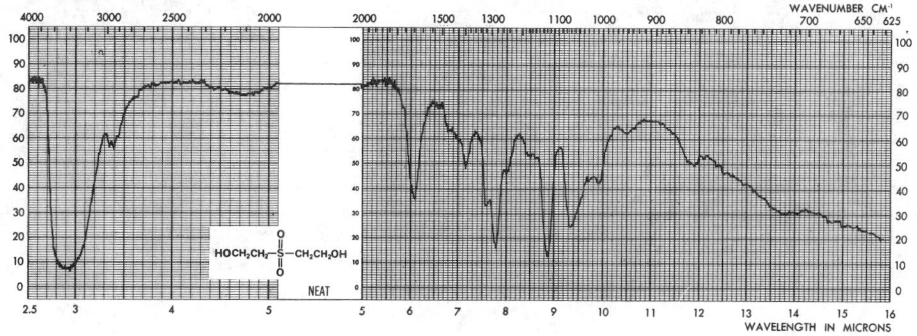

18,436-5
(Methylsulfonyl)acetonitrile
$CH_3SO_2CH_2CN$
M.W. 119.14 m.p. 81-84°

NUJOL MULL

H

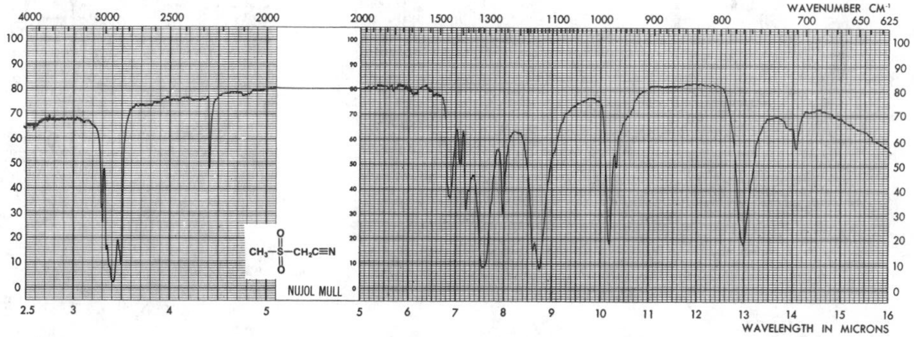

T2220-9 **Tetramethylene sulfone** (sulfolane, tetrahydrothiophene-1,1-dioxide)
M.W. 120.17 n_D^{20} 1.4835
b.p. 285-288°/743 mm. ....

MELT

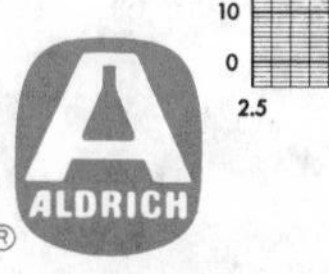

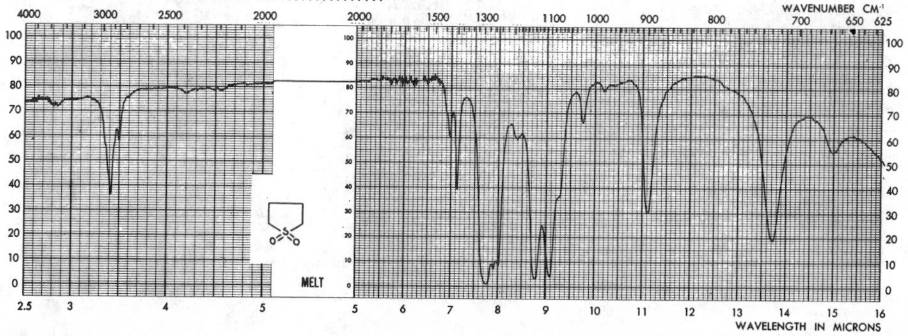

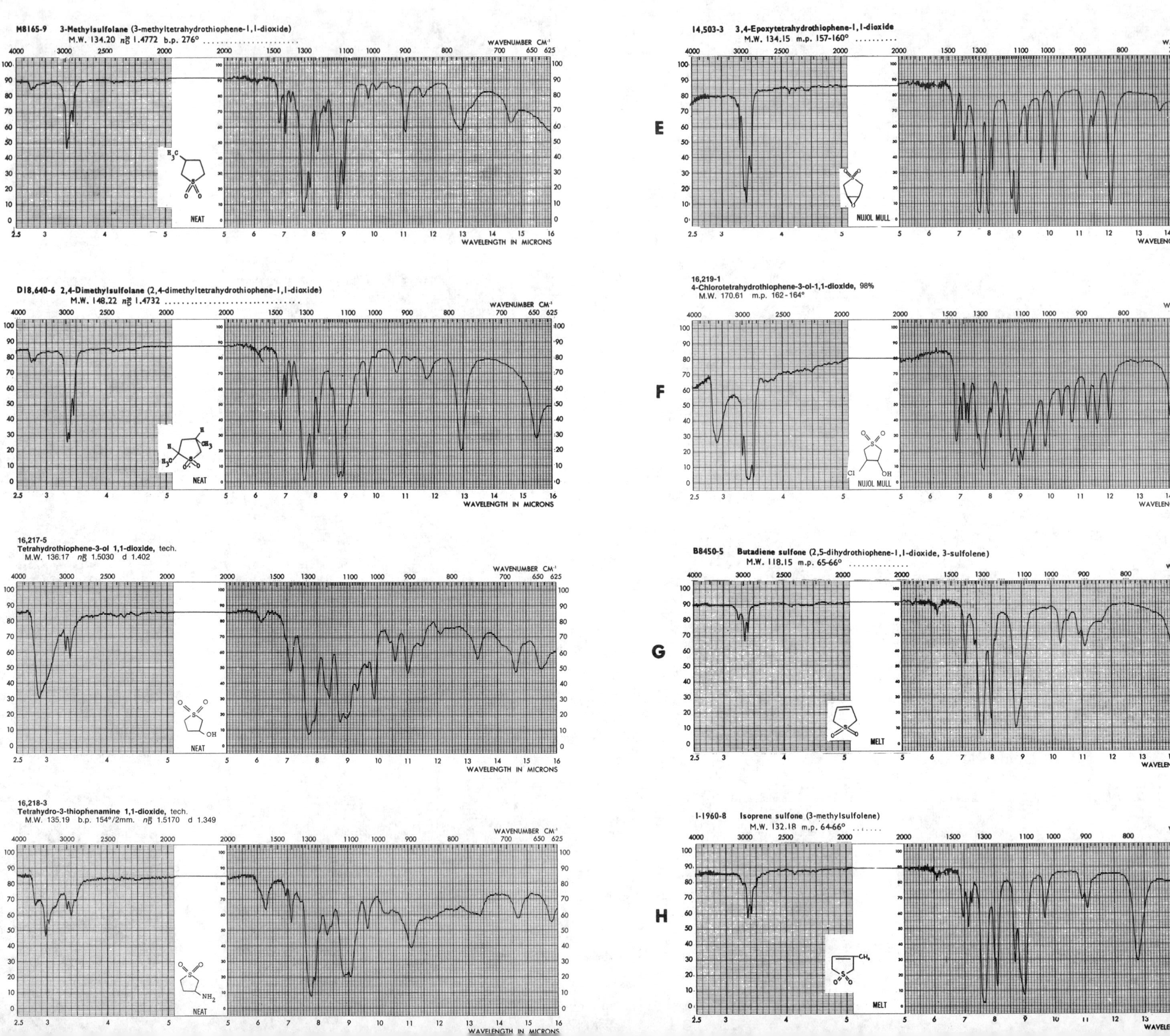
ALDRICH
A
M8165-9 3-Methylsulfolane (3-methyltetrahydrothiophene-1,1-dioxide)
M.W. 134.20 n_D^{20} 1.4772 b.p. 276°
NEAT
B
D18,640-6 2,4-Dimethylsulfolane (2,4-dimethyltetrahydrothiophene-1,1-dioxide)
M.W. 148.22 n_D^{20} 1.4732
NEAT
C
16,217-5
Tetrahydrothiophene-3-ol 1,1-dioxide, tech.
M.W. 136.17 n_D^{20} 1.5030 d 1.402
NEAT
D
16,218-3
Tetrahydro-3-thiophenamine 1,1-dioxide, tech.
M.W. 135.19 b.p. 154°/2mm. n_D^{20} 1.5170 d 1.349
NEAT
E
14,503-3 3,4-Epoxytetrahydrothiophene-1,1-dioxide
M.W. 134.15 m.p. 157-160°
NUJOL MULL
F
16,219-1
4-Chlorotetrahydrothiophene-3-ol-1,1-dioxide, 98%
M.W. 170.61 m.p. 162-164°
NUJOL MULL
G
B8450-5 Butadiene sulfone (2,5-dihydrothiophene-1,1-dioxide, 3-sulfolene)
M.W. 118.15 m.p. 65-66°
MELT
H
I-1960-8 Isoprene sulfone (3-methylsulfolene)
M.W. 132.18 m.p. 64-66°
MELT
WAVENUMBER CM⁻¹
WAVELENGTH IN MICRONS

A

18,776-3
3-Ethyl-2,5-dihydrothiophene-1,1-dioxide, 98%
(3-ethyl-3-sulfolene)
FW 146.21 mp 58-62° Disp. C

MELT

B

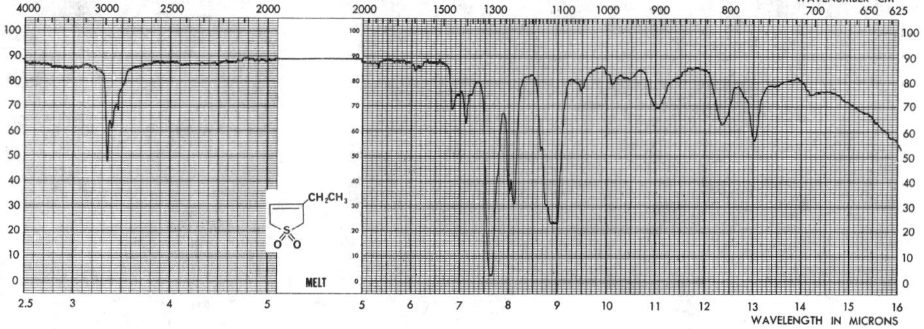

D18,660-0 2,4-Dimethyl-3-sulfolene
M.W. 146.21 m.p. 40-43°

MELT

C

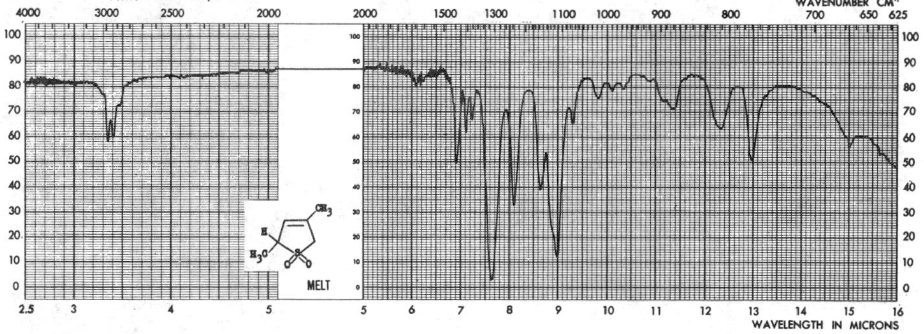

S656-8 Sulfonyldiacetic acid
$O_2S(CH_2CO_2H)_2$ M.W. 182.15 m.p. 184-186°

NUJOL MULL

D

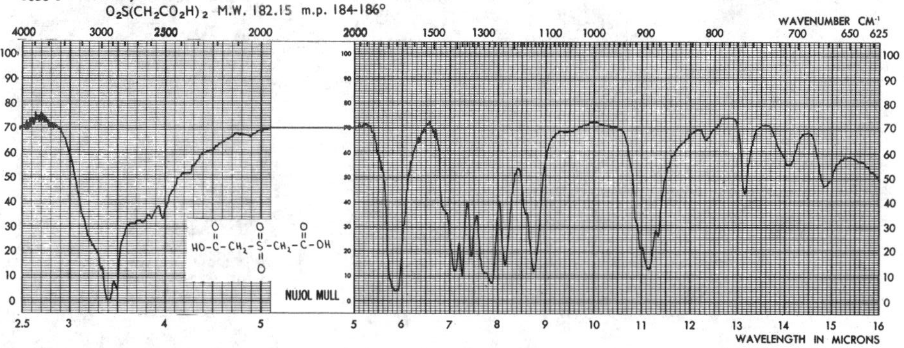

10,861-8 Dimethyl sulfite
$(CH_3O)_2SO$ M.W. 110.13 n_D^{20} 1.4083
b.p. 126-127° ....

NEAT

E

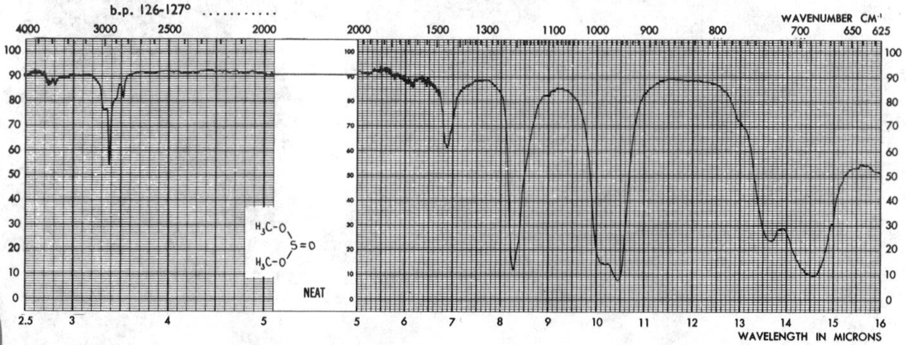

10,863-4 Diethyl sulfite
$(C_2H_5O)_2SO$ M.W. 138.19 n_D^{20} 1.4140
b.p. 158-160° ....

NEAT

F

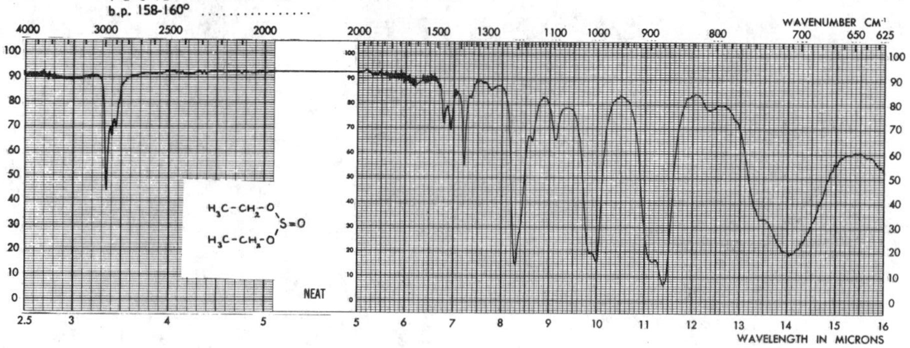

G720-8 Glycol sulfite (ethylene sulfite)
M.W. 108.12 n_D^{20} 1.4452 b.p. 69°/20 mm.

NEAT

G

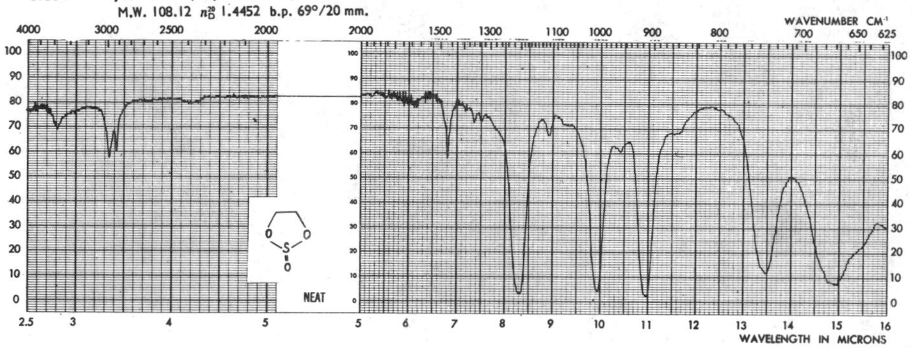

14,331-6 4,5-Dimethyl-2-oxo-1,3,2-dioxathiolane
M.W. 136.17 n_D^{20} 1.4345 b.p. 158° ...

NEAT

H

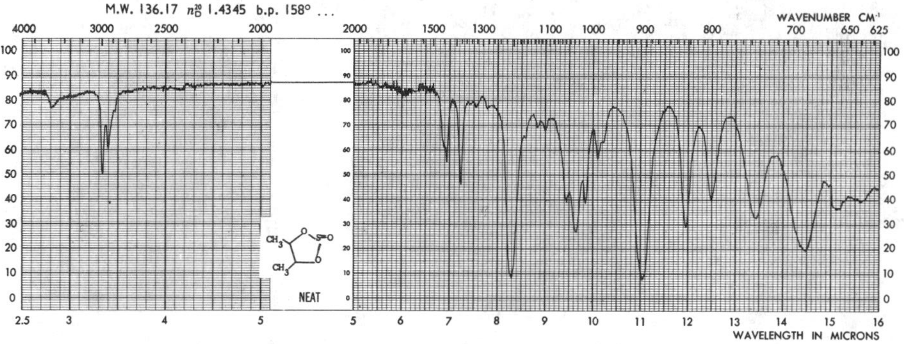

M860-6 Methanesulfonic acid
CH_3SO_3H M.W. 96.10 n_D^{20} 1.4303

NEAT

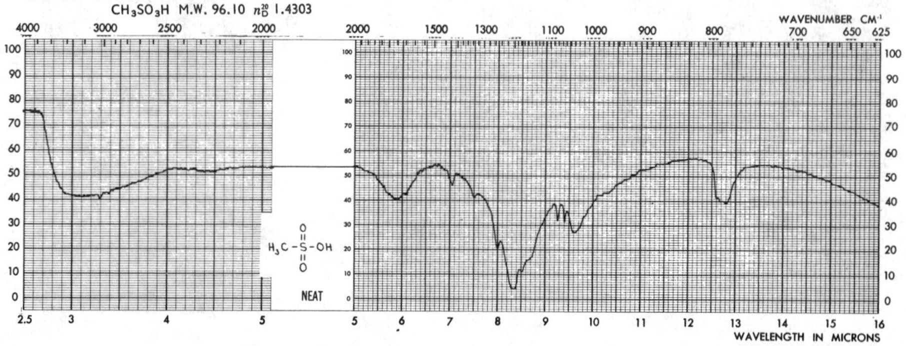

ALDRICH

A 18,626-0
Ethanesulfonic acid
$C_2H_5SO_3H$ FW 110.13 mp -17° bp 123°/0mm.
n_D^{20} 1.4335 d 1.350 *Beil.* **4**,5 Disp. I

B 14,792-3 *dl*-**10-Camphorsulfonic acid**
M.W. 232.30 m.p. 200-203°(dec.)

C C210-7 *d*-**10-Camphorsulfonic acid**
M.W. 232.30 m.p. 194° (dec.)

D M870-3 **Methanesulfonic acid, silver salt**
CH_3SO_3Ag M.W. 202.97 m.p. 267-269°

E 17,643-5
Silver trifluoromethanesulfonate (silver triflate, trifluoromethanesulfonic acid, silver salt)
CF_3SO_3Ag FW 256.94 *Fieser* **6**,520 **7**,324
Disp. K

F 22,151-1
1-Butanesulfonic acid, sodium salt monohydrate, 98%
$CH_3(CH_2)_3SO_3Na \cdot H_2O$ FW 178.18 mp >300°
Beil. **4**,8 Disp. L

G 22,153-8
1-Pentanesulfonic acid, sodium salt monohydrate, 98%
$CH_3(CH_2)_4SO_3Na \cdot H_2O$ FW 192.22 mp >300°
Beil. **4**(3),23 Disp. L

H 22,154-6
1-Hexanesulfonic acid, sodium salt monohydrate, 98%
$CH_3(CH_2)_5SO_3Na \cdot H_2O$ FW 188.22 mp >300°
Beil. **4**(4),54 Disp. L

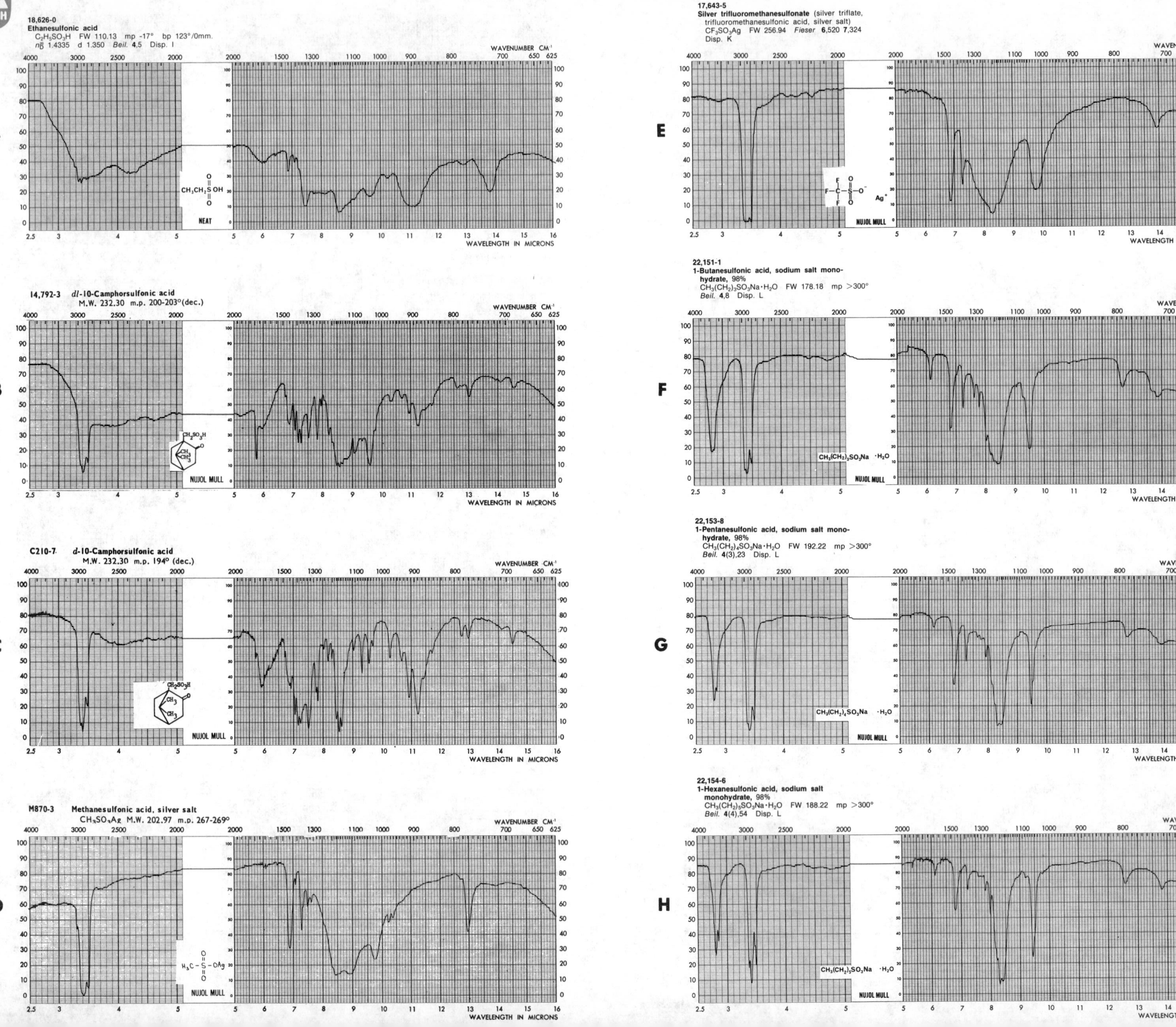

A

22,155-4
1-Heptanesulfonic acid, sodium salt monohydrate, 98%
$CH_3(CH_2)_6SO_3Na \cdot H_2O$ FW 220.26 mp >300°
Beil. **4**(4),57 Disp. L

B

10,645-3 1-Octanesulfonic acid, sodium salt, puriss.
$CH_3(CH_2)_7SO_3Na$ M.W. 216.28 m.p. > 300°

C

22,156-2
1-Octanesulfonic acid, sodium salt monohydrate, 98%
$CH_3(CH_2)_7SO_3Na$ FW 234.30 mp >300°
Beil. **4**(3),25 Disp. L

D

12,175-4 1-Nonanesulfonic acid, sodium salt, puriss.
$CH_3(CH_2)_8SO_3Na$ M.W. 230.30
m.p. > 300°

E

10,644-5 1-Decanesulfonic acid, sodium salt, puriss.
$CH_3(CH_2)_9SO_3Na$ M.W. 244.33 m.p. > 300°

F

12,176-2 1-Undecanesulfonic acid, sodium salt, puriss.
$CH_3(CH_2)_{10}SO_3Na$ M.W. 258.36
m.p. > 300°

G

10,643-7 1-Dodecanesulfonic acid, sodium salt, puriss.
$CH_3(CH_2)_{11}SO_3Na$ M.W. 272.38 m.p. > 300°

H

12,177-0 1-Tridecanesulfonic acid, sodium salt, puriss.
$CH_3(CH_2)_{12}SO_3Na$ M.W. 286.41
m.p. > 300°

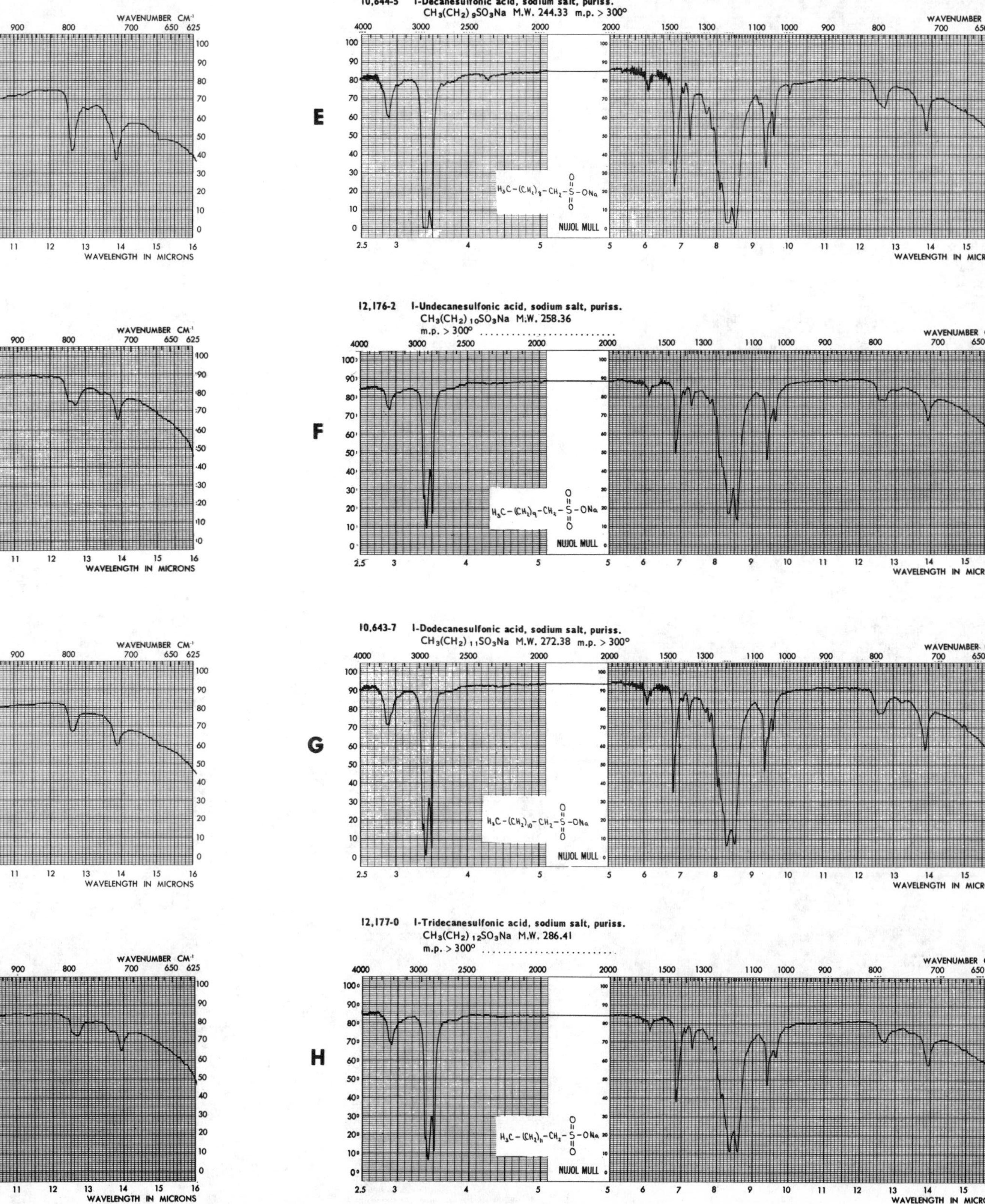

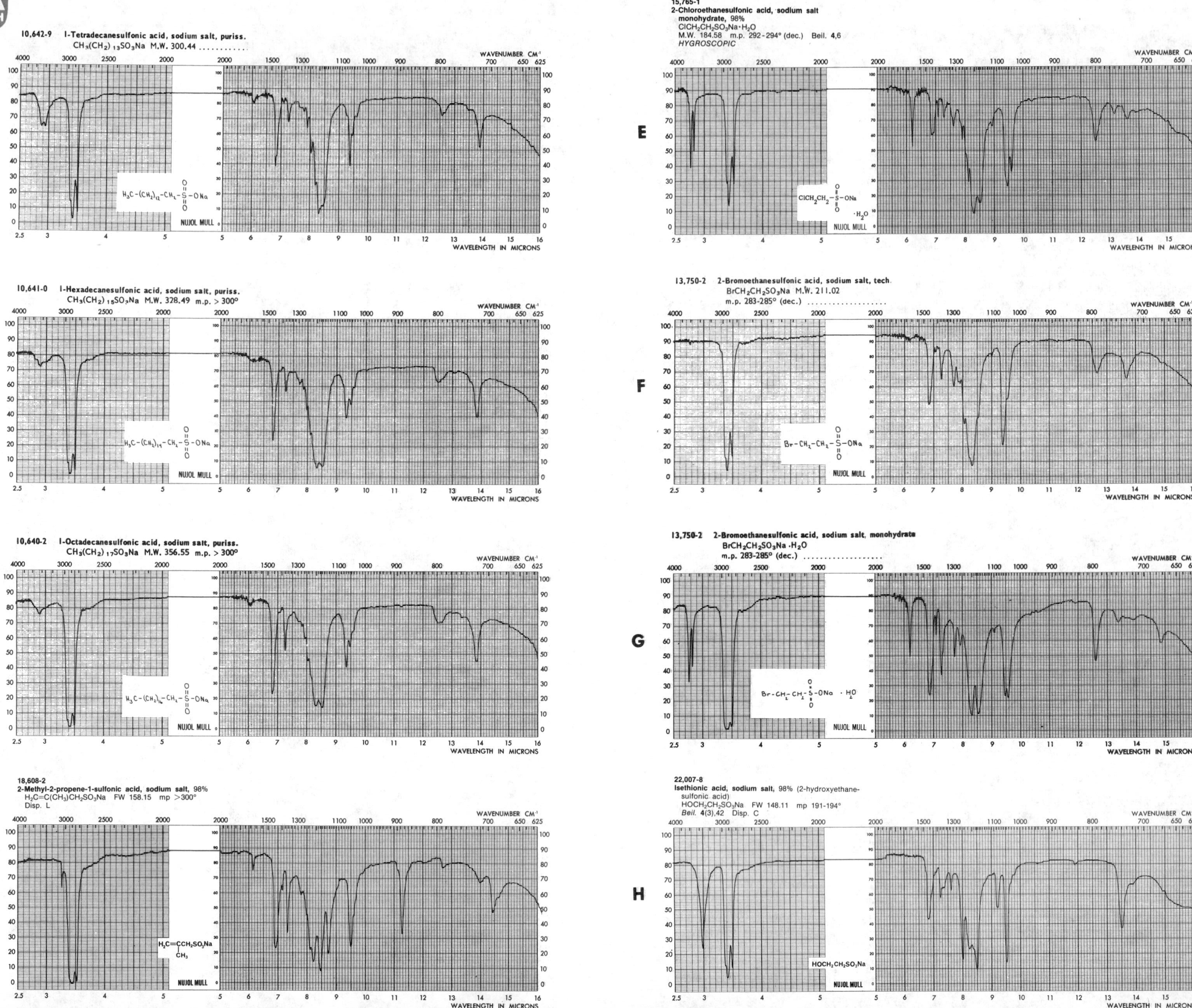

A

10,642-9 1-Tetradecanesulfonic acid, sodium salt, puriss.
$CH_3(CH_2)_{13}SO_3Na$ M.W. 300.44

E

15,765-1
2-Chloroethanesulfonic acid, sodium salt monohydrate, 98%
$ClCH_2CH_2SO_3Na \cdot H_2O$
M.W. 184.58 m.p. 292-294° (dec.) Beil. 4,6
HYGROSCOPIC

B

10,641-0 1-Hexadecanesulfonic acid, sodium salt, puriss.
$CH_3(CH_2)_{15}SO_3Na$ M.W. 328.49 m.p. > 300°

F

13,750-2 2-Bromoethanesulfonic acid, sodium salt, tech.
$BrCH_2CH_2SO_3Na$ M.W. 211.02
m.p. 283-285° (dec.)

C

10,640-2 1-Octadecanesulfonic acid, sodium salt, puriss.
$CH_3(CH_2)_{17}SO_3Na$ M.W. 356.55 m.p. > 300°

G

13,750-2 2-Bromoethanesulfonic acid, sodium salt, monohydrate
$BrCH_2CH_2SO_3Na \cdot H_2O$
m.p. 283-285° (dec.)

D

18,608-2
2-Methyl-2-propene-1-sulfonic acid, sodium salt, 98%
$H_2C{=}C(CH_3)CH_2SO_3Na$ FW 158.15 mp >300°
Disp. L

H

22,007-8
Isethionic acid, sodium salt, 98% (2-hydroxyethanesulfonic acid)
$HOCH_2CH_2SO_3Na$ FW 148.11 mp 191-194°
Beil. 4(3),42 Disp. C

A

A7612-5 **3-Aminopropanesulfonic acid, sodium salt**
$H_2N(CH_2)_3SO_3Na$ M.W. 161.16
m.p. 159° (dec.)

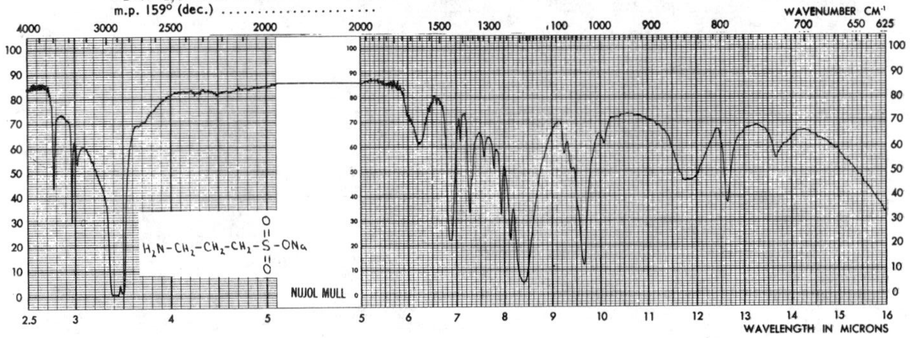

NUJOL MULL

B

21,313-6
Hydroxylamine-O-sulfonic acid
H_2NOSO_3H FW 113.09 mp 210° (dec.)
Fieser 1,481 2,217 3,156 4,256 5,343 6,290
Disp. L,C

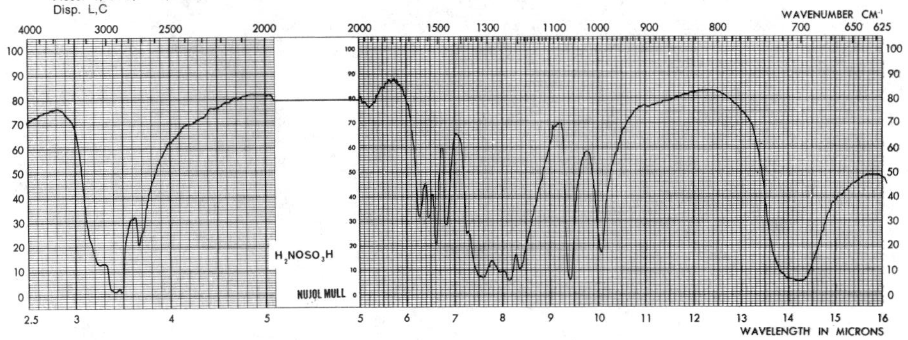

NUJOL MULL

C

12,744-2 **Aminomethanesulfonic acid**
$H_2NCH_2SO_3H$ M.W. 111.12
m.p. 184-185° (dec.)

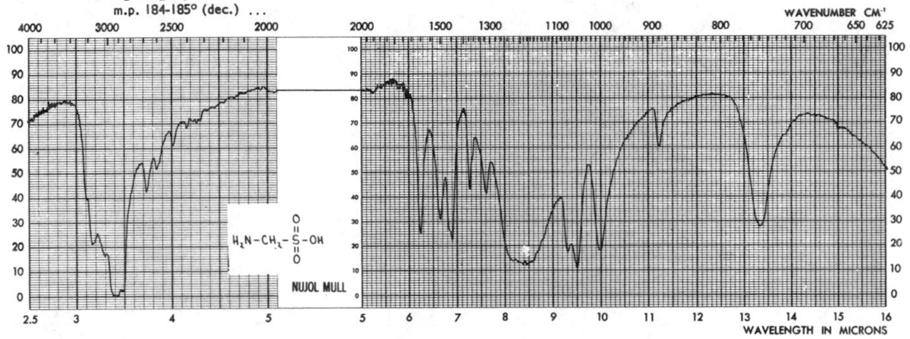

NUJOL MULL

D

15,224-2 **Taurine** (2-aminoethanesulfonic acid)
$H_2NCH_2CH_2SO_3H$ M.W. 125.15
m.p. >300°

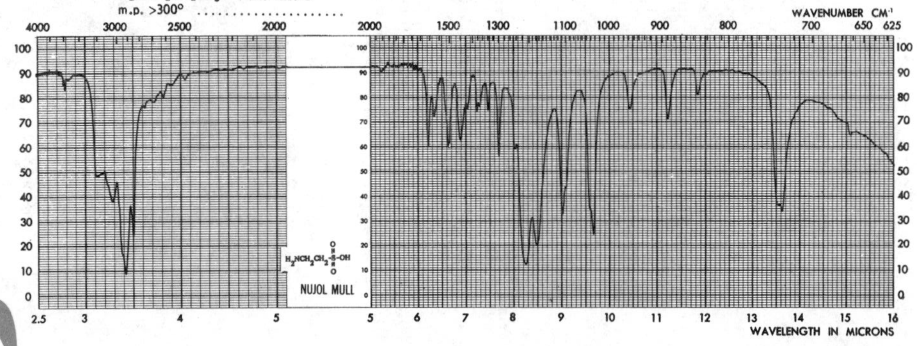

NUJOL MULL

E

A7610-9 **3-Aminopropanesulfonic acid, puriss.**
$H_2N(CH_2)_3SO_3H$ M.W. 139.17
m.p. > 290° (dec.)

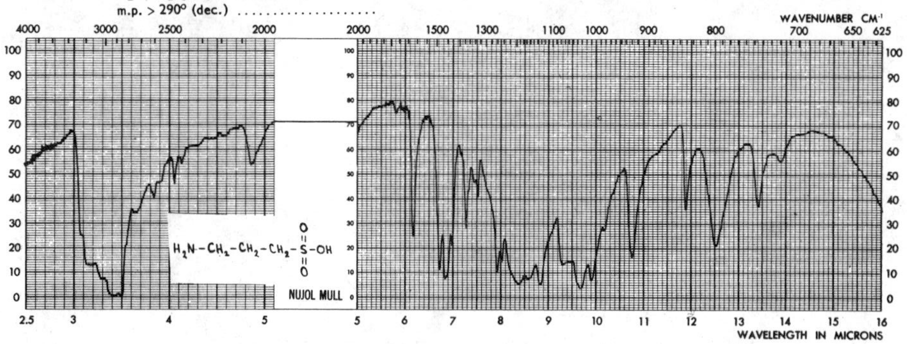

NUJOL MULL

F

85,570-7
DL-Cysteic acid (β-sulfo-DL-alanine)
$HO_3SCH_2CH(NH_2)CO_2H$
M.W. 169.16 m.p. 265° (dec.) Beil. 4,533

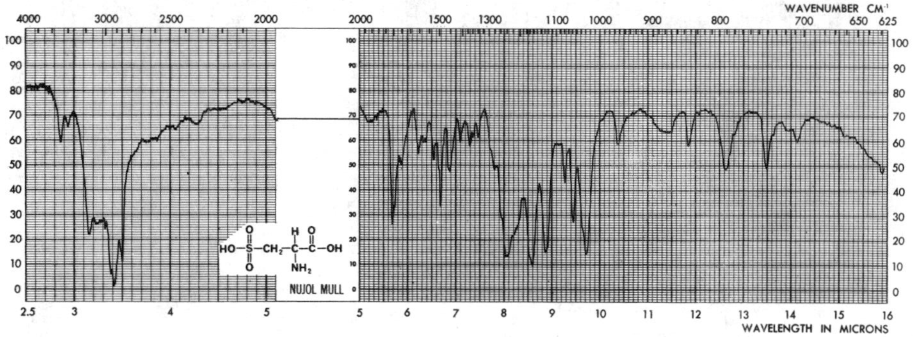

NUJOL MULL

G

85,189-2
L-Cysteic acid monohydrate (β-sulfo-L-alanine)
$HO_3SCH_2CH(NH_2)CO_2H \cdot H_2O$
M.W. 187.17 m.p. 267-269° (dec.)
$[\alpha]^{24}$ +8.2° (c=7.5, H_2O) Beil. 4,533

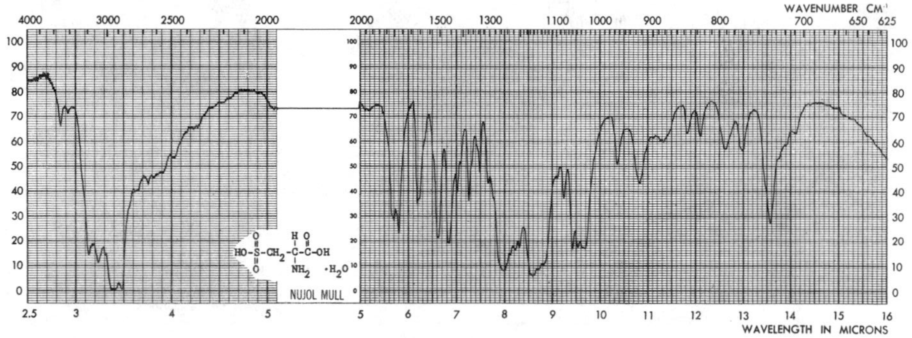

NUJOL MULL

H

21,974-6
DL-Homocysteic acid, 98%
$HO_3SCH_2CH_2CH(NH_2)CO_2H$ FW 183.18
mp 273° (dec.) *Beil.* 4(3),1714 Disp. I

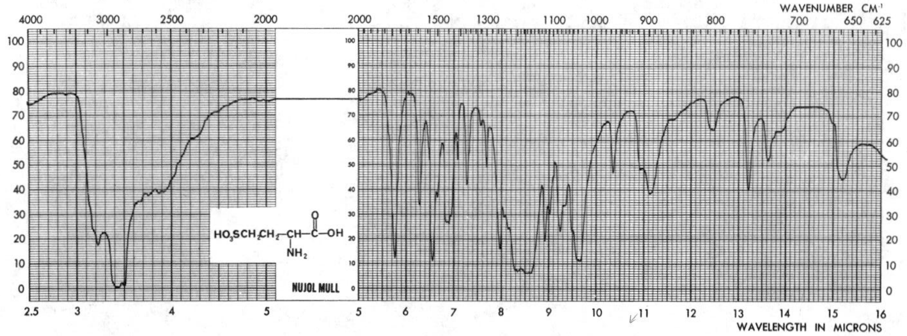

NUJOL MULL

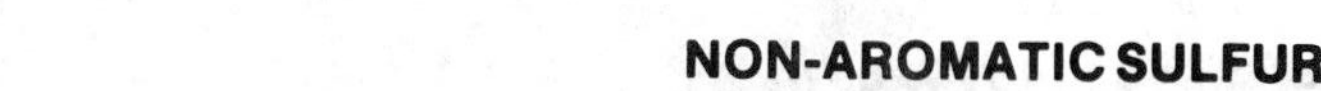

NON-AROMATIC SULFUR OXYGEN

A — 16,377-5
MOPS, 99% (4-morpholinepropanesulfonic acid)
M.W. 209.26 m.p. 277-280° (dec.)

B — 22,403-0
CHES [2-(cyclohexylamino)ethanesulfonic acid]
$C_6H_{11}NHCH_2CH_2SO_3H$ FW 207.29 mp >300°
Disp. C

C — 16,376-7
CAPS, 99% (3-cyclohexylamino-1-propanesulfonic acid)
$C_6H_{11}NH(CH_2)_3SO_3H$
M.W. 221.32 m.p. >300°

D — 16,372-4
BES, 99+% [N,N-bis-(2-hydroxyethyl)-2-aminoethanesulfonic acid]
$(HOCH_2CH_2)_2NCH_2CH_2SO_3H$
M.W. 213.25 m.p. 152-154°

E — 16,373-2
MES (4-morpholineethanesulfonic acid)
M.W. 195.24 m.p. >300°

F — 16,371-6
HEPES, 99% [4-(2-hydroxyethyl)-1-piperazine-ethanesulfonic acid]
M.W. 238.31 m.p. 210-215° (dec.)

G — 16,374-0
EPPS, 99% [4-(2-hydroxyethyl)-1-piperazinepropane-sulfonic acid]
M.W. 252.33 m.p. 231° (dec.)

H — 16,375-9
PIPES [1,4-piperazinebis-(ethanesulfonic acid)]
M.W. 302.37 m.p. >300°

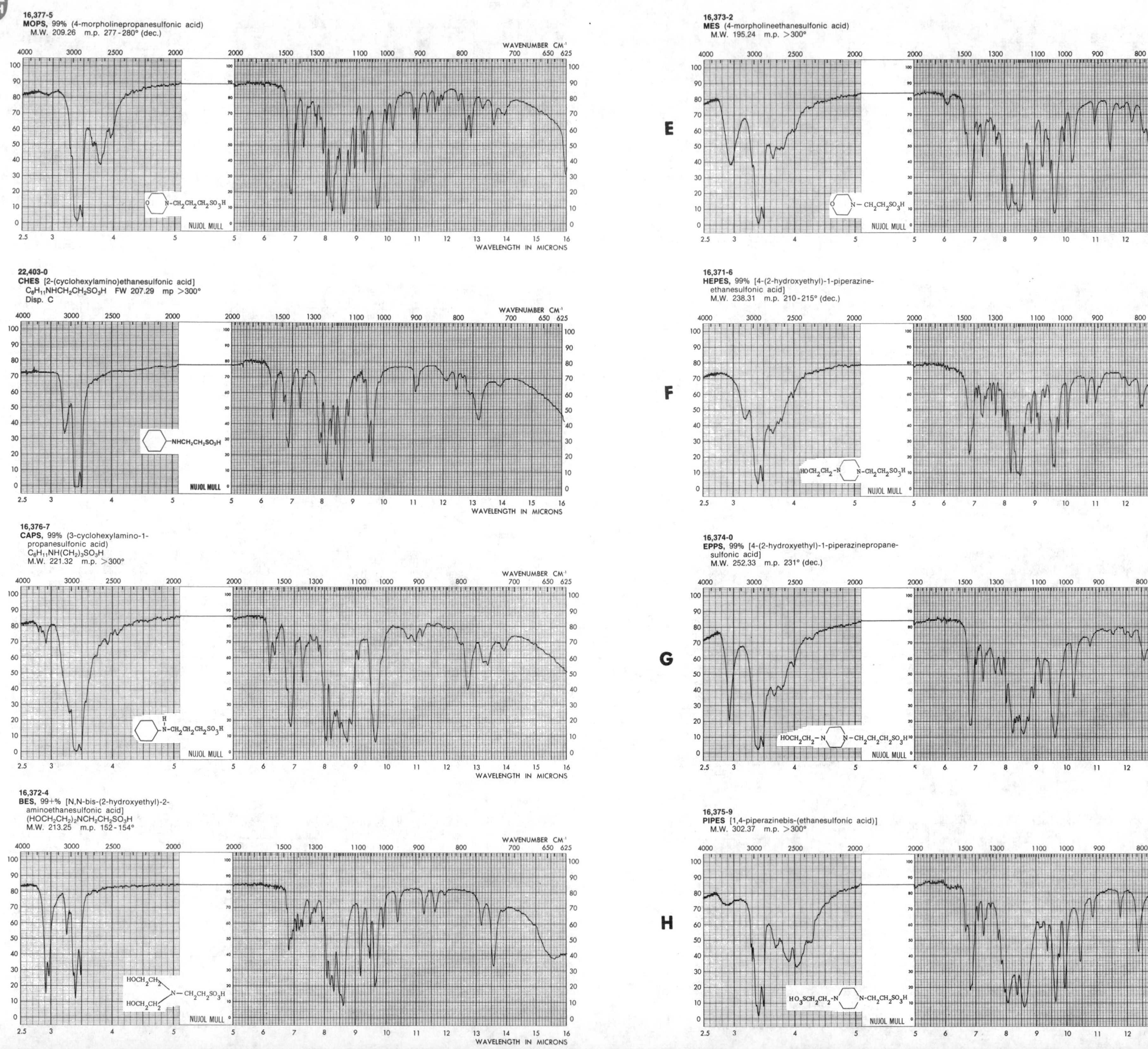

A

TES, 99% (2-[tris(hydroxymethyl)methylamino]-1-ethanesulfonic acid)
$(HOCH_2)_3CNHCH_2CH_2SO_3H$ FW 229.25
mp 223-225° Disp. C

NUJOL MULL

B

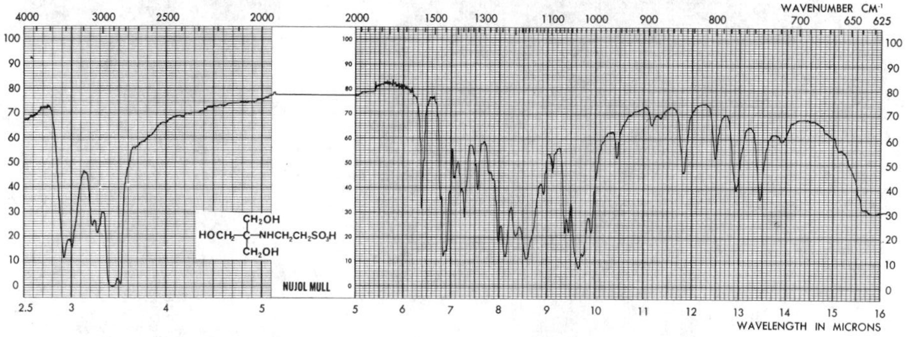

21,993-2
TAPS, 99% (3-[tris(hydroxymethyl)methylamino]-1-propanesulfonic acid)
$(HOCH_2)_3CNH(CH_2)_3SO_3H$ FW 243.28
mp 240° (dec.) Disp. C

NUJOL MULL

C

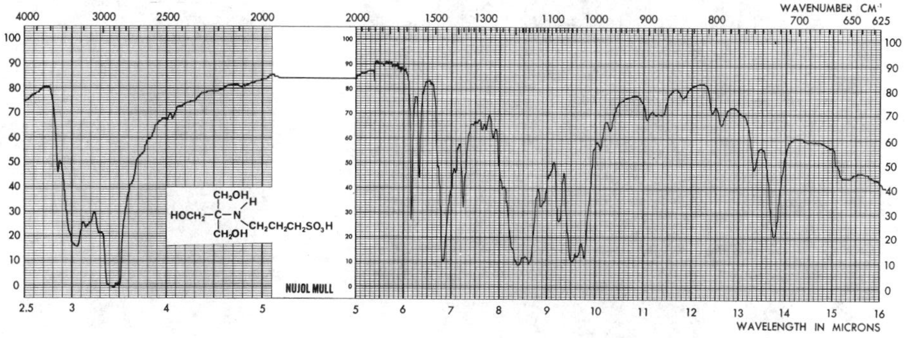

85,759-9
ACES [N-(2-acetamido)-2-aminoethanesulfonic acid, N-(carbamoylmethyl)-taurine]
$H_2NCOCH_2NHCH_2CH_2SO_3H$
M.W. 182.2 m.p. > 220° (dec.)

NUJOL MULL

D

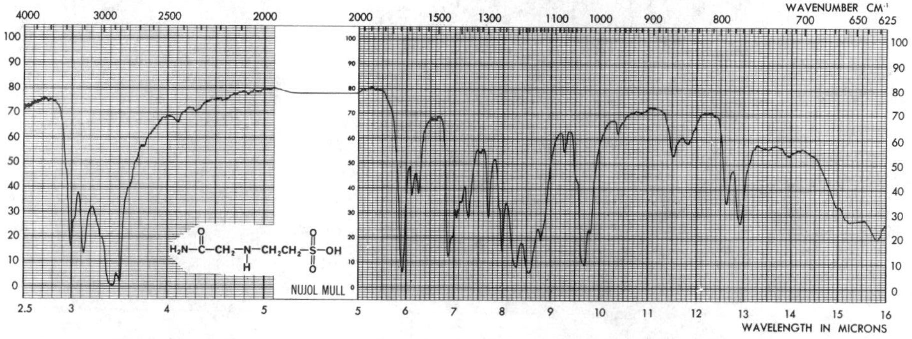

F1600-1 **Formamidinesulfinic acid** (aminoiminomethanesulfinic acid)
$H_2NC(:NH)SO_2H$ M.W. 108.12 m.p. 126° (dec.)

NUJOL MULL

E

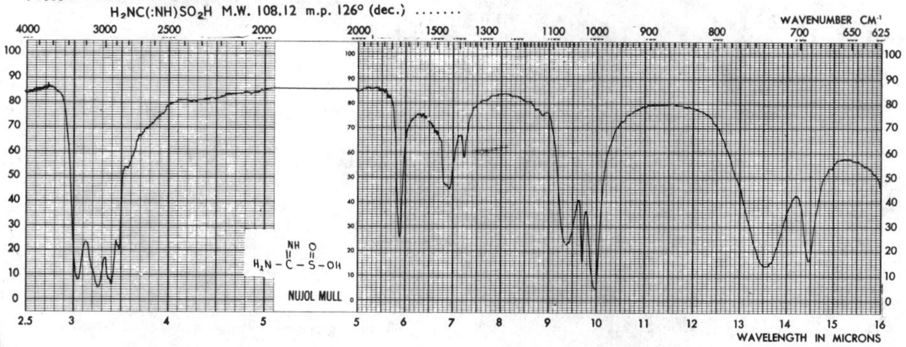

10,959-2 **Sodium formaldehydesulfoxylate**
$HOCH_2OSONa$ M.W. 118.09
m.p. 131° (dec.)

NUJOL MULL

F

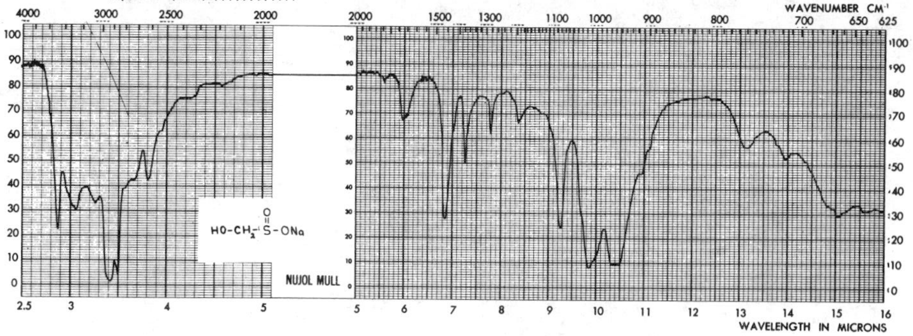

11,270-4 **Formaldehyde sodium bisulfite addition compound** (sodium formaldehyde bisulfite)
$HOCH_2SO_3Na$ M.W. 134.09 m.p. 200° (dec.)

NUJOL MULL

G

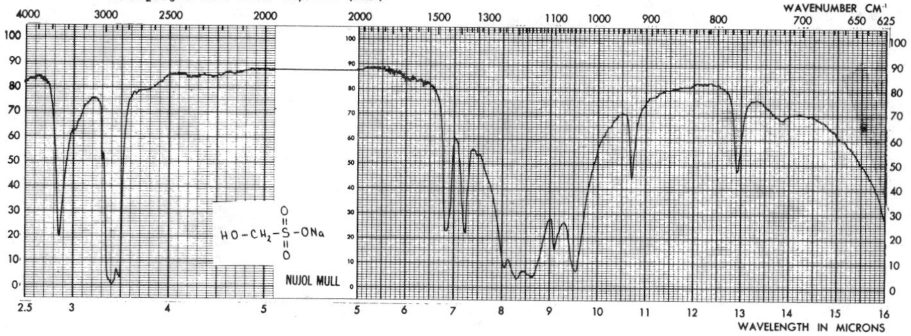

10,878-2 **Acetone sodium bisulfite addition compound** (2-hydroxy-2-propanesulfonic acid, sodium salt)
$(CH_3)_2C(OH)SO_3Na$ M.W. 162.14
m.p. > 300°

NUJOL MULL

H

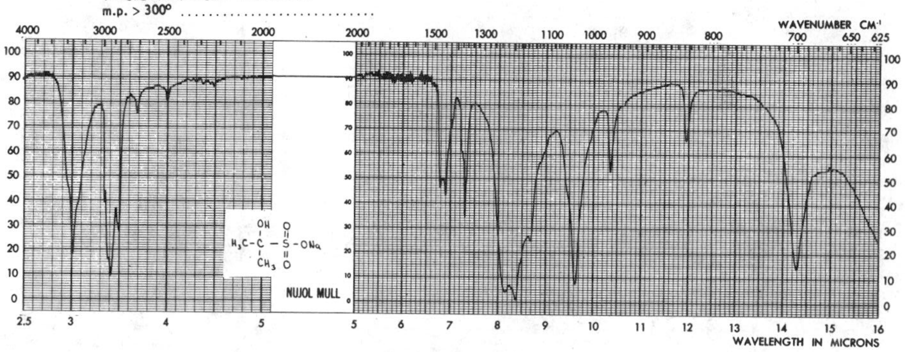

H5450-6 **3-Hydroxy-1-propanesulfonic acid, sodium salt**
$HO(CH_2)_3SO_3Na$ M.W. 162.15
m.p. 227° (dec.)

NUJOL MULL

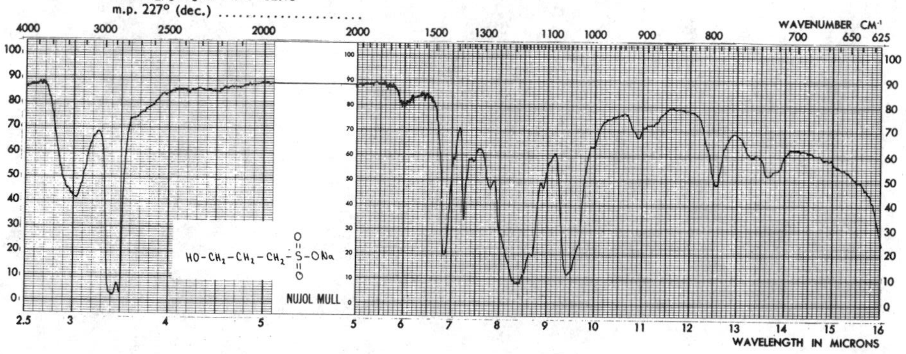

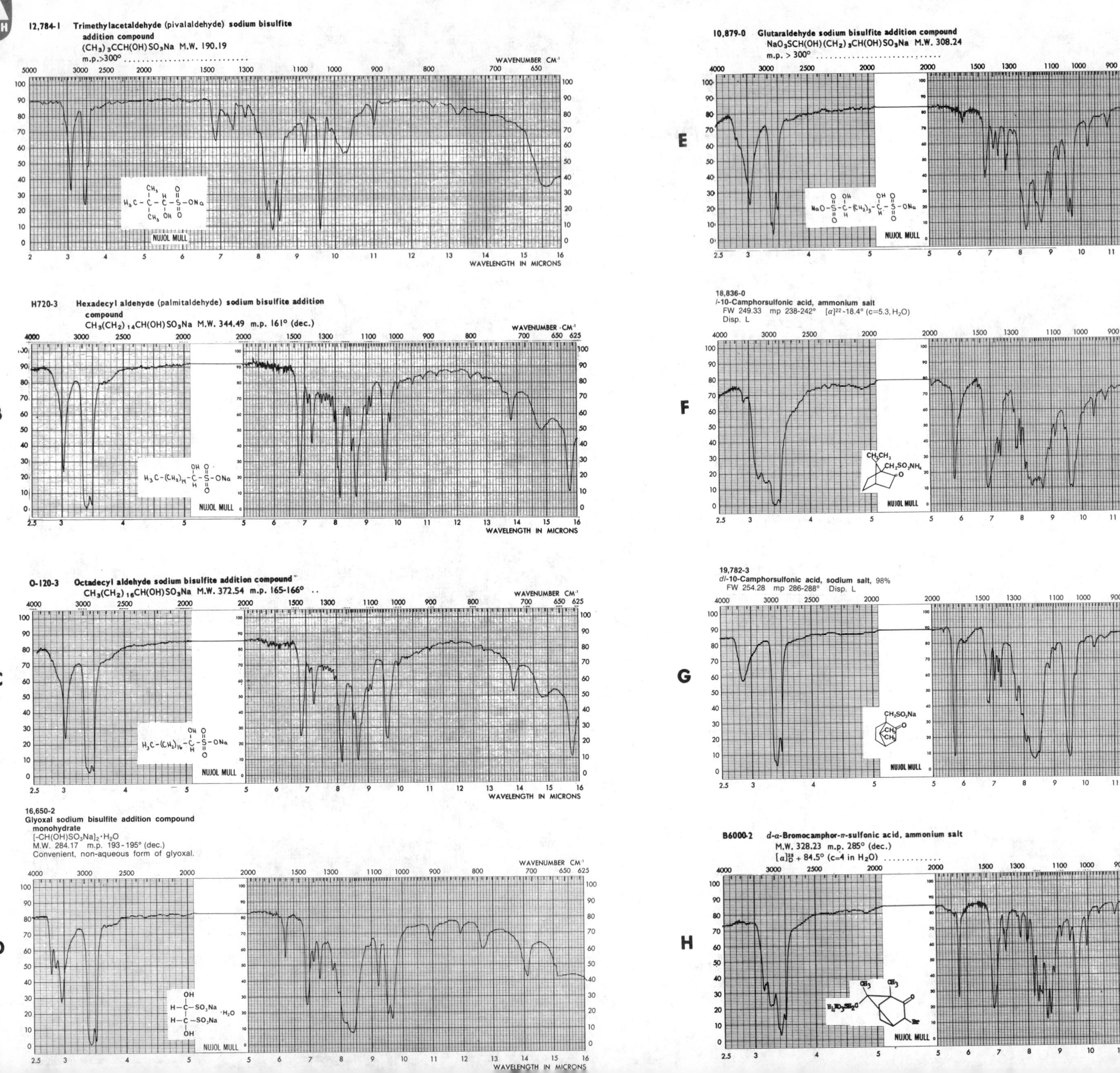
A
12,784-1 Trimethylacetaldehyde (pivalaldehyde) sodium bisulfite addition compound
(CH3)3CCH(OH)SO3Na M.W. 190.19
m.p.>300°
NUJOL MULL
B
H720-3 Hexadecyl aldehyde (palmitaldehyde) sodium bisulfite addition compound
CH3(CH2)14CH(OH)SO3Na M.W. 344.49 m.p. 161° (dec.)
NUJOL MULL
C
O-120-3 Octadecyl aldehyde sodium bisulfite addition compound
CH3(CH2)16CH(OH)SO3Na M.W. 372.54 m.p. 165-166°
NUJOL MULL
D
16,650-2
Glyoxal sodium bisulfite addition compound monohydrate
[-CH(OH)SO3Na]2·H2O
M.W. 284.17 m.p. 193-195° (dec.)
Convenient, non-aqueous form of glyoxal.
NUJOL MULL
E
10,879-0 Glutaraldehyde sodium bisulfite addition compound
NaO3SCH(OH)(CH2)3CH(OH)SO3Na M.W. 308.24
m.p. > 300°
NUJOL MULL
F
18,836-0
l-10-Camphorsulfonic acid, ammonium salt
FW 249.33 mp 238-242° [α]22 -18.4° (c=5.3, H2O)
Disp. L
NUJOL MULL
G
19,782-3
dl-10-Camphorsulfonic acid, sodium salt, 98%
FW 254.28 mp 286-288° Disp. L
NUJOL MULL
H
B6000-2 d-α-Bromocamphor-π-sulfonic acid, ammonium salt
M.W. 328.23 m.p. 285° (dec.)
[α]D + 84.5° (c=4 in H2O)
NUJOL MULL
WAVENUMBER CM⁻¹
WAVELENGTH IN MICRONS

A

12,402-8 *l*-α-Bromocamphor-π-sulfonic acid, ammonium salt
M.W. 328.23 m.p. 291-293° (dec.)

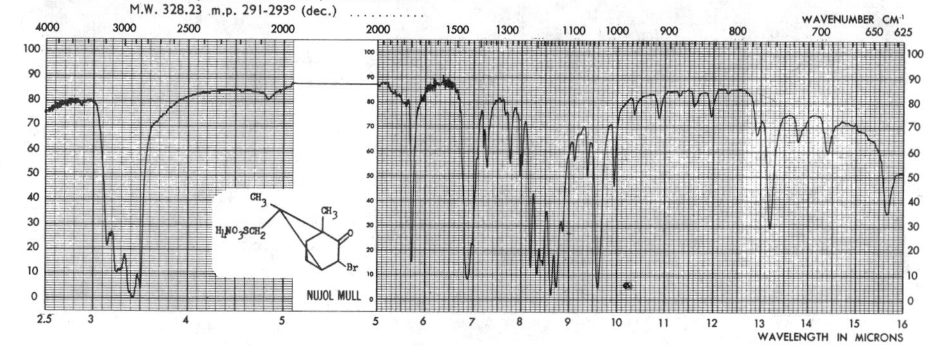

NUJOL MULL

B

D20,117-0 Dioctyl sulfosuccinate [bis-(2-ethylhexyl)sulfosuccinate], sodium salt
$CH_3(CH_2)_3CH(C_2H_5)CH_2O_2CCH_2CH(SO_3Na)CO_2CH_2CH(C_2H_5)(CH_2)_3CH_3$ M.W. 444.55 m.p. 145-150°

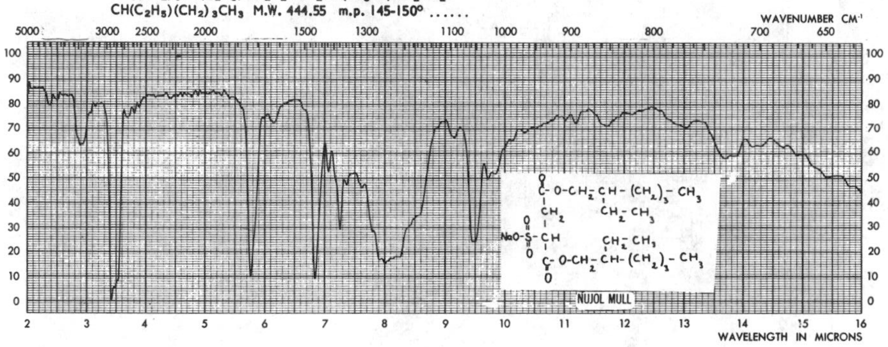

NUJOL MULL

C

16,048-2
Magic Methyl®, 97% (methyl fluorosulfonate)
FSO_3CH_3
M.W. 114.09 b.p. 92-94° n_D^{20} 1.3326 d 1.412
Fieser 3,202 *SEVERE POISON*

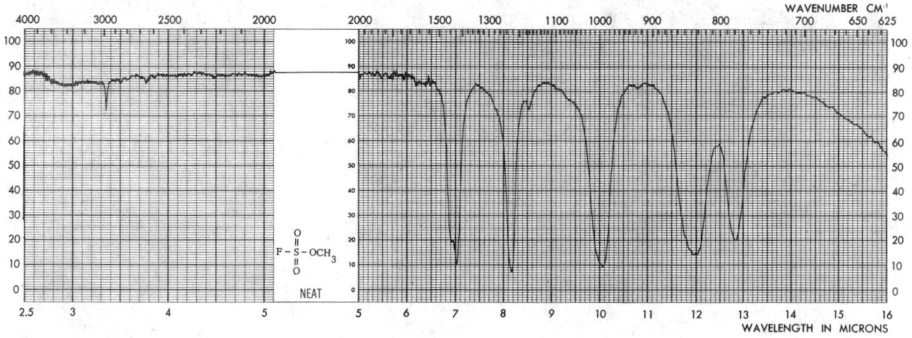

NEAT

D

17,759-8
Ethyl fluorosulfonate
$FSO_3C_2H_5$
M.W. 128.12 *CORROSIVE*

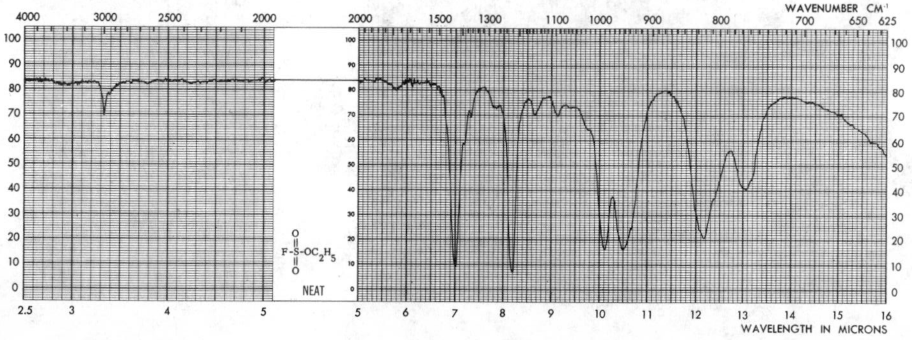

NEAT

E

12,992-5 **Methyl methanesulfonate**
$CH_3OSO_2CH_3$ M.W. 110.13 n_D^{20} 1.4138
b.p. 202.7-203°

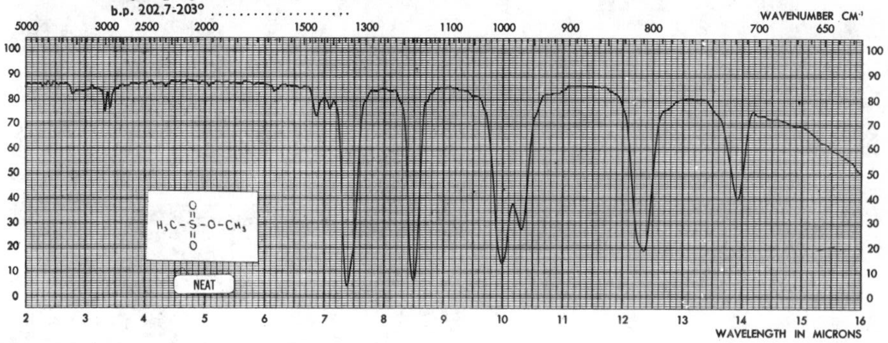

NEAT

F

22,050-7
Ethyl methanesulfonate, 99%
$CH_3SO_3C_2H_5$ FW 124.16 bp 85-86°/10mm.
n_D^{20} 1.4180 d 1.167 *Beil.* 4,5 Disp. K

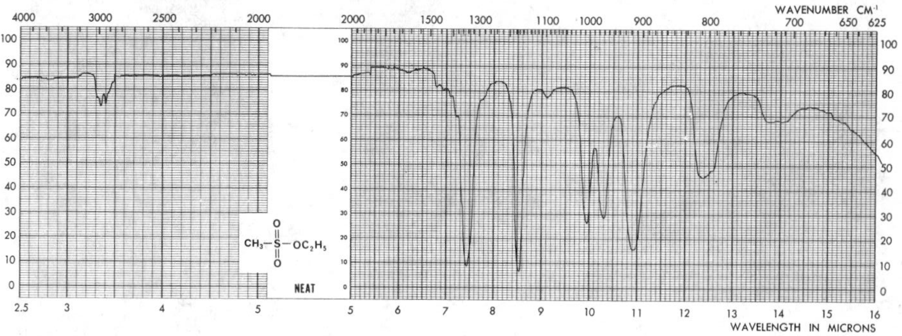

NEAT

G

15,806-2
Methoxymethyl methanesulfonate
$CH_3SO_3CH_2OCH_3$
M.W. 140.16 n_D^{20} 1.4240 Fieser 3,198
CORROSIVE

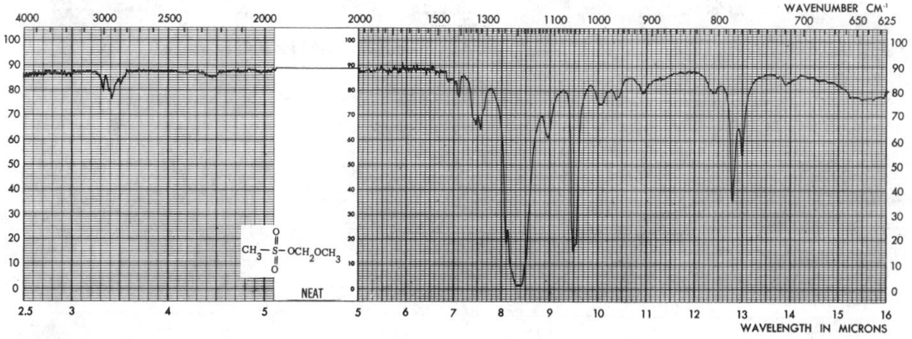

NEAT

H

16,428-3
Methyl trifluoromethanesulfonate, 99+%,
GOLD LABEL
$CF_3SO_3CH_3$
M.W. 164.1 n_D^{20} 1.3244 *CORROSIVE*

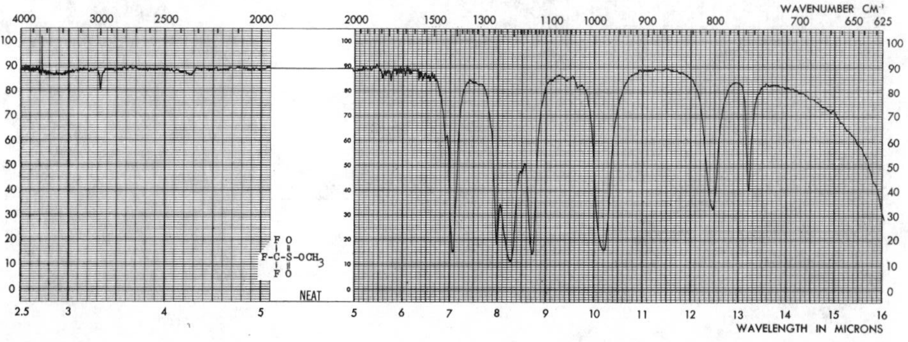

NEAT

A

17,617-6
Trifluoromethanesulfonic anhydride
$(CF_3SO_2)_2O$
M.W. 282.13 n_D^{20} 1.3212

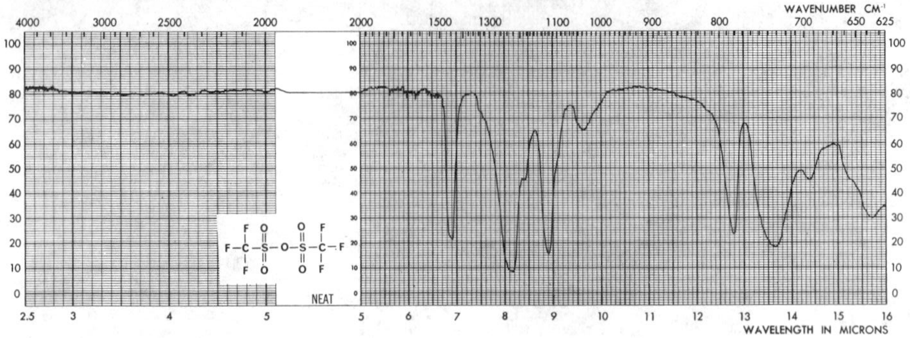

NEAT

B

15,060-6 **Busulfan** (1,4-butanediol dimethanesulfonate)
$CH_3SO_2O(CH_2)_4OSO_2CH_3$ M.W. 246.30
m.p. 115-117.5°

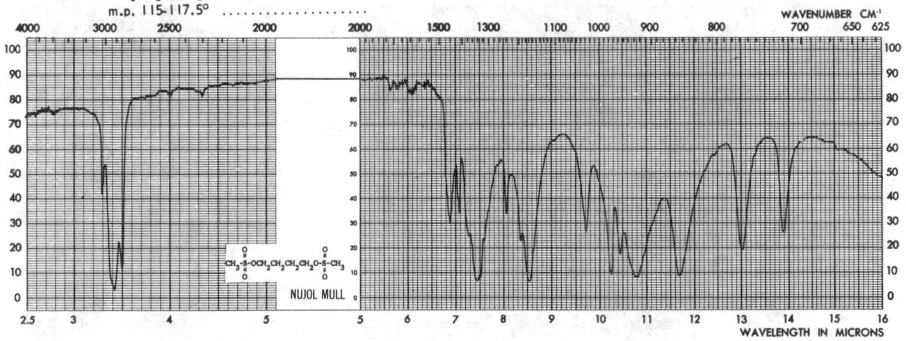

NUJOL MULL

C

C4170-3 **2-Chloroethyl methanesulfonate, puriss.**
$CH_3SO_3CH_2CH_2Cl$ M.W. 158.60 n_D^{20} 1.4562

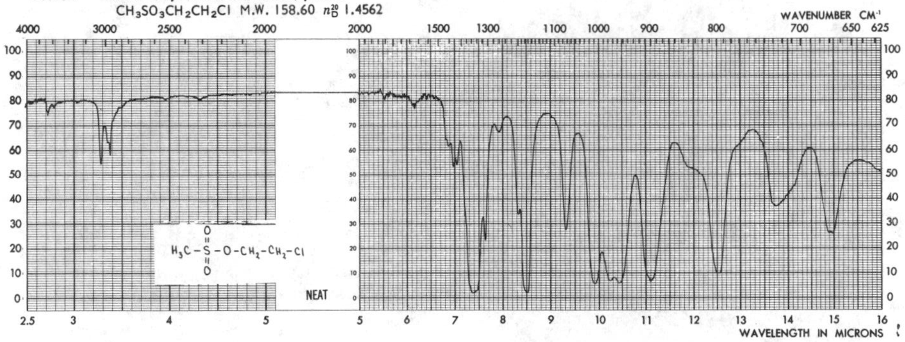

NEAT

D

P5070-6 **1,3-Propane sultone**
M.W. 122.14 m.p. 31.5-34°

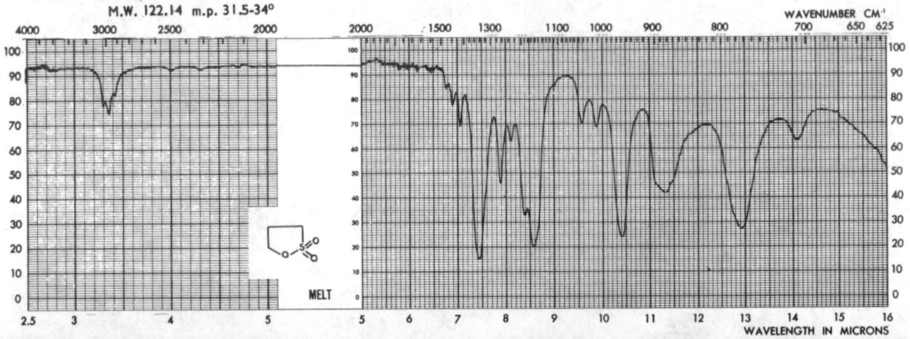

MELT

E

B8550-1 **1,4-Butane sultone** (4-hydroxy-1-butanesulfonic acid δ-sultone)
M.W. 136.17 n_D^{20} 1.4621

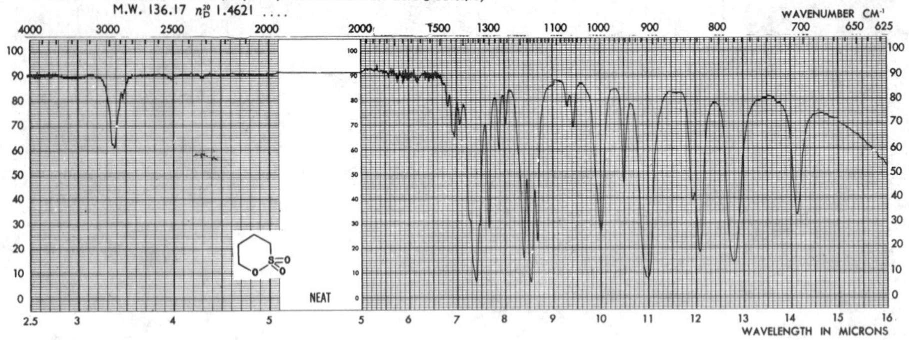

NEAT

F

M3355-7 **Methyl α-d-camphorsulfonate**
M.W. 246.33 m.p. 78-80°

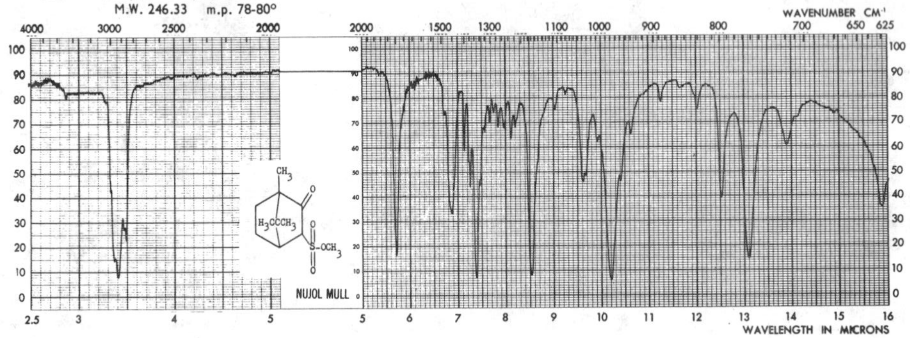

NUJOL MULL

G

15,780-5
Thionyl chloride, 97%
$SOCl_2$
M.W. 118.97 m.p. -105° b.p. 79° n_D^{20} 1.5206
d 1.631 Fieser 1,1158 2,412 3,290
LACHRYMATOR

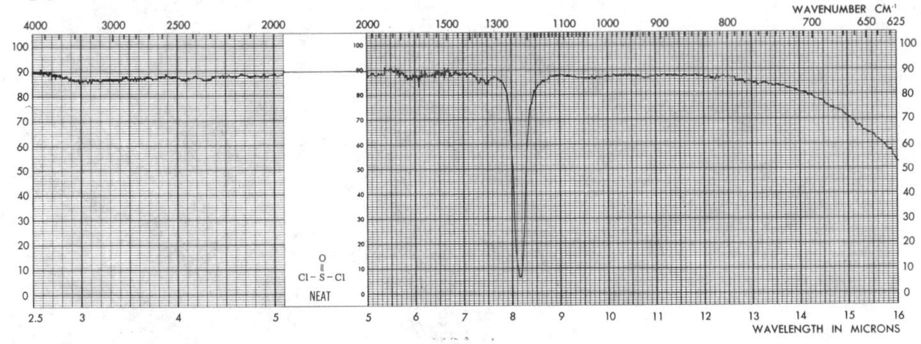

NEAT

H

15,776-7
Sulfuryl chloride, 97%
SO_2Cl_2
M.W. 134.97 m.p. -54° b.p. 68-70° n_D^{20} 1.4430
d 1.68 Fieser 1,1128 2,394 3,276 *CORROSIVE*

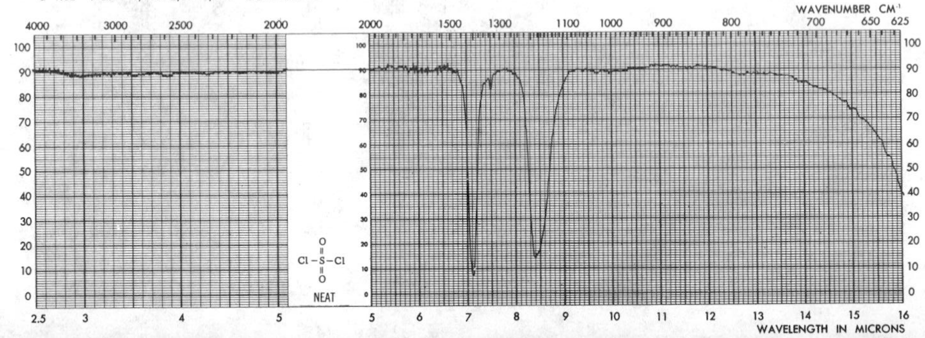

NEAT

A

18,630-9
Chlorosulfonic acid, 99%
$ClSO_3H$
M.W. 116.52 b.p. 151-152°/755mm. n_D^{20} 1.4331
d 1.753

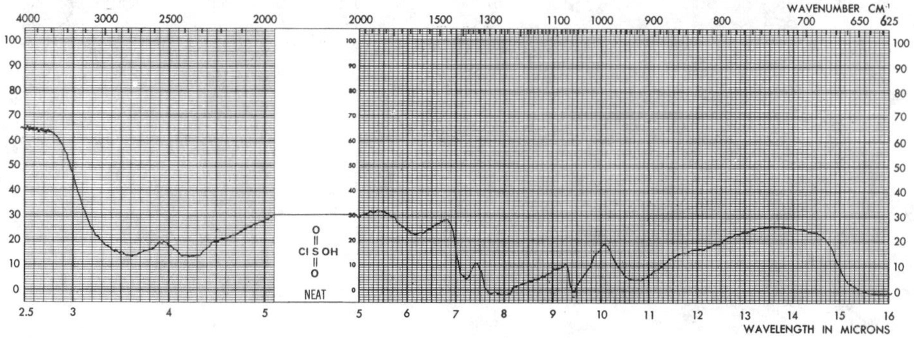

NEAT

B

M880-0 Methanesulfonyl chloride (mesyl chloride)
CH_3SO_2Cl M.W. 114.55 n_D^{20} 1.4518

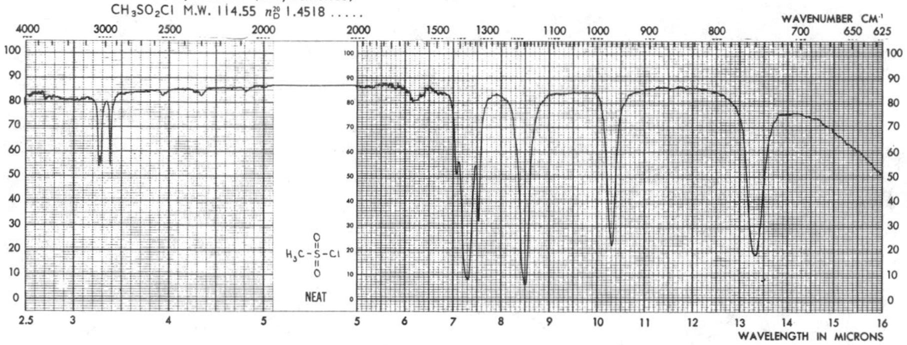

NEAT

C

16,479-8
Trifluoromethanesulfonyl chloride, 99+%,
GOLD LABEL
CF_3SO_2Cl
M.W. 168.52 n_D^{20} 1.3344

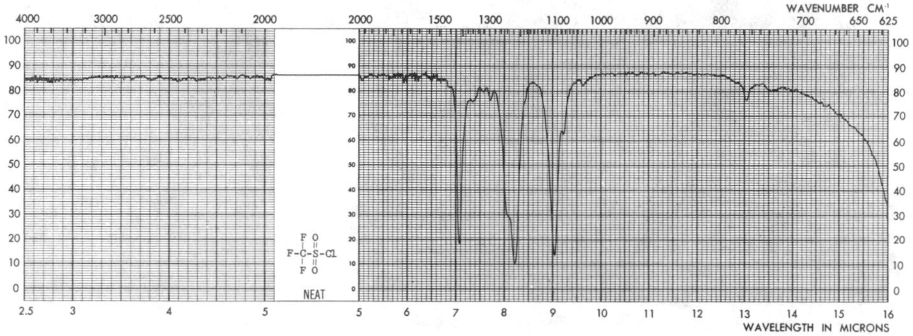

NEAT

D

H676-2 1-Hexadecanesulfonyl chloride
$CH_3(CH_2)_{15}SO_2Cl$ M.W. 324.96 m.p. 55-57°

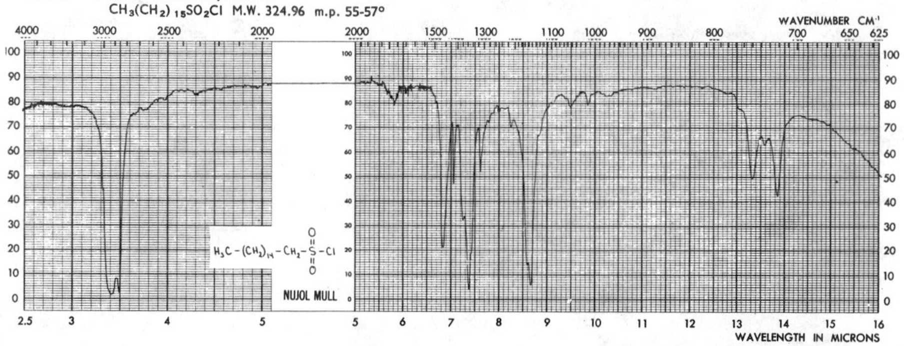

NUJOL MULL

E

12,519-9 3-Chloropropanesulfonyl chloride
$Cl(CH_2)_3SO_2Cl$ M.W. 177.05 n_D^{20} 1.4868
b.p. 70°/0.5 mm.

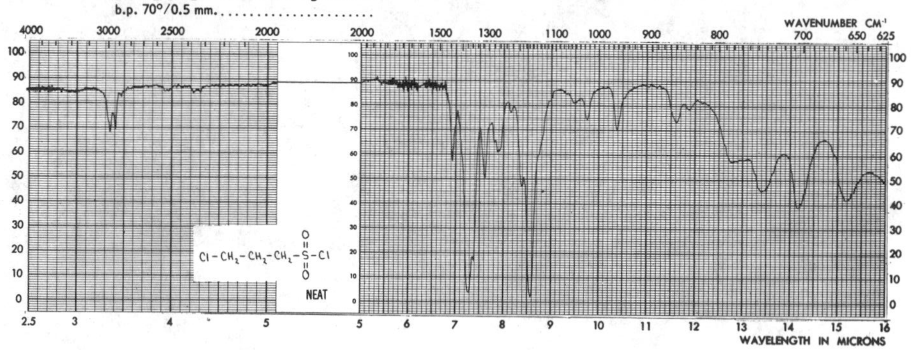

NEAT

F

21,957-6
***d*-10-Camphorsulfonyl chloride, 97%**
FW 250.75 mp 65-67° $[\alpha]^{22}$ +33° (c=1, $CHCl_3$)
Beil. **11**,316 *Fieser* **1**,109 Disp. S

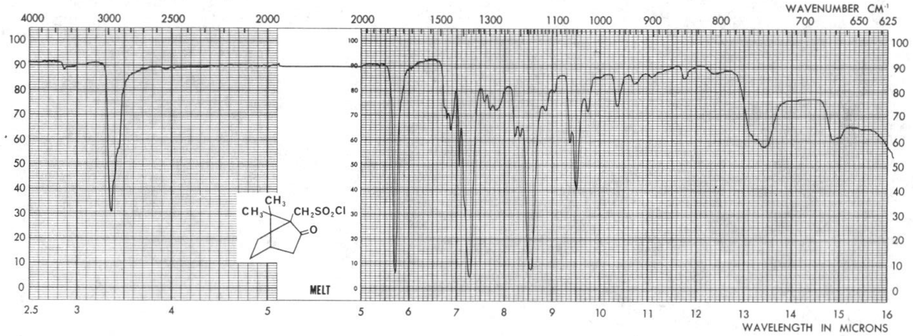

MELT

G

16,193-4
Sulfamoyl chloride, 98%
H_2NSO_2Cl
M.W. 115.54 m.p. 37-39° *IRRITANT*

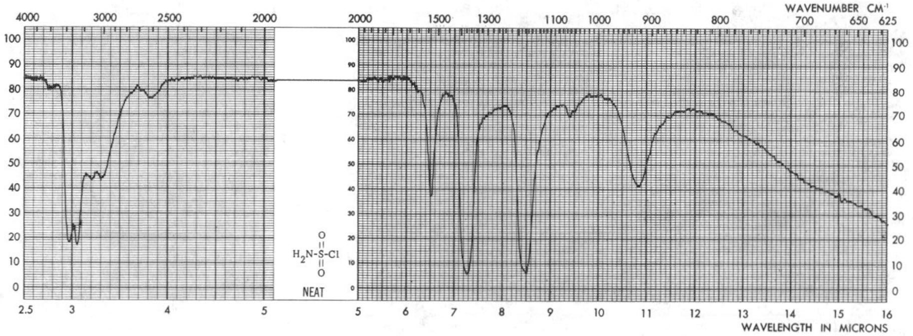

NEAT

H

D18,625-2 Dimethylsulfamoyl chloride
$(CH_3)_2NSO_2Cl$ M.W. 143.59 n_D^{20} 1.4518

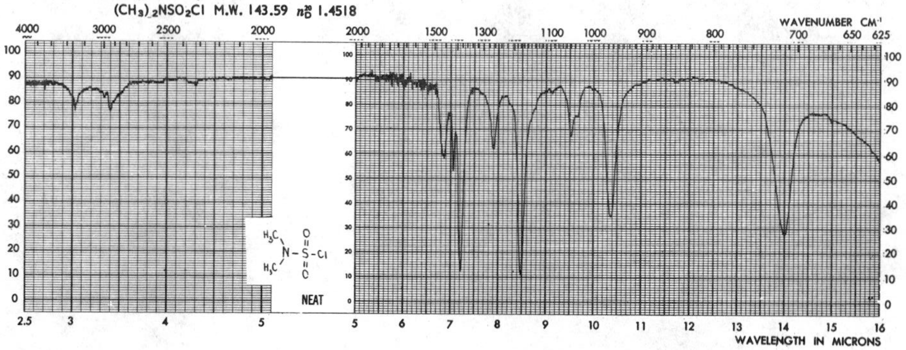

NEAT

ALDRICH ®

A 14,266-2 **Chlorosulfonyl isocyanate**
$ClSO_2NCO$ M.W. 141.53 n_D^{20} 1.4478
b.p. 107°

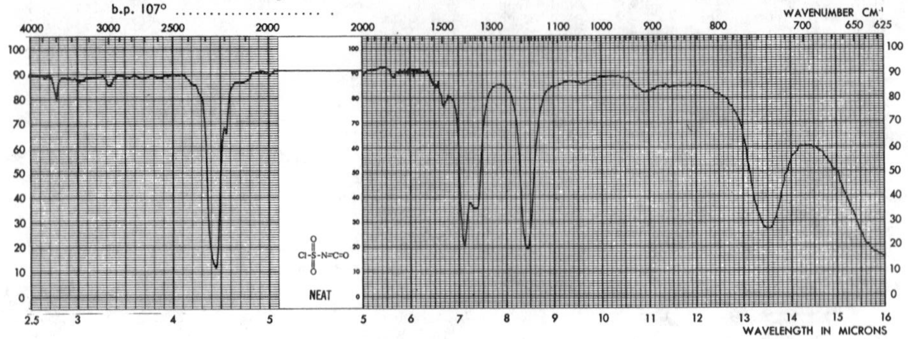

NEAT

B 13,587-9 **Sulfur trioxide trimethylamine complex**
$(CH_3)_3N{\cdot}SO_3$ M.W. 139.17
m.p. 232-238° (dec.)

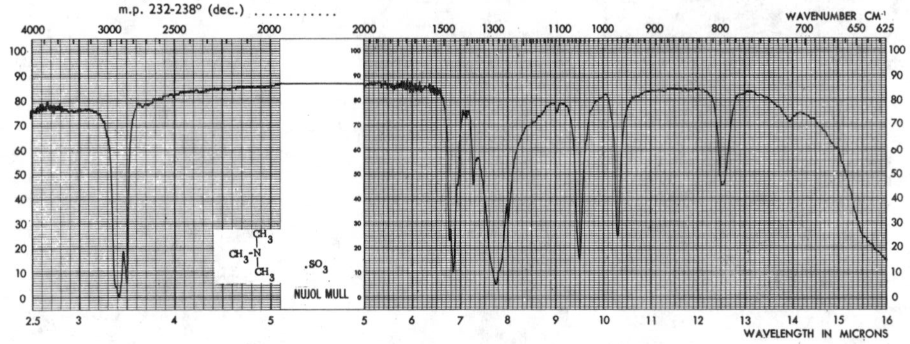

NUJOL MULL

C H674-6 **1-Hexadecanesulfonic acid hydrazide, tech.**
$CH_3(CH_2)_{15}SO_2NHNH_2$ M.W. 320.54

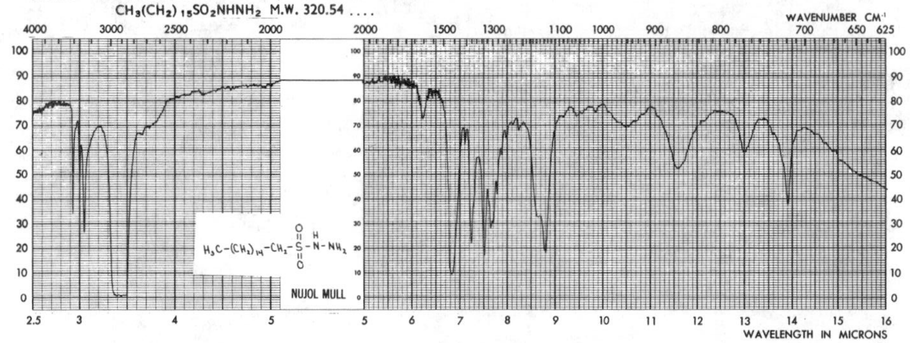

NUJOL MULL

D C10,840-5 **Cyclohexylsulfamic acid** (cyclohexanesulfamic acid), **puriss.**
$C_6H_{11}NHSO_3H$ M.W. 179.24
m.p. 184° (dec.)

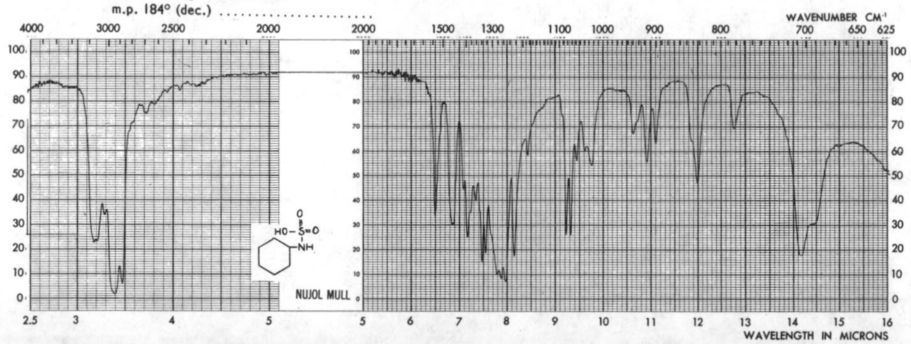

NUJOL MULL

E 13,830-4 **Cyclohexylsulfamic acid** (cyclohexanesulfamic acid), **sodium salt**
$C_6H_{11}NHSO_3Na$ M.W. 201.22
m.p. > 310° (dec.)

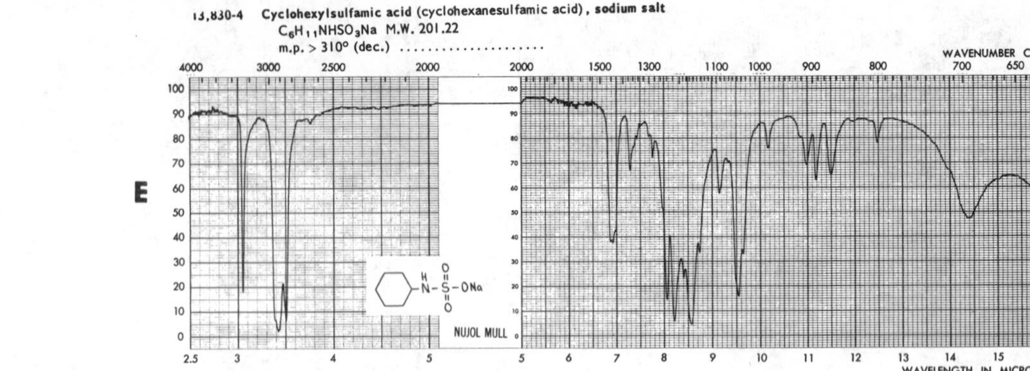

F 13,831-2 **Cyclohexylsulfamic acid** (cyclohexanesulfamic acid), **calcium salt dihydrate**
$(C_6H_{11}NHSO_3)_2Ca{\cdot}2H_2O$ M.W. 368.45
m.p. > 360°

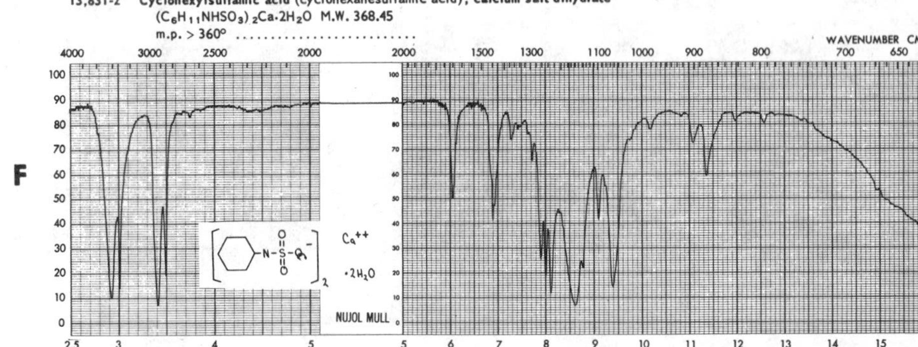

G D18,630-9 **Dimethyl sulfate, puriss.**
$(CH_3O)_2SO_2$ M.W. 126.13 n_D^{20} 1.3865
b.p. 75-77°/15 mm.

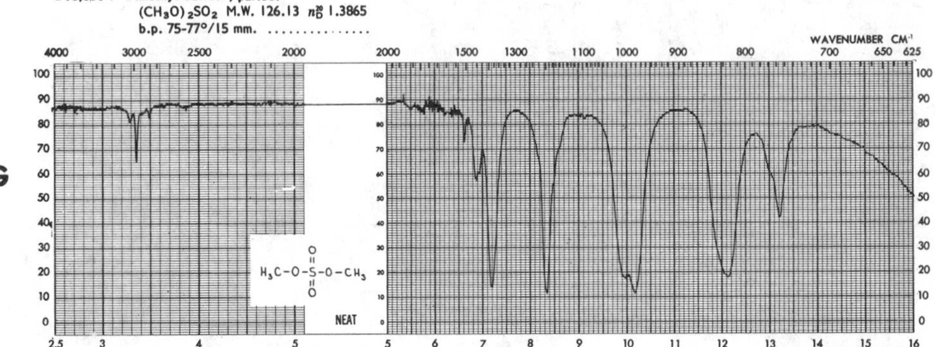

H D10,070-6 **Diethyl sulfate**
$(C_2H_5O)_2SO_2$ M.W. 154.18 n_D^{20} 1.3989

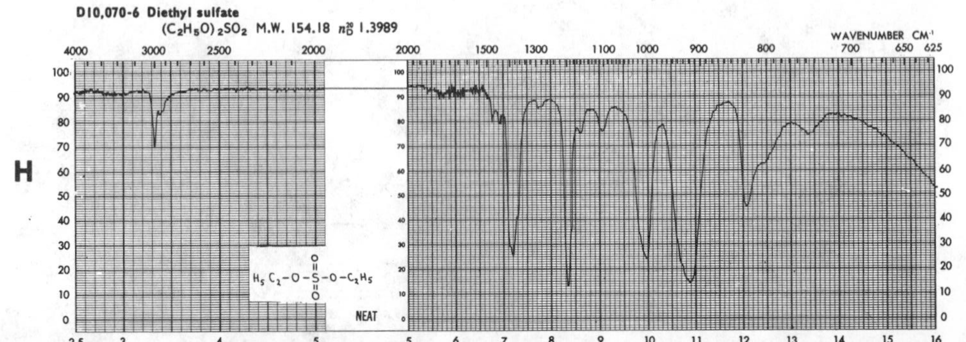

A

M4615 **Methylene sulfate** (1,3,5,7,2,6-tetraoxadithiocane 2,2,6,6-tetraoxide)
M.W. 104.99

B

A5440-7 **2-Aminoethyl hydrogen sulfate**
$H_2NCH_2CH_2OSO_3H$ M.W. 141.15 m.p. 289° (dec.)

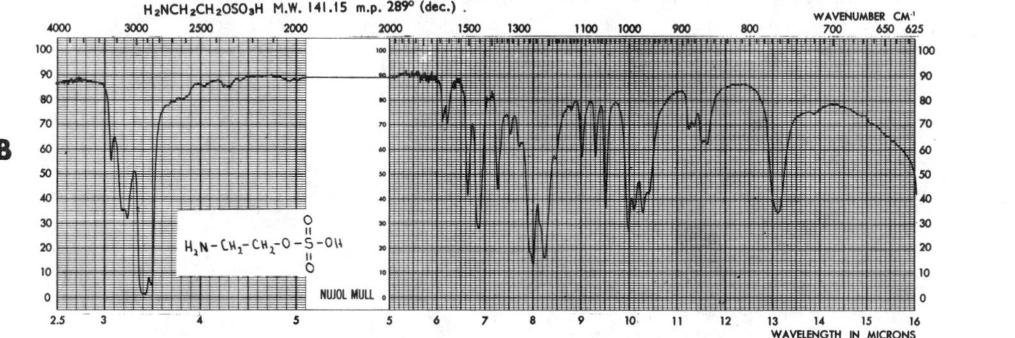

C

85,192-2
Dodecyl sulfate, sodium salt (sodium lauryl sulfate)
$CH_3(CH_2)_{11}OSO_3Na$
M.W. 288.38 m.p. 204-207°

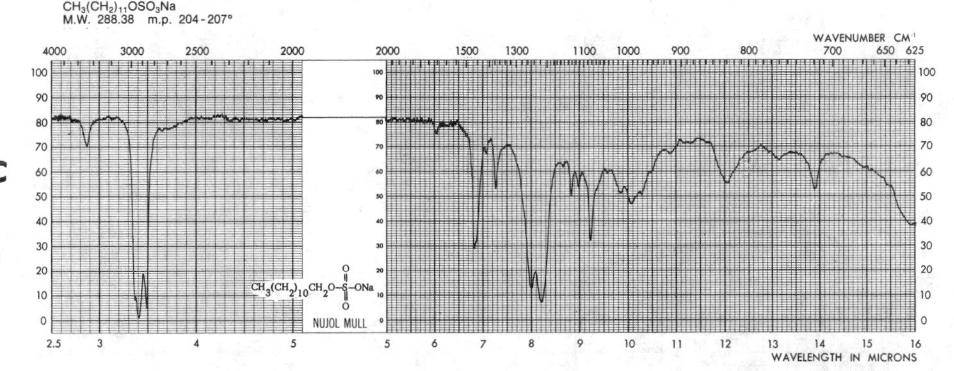

D

S330-5 **Sinigrin** (for the analysis of Vitamin C)
$(C_6H_{11}O_5)SC(CH_2CH:CH_2):NOSO_3K$
M.W. 397.47

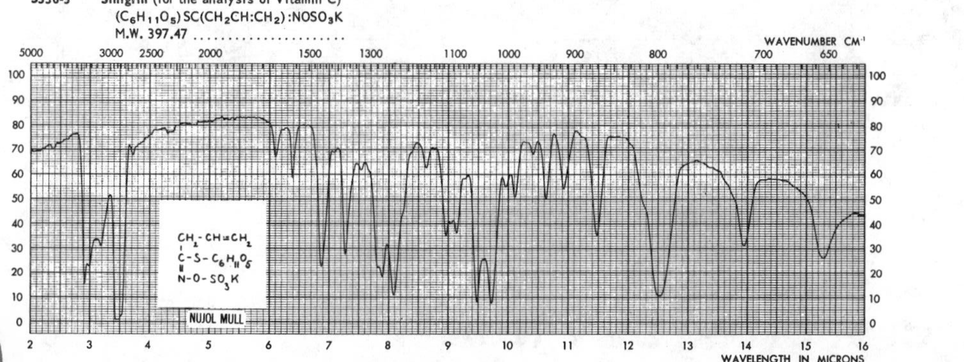

E

85,589-8
L-Methionine sulfoximine
$CH_3S(O)(=NH)CH_2CH_2CH(NH_2)CO_2H$
M.W. 180.23 m.p. >210° (dec.)

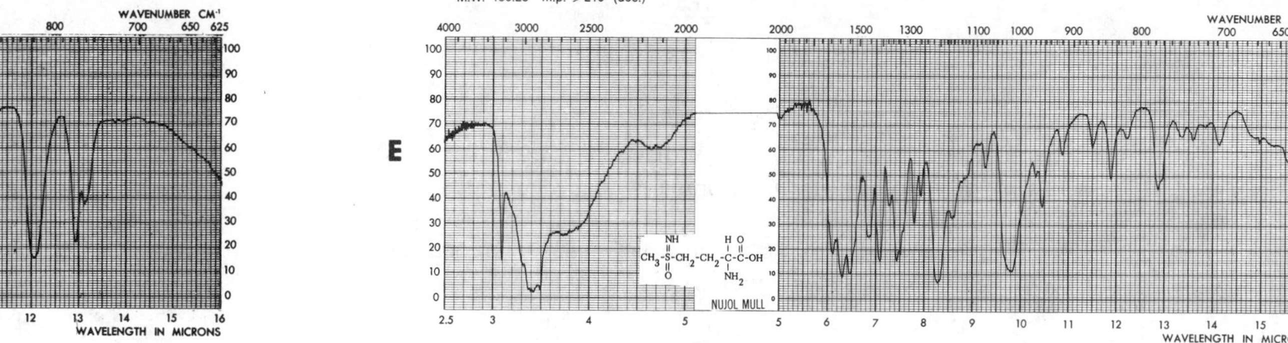

NON-AROMATIC PHOSPHORUS COMPOUNDS

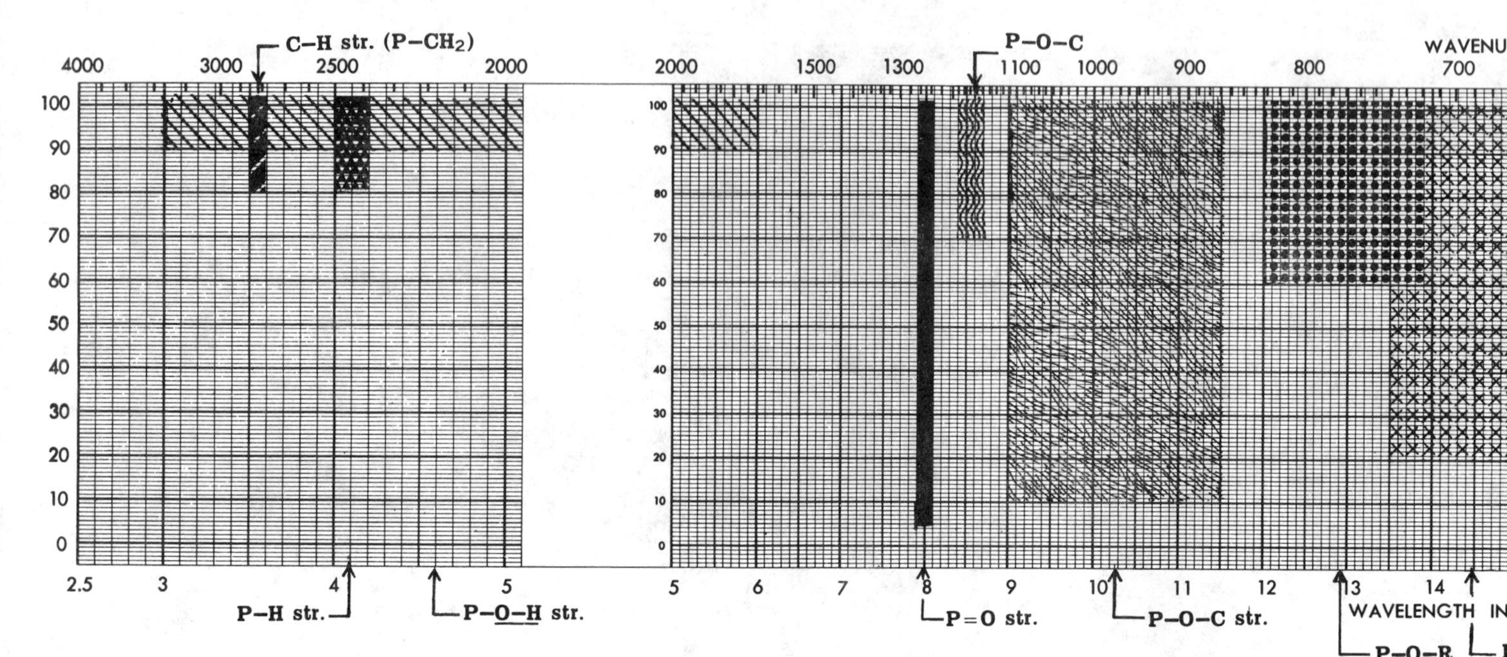

1.) Phosphines 546A-547H
2.) Phosphites....... 548B-550E
3.) Phosphonates 550F-552E
4.) Phosphoramides . 552F-554A
5.) Chlorophosphates 554B-555A
6.) Thiophosphates... 555B-556A
7.) Phosphates 556B-558G

The phosphorus-carbon linkage of the phosphines does not display any characteristic bands. The CH_2 deformation of the P–CH_2 is buried within the C–H bending absorption at 6.8 μ (1470 cm^{-1}). The phosphorus attached to the CH_2 group also affects the CH_2 stretch band by displaying a weak shoulder at 3.55 μ (2815 cm^{-1}).

The P–O–C group absorbs very strongly between 9 and 10 μ (1110 – 1000 cm^{-1}), with the exception of P–O–CH_3. A second strong band appears between 10 and 11.5 μ (1000 – 870 cm^{-1}) usually fused to the 9 μ (1110 cm^{-1}) band. Also associated with the P–O–C group is a medium intensity band between 12 and 14 μ (835 – 715 cm^{-1}) which becomes quite weak for aliphatic groups beyond methyl and ethyl substituents. (See spectra 548B–550E). A weak but characteristic absorption also appears between 8.4 and 8.7 μ (1190 – 1150 cm^{-1}).

The P=O group absorbs strongly near 8 μ (1250 cm^{-1}). It is shifted to near 7.7 μ (1300 cm^{-1}) when attached to chlorine. (See spectra 554B—555A).

The P–H bond absorbs at 4.1 μ (2440 cm^{-1}) in an area usually unoccupied by the bands of interfering groups. The P–O–H function absorbs very strongly between 3 and 6.5 μ (3335 – 1540 cm^{-1}) with three broad maxima; one appearing near 3.8, one at 4.5 and the third at 6 μ (2630, 2220 and 1665 cm^{-1}). (See spectra 550F, and 557B).

The P=S group absorbs between 13.5 μ (740 cm^{-1}) to beyond 16 μ (625 cm^{-1}).

The band shapes and overall spectral appearance of the phosphorus-oxygen compounds are quite similar to those of the sulfur-oxygen collection. For a totally unknown compound, a qualitative phosphorus-sulfur test is most helpful, along with careful attention to absorption positions.

A 16,355-4
Cyclohexylphosphine
$C_6H_{11}PH_2$
M.W. 116.14 b.p. 145° n_D^{20} 1.4903
PYROPHORIC

B 16,356-2
Dicyclohexylphosphine
$(C_6H_{11})_2PH$
M.W. 198.29 b.p. 129°/8mm. n_D^{20} 1.5163
PYROPHORIC

C 16,358-9
Triethylphosphine
$(C_2H_5)_3P$
M.W. 118.16 b.p. 127° n_D^{20} 1.4599 d 0.81
Beil. 4,582 *PYROPHORIC*

D 17,788-1
Tris-(hydroxymethyl)-phosphine (phosphinidyne-trimethanol)
$(HOCH_2)_3P$
M.W. 124.08 m.p. 48-50° b.p. 111-113°/2.5mm.

E 16,346-5
(2-Cyanoethyl)-phosphine (3-phosphinopropionitrile)
$NCCH_2CH_2PH_2$
M.W. 87.06 b.p. 130°/79mm. n_D^{20} 1.4840 d 0.94
PYROPHORIC

F 16,353-8
Bis-(2-cyanoethyl)-phosphine, 98%
(3,3'-phosphinidenedipropionitrile)
$(NCCH_2CH_2)_2PH$
M.W. 140.13 m.p. -8° b.p. 158°/0.3mm.
n_D^{20} 1.5101 d 1.08 *PYROPHORIC*

G T4948-4 **Tri-n-butylphosphine**
$[CH_3(CH_2)_3]_3P$ M.W. 202.32 n_D^{20} 1.4619
b.p. 150°/50 mm.

H 14,480-0 **Tetrabutylphosphonium chloride**
$[CH_3(CH_2)_3]_4PCl$ M.W. 294.89.

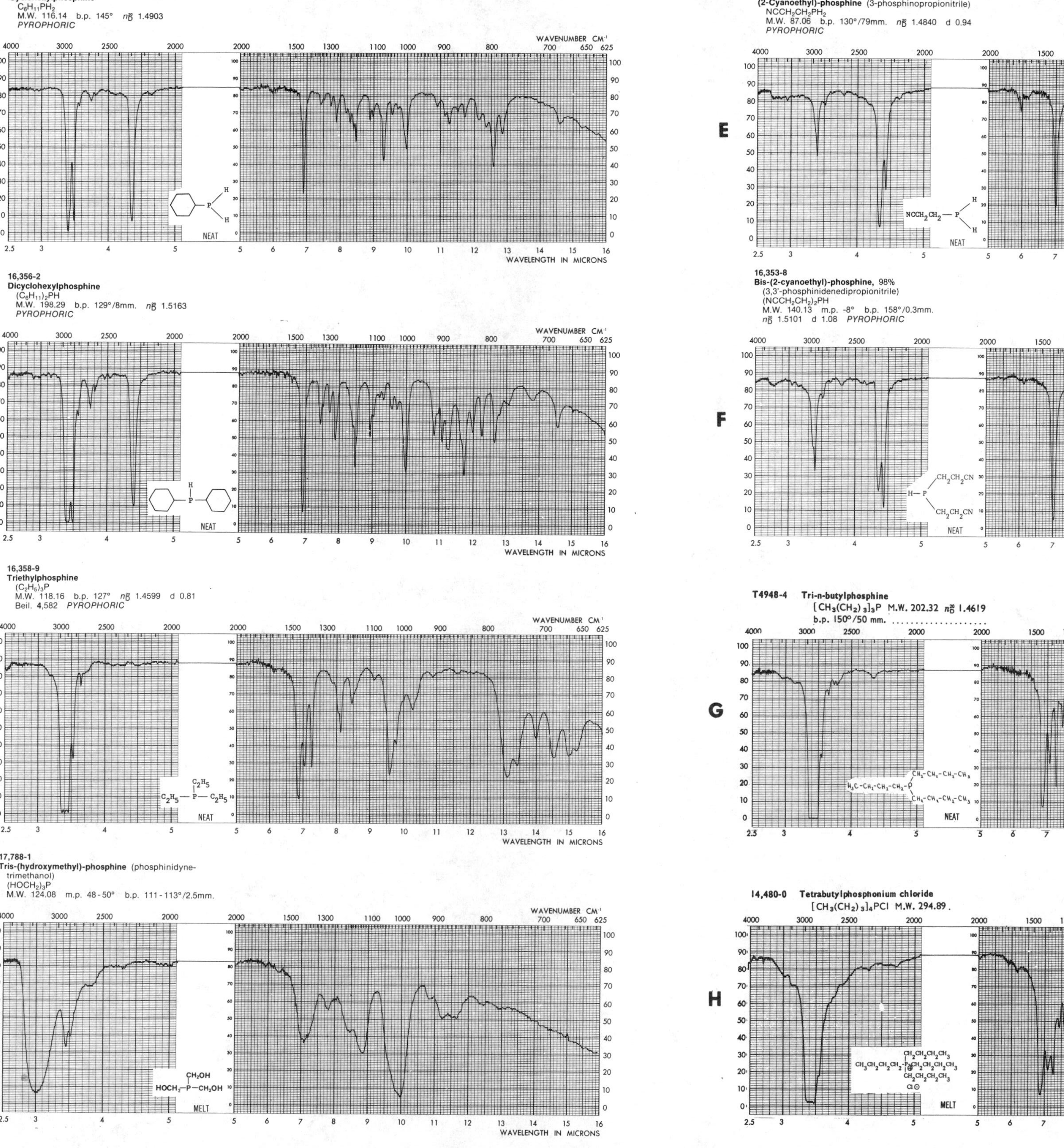

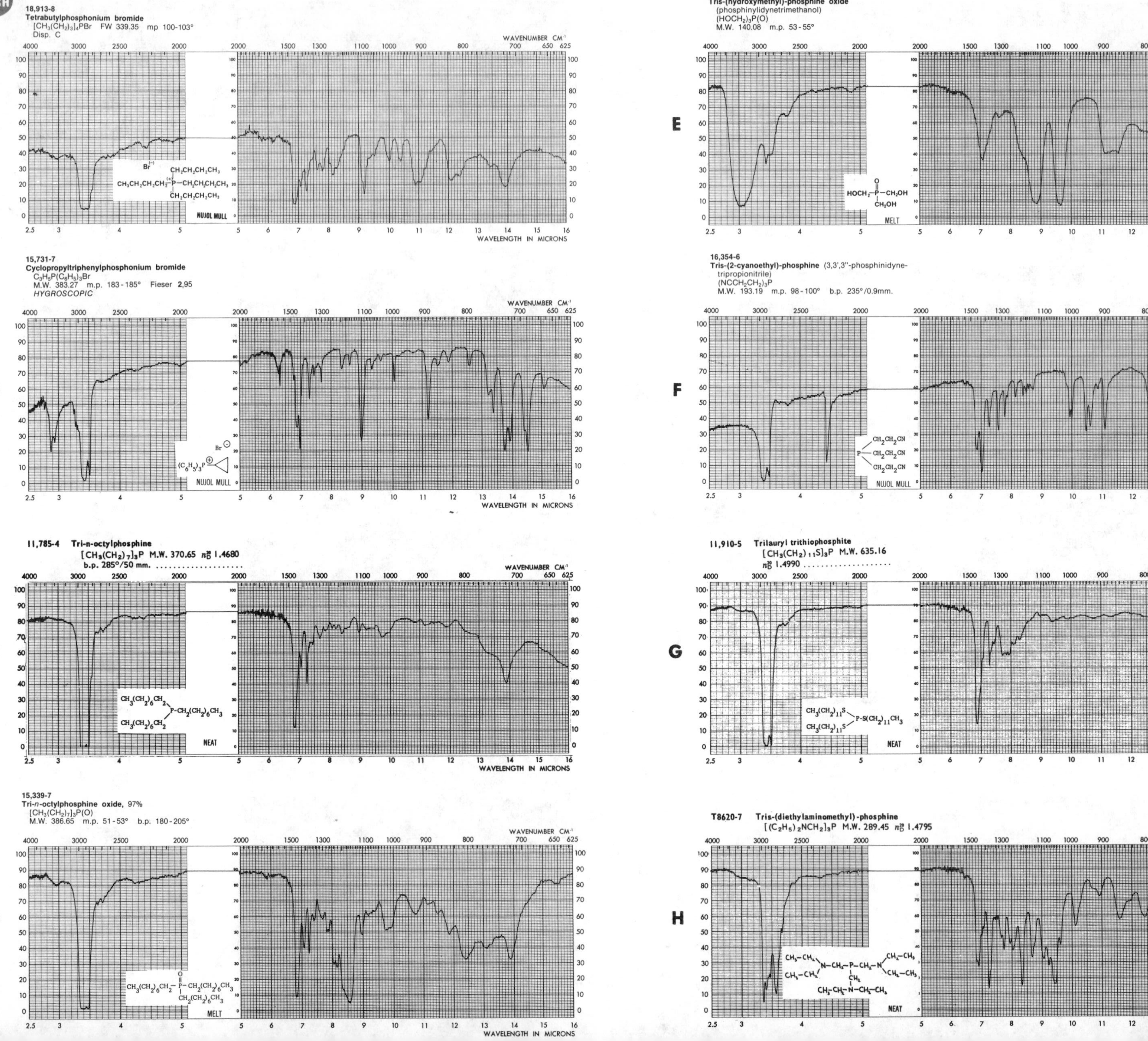

A 18,913-8
Tetrabutylphosphonium bromide
$[CH_3(CH_2)_3]_4PBr$ FW 339.35 mp 100-103°
Disp. C
NUJOL MULL

B 15,731-7
Cyclopropyltriphenylphosphonium bromide
$C_3H_5P(C_6H_5)_3Br$
M.W. 383.27 m.p. 183-185° Fieser 2,95
HYGROSCOPIC
NUJOL MULL

C 11,785-4 **Tri-n-octylphosphine**
$[CH_3(CH_2)_7]_3P$ M.W. 370.65 n_D^{20} 1.4680
b.p. 285°/50 mm.
NEAT

D 15,339-7
Tri-*n*-octylphosphine oxide, 97%
$[CH_3(CH_2)_7]_3P(O)$
M.W. 386.65 m.p. 51-53° b.p. 180-205°
MELT

E 17,790-3
Tris-(hydroxymethyl)-phosphine oxide
(phosphinylidynetrimethanol)
$(HOCH_2)_3P(O)$
M.W. 140.08 m.p. 53-55°
MELT

F 16,354-6
Tris-(2-cyanoethyl)-phosphine (3,3',3''-phosphinidyne-tripropionitrile)
$(NCCH_2CH_2)_3P$
M.W. 193.19 m.p. 98-100° b.p. 235°/0.9mm.
NUJOL MULL

G 11,910-5 **Trilauryl trithiophosphite**
$[CH_3(CH_2)_{11}S]_3P$ M.W. 635.16
n_D^{20} 1.4990
NEAT

H T8620-7 **Tris-(diethylaminomethyl)-phosphine**
$[(C_2H_5)_2NCH_2]_3P$ M.W. 289.45 n_D^{20} 1.4795
NEAT

A

16,357-0
Tris-(2-carbamoylethyl)-phosphine oxide, 98%
(3,3',3''-phosphinylidynetripropionamide)
$(H_2NCOCH_2CH_2)_3P(O)$
M.W. 263.23 m.p. 211-213° *HYGROSCOPIC*

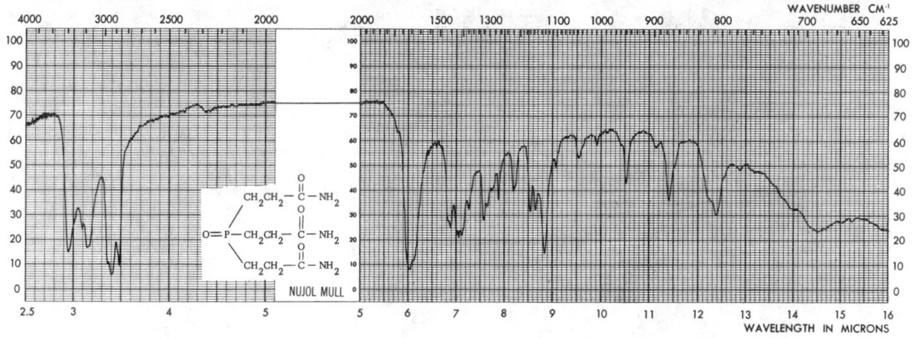

NUJOL MULL

B

T7970-7 **Trimethyl phosphite** (methyl phosphite)
$(CH_3O)_3P$ M.W. 124.08 n_D^{20} 1.4057

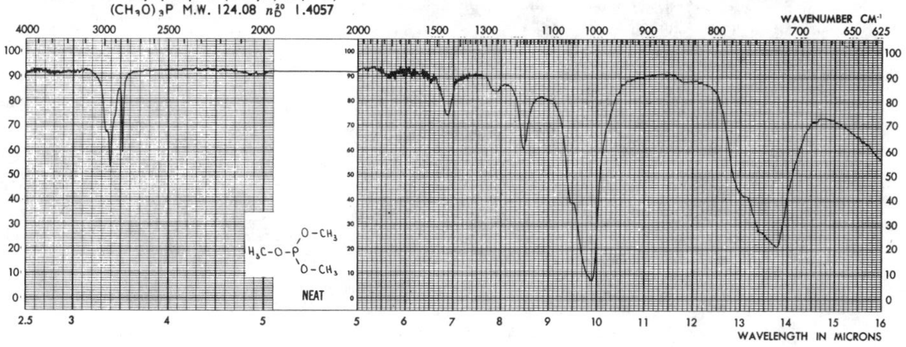

NEAT

C

T6120-4 **Triethyl phosphite**
$(C_2H_5O)_3P$ M.W. 166.16 n_D^{20} 1.4133
b.p. 156.5°

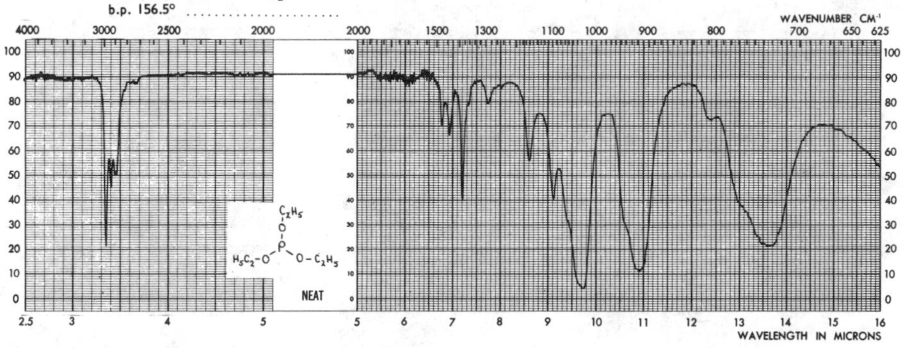

NEAT

D

T6780-6 **Triisopropyl phosphite**
$[(CH_3)_2CHO]_3P$ M.W. 208.24 n_D^{20} 1.4101
b.p. 63-64°/11 mm.

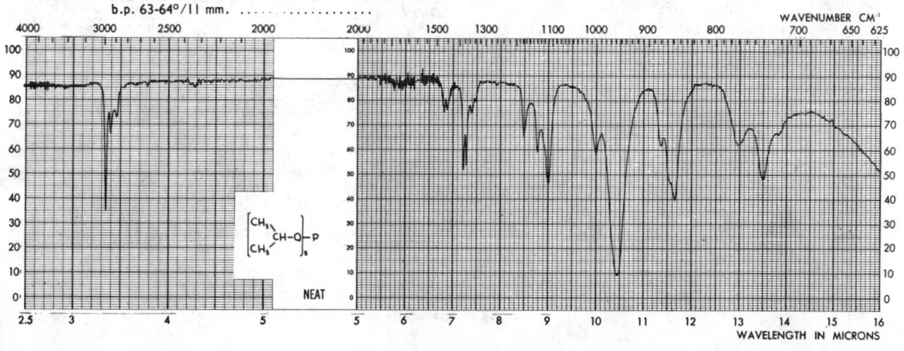

NEAT

E

15,860-7
Tributyl phosphite
$[CH_3(CH_2)_3O]_3P$
M.W. 250.32 b.p. 118-125°/7mm. n_D^{20} 1.4326
d 0.925 Beil. **1**(1),187

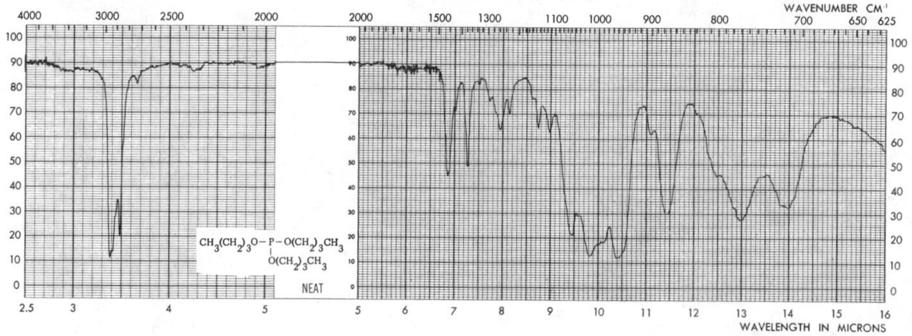

NEAT

F

T8540-5 **Tris-(2-chloroethyl) phosphite, tech.**
$(ClCH_2CH_2O)_3P$ M.W. 269.49 n_D^{20} 1.4868
b.p. 119°/0.15 mm.

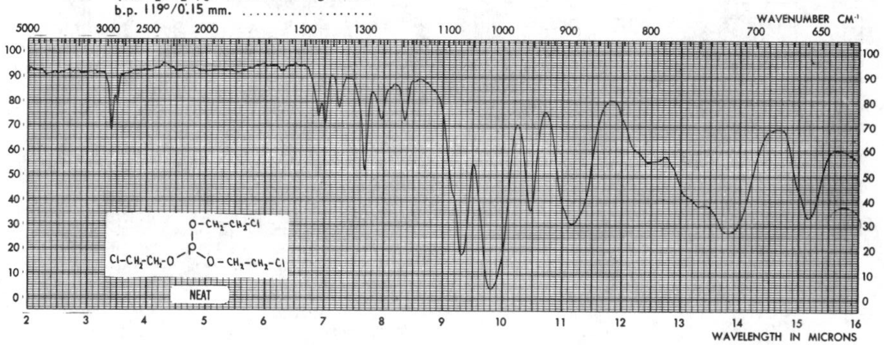

NEAT

G

T4560-8 **Triallyl phosphite**
$(H_2C{:}CHCH_2O)_3P$ M.W. 202.19 n_D^{20} 1.4579
b.p. 84°/12 mm.

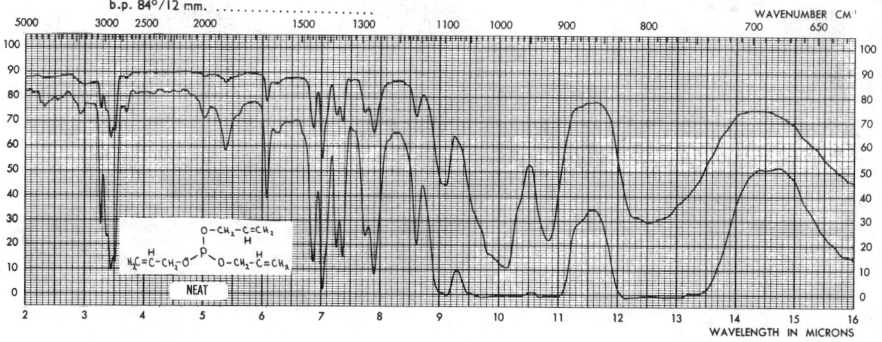

NEAT

H

15,505-5 **4-Ethyl-1-phospha-2,6,7-trioxabicyclo[2.2.2]octane**
(2-ethyl-2-hydroxymethyl-1,3-propanediol cyclic phosphite)
M.W. 162.13 m.p. 51-53°

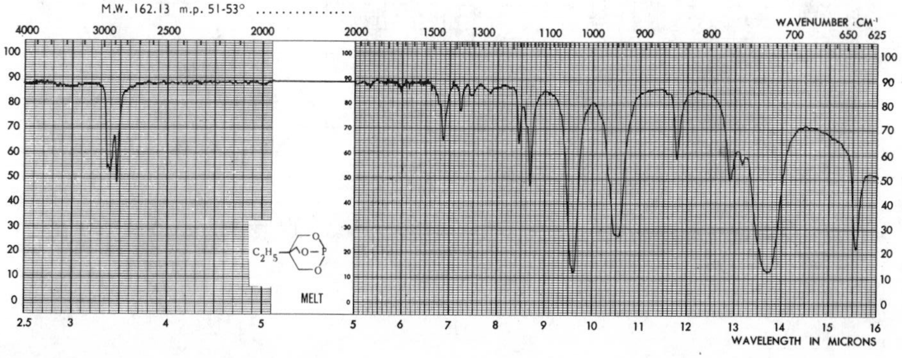

MELT

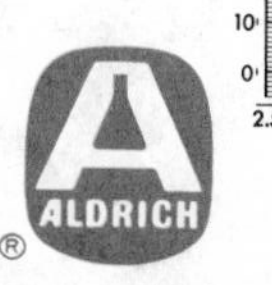

A D9165-9 **Diethyl chlorophosphite** (diethyl chlorophosphonite, diethyl phosphorochloridite)
$(C_2H_5O)_2PCl$ M.W. 156.55
n_D^{20} 1.4341
NEAT

B 19,747-5
Ethyl dichlorophosphite (ethyl phosphorodichloridite)
$C_2H_5OPCl_2$ FW 146.94 bp 117-118° n_D^{20} 1.4645
d 1.286 *Beil.* 1,331 Disp. C
NEAT

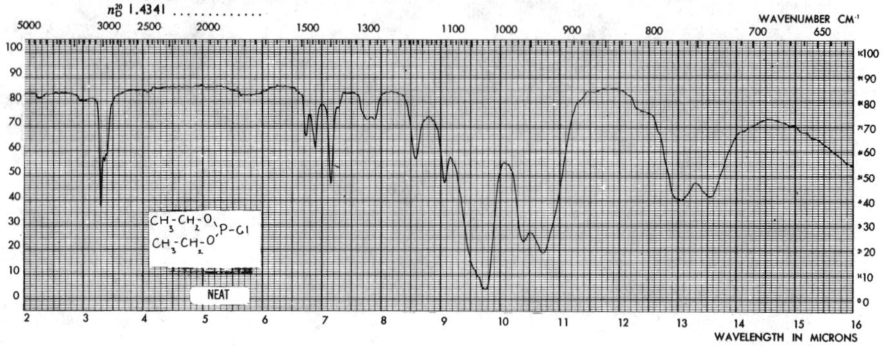

C 21,954-1
2,2,2-Trichloroethyl phosphorodichloridite, 97%
$CCl_3CH_2OPCl_2$ bp 42°/0.100mm. n_D^{20} 1.5211
d 1.606 Disp. K
NEAT

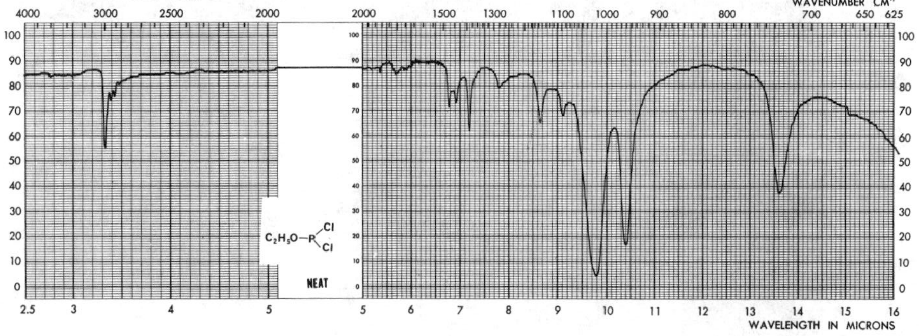

D D17,845-4 **Dimethyl phosphite**
$(CH_3O)_2P(O)H$ M.W. 110.05 n_D^{20} 1.4009
NEAT

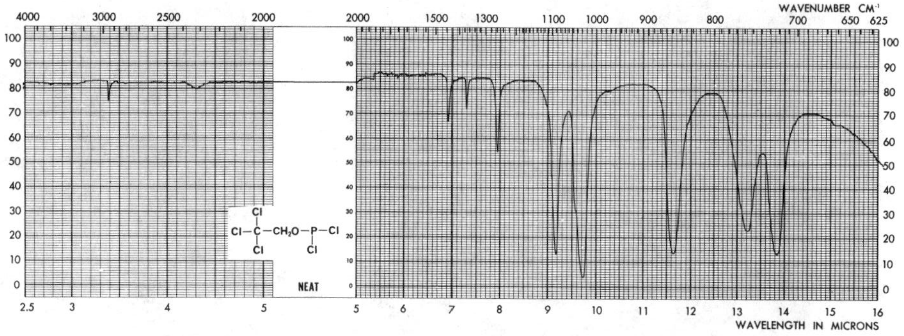

E E2760-2 **Ethylene phosphite**
M.W. 108.03 n_D^{20} 1.4848
NEAT

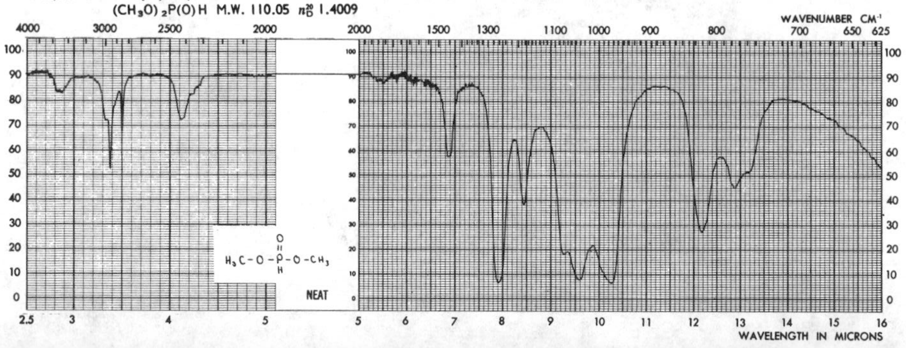

F D9923-4 **Diethyl phosphite**
$(C_2H_5O)_2P(O)H$ M.W. 138.10 n_D^{20} 1.4076
NEAT

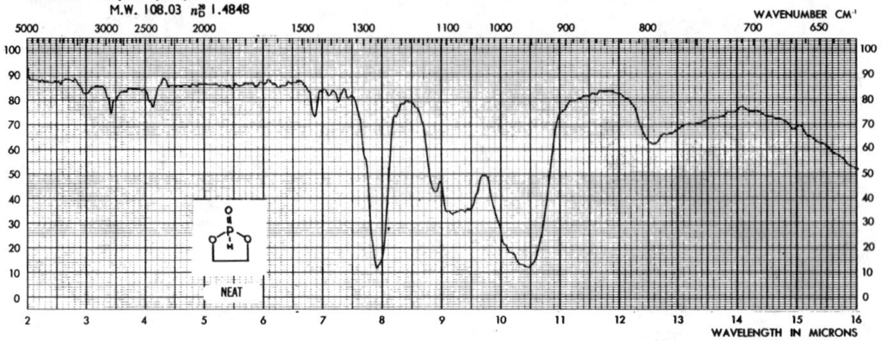

G D21,610 **Di-n-propyl phosphite**
$(C_3H_7O)_2P(O)H$ M.W. 166.16 n_D^{20} 1.4162
NEAT

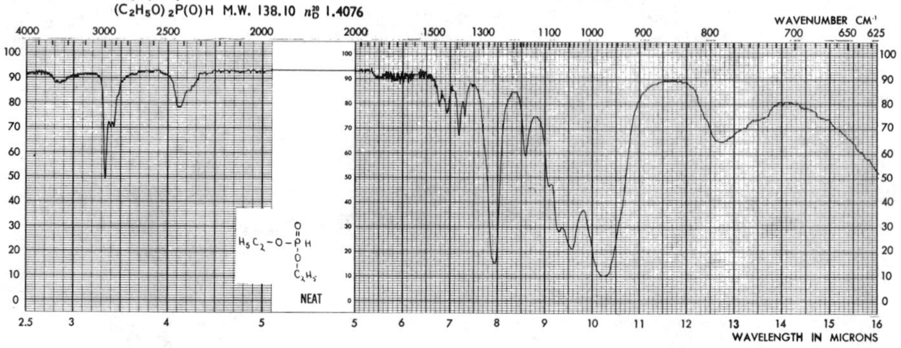

H D12,670-5 **Diisopropyl phosphite**
$[(CH_3)_2CHO]_2P(O)H$ M.W. 166.16 n_D^{20} 1.4070
NEAT

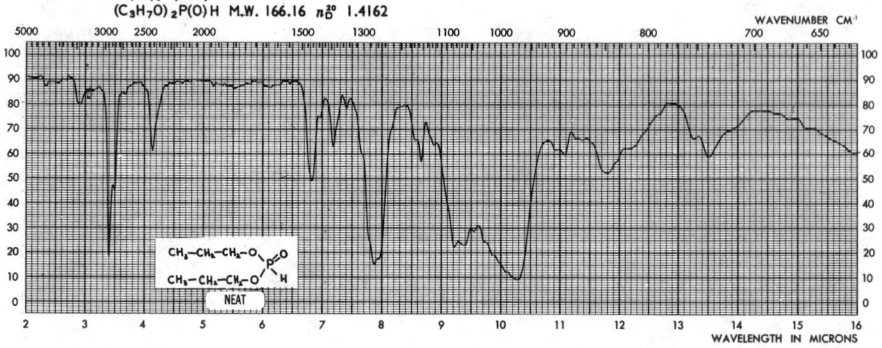

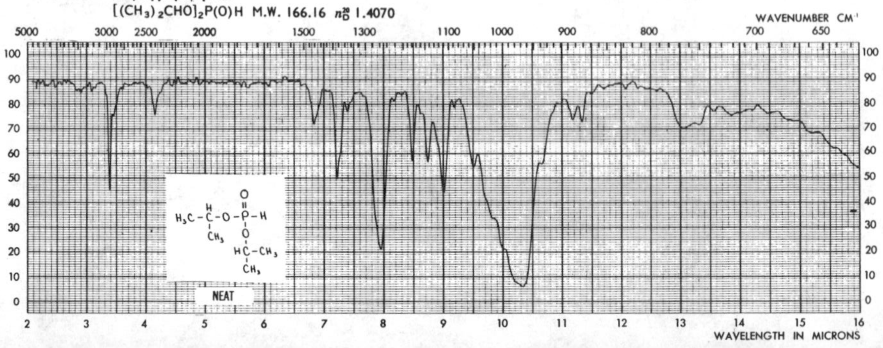

A 12,593-8 Dibutyl phosphite
$[CH_3(CH_2)_3O]_2P(O)H$ M.W. 194.21
n_D^{20} 1.4231 NEAT

B D12,800-7 Dilauryl phosphite
$[CH_3(CH_2)_{11}O]_2P(O)H$ M.W. 418.64
n_D^{20} 1.4520 NEAT

C 11,909-1 Di-n-octadecyl phosphite
$[CH_3(CH_2)_{17}O]_2P(O)H$ M.W. 586.97
m.p. 56.5-59.5° NUJOL MULL

D 15,858-5
Diallyl phosphite, 95%
$(H_2C{=}CHCH_2O)_2P(O)H$
M.W. 162.13 b.p. 62°/1mm. n_D^{20} 1.4487
IRRITANT NEAT

E 15,856-9
Triallyl phosphite, 95%
$(H_2C{=}CHCH_2O)_3P$
M.W. 202.19 b.p. 84°/12mm. n_D^{20} 1.4610
IRRITANT NEAT

F T5510-7 Trichloromethylphosphonic acid
$CCl_3P(O)(OH)_2$ M.W. 199.36 m.p. 84-87° NUJOL MULL

G D16,910-2 Dimethyl methylphosphonate
$(CH_3O)_2P(O)CH_3$ M.W. 124.08
n_D^{20} 1.4117 NEAT

H D9115-2 Diethyl 2-bromoethylphosphonate
$(C_2H_5O)_2P(O)CH_2CH_2Br$ M.W. 245.07
n_D^{20} 1.4600 NEAT

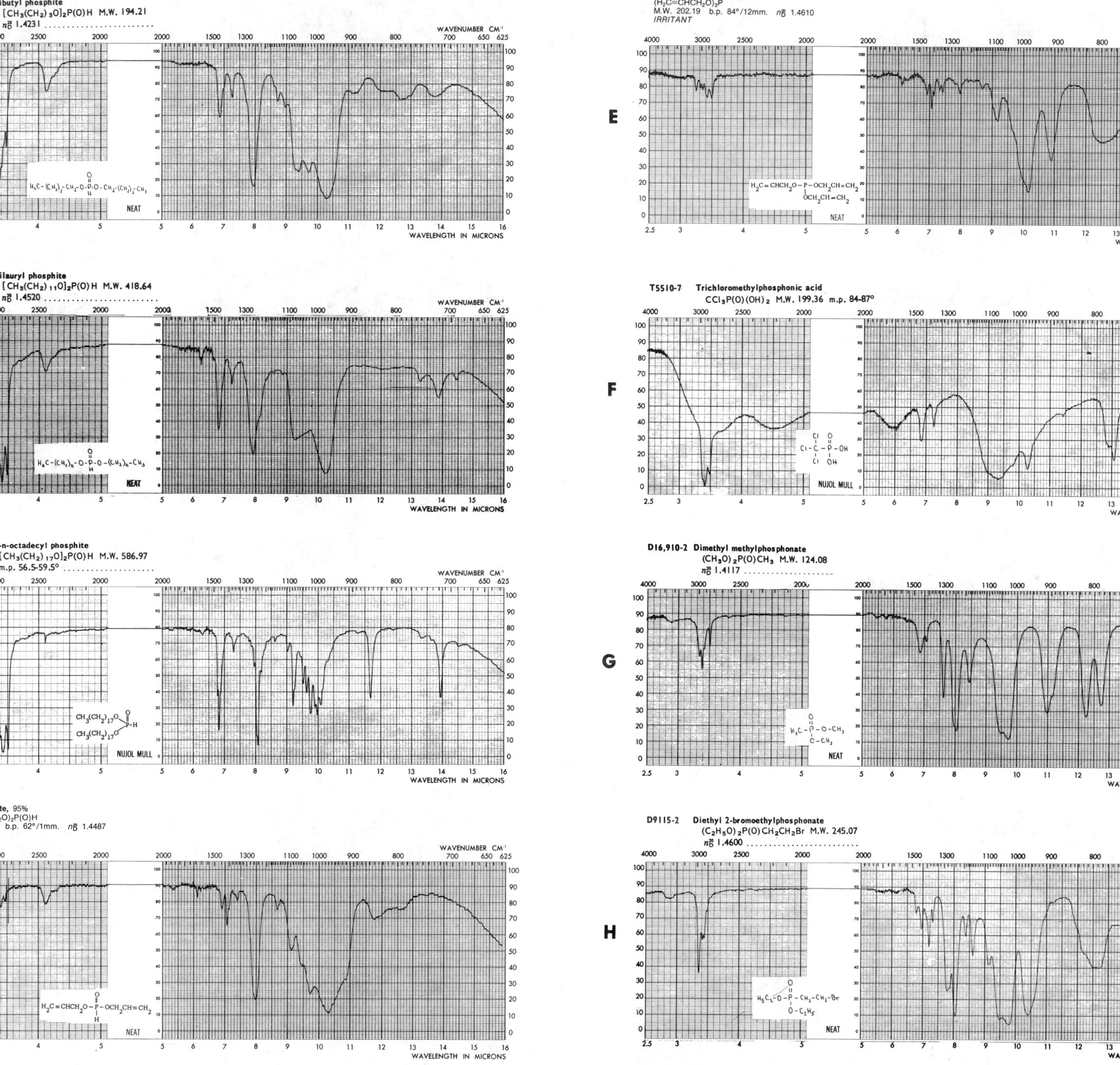

A

15,653-1
Diethyl (ethylthiomethyl)-phosphonate
$C_2H_5SCH_2P(O)(OC_2H_5)_2$
M.W. 212.25 n_D^{20} 1.4640

NEAT

B

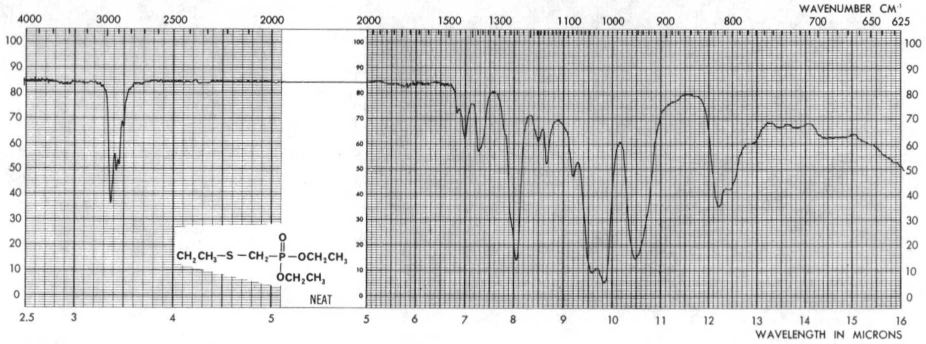

D9925-0 **Diethyl phosphonoacetaldehyde diethyl acetal**
$(C_2H_5O)_2P(O)CH_2CH(OC_2H_5)_2$ M.W. 254.26
n_D^{20} 1.4275

NEAT

C

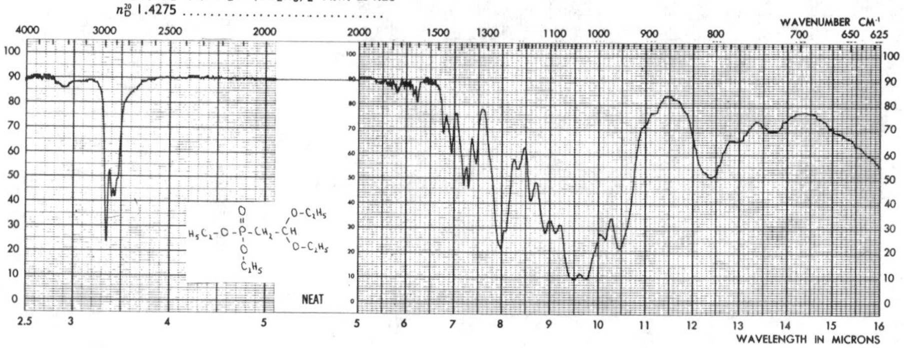

11,613-0 **Diethyl vinylphosphonate**
$(C_2H_5O)_2P(O)CH{:}CH_2$ M.W. 164.14
n_D^{20} 1.4268 b.p. 260°/2 mm.

NEAT

D

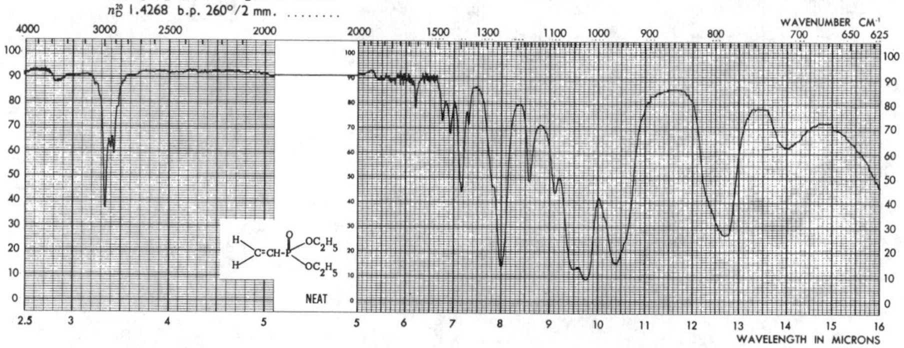

D940-9 **Diallyl allylphosphonate**
$(H_2C{:}CHCH_2O)_2P(O)CH_2CH{:}CH_2$ M.W. 202.19 n_D^{20} 1.4617

NEAT

E

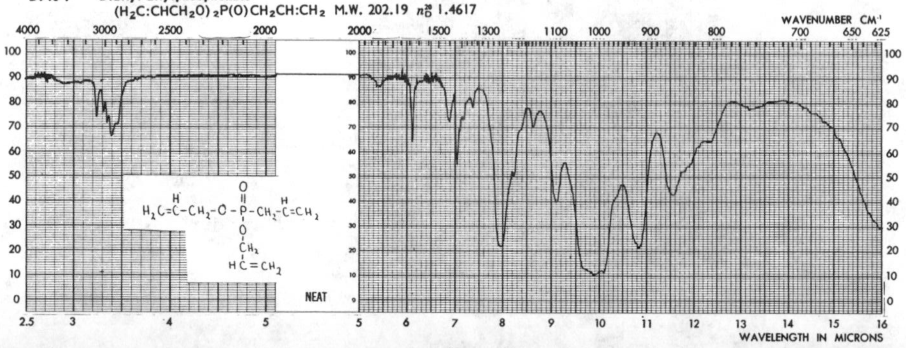

18,069-6
Dimethyl (2-oxopropyl)phosphonate, 95%
$CH_3COCH_2P(O)(OCH_3)_2$ FW 166.02
bp 76-79°/3mm. n_D^{20} 1.4391 Disp. C

NEAT

F

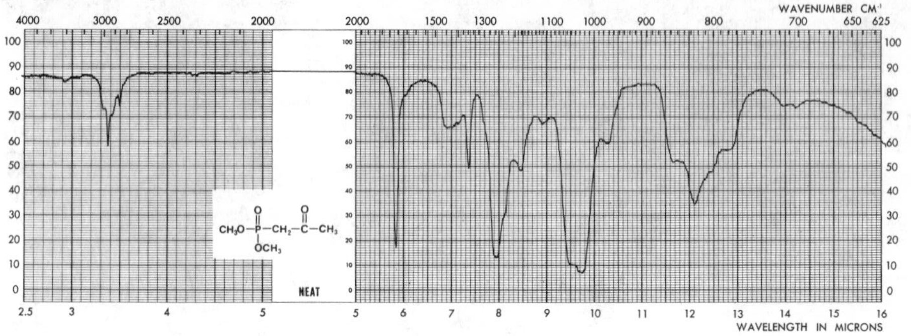

15,793-7
Dimethyl (2-oxoheptyl)-phosphonate
$CH_3(CH_2)_4COCH_2P(O)(OCH_3)_2$
M.W. 222.22 b.p. 109°/0.4mm. n_D^{20} 1.4450

NEAT

G

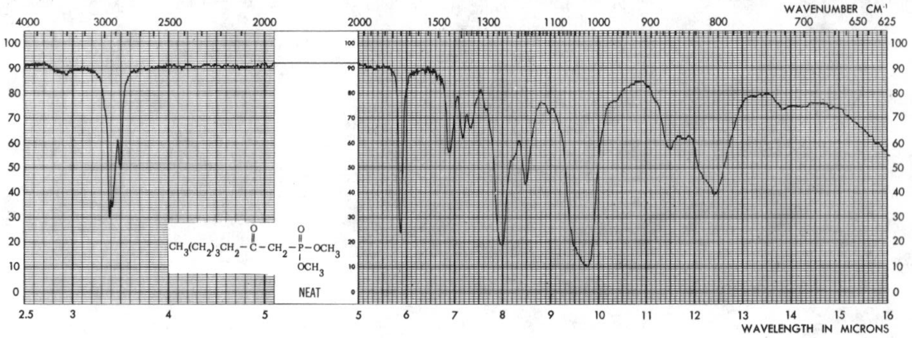

13,511-9 **Ethyl diethoxyphosphinylformate**
$(C_2H_5O)_2P(O)CO_2C_2H_5$ M.W. 210.17
n_D^{20} 1.4230

NEAT

H

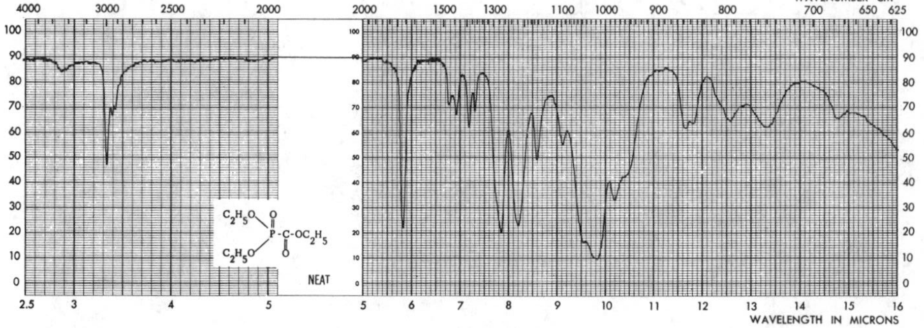

T7975-8 **Trimethyl phosphonoacetate**
$(CH_3O)_2P(O)CH_2CO_2CH_3$ M.W. 182.12
n_D^{20} 1.4370

NEAT

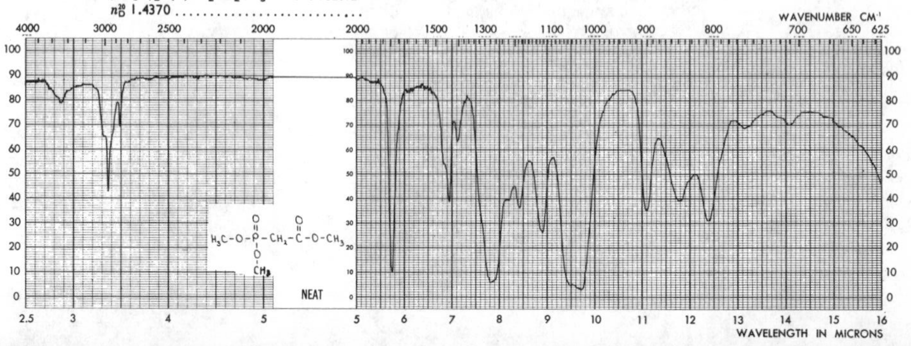

A

15,876-3
Methyl diethylphosphonoacetate, 98%
$(C_2H_5O)_2P(O)CH_2CO_2CH_3$
M.W. 210.17 b.p. 127-131°/9mm. n_D^{20} 1.4335
Beil. **4**(2),976

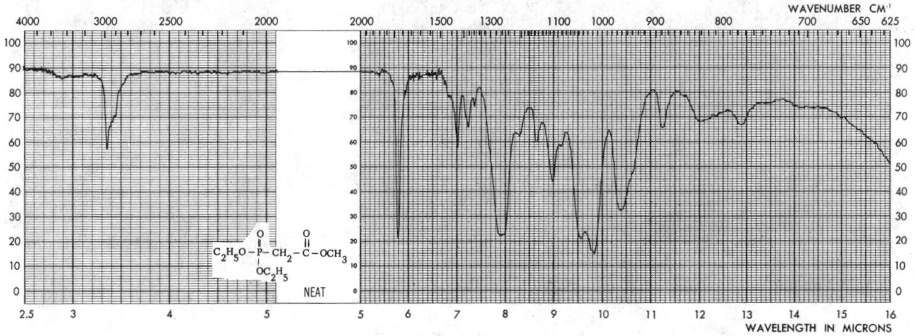

NEAT

B

T6130-1 **Triethyl phosphonoacetate**
$(C_2H_5O)_2P(O)CH_2CO_2C_2H_5$ M.W. 224.19 n_D^{20} 1.4315
b.p. 142.5-145.5°/9 mm.

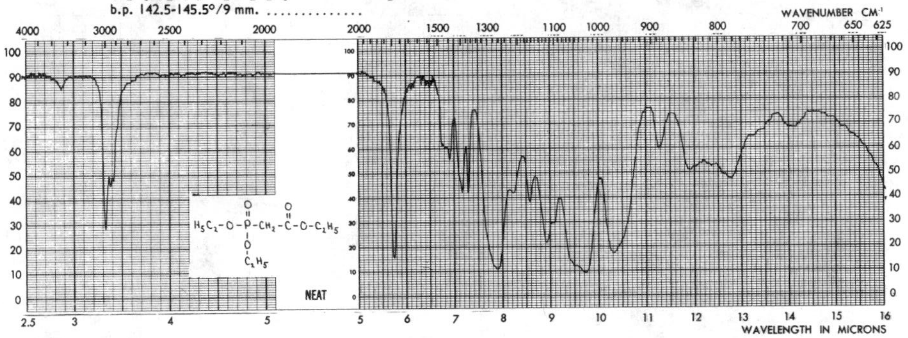

NEAT

C

17,465-3
Triethyl 2-phosphonopropionate
$(C_2H_5O)_2P(O)CH(CH_3)CO_2C_2H_5$ FW 238.22
bp 143-144°/12mm. n_D^{20} 1.4320 d 1.111
Beil. **4**(1),573 Disp. C

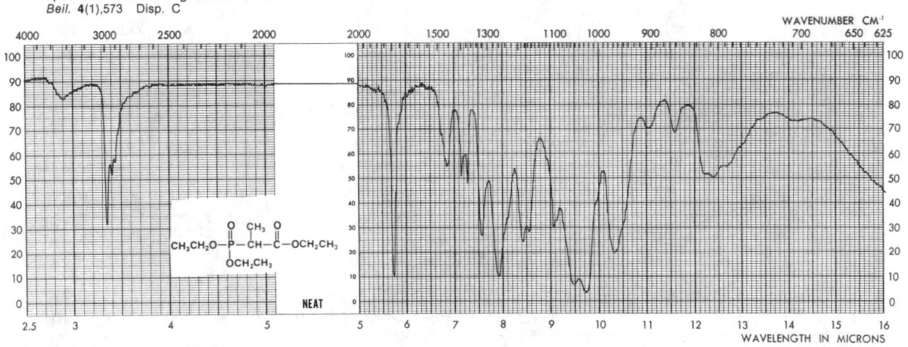

NEAT

D

11,609-2 **Triethyl 4-phosphonocrotonate**
$(C_2H_5O)_2P(O)CH_2CH:CHCO_2C_2H_5$ M.W. 250.23
n_D^{20} 1.4532 b.p. 135°/0.4 mm.

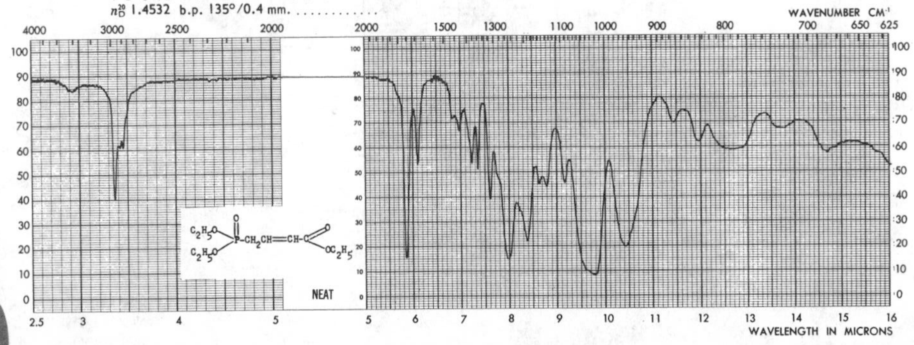

NEAT

E

D9170-5 **Diethyl cyanomethylphosphonate**
$(C_2H_5O)_2P(O)CH_2CN$ M.W. 177.14
n_D^{20} 1.4312

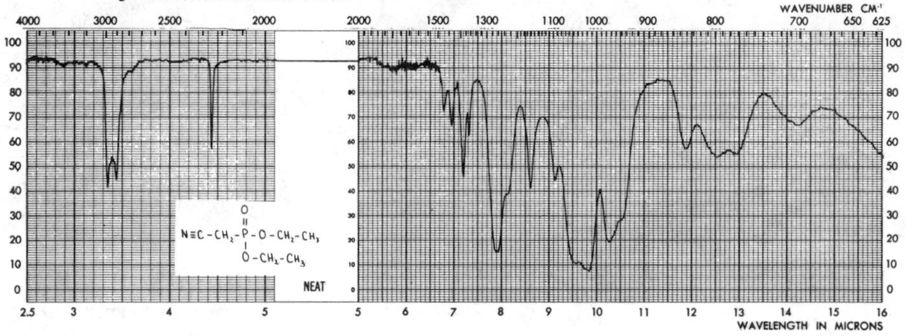

NEAT

F

19,569-3
2,2,2-Tribromoethyl phosphoromorpholinochloridate
FW 450.31 mp 80-83° Disp. C

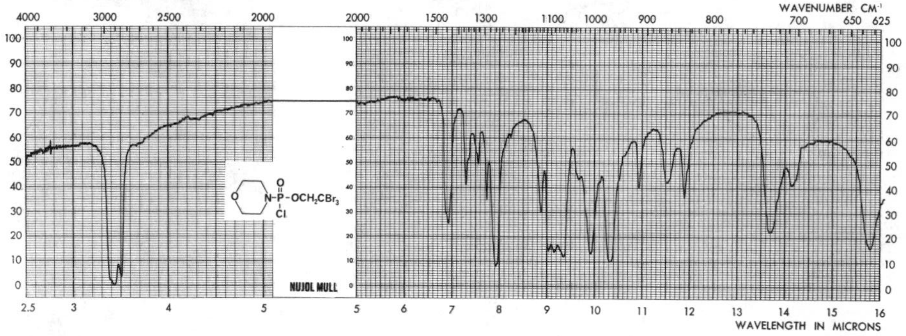

NUJOL MULL

G

21,870-7
Cyclophosphamide monohydrate, 98+%
FW 279.10 mp 49-51° Disp. C

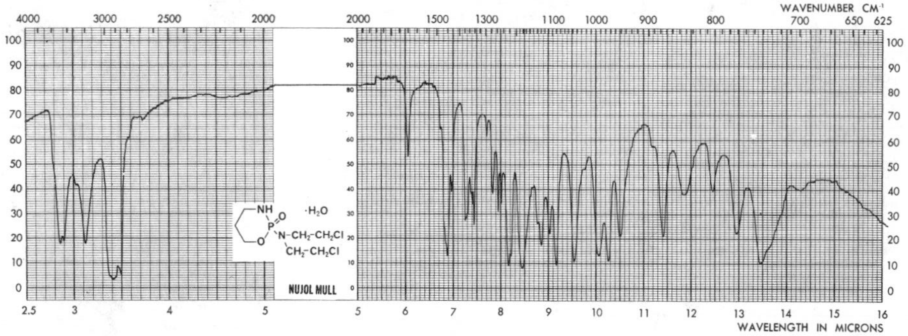

NUJOL MULL

H

16,393-7
Bis-(dimethylamino)-phosphorochloridate, tech., 90%
(tetramethylphosphorodiamidic chloride)
$[(CH_3)_2N]_2P(O)Cl$
M.W. 170.58 n_D^{20} 1.4656 *CORROSIVE*

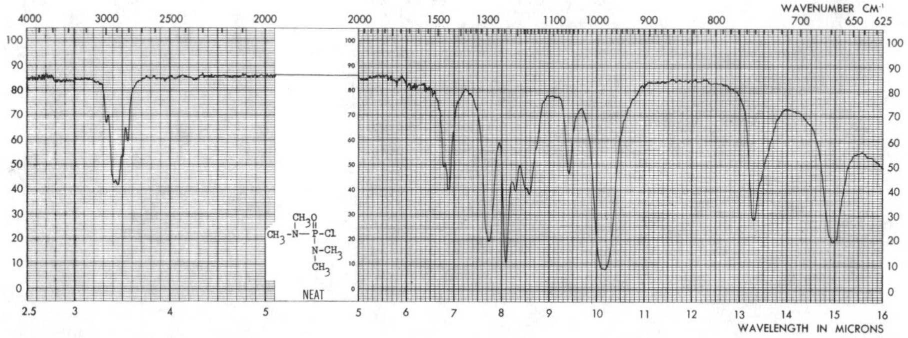

NEAT

WAVENUMBER CM⁻¹ — WAVELENGTH IN MICRONS

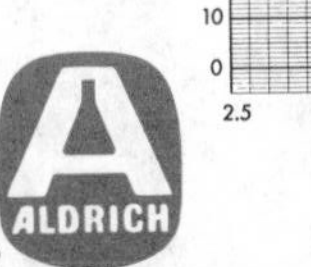

A 14,355-3 **Hexamethylphosphorous triamide**
(send for data sheet)
$[(CH_3)_2N]_3P$ M.W. 163.20 n_D^{20} 1.4633
b.p. 55-58°/15 mm.

B H1160-2 **Hexamethylphosphoramide** (hexamethylphosphoric triamide)
$[(CH_3)_2N]_3P(O)$ M.W. 179.20 n_D^{20} 1.4579
b.p. 66°/0.5 mm.

C 21,625-9
Tripiperidinophosphine oxide, 98%
FW 299.40 mp 40-42° *Beil.* **20**,88 Disp. C

D 11,424-3 **Diethyl methylamidophosphate** (diethyl methylphosphoramidate)
$(C_2H_5O)_2P(O)NHCH_3$ M.W. 167.15
n_D^{20} 1.4228 b.p. 102-105°/3 mm.

E 10,028-5 **Diethyl ethylamidophosphate** (diethyl ethylphosphoramidate)
$(C_2H_5O)_2P(O)NHC_2H_5$ M.W. 181.17 n_D^{20} 1.4220
b.p. 120°/3 mm.

F 11,652-1 **Diethyl isopropylamidophosphate** (diethyl isopropylphosphoramidate)
$(C_2H_5O)_2P(O)NHCH(CH_3)_2$ M.W. 195.20 n_D^{20} 1.4235
b.p. 100°/1 mm.

G 11,559-2 **Diethyl tert.-butylamidophosphate** (diethyl tert.-butylphosphoramidate)
$(C_2H_5O)_2P(O)NHC(CH_3)_3$ M.W. 209.23
n_D^{20} 1.4271 b.p. 25°/1 mm.

H 11,654-8 **Diethyl n-hexylamidophosphate** (diethyl n-hexylphosphoramidate)
$(C_2H_5O)_2P(O)NH(CH_2)_5CH_3$ M.W. 237.28
b.p. 118-120°/0.3 mm.

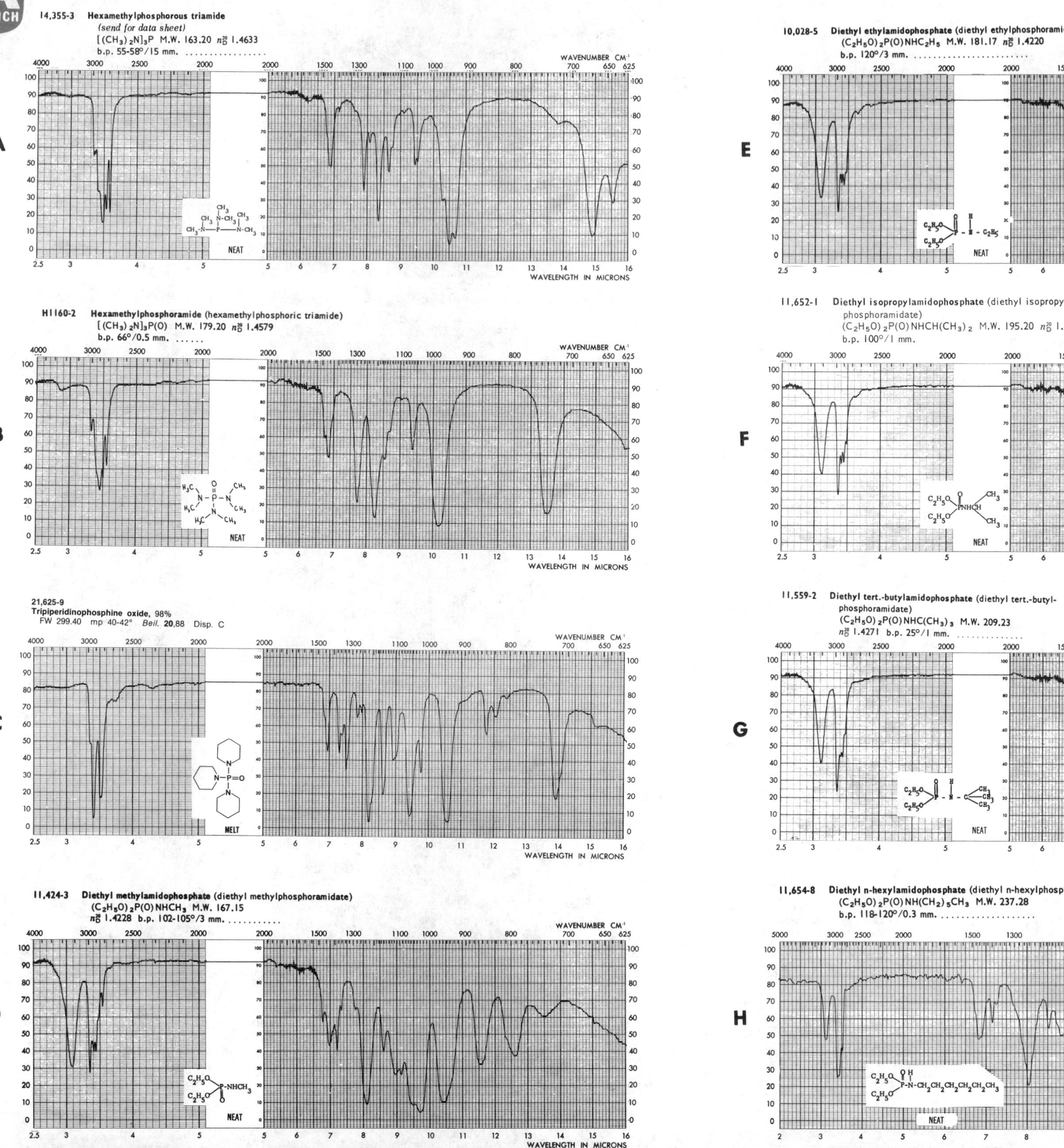

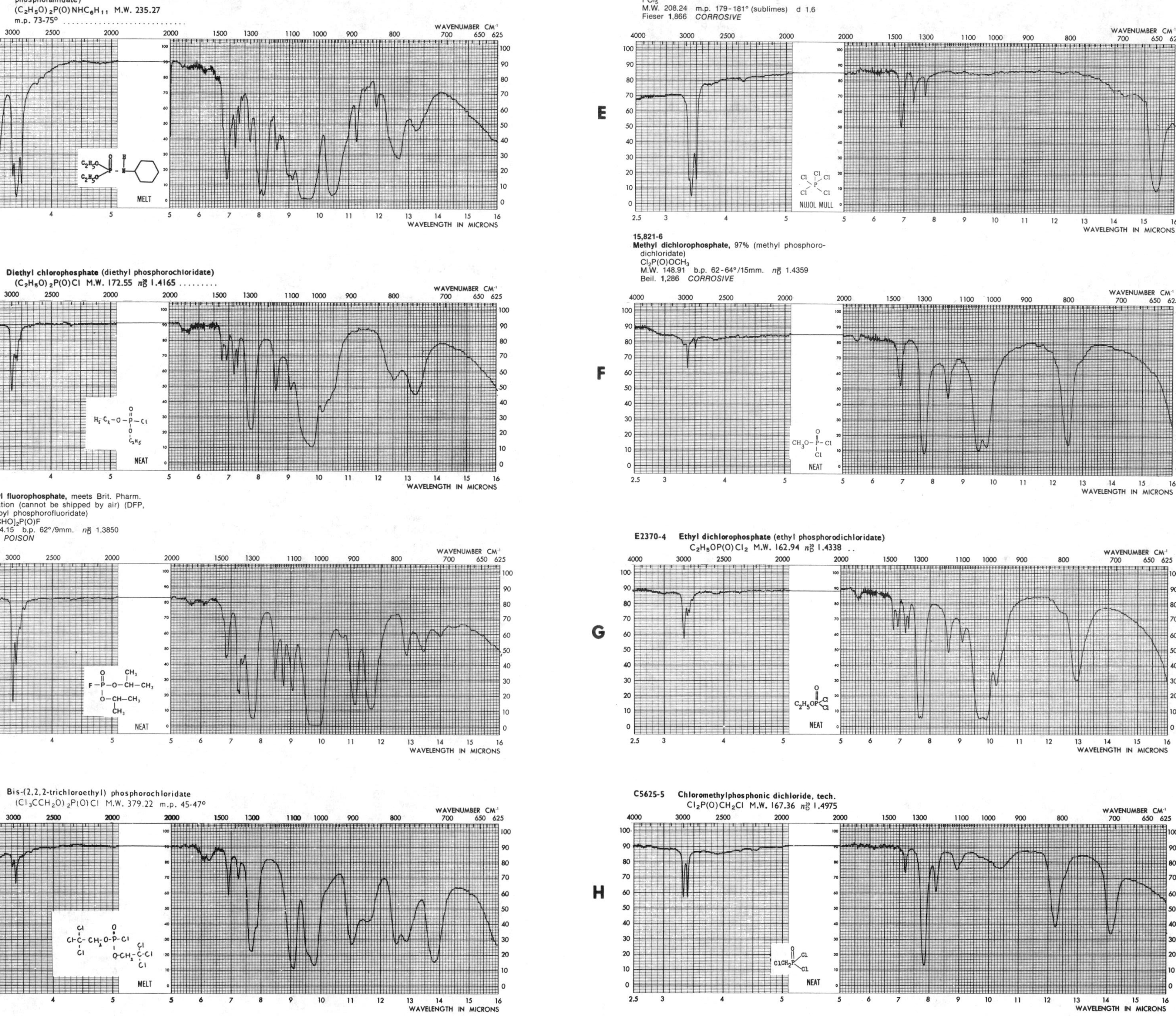

A

10,295-4 **Diethyl cyclohexylamidophosphate** (diethyl cyclohexylphosphoramidate)
$(C_2H_5O)_2P(O)NHC_6H_{11}$ M.W. 235.27
m.p. 73-75°

MELT

B

D9163-2 **Diethyl chlorophosphate** (diethyl phosphorochloridate)
$(C_2H_5O)_2P(O)Cl$ M.W. 172.55 n_D^{20} 1.4165

NEAT

C

D12,600-4
Diisopropyl fluorophosphate, meets Brit. Pharm. specification (cannot be shipped by air) (DFP, diisopropyl phosphorofluoridate)
$[(CH_3)_2CHO]_2P(O)F$
M.W. 184.15 b.p. 62°/9mm. n_D^{20} 1.3850
SEVERE POISON

NEAT

D

15,537-3 **Bis-(2,2,2-trichloroethyl) phosphorochloridate**
$(Cl_3CCH_2O)_2P(O)Cl$ M.W. 379.22 m.p. 45-47°

MELT

E

15,777-5
Phosphorus pentachloride
PCl_5
M.W. 208.24 m.p. 179-181° (sublimes) d 1.6
Fieser 1,866 *CORROSIVE*

NUJOL MULL

F

15,821-6
Methyl dichlorophosphate, 97% (methyl phosphorodichloridate)
$Cl_2P(O)OCH_3$
M.W. 148.91 b.p. 62-64°/15mm. n_D^{20} 1.4359
Beil. 1,286 *CORROSIVE*

NEAT

G

E2370-4 **Ethyl dichlorophosphate** (ethyl phosphorodichloridate)
$C_2H_5OP(O)Cl_2$ M.W. 162.94 n_D^{20} 1.4338

NEAT

H

C5625-5 **Chloromethylphosphonic dichloride, tech.**
$Cl_2P(O)CH_2Cl$ M.W. 167.36 n_D^{20} 1.4975

NEAT

WAVENUMBER CM⁻¹
WAVELENGTH IN MICRONS

A

D15,295-1 **Dimethyl chlorothiophosphate** (dimethyl phosphorochloridothionate)
$(CH_3O)_2P(S)Cl$ M.W. 160.56 n_D^{20} 1.4819

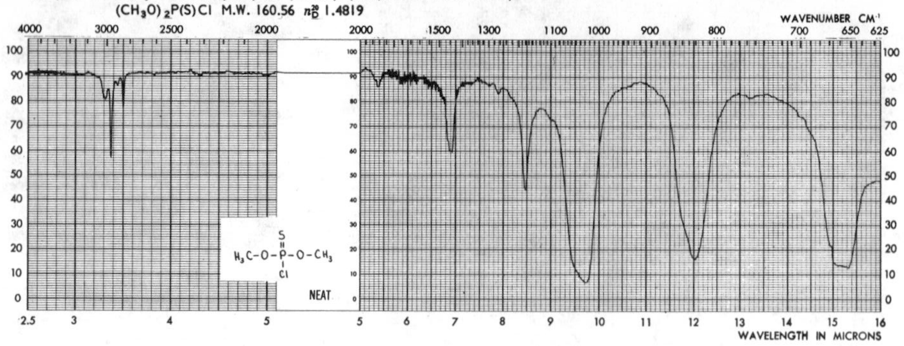

NEAT

B

D9168-3 **Diethyl chlorothiophosphate** (diethyl phosphorochloridothionate)
$(C_2H_5O)_2P(S)Cl$ M.W. 188.61 n_D^{20} 1.4715

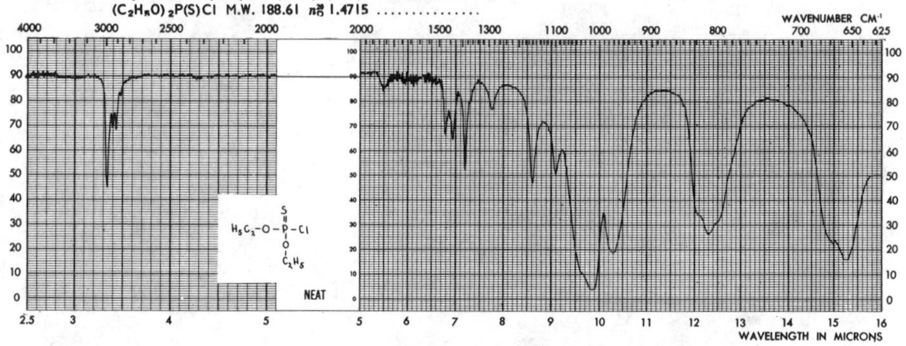

NEAT

C

D21,550 **Di-n-propyl chlorothiophosphate** (di-n-propyl phosphorochloridothionate)
$(C_3H_7O)_2P(S)Cl$ M.W. 216.67 n_D^{20} 1.4691

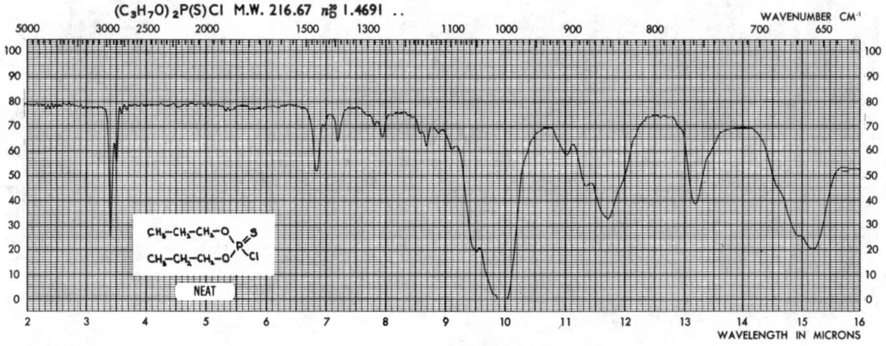

NEAT

D

22,429-4
Thiophosphoryl chloride, 98% (phosphorus sulfochloride)
$PSCl_3$ FW 169.40 mp -35° bp 125° n_D^{20} 1.6350
d 1.668 Disp. W

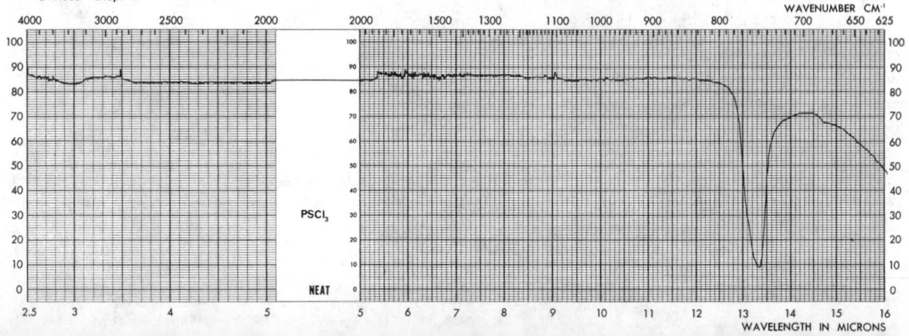

$PSCl_3$

NEAT

E

E2390-9 **Ethyl dichlorothiophosphate** (ethyl phosphorodichloridothionate)
$C_2H_5OP(S)Cl_2$ M.W. 179.01 n_D^{20} 1.5065

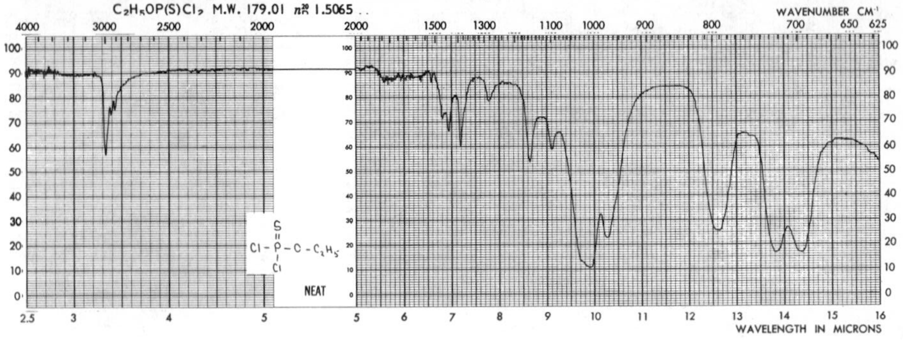

NEAT

F

D9360-0 **Diethyl dithiophosphate, tech.**
$(C_2H_5O)_2P(S)SH$ M.W. 186.23
n_D^{20} 1.5141

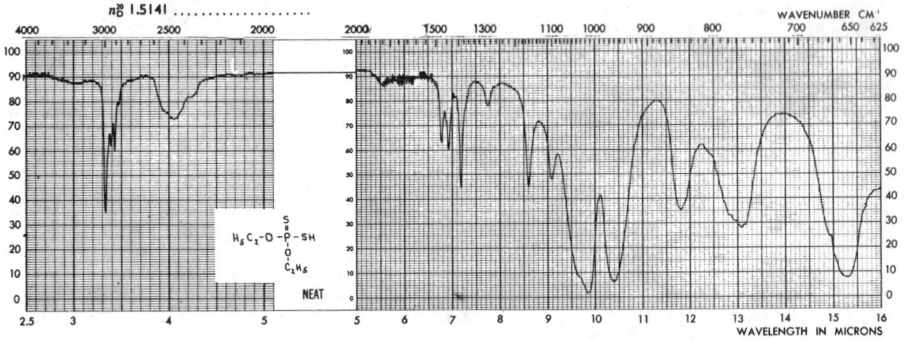

NEAT

G

14,182-8 **Methyl (dimethoxyphosphinothioylthio)-acetate**
$(CH_3O)_2P(S)SCH_2CO_2CH_3$ M.W. 230.24
n_D^{20} 1.5134

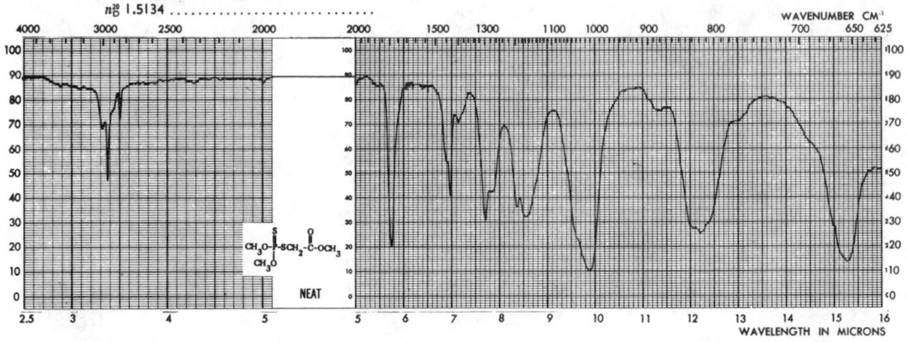

NEAT

H

11,248-8 **Trimethyl thiophosphate**
$(CH_3O)_3P(S)$ M.W. 156.14 n_D^{20} 1.4540

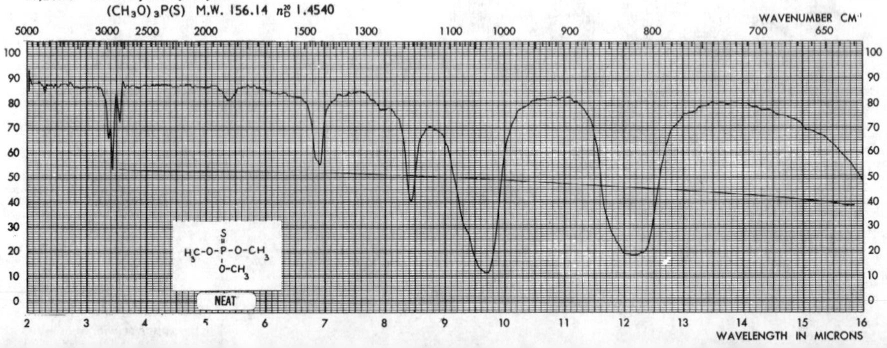

NEAT

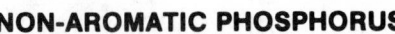

A

T6170-0 **Triethyl thiophosphate** (O,O,O-triethyl phosphorothioate)
$(C_2H_5O)_3P(S)$ M.W. 198.22 n_D^{20} 1.4463 b.p. 94°/10 mm

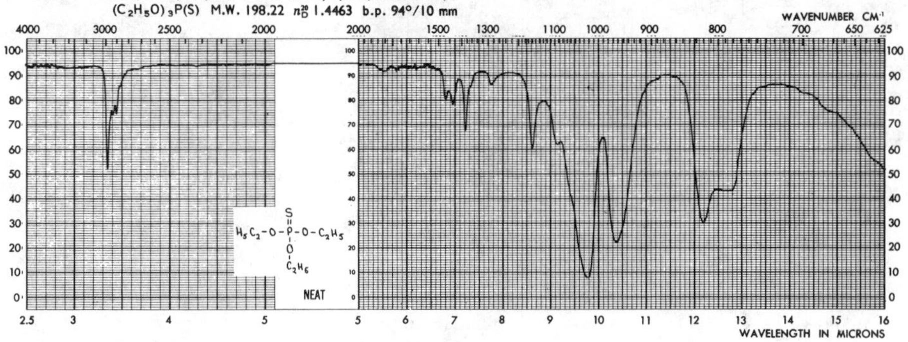

NEAT

B

13,219-5 **Trimethyl phosphate**
$(CH_3O)_3P(O)$ M.W. 140.08 n_D^{20} 1.3958
b.p. 197.2°

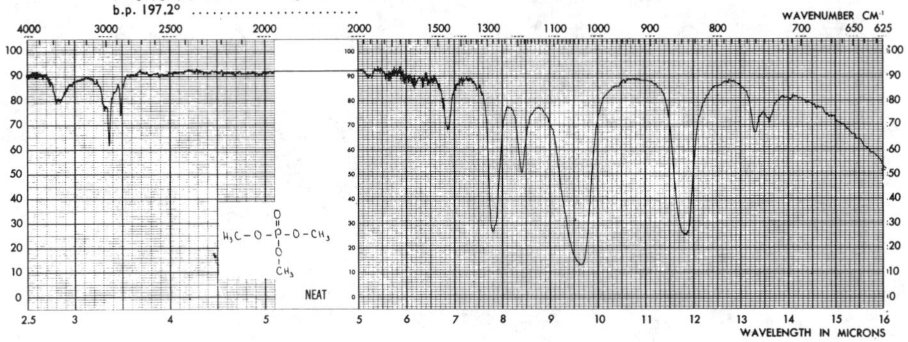

NEAT

C

T6110-7 **Triethyl phosphate (ethyl phosphate)**
$(C_2H_5O)_3P(O)$ M.W. 182.16 n_D^{20} 1.4038

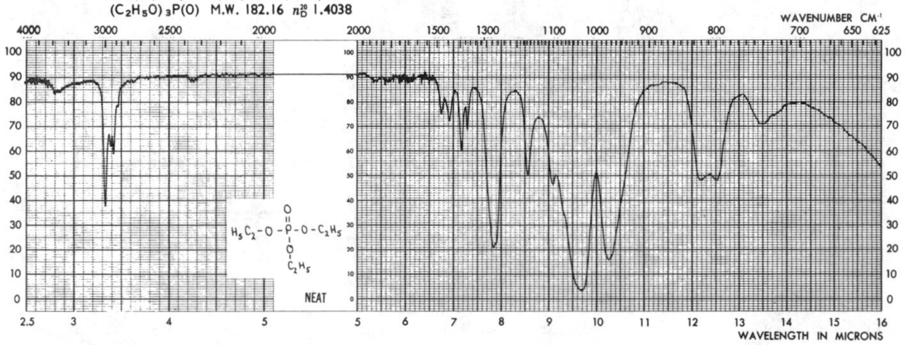

NEAT

D

15,861-5
Tributyl phosphate
$[CH_3(CH_2)_3O]_3P(O)$
M.W. 266.32 b.p. 180-183°/22mm. n_D^{20} 1.4245
d 0.979 Beil. **1**(2),397 *IRRITANT*

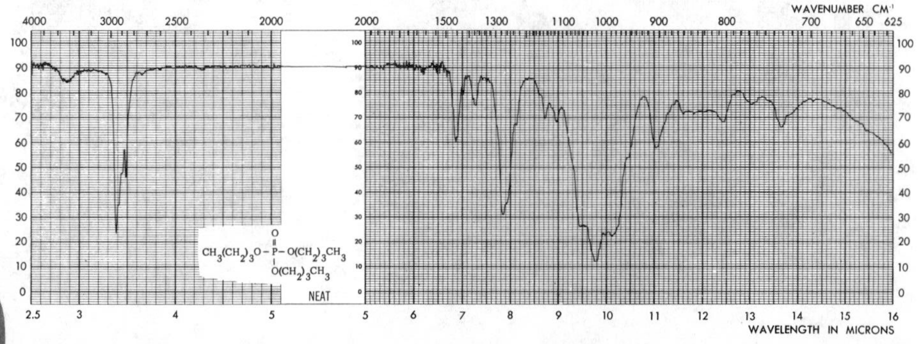

NEAT

E

11,966-0 **Tris-(2-chloroethyl) phosphate**
$(ClCH_2CH_2O)_3P(O)$ M.W. 285.49 n_D^{20} 1.4721
b.p. 214°/25 mm.

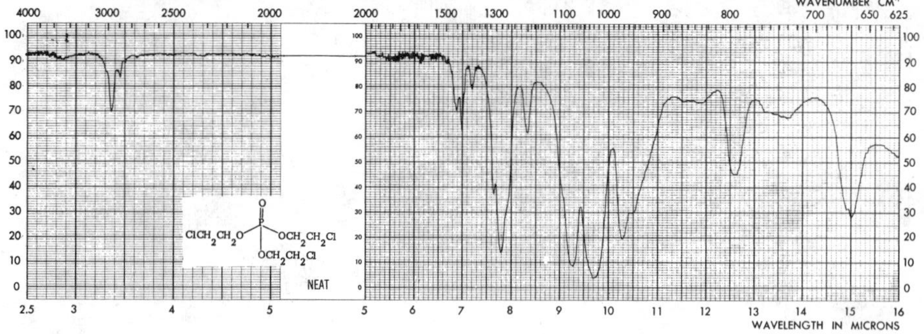

NEAT

F

17,168-9
Tris-(2,3-dibromopropyl) phosphate, 97%
$[BrCH_2CH(Br)CH_2O]_3P(O)$
M.W. 697.64 n_D^{20} 1.5755 d 2.24
Flame retardant and pesticide.

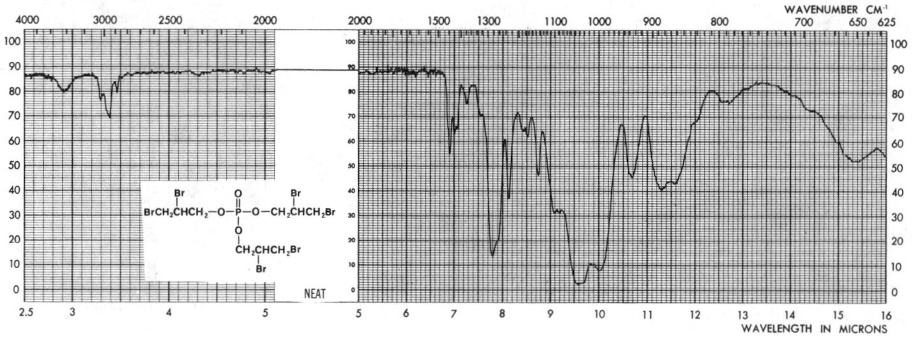

NEAT

G

13,059-1 **Tris-(butoxyethyl) phosphate**
$[CH_3(CH_2)_3OCH_2CH_2O]_3P(O)$ M.W. 398.48
n_D^{20} 1.4359

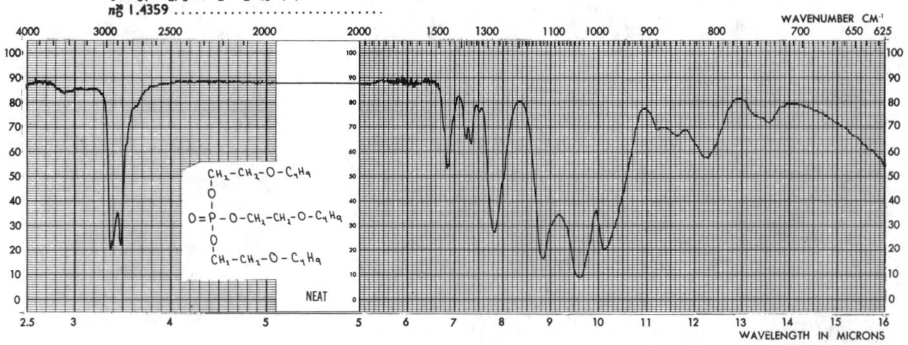

NEAT

H

T4540-3 **Triallyl phosphate**
$(H_2C{:}CHCH_2O)_3P(O)$ M.W. 218.19 n_D^{20} 1.4498
b.p. 80-82°/0.1 mm.

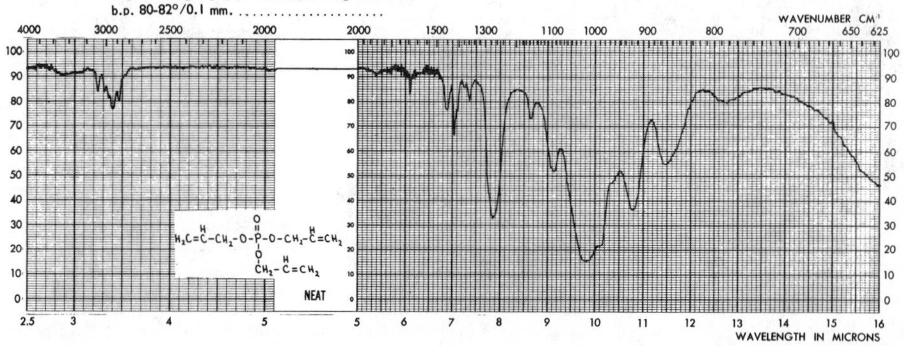

NEAT

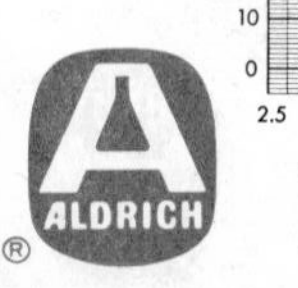

ALDRICH ®

A 15,541-1 **Tetraethyl pyrophosphite**
$(C_2H_5O)_2POP(OC_2H_5)_2$ M.W. 258.19
NEAT

B 10,505-8 **Dimethyl acid pyrophosphate**
$[CH_3OP(OH)(O)]_2O$ M.W. 206.03 n_D^{20} 1.4262
NEAT

C T1100 **Tetraethyl dithiopyrophosphate**
$[(C_2H_5O)_2P(S)]_2O$
NEAT

D D20,110-3 **Di-n-octadecyl phosphate**
$[CH_3(CH_2)_{17}O]_2P(O)OH$ M.W. 602.97 m.p. 79-82°
NUJOL MULL

E 14,623-4 **2-Cyanoethyl phosphate, barium salt dihydrate** (contaminated with barium acetate)
$NCCH_2CH_2OPO_3Ba{\cdot}2H_2O$ M.W. 322.41
m.p. > 300°
NUJOL MULL

F 17,778-4
Dimethyl dithiophosphate, ammonium salt, 95%
$(CH_3O)_2P(S)SNH_4$
M.W. 175.21 m.p. 143-145° (dec.)
NUJOL MULL

G 17,779-2
Diethyl dithiophosphate, ammonium salt, 95%
$(C_2H_5O)_2P(S)SNH_4$
M.W. 203.26 m.p. 164-166°
NUJOL MULL

H 16,359-7
Dicyclohexyldithiophosphinic acid, ammonium salt hydrate (dicyclohexylphosphinodithioic acid)
$(C_6H_{11})_2PS_2NH_4{\cdot}xH_2O$
M.W. 279.45 m.p. 190-194° (dec.)
NUJOL MULL

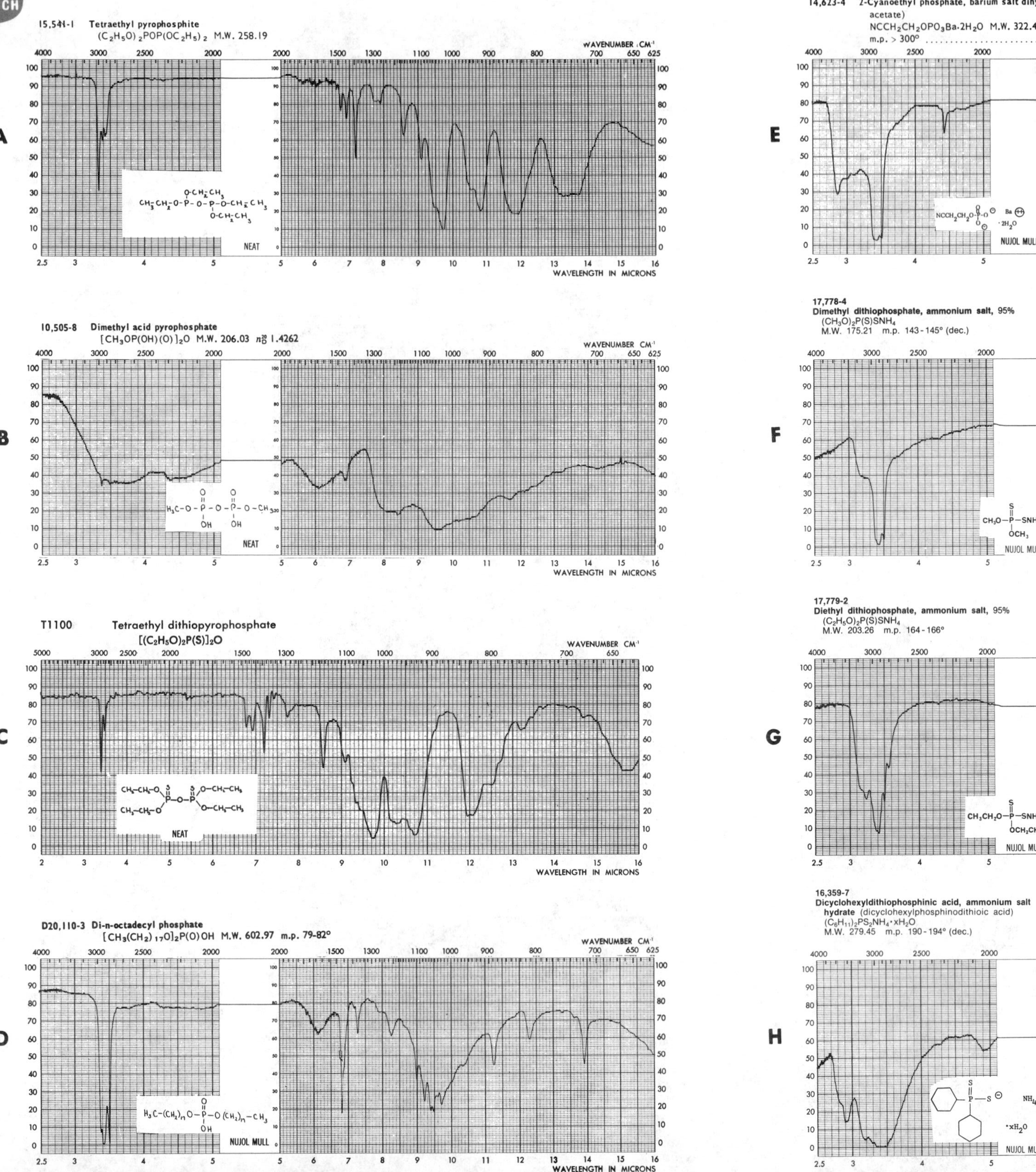

A

15,543-8 p-Dioxane diphosphate
M.W. 284.10 ....

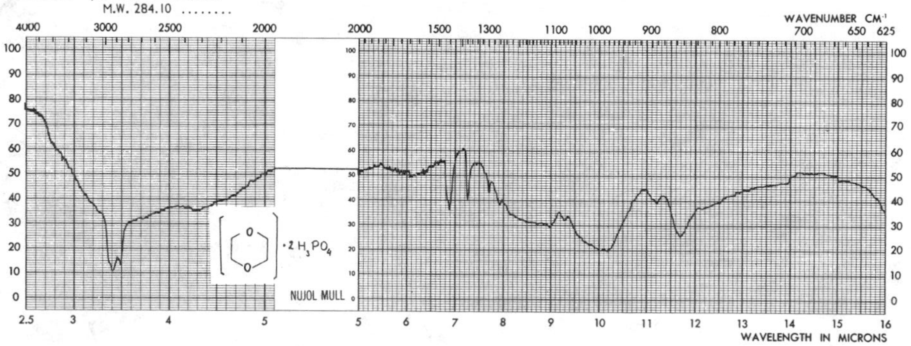

B

86,007-7
Phosphoenolpyruvic acid, monopotassium salt, 99% (PEP)
KOP(O)(OH)OC(=CH_2)CO_2H FW 206.14
mp 175-179° (dec.) *Fieser* 7,3 Disp. L

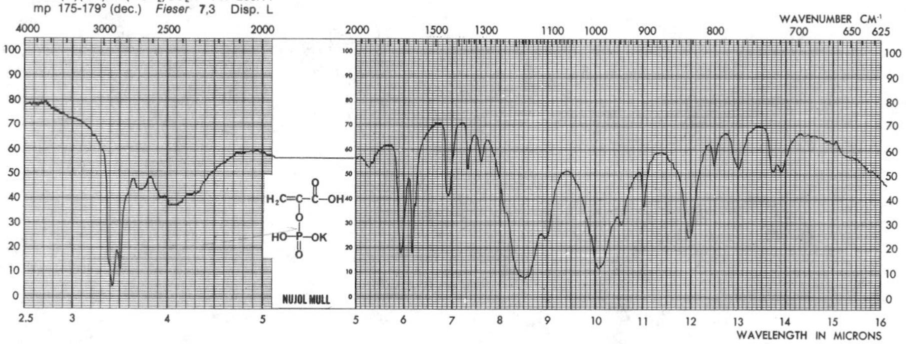

C

85,858-7
Phosphoenolpyruvic acid, tri(cyclohexylamine) salt (PEP)
$(C_6H_{11}NH_3)_3[O_2P(O)OC(=CH_2)CO_2]$
M.W. 465.58 m.p. 197-198° (dec.)

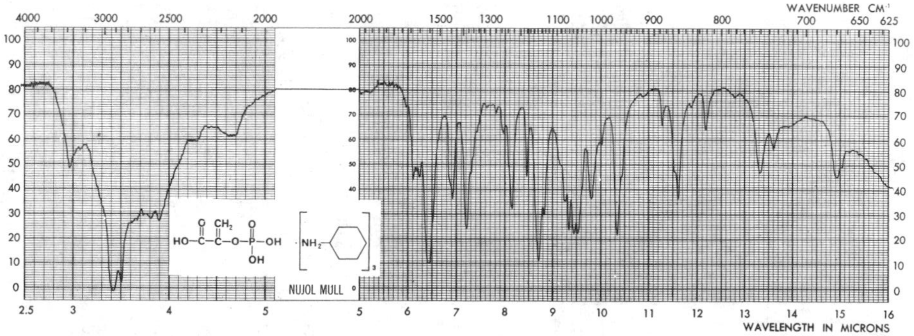

D

85,912-5
D-Fructose-1,6-diphosphate, disodium salt,
tech., 80+%
M.W. 384.08 m.p. 134° (dec.)

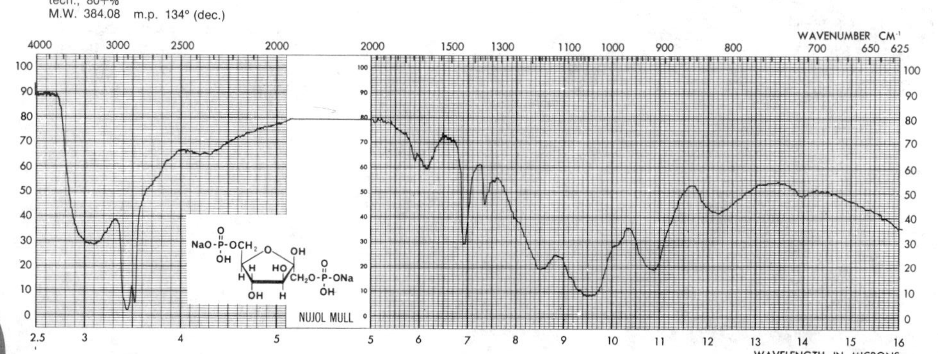

E

85,984-2
D-Fructose-1,6-diphosphate, trisodium salt octahydrate
FW 550.19 mp 71-74° Disp. L

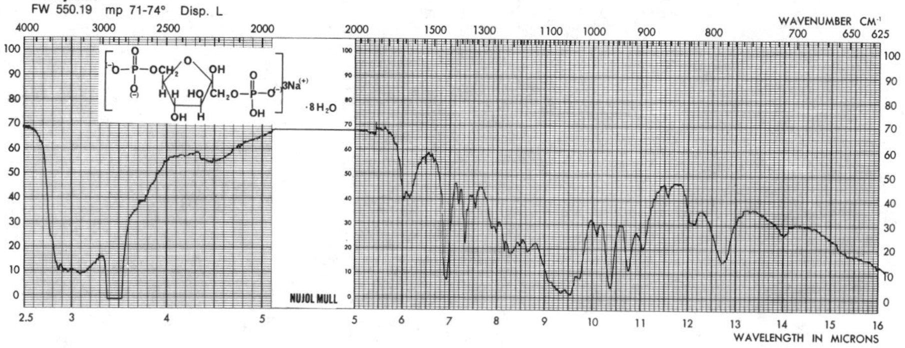

F

85,887-0
α-D-Glucose-1-phosphate, dipotassium salt dihydrate
(Cori ester)
M.W. 372.36 m.p. 209° (dec.)

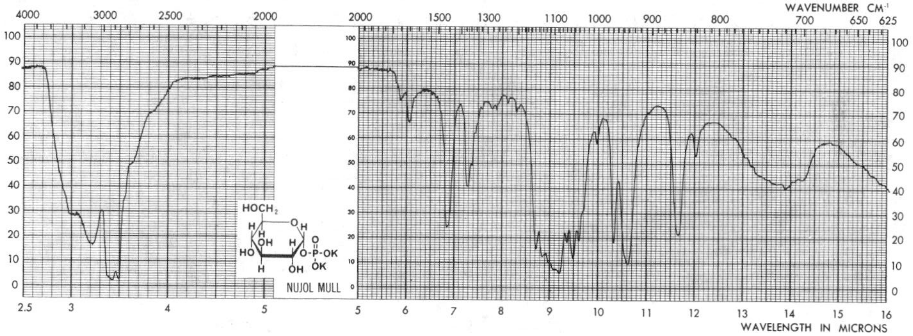

G

85,661-4
D-Fructose-1,6-diphosphate, disodium salt hydrate
M.W. 384.08

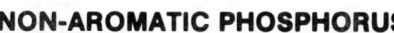

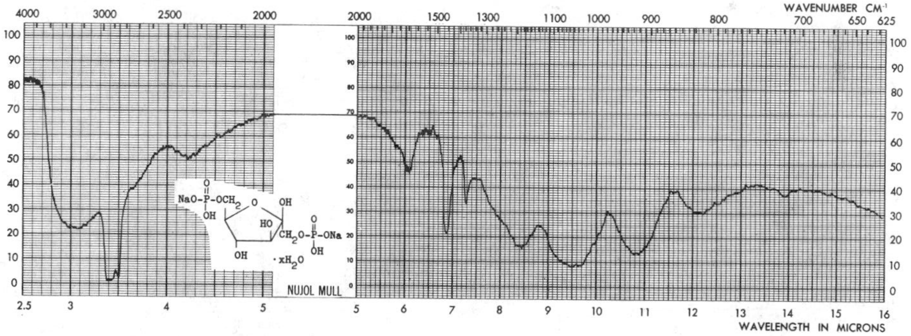

ALDRICH

AROMATIC HYDROCARBONS

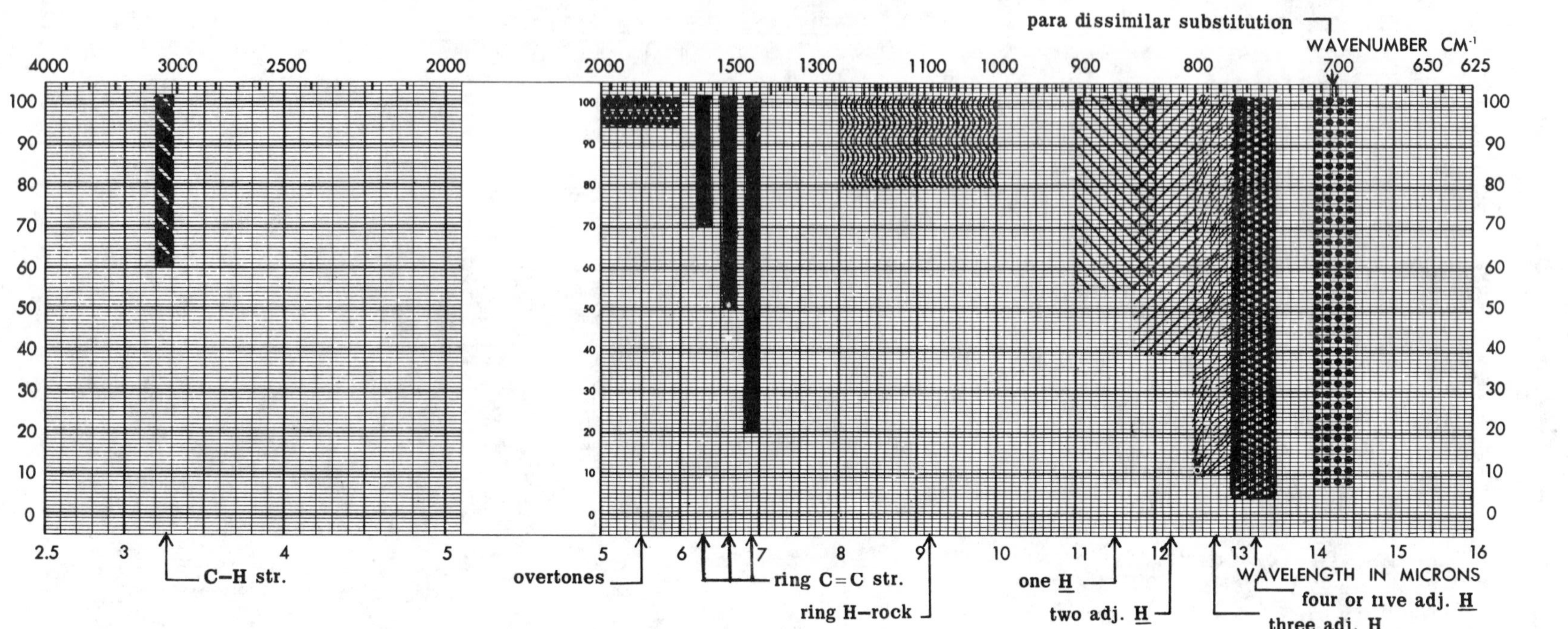

The benzene ring displays significant absorptions in five areas of the infrared spectrum:

1.) the carbon-hydrogen stretch vibration between 3.2 and 3.3 μ (3125 – 3030 cm^{-1}),
2.) the overtone and combination bands indicating ring substitution between 5 and 6 μ (2000 – 1665 cm^{-1}),
3.) the C=C stretch vibrations between 6 and 7 μ (1665 – 1430 cm^{-1}) with two distinct sets of bands; one set near 6.25 μ (1600 cm^{-1}), the other near 6.6 and 7 μ (1515 and 1430 cm^{-1}),
4.) ring hydrogen rocking vibrations between 8 and 10 μ (1250 – 1000 cm^{-1}),
5.) ring substitution bands between 11 and 15 μ (910 – 665 cm^{-1}).

The carbon-hydrogen stretch bands between 3.2 and 3.3 μ (3125 – 3030 cm^{-1}) usually consist of several weak to medium absorptions. However, grating optics are usually required to resolve them into individual bands.

The 5 to 6 μ (2000 – 1665 cm^{-1}) region of overtone and combination bands is quite useful in identifying the type of substitution on the benzene ring. The following spectral portions are of the various methylated benzene compounds. The spectra were run neat and include the C=C stretch vibrations between 6 and 7 μ (1665 – 1430 cm^{-1}) to reflect the relative thickness of the cell used to obtain the intensity of these overtones.

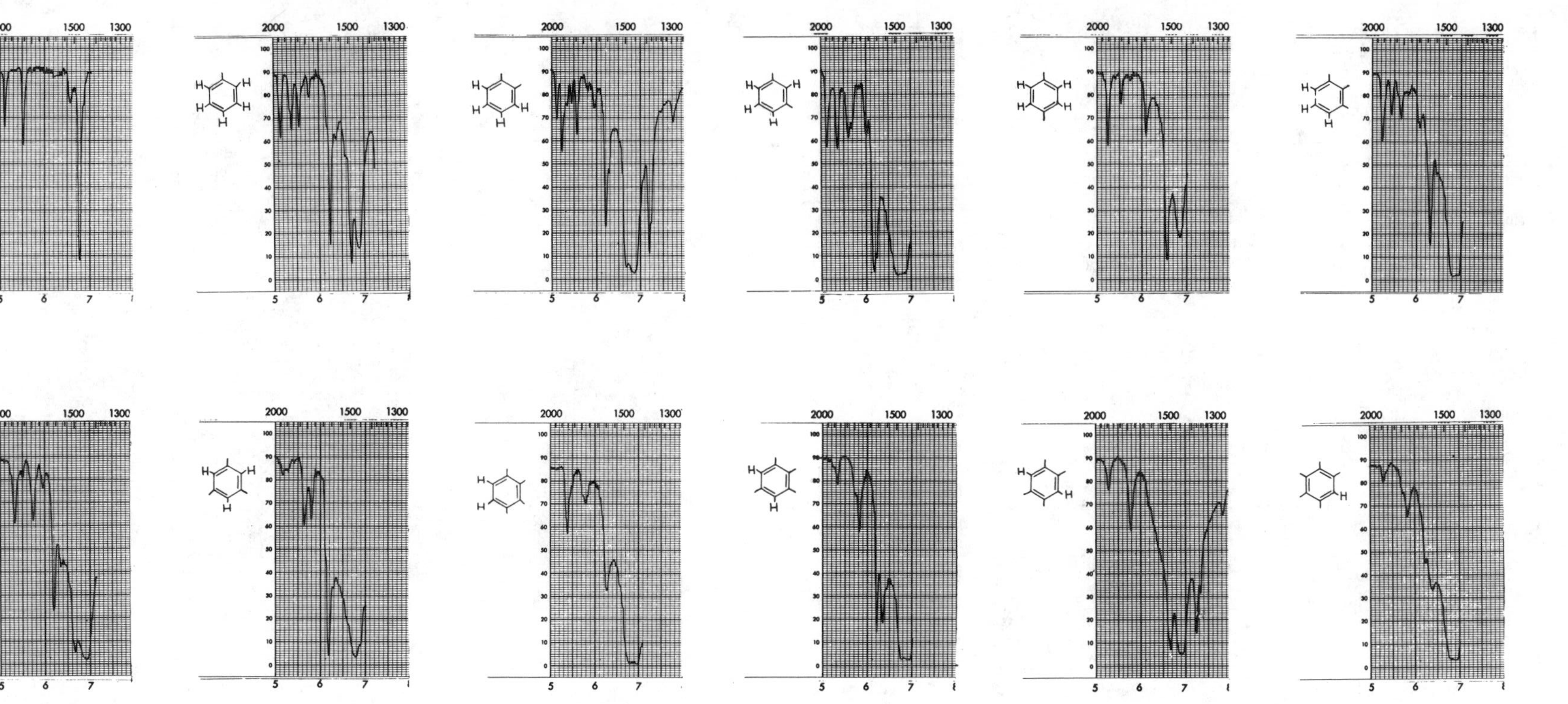

The absorption at 6.6 – 6.7 μ (1515 – 1495 cm^{-1}) is accompanied by an absorption at 7 μ (1430 cm^{-1}). Both are highly variable in intensity and dependent on the benzene ring substituents. The bands between 6.2 and 6.3 μ (1615 – 1585 cm^{-1}) are also variable in intensity and position and often split. When identical groups are para, such as in p-xylene, durene and hexamethylbenzene, these bands do not appear.

The fourth aromatic region, 8 to 10 μ (1250 – 1000 cm^{-1}), displays several weak to medium bands which in general are not useful in diagnosing substitution positions of the benzene ring, but can be helpful in determining the identity of substituents.

The fifth region, between 11 and 15 μ (910 – 665 cm^{-1}), is most important in determining the group positions on the aromatic ring by indicating the number of adjacent hydrogen atoms. A *single hydrogen* as in the 1,3-di-, 1,2,4-tri-, 1,2,3,5-tetra-, 1,2,4,5-tetra- and the penta-substituted benzene rings absorbs between 11 and 12 μ (910 – 835 cm^{-1}). *Two adjacent hydrogen* atoms as in 1,4-di-, 1,2,4-tri- and 1,2,3,4-tetra-substituted benzenes absorb between 11.7 and 12.5 μ (855 – 800 cm^{-1}). *Three adjacent hydrogens* as in 1,3-di-, and 1,2,3-tri-substituted benzenes absorb between 12.5 and 13.1 μ (800 – 765 cm^{-1}). *Four and five adjacent hydrogen* atoms as in 1,2-di- and mono-substituted benzenes absorb between 13 and 13.5 μ (770 – 740 cm^{-1}). These bands are joined by a second absorption between 14 and 14.5 μ (715 – 690 cm^{-1}) only when *dissimilar* groups are positioned *opposite* each other on the benzene ring. This absorption can be seen most outstandingly in the mono-, meta-, 1,2,3-tri- and 1,3,5-tri-substituted benzene compounds. The ortho di-substituted molecule is an exception to this rule.

The substitution absorptions between 11 and 15 μ (910 – 665 cm^{-1}) are highly variable. Groups other than an alkyl group can be disruptive to the substitution patterns displayed by the benzene ring. Some attempt will be made in subsequent aromatic sections to point out these interfering groups.

Fused rings, such as those from spectrum 575G on, follow the same general rules established by the single ring benzene molecules. The bands near 6.2 and 6.7 μ (1615 and 1495 cm^{-1}) are generally weaker than in the single ring benzene compounds. Substitution patterns established for the benzene ring, however, carry through to the aromatic polycyclic compounds.

A

15,462-8 **Benzene, spectrophotometric grade, GOLD LABEL**
(meets A.C.S. spectrophotometric requirements)
C_6H_6 M.W. 78.12 b.p. 80° ....

NEAT

B

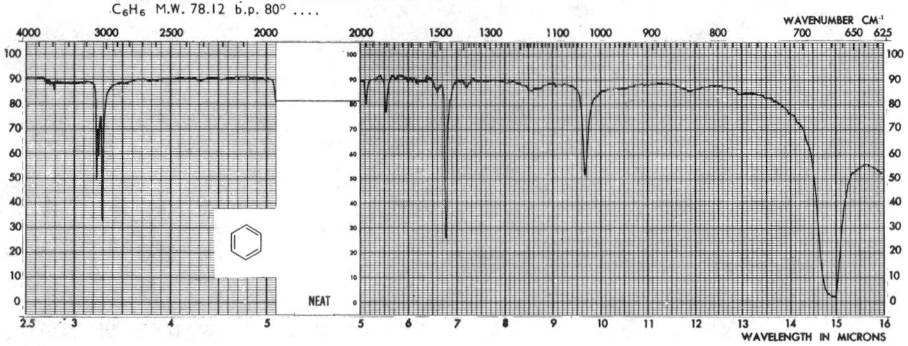

15,500-4 **Toluene, spectrophotometric grade, GOLD LABEL**
(meets A.C.S. spectrophotometric requirements)
$C_6H_5CH_3$ M.W. 92.14 b.p. 110-111°

NEAT

C

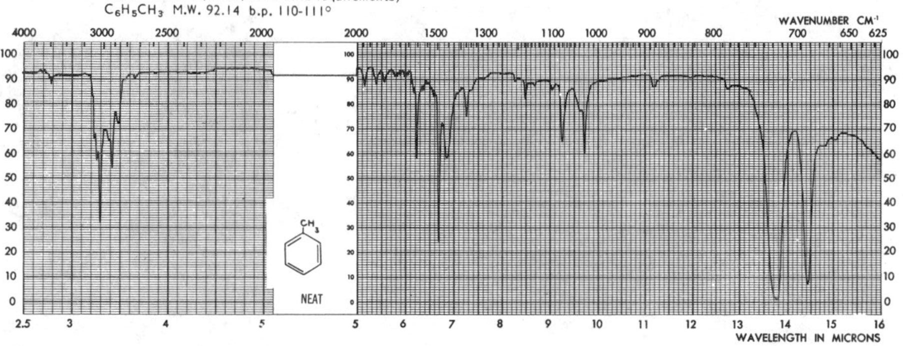

E1250-8 **Ethylbenzene**
$C_6H_5C_2H_5$ M.W. 106.17 n_D^{20} 1.4952

NEAT

D

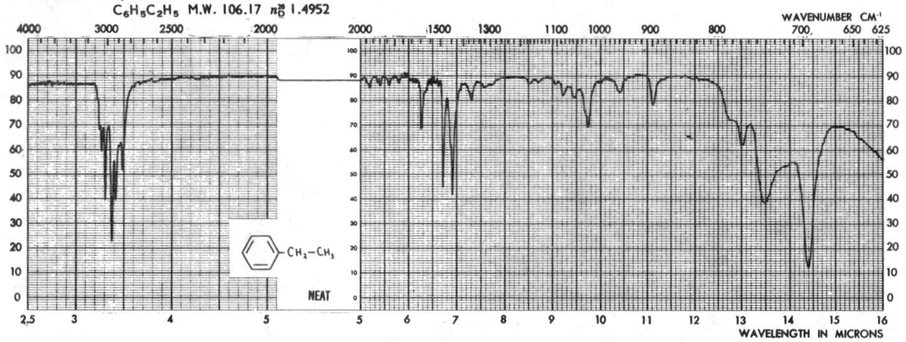

P5240-7 **n-Propylbenzene**
$C_6H_5CH_2CH_2CH_3$ M.W. 120.20 n_D^{20} 1.4912
b.p. 159° ....

NEAT

E

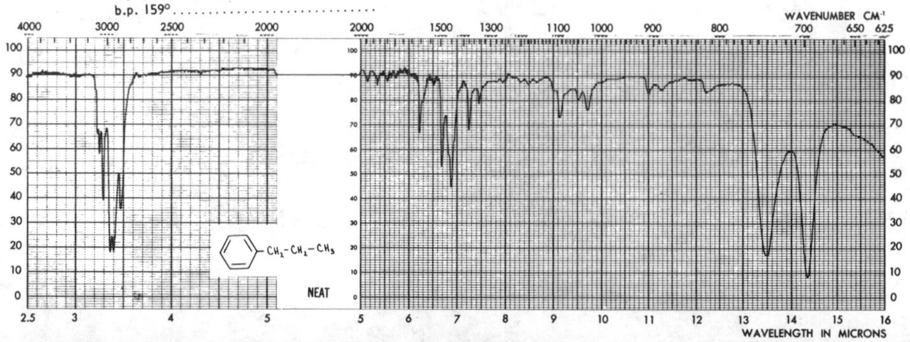

C8765-7 **Cumene** (isopropylbenzene)
$C_6H_5CH(CH_3)_2$ M.W. 120.20 n_D^{20} 1.4917

NEAT

F

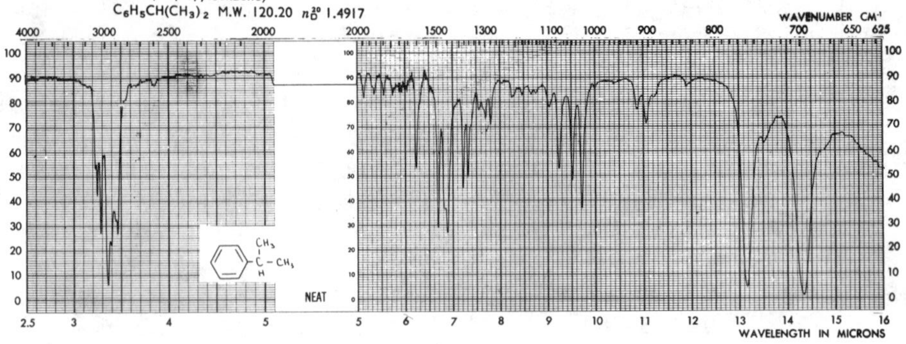

B9020-3 **n-Butylbenzene, puriss.**
$C_6H_5(CH_2)_3CH_3$ M.W. 134.22 n_D^{20} 1.4895

NEAT

G

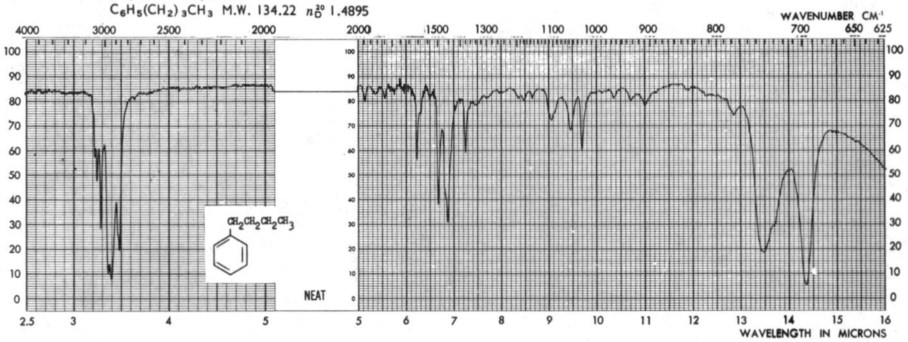

B9040-8 **sec.-Butylbenzene, puriss.**
$C_6H_5CH(CH_3)C_2H_5$ M.W. 134.22 n_D^{20} 1.4890
b.p. 173-174° ....

NEAT

H

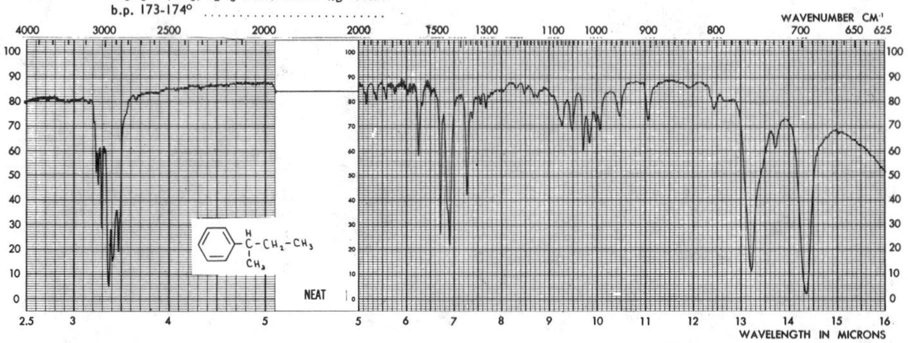

11,316-6 **Isobutylbenzene**
$C_6H_5CH_2CH(CH_3)_2$ M.W. 134.22 n_D^{20} 1.4859
b.p. 170°/736 mm. ....

NEAT

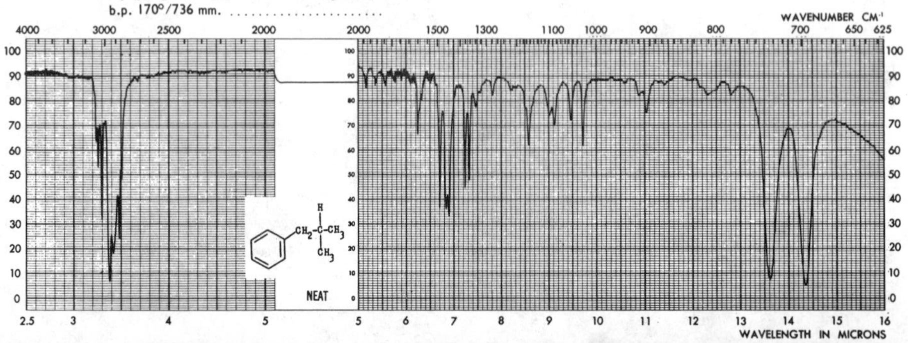

A

B9060-2 tert.-Butylbenzene
$C_6H_5C(CH_3)_3$ M.W. 134.22 n_D^{20} 1.4920

NEAT

B

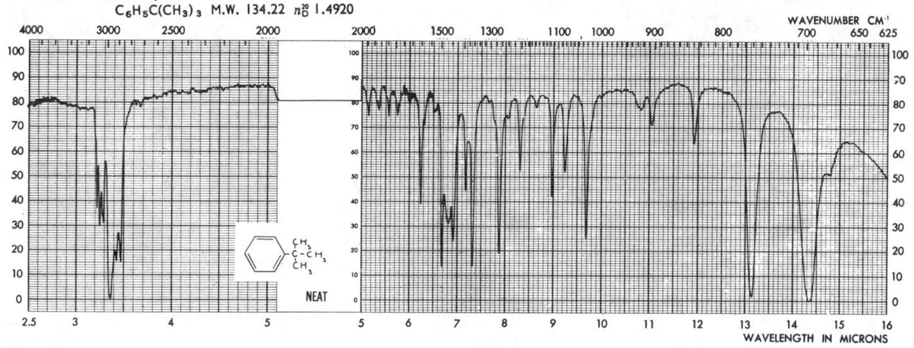

C12,080-4 Cyclopropylphenylmethane (α-cyclopropyltoluene)
$C_6H_5CH_2C_3H_5$ M.W. 132.21 n_D^{20} 1.5151

NEAT

C

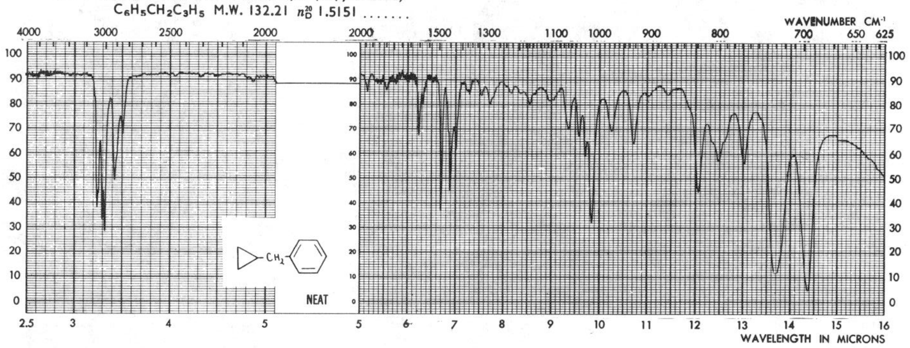

11,317-4 n-Amylbenzene
$C_6H_5(CH_2)_4CH_3$ M.W. 148.25 n_D^{20} 1.4870
b.p. 205°

NEAT

D

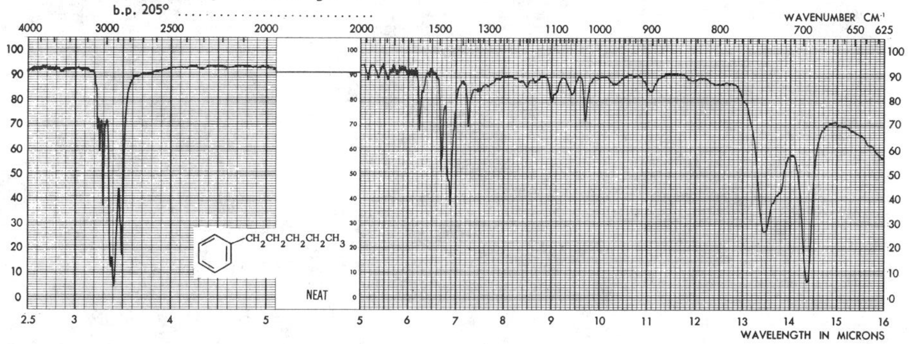

11,129-5 tert.-Amylbenzene
$C_6H_5C(CH_3)_2C_2H_5$ M.W. 148.25
n_D^{20} 1.4945 b.p. 188-191°

NEAT

E

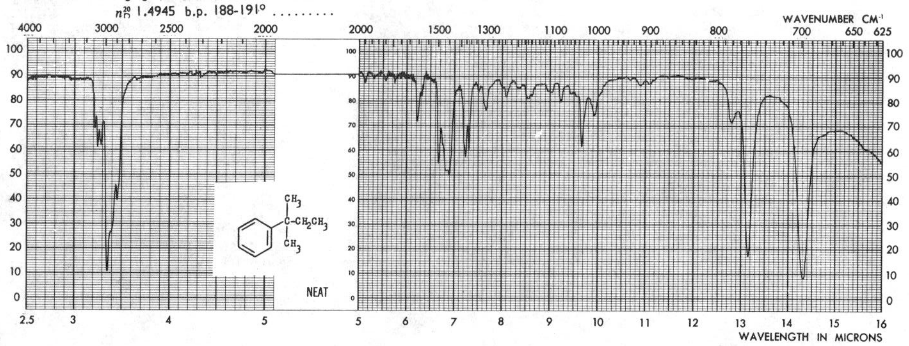

P2570-1 1-Phenylhexane (n-hexylbenzene)
$C_6H_5(CH_2)_5CH_3$ M.W. 162.28 n_D^{20} 1.4865

NEAT

F

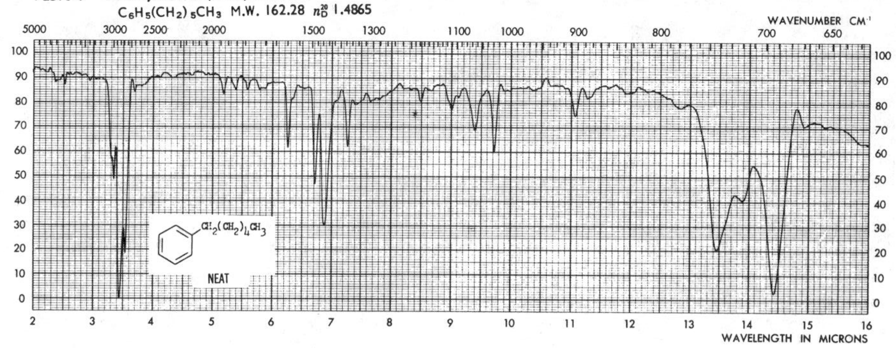

11,318-2 1-Phenylheptane
$C_6H_5(CH_2)_6CH_3$ M.W. 176.30 n_D^{20} 1.4842
b.p. 233°

NEAT

G

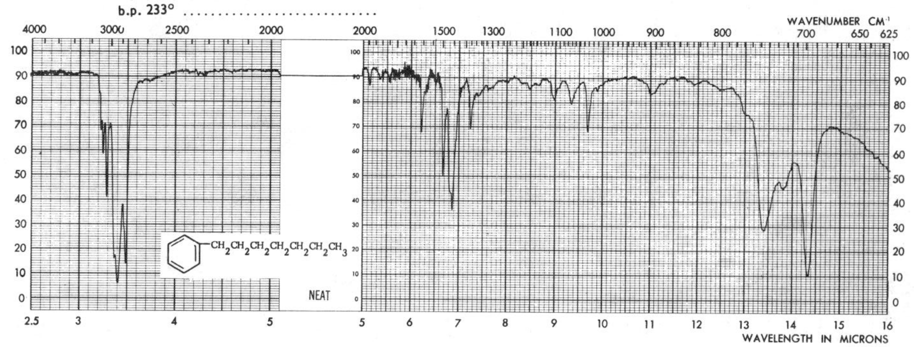

11,319-0 1-Phenyloctane
$C_6H_5(CH_2)_7CH_3$ M.W. 190.33 n_D^{20} 1.4801

NEAT

H

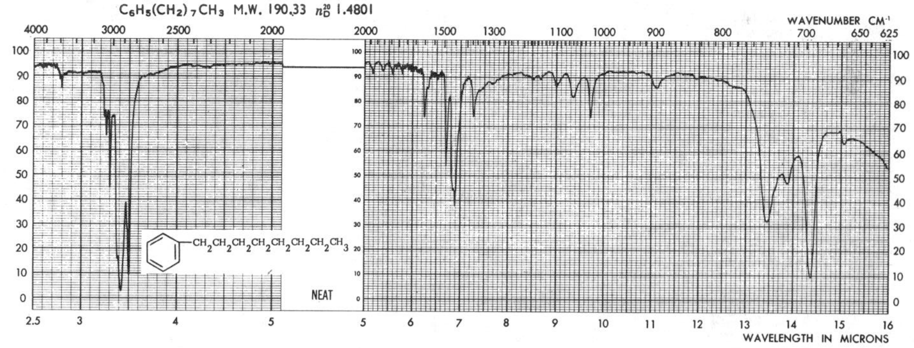

11,320-4 1-Phenylnonane
$C_6H_5(CH_2)_8CH_3$ M.W. 204.36 n_D^{20} 1.4816

NEAT

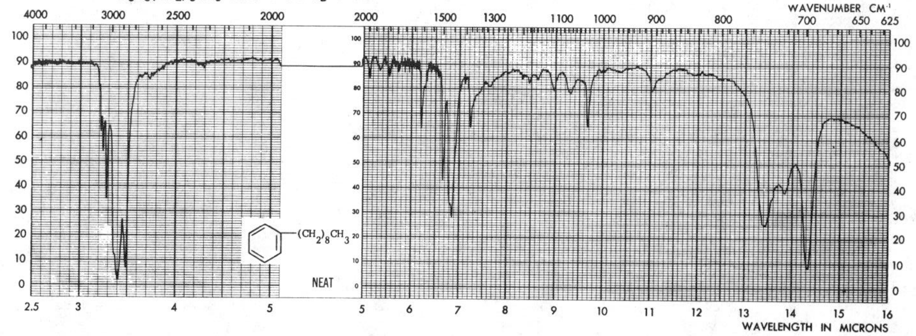

ALDRICH ®

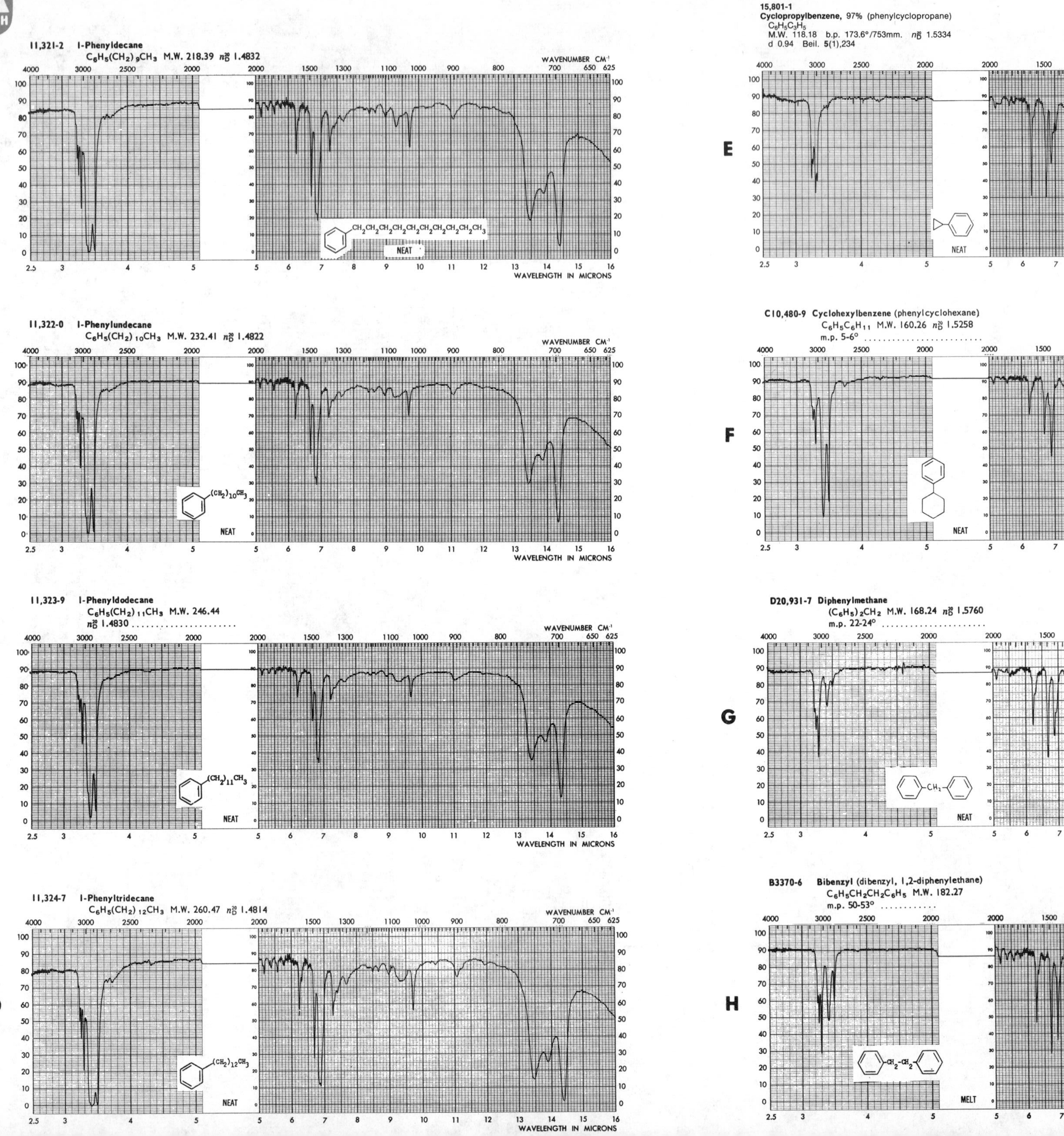

A 11,321-2 **1-Phenyldecane** $C_6H_5(CH_2)_9CH_3$ M.W. 218.39 n_D^{20} 1.4832 — NEAT

B 11,322-0 **1-Phenylundecane** $C_6H_5(CH_2)_{10}CH_3$ M.W. 232.41 n_D^{20} 1.4822 — NEAT

C 11,323-9 **1-Phenyldodecane** $C_6H_5(CH_2)_{11}CH_3$ M.W. 246.44 n_D^{20} 1.4830 — NEAT

D 11,324-7 **1-Phenyltridecane** $C_6H_5(CH_2)_{12}CH_3$ M.W. 260.47 n_D^{20} 1.4814 — NEAT

E 15,801-1 **Cyclopropylbenzene**, 97% (phenylcyclopropane) $C_6H_5C_3H_5$ M.W. 118.18 b.p. 173.6°/753mm. n_D^{20} 1.5334 d 0.94 Beil. 5(1),234 — NEAT

F C10,480-9 **Cyclohexylbenzene** (phenylcyclohexane) $C_6H_5C_6H_{11}$ M.W. 160.26 n_D^{20} 1.5258 m.p. 5-6° — NEAT

G D20,931-7 **Diphenylmethane** $(C_6H_5)_2CH_2$ M.W. 168.24 n_D^{20} 1.5760 m.p. 22-24° — NEAT

H B3370-6 **Bibenzyl** (dibenzyl, 1,2-diphenylethane) $C_6H_5CH_2CH_2C_6H_5$ M.W. 182.27 m.p. 50-53° — MELT

A

D21,150-8 2,2-Diphenylpropane
$CH_3C(C_6H_5)_2CH_3$ M.W. 196.29 m.p. 29°

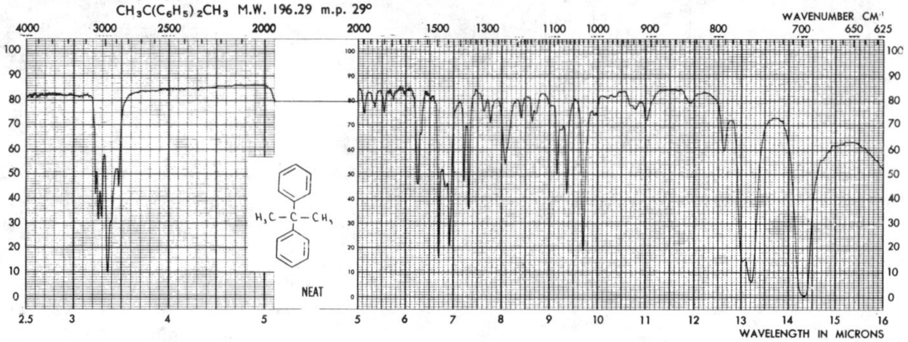

NEAT

B

10,130-3 Triphenylmethane
$(C_6H_5)_3CH$ M.W. 244.34 m.p. 93-94°

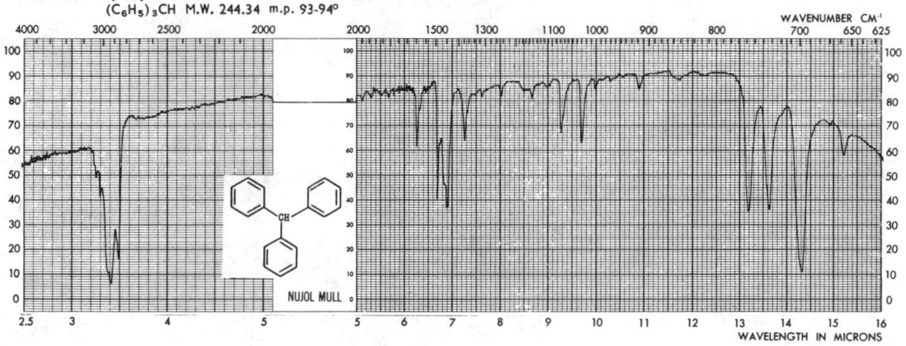

NUJOL MULL

C

T2650-6 Tetraphenylmethane
$(C_6H_5)_4C$ M.W. 320.44 m.p. 280-282°

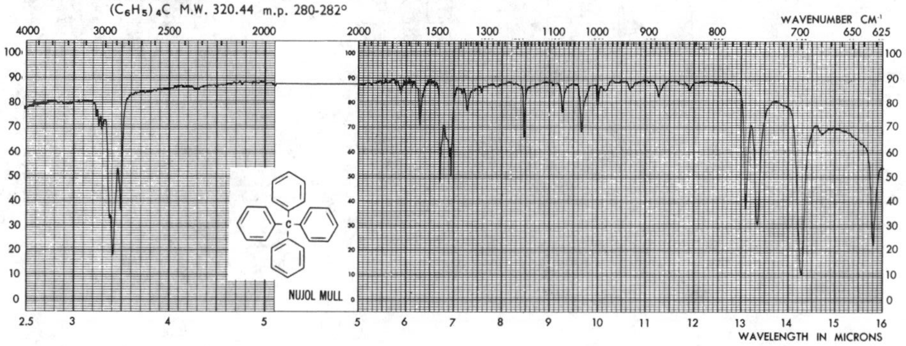

NUJOL MULL

D

X104-0 o-Xylene, 99+%
$C_6H_4(CH_3)_2$ M.W. 106.17 n_D^{20} 1.5027 m.p. -25 to -23°
b.p. 143.5-144.5°

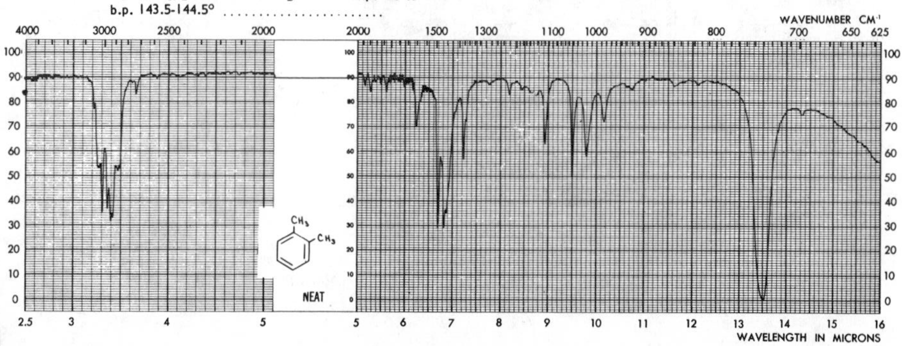

NEAT

E

E4940-1 o-Ethyltoluene
$C_2H_5C_6H_4CH_3$ M.W. 120.20 n_D^{20} 1.5039

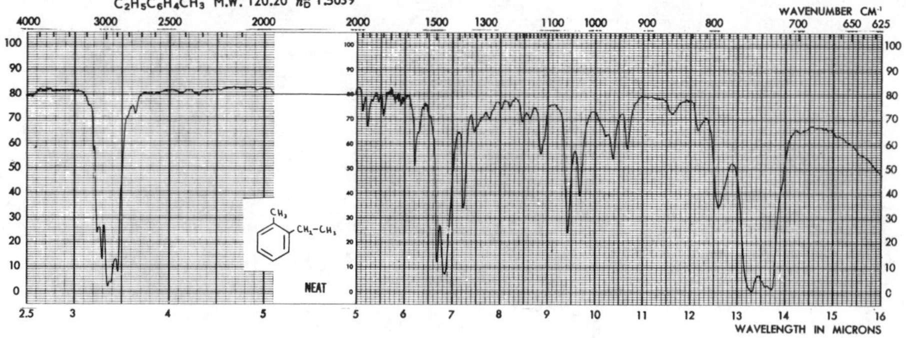

NEAT

F

D9060-1 o-Diethylbenzene
$C_6H_4(C_2H_5)_2$ M.W. 134.22 n_D^{20} 1.5022

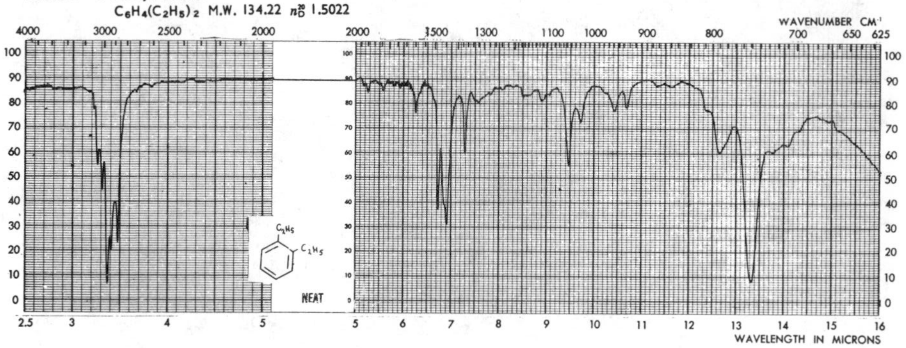

NEAT

G

I-180-4 Indan
M.W. 118.18 n_D^{20} 1.5380 b.p. 70°/20 mm.

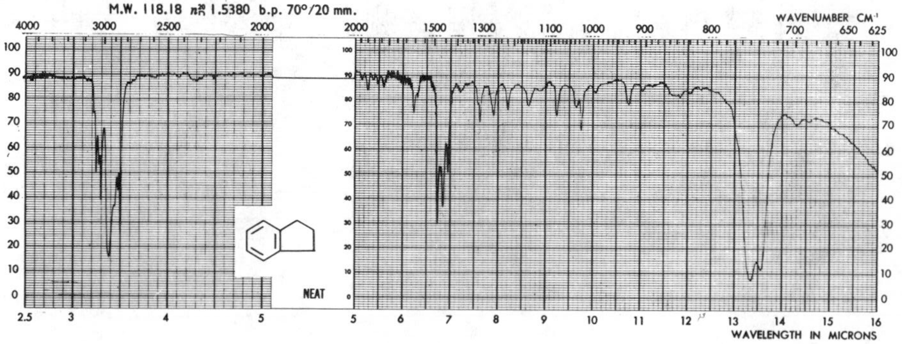

NEAT

H

10,241-5 1,2,3,4-Tetrahydronaphthalene
$C_{10}H_{12}$ M.W. 132.21 n_D^{20} 1.5411 b.p. 207°

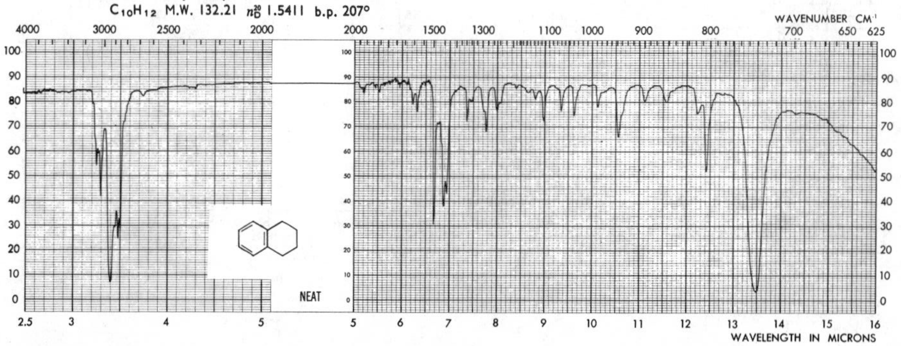

NEAT

A 13,490-2 **m-Xylene**
$C_6H_4(CH_3)_2$ M.W. 106.17 n_D^{20} 1.4970
b.p. 138-139°
NEAT

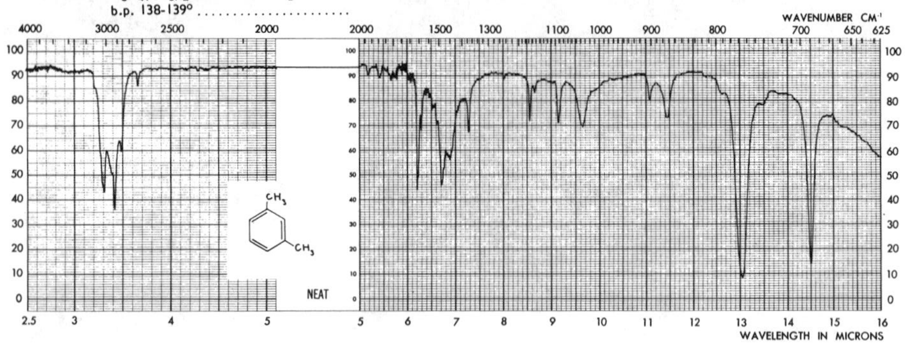

B E4960-6 **m-Ethyltoluene**
$C_2H_5C_6H_4CH_3$ M.W. 120.20 n_D^{20} 1.4956
NEAT

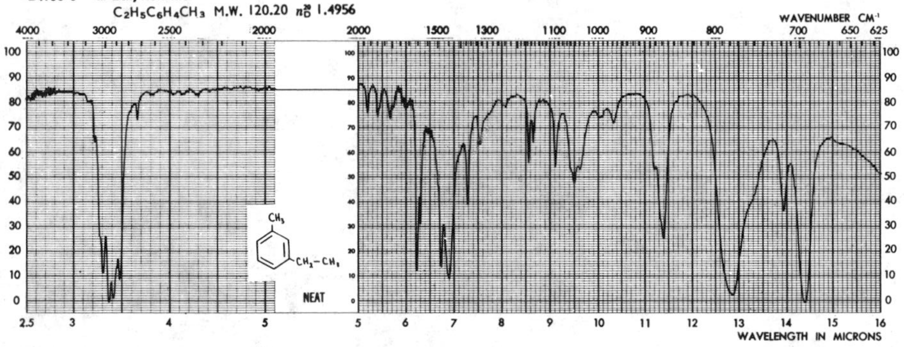

C D9080-6 **m-Diethylbenzene, puriss.**
$C_6H_4(C_2H_5)_2$ M.W. 134.22 n_D^{20} 1.4930
NEAT

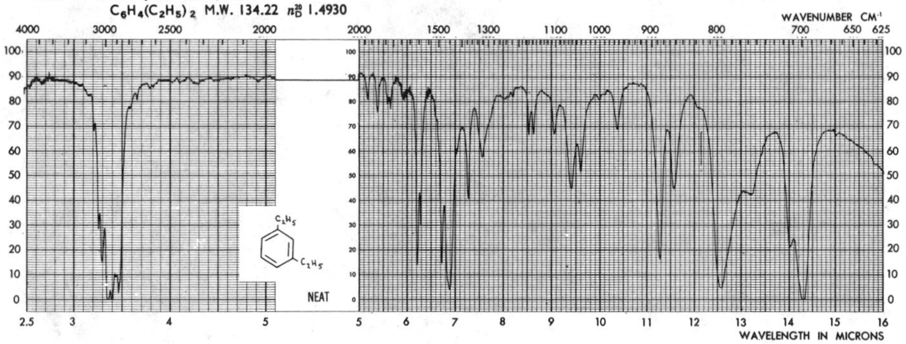

D 11,326-3 **m-Diisopropylbenzene**
$C_6H_4[CH(CH_3)_2]_2$ M.W. 162.28
n_D^{20} 1.4878
NEAT

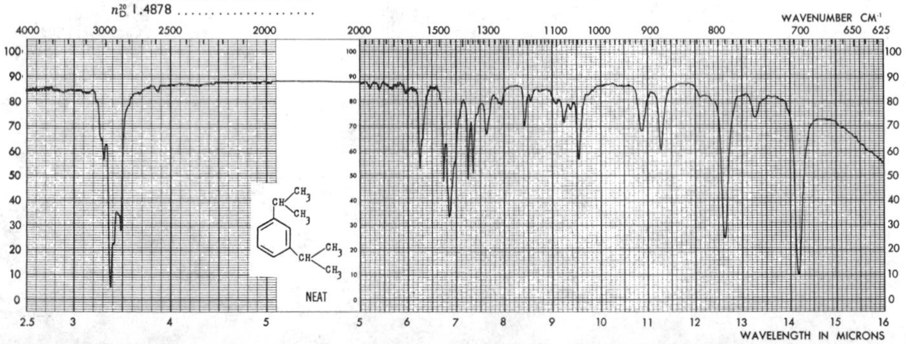

E 13,444-9 **p-Xylene**
$C_6H_4(CH_3)_2$ M.W. 106.17 n_D^{20} 1.4954 m.p. 12-13°
b.p. 138°
NEAT

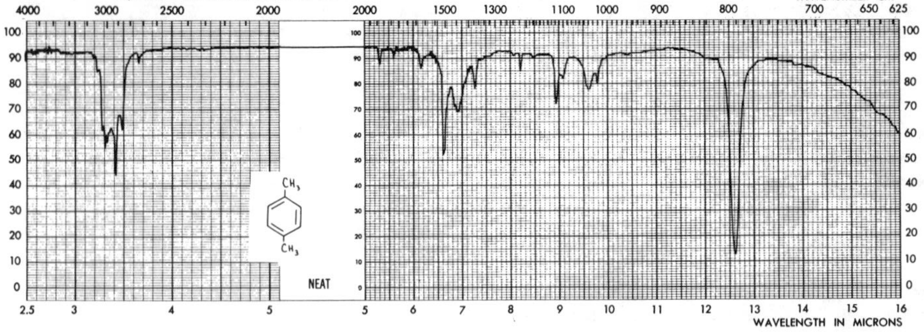

F E4980-0 **p-Ethyltoluene**
$C_2H_5C_6H_4CH_3$ M.W. 120.20
n_D^{20} 1.4939
NEAT

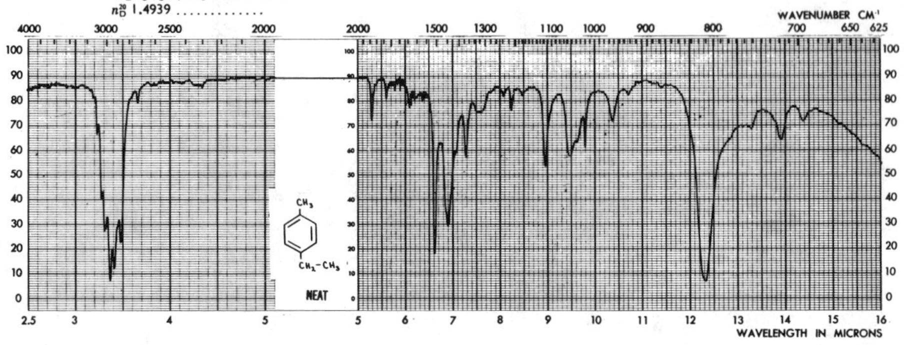

G D9100-4 **p-Diethylbenzene**
$C_6H_4(C_2H_5)_2$ M.W. 134.22 n_D^{20} 1.4940
NEAT

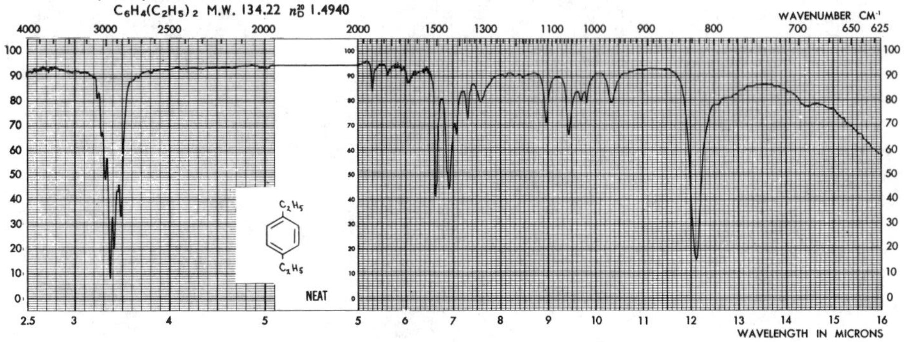

H C12,145-2 **p-Cymene (p-isopropyltoluene), puriss.**
$CH_3C_6H_4CH(CH_3)_2$ M.W. 134.22 n_D^{20} 1.4897
NEAT

WAVENUMBER CM⁻¹: 4000 3000 2500 2000 2000 1500 1300 1100 1000 900 800 700 650 625
WAVELENGTH IN MICRONS: 2.5 3 4 5 5 6 7 8 9 10 11 12 13 14 15 16

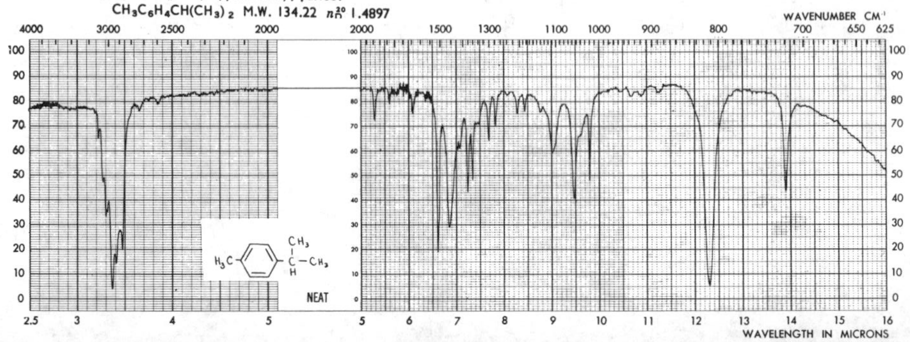

A

B10,262-8 **4-tert.-Butyltoluene**
$(CH_3)_3CC_6H_4CH_3$ M.W. 148.25
n_D^{20} 1.4897

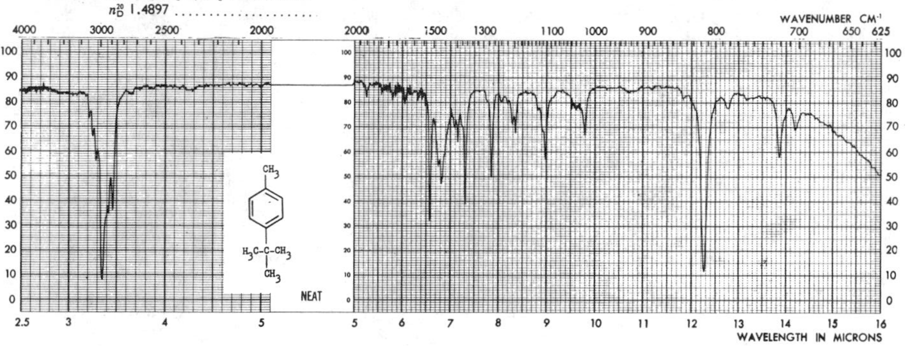

NEAT

B

12,627-6 **p-Diisopropylbenzene**
$C_6H_4[CH(CH_3)_2]_2$ M.W. 162.28
n_D^{20} 1.4889

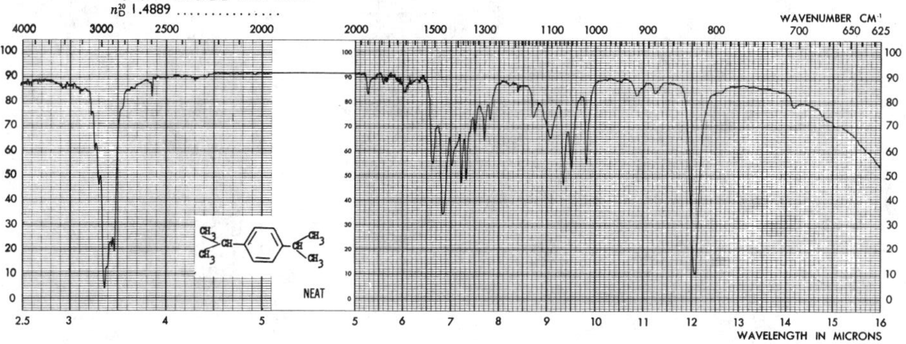

NEAT

C

11,335-2 **p-Di-tert.-butylbenzene**
$C_6H_4[C(CH_3)_3]_2$ M.W. 190.33
m.p. 80-81°

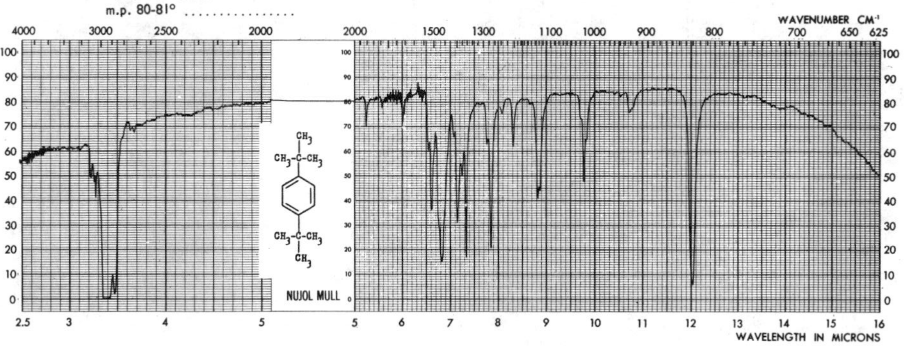

NUJOL MULL

D

12,144-4 **1,2-Di-p-tolylethane**
$CH_3C_6H_4CH_2CH_2C_6H_4CH_3$ M.W. 210.32
m.p. 81.5-82.5°

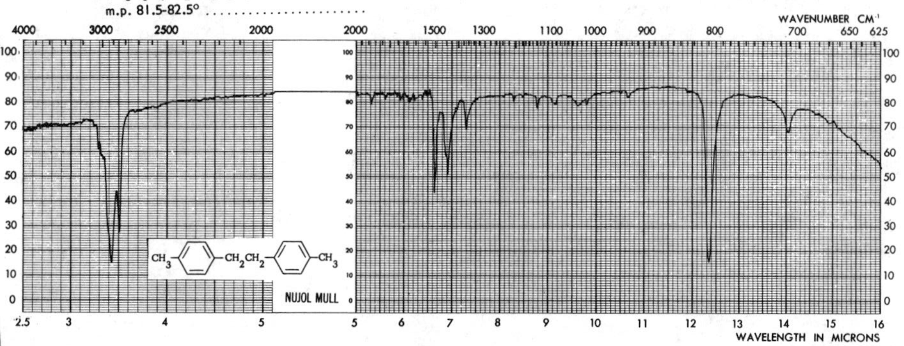

NUJOL MULL

E

P22-5 **[2.2]Paracyclophane** (tricyclo[8.2.2.2^{4,7}]hexadeca-4,6,10,12,13,15-hexaene)
M.W. 208.31 m.p. 285-288°

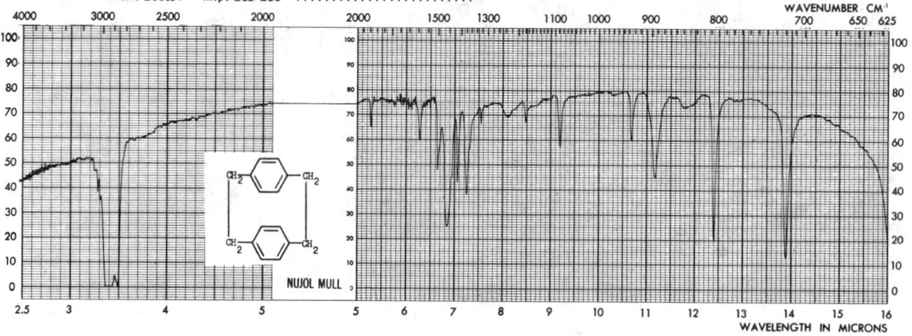

NUJOL MULL

F

17,958-2
p-Dicyclohexylbenzene, 99%
$C_6H_{11}C_6H_4C_6H_{11}$
M.W. 242.41 m.p. 103-105°

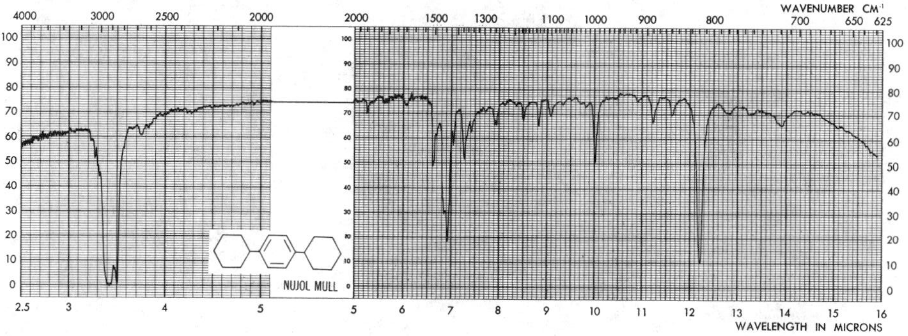

NUJOL MULL

G

D22,050-7 **Di-p-tolylmethane**
$(CH_3C_6H_4)_2CH_2$ M.W. 196.29
n_D^{20} 1.5609

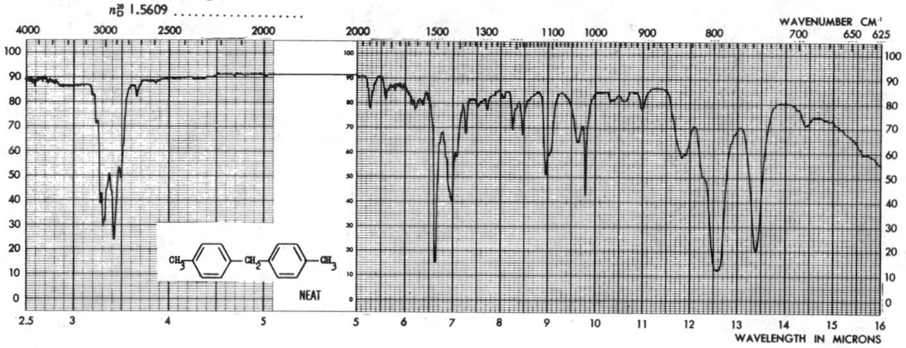

NEAT

H

21,473-6
Xylenes, mixed
$C_6H_4(CH_3)_2$ FW 106.17 bp 137-140° n_D^{20} 1.4975
d 0.860 *Beil.* 5,360 Disp. C

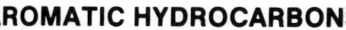

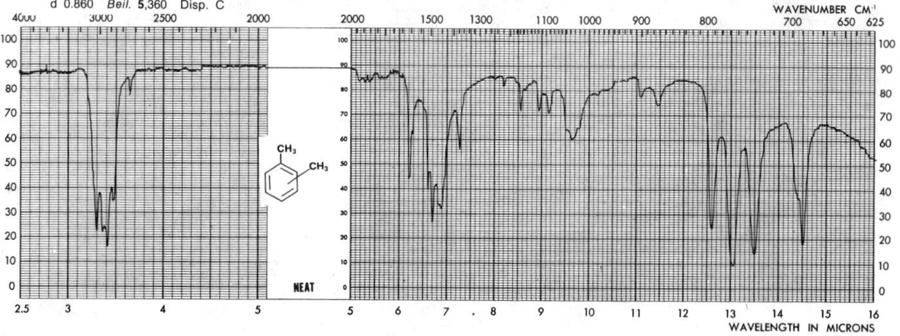

NEAT

ALDRICH

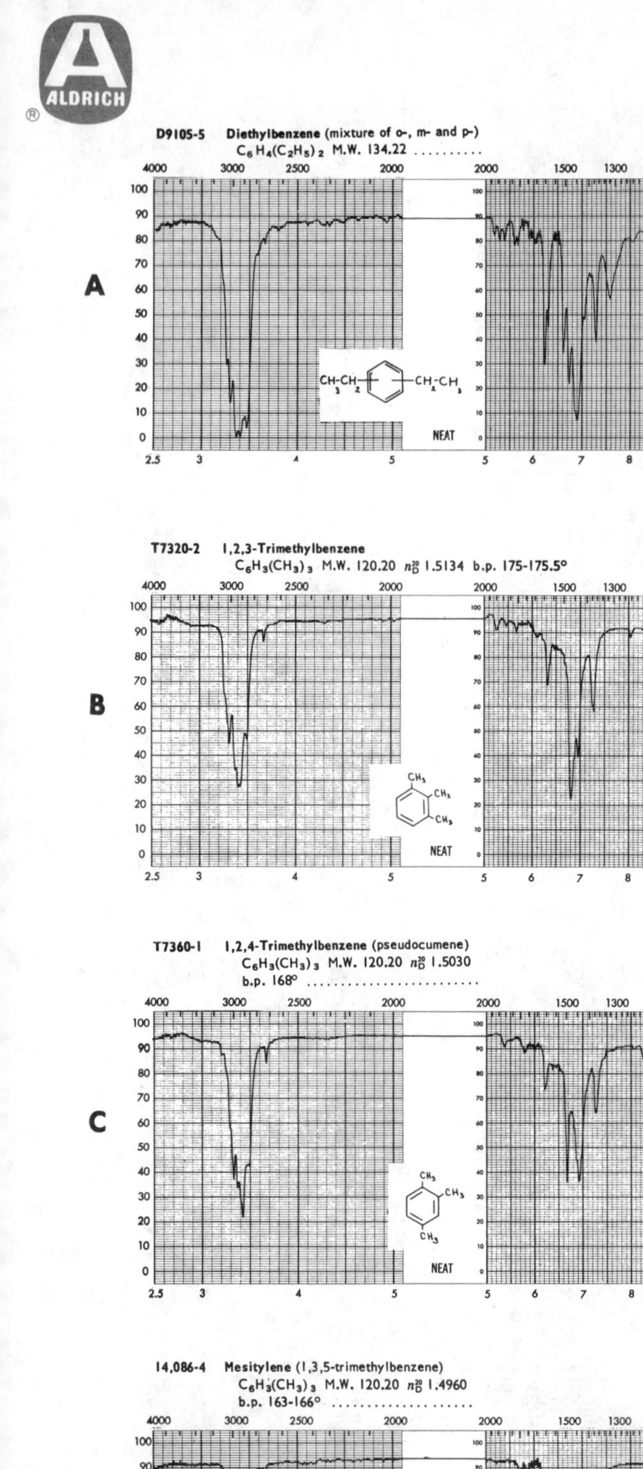

A

D9105-5 **Diethylbenzene** (mixture of o-, m- and p-)
$C_6H_4(C_2H_5)_2$ M.W. 134.22 ....

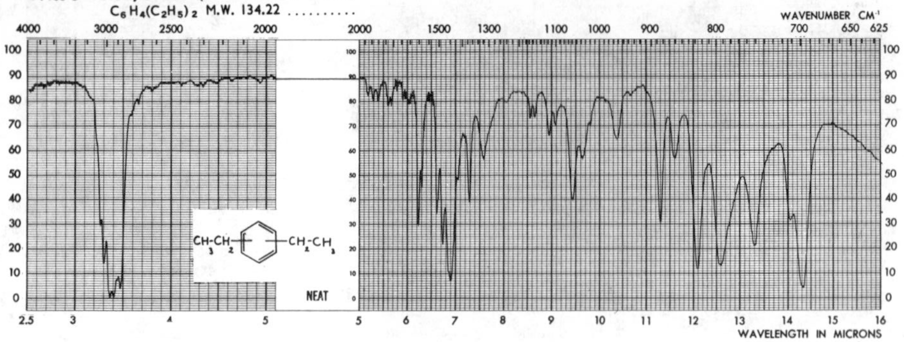

NEAT

B

T7320-2 **1,2,3-Trimethylbenzene**
$C_6H_3(CH_3)_3$ M.W. 120.20 n_D^{20} 1.5134 b.p. 175-175.5°

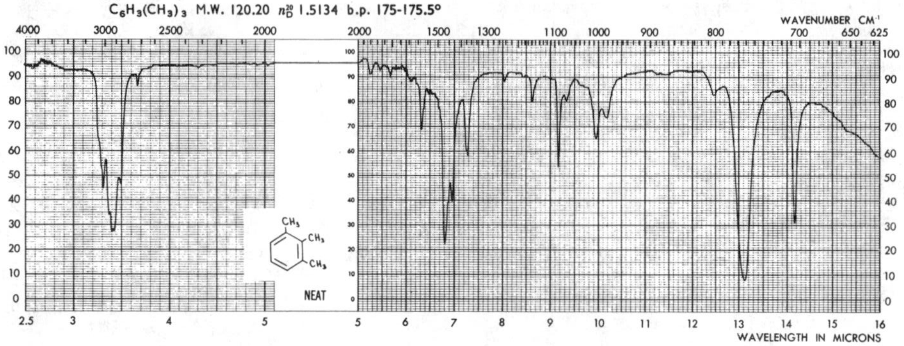

NEAT

C

T7360-1 **1,2,4-Trimethylbenzene** (pseudocumene)
$C_6H_3(CH_3)_3$ M.W. 120.20 n_D^{20} 1.5030
b.p. 168° ....

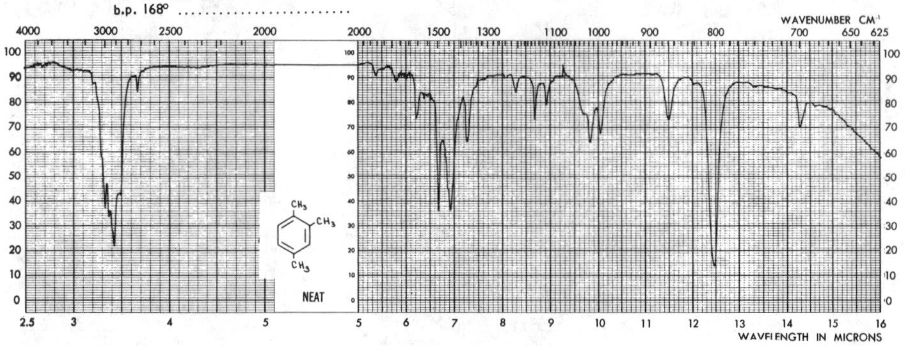

NEAT

D

14,086-4 **Mesitylene** (1,3,5-trimethylbenzene)
$C_6H_3(CH_3)_3$ M.W. 120.20 n_D^{20} 1.4960
b.p. 163-166° ....

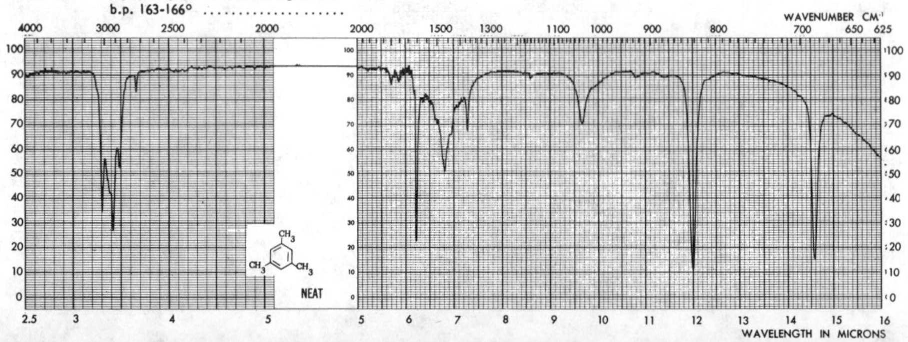

NEAT

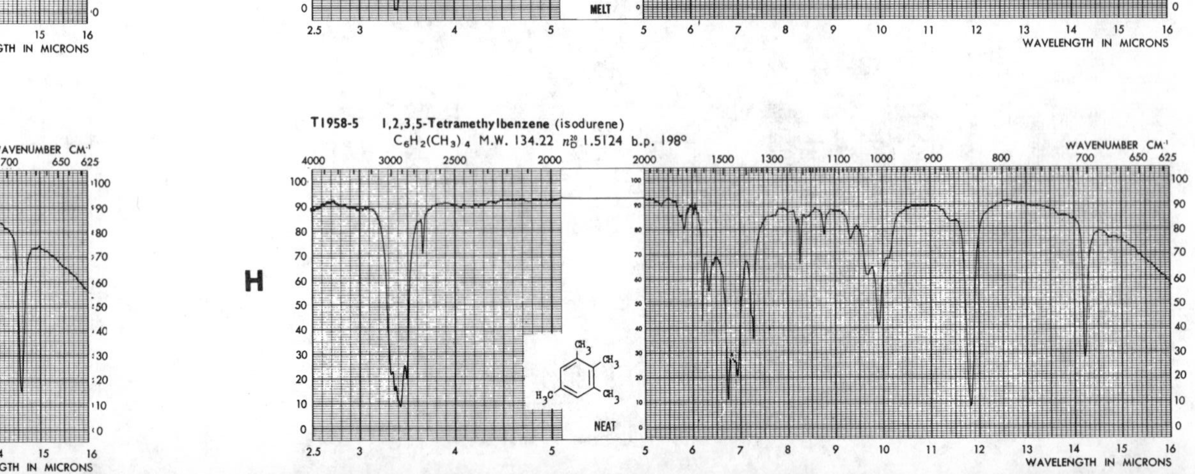

E

13,207-1 **1,3,5-Triethylbenzene**
$C_6H_3(C_2H_5)_3$ M.W. 162.28 n_D^{20} 1.4960 b.p. 217°

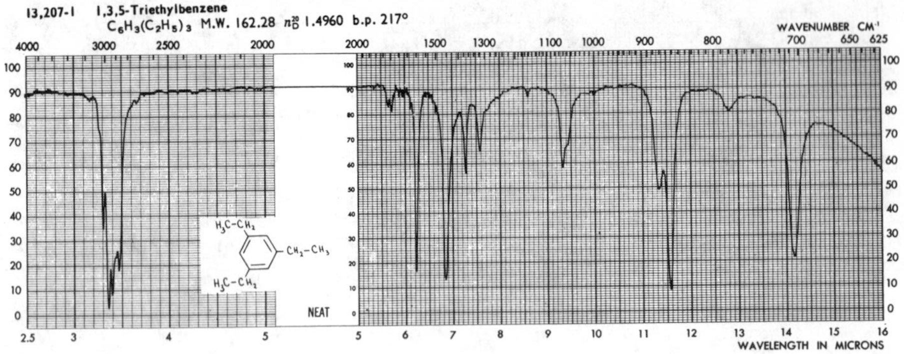

NEAT

F

T6765 **1,3,5-Triisopropylbenzene**
$C_6H_3[CH(CH_3)_2]_3$ M.W. 204.36 n_D^{20} 1.4870

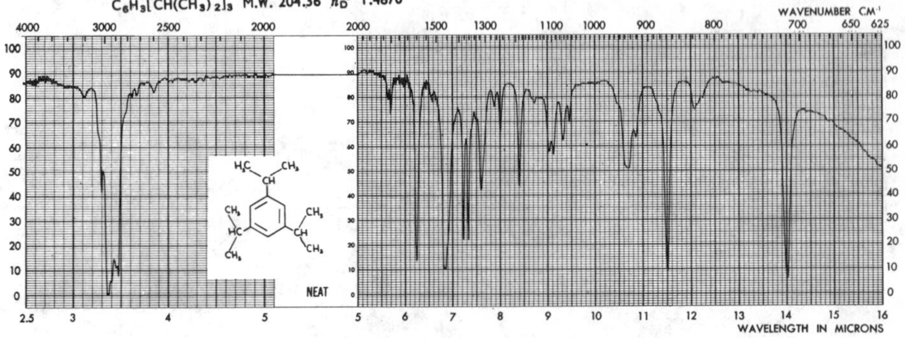

NEAT

G

22,377-8
1,3,5-Tri-*tert*-butylbenzene, 97%
$C_6H_3[C(CH_3)_3]_3$ FW 246.44 mp 69-71°
bp 121-122°/12mm. *Beil.* 5(3),1105 Disp. C

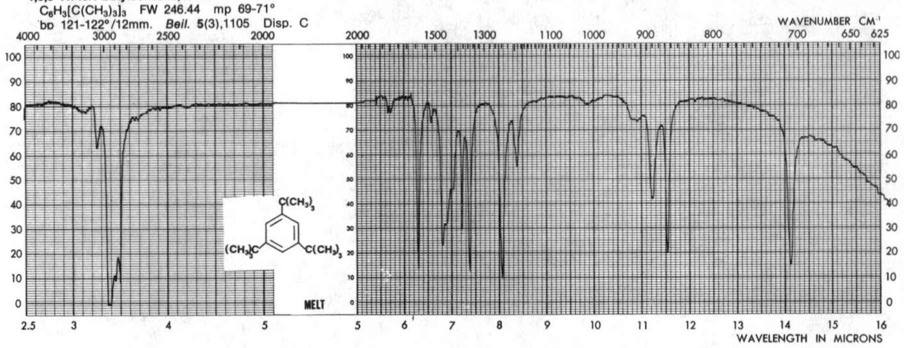

MELT

H

T1958-5 **1,2,3,5-Tetramethylbenzene** (isodurene)
$C_6H_2(CH_3)_4$ M.W. 134.22 n_D^{20} 1.5124 b.p. 198°

NEAT

A

T1960-7 **1,2,4,5-Tetramethylbenzene** (durene)
$C_6H_2(CH_3)_4$ M.W. 134.22 m.p. 75-77°

NUJOL MULL

B

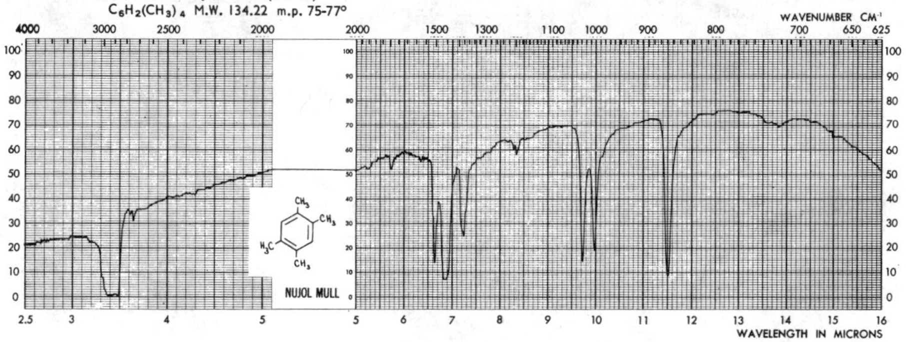

13,539-9 **4,6-Diisopropyl-1,3-dimethylbenzene**
$[(CH_3)_2CH]_2C_6H_2(CH_3)_2$ M.W. 190.33
n_D^{20} 1.4981

NEAT

C

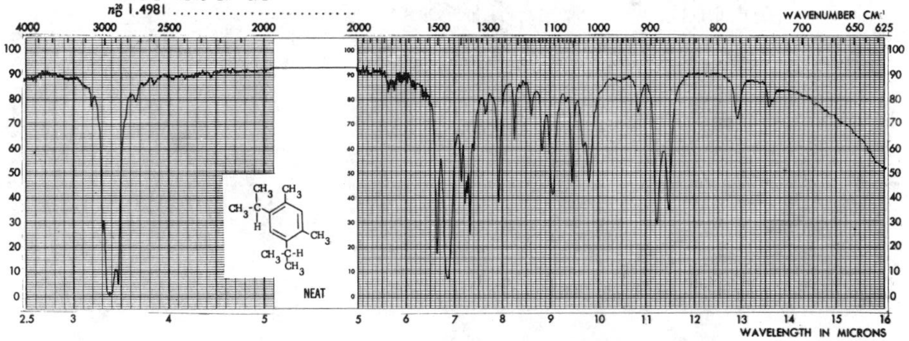

T1830-9 **1,2,4,5-Tetraisopropylbenzene**
$C_6H_2[CH(CH_3)_2]_4$ M.W. 246.42 m.p. 117-118.5°

NUJOL MULL

D

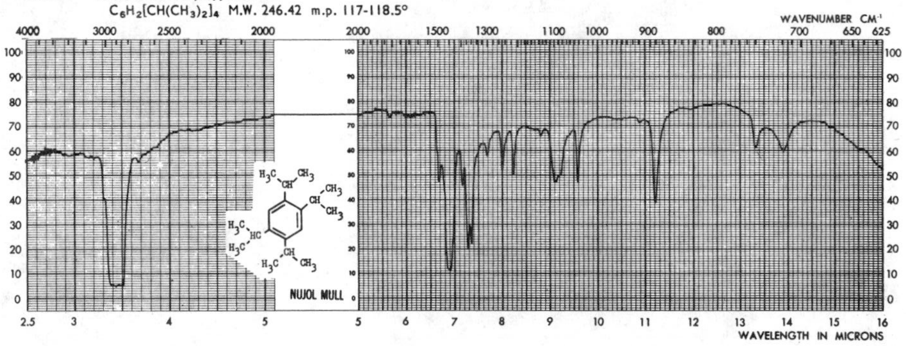

15,360-5 **1,2,3,4-Tetramethylbenzene** (prehnitene)
$C_6H_2(CH_3)_4$ M.W. 134.22 n_D^{20} 1.5187
b.p. 204-205°

NEAT

E

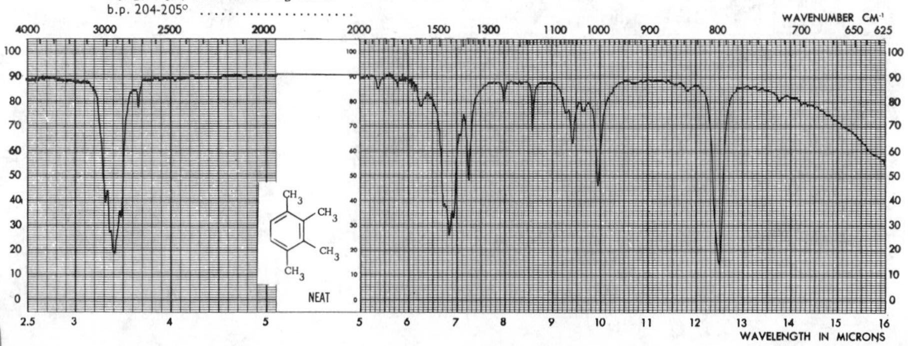

O-280-3 **1,2,3,4,5,6,7,8-Octahydroanthracene**
M.W. 186.30 m.p. 71-73°

MELT

F

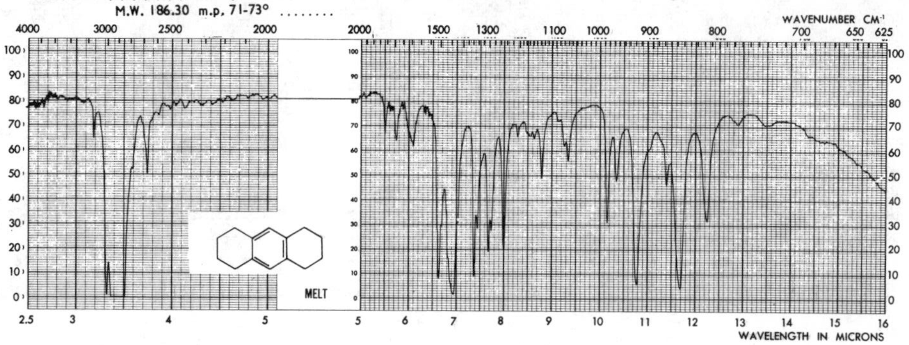

O-300-1 **1,2,3,4,5,6,7,8-Octahydrophenanthrene**
M.W. 186.30 n_D^{20} 1.5667

NEAT

G

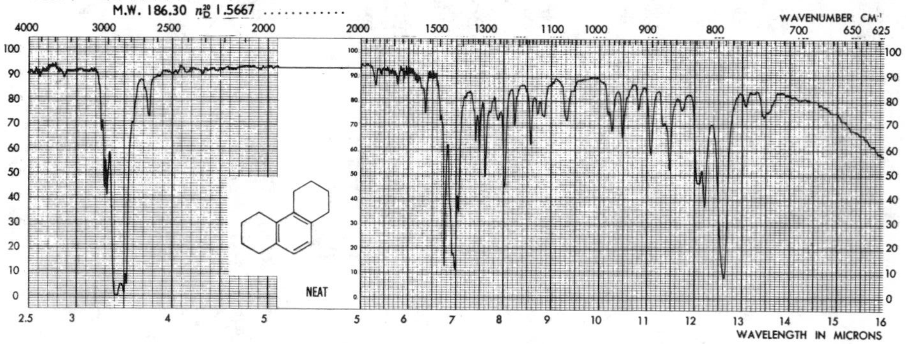

15,361-3
Pentamethylbenzene, 99%
$C_6H(CH_3)_5$
M.W. 148.25 m.p. 50-51.5° b.p. 231° d 0.917
Beil. 5,443

NUJOL MULL

H

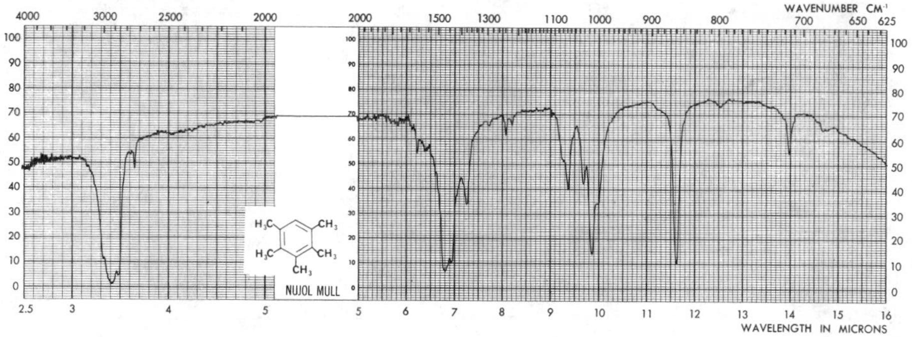

15,361-3 **Pentamethylbenzene**
$C_6H(CH_3)_5$ M.W. 148.25 m.p. 50-51.5°

MELT

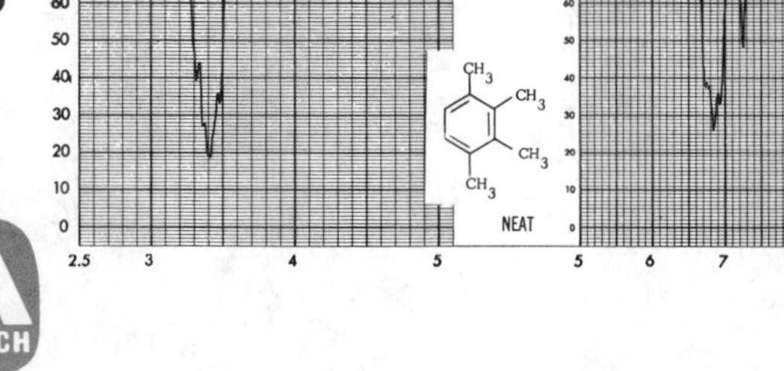

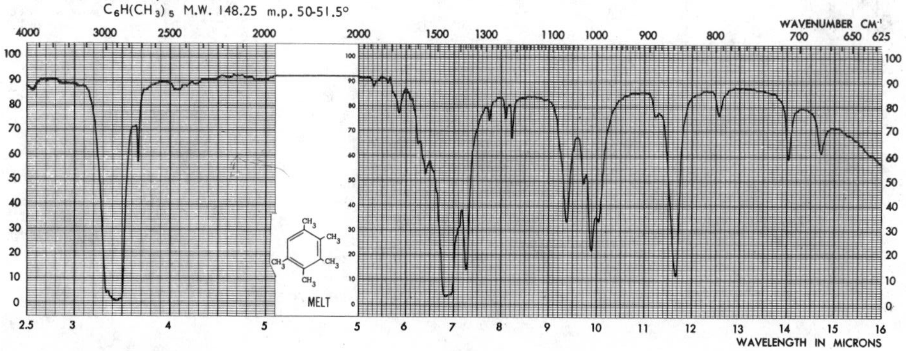

A

H998-2 **Hexamethylbenzene**
$C_6(CH_3)_6$ M.W. 162.28 m.p. 162-164°
NUJOL MULL

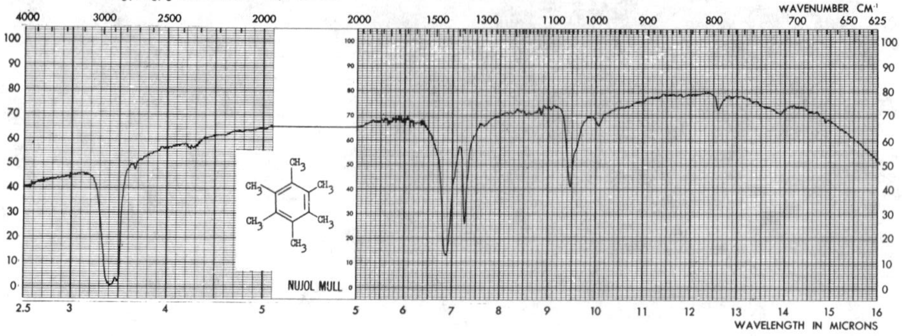

B

10,651-8 **Dodecahydrotriphenylene**
M.W. 240.39 m.p. 232-235°
NUJOL MULL

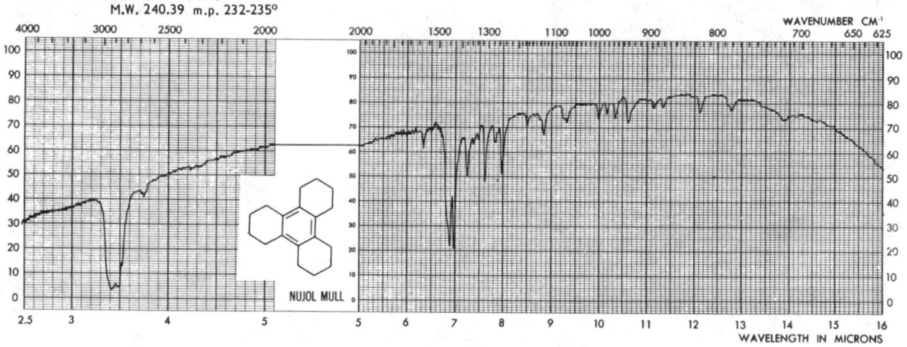

C

S497-2 **Styrene**
$C_6H_5CH{:}CH_2$ M.W. 104.15 n_D^{20} 1.5458
b.p. 145-146°
NEAT

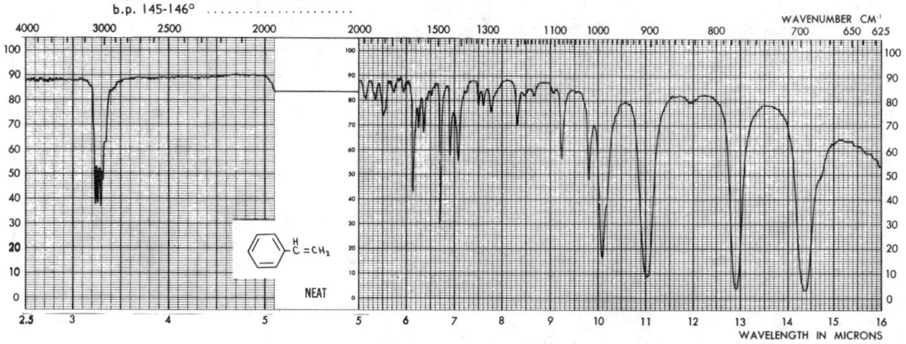

D

M8090-3 **α-Methylstyrene**
$C_6H_5C(CH_3){:}CH_2$ M.W. 118.18 n_D^{20} 1.5363
b.p. 161-163°
NEAT

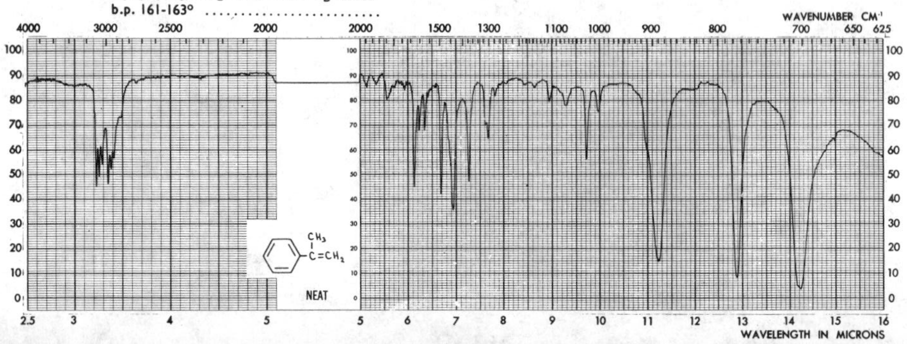

E

11,184-8 ***trans*-β-Methylstyrene**
$C_6H_5CH{:}CHCH_3$ M.W. 118.18 n_D^{20} 1.5485
b.p. 175°
NEAT

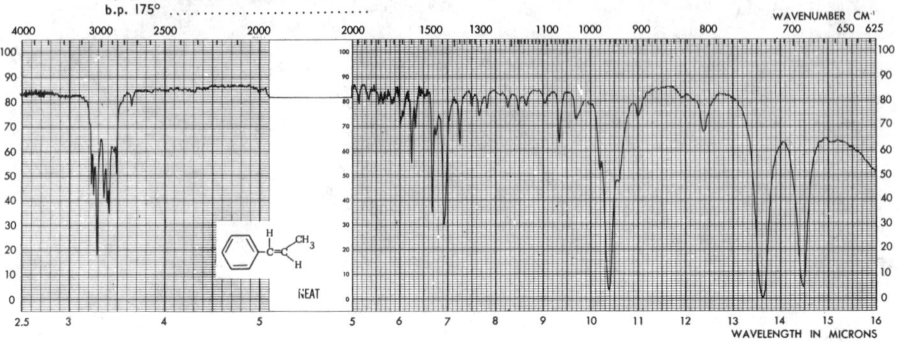

F

A2940-2 **Allylbenzene**
$C_6H_5CH_2CH{:}CH_2$ M.W. 118.18 n_D^{20} 1.5122
b.p. 64-66°/20 mm.
NEAT

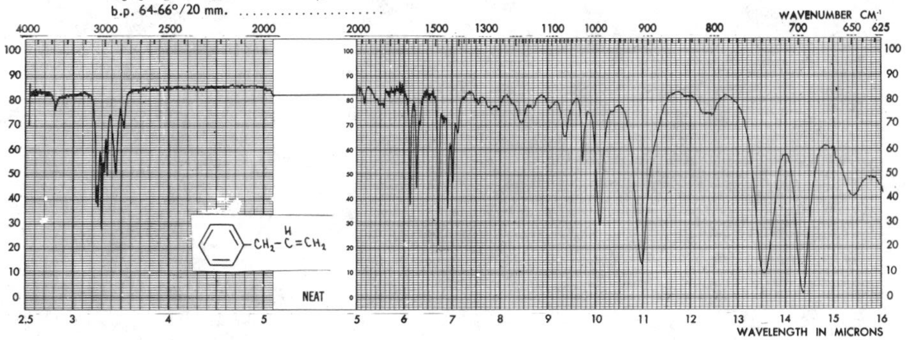

G

P2040-8 **1-Phenyl-2-butene**
$C_6H_5CH_2CH{:}CHCH_3$ M.W. 132.21
n_D^{20} 1.5140
NEAT

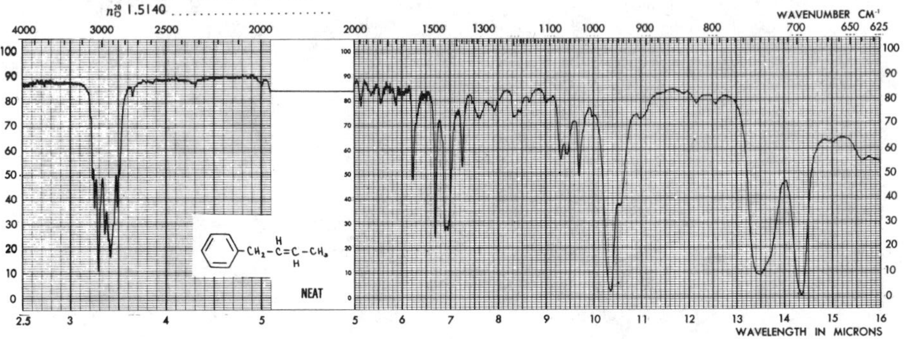

H

11,092-2 **Methallylbenzene** (2-methyl-3-phenyl-1-propene)
$C_6H_5CH_2C(CH_3){:}CH_2$ M.W. 132.21 n_D^{20} 1.5069
NEAT

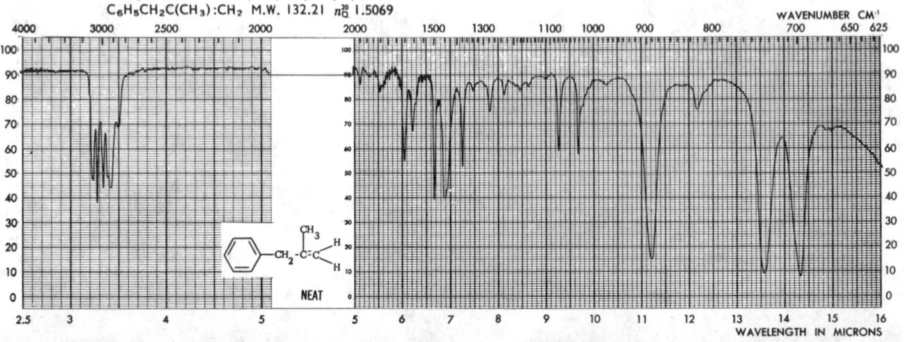

A P2060-2 4-Phenyl-1-butene
$C_6H_5CH_2CH_2CH{:}CH_2$ M.W. 132.21 n_D^{20} 1.5071
b.p. 175-177°
NEAT

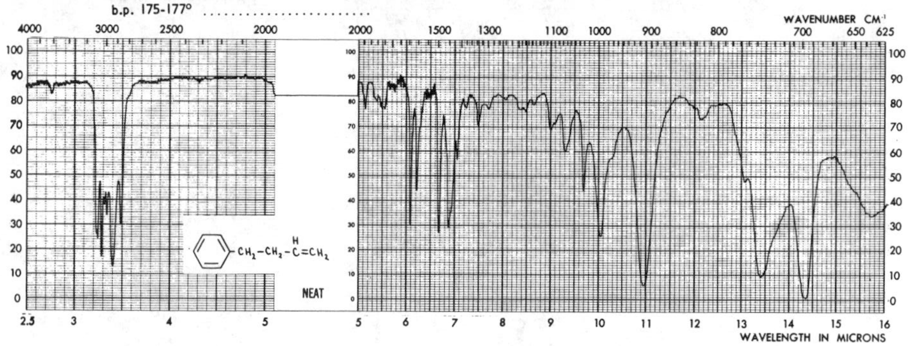

B 11,873-7 2-Methyl-4-phenyl-1-butene
$C_6H_5CH_2CH_2C(CH_3){:}CH_2$ M.W. 146.23
n_D^{20} 1.5048
NEAT

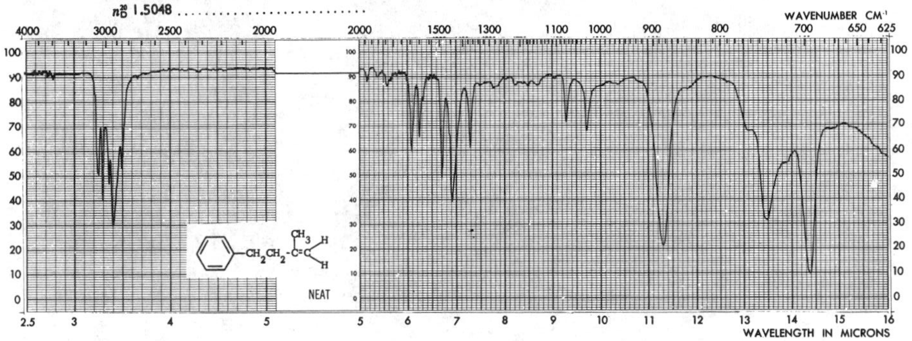

C 11,074-4 1-Phenylcyclopentene
$C_6H_5C_5H_7$ M.W. 144.22 n_D^{20} 1.5706
NEAT

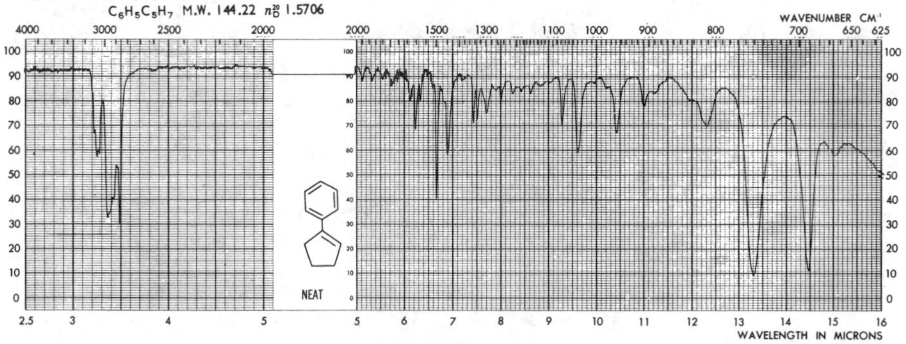

D P2230-3 1-Phenyl-1-cyclohexene
$C_6H_5C_6H_9$ M.W. 158.24 n_D^{20} 1.5665
NEAT

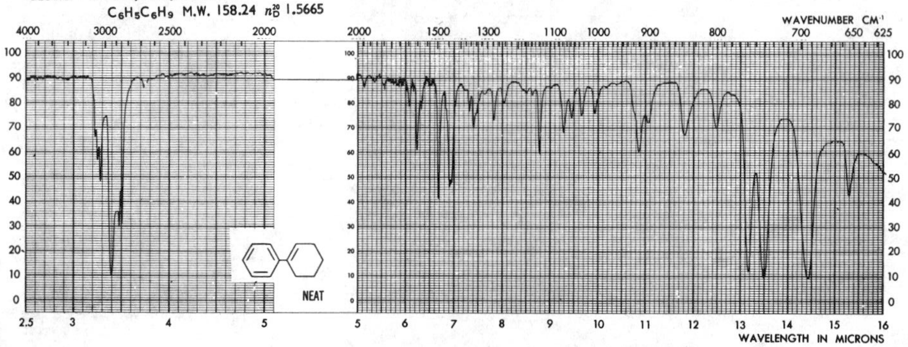

E 13,241-1 2-Phenyl-2-norbornene
M.W. 170.26 n_D^{20} 1.5804
NEAT

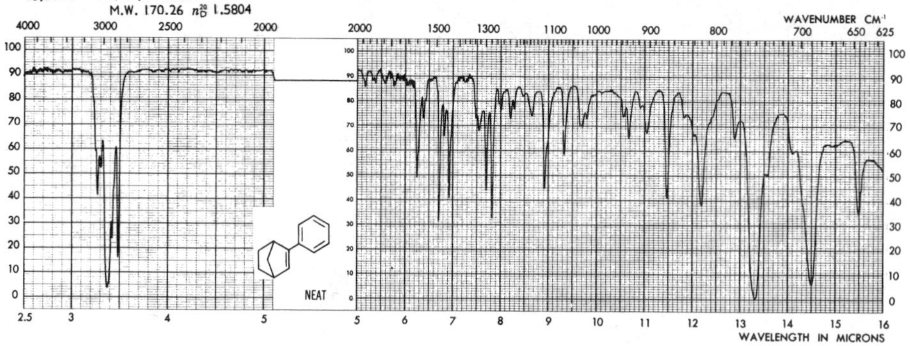

F D10,593-7 1,2-Dihydronaphthalene, tech., 75%
$C_{10}H_{10}$ M.W. 130.19 n_D^{20} 1.5784
NEAT

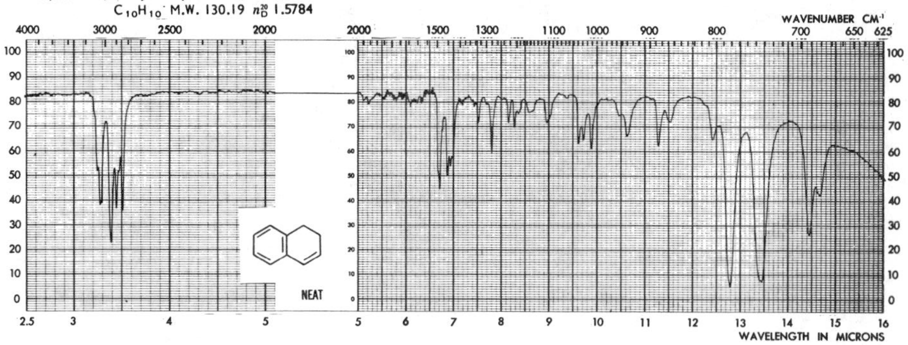

G 11,920-2 1-(o-Tolyl)-cycloheptene
$CH_3C_6H_4C_7H_{11}$ M.W. 186.30 n_D^{20} 1.5411
NEAT

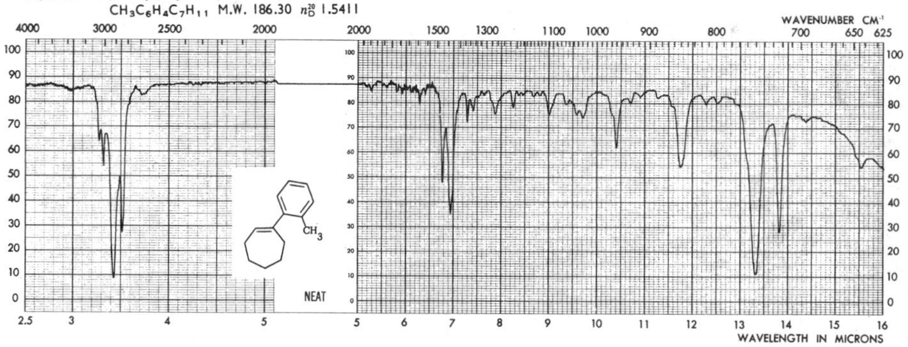

H M8080-6 4-Methylstyrene
$CH_3C_6H_4CH{:}CH_2$ M.W. 118.18 n_D^{20} 1.5412 b.p. 170-175°
NEAT

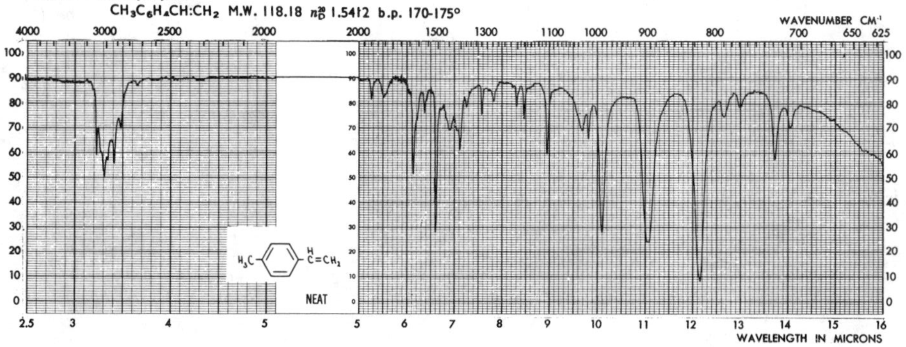

A

16,909-9
Divinylbenzene, mixed isomers, tech., 55%
$C_6H_4(CH{=}CH_2)_2$
M.W. 130.19 b.p. 87° d 0.918

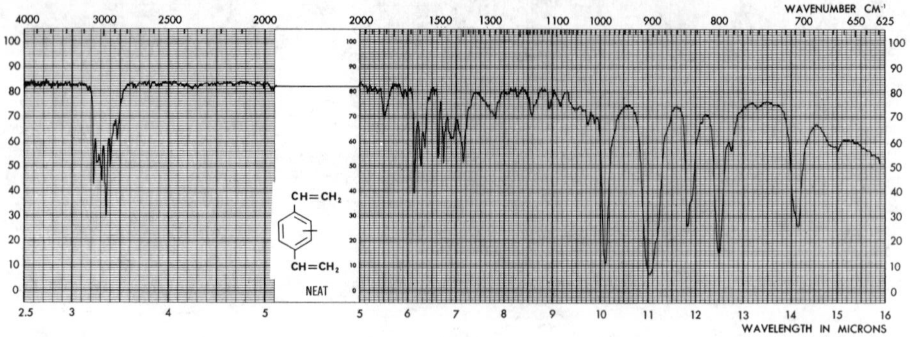

NEAT

B

I-1965-9 **p-Isopropenylisopropylbenzene (p-isopropyl-α-methylstyrene)**
$(CH_3)_2CHC_6H_4C(CH_3){:}CH_2$ M.W. 160.26 n_D^{20} 1.5232 ....

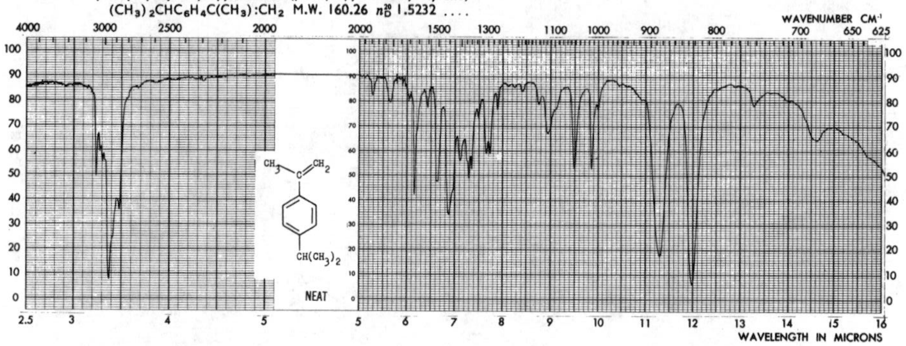

NEAT

C

D12,475-3 **p-Diisopropenylbenzene**
$C_6H_4[C(CH_3){:}CH_2]_2$ M.W. 158.23 m.p. 59.5-63°

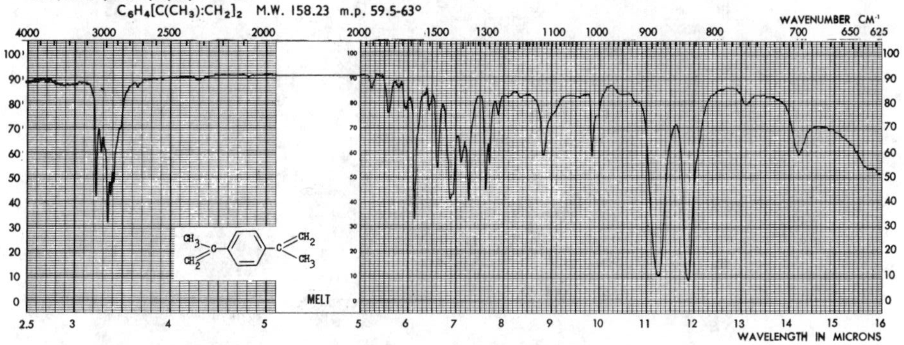

MELT

D

D18,580-9 **2,6-Dimethylstyrene**
$(CH_3)_2C_6H_3CH{:}CH_2$ M.W. 132.21
n_D^{20} 1.5309 ....

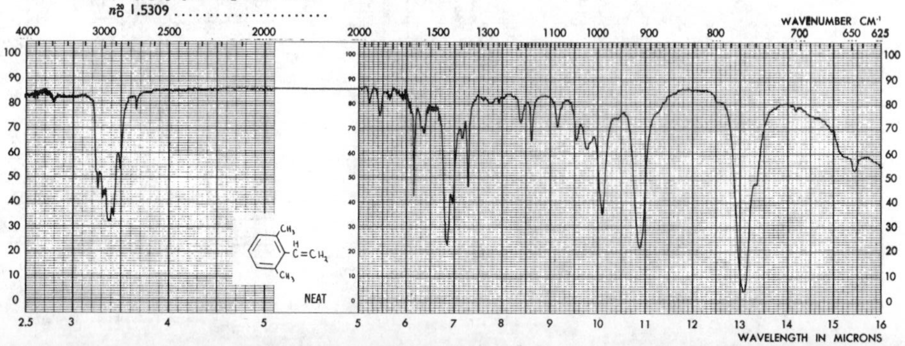

NEAT

E

10,421-3 **Biphenyl, zone refined**
$C_6H_5C_6H_5$ M.W. 154.21 m.p. 68.95°

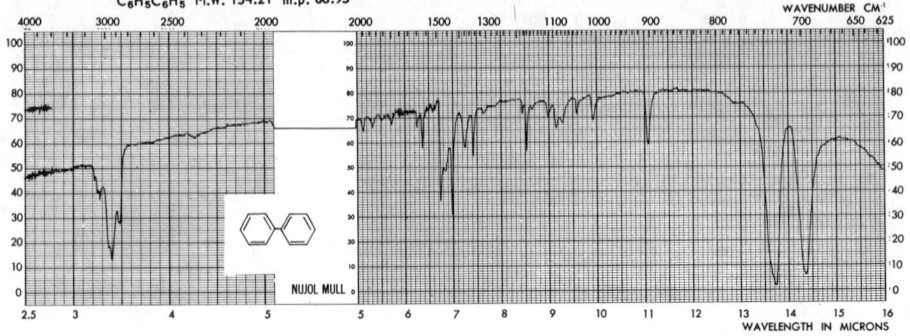

NUJOL MULL

F

T280-0 **o-Terphenyl**
$C_6H_5C_6H_4C_6H_5$ M.W. 230.31 m.p. 53-55°

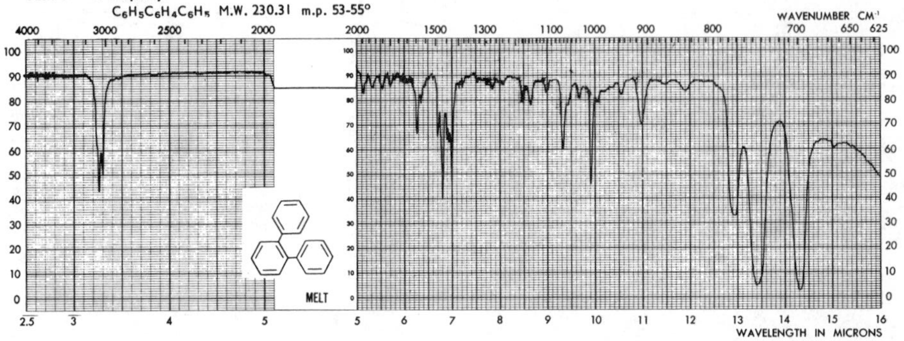

MELT

G

T300 **m-Terphenyl** ....

NUJOL MULL

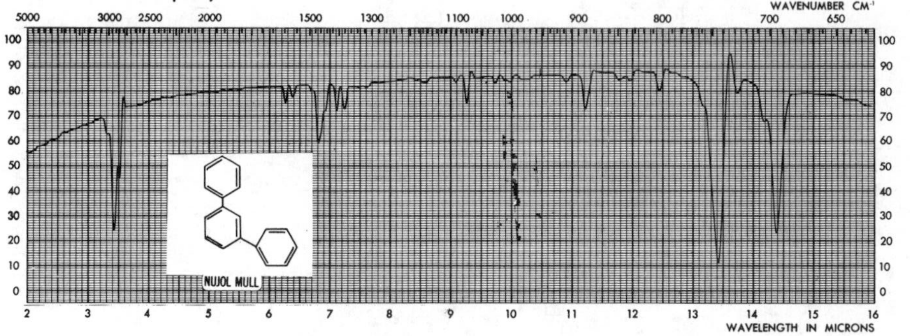

H

15,102-5 **p-Terphenyl, zone refined, 99.9+%, GOLD LABEL**
$C_6H_5C_6H_4C_6H_5$ M.W. 230.31 m.p. 212.48°

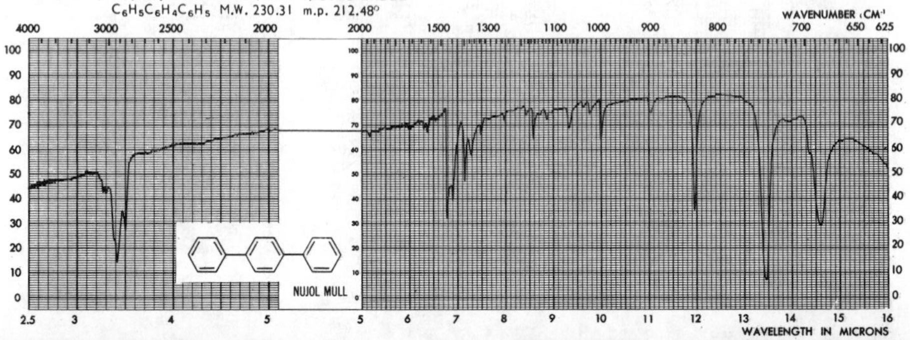

NUJOL MULL

WAVENUMBER CM⁻¹ / WAVELENGTH IN MICRONS

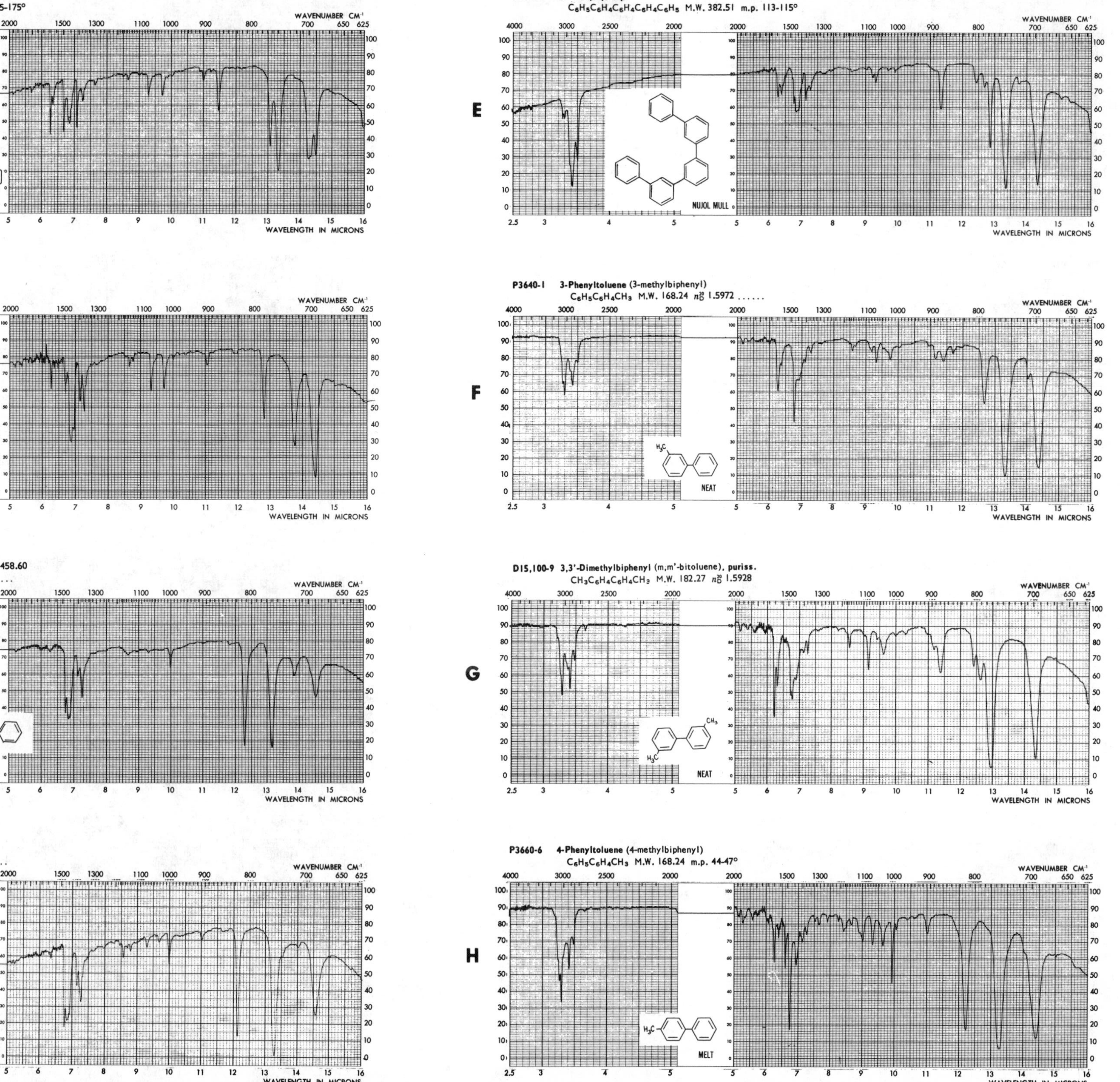
A
T8200-7 1,3,5-Triphenylbenzene
$(C_6H_5)_3C_6H_3$ M.W. 306.41 m.p. 171.5-175°
NUJOL MULL
B
14,945-4
Hexaphenylbenzene, 98%
$C_6(C_6H_5)_6$
M.W. 534.7 m.p. >300°
NUJOL MULL
C
10,855-3 p-Sexiphenyl
$C_6H_5C_6H_4C_6H_4C_6H_4C_6H_4C_6H_5$ M.W. 458.60
m.p. > 300°
NUJOL MULL
D
Q20-5 p-Quaterphenyl
$C_6H_5C_6H_4C_6H_4C_6H_5$ M.W. 306.41
m.p. 310-312°
NUJOL MULL
E
Q180-8 m-Quinquephenyl
$C_6H_5C_6H_4C_6H_4C_6H_4C_6H_5$ M.W. 382.51 m.p. 113-115°
NUJOL MULL
F
P3640-1 3-Phenyltoluene (3-methylbiphenyl)
$C_6H_5C_6H_4CH_3$ M.W. 168.24 n_D^{20} 1.5972
NEAT
G
D15,100-9 3,3'-Dimethylbiphenyl (m,m'-bitoluene), puriss.
$CH_3C_6H_4C_6H_4CH_3$ M.W. 182.27 n_D^{20} 1.5928
NEAT
H
P3660-6 4-Phenyltoluene (4-methylbiphenyl)
$C_6H_5C_6H_4CH_3$ M.W. 168.24 m.p. 44-47°
MELT
WAVENUMBER CM⁻¹
WAVELENGTH IN MICRONS
ALDRICH

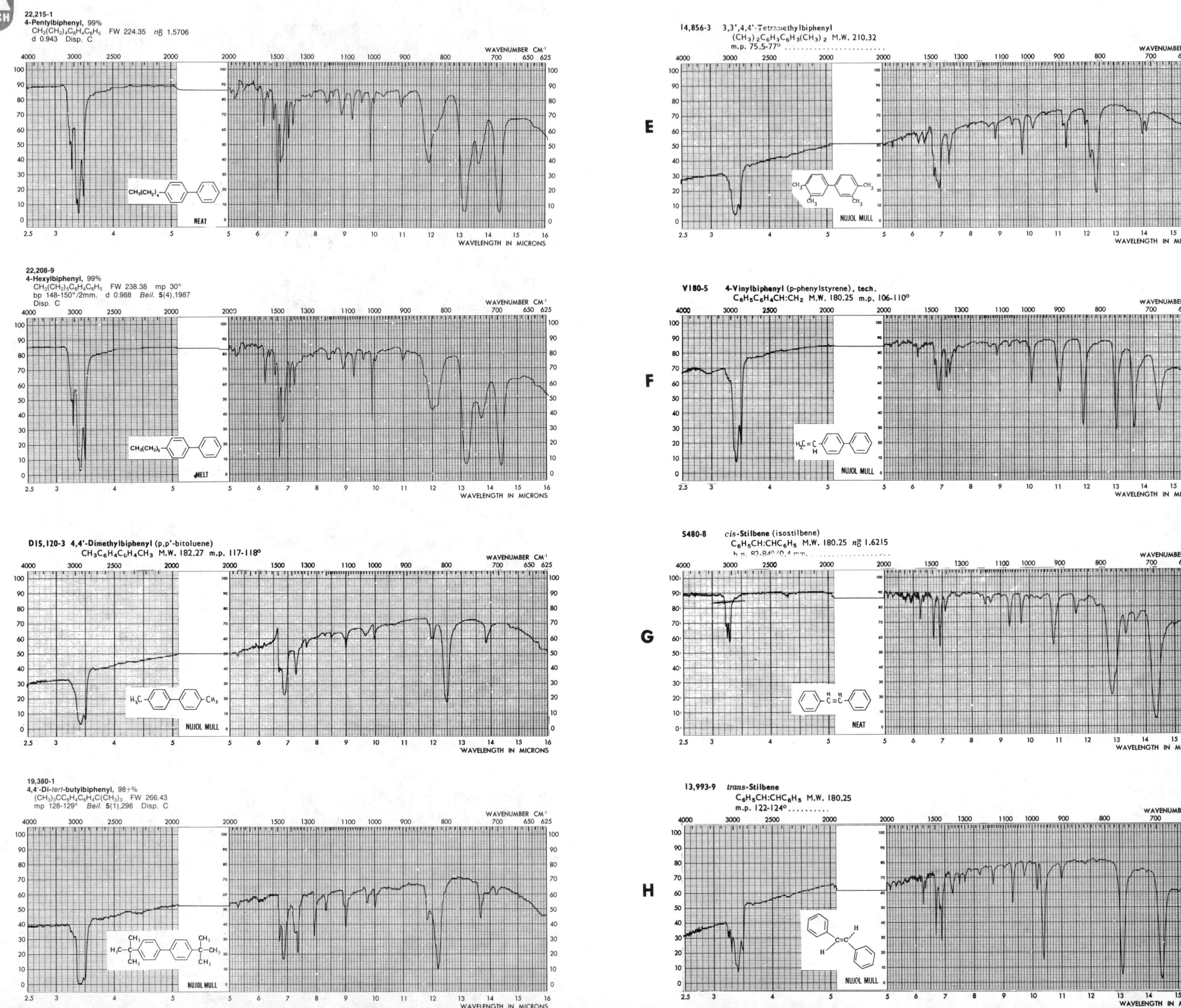
ALDRICH
A
22,215-1
4-Pentylbiphenyl, 99%
$CH_3(CH_2)_4C_6H_4C_6H_5$ FW 224.35 n_D^{20} 1.5706
d 0.943 Disp. C
NEAT
B
22,208-9
4-Hexylbiphenyl, 99%
$CH_3(CH_2)_5C_6H_4C_6H_5$ FW 238.38 mp 30°
bp 148-150°/2mm. d 0.988 Beil. 5(4),1987
Disp. C
MELT
C
D15,120-3 4,4'-Dimethylbiphenyl (p,p'-bitoluene)
$CH_3C_6H_4C_6H_4CH_3$ M.W. 182.27 m.p. 117-118°
NUJOL MULL
D
19,380-1
4,4'-Di-tert-butylbiphenyl, 98+%
$(CH_3)_3CC_6H_4C_6H_4C(CH_3)_3$ FW 266.43
mp 128-129° Beil. 5(1),298 Disp. C
NUJOL MULL
E
14,856-3 3,3',4,4'-Tetramethylbiphenyl
$(CH_3)_2C_6H_3C_6H_3(CH_3)_2$ M.W. 210.32
m.p. 75.5-77°
NUJOL MULL
F
V180-5 4-Vinylbiphenyl (p-phenylstyrene), tech.
$C_6H_5C_6H_4CH:CH_2$ M.W. 180.25 m.p. 106-110°
NUJOL MULL
G
S480-8 cis-Stilbene (isostilbene)
$C_6H_5CH:CHC_6H_5$ M.W. 180.25 n_D^{20} 1.6215
NEAT
H
13,993-9 trans-Stilbene
$C_6H_5CH:CHC_6H_5$ M.W. 180.25
m.p. 122-124°
NUJOL MULL
WAVENUMBER CM⁻¹
WAVELENGTH IN MICRONS

A

D21,375-6 *trans*-p,p'-Diphenylstilbene (DPS)
$C_6H_5C_6H_4CH{:}CHC_6H_4C_6H_5$ M.W. 332.45
m.p. 300° (dec.)

NUJOL MULL

B

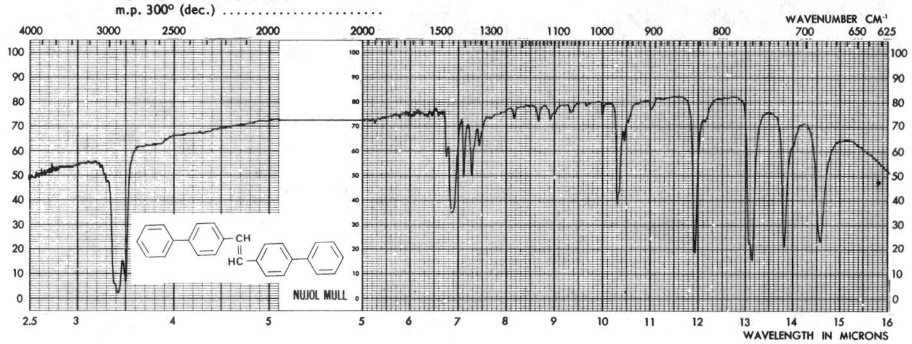

D20,600-8 1,4-Diphenyl-1,3-butadiene
$C_6H_5CH{:}CHCH{:}CHC_6H_5$ M.W. 206.29
m.p. 151-153°

NUJOL MULL

C

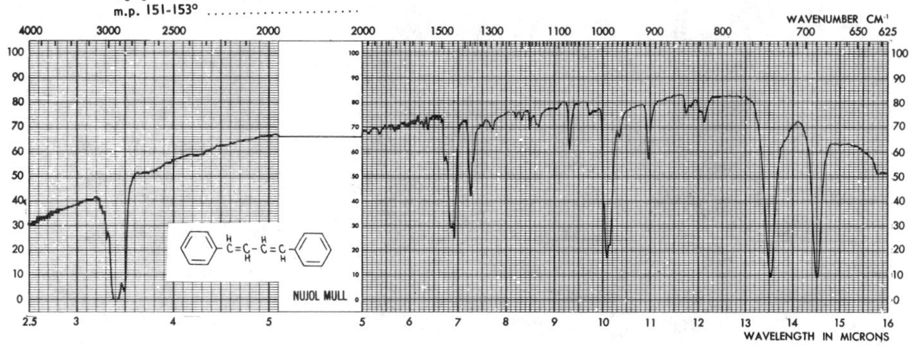

D20,800-0 1,6-Diphenylhexatriene
$C_6H_5CH{:}CHCH{:}CHCH{:}CHC_6H_5$ M.W. 232.33
m.p. 199-203°

NUJOL MULL

D

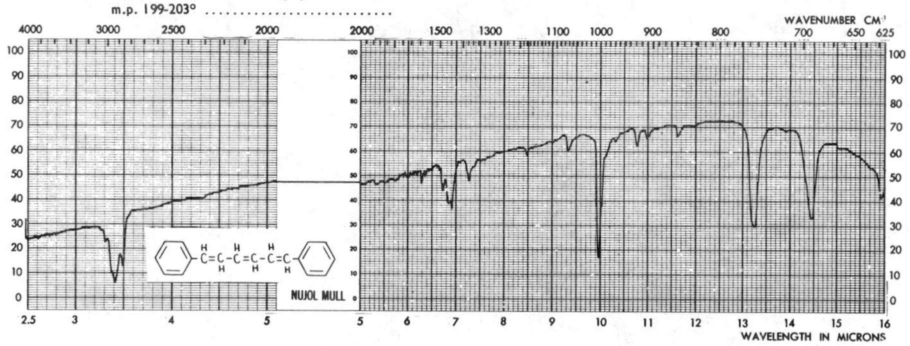

D21,000-5 1,8-Diphenyl-1,3,5,7-octatetraene
$C_6H_5CH{:}CHCH{:}CHCH{:}CHCH{:}CHC_6H_5$ M.W. 258.36
m.p. 235-237°

NUJOL MULL

E

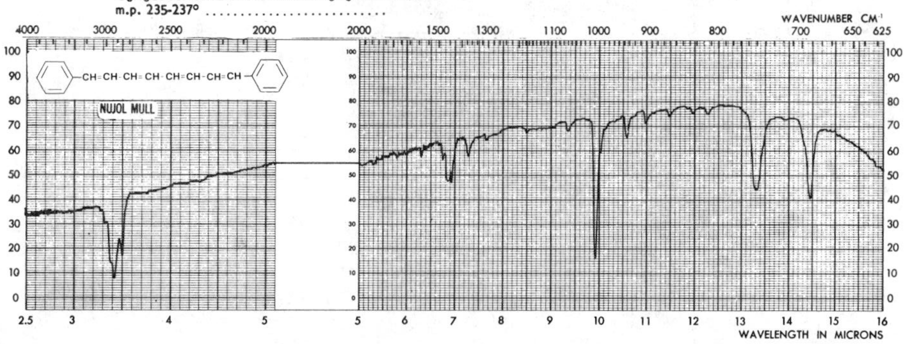

D20,680-6 1,1-Diphenylethylene
$(C_6H_5)_2C{:}CH_2$ M.W. 180.25 n_D^{20} 1.6083

NEAT

F

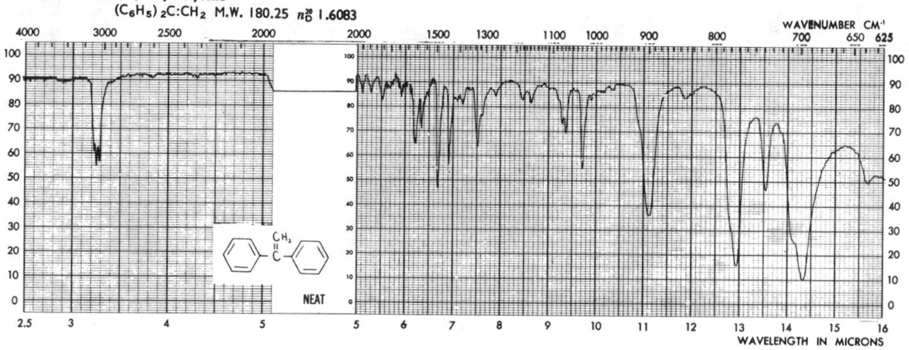

D20,770-5 Diphenylfulvene
M.W. 230.31 m.p. 78-80°

NUJOL MULL

G

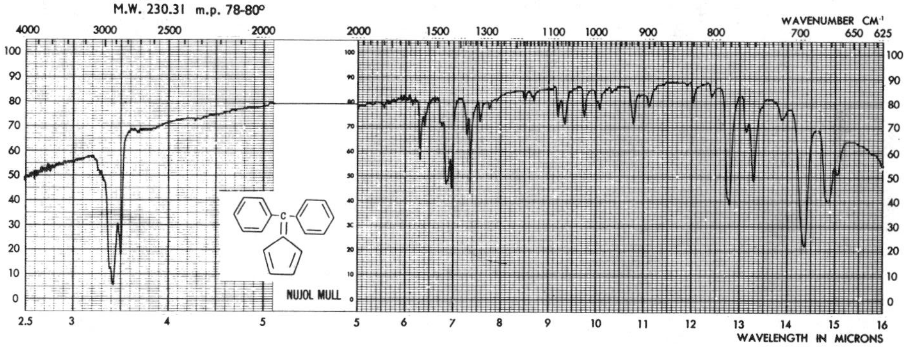

T8280-5 Triphenylethylene
$C_6H_5CH{:}C(C_6H_5)_2$ M.W. 256.35 m.p. 66-69°

MELT

H

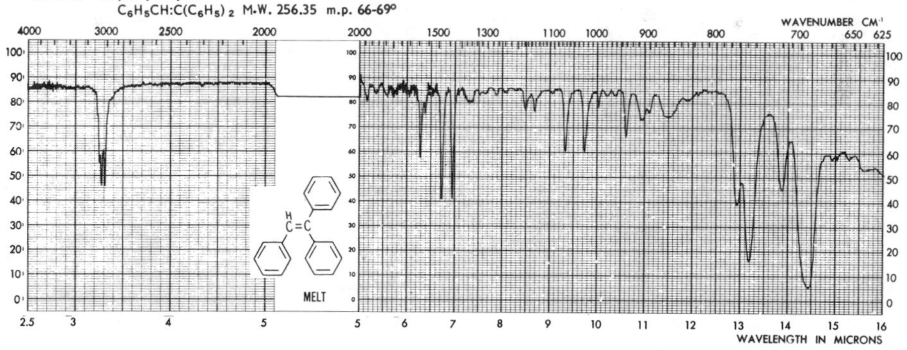

T2620-4 Tetraphenylethylene
$(C_6H_5)_2C{:}C(C_6H_5)_2$ M.W. 332.45
m.p. 222-224°

NUJOL MULL

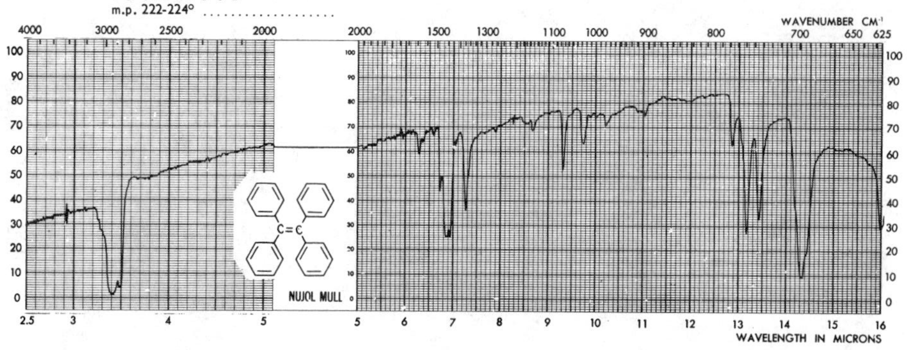

A

T8230-9 1,1,4-Triphenylbutadiene
$C_6H_5CH{:}CHCH{:}C(C_6H_5)_2$ M.W. 282.39 m.p. 100-103°

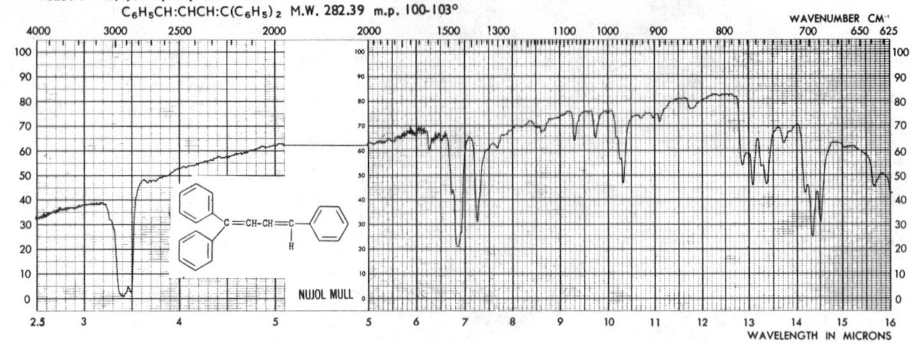

NUJOL MULL

B

18,521-3
1,1,4,4-Tetraphenyl-1,3-butadiene, scintillation grade, 99+%, GOLD LABEL
$(C_6H_5)_2C{=}CHCH{=}C(C_6H_5)_2$
M.W. 358.49 m.p. 207-209° Beil. **5**,750

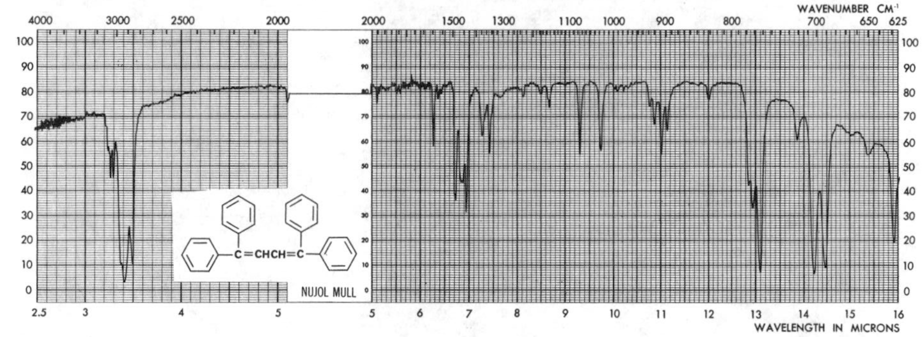

NUJOL MULL

C

17,870-5
1,1,4,4-Tetraphenyl-1,3-butadiene, 99%
$(C_6H_5)_2C{=}CHCH{=}C(C_6H_5)_2$
M.W. 358.49 m.p. 196-198° Beil. **5**,750

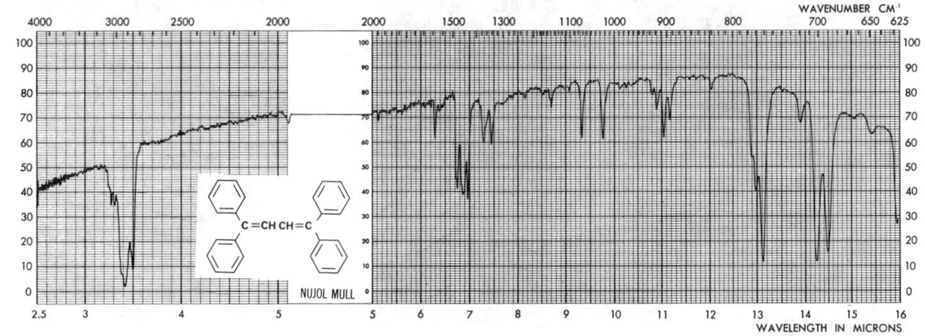

NUJOL MULL

D

22,244-5
***p*-Bis(*o*-methylstyryl)benzene,** 99%
$(CH_3C_6H_4CH{=}CH)_2C_6H_4$ FW 310.44 mp 178-180°
Disp. C

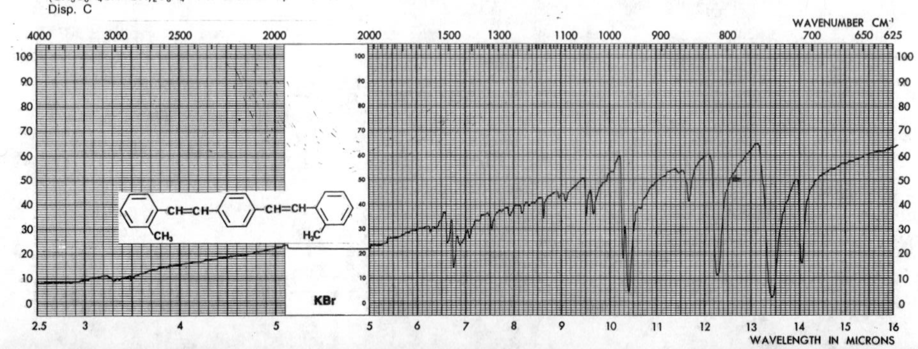

KBr

E

13,467-8 Tetraphenylbutatriene
$(C_6H_5)_2C{:}C{:}C{:}C(C_6H_5)_2$ M.W. 356.47
m.p. 235-238° (dec.)

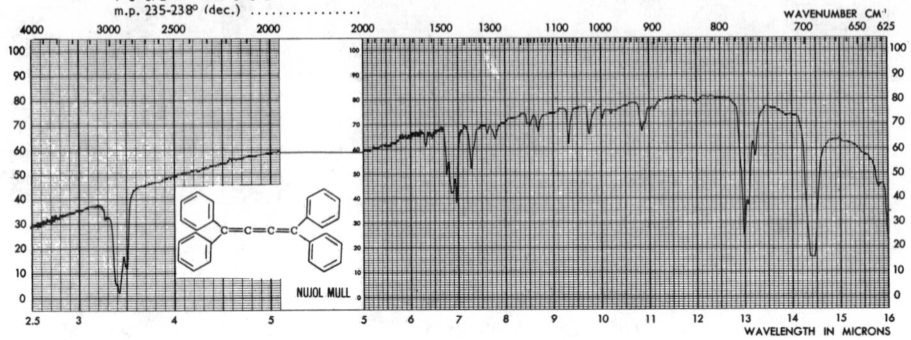

NUJOL MULL

F

T2575-5 1,2,3,4-Tetraphenyl-1,3-cyclopentadiene
M.W. 370.50 m.p. 177-180°

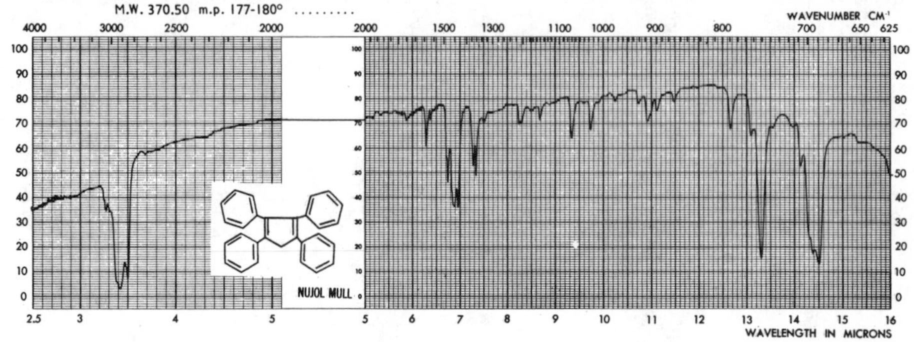

NUJOL MULL

G

I-280-0 Indene, tech., 90+%
M.W. 116.16 n_D^{20} 1.5740 m.p. -5 to -3°
b.p. 181°

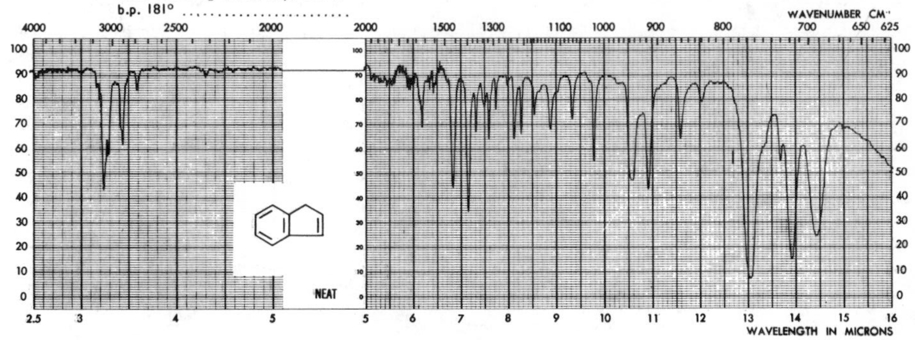

NEAT

H

19,382-8
Indene, 99+%, GOLD LABEL
FW 116.16 mp -2° bp 181.6° n_D^{20} 1.5762
d 0.996 *Beil.* **5**,515 Disp. C

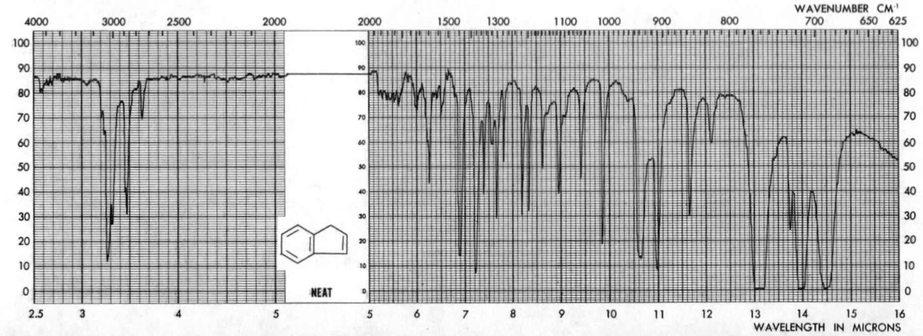

NEAT

A

A9720-3 Azulene
M.W. 128.17 m.p. 99-100.5°

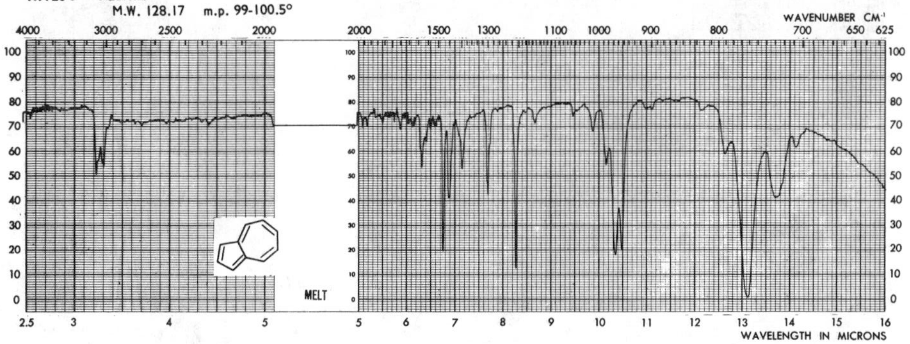

MELT

B

G1100-4 Guaiazulene (1,4-dimethyl-7-isopropylazulene)
M.W. 198.31 ....

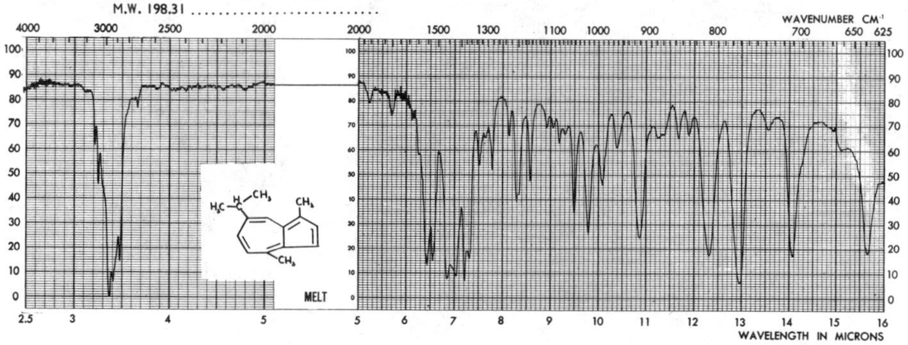

MELT

C

11,390-5 Naphthalene, zone refined
$C_{10}H_8$ M.W. 128.18 m.p. 80.20°

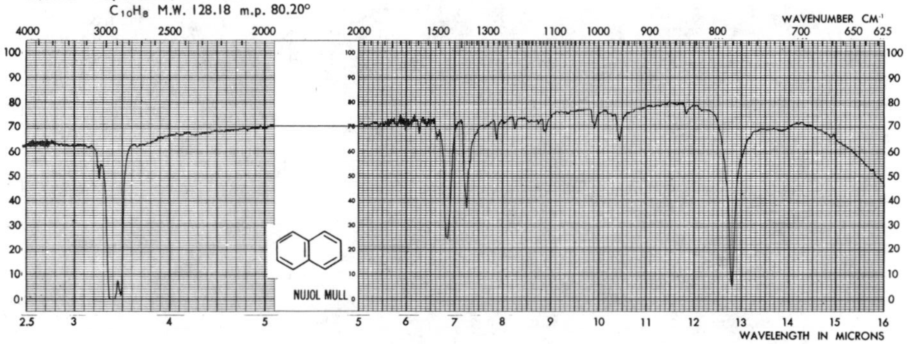

NUJOL MULL

D

M5680-8 1-Methylnaphthalene, puriss.
$C_{10}H_7CH_3$ M.W. 142.20 n_D^{20} 1.6159
b.p. 240-243° ....

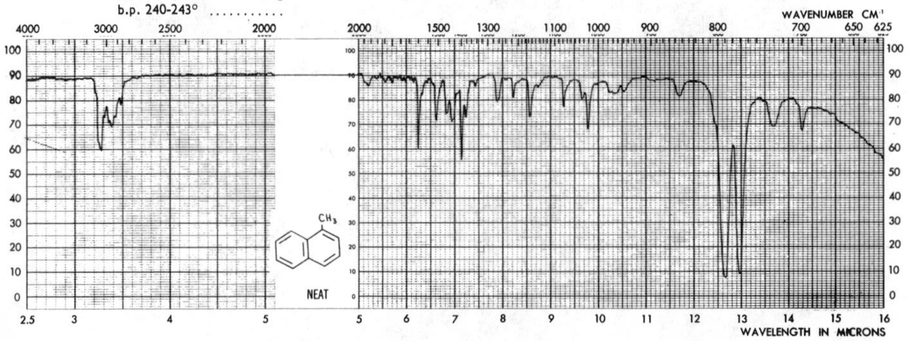

NEAT

E

M5700-6 2-Methylnaphthalene, puriss.
$C_{10}H_7CH_3$ M.W. 142.20 m.p. 34-36°

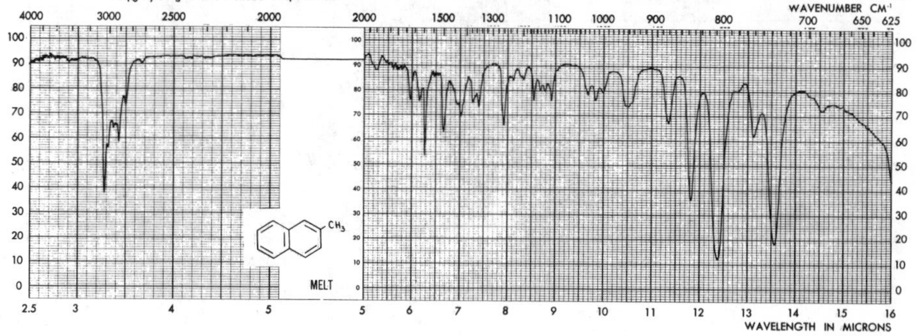

MELT

F

E4000-5 2-Ethylnaphthalene, puriss.
$C_{10}H_7C_2H_5$ M.W. 156.23 n_D^{20} 1.5984

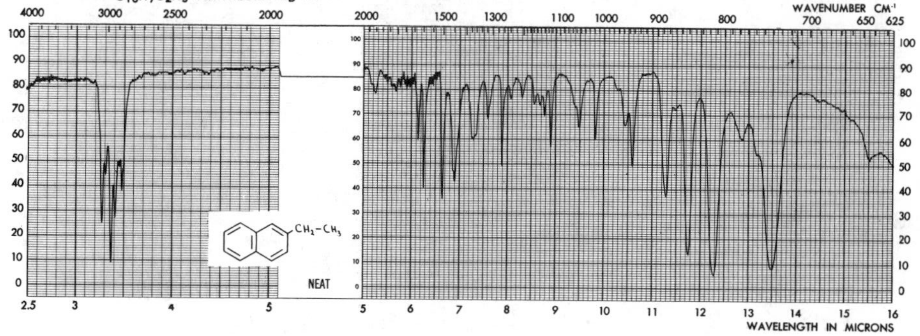

NEAT

G

D17,020-8 1,3-Dimethylnaphthalene
$C_{10}H_6(CH_3)_2$ M.W. 156.23 n_D^{20} 1.6009

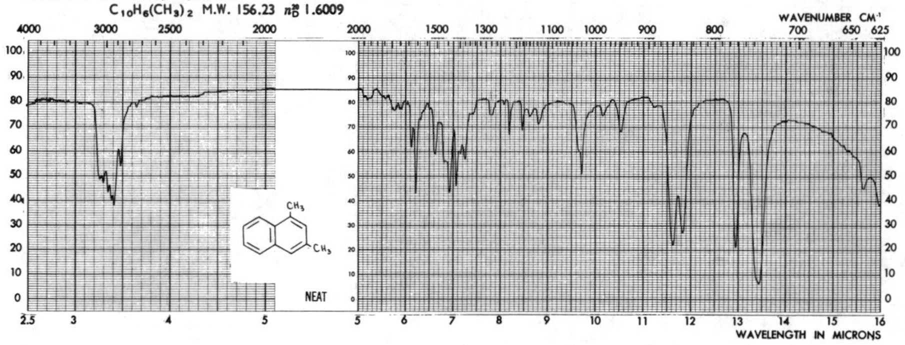

NEAT

H

D17,080-1 2,3-Dimethylnaphthalene, puriss.
$C_{10}H_6(CH_3)_2$ M.W. 156.23 m.p. 102-104°

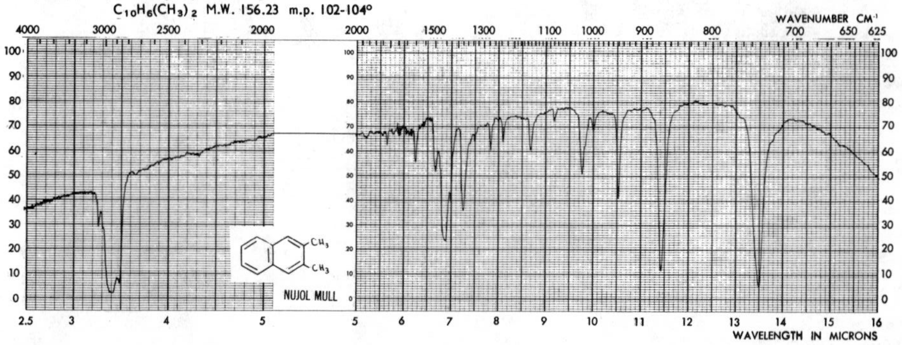

NUJOL MULL

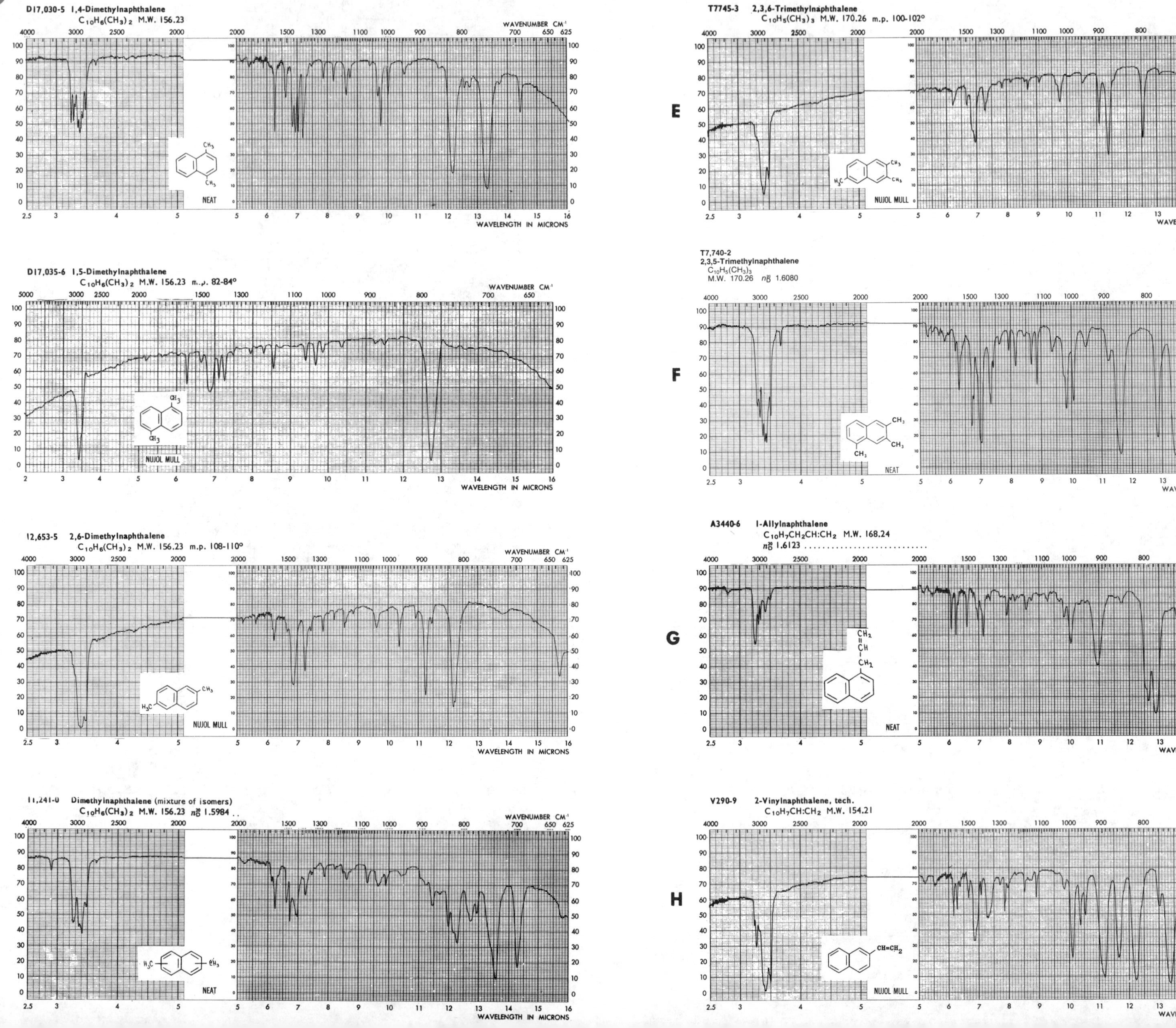
ALDRICH
A
D17,030-5 1,4-Dimethylnaphthalene
$C_{10}H_6(CH_3)_2$ M.W. 156.23
NEAT
B
D17,035-6 1,5-Dimethylnaphthalene
$C_{10}H_6(CH_3)_2$ M.W. 156.23 m.p. 82-84°
NUJOL MULL
C
12,653-5 2,6-Dimethylnaphthalene
$C_{10}H_6(CH_3)_2$ M.W. 156.23 m.p. 108-110°
NUJOL MULL
D
11,241-0 Dimethylnaphthalene (mixture of isomers)
$C_{10}H_6(CH_3)_2$ M.W. 156.23 n_D^{20} 1.5984
NEAT
E
T7745-3 2,3,6-Trimethylnaphthalene
$C_{10}H_5(CH_3)_3$ M.W. 170.26 m.p. 100-102°
NUJOL MULL
F
T7,740-2
2,3,5-Trimethylnaphthalene
$C_{10}H_5(CH_3)_3$
M.W. 170.26 n_D^{20} 1.6080
NEAT
G
A3440-6 1-Allylnaphthalene
$C_{10}H_7CH_2CH{:}CH_2$ M.W. 168.24
n_D^{20} 1.6123
NEAT
H
V290-9 2-Vinylnaphthalene, tech.
$C_{10}H_7CH{:}CH_2$ M.W. 154.21
NUJOL MULL
WAVENUMBER CM⁻¹
WAVELENGTH IN MICRONS

A

P2740-2 **1-Phenylnaphthalene**
$C_{10}H_7C_6H_5$ M.W. 204.27 n_D^{20} 1.6644 b.p. 324-325°

NEAT

B

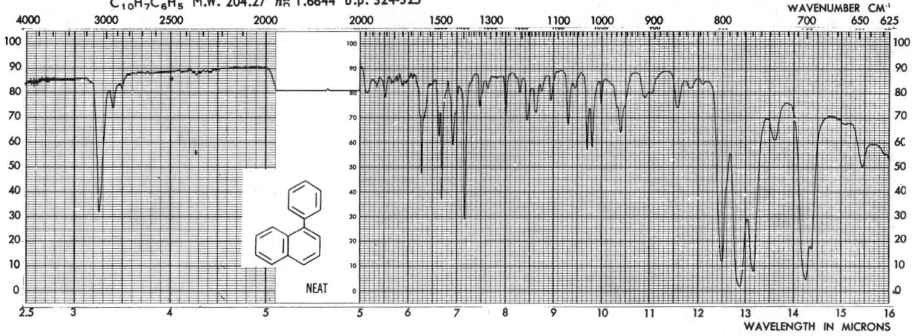

P2260-5 **1-Phenyl-3,4-dihydronaphthalene** (1,2-dihydro-4-phenylnaphthalene)
$C_6H_5C_{10}H_9$ M.W. 206.29 n_D^{20} 1.6303
b.p. 175-177°/12 mm.

NEAT

C

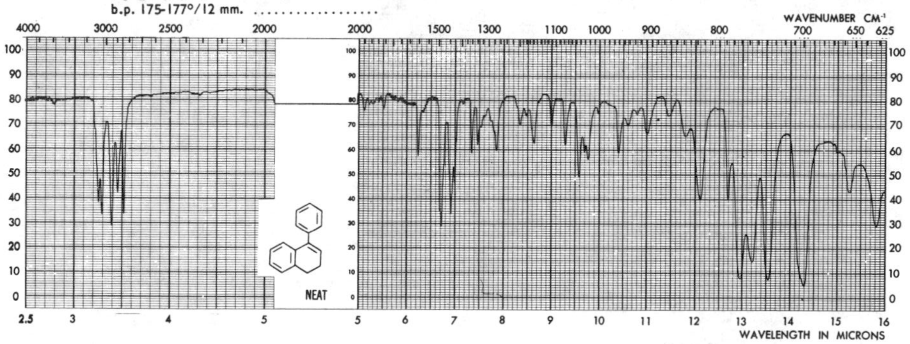

B3514-8 ***trans*-1-(4-Biphenylyl)-2-(1-naphthyl)-ethylene**
(aNBE), scintillation grade
$C_6H_5C_6H_4CH{:}CHC_{10}H_7$ M.W. 306.41 m.p. 144-146°

NUJOL MULL

D

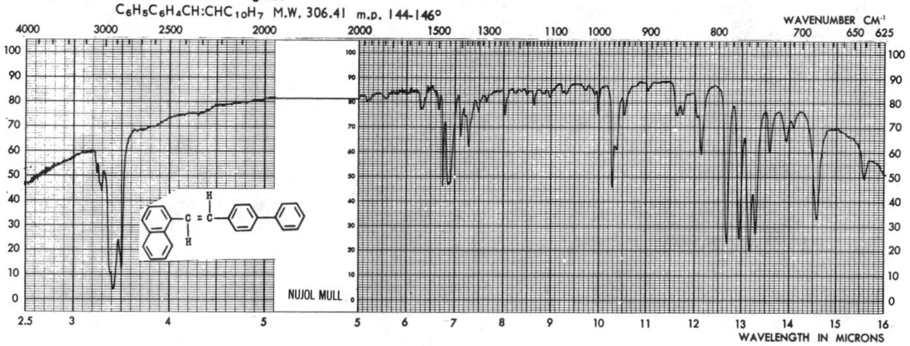

12,833-3 **Fluorene, 98%**
M.W. 166.22 m.p. 112-115°

NUJOL MULL

E

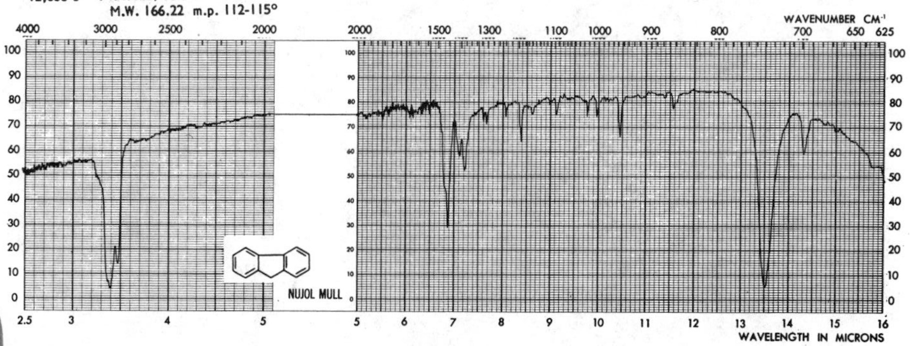

M4659-4 **1-Methylfluorene**
M.W. 180.25 m.p. 86-88°

NUJOL MULL

F

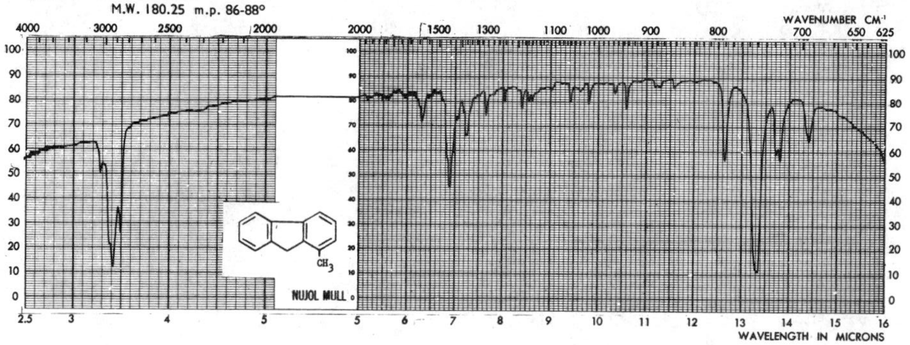

21,685-2
9-Ethylfluorene, 97%
FW 194.28 bp 123-124°/1mm. n_D^{20} 1.6200
d 1.047 *Beil.* **5**,645 Disp. C

NEAT

G

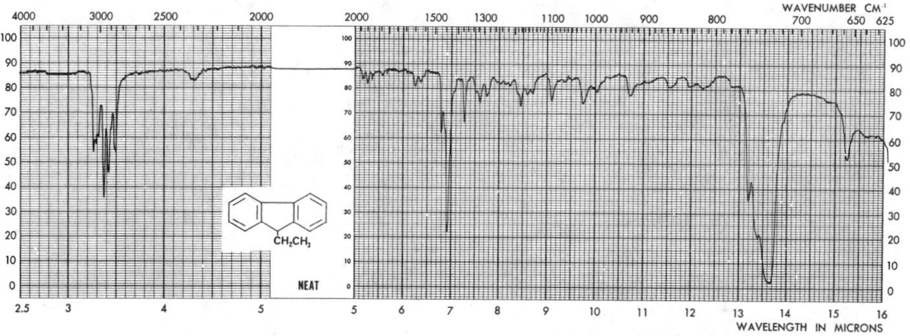

E3270-3 **9-Ethylidenefluorene**
M.W. 192.26 m.p. 102-105°

NUJOL MULL

H

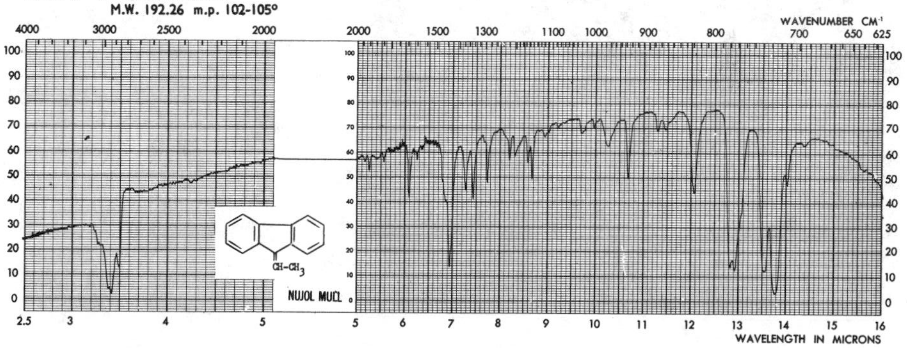

12,378-1 **9,9'-Bifluorene** (difluorenyl)
M.W. 330.43 m.p. 240-242°

NUJOL MULL

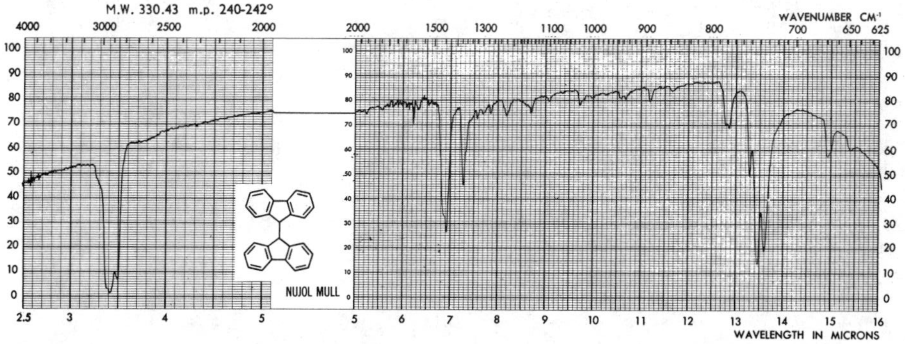

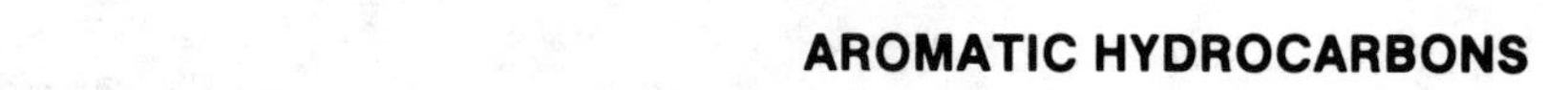

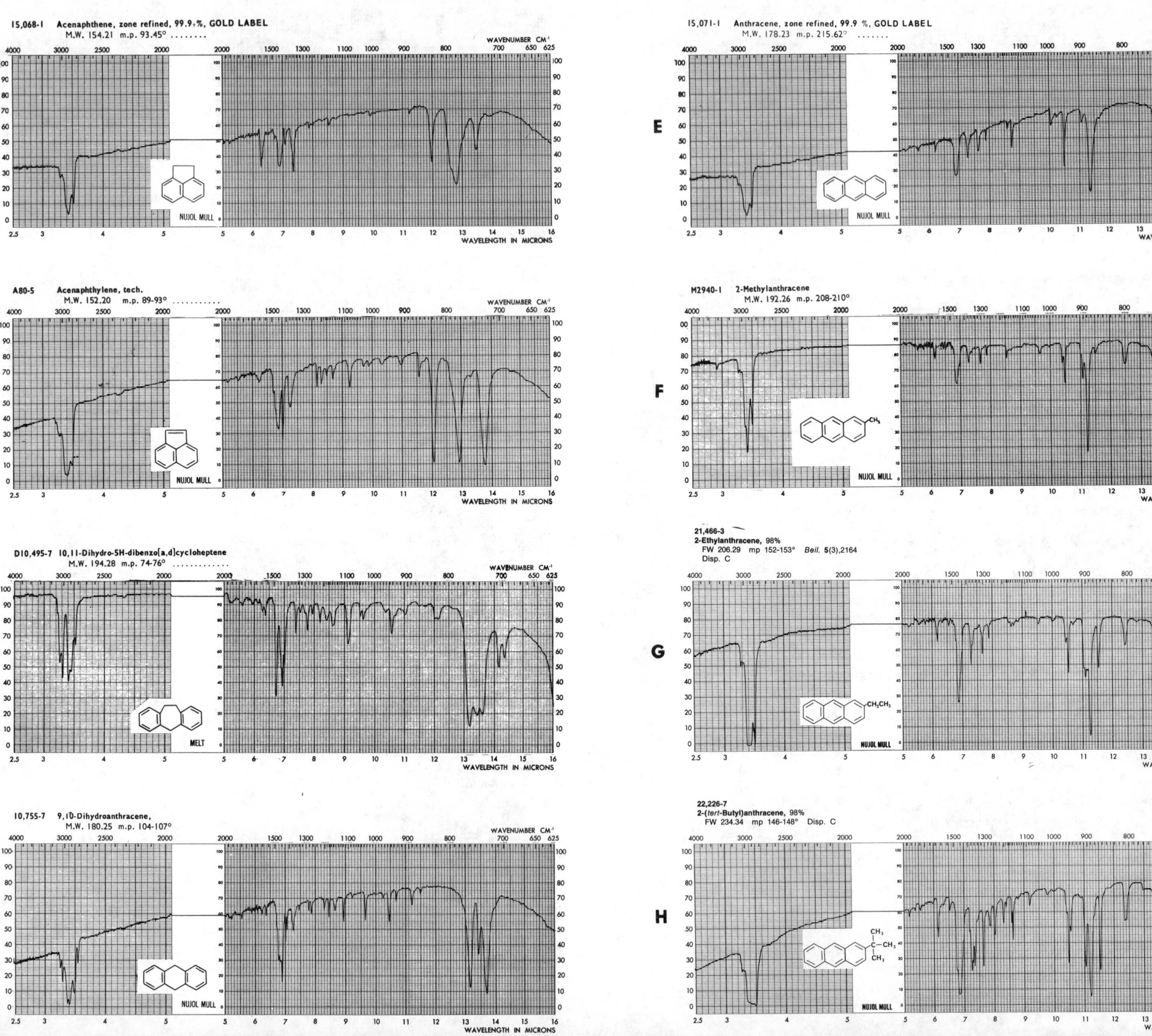
ALDRICH
A
15,068-1 Acenaphthene, zone refined, 99.9+%, GOLD LABEL
M.W. 154.21 m.p. 93.45° ....
NUJOL MULL
B
A80-5 Acenaphthylene, tech.
M.W. 152.20 m.p. 89-93° ....
NUJOL MULL
C
D10,495-7 10,11-Dihydro-5H-dibenzo[a,d]cycloheptene
M.W. 194.28 m.p. 74-76° ....
MELT
D
10,755-7 9,10-Dihydroanthracene,
M.W. 180.25 m.p. 104-107°
NUJOL MULL
E
15,071-1 Anthracene, zone refined, 99.9 %, GOLD LABEL
M.W. 178.23 m.p. 215.62° ......
NUJOL MULL
F
M2940-1 2-Methylanthracene
M.W. 192.26 m.p. 208-210°
CH₃
NUJOL MULL
G
21,466-3
2-Ethylanthracene, 98%
FW 206.29 mp 152-153° Beil. 5(3),2164
Disp. C
CH₂CH₃
NUJOL MULL
H
22,226-7
2-(tert-Butyl)anthracene, 98%
FW 234.34 mp 146-148° Disp. C
NUJOL MULL
WAVENUMBER CM⁻¹
WAVELENGTH IN MICRONS

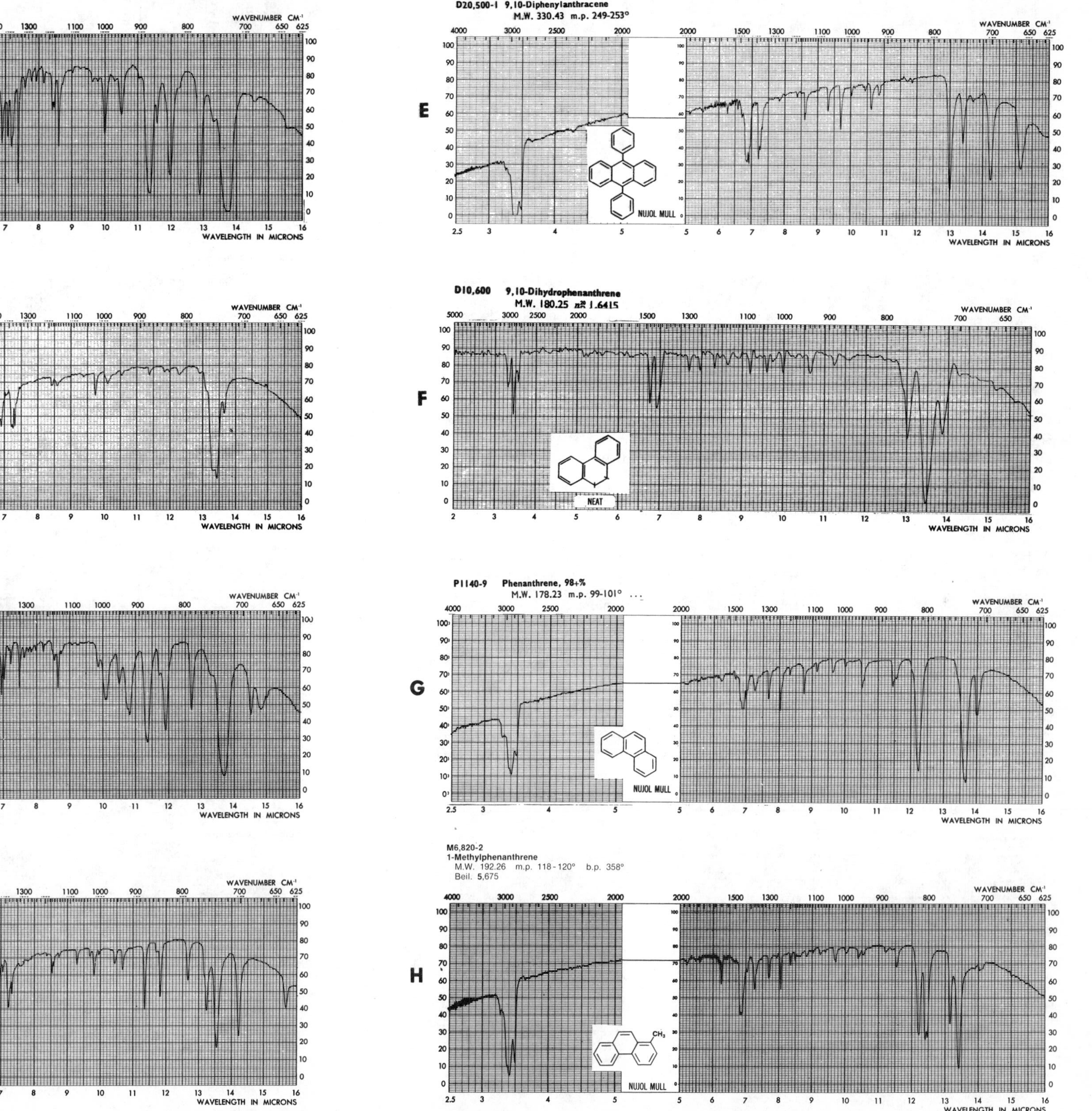
A
M2960-6 9-Methylanthracene
M.W. 192.26 m.p. 79-81°
MELT
B
D14,670-6 9,10-Dimethylanthracene
M.W. 196.21 m.p. 182-184°
NUJOL MULL
C
V170-8 9-Vinylanthracene
M.W. 204.27 m.p. 65-67°
MELT
D
P1800-4 9-Phenylanthracene
M.W. 254.33 m.p. 154-156°
NUJOL MULL
E
D20,500-1 9,10-Diphenylanthracene
M.W. 330.43 m.p. 249-253°
NUJOL MULL
F
D10,600 9,10-Dihydrophenanthrene
M.W. 180.25 n_D^{20} 1.6415
NEAT
G
P1140-9 Phenanthrene, 98+%
M.W. 178.23 m.p. 99-101°
NUJOL MULL
H
M6,820-2
1-Methylphenanthrene
M.W. 192.26 m.p. 118-120° b.p. 358°
Beil. 5,675
NUJOL MULL
WAVENUMBER CM⁻¹
WAVELENGTH IN MICRONS

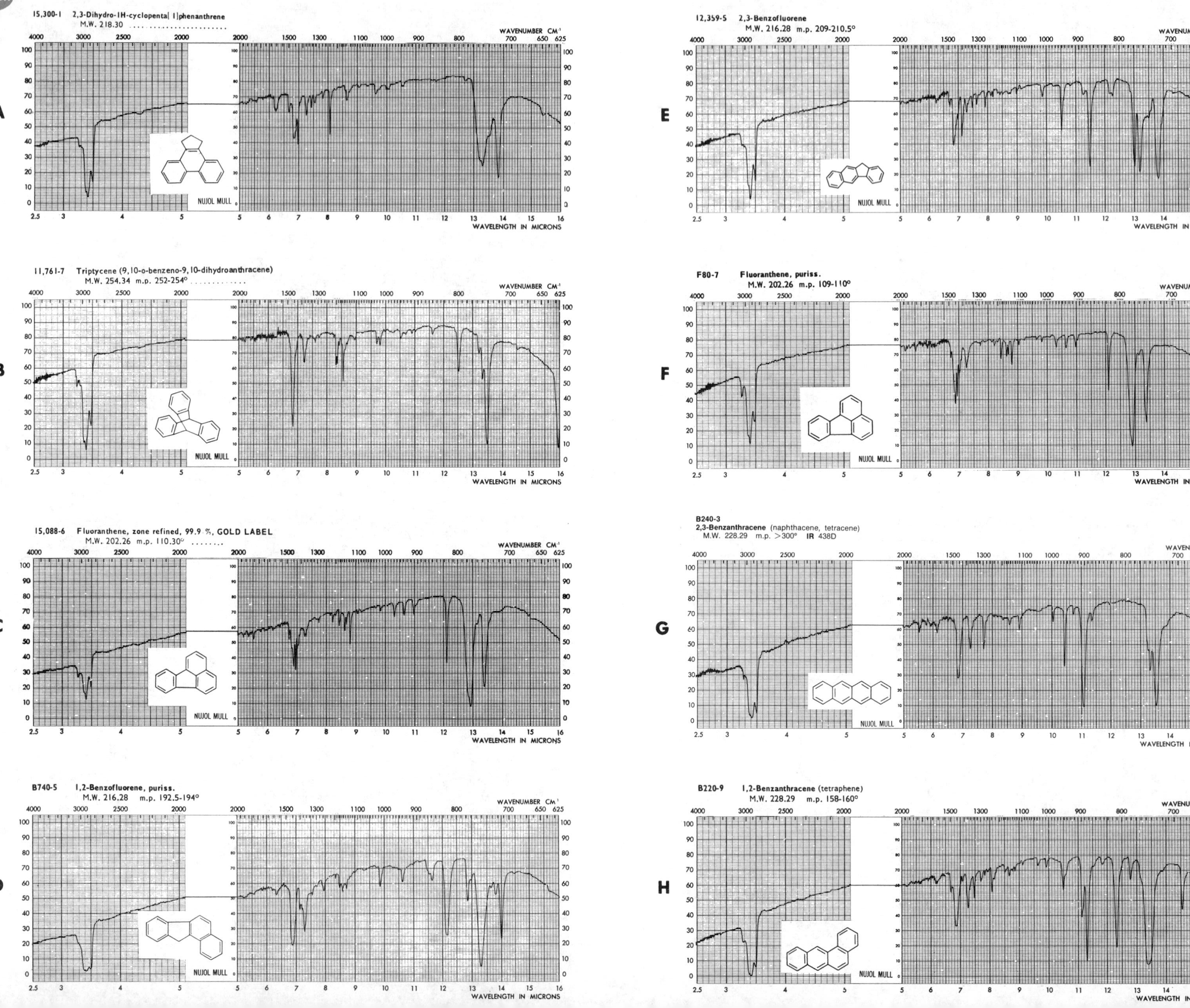
ALDRICH

A
15,300-1 2,3-Dihydro-1H-cyclopenta[l]phenanthrene
M.W. 218.30
NUJOL MULL

B
11,761-7 Triptycene (9,10-o-benzeno-9,10-dihydroanthracene)
M.W. 254.34 m.p. 252-254°
NUJOL MULL

C
15,088-6 Fluoranthene, zone refined, 99.9 %, GOLD LABEL
M.W. 202.26 m.p. 110.30°
NUJOL MULL

D
B740-5 1,2-Benzofluorene, puriss.
M.W. 216.28 m.p. 192.5-194°
NUJOL MULL

E
12,359-5 2,3-Benzofluorene
M.W. 216.28 m.p. 209-210.5°
NUJOL MULL

F
F80-7 Fluoranthene, puriss.
M.W. 202.26 m.p. 109-110°
NUJOL MULL

G
B240-3
2,3-Benzanthracene (naphthacene, tetracene)
M.W. 228.29 m.p. >300° IR 438D
NUJOL MULL

H
B220-9 1,2-Benzanthracene (tetraphene)
M.W. 228.29 m.p. 158-160°
NUJOL MULL

WAVENUMBER CM⁻¹
WAVELENGTH IN MICRONS

A

21,626-7
7,12-Dimethylbenz[*b*]anthracene, 97%
FW 256.35 mp 121-123° *Beil.* **5**(3),2413
Disp. C

KBr

B

21,394-2
3-Methylcholanthrene, 99%
FW 268.36 mp 178-180° bp 280°/80mm.
Beil. **5**(3),2484

NUJOL MULL

C

C8000-8 Chrysene, puriss.
M.W. 228.29 m.p. 256°

NUJOL MULL

D

14,979-9 1,2,3,4-Tetraphenylnaphthalene
$C_{10}H_4(C_6H_5)_4$ M.W. 432.57 ......

NUJOL MULL

E

15,097-5 Pyrene, zone refined, 99.9+%, GOLD LABEL
M.W. 202.26 m.p. 150.49° ....

NUJOL MULL

F

T8260-0 Triphenylene
M.W. 228.29 m.p. 197-200°

NUJOL MULL

G

R220-6 Rubrene (5,6,11,12-tetraphenylnaphthacene)
M.W. 532.69 m.p. > 300° ....

NUJOL MULL

H

T2665-4 1,3,6,8-Tetraphenylpyrene
M.W. 506.65 m.p. 295-298°

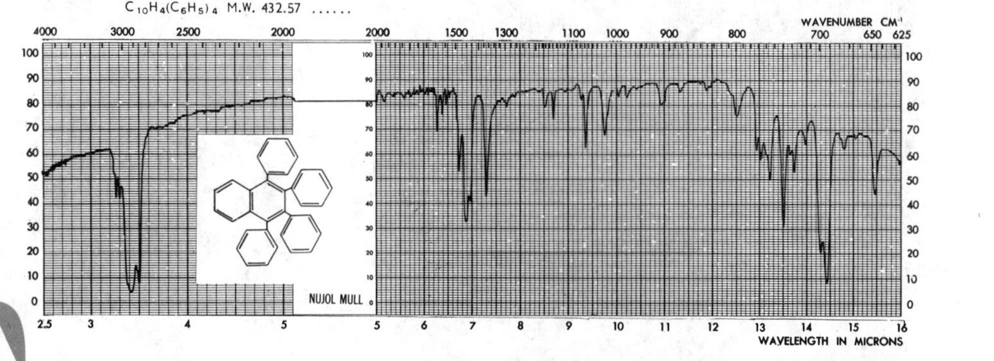

NUJOL MULL

ALDRICH ®

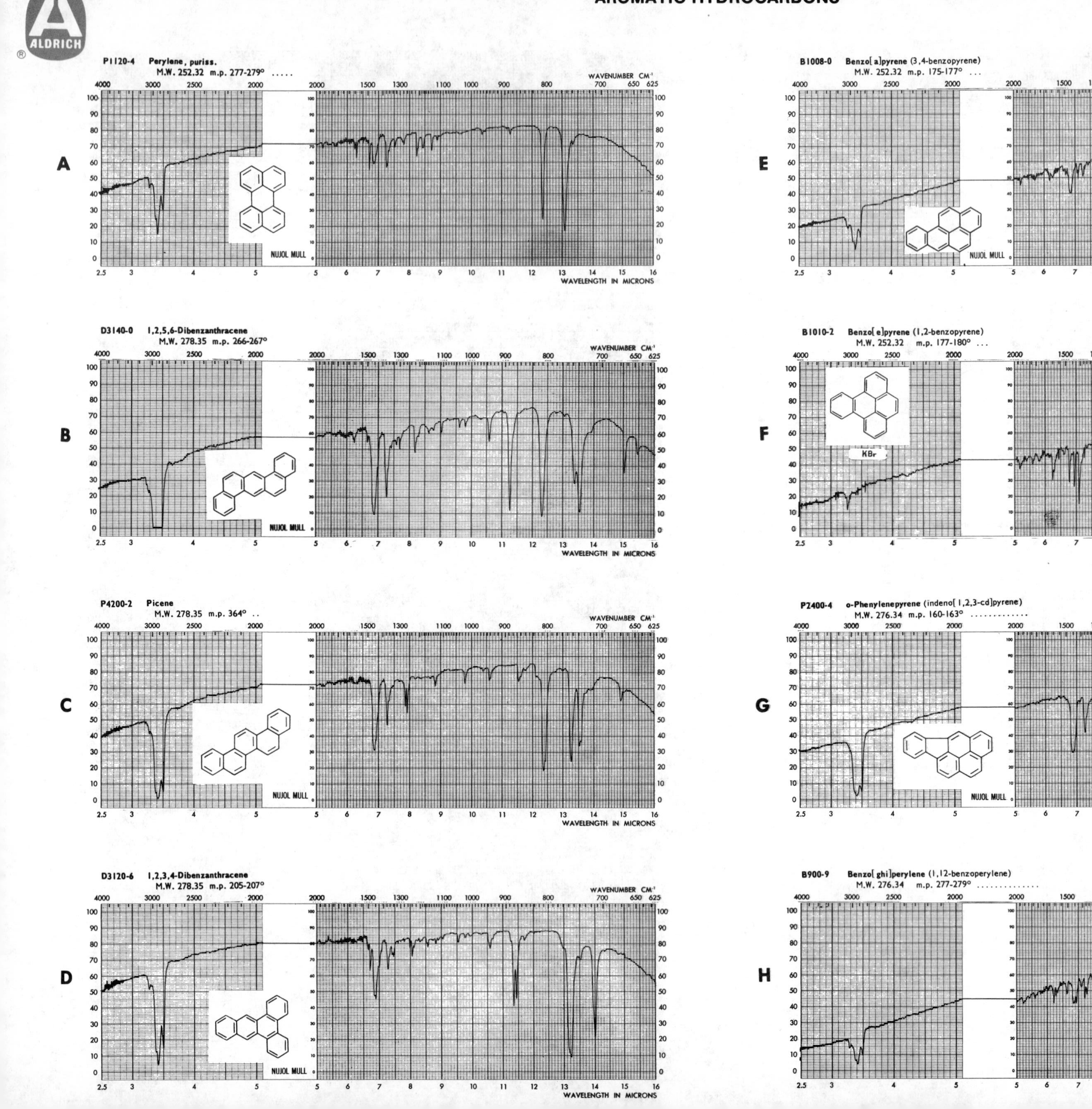
ALDRICH
A
P1120-4 Perylene, puriss.
M.W. 252.32 m.p. 277-279° .....
NUJOL MULL
B
D3140-0 1,2,5,6-Dibenzanthracene
M.W. 278.35 m.p. 266-267°
NUJOL MULL
C
P4200-2 Picene
M.W. 278.35 m.p. 364° ..
NUJOL MULL
D
D3120-6 1,2,3,4-Dibenzanthracene
M.W. 278.35 m.p. 205-207°
NUJOL MULL
E
B1008-0 Benzo[a]pyrene (3,4-benzopyrene)
M.W. 252.32 m.p. 175-177° ...
NUJOL MULL
F
B1010-2 Benzo[e]pyrene (1,2-benzopyrene)
M.W. 252.32 m.p. 177-180° ...
KBr
G
P2400-4 o-Phenylenepyrene (indeno[1,2,3-cd]pyrene)
M.W. 276.34 m.p. 160-163° ....
NUJOL MULL
H
B900-9 Benzo[ghi]perylene (1,12-benzoperylene)
M.W. 276.34 m.p. 277-279° ....
NUJOL MULL
WAVENUMBER CM⁻¹
WAVELENGTH IN MICRONS

A 13,182-2 1,2,3,4,5,6,7,8-Tetrabenznaphthalene (dibenzo[g,p]chrysene)
M.W. 328.41 m.p. 215-219.5°

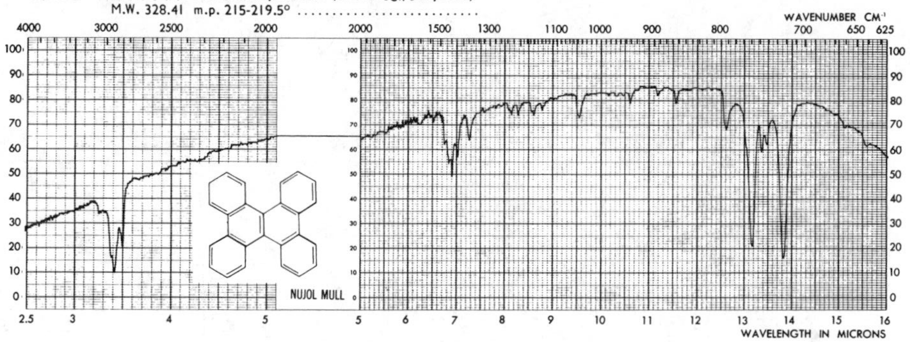

NUJOL MULL

B B897-5 Benzo[rst]pentaphene (dibenzo[a,i]pyrene)
M.W. 302.38 m.p. 270° (dec.)

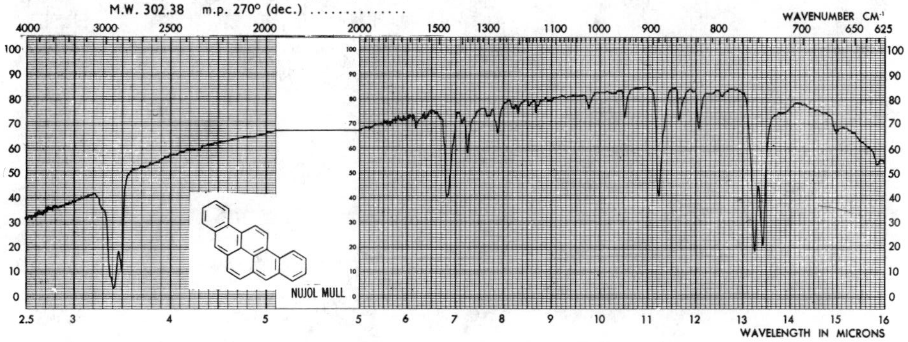

NUJOL MULL

C 13,223-3 Truxene (10,15-dihydro-5H-diindeno[1,2-a:1',2'-c]fluorene)
M.W. 342.44 m.p. > 330°

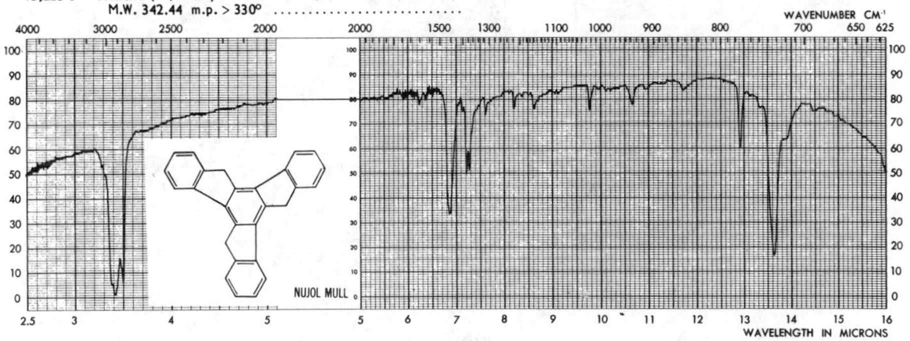

NUJOL MULL

D T4640 1,2,4,5,8,9-Tribenzopyrene (dibenzo[h,rst]pentaphene)
M.W. 352.44 m.p. 330-331°

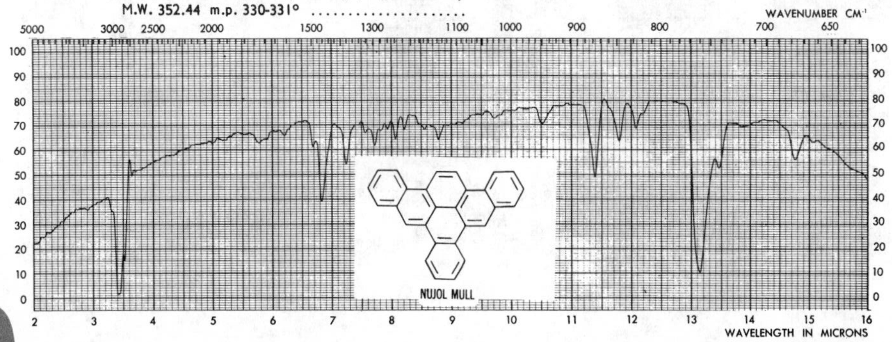

NUJOL MULL

E C8480-1 Coronene
M.W. 300.36 m.p. > 360°

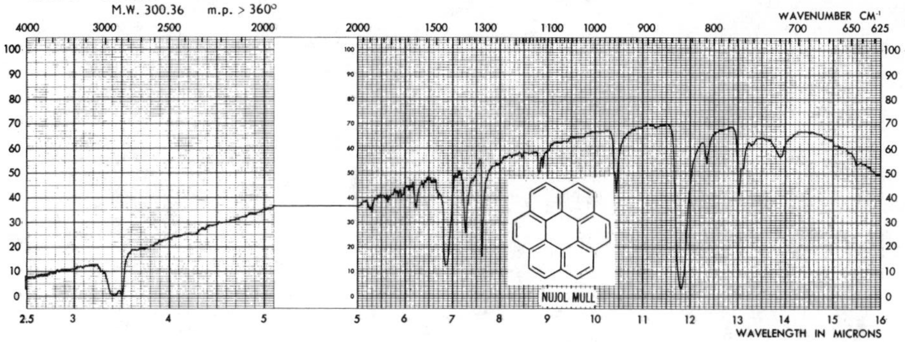

NUJOL MULL

F D12,235-1 Diindeno[1,2,3-cd:1',2',3'-lm]perylene (periflanthene)
M.W. 400.48

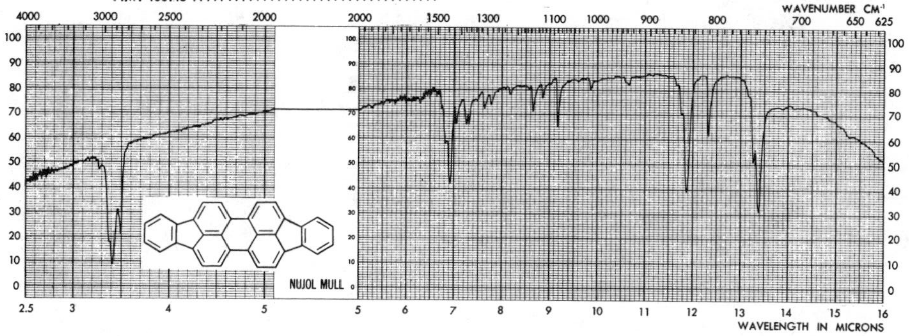

NUJOL MULL

G D20-0 Decacyclene
M.W. 450.54 m.p. > 325°

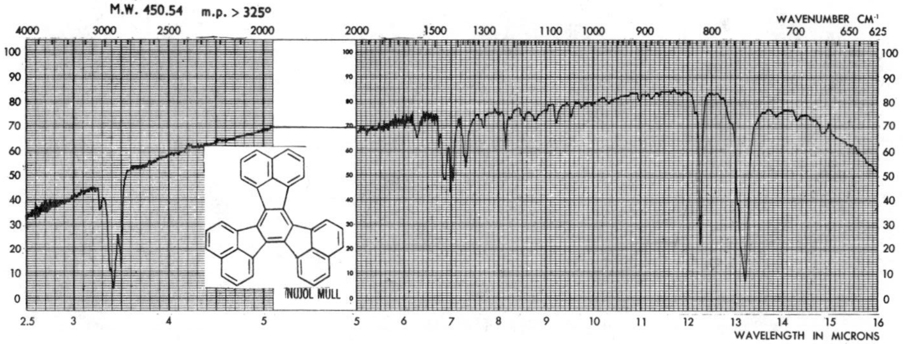

NUJOL MULL

H O-865-8 Ovalene
M.W. 398.47 m.p. > 325°

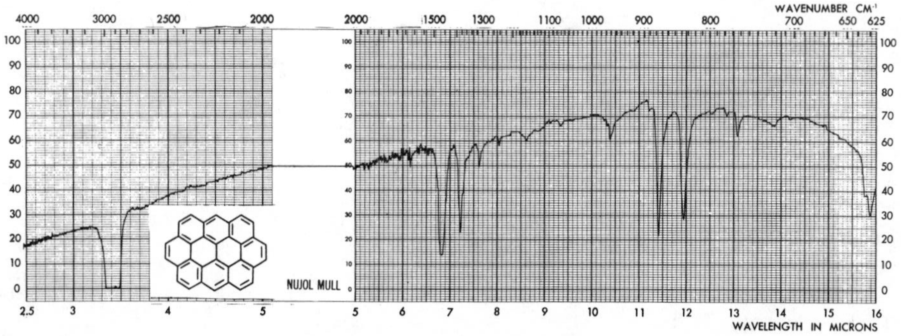

NUJOL MULL

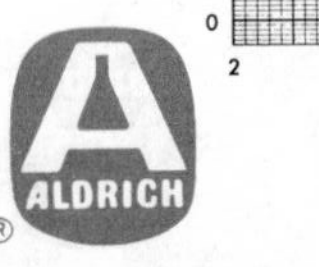

A

15,256-0 BDPA (α,γ-bisdiphenylene-β-phenylallyl), free radical
M.W. 495.65 m.p. 208-214° ....

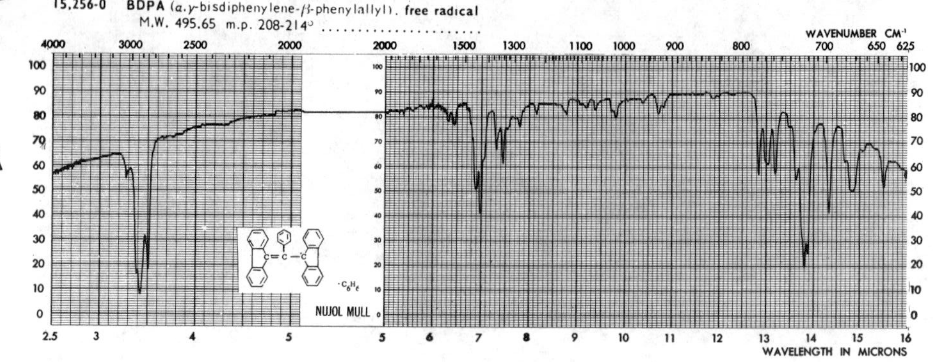

B

19,167-1
Indene-camphor-cyclohexanone, 98.4 to 0.8 to 0.8 mixture, GOLD LABEL
Fieser 7,400 Disp. C

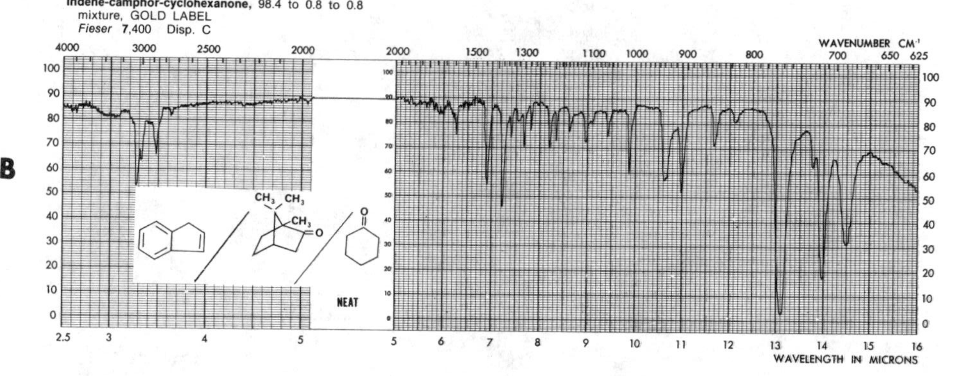

C

19,148-5
Indene-camphor-cyclohexanone, 1 to 1 to 1 mixture, GOLD LABEL
Fieser 7,400 Disp. C

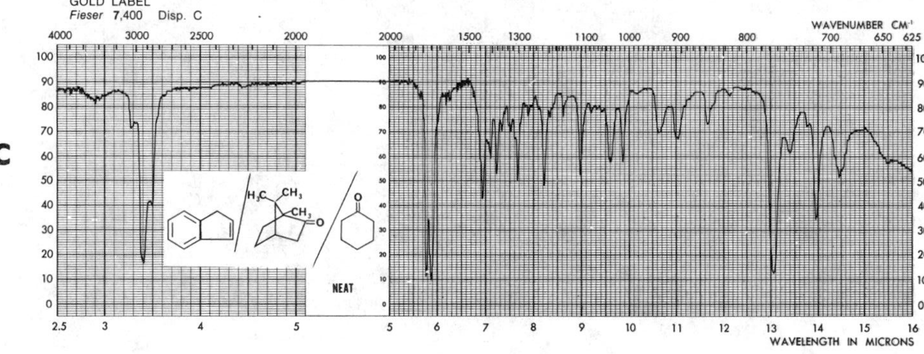

ALDRICH

AROMATIC HALOGENATED HYDROCARBONS

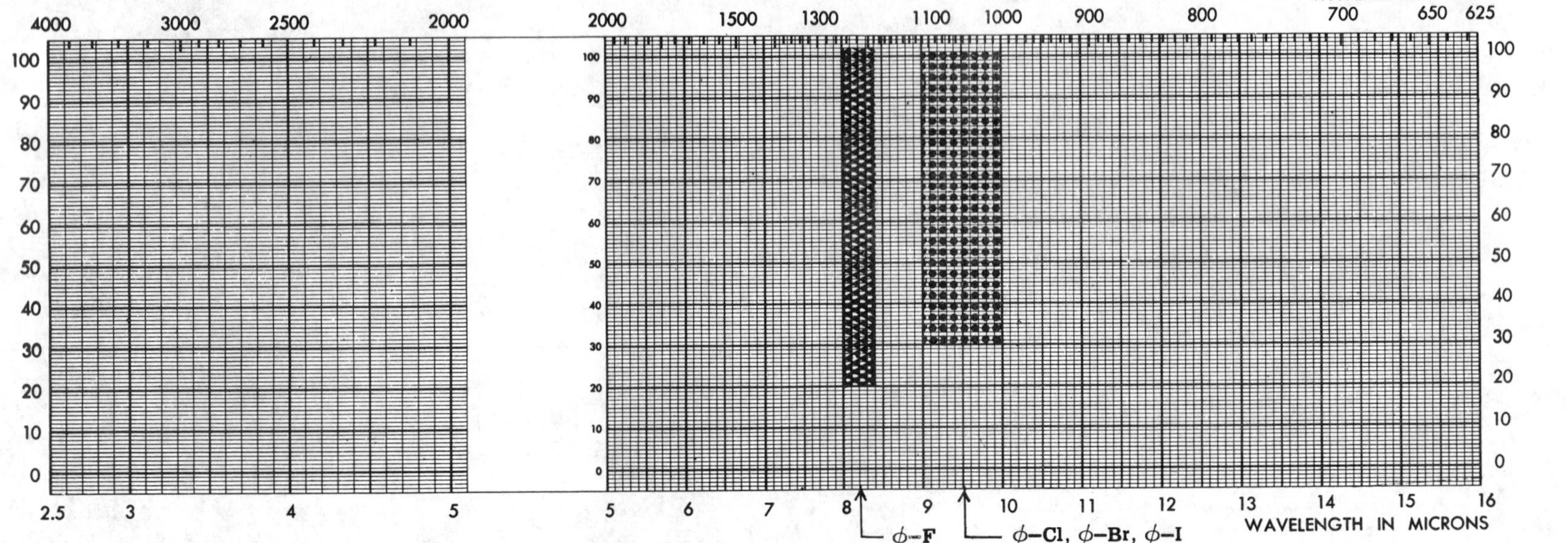

Fluorine attached directly to the aromatic ring exhibits a C–F band near 8 μ (1250 cm^{-1}). Chlorine, bromine and iodine similarly attached absorb between 8.5 and 10 μ (1175 – 1000 cm^{-1}). The position of these bands in various series such as the o, m, p-difluoro, dichloro, dibromo and diiodobenzenes as well as the o, m, p-fluoro, chloro, bromo and iodotoluene series should be noted.

The position of the aromatic fluorine band near 8 μ (1250 cm^{-1}) is in an area also occupied by a number of other absorptions such as the CH_2 wag band of the CH_2–Cl, CH_2–Br or CH_2–I groups, the aromatic C–O stretch absorption, P=O, etc.. Likewise, the other aromatic halogen bands between 8.5 and 10 μ (1175 – 1000 cm^{-1}), are difficult to see due to other groups commonly absorbing in that area. The polyfluorinated benzene compounds do not absorb at 8 μ (1250 cm^{-1}) but show a strong absorption between 9 and 11.2 μ (1110 – 895 cm^{-1}). (See spectra 607H—609D).

The substitution patterns between 11 and 15 μ (910 – 665 cm^{-1}) do, for the most part, follow those observed in the aromatic hydrocarbon section except that the appearance of the band around 14 μ (715 cm^{-1}) caused by dissimilar groups opposite each other on the benzene ring does not always follow the rule established in the aromatic hydrocarbon series.

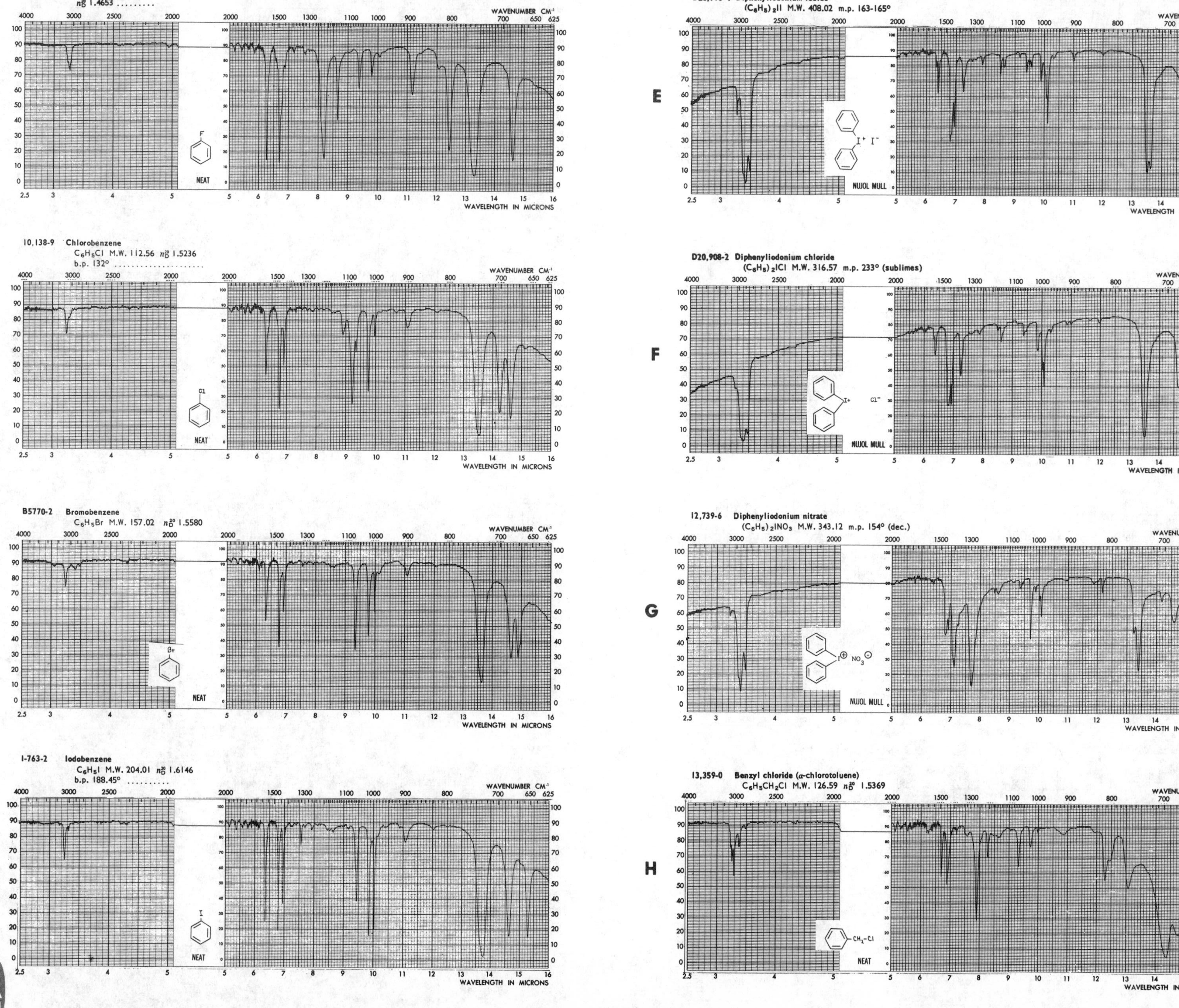

A
F600-1 Fluorobenzene
C_6H_5F M.W. 96.10
n_D^{20} 1.4653
NEAT
B
10,138-9 Chlorobenzene
C_6H_5Cl M.W. 112.56 n_D^{20} 1.5236
b.p. 132°
NEAT
C
B5770-2 Bromobenzene
C_6H_5Br M.W. 157.02 n_D^{20} 1.5580
NEAT
D
I-763-2 Iodobenzene
C_6H_5I M.W. 204.01 n_D^{20} 1.6146
b.p. 188.45°
NEAT
E
D20,910-4 Diphenyliodonium iodide
$(C_6H_5)_2II$ M.W. 408.02 m.p. 163-165°
NUJOL MULL
F
D20,908-2 Diphenyliodonium chloride
$(C_6H_5)_2ICl$ M.W. 316.57 m.p. 233° (sublimes)
NUJOL MULL
G
12,739-6 Diphenyliodonium nitrate
$(C_6H_5)_2INO_3$ M.W. 343.12 m.p. 154° (dec.)
NUJOL MULL
H
13,359-0 Benzyl chloride (α-chlorotoluene)
$C_6H_5CH_2Cl$ M.W. 126.59 n_D^{20} 1.5369
NEAT
WAVENUMBER CM⁻¹
WAVELENGTH IN MICRONS
ALDRICH

AROMATIC HALOGENS

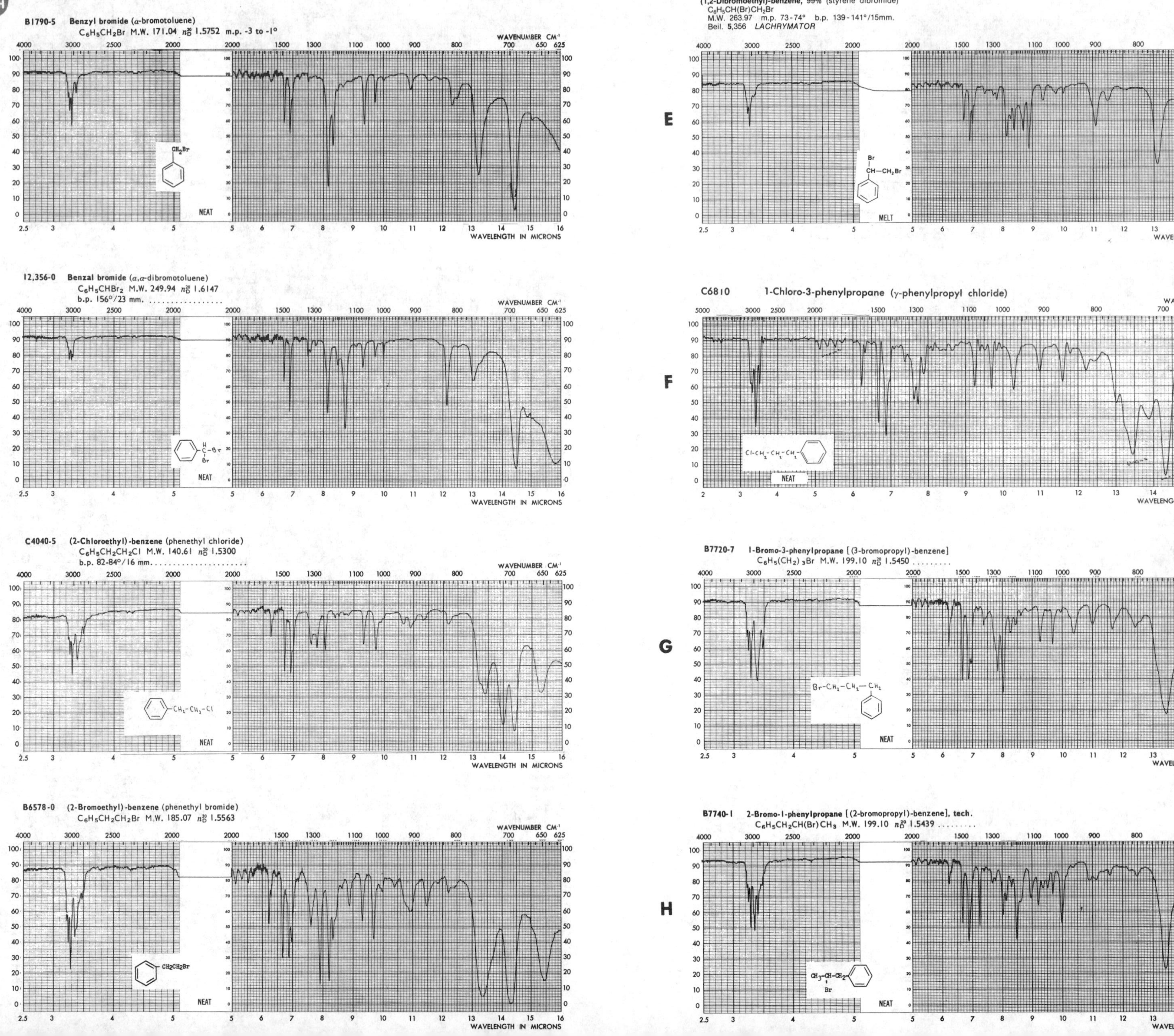
ALDRICH
A
B1790-5 Benzyl bromide (α-bromotoluene)
$C_6H_5CH_2Br$ M.W. 171.04 n_D^{20} 1.5752 m.p. -3 to -1°
NEAT
B
12,356-0 Benzal bromide (α,α-dibromotoluene)
$C_6H_5CHBr_2$ M.W. 249.94 n_D^{20} 1.6147
b.p. 156°/23 mm.
NEAT
C
C4040-5 (2-Chloroethyl)-benzene (phenethyl chloride)
$C_6H_5CH_2CH_2Cl$ M.W. 140.61 n_D^{20} 1.5300
b.p. 82-84°/16 mm.
NEAT
D
B6578-0 (2-Bromoethyl)-benzene (phenethyl bromide)
$C_6H_5CH_2CH_2Br$ M.W. 185.07 n_D^{20} 1.5563
NEAT
E
17,801-2
(1,2-Dibromoethyl)-benzene, 99% (styrene dibromide)
$C_6H_5CH(Br)CH_2Br$
M.W. 263.97 m.p. 73-74° b.p. 139-141°/15mm.
Beil. 5,356 LACHRYMATOR
MELT
F
C6810 1-Chloro-3-phenylpropane (γ-phenylpropyl chloride)
NEAT
G
B7720-7 1-Bromo-3-phenylpropane [(3-bromopropyl)-benzene]
$C_6H_5(CH_2)_3Br$ M.W. 199.10 n_D^{20} 1.5450
NEAT
H
B7740-1 2-Bromo-1-phenylpropane [(2-bromopropyl)-benzene], tech.
$C_6H_5CH_2CH(Br)CH_3$ M.W. 199.10 n_D^{20} 1.5439
NEAT
WAVENUMBER CM⁻¹
WAVELENGTH IN MICRONS

A

14,093-7 β-Bromoisopropylbenzene (β-bromocumene)
$C_6H_5CH(CH_3)CH_2Br$ M.W. 199.10 n_D^{20} 1.5480
b.p. 106-108°/18 mm.

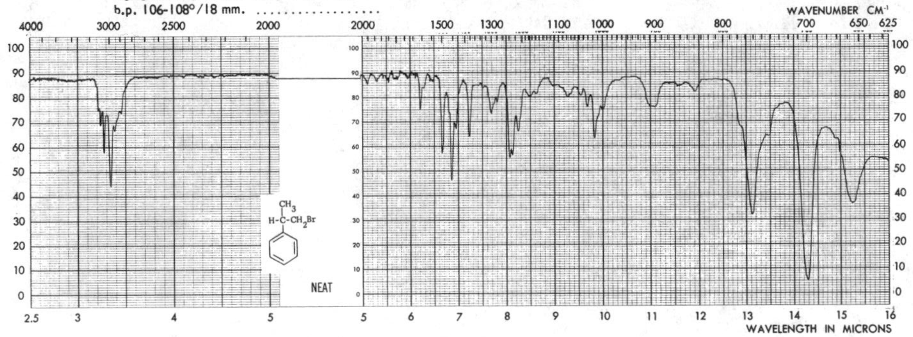

NEAT

B

17,844-6
(2,2-Dichlorocyclopropyl)-benzene, 97%
$C_6H_5C_3H_3Cl_2$
M.W. 187.07 b.p. 103°/10mm. n_D^{20} 1.5514

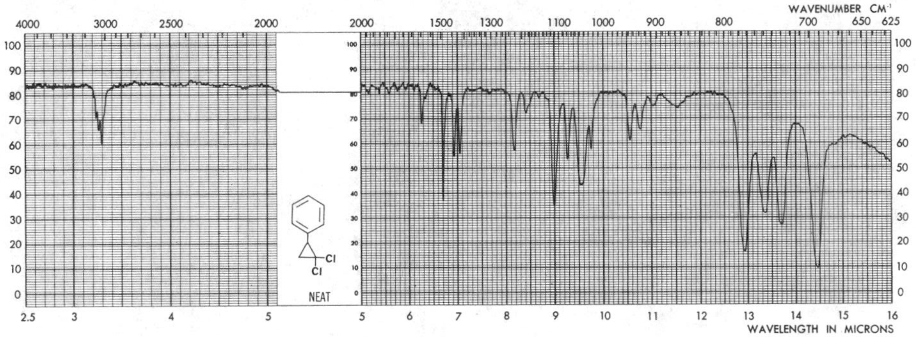

NEAT

C

17,845-4
(2,2-Dichloro-1-methylcyclopropyl)-benzene, 97%
$C_6H_5C_3H_2(CH_3)Cl_2$
M.W. 201.1 n_D^{20} 1.5393

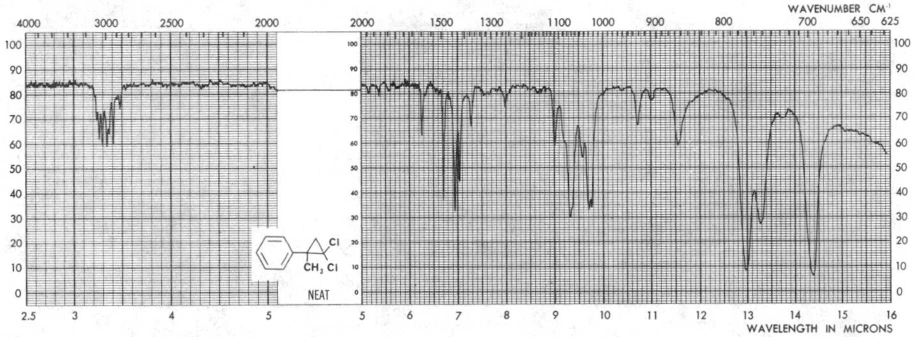

NEAT

D

12,615-2 o-Difluorobenzene
$C_6H_4F_2$ M.W. 114.09 n_D^{20} 1.4427

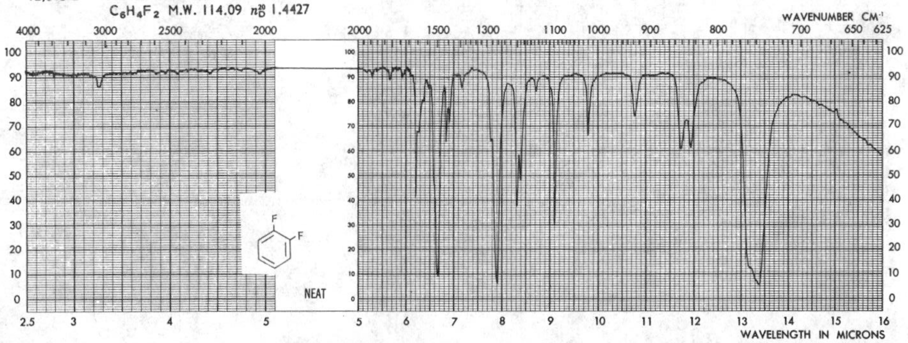

NEAT

E

D5680-2 o-Dichlorobenzene
$C_6H_4Cl_2$ M.W. 147.00
n_D^{20} 1.5504

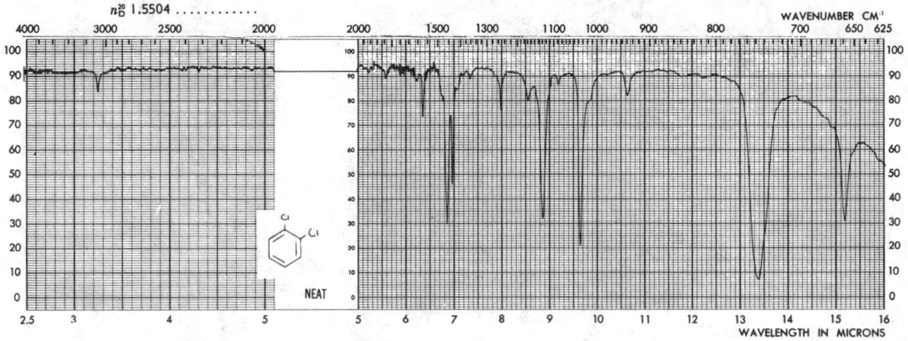

NEAT

F

16,230-2
1-Chloro-2-fluorobenzene, 99%
ClC_6H_4F
M.W. 130.55 m.p. -42.5° b.p. 137-138°
n_D^{20} 1.5010 d 1.244 Beil. 5(1),110 *IRRITANT*

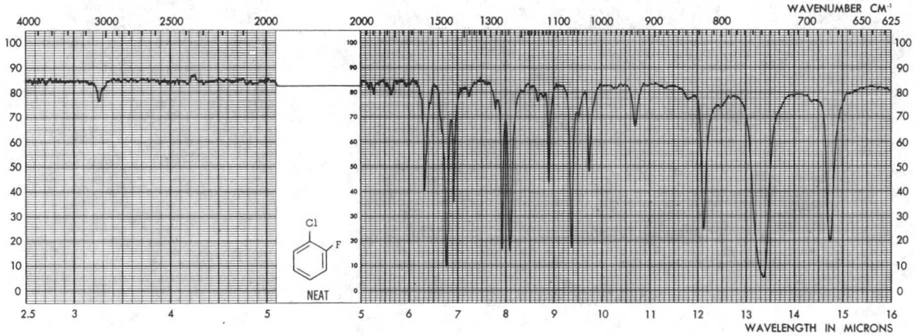

NEAT

G

D3900-2 o-Dibromobenzene
$C_6H_4Br_2$ M.W. 235.92 n_D^{20} 1.6101 m.p. 4-6°

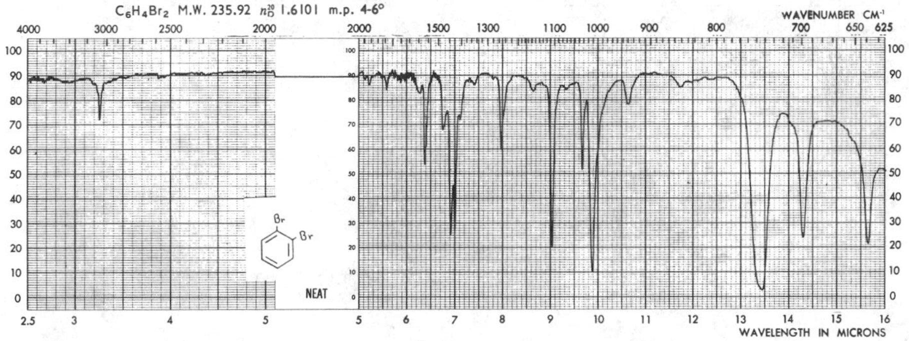

NEAT

H

B6,040-1
2-Bromochlorobenzene, 98.5%
BrC_6H_4Cl
M.W. 191.46 b.p. 204° n_D^{20} 1.5809 d 1.638
Beil. 5,209

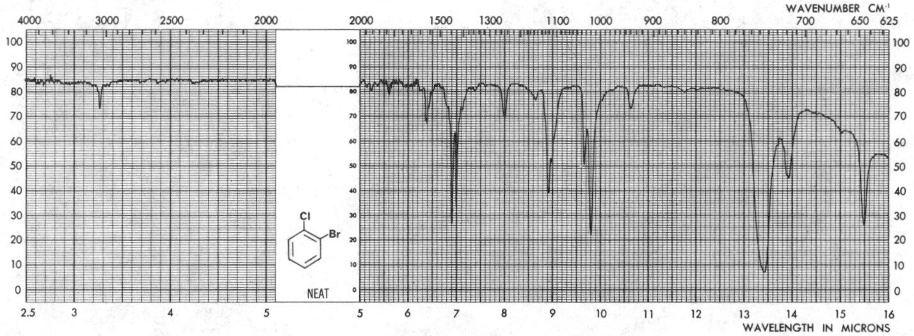

NEAT

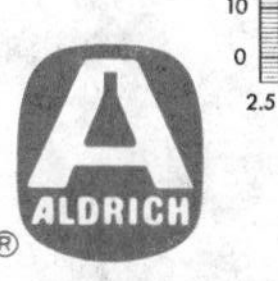

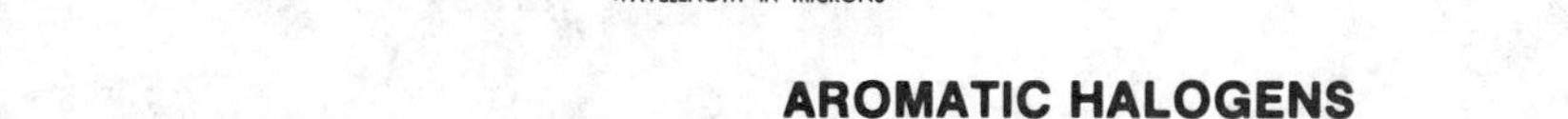

A

B6680-9 **2-Bromofluorobenzene**
BrC_6H_4F M.W. 175.01 n_D^{20} 1.5337

NEAT

B

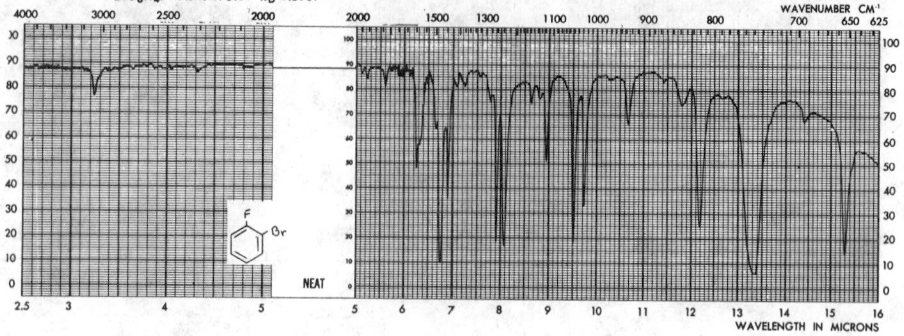

21,940-1
o-Fluoroiodobenzene, 99%
FC_6H_4I FW 222.00 mp -41.50° bp 188-189°
n_D^{20} 1.5909 d 1.903 *Beil.* **5**(1),119 Disp. C

NEAT

C

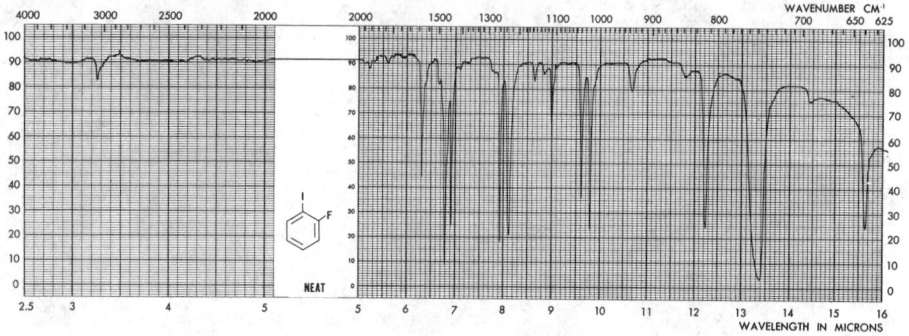

F1532-3 **o-Fluorotoluene**
$CH_3C_6H_4F$ M.W. 110.13 n_D^{20} 1.4727

NEAT

D

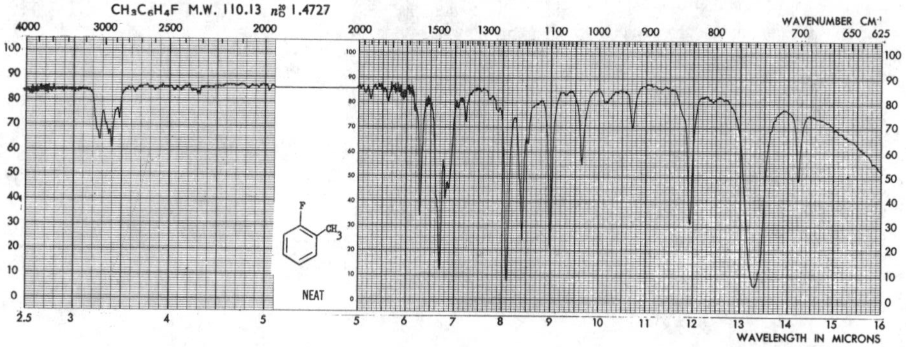

11,191-0 **o-Chlorotoluene**
$CH_3C_6H_4Cl$ M.W. 126.59 n_D^{20} 1.5250
b.p. 157-159°

NEAT

E

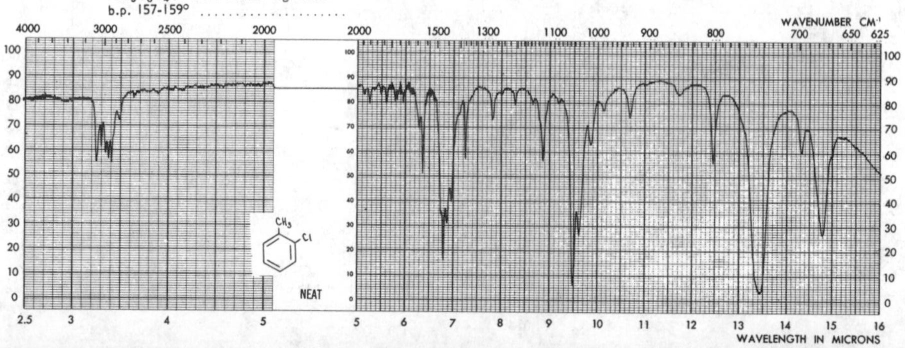

B8200-6 **2-Bromotoluene**
$CH_3C_6H_4Br$ M.W. 171.04 n_D^{20} 1.5552

NEAT

F

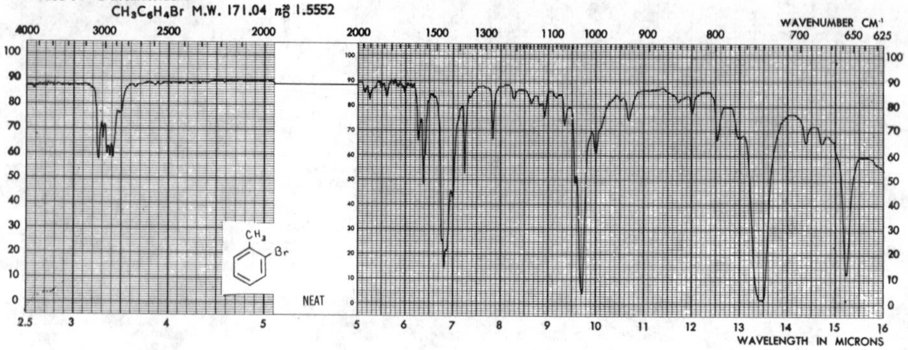

B6580-2 **o-Bromoethylbenzene**
$C_2H_5C_6H_4Br$ M.W. 185.07 n_D^{20} 1.5473

NEAT

G

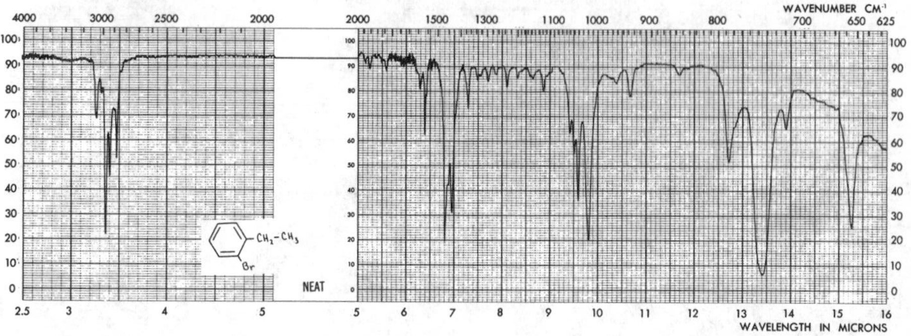

I-1170-4 **o-Iodotoluene**
$CH_3C_6H_4I$ M.W. 218.04 n_D^{20} 1.6079
b.p. 73-75°/7 mm.

NEAT

H

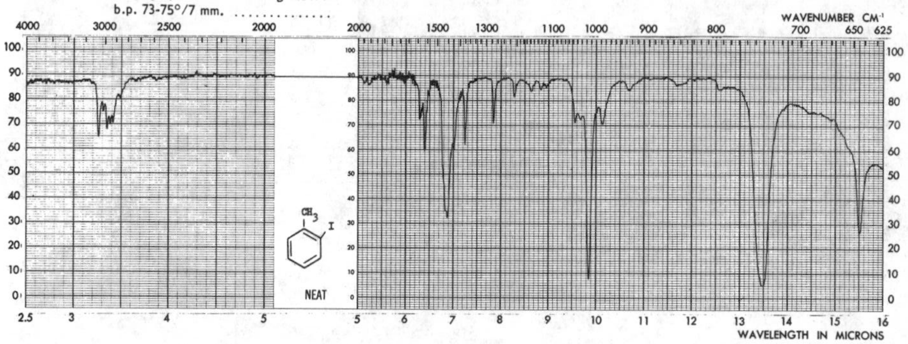

F760-1 **2-Fluorobenzyl chloride (α-chloro-o-fluorotoluene)**
$FC_6H_4CH_2Cl$ M.W. 144.58 n_D^{20} 1.5130

NEAT

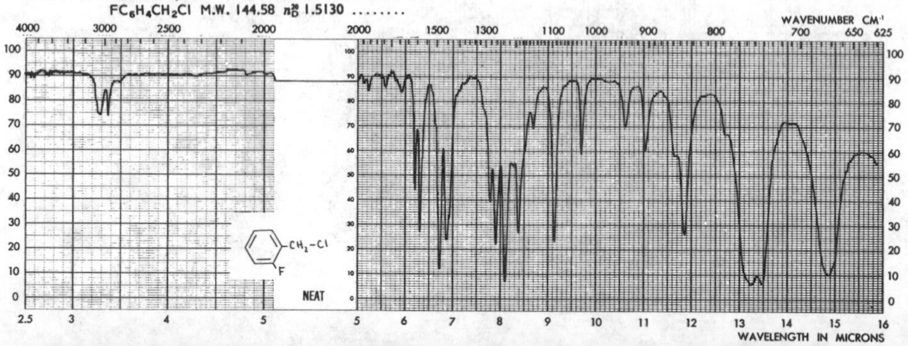

A

C7330-3 *α*-Chloro-o-xylene (2-methylbenzyl chloride)
$CH_3C_6H_4CH_2Cl$ M.W. 140.61 n_D^{20} 1.5408

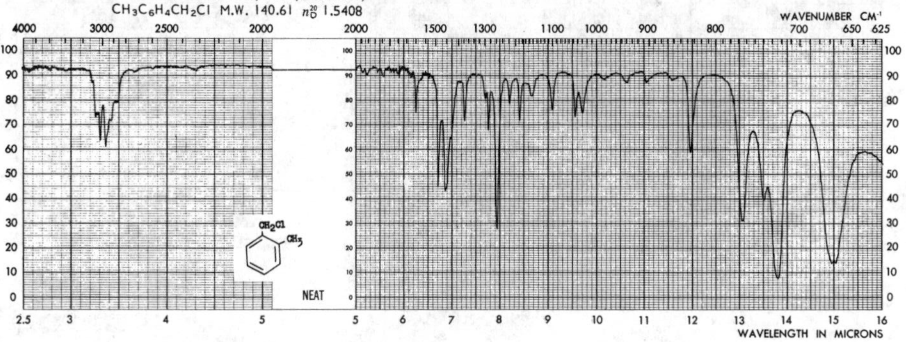

NEAT

B

11,195-3 *α*,o-Dichlorotoluene (o-chlorobenzyl chloride)
$ClC_6H_4CH_2Cl$ M.W. 161.03 n_D^{20} 1.5592
b.p. 214°

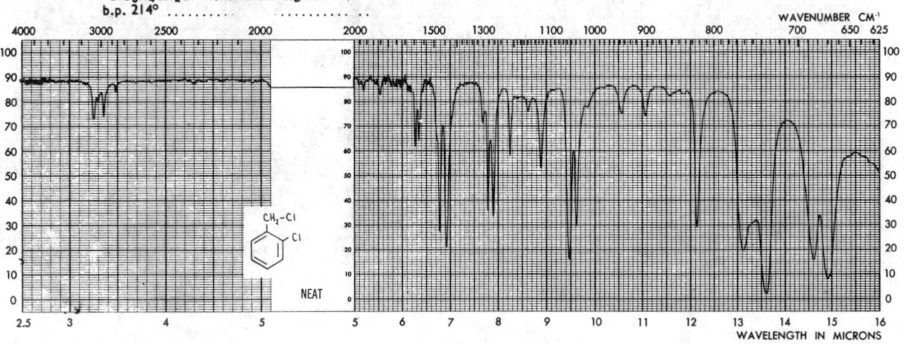

NEAT

C

19,349-6
o-Iodobenzyl chloride, 98% (*α*-chloro-o-iodotoluene)
$IC_6H_4CH_2Cl$ FW 252.48 bp 147-149°/32mm.
n_D^{20} 1.6349 *Beil.* 5(3),726 Disp. C

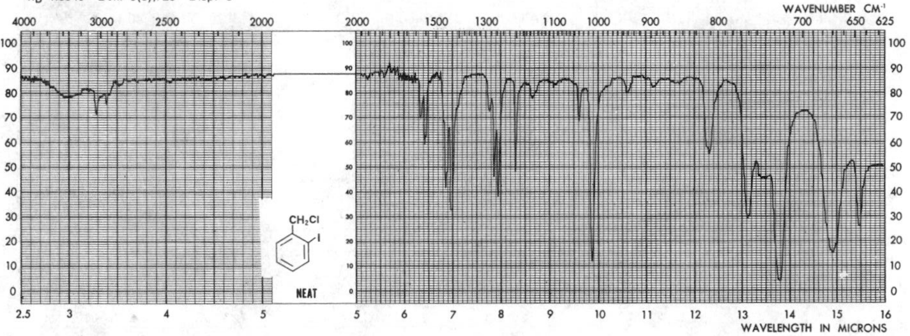

NEAT

D

12,388-9 1,2-Bis-(chloromethyl)-benzene (*α*,*α*'-dichloro-o-xylene)
$C_6H_4(CH_2Cl)_2$ M.W. 175.06 m.p. 56.5-59°

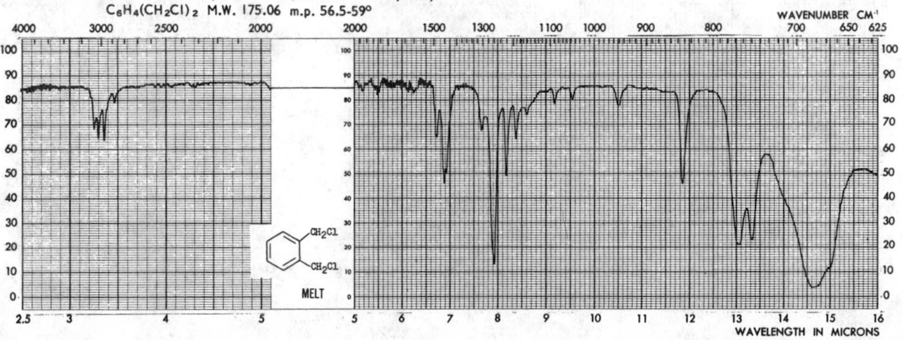

MELT

E

B8340-1 *α*-Bromo-o-xylene (2-methylbenzyl bromide)
$CH_3C_6H_4CH_2Br$ M.W. 185.07 n_D^{20} 1.5742 m.p. 18-20°

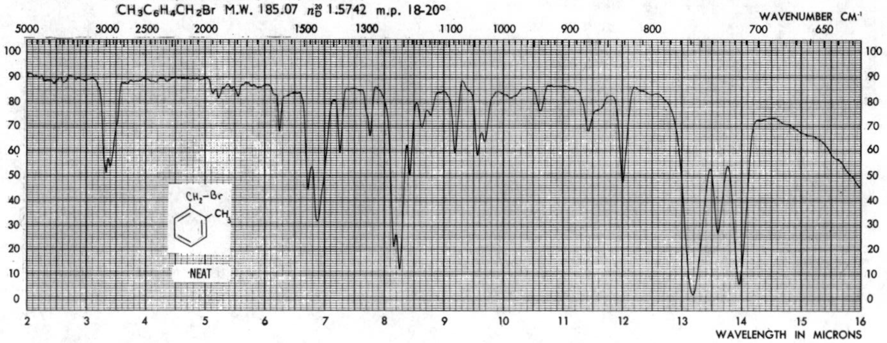

NEAT

F

20,951-1
2-Fluorobenzyl bromide, 98% (*α*-bromo-o-fluorotoluene)
$FC_6H_4CH_2Br$ FW 189.03 bp 84-85°/15mm.
n_D^{20} 1.5525 d 1.567 *Beil.* 5(2),238 Disp. C

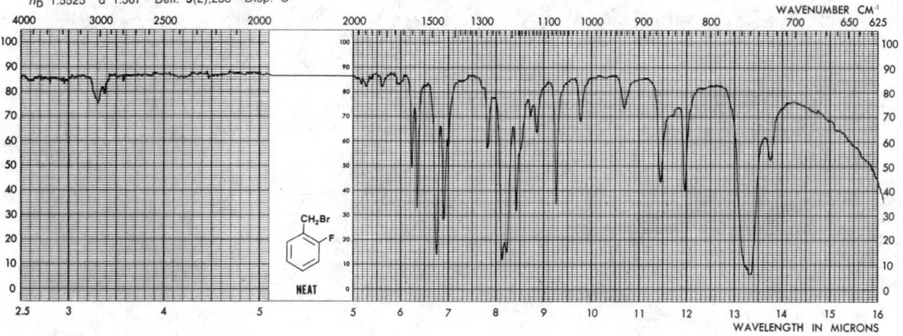

NEAT

G

18,707-0
o-Bromobenzyl bromide, 98% (*α*,o-dibromotoluene)
$BrC_6H_4CH_2Br$ FW 249.94 bp 129°/19mm.
n_D^{20} 1.6193 *Beil.* 5,308 Disp. C

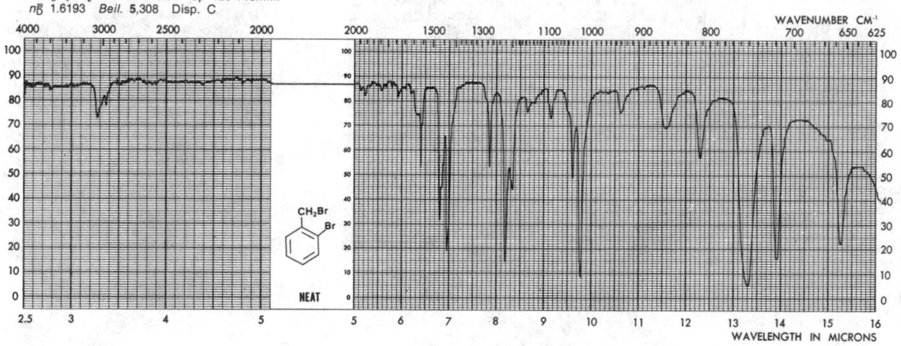

NEAT

H

D4440-5 *α*,*α*'-Dibromo-o-xylene
$C_6H_4(CH_2Br)_2$ M.W. 263.97
m.p. 92-94°

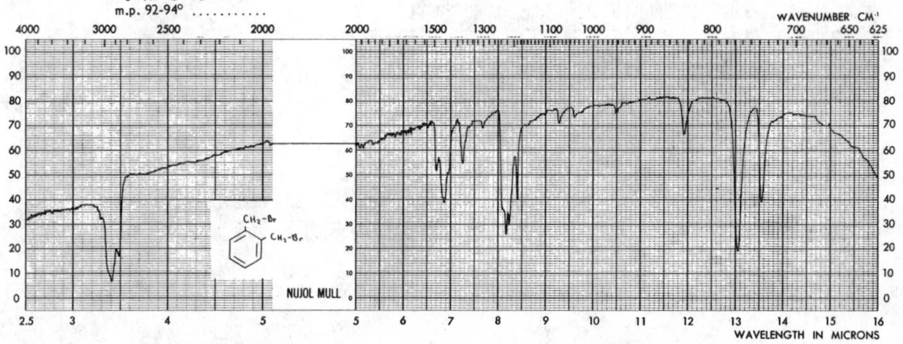

NUJOL MULL

A

T560-5 α,α,α',α'-Tetrabromo-o-xylene
$C_6H_4(CHBr_2)_2$ M.W. 421.77 m.p. 115-118°
NUJOL MULL

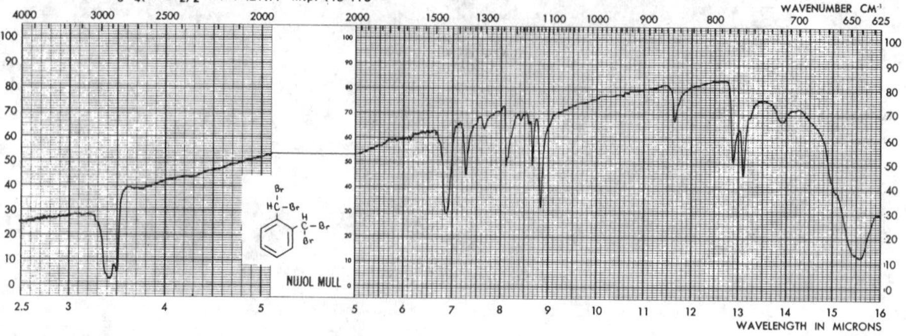

B

D10,200-8 m-Difluorobenzene
$C_6H_4F_2$ M.W. 114.09 n_D^{20} 1.4383
NEAT

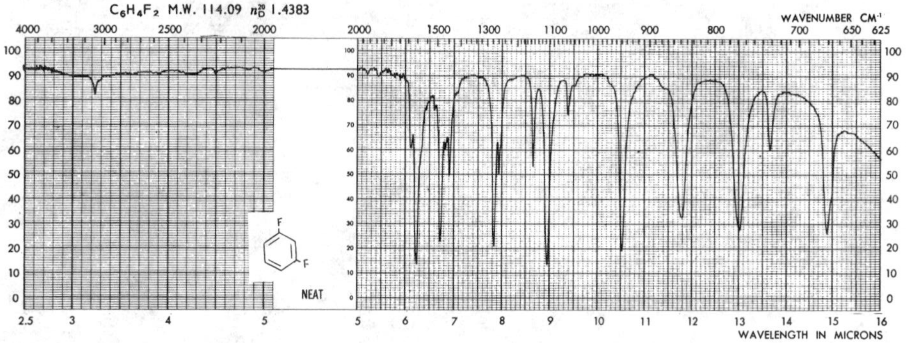

C

11,380-8 m-Dichlorobenzene
$C_6H_4Cl_2$ M.W. 147.00 n_D^{20} 1.5457
b.p. 172°
NEAT

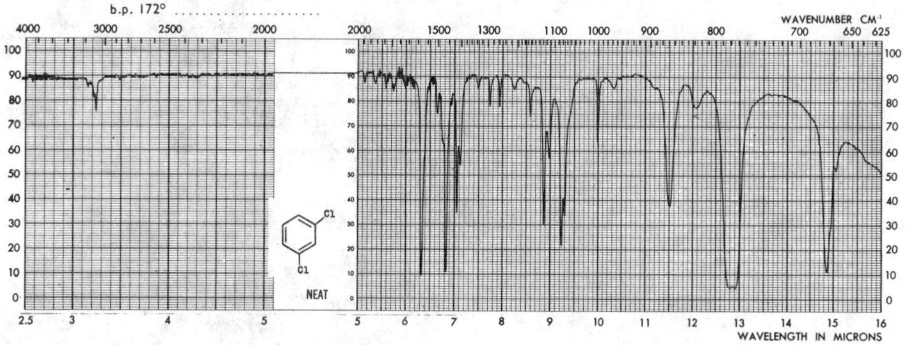

D

16,229-9
1-Chloro-3-fluorobenzene, 99%
ClC_6H_4F
M.W. 130.55 b.p. 126-128° n_D^{20} 1.4935 d 1.219
IRRITANT
NEAT

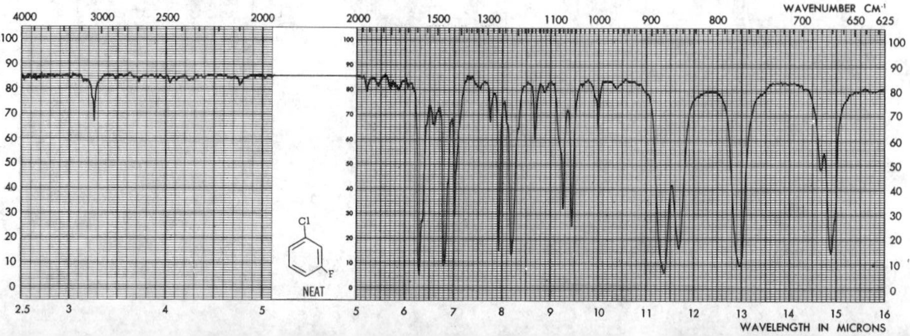

E

B6700-7 3-Bromofluorobenzene
BrC_6H_4F M.W. 175.01 n_D^{20} 1.5257
NEAT

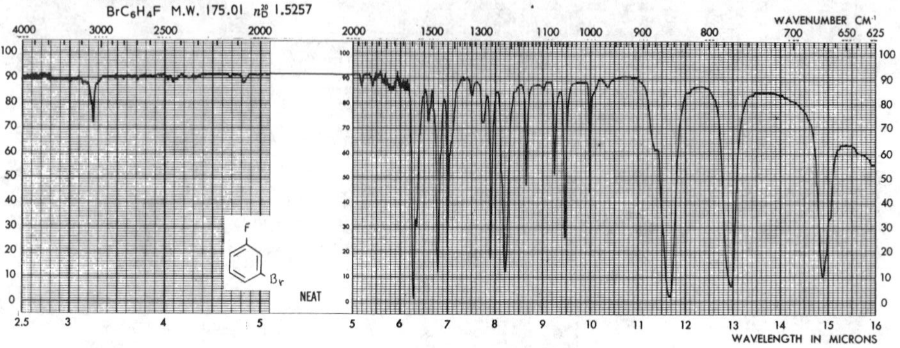

F

21,939-8
m-Fluoroiodobenzene, 99%
FC_6H_4I FW 222.00 bp 77-78°/19mm. n_D^{20} 1.5837
d 1.890 *Beil.* 5(3),578 Disp. C
NEAT

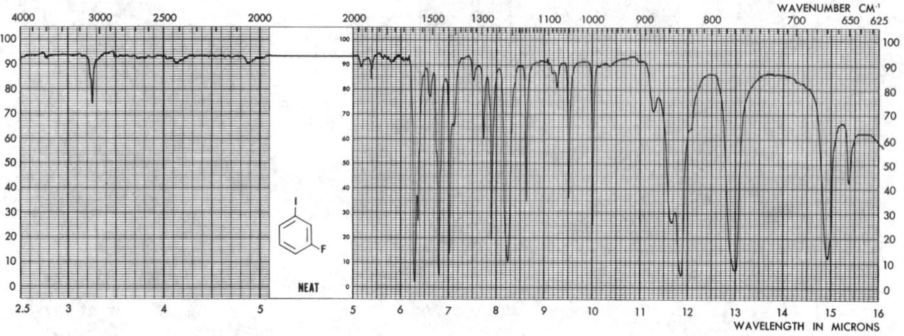

G

12,403-6 3-Bromochlorobenzene
BrC_6H_4Cl M.W. 191.46 n_D^{20} 1.5771
NEAT

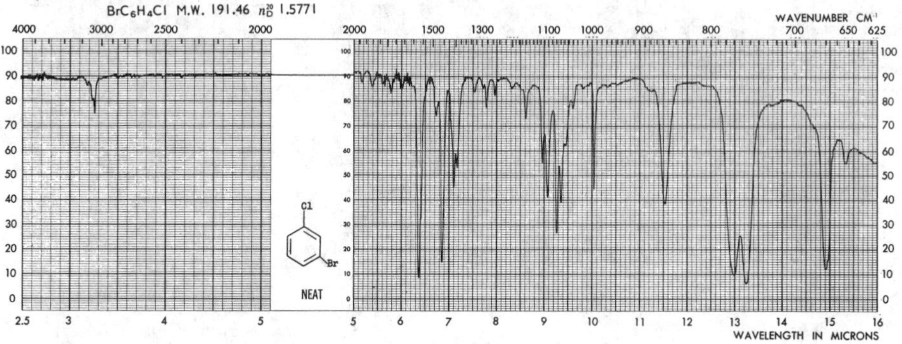

H

19,439-5
m-Dibromobenzene, 97%
$C_6H_4Br_2$ FW 235.92 mp -7° bp 218-219°
n_D^{20} 1.6053 d 1.952 *Beil.* 5,211 Disp. C
NEAT

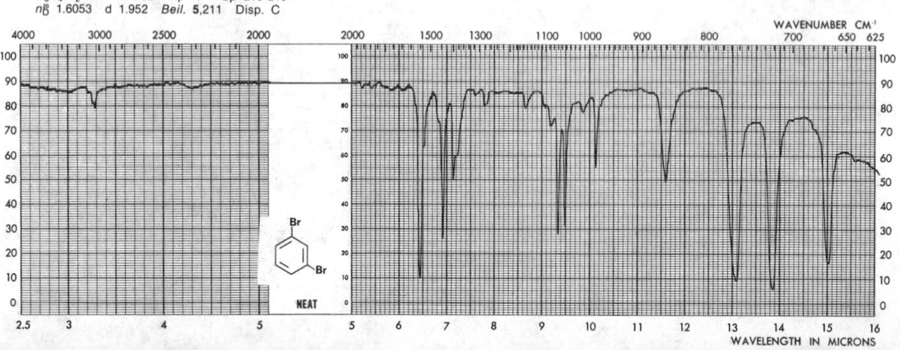

A

16,232-9
m-Fluorotoluene, 99%
$CH_3C_6H_4F$
M.W. 110.13 b.p. 115° n_D^{20} 1.4691 d 0.991
Beil. 5,290

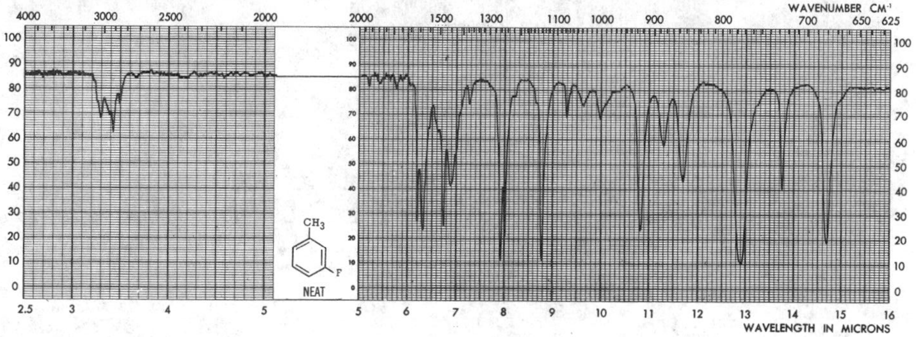

NEAT

B

13,850-9 **m-Chlorotoluene**
$CH_3C_6H_4Cl$ M.W. 126.59 n_D^{20} 1.5218
b.p. 160-162° ....

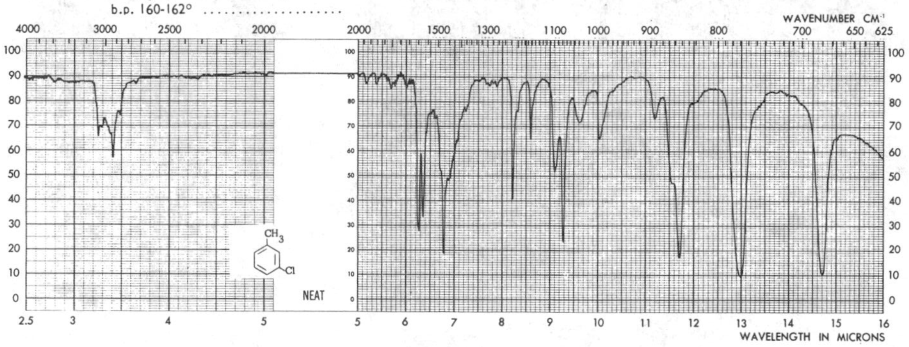

NEAT

C

16,721-5
3-Bromotoluene, 99%
$CH_3C_6H_4Br$
M.W. 171.04 m.p. -40° b.p. 183.7° n_D^{20} 1.5517
d 1.41 Beil. 5,305

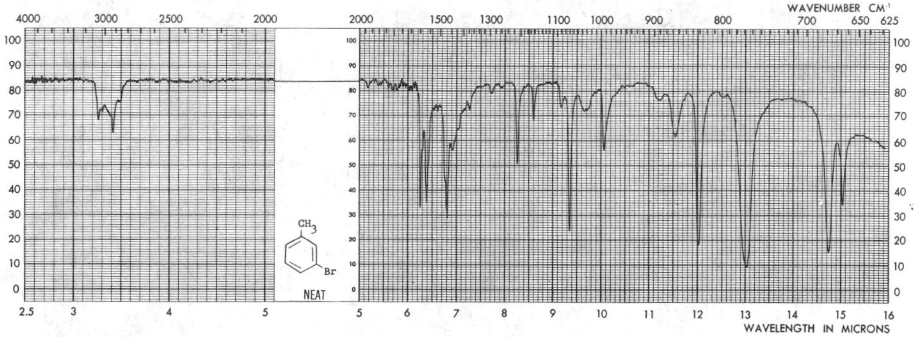

NEAT

D

13,073-7 **m-Iodotoluene**
$CH_3C_6H_4I$ M.W. 218.04 n_D^{20} 1.6032
b.p. 80-82°/10 mm. ....

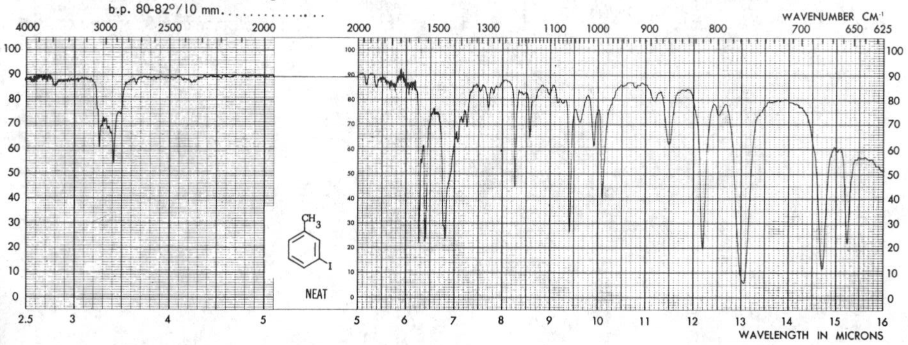

NEAT

E

C7335-4 **α-Chloro-m-xylene** (3-methylbenzyl chloride)
$CH_3C_6H_4CH_2Cl$ M.W. 140.61 n_D^{20} 1.5350
b.p. 195-196° ....

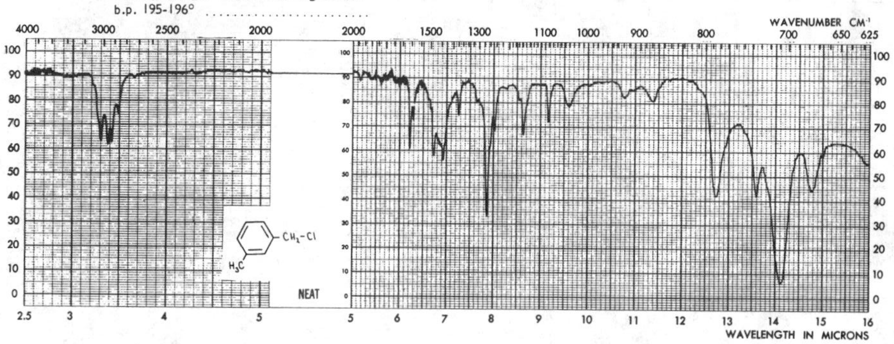

NEAT

F

B8350-9 **α-Bromo-m-xylene** (3-methylbenzyl bromide)
$CH_3C_6H_4CH_2Br$ M.W. 185.07 n_D^{20} 1.5660

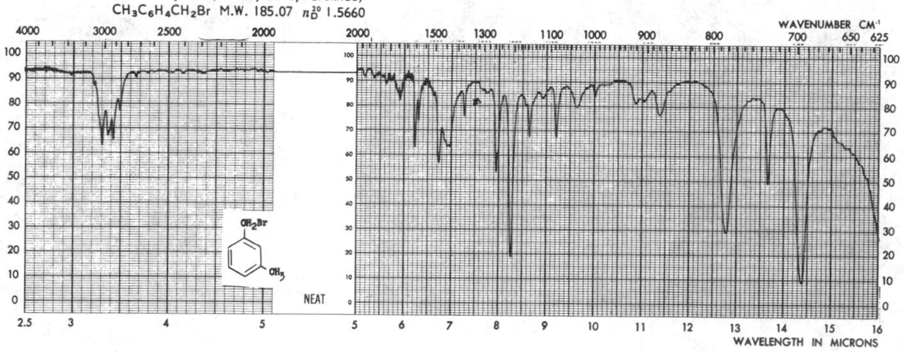

NEAT

G

F780-6 **3-Fluorobenzyl chloride** (α-chloro-m-fluorotoluene)
$FC_6H_4CH_2Cl$ M.W. 144.58 n_D^{20} 1.5131 ....

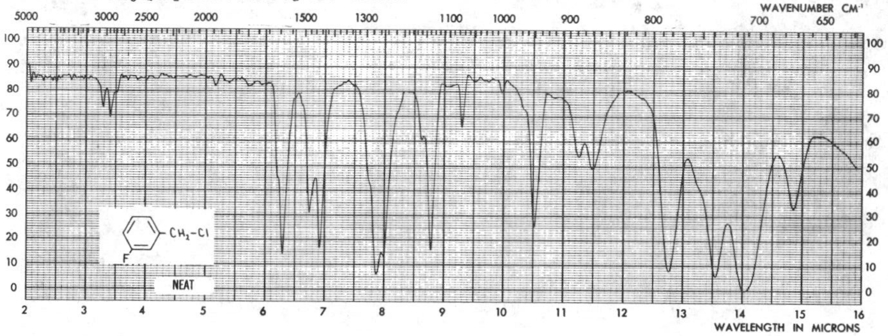

NEAT

H

F750-4 **3-Fluorobenzyl bromide** (α-bromo-m-fluorotoluene)
$FC_6H_4CH_2Br$ M.W. 189.03 n_D^{20} 1.5474 ......

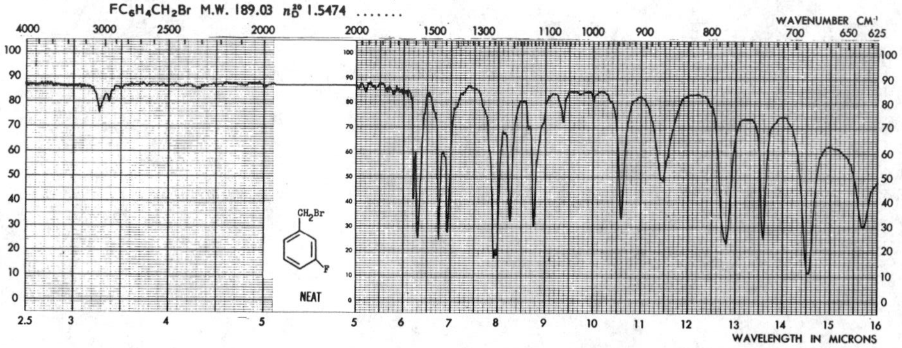

NEAT

ALDRICH

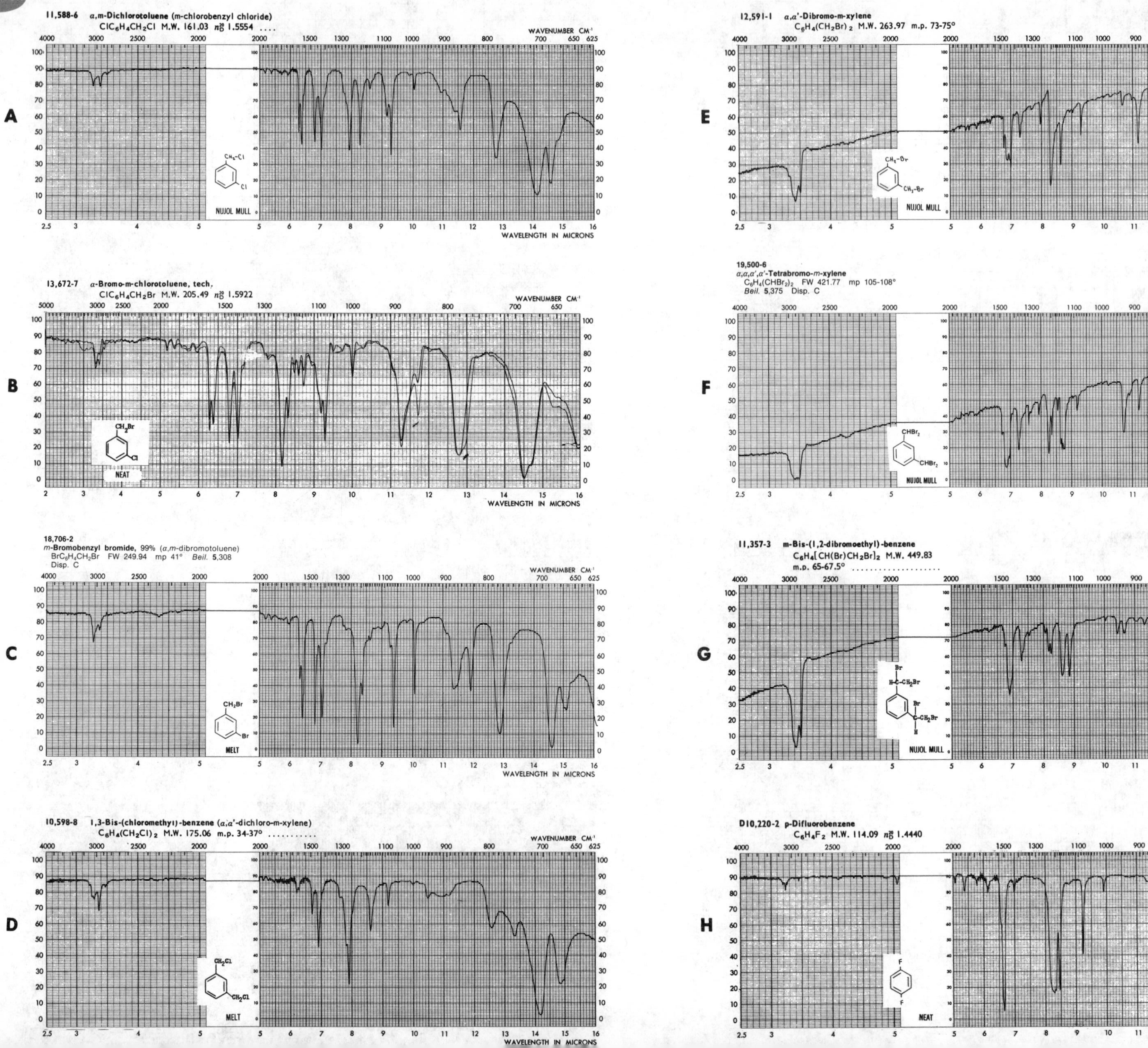
ALDRICH
A
11,588-6 α,m-Dichlorotoluene (m-chlorobenzyl chloride)
ClC6H4CH2Cl M.W. 161.03 n20D 1.5554
NUJOL MULL
B
13,672-7 α-Bromo-m-chlorotoluene, tech.
ClC6H4CH2Br M.W. 205.49 n20D 1.5922
NEAT
C
18,706-2
m-Bromobenzyl bromide, 99% (α,m-dibromotoluene)
BrC6H4CH2Br FW 249.94 mp 41° Beil. 5,308
Disp. C
MELT
D
10,598-8 1,3-Bis-(chloromethyl)-benzene (α,α'-dichloro-m-xylene)
C6H4(CH2Cl)2 M.W. 175.06 m.p. 34-37°
MELT
E
12,591-1 α,α'-Dibromo-m-xylene
C6H4(CH2Br)2 M.W. 263.97 m.p. 73-75°
NUJOL MULL
F
19,500-6
α,α,α',α'-Tetrabromo-m-xylene
C6H4(CHBr2)2 FW 421.77 mp 105-108°
Beil. 5,375 Disp. C
NUJOL MULL
G
11,357-3 m-Bis-(1,2-dibromoethyl)-benzene
C6H4[CH(Br)CH2Br]2 M.W. 449.83
m.p. 65-67.5°
NUJOL MULL
H
D10,220-2 p-Difluorobenzene
C6H4F2 M.W. 114.09 n20D 1.4440
NEAT
WAVENUMBER CM-1
WAVELENGTH IN MICRONS

A 10,424-8 p-Dichlorobenzene, zone refined
$C_6H_4Cl_2$ M.W. 147.00 m.p. 54.17°
MELT

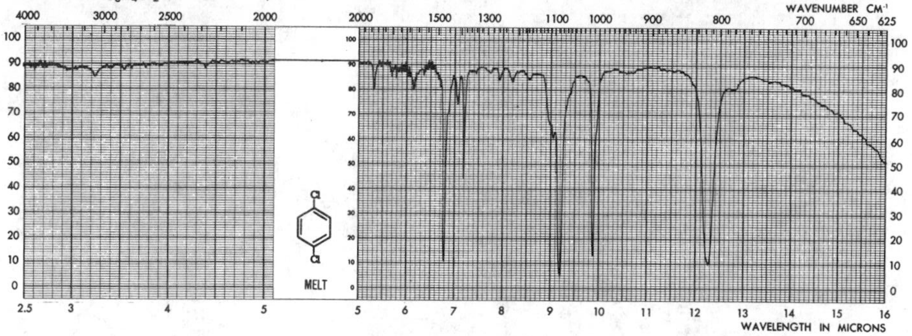

B 10,422-1 p-Dibromobenzene, zone refined
$C_6H_4Br_2$ M.W. 235.92 m.p. 87.33°
NUJOL MULL

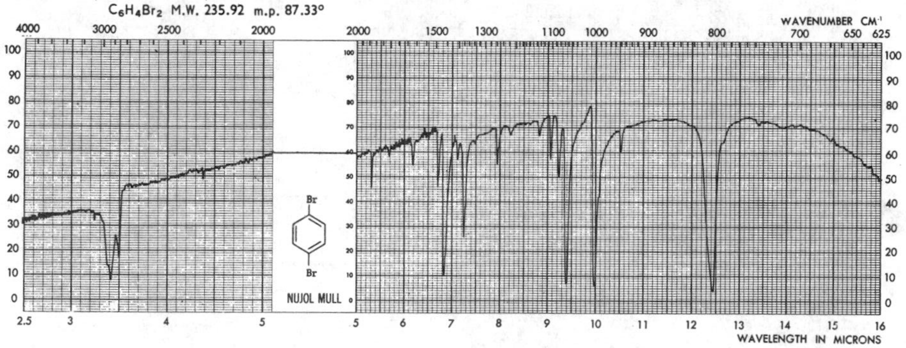

C B6,042-8
4-Bromochlorobenzene, 99%
BrC_6H_4Cl
M.W. 191.46 m.p. 66-68° b.p. 196° Beil. 5,209
NUJOL MULL

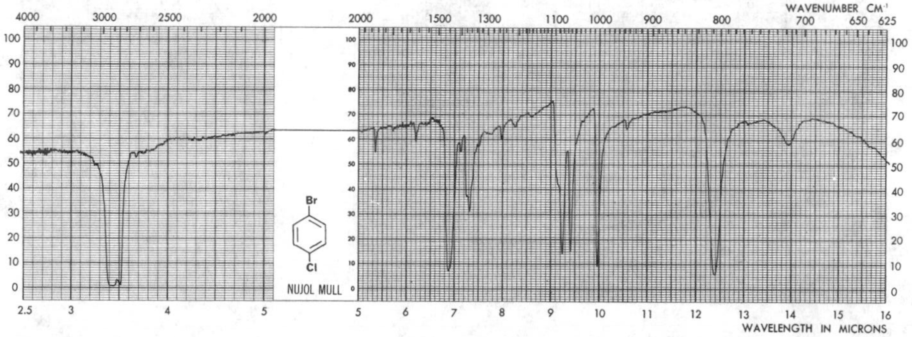

D 22,405-7
1-Chloro-4-fluorobenzene, 98%
ClC_6H_4F FW 130.55 mp -27 to 26° bp 129-130°
n_D^{20} 1.4950 d 1.226 *Beil.* 5,201 Disp. C
NEAT

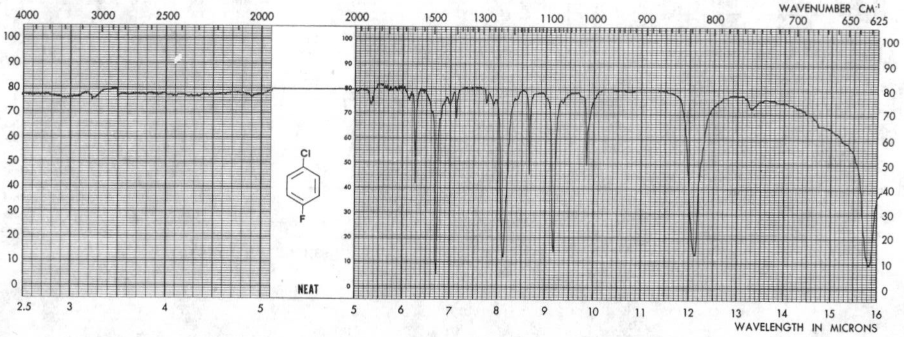

E B6720-1 4-Bromofluorobenzene
BrC_6H_4F M.W. 175.01 n_D^{20} 1.5269
NEAT

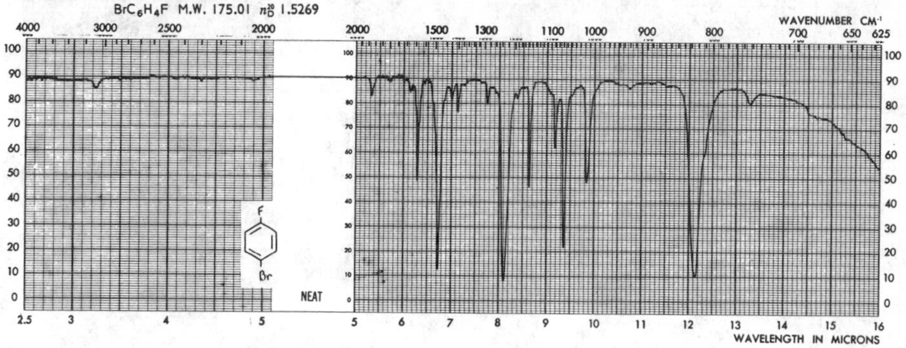

F 21,942-8
p-Fluoroiodobenzene, 99%
FC_6H_4I FW 222.00 mp -20° bp 182-184°
n_D^{20} 1.5832 d 1.925 *Beil.* 5,220 Disp. C
NEAT

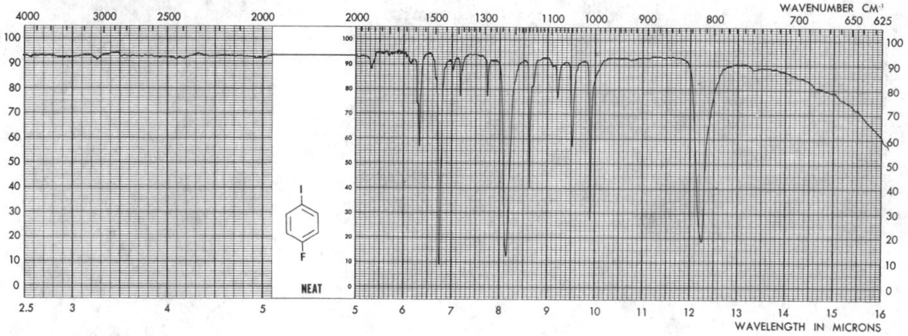

G 19,352-6
p-Diiodobenzene, 98%
$C_6H_4I_2$ FW 329.91 mp 131-133° bp 285°
Beil. 5,227 Disp. C
NUJOL MULL

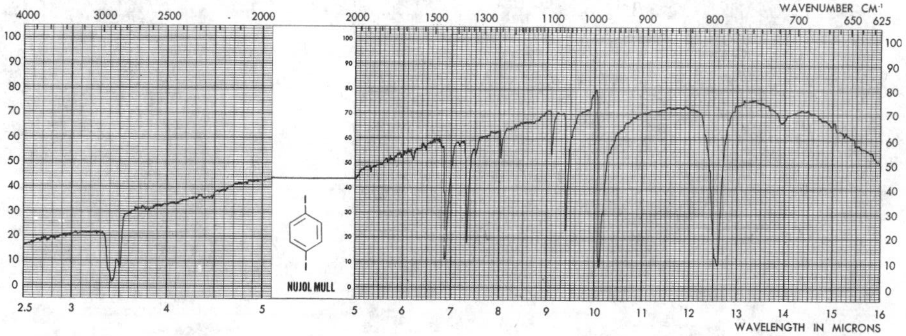

H 10,160-5 1-Chloro-4-iodobenzene
ClC_6H_4I M.W. 238.46 m.p. 53-54°
MELT

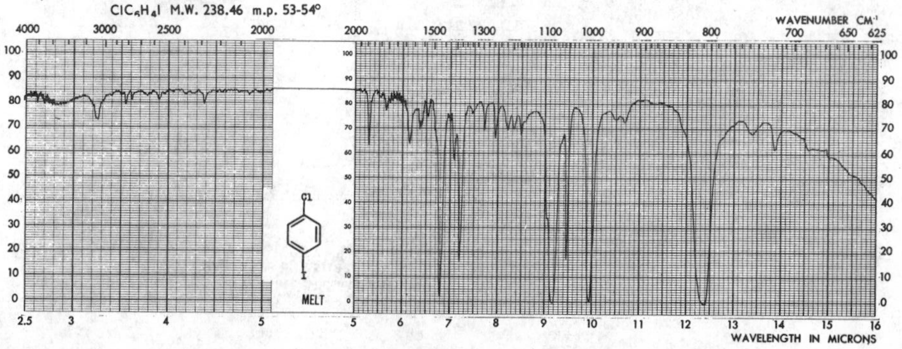

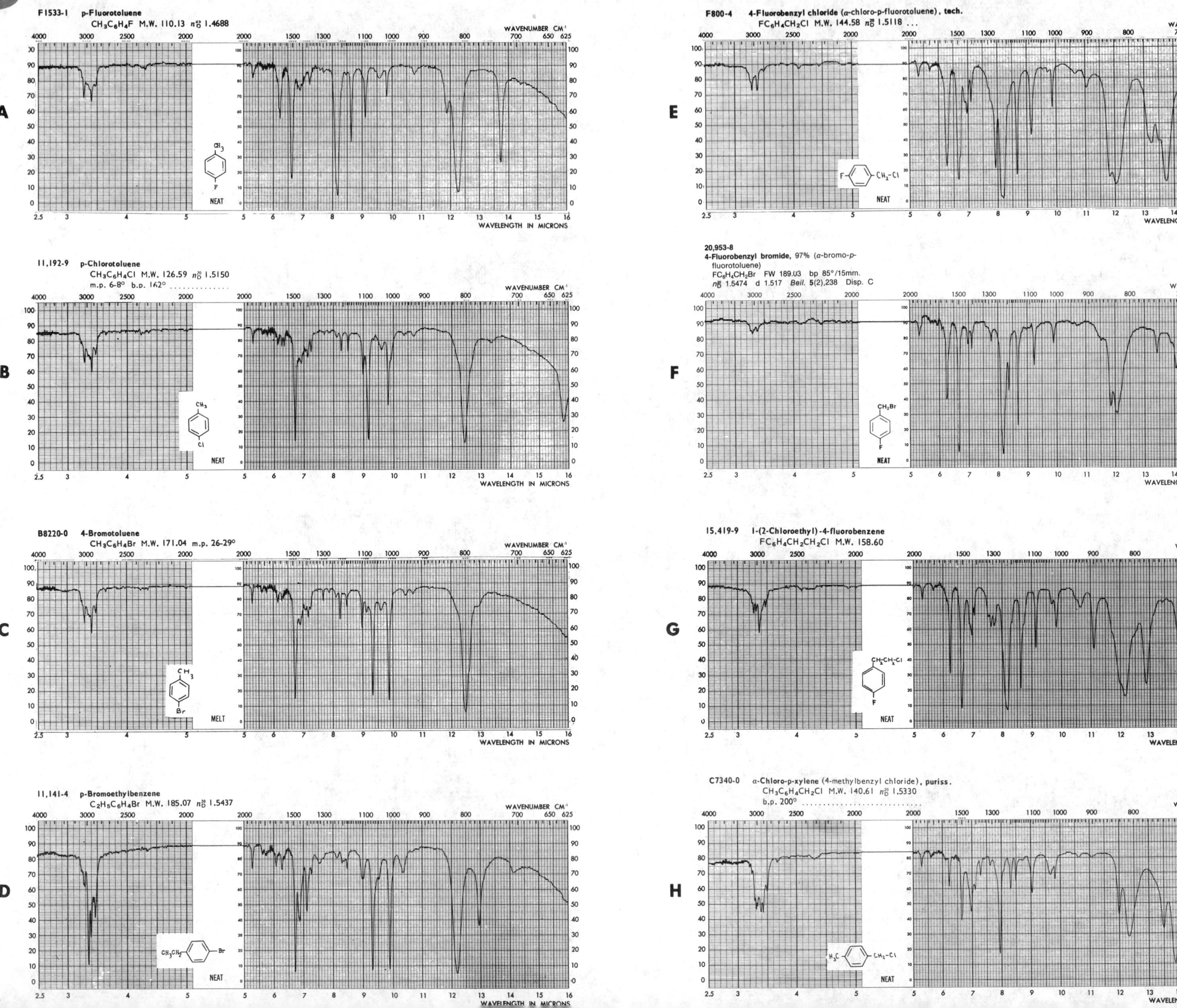

A F1533-1 **p-Fluorotoluene**
$CH_3C_6H_4F$ M.W. 110.13 n_D^{20} 1.4688 — NEAT

B 11,192-9 **p-Chlorotoluene**
$CH_3C_6H_4Cl$ M.W. 126.59 n_D^{20} 1.5150
m.p. 6-8° b.p. 162° — NEAT

C B8220-0 **4-Bromotoluene**
$CH_3C_6H_4Br$ M.W. 171.04 m.p. 26-29° — MELT

D 11,141-4 **p-Bromoethylbenzene**
$C_2H_5C_6H_4Br$ M.W. 185.07 n_D^{20} 1.5437 — NEAT

E F800-4 **4-Fluorobenzyl chloride** (α-chloro-p-fluorotoluene), **tech.**
$FC_6H_4CH_2Cl$ M.W. 144.58 n_D^{20} 1.5118 — NEAT

F 20,953-8
4-Fluorobenzyl bromide, 97% (α-bromo-p-fluorotoluene)
$FC_6H_4CH_2Br$ FW 189.03 bp 85°/15mm.
n_D^{20} 1.5474 d 1.517 *Beil.* 5(2),238 Disp. C — NEAT

G 15,419-9 **1-(2-Chloroethyl)-4-fluorobenzene**
$FC_6H_4CH_2CH_2Cl$ M.W. 158.60 — NEAT

H C7340-0 **α-Chloro-p-xylene** (4-methylbenzyl chloride), **puriss.**
$CH_3C_6H_4CH_2Cl$ M.W. 140.61 n_D^{20} 1.5330
b.p. 200° — NEAT

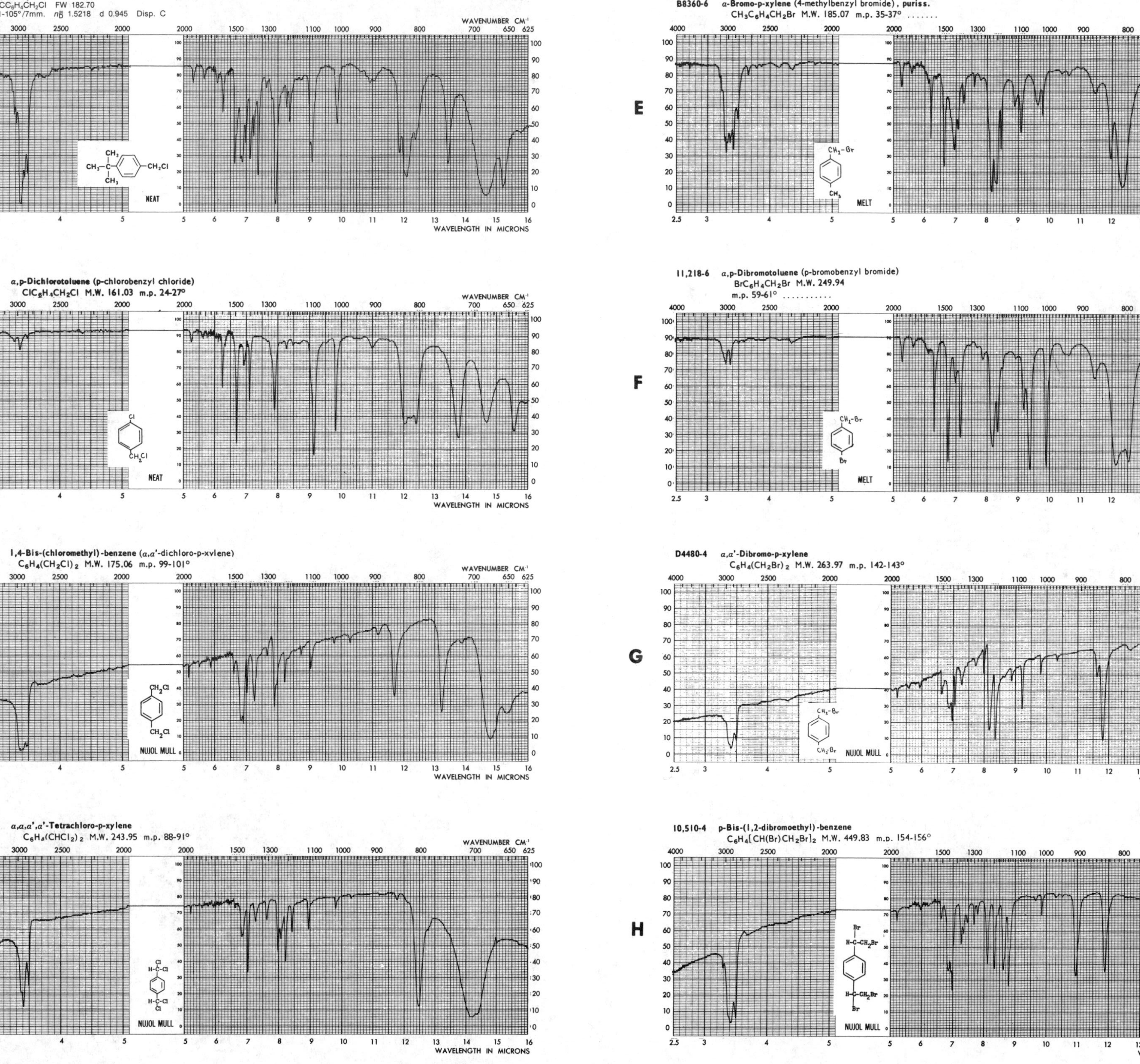
A
19,153-1
p-(tert-Butyl)benzyl chloride [p-(tert-butyl)-α-chlorotoluene]
(CH3)3CC6H4CH2Cl FW 182.70
bp 101-105°/7mm. n 1.5218 d 0.945 Disp. C
NEAT
B
11,196-1 α,p-Dichlorotoluene (p-chlorobenzyl chloride)
ClC6H4CH2Cl M.W. 161.03 m.p. 24-27°
NEAT
C
10,574-0 1,4-Bis-(chloromethyl)-benzene (α,α'-dichloro-p-xylene)
C6H4(CH2Cl)2 M.W. 175.06 m.p. 99-101°
NUJOL MULL
D
14,140-2 α,α,α',α'-Tetrachloro-p-xylene
C6H4(CHCl2)2 M.W. 243.95 m.p. 88-91°
NUJOL MULL
E
B8360-6 α-Bromo-p-xylene (4-methylbenzyl bromide), puriss.
CH3C6H4CH2Br M.W. 185.07 m.p. 35-37°
MELT
F
11,218-6 α,p-Dibromotoluene (p-bromobenzyl bromide)
BrC6H4CH2Br M.W. 249.94
m.p. 59-61°
MELT
G
D4480-4 α,α'-Dibromo-p-xylene
C6H4(CH2Br)2 M.W. 263.97 m.p. 142-143°
NUJOL MULL
H
10,510-4 p-Bis-(1,2-dibromoethyl)-benzene
C6H4[CH(Br)CH2Br]2 M.W. 449.83 m.p. 154-156°
NUJOL MULL
WAVENUMBER CM⁻¹
WAVELENGTH IN MICRONS
ALDRICH

A

T6370-3 *α,α,α*-**Trifluorotoluene** (benzotrifluoride)
$C_6H_5CF_3$ M.W. 146.11 n_D^{20} 1.4145 b.p. 102°

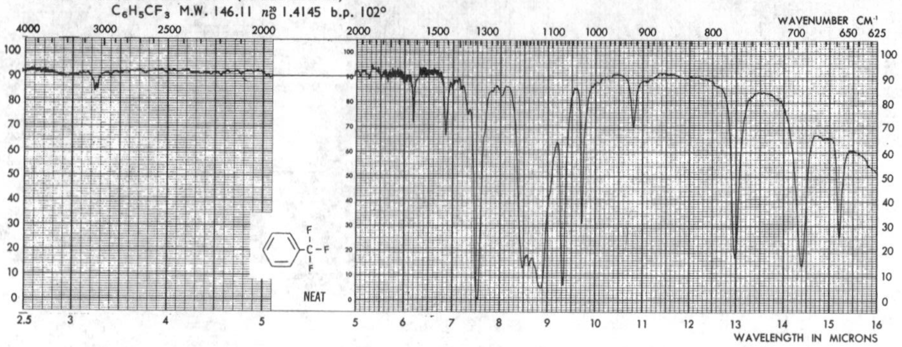

NEAT

B

14,789-3 *α,α,α*-**Trichlorotoluene** (benzotrichloride)
$C_6H_5CCl_3$ M.W. 195.48 n_D^{20} 1.5570
b.p. 219-223° . . . .

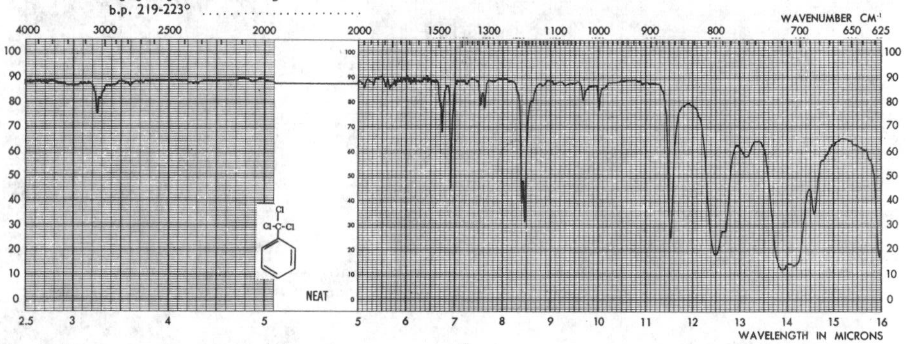

NEAT

C

21,936-3
o-**Fluorobenzotrifluoride**, 99% (*α,α,α,o*-tetra-
fluorotoluene)
$FC_6H_4CF_3$ FW 164.10 bp 114-115°/750mm.
n_D^{20} 1.4065 d 1.293 *Beil.* 5(3),679 Disp. C

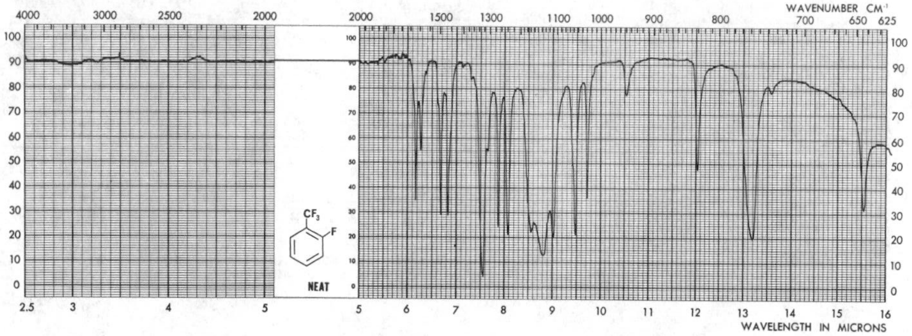

NEAT

D

C2600-3 **2-Chlorobenzotrifluoride** (o-chloro-*α,α,α*-trifluorotoluene)
$ClC_6H_4CF_3$ M.W. 180.56 n_D^{20} 1.4550 . . . .

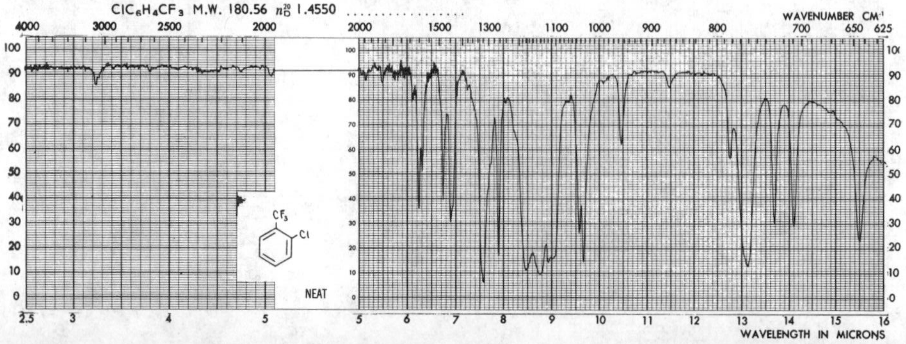

NEAT

E

B5880-6 **2-Bromobenzotrifluoride** (o-bromo-*α,α,α*-trifluorotoluene)
$BrC_6H_4CF_3$ M.W. 225.01 n_D^{20} 1.4852 . . . .

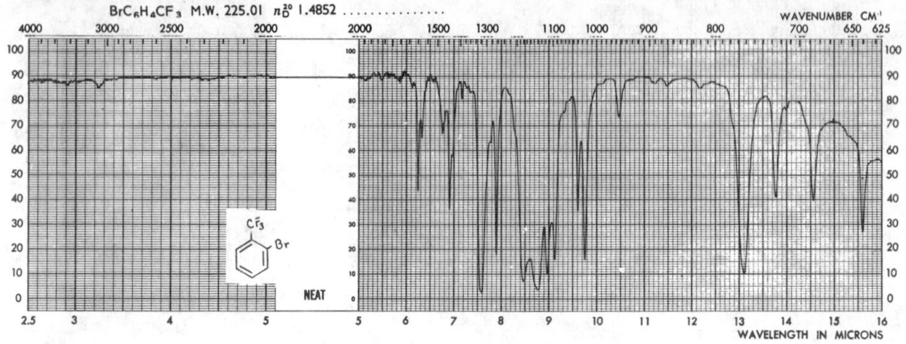

NEAT

F

22,003-5
o-**Iodo**-*α,α,α*-**trifluorotoluene**, 99%
(*o*-iodobenzotrifluoride)
$IC_6H_4CF_3$ FW 272.01 bp 197-198°/750mm.
d 1.939 *Beil.* 5(3),725 Disp. C

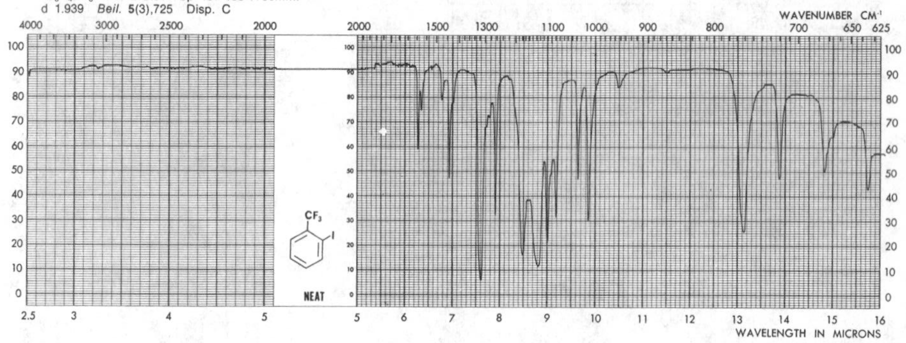

NEAT

G

14,628-5 **o-Fluoro**-*α,α,α*-**trichlorotoluene** (1-trichloromethyl-2-fluorobenzene)
$FC_6H_4CCl_3$ M.W. 213.47 n_D^{20} 1.5432
b.p. 75°/5 mm. . . . .

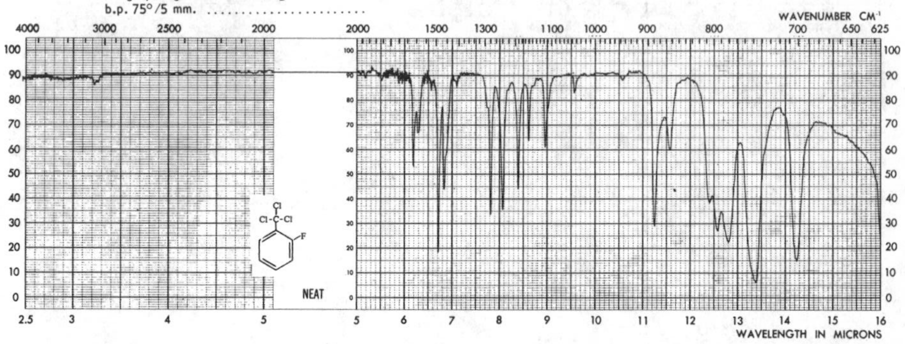

NEAT

H

C2540-6 **2-Chlorobenzotrichloride** (*α,α,α,o*-tetrachlorotoluene)
$ClC_6H_4CCl_3$ M.W. 229.92 m.p. 31-32.5° . .

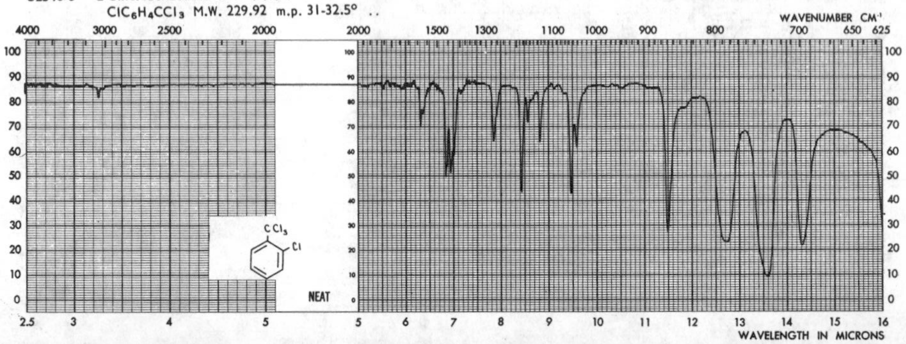

NEAT

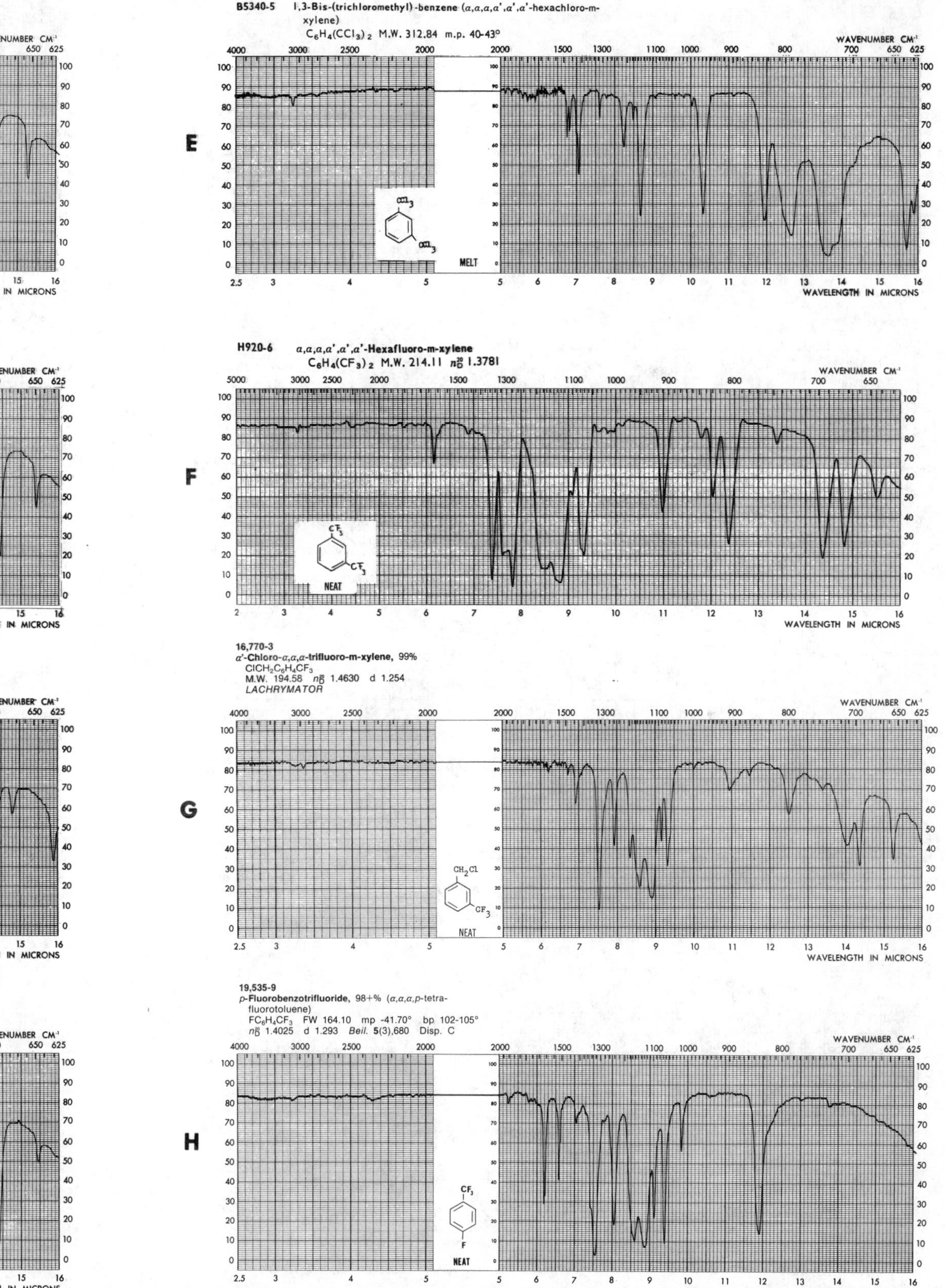

A

21,937-1
m-**Fluorobenzotrifluoride**, 99% (α,α,α,*m*-tetrafluorotoluene)
$FC_6H_4CF_3$ FW 164.10 bp 101-102° n_D^{20} 1.4007
d 1.302 *Beil.* 5(2),224 Disp. C

B

C2620-8 **3-Chlorobenzotrifluoride** (*m*-chloro-α,α,α-trifluorotoluene)
$ClC_6H_4CF_3$ M.W. 180.56 n_D^{20} 1.4461

C

C2560-0 **3-Chlorobenzotrichloride** (α,α,α,m-tetrachlorotoluene
$ClC_6H_4CCl_3$ M.W. 229.92 n_D^{20} 1.5705

D

B5900-4 **3-Bromobenzotrifluoride** (m-bromo-α,α,α-trifluorotoluene)
$BrC_6H_4CF_3$ M.W. 225.01 n_D^{20} 1.4716

E

B5340-5 **1,3-Bis-(trichloromethyl)-benzene** (α,α,α,α',α',α'-hexachloro-m-xylene)
$C_6H_4(CCl_3)_2$ M.W. 312.84 m.p. 40-43°

F

H920-6 **α,α,α,α',α',α'-Hexafluoro-m-xylene**
$C_6H_4(CF_3)_2$ M.W. 214.11 n_D^{20} 1.3781

G

16,770-3
α'-**Chloro-α,α,α-trifluoro-m-xylene**, 99%
$ClCH_2C_6H_4CF_3$
M.W. 194.58 n_D^{20} 1.4630 d 1.254
LACHRYMATOR

H

19,535-9
p-**Fluorobenzotrifluoride**, 98+% (α,α,α,*p*-tetrafluorotoluene)
$FC_6H_4CF_3$ FW 164.10 mp -41.70° bp 102-105°
n_D^{20} 1.4025 d 1.293 *Beil.* 5(3),680 Disp. C

A

C2640-2 **4-Chlorobenzotrifluoride** (p-chloro-α,α,α-trifluorotoluene)
$ClC_6H_4CF_3$ M.W. 180.56 n_D^{20} 1.4463

NEAT

B

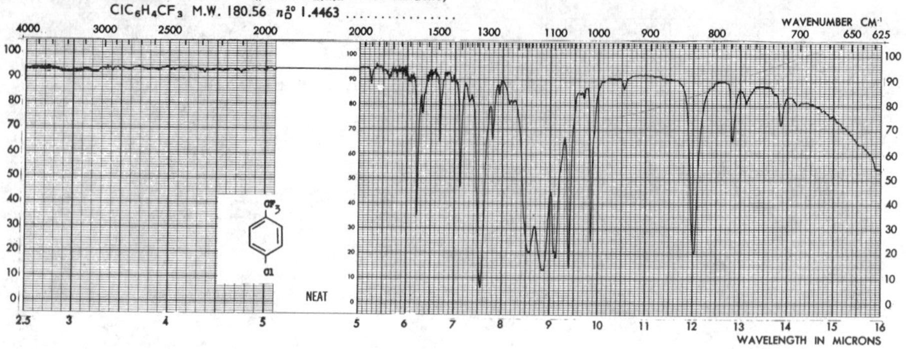

15,269-2 **4-Bromobenzotrifluoride** (p-bromo-α,α,α-trifluorotoluene)
$BrC_6H_4CF_3$ M.W. 225.01 n_D^{20} 1.4725 b.p. 154-155°

NEAT

C

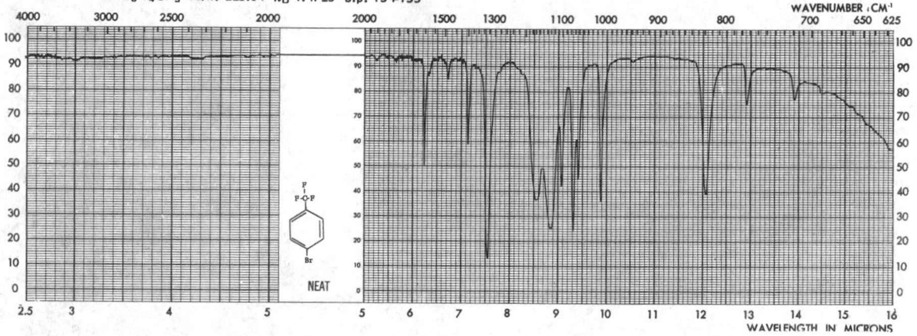

14,627-7 **p-Fluoro-α,α,α-trichlorotoluene** (1-trichloromethyl-4-fluorobenzene)
$FC_6H_4CCl_3$ M.W. 213.47 n_D^{20} 1.5334
b.p. 98°/16 mm.

NEAT

D

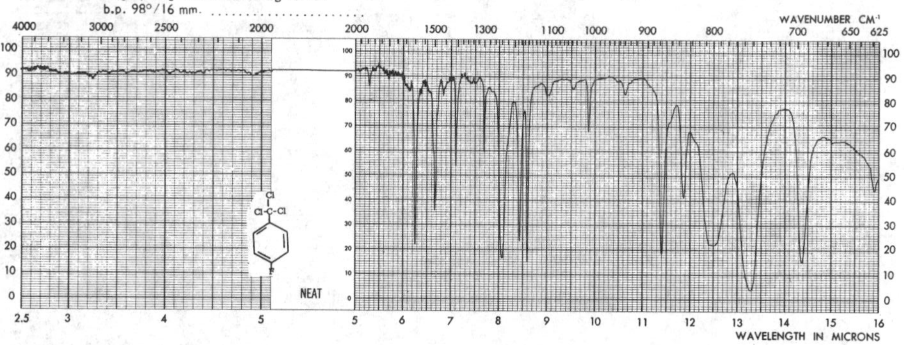

C2580-5 **4-Chlorobenzotrichloride** (α,α,α,p-tetrachlorotoluene)
$ClC_6H_4CCl_3$ M.W. 229.92 n_D^{20} 1.5710
b.p. 250-254°

NEAT

E

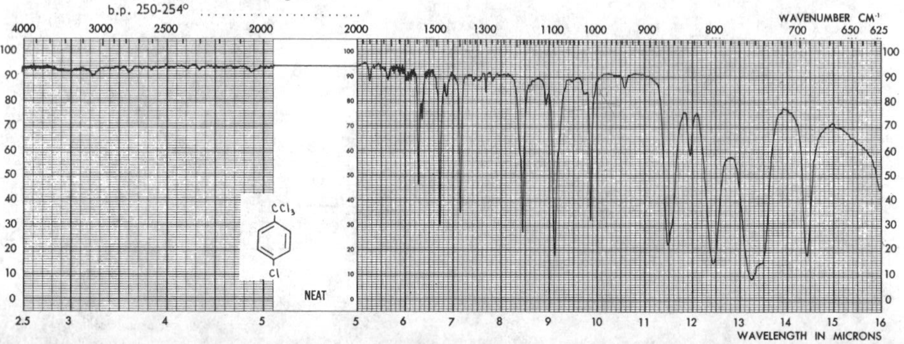

12,397-8 **1,4-Bis-(trichloromethyl)-benzene** (α,α,α,α',α',α'-hexachloro-p-xylene)
$C_6H_4(CCl_3)_2$ M.W. 312.84 m.p. 110-111°

NUJOL MULL

F

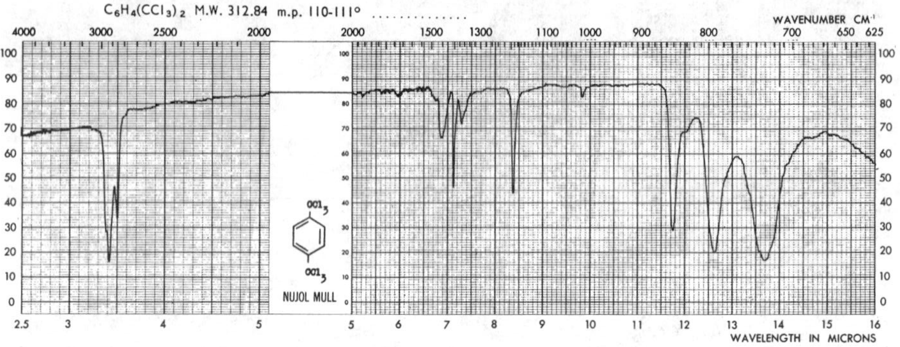

F1554-4 **3-Fluoro-o-xylene**
$(CH_3)_2C_6H_3F$ M.W. 124.16 n_D^{20} 1.4846

NEAT

G

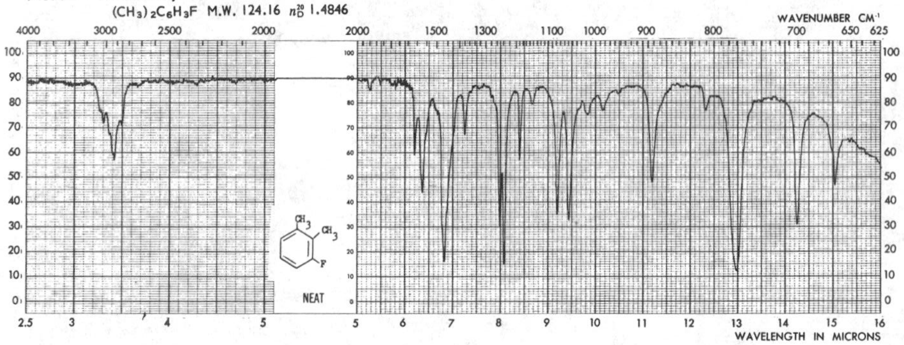

14,122-4 **2-Chloro-6-fluorotoluene**
$CH_3C_6H_3(Cl)F$ M.W. 144.58 n_D^{20} 1.5026
b.p. 154-156°

NEAT

H

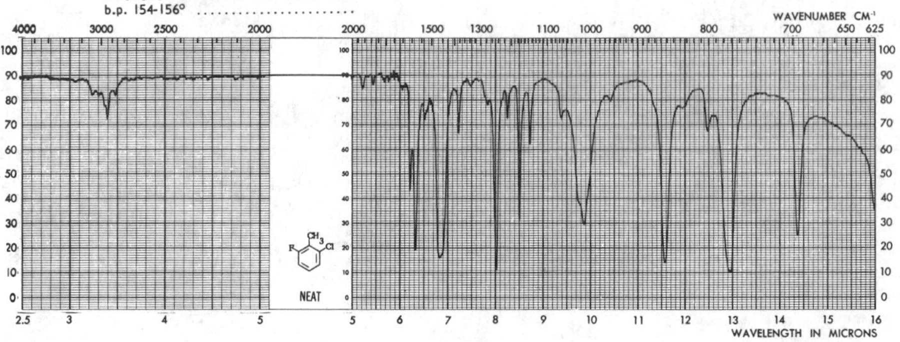

21,811-1
2-Chloro-6-fluorobenzyl chloride, 98%
$ClC_6H_3(F)CH_2Cl$ FW 179.02 n_D^{20} 1.5372 d 1.401
Disp. C

NEAT

(Each spectrum: WAVENUMBER CM⁻¹ 4000–625; WAVELENGTH IN MICRONS 2.5–16; transmittance 0–100)

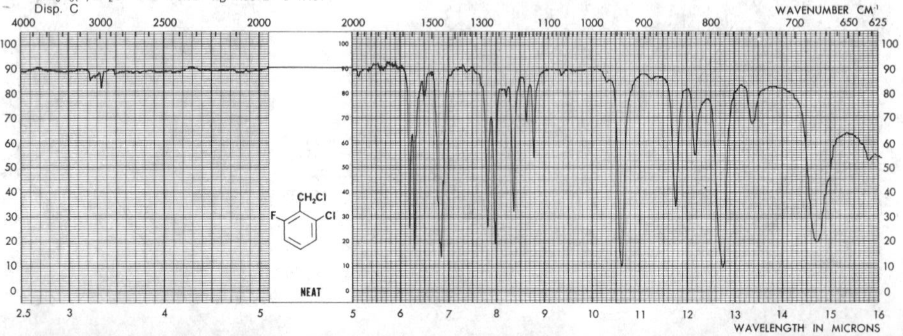

A 14,184-4 **2-Chloro-6-fluorobenzal chloride** (6-fluoro-α,α,2-trichlorotoluene)
$ClC_6H_3(F)CHCl_2$ M.W. 213.47 n_D^{20} 1.5520
b.p. 235°

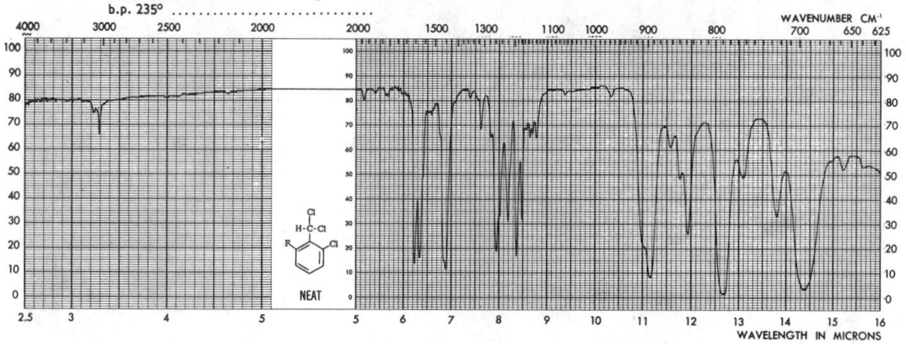

NEAT

B 21,813-8
α,α,α,2-Tetrachloro-6-fluorotoluene, 98% (2-chloro-6-fluorobenzotrichloride)
$ClC_6H_3(F)CCl_3$ FW 247.91 mp 36-40° Disp. C

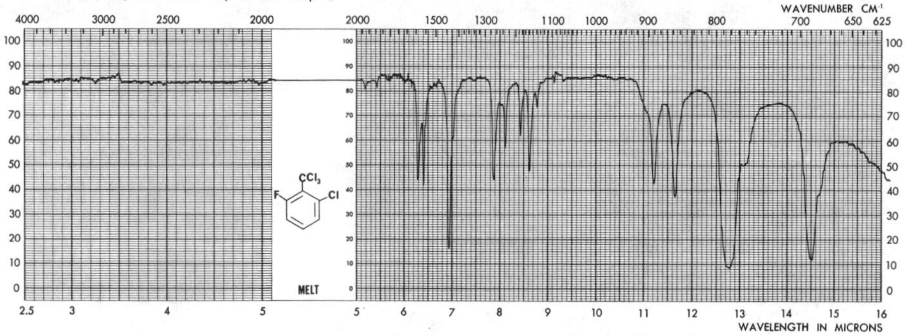

MELT

C T5440-2 **1,2,3-Trichlorobenzene**
$C_6H_3Cl_3$ M.W. 181.45 m.p. 53-54°

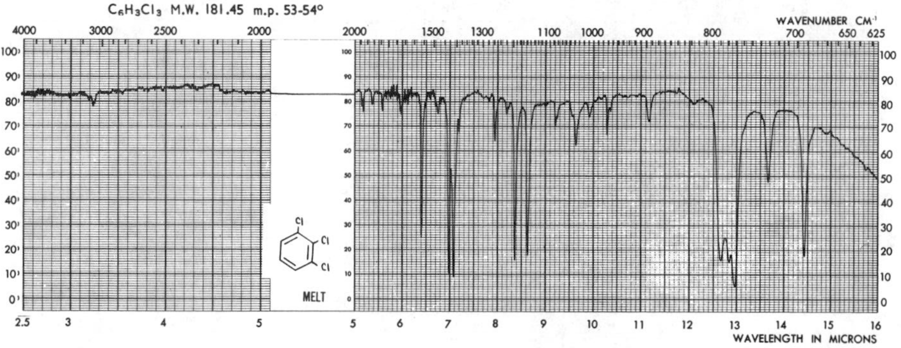

MELT

D D7600-5 **2,6-Dichlorotoluene, puriss.**
$CH_3C_6H_3Cl_2$ M.W. 161.03 n_D^{20} 1.5507

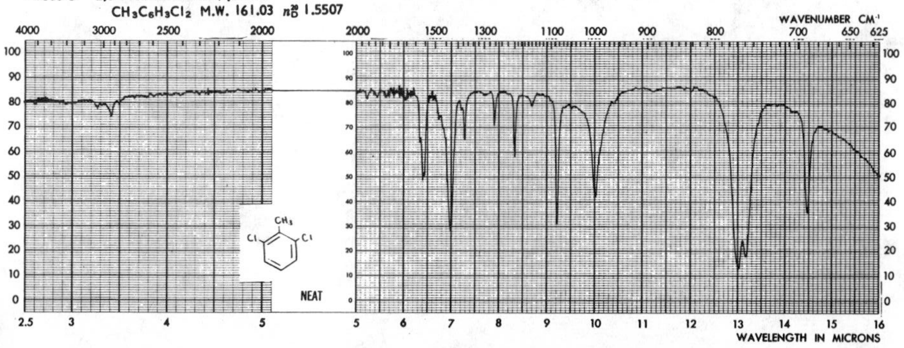

NEAT

E 16,065-2
1-Bromo-2,6-dichlorobenzene, 99%
$BrC_6H_3Cl_2$
M.W. 225.91 m.p. 65-67° b.p. 242°/765mm.
Beil. 5,210

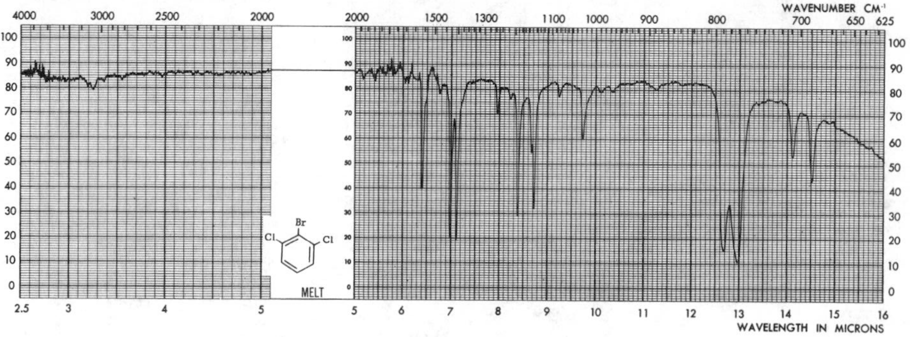

MELT

F T5630-8 **α,2,6-Trichlorotoluene** (2,6-dichlorobenzyl chloride)
$Cl_2C_6H_3CH_2Cl$ M.W. 195.48 m.p. 36-39°

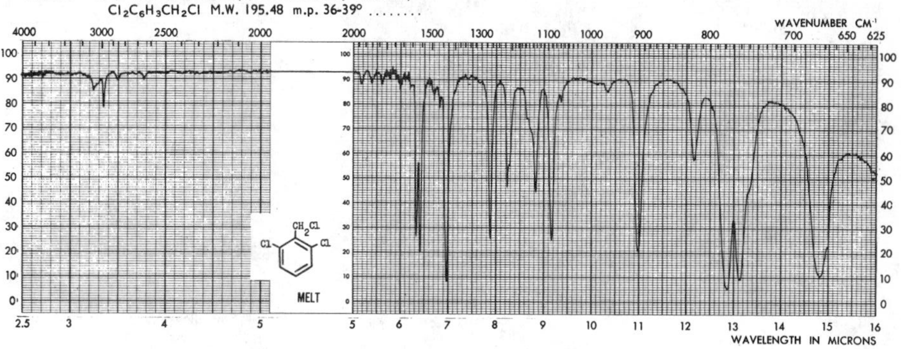

MELT

G T850-7 **α,α,2,6-Tetrachlorotoluene, 97%**
$Cl_2C_6H_3CHCl_2$ M.W. 229.92 n_D^{20} 1.5844

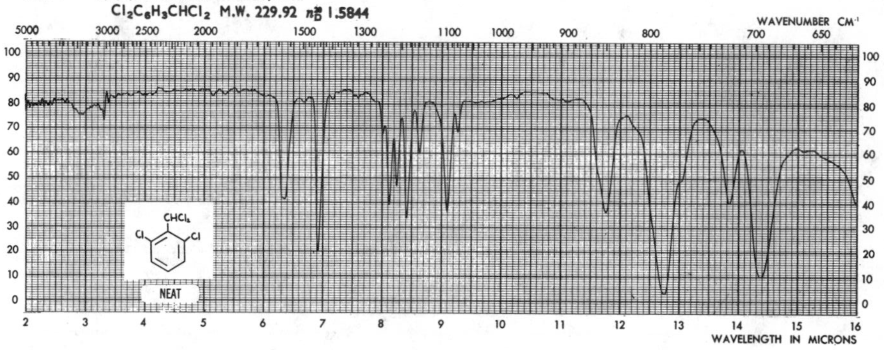

NEAT

H 10,030-7 **α-Bromo-2,6-dichlorotoluene** (2,6-dichlorobenzyl bromide)
$Cl_2C_6H_3CH_2Br$ M.W. 239.93 m.p. 54-55°

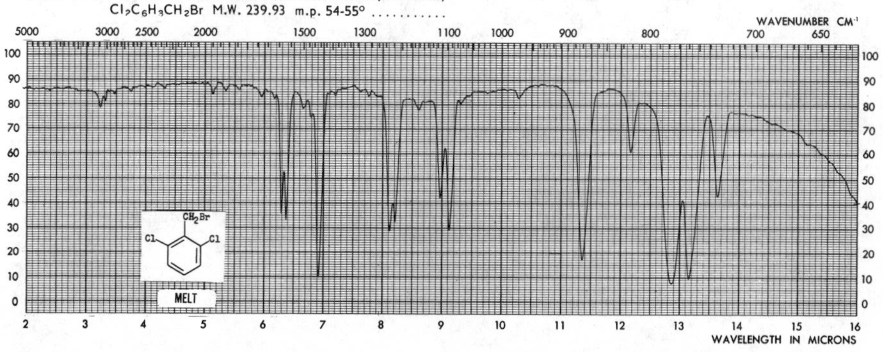

MELT

A

11,585-1 **2-Bromo-m-xylene**
$(CH_3)_2C_6H_3Br$ M.W. 185.07 n_D^{20} 1.5541

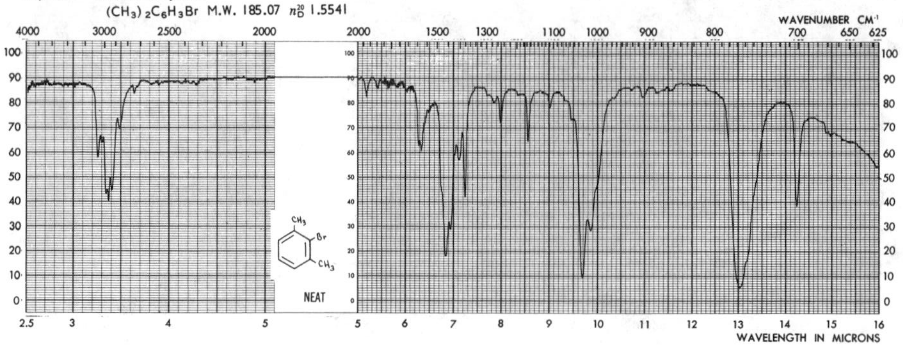

NEAT

B

B8378-9 **3-Bromo-o-xylene**
$(CH_3)_2C_6H_3Br$ M.W. 185.07

NEAT

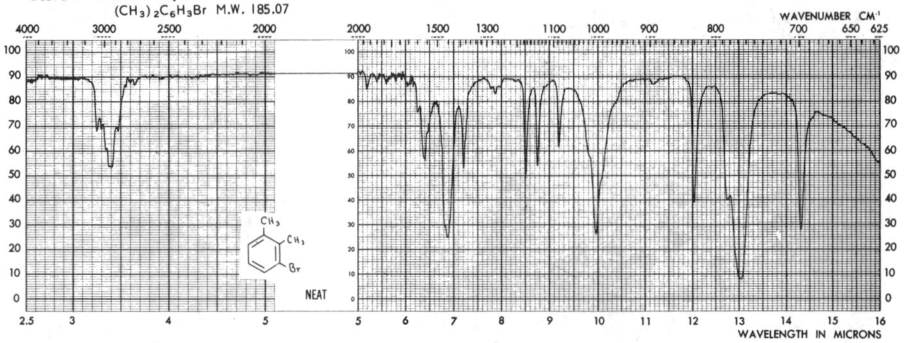

C

19,684-3
1,2,4-Trifluorobenzene, 97+%
$C_6H_3F_3$ FW 132.09 bp 88° n_D^{20} 1.4225 d 1.264
Beil. 5(2),148 Disp. C

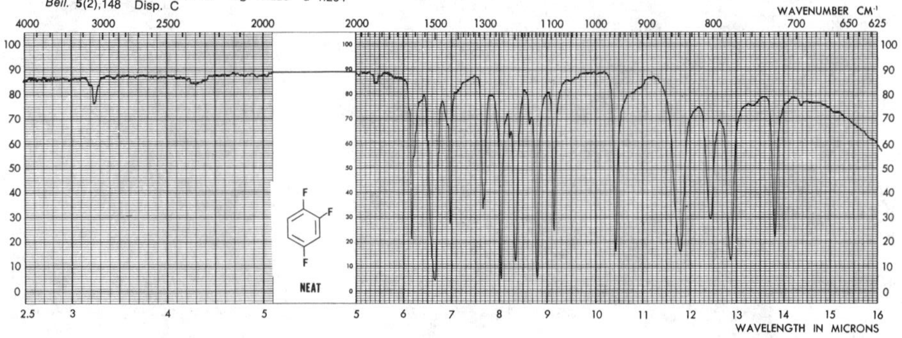

NEAT

D

13,204-7 **1,2,4-Trichlorobenzene**
$C_6H_3Cl_3$ M.W. 181.45 n_D^{20} 1.5707
b.p. 213-214°

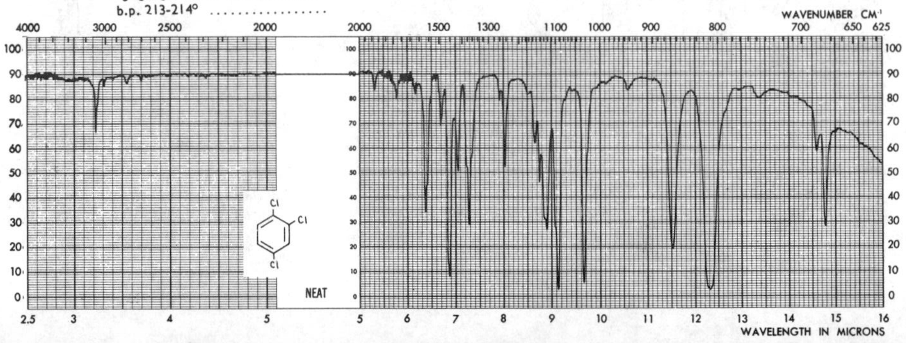

NEAT

E

13,275-6 **1,2,4-Tribromobenzene**
$C_6H_3Br_3$ M.W. 314.82 m.p. 41-43°

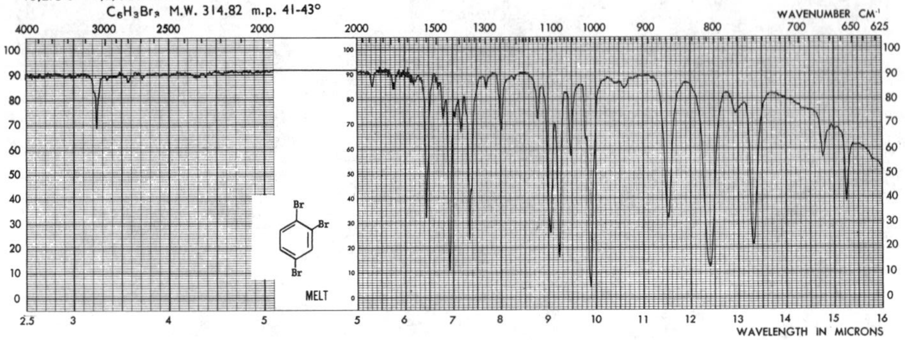

MELT

F

16,136-5
3,4-Dichlorotoluene, 97%
$CH_3C_6H_3Cl_2$
M.W. 161.03 b.p. 200.5°/741mm. n_D^{20} 1.5472
d 1.251 Beil. 5,296

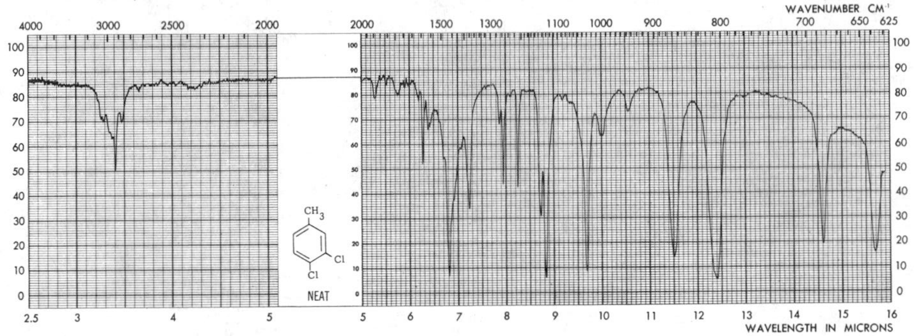

NEAT

G

13,925-4 **α,2,4-Trichlorotoluene** (2,4-dichlorobenzyl chloride), **tech.**
$Cl_2C_6H_3CH_2Cl$ M.W. 195.48 n_D^{20} 1.5757
b.p. 118-119°/13 mm.

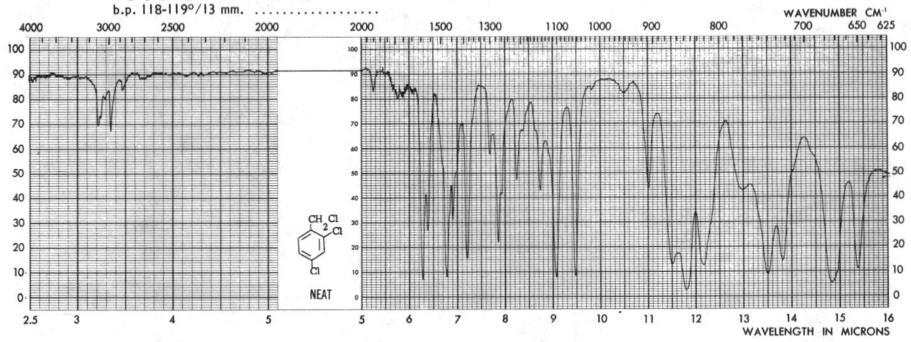

NEAT

H

14,500-9 **2,4-Dichlorotoluene**
$CH_3C_6H_3Cl_2$ M.W. 161.03 n_D^{20} 1.5454
b.p. 200°

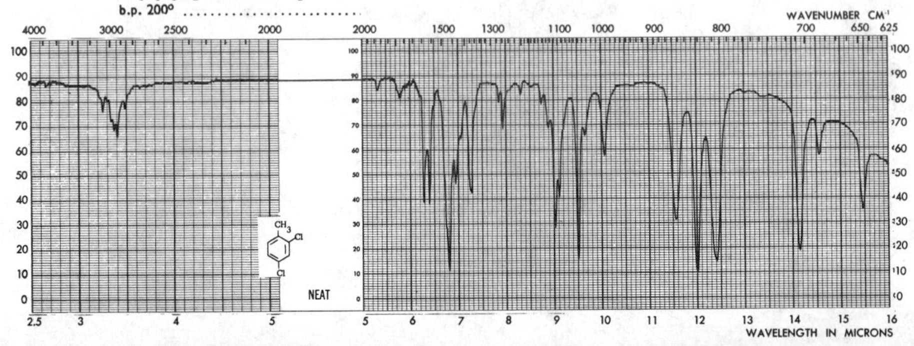

NEAT

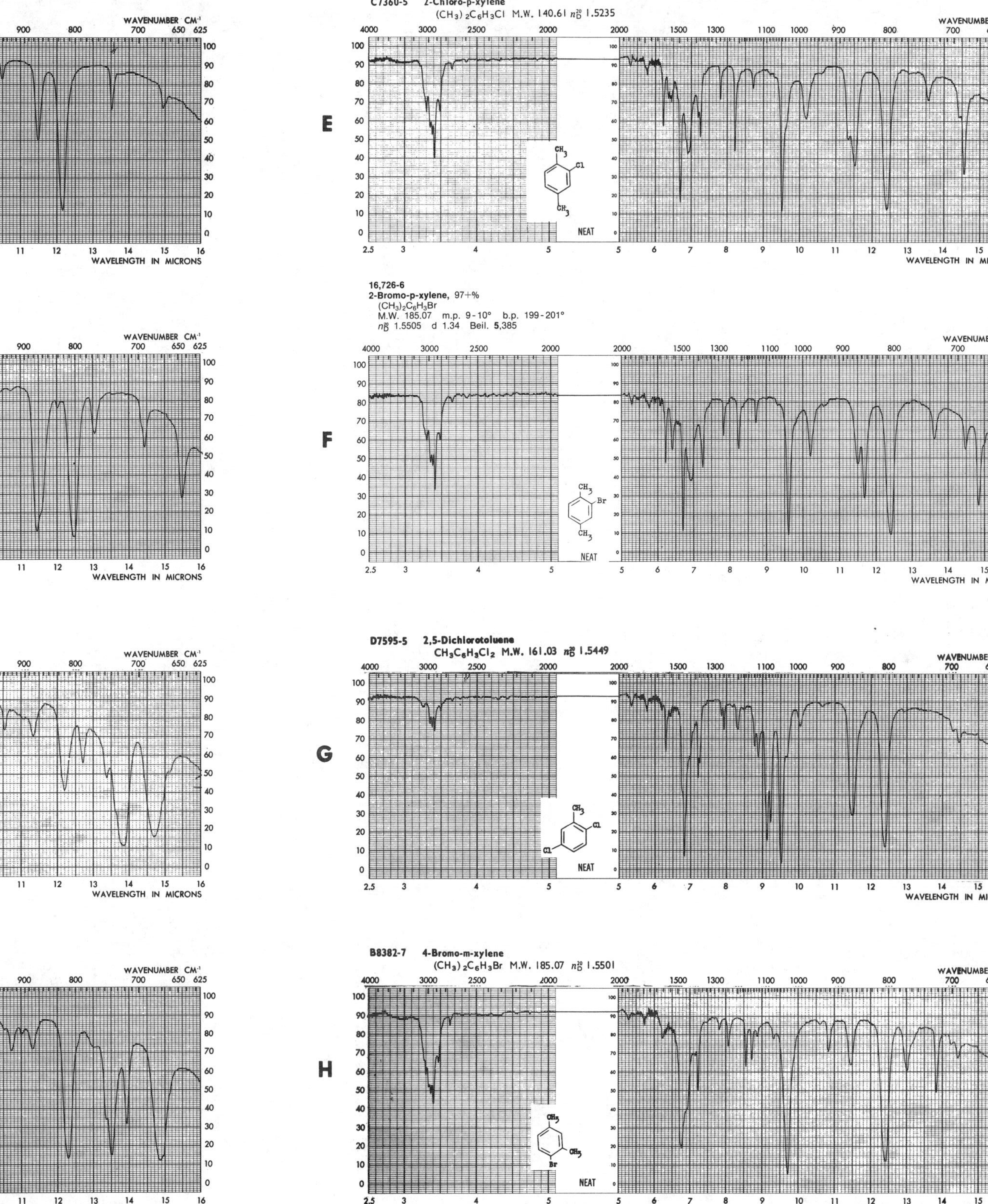

A 15,225-0 **2,4-Dichlorobenzotrifluoride** (2,4-dichloro-α,α,α-trifluorotoluene)
$Cl_2C_6H_3CF_3$ M.W. 215.00 n_D^{20} 1.4802 .....
NEAT

B 13,775-8 **4-Chloro-o-xylene**
$(CH_3)_2C_6H_3Cl$ M.W. 140.61 n_D^{20} 1.5283
b.p. 84-85°/20 mm. ....
NEAT

C D15,060-6 **3,4-Dimethylbenzyl chloride** (1-chloromethyl-3,4-dimethylbenzene), tech., 75%
$(CH_3)_2C_6H_3CH_2Cl$ M.W. 154.64 n_D^{20} 1.5402
b.p. 100°/12 mm. ....
NEAT

D 12,640-3 **2,5-Dimethylbenzyl chloride** (1-chloromethyl-2,5-dimethylbenzene)
$(CH_3)_2C_6H_3CH_2Cl$ M.W. 154.64 n_D^{20} 1.5374 ....
NEAT

E C7360-5 **2-Chloro-p-xylene**
$(CH_3)_2C_6H_3Cl$ M.W. 140.61 n_D^{20} 1.5235
NEAT

F 16,726-6 **2-Bromo-p-xylene**, 97+%
$(CH_3)_2C_6H_3Br$
M.W. 185.07 m.p. 9-10° b.p. 199-201°
n_D^{20} 1.5505 d 1.34 Beil. 5,385
NEAT

G D7595-5 **2,5-Dichlorotoluene**
$CH_3C_6H_3Cl_2$ M.W. 161.03 n_D^{20} 1.5449
NEAT

H B8382-7 **4-Bromo-m-xylene**
$(CH_3)_2C_6H_3Br$ M.W. 185.07 n_D^{20} 1.5501
NEAT

A

B8380-0 4-Bromo-o-xylene, tech.
$(CH_3)_2C_6H_3Br$ M.W. 185.07 n_D^{20} 1.5530

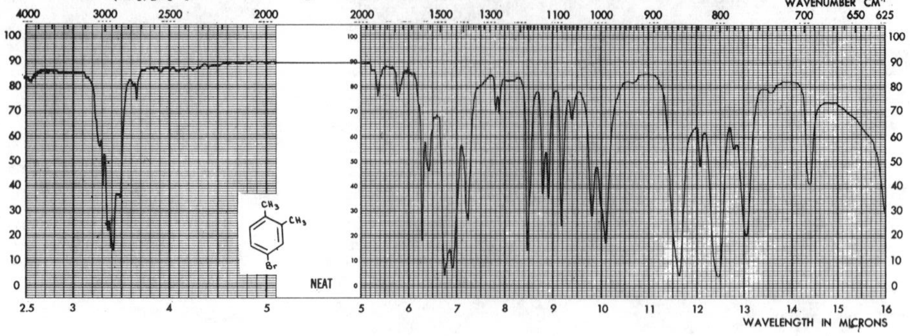

NEAT

B

D5800 2,5-Dichlorobenzotrifluoride
$Cl_2C_6H_3CF_3$ M.W. 215.00 n_D^{20} 1.4810

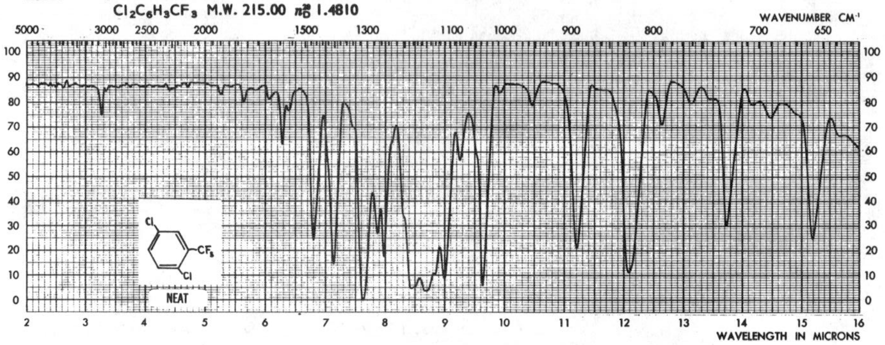

NEAT

C

15,128-9 5-Bromo-2-chlorobenzotrifluoride (5-bromo-2-chloro-α,α,α-trifluorotoluene), tech.
$BrC_6H_3(Cl)CF_3$ M.W. 259.46 n_D^{20} 1.5062 ...

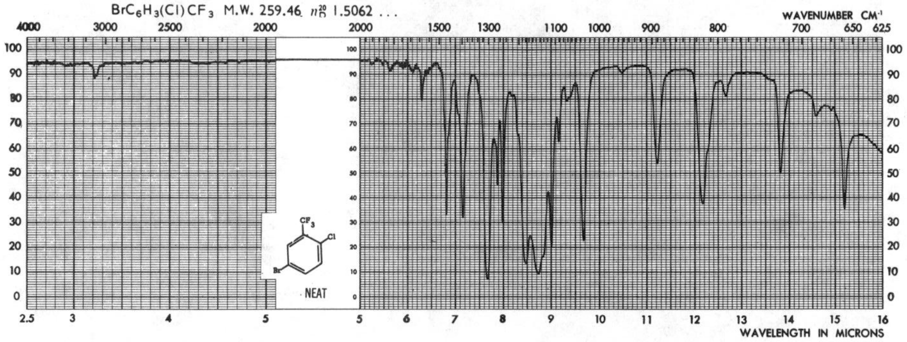

NEAT

D

14,557-2 2,4-Dibromo-1-fluorobenzene
$Br_2C_6H_3F$ M.W. 253.91 n_D^{20} 1.5828
b.p. 105-110°/22 mm. ....

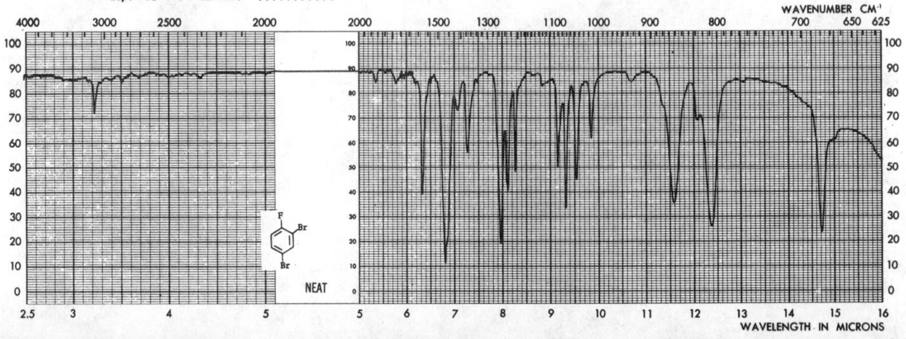

NEAT

E

F940 4-Fluoro-2-iodotoluene

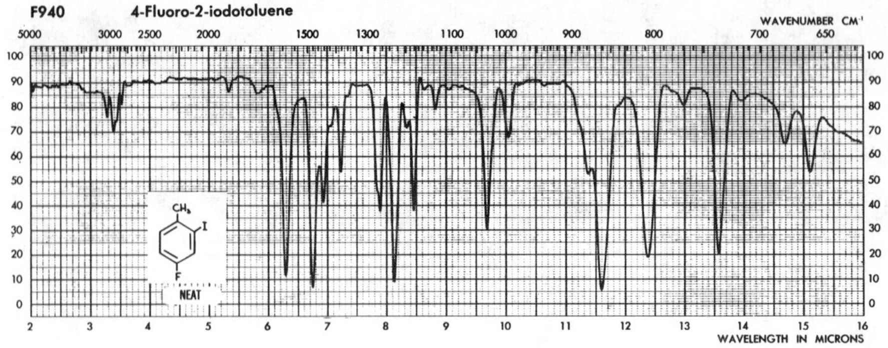

NEAT

F

17,755-5
1,4-Dichloro-2-iodobenzene, 98%
$Cl_2C_6H_3I$
M.W. 272.9 m.p. 21° b.p. 255-256°/742mm.
n_D^{20} 1.6461 Beil. 5,221

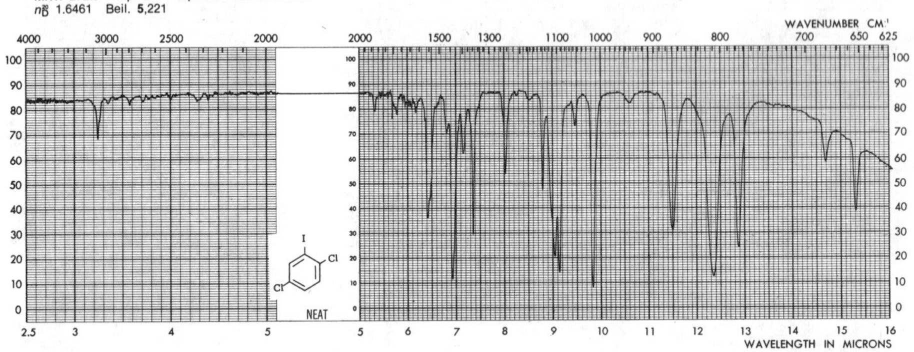

NEAT

G

19,685-1
1,3,5-Trifluorobenzene, 98+%
$C_6H_3F_3$ FW 132.09 mp -5.50° bp 75-76°
n_D^{20} 1.4140 d 1.277 Disp. C

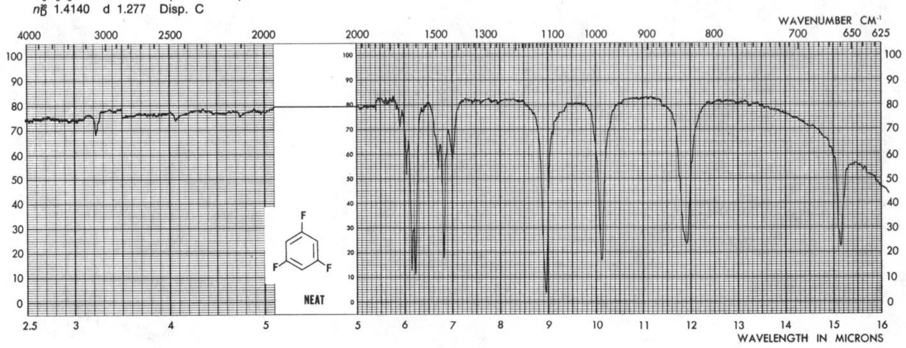

NEAT

H

T5460-7 1,3,5-Trichlorobenzene
$C_6H_3Cl_3$ M.W. 181.45 m.p. 63-65°

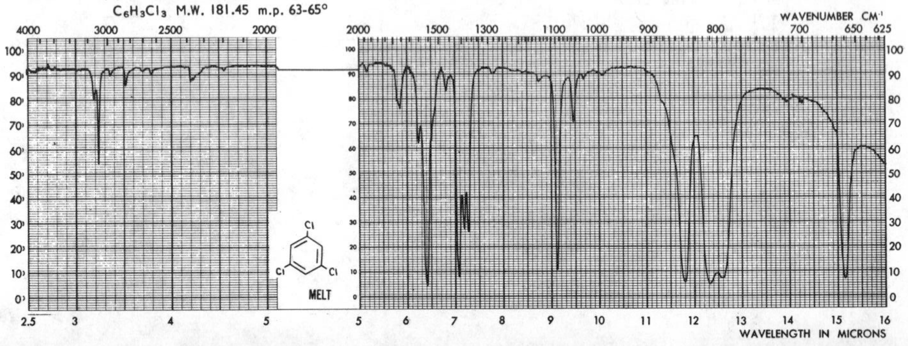

MELT

A

14,006-6 1,3,5-Tribromobenzene
$C_6H_3Br_3$ M.W. 314.82 m.p. 121-124°

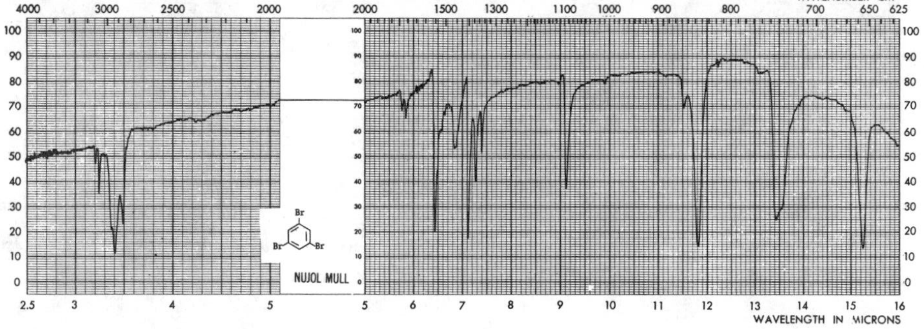

NUJOL MULL

B

19,254-6
1,3-Dichloro-5-iodobenzene, 99%
$Cl_2C_6H_3I$ FW 272.90 mp 56-58° *Beil.* **5**(1),120
Disp. C

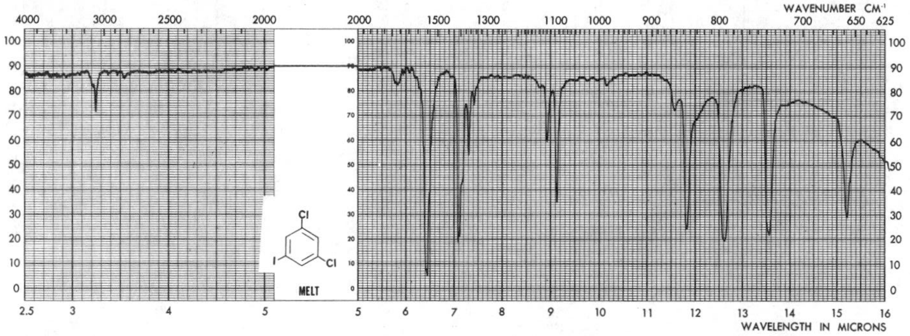

MELT

C

11,395-6 3,5-Difluoroiodobenzene
$F_2C_6H_3I$ M.W. 239.99 n_D^{20} 1.5531 b.p. 58-60°/17 mm.

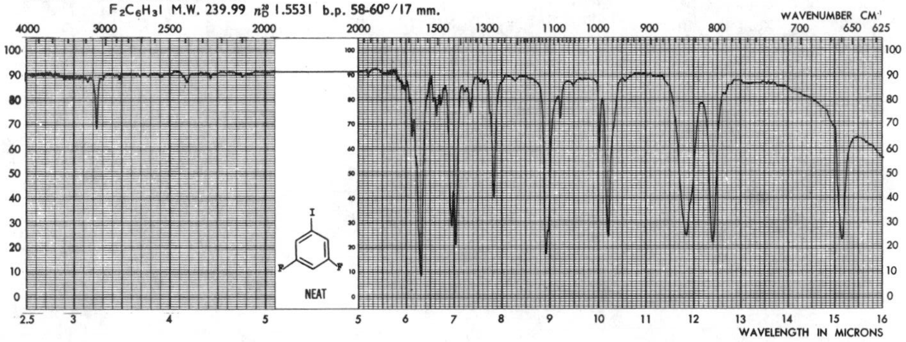

NEAT

D

T1163-0 1,2,3,4-Tetrafluorobenzene
$C_6H_2F_4$ M.W. 150.07 n_D^{20} 1.4066

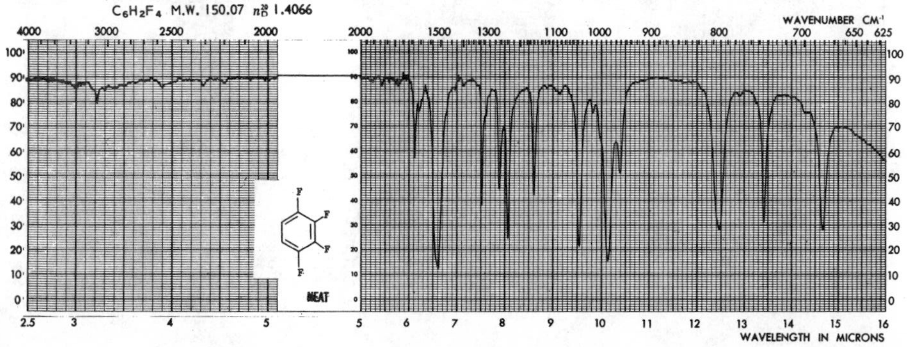

NEAT

E

13,184-9 1,2,3,4-Tetrachlorobenzene
$C_6H_2Cl_4$ M.W. 215.90 m.p. 45-46°

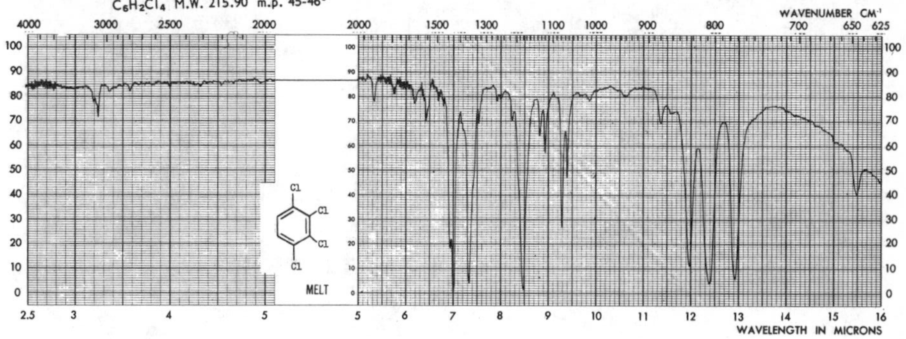

MELT

F

T1164-9 1,2,3,5-Tetrafluorobenzene, puriss.
$C_6H_2F_4$ M.W. 150.07 n_D^{20} 1.4035

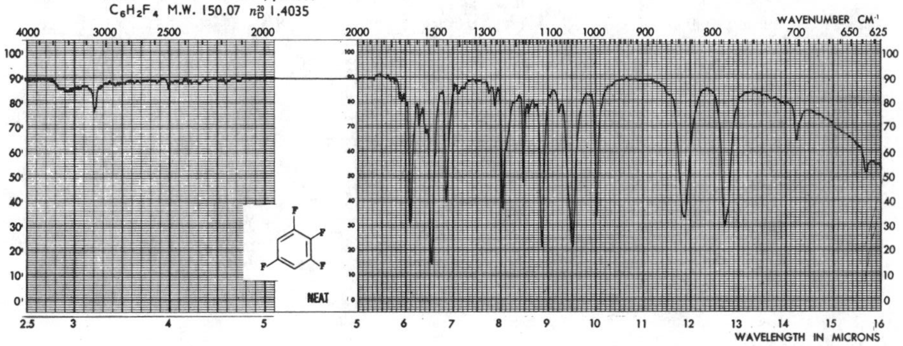

NEAT

G

15,348-6 1,2,3,5-Tetrachlorobenzene
$C_6H_2Cl_4$ M.W. 215.90 m.p. 50-52.5°

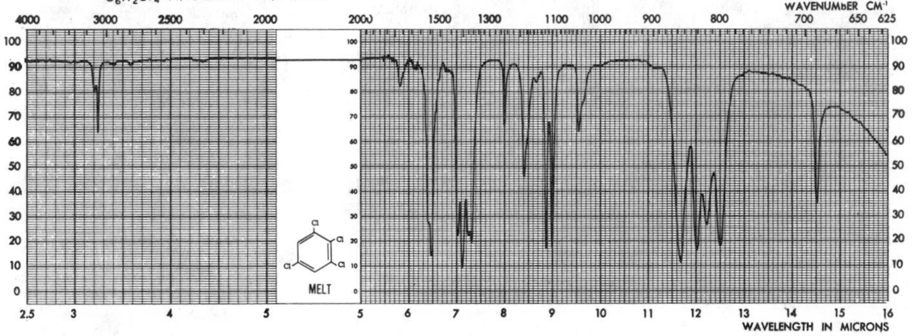

MELT

H

13,698-0 α^2-Chloroisodurene (2,4,6-trimethylbenzyl chloride)
$(CH_3)_3C_6H_2CH_2Cl$ M.W. 168.67
m.p. 34-36°

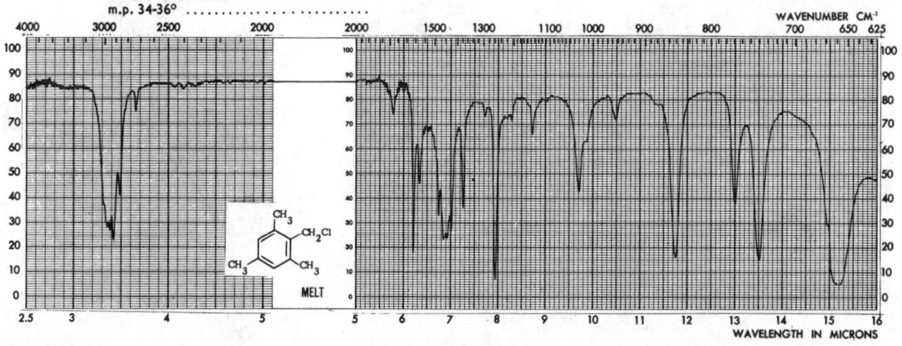

MELT

A

B7160-8 2-Bromomesitylene
1,3,5-$(CH_3)_3C_6H_2Br$ M.W. 199.10 n_D^{20} 1.5511
m.p. 0-2°

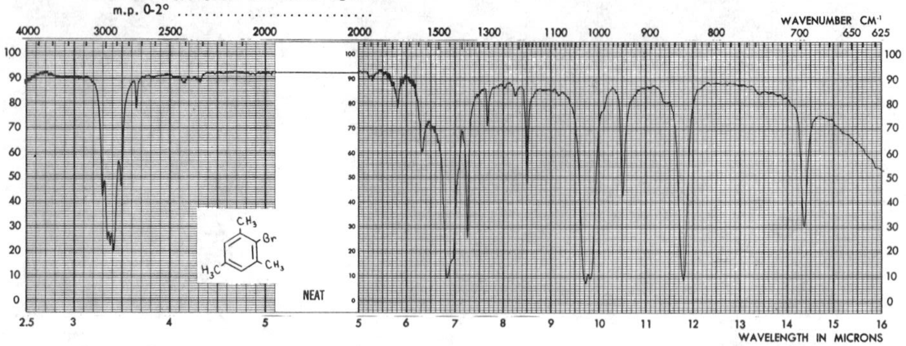

NEAT

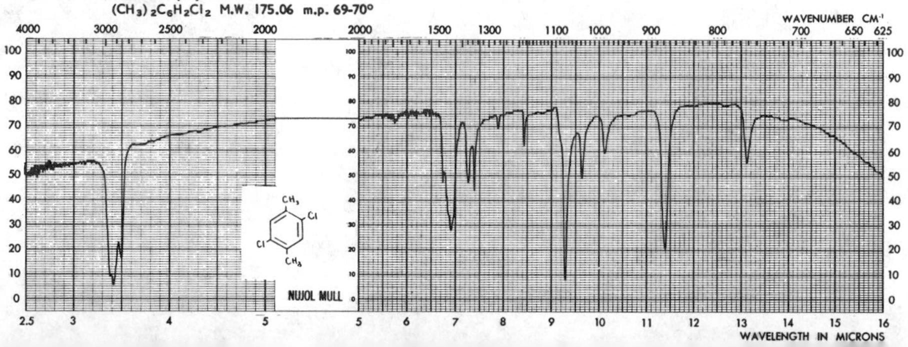

E

13,707-3 2,4,5-Trichlorotoluene
$CH_3C_6H_2Cl_3$ M.W. 195.48 m.p. 79-81°

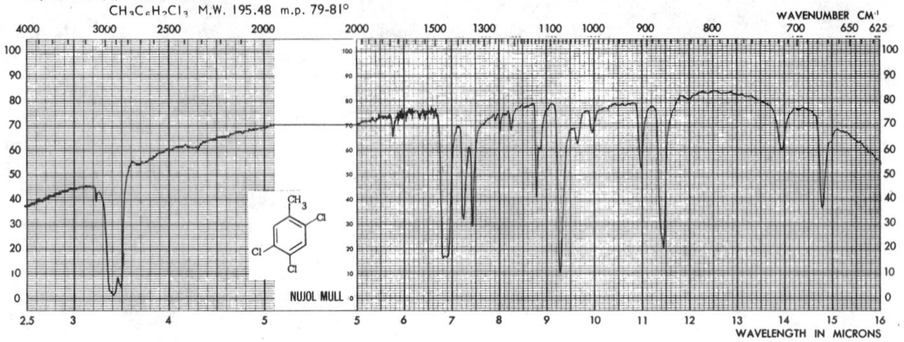

NUJOL MULL

B

T1165-7 1,2,4,5-Tetrafluorobenzene
$C_6H_2F_4$ M.W. 150.07 n_D^{20} 1.4069

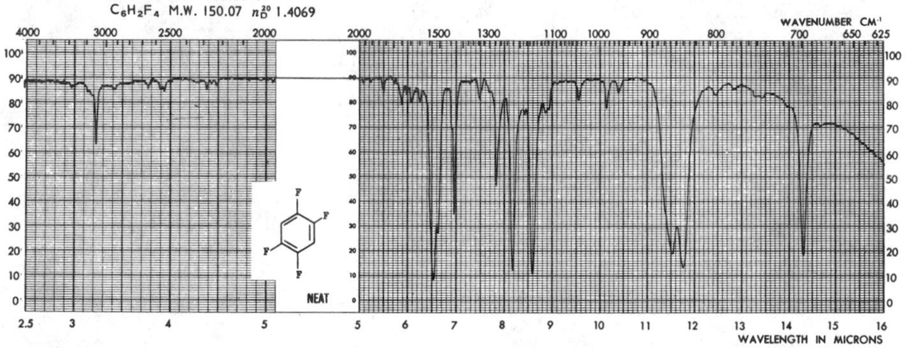

NEAT

F

21,141-9
5-Bromo-1,2,4-trimethylbenzene, 99% (5-bromo-pseudocumene)
$BrC_6H_2(CH_3)_3$ FW 199.10 mp 71-73°
bp 233-235° *Beil.* 5,403 Disp. C

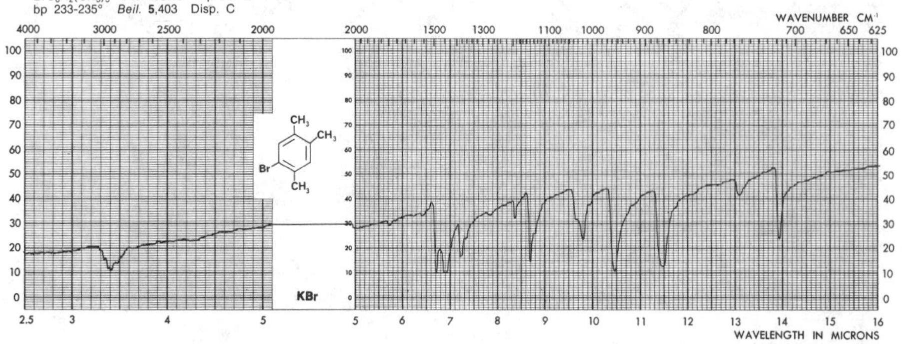

KBr

C

13,185-7 1,2,4,5-Tetrachlorobenzene
$C_6H_2Cl_4$ M.W. 215.90 m.p. 138-140°

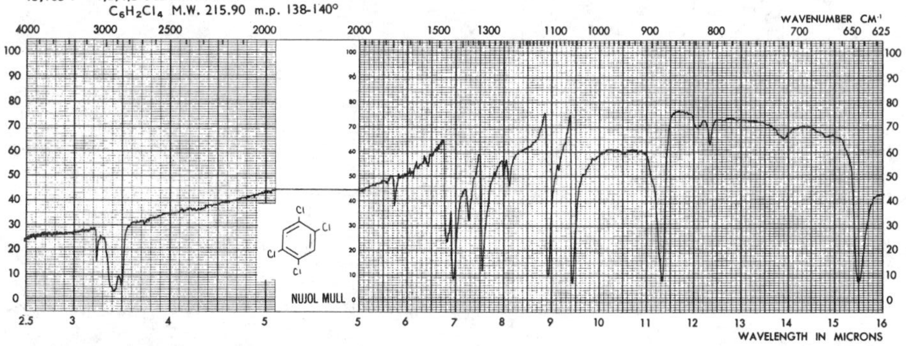

NUJOL MULL

G

11,615-7 2,5-Dibromo-p-xylene
$Br_2C_6H_2(CH_3)_2$ M.W. 263.97 m.p. 72-74°

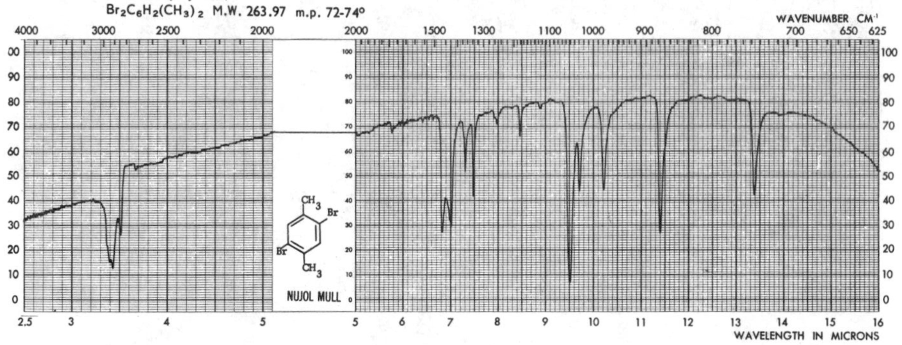

NUJOL MULL

D

D7640-4 2,5-Dichloro-p-xylene
$(CH_3)_2C_6H_2Cl_2$ M.W. 175.06 m.p. 69-70°

NUJOL MULL

H

P530-1 Pentafluorobenzene
C_6HF_5 M.W. 168.06 n_D^{20} 1.3880 b.p. 85°

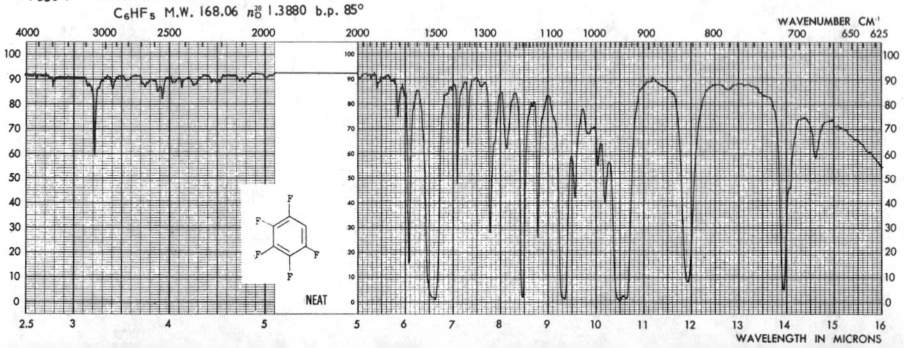

NEAT

A 13,132-6 **Pentachlorobenzene, tech.**
C_6HCl_5 M.W. 250.34 m.p. 82-85°
NUJOL MULL

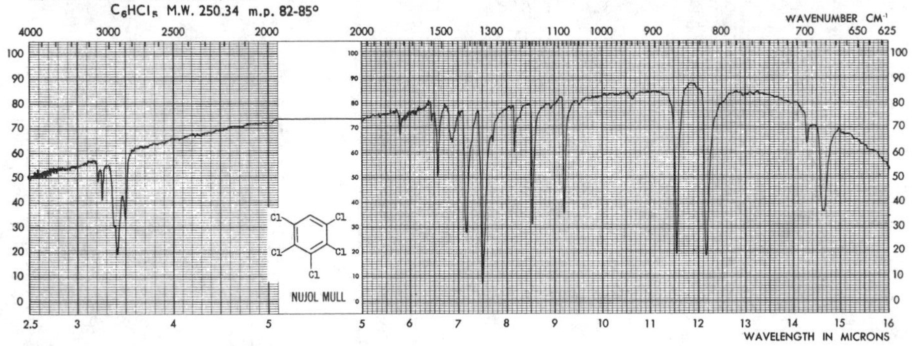

B 10,707-7
1-Bromo-2,3,4,5-tetrafluorobenzene, 97%
BrC_6HF_4
M.W. 228.98 n_D^{20} 1.4653
NEAT

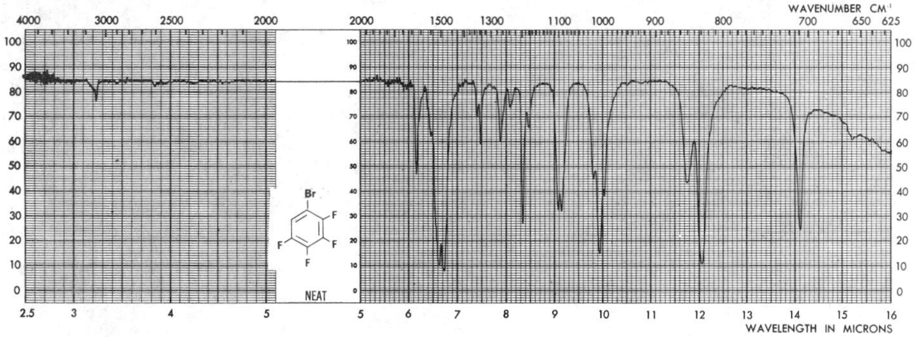

C 10,706-9
1-Bromo-2,3,5,6-tetrafluorobenzene, 97%
BrC_6HF_4
M.W. 228.98 n_D^{20} 1.4689
NEAT

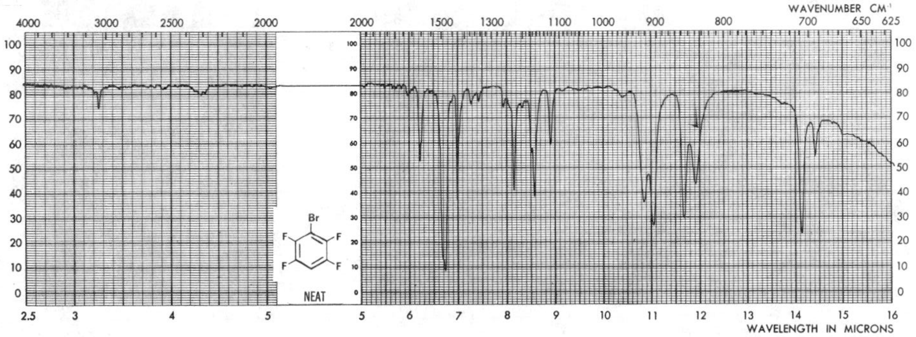

D H870-6 **Hexafluorobenzene**
C_6F_6 M.W. 186.05 n_D^{20} 1.3769
b.p. 81-82°/743 mm.
NEAT

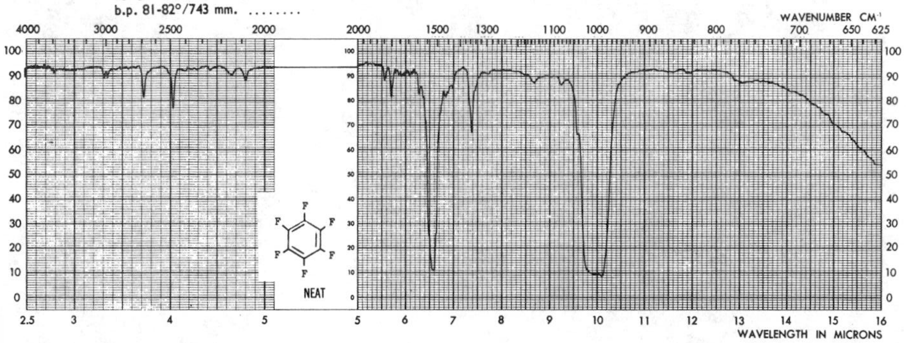

E 10,397-7 **2,3,4,5,6-Pentafluorotoluene, puriss.**
$C_6F_5CH_3$ M.W. 182.09 n_D^{20} 1.4023 b.p. 117°
NEAT

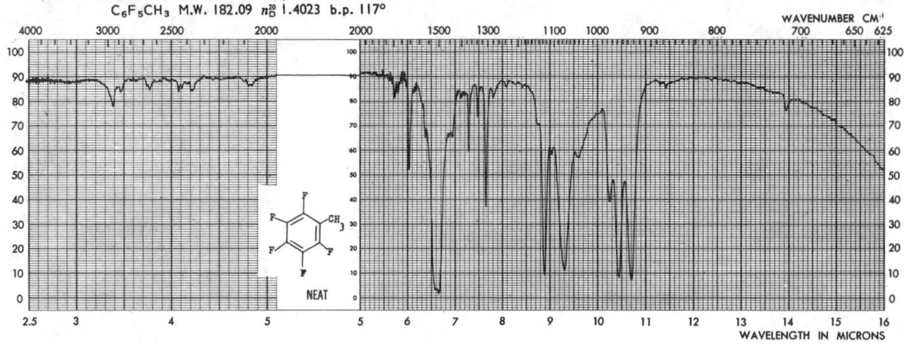

F O—270-6
Octafluorotoluene, 99% (perfluorotoluene)
$C_6F_5CF_3$
M.W. 236.06 b.p. 104° n_D^{20} 1.3670
NEAT

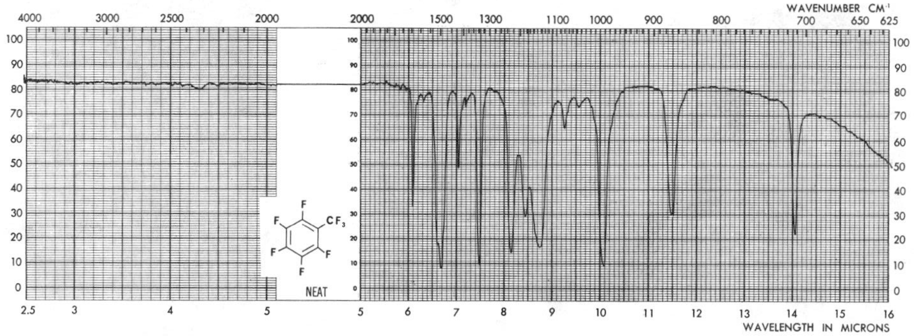

G 10,105-2 **α-Bromo-2,3,4,5,6-pentafluorotoluene** (bromomethylpentafluorobenzene), **puriss.**
$C_6F_5CH_2Br$ M.W. 260.99 n_D^{20} 1.4720
NEAT

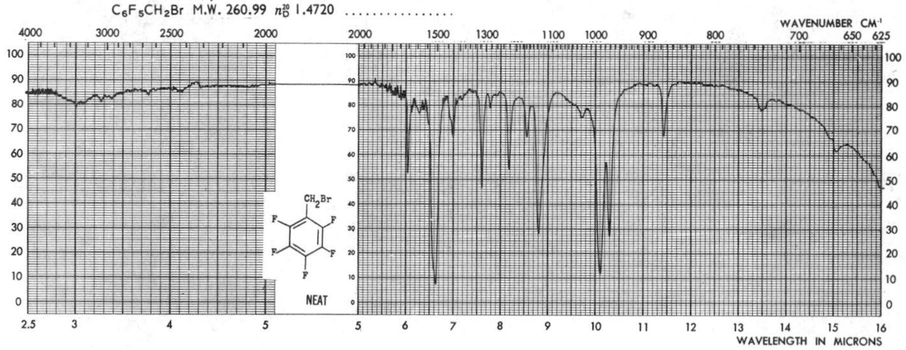

H 19,366-6
Chloropentafluorobenzene, 95%
ClC_6F_5 FW 202.51 bp 122-123°/750mm.
n_D^{20} 1.4206 d 1.568 Disp. D
NEAT

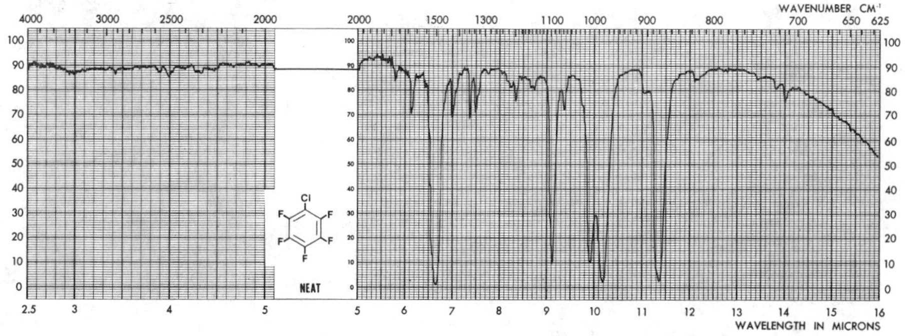

A B7515-8 Bromopentafluorobenzene
BrC_6F_5 M.W. 246.97 n_D^{20} 1.4490

B 10,016-1 1,2-Dibromotetrafluorobenzene
$C_6Br_2F_4$ M.W. 307.88 n_D^{20} 1.5171 b.p. 198°

C 10,201-6 1,3-Dibromotetrafluorobenzene
$C_6Br_2F_4$ M.W. 307.88 n_D^{20} 1.5183

D 10,313-6 Iodopentafluorobenzene, puriss.
C_6F_5I M.W. 293.96 n_D^{20} 1.4980 b.p. 166°

E 10,086-2 3,6-Bis-(chloromethyl)-durene [1,4-bis-(chloromethyl)-2,3,5,6-tetramethylbenzene]
$(CH_3)_4C_6(CH_2Cl)_2$ M.W. 231.17 m.p. 194-196°

F 15,302-8 2,4,6-Tris-(chloromethyl)-mesitylene
$(CH_3)_3C_6(CH_2Cl)_3$ M.W. 265.61

G 11,375-1 2,4,5,6-Tetrachloro-m-xylene
$C_6Cl_4(CH_3)_2$ M.W. 243.95 m.p. 220-222°

H T860-4 2,3,5,6-Tetrachloro-p-xylene
$C_6Cl_4(CH_3)_2$ M.W. 243.95 m.p. 221-229°

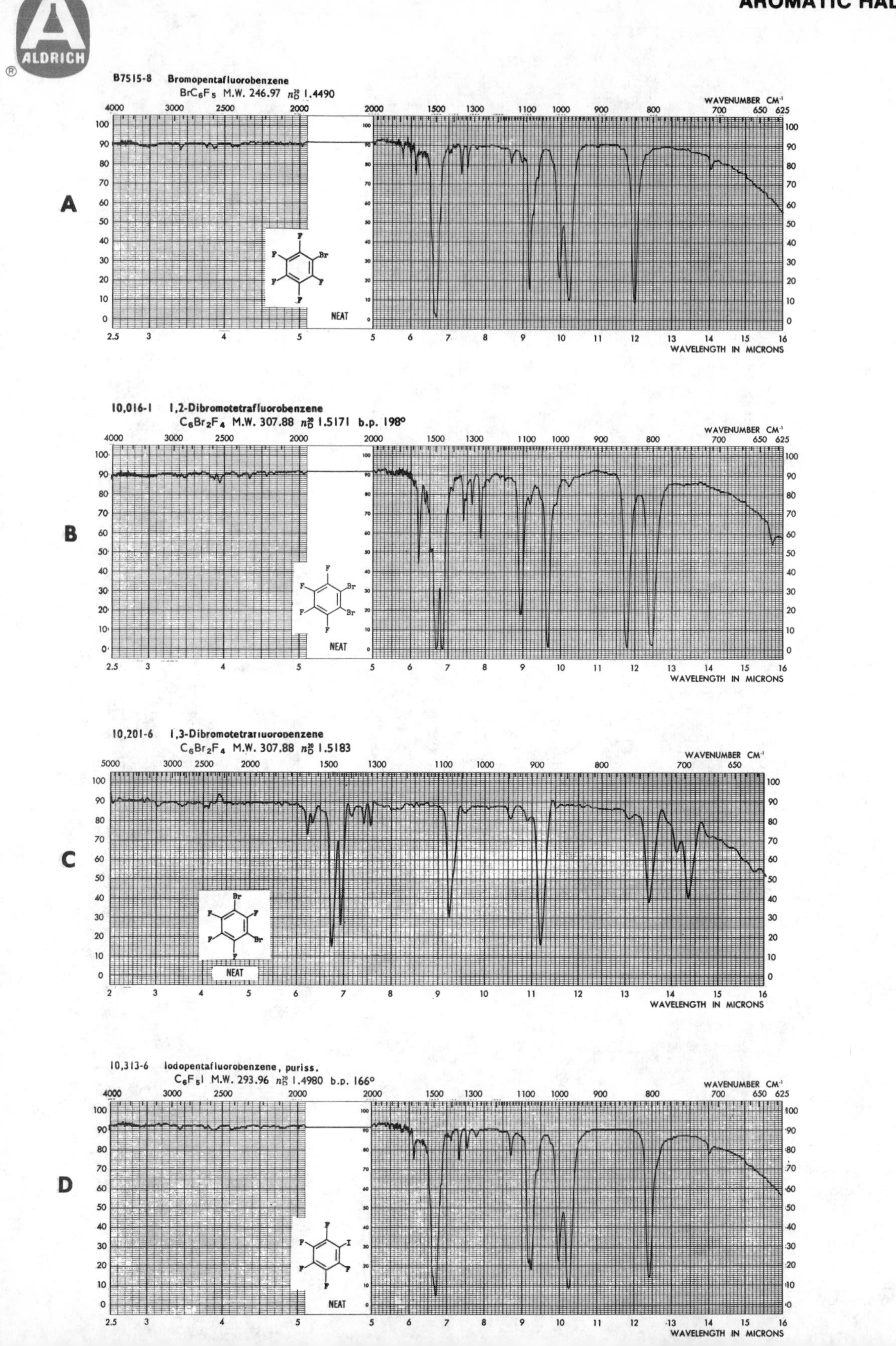

A 11,377-8 α,α',2,4,5,6-Hexachloro-m-xylene
$C_6Cl_4(CH_2Cl)_2$ M.W. 312.84 m.p. 138-140°
NUJOL MULL

B 14,725-7 α,α',2,3,5,6-Hexachloro-p-xylene
$C_6Cl_4(CH_2Cl)_2$ M.W. 312.84 m.p. 178-180°
NUJOL MULL

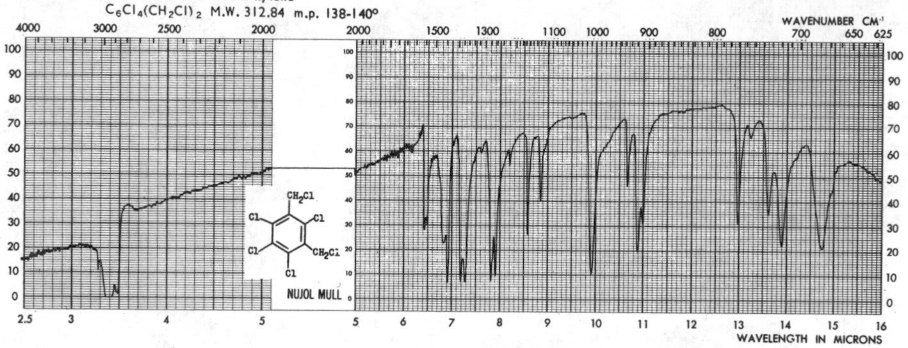

C 11,378-6 α,α,α',α',2,3,5,6-Octachloro-p-xylene, puriss.
$C_6Cl_4(CHCl_2)_2$ M.W. 381.73 m.p. 122-124°
NUJOL MULL

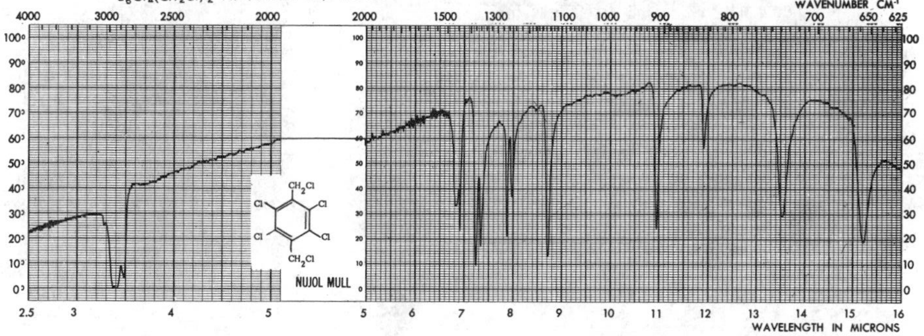

D 17,105-0
Hexachlorobenzene, 97%
C_6Cl_6 FW 284.78 mp 227-229° bp 332°
Beil. 5,205 Disp. C,D
NUJOL MULL

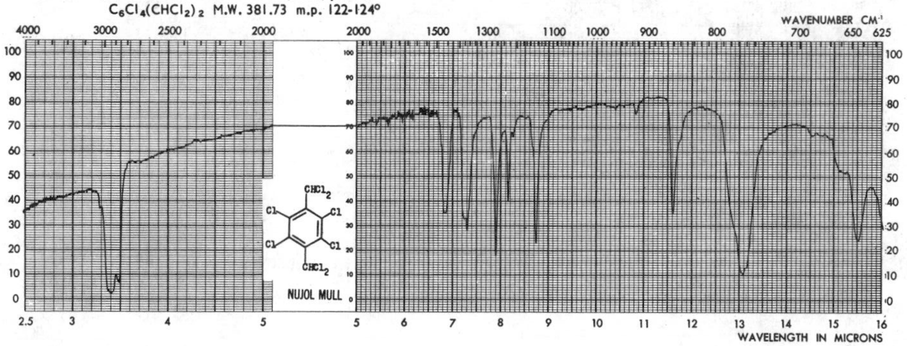

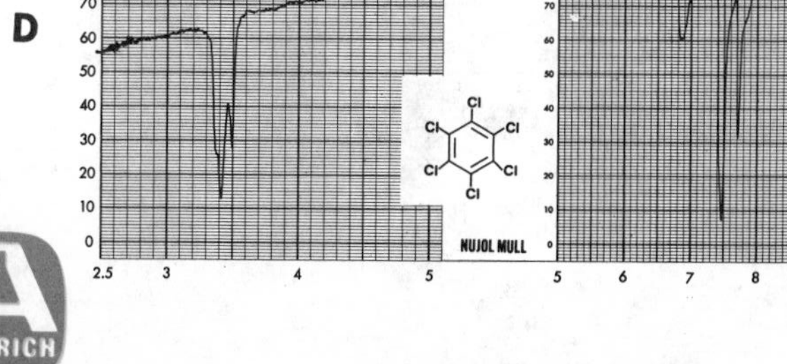

E 10,713-1 Hexabromobenzene
C_6Br_6 M.W. 551.52 m.p. 322-325°
NUJOL MULL

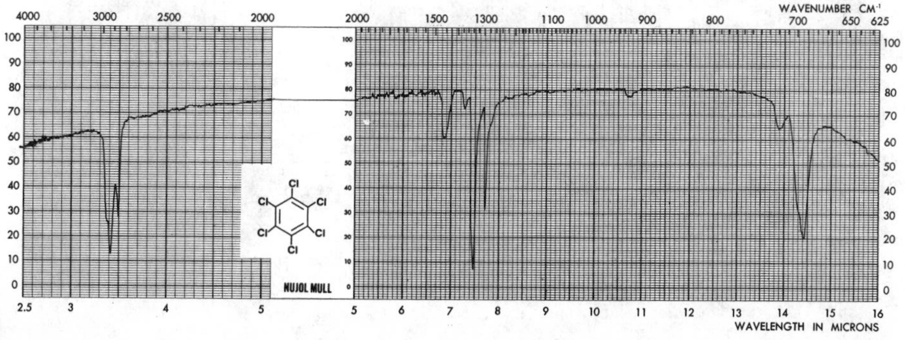

F 19,444-1
2,3,4,5,6-Pentabromoethylbenzene, 98%
$C_6Br_5C_2H_5$ FW 500.67 mp 137-139° *Beil.* 5,357
Disp. D
KBr

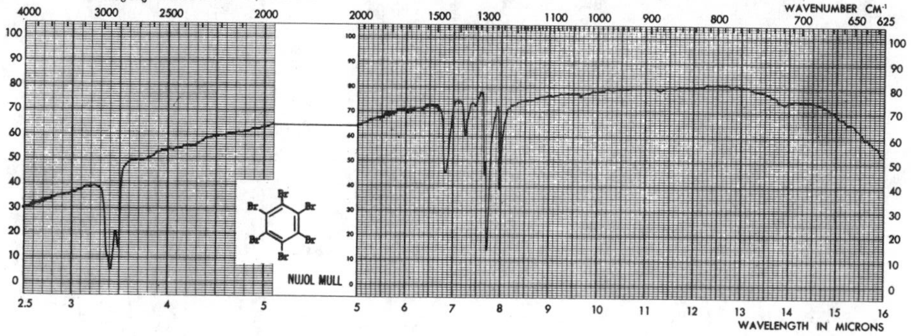

G 15,744-9
β-Bromostyrene
$C_6H_5CH{=}CHBr$
M.W. 183.05 m.p. 7° b.p. 110-112°/20mm.
n_D^{20} 1.6066 d 1.427 Beil. 5,477
NEAT

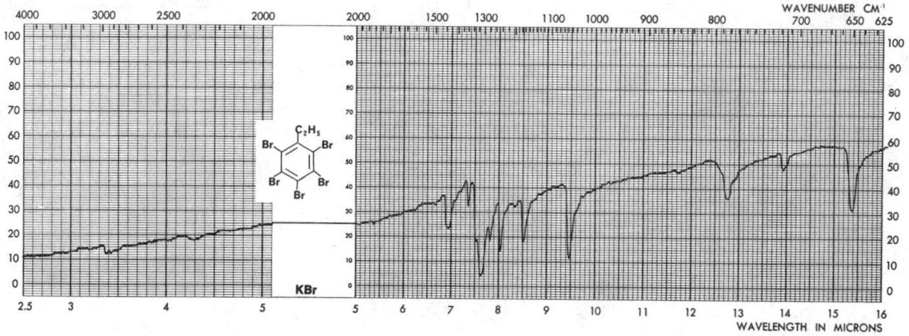

H C8121-7 Cinnamyl bromide (3-bromo-1-phenyl-1-propene)
$C_6H_5CH{:}CHCH_2Br$ M.W. 197.08 m.p. 26-29°
MELT

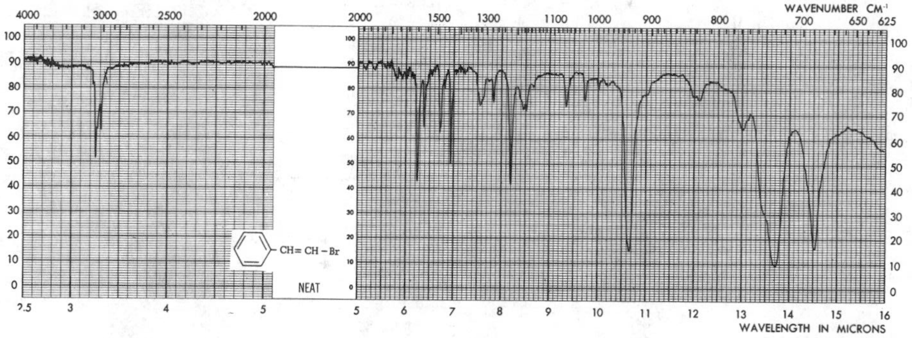

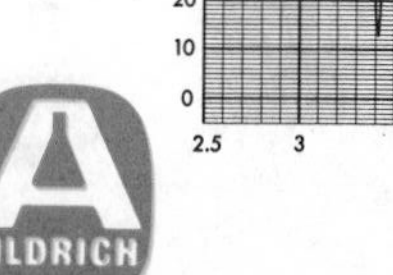

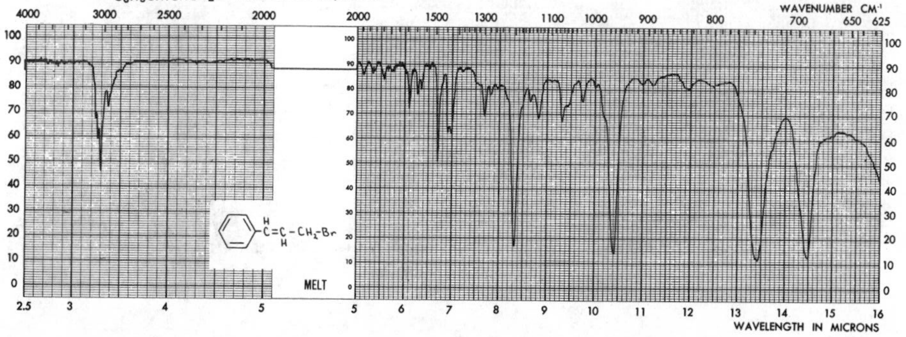

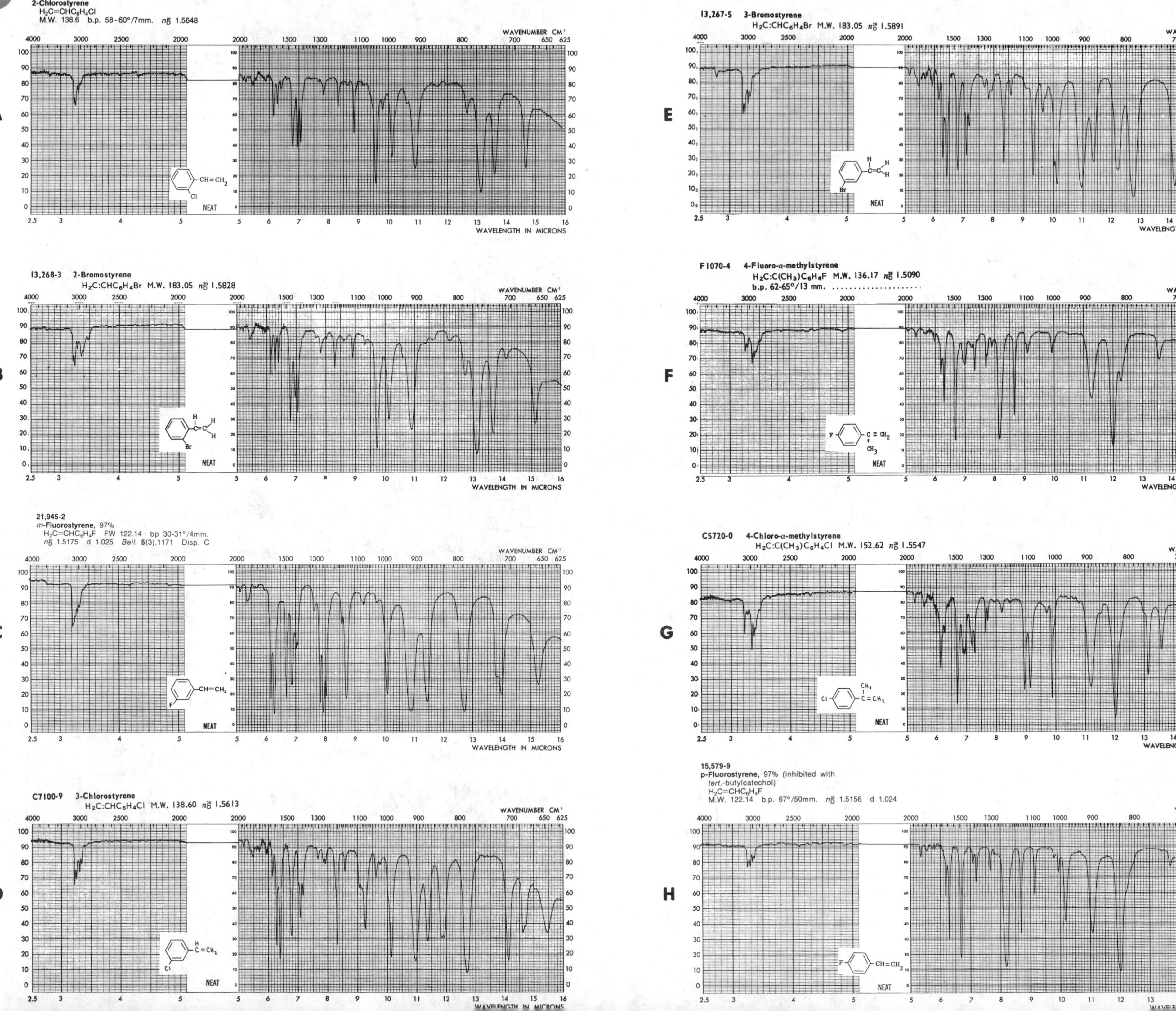
ALDRICH
A
16,067-9
2-Chlorostyrene
$H_2C{=}CHC_6H_4Cl$
M.W. 138.6 b.p. 58-60°/7mm. n_D^{20} 1.5648
NEAT
B
13,268-3 2-Bromostyrene
$H_2C{:}CHC_6H_4Br$ M.W. 183.05 n_D^{20} 1.5828
NEAT
C
21,945-2
m-Fluorostyrene, 97%
$H_2C{=}CHC_6H_4F$ FW 122.14 bp 30-31°/4mm.
n_D^{20} 1.5175 d 1.025 Beil. 5(3),1171 Disp. C
NEAT
D
C7100-9 3-Chlorostyrene
$H_2C{:}CHC_6H_4Cl$ M.W. 138.60 n_D^{20} 1.5613
NEAT
E
13,267-5 3-Bromostyrene
$H_2C{:}CHC_6H_4Br$ M.W. 183.05 n_D^{20} 1.5891
NEAT
F
F1070-4 4-Fluoro-α-methylstyrene
$H_2C{:}C(CH_3)C_6H_4F$ M.W. 136.17 n_D^{20} 1.5090
b.p. 62-65°/13 mm.
NEAT
G
C5720-0 4-Chloro-α-methylstyrene
$H_2C{:}C(CH_3)C_6H_4Cl$ M.W. 152.62 n_D^{20} 1.5547
NEAT
H
15,579-9
p-Fluorostyrene, 97% (inhibited with
tert.-butylcatechol)
$H_2C{=}CHC_6H_4F$
M.W. 122.14 b.p. 67°/50mm. n_D^{20} 1.5156 d 1.024
NEAT
WAVENUMBER CM⁻¹
WAVELENGTH IN MICRONS

A

C7120-3 **4-Chlorostyrene**
$H_2C{:}CHC_6H_4Cl$ M.W. 138.60 n_D^{20} 1.5615
NEAT

B

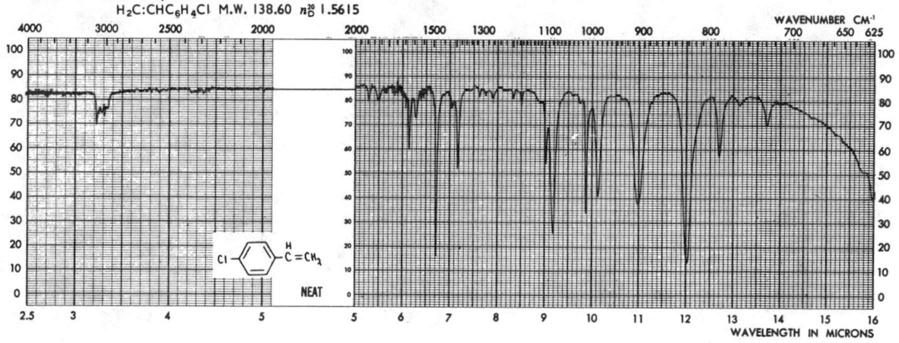

12,414-1 **4-Bromostyrene**
$H_2C{:}CHC_6H_4Br$ M.W. 183.05 n_D^{20} 1.5955
NEAT

C

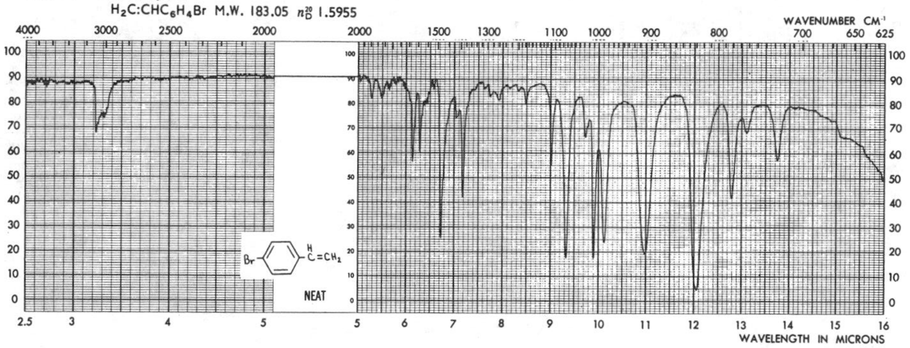

13,039-7 **4-Chloro-β,β-dimethylstyrene**
$(CH_3)_2C{:}CHC_6H_4Cl$ M.W. 166.65
n_D^{20} 1.5543
NEAT

D

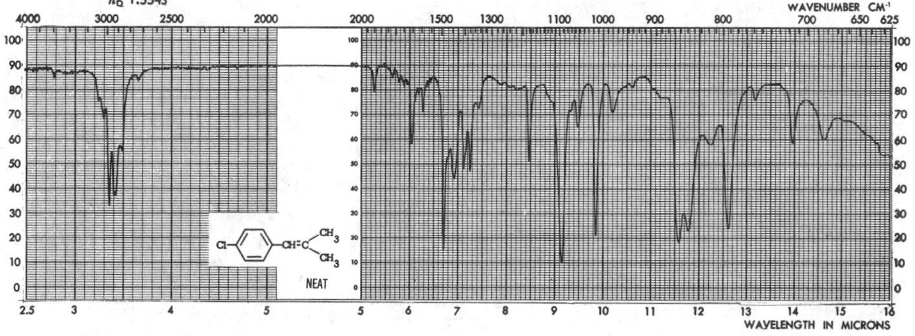

D7450-9 **2,6-Dichlorostyrene**
$H_2C{:}CHC_6H_3Cl_2$ M.W. 173.04 n_D^{20} 1.5740
NEAT

E

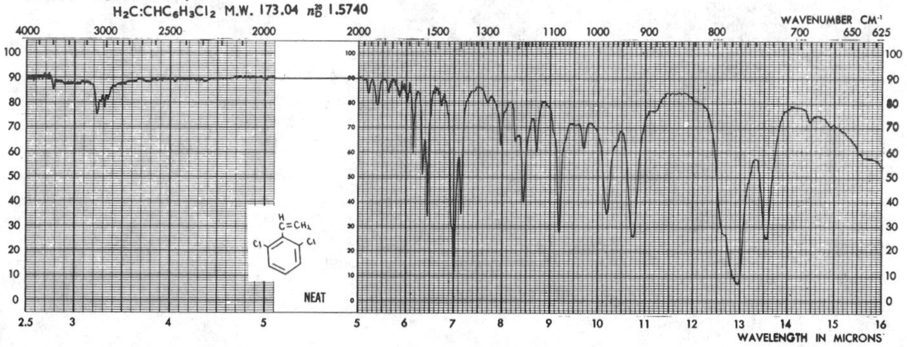

19,691-6
2,3,4,5,6-Pentafluorostyrene
$C_6F_5CH{=}CH_2$ FW 194.10 bp 62-63°/50mm.
n_D^{20} 1.4455 d 1.406 Disp. C
NEAT

F

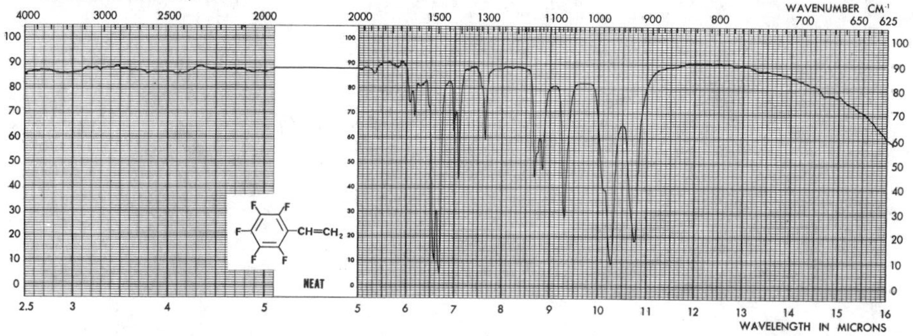

10,338-1 **α-Methyl-2,3,4,5,6-pentafluorostyrene,** 99%
[2-(pentafluorophenyl)-1-propene]
$C_6F_5C(CH_3){=}CH_2$ M.W. 208.13 b.p. 144-145°
n_D^{20} 1.4329 *NMR* 4,71B Disp. C
NEAT

G

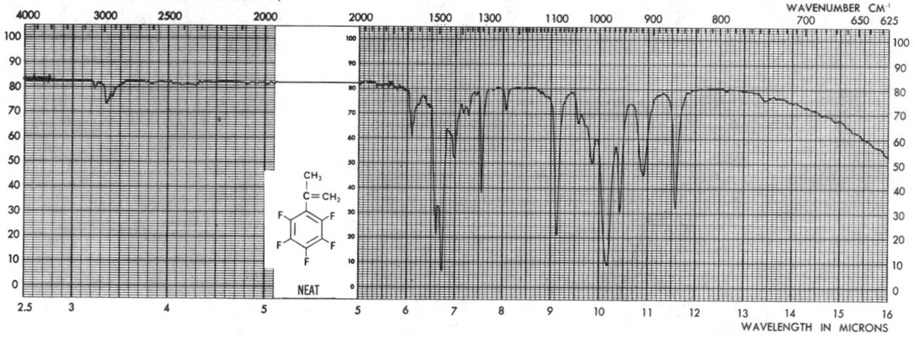

A3475 **Allylpentafluorobenzene** [3-(pentafluorophenyl)-1-propene]
$C_6F_5CH_2CH{:}CH_2$ M.W. 208.13 n_D^{20} 1.4262
NEAT

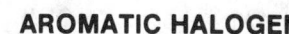

H

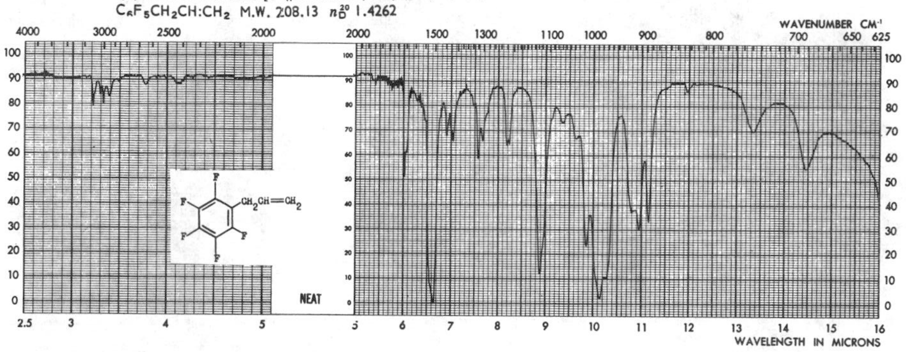

10,274-1 **2-Fluorobiphenyl**
$C_6H_5C_6H_4F$ M.W. 172.20 m.p. 73-74.5°
NUJOL MULL

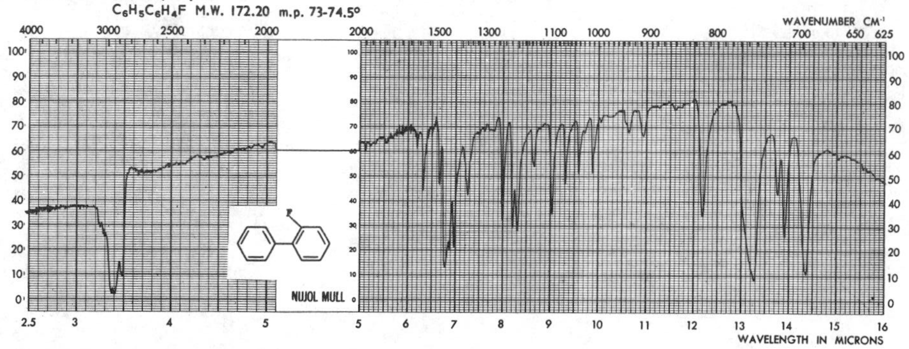

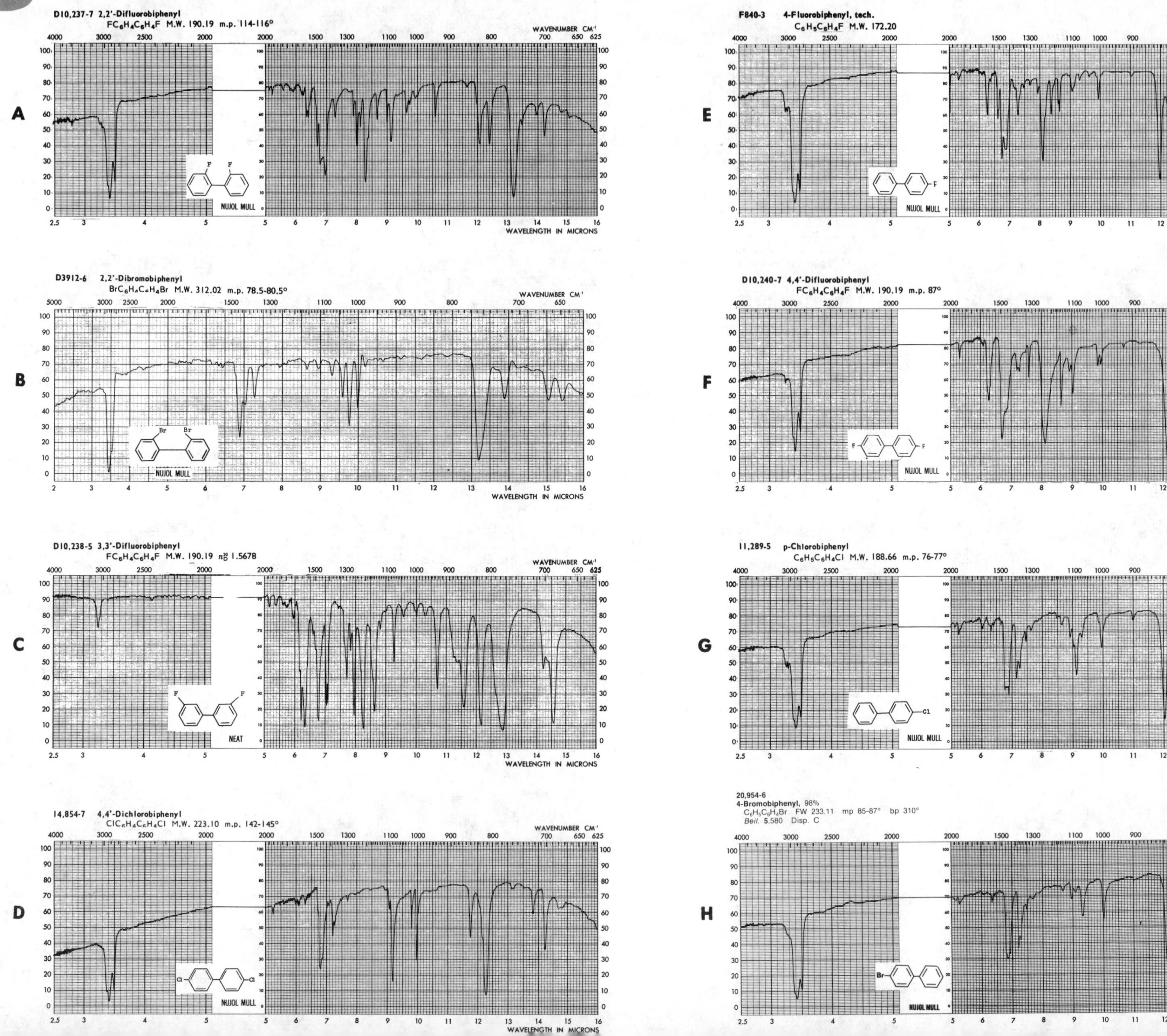

ALDRICH
A
D10,237-7 2,2'-Difluorobiphenyl
$FC_6H_4C_6H_4F$ M.W. 190.19 m.p. 114-116°
NUJOL MULL
B
D3912-6 2,2'-Dibromobiphenyl
$BrC_6H_4C_6H_4Br$ M.W. 312.02 m.p. 78.5-80.5°
NUJOL MULL
C
D10,238-5 3,3'-Difluorobiphenyl
$FC_6H_4C_6H_4F$ M.W. 190.19 n_D^{20} 1.5678
NEAT
D
14,854-7 4,4'-Dichlorobiphenyl
$ClC_6H_4C_6H_4Cl$ M.W. 223.10 m.p. 142-145°
NUJOL MULL
E
F840-3 4-Fluorobiphenyl, tech.
$C_6H_5C_6H_4F$ M.W. 172.20
NUJOL MULL
F
D10,240-7 4,4'-Difluorobiphenyl
$FC_6H_4C_6H_4F$ M.W. 190.19 m.p. 87°
NUJOL MULL
G
11,289-5 p-Chlorobiphenyl
$C_6H_5C_6H_4Cl$ M.W. 188.66 m.p. 76-77°
NUJOL MULL
H
20,954-6
4-Bromobiphenyl, 98%
$C_6H_5C_6H_4Br$ FW 233.11 mp 85-87° bp 310°
Beil. 5,580 Disp. C
NUJOL MULL
WAVENUMBER CM⁻¹
WAVELENGTH IN MICRONS

A

C5227-6 4-Chloromethylbiphenyl (p-phenylbenzyl chloride)
$C_6H_5C_6H_4CH_2Cl$ M.W. 202.68
m.p. 71-73°

NUJOL MULL

B

B6730-9 4-Bromo-4'-fluorobiphenyl
$BrC_6H_4C_6H_4F$ M.W. 251.11 m.p. 97-100.5°

NUJOL MULL

C

D12,240-8 4,4'-Diiodobiphenyl, tech.
$IC_6H_4C_6H_4I$ M.W. 406.00 m.p. 196° (dec.)

NUJOL MULL

D

19,663-0
2,2',3,3',5,5',6,6'-Octafluorobiphenyl, 98%
$HC_6F_4C_6F_4H$ FW 298.14 mp 84-86° Disp. D

NUJOL MULL

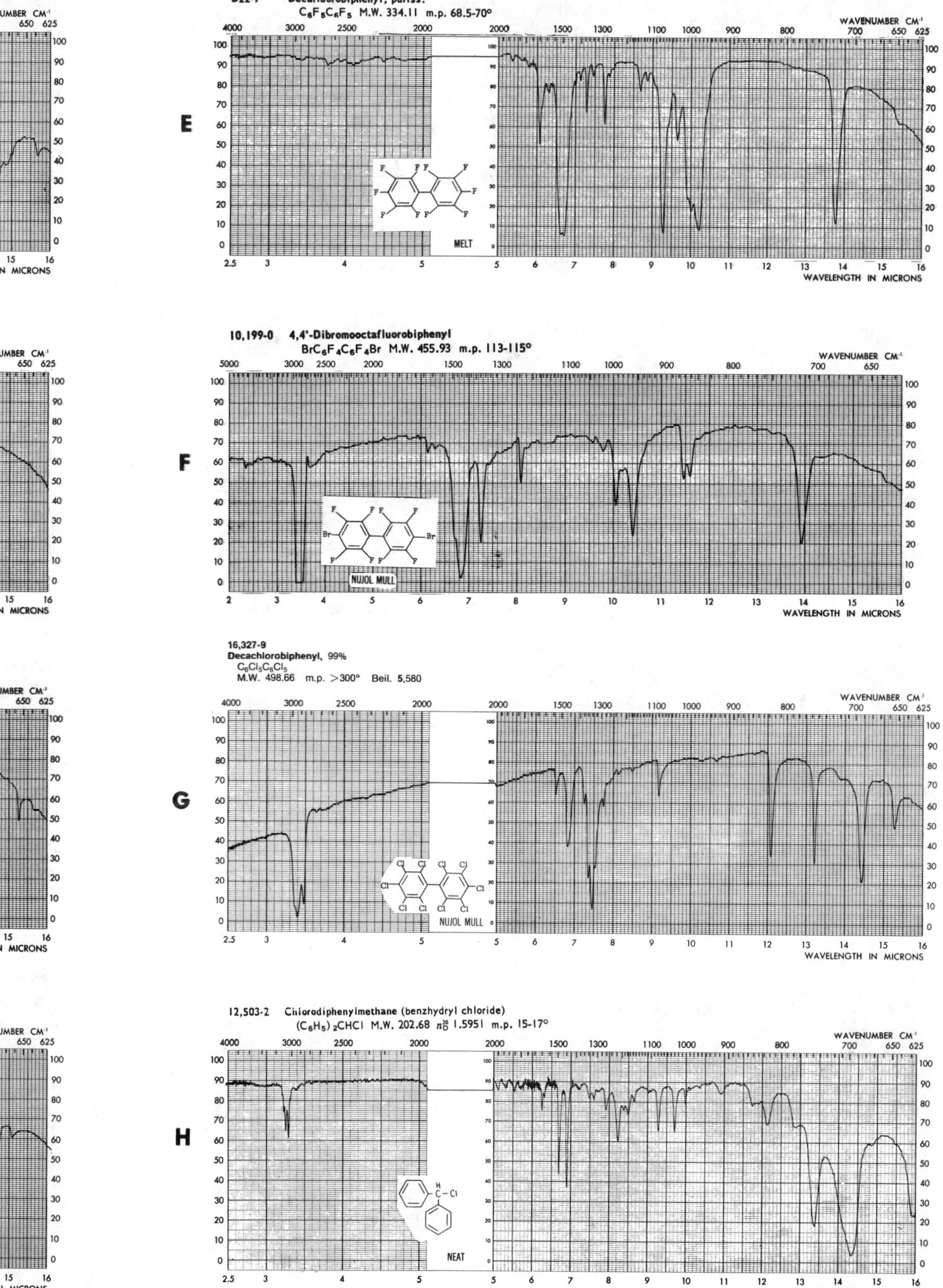

E

D22-7 Decafluorobiphenyl, puriss.
$C_6F_5C_6F_5$ M.W. 334.11 m.p. 68.5-70°

MELT

F

10,199-0 4,4'-Dibromooctafluorobiphenyl
$BrC_6F_4C_6F_4Br$ M.W. 455.93 m.p. 113-115°

NUJOL MULL

G

16,327-9
Decachlorobiphenyl, 99%
$C_6Cl_5C_6Cl_5$
M.W. 498.66 m.p. >300° Beil. 5,580

NUJOL MULL

H

12,503-2 Chlorodiphenylmethane (benzhydryl chloride)
$(C_6H_5)_2CHCl$ M.W. 202.68 n_D^{20} 1.5951 m.p. 15-17°

NEAT

A

B6550-0 **1-Bromo-3,3-diphenylpropane**
$(C_6H_5)_2CHCH_2CH_2Br$ M.W. 275.19 m.p. 42-43°
MELT

B

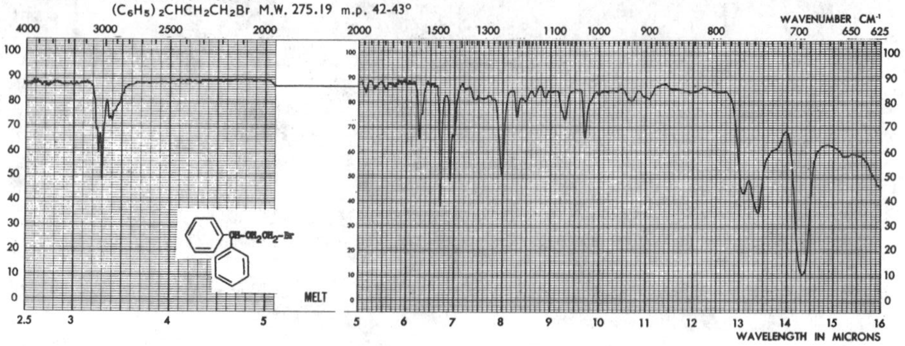

B6540-3 **Bromodiphenylmethane** (benzhydryl bromide)
$(C_6H_5)_2CHBr$ M.W. 247.14 m.p. 38.5-40°
MELT

C

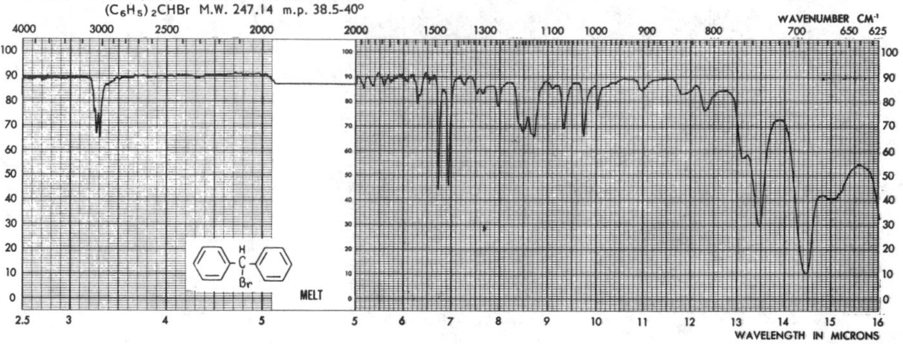

10,655-0 **1,2-Dibromo-1,2-diphenylethane** (stilbene dibromide)
$C_6H_5CH(Br)CH(Br)C_6H_5$ M.W. 340.07
m.p. 241° (dec.)
NUJOL MULL

D

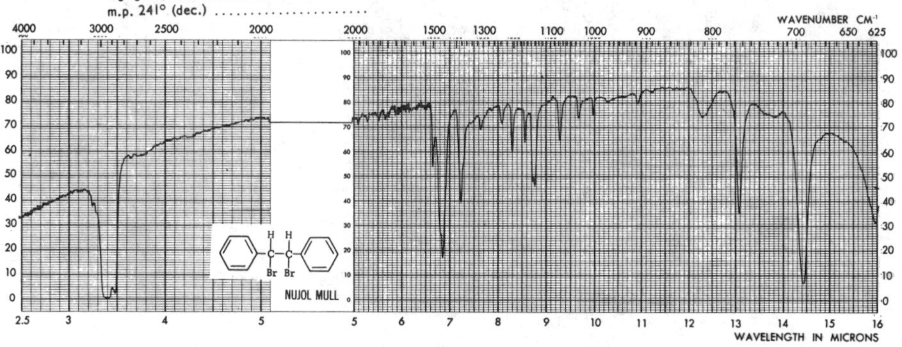

D6140-7 **Dichlorodiphenylmethane**
$(C_6H_5)_2CCl_2$ M.W. 237.13
n_D^{20} 1.6025
NEAT

E

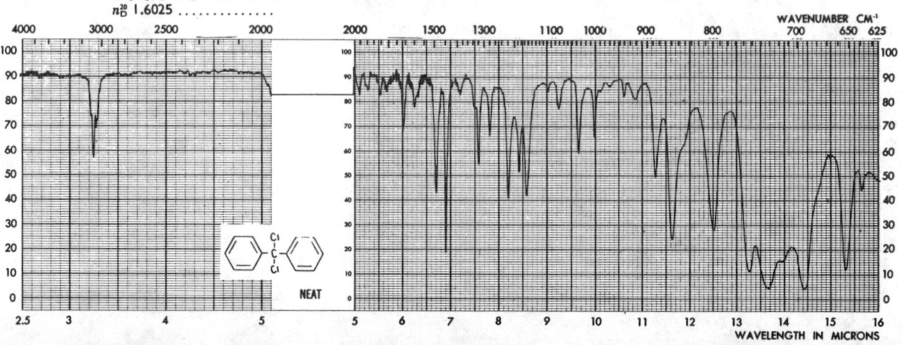

T8380-1 **Triphenylmethyl chloride** (trityl chloride, chlorotriphenylmethane)
$(C_6H_5)_3CCl$ M.W. 278.78 m.p. 111-114°
NUJOL MULL

F

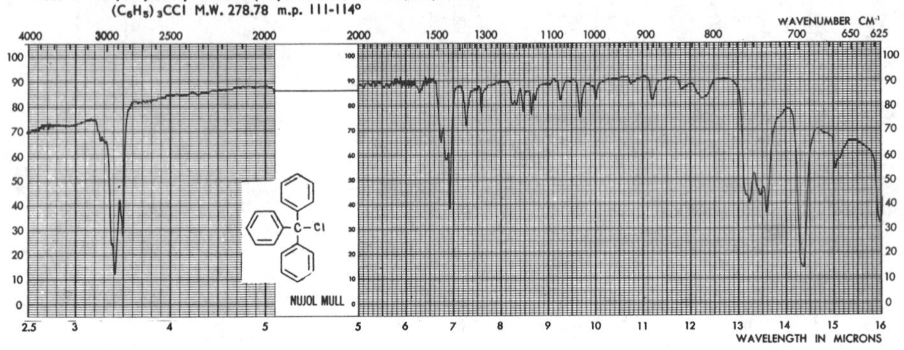

T8360-7 **Triphenylmethyl bromide** (trityl bromide, bromotriphenylmethane)
$(C_6H_5)_3CBr$ M.W. 323.24 m.p. 152-154°
NUJOL MULL

G

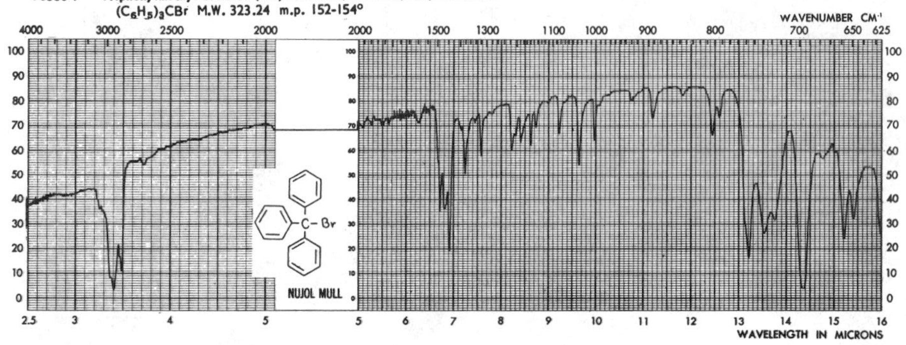

10,331-4 **Chloro-(p-chlorophenyl)-phenylmethane** (p-chlorobenzhydryl chloride)
$ClC_6H_4CH(C_6H_5)Cl$ M.W. 237.13
n_D^{20} 1.6011
NEAT

H

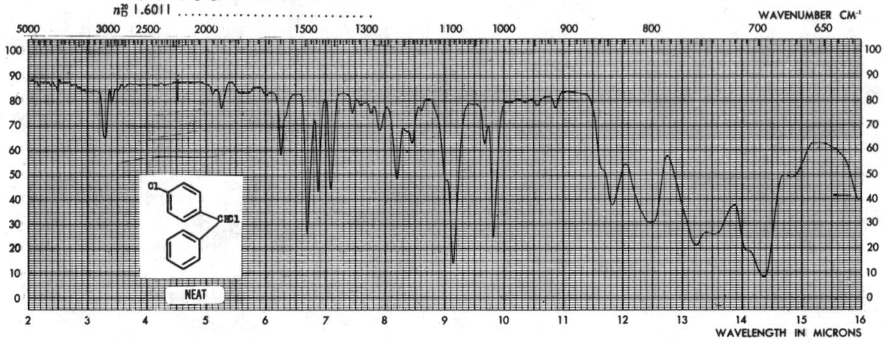

B7712 **(p-Bromophenyl)-phenylmethane**
$C_6H_5CH_2C_6H_4Br$ M.W. 247.14 n_D^{20} 1.6029
NEAT

WAVENUMBER CM⁻¹ — WAVELENGTH IN MICRONS

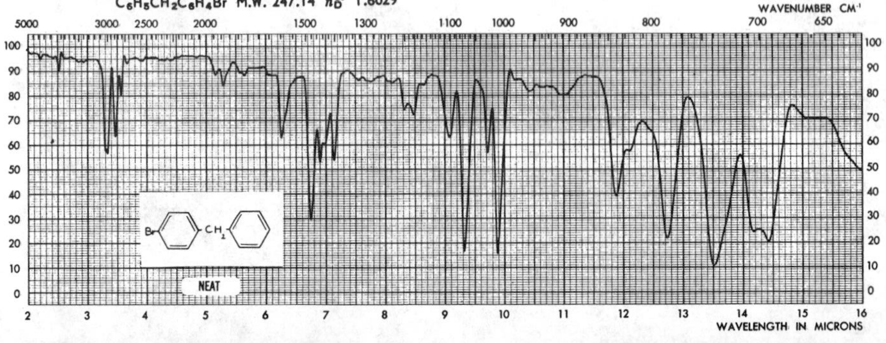

A

D4070-1 4,4'-Dibromodiphenylmethane
$CH_2(C_6H_4Br)_2$ M.W. 326.04 m.p. 65-67°

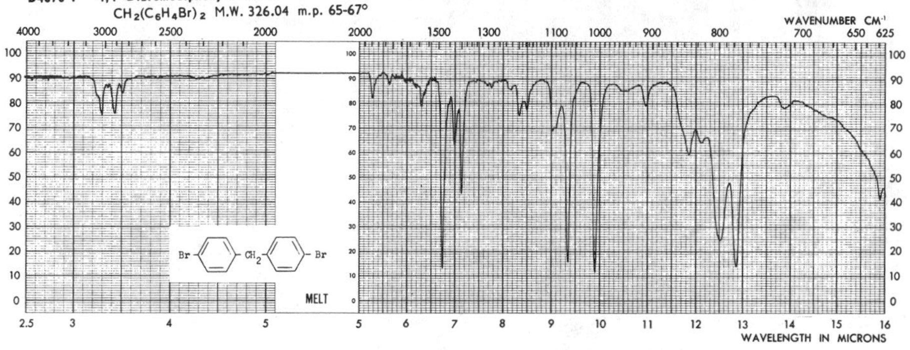

MELT

B

12,676-4 1,1-Diphenyl-2,2,2-trichloroethane
$(C_6H_5)_2CHCCl_3$ M.W. 285.60 m.p. 63-64°

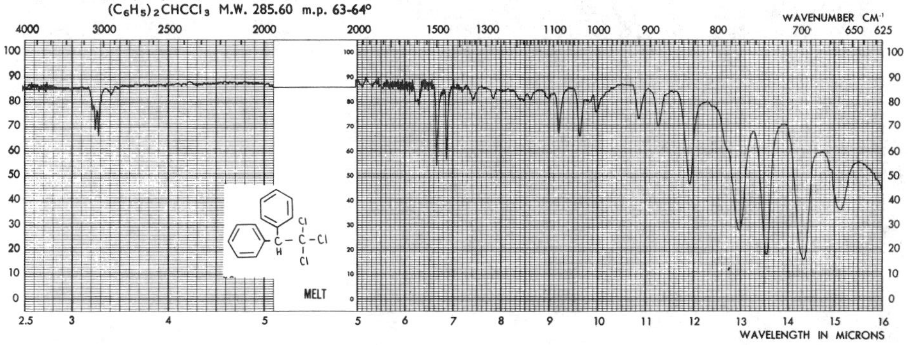

MELT

C

C6380-4 1-(o-Chlorophenyl)-1-(p-chlorophenyl)-2,2-dichloroethane
(o,p'-DDD)
$(ClC_6H_4)_2CHCHCl_2$ M.W. 320.05
m.p. 77-78°

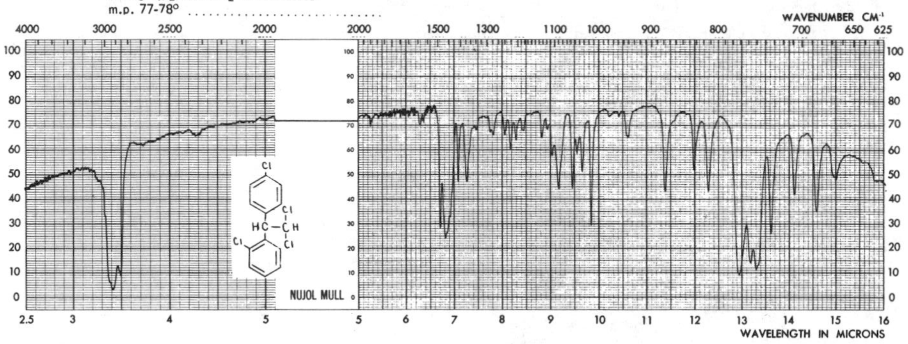

NUJOL MULL

D

10,464-7 1-(o-Chlorophenyl)-1-(p-chlorophenyl)-2,2,2-trichloroethane
(o,p'-DDT), puriss.
$(ClC_6H_4)_2CHCCl_3$ M.W. 354.49 m.p. 75°

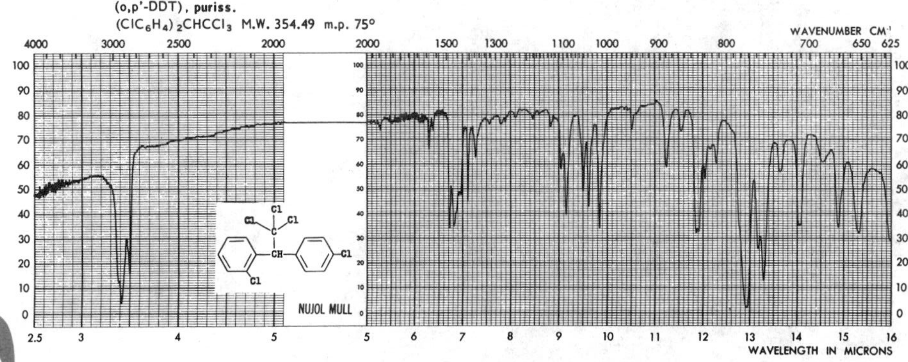

NUJOL MULL

E

C6385-5 1-(m-Chlorophenyl)-1-(p-chlorophenyl)-2,2-dichloroethane
(m,p'-DDD)
$(ClC_6H_4)_2CHCHCl_2$ M.W. 320.05 m.p. 53-55°

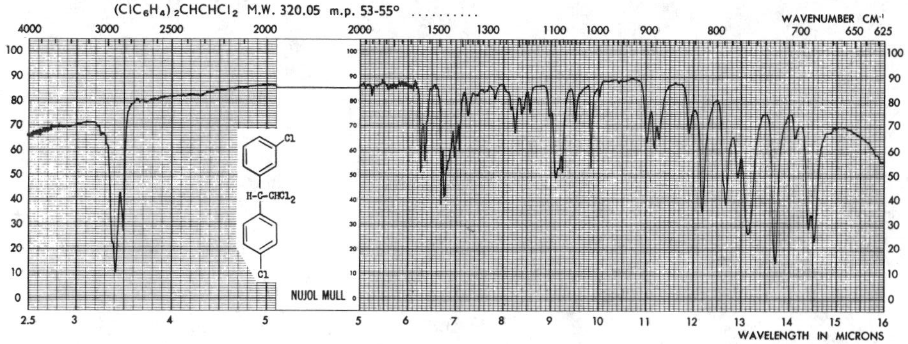

NUJOL MULL

F

B4430-9 1,1-Bis-(4-fluorophenyl)-2,2-dichloroethane (p,p'-difluoro-DDD)
$(FC_6H_4)_2CHCHCl_2$ M.W. 287.14 m.p. 77.5-79.5°

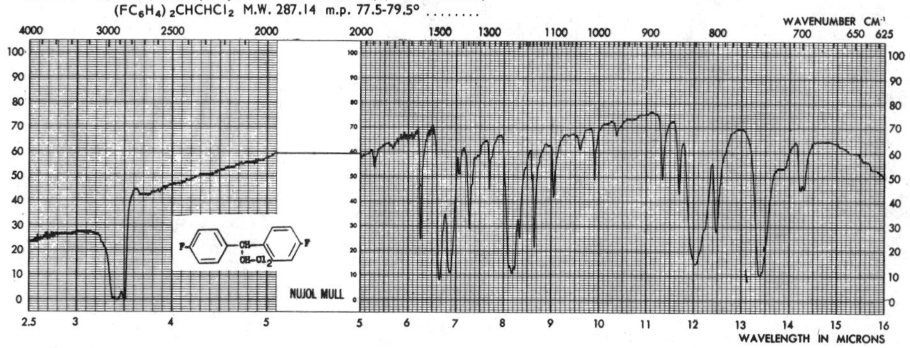

NUJOL MULL

G

16,370-8
1,1-Bis-(p-fluorophenyl)-3-chloropropane, 97%
[3,3-bis-(p-fluorophenyl)-propyl chloride]
$(FC_6H_4)_2CHCH_2CH_2Cl$
M.W. 266.72 n_D^{20} 1.5458 d 1.213

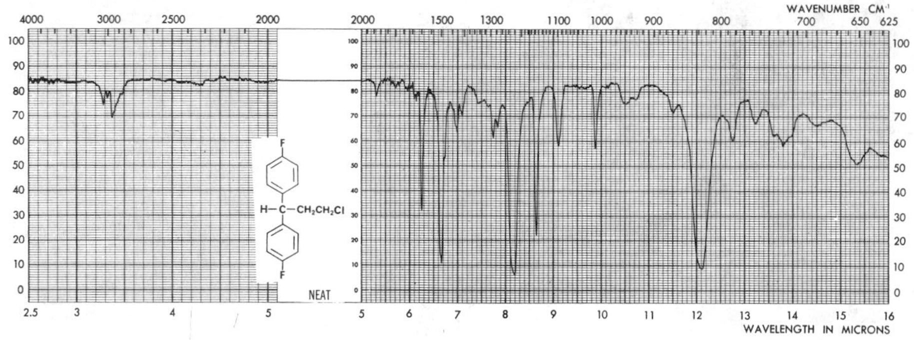

NEAT

H

B3960-7 2,2-Bis-(p-chlorophenyl)-1,1-dichloroethane (p,p'-DDD), tech.
$(ClC_6H_4)_2CHCHCl_2$ M.W. 320.06

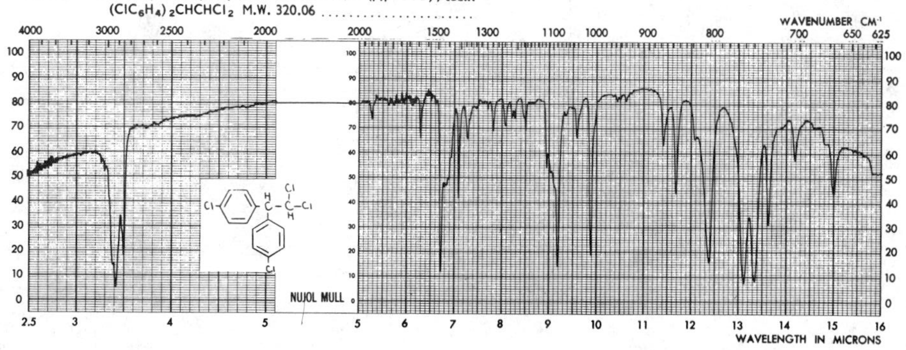

NUJOL MULL

A

10,002-1 **1,1-Bis-(p-chlorophenyl)-2,2,2-trichloroethane (p,p'-DDT), puriss.**
$(ClC_6H_4)_2CHCCl_3$ M.W. 354.49 m.p. 108-108.5°

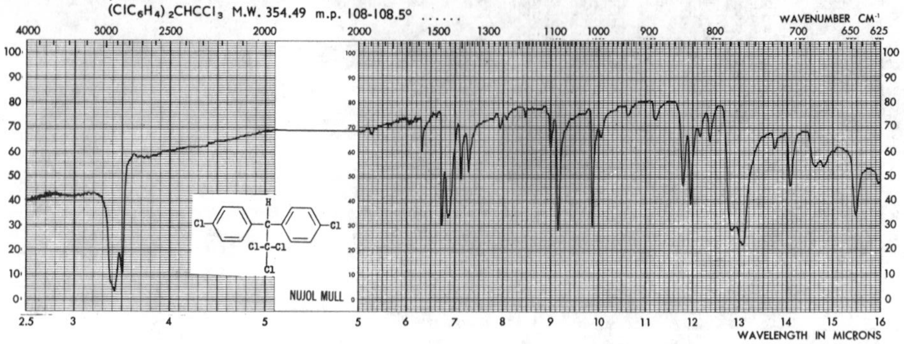

NUJOL MULL

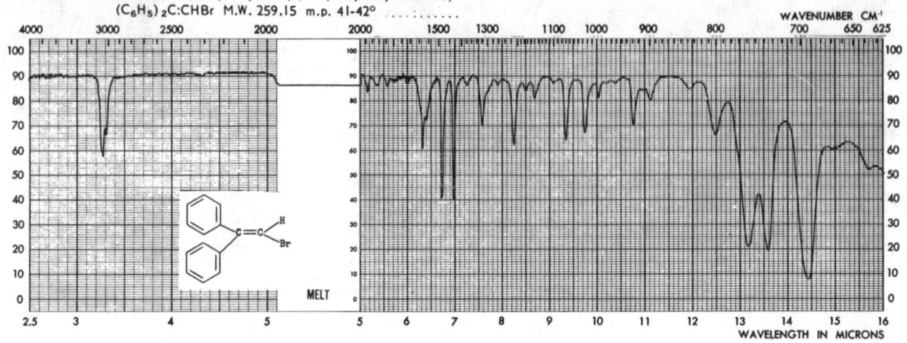

B

14,176-3 **1,1-Bis-(p-chlorophenyl)-1,2,2,2-tetrachloroethane**
$(ClC_6H_4)_2CClCCl_3$ M.W. 388.94
m.p. 82-85°

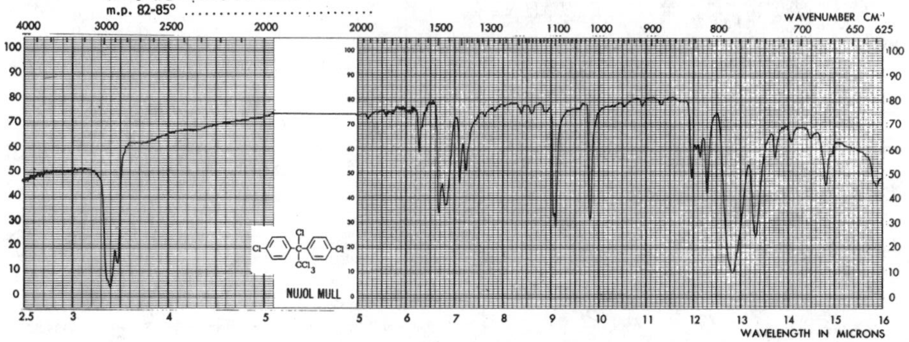

NUJOL MULL

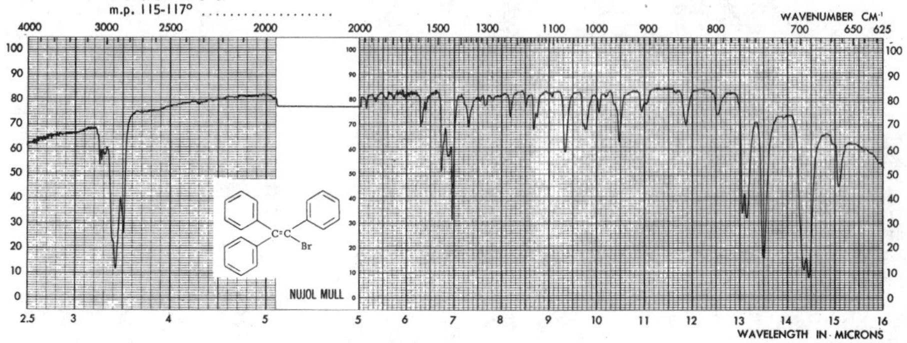

C

11,550-9 **2,2-Bis-(p-chlorophenyl)-1,1,1-trifluoroethane**
$(ClC_6H_4)_2CHCF_3$ M.W. 305.13 m.p. 43-45.5°

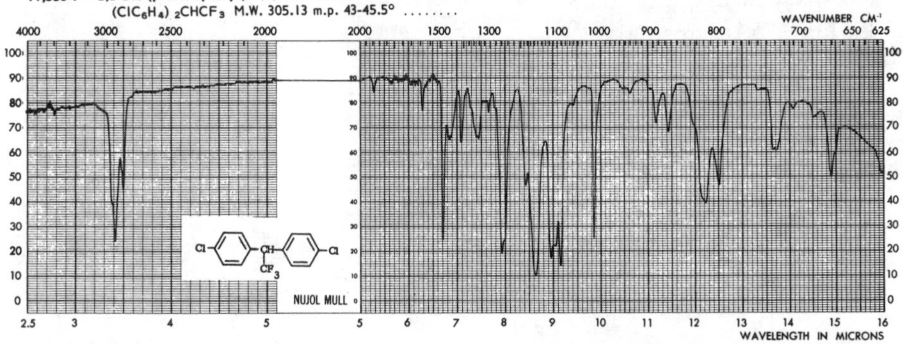

NUJOL MULL

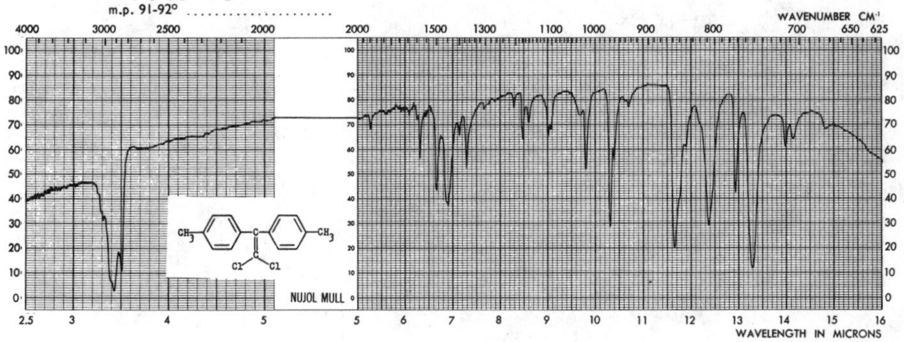

D

18,718-6
Cinnamyl chloride, 95% [(3-chloropropenyl)benzene]
$C_6H_5CH{=}CHCH_2Cl$

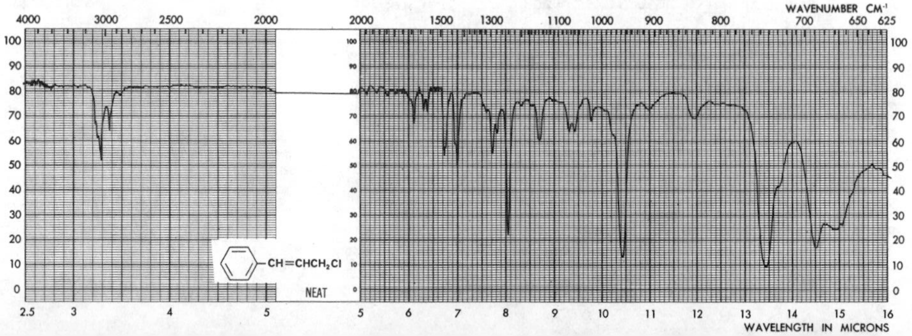

NEAT

E

B6530-6 **2-Bromo-1,1-diphenylethylene** (2,2-diphenylvinyl bromide)
$(C_6H_5)_2C{:}CHBr$ M.W. 259.15 m.p. 41-42°

MELT

F

12,185-1 **Bromotriphenylethylene**
$(C_6H_5)_2C{:}C(C_6H_5)Br$ M.W. 335.25
m.p. 115-117°

NUJOL MULL

G

11,551-7 **1,1-Dichloro-2,2-di-(p-tolyl)-ethylene**
$(CH_3C_6H_4)_2C{:}CCl_2$ M.W. 277.20
m.p. 91-92°

NUJOL MULL

H

14,498-3 **1-(o-Chlorophenyl)-1-(p-chlorophenyl)-2,2-dichloroethylene (o,p'-DDE), puriss.**
$(ClC_6H_4)_2C{:}CCl_2$ M.W. 318.03
m.p. 75-78°

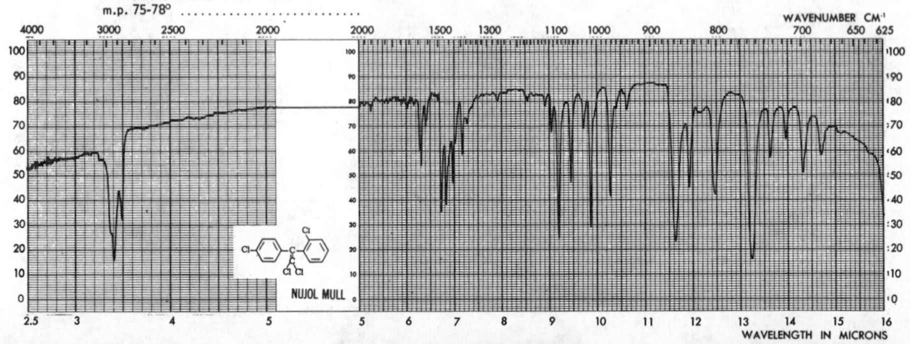

NUJOL MULL

A

12,389-7 **2,2-Bis-(p-chlorophenyl)-1,1-dichloroethylene** (p,p'-DDE)
$(ClC_6H_4)_2C:CCl_2$ M.W. 318.03 m.p. 88-90°

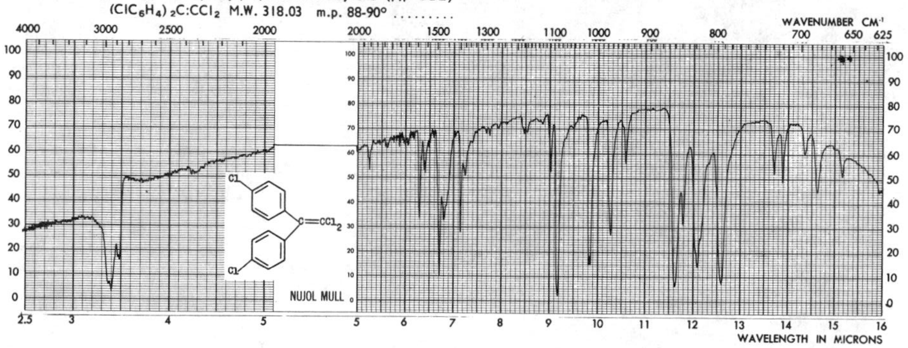

NUJOL MULL

B

14,971-3 **1-Fluoronaphthalene**
$C_{10}H_7F$ M.W. 146.16 n_D^{20} 1.5928
b.p. 93-94°/14 mm.

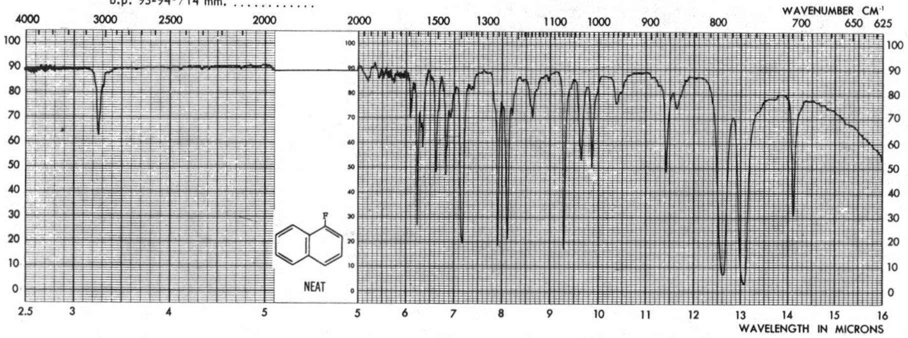

NEAT

C

C5765-0 **1-Chloronaphthalene**
$C_{10}H_7Cl$ M.W. 162.62 n_D^{20} 1.6349

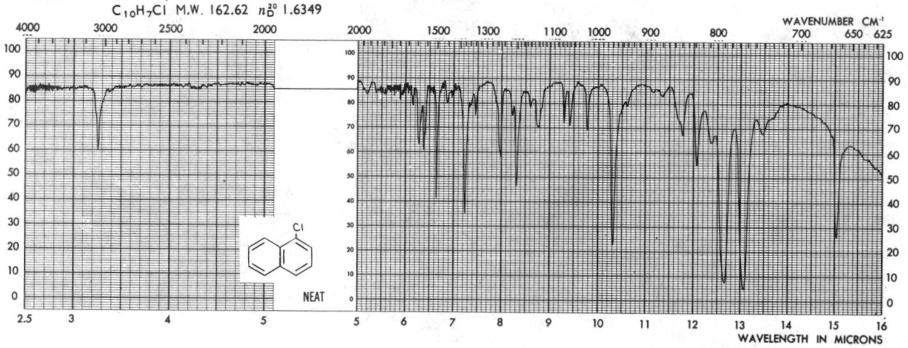

NEAT

D

B7310-4 **1-Bromonaphthalene**
$C_{10}H_7Br$ M.W. 207.08 n_D^{20} 1.6576
m.p. 2-4°

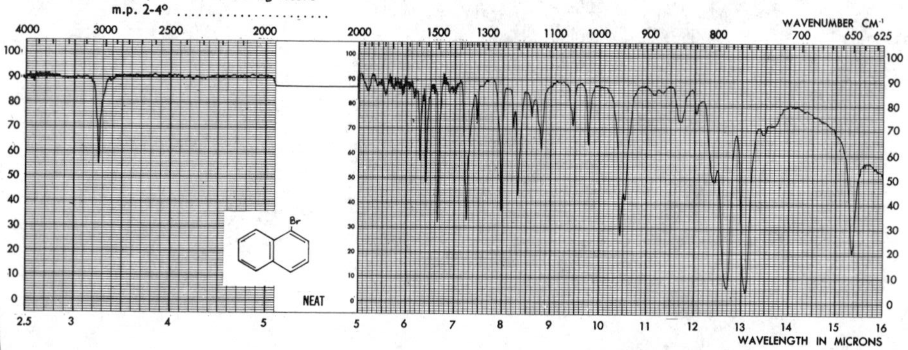

NEAT

E

18,505-1
2,3-Dibromonaphthalene
$C_{10}H_6Br_2$
M.W. 285.98 m.p. 140-141°

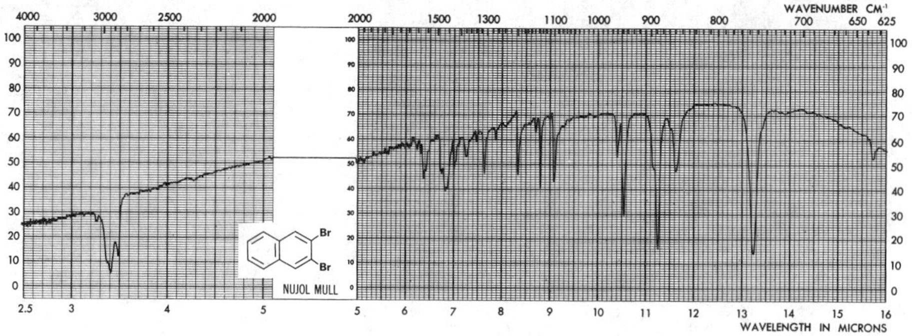

NUJOL MULL

F

F1075-5 **2-Fluoronaphthalene**
$C_{10}H_7F$ M.W. 146.16 m.p. 60-61°

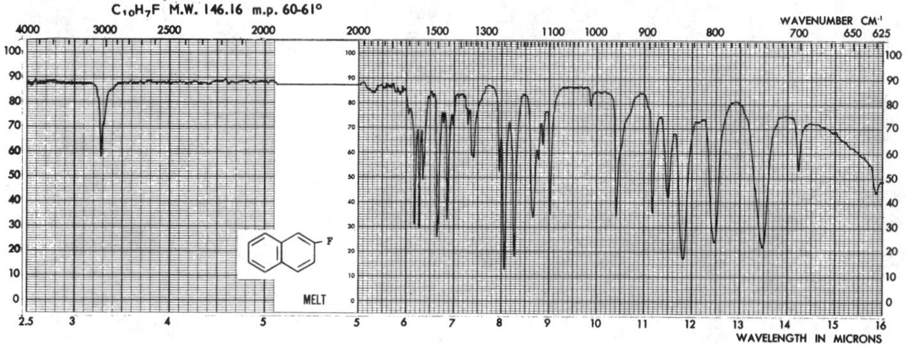

MELT

G

18,364-4
2-Bromonaphthalene, 97%
$C_{10}H_7Br$
M.W. 207.08 m.p. 52-55° b.p. 281-282°
Beil. 5,548

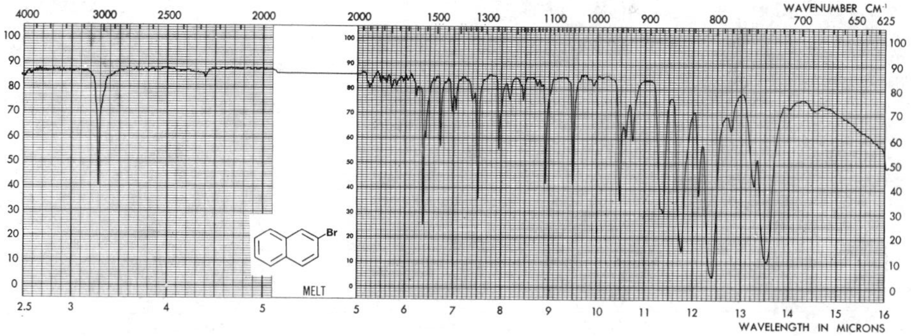

MELT

H

C5420-1 **1-(Chloromethyl)-naphthalene**
$C_{10}H_7CH_2Cl$ M.W. 176.65 n_D^{20} 1.6380

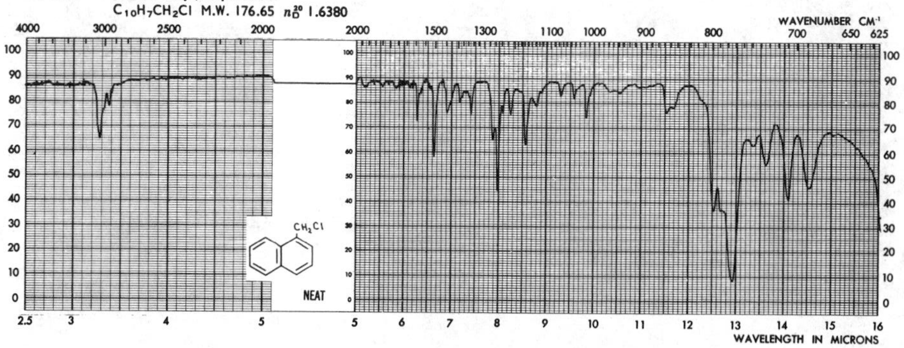

NEAT

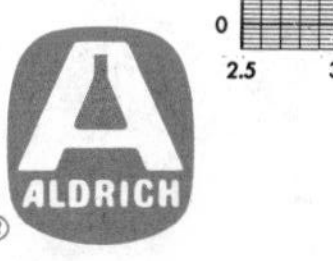

ALDRICH

A

14,367-7 2-(Bromomethyl)-naphthalene
$C_{10}H_7CH_2Br$ M.W. 221.10 m.p. 55-57°
MELT

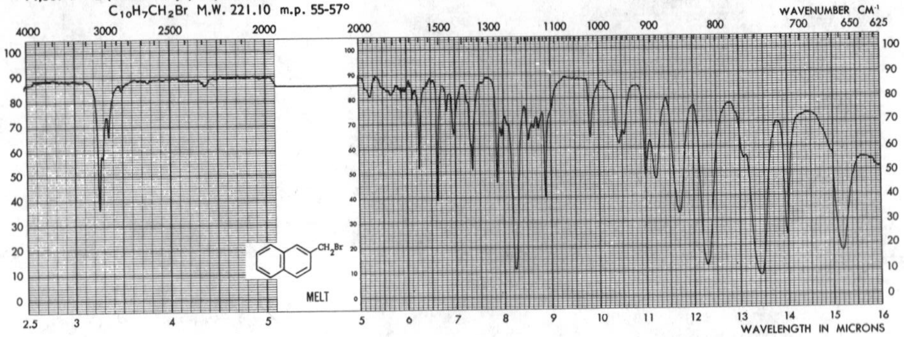

B

C5320-5 1-Chloromethyl-2-methylnaphthalene
$CH_3C_{10}H_6CH_2Cl$ M.W. 190.67 m.p. 59.5-62°
MELT

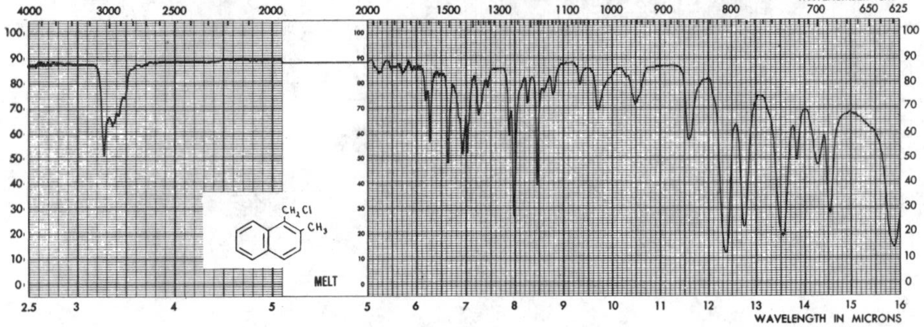

C

12,410-9 1-Bromo-2-methylnaphthalene
$CH_3C_{10}H_6Br$ M.W. 221.10 n_D^{20} 1.6484
NEAT

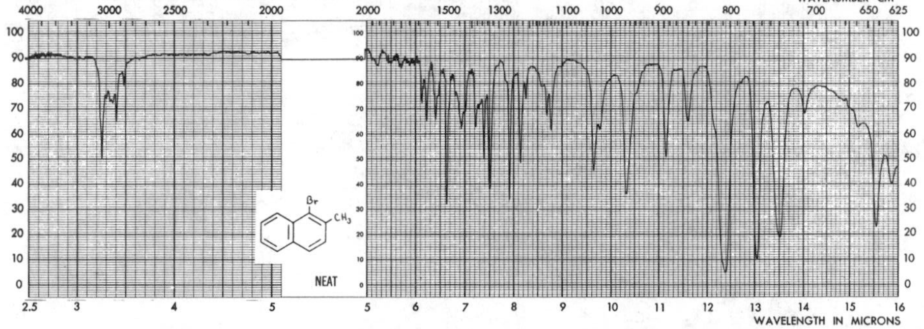

D

B7260-4 1-Bromo-4-methylnaphthalene
$CH_3C_{10}H_6Br$ M.W. 221.10 n_D^{20} 1.6512
NEAT

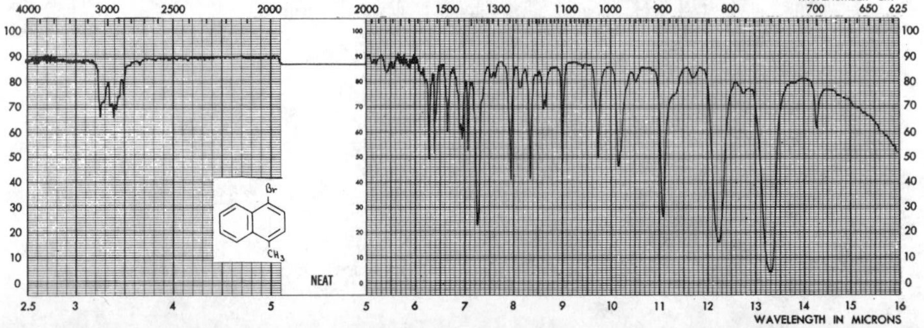

E

18,500-0
1,2,3,4-Tetrachloronaphthalene
$C_{10}H_4Cl_4$
M.W. 265.95 m.p. 198-200°
NUJOL MULL

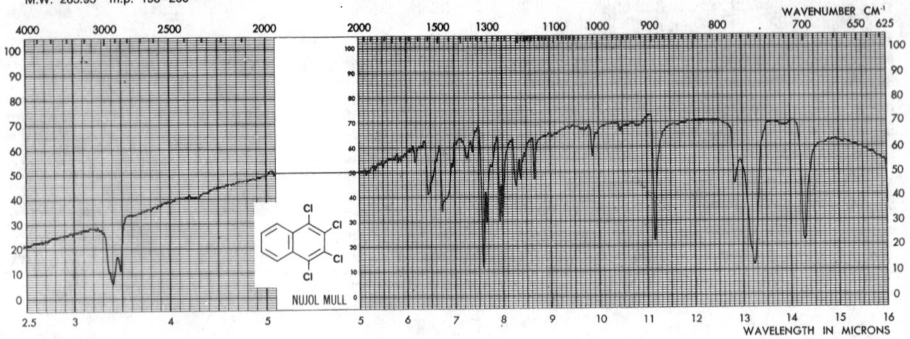

F

O-258-7 Octafluoronaphthalene (perfluoronaphthalene)
$C_{10}F_8$ M.W. 272.09 m.p. 86-88°
NUJOL MULL

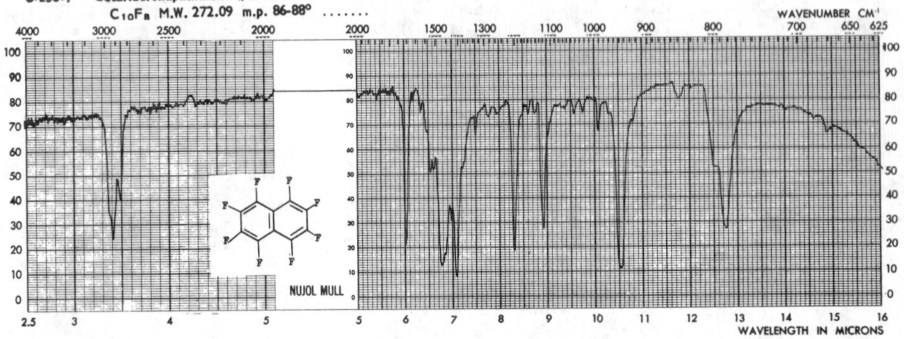

G

B5600-5 5-Bromoacenaphthene
M.W. 233.11 m.p. 54-56°
MELT

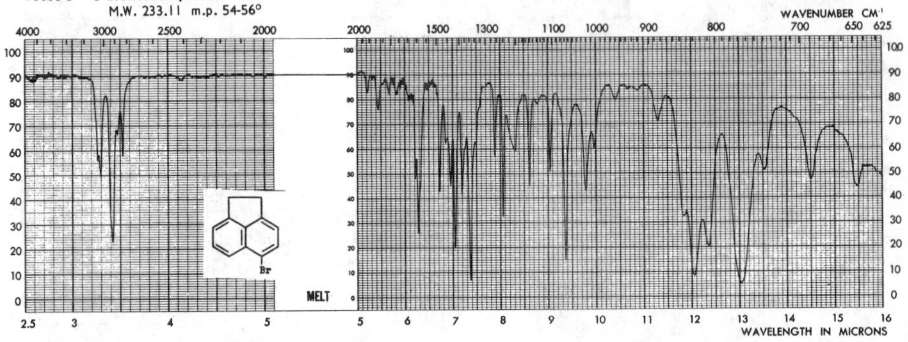

H

C4300-5 9-Chlorofluorene
M.W. 200.67 m.p. 88-89°
NUJOL MULL

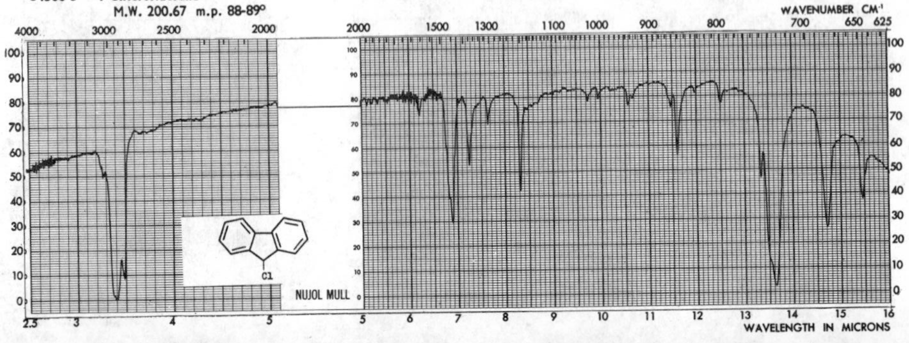

A B6660-4 9-Bromofluorene
M.W. 245.12 m.p. 102.5-105°
NUJOL MULL

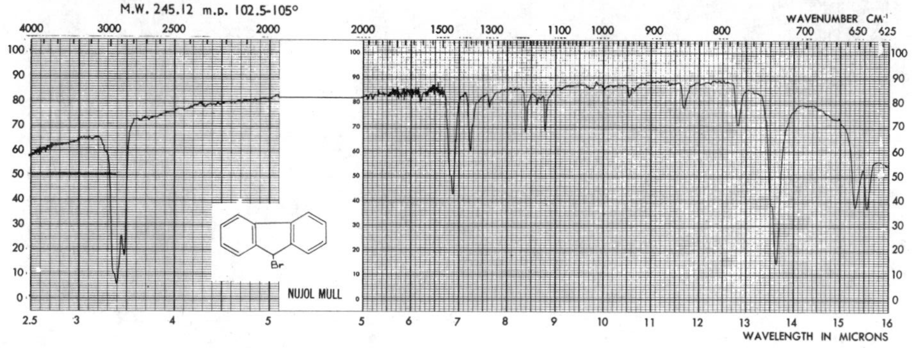

B 11,498-7 9-Bromo-9-bromomethylfluorene
M.W. 338.05 m.p. 143-144°
NUJOL MULL

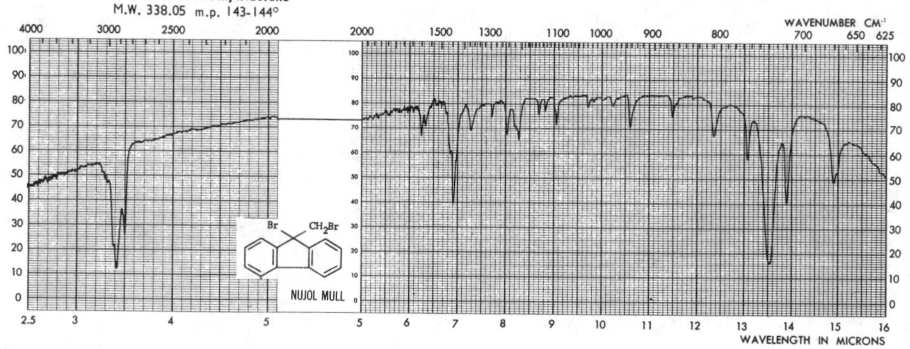

C 12,406-0 2-Bromofluorene
M.W. 245.12 m.p. 112-114°
NUJOL MULL

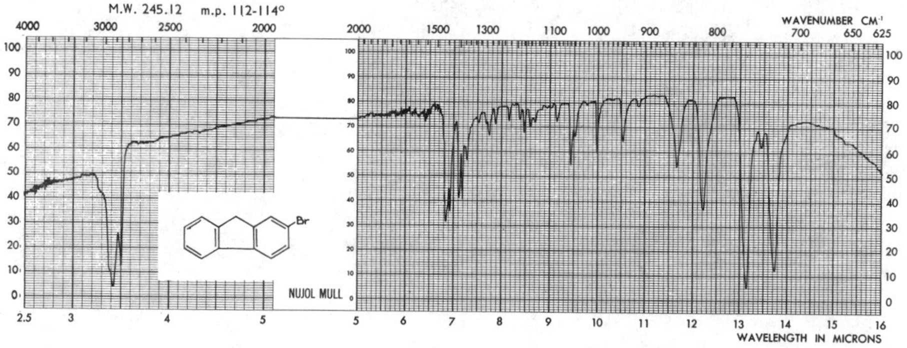

D 15,390-7 2-Iodofluorene
M.W. 292.12 m.p. 229-231°
NUJOL MULL

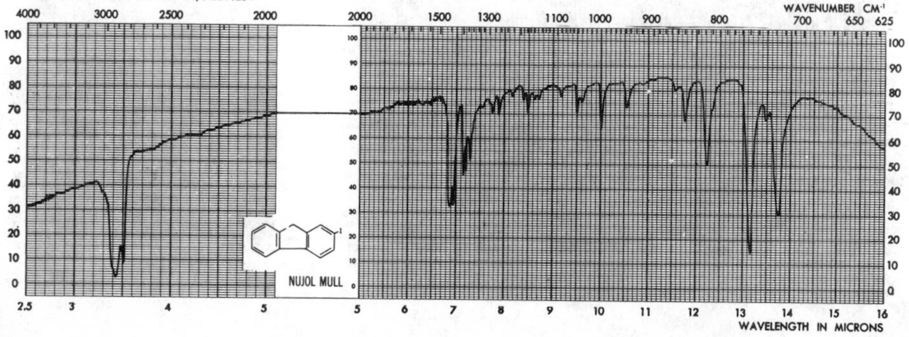

E C3430-8 5-Chloro-10,11-dihydro-5H-dibenzo[a,d]cycloheptene
M.W. 228.73 m.p. 106-107°
NUJOL MULL

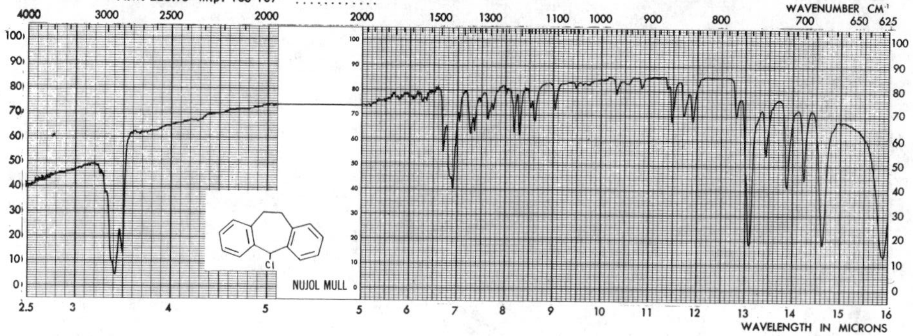

F 18,771-2
1-Chloroanthracene
FW 212.68 mp 77-80° d 1.171 *Beil.* **5**(1),324
Disp. C
NUJOL MULL

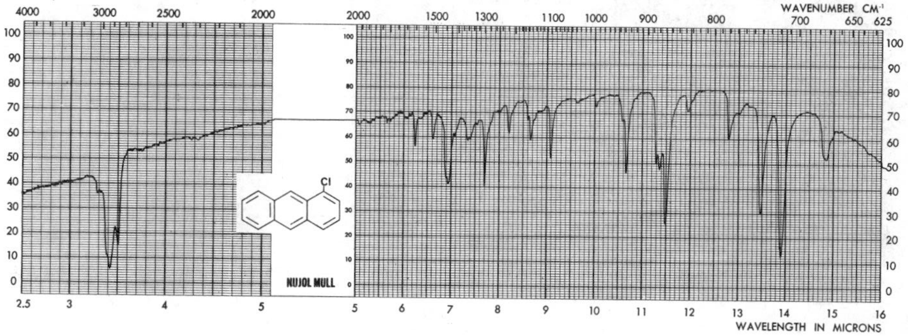

G 18,772-0
2-Chloroanthracene, 95%
FW 212.68 mp 221-223° Disp. C
NUJOL MULL

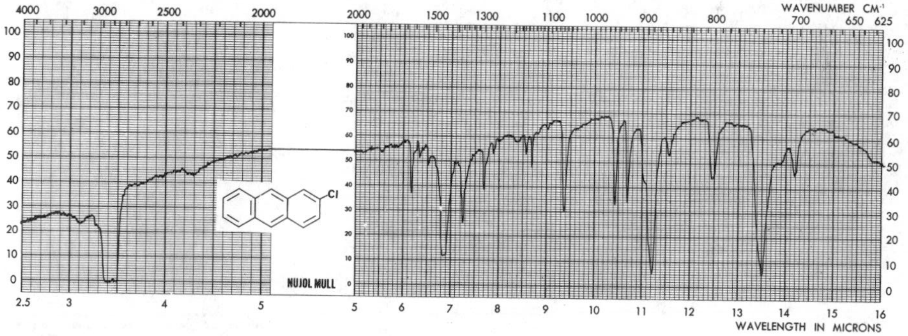

H 19,651-7
9-(Chloromethyl)anthracene, 98+%
FW 226.71 mp 138-140° Disp. C
NUJOL MULL

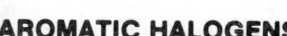

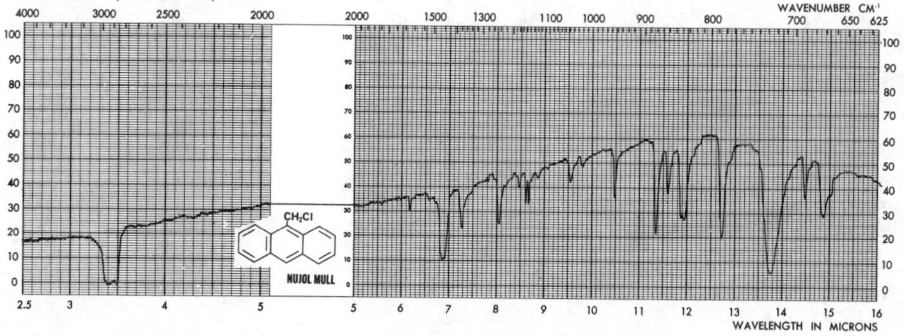

A

B5660-9 **9-Bromoanthracene**
M.W. 257.14 m.p. 94-97°

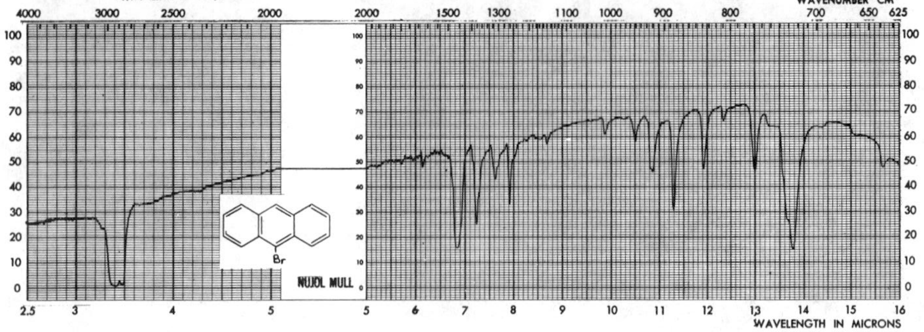

NUJOL MULL

B

D3885-5 **9,10-Dibromoanthracene**
M.W. 336.04 m.p. 223.5-224.5°

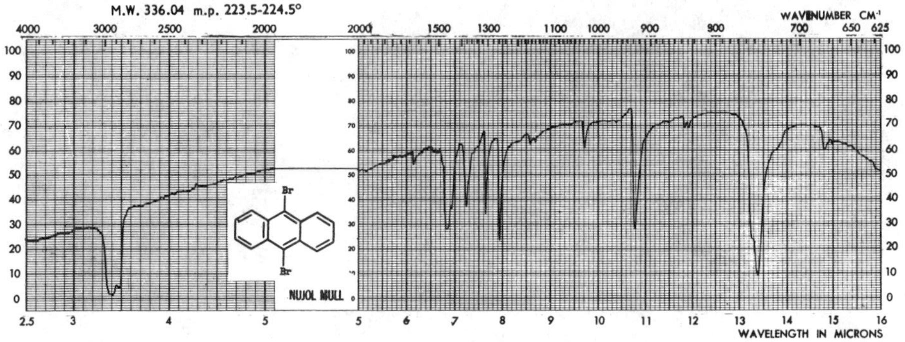

NUJOL MULL

C

20,659-8
9-Chlorophenanthrene, 98%
FW 212.68 mp 47-49° *Beil.* **5**(1),329 Disp. C

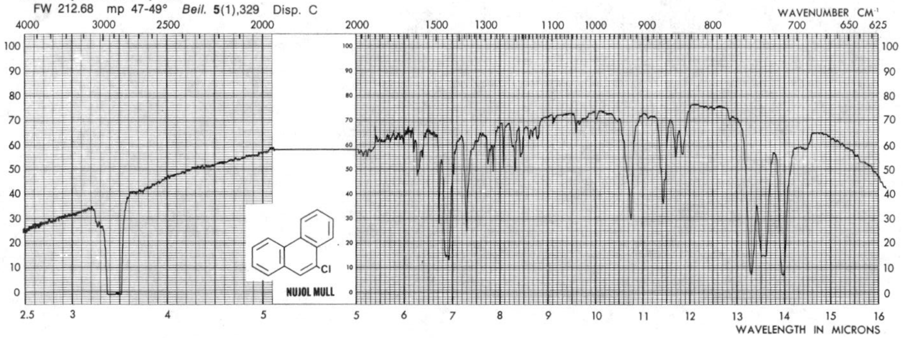

NUJOL MULL

D

B7540-9 **9-Bromophenanthrene**
M.W. 257.14 m.p. 54-58°

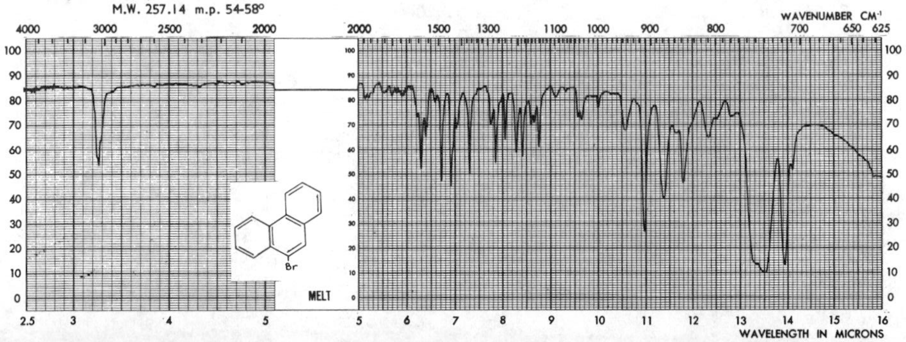

MELT

E

T810-8 **1,3,6,8-Tetrachloropyrene, tech.**
M.W. 340.04 m.p. > 330° ....

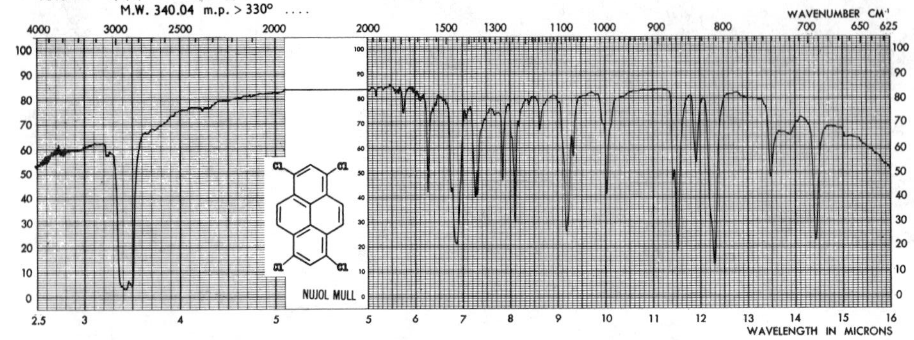

NUJOL MULL

F

18,488-8
Naphthalene-bis(hexachlorocyclopentadiene) adduct,
tech., 95%
M.W. 673.72 m.p. 208-210°
Precursor to substituted naphthalenes which are otherwise difficult to synthesize.

NUJOL MULL

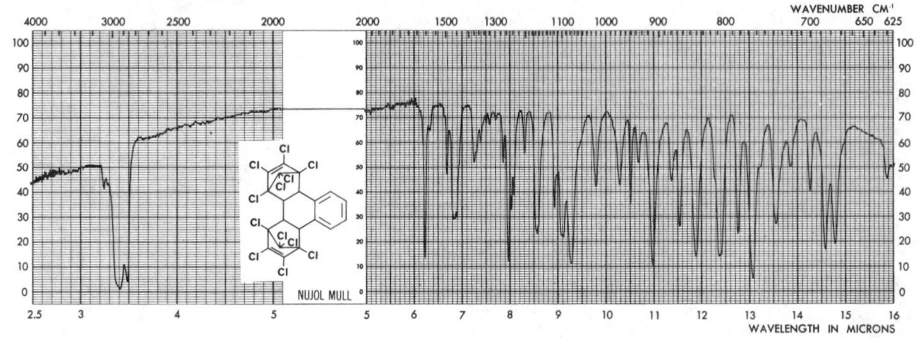

G

18,489-6
2-Methylnaphthalene-bis(hexachlorocyclopentadiene) adduct, 97%
M.W. 687.75 m.p. 162-165°

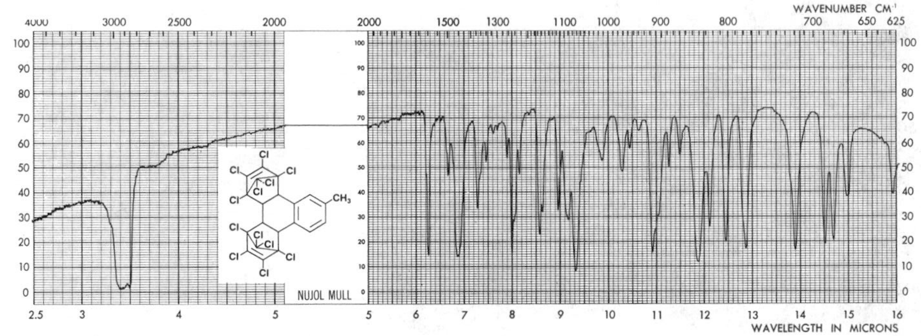

NUJOL MULL

H

18,493-4
2-Bromonaphthalene-bis(hexachlorocyclopentadiene) adduct
M.W. 752.62 m.p. 189-192°
Precursor to substituted naphthalenes which are otherwise difficult to synthesize.

NUJOL MULL

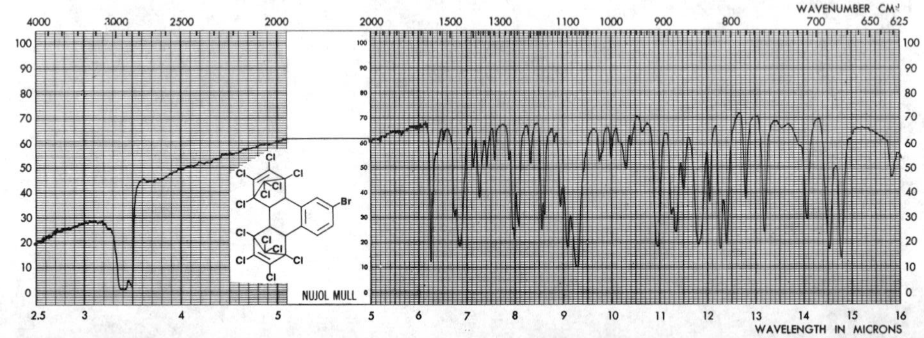

A

1,2,3,4-Tetrachloronaphthalene-bis(hexachlorocyclopentadiene) adduct
M.W. 811.5 m.p. 230-231°
Precursor to substituted naphthalenes which are otherwise difficult to synthesize.

NUJOL MULL

B

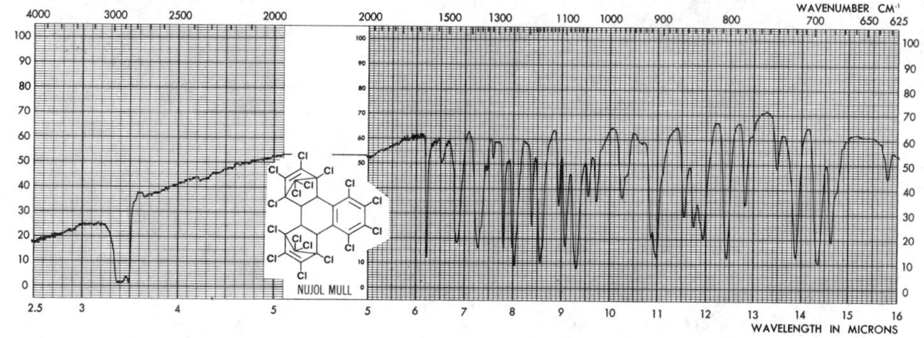

22,465-0 3-Bromobenzotrifluoride

NEAT

C

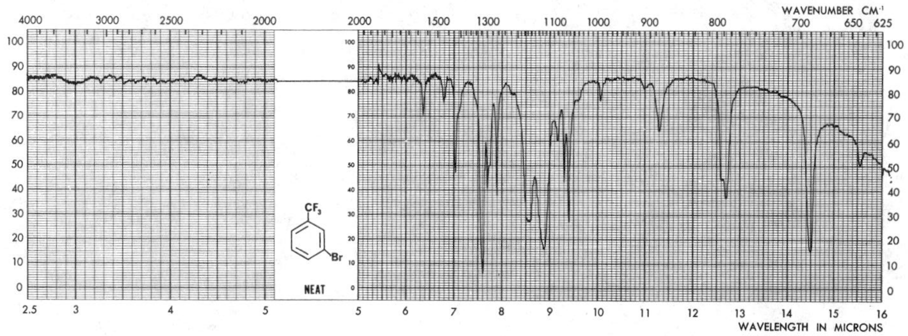

22,532-0
2,3-Dichlorotoluene, 98%
$CH_3C_6H_3Cl_2$ FW 161.03 mp 6° bp 207-208°
n_D^{20} 1.5517 d 1.228 *Beil.* **5**,295 Disp. C

NEAT

D

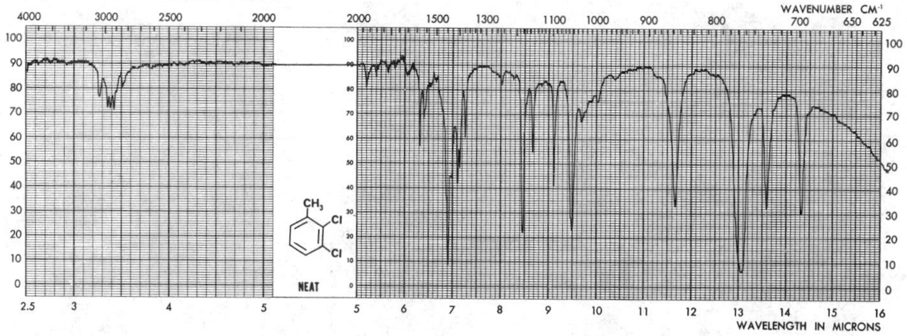

22,514-2
Bromotriphenylethylene, 98%
$(C_6H_5)_2C{=}C(C_6H_5)Br$ FW 335.25 mp 115-117°
Beil. **5**,722 *IR* **2**,550B Disp. C

NUJOL MULL

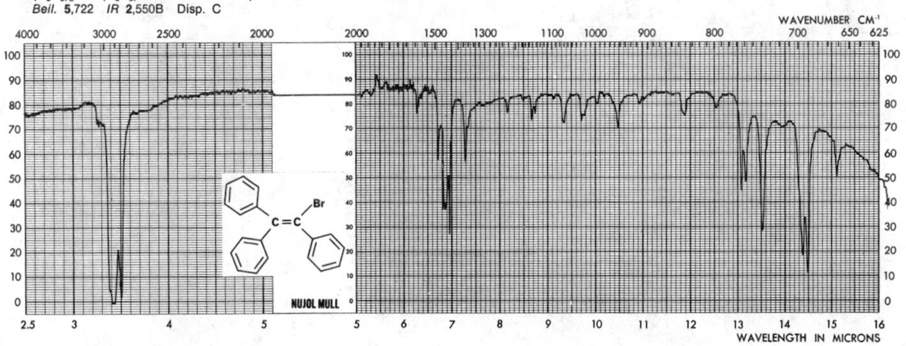

AROMATIC ETHERS

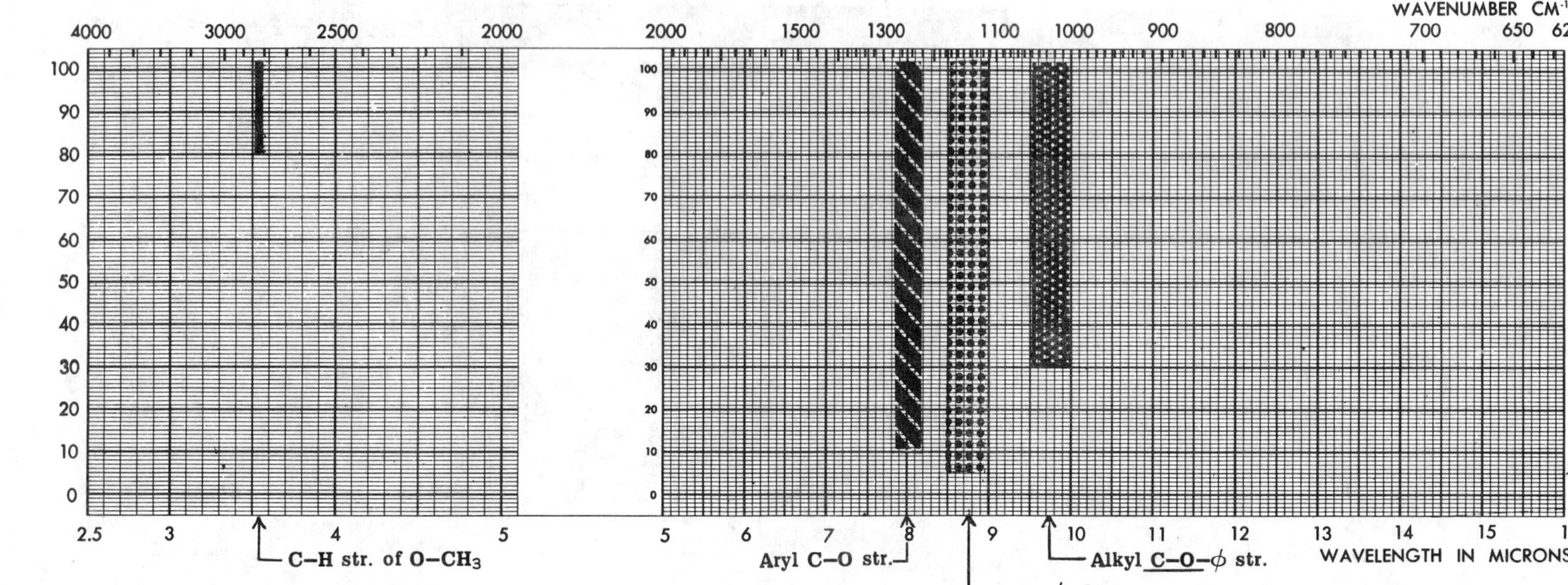

The aromatic carbon-oxygen vibration appears as a strong band near 8 μ (1250 cm^{-1}). The aliphatic portion of the ether linkage displays its absorption between 9.5 and 10 μ (1055 – 1000 cm^{-1}). This band is missing, of course, in the spectra of the all-aromatic ethers (spectra 634H—635E). The bands that do appear are due to aromatic ring vibrations.

An absorption between 8.5 and 9 μ (1175 – 1110 cm^{-1}) will also be noted. It is particularly strong when the benzene ring is substituted in three or more positions.

In spectra 632D-E and 632F the ether band at 8 μ (1250 cm^{-1}) is absent.

The methoxy group displays a C–H stretch band at 3.53 μ (2835 cm^{-1}) distinctly separate from the other C–H bands and different from other ether groups. This band can be obscured when the sample is prepared as a nujol mull. (See spectra 627F and G).

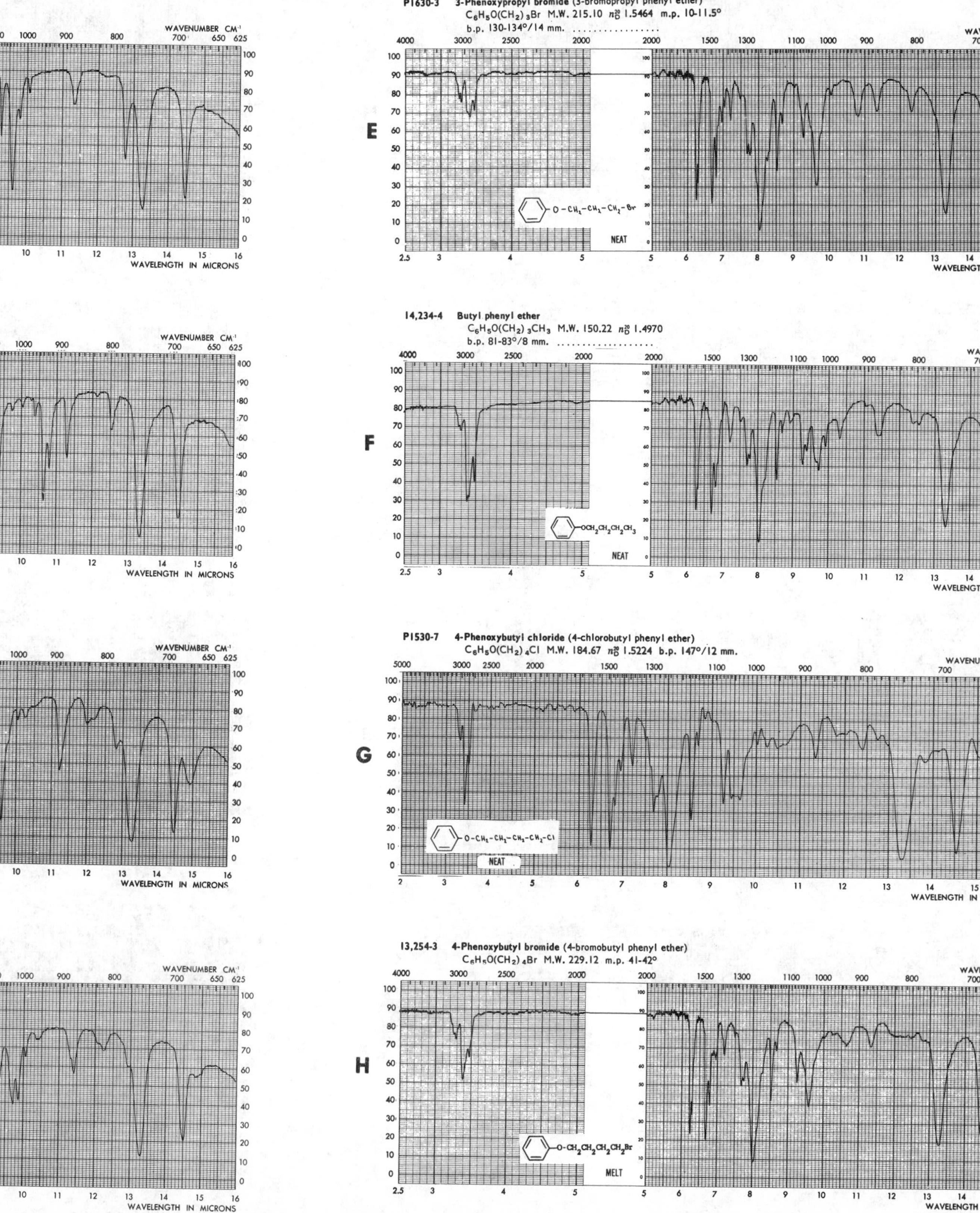

A 12,322-6 **Anisole**
$C_6H_5OCH_3$ M.W. 108.14 n_D^{20} 1.5151
NEAT

B 14,028-7 **1,2-Diphenoxyethane**
$C_6H_5OCH_2CH_2OC_6H_5$ M.W. 214.26
m.p. 94-96°
NUJOL MULL

C 11,427-8 **β-Chlorophenetole** (2-chloroethyl phenyl ether)
$C_6H_5OCH_2CH_2Cl$ M.W. 132.59
NEAT

D B7,550-6
β-Bromophenetole, 98% (2-bromoethyl phenyl ether)
$C_6H_5OCH_2CH_2Br$
M.W. 201.07 m.p. 33.5-34° b.p. 144°/40mm.
Beil. 6,142
NEAT

E P1630-3 **3-Phenoxypropyl bromide** (3-bromopropyl phenyl ether)
$C_6H_5O(CH_2)_3Br$ M.W. 215.10 n_D^{20} 1.5464 m.p. 10-11.5°
b.p. 130-134°/14 mm.
NEAT

F 14,234-4 **Butyl phenyl ether**
$C_6H_5O(CH_2)_3CH_3$ M.W. 150.22 n_D^{20} 1.4970
b.p. 81-83°/8 mm.
NEAT

G P1530-7 **4-Phenoxybutyl chloride** (4-chlorobutyl phenyl ether)
$C_6H_5O(CH_2)_4Cl$ M.W. 184.67 n_D^{20} 1.5224 b.p. 147°/12 mm.
NEAT

H 13,254-3 **4-Phenoxybutyl bromide** (4-bromobutyl phenyl ether)
$C_6H_5O(CH_2)_4Br$ M.W. 229.12 m.p. 41-42°
MELT

A M2935-5 **o-Methylanisole**
$CH_3C_6H_4OCH_3$ M.W. 122.17 n_D^{20} 1.5161

B 14,015-5 **Veratrole** (o-dimethoxybenzene), **puriss.**
$C_6H_4(OCH_3)_2$ M.W. 138.17 n_D^{20} 1.5337
b.p. 206-207°

C 15,916-6
1,3-Benzodioxole, 99% (1,2-methylenedioxybenzene)
M.W. 122.12 b.p. 172-173° n_D^{20} 1.5398 d 1.064
Beil. **19**,20

D 17,687-7
Phthalan, 97% (o-xylylene oxide)
M.W. 120.15 b.p. 192° n_D^{20} 1.5457 d 1.098
Beil. **17**,51

E 18,396-2
2,3-Dihydrobenzofuran, 98% (coumaran)
M.W. 120.15 b.p. 188-189° n_D^{20} 1.5497 d 1.065
Beil. **17**,50

F 17,900-0
1,4-Benzodioxan, 97%
M.W. 136.15 b.p. 103°/6mm. n_D^{20} 1.5485 d 1.142

G 15,839-9
Dibenzo-18-crown-6, 98% (2,3,11,12-dibenzo-1,4,7,10,13,16-hexaoxacyclooctadeca-2,11-diene)
M.W. 360.41 m.p. 162-164° *IRRITANT*

H F420-3 **2-Fluoroanisole**
$FC_6H_4OCH_3$ M.W. 126.13 n_D^{20} 1.4935

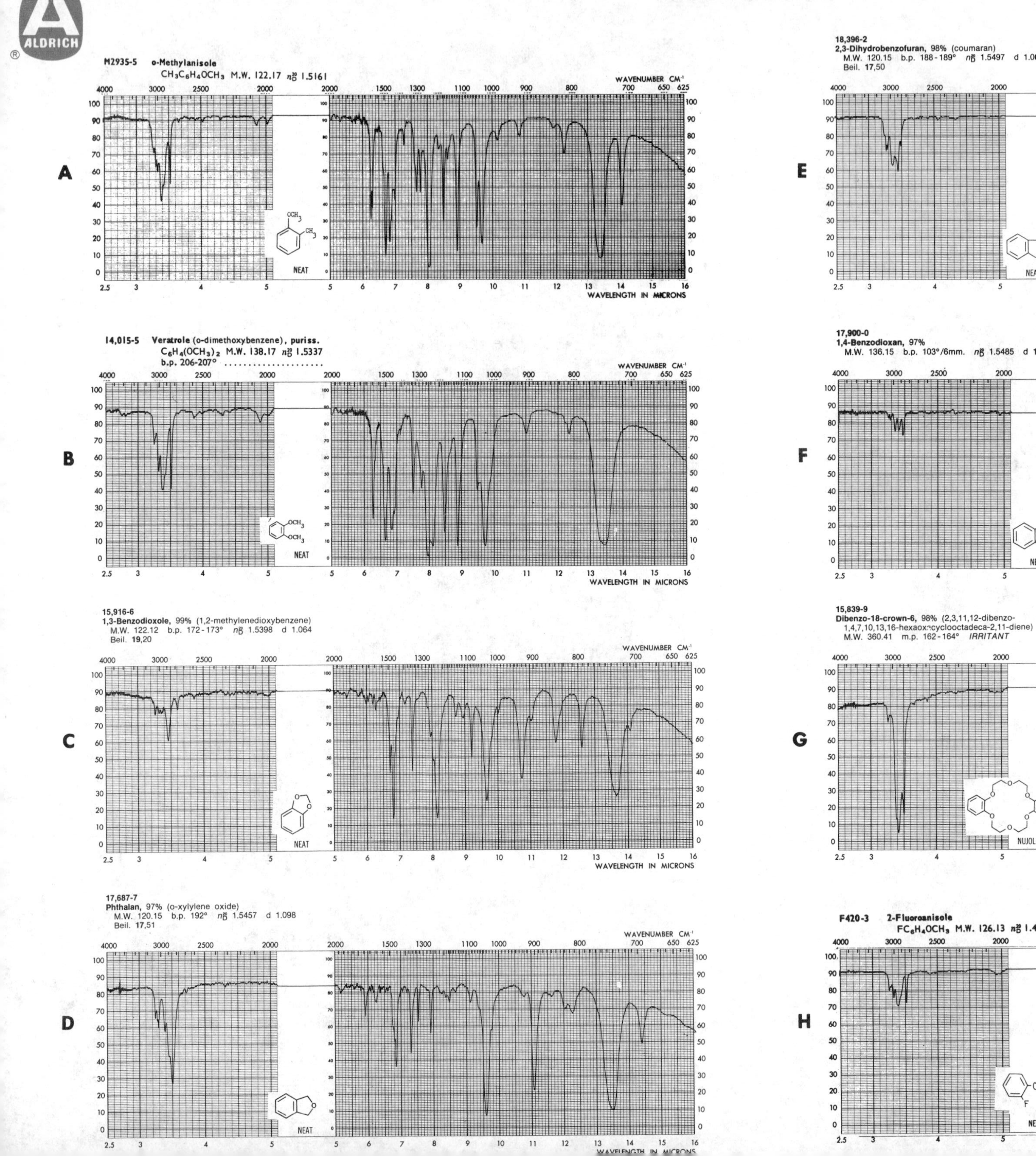

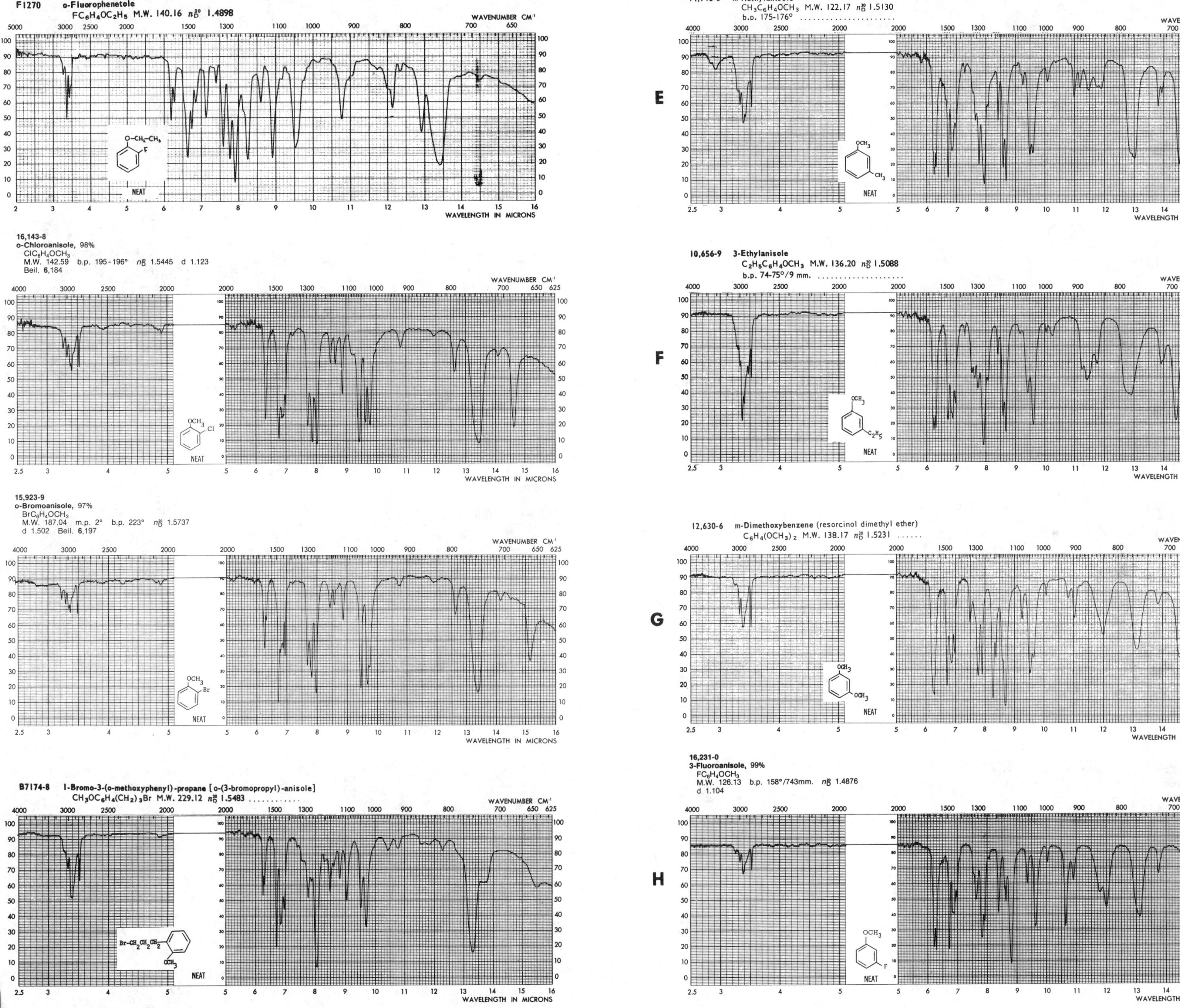

A — F1270 **o-Fluorophenetole**
$FC_6H_4OC_2H_5$ M.W. 140.16 n_D^{20} 1.4898
NEAT

B — 16,143-8 **o-Chloroanisole**, 98%
$ClC_6H_4OCH_3$
M.W. 142.59 b.p. 195-196° n_D^{20} 1.5445 d 1.123
Beil. **6**,184
NEAT

C — 15,923-9 **o-Bromoanisole**, 97%
$BrC_6H_4OCH_3$
M.W. 187.04 m.p. 2° b.p. 223° n_D^{20} 1.5737
d 1.502 Beil. **6**,197
NEAT

D — B7174-8 **1-Bromo-3-(o-methoxyphenyl)-propane** [o-(3-bromopropyl)-anisole]
$CH_3OC_6H_4(CH_2)_3Br$ M.W. 229.12 n_D^{20} 1.5483
NEAT

E — 14,916-0 **m-Methylanisole**
$CH_3C_6H_4OCH_3$ M.W. 122.17 n_D^{20} 1.5130
b.p. 175-176°
NEAT

F — 10,656-9 **3-Ethylanisole**
$C_2H_5C_6H_4OCH_3$ M.W. 136.20 n_D^{20} 1.5088
b.p. 74-75°/9 mm.
NEAT

G — 12,630-6 **m-Dimethoxybenzene** (resorcinol dimethyl ether)
$C_6H_4(OCH_3)_2$ M.W. 138.17 n_D^{20} 1.5231
NEAT

H — 16,231-0 **3-Fluoroanisole**, 99%
$FC_6H_4OCH_3$
M.W. 126.13 b.p. 158°/743mm. n_D^{20} 1.4876
d 1.104
NEAT

A

21,310-1
***m*-(Trifluoromethyl)anisole, 99%**
$CF_3C_6H_4OCH_3$ FW 176.14 n_D^{20} 1.4434 d 1.217
Disp. C

NEAT

B

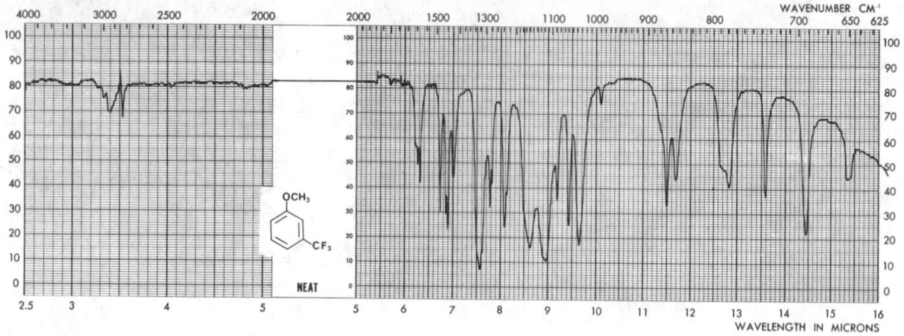

15,733-3
m-Chloroanisole
$ClC_6H_4OCH_3$
M.W. 142.59 b.p. 193° n_D^{20} 1.5362 Beil. 6,185

NEAT

C

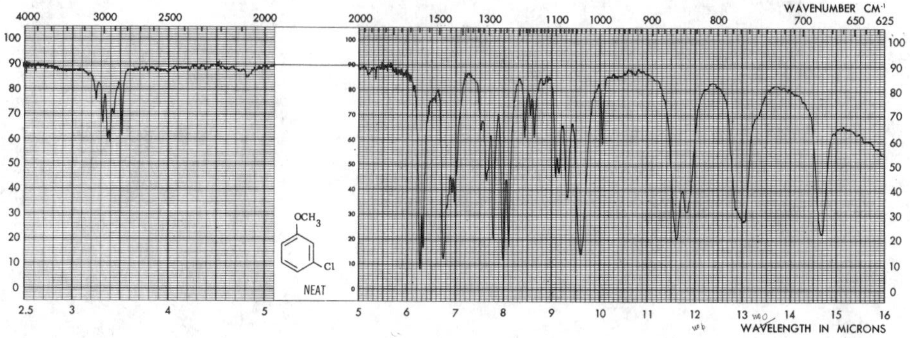

20,938-4
***m*-Methoxybenzyl chloride, 97%**
[*m*-(chloromethyl)anisole]
$CH_3OC_6H_4CH_2Cl$ FW 156.61 bp 124°/13mm.
n_D^{20} 1.5446 d 1.078 *Beil.* 6(1),189 Disp. C

NEAT

D

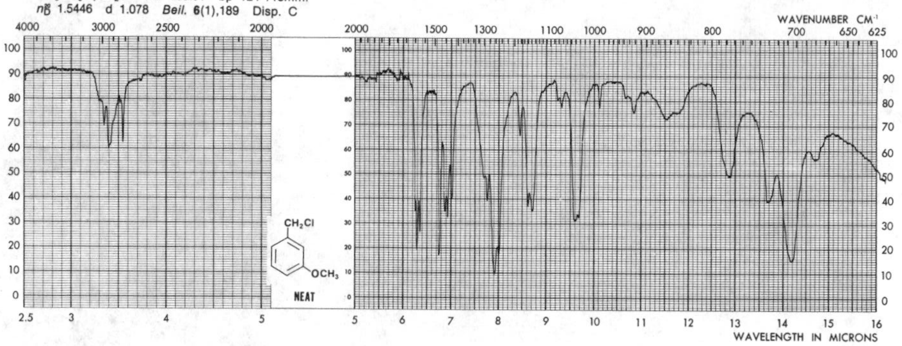

B5649-8 **m-Bromoanisole**
$BrC_6H_4OCH_3$ M.W. 187.04 n_D^{20} 1.5635

NEAT

E

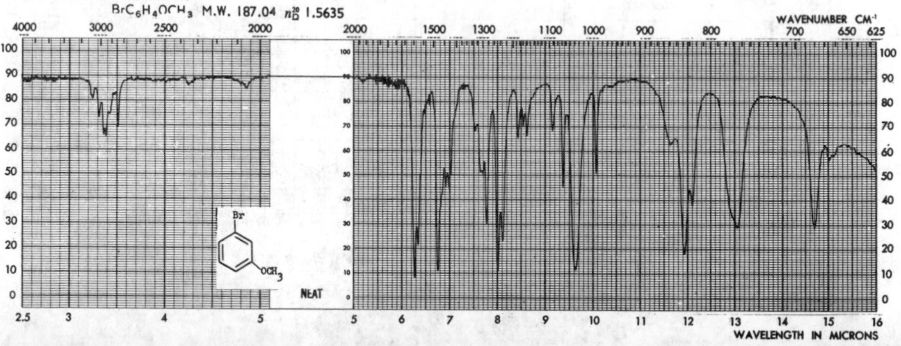

14,809-1 **p-Methylanisole**
$CH_3C_6H_4OCH_3$ M.W. 122.17 n_D^{20} 1.5112
b.p. 174°

NEAT

F

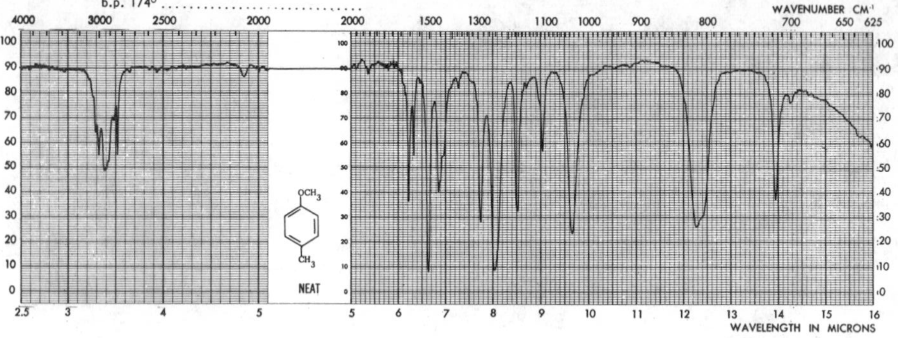

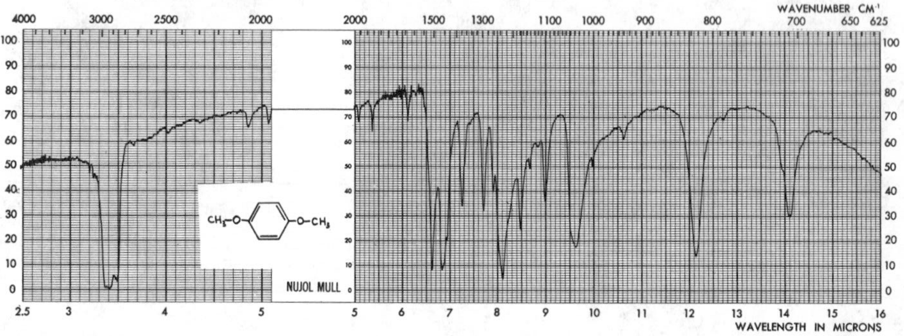

D13,135-0 **p-Dimethoxybenzene** (hydroquinone dimethyl ether)
$C_6H_4(OCH_3)_2$ M.W. 138.17 m.p. 56-60°

NUJOL MULL

G

D13,135-0 **p-Dimethoxybenzene** (hydroquinone dimethyl ether)
$C_6H_4(OCH_3)_2$ M.W. 138.17 m.p. 56-60°

MELT

H

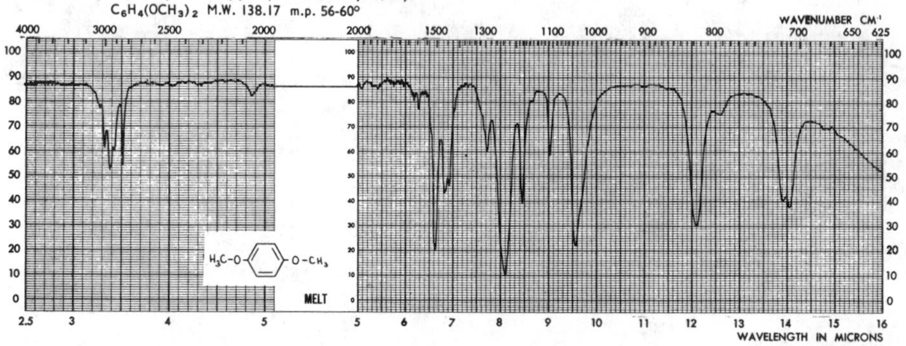

F460-2 **4-Fluoroanisole**
$FC_6H_4OCH_3$ M.W. 126.13 n_D^{20} 1.4877
b.p. 156-157°

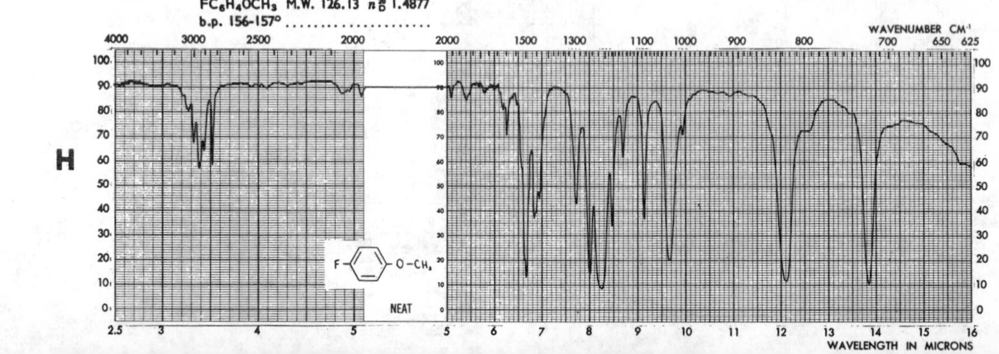

A 15,907-7
α,p-**Dichloroanisole,** 97%
$ClC_6H_4OCH_2Cl$
M.W. 177.03 m.p. 29-30° b.p. 120-124°/18mm.
n_D^{20} 1.5515

B 15,906-9
p-Chloroanisole
$ClC_6H_4OCH_3$
M.W. 142.59 m.p. -18° b.p. 198-202°
n_D^{20} 1.5358 Beil. **6**,186

C B5650-1 **p-Bromoanisole**
$BrC_6H_4OCH_3$ M.W. 187.04 n_D^{20} 1.5620 m.p. 13-14°

D 21,144-3
p-**Bromophenetole,** 99% (*p*-bromophenyl ethyl ether)
$BrC_6H_4OC_2H_5$ FW 201.07 mp 4° bp 233°
n_D^{20} 1.5510 d 1.407 *Beil.* **6**,199 Disp. C

E 19,875-7
p-**Bromophenyl 2-chloroethyl ether**
$BrC_6H_4OCH_2CH_2Cl$ FW 235.51 mp 55-57°
Beil. **6**(3),742 Disp. C

F 10,564-3 **2-Bromoethyl p-bromophenyl ether** (*β,p*-dibromophenetole), **tech.**
$BrC_6H_4OCH_2CH_2Br$ M.W. 279.97
m.p. 55-59°

G I-760-8 **4-Iodoanisole**
$IC_6H_4OCH_3$ M.W. 234.04
m.p. 48-50°

H 11,408-1 **p-Benzyloxybenzyl chloride** (*p*-chloromethyl-*α*-phenylanisole)
$C_6H_5CH_2OC_6H_4CH_2Cl$ M.W. 232.71
m.p. 79-81°

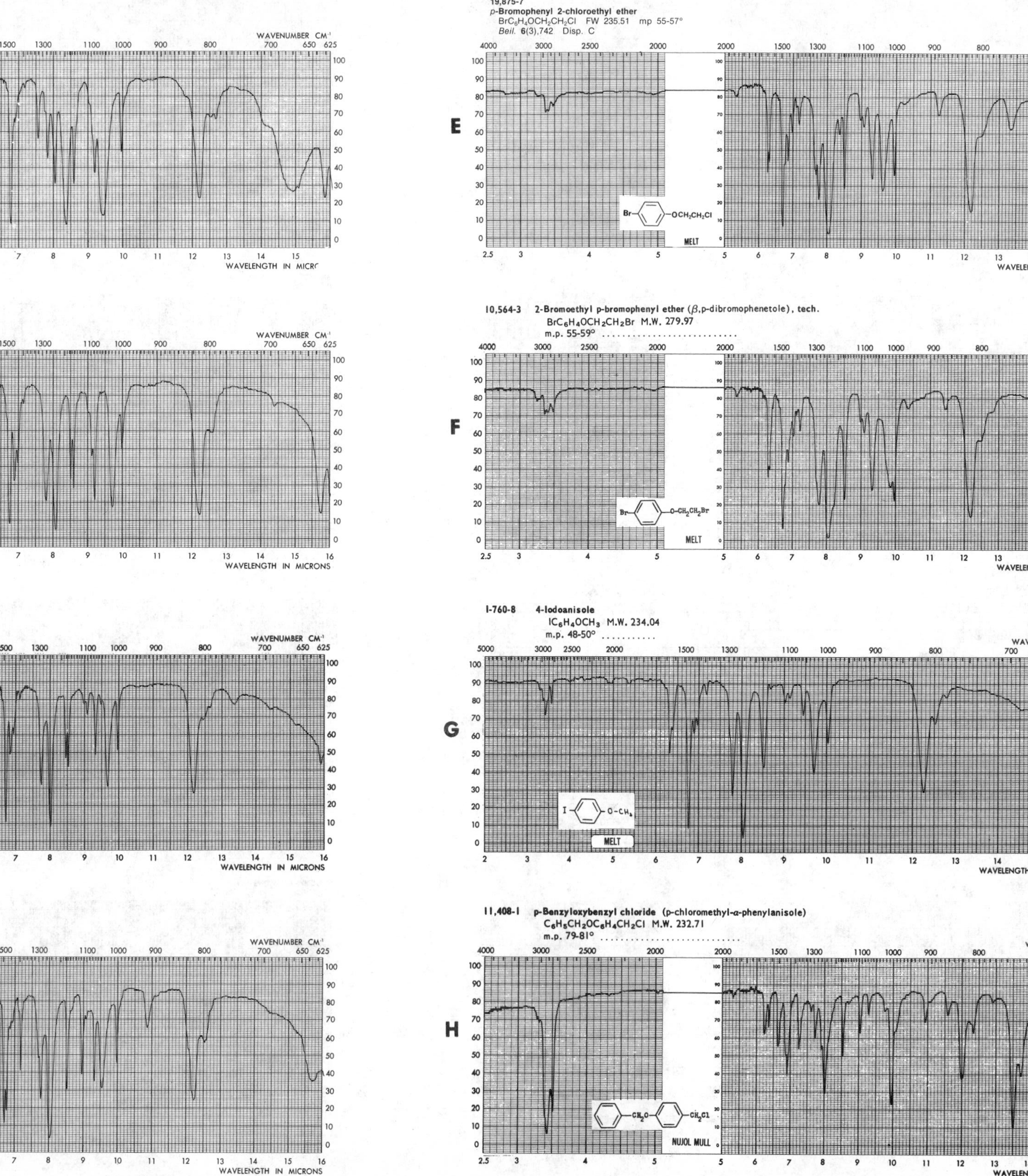

A

D14,640-4 2,6-Dimethylanisole
$(CH_3)_2C_6H_3OCH_3$ M.W. 136.19
n_D^{20} 1.5037 ....

NEAT

B

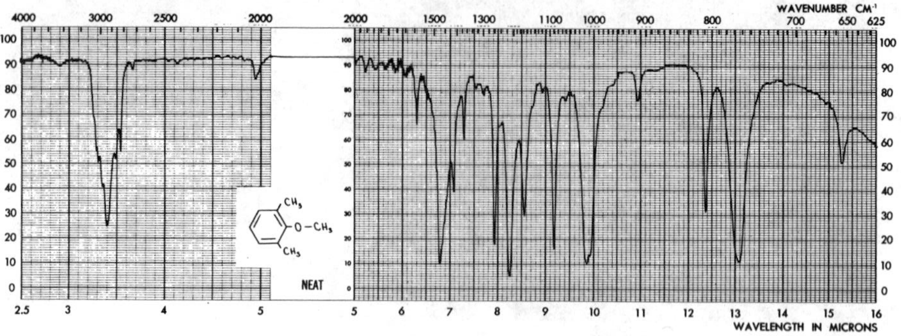

15,732-5
2,6-Dichloroanisole, 99%
$Cl_2C_6H_3OCH_3$
M.W. 177.03 m.p. 10.1° n_D^{20} 1.5436
Beil. **6**(1),103

NEAT

C

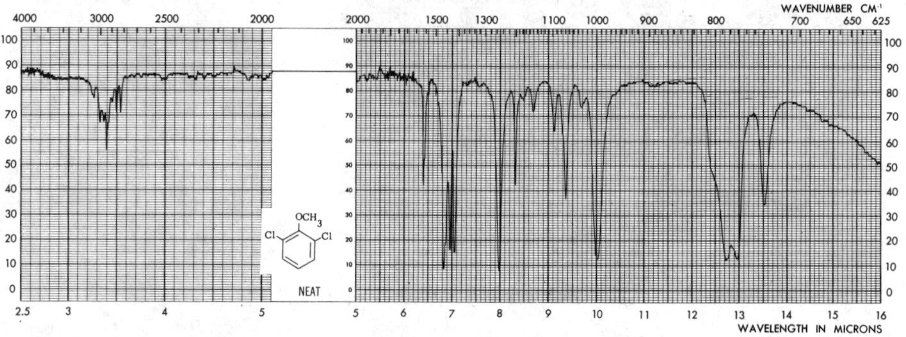

13,746-4 2,3-Dimethylanisole
$(CH_3)_2C_6H_3OCH_3$ M.W. 136.19

NEAT

D

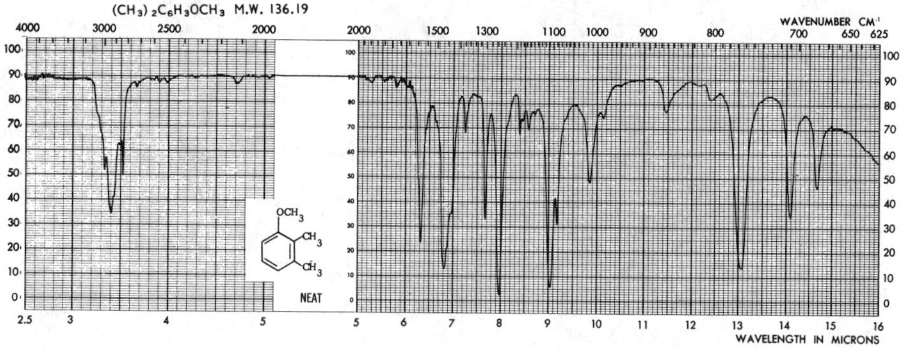

15,675-2
2,3-Dichloroanisole
$Cl_2C_6H_3OCH_3$
M.W. 177.03 m.p. 31-33° Beil. **6**(1),102

MELT

E

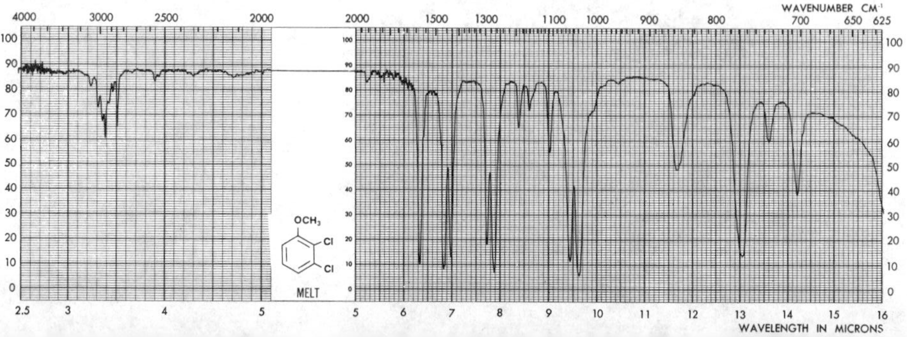

11,587-8 3-Methylveratrole
$CH_3C_6H_3$-1,2-$(OCH_3)_2$ M.W. 152.19 n_D^{20} 1.5128

NEAT

F

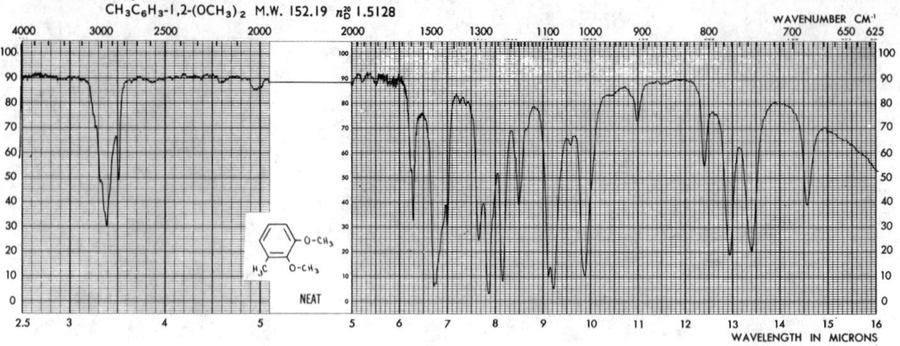

D13,720-0 2,6-Dimethoxytoluene
$CH_3C_6H_3(OCH_3)_2$ M.W. 152.19 m.p. 39-41°

MELT

G

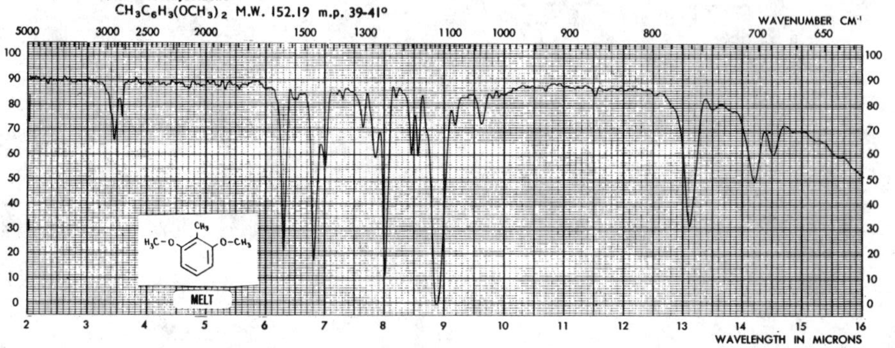

15,754-6
1-Bromo-2,6-dimethoxybenzene, 99%
$BrC_6H_3(OCH_3)_2$
M.W. 217.07 m.p. 92-94°

NUJOL MULL

H

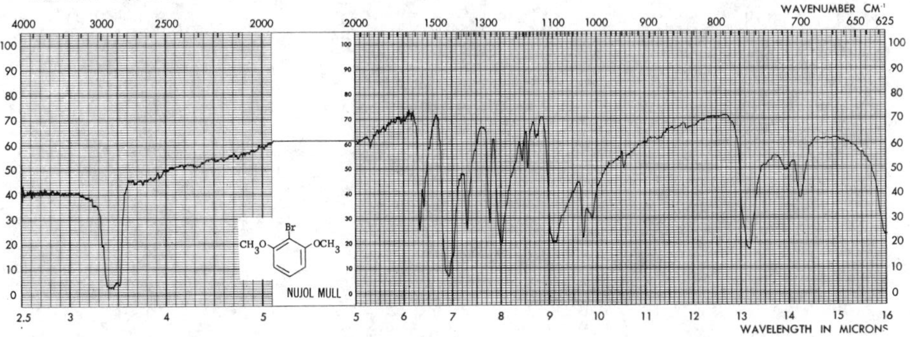

13,799-5 1,2,3-Trimethoxybenzene
$C_6H_3(OCH_3)_3$ M.W. 168.19 m.p. 40-44°

MELT

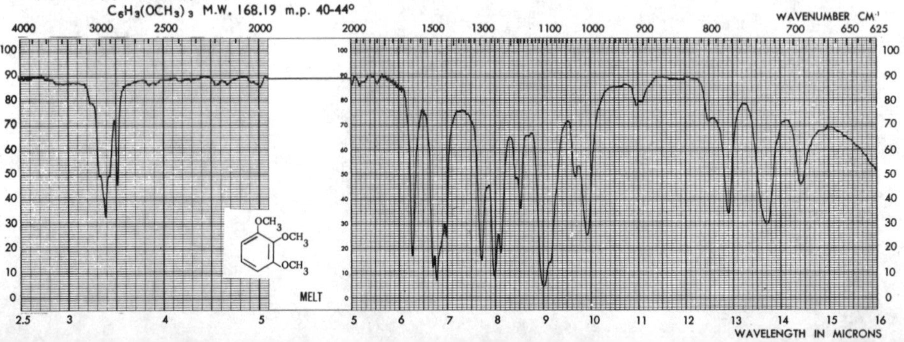

A 13,749-9 **3,4-Dimethylanisole**
$(CH_3)_2C_6H_3OCH_3$ M.W. 136.19 n_D^{20} 1.5184
b.p. 200°

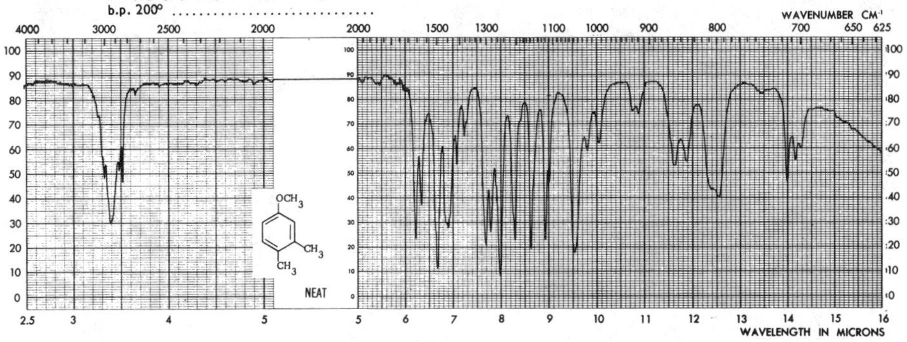

NEAT

B 18,325-3
6-Methoxy-1,2,3,4-tetrahydronaphthalene, tech., 85%
M.W. 162.23 b.p. 90-95°/1mm. n_D^{20} 1.5402

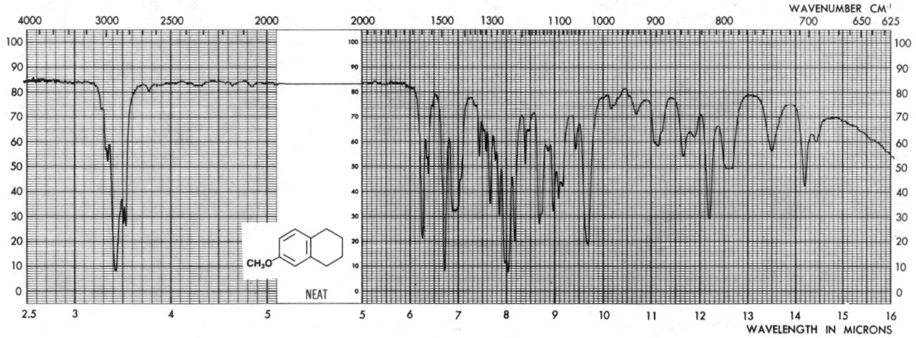

NEAT

C 13,747-2 **2,4-Dimethylanisole**
$(CH_3)_2C_6H_3OCH_3$ M.W. 136.19 n_D^{20} 1.5144
b.p. 191°

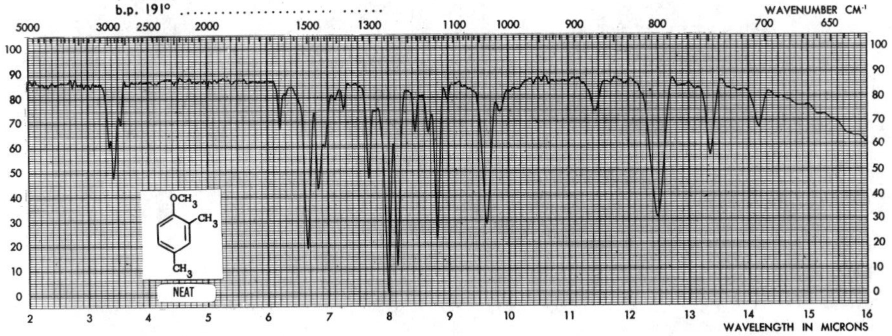

NEAT

D 13,748-0 **2,5-Dimethylanisole**
$(CH_3)_2C_6H_3OCH_3$ M.W. 136.19 n_D^{20} 1.5149
b.p. 190°

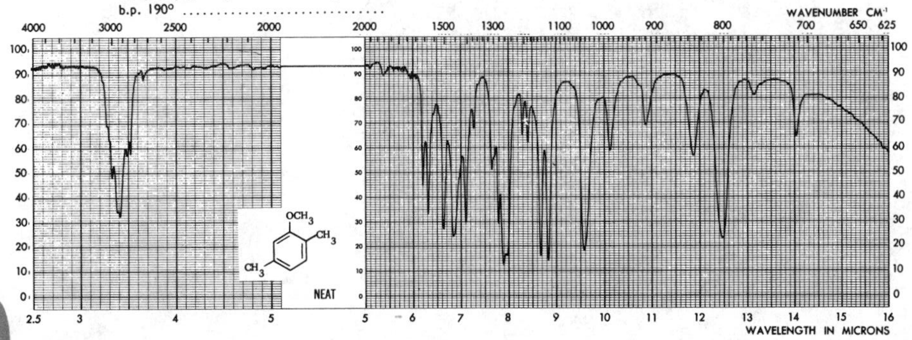

NEAT

E C3520 **2-Chloro-1,4-dimethoxybenzene**

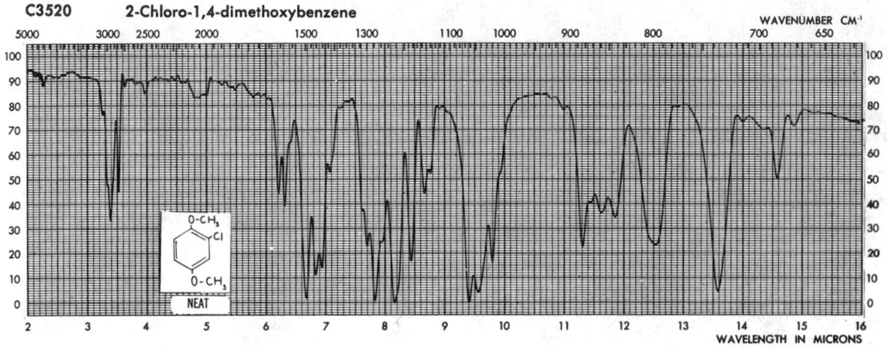

NEAT

F B8335-5 **4-Bromoveratrole**
BrC_6H_3-1,2-$(OCH_3)_2$ M.W. 217.07
n_D^{20} 1.5742

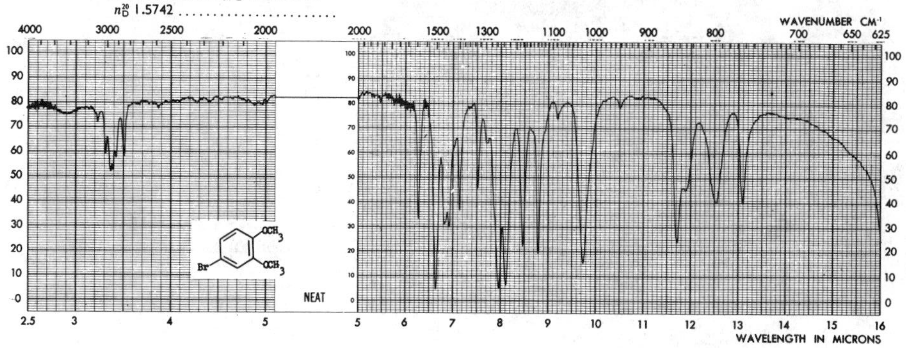

NEAT

G 15,755-4
1-Bromo-2,4-dimethoxybenzene, 97%
$BrC_6H_3(OCH_3)_2$
M.W. 217.07 b.p. 147°/18mm. n_D^{20} 1.5650
d 1.495

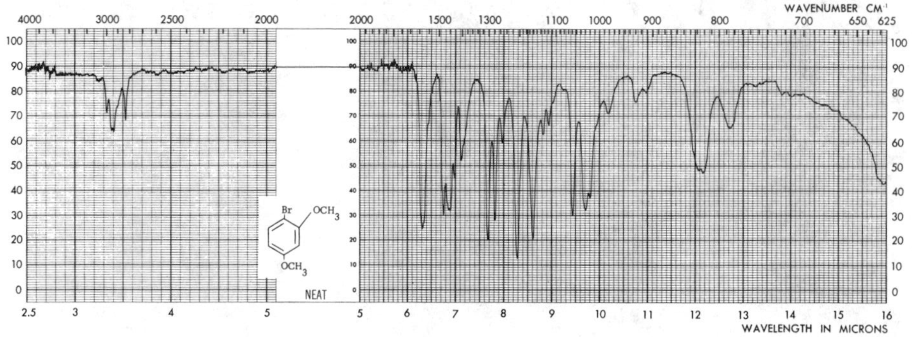

NEAT

H T6880-2 **1,2,4-Trimethoxybenzene**
$C_6H_3(OCH_3)_3$ M.W. 168.19 n_D^{20} 1.5330

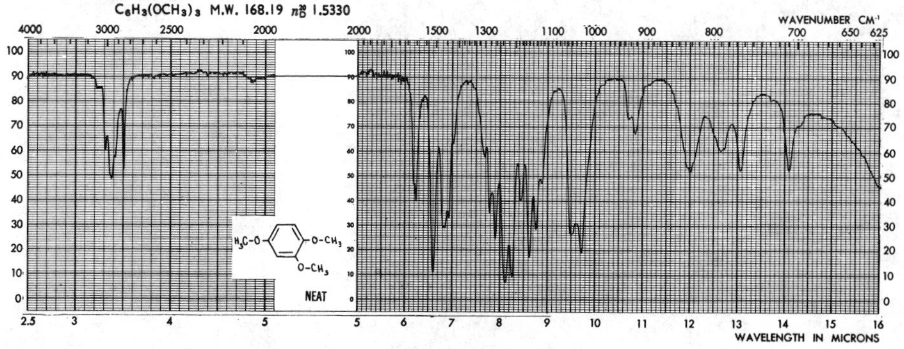

NEAT

ALDRICH ®

A

13,884-3 1,2,4-Triethoxybenzene
$C_6H_3(OC_2H_5)_3$ M.W. 210.27 m.p. 30-33°
MELT

B

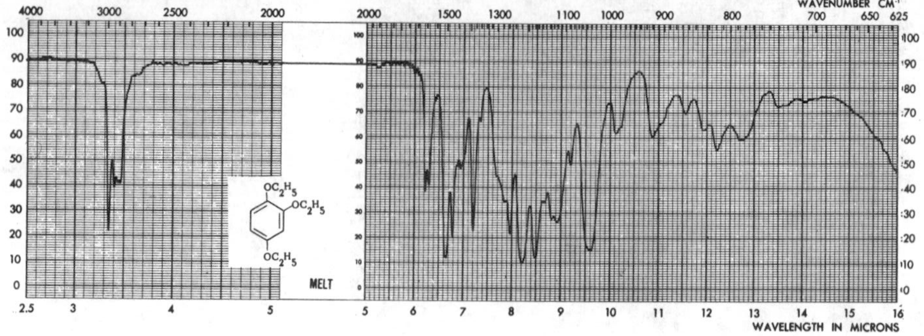

D14,660-9 3,5-Dimethylanisole, puriss.
$(CH_3)_2C_6H_3OCH_3$ M.W. 136.19 n_D^{20} 1.5127
NEAT

C

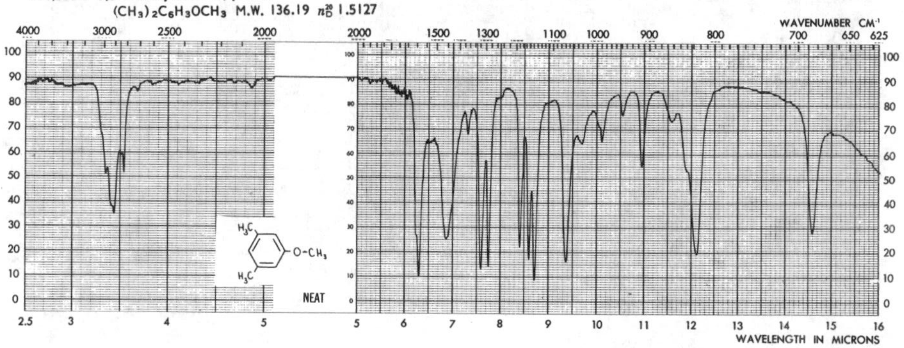

15,734-1
3,5-Dichloroanisole, 99%
$Cl_2C_6H_3OCH_3$
M.W. 177.03 m.p. 40-42° Beil. 6,190
MELT

D

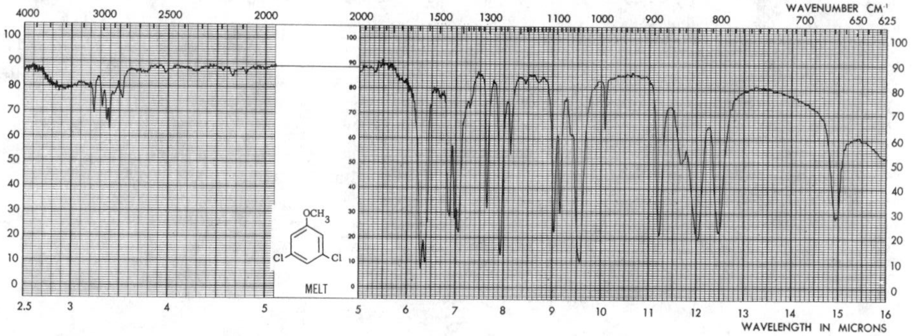

20,925-2
5-Chloro-1,3-dimethoxybenzene, 97+%
$ClC_6H_3(OCH_3)_2$ FW 172.61 mp 34-36°
Beil. 6(3),4335 Disp. C
MELT

E

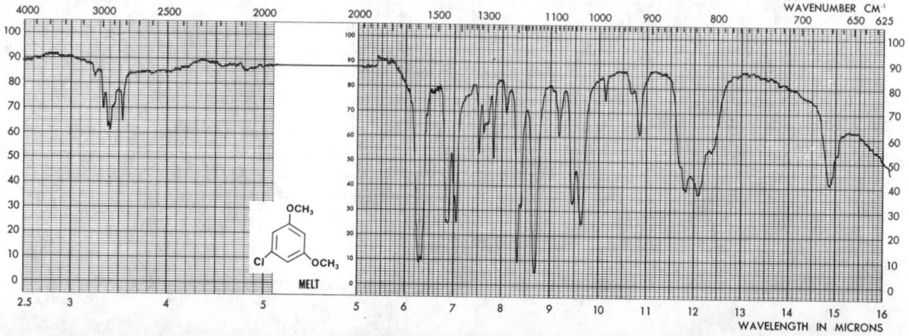

13,882-7 1,3,5-Trimethoxybenzene
$C_6H_3(OCH_3)_3$ M.W. 168.19 m.p. 51-53°
NUJOL MULL

F

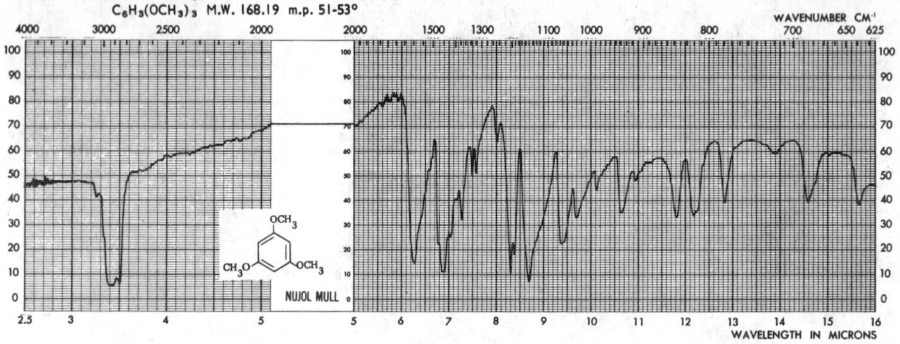

13,881-9 2,4,6-Trimethoxytoluene
$CH_3C_6H_2(OCH_3)_3$ M.W. 182.22
NEAT

G

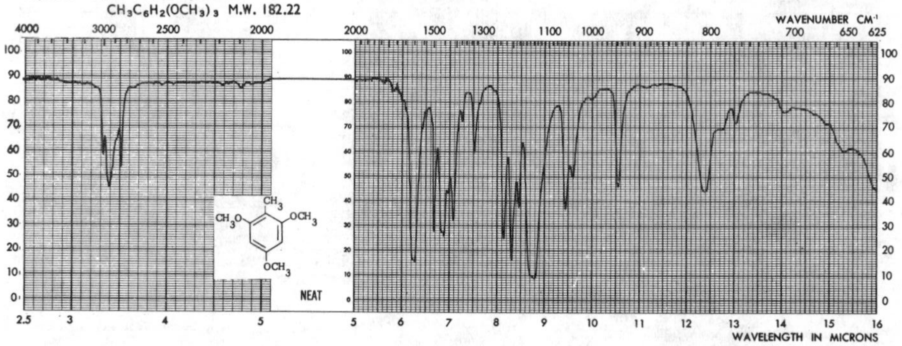

13,878-9 1-Ethyl-2,4,6-trimethoxybenzene
$C_2H_5C_6H_2(OCH_3)_3$ M.W. 196.25 m.p. 33-34°
MELT

H

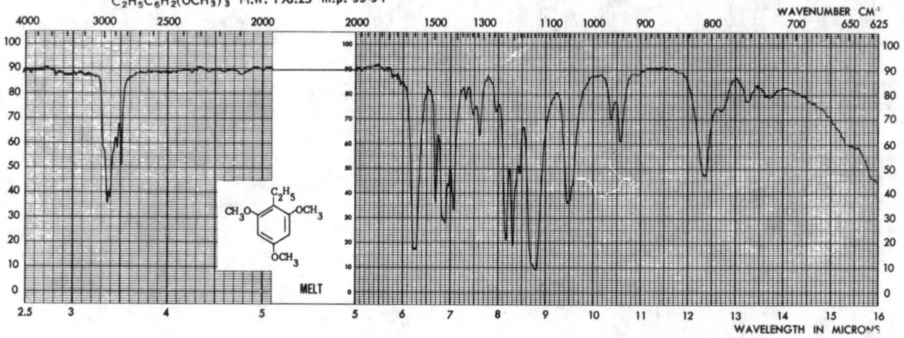

13,877-0 2,4,6-Trimethoxydiphenylmethane
$C_6H_5CH_2C_6H_2(OCH_3)_3$ M.W. 258.32
m.p. 90.5-92.5°
NUJOL MULL

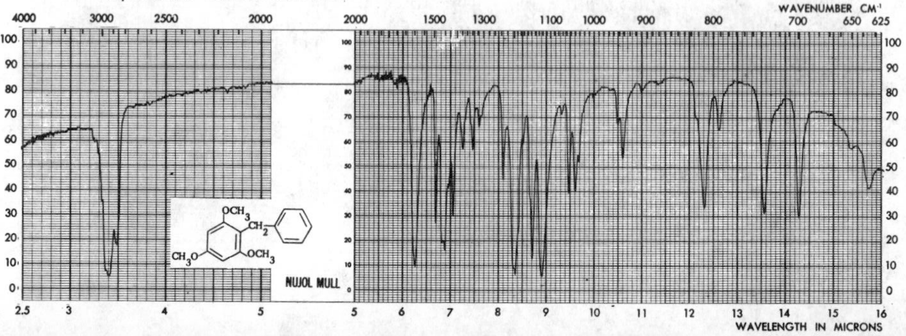

A

12,008-1 β-**Bromo-2,4,6-triiodophenetole** (2-bromoethyl 2,4,6-triiodophenyl ether)
$I_3C_6H_2OCH_2CH_2Br$ M.W. 578.76 m.p. 127-130° ....

NUJOL MULL

B

15,736-8
2,3,4-Trichloroanisole, 98%
$Cl_3C_6H_2OCH_3$
M.W. 211.48 m.p. 69-71° Beil. **6**(2),179

MELT

C

15,737-6
2,3,6-Trichloroanisole, 98%
$Cl_3C_6H_2OCH_3$
M.W. 211.48 m.p. 44-46° Beil. **6**(2),180

MELT

D

19,676-2
2,3,5,6-Tetrafluoroanisole, 97+%
$HC_6F_4OCH_3$ FW 180.10 bp 138° n_D^{20} 1.4287
d 1.293 Disp. C

NEAT

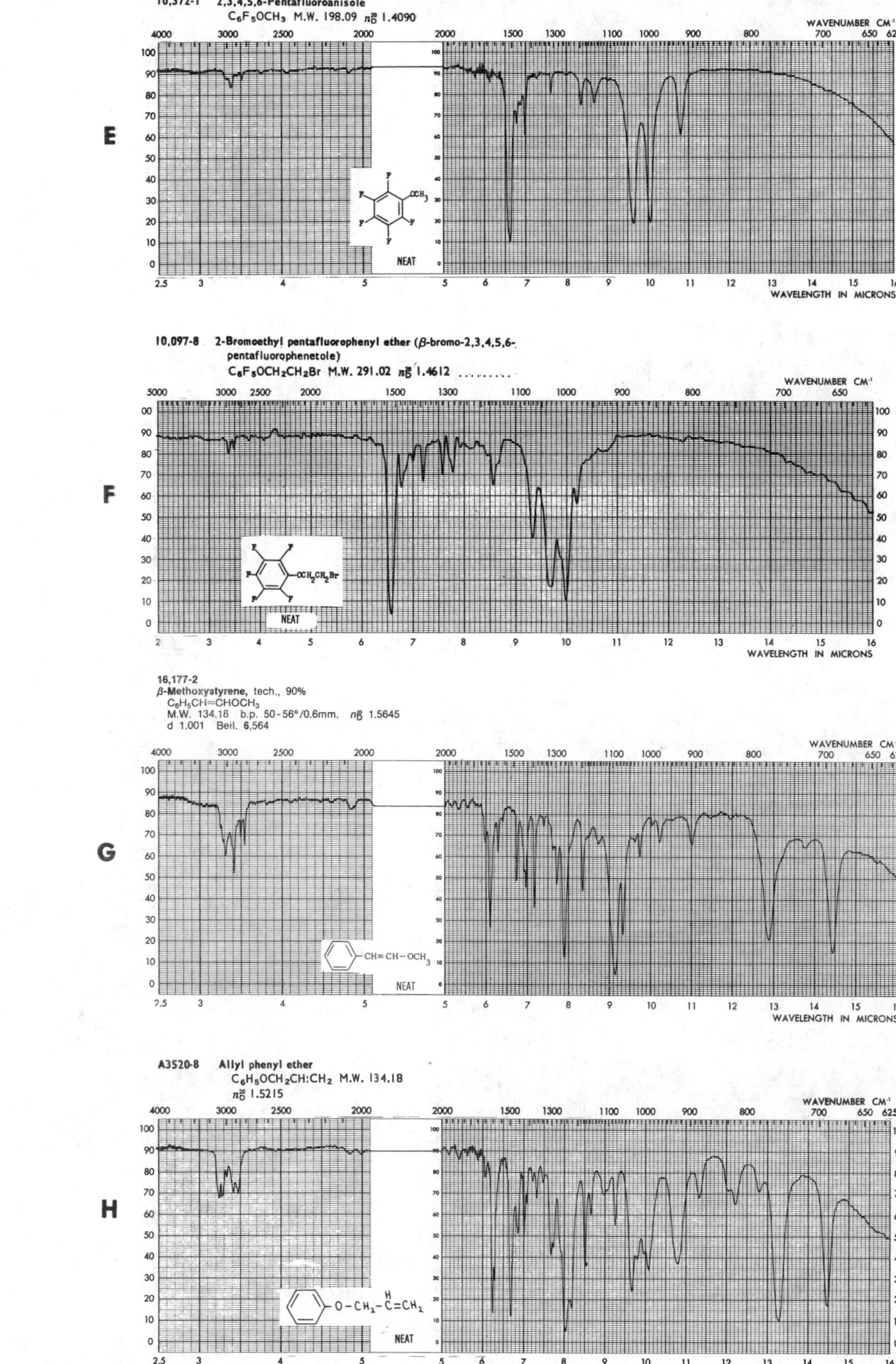

E

10,372-1 **2,3,4,5,6-Pentafluoroanisole**
$C_6F_5OCH_3$ M.W. 198.09 n_D^{20} 1.4090

NEAT

F

10,097-8 **2-Bromoethyl pentafluorophenyl ether** (β-bromo-2,3,4,5,6-pentafluorophenetole)
$C_6F_5OCH_2CH_2Br$ M.W. 291.02 n_D^{20} 1.4612 ....

NEAT

G

16,177-2
β-**Methoxystyrene,** tech., 90%
$C_6H_5CH{=}CHOCH_3$
M.W. 134.18 b.p. 50-56°/0.6mm. n_D^{20} 1.5645
d 1.001 Beil. **6**,564

NEAT

H

A3520-8 **Allyl phenyl ether**
$C_6H_5OCH_2CH{:}CH_2$ M.W. 134.18
n_D^{20} 1.5215

NEAT

ALDRICH ®

A

12,562-8 **Allyl o-tolyl ether**
$CH_3C_6H_4OCH_2CH{:}CH_2$ M.W. 148.21 n_D^{20} 1.5179
b.p. 80-82°/12 mm.

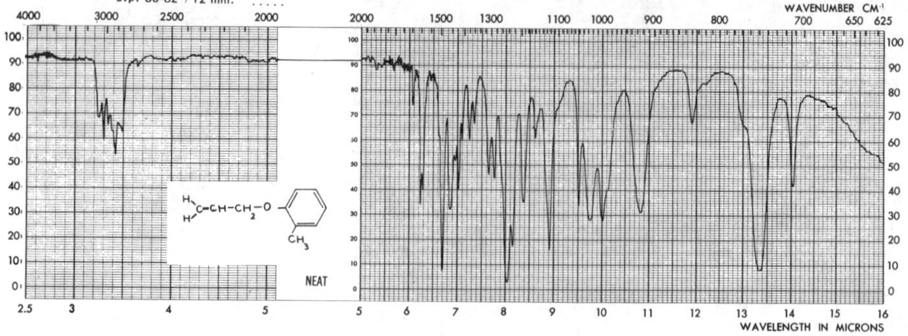

NEAT

B

14,100-3
4-Vinylanisole, 99%
$H_2C{=}CHC_6H_4OCH_3$
M.W. 134.18 b.p. 41-42°/0.5mm. n_D^{20} 1.5622
d 1.009 Beil. **6**,561

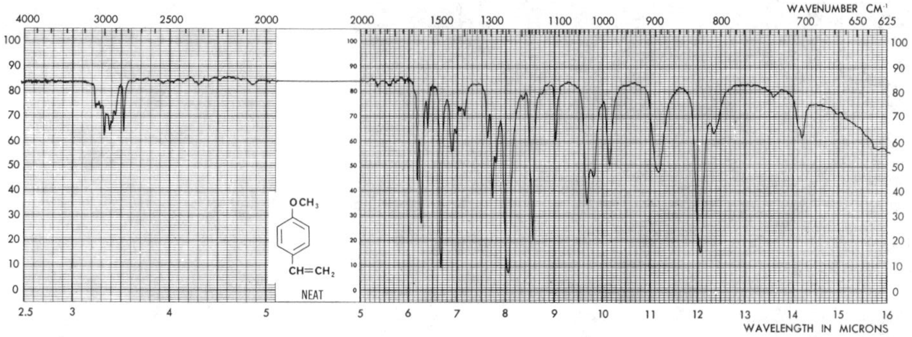

NEAT

C

11,787-0 **Anethole (p-propenylanisole), U.S.P.**
$CH_3CH{:}CHC_6H_4OCH_3$ M.W. 148.21 n_D^{20} 1.5591
b.p. 234-237°

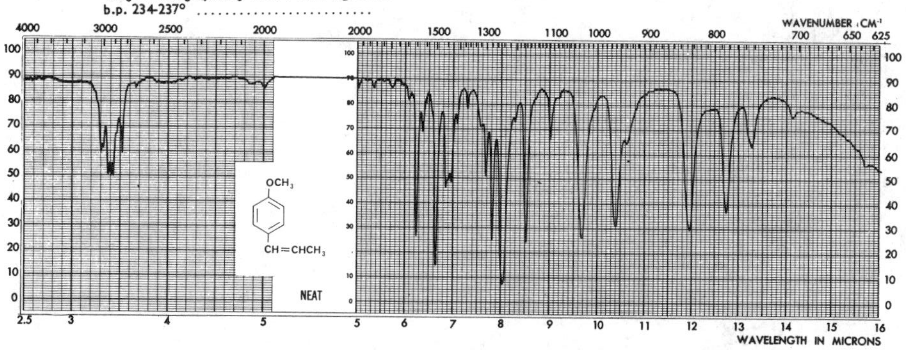

NEAT

D

20,557-5
4-Benzyloxy-3-methoxystyrene, 95%
$C_6H_5CH_2OC_6H_3(OCH_3)CH{=}CH_2$ FW 240.30
mp 48-51° Disp. C

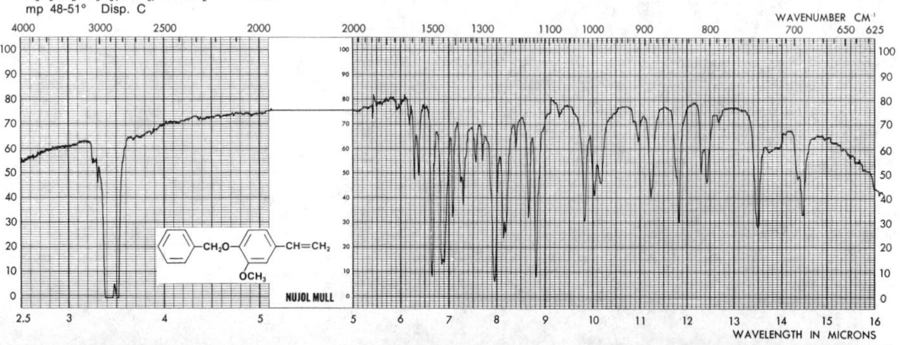

NUJOL MULL

E

A2920-8 **4-Allylanisole (estragole)**
$H_2C{:}CHCH_2C_6H_4OCH_3$ M.W. 148.21
n_D^{20} 1.5259

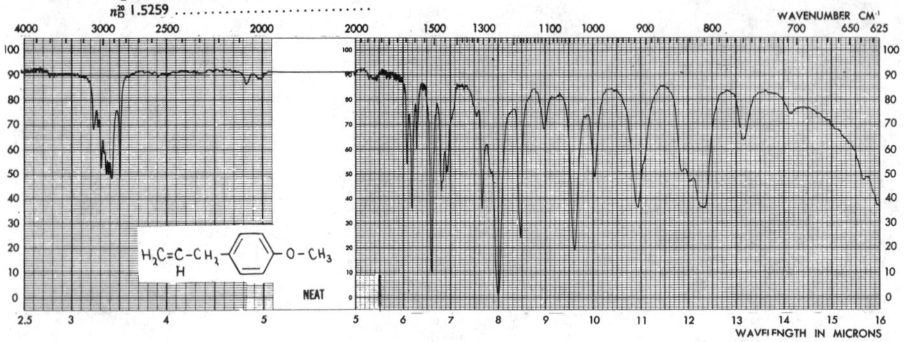

NEAT

F

12,777-9 **Allyl p-tolyl ether**
$CH_3C_6H_4OCH_2CH{:}CH_2$ M.W. 148.21 n_D^{20} 1.5168
b.p. 90-92°/10 mm.

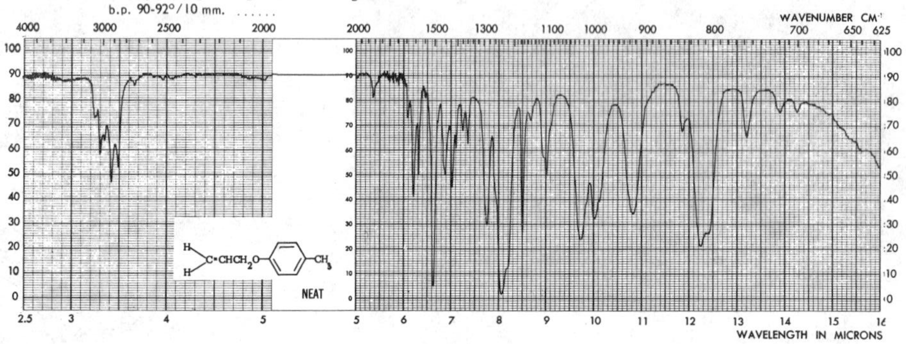

NEAT

G

17,820-9
2,2-Bis-[p-(allyloxy)-phenyl]-propane
$(H_2C{=}CHCH_2OC_6H_4)_2C(CH_3)_2$
M.W. 308.42 n_D^{20} 1.5636 d 1.022

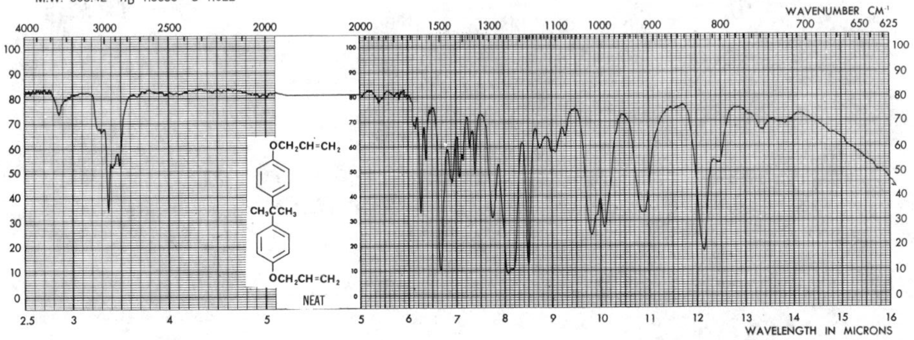

NEAT

H

15,446-6 **3,4-Dimethoxystyrene**
$(CH_3O)_2C_6H_3CH{:}CH_2$ M.W. 164.20 n_D^{20} 1.5711

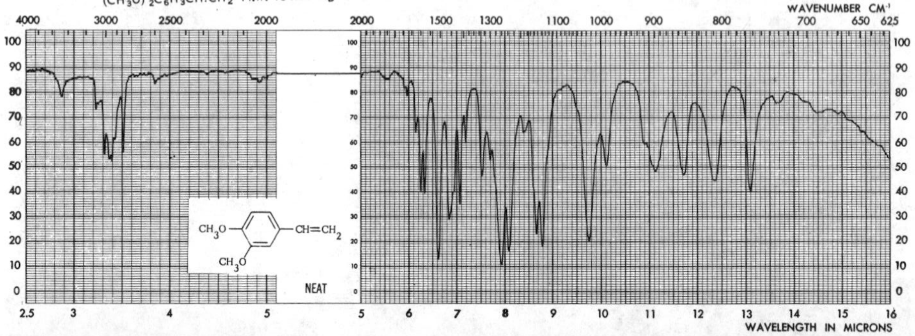

NEAT

A

D13,690-5 1,2-Dimethoxy-4-propenylbenzene
$CH_3CH{:}CHC_6H_3(OCH_3)_2$ M.W. 178.23 n_D^{20} 1.5680

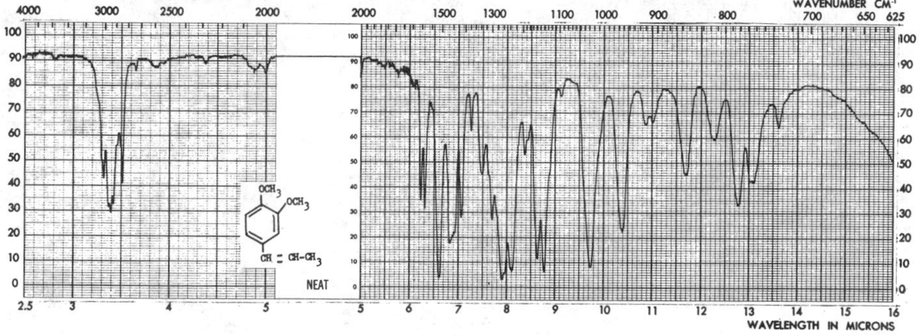

NEAT

B

S20-8 Safrole
M.W. 162.19 n_D^{20} 1.5379 b.p. 232-234°

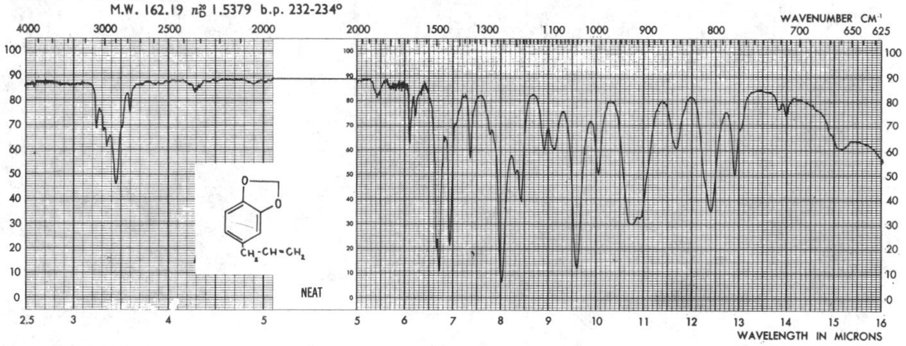

NEAT

C

22,107-4
2,4,5-Trimethoxypropenylbenzene (β-asarone)
$(CH_3O)_3C_6H_2CH{=}CHCH_3$ FW 208.26 n_D^{20} 1.5614
d 1.073 *Beil.* **6**(3),6440 Disp. C

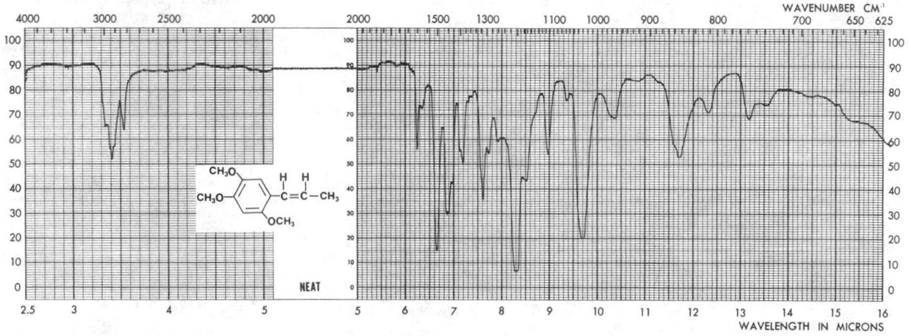

NEAT

D

21,461-2
4-Methoxystilbene, 98+%
$C_6H_5CH{=}CHC_6H_4OCH_3$ FW 210.28 mp 136-138°
Beil. **6**,693 Disp. C

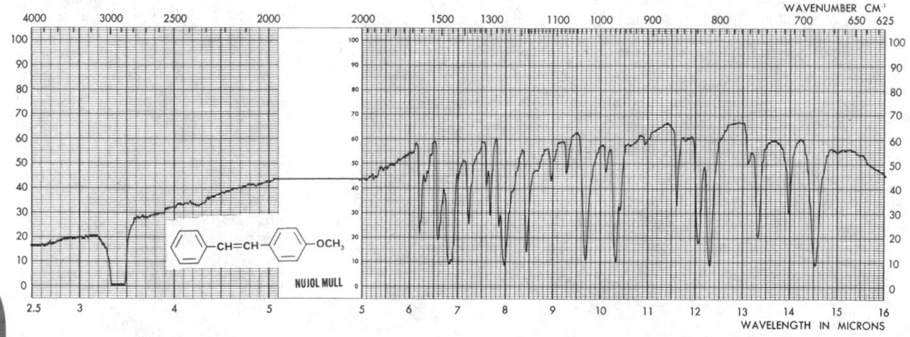

NUJOL MULL

E

D13,705-7 4,4'-Dimethoxystilbene
$CH_3OC_6H_4CH{:}CHC_6H_4OCH_3$ M.W. 240.30 m.p. 211-213°

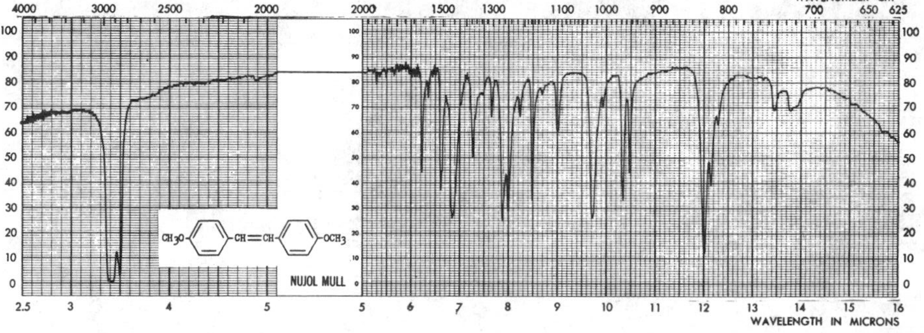

NUJOL MULL

F

16,408-9
trans-**4-Butyl-α-chloro-4'-ethoxystilbene**, 99+%,
GOLD LABEL
$CH_3(CH_2)_3C_6H_4C(Cl){=}CHC_6H_4OC_2H_5$
M.W. 314.86 m.p. 29°°

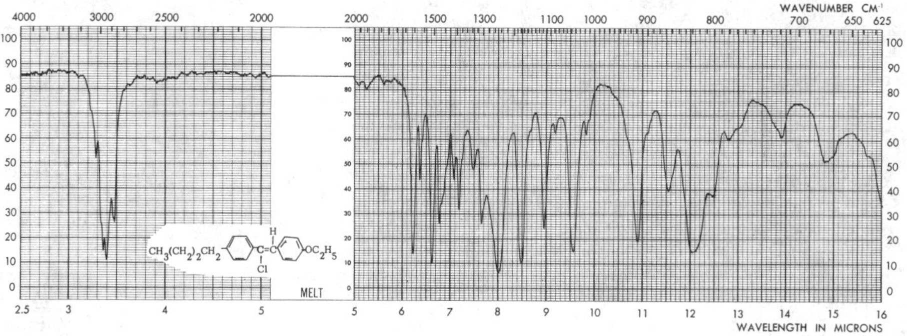

MELT

G

16,407-0
trans-**4-Octyl-α-chloro-4'-ethoxystilbene**, 99+%,
GOLD LABEL
$CH_3(CH_2)_7C_6H_4C(Cl){=}CHC_6H_4OC_2H_5$
M.W. 370.96 m.p. 32°°

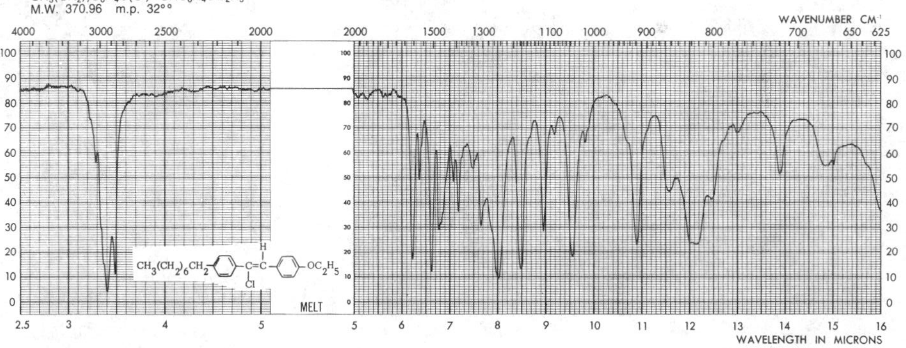

MELT

H

P2410-1 Phenyl ether
$(C_6H_5)_2O$ M.W. 170.21 m.p. 27-28.5° . . . . .

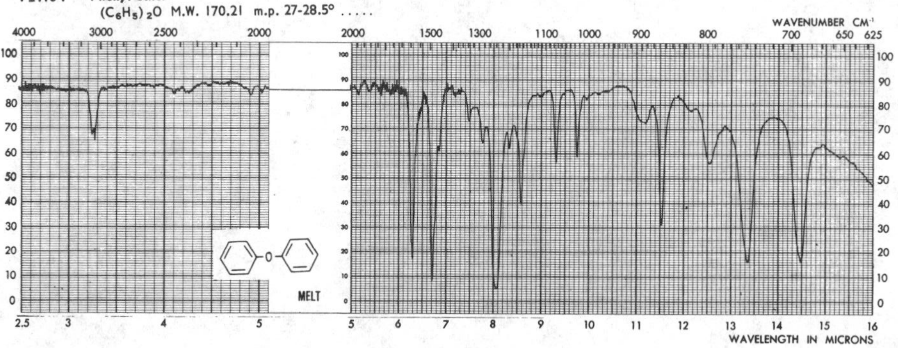

MELT

WAVENUMBER CM⁻¹ — WAVELENGTH IN MICRONS

A 19,222-8
***m*-Phenoxytoluene** (phenyl *m*-tolyl ether)
$C_6H_5OC_6H_4CH_3$ FW 184.24 bp 271-273°
n_D^{20} 1.5727 d 1.051 *Beil.* **6**,377 Disp. C

B B6520-9 **4-Bromodiphenyl ether** (p-bromophenyl phenyl ether), puriss.
$BrC_6H_4OC_6H_5$ M.W. 249.11 n_D^{20} 1.6070
m.p. 17-19° b.p. 305°

C 11,727-7 **4-Bromophenyl ether**
$(BrC_6H_4)_2O$ M.W. 328.02 m.p. 57.5-61°

D 19,442-5
Pentabromophenyl ether, 98%
$(C_6Br_5)_2O$ FW 959.22 mp >300° *Beil.* **6**(1),108
Disp. D

E X20-1 **Xanthene**
M.W. 182.22 m.p. 101-102°

F I-1580-7 **Isochroman**
M.W. 134.18 n_D^{20} 1.5444

G 18,695-3
2,3-Dihydro-2-methylbenzofuran, 99%
n_D^{20} 1.5308

H 10,665-8 **2-Bromomethyl-5-methylcoumaran**
M.W. 227.11 m.p. 34-37°

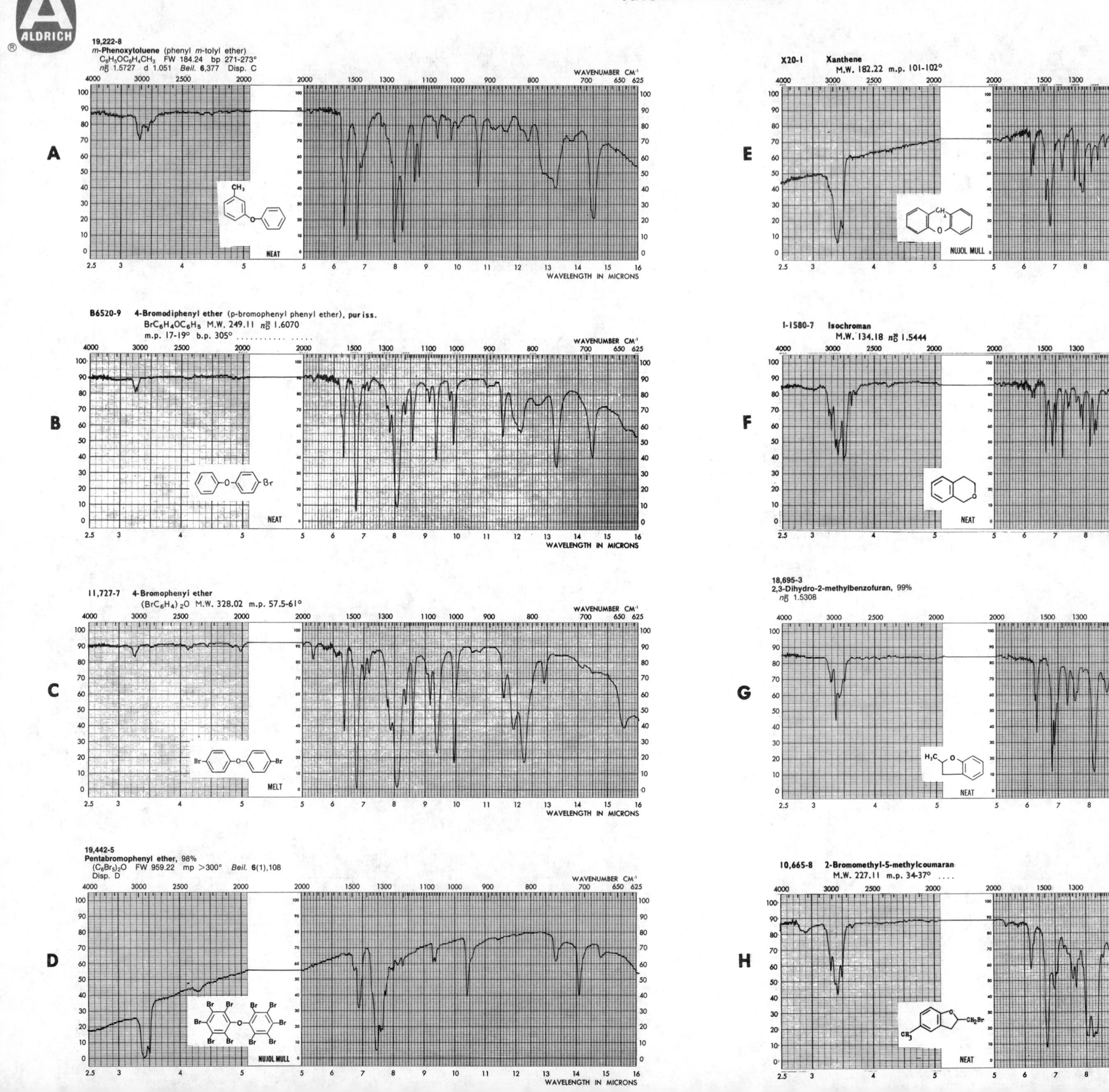

A

Piperonyl chloride, 98% [4-chloromethyl-1,2-(methylenedioxy)benzene]
FW 170.60 mp 20-21° bp 134-135°/14mm.
n_D^{20} 1.5660 d 1.312 *Beil.* **19**,22 *Fieser* **7**,10
Disp. C

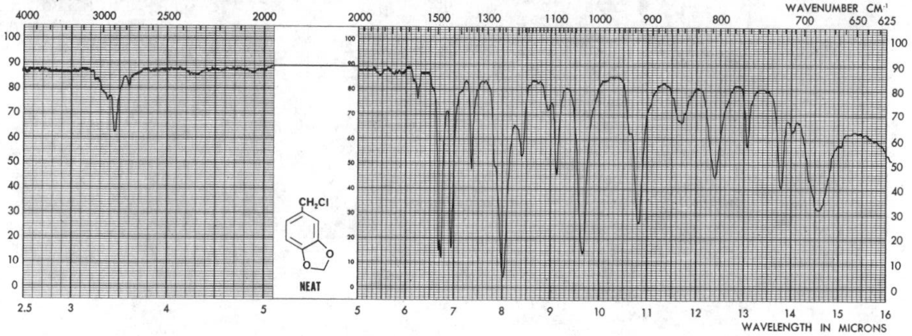

NEAT

B

14,748-6 6-Chloropiperonyl chloride
M.W. 205.04 m.p. 62.5-65.5°

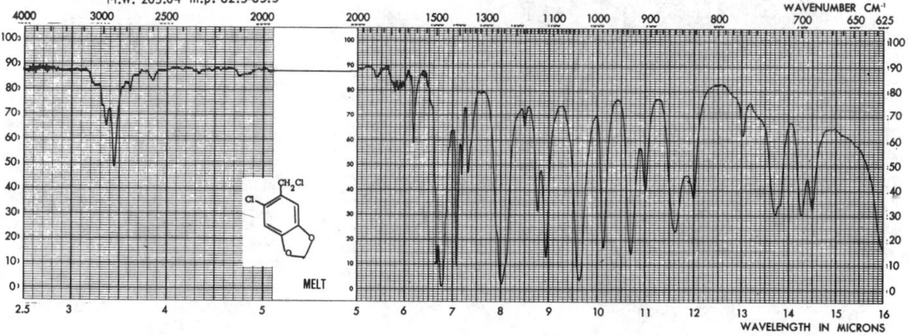

MELT

C

12,340-4 4-Phenyl-1,3-dioxane
M.W. 164.21 n_D^{20} 1.5298 b.p. 245°

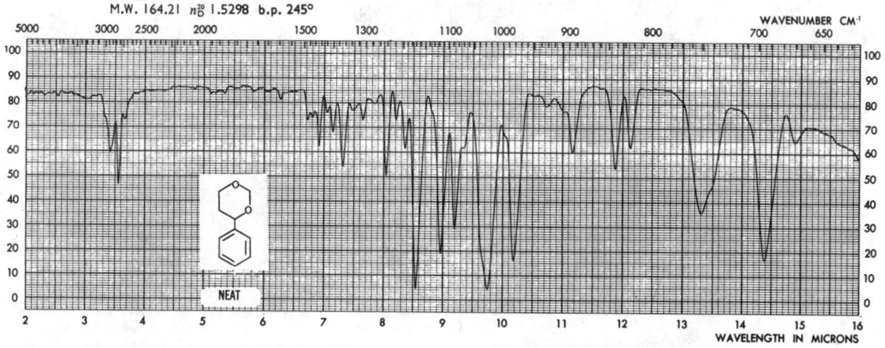

NEAT

D

11,891-5 2-(p-Fluorophenyl)-1,3-dioxolane
M.W. 168.17 n_D^{20} 1.5025 ....

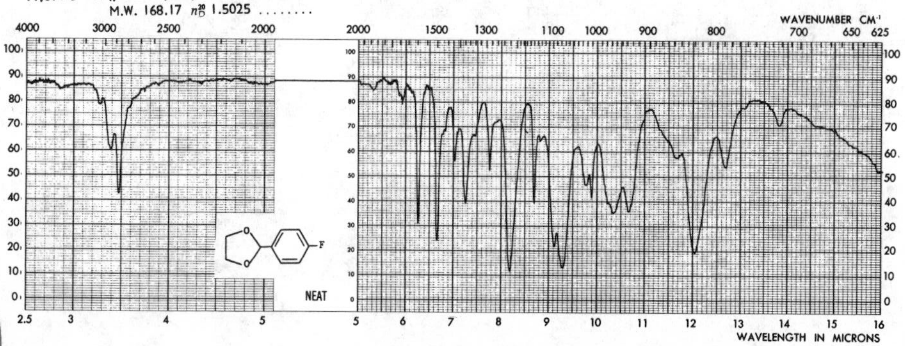

NEAT

E

19,761-0
2-(m-Bromophenyl)-1,3-dioxolane, 95%
FW 229.08 bp 132-133° n_D^{20} 1.5627 d 1.514
Disp. C

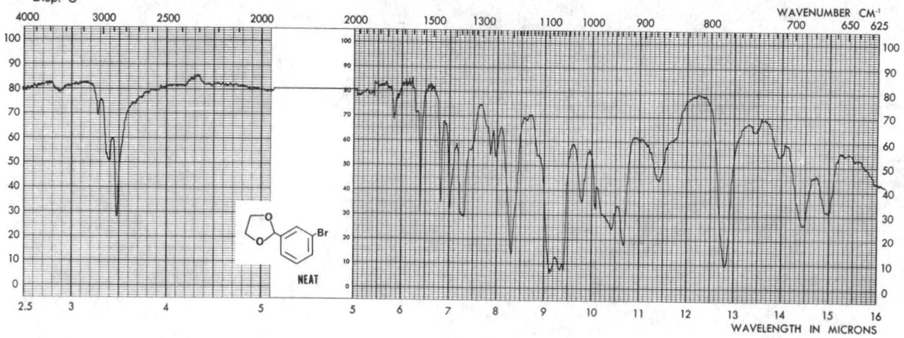

NEAT

F

C5220-9 2-Chloromethyl-1,4-benzodioxane
M.W. 184.62 n_D^{20} 1.5539 .....

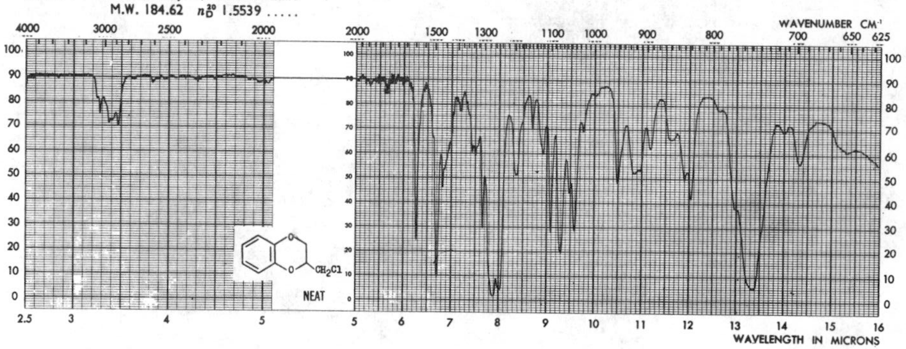

NEAT

G

14,017-1 Disalicylaldehyde (3,4,7,8-dibenzo-2,6,9-trioxabicyclo[3.3.1]nona-3,7-diene)
M.W. 226.23 m.p. 130-132° ....

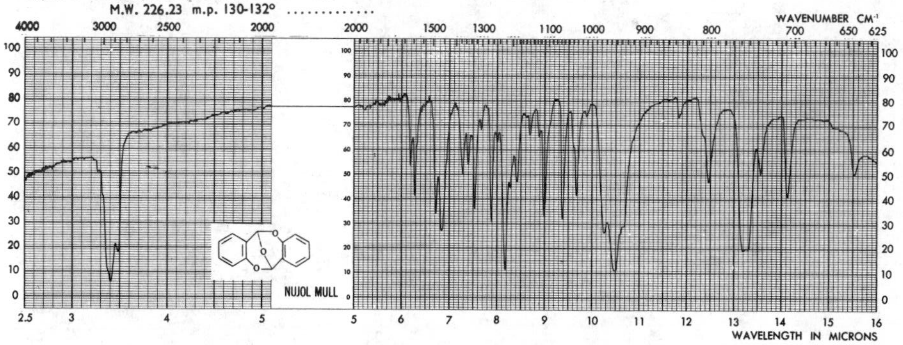

NUJOL MULL

H

12,392-7 2,2-Bis-(p-fluorophenyl)-tetrahydrofuran
M.W. 260.29 m.p. 44-45° ....

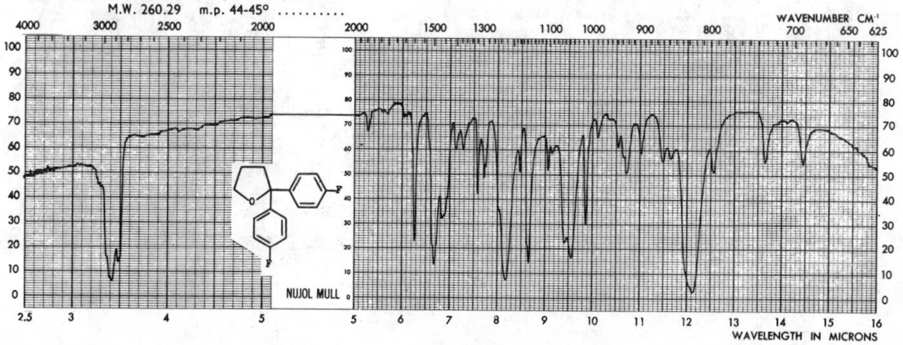

NUJOL MULL

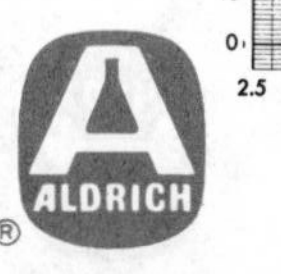

A

10,801-4 **Benzyl ether**
$(C_6H_5CH_2)_2O$ M.W. 198.27 n_D^{20} 1.5591
m.p. 1.5-3.5° b.p. 298°
NEAT

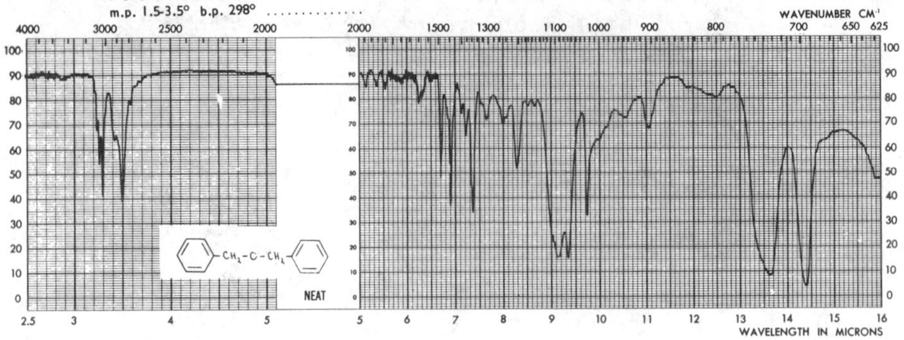

B

13,313-2 **1,4-Benzenedimethanol dimethyl ether**
$C_6H_4(CH_2OCH_3)_2$ M.W. 166.22
n_D^{20} 1.5035
NEAT

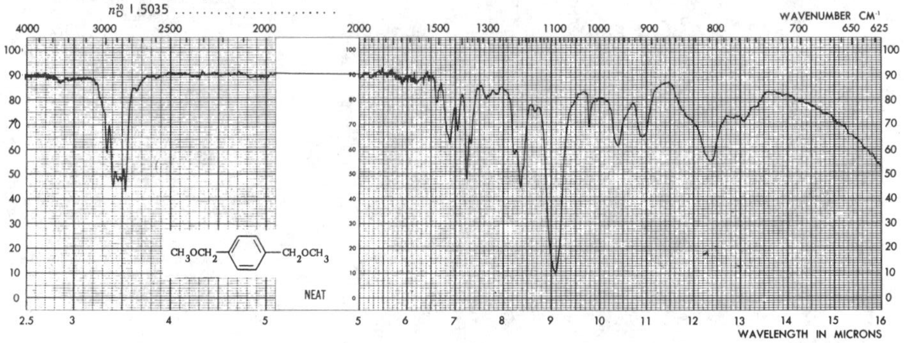

C

13,314-0 **1,4-Benzenedimethanol diethyl ether**
$C_6H_4(CH_2OC_2H_5)_2$ M.W. 194.28
n_D^{20} 1.4922
NEAT

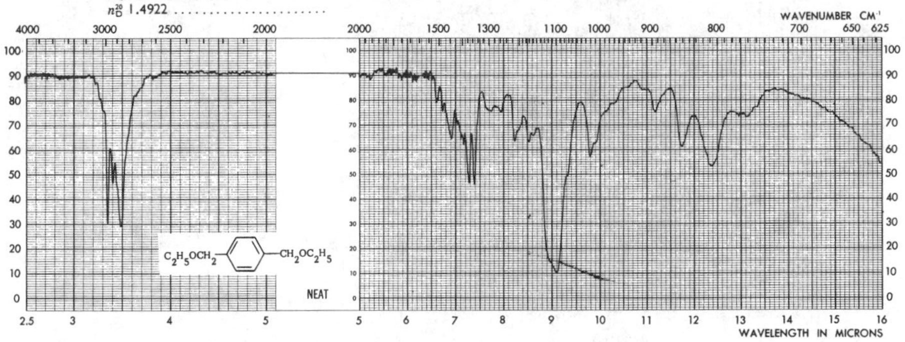

D

11,356-5 **2,6-Dichlorobenzyl methyl ether**
$C_8H_8Cl_2O$ M.W. 191.06 n_D^{20} 1.5429
NEAT

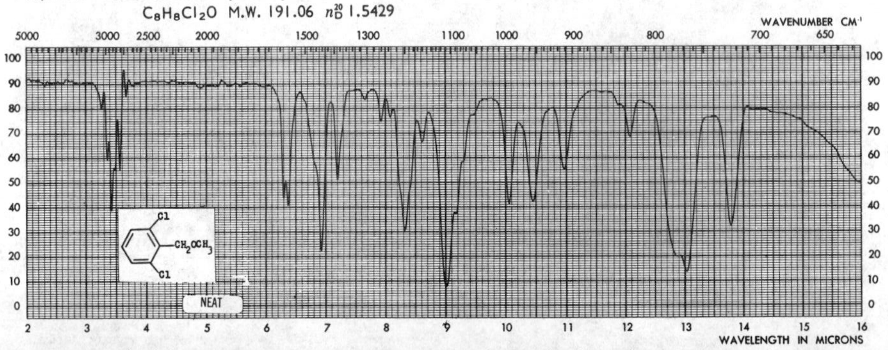

E

11,358-1 **2,6-Dichlorobenzyl ether**
$(Cl_2C_6H_3CH_2)_2O$ M.W. 336.05 m.p. 125-127°
NUJOL MULL

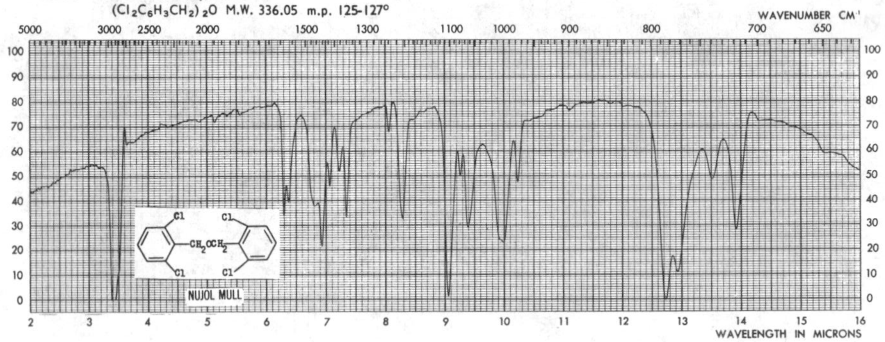

F

18,725-9
3,4-Dibenzyloxybenzyl chloride
$(C_6H_5CH_2O)_2C_6H_3CH_2Cl$ FW 338.83 mp 41-43°
Disp. C
MELT

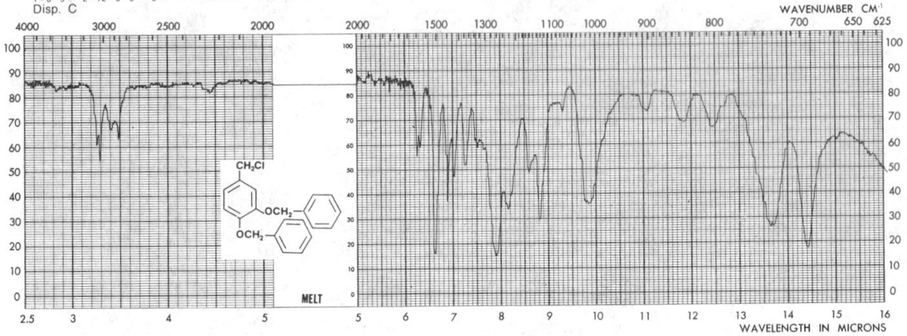

G

11,599-1 **2,5-Bis-(methoxymethyl)-p-xylene**
$(CH_3)_2C_6H_2(CH_2OCH_3)_2$ M.W. 194.28
m.p. 66-69.5°
NUJOL MULL

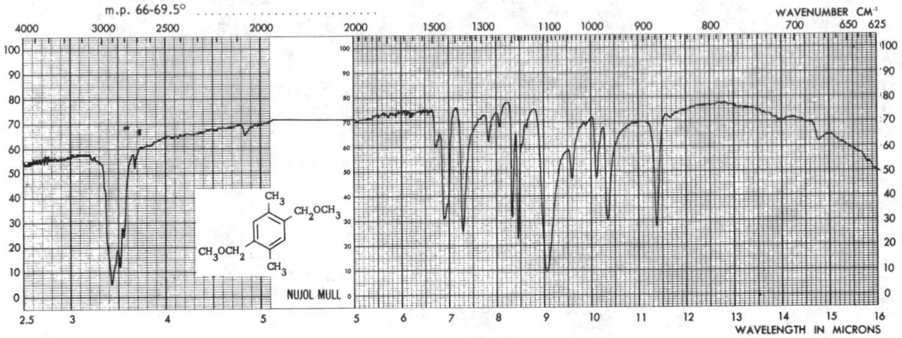

H

11,600-9 **3,6-Bis-(methoxymethyl)-durene**
$(CH_3)_4C_6(CH_2OCH_3)_2$ M.W. 222.33
m.p. 113-115.5°
NUJOL MULL

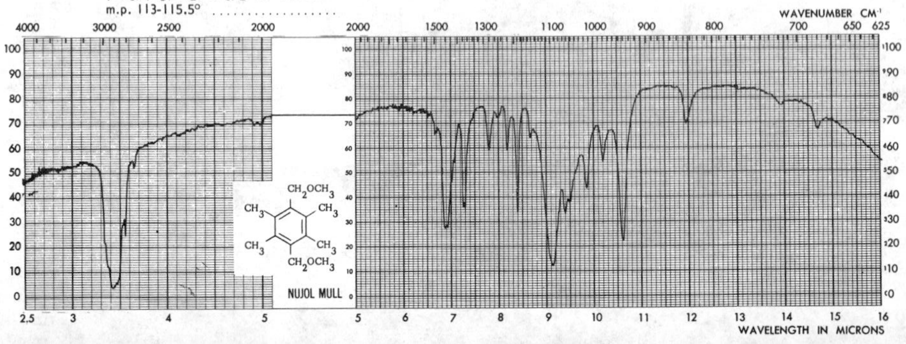

A 17,814-4
[(Tetramethyl-p-phenylene)dimethylene]-bis(*tert*.-butyl peroxide)
M.W. 338.49 m.p. 120-122°

B 19,646-0
o-Methoxybiphenyl (o-phenylanisole)
$C_6H_5C_6H_4OCH_3$ FW 184.24 bp 274° n_D^{20} 1.6105
d 1.023 *Beil.* **6**,672 Disp. C

C D13,320-5 3,3'-Dimethoxybiphenyl (3,3'-bianisole)
$CH_3OC_6H_4C_6H_4OCH_3$ M.W. 214.26 m.p. 34.5-36°

D 14,853-9 4,4'-Dimethoxybiphenyl (4,4'-bianisole)
$CH_3OC_6H_4C_6H_4OCH_3$ M.W. 214.26
m.p. 176-178°

E 13,142-3 2-Phenyloxybiphenyl (2-biphenylyl phenyl ether)
$C_6H_5C_6H_4OC_6H_5$ M.W. 246.31 m.p. 49-50.5°

F 15,457-1
1-Methoxynaphthalene
$C_{10}H_7OCH_3$
M.W. 158.2 b.p. 135-137°/12mm. n_D^{20} 1.6220
d 1.09 Beil. **6**,606

G 19,258-9
1-Ethoxynaphthalene, 99%
$C_{10}H_7OC_2H_5$ FW 172.23 bp 280° n_D^{20} 1.6040
d 1.060 *Beil.* **6**,606 Disp. C

H 14,824-5 2-Methoxynaphthalene
$C_{10}H_7OCH_3$ M.W. 158.19 m.p. 73-75°

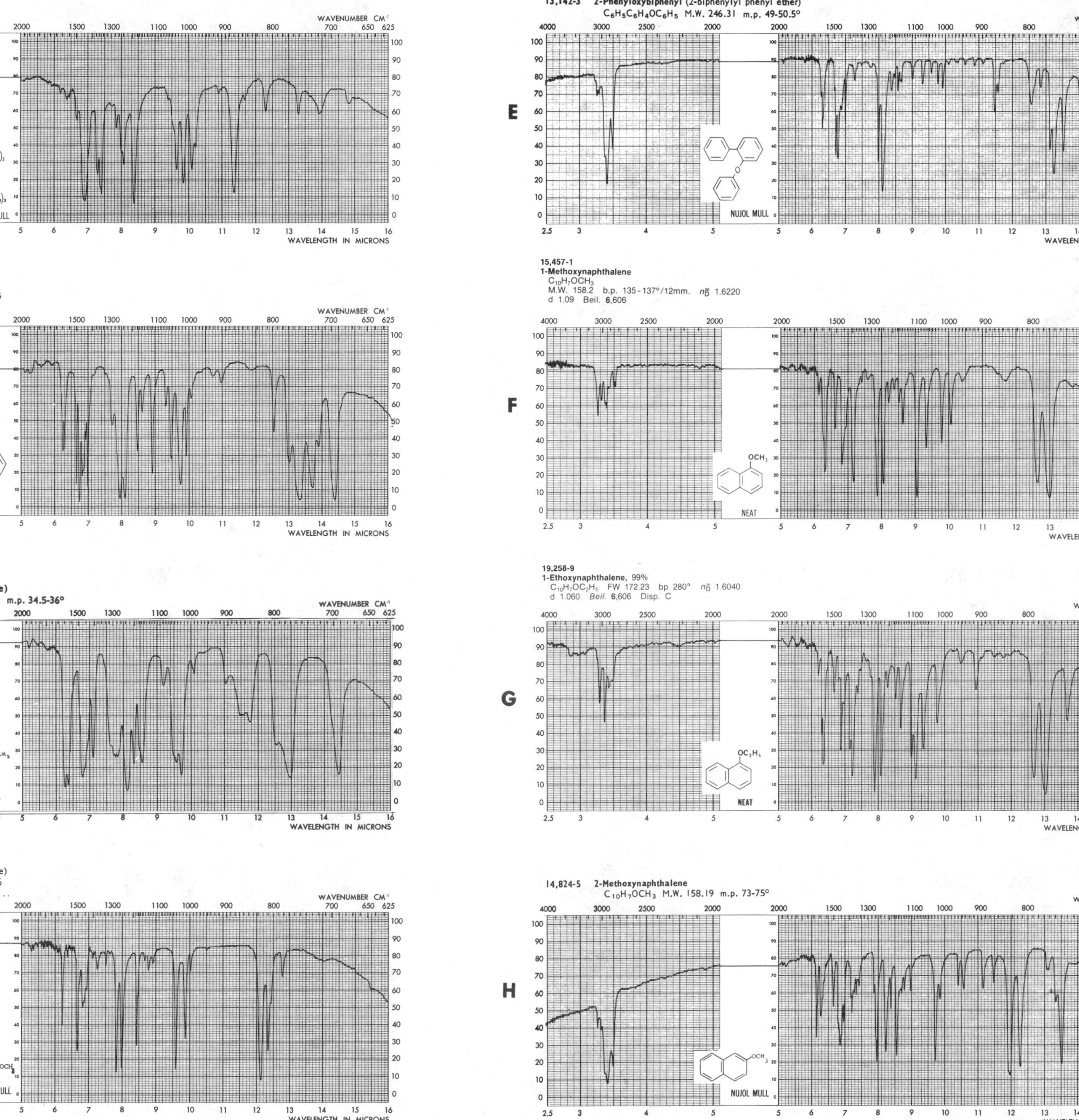

A

12,479-6 **1-Chloro-4-methoxynaphthalene**
$ClC_{10}H_6OCH_3$ M.W. 192.65 n_D^{20} 1.6313
NEAT

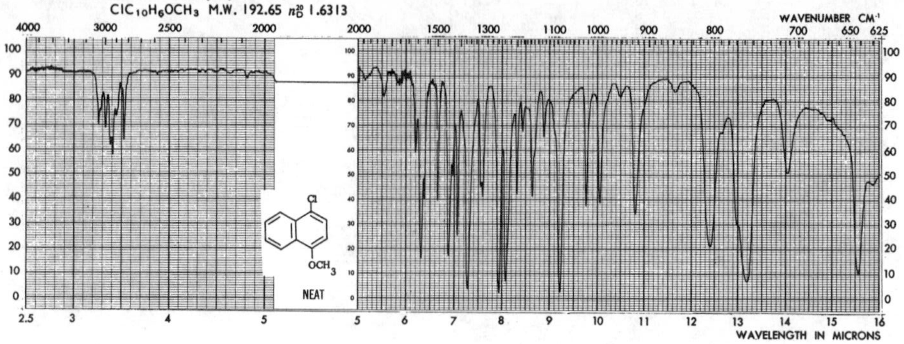

B

15,756-2
1-Bromo-4-methoxynaphthalene, 98%
$BrC_{10}H_6OCH_3$
M.W. 237.1 b.p. 148-150°/0.1mm. n_D^{20} 1.6526
d 1.472 Beil. **6**(2),582
NEAT

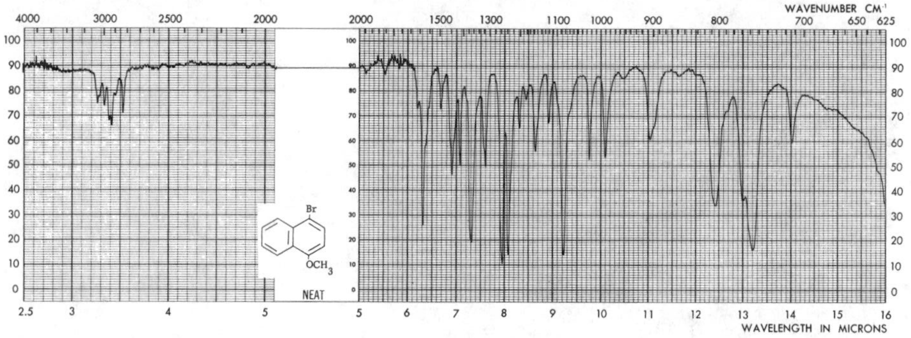

C

20,017-4
2-Bromo-6-methoxynaphthalene, 97%
$BrC_{10}H_6OCH_3$ FW 237.10 mp 108-111°
Beil. **6**,651 Disp. C
NUJOL MULL

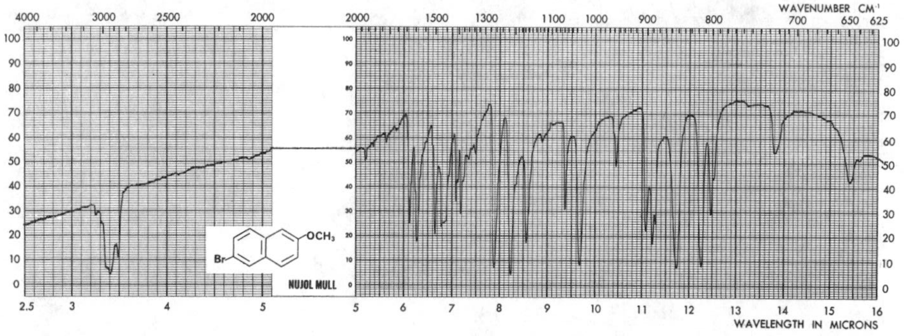

D

D13,480-5 **1,7-Dimethoxynaphthalene**
$C_{10}H_6(OCH_3)_2$ M.W. 188.23 n_D^{22} 1.6154
NEAT

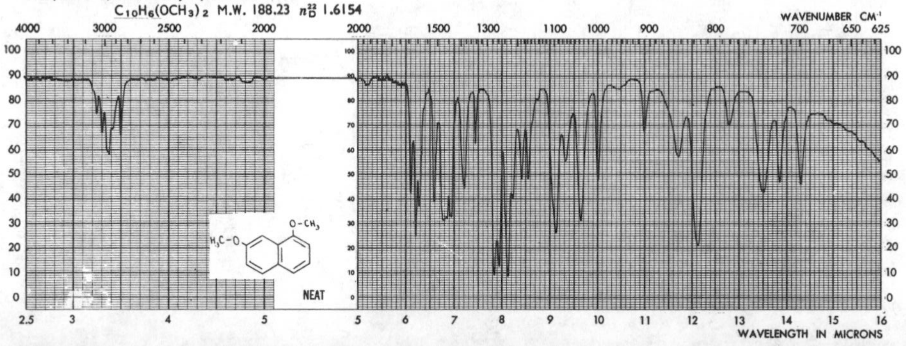

E

D13,485-6 **2,6-Dimethoxynaphthalene**
$C_{10}H_6(OCH_3)_2$ M.W. 188.23
m.p. 152.5-153.5°
NUJOL MULL

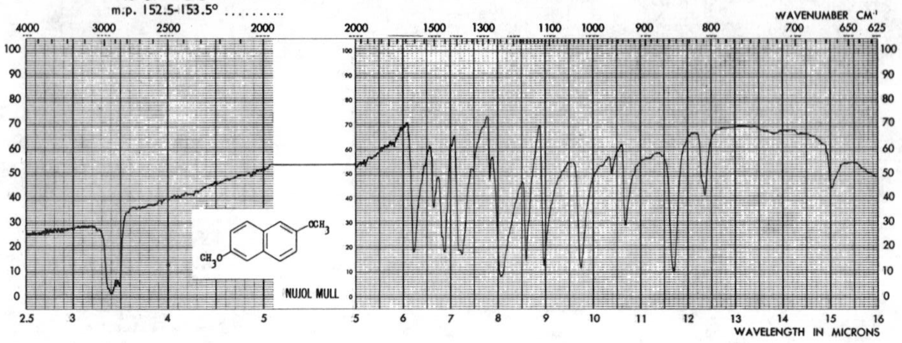

F

21,315-2
2,7-Dimethoxynaphthalene, 98%
$C_{10}H_6(OCH_3)_2$ FW 188.23 mp 137-139°
Beil. **6**,986 Disp. C
NUJOL MULL

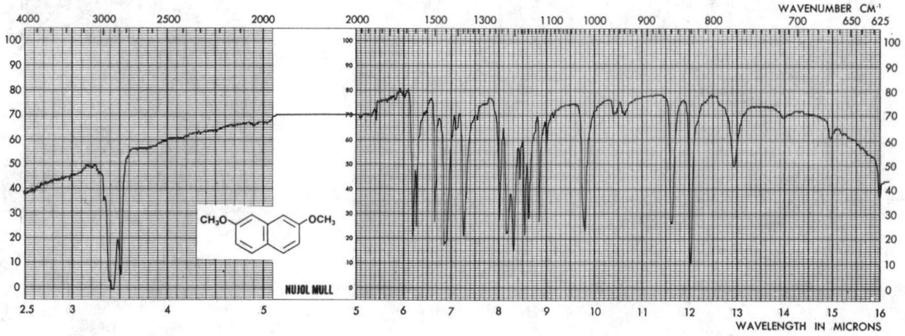

G

18,504-3
1,2,3,4,5,6-Hexachloro-7-methoxynaphthalene, tech.
$Cl_6C_{10}HOCH_3$
M.W. 364.87 m.p. 197-200°
NUJOL MULL

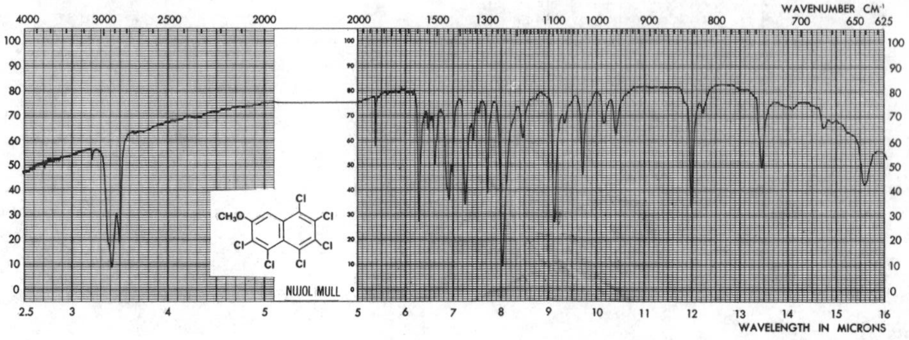

H

M1480-3 **2-Methoxyfluorene**
M.W. 196.25 m.p. 111-112°
NUJOL MULL

WAVENUMBER CM⁻¹ — WAVELENGTH IN MICRONS

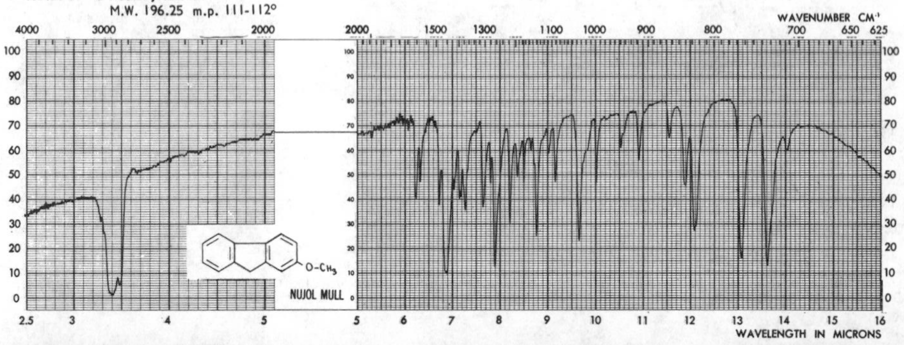

A

M1478-1 **1-Methoxyfluorene**
M.W. 196.25 m.p. 85-87°

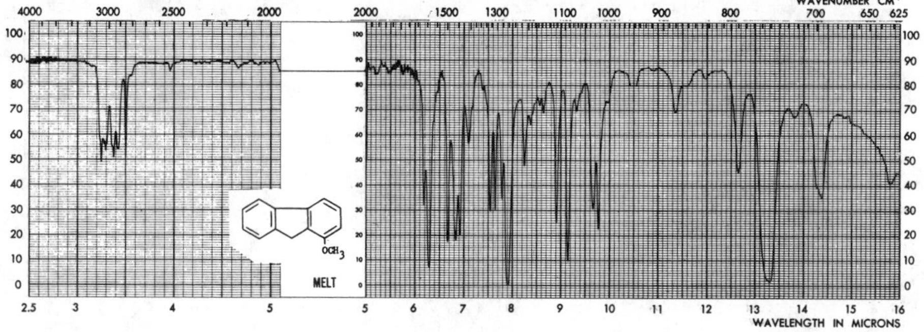

MELT

B

12,920-8 **p-Anisylchlorodiphenylmethane** (p-methoxytriphenylmethyl chloride, p-methoxytrityl chloride)
$CH_3OC_6H_4C(C_6H_5)_2Cl$ M.W. 308.81
m.p. 122-124°

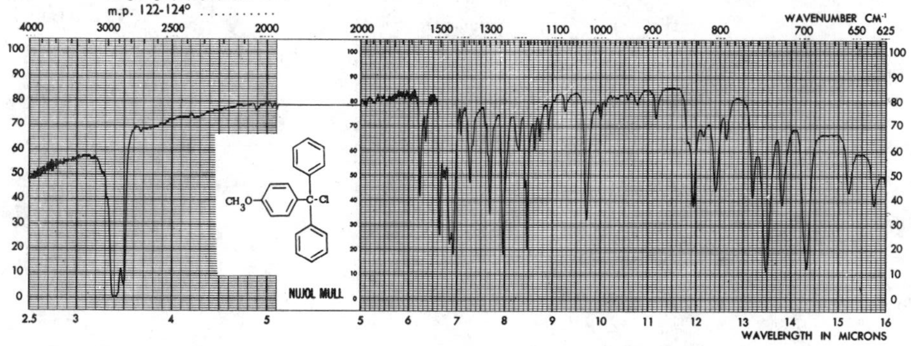

NUJOL MULL

C

10,001-3 **4,4'-Dimethoxytrityl chloride** (p,p'-dimethoxytriphenylmethyl chloride)
$C_6H_5C(C_6H_4OCH_3)_2Cl$ M.W. 338.83
m.p. 119-123°

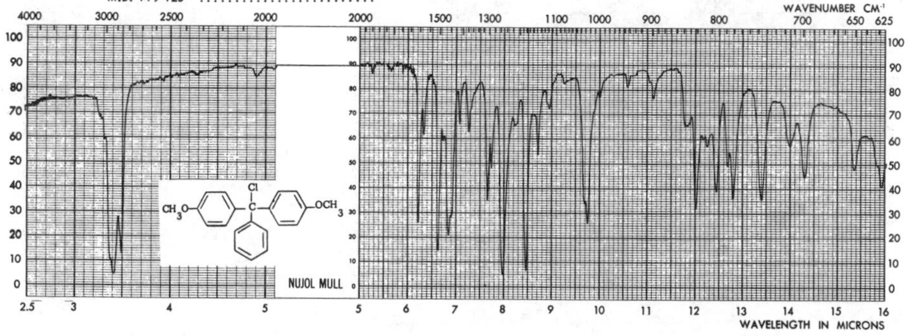

NUJOL MULL

D

14,405-3 **4,4',4''-Trimethoxytrityl chloride**
$(CH_3OC_6H_4)_3CCl$ M.W. 368.86
m.p. 155-157°

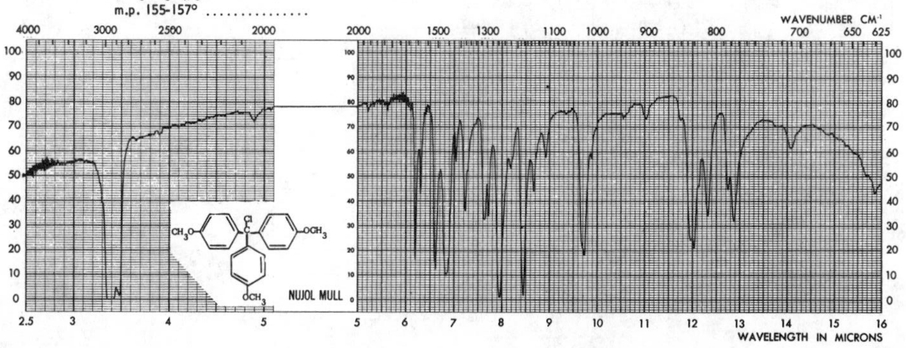

NUJOL MULL

E

19,585-5
Precocene I, 99% (7-methoxy-2,2-dimethylchromene)
FW 190.24 bp 68°/0.100mm. n_D^{20} 1.5595 d 1.052
Disp. C

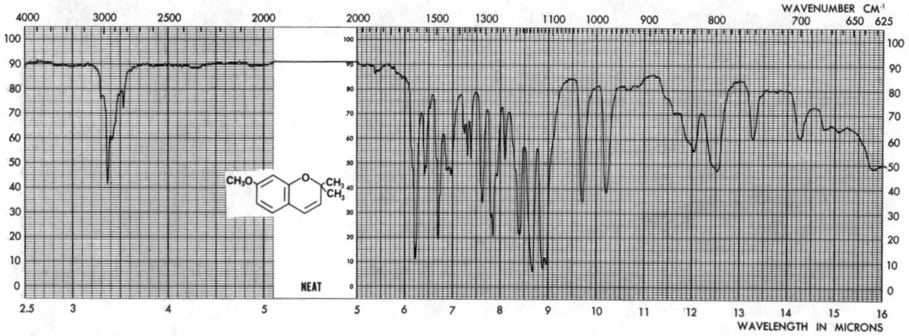

NEAT

F

19,491-3
Precocene II, 99% (6,7-dimethoxy-2,2-dimethyl-3-chromene)
FW 220.27 mp 46-47° Disp. C

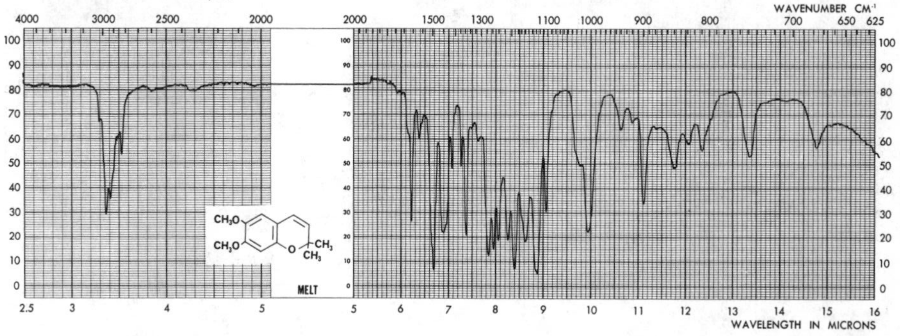

MELT

G

21,753-0
7-Ethoxy-6-methoxy-2,2-dimethylchromene, 99% (ethoxy-Precocene)
FW 234.30 n_D^{20} 1.5560 d 0.929 Disp. C

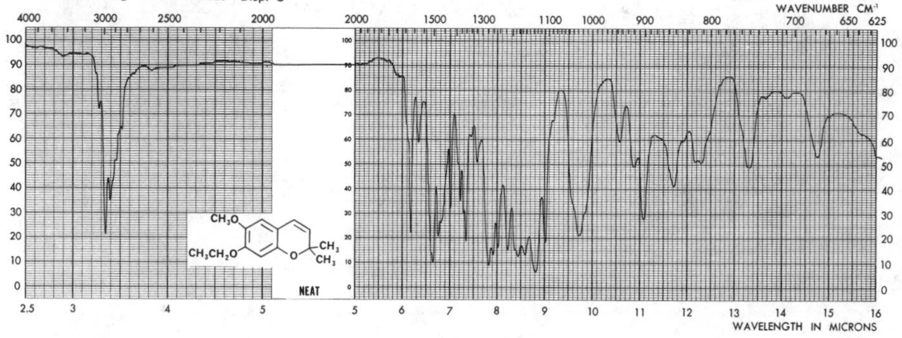

NEAT

H

S500-6 **Styrene oxide** (1,2-epoxyethylbenzene)
M.W. 120.15 n_D^{20} 1.5342 b.p. 194.1°

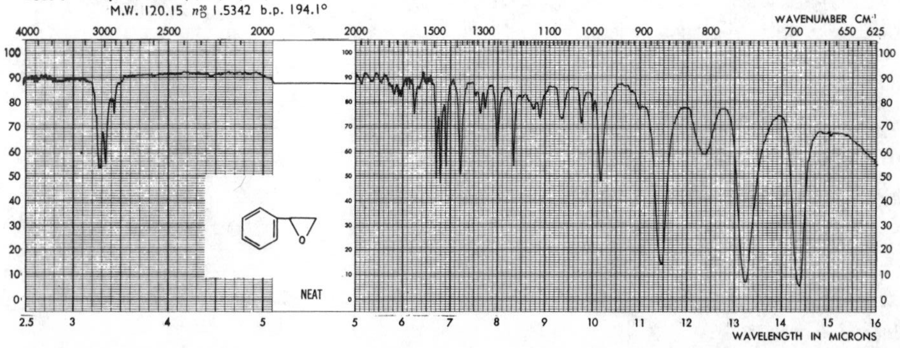

NEAT

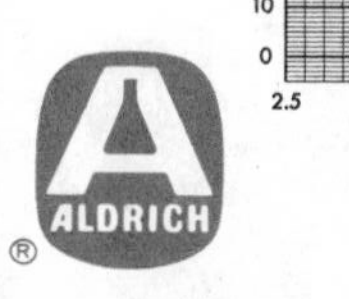

A

S492-1 *trans*-**Stilbene oxide**
M.W. 196.25 m.p. 65-67°
MELT

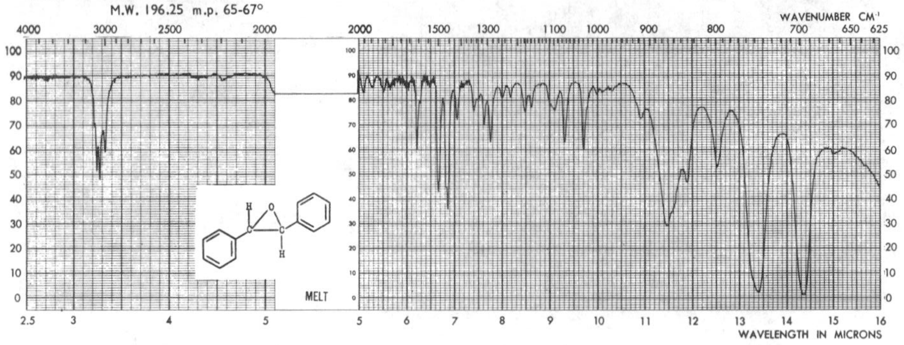

B

14,831-8 **2,3-Epoxypropyl p-ethylphenyl ether** (p-ethylphenyl glycidyl ether)
M.W. 178.23 n_D^{20} 1.5214 b.p. 145-150°/12 mm.
NEAT

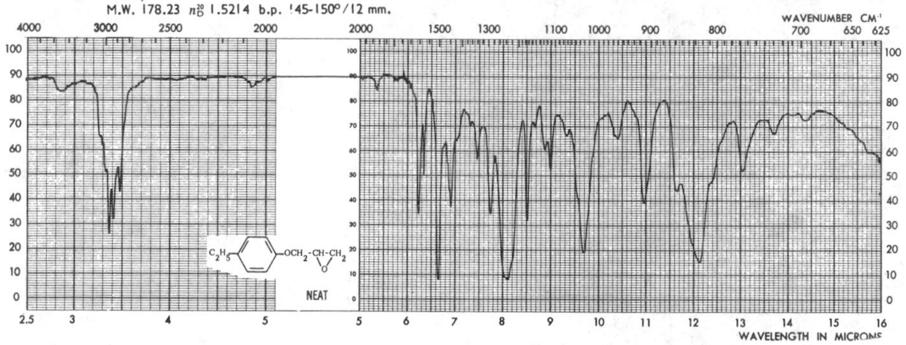

C

C6480-0 **p-Chlorophenyl 2,3-epoxypropyl ether** (p-chlorophenyl glycidyl ether)
M.W. 184.62 n_D^{20} 1.5450
MELT

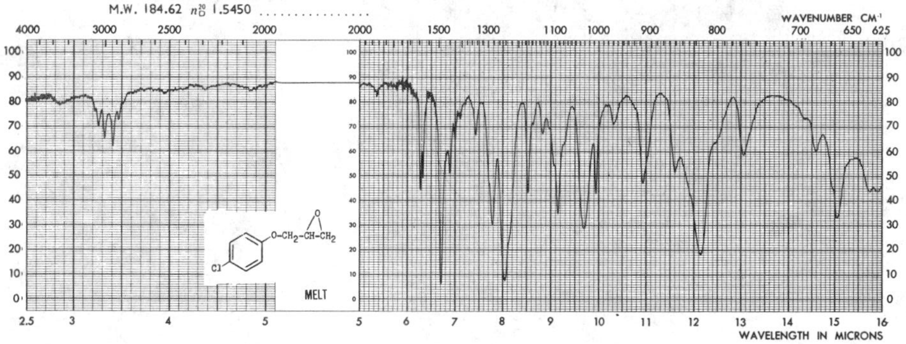

D

14,754-0 **p-Bromophenyl 2,3-epoxypropyl ether** (p-bromophenyl glycidyl ether)
M.W. 229.08 m.p. 43-46°
MELT

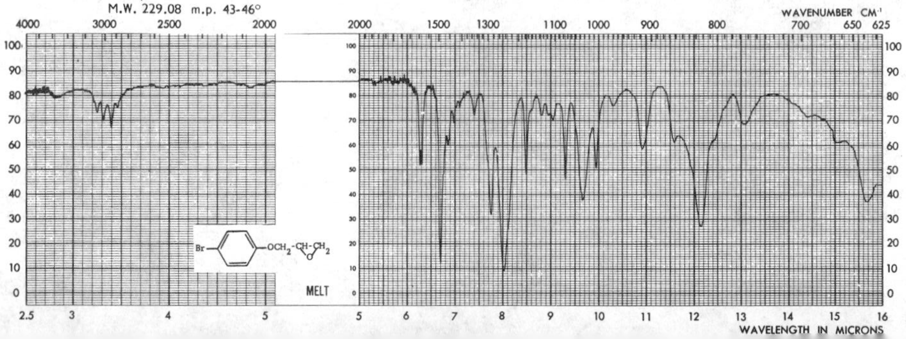

E

14,806-7 **2,3-Epoxypropyl p-methoxyphenyl ether** (glycidyl p-methoxyphenyl ether)
M.W. 180.20 m.p. 45-48.5°
MELT

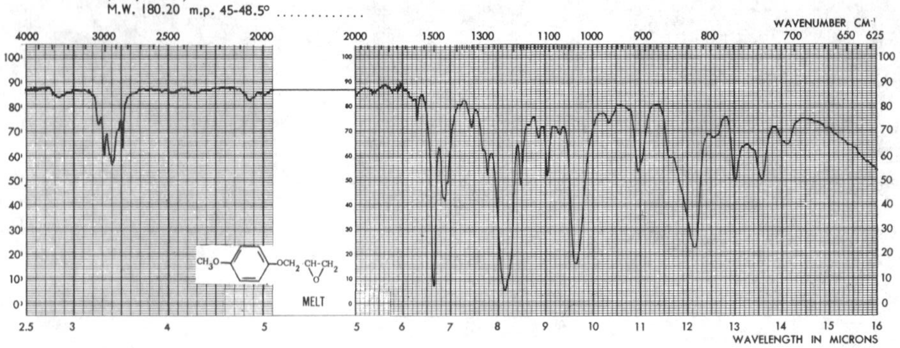

F

14,805-9 **p-*tert*.-Butylphenyl 2,3-epoxypropyl ether**, 99%
(p-*tert*.-butylphenyl glycidyl ether)
M.W. 206.29 b.p. 165 - 170°/14mm. n_D^{20} 1.5145
NMR 4,104D
NEAT

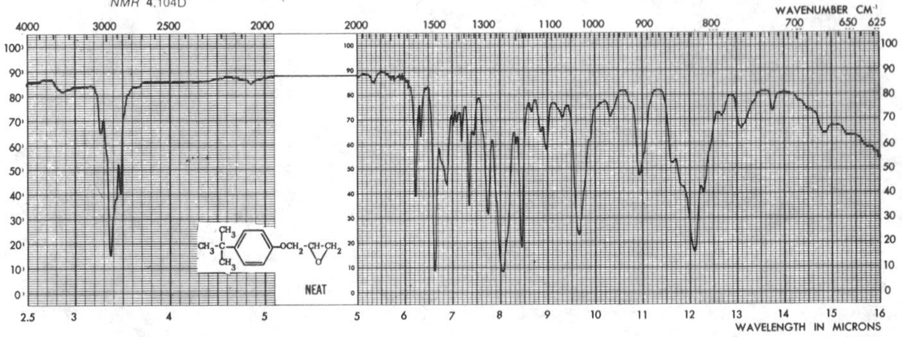

G

19,650-9
o-Biphenylyl glycidyl ether, 95% [3-(o-biphenylyloxy)-1,2-epoxypropane]
FW 226.28 mp 30-32° bp 120°/0.100mm.
Disp. C
MELT

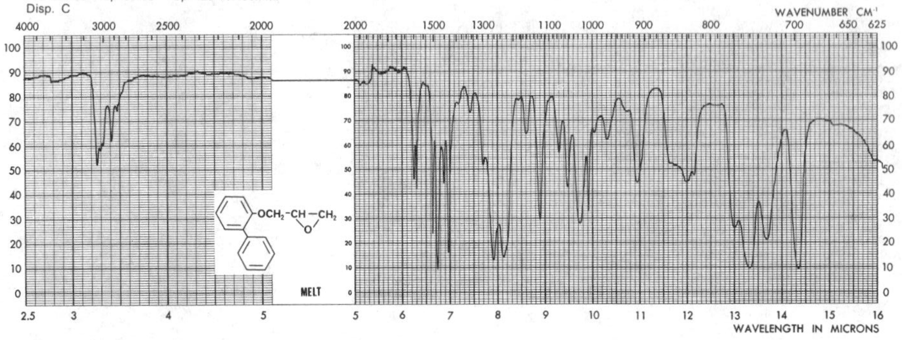

H

16,453-4
Trimethyl orthobenzoate
$C_6H_5C(OCH_3)_3$
M.W. 182.22 b.p. 87-88°/7mm. n_D^{20} 1.4887
NEAT

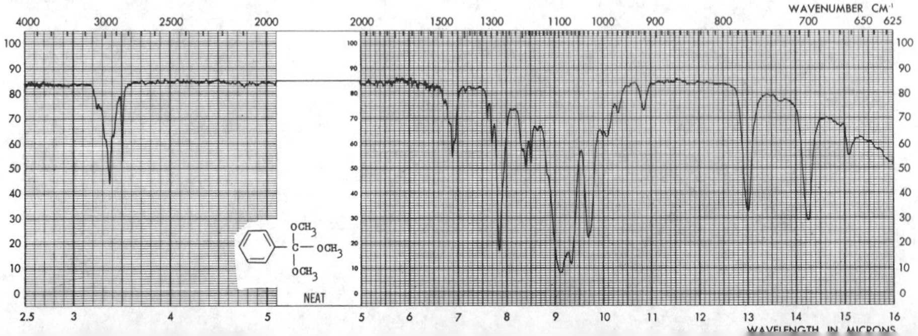

B950-5
Benzophenone dimethyl ketal
(dimethoxydiphenylmethane)
$(C_6H_5)_2C(OCH_3)_2$
M.W. 228.29 m.p. 105-107° b.p. 288-290°
Beil. 7,415

A

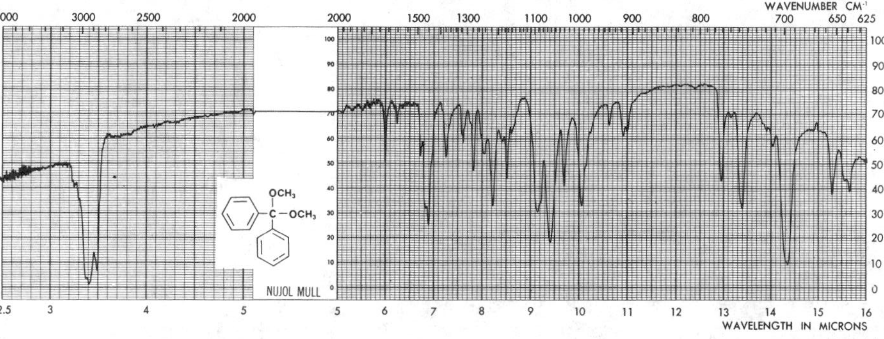

P1660-5 **Phenylacetaldehyde dimethyl acetal**
$C_6H_5CH_2CH(OCH_3)_2$ M.W. 166.22 n_D^{20} 1.4932
b.p. 220°

B

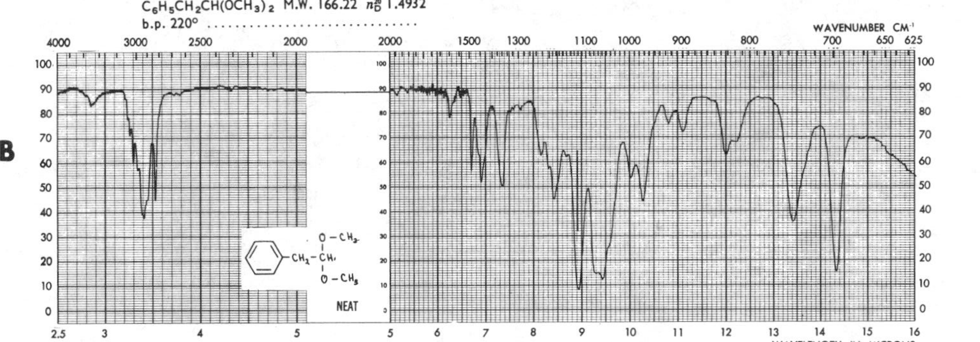

P1490-4 **Phenoxyacetaldehyde diethyl acetal**
$C_6H_5OCH_2CH(OC_2H_5)_2$ M.W. 210.27 n_D^{20} 1.4886
b.p. 254-256°

C

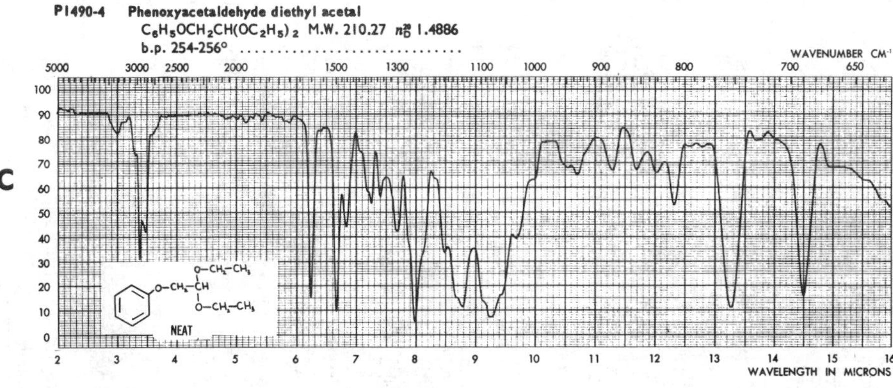

15,848-8
Diethyl phenyl orthoformate
$C_6H_5OCH(OC_2H_5)_2$
M.W. 196.25 b.p. 103-104°/10mm. n_D^{20} 1.4822
Fieser 3,97

D

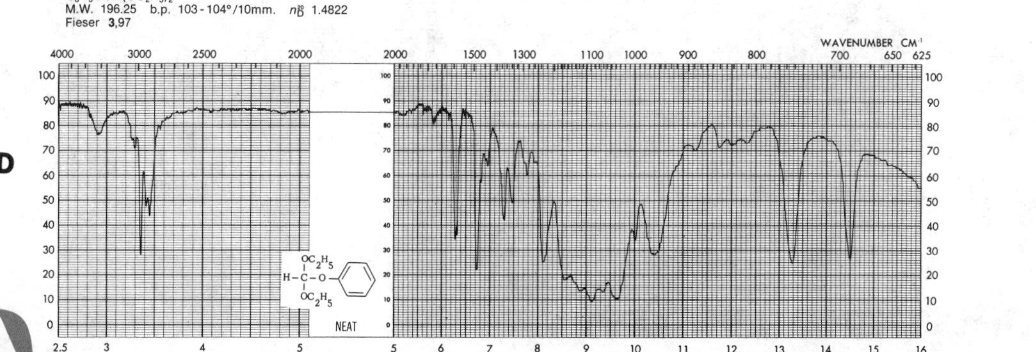

AROMATIC ALCOHOLS AND PHENOLS

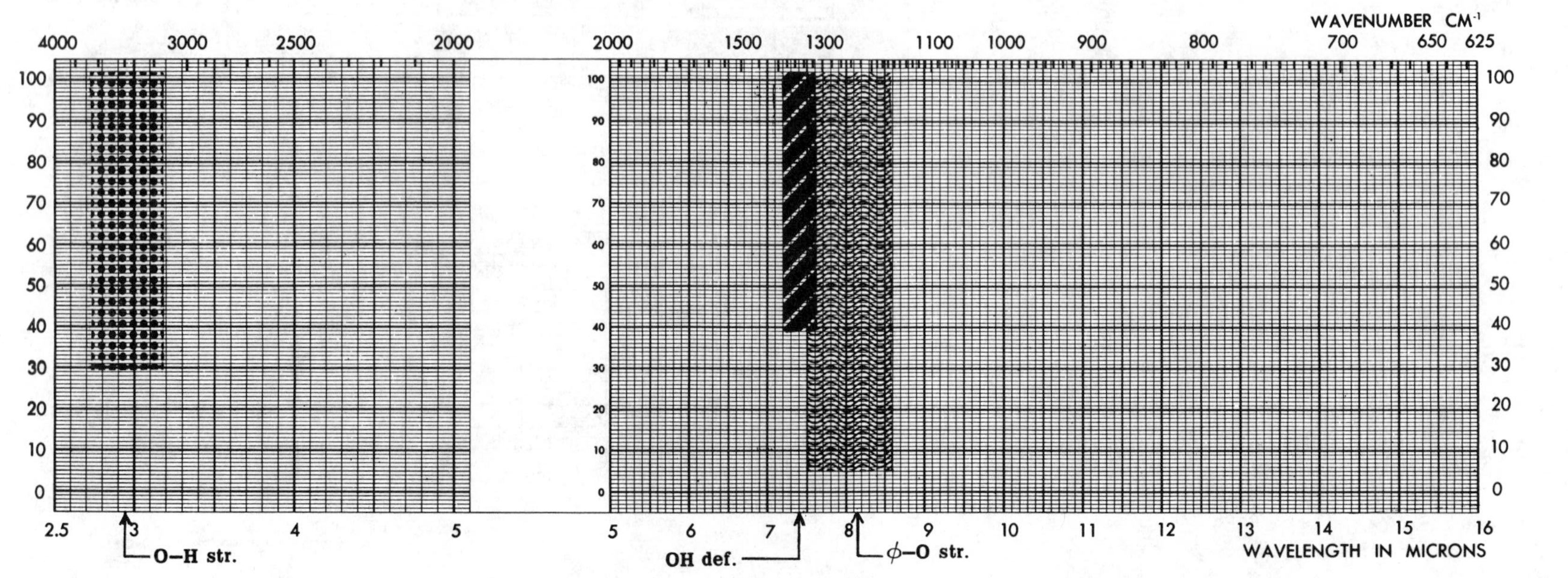

The phenolic O–H stretch absorbs between 2.7 and 3.2 μ (3705 – 3125 cm^{-1}). This absorption is strong and usually broad due to hydrogen bonding. It becomes sharp and shifts to 2.7 μ (3705 cm^{-1}) when neighboring groups sterically hinder hydrogen bonding. This can be seen in spectra 650D—651C and particularly in spectra 650H and 658A.

Phenols also absorb near 7.2 – 7.6 μ (1390 – 1315 cm^{-1}), the OH deformation, and between 7.5 and 8.6 μ (1335 – 1165 cm^{-1}), the aromatic C–O stretch. The 7.5 to 8.6 μ (1335 – 1165 cm^{-1}) band is usually split with a number of maxima.

In general, the aromatic substitution bands are not altered by the attachment of the hydroxyl group. However, medium to strong bands often do accompany the main substitution bands between 11 and 15 μ (910 – 665 cm^{-1}).

The absorptions already discussed in the non-aromatic alcohol section can be seen in spectra 673F—703E where the OH is no longer attached to the aromatic ring.

A 15,099-1 Phenol, zone refined, 99.9+%, GOLD LABEL
C_6H_5OH M.W. 94.11 m.p. 40.68°...

MELT

B C8570-0 o-Cresol, puriss.
$CH_3C_6H_4OH$ M.W. 108.14 m.p. 32-33.5°

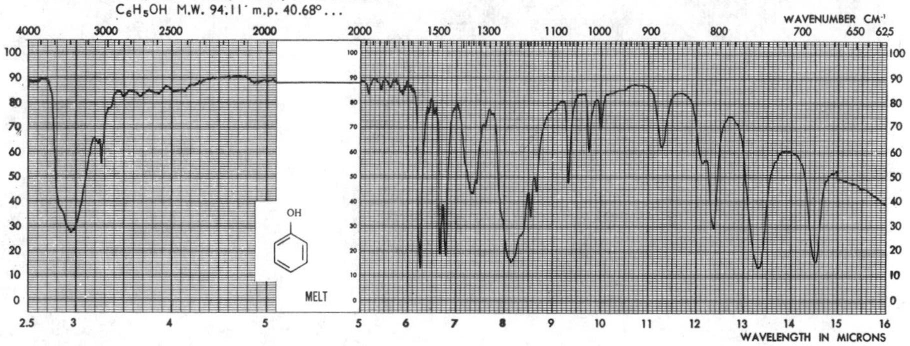

MELT

C E4400-0 2-Ethylphenol
$C_2H_5C_6H_4OH$ M.W. 122.17 n_D^{20} 1.5372

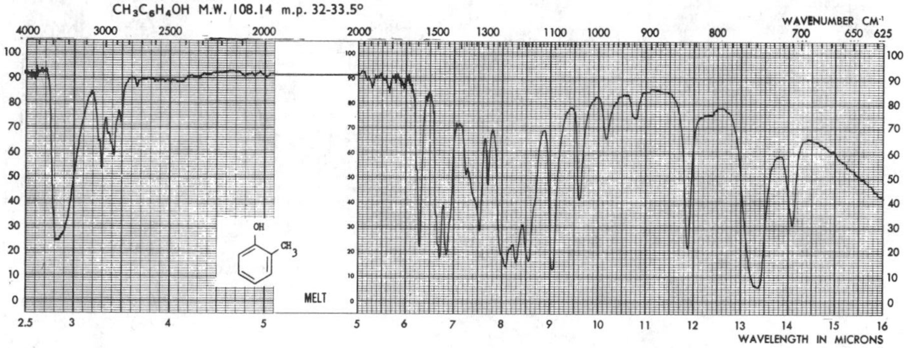

NEAT

D P5360-8 2-n-Propylphenol
$CH_3CH_2CH_2C_6H_4OH$ M.W. 136.19 n_D^{20} 1.5244
b.p. 224.6-226.6°

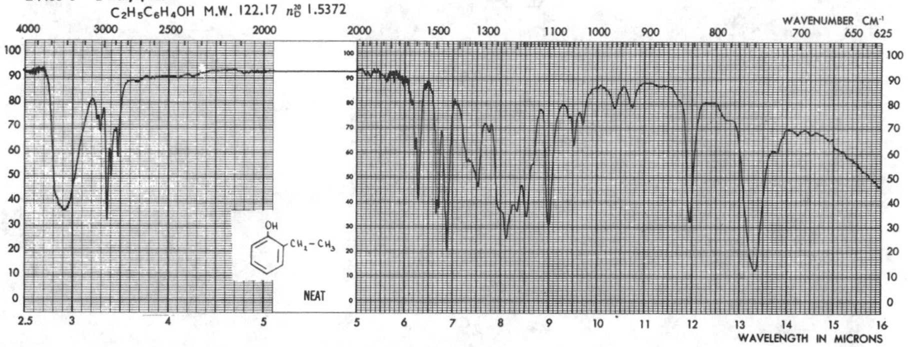

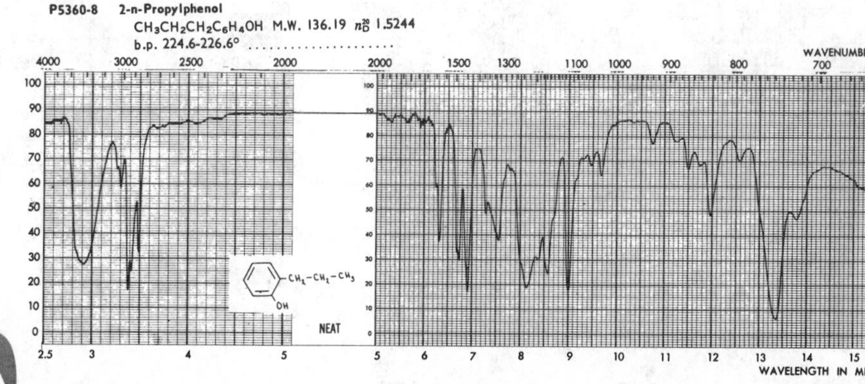

NEAT

E 12,952-6 2-Isopropylphenol
$(CH_3)_2CHC_6H_4OH$ M.W. 136.19 n_D^{20} 1.5259
b.p. 212-212.5°

NEAT

F B9900-6 2-sec.-Butylphenol
$C_2H_5CH(CH_3)C_6H_4OH$ M.W. 150.22 n_D^{20} 1.5222

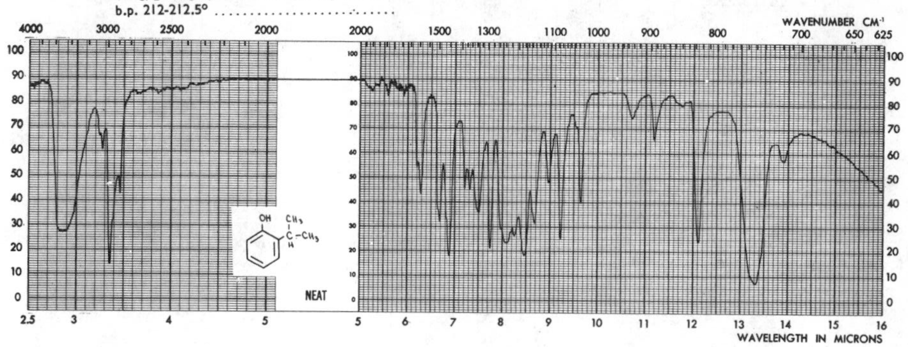

NEAT

G B9940-5 2-tert.-Butylphenol
$(CH_3)_3CC_6H_4OH$ M.W. 150.22 n_D^{20} 1.5228

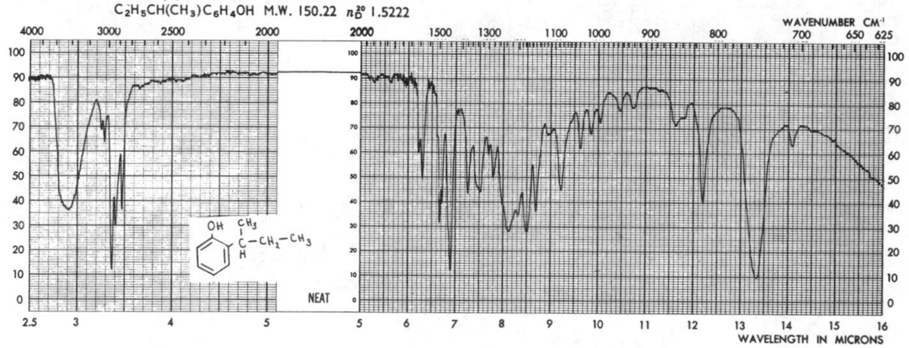

NEAT

H C10,720-4 2-Cyclohexylphenol
$C_6H_{11}C_6H_4OH$ M.W. 176.26 m.p. 56-57°

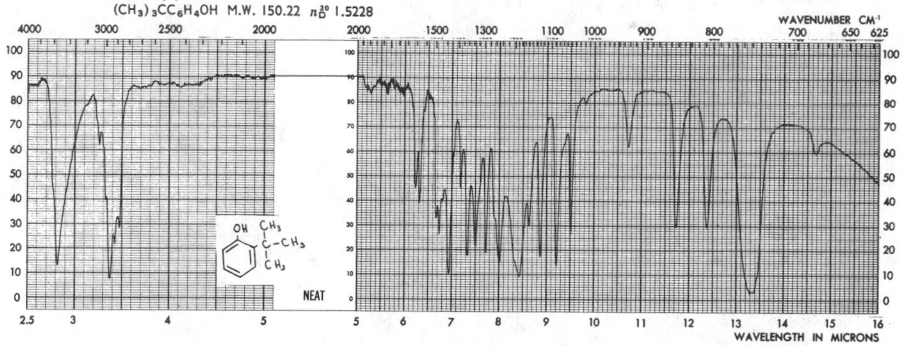

MELT

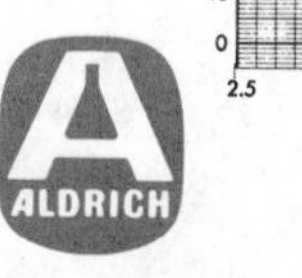

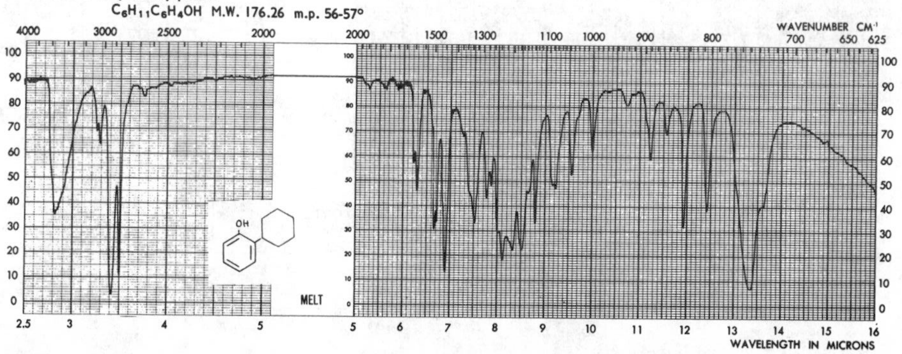

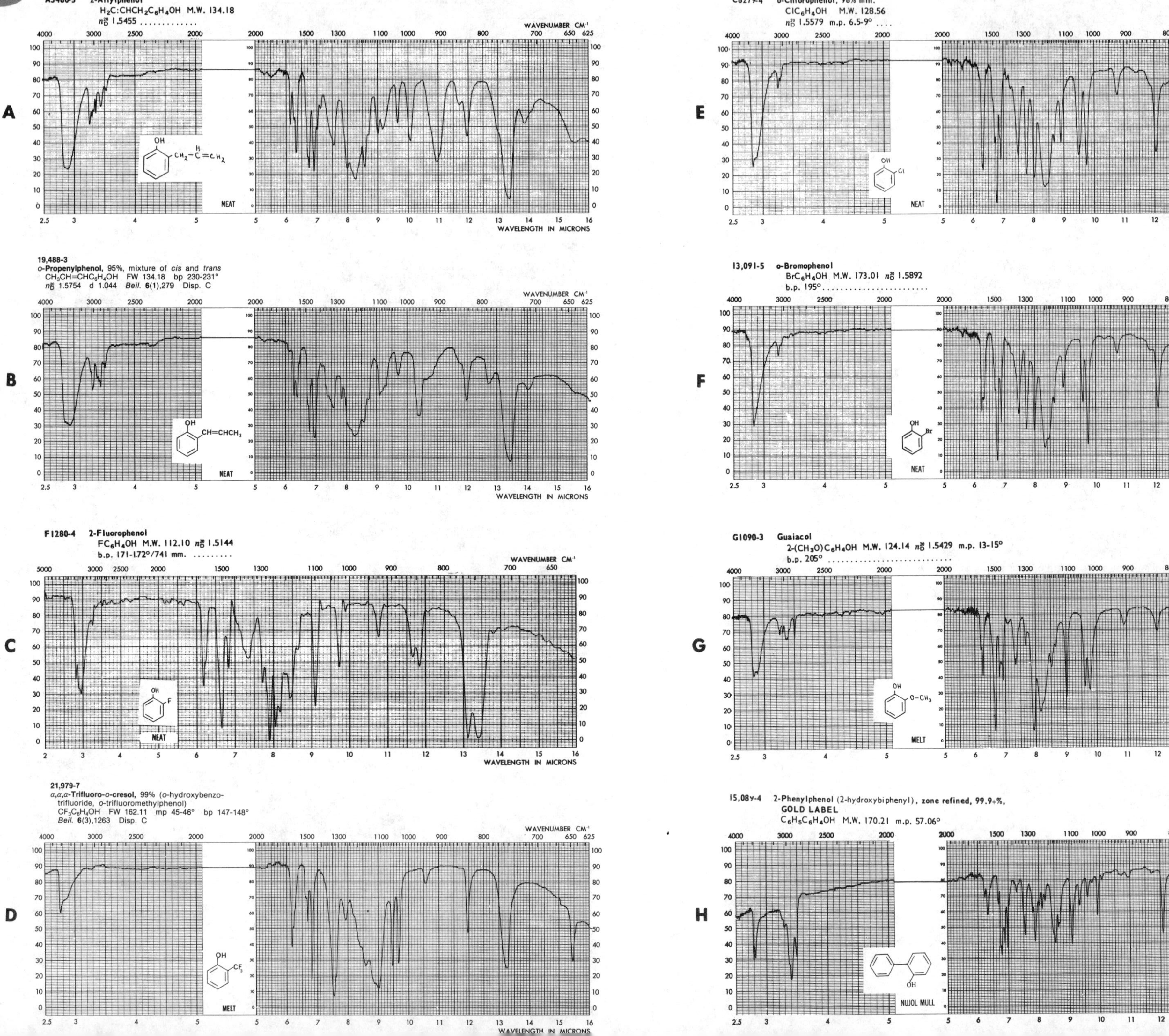
A
A3480-5 2-Allylphenol
$H_2C{:}CHCH_2C_6H_4OH$ M.W. 134.18
n_D^{20} 1.5455
NEAT
B
19,488-3
o-Propenylphenol, 95%, mixture of *cis* and *trans*
$CH_3CH{=}CHC_6H_4OH$ FW 134.18 bp 230-231°
n_D^{20} 1.5754 d 1.044 *Beil.* **6**(1),279 Disp. C
NEAT
C
F1280-4 2-Fluorophenol
FC_6H_4OH M.W. 112.10 n_D^{20} 1.5144
b.p. 171-172°/741 mm.
NEAT
D
21,979-7
α,α,α-Trifluoro-o-cresol, 99% (o-hydroxybenzotrifluoride, o-trifluoromethylphenol)
$CF_3C_6H_4OH$ FW 162.11 mp 45-46° bp 147-148°
Beil. 6(3),1263 Disp. C
MELT
E
C6279-4 o-Chlorophenol, 98% min.
ClC_6H_4OH M.W. 128.56
n_D^{20} 1.5579 m.p. 6.5-9°
NEAT
F
13,091-5 o-Bromophenol
BrC_6H_4OH M.W. 173.01 n_D^{20} 1.5892
b.p. 195°
NEAT
G
G1090-3 Guaiacol
$2\text{-}(CH_3O)C_6H_4OH$ M.W. 124.14 n_D^{20} 1.5429 m.p. 13-15°
b.p. 205°
MELT
H
15,08y-4 2-Phenylphenol (2-hydroxybiphenyl), zone refined, 99.9+%,
GOLD LABEL
$C_6H_5C_6H_4OH$ M.W. 170.21 m.p. 57.06°
NUJOL MULL
WAVENUMBER CM⁻¹
WAVELENGTH IN MICRONS

A

11,581-9 **o,o'-Biphenol** (2,2'-dihydroxybiphenyl)
$HOC_6H_4C_6H_4OH$ M.W. 186.21
m.p. 110-112° . . . .

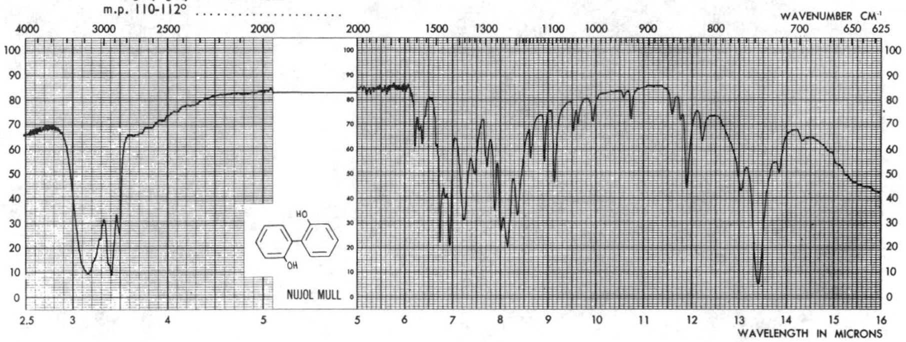

NUJOL MULL

B

C8572-7 **m-Cresol, puriss.**
$CH_3C_6H_4OH$ M.W. 108.14 n_D^{20} 1.5409 m.p. 8-10°

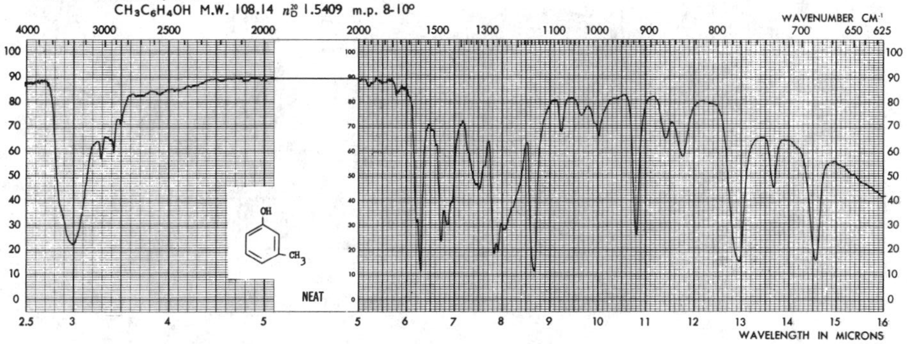

NEAT

C

E4410-8 **3-Ethylphenol**
$C_2H_5C_6H_4OH$ M.W. 122.17
n_D^{20} 1.5310 . . . .

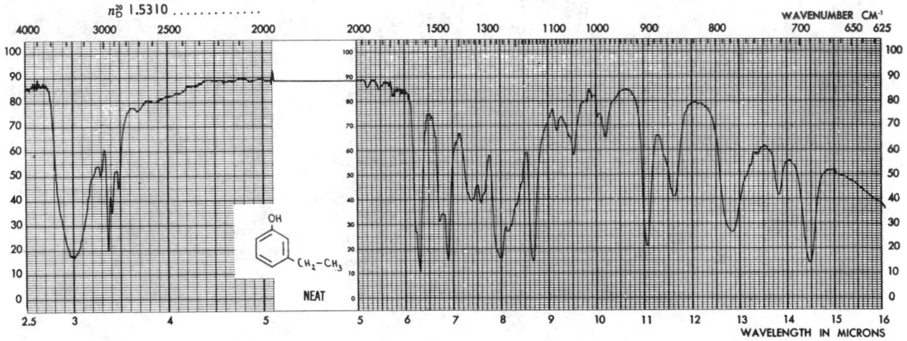

NEAT

D

I—2,650-7
3-Isopropylphenol, tech., 60%
$(CH_3)_2CHC_6H_4OH$
M.W. 136.19 b.p. 228° Beil. **6**,505 *IRRITANT*

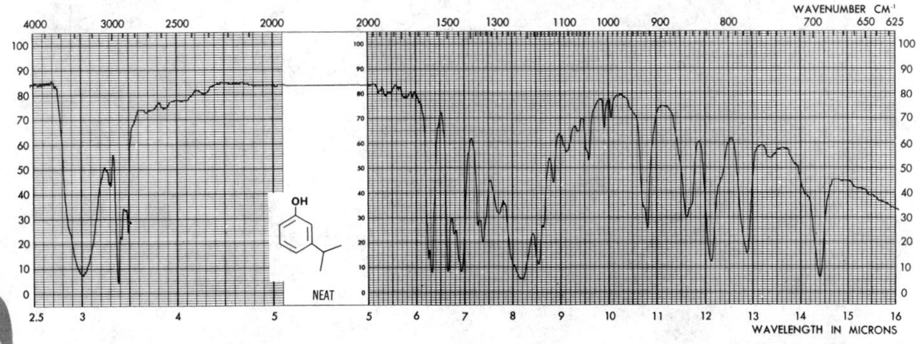

NEAT

E

12,428-1 **3-tert.-Butylphenol**
$(CH_3)_3CC_6H_4OH$ M.W. 150.22 m.p. 40-42°

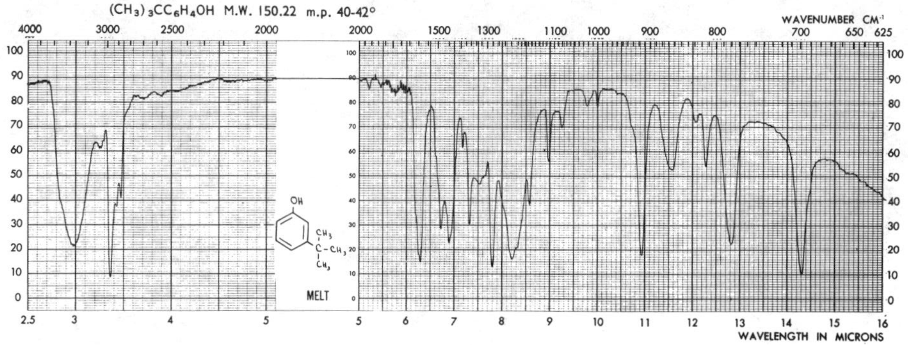

MELT

F

17,132-8
3-n-Pentadecylphenol, 97%
$CH_3(CH_2)_{14}C_6H_4OH$
M.W. 304.52 m.p. 49-52° Beil. **6**(2),518

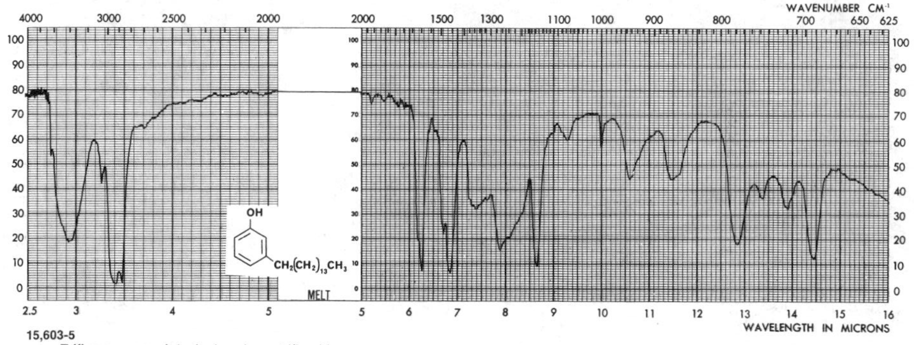

MELT

G

15,603-5
α,α,α-Trifluoro-m-cresol (m-hydroxybenzotrifluoride.
m-trifluoromethylphenol)
$CF_3C_6H_4OH$
M.W. 162.11 m.p. -1.8° b.p. 178-179°
n_D^{20} 1.4588 Beil. **6**(1),187

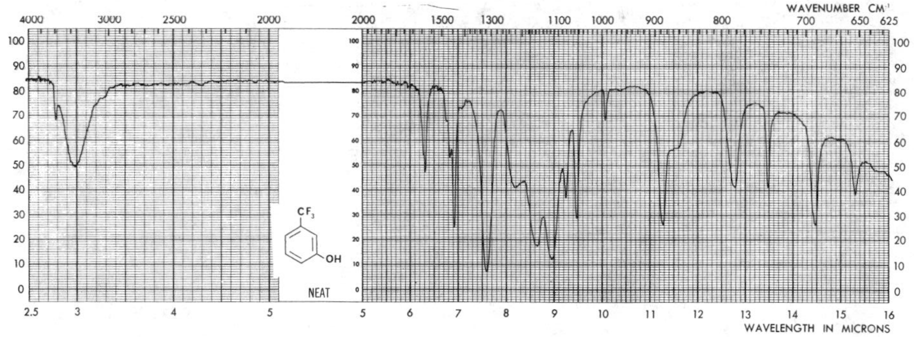

NEAT

H

F1300-2 **3-Fluorophenol**
FC_6H_4OH M.W. 112.10 n_D^{20} 1.5128

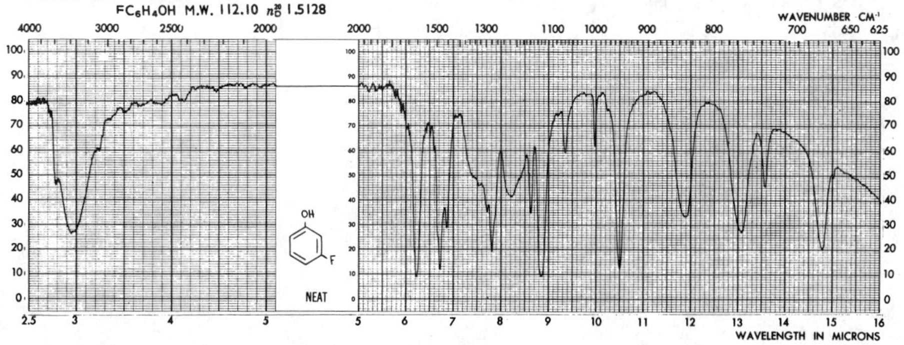

NEAT

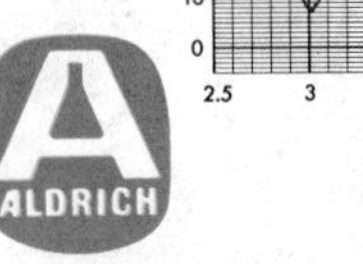

A C6280-8 m-Chlorophenol
ClC_6H_4OH M.W. 128.56
m.p. 35-36°
MELT

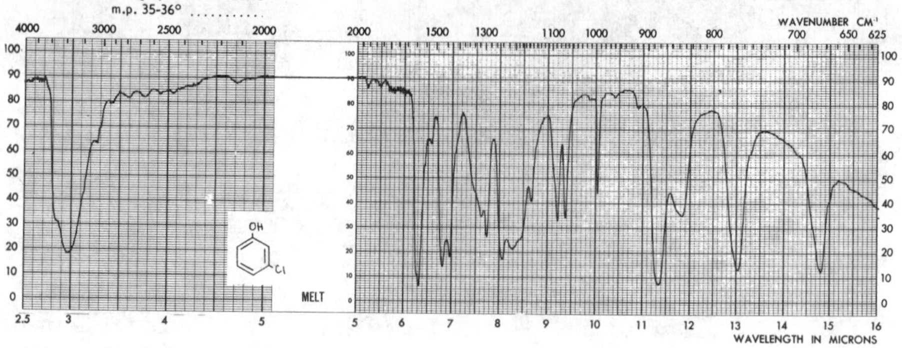

B 10,107-9 m-Bromophenol
BrC_6H_4OH M.W. 173.01 m.p. 30-32°
NEAT

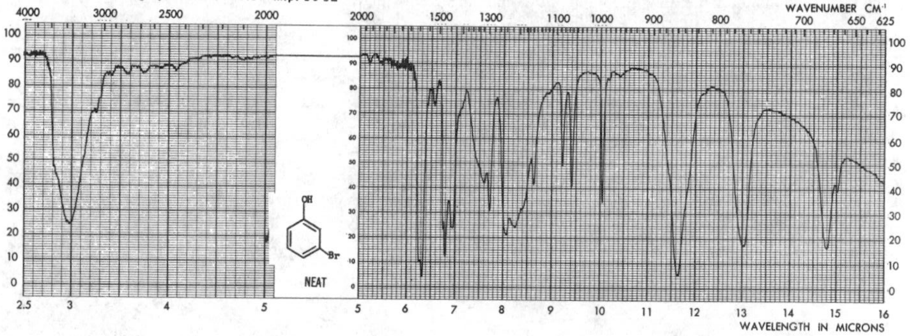

C I-1000 3-Iodophenol
MELT

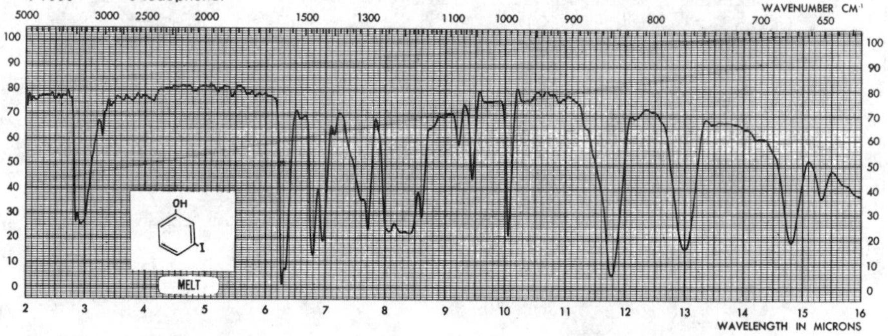

D 13,996-3 m-Methoxyphenol
$CH_3OC_6H_4OH$ M.W. 124.14 n_D^{20} 1.5520
b.p. 113-115°/5 mm.
NEAT

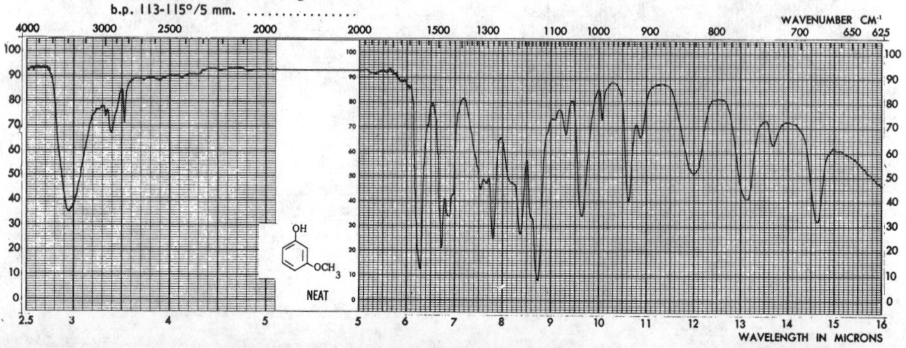

E C8575-1 p-Cresol, puriss.
$CH_3C_6H_4OH$ M.W. 108.14 m.p. 32-34°
MELT

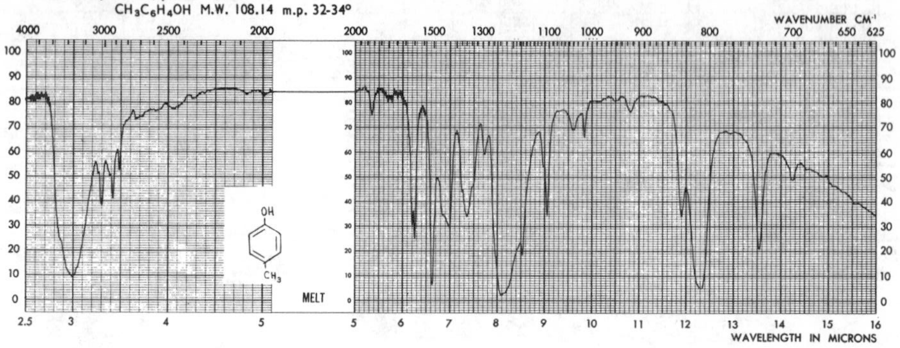

F E4420-5 4-Ethylphenol
$C_2H_5C_6H_4OH$ M.W. 122.17 m.p. 42-45°
MELT

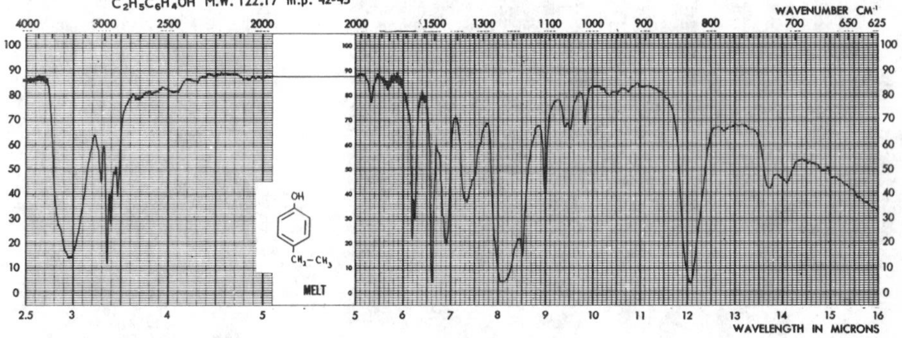

G P5380-2 4-n-Propylphenol
$CH_3CH_2CH_2C_6H_4OH$ M.W. 136.19
n_D^{20} 1.5086
NEAT

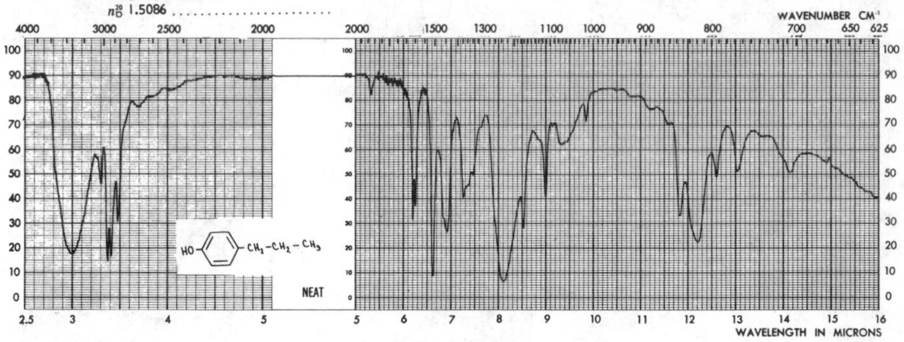

H 17,540-4
4-Isopropylphenol, 98%
$(CH_3)_2CHC_6H_4OH$
M.W. 136.19 m.p. 59-61° b.p. 212-212.5°
Beil. 6,505
NUJOL MULL

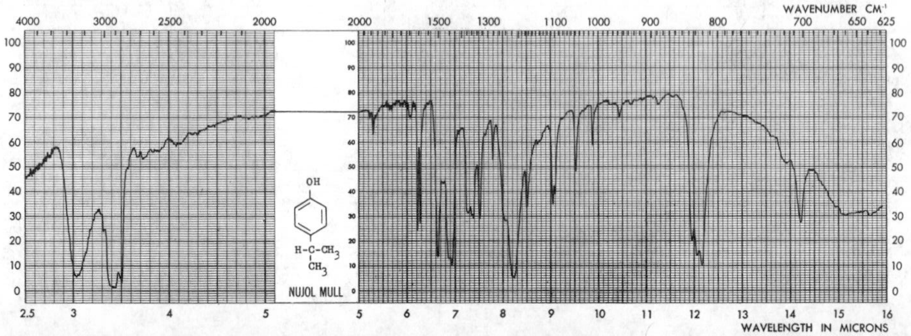

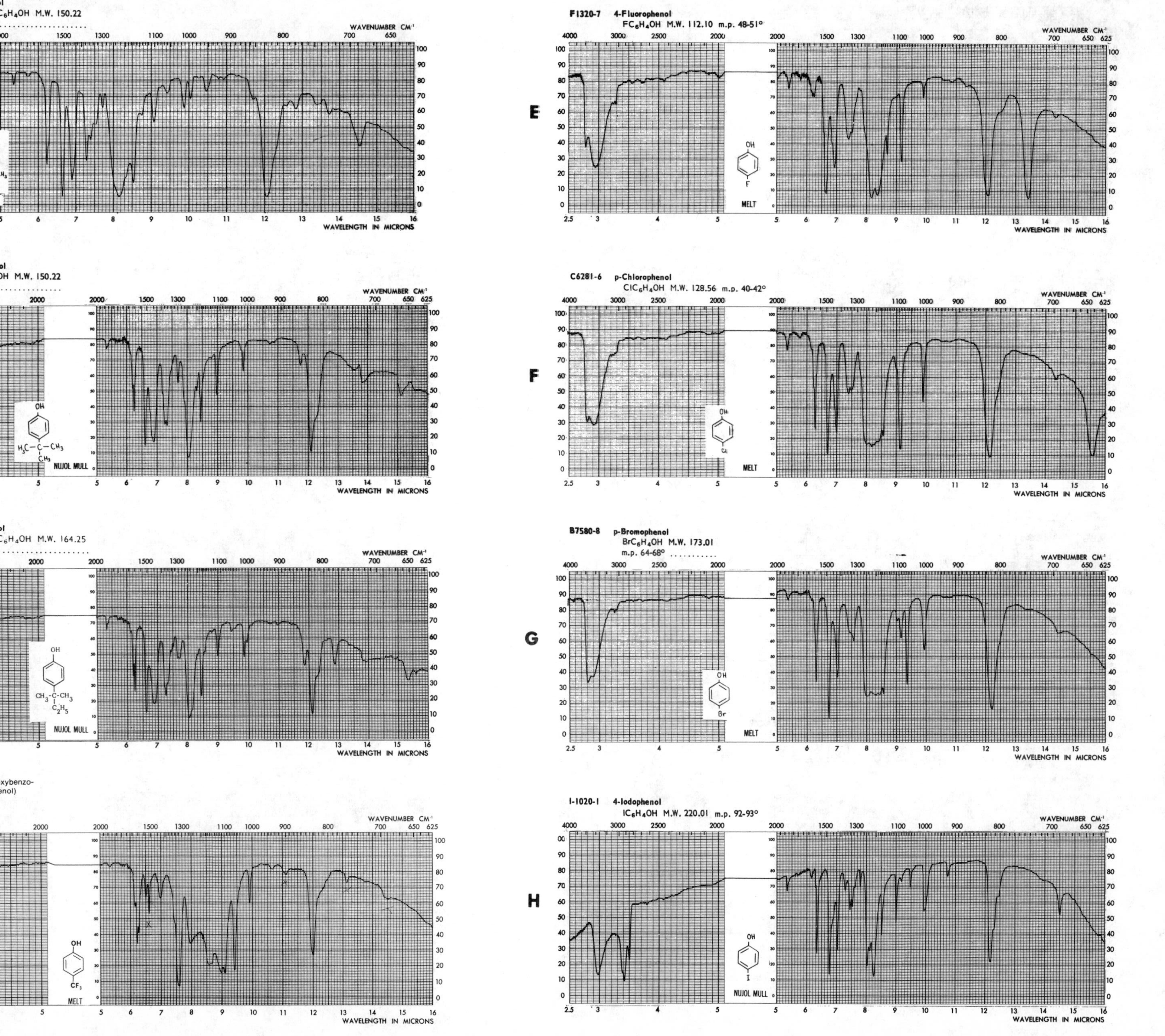

A
13,528-3 4-sec.-Butylphenol
$C_2H_5CH(CH_3)C_6H_4OH$ M.W. 150.22
m.p. 54-58°
MELT
B
B9990-1 4-tert.-Butylphenol
$(CH_3)_3CC_6H_4OH$ M.W. 150.22
m.p. 98-101°
NUJOL MULL
C
15,384-2 p-tert.-Amylphenol
$C_2H_5C(CH_3)_2C_6H_4OH$ M.W. 164.25
m.p. 88-89°
NUJOL MULL
D
17,847-0
α,α,α-Trifluoro-p-cresol, (p-hydroxybenzotrifluoride, p-trifluoromethylphenol)
$CF_3C_6H_4OH$
M.W. 162.11 m.p. 45-47°
MELT
E
F1320-7 4-Fluorophenol
FC_6H_4OH M.W. 112.10 m.p. 48-51°
MELT
F
C6281-6 p-Chlorophenol
ClC_6H_4OH M.W. 128.56 m.p. 40-42°
MELT
G
B7580-8 p-Bromophenol
BrC_6H_4OH M.W. 173.01
m.p. 64-68°
MELT
H
I-1020-1 4-Iodophenol
IC_6H_4OH M.W. 220.01 m.p. 92-93°
NUJOL MULL
WAVENUMBER CM⁻¹
WAVELENGTH IN MICRONS
ALDRICH

A

M1865-5 **p-Methoxyphenol**
$CH_3OC_6H_4OH$ M.W. 124.14
m.p. 55-57° ....

MELT

B

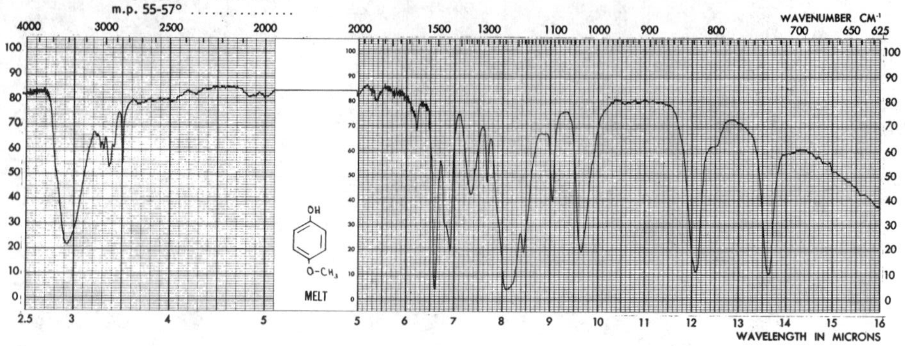

B8780-6 **4-n-Butoxyphenol**
$CH_3(CH_2)_3OC_6H_4OH$ M.W. 166.22 m.p. 65-66°

NUJOL MULL

C

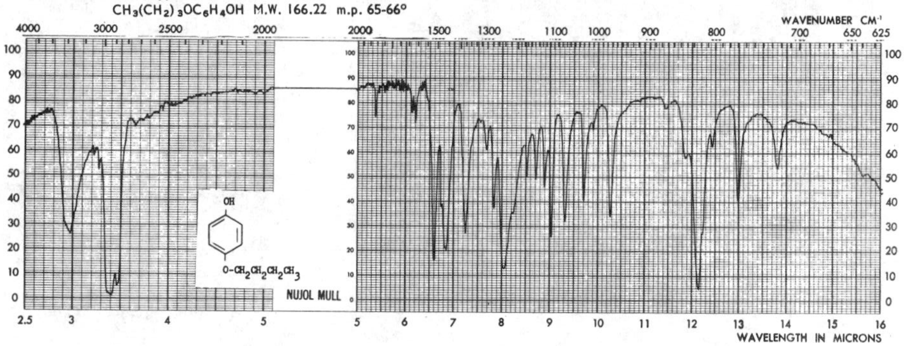

22,219-4
4-Pentyloxyphenol, 99%
$CH_3(CH_2)_4OC_6H_4OH$ FW 180.25 mp 48-50°
Beil. **6**(3),4389 Disp. C

MELT

D

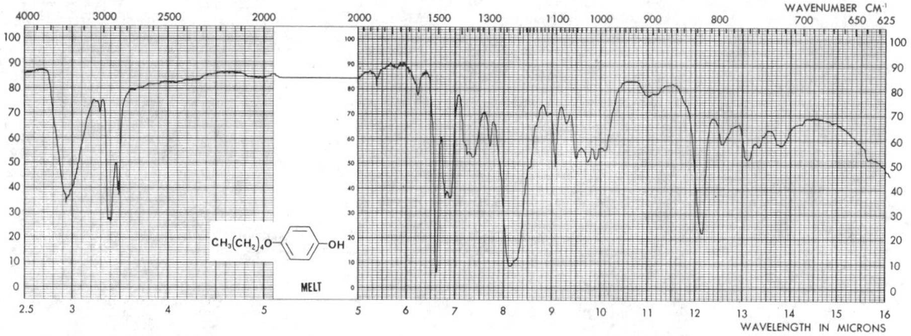

22,212-7
4-Hexyloxyphenol, 99%
$CH_3(CH_2)_5OC_6H_4OH$ FW 194.27 mp 45-47°
Beil. **6**(3),4390 Disp. C

MELT

E

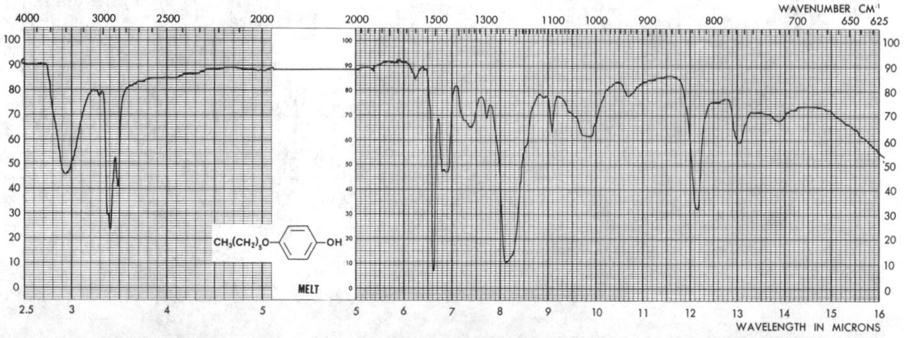

22,207-0
4-Heptyloxyphenol, 99%
$CH_3(CH_2)_6OC_6H_4OH$ FW 208.30 mp 60-63°
Beil. **6**(3),4391 Disp. C

MELT

F

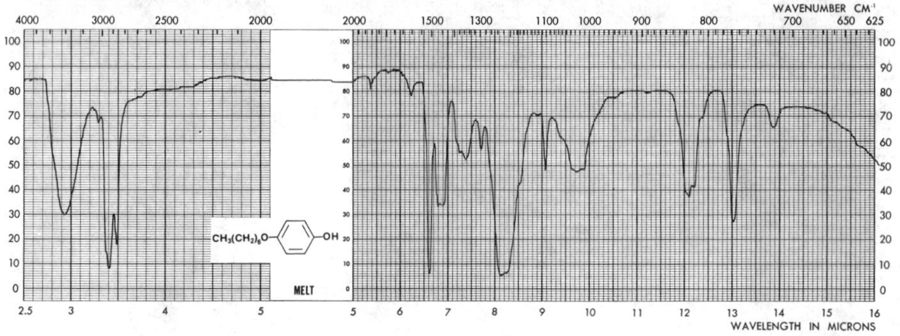

D17,400-9 **2,3-Dimethylphenol**
$(CH_3)_2C_6H_3OH$ M.W. 122.17 m.p. 73-75.5°

NUJOL MULL

G

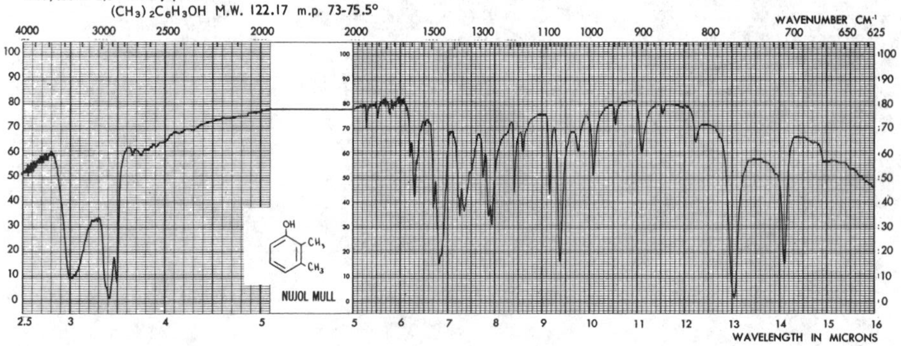

16,080-6
4-Indanol, 98%
M.W. 134.18 m.p. 47-49° b.p. 244-246°
Beil. **6**,574

MELT

H

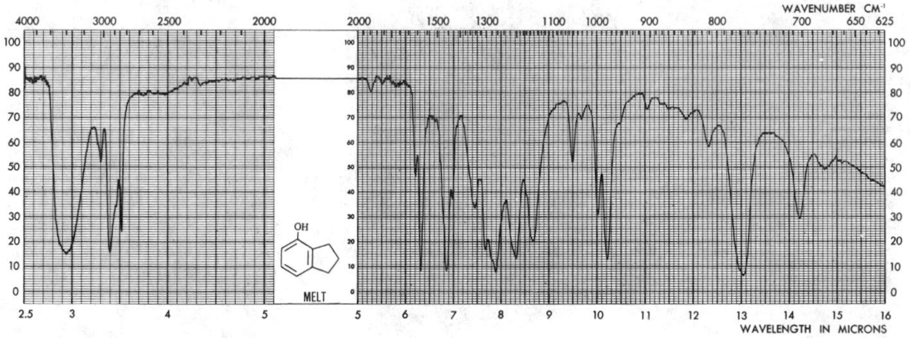

T1340-4 **5,6,7,8-Tetrahydro-1-naphthol**
M.W. 148.21 m.p. 69-71° ...

NUJOL MULL

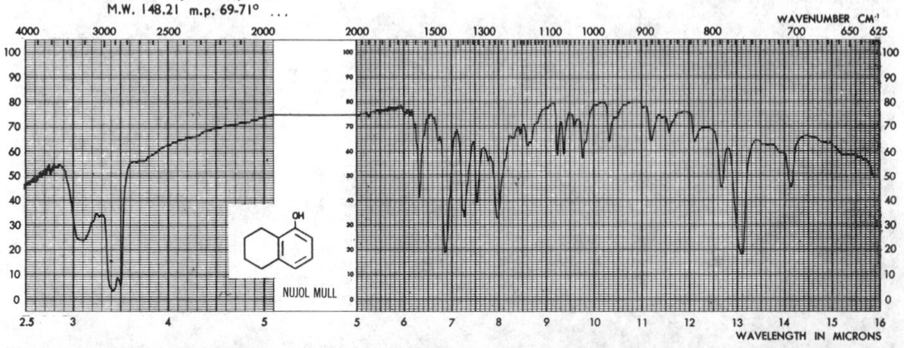

A

D6980-7 2,3-Dichlorophenol
$Cl_2C_6H_3OH$ M.W. 163.00
m.p. 57-59° ....

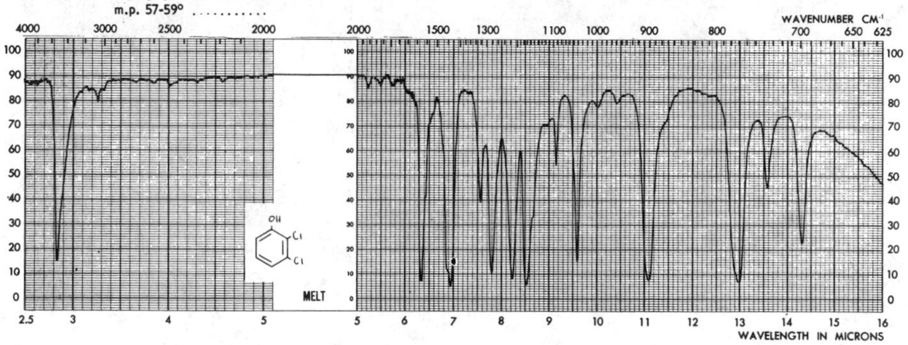

MELT

B

M1600-8 3-Methoxy-2-methylphenol (3-methoxy-o-cresol)
$CH_3OC_6H_3(CH_3)OH$ M.W. 138.17 m.p. 45-47°

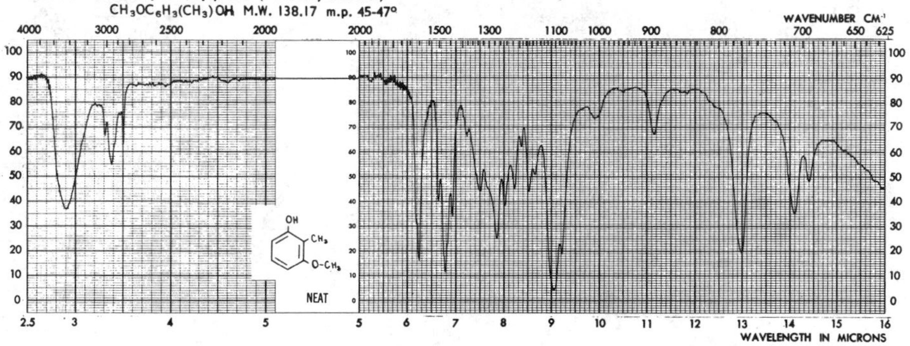

NEAT

C

12,633-0 2,3-Dimethoxyphenol
$(CH_3O)_2C_6H_3OH$ M.W. 154.17 n_D^{20} 1.5392 .

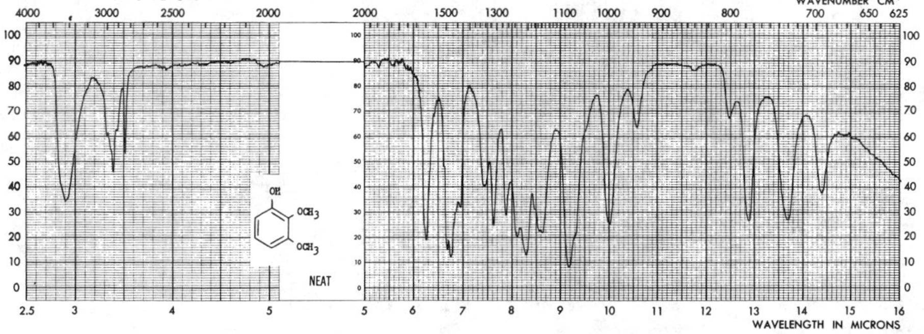

NEAT

D

D17,490-4 2,6-Dimethylphenol, puriss.
$(CH_3)_2C_6H_3OH$ M.W. 122.17 m.p. 46°

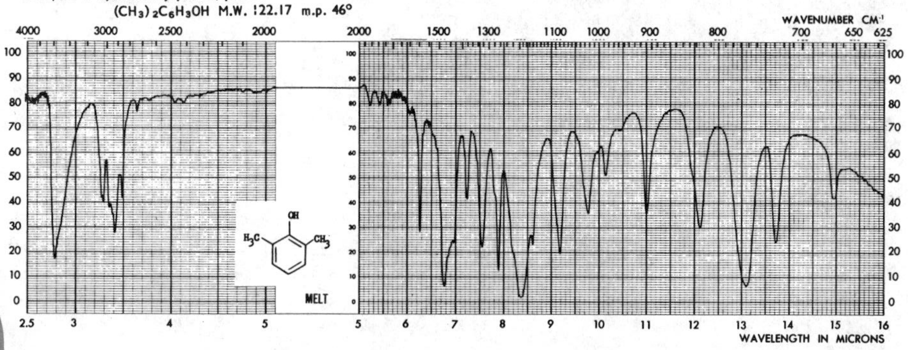

MELT

E

D12,660-8 2,6-Diisopropylphenol
$[(CH_3)_2CH]_2C_6H_3OH$ M.W. 178.28 n_D^{20} 1.5125

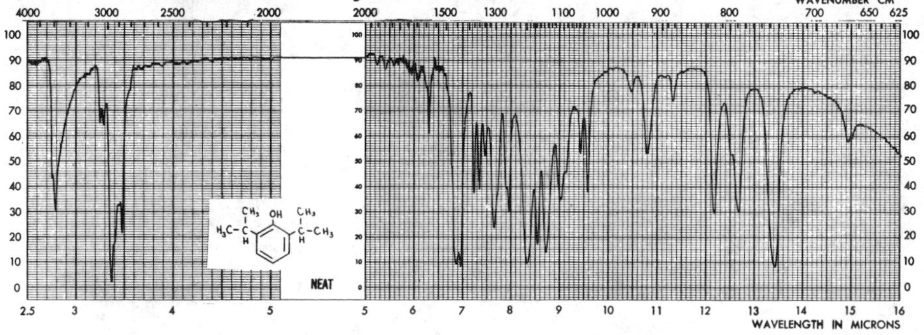

NEAT

F

11,971-7 2,6-Di-sec.-butylphenol
$[C_2H_5CH(CH_3)]_2C_6H_3OH$ M.W. 206.33
n_D^{20} 1.5049 ....

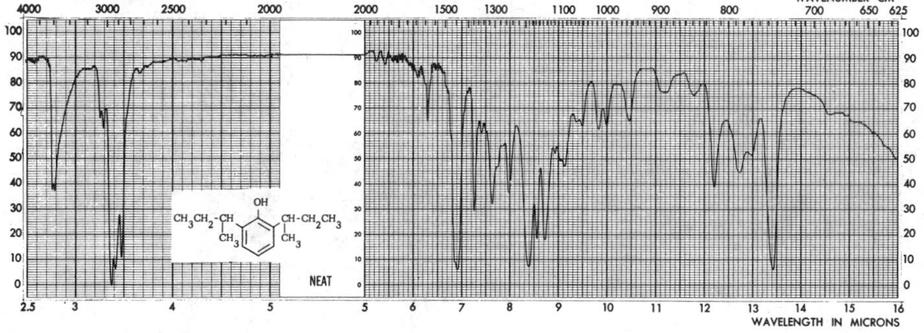

NEAT

G

B9760-7 2-tert.-Butyl-6-methylphenol (6-tert.-butyl-o-cresol)
$(CH_3)_3CC_6H_3(CH_3)OH$ M.W. 164.25 m.p. 30-32°

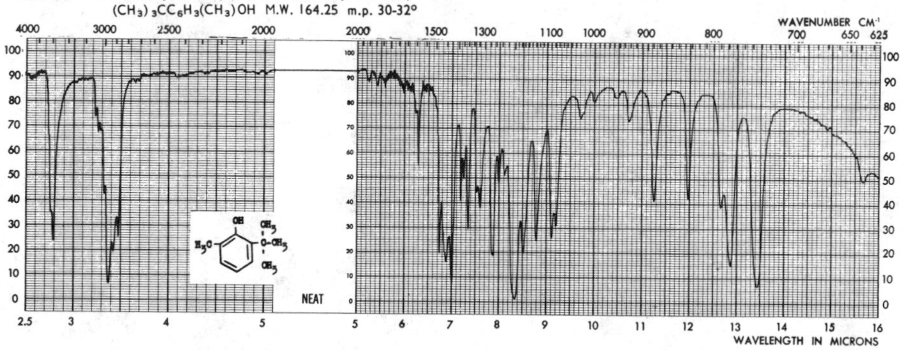

NEAT

H

D4840-0 2,6-Di-tert.-butylphenol, puriss.
$[(CH_3)_3C]_2C_6H_3OH$ M.W. 206.33
m.p. 35-38° ....

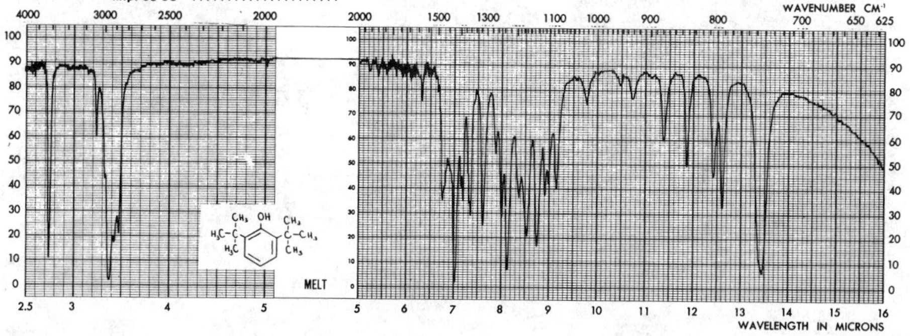

MELT

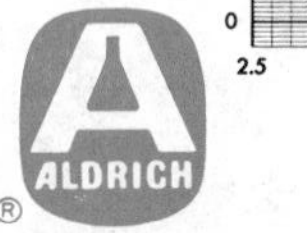

A

A3400-7 **2-Allyl-6-methylphenol**
$H_2C:CHCH_2C_6H_3(CH_3)OH$ M.W. 148.21
n_D^{20} 1.5377

NEAT

B

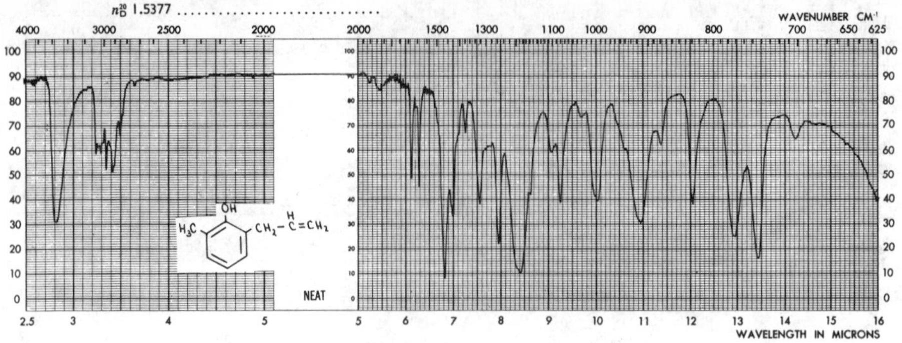

C5500-3 2-Chloro-6-methylphenol (6-chloro-o-cresol), tech., 80%
$ClC_6H_3(CH_3)OH$ M.W. 142.59
n_D^{20} 1.5449

NEAT

C

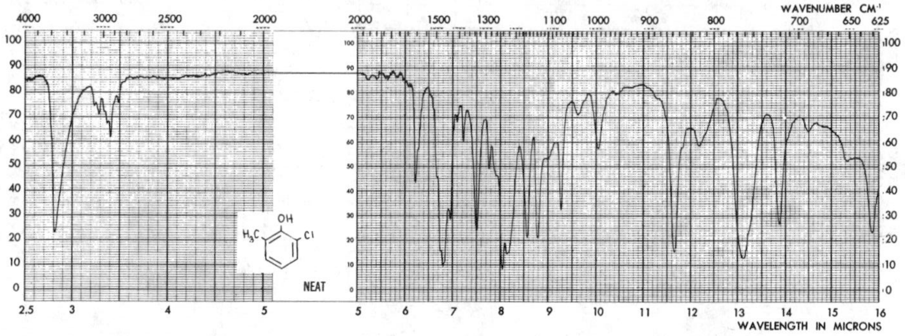

D7020-1 **2,6-Dichlorophenol**
$Cl_2C_6H_3OH$ M.W. 163.00 m.p. 65-66°

NUJOL MULL

D

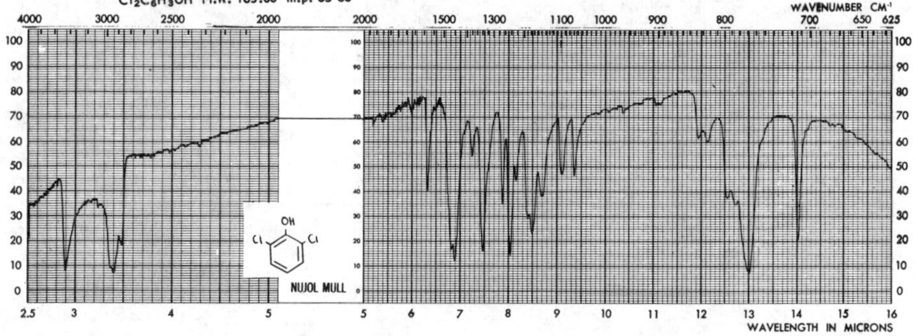

D13,555-0 **2,6-Dimethoxyphenol**
$(CH_3O)_2C_6H_3OH$ M.W. 154.17 m.p. 56-57°

MELT

E

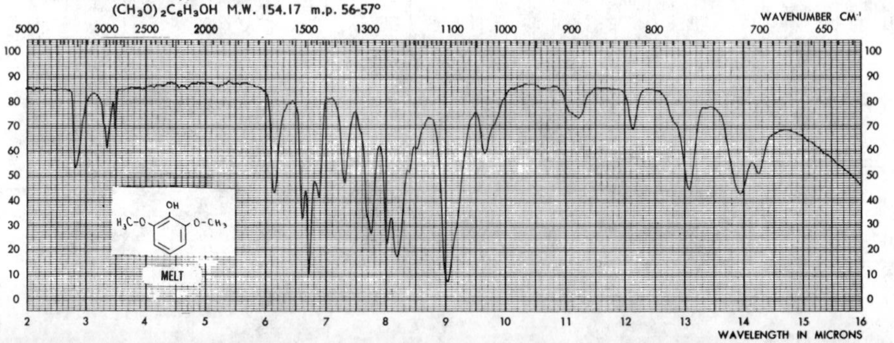

15,085-1 3,5-Dimethylphenol, zone refined, 99.9+%, GOLD LABEL
$(CH_3)_2C_6H_3OH$ M.W. 122.17

NUJOL MULL

F

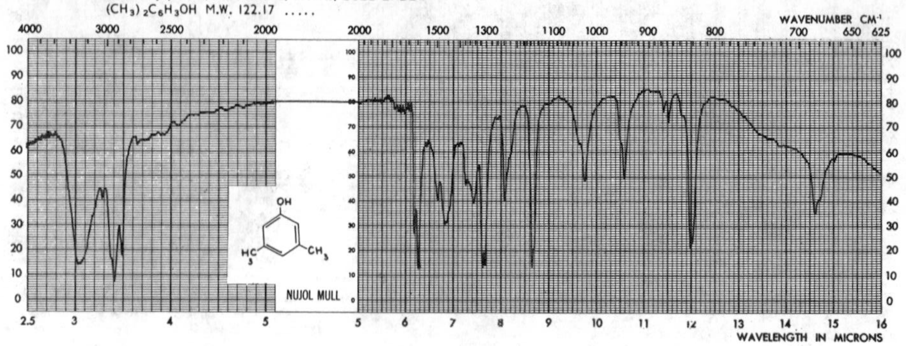

B9770-4 **3-tert.-Butyl-5-methylphenol** (5-tert.-butyl-m-cresol), tech.
$(CH_3)_3CC_6H_3(CH_3)OH$ M.W. 164.25

MELT

G

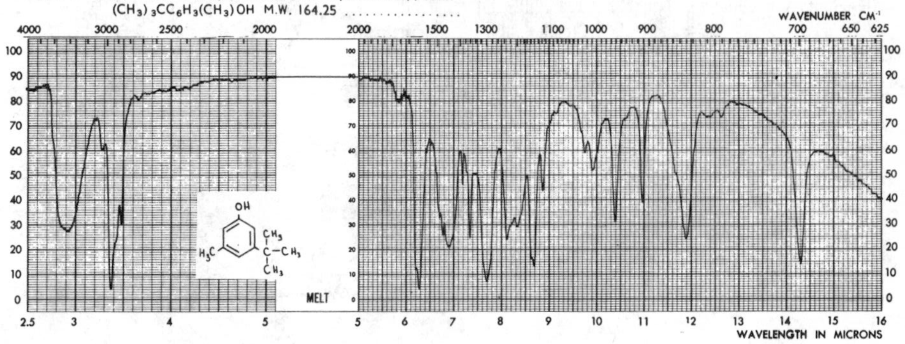

11,710-2
3,5-Diisopropylphenol
$[(CH_3)_2CH]_2C_6H_3OH$
M.W. 178.28 m.p. 51-53° *IRRITANT*

MELT

H

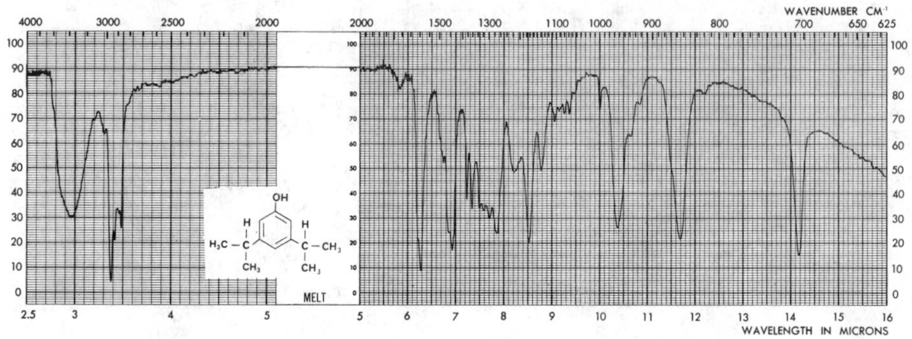

D4850-8 **3,5-Di-tert.-butylphenol**
$[(CH_3)_3C]_2C_6H_3OH$ M.W. 206.33
m.p. 87-89°

NUJOL MULL

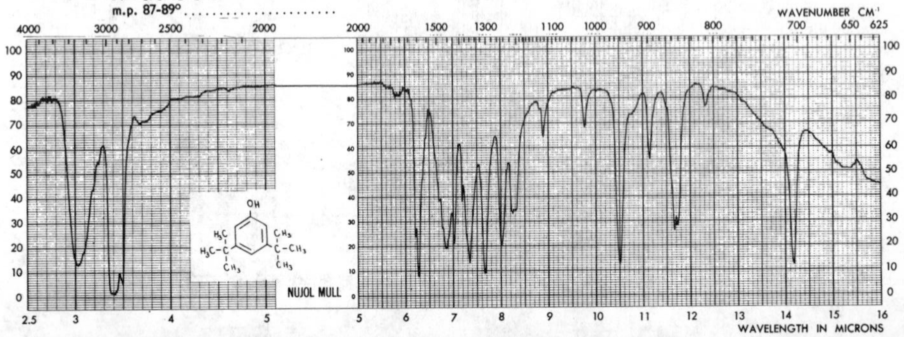

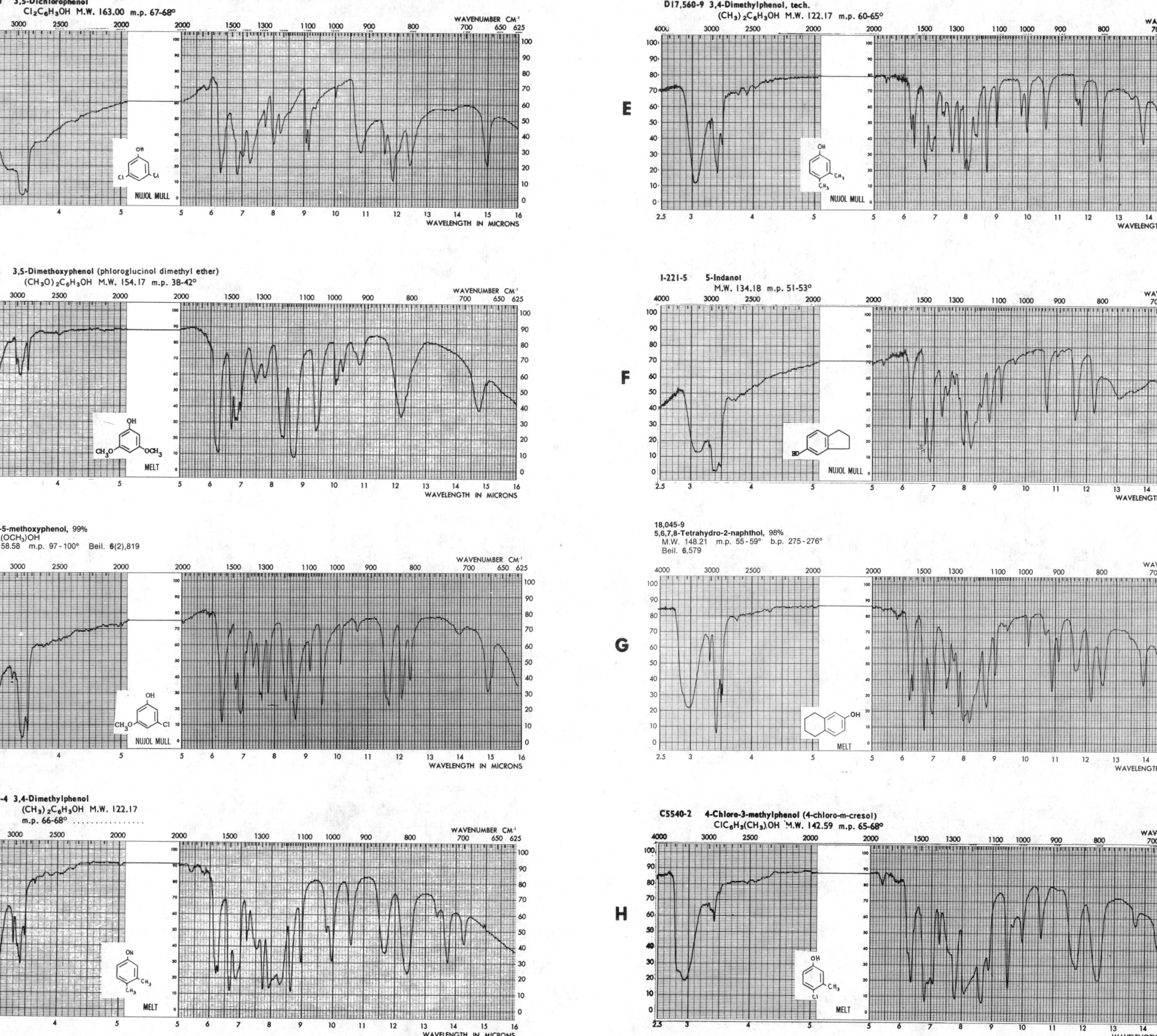
A
D7060-0 3,5-Dichlorophenol
$Cl_2C_6H_3OH$ M.W. 163.00 m.p. 67-68°
NUJOL MULL
B
13,263-2 3,5-Dimethoxyphenol (phloroglucinol dimethyl ether)
$(CH_3O)_2C_6H_3OH$ M.W. 154.17 m.p. 38-42°
MELT
C
16,057-1
3-Chloro-5-methoxyphenol, 99%
$ClC_6H_3(OCH_3)OH$
M.W. 158.58 m.p. 97-100° Beil. 6(2),819
NUJOL MULL
D
D17,540-4 3,4-Dimethylphenol
$(CH_3)_2C_6H_3OH$ M.W. 122.17
m.p. 66-68°
MELT
E
D17,560-9 3,4-Dimethylphenol, tech.
$(CH_3)_2C_6H_3OH$ M.W. 122.17 m.p. 60-65°
NUJOL MULL
F
I-221-5 5-Indanol
M.W. 134.18 m.p. 51-53°
NUJOL MULL
G
18,045-9
5,6,7,8-Tetrahydro-2-naphthol, 98%
M.W. 148.21 m.p. 55-59° b.p. 275-276°
Beil. 6,579
MELT
H
C5540-2 4-Chloro-3-methylphenol (4-chloro-m-cresol)
$ClC_6H_3(CH_3)OH$ M.W. 142.59 m.p. 65-68°
MELT
WAVENUMBER CM⁻¹
WAVELENGTH IN MICRONS
ALDRICH

A

D7040-6 3,4-Dichlorophenol
$Cl_2C_6H_3OH$ M.W. 163.00 m.p. 66-68°

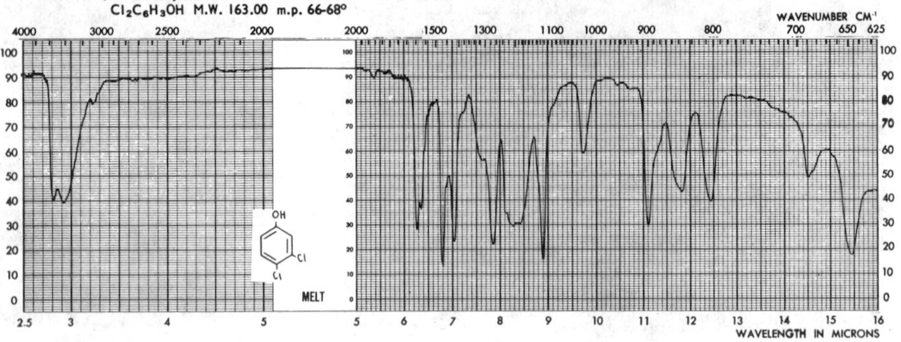

MELT

B

D17,420-3 2,4-Dimethylphenol
$(CH_3)_2C_6H_3OH$ M.W. 122.17
m.p. 23-25°

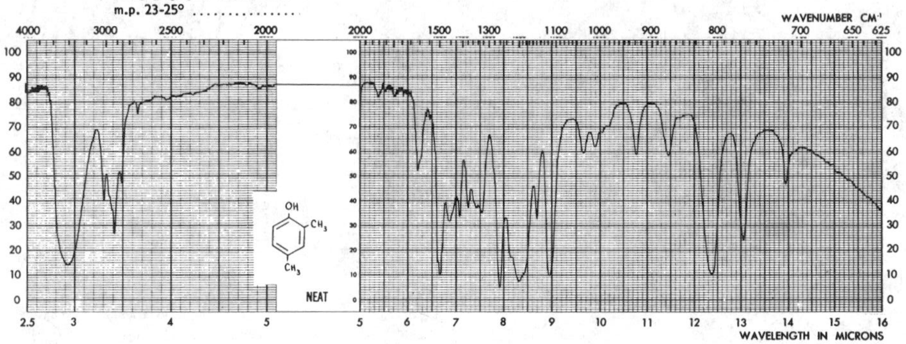

NEAT

C

E2870 4-Ethylguaiacol (4-ethyl-2-methoxyphenol)
$C_2H_5C_6H_3(OCH_3)OH$ M.W. 152.18 n_D^{20} 1.5281

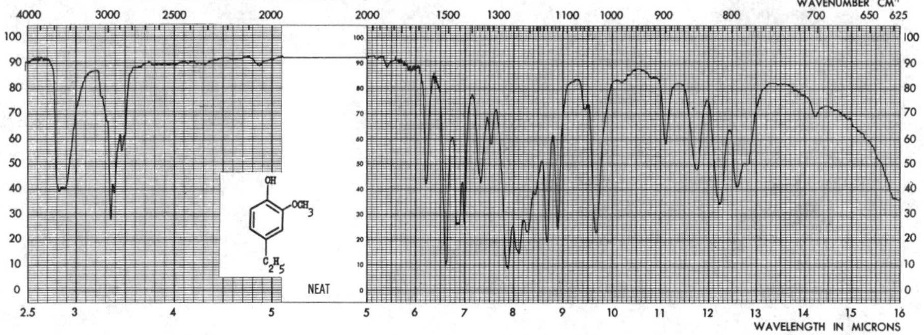

NEAT

D

D17,460-2 2,5-Dimethylphenol
$(CH_3)_2C_6H_3OH$ M.W. 122.17
m.p. 71-73°

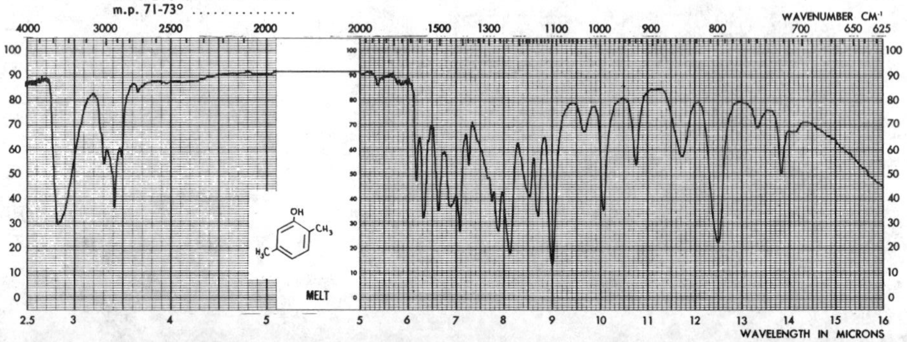

MELT

E

D17,480-7 2,5-Dimethylphenol, tech.
$(CH_3)_2C_6H_3OH$ M.W. 122.17 m.p. 64.5-71°

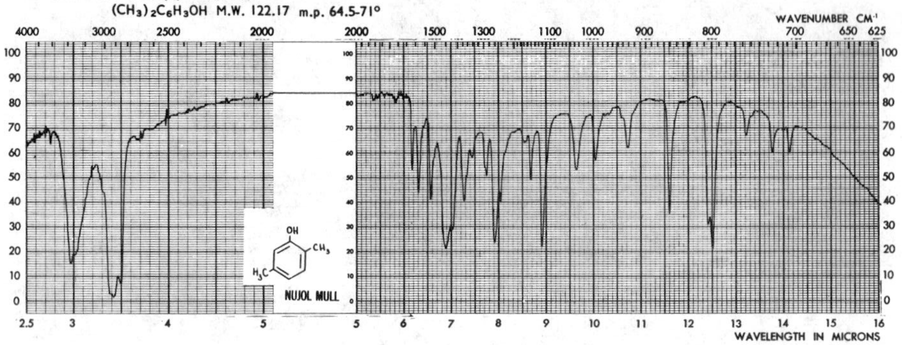

NUJOL MULL

F

11,209-7 Thymol
$2\text{-}[(CH_3)_2CH]C_6H_3\text{-}5\text{-}(CH_3)OH$ M.W. 150.22
m.p. 49-51°

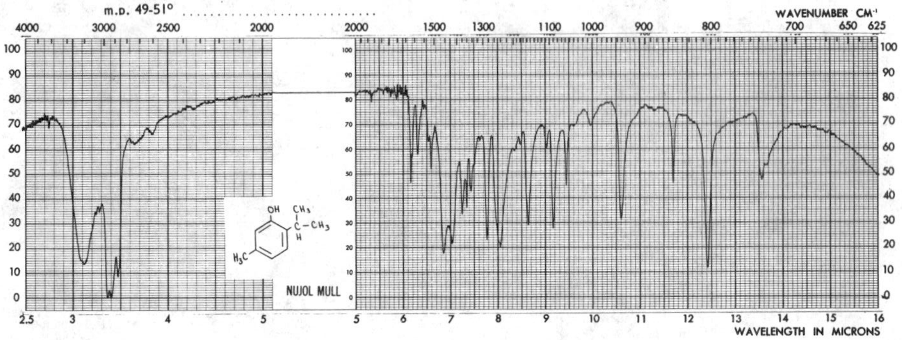

NUJOL MULL

G

11,712-9 2,4-Diisopropylphenol, tech.
$[(CH_3)_2CH]_2C_6H_3OH$ M.W. 178.28

NEAT

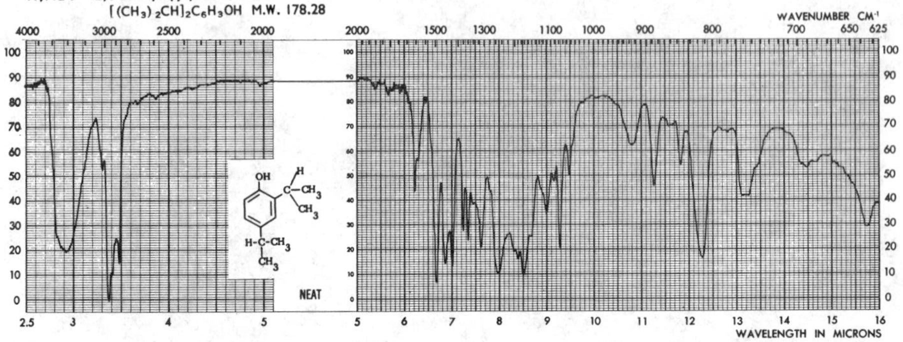

H

11,711-0 2,5-Diisopropylphenol, tech.
$[(CH_3)_2CH]_2C_6H_3OH$ M.W. 178.28

NEAT

WAVENUMBER CM⁻¹

WAVELENGTH IN MICRONS

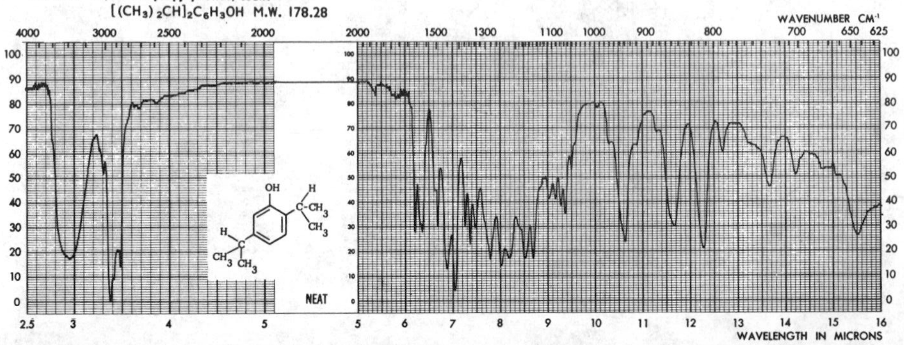

A B9740-2 **2-tert.-Butyl-5-methylphenol** (6-tert.-butyl-m-cresol)
$(CH_3)_3CC_6H_3(CH_3)OH$ M.W. 164.25
n_D^{20} 1.5150
NEAT

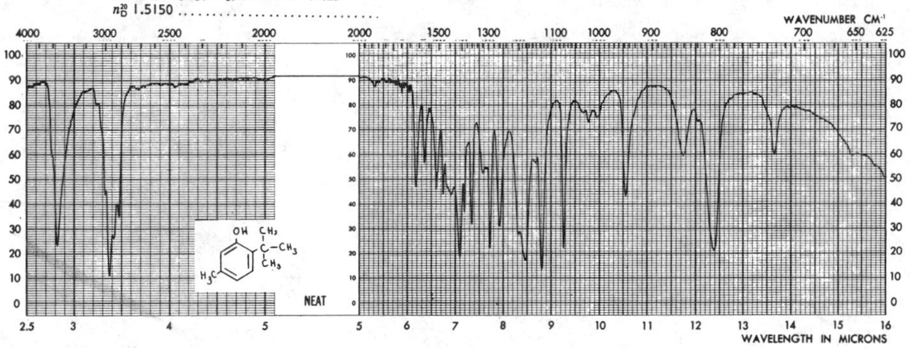

B B9780-1 **4-tert.-Butyl-2-methylphenol** (4-tert.-butyl-o-cresol)
$(CH_3)_3CC_6H_3(CH_3)OH$ M.W. 164.25 n_D^{20} 1.5232
NEAT

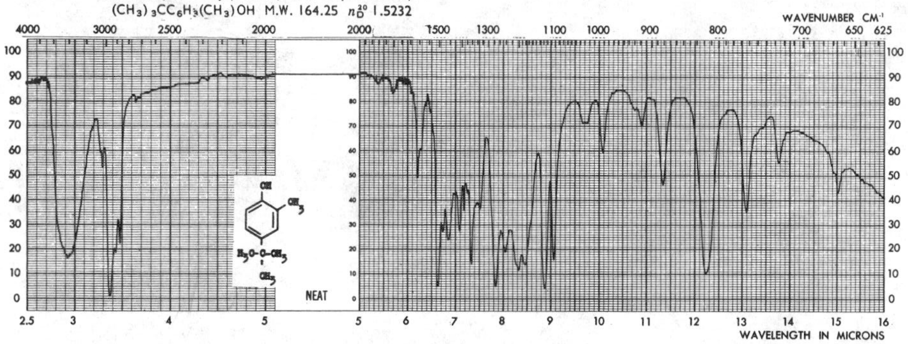

C B9720-8 **2-tert.-Butyl-4-methylphenol** (2-tert.-butyl-p-cresol)
$(CH_3)_3CC_6H_3(CH_3)OH$ M.W. 164.25 m.p. 51-52°
MELT

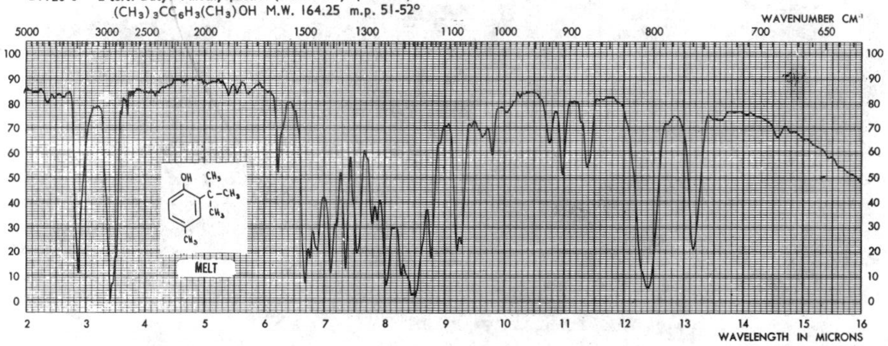

D 13,773-1 **2,4-Di-tert.-butylphenol**
$[(CH_3)_3C]_2C_6H_3OH$ M.W. 206.33
m.p. 52-57°
MELT

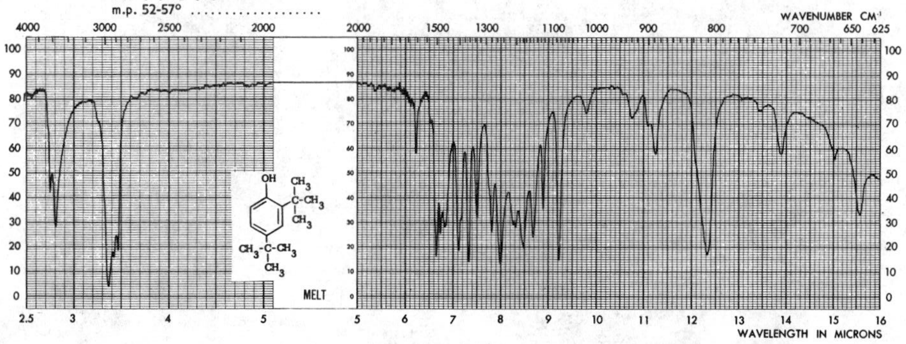

E D4830-3 **2,5-Di-tert.-butylphenol**
$[(CH_3)_3C]_2C_6H_3OH$ M.W. 206.33
m.p. 121-123.5°
NUJOL MULL

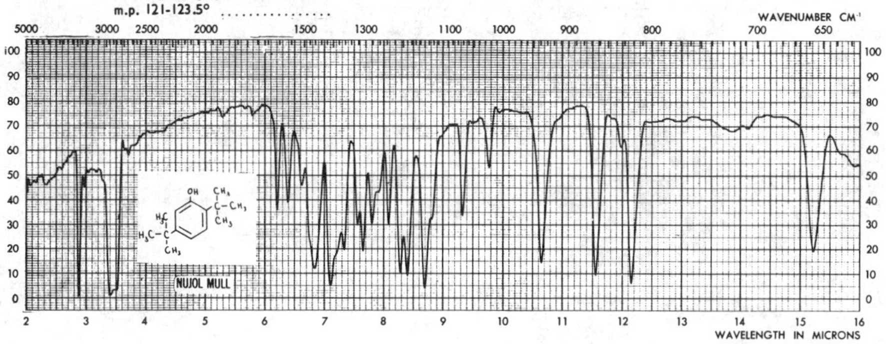

F C5520-8 **4-Chloro-2-methylphenol** (4-chloro-o-cresol)
$ClC_6H_3(CH_3)OH$ M.W. 142.59 m.p. 45-48°
MELT

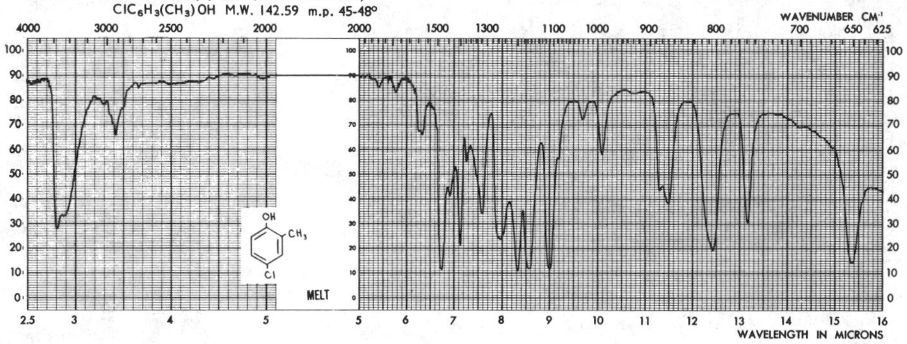

G B7280-9 **2-Bromo-4-methylphenol** (2-bromo-p-cresol)
$BrC_6H_3(CH_3)OH$ M.W. 187.04 n_D^{20} 1.5772
NEAT

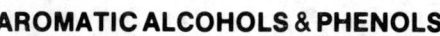

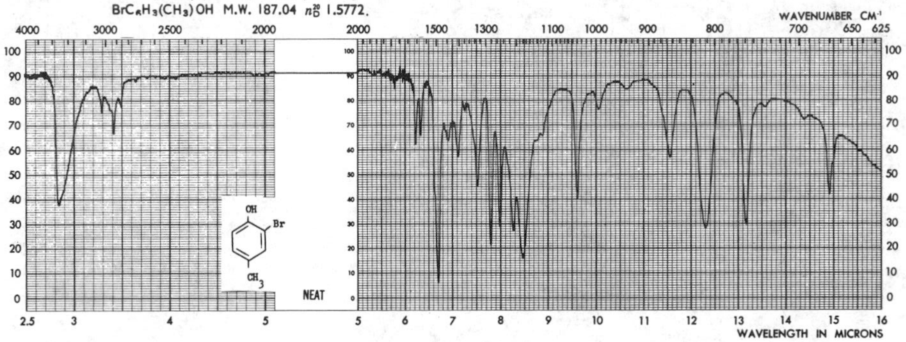

H 11,708-0 **4-tert.-Butyl-2-chlorophenol**
$(CH_3)_3CC_6H_3(Cl)OH$ M.W. 184.67
n_D^{20} 1.5315
NEAT

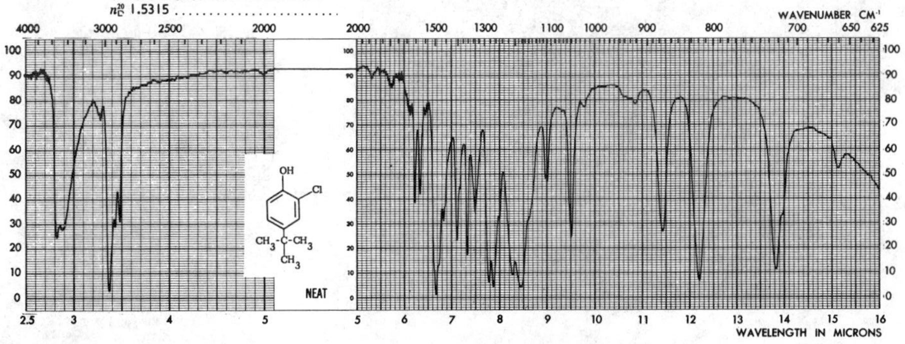

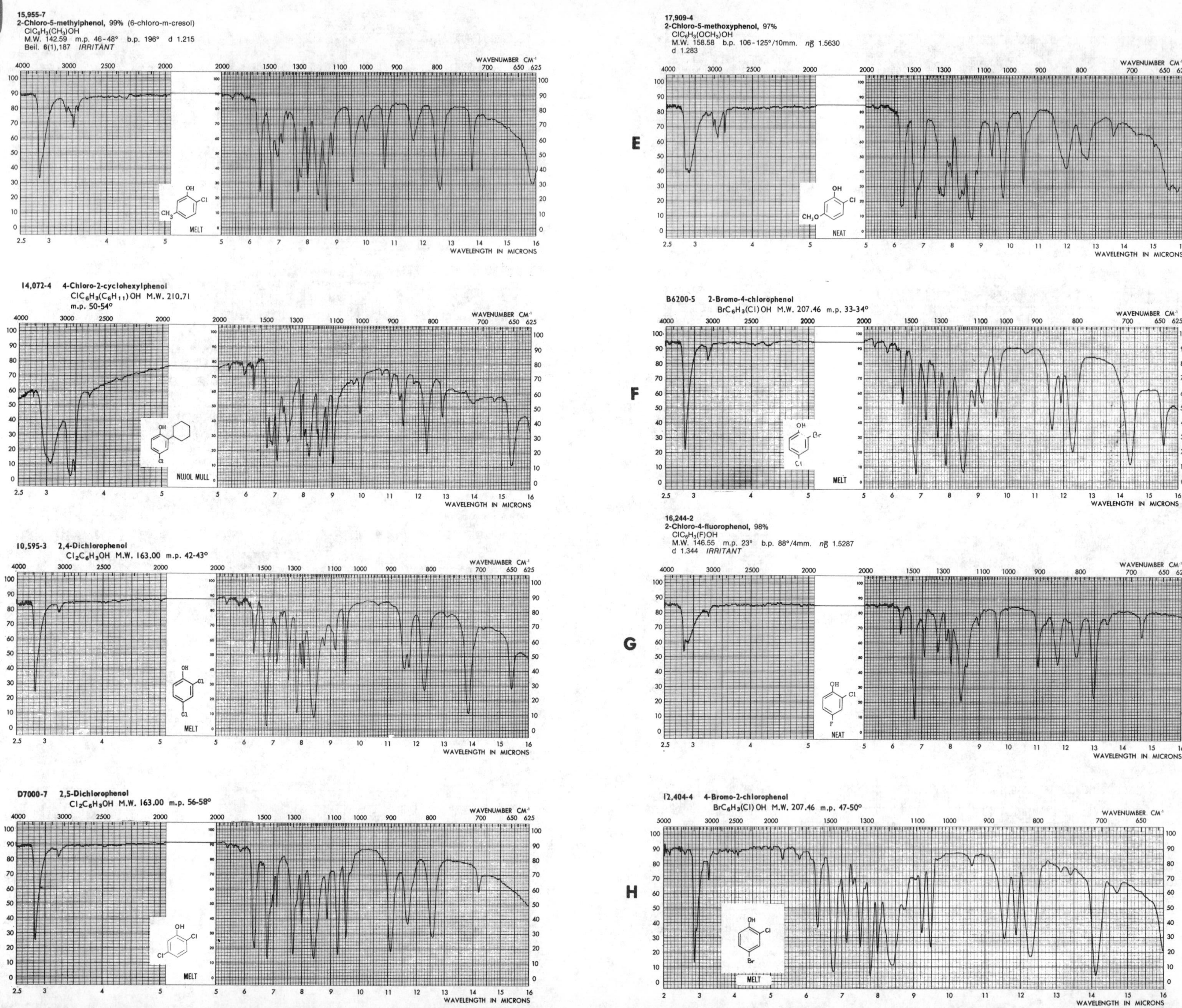

ALDRICH
15,955-7
2-Chloro-5-methylphenol, 99% (6-chloro-m-cresol)
$ClC_6H_3(CH_3)OH$
M.W. 142.59 m.p. 46-48° b.p. 196° d 1.215
Beil. 6(1),187 IRRITANT
A
MELT
14,072-4 4-Chloro-2-cyclohexylphenol
$ClC_6H_3(C_6H_{11})OH$ M.W. 210.71
m.p. 50-54°
B
NUJOL MULL
10,595-3 2,4-Dichlorophenol
$Cl_2C_6H_3OH$ M.W. 163.00 m.p. 42-43°
C
MELT
D7000-7 2,5-Dichlorophenol
$Cl_2C_6H_3OH$ M.W. 163.00 m.p. 56-58°
D
MELT
17,909-4
2-Chloro-5-methoxyphenol, 97%
$ClC_6H_3(OCH_3)OH$
M.W. 158.58 b.p. 106-125°/10mm. n_D^{20} 1.5630
d 1.283
E
NEAT
B6200-5 2-Bromo-4-chlorophenol
$BrC_6H_3(Cl)OH$ M.W. 207.46 m.p. 33-34°
F
MELT
16,244-2
2-Chloro-4-fluorophenol, 98%
$ClC_6H_3(F)OH$
M.W. 146.55 m.p. 23° b.p. 88°/4mm. n_D^{20} 1.5287
d 1.344 IRRITANT
G
NEAT
12,404-4 4-Bromo-2-chlorophenol
$BrC_6H_3(Cl)OH$ M.W. 207.46 m.p. 47-50°
H
MELT
WAVENUMBER CM⁻¹
WAVELENGTH IN MICRONS

A

A3380-9 **2-Allyl-4-methylphenol**
$H_2C{:}CHCH_2C_6H_3(CH_3)OH$ M.W. 148.21
n_D^{20} 1.5385

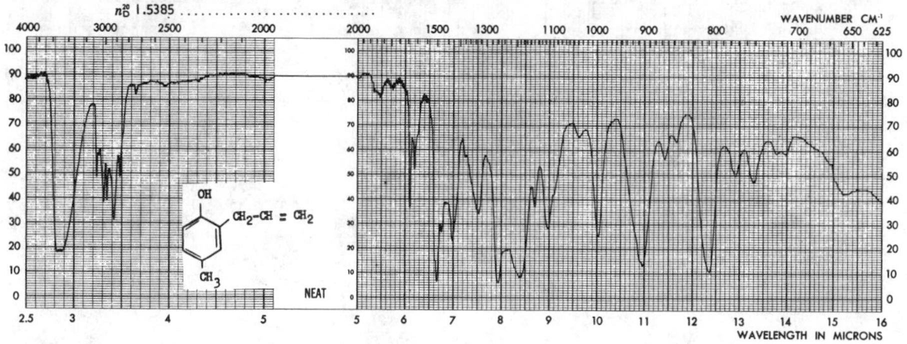

NEAT

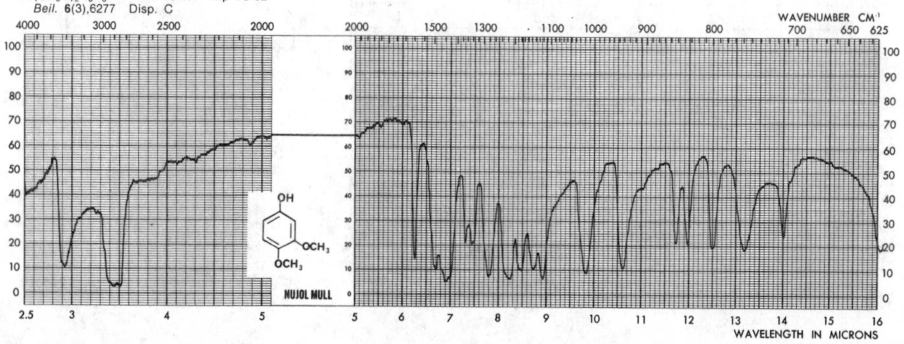

E

22,224-0
3-Ethoxy-4-methoxyphenol monohydrate, 99%
$C_2H_5OC_6H_3(OCH_3)OH{\cdot}H_2O$ FW 186.21
mp 91-95° *Beil.* **6**(3),6279 Disp. C

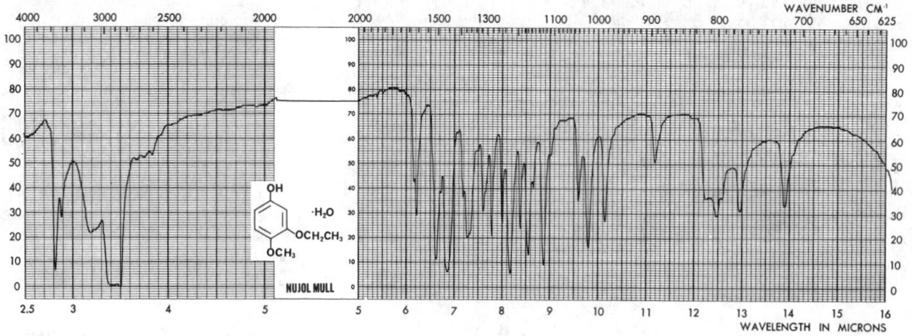

NUJOL MULL

B

E5179-1 **Eugenol**
$4\text{-}(H_2C{:}CHCH_2)C_6H_3\text{-}2\text{-}(OCH_3)OH$ M.W. 164.20
n_D^{20} 1.5396 m.p. -12 to -10°

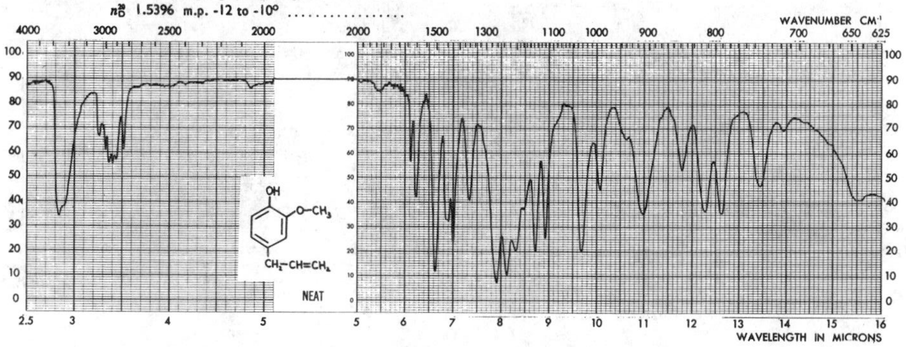

NEAT

F

A3,160-1
4-Allyl-2,6-dimethoxyphenol, tech., 90+%
$H_2C{=}CHCH_2C_6H_2(OCH_3)_2OH$
M.W. 194.23 b.p. 168-169°/11mm. n_D^{20} 1.5480
Beil. **6**(1),556

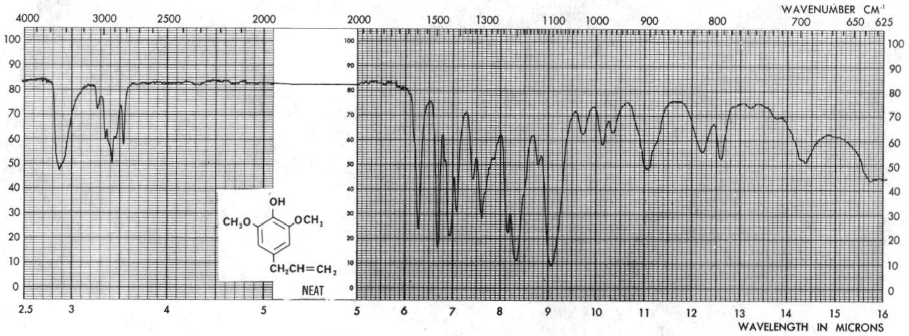

NEAT

C

I-1720-6 **Isoeugenol**
$4\text{-}(CH_3CH{:}CH)C_6H_3\text{-}2\text{-}(OCH_3)OH$ M.W. 164.20
n_D^{20} 1.5748 m.p. 16-19° b.p. 266°

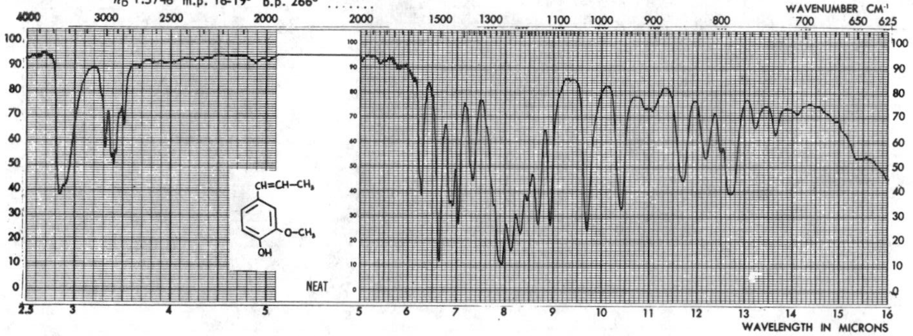

NEAT

G

S300-3 **Sesamol** (3,4-methylenedioxyphenol)
M.W. 138.12 m.p. 63-65°

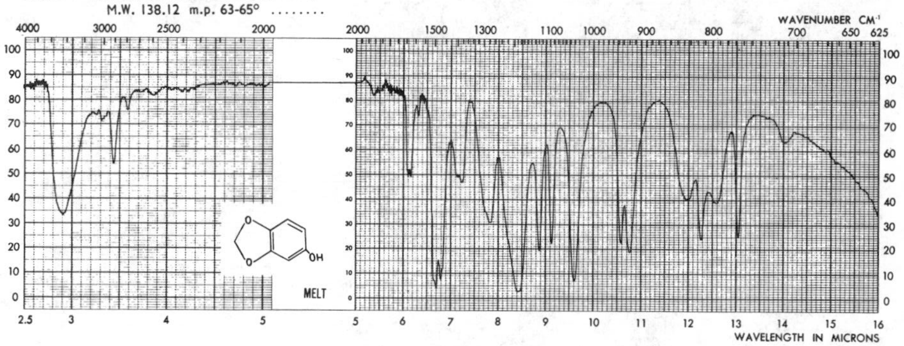

MELT

D

19,446-8
3,4-Dimethoxyphenol, 97%
$(CH_3O)_2C_6H_3OH$ FW 154.17 mp 79-82°
Beil. **6**(3),6277 Disp. C

NUJOL MULL

H

T7870-0 **2,3,6-Trimethylphenol**
$(CH_3)_3C_6H_2OH$ M.W. 136.19 m.p. 62-64°

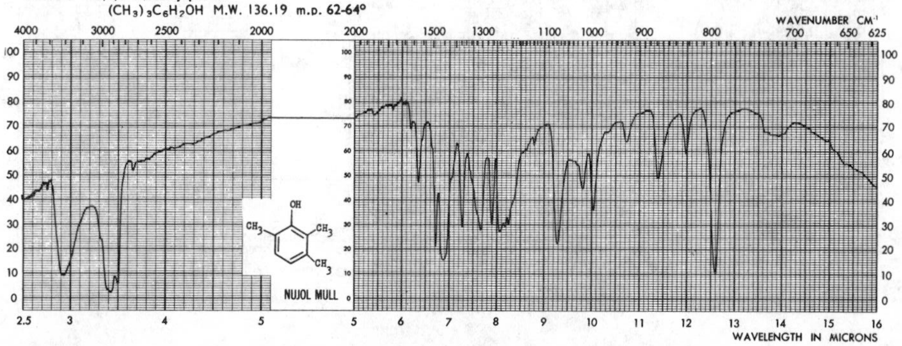

NUJOL MULL

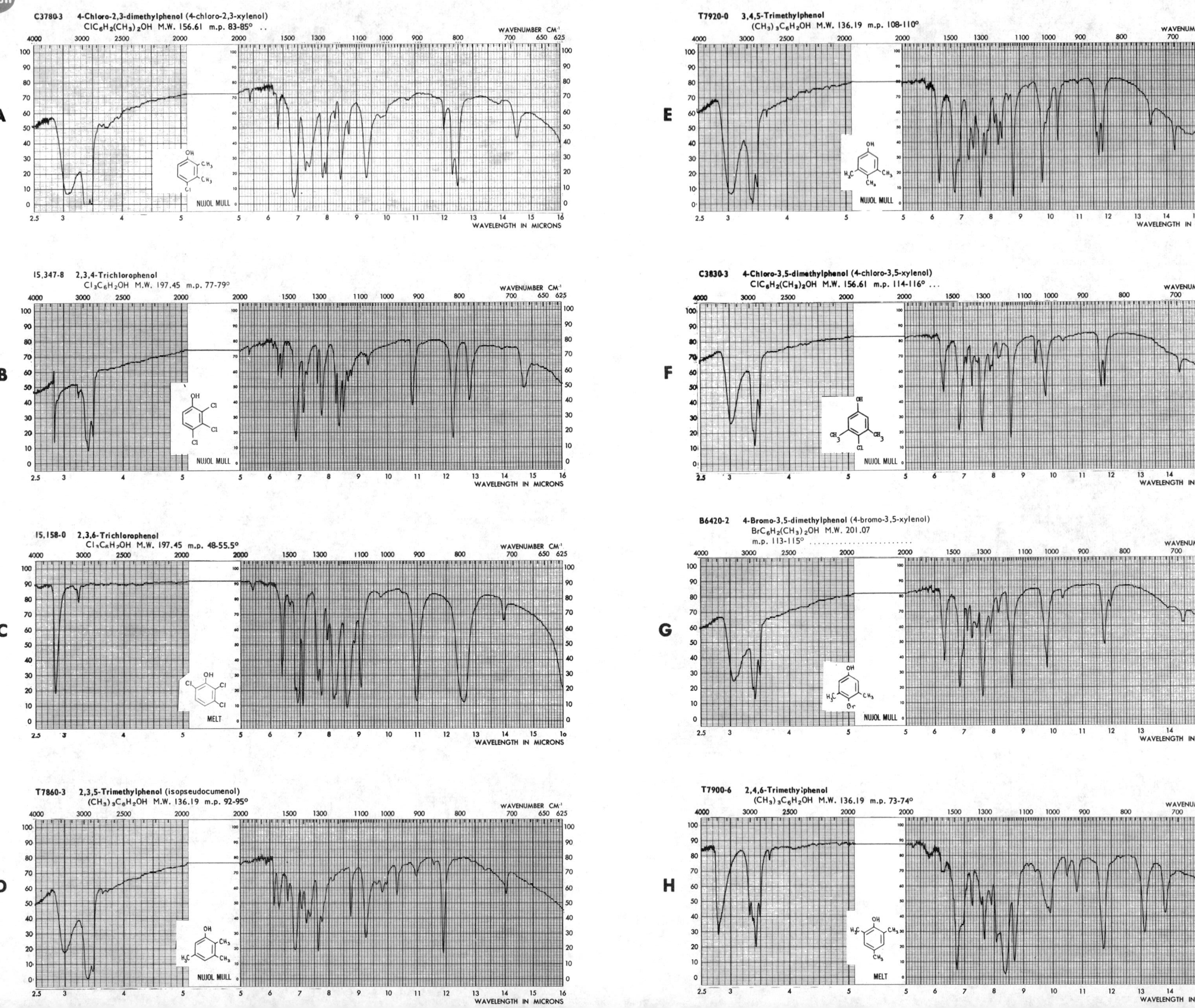

ALDRICH
A
C3780-3 4-Chloro-2,3-dimethylphenol (4-chloro-2,3-xylenol)
$ClC_6H_2(CH_3)_2OH$ M.W. 156.61 m.p. 83-85° ..
NUJOL MULL
B
15,347-8 2,3,4-Trichlorophenol
$Cl_3C_6H_2OH$ M.W. 197.45 m.p. 77-79°
NUJOL MULL
C
15,158-0 2,3,6-Trichlorophenol
$Cl_3C_6H_2OH$ M.W. 197.45 m.p. 48-55.5°
MELT
D
T7860-3 2,3,5-Trimethylphenol (isopseudocumenol)
$(CH_3)_3C_6H_2OH$ M.W. 136.19 m.p. 92-95°
NUJOL MULL
E
T7920-0 3,4,5-Trimethylphenol
$(CH_3)_3C_6H_2OH$ M.W. 136.19 m.p. 108-110°
NUJOL MULL
F
C3830-3 4-Chloro-3,5-dimethylphenol (4-chloro-3,5-xylenol)
$ClC_6H_2(CH_3)_2OH$ M.W. 156.61 m.p. 114-116° ...
NUJOL MULL
G
B6420-2 4-Bromo-3,5-dimethylphenol (4-bromo-3,5-xylenol)
$BrC_6H_2(CH_3)_2OH$ M.W. 201.07
m.p. 113-115°
NUJOL MULL
H
T7900-6 2,4,6-Trimethylphenol
$(CH_3)_3C_6H_2OH$ M.W. 136.19 m.p. 73-74°
MELT
WAVENUMBER CM⁻¹
WAVELENGTH IN MICRONS

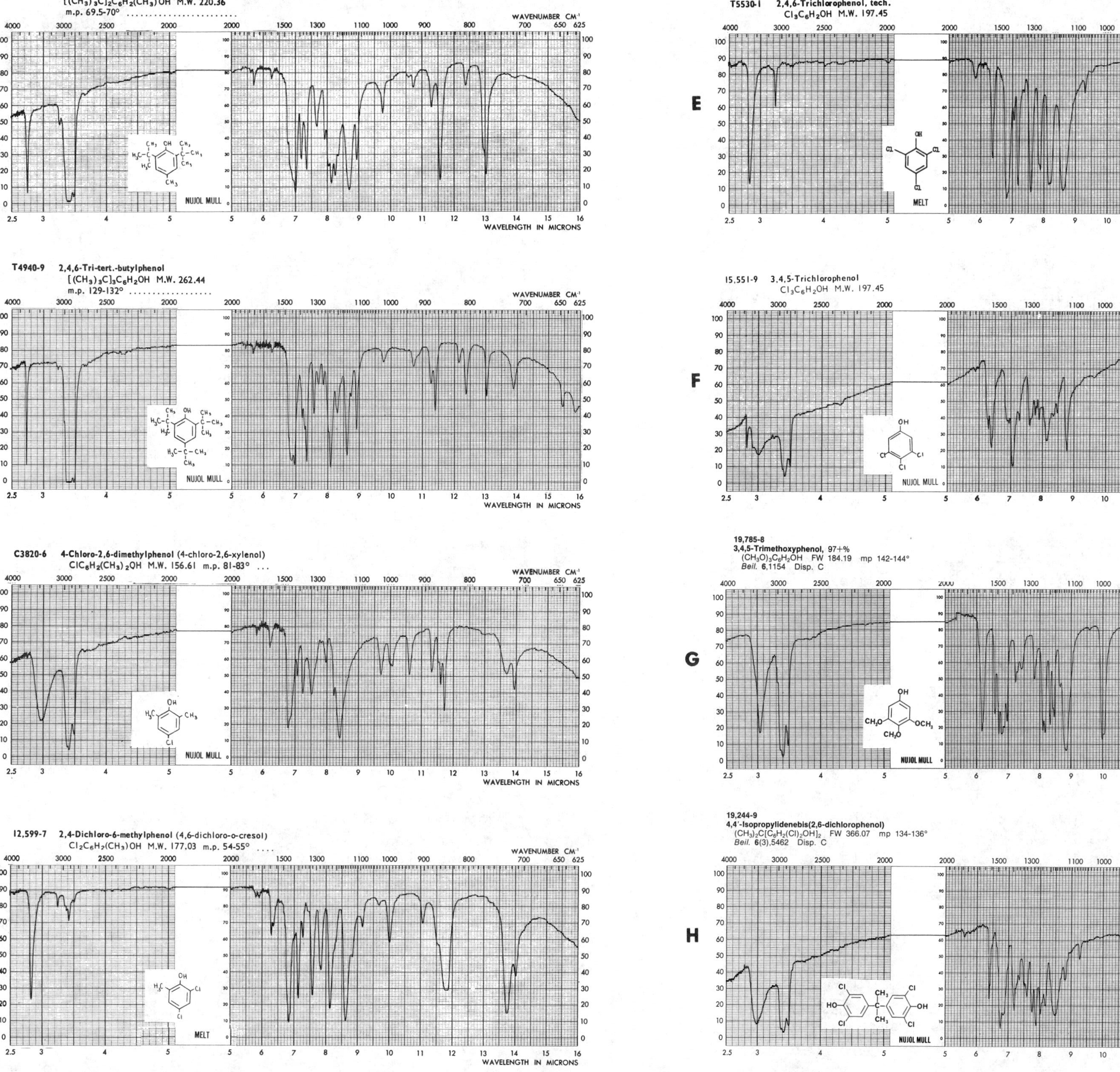
A
D4740-4 2,6-Di-tert.-butyl-4-methylphenol (2,6-di-tert.-butyl-p-cresol)
[(CH3)3C]2C6H2(CH3)OH M.W. 220.36
m.p. 69.5-70°
NUJOL MULL
B
T4940-9 2,4,6-Tri-tert.-butylphenol
[(CH3)3C]3C6H2OH M.W. 262.44
m.p. 129-132°
NUJOL MULL
C
C3820-6 4-Chloro-2,6-dimethylphenol (4-chloro-2,6-xylenol)
ClC6H2(CH3)2OH M.W. 156.61 m.p. 81-83°
NUJOL MULL
D
12,599-7 2,4-Dichloro-6-methylphenol (4,6-dichloro-o-cresol)
Cl2C6H2(CH3)OH M.W. 177.03 m.p. 54-55°
MELT
E
T5530-1 2,4,6-Trichlorophenol, tech.
Cl3C6H2OH M.W. 197.45
MELT
F
15,551-9 3,4,5-Trichlorophenol
Cl3C6H2OH M.W. 197.45
NUJOL MULL
G
19,785-8
3,4,5-Trimethoxyphenol, 97+%
(CH3O)3C6H2OH FW 184.19 mp 142-144°
Beil. 6,1154 Disp. C
NUJOL MULL
H
19,244-9
4,4'-Isopropylidenebis(2,6-dichlorophenol)
(CH3)2C[C6H2(Cl)2OH]2 FW 366.07 mp 134-136°
Beil. 6(3),5462 Disp. C
NUJOL MULL
WAVENUMBER CM⁻¹
WAVELENGTH IN MICRONS

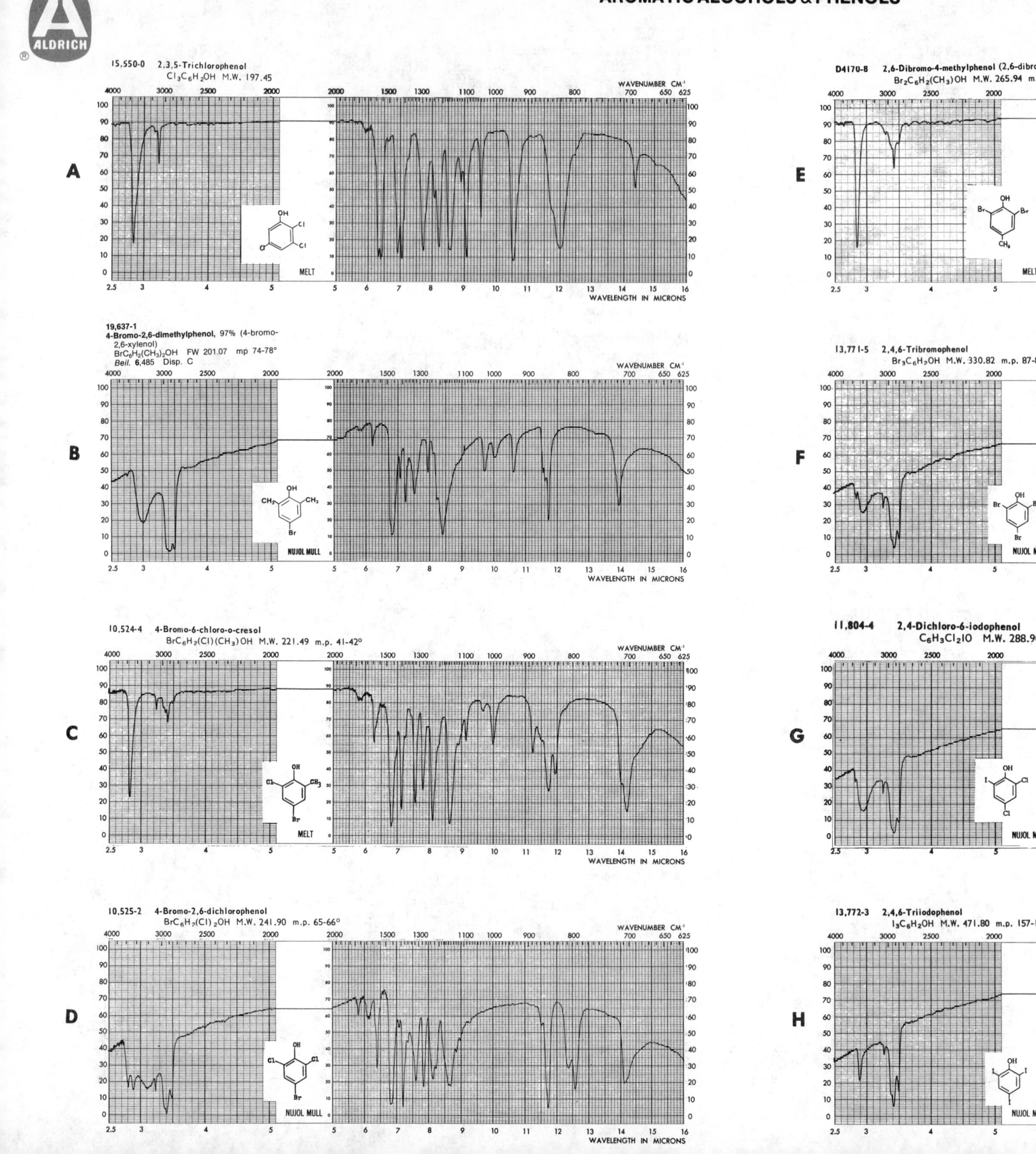
A
15,550-0 2,3,5-Trichlorophenol
$Cl_3C_6H_2OH$ M.W. 197.45
MELT
B
19,637-1
4-Bromo-2,6-dimethylphenol, 97% (4-bromo-2,6-xylenol)
$BrC_6H_2(CH_3)_2OH$ FW 201.07 mp 74-78°
Beil. 6,485 Disp. C
NUJOL MULL
C
10,524-4 4-Bromo-6-chloro-o-cresol
$BrC_6H_2(Cl)(CH_3)OH$ M.W. 221.49 m.p. 41-42°
MELT
D
10,525-2 4-Bromo-2,6-dichlorophenol
$BrC_6H_2(Cl)_2OH$ M.W. 241.90 m.p. 65-66°
NUJOL MULL
E
D4170-8 2,6-Dibromo-4-methylphenol (2,6-dibromo-p-cresol)
$Br_2C_6H_2(CH_3)OH$ M.W. 265.94 m.p. 49-50°
MELT
F
13,771-5 2,4,6-Tribromophenol
$Br_3C_6H_2OH$ M.W. 330.82 m.p. 87-89°
NUJOL MULL
G
11,804-4 2,4-Dichloro-6-iodophenol
$C_6H_3Cl_2IO$ M.W. 288.90 m.p. 53-57°
NUJOL MULL
H
13,772-3 2,4,6-Triiodophenol
$I_3C_6H_2OH$ M.W. 471.80 m.p. 157-159°
NUJOL MULL
WAVENUMBER CM⁻¹
WAVELENGTH IN MICRONS

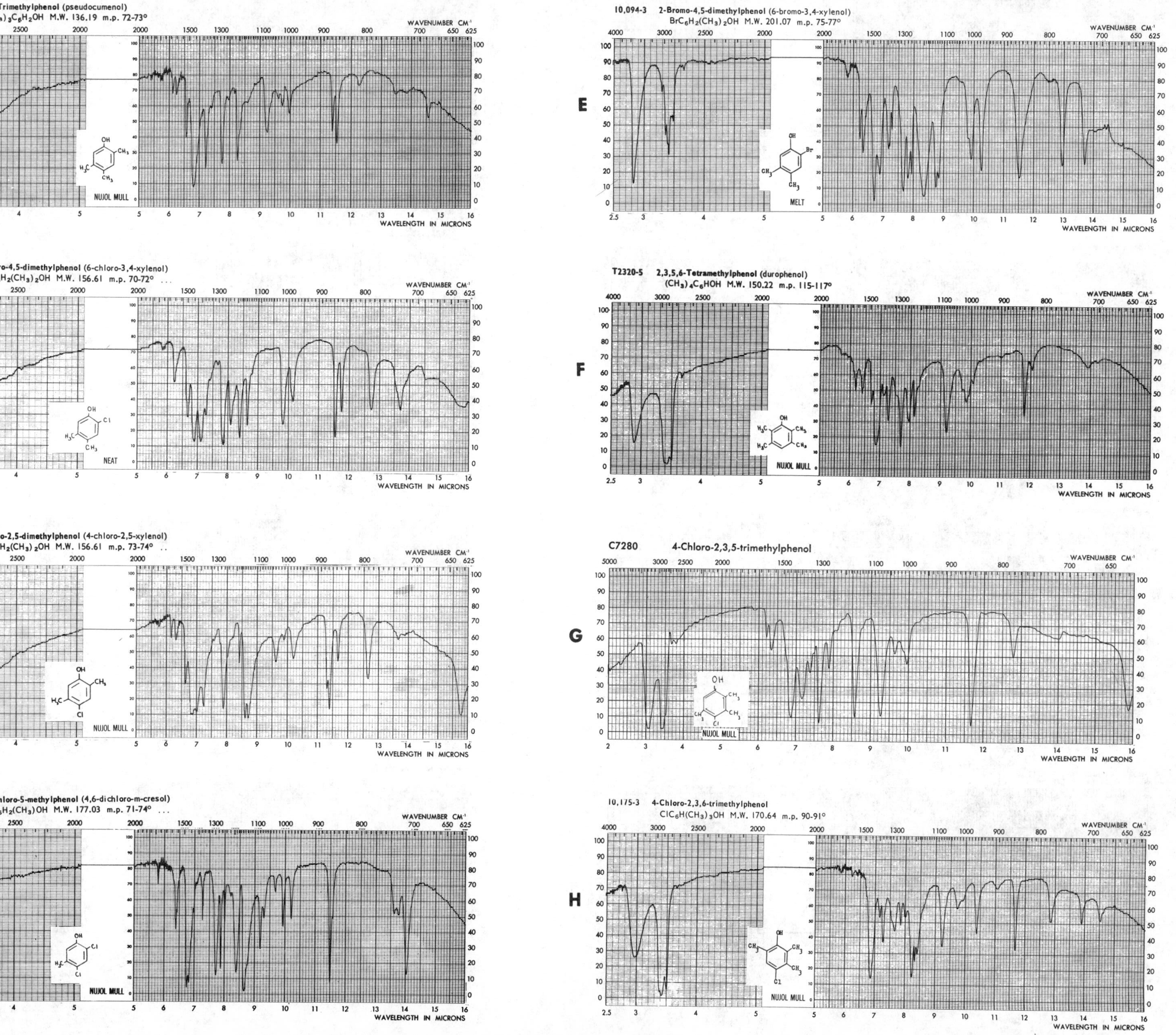
T7880-8 2,4,5-Trimethylphenol (pseudocumenol)
(CH₃)₃C₆H₂OH M.W. 136.19 m.p. 72-73°
NUJOL MULL
C3760-9 2-Chloro-4,5-dimethylphenol (6-chloro-3,4-xylenol)
ClC₆H₂(CH₃)₂OH M.W. 156.61 m.p. 70-72°
NEAT
C3800-1 4-Chloro-2,5-dimethylphenol (4-chloro-2,5-xylenol)
ClC₆H₂(CH₃)₂OH M.W. 156.61 m.p. 73-74°
NUJOL MULL
D6580-1 2,4-Dichloro-5-methylphenol (4,6-dichloro-m-cresol)
Cl₂C₆H₂(CH₃)OH M.W. 177.03 m.p. 71-74°
NUJOL MULL
10,094-3 2-Bromo-4,5-dimethylphenol (6-bromo-3,4-xylenol)
BrC₆H₂(CH₃)₂OH M.W. 201.07 m.p. 75-77°
MELT
T2320-5 2,3,5,6-Tetramethylphenol (durophenol)
(CH₃)₄C₆HOH M.W. 150.22 m.p. 115-117°
NUJOL MULL
C7280 4-Chloro-2,3,5-trimethylphenol
NUJOL MULL
10,175-3 4-Chloro-2,3,6-trimethylphenol
ClC₆H(CH₃)₃OH M.W. 170.64 m.p. 90-91°
NUJOL MULL
WAVENUMBER CM⁻¹
WAVELENGTH IN MICRONS
A
B
C
D
E
F
G
H

ALDRICH

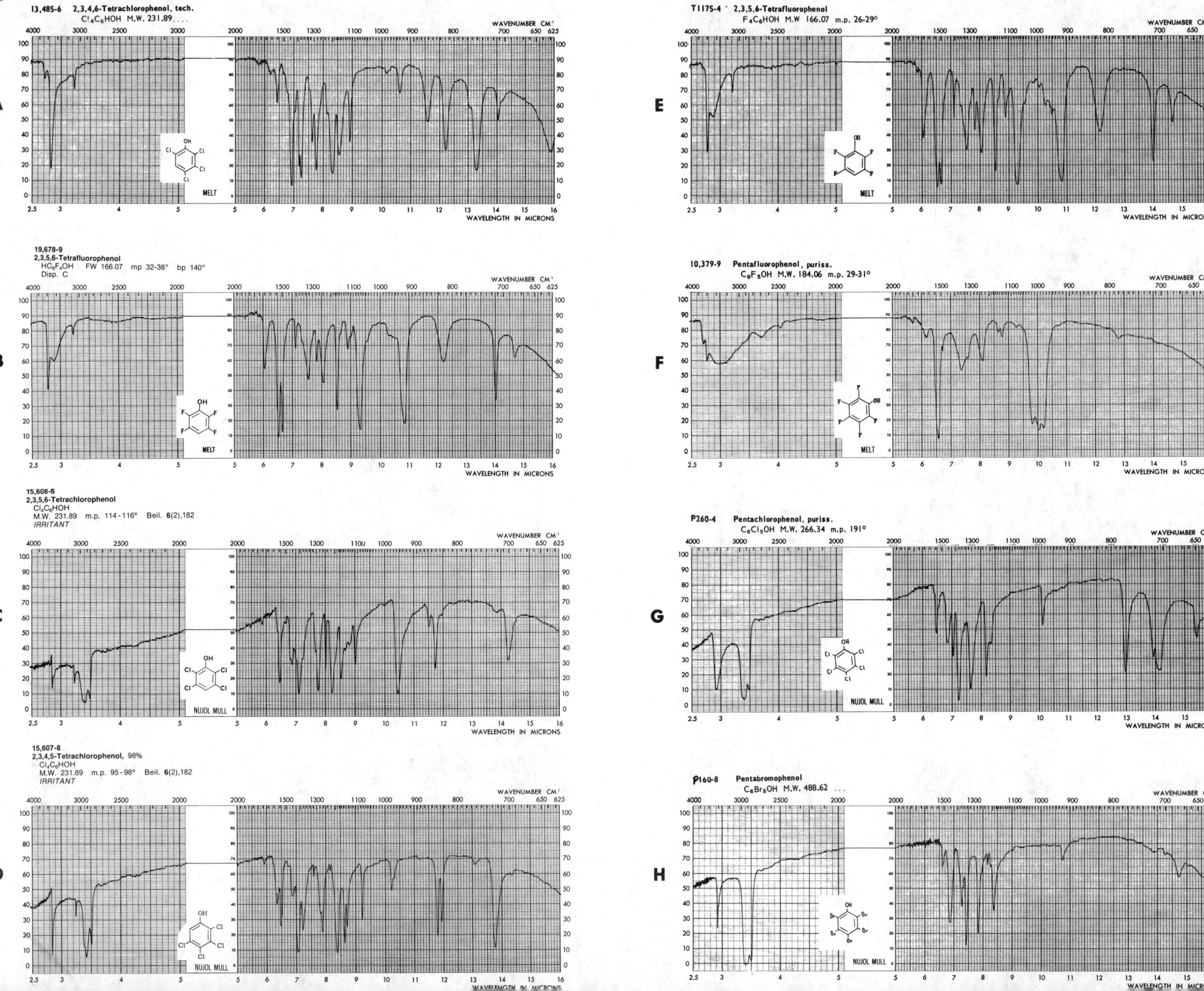
ALDRICH
A
13,485-6 2,3,4,6-Tetrachlorophenol, tech.
Cl_4C_6HOH M.W. 231.89....
MELT
B
19,678-9
2,3,5,6-Tetrafluorophenol
HC_6F_4OH FW 166.07 mp 32-38° bp 140°
Disp. C
MELT
C
15,608-6
2,3,5,6-Tetrachlorophenol
Cl_4C_6HOH
M.W. 231.89 m.p. 114-116° Beil. 6(2),182
IRRITANT
NUJOL MULL
D
15,607-8
2,3,4,5-Tetrachlorophenol, 98%
Cl_4C_6HOH
M.W. 231.89 m.p. 95-98° Beil. 6(2),182
IRRITANT
NUJOL MULL
E
T1175-4 2,3,5,6-Tetrafluorophenol
F_4C_6HOH M.W 166.07 m.p. 26-29°
MELT
F
10,379-9 Pentafluorophenol, puriss.
C_6F_5OH M.W. 184.06 m.p. 29-31°
MELT
G
P260-4 Pentachlorophenol, puriss.
C_6Cl_5OH M.W. 266.34 m.p. 191°
NUJOL MULL
H
P160-8 Pentabromophenol
C_6Br_5OH M.W. 488.62 ...
NUJOL MULL
WAVENUMBER CM⁻¹
WAVELENGTH IN MICRONS

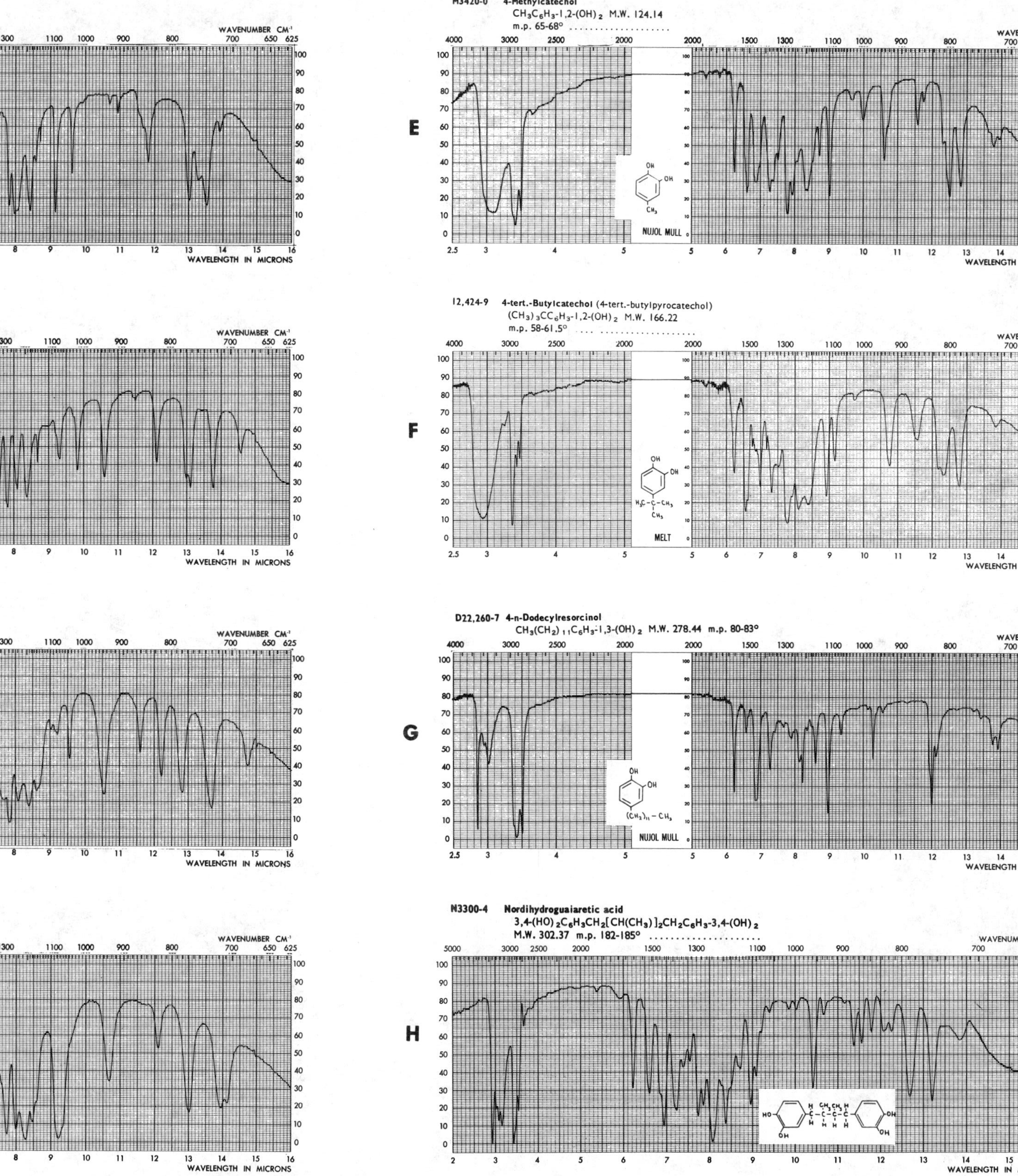

A 13,501-1 **Catechol** (pyrocatechol), 99+%
C_6H_4-1,2-$(OH)_2$ M.W. 110.11
m.p. 104-106°
NUJOL MULL

B M3400-6 **3-Methylcatechol**
$CH_3C_6H_3$-1,2-$(OH)_2$ M.W. 124.14 m.p. 67-69°
NUJOL MULL

C I-2160-2 **3-Isopropylcatechol** (3-isopropylpyrocatechol)
$(CH_3)_2CHC_6H_3$-1,2-$(OH)_2$ M.W. 152.19
m.p. 49-51°
MELT

D M1320-3 **3-Methoxycatechol** (pyrogallol monomethyl ether)
$CH_3OC_6H_3$-1,2-$(OH)_2$ M.W. 140.14
m.p. 43-44°
MELT

E M3420-0 **4-Methylcatechol**
$CH_3C_6H_3$-1,2-$(OH)_2$ M.W. 124.14
m.p. 65-68°
NUJOL MULL

F 12,424-9 **4-tert.-Butylcatechol** (4-tert.-butylpyrocatechol)
$(CH_3)_3CC_6H_3$-1,2-$(OH)_2$ M.W. 166.22
m.p. 58-61.5°
MELT

G D22,260-7 **4-n-Dodecylresorcinol**
$CH_3(CH_2)_{11}C_6H_3$-1,3-$(OH)_2$ M.W. 278.44 m.p. 80-83°
NUJOL MULL

H N3300-4 **Nordihydroguaiaretic acid**
3,4-$(HO)_2C_6H_3CH_2[CH(CH_3)]_2CH_2C_6H_3$-3,4-$(OH)_2$
M.W. 302.37 m.p. 182-185°

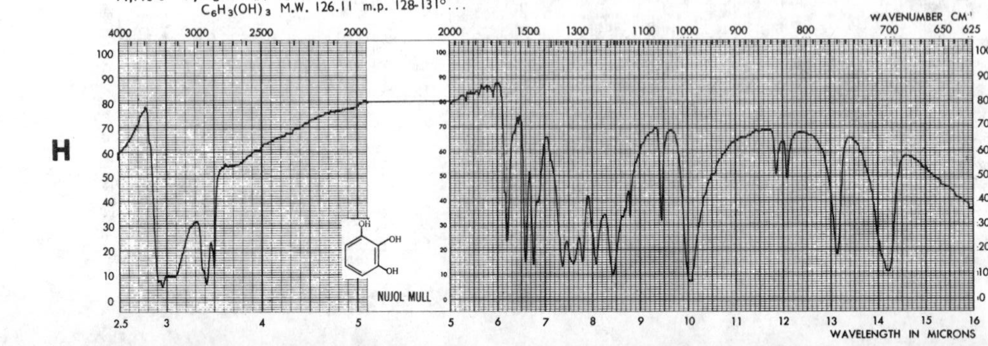

A

14,878-4 **DL-3,4-Dihydroxyphenylglycol** (DL-β,3,4-trihydroxyphenethyl alcohol)
$(HO)_2C_6H_3CH(OH)CH_2OH$ M.W. 170.17
m.p. 116-117°

NUJOL MULL

B

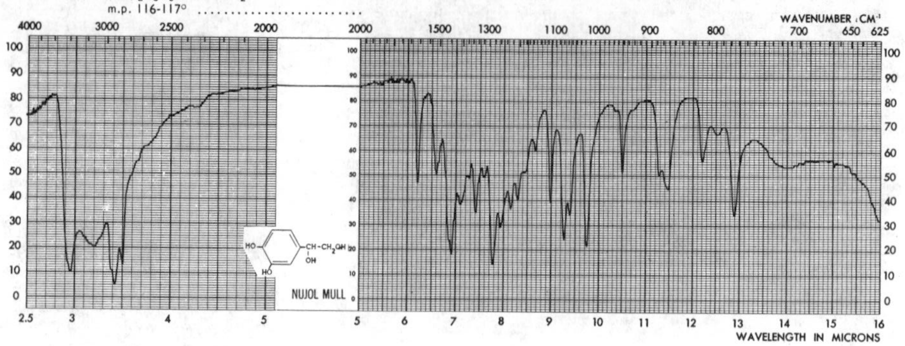

14,879-2 **DL-4-Hydroxy-3-methoxyphenylglycol** (DL-β,4-dihydroxy-3-methoxyphenethyl alcohol)
$[HOC_6H_3(OCH_3)CH(OH)CH_2OH]_2$

NEAT

C

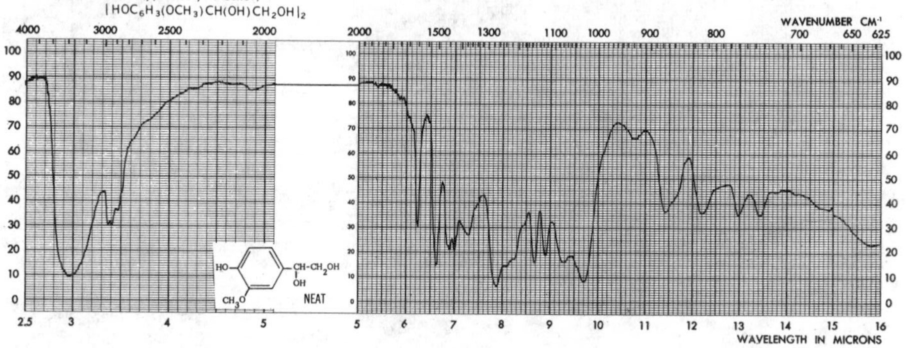

D12,562-8 **3,6-Diisopropylcatechol** (3,6-diisopropylpyrocatechol)
$[(CH_3)_2CH]_2C_6H_2$-1,2-$(OH)_2$ M.W. 194.27 m.p. 75-76°

MELT

D

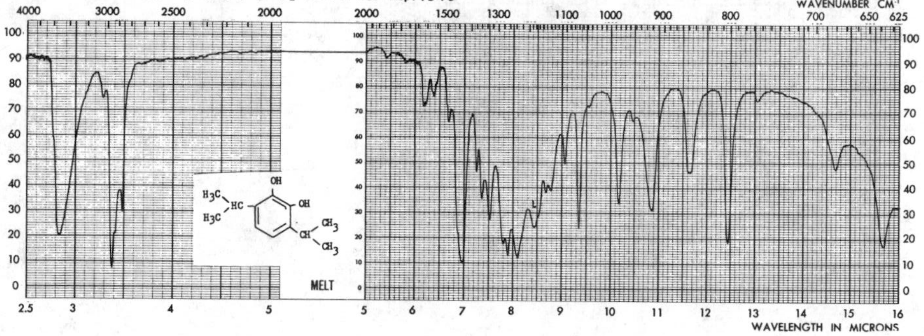

D12,560-1 **3,5-Diisopropylcatechol** (3,5-diisopropylpyrocatechol)
$[(CH_3)_2CH]_2C_6H_2$-1,2-$(OH)_2$ M.W. 194.27 m.p. 62-65°

MELT

E

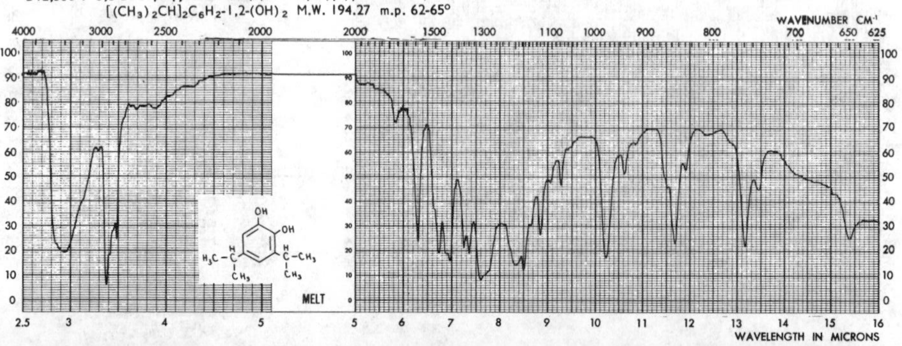

D4580-0 **3,5-Di-tert.-butylcatechol**
$[(CH_3)_3C]_2C_6H_2$-1,2-$(OH)_2$ M.W. 222.33 m.p. 96-99°

NUJOL MULL

F

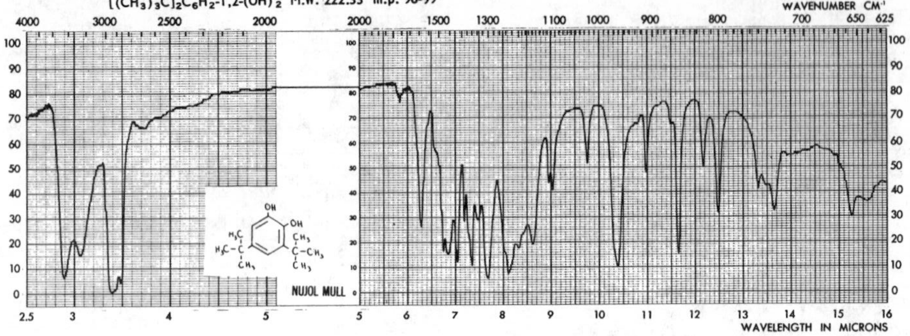

T690-3 **Tetrachlorocatechol** (tetrachloropyrocatechol) **monohydrate**
C_6Cl_4-1,2-$(OH)_2 \cdot H_2O$ M.W. 265.91 m.p. 189-191°

NUJOL MULL

G

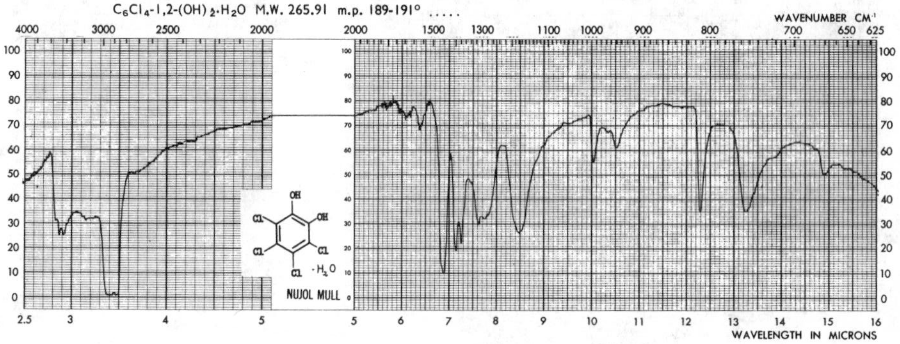

T480-3 **Tetrabromocatechol** (tetrabromopyrocatechol)
C_6Br_4-1,2-$(OH)_2$ M.W. 425.72 m.p. 188-193°

NUJOL MULL

H

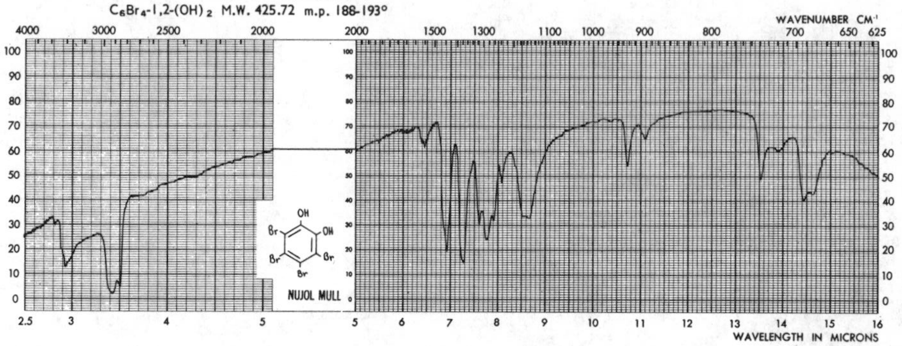

14,795-8 **Pyrogallol** (pyrogallic acid, 1,2,3-trihydroxybenzene)
$C_6H_3(OH)_3$ M.W. 126.11 m.p. 128-131°

NUJOL MULL

A

17,340-1
1,2,4-Benzenetriol, 99% (hydroxyhydroquinone)
$C_6H_3(OH)_3$
M.W. 126.11 m.p. 140° (sublimes) Beil. **6**,1087

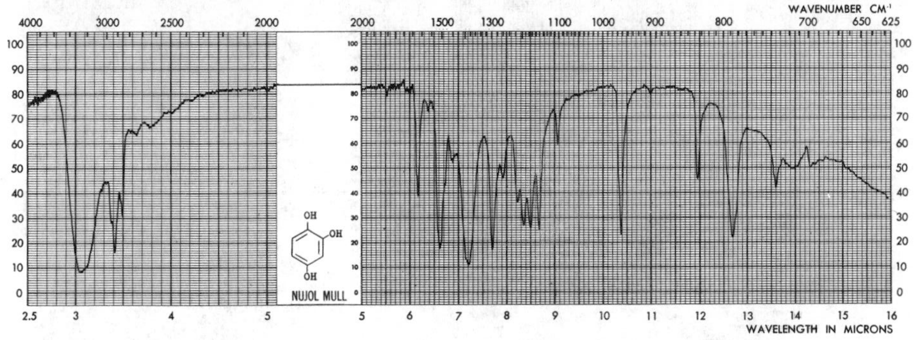

NUJOL MULL

B

P3800-5 **Phloroglucinol dihydrate**
C_6H_3-1,3,5-$(OH)_3 \cdot 2H_2O$ M.W. 162.14 m.p. 218-221°

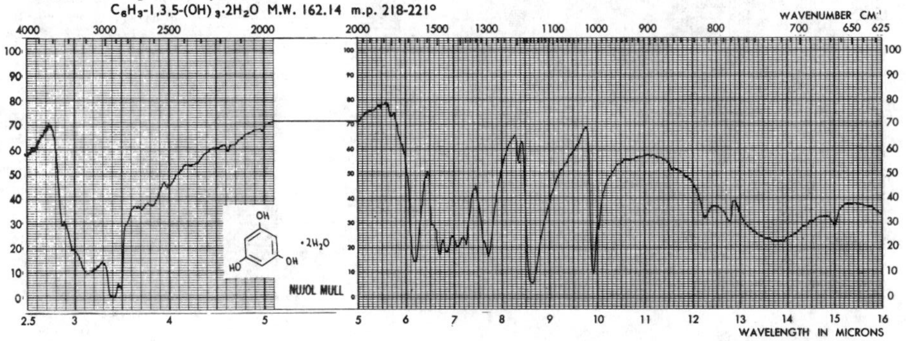

NUJOL MULL

C

13,072-9 **Benzenehexol** (hexahydroxybenzene)
$C_6H_6O_6$ M.W. 174.11 m.p. > 300°

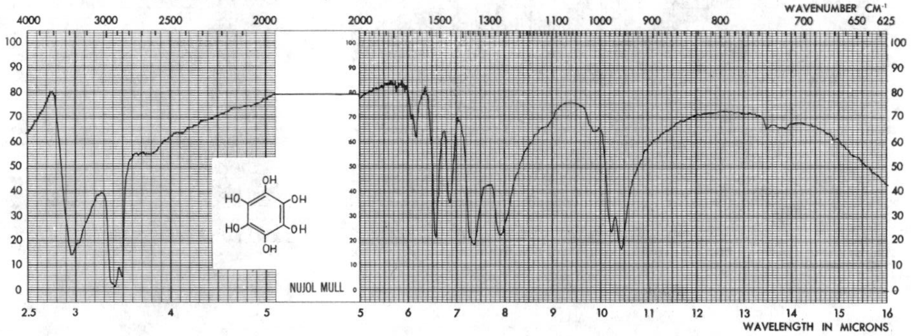

NUJOL MULL

D

R40-6 **Resorcinol**
C_6H_4-1,3-$(OH)_2$ M.W. 110.11 m.p. 109-110°

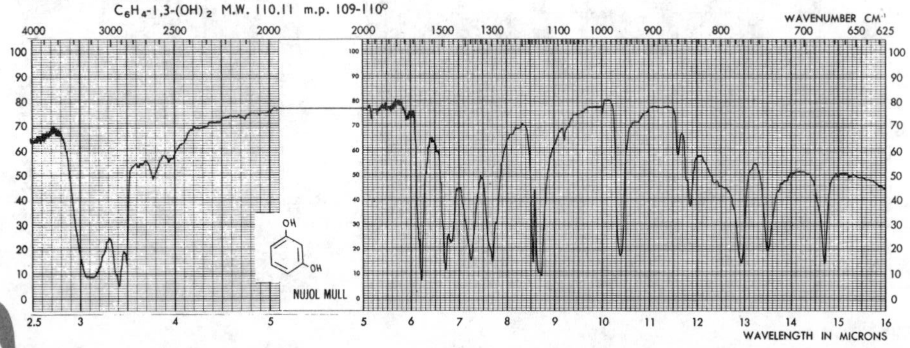

NUJOL MULL

E

M8040-7 **2-Methylresorcinol** (2,6-dihydroxytoluene)
$CH_3C_6H_3(OH)_2$ M.W. 124.14
m.p. 115-118° ....

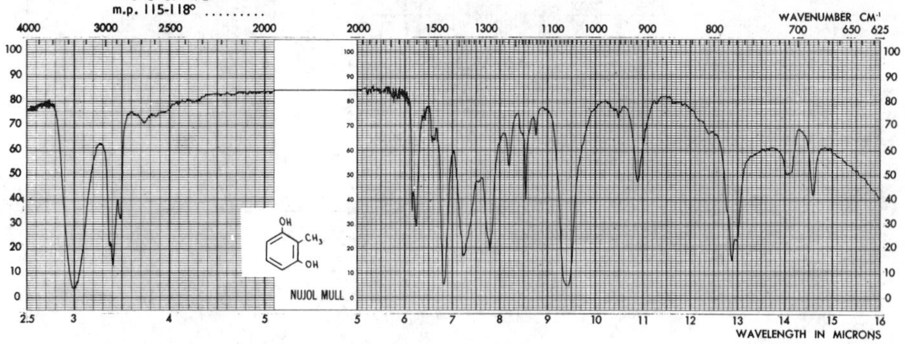

NUJOL MULL

F

19,119-1
4-Methylresorcinol, 97% (2,4-dihydroxytoluene)
$CH_3C_6H_3(OH)_2$ FW 124.14 mp 106-108°
bp 267-270° *Beil.* **6**,872 Disp. C

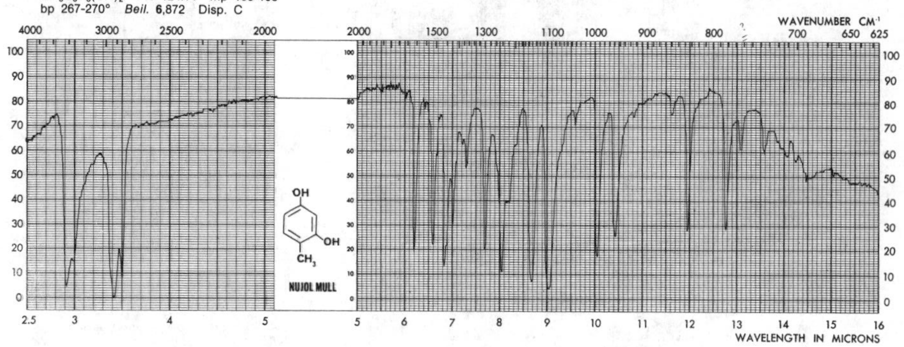

NUJOL MULL

G

E4820-0 **4-Ethylresorcinol**
$C_2H_5C_6H_3$-1,3-$(OH)_2$ M.W. 138.17 m.p. 95-98°

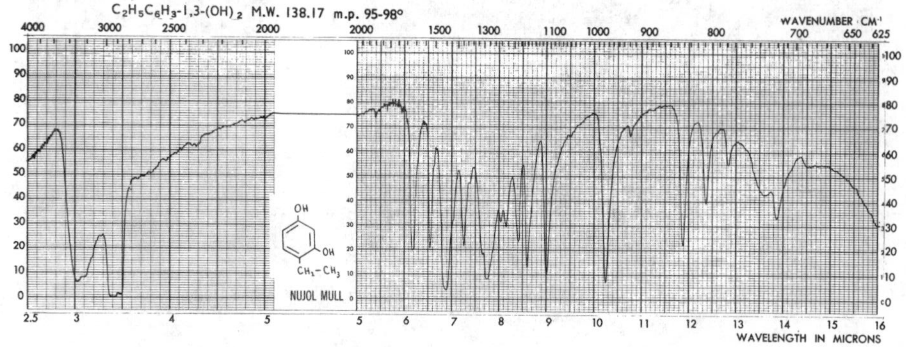

NUJOL MULL

H

P5420-5 **4-n-Propylresorcinol**
$CH_3CH_2CH_2C_6H_3$-1,3-$(OH)_2$ M.W. 152.19 m.p. 65-70° ...

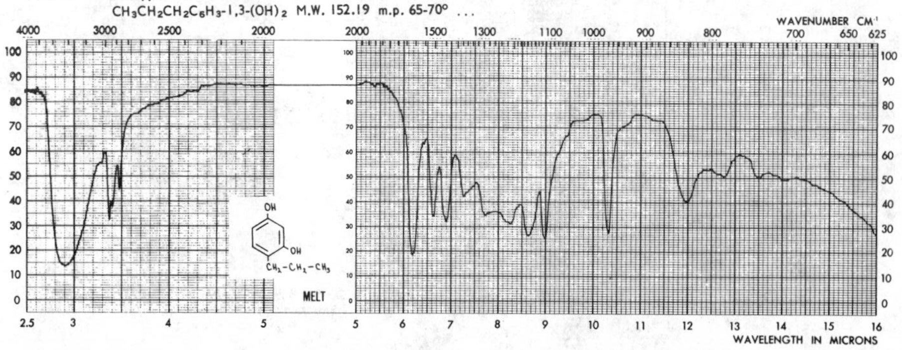

MELT

ALDRICH ®

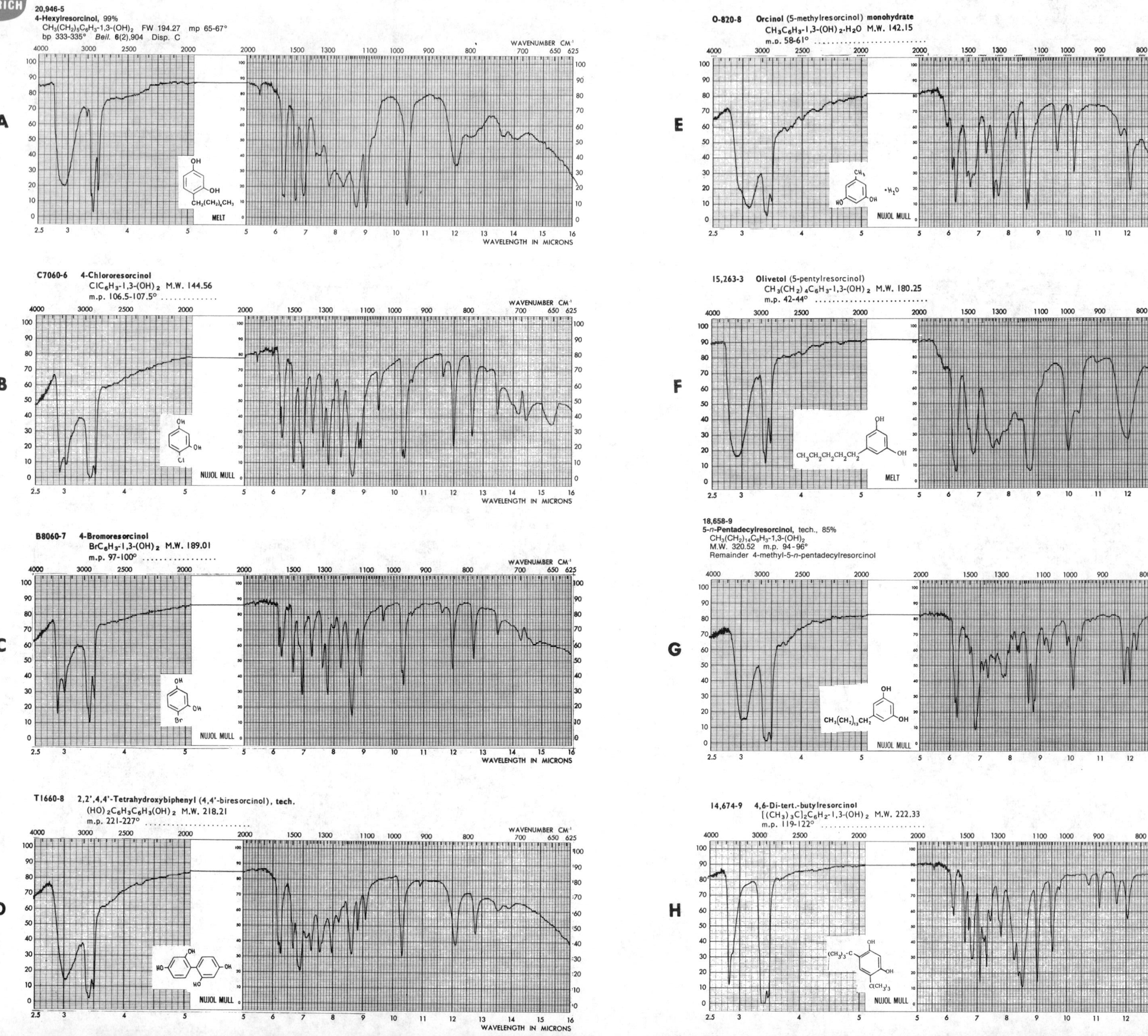
A
20,946-5
4-Hexylresorcinol, 99%
$CH_3(CH_2)_5C_6H_3$-1,3-$(OH)_2$ FW 194.27 mp 65-67°
bp 333-335° Beil. 6(2),904 Disp. C
MELT
B
C7060-6 4-Chlororesorcinol
ClC_6H_3-1,3-$(OH)_2$ M.W. 144.56
m.p. 106.5-107.5°
NUJOL MULL
C
B8060-7 4-Bromoresorcinol
BrC_6H_3-1,3-$(OH)_2$ M.W. 189.01
m.p. 97-100°
NUJOL MULL
D
T1660-8 2,2',4,4'-Tetrahydroxybiphenyl (4,4'-biresorcinol), tech.
$(HO)_2C_6H_3C_6H_3(OH)_2$ M.W. 218.21
m.p. 221-227°
NUJOL MULL
E
O-820-8 Orcinol (5-methylresorcinol) monohydrate
$CH_3C_6H_3$-1,3-$(OH)_2 \cdot H_2O$ M.W. 142.15
m.p. 58-61°
NUJOL MULL
F
15,263-3 Olivetol (5-pentylresorcinol)
$CH_3(CH_2)_4C_6H_3$-1,3-$(OH)_2$ M.W. 180.25
m.p. 42-44°
MELT
G
18,658-9
5-n-Pentadecylresorcinol, tech., 85%
$CH_3(CH_2)_{14}C_6H_3$-1,3-$(OH)_2$
M.W. 320.52 m.p. 94-96°
Remainder 4-methyl-5-n-pentadecylresorcinol
NUJOL MULL
H
14,674-9 4,6-Di-tert.-butylresorcinol
$[(CH_3)_3C]_2C_6H_2$-1,3-$(OH)_2$ M.W. 222.33
m.p. 119-122°
NUJOL MULL
WAVENUMBER CM⁻¹
WAVELENGTH IN MICRONS

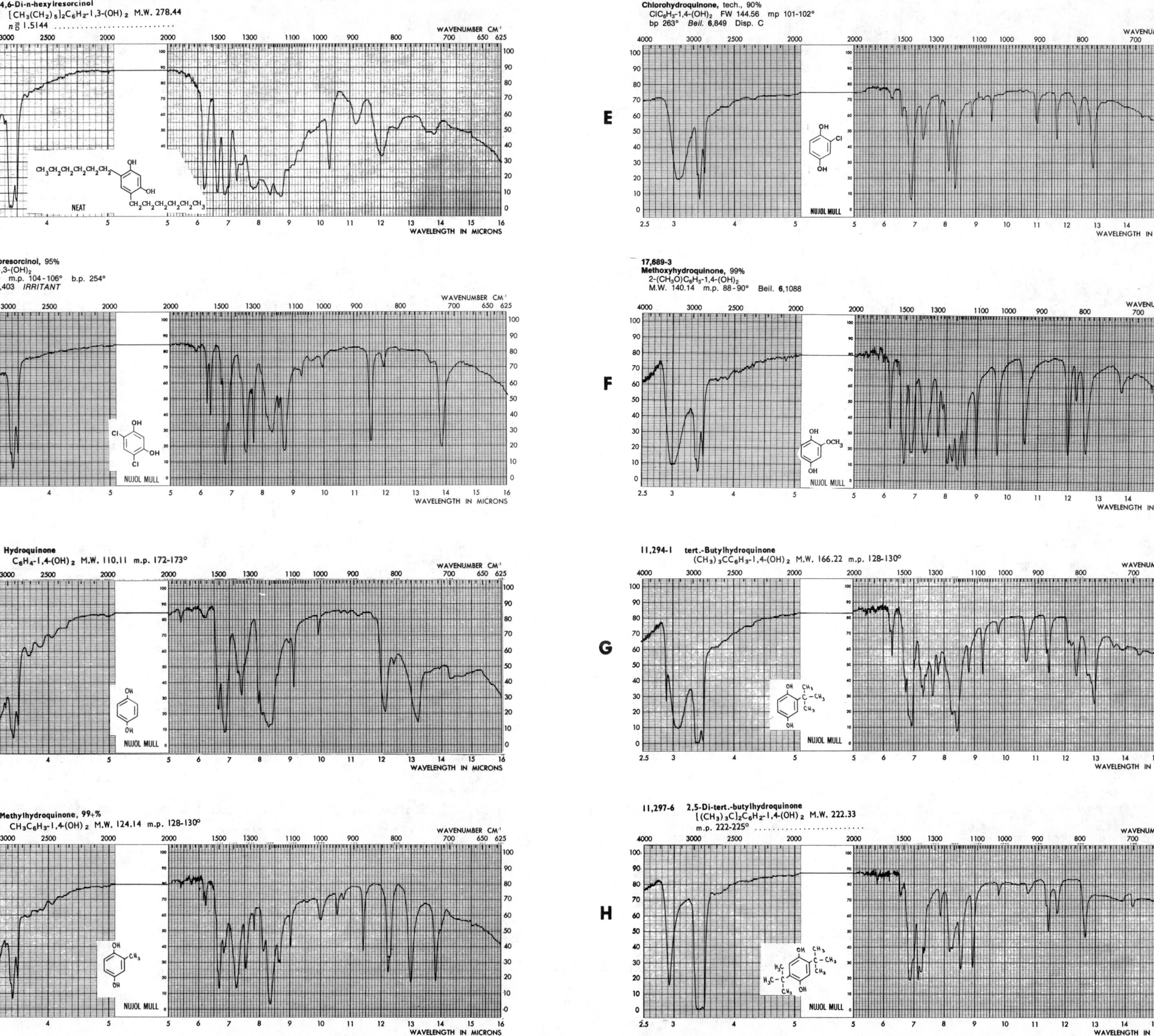
A
12,675-6 4,6-Di-n-hexylresorcinol
$[CH_3(CH_2)_5]_2C_6H_2$-1,3-$(OH)_2$ M.W. 278.44
n_D^{20} 1.5144
NEAT
B
13,098-2
4,6-Dichlororesorcinol, 95%
$Cl_2C_6H_2$-1,3-$(OH)_2$
M.W. 179 m.p. 104-106° b.p. 254°
Beil. 6(1),403 IRRITANT
NUJOL MULL
C
H1790-2 Hydroquinone
C_6H_4-1,4-$(OH)_2$ M.W. 110.11 m.p. 172-173°
NUJOL MULL
D
11,296-8 Methylhydroquinone, 99+%
$CH_3C_6H_3$-1,4-$(OH)_2$ M.W. 124.14 m.p. 128-130°
NUJOL MULL
E
22,408-1
Chlorohydroquinone, tech., 90%
ClC_6H_3-1,4-$(OH)_2$ FW 144.56 mp 101-102°
bp 263° Beil. 6,849 Disp. C
NUJOL MULL
F
17,689-3
Methoxyhydroquinone, 99%
2-$(CH_3O)C_6H_3$-1,4-$(OH)_2$
M.W. 140.14 m.p. 88-90° Beil. 6,1088
NUJOL MULL
G
11,294-1 tert.-Butylhydroquinone
$(CH_3)_3CC_6H_3$-1,4-$(OH)_2$ M.W. 166.22 m.p. 128-130°
NUJOL MULL
H
11,297-6 2,5-Di-tert.-butylhydroquinone
$[(CH_3)_3C]_2C_6H_2$-1,4-$(OH)_2$ M.W. 222.33
m.p. 222-225°
NUJOL MULL
WAVENUMBER CM⁻¹
WAVELENGTH IN MICRONS
ALDRICH

AROMATIC ALCOHOLS & PHENOLS

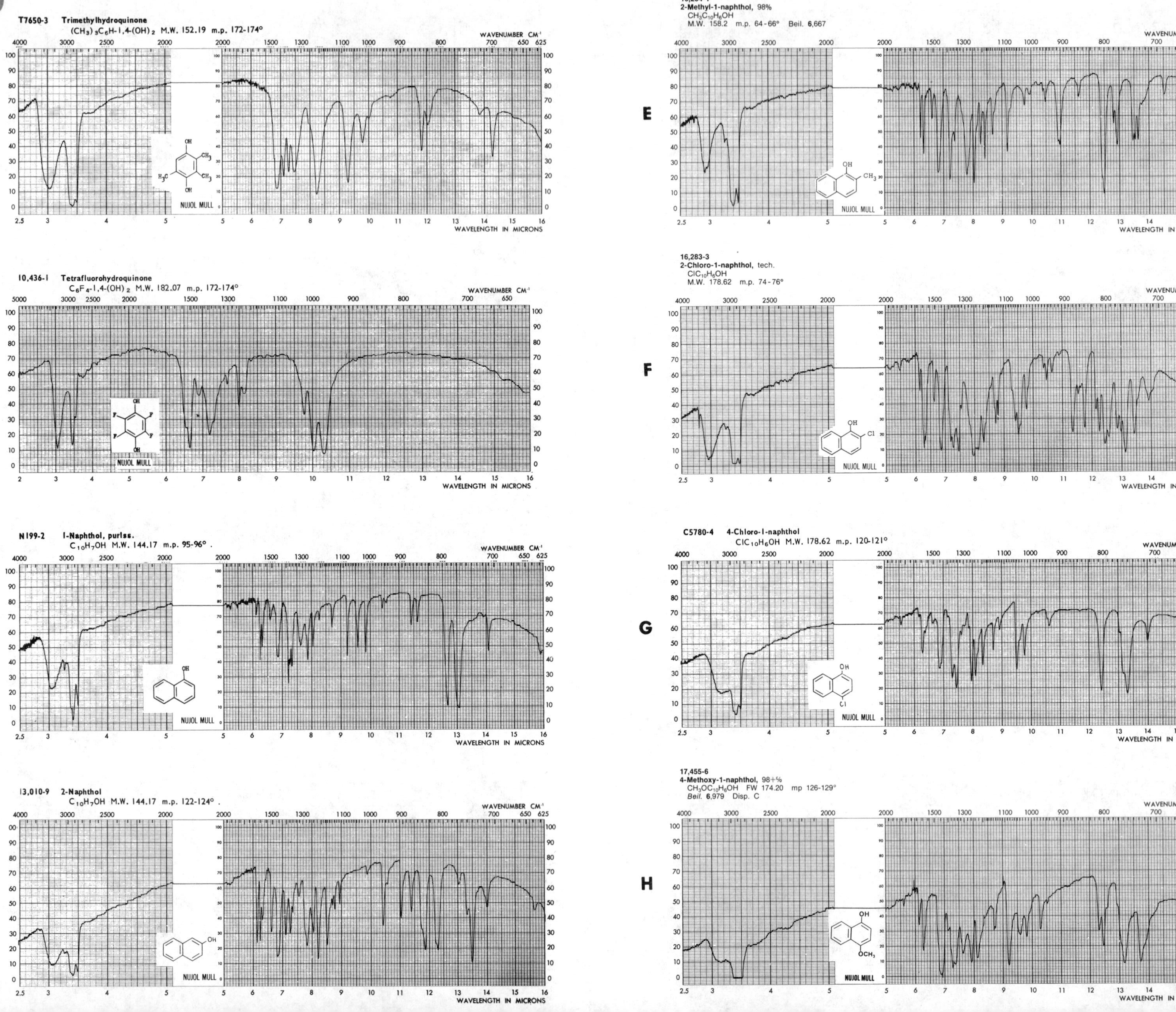

ALDRICH
A
T7650-3 Trimethylhydroquinone
$(CH_3)_3C_6H$-1,4-$(OH)_2$ M.W. 152.19 m.p. 172-174°
B
10,436-1 Tetrafluorohydroquinone
C_6F_4-1,4-$(OH)_2$ M.W. 182.07 m.p. 172-174°
C
N199-2 1-Naphthol, puriss.
$C_{10}H_7OH$ M.W. 144.17 m.p. 95-96°
D
13,010-9 2-Naphthol
$C_{10}H_7OH$ M.W. 144.17 m.p. 122-124°
E
16,284-1
2-Methyl-1-naphthol, 98%
$CH_3C_{10}H_6OH$
M.W. 158.2 m.p. 64-66° Beil. 6,667
F
16,283-3
2-Chloro-1-naphthol, tech.
$ClC_{10}H_6OH$
M.W. 178.62 m.p. 74-76°
G
C5780-4 4-Chloro-1-naphthol
$ClC_{10}H_6OH$ M.W. 178.62 m.p. 120-121°
H
17,455-6
4-Methoxy-1-naphthol, 98+%
$CH_3OC_{10}H_6OH$ FW 174.20 mp 126-129°
Beil. 6,979 Disp. C
NUJOL MULL
WAVENUMBER CM⁻¹
WAVELENGTH IN MICRONS

A B7320-1 1-Bromo-2-naphthol
$BrC_{10}H_6OH$ M.W. 223.07 m.p. 75-78°
MELT

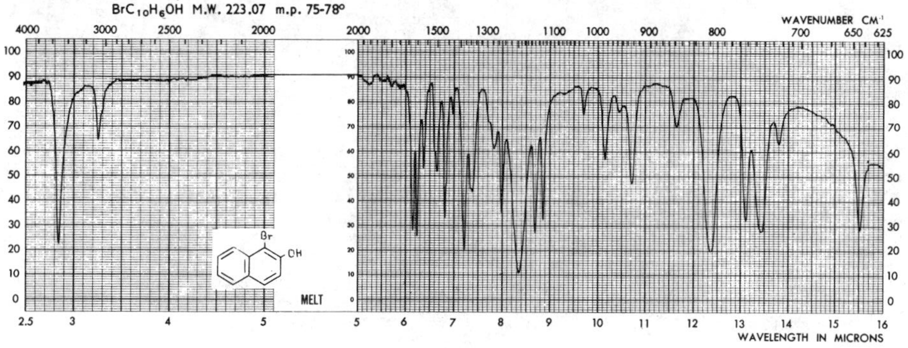

B 13,560-7 1-Iodo-2-naphthol
$IC_{10}H_6OH$ M.W. 270.07 m.p. 92-94°
NUJOL MULL

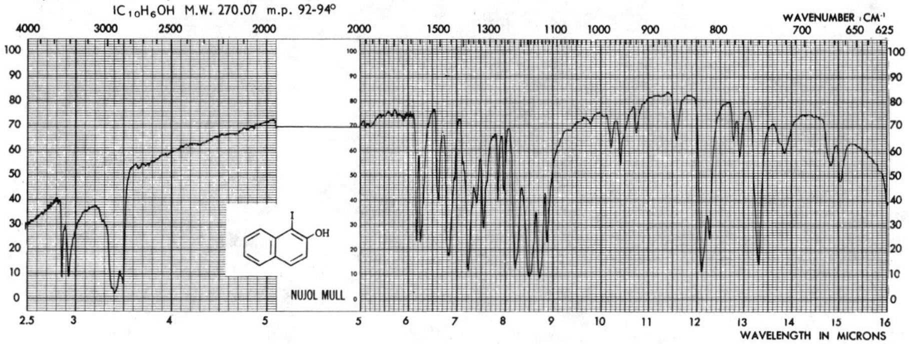

C 10,465-5 1,1'-Bi-2-naphthol (1,1'-di-2-naphthol)
$HOC_{10}H_6C_{10}H_6OH$ M.W. 286.33 m.p. 208-210°
NUJOL MULL

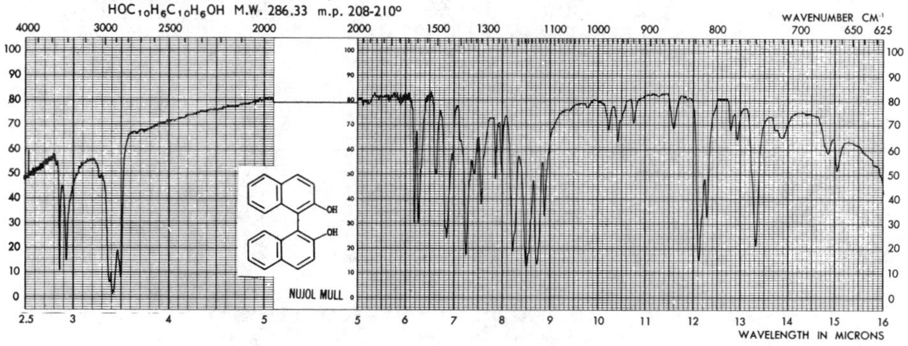

D 12,047-2 1,1'-Methylenedi-2-naphthol
$CH_2(C_{10}H_6OH)_2$ M.W. 300.36 m.p. 200-203°
NUJOL MULL

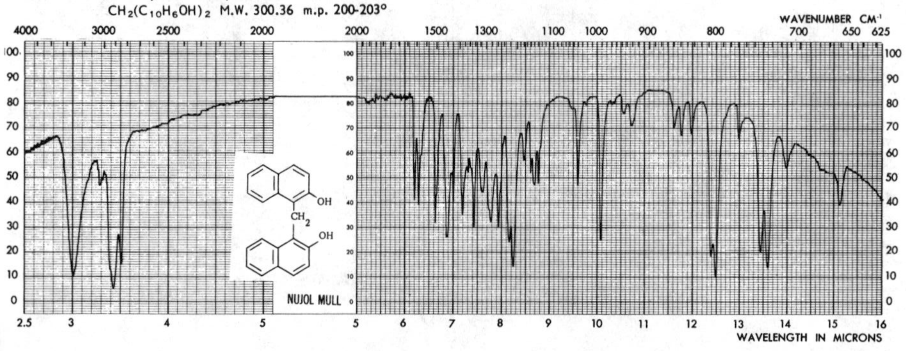

E B7340-6 6-Bromo-2-naphthol
$BrC_{10}H_6OH$ M.W. 223.07
m.p. 121-125°
NUJOL MULL

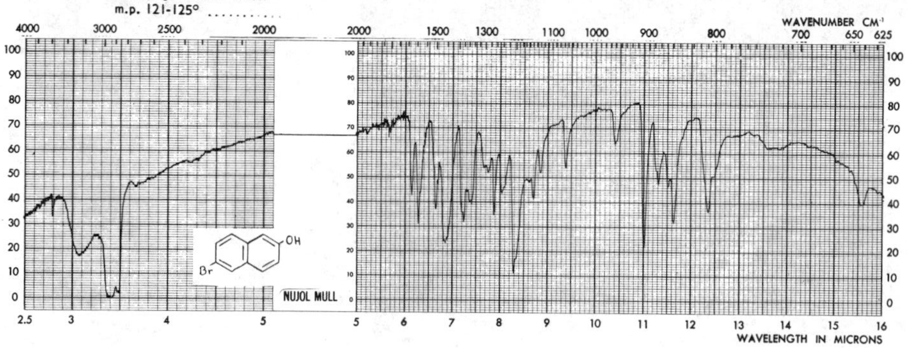

F M5729-4 6-Methyl-2-naphthol
$CH_3C_{10}H_6OH$ M.W. 158.19 m.p. 126-128°
NUJOL MULL

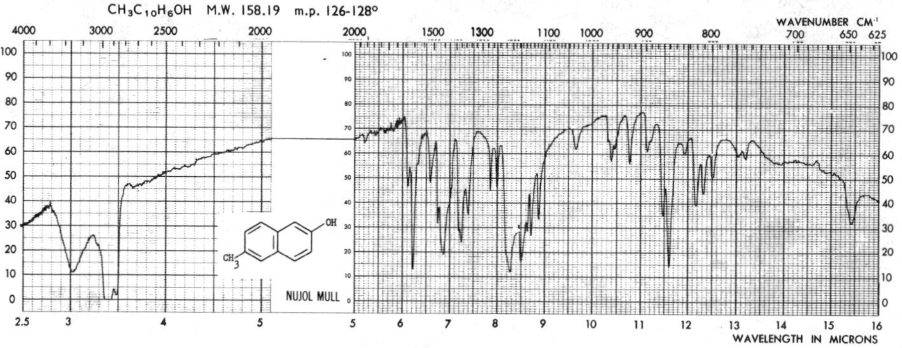

G M5730-8 7-Methyl-2-naphthol
$CH_3C_{10}H_6OH$ M.W. 158.19 m.p. 98-100°
NUJOL MULL

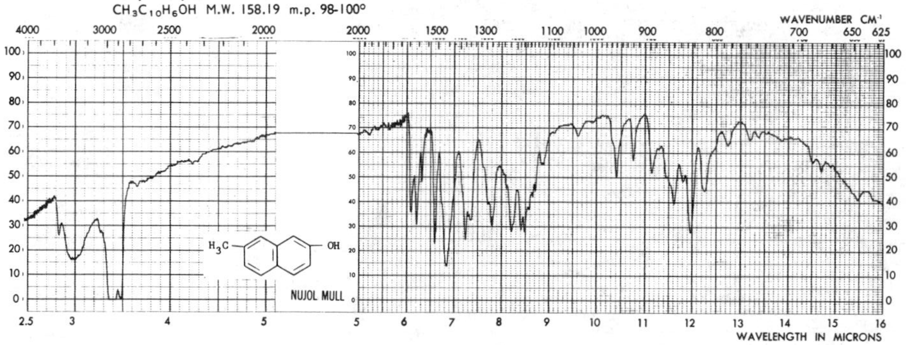

H D4180-5 1,6-Dibromo-2-naphthol
$Br_2C_{10}H_5OH$ M.W. 301.98 m.p. 105-107°
NUJOL MULL

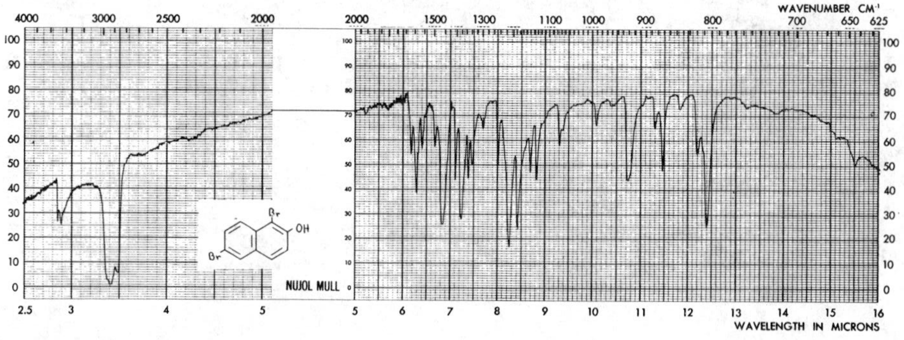

A

D11,600-9 2,3-Dihydroxynaphthalene (2,3-naphthalenediol)
$C_{10}H_6(OH)_2$ M.W. 160.17 m.p. 160-164°
NUJOL MULL

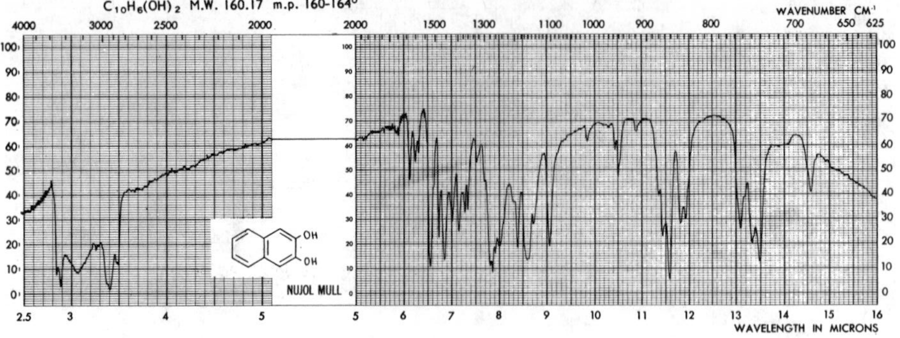

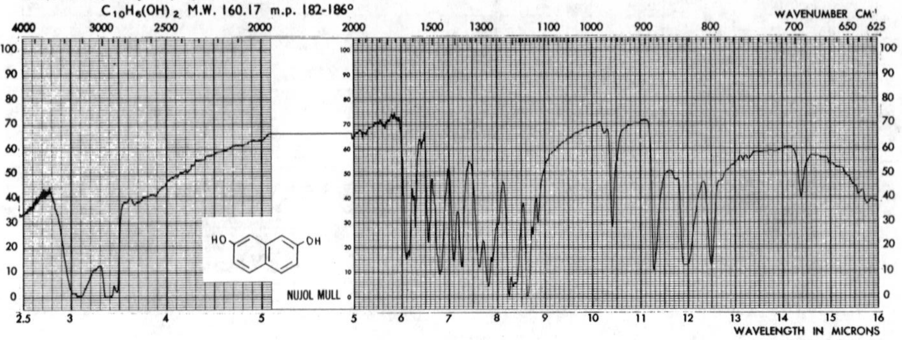

B

14,529-7 1,3-Dihydroxynaphthalene (1,3-naphthalenediol, naphthoresorcinol)
$C_{10}H_6(OH)_2$ M.W. 160.17
m.p. 123-125°
NUJOL MULL

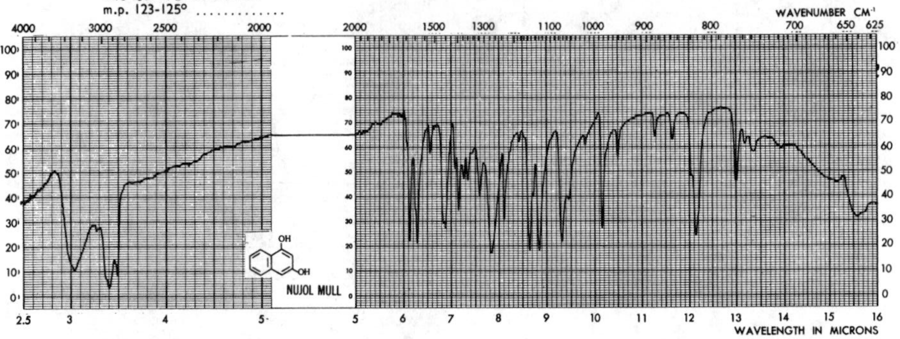

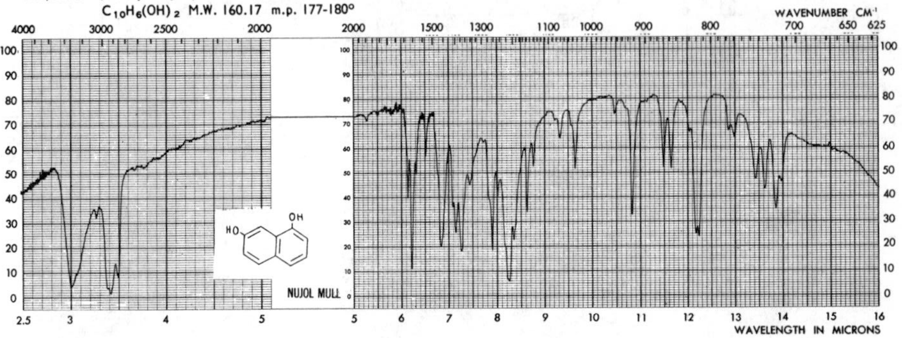

C

D11,560-6 1,5-Dihydroxynaphthalene (1,5-naphthalenediol)
$C_{10}H_6(OH)_2$ M.W. 160.17 m.p. 259-261° (dec.)
NUJOL MULL

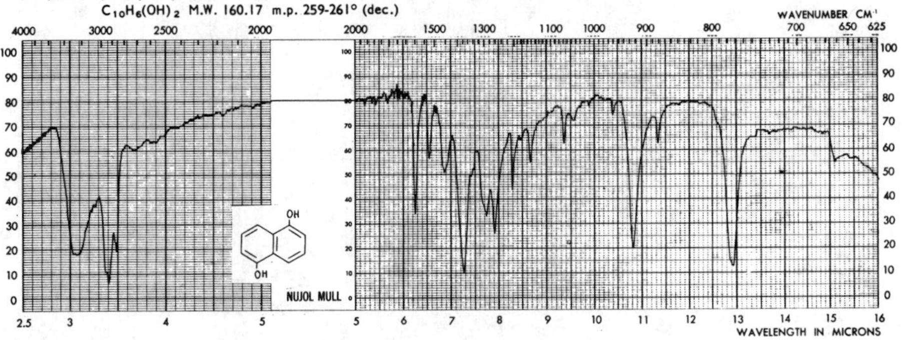

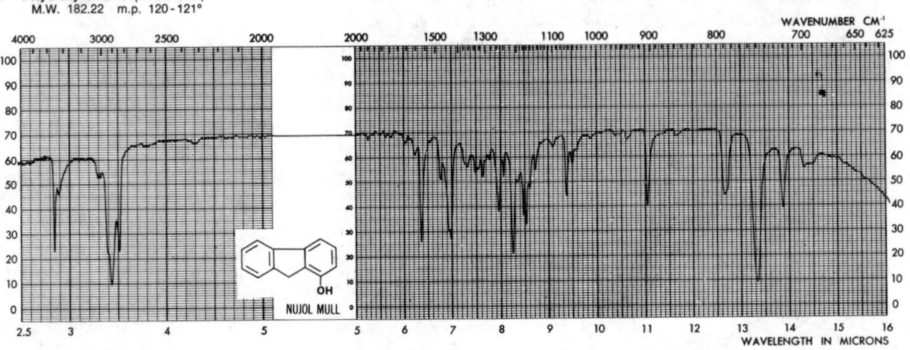

D

D11,620-3 2,6-Dihydroxynaphthalene (2,6-naphthalenediol)
$C_{10}H_6(OH)_2$ M.W. 160.17 m.p. 211-217°
NUJOL MULL

E

D11,640-8 2,7-Dihydroxynaphthalene (2,7-naphthalenediol)
$C_{10}H_6(OH)_2$ M.W. 160.17 m.p. 182-186°
NUJOL MULL

F

D11,580-0 1,7-Dihydroxynaphthalene (1,7-naphthalenediol)
$C_{10}H_6(OH)_2$ M.W. 160.17 m.p. 177-180°
NUJOL MULL

G

H3,070-4
1-Hydroxyfluorene (1-fluorenol)
M.W. 182.22 m.p. 120-121°
NUJOL MULL

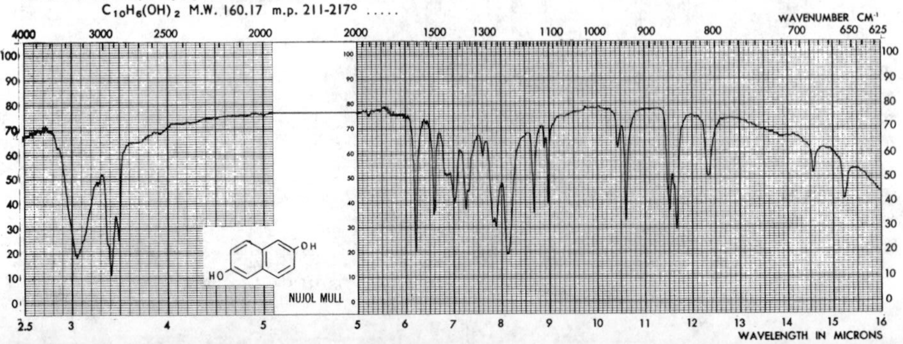

H

A9100-0 Anthrarobin (desoxyalizarin, 3,4-dihydroxy-9-anthranol)
M.W. 226.23
NUJOL MULL

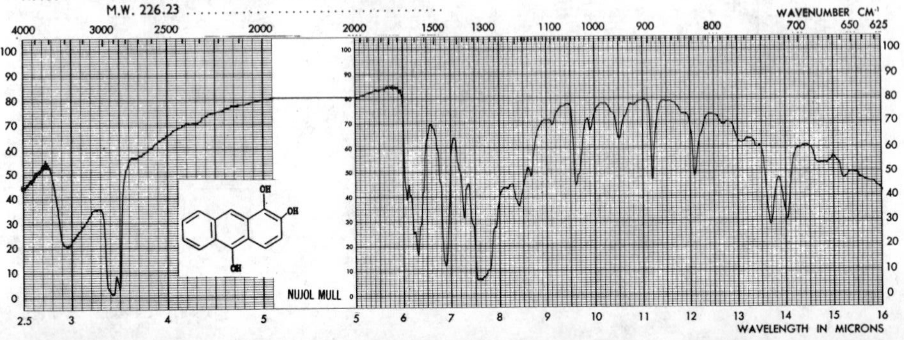

A

T1600-4 **1,4,9,10-Tetrahydroxyanthracene** (leucoquinizarin), tech.
M.W. 242.23 m.p. 147.2-149.2°

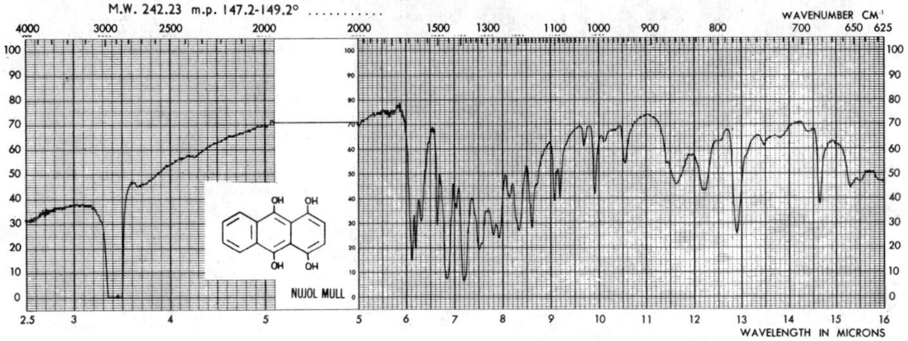

NUJOL MULL

B

21,128-1
9-Phenanthrol (9-hydroxyphenanthrene)
FW 194.23 mp 139-143° *Beil.* **6**,706 Disp. C

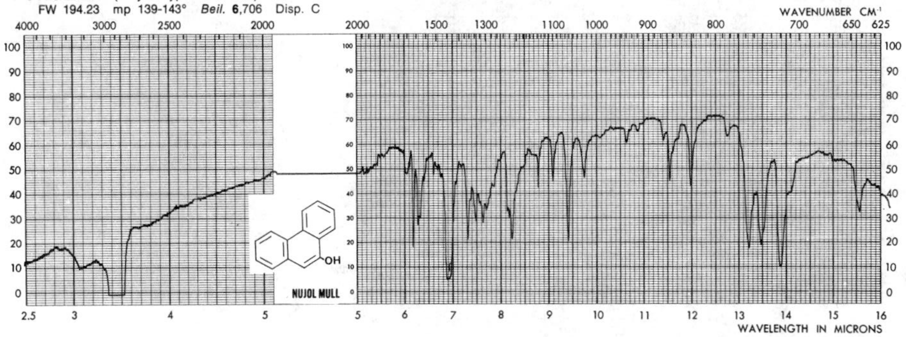

NUJOL MULL

C

14,252-2 **2-Hydroxydiphenylmethane** (α-phenyl-o-cresol)
$C_6H_5CH_2C_6H_4OH$ M.W. 184.24 m.p. 53-54.5°

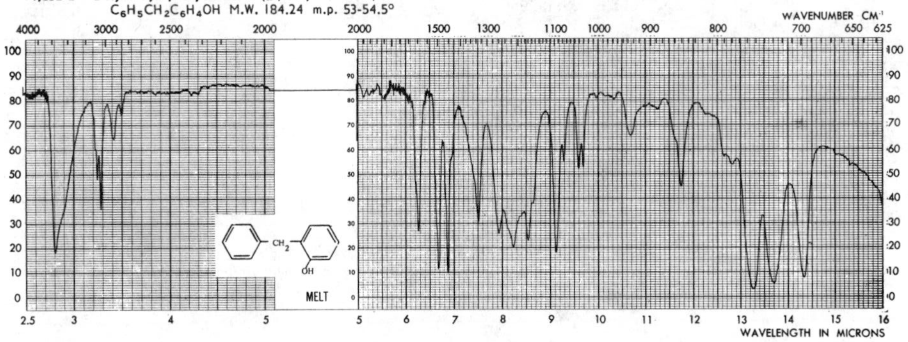

MELT

D

18,304-0
o-(Benzyloxy)-phenol, 99%
$C_6H_5CH_2OC_6H_4OH$
M.W. 200.24 n_D^{20} 1.5906

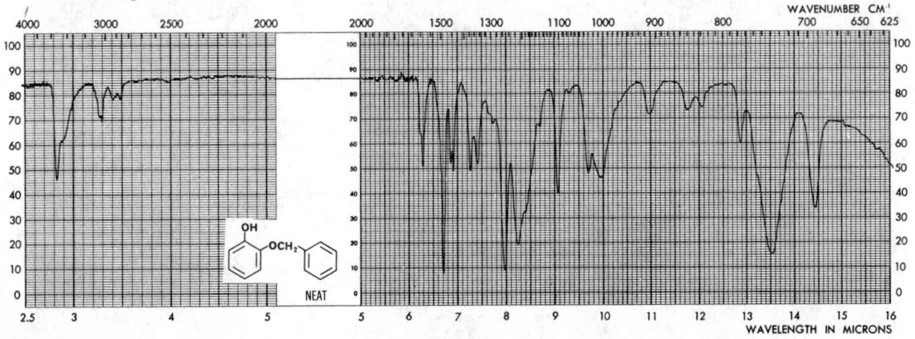

NEAT

E

B4680-8 **Bis-(2-hydroxyphenyl)-methane** (2,2'-methylenediphenol)
$CH_2(C_6H_4OH)_2$ M.W. 200.24 m.p. 115-117°

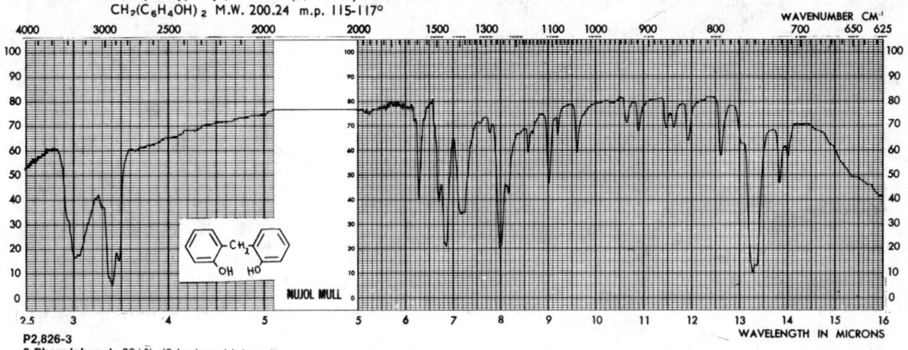

NUJOL MULL

F

P2,826-3
2-Phenylphenol, 99+% (2-hydroxybiphenyl)
$C_6H_5C_6H_4OH$
M.W. 170.21 m.p. 56.5-57.5° b.p. 282° d 1.213
Beil. **6**(2),623 *IRRITANT*
Deoxyribonuclease inhibitor. *Biochim. Biophys. Acta*, **228**, 365 (1971).

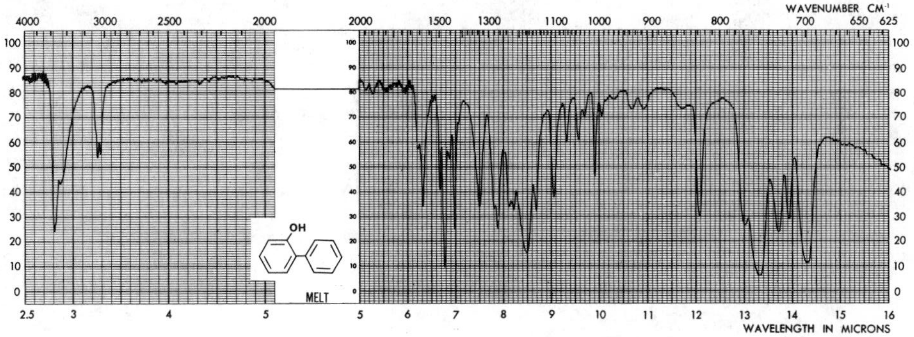

MELT

G

13,434-1 **4-Phenylphenol** (4-hydroxybiphenyl)
$C_6H_5C_6H_4OH$ M.W. 170.21 m.p. 165-167°

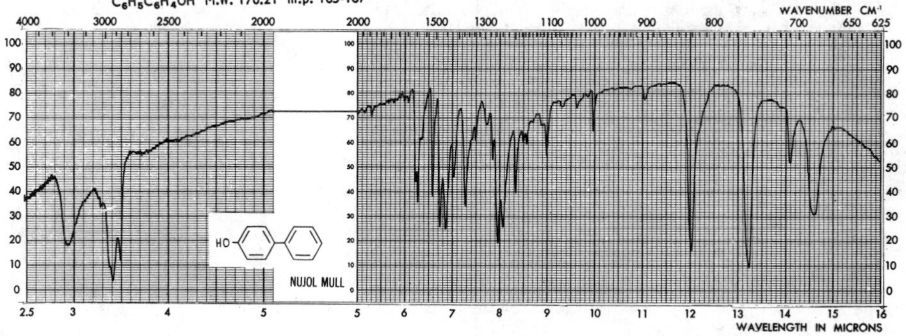

NUJOL MULL

H

16,873-4
p,p'-Biphenol, 97% (4,4'-dihydroxybiphenyl)
$HOC_6H_4C_6H_4OH$
M.W. 186.21 m.p. 278° (dec.) Beil. **6**,991

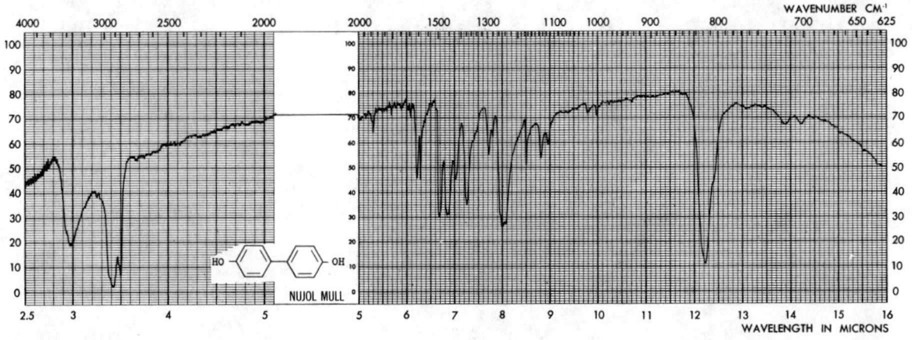

NUJOL MULL

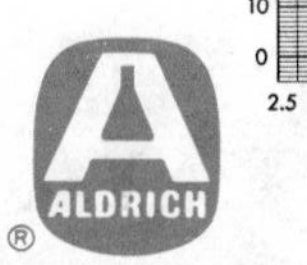

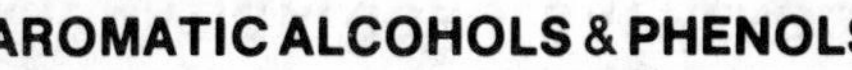

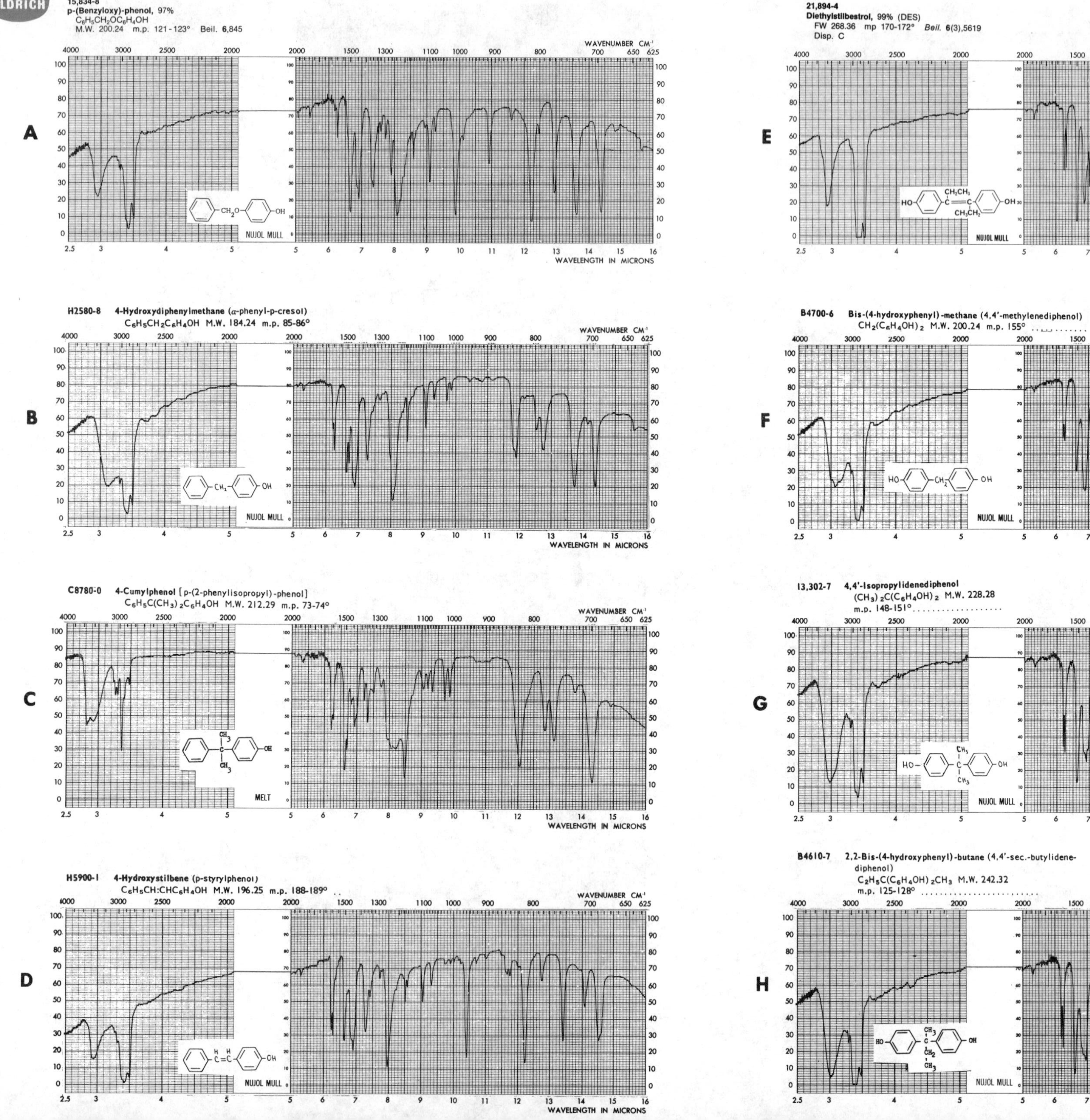

A 15,834-8
p-(Benzyloxy)-phenol, 97%
$C_6H_5CH_2OC_6H_4OH$
M.W. 200.24 m.p. 121-123° Beil. 6,845
NUJOL MULL

B H2580-8 **4-Hydroxydiphenylmethane** (α-phenyl-p-cresol)
$C_6H_5CH_2C_6H_4OH$ M.W. 184.24 m.p. 85-86°
NUJOL MULL

C C8780-0 **4-Cumylphenol** [p-(2-phenylisopropyl)-phenol]
$C_6H_5C(CH_3)_2C_6H_4OH$ M.W. 212.29 m.p. 73-74°
MELT

D H5900-1 **4-Hydroxystilbene** (p-styrylphenol)
$C_6H_5CH{:}CHC_6H_4OH$ M.W. 196.25 m.p. 188-189°
NUJOL MULL

E 21,894-4
Diethylstilbestrol, 99% (DES)
FW 268.36 mp 170-172° *Beil.* 6(3),5619
Disp. C
NUJOL MULL

F B4700-6 **Bis-(4-hydroxyphenyl)-methane** (4,4'-methylenediphenol)
$CH_2(C_6H_4OH)_2$ M.W. 200.24 m.p. 155°
NUJOL MULL

G 13,302-7 **4,4'-Isopropylidenediphenol**
$(CH_3)_2C(C_6H_4OH)_2$ M.W. 228.28
m.p. 148-151°
NUJOL MULL

H B4610-7 **2,2-Bis-(4-hydroxyphenyl)-butane** (4,4'-sec.-butylidenediphenol)
$C_2H_5C(C_6H_4OH)_2CH_3$ M.W. 242.32
m.p. 125-128°
NUJOL MULL

A

21,968-1
meso-**Hexestrol**, 99% [4,4'-(1,2-diethylethylene)diphenol]
[-CH(C_2H_5)C_6H_4OH]$_2$ FW 270.37 mp 186-189°
Beil. 6(3),5503 Disp. C

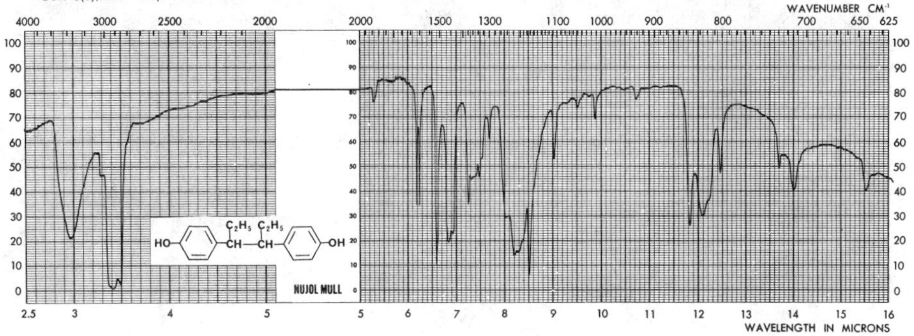

NUJOL MULL

B

20,981-3
1,1,2,2-Tetrakis(*p*-hydroxyphenyl)ethane, 98% (1,1,2,2-ethanetetra-*p*-phenol)
[-CH(C_6H_4OH)$_2$]$_2$ FW 398.46 mp 300-302°
Beil. 6,1182 Disp. C

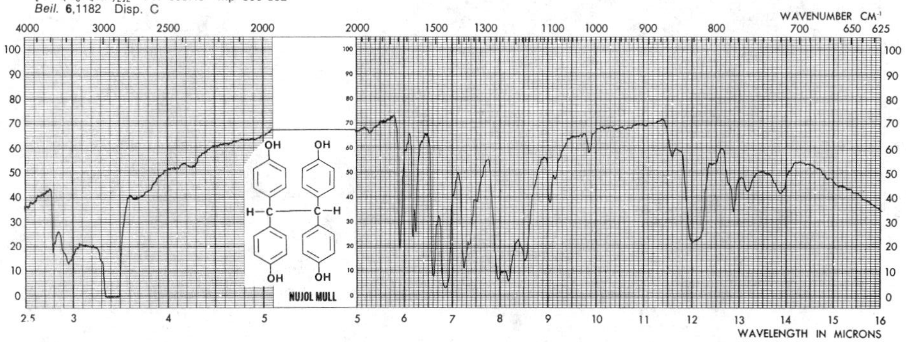

NUJOL MULL

C

15,761-9
Nordihydroguaiaretic acid [4,4'-(2,3-dimethyltetramethylene)-dipyrocatechol]
[-CH(CH_3)$CH_2C_6H_3$(OH)$_2$]$_2$
M.W. 302.37 m.p. 188-190°

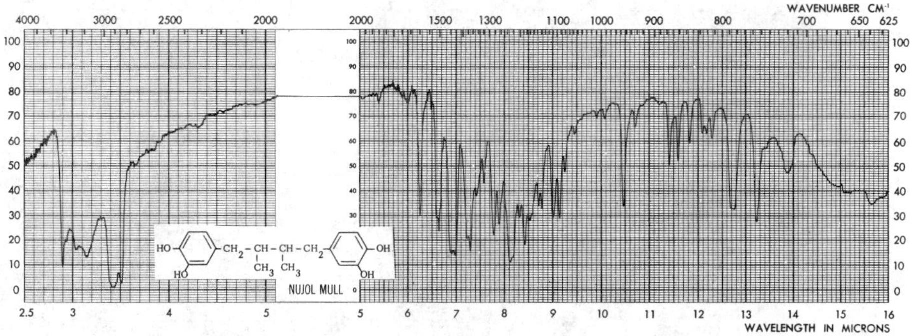

NUJOL MULL

D

B4620-4 **1,1-Bis-(4-hydroxyphenyl)-cyclohexane** (4,4'-cyclohexylidenediphenol)
$C_6H_{10}(C_6H_4OH)_2$ M.W. 268.36 m.p. 186-188°

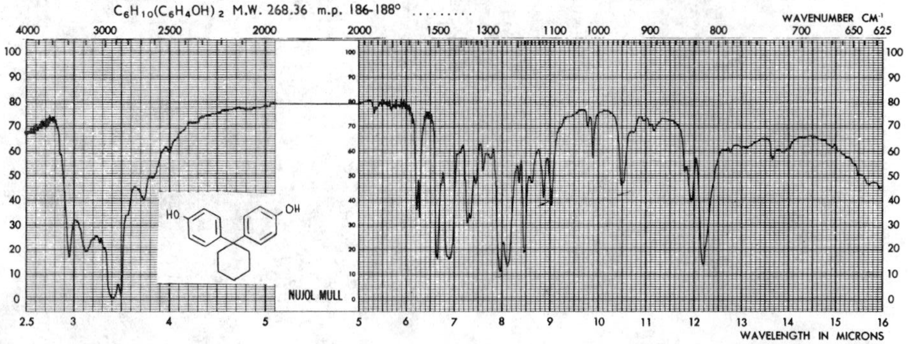

NUJOL MULL

E

13,375-2 **2-Chloro-6-phenylphenol**
$ClC_6H_3(C_6H_5)OH$ M.W. 204.66 m.p. 74-76°

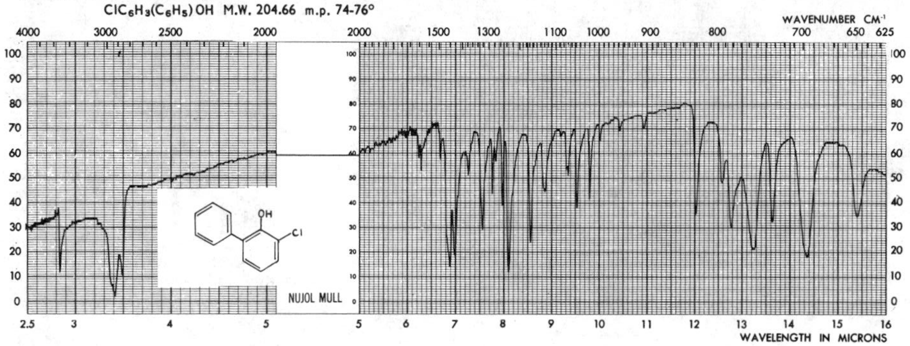

NUJOL MULL

F

13,486-4 **2-Chloro-4-phenylphenol**
$ClC_6H_3(C_6H_5)OH$ M.W. 204.66
m.p. 76-78°

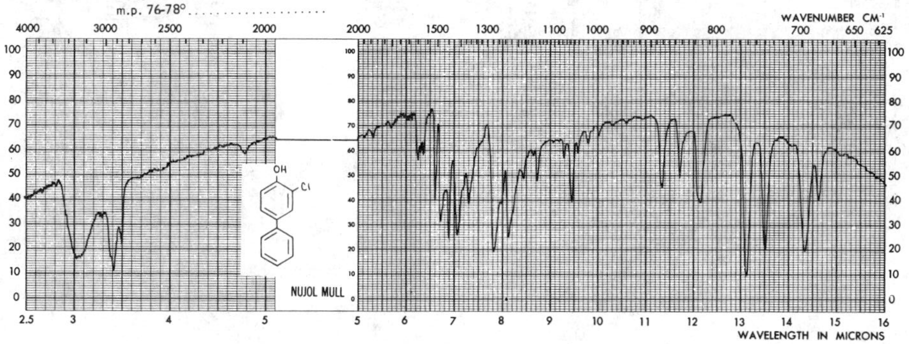

NUJOL MULL

G

B1900 **2-Benzyl-4-chlorophenol (5-chloro-2-hydroxydiphenylmethane)**
$C_6H_5CH_2C_6H_3(Cl)OH$ M.W. 218.68 m.p. 44-49°

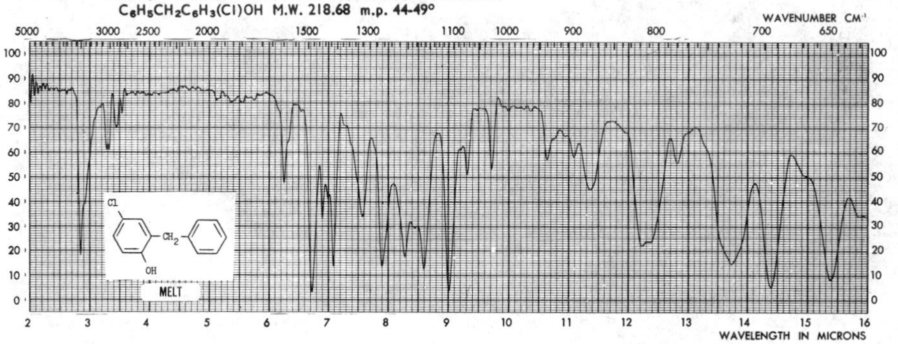

MELT

H

13,322-1 **2,2'-Methylenebis-(4-chlorophenol)**
$CH_2[C_6H_3(Cl)OH]_2$ M.W. 269.13
m.p. 165-168°

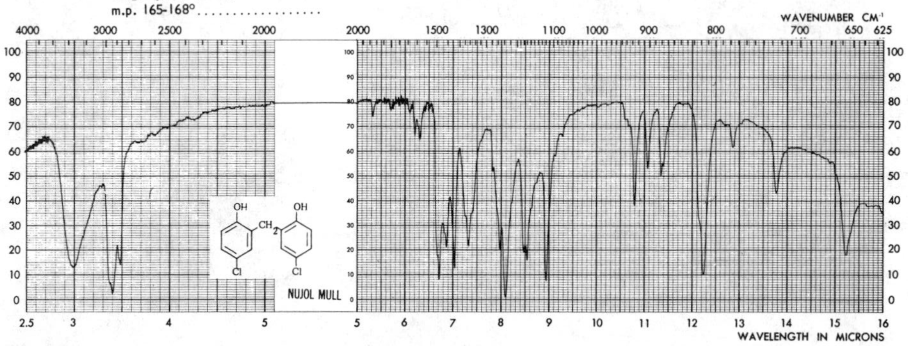

NUJOL MULL

A

H1770-8 **Hydrocoerulignone** (4,4'-dihydroxy-3,3',5,5'-tetramethoxybiphenyl)
$(CH_3O)_2C_6H_2(OH)C_6H_2(OCH_3)_2OH$ M.W. 306.31
m.p. 191-193°

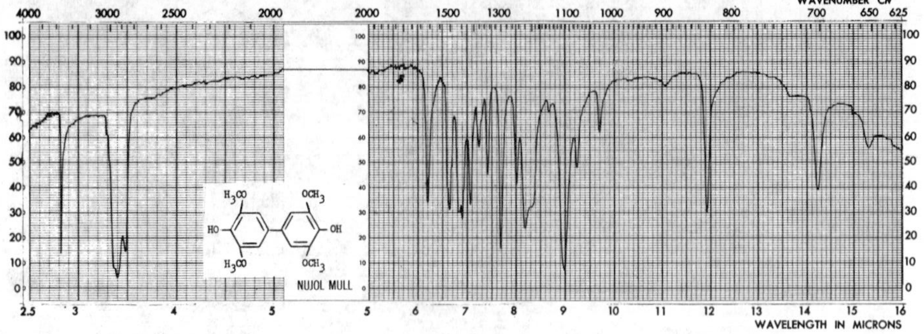

NUJOL MULL

B

10,854-5 **p-Tritylphenol**
$(C_6H_5)_3CC_6H_4OH$ M.W. 336.43 m.p. 280-283°

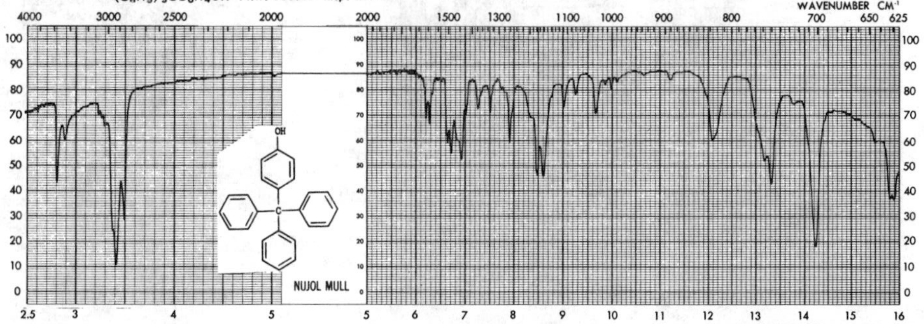

NUJOL MULL

C

D20,937-6 **4,4'-(Diphenylmethylene)-diphenol** (4,4'-dihydroxytetraphenylmethane)
$(C_6H_5)_2C(C_6H_4OH)_2$ M.W. 352.44 m.p. 298-301°

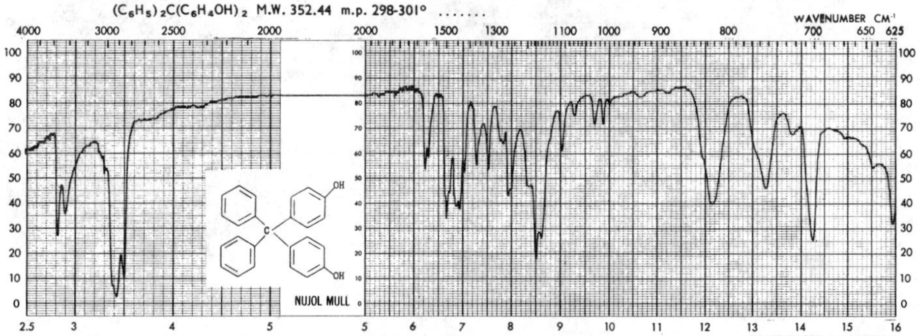

NUJOL MULL

D

R93 **Rhaponticin** (rhapontin, ponticin)
M.W. 420.40 m.p. 230-232.5°

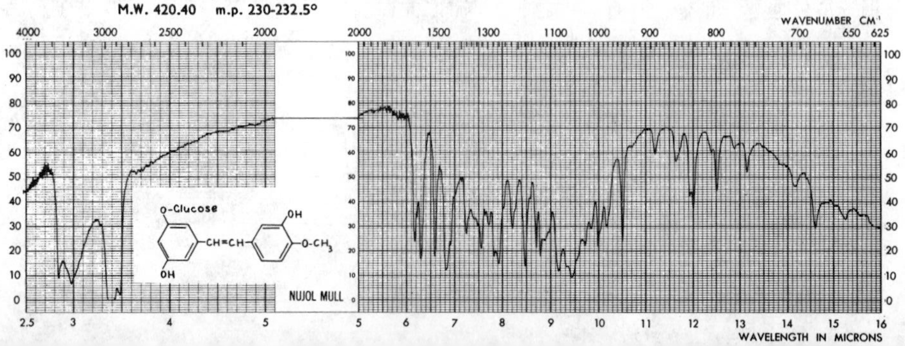

NUJOL MULL

E

85,523-5
l-Epicatechin
M.W. 290.27 m.p. 240° (dec.) Beil. **17**,214

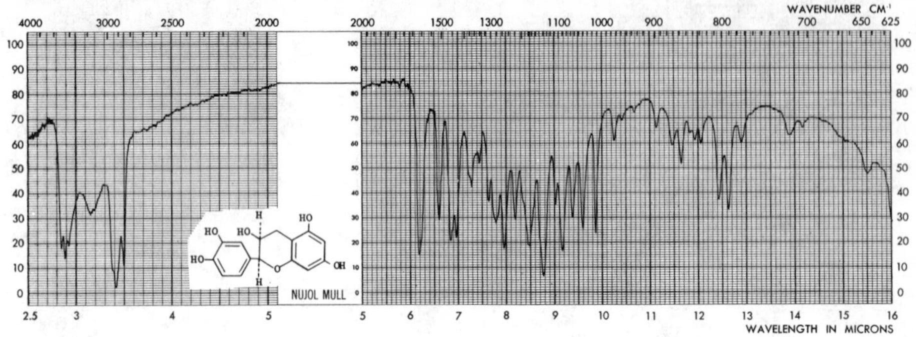

NUJOL MULL

F

85,599-5
6-Bromo-2-naphthyl-β-D-galactopyranoside
M.W. 385.22 m.p. 218-220°
$[\alpha]^{23}$ -50.3° (c=1.1, pyridine)

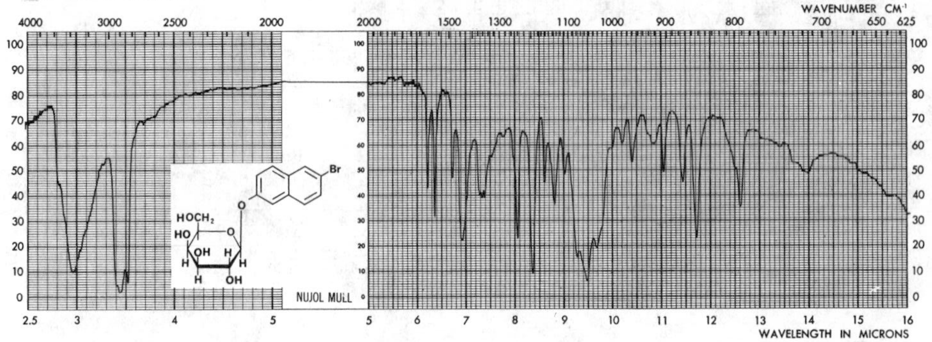

NUJOL MULL

G

85,886-2
6-Bromo-2-naphthyl-β-D-glucopyranoside
M.W. 385.22 m.p. 210-212°

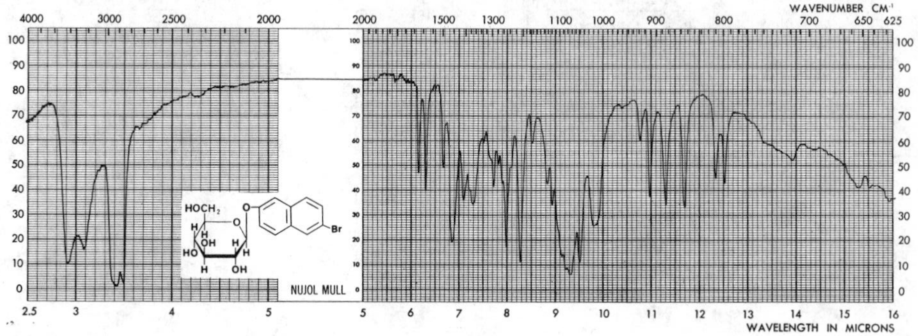

NUJOL MULL

H

M170-9 **Malvin** (malvin chloride, malvoside)
M.W. 691.04 m.p. 152° (dec.)

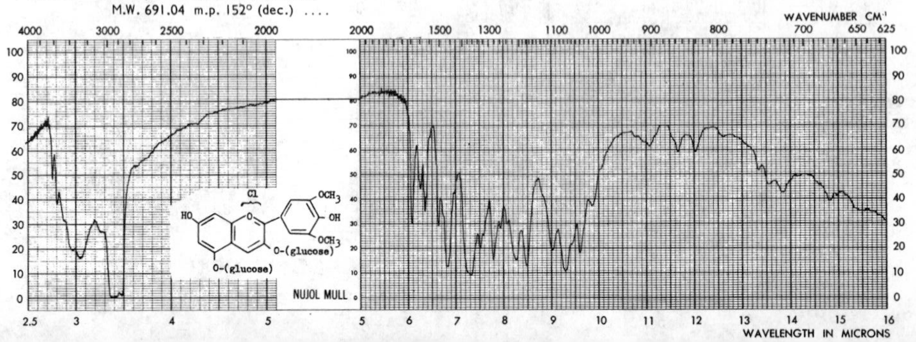

NUJOL MULL

A

85,614-2
Cubebin
M.W. 356.37 m.p. 132-135°

NUJOL MULL

B

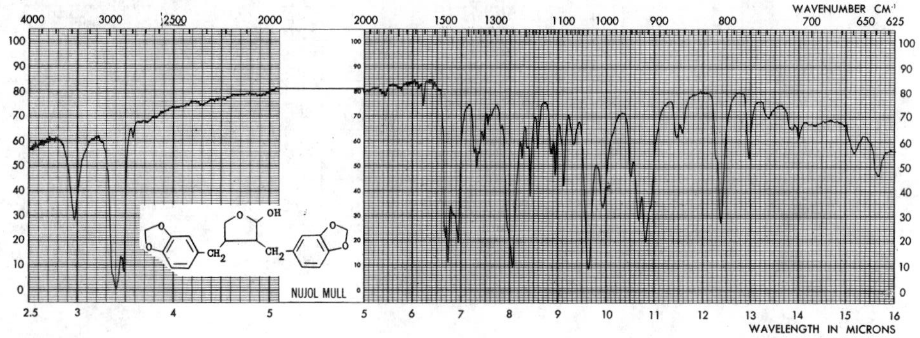

85,844-7
Podophyllotoxin
M.W. 414.41

NUJOL MULL

C

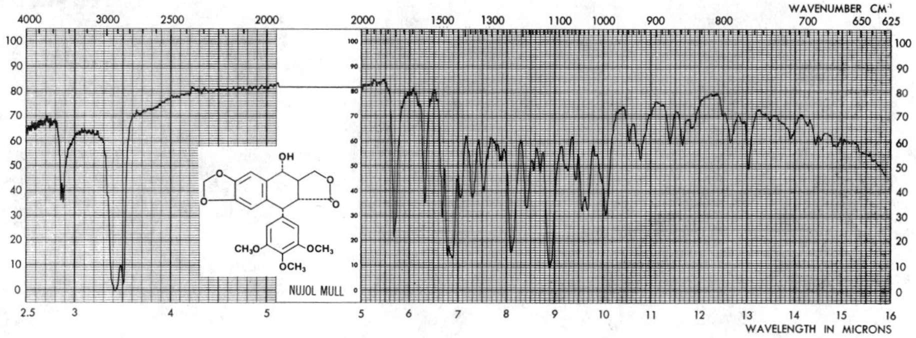

B1620-8 **Benzyl alcohol, puriss.**
$C_6H_5CH_2OH$ M.W. 108.14 n_D^{20} 1.5403

NEAT

D

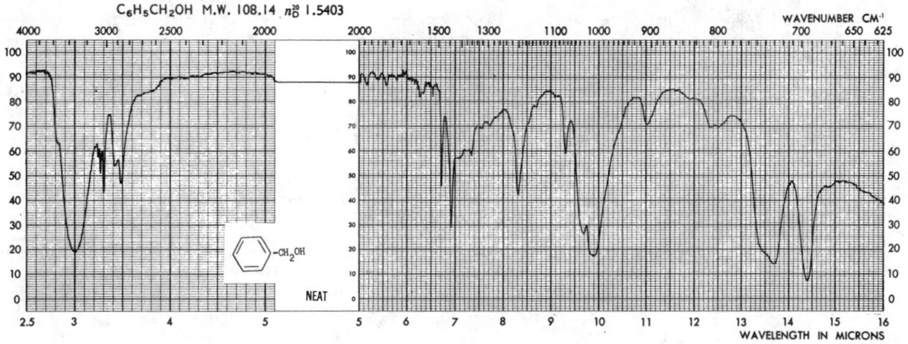

P1380-0 **sec.-Phenethyl alcohol** (α-methylbenzyl alcohol)
$C_6H_5CH(CH_3)OH$ M.W. 122.17 n_D^{20} 1.5249
b.p. 202-204° ....

NEAT

E

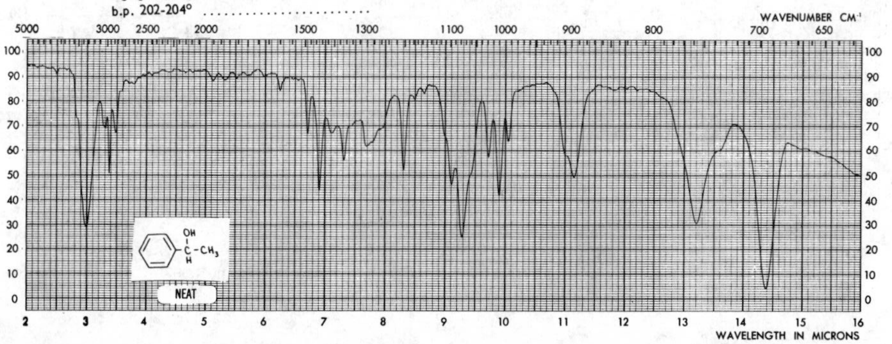

P3080-2 **2-Phenyl-2-propanol** (α,α-dimethylbenzyl alcohol)
$C_6H_5C(CH_3)_2OH$ M.W. 136.19 n_D^{22} 1.5196 b.p. 202°

MELT

F

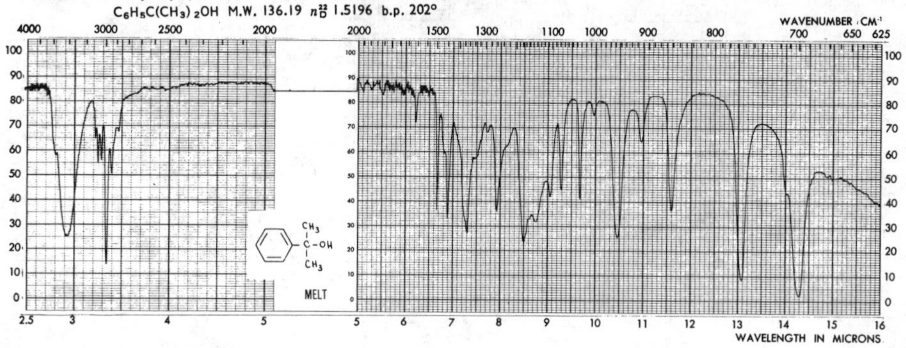

11,130-9 **1-Phenyl-1-propanol** (α-ethylbenzyl alcohol)
$C_2H_5CH(C_6H_5)OH$ M.W. 136.19 n_D^{20} 1.5202
b.p. 103°/14 mm. ....

NEAT

G

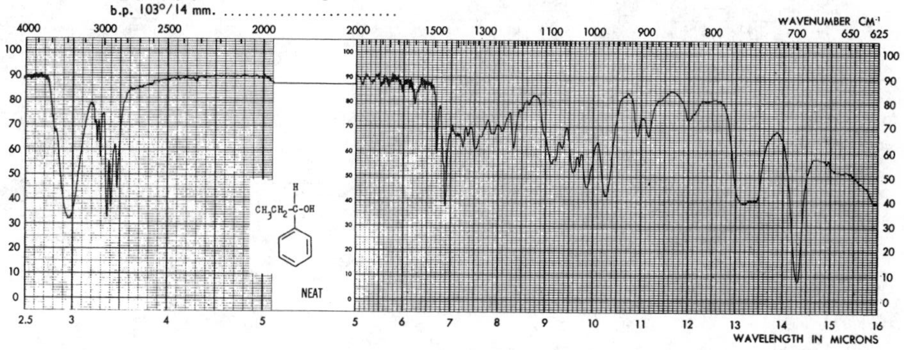

11,182-1 **1-Phenyl-1-butanol**
$CH_3(CH_2)_2CH(C_6H_5)OH$ M.W. 150.22 n_D^{20} 1.5160

NEAT

H

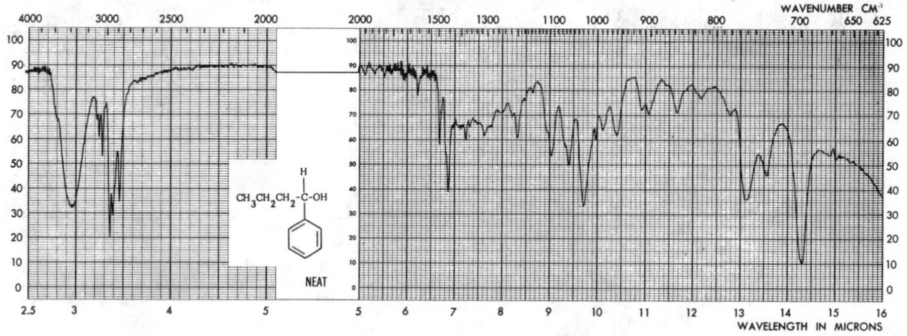

14,218-2 **1-Phenyl-1-pentanol** (α-butylbenzyl alcohol)
$CH_3(CH_2)_3CH(C_6H_5)OH$ M.W. 164.25
n_D^{20} 1.5090 ....

NEAT

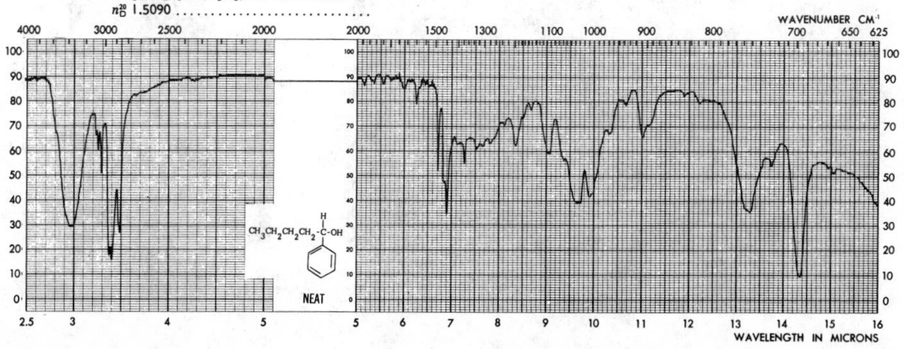

ALDRICH

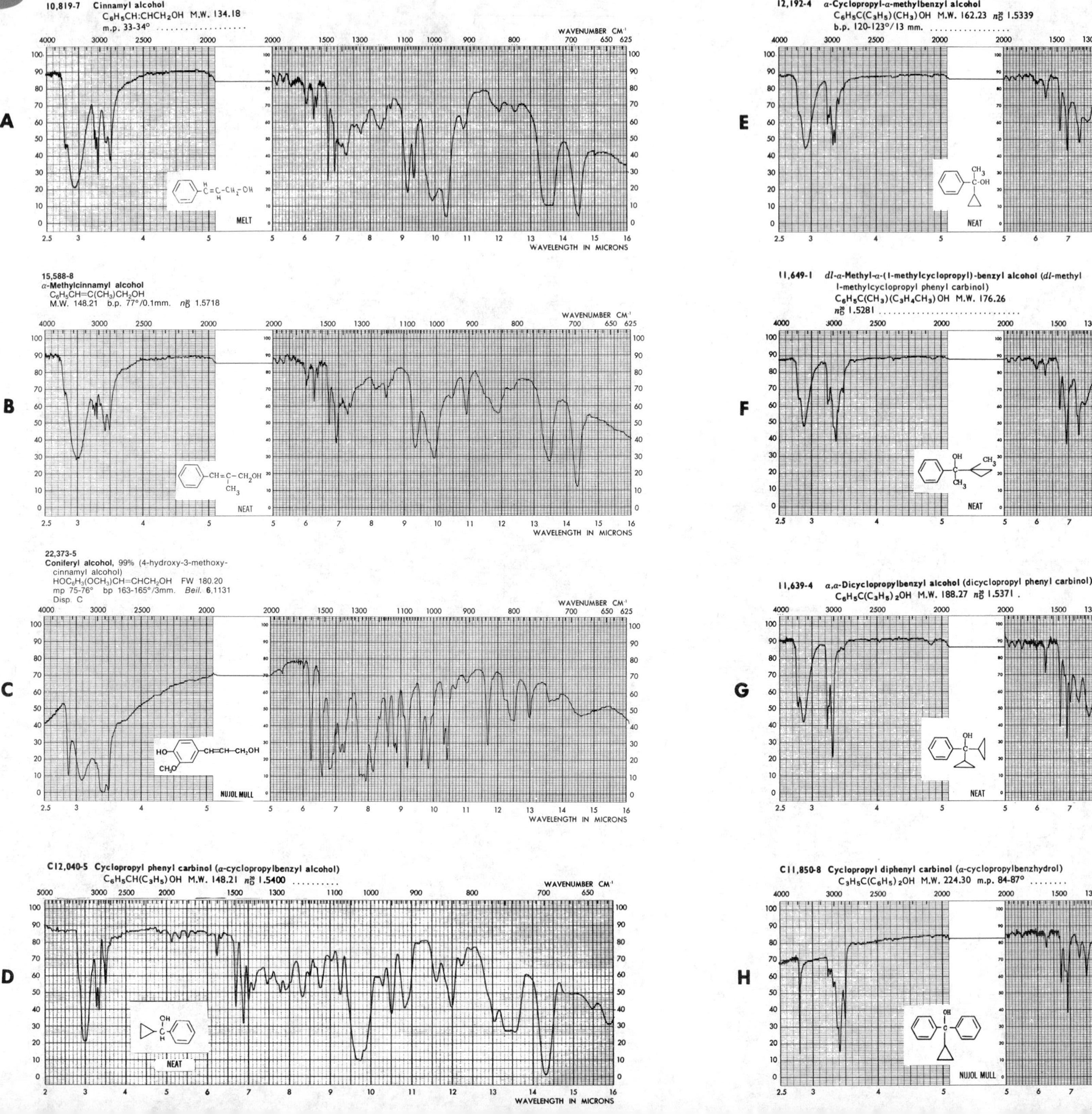

A 10,819-7 **Cinnamyl alcohol**
$C_6H_5CH{:}CHCH_2OH$ M.W. 134.18
m.p. 33-34°

B 15,588-8
α-Methylcinnamyl alcohol
$C_6H_5CH{=}C(CH_3)CH_2OH$
M.W. 148.21 b.p. 77°/0.1mm. n_D^{20} 1.5718

C 22,373-5
Coniferyl alcohol, 99% (4-hydroxy-3-methoxy-cinnamyl alcohol)
$HOC_6H_3(OCH_3)CH{=}CHCH_2OH$ FW 180.20
mp 75-76° bp 163-165°/3mm. *Beil.* **6**,1131
Disp. C

D C12,040-5 **Cyclopropyl phenyl carbinol** (α-cyclopropylbenzyl alcohol)
$C_6H_5CH(C_3H_5)OH$ M.W. 148.21 n_D^{20} 1.5400

E 12,192-4 **α-Cyclopropyl-α-methylbenzyl alcohol**
$C_6H_5C(C_3H_5)(CH_3)OH$ M.W. 162.23 n_D^{20} 1.5339
b.p. 120-123°/13 mm.

F 11,649-1 ***dl*-α-Methyl-α-(1-methylcyclopropyl)-benzyl alcohol** (*dl*-methyl 1-methylcyclopropyl phenyl carbinol)
$C_6H_5C(CH_3)(C_3H_4CH_3)OH$ M.W. 176.26
n_D^{20} 1.5281

G 11,639-4 **α,α-Dicyclopropylbenzyl alcohol** (dicyclopropyl phenyl carbinol)
$C_6H_5C(C_3H_5)_2OH$ M.W. 188.27 n_D^{20} 1.5371

H C11,850-8 **Cyclopropyl diphenyl carbinol** (α-cyclopropylbenzhydrol)
$C_3H_5C(C_6H_5)_2OH$ M.W. 224.30 m.p. 84-87°

A

13,920-3 **Cyclohexyl phenyl carbinol (α-cyclohexylbenzyl alcohol), tech.**
$C_6H_5CH(C_6H_{11})OH$ M.W. 190.29
m.p. 42-45°

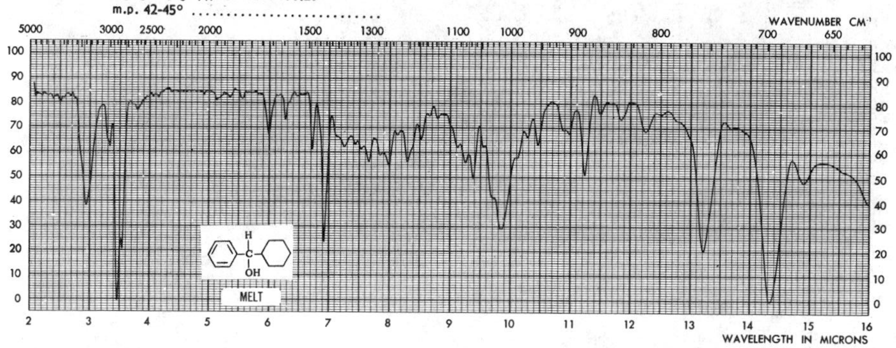

MELT

B

P2225-7 **1-Phenyl-1-cyclohexanol**
$C_6H_5C_6H_{10}OH$ M.W. 176.26 m.p. 60-63°

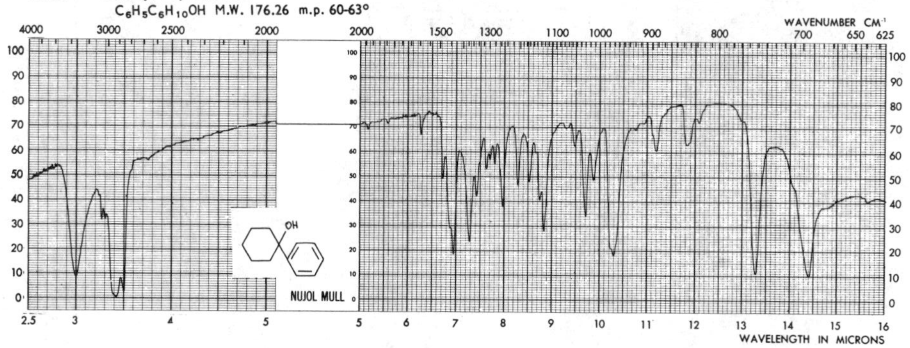

NUJOL MULL

C

17,905-1
trans-**2-Phenyl-1-cyclohexanol,** 99%
$C_6H_5C_6H_{10}OH$
M.W. 176.26 m.p. 53-55° b.p. 152-155°/16mm.
Beil. **6**(2),548

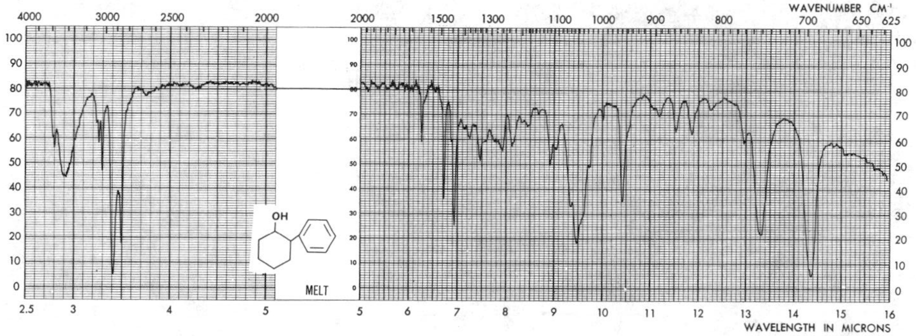

MELT

D

B485-6 **Benzhydrol,** 99%
$(C_6H_5)_2CHOH$ M.W. 184.24 m.p. 66.5-66.7°
b.p. 297-298° *Beil.* **6**,678 *Merck Index* **8**,132

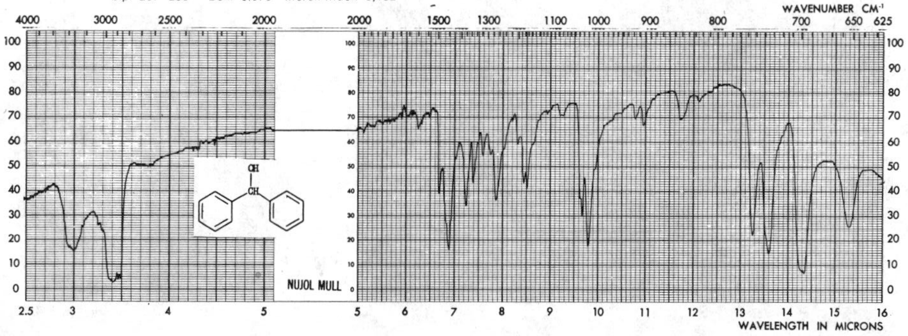

NUJOL MULL

E

15,214-5 **1,1-Diphenylethanol**
$CH_3C(C_6H_5)_2OH$ M.W. 198.27 m.p. 77-81°

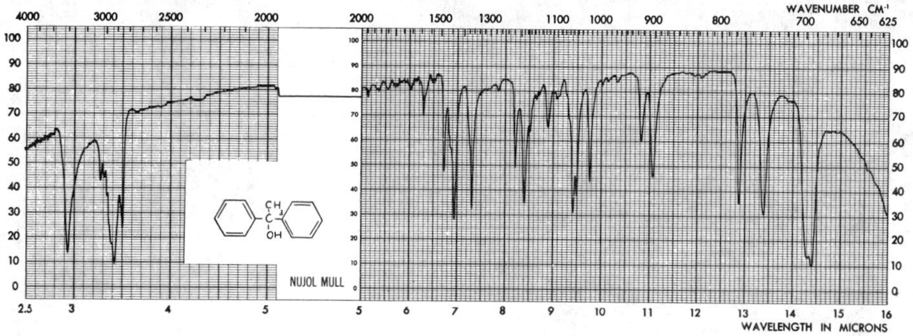

NUJOL MULL

F

13,484-8 **Triphenylmethanol**
$(C_6H_5)_3COH$ M.W. 260.34 m.p. 163-164°

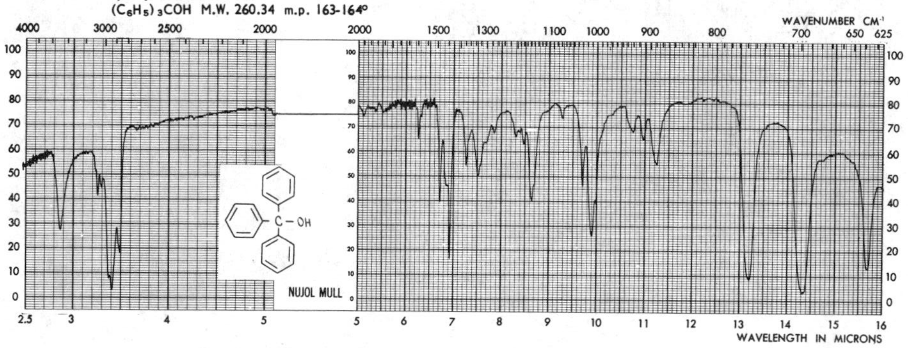

NUJOL MULL

G

12,158-4 **α-Benzylbenzhydrol (1,1,2-triphenylethanol)**
$(C_6H_5)_2C(CH_2C_6H_5)OH$ M.W. 274.36
m.p. 86-89°

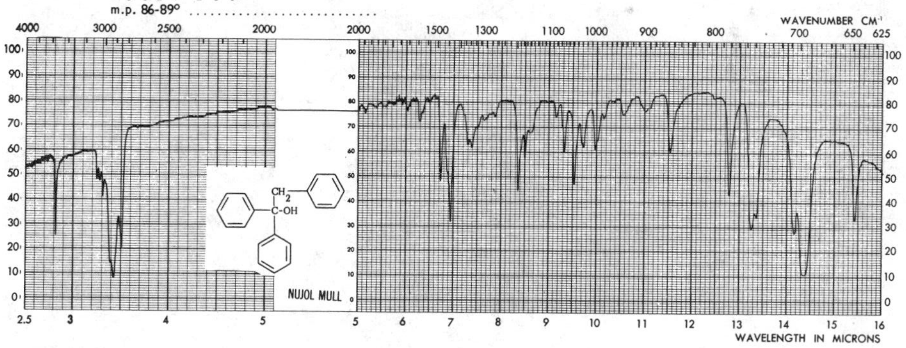

NUJOL MULL

H

18,478-0
o-Phenethylbenzyl alcohol, 98%
$C_6H_5CH_2CH_2C_6H_4CH_2OH$
M.W. 212.29 m.p. 56-59°

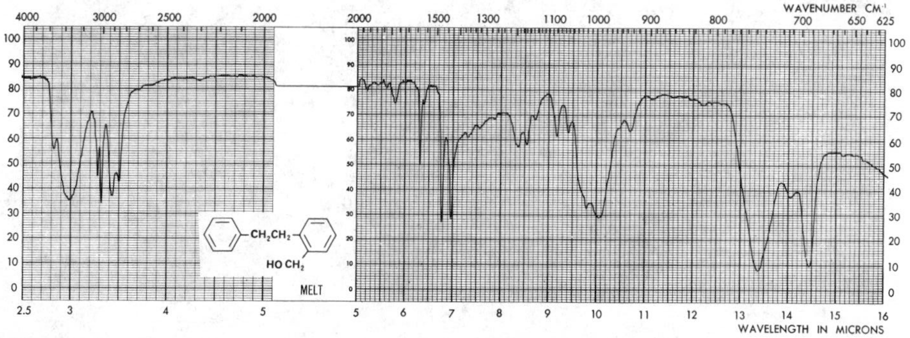

MELT

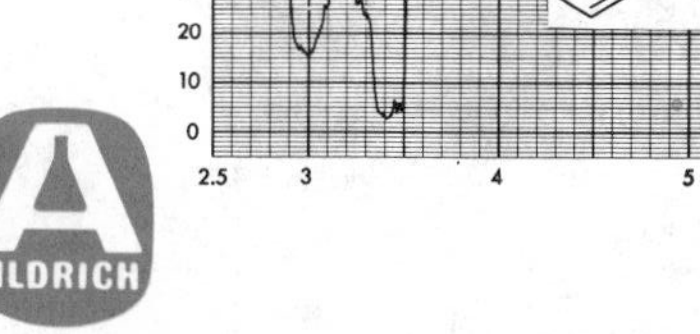

A

B980-7 **Benzopinacole** (1,1,2,2-tetraphenyl-1,2-ethanediol)
$(C_6H_5)_2C(OH)C(OH)(C_6H_5)_2$ M.W. 366.46
m.p. 182-183°

NUJOL MULL

B

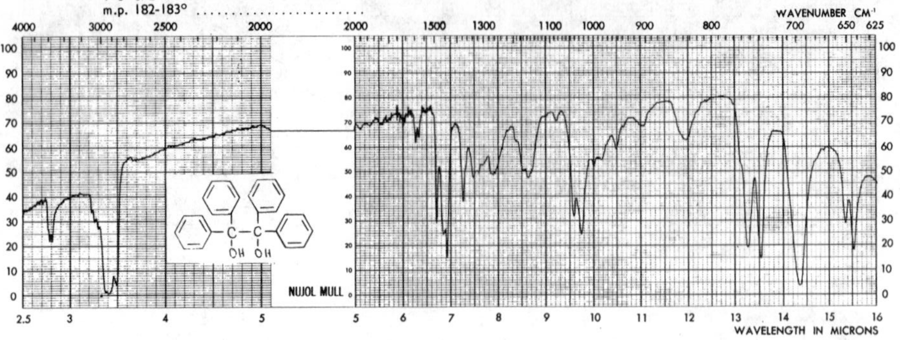

T2565-8 **1,1,4,4-Tetraphenyl-1,4-butanediol**
$HOC(C_6H_5)_2CH_2CH_2C(C_6H_5)_2OH$ M.W. 394.52
m.p. 205-207°

NUJOL MULL

C

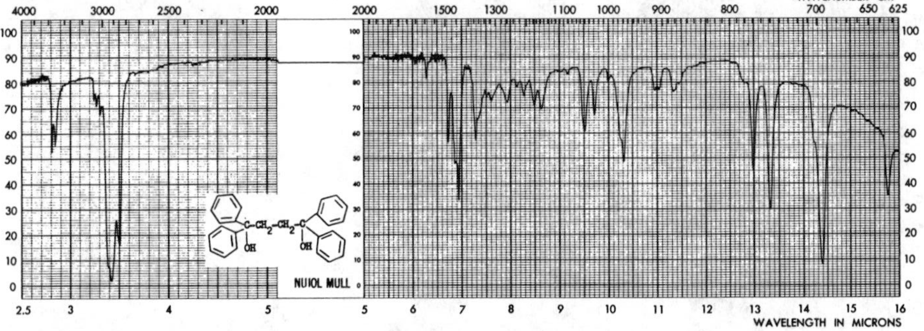

18,328-8
3,4-Bis(p-hydroxyphenyl)-3,4-hexanediol, tech.
$[HOC_6H_4C(C_2H_5)(OH)-]_2$
M.W. 302.37 m.p. 196-198°

NUJOL MULL

D

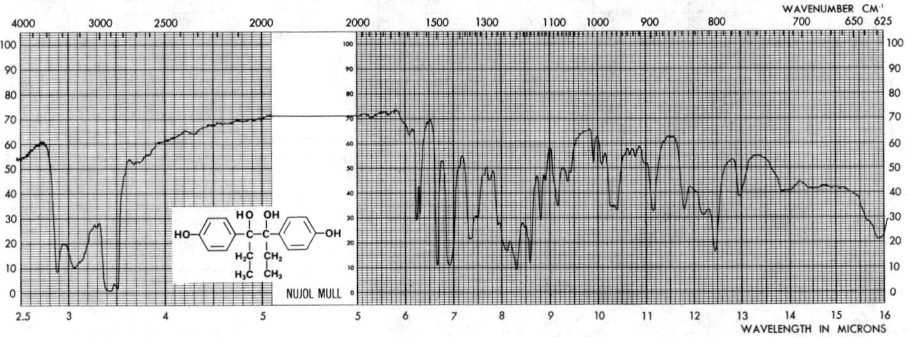

10,756-5 **1,1,1,3,3,3-Hexafluoro-2-phenyl-2-propanol**
$(CF_3)_2C(C_6H_5)OH$ M.W. 244.13 n_D^{20} 1.4148

NEAT

E

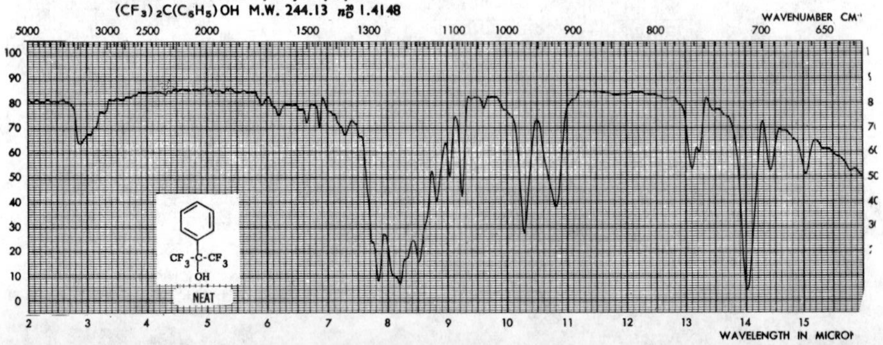

18,847-6
o-Methylbenzyl alcohol, 98%
$CH_3C_6H_4CH_2OH$ FW 122.17 mp 36-39° Disp. C

MELT

F

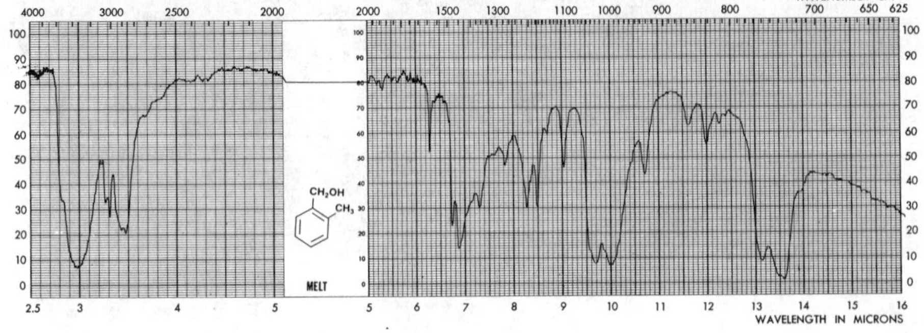

16,251-5
2-Fluorobenzyl alcohol, 98%
$FC_6H_4CH_2OH$
M.W. 126.13 n_D^{20} 1.5136 d 1.173 Beil. **6**(1),222

NEAT

G

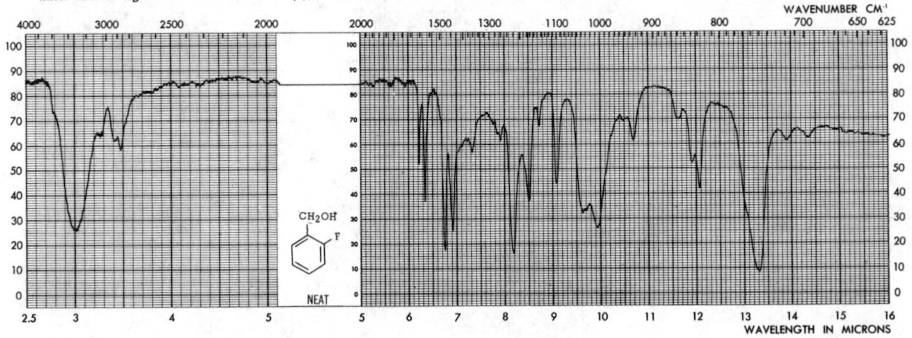

14,546-7 **o-Chlorobenzyl alcohol**
$ClC_6H_4CH_2OH$ M.W. 142.59 m.p. 69-71°

MELT

H

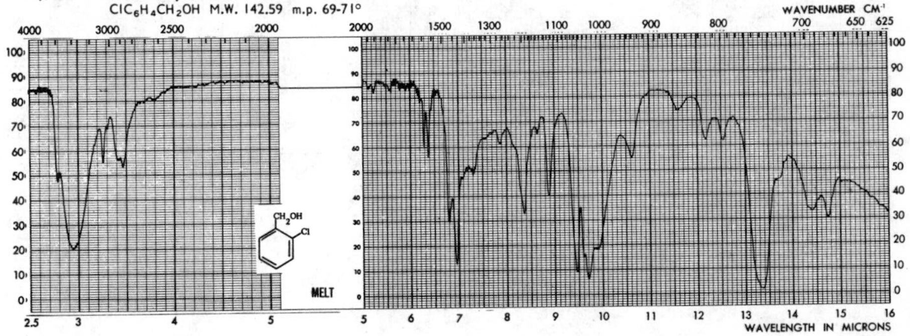

18,427-6
o-Bromobenzyl alcohol, 98%
$BrC_6H_4CH_2OH$
M.W. 187.04 m.p. 79-82° Beil. **6**,445

NUJOL MULL

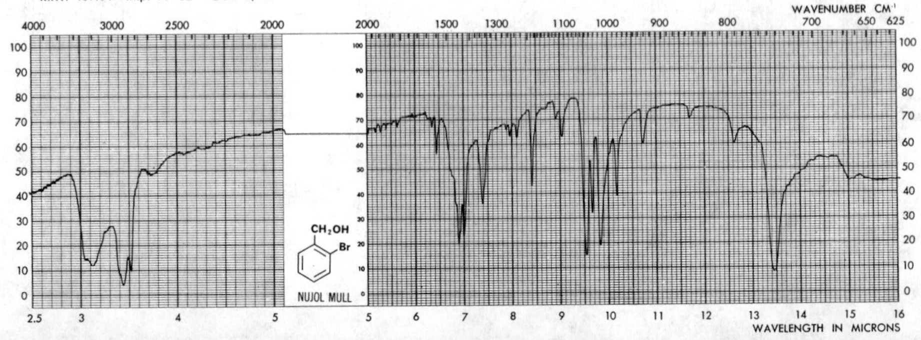

A

18,363-6
o-Iodobenzyl alcohol, 99%
$IC_6H_4CH_2OH$
M.W. 234.04 m.p. 91-93° Beil. **6**(2),424

NUJOL MULL

B

12,412-5 **2-Bromophenyl methyl carbinol** (2-bromo-α-methylbenzyl alcohol)
$BrC_6H_4CH(CH_3)OH$ M.W. 201.07 n_D^{20} 1.5747

NEAT

C

16,695-2
2-Hydroxybenzyl alcohol, 97% (salicyl alcohol)
$HOC_6H_4CH_2OH$
M.W. 124.14 m.p. 86-87° Beil. **6**,891

NUJOL MULL

D

M1,080-8
2-Methoxybenzyl alcohol, 99% (o-anisyl alcohol)
$CH_3OC_6H_4CH_2OH$
M.W. 138.17 b.p. 248-250° n_D^{20} 1.5475 d 1.039
Beil. **6**,893

NEAT

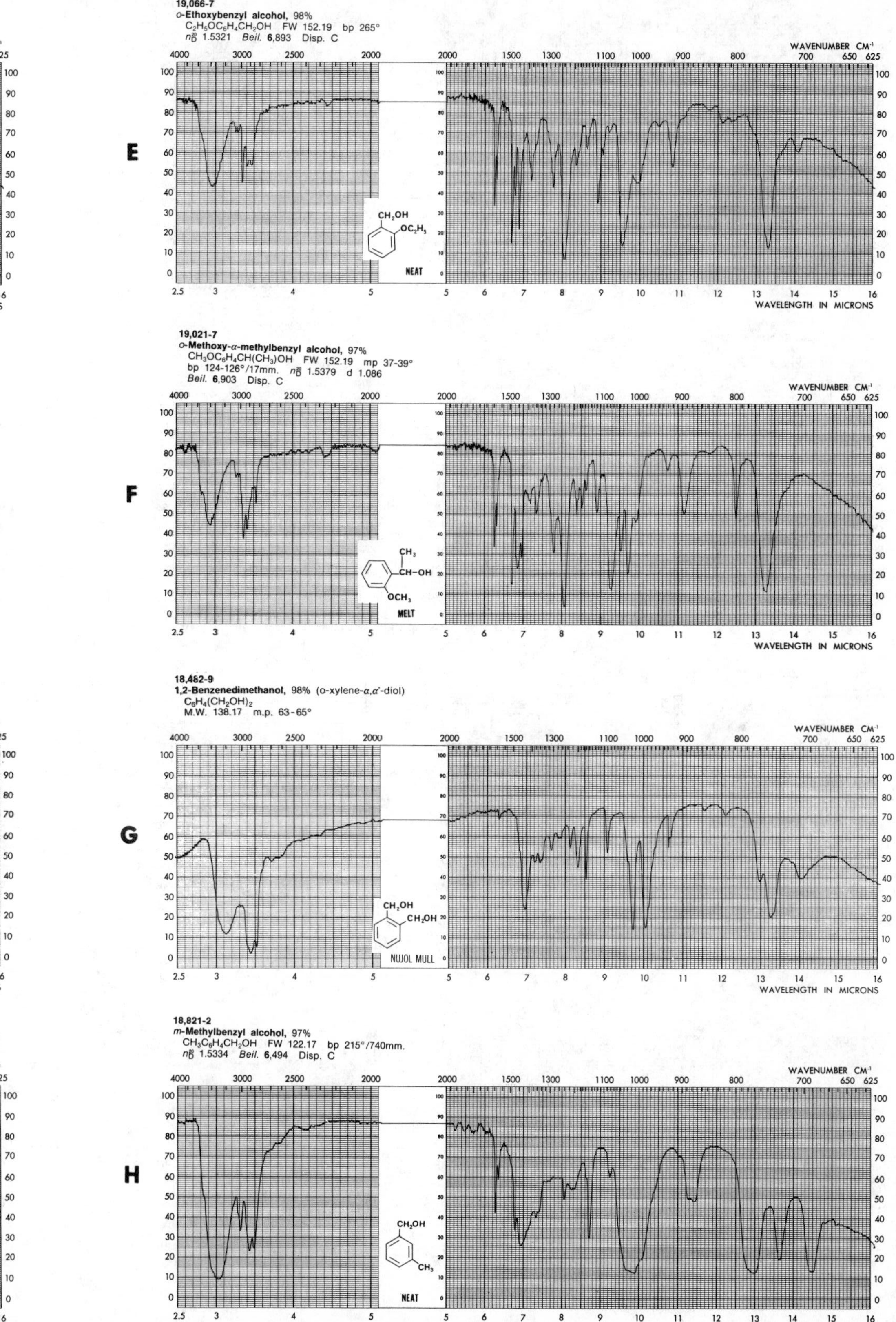

E

19,066-7
o-Ethoxybenzyl alcohol, 98%
$C_2H_5OC_6H_4CH_2OH$ FW 152.19 bp 265°
n_D^{20} 1.5321 *Beil.* **6**,893 Disp. C

NEAT

F

19,021-7
o-Methoxy-α-methylbenzyl alcohol, 97%
$CH_3OC_6H_4CH(CH_3)OH$ FW 152.19 mp 37-39°
bp 124-126°/17mm. n_D^{20} 1.5379 d 1.086
Beil. **6**,903 Disp. C

MELT

G

18,462-9
1,2-Benzenedimethanol, 98% (o-xylene-α,α′-diol)
$C_6H_4(CH_2OH)_2$
M.W. 138.17 m.p. 63-65°

NUJOL MULL

H

18,821-2
m-Methylbenzyl alcohol, 97%
$CH_3C_6H_4CH_2OH$ FW 122.17 bp 215°/740mm.
n_D^{20} 1.5334 *Beil.* **6**,494 Disp. C

NEAT

ALDRICH

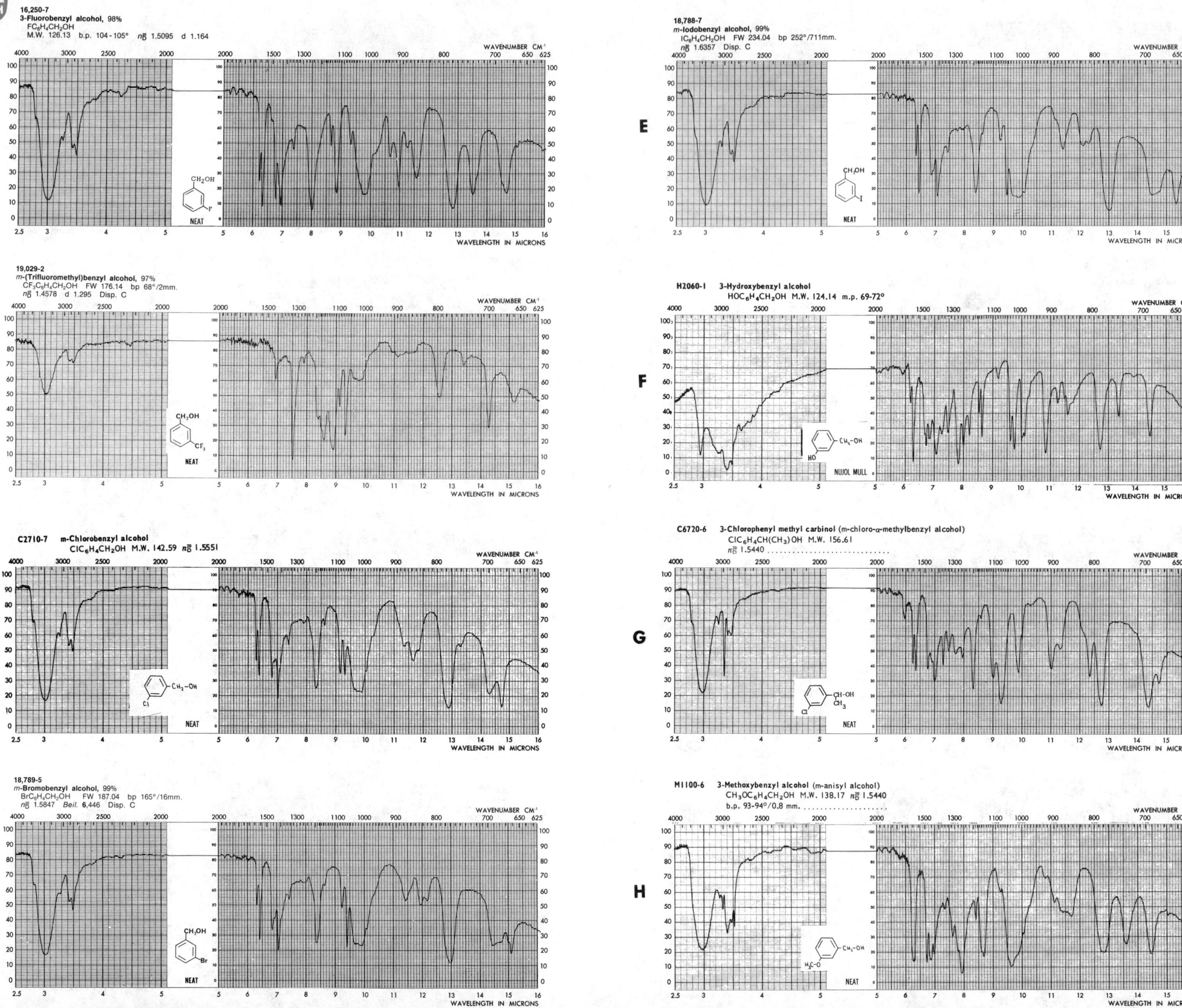
ALDRICH
A
16,250-7
3-Fluorobenzyl alcohol, 98%
FC6H4CH2OH
M.W. 126.13 b.p. 104-105° nD20 1.5095 d 1.164
NEAT
B
19,029-2
m-(Trifluoromethyl)benzyl alcohol, 97%
CF3C6H4CH2OH FW 176.14 bp 68°/2mm.
nD20 1.4578 d 1.295 Disp. C
NEAT
C
C2710-7 m-Chlorobenzyl alcohol
ClC6H4CH2OH M.W. 142.59 nD20 1.5551
NEAT
D
18,789-5
m-Bromobenzyl alcohol, 99%
BrC6H4CH2OH FW 187.04 bp 165°/16mm.
nD20 1.5847 Beil. 6,446 Disp. C
NEAT
E
18,788-7
m-Iodobenzyl alcohol, 99%
IC6H4CH2OH FW 234.04 bp 252°/711mm.
nD20 1.6357 Disp. C
NEAT
F
H2060-1 3-Hydroxybenzyl alcohol
HOC6H4CH2OH M.W. 124.14 m.p. 69-72°
NUJOL MULL
G
C6720-6 3-Chlorophenyl methyl carbinol (m-chloro-α-methylbenzyl alcohol)
ClC6H4CH(CH3)OH M.W. 156.61
nD20 1.5440
NEAT
H
M1100-6 3-Methoxybenzyl alcohol (m-anisyl alcohol)
CH3OC6H4CH2OH M.W. 138.17 nD20 1.5440
b.p. 93-94°/0.8 mm.
NEAT
WAVENUMBER CM-1
WAVELENGTH IN MICRONS

A

19,036-5
m-**Methoxy-α-methylbenzyl alcohol,** 97%
$CH_3OC_6H_4CH(CH_3)OH$ FW 152.19
bp 132°/12mm. n_D^{20} 1.5322 d 1.078 *Beil.* **6**,903
Disp. C

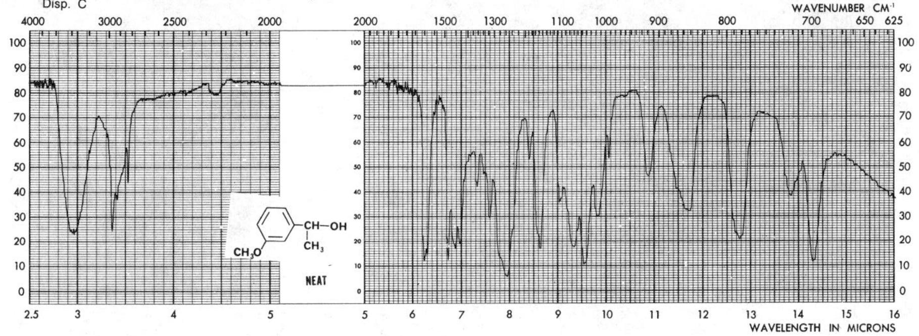

NEAT

B

19,653-3
1,3-Benzenedimethanol, 98% (*m*-xylene-α,α′-diol)
$C_6H_4(CH_2OH)_2$ FW 138.17 mp 56-60°
bp 154-159°/13mm. *Beil.* **6**,914 Disp. C

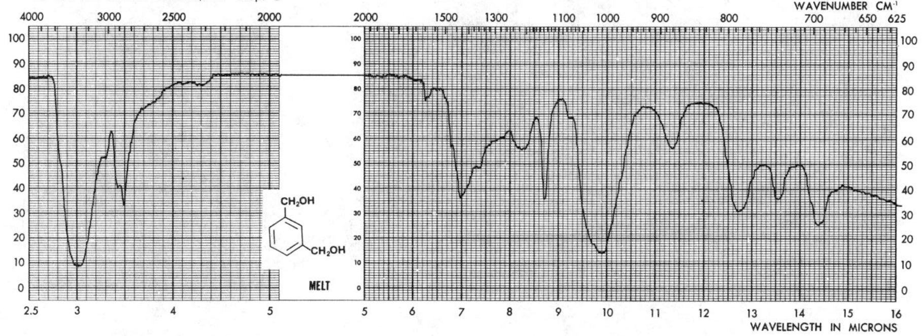

MELT

C

C6425 1-(m-Chlorophenyl)-2,2-dichloroethanol [m-chloro-α-(dichloromethyl)-benzyl alcohol]
$ClC_6H_4CH(OH)CHCl_2$ M.W. 225.52
n_D^{20} 1.5719

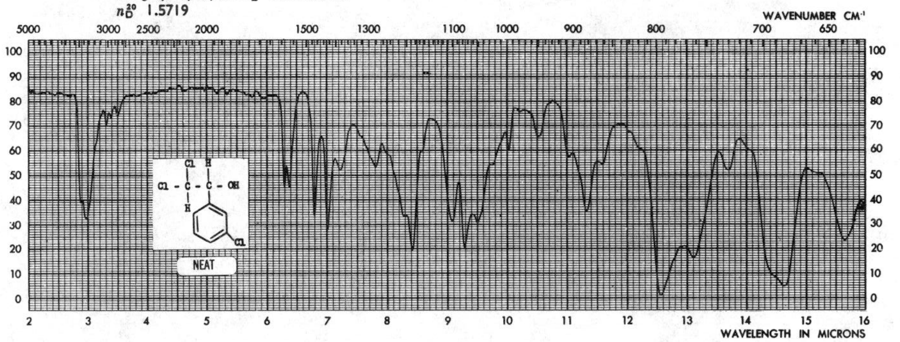

NEAT

D

19,139-6
m-**Aminobenzyl alcohol,** 97%
$H_2NC_6H_4CH_2OH$ FW 123.16 mp 93-95°
Beil. **13**,619 Disp. C

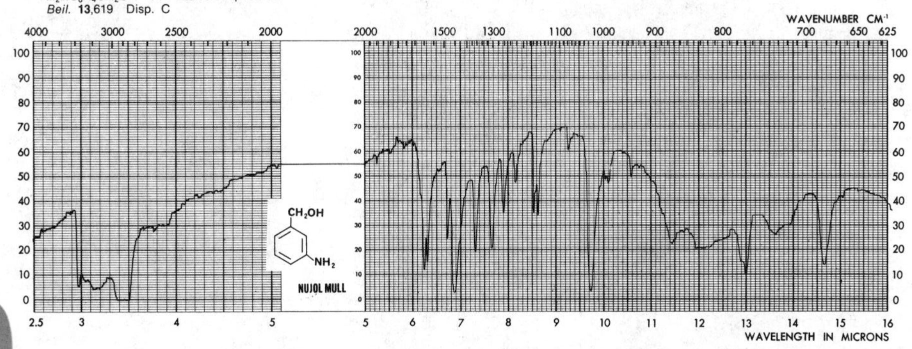

NUJOL MULL

E

19,028-4
m-**Phenoxybenzyl alcohol,** 98%
$C_6H_5OC_6H_4CH_2OH$ FW 200.24 bp 135-140°/1mm.
n_D^{20} 1.5935 Disp. C

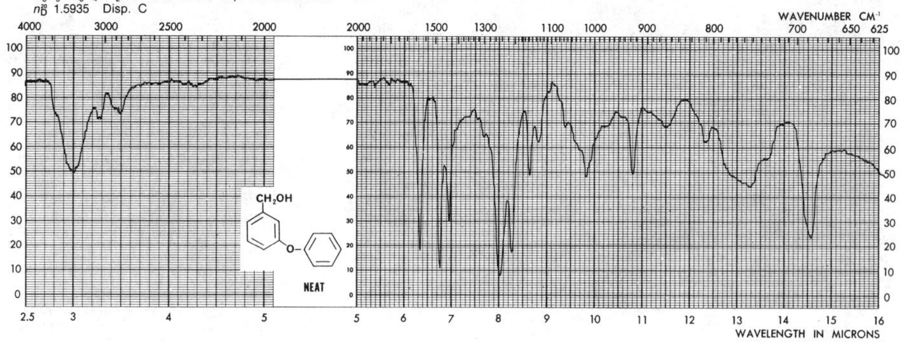

NEAT

F

12,780-9 p-Methylbenzyl alcohol
$CH_3C_6H_4CH_2OH$ M.W. 122.17 m.p. 60-61°

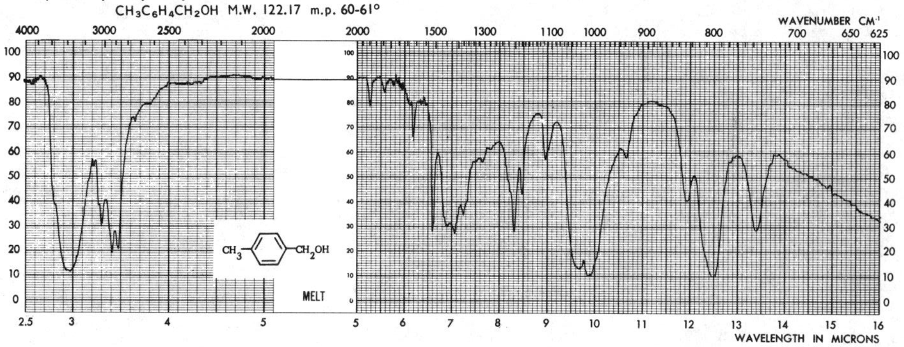

MELT

G

20,544-3
4-Ethylbenzyl alcohol, 99%
$C_2H_5C_6H_4CH_2OH$ FW 136.19 bp 115-117°/9mm.
d 1.028 *Beil.* **6**(2),479 Disp. C

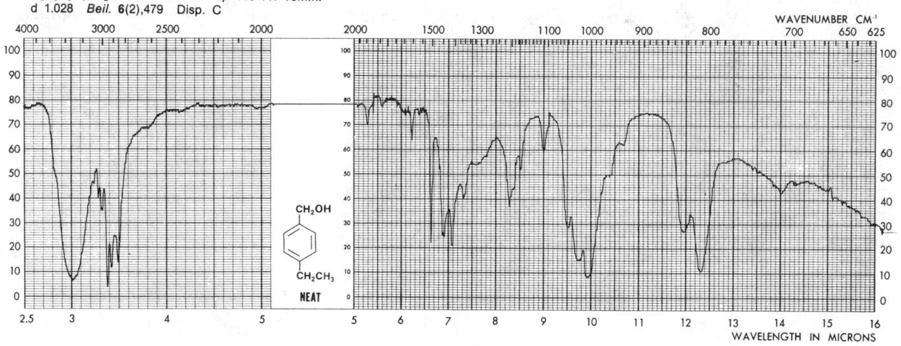

NEAT

H

19,603-7
p-**Isopropylbenzyl alcohol** (cumic alcohol)
$(CH_3)_2CHC_6H_4CH_2OH$ FW 150.22 mp 28°
bp 135-136°/26mm. n_D^{20} 1.5206 d 0.982
Beil. **6**(3),1911 Disp. C

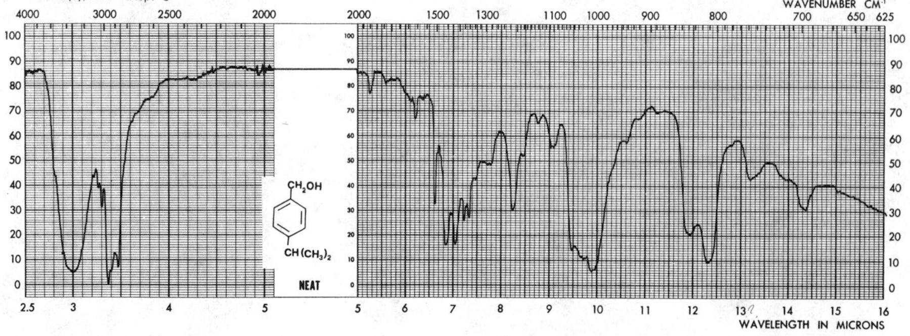

NEAT

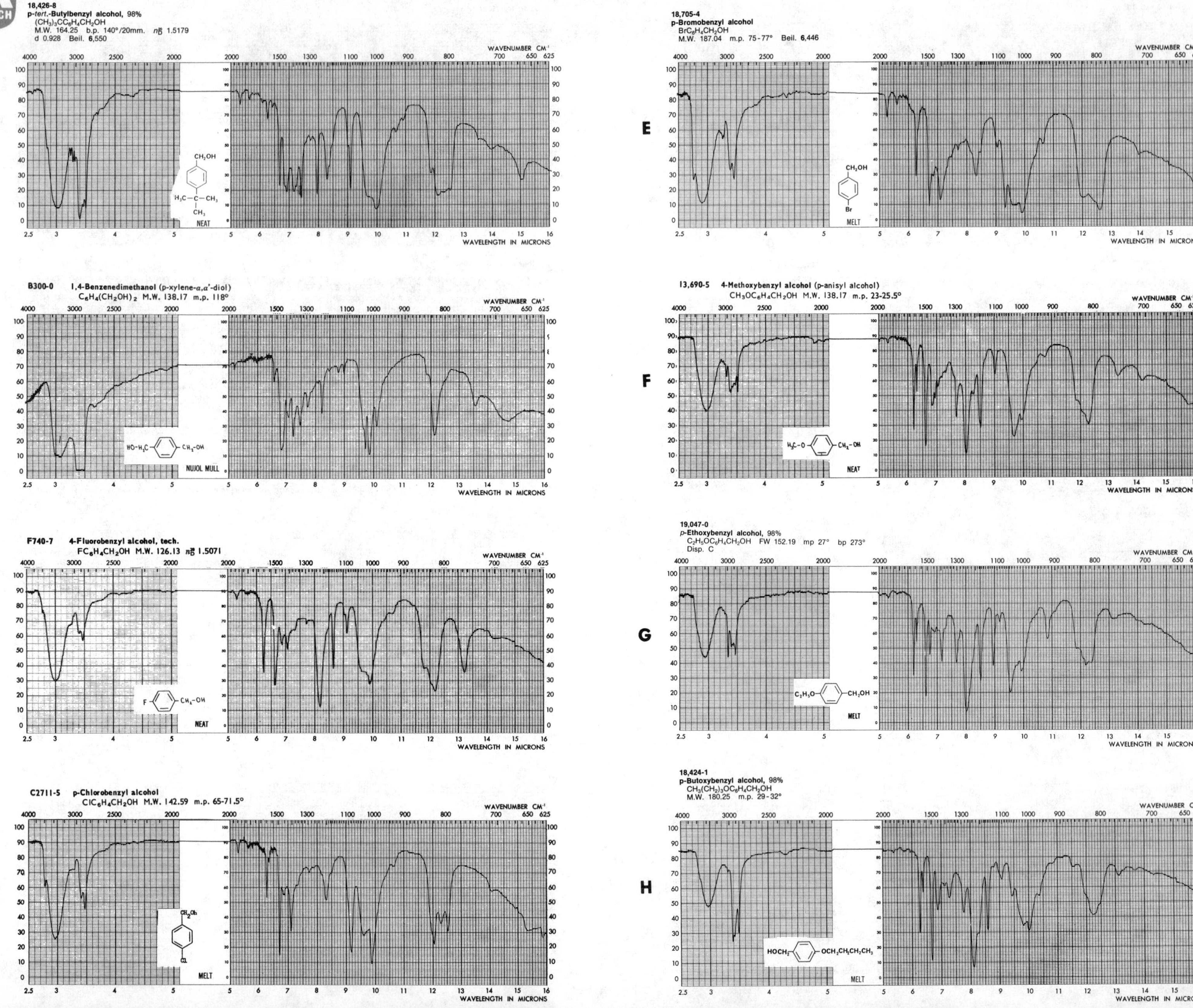
ALDRICH
A
18,426-8
p-tert.-Butylbenzyl alcohol, 98%
(CH3)3CC6H4CH2OH
M.W. 164.25 b.p. 140°/20mm. nD 1.5179
d 0.928 Beil. 6,550
NEAT
B
B300-0 1,4-Benzenedimethanol (p-xylene-α,α'-diol)
C6H4(CH2OH)2 M.W. 138.17 m.p. 118°
NUJOL MULL
C
F740-7 4-Fluorobenzyl alcohol, tech.
FC6H4CH2OH M.W. 126.13 nD 1.5071
NEAT
D
C2711-5 p-Chlorobenzyl alcohol
ClC6H4CH2OH M.W. 142.59 m.p. 65-71.5°
MELT
E
18,705-4
p-Bromobenzyl alcohol
BrC6H4CH2OH
M.W. 187.04 m.p. 75-77° Beil. 6,446
MELT
F
13,690-5 4-Methoxybenzyl alcohol (p-anisyl alcohol)
CH3OC6H4CH2OH M.W. 138.17 m.p. 23-25.5°
NEAT
G
19,047-0
p-Ethoxybenzyl alcohol, 98%
C2H5OC6H4CH2OH FW 152.19 mp 27° bp 273°
Disp. C
MELT
H
18,424-1
p-Butoxybenzyl alcohol, 98%
CH3(CH2)3OC6H4CH2OH
M.W. 180.25 m.p. 29-32°
MELT
WAVENUMBER CM⁻¹
WAVELENGTH IN MICRONS

A H2080-6 **4-Hydroxybenzyl alcohol**
$HOC_6H_4CH_2OH$ M.W. 124.14 m.p. 116-119°
NUJOL MULL

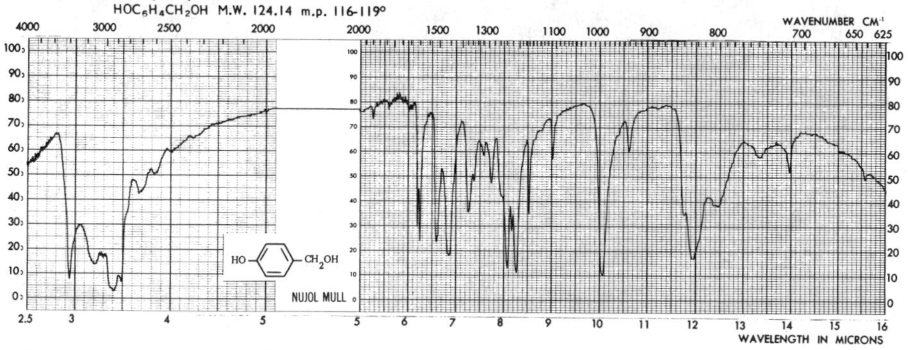

B 19,155-8
p-Aminobenzyl alcohol
$H_2NC_6H_4CH_2OH$ FW 123.16 mp 61-63°
Beil. 13,620 Disp. C
MELT

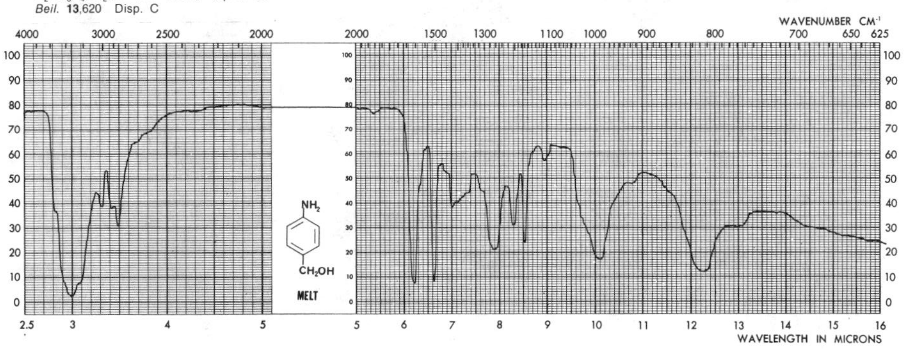

C 12,212-2 **α,p-Dimethylbenzyl alcohol** (methyl p-tolyl carbinol)
$CH_3C_6H_4CH(CH_3)OH$ M.W. 136.19 n_D^{20} 1.5223
b.p. 220°
NEAT

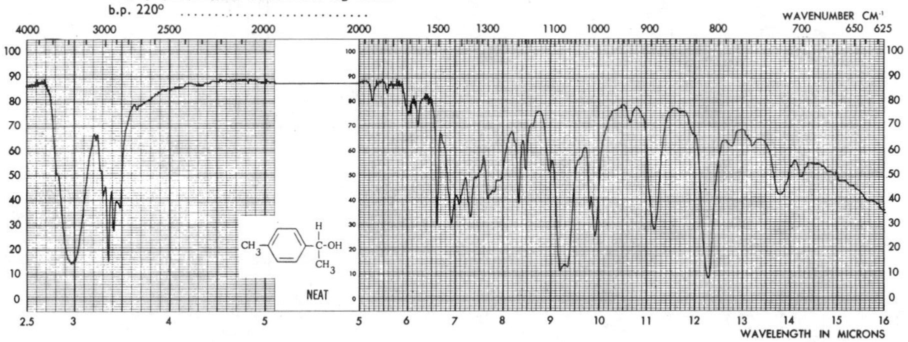

D 11,492-8 ***dl*-p-Methyl-α-(n-propyl)-benzyl alcohol** (*dl*-n-propyl p-tolyl carbinol)
$CH_3C_6H_4CH(CH_2CH_2CH_3)OH$ M.W. 164.25
n_D^{20} 1.5098
NEAT

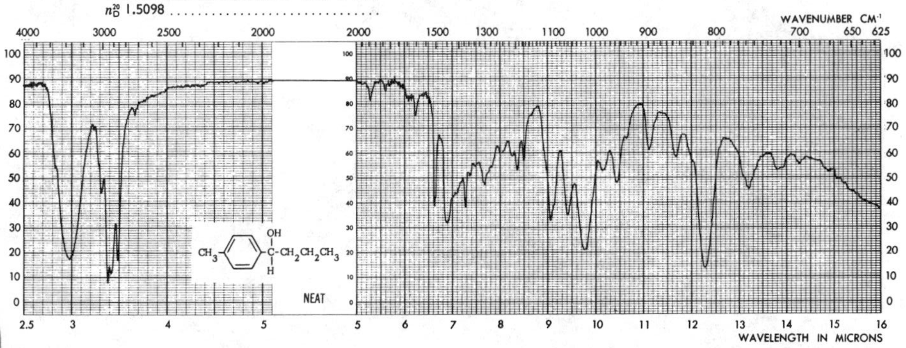

E 13,270-5 **p-Fluoro-α-methylbenzyl alcohol, tech.**
$FC_6H_4CH(CH_3)OH$ M.W. 140.16 n_D^{20} 1.5011
b.p. 90-92°/7 mm.
NEAT

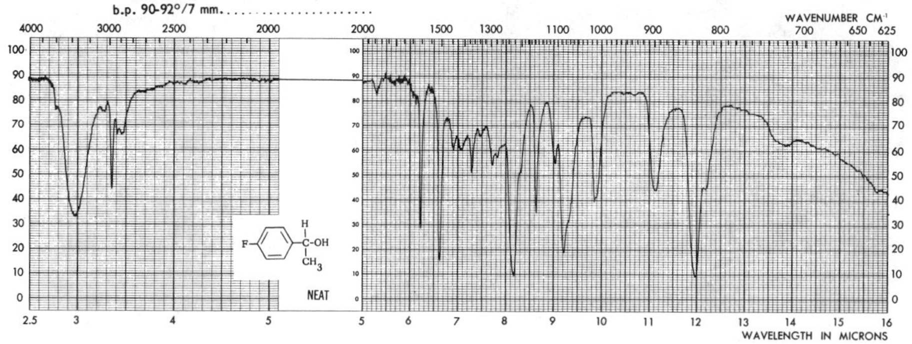

F 15,412-1 **α-Ethyl-p-fluorobenzyl alcohol**
$FC_6H_4CH(C_2H_5)OH$ M.W. 154.19
n_D^{20} 1.4980
NEAT

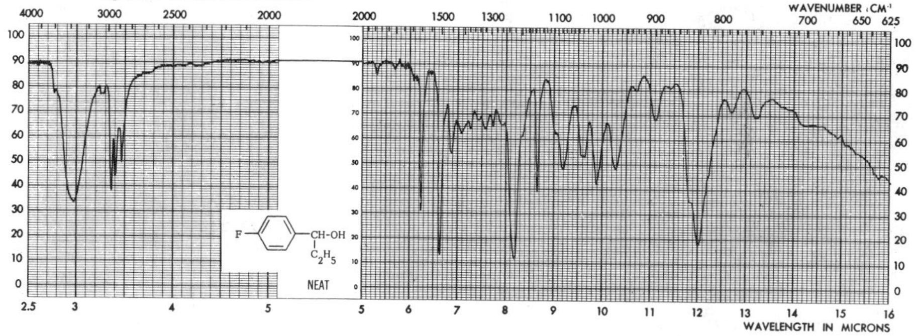

G 11,493-6 ***dl*-p-Fluoro-α-(n-propyl)-benzyl alcohol** (*dl*-p-fluorophenyl n-propyl carbinol)
$FC_6H_4CH(CH_2CH_2CH_3)OH$ M.W. 168.21
m.p. 32-34°
NEAT

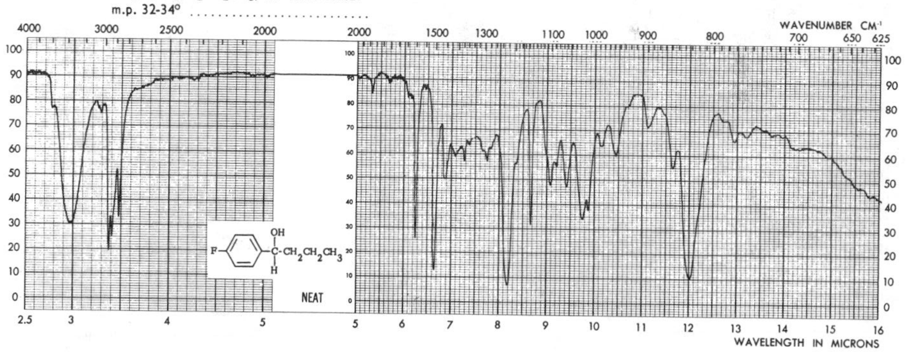

H 14,755-9 **4-Chlorophenyl methyl carbinol** (p-chloro-α-methylbenzyl alcohol)
$ClC_6H_4CH(CH_3)OH$ M.W. 156.61 n_D^{20} 1.5410
b.p. 119°/10 mm.
NEAT

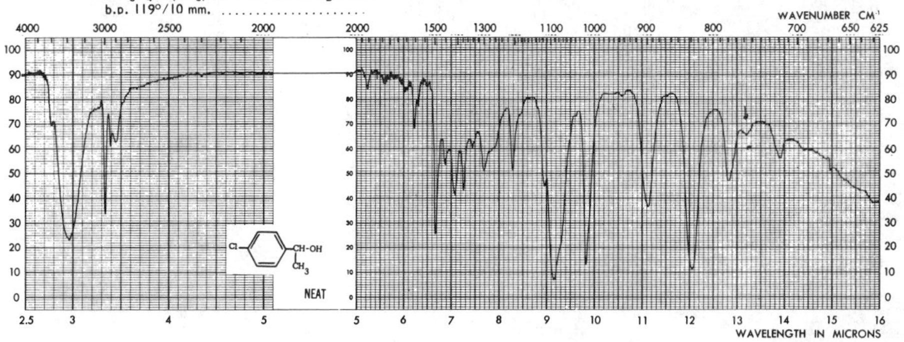

A

15,414-8 **p-Chloro-α-ethylbenzyl alcohol**
$ClC_6H_4CH(C_2H_5)OH$ M.W. 170.64
n_D^{20} 1.5371

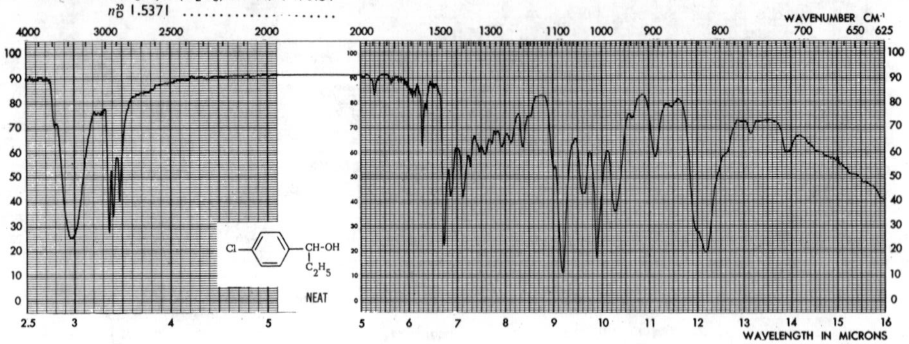

NEAT

B

11,494-4 ***dl*-p-Chloro-α-(n-propyl)-benzyl alcohol** (*dl*-p-chlorophenyl n-propyl carbinol)
$ClC_6H_4CH(CH_2CH_2CH_3)OH$ M.W. 184.67
n_D^{20} 1.5278

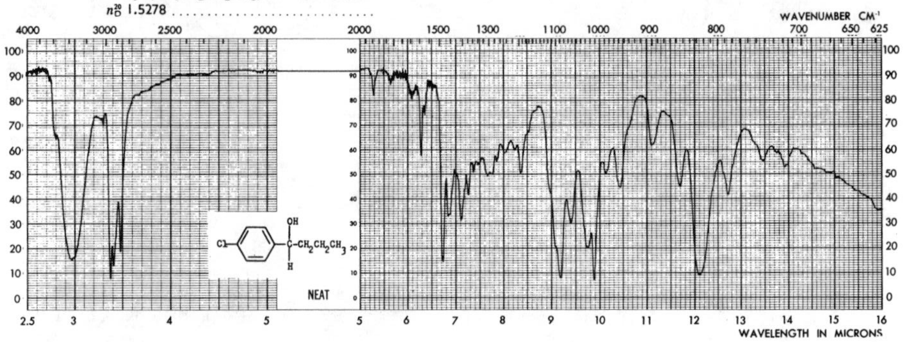

NEAT

C

22,268-2
4,4'-Difluorobenzhydrol, 98%
$(FC_6H_4)_2CHOH$ FW 220.22 mp 47-48°
bp 143°/3mm. *Beil.* **6**(3),3375 Disp. C

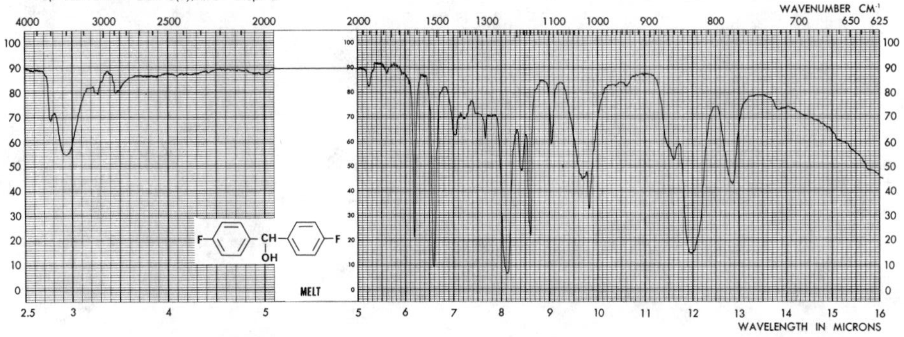

MELT

D

11,313-1 **4,4'-Dichlorobenzhydrol**
$(ClC_6H_4)_2CHOH$ M.W. 253.12 m.p. 91-93°

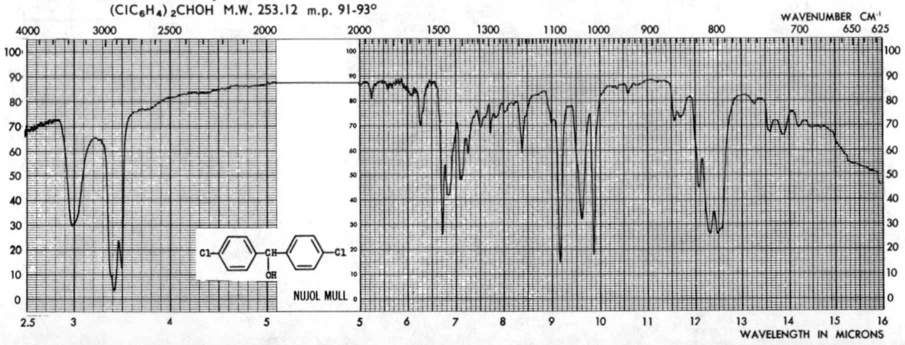

NUJOL MULL

E

19,132-9
4,4'-Dichloro-α-methylbenzhydrol
$(ClC_6H_4)_2C(CH_3)OH$ FW 267.16 mp 69-71°
Beil. **6**(3),3396 Disp. C

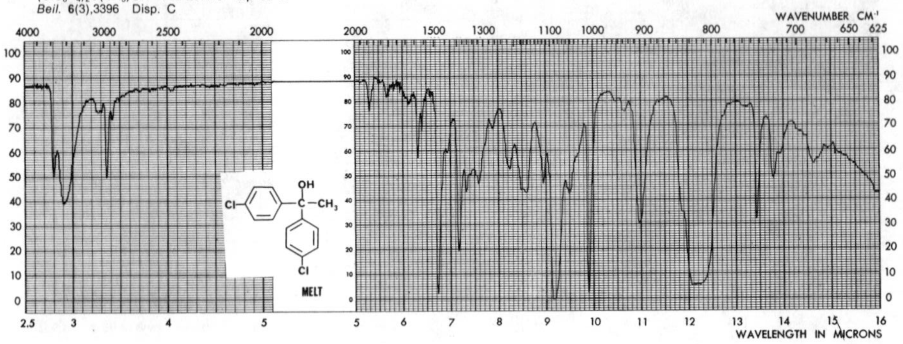

MELT

F

16,258-2
4,4'-Dimethoxybenzhydrol
$(CH_3OC_6H_4)_2CHOH$
M.W. 244.29 m.p. 69-71° Beil. **6**,1136
Fieser **3**,102

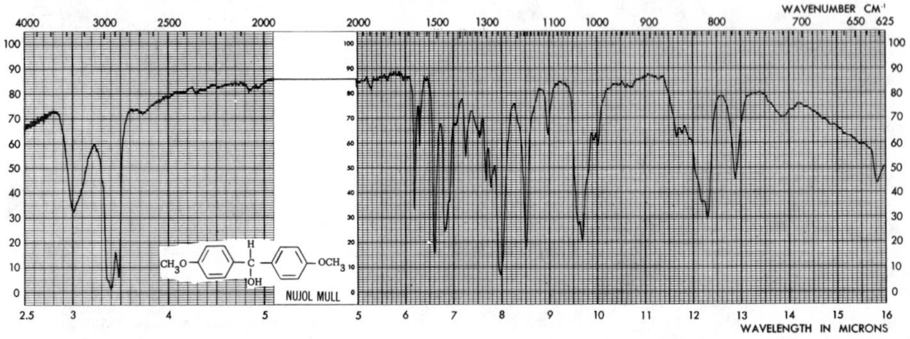

NUJOL MULL

G

18,613-9
o-Phenoxybenzyl alcohol, 99%
$C_6H_5OC_6H_4CH_2OH$
M.W. 200.24 b.p. 125°/0.1mm. n_D^{20} 1.5925

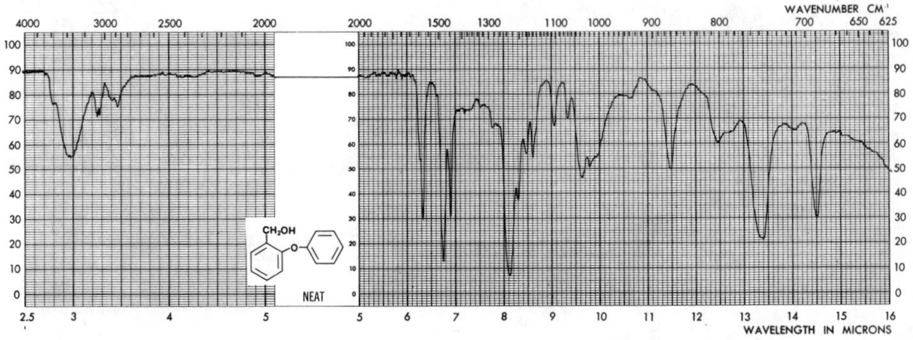

NEAT

H

14,576-9 **4-Bromophenyl methyl carbinol** (4-bromo-α-methylbenzyl alcohol)
$BrC_6H_4CH(CH_3)OH$ M.W. 201.07 n_D^{20} 1.5685
b.p. 119-121°/7 mm.

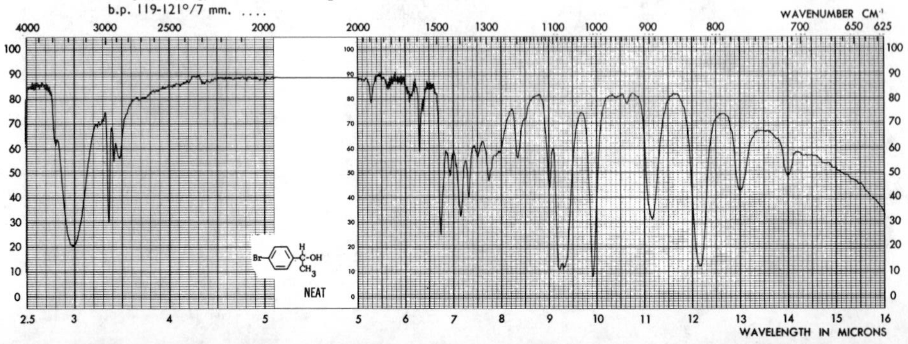

NEAT

A

15,415-6 **p-Bromo-α-ethylbenzyl alcohol**
$BrC_6H_4CH(C_2H_5)OH$ M.W. 215.10
n_D^{20} 1.5560

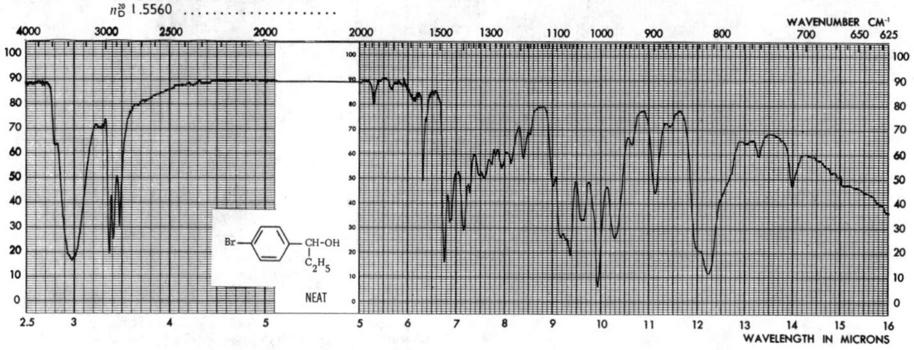

NEAT

B

11,495-2 *dl*-**p-Bromo-α-(n-propyl)-benzyl alcohol** (*dl*-p-bromophenyl n-propyl carbinol)
$BrC_6H_4CH(CH_2CH_2CH_3)OH$ M.W. 229.12
n_D^{20} 1.5480

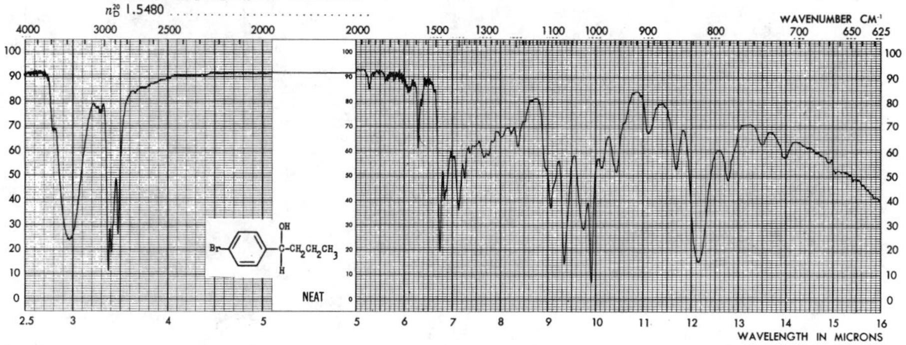

NEAT

C

10,110-9 **1-(p-Bromophenyl)-2,2,2-trichloroethanol** [p-bromo-α-(trichloromethyl)-benzyl alcohol]
$BrC_6H_4CH(OH)CCl_3$ M.W. 304.40 m.p. 55.5-57°

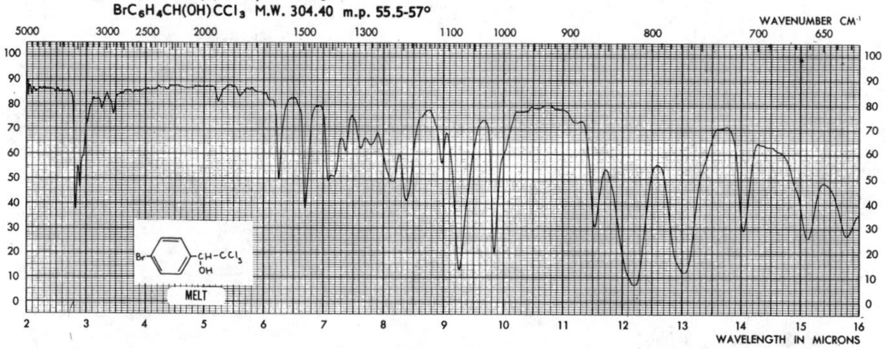

MELT

D

15,411-3 **p-Methoxy-α-methylbenzyl alcohol**
$CH_3OC_6H_4CH(CH_3)OH$ M.W. 152.19
n_D^{20} 1.5348

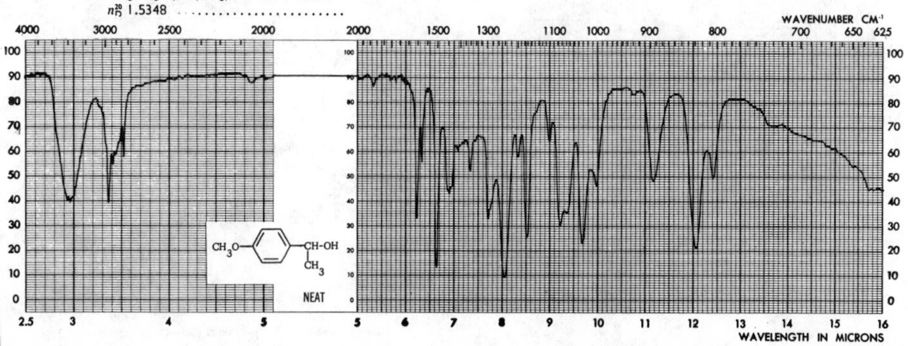

NEAT

E

15,416-4 **α-Ethyl-p-methoxybenzyl alcohol**
$CH_3OC_6H_4CH(C_2H_5)OH$ M.W. 166.22
n_D^{20} 1.5277

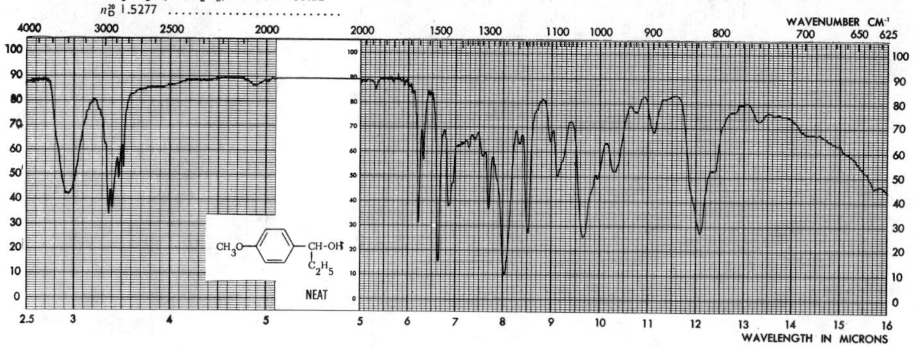

NEAT

F

11,188-0 **α-Cyclopropyl-p-methylbenzyl alcohol** (cyclopropyl p-tolyl carbinol)
$CH_3C_6H_4CH(C_3H_5)OH$ M.W. 162.23

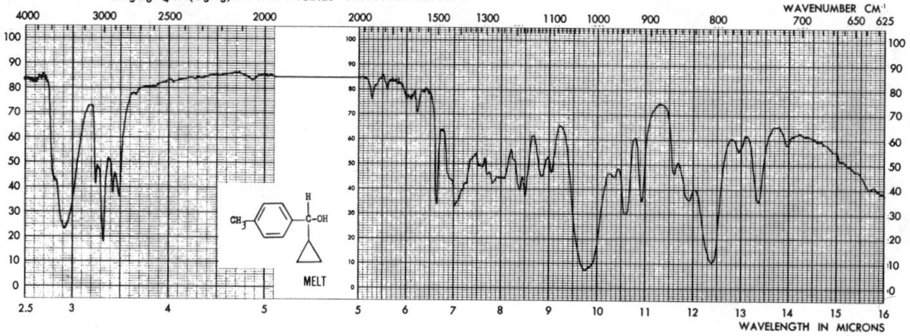

MELT

G

10,185-0 *dl*-**α-Cyclopropyl-α,p-dimethylbenzyl alcohol** (*dl*-cyclopropyl methyl p-tolyl carbinol)
$CH_3C_6H_4C(CH_3)(C_3H_5)OH$ M.W. 176.26 n_D^{20} 1.5310
b.p. 131-133°/12 mm.

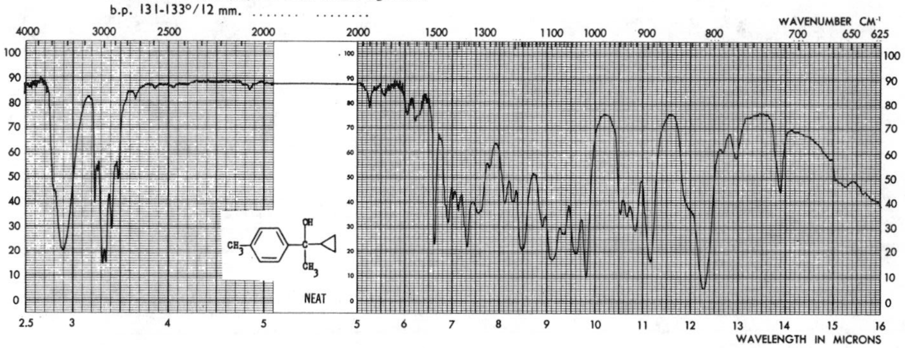

NEAT

H

11,650-5 *dl*-**α,p-Dimethyl-α-(1-methylcyclopropyl)-benzyl alcohol** (*dl*-methyl 1-methylcyclopropyl 4-tolyl carbinol)
$CH_3C_6H_4C(CH_3)(C_3H_4CH_3)OH$ M.W. 190.29
n_D^{20} 1.5255

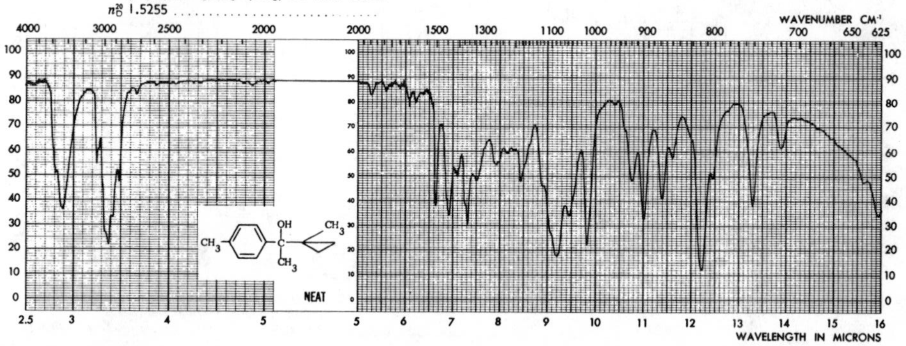

NEAT

ALDRICH

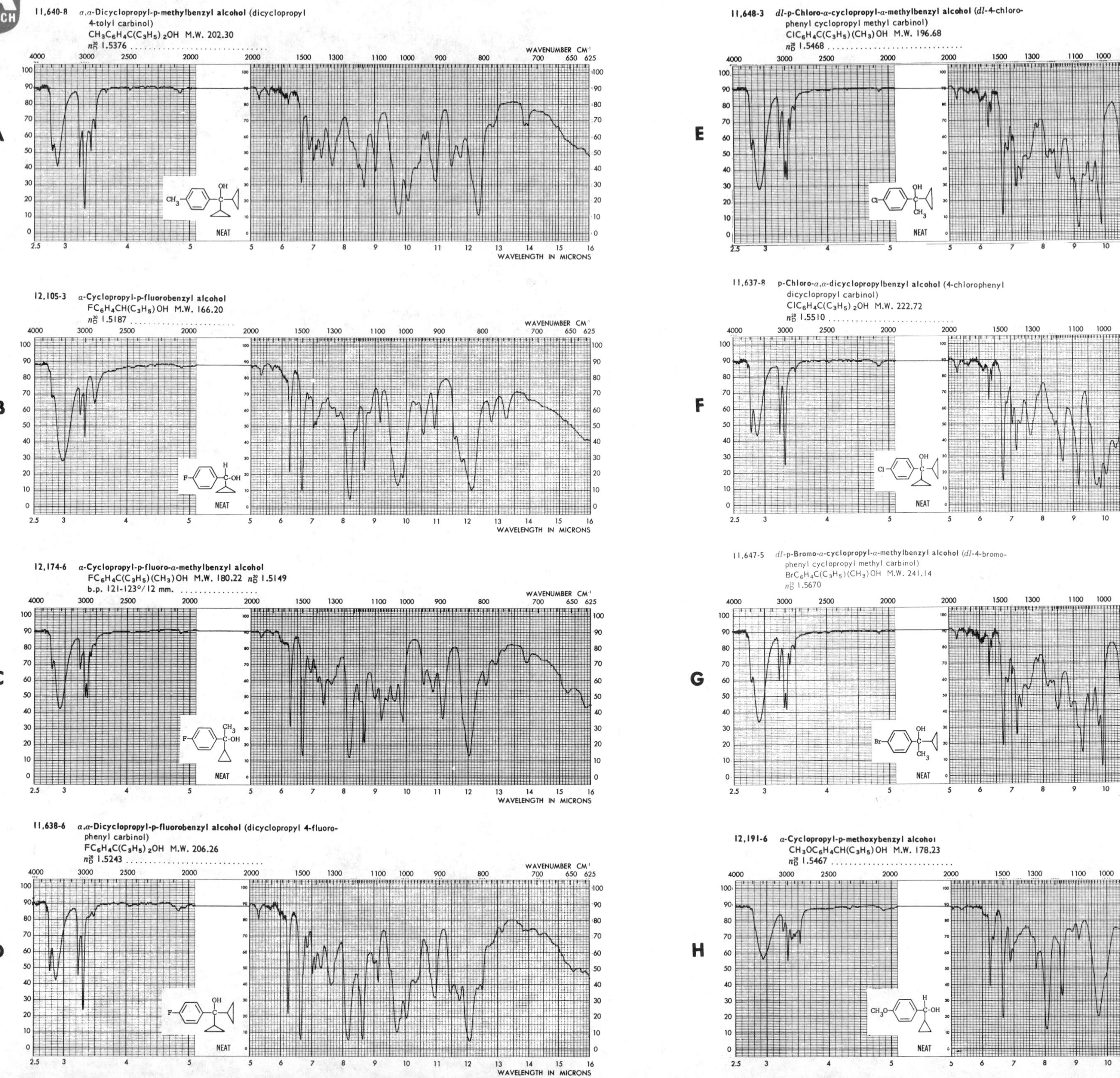

A 11,640-8 **α,α-Dicyclopropyl-p-methylbenzyl alcohol** (dicyclopropyl 4-tolyl carbinol)
$CH_3C_6H_4C(C_3H_5)_2OH$ M.W. 202.30
n_D^{20} 1.5376

B 12,105-3 **α-Cyclopropyl-p-fluorobenzyl alcohol**
$FC_6H_4CH(C_3H_5)OH$ M.W. 166.20
n_D^{20} 1.5187

C 12,174-6 **α-Cyclopropyl-p-fluoro-α-methylbenzyl alcohol**
$FC_6H_4C(C_3H_5)(CH_3)OH$ M.W. 180.22 n_D^{20} 1.5149
b.p. 121-123°/12 mm.

D 11,638-6 **α,α-Dicyclopropyl-p-fluorobenzyl alcohol** (dicyclopropyl 4-fluorophenyl carbinol)
$FC_6H_4C(C_3H_5)_2OH$ M.W. 206.26
n_D^{20} 1.5243

E 11,648-3 ***dl*-p-Chloro-α-cyclopropyl-α-methylbenzyl alcohol** (*dl*-4-chlorophenyl cyclopropyl methyl carbinol)
$ClC_6H_4C(C_3H_5)(CH_3)OH$ M.W. 196.68
n_D^{20} 1.5468

F 11,637-8 **p-Chloro-α,α-dicyclopropylbenzyl alcohol** (4-chlorophenyl dicyclopropyl carbinol)
$ClC_6H_4C(C_3H_5)_2OH$ M.W. 222.72
n_D^{20} 1.5510

G 11,647-5 *dl*-p-Bromo-α-cyclopropyl-α-methylbenzyl alcohol (*dl*-4-bromophenyl cyclopropyl methyl carbinol)
$BrC_6H_4C(C_3H_5)(CH_3)OH$ M.W. 241.14
n_D^{20} 1.5670

H 12,191-6 **α-Cyclopropyl-p-methoxybenzyl alcohol**
$CH_3OC_6H_4CH(C_3H_5)OH$ M.W. 178.23
n_D^{20} 1.5467

A

18,762-3
2-Chloro-6-fluorobenzyl alcohol, 97%
$ClC_6H_3(F)CH_2OH$ FW 160.58 mp 42-44°
Disp. C

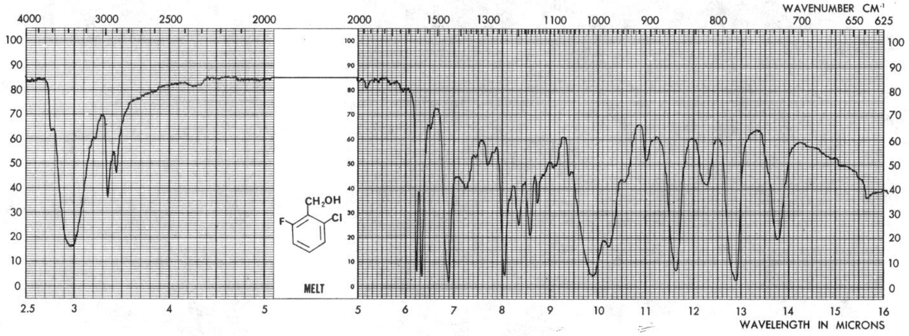

MELT

B

10,029-3 **2,6-Dichlorobenzyl alcohol**
$Cl_2C_6H_3CH_2OH$ M.W. 177.03 m.p. 96-98°

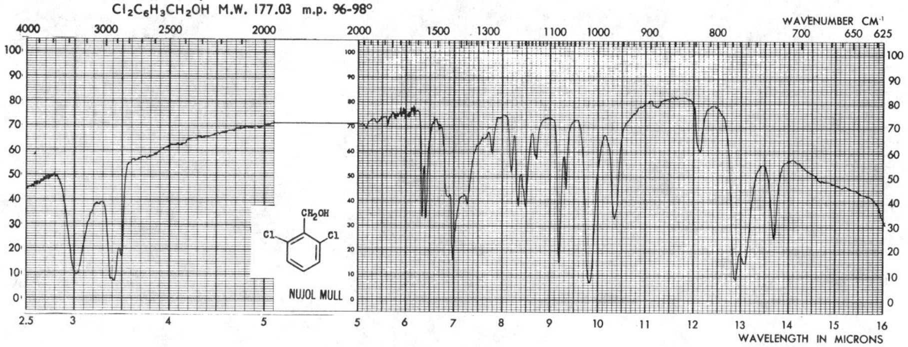

NUJOL MULL

C

12,631-4 **2,3-Dimethoxybenzyl alcohol**
$(CH_3O)_2C_6H_3CH_2OH$ M.W. 168.19 m.p. 48-51°

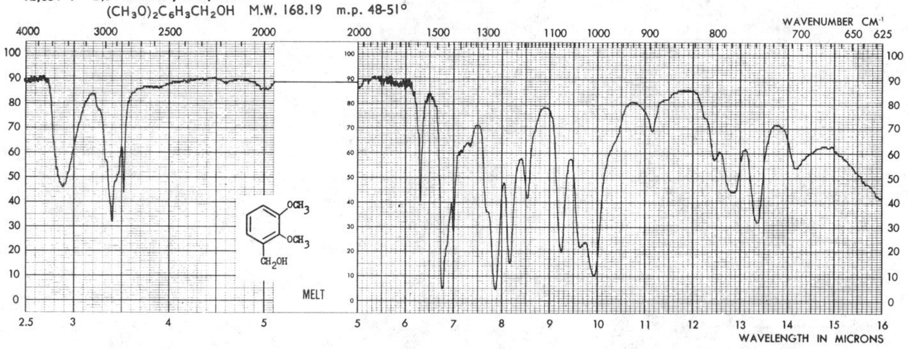

MELT

D

18,878-6
2,4-Dimethylbenzyl alcohol, 97%
$(CH_3)_2C_6H_3CH_2OH$ FW 136.19 bp 120°/13mm.
n_D^{20} 1.5339 Disp. C

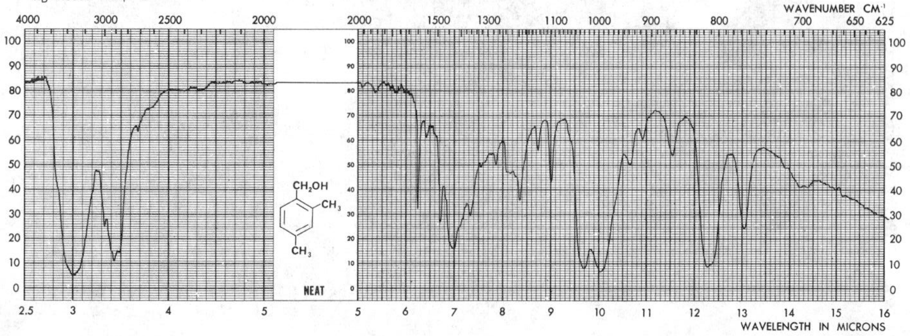

NEAT

E

18,879-4
3,4-Dimethylbenzyl alcohol, 99%
$(CH_3)_2C_6H_3CH_2OH$ FW 136.19 mp 62-65°
bp 218-221° *Beil.* **6**,521 Disp. C

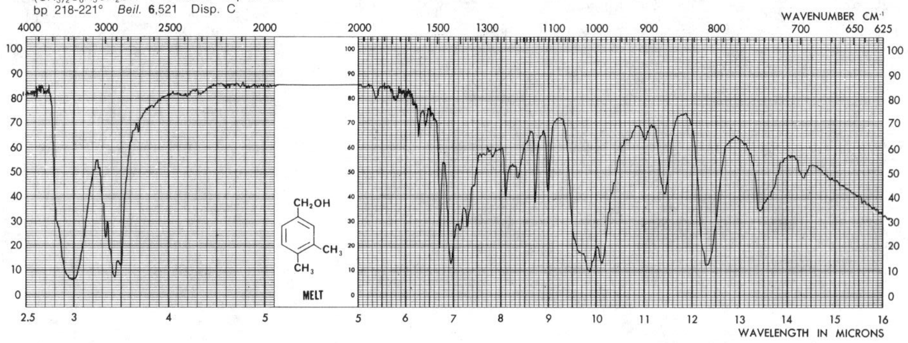

MELT

F

18,932-4
2,5-Dimethylbenzyl alcohol, 98%
$(CH_3)_2C_6H_3CH_2OH$ FW 136.19 bp 232-234°
n_D^{20} 1.5364 *Beil.* **6**,518 Disp. C

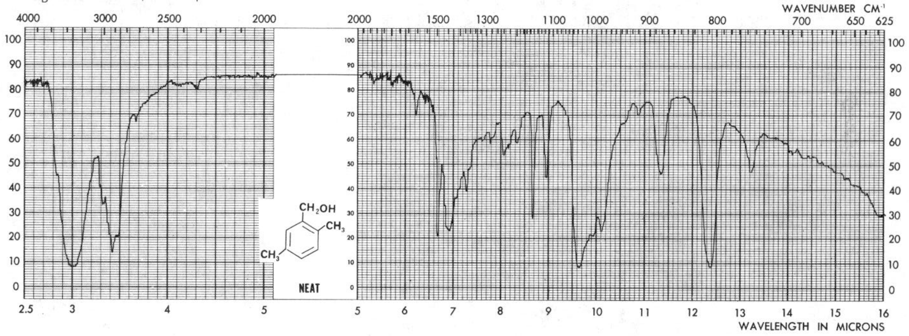

NEAT

G

14,666-8 **2,4-Dichlorobenzyl alcohol**
$Cl_2C_6H_3CH_2OH$ M.W. 177.03 m.p. 55-58°

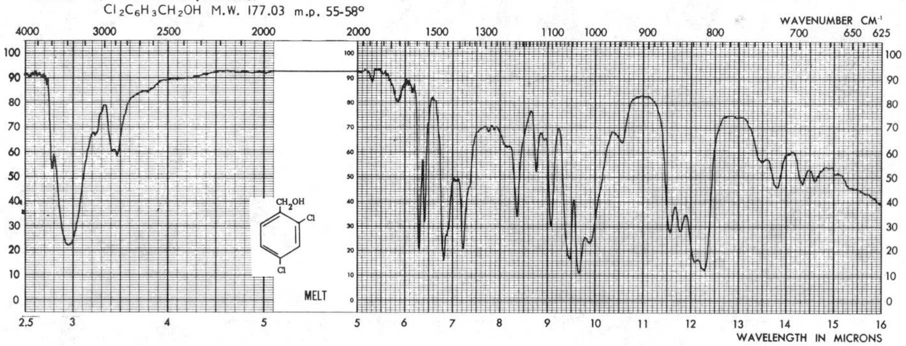

MELT

H

18,661-9
5-Chloro-2-methoxybenzyl alcohol, 98%
$ClC_6H_3(OCH_3)CH_2OH$
M.W. 172.61 m.p. 56-58°
b.p. 104-105°/0.06mm.

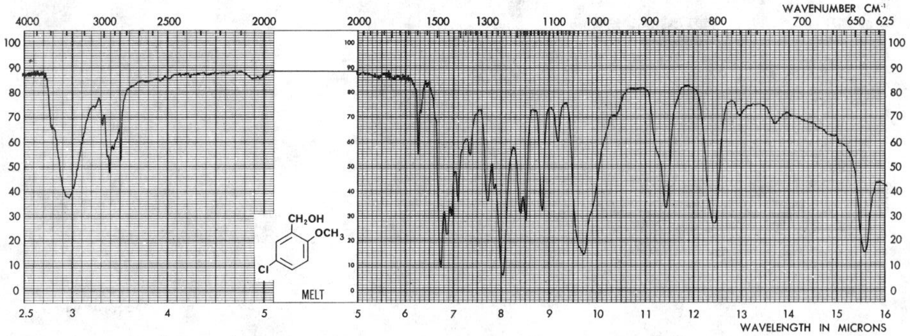

MELT

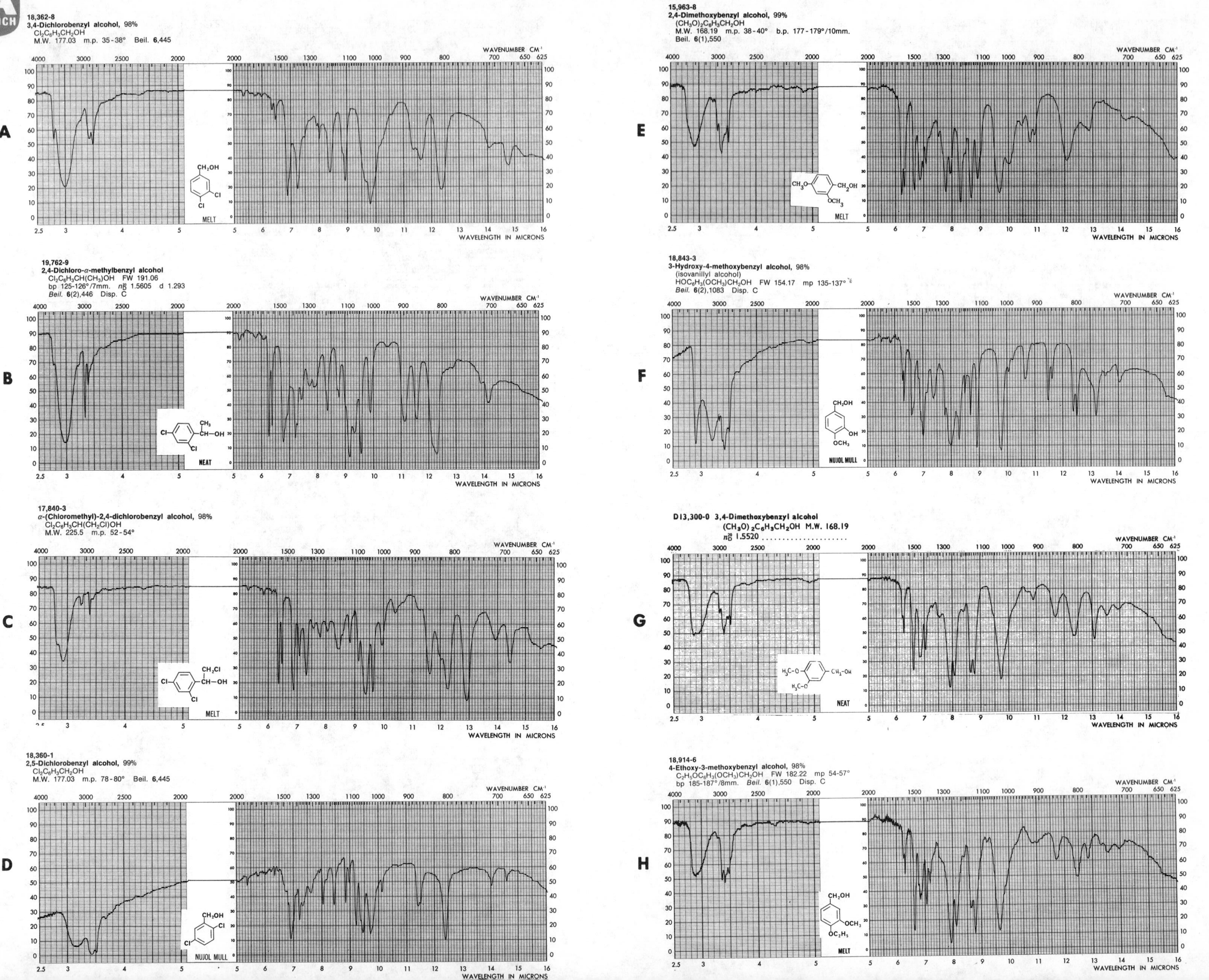
ALDRICH
A
18,362-8
3,4-Dichlorobenzyl alcohol, 98%
$Cl_2C_6H_3CH_2OH$
M.W. 177.03 m.p. 35-38° Beil. 6,445
MELT
B
19,762-9
2,4-Dichloro-α-methylbenzyl alcohol
$Cl_2C_6H_3CH(CH_3)OH$ FW 191.06
bp 125-126°/7mm. n_D^{20} 1.5605 d 1.293
Beil. 6(2),446 Disp. C
NEAT
C
17,840-3
α-(Chloromethyl)-2,4-dichlorobenzyl alcohol, 98%
$Cl_2C_6H_3CH(CH_2Cl)OH$
M.W. 225.5 m.p. 52-54°
MELT
D
18,360-1
2,5-Dichlorobenzyl alcohol, 99%
$Cl_2C_6H_3CH_2OH$
M.W. 177.03 m.p. 78-80° Beil. 6,445
NUJOL MULL
E
15,963-8
2,4-Dimethoxybenzyl alcohol, 99%
$(CH_3O)_2C_6H_3CH_2OH$
M.W. 168.19 m.p. 38-40° b.p. 177-179°/10mm.
Beil. 6(1),550
MELT
F
18,843-3
3-Hydroxy-4-methoxybenzyl alcohol, 98%
(isovanillyl alcohol)
$HOC_6H_3(OCH_3)CH_2OH$ FW 154.17 mp 135-137°
Beil. 6(2),1083 Disp. C
NUJOL MULL
G
D13,300-0 3,4-Dimethoxybenzyl alcohol
$(CH_3O)_2C_6H_3CH_2OH$ M.W. 168.19
n_D^{20} 1.5520
NEAT
H
18,914-6
4-Ethoxy-3-methoxybenzyl alcohol, 98%
$C_2H_5OC_6H_3(OCH_3)CH_2OH$ FW 182.22 mp 54-57°
bp 185-187°/8mm. Beil. 6(1),550 Disp. C
MELT
WAVENUMBER CM⁻¹
WAVELENGTH IN MICRONS

A

18,787-9
2,5-Dimethoxybenzyl alcohol
$(CH_3O)_2C_6H_3CH_2OH$ FW 168.19
bp 122-125°/1mm. n_D^{20} 1.5474 Disp. C

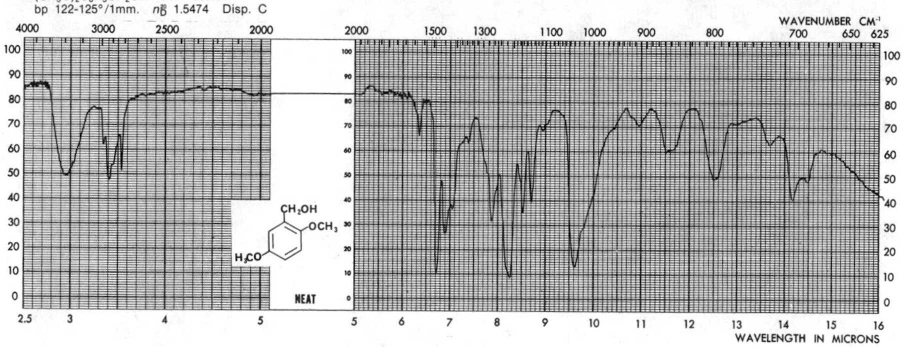

NEAT

B

19,700-9
5-Bromo-2-hydroxybenzyl alcohol, 98+% (5-bromo-salicyl alcohol, bromosaligenin)
$BrC_6H_3(OH)CH_2OH$ FW 203.04 mp 110-112°
Beil. **6**,893 Disp. C

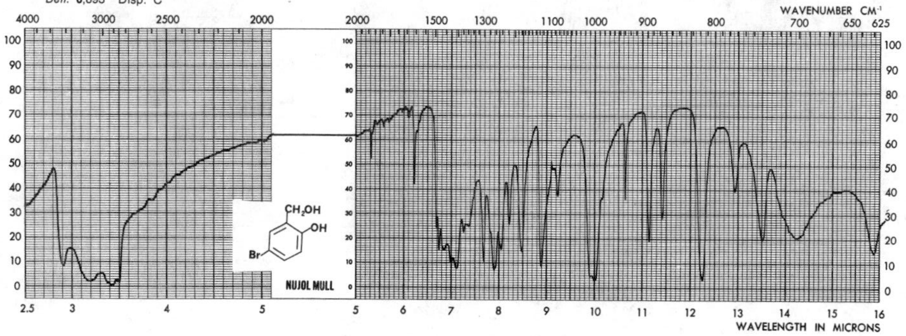

NUJOL MULL

C

18,969-3
5-Bromo-2-methoxybenzyl alcohol, 97%
$BrC_6H_3(OCH_3)CH_2OH$ FW 217.07 mp 68-71°
Beil. **6**,894 Disp. C

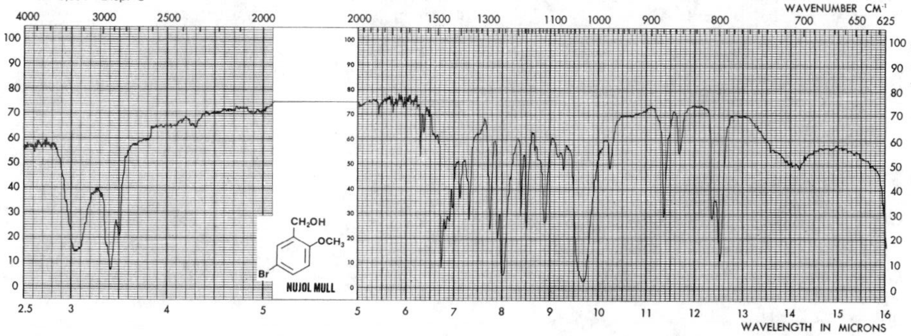

NUJOL MULL

D

P4940-6 Piperonyl alcohol (3,4-methylenedioxyphenylmethanol)
M.W. 152.15 m.p. 55-56°

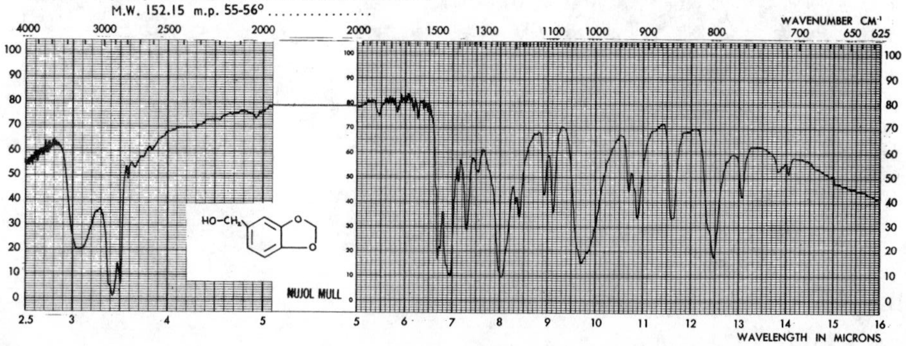

NUJOL MULL

E

17,553-6
4-Hydroxy-3-methoxybenzyl alcohol, 99%
(vanillyl alcohol)
$HOC_6H_3(OCH_3)CH_2OH$
M.W. 154.17 m.p. 113-115° Beil. **6**,1113

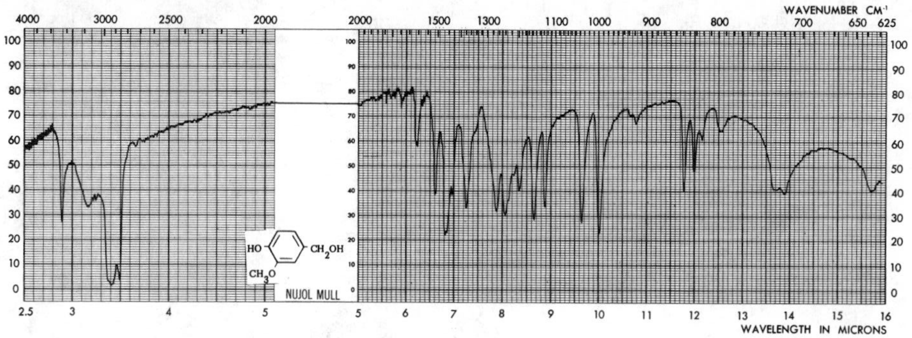

NUJOL MULL

F

I-2905-0 Isovanillyl alcohol (3-hydroxy-4-methoxybenzyl alcohol)
$HOC_6H_3(OCH_3)CH_2OH$ M.W. 154.17 m.p. 130-134°

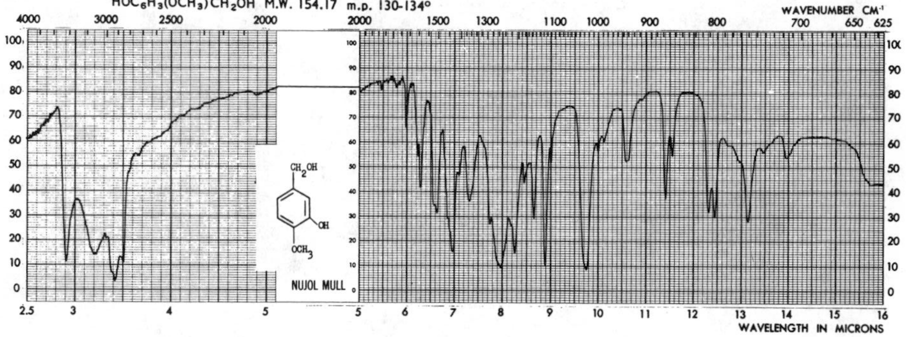

NUJOL MULL

G

19,999-0
3,5-Dimethylbenzyl alcohol, 98%
$(CH_3)_2C_6H_3CH_2OH$ FW 136.19 bp 218-221°
n_D^{20} 1.5312 d 0.927 *Beil.* **6**,521 Disp. C

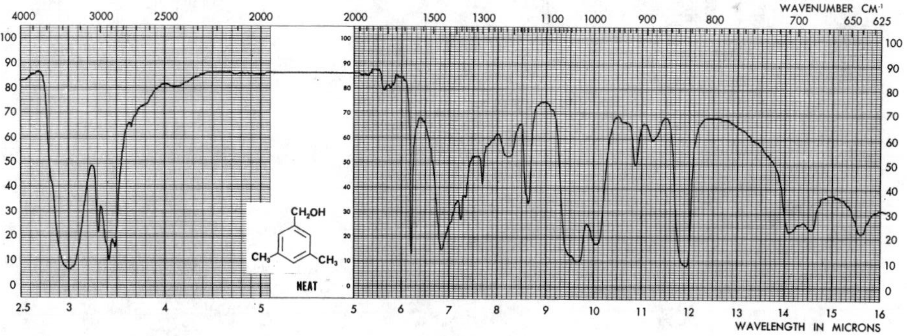

NEAT

H

19,163-9
2,4,6-Trimethylbenzyl alcohol, 98%
$(CH_3)_3C_6H_2CH_2OH$ FW 150.22 mp 87-89°
bp 140°/15mm. *Beil.* **6**(1),268 Disp. C

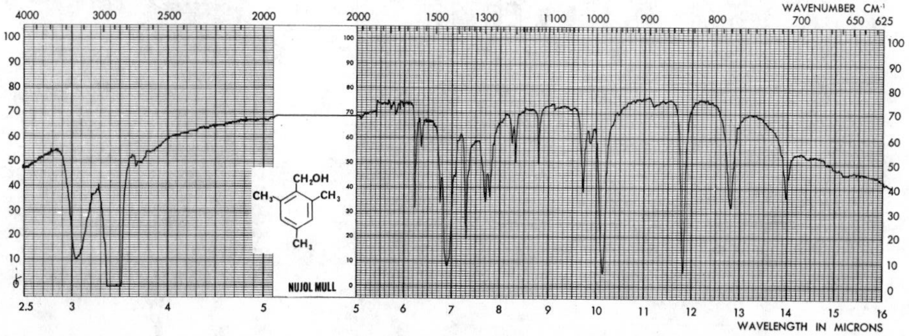

NUJOL MULL

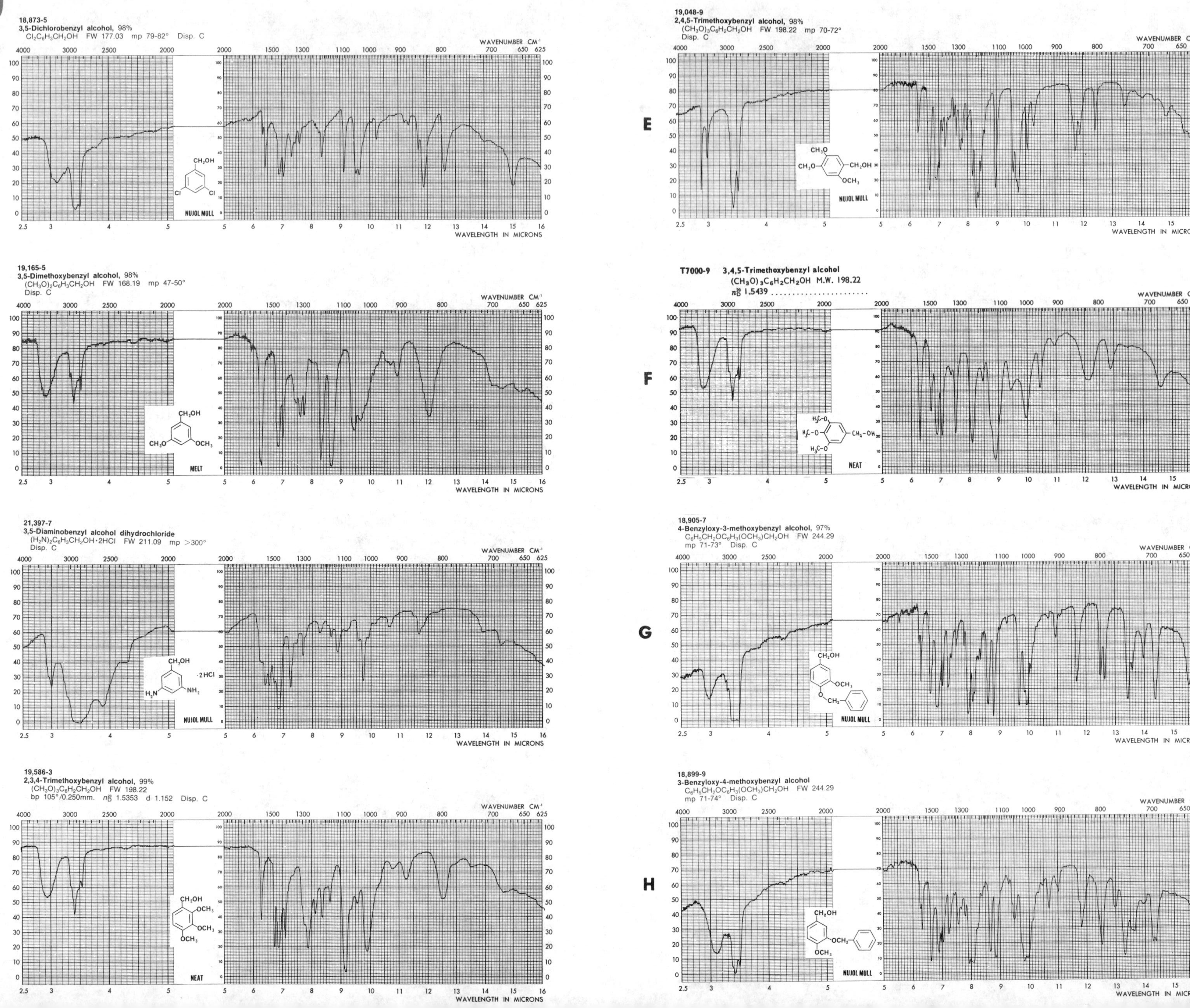
ALDRICH
A
18,873-5
3,5-Dichlorobenzyl alcohol, 98%
$Cl_2C_6H_3CH_2OH$ FW 177.03 mp 79-82° Disp. C
NUJOL MULL
B
19,165-5
3,5-Dimethoxybenzyl alcohol, 98%
$(CH_3O)_2C_6H_3CH_2OH$ FW 168.19 mp 47-50°
Disp. C
MELT
C
21,397-7
3,5-Diaminobenzyl alcohol dihydrochloride
$(H_2N)_2C_6H_3CH_2OH \cdot 2HCl$ FW 211.09 mp >300°
Disp. C
NUJOL MULL
D
19,586-3
2,3,4-Trimethoxybenzyl alcohol, 99%
$(CH_3O)_3C_6H_2CH_2OH$ FW 198.22
bp 105°/0.250mm. n_D^{20} 1.5353 d 1.152 Disp. C
NEAT
E
19,048-9
2,4,5-Trimethoxybenzyl alcohol, 98%
$(CH_3O)_3C_6H_2CH_2OH$ FW 198.22 mp 70-72°
Disp. C
NUJOL MULL
F
T7000-9 3,4,5-Trimethoxybenzyl alcohol
$(CH_3O)_3C_6H_2CH_2OH$ M.W. 198.22
n_D^{20} 1.5439
NEAT
G
18,905-7
4-Benzyloxy-3-methoxybenzyl alcohol, 97%
$C_6H_5CH_2OC_6H_3(OCH_3)CH_2OH$ FW 244.29
mp 71-73° Disp. C
NUJOL MULL
H
18,899-9
3-Benzyloxy-4-methoxybenzyl alcohol
$C_6H_5CH_2OC_6H_3(OCH_3)CH_2OH$ FW 244.29
mp 71-74° Disp. C
NUJOL MULL
WAVENUMBER CM⁻¹
WAVELENGTH IN MICRONS

A

18,892-1
3,4-Dibenzyloxybenzyl alcohol
$(C_6H_5CH_2O)_2C_6H_3CH_2OH$ FW 320.39 mp 72-75°
Disp. C

NUJOL MULL

B

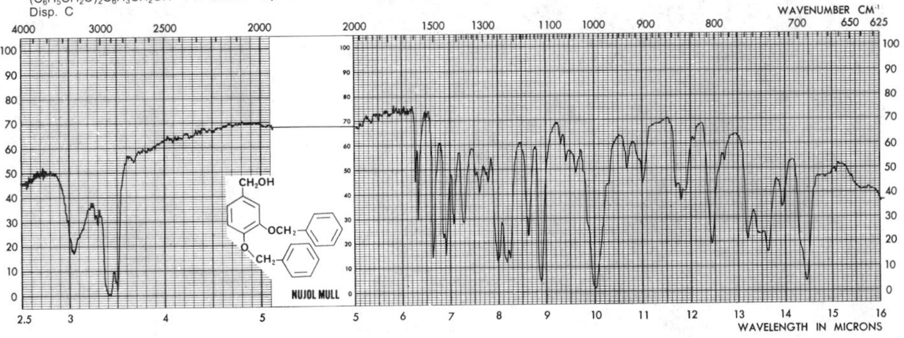

16,220-5
2,3,5,6-Tetramethyl-p-xylene-α,α'-diol, 98%
$(CH_3)_4C_6(CH_2OH)_2$
M.W. 194.27 m.p. 246-248°

NUJOL MULL

C

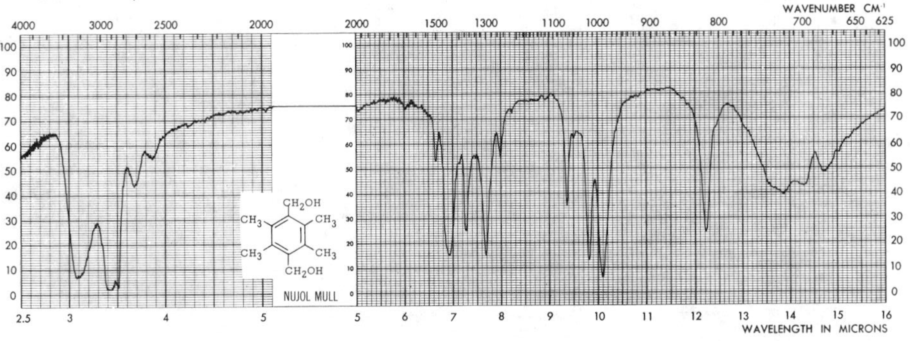

11,374-3 **2,4,5,6-Tetrachlorobenzene-1,3-dimethanol** (2,4,5,6-tetrachloro-m-xylene-α,α'-diol)
$C_6Cl_4(CH_2OH)_2$ M.W. 275.95 m.p. 228-230°

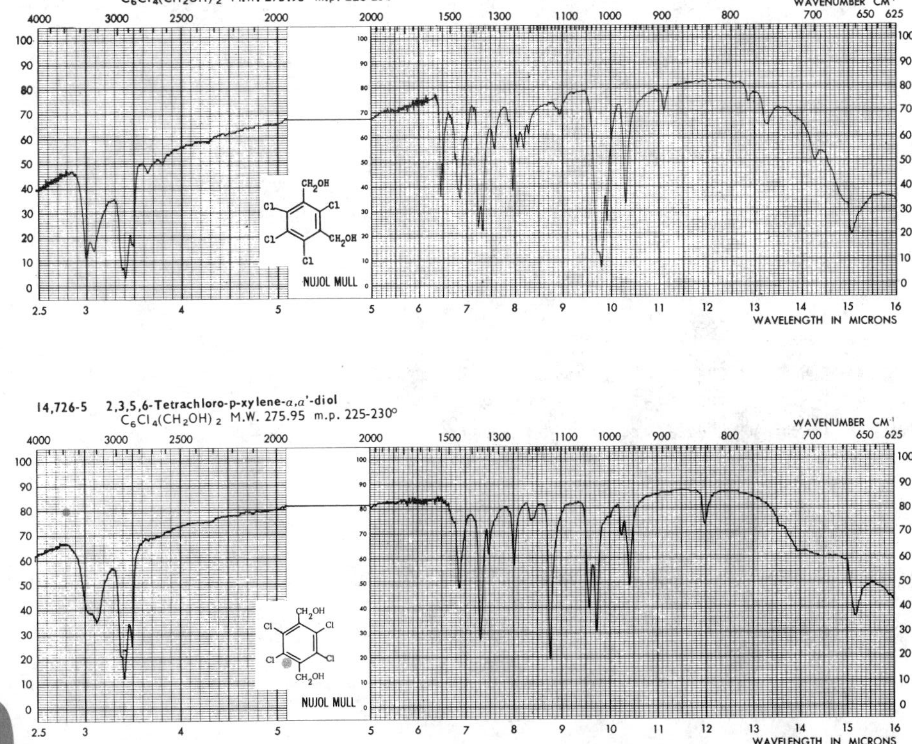

D

14,726-5 **2,3,5,6-Tetrachloro-p-xylene-α,α'-diol**
$C_6Cl_4(CH_2OH)_2$ M.W. 275.95 m.p. 225-230°

E

12,383-8 **4-Biphenylmethanol** (p-phenylbenzyl alcohol)
$C_6H_5C_6H_4CH_2OH$ M.W. 184.24
m.p. 99-101°

NUJOL MULL

F

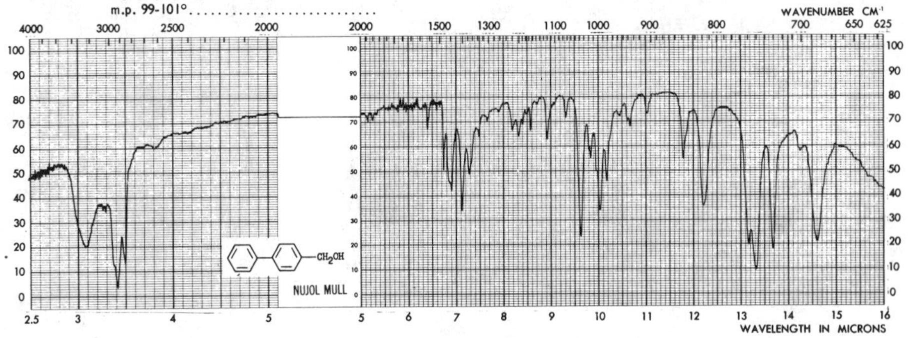

18,737-2
p-Benzyloxybenzyl alcohol, 99%
$C_6H_5CH_2OC_6H_4CH_2OH$
M.W. 214.26 m.p. 86-87°

NUJOL MULL

G

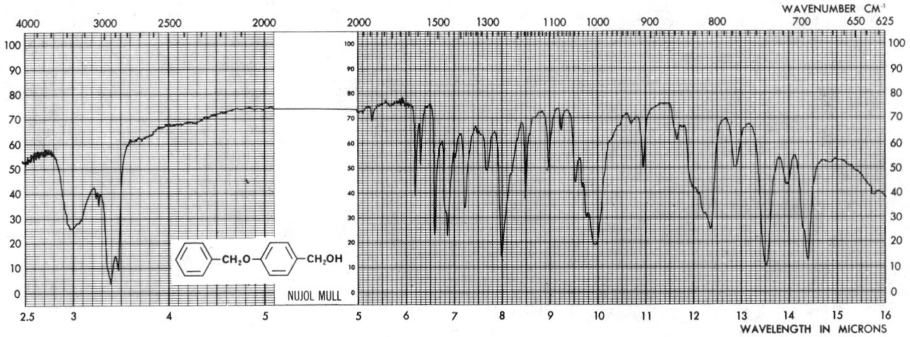

18,732-1
m-Benzyloxybenzyl alcohol, 97%
$C_6H_5CH_2OC_6H_4CH_2OH$
M.W. 214.26 m.p. 48°

MELT

H

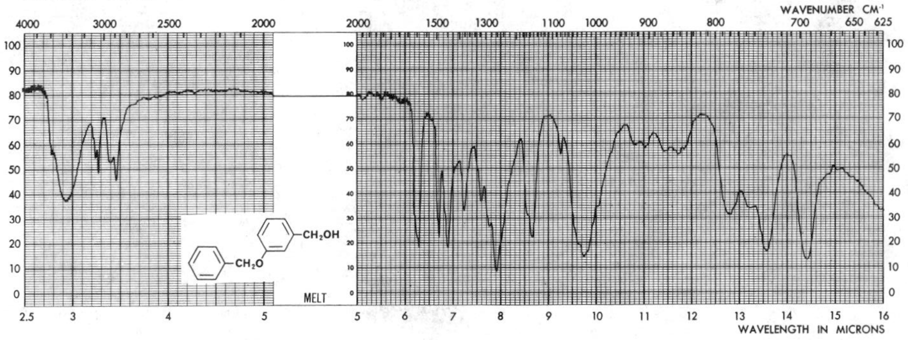

18,996-0
2-Methylbenzhydrol, 98+%
$CH_3C_6H_4CH(C_6H_5)OH$ FW 198.27 mp 93-95°
bp 323° *Beil.* **6**(1),330 Disp. C

NUJOL MULL

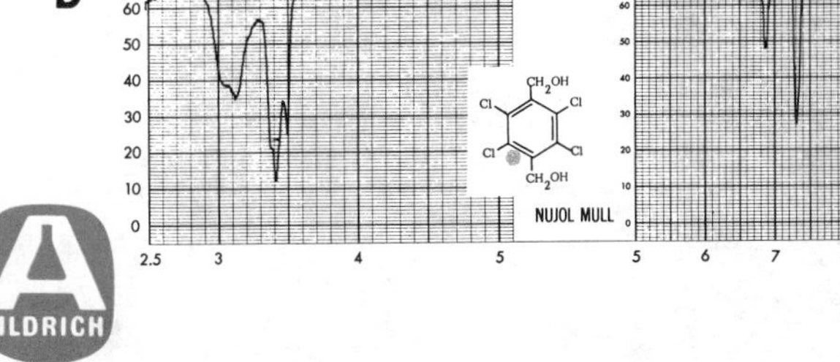

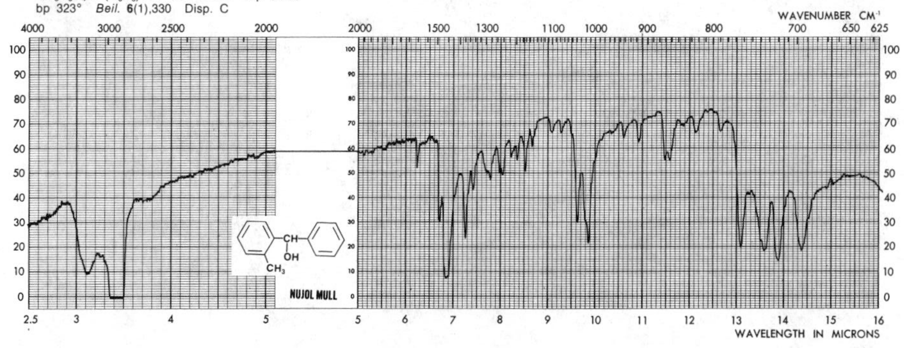

ALDRICH

A

18,995-2
4-Methylbenzhydrol
$CH_3C_6H_4CH(C_6H_5)OH$ FW 198.27 mp 50-54°
Beil. 6,686 Disp. C

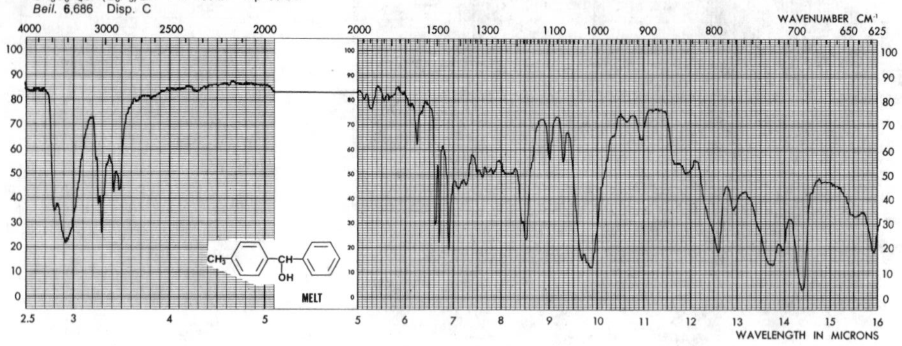

B

12,498-2 **4-Chlorobenzhydrol**
$ClC_6H_4CH(C_6H_5)OH$ M.W. 218.68 m.p. 59-61° ...

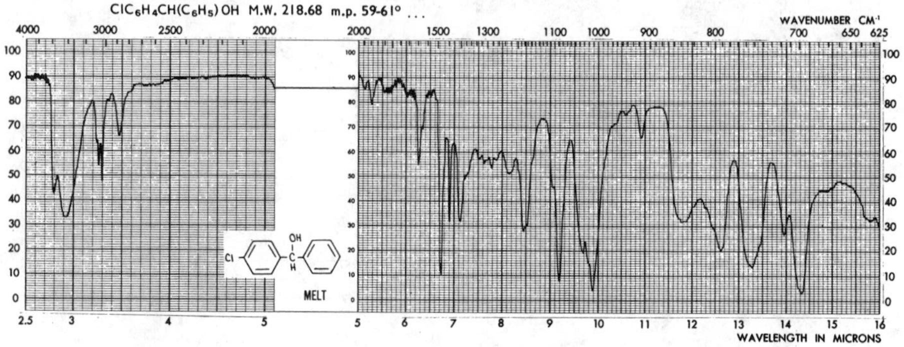

C

12,007-3 **p-Bromobenzhydrol**
$BrC_6H_4CH(C_6H_5)OH$ M.W. 263.14 m.p. 64.5-66.5° ....

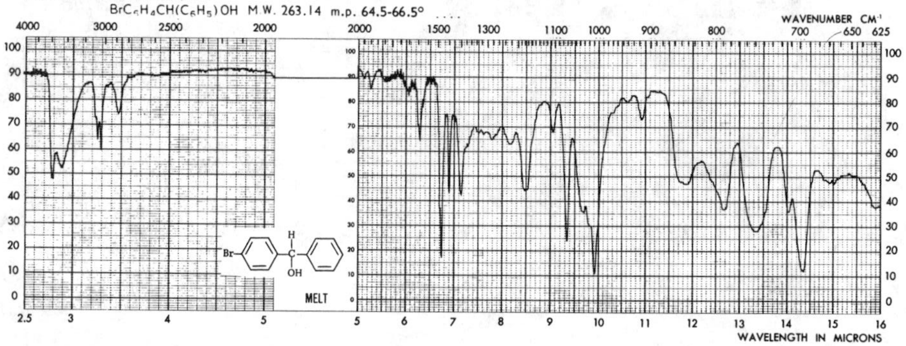

D

19,658-4
Decafluorobenzhydrol, 97+% [bis(pentafluoro-phenyl)methanol]
$(C_6F_5)_2CHOH$ FW 364.14 mp 77-80° Disp. C

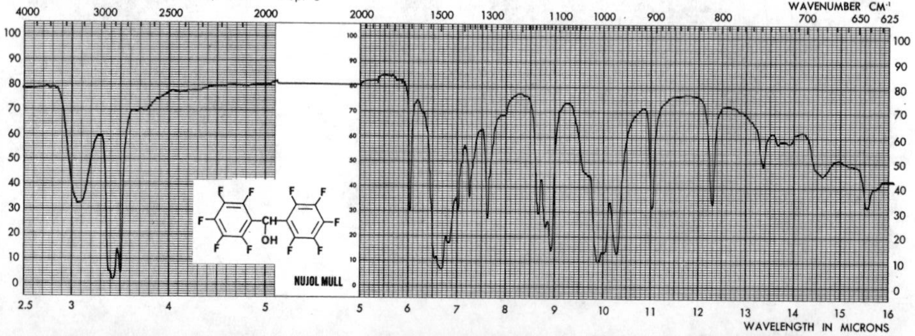

E

18,874-3
o-Benzylbenzyl alcohol, 97%
$C_6H_5CH_2C_6H_4CH_2OH$ FW 198.27 bp 154°/1mm.
n_D^{20} 1.5961 Disp. C

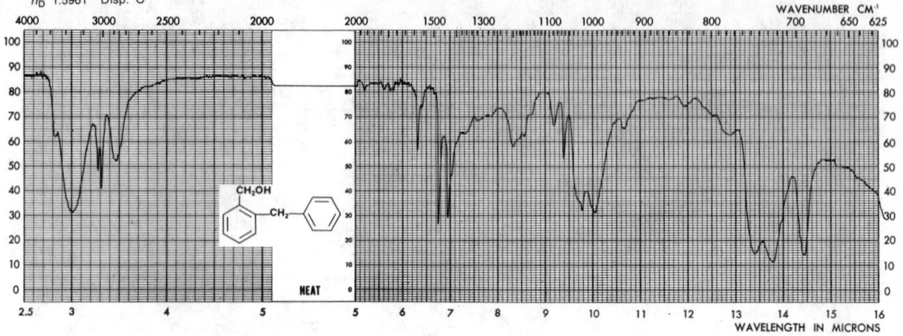

F

13,429-5 **Phenolphthalol** [o-[bis-(p-hydroxyphenyl)-methyl]-benzyl alcohol]
$(HOC_6H_4)_2CHC_6H_4CH_2OH$ M.W. 306.36
m.p. 200-201.5° ....

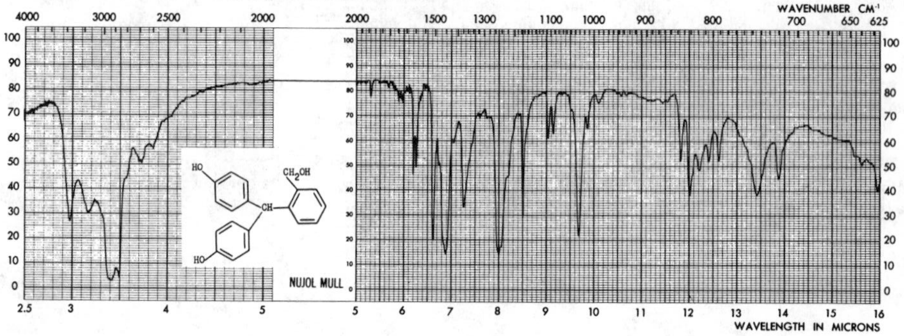

G

19,373-9
1-Indanol, 98%
FW 134.18 mp 50-54° *Beil.* 6,574 Disp. C

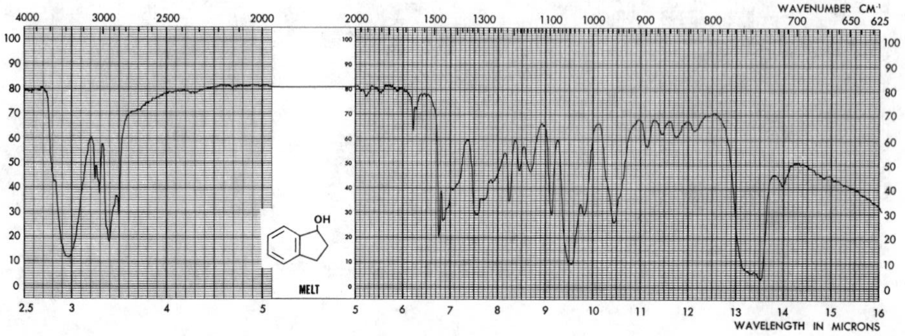

H

B6840-2 **2-Bromo-1-indanol** (indene bromohydrin)
M.W. 213.08 m.p. 130-131° ....

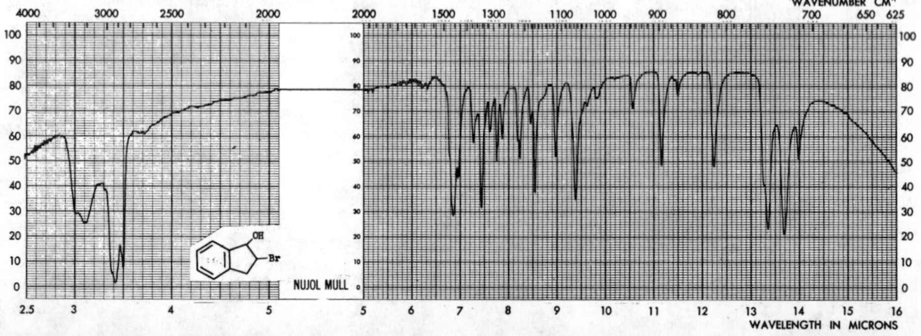

A
19,372-0
1-Methoxy-2-indanol, 98%
FW 164.20 bp 146-148°/11mm. n_D^{20} 1.5482
Beil. **6**,970 Disp. C
NEAT

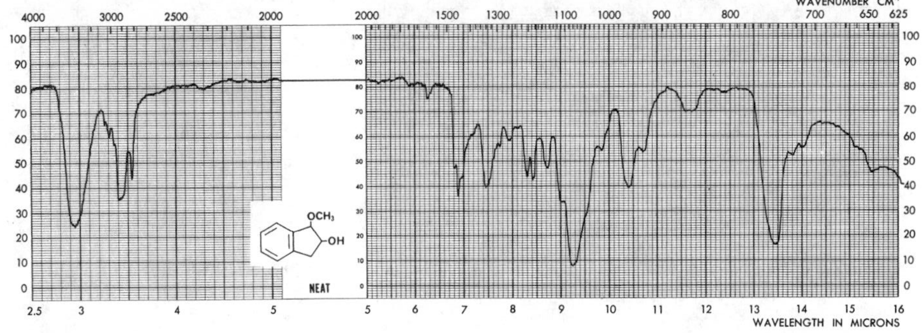

B
12,240-8 **1,2,3,4-Tetrahydro-1-naphthol** (α-tetralol), **tech.**
M.W. 148.21 n_D^{20} 1.5658 b.p. 102-104°/2 mm.
NEAT

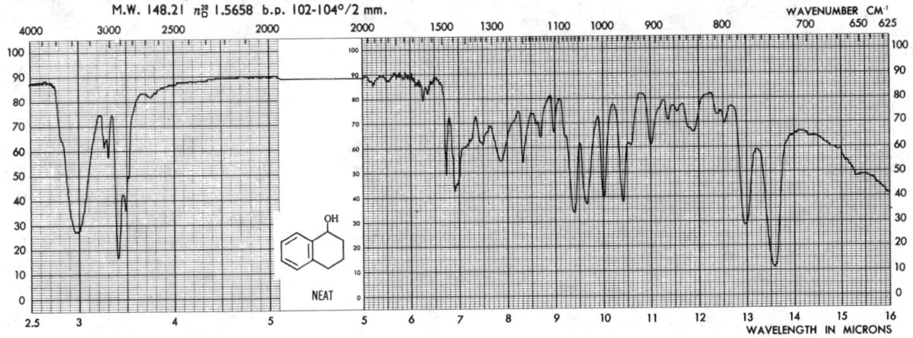

C
10,915-0 **1,5-Dihydroxy-1,2,3,4-tetrahydronaphthalene** (1,2,3,4-tetrahydro-1,5-naphthalenediol)
M.W. 164.20 m.p. 132-134°
NUJOL MULL

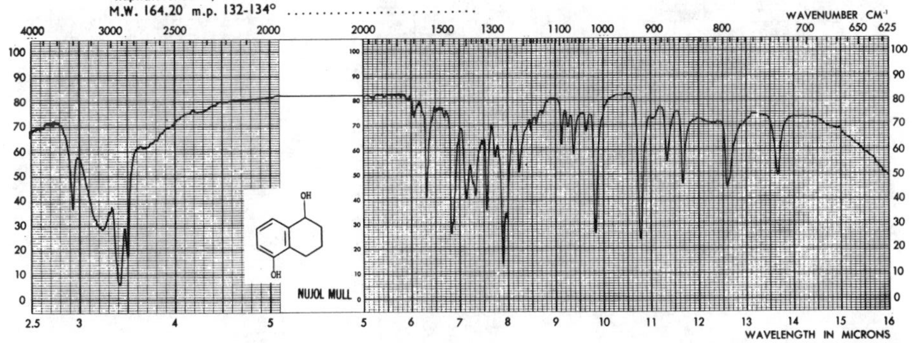

D
12,234-3 4-Chromanol
M.W. 150.18 m.p. 36.5 - 39.5° *NMR* **5**,18C
MELT

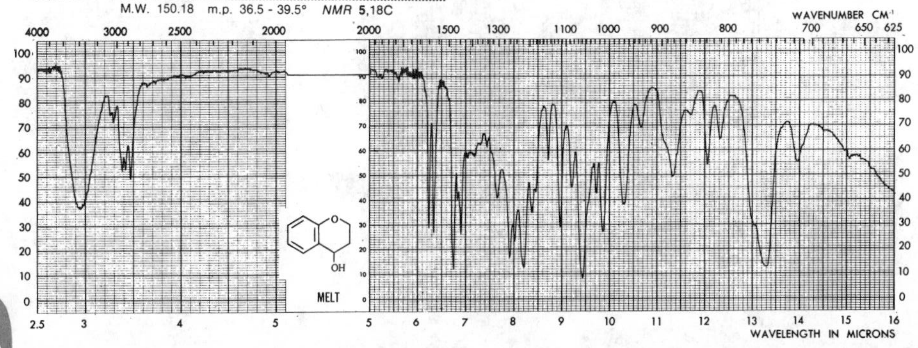

E
H3,840-3
2-Hydroxymethyl-1,4-benzodioxan, 97%
(1,4-benzodioxan-2-methanol)
M.W. 166.18 m.p. 87-90°
NUJOL MULL

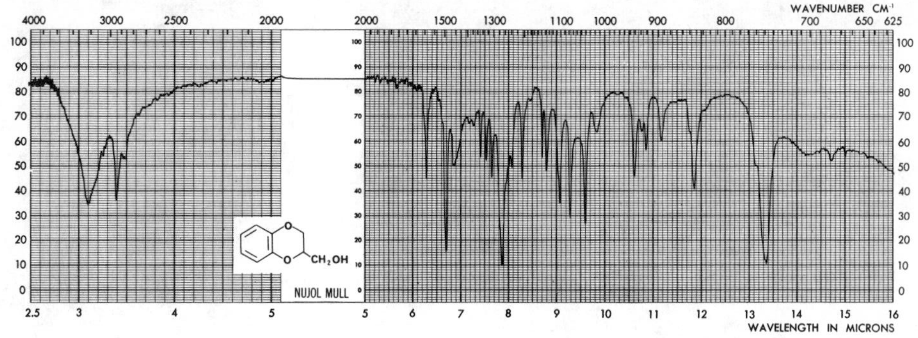

F
21,886-3
9-Phenylxanthen-9-ol, 98%
FW 274.32 mp 160-162° *Beil.* **17**,138 Disp. C
NUJOL MULL

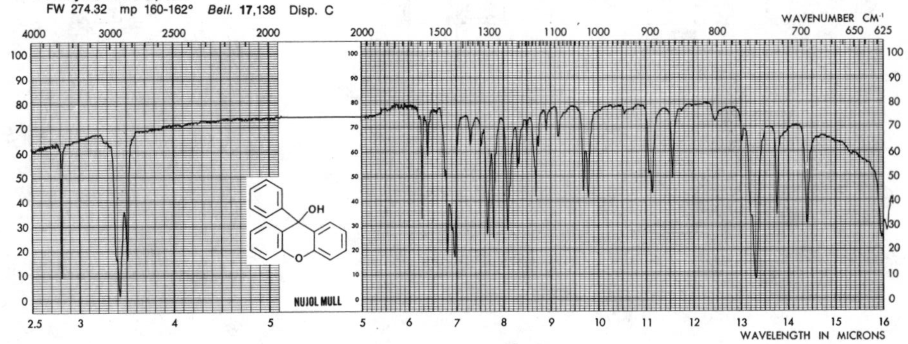

G
18,882-4
2-Biphenylmethanol, 98% (o-phenylbenzyl alcohol)
$C_6H_5C_6H_4CH_2OH$ FW 184.24 mp 46-48°
bp 96°/0mm. Disp. C
MELT

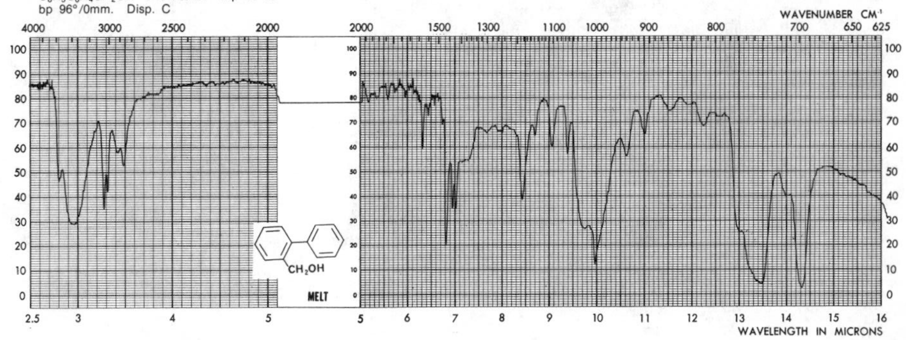

H
1-Naphthalenemethanol, 98%
$C_{10}H_7CH_2OH$
M.W. 158.2 m.p. 61-63° b.p. 301°/715mm.
Beil. **6**,667
MELT

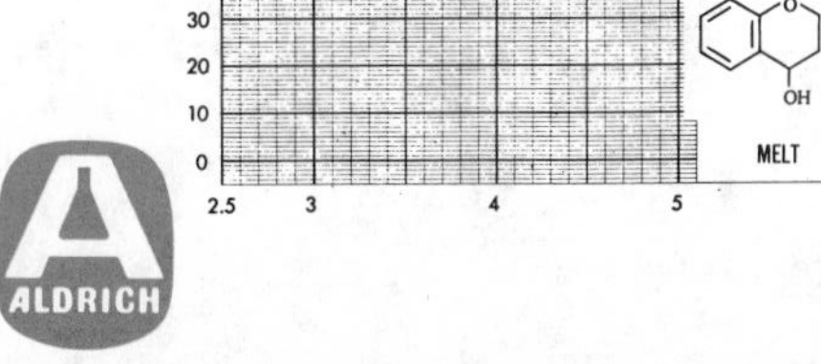

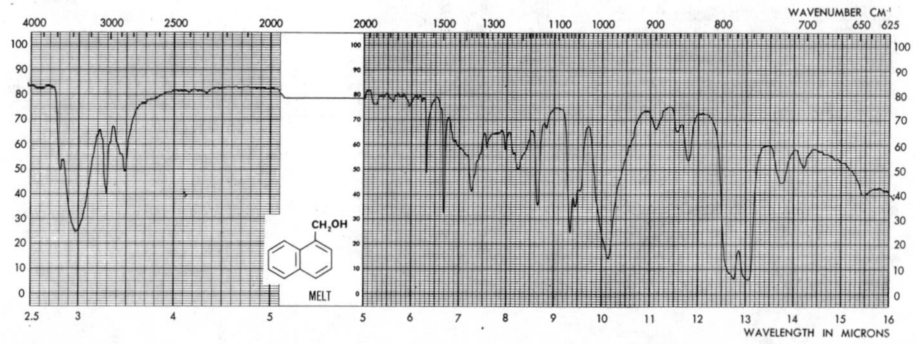

A

18,731-3
2-Naphthalenemethanol, 96%
$C_{10}H_7CH_2OH$
M.W. 158.2 m.p. 74-77° Beil. **6**,668

NUJOL MULL

B

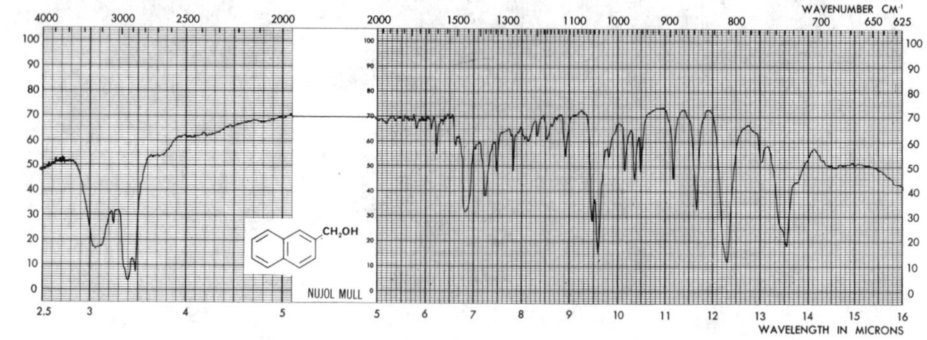

16,050-4
9-Fluorenemethanol, 99%
M.W. 196.25 m.p. 102-104°

NUJOL MULL

C

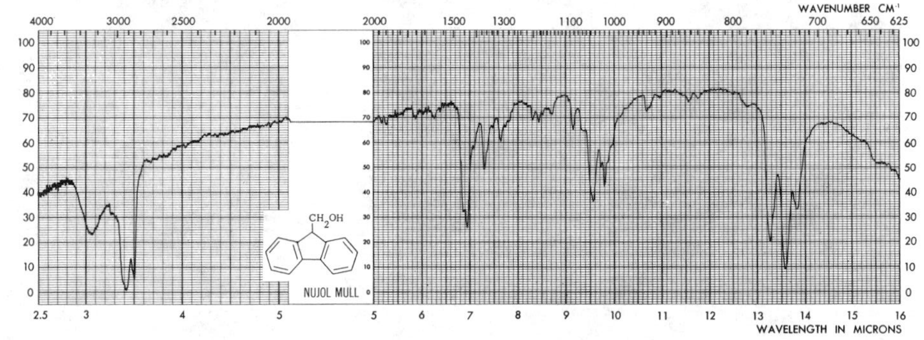

10,711-5 **1-Fluorenemethanol**
M.W. 196.25 m.p. 147-149°

NUJOL MULL

D

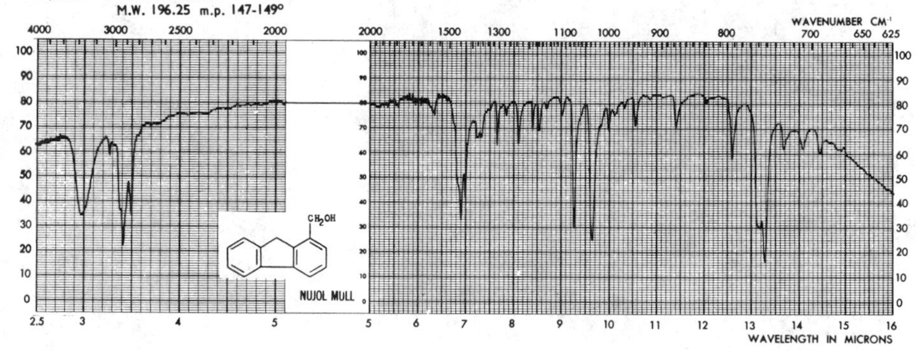

H3120-4 **9-Hydroxyfluorene** (9-fluorenol)
M.W. 182.22 m.p. 153-154°

NUJOL MULL

E

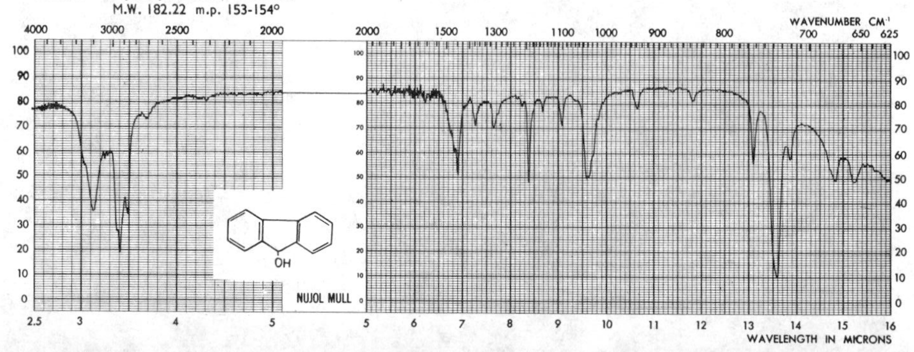

A40-6 **1-Acenaphthenol**
M.W. 170.21 m.p. 147-148°

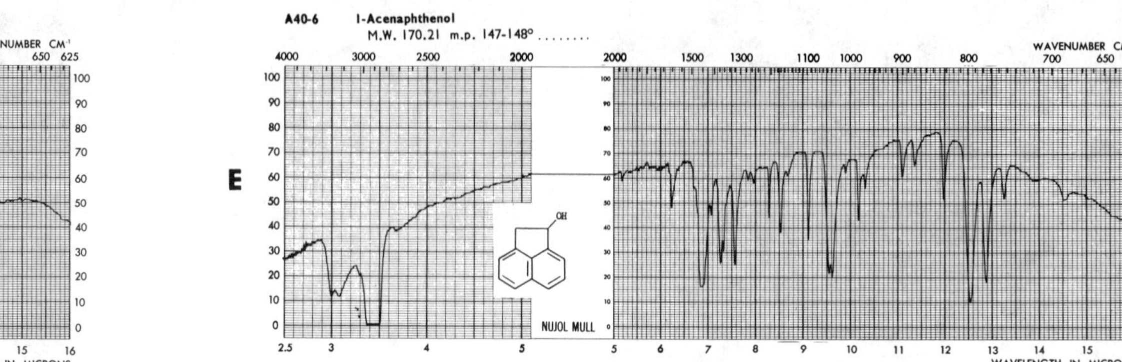

F

D10,497-3 **10,11-Dihydro-5H-dibenzo[a,d]cyclohepten-5-ol**
(dibenzosuberol)
M.W. 210.28 m.p. 86-91°

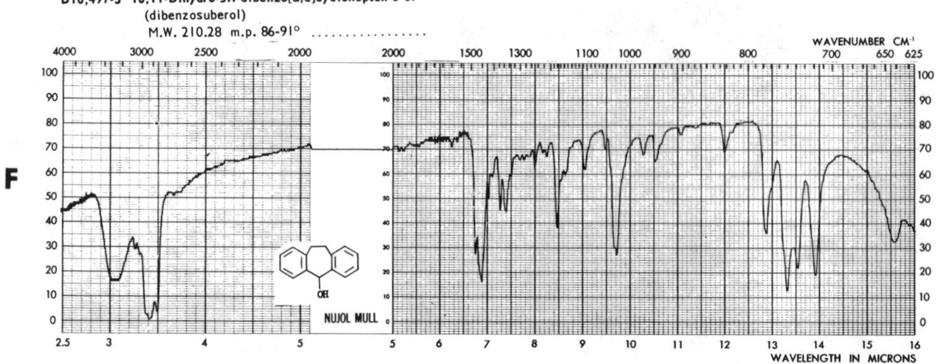

G

D3172-9 **5H-Dibenzo[a,d]cyclohepten-5-ol**
M.W. 208.25 m.p. 122.5-124°

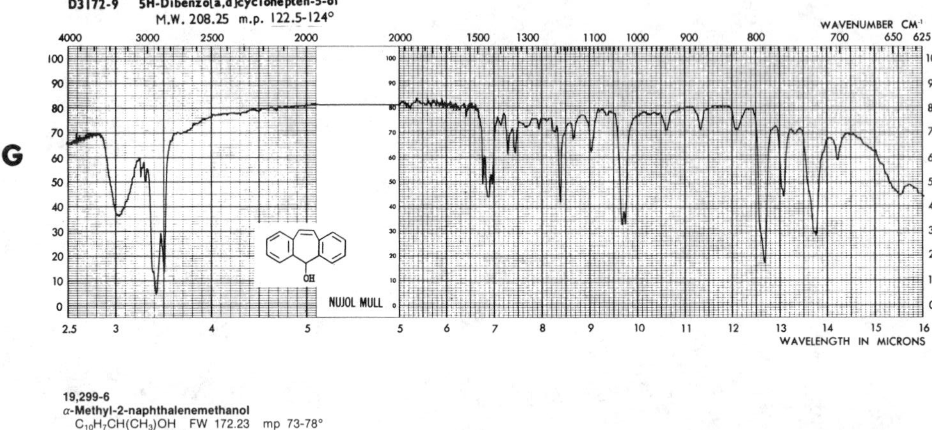

H

19,299-6
α-Methyl-2-naphthalenemethanol
$C_{10}H_7CH(CH_3)OH$ FW 172.23 mp 73-78°
Beil. **6**(3),3041 Disp. C

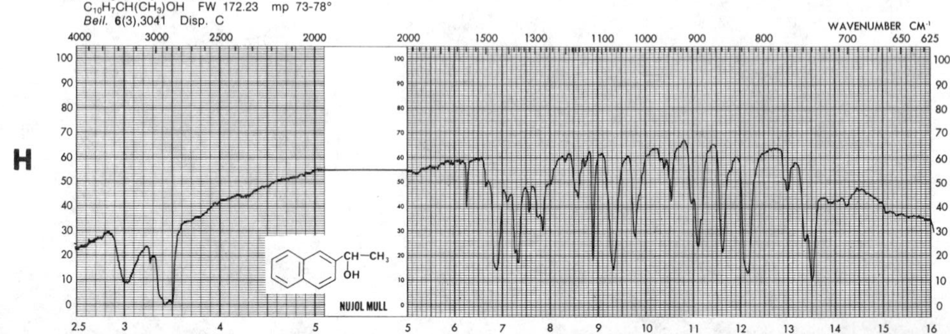

A

18,724-0
9-Anthracenemethanol
M.W. 208.26 m.p. 162-164°

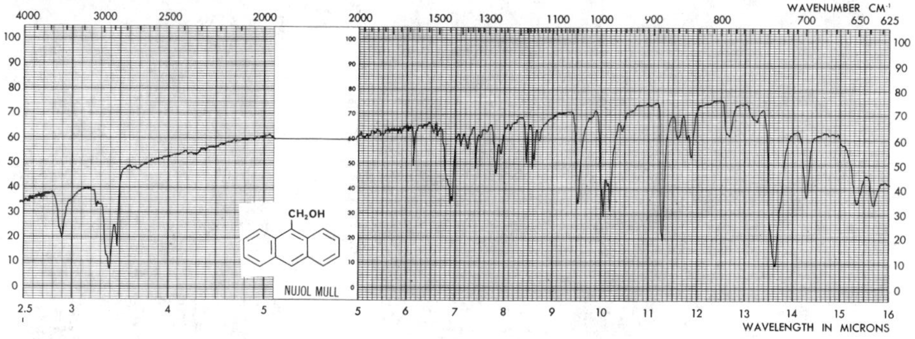

NUJOL MULL

B

19,731-9
10-Chloro-9-anthracenemethanol, 97%
FW 242.71 mp 206-209° Disp. C

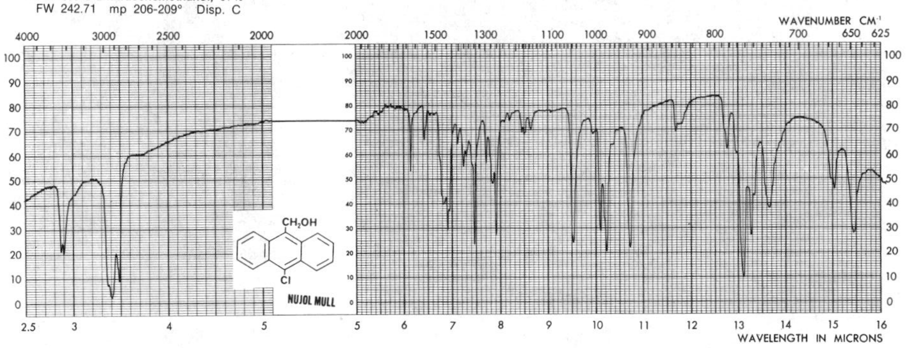

NUJOL MULL

C

21,134-6
(+)-2,2,2-Trifluoro-1-(9-anthryl)ethanol, 98+%
[α-(trifluoromethyl)-9-anthracenemethanol]
FW 276.26 mp 132-136°
$[\alpha]^{25}$ +29° (c=6.3, $CHCl_3$) Disp. C

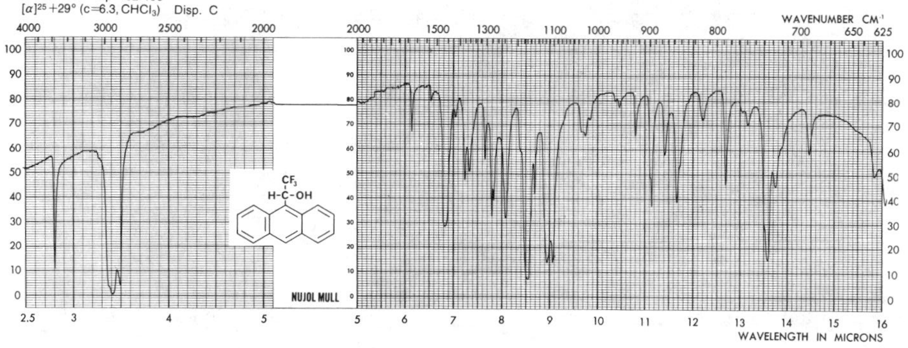

NUJOL MULL

D

21,135-4
(-)-2,2,2-Trifluoro-1-(9-anthryl)ethanol, 98+%
[α-(trifluoromethyl)-9-anthracenemethanol]
FW 276.26 mp 132-135° $[\alpha]^{25}$ -29° (c=6.0, $CHCl_3$)
Disp. C

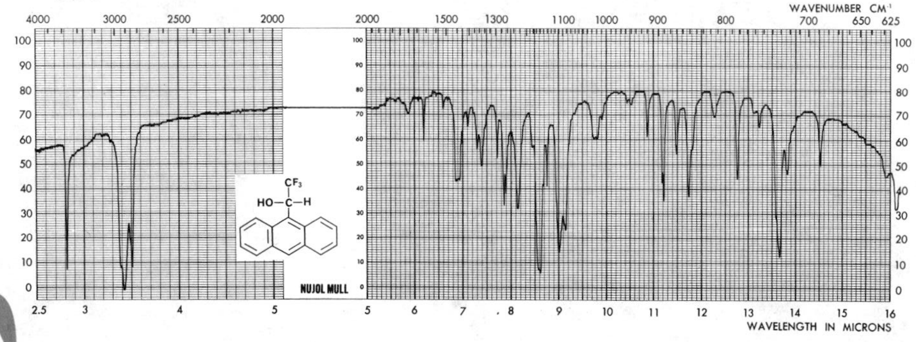

NUJOL MULL

E

P1360-6 **Phenethyl alcohol, puriss.**
$C_6H_5CH_2CH_2OH$ M.W. 122.17 n_D^{20} 1.5317 b.p. 219° ....

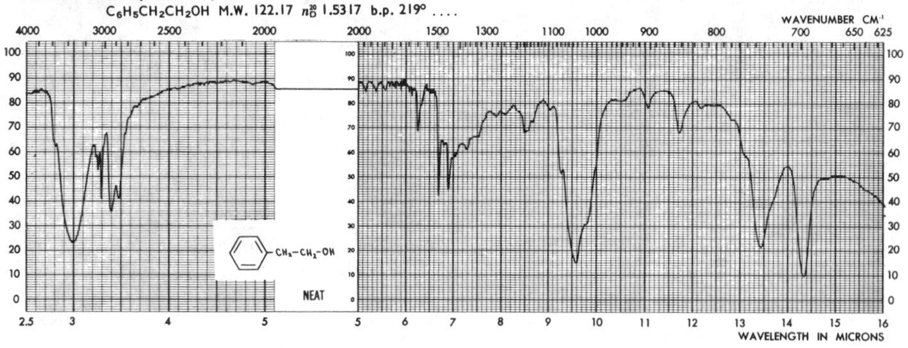

NEAT

F

18,929-4
1,3-Diphenyl-2-propanol, 98%
$C_6H_5CH_2CH(OH)CH_2C_6H_5$ FW 212.29
bp 198°/20mm. n_D^{20} 1.5727 d 1.062 *Beil.* **6**,686
Disp. C

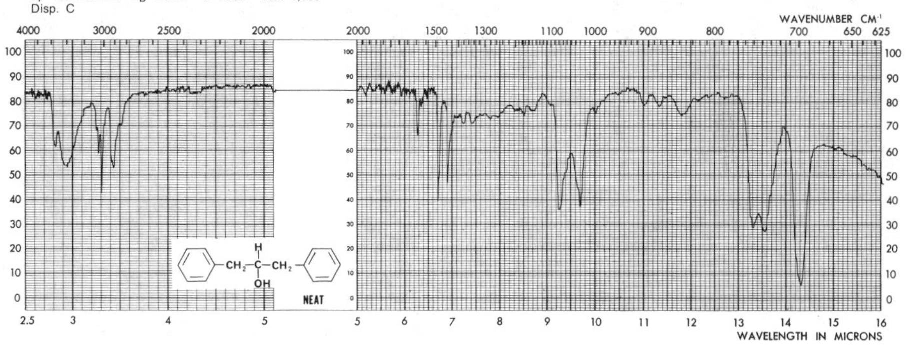

NEAT

G

18,923-5
DL-1-Phenyl-2-propanol, 99% (α-methylphenethyl alcohol)
$C_6H_5CH_2CH(OH)CH_3$ FW 136.19 bp 219-222°
n_D^{20} 1.5220 d 0.973 *Beil.* **6**,503 Disp. C

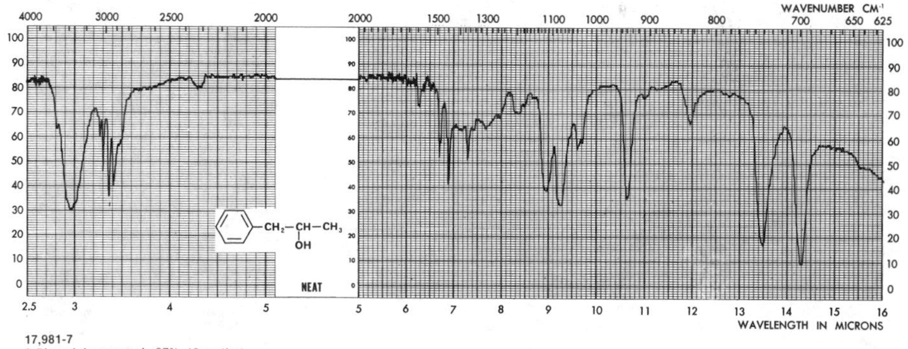

NEAT

H

17,981-7
2-Phenyl-1-propanol, 97% (β-methylphenethyl alcohol)
$CH_3CH(C_6H_5)CH_2OH$
M.W. 136.19 b.p. 110-111°/10mm. n_D^{20} 1.5262
d 0.975

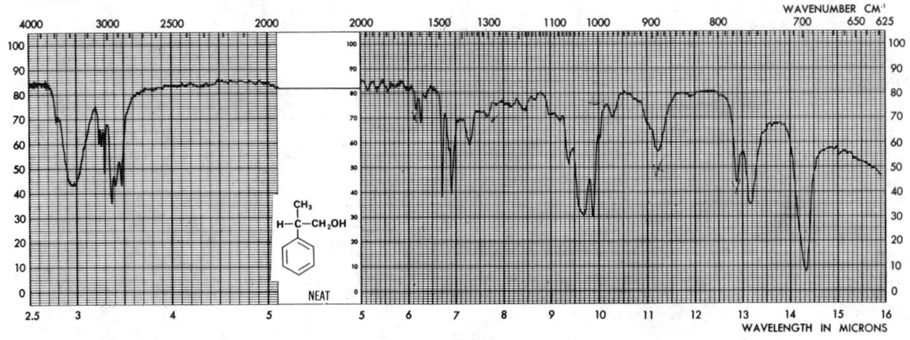

NEAT

ALDRICH

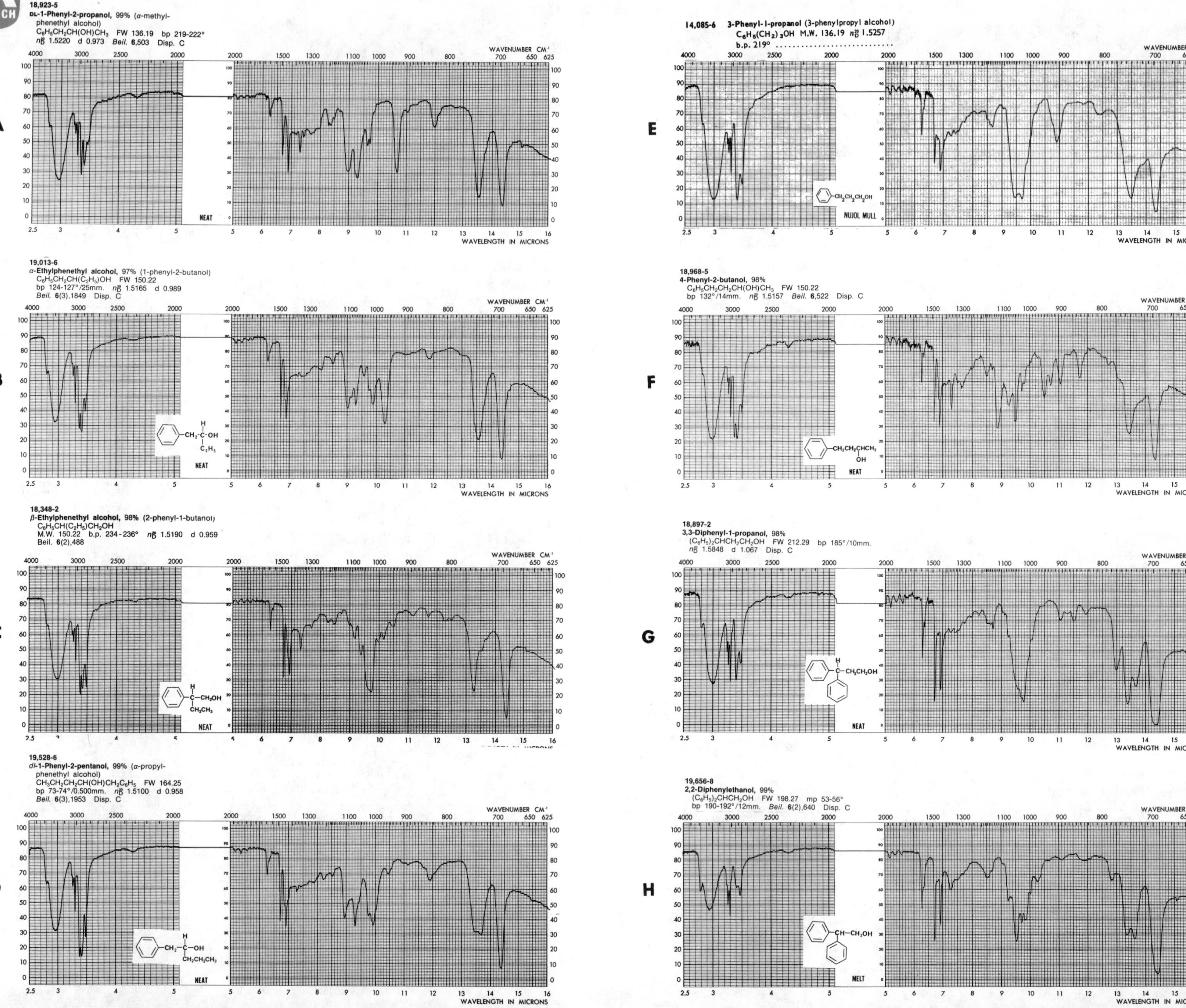
ALDRICH

A
18,923-5
DL-1-Phenyl-2-propanol, 99% (α-methylphenethyl alcohol)
$C_6H_5CH_2CH(OH)CH_3$ FW 136.19 bp 219-222°
n_D^{20} 1.5220 d 0.973 Beil. 6,503 Disp. C
NEAT

B
19,013-6
α-Ethylphenethyl alcohol, 97% (1-phenyl-2-butanol)
$C_6H_5CH_2CH(C_2H_5)OH$ FW 150.22
bp 124-127°/25mm. n_D^{20} 1.5165 d 0.989
Beil. 6(3),1849 Disp. C
NEAT

C
18,348-2
β-Ethylphenethyl alcohol, 98% (2-phenyl-1-butanol)
$C_6H_5CH(C_2H_5)CH_2OH$
M.W. 150.22 b.p. 234-236° n_D^{20} 1.5190 d 0.959
Beil. 6(2),488
NEAT

D
19,528-6
dl-1-Phenyl-2-pentanol, 99% (α-propylphenethyl alcohol)
$CH_3CH_2CH_2CH(OH)CH_2C_6H_5$ FW 164.25
bp 73-74°/0.500mm. n_D^{20} 1.5100 d 0.958
Beil. 6(3),1953 Disp. C
NEAT

E
14,085-6 3-Phenyl-1-propanol (3-phenylpropyl alcohol)
$C_6H_5(CH_2)_3OH$ M.W. 136.19 n_D^{20} 1.5257
b.p. 219°
NUJOL MULL

F
18,968-5
4-Phenyl-2-butanol, 98%
$C_6H_5CH_2CH_2CH(OH)CH_3$ FW 150.22
bp 132°/14mm. n_D^{20} 1.5157 Beil. 6,522 Disp. C
NEAT

G
18,897-2
3,3-Diphenyl-1-propanol, 98%
$(C_6H_5)_2CHCH_2CH_2OH$ FW 212.29 bp 185°/10mm.
n_D^{20} 1.5848 d 1.067 Disp. C
NEAT

H
19,656-8
2,2-Diphenylethanol, 99%
$(C_6H_5)_2CHCH_2OH$ FW 198.27 mp 53-56°
bp 190-192°/12mm. Beil. 6(2),640 Disp. C
MELT

WAVENUMBER CM⁻¹
WAVELENGTH IN MICRONS

A

19,075-6
1,1-Diphenyl-2-propanol, 98%
$(C_6H_5)_2CHCH(OH)CH_3$ FW 212.29 mp 59-62°
Disp. C

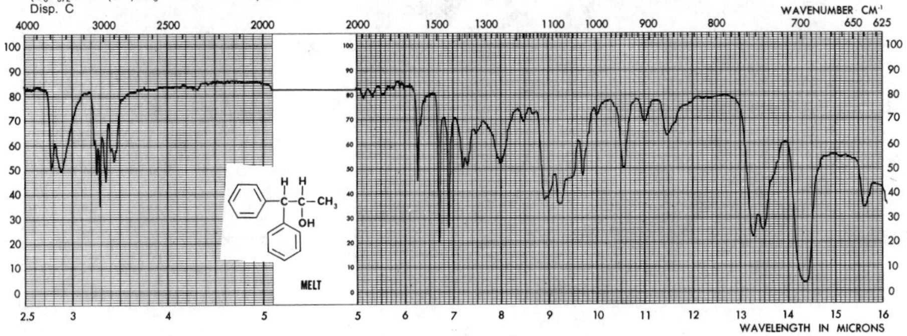

MELT

B

13,478-3 **2,2-Diphenyl-1,3-propanediol**
$HOCH_2C(C_6H_5)_2CH_2OH$ M.W. 228.29
m.p. 102-104°

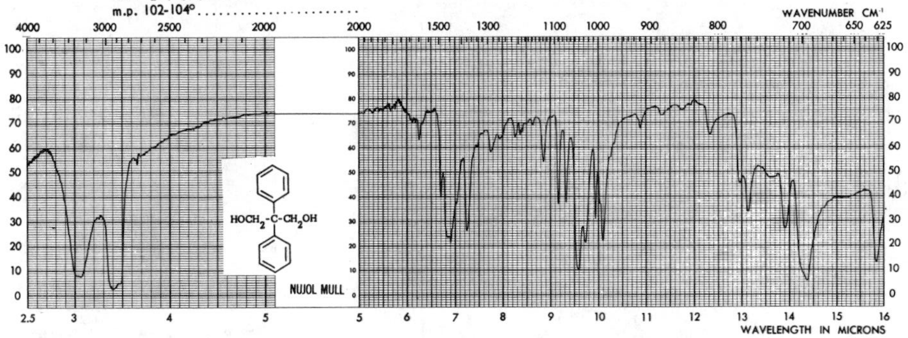

NUJOL MULL

C

19,355-0
β-Methoxy-α-phenylphenethyl alcohol, tech.
$C_6H_5CH(OCH_3)CH(C_6H_5)OH$ FW 228.29
Beil. **6**,1004 Disp. C

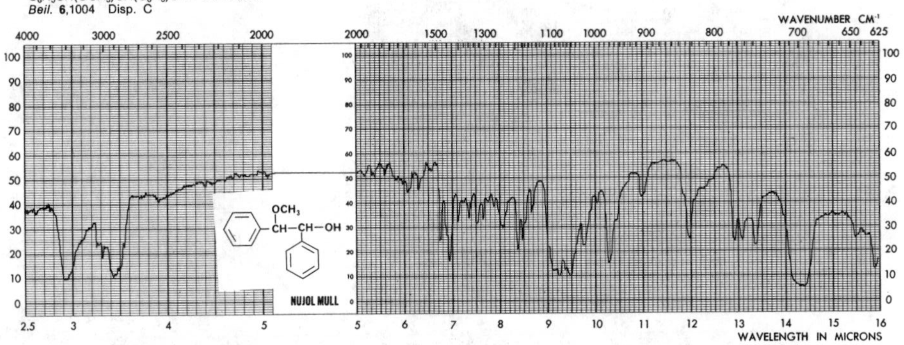

NUJOL MULL

D

B1800-6 **Benzyl-tert.-butanol (dimethyl phenethyl carbinol)**
$C_6H_5CH_2CH_2C(CH_3)_2OH$ M.W. 164.25
m.p. 31-33°

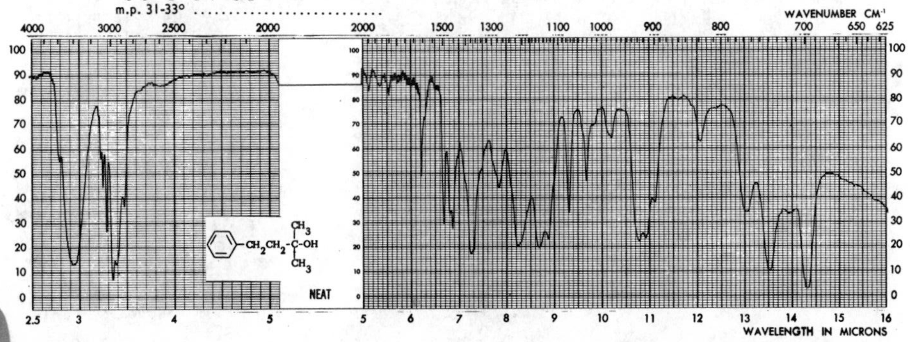

NEAT

E

18,475-6
4-Phenyl-1-butanol, 99%
$C_6H_5(CH_2)_4OH$ FW 150.22 bp 140°/14mm.
n_D^{20} 1.5214 *Beil.* **6**(2),487 Disp. C

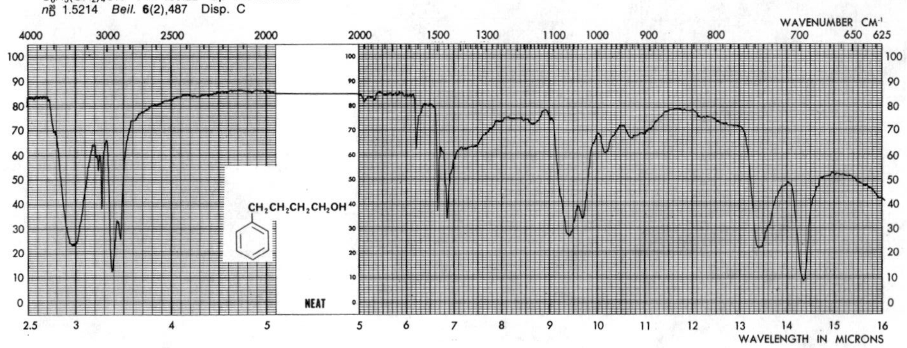

NEAT

F

18,797-6
3-Phenyl-1-butanol, 99%
$CH_3CH(C_6H_5)CH_2CH_2OH$ FW 150.22
bp 138-140°/33mm. n_D^{20} 1.5158 Disp. C

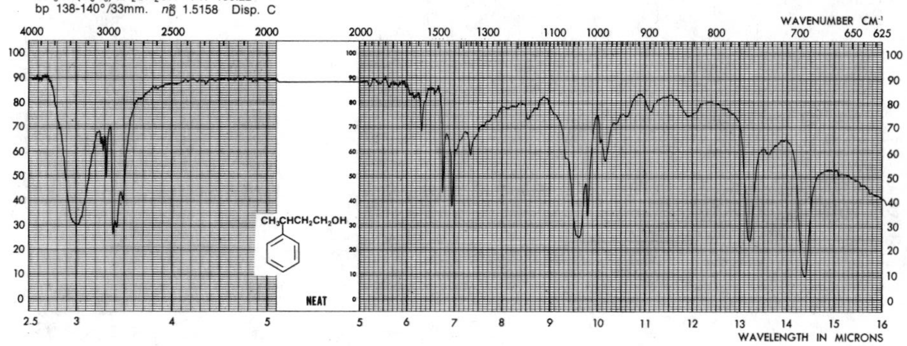

NEAT

G

18,822-0
5-Phenyl-1-pentanol, 99%
$C_6H_5(CH_2)_5OH$ FW 164.25 bp 155°/20mm.
n_D^{20} 1.5162 Disp. C

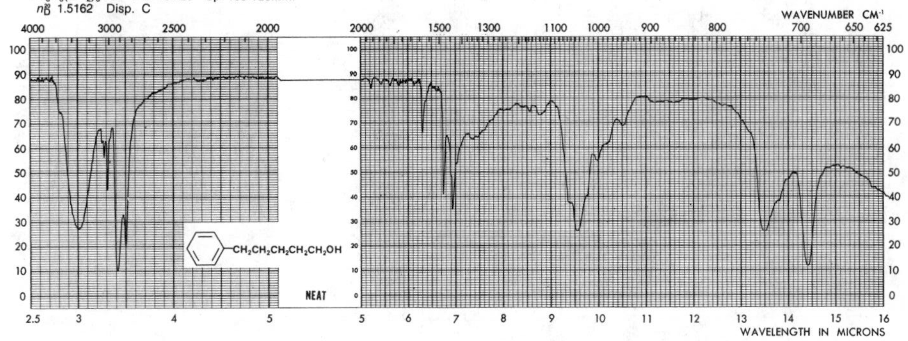

NEAT

H

P2405-5 **1-Phenyl-1,2-ethanediol (styrene glycol)**
$HOCH_2CH(C_6H_5)OH$ M.W. 138.17 m.p. 67.5-69°

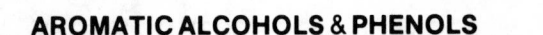

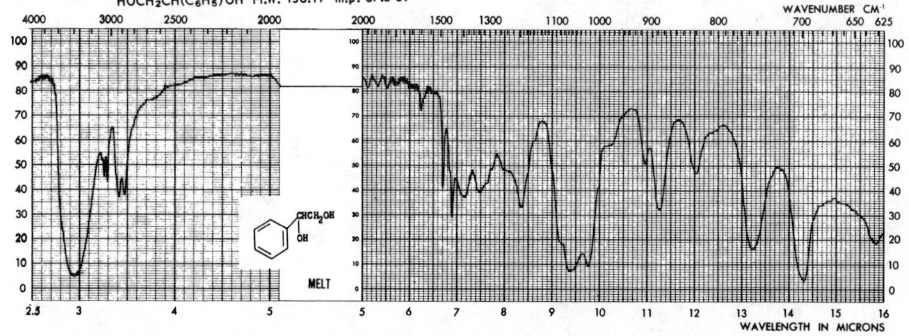

MELT

A

P1560-9 **2-Phenoxyethanol**
$C_6H_5OCH_2CH_2OH$ M.W. 138.17 n_D^{20} 1.5387 m.p. 11-13°
b.p. 237°

NEAT

B

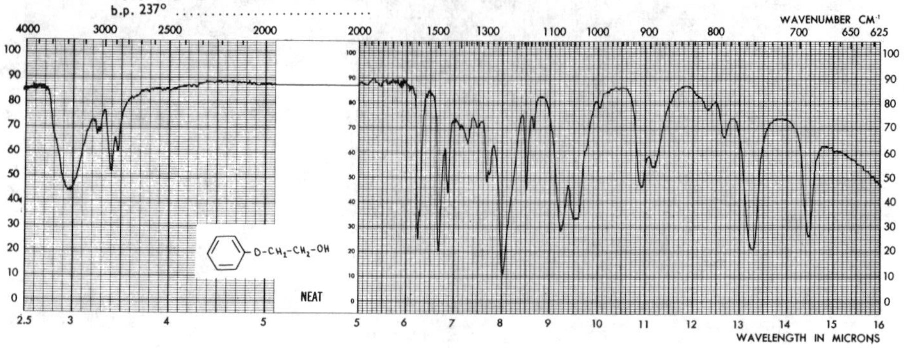

19,485-9
3-Phenoxy-1-propanol, 97%
$C_6H_5O(CH_2)_3OH$ FW 152.19 bp 83-85°/0mm.
n_D^{20} 1.5290 d 1.045 *Beil.* **6**,147 Disp. C

NEAT

C

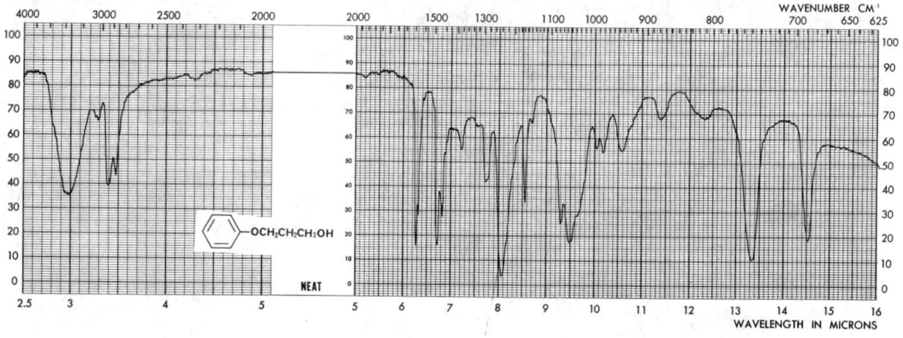

H2,960-9
O-Hydroxyethylresorcinol [2-(m-hydroxy-phenoxy)-ethanol]
3-$(HOCH_2CH_2O)C_6H_4OH$
M.W. 154.17 m.p. 83-86°

NUJOL MULL

D

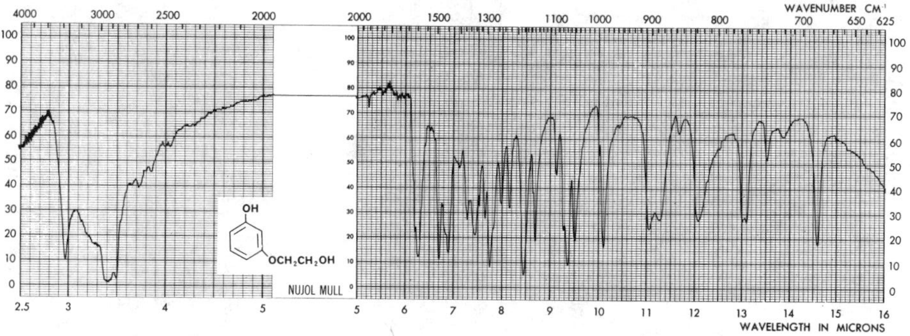

18,872-7
trans-**2-Phenyl-1-cyclopropanemethanol**, 97%
$C_6H_5C_3H_4CH_2OH$ FW 148.21 bp 264° n_D^{20} 1.5522
Disp. C

NEAT

E

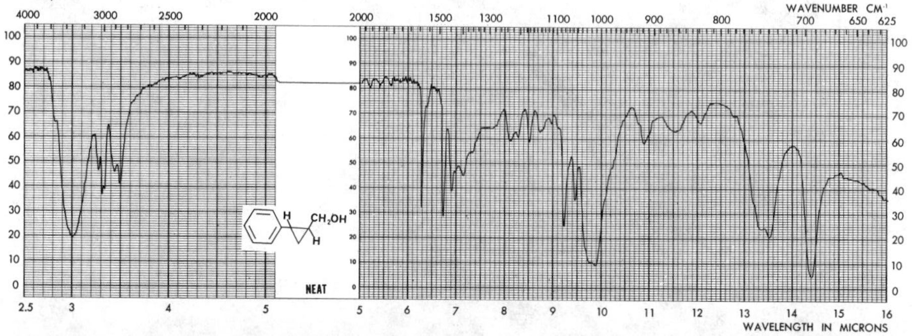

18,809-3
1-Phenylcyclopropanemethanol, 99%
$C_6H_5C_3H_4CH_2OH$ FW 148.21 mp 35-37°
bp 117-122°/112mm. n_D^{20} 1.5457 Disp. C

NEAT

F

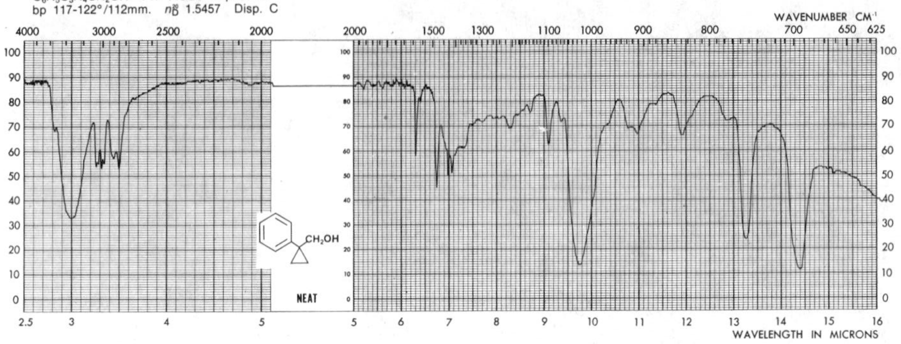

18,867-0
1-Phenyl-1-cyclopentanemethanol, 98%
$C_6H_5C_5H_8CH_2OH$ FW 176.26 mp 44-46°
Disp. C

MELT

G

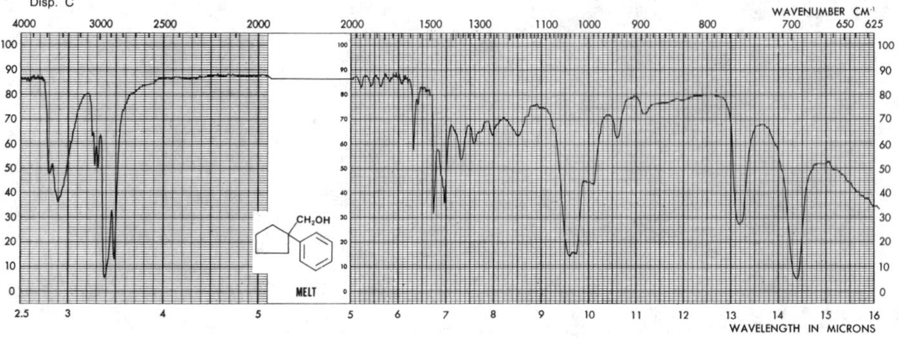

19,348-8
β-**Phenylcyclopentaneethanol**, 99%
$C_5H_9CH(C_6H_5)CH_2OH$ FW 190.29 n_D^{20} 1.5369
d 1.021 Disp. C

NEAT

H

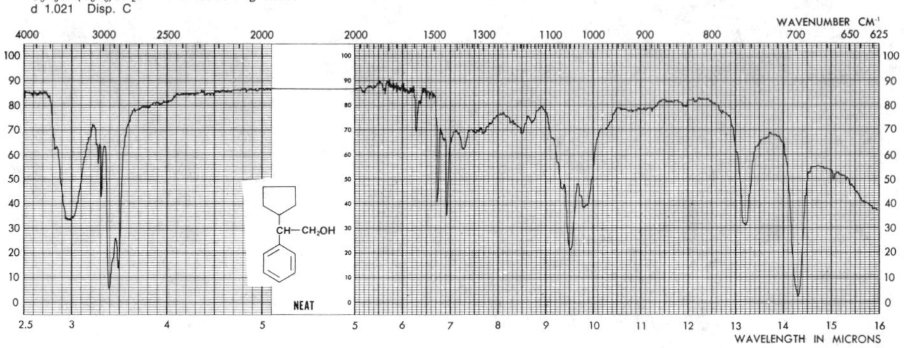

18,035-1
2-Indanol, 99%
M.W. 134.18 m.p. 68-71°

NUJOL MULL

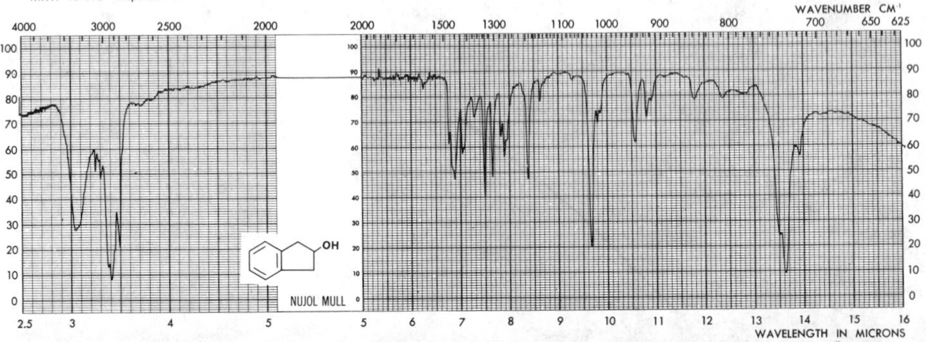

A

P2226-5 **2-Phenyl-1-cyclohexanol** (mixture of *cis* and *trans*)
$C_6H_5C_6H_{10}OH$ M.W. 176.26 b.p. 276-281°

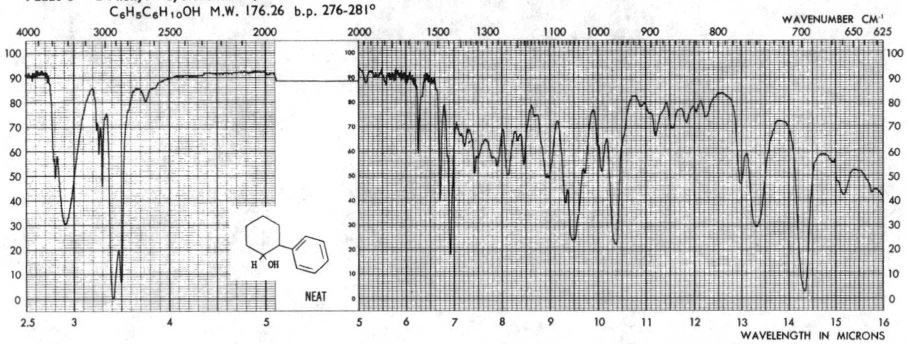

NEAT

B

18,868-9
1-Phenyl-1-cyclohexanemethanol, 98%
$C_6H_5C_6H_{10}CH_2OH$ FW 190.29 mp 61-64°
Disp. C

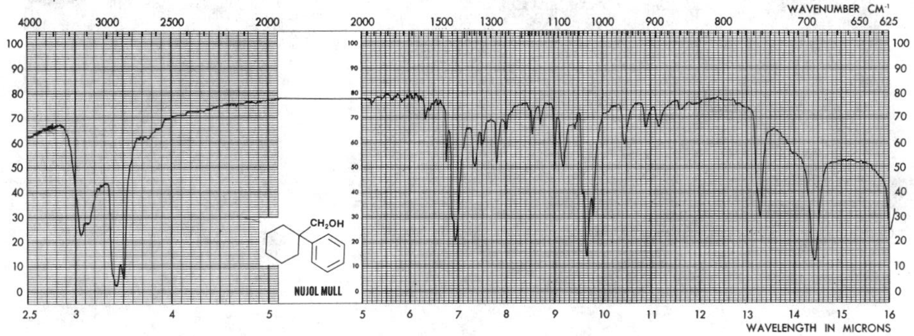

NUJOL MULL

C

17,693-1
***cis*-2-Phenyl-1-cyclohexanol**
$C_6H_5C_6H_{10}OH$
M.W. 176.26 b.p. 141°/16mm. n_D^{20} 1.5426
d 1.035 Beil. **6**(2),548

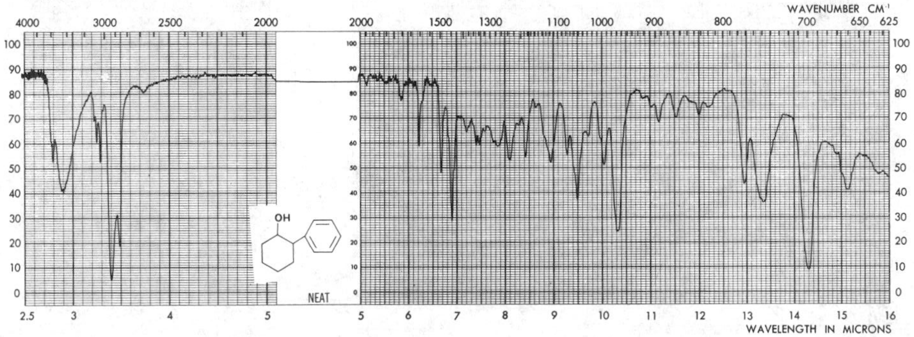

NEAT

D

18,812-3
***o*-Methylphenethyl alcohol,** 98%
$CH_3C_6H_4CH_2CH_2OH$ FW 136.19 bp 243-244°
n_D^{20} 1.5355 d 1.016 *Beil.* **6**,508 Disp. C

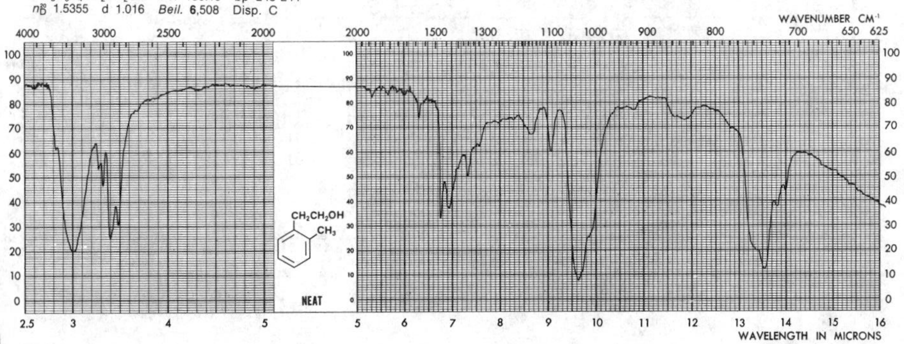

NEAT

E

19,384-4
***o*-Chlorophenethyl alcohol,** 98%
$ClC_6H_4CH_2CH_2OH$ FW 156.61 bp 84-85°/3mm.
n_D^{20} 1.5510 d 1.190 Disp. C

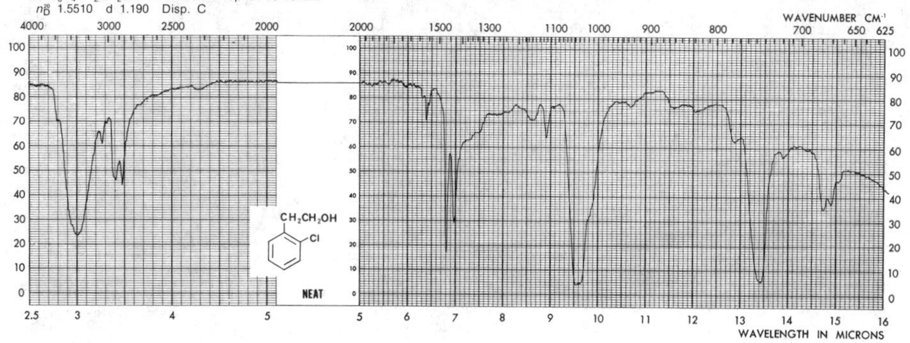

NEAT

F

18,792-5
***o*-Methoxyphenethyl alcohol,** 99%
$CH_3OC_6H_4CH_2CH_2OH$ FW 152.19
bp 133-135°/10mm. n_D^{20} 1.5402 Disp. C

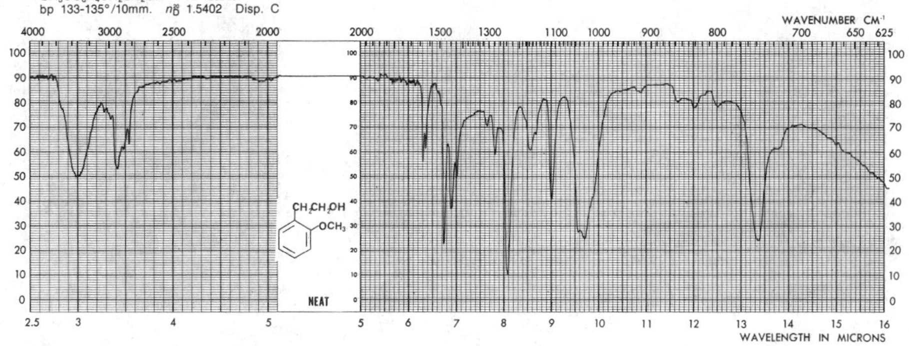

NEAT

G

18,824-7
***o*-Hydroxyphenethyl alcohol,** 99%
$HOC_6H_4CH_2CH_2OH$ FW 138.17
bp 168-169°/2mm. n_D^{20} 1.5592 *Beil.* **6**,906
Disp. C

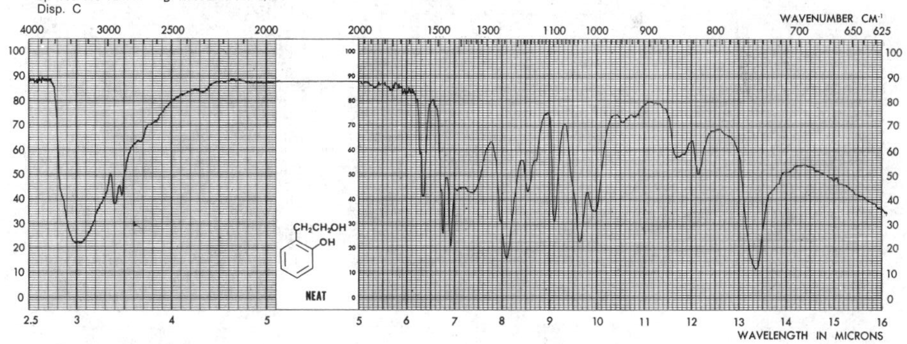

NEAT

H

S30-5 **Salicin**
2-[$(C_6H_{11}O_5)O$]$C_6H_4CH_2OH$ M.W. 286.28 m.p. 138-140°

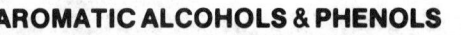

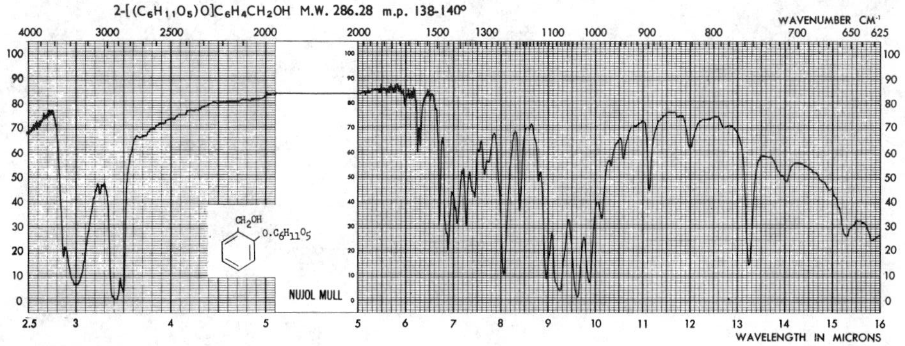

NUJOL MULL

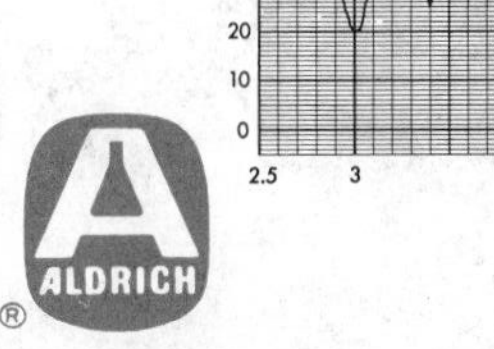

ALDRICH ®

A M2344-6 **3-(o-Methoxyphenyl)-propanol**
$CH_3OC_6H_4(CH_2)_3OH$ M.W. 166.22 n_D^{20} 1.5329
b.p. 147°/10 mm.

B 18,813-1
m-**Methylphenethyl alcohol,** 98%
$CH_3C_6H_4CH_2CH_2OH$ FW 136.19 bp 242-243°
n_D^{20} 1.5294 *Beil.* **6**,508 Disp. C

C 19,351-8
m-**Chlorophenethyl alcohol,** 98%
$ClC_6H_4CH_2CH_2OH$ FW 156.61
bp 135-137°/13mm. n_D^{20} 1.5491 d 1.181 Disp. C

D 18,793-3
m-**Methoxyphenethyl alcohol,** 97%
$CH_3OC_6H_4CH_2CH_2OH$ FW 152.19
bp 141-143°/12mm. n_D^{20} 1.5381 Disp. C

E 19,902-8
m-**Hydroxyphenethyl alcohol,** 99%
$HOC_6H_4CH_2CH_2OH$ FW 138.17
bp 168-173°/4mm. n_D^{20} 1.5643 d 1.082 Disp. C

F M2345-4 **3-(m-Methoxyphenyl)-propanol**
$CH_3OC_6H_4(CH_2)_3OH$ M.W. 166.22 n_D^{20} 1.5305
b.p. 132°/0.4 mm.

G 18,815-8
p-**Methylphenethyl alcohol,** 99%
$CH_3C_6H_4CH_2CH_2OH$ FW 136.19 bp 244-245°
n_D^{20} 1.5267 Disp. C

H 15,417-2
p-Fluorophenethyl alcohol, 97+%
$FC_6H_4CH_2CH_2OH$
M.W. 140.16 n_D^{20} 1.5075

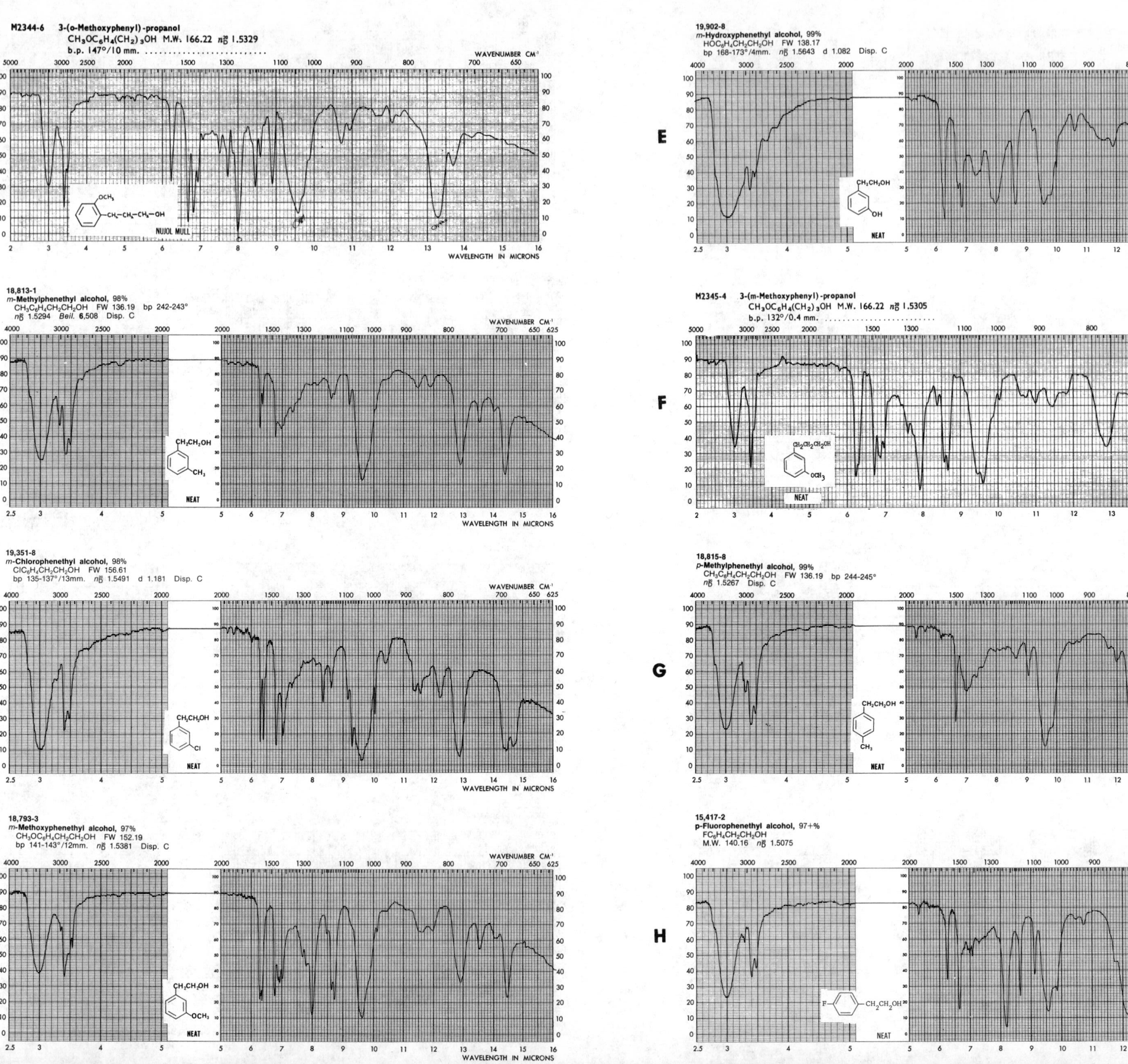

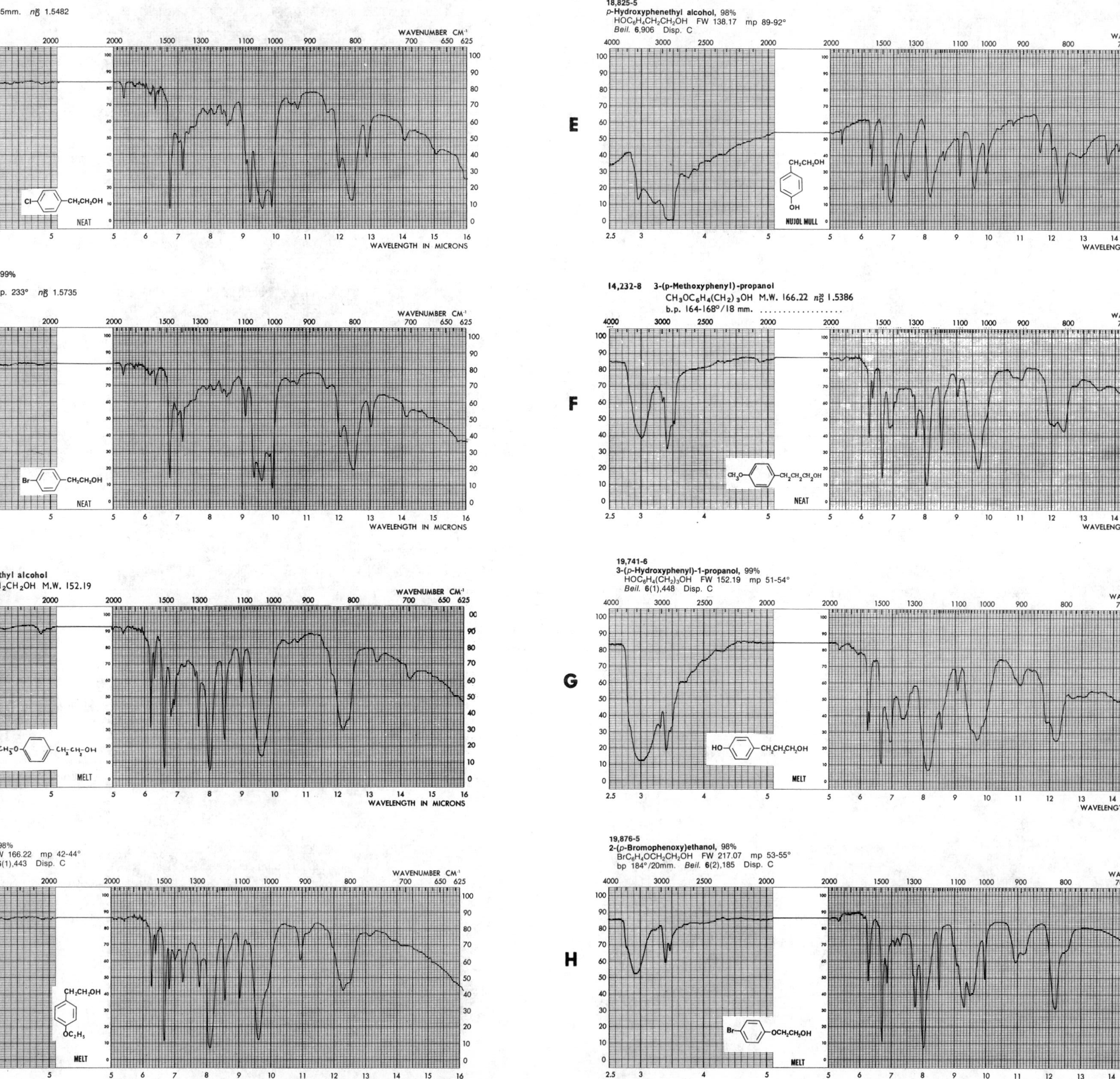
A
18,342-3
p-Chlorophenethyl alcohol, 99%
$ClC_6H_4CH_2CH_2OH$
M.W. 156.61 b.p. 110°/0.5mm. n_D^{20} 1.5482
d 1.157
NEAT
B
18,343-1
p-Bromophenethyl alcohol, 99%
$BrC_6H_4CH_2CH_2OH$
M.W. 201.07 m.p. 4° b.p. 233° n_D^{20} 1.5735
d 1.436 Beil. 6,199
NEAT
C
15,418-0 p-Methoxyphenethyl alcohol
$CH_3OC_6H_4CH_2CH_2OH$ M.W. 152.19
MELT
D
18,796-8
p-Ethoxyphenethyl alcohol, 98%
$C_2H_5OC_6H_4CH_2CH_2OH$ FW 166.22 mp 42-44°
bp 135-140°/7mm. Beil. 6(1),443 Disp. C
MELT
E
18,825-5
p-Hydroxyphenethyl alcohol, 98%
$HOC_6H_4CH_2CH_2OH$ FW 138.17 mp 89-92°
Beil. 6,906 Disp. C
NUJOL MULL
F
14,232-8 3-(p-Methoxyphenyl)-propanol
$CH_3OC_6H_4(CH_2)_3OH$ M.W. 166.22 n_D^{20} 1.5386
b.p. 164-168°/18 mm.
NEAT
G
19,741-6
3-(p-Hydroxyphenyl)-1-propanol, 99%
$HOC_6H_4(CH_2)_3OH$ FW 152.19 mp 51-54°
Beil. 6(1),448 Disp. C
MELT
H
19,876-5
2-(p-Bromophenoxy)ethanol, 98%
$BrC_6H_4OCH_2CH_2OH$ FW 217.07 mp 53-55°
bp 184°/20mm. Beil. 6(2),185 Disp. C
MELT
WAVENUMBER CM⁻¹
WAVELENGTH IN MICRONS

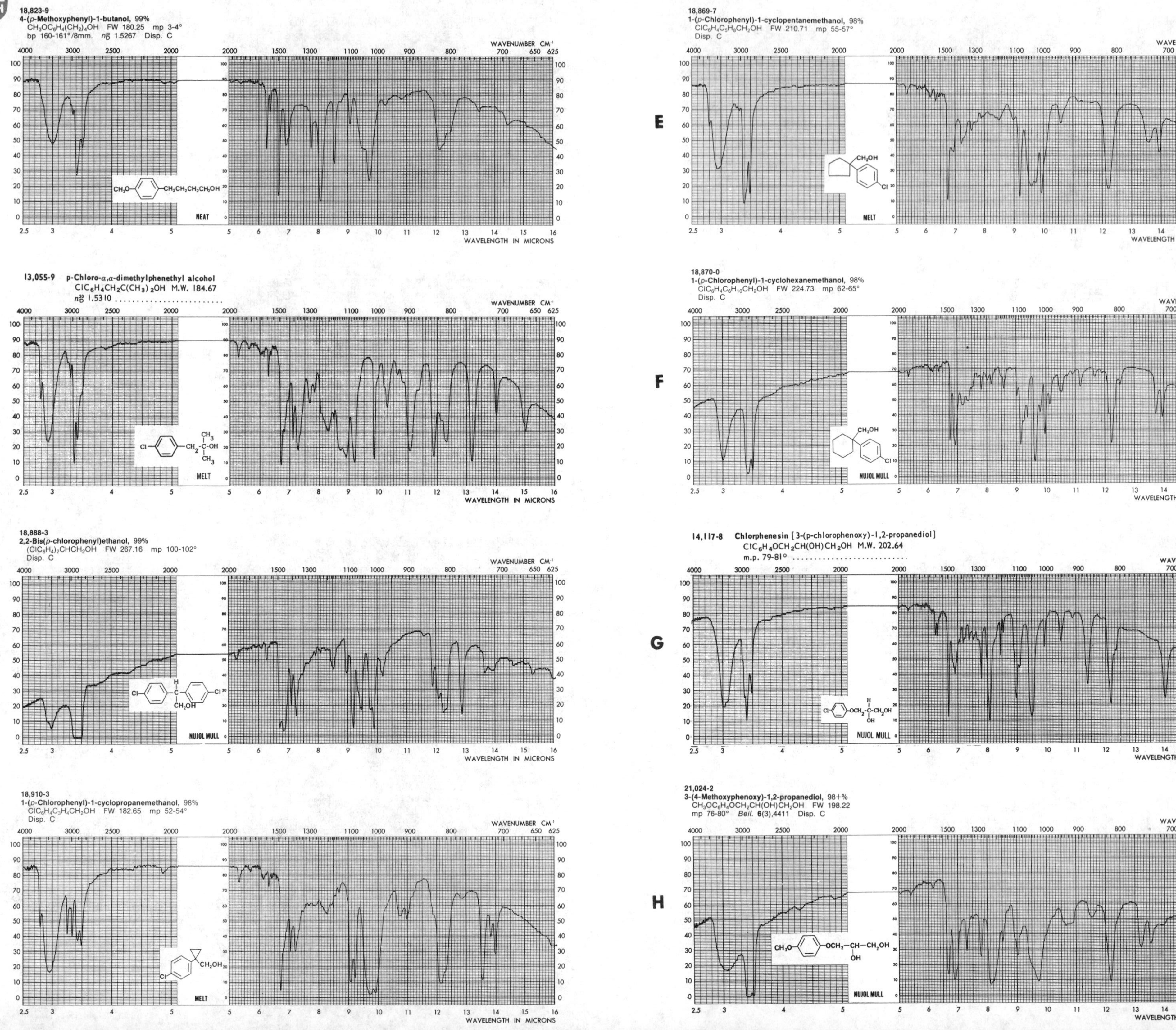
A
18,823-9
4-(p-Methoxyphenyl)-1-butanol, 99%
$CH_3OC_6H_4(CH_2)_4OH$ FW 180.25 mp 3-4°
bp 160-161°/8mm. n_D^{20} 1.5267 Disp. C
NEAT
B
13,055-9 p-Chloro-α,α-dimethylphenethyl alcohol
$ClC_6H_4CH_2C(CH_3)_2OH$ M.W. 184.67
n_D^{20} 1.5310
MELT
C
18,888-3
2,2-Bis(p-chlorophenyl)ethanol, 99%
$(ClC_6H_4)_2CHCH_2OH$ FW 267.16 mp 100-102°
Disp. C
NUJOL MULL
D
18,910-3
1-(p-Chlorophenyl)-1-cyclopropanemethanol, 98%
$ClC_6H_4C_3H_4CH_2OH$ FW 182.65 mp 52-54°
Disp. C
MELT
E
18,869-7
1-(p-Chlorophenyl)-1-cyclopentanemethanol, 98%
$ClC_6H_4C_5H_8CH_2OH$ FW 210.71 mp 55-57°
Disp. C
MELT
F
18,870-0
1-(p-Chlorophenyl)-1-cyclohexanemethanol, 98%
$ClC_6H_4C_6H_{10}CH_2OH$ FW 224.73 mp 62-65°
Disp. C
NUJOL MULL
G
14,117-8 Chlorphenesin [3-(p-chlorophenoxy)-1,2-propanediol]
$ClC_6H_4OCH_2CH(OH)CH_2OH$ M.W. 202.64
m.p. 79-81°
NUJOL MULL
H
21,024-2
3-(4-Methoxyphenoxy)-1,2-propanediol, 98+%
$CH_3OC_6H_4OCH_2CH(OH)CH_2OH$ FW 198.22
mp 76-80° Beil. 6(3),4411 Disp. C
NUJOL MULL
WAVENUMBER CM⁻¹
WAVELENGTH IN MICRONS

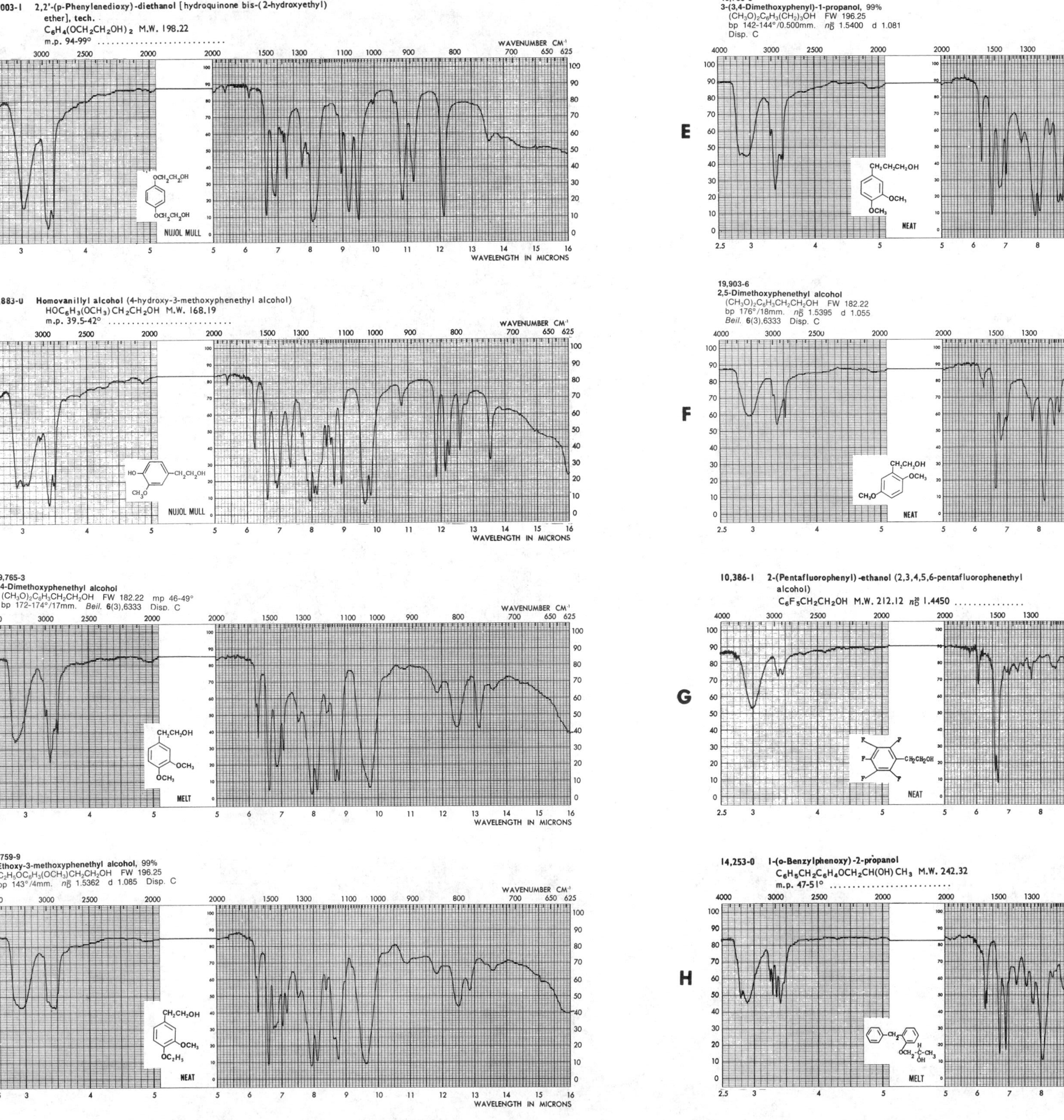

A 14,003-1 **2,2'-(p-Phenylenedioxy)-diethanol [hydroquinone bis-(2-hydroxyethyl) ether], tech.**
$C_6H_4(OCH_2CH_2OH)_2$ M.W. 198.22
m.p. 94-99° — NUJOL MULL

B 14,883-0 **Homovanillyl alcohol** (4-hydroxy-3-methoxyphenethyl alcohol)
$HOC_6H_3(OCH_3)CH_2CH_2OH$ M.W. 168.19
m.p. 39.5-42° — NUJOL MULL

C 19,765-3
3,4-Dimethoxyphenethyl alcohol
$(CH_3O)_2C_6H_3CH_2CH_2OH$ FW 182.22 mp 46-49°
bp 172-174°/17mm. *Beil.* **6**(3),6333 Disp. C — MELT

D 19,759-9
4-Ethoxy-3-methoxyphenethyl alcohol, 99%
$C_2H_5OC_6H_3(OCH_3)CH_2CH_2OH$ FW 196.25
bp 143°/4mm. n_D^{20} 1.5362 d 1.085 Disp. C — NEAT

E 19,768-8
3-(3,4-Dimethoxyphenyl)-1-propanol, 99%
$(CH_3O)_2C_6H_3(CH_2)_3OH$ FW 196.25
bp 142-144°/0.500mm. n_D^{20} 1.5400 d 1.081
Disp. C — NEAT

F 19,903-6
2,5-Dimethoxyphenethyl alcohol
$(CH_3O)_2C_6H_3CH_2CH_2OH$ FW 182.22
bp 176°/18mm. n_D^{20} 1.5395 d 1.055
Beil. **6**(3),6333 Disp. C — NEAT

G 10,386-1 **2-(Pentafluorophenyl)-ethanol** (2,3,4,5,6-pentafluorophenethyl alcohol)
$C_6F_5CH_2CH_2OH$ M.W. 212.12 n_D^{20} 1.4450 — NEAT

H 14,253-0 **1-(o-Benzylphenoxy)-2-propanol**
$C_6H_5CH_2C_6H_4OCH_2CH(OH)CH_3$ M.W. 242.32
m.p. 47-51° — MELT

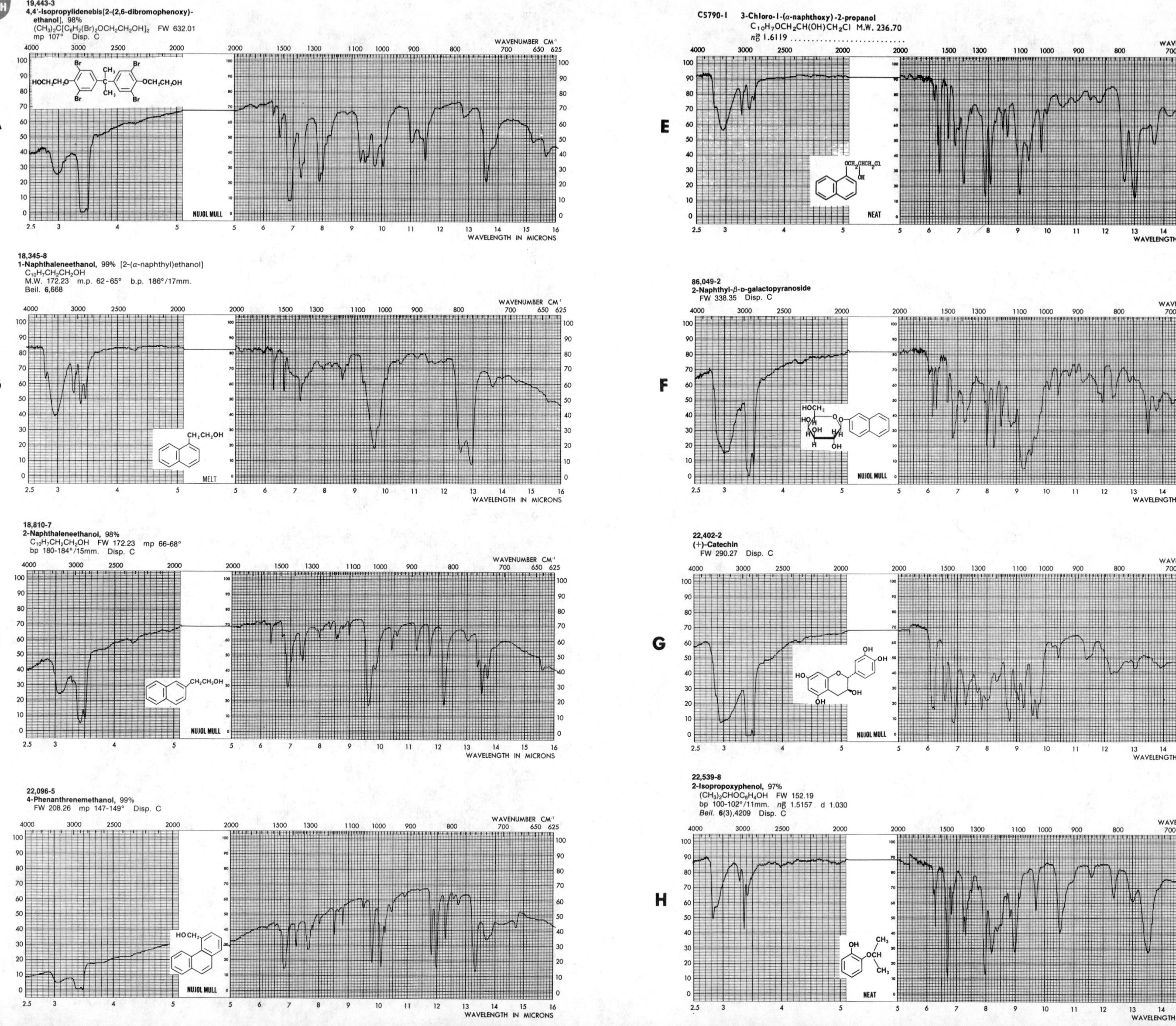

A 19,443-3
4,4'-Isopropylidenebis[2-(2,6-dibromophenoxy)-ethanol], 98%
$(CH_3)_2C[C_6H_2(Br)_2OCH_2CH_2OH]_2$ FW 632.01
mp 107° Disp. C
NUJOL MULL

B 18,345-8
1-Naphthaleneethanol, 99% [2-(α-naphthyl)ethanol]
$C_{10}H_7CH_2CH_2OH$
M.W. 172.23 m.p. 62-65° b.p. 186°/17mm.
Beil. 6,668
MELT

C 18,810-7
2-Naphthaleneethanol, 98%
$C_{10}H_7CH_2CH_2OH$ FW 172.23 mp 66-68°
bp 180-184°/15mm. Disp. C
NUJOL MULL

D 22,096-5
4-Phenanthrenemethanol, 99%
FW 208.26 mp 147-149° Disp. C
NUJOL MULL

E C5790-1 **3-Chloro-1-(α-naphthoxy)-2-propanol**
$C_{10}H_7OCH_2CH(OH)CH_2Cl$ M.W. 236.70
n_D^{20} 1.6119
NEAT

F 86,049-2
2-Naphthyl-β-D-galactopyranoside
FW 338.35 Disp. C
NUJOL MULL

G 22,402-2
(+)-Catechin
FW 290.27 Disp. C
NUJOL MULL

H 22,539-8
2-Isopropoxyphenol, 97%
$(CH_3)_2CHOC_6H_4OH$ FW 152.19
bp 100-102°/11mm. n_D^{20} 1.5157 d 1.030
Beil. 6(3),4209 Disp. C
NEAT

A

22,408-1
Chlorohydroquinone, tech., 90%
ClC_6H_3-1,4-$(OH)_2$ FW 144.56 mp 101-102°
bp 263° *Beil.* 6,849 Disp. C

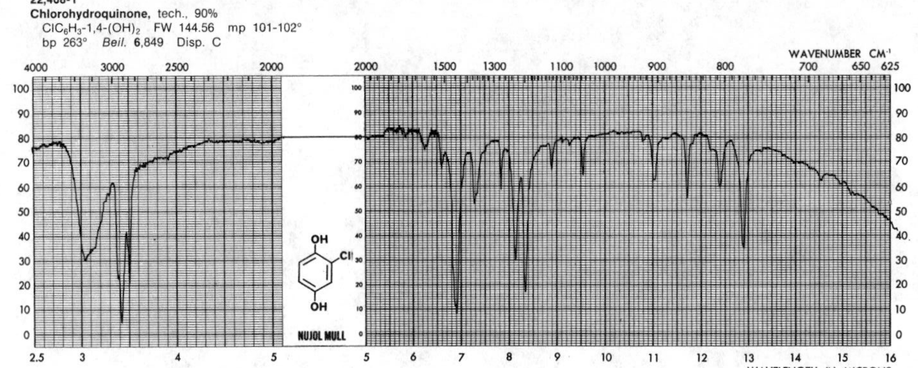

B

21,802-2
2,2,2-Trifluoro-1-(9-anthryl)ethanol, 98+%
[α-(trifluoromethyl)-9-anthracenemethanol]
FW 276.26 mp 142-144° Disp. C

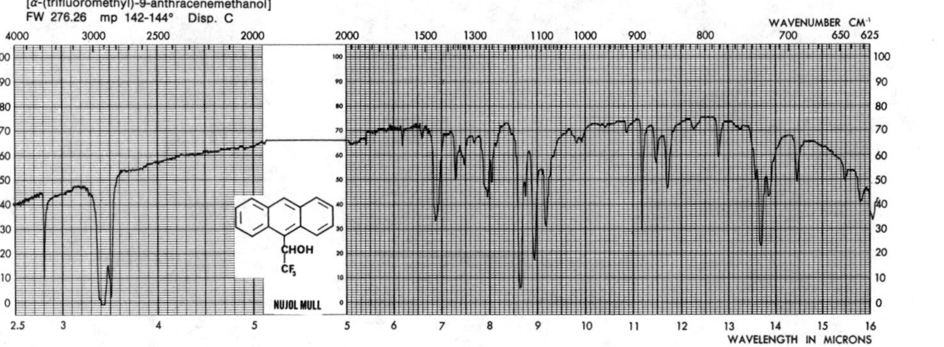

AROMATIC MERCAPTANS AND SULFIDES

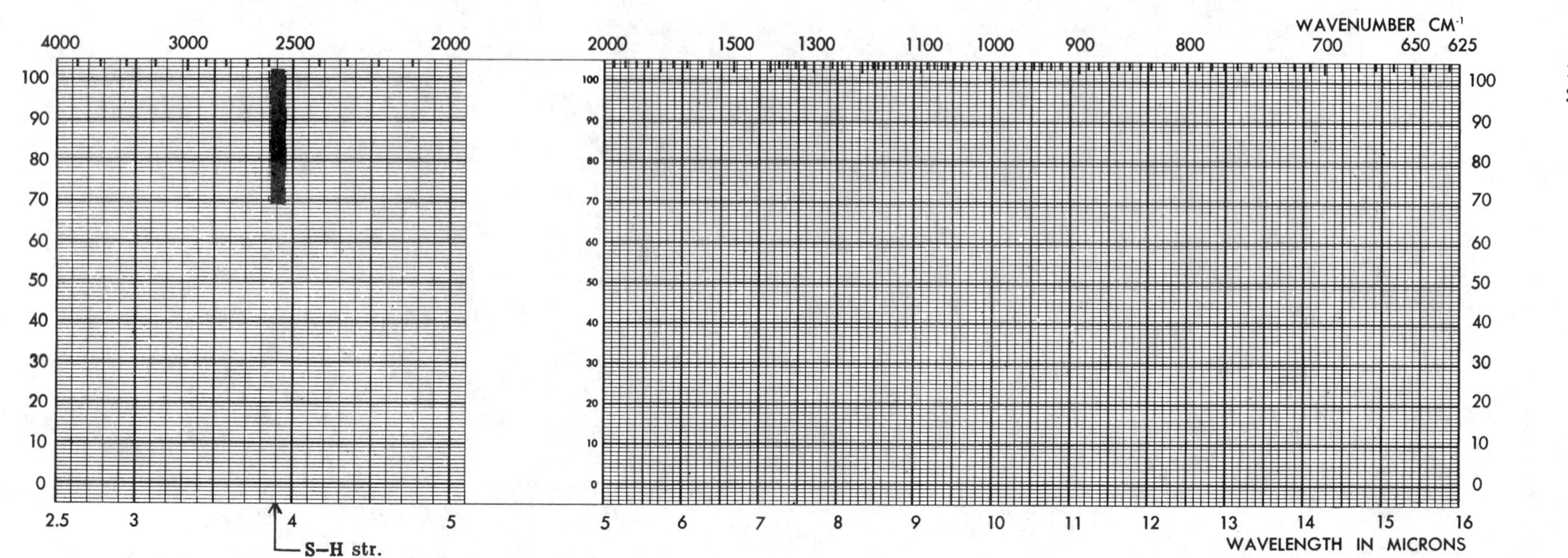

The presence of sulfur on the aromatic ring adds very little to the absorption pattern of the ring itself. It also does not interfere with the substitution patterns between 11 and 15 μ (910 – 665 cm^{-1}). The normal position of the S–H stretch band at 3.9 μ (2565 cm^{-1}) is maintained.

A T3280-8 **Thiophenol** (benzenethiol)
C_6H_5SH M.W. 110.18 n_D^{20} 1.5890 b.p. 169.5°

B 18,334-2
Phenylselenenyl chloride, 98% (benzeneselenenyl chloride)
C_6H_5SeCl
M.W. 191.52

C B2540-1 **Benzyl mercaptan** (α-toluenethiol)
$C_6H_5CH_2SH$ M.W. 124.21 n_D^{20} 1.5751

D T8410-7 **Triphenylmethyl mercaptan**
$(C_6H_5)_3CSH$ M.W. 276.40 m.p. 105-108°

E P3260-0 **3-Phenylpropyl mercaptan** (3-phenyl-1-propanethiol)
$C_6H_5(CH_2)_3SH$ M.W. 152.26 n_D^{20} 1.5494
b.p. 109°/10 mm.

F T2850-9 **o-Thiocresol** (o-toluenethiol)
$CH_3C_6H_4SH$ M.W. 124.21 n_D^{20} 1.5800 m.p. 10-12°
b.p. 194.3°

G 18,405-5
o-Methoxybenzenethiol
$CH_3OC_6H_4SH$ FW 140.20 bp 99°/8mm.
n_D^{20} 1.5918 Disp. C

H T2851-7 **m-Thiocresol** (m-toluenethiol)
$CH_3C_6H_4SH$ M.W. 124.21 n_D^{20} 1.5752
b.p. 195.4°

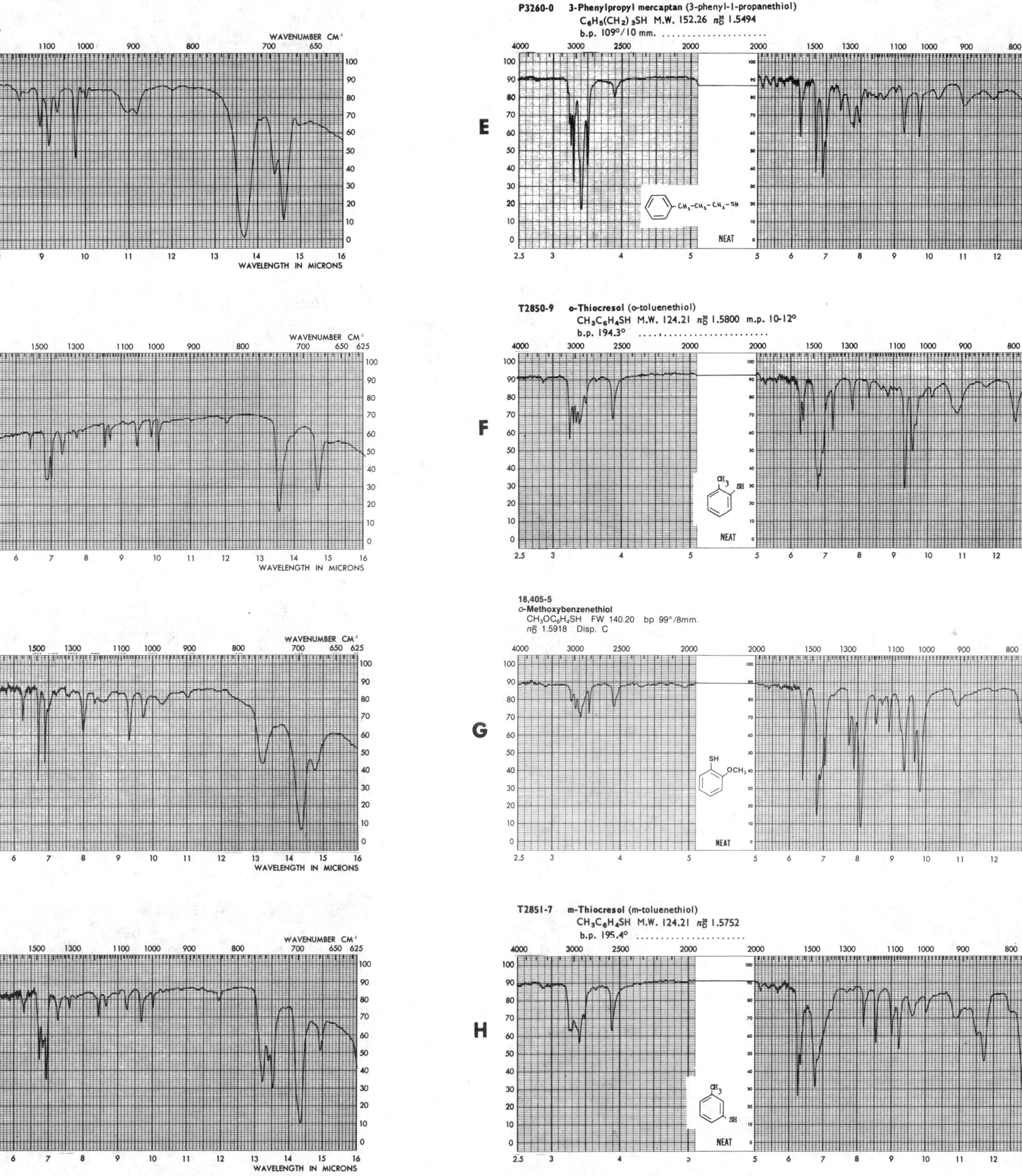

A

15,570-5 **m-Methoxybenzenethiol**
$CH_3OC_6H_4SH$ M.W. 140.20 n_D^{20} 1.5874
b.p. 223-226° ....

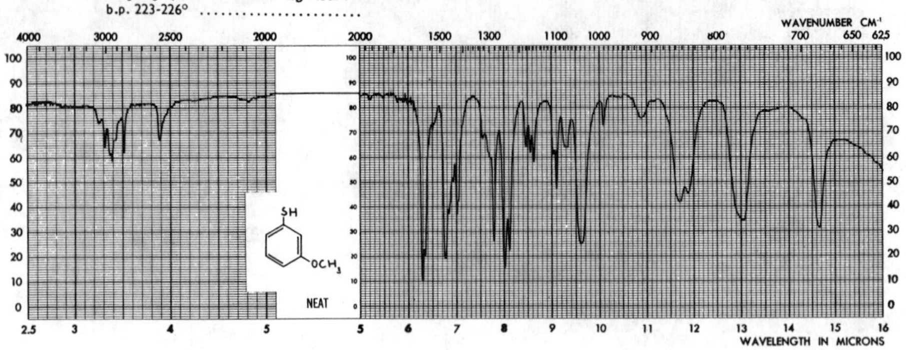

NEAT

B

T2852-5 **p-Thiocresol** (p-toluenethiol)
$CH_3C_6H_4SH$ M.W. 124.21 ....

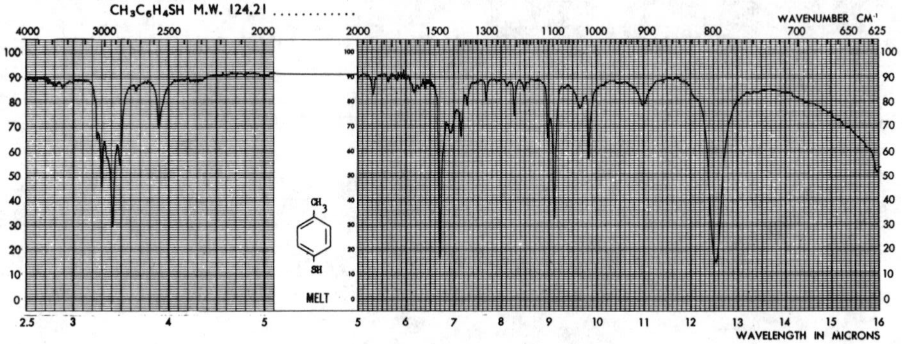

MELT

C

C2870-7 **4-Chlorobenzyl mercaptan** (p-chloro-α-toluenethiol)
$ClC_6H_4CH_2SH$ M.W. 158.65 n_D^{20} 1.5890 ...

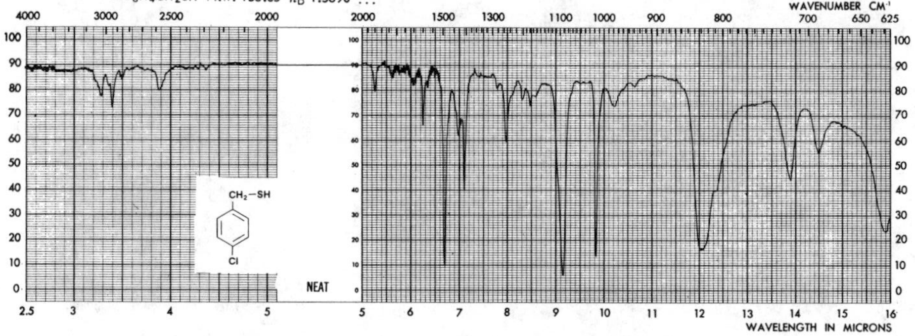

NEAT

D

B8195-6 **4-Bromothiophenol** (p-bromobenzenethiol)
BrC_6H_4SH M.W. 189.08 m.p. 71-76° ..

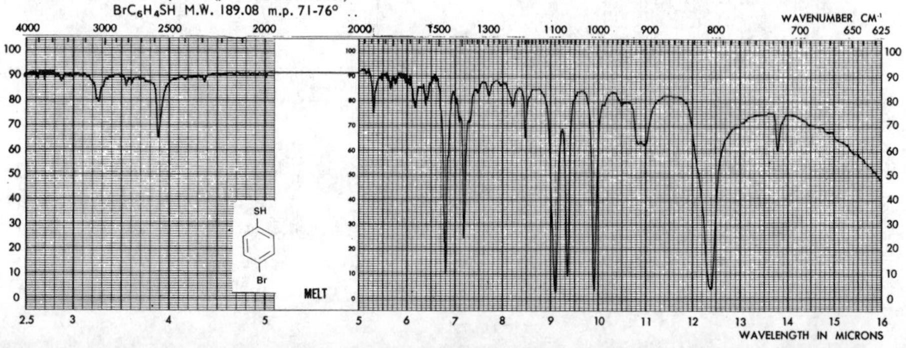

MELT

E

14,727-3 **p-Xylene-α,α'-dithiol** (α,α'-dimercapto-p-xylene)
$C_6H_4(CH_2SH)_2$ M.W. 170.30 m.p. 42.5-45°

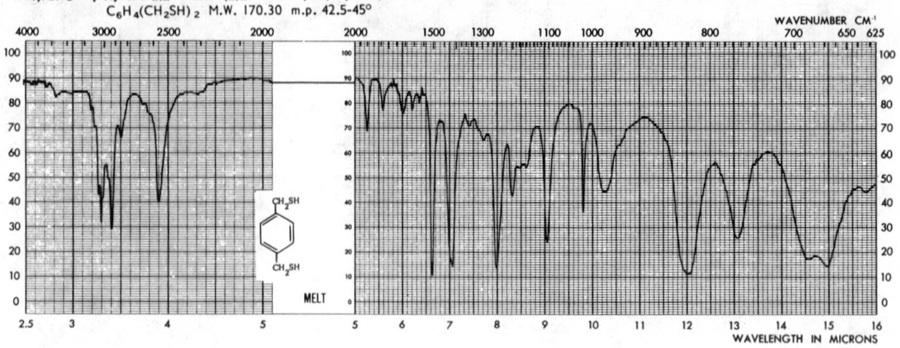

MELT

F

B10,250-4 **4-tert.-Butylthiophenol** (p-tert.-butylbenzenethiol)
$(CH_3)_3CC_6H_4SH$ M.W. 166.29 n_D^{25} 1.5475

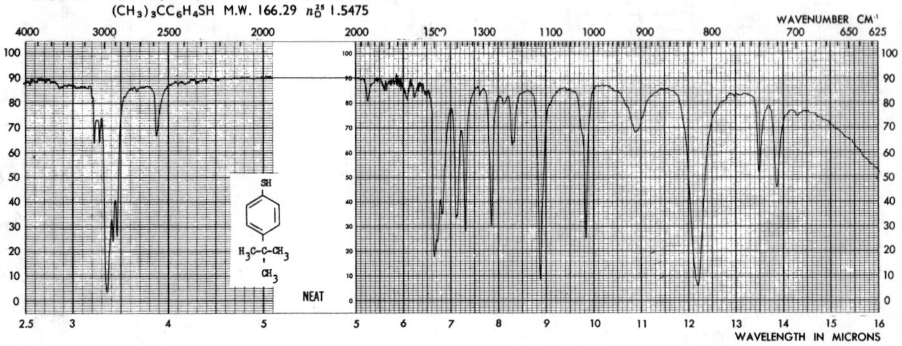

NEAT

G

F1531-5 **4-Fluorothiophenol** (p-fluorobenzenethiol)
FC_6H_4SH M.W. 128.17 n_D^{20} 1.5496 ....

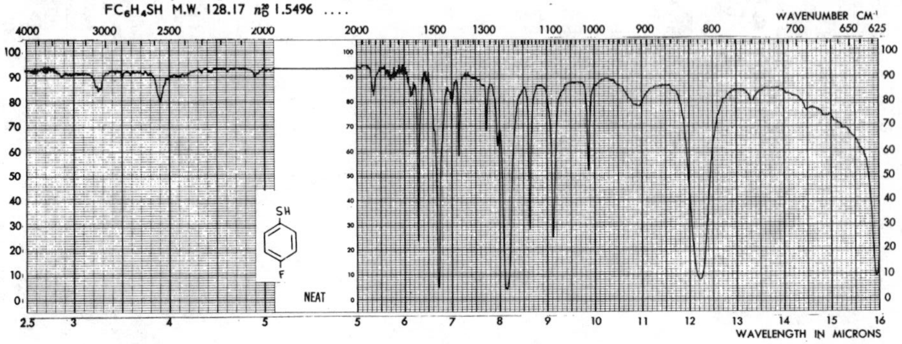

NEAT

H

12,523-7 **p-Chlorothiophenol** (p-chlorobenzenethiol)
ClC_6H_4SH M.W. 144.62 m.p. 49-51° ...

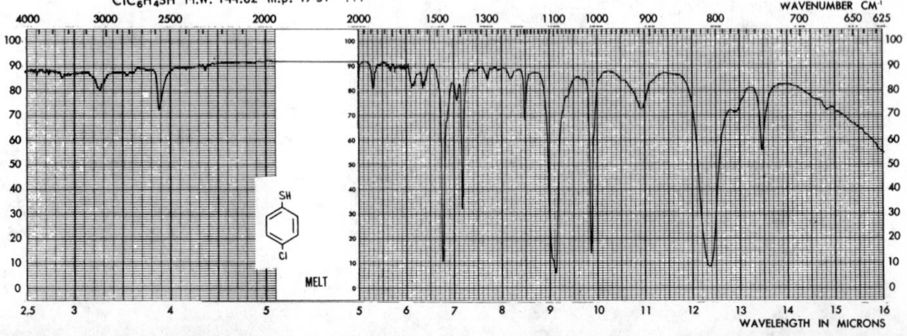

MELT

A

10,952-5 **p-Methoxybenzenethiol**
$CH_3OC_6H_4SH$ M.W. 140.20 n_D^{20} 1.5831
b.p. 100-103°/13 mm.

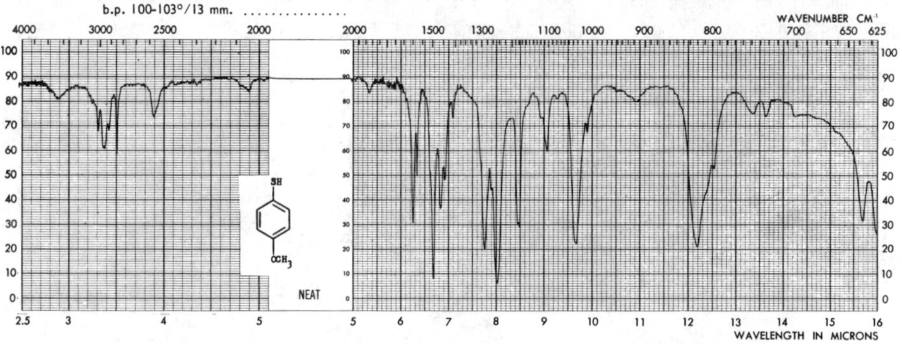

NEAT

B

11,315-8 **p-Methoxy-α-toluenethiol, tech.**
$CH_3OC_6H_4CH_2SH$ M.W. 154.23 n_D^{20} 1.5730
b.p. 90-95°/0.5 mm.

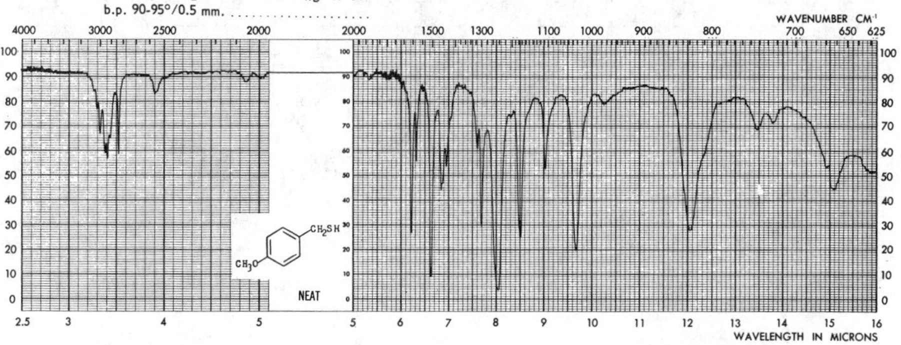

NEAT

C

13,934-3 **4-Bromo-m-thiocresol**
$BrC_6H_3(CH_3)SH$ M.W. 203.11 n_D^{20} 1.6247

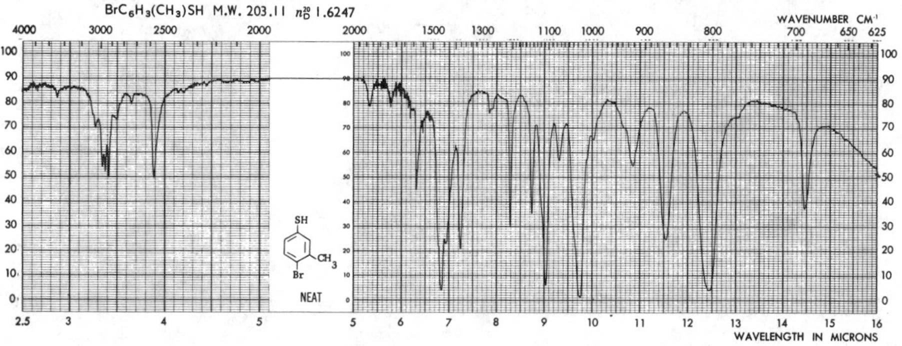

NEAT

D

14,427-4 **2,5-Dichlorobenzenethiol**
$Cl_2C_6H_3SH$ M.W. 179.07

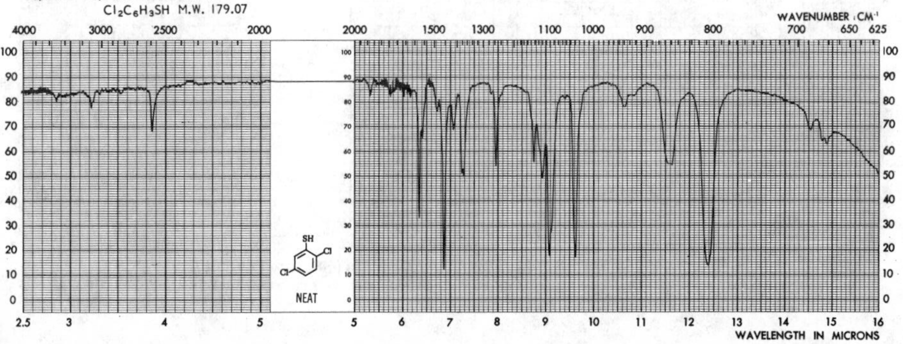

NEAT

E

14,426-6
3,4-Dichlorobenzenethiol, 97%
$Cl_2C_6H_3SH$
M.W. 179.07 n_D^{20} 1.6250 *STENCH*

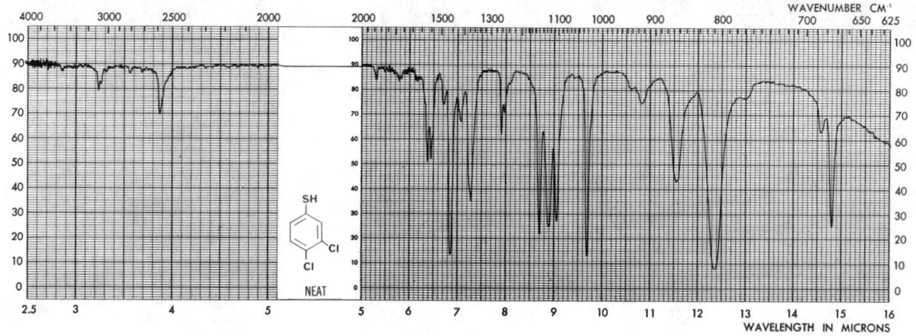

NEAT

F

16,494-1
2,4,5-Trichlorothiophenol (2,4,5-trichlorobenzenethiol)
$Cl_3C_6H_2SH$
M.W. 213.51 m.p. 110-113° *STENCH*

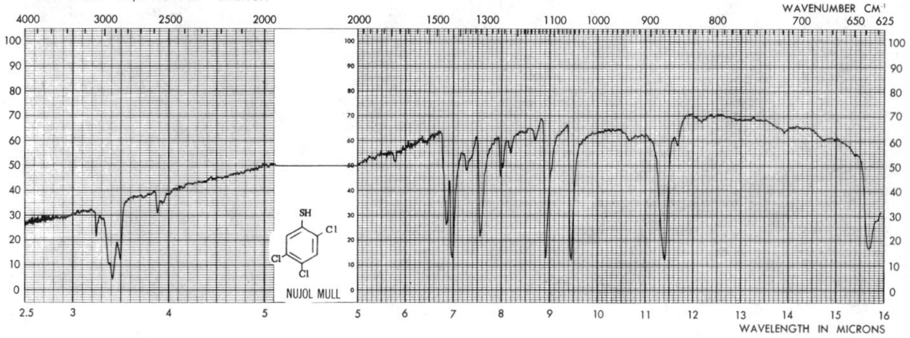

NUJOL MULL

G

18,407-1
Durene-α_1,α_2-dithiol, 97% (4,5-dimethyl-o-xylene-α,α'-dithiol)
$(CH_3)_2C_6H_2(CH_2SH)_2$
M.W. 198.35 m.p. 65-67°

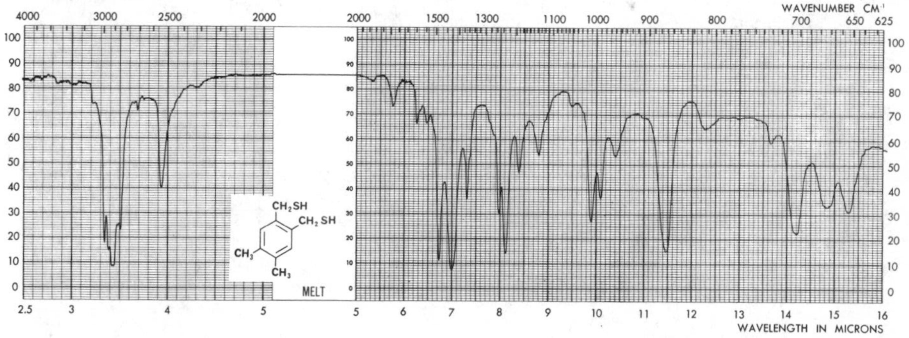

MELT

H

10,018-8 **2,3,5,6-Tetrafluorothiophenol** (2,3,5,6-tetrafluorobenzenethiol)
F_4C_6HSH M.W. 182.14 n_D^{20} 1.4865

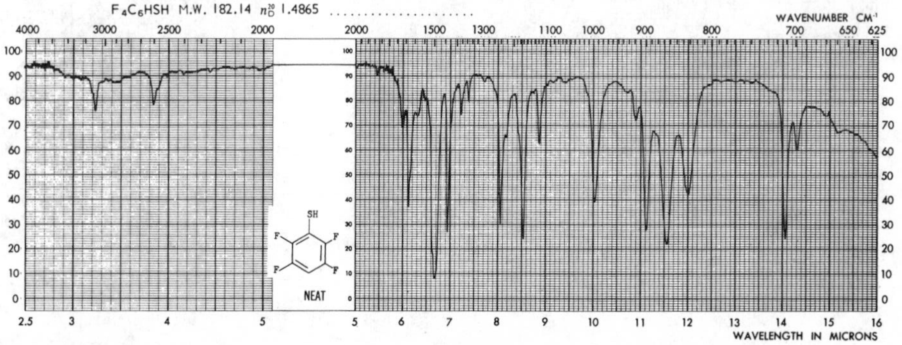

NEAT

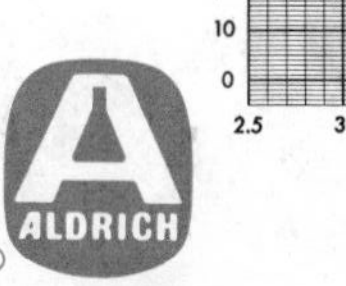

A

P565-4 **Pentafluorothiophenol** (pentafluorobenzenethiol)
C_6F_5SH M.W. 200.13 n_D^{20} 1.4629 b.p. 143° ..

NEAT

B

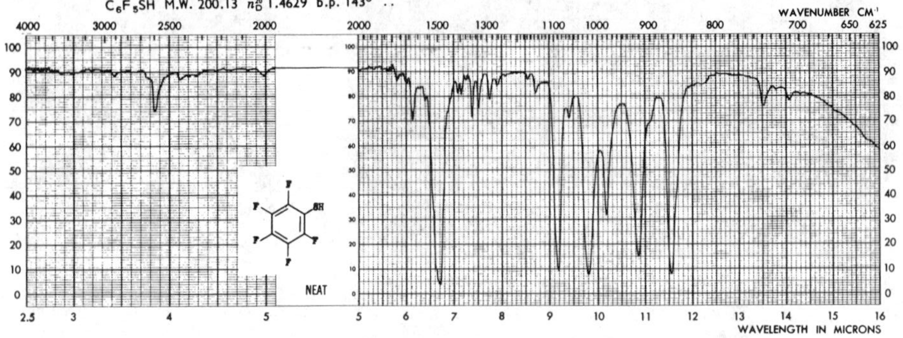

10,220-2 **4,4'-Dimercaptooctafluorobiphenyl** (octafluoro-4,4'-biphenyldithiol)
$HSC_6F_4C_6F_4SH$ M.W. 362.26 m.p. 125-127° ....

NUJOL MULL

C

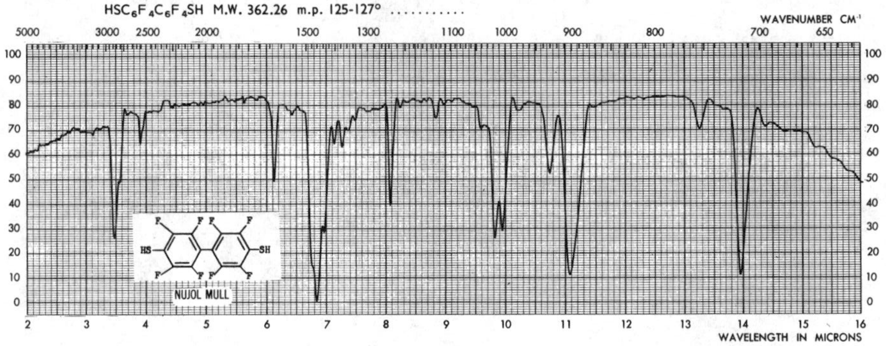

P300-7 **Pentachlorothiophenol** (pentachlorobenzenethiol), **tech.**
C_6Cl_5SH M.W. 282.40 m.p. 228-232° ....

NUJOL MULL

D

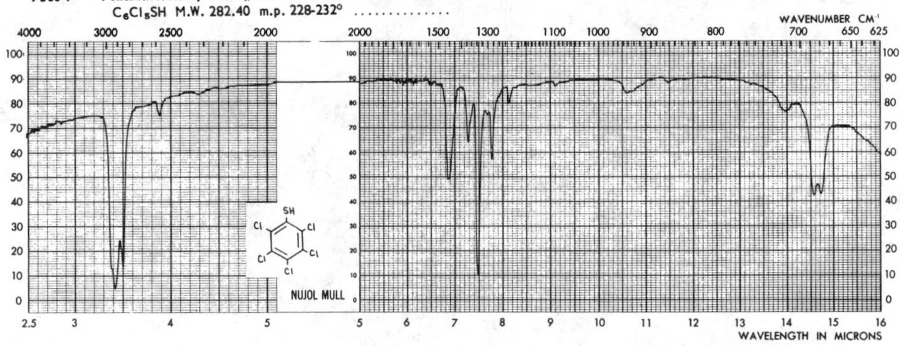

D12,920-8 **3,4-Dimercaptotoluene** (3,4-toluenedithiol)
$CH_3C_6H_3(SH)_2$ M.W. 156.27
n_D^{20} 1.6378 ....

MELT

E

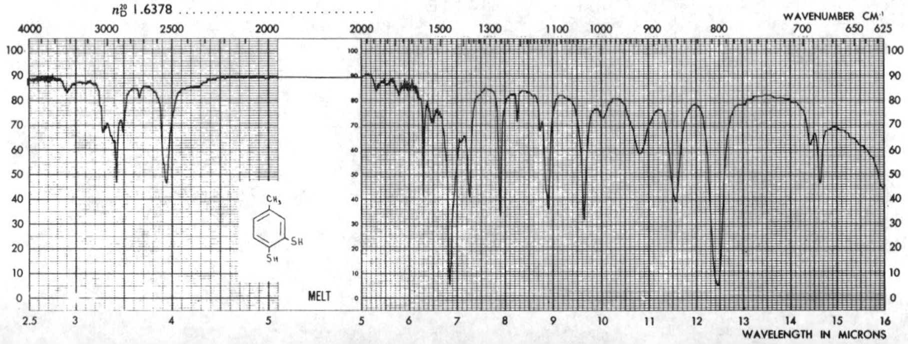

14,428-2 **4-Chloro-m-benzenedithiol**
$ClC_6H_3(SH)_2$ M.W. 176.69 n_D^{20} 1.6704

NEAT

F

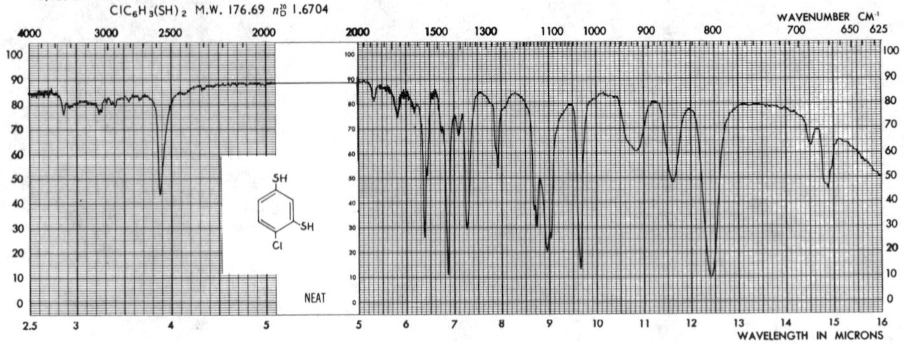

T2800-2 **Thioanisole** (methyl phenyl sulfide)
$C_6H_5SCH_3$ M.W. 124.21 n_D^{20} 1.5852
b.p. 188° ....

NEAT

G

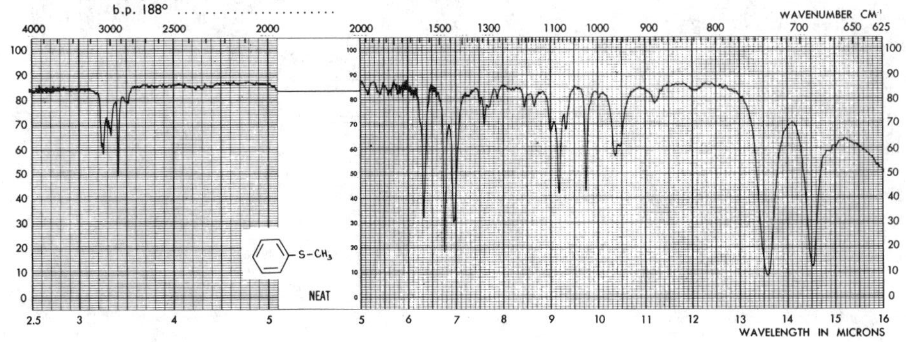

21,663-1
Chloromethyl phenyl sulfide, 98%
$C_6H_5SCH_2Cl$ FW 158.65 bp 66°/0.200mm.
n_D^{20} 1.5950 d 1.184 *Beil.* **6**(3),1002 Disp. C

NEAT

H

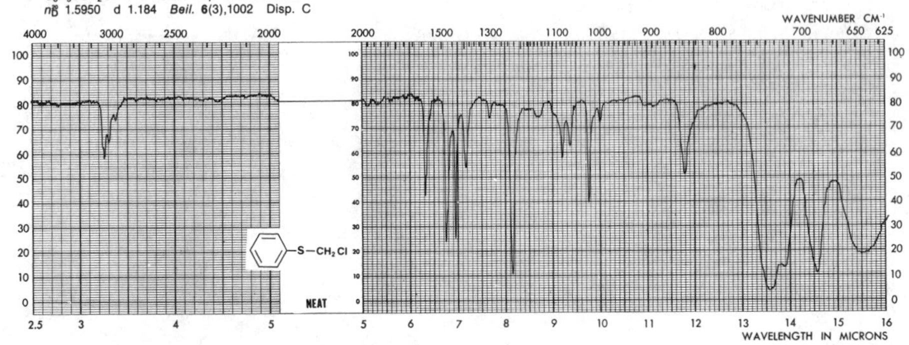

19,652-5
p-**Bromothioanisole,** 97% (*p*-bromophenyl methyl sulfide)
$BrC_6H_4SCH_3$ FW 203.11 mp 38-40° *Beil.* **6**,330
Disp. C

MELT

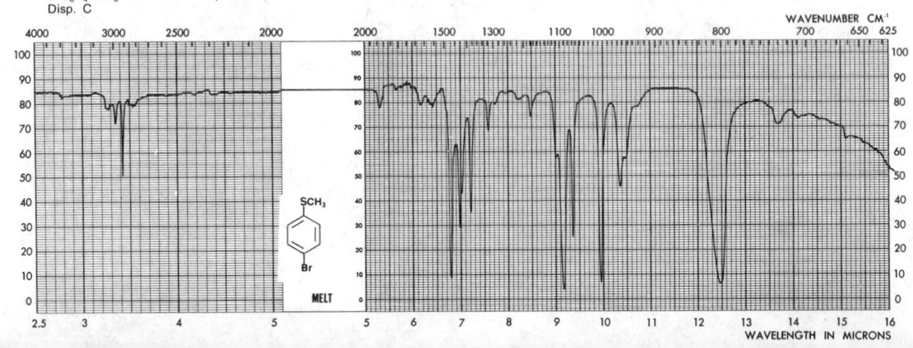

A E4522 **Ethyl phenyl disulfide**
$C_6H_5SSC_2H_5$ M.W. 170.30 n_D^{20} 1.6012
NEAT

B P3531-6 **Phenyl sulfide, puriss.**
$(C_6H_5)_2S$ M.W. 186.27
n_D^{20} 1.6327
NEAT

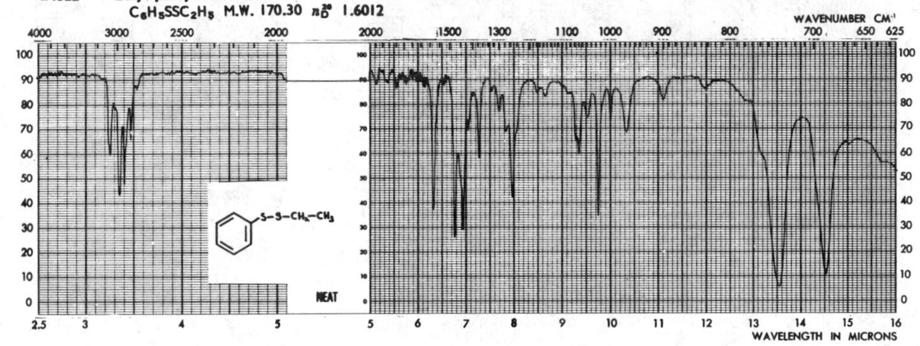

C 16,902-1
Phenyl disulfide, 99% (diphenyl disulfide)
$(C_6H_5S-)_2$ FW 218.34 mp 58-60° *Beil.* 6,323
Fieser 5,276 6,235 Disp. C
MELT

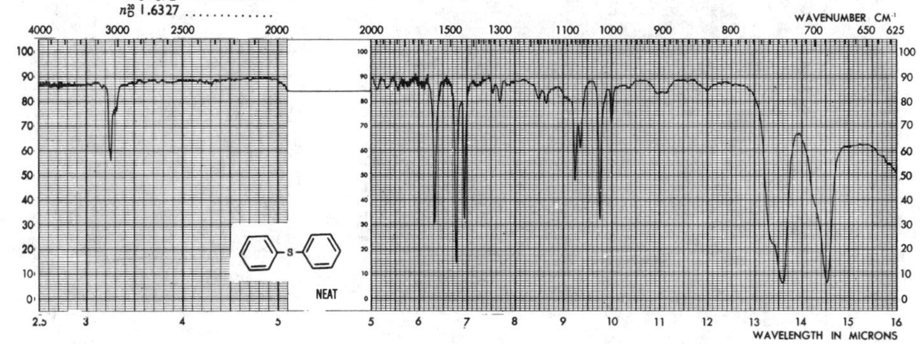

D 18,062-9
Diphenyl diselenide, 99% (phenyl diselenide)
$(C_6H_5)_2Se_2$
M.W. 312.13 m.p. 61-63° Beil. 6,346
MELT

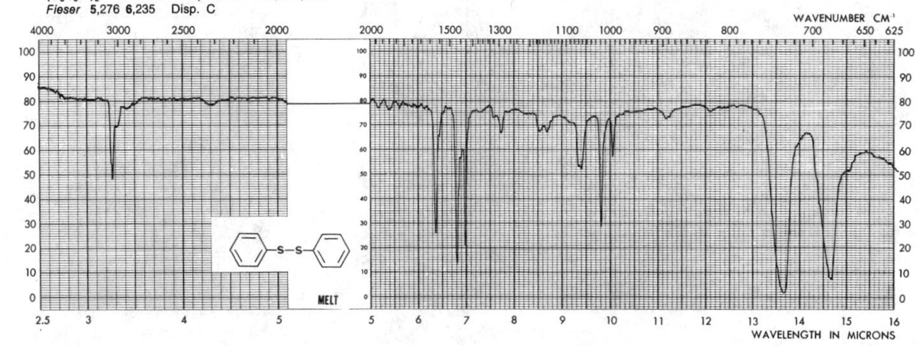

E 10,078-1 **Benzyl methyl sulfide**
$C_6H_5CH_2SCH_3$ M.W. 138.23 n_D^{20} 1.5644
NEAT

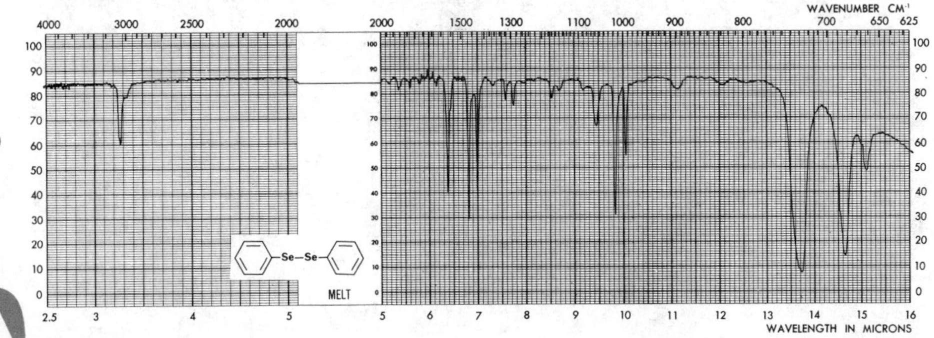

F B2920-2 **Benzyl phenyl sulfide**
$C_6H_5CH_2SC_6H_5$ M.W. 200.30 m.p. 41-43.5°
MELT

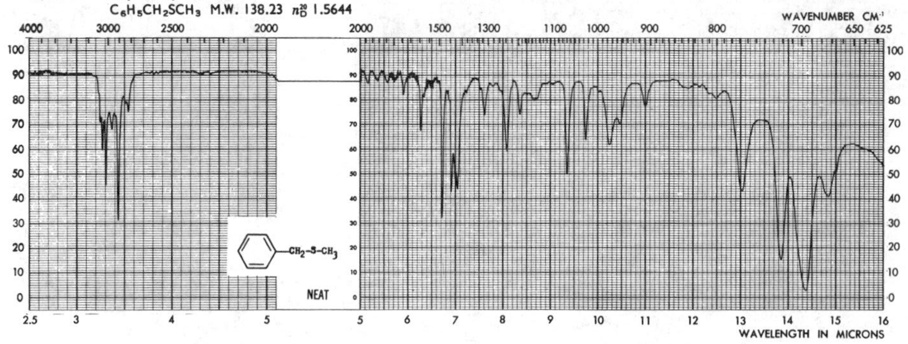

G B2180-5 **Benzyl disulfide**
$(C_6H_5CH_2)_2S_2$ M.W. 246.39
m.p. 70-72°
MELT

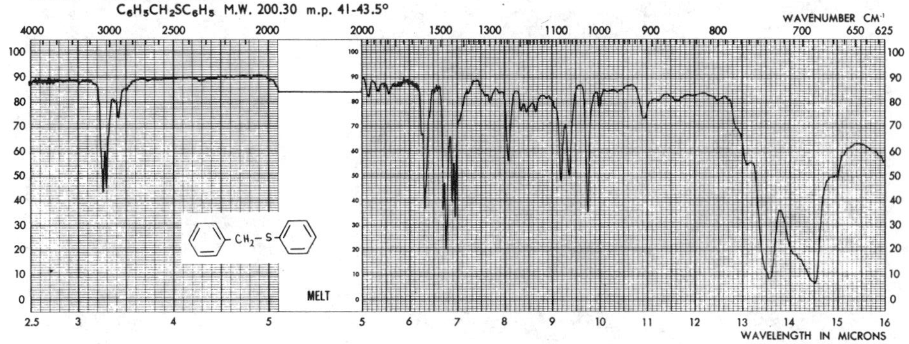

H T3980-2 **p-Tolyl disulfide**
$(CH_3C_6H_4)_2S_2$ M.W. 246.39 m.p. 45-49°
MELT

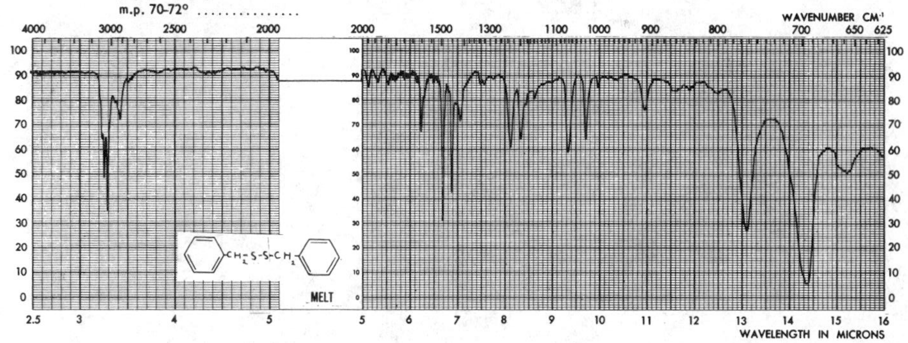

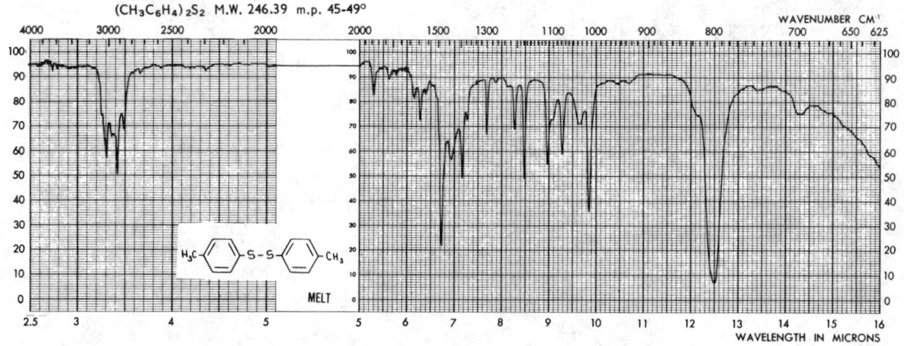

A

B7650-2 **p-Bromophenyl disulfide**
$(BrC_6H_4)_2S_2$ M.W. 376.14 m.p. 92-95°
NUJOL MULL

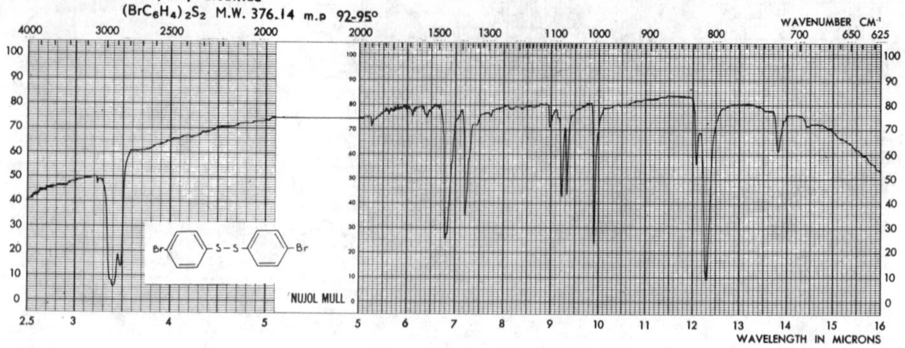

B

13,634-4 **Chloromethyl p-chlorophenyl sulfide**
$ClC_6H_4SCH_2Cl$ M.W. 193.10 n_D^{20} 1.6052
b.p. 128-129°/12 mm.
NEAT

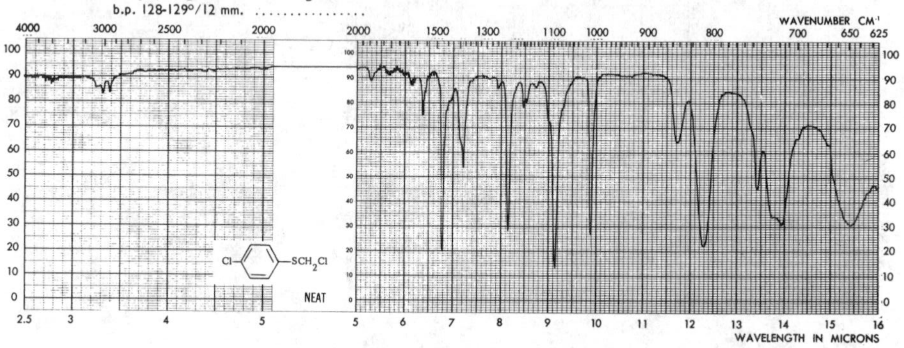

C

12,905-4 **p-Chlorophenyl difluoromethyl sulfide**
$ClC_6H_4SCHF_2$ M.W. 194.63 n_D^{20} 1.5329
b.p. 52°/1 mm.
NEAT

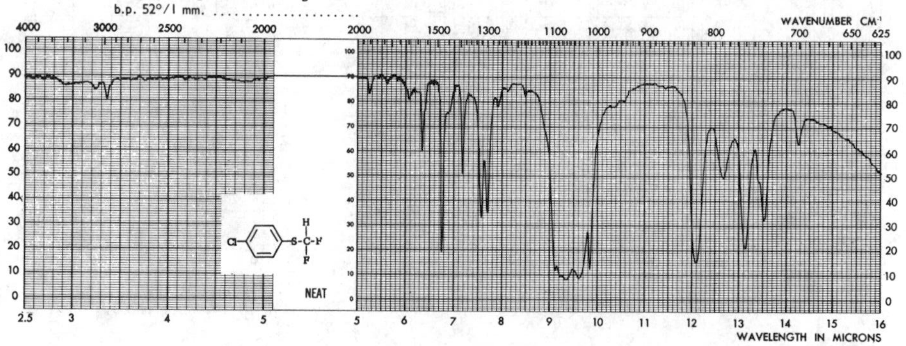

D

M5552-6 **4-(Methylmercapto)-phenol**
$CH_3SC_6H_4OH$ M.W. 140.20 m.p. 77-80°
NUJOL MULL

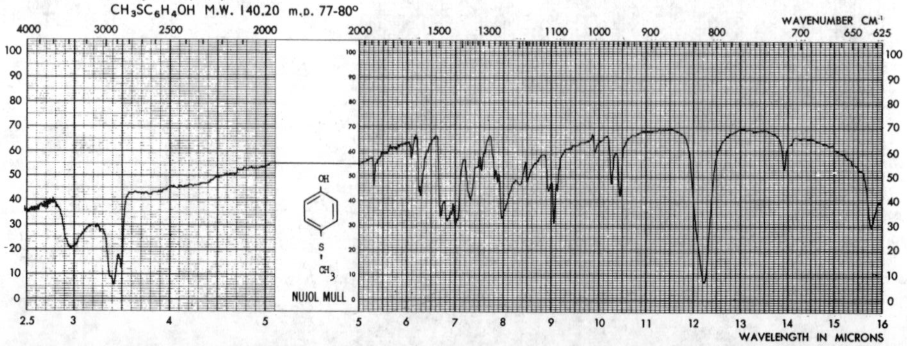

E

15,512-8 **4-(Methylthio)-m-cresol**
$CH_3SC_6H_3(CH_3)OH$ M.W. 154.23 m.p. 53-54°
MELT

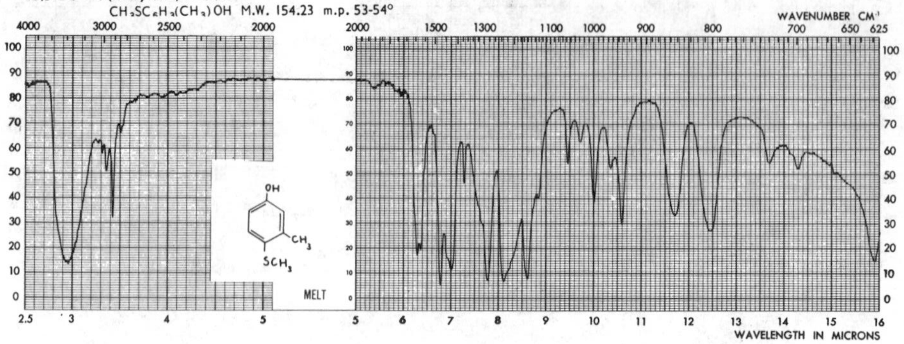

F

14,429-0 **2,4-Bis-(methylthio)-1-chlorobenzene**
$(CH_3S)_2C_6H_3Cl$ M.W. 204.74 n_D^{20} 1.6512
NEAT

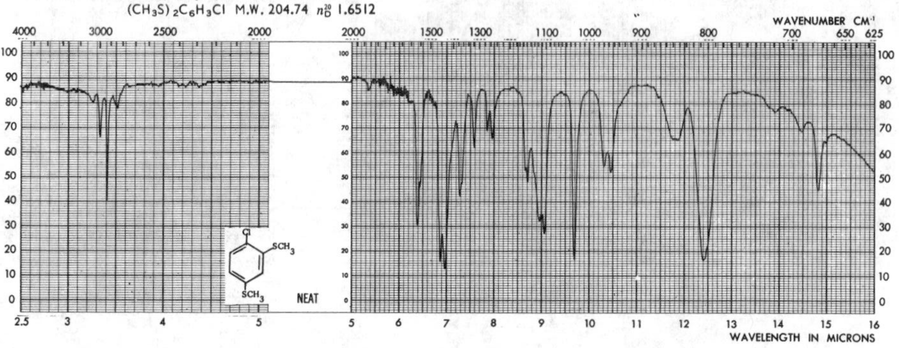

G

18,694-5
Methyl 2,4,5-trichlorophenyl sulfide, 97%
$Cl_3C_6H_2SCH_3$ FW 227.54 mp 51-55° Disp. C
MELT

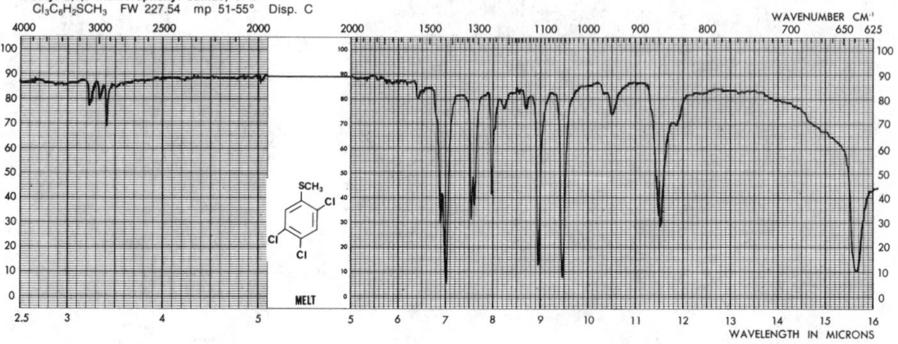

H

21,617-8
4,4'-Thiodiphenol, 99% (4-hydroxyphenyl sulfide)
$S(C_6H_4OH)_2$ FW 218.27 mp 150-155°
Beil. 6,860 Disp. C
NUJOL MULL

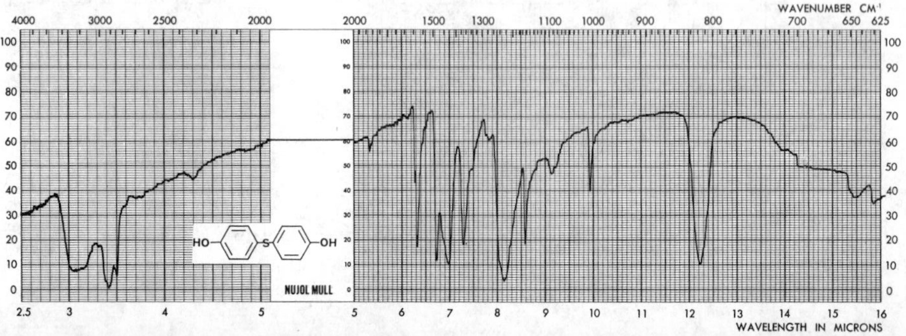

A

D11,820-6 2,4-Dihydroxyphenyl sulfide (4,4'-thiodiresorcinol)
$[(HO)_2C_6H_3]_2S$ M.W. 250.27
m.p. 171-177° ....

NUJOL MULL

B

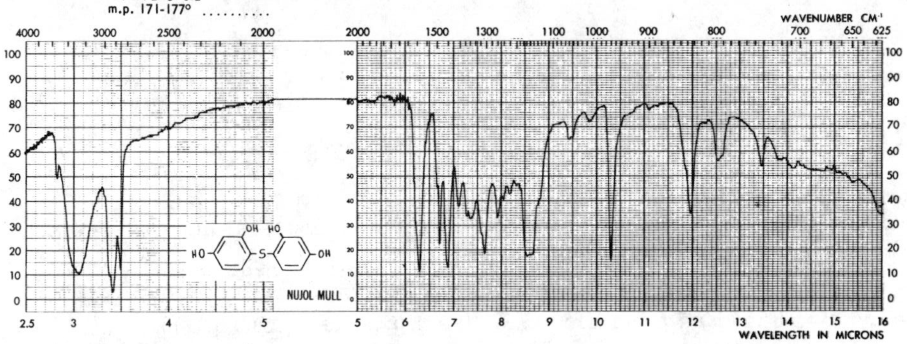

12,426-5 3-tert.-Butyl-4-hydroxy-5-methylphenyl sulfide [4,4'-thiobis-(2-tert.-butyl-6-methylphenol)], tech.
$[(CH_3)_3CC_6H_2(CH_3)OH]_2S$ M.W. 358.54 m.p. 110-115°

NUJOL MULL

C

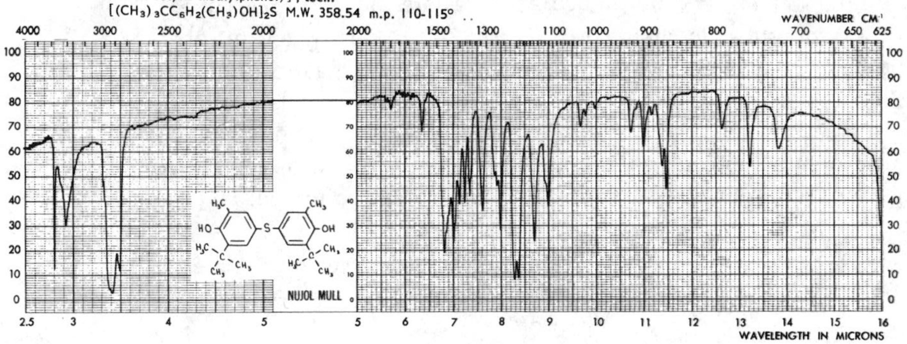

20,002-6
2,4,5-Trichlorophenyl disulfide, 98%
$(Cl_3C_6H_2)_2S_2$ FW 425.01 mp 140-144° Disp. D

NUJOL MULL

D

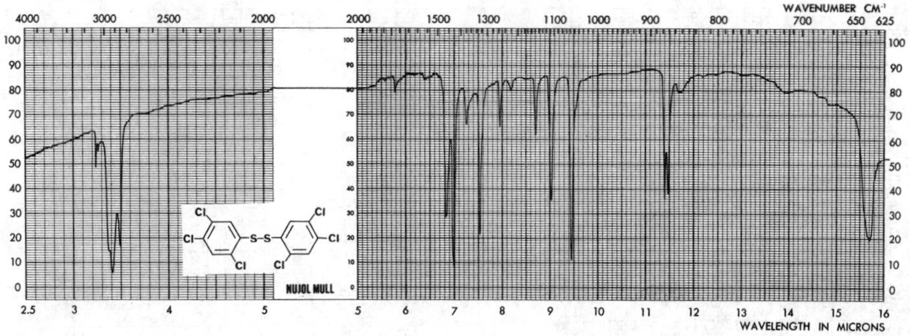

12,238-6 Thiochroman-4-ol
M.W. 166.24 m.p. 68-70°

NUJOL MULL

E

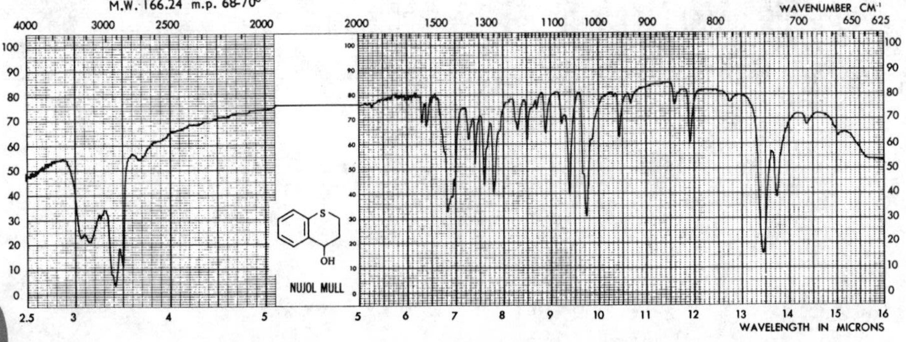

T3380-4 Thioxanthene
M.W. 198.29 m.p. 126-129°

NUJOL MULL

F

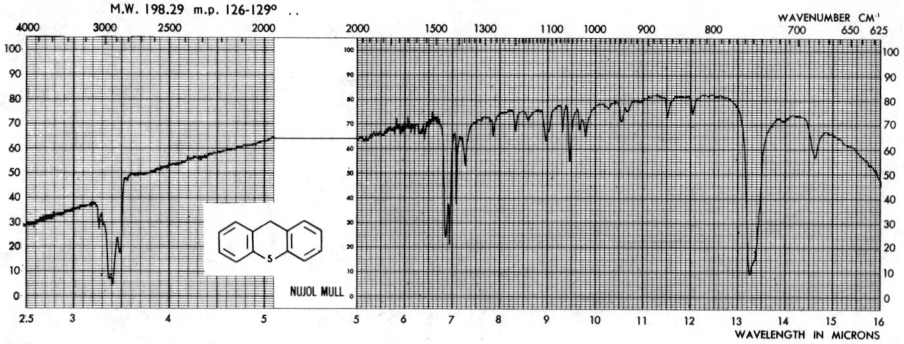

12,244-0 Thianthrene
M.W. 216.33 m.p. 154-156.5°

NUJOL MULL

G

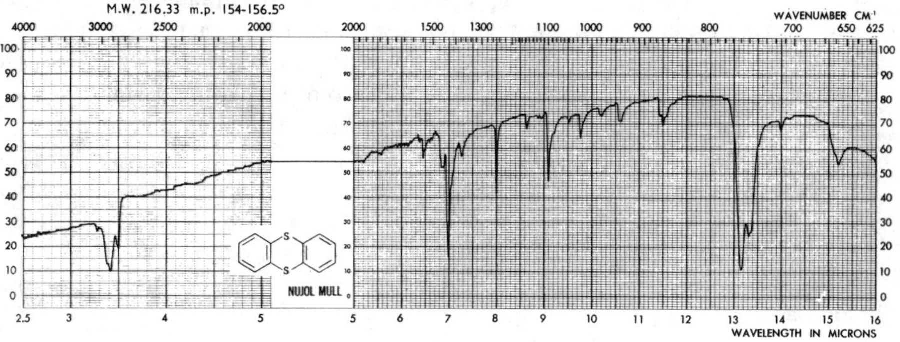

C7235-8 2-Chlorothioxanthene
M.W. 230.74 m.p. 101-102°

NUJOL MULL

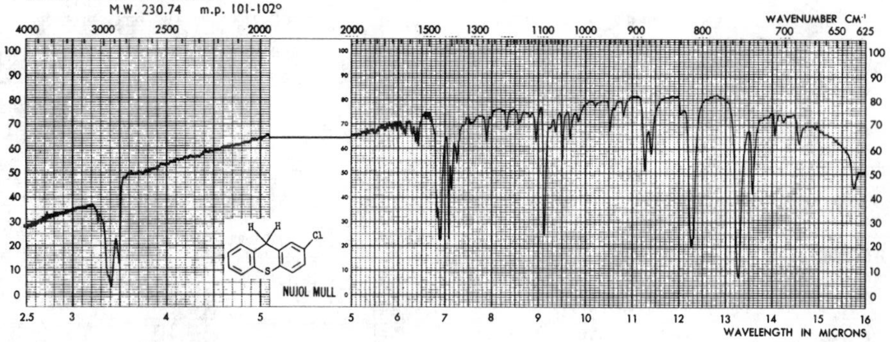

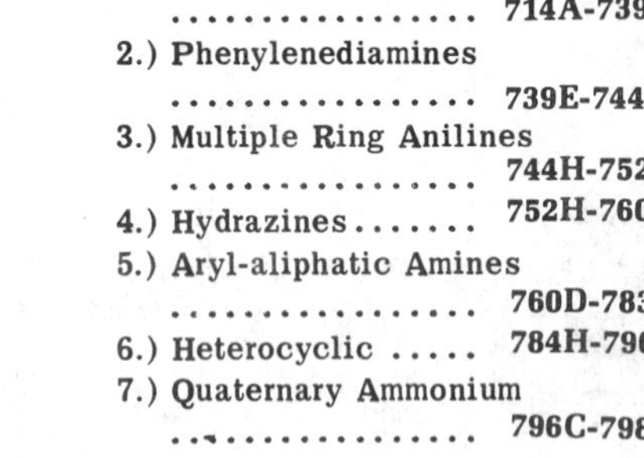

AROMATIC AMINES

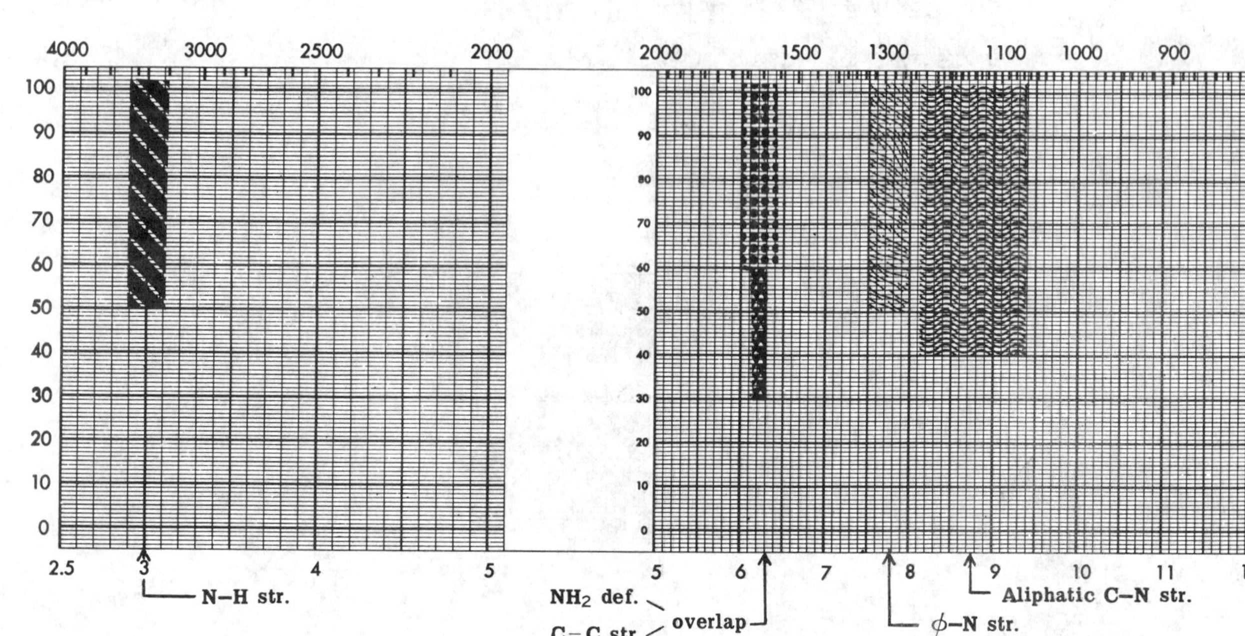

1.) Single Ring Anilines 714A-739D
2.) Phenylenediamines 739E-744G
3.) Multiple Ring Anilines 744H-752G
4.) Hydrazines....... 752H-760C
5.) Aryl-aliphatic Amines 760D-783G
6.) Heterocyclic 784H-796B
7.) Quaternary Ammonium 796C-798C

The spectra of amine salts are dispersed among the spectra of the free amines in the same manner as in the non-aromatic amine section.

The N–H stretch of the primary aromatic amine absorbs at slightly lower wavelengths than the aliphatic amine [2.9 and 2.95 μ (3450 and 3390 cm^{-1}) with a minor band at 3.1 μ (3225 cm^{-1})]. The aromatic carbon-nitrogen stretch vibration appears between 7.5 and 8 μ (1335 – 1250 cm^{-1}) and is not as intense as the corresponding oxygen-carbon stretch band at 8 μ (1250 cm^{-1}). It is interesting to note the disappearance of this band in the protonated molecules. (See spectra 714A vs. B, 724A vs. D, 725F vs. G, etc.)

In secondary amines, the N–H absorption is considerably sharper near 2.9 μ (3450 cm^{-1}) than in the aliphatic secondary amines.

The normal positions and intensities of the aromatic bands are in general not disturbed by the amine attached directly to the ring. The 6.2 μ (1615 cm^{-1}) ring band and the 6,2 μ (1615 cm^{-1}) NH_2 deformation band overlap and either may hide the other completely. The substitution bands between 11 and 15 μ (910 – 665 cm^{-1}) are embedded within the gentle sloping NH_2 wagging bands between 12 and 16 μ (835 – 625 cm^{-1}). Various breaks in the slope look like negative absorptions. [See spectra 723D at 14.3 μ (700 cm^{-1}), 724E at 14.2 μ (705 cm^{-1}), 724G at 14.2 μ (705 cm^{-1}) 726G at 15 μ (665 cm^{-1}), etc.]

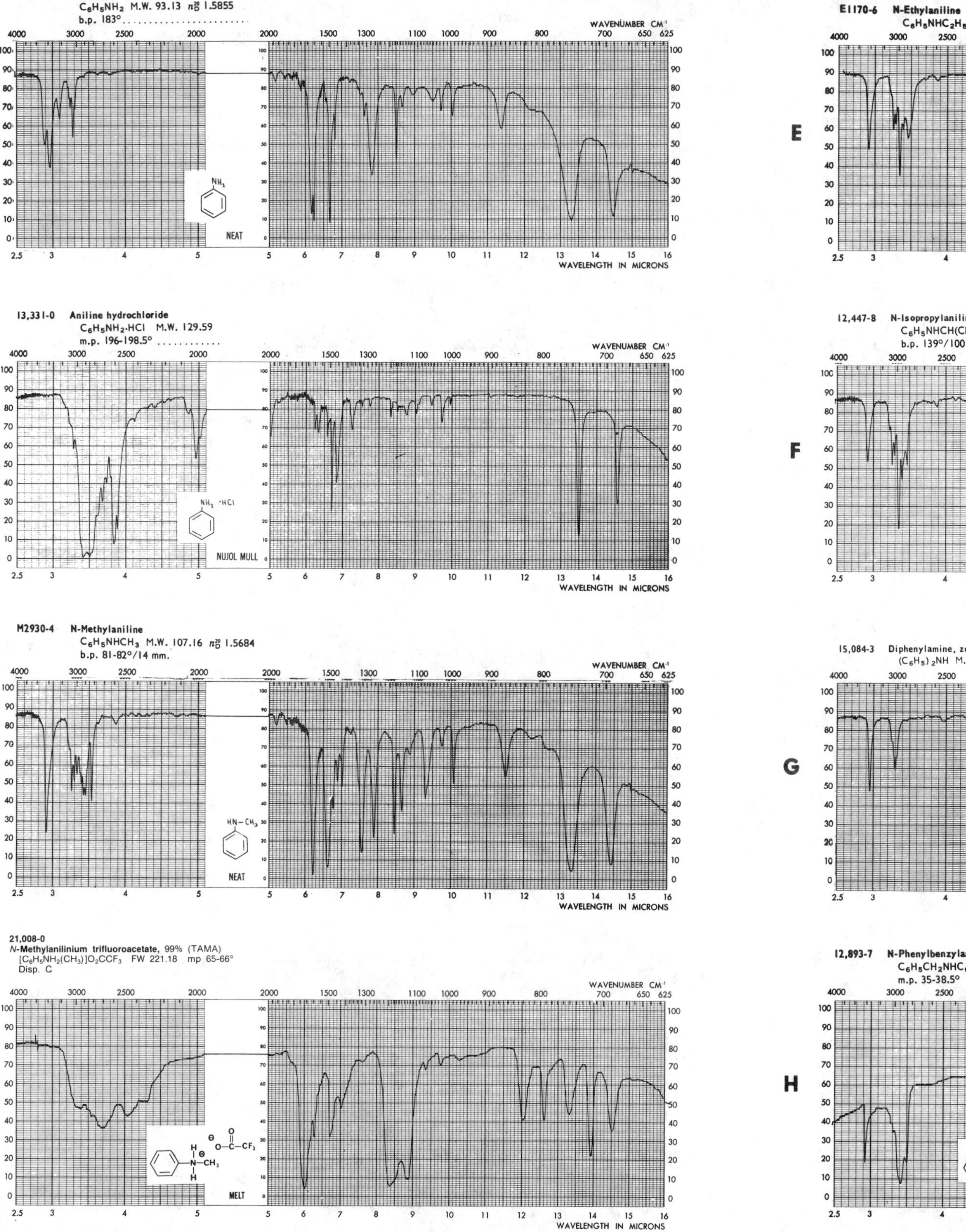

A 13,293-4 Aniline, 99.9+%
$C_6H_5NH_2$ M.W. 93.13 n_D^{20} 1.5855
b.p. 183°

NEAT

B 13,331-0 Aniline hydrochloride
$C_6H_5NH_2{\cdot}HCl$ M.W. 129.59
m.p. 196-198.5°

NUJOL MULL

C M2930-4 N-Methylaniline
$C_6H_5NHCH_3$ M.W. 107.16 n_D^{20} 1.5684
b.p. 81-82°/14 mm.

NEAT

D 21,008-0
N-Methylanilinium trifluoroacetate, 99% (TAMA)
$[C_6H_5NH_2(CH_3)]O_2CCF_3$ FW 221.18 mp 65-66°
Disp. C

MELT

E E1170-6 N-Ethylaniline
$C_6H_5NHC_2H_5$ M.W. 121.18 n_D^{20} 1.5520

NEAT

F 12,447-8 N-Isopropylaniline
$C_6H_5NHCH(CH_3)_2$ M.W. 135.21 n_D^{20} 1.5382
b.p. 139°/100 mm.

NEAT

G 15,084-3 Diphenylamine, zone refined, 99.9+%, GOLD LABEL
$(C_6H_5)_2NH$ M.W. 169.23 m.p. 52.99°

MELT

H 12,893-7 N-Phenylbenzylamine, puriss.
$C_6H_5CH_2NHC_6H_5$ M.W. 183.26
m.p. 35-38.5°

NUJOL MULL

A

D2700-4 **1,2-Dianilinoethane (N,N'-diphenylethylenediamine, Wanzlick's Reagent f aldehydes), tech.**
$C_6H_5NHCH_2CH_2NHC_6H_5$ M.W. 212.30

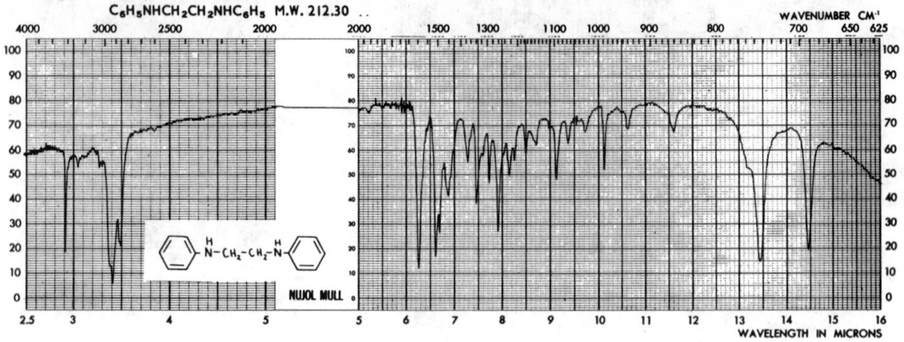

NUJOL MULL

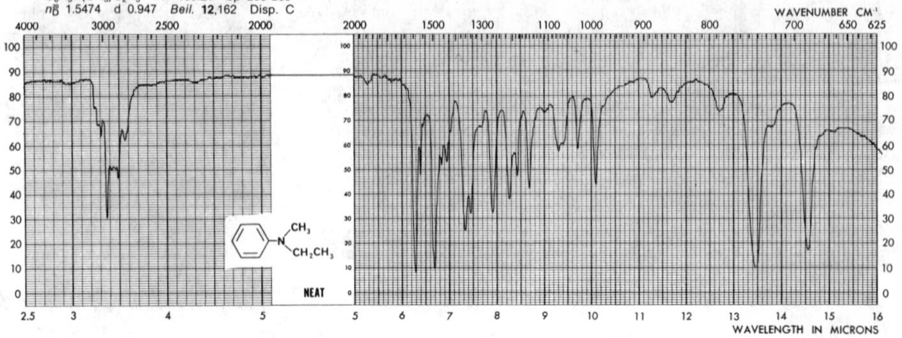

B

A2900-3 **N-Allylaniline, tech.**
$C_6H_5NHCH_2CH{:}CH_2$ M.W. 133.19
n_D^{20} 1.5630

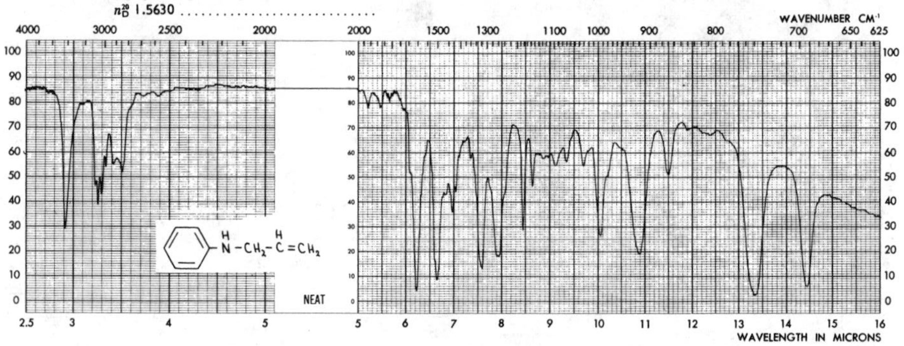

NEAT

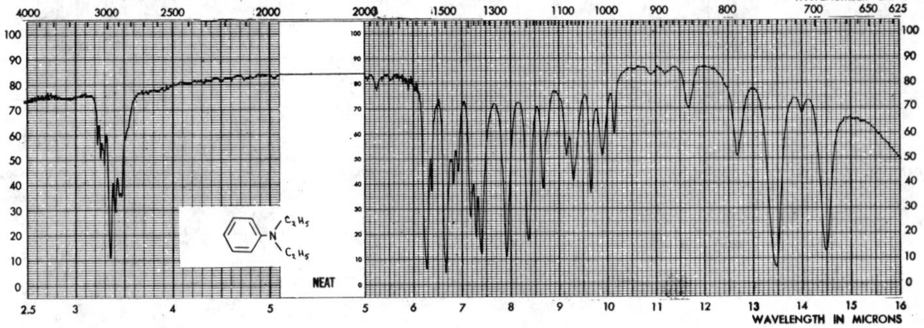

C

C8620 N-Crotylaniline

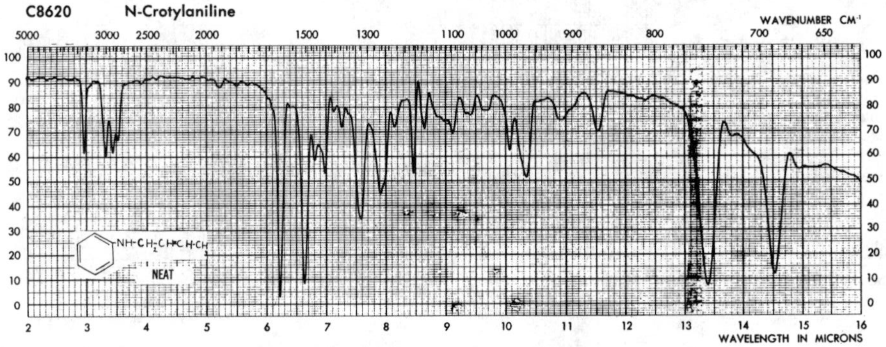

NEAT

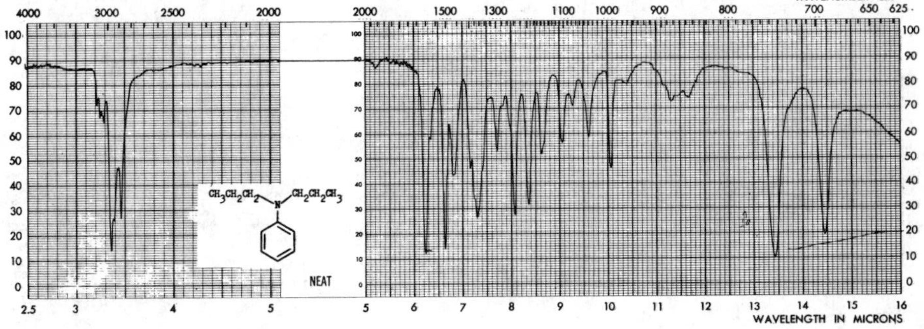

D

D14,575-0 **N,N-Dimethylaniline**
$C_6H_5N(CH_3)_2$ M.W. 121.18
n_D^{20} 1.5581 m.p. 1.5-2.5°

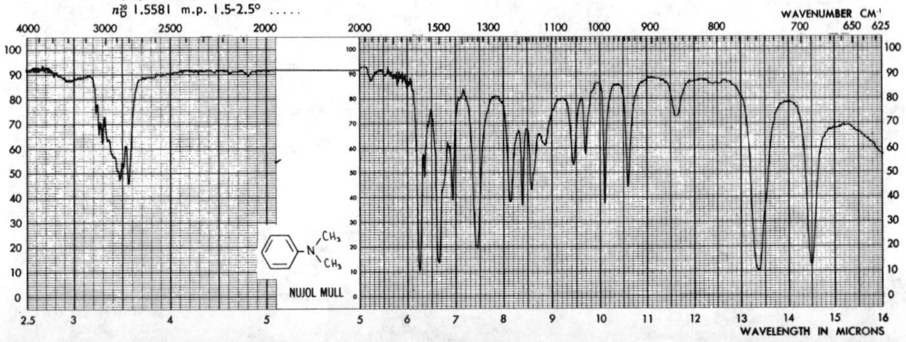

NUJOL MULL

E

21,348-9
***N*-Ethyl-*N*-methylaniline, 95+%** (*N*-methyl-*N*-ethylaniline)
$C_6H_5N(CH_3)C_2H_5$ FW 135.21 bp 203-205°
n_D^{20} 1.5474 d 0.947 *Beil.* **12**,162 Disp. C

NEAT

F

D8990-5 **N,N-Diethylaniline**
$C_6H_5N(C_2H_5)_2$ M.W. 149.24 n_D^{20} 1.5409

NEAT

G

D21,530-9 **N,N-Di-n-propylaniline**
$C_6H_5N(CH_2CH_2CH_3)_2$ M.W. 177.29
n_D^{20} 1.5271

NEAT

H

T8160-4 **Triphenylamine**
$(C_6H_5)_3N$ M.W. 245.33 m.p. 126-128°

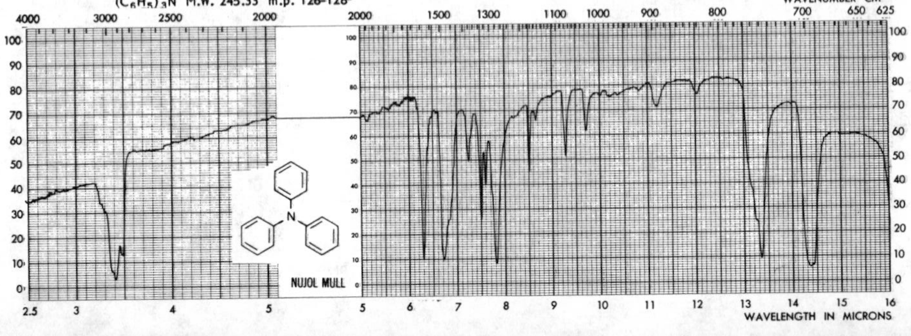

NUJOL MULL

A

10,195-8 **N,N-Dibenzylaniline** (N-phenyldibenzylamine)
$(C_6H_5CH_2)_2NC_6H_5$ M.W. 273.38 m.p. 69-71°

NUJOL MULL

B

10,254-7 **N-Benzyl-N-ethylaniline** (N-ethyl-N-phenylbenzylamine), **puriss.**
$C_6H_5CH_2N(C_2H_5)C_6H_5$ M.W. 211.31 n_D^{20} 1.5930
b.p. 309-318°

NEAT

C

A3360-4 **N-Allyl-N-methylaniline**
$C_6H_5N(CH_3)CH_2CH{:}CH_2$ M.W. 147.22
n_D^{20} 1.5561

NEAT

D

15,687-6
2-Anilinoethanol, 98% (N-phenylethanolamine)
$C_6H_5NHCH_2CH_2OH$
M.W. 137.18 b.p. 150-152°/10mm. n_D^{20} 1.5793
d 1.085 Beil. **12**,182 *IRRITANT*

NEAT

E

11,768-4 **2-(N-Ethylanilino)-ethanol**
$C_2H_5N(C_6H_5)(CH_2)_2OH$ M.W. 165.24
m.p. 34-37°

MELT

F

P2240-0 **N-Phenyldiethanolamine** [2,2'-(phenylimino)-diethanol]
$(HOCH_2CH_2)_2NC_6H_5$ M.W. 181.24
m.p. 52-55°

MELT

G

T3710-9 **o-Toluidine, puriss.**
$CH_3C_6H_4NH_2$ M.W. 107.16 n_D^{20} 1.5709
b.p. 200.2°

NEAT

H

22,275-5
2,2'-Ethylenedianiline diphosphate, 96% (α,α'-bi-o-toluidine, 2,2'-diaminobibenzyl)
$H_2NC_6H_4CH_2CH_2C_6H_4NH_2 \cdot 2H_3PO_4$ FW 310.30
mp 245° (dec.) Disp. C

NUJOL MULL

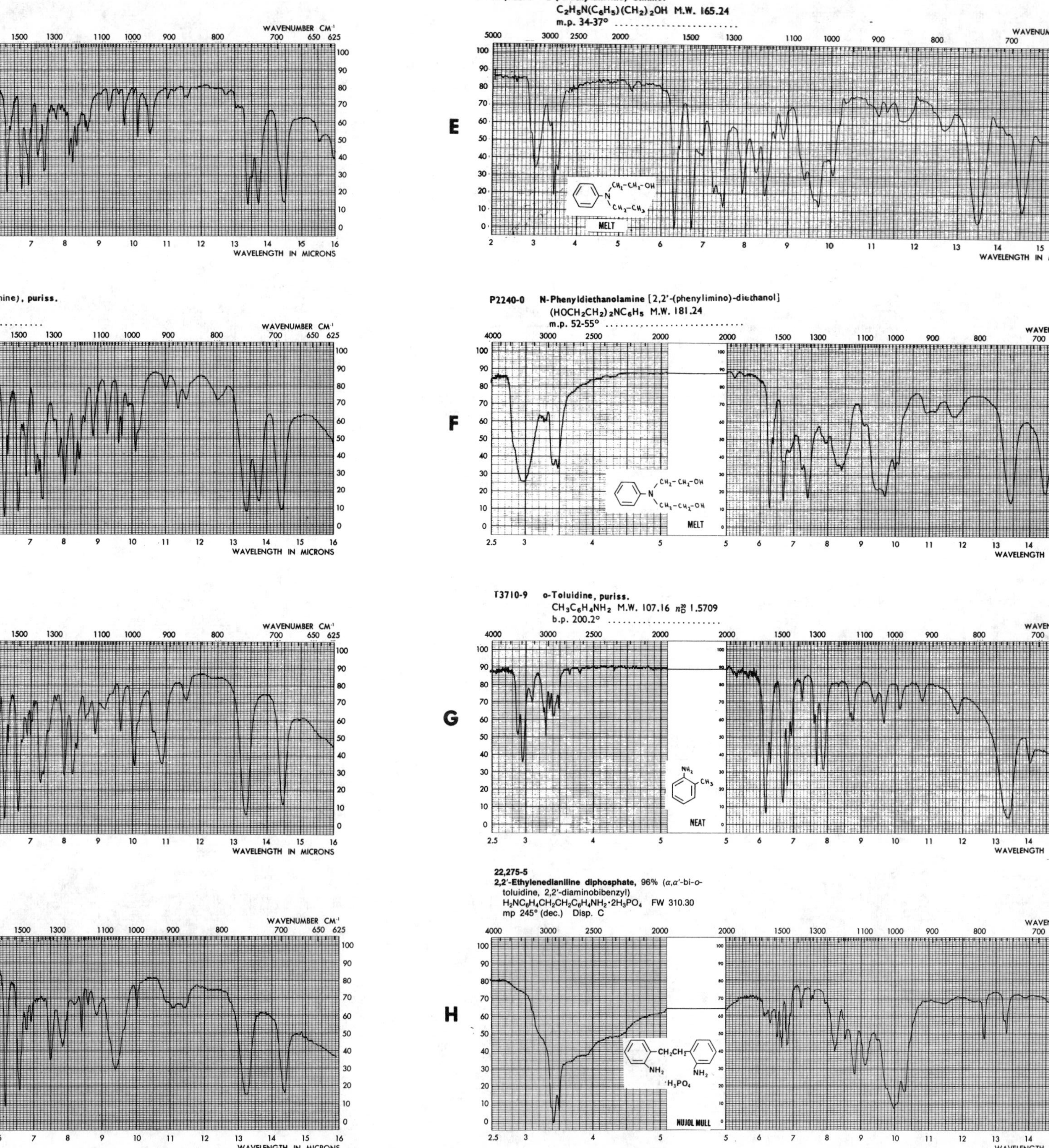

ALDRICH

A

E1180-3 **o-Ethylaniline**
$C_2H_5C_6H_4NH_2$ M.W. 121.18 n_D^{20} 1.5603
NEAT

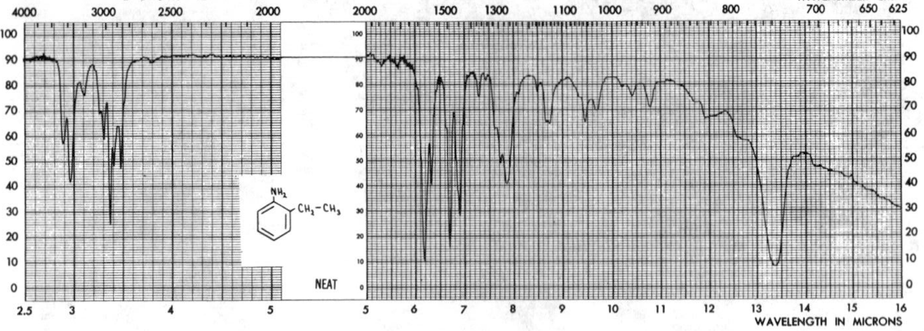

B

F340-1 **2-Fluoroaniline**
$FC_6H_4NH_2$ M.W. 111.12 n_D^{20} 1.5421
NEAT

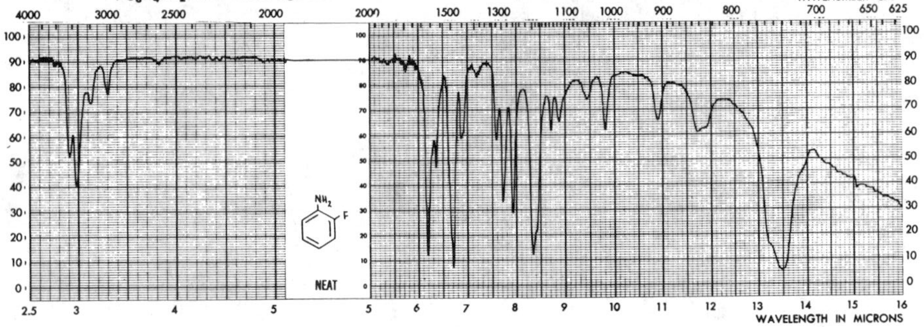

C

A4160-7 **2-Aminobenzotrifluoride** (α,α,α-trifluoro-o-toluidine)
$H_2NC_6H_4CF_3$ M.W. 161.13 n_D^{20} 1.4795
NEAT

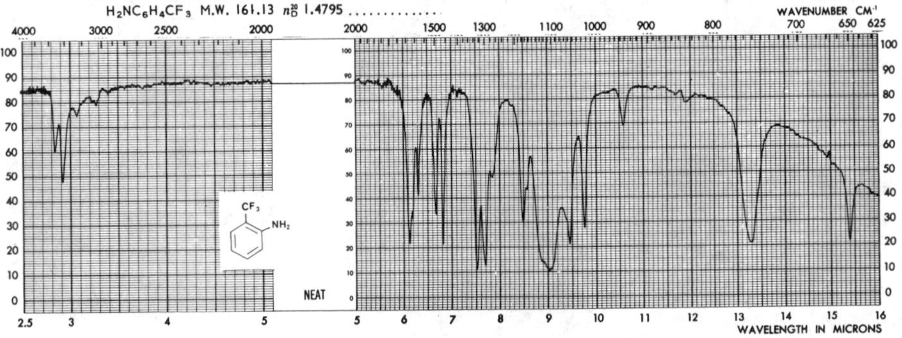

D

20,936-8
o-(2-Chloro-1,1,2-trifluoroethylthio)aniline, 98+%
$ClCHFCF_2SC_6H_4NH_2$ FW 241.66 n_D^{20} 1.5441
d 1.281 Disp. C
NEAT

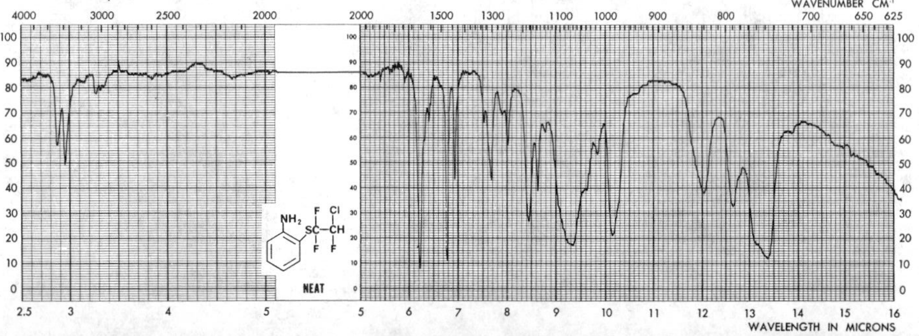

E

C2239-3 **2-Chloroaniline**
$ClC_6H_4NH_2$ M.W. 127.57 n_D^{20} 1.5877
m.p. -2 to -1°
NEAT

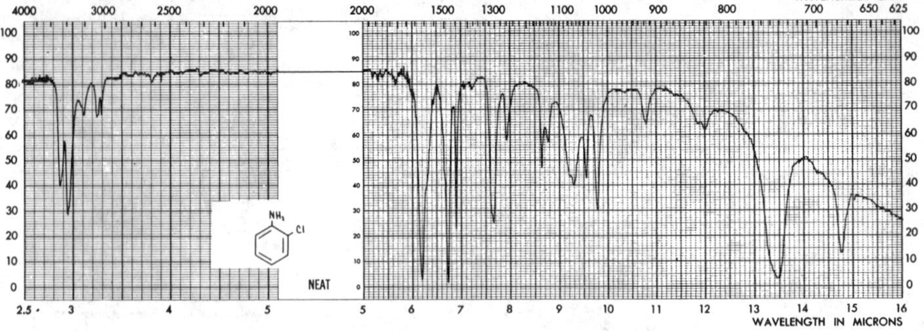

F

B5642-0 **o-Bromoaniline**
$BrC_6H_4NH_2$ M.W. 172.03
m.p. 29.5-31°
MELT

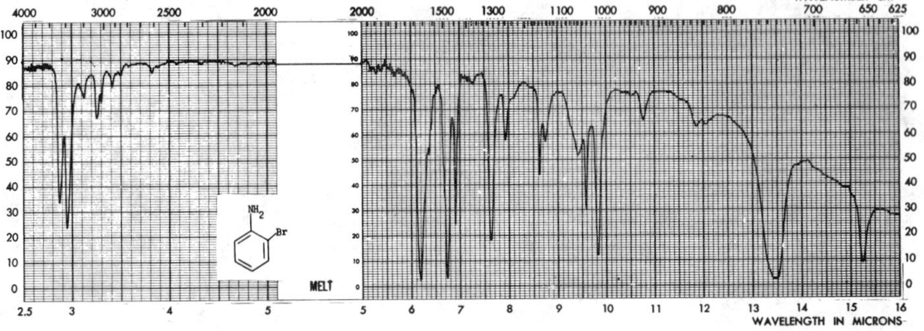

G

I-700-4 **2-Iodoaniline**
$IC_6H_4NH_2$ M.W. 219.03 m.p. 55-58°
MELT

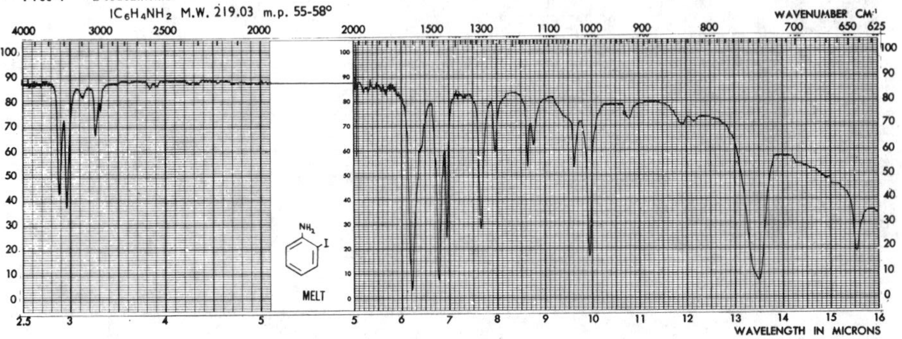

H

A8818-2 **o-Anisidine** (o-methoxyaniline), **puriss.**
$CH_3OC_6H_4NH_2$ M.W. 123.16
n_D^{20} 1.5713 m.p. 5-6°
NEAT

WAVENUMBER CM⁻¹ / WAVELENGTH IN MICRONS

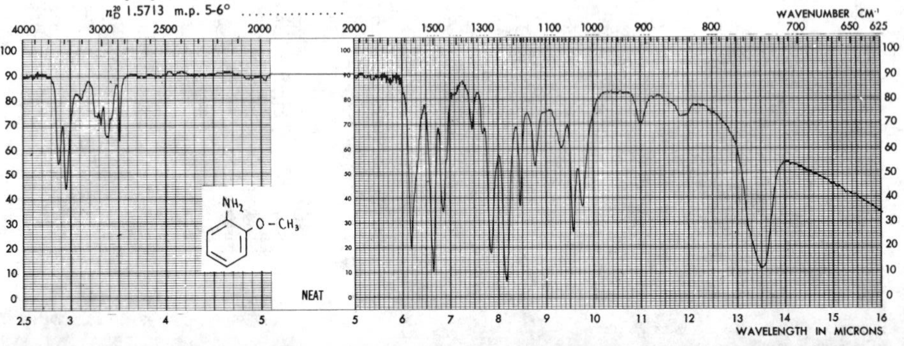

A 10,592-9 **o-Phenetidine**
$C_2H_5OC_6H_4NH_2$ M.W. 137.18 n_D^{20} 1.5560
b.p. 231-233°
NEAT

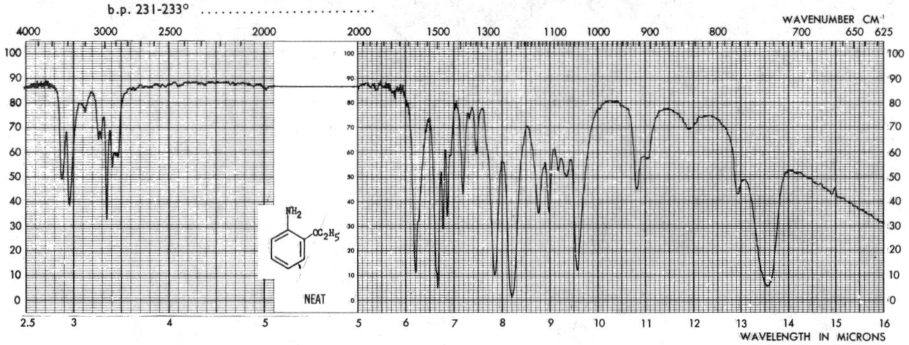

B A7130-1 **o-Aminophenol**
$H_2NC_6H_4OH$ M.W. 109.13 m.p. 171-174°
NUJOL MULL

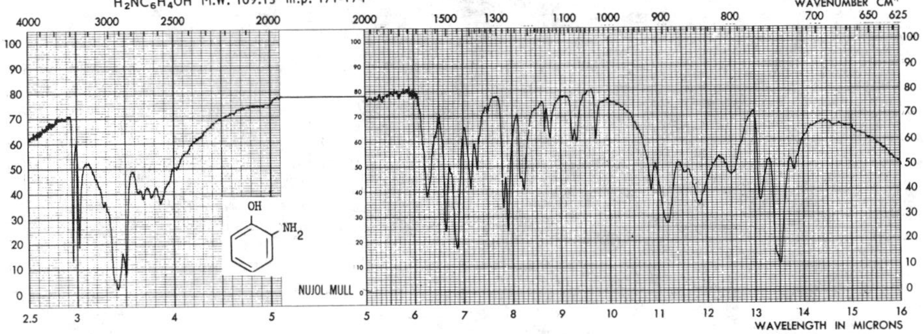

C 12,283-1 **o-Aminobenzyl alcohol**
$H_2NC_6H_4CH_2OH$ M.W. 123.16 m.p. 84-85°
NUJOL MULL

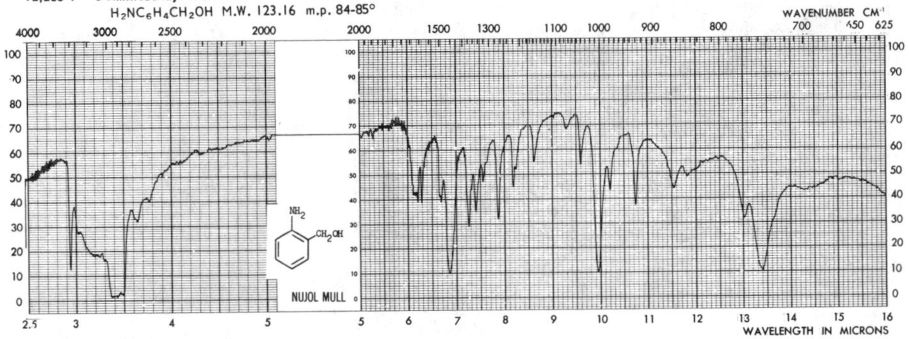

D 19,260-0
o-Aminophenethyl alcohol
$H_2NC_6H_4CH_2CH_2OH$ FW 137.18
bp 147-148°/3.500mm. n_D^{20} 1.5849 d 1.045
Beil. 13(3),1679 Disp. C
NEAT

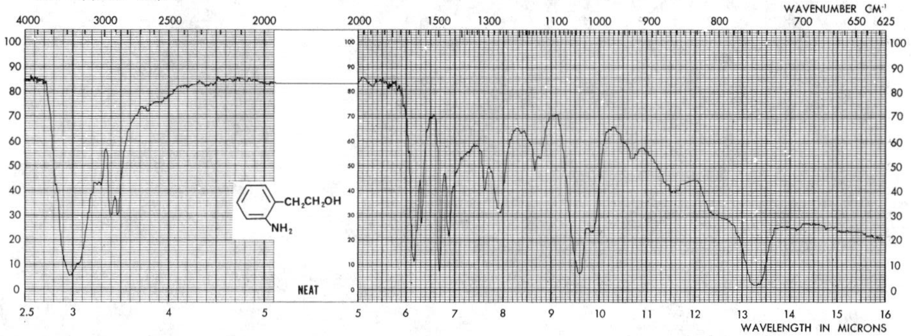

E 12,313-7 **2-Aminothiophenol** (2-aminobenzenethiol)
$H_2NC_6H_4SH$ M.W. 125.19 n_D^{20} 1.6406
NEAT

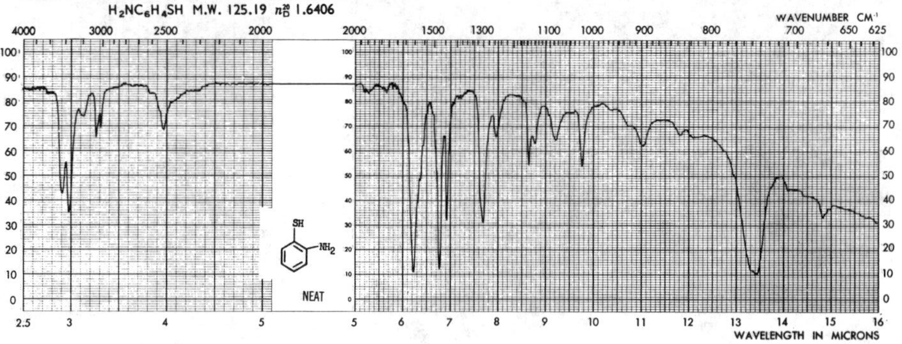

F M5420-1 **2-Methylmercaptoaniline** [o-(methylthio)-aniline]
$CH_3SC_6H_4NH_2$ M.W. 139.22 n_D^{20} 1.6239
b.p. 234° (some dec.)
NEAT

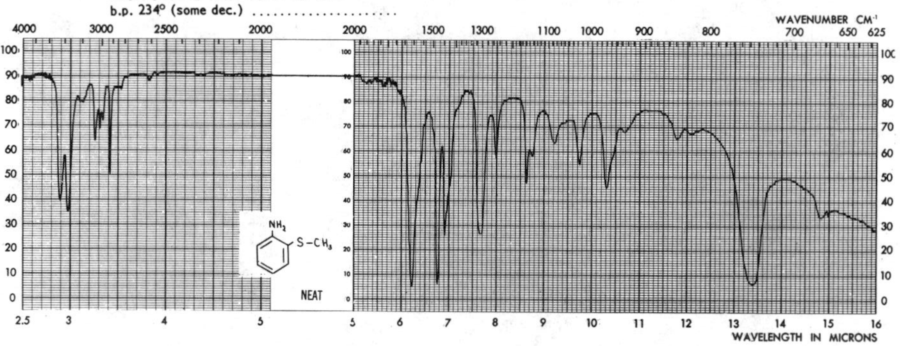

G 10,830-8 **N-Ethyl-o-toluidine**
$CH_3C_6H_4NHC_2H_5$ M.W. 135.21 n_D^{20} 1.5456
b.p. 218°
NEAT

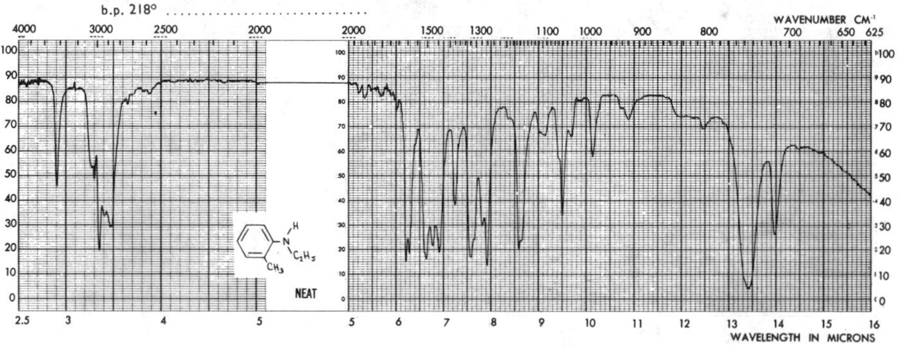

H 12,281-5 **N-Allyl-o-toluidine**
$CH_3C_6H_4NHCH_2CH:CH_2$ M.W. 147.22
b.p. 236-238°
NEAT

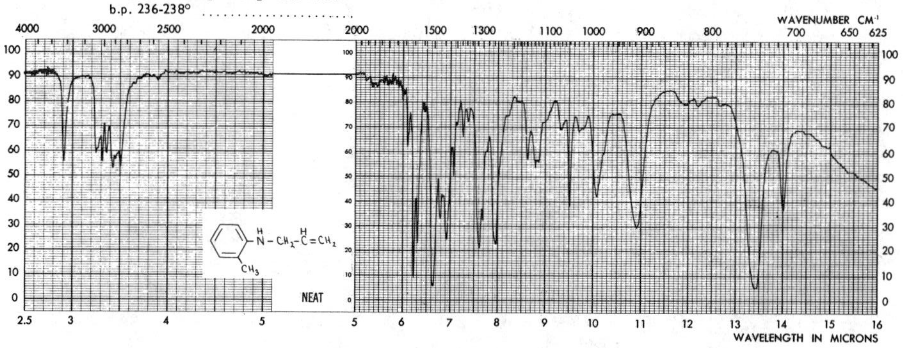

ALDRICH

19,421-2
o-Isopropenylaniline, 98+%
$H_2C{=}C(CH_3)C_6H_4NH_2$ FW 133.19 bp 95°/13mm.
n_D^{20} 1.5722 d 0.978 *Beil.* **12**(3),2793 Disp. C

13,201-2 **m-Toluidine**
$CH_3C_6H_4NH_2$ M.W. 107.16 n_D^{20} 1.5669
b.p. 203°

17,549-8
m-Ethylaniline, 98%
$C_2H_5C_6H_4NH_2$
M.W. 121.18 m.p. -8° b.p. 212° n_D^{20} 1.5556
d 0.975 Beil. **12**,1090

18,077-7
N,N-Dimethyl-m-toluidine, 97%
$CH_3C_6H_4N(CH_3)_2$
M.W. 135.21 b.p. 215° n_D^{20} 1.5506 Beil. **12**,857

F360-6 **3-Fluoroaniline**
$FC_6H_4NH_2$ M.W. 111.12 n_D^{20} 1.5436.

A4180-1 **3-Aminobenzotrifluoride** (α,α,α-trifluoro-m-toluidine)
$H_2NC_6H_4CF_3$ M.W. 161.13 n_D^{20} 1.4787

C2240-7 **3-Chloroaniline**
$ClC_6H_4NH_2$ M.W. 127.57 n_D^{25} 1.5900 m.p. -11 to -9°

18,002-5
m-Bromoaniline, 98%
$BrC_6H_4NH_2$
M.W. 172.03 m.p. 16.8° b.p. 251° n_D^{20} 1.6250
Beil. **12**,633

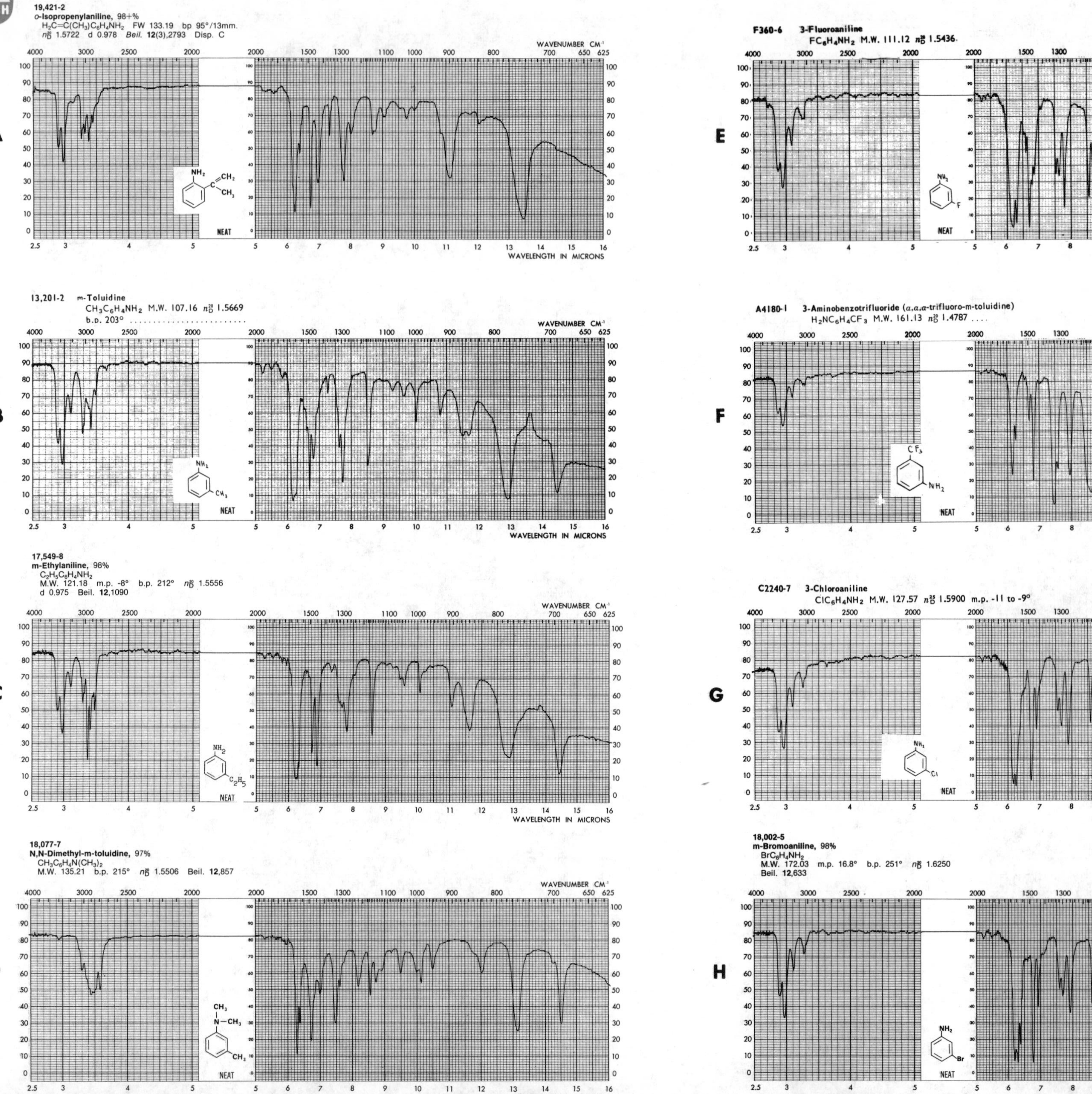

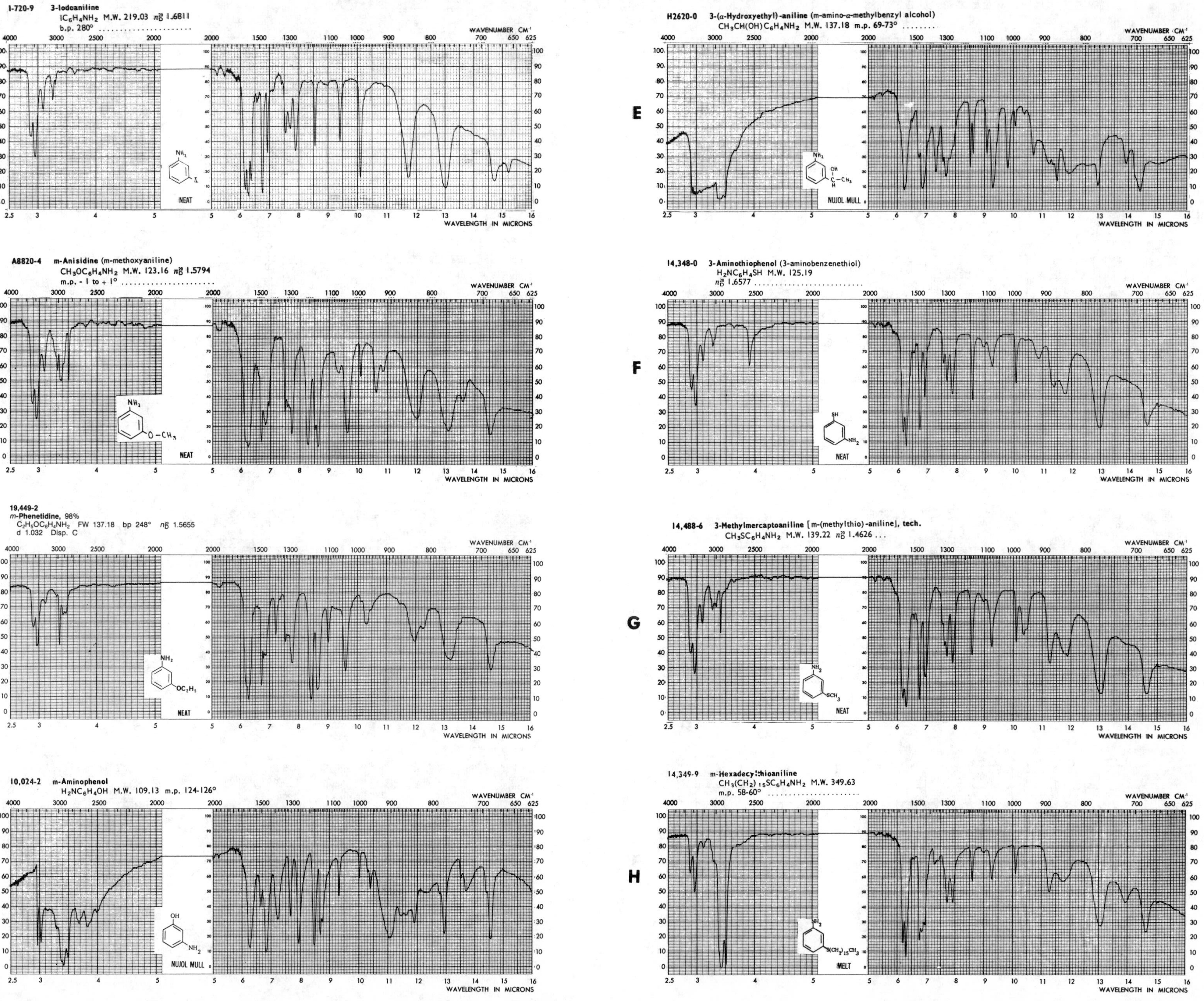
A
I-720-9 3-Iodoaniline
$IC_6H_4NH_2$ M.W. 219.03 n_D^{20} 1.6811
b.p. 280°
NEAT
B
A8820-4 m-Anisidine (m-methoxyaniline)
$CH_3OC_6H_4NH_2$ M.W. 123.16 n_D^{20} 1.5794
m.p. - 1 to + 1°
NEAT
C
19,449-2
m-Phenetidine, 98%
$C_2H_5OC_6H_4NH_2$ FW 137.18 bp 248° n_D^{20} 1.5655
d 1.032 Disp. C
NEAT
D
10,024-2 m-Aminophenol
$H_2NC_6H_4OH$ M.W. 109.13 m.p. 124-126°
NUJOL MULL
E
H2620-0 3-(α-Hydroxyethyl)-aniline (m-amino-α-methylbenzyl alcohol)
$CH_3CH(OH)C_6H_4NH_2$ M.W. 137.18 m.p. 69-73°
NUJOL MULL
F
14,348-0 3-Aminothiophenol (3-aminobenzenethiol)
$H_2NC_6H_4SH$ M.W. 125.19
n_D^{20} 1.6577
NEAT
G
14,488-6 3-Methylmercaptoaniline [m-(methylthio)-aniline], tech.
$CH_3SC_6H_4NH_2$ M.W. 139.22 n_D^{20} 1.4626
NEAT
H
14,349-9 m-Hexadecylthioaniline
$CH_3(CH_2)_{15}SC_6H_4NH_2$ M.W. 349.63
m.p. 58-60°
MELT
WAVENUMBER CM⁻¹
WAVELENGTH IN MICRONS
ALDRICH

A

10,272-5 **N-Ethyl-m-toluidine**
$CH_3C_6H_4NHC_2H_5$ M.W. 135.21 n_D^{20} 1.5451 b.p. 221°

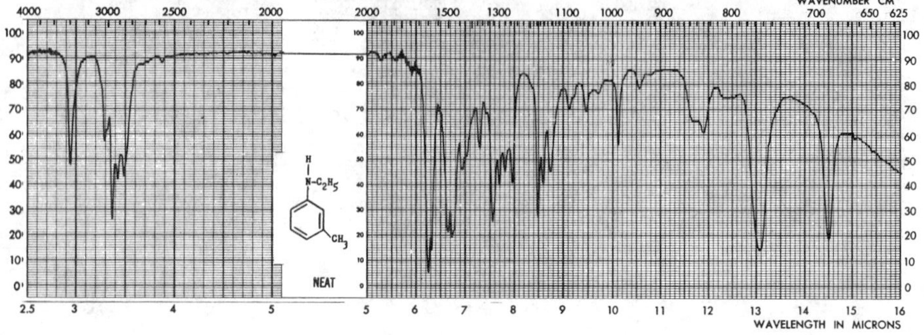

NEAT

B

10,257-1 **N,N-Diethyl-m-toluidine**
$CH_3C_6H_4N(C_2H_5)_2$ M.W. 163.26 n_D^{20} 1.5361 b.p. 231° ...

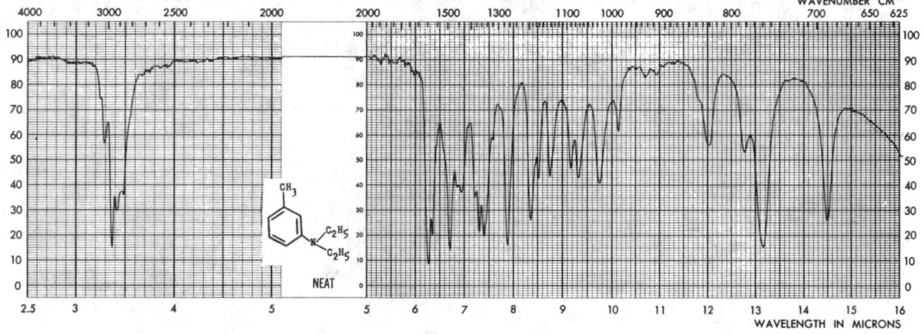

NEAT

C

C3680-7 **3-Chloro-N,N-dimethylaniline, puriss.**
$ClC_6H_4N(CH_3)_2$ M.W. 155.63 n_D^{20} 1.5746

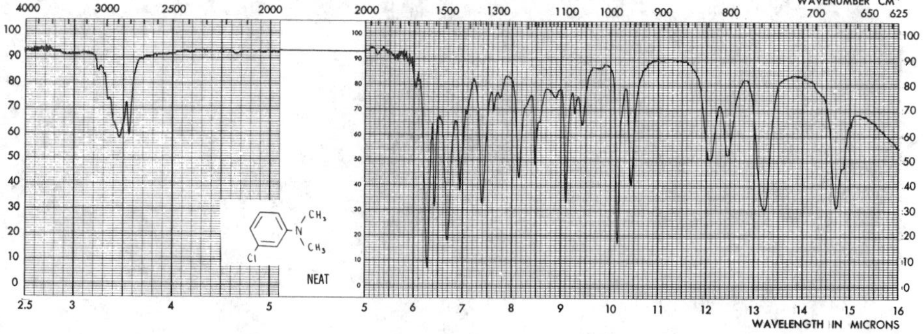

NEAT

D

13,280-2 **3-Chloro-N,N-diethylaniline**
$ClC_6H_4N(C_2H_5)_2$ M.W. 183.68 n_D^{20} 1.5575
b.p. 248-249°/740 mm. ....

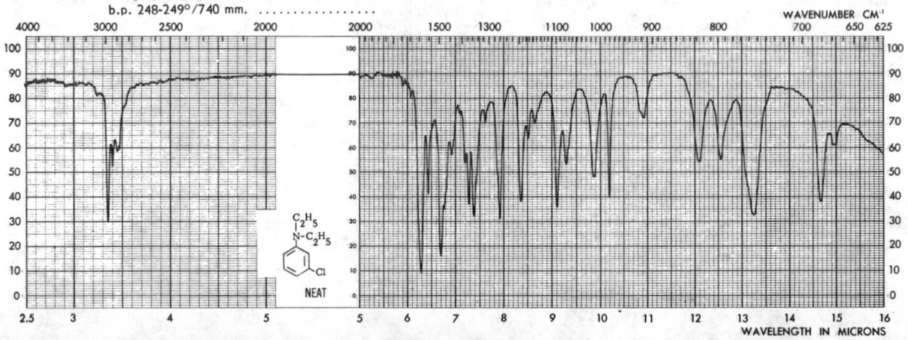

NEAT

E

D14,400-2 **3-Dimethylaminophenol, tech.**
$(CH_3)_2NC_6H_4OH$ M.W. 137.18

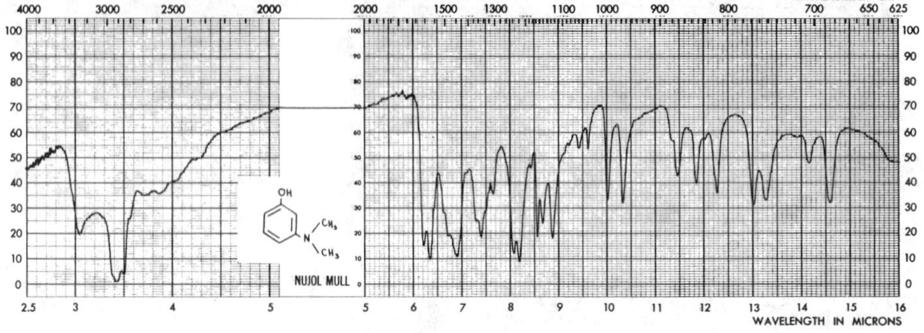

NUJOL MULL

F

10,209-1 **m-Diethylaminophenol**
$(C_2H_5)_2NC_6H_4OH$ M.W. 165.24 m.p. 71-73°

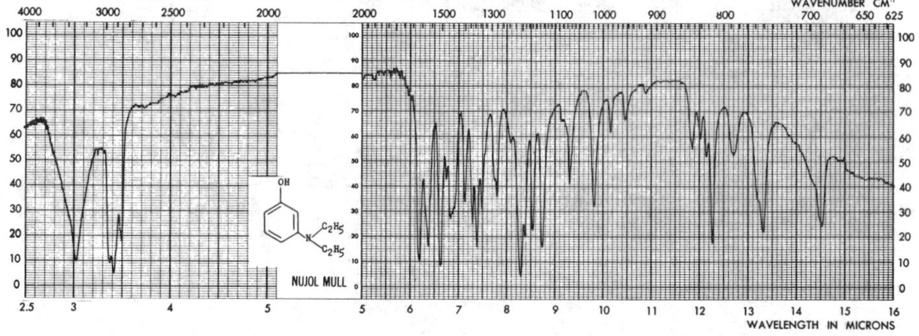

NUJOL MULL

G

12,832-5 **2-(N-Ethyl-m-toluidino)-ethanol,** 99% [N-ethyl-N-(2-hydroxyethyl)-3-toluidine]
$CH_3C_6H_4N(C_2H_5)CH_2CH_2OH$ M.W. 179.26
b.p. 114 - 115°/1mm. n_D^{20} 1.5540 *NMR* 5,48B

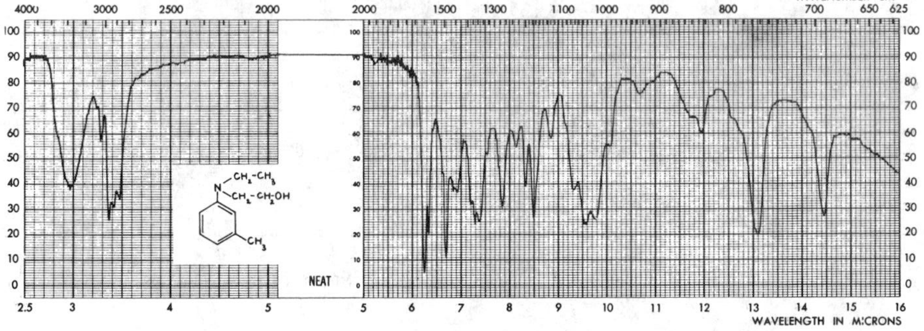

NEAT

H

T3720-6 **p-Toluidine**
$CH_3C_6H_4NH_2$ M.W. 107.16 m.p. 41-44°

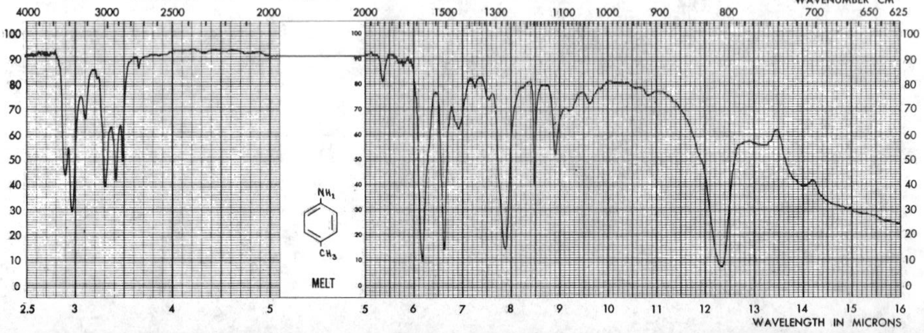

MELT

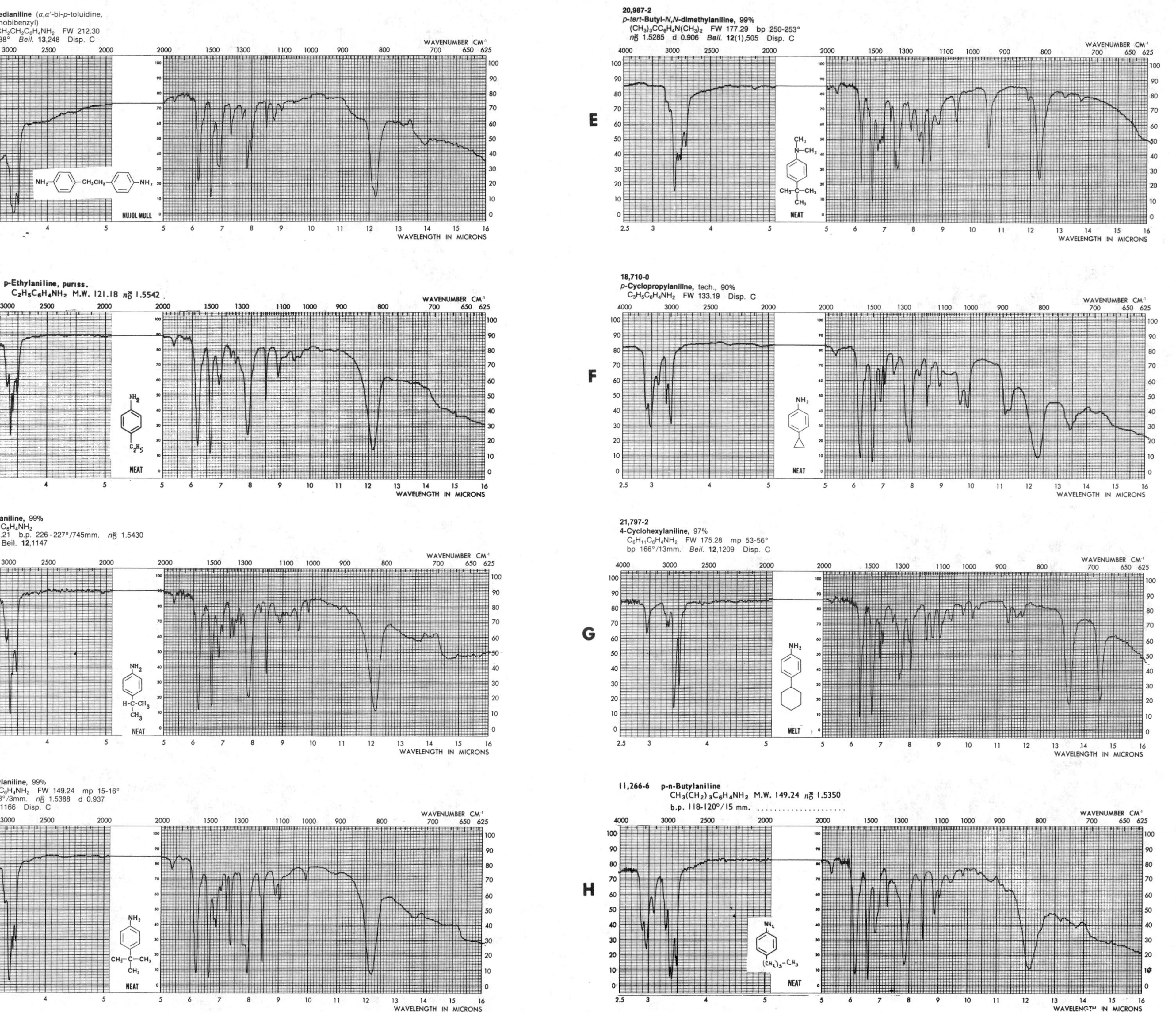

A

19,324-0
4,4'-Ethylenedianiline (α,α'-bi-*p*-toluidine, 4,4'-diaminobibenzyl)
$H_2NC_6H_4CH_2CH_2C_6H_4NH_2$ FW 212.30
mp 136-138° *Beil.* **13**,248 Disp. C
NUJOL MULL

B

E1200-1 **p-Ethylaniline, puriss.**
$C_2H_5C_6H_4NH_2$ M.W. 121.18 n_D^{20} 1.5542
NEAT

C

17,543-9
p-Isopropylaniline, 99%
$(CH_3)_2CHC_6H_4NH_2$
M.W. 135.21 b.p. 226-227°/745mm. n_D^{20} 1.5430
d 0.989 Beil. **12**,1147
NEAT

D

20,986-4
p-tert-**Butylaniline,** 99%
$(CH_3)_3CC_6H_4NH_2$ FW 149.24 mp 15-16°
bp 90-93°/3mm. n_D^{20} 1.5388 d 0.937
Beil. **12**,1166 Disp. C
NEAT

E

20,987-2
p-tert-**Butyl-*N,N*-dimethylaniline,** 99%
$(CH_3)_3CC_6H_4N(CH_3)_2$ FW 177.29 bp 250-253°
n_D^{20} 1.5285 d 0.906 *Beil.* **12**(1),505 Disp. C
NEAT

F

18,710-0
p-**Cyclopropylaniline,** tech., 90%
$C_3H_5C_6H_4NH_2$ FW 133.19 Disp. C
NEAT

G

21,797-2
4-Cyclohexylaniline, 97%
$C_6H_{11}C_6H_4NH_2$ FW 175.28 mp 53-56°
bp 166°/13mm. *Beil.* **12**,1209 Disp. C
MELT

H

11,266-6 **p-n-Butylaniline**
$CH_3(CH_2)_3C_6H_4NH_2$ M.W. 149.24 n_D^{20} 1.5350
b.p. 118-120°/15 mm.
NEAT

A

13,245-4 **4,4'-Methylenedianiline**
$CH_2(C_6H_4NH_2)_2$ M.W. 198.27
m.p. 91-93°

NUJOL MULL

B

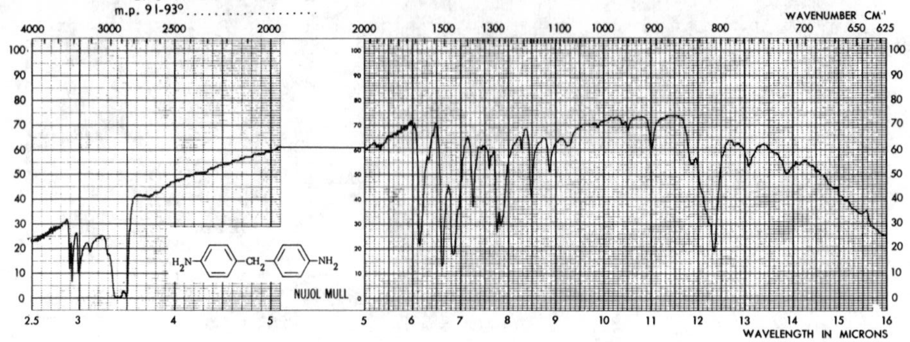

14,730-3 **Benzidine dihydrochloride**
$(-C_6H_4-4-NH_2)_2 \cdot 2HCl$ M.W. 257.16
m.p. >300°

NUJOL MULL

C

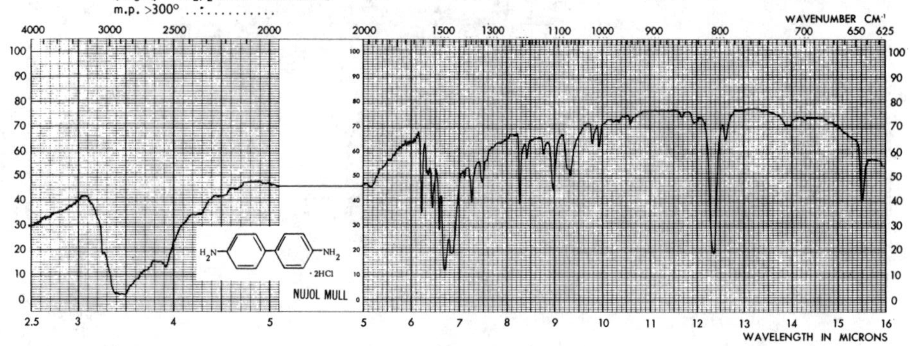

D2520-6 **4,4'-Diaminostilbene (4,4'-vinylenedianiline) dihydrochloride**
$H_2NC_6H_4CH{:}CHC_6H_4NH_2 \cdot 2HCl$ M.W. 283.20 m.p. > 320°

NUJOL MULL

D

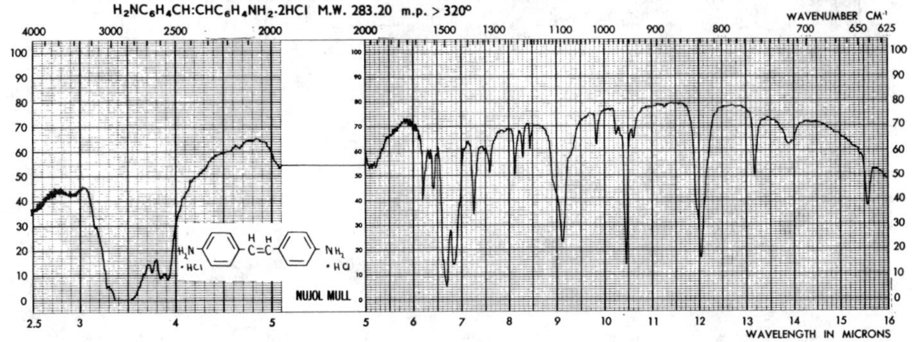

F380-0 **4-Fluoroaniline**
$FC_6H_4NH_2$ M.W. 111.12
n_D^{20} 1.5379

NEAT

E

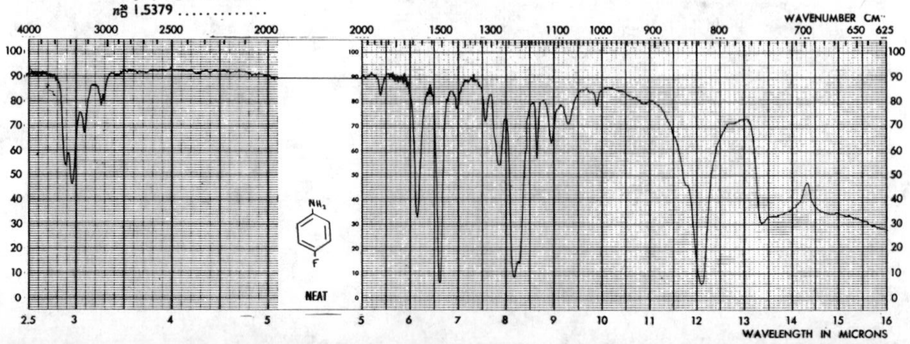

22,306-9
4-Fluoro-*N*-methylaniline, 98%
$FC_6H_4NHCH_3$ FW 125.15 bp 79°/11mm.
n_D^{20} 1.5325 d 1.040 Disp. C

NEAT

F

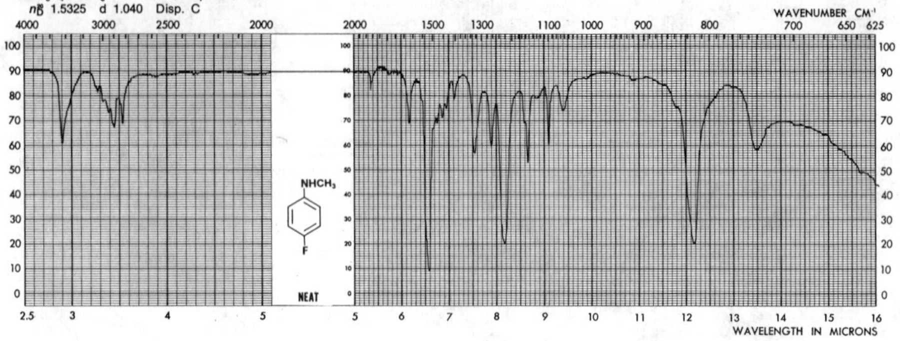

17,287-1
4-Aminobenzotrifluoride, 97% (α,α,α-trifluoro-p-toluidine)
$H_2NC_6H_4CF_3$
M.W. 161.13 m.p. 8-10° b.p. 90-91°/20mm.

NEAT

G

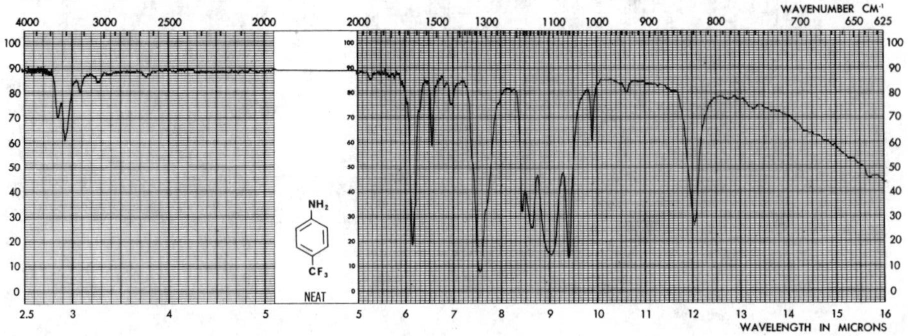

15,145-9 **4-Chloroaniline, 99+%**
$ClC_6H_4NH_2$ M.W. 127.57 m.p. 69-72°

MELT

H

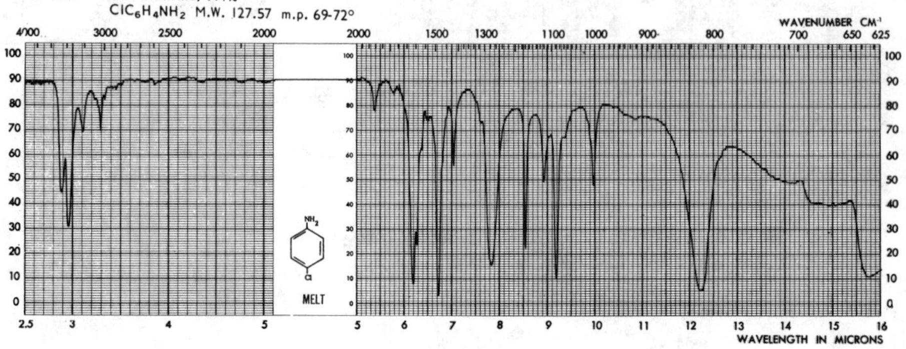

21,035-8
4-Chloro-*N*-methylaniline, 94%
$ClC_6H_4NHCH_3$ FW 141.60 bp 239° n_D^{20} 1.5893
d 1.169 *Beil.* **12**,609 Disp. C

NEAT

WAVENUMBER CM⁻¹ / WAVELENGTH IN MICRONS

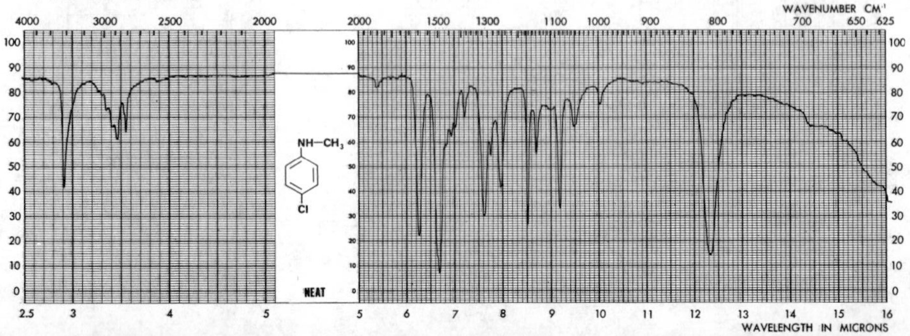

A

10,090-0 p-Bromoaniline
$BrC_6H_4NH_2$ M.W. 172.03 m.p. 62-64°

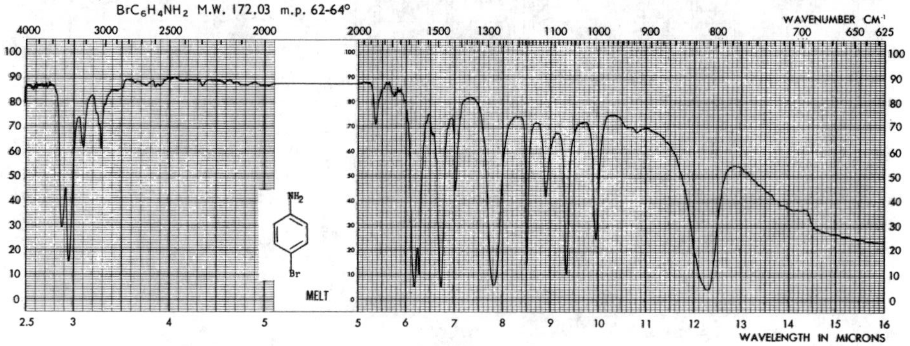

MELT

B

14,129-1 p-Bromoaniline hydrochloride
$BrC_6H_4NH_2 \cdot HCl$ M.W. 208.49
m.p. > 220° (sublimes) ....

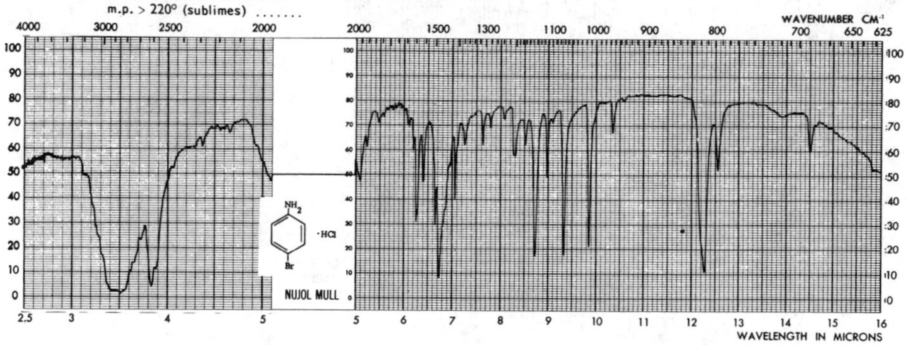

NUJOL MULL

C

14,130-5 p-Bromoaniline hydrobromide
$BrC_6H_4NH_2 \cdot HBr$ M.W. 252.95
m.p. 230° (dec.) ....

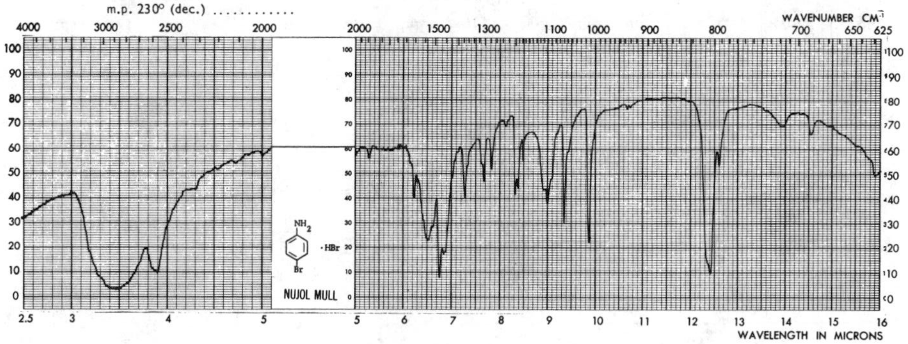

NUJOL MULL

D

12,936-4 4-Iodoaniline
$IC_6H_4NH_2$ M.W. 219.03
m.p. 63-65° ....

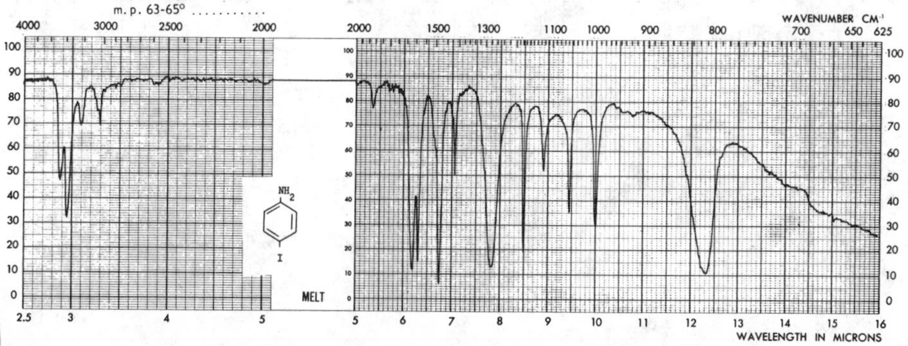

MELT

E

A8825-5 p-Anisidine (p-methoxyaniline)
$CH_3OC_6H_4NH_2$ M.W. 123.16 m.p. 57-60°

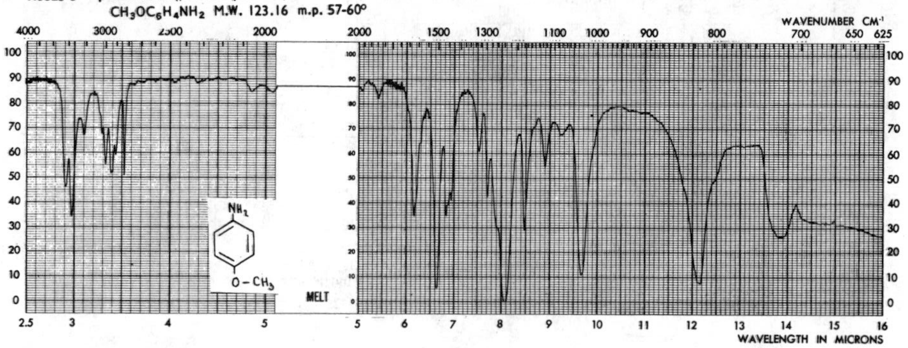

MELT

F

18,003-3
N-Methyl-p-anisidine, 98%
$CH_3OC_6H_4NHCH_3$
M.W. 137.18 m.p. 34-36° b.p. 135-136°/19mm.
Beil. 13,442

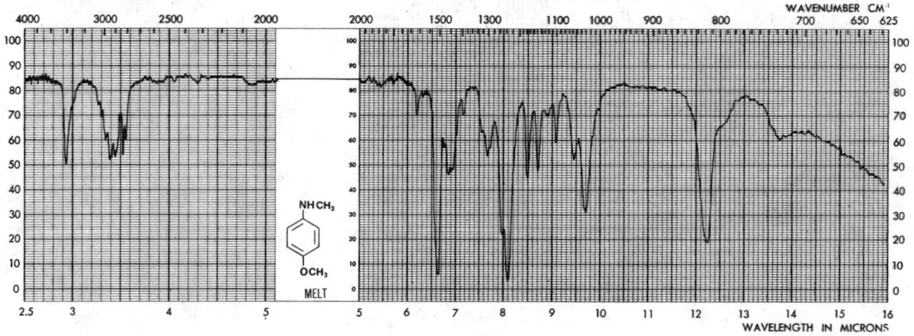

MELT

G

P1481-5 p-Phenetidine
$C_2H_5OC_6H_4NH_2$ M.W. 137.18 n_D^{20} 1.5609

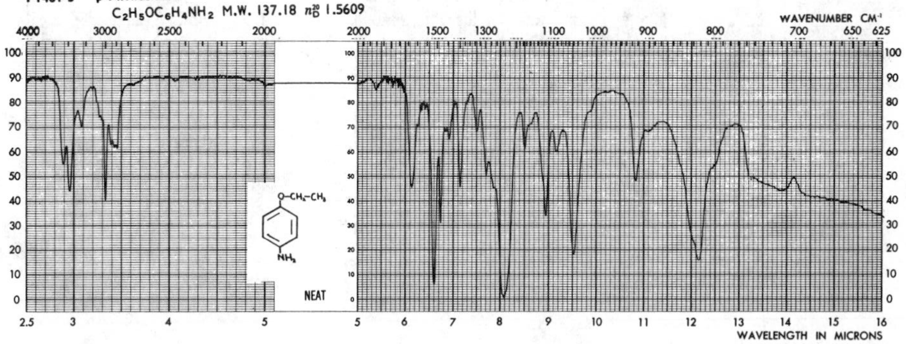

NEAT

H

22,210-0
4-Hexyloxyaniline, 99%
$CH_3(CH_2)_5OC_6H_4NH_2$ FW 193.29 mp 43-45°
bp 155-158°/5mm. *Beil.* 13(3),998 Disp. C

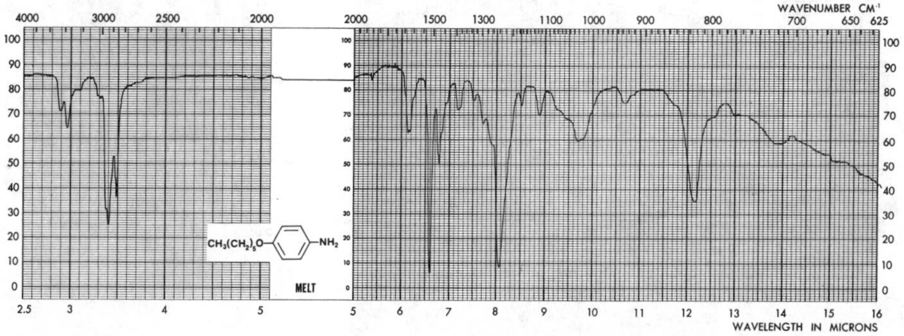

MELT

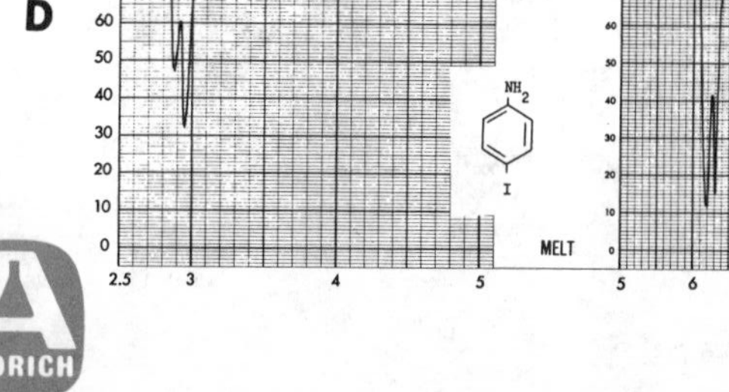

ALDRICH

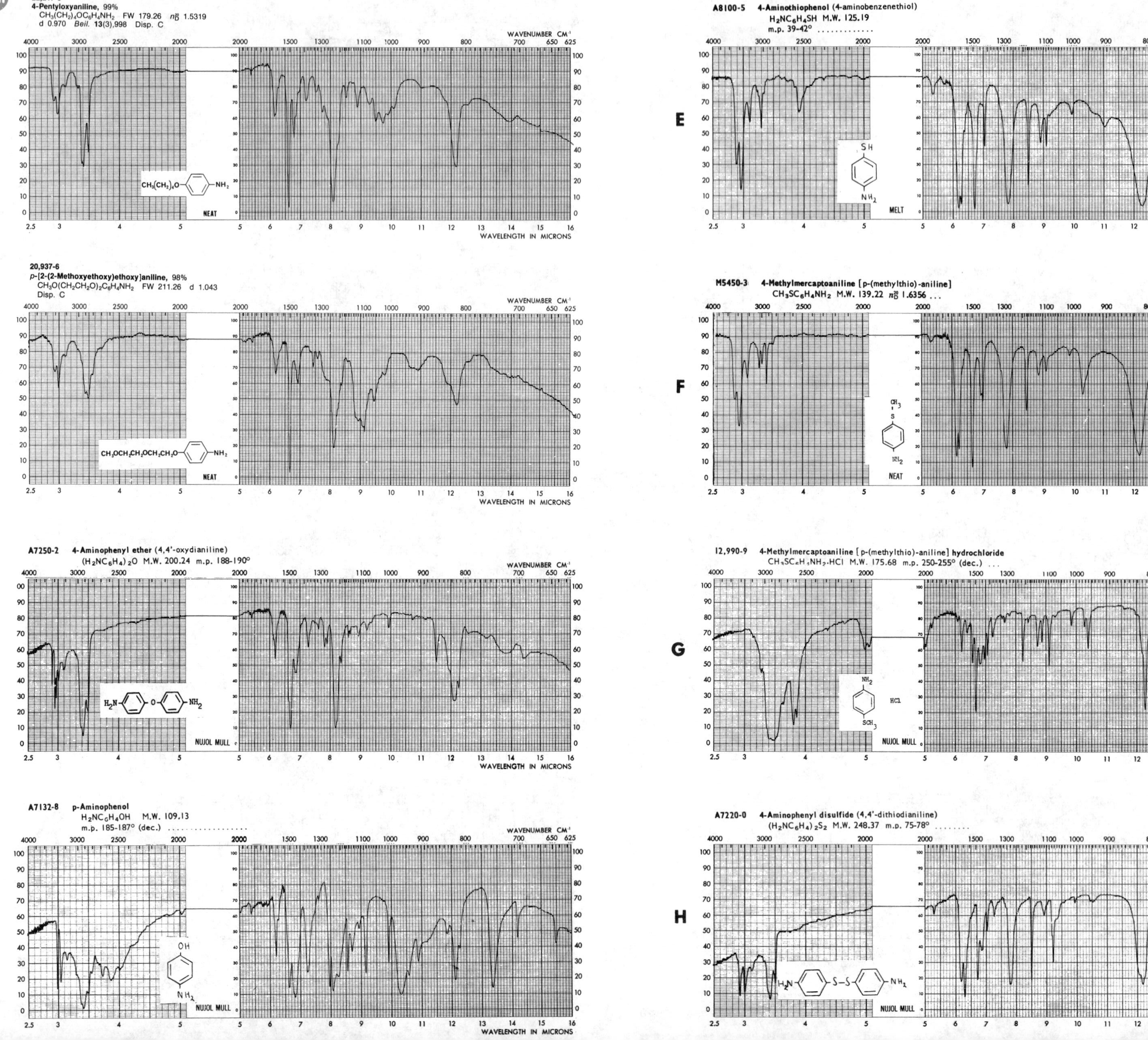
A
22,217-8
4-Pentyloxyaniline, 99%
CH₃(CH₂)₄OC₆H₄NH₂ FW 179.26 n²⁰D 1.5319
d 0.970 Beil. 13(3),998 Disp. C
NEAT
B
20,937-6
p-[2-(2-Methoxyethoxy)ethoxy]aniline, 98%
CH₃O(CH₂CH₂O)₂C₆H₄NH₂ FW 211.26 d 1.043
Disp. C
NEAT
C
A7250-2 4-Aminophenyl ether (4,4'-oxydianiline)
(H₂NC₆H₄)₂O M.W. 200.24 m.p. 188-190°
NUJOL MULL
D
A7132-8 p-Aminophenol
H₂NC₆H₄OH M.W. 109.13
m.p. 185-187° (dec.)
NUJOL MULL
E
A8100-5 4-Aminothiophenol (4-aminobenzenethiol)
H₂NC₆H₄SH M.W. 125.19
m.p. 39-42°
MELT
F
M5450-3 4-Methylmercaptoaniline [p-(methylthio)-aniline]
CH₃SC₆H₄NH₂ M.W. 139.22 n²⁰D 1.6356
NEAT
G
12,990-9 4-Methylmercaptoaniline [p-(methylthio)-aniline] hydrochloride
CH₃SC₆H₄NH₂·HCl M.W. 175.68 m.p. 250-255° (dec.)
HCl
NUJOL MULL
H
A7220-0 4-Aminophenyl disulfide (4,4'-dithiodianiline)
(H₂NC₆H₄)₂S₂ M.W. 248.37 m.p. 75-78°
NUJOL MULL
WAVENUMBER CM⁻¹
WAVELENGTH IN MICRONS

A

D18,900-6 **N,N-Dimethyl-p-toluidine**
$CH_3C_6H_4N(CH_3)_2$ M.W. 135.21 n_D^{20} 1.5458
b.p. 211°

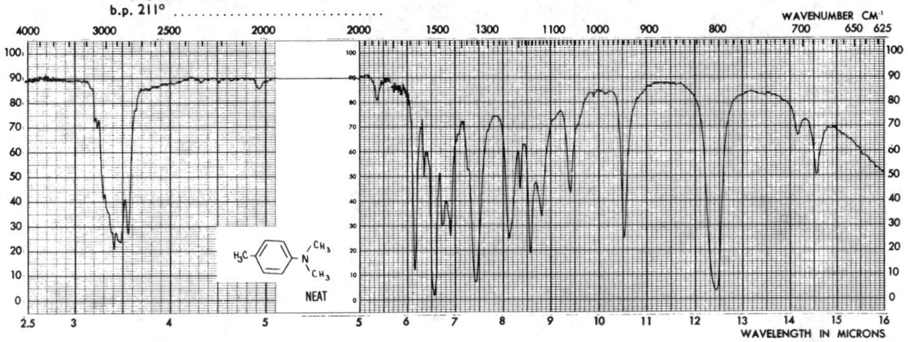

NEAT

B

16,412-7
2,2'-(p-Tolylimino)-diethanol, 97%
$CH_3C_6H_4N(CH_2CH_2OH)_2$
M.W. 195.26 m.p. 50-53° b.p. 338-340°
Beil. **12**,908

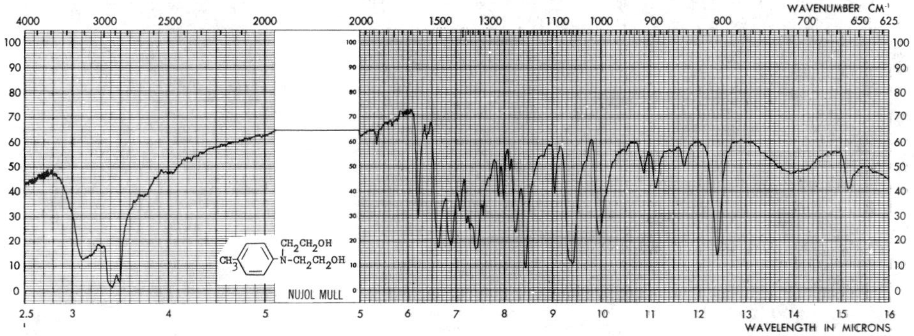

NUJOL MULL

C

T1980-1 **N,N,N',N'-Tetramethylbenzidine, tech.**
4-[$(CH_3)_2N$]$C_6H_4C_6H_4$-4-[$N(CH_3)_2$] M.W. 240.35
m.p. 193-195°

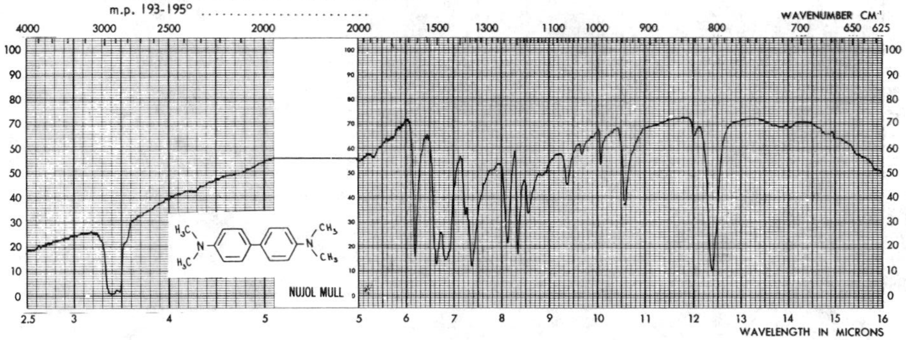

NUJOL MULL

D

13,285-3 **N,N-Diethyl-p-anisidine**
$CH_3OC_6H_4N(C_2H_5)_2$ M.W. 179.26
n_D^{20} 1.5381

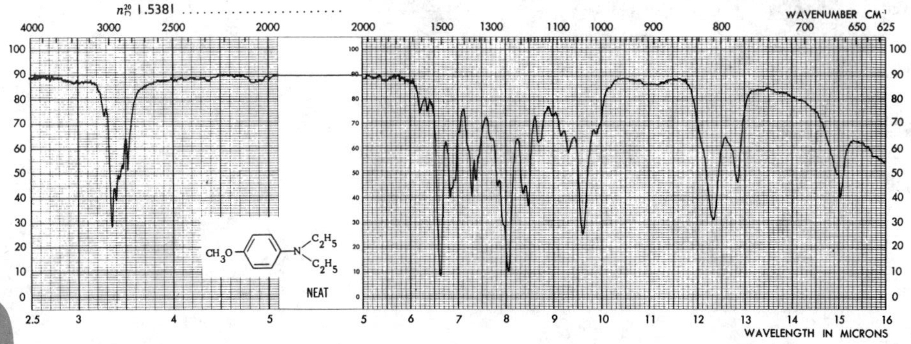

NEAT

E

12,972-0 **p-Methylaminophenol sulfate**
$(CH_3NHC_6H_4OH)_2 \cdot H_2SO_4$ M.W. 344.39
m.p. 245° (dec.)

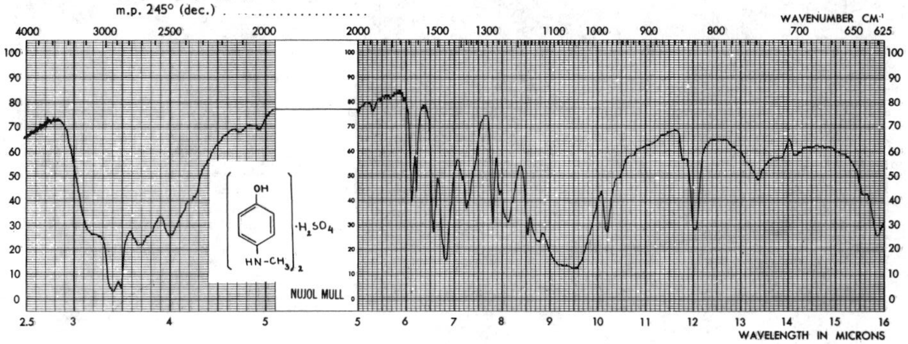

NUJOL MULL

F

F410-6 **2-(p-Fluoroanilino)-ethanethiol**
$FC_6H_4NHCH_2CH_2SH$ M.W. 171.24 n_D^{20} 1.5729

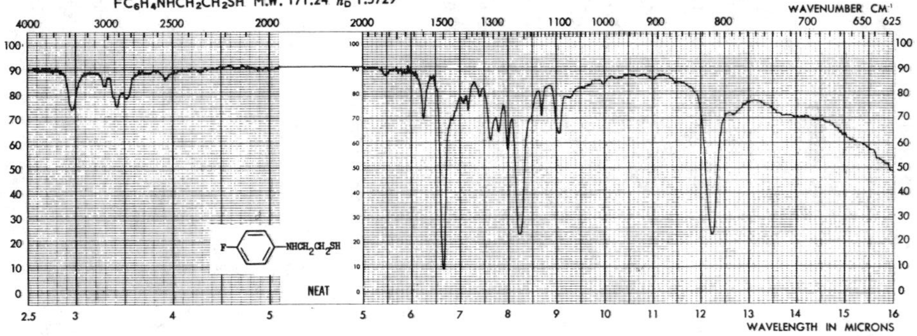

NEAT

G

D14,580-7 **2,3-Dimethylaniline** (2,3-xylidine)
$(CH_3)_2C_6H_3NH_2$ M.W. 121.18 n_D^{20} 1.5673

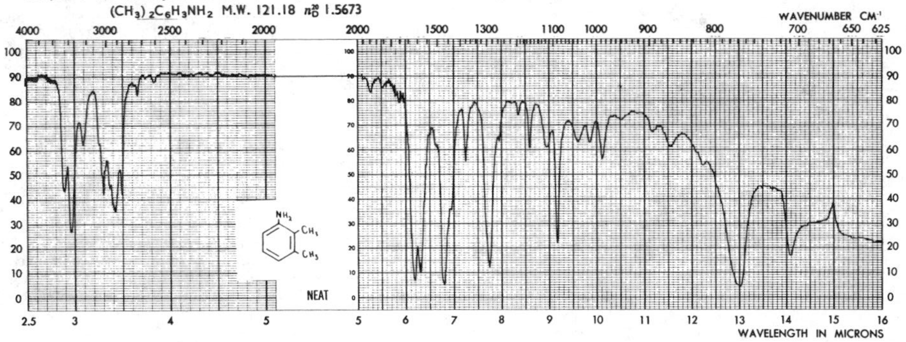

NEAT

H

20,990-2
N-**Ethyl-2,3-xylidine**, 99%
$(CH_3)_2C_6H_3NHC_2H_5$ FW 149.24 bp 227-228°
n_D^{20} 1.5468 d 0.917 *Beil.* **12**,1101 Disp. C

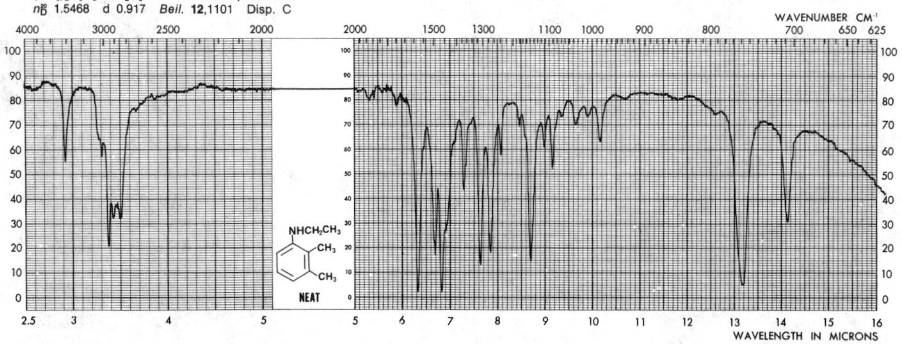

NEAT

A

A8000-9 **1-Amino-5,6,7,8-tetrahydronaphthalene** (5,6,7,8-tetrahydro-1-naphthylamine)
M.W. 147.22 n_D^{20} 1.6050

NEAT

B

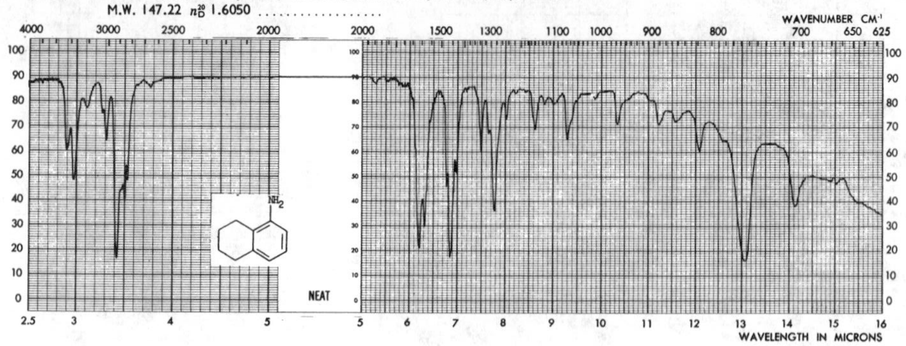

D14,600-5 **2,6-Dimethylaniline** (2,6-xylidine)
$(CH_3)_2C_6H_3NH_2$ M.W. 121.18 n_D^{20} 1.5601
m.p. 10-12°

MELT

C

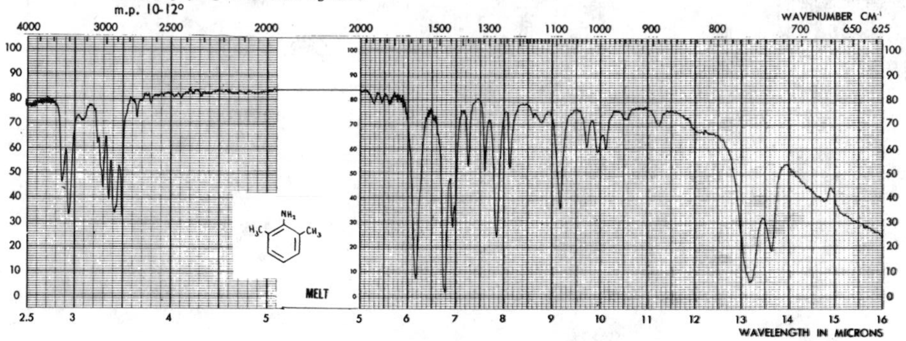

15,772-4
6-Ethyl-o-toluidine, 98+%
$C_2H_5C_6H_3(CH_3)NH_2$
M.W. 135.21 m.p. -33° b.p. 231° n_D^{20} 1.5525
d 0.968 *IRRITANT*

NEAT

D

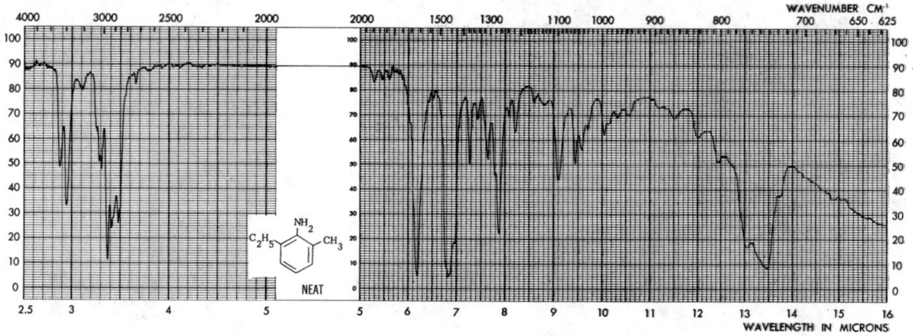

14,938-1 **2,6-Diethylaniline**
$(C_2H_5)_2C_6H_3NH_2$ M.W. 149.24 n_D^{20} 1.5452
b.p. 243°

NEAT

E

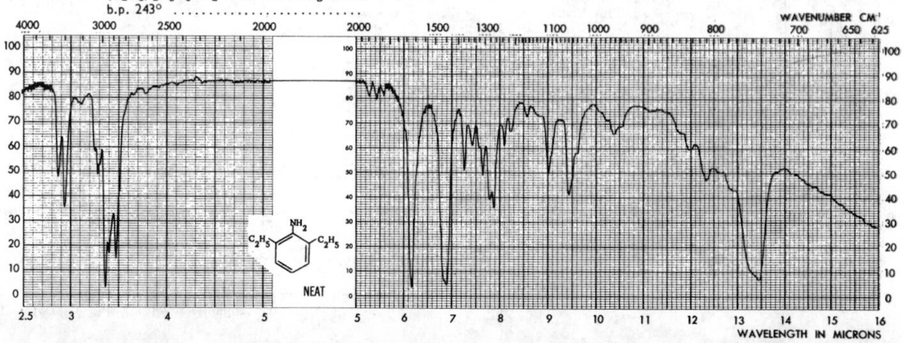

15,771-6
2,6-Diisopropylaniline, 95%
$[(CH_3)_2CH]_2C_6H_3NH_2$
M.W. 177.29 m.p. -45° b.p. 257° n_D^{20} 1.5332
d 0.94 Beil. **12**,168 *IRRITANT*

NEAT

F

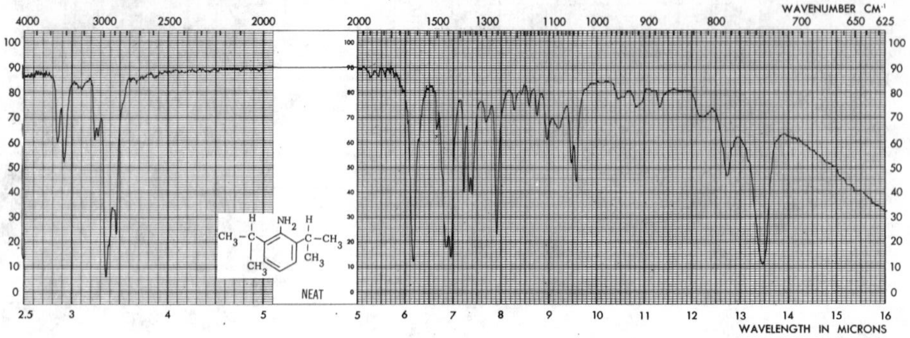

10,162-1 **3-Chloro-2-methylaniline** (3-chloro-o-toluidine), **puriss.**
$ClC_6H_3(CH_3)NH_2$ M.W. 141.60 n_D^{20} 1.5880 m.p. 0-2°

NEAT

G

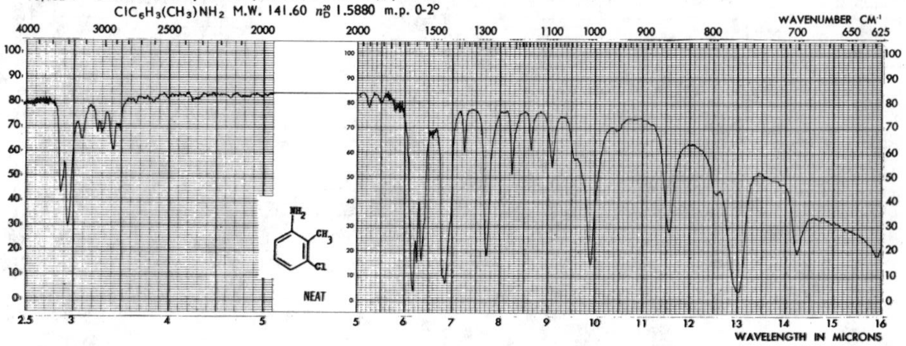

C5100-8 **2-Chloro-6-methylaniline** (6-chloro-o-toluidine)
$ClC_6H_3(CH_3)NH_2$ M.W. 141.60 n_D^{20} 1.5761

NEAT

H

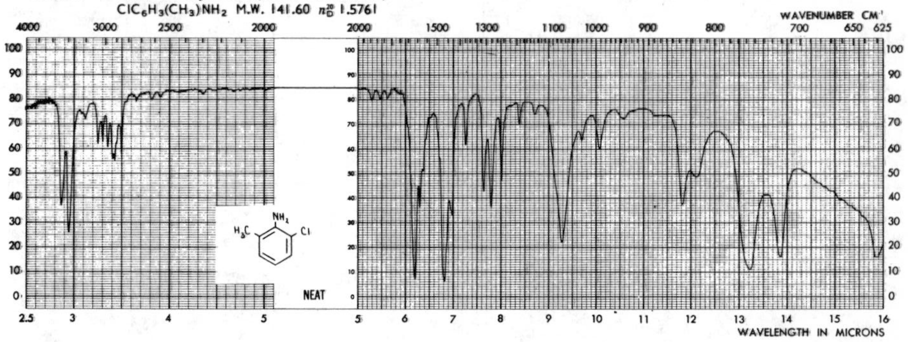

19,661-4
2,6-Difluoroaniline, 97+%
$F_2C_6H_3NH_2$ FW 129.11 bp 51-52°/15mm.
n_D^{20} 1.5084 d 1.199 Disp. C

NEAT

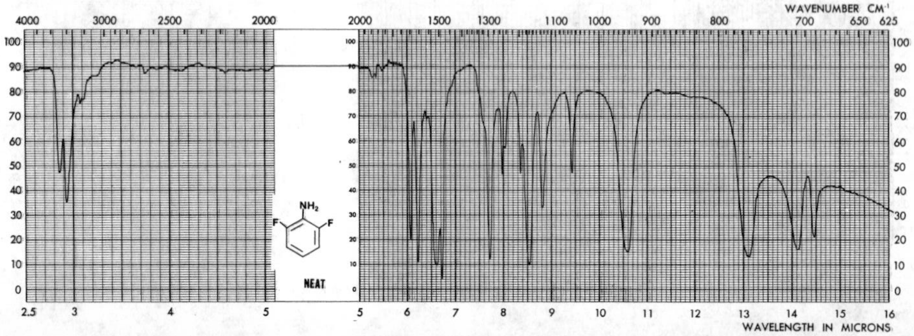

A D5550-4 2,6-Dichloroaniline
$Cl_2C_6H_3NH_2$ M.W. 162.02
m.p. 38-41°

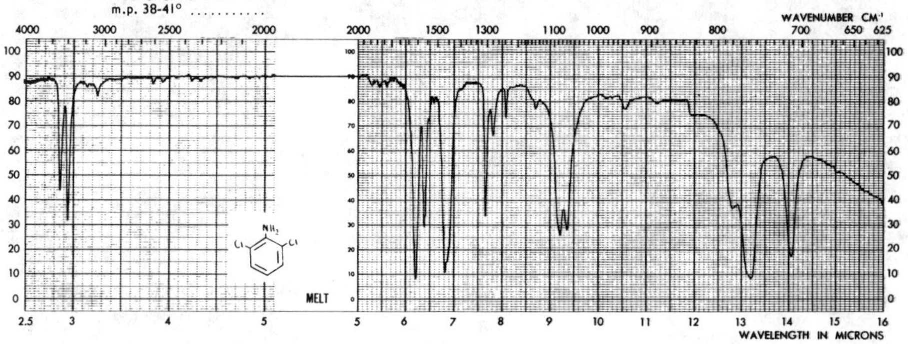

MELT

B D5540-7 2,3-Dichloroaniline
$Cl_2C_6H_3NH_2$ M.W. 162.02

MELT

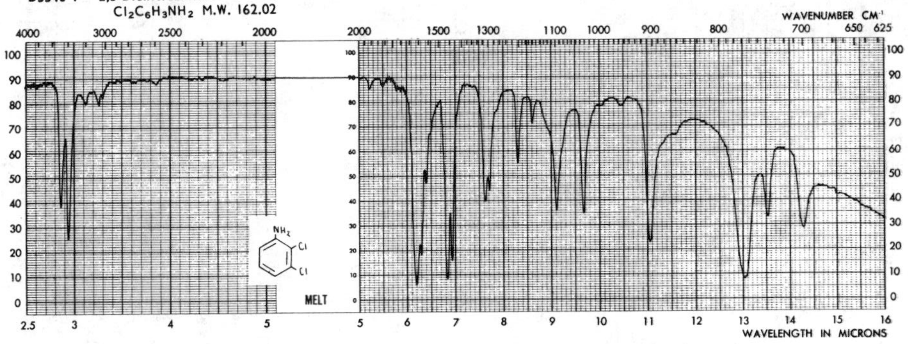

C D3880-4 2,6-Dibromoaniline
$Br_2C_6H_3NH_2$ M.W. 250.93 m.p. 80°

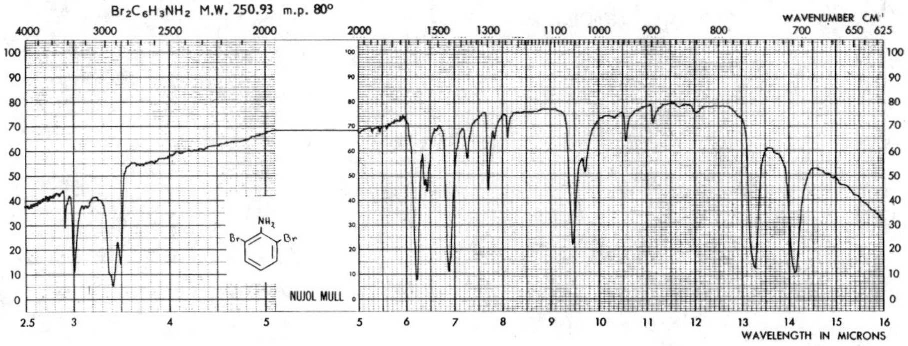

NUJOL MULL

D 14,994-2 3-Chloro-o-anisidine (3-chloro-2-methoxyaniline)
$ClC_6H_3(OCH_3)NH_2$ M.W. 157.60 n_D^{20} 1.5742
b.p. 246°

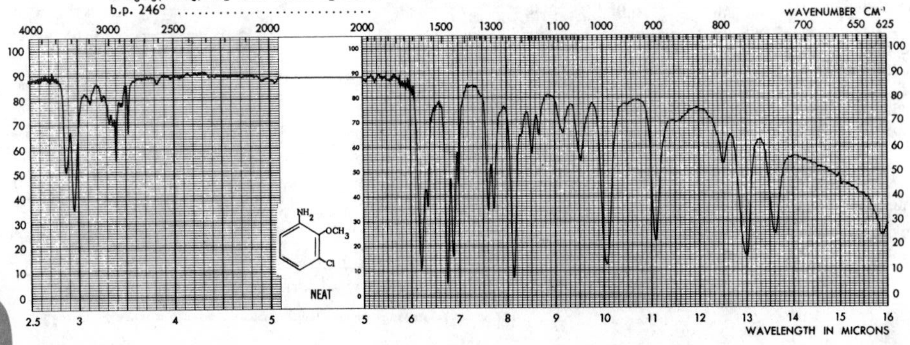

NEAT

E 12,637-3 3,4-Dimethylaniline (3,4-xylidine)
$(CH_3)_2C_6H_3NH_2$ M.W. 121.18
m.p. 49-52°

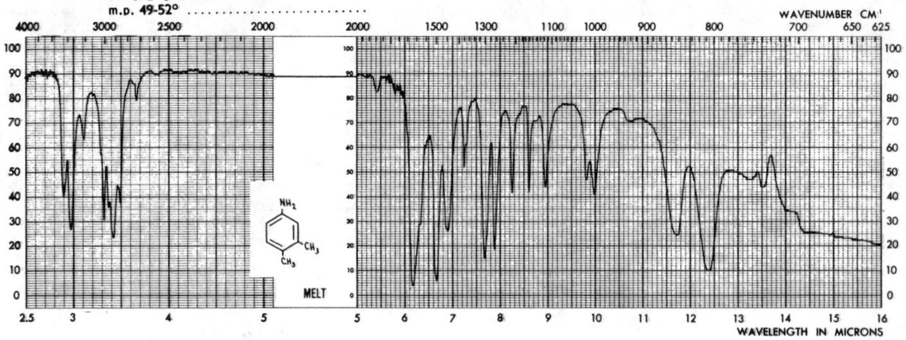

MELT

F 13,087-7 5-Aminoindan (5-indanamine)
M.W. 133.19 m.p. 32.5-34.5°

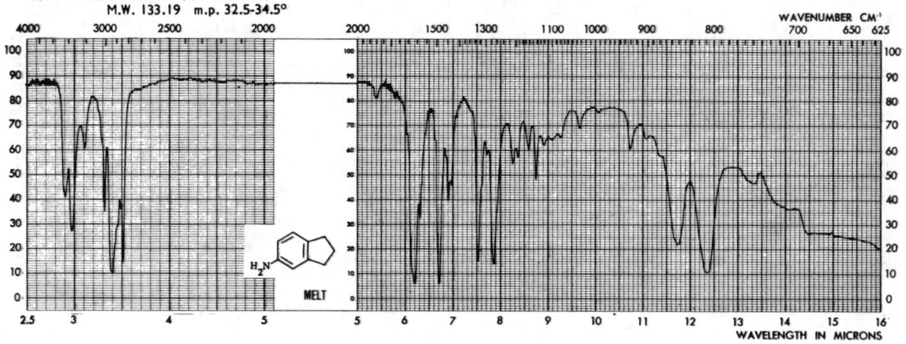

MELT

G 10,225-3 2,5-Dimethylaniline (2,5-xylidine)
$(CH_3)_2C_6H_3NH_2$ M.W. 121.18 n_D^{20} 1.5592 m.p. 13-14°
b.p. 218.5°

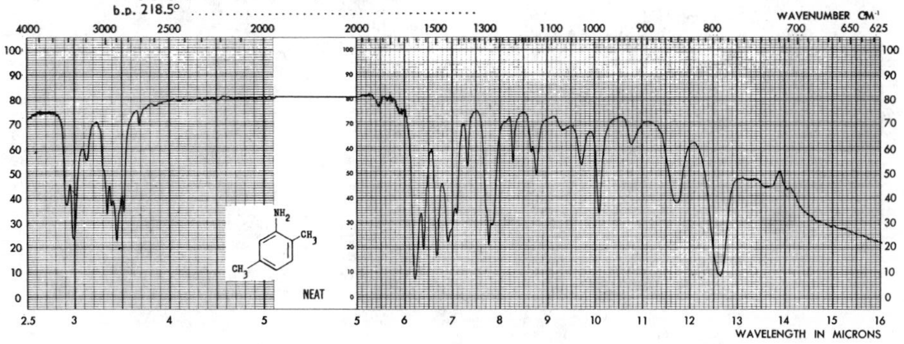

NEAT

H 10,829-4 2,4-Dimethylaniline (2,4-xylidine)
$(CH_3)_2C_6H_3NH_2$ M.W. 121.18 n_D^{20} 1.5586
b.p. 212°

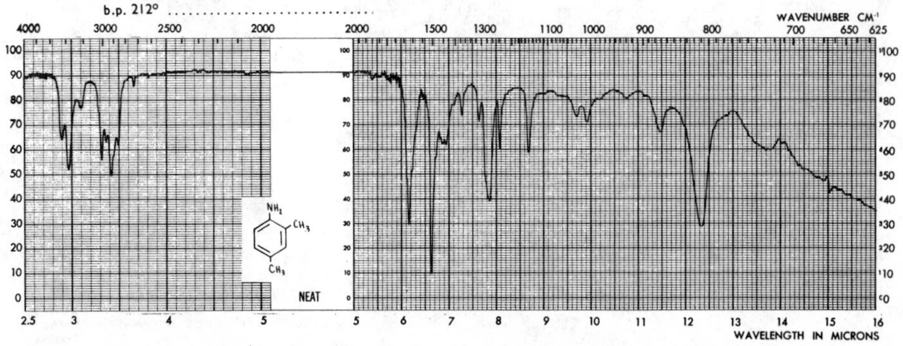

NEAT

WAVENUMBER CM⁻¹ / WAVELENGTH IN MICRONS

A

14,865-2 **2-Amino-p-cymene** (carvacrylamine, 2-methyl-5-isopropylaniline), tech.
$(CH_3)_2CHC_6H_3(CH_3)NH_2$ M.W. 149.24 n_D^{20} 1.5389
b.p. 118-120°/10 mm.

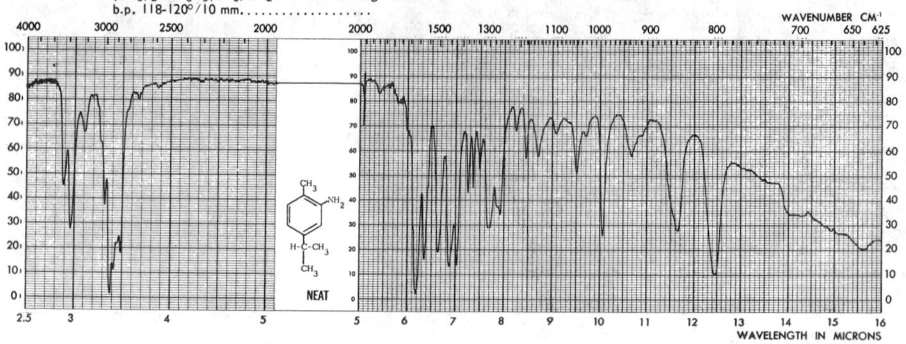

NEAT

B

T3547-5 **o-Tolidine**
$4\text{-}(H_2N)C_6H_3(CH_3)C_6H_3(CH_3)\text{-}4\text{-}(NH_2)$ M.W. 212.30
m.p. 130-133°

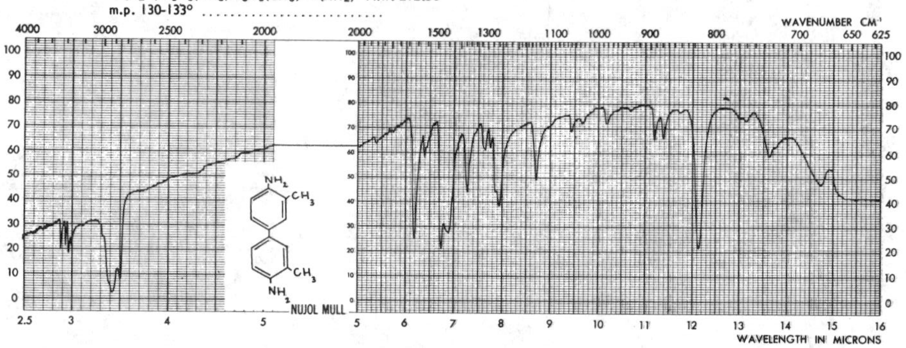

NUJOL MULL

C

T3548-3 **o-Tolidine dihydrochloride**
$4\text{-}(H_2N)C_6H_3(CH_3)C_6H_3(CH_3)\text{-}4\text{-}(NH_2)\cdot 2HCl$ M.W. 285.22
m.p. > 320°

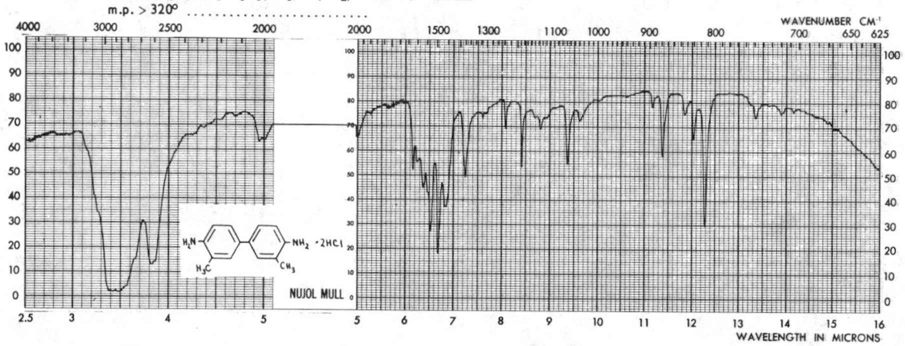

NUJOL MULL

D

19,325-9
4,4'-Ethylenedi-*m*-toluidine (4,4'-diamino-2,2'-dimethylbibenzyl)
$[\text{-}CH_2C_6H_3(CH_3)NH_2]_2$ FW 240.35 mp 170-173°
Disp. C

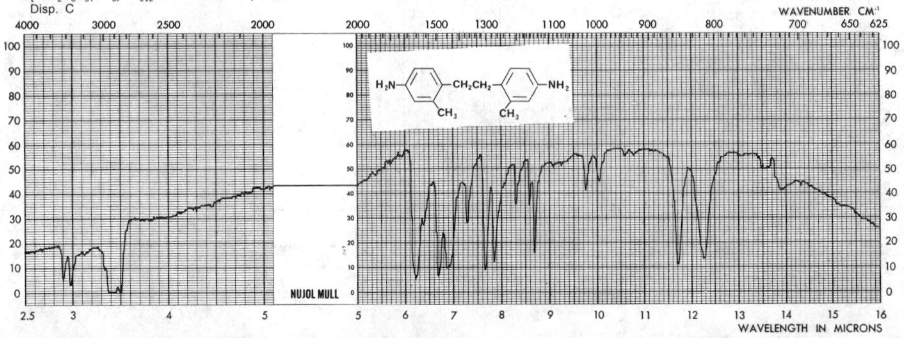

NUJOL MULL

E

22,266-6
3-Fluoro-4-methylaniline, 99% (3-fluoro-*p*-toluidine)
$FC_6H_3(CH_3)NH_2$ FW 125.15 mp 30-32°
n_D^{20} 1.5405 d 1.093 *Beil.* **12**(3),2151 *IR* **2**,643A
Disp. C

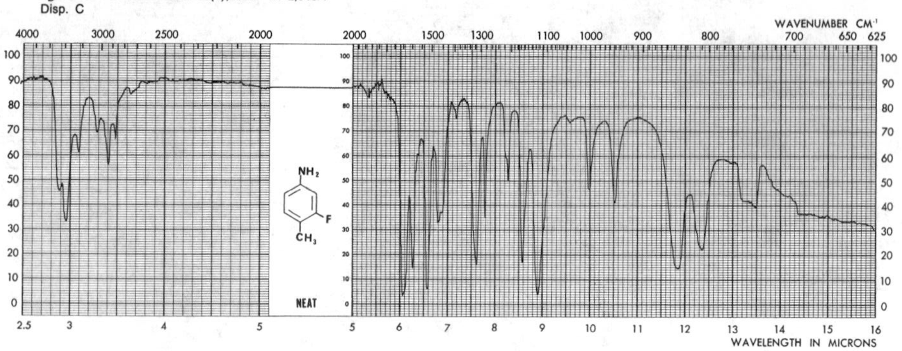

NEAT

F

F960-4 **2-Fluoro-4-methylaniline** (2-fluoro-p-toluidine)
$FC_6H_3(CH_3)NH_2$ M.W. 125.15 n_D^{20} 1.5347

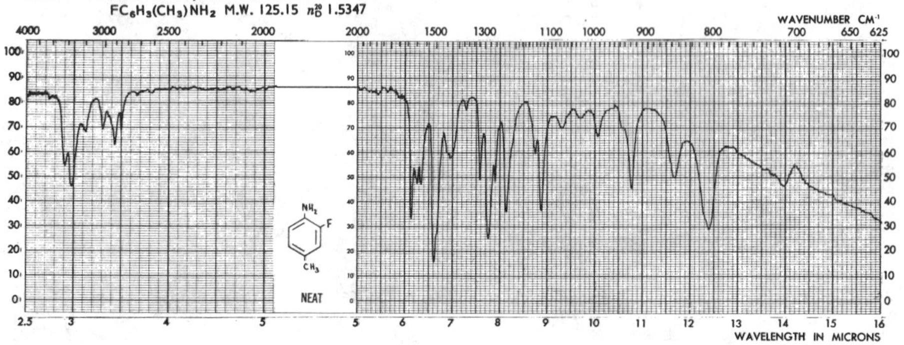

NEAT

G

F1040-2 **5-Fluoro-2-methylaniline** (5-fluoro-o-toluidine)
$FC_6H_3(CH_3)NH_2$ M.W. 125.15 m.p. 38-40°

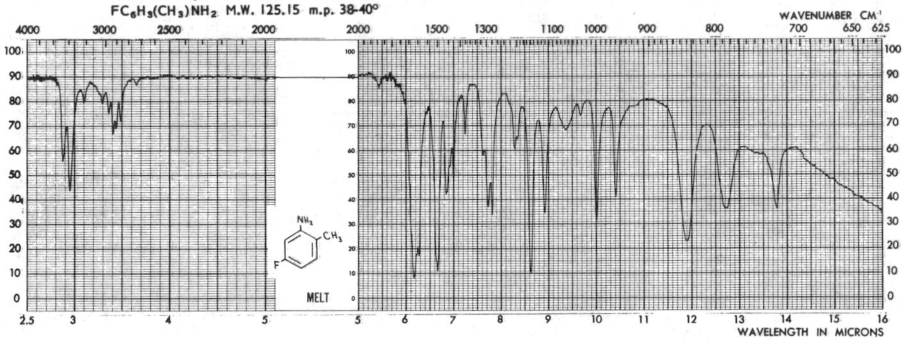

MELT

H

10,135-4 **2-Fluoro-5-methylaniline** (6-fluoro-m-toluidine)
$FC_6H_3(CH_3)NH_2$ M.W. 125.15 n_D^{20} 1.5350

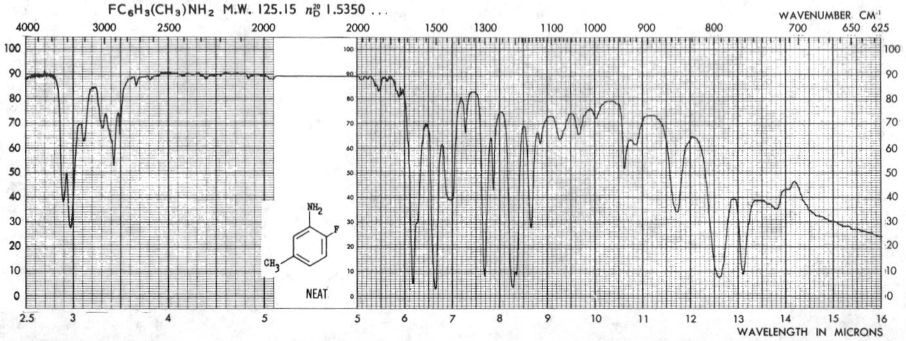

NEAT

A 16,233-7 **4-Fluoro-3-methylaniline**, 96% (4-fluoro-m-toluidine)
$FC_6H_3(CH_3)NH_2$
M.W. 125.15 n_D^{20} 1.5346 d 1.119 *IRRITANT*
MELT

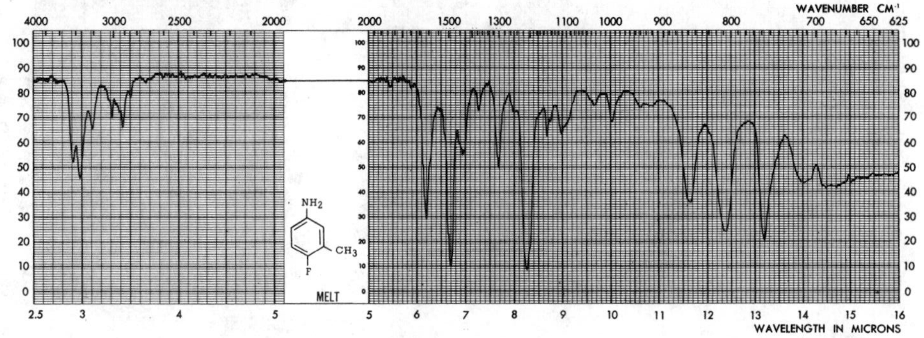

B D10,140-0 **2,4-Difluoroaniline**
$F_2C_6H_3NH_2$ M.W. 129.11 n_D^{20} 1.5063
NEAT

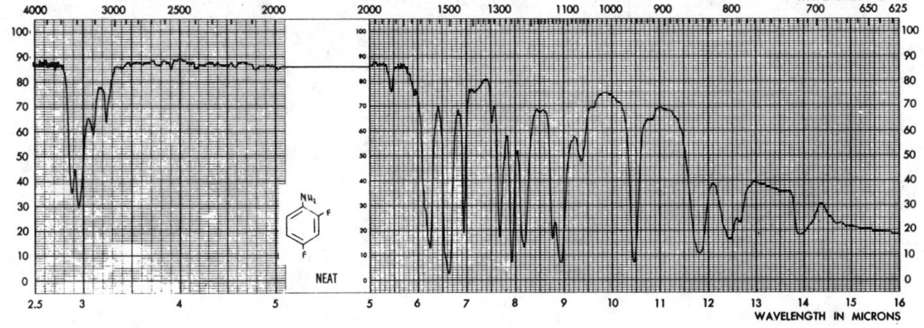

C D10,160-5 **2,5-Difluoroaniline**
$F_2C_6H_3NH_2$ M.W. 129.11 n_D^{20} 1.5121
NEAT

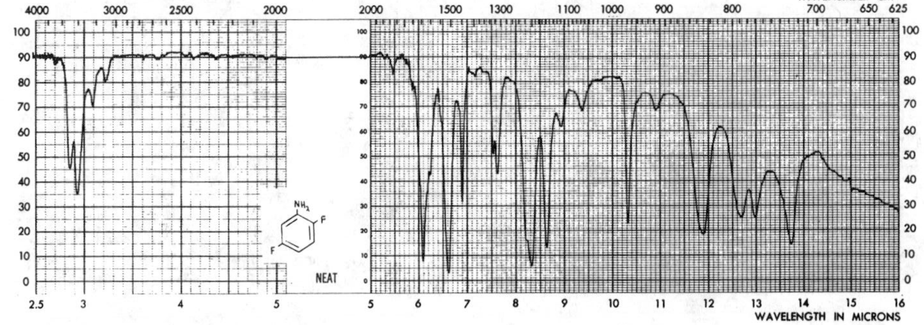

D 10,164-8 **3-Chloro-4-methylaniline** (3-chloro-p-toluidine), **puriss.**
$ClC_6H_3(CH_3)NH_2$ M.W. 141.60 m.p. 24-25°
NEAT

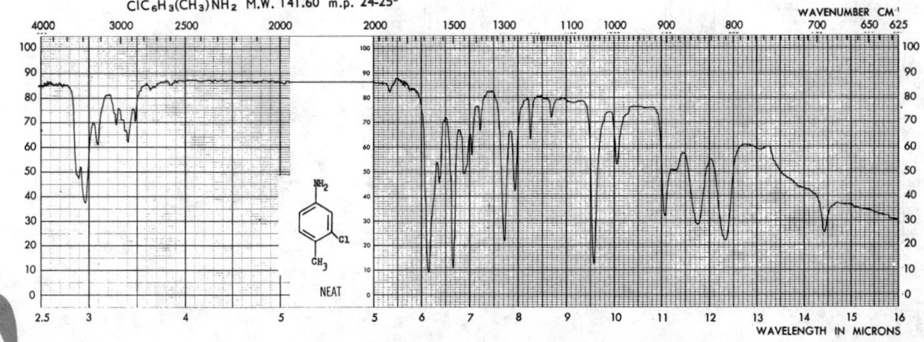

E 12,507-5 **2-Chloro-4-methylaniline** (2-chloro-p-toluidine)
$ClC_6H_3(CH_3)NH_2$ M.W. 141.60 $n_D^{21.6}$ 1.5748
NEAT

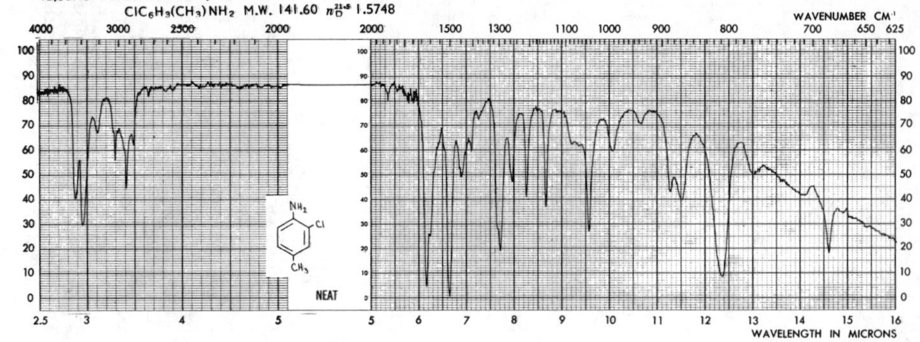

F 11,732-3 **4,4'-Methylenebis-(o-chloroaniline)**
$CH_2[C_6H_3(Cl)NH_2]_2$ M.W. 267.16
m.p. 106-108° . . . .
NUJOL MULL

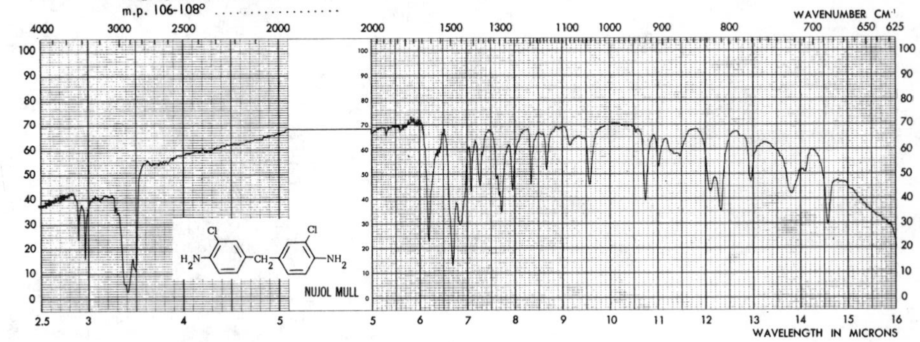

G C5120-2 **5-Chloro-2-methylaniline** (5-chloro-o-toluidine)
$ClC_6H_3(CH_3)NH_2$ M.W. 141.60 m.p. 22° . . .
MELT

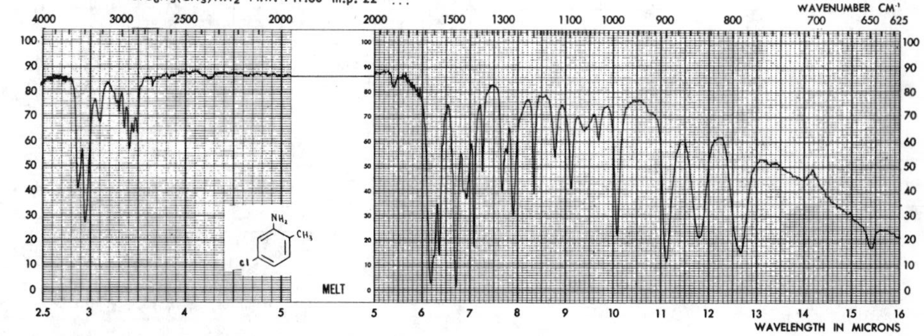

H C5110-5 **4-Chloro-2-methylaniline** (4-chloro-o-toluidine)
$ClC_6H_3(CH_3)NH_2$ M.W. 141.60 m.p. 27° . . .
NEAT

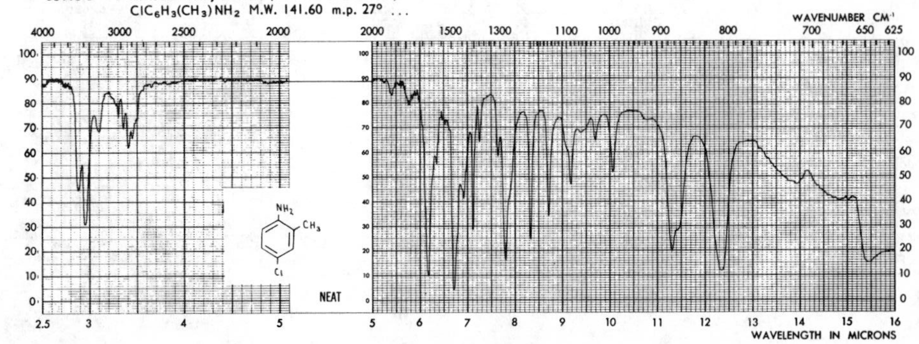

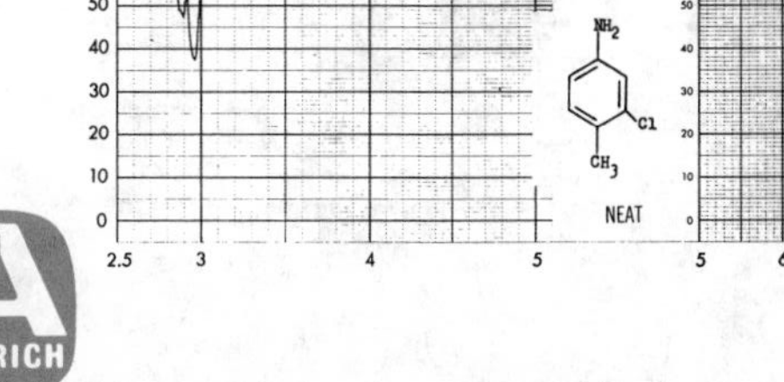

A

D5560-1 **3,4-Dichloroaniline**
$Cl_2C_6H_3NH_2$ M.W. 162.02 m.p. 70-72.5°

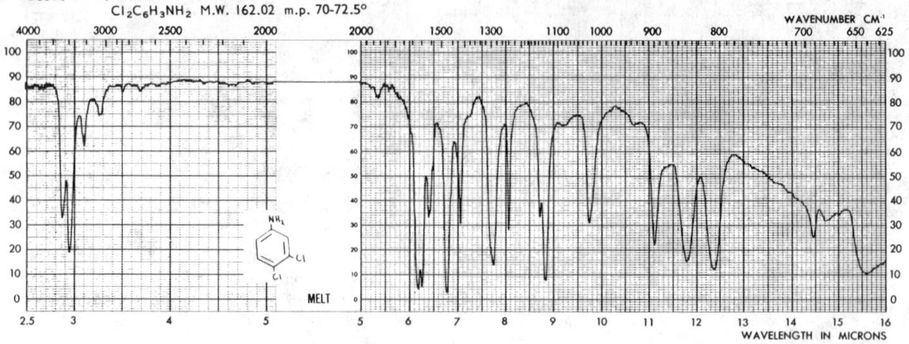

MELT

B

11,215-1 **2,4-Dichloroaniline**
$Cl_2C_6H_3NH_2$ M.W. 162.02 m.p. 62-64°

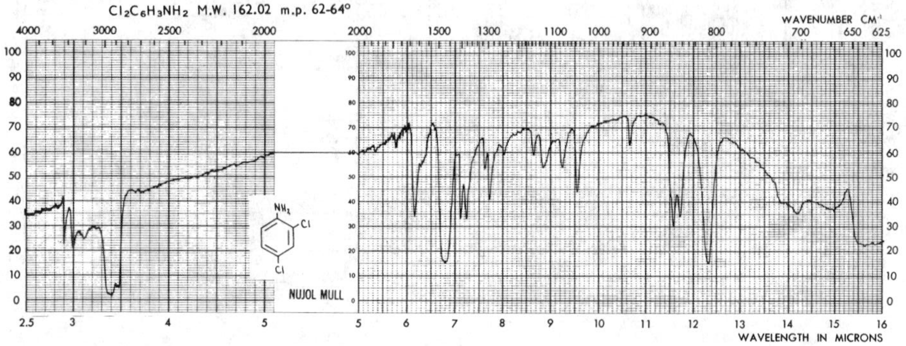

NUJOL MULL

C

10,202-4 **2,5-Dichloroaniline**
$Cl_2C_6H_3NH_2$ M.W. 162.02 m.p. 49-51°

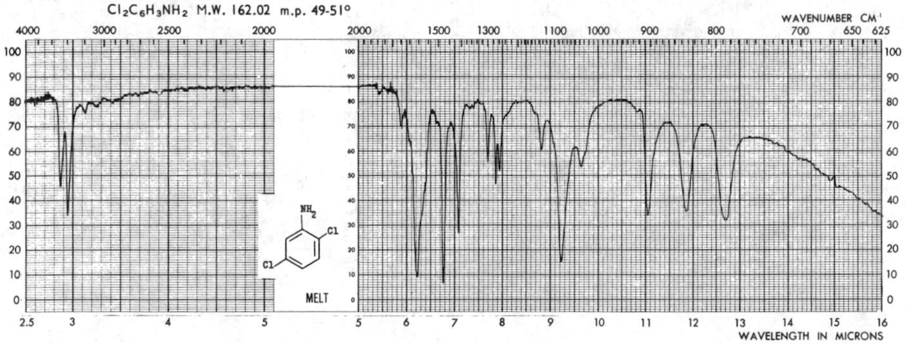

MELT

D

15,425-3 **4-Bromo-2-methylaniline** (4-bromo-o-toluidine)
$BrC_6H_3(CH_3)NH_2$ M.W. 186.07 m.p. 52-56°

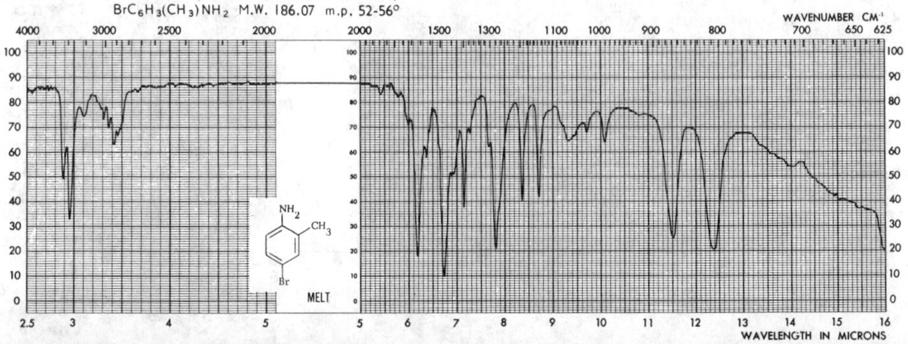

MELT

E

15,426-1 **4-Bromo-3-methylaniline** (4-bromo-m-toluidine)
$BrC_6H_3(CH_3)NH_2$ M.W. 186.07
m.p. 79.5-81.5°

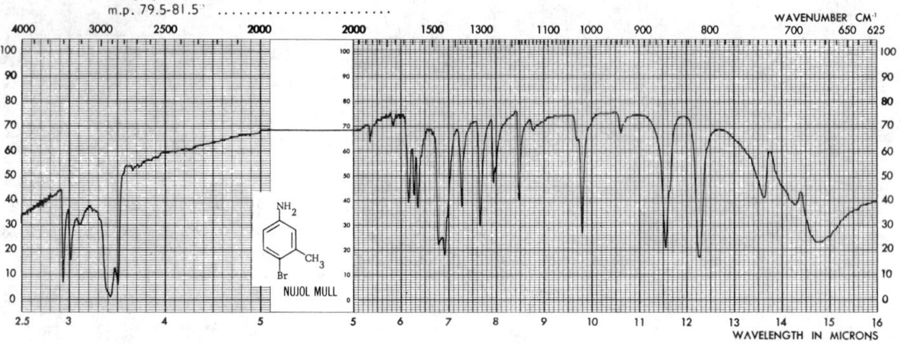

NUJOL MULL

F

12,406-7 **2-Bromo-4-methylaniline** (2-bromo-p-toluidine)
$BrC_6H_3(CH_3)NH_2$ M.W. 186.07
n_D^{20} 1.5999 m.p. 14-16°

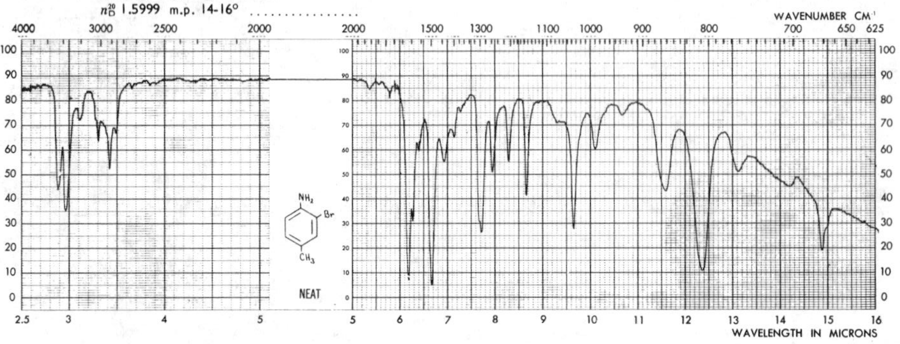

NEAT

G

15,424-5
4-Bromo-2-chloroaniline
$BrC_6H_3(Cl)NH_2$
M.W. 206.48 m.p. 70-72° Beil. **12**,652

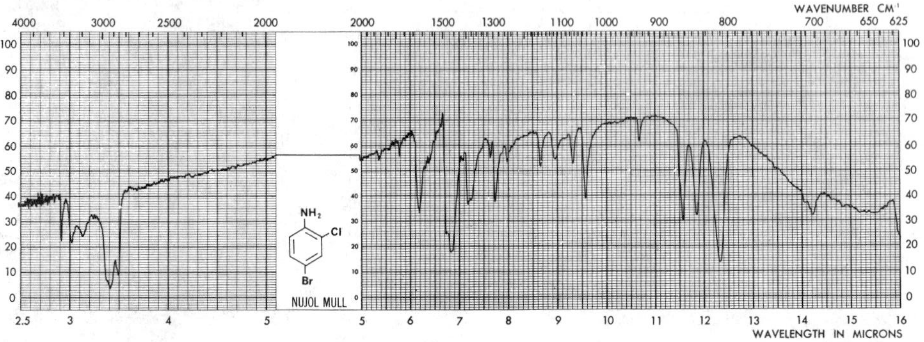

NUJOL MULL

H

D3840-5 **2,4-Dibromoaniline**
$Br_2C_6H_3NH_2$ M.W. 250.93 m.p. 72-76°

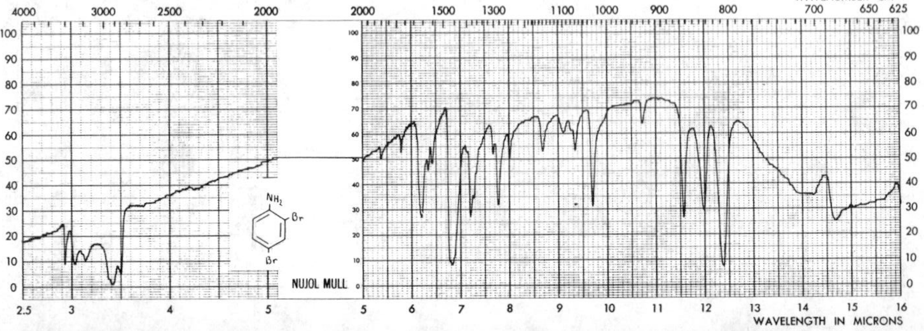

NUJOL MULL

A

12,588-1 **2,5-Dibromoaniline**
$Br_2C_6H_3NH_2$ M.W. 250.93 m.p. 53-55°

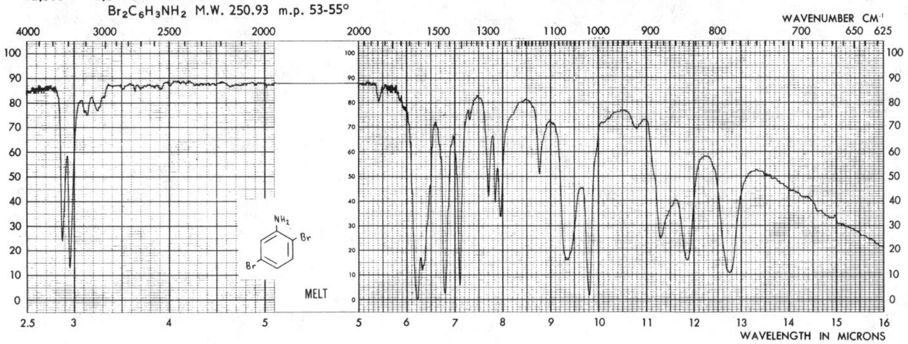

MELT

B

I-860-4 **3-Iodo-4-methylaniline**
$IC_6H_3(CH_3)NH_2$ M.W. 233.05
m.p. 36.5-40.5°

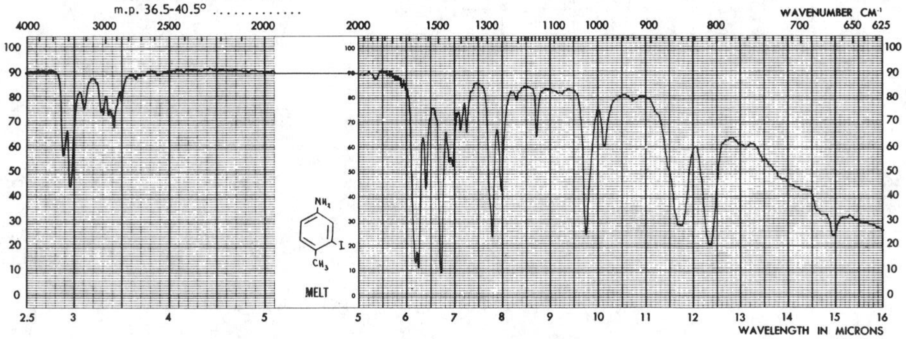

MELT

C

21,775-1
α,α,α,4-Tetrafluoro-*o*-toluidine, 99%
$FC_6H_3(CF_3)NH_2$ FW 179.12 bp 70-72°/17.500mm.
n_D^{20} 1.4638 d 1.380 *Beil.* **12**(3),1909 Disp. C

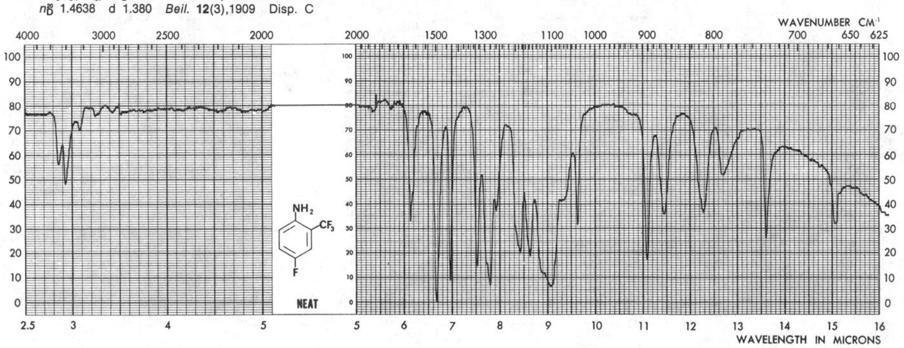

NEAT

D

21,777-8
α,α,α,4-Tetrafluoro-*m*-toluidine, 99%
$FC_6H_3(CF_3)NH_2$ FW 179.12 bp 207-208°
n_D^{20} 1.4661 d 1.393 Disp. C

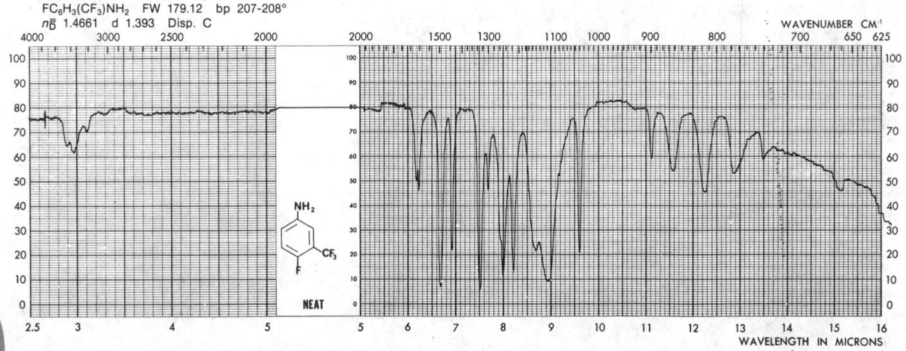

NEAT

E

A4565-3 **5-Amino-2-chlorobenzotrifluoride** (4-chloro-α,α,α-trifluoro-m-toluidine), tech.
$H_2NC_6H_3(Cl)CF_3$ M.W. 195.57 m.p. 34-36°

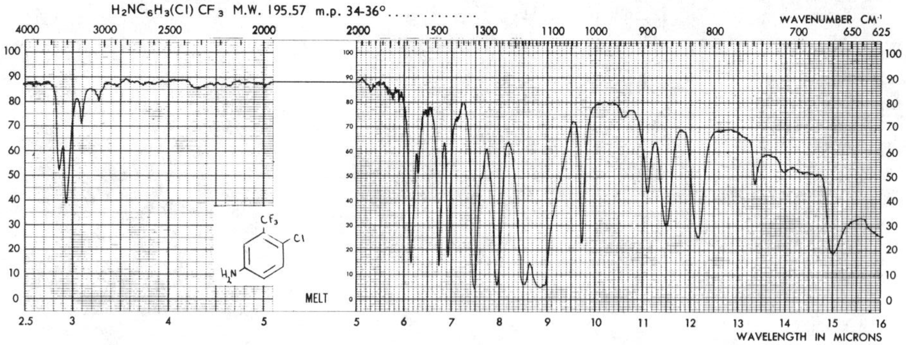

MELT

F

21,772-7
4-Chloro-α,α,α-trifluoro-*o*-toluidine, 97% (2-amino-5-chlorobenzotrifluoride)
$H_2NC_6H_3(Cl)CF_3$ FW 195.57 bp 66-67°/3mm.
n_D^{20} 1.5069 d 1.386 *Beil.* **12**(3),1921 Disp. C

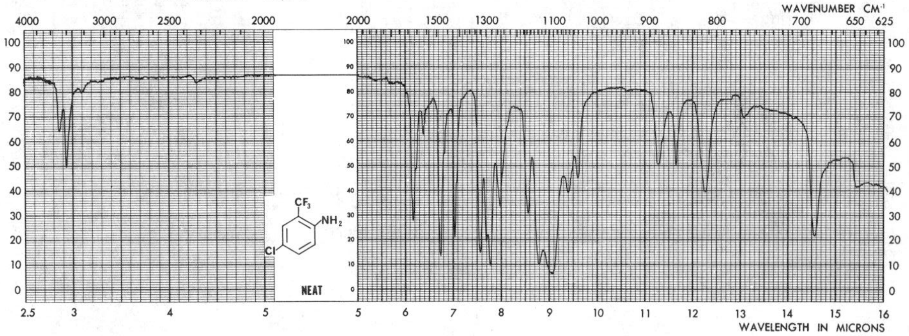

NEAT

G

21,785-9
4-Bromo-α,α,α-trifluoro-*o*-toluidine
$BrC_6H_3(CF_3)NH_2$ FW 240.03 Disp. C

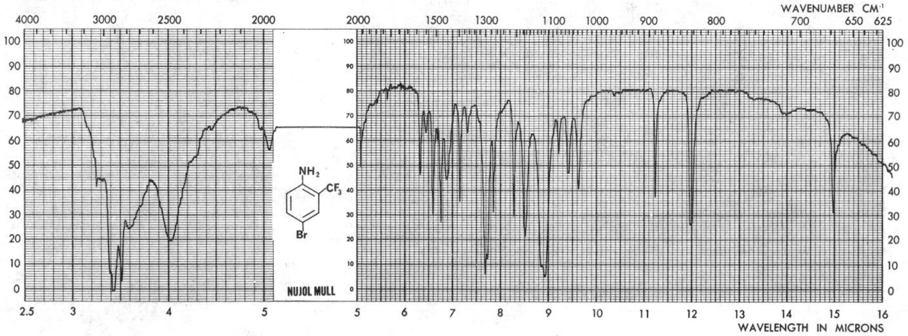

NUJOL MULL

H

21,786-7
6-Bromo-α,α,α-trifluoro-*m*-toluidine, 97%
$BrC_6H_3(CF_3)NH_2$ FW 240.03 n_D^{20} 1.5209 d 1.675
Disp. C

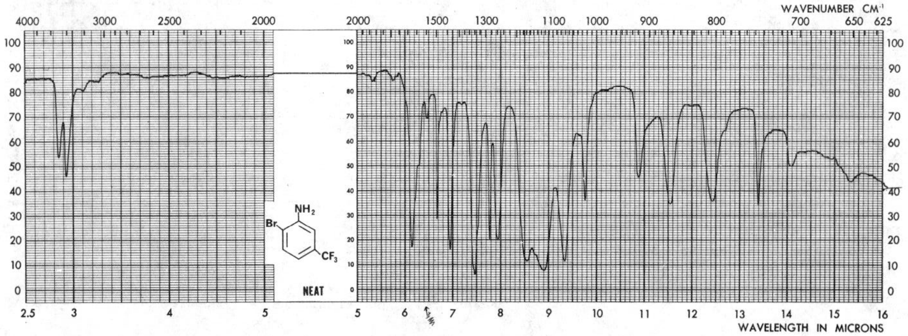

NEAT

A

A4560-2 **3-Amino-4-chlorobenzotrifluoride** (6-chloro-α,α,α-trifluoro-m-toluidine)
$H_2NC_6H_3(Cl)CF_3$ M.W. 195.57 n_D^{23} 1.4965

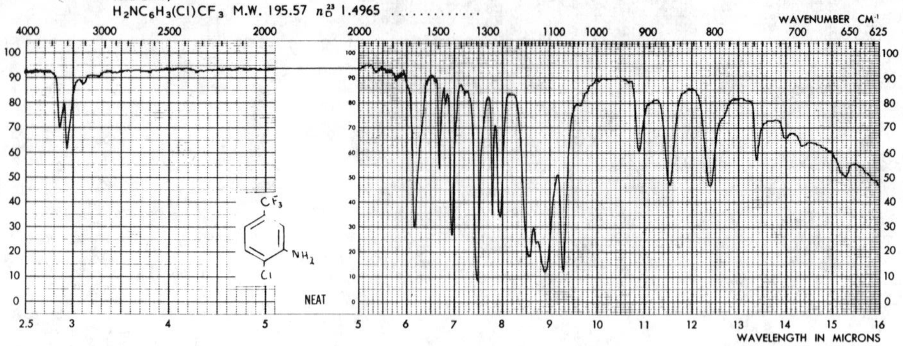

NEAT

B

M1500-1 **4-Methoxy-2-methylaniline** (2-methyl-p-anisidine)
$CH_3OC_6H_3(CH_3)NH_2$ M.W. 137.18 n_D^{20} 1.5647
b.p. 146-147°/23 mm.

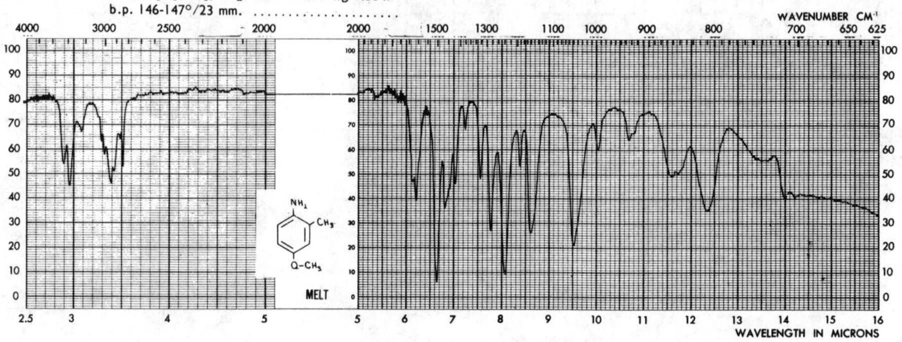

MELT

C

10,328-4 **2-Methoxy-5-methylaniline** (5-methyl-o-anisidine)
$CH_3OC_6H_3(CH_3)NH_2$ M.W. 137.18
m.p. 52-54°

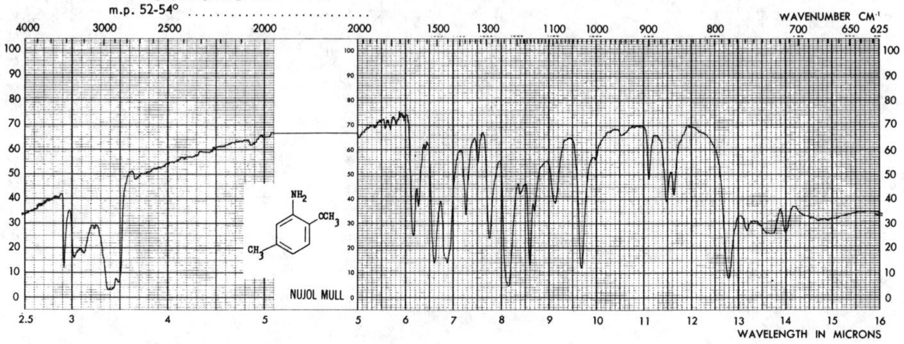

NUJOL MULL

D

10,259-8 **3,3'-Dimethoxybenzidine** (o-dianisidine)
$4\text{-}(H_2N)C_6H_3(OCH_3)C_6H_3(OCH_3)\text{-}4\text{-}(NH_2)$ M.W. 244.29
m.p. 136-137°

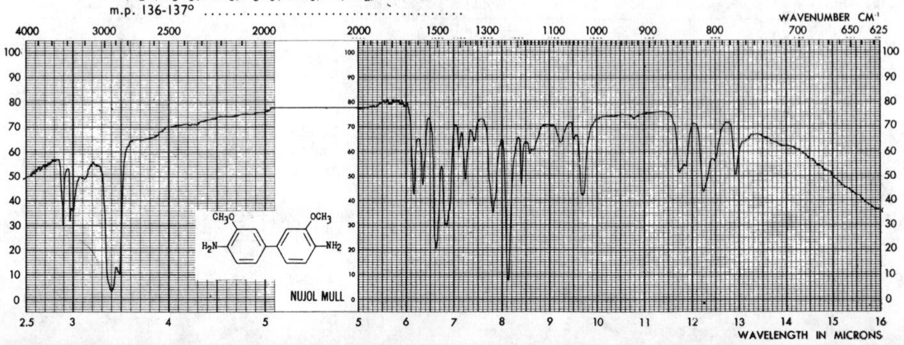

NUJOL MULL

E

15,160-2 **6-Chloro-m-anisidine** (2-chloro-5-methoxyaniline) **hydrochloride**
$ClC_6H_3(OCH_3)NH_2 \cdot HCl$ M.W. 194.06
m.p. 207° (dec.)

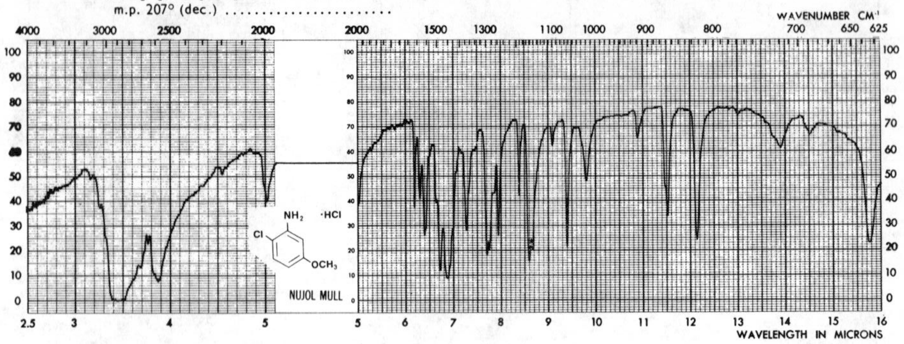

NUJOL MULL

F

A8300-8 **4-Aminoveratrole** (3,4-dimethoxyaniline)
$H_2NC_6H_3(OCH_3)_2$ M.W. 153.18
m.p. 84-87°

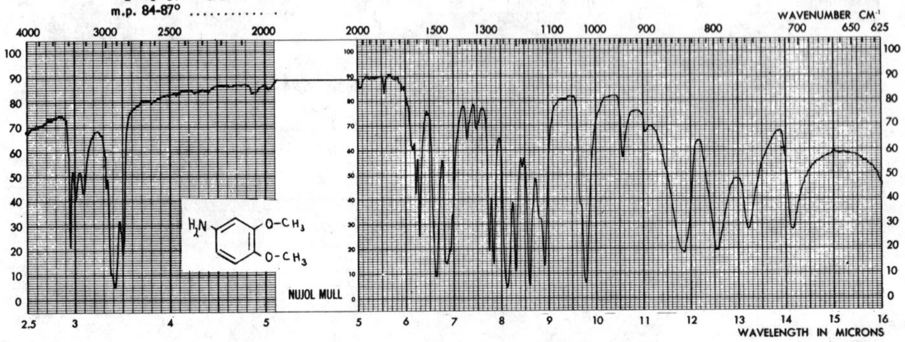

NUJOL MULL

G

16,149-7
3,4-(Methylenedioxy)-aniline, 97%
M.W. 137.14 m.p. 39-41° b.p. 144°/16mm.

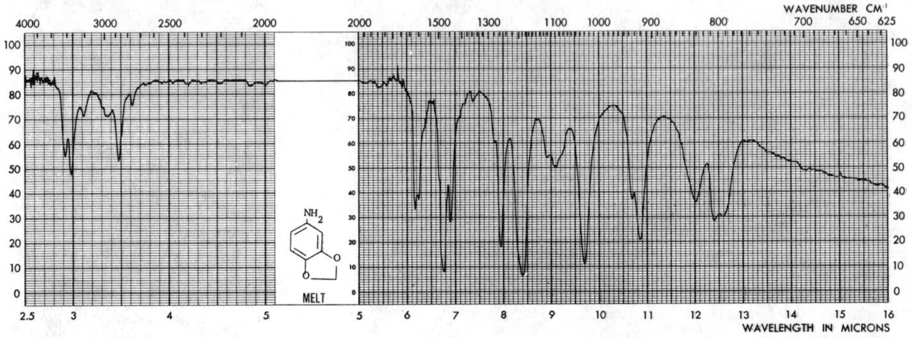

MELT

H

19,323-2
1,4-Benzodioxan-6-amine, 99% (6-amino-1,4-benzodioxan)
FW 151.17 n_D^{20} 1.5987 d 1.231 Disp. C

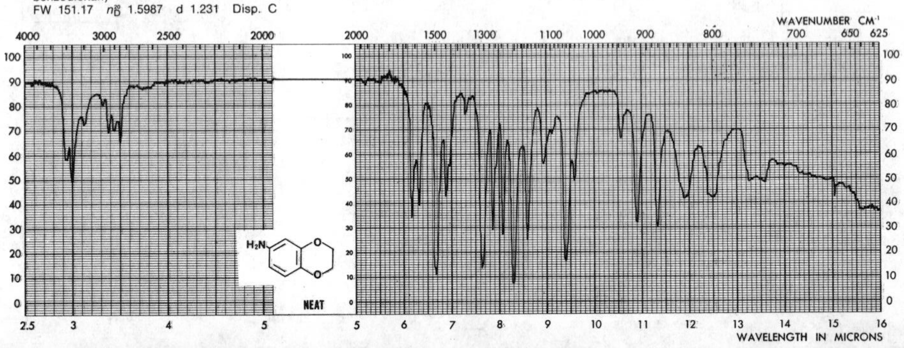

NEAT

A

D8335-4 3,4-Diethoxyaniline
$(C_2H_5O)_2C_6H_3NH_2$ M.W. 181.24 m.p. 47-49°

NUJOL MULL

B

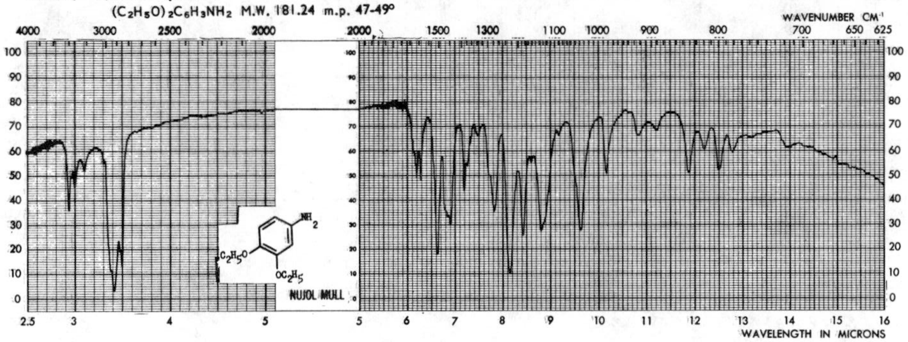

D12,980-1 2,4-Dimethoxyaniline
$(CH_3O)_2C_6H_3NH_2$ M.W. 153.18 m.p. 34-37°

MELT

C

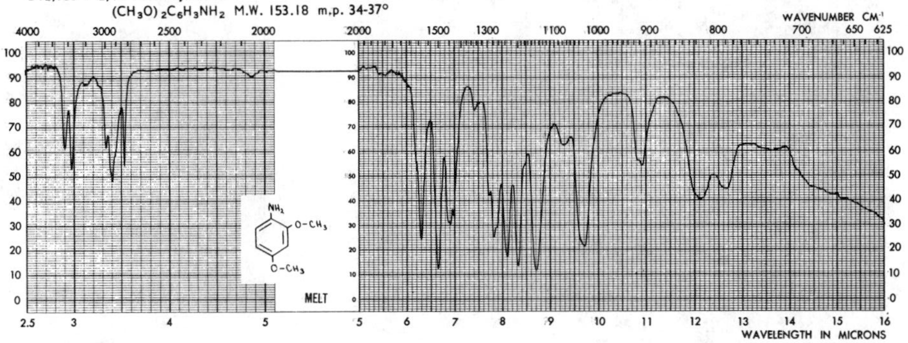

16,317-1
4-Aminoresorcinol hydrochloride, 97%
$H_2NC_6H_3$-1,3-$(OH)_2 \cdot HCl$
M.W. 161.59 m.p. 220° (dec.) Beil. **13**,783

NUJOL MULL

D

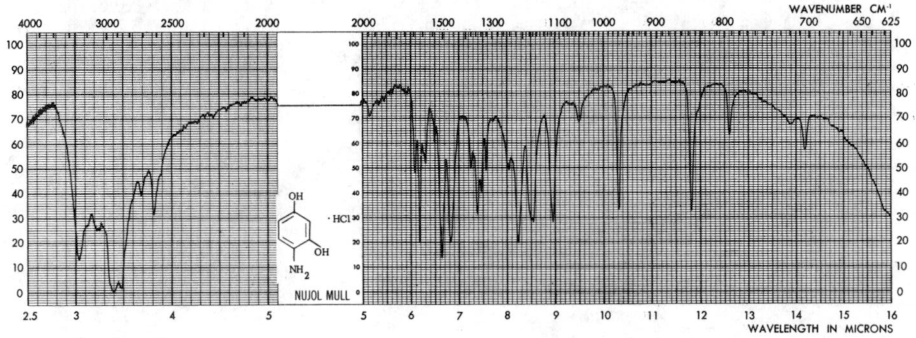

11,298-4 2,5-Dimethoxyaniline, puriss.
$(CH_3O)_2C_6H_3NH_2$ M.W. 153.18 m.p. 80-82°

NUJOL MULL

E

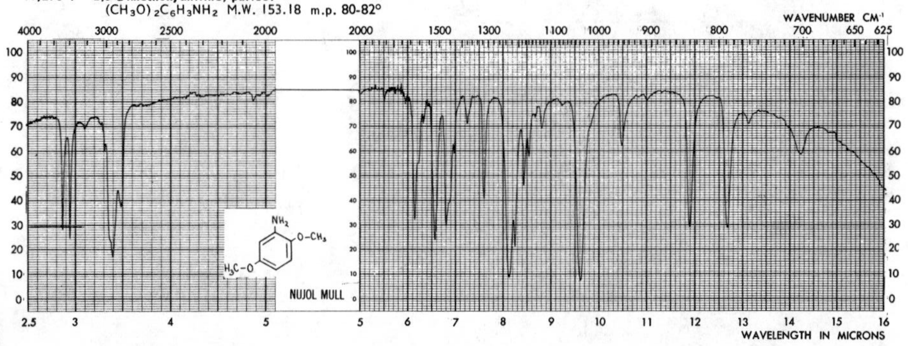

13,671-9 5-Amino-o-cresol (5-amino-2-methylphenol)
$H_2NC_6H_3(CH_3)OH$ M.W. 123.16
m.p. 157-159°

NUJOL MULL

F

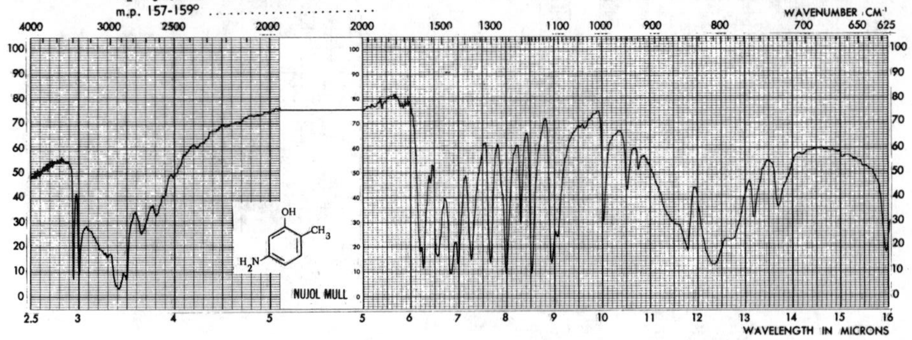

14,490-8 2-Amino-p-cresol (2-amino-4-methylphenol)
$H_2NC_6H_3(CH_3)OH$ M.W. 123.16
m.p. 135-137.5°

NUJOL MULL

G

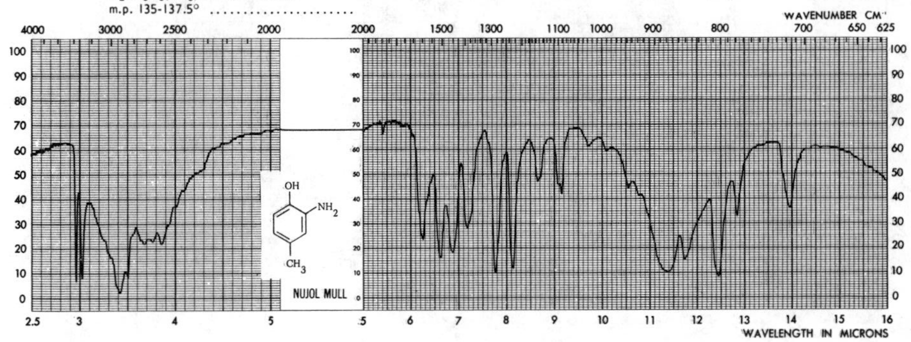

19,328-3
2-Amino-4-*tert*-butylphenol
$(CH_3)_3CC_6H_3(NH_2)OH$ FW 165.24 mp 160-163°
Disp. C

NUJOL MULL

H

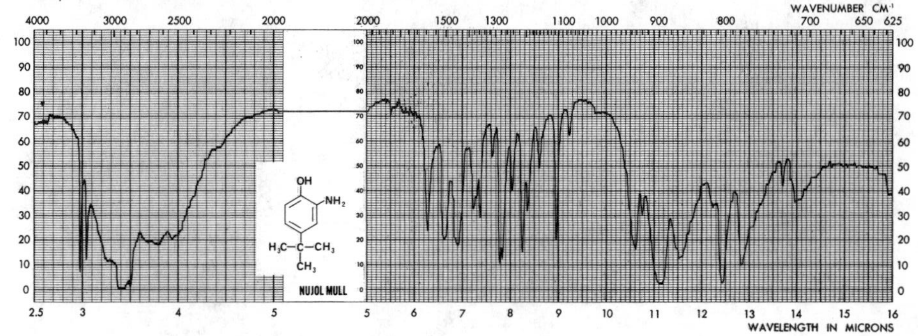

14,491-6 6-Amino-m-cresol (2-amino-5-methylphenol)
$H_2NC_6H_3(CH_3)OH$ M.W. 123.16
m.p. 156-159°

NUJOL MULL

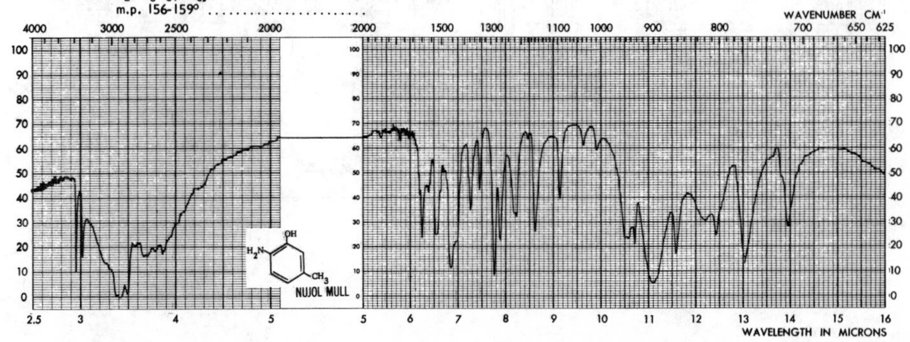

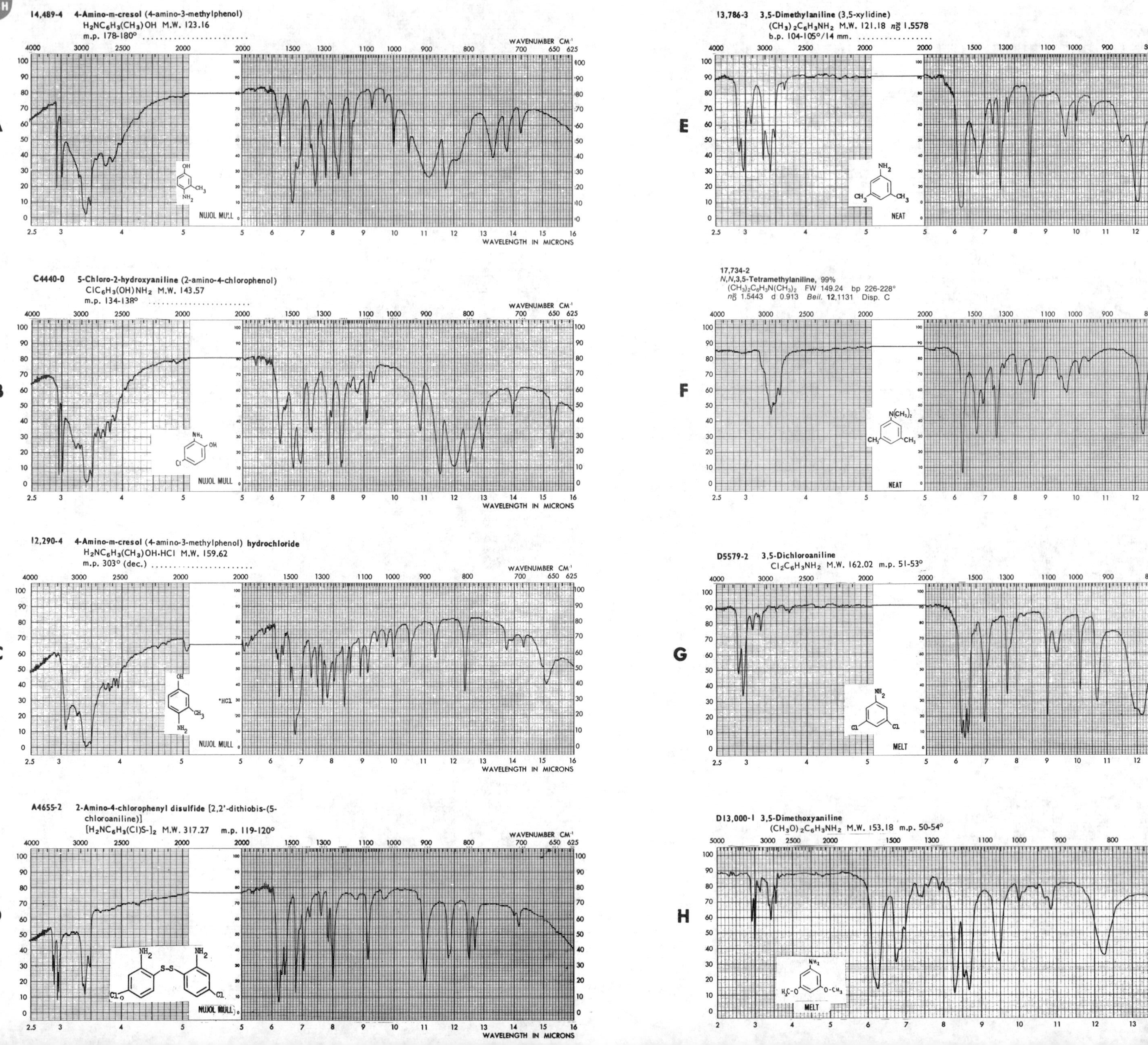
ALDRICH
A
14,489-4 4-Amino-m-cresol (4-amino-3-methylphenol)
$H_2NC_6H_3(CH_3)OH$ M.W. 123.16
m.p. 178-180°
NUJOL MULL
B
C4440-0 5-Chloro-2-hydroxyaniline (2-amino-4-chlorophenol)
$ClC_6H_3(OH)NH_2$ M.W. 143.57
m.p. 134-138°
NUJOL MULL
C
12,290-4 4-Amino-m-cresol (4-amino-3-methylphenol) hydrochloride
$H_2NC_6H_3(CH_3)OH{\cdot}HCl$ M.W. 159.62
m.p. 303° (dec.)
·HCl
NUJOL MULL
D
A4655-2 2-Amino-4-chlorophenyl disulfide [2,2'-dithiobis-(5-chloroaniline)]
$[H_2NC_6H_3(Cl)S\text{-}]_2$ M.W. 317.27 m.p. 119-120°
NUJOL MULL
E
13,786-3 3,5-Dimethylaniline (3,5-xylidine)
$(CH_3)_2C_6H_3NH_2$ M.W. 121.18 n_D^{20} 1.5578
b.p. 104-105°/14 mm.
NEAT
F
17,734-2
N,N,3,5-Tetramethylaniline, 99%
$(CH_3)_2C_6H_3N(CH_3)_2$ FW 149.24 bp 226-228°
n_D^{20} 1.5443 d 0.913 Beil. 12,1131 Disp. C
NEAT
G
D5579-2 3,5-Dichloroaniline
$Cl_2C_6H_3NH_2$ M.W. 162.02 m.p. 51-53°
MELT
H
D13,000-1 3,5-Dimethoxyaniline
$(CH_3O)_2C_6H_3NH_2$ M.W. 153.18 m.p. 50-54°
MELT
WAVENUMBER CM⁻¹
WAVELENGTH IN MICRONS

A

19,693-2
5-Methoxy-α,α,α-trifluoro-*m*-toluidine
$CH_3OC_6H_3(CF_3)NH_2$ FW 191.15 mp 45-50°
Fieser **7**,30 Disp. C

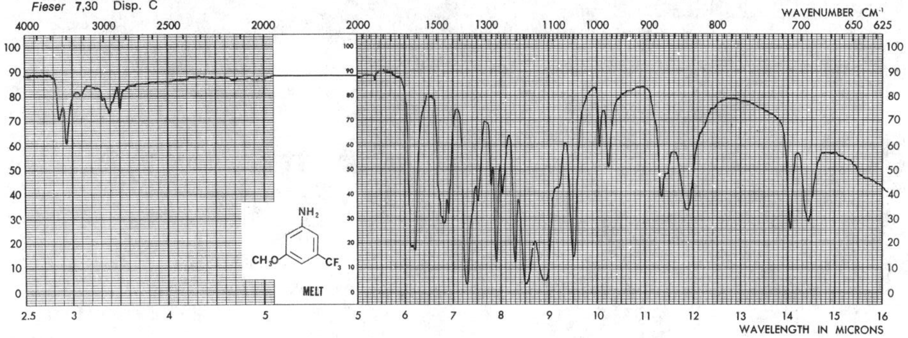

MELT

B

19,313-5
3,5-Bis(trifluoromethyl)aniline, 98+% (α,α,α,α',α',α'-hexafluoro-3,5-xylidine)
$(CF_3)_2C_6H_3NH_2$ FW 229.13 bp 85°/15mm.
n_D^{20} 1.4325 d 1.467 Disp. C

NEAT

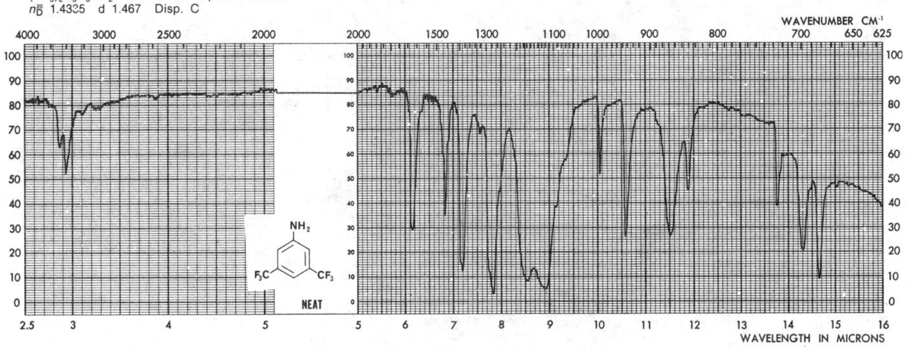

C

19,683-5
2,4,6-Trifluoroaniline, 97+%
$F_3C_6H_2NH_2$ FW 147.10 mp 33-37°
bp 57°/22mm. Disp. C

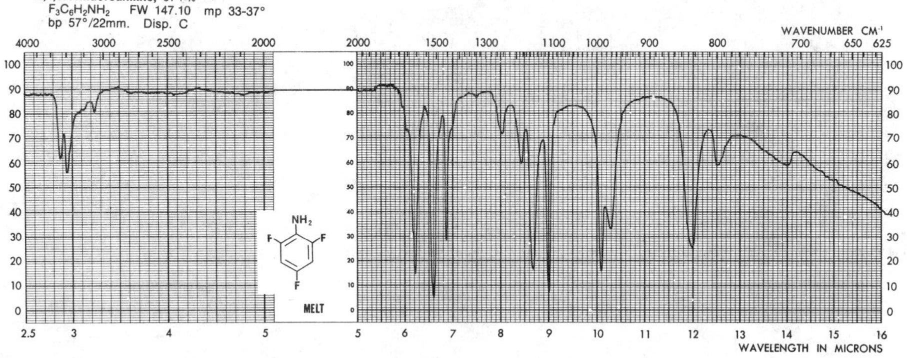

MELT

D

19,706-8
2,6-Dibromo-4-methylaniline, 98+% (2,6-dibromo-*p*-toluidine)
$Br_2C_6H_2(CH_3)NH_2$ FW 264.96 mp 75-77°
Beil. **12**,993 Disp. C

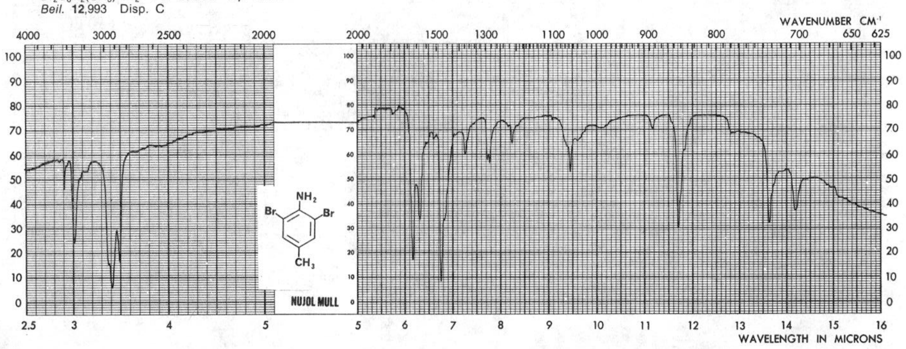

NUJOL MULL

E

19,237-6
4-Bromo-2,6-dimethylaniline, 98% (4-bromo-2,6-xylidine)
$BrC_6H_2(CH_3)_2NH_2$ FW 200.09 mp 50-52°
Beil. **12**,1110 Disp. C

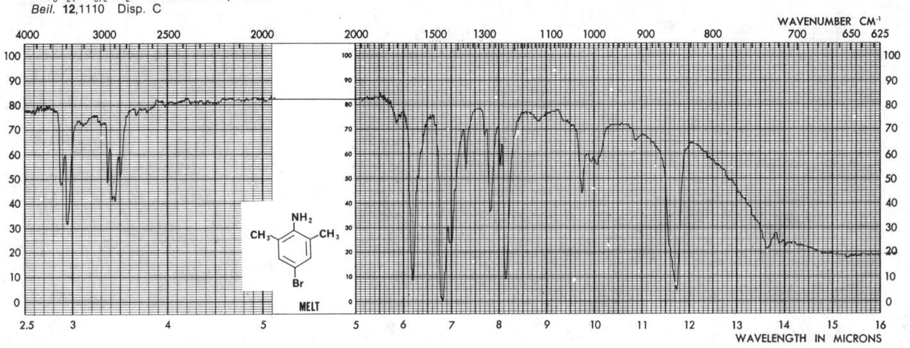

MELT

F

19,327-5
6-Amino-2,4-dimethylphenol (6-amino-2,4-xylenol)
$H_2NC_6H_2(CH_3)_2OH$ FW 137.18 mp 135-136°
Beil. **13**,630 Disp. C

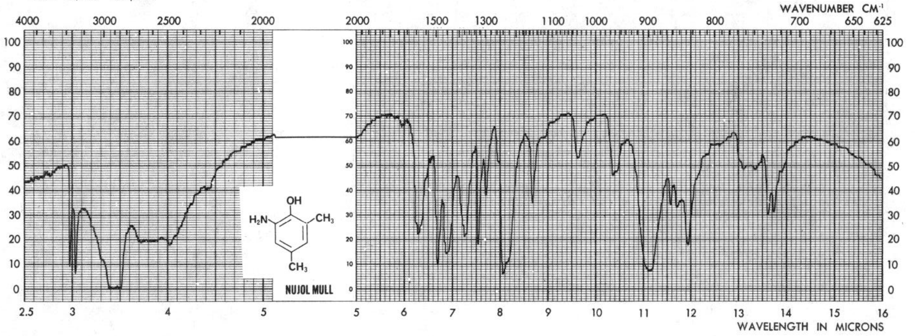

NUJOL MULL

G

A4840-7 **4-Amino-2,6-dichlorophenol**
$H_2NC_6H_2(Cl)_2OH$ M.W. 178.02
m.p. 165-172° (dec.)

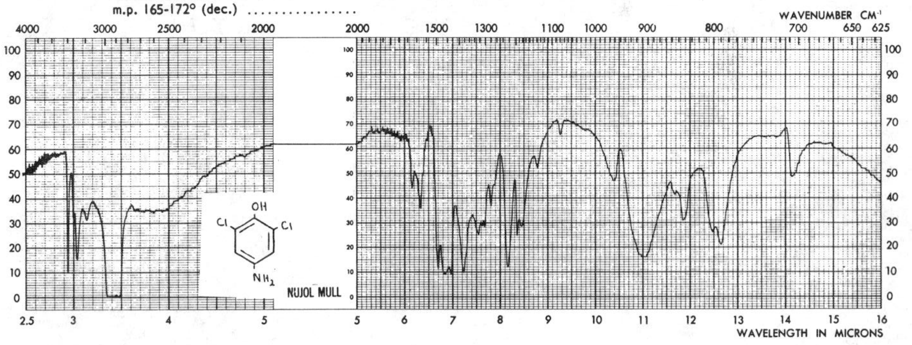

NUJOL MULL

H

18,607-4
4-Amino-2,6-dimethylphenol hydrochloride monohydrate, 97% (4-amino-2,6-xylenol)
$H_2NC_6H_2(CH_3)_2OH·HCl·H_2O$ FW 191.66
mp 270-275° (dec.) Disp. C

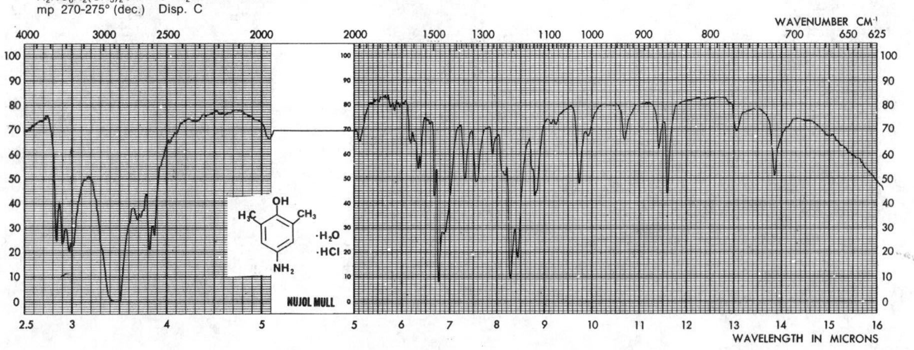

NUJOL MULL

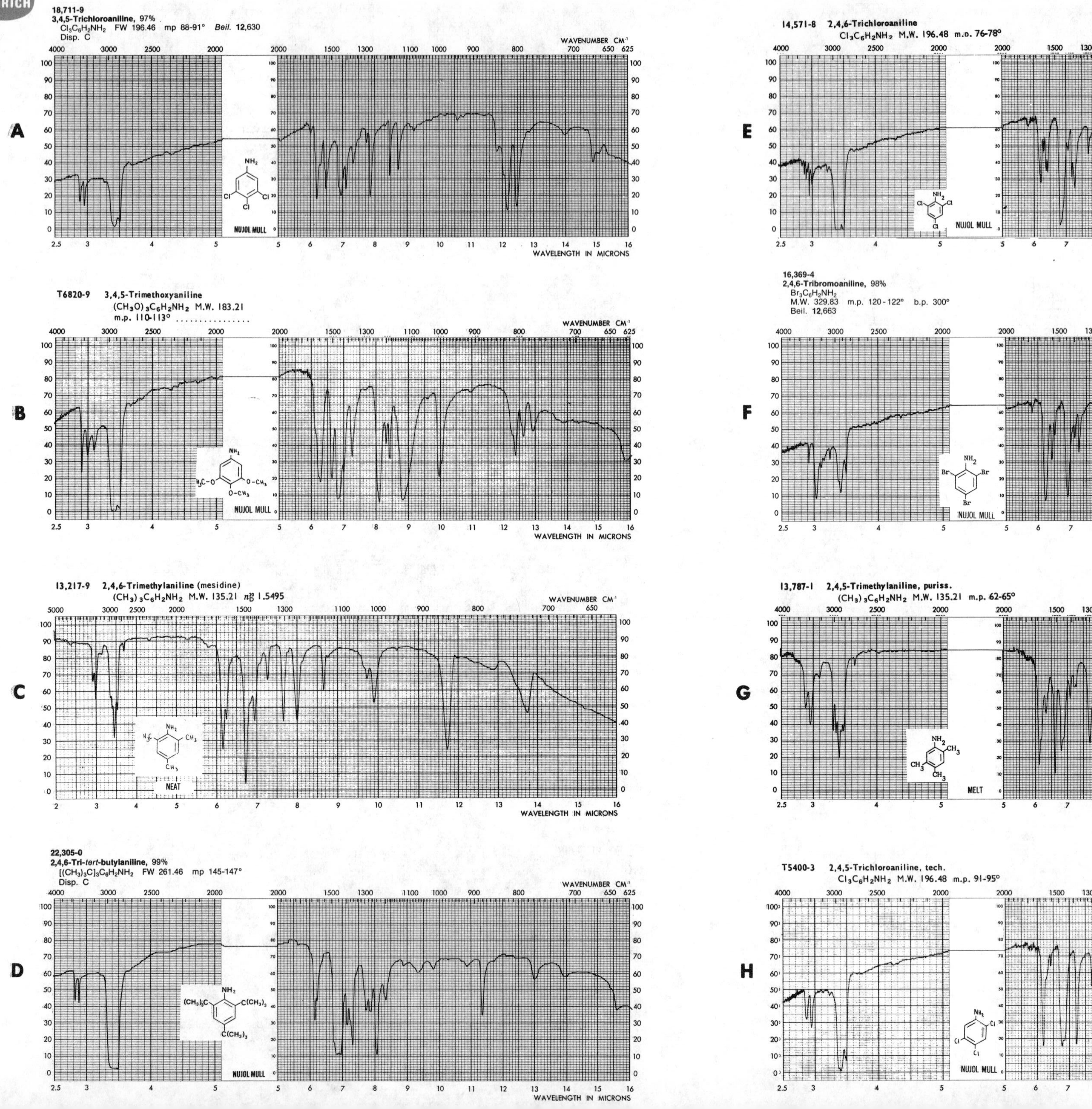
A
18,711-9
3,4,5-Trichloroaniline, 97%
$Cl_3C_6H_2NH_2$ FW 196.46 mp 88-91° Beil. 12,630
Disp. C
NUJOL MULL
B
T6820-9 3,4,5-Trimethoxyaniline
$(CH_3O)_3C_6H_2NH_2$ M.W. 183.21
m.p. 110-113°
NUJOL MULL
C
13,217-9 2,4,6-Trimethylaniline (mesidine)
$(CH_3)_3C_6H_2NH_2$ M.W. 135.21 n_D^{20} 1.5495
NEAT
D
22,305-0
2,4,6-Tri-tert-butylaniline, 99%
$[(CH_3)_3C]_3C_6H_2NH_2$ FW 261.46 mp 145-147°
Disp. C
NUJOL MULL
E
14,571-8 2,4,6-Trichloroaniline
$Cl_3C_6H_2NH_2$ M.W. 196.48 m.p. 76-78°
NUJOL MULL
F
16,369-4
2,4,6-Tribromoaniline, 98%
$Br_3C_6H_2NH_2$
M.W. 329.83 m.p. 120-122° b.p. 300°
Beil. 12,663
NUJOL MULL
G
13,787-1 2,4,5-Trimethylaniline, puriss.
$(CH_3)_3C_6H_2NH_2$ M.W. 135.21 m.p. 62-65°
MELT
H
T5400-3 2,4,5-Trichloroaniline, tech.
$Cl_3C_6H_2NH_2$ M.W. 196.48 m.p. 91-95°
NUJOL MULL
WAVENUMBER CM⁻¹
WAVELENGTH IN MICRONS

A C3500-2 5-Chloro-2,4-dimethoxyaniline
$ClC_6H_2(OCH_3)_2NH_2$ M.W. 187.63 m.p. 90-92°
NUJOL MULL

B C3480-4 4-Chloro-2,5-dimethoxyaniline
$ClC_6H_2(OCH_3)_2NH_2$ M.W. 187.63 m.p. 117-118°
NUJOL MULL

C 12,649-7 4-Amino-2,5-dimethylphenol (4-amino-2,5-xylenol)
$H_2NC_6H_2(CH_3)_2OH$ M.W. 137.18 m.p. 142-143°
NUJOL MULL

D 12,211-4 4-Aminothymol hydrochloride
$H_2NC_6H_2$-2-[$CH(CH_3)_2$]-5-(CH_3)OH·HCl M.W. 201.70
m.p. 255-260°
NUJOL MULL

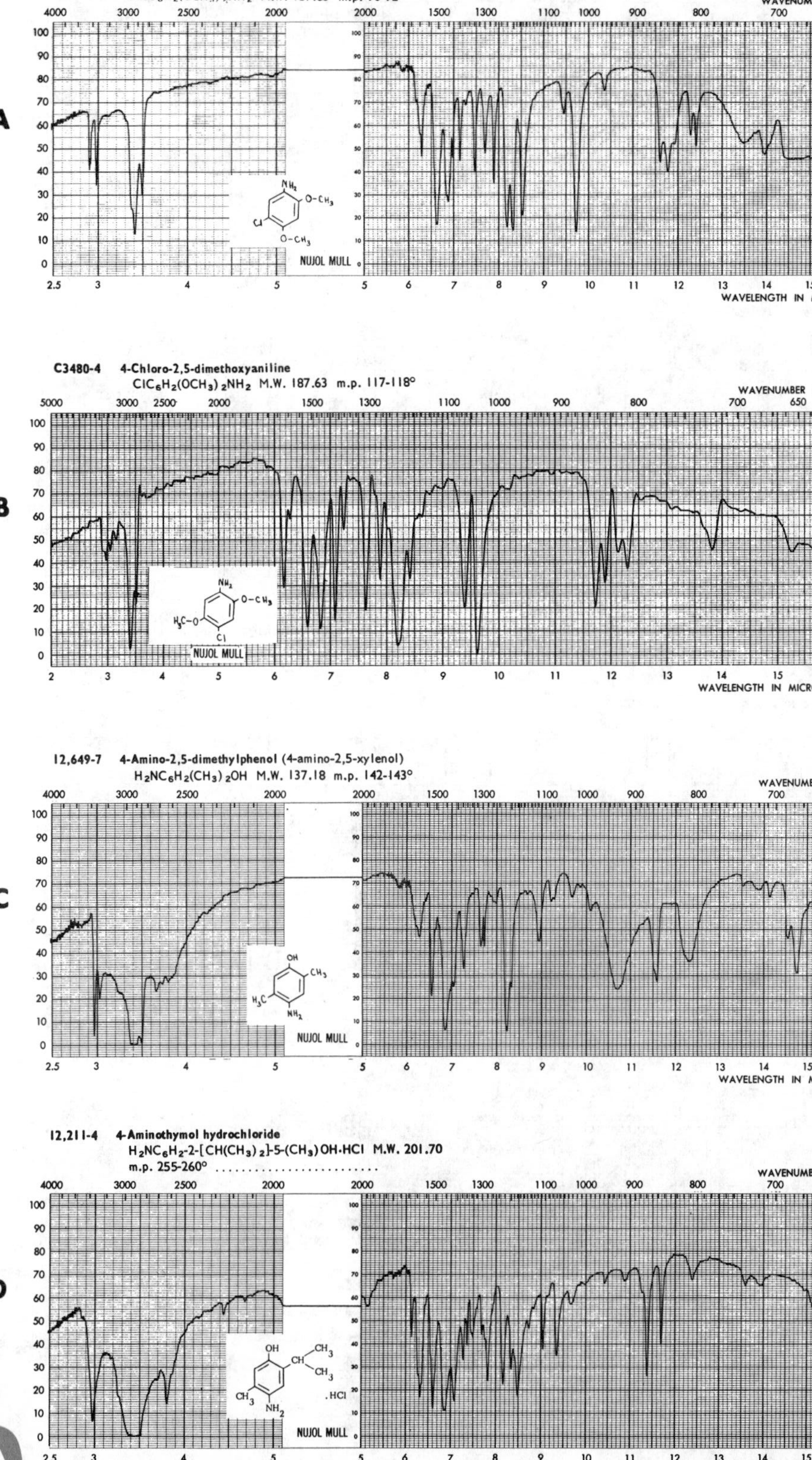

E 22,195-3
2,6-Dichloro-3-methylaniline, 99+%
$Cl_2C_6H_2(CH_3)NH_2$ FW 176.05 mp 37-39°
Disp. C
MELT

F 17,698-2
2,3,4-Trichloroaniline, 97%
$Cl_3C_6H_2NH_2$
M.W. 196.46 m.p. 65-67° b.p. 292°/774mm.
Beil. 12,626
MELT

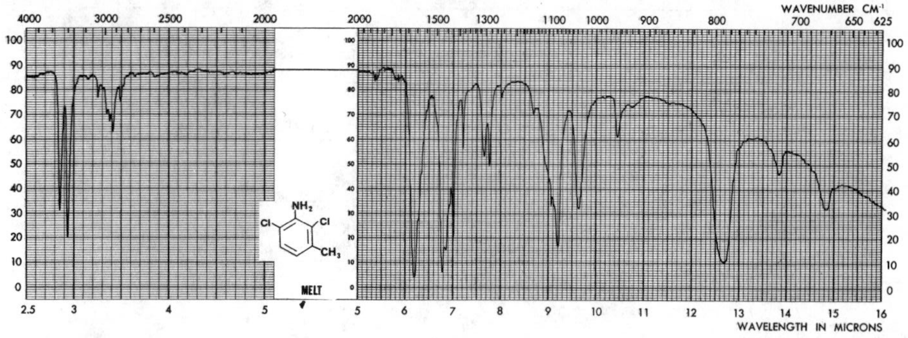

G 15,609-4
2,3,5,6-Tetrachloroaniline
$Cl_4C_6HNH_2$
M.W. 230.91 m.p. 106-108° Beil. 12(2),340
NUJOL MULL

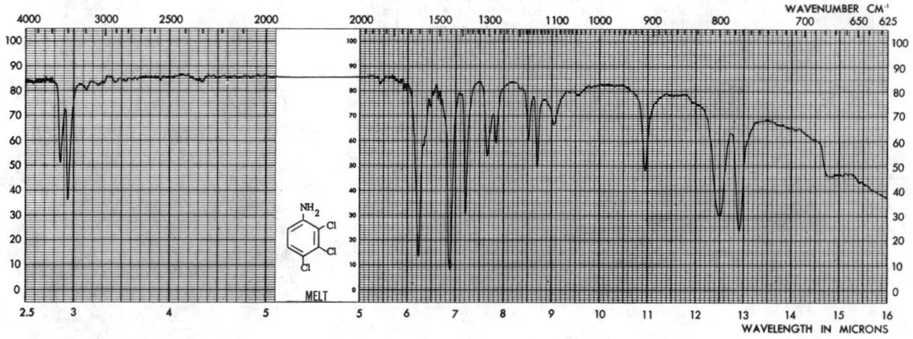

H 10,434-5 2,3,5,6-Tetrafluoroaniline
$F_4C_6HNH_2$ M.W. 165.09 m.p. 31-32°
MELT

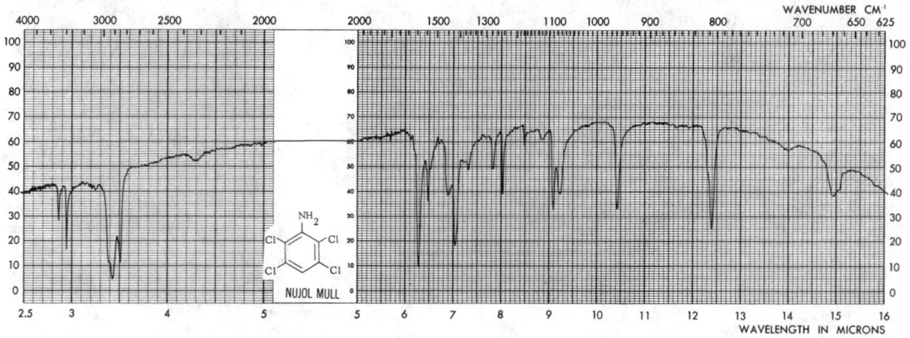

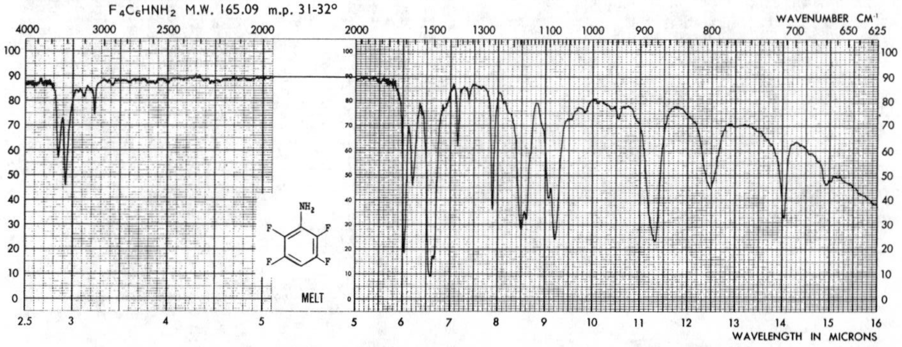

WAVENUMBER CM^{-1} / WAVELENGTH IN MICRONS

A

15,610-8
2,3,4,5-Tetrachloroaniline, 98+%
$Cl_4C_6HNH_2$

NUJOL MULL

B

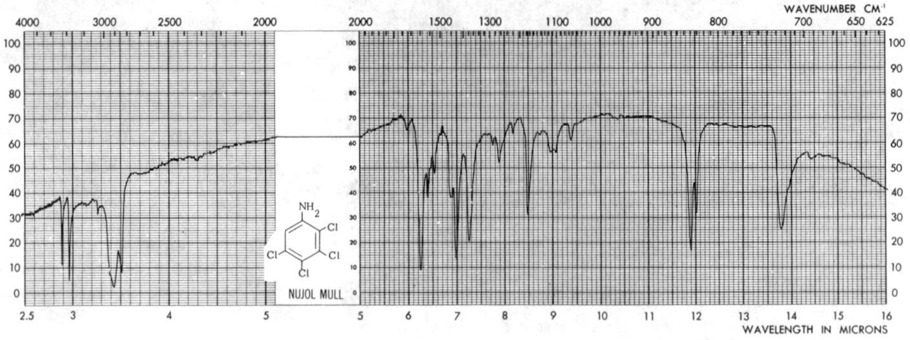

10,432-9 2,3,4,5-Tetrafluoroaniline
$HC_6F_4NH_2$ M.W. 165.09

NEAT

C

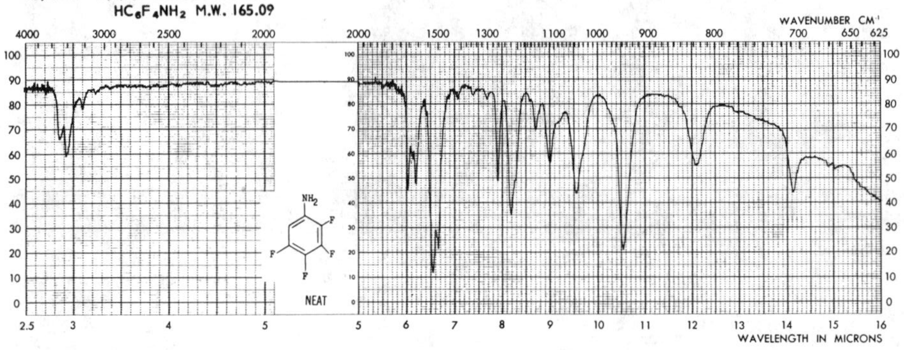

19,675-4
2,3,4,6-Tetrafluoroaniline, 97+%
$HC_6F_4NH_2$ FW 165.09 bp 80°/50mm. n_D^{20} 1.4630
d 1.481 Disp. C

NEAT

D

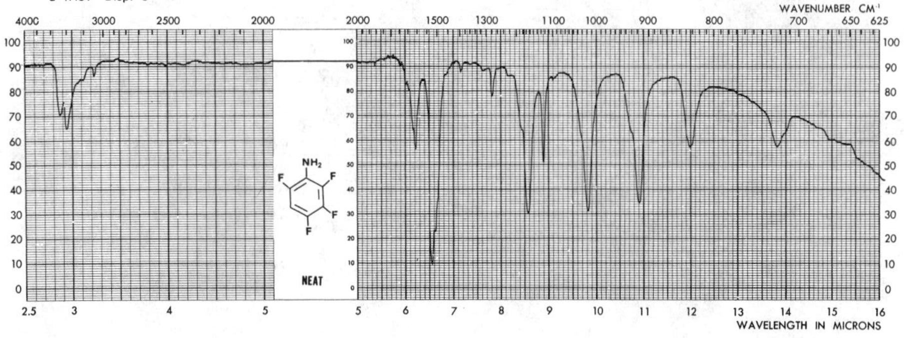

10,371-3 2,3,4,5,6-Pentafluoroaniline
$C_6F_5NH_2$ M.W. 183.08 m.p. 35-36°

MELT

E

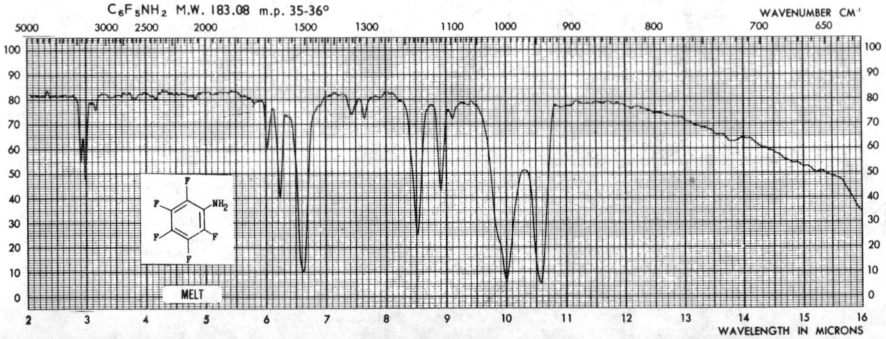

19,659-2
4,4'-Diaminooctafluorobiphenyl, 98% (octafluoro-benzidine)
$H_2NC_6F_4C_6F_4NH_2$ FW 328.16 mp 175-177°
Disp. D

NUJOL MULL

F

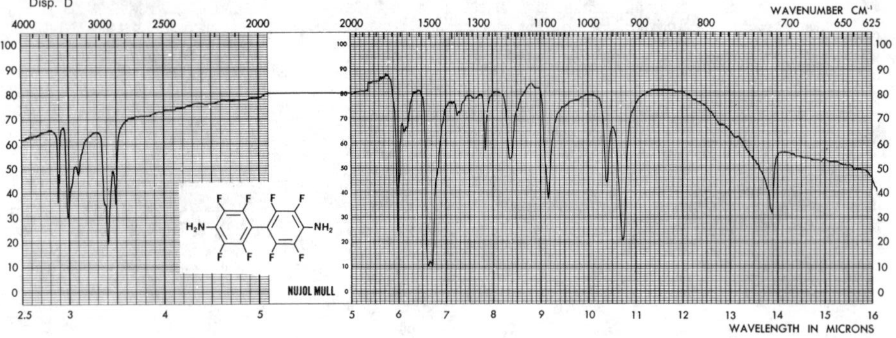

19,716-5
Pentachloroaniline, 98%
$C_6Cl_5NH_2$ FW 265.36 mp 232-235° *Beil.* 12,631
Disp. D

NUJOL MULL

G

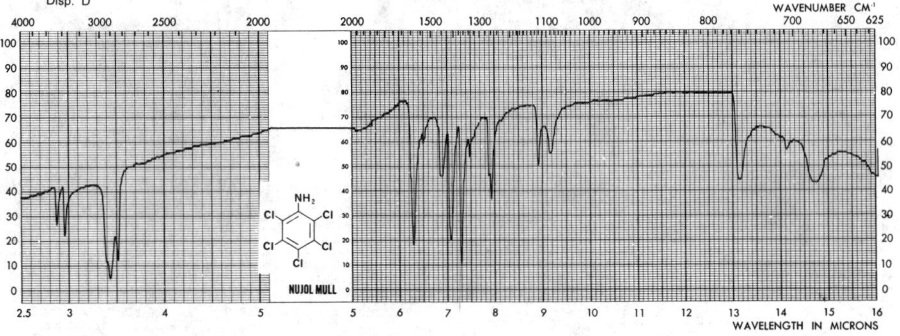

P2393-8 o-Phenylenediamine
$C_6H_4(NH_2)_2$ M.W. 108.14 m.p. 98-103.5°

NUJOL MULL

H

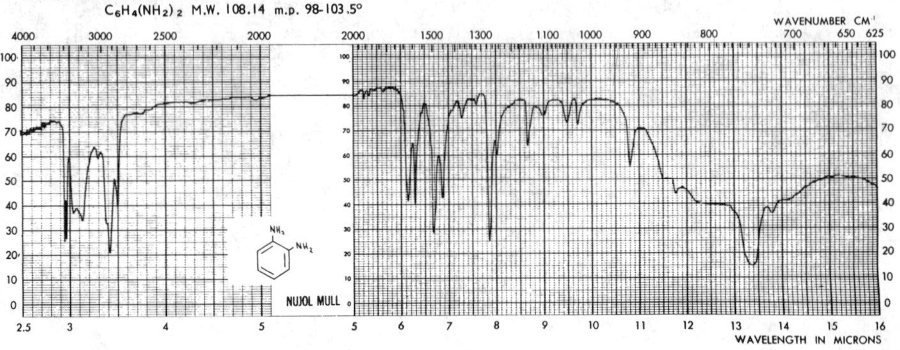

D2602-4 3,4-Diaminotoluene (3,4-toluenediamine)
$CH_3C_6H_3(NH_2)_2$ M.W. 122.17 m.p. 88-90°

NUJOL MULL

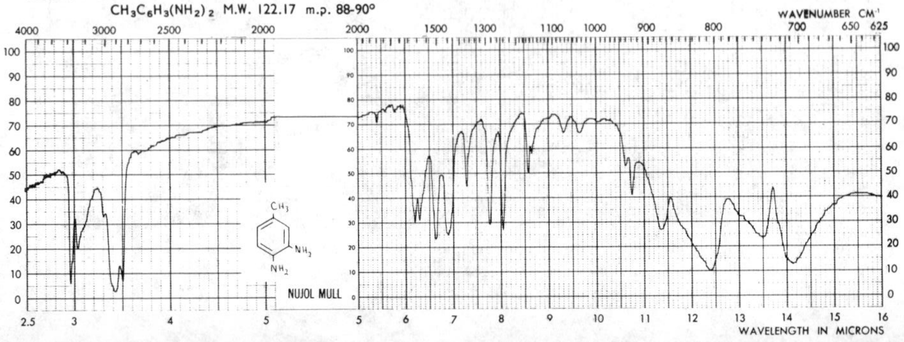

A D2603-2 3,4-Diaminotoluene (3,4-toluenediamine) dihydrochloride
$CH_3C_6H_3(NH_2)_2 \cdot 2HCl$ M.W. 195.09 m.p. 266-268° (dec.)

NUJOL MULL

B D1238-4 3,3'-Diaminobenzidine (3,3',4,4'-biphenyltetramine), tech.
$(H_2N)_2C_6H_3C_6H_3(NH_2)_2$ M.W. 214.28
m.p. 178-180°

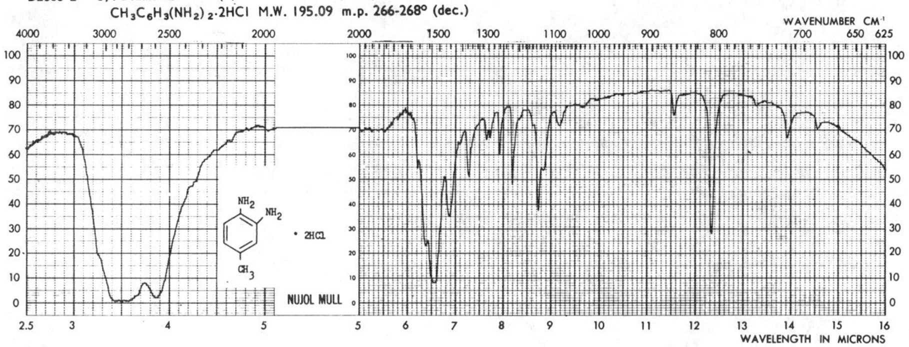

NUJOL MULL

C D1240-6 3,3'-Diaminobenzidine (3,3',4,4'-biphenyltetramine) tetrahydrochloride dihydrate
$(H_2N)_2C_6H_3C_6H_3(NH_2)_2 \cdot 4HCl \cdot 2H_2O$ M.W. 396.15
m.p. 328-330° (dec.)

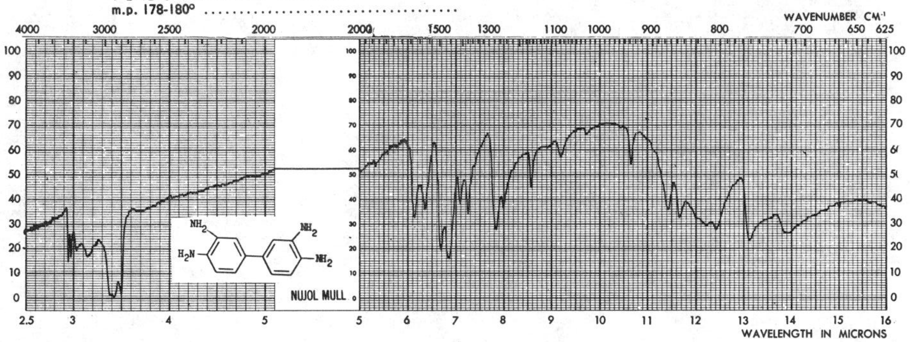

NUJOL MULL

D 86,033-6
3,3',5,5'-Tetramethylbenzidine, 99+%, GOLD LABEL (TMB)
$[-C_6H_2(CH_3)_2\text{-}4\text{-}NH_2]_2$ FW 240.35 mp 168-169°
Disp. C

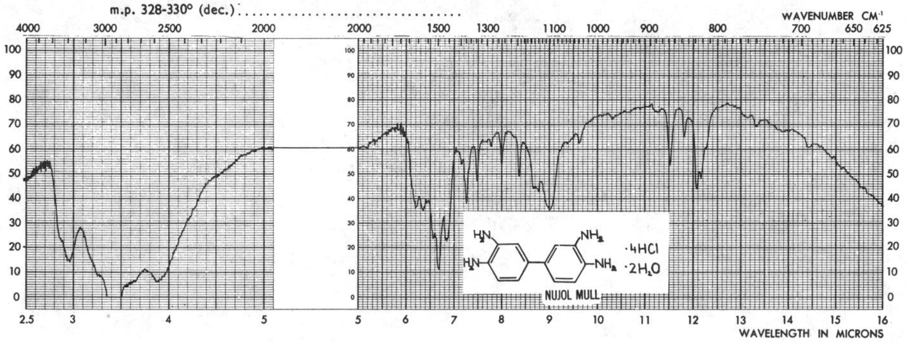

NUJOL MULL

E 86,151-0
3,3',5,5'-Tetramethylbenzidine dihydrochloride (TMB)
$[-C_6H_2(CH_3)_2\text{-}4\text{-}NH_2]_2 \cdot 2HCl$ FW 313.27 Disp. C

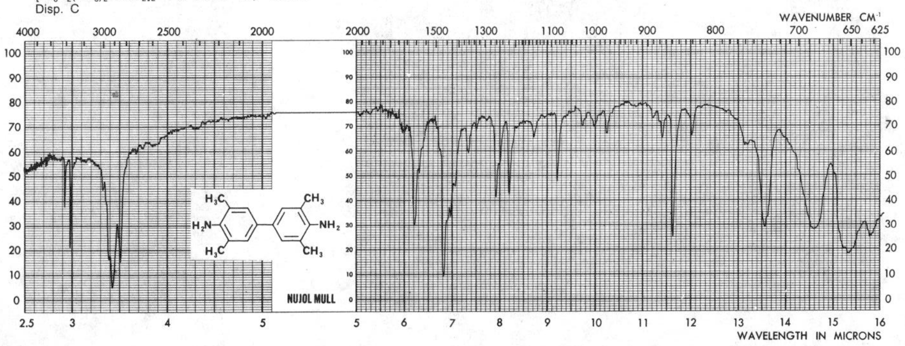

NUJOL MULL

F 10,887-1 4-Chloro-o-phenylenediamine
$ClC_6H_3(NH_2)_2$ M.W. 142.59 m.p. 72-74°

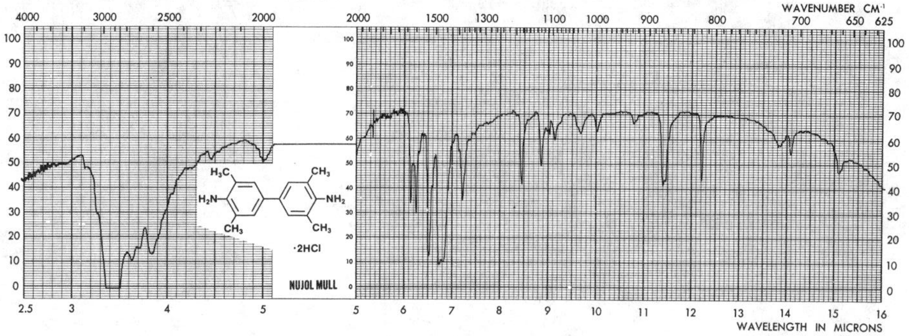

NUJOL MULL

G M2040-4 4-Methoxy-o-phenylenediamine
$CH_3OC_6H_3(NH_2)_2$ M.W. 138.17 b.p. 140-141°/5 mm.

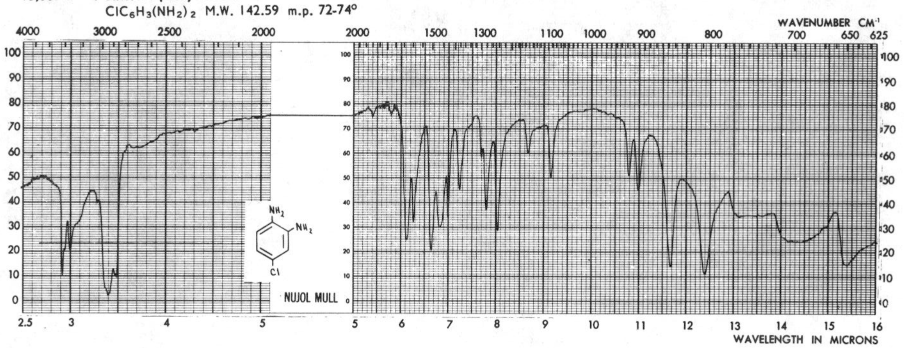

MELT

H D17,660-5 4,5-Dimethyl-o-phenylenediamine (4,5-diamino-o-xylene)
$(CH_3)_2C_6H_2(NH_2)_2$ M.W. 136.20
m.p. 127-129°

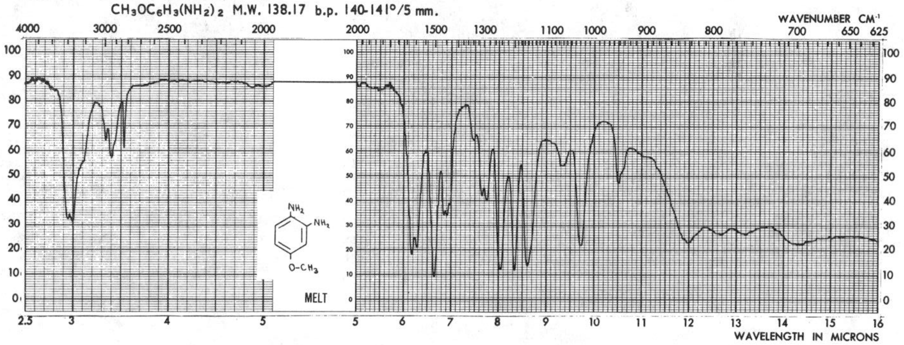

NUJOL MULL

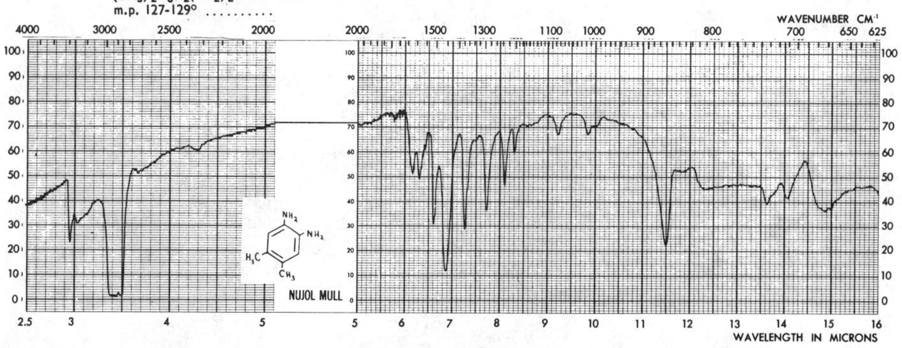

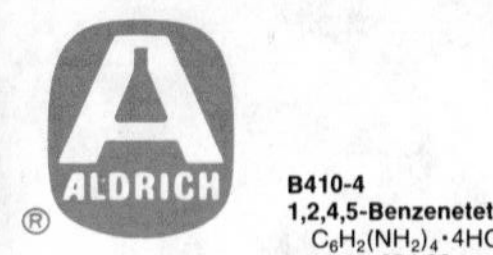

A

B410-4
1,2,4,5-Benzenetetramine tetrahydrochloride, 98%
$C_6H_2(NH_2)_4 \cdot 4HCl$
M.W. 284.02 m.p. >300° Beil. **13**,337

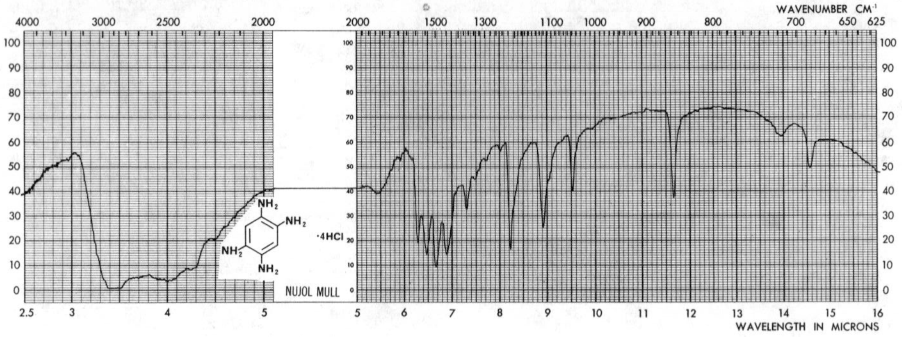

NUJOL MULL

B

D7160-7 **4,5-Dichloro-o-phenylenediamine**
$Cl_2C_6H_2(NH_2)_2$ M.W. 177.03 m.p. 160-164°

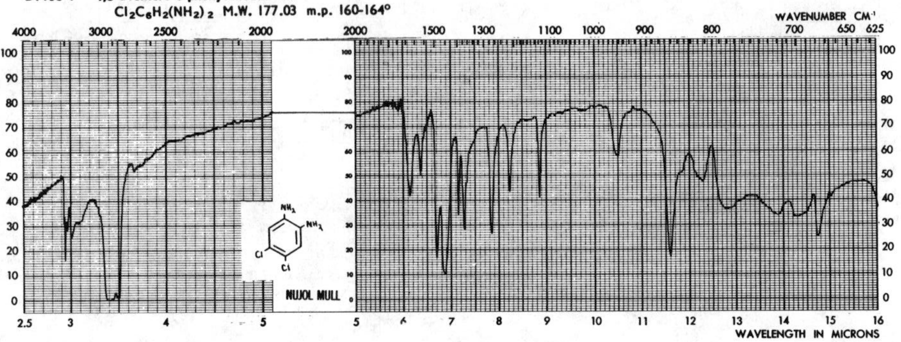

NUJOL MULL

C

P2835-2 **N-Phenyl-o-phenylenediamine** (o-aminodiphenylamine)
$C_6H_5NHC_6H_4NH_2$ M.W. 184.24
m.p. 79.5-82.5°

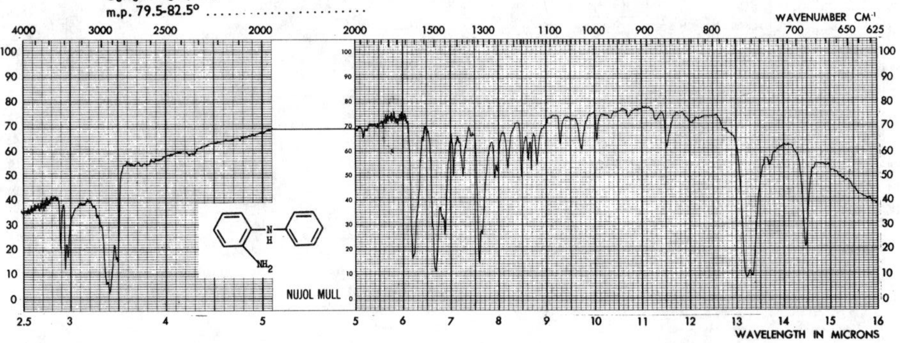

NUJOL MULL

D

P2395-4 **m-Phenylenediamine, puriss.**
$C_6H_4(NH_2)_2$ M.W. 108.14 m.p. 62-64°

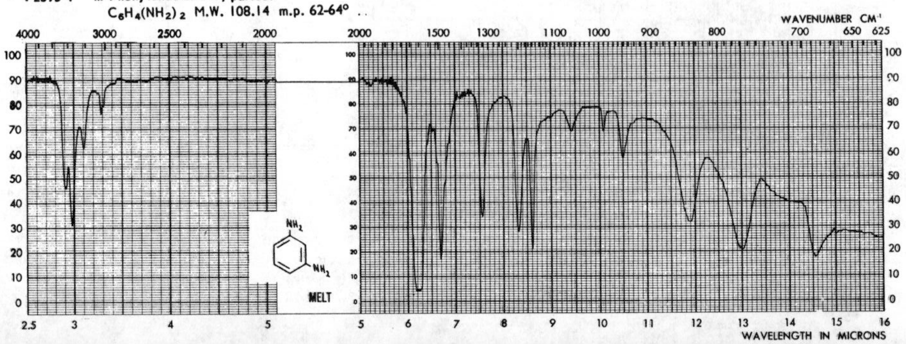

MELT

E

21,922-3
***N,N*-Dimethyl-*m*-phenylenediamine dihydrochloride**, 99%
$(CH_3)_2NC_6H_4NH_2 \cdot 2HCl$ FW 209.12
mp 217° (dec.) *Beil.* **13**,40 Disp. C

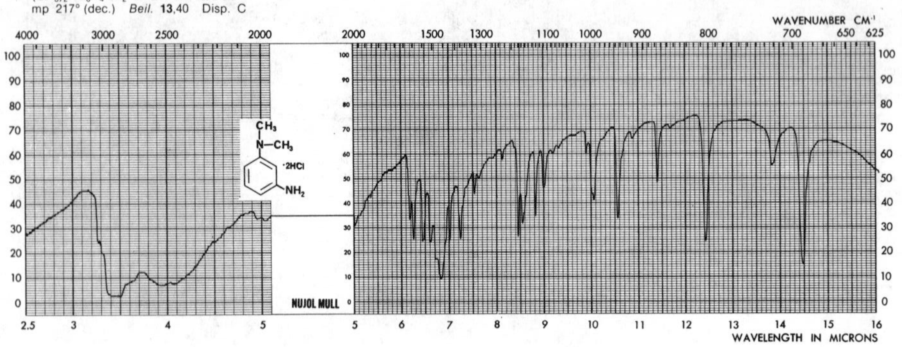

NUJOL MULL

F

14,811-3 **2,6-Diaminotoluene** (2,6-toluenediamine)
$CH_3C_6H_3(NH_2)_2$ M.W. 122.17 m.p. 104-106°

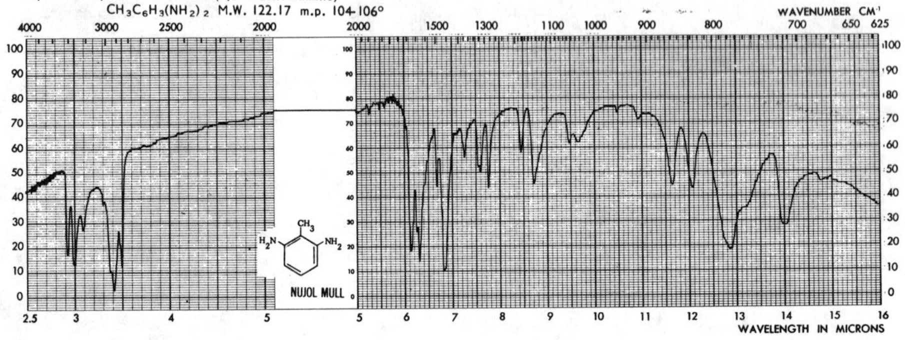

NUJOL MULL

G

10,191-5 **2,4-Diaminotoluene** (2,4-toluenediamine)
$CH_3C_6H_3(NH_2)_2$ M.W. 122.17 m.p. 97-99°

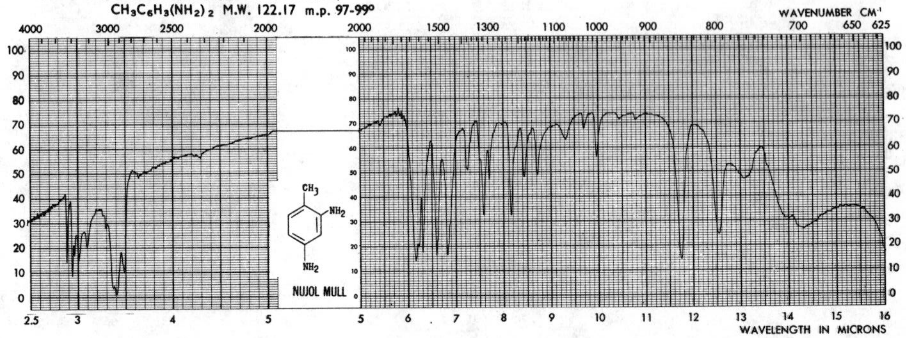

NUJOL MULL

H

A5,968-9
6-Aminoindoline dihydrochloride
M.W. 207.11 m.p. 274-275° (dec.)

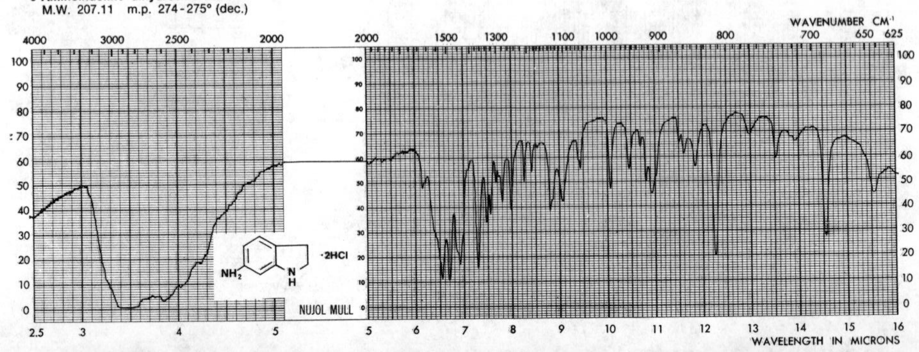

NUJOL MULL

A

12,517-2 **4-Chloro-m-phenylenediamine**
$ClC_6H_3(NH_2)_2$ M.W. 142.59 m.p. 87-90°

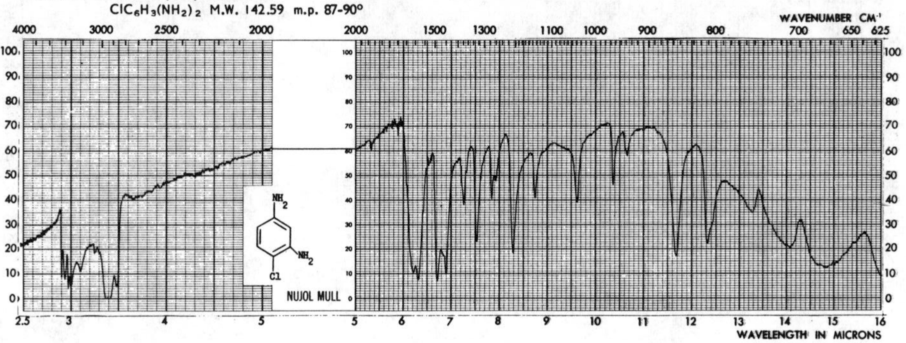

NUJOL MULL

B

18,332-6
4-Methoxy-m-phenylenediamine disulfate
$CH_3OC_6H_3(NH_2)_2 \cdot 2H_2SO_4$
M.W. 334.33 m.p. 189-192° (dec.)

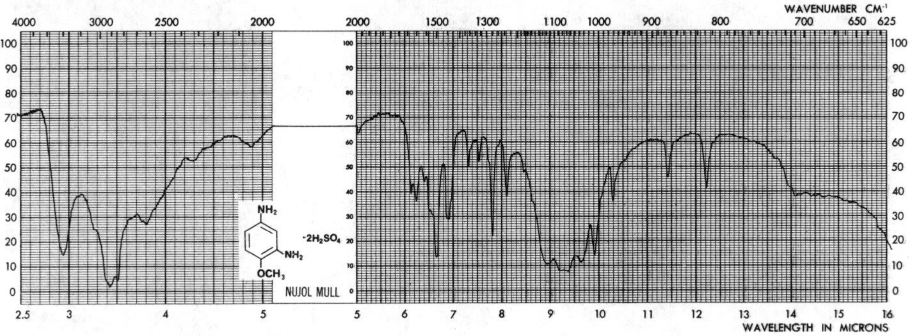

NUJOL MULL

C

19,914-1
2,4-Diamino-6-methylphenol dihydrochloride, tech.
(4,6-diamino-o-cresol)
$CH_3C_6H_2(NH_2)_2OH \cdot 2HCl$ FW 211.09
mp 294° (dec.) *Beil.* **13**,588 Disp. C

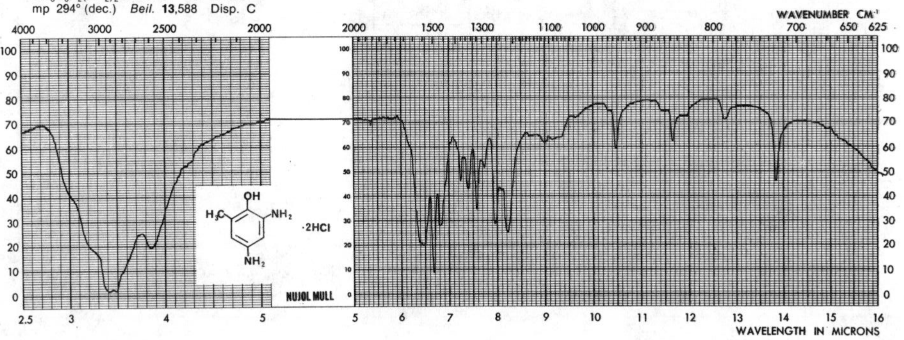

NUJOL MULL

D

20,015-8
4-Ethoxy-1,3-phenylenediamine dihydrochloride
$C_2H_5OC_6H_3(NH_2)_2 \cdot 2HCl$ FW 225.12
mp 228° (dec.) *Beil.* **13**(2),308 *Fieser* **7**,30
Disp. C

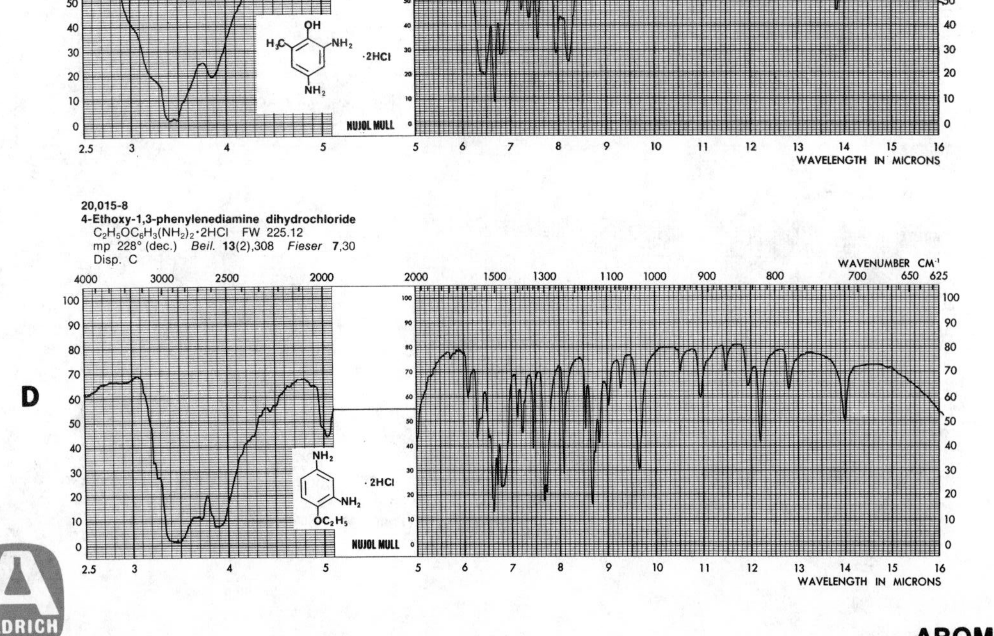

NUJOL MULL

E

20,911-2
4-Ethoxy-1,3-phenylenediamine sulfate monohydrate, 97+%
$C_2H_5OC_6H_3(NH_2)_2 \cdot H_2SO_4 \cdot H_2O$ FW 268.29
Beil. **13**(1),204 Disp. C

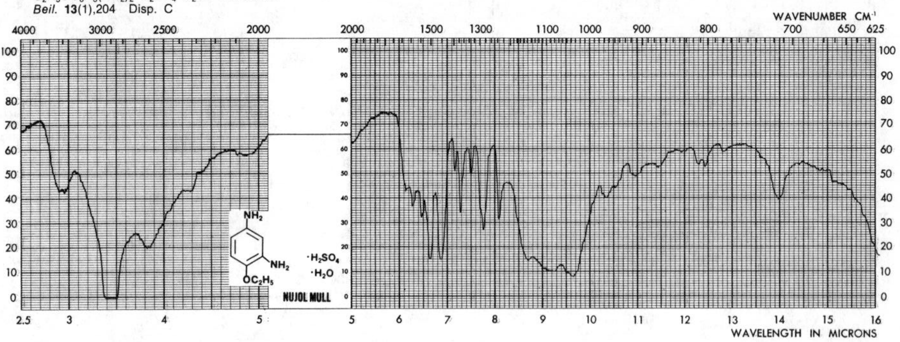

NUJOL MULL

F

20,016-6
4-(2-Hydroxyethoxy)-1,3-phenylenediamine dihydrochloride [2-(2,4-diaminophenoxy)ethanol]
$HOCH_2CH_2OC_6H_3(NH_2)_2 \cdot 2HCl$ FW 241.12
mp 262° (dec.) Disp. C

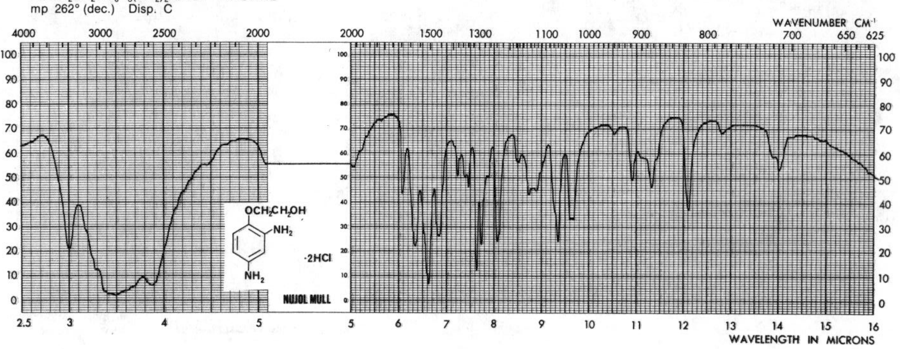

NUJOL MULL

G

21,125-7
4-(2-Hydroxyethoxy)-1,3-phenylenediamine sulfate dihydrate, 97+% [2-(2,4-diaminophenoxy)ethanol]
$HOCH_2CH_2OC_6H_3(NH_2)_2 \cdot H_2SO_4 \cdot 2H_2O$ FW 302.30
mp >300° Disp. C

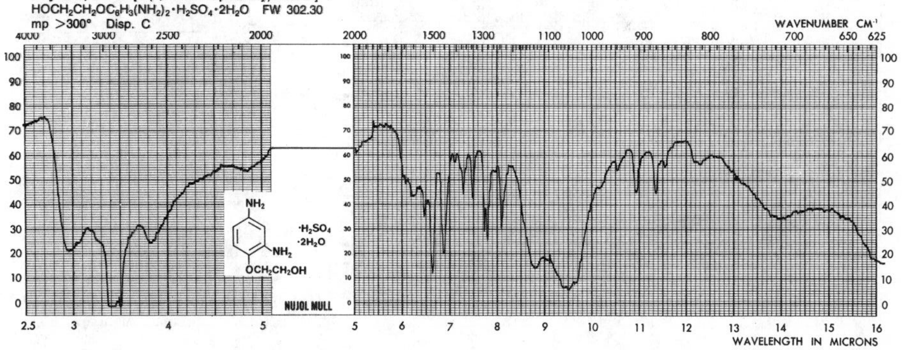

NUJOL MULL

H

20,923-6
4-(2-Hydroxyethylthio)-1,3-phenylenediamine dihydrochloride [2-(2,4-diaminophenylthio)ethanol]
$HOCH_2CH_2SC_6H_3(NH_2)_2 \cdot 2HCl$ FW 257.18
mp 180° (dec.) Disp. C

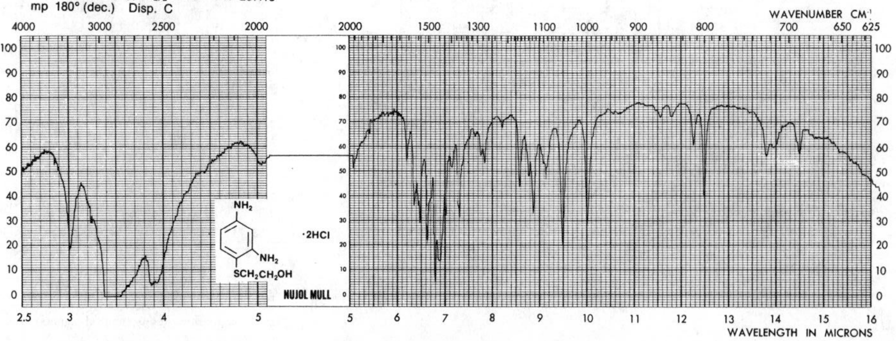

NUJOL MULL

A

P2396-2 **p-Phenylenediamine**
$C_6H_4(NH_2)_2$ M.W. 108.14 m.p. 138-143°

NUJOL MULL

B

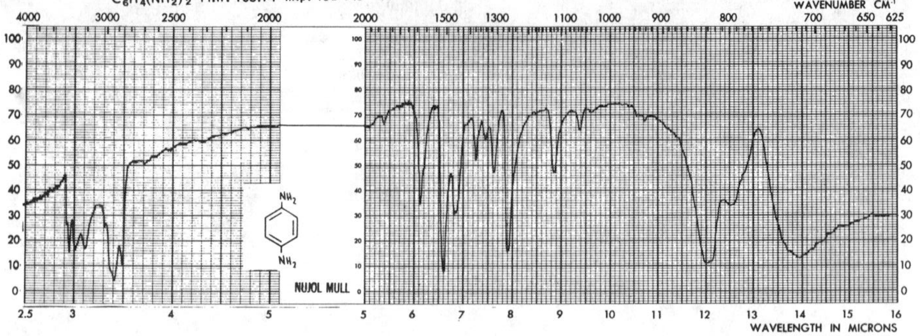

13,769-3 **p-Phenylenediamine dihydrochloride**
$C_6H_4(NH_2)_2 \cdot 2HCl$ M.W. 181.07 m.p. > 360°

NUJOL MULL

C

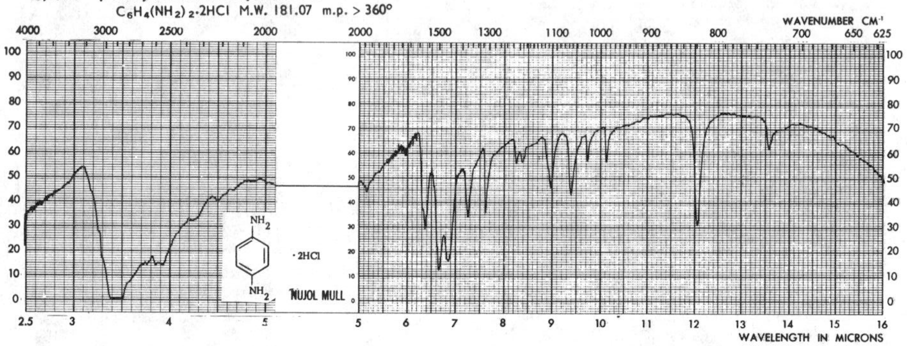

19,399-2
***N,N*-Dimethyl-*p*-phenylenediamine**
$(CH_3)_2NC_6H_4NH_2$ FW 136.20 mp 34-36°
bp 262° *Beil.* **13**,72 Disp. C

MELT

D

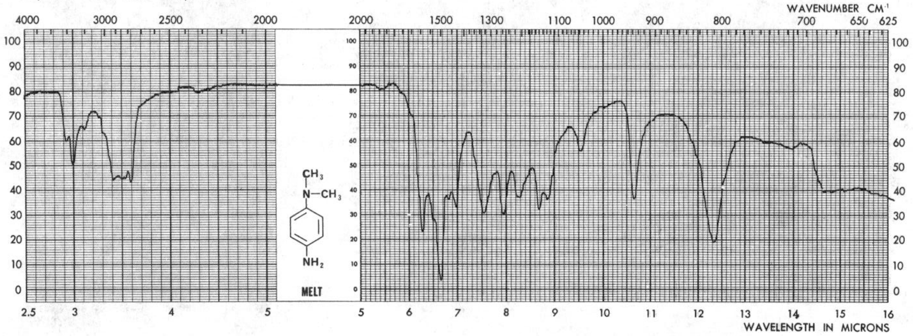

21,923-1
***N,N*-Dimethyl-*p*-phenylenediamine dihydrochloride**, 99%
$(CH_3)_2NC_6H_4NH_2 \cdot 2HCl$ FW 209.12
mp 222° (dec.) *Beil.* **13**,73 *Fieser* **1**,293 Disp. C

NUJOL MULL

E

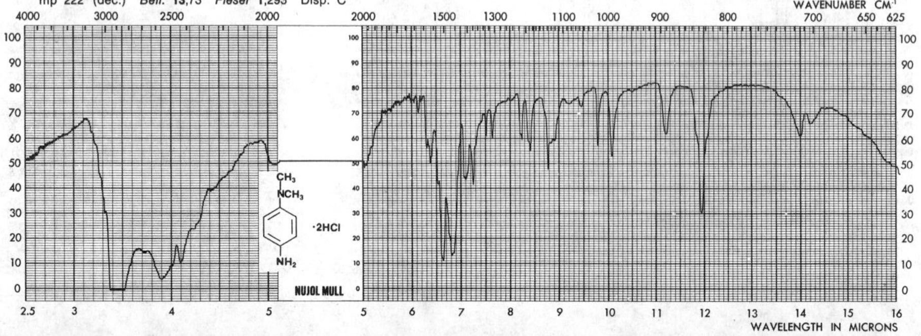

18,638-4
N,N-Dimethyl-p-phenylenediamine sulfate, tech.
$(CH_3)_2NC_6H_4NH_2 \cdot H_2SO_4$
M.W. 234.28 m.p. 234-236° (dec.) b.p. 495°
Beil. **13**,72 *CARCINOGEN*

NUJOL MULL

F

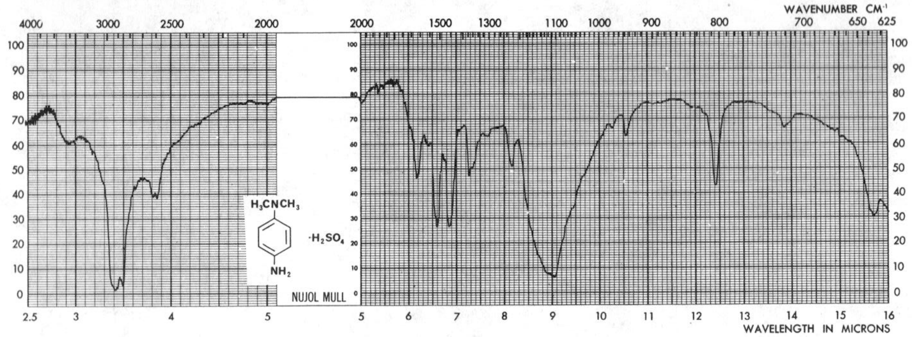

16,020-2
N,N,N',N'-Tetramethyl-p-phenylenediamine, 98%
$C_6H_4[N(CH_3)_2]_2$
M.W. 164.25 m.p. 49-51° b.p. 260° Beil. **13**,74

MELT

G

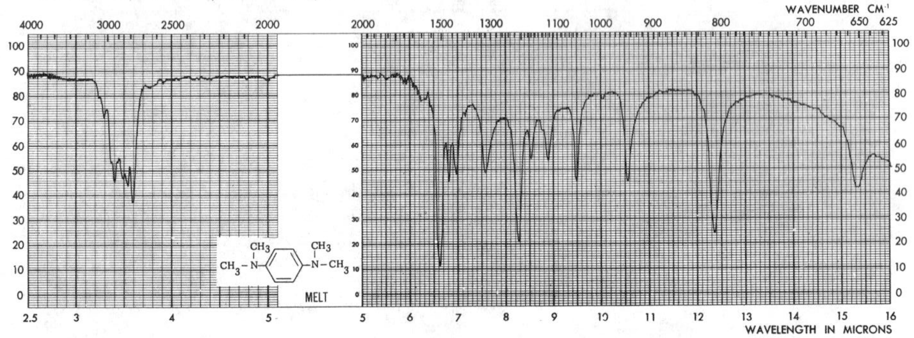

21,120-6
***N,N*-Bis(2-hydroxyethyl)-*p*-phenylenediamine sulfate monohydrate,** 97%
$H_2NC_6H_4N(CH_2CH_2OH)_2 \cdot H_2SO_4 \cdot H_2O$ FW 312.34
mp 145° (dec.) Disp. C

NUJOL MULL

H

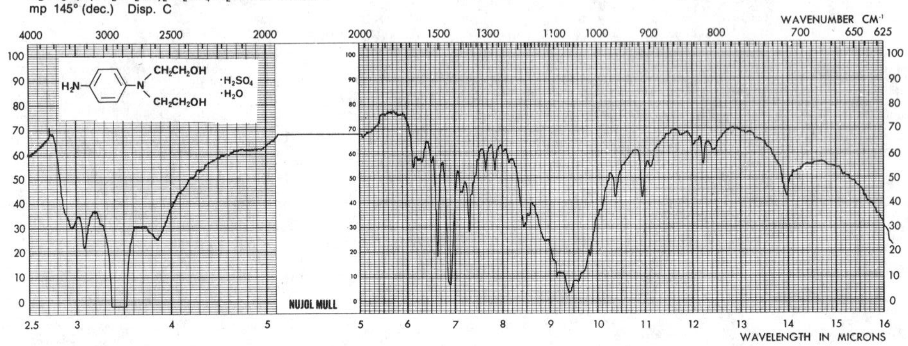

D2600-8 **2,5-Diaminotoluene (2,5-toluenediamine), dihydrochloride**
$CH_3C_6H_3(NH_2)_2 \cdot 2HCl$ M.W. 195.09 m.p. 250° (dec.)

NUJOL MULL

WAVENUMBER CM⁻¹ — WAVELENGTH IN MICRONS

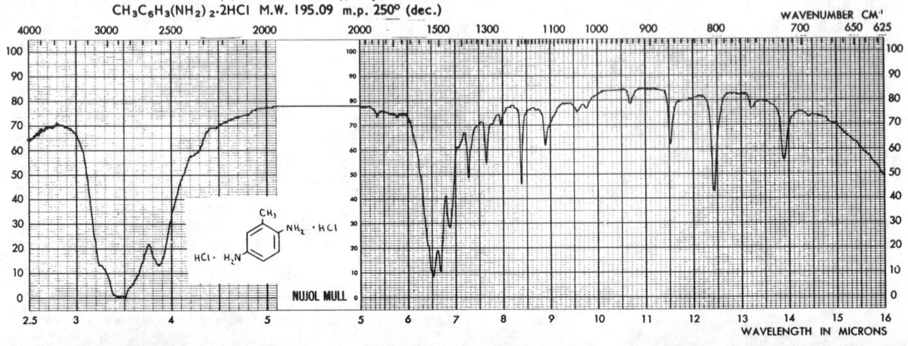

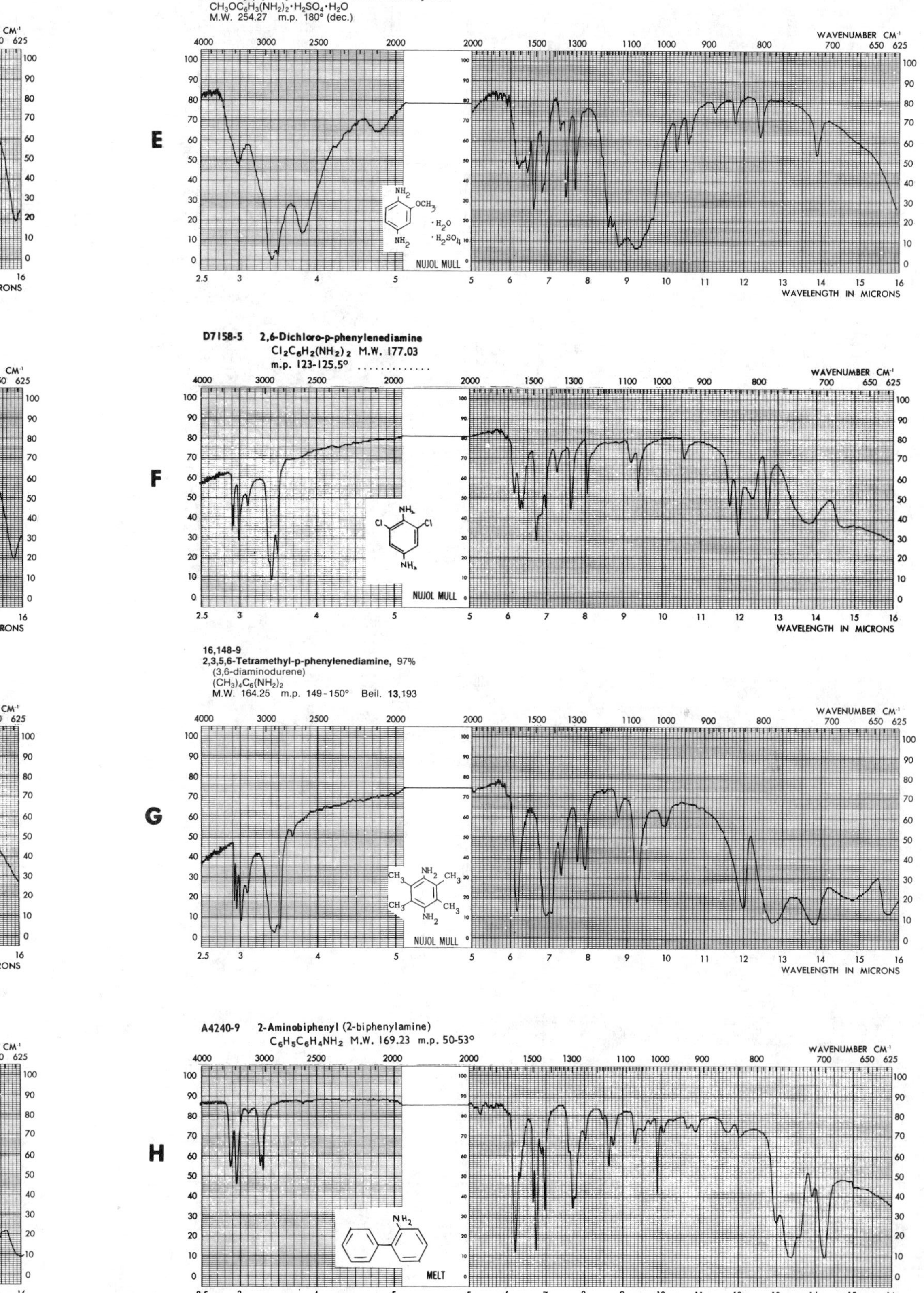

A 15,433-4 **2,5-Diaminotoluene** (2,5-toluenediamine) sulfate
$CH_3C_6H_3(NH_2)_2 \cdot H_2SO_4$ M.W. 220.25
m.p. 300° ....
NUJOL MULL

B 17,823-3
2-Chloro-p-phenylenediamine sulfate, 98%
$ClC_6H_3(NH_2)_2 \cdot H_2SO_4$
M.W. 240.67 m.p. 251-253° Beil. **13**,117
NUJOL MULL

C 14,784-2 **2-Chloro-N¹,N¹-diethyl-p-phenylenediamine monohydrochloride monohydrate**
$ClC_6H_3(NH_2)N(C_2H_5)_2 \cdot HCl \cdot H_2O$ M.W. 253.18
m.p. 202-203° (dec.) ....
NUJOL MULL

D 21,149-4
2,5-Dichloro-*p*-phenylenediamine
$Cl_2C_6H_2(NH_2)_2$ FW 177.03 mp 165° (dec.)
Beil. **13**,118 Disp. C
NUJOL MULL

E 17,006-2
2-Methoxy-p-phenylenediamine sulfate monohydrate
$CH_3OC_6H_3(NH_2)_2 \cdot H_2SO_4 \cdot H_2O$
M.W. 254.27 m.p. 180° (dec.)
NUJOL MULL

F D7158-5 **2,6-Dichloro-p-phenylenediamine**
$Cl_2C_6H_2(NH_2)_2$ M.W. 177.03
m.p. 123-125.5° ....
NUJOL MULL

G 16,148-9
2,3,5,6-Tetramethyl-p-phenylenediamine, 97%
(3,6-diaminodurene)
$(CH_3)_4C_6(NH_2)_2$
M.W. 164.25 m.p. 149-150° Beil. **13**,193
NUJOL MULL

H A4240-9 **2-Aminobiphenyl** (2-biphenylamine)
$C_6H_5C_6H_4NH_2$ M.W. 169.23 m.p. 50-53°
MELT

WAVENUMBER CM⁻¹ — WAVELENGTH IN MICRONS

A

A4242-5 **4-Aminobiphenyl (4-biphenylamine)**
$C_6H_5C_6H_4NH_2$ M.W. 169.23 m.p. 52-54°
MELT

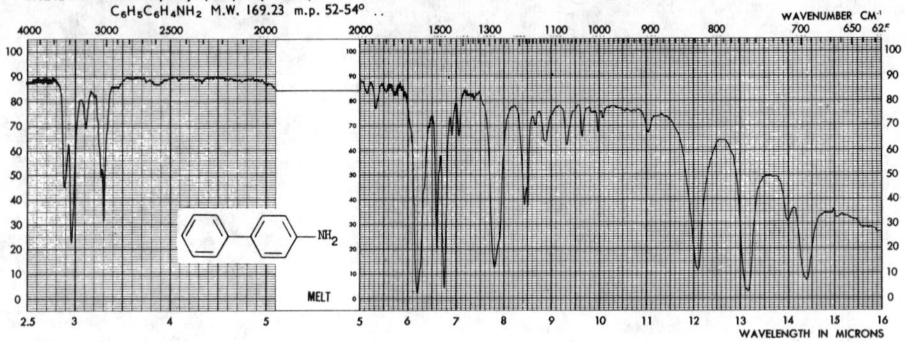

B

20,988-0
5-Phenyl-o-anisidine, 98+% (2-methoxy-5-phenylaniline)
$C_6H_5C_6H_3(OCH_3)NH_2$ FW 199.25 mp 82-83°
Beil. 13(3),1946 Disp. C
NUJOL MULL

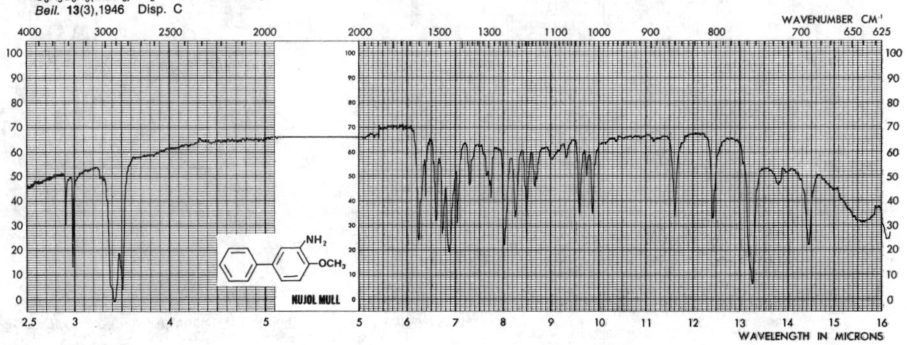

C

D20,520-6 **N,N'-Diphenylbenzidine**
4-$(C_6H_5NH)C_6H_4C_6H_4$-4-(NHC_6H_5) M.W. 336.44
m.p. 246-248°
NUJOL MULL

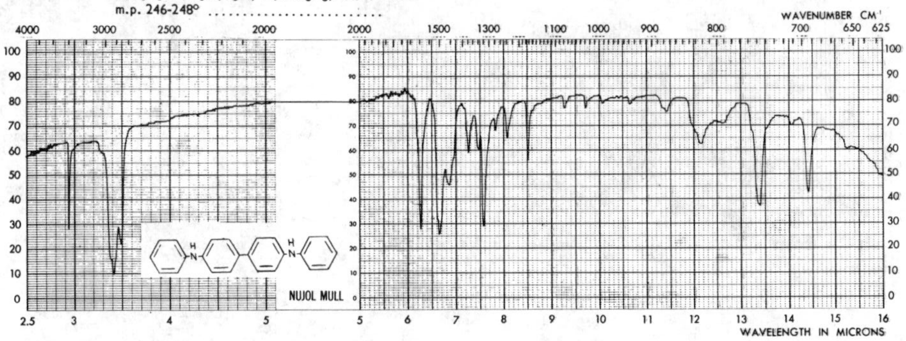

D

M4445-1 **4,4'-Methylenebis-(N,N-dimethylaniline)**
$CH_2[C_6H_4N(CH_3)_2]_2$ M.W. 254.38
m.p. 88-89°
NUJOL MULL

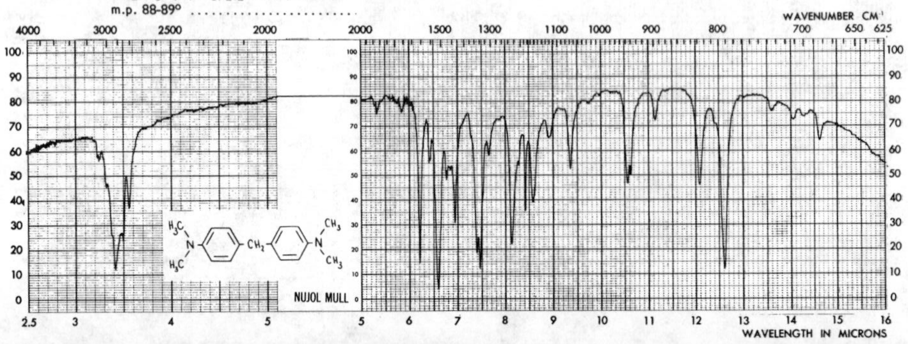

E

85,855-2
4,4'-Bis(dimethylamino)benzhydrol [4,4'-bis-(dimethylamino)diphenyl carbinol]
$[(CH_3)_2NC_6H_4]_2CHOH$
M.W. 270.38 m.p. 100-102° Beil. **13**,698
NUJOL MULL

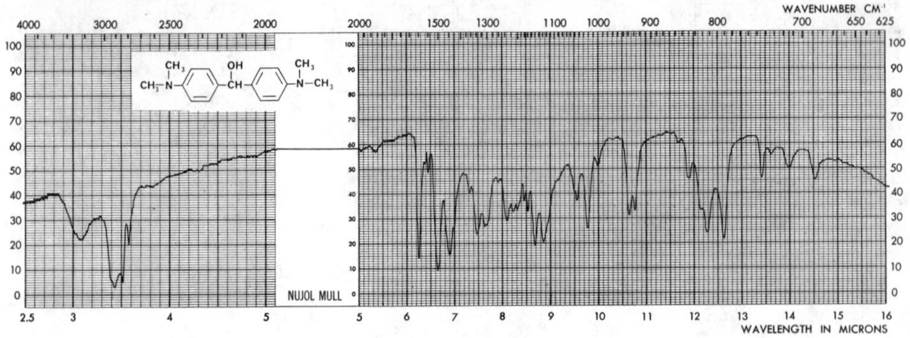

F

15,950-6
p-Tritylaniline, 98%
$(C_6H_5)_3CC_6H_4NH_2$
M.W. 335.45 m.p. 253-255°
NUJOL MULL

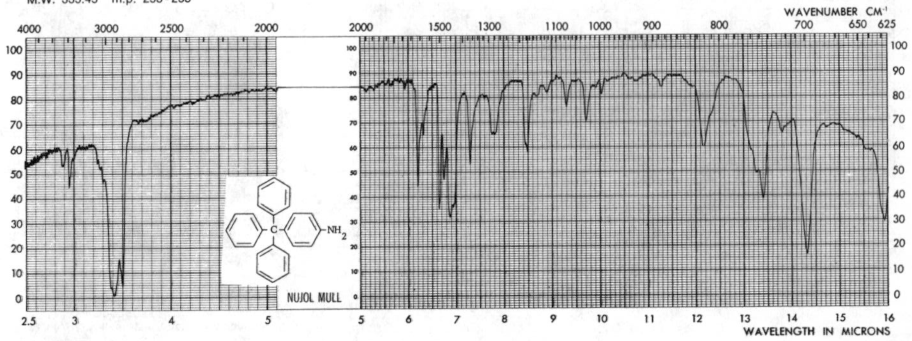

G

21,560-0
Pararosaniline base (C.I. 42500)
FW 305.38 mp 205° (dec.) *Beil.* **13**,733
Disp. C,D
NUJOL MULL

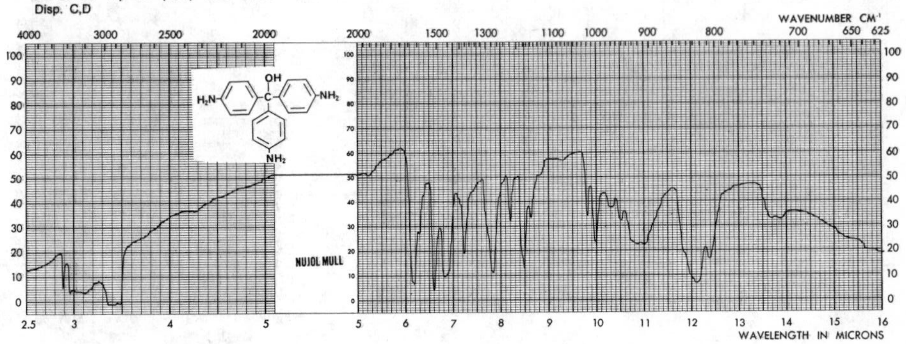

H

14,781-8 *trans*-**2',5'-Dimethoxy-4-stilbenamine**
$(CH_3O)_2C_6H_3CH{:}CHC_6H_4NH_2$ M.W. 255.32
m.p. 86-88°
NUJOL MULL

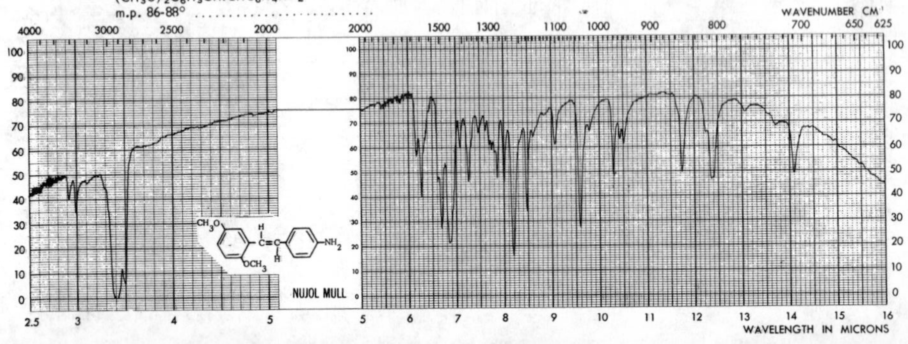

A

P1510-2 p-Phenoxyaniline (4-aminophenyl phenyl ether)
$C_6H_5OC_6H_4NH_2$ M.W. 185.23
m.p. 85-86°

NUJOL MULL

B

17,888-8
p-(p-Aminophenoxy)-phenol
$H_2NC_6H_4OC_6H_4OH$
M.W. 201.23 m.p. 150-152°

NUJOL MULL

C

17,885-3
4,4'-(p-Phenylenedioxy)-dianiline, 97%
$C_6H_4(OC_6H_4NH_2)_2$
M.W. 292.34 m.p. 169-171°

NUJOL MULL

D

17,861-6
3,3'-Dimethoxybenzidine, 82%, remainder moisture
(o-dianisidine)
$4\text{-}(H_2N)C_6H_3(OCH_3)C_6H_3(OCH_3)\text{-}4\text{-}(NH_2)$
M.W. 244.29 m.p. 137-139° Beil. **13**,807

NUJOL MULL

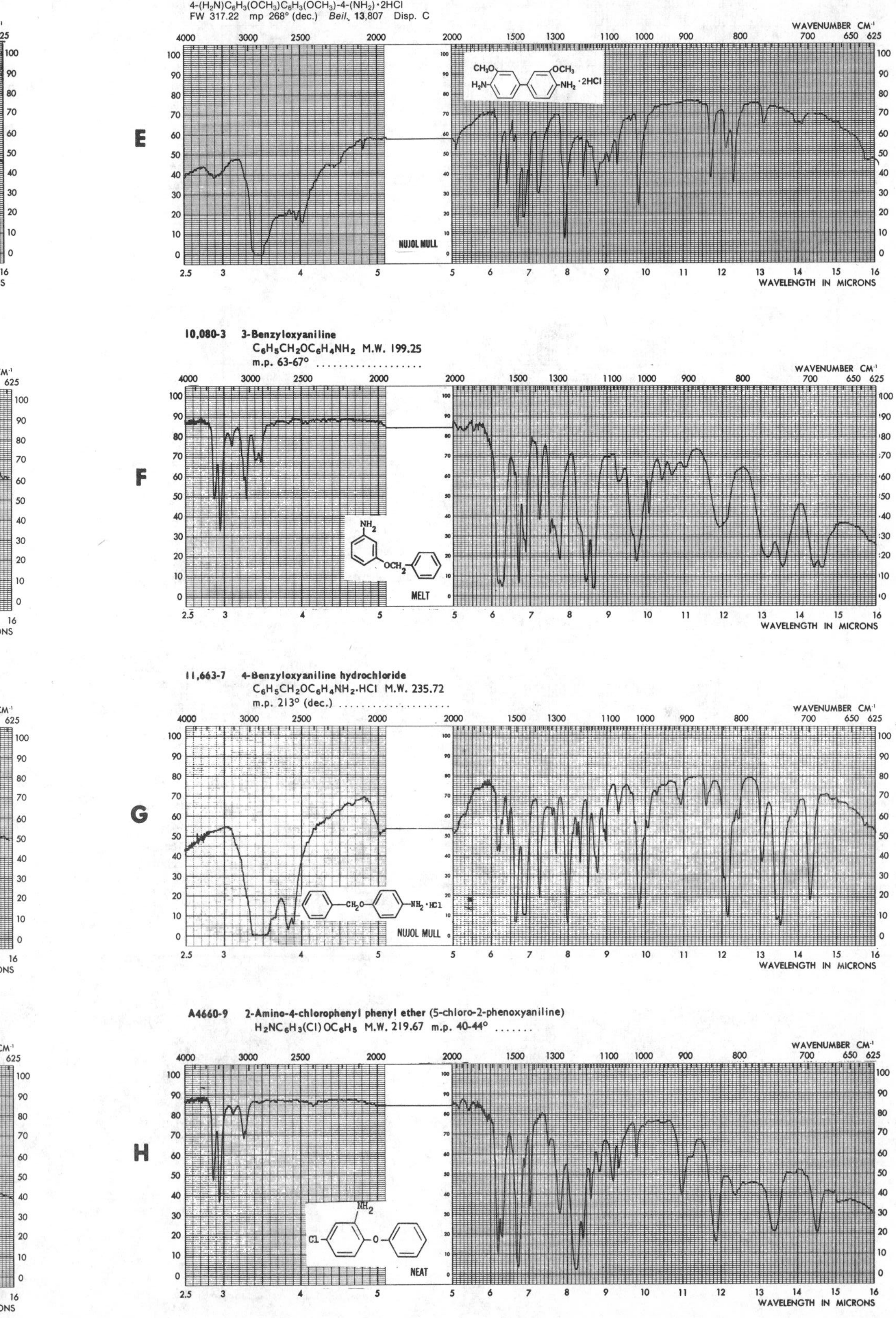

E

19,124-8
3,3'-Dimethoxybenzidine dihydrochloride, tech., 88%
(o-dianisidine)
$4\text{-}(H_2N)C_6H_3(OCH_3)C_6H_3(OCH_3)\text{-}4\text{-}(NH_2)\cdot 2HCl$
FW 317.22 mp 268° (dec.) *Beil.* **13**,807 Disp. C

NUJOL MULL

F

10,080-3 3-Benzyloxyaniline
$C_6H_5CH_2OC_6H_4NH_2$ M.W. 199.25
m.p. 63-67°

MELT

G

11,663-7 4-Benzyloxyaniline hydrochloride
$C_6H_5CH_2OC_6H_4NH_2\cdot HCl$ M.W. 235.72
m.p. 213° (dec.)

NUJOL MULL

H

A4660-9 2-Amino-4-chlorophenyl phenyl ether (5-chloro-2-phenoxyaniline)
$H_2NC_6H_3(Cl)OC_6H_5$ M.W. 219.67 m.p. 40-44°

NEAT

A

10,253-9 **N-Benzyl-N-ethyl-m-toluidine** (N-ethyl-N-m-tolylbenzylamine)
$C_6H_5CH_2N(C_2H_5)C_6H_4CH_3$ M.W. 225.34 n_D^{20} 1.5851

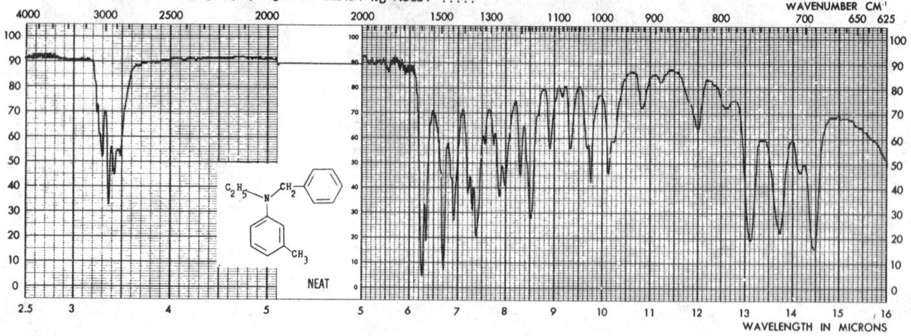

NEAT

B

18,351-2
3-Methyldiphenylamine, 98%
$CH_3C_6H_4NHC_6H_5$
M.W. 183.25 b.p. 315°/724mm. n_D^{20} 1.6350
Beil. **12**,857

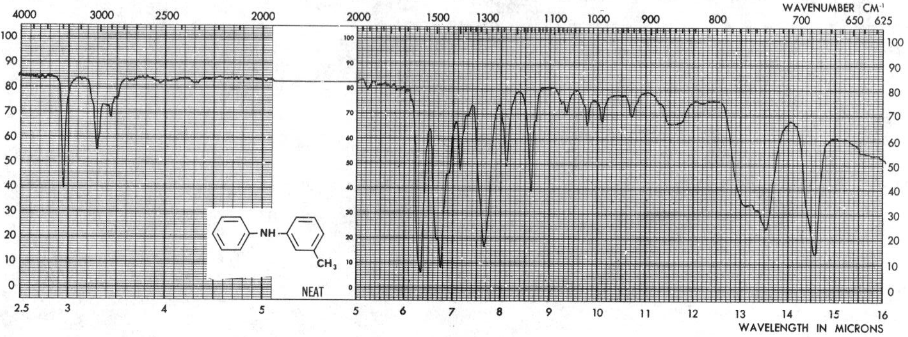

NEAT

C

13,095-8 **3-Chlorodiphenylamine**
$ClC_6H_4NHC_6H_5$ M.W. 203.67 n_D^{20} 1.6513

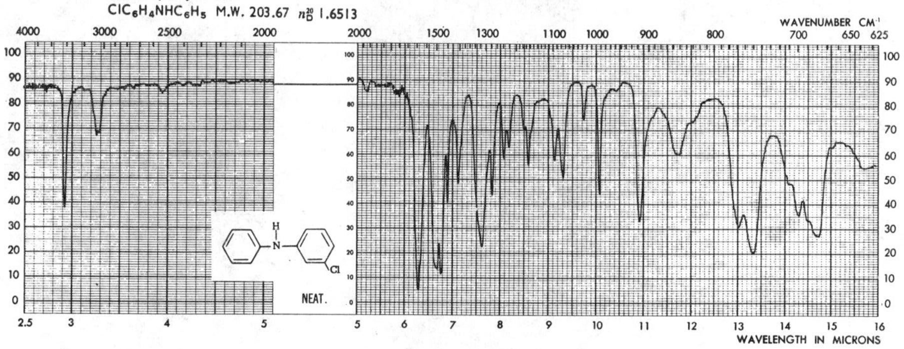

NEAT.

D

12,472-9 **N-Phenyl-α,α,α-trifluoro-m-toluidine**
$CF_3C_6H_4NHC_6H_5$ M.W. 237.23
n_D^{20} 1.5662

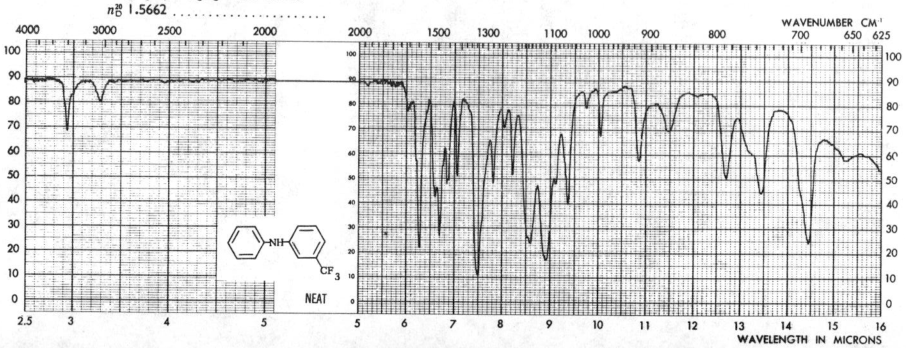

NEAT

E

17,986-8
m-(o-Toluidino)-phenol, tech. (3-hydroxy-2'-methyl-diphenylamine)
$CH_3C_6H_4NHC_6H_4OH$
M.W. 199.25 m.p. 52-54°

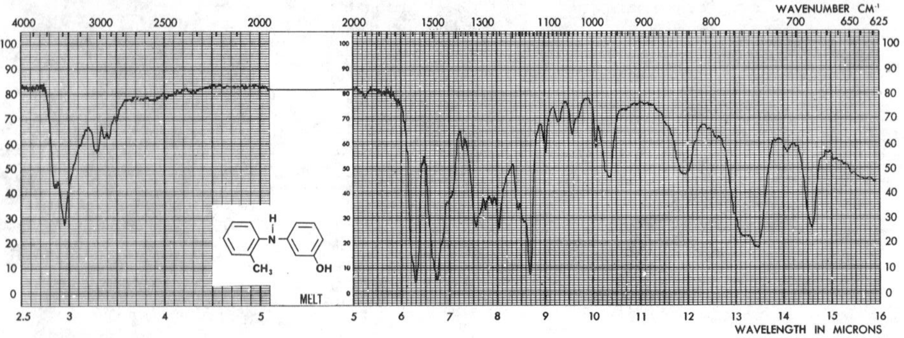

MELT

F

21,702-6
***N*-(4-Methoxyphenyl)-*p*-phenylenediamine hydrochloride**
$CH_3OC_6H_4NHC_6H_4NH_2 \cdot HCl$ FW 250.73
mp 249-255° *Beil.* **13**(3),1161 Disp. C

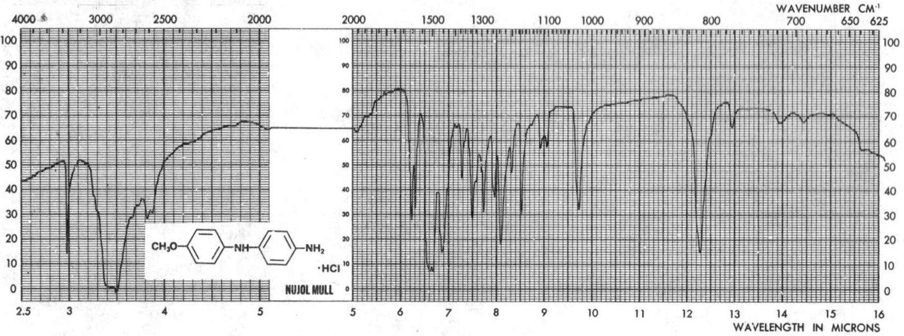

NUJOL MULL

G

12,315-3 **p-(4-Amino-m-toluidino)-phenol**
$H_2NC_6H_3(CH_3)NHC_6H_4OH$ M.W. 214.27 m.p. 159-163°

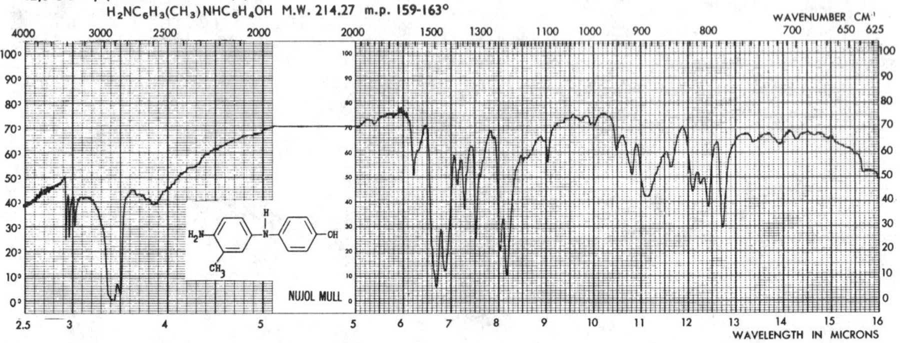

NUJOL MULL

H

15,326-5 2-(p-Tolylthio)-aniline
$CH_3C_6H_4SC_6H_4NH_2$ M.W. 215.32 m.p. 44-46°

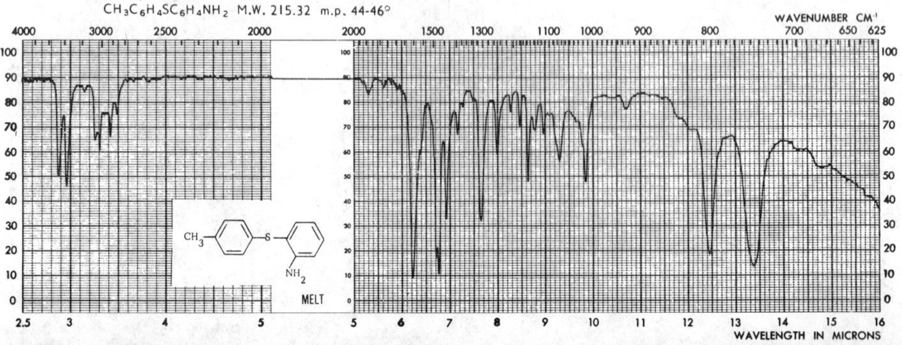

MELT

A

A6639-1 **1-Aminonaphthalene** (α-naphthylamine)
$C_{10}H_7NH_2$ M.W. 143.19 m.p. 48-50°
MELT

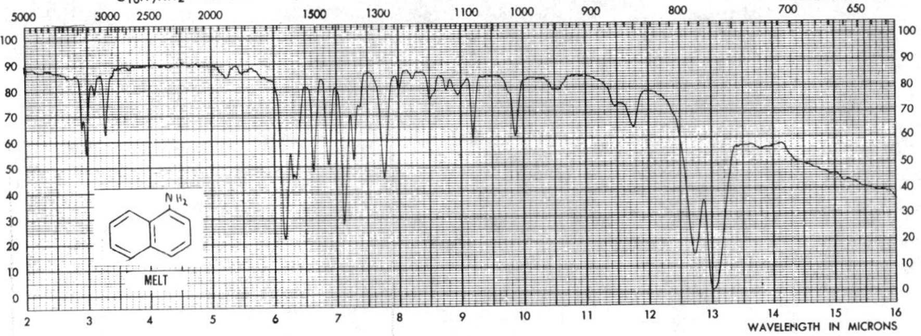

B

10,270-9 **N-Ethyl-1-naphthylamine**
$C_{10}H_7NHC_2H_5$ M.W. 171.24 n_D^{20} 1.6475
NEAT

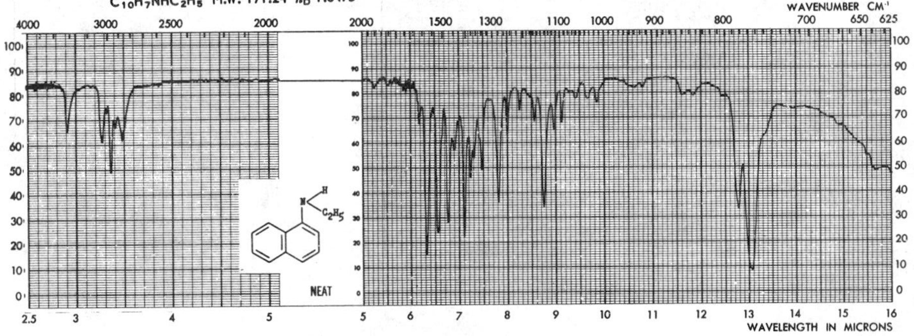

C

21,899-5
***N,N*-Dimethyl-1-naphthylamine,** 99%
$C_{10}H_7N(CH_3)_2$ FW 171.24 bp 139-140°/13mm.
n_D^{20} 1.6227 d 1.042 *Beil.* **12**,1221 Disp. C
NEAT

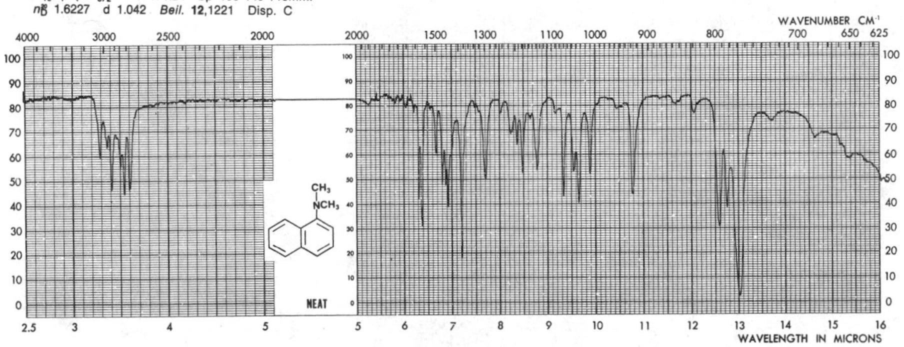

D

22,248-8
***N*-(1-Naphthyl)ethylenediamine dihydrochloride**
$C_{10}H_7NHCH_2CH_2NH_2 \cdot 2HCl$ FW 259.18 Disp. C
NUJOL MULL

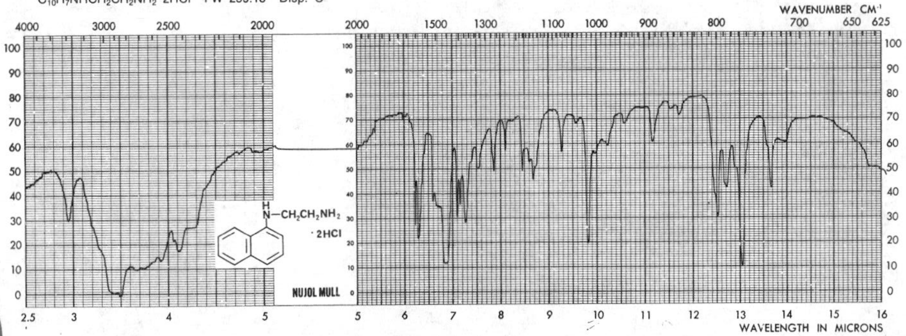

E

10,404-3 **N-Phenyl-1-naphthylamine** (N-1-naphthylaniline)
$C_{10}H_7NHC_6H_5$ M.W. 219.29 m.p. 56-58°
MELT

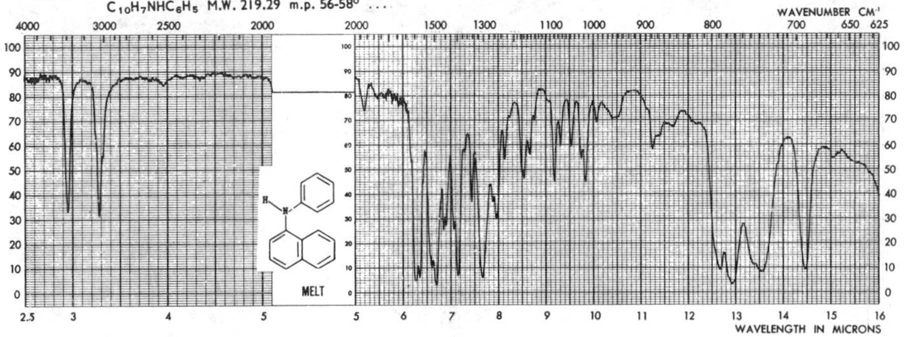

F

17,805-5
N-Phenyl-2-naphthylamine, 98% (N-2-naphthylaniline)
$C_{10}H_7NHC_6H_5$
M.W. 219.29 m.p. 107-109° b.p. 305-395.5°
Beil. **12**,1275
NUJOL MULL

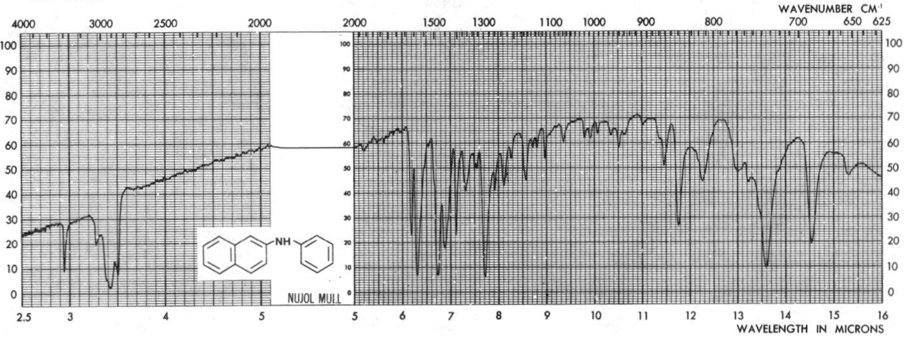

G

16,414-3
N-(p-Hydroxyphenyl)-2-naphthylamine, 95%
[p-(2-naphthylamino)-phenol]
$C_{10}H_7NHC_6H_4OH$
M.W. 235.29 m.p. 139-142° Beil. **13**,450
NUJOL MULL

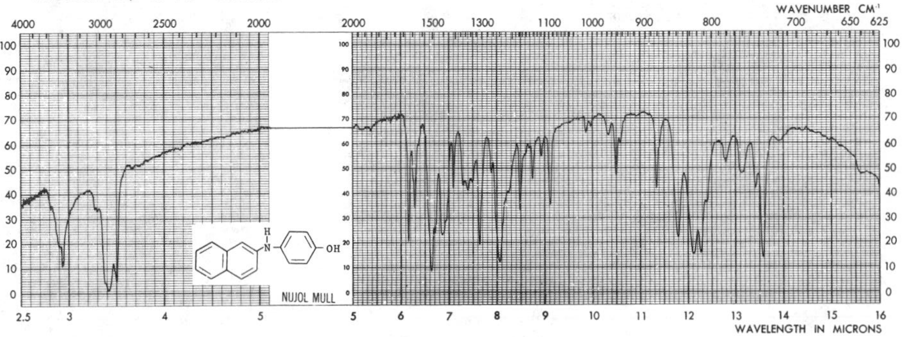

H

A6640-5 **2-Aminonaphthalene** (β-naphthylamine)
$C_{10}H_7NH_2$ M.W. 143.19 m.p. 110-111°
NUJOL MULL

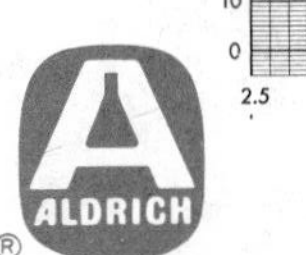

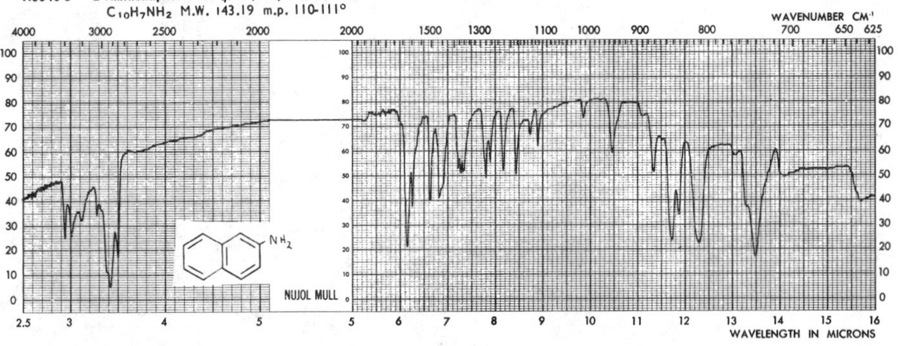

A

D19,200-7 Di-2-naphthylamine
$(C_{10}H_7)_2NH$ M.W. 269.35 m.p. 171-175°

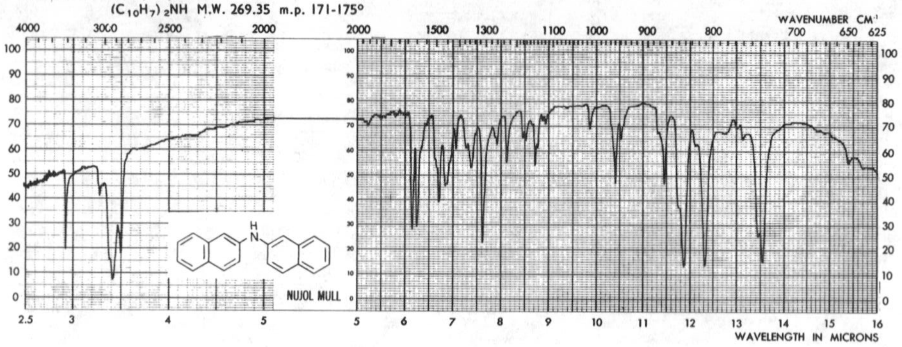

NUJOL MULL

B

16,164-0
6,13-Dihydrodibenzo[b,i]phenazine, tech.
M.W. 282.35 m.p. >300°

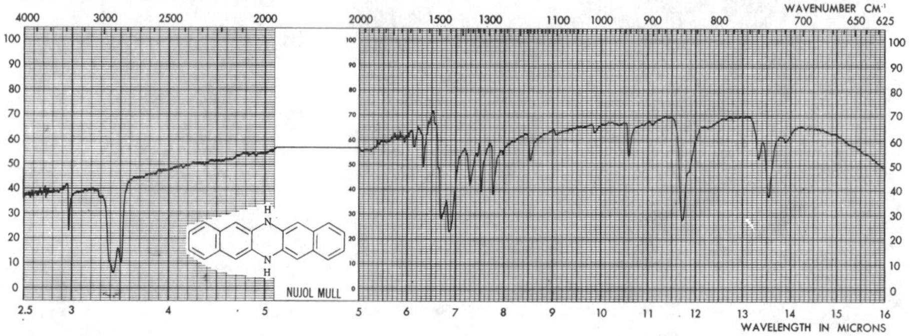

NUJOL MULL

C

A4640-4 1-Amino-4-chloronaphthalene (4-chloro-1-naphthylamine)
$ClC_{10}H_6NH_2$ M.W. 177.63 m.p. 98-100°

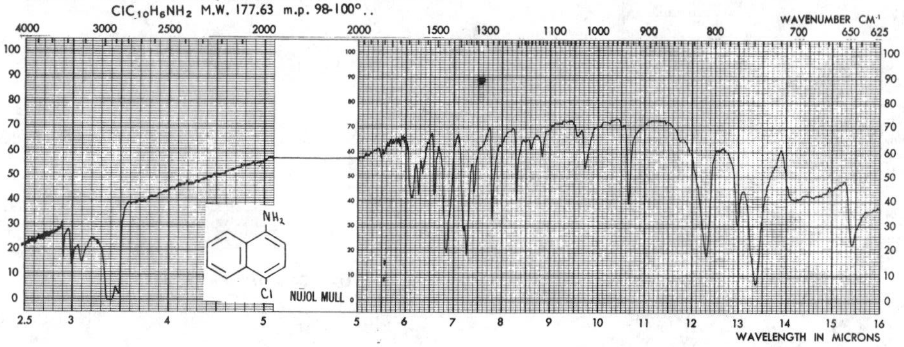

NUJOL MULL

D

A4340-5 1-Amino-4-bromonaphthalene (4-bromo-1-naphthylamine)
$BrC_{10}H_6NH_2$ M.W. 222.09
m.p. 98-100°

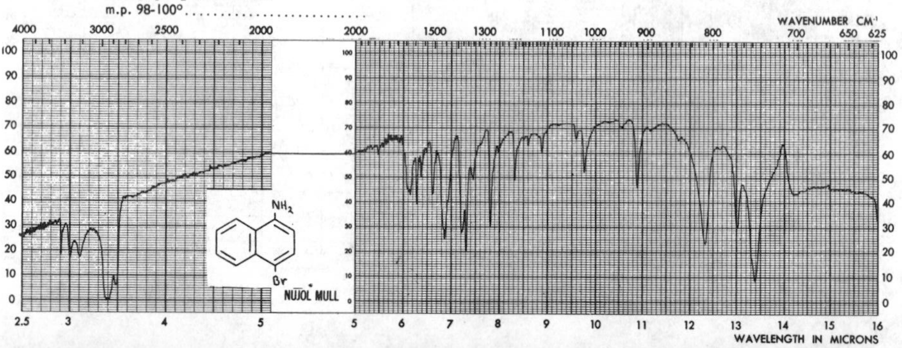

NUJOL MULL

E

13,347-7 1-Amino-2-naphthol hydrochloride
$H_2NC_{10}H_6OH{\cdot}HCl$ M.W. 195.65
m.p. > 250° (dec.)

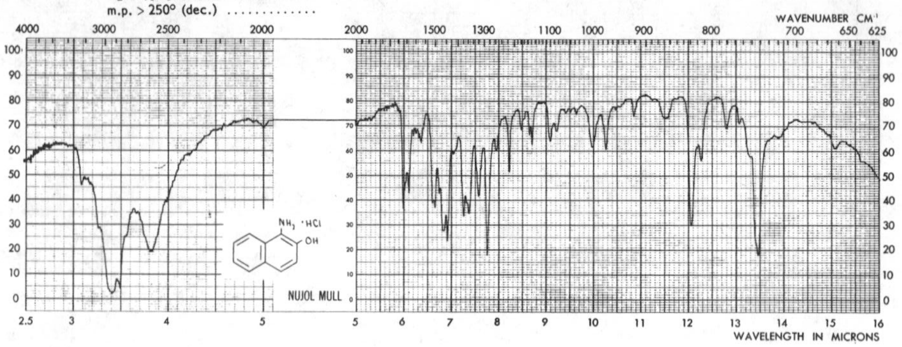

NUJOL MULL

F

13,348-5 4-Amino-1-naphthol hydrochloride, tech.
$H_2NC_{10}H_6OH{\cdot}HCl$ M.W. 195.65 m.p. > 245° (dec.)

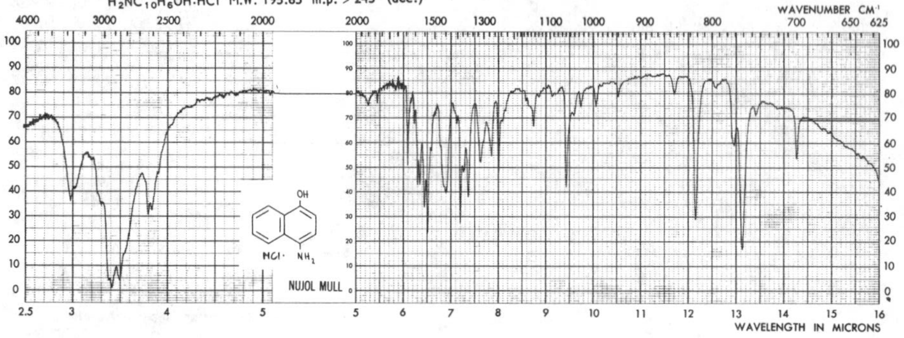

NUJOL MULL

G

13,349-3 7-Amino-2-naphthol hydrochloride, tech.
$H_2NC_{10}H_6OH{\cdot}HCl$ M.W. 195.65
m.p. 262-263° (dec.)

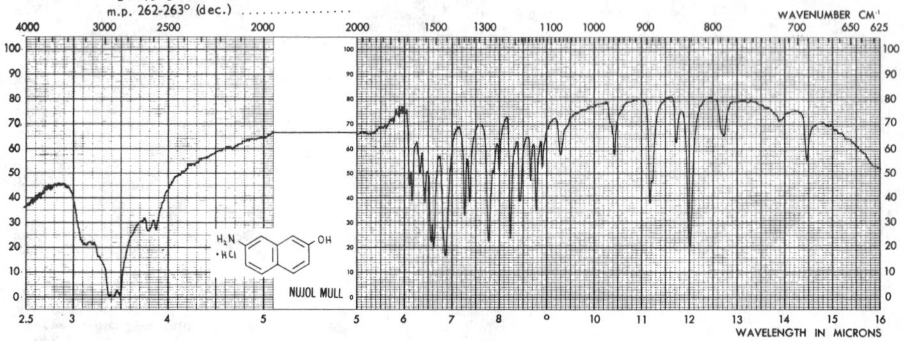

NUJOL MULL

H

14,582-3 8-Amino-2-naphthol, tech., 87%
$H_2NC_{10}H_6OH$ M.W. 159.19
m.p. 204-207°

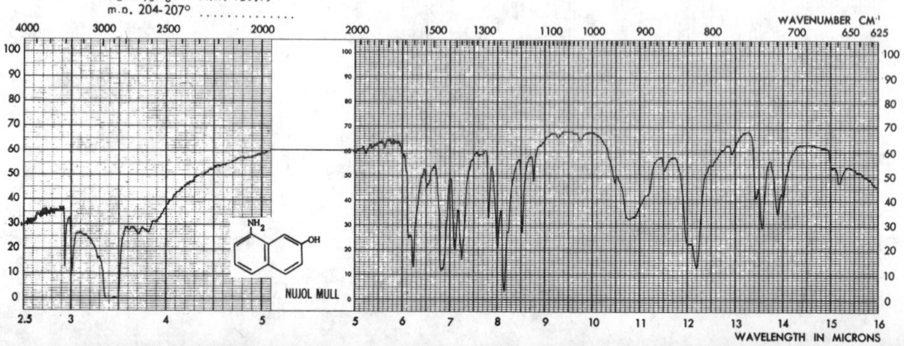

NUJOL MULL

A

D2100-6 **1,2-Diaminonaphthalene** (1,2-naphthalenediamine)
$C_{10}H_6(NH_2)_2$ M.W. 158.20 m.p. 95-98°

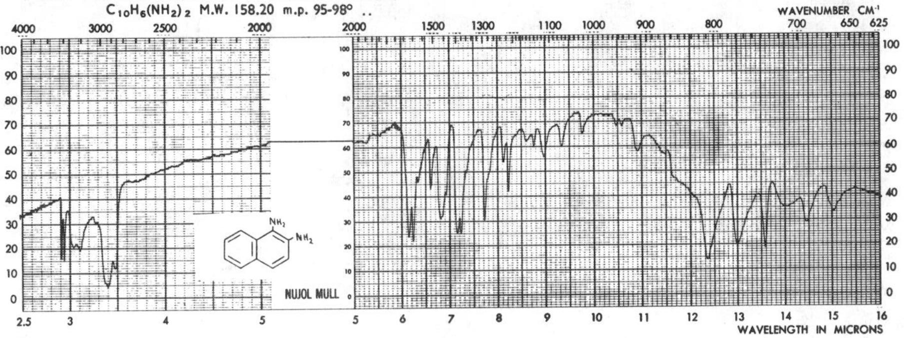

NUJOL MULL

B

16,426-7
3-Amino-2-naphthol, 99%
$H_2NC_{10}H_6OH$
M.W. 159.19 m.p. 225° (dec.) Beil. **13**,681

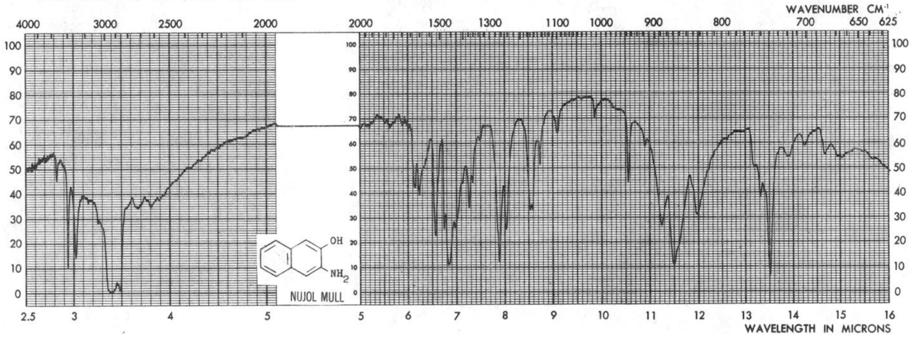

NUJOL MULL

C

13,653-0 **2,3-Diaminonaphthalene** (2,3-naphthalenediamine)
(send for data sheet)
$C_{10}H_6(NH_2)_2$ M.W. 158.20 m.p. 195-198°

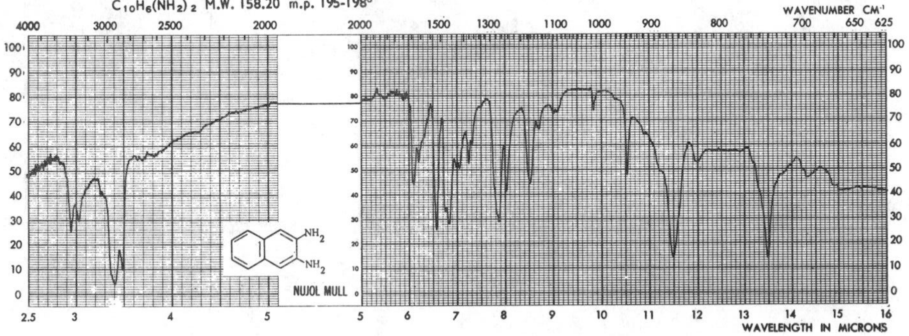

NUJOL MULL

D

17,613-3
2,3-Diaminonaphthalene dihydrochloride, 99%
(2,3-naphthalenediamine)
$C_{10}H_6(NH_2)_2 \cdot 2HCl$
M.W. 231.13 m.p. >300° *IRRITANT*

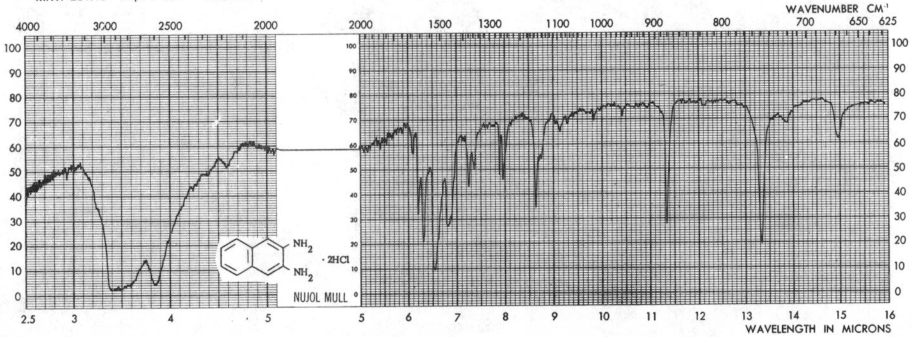

NUJOL MULL

E

D2120-0 **1,5-Diaminonaphthalene** (1,5-naphthalenediamine)
$C_{10}H_6(NH_2)_2$ M.W. 158.20 m.p. 188-190°

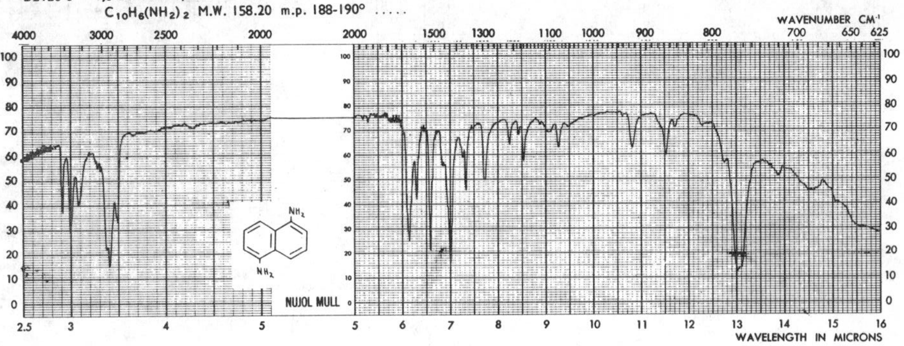

NUJOL MULL

F

D2140-5 **1,8-Diaminonaphthalene** (1,8-naphthalenediamine)
$C_{10}H_6(NH_2)_2$ M.W. 158.20 m.p. 61.5-64°

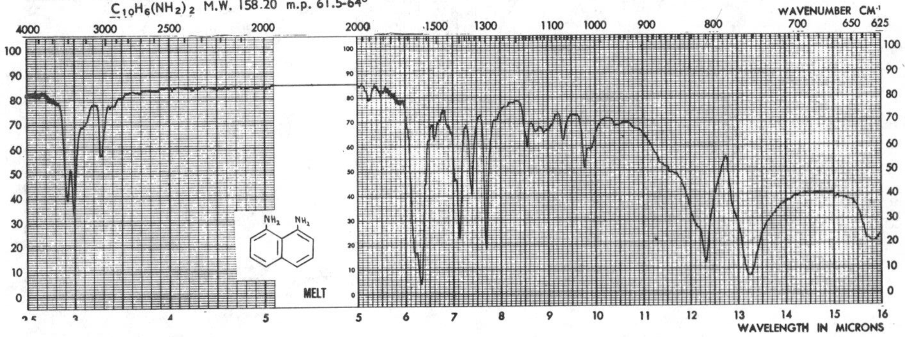

MELT

G

15,849-6
Proton Sponge® [1,8-bis-(dimethylamino)-naphthalene, N,N,N',N'-tetramethyl-1,8-naphthalenediamine]
$C_{10}H_6[N(CH_3)_2]_2$
M.W. 214.31 m.p. 49-51° Fieser **3**,22

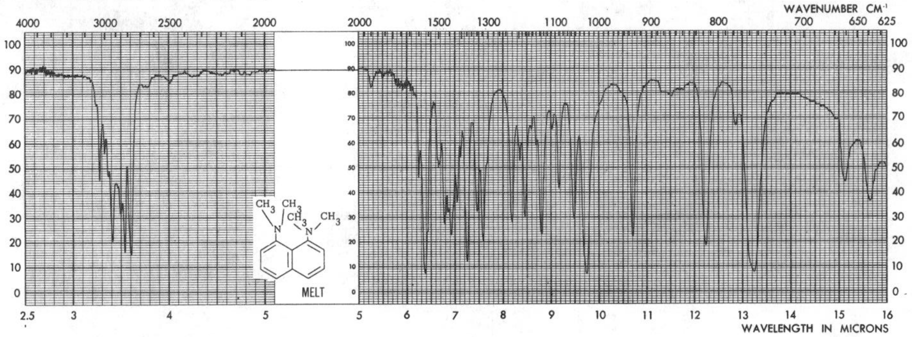

MELT

H

A3710-3 **5-Aminoacenaphthene** (5-acenaphthenamine)
M.W. 169.23 m.p. 106-107°

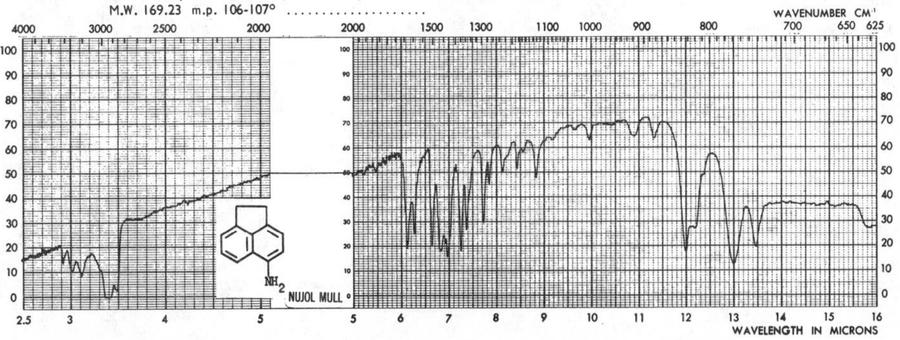

NUJOL MULL

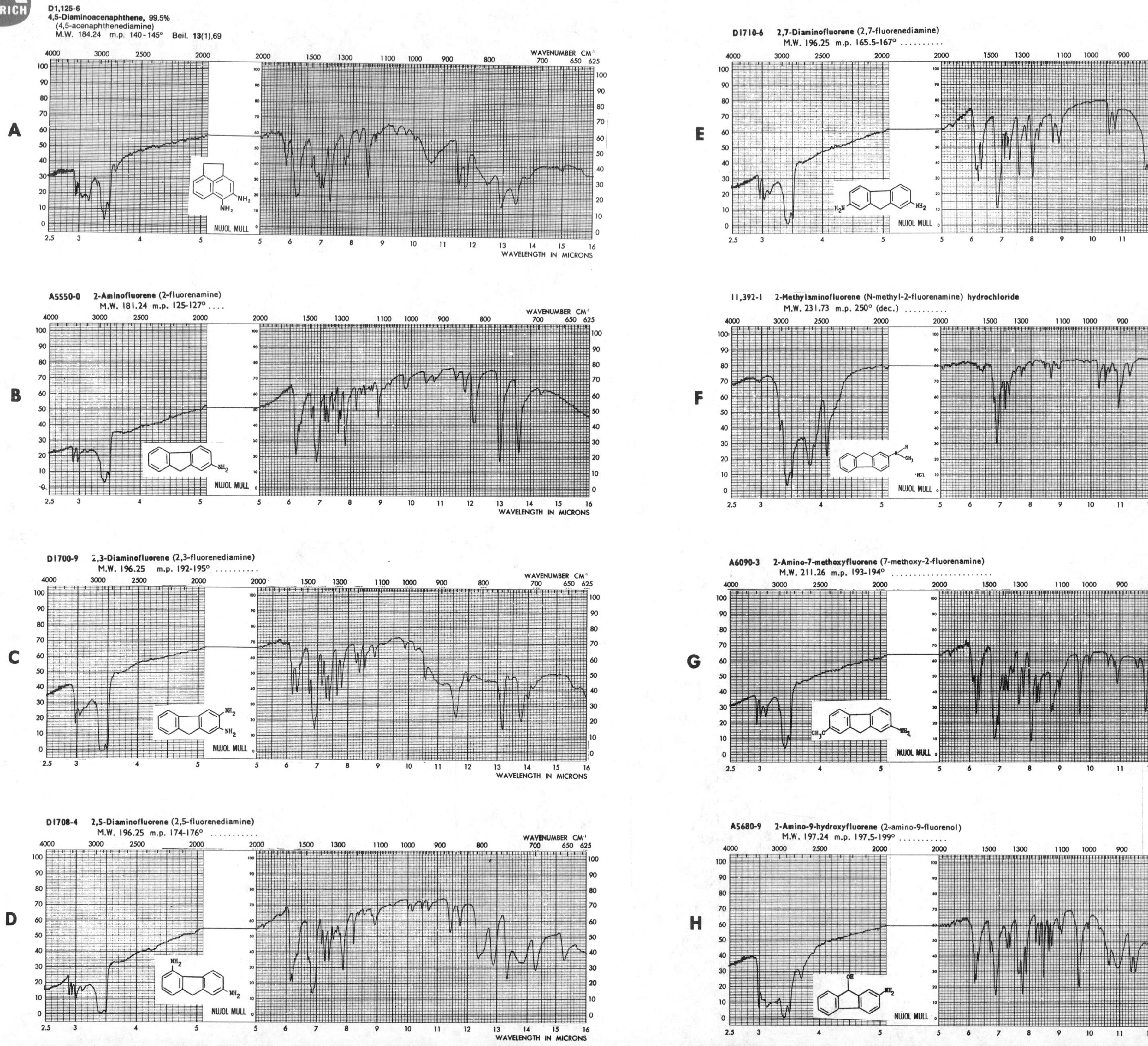
A
D1,125-6
4,5-Diaminoacenaphthene, 99.5%
(4,5-acenaphthenediamine)
M.W. 184.24 m.p. 140-145° Beil. 13(1),69
NUJOL MULL
B
A5550-0 2-Aminofluorene (2-fluorenamine)
M.W. 181.24 m.p. 125-127° ....
NUJOL MULL
C
D1700-9 2,3-Diaminofluorene (2,3-fluorenediamine)
M.W. 196.25 m.p. 192-195° ....
NUJOL MULL
D
D1708-4 2,5-Diaminofluorene (2,5-fluorenediamine)
M.W. 196.25 m.p. 174-176° ....
NUJOL MULL
E
D1710-6 2,7-Diaminofluorene (2,7-fluorenediamine)
M.W. 196.25 m.p. 165.5-167° ....
NUJOL MULL
F
11,392-1 2-Methylaminofluorene (N-methyl-2-fluorenamine) hydrochloride
M.W. 231.73 m.p. 250° (dec.) ....
NUJOL MULL
G
A6090-3 2-Amino-7-methoxyfluorene (7-methoxy-2-fluorenamine)
M.W. 211.26 m.p. 193-194° ....
NUJOL MULL
H
A5680-9 2-Amino-9-hydroxyfluorene (2-amino-9-fluorenol)
M.W. 197.24 m.p. 197.5-199° ....
NUJOL MULL
WAVENUMBER CM⁻¹
WAVELENGTH IN MICRONS

A A3860-8 **1-Aminoanthracene** (1-anthramine)
M.W. 193.25 m.p. 112-117° ....
NUJOL MULL

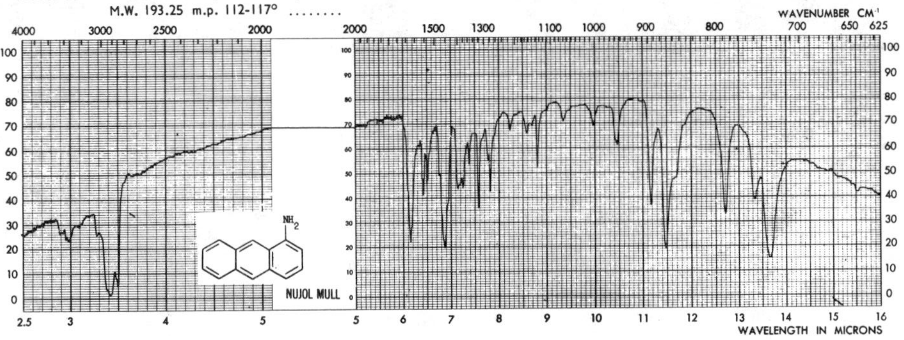

B A3880-0 **2-Aminoanthracene** (2-anthramine)
M.W. 193.25 m.p. 238-241° ....
NUJOL MULL

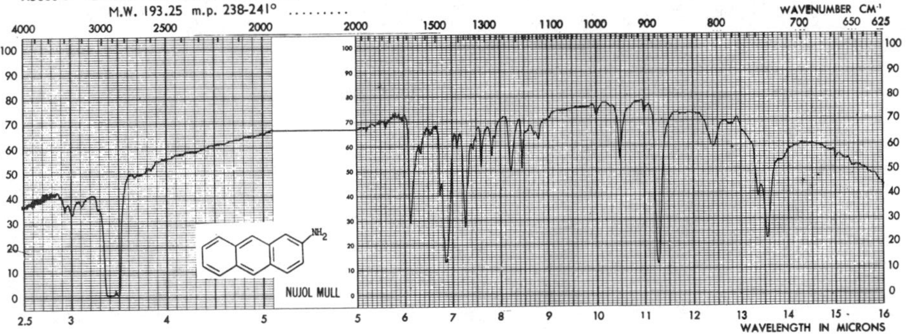

C 14,910-1 **9-Aminophenanthrene** (9-phenanthrenamine)
M.W. 193.25 m.p. 137-139° ....
NUJOL MULL

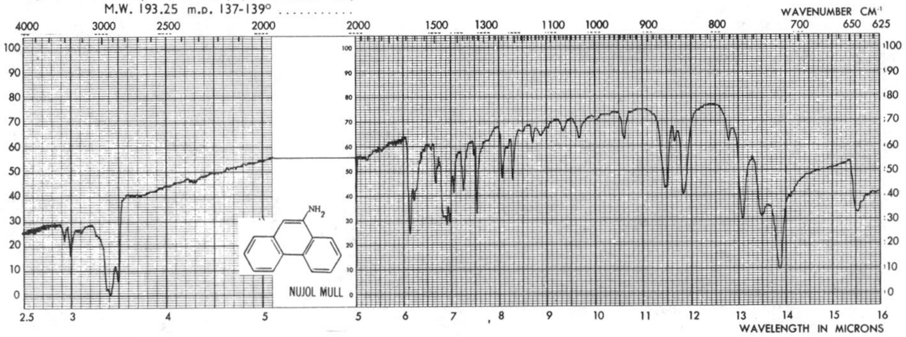

D D2290-8 **9,10-Diaminophenanthrene** (9,10-phenanthrenediamine)
M.W. 208.27 m.p. 164-166° ....
NUJOL MULL

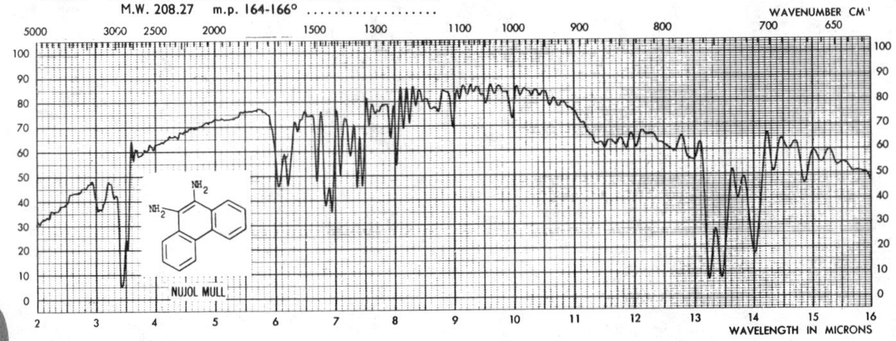

E A5540-3 **3-Aminofluoranthene** (3-fluoranthenamine)
M.W. 217.27 m.p. 115-117° ....
NUJOL MULL

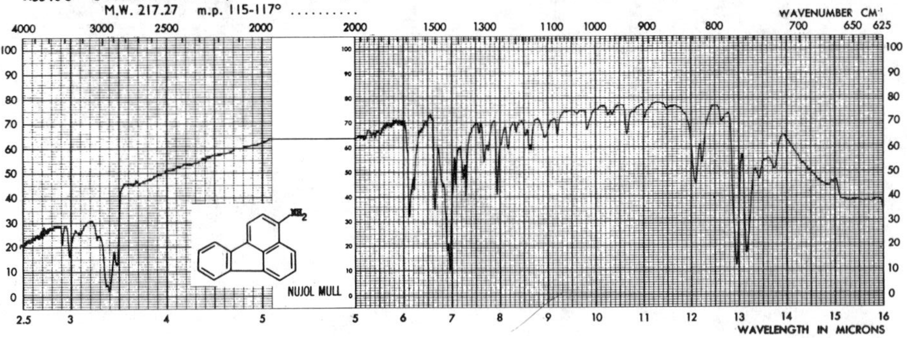

F A7790-3 **1-Aminopyrene** (1-pyrenamine)
M.W. 217.27 m.p. 116-118°
NUJOL MULL

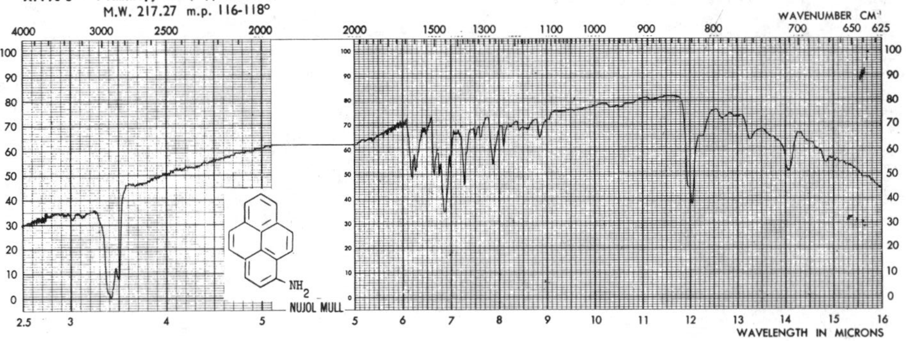

G A4705-2 **6-Aminochrysene** (6-chrysenamine)
M.W. 243.31 m.p. 209-211.5° ...
NUJOL MULL

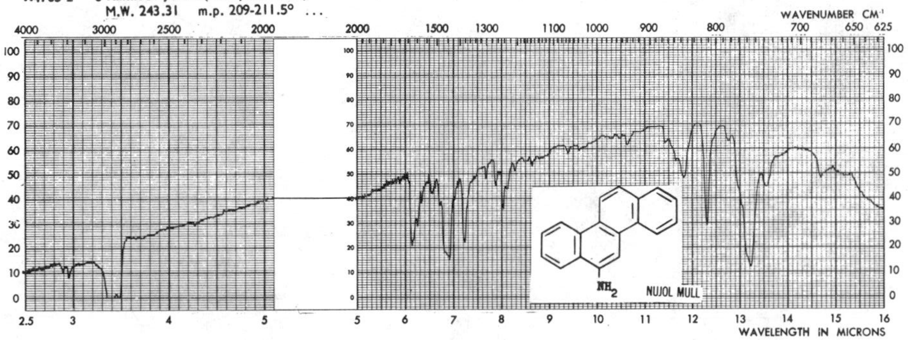

H P2625-2 **Phenylhydrazine**
$C_6H_5NHNH_2$ M.W. 108.14 n_D^{20} 1.6049
b.p. 243.5° ....
NEAT

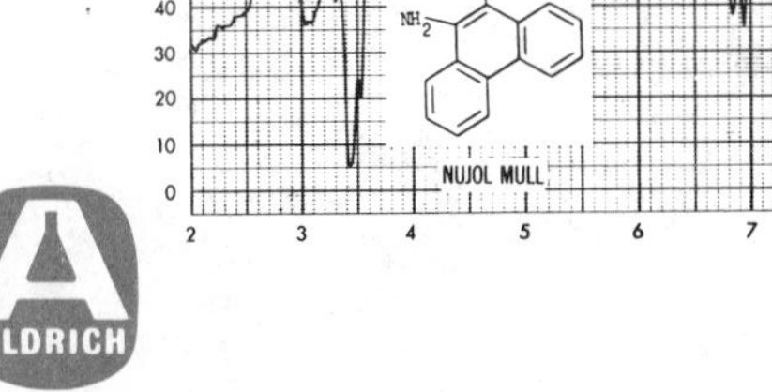

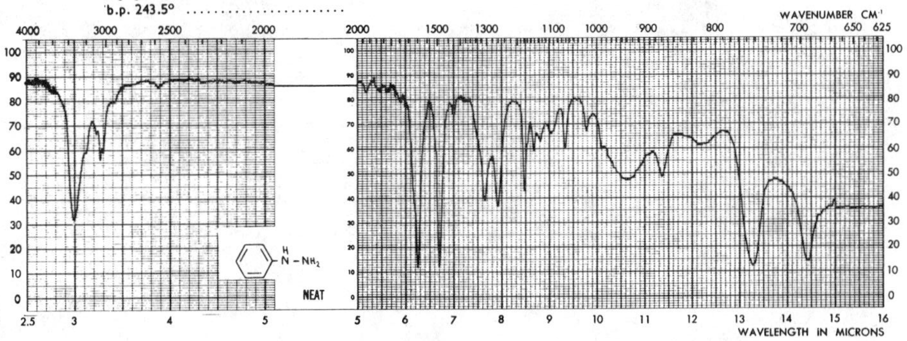

A 11,471-5 **Phenylhydrazine hydrochloride**
$C_6H_5NHNH_2 \cdot HCl$ M.W. 144.61
m.p. 242° (dec.)
NUJOL MULL

B 11,459-6 **1,1-Diphenylhydrazine hydrochloride**
$(C_6H_5)_2NNH_2 \cdot HCl$ M.W. 220.70
m.p. 282°
NUJOL MULL

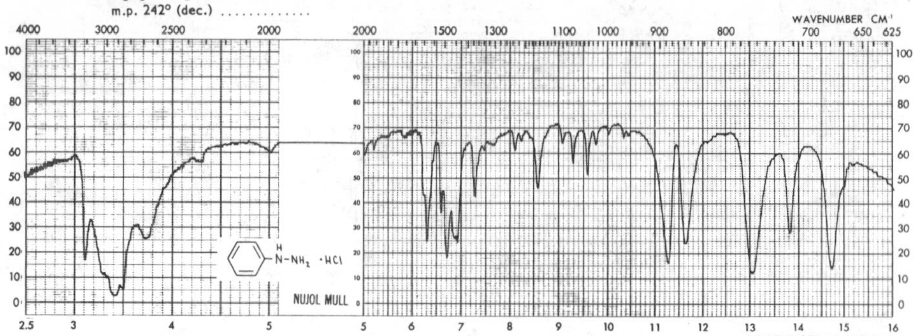

C 12,672-1 **1,2-Diphenylhydrazine** (hydrazobenzene)
$C_6H_5NHNHC_6H_5$ M.W. 184.24 m.p. 123-127°
NUJOL MULL

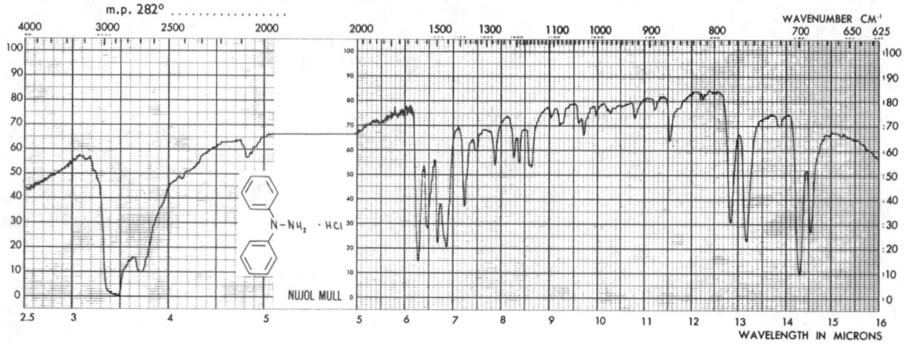

D M6960-8 **1-Methyl-1-phenylhydrazine**
$C_6H_5N(CH_3)NH_2$ M.W. 122.17 n_D^{20} 1.5691 b.p. 227°
NEAT

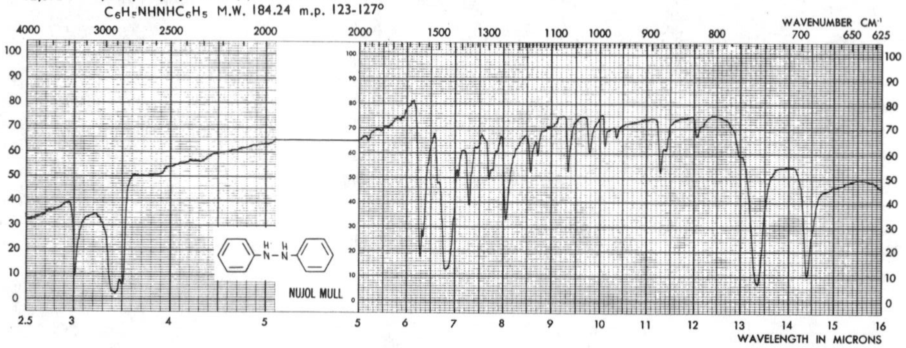

E 14,291-3 **1-Methyl-1-phenylhydrazine sulfate dihydrate**
$[C_6H_5N(CH_3)NH_2]_2 \cdot H_2SO_4 \cdot 2H_2O$ M.W. 378.45
m.p. 180-181.5° (dec.)
NUJOL MULL

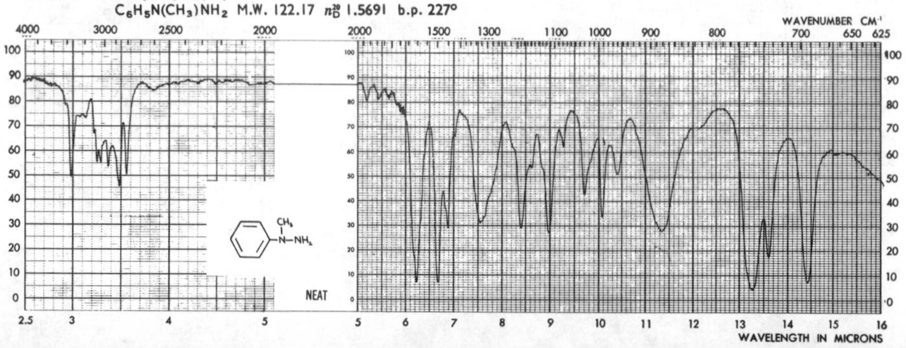

F B2285-2 **Benzylhydrazine dihydrochloride**
$C_6H_5CH_2NHNH_2 \cdot 2HCl$ M.W. 195.09
m.p. 143-144° (dec.)
NUJOL MULL

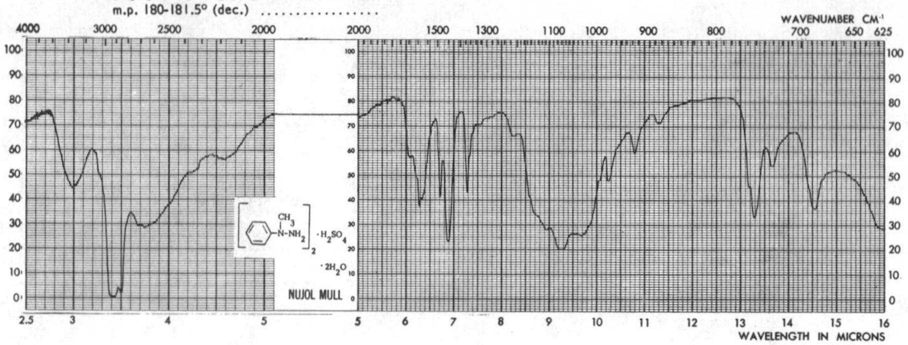

G P2460-8 **2-Phenylethylhydrazine sulfate**
$C_6H_5CH_2CH_2NHNH_2 \cdot H_2SO_4$ M.W. 234.27
m.p. 170-172°
NUJOL MULL

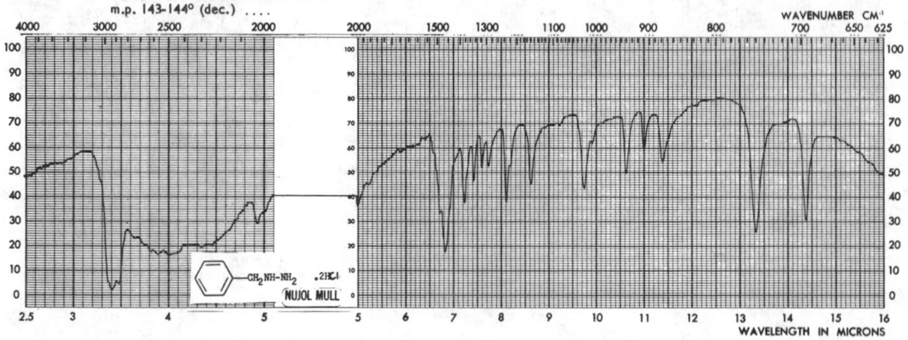

H T4020-7 **o-Tolylhydrazine hydrochloride**
$CH_3C_6H_4NHNH_2 \cdot HCl$ M.W. 158.63 m.p. 187° (dec.)
NUJOL MULL

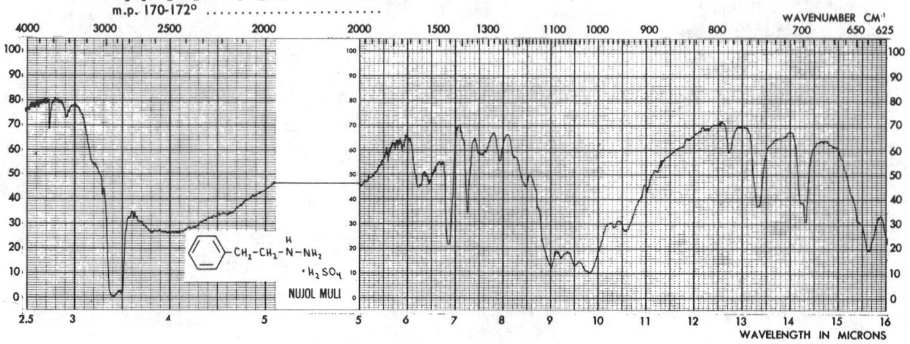

WAVENUMBER CM⁻¹ / WAVELENGTH IN MICRONS

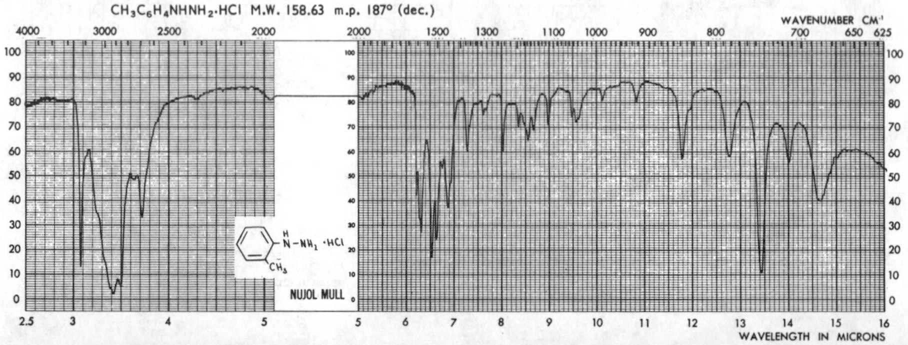

A

15,342-7
2-Fluorophenylhydrazine hydrochloride
$FC_6H_4NHNH_2 \cdot HCl$
M.W. 162.6 m.p. 205° (dec.)

NUJOL MULL

B

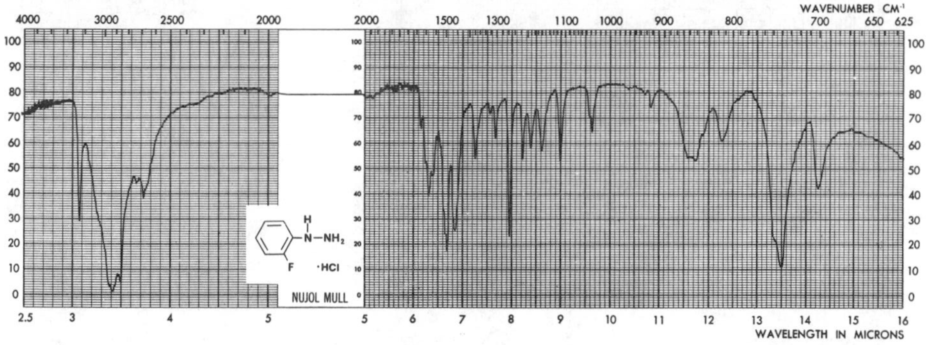

10,950-9 2-Chlorophenylhydrazine hydrochloride
$ClC_6H_4NHNH_2 \cdot HCl$ M.W. 179.05
m.p. 187-188°

NUJOL MULL

C

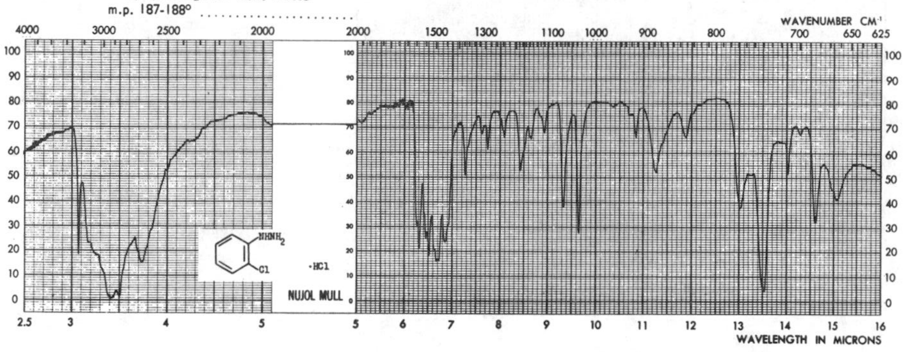

15,362-1 2-Bromophenylhydrazine hydrochloride, 95%
$BrC_6H_4NHNH_2 \cdot HCl$ M.W. 223.51
m.p. 189° (dec.)

NUJOL MULL

D

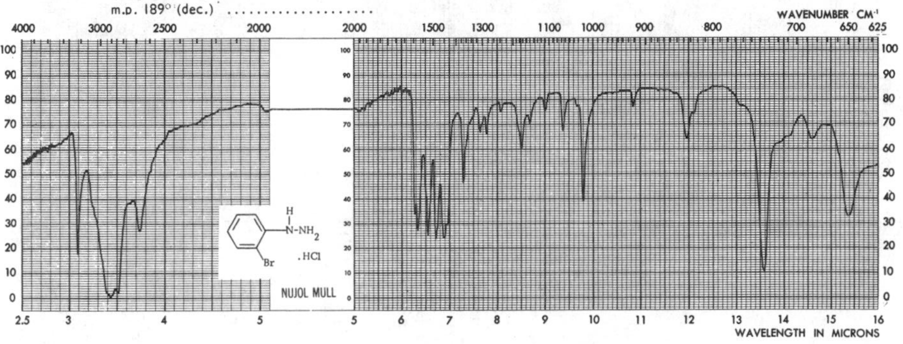

C2810-3 N-(o-Chlorobenzyl)-hydrazine hydrochloride
$ClC_6H_4CH_2NHNH_2 \cdot 2HCl$ M.W. 229.54
m.p. 145-146°

NUJOL MULL

E

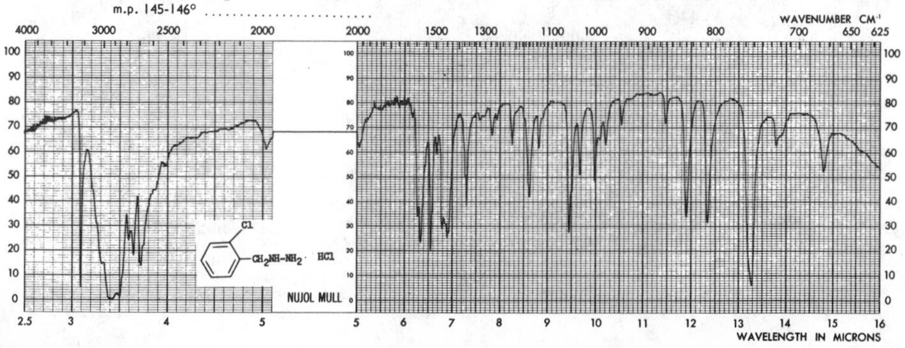

M2100-1 o-Methoxyphenylhydrazine hydrochloride
$CH_3OC_6H_4NHNH_2 \cdot HCl$ M.W. 174.63 m.p. 152° (dec.)

NUJOL MULL

F

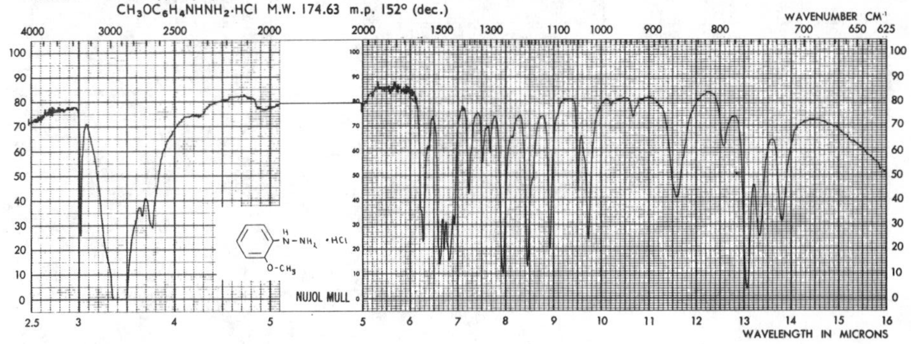

17,752-0
(o-Aminophenyl)-hydrazine dihydrochloride
$H_2NC_6H_4NHNH_2 \cdot 2HCl$
M.W. 196.08 m.p. >300°

NUJOL MULL

G

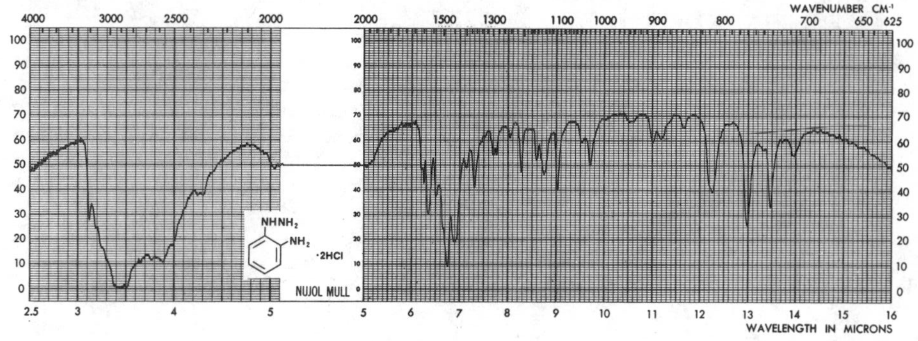

T4040-1 m-Tolylhydrazine hydrochloride
$CH_3C_6H_4NHNH_2 \cdot HCl$ M.W. 158.63 m.p. 184° (dec.)

NUJOL MULL

H

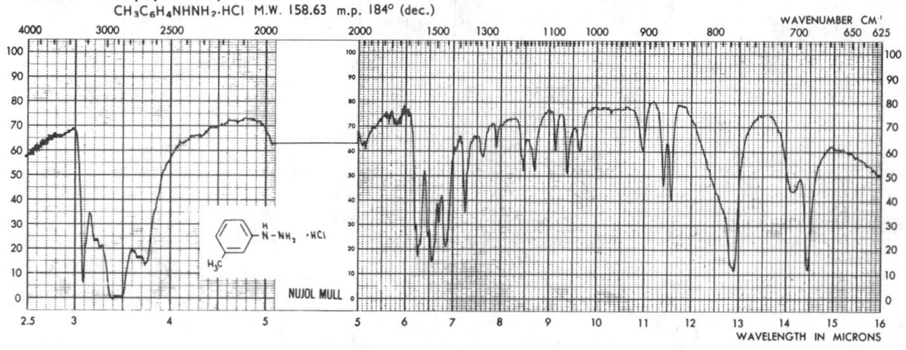

15,396-6 3-Chlorophenylhydrazine hydrochloride
$ClC_6H_4NHNH_2 \cdot HCl$ M.W. 179.05
m.p. 242° (dec.)

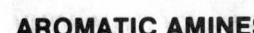

NUJOL MULL

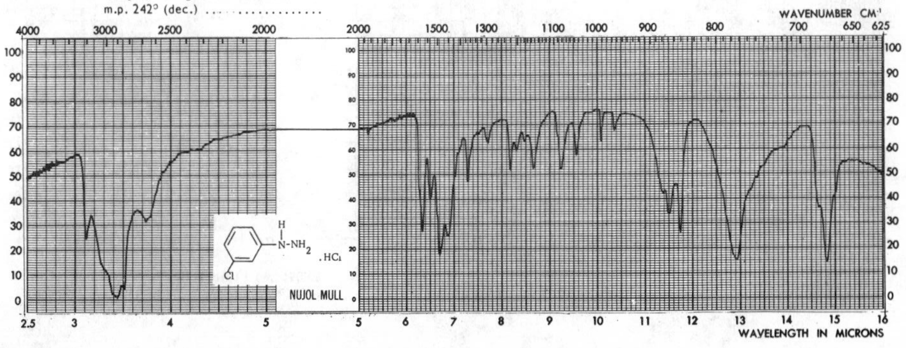

A

15,395-8 **3-Bromophenylhydrazine hydrochloride**
$BrC_6H_4NHNH_2 \cdot HCl$ M.W. 223.51
m.p. 227-231° (dec.)

NUJOL MULL

B

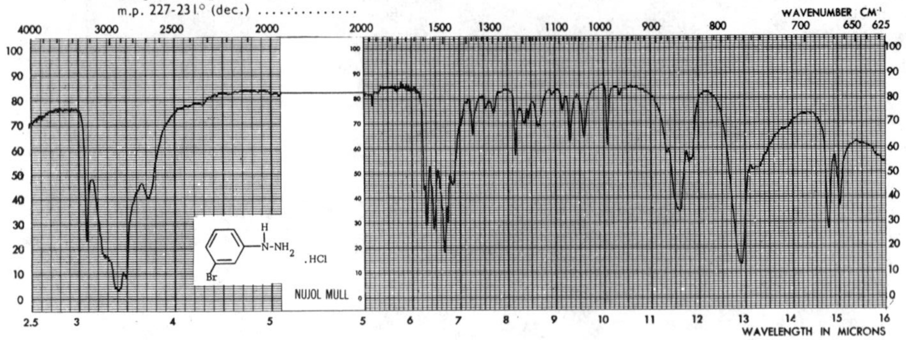

15,397-4 **3-Fluorophenylhydrazine hydrochloride**
$FC_6H_4NHNH_2 \cdot HCl$ M.W. 162.60
m.p. 268° (dec.)

NUJOL MULL

C

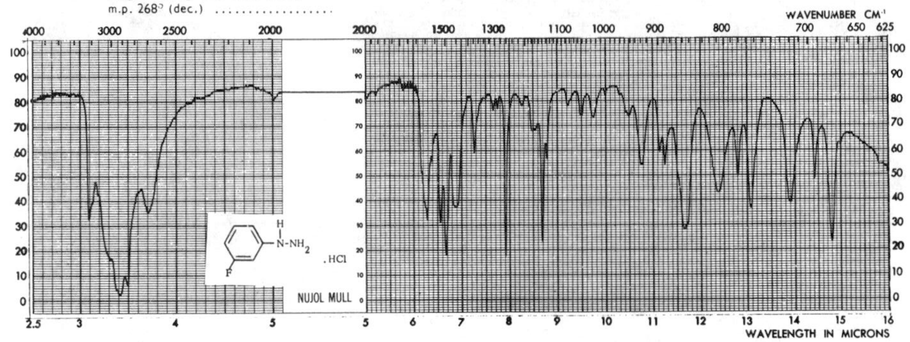

16,174-8
m-Methoxyphenylhydrazine hydrochloride, 97%
$CH_3OC_6H_4NHNH_2 \cdot HCl$
M.W. 174.63 m.p. 142° (dec.)

NUJOL MULL

D

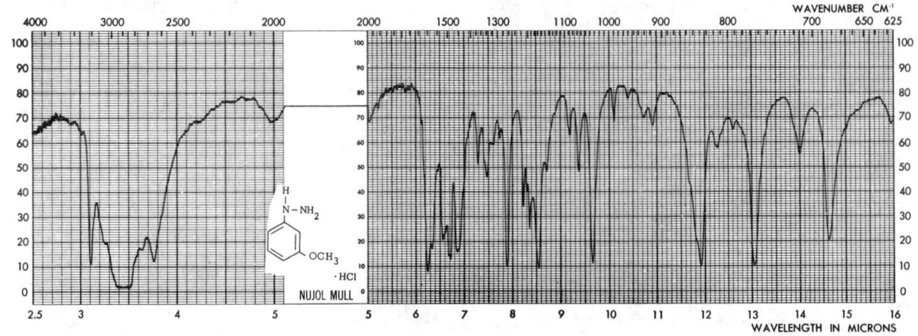

14,332-4 **m-(Hexadecylthio)-phenylhydrazine hydrochloride, tecn.**
$CH_3(CH_2)_{15}SC_6H_4NHNH_2 \cdot HCl$ M.W. 401.10

NUJOL MULL

E

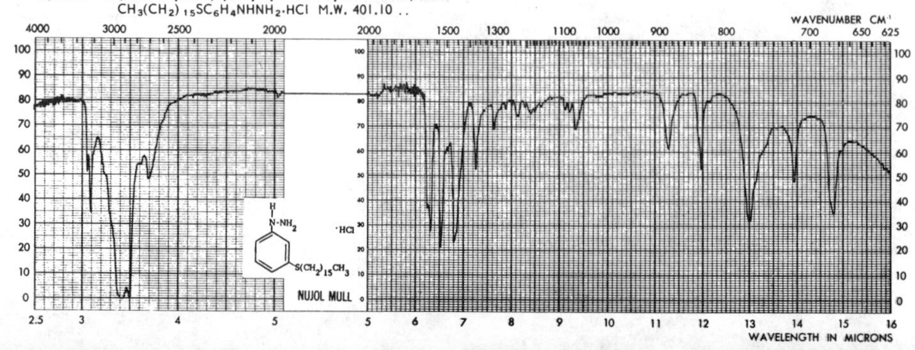

T4060-6 **p-Tolylhydrazine hydrochloride**
$CH_3C_6H_4NHNH_2 \cdot HCl$ M.W. 158.63
m.p. > 200° (dec.)

NUJOL MULL

F

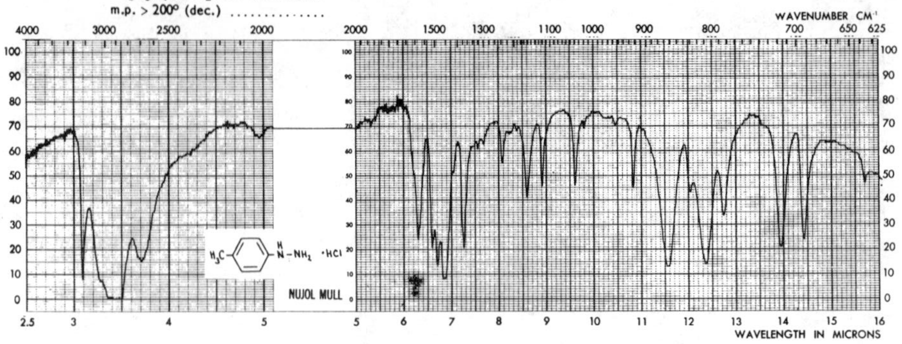

F1420-3 **4-Fluorophenylhydrazine hydrochloride**
$FC_6H_4NHNH_2 \cdot HCl$ M.W. 162.60
m.p. > 300°

NUJOL MULL

G

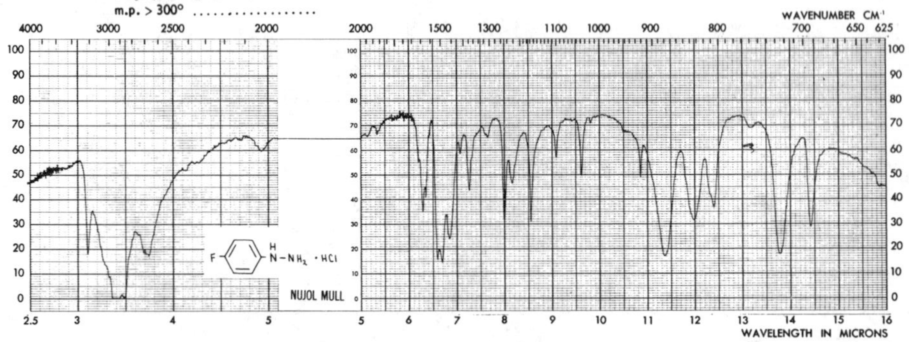

C6580-7 **4-Chlorophenylhydrazine hydrochloride**
$ClC_6H_4NHNH_2 \cdot HCl$ M.W. 179.05
m.p. 220° (dec.)

NUJOL MULL

H

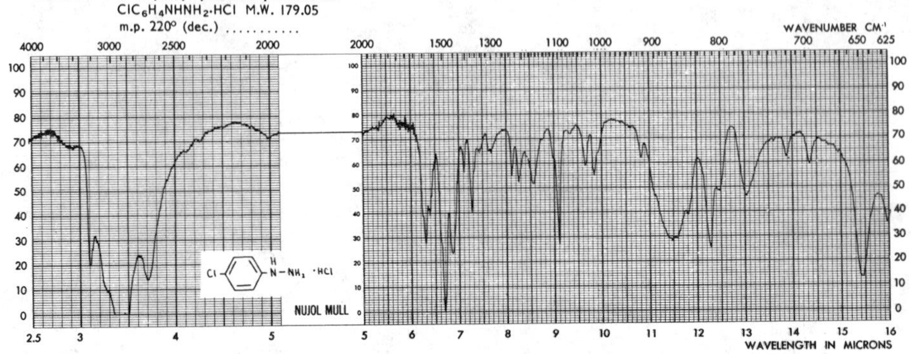

14,321-9 **4-Bromophenylhydrazine hydrochloride**
$BrC_6H_4NHNH_2 \cdot HCl$ M.W. 223.51
m.p. 209° (dec.)

NUJOL MULL

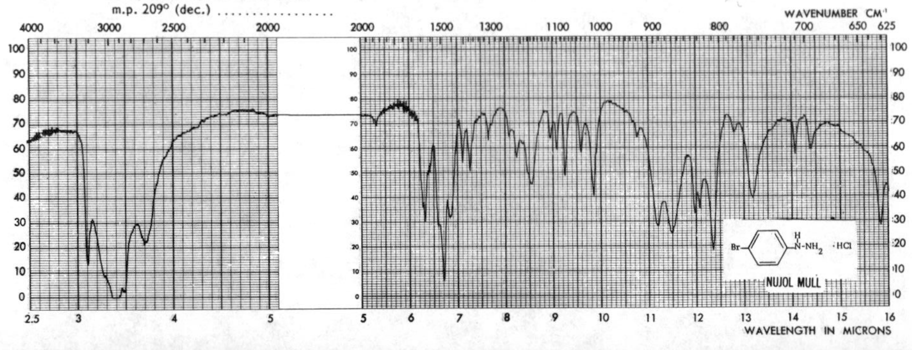

15,213-7 **p-Methoxyphenylhydrazine hydrochloride**
$CH_3OC_6H_4NHNH_2 \cdot HCl$ M.W. 174.63
m.p. 153-153.5° (dec.)

15,283-8 4-Chloro-o-tolylhydrazine hydrochloride
$ClC_6H_3(CH_3)NHNH_2 \cdot HCl$ M.W. 193.08
m.p. 207° (dec.)

15,343-5 3-Chloro-p-tolylhydrazine hydrochloride
$ClC_6H_3(CH_3)NHNH_2 \cdot HCl$ M.W. 193.08
m.p. 247° (dec.)

16,070-9
6-Methoxy-m-tolylhydrazine hydrochloride, 98%
$CH_3OC_6H_3(CH_3)NHNH_2 \cdot HCl$
M.W. 188.66 m.p. 155-156° (dec.) Beil. 15,607

15,236-6
2-Chloro-5-methoxyphenylhydrazine
$ClC_6H_3(OCH_3)NHNH_2$
M.W. 172.62 m.p. 70-72°

15,399-0
3-Chloro-o-tolylhydrazine hydrochloride
$ClC_6H_3(CH_3)NHNH_2 \cdot HCl$
M.W. 193.08 m.p. 244-246° (dec.)

15,340-0 2,3-Dichlorophenylhydrazine hydrochloride
$Cl_2C_6H_3NHNH_2 \cdot HCl$ M.W. 213.50
m.p. 234-235° (dec.)

15,341-9 2,6-Dichlorophenylhydrazine hydrochloride
$Cl_2C_6H_3NHNH_2 \cdot HCl$ M.W. 213.50
m.p. 225-235° (dec.)

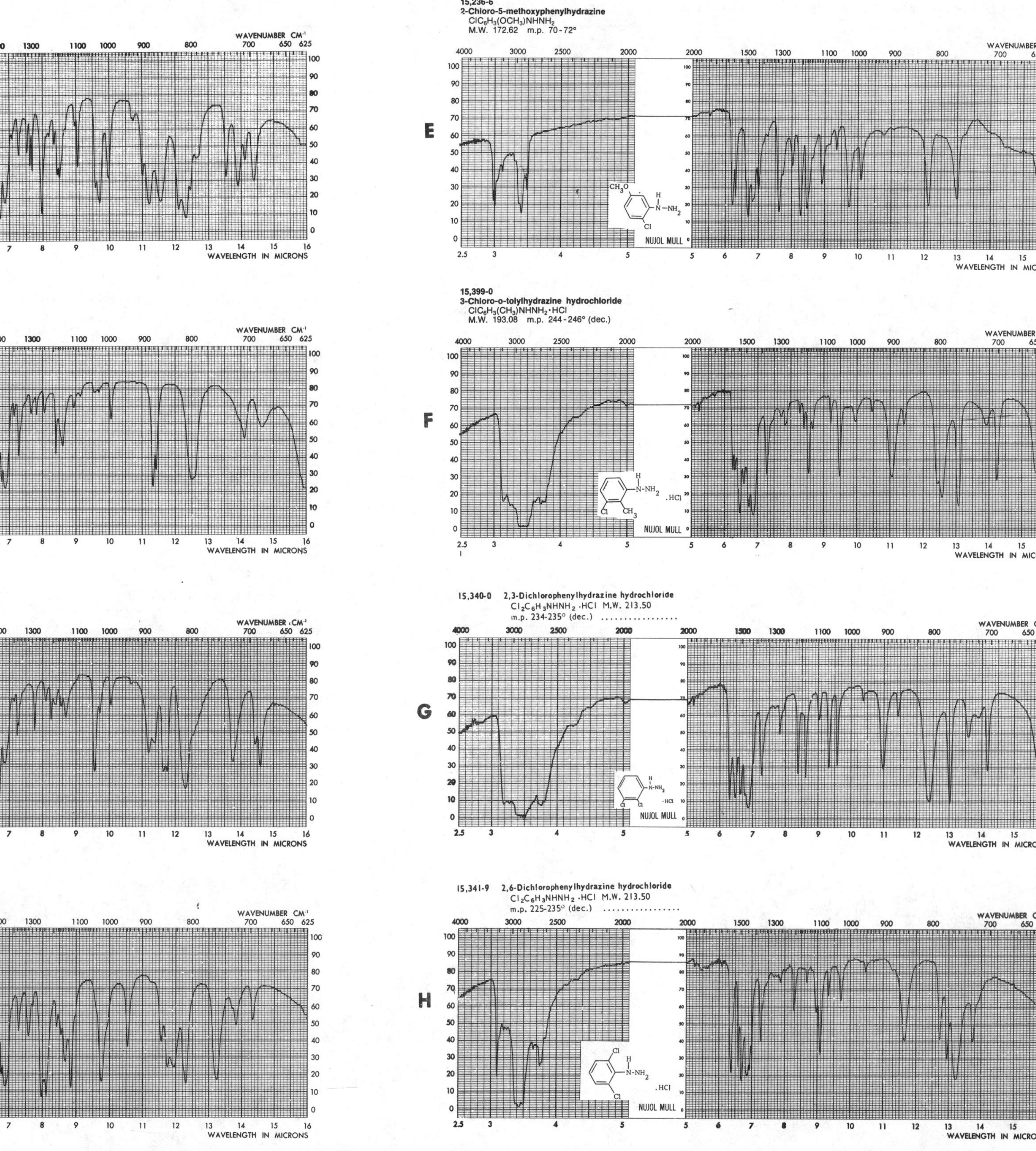

ALDRICH

A

15,280-3 2,4-Dichlorophenylhydrazine hydrochloride
$Cl_2C_6H_3NHNH_2 \cdot HCl$ M.W. 213.50
m.p. 217-218° (dec.)

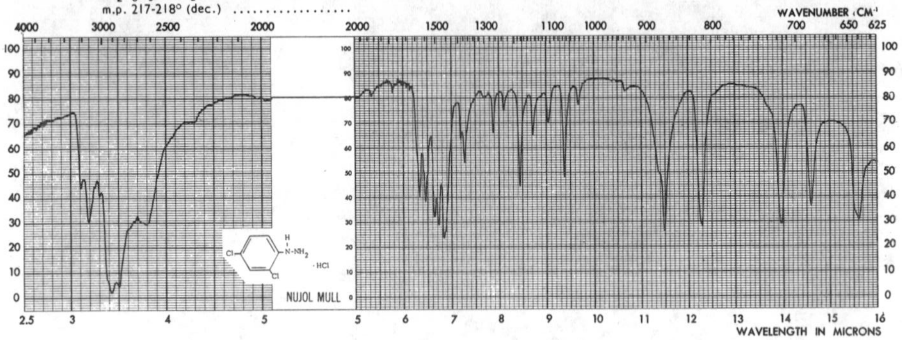

NUJOL MULL

B

15,011-8 2,5-Dichlorophenylhydrazine
$Cl_2C_6H_3NHNH_2$ M.W. 177.03
m.p. 102-103°

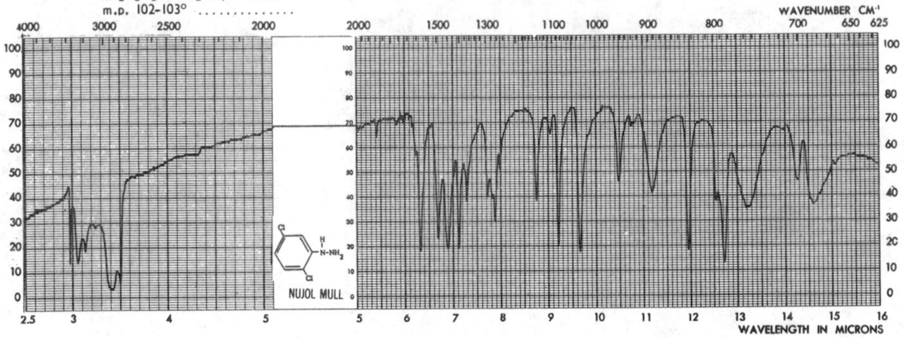

NUJOL MULL

C

15,278-1 2,5-Dichlorophenylhydrazine hydrochloride
$Cl_2C_6H_3NHNH_2 \cdot HCl$ M.W. 213.50
m.p. 208° (dec.)

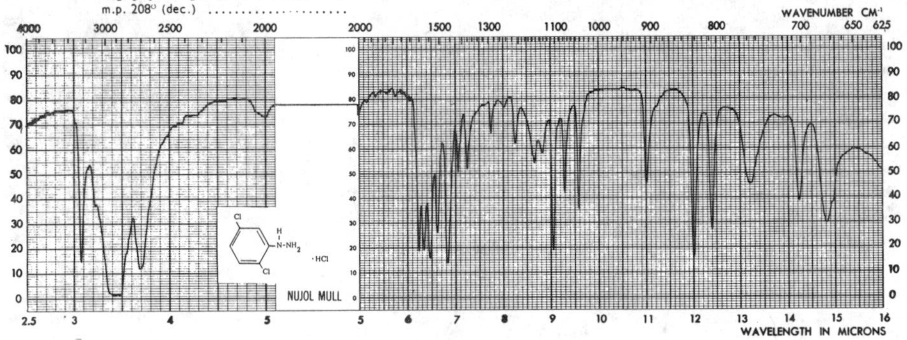

NUJOL MULL

D

15,281-1 3,4-Dichlorophenylhydrazine hydrochloride
$Cl_2C_6H_3NHNH_2 \cdot HCl$ M.W. 213.50
m.p. 230° (dec.)

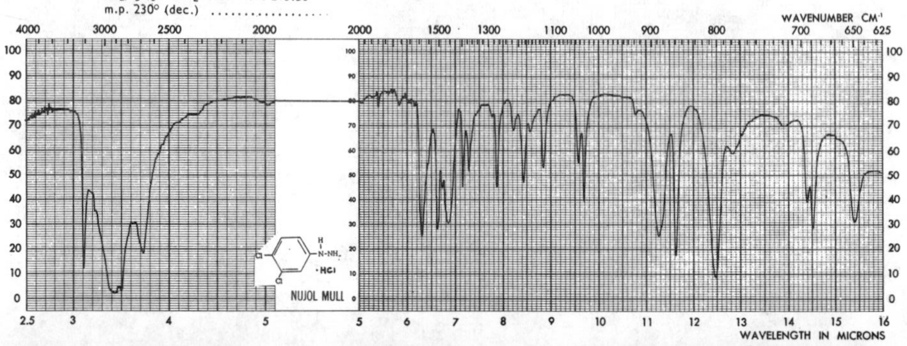

NUJOL MULL

E

15,364-8
3,5-Dichlorophenylhydrazine hydrochloride, 95%
$Cl_2C_6H_3NHNH_2 \cdot HCl$
M.W. 213.5 m.p. 208-210° (dec.) Beil. 15(1),116

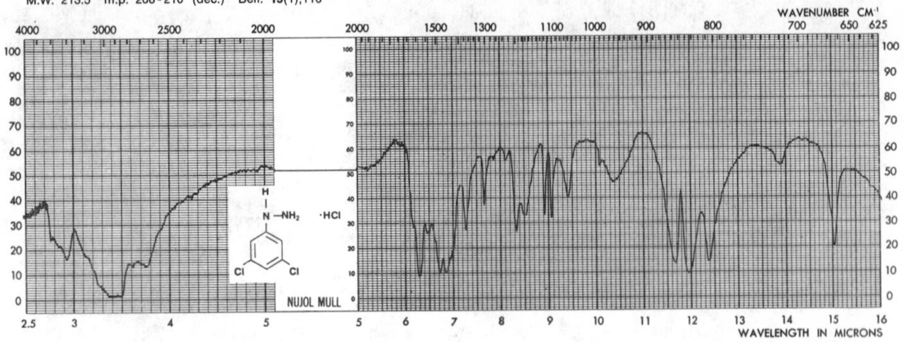

NUJOL MULL

F

13,514-3 2,4,6-Trichlorophenylhydrazine, tech., 70%
$Cl_3C_6H_2NHNH_2$ M.W. 211.48
m.p. 128-132° (dec.)

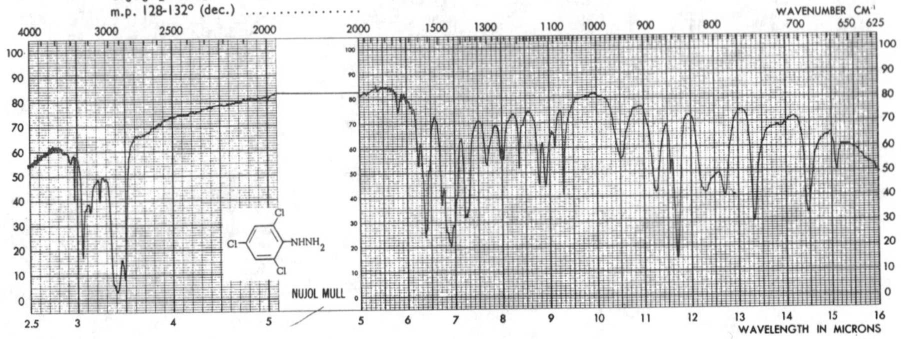

NUJOL MULL

G

19,679-7
2,3,5,6-Tetrafluorophenylhydrazine, 97+%
$HC_6F_4NHNH_2$ FW 180.10 mp 91-93° Disp. C

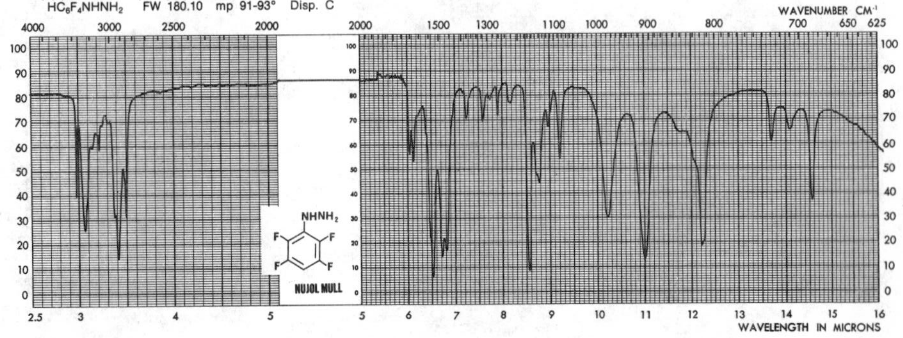

NUJOL MULL

H

15,638-8
Pentafluorophenylhydrazine, tech.
$C_6F_5NHNH_2$
M.W. 198.09 m.p. 74-76°

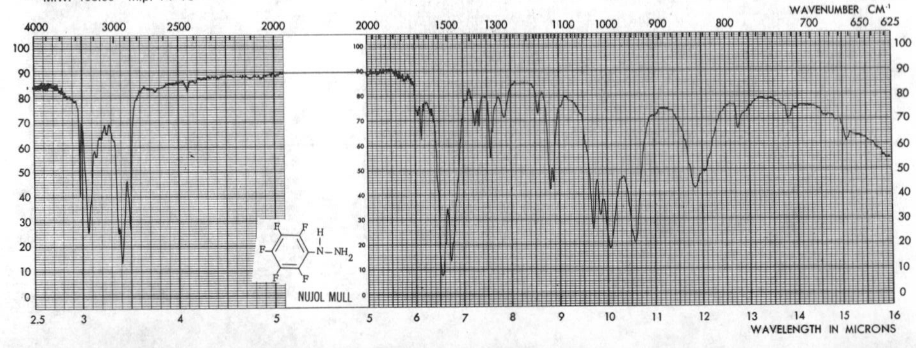

NUJOL MULL

A 10,015-3
4,4'-Dihydrazinooctafluorobiphenyl
$H_2NNHC_6F_4C_6F_4NHNH_2$
M.W. 358.19 m.p. 206-208°

B 15,785-6
2-Naphthylhydrazine hydrochloride
$C_{10}H_7NHNH_2 \cdot HCl$
M.W. 194.67 m.p. 236-238° (dec.) Beil. 15,568

C B960-2
Benzophenone hydrazone, 96%
$(C_6H_5)_2C{=}NNH_2$
M.W. 196.25 m.p. 95-98° b.p. 225-230°/55mm.
Beil. 7,417

D B517-8 **Benzil dihydrazone**
$C_6H_5C(:NNH_2)C(:NNH_2)C_6H_5$ M.W. 238.29 m.p. 148-150°

E F157-3 **9-Fluorenone hydrazone**
M.W. 194.24 m.p. 148-150°

F 13,135-0 **Perinaphthenone hydrazone**
M.W. 194.24 m.p. 139-142°

G 12,181-9 **Benzophenone phenylhydrazone**
$(C_6H_5)_2C{:}NNHC_6H_5$ M.W. 272.35
m.p. 136-138°

H 12,973-9 **3-Methyl-2-benzothiazolinone hydrazone hydrochloride monohydrate**
M.W. 233.72 m.p. 270° (dec.)

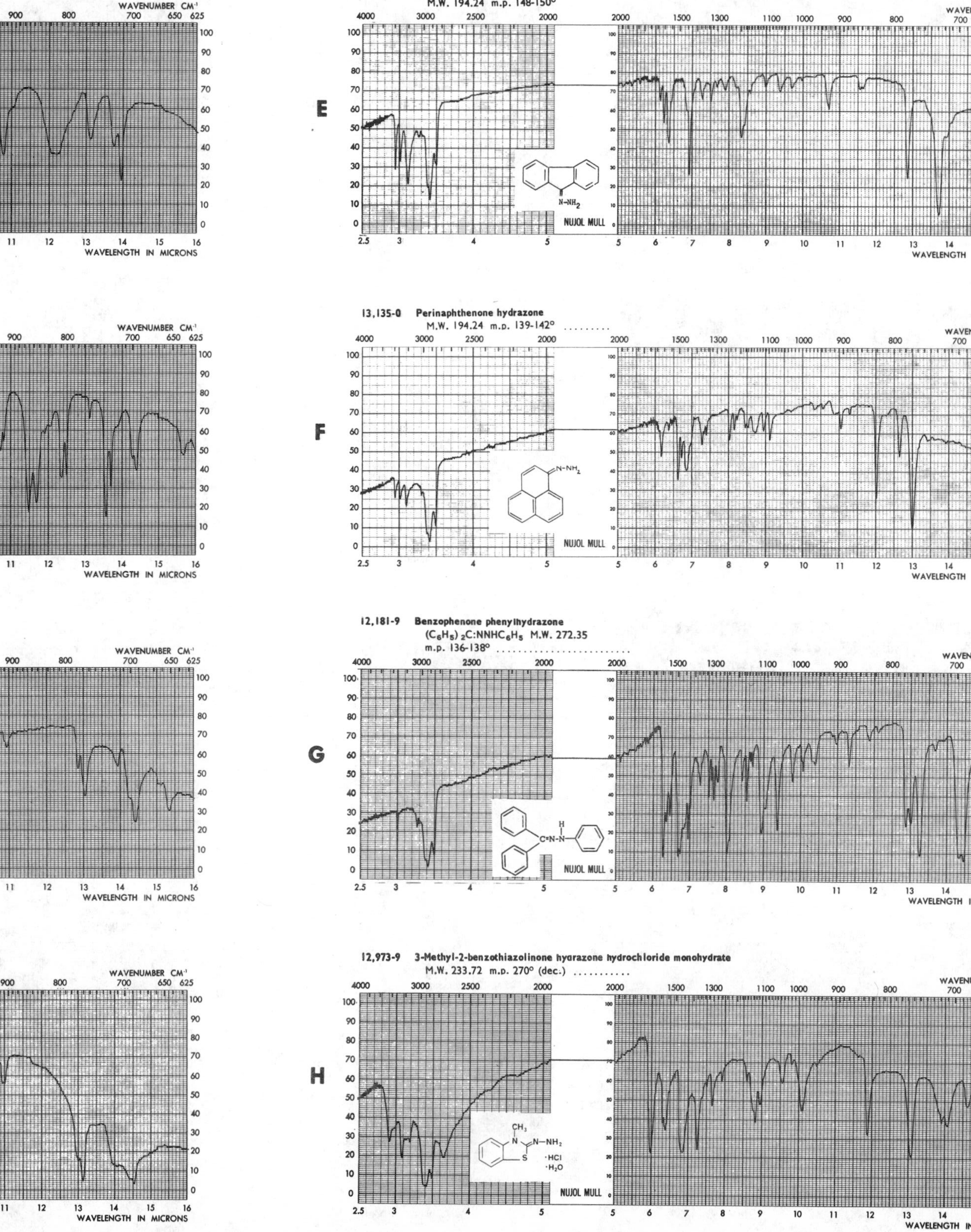

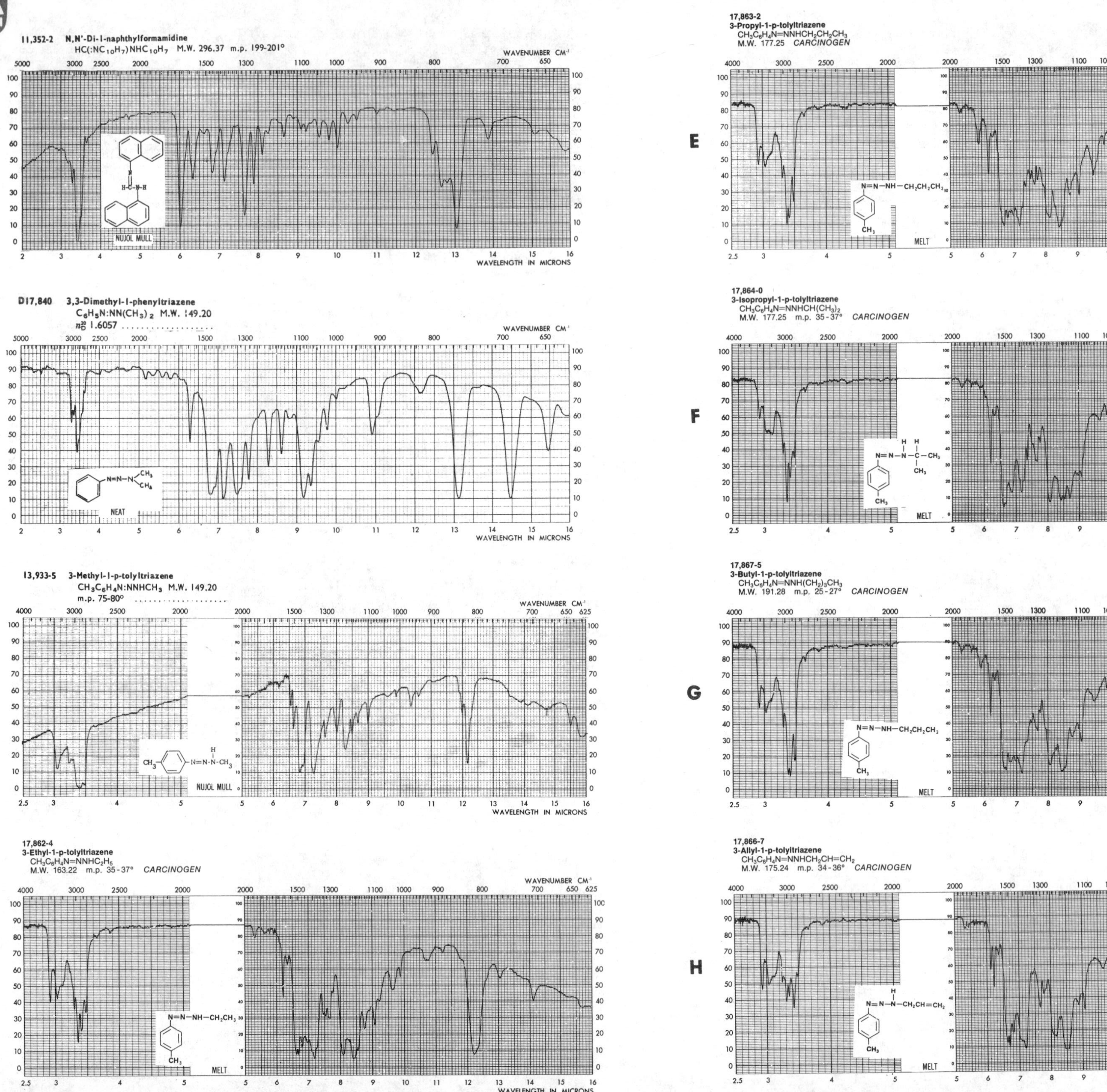
ALDRICH
A
11,352-2 N,N'-Di-1-naphthylformamidine
HC(:NC10H7)NHC10H7 M.W. 296.37 m.p. 199-201°
NUJOL MULL
B
D17,840 3,3-Dimethyl-1-phenyltriazene
C6H5N:NN(CH3)2 M.W. 149.20
n20D 1.6057
NEAT
C
13,933-5 3-Methyl-1-p-tolyltriazene
CH3C6H4N:NNHCH3 M.W. 149.20
m.p. 75-80°
NUJOL MULL
D
17,862-4
3-Ethyl-1-p-tolyltriazene
CH3C6H4N=NNHC2H5
M.W. 163.22 m.p. 35-37° CARCINOGEN
MELT
E
17,863-2
3-Propyl-1-p-tolyltriazene
CH3C6H4N=NNHCH2CH2CH3
M.W. 177.25 CARCINOGEN
MELT
F
17,864-0
3-Isopropyl-1-p-tolyltriazene
CH3C6H4N=NNHCH(CH3)2
M.W. 177.25 m.p. 35-37° CARCINOGEN
MELT
G
17,867-5
3-Butyl-1-p-tolyltriazene
CH3C6H4N=NNH(CH2)3CH3
M.W. 191.28 m.p. 25-27° CARCINOGEN
MELT
H
17,866-7
3-Allyl-1-p-tolyltriazene
CH3C6H4N=NNHCH2CH=CH2
M.W. 175.24 m.p. 34-36° CARCINOGEN
MELT
WAVENUMBER CM⁻¹
WAVELENGTH IN MICRONS

A

17,865-9
3-Benzyl-1-p-tolyltriazene
$CH_3C_6H_4N{=}NNHCH_2C_6H_5$
M.W. 225.3 m.p. 77-79° *CARCINOGEN*

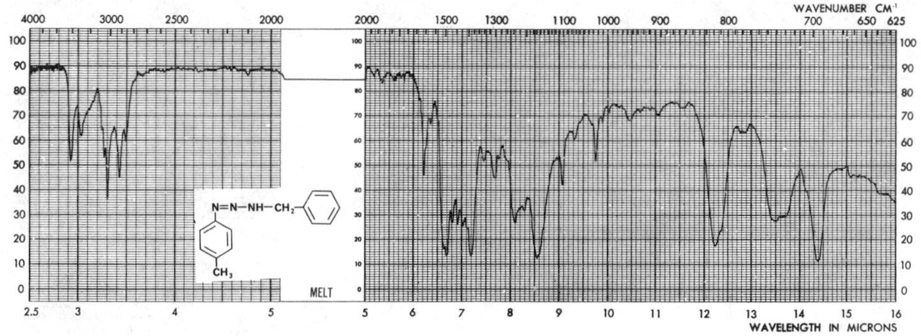

MELT

B

D11,540-1 **2,2'-Dihydroxy-1,1'-naphthalazine** (2-hydroxy-1-naphthaldehyde azine)
M.W. 340.38 m.p. 303-305°

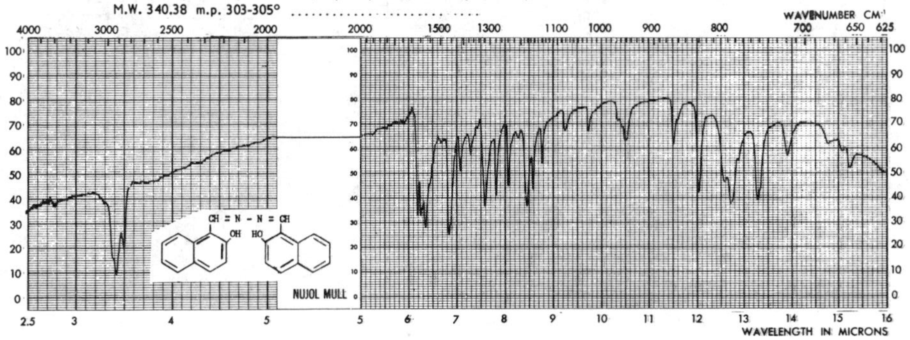

NUJOL MULL

C

T8300-3 **Triphenylformazan**
$C_6H_5C({:}NNHC_6H_5)N{:}NC_6H_5$ M.W. 300.37
m.p. 165-168°

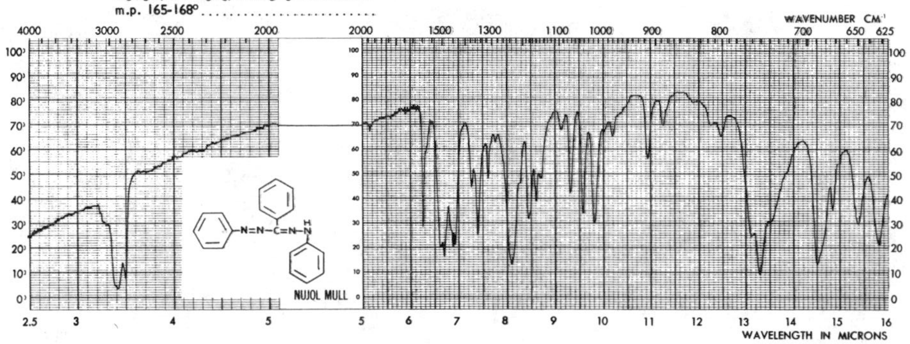

NUJOL MULL

D

B1630-5 **Benzylamine**
$C_6H_5CH_2NH_2$ M.W. 107.16 n_D^{20} 1.5424

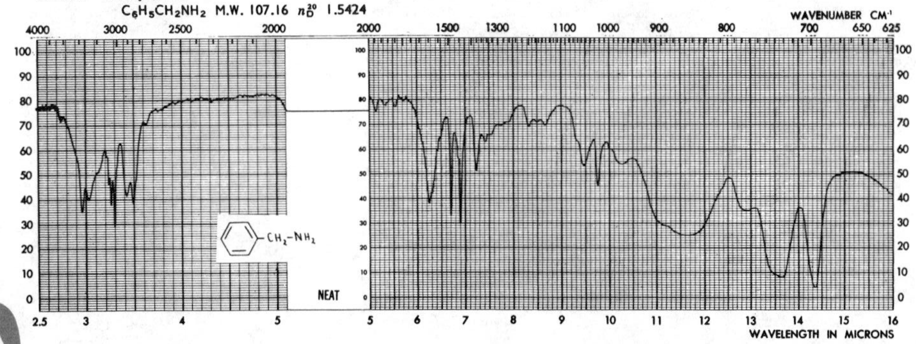

NEAT

E

21,425-6
Benzylamine hydrochloride, 99%
$C_6H_5CH_2NH_2 \cdot HCl$ FW 143.62 mp 262-263°
Beil. **12**,1017 Disp. C

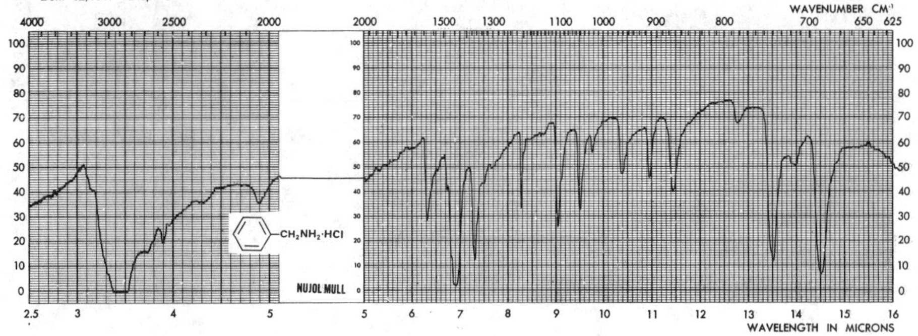

NUJOL MULL

F

B2298-4 **O-Benzylhydroxylamine** (benzyloxyamine) **hydrochloride**
$C_6H_5CH_2ONH_2 \cdot HCl$ M.W. 159.62 m.p. 238° (sublimes)

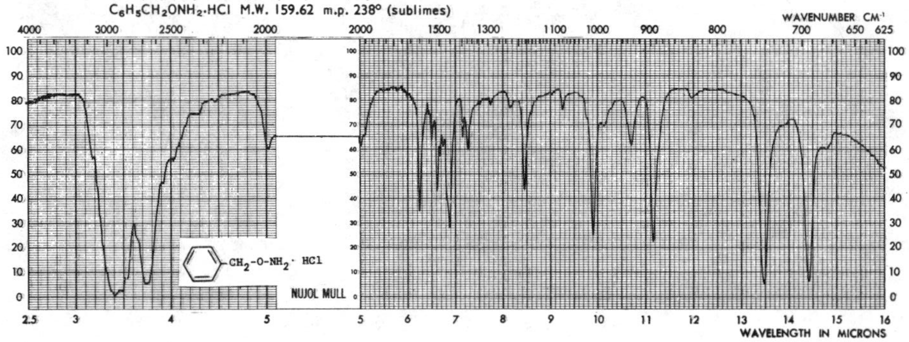

NUJOL MULL

G

19,448-4
O-(2,3,4,5,6-Pentafluorobenzyl)hydroxylamine hydrochloride, 99+%, GOLD LABEL
$C_6F_5CH_2ONH_2 \cdot HCl$ FW 249.57
mp 227° (sublimes) Disp. C

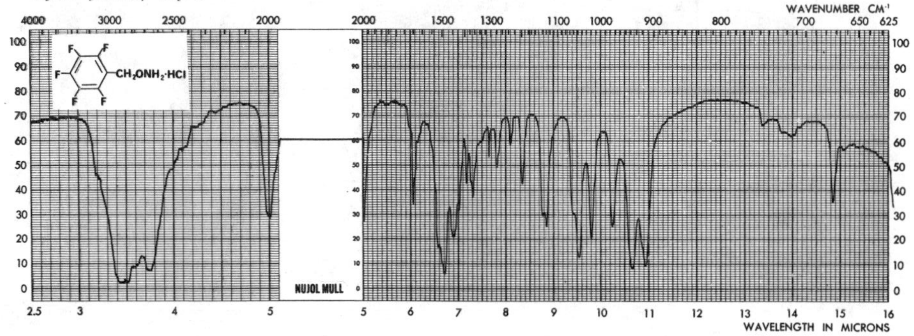

NUJOL MULL

H

M3110-4 *dl*-α-**Methylbenzylamine** (α-phenylethylamine)
$C_6H_5CH(CH_3)NH_2$ M.W. 121.18
n_D^{20} 1.5253

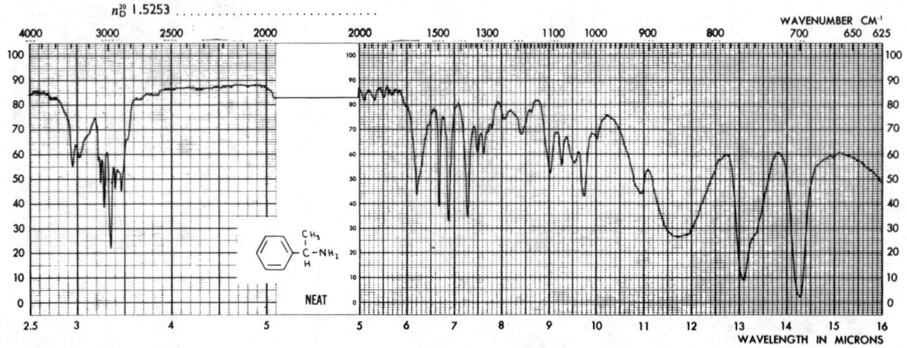

NEAT

ALDRICH

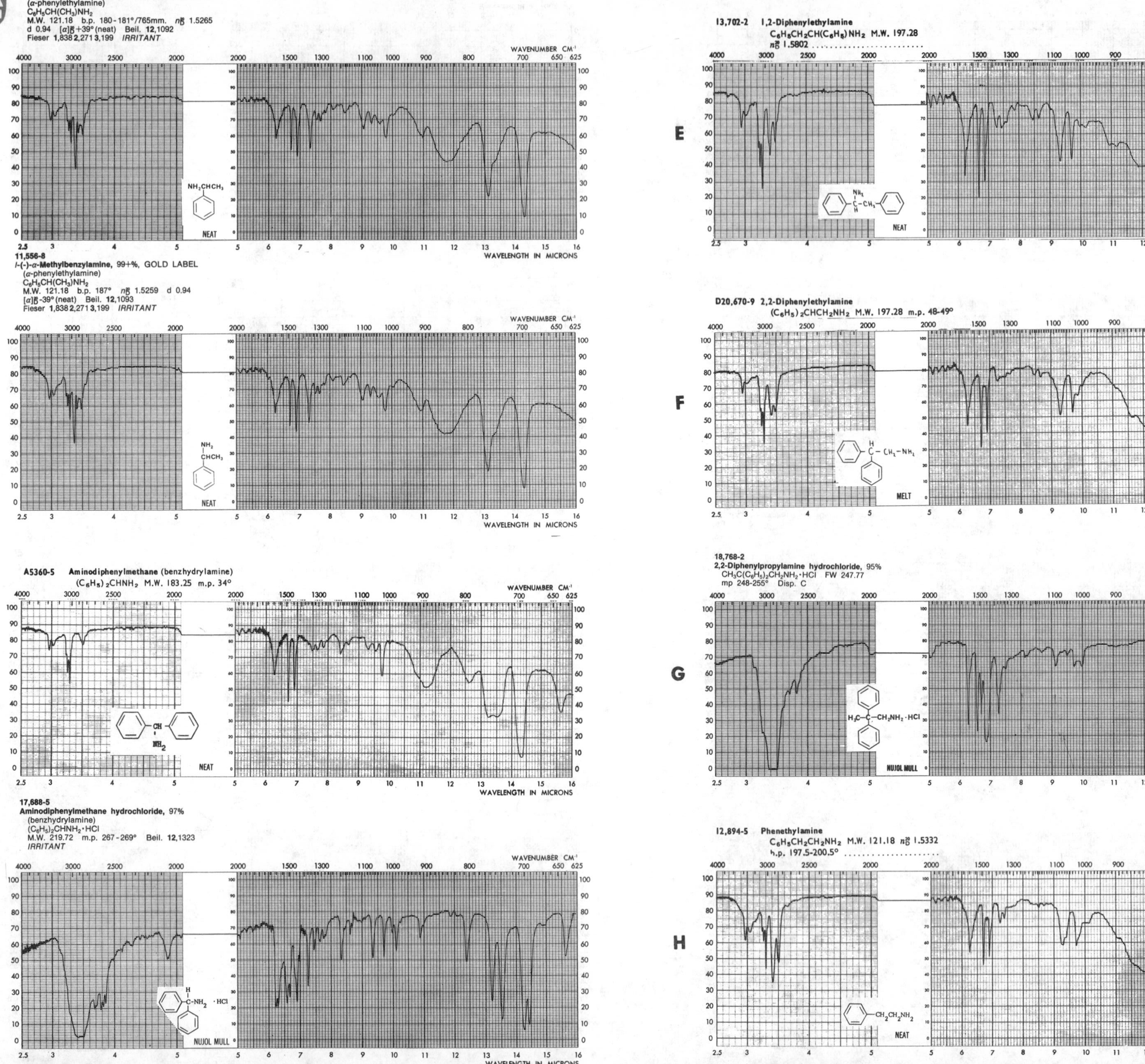
ALDRICH
A
11,554-1
d-(+)-α-Methylbenzylamine, 99+%, GOLD LABEL
(α-phenylethylamine)
C6H5CH(CH3)NH2
M.W. 121.18 b.p. 180-181°/765mm. n20D 1.5265
d 0.94 [α]20D +39° (neat) Beil. 12,1092
Fieser 1,838 2,271 3,199 IRRITANT
NEAT
B
11,556-8
l-(-)-α-Methylbenzylamine, 99+%, GOLD LABEL
(α-phenylethylamine)
C6H5CH(CH3)NH2
M.W. 121.18 b.p. 187° n20D 1.5259 d 0.94
[α]20D -39° (neat) Beil. 12,1093
Fieser 1,838 2,271 3,199 IRRITANT
NEAT
C
A5360-5 Aminodiphenylmethane (benzhydrylamine)
(C6H5)2CHNH2 M.W. 183.25 m.p. 34°
NEAT
D
17,688-5
Aminodiphenylmethane hydrochloride, 97%
(benzhydrylamine)
(C6H5)2CHNH2·HCl
M.W. 219.72 m.p. 267-269° Beil. 12,1323
IRRITANT
NUJOL MULL
E
13,702-2 1,2-Diphenylethylamine
C6H5CH2CH(C6H5)NH2 M.W. 197.28
n20D 1.5802
NEAT
F
D20,670-9 2,2-Diphenylethylamine
(C6H5)2CHCH2NH2 M.W. 197.28 m.p. 48-49°
MELT
G
18,768-2
2,2-Diphenylpropylamine hydrochloride, 95%
CH3C(C6H5)2CH2NH2·HCl FW 247.77
mp 248-255° Disp. C
NUJOL MULL
H
12,894-5 Phenethylamine
C6H5CH2CH2NH2 M.W. 121.18 n20D 1.5332
b.p. 197.5-200.5°
NEAT
WAVENUMBER CM⁻¹
WAVELENGTH IN MICRONS

A A8310-5 *d*-Amphetamine (*d*-α-methylphenethylamine) puriss.
$C_6H_5CH_2CH(CH_3)NH_2$ M.W. 135.21
n_D^{20} 1.5163 $[\alpha]_D^{20}$ + 33.0° (neat)

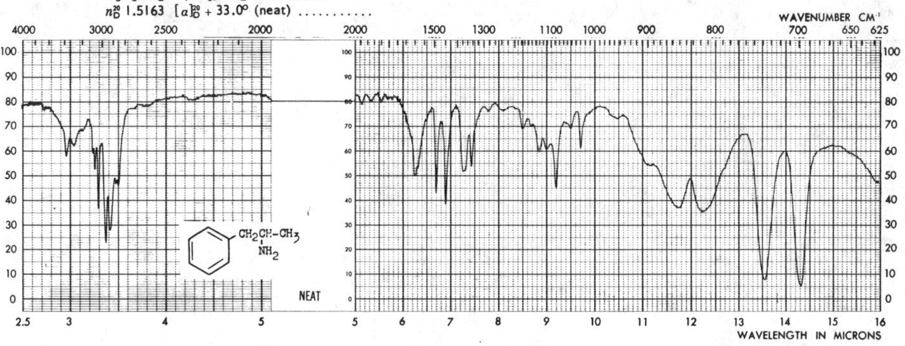

NEAT

B 13,674-3 *l*-Amphetamine (*l*-α-methylphenethylamine), puriss.
$C_6H_5CH_2CH(CH_3)NH_2$ M.W. 135.21 n_D^{20} 1.5182
$[\alpha]_D^{20}$ - 33.0° (neat)

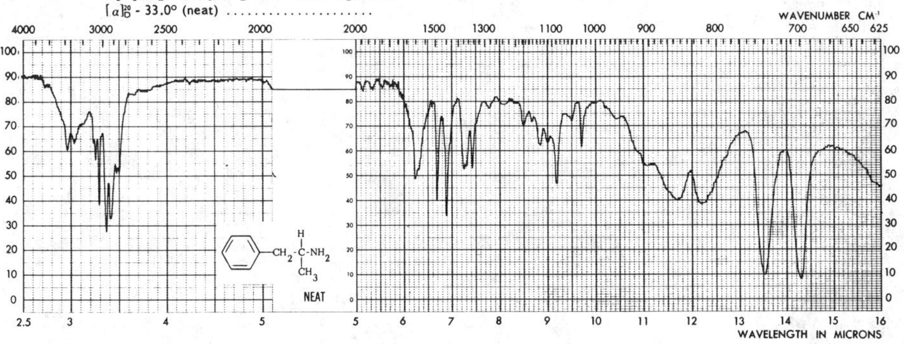

NEAT

C 13,675-1 *l*-Amphetamine (*l*-α-methylphenethylamine) sulfate
$[C_6H_5CH_2CH(CH_3)NH_2]_2 \cdot H_2SO_4$ M.W. 368.50
m.p. 330° (dec.) $[\alpha]_D^{22}$ - 17° (c=4.5, H_2O)

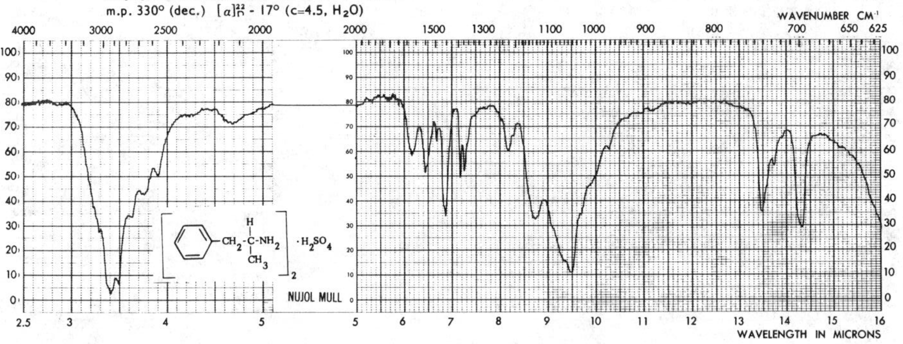

NUJOL MULL

D 18,614-7
2-Amino-3-phenyl-1-propanol
$C_6H_5CH_2CH(NH_2)CH_2OH$
M.W. 151.21 m.p. 147-151° Beil. **13**(3).1757

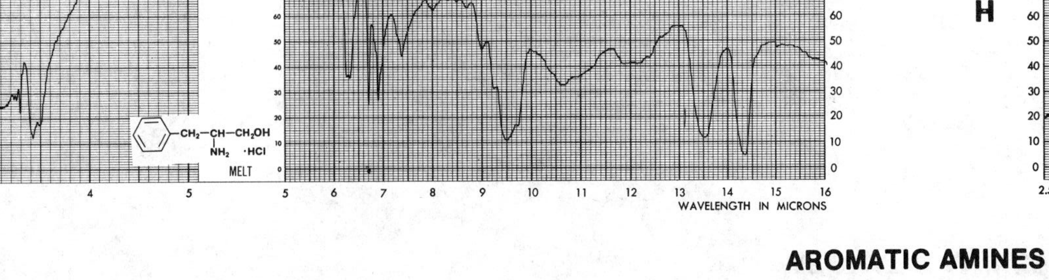

MELT

E D17,388-6 α,α-Dimethylphenethylamine
$C_6H_5CH_2C(CH_3)_2NH_2$ M.W. 149.24
n_D^{20} 1.5158

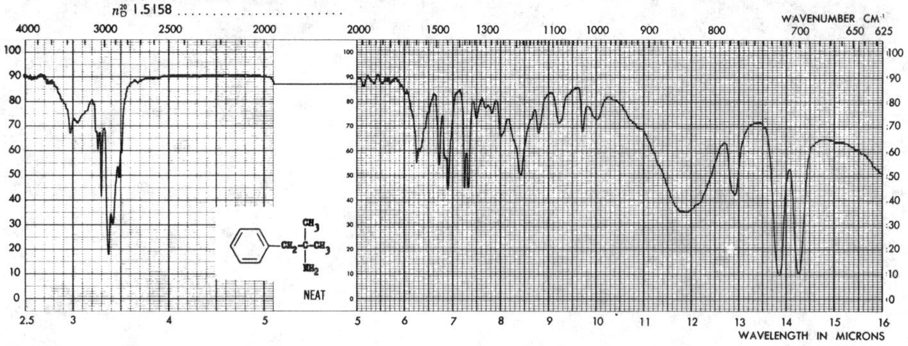

NEAT

F 14,943-8 α,α-Dimethylphenethylamine hydrochloride
$C_6H_5CH_2C(CH_3)_2NH_2 \cdot HCl$ M.W. 185.70
m.p. 197-199°

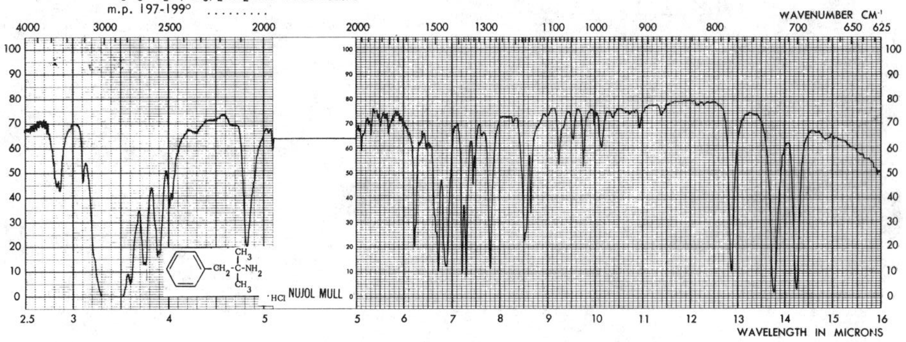

NUJOL MULL

G P2237-0 *trans*-2-Phenylcyclopropylamine
$C_6H_5C_3H_4NH_2$ M.W. 133.19 m.p. 43-46°

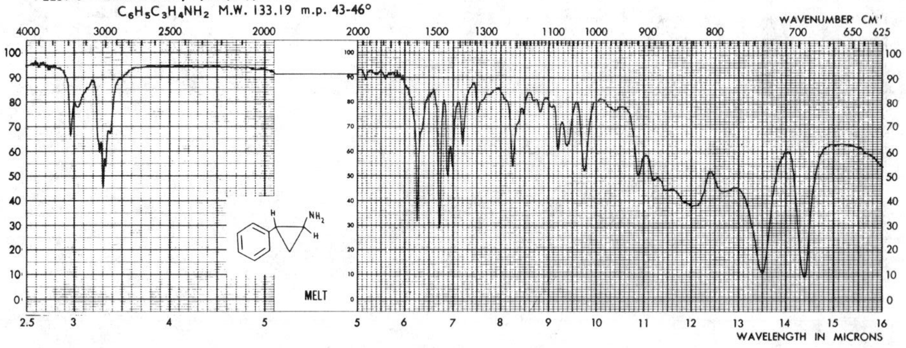

MELT

H 18,769-0
1-Phenylcyclopropanemethylamine hydrochloride, 99%
$C_6H_5C_3H_4CH_2NH_2 \cdot HCl$ FW 183.68 mp 170-172°
Disp. C

NUJOL MULL

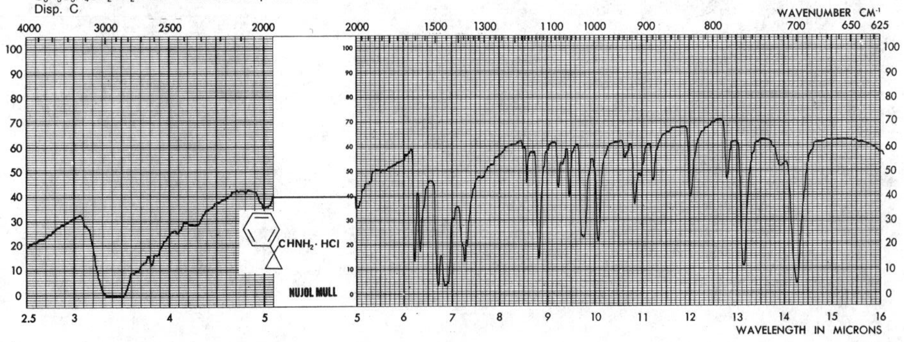

A 10,400-0 1-Phenylcyclohexylamine
$C_6H_5C_6H_{10}NH_2$ M.W. 175.28 n_D^{20} 1.5486
NEAT

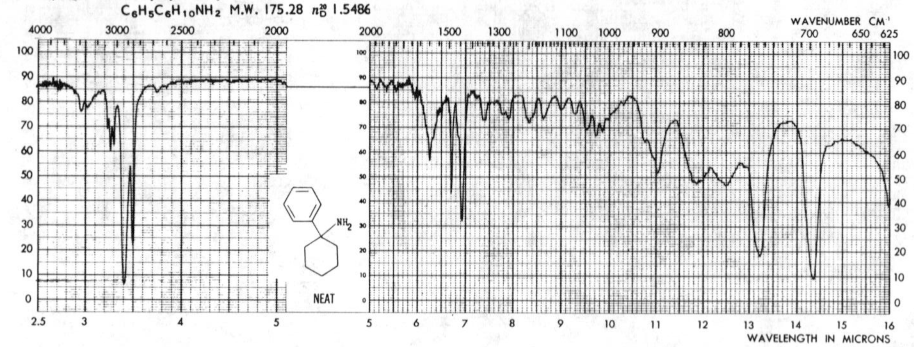

B P3240-6 3-Phenyl-1-propylamine, tech.
$C_6H_5(CH_2)_3NH_2$ M.W. 135.21
b.p. 221.5°/755 mm.
NEAT

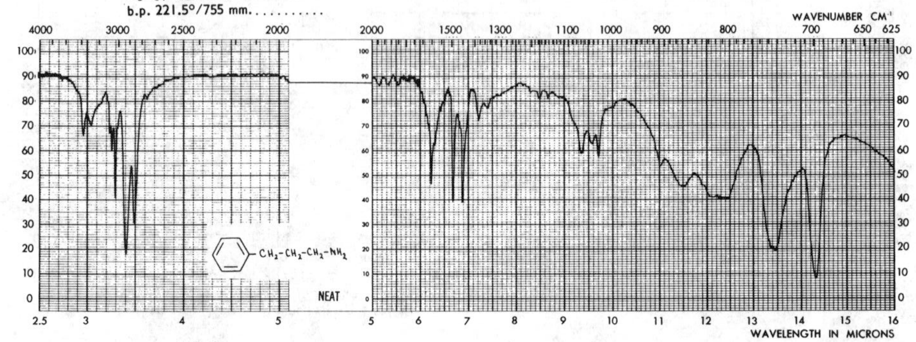

C 13,629-8 3,3-Diphenylpropylamine
$(C_6H_5)_2CHCH_2CH_2NH_2$ M.W. 211.31
m.p. 29-31°
NEAT

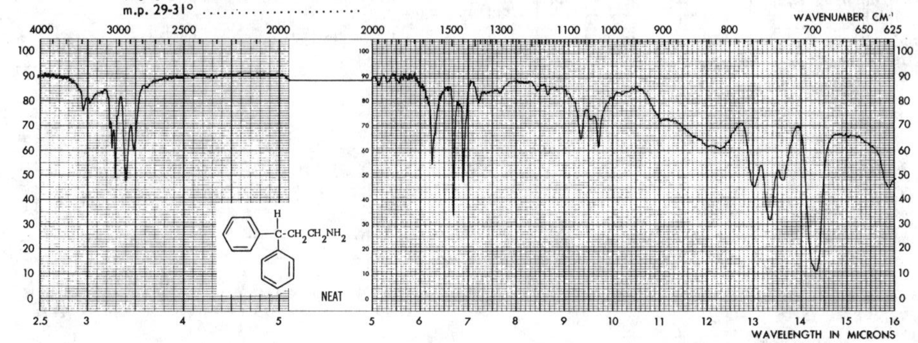

D M7053 1-Methyl-3-phenylpropylamine
$C_6H_5(CH_2)_2CH(CH_3)NH_2$ M.W. 149.24 n_D^{20} 1.5123
NEAT

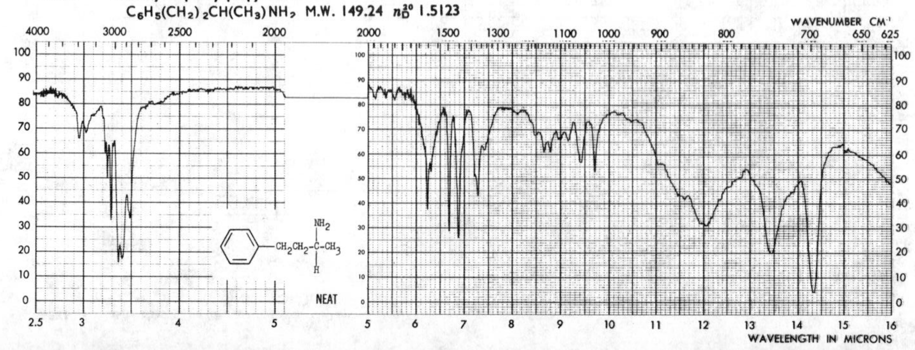

E 14,539-4 4-Phenylbutylamine
$C_6H_5(CH_2)_4NH_2$ M.W. 149.24 n_D^{20} 1.5195
NEAT

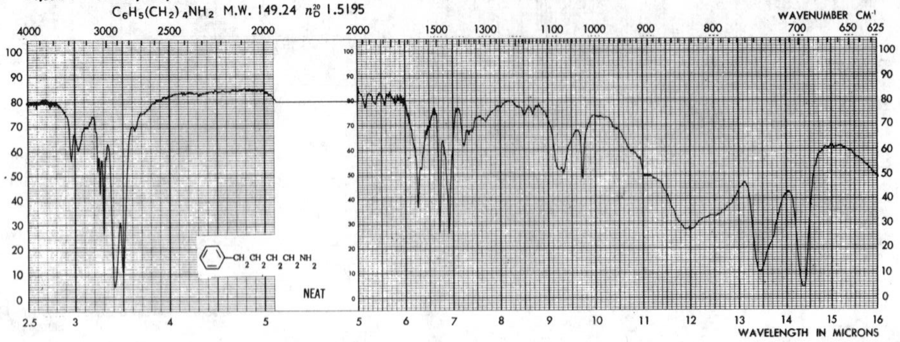

F P2415-2 N-Phenylethylenediamine
$C_6H_5NHCH_2CH_2NH_2$ M.W. 136.20
n_D^{20} 1.5836
NEAT

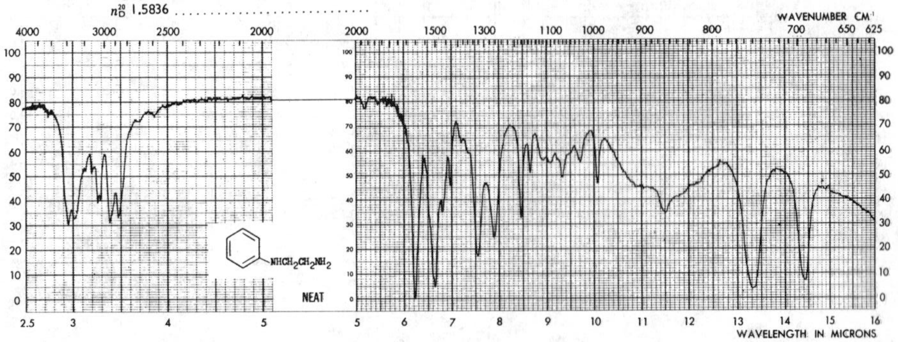

G 12,005-7 2-(Benzyloxy)-ethylamine
$C_6H_5CH_2OCH_2CH_2NH_2$ M.W. 151.21 n_D^{20} 1.5222
b.p. 114-117°/11 mm.
NEAT

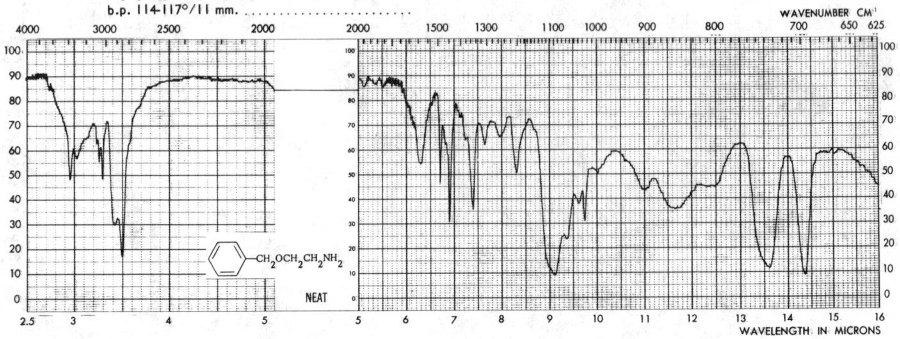

H 15,028-2 1-Methyl-2-phenoxyethylamine
$C_6H_5OCH_2CH(CH_3)NH_2$ M.W. 151.21
n_D^{20} 1.5209
NEAT

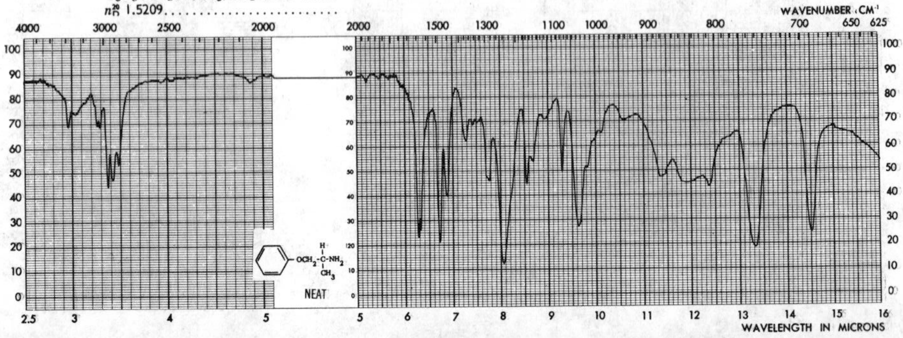

A

A7240-5 **2-Amino-1-phenylethanol** [α-(aminomethyl)-benzyl alcohol]
$H_2NCH_2CH(C_6H_5)OH$ M.W. 137.18
m.p. 57-59°

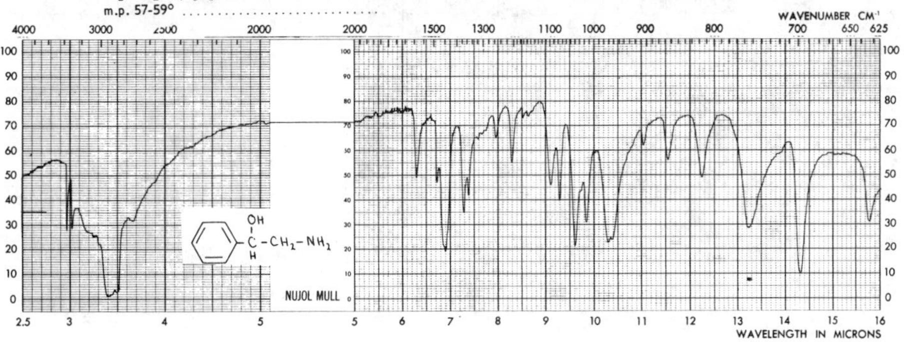

NUJOL MULL

B

19,035-7
D-(-)-α-**Phenylglycinol**, 98% (2-amino-2-phenylethanol)
$C_6H_5CH(NH_2)CH_2OH$ FW 137.18 mp 75-77°
$[\alpha]^{24}$ -31.7° (c=0.76, 1*N* HCl) Disp. C

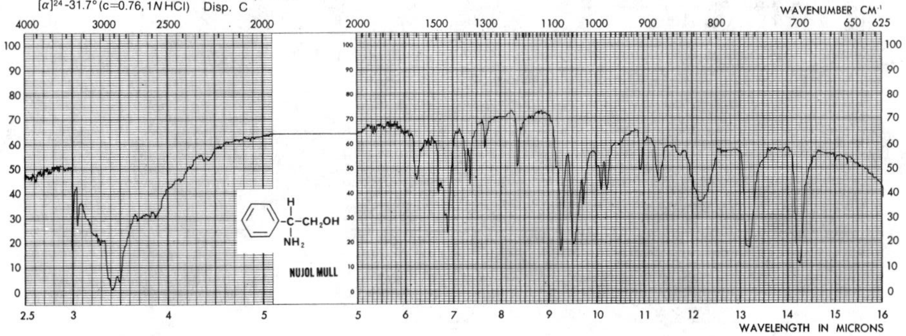

NUJOL MULL

C

19,043-8
L-**2-Amino-3-phenyl-1-propanol**, 98%
(L-phenylalaninol)
$C_6H_5CH_2CH(NH_2)CH_2OH$ FW 151.21 mp 92-94°
$[\alpha]^{22}$ -22.8° (c=1.2, 1*N* HCl) Disp. C

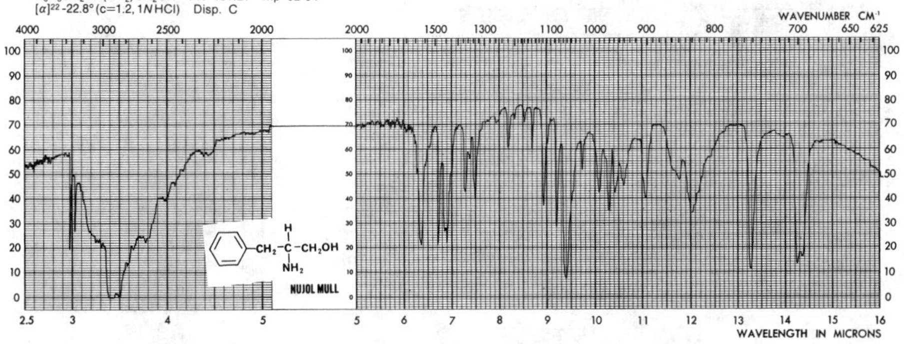

NUJOL MULL

D

13,143-1 **Phenylpropanolamine** (norephedrine) **hydrochloride, puriss.**
$C_6H_5CH(OH)CH(CH_3)NH_2 \cdot HCl$ M.W. 187.67
m.p. 198-199°

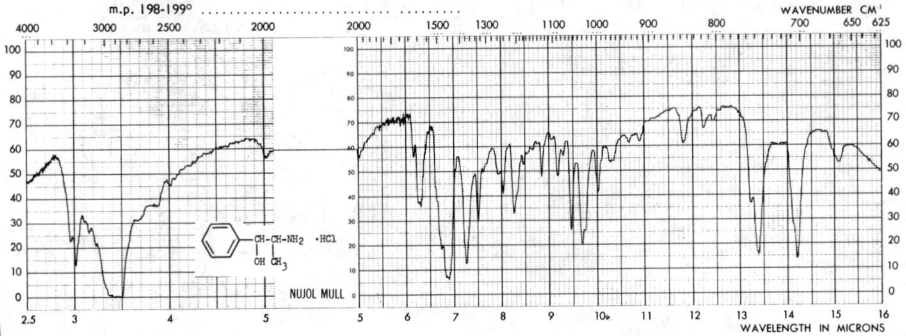

NUJOL MULL

E

19,362-3
(+)-**Norephedrine hydrochloride** [*erythro*-α-(1-aminoethyl)benzyl alcohol, phenylpropanolamine]
$C_6H_5CH(OH)CH(CH_3)NH_2 \cdot HCl$ FW 187.67
mp 174-176° $[\alpha]^{23}$ +33.4° (c=7, H_2O)
Beil. **13**(2),371 Disp. C

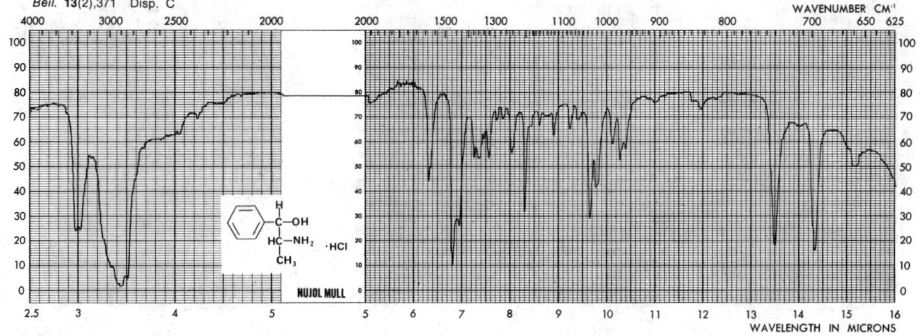

NUJOL MULL

F

19,363-1
(-)-**Norpseudoephedrine hydrochloride** [*threo*-α-(1-aminoethyl)benzyl alcohol]
$C_6H_5CH(OH)CH(CH_3)NH_2 \cdot HCl$ FW 187.67
mp 180-183° $[\alpha]^{23}$ -41.7° (c=7, H_2O)
Beil. **13**(2),372 Disp. C

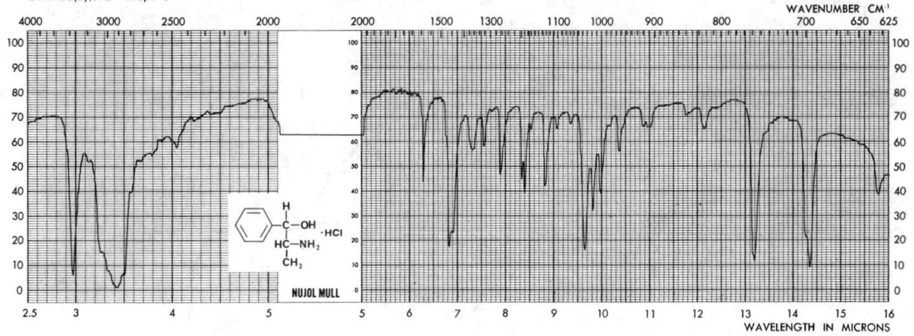

NUJOL MULL

G

15,030-4 **L-(+)-*threo*-2-Amino-1-phenyl-1,3-propanediol**
$C_6H_5CH(OH)CH(NH_2)CH_2OH$ M.W. 167.21
m.p. 109-113° $[\alpha]_D^{22}$ + 32.4° (c=1, CH_3OH)

NUJOL MULL

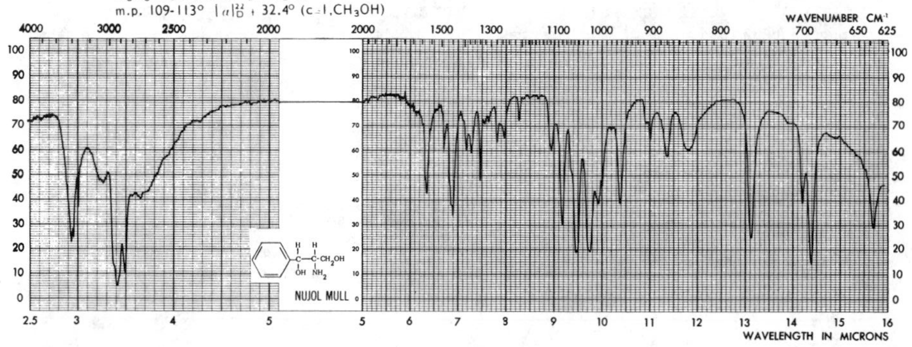

H

B2560-6 **Benzylmethylamine** (N-methylbenzylamine)
$C_6H_5CH_2NHCH_3$ M.W. 121.18 n_D^{20} 1.5224

NEAT

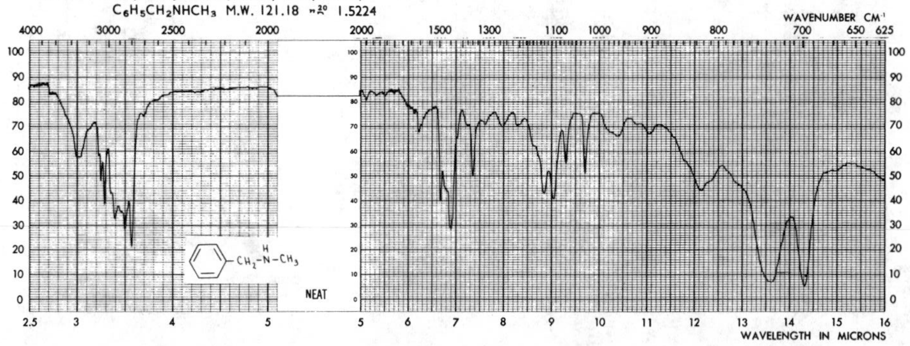

A

12,699-3 **N-Ethylbenzylamine, puriss.**
$C_6H_5CH_2NHC_2H_5$ M.W. 135.21 n_D^{20} 1.5117
b.p. 191-194°

NEAT

B

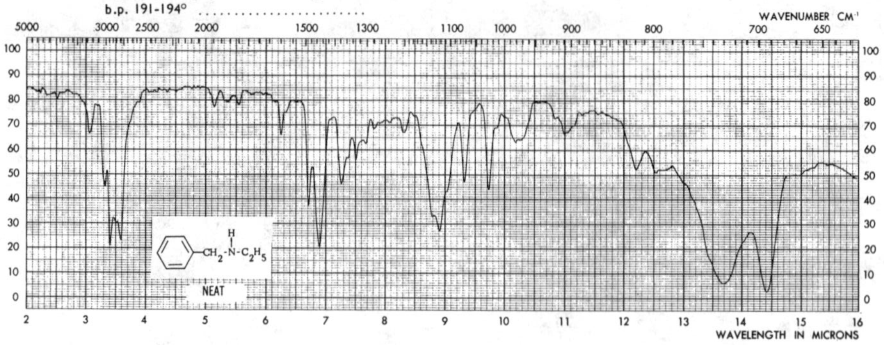

12,704-3 **N-(n-Propyl)-benzylamine, puriss.**
$C_6H_5CH_2NHCH_2CH_2CH_3$ M.W. 149.24 n_D^{20} 1.5061
b.p. 210°

NEAT

C

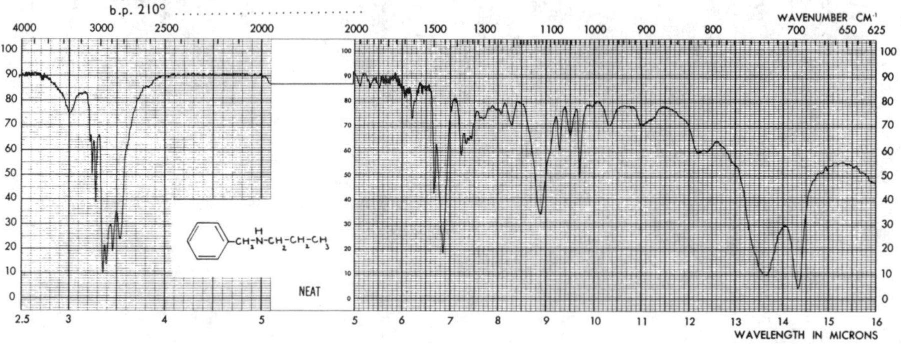

13,696-4 **N-Isopropylbenzylamine** (N-benzylisopropylamine)
$C_6H_5CH_2NHCH(CH_3)_2$ M.W. 149.24 n_D^{20} 1.5039

NEAT

D

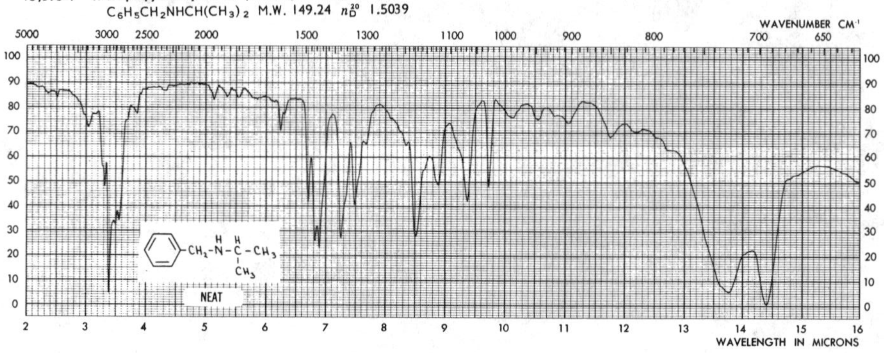

12,693-4 **N-(n-Butyl)-benzylamine, puriss.**
$C_6H_5CH_2NH(CH_2)_3CH_3$ M.W. 163.26 n_D^{20} 1.5016
b.p. 226-230°/715 mm.

NEAT

E

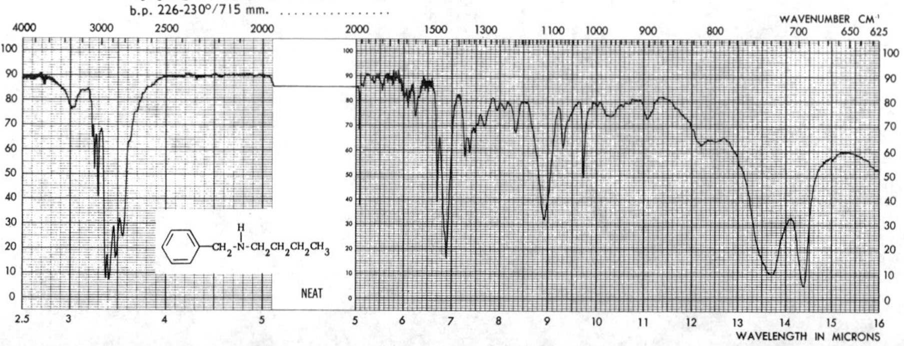

21,920-7
N-(*tert*-Butyl)benzylamine, 99%
$C_6H_5CH_2NHC(CH_3)_3$ FW 163.27 bp 80°/5mm.
n_D^{20} 1.4968 d 0.881 *Beil.* **12**,1022 Disp. C

NEAT

F

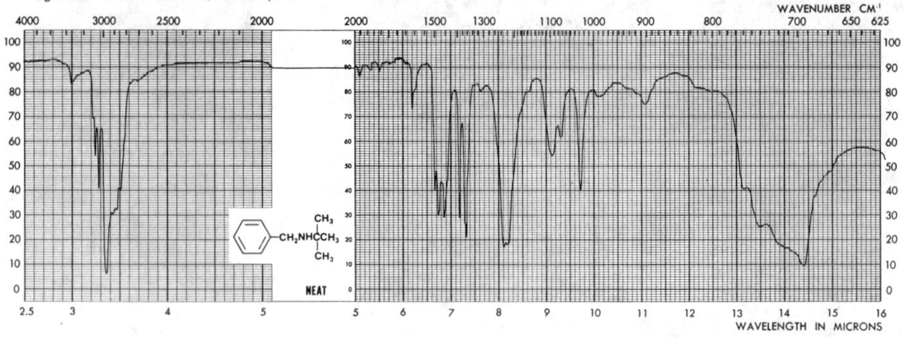

D3410-8 **Dibenzylamine**
$(C_6H_5CH_2)_2NH$ M.W. 197.28 n_D^{20} 1.5731

NEAT

G

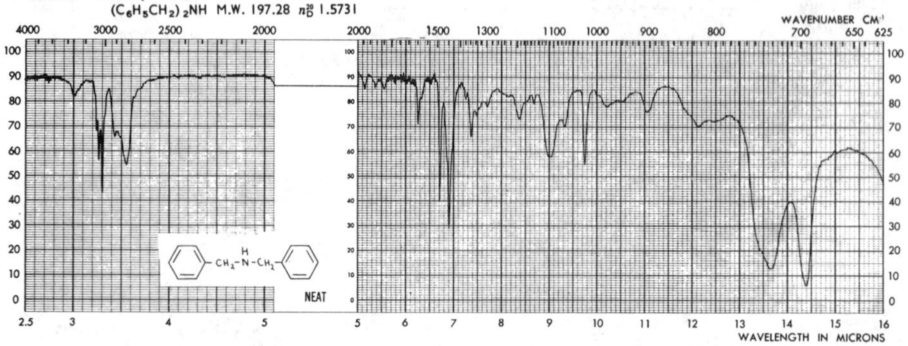

D15,040 **Di-(α-methylbenzyl)-amine**

NEAT

H

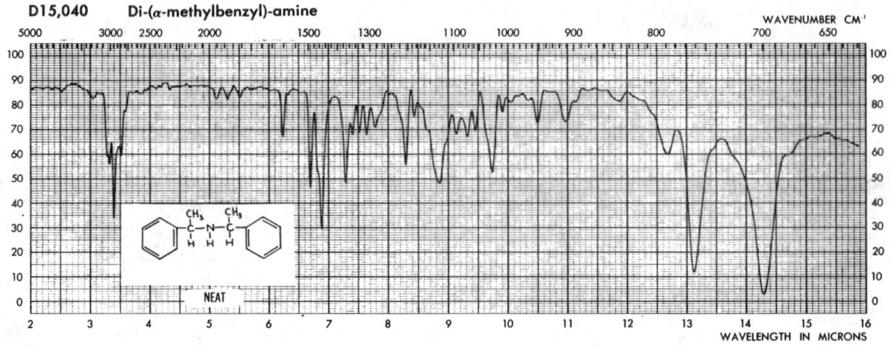

D3520-1 **N,N'-Dibenzylethylenediamine**
$C_6H_5CH_2NHCH_2CH_2NHCH_2C_6H_5$ M.W. 240.35
n_D^{20} 1.5615

NEAT

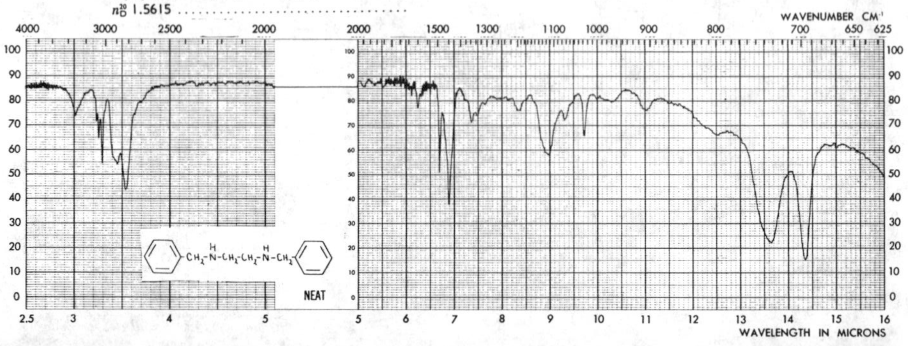

A

M6842-3 **N-Methylphenethylamine**
$C_6H_5CH_2CH_2NHCH_3$ M.W. 135.21
n_D^{20} 1.5162

NEAT

B

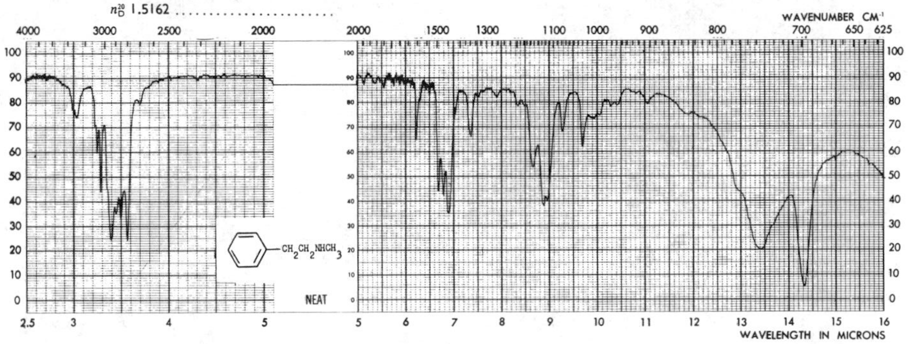

18,007-6
β-Methylphenethylamine, 99% (1-amino-2-phenylpropane)
$C_6H_5CH(CH_3)CH_2NH_2$
M.W. 135.21 b.p. 80°/10mm. n_D^{20} 1.5241 d 0.93

NEAT

C

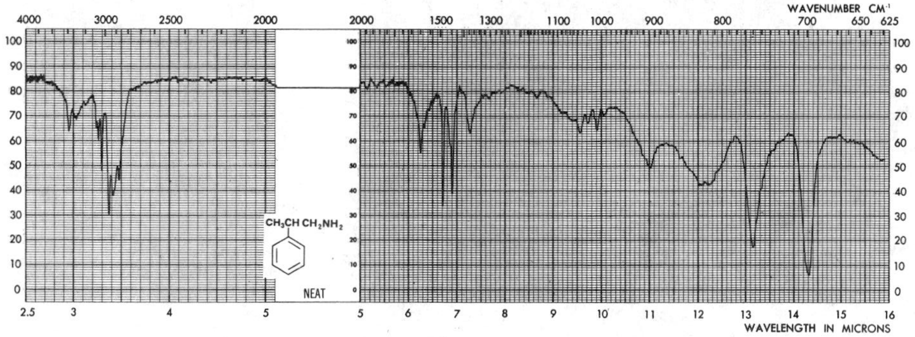

D570-5 **d-Desoxyephedrine** (*d*-N,α-dimethylphenethylamine)
$C_6H_5CH_2CH(CH_3)NHCH_3$ M.W. 149.24
n_D^{20} 1.5073

NEAT

D

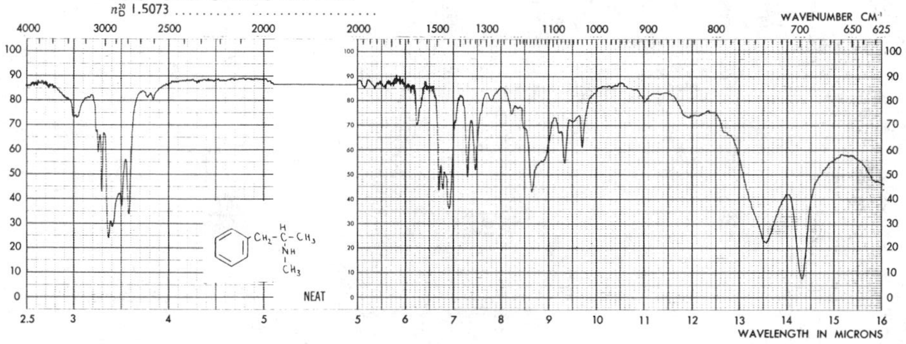

D571-3 **d-Desoxyephedrine** (*d*-N,α-dimethylphenethylamine) **hydrochloride**
$C_6H_5CH_2CH(CH_3)NHCH_3 \cdot HCl$ M.W. 185.70 m.p. 169.5-173°
$[\alpha]_D^{20}$ + 18.0° (c=2, H_2O)

NUJOL MULL

E

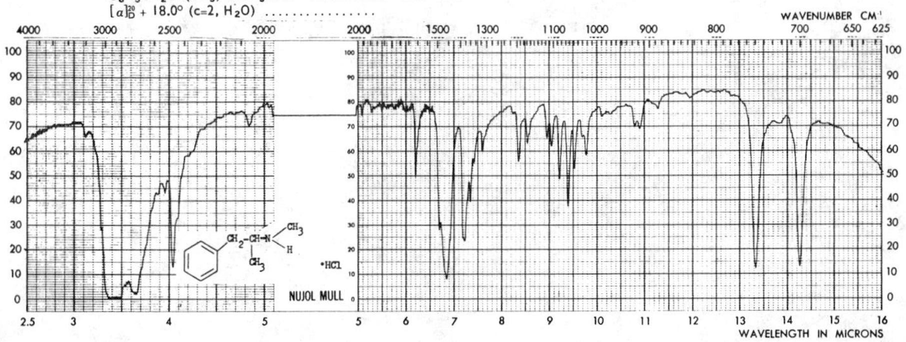

12,368-4 **2-(Benzylamino)-norbornane** (N-benzyl-2-norbornanamine)
M.W. 201.31 n_D^{20} 1.5411

NEAT

F

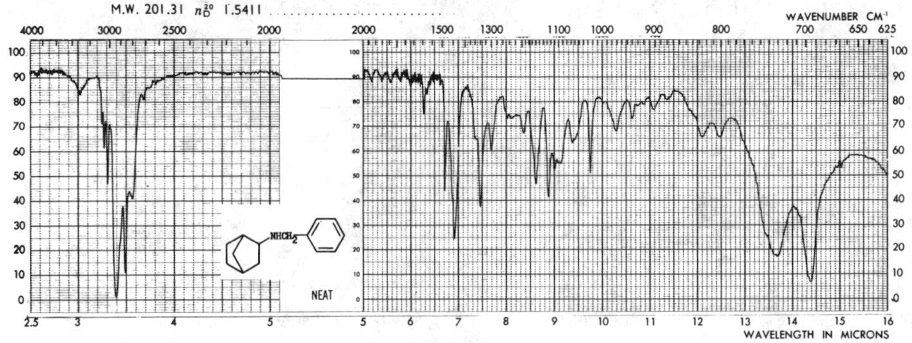

P1395 **2-(Phenethylamino)-norbornane** (N-phenethyl-2-norbornanamine)
M.W. 215.34 n_D^{20} 1.5339

NEAT

G

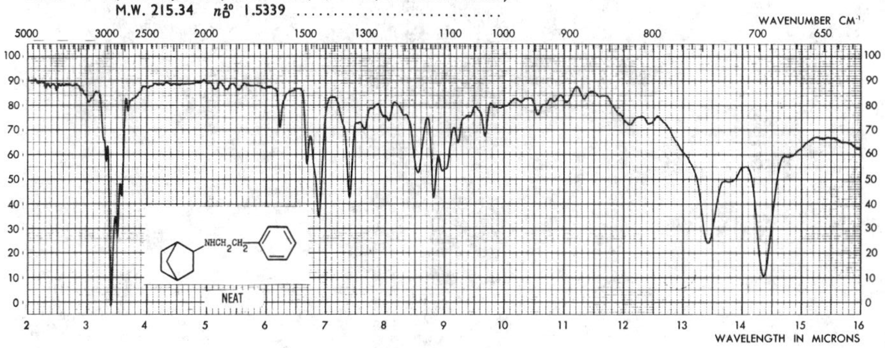

12,719-1 **N'-Benzyl-N,N-dimethylethylenediamine, tech.**
$C_6H_5CH_2NHCH_2CH_2N(CH_3)_2$ M.W. 178.28
n_D^{20} 1.5089 b.p. 122-124°/11 mm.

NEAT

H

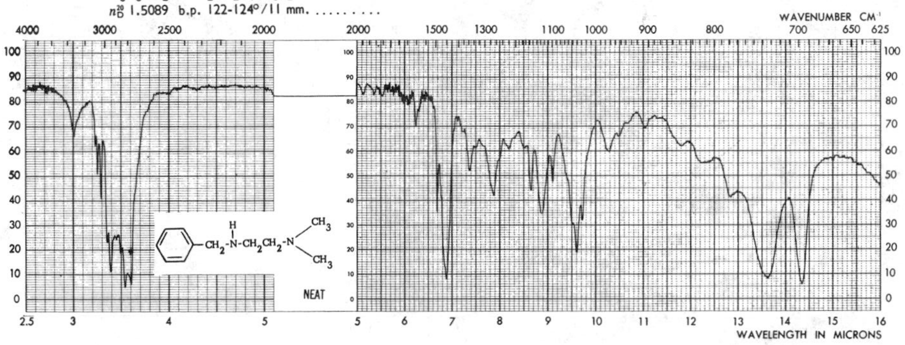

B2200-3 **N-Benzylethanolamine** (2-benzylaminoethanol), **puriss.**
$C_6H_5CH_2NHCH_2CH_2OH$ M.W. 151.21 n_D^{20} 1.5435

NEAT

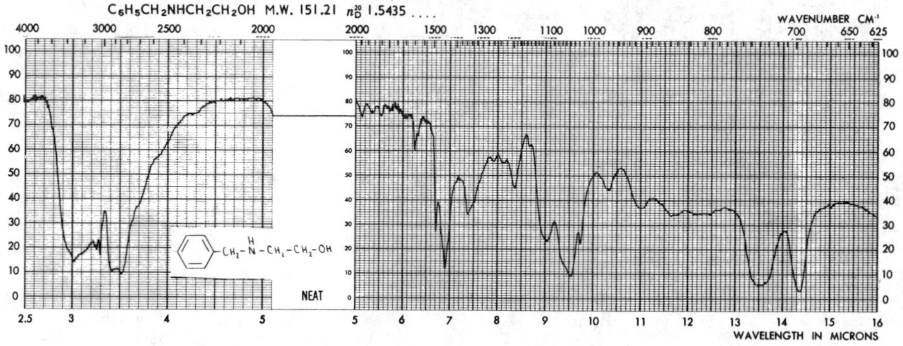

A

11,496-0 **3-Benzylamino-1-propanol**
$C_6H_5CH_2NH(CH_2)_3OH$ M.W. 165.24
n_D^{20} 1.5365

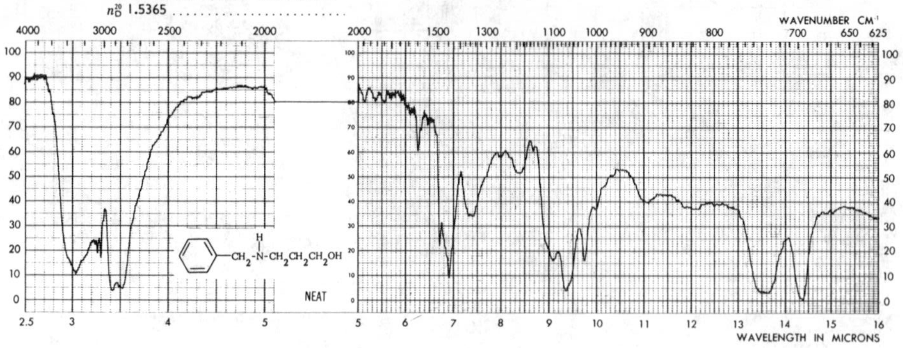

NEAT

B

11,497-9 *dl*-**1-Benzylamino-2-propanol**
$C_6H_5CH_2NHCH_2CH(OH)CH_3$ M.W. 165.24
n_D^{20} 1.5270

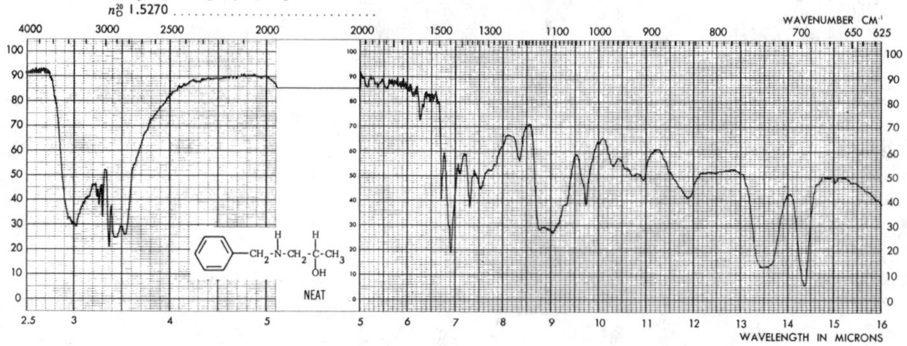

NEAT

C

B1660-7 **DL-2-Benzylamino-1-propanol**
$CH_3CH(NHCH_2C_6H_5)CH_2OH$ M.W. 165.24 m.p. 68-70°

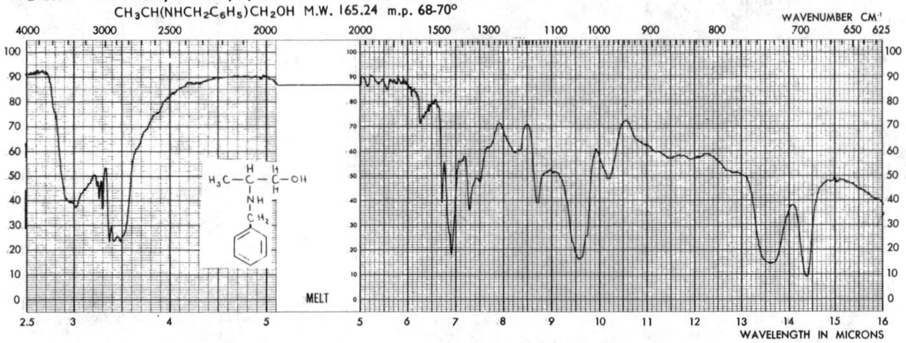

MELT

D

20,984-8
dl-**α-(Methylaminomethyl)benzyl alcohol,** 99%
(Halostachine)
$C_6H_5CH(CH_2NHCH_3)OH$ FW 151.21 mp 73-75°
Disp. C

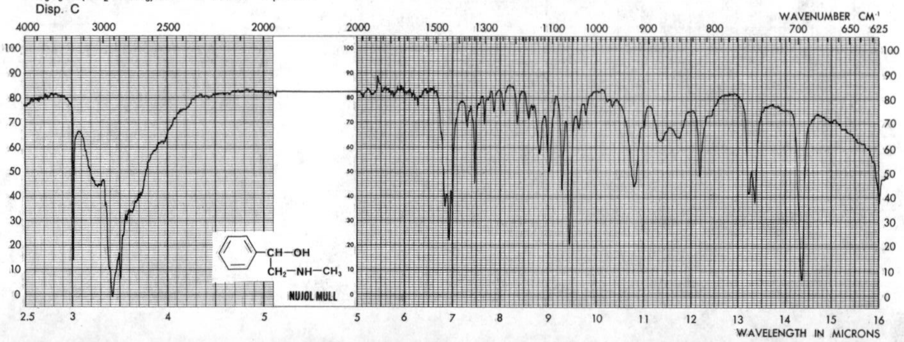

NUJOL MULL

E

18,742-9
d-**Ephedrine,** 99%, anhydrous [*d*-α-(1-methylamino-ethyl)benzyl alcohol]
$C_6H_5CH[CH(NHCH_3)CH_3]OH$ FW 165.24
mp 38-41° bp 225° $[\alpha]_D^{25}$ +13.0° (c=4, H_2O)
Fieser 5,289 Disp. C

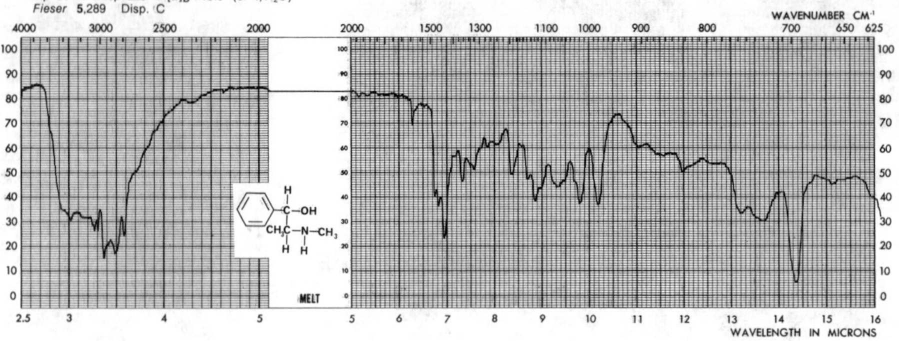

MELT

F

13,491-0 *l*-**Ephedrine** [*l*-α-(1-methylaminoethyl)-benzyl alcohol]
$C_6H_5CH[CH(NHCH_3)CH_3]OH$ M.W. 165.24 m.p. 37-39°
$[\alpha]_D^{18}$ - 41° (c=5, H_2O-HCl)

MELT

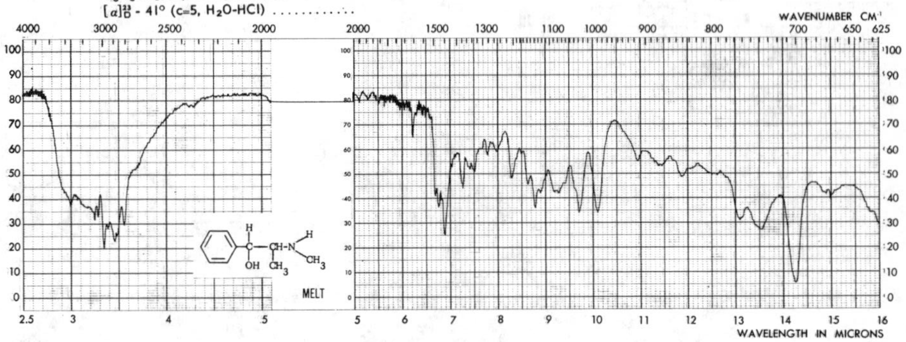

G

86,039-5
l-**Ephedrine nitrate,** 99% [α-(1-methylaminoethyl)-benzyl alcohol]
$C_6H_5CH[CH(NHCH_3)CH_3]OH \cdot HNO_3$ FW 228.25
mp 126-128° $[\alpha]^{21}$ -31° (c=5, H_2O) Disp. C

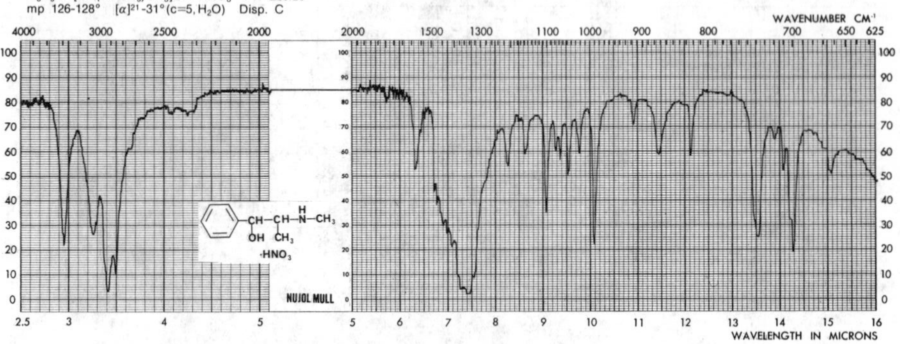

NUJOL MULL

H

12,038-3 *dl*-**Ephedrine** [*dl*-α-(1-methylaminoethyl)-benzyl alcohol] **hydrochloride**
$C_6H_5CH[CH(NHCH_3)CH_3]OH \cdot HCl$ M.W. 201.70
m.p. 191-193.5°

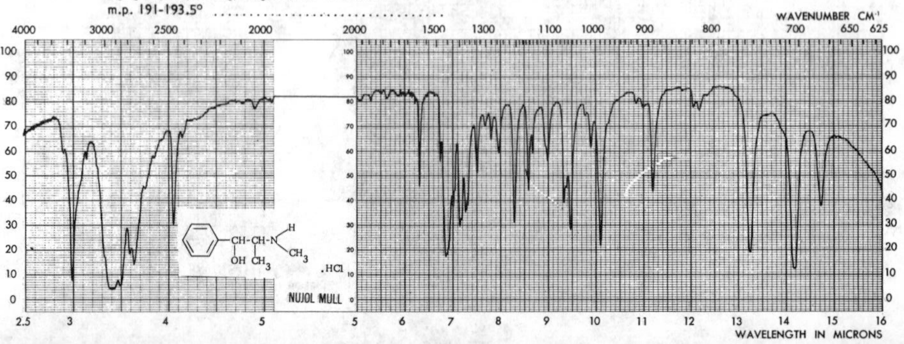

NUJOL MULL

A

85,733-5
d-**Ephedrine hydrochloride** [*d*-α-(1-methylamino-ethyl)-benzyl alcohol]
$C_6H_5CH[CH(NHCH_3)CH_3]OH \cdot HCl$
M.W. 201.7 m.p. 218-220° $[\alpha]^{23}$ +34.3° (c=5, H_2O)

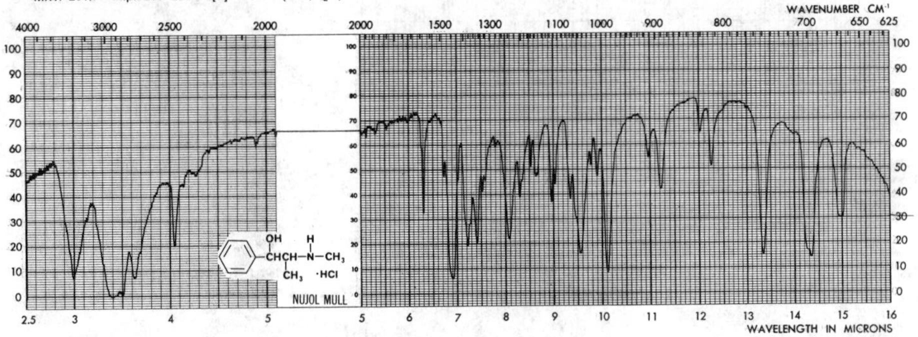

NUJOL MULL

B

18,654-6
1S,2S-(+)-2-Amino-1-phenyl-1,3-propanediol, 98%
$C_6H_5CH(OH)CH(NH_2)CH_2OH$
M.W. 167.21 m.p. 109-113°
$[\alpha]_D^{25}$ +25.7° (c=1, CH_3OH)

NUJOL MULL

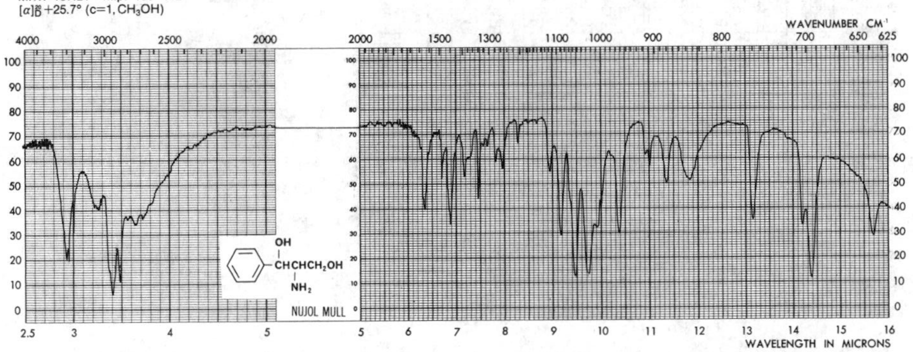

C

21,347-0
α-(Methylaminomethyl)benzyl alcohol, benzoate salt, 99%
$C_6H_5CH(CH_2NHCH_3)OH \cdot C_6H_5CO_2H$ FW 273.33
mp 101-102° Disp. C

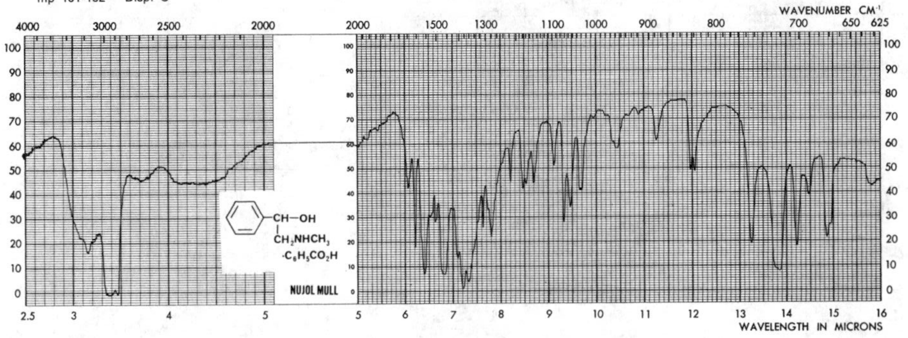

NUJOL MULL

D

21,850-2
3-(*N*-Benzyl-*N*-methylamino)-1,2-propanediol, 96+%
$C_6H_5CH_2N(CH_3)CH_2CH(OH)CH_2OH$ FW 195.26
bp 206°/30mm. n_D^{20} 1.5341 d 1.084 Disp. C

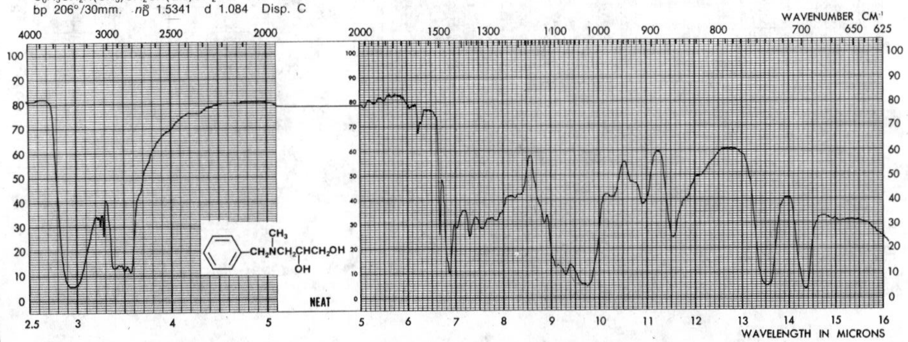

NEAT

E

B1636-4 **2-Benzylaminoethanethiol**
$C_6H_5CH_2NHCH_2CH_2SH$ M.W. 167.28 n_D^{20} 1.5621

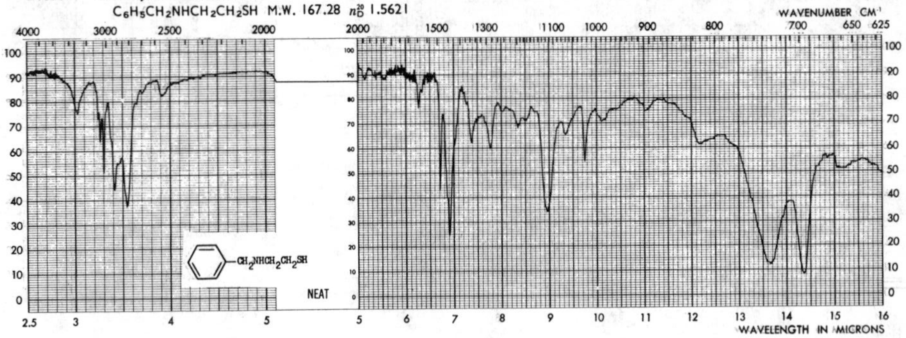

NEAT

F

P1390-8 **2-(β-Phenethylamino)-ethanethiol**
$C_6H_5CH_2CH_2NHCH_2CH_2SH$ M.W. 181.30 n_D^{20} 1.5514

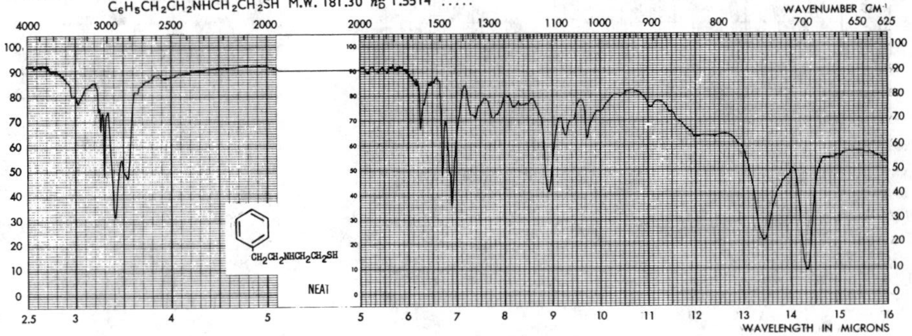

NEAT

G

B2415-4 **N-Benzylidenemethylamine**
$C_6H_5CH{:}NCH_3$ M.W. 119.17 n_D^{20} 1.5526

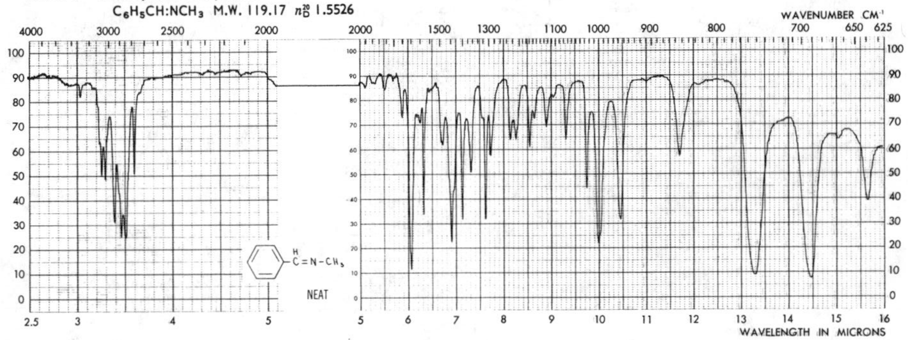

NEAT

H

13,692-1 **N,N-Dimethylbenzylamine** (benzyldimethylamine)
$C_6H_5CH_2N(CH_3)_2$ M.W. 135.21
n_D^{20} 1.5011

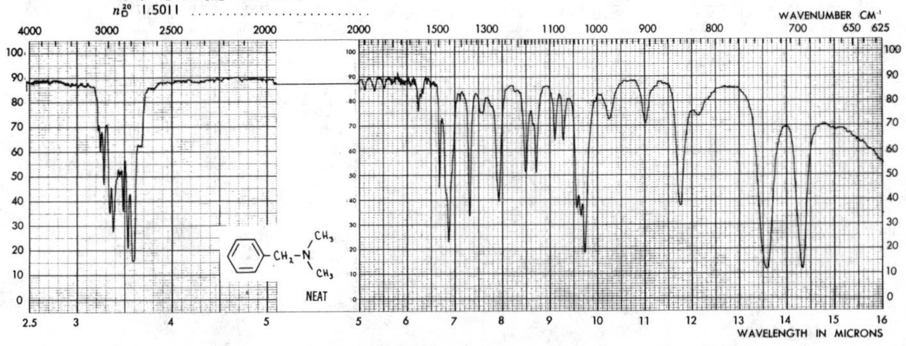

NEAT

A

10,232-6 N,N-Dimethyl-1-phenylcyclohexylamine
$C_6H_5C_6H_{10}N(CH_3)_2$ M.W. 203.33 m.p. 41-44°

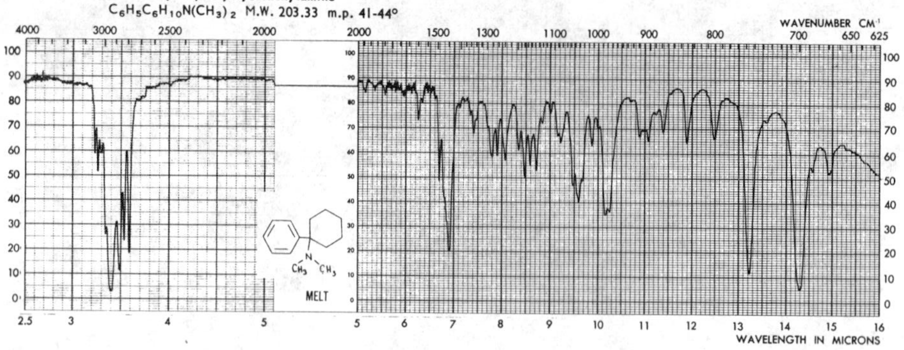

MELT

B

D3545-7 N,N-Dibenzylhydroxylamine
$(C_6H_5CH_2)_2NOH$ M.W. 213.28 m.p. 122-123°

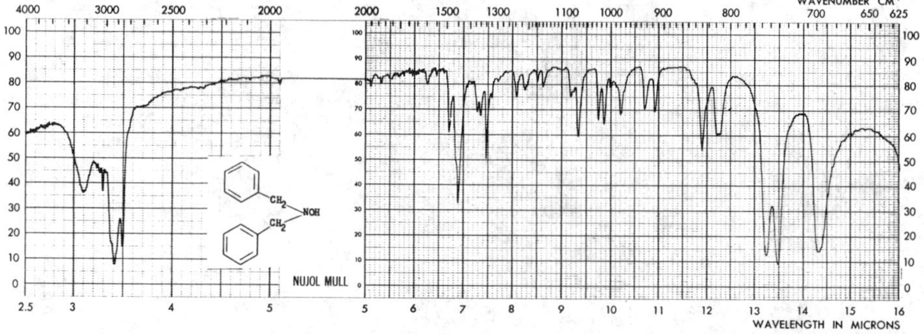

NUJOL MULL

C

12,892-9 Tribenzylamine, puriss.
$(C_6H_5CH_2)_3N$ M.W. 287.41 m.p. 91-94°

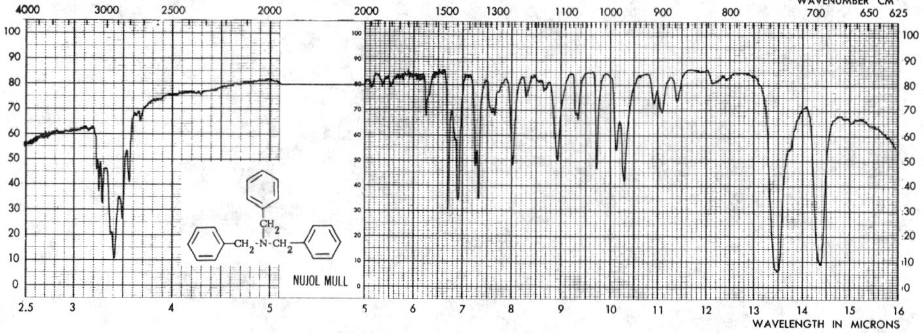

NUJOL MULL

D

13,929-7 N-(2-Chloroethyl)-N-methylbenzylamine hydrochloride
$C_6H_5CH_2N(CH_3)CH_2CH_2Cl{\cdot}HCl$ M.W. 220.14
m.p. 143-147°

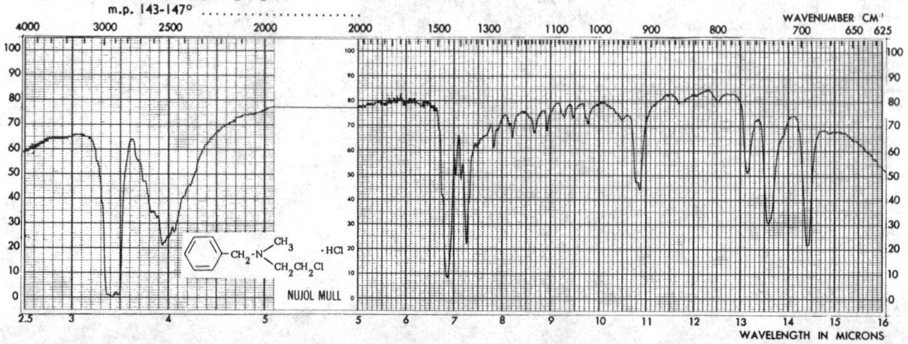

NUJOL MULL

E

C6950-0 N-(3-Chloropropyl)-N-methylbenzylamine hydrochloride
$C_6H_5CH_2N(CH_3)(CH_2)_3Cl{\cdot}HCl$ M.W. 234.17
m.p. 89-90°

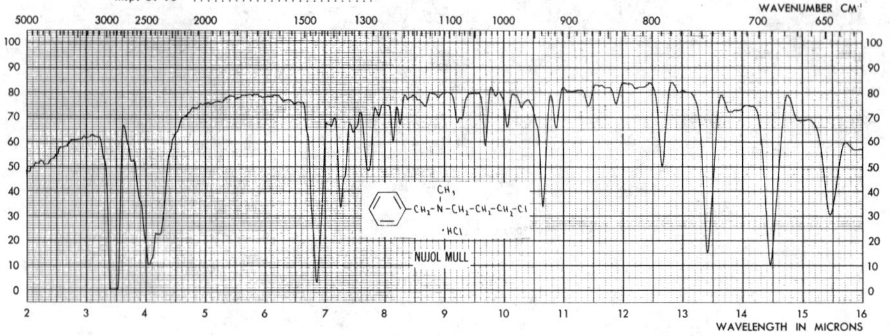

NUJOL MULL

F

12,013-8 N-(2-Chloroethyl)-N-(2-methoxyethyl)-benzylamine hydrochloride
$C_6H_5CH_2N(CH_2CH_2Cl)CH_2CH_2OCH_3{\cdot}HCl$ M.W. 264.20
m.p. 119-122°

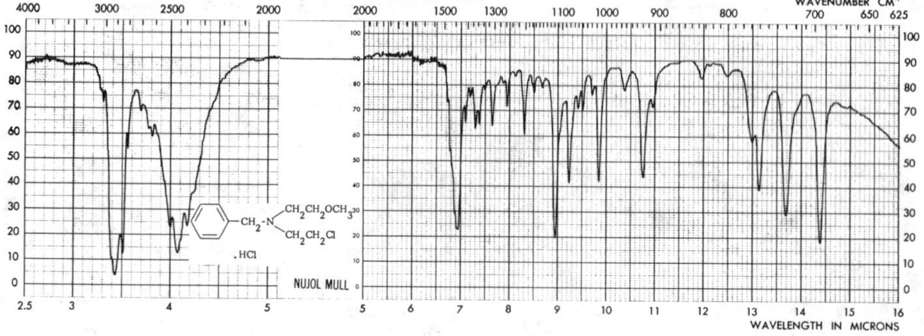

NUJOL MULL

G

B2580-0 N-Benzyl-N-methylethanolamine [2-(benzylmethylamino)-ethanol]
$C_6H_5CH_2N(CH_3)CH_2CH_2OH$ M.W. 165.24 n_D^{20} 1.5272

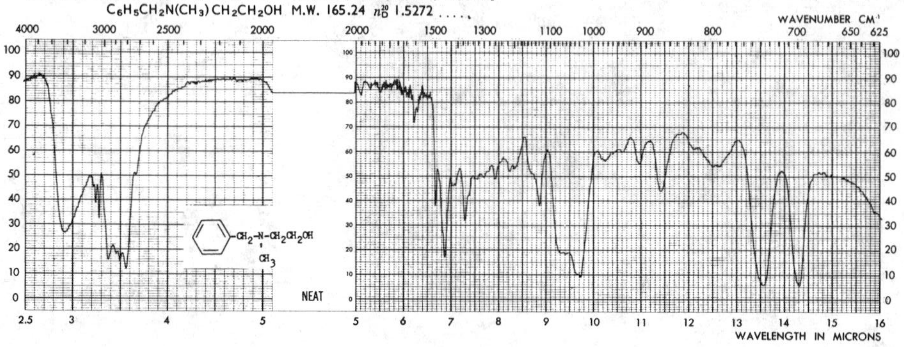

NEAT

H

B2570-3 3-(Benzylmethylamino)-1-propanol
$C_6H_5CH_2N(CH_3)(CH_2)_3OH$ M.W. 179.26
n_D^{20} 1.4251

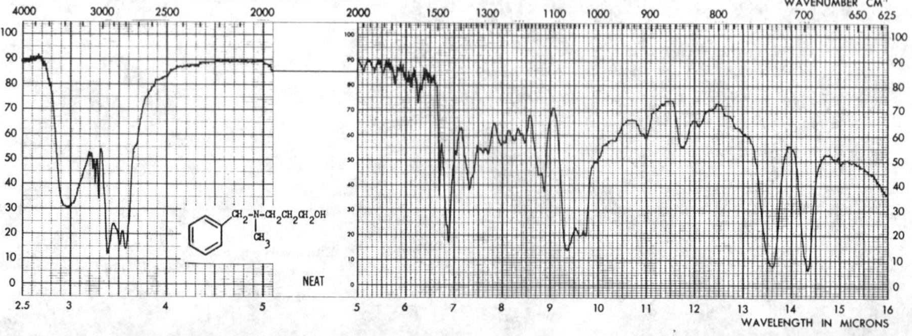

NEAT

A 13,697-2 2,2'-(Benzylimino)-diethanol (N-benzyldiethanolamine), puriss.
$C_6H_5CH_2N(CH_2CH_2OH)_2$ M.W. 195.26
n_D^{20} 1.5378 b.p. 155-165°/2 mm.
NEAT

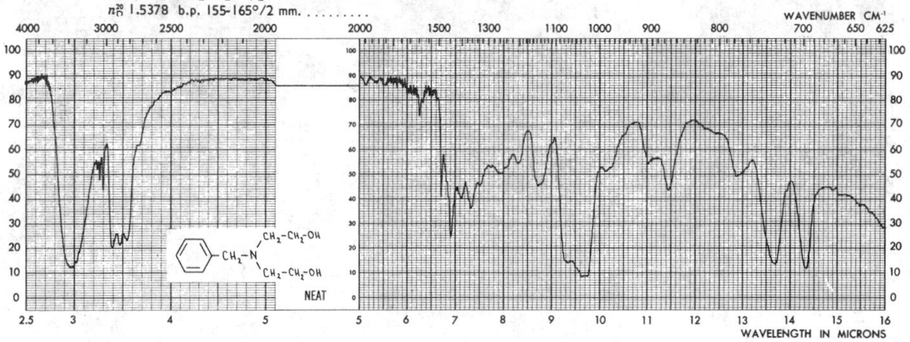

B D3500-7 N,N-Dibenzylethanolamine (2-dibenzylaminoethanol)
$(C_6H_5CH_2)_2NCH_2CH_2OH$ M.W. 241.33
m.p. 44-46°
NUJOL MULL

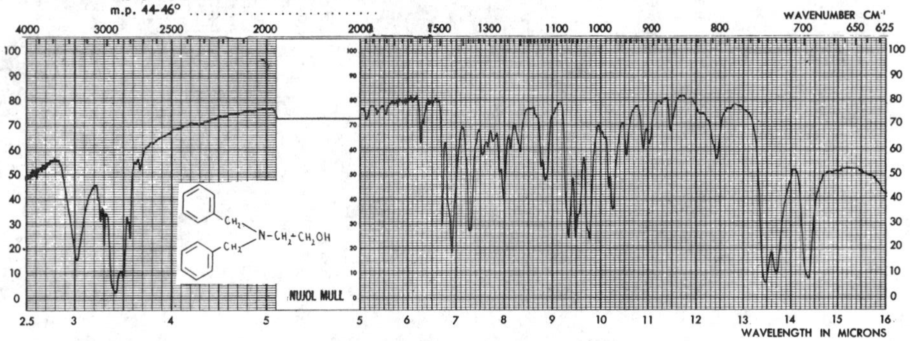

C 13,128-8 Orphenadrine [N,N-dimethyl-2-(o-methyl-α-phenylbenzyloxy)-ethylamine] hydrochloride
$CH_3C_6H_4CH(C_6H_5)OCH_2CH_2N(CH_3)_2 \cdot HCl$ M.W. 305.85
m.p. 163-166°
NUJOL MULL

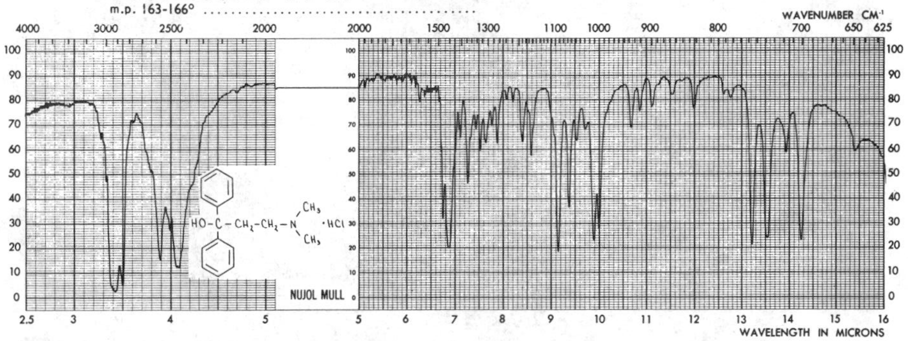

D 11,897-4 *dl*-4-Dimethylamino-1,2-diphenyl-3-methyl-2-butanol hydrochloride
$(CH_3)_2NCH_2CH(CH_3)C(C_6H_5)(OH)CH_2C_6H_5 \cdot HCl$ M.W. 319.88
m.p. 235-237.5°
NUJOL MULL

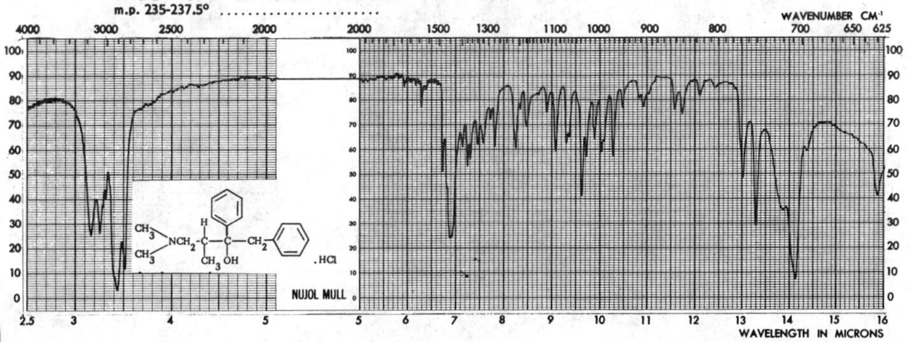

E 11,898-2 *d*-4-Dimethylamino-1,2-diphenyl-3-methyl-2-butanol hydrochloride
$(CH_3)_2NCH_2CH(CH_3)C(C_6H_5)(OH)CH_2C_6H_5 \cdot HCl$ M.W. 319.88
m.p. 245-246.5° $[\alpha]_D^{25}$ + 46° (c=0.55, H_2O)
NUJOL MULL

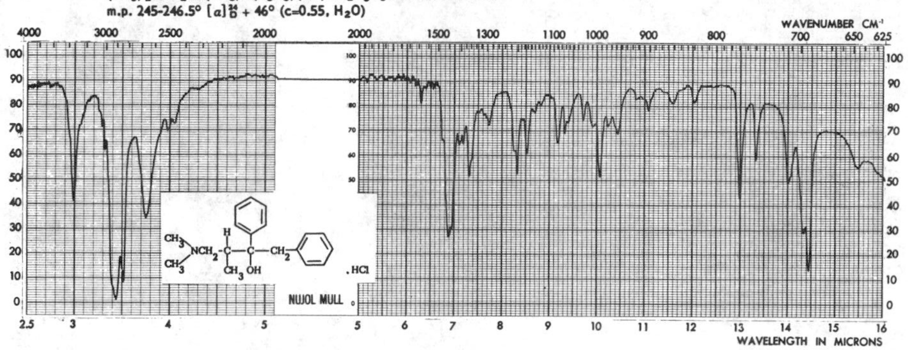

F 11,899-0 *l*-4-Dimethylamino-1,2-diphenyl-3-methyl-2-butanol hydrochloride
$(CH_3)_2NCH_2CH(CH_3)C(C_6H_5)(OH)CH_2C_6H_5 \cdot HCl$ M.W. 319.88
m.p. 243-245° $[\alpha]_D^{25}$ - 46° (c=0.55, H_2O)
NUJOL MULL

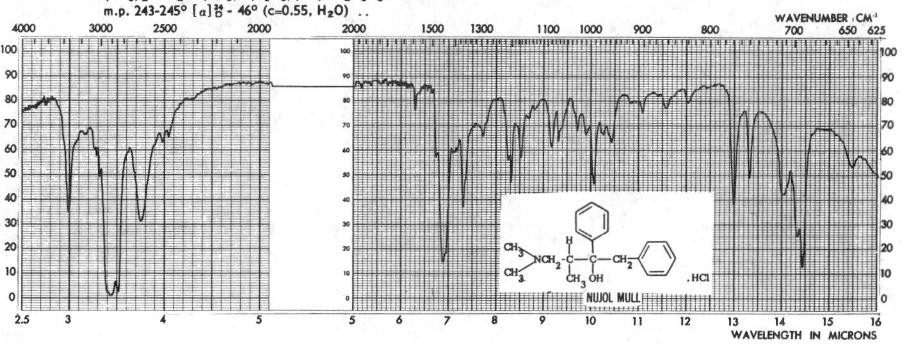

G 12,713-2 2-Methylbenzylamine
$CH_3C_6H_4CH_2NH_2$ M.W. 121.18 n_D^{20} 1.5428
b.p. 199°
NEAT

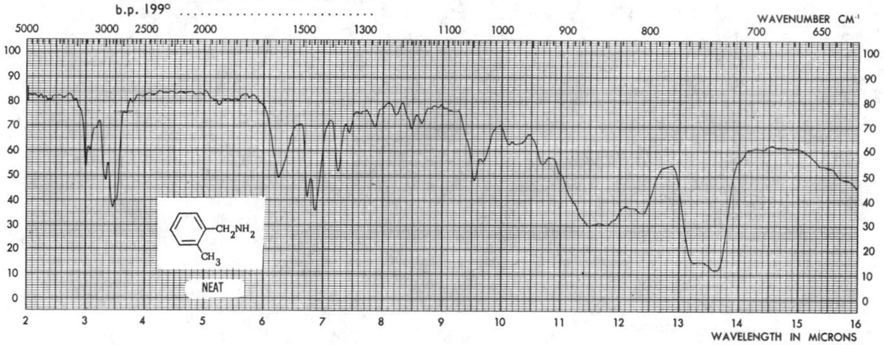

H A5950-6 1-Aminoindan (1-indanamine)
M.W. 133.19 n_D^{20} 1.5613
NEAT

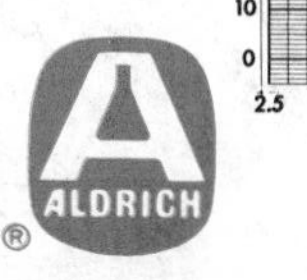

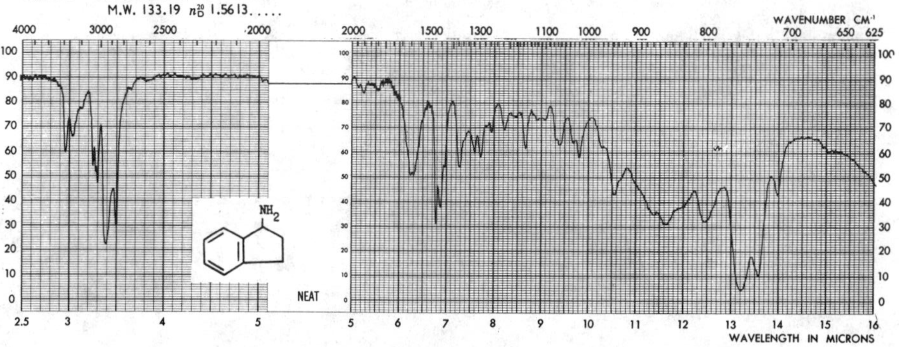

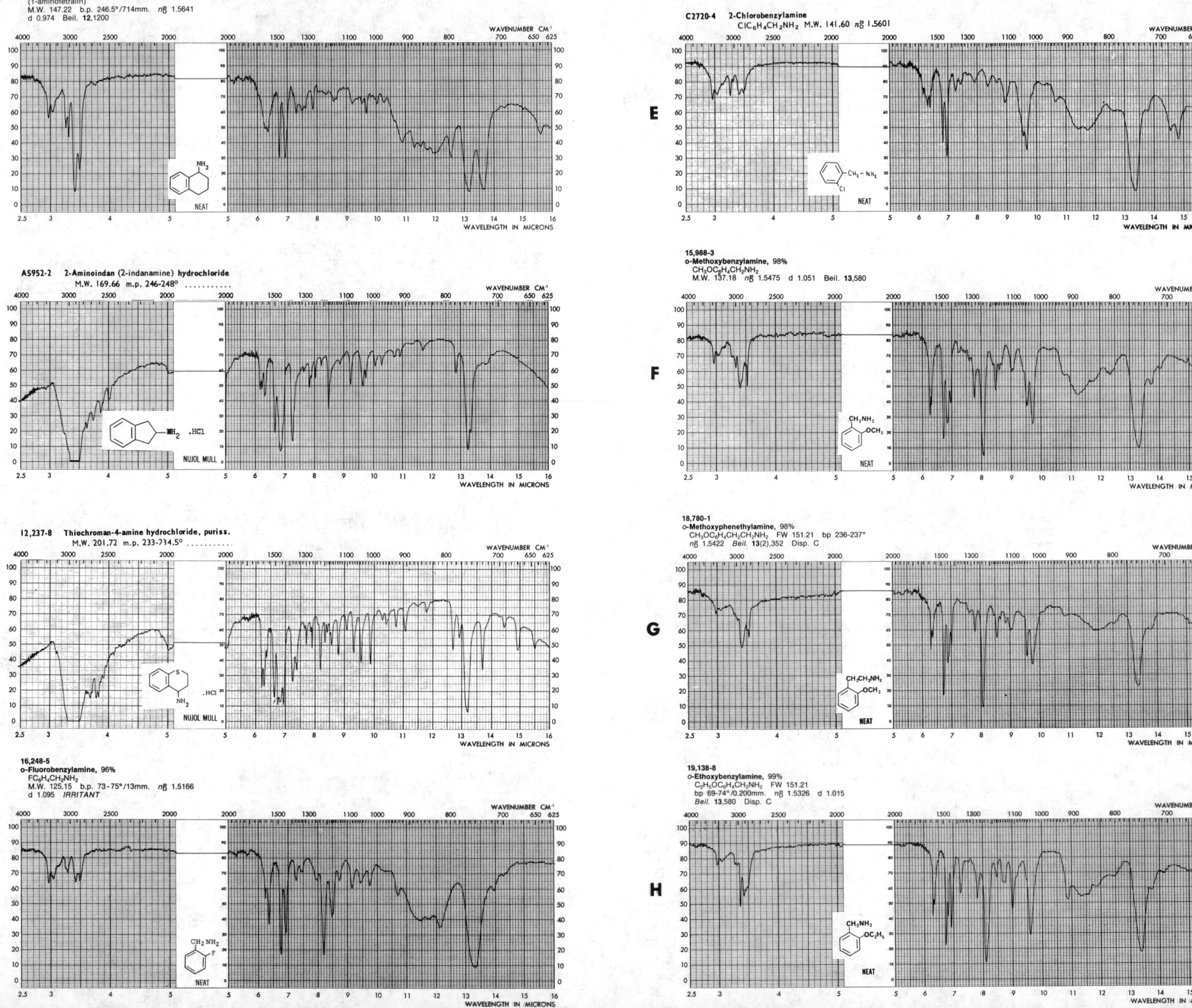

A

17,735-0
1,2,3,4-Tetrahydro-1-naphthylamine, 98%
(1-aminotetralin)
M.W. 147.22 b.p. 246.5°/714mm. n_D^{20} 1.5641
d 0.974 Beil. **12**,1200
NEAT

B

A5952-2 **2-Aminoindan (2-indanamine) hydrochloride**
M.W. 169.66 m.p. 246-248°
NUJOL MULL

C

12,237-8 **Thiochroman-4-amine hydrochloride, puriss.**
M.W. 201.72 m.p. 233-234.5°
NUJOL MULL

D

16,248-5
o-Fluorobenzylamine, 96%
$FC_6H_4CH_2NH_2$
M.W. 125.15 b.p. 73-75°/13mm. n_D^{20} 1.5166
d 1.095 *IRRITANT*
NEAT

E

C2720-4 **2-Chlorobenzylamine**
$ClC_6H_4CH_2NH_2$ M.W. 141.60 n_D^{20} 1.5601
NEAT

F

15,988-3
o-Methoxybenzylamine, 98%
$CH_3OC_6H_4CH_2NH_2$
M.W. 137.18 n_D^{20} 1.5475 d 1.051 Beil. **13**,580
NEAT

G

18,780-1
o-**Methoxyphenethylamine**, 98%
$CH_3OC_6H_4CH_2CH_2NH_2$ FW 151.21 bp 236-237°
n_D^{20} 1.5422 *Beil.* **13**(2),352 Disp. C
NEAT

H

19,138-8
o-**Ethoxybenzylamine**, 99%
$C_2H_5OC_6H_4CH_2NH_2$ FW 151.21
bp 69-74°/0.200mm. n_D^{20} 1.5326 d 1.015
Beil. **13**,580 Disp. C
NEAT

A

D10,493-0 10,11-Dihydro-5H-dibenzo[a,d]cyclohepten-5-amine
M.W. 209.29 m.p. 89-91°

MELT

B

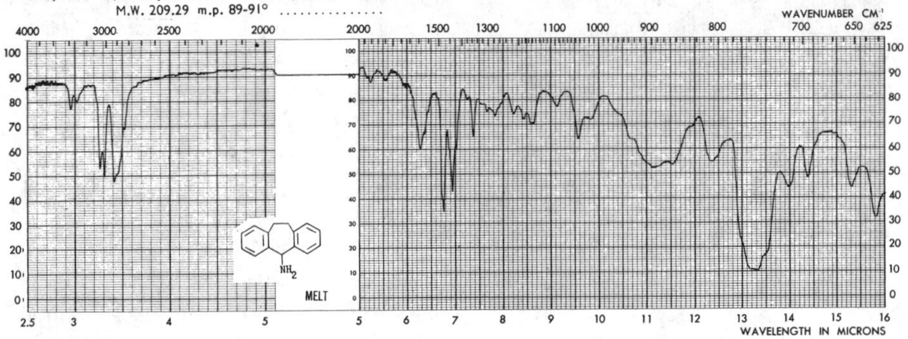

21,883-9
Benextramine tetrahydrochloride monohydrate [BHC, *N,N''*-(dithiodi-2,1-ethanediyl)bis[*N'*-(2-methoxyphenyl)methyl]-1,6-hexanediamine]
FW 754.80 Disp. C

NUJOL MULL

C

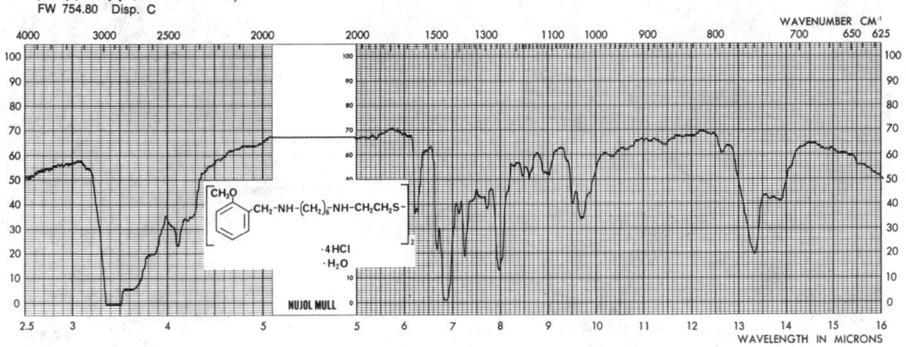

12,682-9 3-Methylbenzylamine
$CH_3C_6H_4CH_2NH_2$ M.W. 121.18 n_D^{20} 1.5354
b.p. 202-205°

NEAT

D

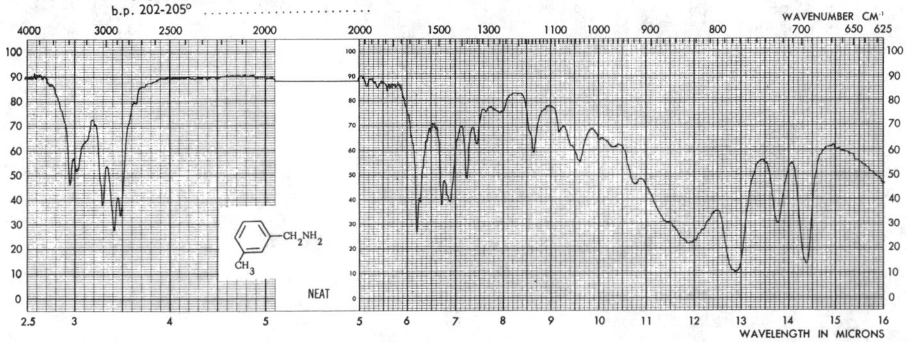

X120-2 m-Xylylenediamine
$C_6H_4(CH_2NH_2)_2$ M.W. 136.20
n_D^{20} 1.5709

NEAT

E

12,689-6 m-Fluorobenzylamine
$FC_6H_4CH_2NH_2$ M.W. 125.15 n_D^{20} 1.5152

NEAT

F

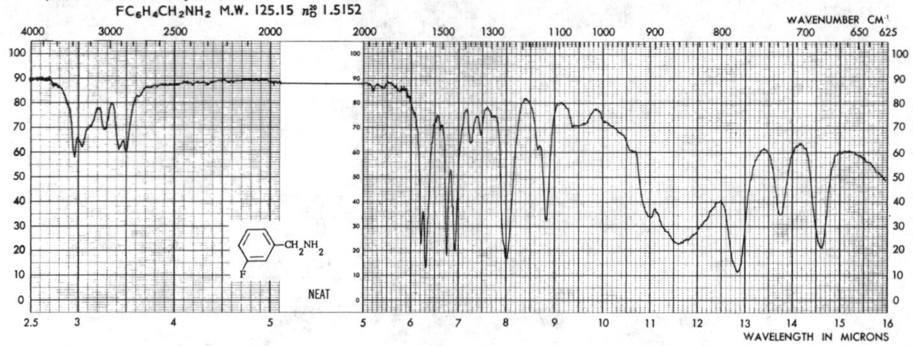

12,716-7 3-Chlorobenzylamine
$ClC_6H_4CH_2NH_2$ M.W. 141.60 n_D^{20} 1.5591

NEAT

G

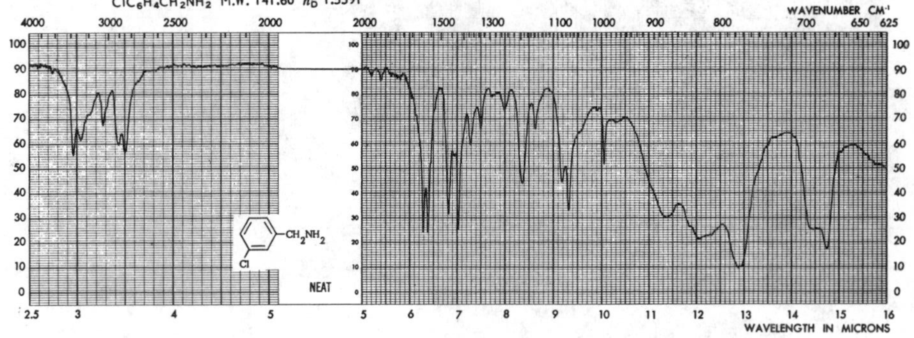

10,006-4 m-Iodobenzylamine
$IC_6H_4CH_2NH_2$ M.W. 233.05 n_D^{20} 1.6157

NEAT

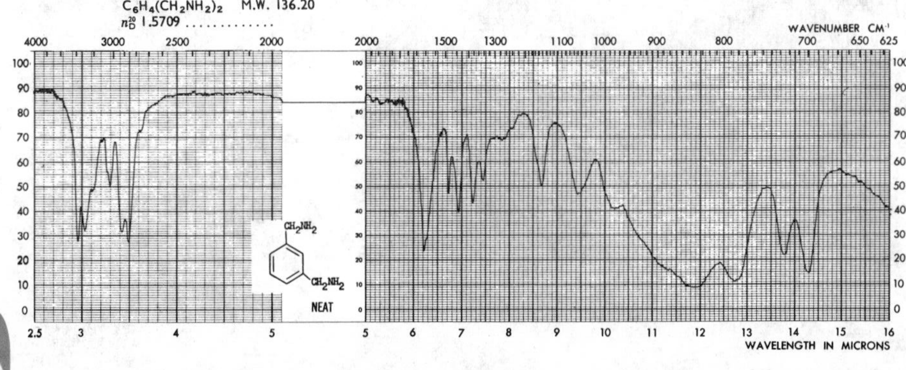

H

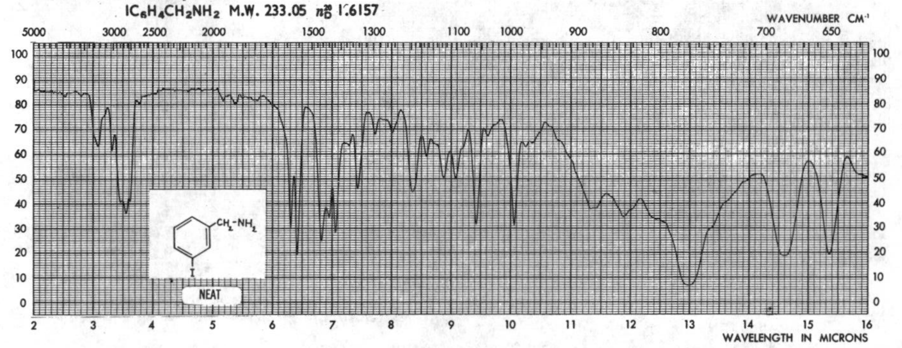

13,499-6 m-Iodobenzylamine hydrochloride
$IC_6H_4CH_2NH_2 \cdot HCl$ M.W. 269.51
m.p. 188-190°

NUJOL MULL

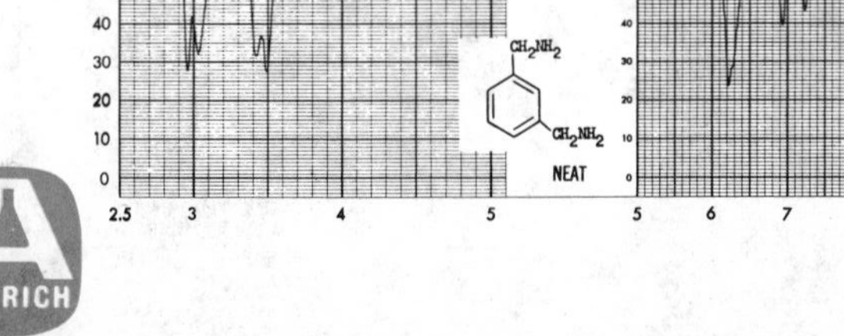

AROMATIC AMINES

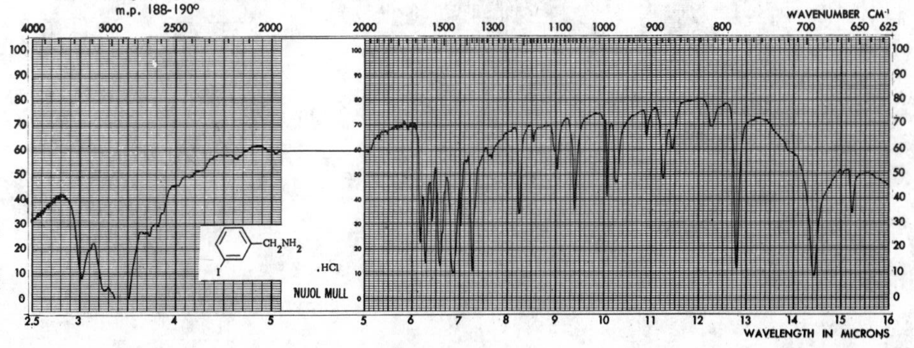

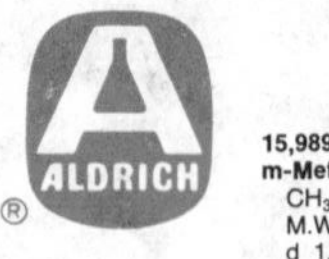

A

15,989-1
m-Methoxybenzylamine, 98%
$CH_3OC_6H_4CH_2NH_2$
M.W. 137.18 b.p. 140°/37mm. n_D^{20} 1.5487
d 1.072 Beil. **13**(1),226

NEAT

B

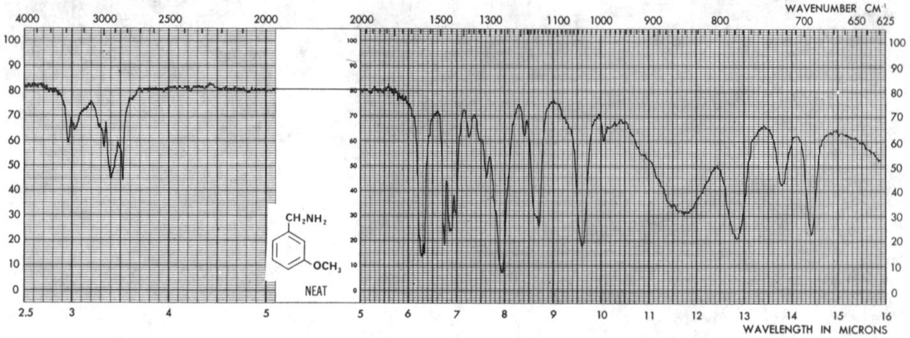

85,992-3
m-**Hydroxybenzylhydrazine dihydrochloride,** 99%
(α-hydrazino-*m*-cresol)
$HOC_6H_4CH_2NHNH_2 \cdot 2HCl$ FW 211.09
mp 138° (dec.) Disp. C

NUJOL MULL

C

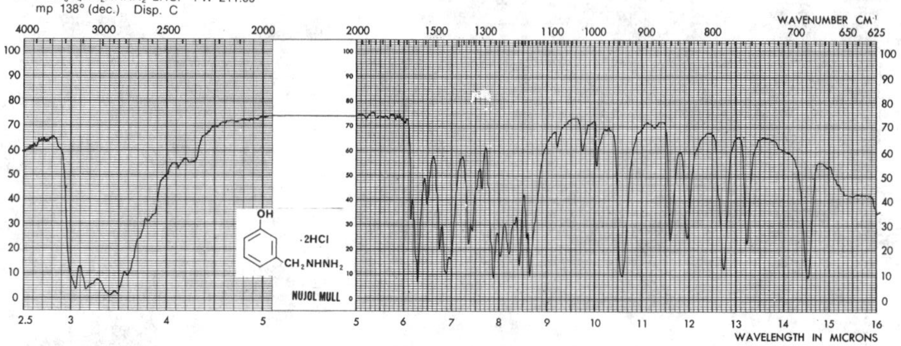

16,483-6
2-Amino-1-(m-chlorophenyl)-ethanol hydrochloride
(m-chloro-β-hydroxyphenethylamine)
$H_2NCH_2CH(C_6H_4Cl)OH \cdot HCl$
M.W. 208.09 m.p. 251° (dec.)

NUJOL MULL

D

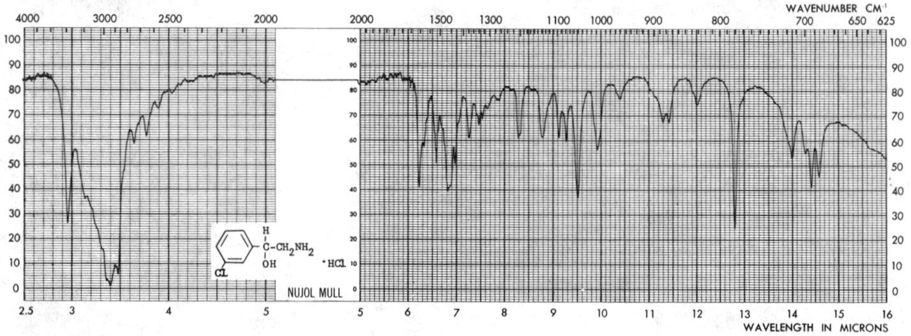

11,372-7 **Norphenylephrine** (α-aminomethyl-m-hydroxybenzyl alcohol) **hydrochloride**
$HOC_6H_4CH(CH_2NH_2)OH \cdot HCl$ M.W. 189.64
m.p. 162-164°

NUJOL MULL

E

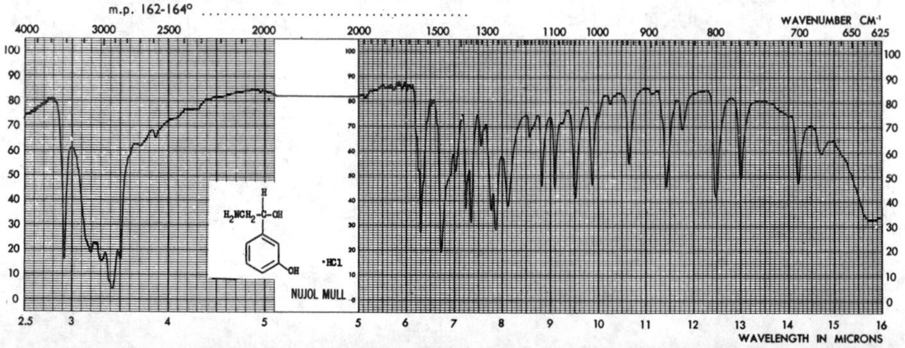

22,289-5
l-**Phenylephrine hydrochloride,** 99% [*m*-hydroxy-α-(methylaminomethyl)benzyl alcohol]
$HOC_6H_4CH(CH_2NHCH_3)OH \cdot HCl$ FW 203.67
mp 143-145° $[\alpha]^{25}$ -43.5° (c=5, H_2O) Disp. C

KBr

F

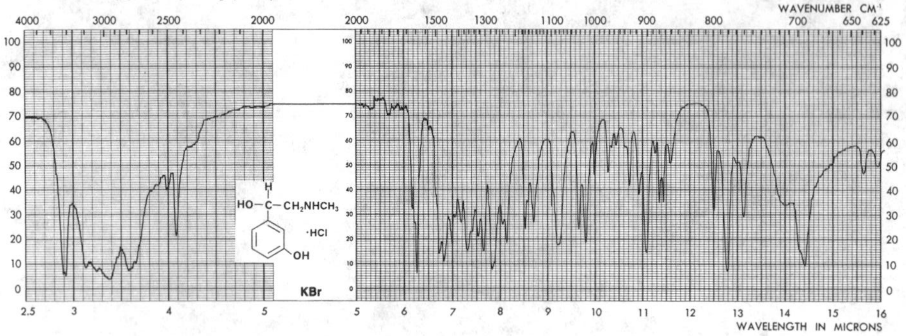

12,901-1 *dl*-**N-Ethylnorphenylephrine** [*dl*-α-(ethylaminomethyl)-m-hydroxybenzyl alcohol] **hydrochloride**
$HOC_6H_4CH(CH_2NHC_2H_5)OH \cdot HCl$ M.W. 217.70
m.p. 119-120.5°

NUJOL MULL

G

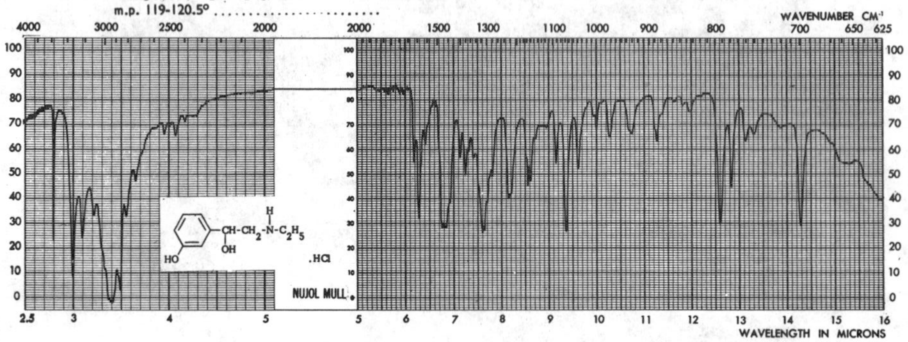

M3120-1 **4-Methylbenzylamine**
$CH_3C_6H_4CH_2NH_2$ M.W. 121.18 n_D^{20} 1.5327
b.p. 195°

NEAT

H

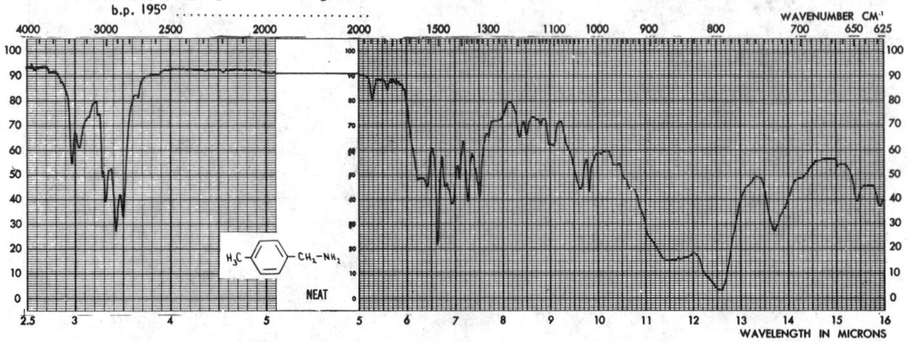

13,202-0 **2-(p-Tolyl)-ethylamine** (p-methylphenethylamine)
$CH_3C_6H_4CH_2CH_2NH_2$ M.W. 135.21 n_D^{20} 1.5257 b.p. 214.5°

NEAT

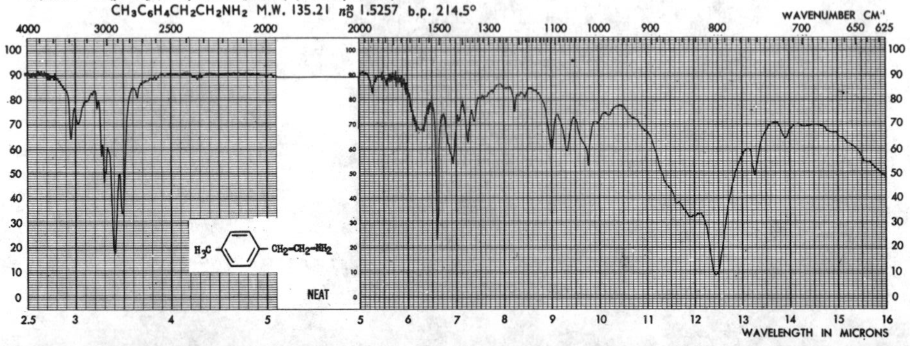

A

16,249-3
p-Fluorobenzylamine, tech., 92%
$FC_6H_4CH_2NH_2$
M.W. 125.15 b.p. 183° n_D^{20} 1.5117 d 1.095
IRRITANT

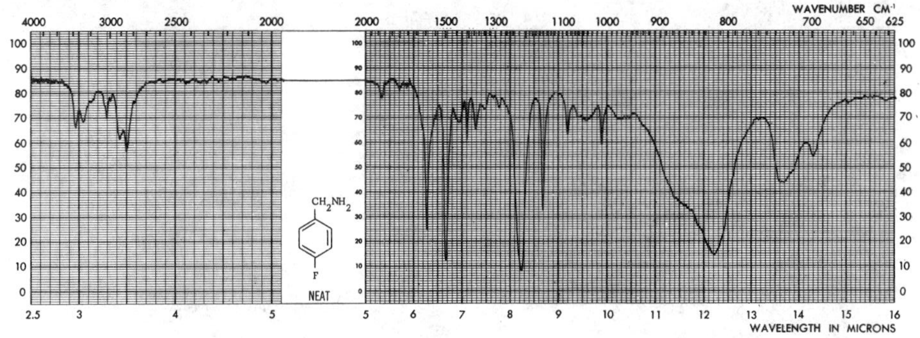

NEAT

B

19,470-0
p-**Fluorobenzylamine hydrochloride**, 97+%
$FC_6H_4CH_2NH_2 \cdot HCl$ FW 161.61 mp 287-290°
Disp. C

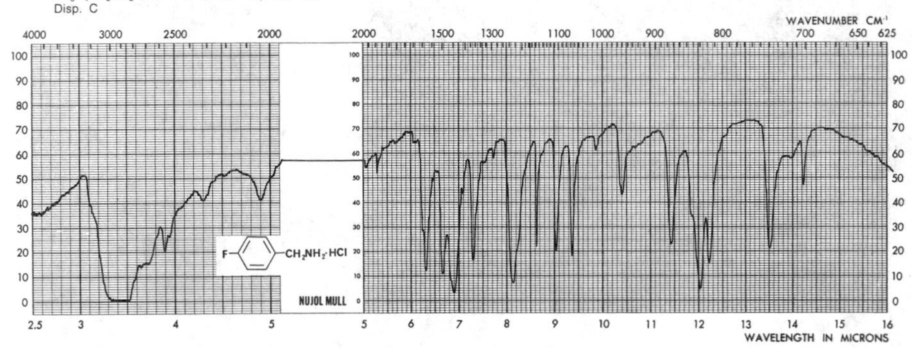

NUJOL MULL

C

C2740-9 **4-Chlorobenzylamine**
$ClC_6H_4CH_2NH_2$ M.W. 141.60 n_D^{20} 1.5579

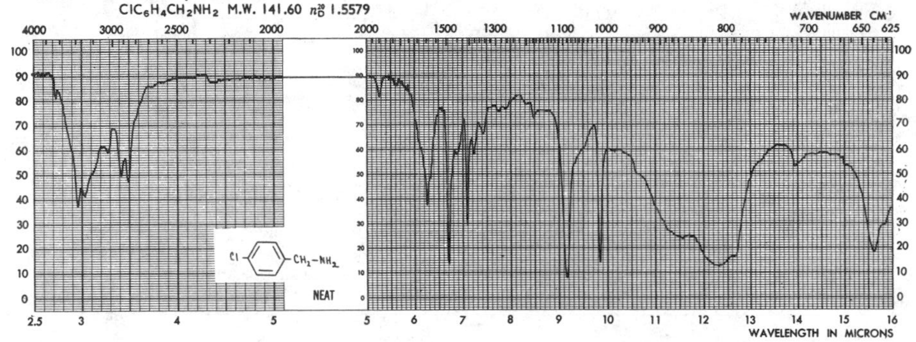

NEAT

D

15,405-9 **p-Chloro-α-methylbenzylamine**
$ClC_6H_4CH(CH_3)NH_2$ M.W. 155.63 n_D^{20} 1.5424

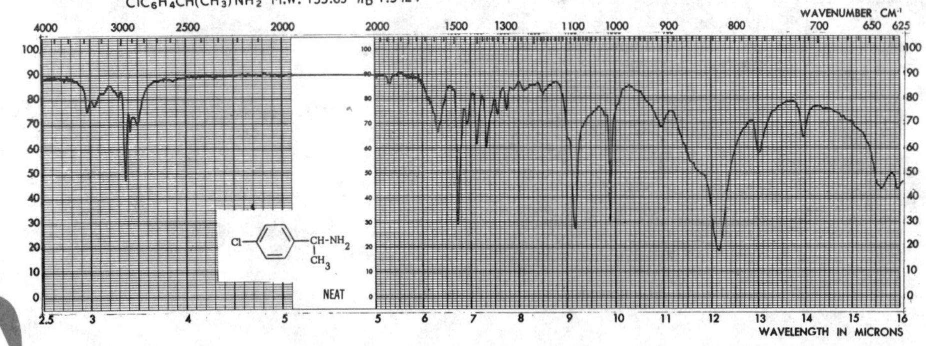

NEAT

E

20,521-4
4-Bromobenzylamine hydrochloride, 98%
$BrC_6H_4CH_2NH_2 \cdot HCl$ FW 222.52 mp 274-276°
Beil. **12**,1075 Disp. C

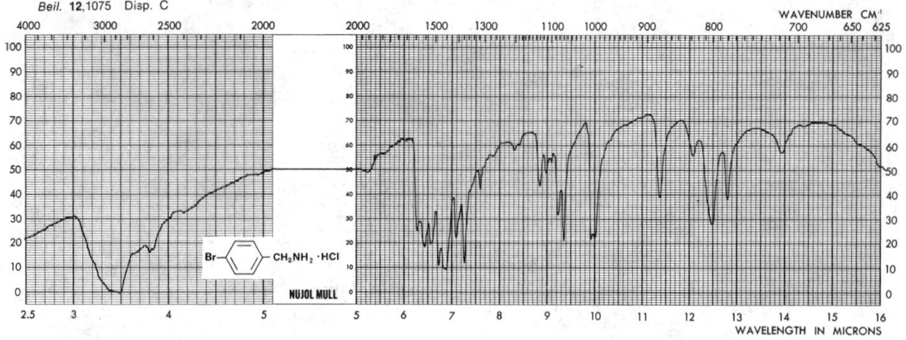

NUJOL MULL

F

18,930-8
p-**Bromophenethylamine**, 98%
$BrC_6H_4CH_2CH_2NH_2$ FW 200.09
bp 63-72°/0.200mm. n_D^{20} 1.5750 d 1.290 Disp. C

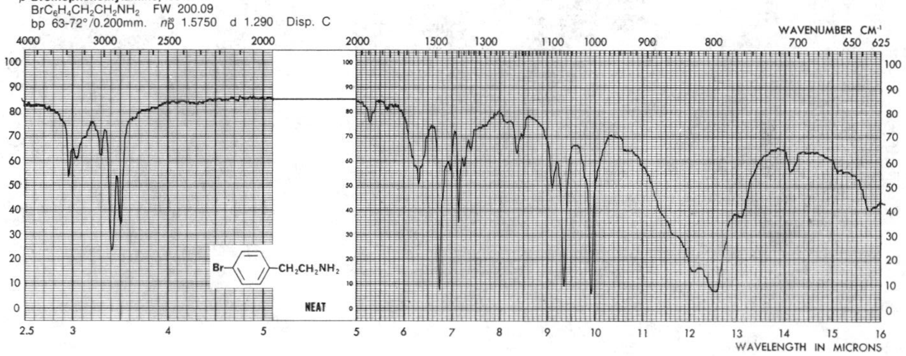

NEAT

G

15,406-7 **p-Bromo-α-methylbenzylamine**
$BrC_6H_4CH(CH_3)NH_2$ M.W. 200.09
n_D^{20} 1.5657

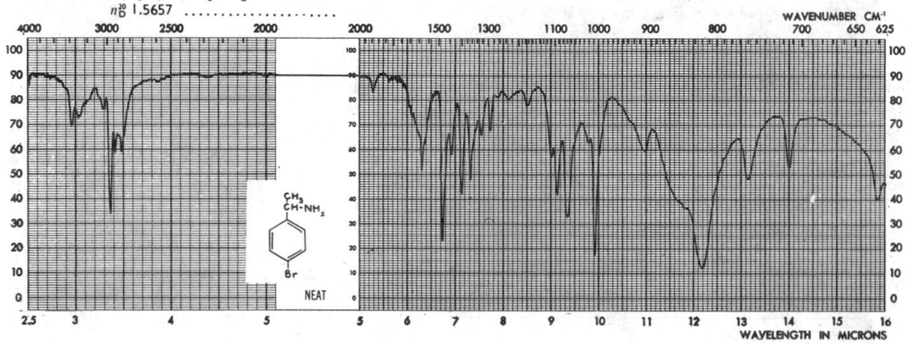

NEAT

H

15,404-0 **p-Fluoro-α-methylbenzylamine**
$FC_6H_4CH(CH_3)NH_2$ M.W. 139.17

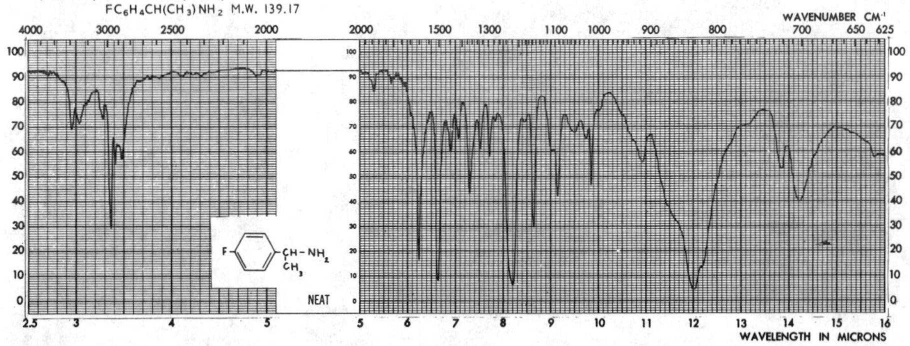

NEAT

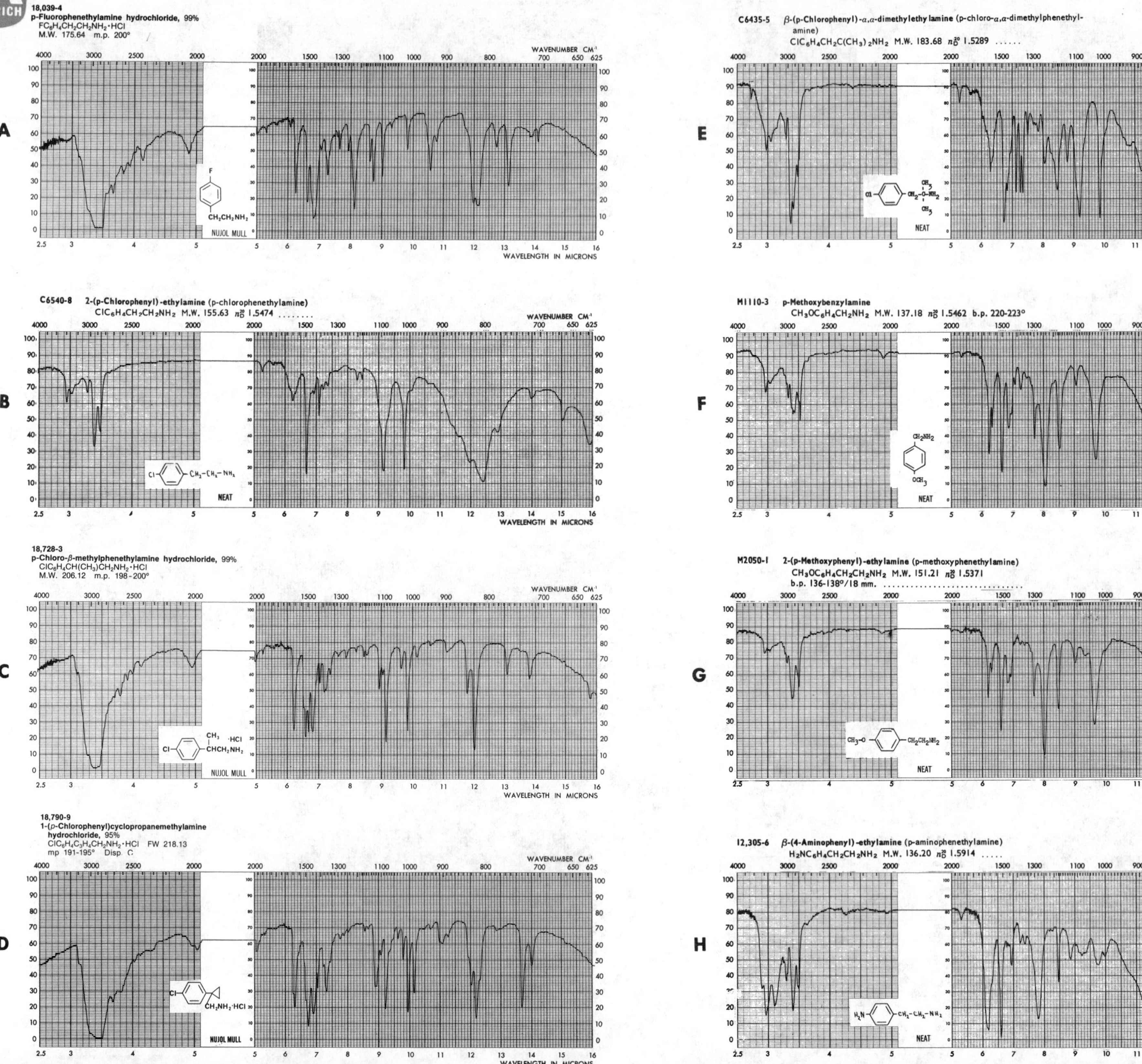
ALDRICH
A
18,039-4
p-Fluorophenethylamine hydrochloride, 99%
$FC_6H_4CH_2CH_2NH_2 \cdot HCl$
M.W. 175.64 m.p. 200°
NUJOL MULL
B
C6540-8 2-(p-Chlorophenyl)-ethylamine (p-chlorophenethylamine)
$ClC_6H_4CH_2CH_2NH_2$ M.W. 155.63 n_D^{20} 1.5474
NEAT
C
18,728-3
p-Chloro-β-methylphenethylamine hydrochloride, 99%
$ClC_6H_4CH(CH_3)CH_2NH_2 \cdot HCl$
M.W. 206.12 m.p. 198-200°
NUJOL MULL
D
18,790-9
1-(p-Chlorophenyl)cyclopropanemethylamine hydrochloride, 95%
$ClC_6H_4C_3H_4CH_2NH_2 \cdot HCl$ FW 218.13
mp 191-195° Disp. C
NUJOL MULL
E
C6435-5 β-(p-Chlorophenyl)-α,α-dimethylethylamine (p-chloro-α,α-dimethylphenethylamine)
$ClC_6H_4CH_2C(CH_3)_2NH_2$ M.W. 183.68 n_D^{20} 1.5289
NEAT
F
M1110-3 p-Methoxybenzylamine
$CH_3OC_6H_4CH_2NH_2$ M.W. 137.18 n_D^{20} 1.5462 b.p. 220-223°
NEAT
G
M2050-1 2-(p-Methoxyphenyl)-ethylamine (p-methoxyphenethylamine)
$CH_3OC_6H_4CH_2CH_2NH_2$ M.W. 151.21 n_D^{20} 1.5371
b.p. 136-138°/18 mm.
NEAT
H
12,305-6 β-(4-Aminophenyl)-ethylamine (p-aminophenethylamine)
$H_2NC_6H_4CH_2CH_2NH_2$ M.W. 136.20 n_D^{20} 1.5914
NEAT
WAVENUMBER CM⁻¹
WAVELENGTH IN MICRONS

A

T9034-4 **Tyramine [p-(2-aminoethyl)-phenol]**
$HOC_6H_4CH_2CH_2NH_2$ M.W. 137.18 m.p. 162-163°

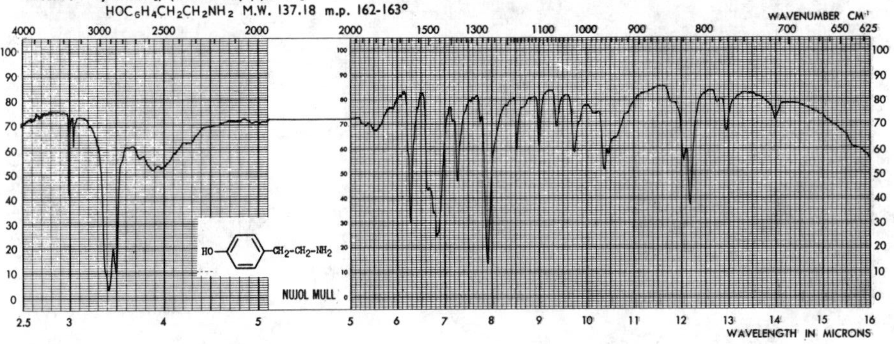

NUJOL MULL

B

T9035-2 **Tyramine [p-(2-aminoethyl)-phenol] hydrochloride**
$HOC_6H_4CH_2CH_2NH_2 \cdot HCl$ M.W. 173.65 m.p. 271-274°

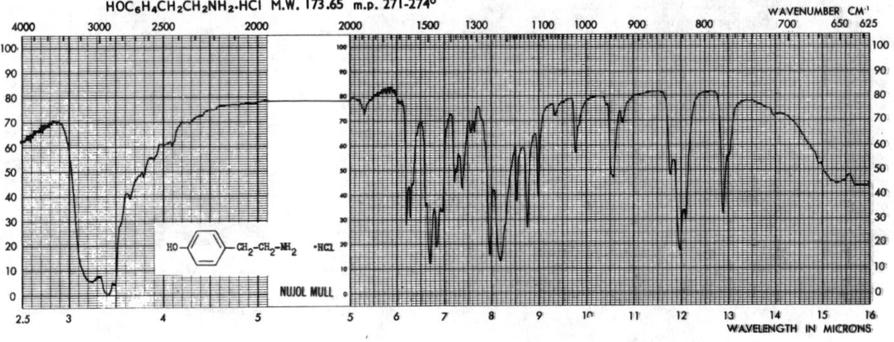

NUJOL MULL

C

A7682 **p-(2-Aminopropyl)-phenol (hydroxyamphetamine) hydrobromide**
$HOC_6H_4CH_2CH(NH_2)CH_3 \cdot HBr$ M.W. 232.14 m.p. 190-193°

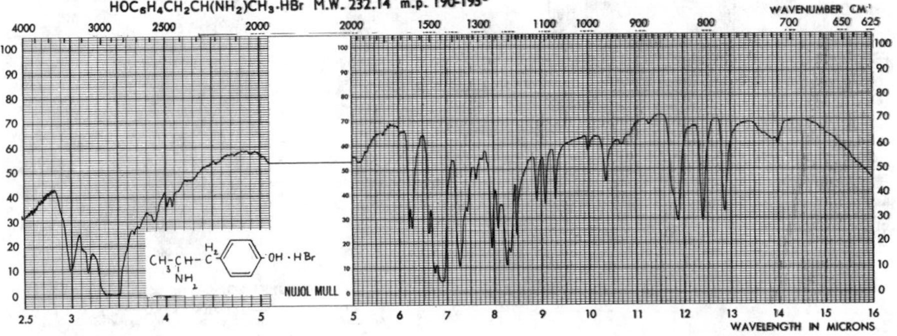

NUJOL MULL

D

10,283-0 **1-(p-Fluorophenyl)-cyclohexylamine**
$FC_6H_4C_6H_{10}NH_2$ M.W. 193.27 n_D^{20} 1.5280
b.p. 84-85°/0.8 mm

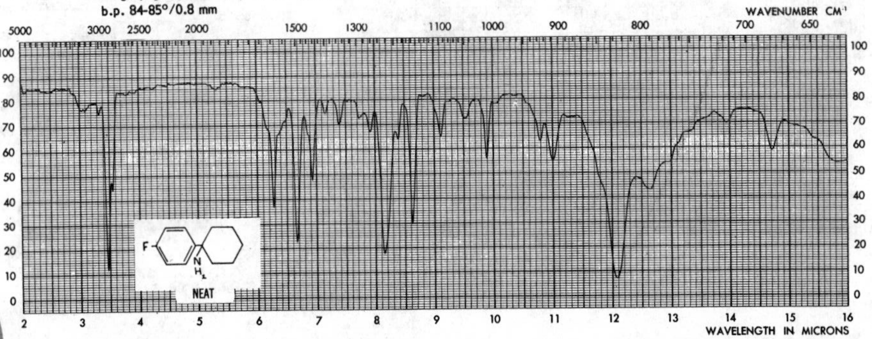

NEAT

E

10,287-3 **1-(p-Fluorophenyl)-N-methylcyclohexylamine**
$FC_6H_4C_6H_{10}NHCH_3$ M.W. 207.29 n_D^{20} 1.5220

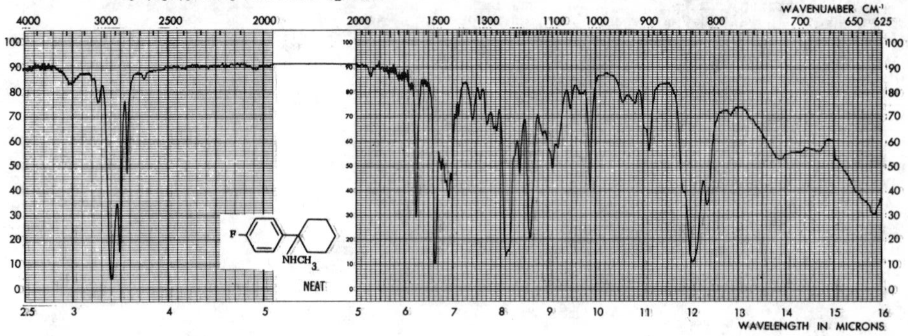

NEAT

F

A5445-8 **α-(1-Aminoethyl)-p-hydroxybenzyl alcohol**
(p-hydroxynorephedrine) hydrochloride, puriss.
$HOC_6H_4CH[CH(NH_2)CH_3]OH \cdot HCl$ M.W. 203.67
m.p. 195° (dec.)

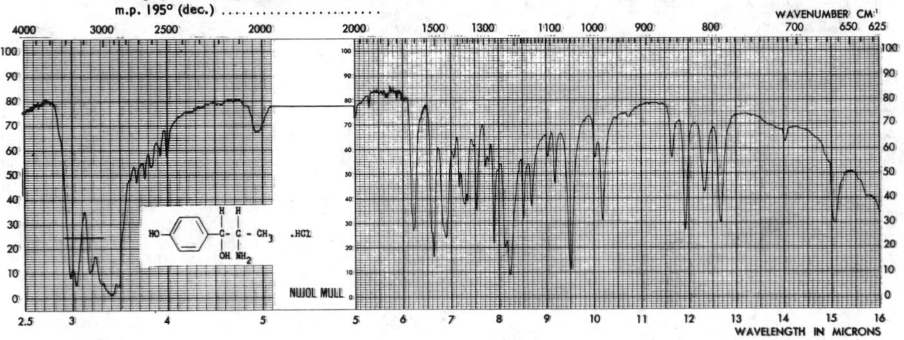

NUJOL MULL

G

19,117-5
DL-p-Chlorophenylalaninol, 99% [2-amino-3-(p-chlorophenyl)-1-propanol]
$ClC_6H_4CH_2CH(NH_2)CH_2OH$ FW 185.66
mp 80-82° Disp. C

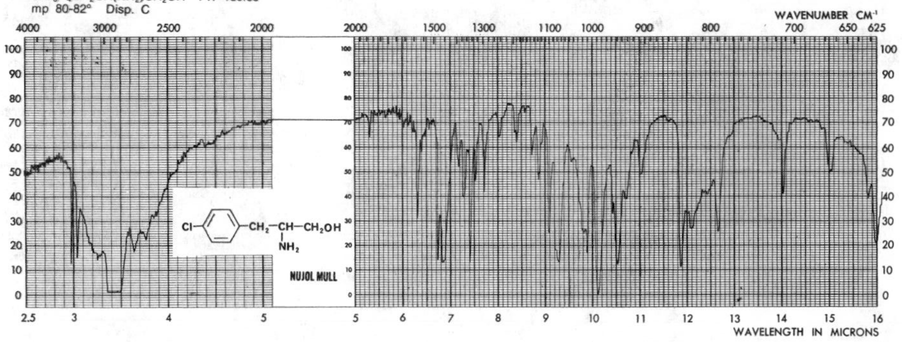

NUJOL MULL

H

13,051-6 *dl*-**Octopamine** [*dl*-α-(aminomethyl)-p-hydroxybenzyl alcohol]
hydrochloride
$HOC_6H_4CH(CH_2NH_2)OH \cdot HCl$ M.W. 189.64
m.p. 169-170° (dec.)

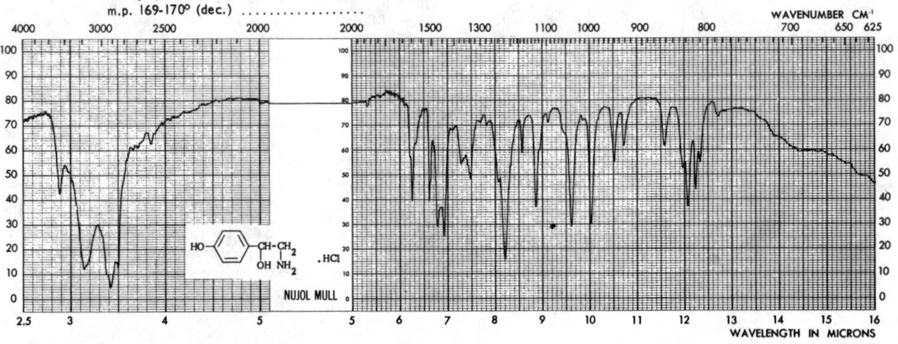

NUJOL MULL

ALDRICH

A

13,050-8 *dl*-p-Hydroxy-α-(methylaminomethyl)-benzyl alcohol *d*-tartrate
$[HOC_6H_4CH(CH_2NHCH_3)OH]_2 \cdot C_4H_6O_6$ M.W. 484.51
m.p. 190-192° (dec.)

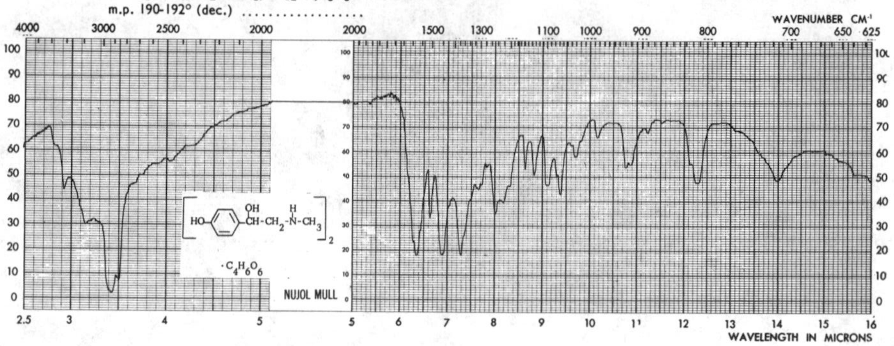

NUJOL MULL

B

10,615-1 p-Hydroxyephedrine [p-hydroxy-α-(1-methylaminoethyl)-benzyl alcohol] hydrochloride, puriss.
$HOC_6H_4CH(OH)CH(CH_3)NHCH_3 \cdot HCl$ M.W. 217.70
m.p. 166-168°

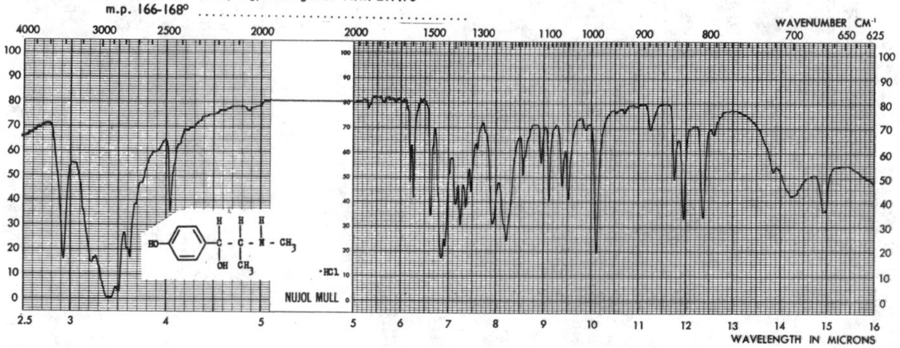

NUJOL MULL

C

D14,140-2 4-(β-Dimethylaminoethyl)-phenol (hordenine) sulfate dihydrate
$[(CH_3)_2NCH_2CH_2C_6H_4OH]_2 \cdot H_2SO_4 \cdot 2H_2O$ M.W. 464.58
m.p. 204-206° (after dehydration)

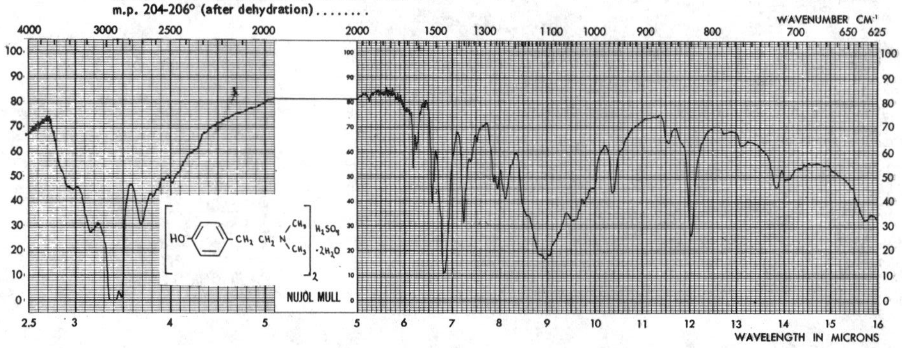

NUJOL MULL

D

12,697-7 2,4-Dimethylbenzylamine
$(CH_3)_2C_6H_3CH_2NH_2$ M.W. 135.21 n_D^{20} 1.5377
b.p. 218-219°

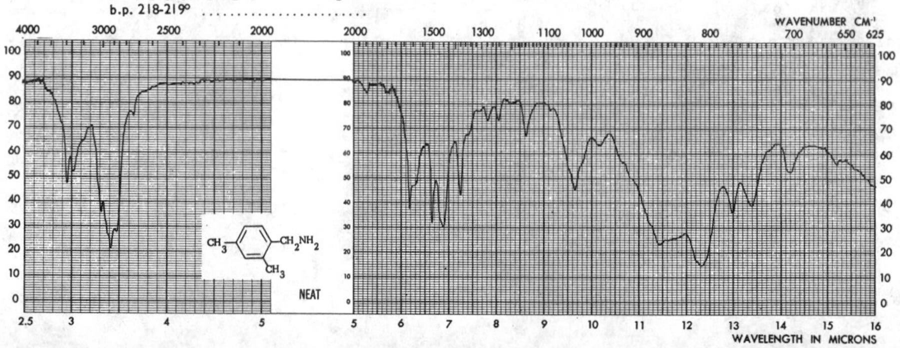

NEAT

E

12,695-0 2,5-Dimethylbenzylamine
$(CH_3)_2C_6H_3CH_2NH_2$ M.W. 135.21 n_D^{20} 1.5377
b.p. 225-226°

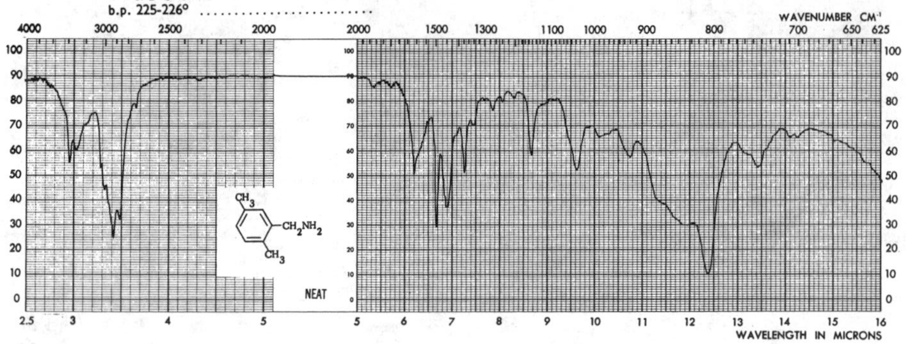

NEAT

F

D5840-6 2,4-Dichlorobenzylamine
$Cl_2C_6H_3CH_2NH_2$ M.W. 176.05 n_D^{20} 1.5794

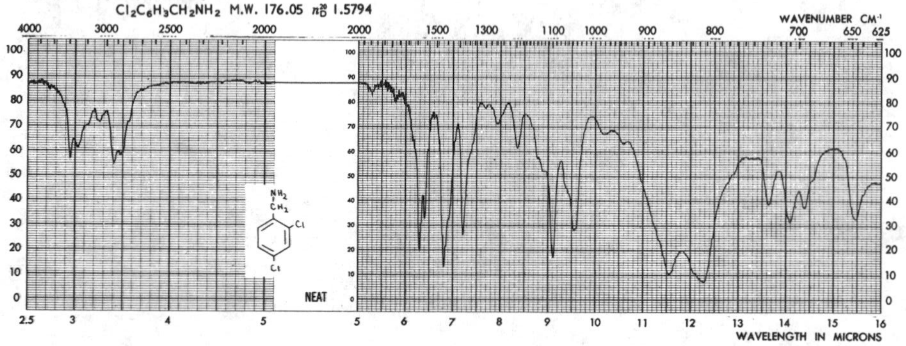

NEAT

G

D5860-0 3,4-Dichlorobenzylamine
$Cl_2C_6H_3CH_2NH_2$ M.W. 176.05 n_D^{20} 1.5764

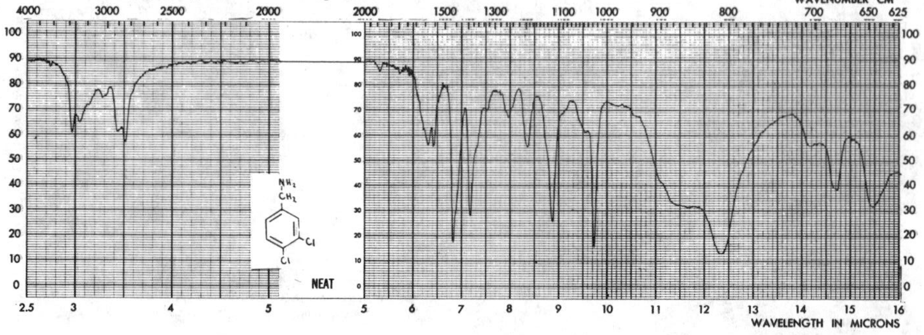

NEAT

H

18,985-5
2,3-Dimethoxybenzylamine, 98+%
$(CH_3O)_2C_6H_3CH_2NH_2$ FW 167.21 bp 137°/11mm.
n_D^{20} 1.5415 *Beil.* **13**(1),319 Disp. C

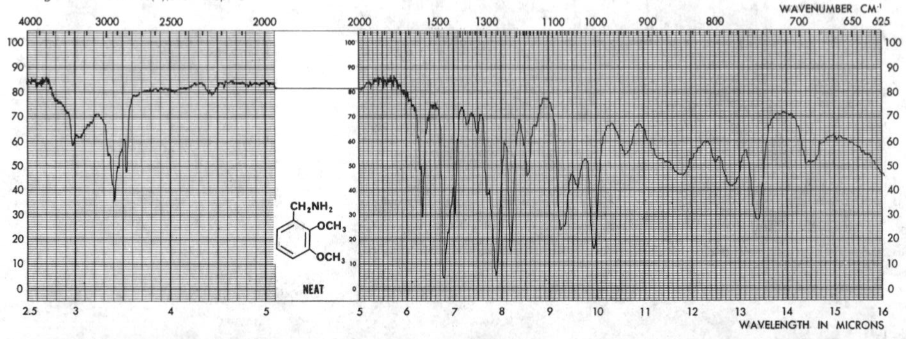

NEAT

A

17,860-8
2,4-Dimethoxybenzylamine hydrochloride, 97%
$(CH_3O)_2C_6H_3CH_2NH_2 \cdot HCl$
M.W. 203.67 m.p. 183-185°

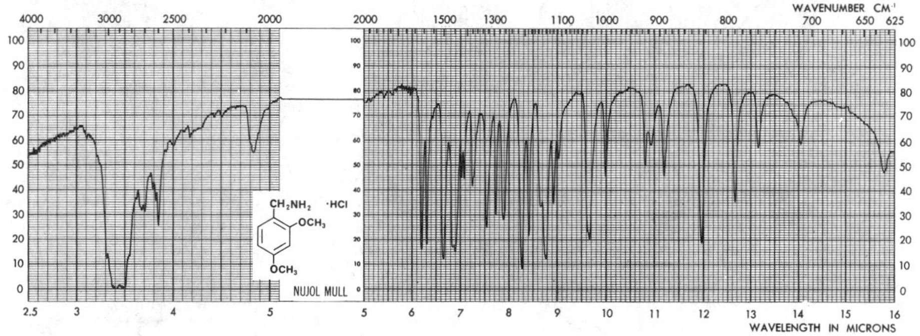

NUJOL MULL

B

V130-9 Veratrylamine
3,4-$(CH_3O)_2C_6H_3CH_2NH_2$ M.W. 167.21 n_D^{20} 1.5556

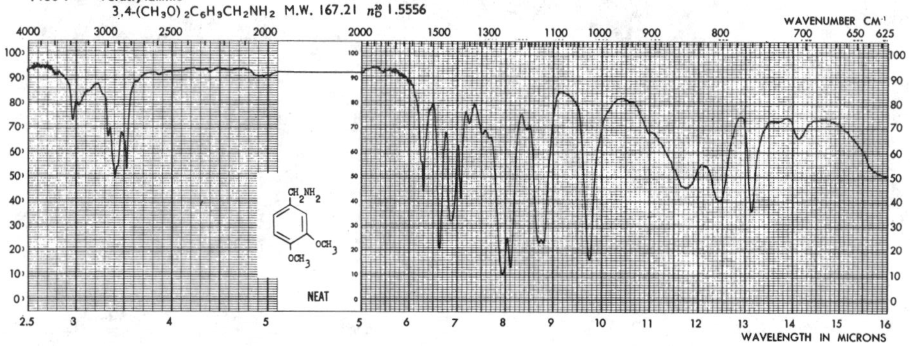

NEAT

C

D13,620-4 β-(3,4-Dimethoxyphenyl)-ethylamine (3,4-dimethoxyphenethylamine, homoveratrylamine)
$(CH_3O)_2C_6H_3CH_2CH_2NH_2$ M.W. 181.24
n_D^{20} 1.5464

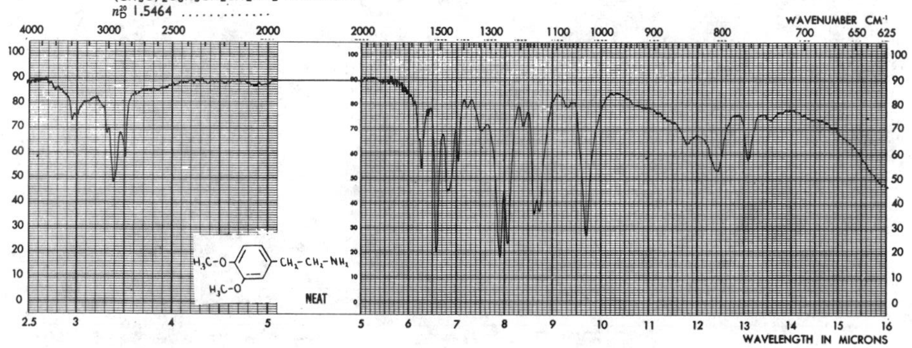

NEAT

D

P4950-3 Piperonylamine
M.W. 151.17 n_D^{20} 1.5635 b.p. 138-139°/13 mm.

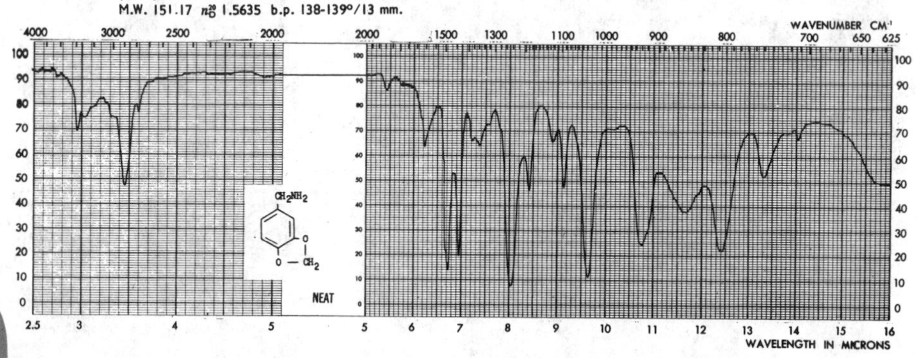

NEAT

E

M4540-7 β-(3,4-Methylenedioxyphenyl)-isopropylamine
M.W. 179.22 n_D^{20} 1.5407

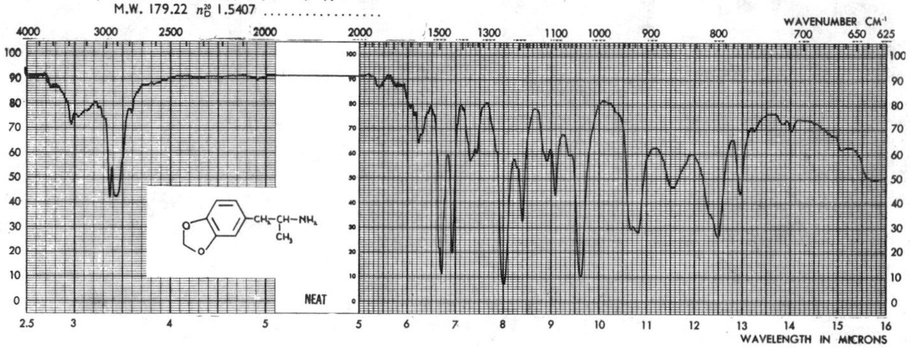

NEAT

F

H3660-5 4-Hydroxy-3-methoxybenzylamine (vanillylamine) hydrochloride
$HOC_6H_3(OCH_3)CH_2NH_2 \cdot HCl$ M.W. 189.64 m.p. 217-220°

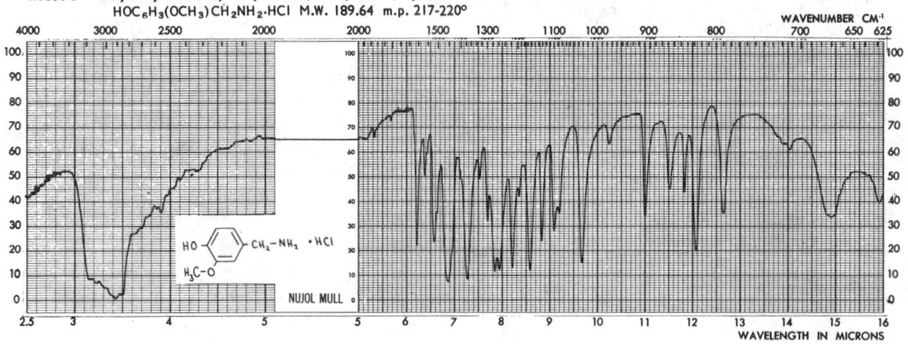

NUJOL MULL

G

15,580-2 α-Ethyl-3-hydroxy-4-methylphenethylamine hydrochloride
$CH_3C_6H_3(OH)CH_2CH(C_2H_5)NH_2 \cdot HCl$ M.W. 215.73
m.p. 160-161°

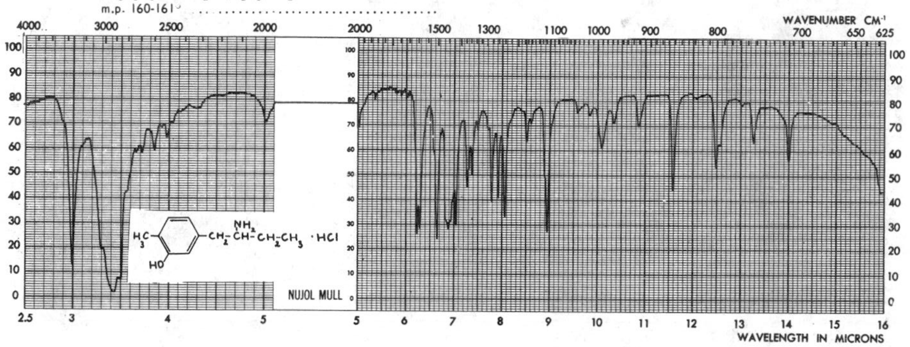

NUJOL MULL

H

15,582-9 α,4-Dimethyl-3-hydroxyphenethylamine hydrochloride
$CH_3C_6H_3(OH)CH_2CH(CH_3)NH_2 \cdot HCl$ M.W. 201.70

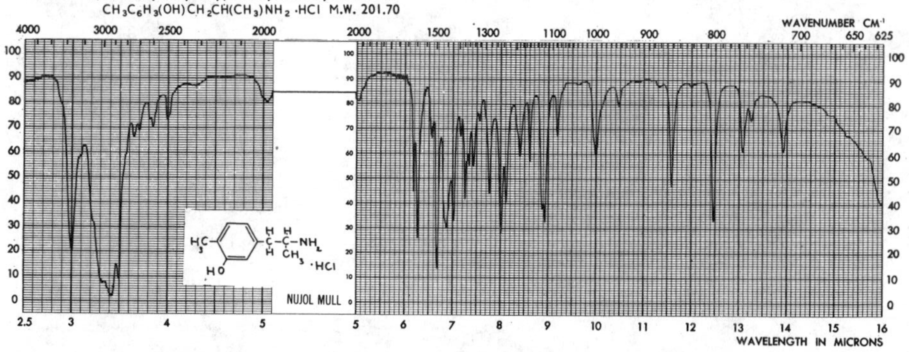

NUJOL MULL

A

85,878-1
3,4-Dihydroxybenzylamine hydrobromide, 98%
[4-(aminomethyl)catechol, DHBA]
$(HO)_2C_6H_3CH_2NH_2 \cdot HBr$ FW 220.07 mp >180°
Beil. **13**,796 Disp. C

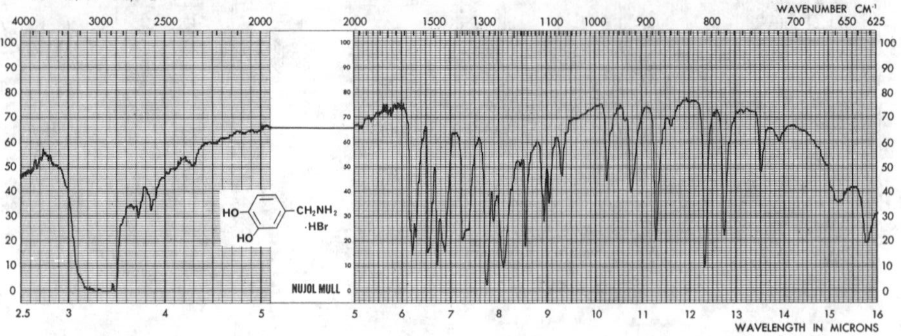

NUJOL MULL

B

H6025-5 **3-Hydroxytyramine** (3,4-dihydroxyphenethylamine, dopamine) **hydrochloride**
$(HO)_2C_6H_3CH_2CH_2NH_2 \cdot HCl$ M.W. 189.64
m.p. 241-243°

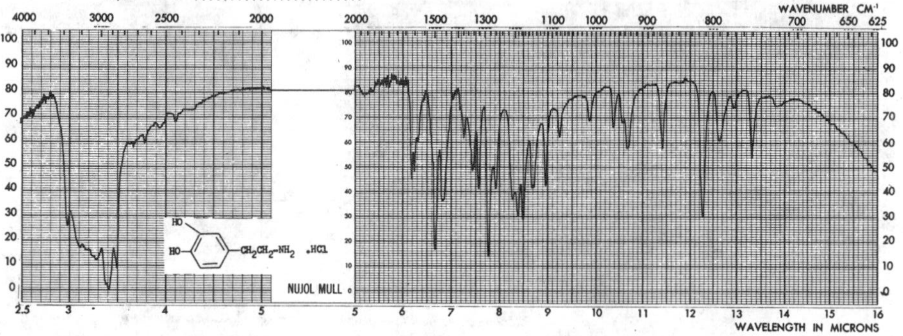

NUJOL MULL

C

16,113-6
3-Hydroxytyramine hydrobromide, 99%
(3,4-dihydroxyphenethylamine, dopamine)
$(HO)_2C_6H_3CH_2CH_2NH_2 \cdot HBr$
M.W. 234.1 m.p. 218-220° Beil. **13**(1),325

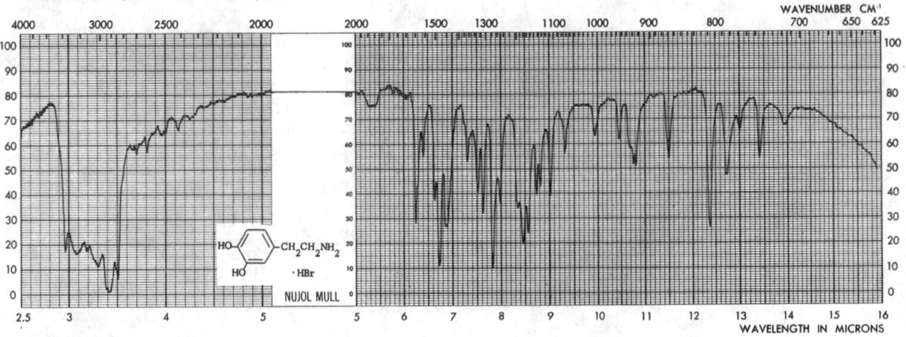

NUJOL MULL

D

16,431-3
3-O-Methyldopamine hydrochloride, 99+%, GOLD LABEL (3-methoxytyramine)
$CH_3OC_6H_3$-4-$(OH)CH_2CH_2NH_2 \cdot HCl$
M.W. 203.67 m.p. 213-215°

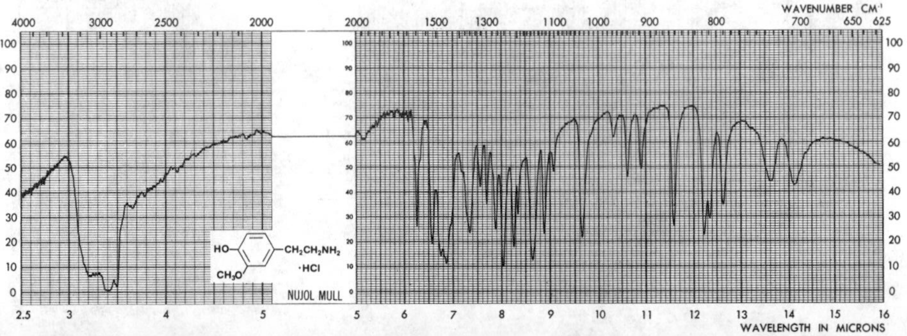

NUJOL MULL

E

19,596-0
4-O-Methyldopamine hydrochloride, 98% (3-hydroxy-4-methoxyphenethylamine)
$CH_3OC_6H_3(OH)CH_2CH_2NH_2 \cdot HCl$ FW 203.67
mp 207-208° Disp. C

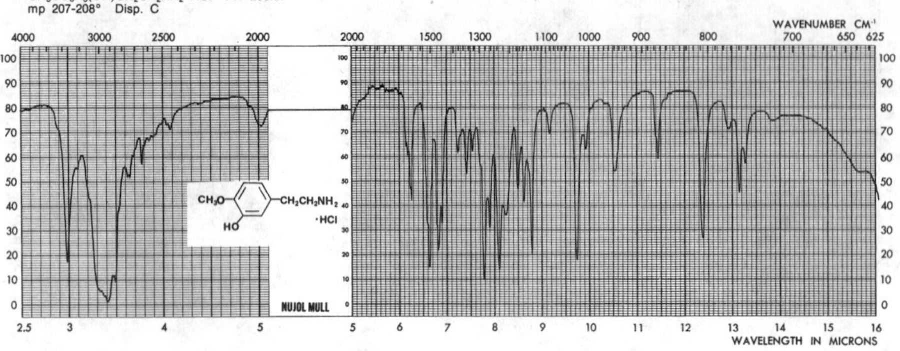

NUJOL MULL

F

16,189-6
3,4-(Dibenzyloxy)-phenethylamine hydrochloride, 99+%, GOLD LABEL
$(C_6H_5CH_2O)_2C_6H_3CH_2CH_2NH_2 \cdot HCl$
M.W. 333.43 m.p. 131-133°

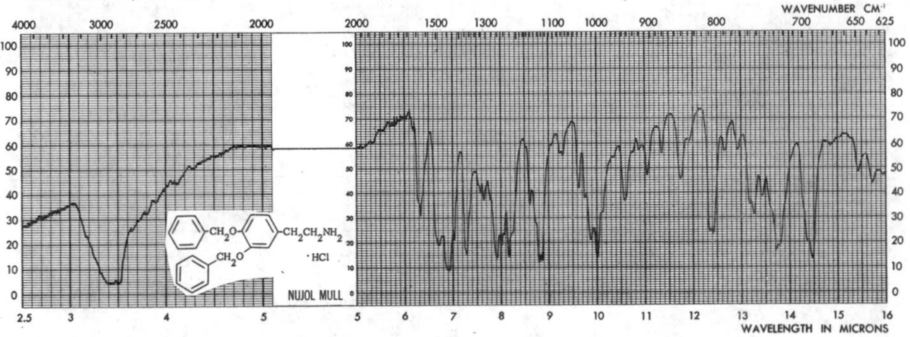

NUJOL MULL

G

12,157-6 *l*-**Arterenol** (*l*-α-aminomethyl-3,4-dihydroxybenzyl alcohol) *d*-**bitartrate monohydrate**
$(HO)_2C_6H_3CH(CH_2NH_2)OH \cdot C_4H_6O_6 \cdot H_2O$ M.W. 337.29
m.p. 95-98° $[\alpha]_D^{23}$ - 12.3° (c=1.6, H_2O)

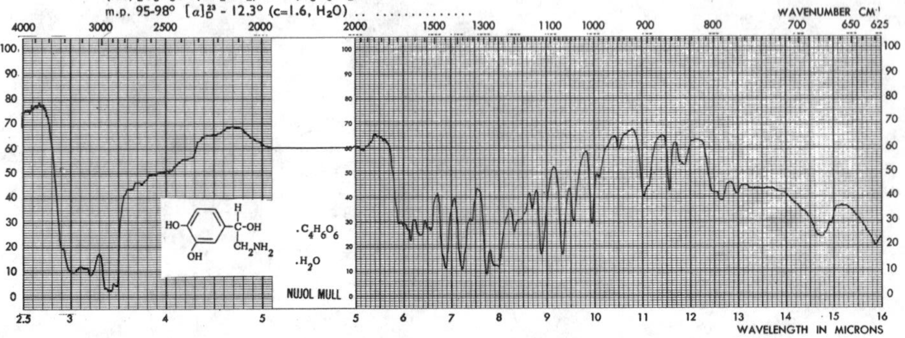

NUJOL MULL

H

85,743-2
dl-**Norepinephrine** [α-(aminomethyl)-3,4-dihydroxybenzyl alcohol]
$(HO)_2C_6H_3CH(CH_2NH_2)OH$
M.W. 169.18 m.p. 189° (dec.)

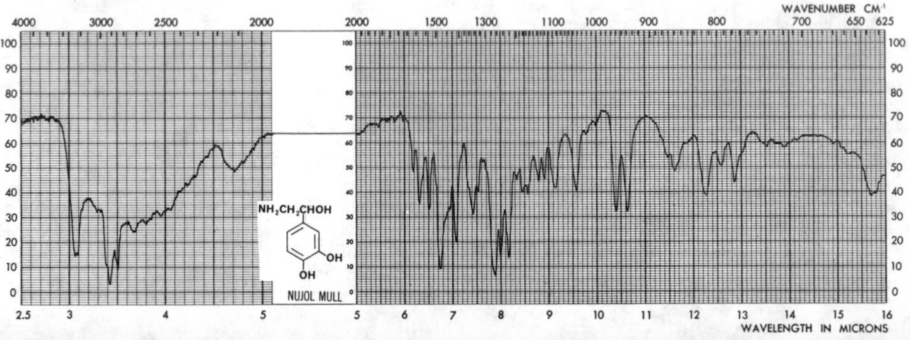

NUJOL MULL

A 17,107-7
dl-**Norepinephrine hydrochloride,** 99%
[α-(aminomethyl)-3,4-dihydroxybenzyl alcohol]
$(HO)_2C_6H_3CH(CH_2NH_2)OH \cdot HCl$
M.W. 205.64 m.p. 145-147°

B 17,106-9
l-**Norepinephrine hydrochloride,** 98%
[α-(aminomethyl)-3,4-dihydroxybenzyl alcohol]
$(HO)_2C_6H_3CH(CH_2NH_2)OH \cdot HCl$
M.W. 205.64 m.p. 146-148° (dec.)

C 21,929-0
dl-**Epinephrine,** 99% [*dl*-3,4-dihydroxy-α-(methylaminomethyl)benzyl alcohol]
$(HO)_2C_6H_3CH(CH_2NHCH_3)OH$ FW 183.21
mp 204° (dec.) *Beil.* **13**,830 Disp. C

D 21,930-4
l-**Epinephrine,** 99% [*l*-3,4-dihydroxy-α-(methylaminomethyl)benzyl alcohol]
$(HO)_2C_6H_3CH(CH_2NHCH_3)OH$ FW 183.21
mp 215° (dec.) $[\alpha]^{25}$ -51° (c=2, 0.5*N* HCl)
Beil. **13**,830 Disp. C

E 15,434-2 *l*-**Isoproterenol hydrochloride**
$3,4\text{-}(HO)_2C_6H_3CH(OH)CH_2NHCH(CH_3)_2 \cdot HCl$
M.W. 247.72 m.p. 153-154°
$[\alpha]^{25}_{D}$ -37.8° (c 1, H_2O)

F I-2790-2 *dl*-**Isoproterenol hydrochloride**
$3,4\text{-}(HO)_2C_6H_3CH(OH)CH_2NHCH(CH_3)_2 \cdot HCl$ M.W. 247.72
m.p. 172.5° (dec.)

G 10,044-7 *dl*-**Isoproterenol sulfate dihydrate**
$3,4\text{-}(HO)_2C_6H_3CH(OH)CH_2NHCH(CH_3)_2 \cdot H_2SO_4 \cdot 2H_2O$ M.W. 345.37
m.p. 130° (dec.)

H 18,881-6
d-**Isoproterenol** *d*-**bitartrate**
$3,4\text{-}(HO)_2C_6H_3CH(OH)CH_2NHCH(CH_3)_2 \cdot HO_2C\text{-}CH(OH)CH(OH)CO_2H$ FW 361.35
mp 165-170° (dec.) $[\alpha]^{22}$ +30.5° (c=1.1, H_2O)
Disp. D

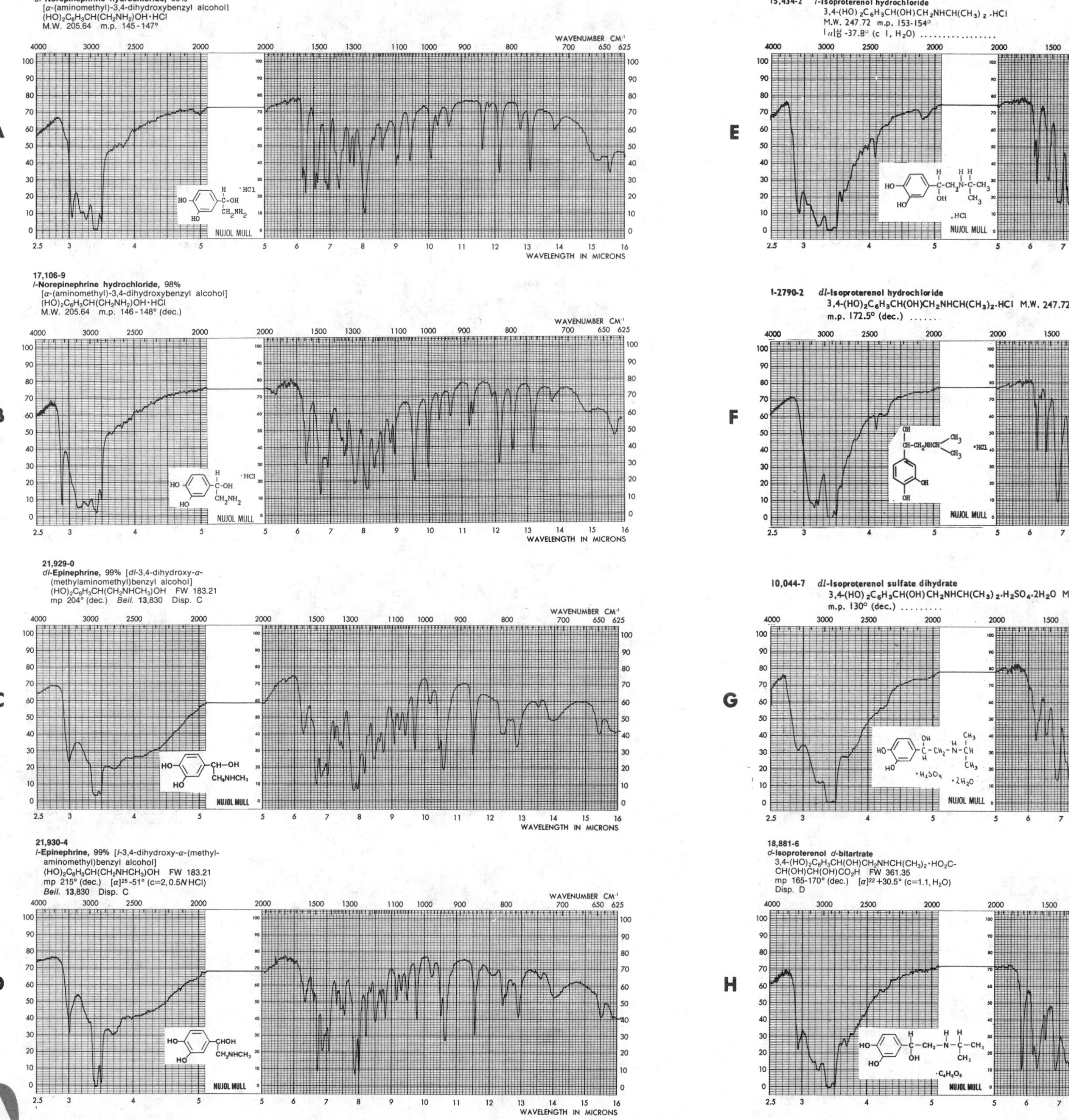

ALDRICH®

A
18,663-5
l-Isoproterenol *d*-bitartrate dihydrate
3,4-$(HO)_2C_6H_3CH(OH)CH_2NH$—
$CH(CH_3)_2 \cdot HO_2CCH(OH)CH(OH)CO_2H \cdot 2H_2O$
M.W. 397.38 m.p. 82-84° $[\alpha]^{22}$ -12.8° (c=2.3, H_2O)
Sympathomimetic for bronchodilation

B
16,482-8
2-Amino-1-(3,4-dichlorophenyl)-ethanol hydrochloride
(3,4-dichloro-β-hydroxyphenethylamine)
$H_2NCH_2CH(C_6H_3Cl_2)OH \cdot HCl$
M.W. 242.53 m.p. 245° (dec.)

C
D7175-5 1-(3',4'-Dichlorophenyl)-2-isopropylaminoethanol (DCI, dichloroisoproterenol) hydrochloride
$(CH_3)_2CHNHCH_2CH(C_6H_3Cl_2)OH \cdot HCl$ M.W. 248.15
m.p. 155-156°

D
14,226-3 4-Amino-α-diethylamino-o-cresol dihydrochloride
$H_2NC_6H_3[CH_2N(C_2H_5)_2]OH \cdot 2HCl$ M.W. 267.20
m.p. 215-218° (dec.)

E
10,519-8 Dehydroabietylamine (1,4a-dimethyl-7-isopropyl-1,2,3,4,4a,9,10,10a-octahydro-1-phenanthrenemethylamine), 90+%
M.W. 285.48 n_D^{20} 1.5478

F
C2445-0 4-Chlorobenzhydrylamine hydrochloride
$ClC_6H_4CH(C_6H_5)NH_2 \cdot HCl$ M.W. 254.16
m.p. 300-305° (dec.)

G
15,156-4 5-Hydroxydopamine (3,4,5-trihydroxyphenethylamine) hydrochloride
$(HO)_3C_6H_2CH_2CH_2NH_2 \cdot HCl$ M.W. 205.64
m.p. 233-234°

H
13,942-4 Mescaline (3,4,5-trimethoxyphenethylamine) hydrochloride
$(CH_3O)_3C_6H_2CH_2CH_2NH_2 \cdot HCl$ M.W. 247.72
m.p. 182-184°

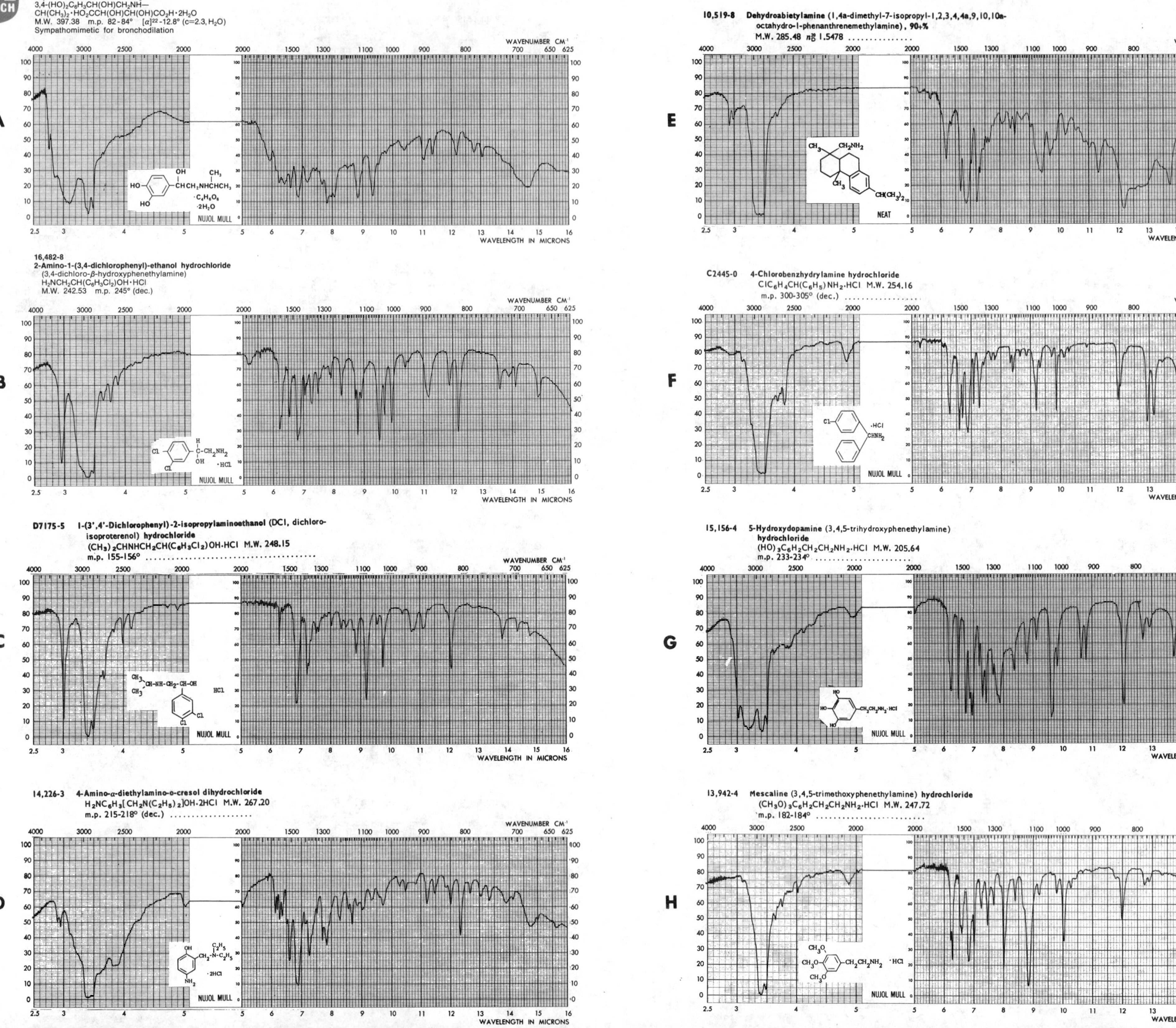

19,707-6
N-(3-Methoxypropyl)-3,4,5-trimethoxybenzylamine, 98+%
$(CH_3O)_3C_6H_2CH_2NH(CH_2)_3OCH_3$ FW 269.34
n_D^{20} 1.5205 d 1.077 Disp. C

14,668-4
4-(Diethylaminomethyl)-2,5-dimethylphenol, 98%
$(C_2H_5)_2NCH_2C_6H_2(CH_3)_2OH$
M.W. 207.32 m.p. 92-94°

T5820-3 2,4,6-Tri-(dimethylaminomethyl)-phenol
$[(CH_3)_2NCH_2]_3C_6H_2OH$ M.W. 265.40 n_D^{20} 1.5181

14,980-2 6-Hydroxydopamine (2,4,5-trihydroxyphenethylamine) hydrochloride
$(HO)_3C_6H_2CH_2CH_2NH_2 \cdot HCl$ M.W. 205.64
m.p. 232-233° (dec.)

16,295-7
6-Hydroxydopamine hydrobromide, 99%
(2,4,5-trihydroxyphenethylamine)
$(HO)_3C_6H_2CH_2CH_2NH_2 \cdot HBr$
M.W. 250.1 m.p. 217-219° (dec.)
HYGROSCOPIC

15,762-7
2,3,4-Trimethoxyphenethylamine hydrochloride
$(CH_3O)_3C_6H_2CH_2CH_2NH_2 \cdot HCl$
M.W. 247.72 m.p. 162-164°

11,373-5 2,4,5,6-Tetrachloro-m-xylylenediamine
$C_6Cl_4(CH_2NH_2)_2$ M.W. 273.98 m.p. 132-134°

T870-1 2,3,5,6-Tetrachloro-p-xylylenediamine
$C_6Cl_4(CH_2NH_2)_2$ M.W. 273.98 m.p. 138-141°

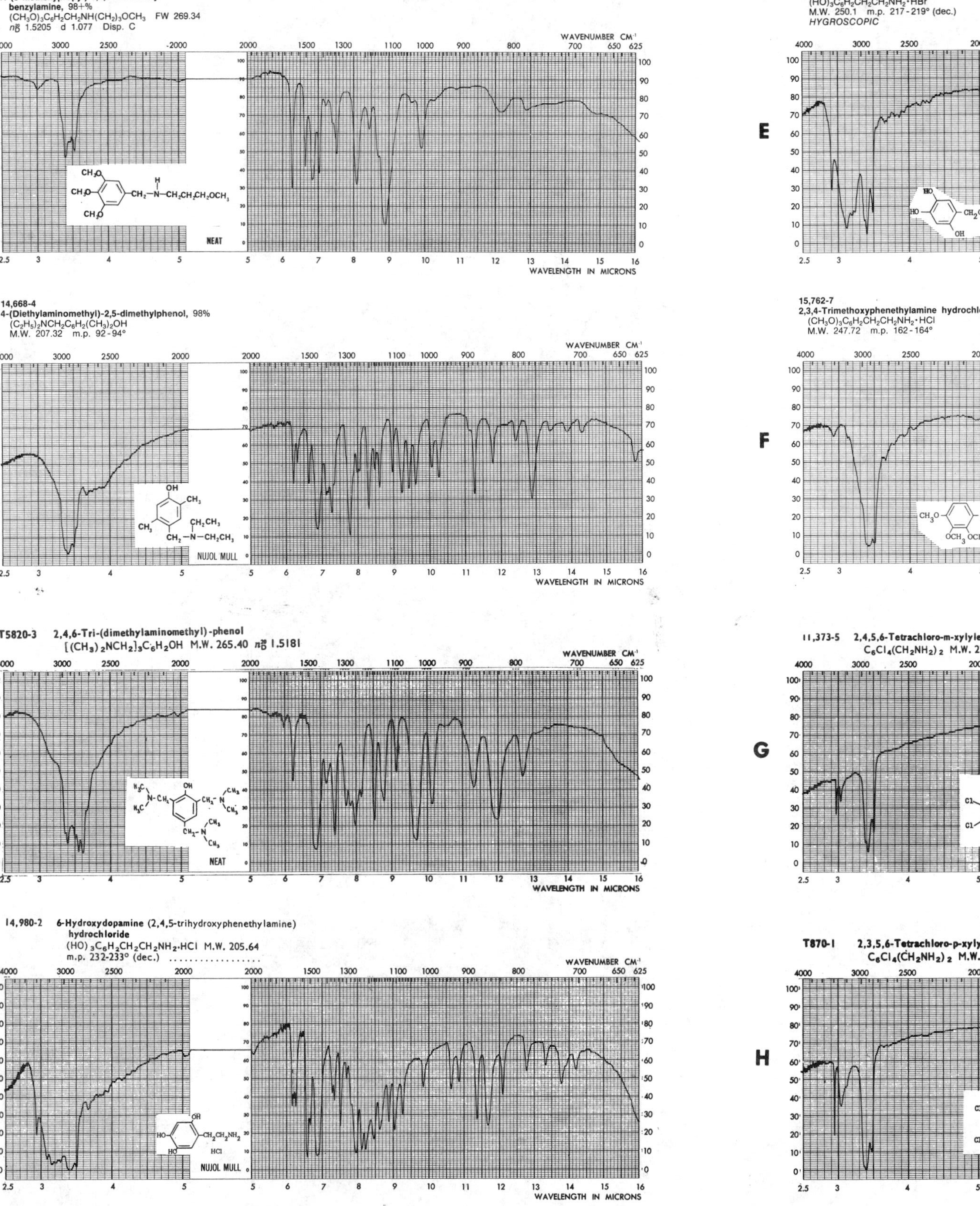

A

12,703-5 **1-Naphthalenemethylamine, tech.**
$C_{10}H_7CH_2NH_2$ M.W. 157.22 n_D^{20} 1.6370
b.p. 138-141°/7 mm.

NEAT

B

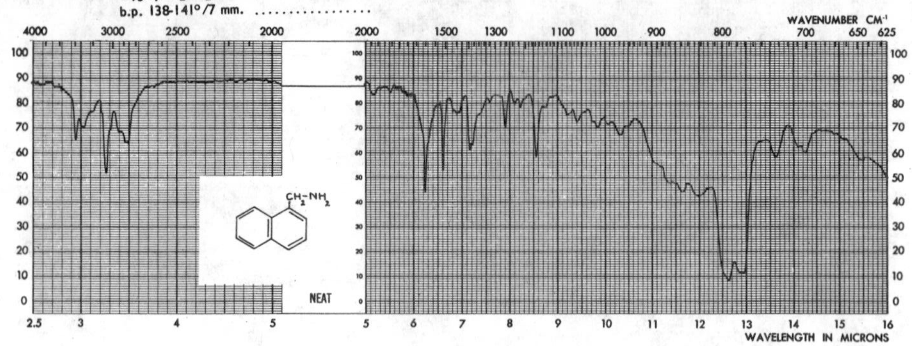

N445-2 ***d*-α-(1-Naphthyl)-ethylamine**
$CH_3CH(C_{10}H_7)NH_2$ M.W. 171.24 n_D^{20} 1.6227 b.p. 156°/15 mm.
$[\alpha]_D^{20}$ +81.35° (neat)

NEAT

C

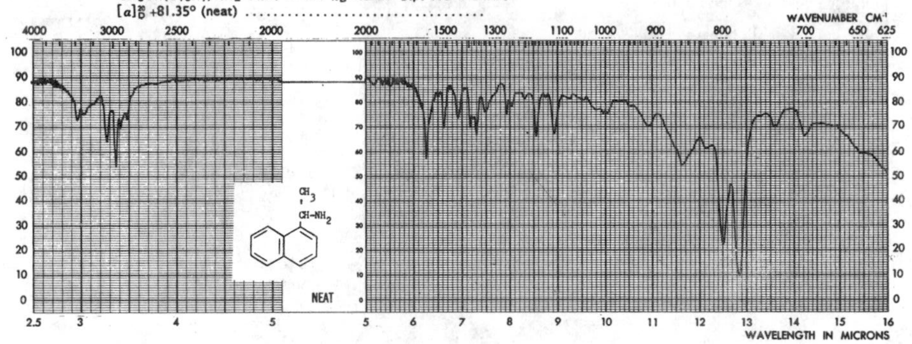

N446-0 ***l*-α-(1-Naphthyl)-ethylamine**
$CH_3CH(C_{10}H_7)NH_2$ M.W. 171.24 n_D^{20} 1.6215
b.p. 156°/15 mm. $[\alpha]_D^{20}$ - 81.35° (neat)

NEAT

D

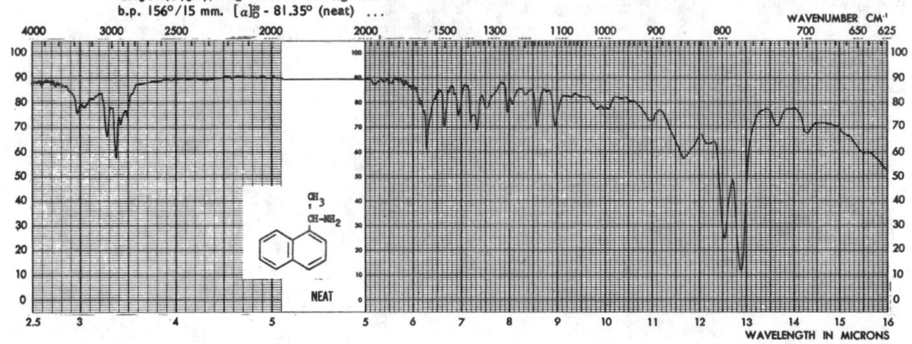

22,298-4
dl-**Propranolol hydrochloride**, 99%
[1-(isopropylamino)-3-(1-naphthyloxy)-2-propanol]
$C_{10}H_7OCH_2CH(OH)CH_2NHCH(CH_3)_2 \cdot HCl$
FW 295.81 mp 163-165° Disp. C

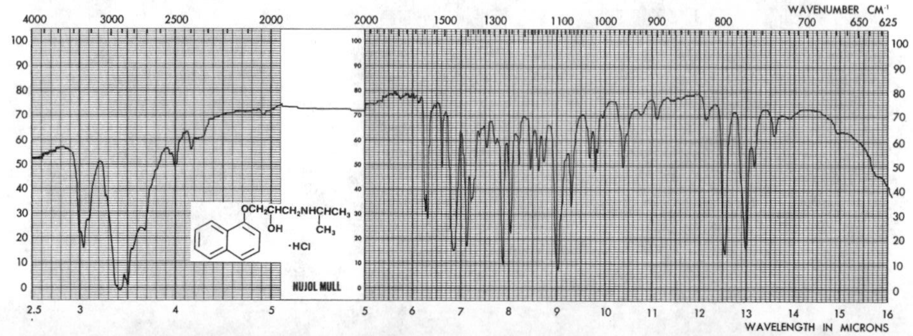

NUJOL MULL

E

I-2065-7 **1-(Isopropylamino)-3-(α-naphthoxy)-2-propanol (propranolol) hydrochloride**
$C_{10}H_7OCH_2CH(OH)CH_2NHCH(CH_3)_2 \cdot HCl$ M.W. 295.81
m.p. 163-164.5°

NUJOL MULL

F

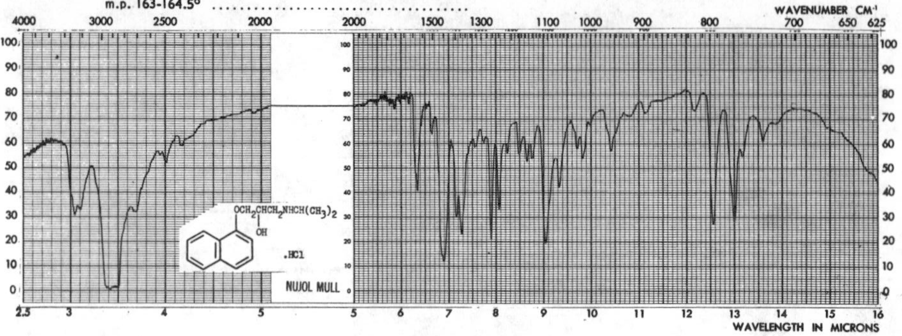

A5560-8 **9-Aminofluorene (9-fluorenamine) hydrochloride**
M.W. 217.70 m.p. 263-264°

NUJOL MULL

G

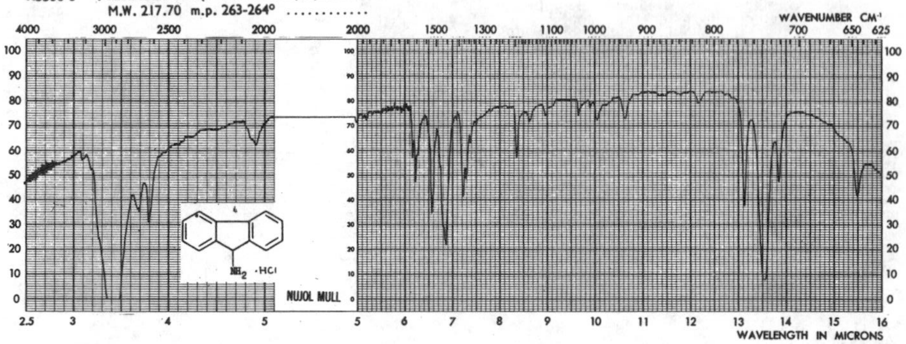

14,308-1 **Phenyl isocyanide dichloride** [N-(dichloromethylene)-aniline], tech.
$C_6H_5N{:}CCl_2$ M.W. 174.03 n_D^{20} 1.5831
b.p. 103-106°/30 mm.

NEAT

H

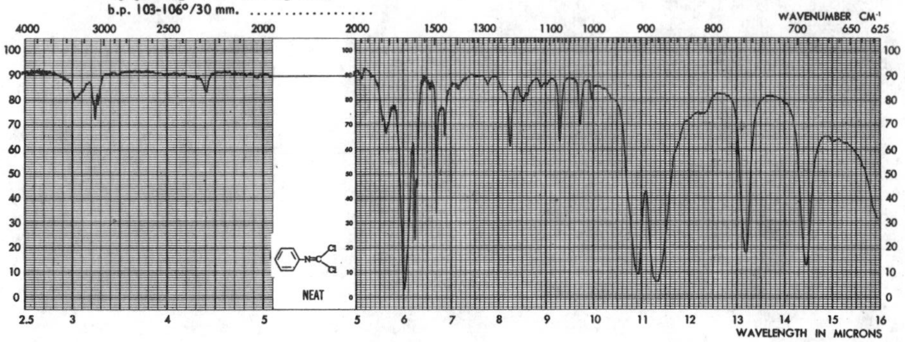

19,136-1
1-Benzylpyrrolidine, 99%
FW 161.25 bp 45°/0.700mm. n_D^{20} 1.5270 d 0.965
Disp. C

NEAT

(Each spectrum: WAVENUMBER CM⁻¹ 4000–625; WAVELENGTH IN MICRONS 2.5–16; transmittance 0–100.)

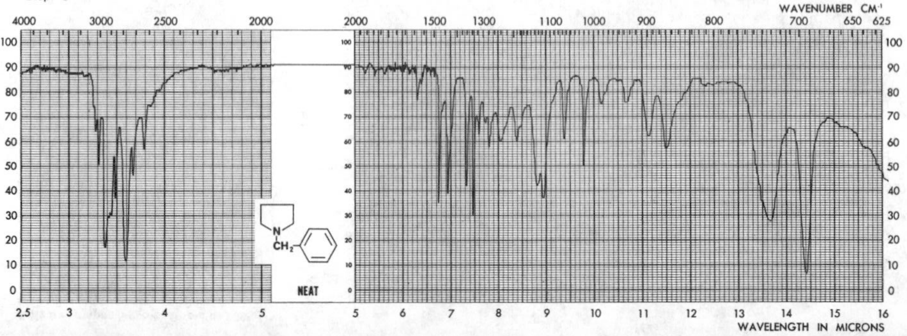

A

19,792-0
1-[2-(*p*-Bromophenoxy)ethyl]pyrrolidine, 95%
FW 270.18 bp 138-140°/1.200mm. n_D^{20} 1.5573
d 1.304 Disp. C

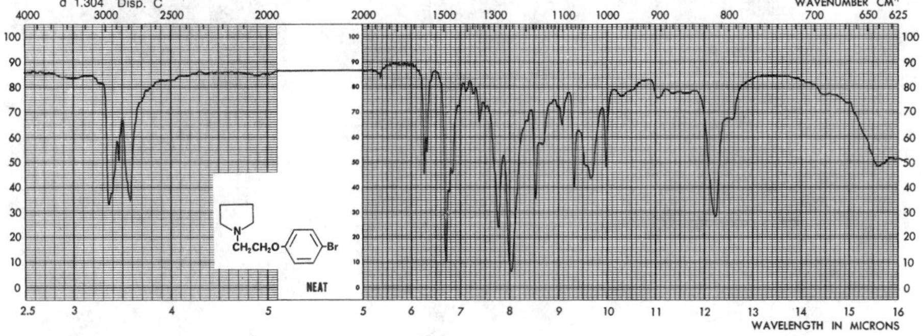

NEAT

B

15,910-7
1-(3,4-Dihydro-2-naphthyl)-pyrrolidine
M.W. 199.3 m.p. 82-84°

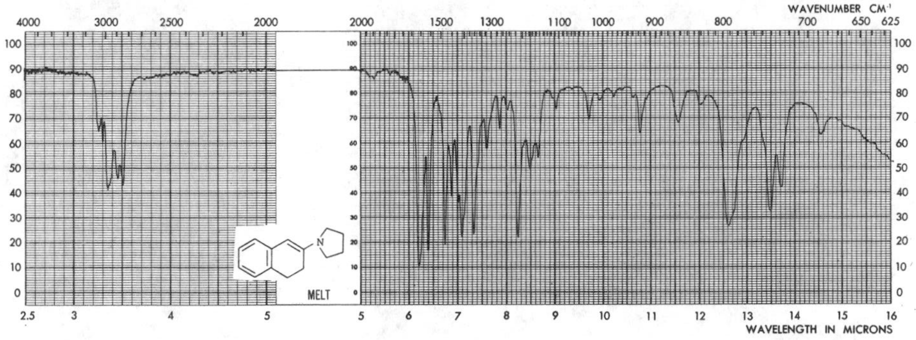

MELT

C

14,186-0 **Hydrastinine chloride monohydrate**
M.W. 243.69 m.p. 208° (dec.)

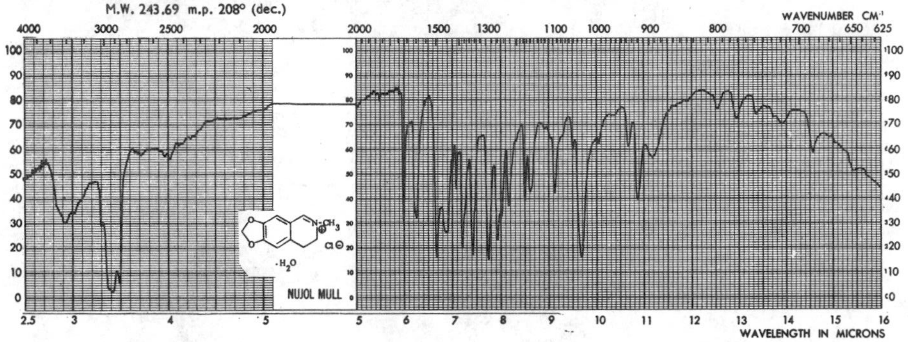

NUJOL MULL

D

17,951-5
N-Ethyl-3-phenyl-2-norbornanamine hydrochloride,
99% (fencamfamine)
M.W. 251.8 m.p. 190-192°

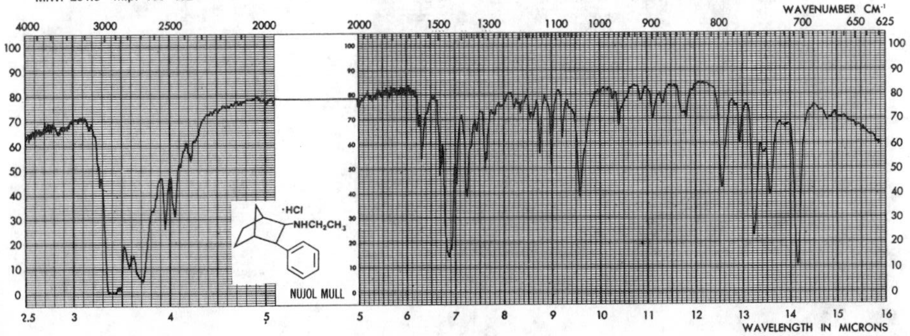

NUJOL MULL

E

19,224-4
1-Phenethylpiperidine, 98%
FW 189.30 mp -13° bp 272° n_D^{20} 1.5238
d 0.945 *Beil.* **20**(2),16 Disp. C

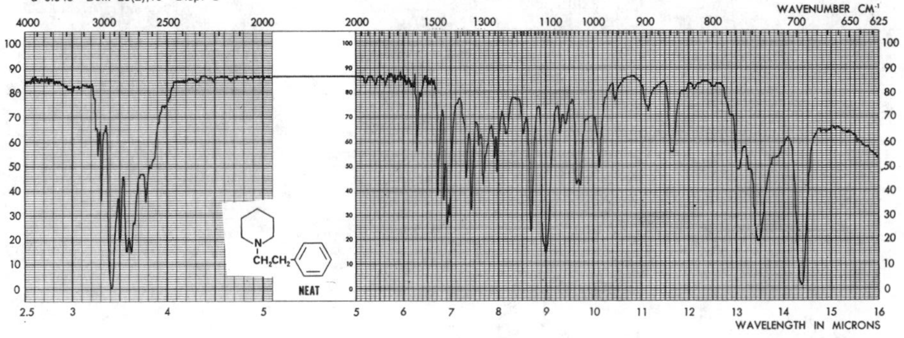

NEAT

F

19,581-2
4-Amino-1-benzylpiperidine, 98+%
FW 190.29 n_D^{20} 1.5430 d 0.933 Disp. C

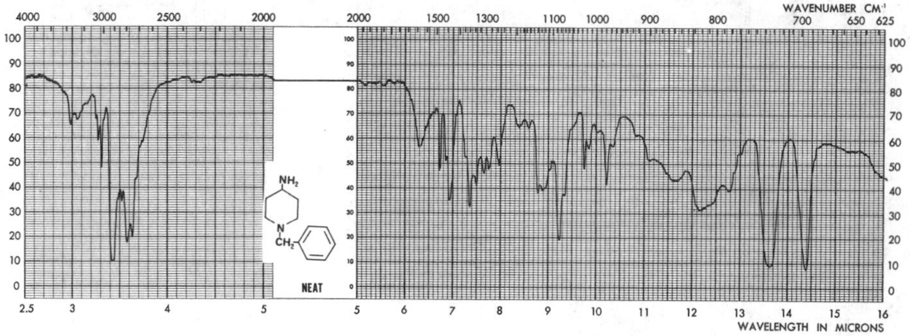

NEAT

G

14,236-0
4-Benzylpiperidine
M.W. 175.28 m.p. 6-7° b.p. 279° n_D^{20} 1.5379
d 0.997 Beil. **20**,296

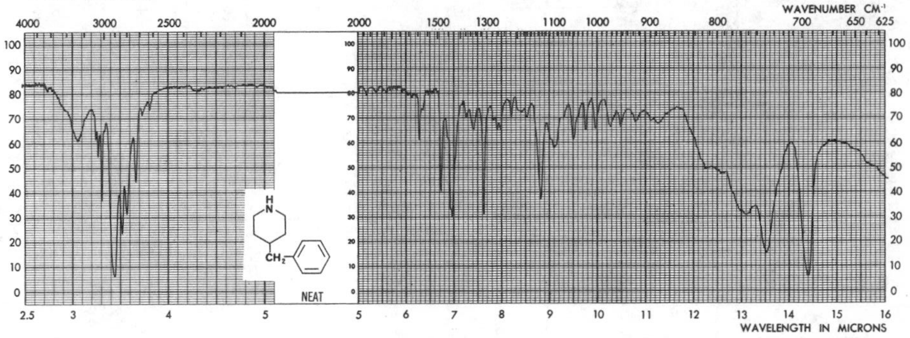

NEAT

H

P3015 **4-Phenylpiperidine**
M.W. 161.25 m.p. 58.5-63

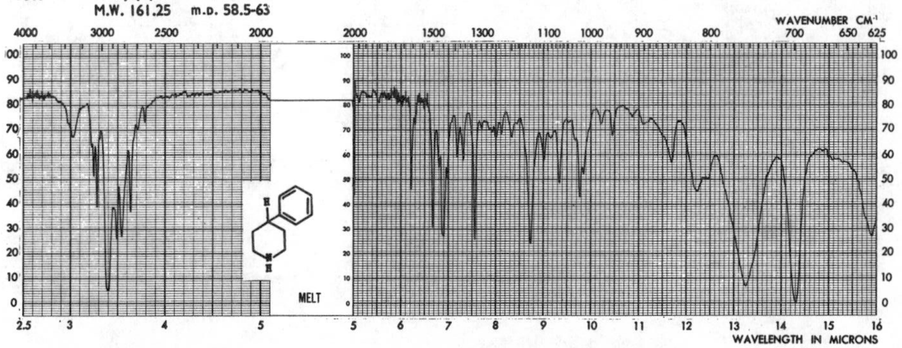

MELT

A

19,268-6
4-Bromo-4-phenylpiperidine hydrobromide
FW 321.07 mp 209-211° Disp. C
NUJOL MULL

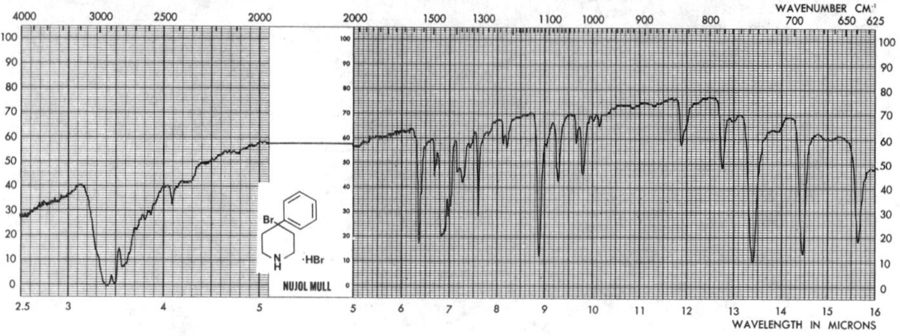

B

11,963-6 4-(3-Phenylpropyl)-piperidine
M.W. 203.33 n_D^{20} 1.5260 b.p. 312°
NEAT

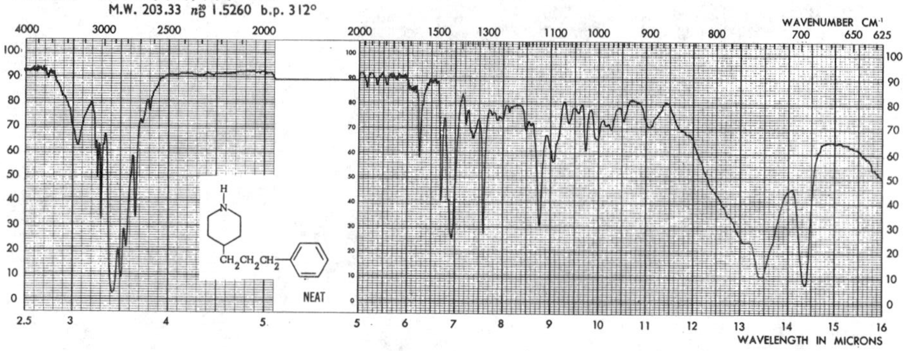

C

D20,950-3 4-Diphenylmethylpiperidine
M.W. 251.36 m.p. 101-103.5°
NUJOL MULL

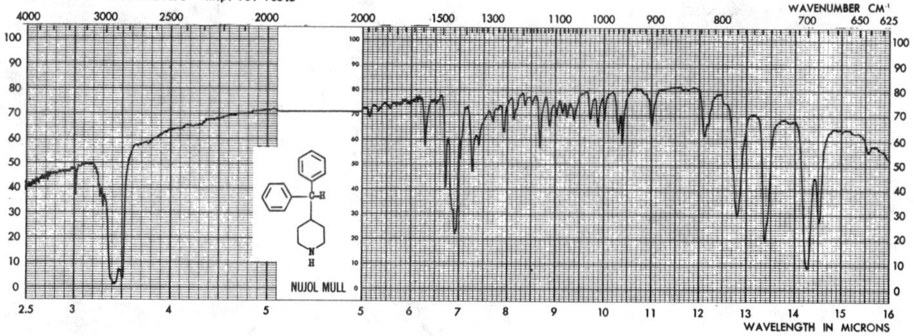

D

13,474-0 4-Phenyl-1,2,3,6-tetrahydropyridine hydrochloride
M.W. 195.69 m.p. 202-203.5° ....
NUJOL MULL

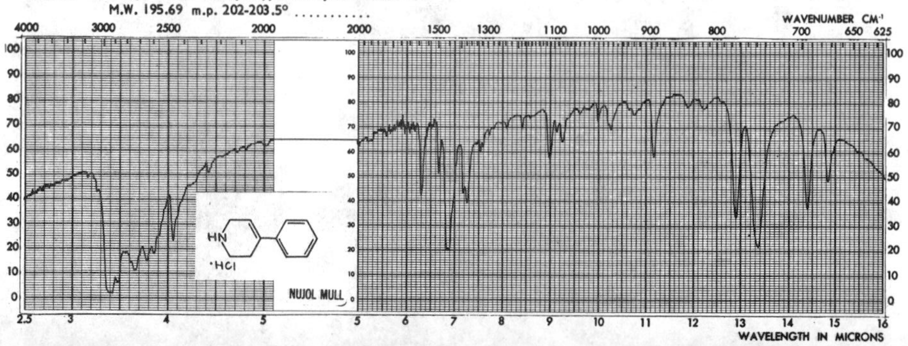

E

14,219-0 N-Methyl-4-phenyl-1,2,3,6-tetrahydropyridine hydrochloride
M.W. 209.72 m.p. 254-257° ....
NUJOL MULL

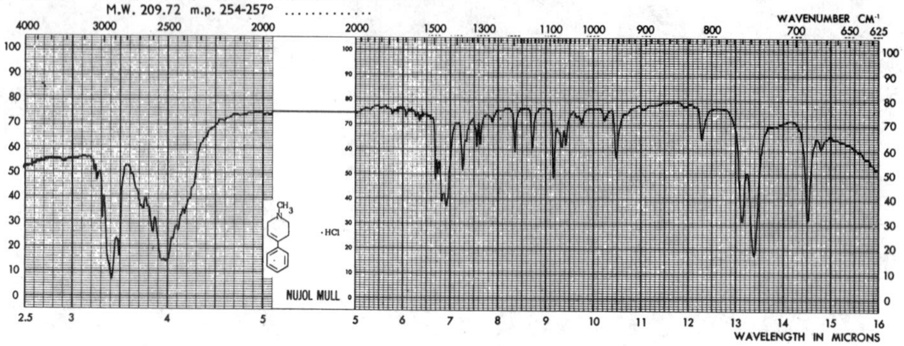

F

13,904-1 N-Benzyl-3-chloropiperidine hydrochloride
M.W. 246.18 m.p. 195-197° ....
NUJOL MULL

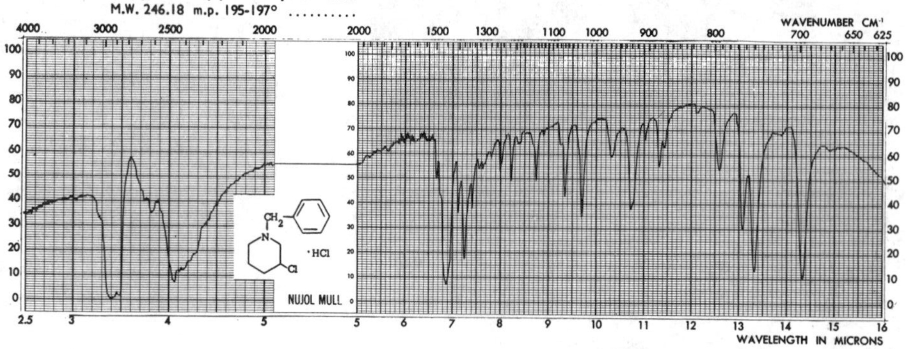

G

19,991-5
N-Methyl-4-phenyl-1,2,3,6-tetrahydropyridine, 97%
FW 173.26 mp 37-40° Disp. C
MELT

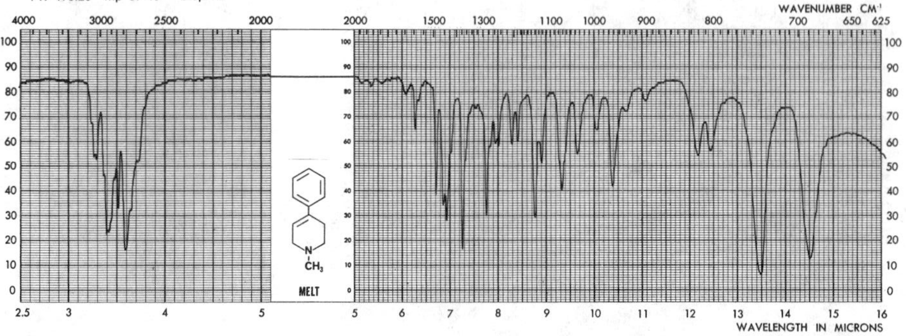

H

F1515-3 4-(p-Fluorophenyl)-1,2,3,6-tetrahydropyridine hydrochloride
M.W. 213.68 m.p. 171-173° ....
NUJOL MULL

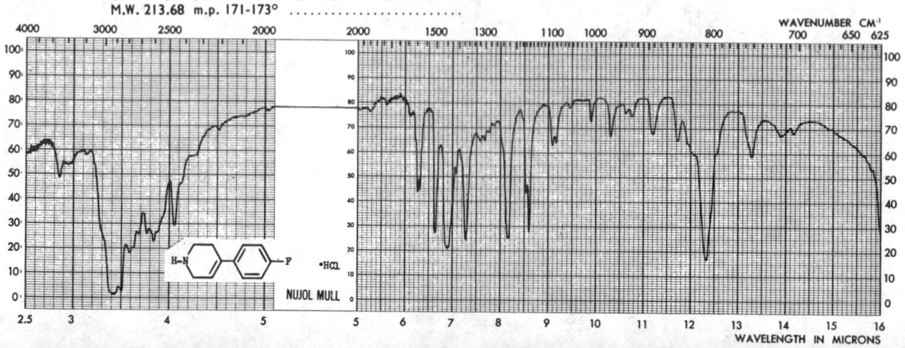

A C6840-7 4-(p-Chlorophenyl)-1,2,3,6-tetrahydropyridine hydrochloride
M.W. 230.14 m.p. 204-206°

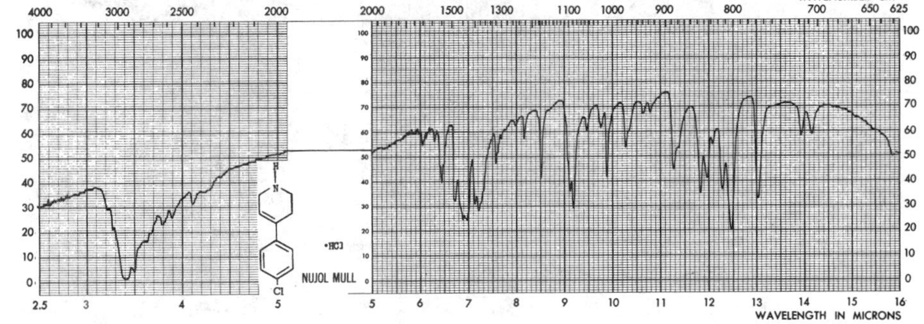

NUJOL MULL

B H5220-1 **4-Hydroxy-4-phenylpiperidine** (4-phenyl-4-piperidinol)
M.W. 177.25 m.p. 158-160°

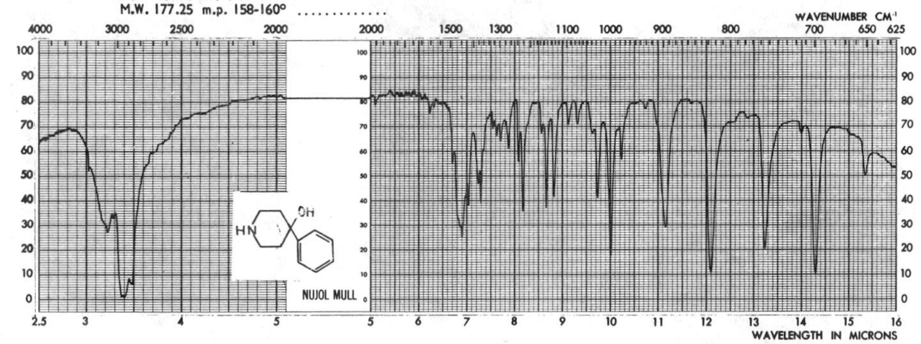

NUJOL MULL

C B2310-7 **4-Benzyl-4-hydroxypiperidine** (4-benzyl-4-piperidinol)
M.W. 191.27 m.p. 84-86.5°

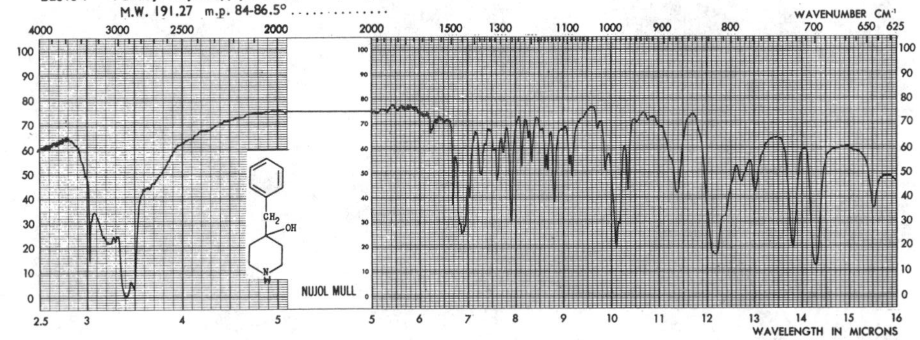

NUJOL MULL

D 13,893-2 **1-Benzyl-3-hydroxypiperidine** (1-benzyl-3-piperidinol)
M.W. 191.27 n_D^{20} 1.5482 b.p. 107°/0.1 mm.

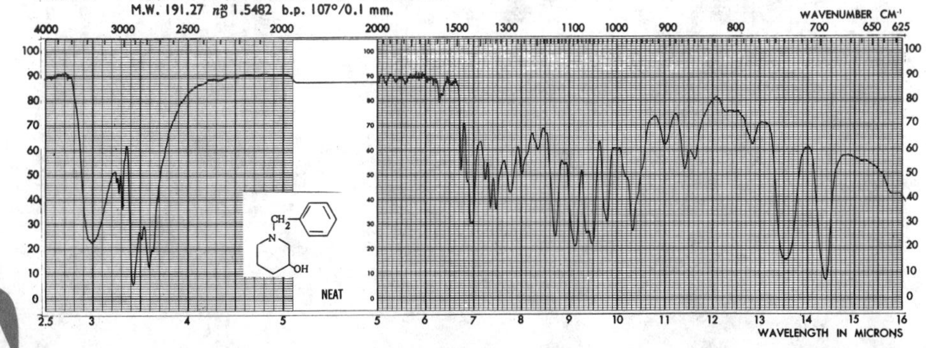

NEAT

E 15,298-6 1-Benzyl-4-hydroxypiperidine (1-benzyl-4-piperidinol)
M.W. 191.27 m.p. 41-44

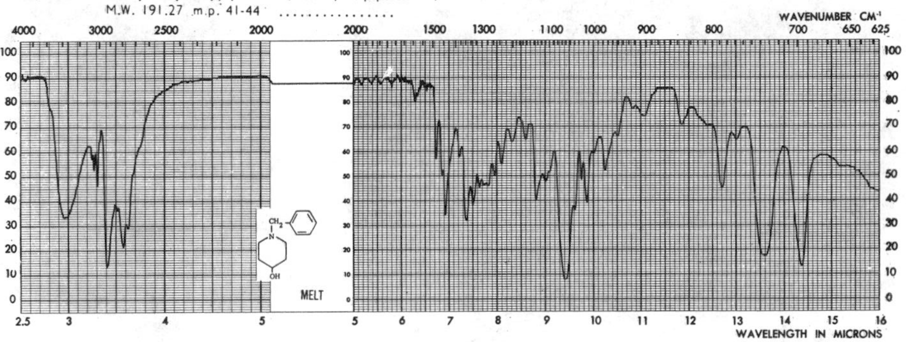

MELT

F H5915 **4-Hydroxy-4-(p-tolyl)-piperidine**

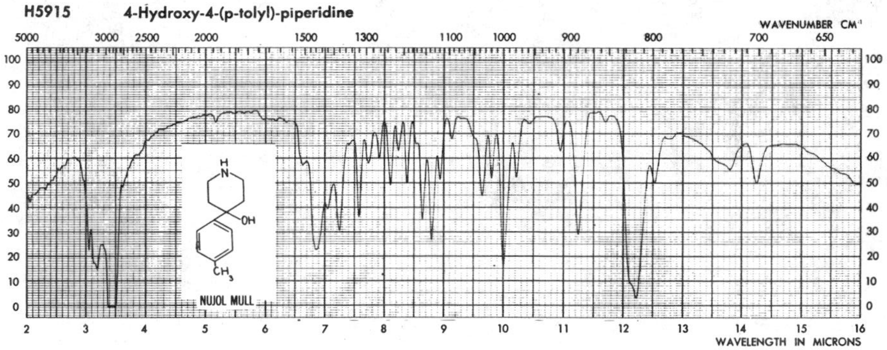

NUJOL MULL

G C6605-6 4-(p-Chlorophenyl)-4-hydroxypiperidine [4-(p-chlorophenyl)-4-piperidinol]
M.W. 211.69 m.p. 137-140°

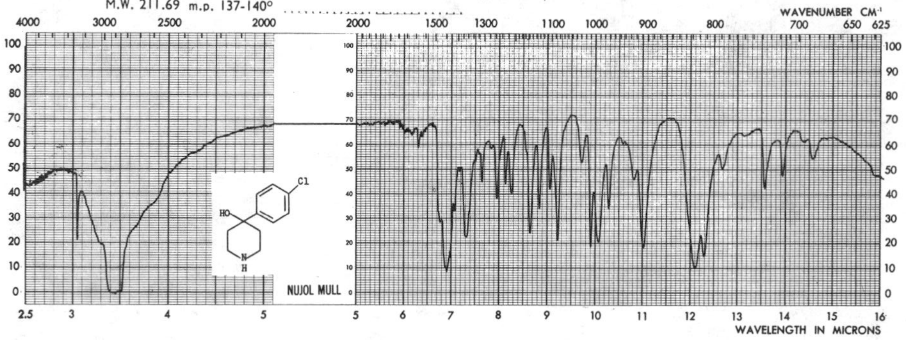

NUJOL MULL

H L323-4 Lobelanidine (α,α'-diphenyl-1-methyl-2,6-piperidinediethanol) hydrochloride
M.W. 375.94 m.p. 136-143° (dec.)

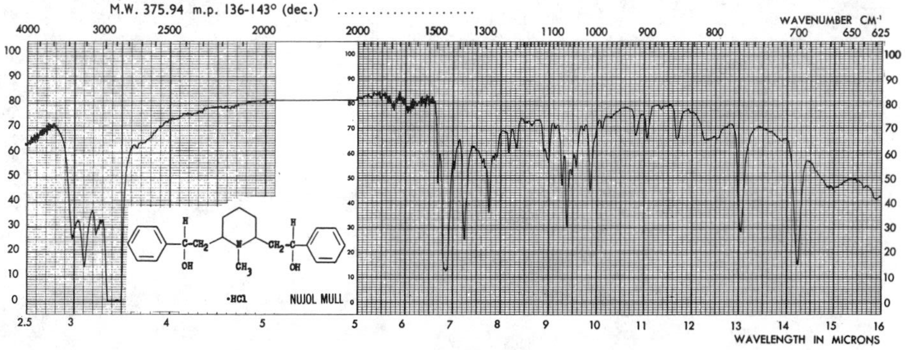

NUJOL MULL

A

21,303-9
2-Phenyl-2-imidazoline, 98+%
FW 146.19 mp 94-99° *Beil.* **23**,154 Disp. C

NUJOL MULL

B

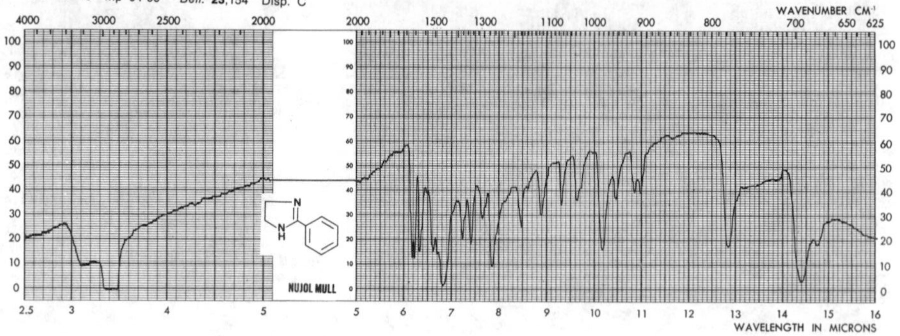

T3546-7 Tolazoline (2-benzyl-2-imidazoline) **hydrochloride**
M.W. 196.68 m.p. 174-177°

NUJOL MULL

C

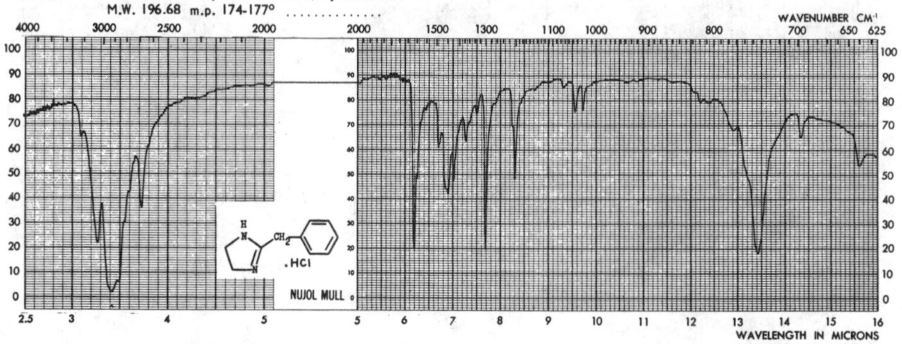

18,352-0
2-(1-Naphthylmethyl)-2-imidazoline hydrochloride, 99%
M.W. 246.74

NUJOL MULL

D

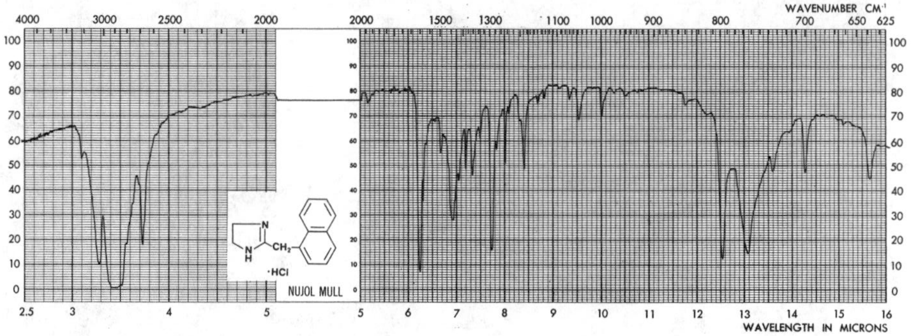

14,678-1 ***dl*-Isoamarine** (*dl*-2,4,5-triphenyl-2-imidazoline)
M.W. 298.39 m.p. 201-203°

NUJOL MULL

E

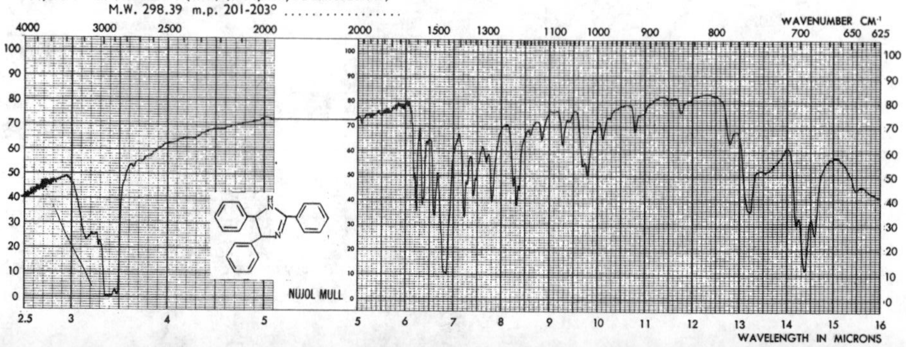

18,766-6
(4*S*,5*S*)-(-)-2-Methyl-5-phenyl-2-oxazoline-4-methanol, 99% (4-hydroxymethyl-2-methyl-5-phenyl-2-oxazoline)
FW 191.23 mp 65-68° Disp. C

MELT

F

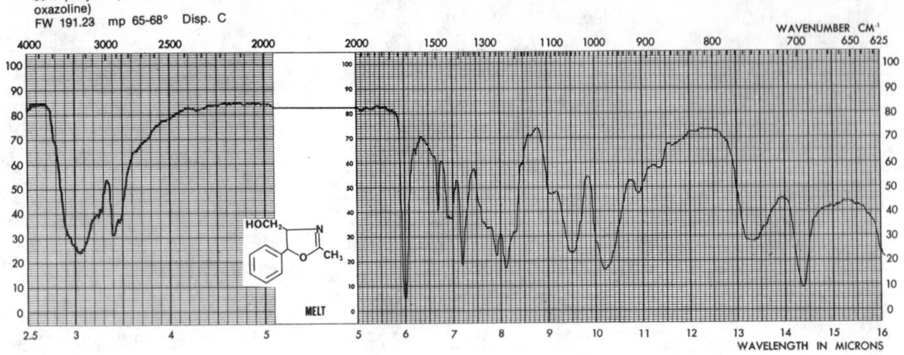

18,774-7
(4*S*,5*S*)-(-)-2-Ethyl-5-phenyl-2-oxazoline-4-methanol
(2-ethyl-4-hydroxymethyl-5-phenyl-2-oxazoline)
FW 205.26 mp 69-71° $[\alpha]^{22}$ -132.6° (c=9.1, $CHCl_3$)
Disp. C

NUJOL MULL

G

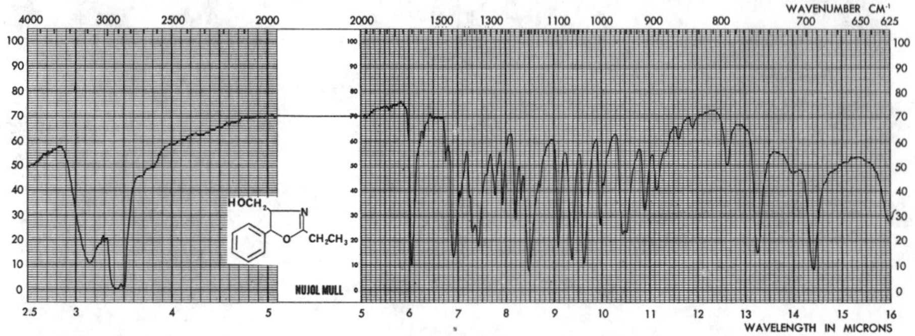

18,765-8
(4*S*,5*S*)-(-)-4-Methoxymethyl-2-methyl-5-phenyl-2-oxazoline
FW 205.26 bp 79-82°/0mm. n_D^{20} 1.5155
$[\alpha]^{22}$ -113.2° (c=10.5, $CHCl_3$) *Fieser* **6**,386
Disp. C

NEAT

H

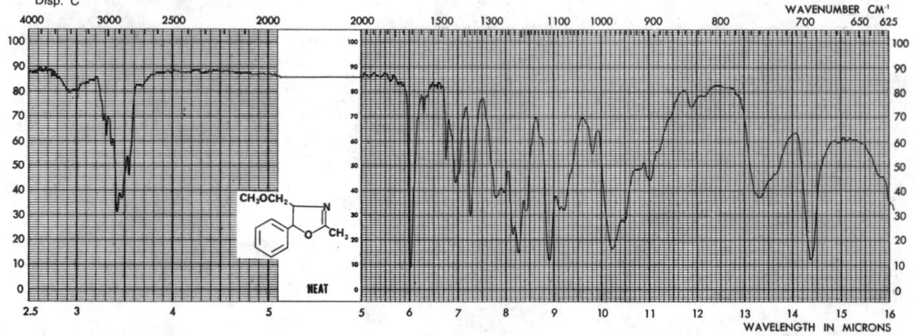

16,072-5
1,3,5-Triphenylverdazyl, free radical, 97%
M.W. 313.38 m.p. 137-139°

NUJOL MULL

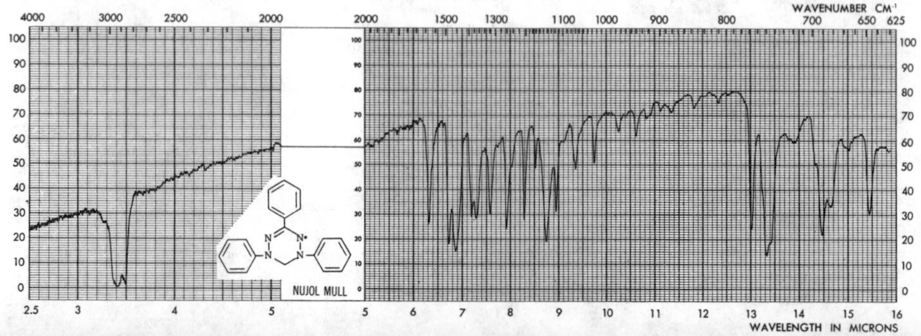

A

19,613-4
Tetramisole hydrochloride, 99+% (DL-2,3,5,6-tetrahydro-6-phenylimidazo[2,1-*b*]thiazole)
FW 240.76 mp 266-267° Disp. C

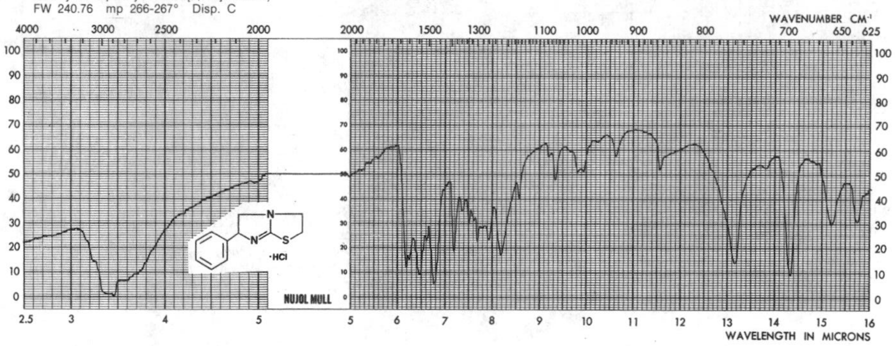

NUJOL MULL

B

19,614-2
Levamisole hydrochloride, 99+% [*l*-(-)-2,3,5,6-tetrahydro-6-phenylimidazo[2,1-*b*]thiazole]
FW 240.76 mp 230-233°
$[\alpha]^{21}$ -127.3° (c=0.9, H_2O) Disp. C

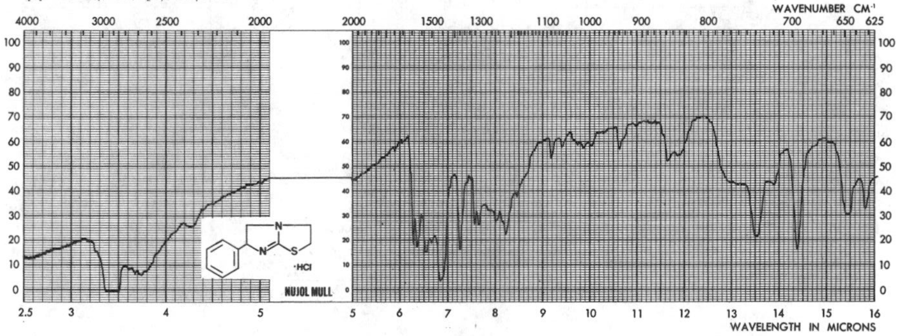

NUJOL MULL

C

19,005-5
d-p-**Bromotetramisole oxalate,** 99%
FW 373.23 mp 192° (dec.)
$[\alpha]^{25}$ +105° (c=0.5, H_2O) Disp. C

19,005-5

NUJOL MULL

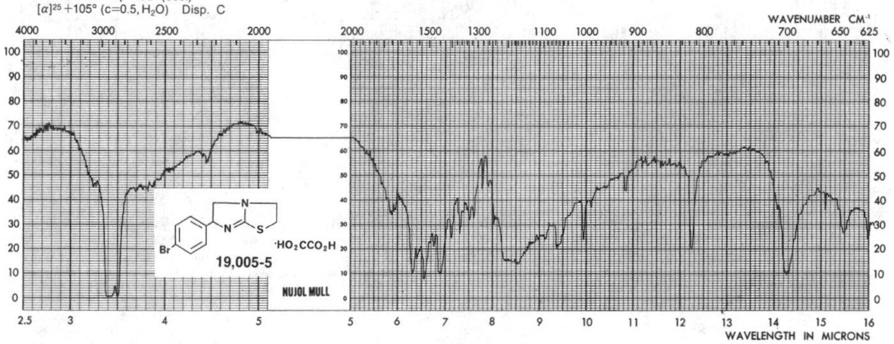

D

19,004-7
l-p-**Bromotetramisole oxalate,** 99% (*p*-bromo-levamisole)
FW 373.23 mp 192° (dec.)
$[\alpha]^{25}$ -105° (c=0.5, H_2O) Disp. C

NUJOL MULL

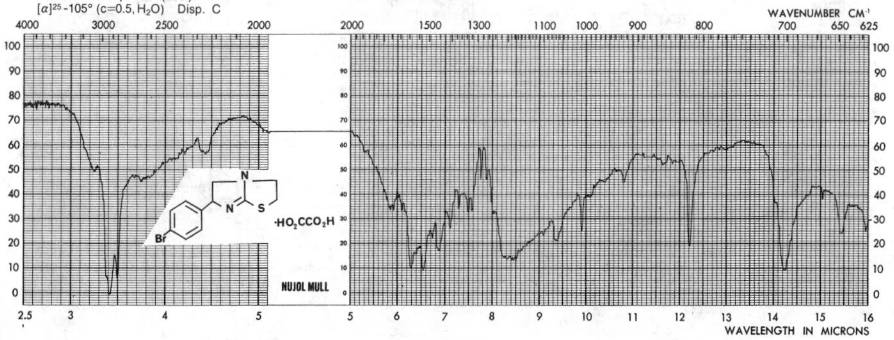

E

21,408-6
3-(*p*-Chlorophenyl)-2-ethyl-2,3,5,6-tetra-hydroimidazo[2,1-*b*]thiazol-3-ol, 97%
FW 282.79 mp 161-163° Disp. C

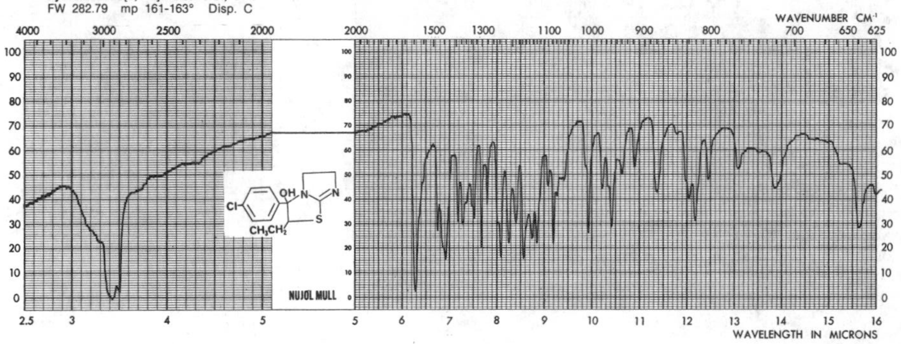

NUJOL MULL

F

P3000-4 N-Phenylpiperazine
M.W. 162.24 n_D^{20} 1.5875 b.p. 286.5°

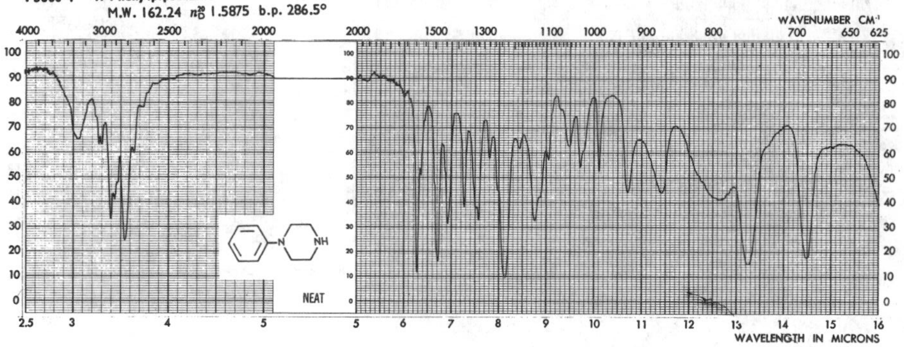

NEAT

G

13,683-2 1-Benzylpiperazine
n_D^{20} 1.5467 ....

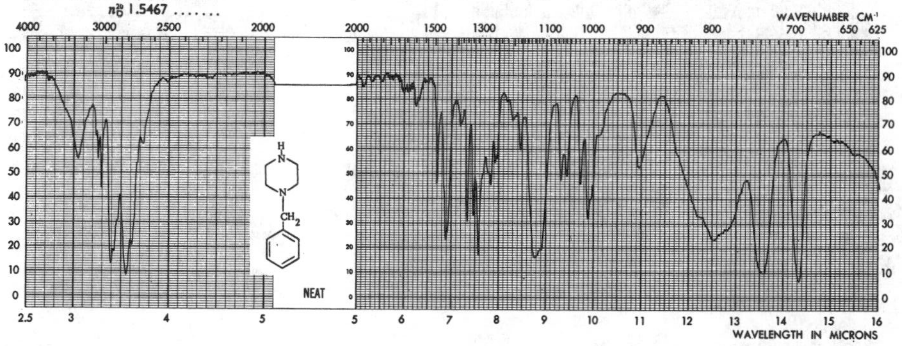

NEAT

H

B2960 1-Benzylpiperazine dihydrochloride
M.W. 249.19 m.p. 288° (dec.)

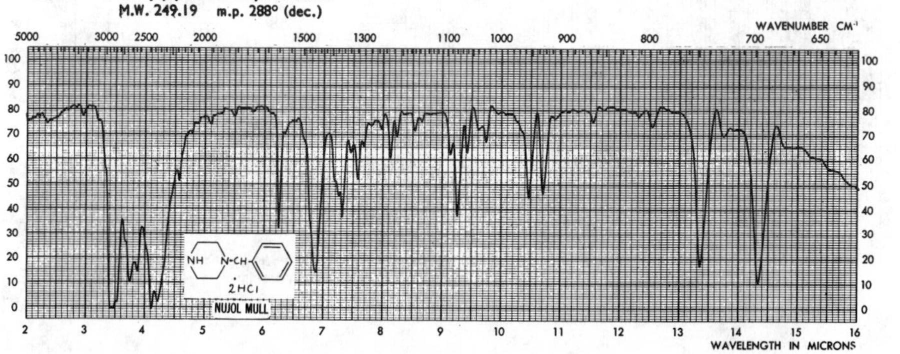

NUJOL MULL

A T4200-5 1-(o-Tolyl)-piperazine dihydrochloride
M.W. 249.19 m.p. 230-235°

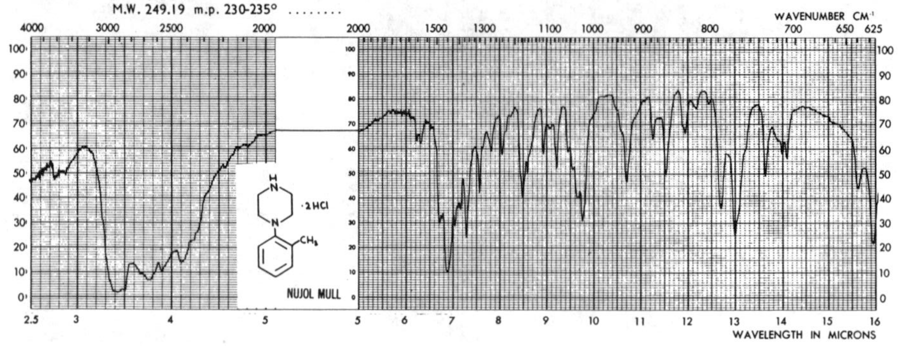

NUJOL MULL

B C6760-5 1-(o-Chlorophenyl)-piperazine hydrochloride hydrate
M.W. 251.16 m.p. 114-117°

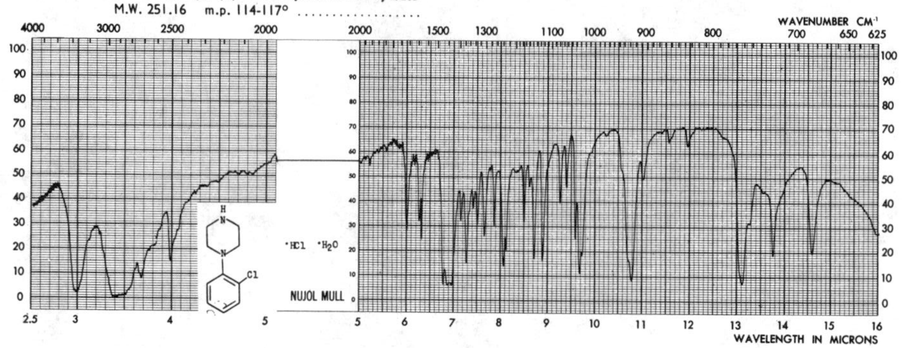

NUJOL MULL

C M2260-1 1-(o-Methoxyphenyl)-piperazine

NEAT

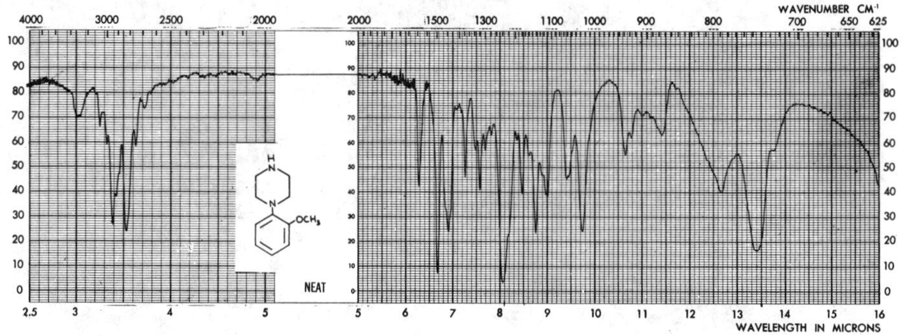

D M2260-1 1-(o-Methoxyphenyl)-piperazine dihydrochloride hydrate
M.W. 265.18 (anhydrous) m.p. 220° (dec.)

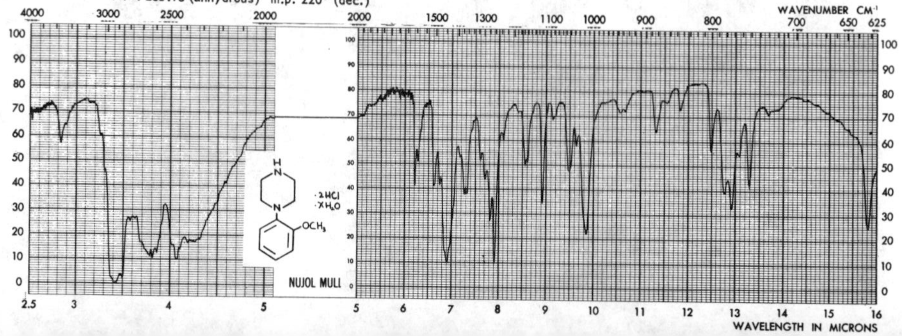

NUJOL MULL

E 13,246-2 1-(m-Tolyl)-piperazine dihydrochloride monohydrate
M.W. 267.20 m.p. 200° (dec.)

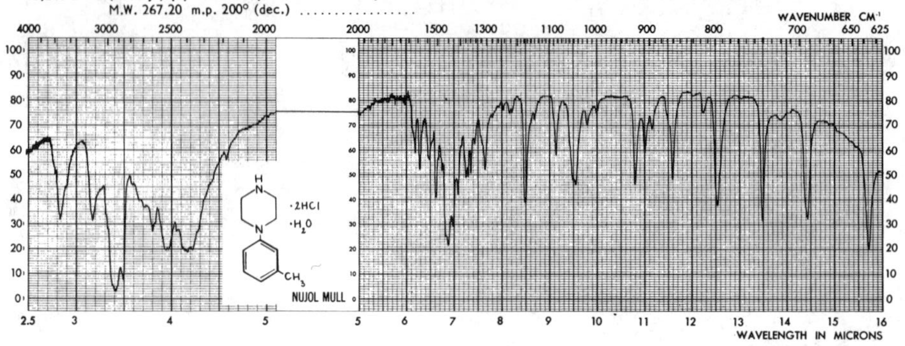

NUJOL MULL

F 10,558-9 2-Methyl-1-m-tolylpiperazine
M.W. 190.29 n_D^{20} 1.5660

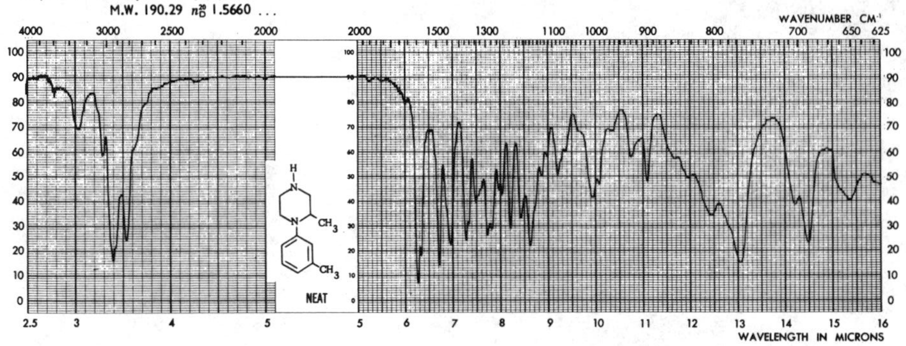

NEAT

G 12,518-0 1-(m-Chlorophenyl)-piperazine dihydrochloride
M.W. 269.60 m.p. 191-196° (dec.)

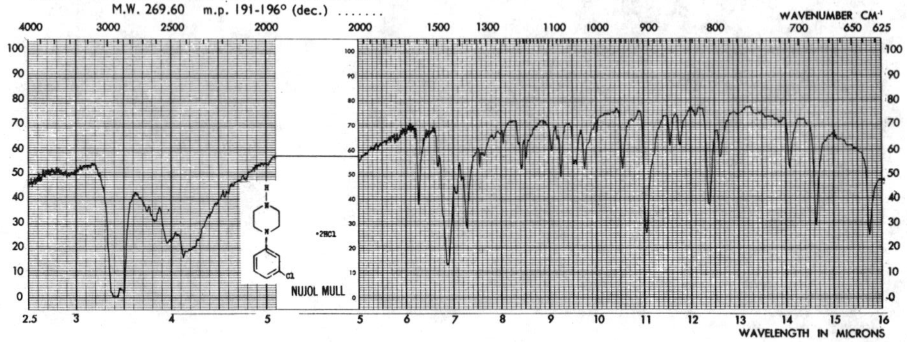

NUJOL MULL

H 10,560-0 1-(m-Chlorophenyl)-2-methylpiperazine
M.W. 210.71 n_D^{20} 1.5885

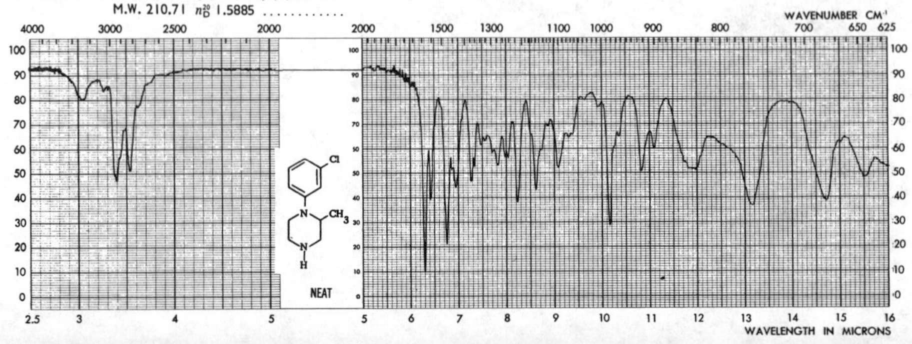

NEAT

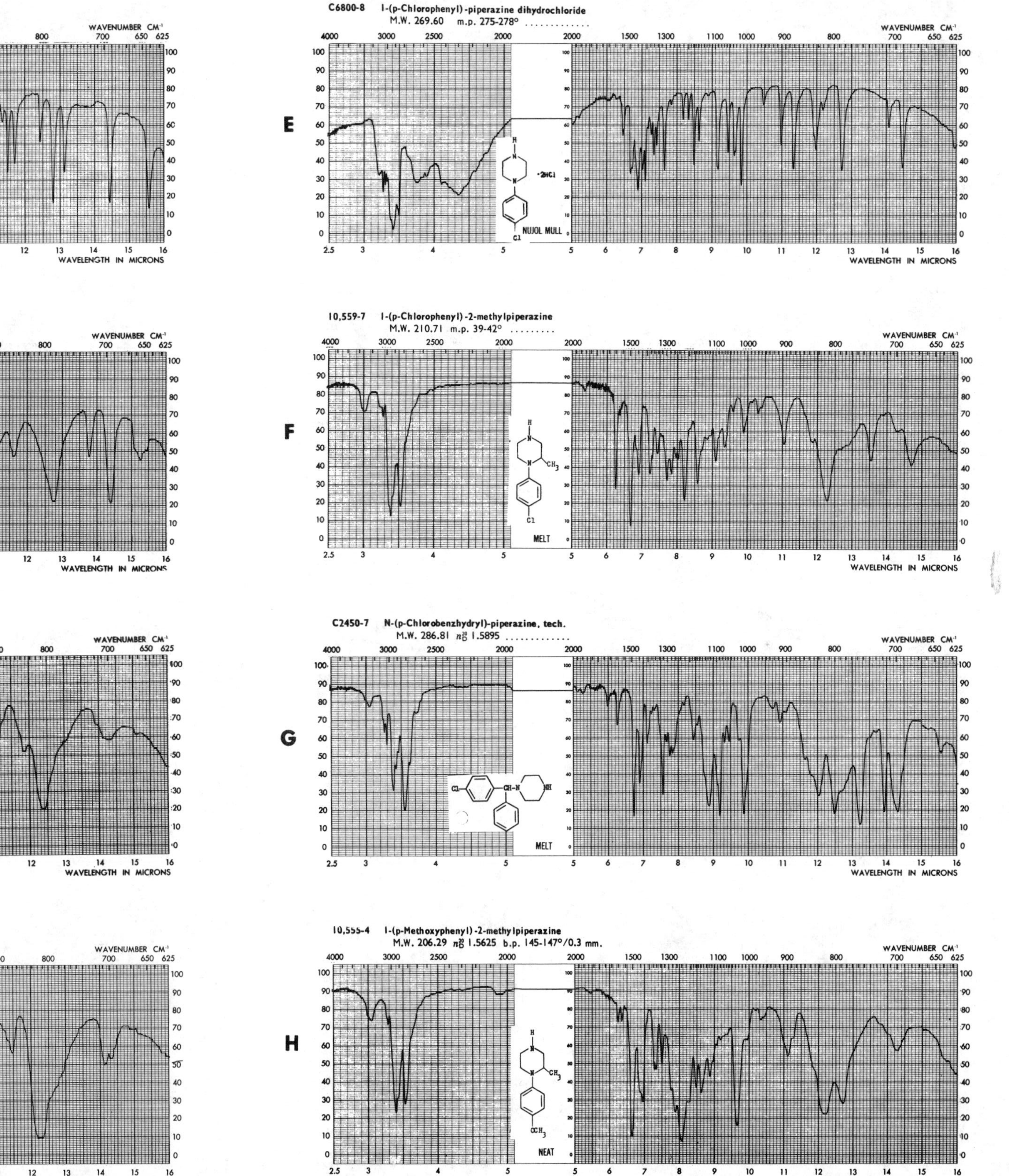

A M2280-6 1-(m-Methoxyphenyl)-piperazine dihydrochloride
M.W. 265.18 m.p. 213° (dec.)
NUJOL MULL

B 14,985-3 N-(α,α,α-Trifluoro-m-tolyl)-piperazine
M.W. 230.24 n_D^{20} 1.5208
NEAT

C 10,557-0 2-Methyl-1-p-tolylpiperazine, puriss.
M.W. 190.29 n_D^{20} 1.5633 b.p. 112-114°/0.4 mm.
NEAT

D 19,133-7
1-(p-Fluorophenyl)piperazine
FW 180.23 mp 30-33° bp 118-123°/0.100mm.
Disp. C
MELT

E C6800-8 1-(p-Chlorophenyl)-piperazine dihydrochloride
M.W. 269.60 m.p. 275-278°
NUJOL MULL

F 10,559-7 1-(p-Chlorophenyl)-2-methylpiperazine
M.W. 210.71 m.p. 39-42°
MELT

G C2450-7 N-(p-Chlorobenzhydryl)-piperazine, tech.
M.W. 286.81 n_D^{20} 1.5895
MELT

H 10,555-4 1-(p-Methoxyphenyl)-2-methylpiperazine
M.W. 206.29 n_D^{20} 1.5625 b.p. 145-147°/0.3 mm.
NEAT

A

M2300-4 1-(p-Methoxyphenyl)-piperazine dihydrochloride
M.W. 265.18 m.p. 258° (dec.)

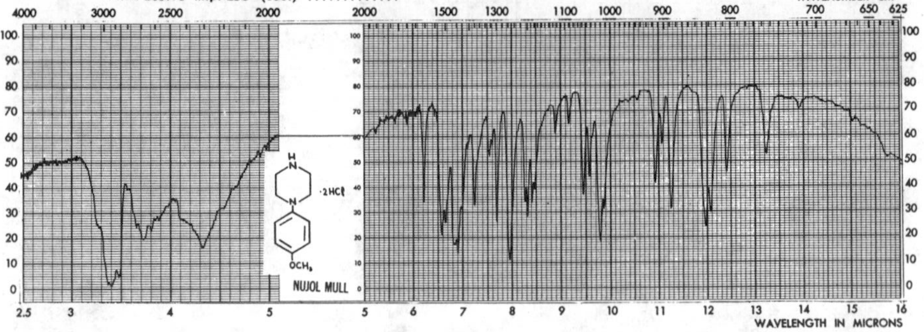

NUJOL MULL

B

21,133-8
4-Phenylmorpholine, 98+%
FW 163.22 mp 51-54° bp 165-170°/45mm.
Beil. 27,6 *Fieser* 1,846 Disp. C

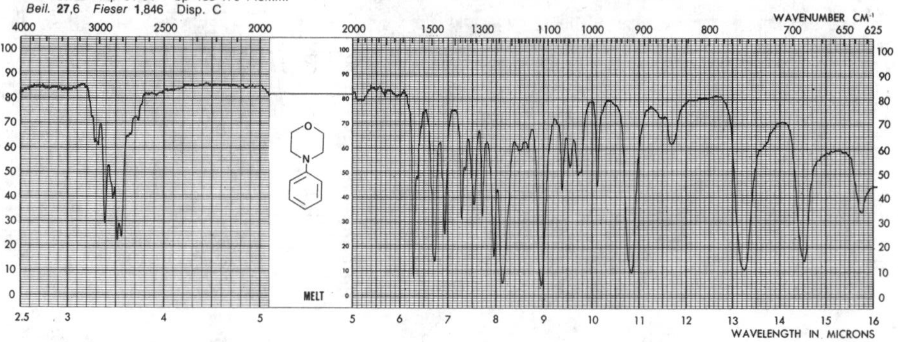

MELT

C

19,715-7
p-Morpholinoaniline, 98+%
FW 178.24 mp 132-135° Disp. C

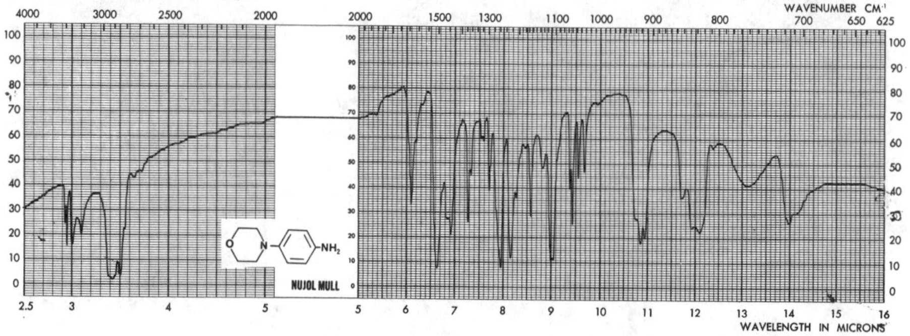

NUJOL MULL

D

13,590-9 D-Phendimetrazine (D-3,4-dimethyl-2-phenylmorpholine) bitartrate
M.W. 341.36 m.p. 190-192°

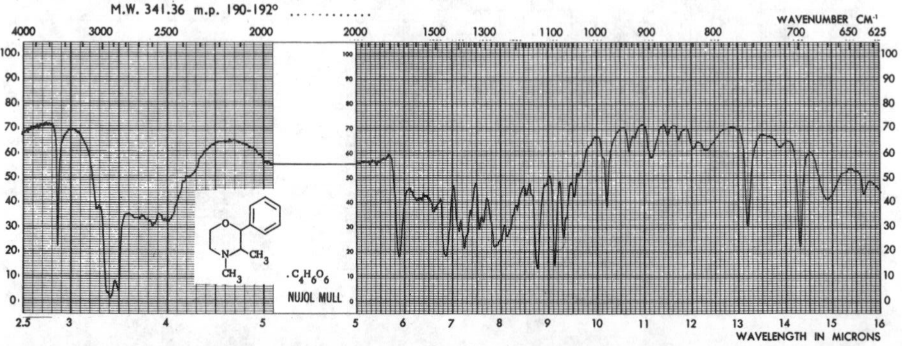

$\cdot C_4H_6O_6$

NUJOL MULL

E

18,671-6
2,5-Dimethyl-4-(morpholinomethyl)phenol hydrochloride monohydrate, 97%
M.W. 275.78 m.p. 180-185°

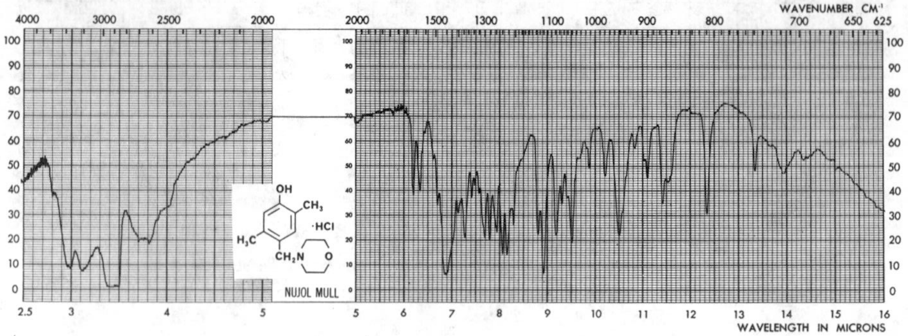

NUJOL MULL

F

I-560-5 Indoline
M.W. 119.17 n_D^{20} 1.5906 b.p. 220-221°

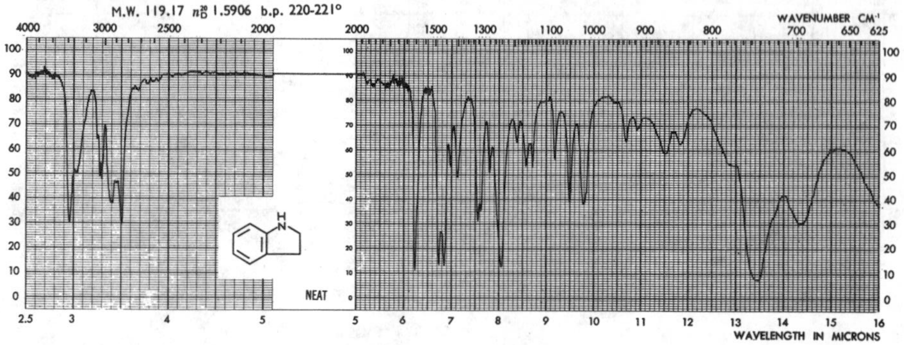

NEAT

G

M5160-1 2-Methylindoline, tech.
M.W. 133.19 n_D^{20} 1.5681 b.p. 228-229°

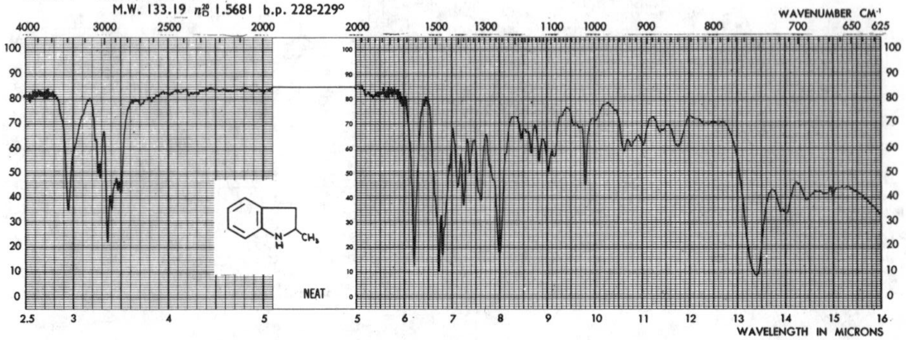

NEAT

H

T1240-8 1,2,3,4-Tetrahydrocarbazole
M.W. 171.24 m.p. 120-124°

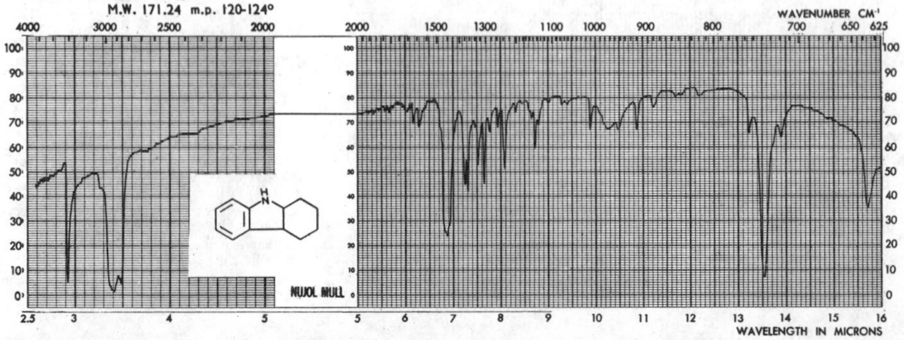

NUJOL MULL

A

D16,680 2,5-Dimethylindoline

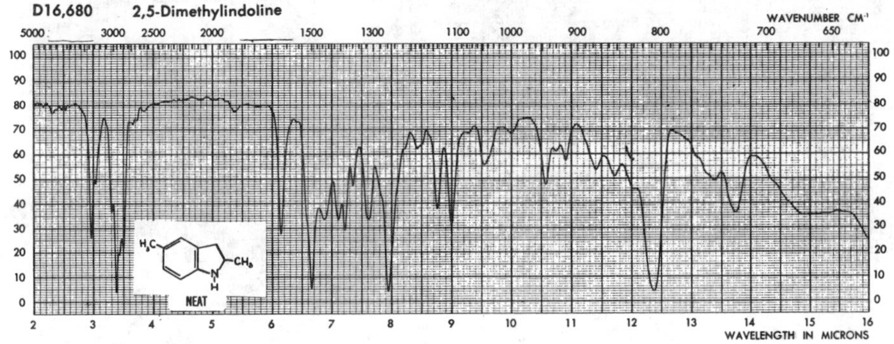

NEAT

B

F919-1 6-Fluoroindoline
M.W. 137.16 n_D^{20} 1.5599

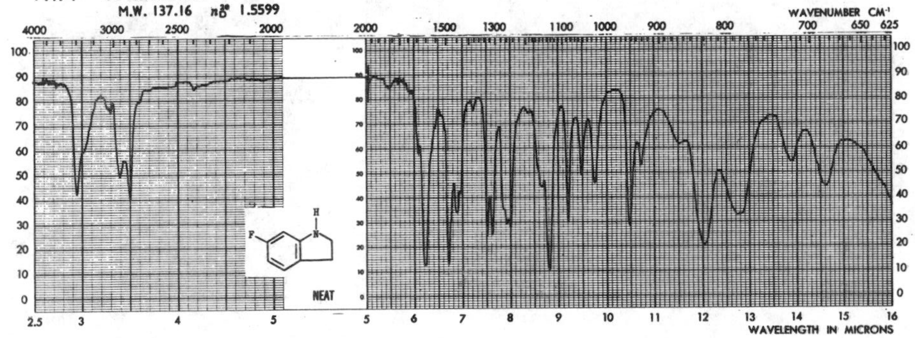

NEAT

C

C4790-6 6-Chloroindoline hydrochloride
M.W. 153.61 m.p. 260-264°

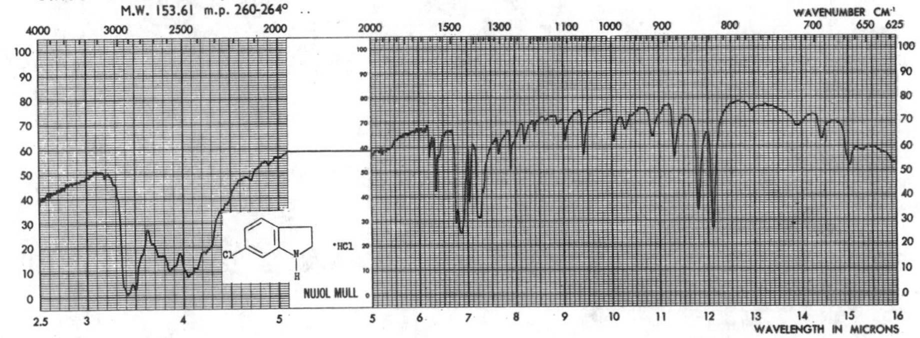

NUJOL MULL

D

M4620-9 2-Methylene-1,3,3-trimethylindoline
M.W. 173.26 n_D^{20} 1.5750 b.p. 243°/746 mm.

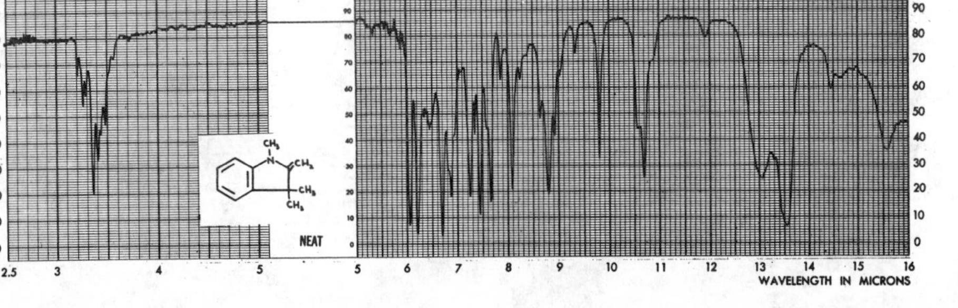

NEAT

E

16,181-0
5-Chloro-2-methylene-1,3,3-trimethylindoline,
tech., 95%
M.W. 207.7 n_D^{20} 1.5937 d 1.083

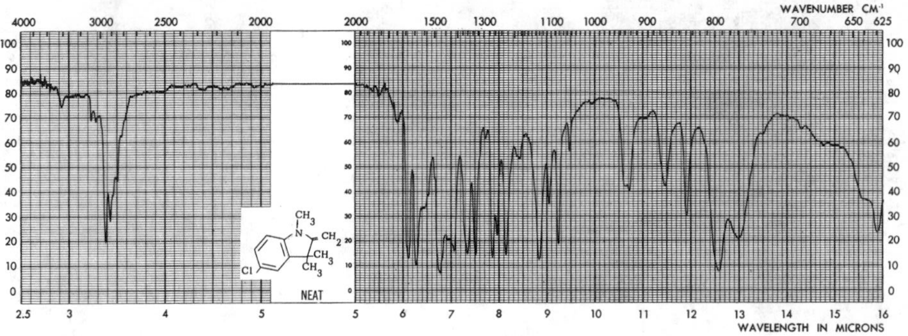

NEAT

F

21,430-2
2'-Methyl-2',3',10,11-tetrahydrospiro[5*H*-dibenzo[*a*,*d*]-cycloheptene-5,1'-[1*H*]isoindole], 98%
FW 311.43 mp 120-126° Disp. C

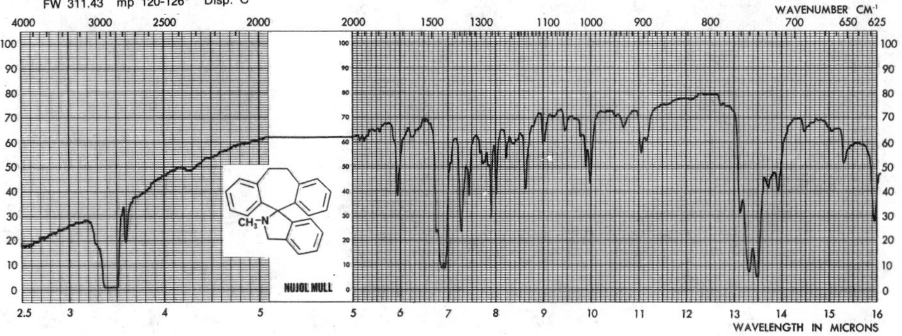

NUJOL MULL

G

D14,980-2 2,2-Dimethylbenzothiazoline
M.W. 165.26 m.p. 48-51°

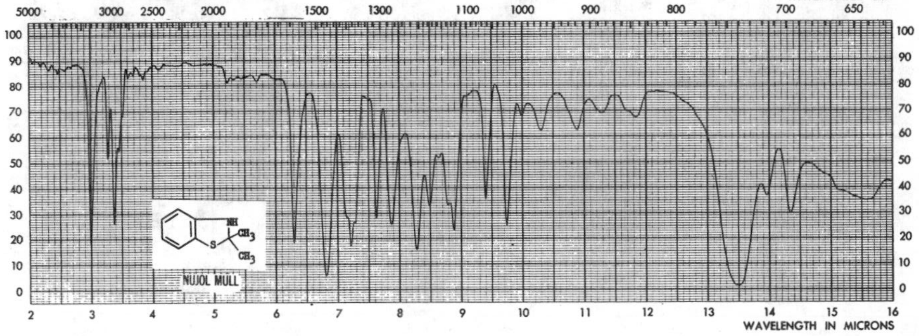

NUJOL MULL

H

T1550-4 1,2,3,4-Tetrahydroquinoline
M.W. 133.19 n_D^{20} 1.5924

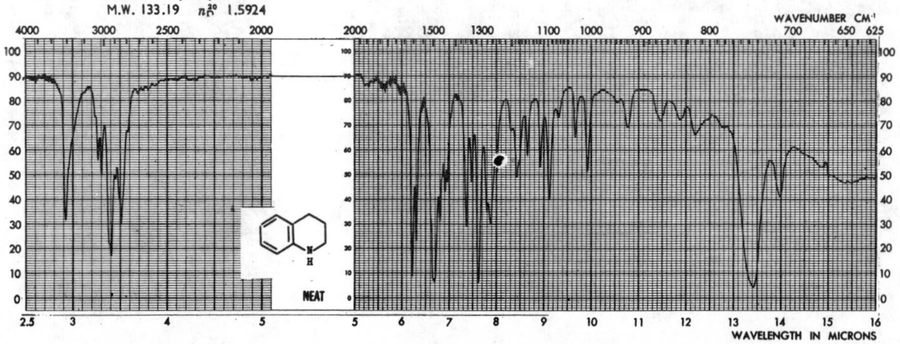

NEAT

A

19,744-0
1,2-Dihydro-2,2,4-trimethylquinoline, 95%
FW 173.26 bp 90-95°/0mm. n_D^{20} 1.5895 d 0.934
Disp. C

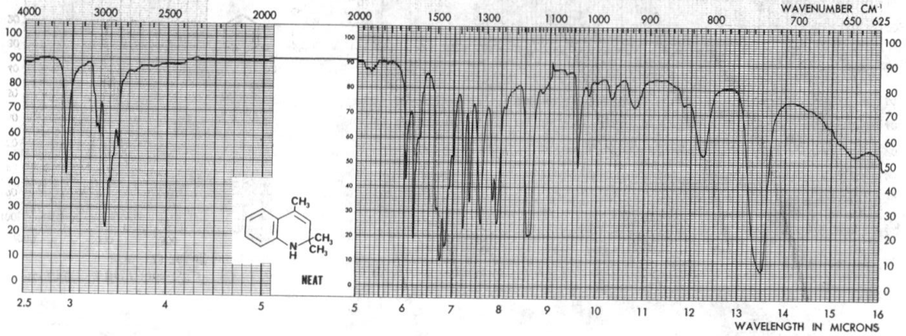

NEAT

B

19,636-3
6-Ethoxy-1,2,3,4-tetrahydro-2,2,4-trimethylquinoline, 97%
FW 219.33 mp 39-43° bp 122°/2mm. Disp. C

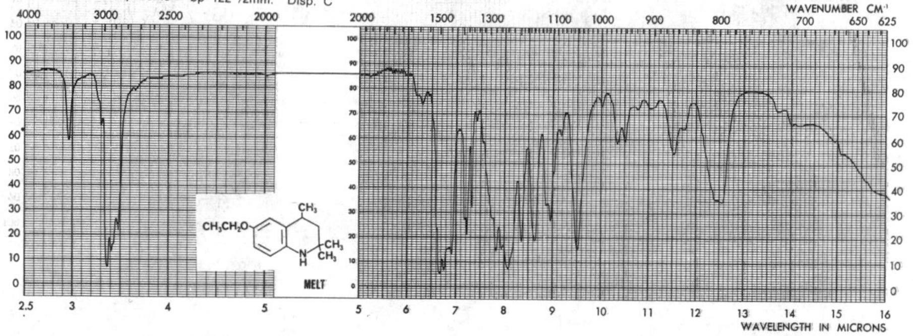

MELT

C

J100-1 **Julolidine** (2,3,6,7-tetrahydro-1H,5H-benzo[ij]quinolizine)
M.W. 173.26 m.p. 35-38°

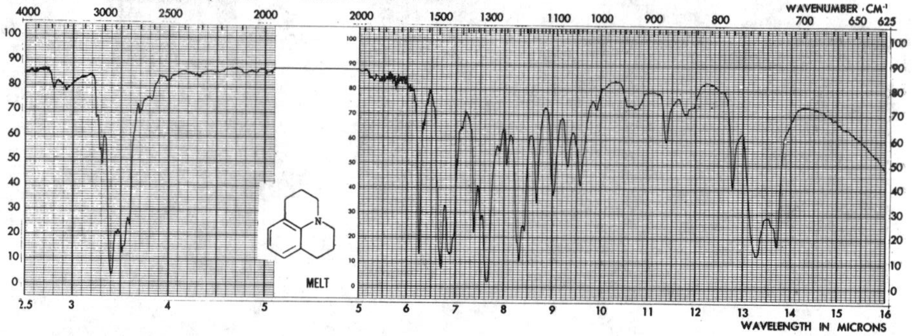

MELT

D

T1300-5 **1,2,3,4-Tetrahydroisoquinoline**
M.W. 133.19 n_D^{20} 1.5668 b.p. 232-233°

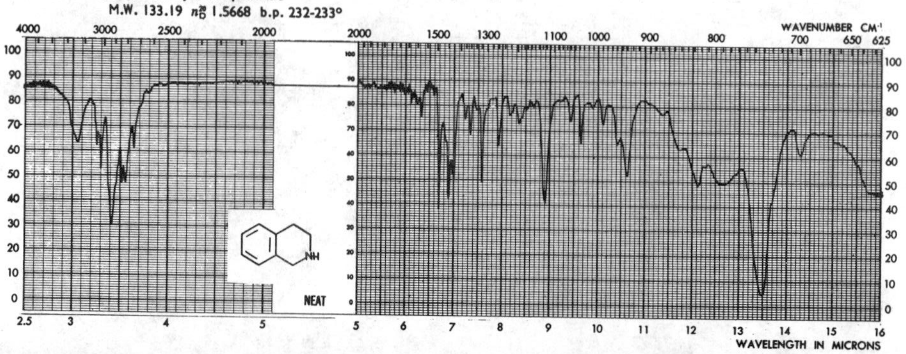

NEAT

E

13,089-3 **Acridan**
M.W. 181.24 m.p. 168-172°

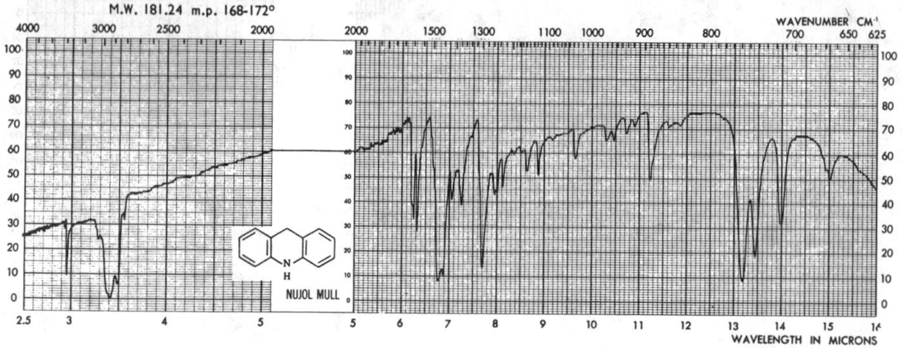

NUJOL MULL

F

I-130-8 **Iminodibenzyl** (10,11-dihydro-5H-dibenz[b,f]azepine)
M.W. 195.27 m.p. 105-108°

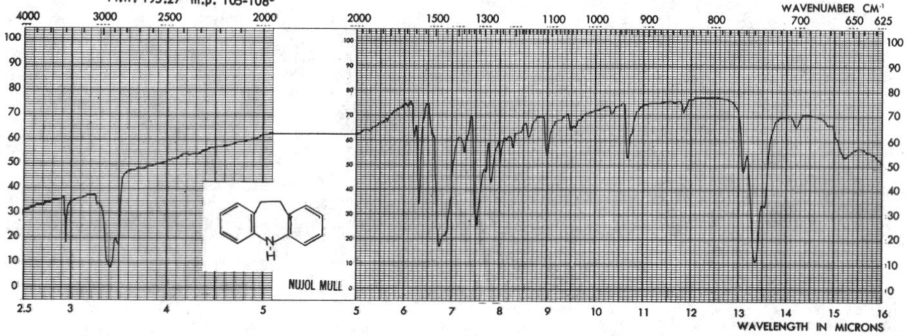

NUJOL MULL

G

H1565-9 **Homoacridan** (5,6-dihydro-11H-dibenz[b,e]azepine)
M.W. 195.25 m.p. 129-132°

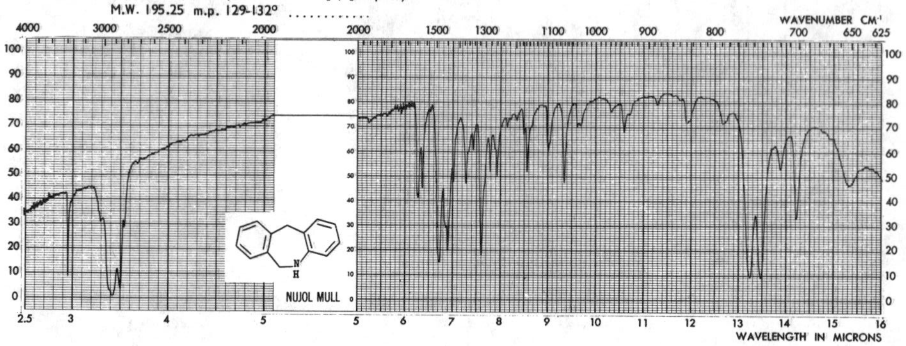

NUJOL MULL

H

18,761-5
5,6,11,12-Tetrahydrodibenz[b,f]azocine
A medicinal building block

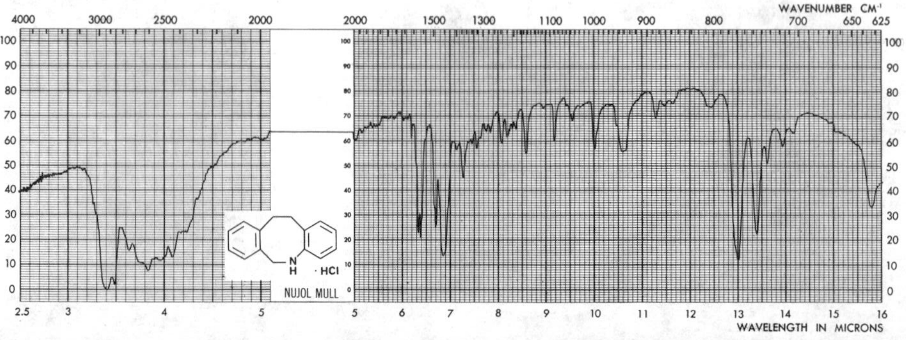

NUJOL MULL

A

P1485-8 Phenoxazine
M.W. 183.21 m.p. 152-155°

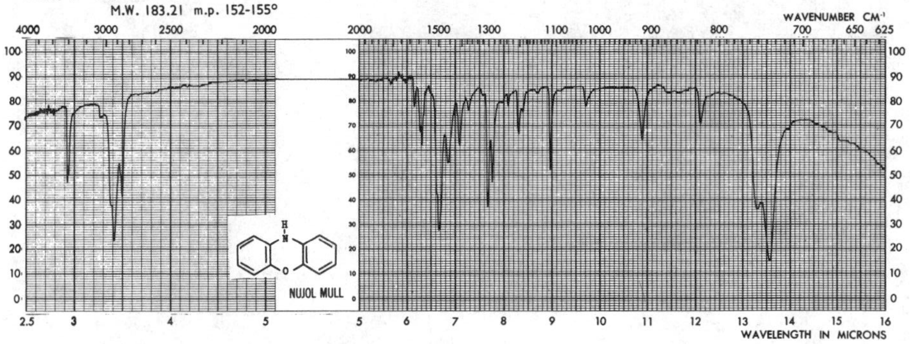

NUJOL MULL

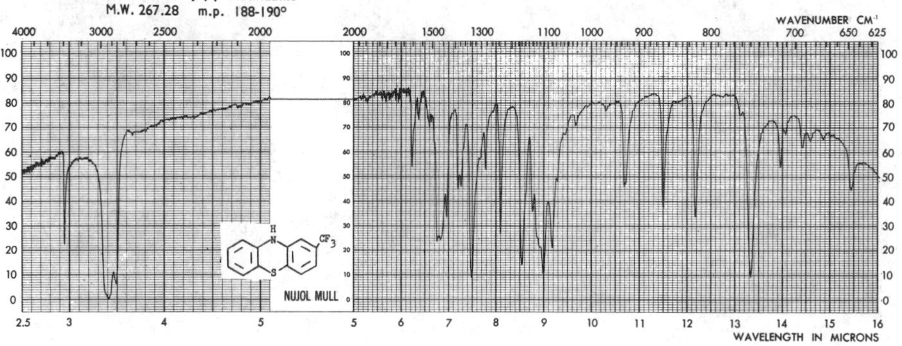

B

P1483-1 Phenothiazine
M.W. 199.28 m.p. 180-185°

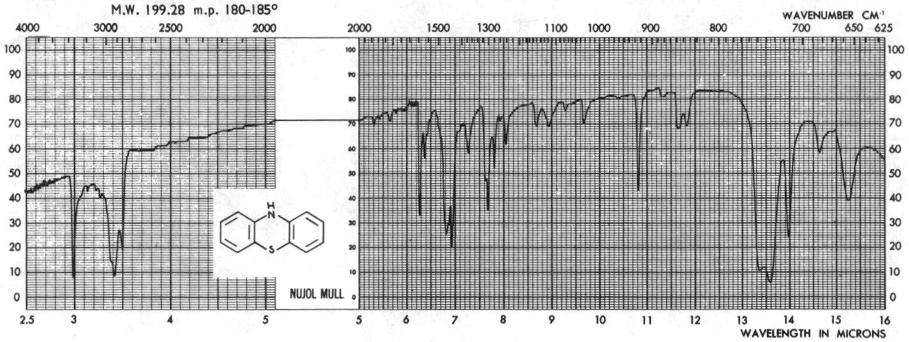

NUJOL MULL

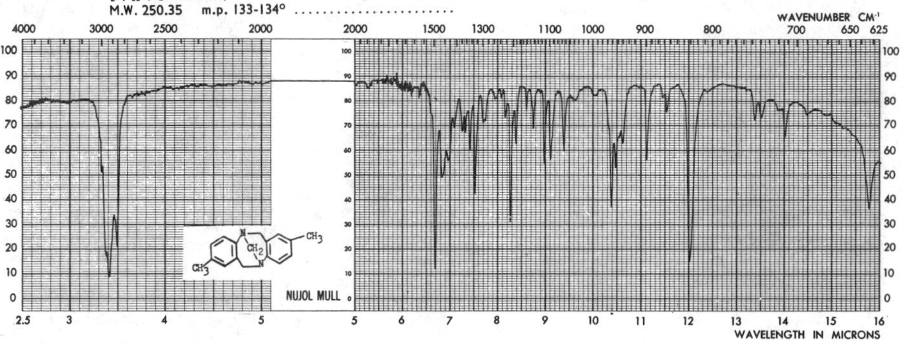

C

C6300-6 2-Chlorophenothiazine
M.W. 233.72 m.p. 196-199° (dec.)

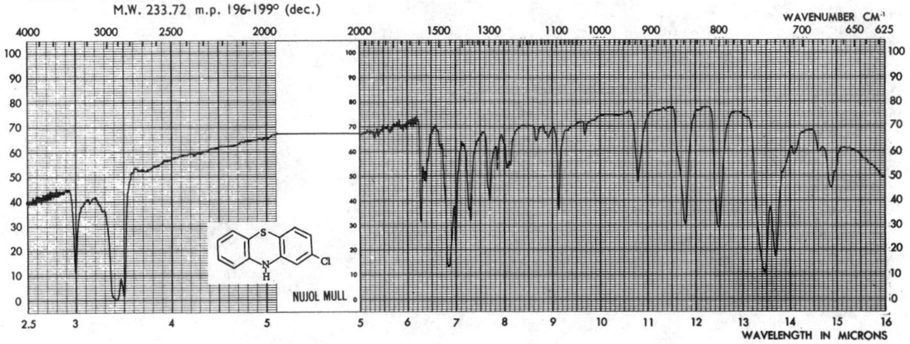

NUJOL MULL

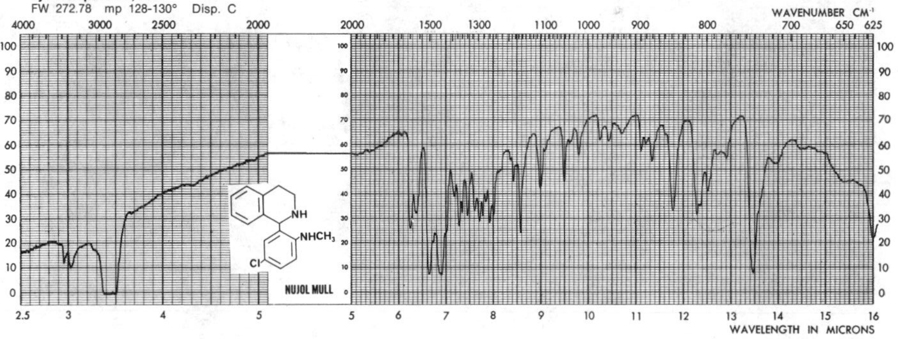

D

M1870-1 2-Methoxyphenothiazine
M.W. 229.30 m.p. 184-187°

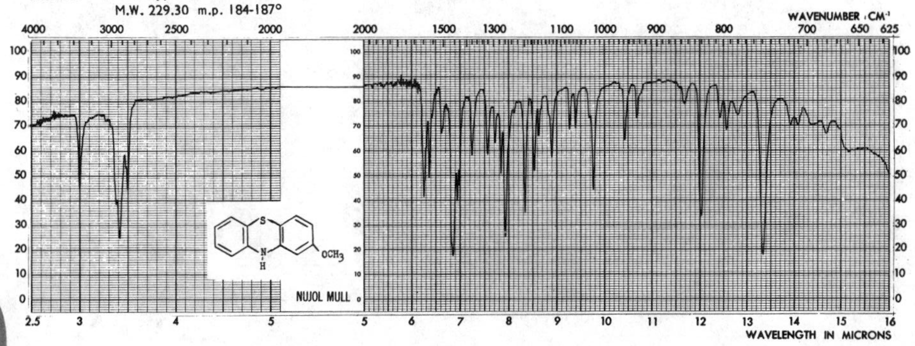

NUJOL MULL

E

T6345-2 2-(Trifluoromethyl)-phenothiazine
M.W. 267.28 m.p. 188-190°

NUJOL MULL

F

13,222-5 Troger's Base (2,8-dimethyl-6H,12H-5,11-methanodibenzo-[b,f][1,5]diazocine)
M.W. 250.35 m.p. 133-134° ....

NUJOL MULL

G

21,412-4
dl-1-[5-Chloro-2-(methylamino)phenyl]-1,2,3,4-tetra-hydroisoquinoline, 97%
FW 272.78 mp 128-130° Disp. C

NUJOL MULL

H

21,434-5
l-1-[5-Chloro-2-(methylamino)phenyl]-1,2,3,4-tetra-hydroisoquinoline *l*-tartrate, 98%
FW 695.65 mp 212° (dec.)
$[\alpha]^{22}$ -25° (c=2, 6N HCl) Disp. C

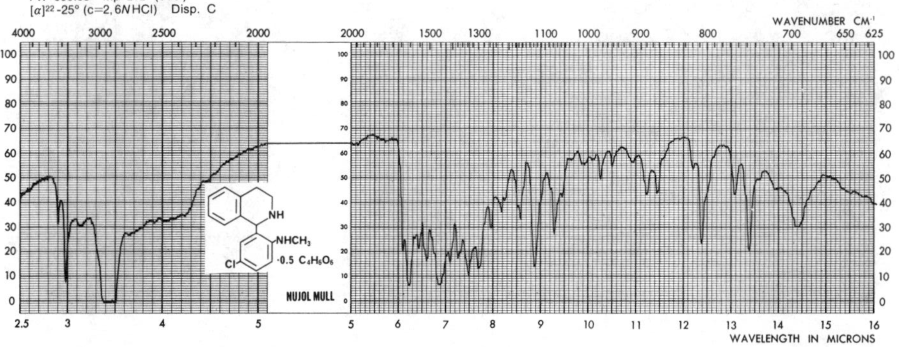

NUJOL MULL

ALDRICH ®

A

19,597-9
2-Methyl-1,2,3,4-tetrahydro-6,7-isoquinolinediol hydrochloride, 98%
FW 215.68 mp 255° (dec.) *Beil.* **21**(1),239
Disp. C

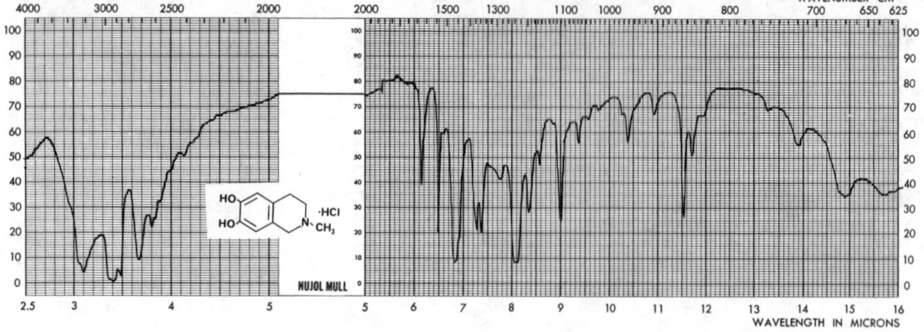

NUJOL MULL

B

S90-9 **Salsolidine hydrochloride dihydrate**
M.W. 279.77 m.p. 236-238°

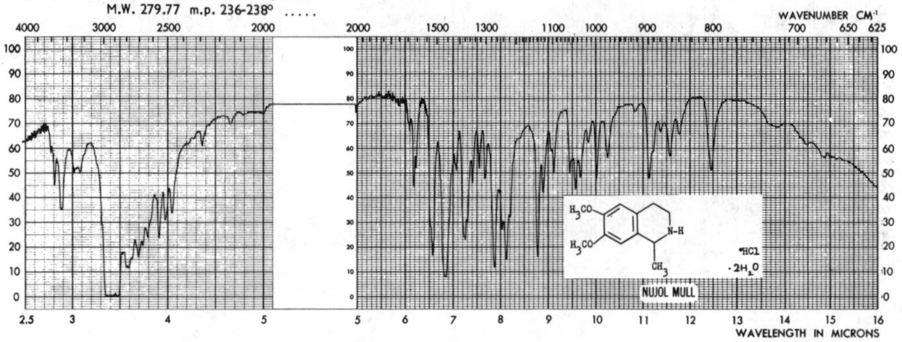

NUJOL MULL

C

12,208-4 **8-Methoxy-*z*-methyl-6,7-methylenedioxy-1,2,3,4-tetrahydroisoquinoline hydrobromide**
M.W. 302.18 m.p. 229-231°

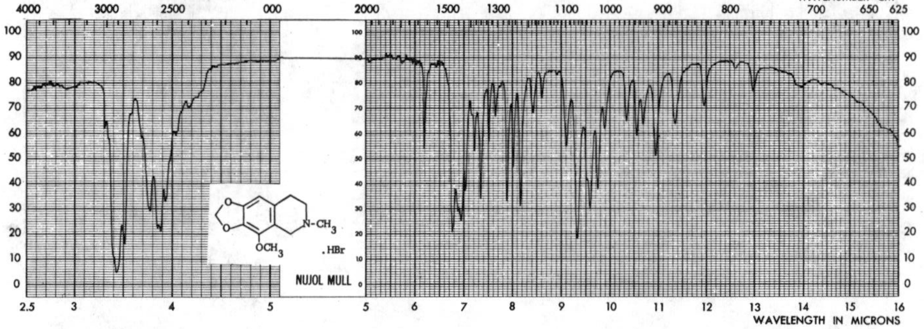

NUJOL MULL

D

14,776-1 **Salsolinol hydrobromide**
M.W. 260.14 m.p. 179-184°

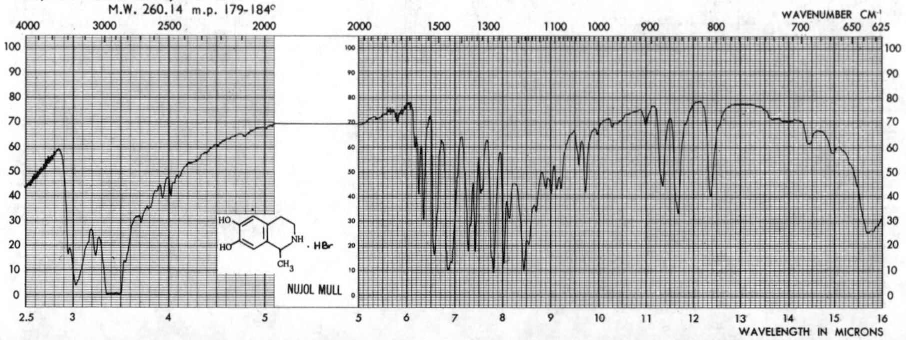

NUJOL MULL

E

11,577-0 **DL-Laudanosoline hydrobromide trihydrate**
M.W. 436.31 m.p. 232-234°

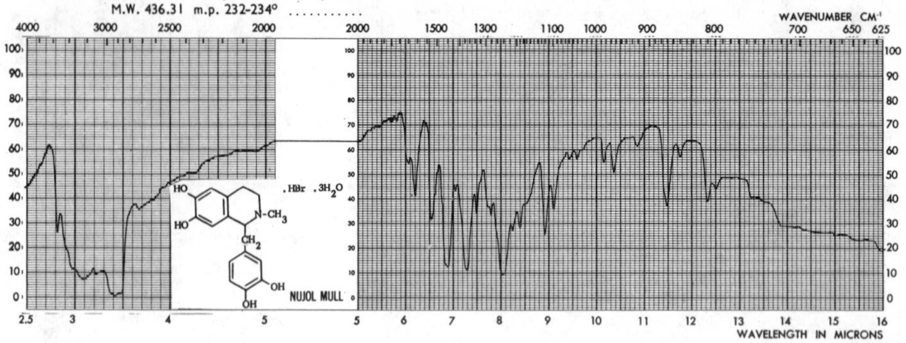

NUJOL MULL

F

10,467-1 **DL-Laudanosine**
M.W. 357.45 m.p. 116-118°

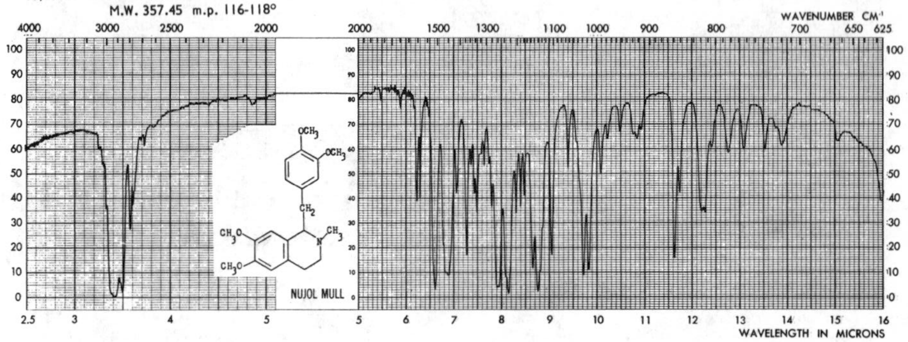

NUJOL MULL

G

85,520-0
***dl*-Tetrahydropalmatine hemihydrochloride**, 90%
M.W. 373.67 m.p. 210° (dec.)

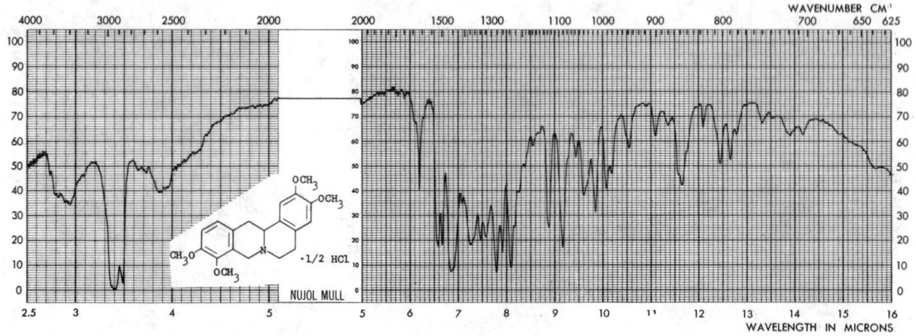

NUJOL MULL

H

85,519-7
***d*-Tetrahydropalmatine hydrochloride**, 95%
M.W. 391.9 m.p. 224° (dec.)

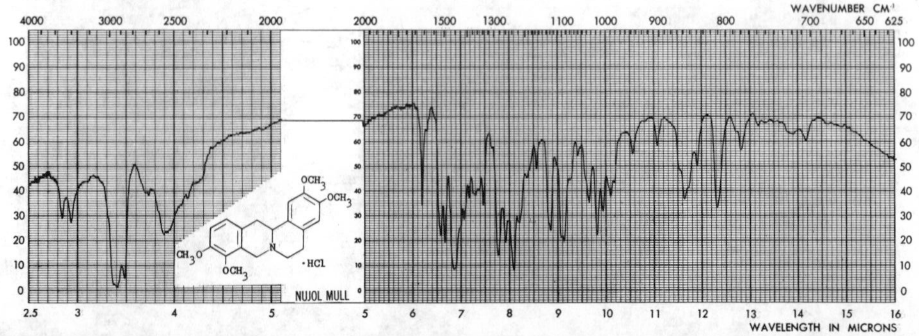

NUJOL MULL

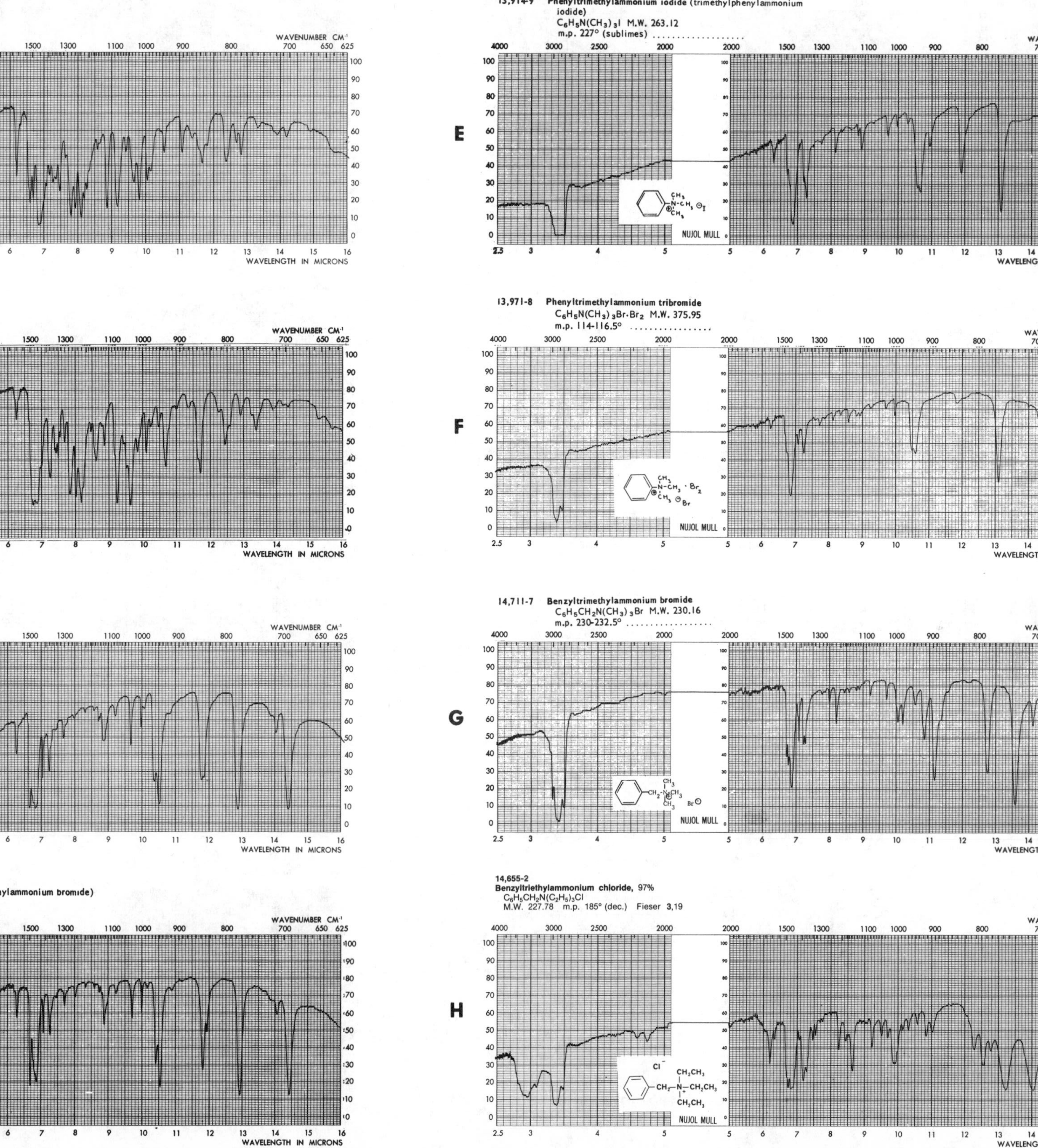

A 85,521-9
l-Tetrahydropalmatine hydrochloride, 85%
M.W. 391.9 m.p. 222° (dec.) Beil. 21,216

B 11,939-3 9-Desoxyberberine, tech.
M.W. 337.38 m.p. 158-163°

C 19,916-8
Phenyltrimethylammonium chloride, 98+% (trimethylphenylammonium chloride)
$C_6H_5N(CH_3)_3Cl$ FW 171.67 mp 237° (sublimes)
Beil. 12,158 Disp. C

D 13,532-1 Phenyltrimethylammonium bromide (trimethylphenylammonium bromide)
$C_6H_5N(CH_3)_3Br$ M.W. 216.13
m.p. 208° (dec.)

E 13,914-9 Phenyltrimethylammonium iodide (trimethylphenylammonium iodide)
$C_6H_5N(CH_3)_3I$ M.W. 263.12
m.p. 227° (sublimes)

F 13,971-8 Phenyltrimethylammonium tribromide
$C_6H_5N(CH_3)_3Br{\cdot}Br_2$ M.W. 375.95
m.p. 114-116.5°

G 14,711-7 Benzyltrimethylammonium bromide
$C_6H_5CH_2N(CH_3)_3Br$ M.W. 230.16
m.p. 230-232.5°

H 14,655-2
Benzyltriethylammonium chloride, 97%
$C_6H_5CH_2N(C_2H_5)_3Cl$
M.W. 227.78 m.p. 185° (dec.) Fieser 3,19

ALDRICH

A

14,712-5 **Benzyltriethylammonium bromide**
$C_6H_5CH_2N(C_2H_5)_3Br$ M.W. 272.24
m.p. 194° (dec.)

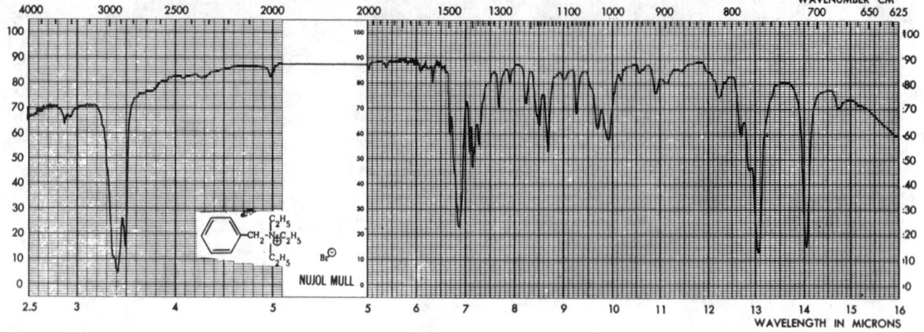

NUJOL MULL

B

19,377-1
Benzyltributylammonium chloride, 98%
$C_6H_5CH_2N[(CH_2)_3CH_3]_3Cl$ FW 312.94
mp 155° (dec.) *Fieser* 6,41 Disp. C

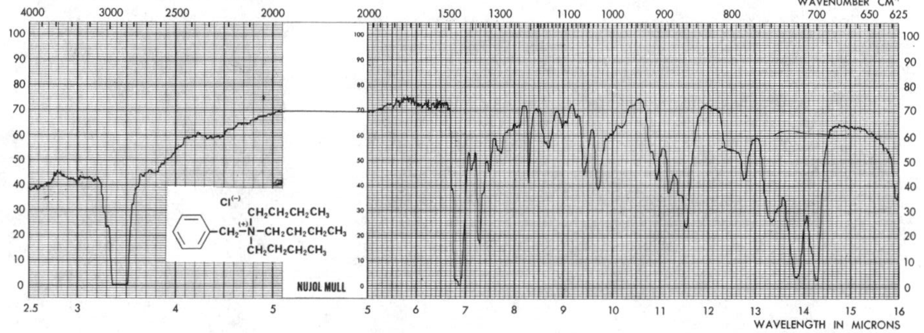

NUJOL MULL

C

B3260-2 **N-Benzyltrimethylammonium hydroxide** (Triton B) (40% in methanol)
$C_6H_5CH_2N(CH_3)_3OH$ M.W. 167.25 (dry basis)

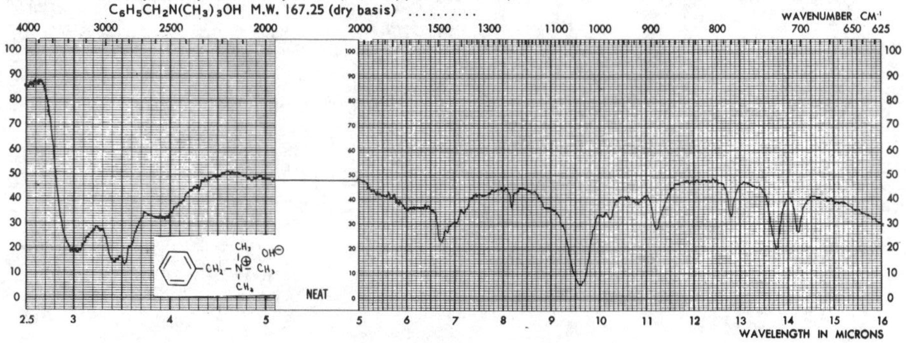

NEAT

D

12,895-3 **Dibenzyldimethylammonium chloride monohydrate, puriss.**
$(C_6H_5CH_2)_2N(CH_3)_2Cl \cdot H_2O$ M.W. 279.81
m.p. 93.5-97°

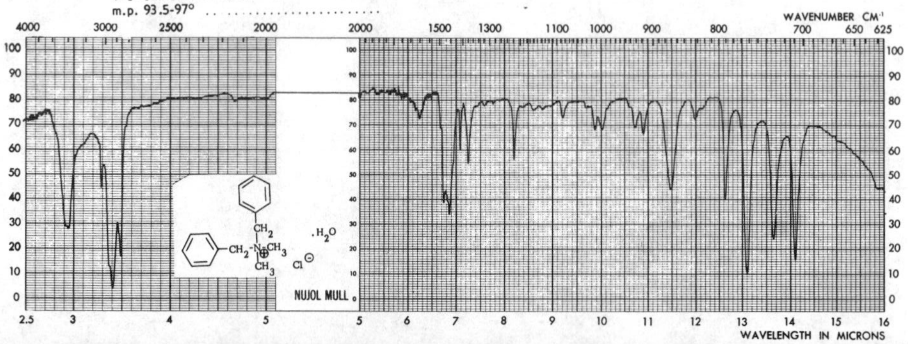

NUJOL MULL

E

11,656-4 **O-Methylcandicine iodide** [(p-methoxyphenethyl)-trimethylammonium iodide]
$CH_3OC_6H_4CH_2CH_2N(CH_3)_3I$ M.W. 337.20 m.p. 211-213°

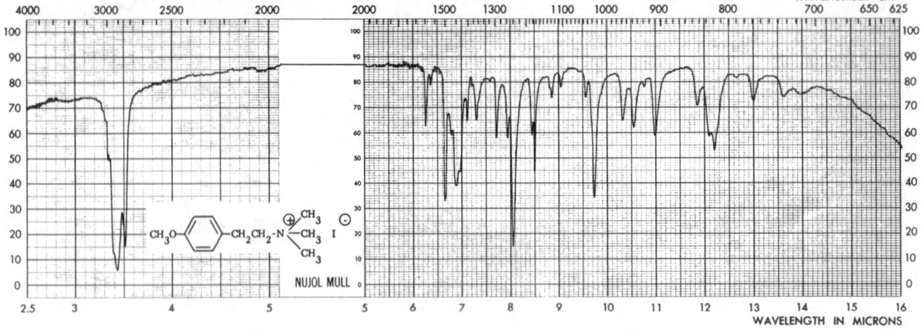

NUJOL MULL

F

11,792-7 **Candicine iodide** [(p-hydroxyphenethyl)-trimethylammonium iodide]
$HOC_6H_4CH_2CH_2N(CH_3)_3I$ M.W. 307.18 m.p. 229-231°

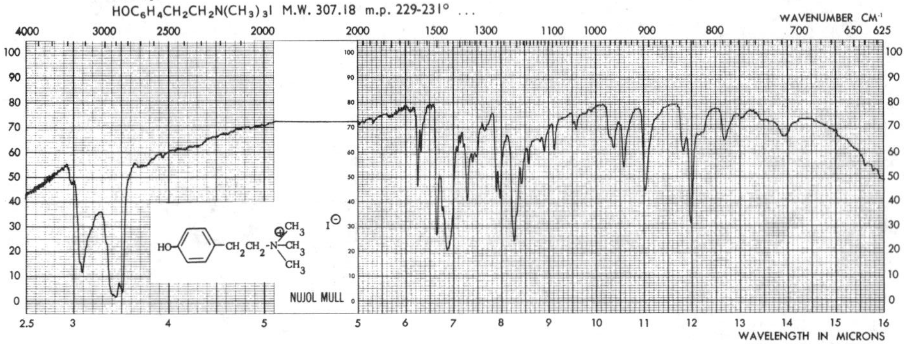

NUJOL MULL

G

14,802-4 [1-(3,4-Dichlorophenyl)-1-hydroxyethyl]dimethylisopropylammonium iodide (DDCI)
$Cl_2C_6H_3C(CH_3)(OH)N(CH_3)_2CH(CH_3)_2I$ M.W. 404.12
m.p. 130-132°

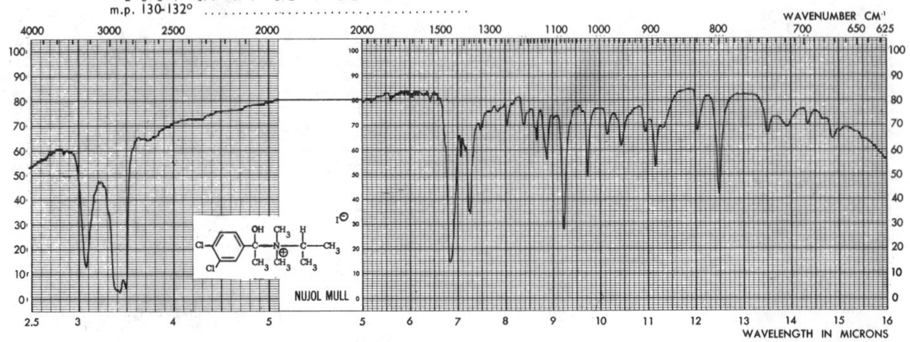

NUJOL MULL

H

B470-8 **Benzethonium chloride monohydrate**
M.W. 466.11

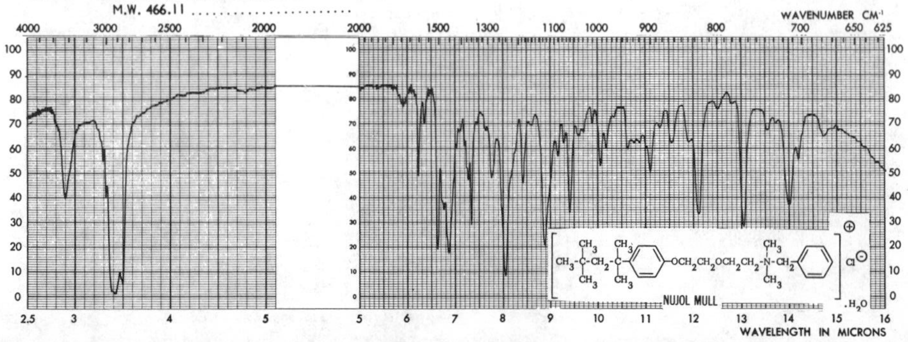

NUJOL MULL

A

11,603-3 **Hemicholinium-15** (4,4-dimethyl-2-hydroxy-2-phenylmorpholinium bromide)
M.W. 288.19 m.p. 189-191° ....
NUJOL MULL

B

D17,750-4 **1,1-Dimethyl-4-phenylpiperazinium iodide** (DMPP)
M.W. 318.20 m.p. 234-238° ....
NUJOL MULL

C

H30-3 **Hemicholinium-3** [2,2'-(4,4'-biphenylene)-bis-(2-hydroxy-4,4-dimethylmorpholinium bromide)]
M.W. 574.36 m.p. 215-218° ....
NUJOL MULL

D

22,493-6
4-Aminobenzotrifluoride, 99% (α,α,α-trifluoro-*p*-toluidine)
$H_2NC_6H_4CF_3$ FW 161.13 bp 83°/12mm.
n_D^{20} 1.4840 d 1.283 *Beil.* **12**(3),2151 Disp. C
NEAT

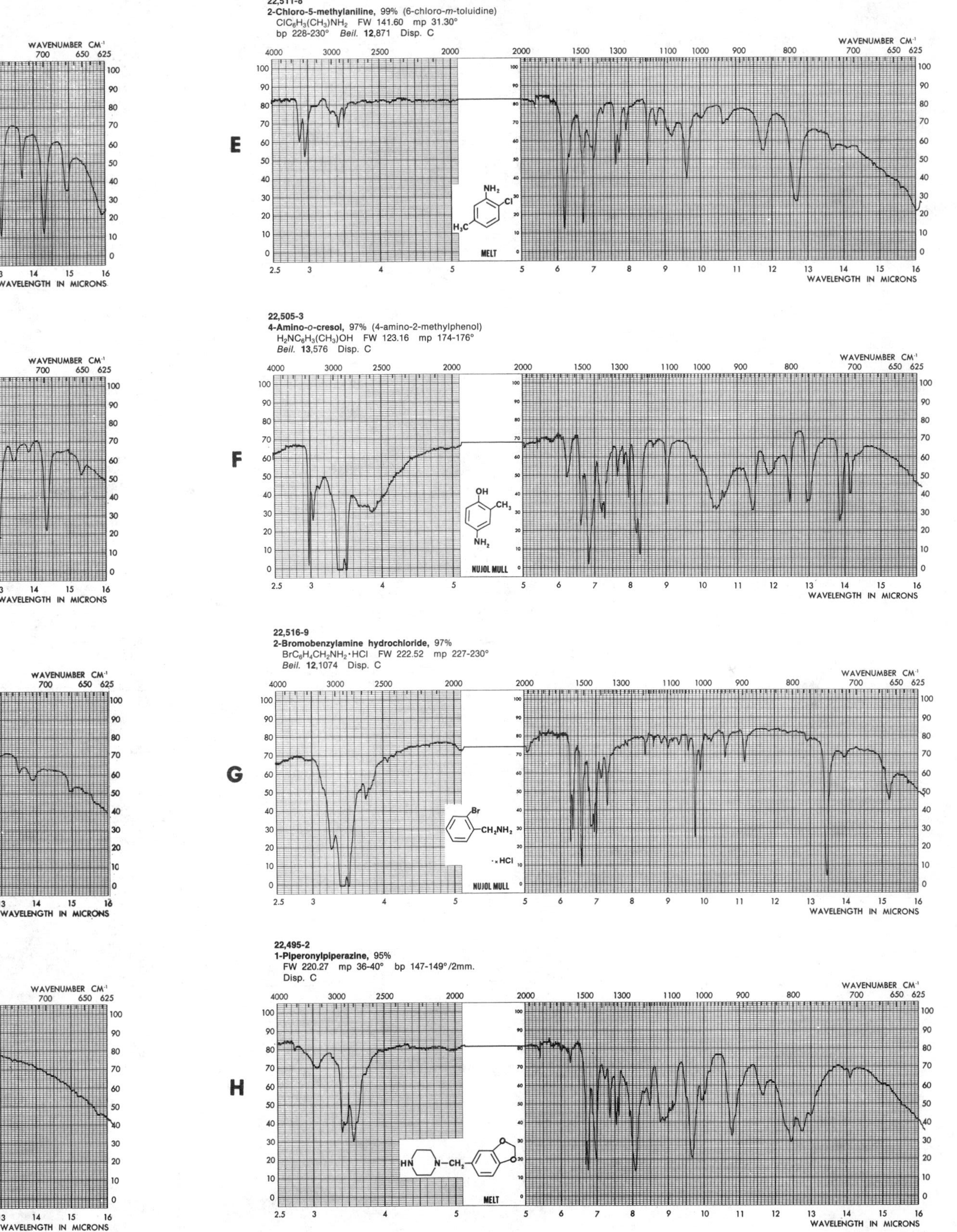

E

22,511-8
2-Chloro-5-methylaniline, 99% (6-chloro-*m*-toluidine)
$ClC_6H_3(CH_3)NH_2$ FW 141.60 mp 31.30°
bp 228-230° *Beil.* **12**,871 Disp. C
MELT

F

22,505-3
4-Amino-*o*-cresol, 97% (4-amino-2-methylphenol)
$H_2NC_6H_3(CH_3)OH$ FW 123.16 mp 174-176°
Beil. **13**,576 Disp. C
NUJOL MULL

G

22,516-9
2-Bromobenzylamine hydrochloride, 97%
$BrC_6H_4CH_2NH_2 \cdot HCl$ FW 222.52 mp 227-230°
Beil. **12**,1074 Disp. C
NUJOL MULL

H

22,495-2
1-Piperonylpiperazine, 95%
FW 220.27 mp 36-40° bp 147-149°/2mm.
Disp. C
MELT

ALDRICH

AROMATIC NITRO AND NITROSO COMPOUNDS

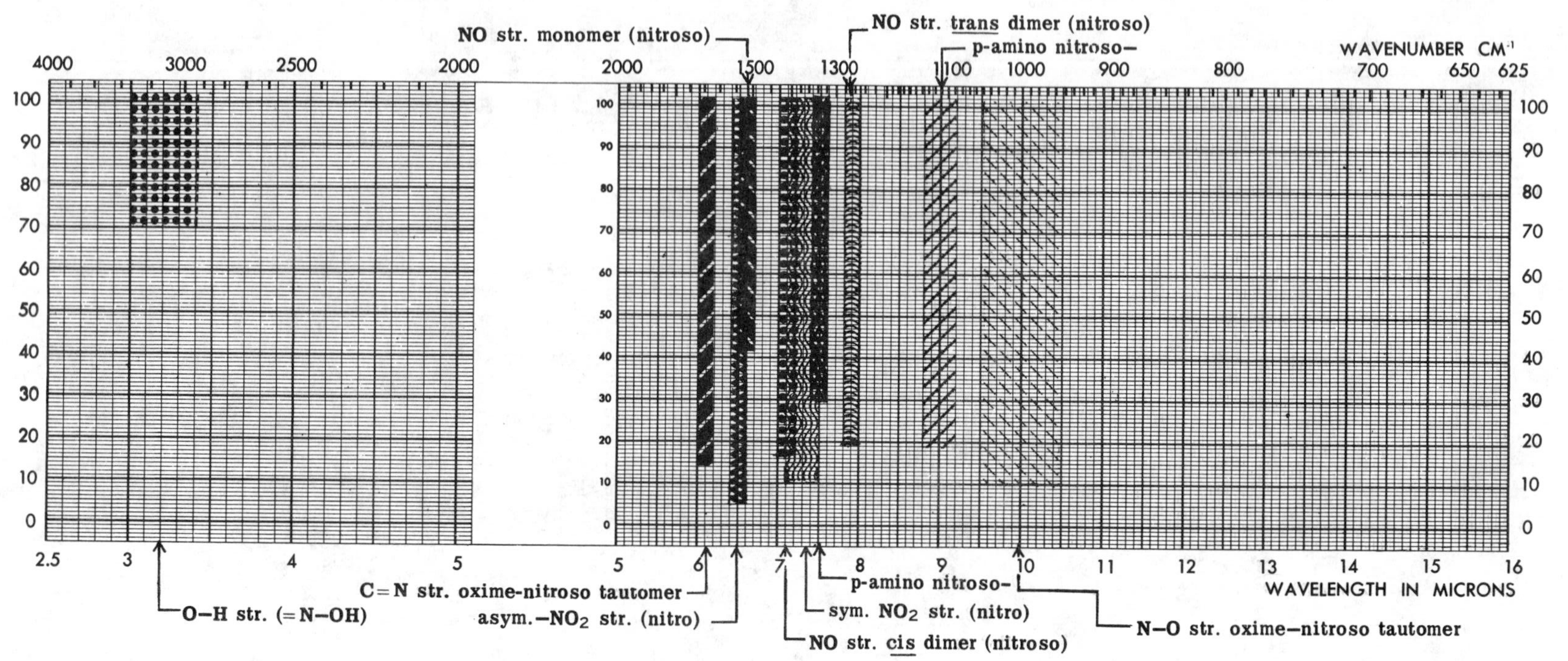

1.) Nitroso 801A-802A
2.) Arylnitroalkenes .. 803B-803E
3.) Ring Nitro 803F-845B

All but two of the nitroso compounds in this section have either an amino or hydroxy group in the ortho or para position. The two para-amino spectra (801C and D) display strong absorptions near 7.5 and 9 μ (1335 and 1110 cm^{-1}). The ortho or para-hydroxy nitroso compounds are usually in the tautomeric benzoquinone monoxime configuration:

or

In these cases the C=N and C=O bands absorb near 6.1 and 6.2 μ (1640 and 1615 cm^{-1}). The hydroxyl group of the oxime absorbs near 3.2 μ (3125 cm^{-1}) along with the N–O stretch vibration between 9.5 and 10.5 μ (1055 – 950 cm^{-1}).

The two normal nitroso spectra (801A and B) are run as mulls and therefore exhibit the absorptions of the nitroso dimer. In spectrum 801A, the dimer is in the *cis* form and absorbs at 7.1 μ

cis

trans

(1410 cm^{-1}). The *trans* form, spectrum 801B, absorbs strongly at 7.9 μ (1265 cm^{-1}). Monomeric aromatic nitroso compounds display their N=O stretch absorption near 6.6 μ (1515 cm^{-1}).

The aromatic nitro group has two strong bands near 6.5 μ (1540 cm^{-1}), asymmetric stretch, and 7.4 μ (1350 cm^{-1}), symmetric stretch. The 7.4 μ (1350 cm^{-1}) band is generally the weaker. When an amino group is situated para to the nitro function, the 7.4 μ (1350 cm^{-1}) band is shifted to 7.6 μ (1315 cm^{-1}), while in the ortho position, the shift is to near 8 μ (1250 cm^{-1}). In both cases, the band is very strong. The relative strength of the nitro bands compared to bands of other functional groups should be carefully noted as they appear in the same molecule.

The substitution bands between 11 and 15 μ (910 – 665 cm^{-1}) are strongly altered by the presence of the nitro group on the ring. Prediction as to band position in any of the various substitution positions is extremely difficult. In general, bands do appear in the approximate vicinity of the expected position; however, numerous other bands accompany these absorptions. One of these bands (medium to strong) usually appears near 13.5 μ (740 cm^{-1}).

The C–H stretch at 3.25 μ (3075 cm^{-1}) is accompanied by a weaker band near 3.5 μ (2855 cm^{-1}). This can be seen in spectra 803H and 804C—805B where mineral oil does not mask the absorption.

A

N2460-9 **Nitrosobenzene**
C_6H_5NO M.W. 107.11
m.p. 67-69°

NUJOL MULL

B

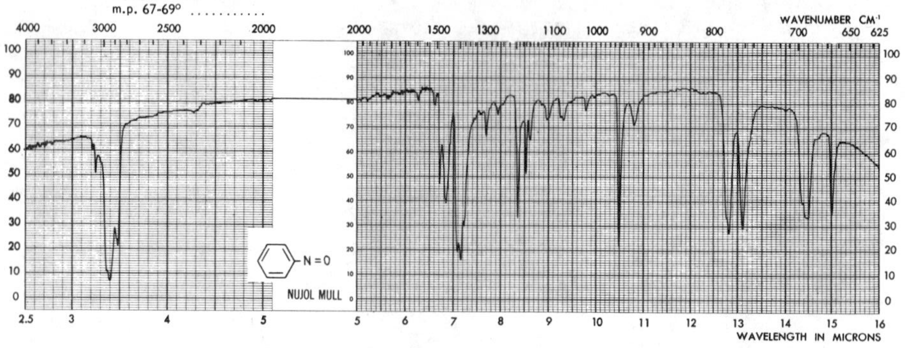

N2640-7 **2-Nitrosotoluene**
$CH_3C_6H_4NO$ M.W. 121.14 m.p. 72-75°

NUJOL MULL

C

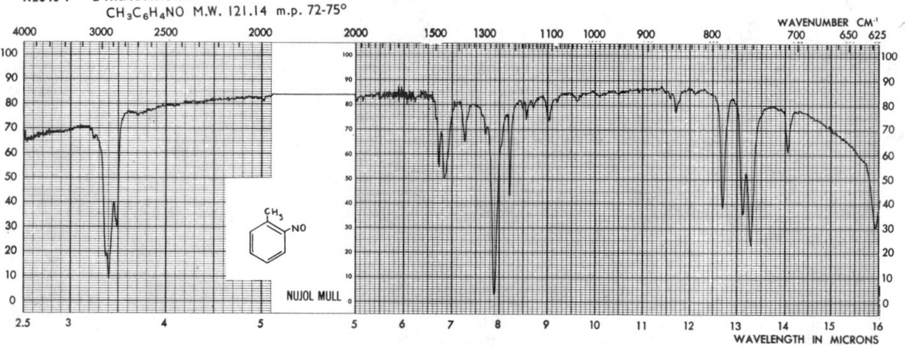

D17,240-5 **N,N-Dimethyl-4-nitrosoaniline** (4-nitroso-N,N-dimethylaniline)
$ONC_6H_4N(CH_3)_2$ M.W. 150.18
m.p. 85-86°

NUJOL MULL

D

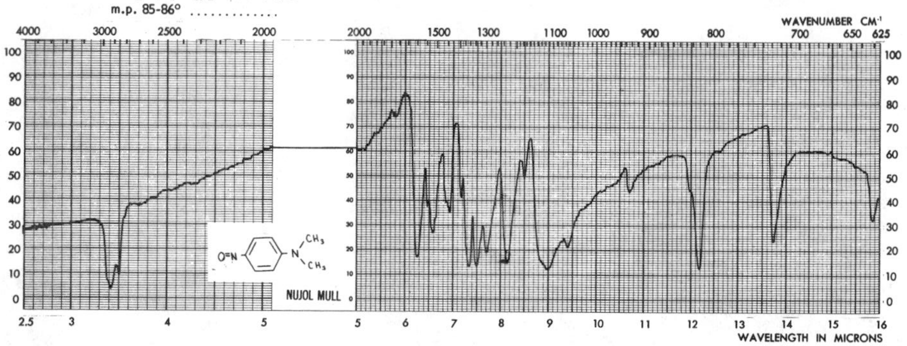

13,473-2 **N,N-Diethyl-4-nitrosoaniline** (4-nitroso-N,N-diethylaniline)
$ONC_6H_4N(C_2H_5)_2$ M.W. 178.24
m.p. 85-86°

NUJOL MULL

E

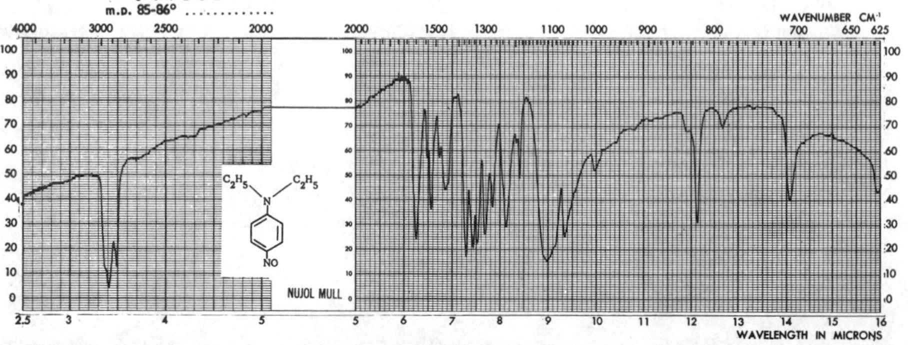

22,378-6
2,4,6-Tri-*tert*-butylnitrosobenzene, 99%
$[(CH_3)_3C]_3C_6H_2NO$ FW 275.44 mp 172-173°
Disp. C

NUJOL MULL

F

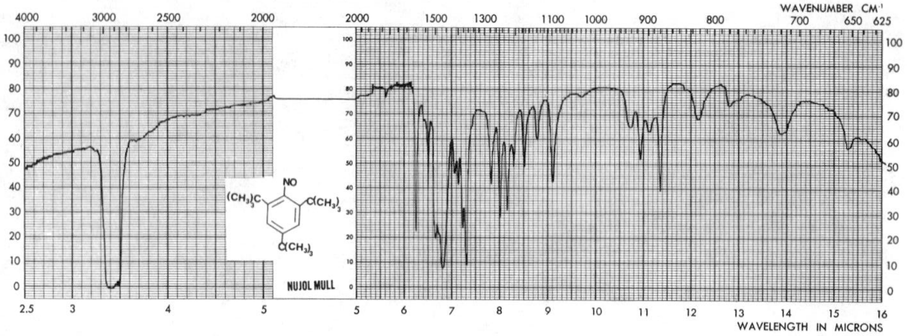

H1212-9 **Hexanitrosobenzene**
$C_6(NO)_6$ M.W. 252.11 m.p. 198-200° (dec.,

NUJOL MULL

G

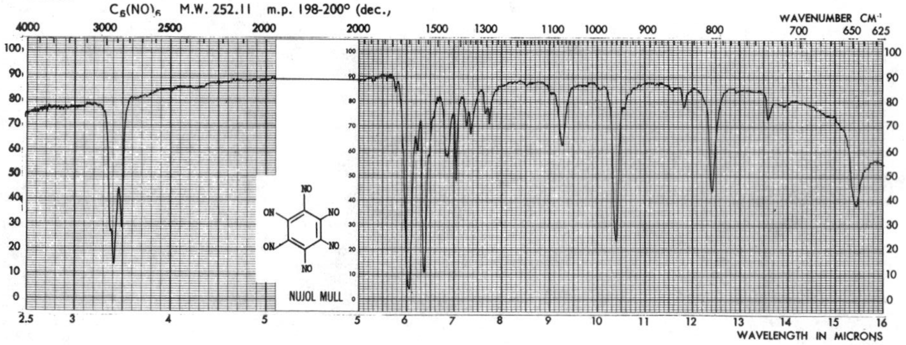

11,709-9 **p-Nitrosophenol**
ONC_6H_4OH M.W. 123.11
m.p. 132-134° (dec.)

NUJOL MULL

H

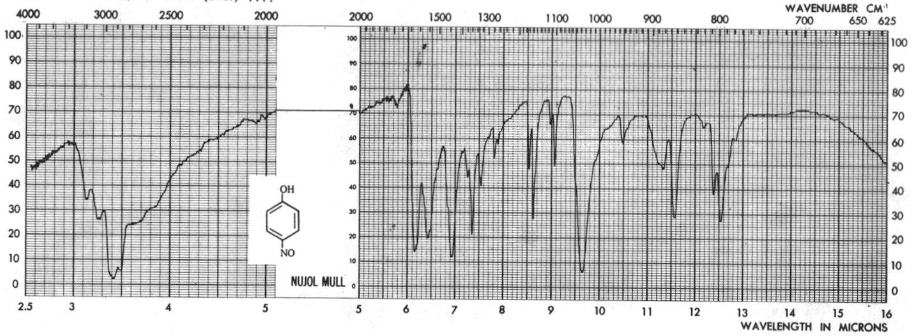

M6420-7 **3-Methyl-4-nitrosophenol** (4-nitroso-m-cresol), tech.
$CH_3C_6H_3(NO)OH$ M.W. 137.14 m.p. 144-146°

NUJOL MULL

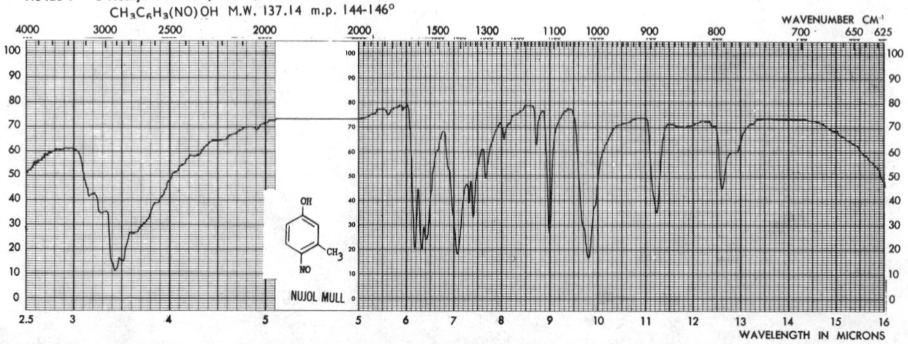

A

10,956-8 2-Methyl-4-nitrosophenol (4-nitroso-o-cresol), tech.
$CH_3C_6H_3(NO)OH$ M.W. 137.14
m.p. 123-125° (dec.)

NUJOL MULL

B

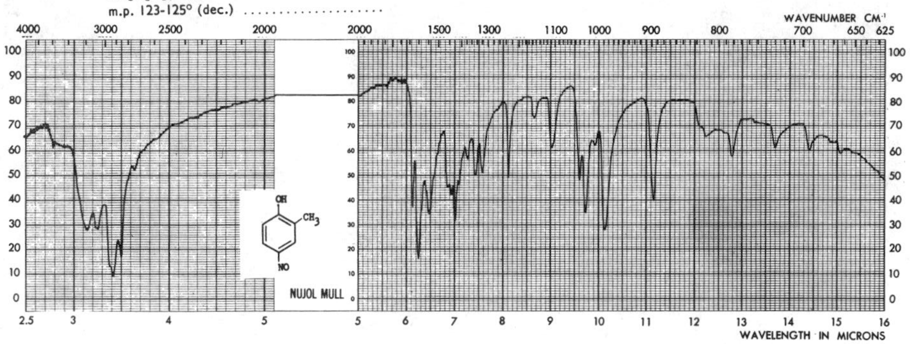

13,272-1 2,6-Dimethyl-4-nitrosophenol
$ONC_6H_2(CH_3)_2OH$ M.W. 151.17 (dry)
m.p. 166-168° (dec.)

NUJOL MULL

C

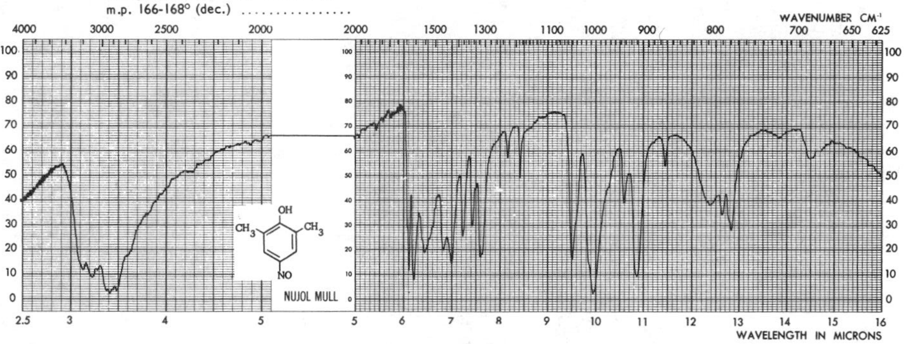

14,991-8 2,6-Di-tert.-butyl-4-nitrosophenol
$ONC_6H_2[C(CH_3)_3]_2OH$ M.W. 235.33
m.p. 214-216° (dec.)

NUJOL MULL

D

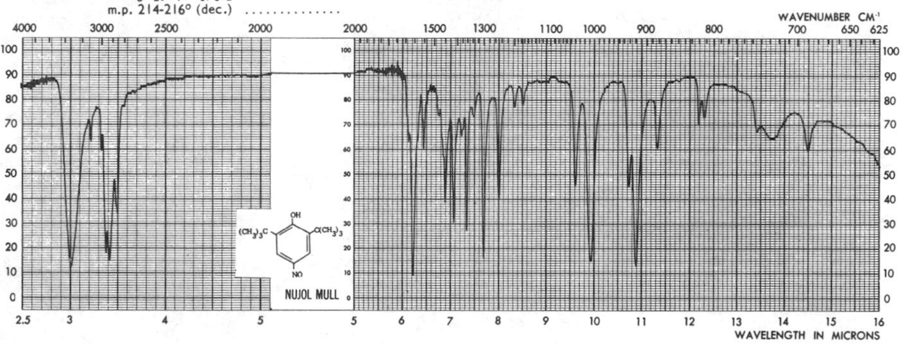

12,224-6 6-Chloro-4-nitroso-o-cresol, tech.
$ClC_6H_2(NO)(CH_3)OH$ M.W. 171.58 (dry)

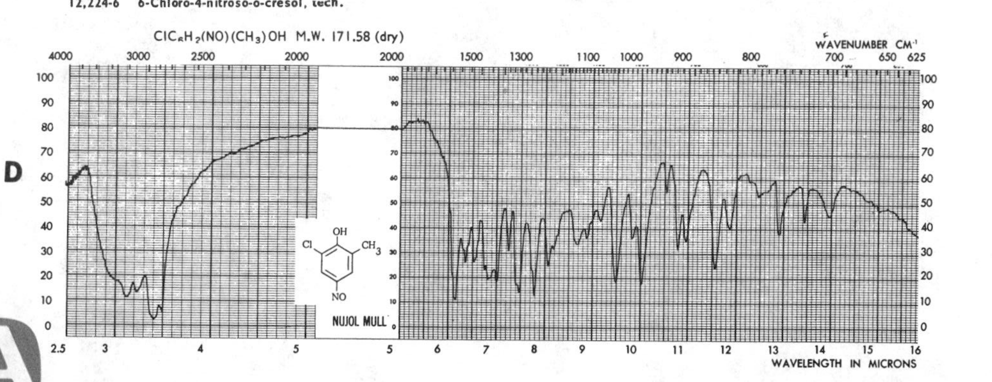

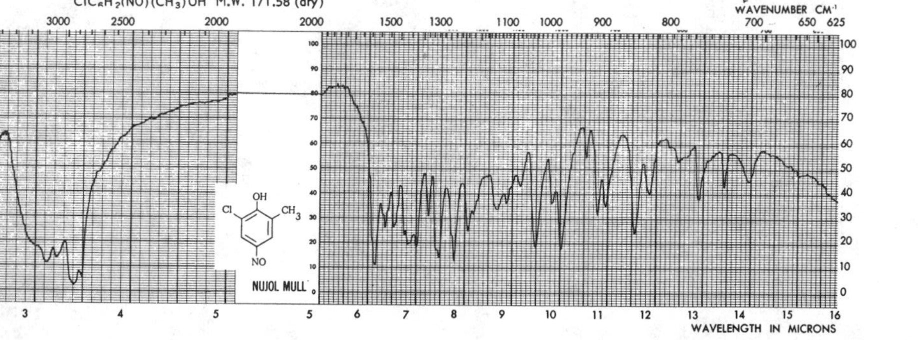

NUJOL MULL

E

12,223-8 2-Chloro-4-nitrosophenol, moist (contains approx. 50% water)
$ClC_6H_3(NO)OH$ M.W. 157.56 (dry)

NUJOL MULL

F

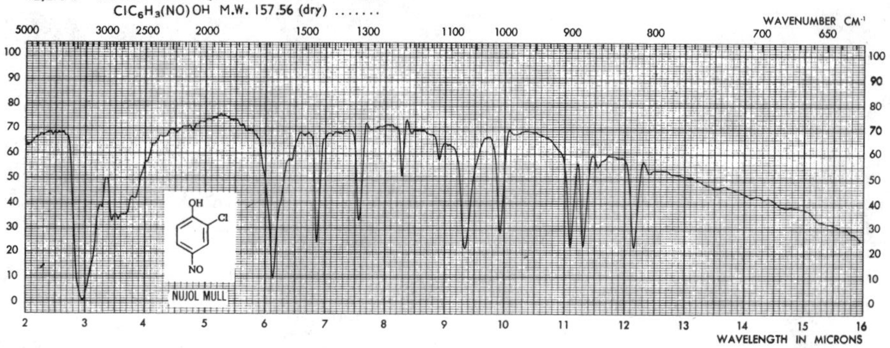

11,469-3 1-Nitroso-2-naphthol
$ONC_{10}H_6OH$ M.W. 173.17 m.p. 106-108°

NUJOL MULL

G

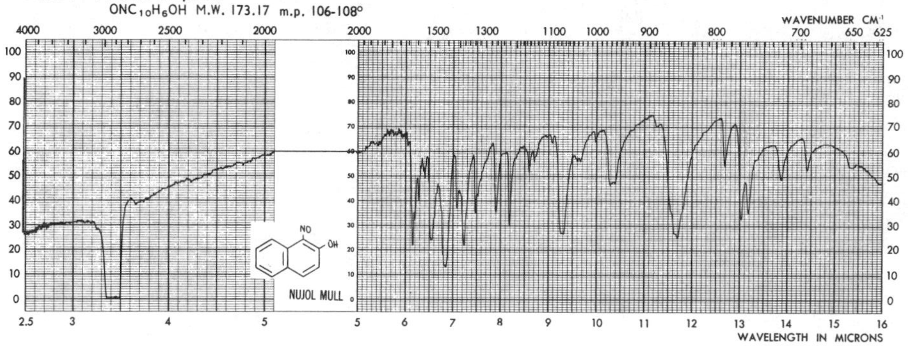

11,470-7 2-Nitroso-1-naphthol
$ONC_{10}H_6OH$ M.W. 173.17 m.p. 165° (dec.)

NUJOL MULL

H

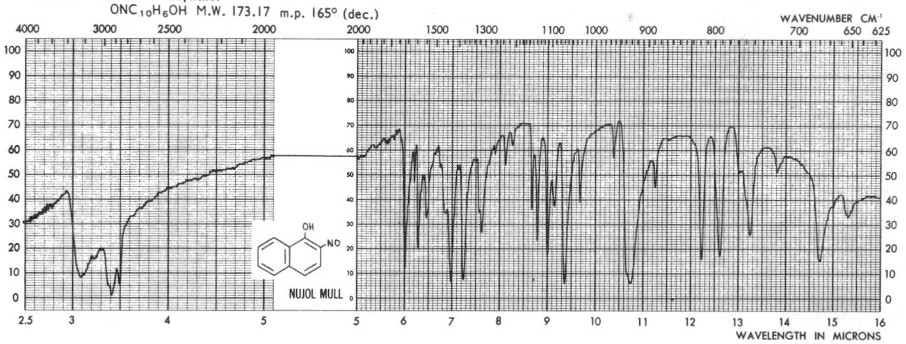

14,646-3 2,4-Dinitroso-1,3-naphthalenediol tetrahydrate
$(ON)_2C_{10}H_4(OH)_2 \cdot 4H_2O$ M.W. 290.23
m.p. 117-120°

NUJOL MULL

ALDRICH

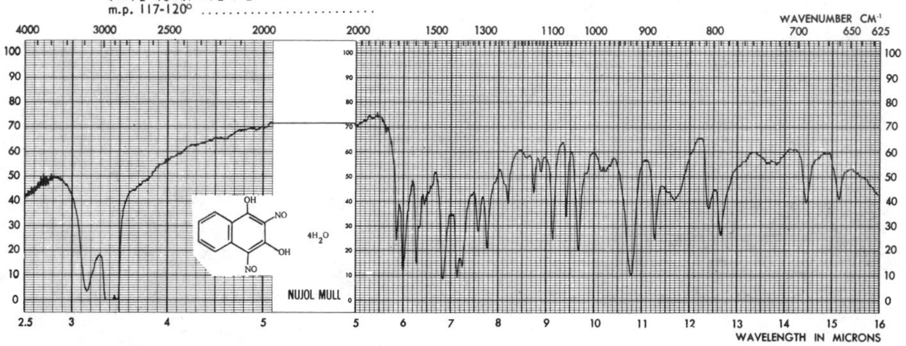

A

20,688-1
Cupferron, A.C.S. reagent
$C_6H_5N(NO)ONH_4$ FW 155.16 mp 154° (dec.)
Beil. **16**(1),395 Disp. C

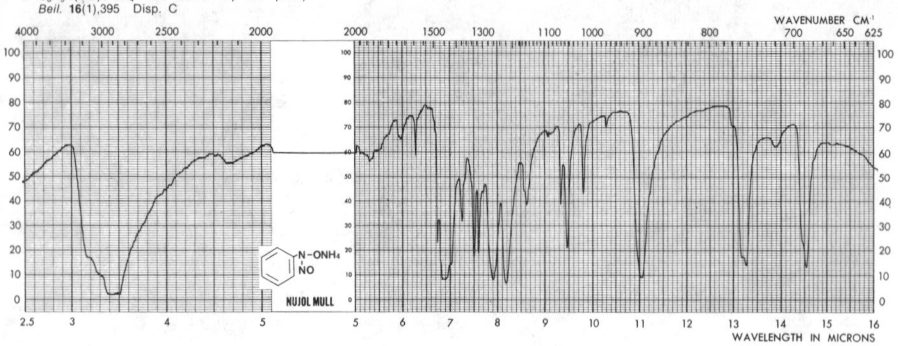

NUJOL MULL

B

N2680-6 **ω-Nitrostyrene**
$C_6H_5CH{:}CHNO_2$ M.W. 149.15 m.p. 55-58°

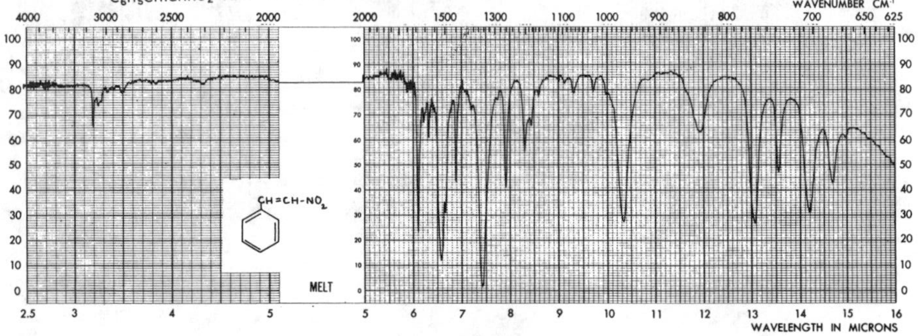

MELT

C

12,257-2 **p-Fluoro-β-nitrostyrene**
$FC_6H_4CH{:}CHNO_2$ M.W. 167.14 m.p. 100-103°

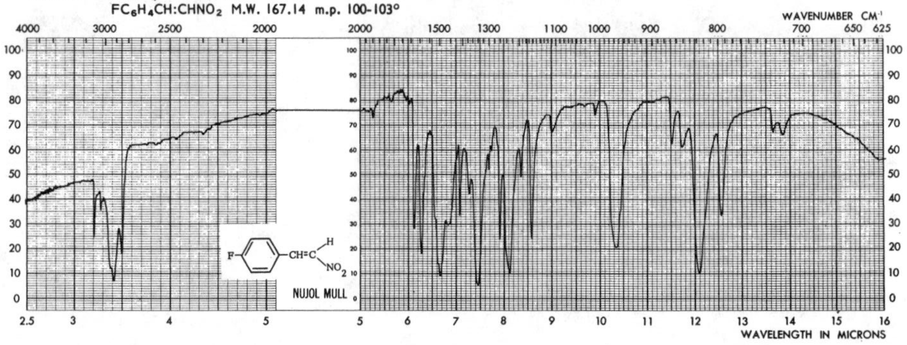

NUJOL MULL

D

11,890-7 **p-Fluoro-β-nitropropenylbenzene**
$FC_6H_4CH{:}C(NO_2)CH_3$ M.W. 181.17
m.p. 65-66°

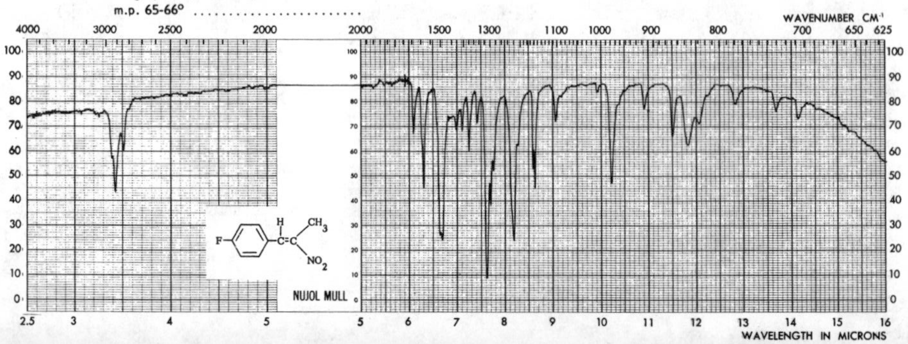

NUJOL MULL

E

14,022-8 **2,5-Dimethoxy-β-methyl-β-nitrostyrene**
$(CH_3O)_2C_6H_3CH{:}C(CH_3)NO_2$ M.W. 223.23
m.p. 73-75°

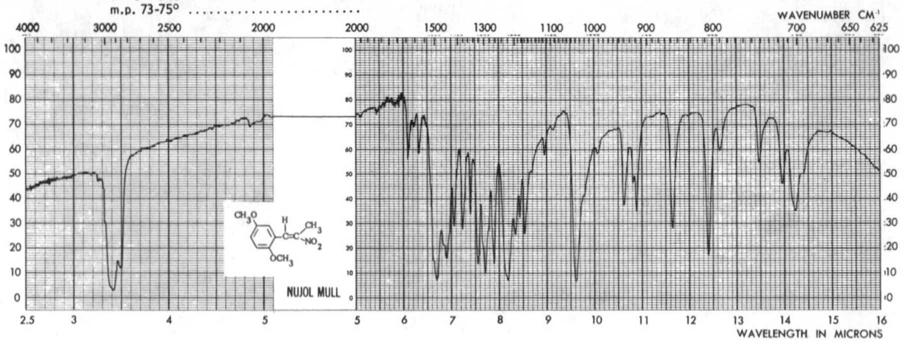

NUJOL MULL

F

18,972-3
9-(ω-Nitrovinyl)anthracene, 98+%
FW 249.27 mp 157-160° Disp. C

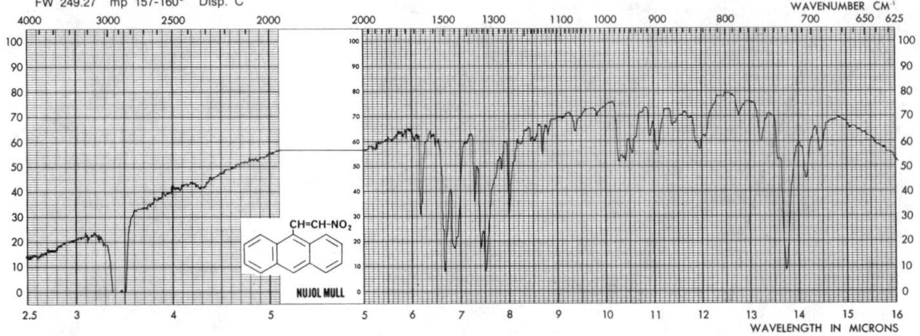

NUJOL MULL

G

N1095-0 **Nitrobenzene**
$C_6H_5NO_2$ M.W. 123.11 n_D^{20} 1.5513 m.p. 5-6°

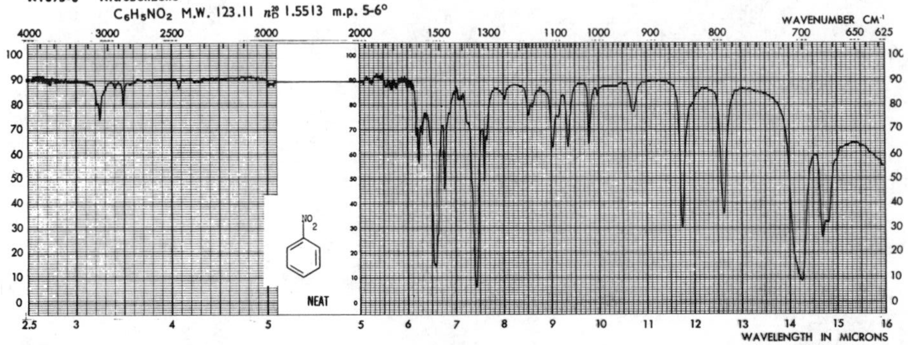

NEAT

H

N2730-6 **2-Nitrotoluene, puriss.**
$CH_3C_6H_4NO_2$ M.W. 137.14 n_D^{20} 1.5450 m.p. -4 to -3°
b.p. 220-225°

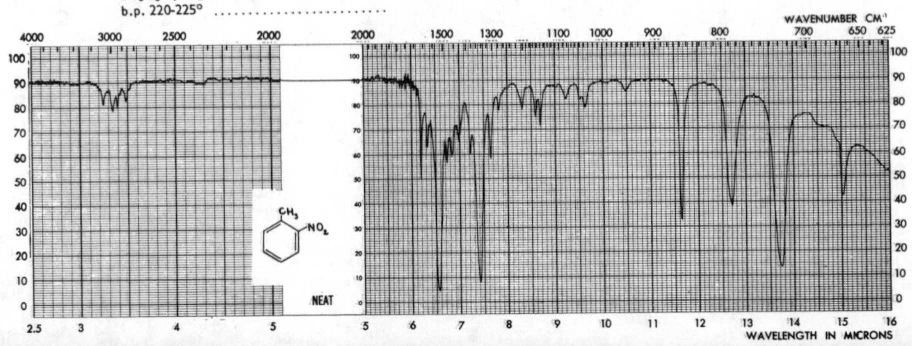

NEAT

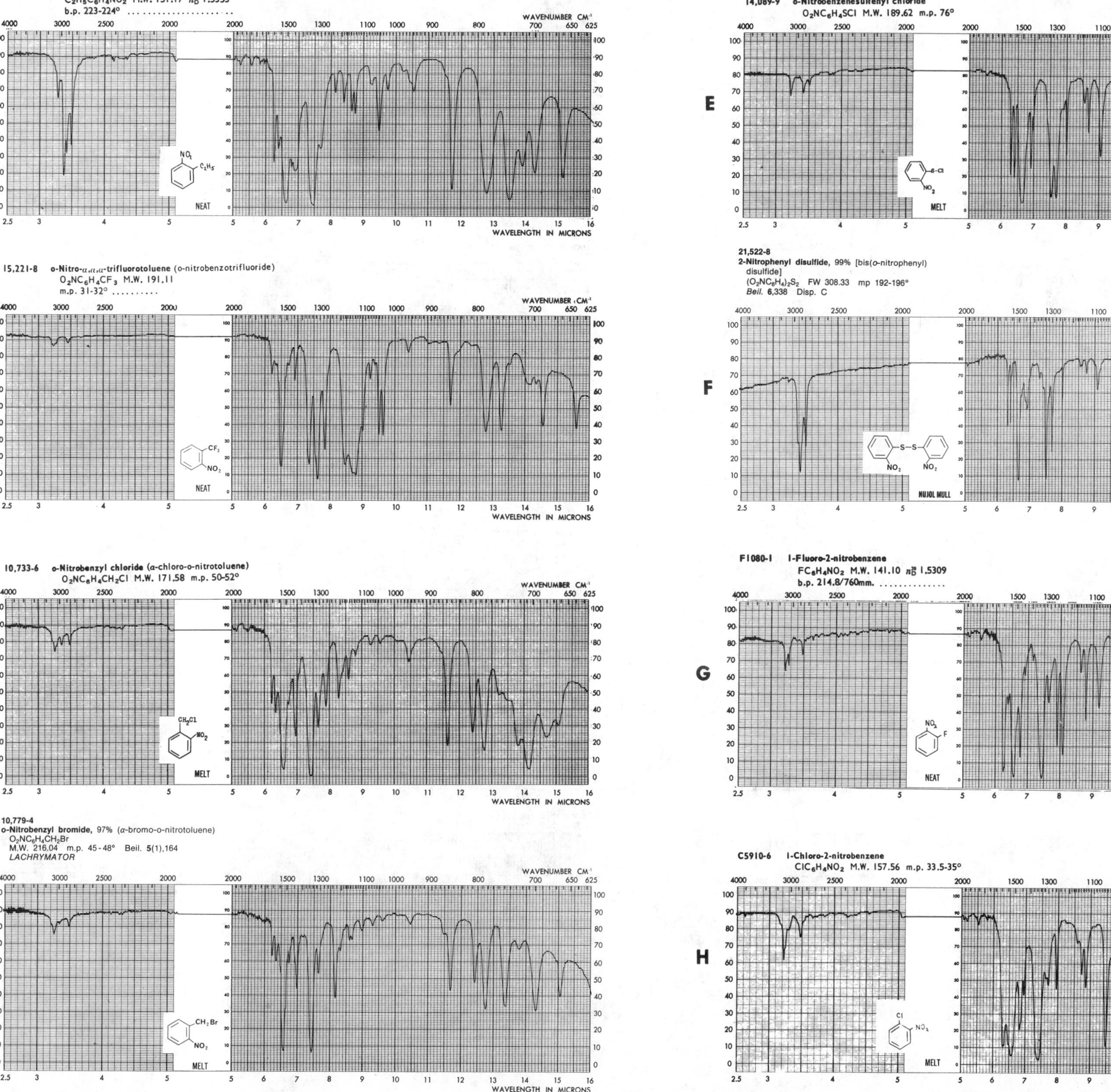

A
13,778-2 2-Ethylnitrobenzene
$C_2H_5C_6H_4NO_2$ M.W. 151.17 n_D^{20} 1.5353
b.p. 223-224°
NEAT
B
15,221-8 o-Nitro-α,α,α-trifluorotoluene (o-nitrobenzotrifluoride)
$O_2NC_6H_4CF_3$ M.W. 191.11
m.p. 31-32°
NEAT
C
10,733-6 o-Nitrobenzyl chloride (α-chloro-o-nitrotoluene)
$O_2NC_6H_4CH_2Cl$ M.W. 171.58 m.p. 50-52°
MELT
D
10,779-4
o-Nitrobenzyl bromide, 97% (α-bromo-o-nitrotoluene)
$O_2NC_6H_4CH_2Br$
M.W. 216.04 m.p. 45-48° Beil. 5(1),164
LACHRYMATOR
MELT
E
14,089-9 o-Nitrobenzenesulfenyl chloride
$O_2NC_6H_4SCl$ M.W. 189.62 m.p. 76°
MELT
F
21,522-8
2-Nitrophenyl disulfide, 99% [bis(o-nitrophenyl) disulfide]
$(O_2NC_6H_4)_2S_2$ FW 308.33 mp 192-196°
Beil. 6,338 Disp. C
NUJOL MULL
G
F1080-1 1-Fluoro-2-nitrobenzene
$FC_6H_4NO_2$ M.W. 141.10 n_D^{20} 1.5309
b.p. 214.8/760mm.
NEAT
H
C5910-6 1-Chloro-2-nitrobenzene
$ClC_6H_4NO_2$ M.W. 157.56 m.p. 33.5-35°
MELT
WAVENUMBER CM⁻¹
WAVELENGTH IN MICRONS
ALDRICH

A 11,211-9 **1-Bromo-2-nitrobenzene**
$BrC_6H_4NO_2$ M.W. 202.01 m.p. 42-43°
MELT

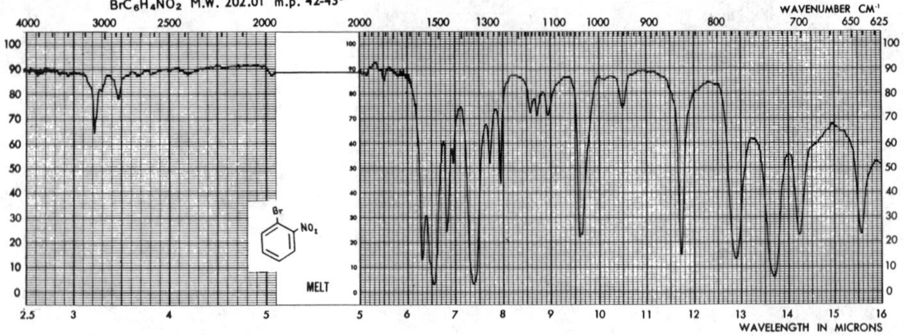

B 13,619-0 **1-Iodo-2-nitrobenzene**
$IC_6H_4NO_2$ M.W. 249.01 m.p. 49-50°
MELT

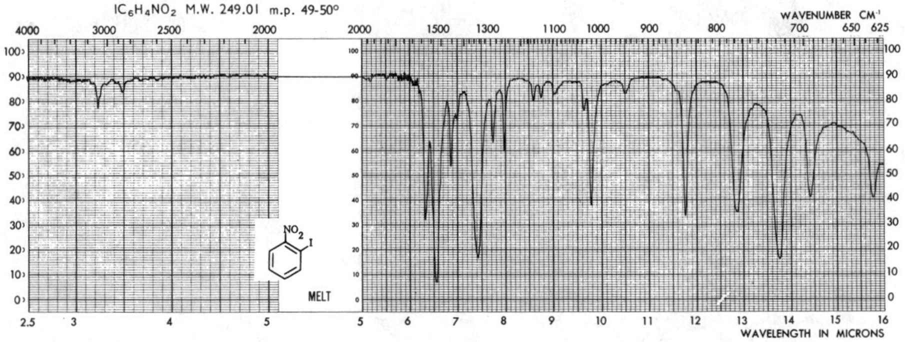

C N1970-2 **2-Nitrophenol**
$O_2NC_6H_4OH$ M.W. 139.11 m.p. 44-46°
MELT

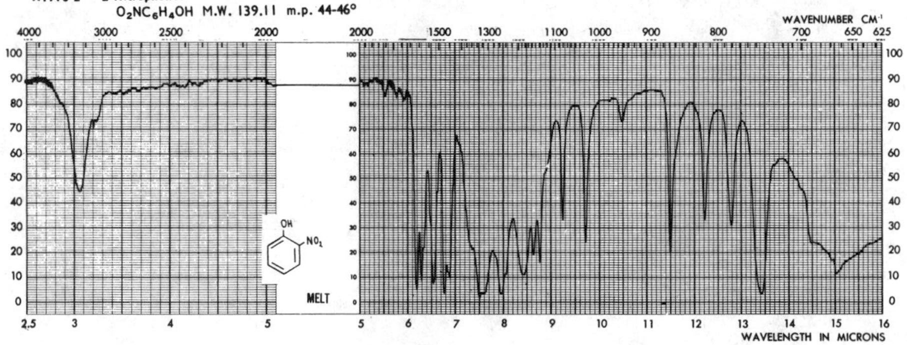

D 10,140-0 **o-Nitroanisole**
$O_2NC_6H_4OCH_3$ M.W. 153.14 n_D^{20} 1.5602
NEAT

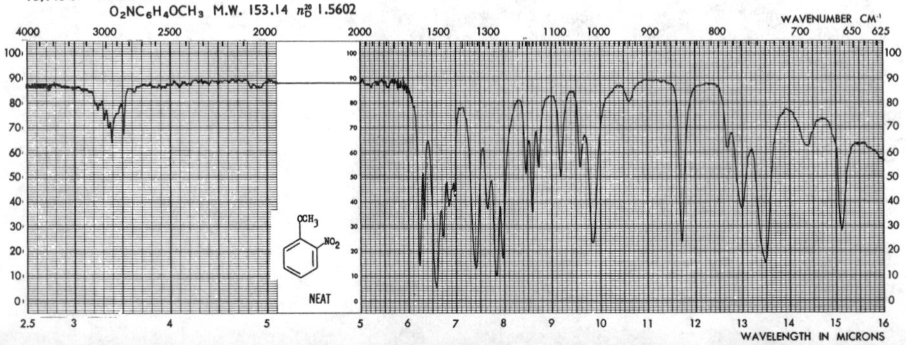

E N1280-5 **o-Nitrobenzyl alcohol**
$O_2NC_6H_4CH_2OH$ M.W. 153.14 m.p. 68-71°
NUJOL MULL

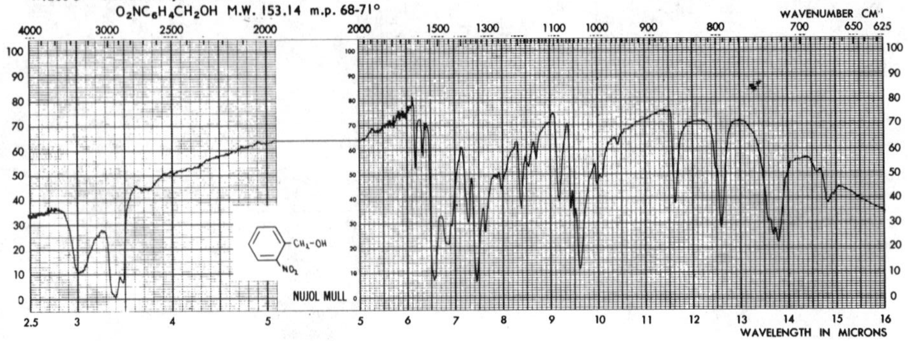

F 18,347-4
o-Nitrophenethyl alcohol, 98%
$O_2NC_6H_4CH_2CH_2OH$
M.W. 167.16 m.p. 2° b.p. 267° n_D^{20} 1.5637
d 1.19 Beil. 6,218
NEAT

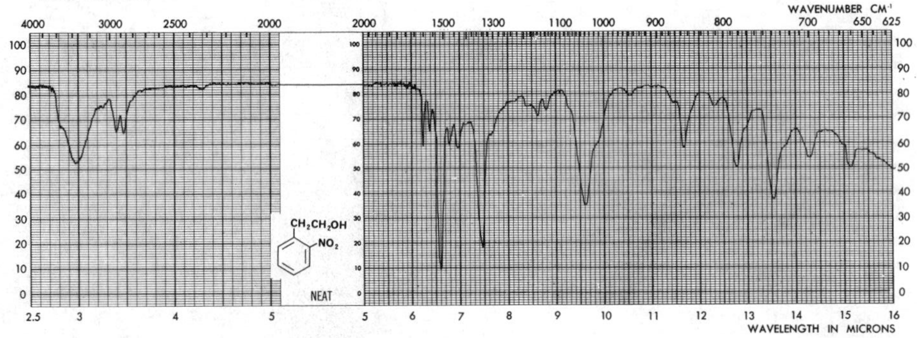

G N2150-2 **o-Nitrophenyl-β-D-galactopyranoside, puriss.**
M.W. 301.26 m.p. 195°
NUJOL MULL

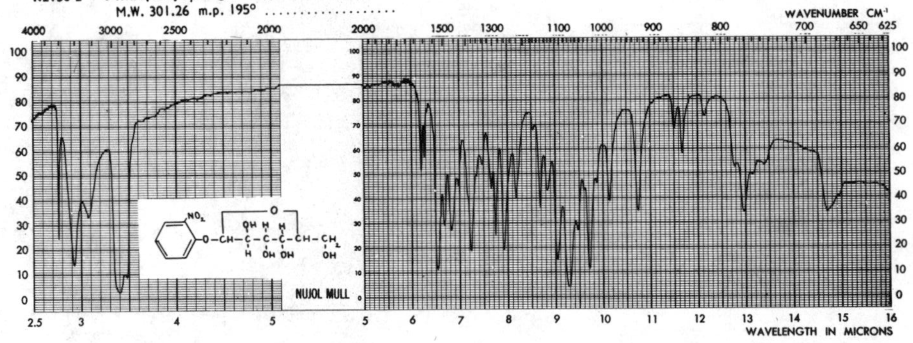

H 86,035-2
o-Nitrophenyl-β-D-thiogalactopyranoside
FW 317.32 mp 201-202° (dec.)
$[\alpha]^{25}$ -229.7° (c=0.71, CH_3OH) Disp. C
NUJOL MULL

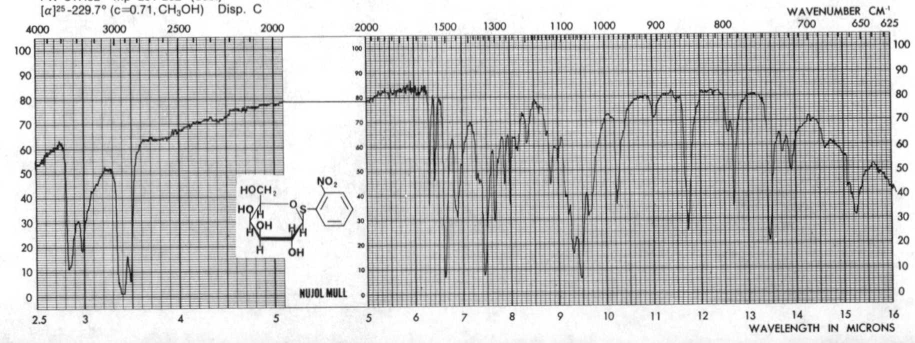

A

N978-0 **o-Nitroaniline**
$O_2NC_6H_4NH_2$ M.W. 138.13 m.p. 74-76°
NUJOL MULL

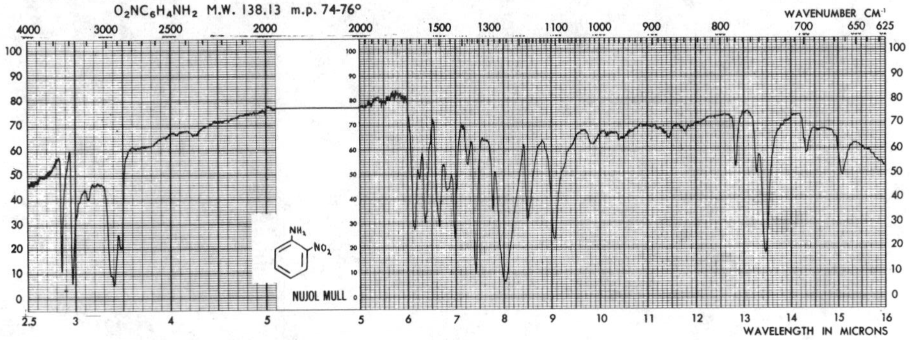

B

N2158-8 **2-Nitrophenylhydrazine**
$O_2NC_6H_4NHNH_2$ M.W. 153.14
m.p. 90-92°
NUJOL MULL

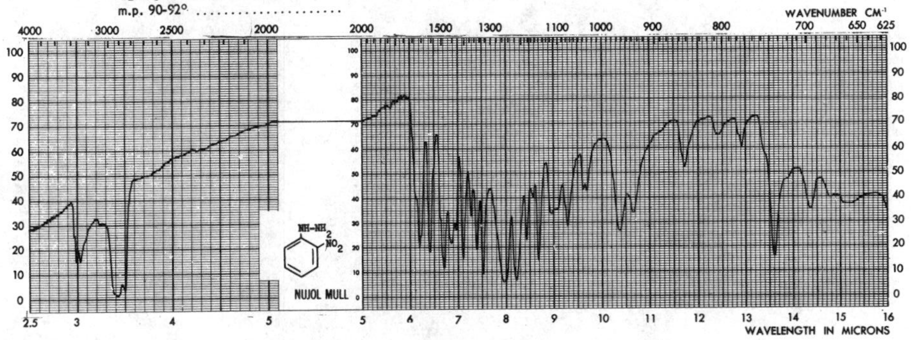

C

19,403-4
***N*-Methyl-*o*-nitroaniline**
$O_2NC_6H_4NHCH_3$ FW 152.15 mp 35-38°
Beil. 12,689 Disp. C
MELT

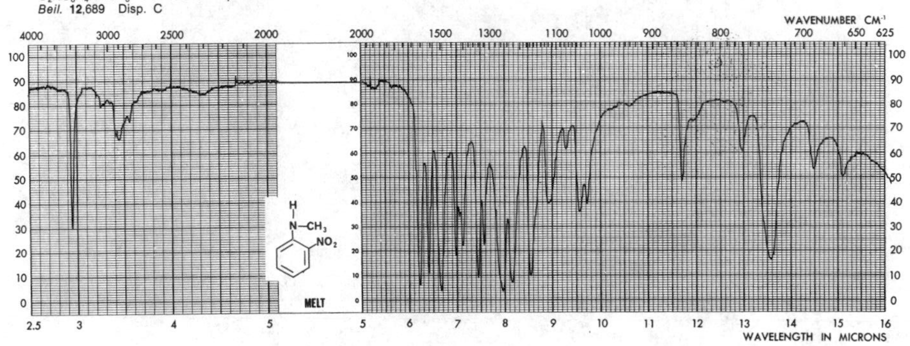

D

12,908-9 **N-Ethyl-2-nitroaniline**
$O_2NC_6H_4NHC_2H_5$ M.W. 166.18
b.p. 168°/20 mm.
NEAT

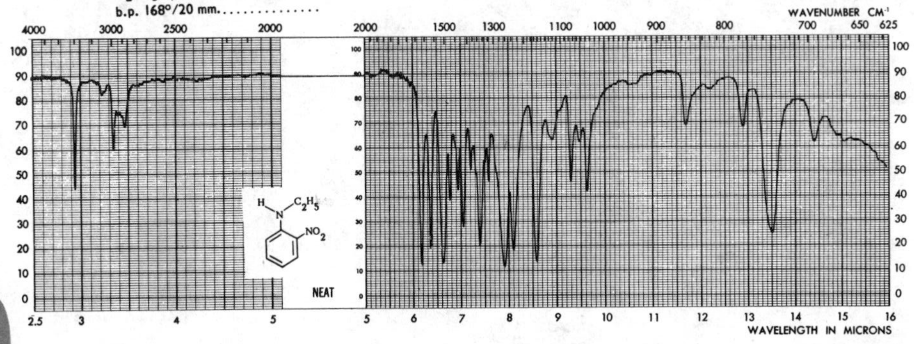

E

12,663-2 **o-Dinitrobenzene**
$C_6H_4(NO_2)_2$ M.W. 168.11 m.p. 116.5-119°
NUJOL MULL

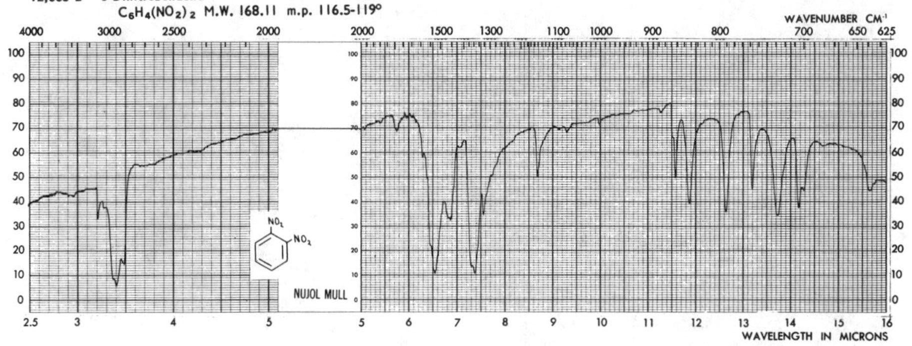

F

N2731-4 **3-Nitrotoluene**
$CH_3C_6H_4NO_2$ M.W. 137.14 n_D^{20} 1.5459 m.p. 15-16°
b.p. 232°
NEAT

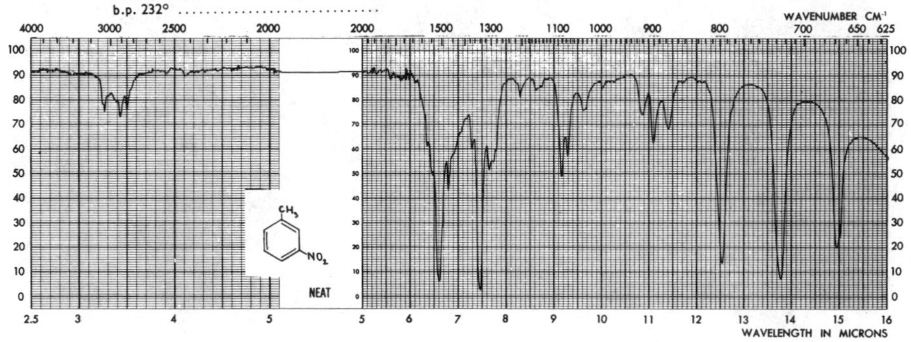

G

19,116-7
***m*-Nitrobenzyl chloride,** 97% (α-chloro-*m*-nitrotoluene)
$O_2NC_6H_4CH_2Cl$ FW 171.58 mp 45-47°
bp 85-87°/5mm. Disp. C
MELT

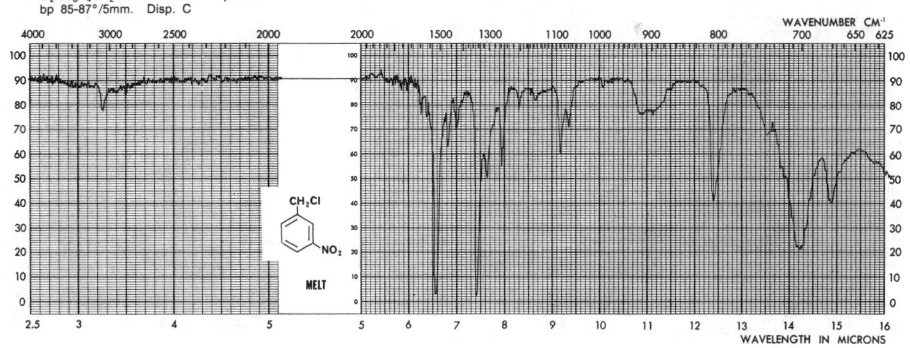

H

17,118-2
m-Nitrobenzyl bromide
M.W. 216.04 m.p. 38-48° Beil. 5,334
NUJOL MULL

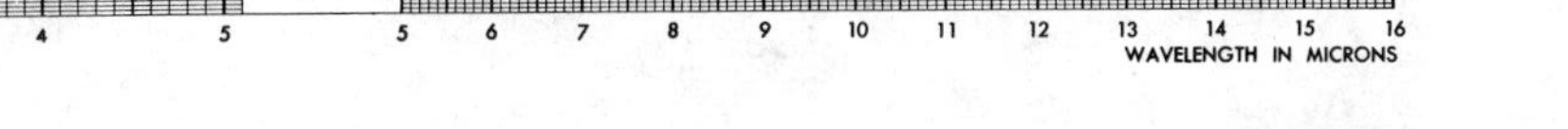

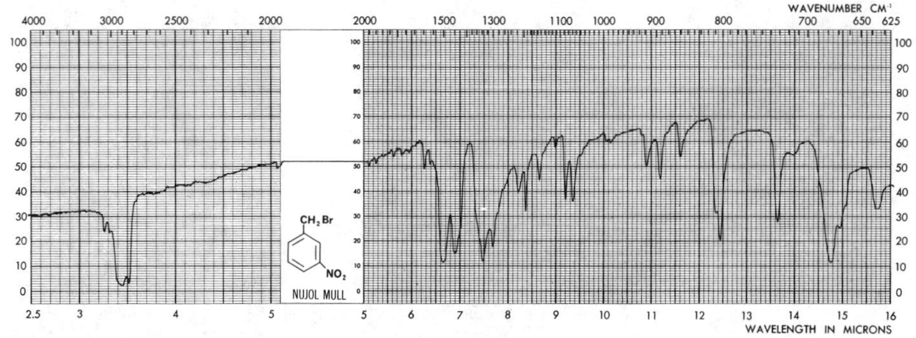

A

22,251-8
m-Nitrobenzyl bromide, 99% (α-bromo-m-nitrotoluene)
$O_2NC_6H_4CH_2Br$ FW 216.04 mp 58-59°
Beil. 5,334 Disp. C

MELT

B

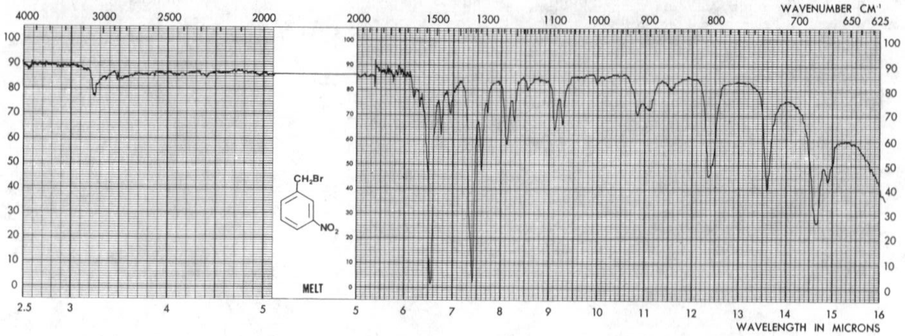

N2660-1 **3-Nitrostyrene**
$H_2C{:}CHC_6H_4NO_2$ M.W. 149.15 n_D^{20} 1.5833

NEAT

C

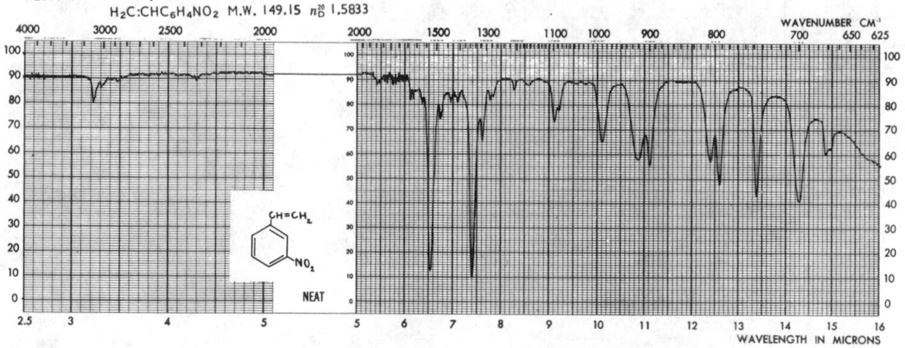

15,307-9 **m-Nitro-α,α,α-trifluorotoluene** (m-nitrobenzotrifluoride)
$O_2NC_6H_4CF_3$ M.W. 191.11 n_D^{20} 1.4715
b.p. 200-205°

NEAT

D

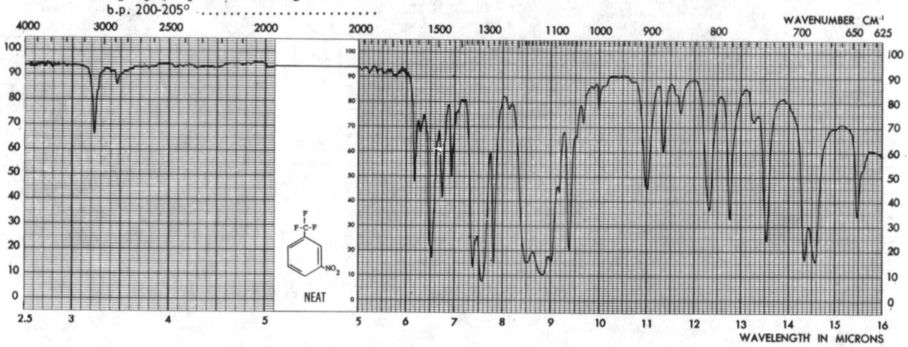

12,839-2 **1-Fluoro-3-nitrobenzene**
$FC_6H_4NO_2$ M.W. 141.10 n_D^{20} 1.5195 b.p. 205°

NEAT

E

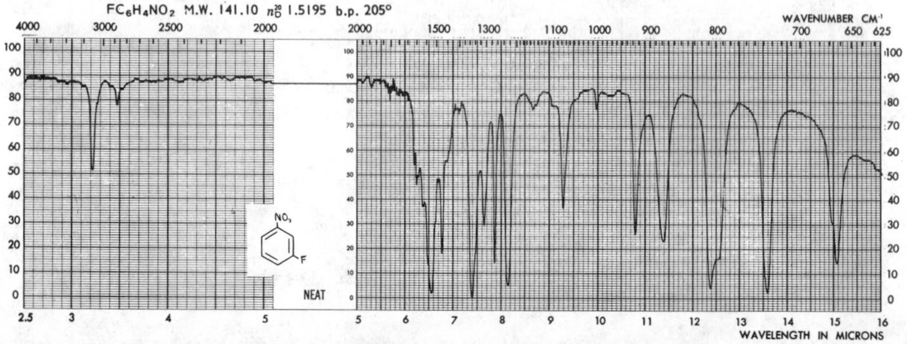

21,875-8
1-Chloro-3-nitrobenzene, 98%
$ClC_6H_4NO_2$ FW 157.56 mp 42-44° bp 236°
d 1.534 *Beil.* 5,243 Disp. C

MELT

F

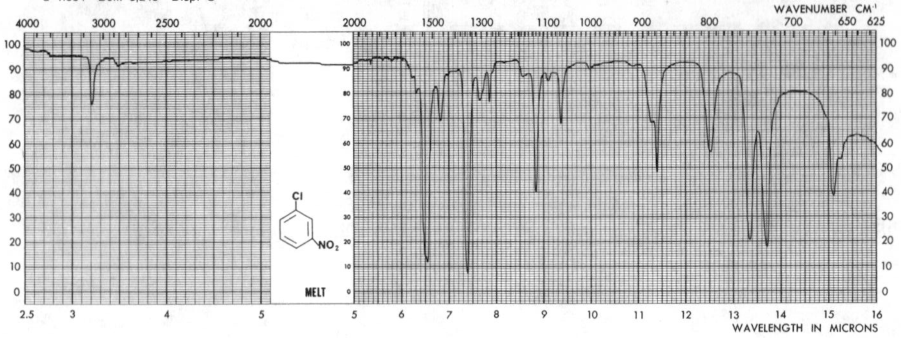

13,834-7 **1-Bromo-3-nitrobenzene**
$BrC_6H_4NO_2$ M.W. 202.01 m.p. 53-55°

MELT

G

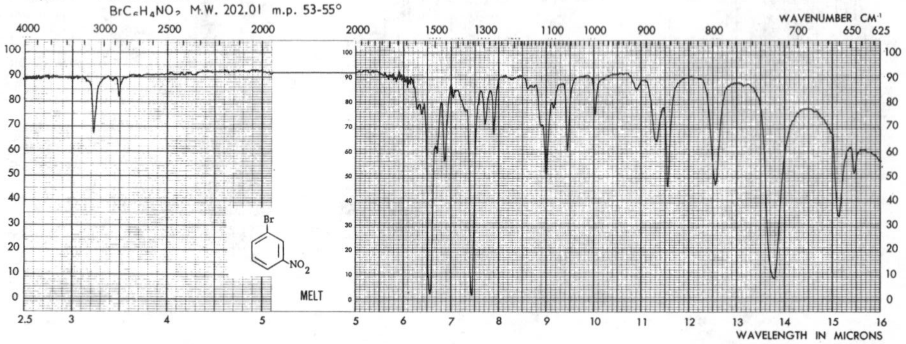

14,449-5 **1-Iodo-3-nitrobenzene**
$IC_6H_4NO_2$ M.W. 249.01 m.p. 33-35°

MELT

H

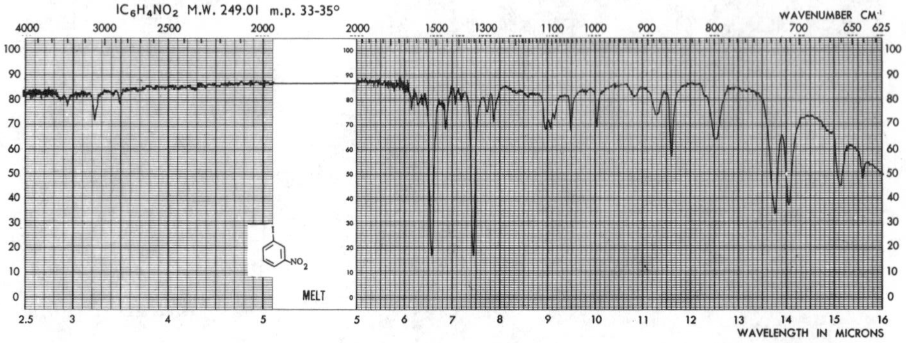

17,098-4
3-Nitrophenol, 95+%
$O_2NC_6H_4OH$
M.W. 139.11 m.p. 95-97° b.p. 197°/70mm.
Beil. 6,222 *IRRITANT*

NUJOL MULL

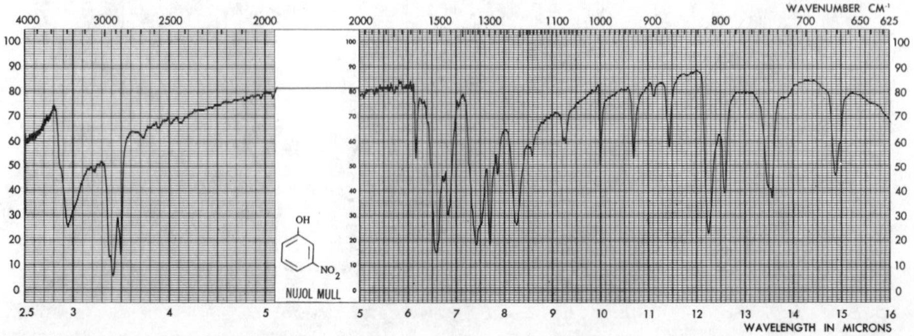

A 14,605-6 m-Nitrobenzyl alcohol
$O_2NC_6H_4CH_2OH$ M.W. 153.14
m.p. 30-32°
MELT

B N982-9 m-Nitroaniline
$O_2NC_6H_4NH_2$ M.W. 138.13 m.p. 112-114°
NUJOL MULL

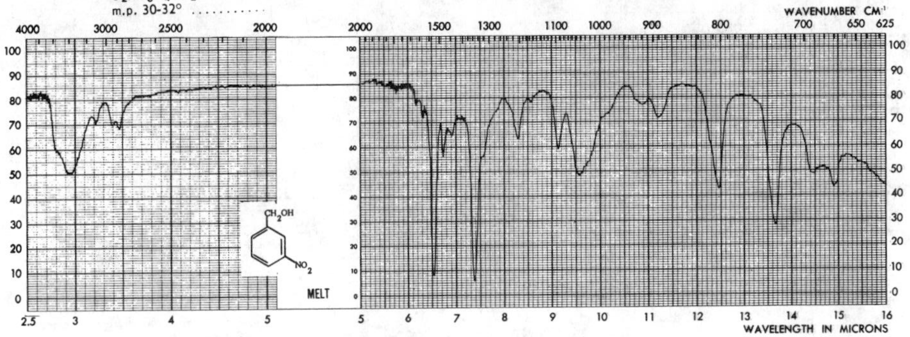

C N2180-4 3-Nitrophenylhydrazine hydrochloride
$O_2NC_6H_4NHNH_2 \cdot HCl$ M.W. 189.60
m.p. 200-210° (dec.)
NUJOL MULL

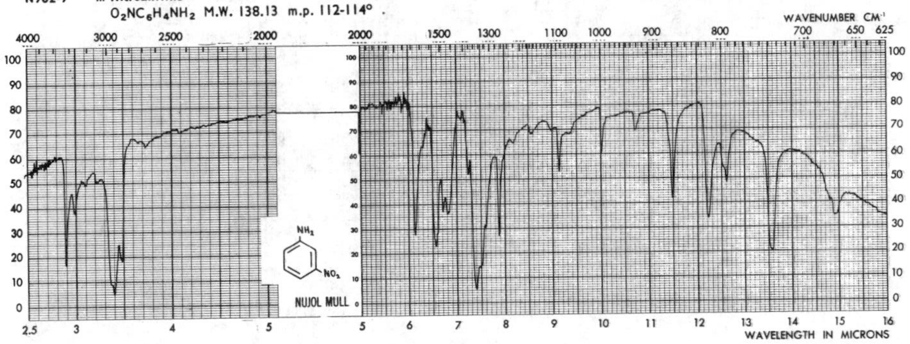

D 19,166-3
m-Nitrobenzylamine hydrochloride, 97%
$O_2NC_6H_4CH_2NH_2 \cdot HCl$ FW 188.62 mp 221-223°
Beil. **12**,1076 Disp. C
NUJOL MULL

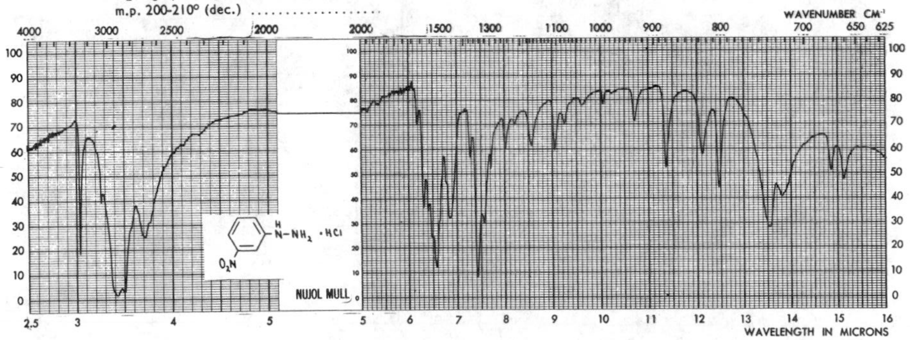

E D17,195-6 N,N-Dimethyl-3-nitroaniline
$O_2NC_6H_4N(CH_3)_2$ M.W. 166.18 m.p. 59-60°
MELT

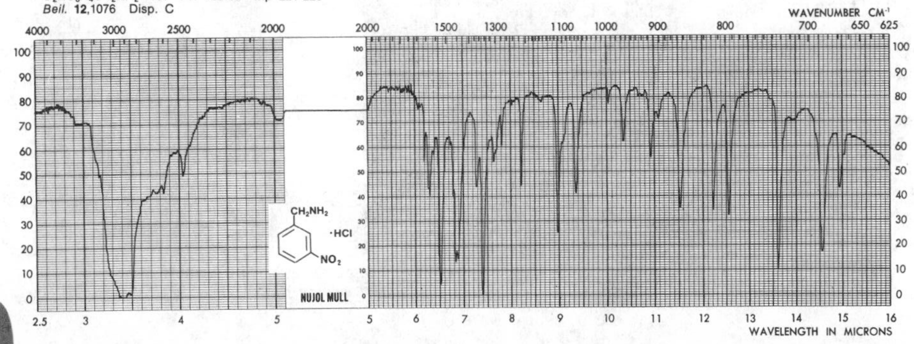

F 11,433-2 m-Dinitrobenzene, zone refined
$C_6H_4(NO_2)_2$ M.W. 168.11 m.p. 90.02°
NUJOL MULL

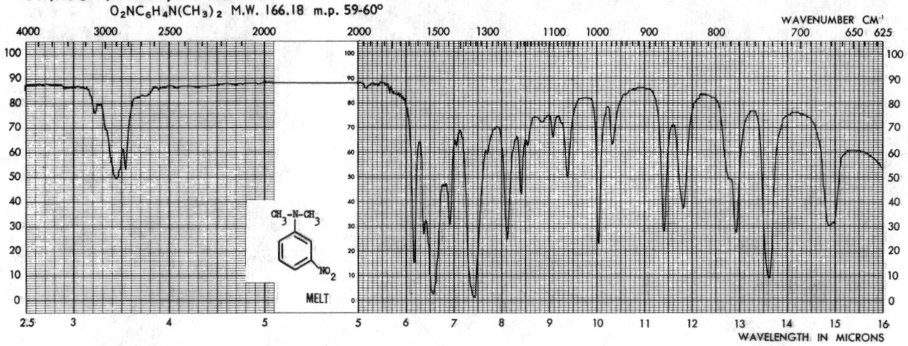

G N2732-2 4-Nitrotoluene
$CH_3C_6H_4NO_2$ M.W. 137.14 m.p. 52.5-53.5°
MELT

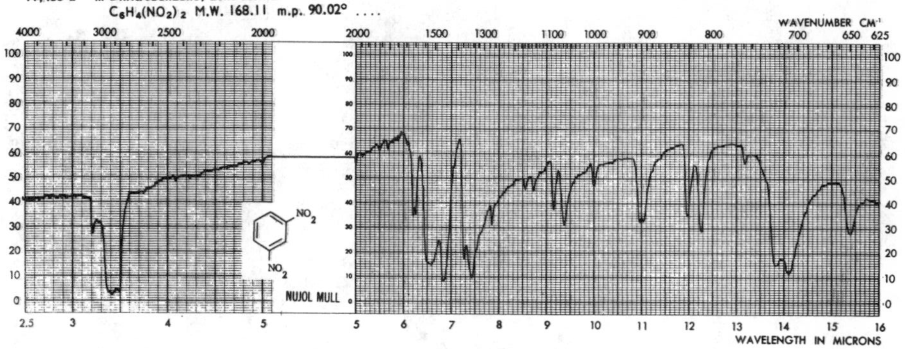

H E4100-1 4-Ethylnitrobenzene, puriss.
$C_2H_5C_6H_4NO_2$ M.W. 151.17 n_D^{20} 1.5445
NEAT

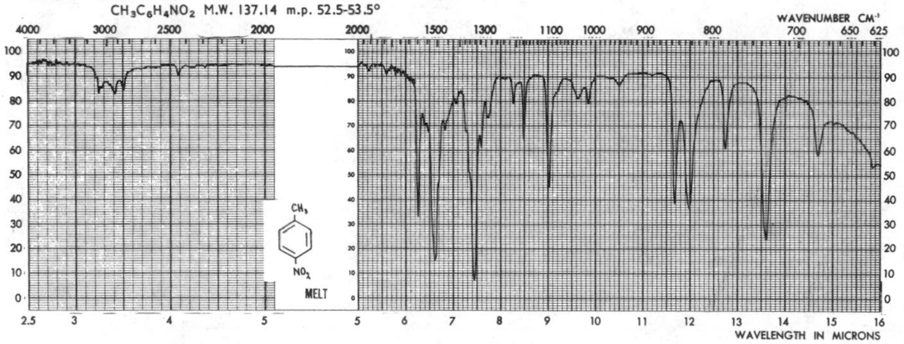

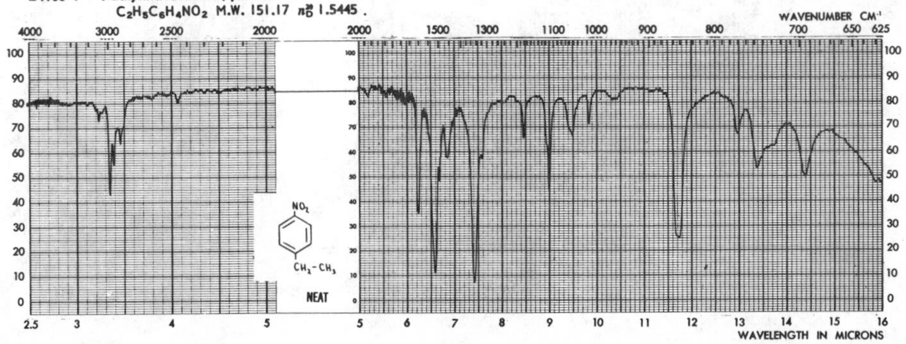

A

14,011-2 **p-Nitrobenzyl chloride** (α-chloro-p-nitrotoluene)
$O_2NC_6H_4CH_2Cl$ M.W. 171.58 m.p. 70-73°

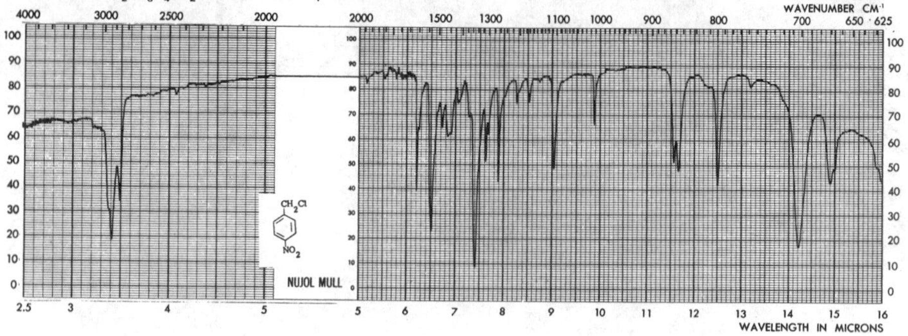

NUJOL MULL

B

N1305-4 **p-Nitrobenzyl bromide** (α-bromo-p-nitrotoluene)
$O_2NC_6H_4CH_2Br$ M.W. 216.04 m.p. 98-100°

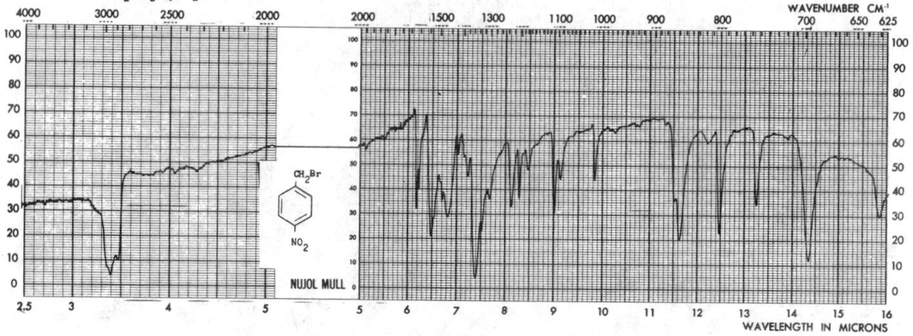

NUJOL MULL

C

11,505-3 **p-Nitrophenethyl bromide** [1-(2-bromoethyl)-4-nitrobenzene]
$O_2NC_6H_4CH_2CH_2Br$ M.W. 230.07
m.p. 67-69°

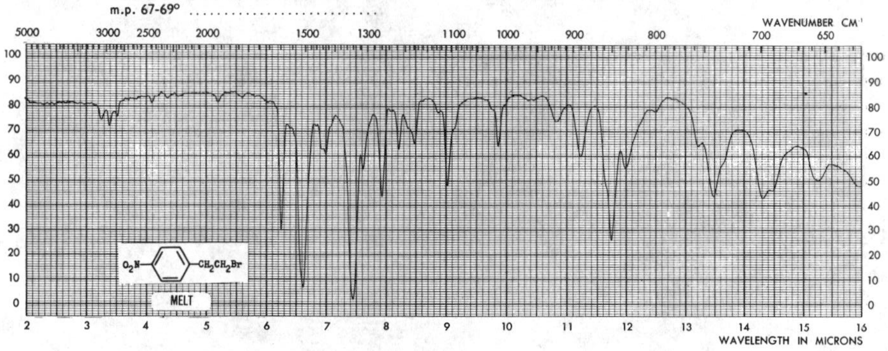

MELT

D

21,178-8
p-**Nitro-α,α,α-trifluorotoluene**, 96% (*p*-nitrobenzotrifluoride)
$O_2NC_6H_4CF_3$ FW 191.11 mp 38-40°
bp 81-83°/10mm. *Beil.* 5(2),251 Disp. C

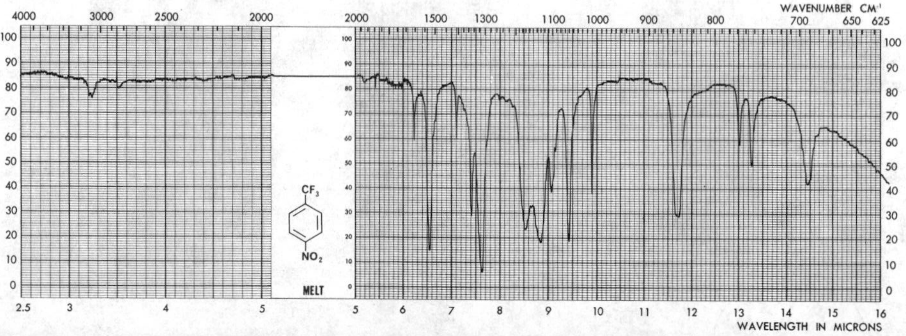

MELT

E

F1120-4 **1-Fluoro-4-nitrobenzene**
$FC_6H_4NO_2$ M.W. 141.10 n_D^{20} 1.5312 b.p. 205°

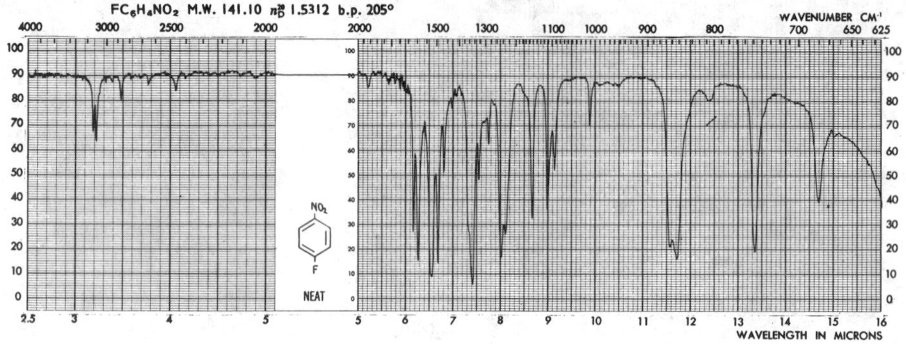

NEAT

F

C5912-2 **1-Chloro-4-nitrobenzene**
$ClC_6H_4NO_2$ M.W. 157.56 m.p. 83-84°

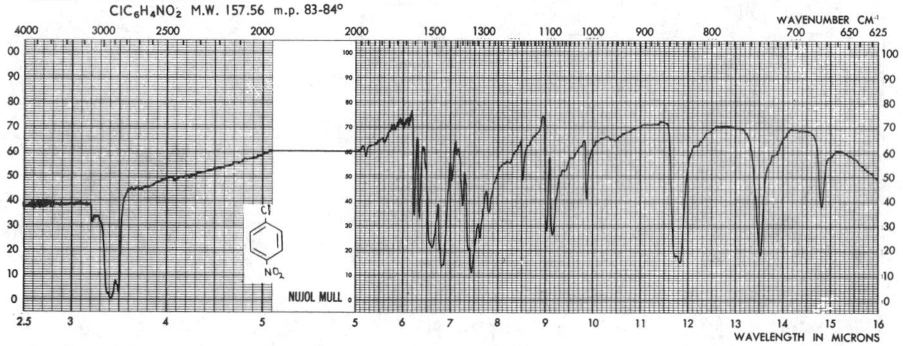

NUJOL MULL

G

16,715-0
1-Bromo-4-nitrobenzene
$BrC_6H_4NO_2$ FW 202.01 mp 125-127°
bp 255-256° *Beil.* 5,248 Disp. C

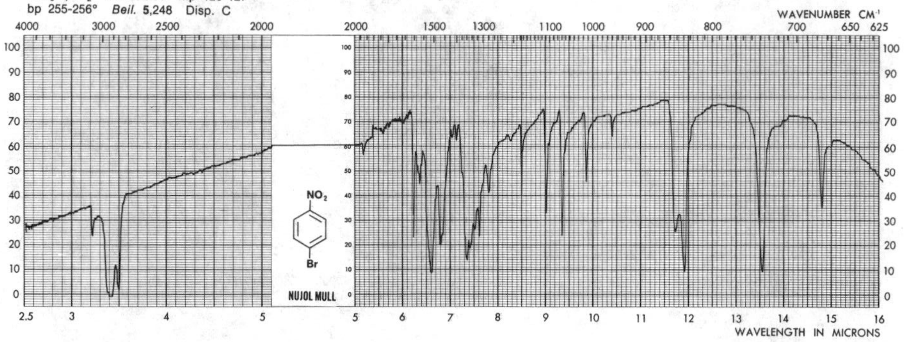

NUJOL MULL

H

1-980-5 **1-Iodo-4-nitrobenzene**
$IC_6H_4NO_2$ M.W. 249.01 m.p. 171-173°

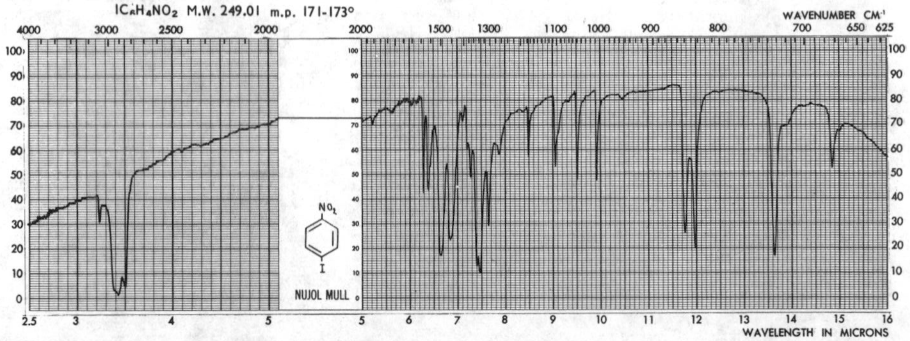

NUJOL MULL

A 10,354-3 **p-Nitroanisole**
$O_2NC_6H_4OCH_3$ M.W. 153.14 m.p. 50-52°
MELT

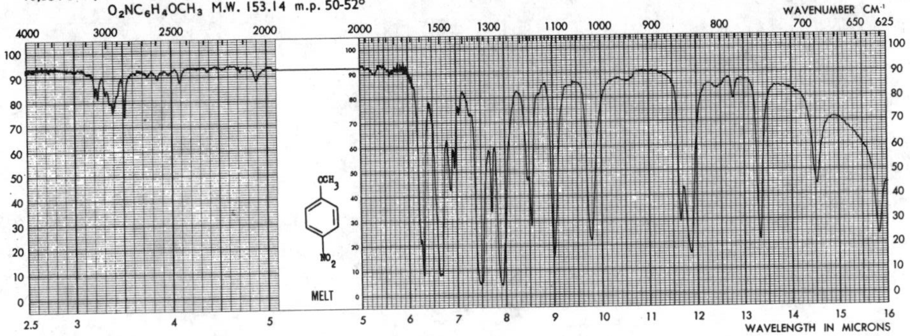

B N2720-9 **4-Nitrothiophenol** (p-nitrobenzenethiol), tech.,
$O_2NC_6H_4SH$ M.W. 155.18 (dry basis)
NUJOL MULL

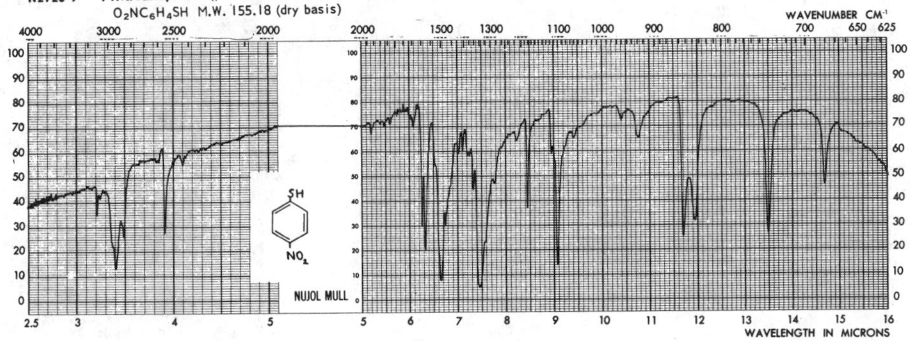

C 13,023-0 **4-Nitrophenol**
$O_2NC_6H_4OH$ M.W. 139.11 m.p. 114-116°
NUJOL MULL

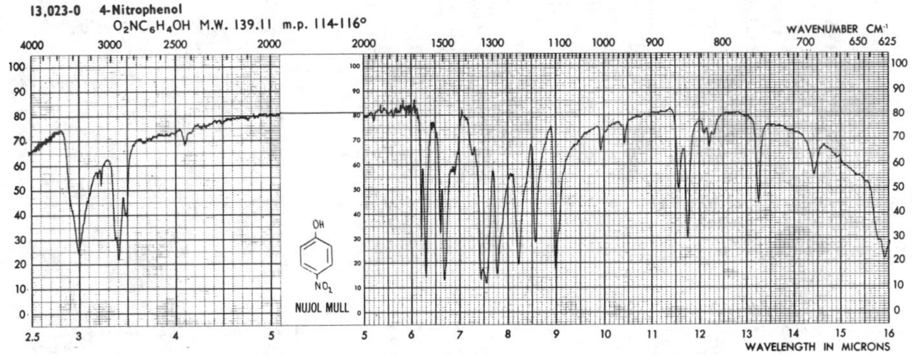

D 16,163-2 **Sodium p-nitrophenoxide,**
(4-nitrophenol, sodium salt)
$O_2NC_6H_4ONa$ M.W. 161.09 m.p. >300°
Beil. **6**,226 Disp. C *HYGROSCOPIC*
NUJOL MULL

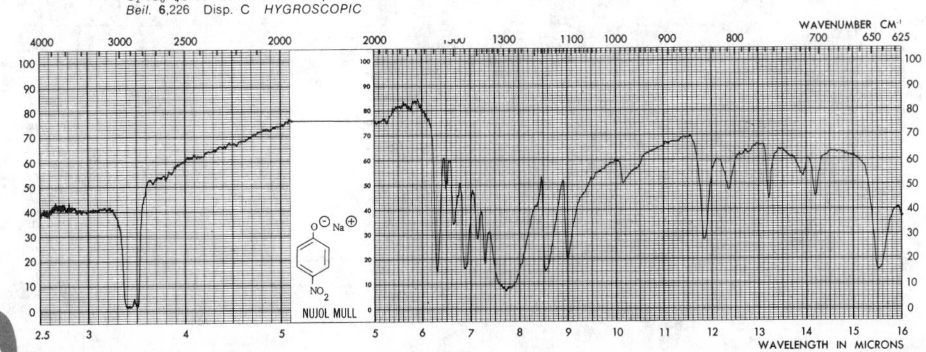

E N1282-1 **p-Nitrobenzyl alcohol**
$O_2NC_6H_4CH_2OH$ M.W. 153.14 m.p. 91-94°
NUJOL MULL

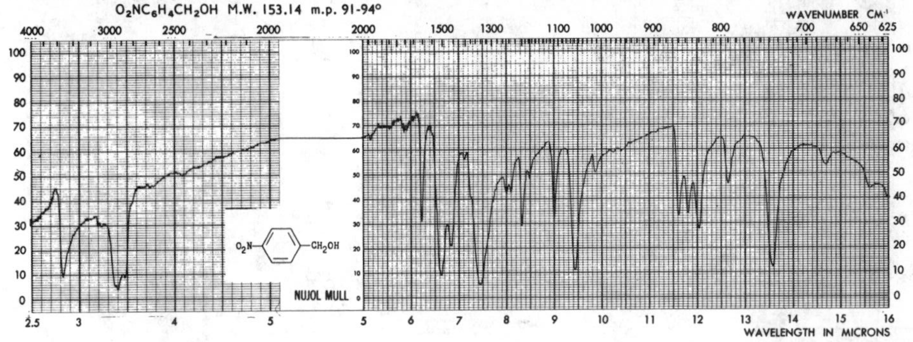

F 18,346-6
p-Nitrophenethyl alcohol, 98%
$O_2NC_6H_4CH_2CH_2OH$
M.W. 167.16 m.p. 62-64° Beil. **6**(2),238
MELT

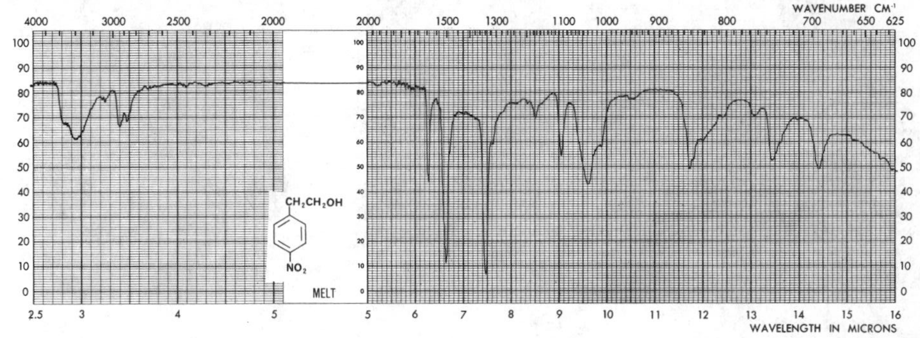

G 18,875-1
4-(*p*-Nitrophenyl)-1-butanol
$O_2NC_6H_4(CH_2)_4OH$ FW 195.22 n_D^{20} 1.5565
Disp. C
NEAT

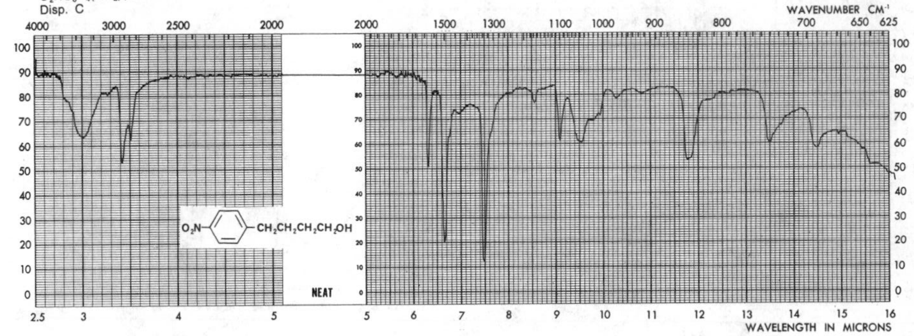

H 19,143-4
***p*-Nitrobenzylamine hydrochloride**
$O_2NC_6H_4CH_2NH_2 \cdot HCl$ FW 188.62 mp 225° (dec.)
Beil. **12**,1084 Disp. C
NUJOL MULL

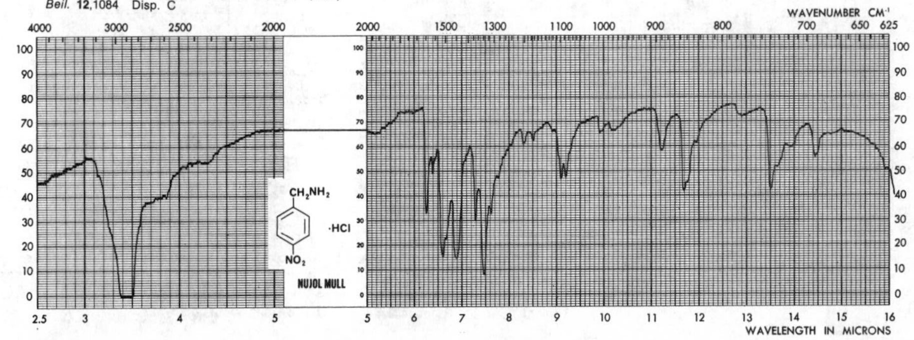

A

18,480-2
p-Nitrophenethylamine hydrochloride
$O_2NC_6H_4CH_2CH_2NH_2 \cdot HCl$
M.W. 202.64

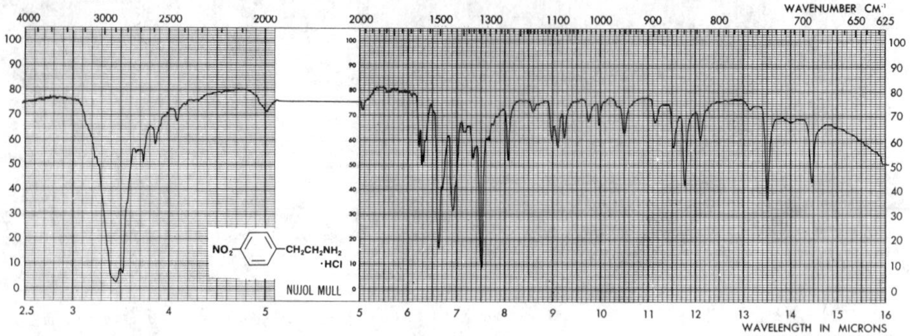

NUJOL MULL

B

22,191-0
4-Nitro-*N*-propylbenzylamine hydrochloride, 98%
$O_2NC_6H_4CH_2NHCH_2CH_2CH_3 \cdot HCl$ FW 230.70
mp 230-232° *Beil.* **12**,1085 *Fieser* **7**,190
Disp. C

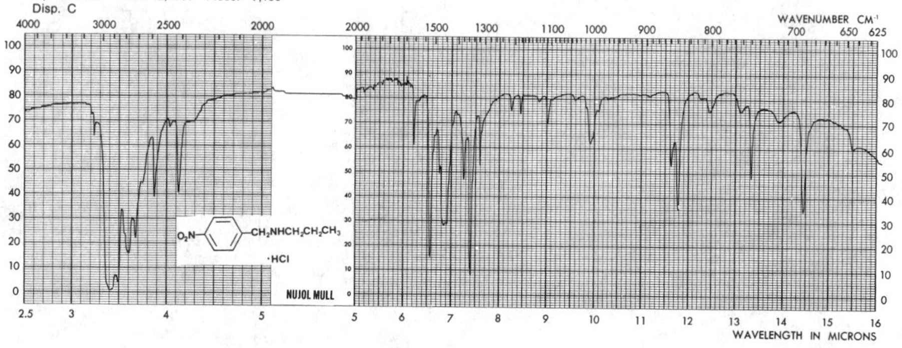

NUJOL MULL

C

N985-3 p-Nitroaniline
$O_2NC_6H_4NH_2$ M.W. 138.13
m.p. 148.5-149.5°

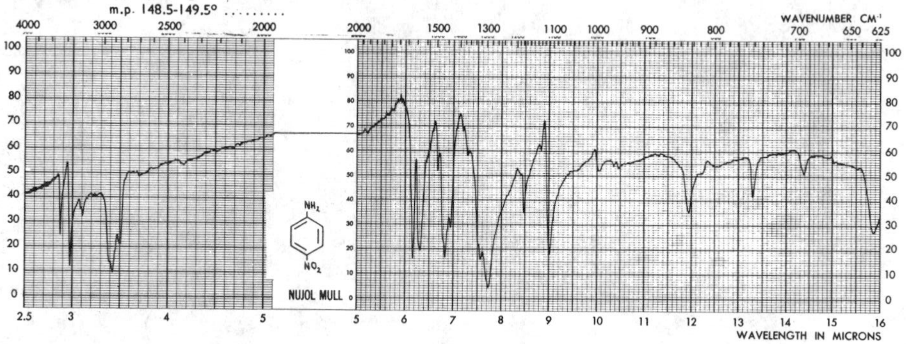

NUJOL MULL

D

11,468-5 4-Nitrophenylhydrazine
$O_2NC_6H_4NHNH_2$ M.W. 153.14
m.p. 154-156°

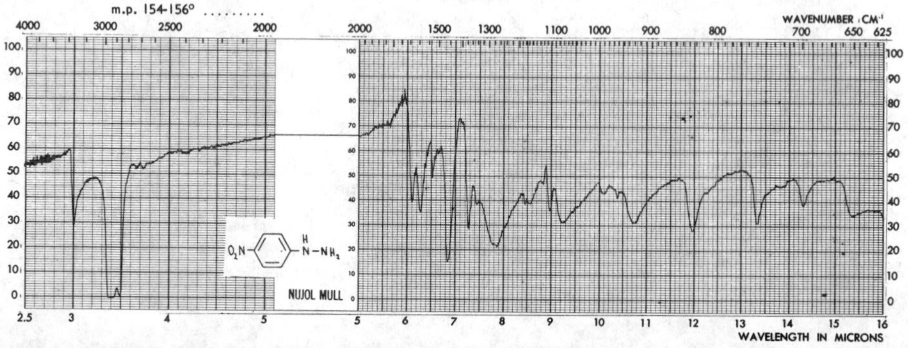

NUJOL MULL

E

A7071 DL-*threo*-2-Amino-1-(p-nitrophenyl)-1,3-propanediol
$HOCH_2CH(NH_2)CH(C_6H_4NO_2)OH$ M.W. 212.21
m.p. 141.5-142.5°

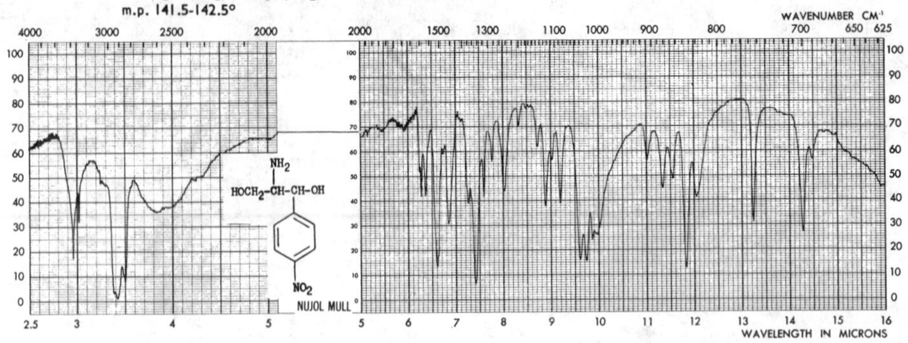

NUJOL MULL

F

A7070-4 D-(-)-*threo*-2-Amino-1-(p-nitrophenyl)-1,3-propanediol
$HOCH_2CH(NH_2)CH(C_6H_4NO_2)OH$ M.W. 212.21
m.p. 163-165°

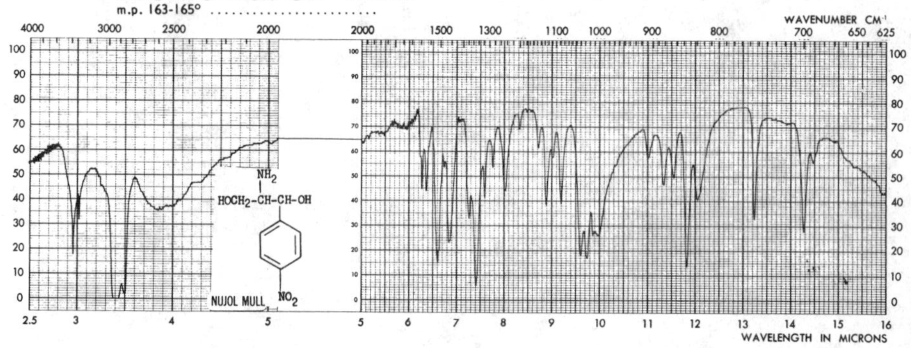

NUJOL MULL

G

13,891-6 N-(p-Nitrophenyl)-morpholine
M.W. 208.22 m.p. 150-152°

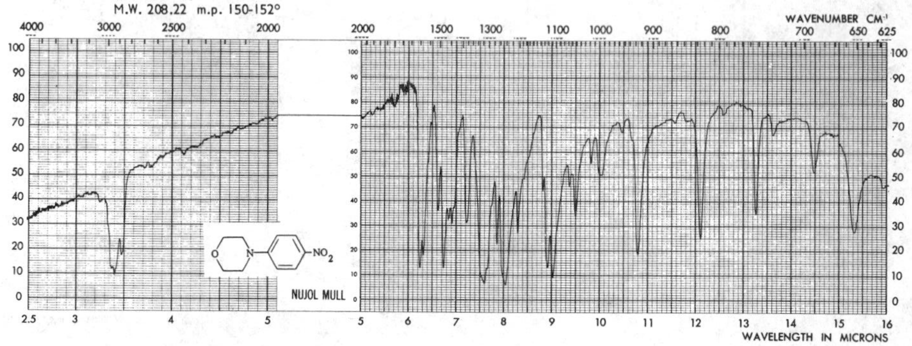

NUJOL MULL

H

10,236-9 p-Dinitrobenzene
$C_6H_4(NO_2)_2$ M.W. 168.11 m.p. 172-174°

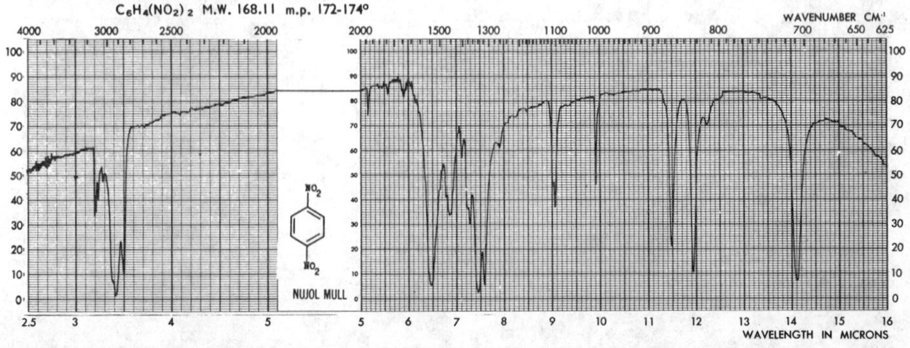

NUJOL MULL

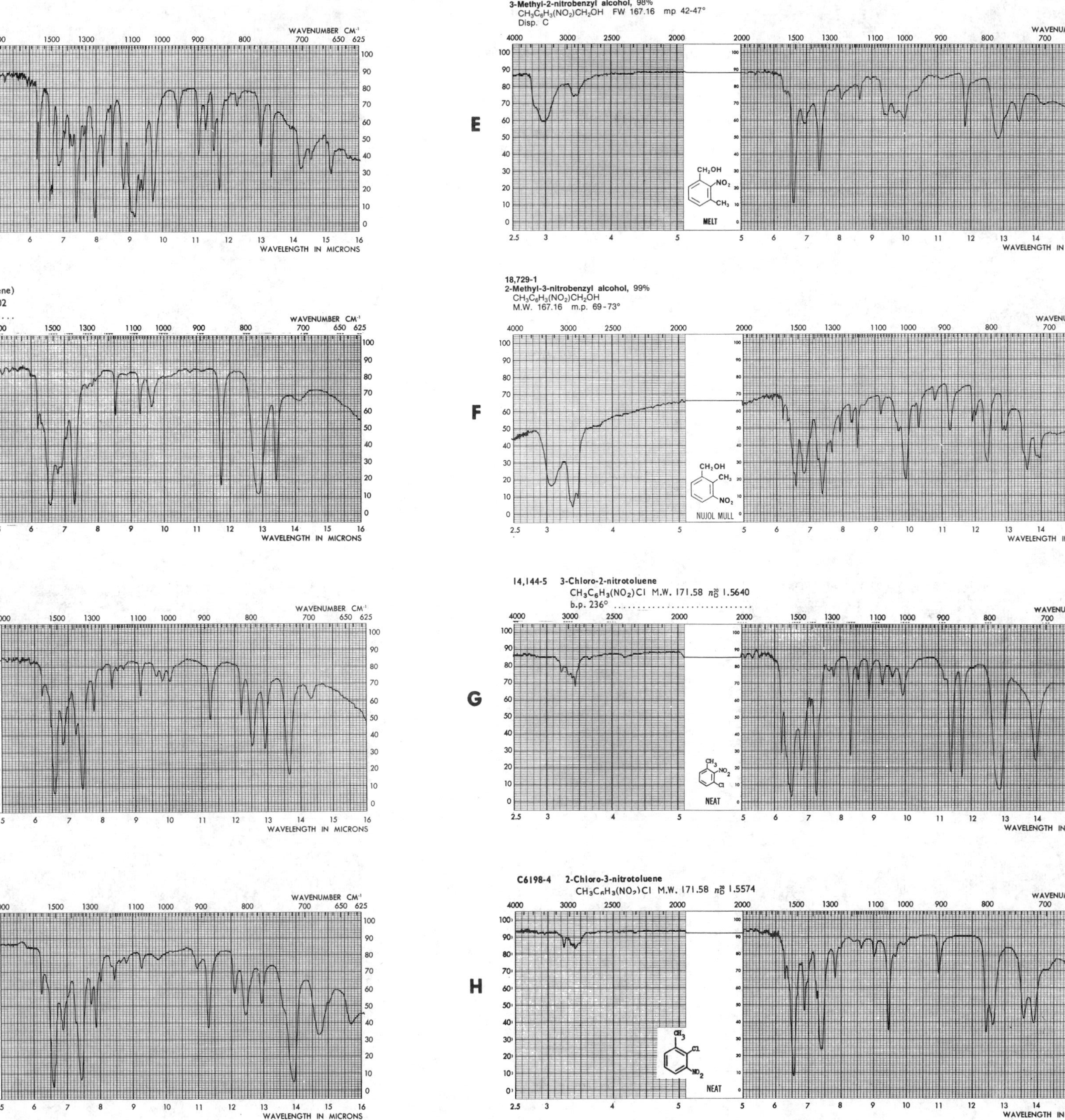

A 86,034-4
p-Nitrophenyl-β-D-galactopyranoside, 98%
FW 301.25 mp 174-177° Disp. L

B N2835-3 **2-Nitro-m-xylene** (1,3-dimethyl-2-nitrobenzene)
$(CH_3)_2C_6H_3NO_2$ M.W. 151.17 n_D^{20} 1.5202
b.p. 225°/744 mm.

C 13,030-3
3-Nitro-o-xylene, 97% (1,2-dimethyl-3-nitrobenzene)
$(CH_3)_2C_6H_3NO_2$
M.W. 151.17 m.p. 7-9° b.p. 245° n_D^{20} 1.5434
Beil. 5,367

D 19,536-7
2-Methyl-3-nitrobenzyl chloride
$CH_3C_6H_3(NO_2)CH_2Cl$ FW 185.61 mp 43-46°
Disp. C

E 18,826-3
3-Methyl-2-nitrobenzyl alcohol, 98%
$CH_3C_6H_3(NO_2)CH_2OH$ FW 167.16 mp 42-47°
Disp. C

F 18,729-1
2-Methyl-3-nitrobenzyl alcohol, 99%
$CH_3C_6H_3(NO_2)CH_2OH$
M.W. 167.16 m.p. 69-73°

G 14,144-5 **3-Chloro-2-nitrotoluene**
$CH_3C_6H_3(NO_2)Cl$ M.W. 171.58 n_D^{20} 1.5640
b.p. 236°

H C6198-4 **2-Chloro-3-nitrotoluene**
$CH_3C_6H_3(NO_2)Cl$ M.W. 171.58 n_D^{20} 1.5574

A

10,169-9 **2-Chloro-6-nitrotoluene**
$CH_3C_6H_3(NO_2)Cl$ M.W. 171.58
m.p. 36.5-40°

MELT

B

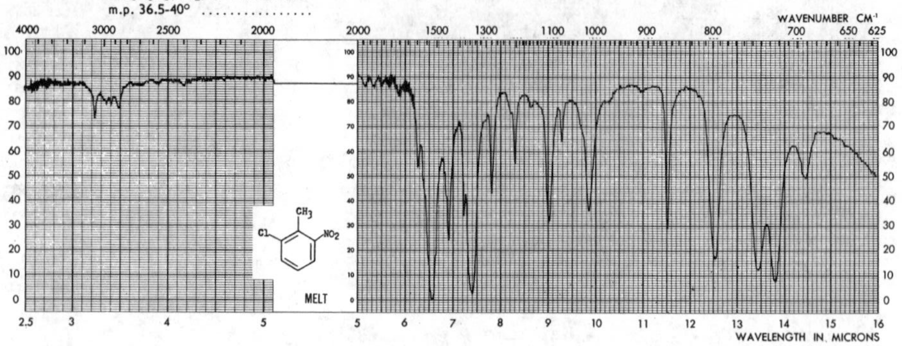

D6820-7 **2,3-Dichloronitrobenzene** (1,2-dichloro-3-nitrobenzene)
$Cl_2C_6H_3NO_2$ M.W. 192.00 m.p. 61-62°

NUJOL MULL

C

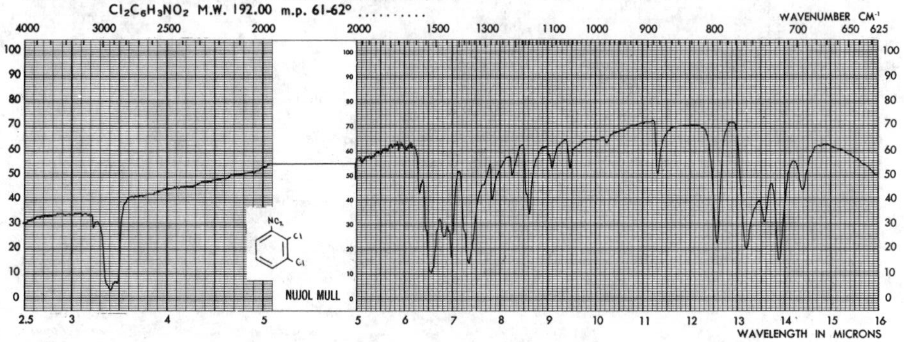

M6020-1 **3-Methyl-2-nitroanisole**
$CH_3C_6H_3(NO_2)OCH_3$ M.W. 167.16
m.p. 48-50°

NUJOL MULL

D

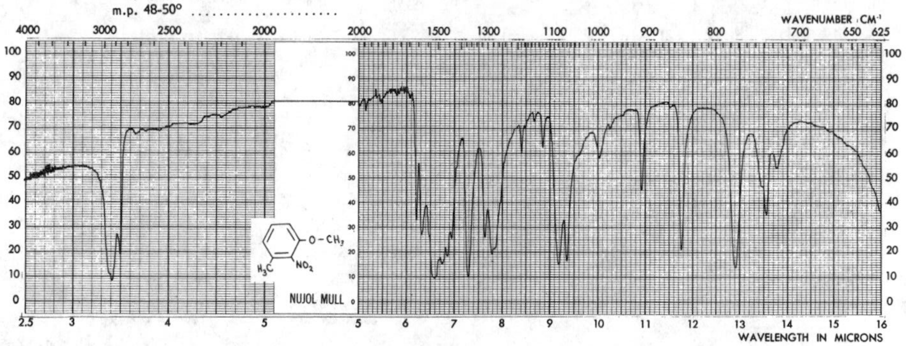

11,542-8 **2-Methyl-3-nitroanisole**
$CH_3C_6H_3(NO_2)OCH_3$ M.W. 167.16
m.p. 49-51°

MELT

E

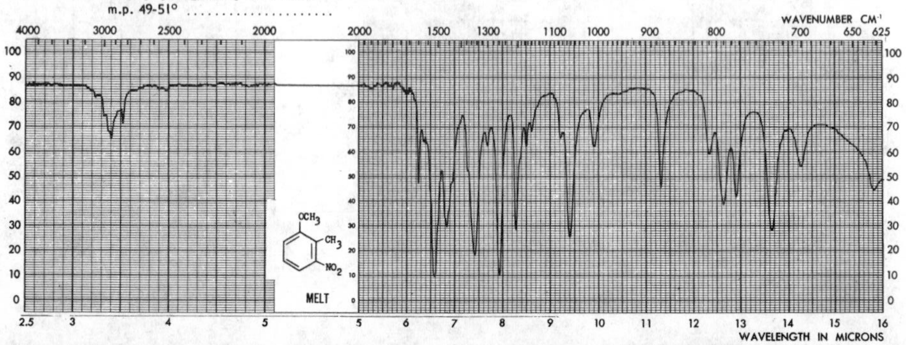

18,846-8
2-Chloro-6-nitroanisole, 99%
$ClC_6H_3(NO_2)OCH_3$ FW 187.58 mp 56-59°
Beil. **6**(1),122 Disp. C

MELT

F

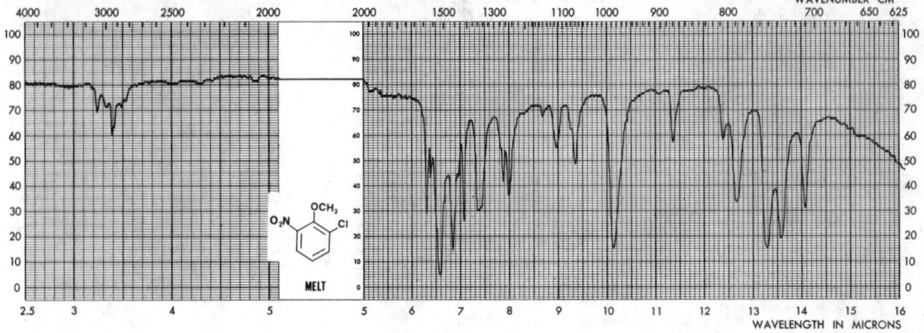

10,694-1
2-Methyl-3-nitrophenol (3-nitro-o-cresol)
$CH_3C_6H_3(NO_2)OH$
M.W. 153.14 m.p. 146-148° Beil. **6**,366

NUJOL MULL

G

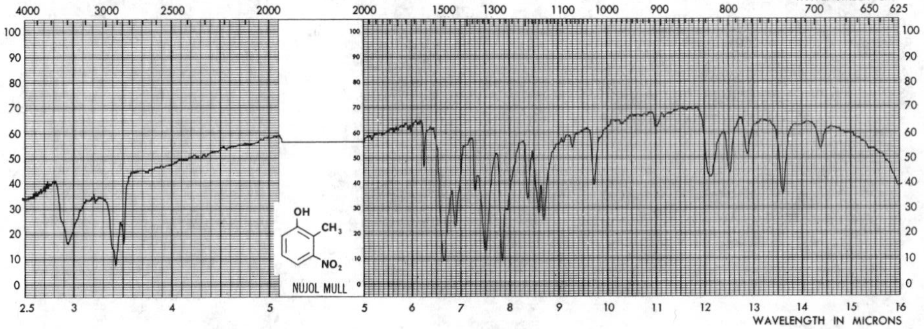

16,074-1
3-Methyl-2-nitrophenol, 99% (2-nitro-m-cresol)
$CH_3C_6H_3(NO_2)OH$
M.W. 153.14 m.p. 35-39° Beil. **6**,385 *IRRITANT*

MELT

H

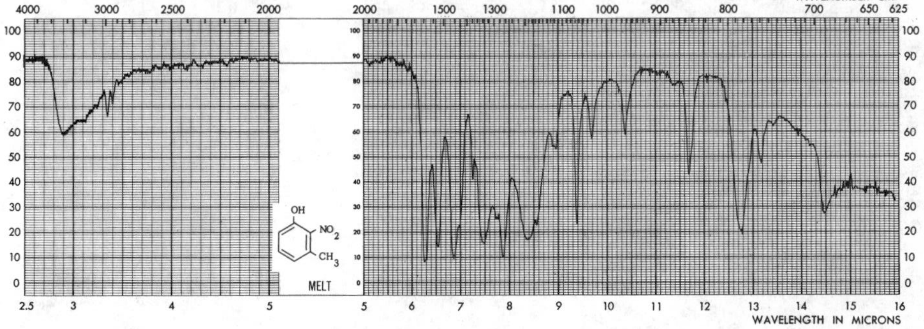

11,584-3 **2-Methyl-3-nitroaniline** (3-nitro-o-toluidine)
$CH_3C_6H_3(NO_2)NH_2$ M.W. 152.15 m.p. 88-90°

NUJOL MULL

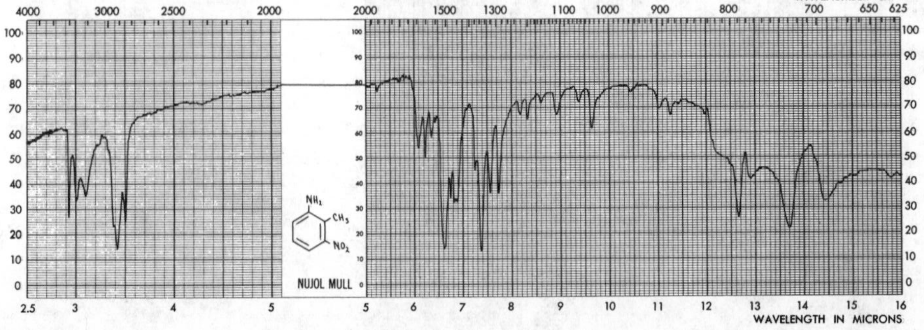

A

M5940-8 **2-Methyl-6-nitroaniline** (6-nitro-o-toluidine)
$CH_3C_6H_3(NO_2)NH_2$ M.W. 152.15
m.p. 93-96°

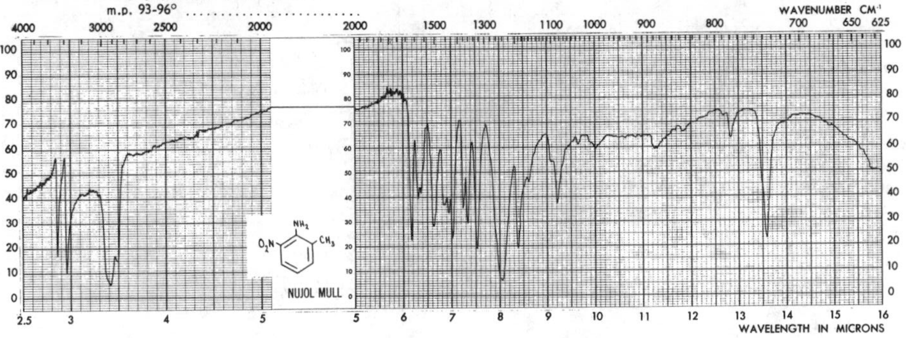

NUJOL MULL

B

17,829-2
2-Chloro-6-nitroaniline, 98%
$ClC_6H_3(NO_2)NH_2$
M.W. 172.57 m.p. 72-75° Beil. **12**(1),356

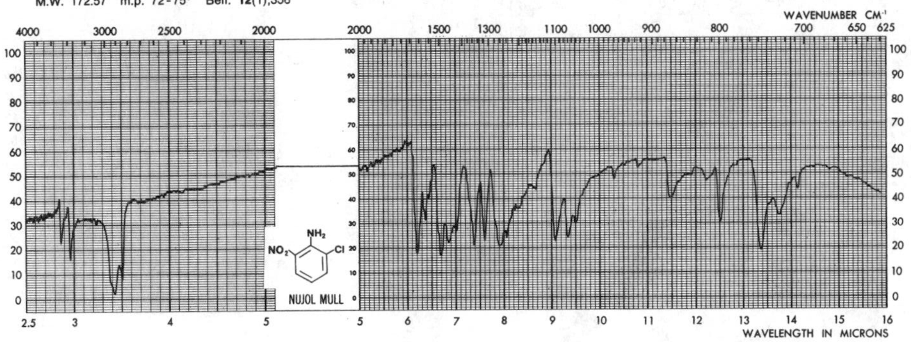

NUJOL MULL

C

N2130-8 **3-Nitro-o-phenylenediamine**
$O_2NC_6H_3(NH_2)_2$ M.W. 153.14 m.p. 157-158°

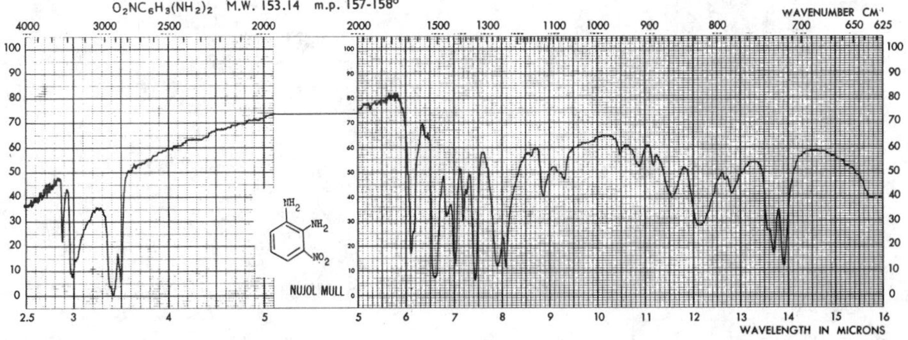

NUJOL MULL

D

A7065-8 **2-Amino-6-nitrophenol**
$H_2NC_6H_3(NO_2)OH$ M.W. 154.13 m.p. 109-112° ..

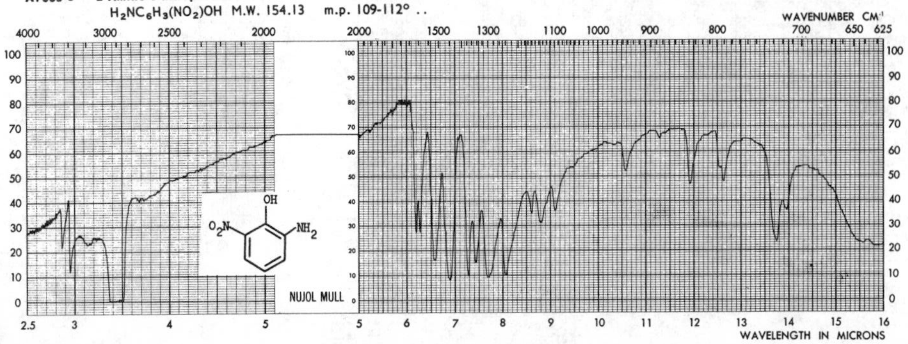

NUJOL MULL

E

14,756-7 **2,3-Dinitrotoluene**
$CH_3C_6H_3(NO_2)_2$ M.W. 182.14 m.p. 59.5-61.5°

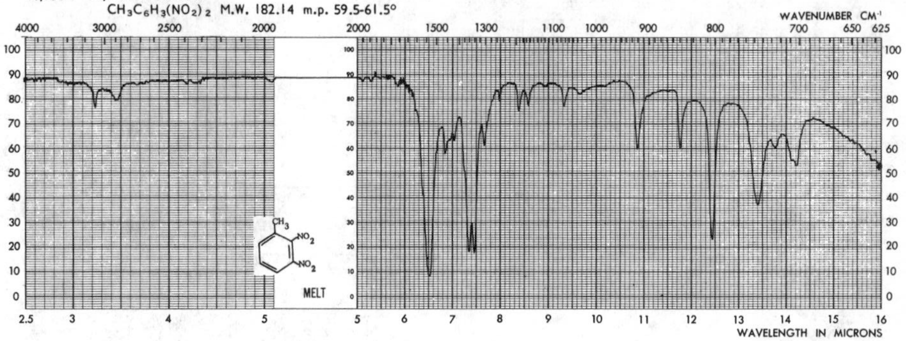

MELT

F

D20,060-3 **2,6-Dinitrotoluene**
$CH_3C_6H_3(NO_2)_2$ M.W. 182.14 m.p. 64-66°

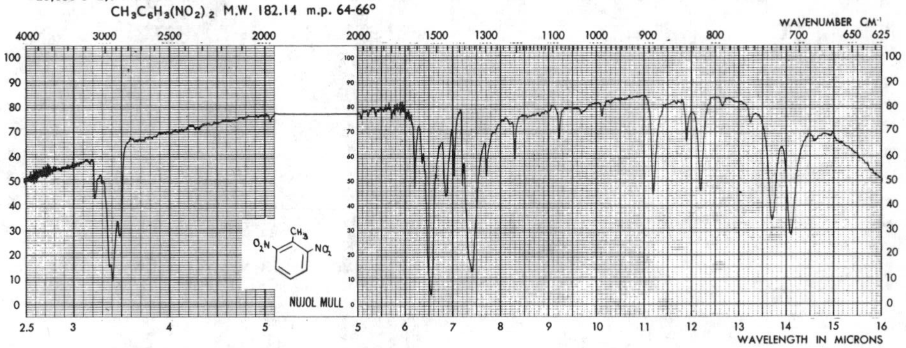

NUJOL MULL

G

C3875-3 **1-Chloro-2,6-dinitrobenzene** (2,6-dinitrochlorobenzene)
$ClC_6H_3(NO_2)_2$ M.W. 202.55 m.p. 85-86° ..

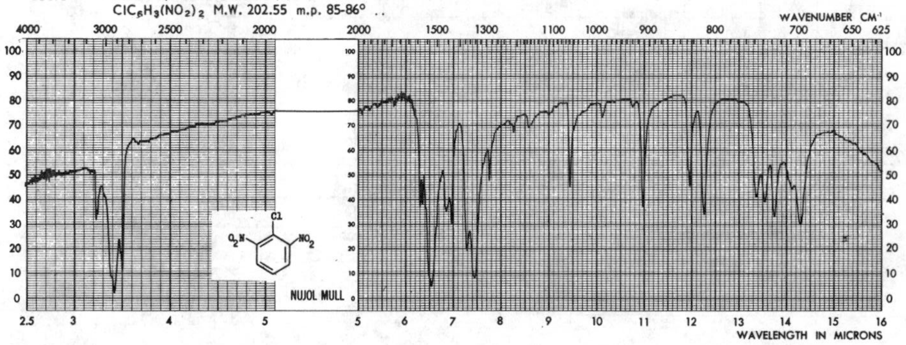

NUJOL MULL

H

D19,880-3 **2,6-Dinitrophenol, moistened with 50% water**
$(O_2N)_2C_6H_3OH$
M.W. 184.11 (dry) ......

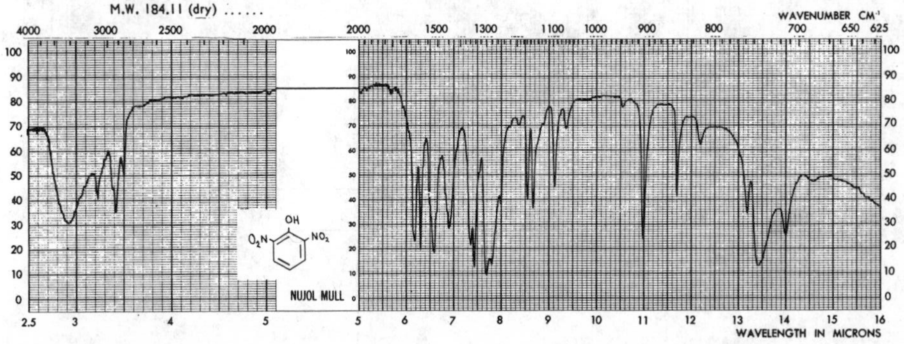

NUJOL MULL

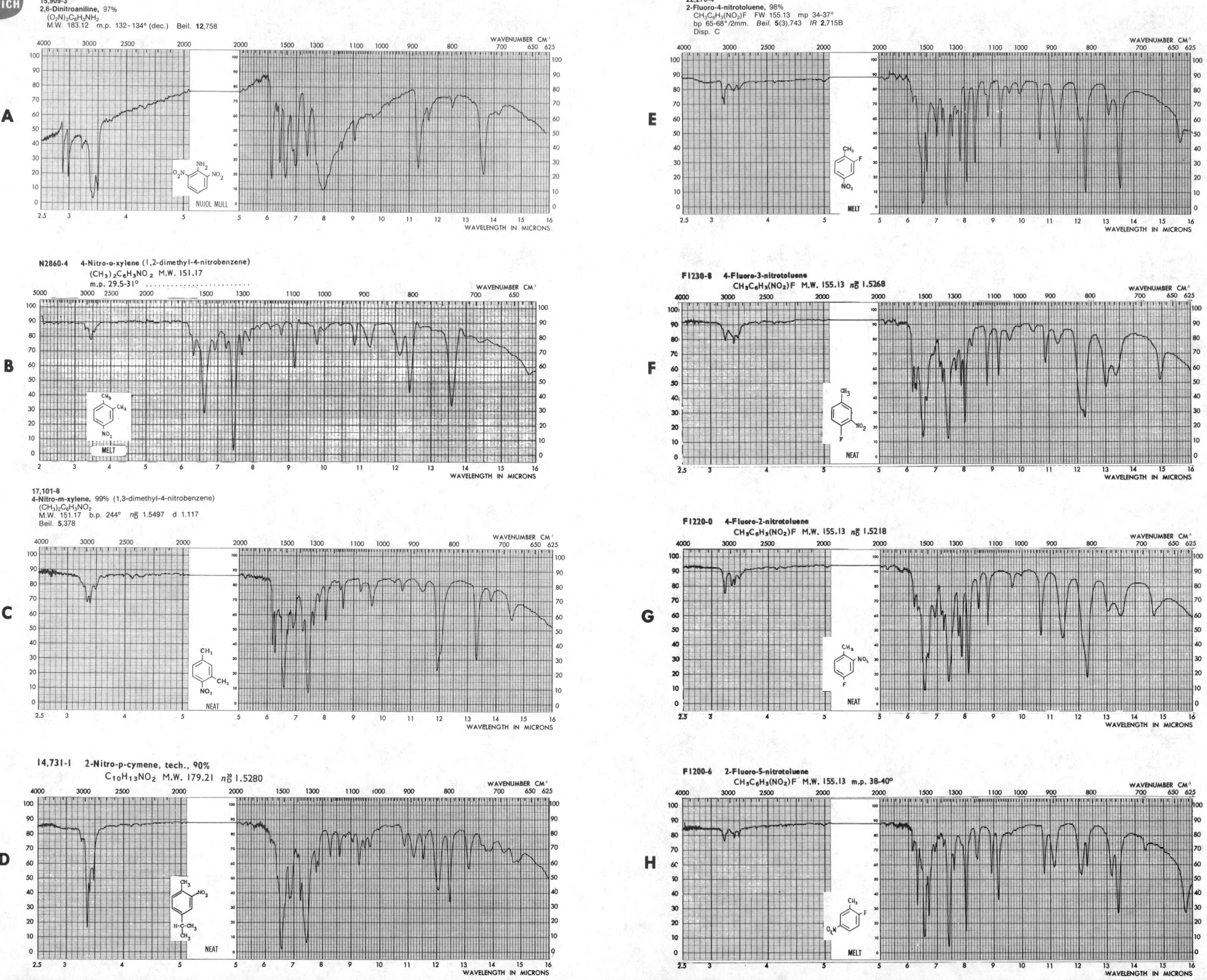
ALDRICH

A
15,909-3
2,6-Dinitroaniline, 97%
$(O_2N)_2C_6H_3NH_2$
M.W. 183.12 m.p. 132-134° (dec.) Beil. 12,758
NUJOL MULL

B
N2860-4 4-Nitro-o-xylene (1,2-dimethyl-4-nitrobenzene)
$(CH_3)_2C_6H_3NO_2$ M.W. 151.17
m.p. 29.5-31°
MELT

C
17,101-8
4-Nitro-m-xylene, 99% (1,3-dimethyl-4-nitrobenzene)
$(CH_3)_2C_6H_3NO_2$
M.W. 151.17 b.p. 244° n_D^{20} 1.5497 d 1.117
Beil. 5,378
NEAT

D
14,731-1 2-Nitro-p-cymene, tech., 90%
$C_{10}H_{13}NO_2$ M.W. 179.21 n_D^{20} 1.5280
NEAT

E
22,270-4
2-Fluoro-4-nitrotoluene, 98%
$CH_3C_6H_3(NO_2)F$ FW 155.13 mp 34-37°
bp 65-68°/2mm. Beil. 5(3),743 IR 2,715B
Disp. C
MELT

F
F1230-8 4-Fluoro-3-nitrotoluene
$CH_3C_6H_3(NO_2)F$ M.W. 155.13 n_D^{20} 1.5268
NEAT

G
F1220-0 4-Fluoro-2-nitrotoluene
$CH_3C_6H_3(NO_2)F$ M.W. 155.13 n_D^{20} 1.5218
NEAT

H
F1200-6 2-Fluoro-5-nitrotoluene
$CH_3C_6H_3(NO_2)F$ M.W. 155.13 m.p. 38-40°
MELT

WAVENUMBER CM⁻¹
WAVELENGTH IN MICRONS

A F1240-5 5-Fluoro-2-nitrotoluene, tech.
$CH_3C_6H_3(NO_2)F$ M.W. 155.13 n_D^{20} 1.5271

B C4380-3 3-Chloro-4-fluoronitrobenzene
$ClC_6H_3(F)NO_2$ M.W. 175.55 m.p. 43-47°

C 12,514-8 2-Chloro-4-nitrotoluene
$CH_3C_6H_3(NO_2)Cl$ M.W. 171.58 m.p. 60.5-62.5°

D 19,531-6
3-Methyl-4-nitrobenzyl chloride, 99%
$CH_3C_6H_3(NO_2)CH_2Cl$ FW 185.61 mp 15°
bp 104-107°/0.400mm. n_D^{20} 1.5745 d 1.251
Disp. C

E 19,232-5
4-Methyl-3-nitrobenzyl chloride, 98%
$CH_3C_6H_3(NO_2)CH_2Cl$ FW 185.61 mp 48-50°
bp 87-88°/0mm. *Fieser* 7,10 Disp. C

F 19,177-9
5-Methyl-2-nitrobenzyl chloride
$CH_3C_6H_3(NO_2)CH_2Cl$ FW 185.61 mp 41-43°
Disp. C

G 18,763-1
3-Methyl-4-nitrobenzyl alcohol, 98%
$CH_3C_6H_3(NO_2)CH_2OH$ FW 167.16 mp 57-58°
Disp. C

H 18,415-2
2-Chloro-4-nitrobenzyl alcohol, 98%
$ClC_6H_3(NO_2)CH_2OH$
M.W. 187.58 m.p. 79-83°

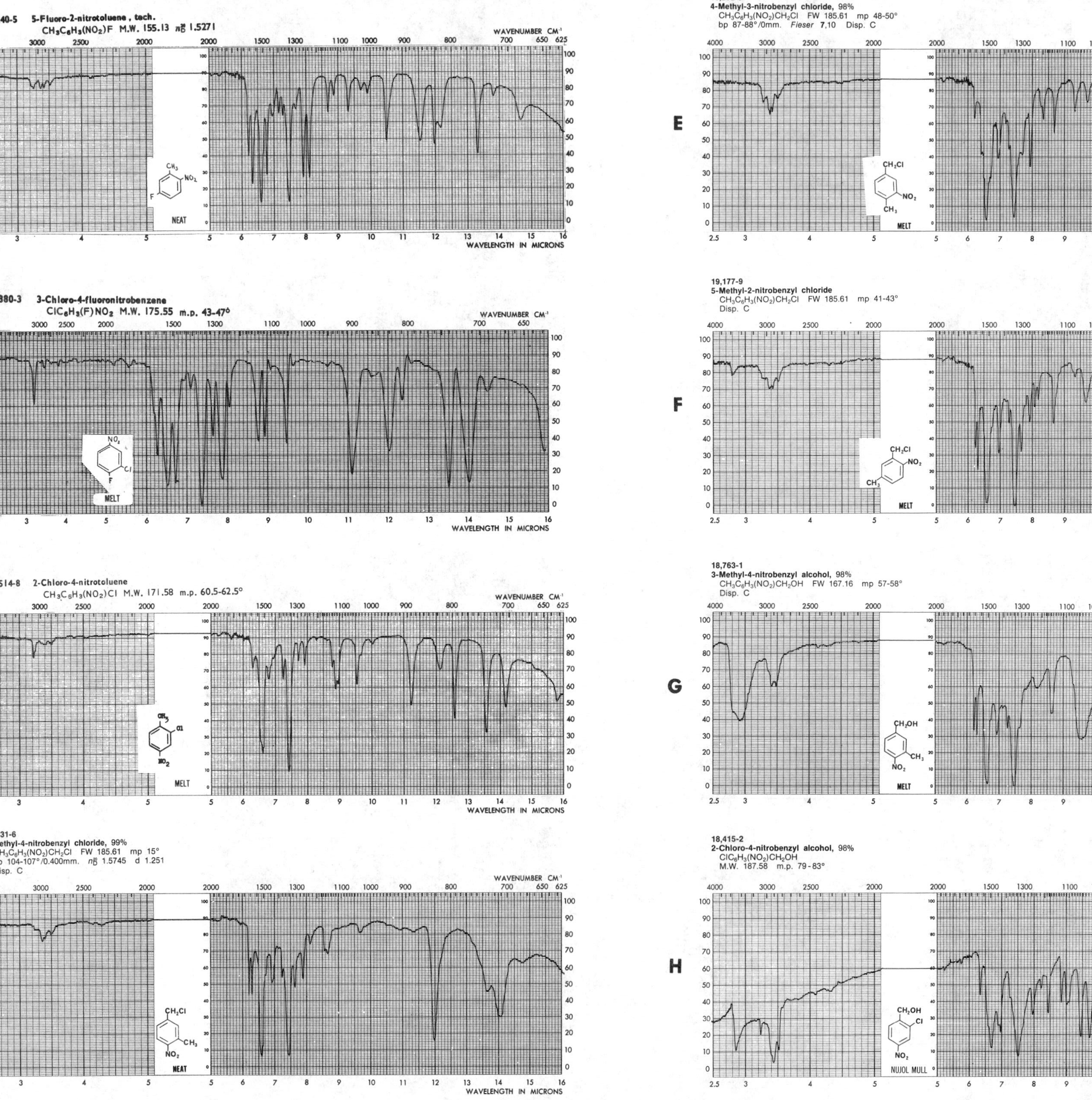

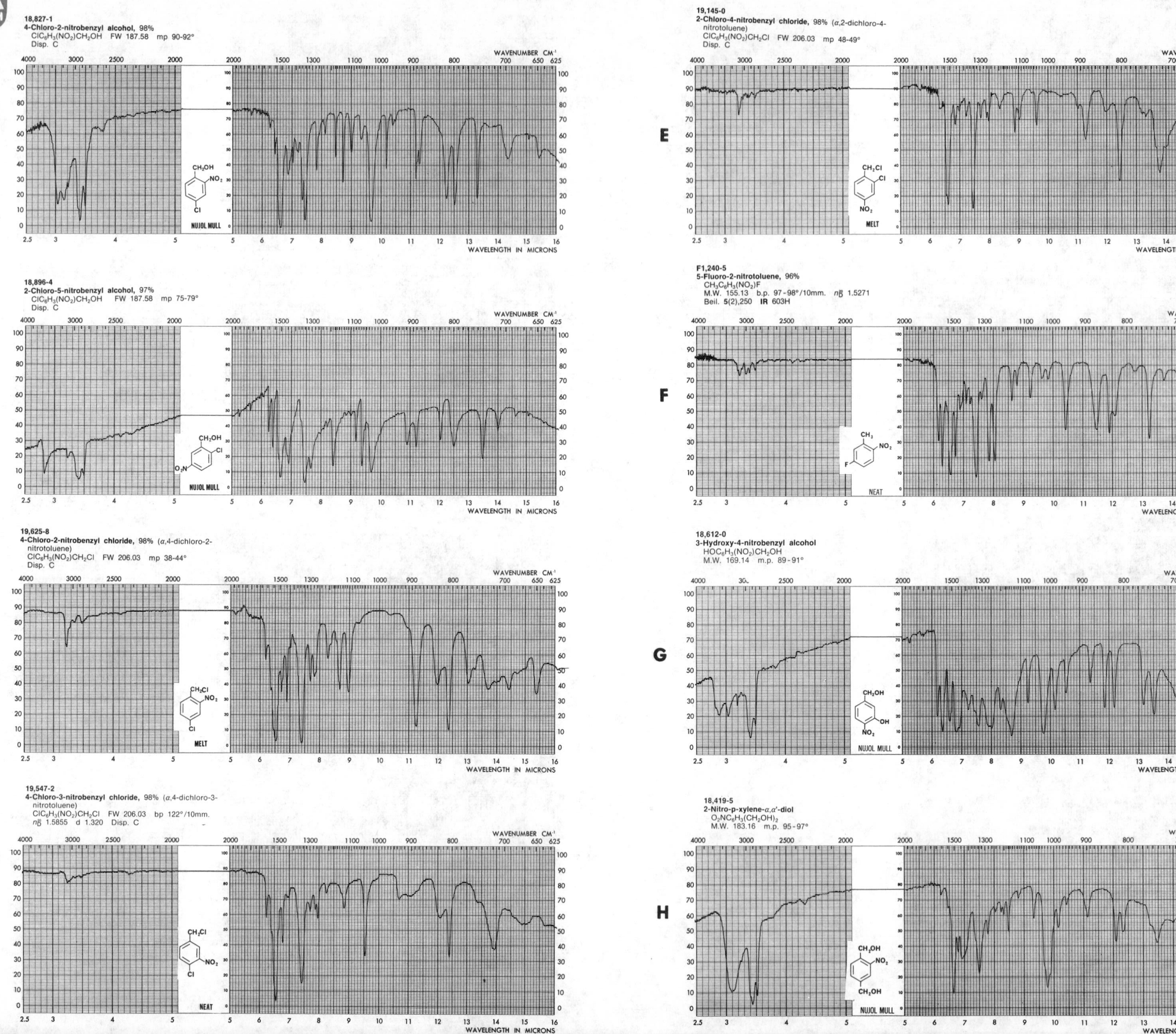

A
18,827-1
4-Chloro-2-nitrobenzyl alcohol, 98%
$ClC_6H_3(NO_2)CH_2OH$ FW 187.58 mp 90-92°
Disp. C
NUJOL MULL

B
18,896-4
2-Chloro-5-nitrobenzyl alcohol, 97%
$ClC_6H_3(NO_2)CH_2OH$ FW 187.58 mp 75-79°
Disp. C
NUJOL MULL

C
19,625-8
4-Chloro-2-nitrobenzyl chloride, 98% (α,4-dichloro-2-nitrotoluene)
$ClC_6H_3(NO_2)CH_2Cl$ FW 206.03 mp 38-44°
Disp. C
MELT

D
19,547-2
4-Chloro-3-nitrobenzyl chloride, 98% (α,4-dichloro-3-nitrotoluene)
$ClC_6H_3(NO_2)CH_2Cl$ FW 206.03 bp 122°/10mm.
n_D^{20} 1.5855 d 1.320 Disp. C
NEAT

E
19,145-0
2-Chloro-4-nitrobenzyl chloride, 98% (α,2-dichloro-4-nitrotoluene)
$ClC_6H_3(NO_2)CH_2Cl$ FW 206.03 mp 48-49°
Disp. C
MELT

F
F1,240-5
5-Fluoro-2-nitrotoluene, 96%
$CH_3C_6H_3(NO_2)F$
M.W. 155.13 b.p. 97-98°/10mm. n_D^{20} 1.5271
Beil. **5**(2),250 **IR** 603H
NEAT

G
18,612-0
3-Hydroxy-4-nitrobenzyl alcohol
$HOC_6H_3(NO_2)CH_2OH$
M.W. 169.14 m.p. 89-91°
NUJOL MULL

H
18,419-5
2-Nitro-p-xylene-α,α'-diol
$O_2NC_6H_3(CH_2OH)_2$
M.W. 183.16 m.p. 95-97°
NUJOL MULL

A. 19,383-6 **3-Methoxy-4-nitrobenzyl alcohol,** 99%
$CH_3OC_6H_3(NO_2)CH_2OH$ FW 183.16

B. 14,145-3 **5-Chloro-2-nitrotoluene**
$CH_3C_6H_3(NO_2)Cl$ M.W. 171.58
m.p. 25-27°

C. 18,740-2 **5-Chloro-2-nitrobenzyl alcohol,** 97%
$ClC_6H_3(NO_2)CH_2OH$
M.W. 187.58 m.p. 78-79°

D. 18,726-7 **4-Methyl-3-nitrobenzyl alcohol,** 99%
$CH_3C_6H_3(NO_2)CH_2OH$
M.W. 167.16 m.p. 39-41°

E. 18,741-0 **5-Methyl-2-nitrobenzyl alcohol,** 99%
$CH_3C_6H_3(NO_2)CH_2OH$
M.W. 167.16 m.p. 66-67°

F. 14,146-1 **3-Chloro-4-nitrotoluene**
$CH_3C_6H_3(NO_2)Cl$ M.W. 171.58 n_D^{20} 1.5400
b.p. 219°

G. 18,715-1 **2-Chloro-4-nitrobenzyl bromide,** tech., 90%
(α-bromo-2-chloro-4-nitrotoluene)
$ClC_6H_3(NO_2)CH_2Br$
M.W. 250.49 m.p. 50° Beil. 5,335

H. 10,170-2 **4-Chloro-2-nitrotoluene**
$CH_3C_6H_3(NO_2)Cl$ M.W. 171.58 m.p. 36-38°

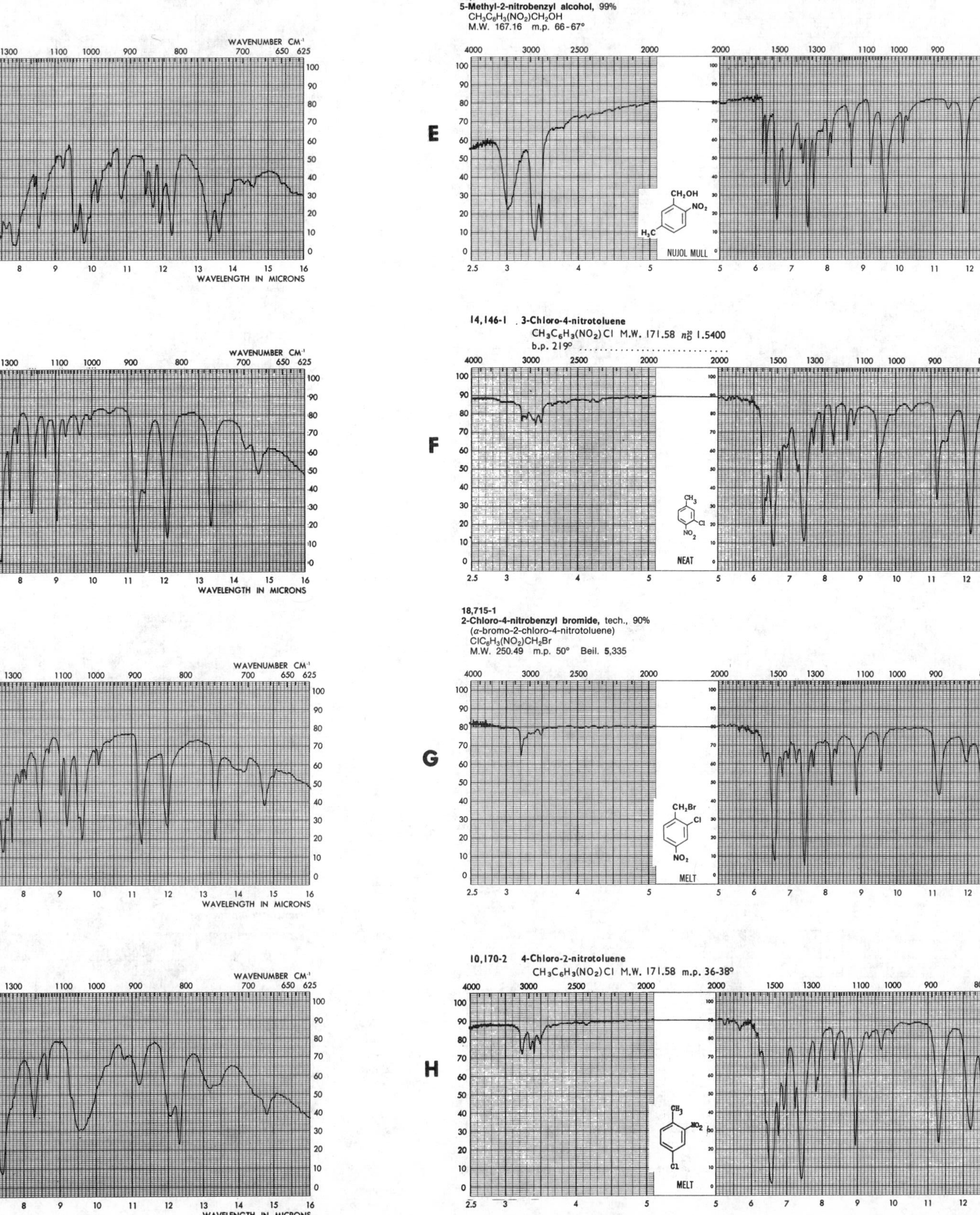

A C6220-4 4-Chloro-3-nitrotoluene
$CH_3C_6H_3(NO_2)Cl$ M.W. 171.58
n_D^{20} 1.5572 m.p. 5-6°
NEAT

B 18,416-0
4-Chloro-3-nitrobenzyl alcohol, 98%
$ClC_6H_3(NO_2)CH_2OH$
m.p. 62-64°
MELT

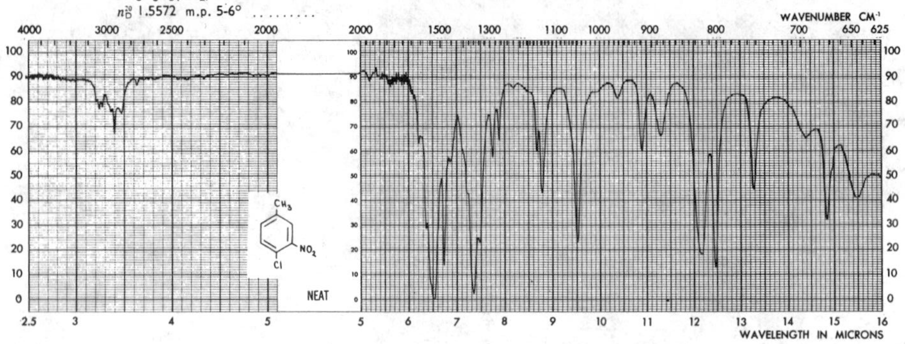

C D6880-0 3,4-Dichloronitrobenzene (1,2-dichloro-4-nitrobenzene)
$Cl_2C_6H_3NO_2$ M.W. 192.00 m.p. 40.5-42°
MELT

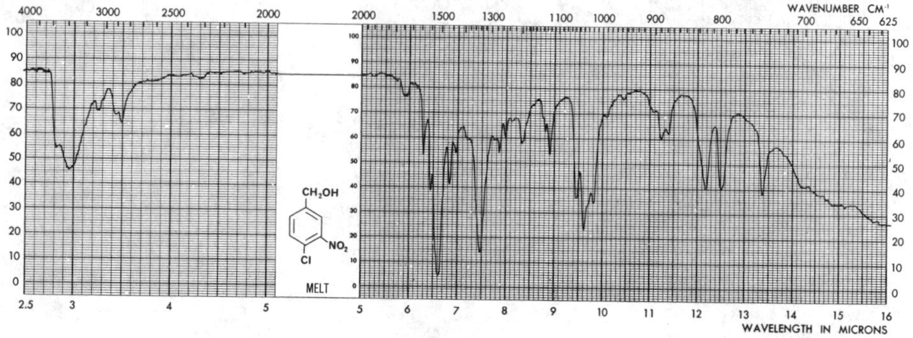

D D6840-1 2,4-Dichloronitrobenzene (1,3-dichloro-4-nitrobenzene)
$Cl_2C_6H_3NO_2$ M.W. 192.00 m.p. 29-32°
MELT

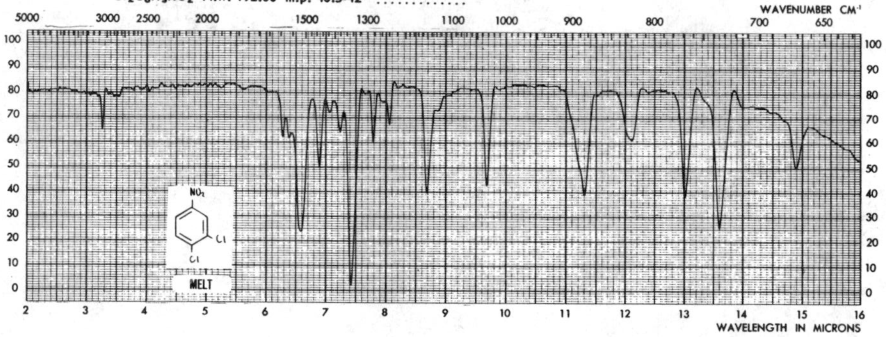

E D6860-6 2,5-Dichloronitrobenzene (1,4-dichloro-2-nitrobenzene)
$Cl_2C_6H_3NO_2$ M.W. 192.00 m.p. 52-54°
MELT

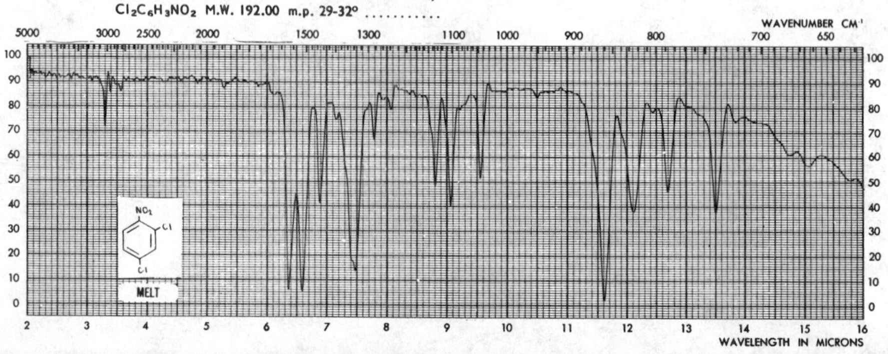

F B7440-2 2-Bromo-4-nitrotoluene
$CH_3C_6H_3(NO_2)Br$ M.W. 216.04 m.p. 76-77°
NUJOL MULL

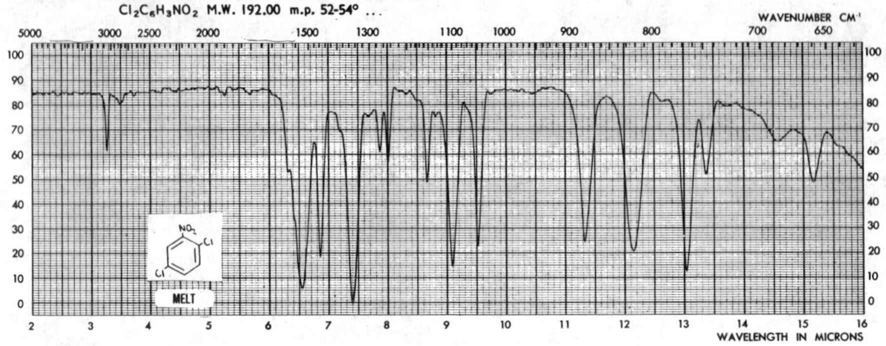

G 15,318-4 1-Bromo-4-chloro-2-nitrobenzene
$BrC_6H_3(Cl)NO_2$ M.W. 236.46
m.p. 67-69°
MELT

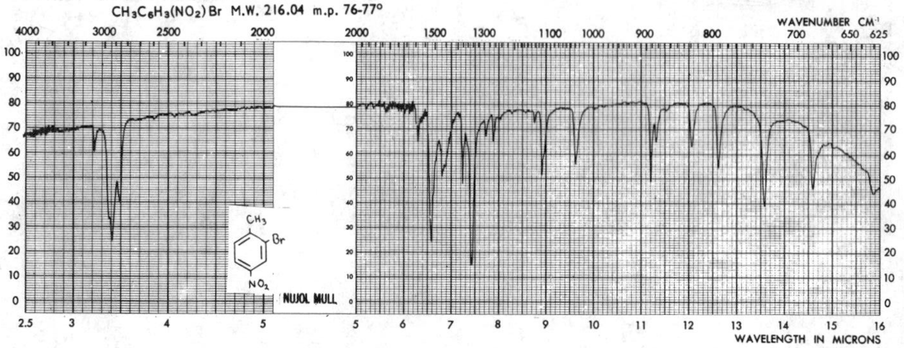

H D4200-3 2,5-Dibromonitrobenzene
$Br_2C_6H_3NO_2$ M.W. 280.91 m.p. 82-84°
MELT

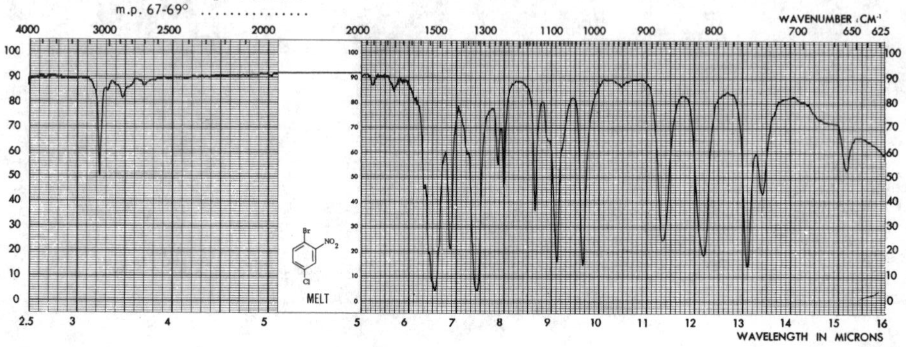

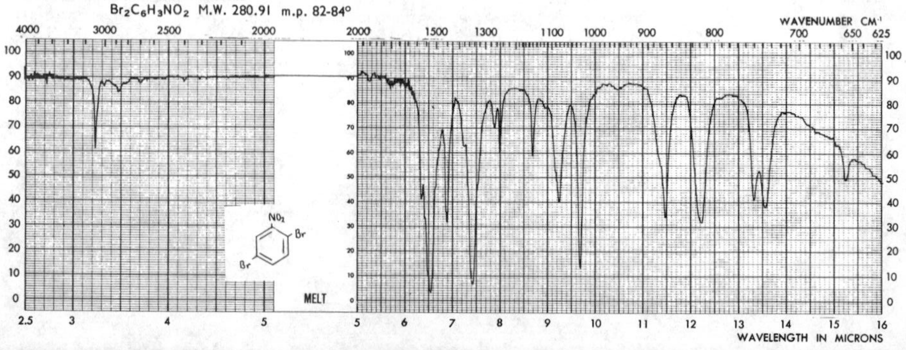

A

12,567-9 2-Iodo-4-nitrotoluene
$CH_3C_6H_3(NO_2)I$ M.W. 263.03 m.p. 51-53°
MELT

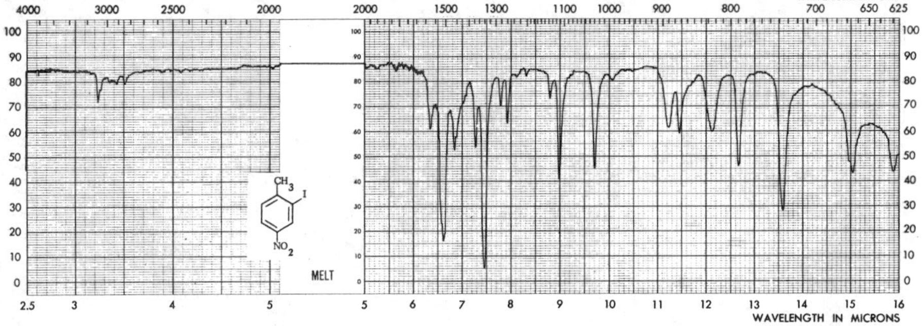

B

C6040-6 2-Chloro-5-nitrobenzotrifluoride (2-chloro-5-nitro-α,α,α-trifluorotoluene)
$ClC_6H_3(NO_2)CF_3$ M.W. 225.55 n_D^{20} 1.5083
NEAT

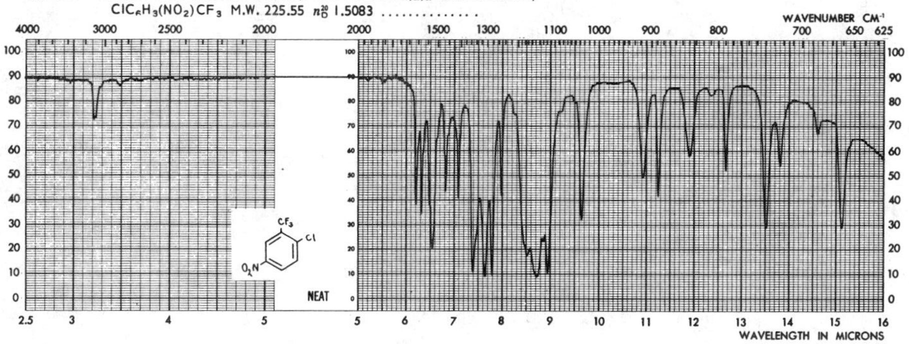

C

21,433-7
4-Fluoro-3-nitrobenzotrifluoride, 99% (3-nitro-α,α,α,4-tetrafluorotoluene)
$FC_6H_3(NO_2)CF_3$ FW 209.10 bp 92°/15mm.
n_D^{20} 1.4625 d 1.494 *Beil.* 5(4),853 Disp. C
NEAT

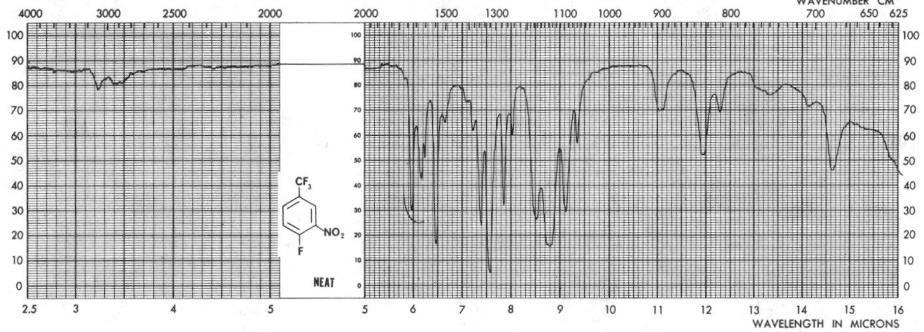

D

C6060-0 4-Chloro-3-nitrobenzotrifluoride (4-chloro-3-nitro-α,α,α-trifluorotoluene)
$ClC_6H_3(NO_2)CF_3$ M.W. 225.55 n_D^{20} 1.4893
NEAT

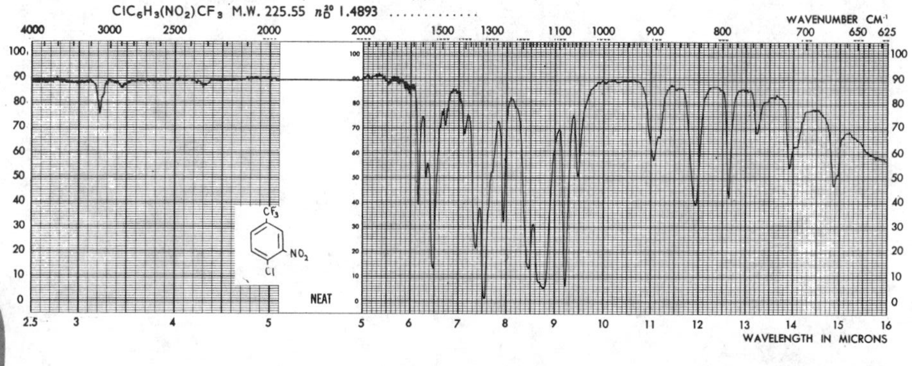

E

C6080-5 5-Chloro-2-nitrobenzotrifluoride (5-chloro-2-nitro-α,α,α-trifluorotoluene), tech.
$ClC_6H_3(NO_2)CF_3$ M.W. 225.55 n_D^{20} 1.4961
NEAT

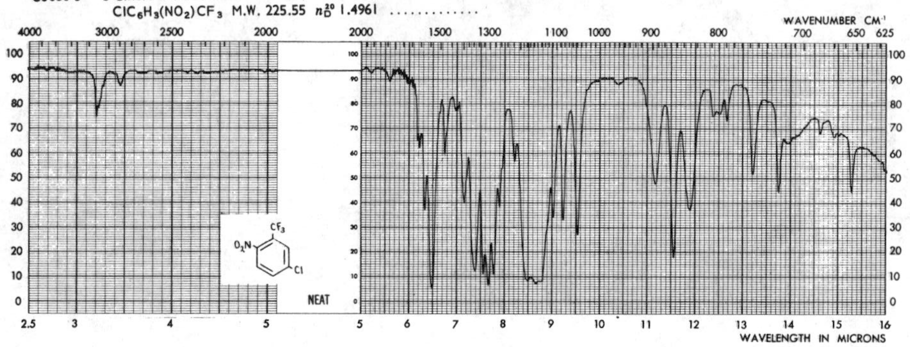

F

22,282-8
4-Methoxy-3-nitrobenzotrifluoride, 99%
$CH_3OC_6H_3(NO_2)CF_3$ FW 221.14 mp 47-49°
Beil. 6(3),1387 Disp. C
MELT

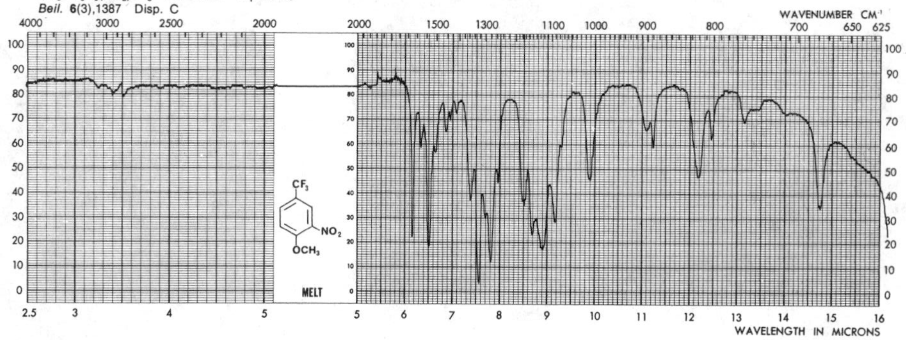

G

13,982-3 4-Methyl-3-nitroanisole
$CH_3C_6H_3(NO_2)OCH_3$ M.W. 167.16 n_D^{20} 1.5530
b.p. 266-267°
NEAT

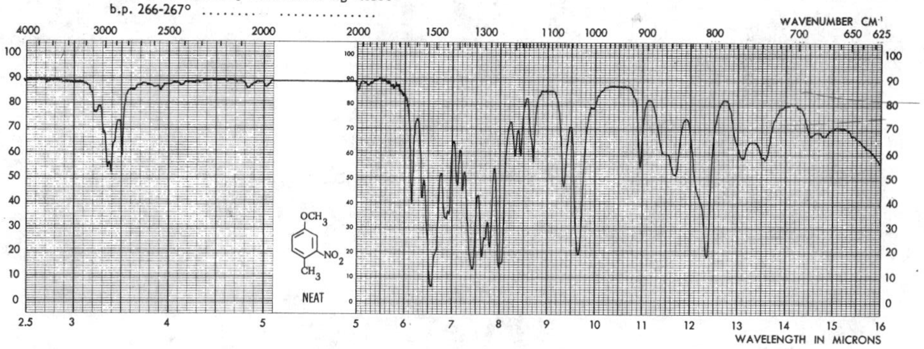

H

15,223-4 3-Methyl-4-nitroanisole
$CH_3C_6H_3(NO_2)OCH_3$ M.W. 167.16
m.p. 48-50°
NUJOL MULL

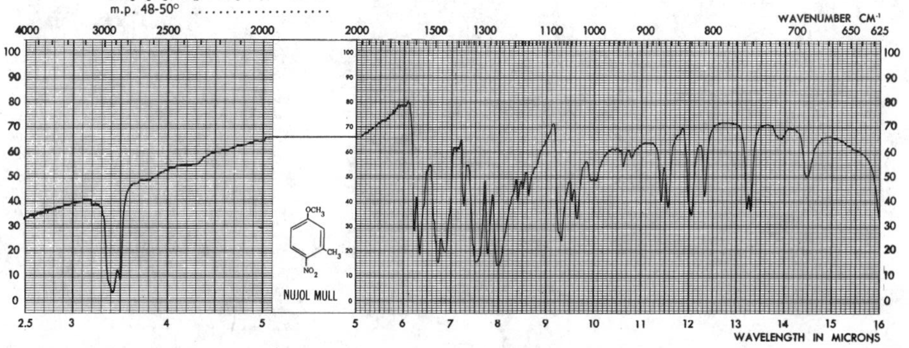

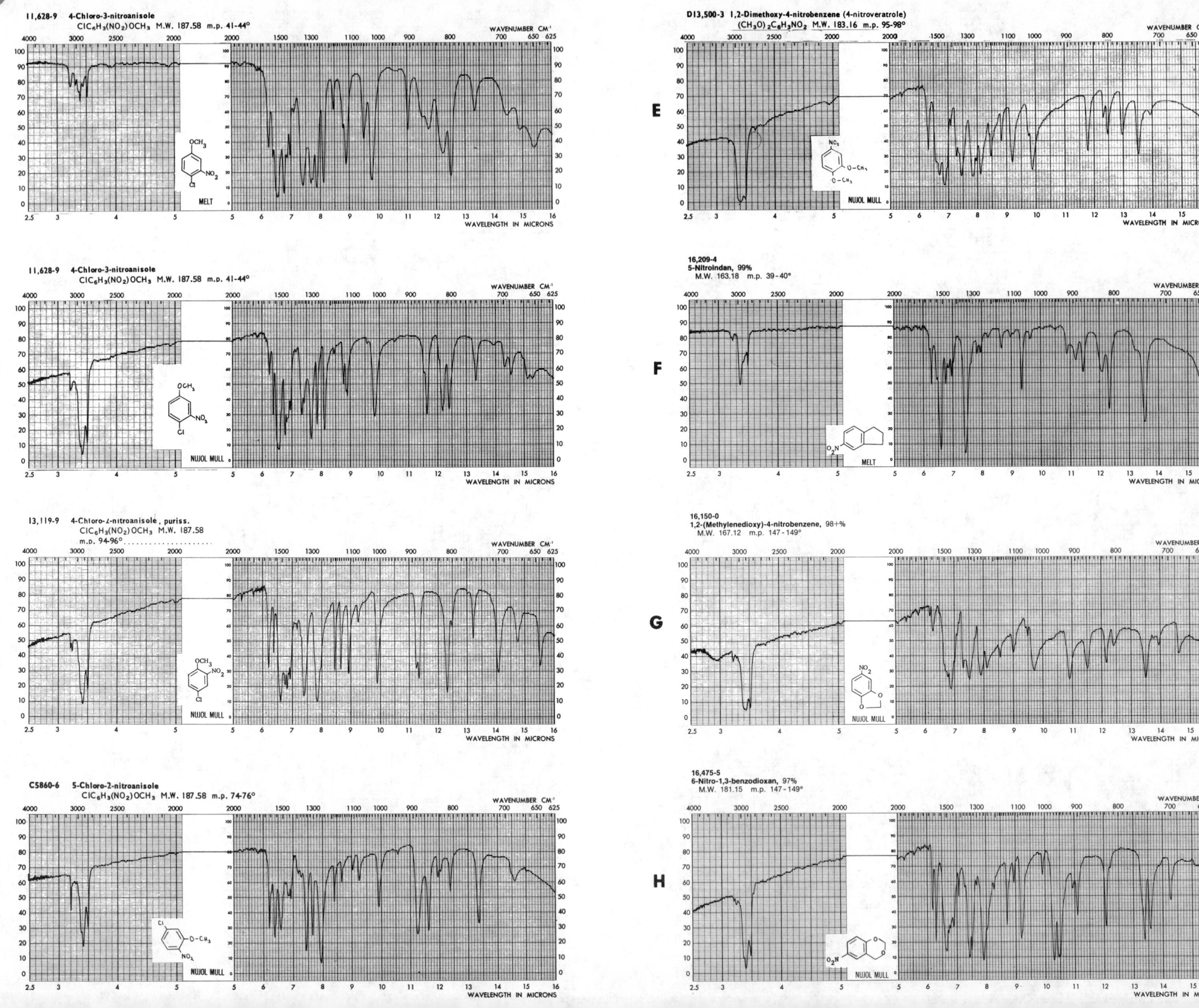
A
11,628-9 4-Chloro-3-nitroanisole
$ClC_6H_3(NO_2)OCH_3$ M.W. 187.58 m.p. 41-44°
MELT
B
11,628-9 4-Chloro-3-nitroanisole
$ClC_6H_3(NO_2)OCH_3$ M.W. 187.58 m.p. 41-44°
NUJOL MULL
C
13,119-9 4-Chloro-2-nitroanisole, puriss.
$ClC_6H_3(NO_2)OCH_3$ M.W. 187.58
m.p. 94-96°
NUJOL MULL
D
C5860-6 5-Chloro-2-nitroanisole
$ClC_6H_3(NO_2)OCH_3$ M.W. 187.58 m.p. 74-76°
NUJOL MULL
E
D13,500-3 1,2-Dimethoxy-4-nitrobenzene (4-nitroveratrole)
$(CH_3O)_2C_6H_3NO_2$ M.W. 183.16 m.p. 95-98°
NUJOL MULL
F
16,209-4
5-Nitroindan, 99%
M.W. 163.18 m.p. 39-40°
MELT
G
16,150-0
1,2-(Methylenedioxy)-4-nitrobenzene, 98+%
M.W. 167.12 m.p. 147-149°
NUJOL MULL
H
16,475-5
6-Nitro-1,3-benzodioxan, 97%
M.W. 181.15 m.p. 147-149°
NUJOL MULL
WAVENUMBER CM⁻¹
WAVELENGTH IN MICRONS

A

12,605-5 **2,5-Diethoxynitrobenzene**
$(C_2H_5O)_2C_6H_3NO_2$ M.W. 211.22 m.p. 48-51°
MELT

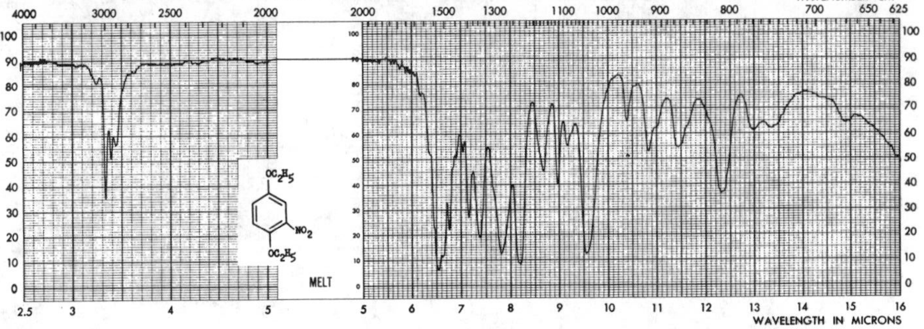

B

M6265-4 **3-Methyl-4-nitrophenol** (4-nitro-m-cresol)
$CH_3C_6H_3(NO_2)OH$ M.W. 153.14 m.p. 125-126°
NUJOL MULL

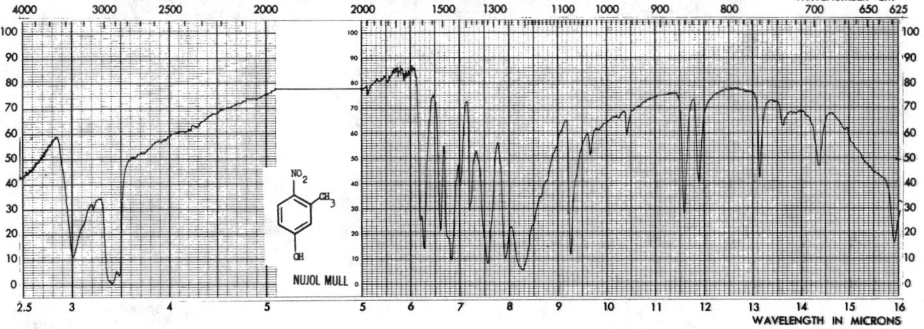

C

13,981-5 **4-Methyl-3-nitrophenol** (3-nitro-p-cresol)
$CH_3C_6H_3(NO_2)OH$ M.W. 153.14
m.p. 78-81°
NUJOL MULL

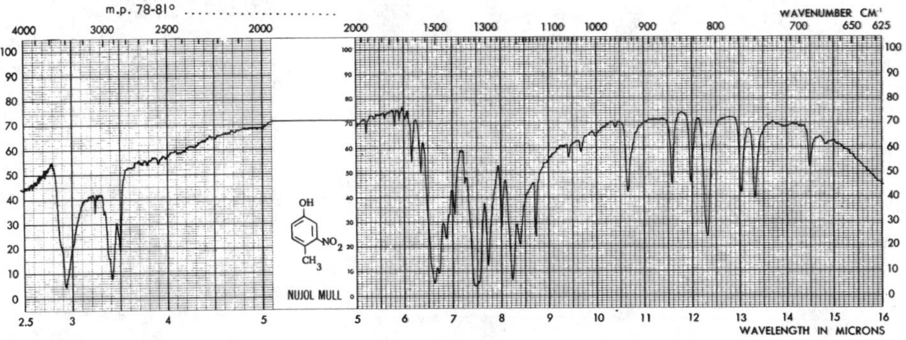

D

M6280-8 **4-Methyl-2-nitrophenol** (2-nitro-p-cresol)
$CH_3C_6H_3(NO_2)OH$ M.W. 153.14 m.p. 35°
MELT

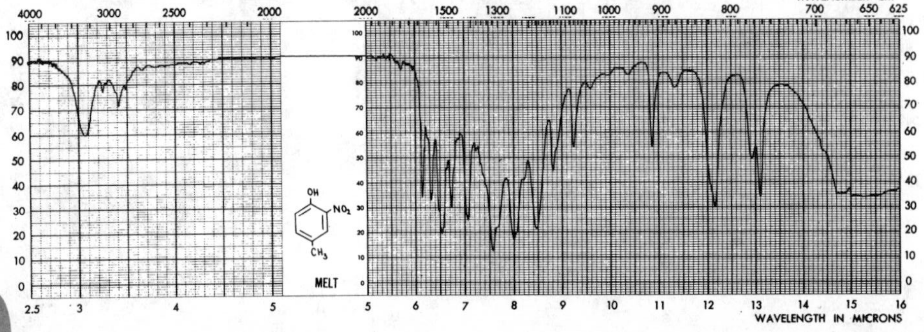

E

13,779-0 **5-Methyl-2-nitrophenol** (6-nitro-m-cresol)
$CH_3C_6H_3(NO_2)OH$ M.W. 153.14
m.p. 53-56°
MELT

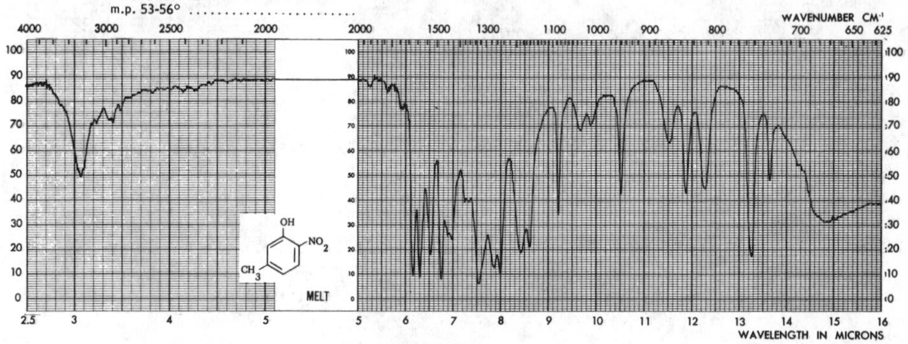

F

C5490-2 **2-Chloromethyl-4-nitrophenol** (α-chloro-4-nitro-o-cresol)
$ClCH_2C_6H_3(NO_2)OH$ M.W. 187.58
m.p. 126-128° (dec.)
NUJOL MULL

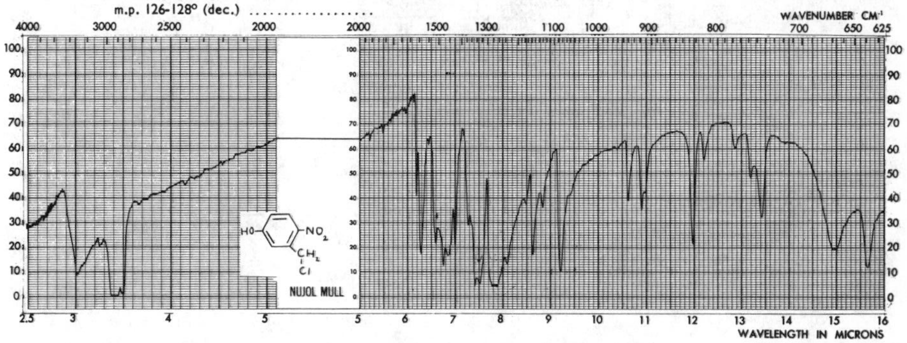

G

B7270-1 **2-Bromomethyl-4-nitrophenol** (α-bromo-4-nitro-o-cresol)
$BrCH_2C_6H_3(NO_2)OH$ M.W. 232.04
m.p. 153-155°
NUJOL MULL

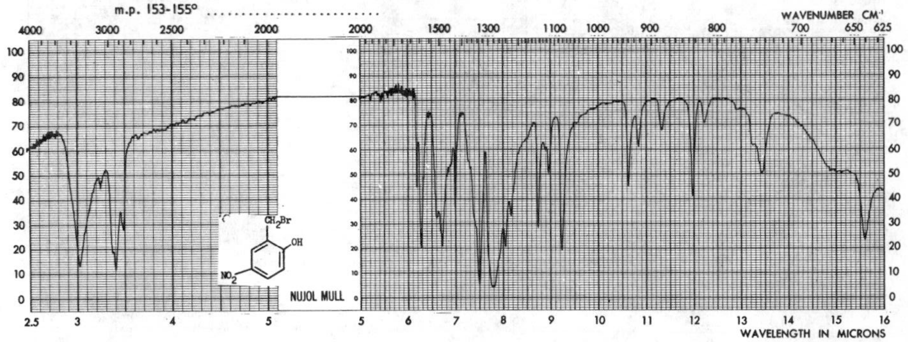

H

16,348-1
2-Methoxy-5-nitrobenzyl bromide (2-bromomethyl-4-nitroanisole, Koshland's Reagent II)
$CH_3OC_6H_3(NO_2)CH_2Br$
M.W. 246.07 m.p. 78-80° *LACHRYMATOR*
NUJOL MULL

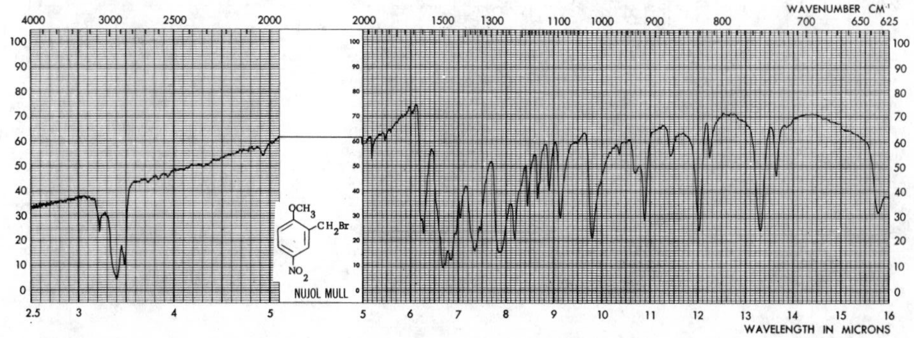

A

N2780-2 **4-Nitro-3-trifluoromethylphenol**
$O_2NC_6H_3(CF_3)OH$ M.W. 207.11 m.p. 77-80°
NUJOL MULL

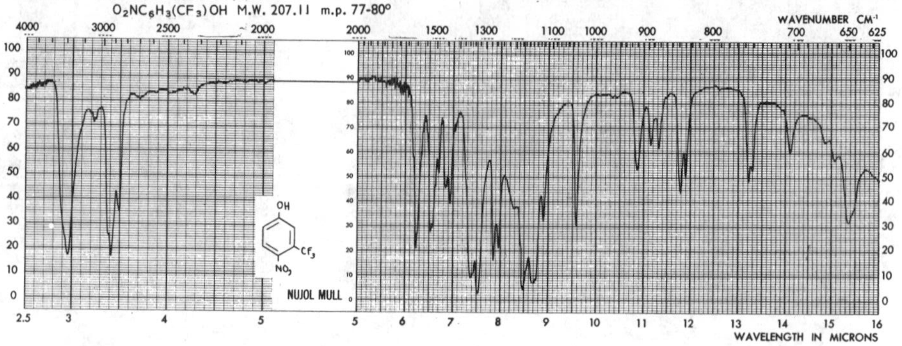

B

18,410-1
5-Fluoro-2-nitrophenol
$FC_6H_3(NO_2)OH$
M.W. 157.1 m.p. 25-28° Beil. **6**(2),225
NEAT

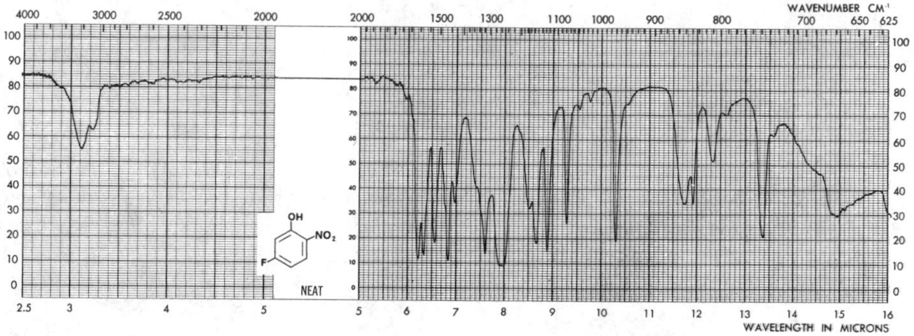

C

18,412-8
3-Fluoro-4-nitrophenol, 98%
$FC_6H_3(NO_2)OH$
M.W. 157.1 m.p. 85-88°
NUJOL MULL

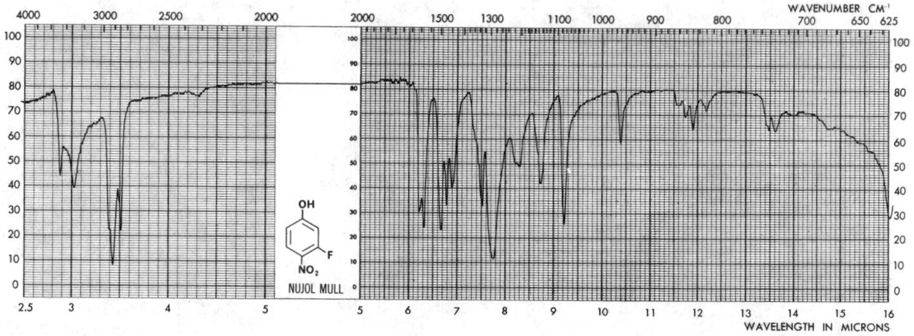

D

C6120-8 **2-Chloro-4-nitrophenol**
$ClC_6H_3(NO_2)OH$ M.W. 173.56
m.p. 105-106°
NUJOL MULL

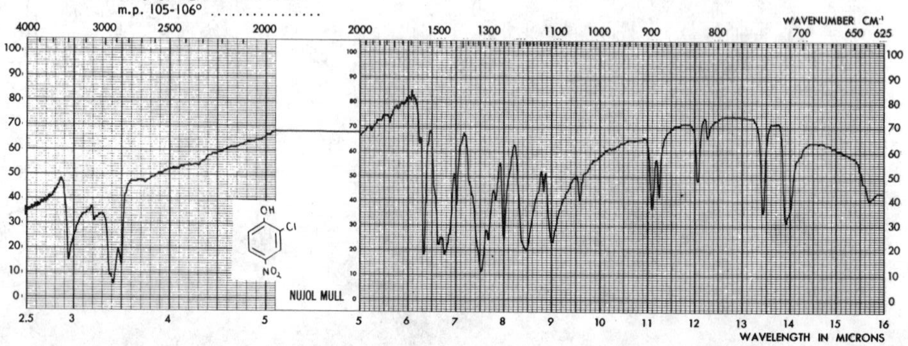

E

N1555-3 **4-Nitrocatechol**, reagent for germanium
$O_2NC_6H_3$-1,2-$(OH)_2$ M.W. 155.11
m.p. 174-176°
NUJOL MULL

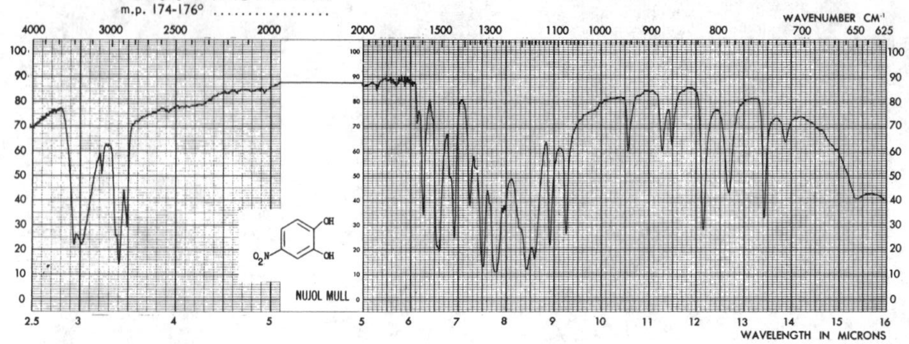

F

A7040-2 **2-Amino-4-nitrophenol**
$H_2NC_6H_3(NO_2)OH$ M.W. 154.13
m.p. 145-147°
NUJOL MULL

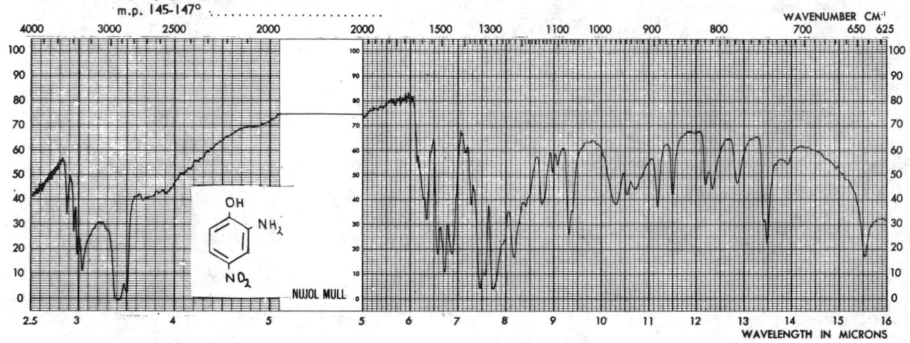

G

A7060-7 **2-Amino-5-nitrophenol, tech.**
$H_2NC_6H_3(NO_2)OH$ M.W. 154.13 m.p. 195-198°
NUJOL MULL

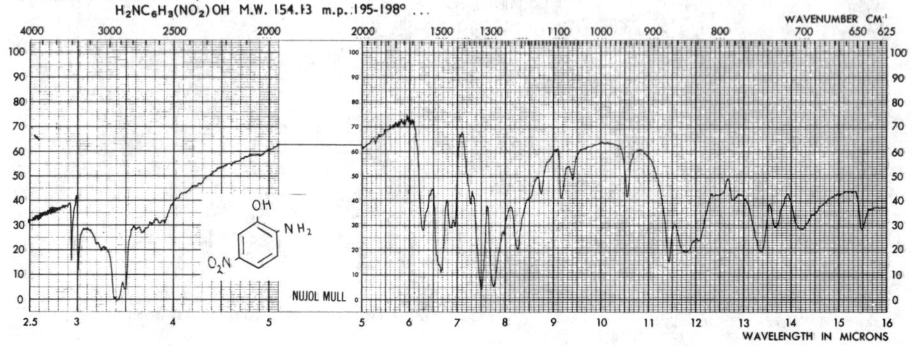

H

14,721-4 **4-Amino-2-nitrophenol** (4-hydroxy-3-nitroaniline)
$H_2NC_6H_3(NO_2)OH$ M.W. 154.13
m.p. 125-127°
NUJOL MULL

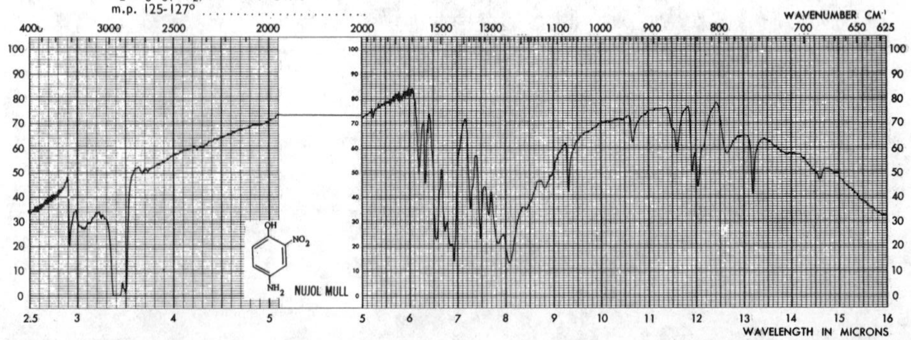

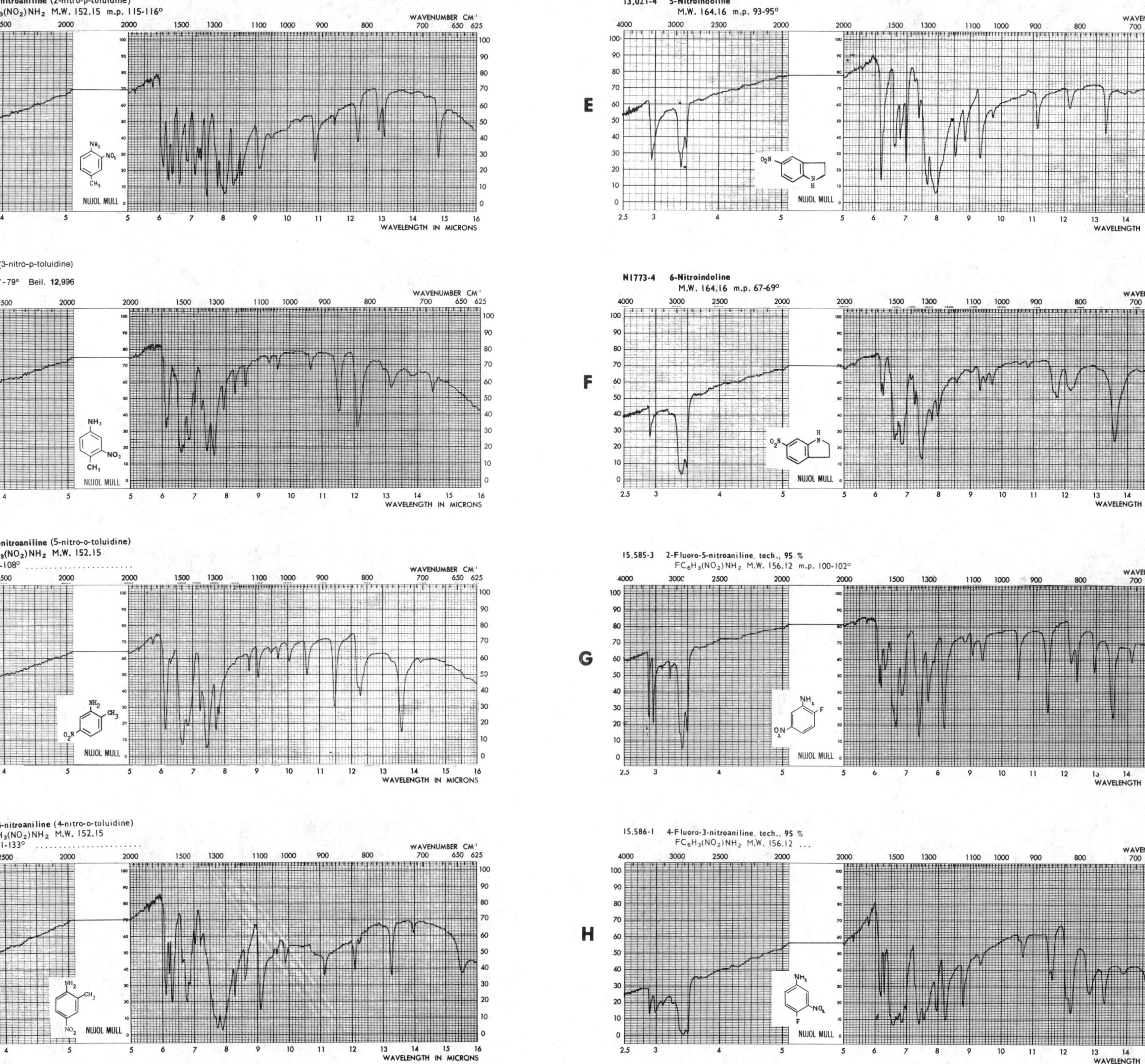
A
M5960-2 4-Methyl-2-nitroaniline (2-nitro-p-toluidine)
$CH_3C_6H_3(NO_2)NH_2$ M.W. 152.15 m.p. 115-116°
NUJOL MULL
B
M5,980-7
4-Methyl-3-nitroaniline (3-nitro-p-toluidine)
$CH_3C_6H_3(NO_2)NH_2$
M.W. 152.15 m.p. 77-79° Beil. 12,996
NUJOL MULL
C
M5938-6 2-Methyl-5-nitroaniline (5-nitro-o-toluidine)
$CH_3C_6H_3(NO_2)NH_2$ M.W. 152.15
m.p. 107-108°
NUJOL MULL
D
14,643-9 2-Methyl-4-nitroaniline (4-nitro-o-toluidine)
$CH_3C_6H_3(NO_2)NH_2$ M.W. 152.15
m.p. 131-133°
NUJOL MULL
E
13,021-4 5-Nitroindoline
M.W. 164.16 m.p. 93-95°
NUJOL MULL
F
N1773-4 6-Nitroindoline
M.W. 164.16 m.p. 67-69°
NUJOL MULL
G
15,585-3 2-Fluoro-5-nitroaniline, tech., 95 %
$FC_6H_3(NO_2)NH_2$ M.W. 156.12 m.p. 100-102°
NUJOL MULL
H
15,586-1 4-Fluoro-3-nitroaniline, tech., 95 %
$FC_6H_3(NO_2)NH_2$ M.W. 156.12 ...
NUJOL MULL
WAVENUMBER CM⁻¹
WAVELENGTH IN MICRONS
ALDRICH

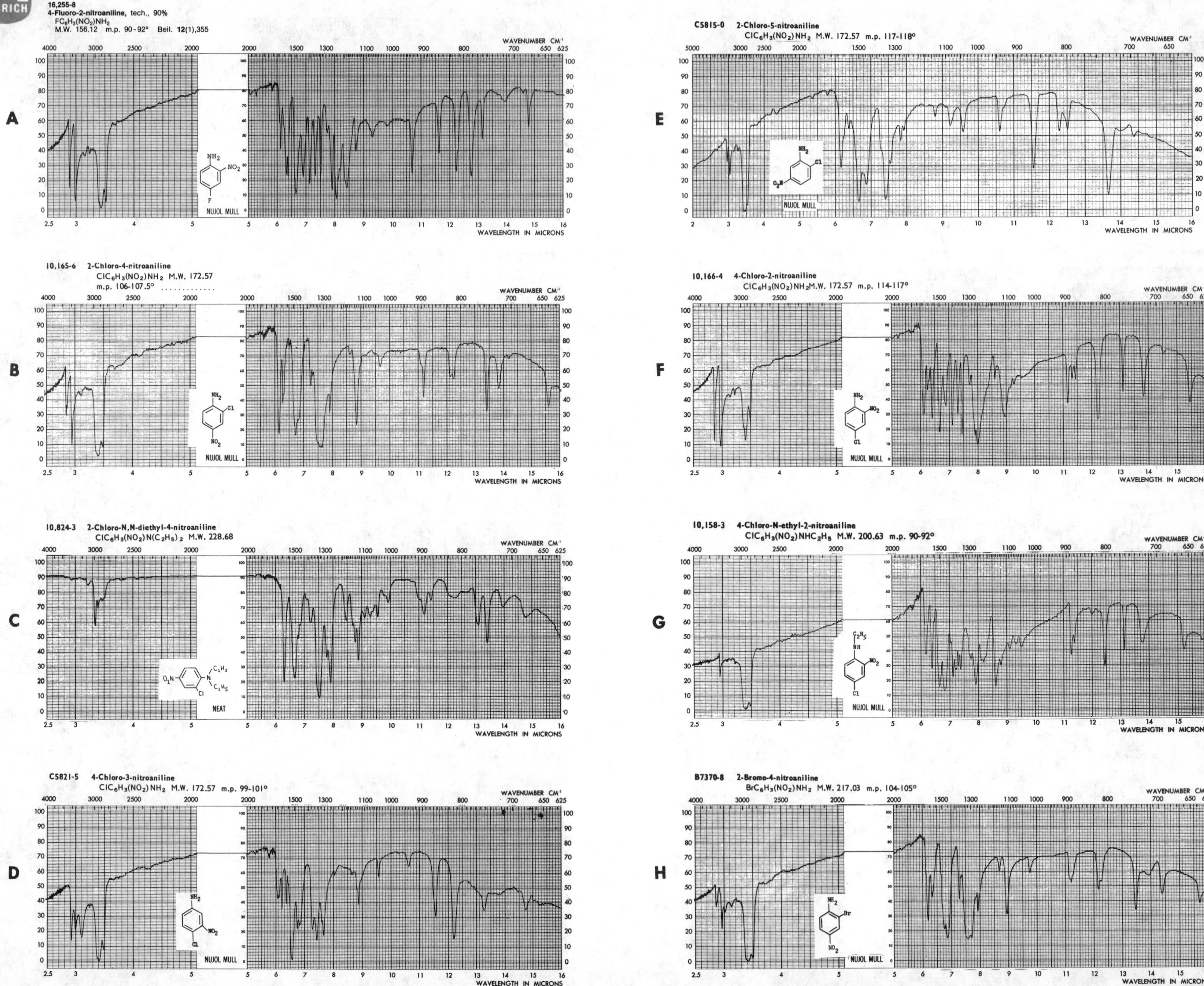
ALDRICH
A
16,255-8
4-Fluoro-2-nitroaniline, tech., 90%
$FC_6H_3(NO_2)NH_2$
M.W. 156.12 m.p. 90-92° Beil. 12(1),355
NUJOL MULL
B
10,165-6 2-Chloro-4-nitroaniline
$ClC_6H_3(NO_2)NH_2$ M.W. 172.57
m.p. 106-107.5°
NUJOL MULL
C
10,824-3 2-Chloro-N,N-diethyl-4-nitroaniline
$ClC_6H_3(NO_2)N(C_2H_5)_2$ M.W. 228.68
NEAT
D
C5821-5 4-Chloro-3-nitroaniline
$ClC_6H_3(NO_2)NH_2$ M.W. 172.57 m.p. 99-101°
NUJOL MULL
E
C5815-0 2-Chloro-5-nitroaniline
$ClC_6H_3(NO_2)NH_2$ M.W. 172.57 m.p. 117-118°
NUJOL MULL
F
10,166-4 4-Chloro-2-nitroaniline
$ClC_6H_3(NO_2)NH_2$ M.W. 172.57 m.p. 114-117°
NUJOL MULL
G
10,158-3 4-Chloro-N-ethyl-2-nitroaniline
$ClC_6H_3(NO_2)NHC_2H_5$ M.W. 200.63 m.p. 90-92°
NUJOL MULL
H
B7370-8 2-Bromo-4-nitroaniline
$BrC_6H_3(NO_2)NH_2$ M.W. 217.03 m.p. 104-105°
NUJOL MULL
WAVENUMBER CM⁻¹
WAVELENGTH IN MICRONS

A A6880-7 **5-Amino-2-nitrobenzotrifluoride** (4-nitro-α,α,α-trifluoro-m-toluidine), tech.
$H_2NC_6H_3(NO_2)CF_3$ M.W. 206.12 m.p. 127-128°

NUJOL MULL

B 19,657-6
2-Amino-5-nitrobenzotrifluoride, 98% (4-nitro-α,α,α-trifluoro-o-toluidine)
$H_2NC_6H_3(NO_2)CF_3$ FW 206.12 mp 90-92°
Disp. C

NUJOL MULL

C A6860-2 **4-Amino-3-nitrobenzotrifluoride** (2-nitro-α,α,α-trifluoro-p-toluidine)
$H_2NC_6H_3(NO_2)CF_3$ M.W. 206.12
m.p. 105-106°

NUJOL MULL

D M1740-3 **4-Methoxy-2-nitroaniline** (2-nitro-p-anisidine)
$CH_3OC_6H_3(NO_2)NH_2$ M.W. 168.15 m.p. 123-126°

NUJOL MULL

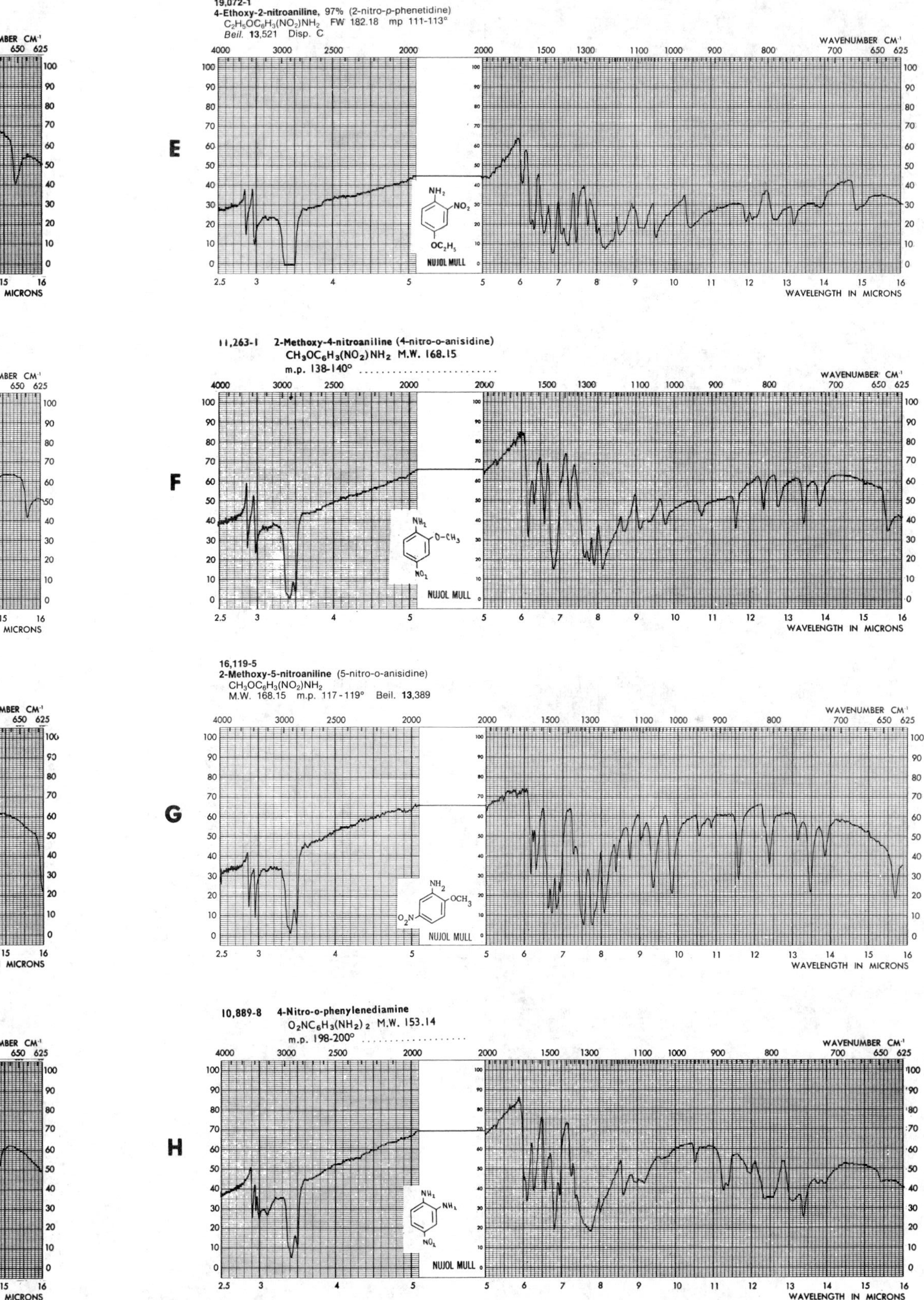

E 19,072-1
4-Ethoxy-2-nitroaniline, 97% (2-nitro-p-phenetidine)
$C_2H_5OC_6H_3(NO_2)NH_2$ FW 182.18 mp 111-113°
Beil. **13**,521 Disp. C

F 11,263-1 **2-Methoxy-4-nitroaniline** (4-nitro-o-anisidine)
$CH_3OC_6H_3(NO_2)NH_2$ M.W. 168.15
m.p. 138-140°

G 16,119-5
2-Methoxy-5-nitroaniline (5-nitro-o-anisidine)
$CH_3OC_6H_3(NO_2)NH_2$
M.W. 168.15 m.p. 117-119° Beil. **13**,389

H 10,889-8 **4-Nitro-o-phenylenediamine**
$O_2NC_6H_3(NH_2)_2$ M.W. 153.14
m.p. 198-200°

ALDRICH ®

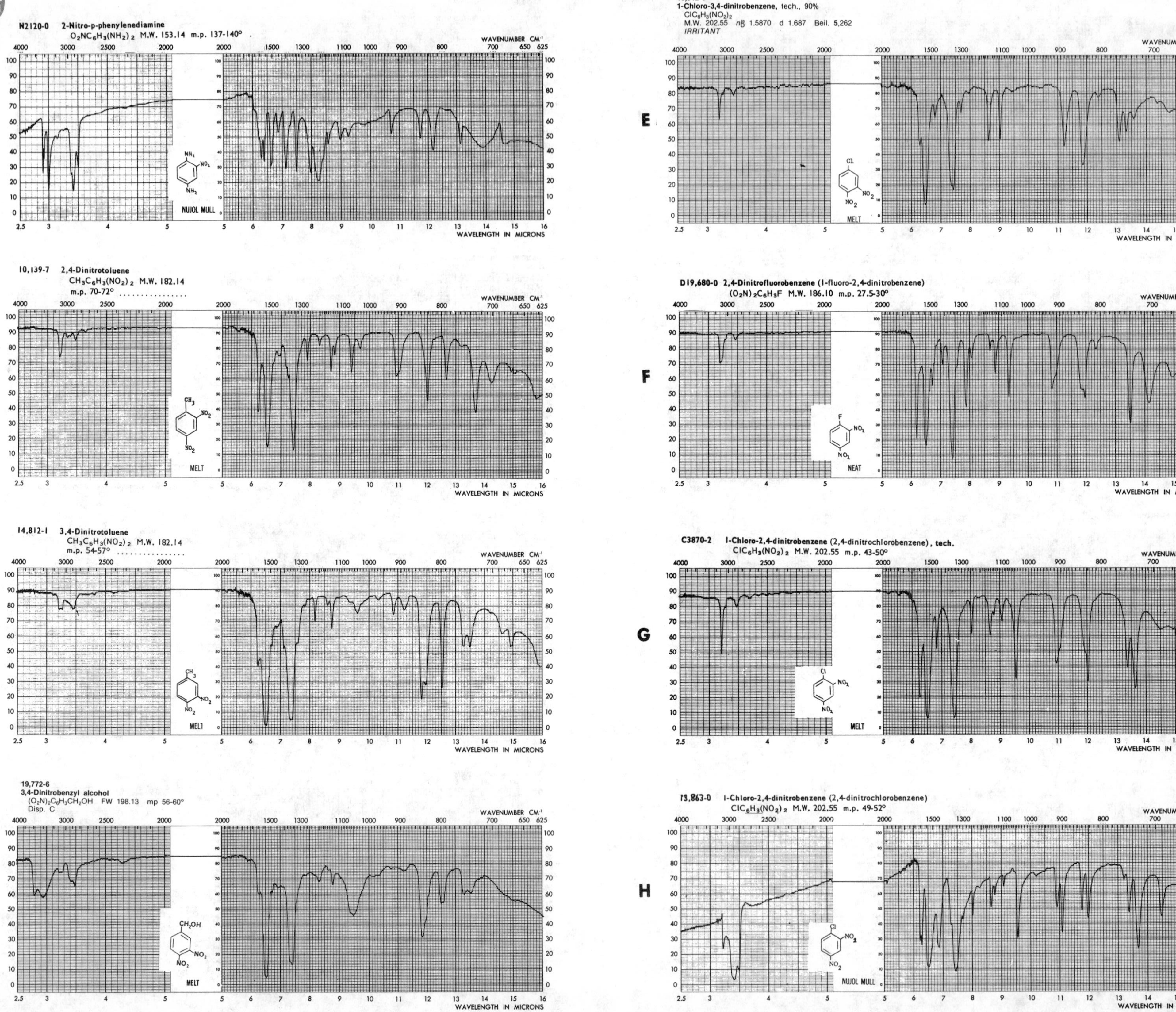
ALDRICH
A
N2120-0 2-Nitro-p-phenylenediamine
$O_2NC_6H_3(NH_2)_2$ M.W. 153.14 m.p. 137-140°
NUJOL MULL
B
10,139-7 2,4-Dinitrotoluene
$CH_3C_6H_3(NO_2)_2$ M.W. 182.14
m.p. 70-72°
MELT
C
14,812-1 3,4-Dinitrotoluene
$CH_3C_6H_3(NO_2)_2$ M.W. 182.14
m.p. 54-57°
MELT
D
19,772-6
3,4-Dinitrobenzyl alcohol
$(O_2N)_2C_6H_3CH_2OH$ FW 198.13 mp 56-60°
Disp. C
MELT
E
16,312-0
1-Chloro-3,4-dinitrobenzene, tech., 90%
$ClC_6H_3(NO_2)_2$
M.W. 202.55 n_D^{20} 1.5870 d 1.687 Beil. 5,262
IRRITANT
MELT
F
D19,680-0 2,4-Dinitrofluorobenzene (1-fluoro-2,4-dinitrobenzene)
$(O_2N)_2C_6H_3F$ M.W. 186.10 m.p. 27.5-30°
NEAT
G
C3870-2 1-Chloro-2,4-dinitrobenzene (2,4-dinitrochlorobenzene), tech.
$ClC_6H_3(NO_2)_2$ M.W. 202.55 m.p. 43-50°
MELT
H
13,863-0 1-Chloro-2,4-dinitrobenzene (2,4-dinitrochlorobenzene)
$ClC_6H_3(NO_2)_2$ M.W. 202.55 m.p. 49-52°
NUJOL MULL
WAVENUMBER CM⁻¹
WAVELENGTH IN MICRONS

A D19,715-7 2,4-Dinitroiodobenzene
$(O_2N)_2C_6H_3I$ M.W. 294.00 m.p. 89-91°
NUJOL MULL

B 10,545-7 2,4-Dinitrobenzenesulfenyl chloride
$(O_2N)_2C_6H_3SCl$ M.W. 234.62 m.p. 94-97°
NUJOL MULL

C 85,775-0
Dimethyl(2-methoxy-5-nitrobenzyl)sulfonium bromide
$CH_3OC_6H_3(NO_2)CH_2S(CH_3)_2Br$
M.W. 308.2 m.p. 149-150° (dec.)
NUJOL MULL

D 85,774-2
Dimethyl(2-hydroxy-5-nitrobenzyl)sulfonium bromide
$HOC_6H_3(NO_2)CH_2S(CH_3)_2Br$
M.W. 294.17 m.p. 172-173° (dec.)
NUJOL MULL

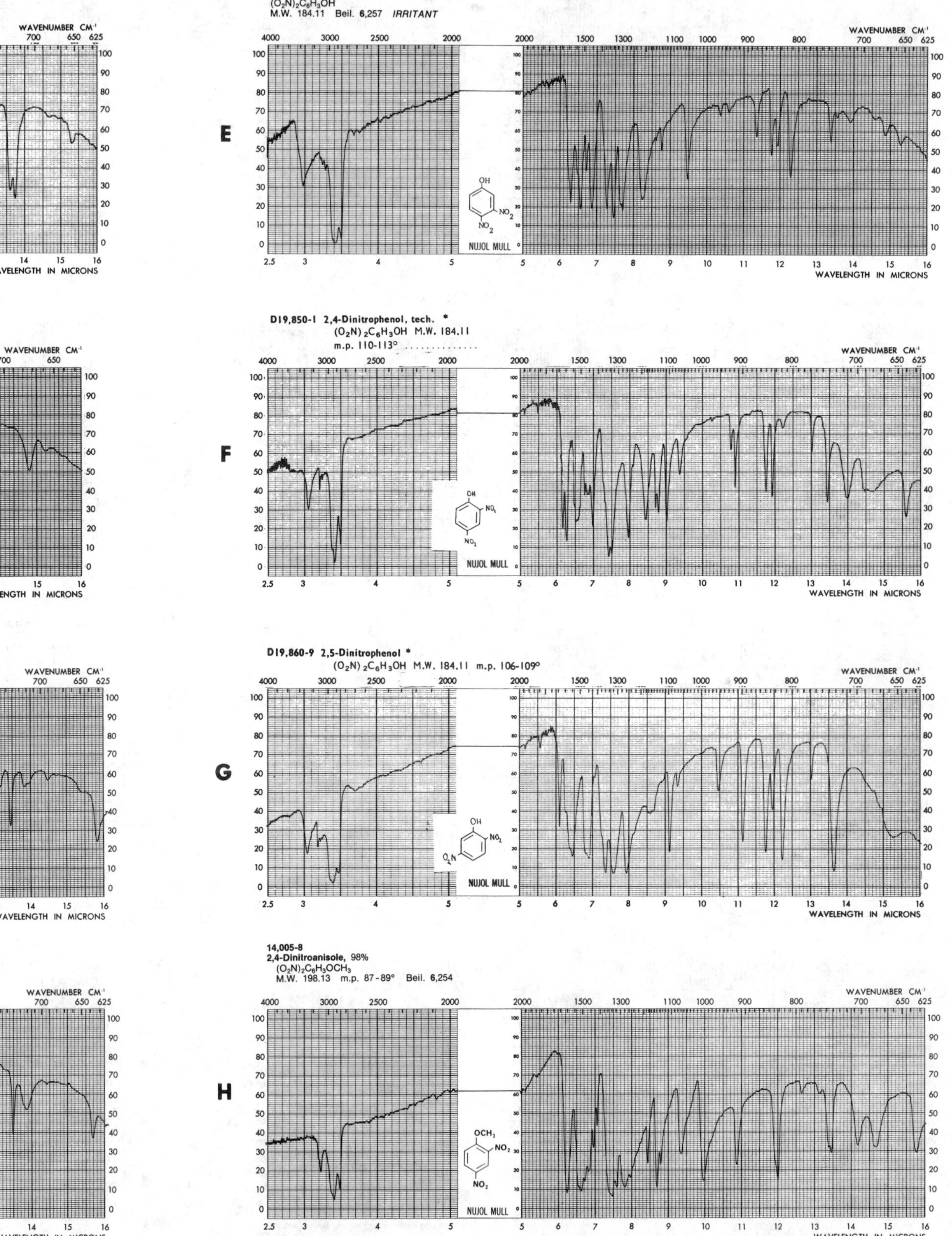

ALDRICH

A

D19,301-1 **2,4-Dinitroaniline**
$(O_2N)_2C_6H_3NH_2$ M.W. 183.12
m.p. 176-178°

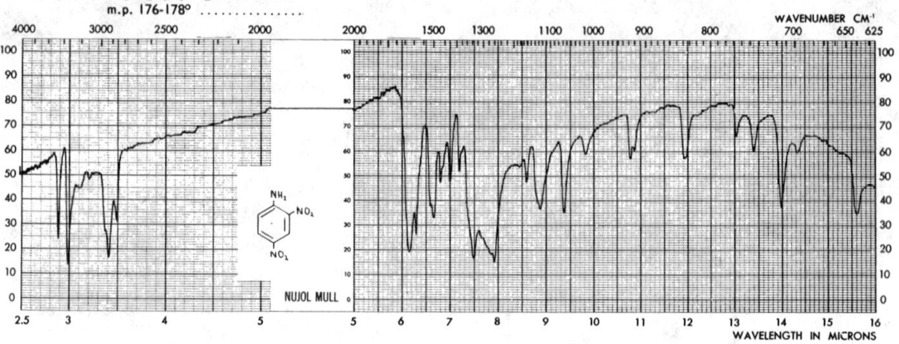

NUJOL MULL

B

19,404-2
2,4-Dinitro-*N*-ethylaniline, 97%
$(O_2N)_2C_6H_3NHC_2H_5$ FW 211.18 mp 110-113°
Beil. **12**,749 Disp. C

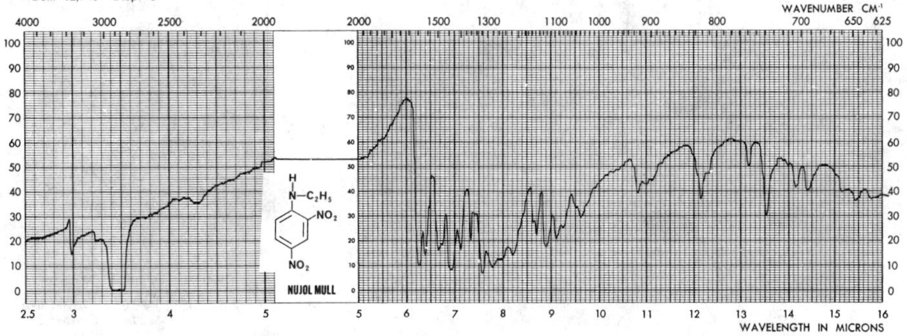

NUJOL MULL

C

D19,930-3 **2,4-Dinitrophenylhydrazine**
$(O_2N)_2C_6H_3NHNH_2$ M.W. 198.14
m.p. 199-202°

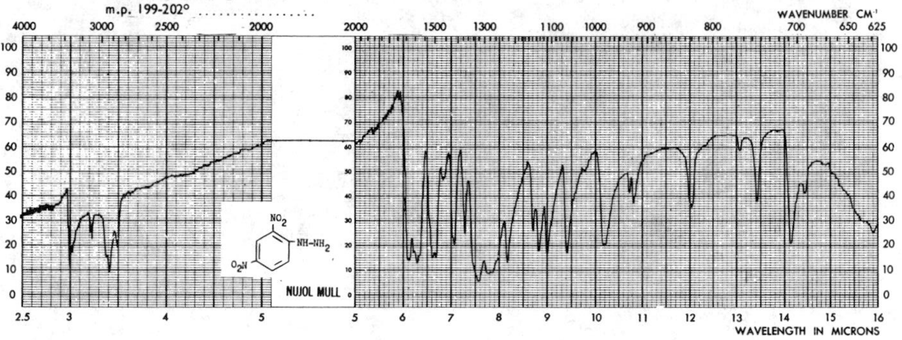

NUJOL MULL

D

14,458-4 **N,N-Dimethyl-2,4-dinitrostyrylamine** (*β*-dimethylamino-2,4-dinitrostyrene)
$(O_2N)_2C_6H_3CH{:}CHN(CH_3)_2$ M.W. 237.22
m.p. 169-170°

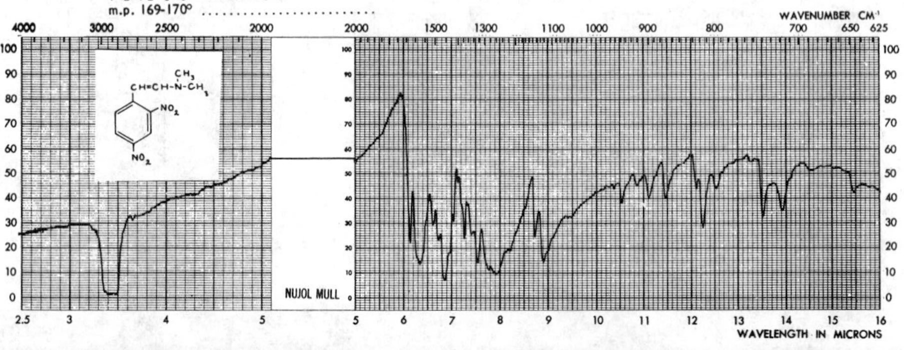

NUJOL MULL

E

19,245-7
Cyclohexanone 2,4-dinitrophenylhydrazone, 99+%,
GOLD LABEL
$C_6H_{10}[=NNHC_6H_3(NO_2)_2]$ FW 278.27
mp 159-160° Disp. C

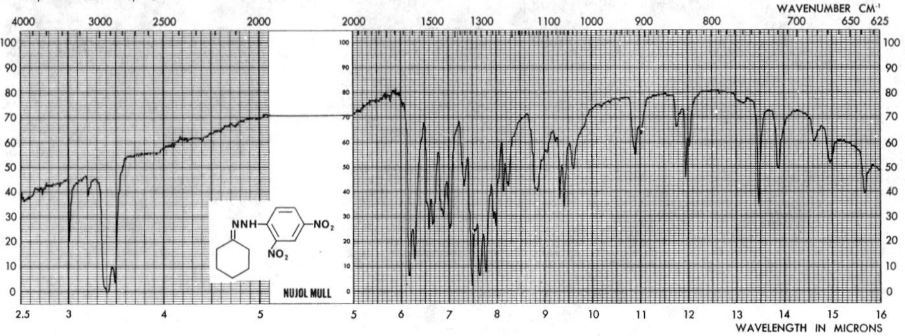

NUJOL MULL

F

13,785-5 **5-Nitro-m-xylene** (1,3-dimethyl-5-nitrobenzene), **puriss.**
$(CH_3)_2C_6H_3NO_2$ M.W. 151.17 m.p. 72-74°

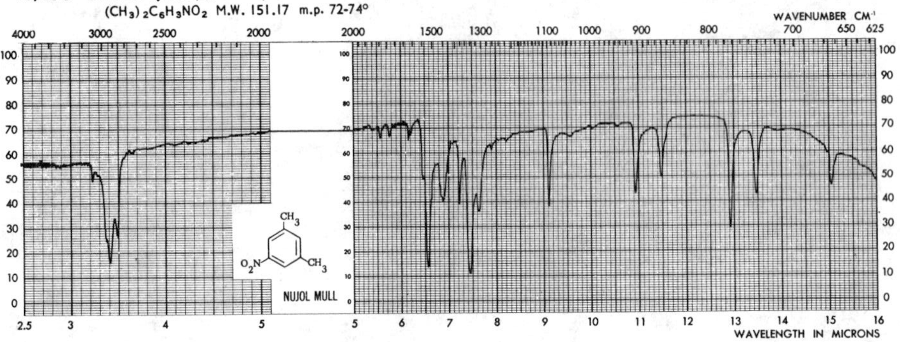

NUJOL MULL

G

19,164-7
3,5-Dinitrobenzyl chloride, 97% (*α*-chloro-3,5-dinitrotoluene)
$(O_2N)_2C_6H_3CH_2Cl$ FW 216.58 mp 79-82°
Fieser **7**,250 Disp. C

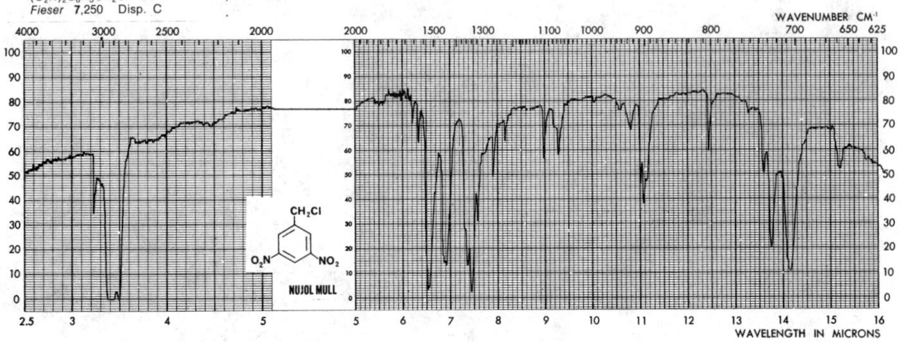

NUJOL MULL

H

18,479-9
5-Nitro-m-xylene-*α*,*α*'-diol
$O_2NC_6H_3(CH_2OH)_2$
M.W. 183.16 m.p. 94-96°

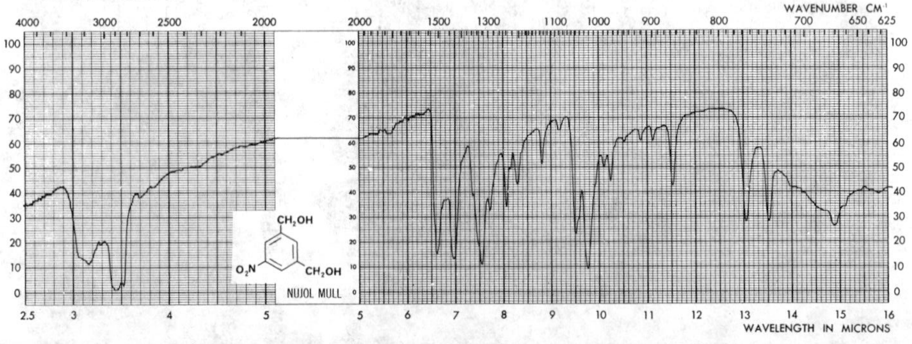

NUJOL MULL

A

I-910-4 3-Iodo-5-nitroaniline
$IC_6H_3(NO_2)NH_2$ M.W. 264.02 m.p. 139.5-141° (dec.)
NUJOL MULL

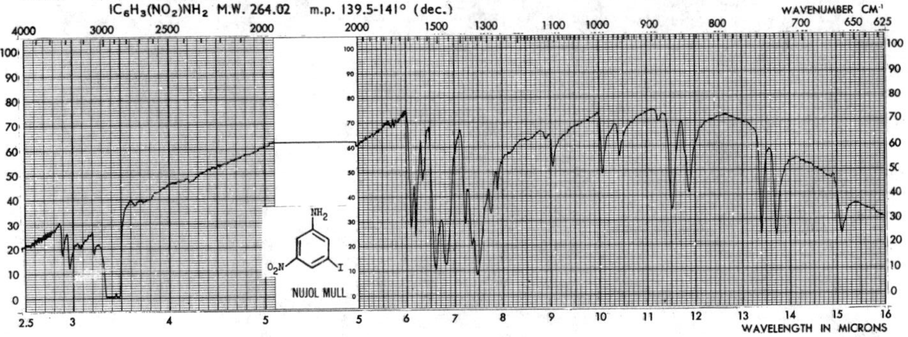

B

18,414-4
3,5-Dinitrobenzyl alcohol
$(O_2N)_2C_6H_3CH_2OH$
M.W. 198.13
MELT

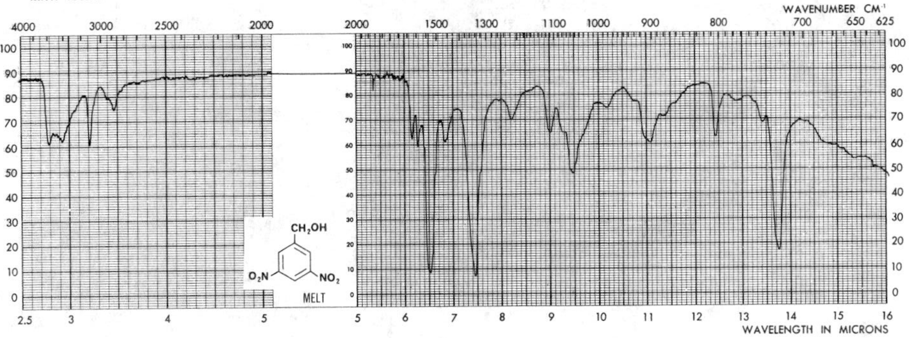

C

19,698-3
3,5-Dinitrobenzotrifluoride, 98+%
$(O_2N)_2C_6H_3CF_3$ FW 236.11 mp 48-52°
Beil. **5**(3),763 Disp. C
MELT

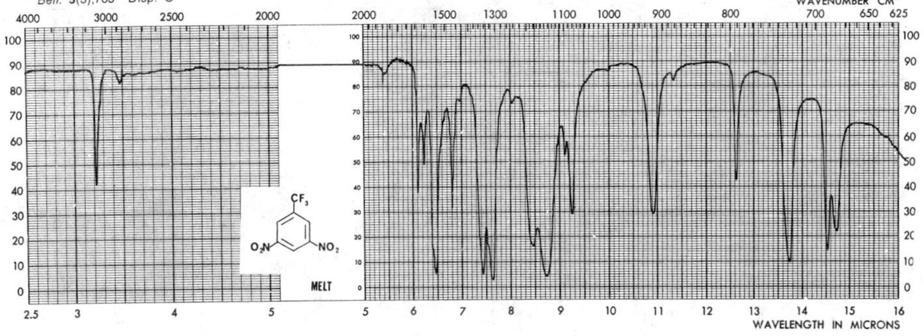

D

19,699-1
3,5-Bis(trifluoromethyl)nitrobenzene, 98+%
$(CF_3)_2C_6H_3NO_2$ FW 259.11 bp 71-72°/7mm.
n_D^{20} 1.4268 d 1.535 *Beil.* **5**(3),841 Disp. C
NEAT

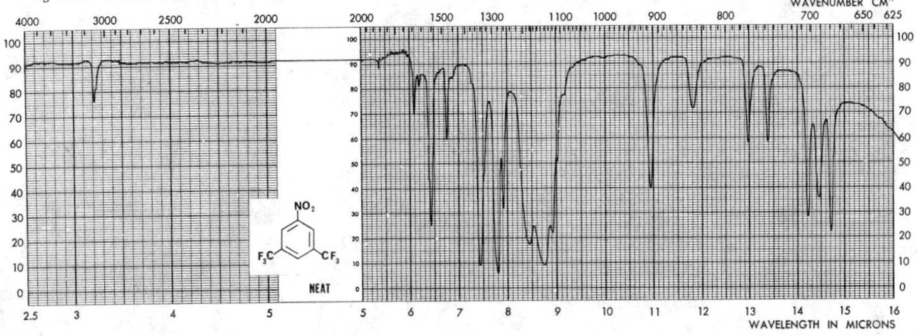

E

D19,340-2 3,5-Dinitroaniline
$(O_2N)_2C_6H_3NH_2$ M.W. 183.12 m.p. 160-162°
NUJOL MULL

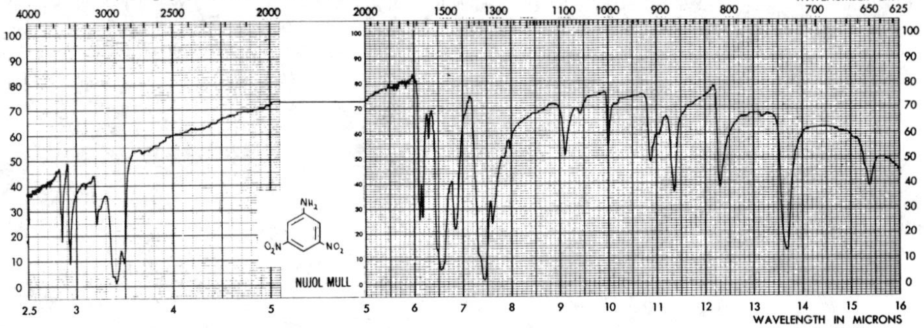

F

13,837-1 3,4-Dinitro-o-xylene
$(CH_3)_2C_6H_2(NO_2)_2$ M.W. 196.16
m.p. 80-82°
NUJOL MULL

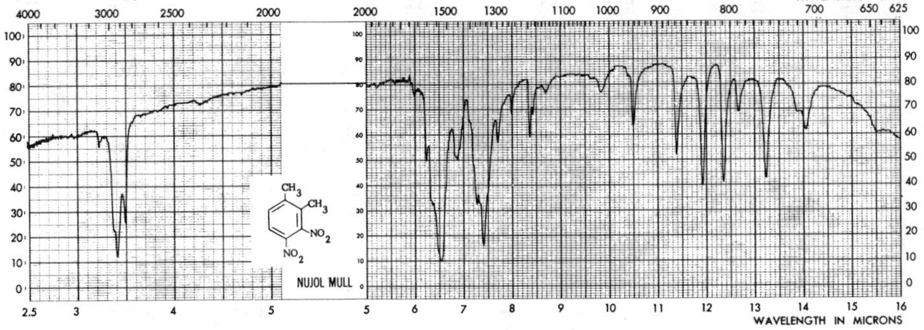

G

14,560-2 2,4-Dinitro-m-xylene
$(CH_3)_2C_6H_2(NO_2)_2$ M.W. 196.16
m.p. 84-86°
NUJOL MULL

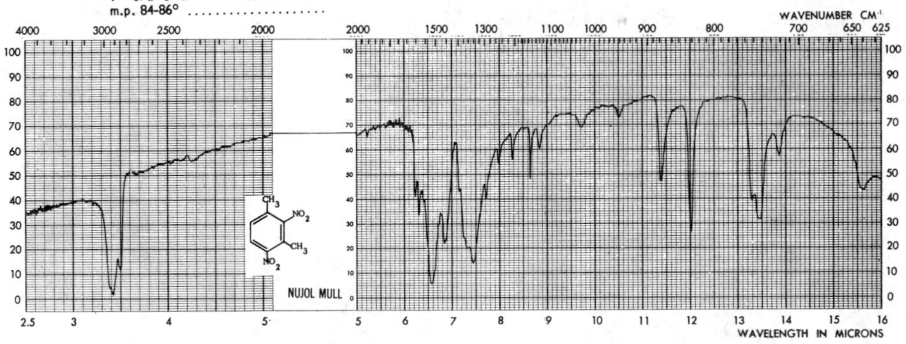

H

11,753-6 2,6-Dichloro-3-nitrotoluene
$Cl_2C_6H_2(NO_2)CH_3$ M.W. 206.03 m.p. 53-55°
MELT

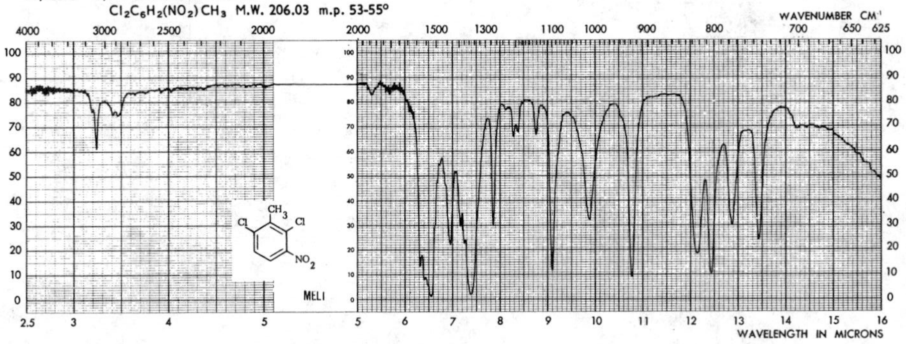

A

T5515-8 1,2,3-Trichloro-4-nitrobenzene
$Cl_3C_6H_2NO_2$ M.W. 226.45 m.p. 55-56°

MELT

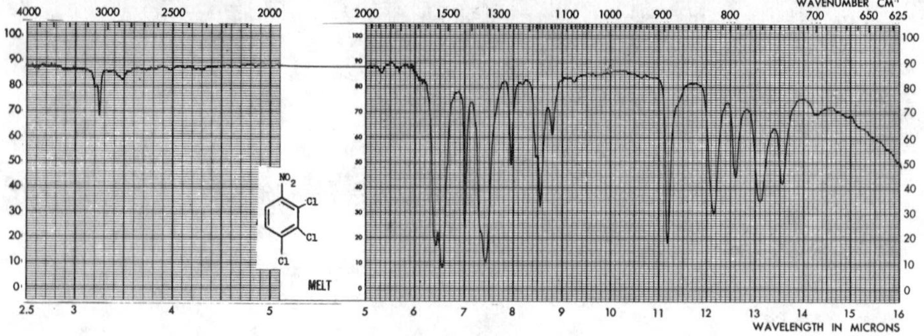

B

T5515-8 1,2,3-Trichloro-4-nitrobenzene
$Cl_3C_6H_2NO_2$ M.W. 226.45 m.p. 55-56°

NUJOL MULL

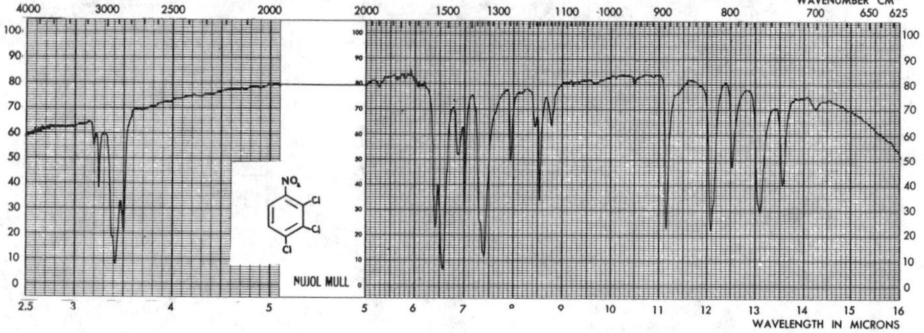

C

20,957-0
2,3-Dimethyl-4-nitroanisole
$O_2NC_6H_2(CH_3)_2OCH_3$ FW 181.19 mp 70-73°
Disp. C

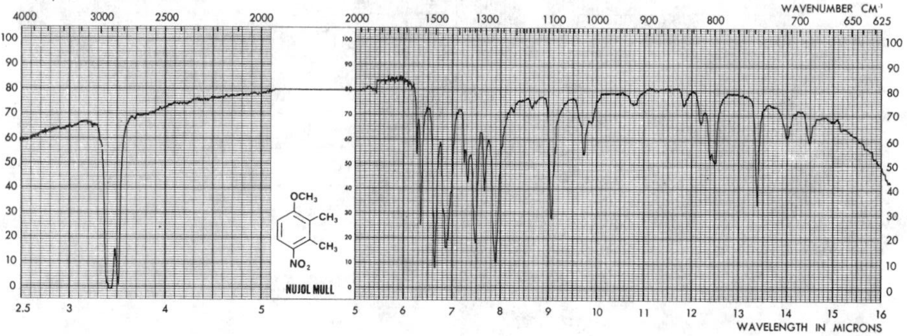

NUJOL MULL

D

15,009-6 1-Fluoro-2,4,6-trinitrobenzene (picryl fluoride)
$FC_6H_2(NO_2)_3$ M.W. 231.10 m.p. 127-130°

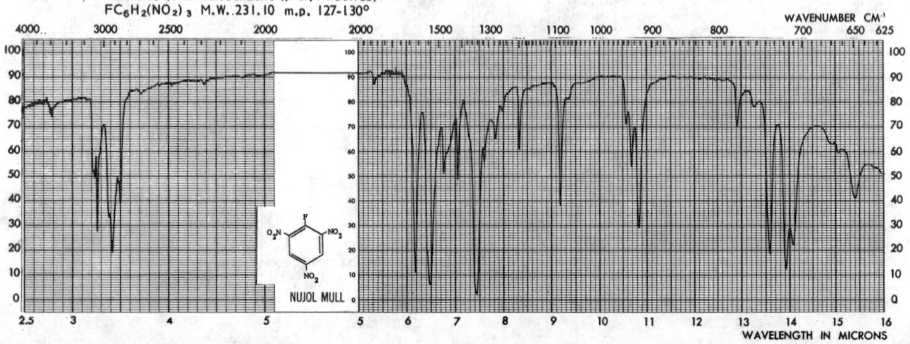

NUJOL MULL

E

14,008-2 1-Chloro-2,4,6-trinitrobenzene (picryl chloride)
$ClC_6H_2(NO_2)_3$ M.W. 247.55 m.p. 80-82°

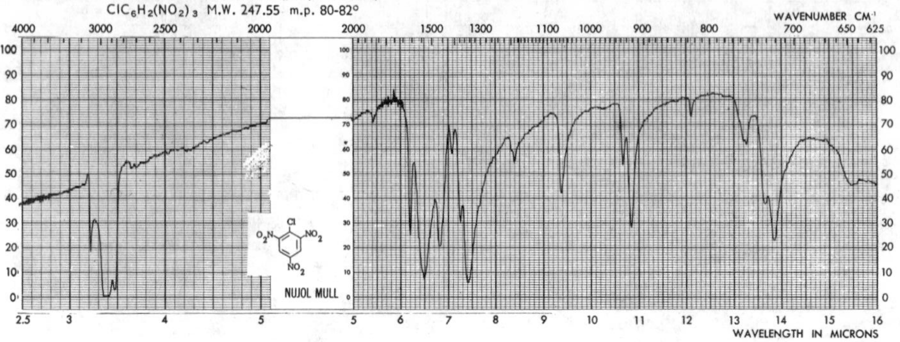

NUJOL MULL

F

14,007-4 2,4,6-Trinitroanisole
$(O_2N)_3C_6H_2OCH_3$ M.W. 243.13 m.p. 66-68°

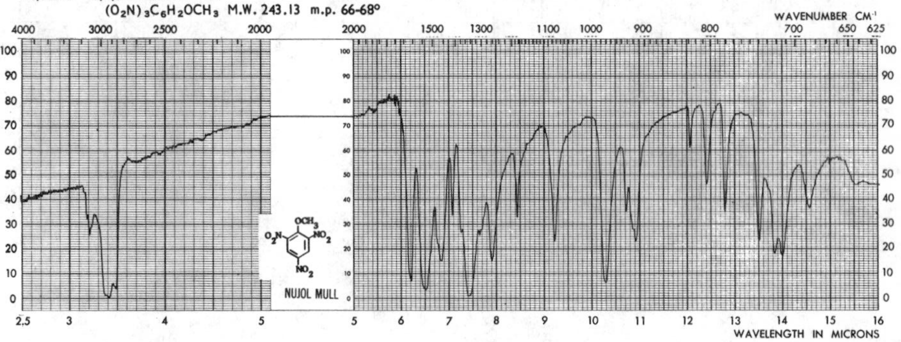

NUJOL MULL

G

N1850-1 2-Nitromesitylene
1,3,5-$(CH_3)_3C_6H_2NO_2$ M.W. 165.19
m.p. 41-44°

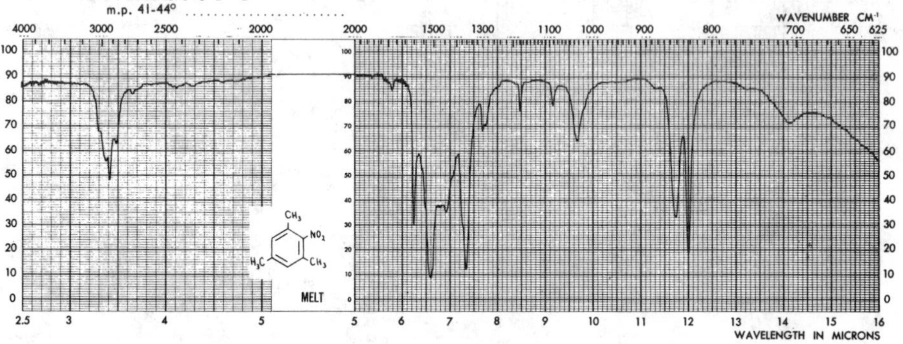

MELT

H

22,304-2
2,4,6-Tri-*tert*-butylnitrobenzene, 99%
$[(CH_3)_3C]_3C_6H_2NO_2$ FW 291.44 mp 205-206°
Beil. 5(4),1207 Disp. C

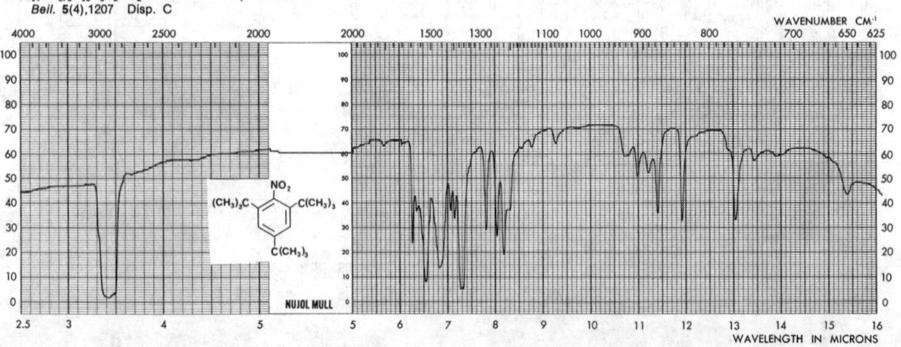

NUJOL MULL

A 13,839-8 3,5-Dinitro-o-xylene, tech.
$(CH_3)_2C_6H_2(NO_2)_2$ M.W. 196.16
m.p. 67-70°

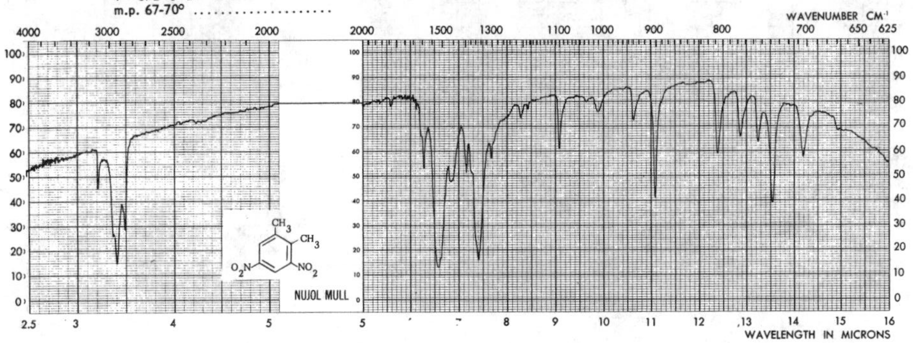

NUJOL MULL

B 13,271-3 2,6-Dimethyl-4-nitrophenol
$O_2NC_6H_2(CH_3)_2OH$ M.W. 167.17
m.p. 167-168° (dec.)

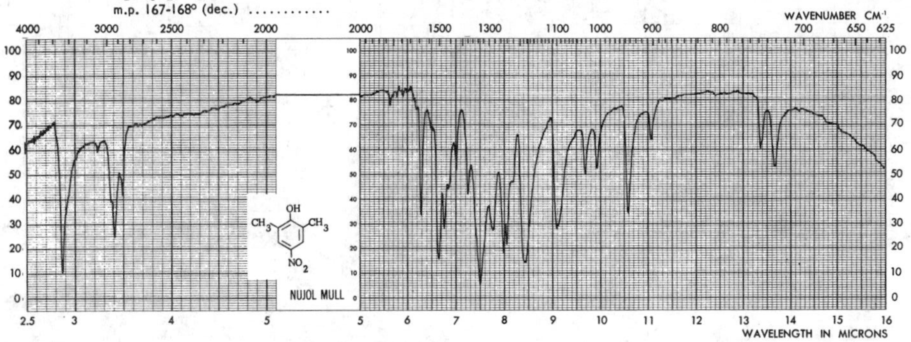

NUJOL MULL

C 10,523-6 6-Chloro-4-nitro-o-cresol
$ClC_6H_2(NO_2)(CH_3)OH$ M.W. 187.58 m.p. 122-124°

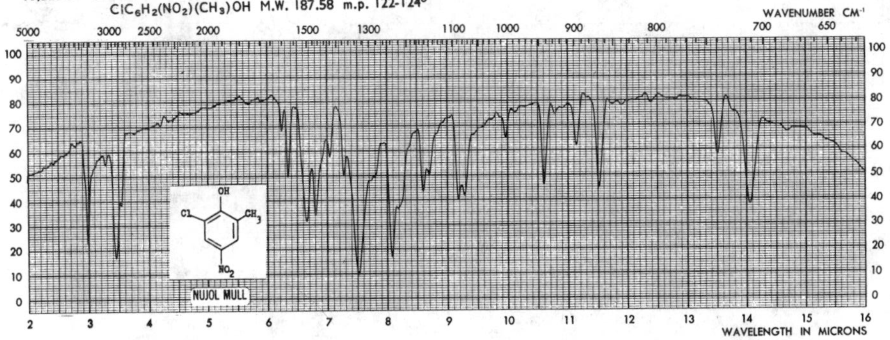

NUJOL MULL

D D6920-3 2,6-Dichloro-4-nitrophenol
$Cl_2C_6H_2(NO_2)OH$ M.W. 208.00
m.p. 121-121.5° (dec.)

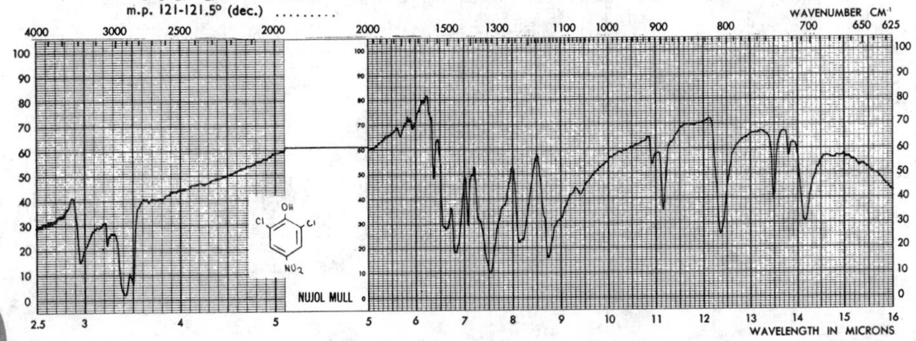

NUJOL MULL

E D4217-8 2,6-Dibromo-4-nitrophenol
$Br_2C_6H_2(NO_2)OH$ M.W. 296.91
m.p. 143-145° (dec.)

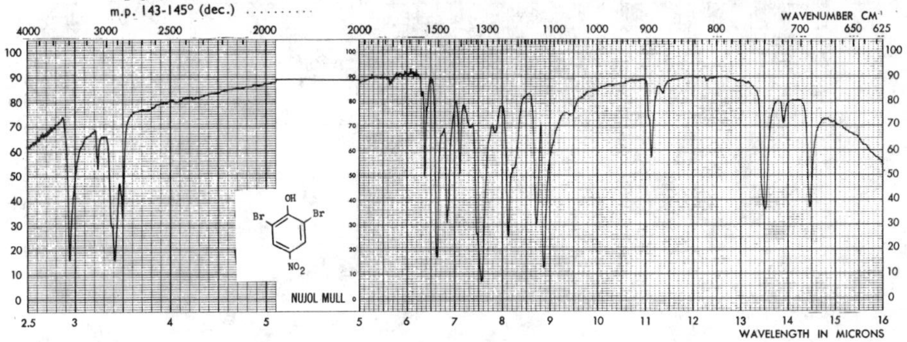

NUJOL MULL

F 14,541-6 2,6-Diiodo-4-nitrophenol
$I_2C_6H_2(NO_2)OH$ M.W. 390.91 m.p. 152-154°

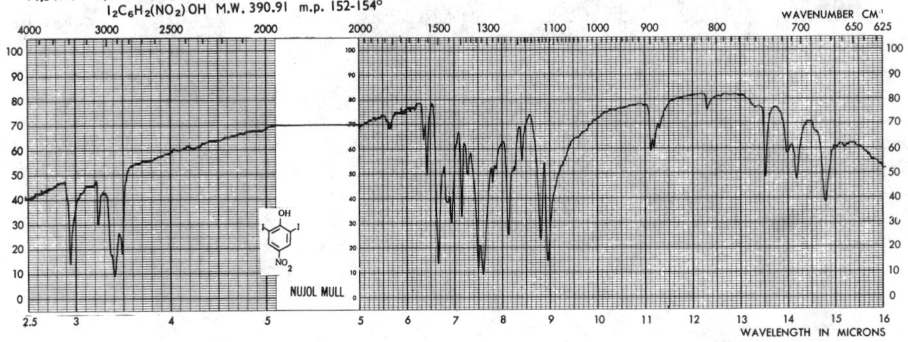

NUJOL MULL

G 12,330-7 2,4-Dibromo-6-nitrophenol
$Br_2C_6H_2(NO_2)OH$ M.W. 296.91
m.p. 106-108°

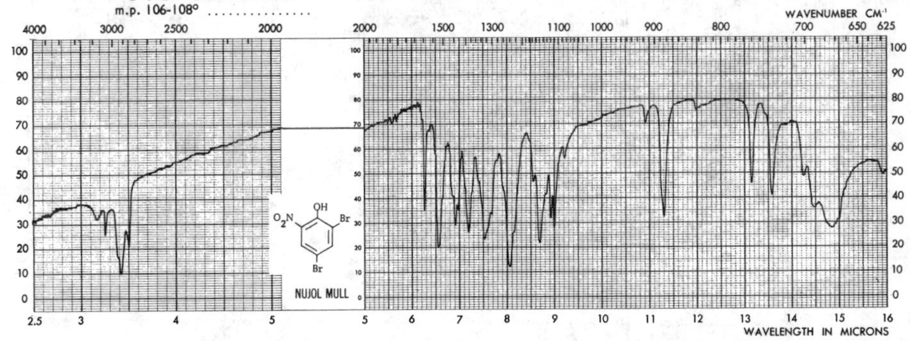

NUJOL MULL

H 19,710-6
4,6-Dinitro-o-cresol
$CH_3C_6H_2(NO_2)_2OH$ FW 198.13 mp 83-85°
Beil. 6,369 Disp. C

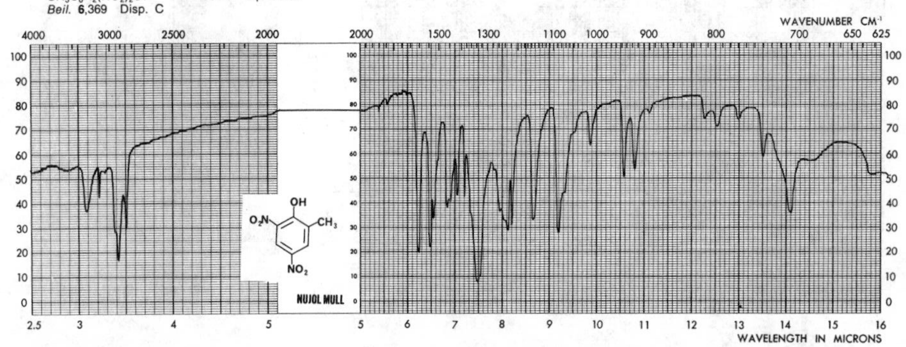

NUJOL MULL

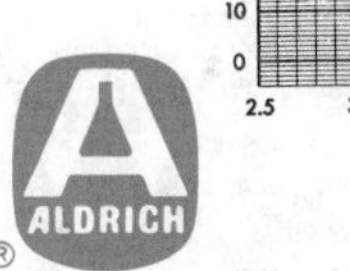

A 12,461-3 **2-Chloro-4,6-dinitrophenol**
$ClC_6H_2(NO_2)_2OH$ M.W. 218.55 (dry)
NUJOL MULL

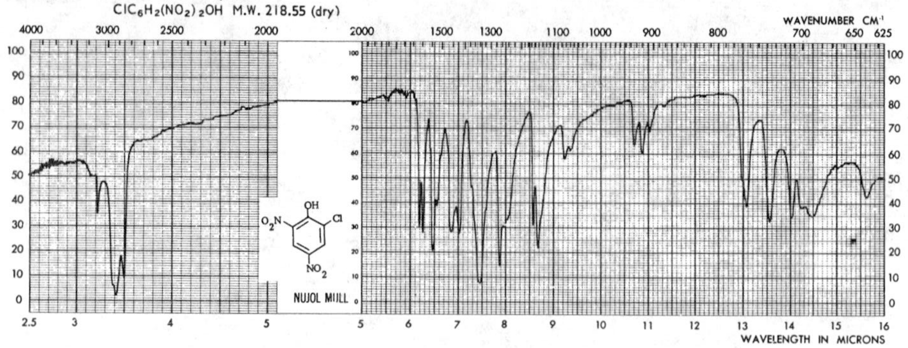

B 19,701-7
4-Chloro-3,5-dinitrobenzotrifluoride
$ClC_6H_2(NO_2)_2CF_3$ FW 270.55 mp 56-58°
Disp. C
MELT

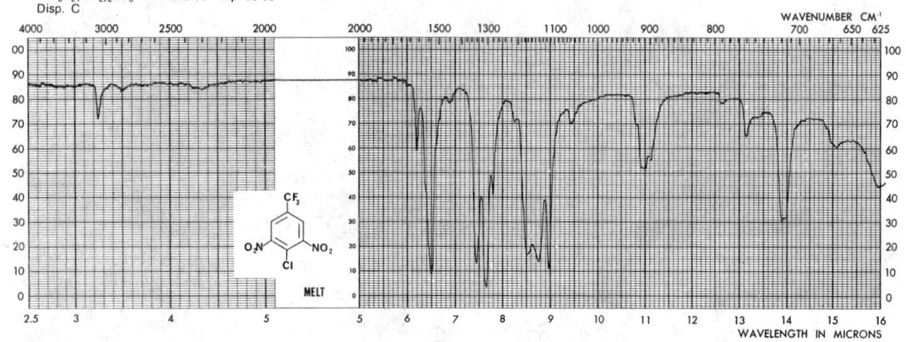

C 12,600-4 **2,4-Dichloro-6-nitroaniline**
$Cl_2C_6H_2(NO_2)NH_2$ M.W. 207.02
m.p. 101-103°
NUJOL MULL

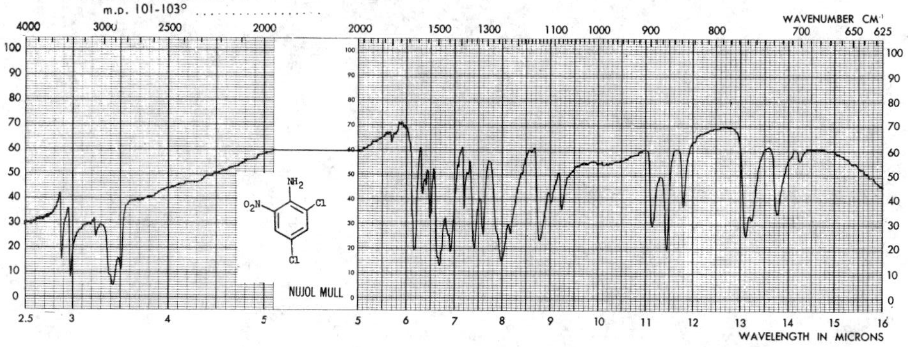

D D6782-0 **2,6-Dichloro-4-nitroaniline**
$Cl_2C_6H_2(NO_2)NH_2$ M.W. 207.02 m.p. 190-192°
NUJOL MULL

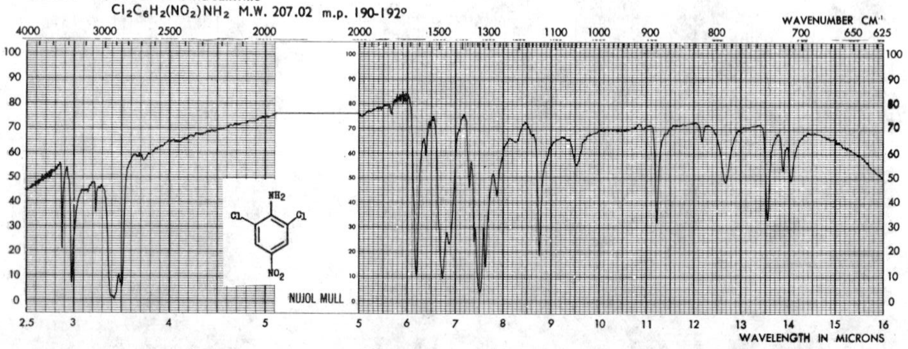

E D12,370-6 **2,6-Diiodo-4-nitroaniline**
$I_2C_6H_2(NO_2)NH_2$ M.W. 389.92 m.p. 251-253°
NUJOL MULL

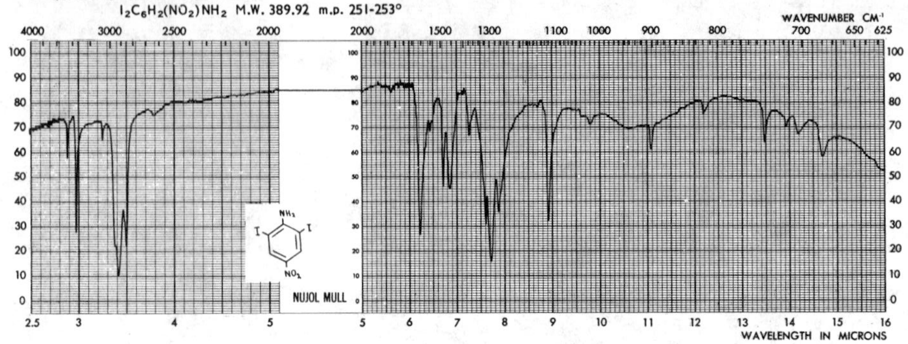

F 19,228-7
2,6-Diamino-4-nitrotoluene, 99% (4-nitro-2,6-toluenediamine)
$CH_3C_6H_2(NH_2)_2NO_2$ FW 167.17 mp 216-218°
Disp. C
NUJOL MULL

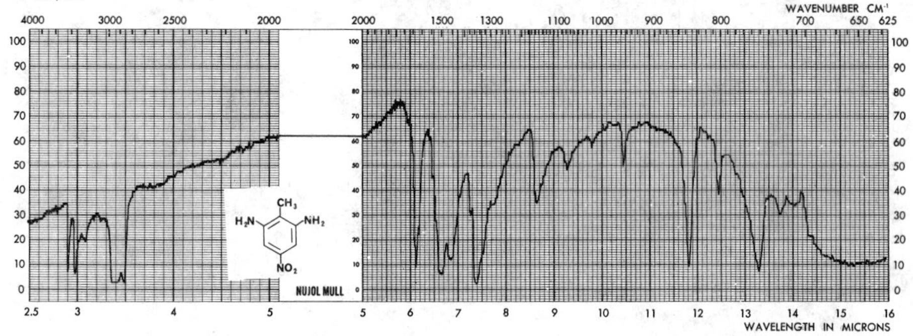

G 19,654-1
3,5-Dinitro-2-methylbenzyl alcohol, 97%
$CH_3C_6H_2(NO_2)_2CH_2OH$ FW 212.16 mp 86-89°
Disp. C
NUJOL MULL

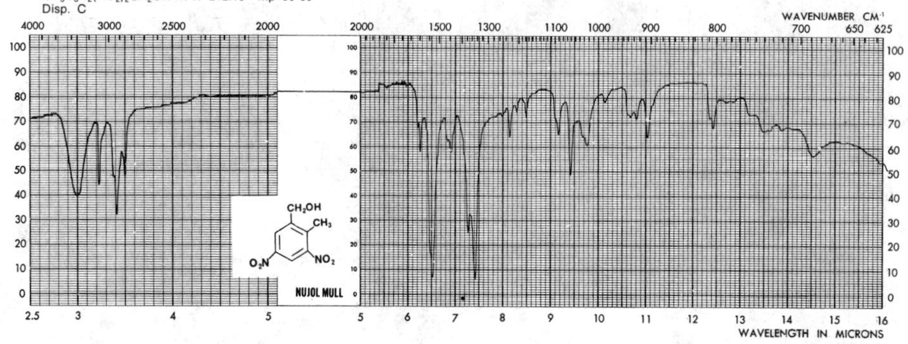

H 19,026-8
2,6-Dibromo-4-nitroaniline, 97+%
$Br_2C_6H_2(NO_2)NH_2$ FW 295.93 mp 206-208°
Beil. 12,743 Disp. C
NUJOL MULL

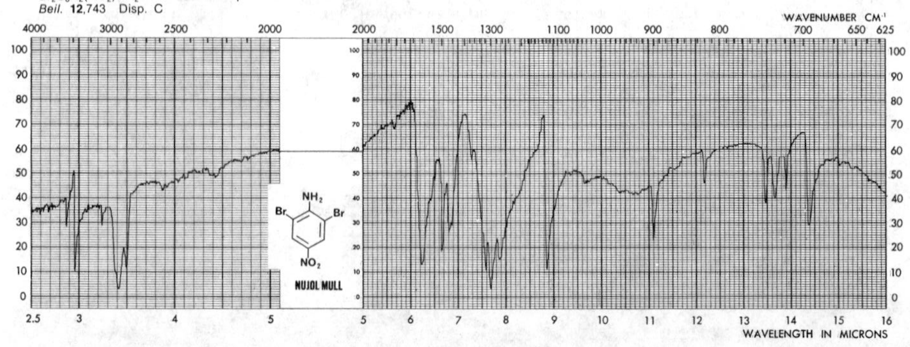

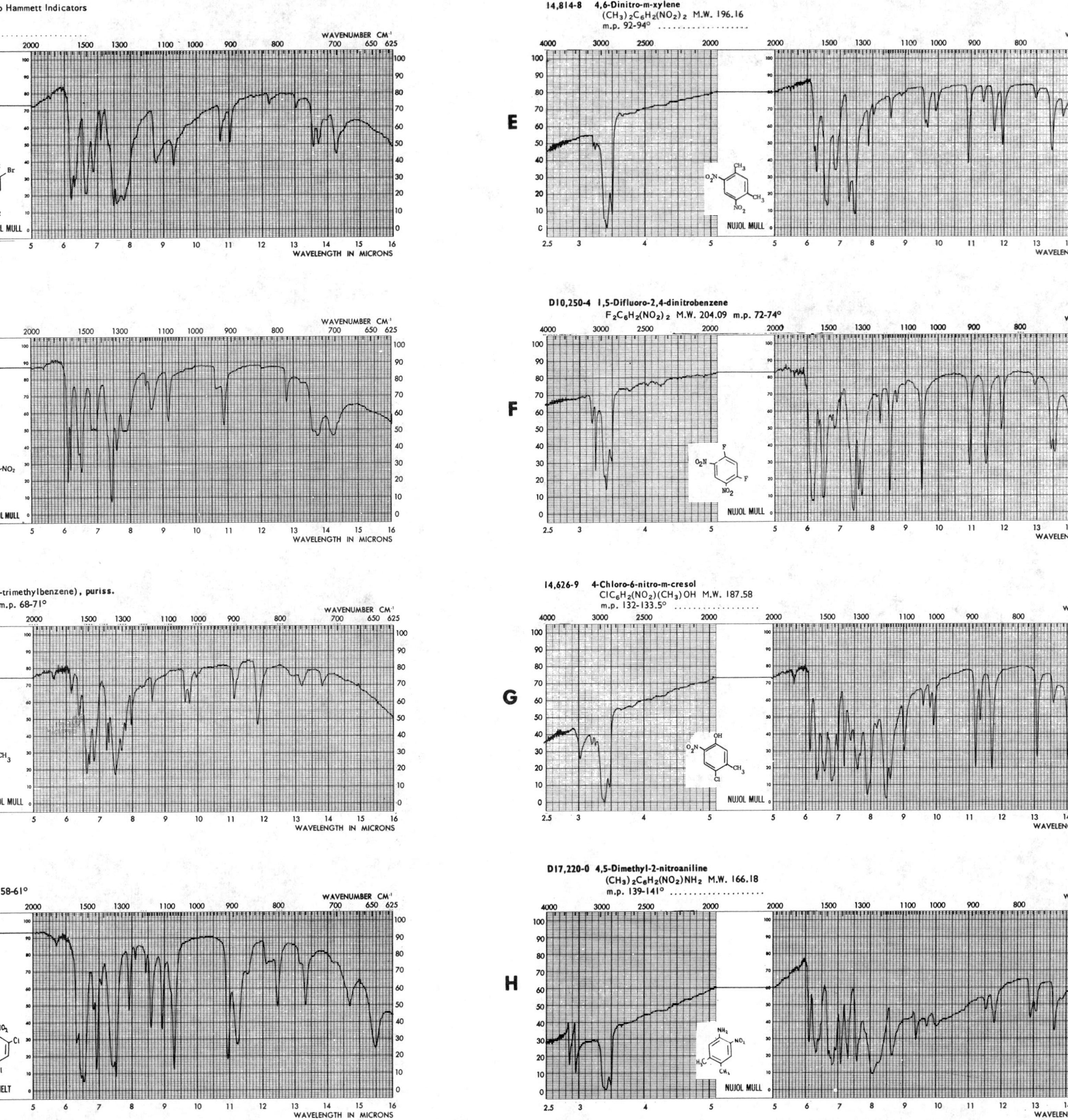
A
11,396-4 2-Bromo-4,6-dinitroaniline, see also Hammett Indicators
$BrC_6H_2(NO_2)_2NH_2$ M.W. 262.03
m.p. 151-154°
NUJOL MULL
B
19,737-8
Picric acid, 75% (2,4,6-trinitrophenol)
$(O_2N)_3C_6H_2OH$ FW 229.11 mp 120-122°
Disp. K
NUJOL MULL
C
13,789-8 5-Nitropseudocumene (5-nitro-1,2,4-trimethylbenzene), puriss.
$(CH_3)_3C_6H_2NO_2$ M.W. 165.19 m.p. 68-71°
NUJOL MULL
D
T5520-4 1,2,4-Trichloro-5-nitrobenzene
$Cl_3C_6H_2NO_2$ M.W. 226.45 m.p. 58-61°
MELT
E
14,814-8 4,6-Dinitro-m-xylene
$(CH_3)_2C_6H_2(NO_2)_2$ M.W. 196.16
m.p. 92-94°
NUJOL MULL
F
D10,250-4 1,5-Difluoro-2,4-dinitrobenzene
$F_2C_6H_2(NO_2)_2$ M.W. 204.09 m.p. 72-74°
NUJOL MULL
G
14,626-9 4-Chloro-6-nitro-m-cresol
$ClC_6H_2(NO_2)(CH_3)OH$ M.W. 187.58
m.p. 132-133.5°
NUJOL MULL
H
D17,220-0 4,5-Dimethyl-2-nitroaniline
$(CH_3)_2C_6H_2(NO_2)NH_2$ M.W. 166.18
m.p. 139-141°
NUJOL MULL
WAVENUMBER CM⁻¹
WAVELENGTH IN MICRONS
ALDRICH

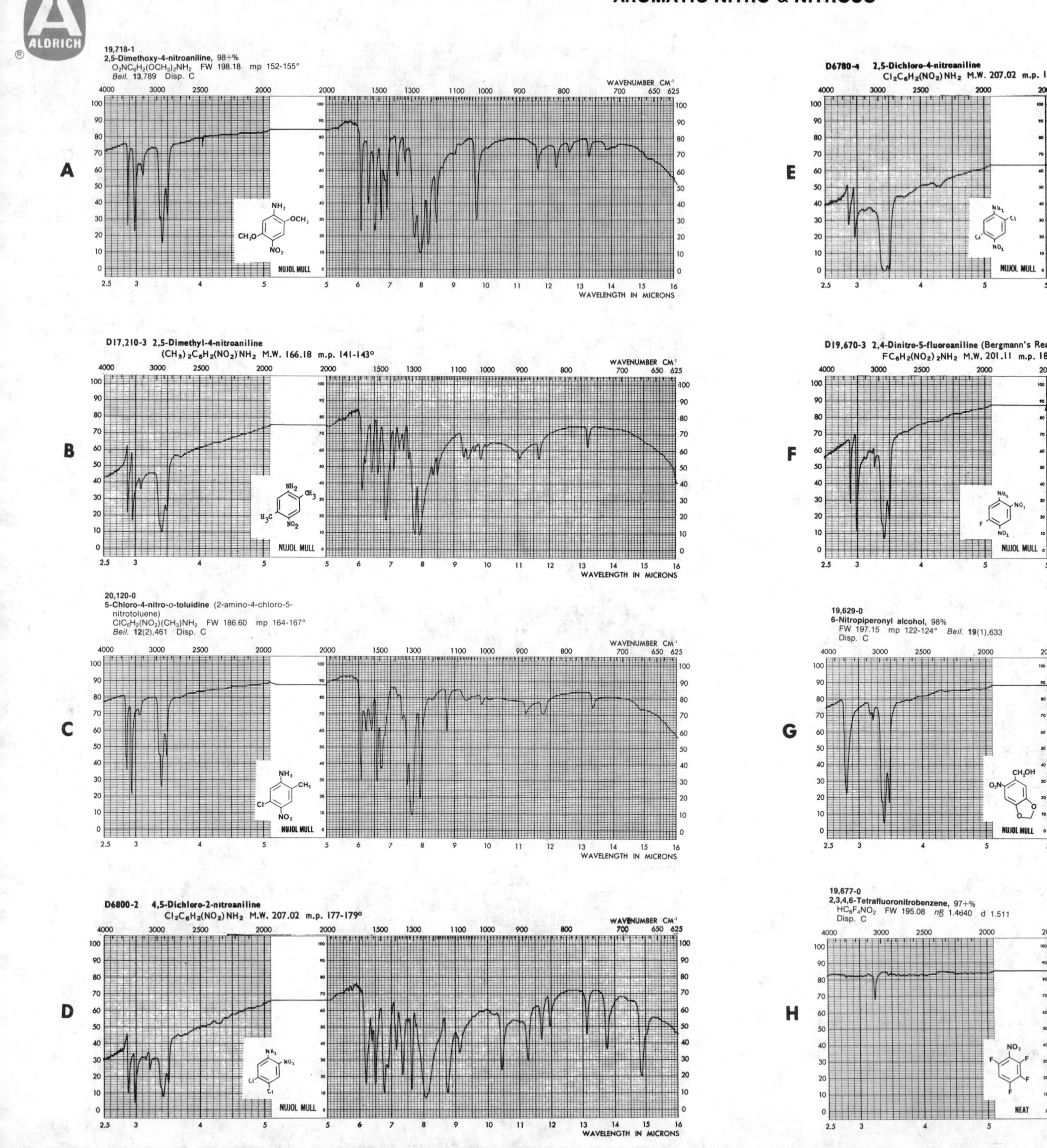
ALDRICH
A
19,718-1
2,5-Dimethoxy-4-nitroaniline, 98+%
$O_2NC_6H_2(OCH_3)_2NH_2$ FW 198.18 mp 152-155°
Beil. 13,789 Disp. C
NUJOL MULL
B
D17,210-3 2,5-Dimethyl-4-nitroaniline
$(CH_3)_2C_6H_2(NO_2)NH_2$ M.W. 166.18 m.p. 141-143°
NUJOL MULL
C
20,120-0
5-Chloro-4-nitro-o-toluidine (2-amino-4-chloro-5-nitrotoluene)
$ClC_6H_2(NO_2)(CH_3)NH_2$ FW 186.60 mp 164-167°
Beil. 12(2),461 Disp. C
NUJOL MULL
D
D6800-2 4,5-Dichloro-2-nitroaniline
$Cl_2C_6H_2(NO_2)NH_2$ M.W. 207.02 m.p. 177-179°
NUJOL MULL
E
D6780-4 2,5-Dichloro-4-nitroaniline
$Cl_2C_6H_2(NO_2)NH_2$ M.W. 207.02 m.p. 148-149°
NUJOL MULL
F
D19,670-3 2,4-Dinitro-5-fluoroaniline (Bergmann's Reagent for amino acids)
$FC_6H_2(NO_2)_2NH_2$ M.W. 201.11 m.p. 180-183°
NUJOL MULL
G
19,629-0
6-Nitropiperonyl alcohol, 98%
FW 197.15 mp 122-124° Beil. 19(1),633
Disp. C
NUJOL MULL
H
19,677-0
2,3,4,6-Tetrafluoronitrobenzene, 97+%
$HC_6F_4NO_2$ FW 195.08 n_D^{20} 1.4640 d 1.511
Disp. C
NEAT
WAVENUMBER CM⁻¹
WAVELENGTH IN MICRONS

A T780-2 2,3,5,6-Tetrachloronitrobenzene
$Cl_4C_6HNO_2$ M.W. 260.89 ....

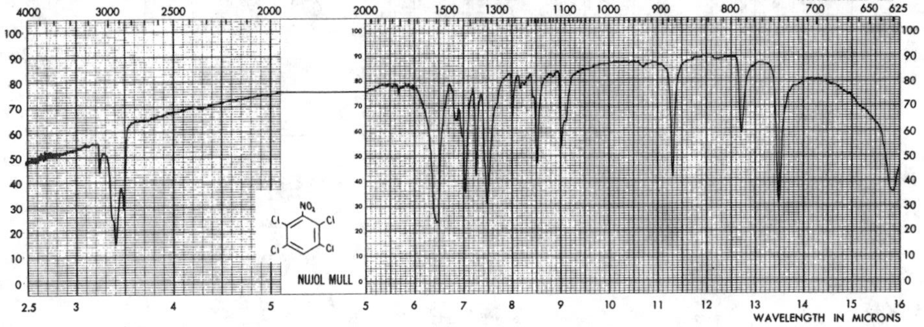

NUJOL MULL

B T770-5 2,3,4,5-Tetrachloronitrobenzene
$Cl_4C_6HNO_2$ M.W. 260.89 m.p. 65-67°

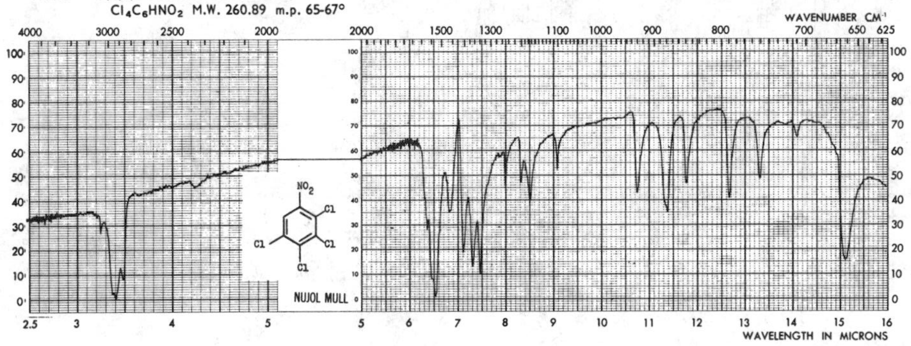

NUJOL MULL

C 14,009-0 1,3-Dichloro-2,4,6-trinitrobenzene
$Cl_2C_6H(NO_2)_3$ M.W. 282.00
m.p. 129-131° ....

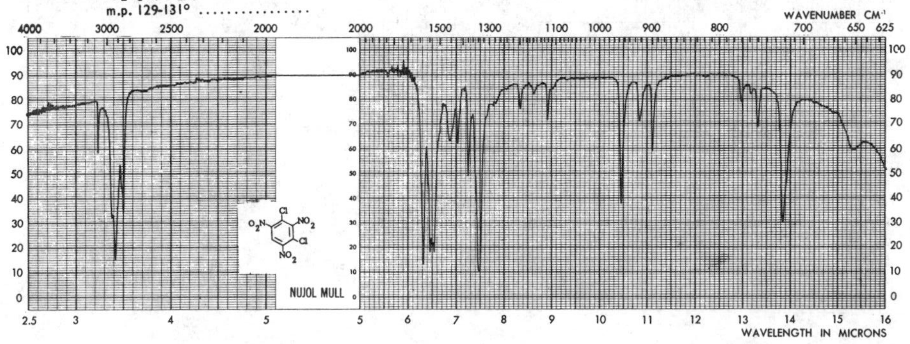

NUJOL MULL

D 13,212-8 3-Trifluoromethyl-2,4,6-trinitrophenol
$CF_3C_6H(NO_2)_3OH$ M.W. 297.10 m.p. 121-123°

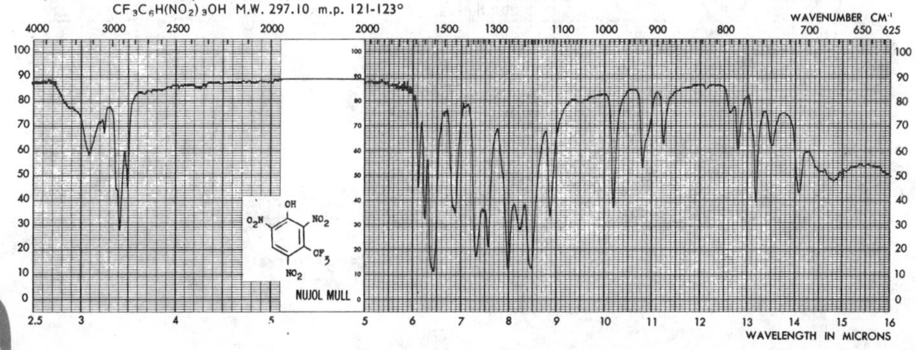

NUJOL MULL

E 14,010-4 2,4,6-Trinitroresorcinol
$(O_2N)_3C_6H$-1,3-$(OH)_2$ M.W. 245.11
m.p. 176-178° (dec.) ....

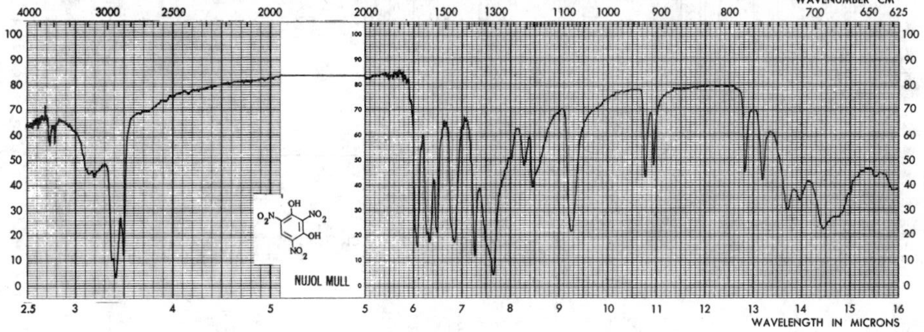

NUJOL MULL

F P220-5 Pentachloronitrobenzene, tech. (contains 1% hexachlorobenzene)
$C_6Cl_5NO_2$ M.W. 295.34 m.p. 146-150° (dec.) ....

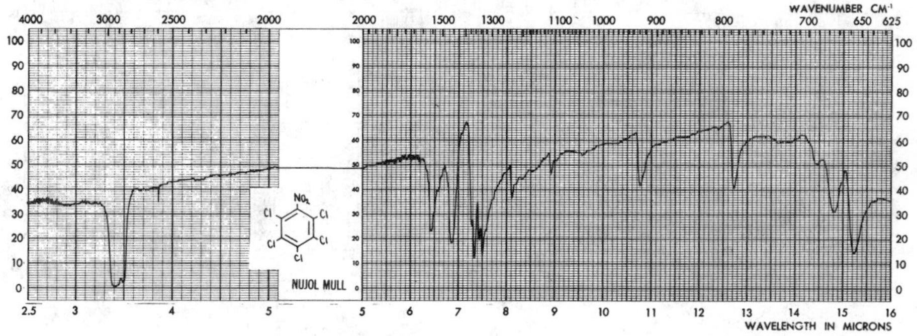

NUJOL MULL

G D19,620-7 Dinitrodurene (1,2,4,5-tetramethyl-3,6-dinitrobenzene)
$(CH_3)_4C_6(NO_2)_2$ M.W. 224.22 m.p. 208-211° .....

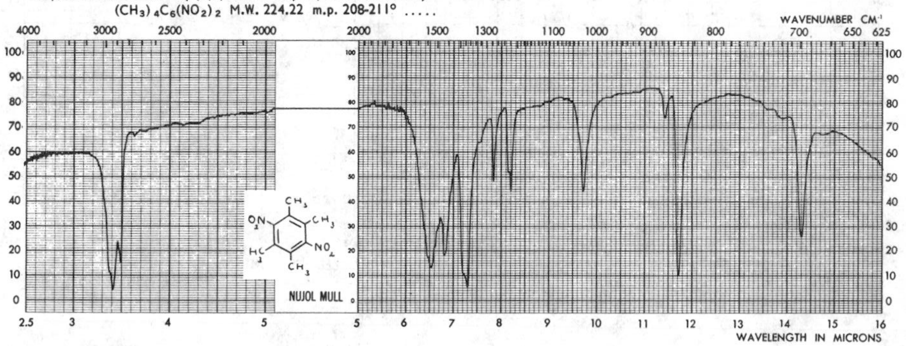

NUJOL MULL

H N1480-8 2-Nitrobiphenyl
$C_6H_5C_6H_4NO_2$ M.W. 199.21 m.p. 36-38°

MELT

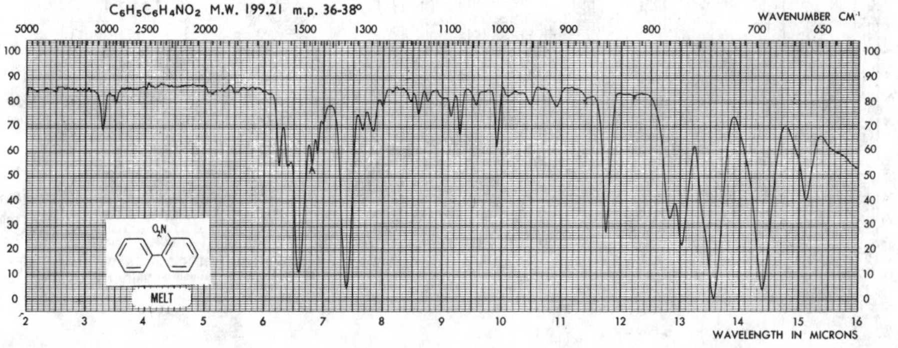

A N1500-6 3-Nitrobiphenyl
$C_6H_5C_6H_4NO_2$ M.W. 199.21 m.p. 58-60°
MELT

B N1520-0 4-Nitrobiphenyl
$C_6H_5C_6H_4NO_2$ M.W. 199.21 m.p. 108-111°
NUJOL MULL

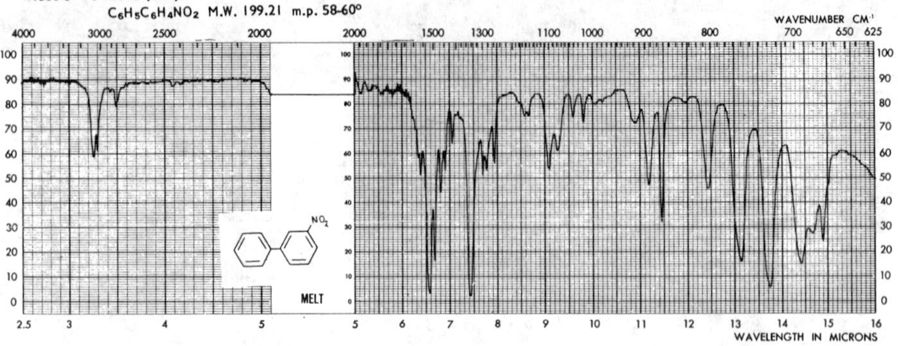

C 11,552-5 4-Nitro-p-terphenyl
$C_6H_5C_6H_4C_6H_4NO_2$ M.W. 275.31
m.p. 209-213°
NUJOL MULL

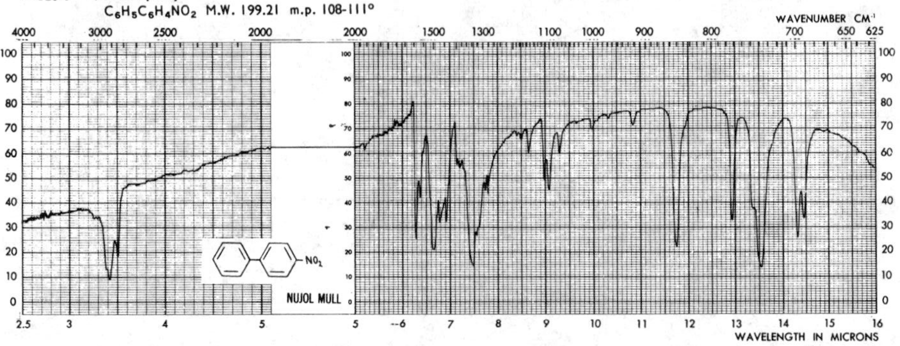

D 12,664-0 2,2'-Dinitrobiphenyl
$O_2NC_6H_4C_6H_4NO_2$ M.W. 244.21
m.p. 124-126°
NUJOL MULL

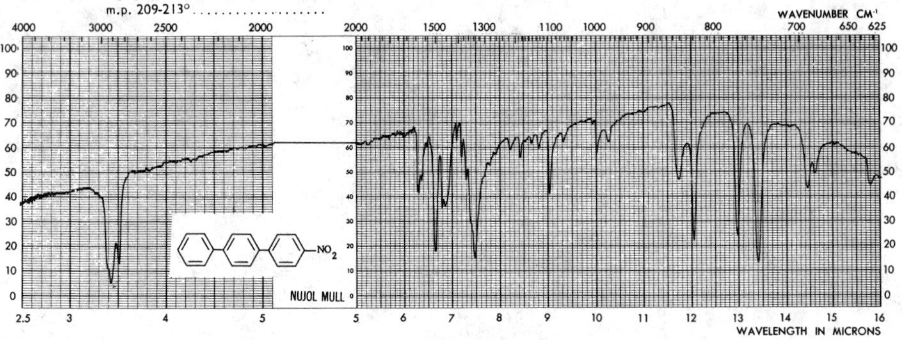

E D19,570-7 4,4'-Dinitrobiphenyl
$O_2NC_6H_4C_6H_4NO_2$ M.W. 244.21 m.p. 235-238°
NUJOL MULL

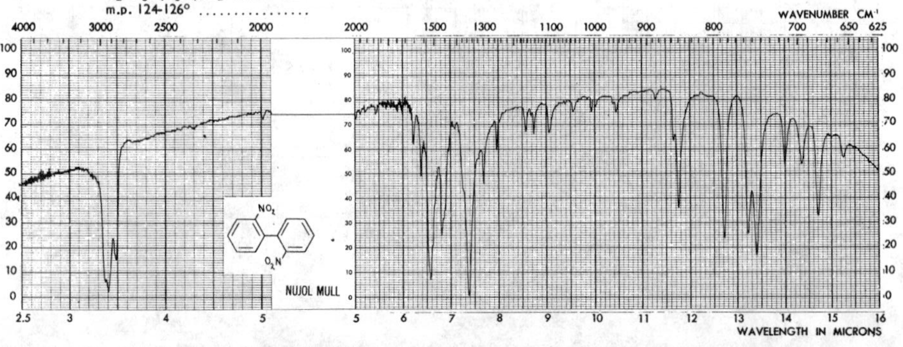

F D19,540-5 4,4'-Dinitrobibenzyl
$O_2NC_6H_4CH_2CH_2C_6H_4NO_2$ M.W. 272.26
NUJOL MULL

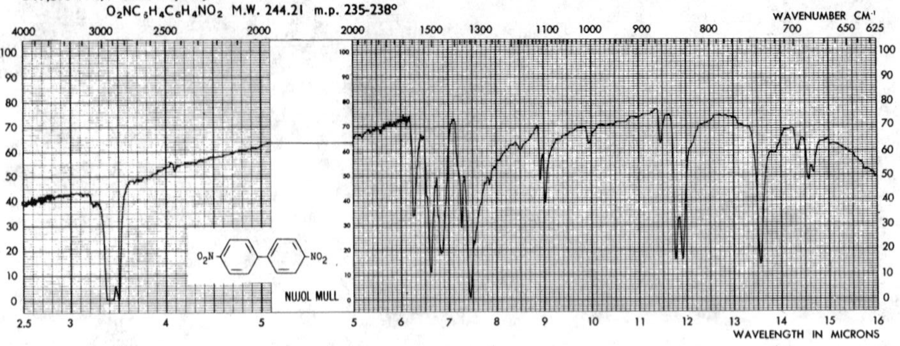

G F1140-9 4-Fluoro-4'-nitrobiphenyl
$FC_6H_4C_6H_4NO_2$ M.W. 217.20 m.p. 125-126°
NUJOL MULL

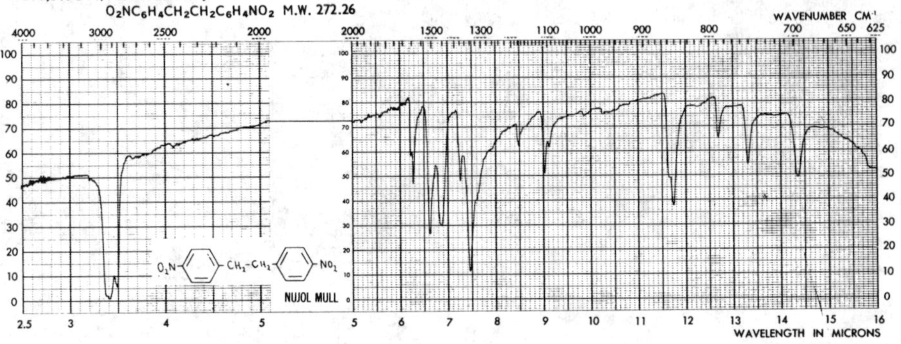

H D10,255-5 4,4'-Difluoro-2,2'-dinitrobibenzyl
$FC_6H_3(NO_2)CH_2CH_2C_6H_3(F)NO_2$ M.W. 308.24 m.p. 155-157°
NUJOL MULL

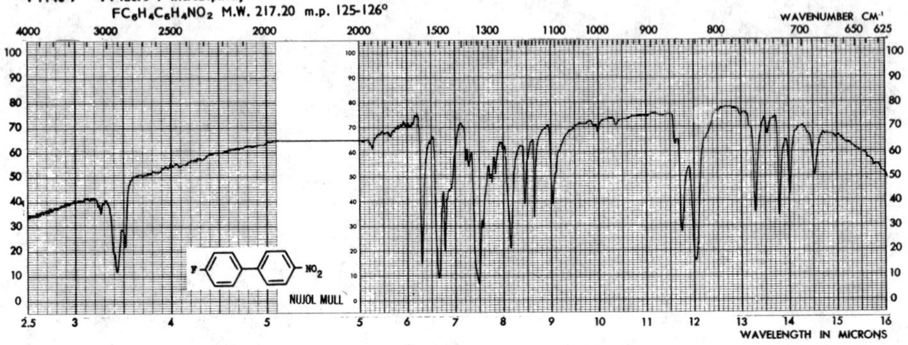

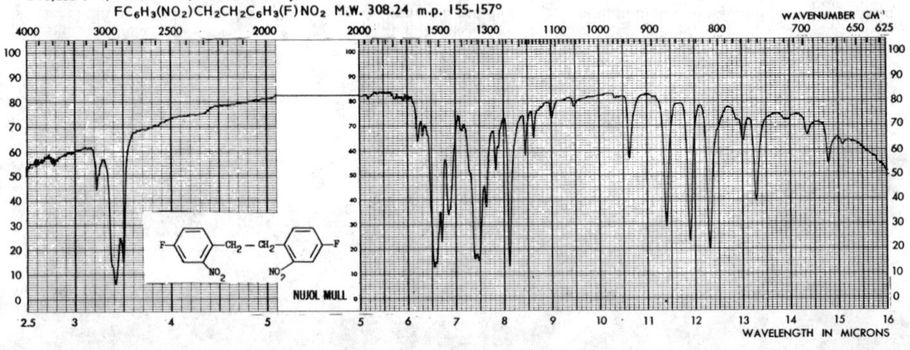

A 11,333-6 **4-Chloro-4'-nitrobiphenyl**
$ClC_6H_4C_6H_4NO_2$ M.W. 233.66
m.p. 137.5-140°
NUJOL MULL

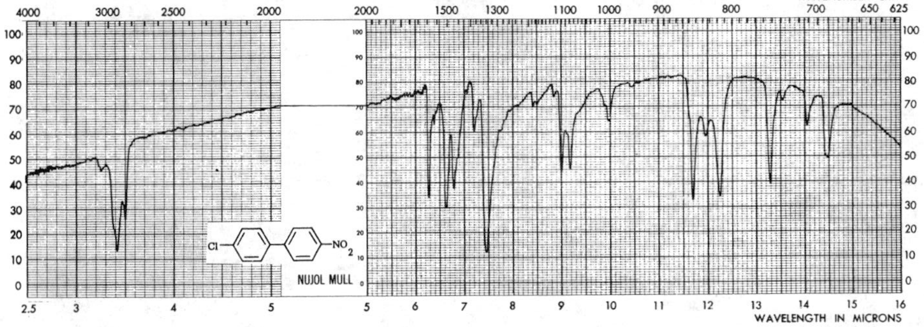

B 15,836-4
4-Iodo-4'-nitrobiphenyl, 98%
$IC_6H_4C_6H_4NO_2$
M.W. 325.11 m.p. 205-207° Beil. **5**(2),490
NUJOL MULL

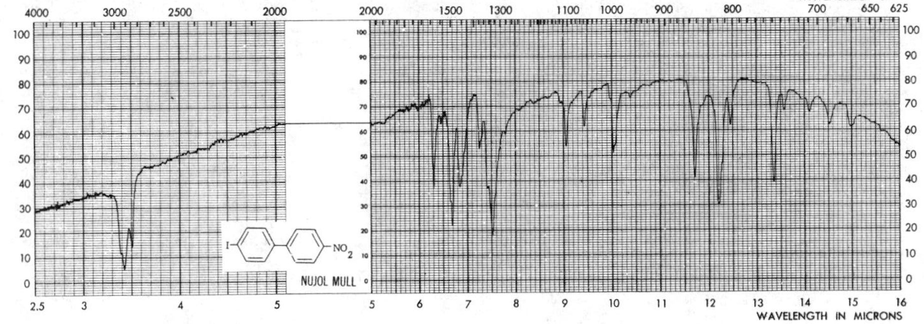

C 10,104-4 **4-Bromo-3-nitrobiphenyl**
$C_6H_5C_6H_3(NO_2)Br$ M.W. 278.11 m.p. 42-44°
MELT

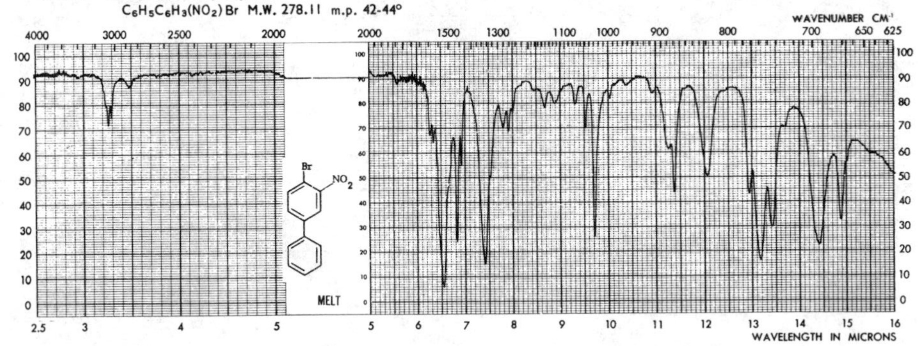

D N2190-1 **p-Nitrophenyl phenyl ether**
$O_2NC_6H_4OC_6H_5$ M.W. 215.21 m.p. 57-58.5°
MELT

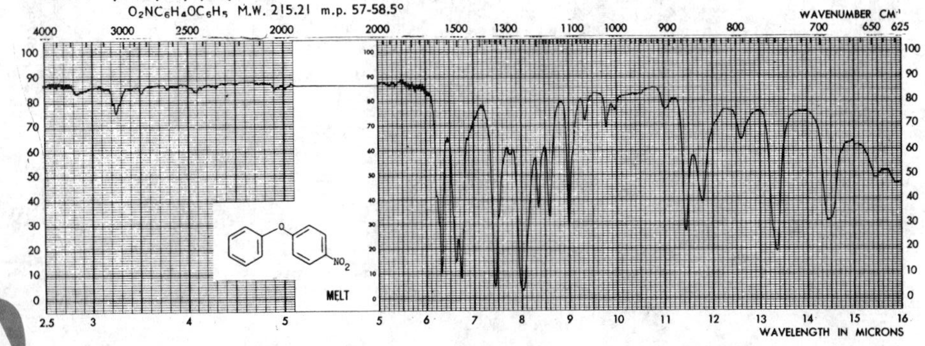

E 17,886-1
p-(p-Nitrophenoxy)-phenol, 97%
$O_2NC_6H_4OC_6H_4OH$
M.W. 231.21 m.p. 170-172°
NUJOL MULL

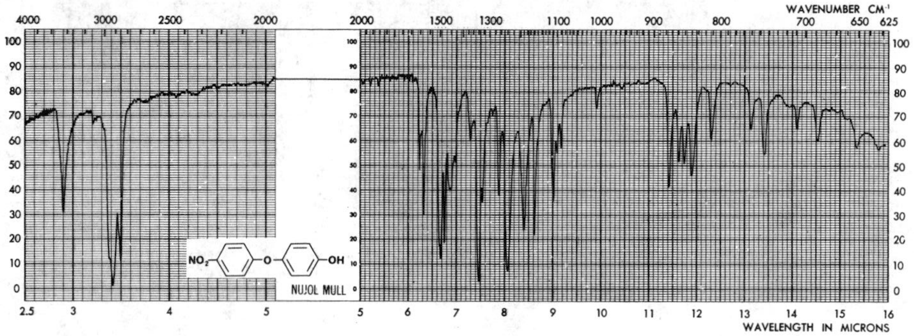

F 15,324-9 **p-Chlorophenyl o-nitrophenyl ether**
$ClC_6H_4OC_6H_4NO_2$ M.W. 249.66
m.p. 42-45°
NUJOL MULL

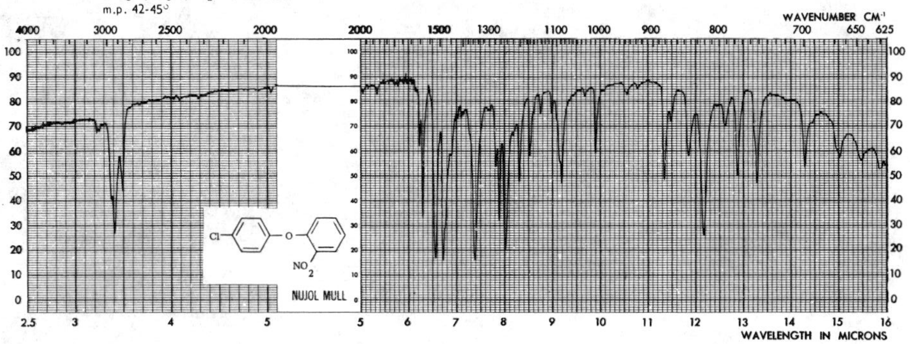

G 13,852-5 **2,5-Dimethoxy-4'-nitrostilbene**
$(CH_3O)_2C_6H_3CH{:}CHC_6H_4NO_2$ M.W. 285.30
m.p. 117-119°
NUJOL MULL

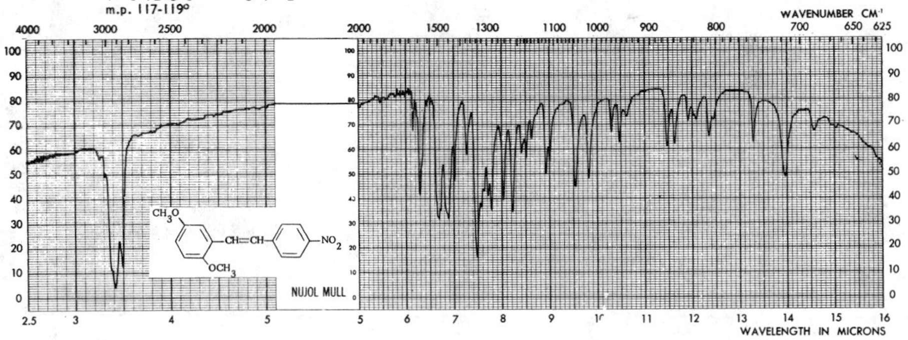

H 15,231-5 **2-Nitrophenyl disulfide** [bis-(o-nitrophenyl) disulfide]
$(O_2NC_6H_4)_2S_2$ M.W. 308.33 m.p. 189-193°
NUJOL MULL

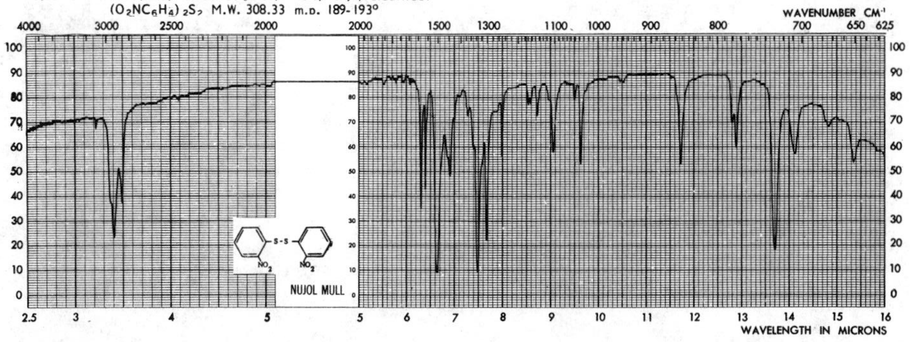

A

N2100-6 **3-Nitrophenyl disulfide** [bis-(m-nitrophenyl) disulfide, nitrophenide]
$(O_2NC_6H_4)_2S_2$ M.W. 308.33 m.p. 79-81°

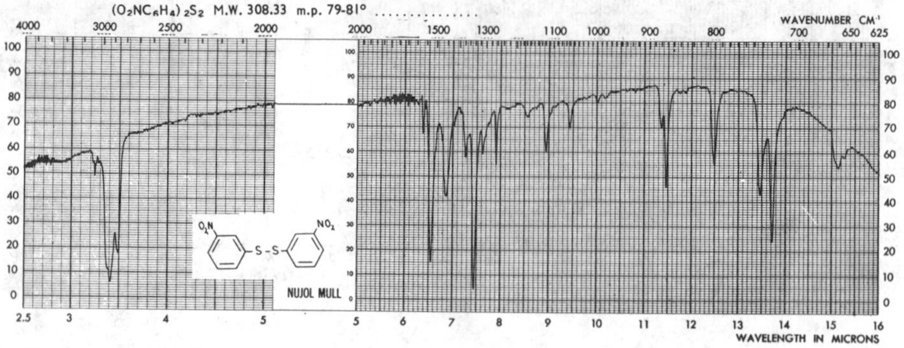

NUJOL MULL

B

18,598-1
p-Nitrophenyl phenyl sulfide, 98%
$C_6H_5SC_6H_4NO_2$
M.W. 231.28 m.p. 56-58° Beil. 6,339

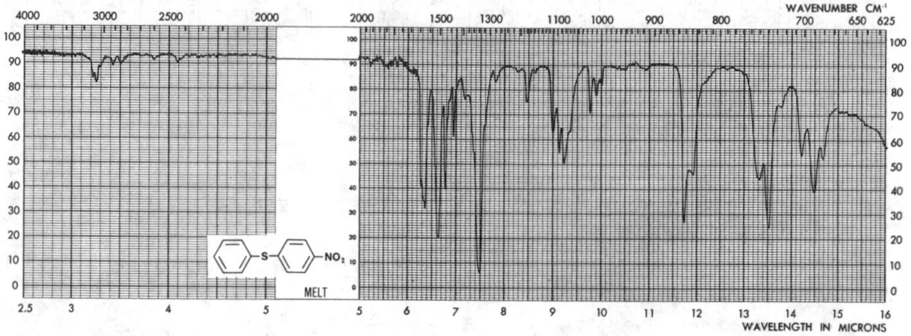

MELT

C

N2260-6 **4-Nitrophenyl sulfide** [bis-(p-nitrophenyl) sulfide]
$(O_2NC_6H_4)_2S$ M.W. 276.27 m.p. 157-159°

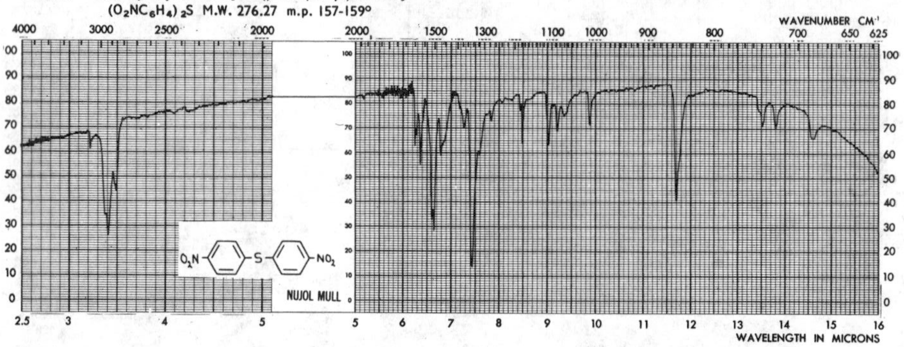

NUJOL MULL

D

N2102-2 **4-Nitrophenyl disulfide** [bis-(p-nitrophenyl) disulfide]
$(O_2NC_6H_4)_2S_2$ M.W. 308.33 m.p. 179-182°

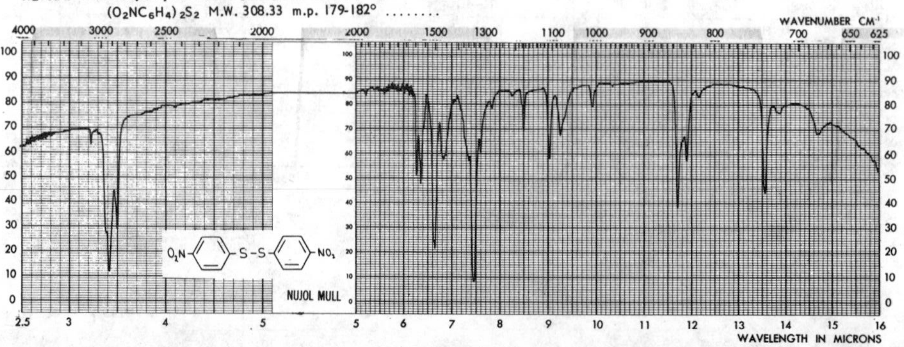

NUJOL MULL

E

12,512-1 **4-Chloro-2-nitrophenyl disulfide** [bis-(4-chloro-2-nitrophenyl) disulfide]
$[ClC_6H_3(NO_2)]_2S_2$ M.W. 377.22 m.p. 215-217° (dec.)

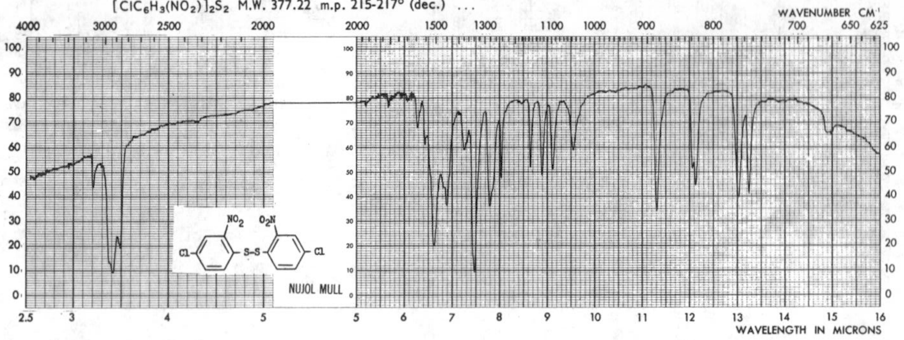

NUJOL MULL

F

11,387-5 **2,4-Dinitrophenyl sulfide**
$[(O_2N)_2C_6H_3]_2S$ M.W. 366.26
m.p. 196.5-198°

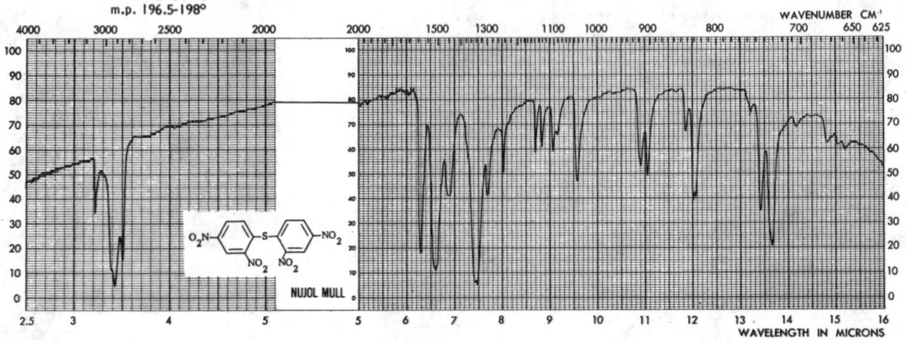

NUJOL MULL

G

A6918-8 **4-Amino-4'-nitrodiphenyl sulfide** [4-(p-nitrophenylthio)-aniline]
$H_2NC_6H_4SC_6H_4NO_2$ M.W. 246.29
m.p. 141.5-142.5°

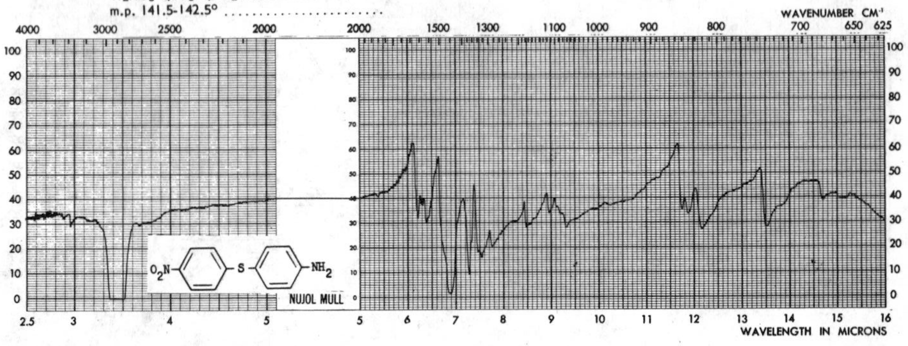

NUJOL MULL

H

10,355-1 **3-Nitro-4-biphenylamine**
$C_6H_5C_6H_3(NO_2)NH_2$ M.W. 214.23 m.p. 170-171°

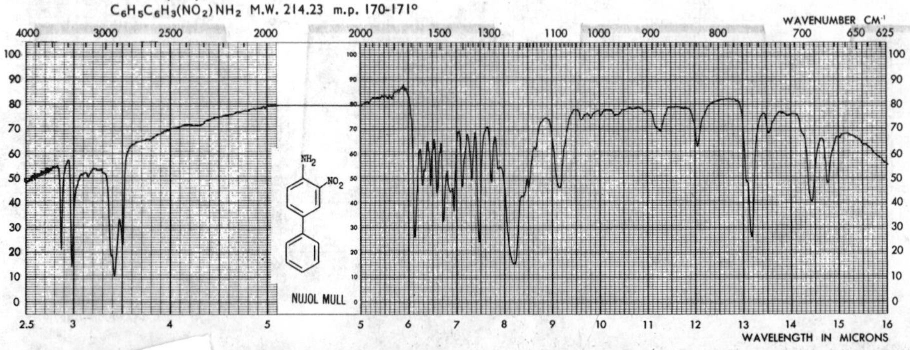

NUJOL MULL

A

$CH_2(C_6H_3(NO_2)NH_2)_2$ M.W. 258.27
m.p. 202-204° (dec.)

E

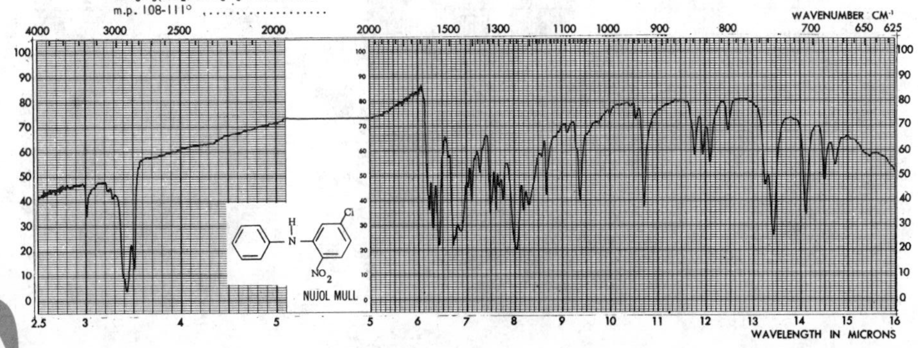

$(O_2N)_2C_6H_3NHC_6H_5$ M.W. 259.22
m.p. 156-158°

B

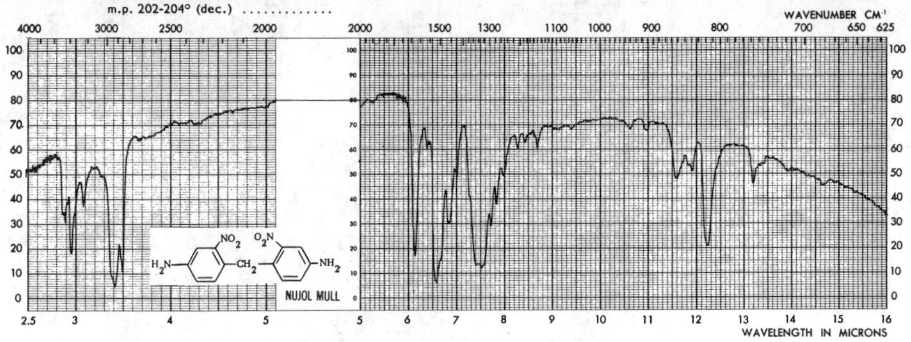

10,357-8 **4-Nitrodiphenylamine**
$C_6H_5NHC_6H_4NO_2$ M.W. 214.23 m.p. 132-135°

F

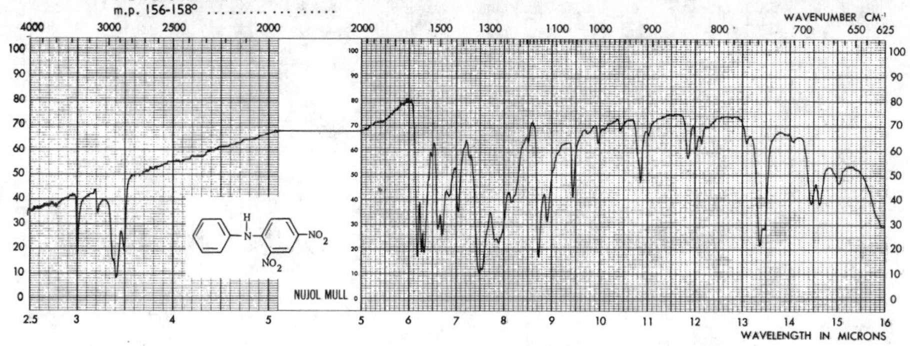

13,556-9 **2,4-Dinitro-2'-methyldiphenylamine**
$CH_3C_6H_4NHC_6H_3(NO_2)_2$ M.W. 273.25
m.p. 121-123°

C

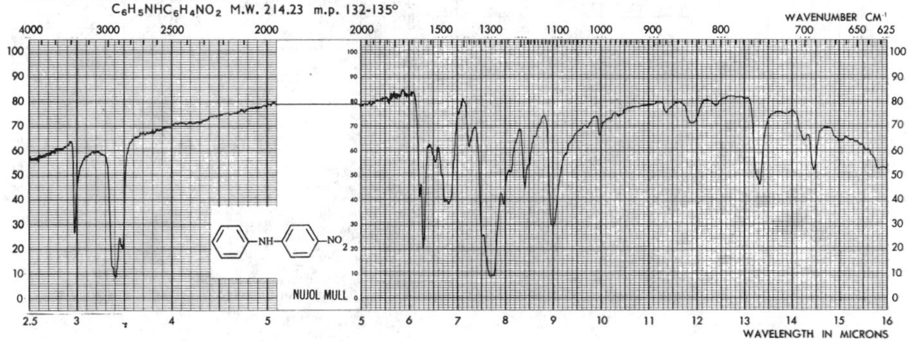

15,717-1
2-Nitrodiphenylamine, 98%
$C_6H_5NHC_6H_4NO_2$
M.W. 214.22 m.p. 76-78° Beil. **12**,690

G

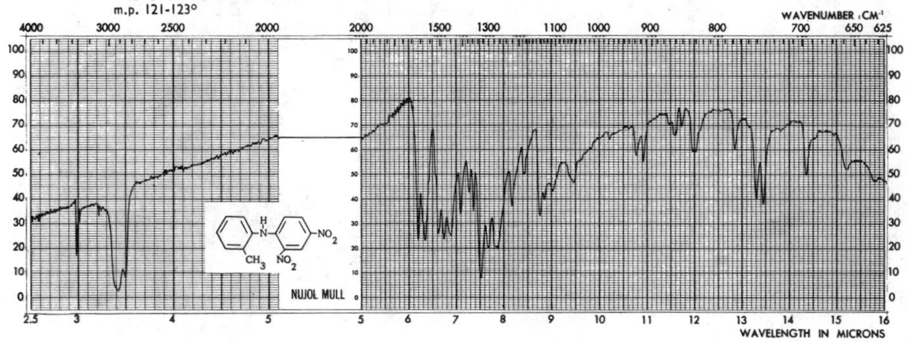

11,800-1 **2,4-Dinitro-3'-methyldiphenylamine**
$CH_3C_6H_4NHC_6H_3(NO_2)_2$ M.W. 273.25
m.p. 159-161°

D

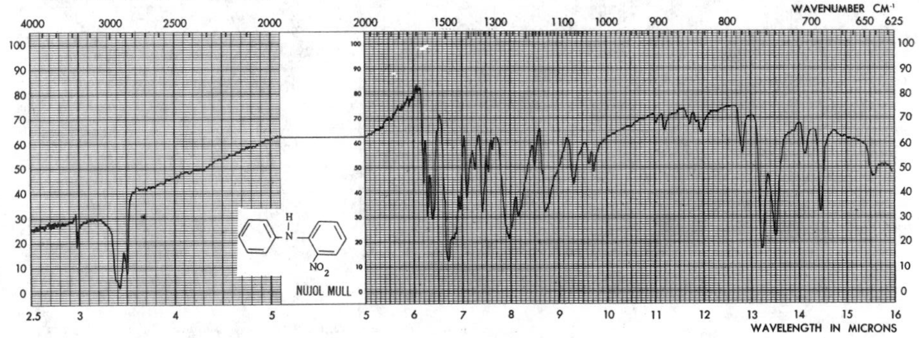

15,322-2 **5-Chloro-2-nitrodiphenylamine**
$ClC_6H_3(NO_2)NHC_6H_5$ M.W. 248.67
m.p. 108-111°

H

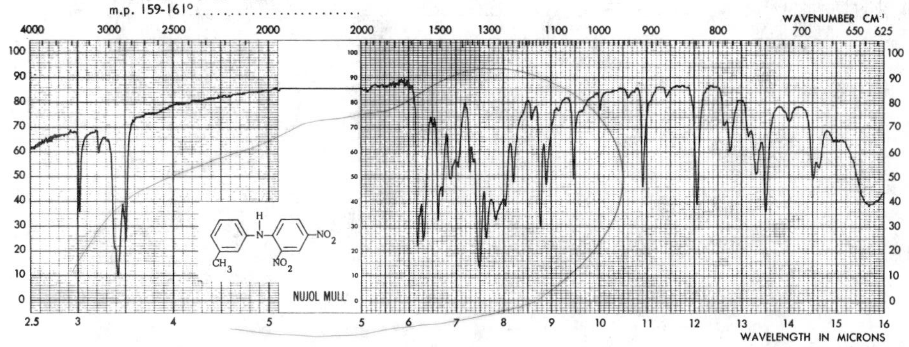

11,798-6 **4'-Chloro-2,4-dinitrodiphenylamine**
$(O_2N)_2C_6H_3NHC_6H_4Cl$ M.W. 293.67
m.p. 164-167°

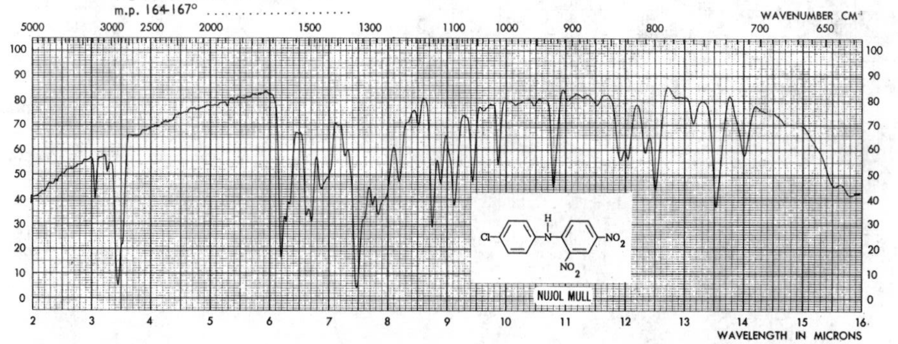

A

11,802-8 **2,4-Dinitro-2'-methoxydiphenylamine**
$(O_2N)_2C_6H_3NHC_6H_4OCH_3$ M.W. 289.25
m.p. 165-167°

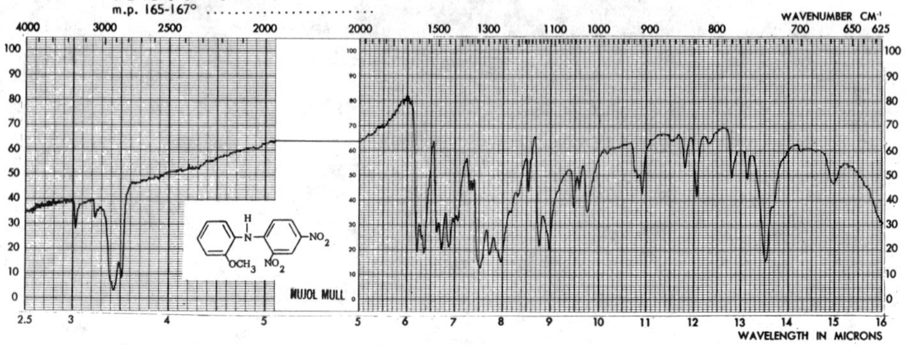

NUJOL MULL

B

12,662-4 **p-(2,4-Dinitroanilino)-phenol** (2,4-dinitro-4'-hydroxydiphenylamine)
$(O_2N)_2C_6H_3NHC_6H_4OH$ M.W. 275.22
m.p. 192-193°

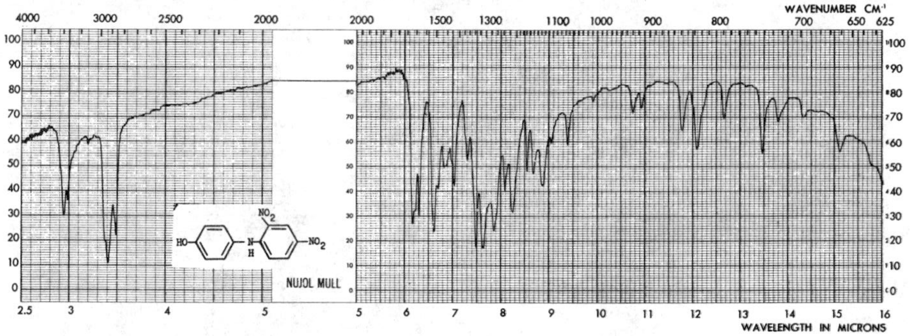

NUJOL MULL

C

13,856-8 **2,3',4,6-Tetranitrodiphenylamine**
$(O_2N)_3C_6H_2NHC_6H_4NO_2$ M.W. 349.22 m.p. 210-211.5°

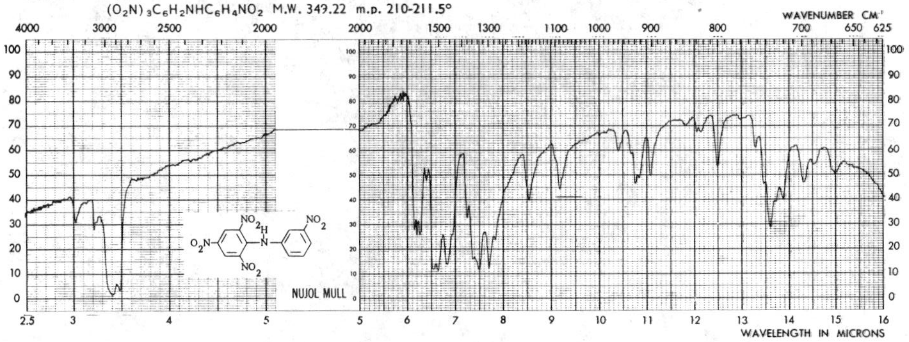

NUJOL MULL

D

13,854-1 **2,4,4',6-Tetranitrodiphenylamine**
$(O_2N)_3C_6H_2NHC_6H_4NO_2$ M.W. 349.22 m.p. 218-221°

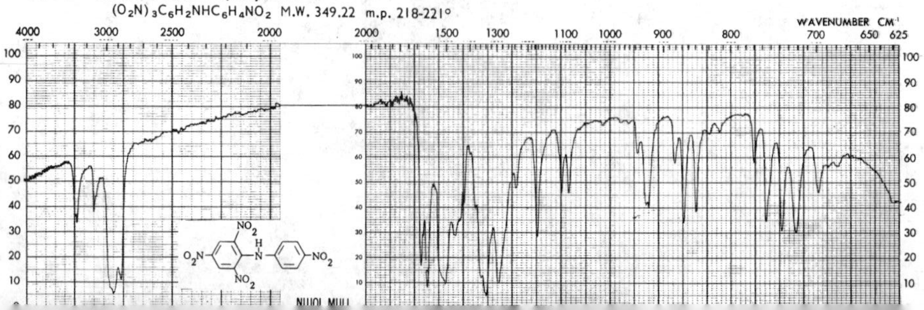

NUJOL MULL

E

H1210-2 **2,2',4,4',6,6'-Hexanitrodiphenylamine** (dipicrylamine), moist, 85%
$[(O_2N)_3C_6H_2]_2NH$ M.W. 439.21 (dry)
m.p. 243-244° (dec.)

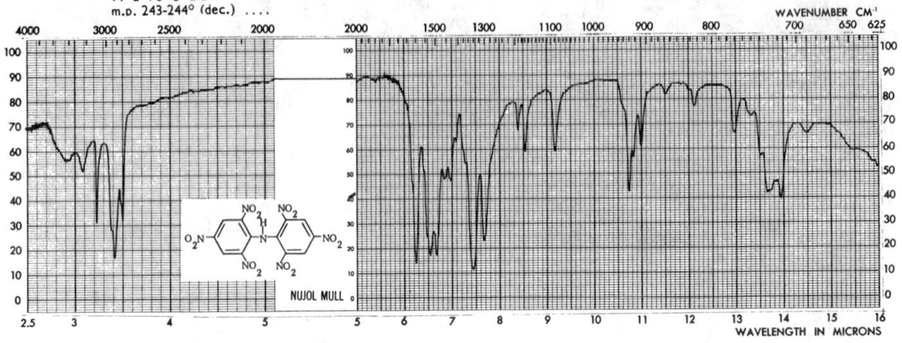

NUJOL MULL

F

D21,140-0 **2,2-Diphenyl-1-picrylhydrazyl** (free radical)
M.W. 394.32 m.p. 132-133°

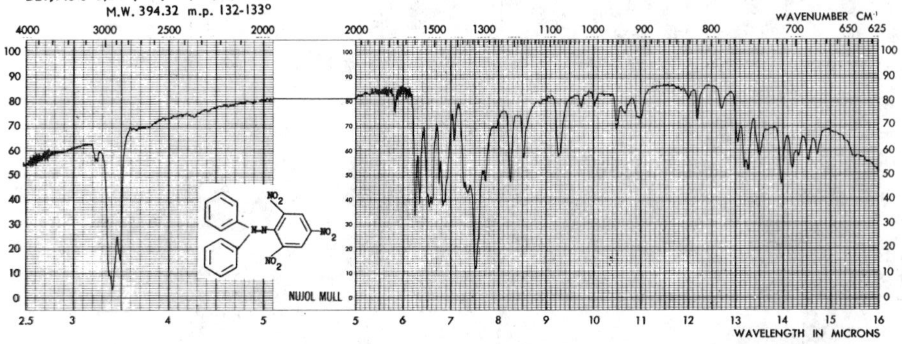

NUJOL MULL

G

10,359-4 **1-Nitronaphthalene**
$C_{10}H_7NO_2$ M.W. 173.17 m.p. 55-56°

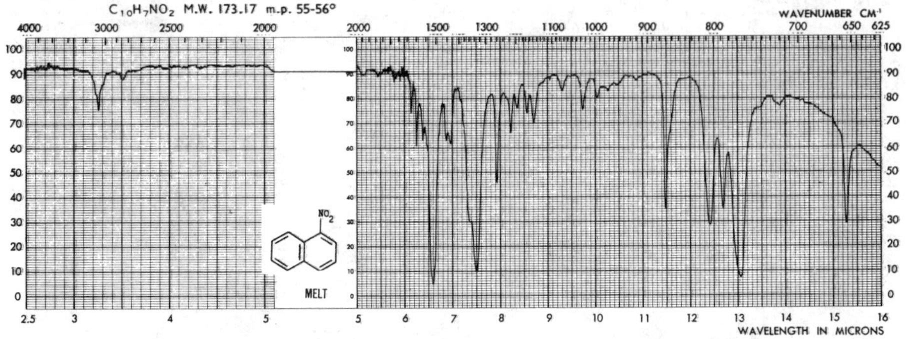

MELT

H

18,484-5
2-Nitronaphthalene, tech.
$C_{10}H_7NO_2$
M.W. 173.17 Beil. 5,555

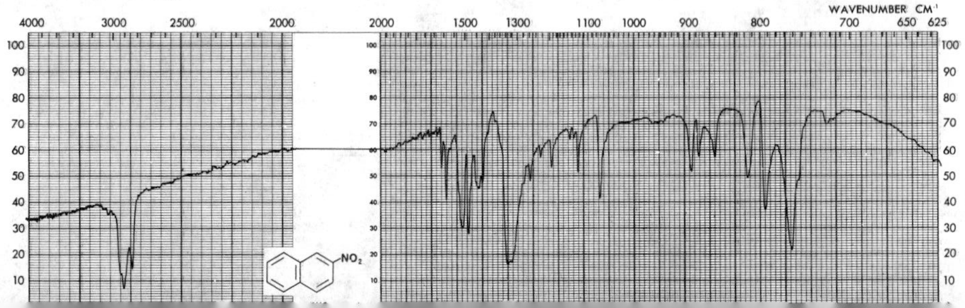

m.p. 79-82° ....

A

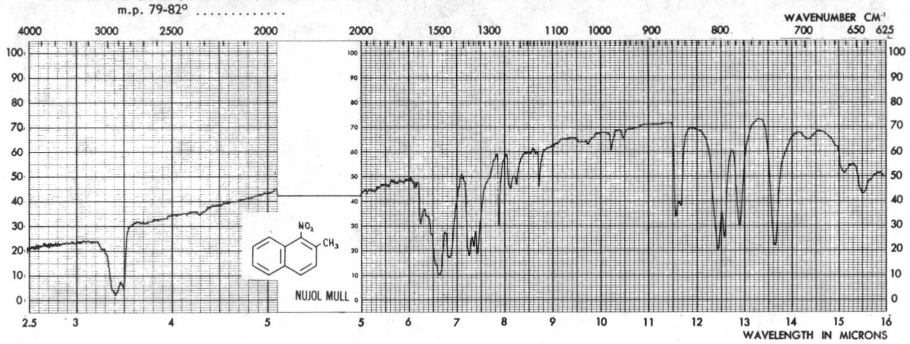

NUJOL MULL

11,631-9 **1-Fluoro-4-nitronaphthalene**
$FC_{10}H_6NO_2$ M.W. 191.16 m.p. 77-78°

B

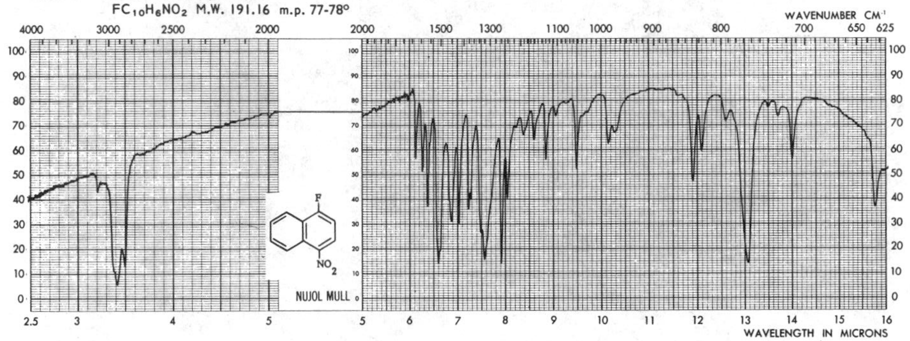

NUJOL MULL

C6100-3 **1-Chloro-8-nitronaphthalene, tech.**
$ClC_{10}H_6NO_2$ M.W. 172.16 .....

C

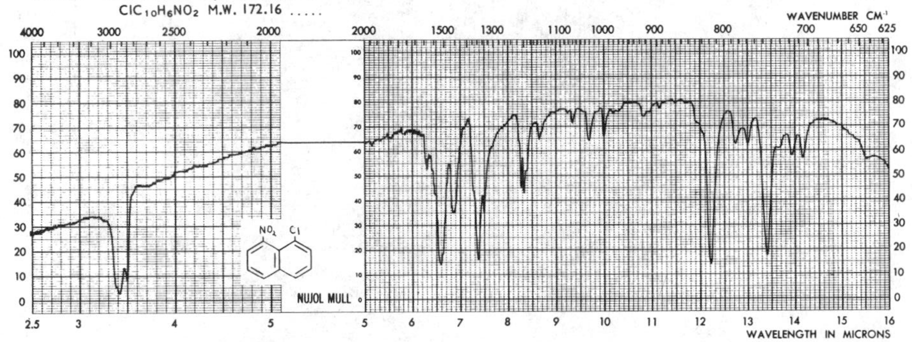

NUJOL MULL

15,757-0
1-Bromo-5-nitronaphthalene, 98%
$BrC_{10}H_6NO_2$
M.W. 252.07 m.p. 119-121° Beil. **5**,557

D

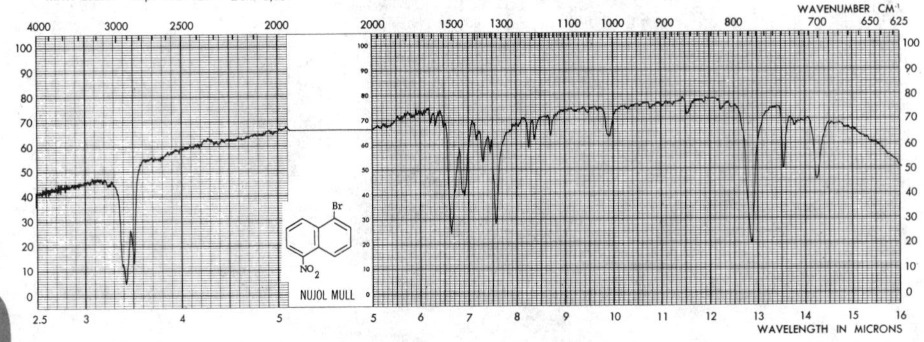

NUJOL MULL

M.W. 242.06 m.p. 122-125°

E

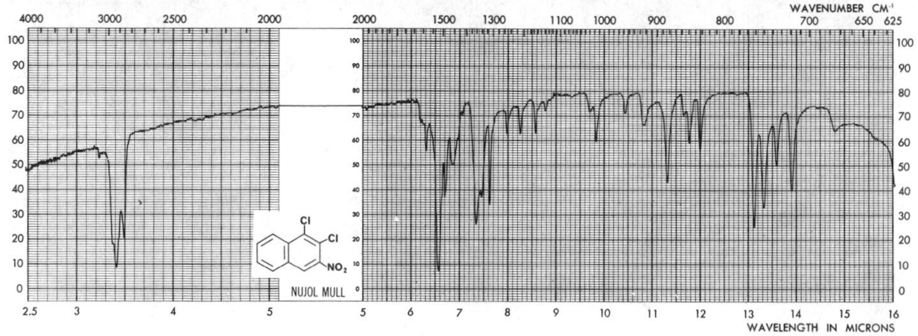

NUJOL MULL

M1800-0 **1-Methoxy-4-nitronaphthalene**
$CH_3OC_{10}H_6NO_2$ M.W. 203.20 m.p. 83-85°

F

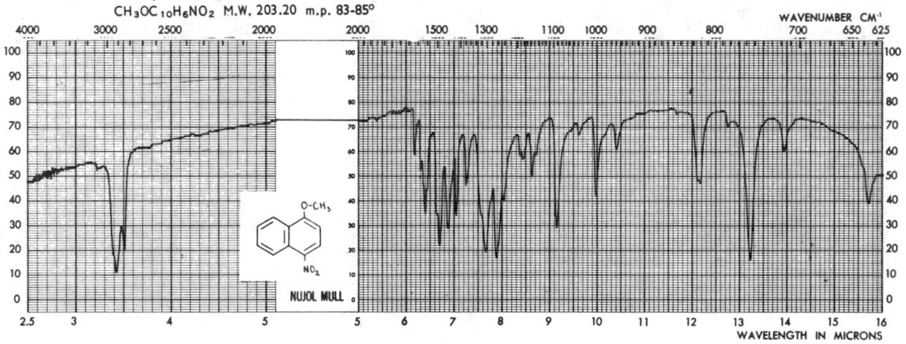

NUJOL MULL

N1930-3 **1-Nitro-2-naphthol**
$O_2NC_{10}H_6OH$ M.W. 189.17 m.p. 103-105°

G

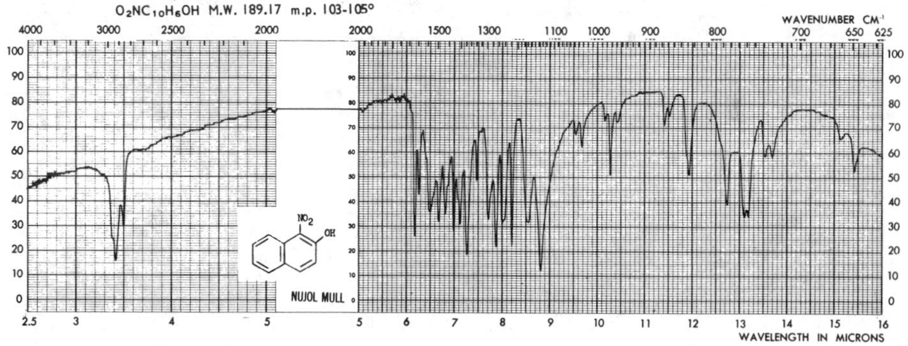

NUJOL MULL

16,115-2
2-Nitro-1-naphthol, 90%, remainder potassium salt
$O_2NC_{10}H_6OH$
M.W. 189.17 m.p. 123-125° Beil. **6**,615

H

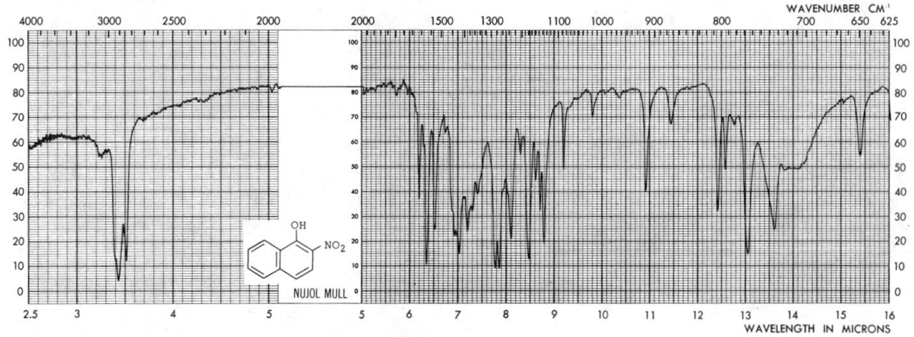

NUJOL MULL

A A7020-8 **2-Amino-1-nitronaphthalene** (1-nitro-2-naphthylamine)
$H_2NC_{10}H_6NO_2$ M.W. 188.19 m.p. 124-127°
NUJOL MULL

B A7000-3 **1-Amino-4-nitronaphthalene** (4-nitro-1-naphthylamine)
$H_2NC_{10}H_6NO_2$ M.W. 188.19 m.p. 185-190°
NUJOL MULL

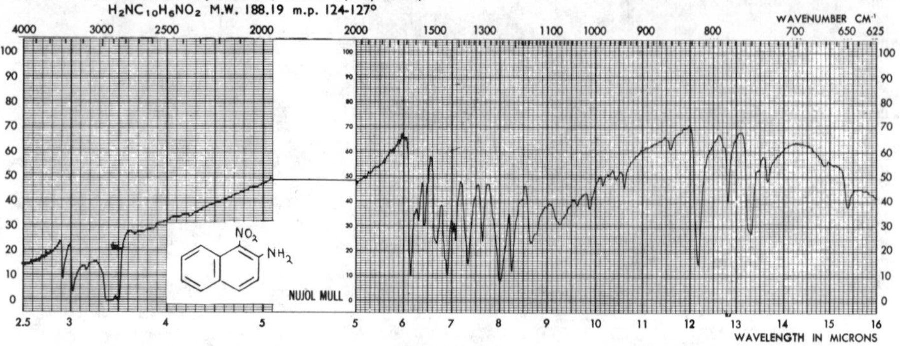

C 16,106-3
1-Amino-5-nitronaphthalene, 98+% (5-nitro-1-naphthylamine)
$H_2NC_{10}H_6NO_2$
M.W. 188.19 m.p. 116-117° (dec.) Beil. **12**,1260
NUJOL MULL

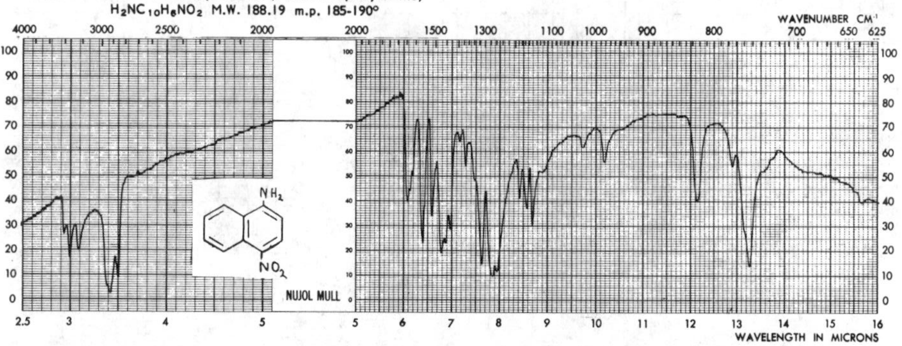

D 12,806-6 **1,3-Dinitronaphthalene**
$C_{10}H_6(NO_2)_2$ M.W. 218.17 m.p. 147-149°
NUJOL MULL

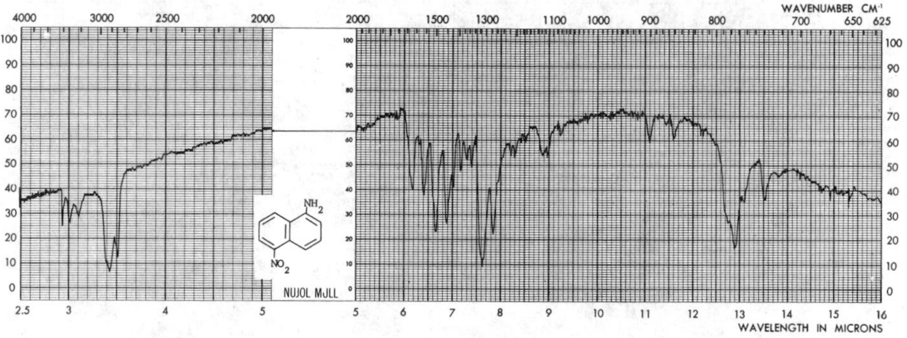

E D19,800-5 **1,4-Dinitronaphthalene**
$C_{10}H_6(NO_2)_2$ M.W. 218.17 m.p. 133°
NUJOL MULL

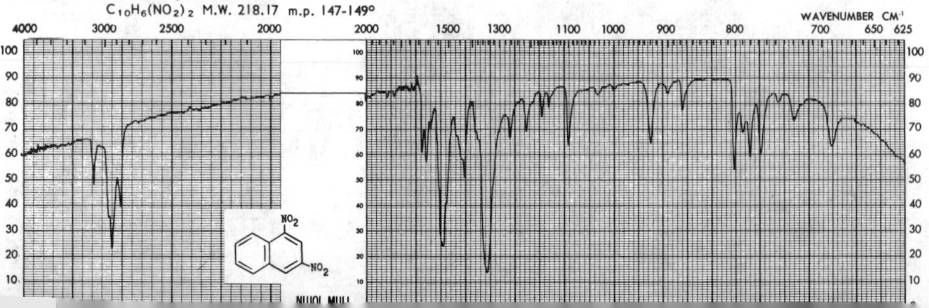

F 18,507-8
2-Bromo-3-nitronaphthalene, tech.
$BrC_{10}H_6NO_2$
M.W. 252.07 m.p. 82-84° Beil. **5**(2),453
NUJOL MULL

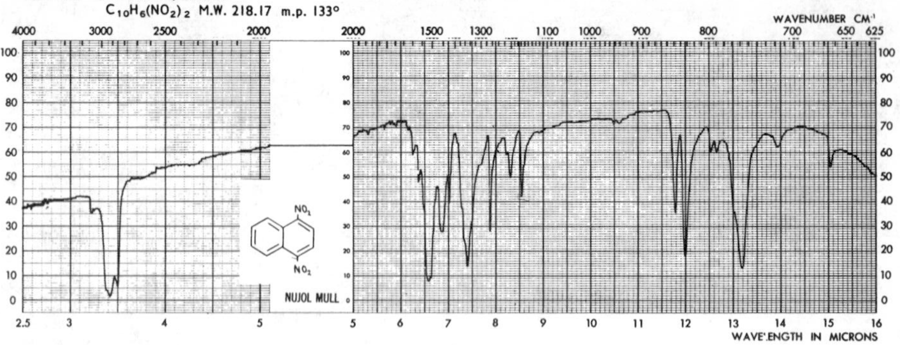

G 18,502-7
2,3-Dinitronaphthalene
$C_{10}H_6(NO_2)_2$
M.W. 218.17 m.p. 171-173°
NUJOL MULL

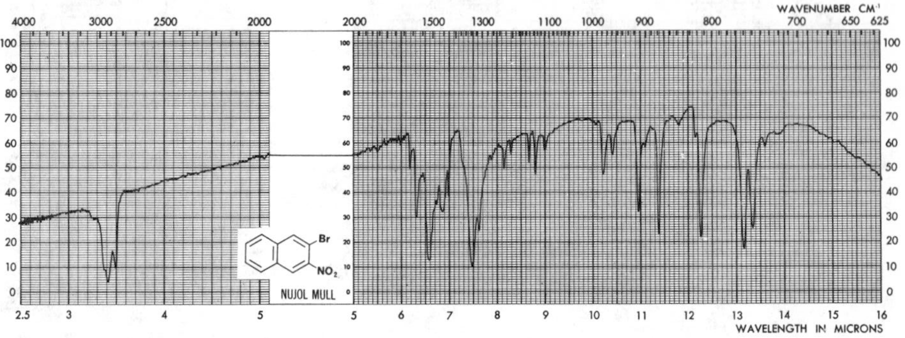

H 12,667-5 **1,5-Dinitronaphthalene**
$C_{10}H_6(NO_2)_2$ M.W. 218.17 m.p. 215-220°
NUJOL MULL

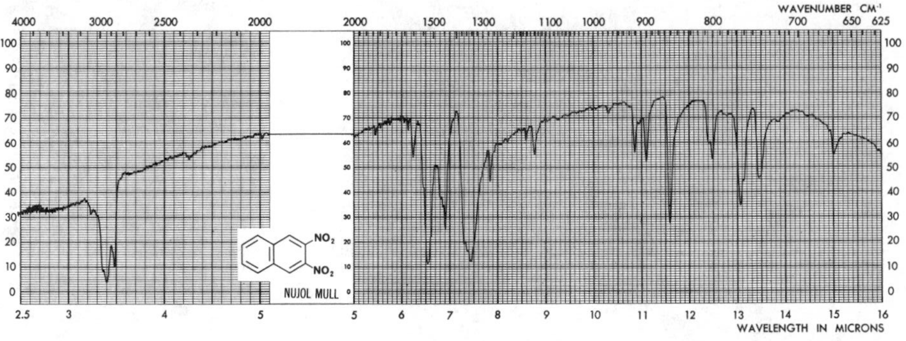

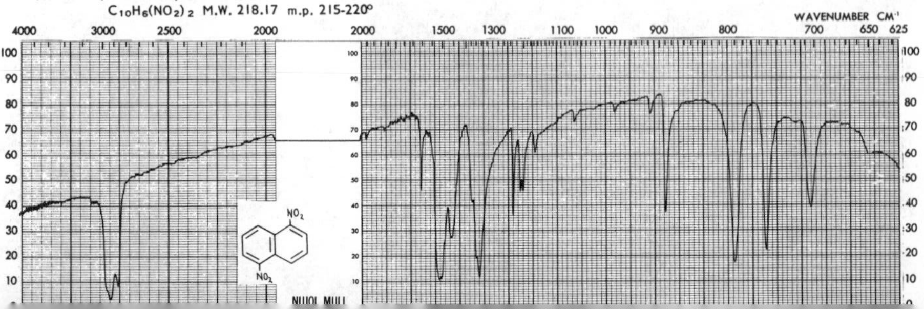

A 14,148-8 **1,8-Dinitronaphthalene**
$C_{10}H_6(NO_2)_2$ M.W. 218.17 m.p. 171-172°
NUJOL MULL

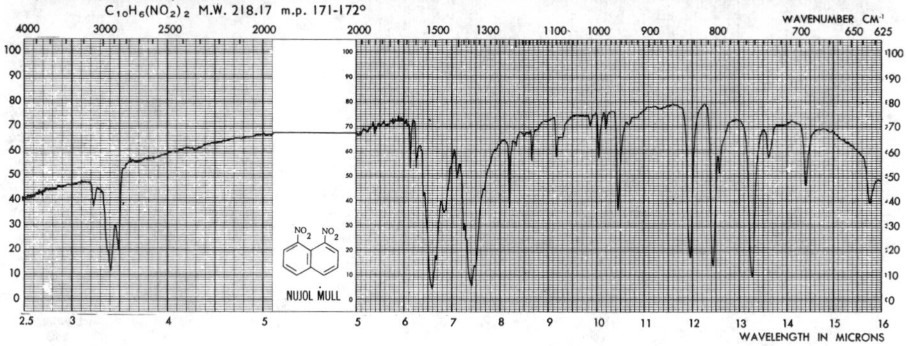

B 16,503-5
1,2,3,4,5,6-Hexachloro-7-nitronaphthalene
$Cl_6C_{10}HNO_2$
M.W. 379.84 m.p. 179-181°
NUJOL MULL

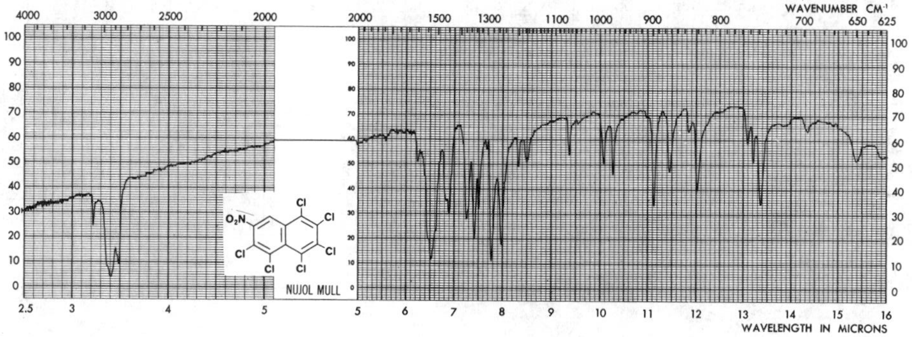

C N1675-4 **2-Nitrofluorene**
M.W. 211.22 m.p. 157-158°
NUJOL MULL

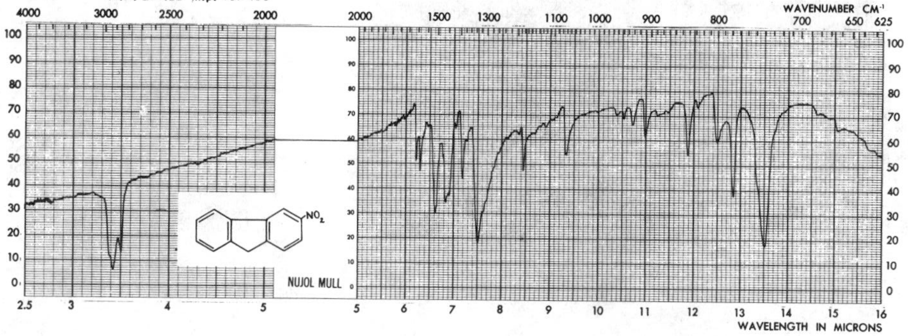

D D19,640-1 **2,7-Dinitrofluorene**
M.W. 256.22 m.p. 290-306° (dec.)
NUJOL MULL

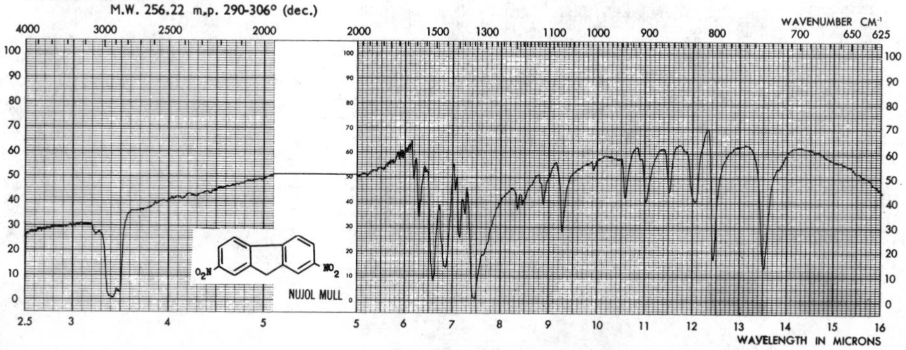

E A6960-9 **2-Amino-7-nitrofluorene**
M.W. 226.24 m.p. 229-231°
NUJOL MULL

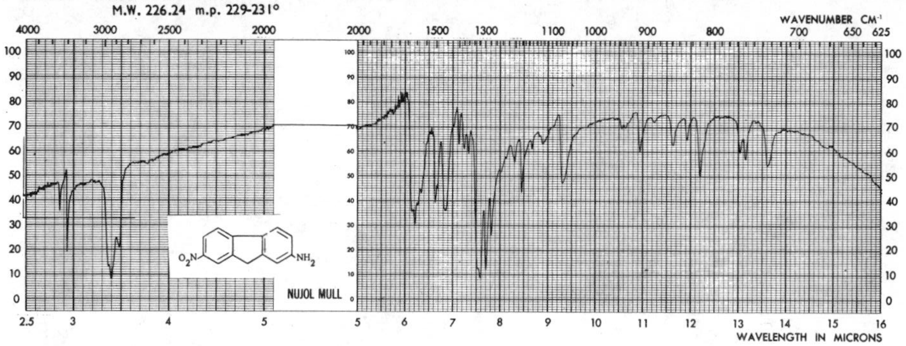

F N1020-9 **9-Nitroanthracene**
M.W. 223.23 m.p. 141-143°
NUJOL MULL

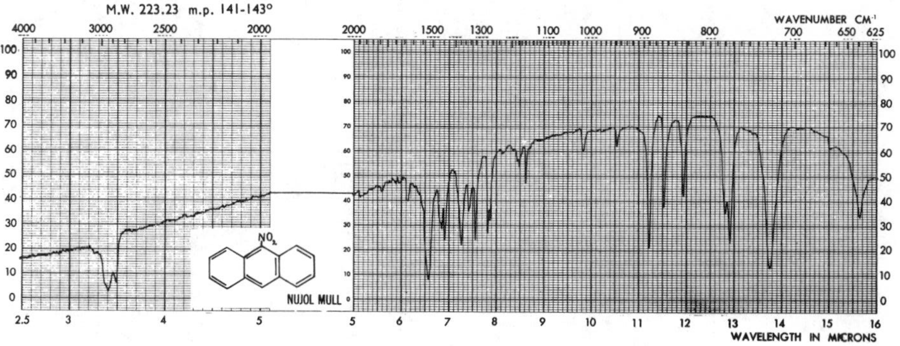

G 13,013-3 **5-Nitroacenaphthene, puriss.**
M.W. 199.21 m.p. 101-102°
NUJOL MULL

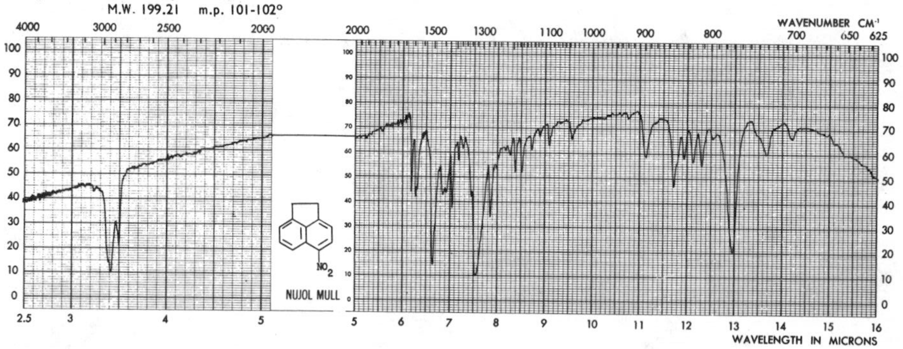

H 18,499-3
2-Nitronaphthalene-bis(hexachlorocyclopentadiene) adduct, tech.
M.W. 718.72 m.p. 217-220°
NUJOL MULL

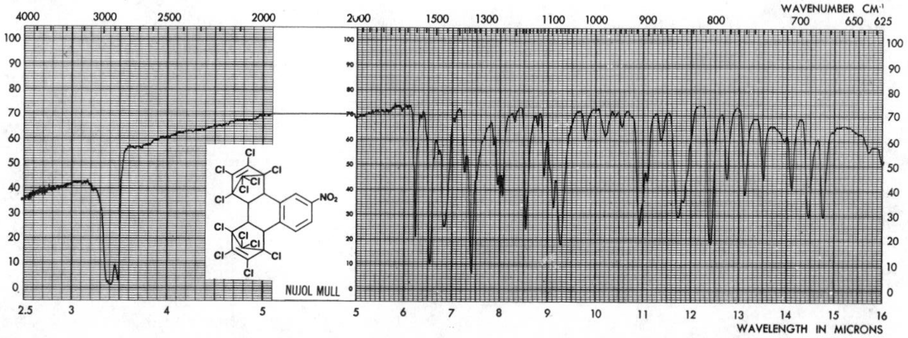

ALDRICH

A

18,498-5
2-Bromo-3-nitronaphthalene-bis(hexachlorocyclopentadiene) adduct
M.W. 797.62 m.p. 243° (dec.)

B

18,494-2
1,2-Dichloro-3-nitronaphthalene-bis(hexachlorocyclopentadiene) adduct, tech.
M.W. 787.61 m.p. 197-204°

C

22,543-6
2,4-Dichloro-6-nitrophenol
$Cl_2C_6H_2(NO_2)OH$ FW 208.00 mp 118-120°
Beil. **6**,241 Disp. T

D

22,542-8
6-Chloro-2,4-dinitroaniline, 97%
$ClC_6H_2(NO_2)_2NH_2$ FW 217.57 mp 157-159°
Beil. **12**(1),367 Disp. C

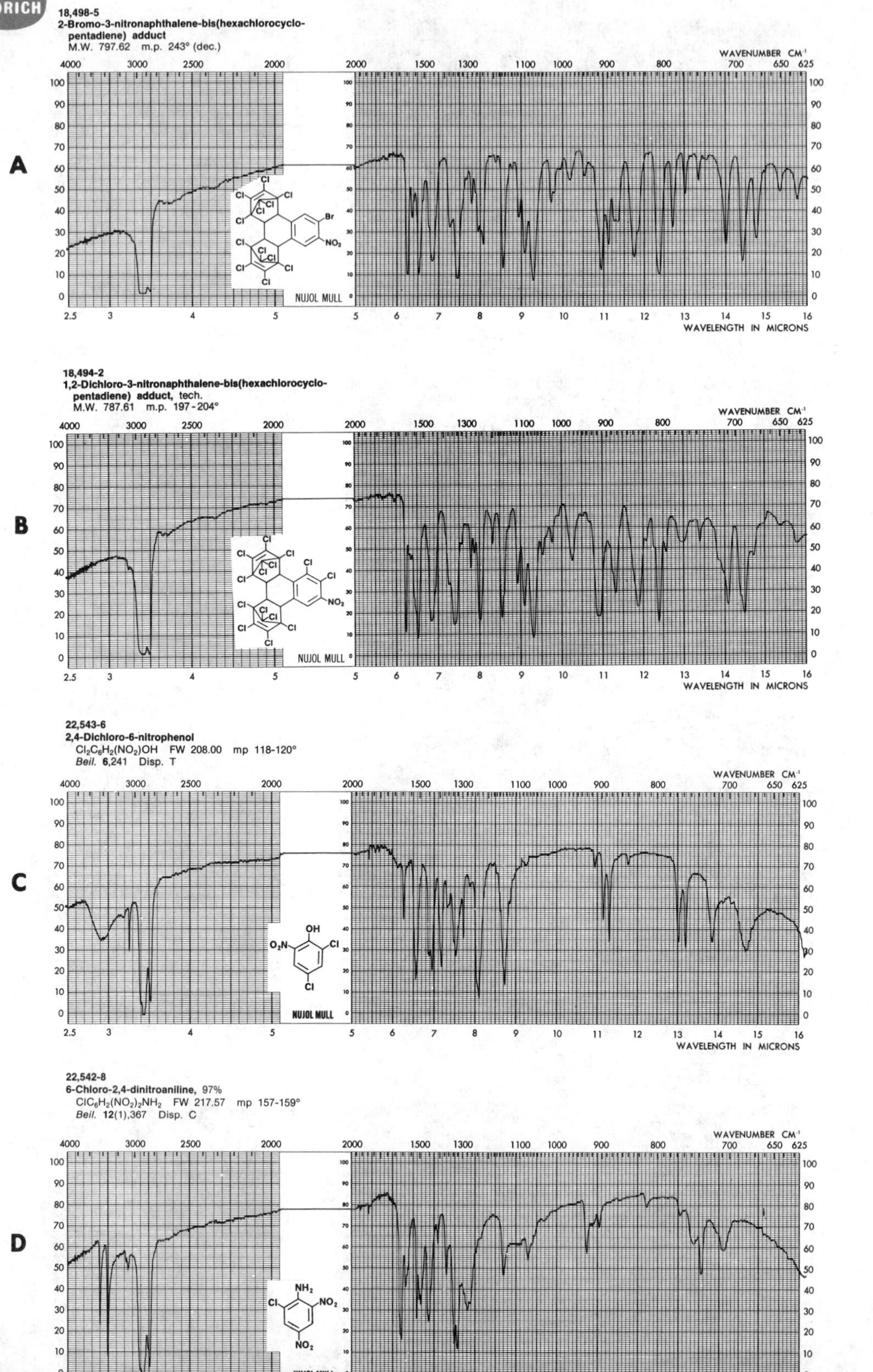

AROMATIC KETONES

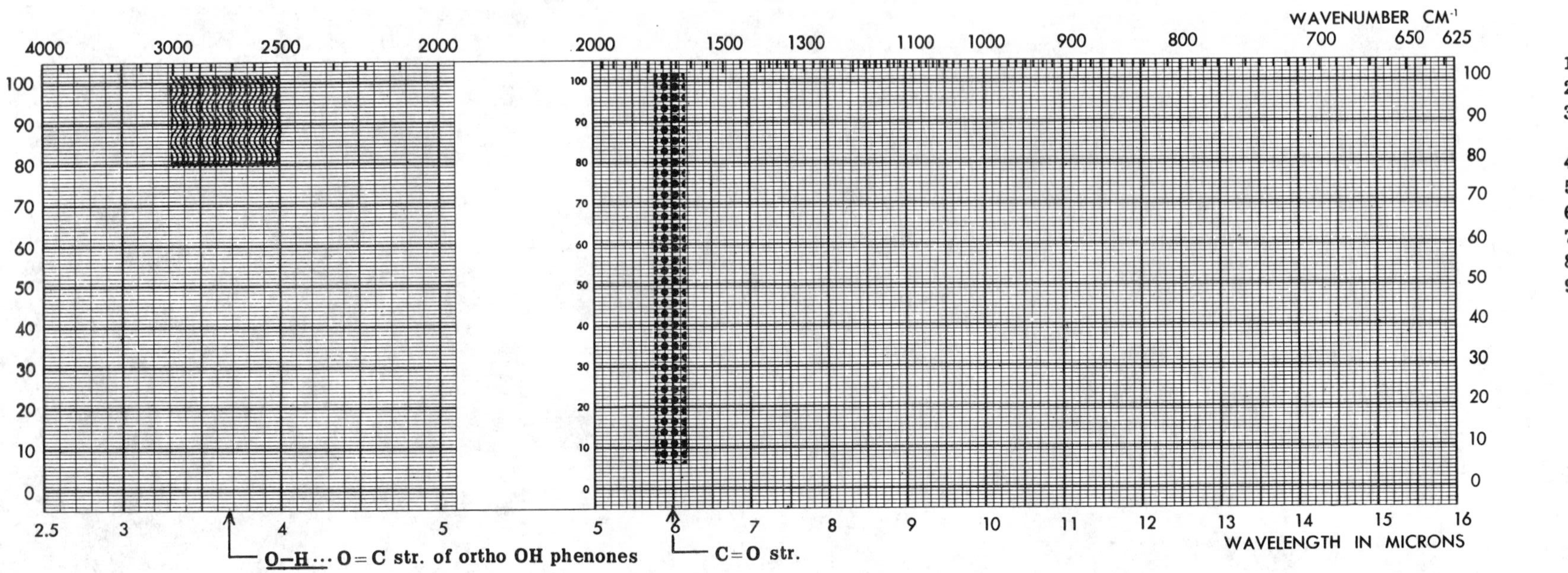

The effect of conjugation on the position of the ketone carbonyl band can be seen as we move from the nonconjugated ketones (from spectrum 848A) through the conjugated acetophenone type ketones (from spectrum 852C) and finally to the doubly conjugated benzophenone type ketones (from spectrum 880B). The normal band position near 5.8 μ (1725 cm^{-1}) is shifted to a higher wavelength near 6 μ (1665 cm^{-1}), and then to 6.2 μ (1615 cm^{-1}), respectively.

When a hydroxyl group is substituted in the ortho position of an acetophenone or benzophenone, there is hydrogen bonding between the carbonyl and hydroxyl group. The OH stretch shifts from its normal position near 3 μ (3335 cm^{-1}) to 3.3 μ (3030 cm^{-1}), and the carbonyl shifts to near 6.1 μ (1640 cm^{-1}). The broad OH stretch band near 3.3 μ (3030 cm^{-1}) is very difficult to see in nujol mull spectra due to the overlap with the mineral oil C–H stretch bands. In the meta and para substituted hydroxyphenones, the OH stretch and C=O stretch bands return to approximately their normal positions.

The substitution pattern of the aromatic ring between 11 and 15 μ (910 – 665 cm^{-1}) is altered somewhat by the influence of the conjugated ketone group. However, this effect is not as great as that seen in the nitro substituted aromatics. Additional bands to those expected from the various substitution configurations do occur quite frequently. Interference is especially prevalent in the benzophenones and the anthraquinones.

A

$C_6H_5CH_2COCH_3$ M.W. 134.18 n_D 1.51..
b.p. 99-102°/13 mm.

NEAT

B

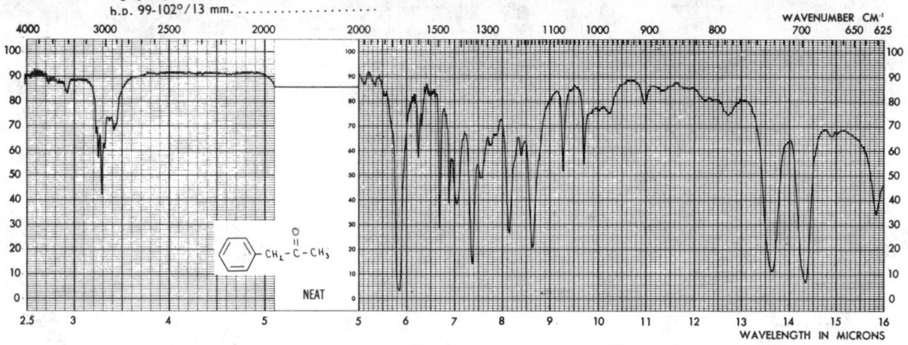

B1,600-3
Benzylacetone (4-phenyl-2-butanone)
$C_6H_5CH_2CH_2COCH_3$
M.W. 148.21 b.p. 235° n_D^{20} 1.5122 d 0.989
Beil. 7,314

NEAT

C

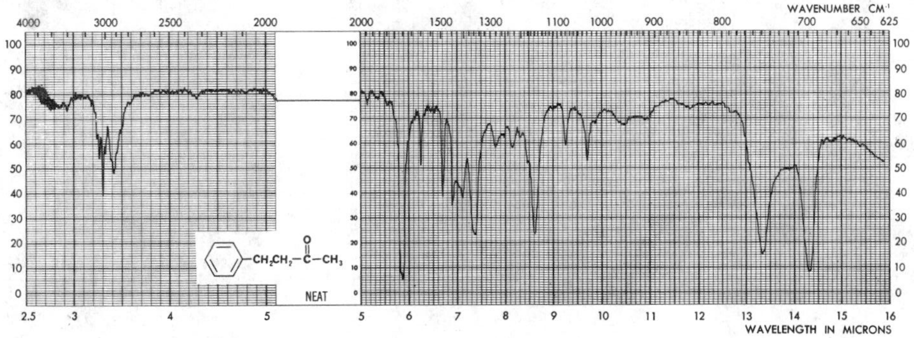

13,722-7 1-Phenyl-2-butanone
$C_6H_5CH_2COC_2H_5$ M.W. 148.21 n_D^{20} 1.5122
b.p. 109-112°/15 mm.

NEAT

D

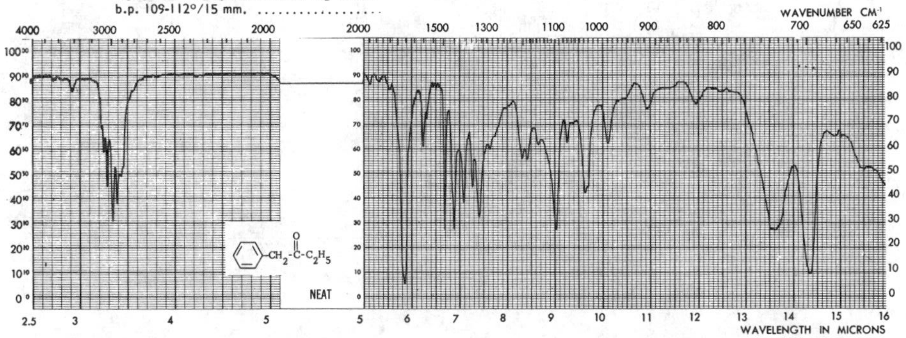

D20,440-4 1,1-Diphenylacetone (1,1-diphenyl-2-propanone)
$(C_6H_5)_2CHCOCH_3$ M.W. 210.28 m.p. 59-63°

MELT

E

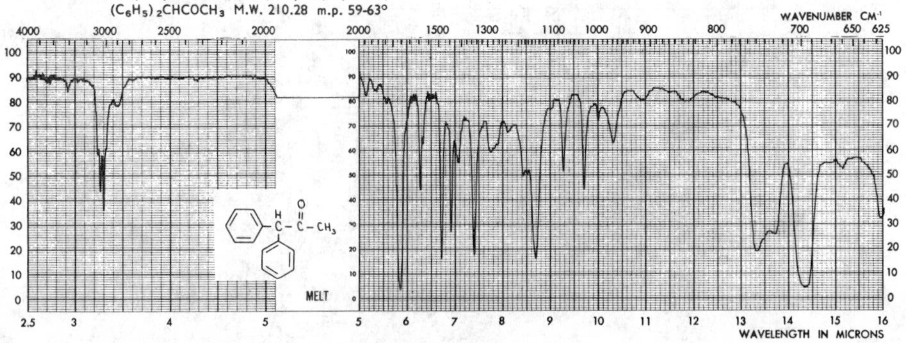

$C_6H_5CH_2COCH_2C_6H_5$ M.W. 210.28
m.p. 34-35°

MELT

F

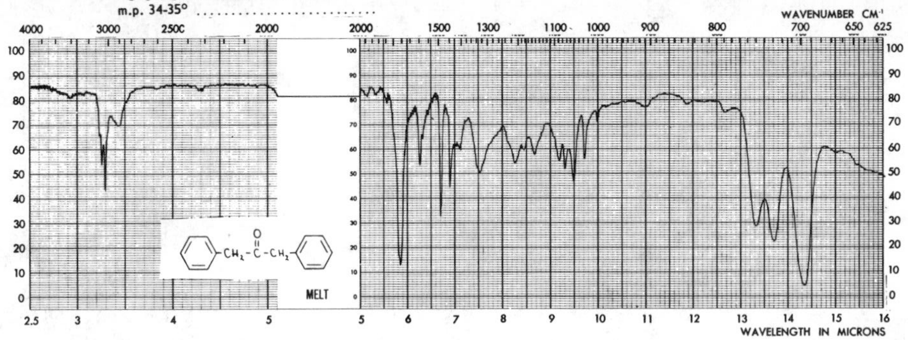

P2227-3 2-Phenylcyclohexanone, tech.
$C_6H_5C_6H_9(:O)$ M.W. 174.24

MELT

G

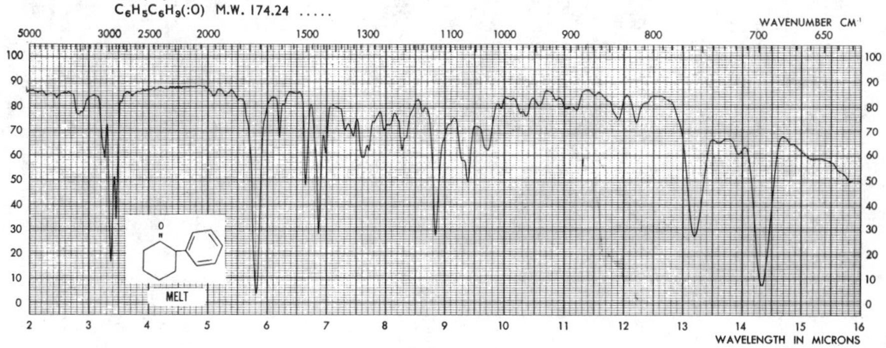

19,623-1
4-Phenylcyclohexanone, 98+%
$C_6H_5C_6H_9(=O)$ FW 174.24 mp 78-80°
Beil. 7(3),1466 Disp. C

NUJOL MULL

H

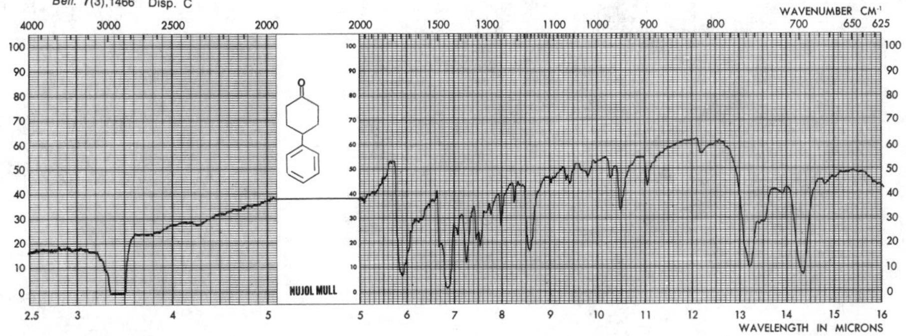

16,432-1
2-(m-Methoxyphenyl)-cyclohexanone
$CH_3OC_6H_4C_6H_9(=O)$
M.W. 204.27 n_D^{20} 1.5470

NEAT

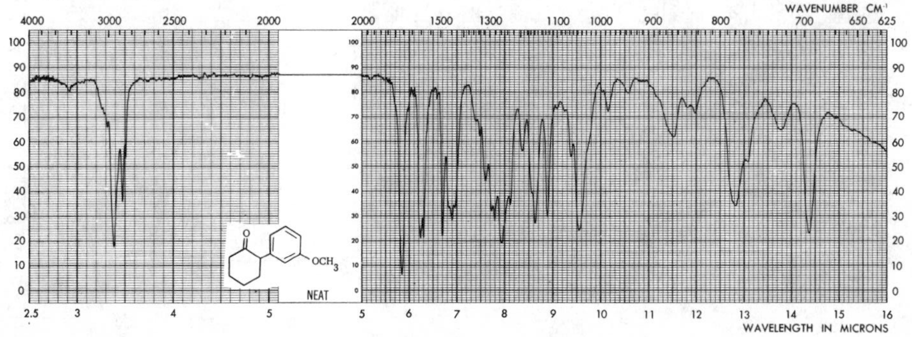

ALDRICH

A P2222-2 2-Phenylcycloheptanone
M.W. 188.27 n_D^{20} 1.5413
NEAT

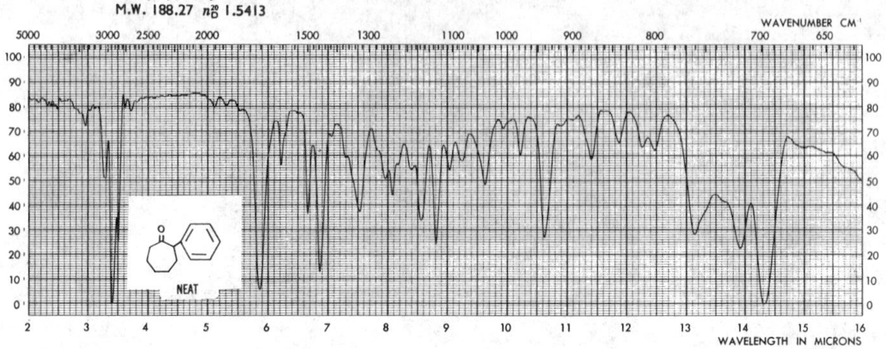

B 14,669-2 2-Indanone
M.W. 132.16 m.p. 57°
MELT

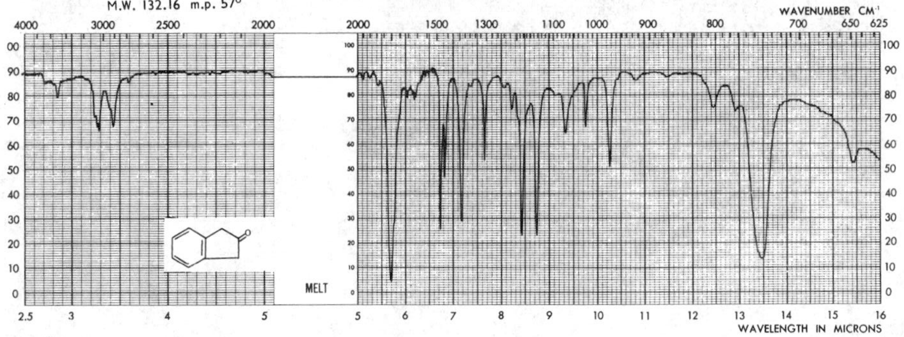

C T1920-8 β-Tetralone [3,4-dihydro-2(1H)-naphthalenone]
M.W. 146.19 n_D^{20} 1.5598
NEAT

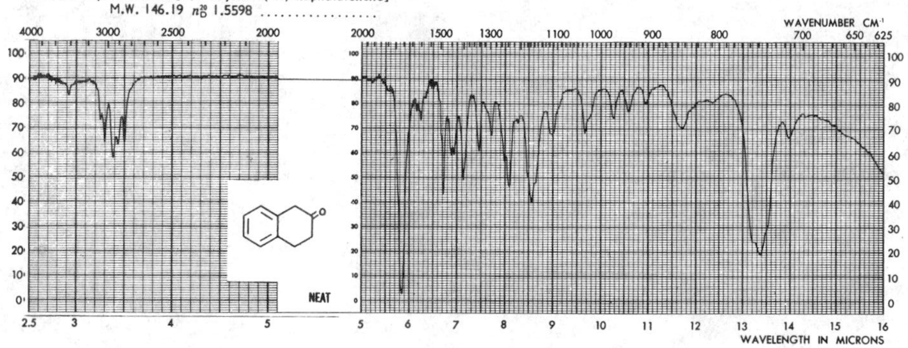

D M8290-6 1-Methyl-2-tetralone
M.W. 160.22 n_D^{20} 1.5530

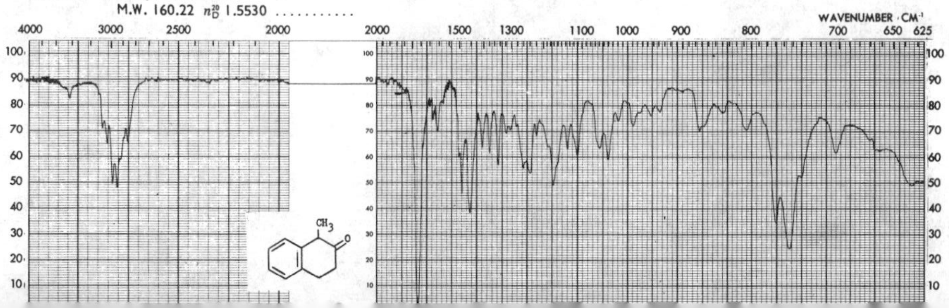

E M2557-0 5-Methoxy-2-tetralone, tech.
M.W. 176.22 n_D^{20} 1.5599 b.p. 120°/0.5 mm.
NEAT

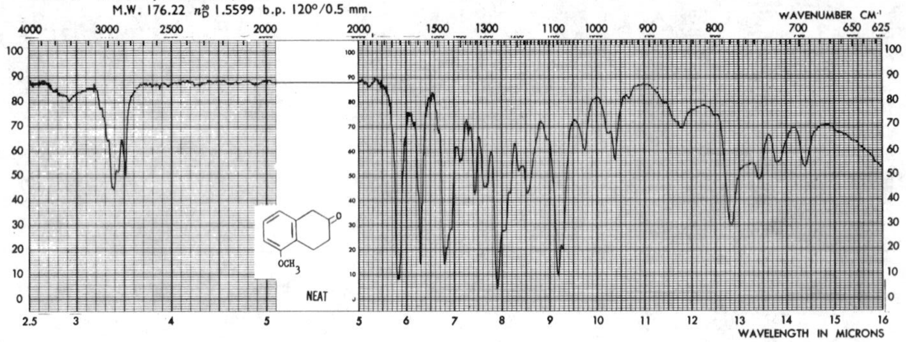

F 18,406-3
6-Methoxy-2-tetralone
M.W. 176.22 n_D^{20} 1.5645
NEAT

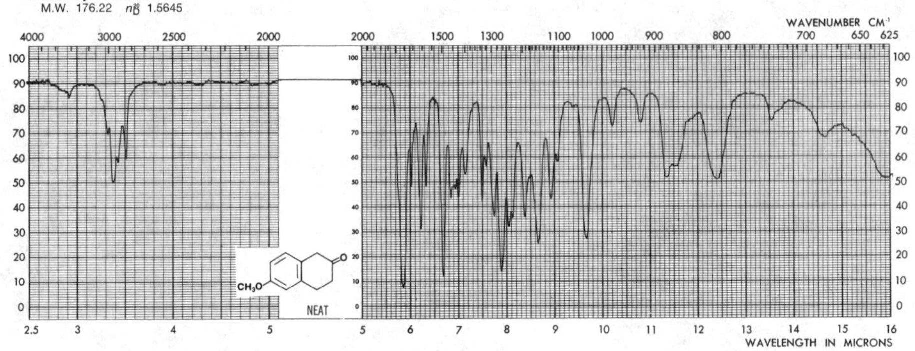

G 16,418-6
7-Methoxy-2-tetralone, 95%
M.W. 176.22 b.p. 124-126°/1.5mm.
MELT

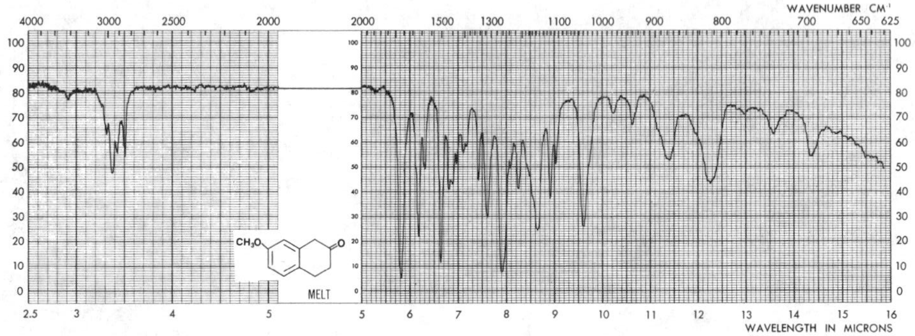

H 20,874-4
(2-Fluorophenyl)acetone, 99%
$FC_6H_4CH_2COCH_3$ FW 152.17 bp 47°/0mm.
n_D^{20} 1.4989 d 1.077 Disp. C

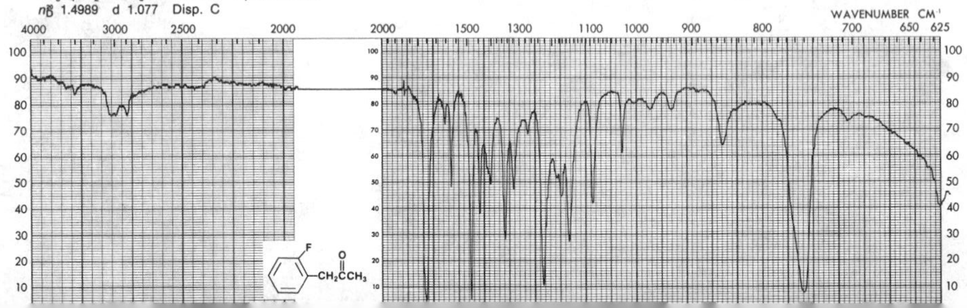

A

(4-Fluorophenyl)acetone, 98%
$FC_6H_4CH_2COCH_3$ FW 152.17 bp 106-107°/18mm.
n_D^{20} 1.4958 d 1.139 *Beil.* 7(3),1040 Disp. C

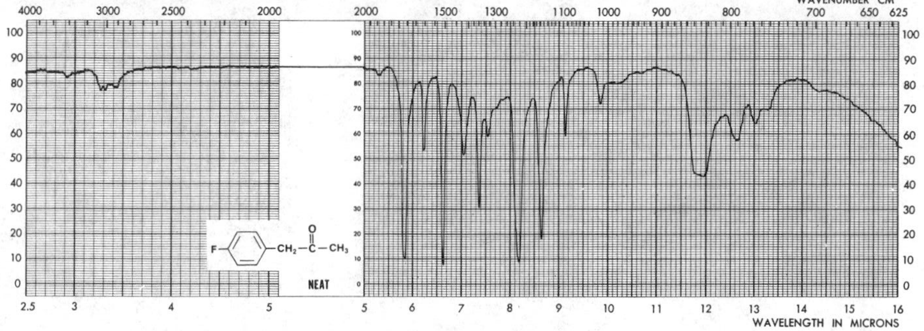

NEAT

B

19,379-8
***m*-(Trifluoromethyl)phenylacetone,** 97% [1-(α,α,α-trifluoro-*m*-tolyl)-2-propanone]
$CF_3C_6H_4CH_2COCH_3$ FW 202.18
bp 89-90°/0.500mm. n_D^{20} 1.4570 d 1.204 Disp. C

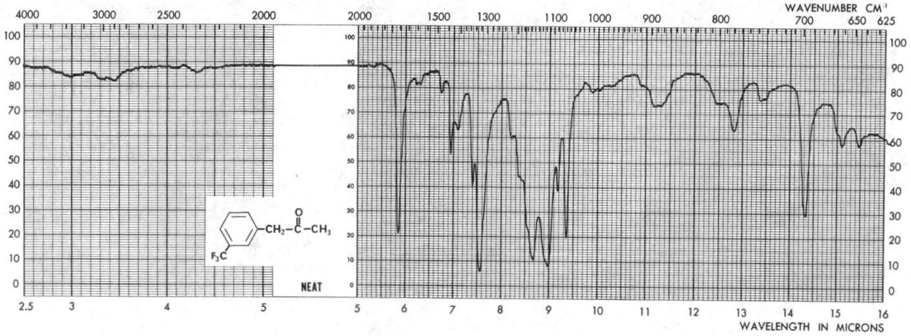

NEAT

C

21,398-5
***o*-Methoxyphenylacetone,** 98%
$CH_3OC_6H_4CH_2COCH_3$ FW 164.20
bp 127-130°/10mm. n_D^{20} 1.5250 d 1.054
Beil. 8(3),397 Disp. C

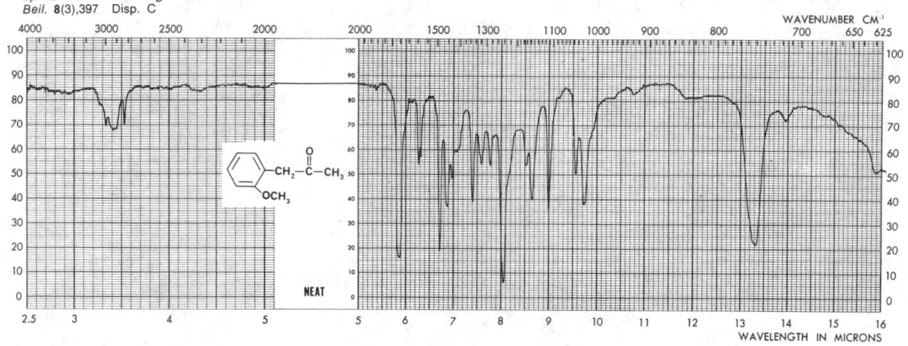

NEAT

D

19,917-6
***p*-Methoxyphenylacetone,** 97+%
$CH_3OC_6H_4CH_2COCH_3$ FW 164.20 bp 145°/25mm.
n_D^{20} 1.5250 d 1.067 *Beil.* **8**,106 Disp. C

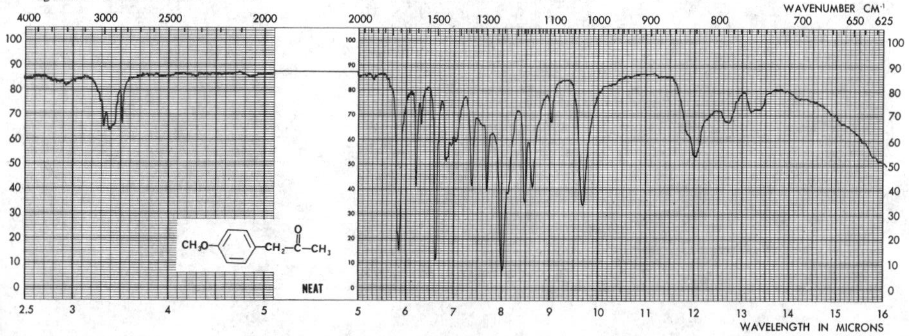

NEAT

E

A8860-3 3-(p-Anisyl)-4-hexanone [4-(p-methoxyphenyl)-3-hexanone]
$C_2H_5CH(C_6H_4OCH_3)COC_2H_5$ M.W. 206.29
n_D^{20} 1.5102

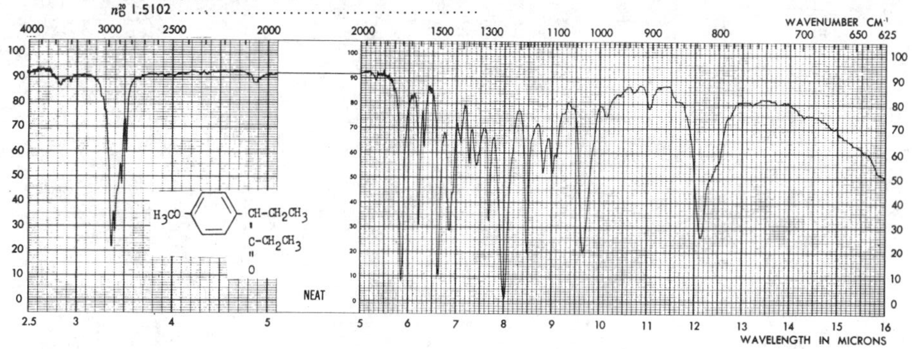

NEAT

F

17,851-9
4-(p-Hydroxyphenyl)-2-butanone
$HOC_6H_4CH_2CH_2COCH_3$
M.W. 164.2 m.p. 82-83°

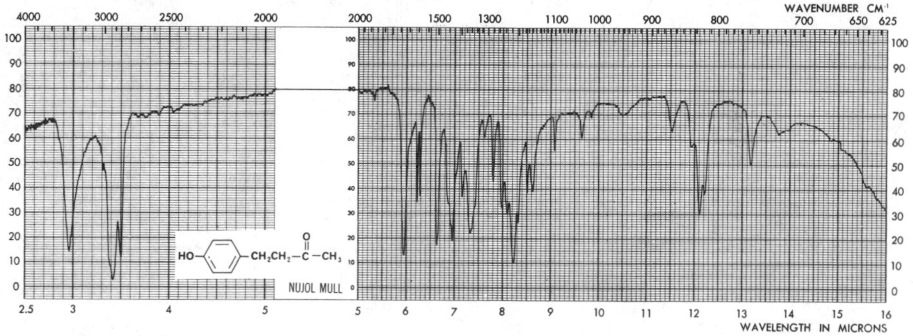

NUJOL MULL

G

14,121-6 3,4-Dimethoxyphenylacetone
$(CH_3O)_2C_6H_3CH_2COCH_3$ M.W. 194.23
n_D^{20} 1.5358

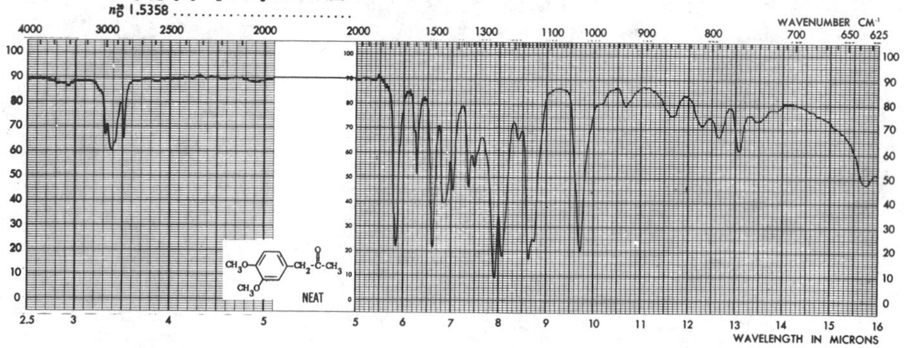

NEAT

H

10,737-9
1-(3,4-Dimethoxyphenyl)-2-butanone
$(CH_3O)_2C_6H_3CH_2COC_2H_5$
M.W. 208.26 b.p. 137-143°/1.1mm. n_D^{20} 1.5355

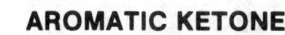

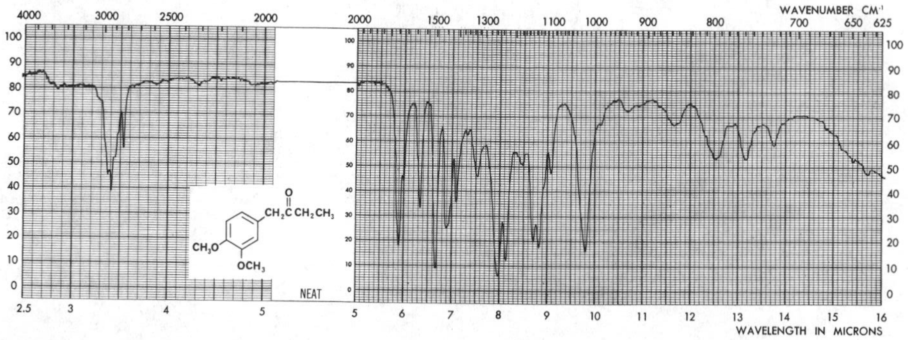

NEAT

A Z50-6 **Zingerone [4-(4-hydroxy-3-methoxyphenyl)-2-butanone], tech.**
$HOC_6H_3(OCH_3)CH_2CH_2COCH_3$ M.W. 194.23
n_D^{20} 1.5407 NEAT

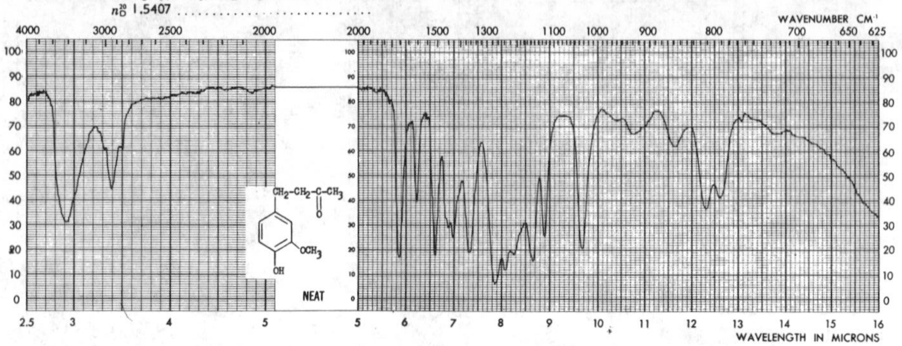

B 15,202-1 **Phenoxy-2-propanone** (phenoxyacetone), **95%**
$C_6H_5OCH_2COCH_3$ M.W. 150.18 n_D^{20} 1.5175
b.p. 120°/19 mm. NEAT

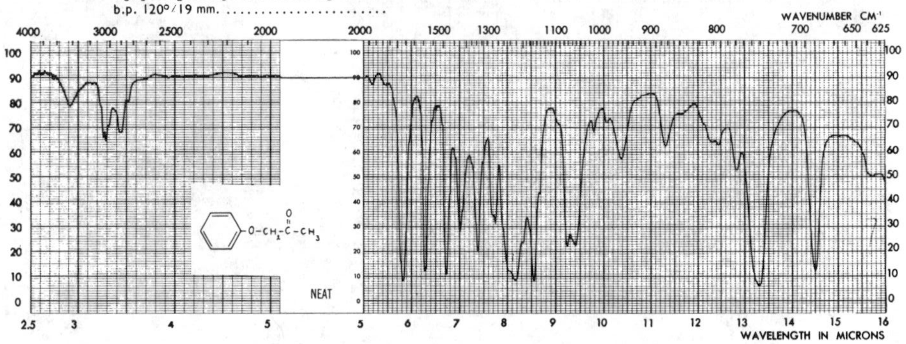

C 12,006-5 **[p-(Benzyloxy)-phenoxy]-2-propanone**
$C_6H_5CH_2OC_6H_4OCH_2COCH_3$ M.W. 256.30 m.p. 75-77° NUJOL MULL

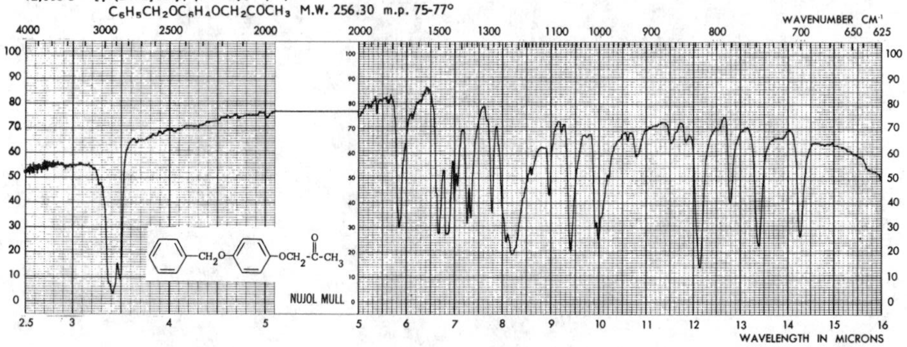

D 17,681-8
7-*syn*-Benzyloxymethyl-5-norbornen-2-one,
tech., ca. 90%
M.W. 228.29 n_D^{20} 1.5375 d 1.082

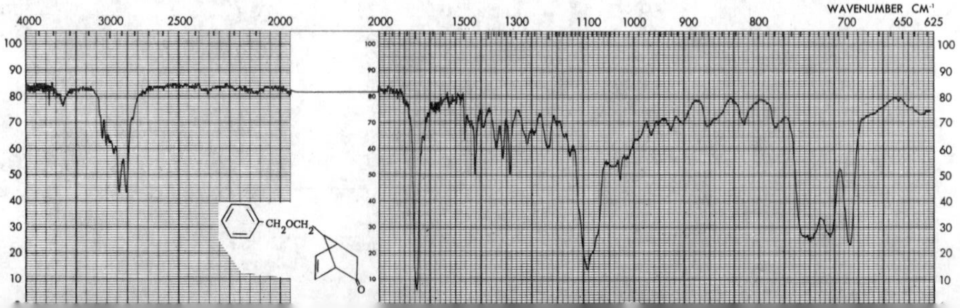

E 18,517-5
1-Benzyl-3-pyrrolidinone
M.W. 175.23 NEAT

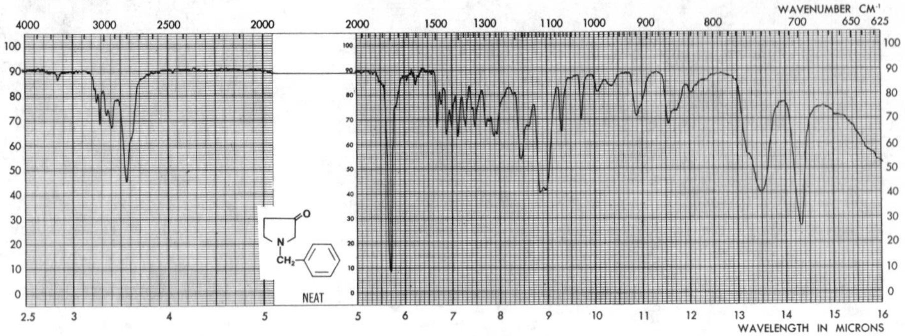

F B2980-6 **1-Benzyl-4-piperidone, puriss.**
M.W. 189.26 n_D^{20} 1.5399 NEAT

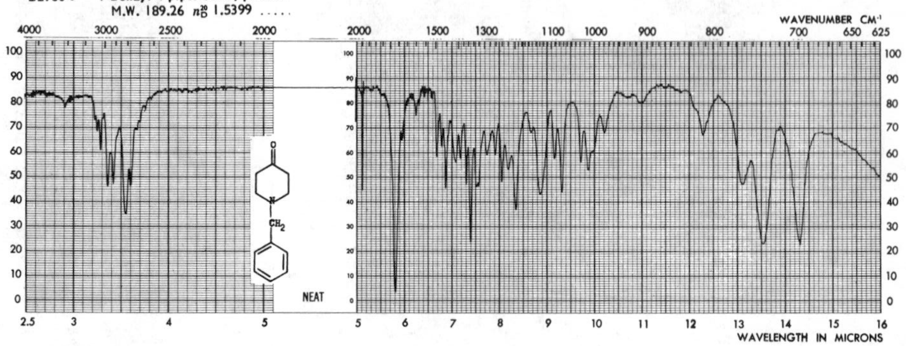

G 13,138-5 **1-(β-Phenethyl)-4-piperidone**
M.W. 203.29 m.p. 57-60° NUJOL MULL

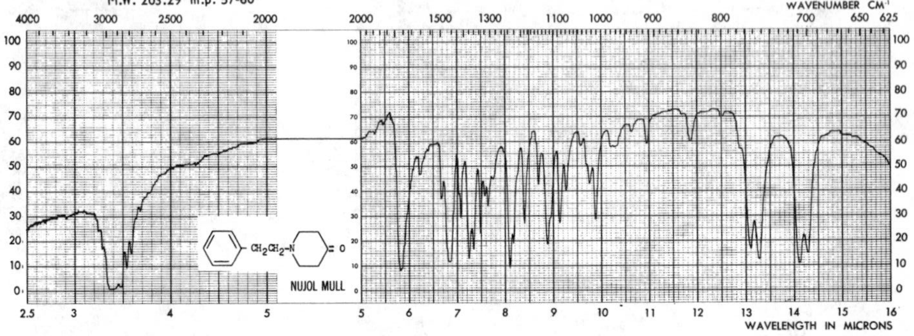

H 12,374-9 **1-Benzyl-3-piperidone**
M.W. 189.26 n_D^{20} 1.5370 NEAT

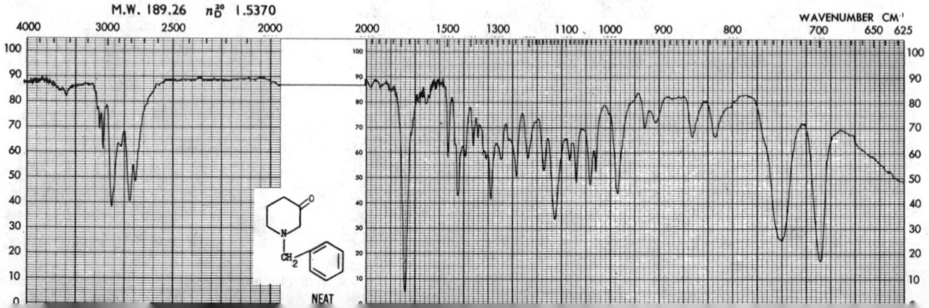

A

M.W. 225.72 m.p. 170-172° (dec.)

NUJOL MULL

B

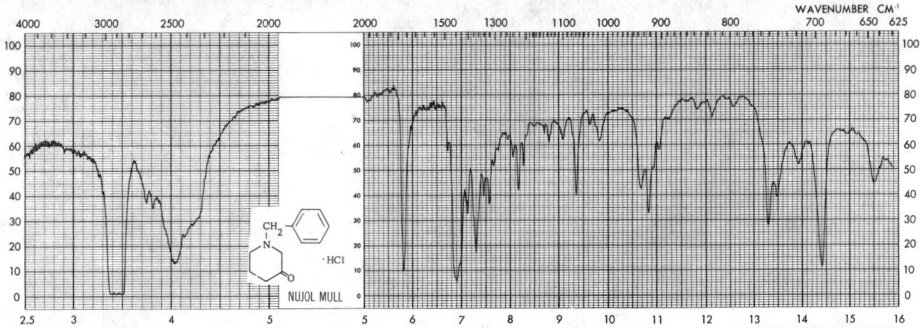

A2,040-5
4-Acetyl-4-phenylpiperidine
M.W. 203.29 m.p. 44-46°

MELT

C

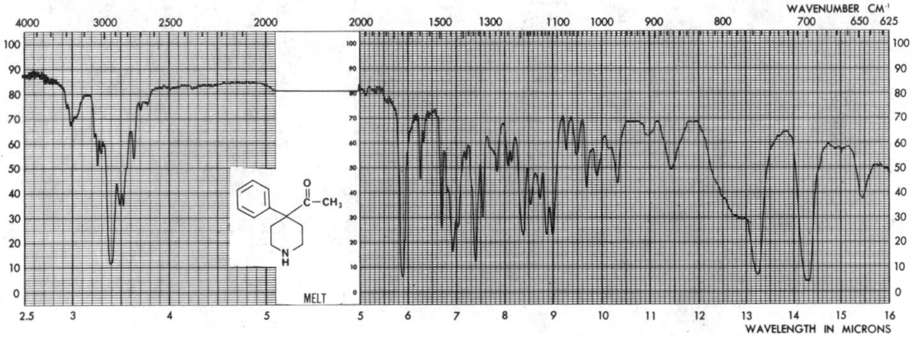

B2435-9 2-Benzylidene-3-quinuclidinone, puriss.
M.W. 213.27 m.p. 131.5-133° ....

NUJOL MULL

D

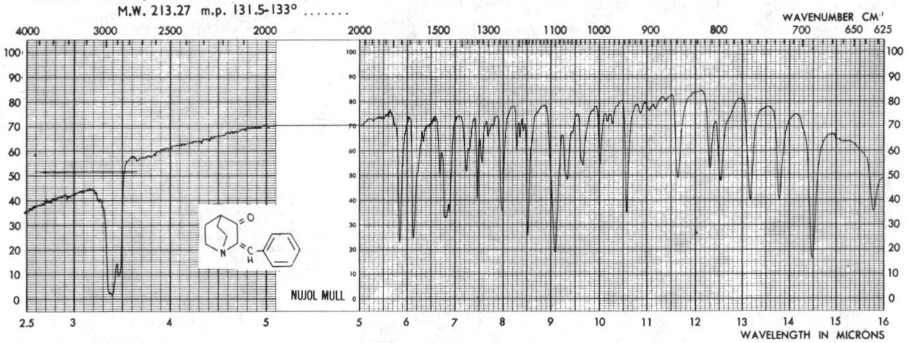

14,788-5 *trans*-4-Phenyl-3-buten-2-one (benzalacetone)
$C_6H_5CH{:}CHCOCH_3$ M.W. 146.19
m.p. 35-39° ....

MELT

E

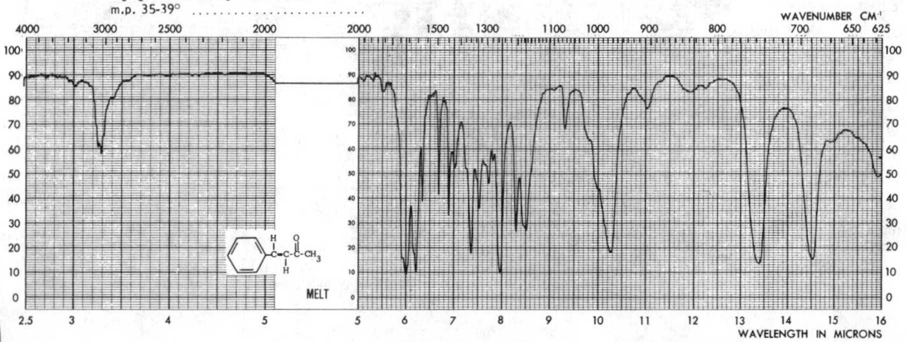

13,724-3 4-(p-Tolyl)-3-buten-2-one
$CH_3C_6H_4CH{:}CHCOCH_3$ M.W. 160.22 .

MELT

F

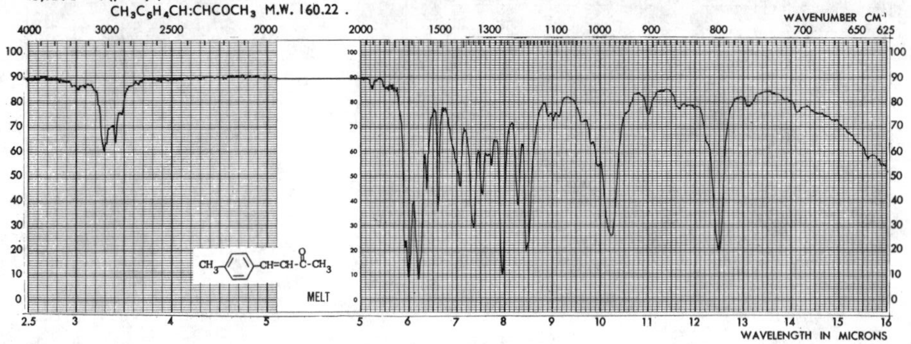

13,999-8 Bis-(p-methylstyryl) ketone (di-p-methylstyryl ketone, 1,5-di-p-tolyl-1,4-pentadien-3-one)
$CH_3C_6H_4CH{:}CHCOCH{:}CHC_6H_4CH_3$ M.W. 262.35
m.p. 173-175°

NUJOL MULL

G

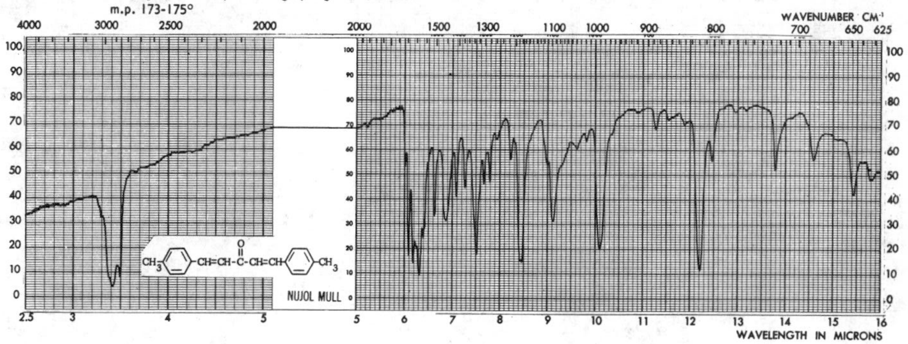

12,037-5 2,6-Divanillylidenecyclohexanone
M.W. 366.41 m.p. 177-179°

NUJOL MULL

H

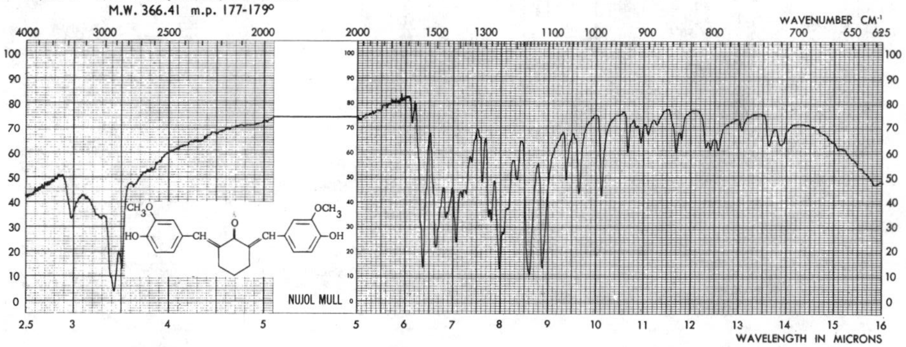

K230-5 7-Keto-13-methyl-5,6,7,9,10,13-hexahydrophenanthrene
M.W. 212.29 m.p. 88-90°

NUJOL MULL

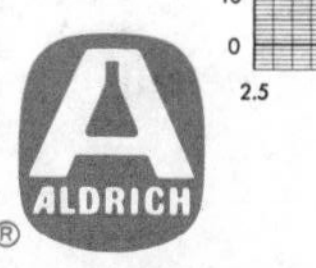

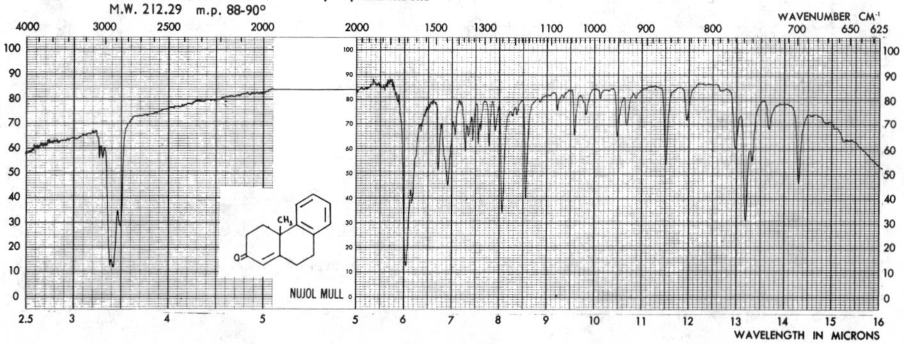

A K225-9 7-Keto-1-methoxy-13-methyl-5,6,7,9,10,13-hexahydrophenanthrene
M.W. 242.32 m.p. 118-121°
NUJOL MULL

B 17,737-7
Diphenylcyclopropenone, 98%
M.W. 206.24 m.p. 119-121°
NUJOL MULL

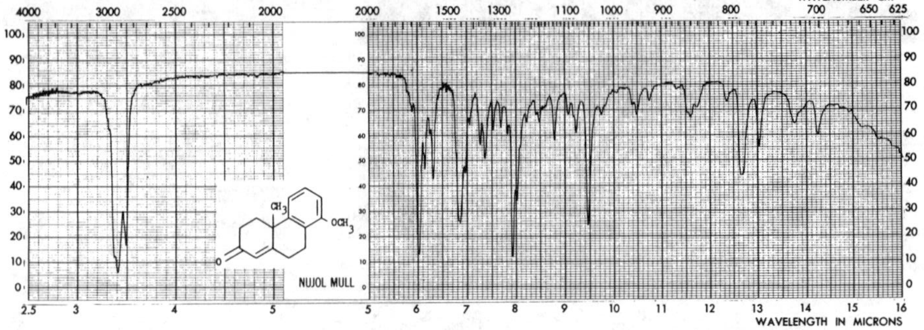

C T2580-1 Tetraphenylcyclopentadienone
M.W. 384.48 m.p. 217-220°
NUJOL MULL

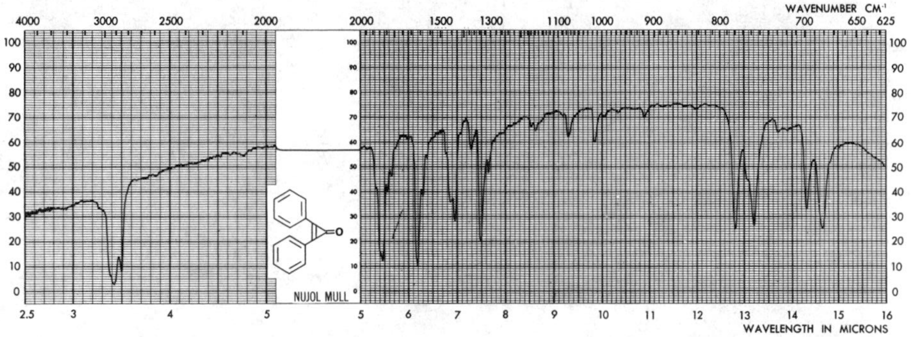

D M2450-7 3-(p-Methoxyphenyl)-2,4,5-triphenylcyclopentadienone
M.W. 414.50 m.p. 212-214°

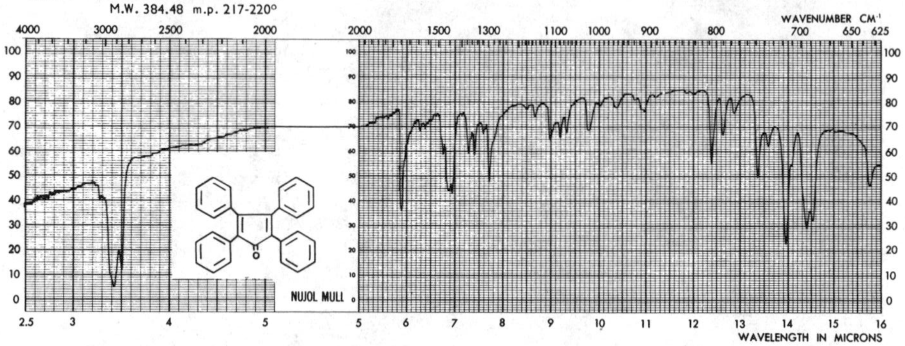

E A1070-1 Acetophenone
$C_6H_5COCH_3$ M.W. 120.15 n_D^{20} 1.5338 m.p. 19-20°
NEAT

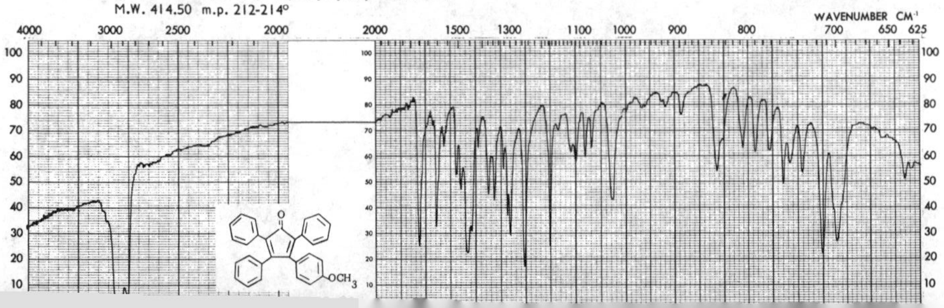

F P5160-5 Propiophenone
$C_6H_5COC_2H_5$ M.W. 134.18 n_D^{20} 1.5258 m.p. 18-19°
NEAT

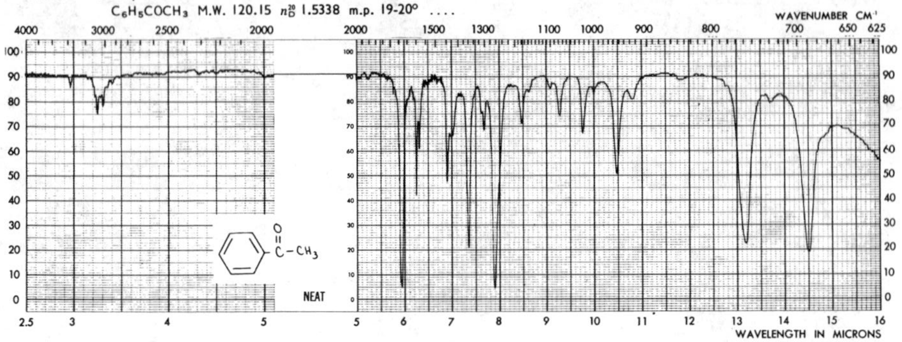

G 12,433-8 n-Butyrophenone
$C_6H_5COCH_2CH_2CH_3$ M.W. 148.21 n_D^{20} 1.5210
m.p. 11.5-13° b.p. 228-229.5°
NEAT

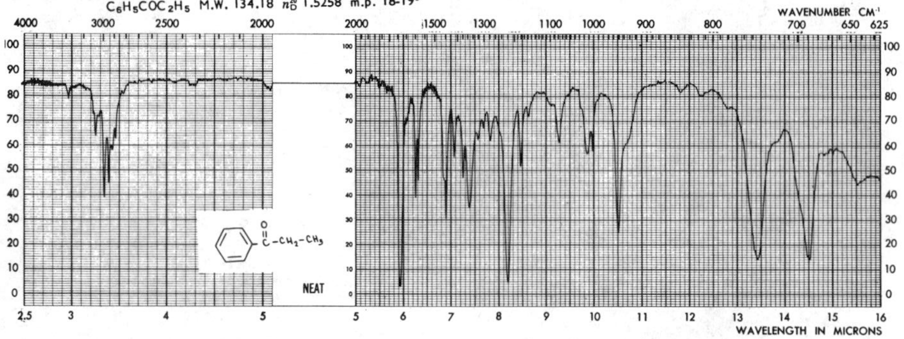

H 13,036-2 Isobutyrophenone
$C_6H_5COCH(CH_3)_2$ M.W. 148.21 n_D^{20} 1.5172
b.p. 217°

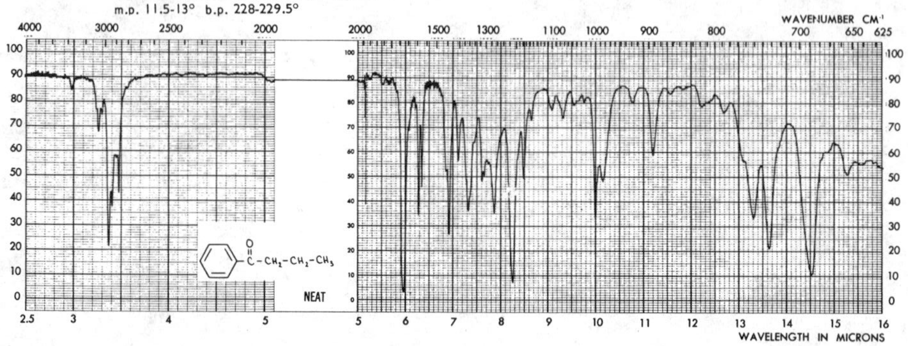

WAVENUMBER CM⁻¹ — WAVELENGTH IN MICRONS

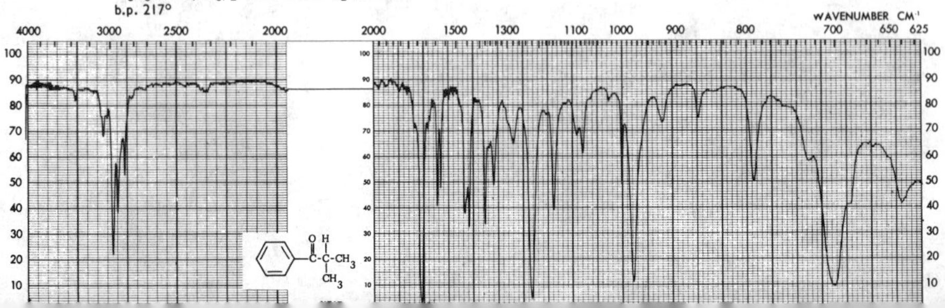

A
$C_6H_5COC_3H_5$ M.W. 146.20 n_D^{20} 1.5534

V65-9 **Valerophenone**
$C_6H_5CO(CH_2)_3CH_3$ M.W. 162.23 n_D^{20} 1.5158
b.p. 105-107°/5 mm.

B

10,836-7 **Cyclobutyl phenyl ketone**
$C_6H_5COC_4H_7$ M.W. 160.22 n_D^{20} 1.5460
b.p. 114-118°/7 mm.

C

18,993-6
Cyclopentyl phenyl ketone, 98%
$C_6H_5COC_5H_9$ FW 174.24 n_D^{20} 1.5428 Disp. C

D

E
$C_6H_5CO(CH_2)_4CH_3$ M.W. 176.26 m.p. 25-26°

15,991-3
Heptanophenone, 97%
$C_6H_5CO(CH_2)_5CH_3$
M.W. 190.29 m.p. 17° b.p. 155°/15mm.
n_D^{20} 1.5077 Beil. 7,337

F

15,992-1
Undecanophenone, 98%
$CH_3(CH_2)_9COC_6H_5$
M.W. 246.39 m.p. 28-30°

G

13,921-1 **Cyclohexyl phenyl ketone**
$C_6H_{11}COC_6H_5$ M.W. 188.27

H

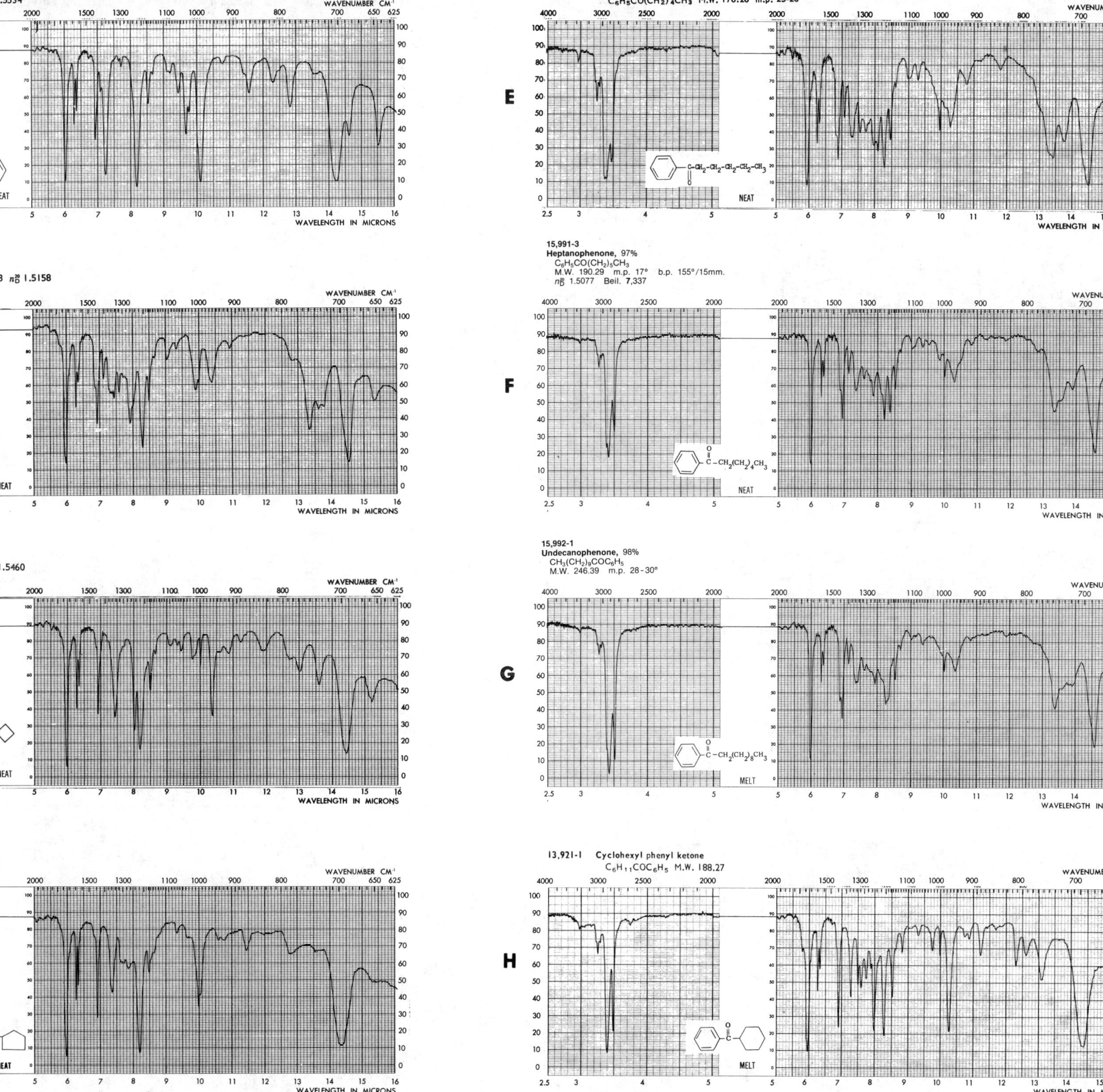

A

11,506-1 **2-Benzoyl-5-norbornene** (5-norbornen-2-yl phenyl ketone), mixture of endo and exo
M.W. 198.27 n_D^{20} 1.5713 b.p. 1[illegible]2-124°/2 mm.

NEAT

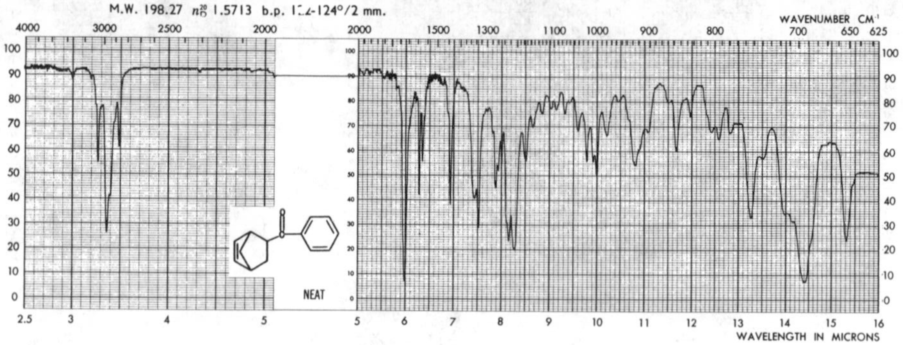

B

14,533-5 **Dimethyl(phenacyl)sulfonium bromide**
$C_6H_5COCH_2S(CH_3)_2Br$ M.W. 261.19
m.p. 140-142° (dec.)

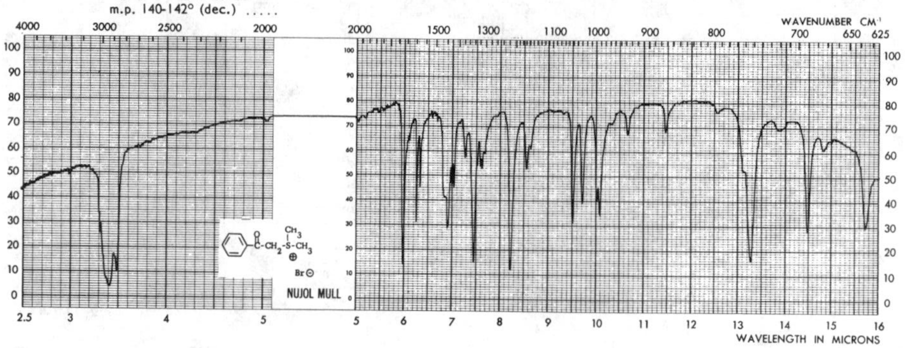

NUJOL MULL

C

D436-9 **Deoxybenzoin** (α-phenylacetophenone)
$C_6H_5CH_2COC_6H_5$ M.W. 196.25
m.p. 55-56.5°

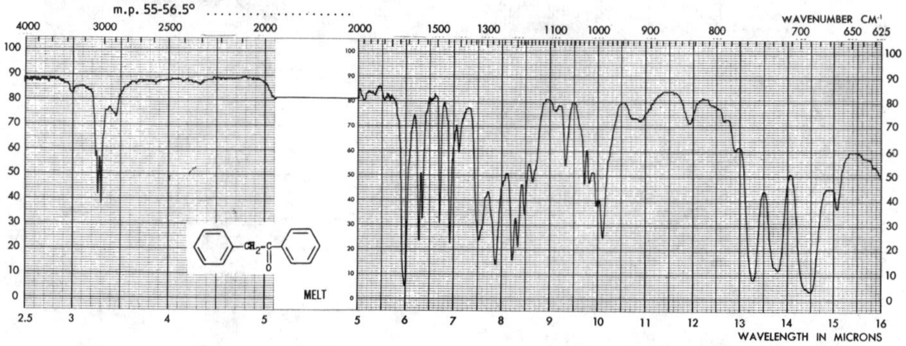

MELT

D

21,669-0
2,2,2-Triphenylacetophenone (benzopinacolone, phenyl trityl ketone)
$(C_6H_5)_3CCOC_6H_5$ FW 348.45 mp 175-177°
Beil. 7,544 Disp. C

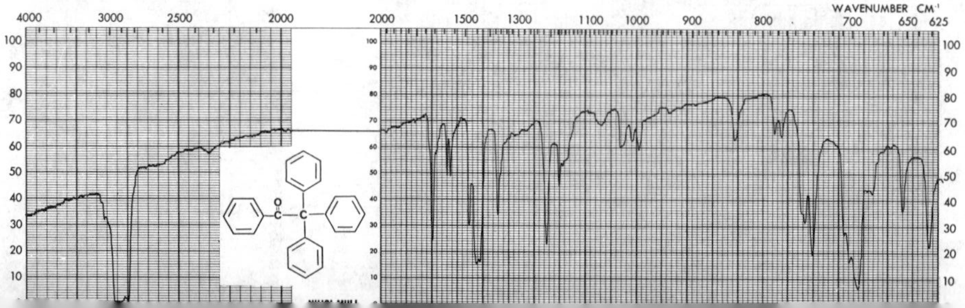

E

15,750-3
Desyl chloride, 95% (2-chloro-2-phenylacetophenone)
$C_6H_5CH(Cl)COC_6H_5$
M.W. 230.69 m.p. 62-63° Beil. 7,436

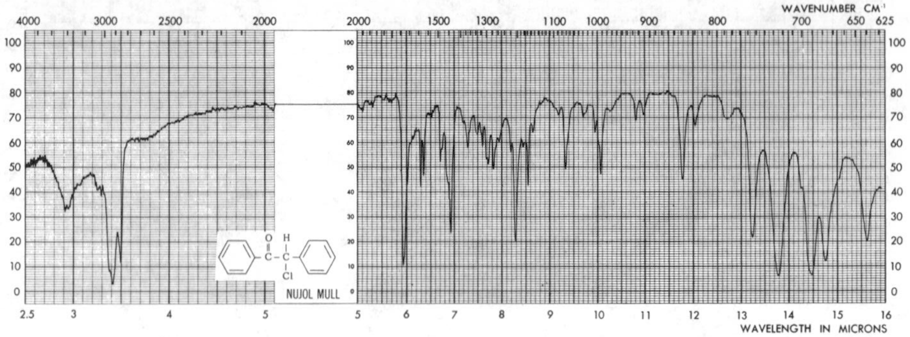

NUJOL MULL

F

13,570-4 **β-Phenylbutyrophenone**
$CH_3CH(C_6H_5)CH_2COC_6H_5$ M.W. 224.30
m.p. 73-74°

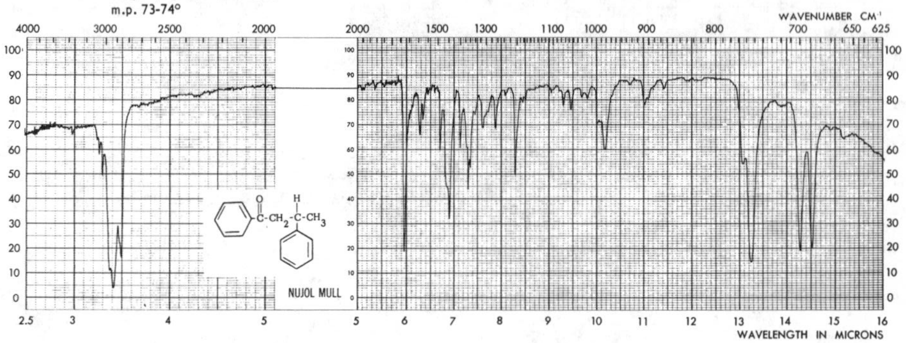

NUJOL MULL

G

P2130-7 **γ-Phenylbutyrophenone**
$C_6H_5(CH_2)_3COC_6H_5$ M.W. 224.30 m.p. 53-57°

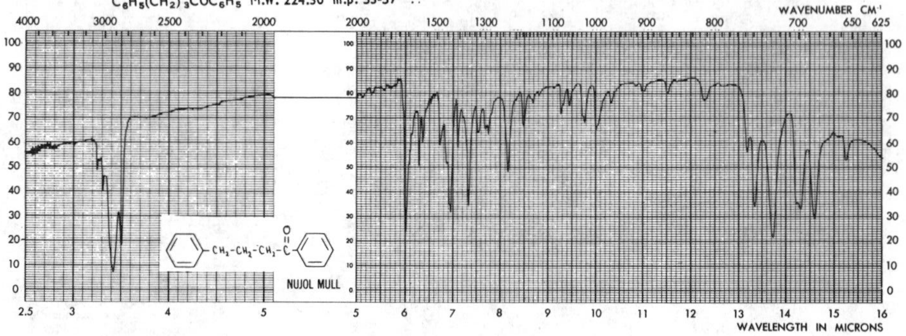

NUJOL MULL

H

D3345-4 **Dibenzoylmethane** (1,3-diphenyl-1,3-propanedione)
$C_6H_5COCH_2COC_6H_5$ M.W. 224.26
m.p. 77.5-79°

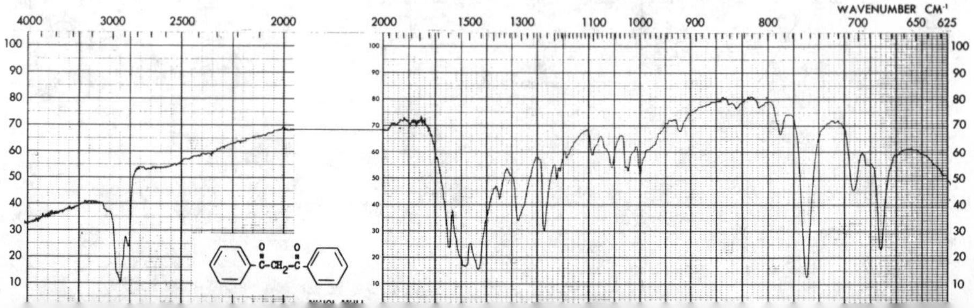

WAVENUMBER CM^{-1} — WAVELENGTH IN MICRONS

A

$C_6H_5CO(CH_2)_4COC_6H_5$ M.W. 266.34
m.p. 104-105°

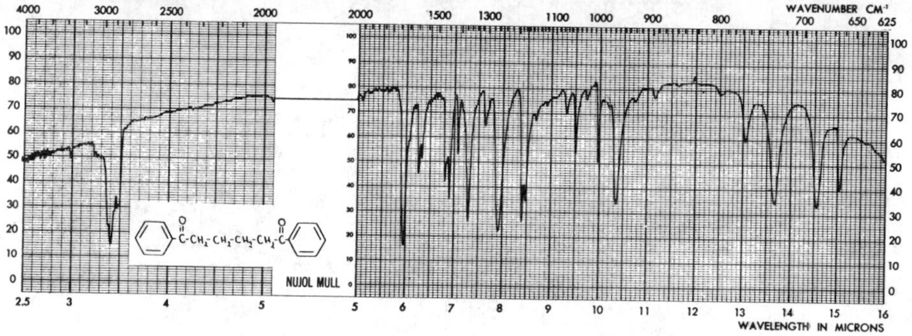

NUJOL MULL

B

15,972-7
2,2,2-Triphenylacetophenone, 99%
$(C_6H_5)_3CCOC_6H_5$
M.W. 348.45 m.p. 181-183° Beil. 7,544

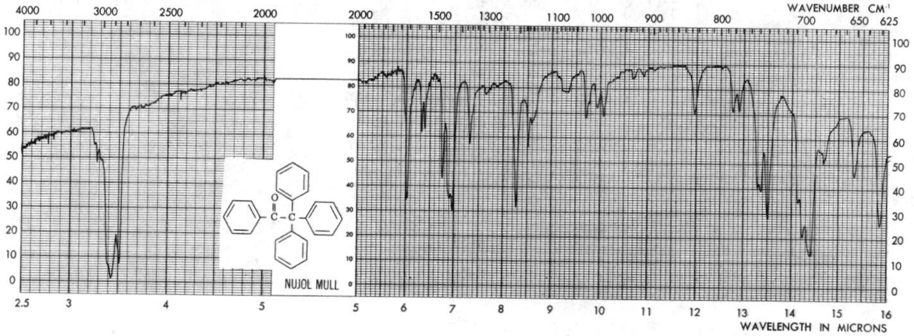

NUJOL MULL

C

M2659-3 o-Methylacetophenone
$CH_3C_6H_4COCH_3$ M.W. 134.18 n_D^{20} 1.5302

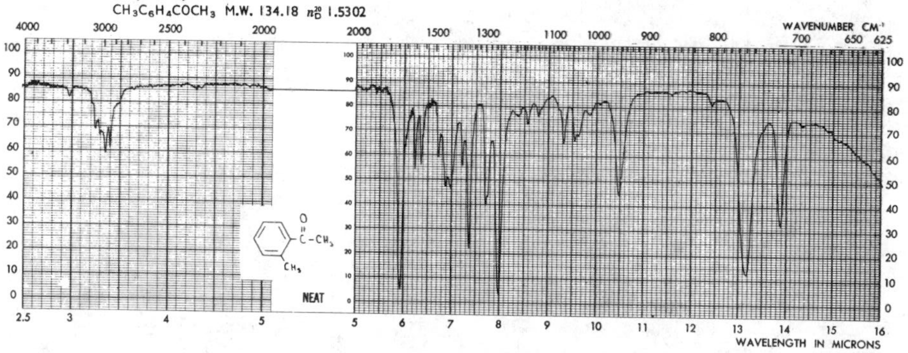

NEAT

D

I-230-4 1-Indanone, puriss.
M.W. 132.16 m.p. 40-42°

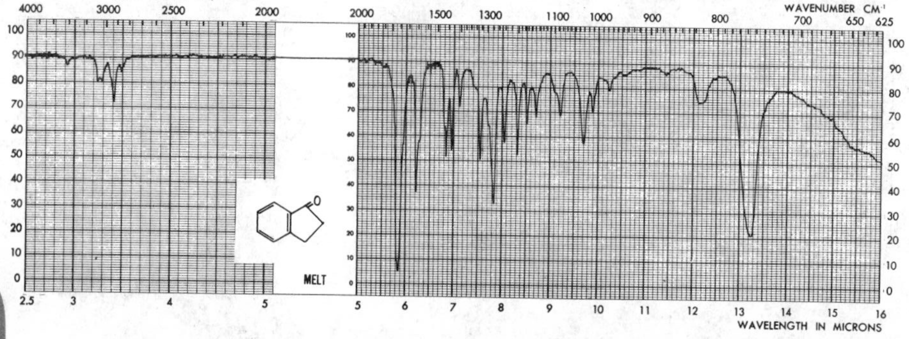

MELT

E

4(7)-Bromo-7(4)-methyl-1-indanone, mixture of isomers
FW 225.09 *Beil.* 7(3),1428 Disp. C

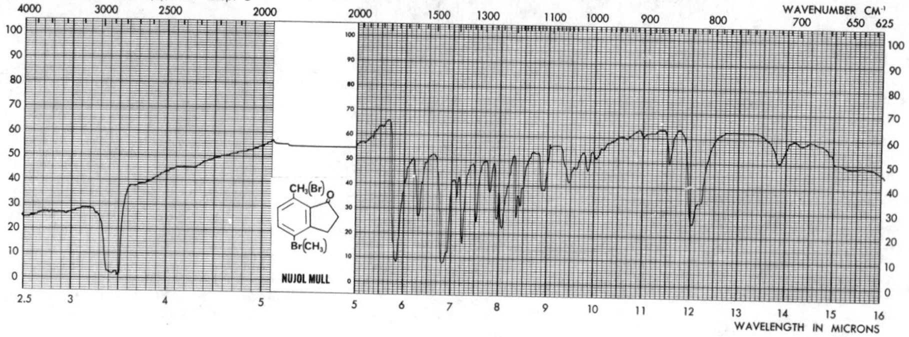

NUJOL MULL

F

18,353-9
5-Methoxy-1-indanone, 98%
M.W. 162.19 m.p. 108-110° Beil. 8(2),152

NUJOL MULL

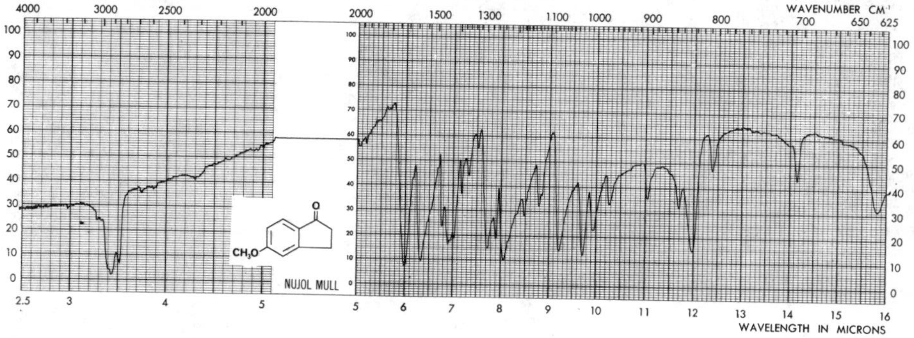

G

17,525-0
6-Methoxy-1-indanone, 99%
M.W. 162.19 m.p. 108-110° Beil. 8(2),152

NUJOL MULL

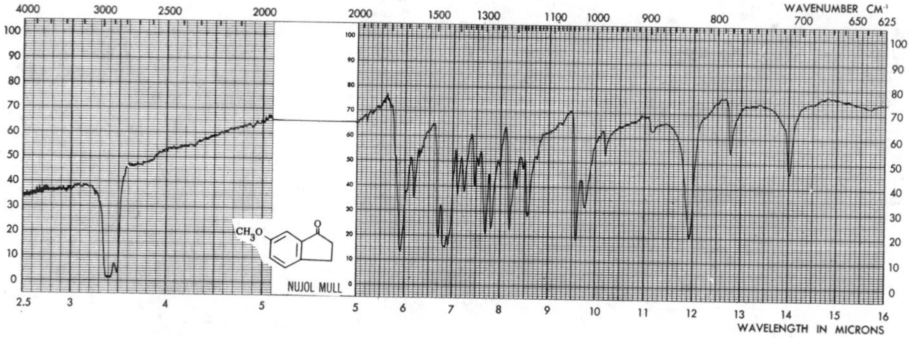

H

T1900-3 α-Tetralone [3,4-dihydro-1(2H)-naphthalenone]
M.W. 146.19 n_D^{20} 1.5672
b.p. 113-116°/6 mm.

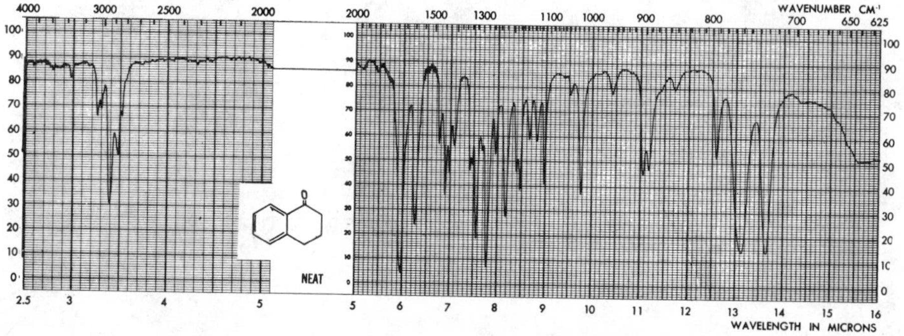

NEAT

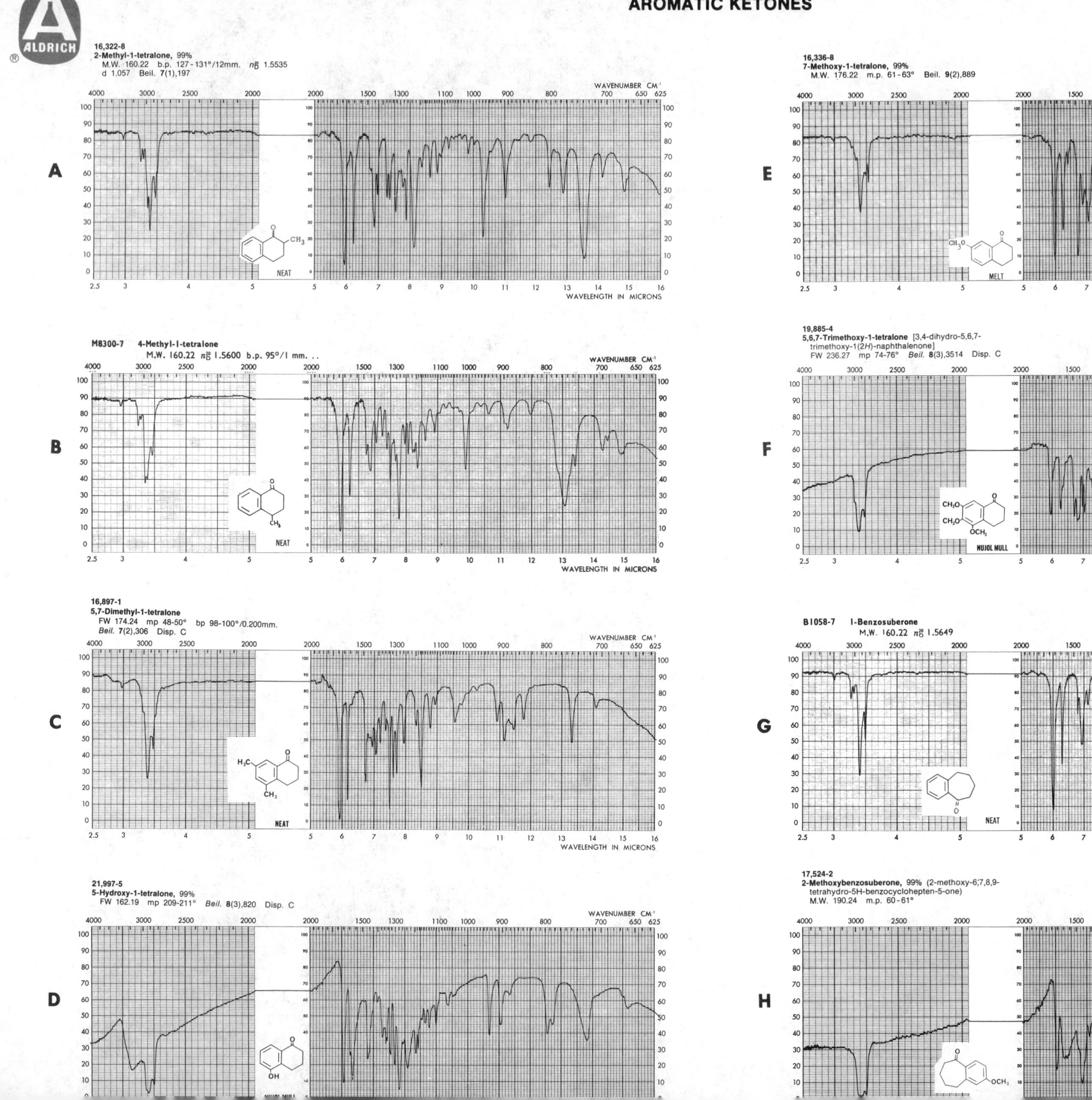
ALDRICH
A
16,322-8
2-Methyl-1-tetralone, 99%
M.W. 160.22 b.p. 127-131°/12mm. n_D^{20} 1.5535
d 1.057 Beil. 7(1),197
NEAT
B
M8300-7 4-Methyl-1-tetralone
M.W. 160.22 n_D^{20} 1.5600 b.p. 95°/1 mm. . .
NEAT
C
16,897-1
5,7-Dimethyl-1-tetralone
FW 174.24 mp 48-50° bp 98-100°/0.200mm.
Beil. 7(2),306 Disp. C
NEAT
D
21,997-5
5-Hydroxy-1-tetralone, 99%
FW 162.19 mp 209-211° Beil. 8(3),820 Disp. C
E
16,336-8
7-Methoxy-1-tetralone, 99%
M.W. 176.22 m.p. 61-63° Beil. 9(2),889
MELT
F
19,885-4
5,6,7-Trimethoxy-1-tetralone [3,4-dihydro-5,6,7-trimethoxy-1(2H)-naphthalenone]
FW 236.27 mp 74-76° Beil. 8(3),3514 Disp. C
NUJOL MULL
G
B1058-7 1-Benzosuberone
M.W. 160.22 n_D^{20} 1.5649
NEAT
H
17,524-2
2-Methoxybenzosuberone, 99% (2-methoxy-6,7,8,9-tetrahydro-5H-benzocyclohepten-5-one)
M.W. 190.24 m.p. 60-61°
WAVENUMBER CM⁻¹
WAVELENGTH IN MICRONS

n_D^{20} 1.5270

A

NEAT

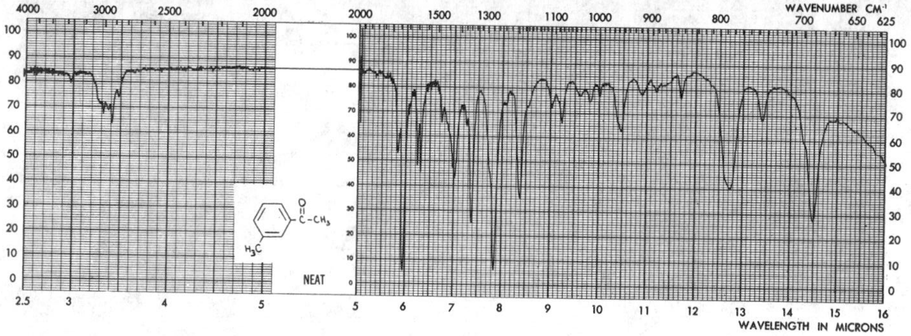

M2661-5 p-Methylacetophenone
$CH_3C_6H_4COCH_3$ M.W. 134.18 n_D^{20} 1.5328
m.p. -24 to -22°

B

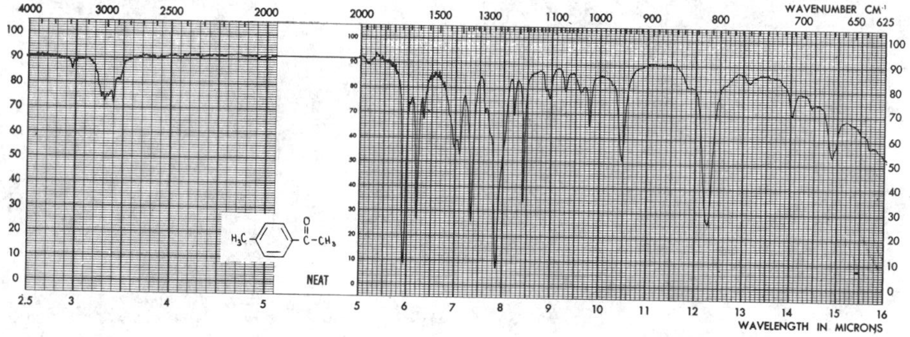

NEAT

15,953-0
2-Bromo-4'-methylacetophenone, 97%
$CH_3C_6H_4COCH_2Br$
M.W. 213.08 m.p. 45-49° Beil. 7,309
LACHRYMATOR

C

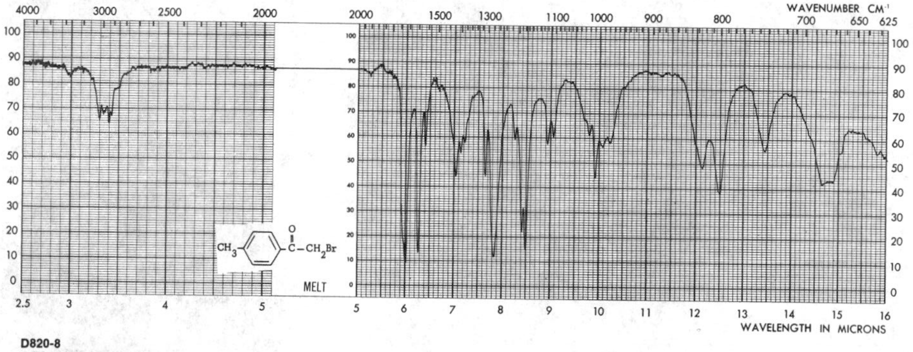

MELT

D820-8
p-Diacetylbenzene, 98%
$C_6H_4(COCH_3)_2$
M.W. 162.19 m.p. 111-113° Beil. 7,686
IR 633E

D

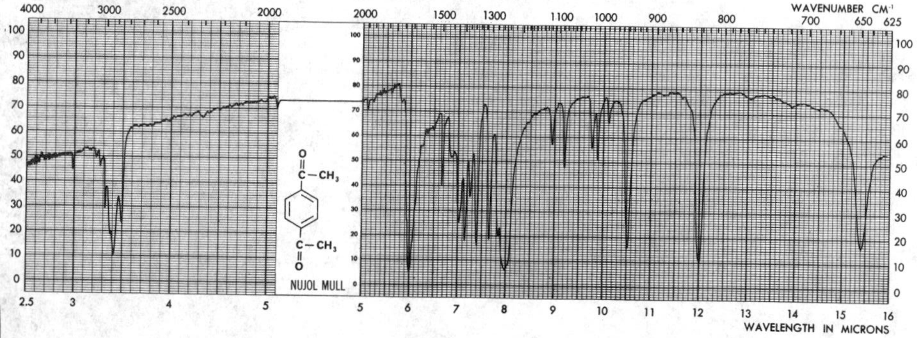

NUJOL MULL

$C_6H_4(COCH_3)_2$
M.W. 162.19 m.p. 31-34°

E

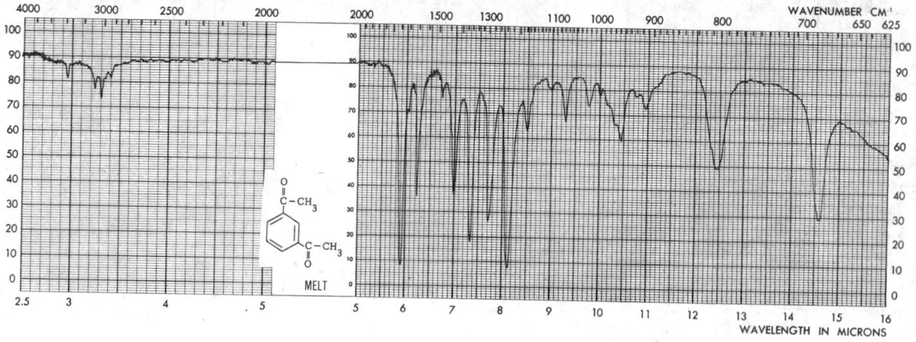

MELT

T4420-2 1,3,5-Triacetylbenzene
$C_6H_3(COCH_3)_3$ M.W. 204.23 m.p. 162-164°

F

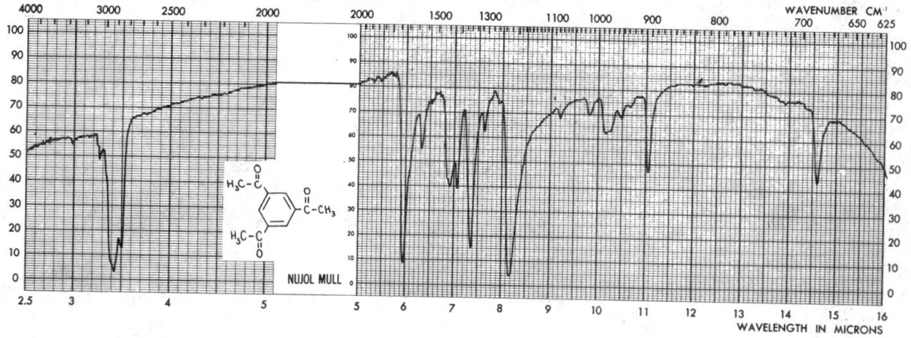

NUJOL MULL

13,723-5 3',4'-Dimethylacetophenone
$(CH_3)_2C_6H_3COCH_3$ M.W. 148.21 n_D^{20} 1.5380
b.p. 243°

G

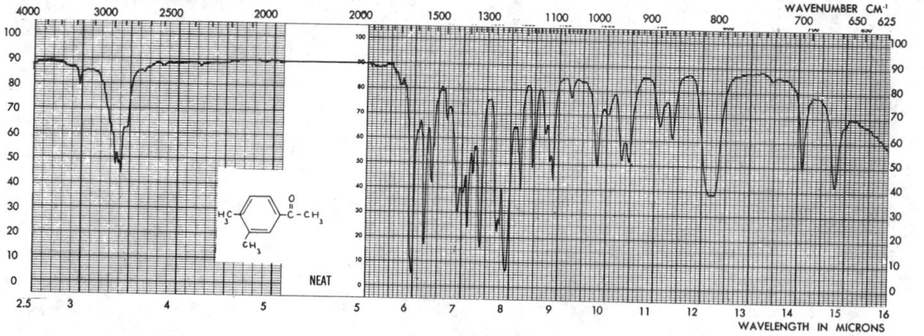

NEAT

12,274-2 5-Acetylindan
M.W. 160.22 n_D^{20} 1.5610

H

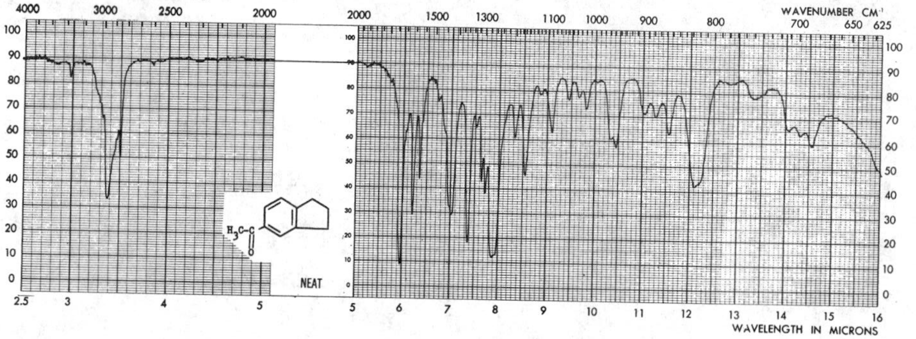

NEAT

ALDRICH

A D13,820-7 2',4'-Dimethylacetophenone, tech.
$(CH_3)_2C_6H_3COCH_3$ M.W. 148.21 n_D^{20} 1.5330
NEAT

B T7240-0 2',4',6'-Trimethylacetophenone
$(CH_3)_3C_6H_2COCH_3$ M.W. 162.23 n_D^{20} 1.5169
b.p. 235-236°
NEAT

C 14,272-7 3,3,6,8-Tetramethyl-1-tetralone [3,4-dihydro-3,3,6,8-tetramethyl-1(2H)-naphthalenone]
M.W. 202.30 m.p. 57-59°
NUJOL MULL

D 12,272-6 4-Acetylbiphenyl
$C_6H_5C_6H_4COCH_3$ M.W. 196.25 m.p. 120-121°
NUJOL MULL

E 13,477-5 2'-Acetonaphthone (methyl 2-naphthyl ketone)
$C_{10}H_7COCH_3$ M.W. 170.21 m.p. 53-55°
MELT

F A1620-3 2-Acetylfluorene
M.W. 208.26 m.p. 128-129°
NUJOL MULL

G A1260-7 9-Acetylanthracene
M.W. 220.27 m.p. 75°
MELT

H A1920-2 2-Acetylphenanthrene
M.W. 220.27 m.p. 144-145°
NUJOL MULL

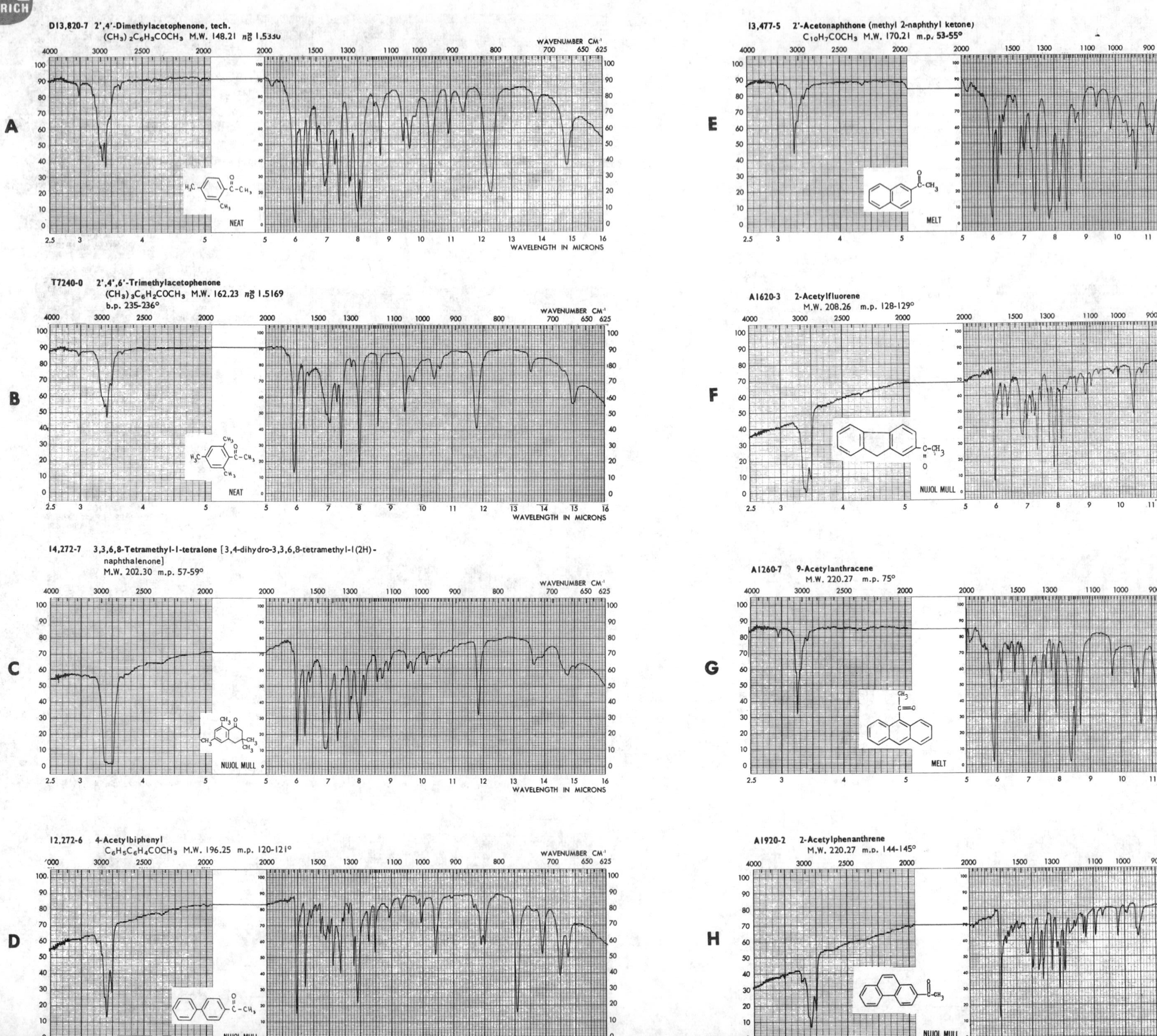

M.W. 220.27 m.p. 67-71°

m.p. 48-51°

A1960-1 9-Acetylphenanthrene
M.W. 220.27 m.p. 73-74°

B7968-4 α-Bromopropiophenone
$C_6H_5COCH(Br)CH_3$ M.W. 213.08
n_D^{17} 1.5718

C1968-6 α-Chloroacetophenone (phenacyl chloride)
$C_6H_5COCH_2Cl$ M.W. 154.60 m.p. 54-56°

B6920-4 α-Bromoisobutyrophenone (α-bromo-α-methylpropiophenone)
$C_6H_5COC(CH_3)_2Br$ M.W. 227.11
n_D^{20} 1.5561

D5485-0 α,α-Dichloroacetophenone
$C_6H_5COCHCl_2$ M.W. 189.04 n_D^{20} 1.5686

14,158-5 β-Chloropropiophenone, tech.
$C_6H_5COCH_2CH_2Cl$ M.W. 168.62
m.p. 40-44°

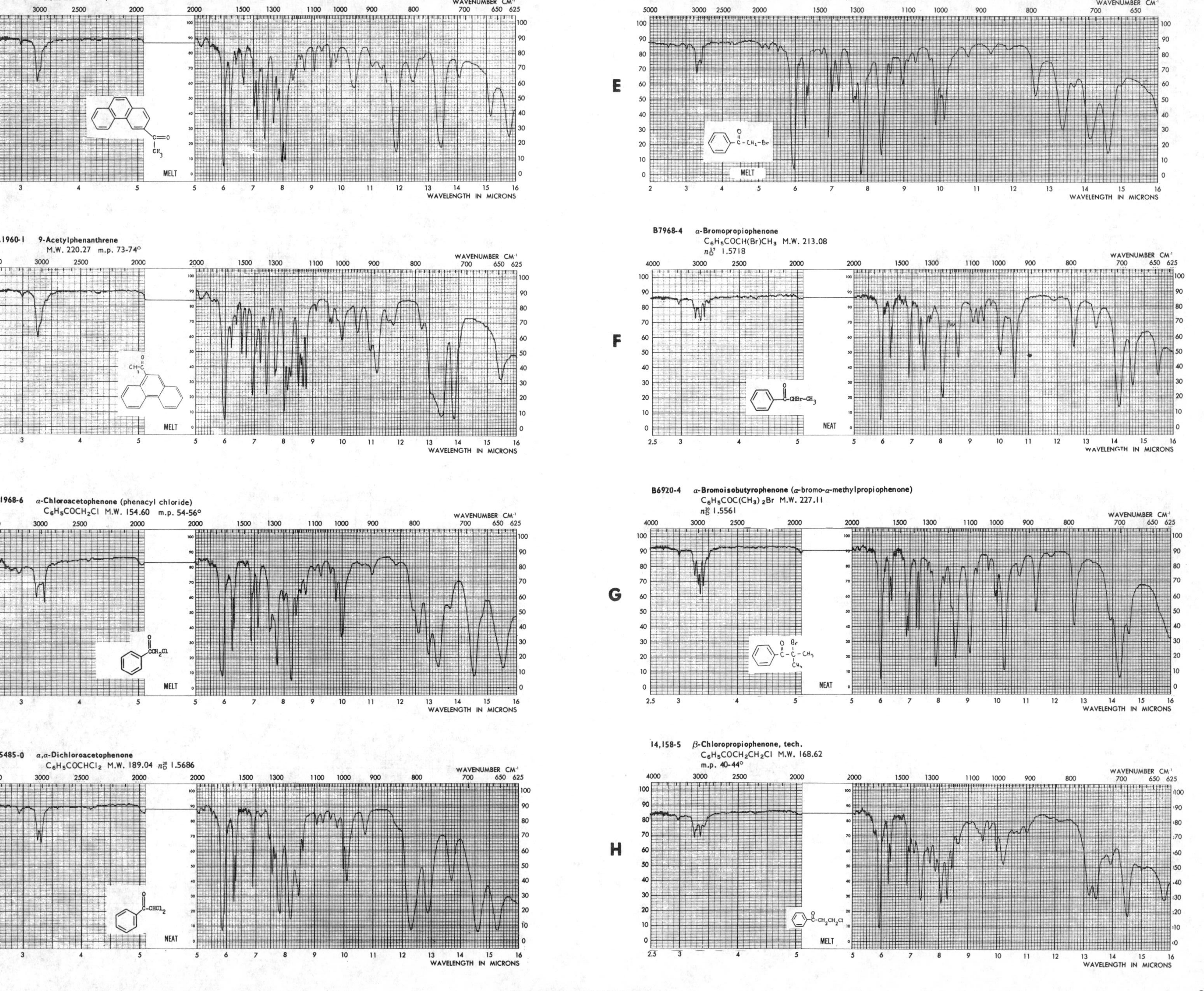

A

C3020-5 **γ-Chlorobutyrophenone**
$C_6H_5CO(CH_2)_3Cl$ M.W. 182.65 n_D^{20} 1.5459

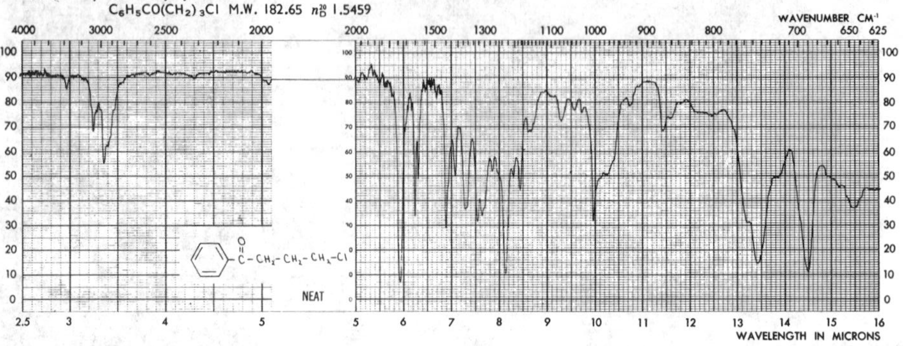

NEAT

B

10,784-0 **α,α,α-Trifluoroacetophenone**
$C_6H_5COCF_3$ M.W. 174.12 n_D^{20} 1.4615 b.p. 165-166°

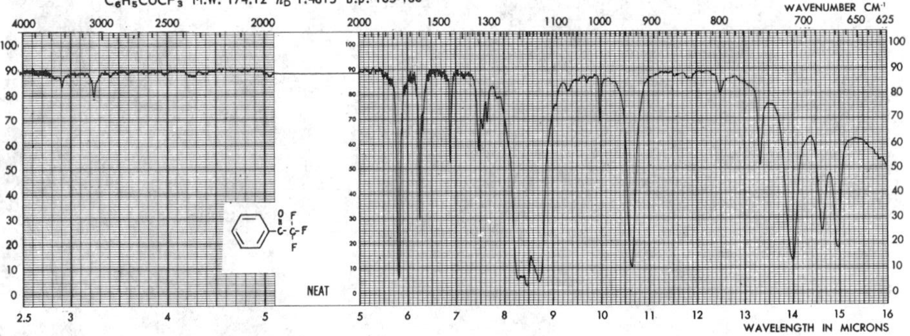

NEAT

C

21,801-4
9-Anthryl trifluoromethyl ketone, 98+%
FW 274.24 mp 84-86° Disp. C

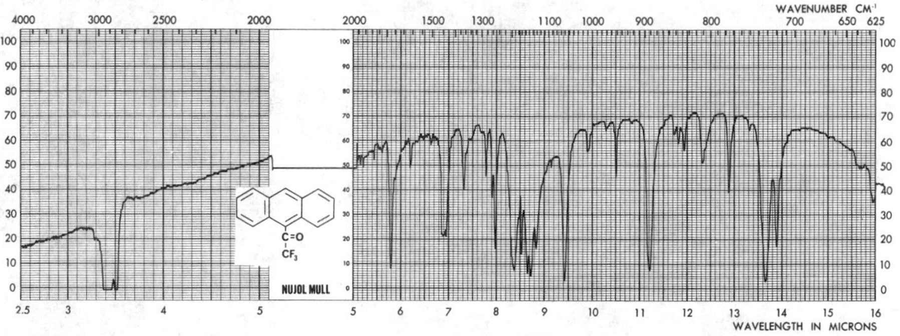

NUJOL MULL

D

B9140-4 **p-tert.-Butyl-γ-chlorobutyrophenone, tech.**
$(CH_3)_3CC_6H_4CO(CH_2)_3Cl$ M.W. 238.76
m.p. 45-47°

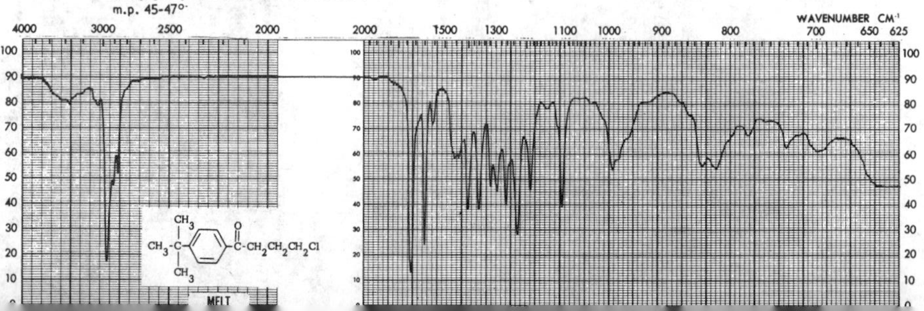

MELT

E

10,108-7 **α-Bromo-p-phenylacetophenone** (p-phenylphenacyl bromide)
$C_6H_5C_6H_4COCH_2Br$ M.W. 275.15 m.p. 125-127°

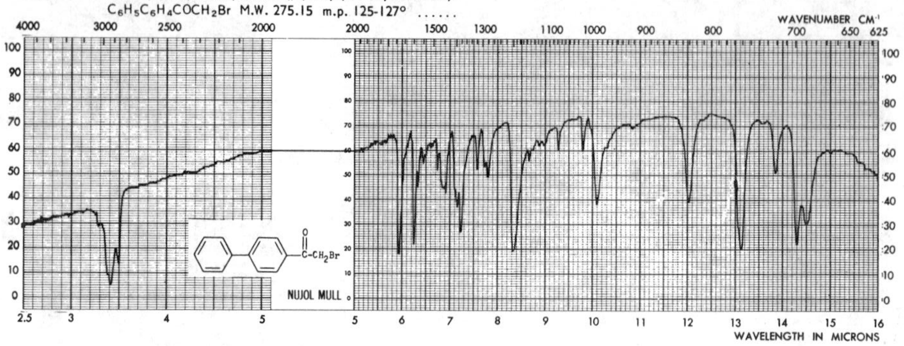

NUJOL MULL

F

10,512-0 **α-Bromo-2'-acetonaphthone** (bromomethyl 2-naphthyl ketone)
$C_{10}H_7COCH_2Br$ M.W. 249.11 m.p. 82-84°

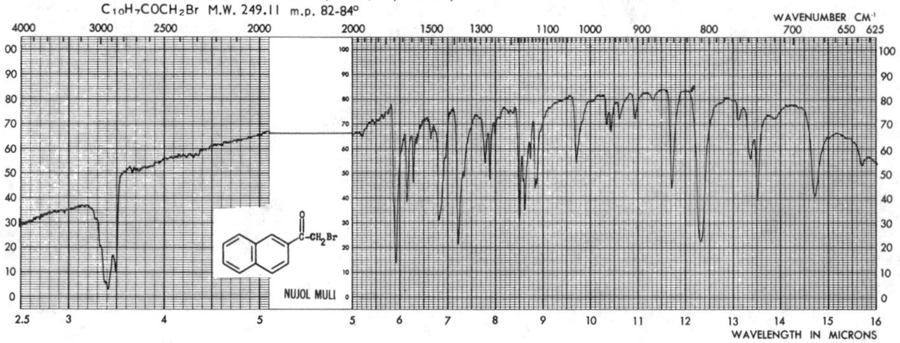

NUJOL MULL

G

18,371-7
o-Fluoroacetophenone, 97%
$FC_6H_4COCH_3$
M.W. 138.14 n_D^{20} 1.5075

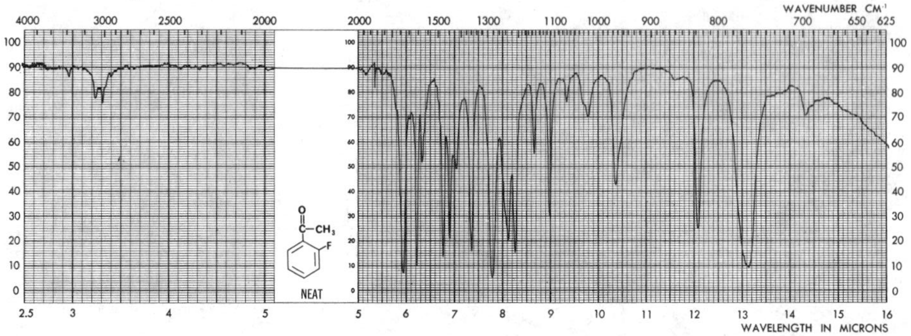

NEAT

H

18,370-9
o-Chloroacetophenone
$ClC_6H_4COCH_3$
M.W. 154.6 n_D^{20} 1.5438 d 1.188 Beil. **7**(1),151

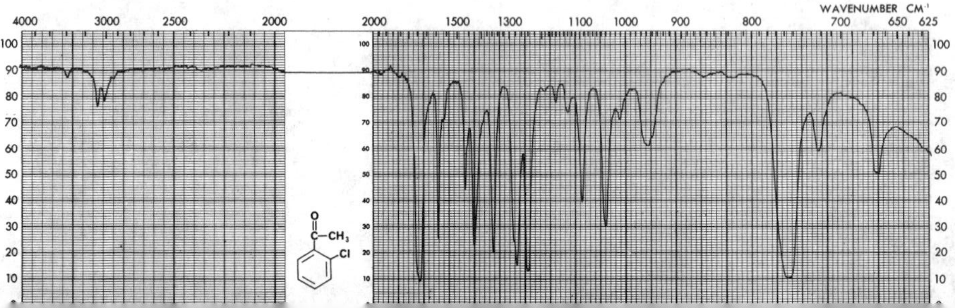

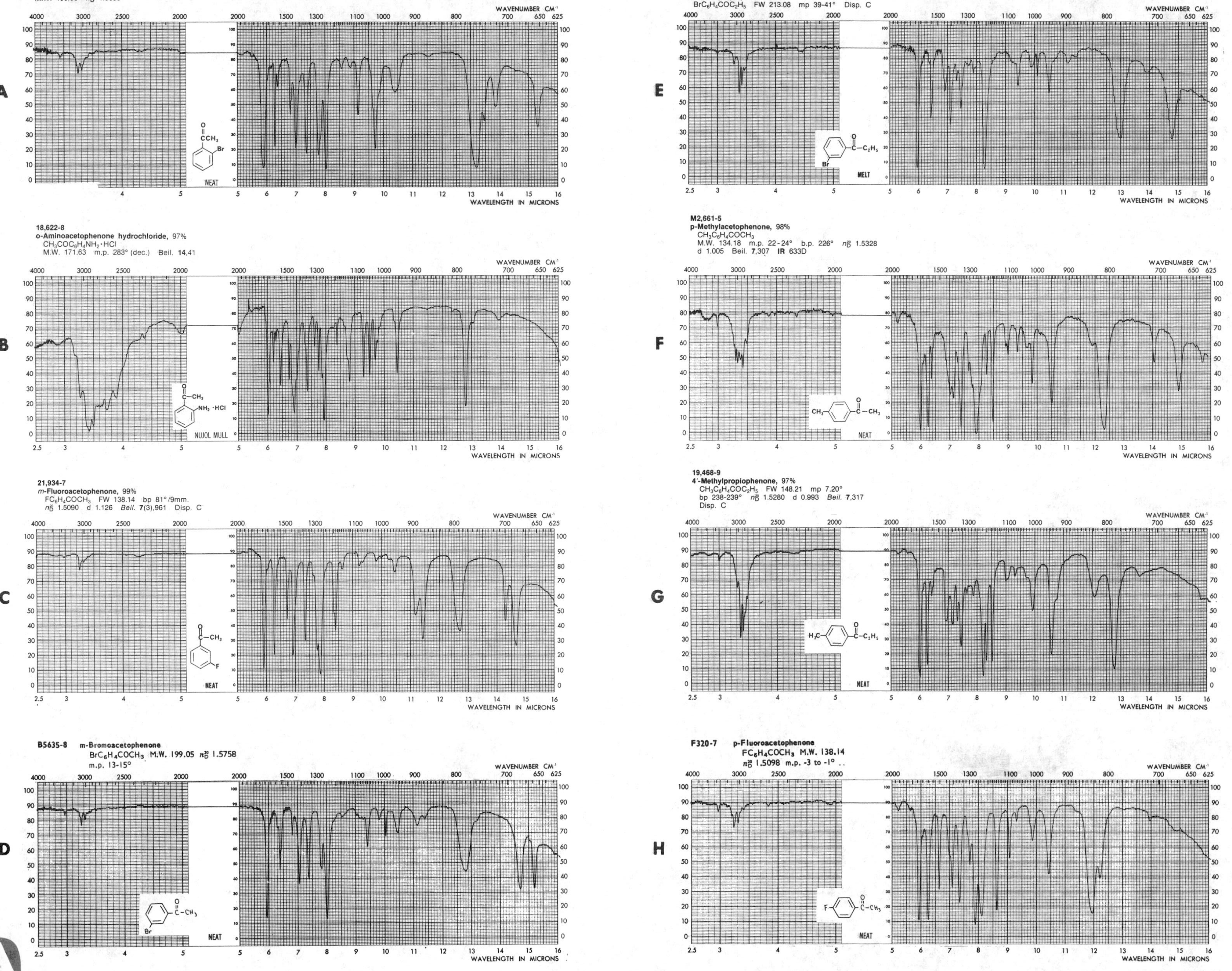
A
$BrC_6H_4COCH_3$
M.W. 199.05 n_D^{20} 1.5680
NEAT
B
18,622-8
o-Aminoacetophenone hydrochloride, 97%
$CH_3COC_6H_4NH_2 \cdot HCl$
M.W. 171.63 m.p. 283° (dec.) Beil. 14,41
NUJOL MULL
C
21,934-7
m-Fluoroacetophenone, 99%
$FC_6H_4COCH_3$ FW 138.14 bp 81°/9mm.
n_D^{20} 1.5090 d 1.126 Beil. 7(3),961 Disp. C
NEAT
D
B5635-8 m-Bromoacetophenone
$BrC_6H_4COCH_3$ M.W. 199.05 n_D^{20} 1.5758
m.p. 13-15°
NEAT
E
19,049-7
m-Bromopropiophenone, 98%
$BrC_6H_4COC_2H_5$ FW 213.08 mp 39-41° Disp. C
MELT
F
M2,661-5
p-Methylacetophenone, 98%
$CH_3C_6H_4COCH_3$
M.W. 134.18 m.p. 22-24° b.p. 226° n_D^{20} 1.5328
d 1.005 Beil. 7,307 IR 633D
NEAT
G
19,468-9
4'-Methylpropiophenone, 97%
$CH_3C_6H_4COC_2H_5$ FW 148.21 mp 7.20°
bp 238-239° n_D^{20} 1.5280 d 0.993 Beil. 7,317
Disp. C
NEAT
H
F320-7 p-Fluoroacetophenone
$FC_6H_4COCH_3$ M.W. 138.14
n_D^{20} 1.5098 m.p. -3 to -1°
NEAT
WAVENUMBER CM⁻¹
WAVELENGTH IN MICRONS
ALDRICH

A 12,841-4 p-Fluoropropiophenone
$FC_6H_4COC_2H_5$ M.W. 152.17 n_D^{20} 1.5059
NEAT

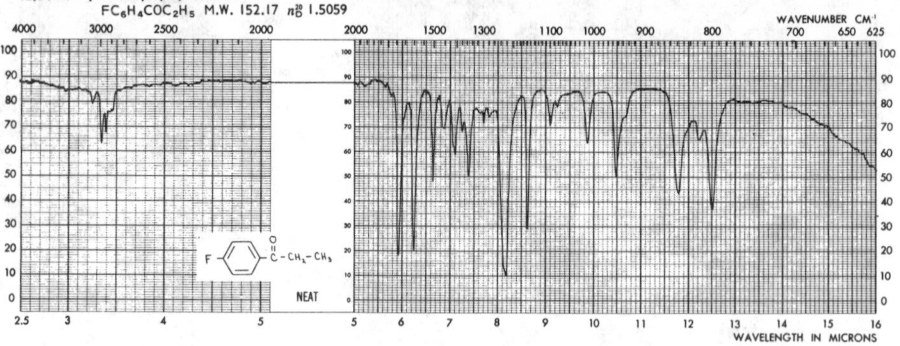

B F850-0 p-Fluorobutyrophenone
$FC_6H_4COCH_2CH_2CH_3$ M.W. 166.20
m.p. 30-32°
MELT

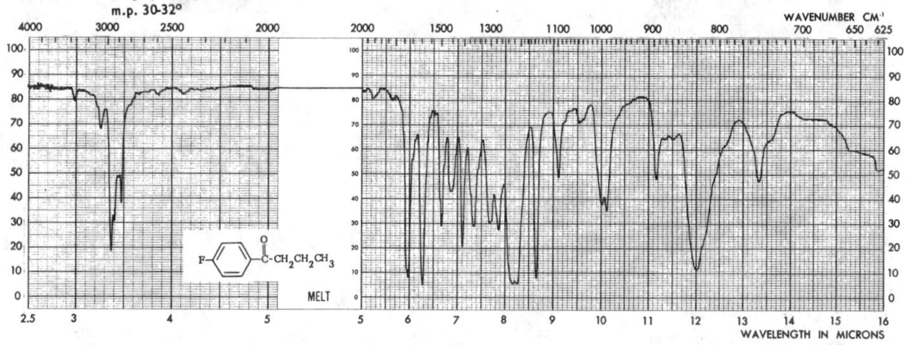

C C11,900-8 Cyclopropyl 4-fluorophenyl ketone
$FC_6H_4COC_3H_5$ M.W. 164.18 n_D^{20} 1.5334
NEAT

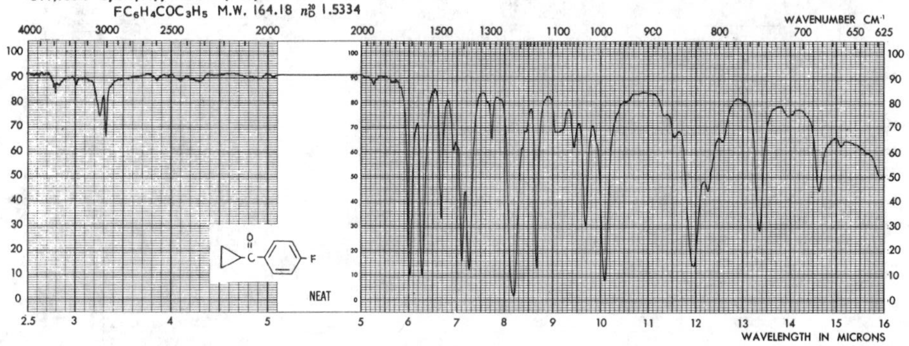

D 12,200-9 Cyclobutyl p-fluorophenyl ketone
$FC_6H_4COC_4H_7$ M.W. 178.21 n_D^{20} 1.5275
b.p. 125-127°/8 mm.

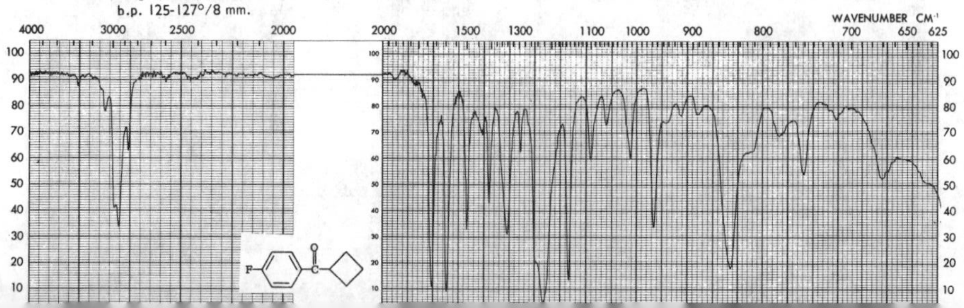

E 13,288-8 α-Chloro-p-fluoroacetophenone
$FC_6H_4COCH_2Cl$ M.W. 172.59 m.p. 47-50°
MELT

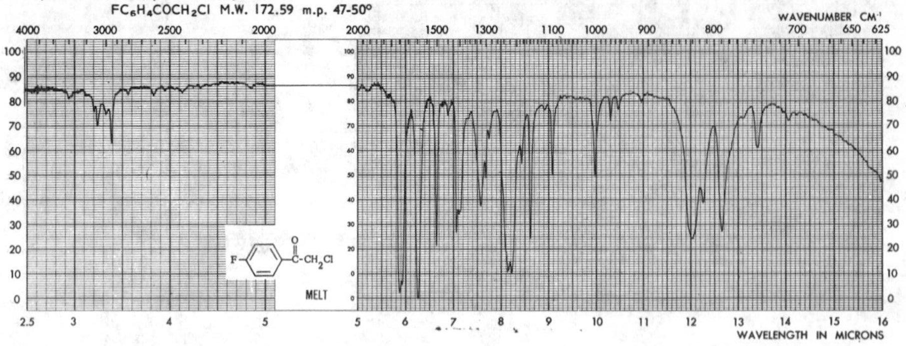

F 13,515-1 β-Chloro-p-fluoropropiophenone
$FC_6H_4COCH_2CH_2Cl$ M.W. 186.61
m.p. 47-47.5°
MELT

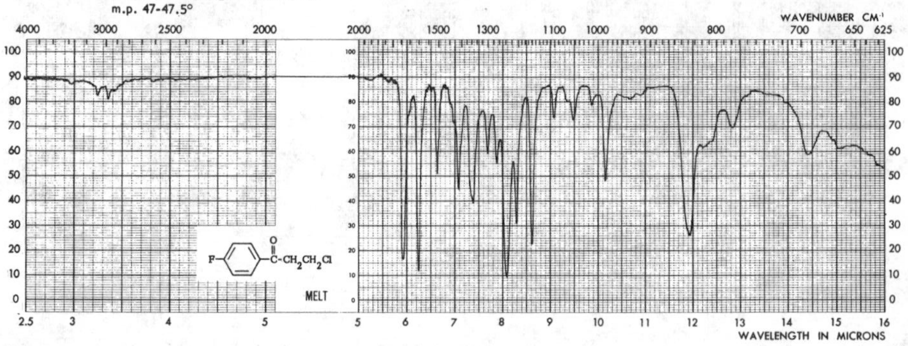

G C4360-9 γ-Chloro-p-fluorobutyrophenone, tech.
$FC_6H_4CO(CH_2)_3Cl$ M.W. 200.64
n_D^{20} 1.5267
NEAT

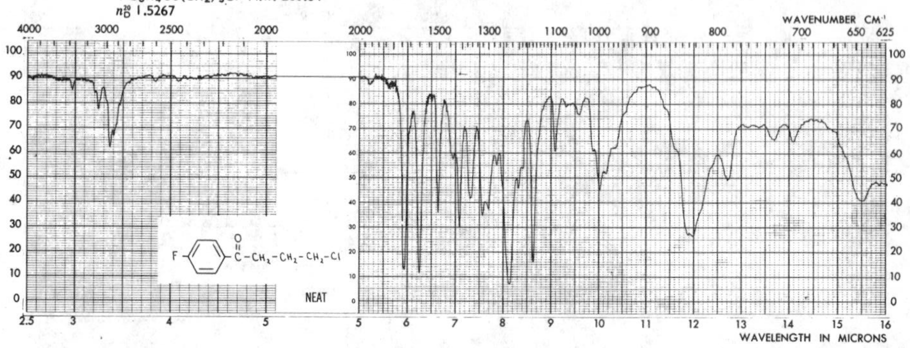

H 13,479-1 4'-Fluorodeoxybenzoin (4'-fluoro-α-phenylacetophenone)
$FC_6H_4COCH_2C_6H_5$ M.W. 214.24
m.p. 77-80°

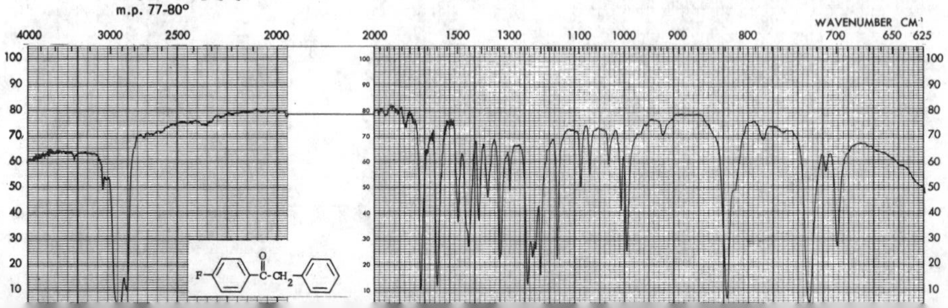

WAVENUMBER CM⁻¹ / WAVELENGTH IN MICRONS

A 2',3',4',5',6'-Pentafluoroacetophenone, 97%
$C_6F_5COCH_3$ FW 210.10 bp 130-131° n_D^{20} 1.4366
d 1.476 Disp. C
NEAT

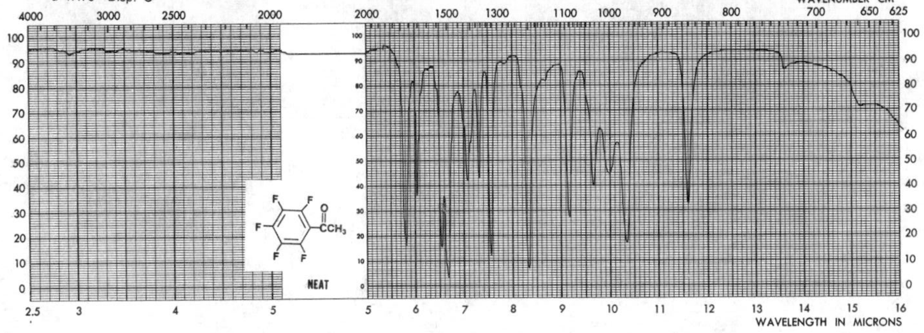

B C1970-8 p-Chloroacetophenone
$ClC_6H_4COCH_3$ M.W. 154.60 n_D^{20} 1.5549 m.p. 15-17°
NEAT

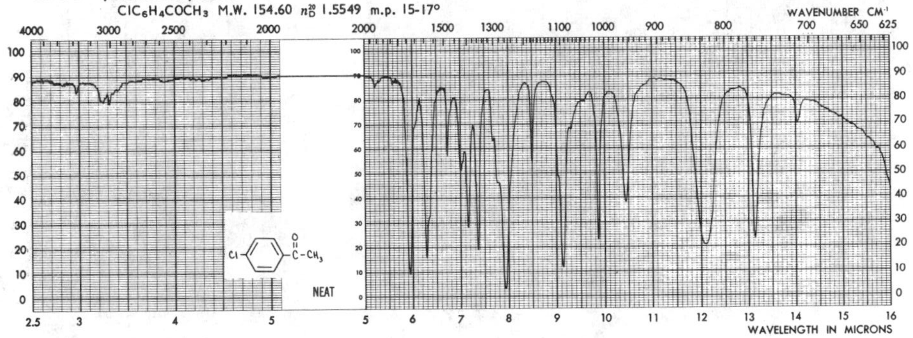

C C6920-9 p-Chloropropiophenone
$ClC_6H_4COC_2H_5$ M.W. 168.62
m.p. 35-37°
MELT

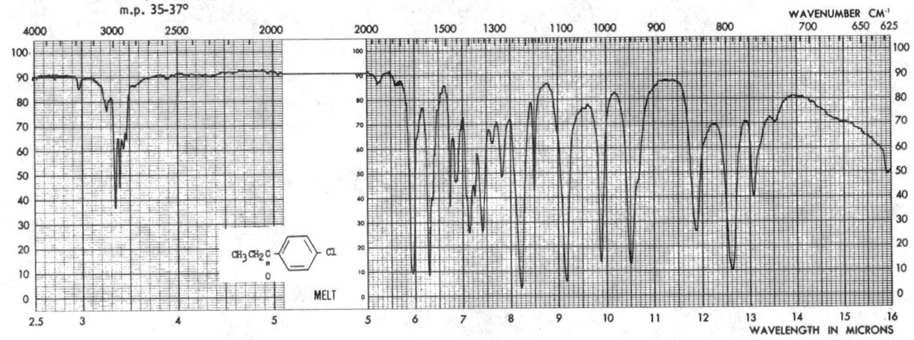

D C3030-2 p-Chlorobutyrophenone
$ClC_6H_4COCH_2CH_2CH_3$ M.W. 182.65
m.p. 37-39°
MELT

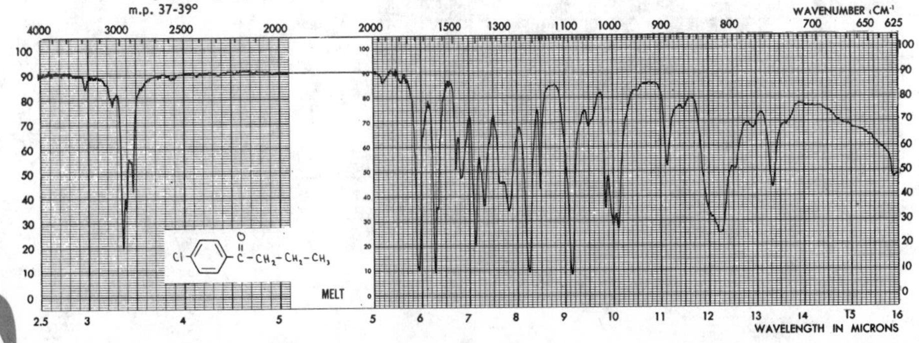

E C6420-7 4-Chlorophenyl cyclopropyl ketone
$ClC_6H_4COC_3H_5$ M.W. 180.63 m.p. 29-31°
NEAT

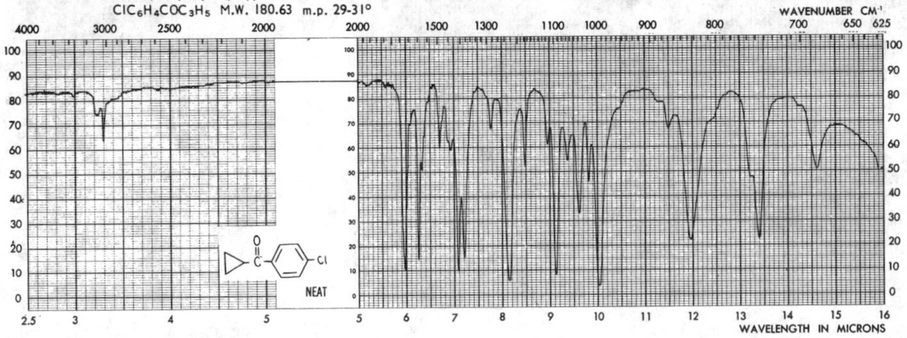

F 10,127-3 α-Bromo-p-chloroacetophenone (p-chlorophenacyl bromide)
$ClC_6H_4COCH_2Br$ M.W. 233.50
m.p. 96-97°
NUJOL MULL

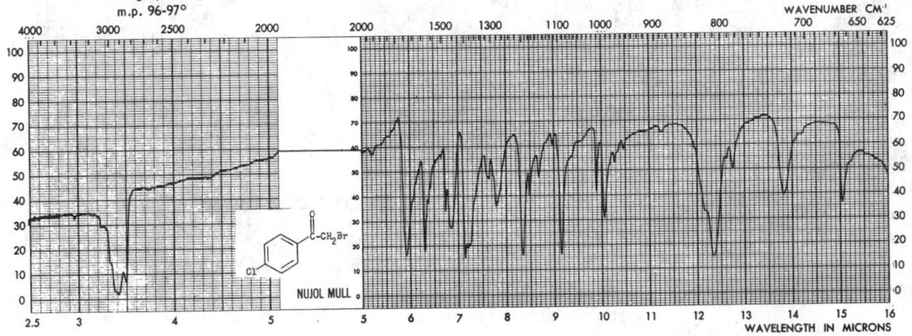

G 14,159-3 β,p-Dichloropropiophenone
$ClC_6H_4COCH_2CH_2Cl$ M.W. 203.07
m.p. 48-51°
MELT

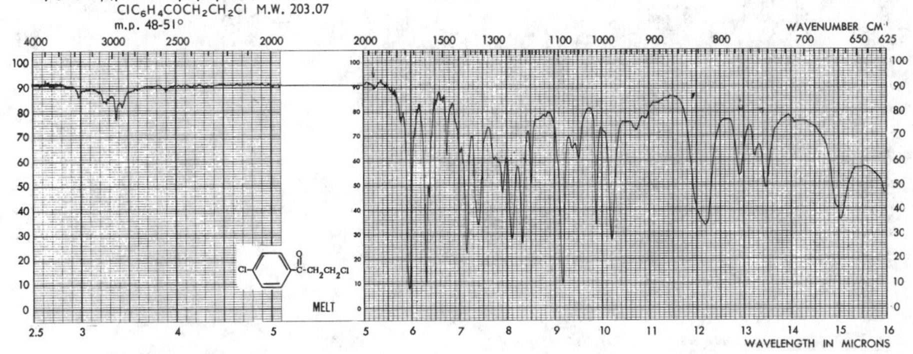

H 11,286-0 p-Chloro-α,α,α-trifluoroacetophenone
$ClC_6H_4COCF_3$ M.W. 208.60 n_D^{20} 1.4911
b.p. 180-183°
NEAT

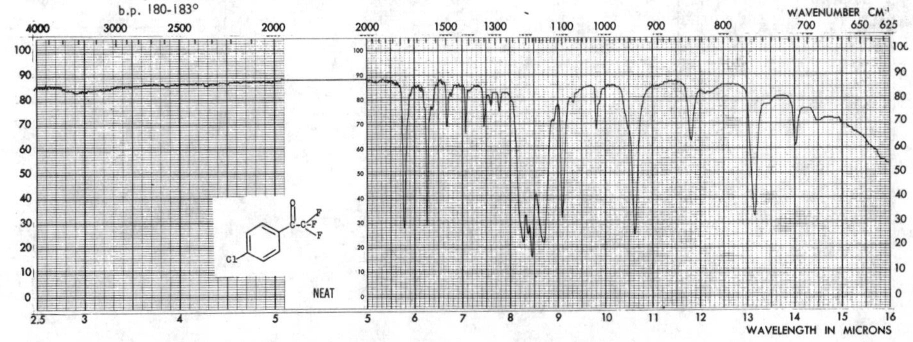

A

17,837-3
2',4'-Dichloroacetophenone
$Cl_2C_6H_3COCH_3$
M.W. 189.04 m.p. 33-34° b.p. 140-150°/15mm.
n_D^{20} 1.5635 Beil. 7(2),219
NEAT

B

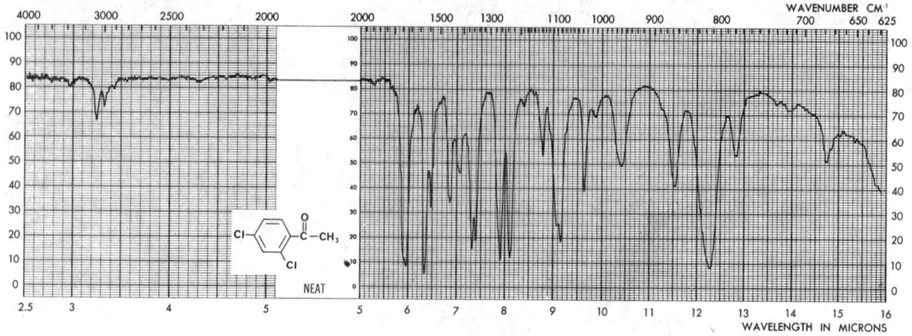

17,838-1
2',3',4'-Trichloroacetophenone
$Cl_3C_6H_2COCH_3$
M.W. 223.49 m.p. 59-64°
MELT

C

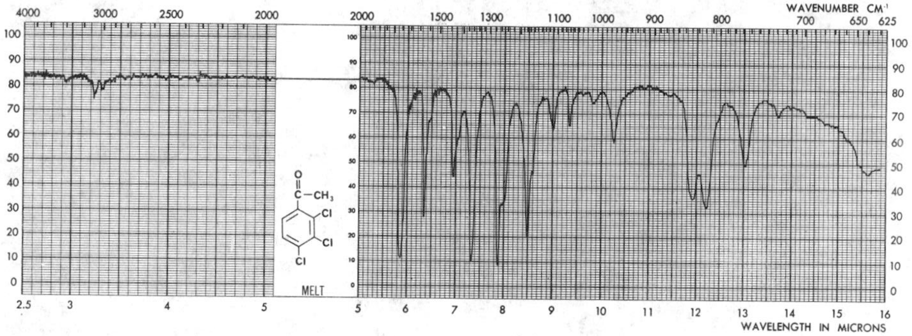

16,052-0
3',4'-Dichloroacetophenone, 99%
$Cl_2C_6H_3COCH_3$
M.W. 189.04 m.p. 72-74° b.p. 135°/12mm.
Beil. 7(2),219
NUJOL MULL

D

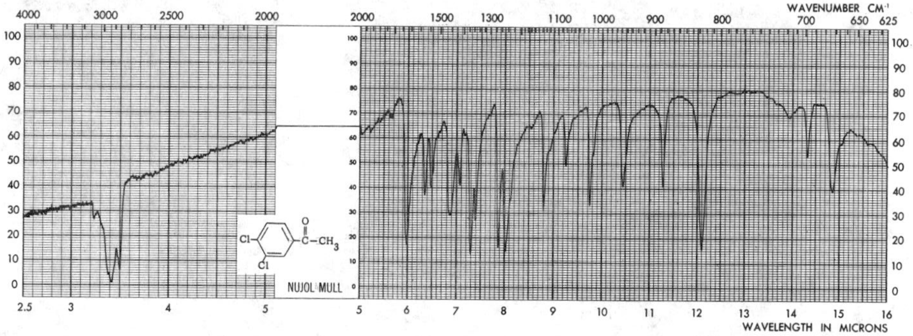

18,341-5
3',4'-Dichloropropiophenone, 99%
$Cl_2C_6H_3COC_2H_5$
M.W. 203.07 m.p. 44-46° b.p. 136-140°/18mm.
NUJOL MULL

E

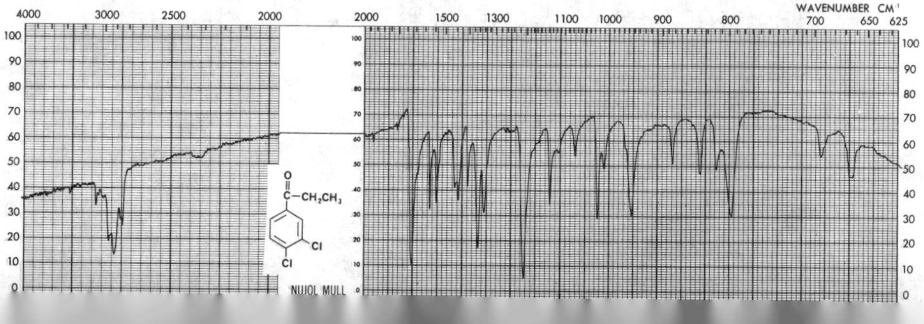

15,925-5
2,2',4'-Trichloroacetophenone, 95%
$Cl_2C_6H_3COCH_2Cl$
M.W. 223.49 m.p. 52-55° Beil. 7,283 *IRRITANT*
MELT

F

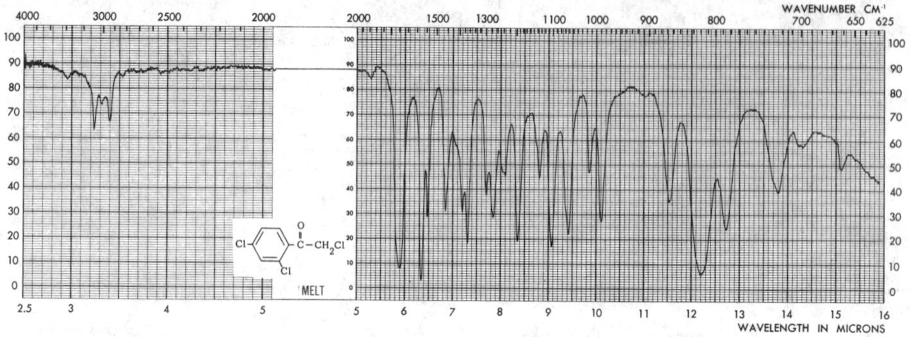

18,319-9
2',5'-Dichloroacetophenone
$Cl_2C_6H_3COCH_3$
M.W. 189.04 m.p. 11-13° n_D^{20} 1.5624
NEAT

G

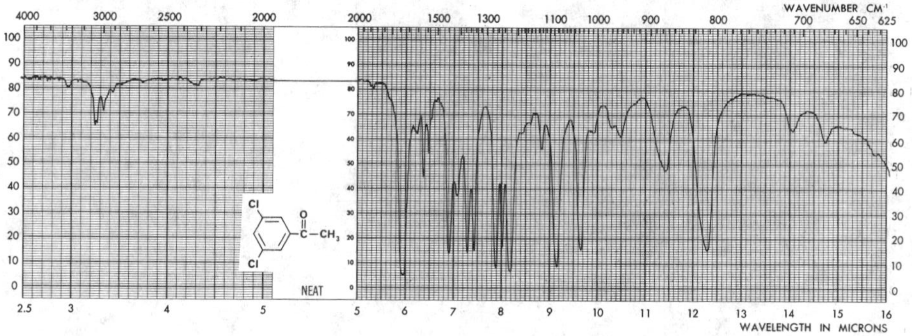

B5640-4 **p-Bromoacetophenone**
$BrC_6H_4COCH_3$ M.W. 199.05 m.p. 48-51°
MELT

H

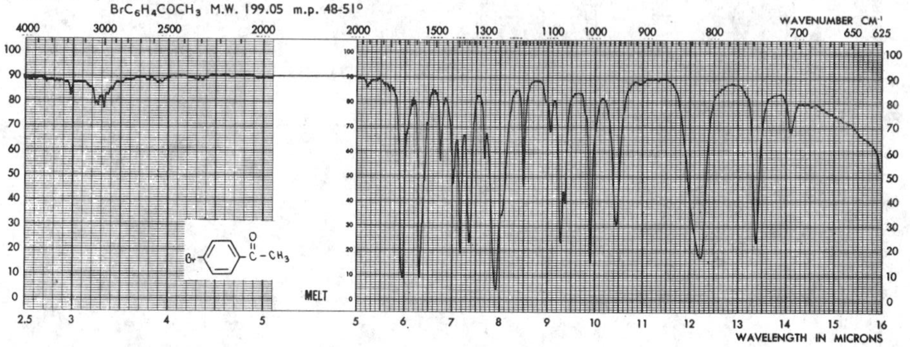

B7970-6 **p-Bromopropiophenone**
$BrC_6H_4COC_2H_5$ M.W. 213.08 m.p. 42-46°
MELT

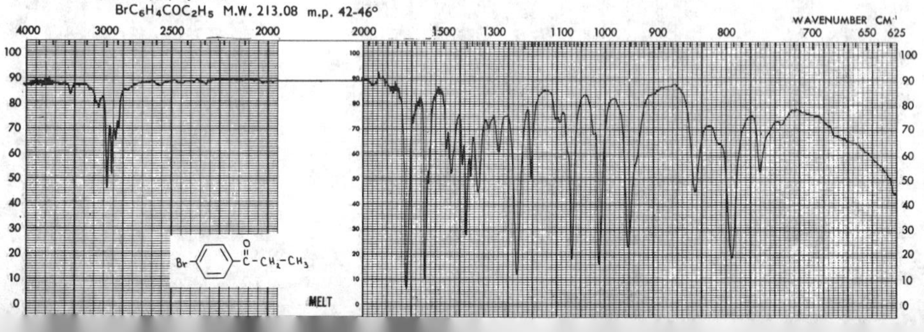

A

$BrC_6H_4COCH_2CH_2CH_3$ M.W. 227.11
m.p. 34-36.5°

MELT

B

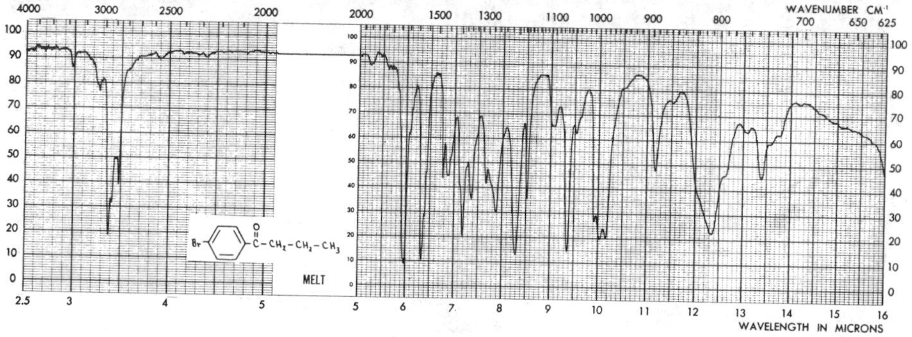

22,141-4
p-**Bromovalerophenone**, 98+%
$BrC_6H_4CO(CH_2)_3CH_3$ FW 241.14 mp 34-36°
bp 168-169°/20mm. *Beil.* 7(3),1116 Disp. C

MELT

C

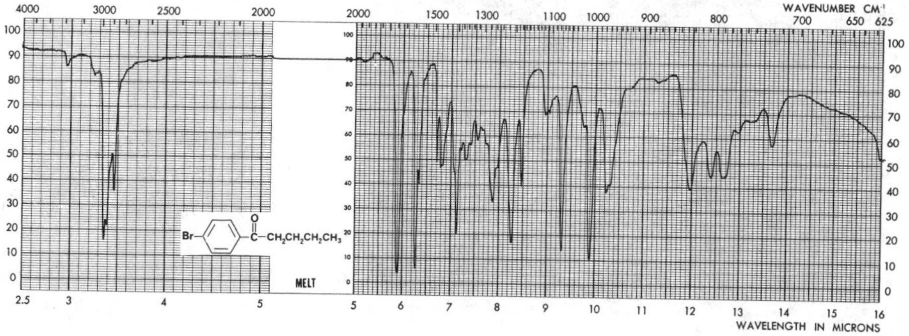

B7640-5 **4-Bromophenyl cyclopropyl ketone**
$BrC_6H_4COC_3H_5$ M.W. 225.09 n_D^{20} 1.5923

MELT

D

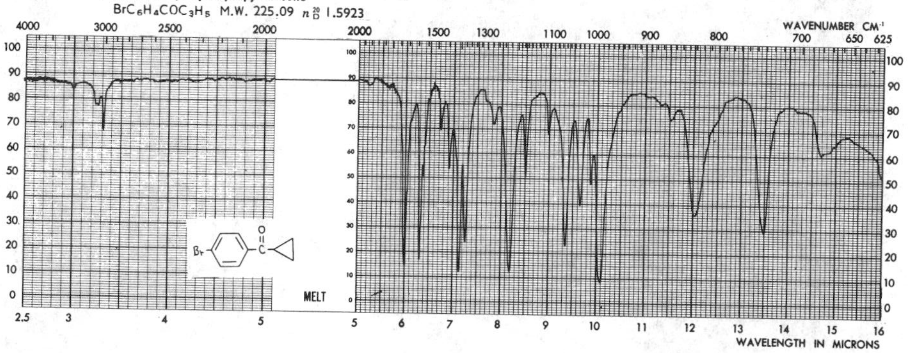

D3830-8 **α,p-Dibromoacetophenone** (p-bromophenacyl bromide)
$BrC_6H_4COCH_2Br$ M.W. 277.95
m.p. 110-112.5°

NUJOL MULL

E

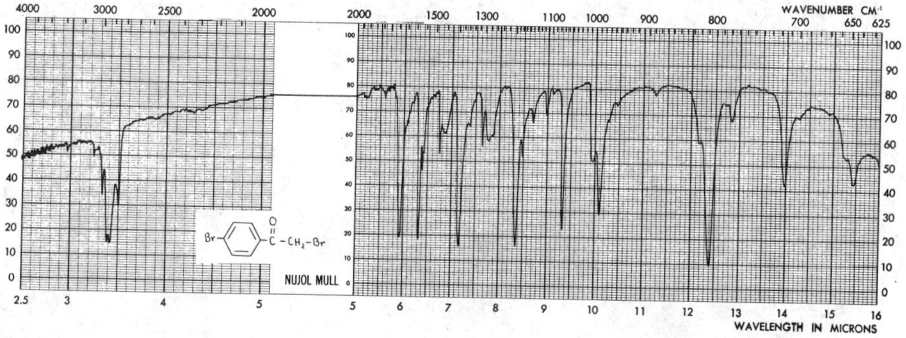

B6100-9 **p-Bromo-γ-chlorobutyrophenone**
$BrC_6H_4CO(CH_2)_3Cl$ M.W. 261.55
m.p. 35.5-38°

MELT

F

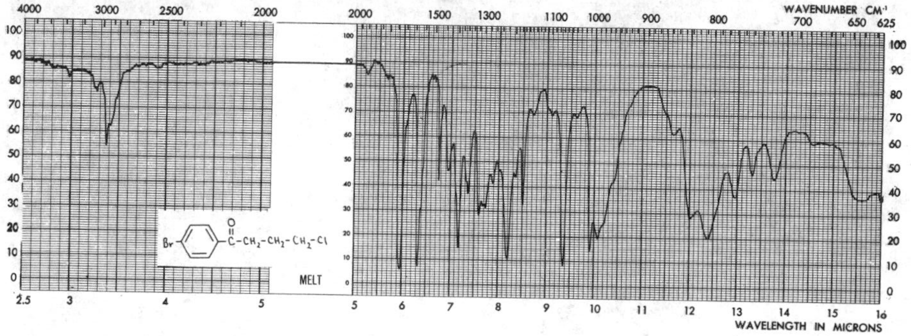

M960-2 **α-Methoxyacetophenone**
$C_6H_5COCH_2OCH_3$ M.W. 150.18 n_D^{20} 1.5346
b.p. 122-123°/18 mm.

NEAT

G

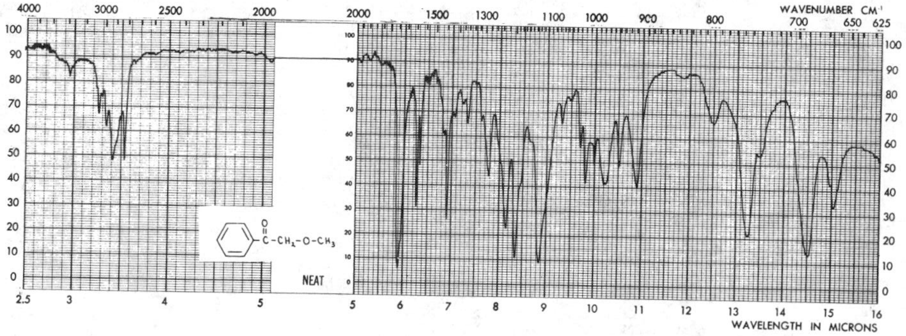

M920-3 **o-Methoxyacetophenone**
$CH_3OC_6H_4COCH_3$ M.W. 150.18 n_D^{20} 1.5393
b.p. 245°

NEAT

H

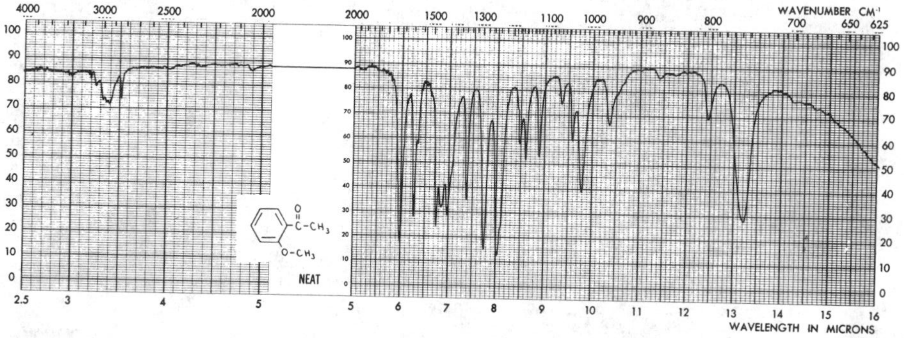

M940-8 **m-Methoxyacetophenone**
$CH_3OC_6H_4COCH_3$ M.W. 150.18 n_D^{20} 1.5410
b.p. 125-128°

NEAT

AROMATIC KETONES

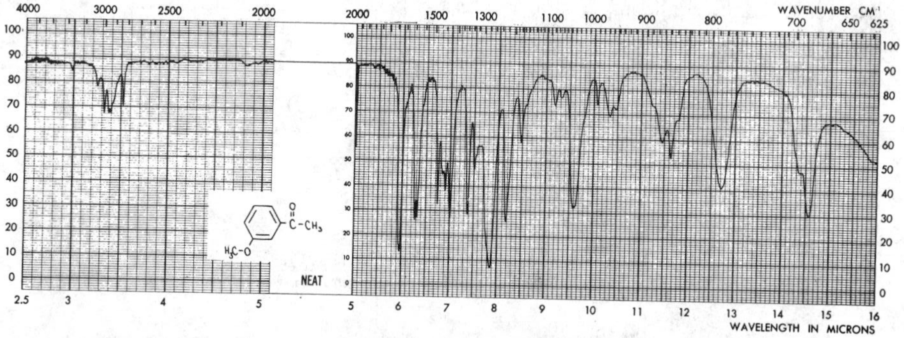

ALDRICH

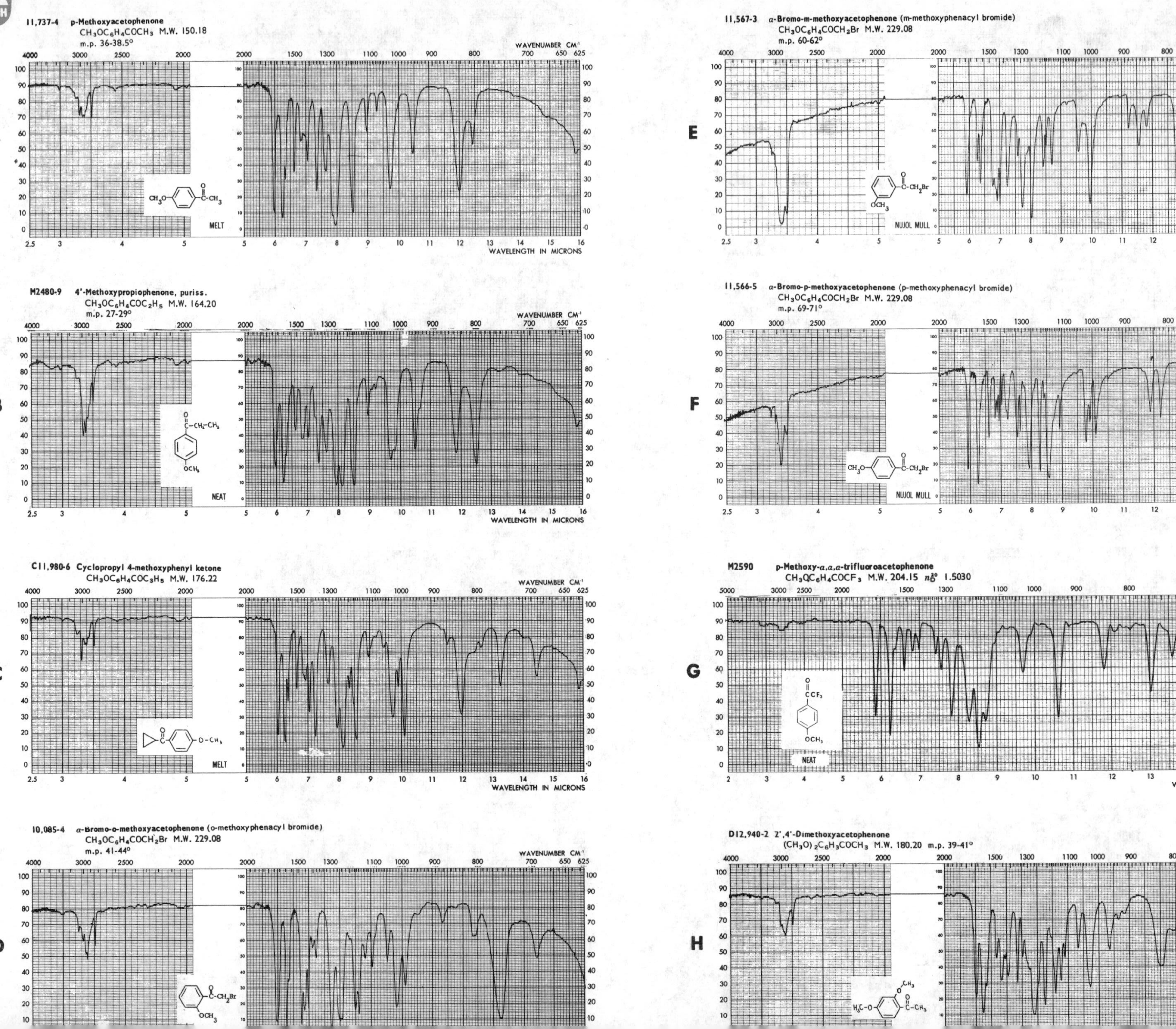

A — 11,737-4 p-Methoxyacetophenone
$CH_3OC_6H_4COCH_3$ M.W. 150.18
m.p. 36-38.5°
MELT

B — M2480-9 4'-Methoxypropiophenone, puriss.
$CH_3OC_6H_4COC_2H_5$ M.W. 164.20
m.p. 27-29°
NEAT

C — C11,980-6 Cyclopropyl 4-methoxyphenyl ketone
$CH_3OC_6H_4COC_3H_5$ M.W. 176.22
MELT

D — 10,085-4 α-Bromo-o-methoxyacetophenone (o-methoxyphenacyl bromide)
$CH_3OC_6H_4COCH_2Br$ M.W. 229.08
m.p. 41-44°

E — 11,567-3 α-Bromo-m-methoxyacetophenone (m-methoxyphenacyl bromide)
$CH_3OC_6H_4COCH_2Br$ M.W. 229.08
m.p. 60-62°
NUJOL MULL

F — 11,566-5 α-Bromo-p-methoxyacetophenone (p-methoxyphenacyl bromide)
$CH_3OC_6H_4COCH_2Br$ M.W. 229.08
m.p. 69-71°
NUJOL MULL

G — M2590 p-Methoxy-α,α,α-trifluoroacetophenone
$CH_3OC_6H_4COCF_3$ M.W. 204.15 n_D^{20} 1.5030
NEAT

H — D12,940-2 2',4'-Dimethoxyacetophenone
$(CH_3O)_2C_6H_3COCH_3$ M.W. 180.20 m.p. 39-41°

A

$(CH_3O)_2C_6H_3COCH_3$ M.W. 180.20 n_D^{20} 1.5441
m.p. 18-20° b.p. 155-158°/14 mm.

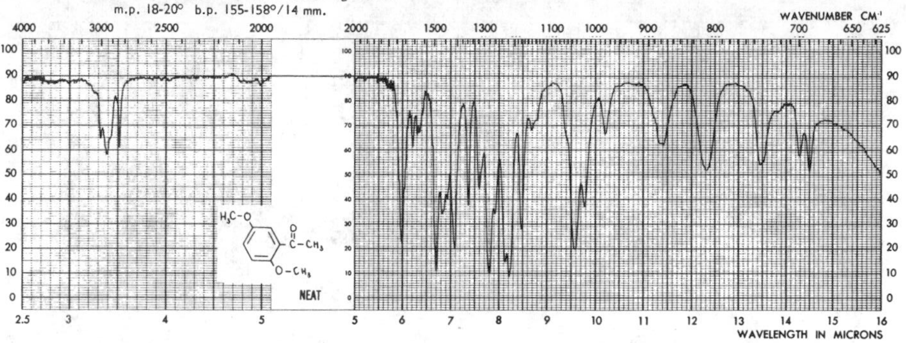

NEAT

E

M.W. 180.2 m.p. 35-34 b.p. 235-237
n_D^{20} 1.5430 Beil. 8,274

MELT

B

10,458-2 α-Bromo-2',5'-dimethoxyacetophenone
$(CH_3O)_2C_6H_3COCH_2Br$ M.W. 259.11
m.p. 82-85.5°

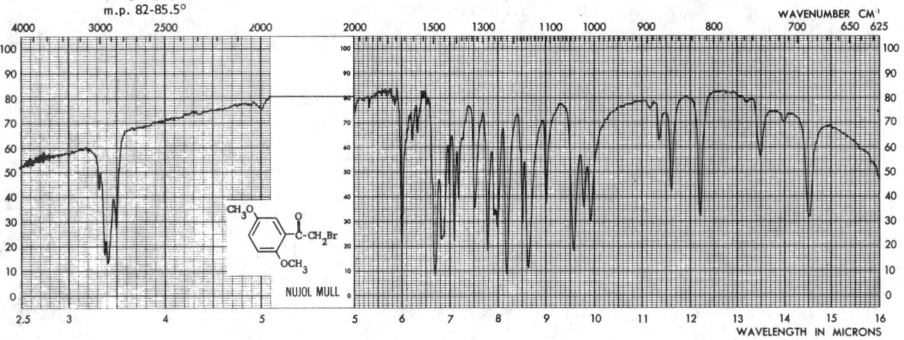

NUJOL MULL

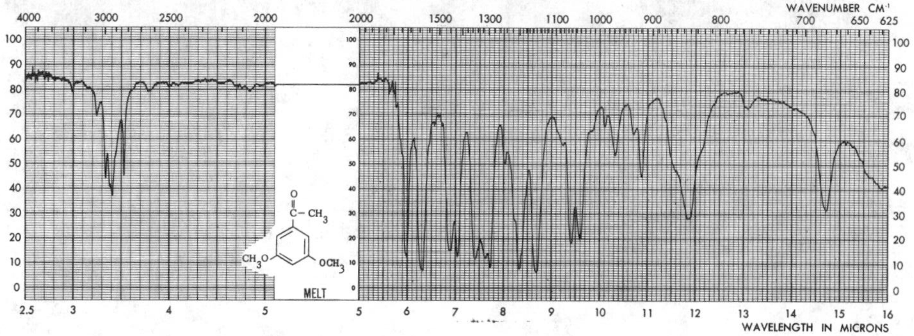

F

21,534-1
3,5-Dibenzyloxyacetophenone, 98%
$(C_6H_5CH_2O)_2C_6H_3COCH_3$ FW 332.40 mp 60-62°
Disp. C

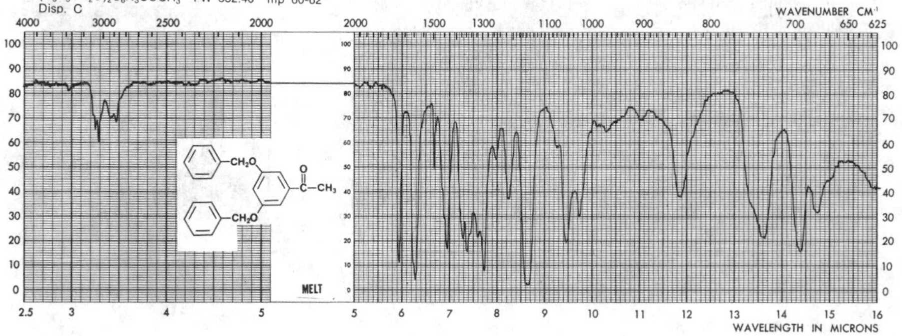

MELT

C

19,948-6
α-Bromo-2',4'-dimethoxyacetophenone, 98%
$(CH_3O)_2C_6H_3COCH_2Br$ FW 259.10 mp 102-104°
Beil. 8,269 Disp. C

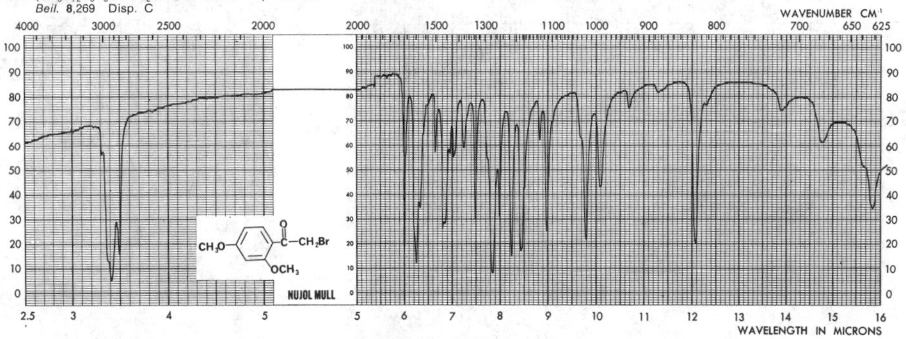

NUJOL MULL

G

T6810-1 3',4',5'-Trimethoxyacetophenone, puriss.
$(CH_3O)_3C_6H_2COCH_3$ M.W. 210.23
m.p. 82°

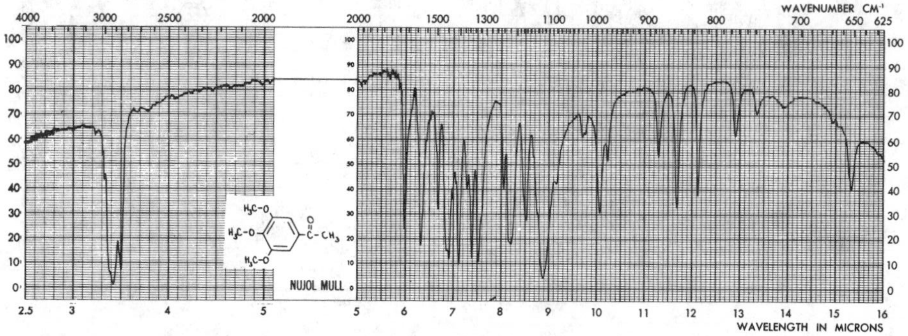

NUJOL MULL

D

17,902-7
1,4-Benzodioxan-6-yl methyl ketone, 98%
M.W. 178.19 m.p. 80-82°

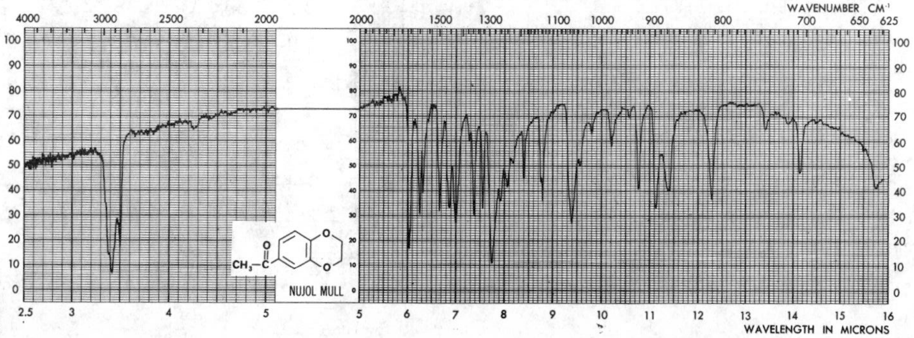

NUJOL MULL

H

18,981-2
2',3',4'-Trimethoxyacetophenone
$(CH_3O)_3C_6H_2COCH_3$ FW 210.23 mp 14-15°
bp 295-297° n_D^{20} 1.5384 *Beil.* 8,393 Disp. C

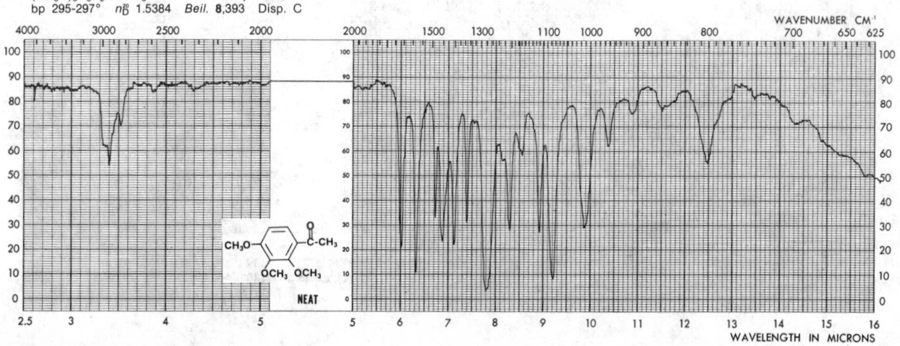

NEAT

(All spectra: WAVENUMBER CM⁻¹ 4000–625; WAVELENGTH IN MICRONS 2.5–16)

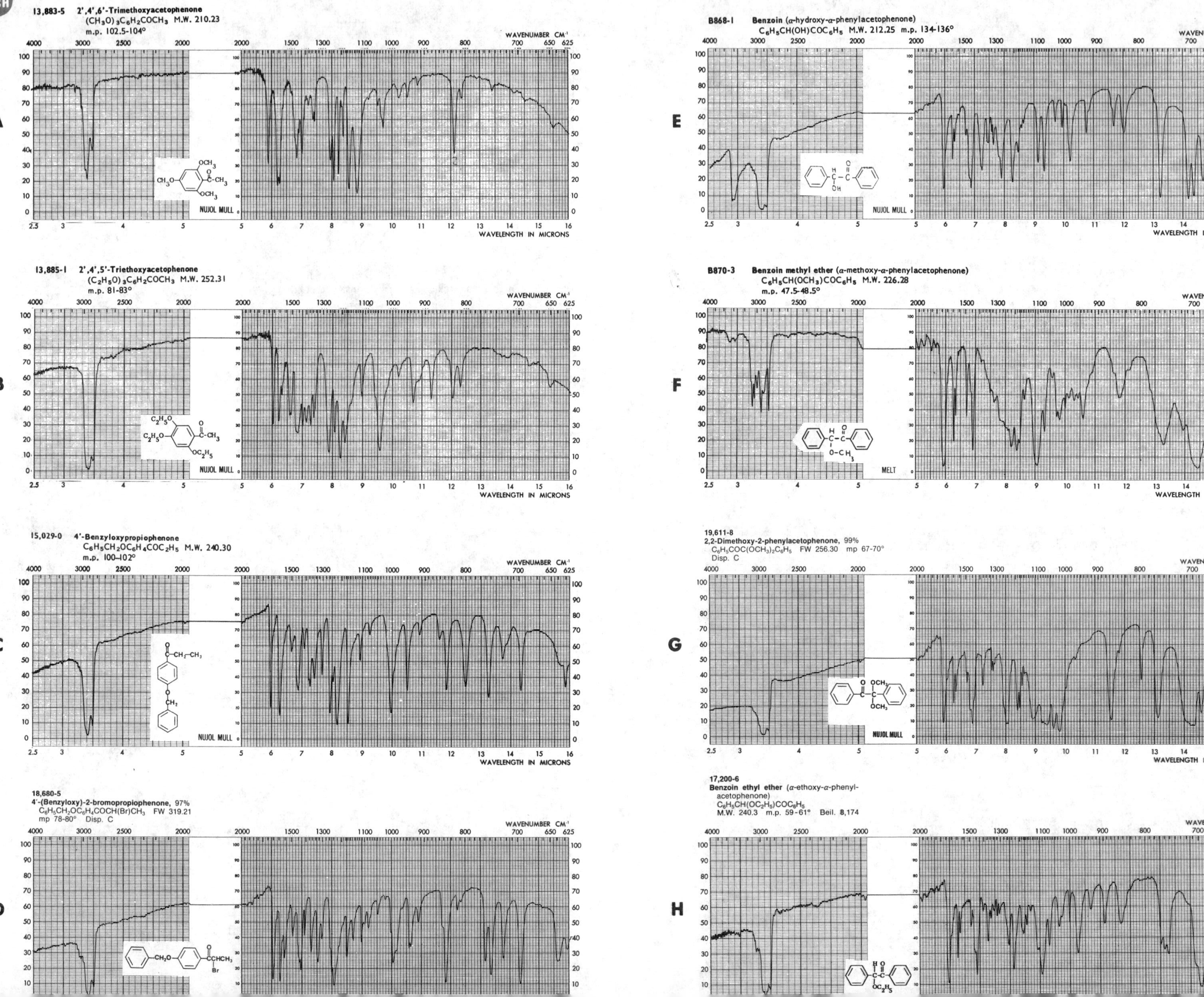

A 13,883-5 **2',4',6'-Trimethoxyacetophenone**
$(CH_3O)_3C_6H_2COCH_3$ M.W. 210.23
m.p. 102.5-104°
NUJOL MULL

B 13,885-1 **2',4',5'-Triethoxyacetophenone**
$(C_2H_5O)_3C_6H_2COCH_3$ M.W. 252.31
m.p. 81-83°
NUJOL MULL

C 15,029-0 **4'-Benzyloxypropiophenone**
$C_6H_5CH_2OC_6H_4COC_2H_5$ M.W. 240.30
m.p. 100-102°
NUJOL MULL

D 18,680-5
4'-(Benzyloxy)-2-bromopropiophenone, 97%
$C_6H_5CH_2OC_6H_4COCH(Br)CH_3$ FW 319.21
mp 78-80° Disp. C

E B868-1 **Benzoin** (α-hydroxy-α-phenylacetophenone)
$C_6H_5CH(OH)COC_6H_5$ M.W. 212.25 m.p. 134-136°
NUJOL MULL

F B870-3 **Benzoin methyl ether** (α-methoxy-α-phenylacetophenone)
$C_6H_5CH(OCH_3)COC_6H_5$ M.W. 226.28
m.p. 47.5-48.5°
MELT

G 19,611-8
2,2-Dimethoxy-2-phenylacetophenone, 99%
$C_6H_5COC(OCH_3)_2C_6H_5$ FW 256.30 mp 67-70°
Disp. C
NUJOL MULL

H 17,200-6
Benzoin ethyl ether (α-ethoxy-α-phenylacetophenone)
$C_6H_5CH(OC_2H_5)COC_6H_5$
M.W. 240.3 m.p. 59-61° Beil. 8,174

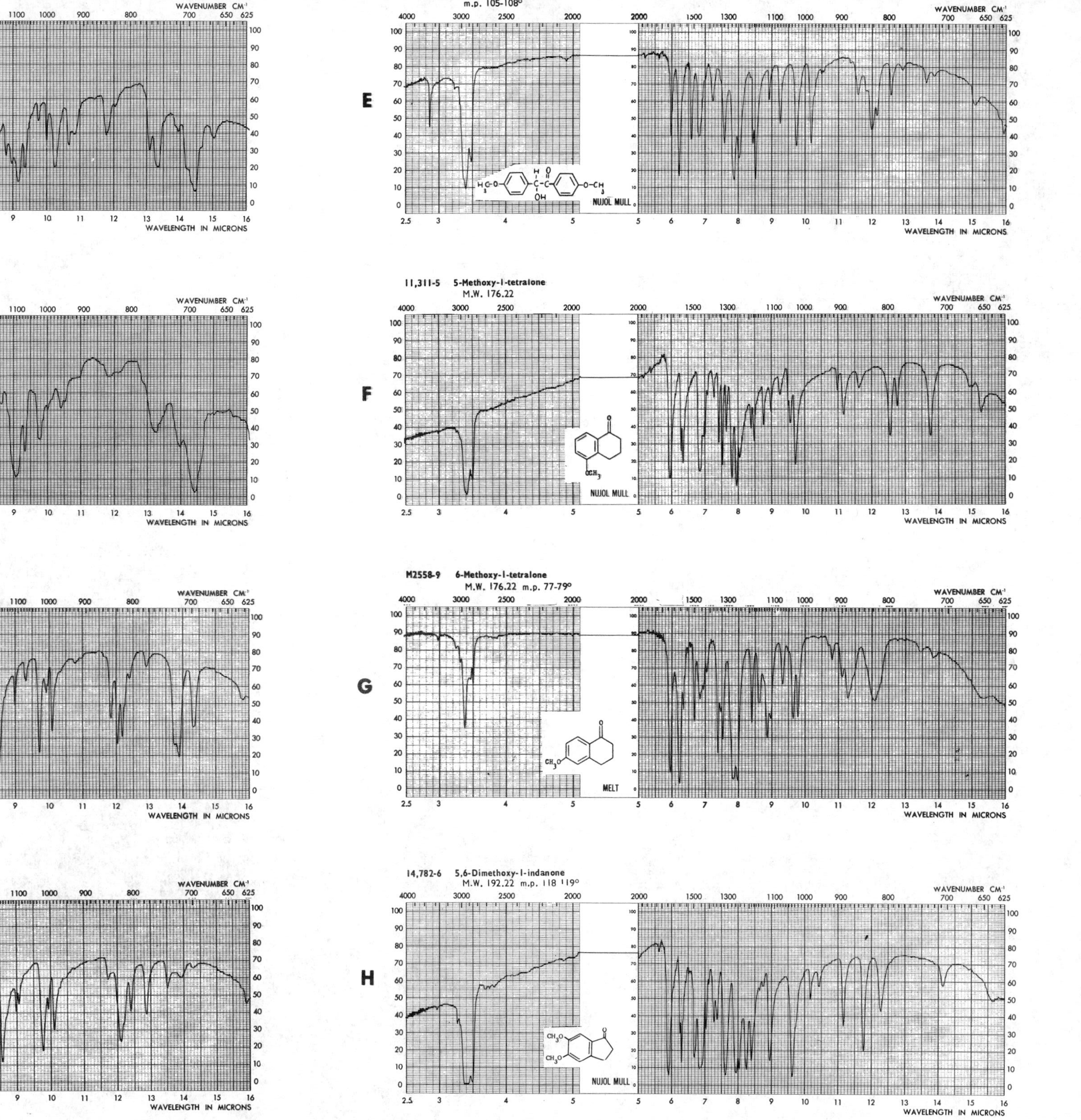

A

Disp. C

19,578-2
Benzoin isobutyl ether, 98% (α-isobutoxy-α-phenylacetophenone)
$C_6H_5CH[OCH_2CH(CH_3)_2]COC_6H_5$ FW 268.36
bp 133°/0.500mm. n_D^{20} 1.5485 d 0.985 Disp. C

B

A8850-6 **p-Anisyl benzyl ketone** (p-methoxy-α-phenylacetophenone, 4'-methoxydeoxybenzoin)
$CH_3OC_6H_4COCH_2C_6H_5$ M.W. 226.28 m.p. 71-74°

C

D560-8 **Desoxyanisoin** [p-methoxy-α-(p-methoxyphenyl)-acetophenone]
$CH_3OC_6H_4CH_2COC_6H_4OCH_3$ M.W. 256.30
m.p. 110-112°

D

E

4-$(CH_3O)C_6H_4CH(OH)COC_6H_4$-4-$(OCH_3)$ M.W. 272.30
m.p. 105-108°

11,311-5 **5-Methoxy-1-tetralone**
M.W. 176.22

F

M2558-9 **6-Methoxy-1-tetralone**
M.W. 176.22 m.p. 77-79°

G

14,782-6 **5,6-Dimethoxy-1-indanone**
M.W. 192.22 m.p. 118 119°

H

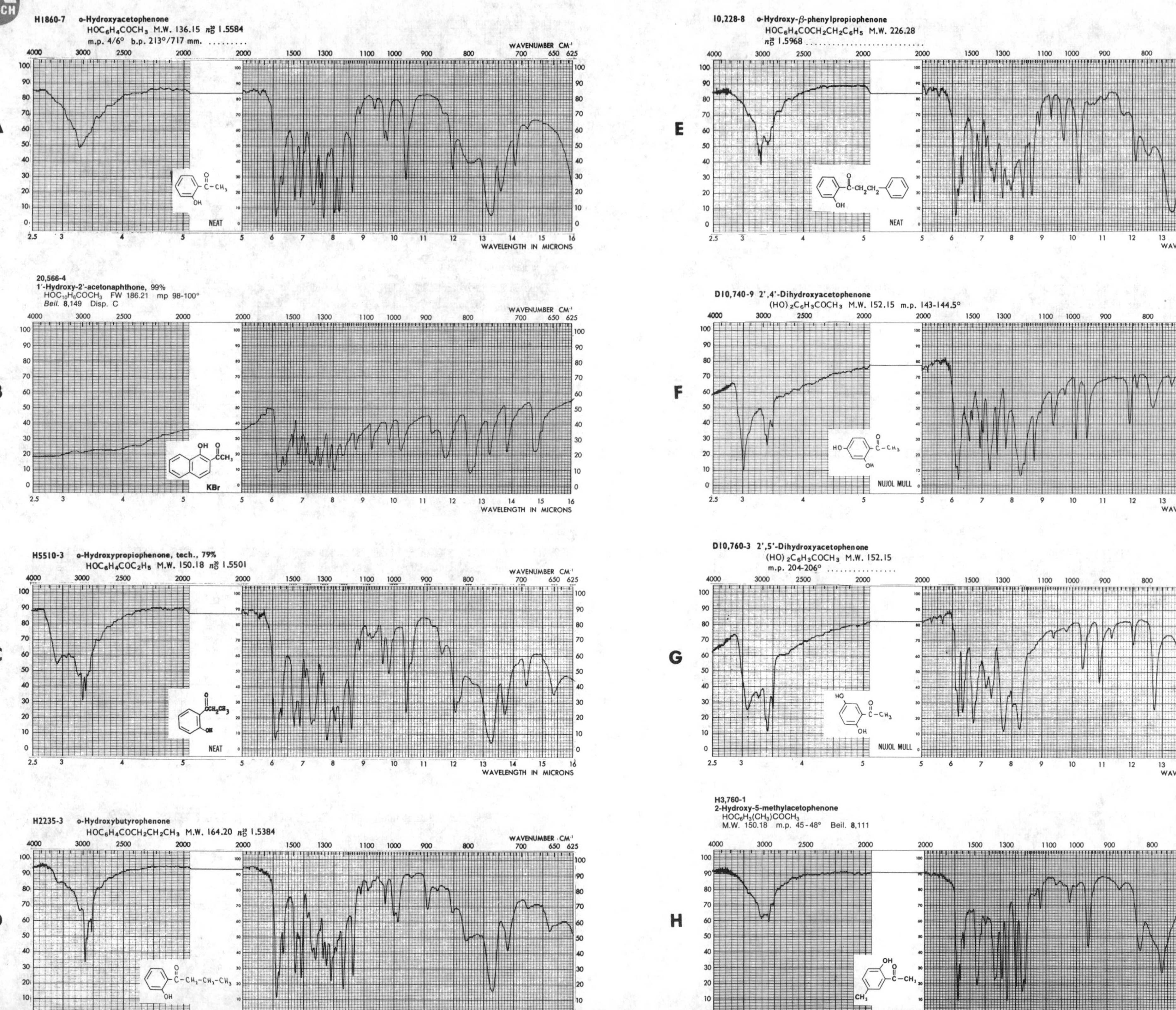
ALDRICH
A
H1860-7 o-Hydroxyacetophenone
$HOC_6H_4COCH_3$ M.W. 136.15 n_D^{20} 1.5584
m.p. 4/6° b.p. 213°/717 mm.
NEAT
B
20,566-4
1'-Hydroxy-2'-acetonaphthone, 99%
$HOC_{10}H_6COCH_3$ FW 186.21 mp 98-100°
Beil. 8,149 Disp. C
KBr
C
H5510-3 o-Hydroxypropiophenone, tech., 79%
$HOC_6H_4COC_2H_5$ M.W. 150.18 n_D^{20} 1.5501
NEAT
D
H2235-3 o-Hydroxybutyrophenone
$HOC_6H_4COCH_2CH_2CH_3$ M.W. 164.20 n_D^{20} 1.5384
E
10,228-8 o-Hydroxy-β-phenylpropiophenone
$HOC_6H_4COCH_2CH_2C_6H_5$ M.W. 226.28
n_D^{20} 1.5968
NEAT
F
D10,740-9 2',4'-Dihydroxyacetophenone
$(HO)_2C_6H_3COCH_3$ M.W. 152.15 m.p. 143-144.5°
NUJOL MULL
G
D10,760-3 2',5'-Dihydroxyacetophenone
$(HO)_2C_6H_3COCH_3$ M.W. 152.15
m.p. 204-206°
NUJOL MULL
H
H3,760-1
2-Hydroxy-5-methylacetophenone
$HOC_6H_3(CH_3)COCH_3$
M.W. 150.18 m.p. 45-48° Beil. 8,111
WAVENUMBER CM⁻¹
WAVELENGTH IN MICRONS

A D11,922 2',5'-Dihydroxypropiophenone
$(HO)_2C_6H_3COCH_2CH_3$ M.W. 166.18 m.p. 96-97°
NUJOL MULL

B D10,780-8 2',6'-Dihydroxyacetophenone
$(HO)_2C_6H_3COCH_3$ M.W. 152.15 m.p. 156-158°
NUJOL MULL

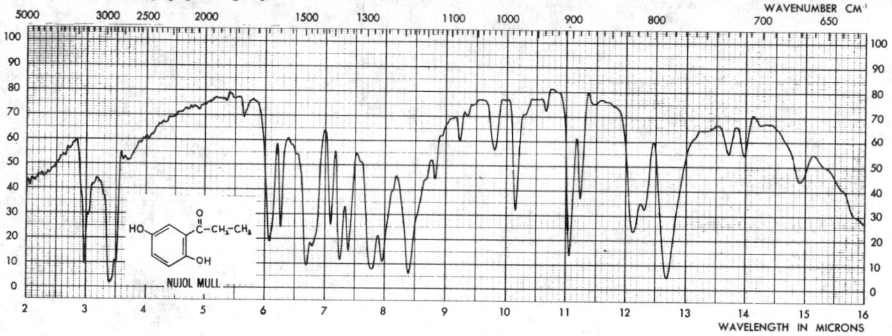

C D11,920-2 2',4'-Dihydroxypropiophenone
$(HO)_2C_6H_3COC_2H_5$ M.W. 166.18 m.p. 100-103°
NUJOL MULL

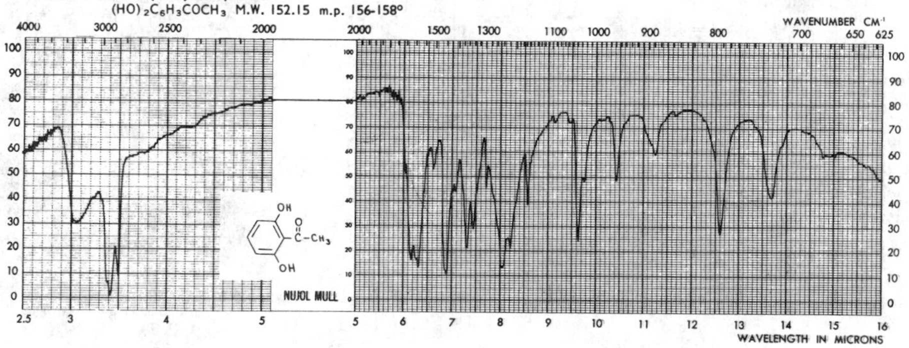

D 20,947-3
4-Hexanoylresorcinol, 98% (2',4'-dihydroxy-hexanophenone)
$CH_3(CH_2)_4COC_6H_3(OH)_2$ FW 208.26 mp 53-56°
bp 217°/14mm. Disp. C
NUJOL MULL

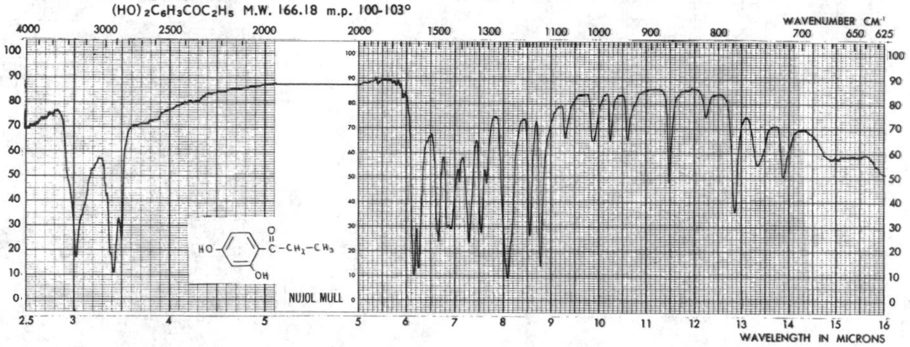

E T6440-8 2',3',4'-Trihydroxyacetophenone (gallacetophenone)
$(HO)_3C_6H_2COCH_3$ M.W. 168.15 m.p. 169-173°
NUJOL MULL

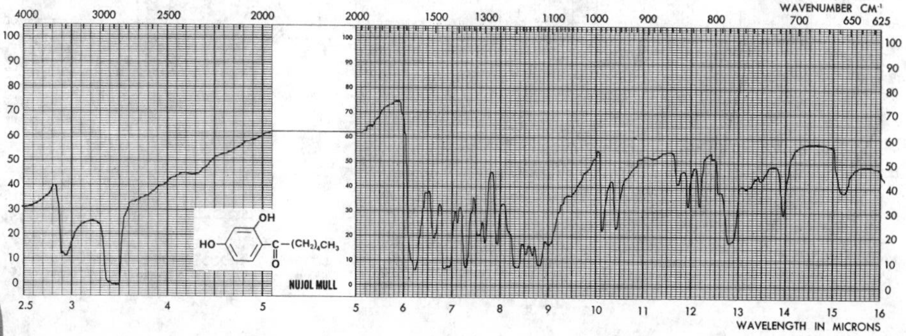

F T6460-2 2',4',6'-Trihydroxyacetophenone (phloroacetophenone)
$(HO)_3C_6H_2COCH_3$ M.W. 168.15
m.p. 222-224°
NUJOL MULL

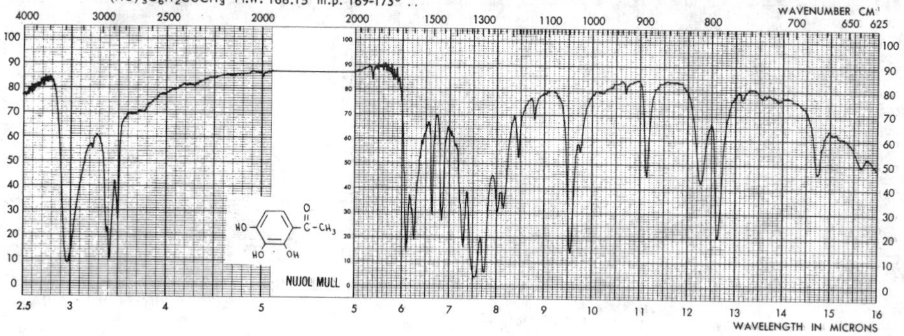

G 16,178-0
2',4',6'-Trihydroxypropiophenone monohydrate, 97%
$(HO)_3C_6H_2COC_2H_5 \cdot H_2O$
M.W. 200.19 m.p. 172-174° Beil. 8(2),448
NUJOL MULL

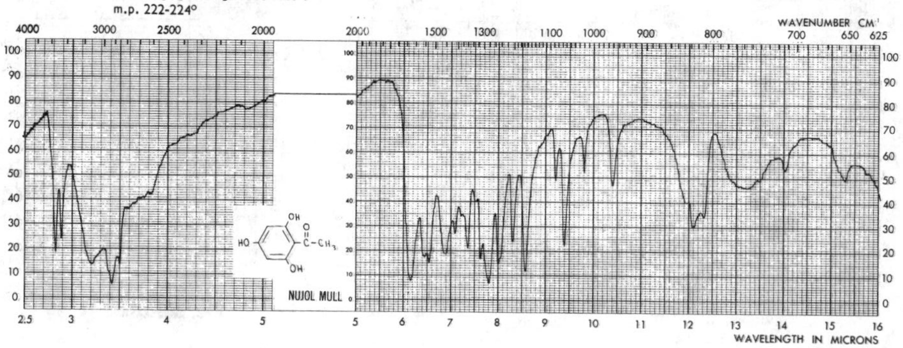

H 18,388-1
2'-Hydroxy-4',6'-dimethylacetophenone, 97%
$HOC_6H_2(CH_3)_2COCH_3$
M.W. 164.2 m.p. 53-57°
MELT

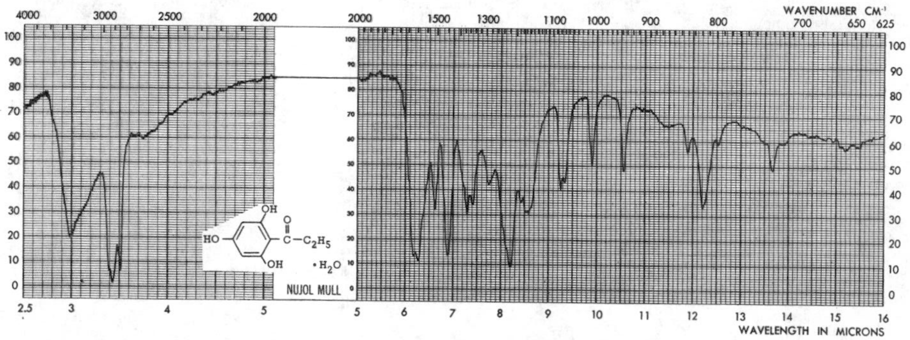

AROMATIC KETONES

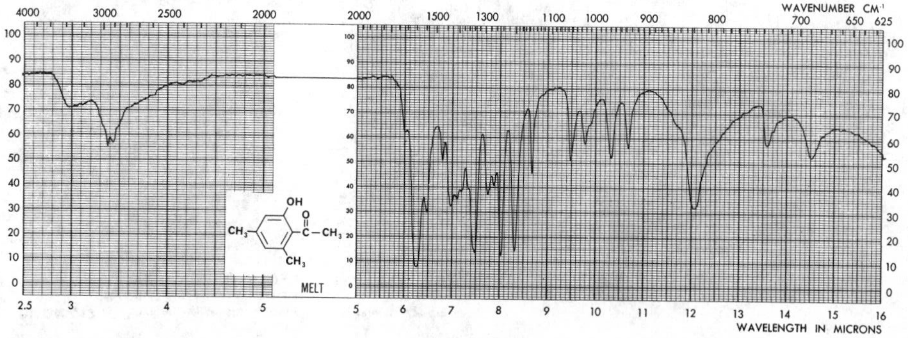

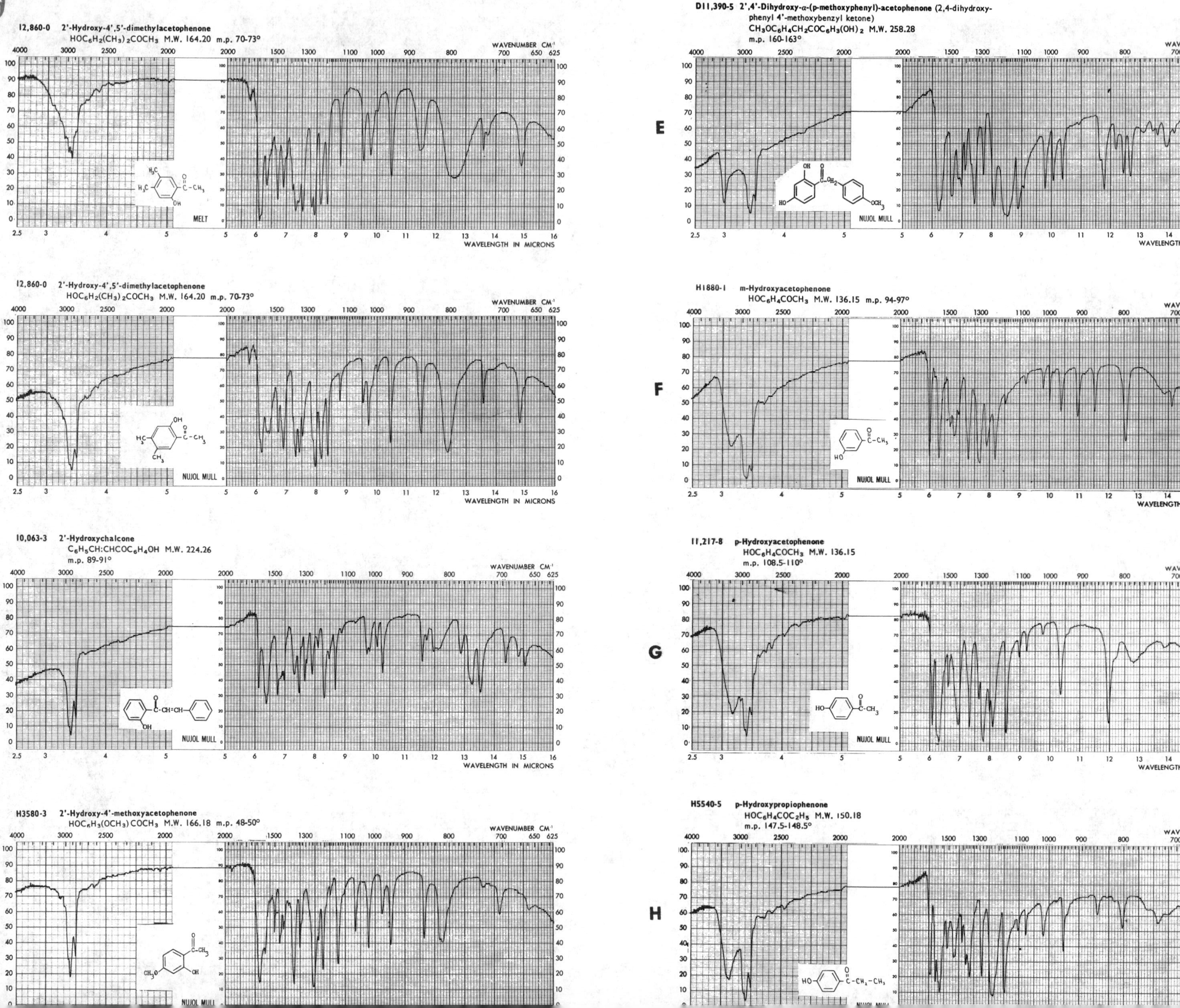
ALDRICH

A
12,860-0 2'-Hydroxy-4',5'-dimethylacetophenone
$HOC_6H_2(CH_3)_2COCH_3$ M.W. 164.20 m.p. 70-73°
MELT

B
12,860-0 2'-Hydroxy-4',5'-dimethylacetophenone
$HOC_6H_2(CH_3)_2COCH_3$ M.W. 164.20 m.p. 70-73°
NUJOL MULL

C
10,063-3 2'-Hydroxychalcone
$C_6H_5CH{:}CHCOC_6H_4OH$ M.W. 224.26
m.p. 89-91°
NUJOL MULL

D
H3580-3 2'-Hydroxy-4'-methoxyacetophenone
$HOC_6H_3(OCH_3)COCH_3$ M.W. 166.18 m.p. 48-50°
NUJOL MULL

E
D11,390-5 2',4'-Dihydroxy-α-(p-methoxyphenyl)-acetophenone (2,4-dihydroxyphenyl 4'-methoxybenzyl ketone)
$CH_3OC_6H_4CH_2COC_6H_3(OH)_2$ M.W. 258.28
m.p. 160-163°
NUJOL MULL

F
H1880-1 m-Hydroxyacetophenone
$HOC_6H_4COCH_3$ M.W. 136.15 m.p. 94-97°
NUJOL MULL

G
11,217-8 p-Hydroxyacetophenone
$HOC_6H_4COCH_3$ M.W. 136.15
m.p. 108.5-110°
NUJOL MULL

H
H5540-5 p-Hydroxypropiophenone
$HOC_6H_4COC_2H_5$ M.W. 150.18
m.p. 147.5-148.5°

WAVENUMBER CM⁻¹
WAVELENGTH IN MICRONS

HOC$_6$H$_4$COCH$_2$CH$_2$CH$_3$ M.W. 164.20 m.p. 92-94°

A

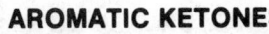

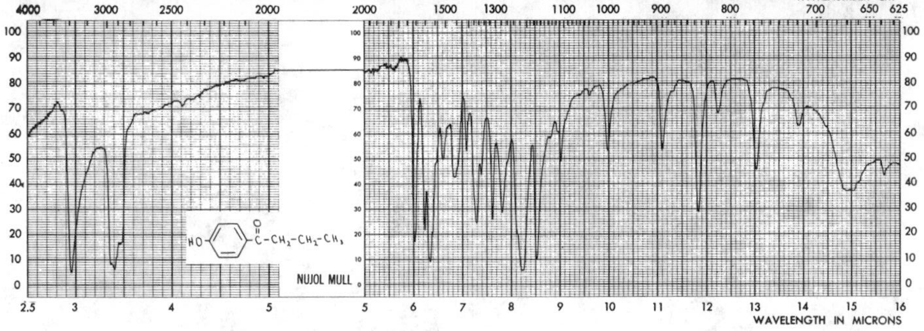

B2307-7 **Benzyl 4-hydroxyphenyl ketone** (4'-hydroxydeoxybenzoin, p-hydroxy-α-phenylacetophenone)
C$_6$H$_5$CH$_2$COC$_6$H$_4$OH M.W. 212.25
m.p. 146-148°

B

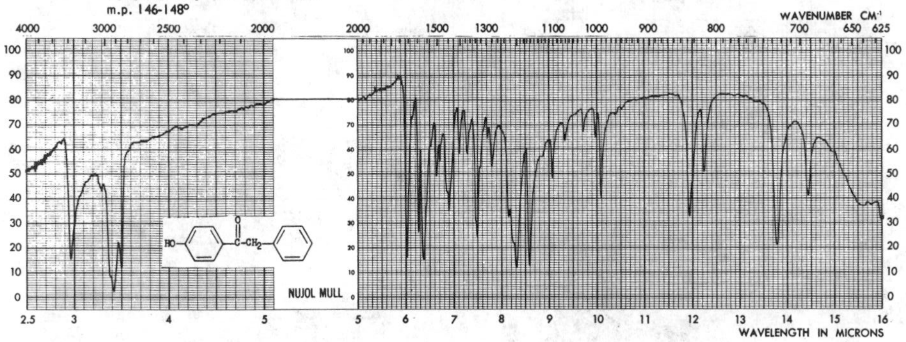

14,094-5 **α-Chloro-p-hydroxyacetophenone, tech.**
HOC$_6$H$_4$COCH$_2$Cl M.W. 170.60
m.p. 145-148°

C

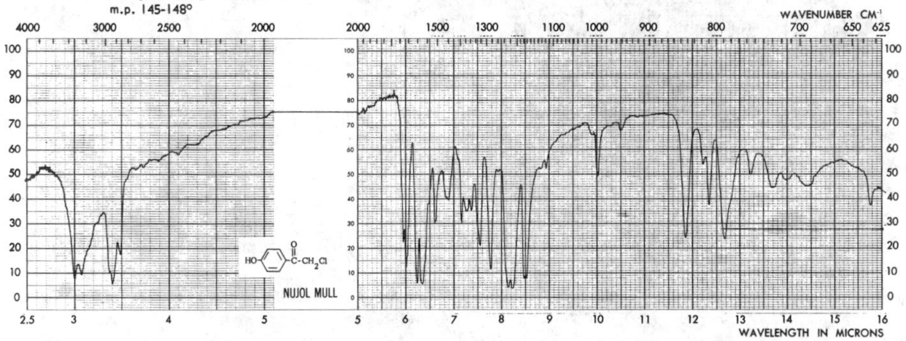

C4490-7 **γ-Chloro-p-hydroxybutyrophenone, tech.**
HOC$_6$H$_4$CO(CH$_2$)$_3$Cl M.W. 198.65
m.p. 113-116.5°

D

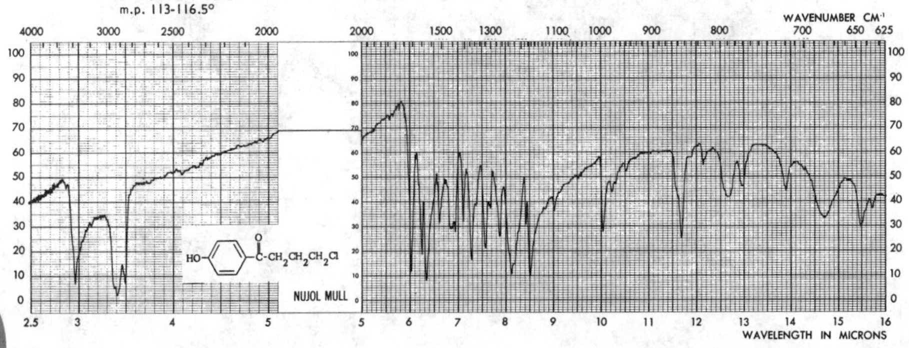

M.W. 150.18 m.p. 107-109° Beil. 8,112

E

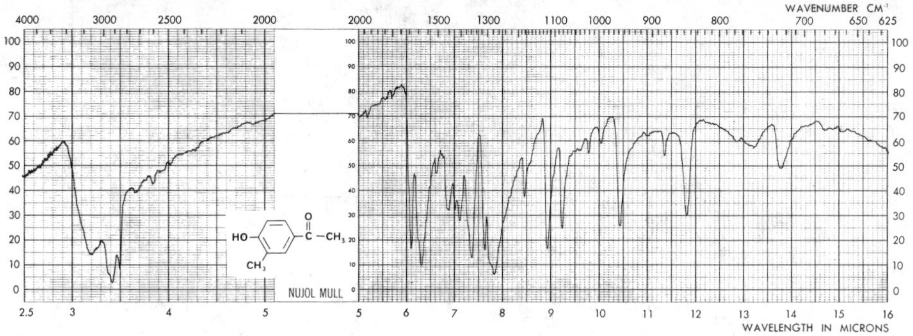

H3,780-6
4-Hydroxy-2-methylacetophenone
HOC$_6$H$_3$(CH$_3$)COCH$_3$
M.W. 150.18 m.p. 127-129° b.p. 313° d 1.059
Beil. 8,111

F

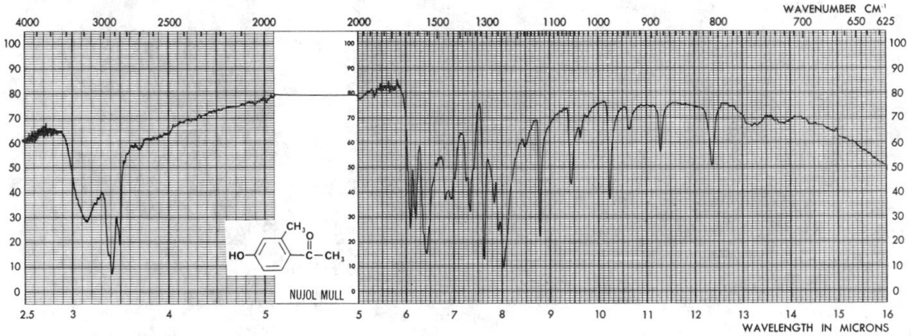

C3440-5 **α-Chloro-3',4'-dihydroxyacetophenone** [4-(chloroacetyl)-catechol]
(HO)$_2$C$_6$H$_3$COCH$_2$Cl M.W. 186.59
m.p. 174-176°

G

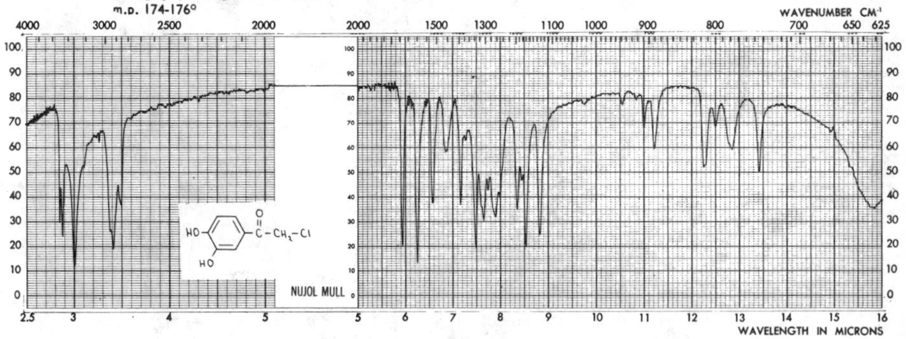

A1080-9 **Acetovanillone** (4'-hydroxy-3'-methoxyacetophenone)
HOC$_6$H$_3$(OCH$_3$)COCH$_3$ M.W. 166.18
m.p. 113-116°

H

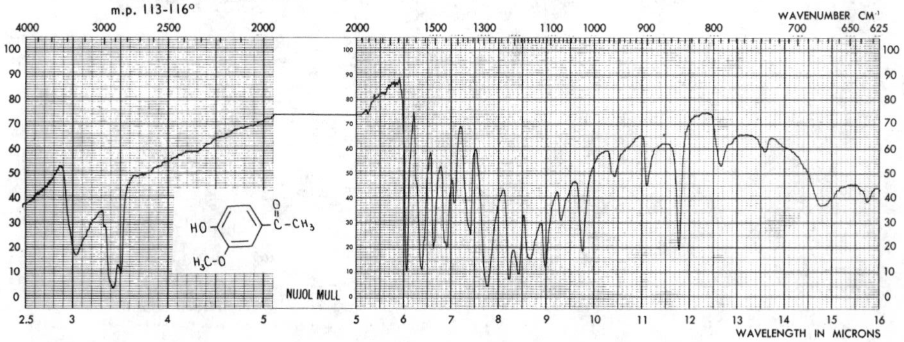

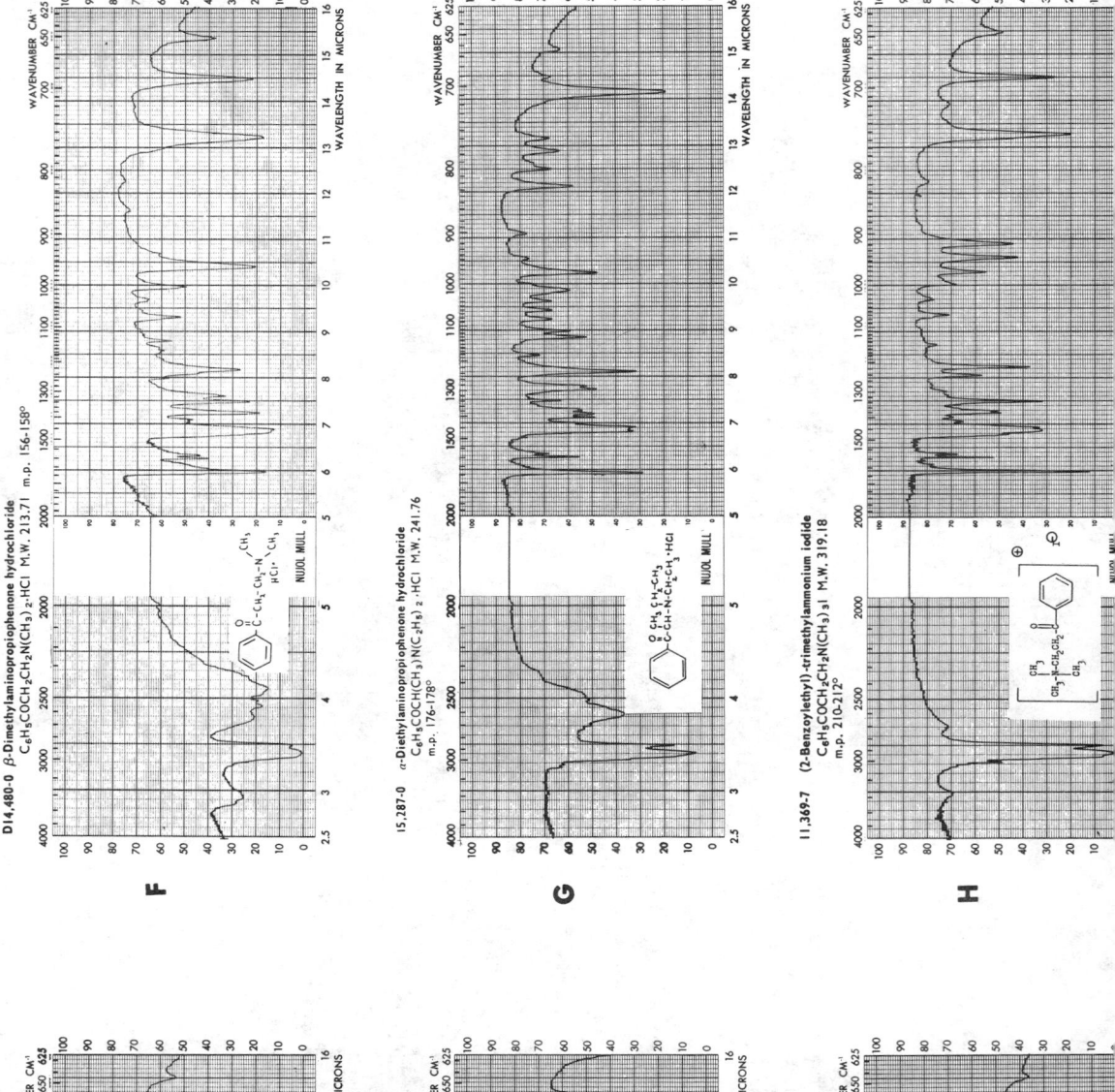

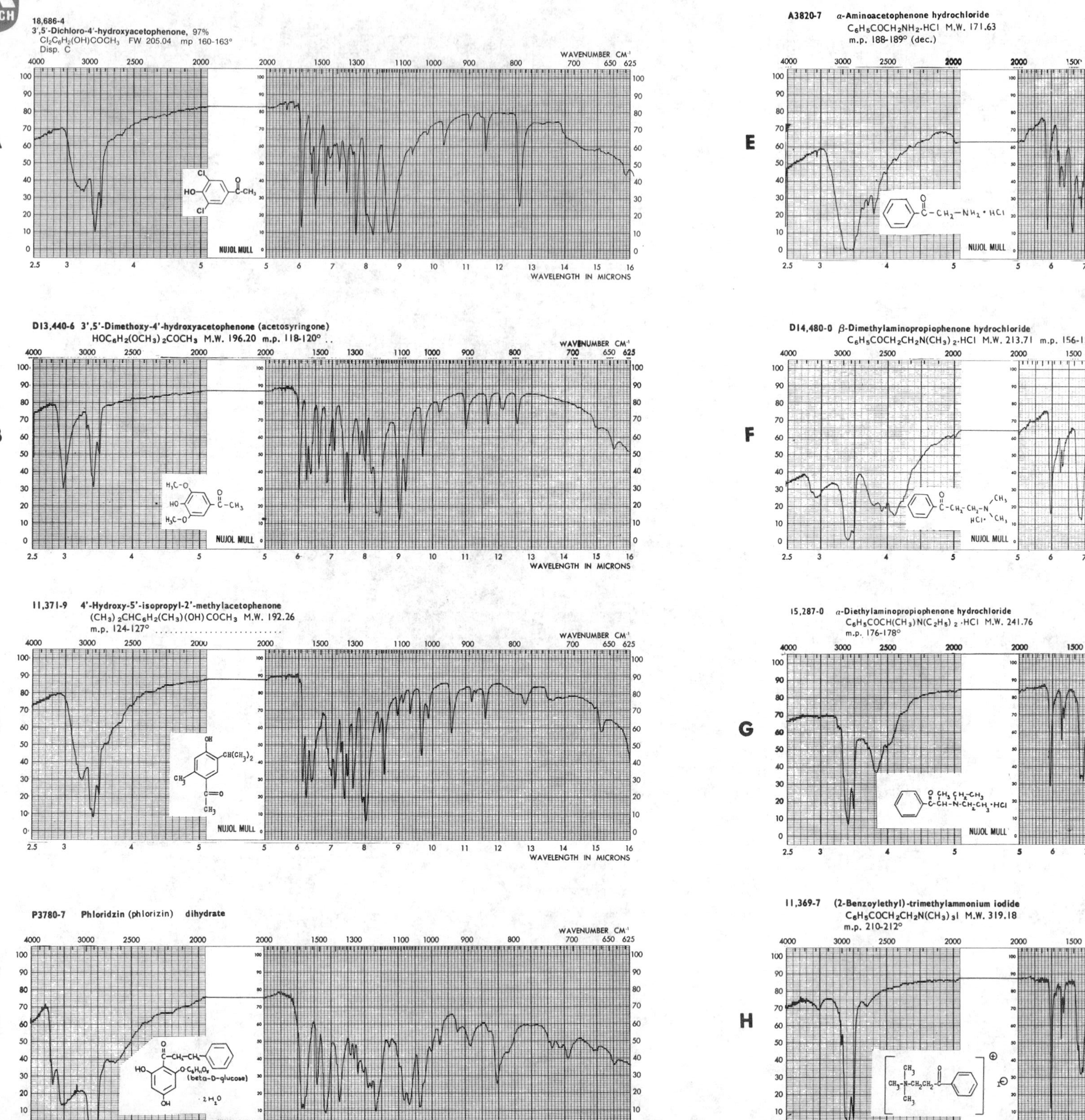

A 18,686-4 3',5'-Dichloro-4'-hydroxyacetophenone, 97% $Cl_2C_6H_2(OH)COCH_3$ FW 205.04 mp 160-163° Disp. C

B D13,440-6 3',5'-Dimethoxy-4'-hydroxyacetophenone (acetosyringone) $HOC_6H_2(OCH_3)_2COCH_3$ M.W. 196.20 m.p. 118-120°

C 11,371-9 4'-Hydroxy-5'-isopropyl-2'-methylacetophenone $(CH_3)_2CHC_6H_2(CH_3)(OH)COCH_3$ M.W. 192.26 m.p. 124-127°

D P3780-7 Phloridzin (phlorizin) dihydrate

E A3820-7 α-Aminoacetophenone hydrochloride $C_6H_5COCH_2NH_2{\cdot}HCl$ M.W. 171.63 m.p. 188-189° (dec.)

F D14,480-0 β-Dimethylaminopropiophenone hydrochloride $C_6H_5COCH_2CH_2N(CH_3)_2{\cdot}HCl$ M.W. 213.71 m.p. 156-158°

G 15,287-0 α-Diethylaminopropiophenone hydrochloride $C_6H_5COCH(CH_3)N(C_2H_5)_2{\cdot}HCl$ M.W. 241.76 m.p. 176-178°

H 11,369-7 (2-Benzoylethyl)-trimethylammonium iodide $C_6H_5COCH_2CH_2N(CH_3)_3I$ M.W. 319.18 m.p. 210-212°

A

M.W. 295.39 m.p. 129-132°

NUJOL MULL

B

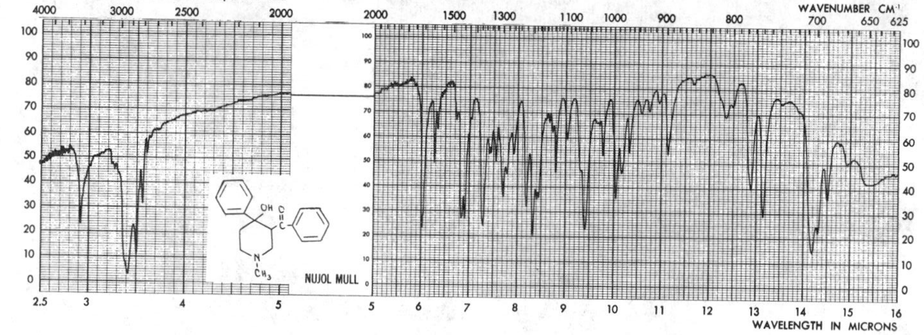

L325-0 **Lobelanine hydrochloride**
M.W. 371.91 m.p. 191-192° (dec.)

NUJOL MULL

C

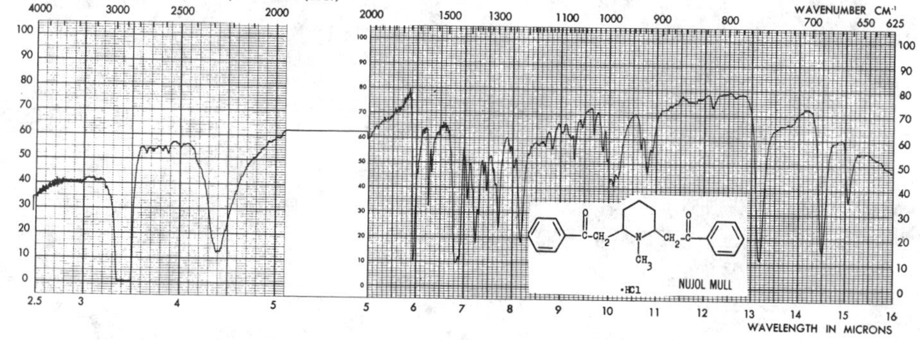

14,187-9 **Lobeline hydrochloride**
M.W. 373.93 m.p. 190-192°

NUJOL MULL

D

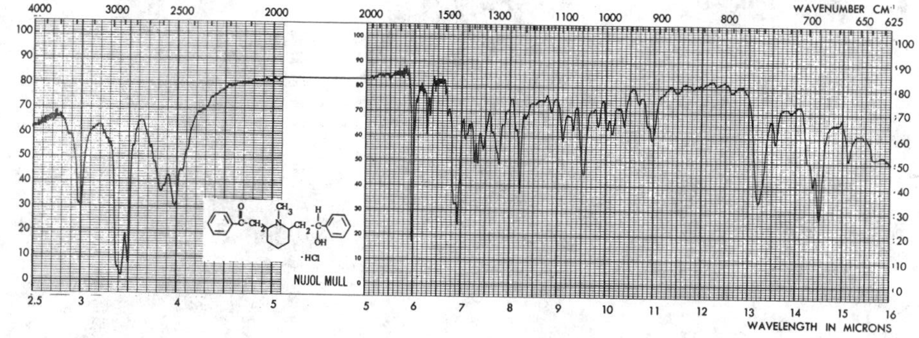

A3780-4 **o-Aminoacetophenone**
$H_2NC_6H_4COCH_3$ M.W. 135.17 n_D^{20} 1.6160
m.p. 16-18°

NEAT

E

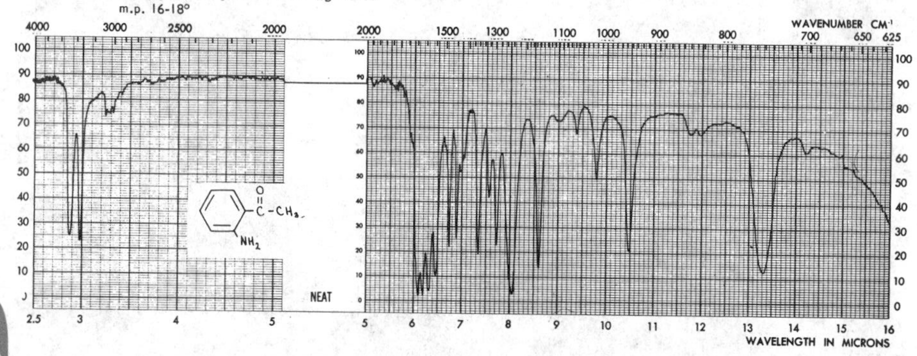

13,935-1 **m-Aminoacetophenone**
$H_2NC_6H_4COCH_3$ M.W. 135.17 m.p. 96-98°

NUJOL MULL

F

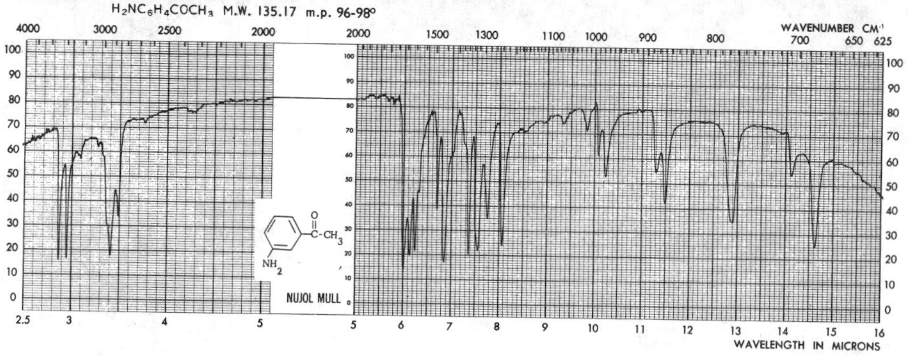

A3800-2 **p-Aminoacetophenone**
$H_2NC_6H_4COCH_3$ M.W. 135.17
m.p. 104-106°

NUJOL MULL

G

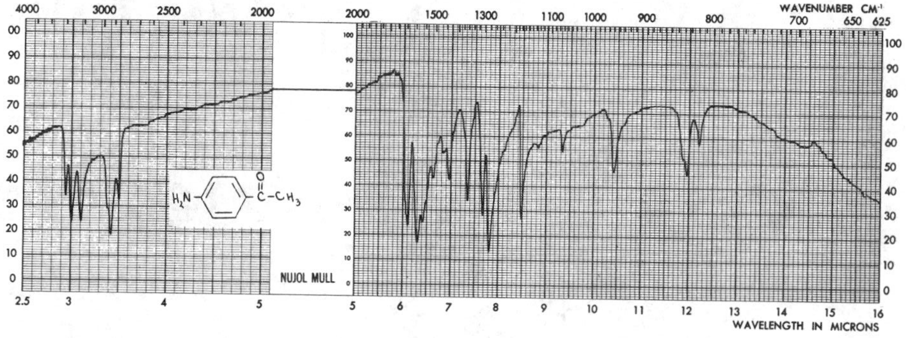

12,171-1 **4'-(γ-Dimethylaminopropylamino)-acetophenone**
$(CH_3)_2N(CH_2)_3NHC_6H_4COCH_3$ M.W. 220.32 n_D^{20} 1.5855
b.p. 150°/0.03 mm.

NEAT

H

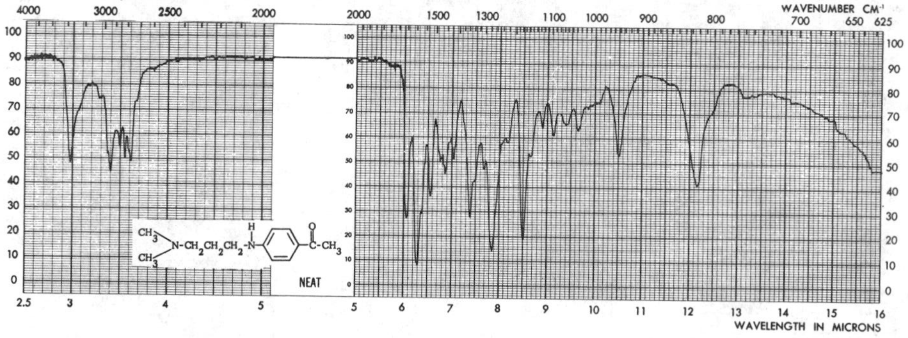

12,792-2 **p-(Phenethylamino)-acetophenone**
$C_6H_5CH_2CH_2NHC_6H_4COCH_3$ M.W. 239.32
m.p. 59-60°

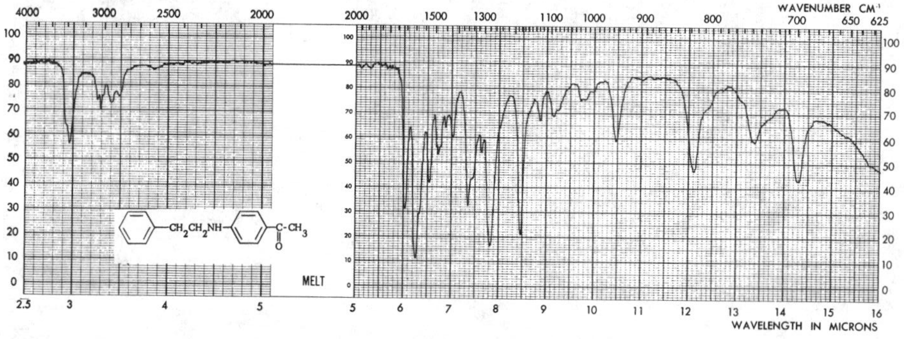

MELT

A — 12,798-1 p-(α-Methylphenethylamino)-acetophenone hydrochloride
$C_6H_5CH_2CH(CH_3)NHC_6H_4COCH_3 \cdot HCl$ M.W. 289.81 m.p. 142-145°

B — D13,947-5 4-Dimethylaminobenzoin (p-dimethylamino-α-hydroxy-α-phenylacetophenone)
$(CH_3)_2NC_6H_4COCH(OH)C_6H_5$ M.W. 255.32 m.p. 161-163°

C — 11,972-5 p-Piperidinoacetophenone
M.W. 203.29 m.p. 85-87°

D — 12,889-9 p-(3-Hydroxypiperidino)-acetophenone
M.W. 219.29 m.p. 93-95°

E — 12,890-2 p-(4-Hydroxypiperidino)-acetophenone
M.W. 219.29 m.p. 125-126.5°

F — 11,986-5 p-Morpholinoacetophenone
M.W. 205.26 m.p. 96-98°

G — 13,617-4 p-Morpholinopropiophenone
M.W. 219.29 m.p. 73-75°

H — 13,633-6 4'-Morpholinodeoxybenzoin (p-morpholino-α-phenylacetophenone)
M.W. 281.36 m.p. 131-135°

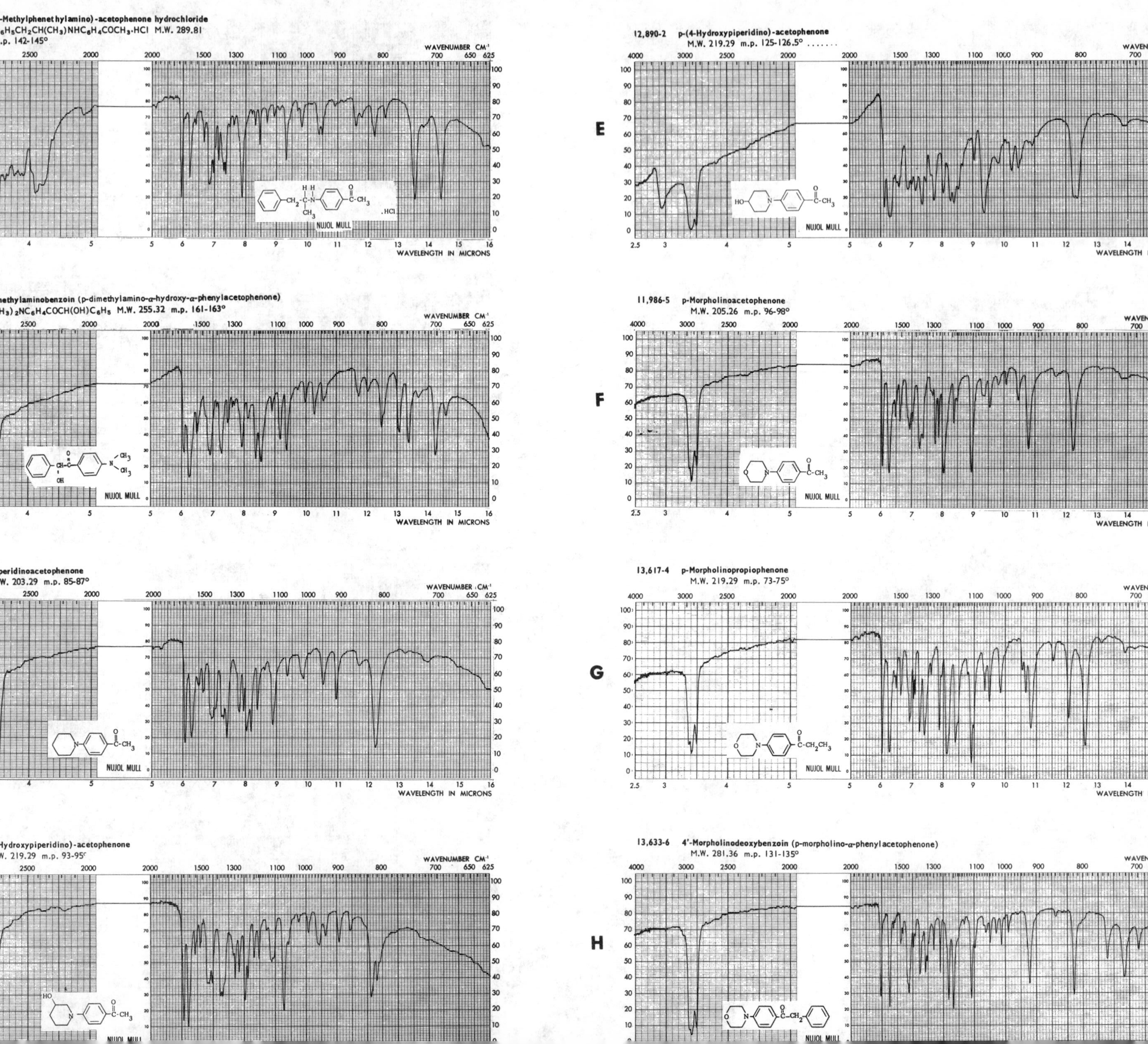

A 13,646-8 p-Piperazinoacetophenone
M.W. 204.27 m.p. 107-110°
NUJOL MULL

B 11,987-3 p-(4-Methylpiperazino)-acetophenone
M.W. 218.30 m.p. 96-98°
NUJOL MULL

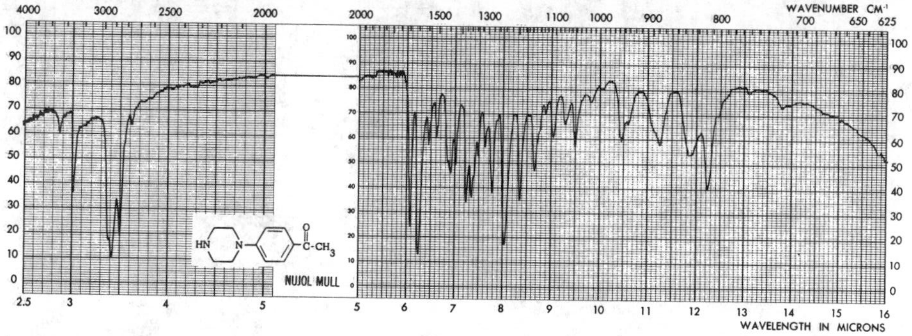

C 12,880-5 p-(N-2-Hydroxyethylpiperazino)-acetophenone
M.W. 248.33 m.p. 128-129.5°
NUJOL MULL

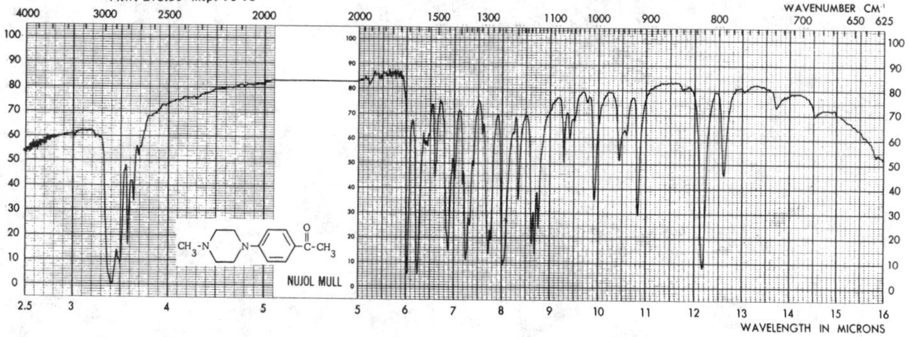

D 13,868-1 N,N'-Piperazinedi-p-acetophenone
M.W. 322.41 m.p. 274-276°
NUJOL MULL

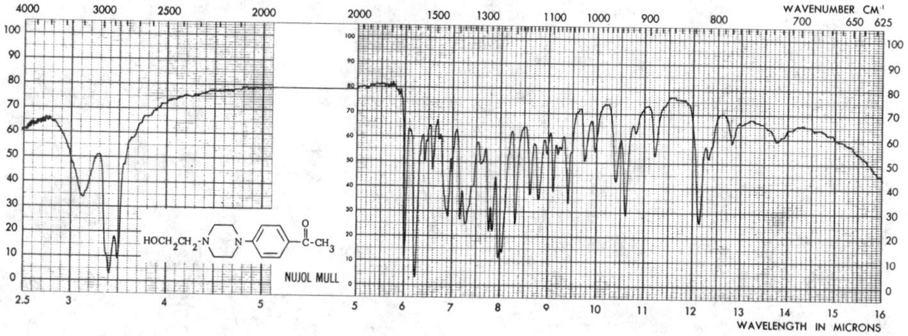

E 17,522-6 2-Acetylphenothiazine, 95%
M.W. 241.31 m.p. 180-185°
NUJOL MULL

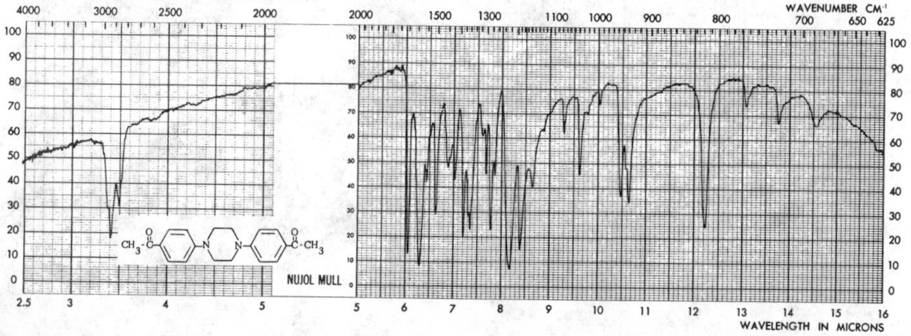

F A1690-4 5-Acetylindoline
M.W. 161.20 m.p. 74-76°
MELT

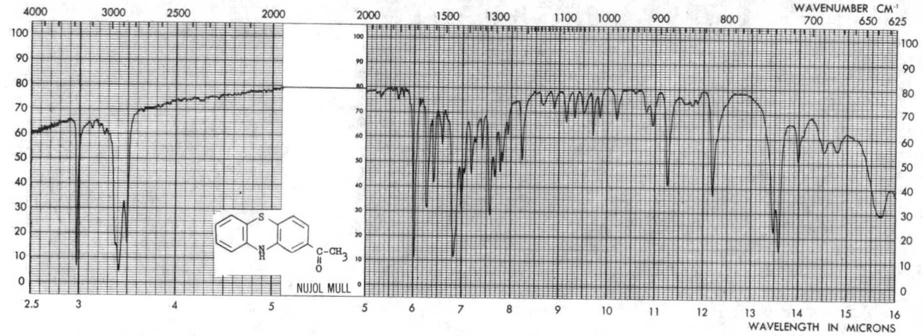

G N920-9 o-Nitroacetophenone
$O_2NC_6H_4COCH_3$ M.W. 165.15 n_D^{20} 1.5510 supercooled,
m.p. 28-30°
NEAT

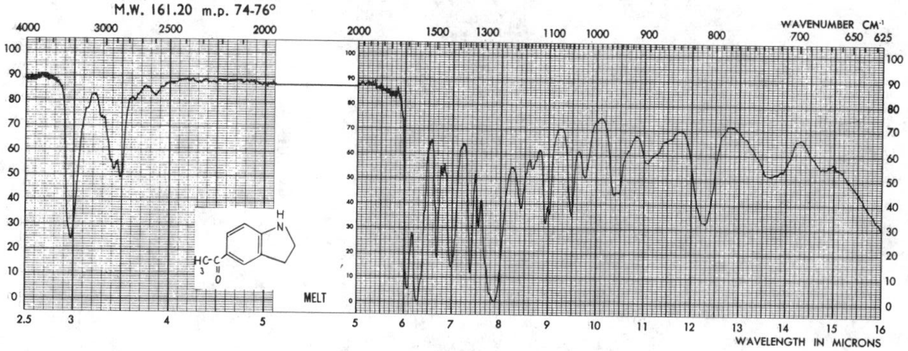

H N938-1 m-Nitroacetophenone
$O_2NC_6H_4COCH_3$ M.W. 165.15 m.p. 74-78°
NUJOL MULL

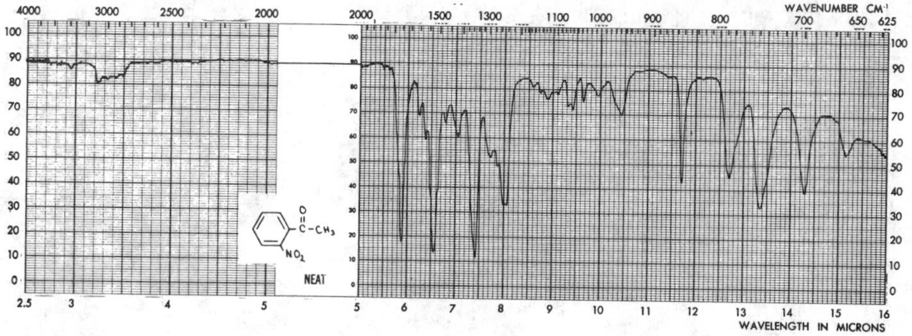

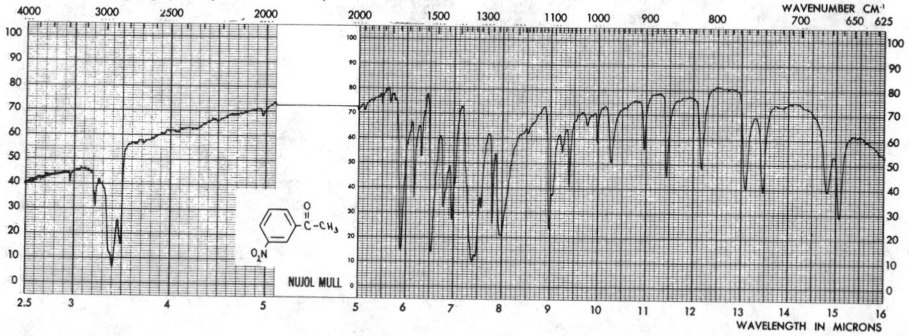

A 13,076-1 **m-Nitropropiophenone**
$O_2NC_6H_4COC_2H_5$ M.W. 179.18
m.p. 97-100°

B N960-8 **p-Nitroacetophenone**
$O_2NC_6H_4COCH_3$ M.W. 165.15 m.p. 80-82°

C 19,396-8
4'-Chloro-3'-nitroacetophenone
$ClC_6H_3(NO_2)COCH_3$ FW 199.60 mp 99-101°
Beil. **7**(3),995 Disp. C

D 12,510-5 **5'-Chloro-2'-nitroacetophenone**
$ClC_6H_3(NO_2)COCH_3$ M.W. 199.60 m.p. 58-60°

E 19,799-8
Methyl 4,5-dimethoxy-2-nitrobenzoate, 97% (methyl 6-nitroveratrate)
$O_2NC_6H_2(OCH_3)_2CO_2CH_3$ FW 241.20
mp 141-144° *Beil.* **10**,403 Disp. C

F 15,912-3
3-(Hexahydro-1H-azepin-1-yl)-3'-nitropropiophenone hydrochloride, 99%
M.W. 312.8 m.p. 172-174°

G 21,368-3
Tilorone Analog R 10,233 DA, 97% [2,7-bis(4-piperidinobutyryl)fluorene]
FW 472.68 mp 163-165° Disp. C

H 21,364-0
Tilorone Analog R 11,645 DA, 98%
[3,9-bis(dimethylaminoacetyl)fluoranthene dihydrochloride hydrate]
FW 445.38 mp >300° Disp. C

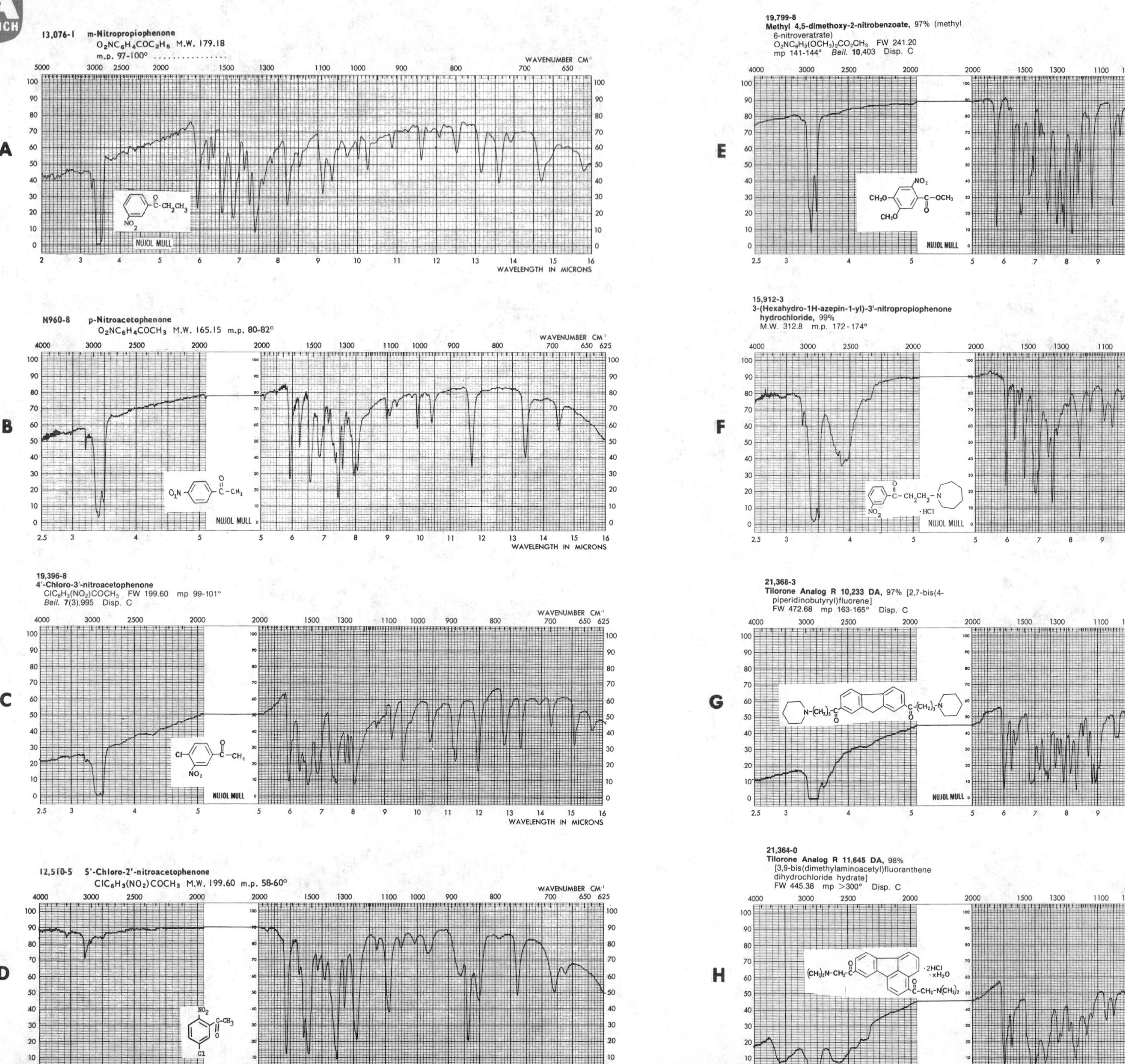

[2,7-bis(dimethylaminoacetyl)-9H-xanthene
dihydrochloride sesquihydrate]
FW 452.38 Disp. C

A

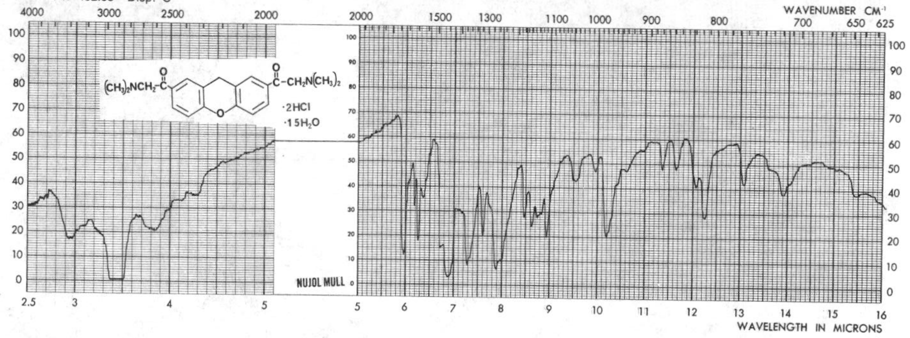

14,211-5
3-Dimethylamino-1-phenyl-2-propen-1-one, 98%
$(CH_3)_2NCH{=}CHCOC_6H_5$
M.W. 175.23 m.p. 92-94°

B

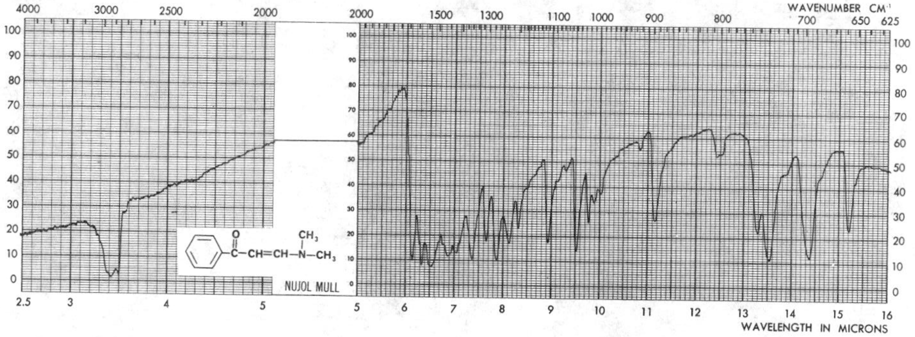

13,612-3 **Chalcone** (benzylideneacetophenone)
$C_6H_5CH{:}CHCOC_6H_5$ M.W. 208.26
m.p. 55-57°

C

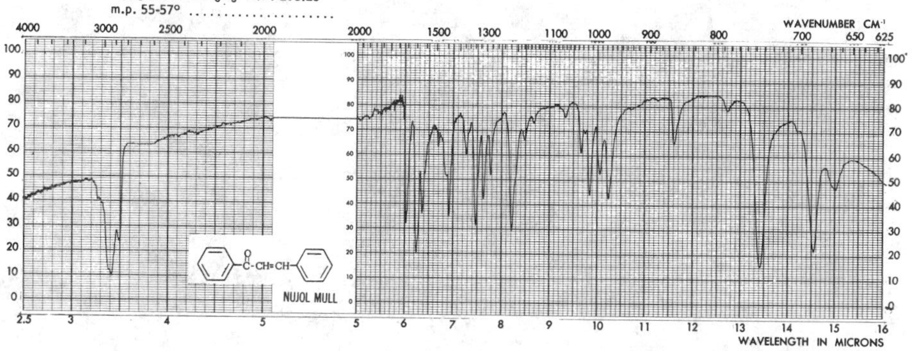

D3320-9 ***trans*-1,2-Dibenzoylethylene** (*trans*-1,4-diphenyl-2-butene-1,4-dione)
$C_6H_5COCH{:}CHCOC_6H_5$ M.W. 236.27 m.p. 108-111°

D

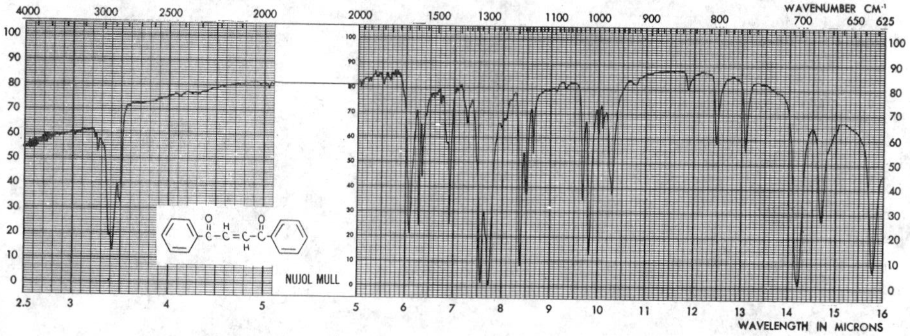

14,387-1 **4'-Fluorochalcone**
$C_6H_5CH{:}CHCOC_6H_4F$ M.W. 226.25
m.p. 79-81°

E

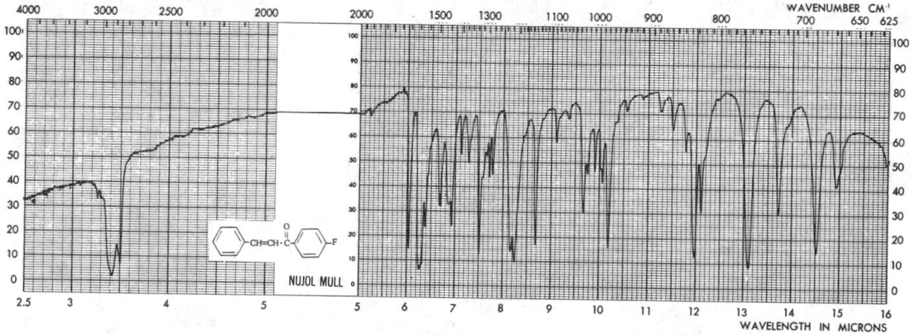

15,747-3
4'-Bromochalcone, 99%
$C_6H_5CH{=}CHCOC_6H_4Br$
M.W. 287.16 m.p. 103-105° Beil. 7(1),263

F

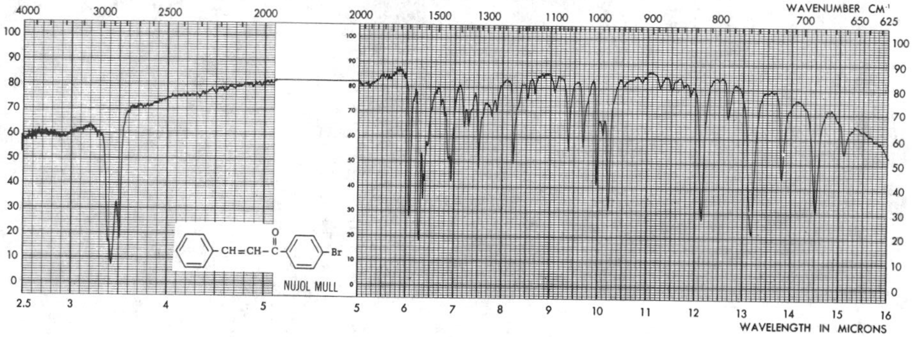

15,746-5
4'-Methoxychalcone, 97%
$C_6H_5CH{=}CHCOC_6H_4OCH_3$
M.W. 238.29 m.p. 101-103° Beil. 8,193

G

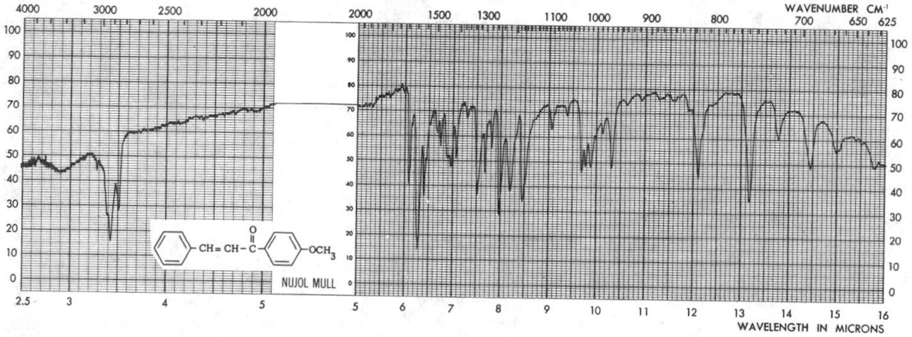

15,758-9
4-Methoxychalcone, 98%
$CH_3OC_6H_4CH{=}CHCOC_6H_5$
M.W. 238.29 m.p. 72-74° Beil. 8,192

H

ALDRICH

AROMATIC KETONES

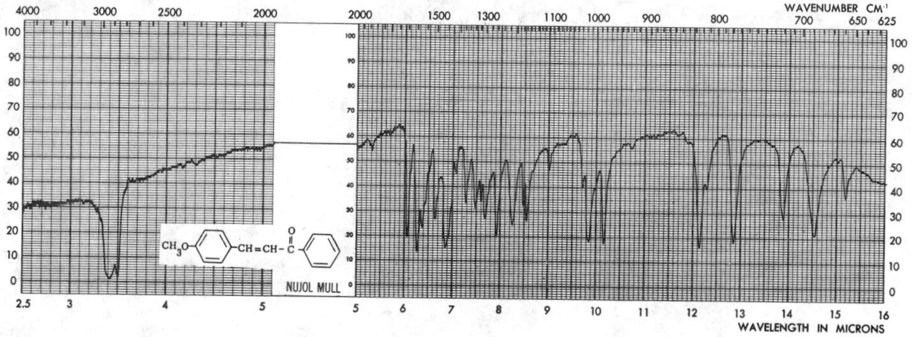

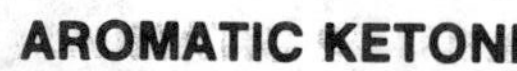

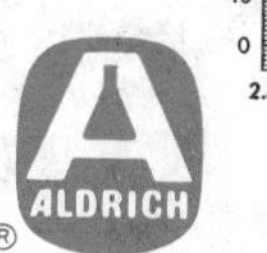

A

14,386-3 **2-Chloro-4'-fluorochalcone**
$ClC_6H_4CH:CHCOC_6H_4F$ M.W. 260.70
m.p. 84-87°

NUJOL MULL

B

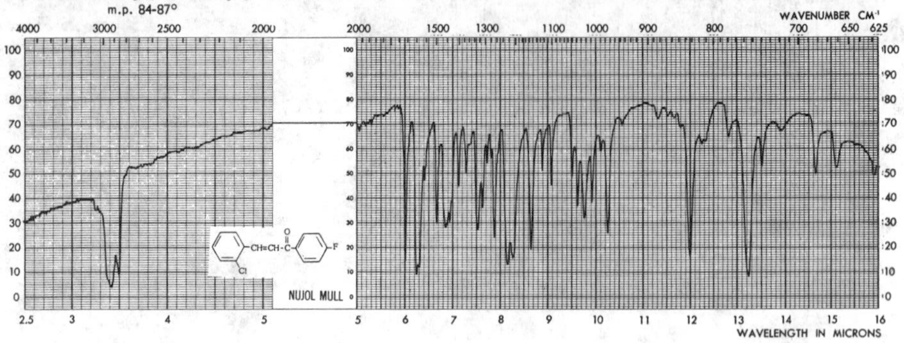

14,389-8 **4'-Fluoro-4-methoxychalcone**
$CH_3OC_6H_4CH:CHCOC_6H_4F$ M.W. 256.28
m.p. 104-107°

NUJOL MULL

C

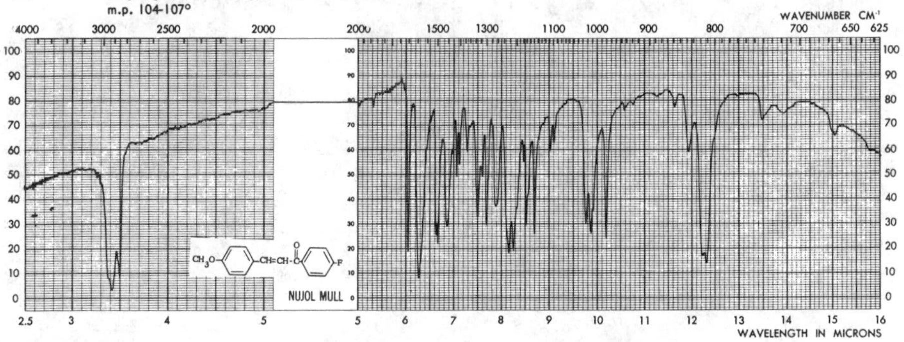

15,748-1
4-Nitrochalcone, 99%
$O_2NC_6H_4CH{=}CHCOC_6H_5$
M.W. 253.26 m.p. 158-160° Beil. 7,482

NUJOL MULL

D

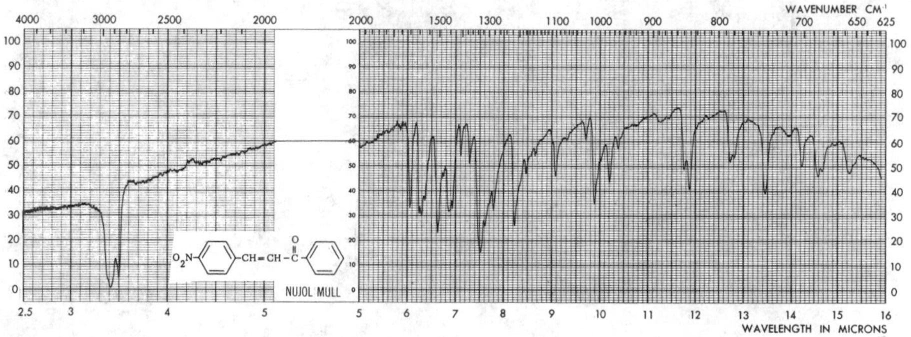

14,525-4 **4-Chloro-4'-fluoro-3-nitrochalcone**
$ClC_6H_3(NO_2)CH:CHCOC_6H_4F$ M.W. 305.70
m.p. 161-163°

E

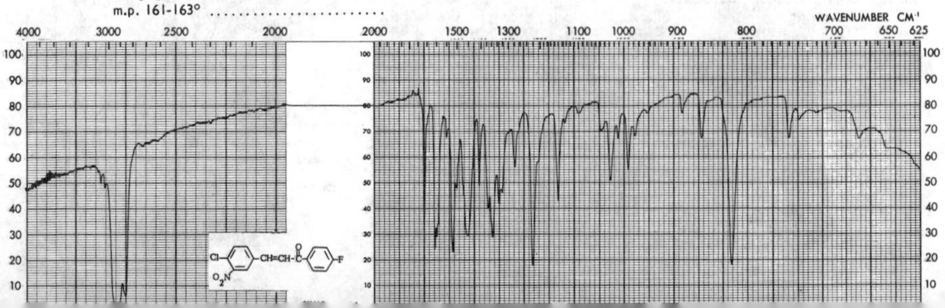

14,212-3 **3-Dimethylamino-1,2-diphenyl-2-propen-1-one**
$(CH_3)_2NCH:C(C_6H_5)COC_6H_5$ M.W. 251.33
m.p. 128-131°

NUJOL MULL

F

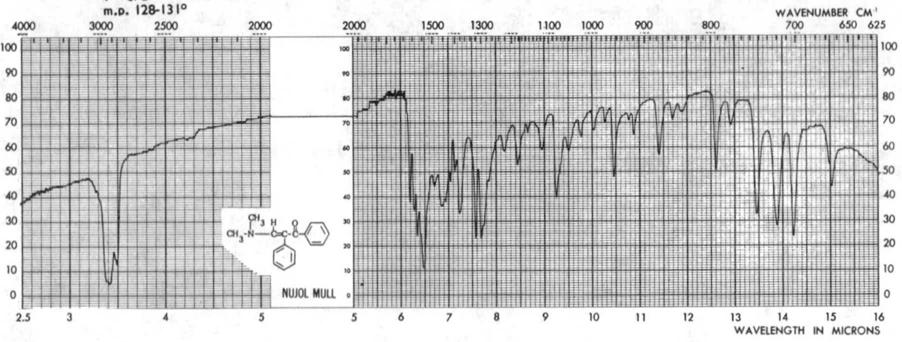

22,303-4
1-Phenyl-1,2-propanedione, 99%
$C_6H_5COCOCH_3$ FW 148.16 bp 103-105°/14mm.
n_D^{20} 1.5350 d 1.101 *Beil.* 7,677 Disp. C

NEAT

G

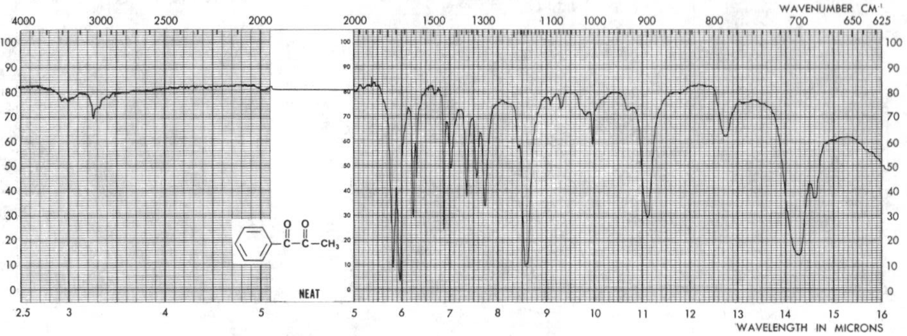

15,078-9 **Benzil, zone refined, 99.9 %, GOLD LABEL**
$C_6H_5COCOC_6H_5$ M.W. 210.23
m.p. 94.86°

NUJOL MULL

H

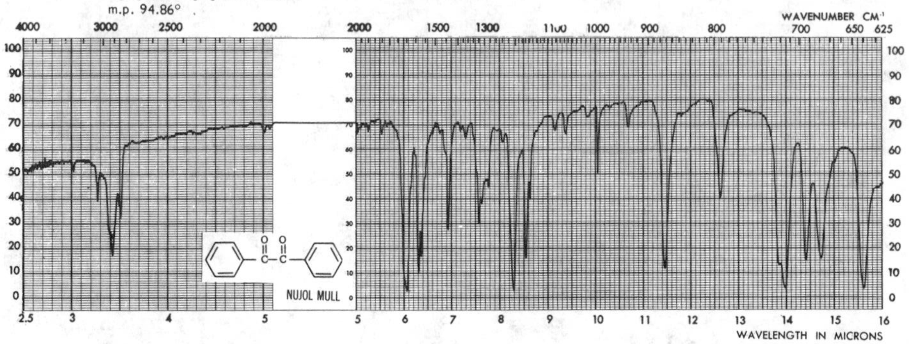

14,670-6 **4,4'-Dimethylbenzil**
$CH_3C_6H_4COCOC_6H_4CH_3$ M.W. 238.29
m.p. 102-103.5°

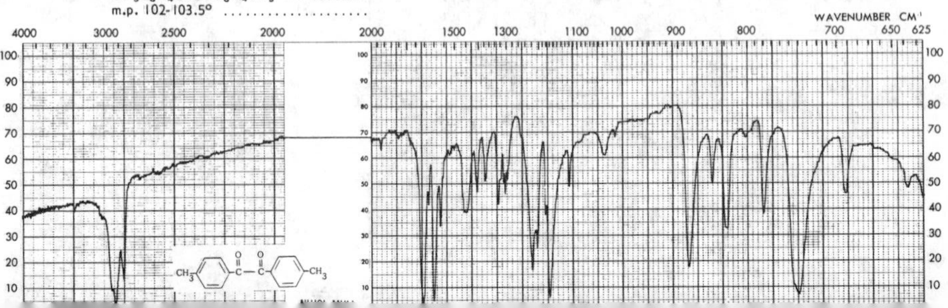

A

$CH_3OC_6H_4COCOC_6H_4OCH_3$
M.W. 270.28 m.p. 132-134° Beil. 8,428

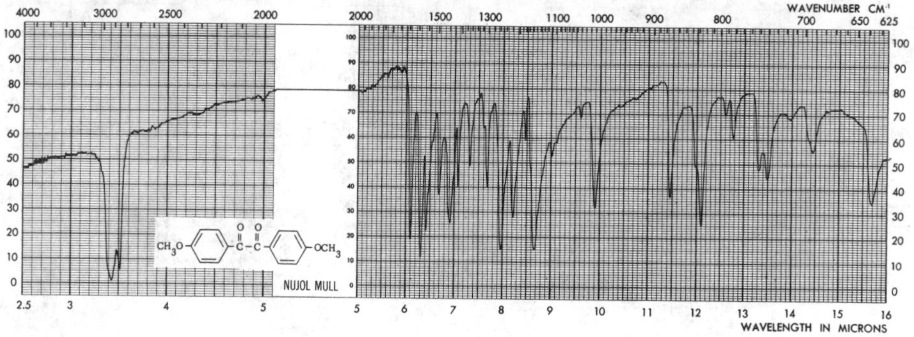

NUJOL MULL

B

B1190-7 **1-Benzoylacetone** (1-phenyl-1,3-butanedione)
$C_6H_5COCH_2COCH_3$ M.W. 162.19 m.p. 58-60°

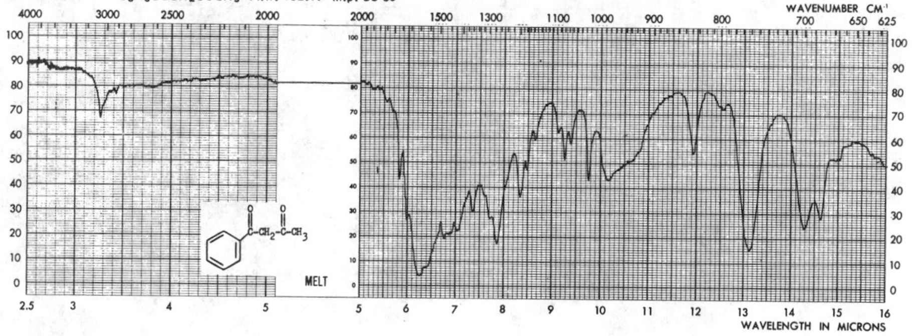

MELT

C

21,704-2
4,4,4-Trifluoro-1-phenyl-1,3-butanedione, 99%
$C_6H_5COCH_2COCF_3$ FW 216.16 mp 38-40°
bp 224° *Beil.* 7(3),3490 Disp. C

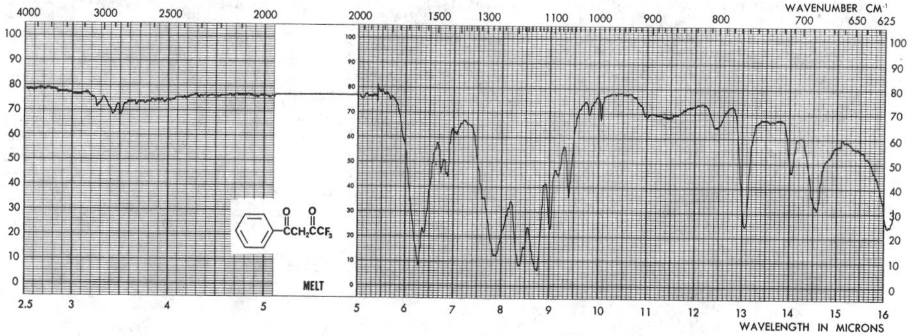

MELT

D

B2420-0 **3-Benzylidene-2,4-pentanedione, puriss.**
$CH_3COC(:CHC_6H_5)COCH_3$ M.W. 188.23
n_D^{20} 1.5821

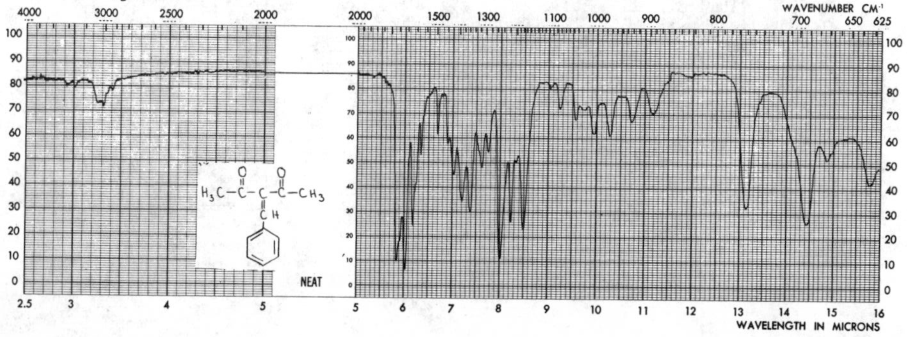

NEAT

E

I-200-2 **1,3-Indandione**
M.W. 146.15 m.p. 129-132°

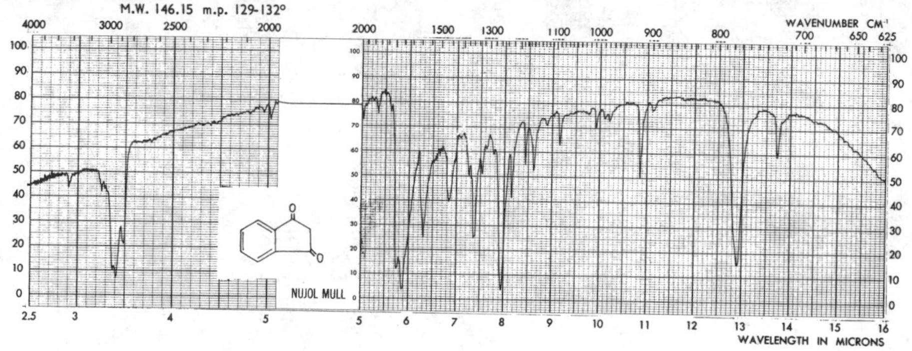

NUJOL MULL

F

N1740-8 **2-Nitro-1,3-indanedione**, reagent for organic bases and amino acids
M.W. 191.14 m.p. 127° (dec.)

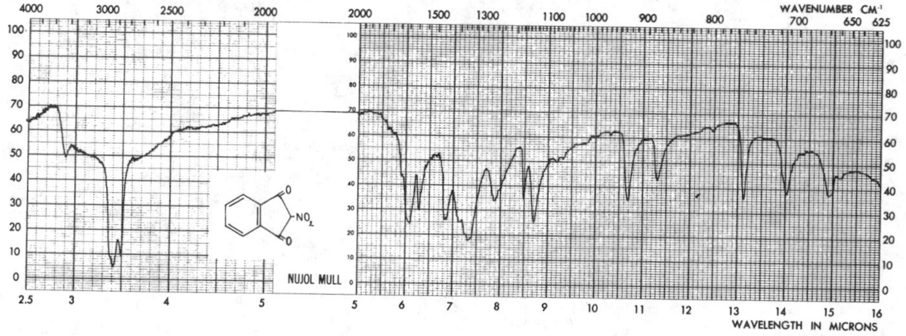

NUJOL MULL

G

P2640-6 **2-Phenyl-1,3-indandione**
M.W. 222.24 m.p. 148-150°

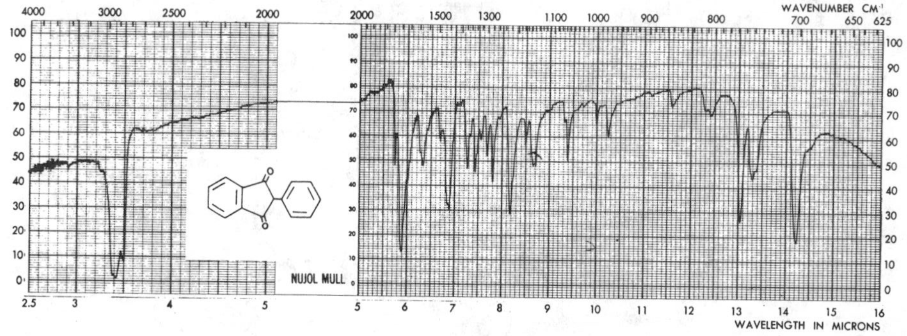

NUJOL MULL

H

B3460-5 **Bindone** (bisindanedione)
M.W. 274.28 m.p. 208-211°

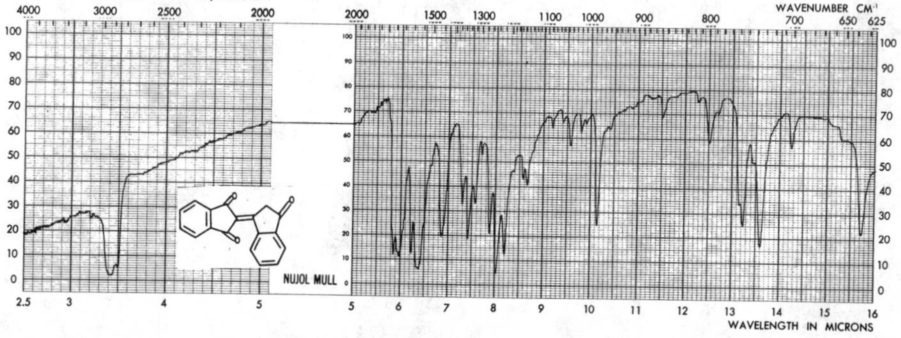

NUJOL MULL

AROMATIC KETONES

A 15,037-1 2-Acetyl-1-tetralone
M.W. 188.23 m.p. 55-57°
MELT

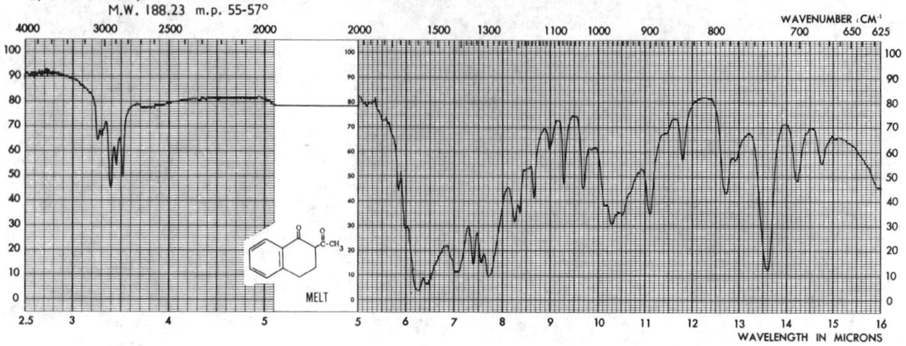

B U340-3 *l*-Usnic acid
M.W. 344.32 m.p. 205-208° $[\alpha]^{23}_{D}$ - 514°
(c=0.7, $CHCl_3$)
NUJOL MULL

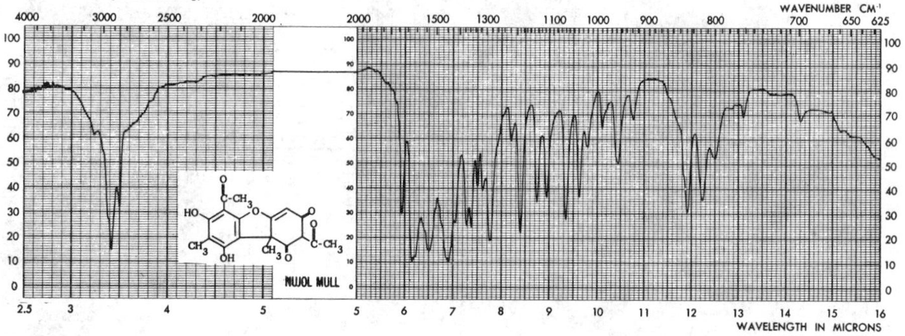

C 15,117-3 Ninhydrin (1,2,3-triketohydrindene hydrate), puriss., spectrophotometric grade
M.W. 178.14 m.p. 250° (dec.)
NUJOL MULL

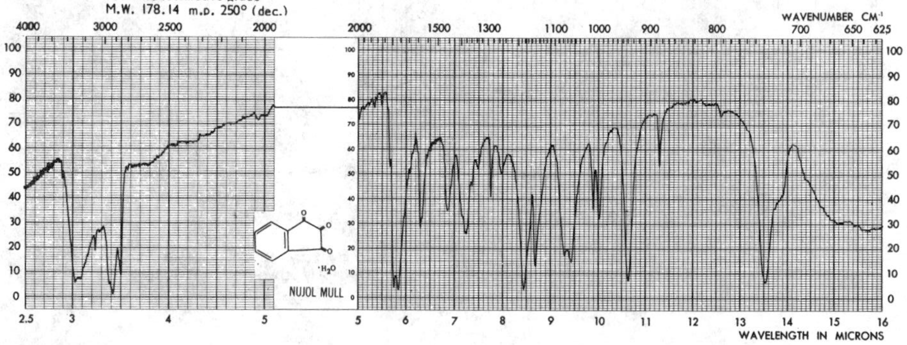

D D20,483-8 2-Diphenylacetyl-1,3-indandione-1-hydrazone
M.W. 354.39 m.p. 241-243°

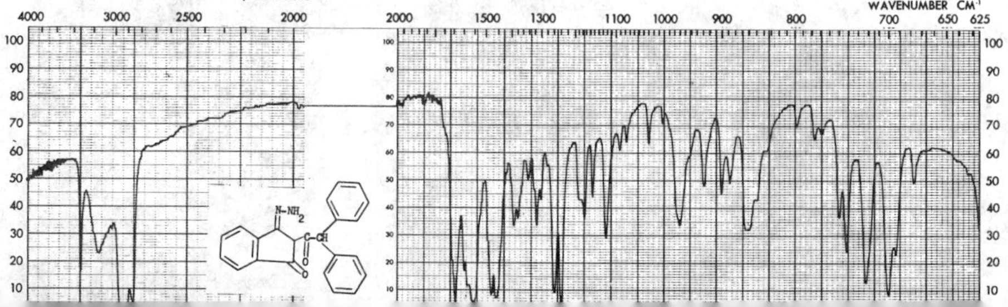

E D20,900-7 2,3-Diphenyl-1-indenone
M.W. 282.34 m.p. 149-152°
NUJOL MULL

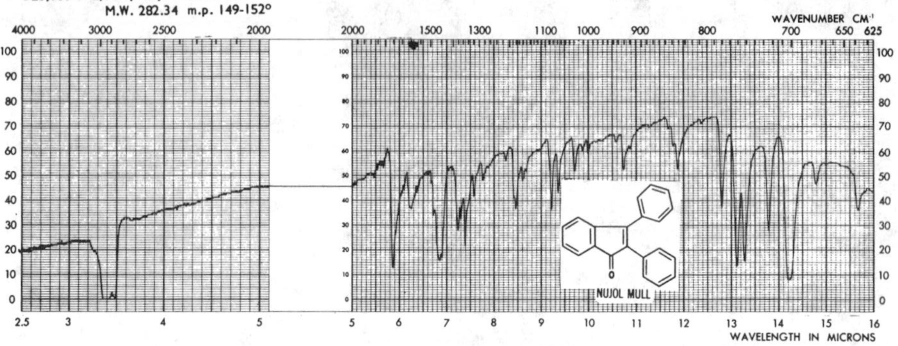

F I-233-9 2-Indanylidene-1-indanone [($\Delta^{1,2'}$-biindan)-1'-one]
M.W. 246.31 m.p. 142-143°
NUJOL MULL

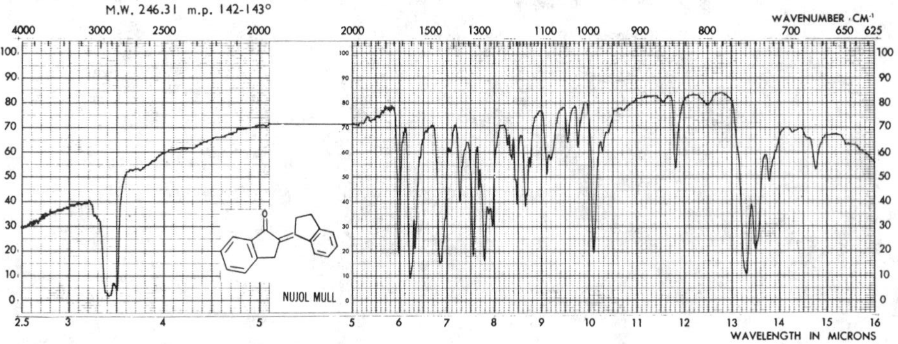

G H1730-9 Hydrindantin (2,2'-dihydroxy-2,2'-biindan-1,1',3,3'-tetrone), anhydrous
M.W. 322.28 m.p. 260-263°
NUJOL MULL

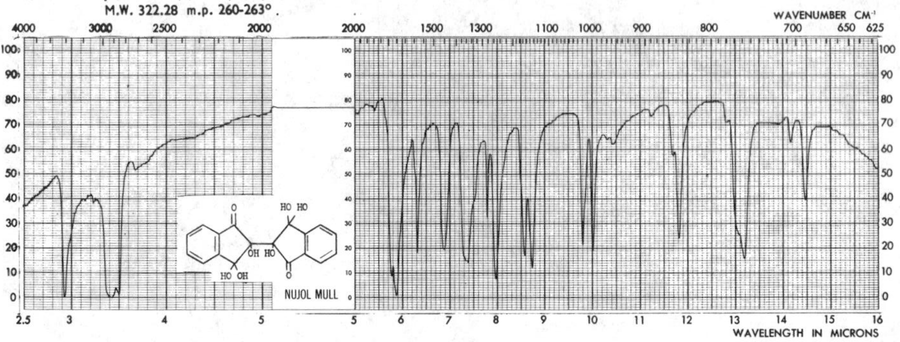

H 13,563-1 Hydrindantin (2,2',3,3,3',3'-hexahydroxy-2,2'-biindan-1,1'-dione) dihydrate
M.W. 358.31 m.p. 258-259°

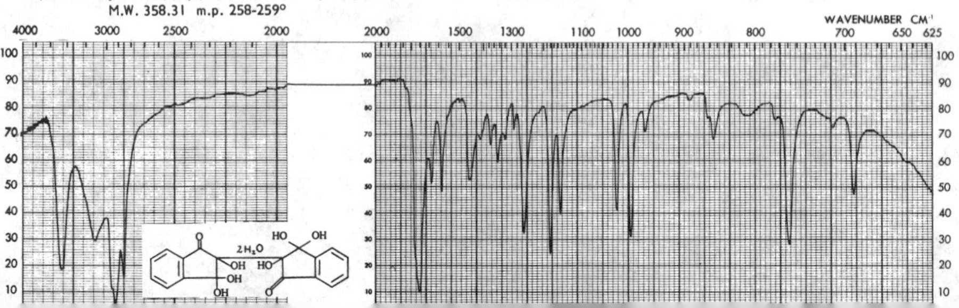

P1080-1 Perinaphthenone
M.W. 180.21 m.p. 153-156°

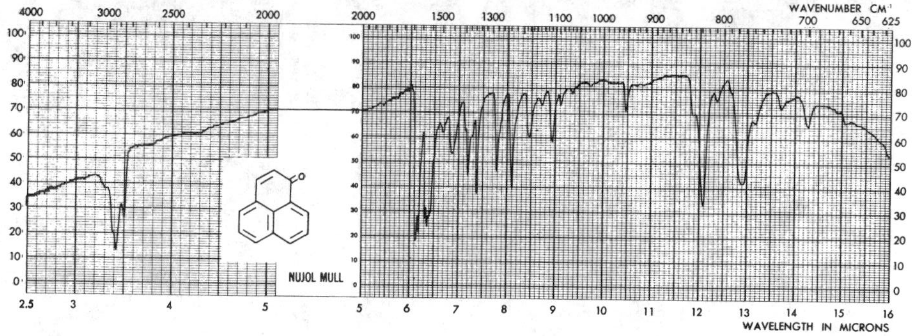

A — NUJOL MULL

22,220-8
5,6,8,9-Tetrahydrobenz[*a*]anthracen-11(10*H*)-one, 99%
FW 248.33 mp 98-99° *Beil.* **7**(3),2586 Disp. C

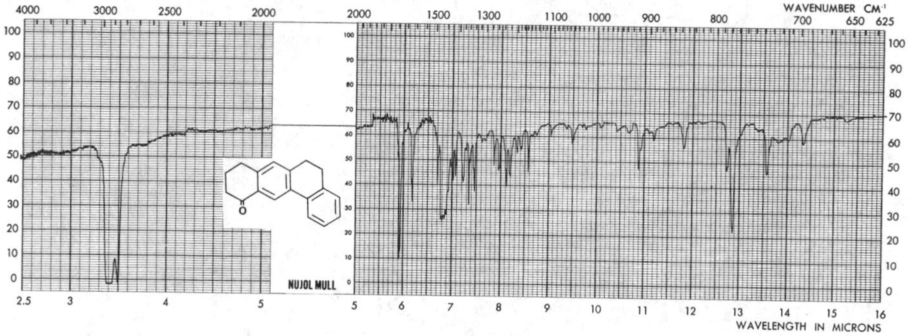

B — NUJOL MULL

18,816-6
3,4-Dihydrobenz[*a*]anthracen-1(2*H*)-one
FW 246.31 mp 113-116° Disp. C

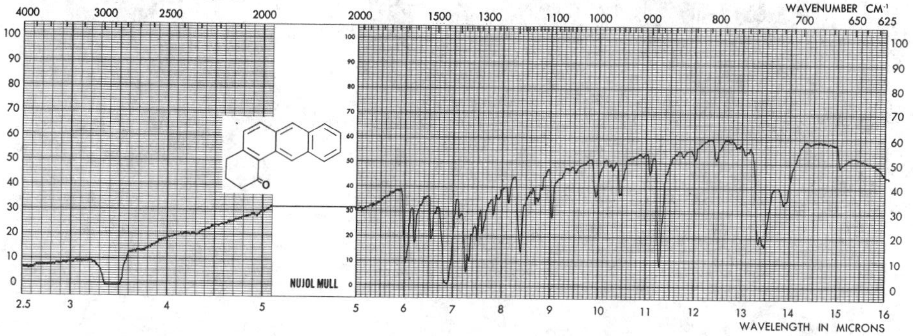

C — NUJOL MULL

19,033-0
1,2,3,6,7,8,11,12-Octahydrobenzo[*e*]pyren-9(10*H*)-one, 99+%
FW 276.38 mp 146-148° Disp. C

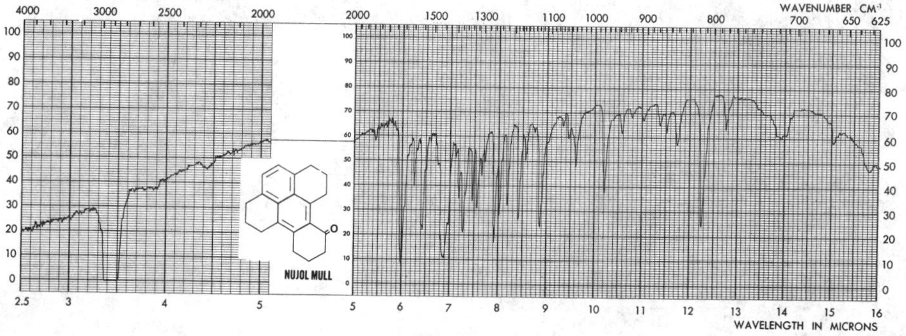

D — NUJOL MULL

B930-0 Benzophenone
$(C_6H_5)_2CO$ M.W. 182.22 m.p. 48-49.5°

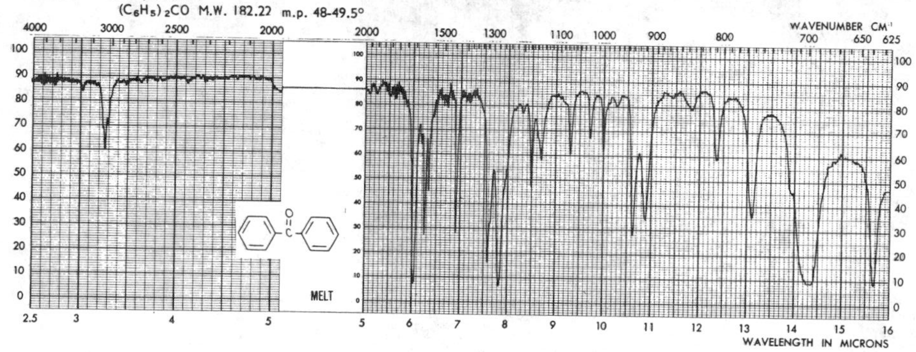

E — MELT

B515-1
Benzil
$C_6H_5COCOC_6H_5$
M.W. 210.23 m.p. 94-95°

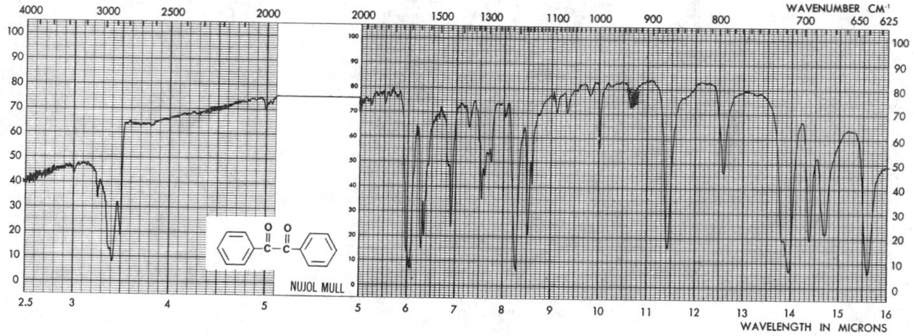

F — NUJOL MULL

D3260-1 o-Dibenzoylbenzene (2-benzoylbenzophenone)
$C_6H_4(COC_6H_5)_2$ M.W. 286.33 m.p. 146-147°

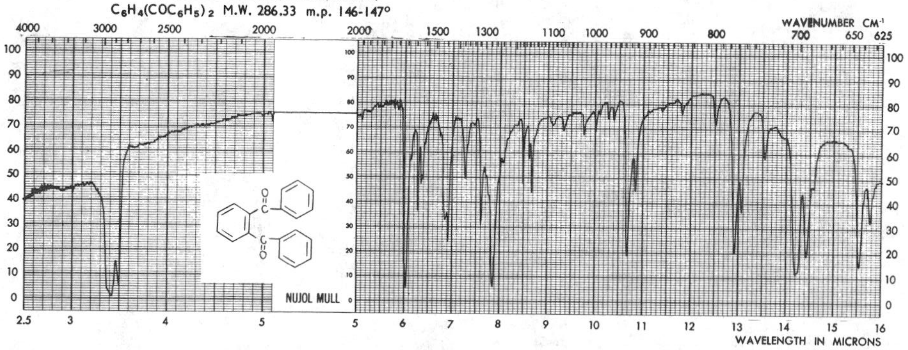

G — NUJOL MULL

B1260-1 4-Benzoylbiphenyl (p-phenylbenzophenone) see also Hammett Indicators
$C_6H_5C_6H_4COC_6H_5$ M.W. 258.32
m.p. 94-100°

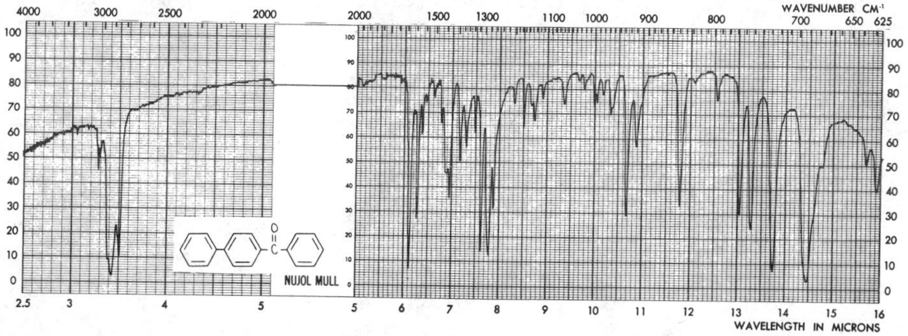

H — NUJOL MULL

AROMATIC KETONES

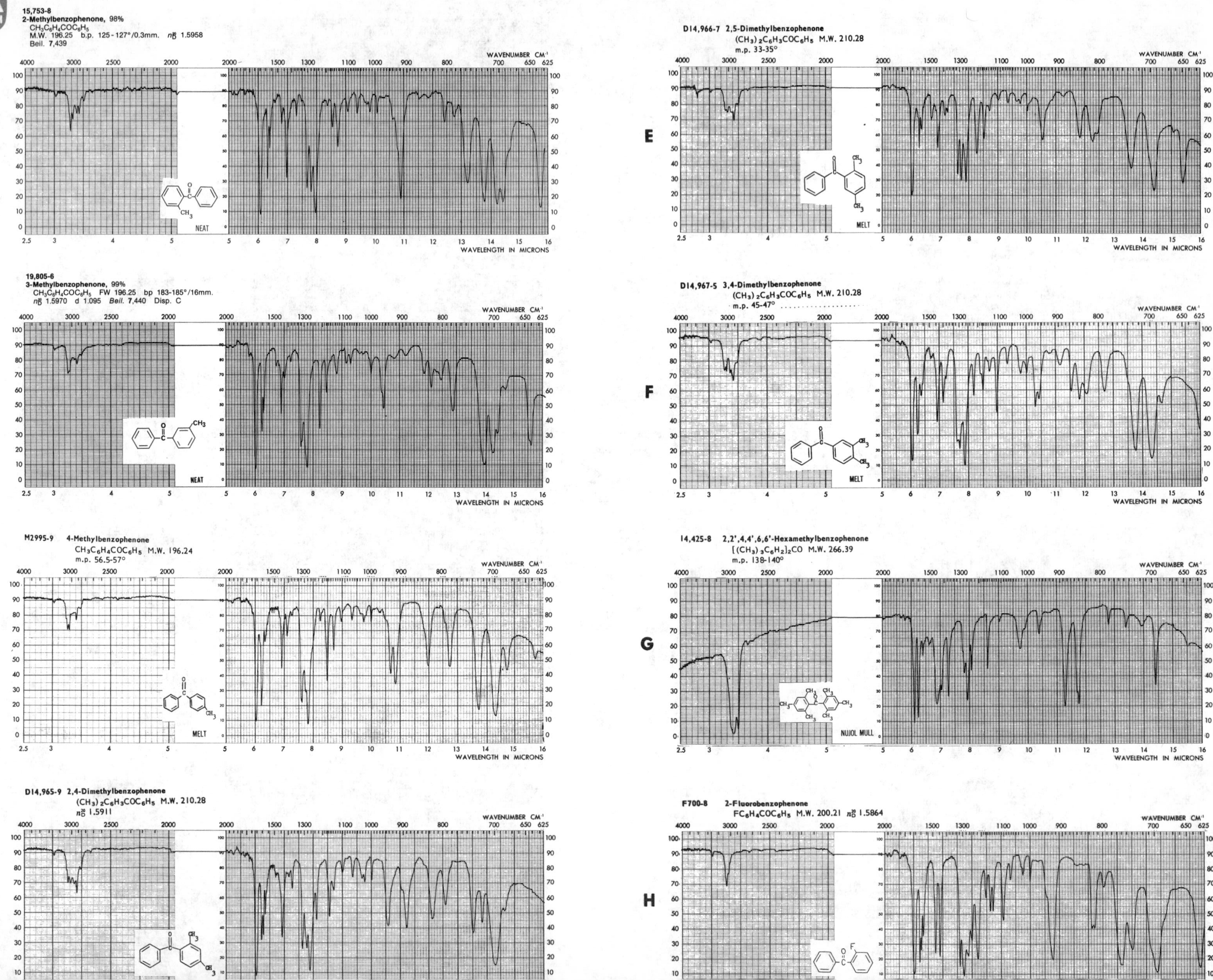

A 15,753-8 **2-Methylbenzophenone, 98%**
$CH_3C_6H_4COC_6H_5$
M.W. 196.25 b.p. 125-127°/0.3mm. n_D^{20} 1.5958
Beil. 7,439
NEAT

B 19,805-6 **3-Methylbenzophenone, 99%**
$CH_3C_6H_4COC_6H_5$ FW 196.25 bp 183-185°/16mm.
n_D^{20} 1.5970 d 1.095 *Beil.* 7,440 Disp. C
NEAT

C M2995-9 **4-Methylbenzophenone**
$CH_3C_6H_4COC_6H_5$ M.W. 196.24
m.p. 56.5-57°
MELT

D D14,965-9 **2,4-Dimethylbenzophenone**
$(CH_3)_2C_6H_3COC_6H_5$ M.W. 210.28
n_D^{20} 1.5911

E D14,966-7 **2,5-Dimethylbenzophenone**
$(CH_3)_2C_6H_3COC_6H_5$ M.W. 210.28
m.p. 33-35°
MELT

F D14,967-5 **3,4-Dimethylbenzophenone**
$(CH_3)_2C_6H_3COC_6H_5$ M.W. 210.28
m.p. 45-47°
MELT

G 14,425-8 **2,2',4,4',6,6'-Hexamethylbenzophenone**
$[(CH_3)_3C_6H_2]_2CO$ M.W. 266.39
m.p. 138-140°
NUJOL MULL

H F700-8 **2-Fluorobenzophenone**
$FC_6H_4COC_6H_5$ M.W. 200.21 n_D^{20} 1.5864

AROMATIC KETONES

A

$FC_6H_4COC_6H_5$ M.W. 200.21 m.p. 43-45°

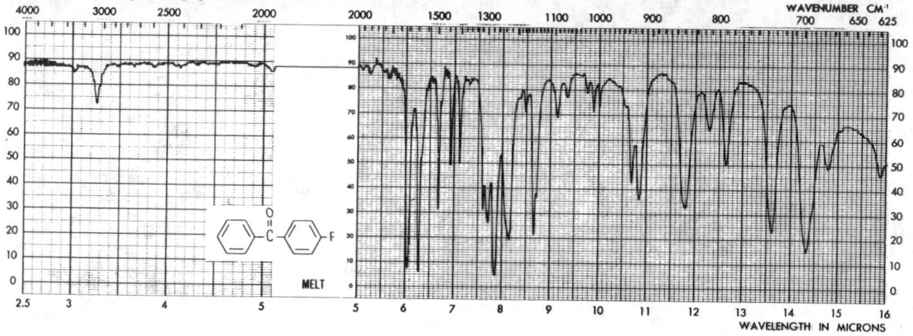

MELT

B

19,438-7
2-Chlorobenzophenone, 99+%
$ClC_6H_4COC_6H_5$ FW 216.67 mp 44-47° bp 330°
Beil. 7,419 Disp. C

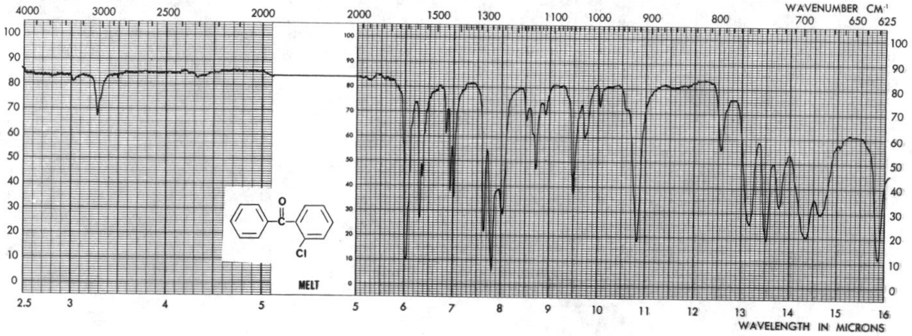

MELT

C

C2500-7 4-Chlorobenzophenone
$ClC_6H_4COC_6H_5$ M.W. 216.67 m.p. 75-77°

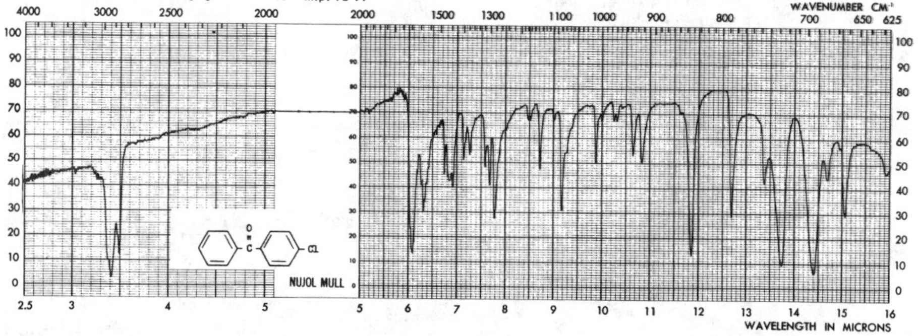

NUJOL MULL

D

B5860-1 4-Bromobenzophenone
$BrC_6H_4COC_6H_5$ M.W. 261.12 m.p. 80-82.5°

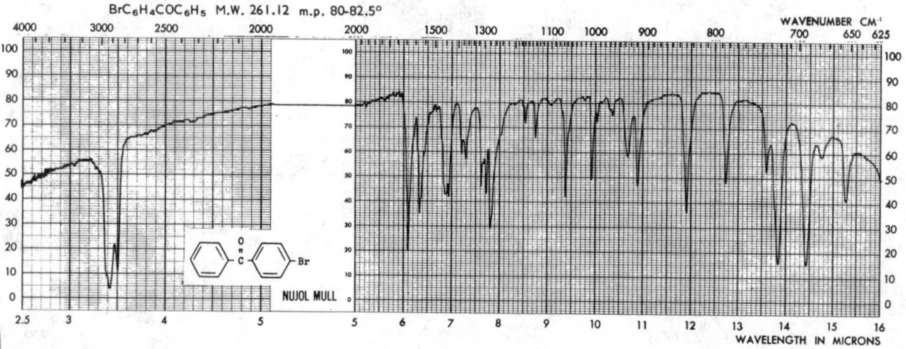

NUJOL MULL

E

11,549-5 4,4'-Difluorobenzophenone
$(FC_6H_4)_2CO$ M.W. 218.21 m.p. 104-108°

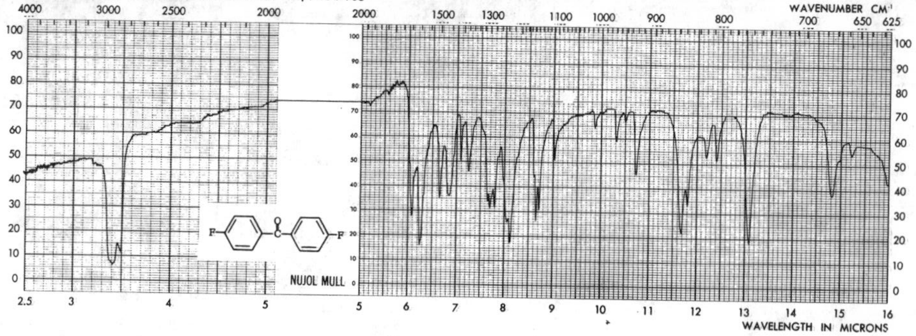

NUJOL MULL

F

11,370-0 4,4'-Dichlorobenzophenone
$(ClC_6H_4)_2CO$ M.W. 251.10 m.p. 147-148°

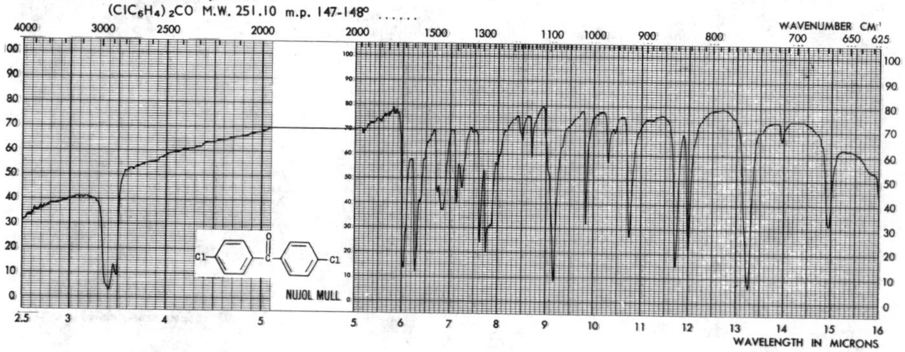

NUJOL MULL

G

11,548-7 4-Bromo-4'-chlorobenzophenone
$BrC_6H_4COC_6H_4Cl$ M.W. 295.57
m.p. 147-148.5°

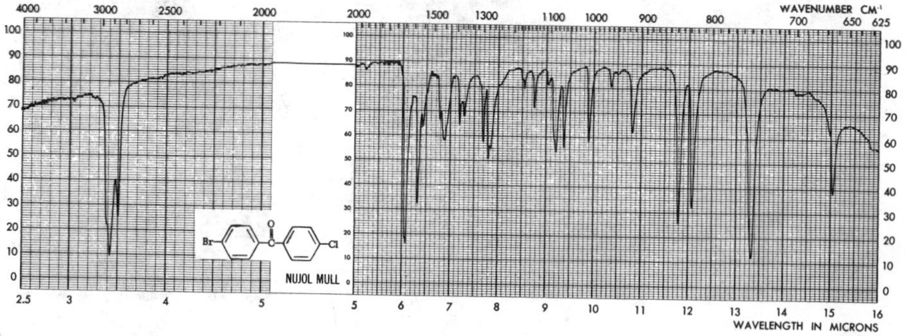

NUJOL MULL

H

13,621-2 2-Chloro-4'-fluorobenzophenone
$ClC_6H_4COC_6H_4F$ M.W. 234.66 m.p. 60-62°

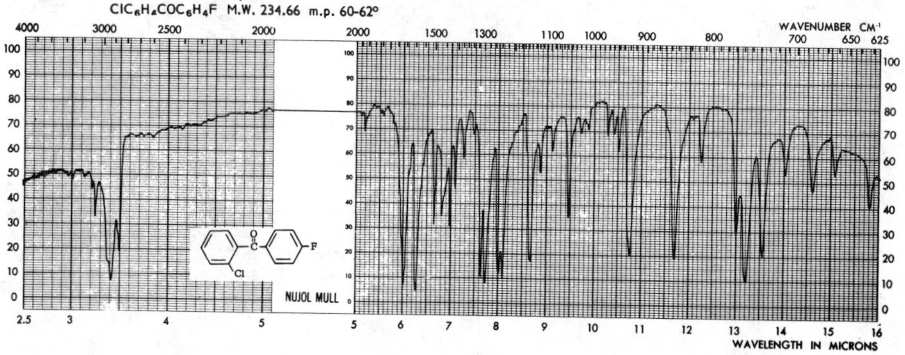

NUJOL MULL

(Each spectrum: WAVENUMBER CM⁻¹ 4000–625; WAVELENGTH IN MICRONS 2.5–16; transmittance 0–100)

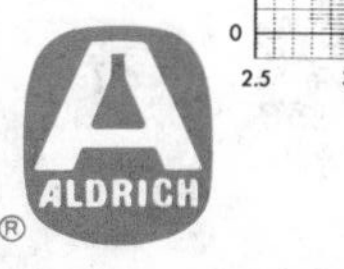

ALDRICH ®

A 22,269-0
2,4'-Difluorobenzophenone, 98%
$(FC_6H_4)_2CO$ FW 218.20 mp 22-24°
bp 176-178°/16mm. n_D^{20} 1.5689 d 1.244
Beil. 7(3),2070 Disp. C
NEAT

B 13,609-3 **2,4-Dichloro-4'-fluorobenzophenone**
$Cl_2C_6H_3COC_6H_4F$ M.W. 269.10 n_D^{20} 1.6015
b.p. 150°/0.1 mm.
NEAT

C 19,673-8
2,3,4,5,6-Pentafluorobenzophenone, 98%
$C_6F_5COC_6H_5$ FW 272.18 mp 36-39°
bp 93°/0.200mm. Disp. C
MELT

D 10,189-3 **Decafluorobenzophenone**
$(C_6F_5)_2CO$ M.W. 362.12 m.p. 92-94.5°
NUJOL MULL

E M1030-1 **4-Methoxybenzophenone**
$CH_3OC_6H_4COC_6H_5$ M.W. 212.25 m.p. 58-60°
MELT

F 14,198-4 **4,4'-Dimethoxybenzophenone**
$(CH_3OC_6H_4)_2CO$ M.W. 242.27
m.p. 141-143°
NUJOL MULL

G 14,101-1
4,4'-Dimethoxythiobenzophenone
$(CH_3OC_6H_4)_2CS$
M.W. 258.34 m.p. 118-120° Beil. 8,319
NUJOL MULL

H 13,870-3 **2,4,6-Trimethoxybenzophenone**
$(CH_3O)_3C_6H_2COC_6H_5$ M.W. 272.30
m.p. 110-113°
NUJOL MULL

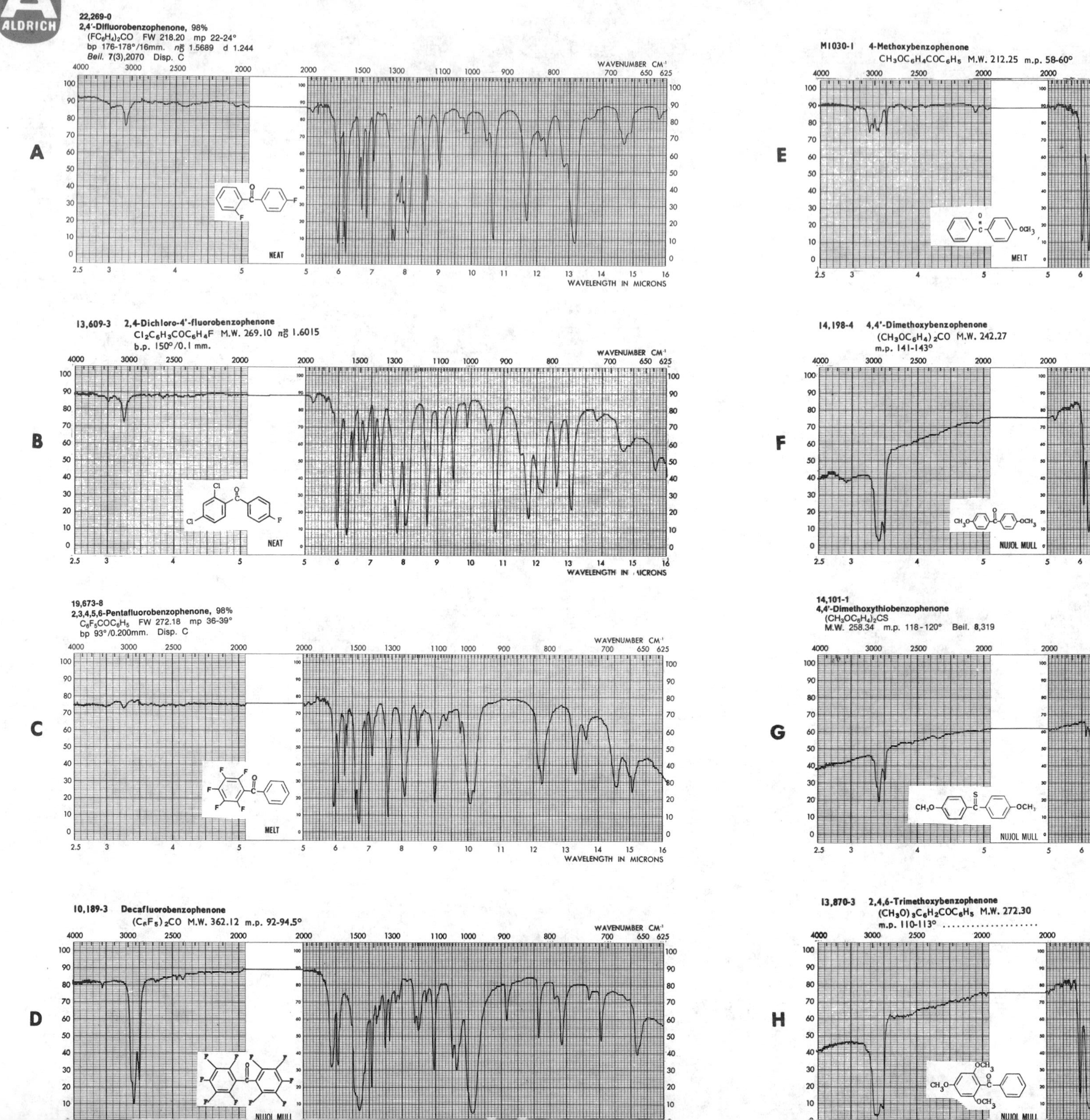

A

$(CH_3O)_3C_6H_2COC_6H_5$ M.W. 272.30
m.p. 93-95°

B

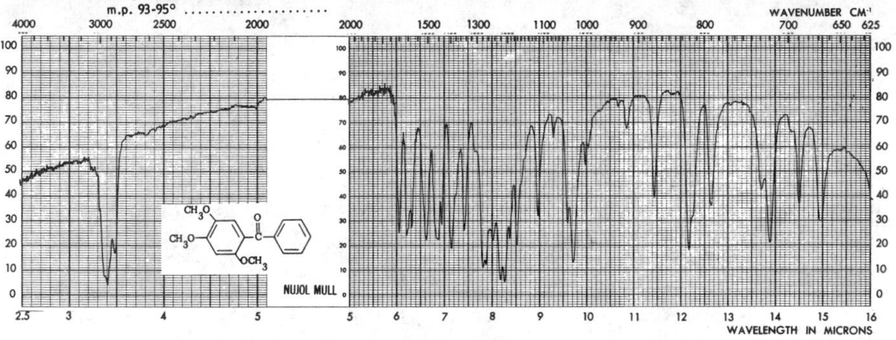

13,888-6 2,4,5-Triethoxybenzophenone
$(C_2H_5O)_3C_6H_2COC_6H_5$ M.W. 314.39
m.p. 125-127°

C

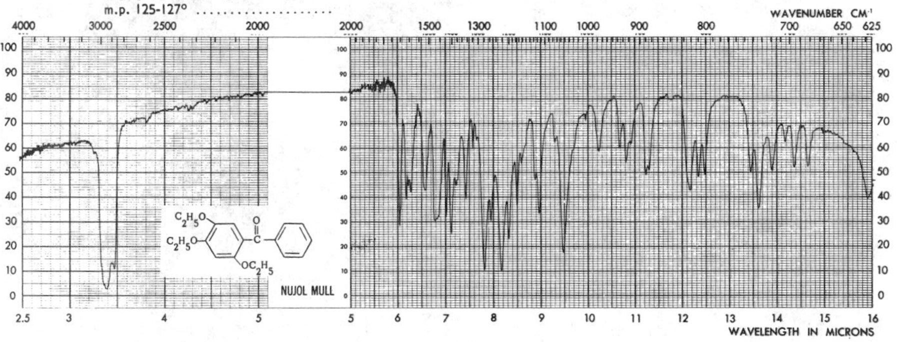

10,316-0 o-Hydroxybenzophenone
$HOC_6H_4COC_6H_5$ M.W. 198.22 m.p. 36-38°

D

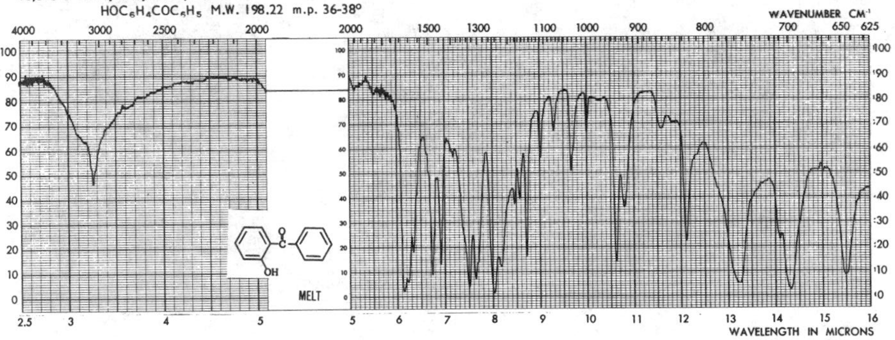

D11,020-5 2,2'-Dihydroxybenzophenone
$(HOC_6H_4)_2CO$ M.W. 214.22 m.p. 61-62.5°

E

12,621-7 2,4-Dihydroxybenzophenone
$(HO)_2C_6H_3COC_6H_5$ M.W. 214.22 m.p. 144.5-147°

F

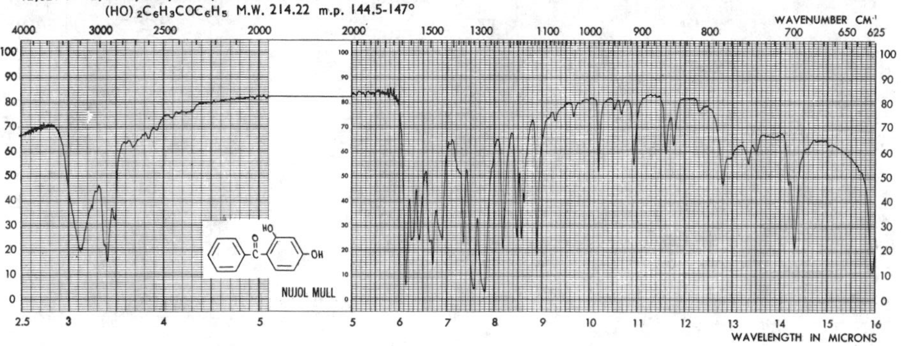

T6570-6 2,4,4'-Trihydroxybenzophenone
$(HO)_2C_6H_3COC_6H_4OH$ M.W. 230.22
m.p. 197-198°

G

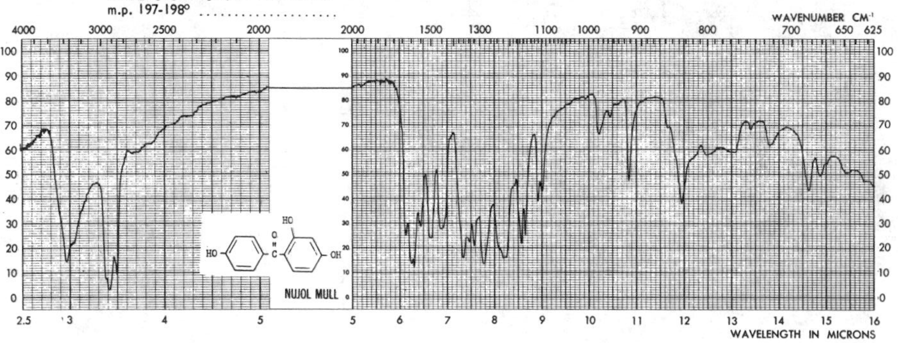

15,829-1
2,4,6-Trihydroxybenzophenone
$(HO)_3C_6H_2COC_6H_5$
M.W. 230.22 m.p. 164-166° Beil. 8(1),701

H

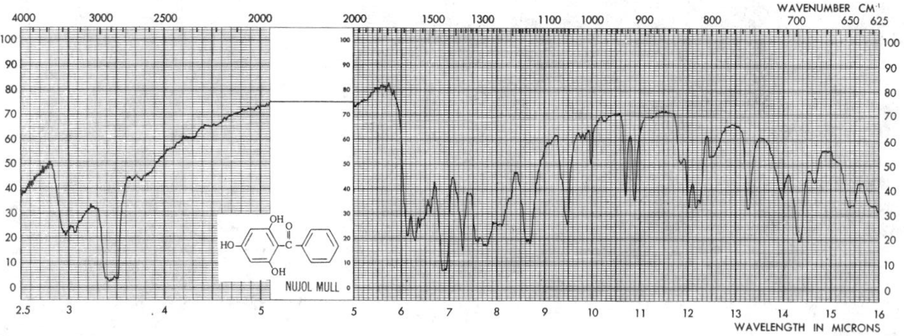

T1640-3 2,2',4,4'-Tetrahydroxybenzophenone
$[(HO)_2C_6H_3]_2CO$ M.W. 246.22
m.p. 196-198°

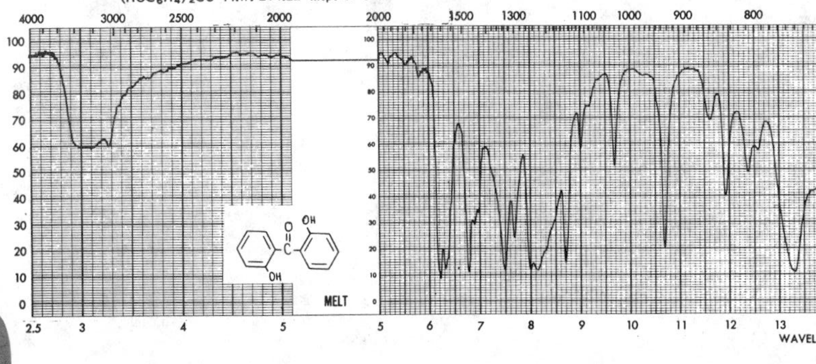

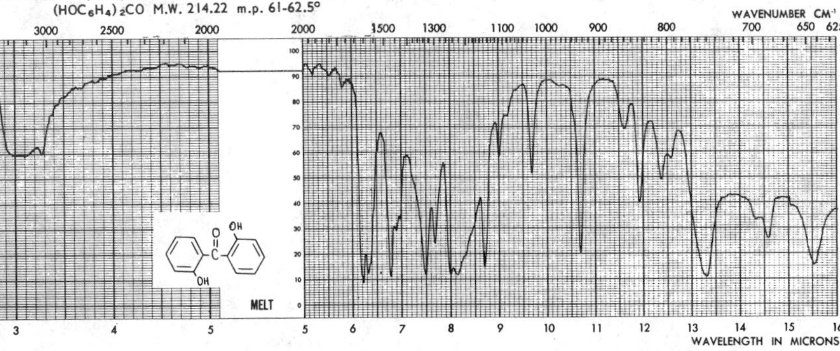

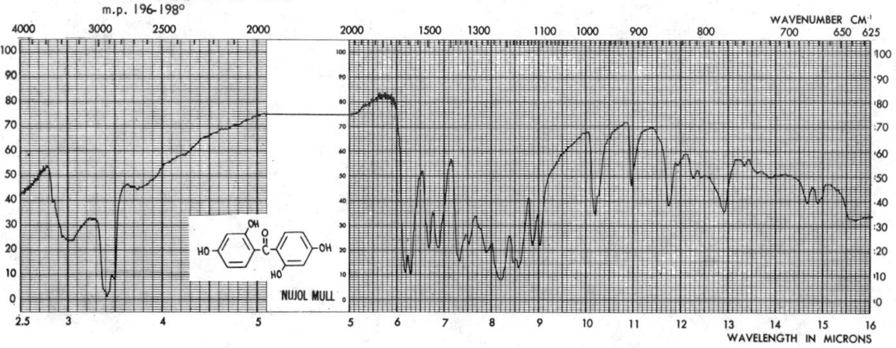

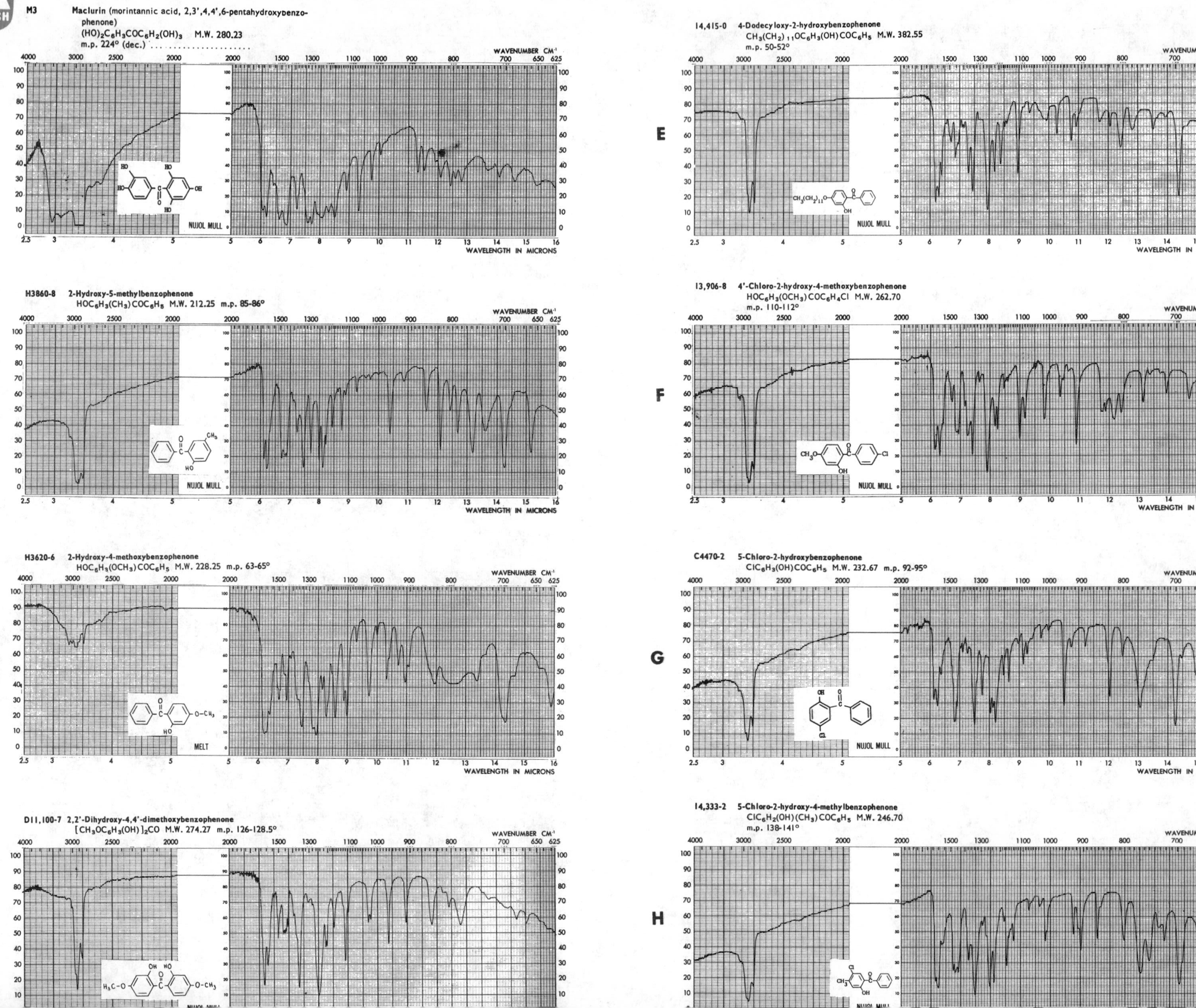

A M3 Maclurin (morintannic acid, 2,3',4,4',6-pentahydroxybenzophenone)
$(HO)_2C_6H_3COC_6H_2(OH)_3$ M.W. 280.23
m.p. 224° (dec.)
NUJOL MULL

B H3860-8 2-Hydroxy-5-methylbenzophenone
$HOC_6H_3(CH_3)COC_6H_5$ M.W. 212.25 m.p. 85-86°
NUJOL MULL

C H3620-6 2-Hydroxy-4-methoxybenzophenone
$HOC_6H_3(OCH_3)COC_6H_5$ M.W. 228.25 m.p. 63-65°
MELT

D D11,100-7 2,2'-Dihydroxy-4,4'-dimethoxybenzophenone
$[CH_3OC_6H_3(OH)]_2CO$ M.W. 274.27 m.p. 126-128.5°

E 14,415-0 4-Dodecyloxy-2-hydroxybenzophenone
$CH_3(CH_2)_{11}OC_6H_3(OH)COC_6H_5$ M.W. 382.55
m.p. 50-52°
NUJOL MULL

F 13,906-8 4'-Chloro-2-hydroxy-4-methoxybenzophenone
$HOC_6H_3(OCH_3)COC_6H_4Cl$ M.W. 262.70
m.p. 110-112°
NUJOL MULL

G C4470-2 5-Chloro-2-hydroxybenzophenone
$ClC_6H_3(OH)COC_6H_5$ M.W. 232.67 m.p. 92-95°
NUJOL MULL

H 14,333-2 5-Chloro-2-hydroxy-4-methylbenzophenone
$ClC_6H_2(OH)(CH_3)COC_6H_5$ M.W. 246.70
m.p. 138-141°

Beil. 8,137 Disp. C

A

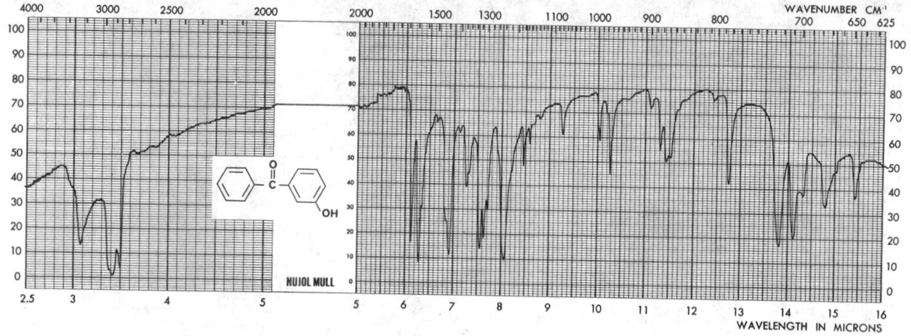

NUJOL MULL

B

H2020-2 p-Hydroxybenzophenone
$HOC_6H_4COC_6H_5$ M.W. 198.22 m.p. 132-135°

NUJOL MULL

C

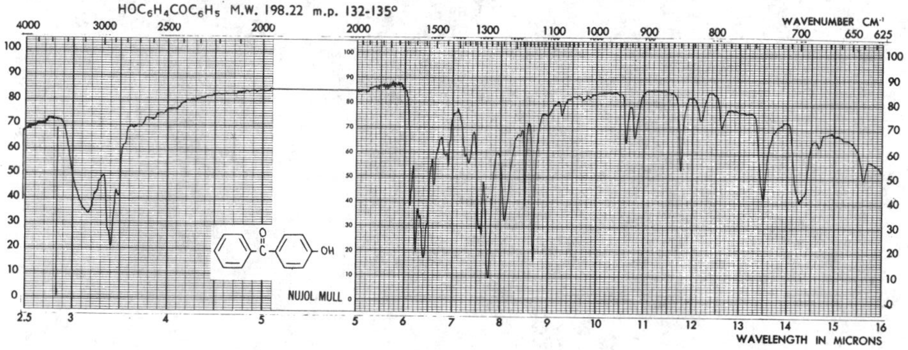

H3900-0 4-Hydroxy-4'-methylbenzophenone
$CH_3C_6H_4COC_6H_4OH$ M.W. 212.25
m.p. 167-170°

NUJOL MULL

D

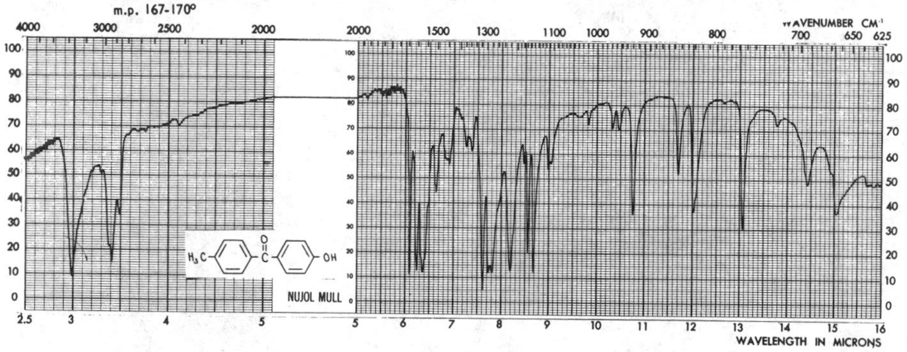

D11,050-7 4,4'-Dihydroxybenzophenone
$(HOC_6H_4)_2CO$ M.W. 214.22 m.p. 207-211°

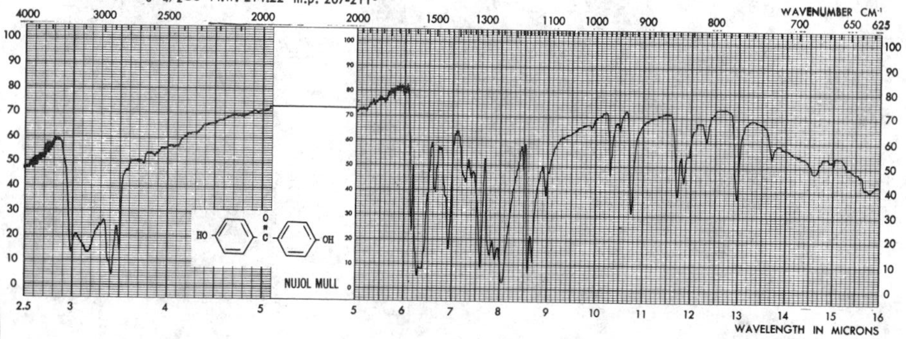

NUJOL MULL

E

3,5-Dichloro-4-hydroxybenzophenone, 98%
$Cl_2C_6H_2(OH)COC_6H_5$ FW 267.11 mp 143-146°
Beil. 8(2),187 Disp. C

NUJOL MULL

F

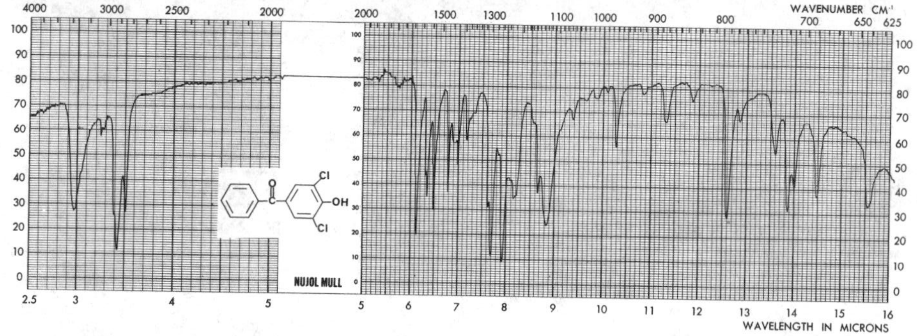

19,060-8
6-Benzoyl-2-naphthol, 98+% (6-hydroxy-2-naphthyl phenyl ketone)
$C_6H_5COC_{10}H_6OH$ FW 248.29 mp 161-162°
Disp. C

NUJOL MULL

G

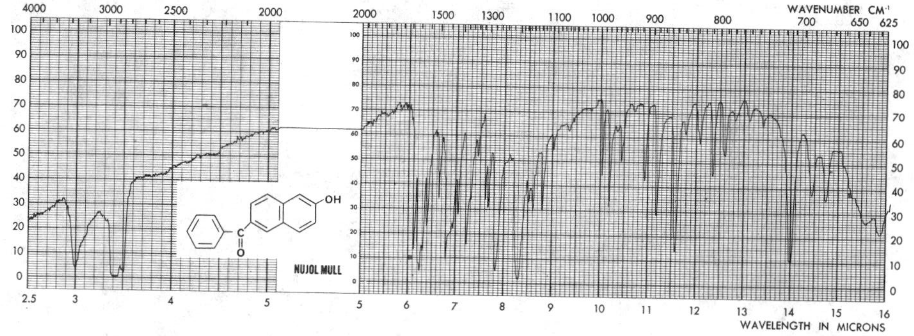

A4120-8 2-Aminobenzophenone
$H_2NC_6H_4COC_6H_5$ M.W. 197.24
m.p. 105-109°

NUJOL MULL

H

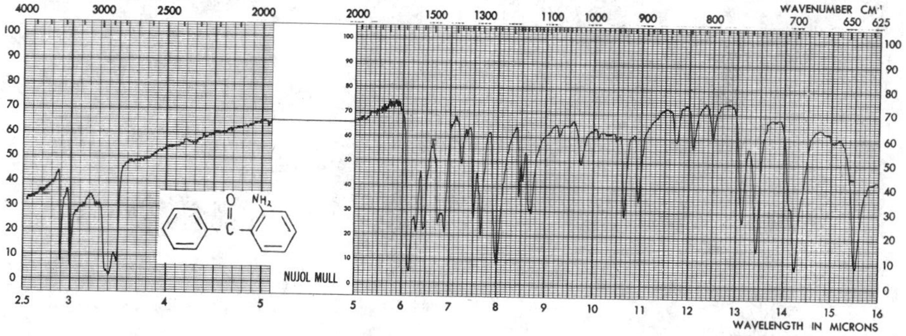

A4140-2 4-Aminobenzophenone
$H_2NC_6H_4COC_6H_5$ M.W. 197.24
m.p. 121-124°

NUJOL MULL

ALDRICH

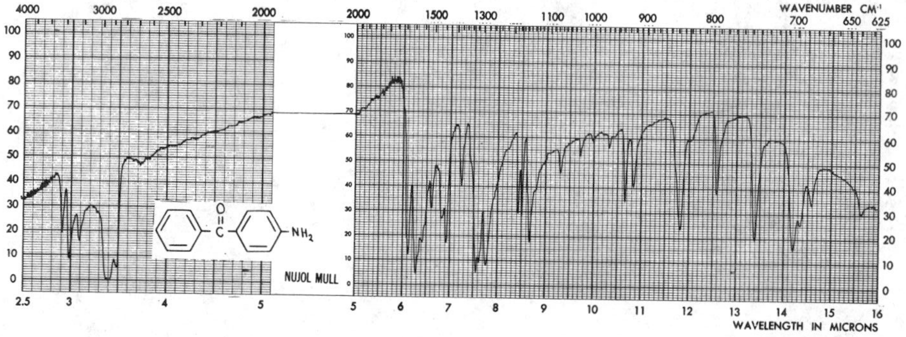

ALDRICH ®

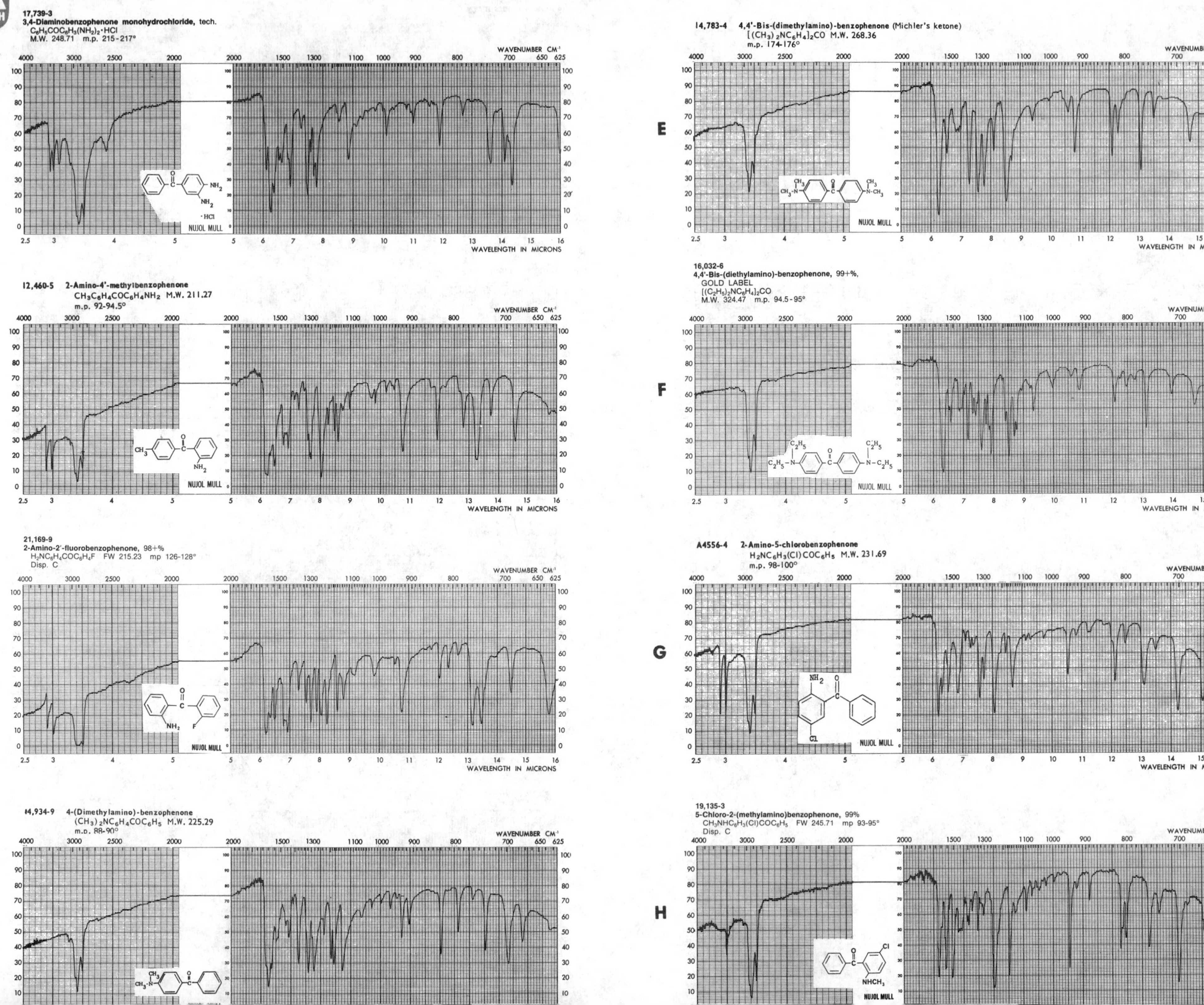

A 17,739-3 3,4-Diaminobenzophenone monohydrochloride, tech. $C_6H_5COC_6H_3(NH_2)_2 \cdot HCl$ M.W. 248.71 m.p. 215-217°

B 12,460-5 2-Amino-4'-methylbenzophenone $CH_3C_6H_4COC_6H_4NH_2$ M.W. 211.27 m.p. 92-94.5°

C 21,169-9 2-Amino-2'-fluorobenzophenone, 98+% $H_2NC_6H_4COC_6H_4F$ FW 215.23 mp 126-128° Disp. C

D 14,934-9 4-(Dimethylamino)-benzophenone $(CH_3)_2NC_6H_4COC_6H_5$ M.W. 225.29 m.p. 88-90°

E 14,783-4 4,4'-Bis-(dimethylamino)-benzophenone (Michler's ketone) $[(CH_3)_2NC_6H_4]_2CO$ M.W. 268.36 m.p. 174-176°

F 16,032-6 4,4'-Bis-(diethylamino)-benzophenone, 99+%, GOLD LABEL $[(C_2H_5)_2NC_6H_4]_2CO$ M.W. 324.47 m.p. 94.5-95°

G A4556-4 2-Amino-5-chlorobenzophenone $H_2NC_6H_3(Cl)COC_6H_5$ M.W. 231.69 m.p. 98-100°

H 19,135-3 5-Chloro-2-(methylamino)benzophenone, 99% $CH_3NHC_6H_3(Cl)COC_6H_5$ FW 245.71 mp 93-95° Disp. C

Beil. 14(1),389 Disp. C

A

NUJOL MULL

10,515-5 **2-Amino-2',5-dichlorobenzophenone**
$H_2NC_6H_3(Cl)COC_6H_4Cl$ M.W. 266.13 m.p. 87-89°

B

NUJOL MULL

13,648-4 **2-Morpholinobenzophenone**
M.W. 267.33 m.p. 114-116°

C

NUJOL MULL

13,620-4 **4-Morpholinobenzophenone**
M.W. 267.33 m.p. 138-141°

D

NUJOL MULL

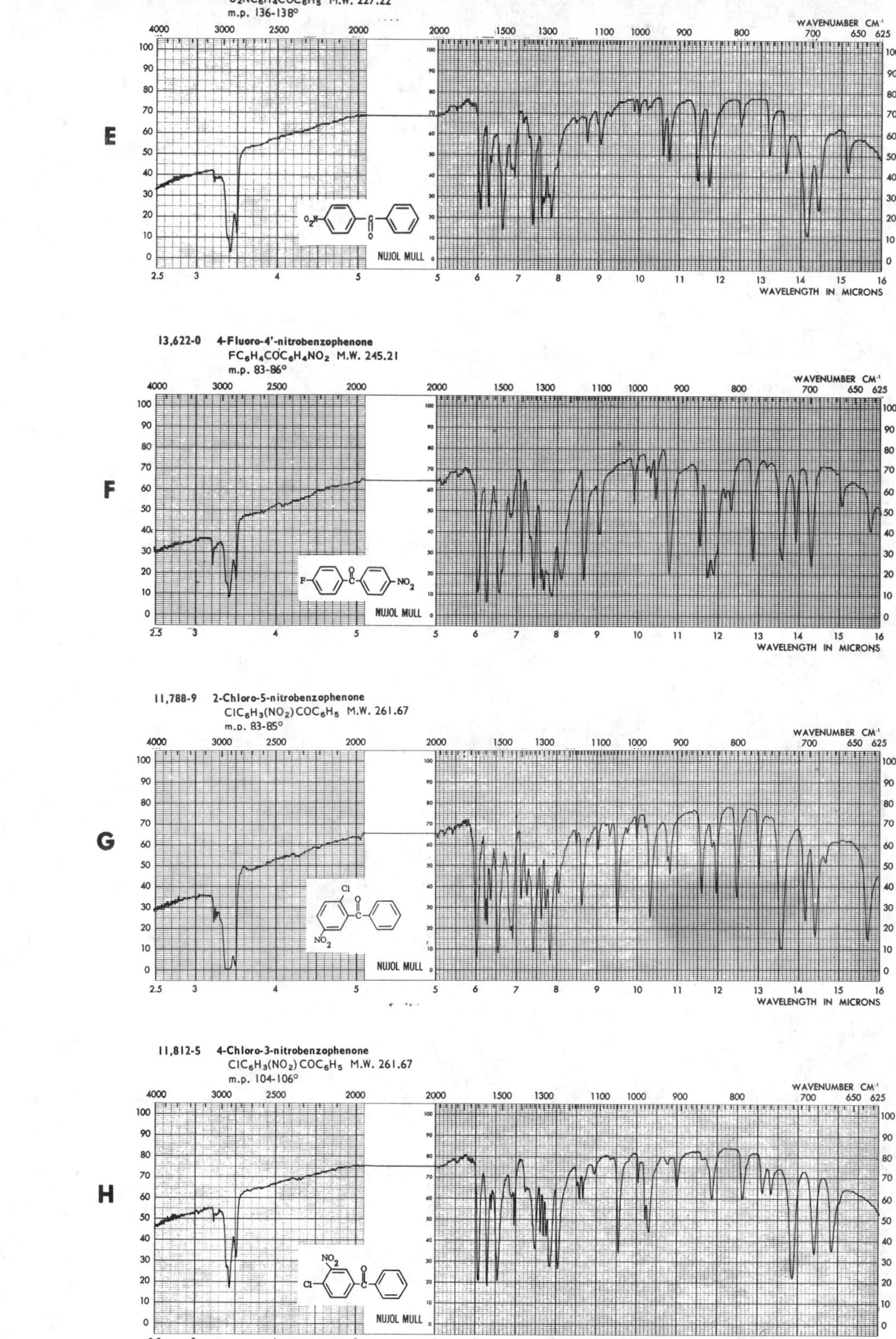

$O_2NC_6H_4COC_6H_5$ M.W. 227.22
m.p. 136-138°

E

13,622-0 **4-Fluoro-4'-nitrobenzophenone**
$FC_6H_4COC_6H_4NO_2$ M.W. 245.21
m.p. 83-86°

F

11,788-9 **2-Chloro-5-nitrobenzophenone**
$ClC_6H_3(NO_2)COC_6H_5$ M.W. 261.67
m.p. 83-85°

G

11,812-5 **4-Chloro-3-nitrobenzophenone**
$ClC_6H_3(NO_2)COC_6H_5$ M.W. 261.67
m.p. 104-106°

H

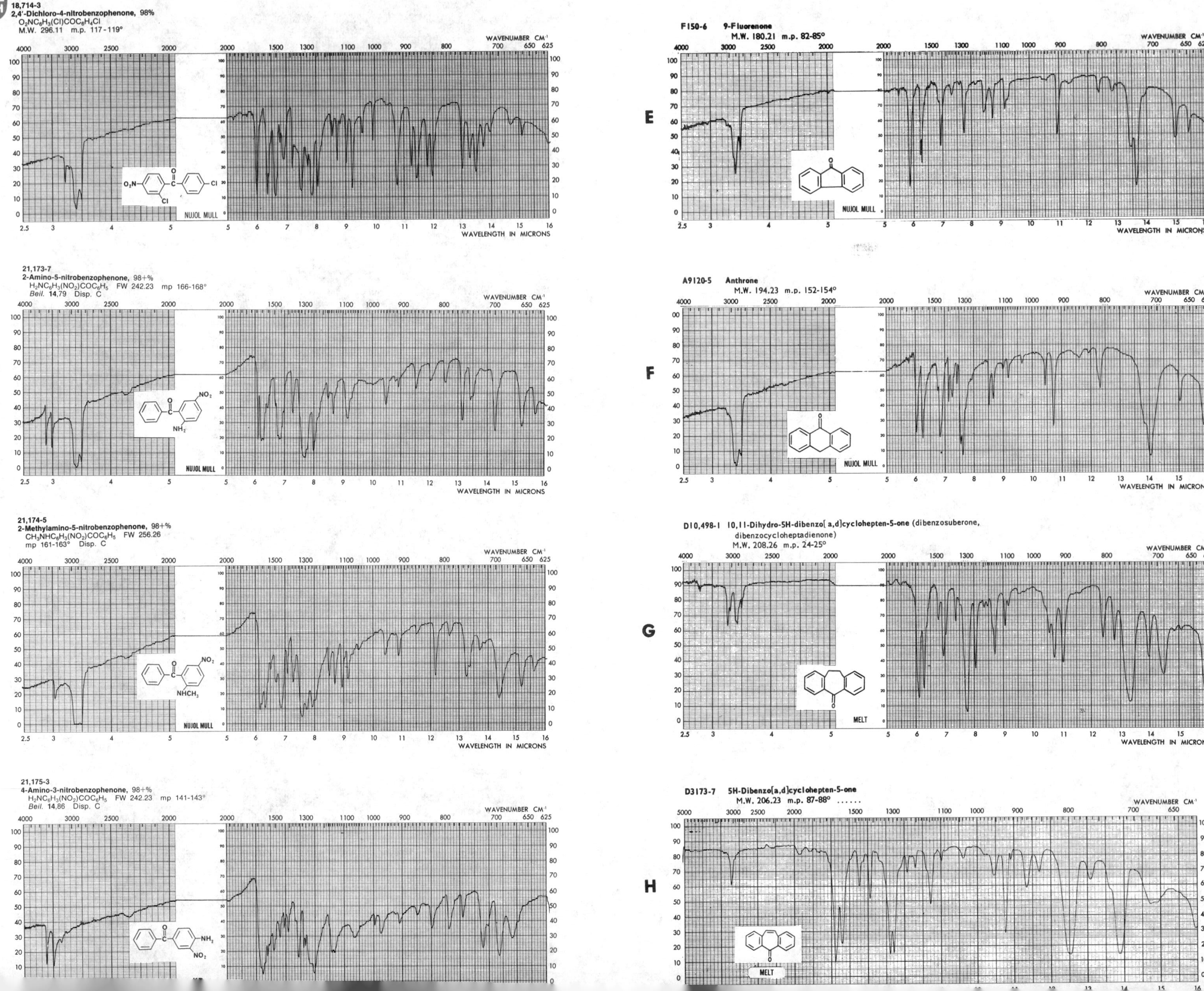
ALDRICH
A
18,714-3
2,4'-Dichloro-4-nitrobenzophenone, 98%
$O_2NC_6H_3(Cl)COC_6H_4Cl$
M.W. 296.11 m.p. 117-119°
NUJOL MULL
B
21,173-7
2-Amino-5-nitrobenzophenone, 98+%
$H_2NC_6H_3(NO_2)COC_6H_5$ FW 242.23 mp 166-168°
Beil. 14,79 Disp. C
NUJOL MULL
C
21,174-5
2-Methylamino-5-nitrobenzophenone, 98+%
$CH_3NHC_6H_3(NO_2)COC_6H_5$ FW 256.26
mp 161-163° Disp. C
NUJOL MULL
D
21,175-3
4-Amino-3-nitrobenzophenone, 98+%
$H_2NC_6H_3(NO_2)COC_6H_5$ FW 242.23 mp 141-143°
Beil. 14,86 Disp. C
E
F150-6 9-Fluorenone
M.W. 180.21 m.p. 82-85°
NUJOL MULL
F
A9120-5 Anthrone
M.W. 194.23 m.p. 152-154°
NUJOL MULL
G
D10,498-1 10,11-Dihydro-5H-dibenzo[a,d]cyclohepten-5-one (dibenzosuberone, dibenzocycloheptadienone)
M.W. 208.26 m.p. 24-25°
MELT
H
D3173-7 5H-Dibenzo[a,d]cyclohepten-5-one
M.W. 206.23 m.p. 87-88°
MELT
WAVENUMBER CM⁻¹
WAVELENGTH IN MICRONS

A 15,271-4 10-Bromo-5H-dibenzo[a,d]cyclohepten-5-one
M.W. 285.15 m.p. 113-115°
NUJOL MULL

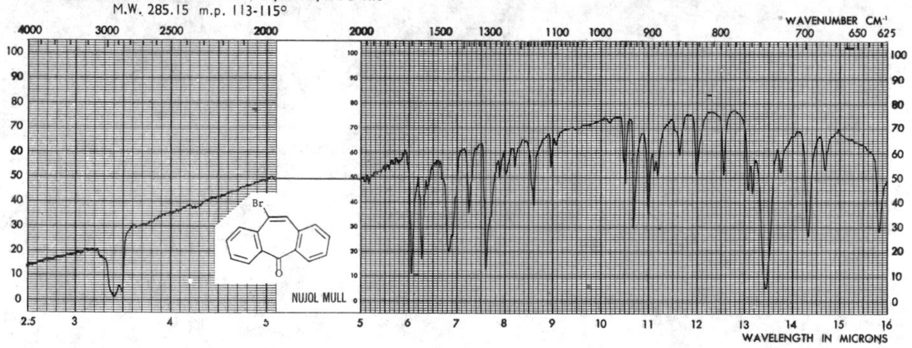

B B260-8 Benzanthrone (7H-benz[de]anthracen-7-one), tech.
M.W. 230.27 m.p. 168-170°
NUJOL MULL

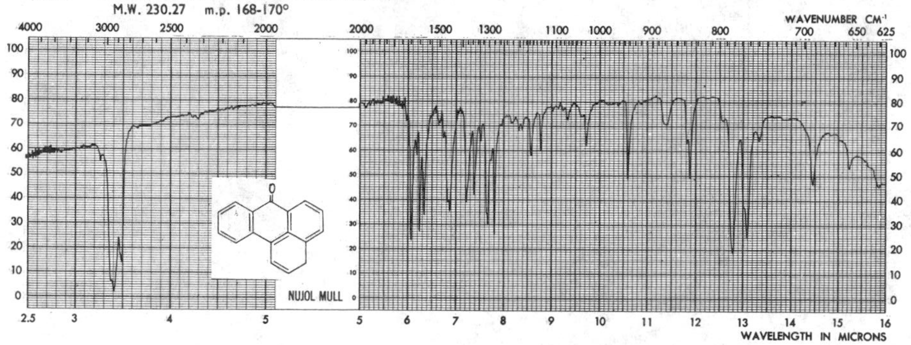

C 10,011-0 3-Bromo-9-fluorenone
M.W. 259.11 m.p. 160-162°
NUJOL MULL

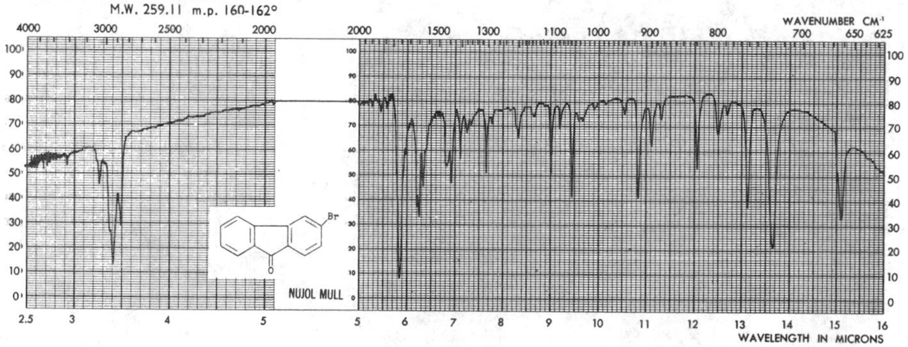

D I-800-0 2-Iodo-9-fluorenone
M.W. 306.10 m.p. 153-155°
NUJOL MULL

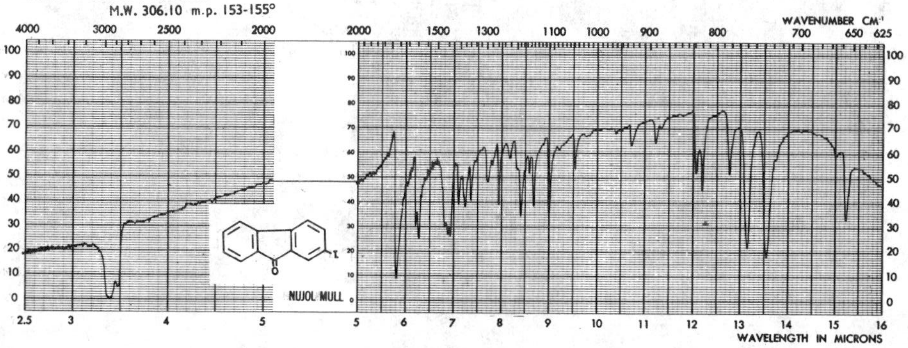

E H3130-1 1-Hydroxy-9-fluorenone
M.W. 196.21 m.p. 117-118°
NUJOL MULL

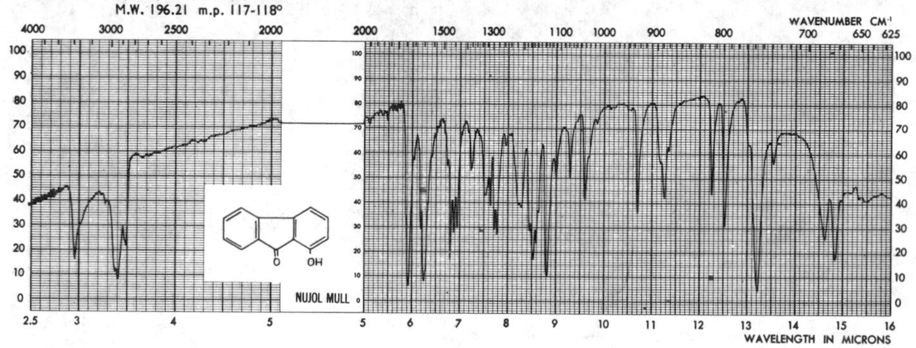

F H3132-8 2-Hydroxy-9-fluorenone
M.W. 196.21 m.p. 207-209°
NUJOL MULL

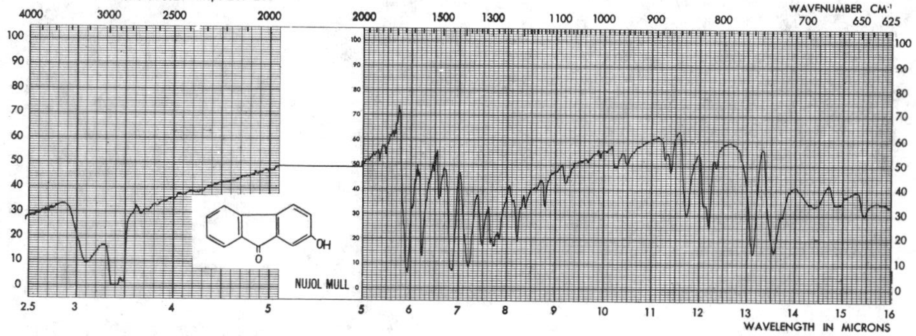

G H3134-4 4-Hydroxy-9-fluorenone
M.W. 196.21 m.p. 245-249°
NUJOL MULL

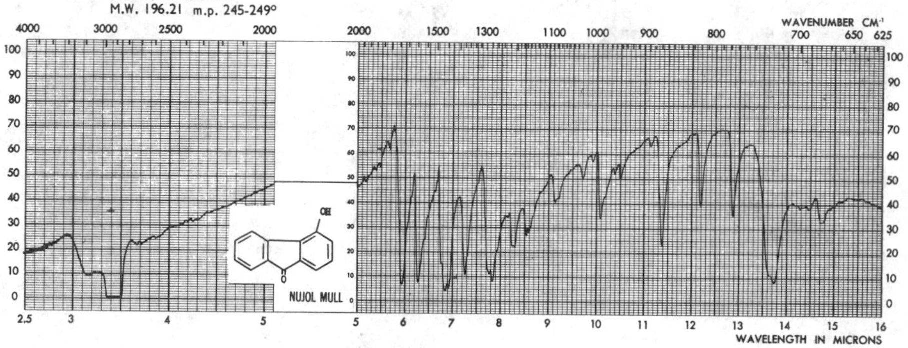

H A5579-9 1-Amino-9-fluorenone
M.W. 195.22 m.p. 118-120°
NUJOL MULL

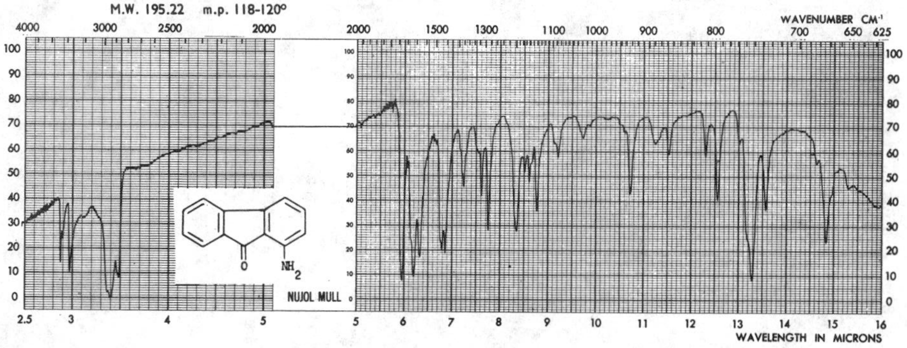

ALDRICH ®

AROMATIC KETONES

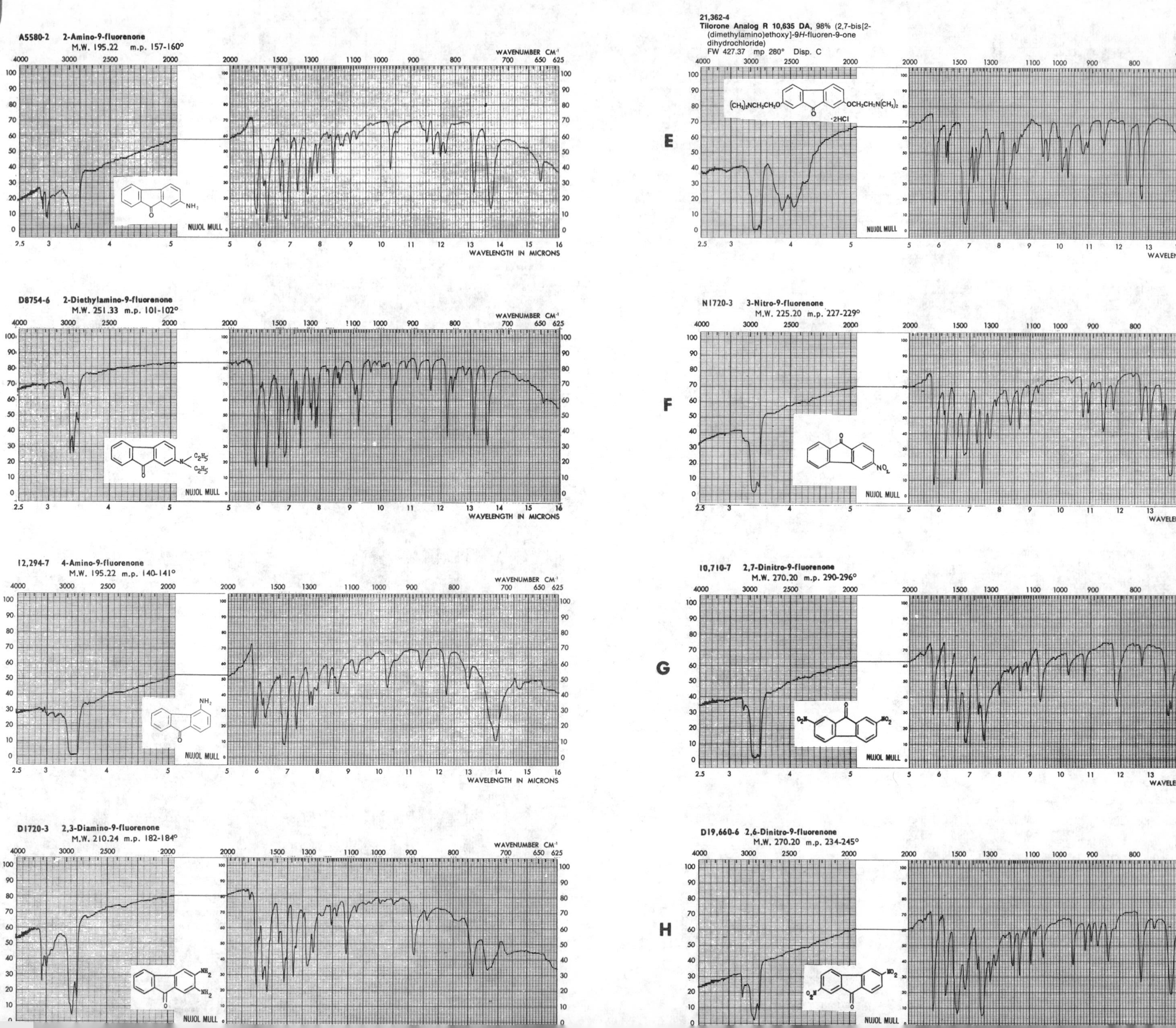
ALDRICH
A5580-2 2-Amino-9-fluorenone
M.W. 195.22 m.p. 157-160°
A
D8754-6 2-Diethylamino-9-fluorenone
M.W. 251.33 m.p. 101-102°
B
12,294-7 4-Amino-9-fluorenone
M.W. 195.22 m.p. 140-141°
C
D1720-3 2,3-Diamino-9-fluorenone
M.W. 210.24 m.p. 182-184°
D
21,362-4
Tilorone Analog R 10,635 DA, 98% (2,7-bis[2-(dimethylamino)ethoxy]-9H-fluoren-9-one dihydrochloride)
FW 427.37 mp 280° Disp. C
E
N1720-3 3-Nitro-9-fluorenone
M.W. 225.20 m.p. 227-229°
F
10,710-7 2,7-Dinitro-9-fluorenone
M.W. 270.20 m.p. 290-296°
G
D19,660-6 2,6-Dinitro-9-fluorenone
M.W. 270.20 m.p. 234-245°
H
WAVENUMBER CM⁻¹
WAVELENGTH IN MICRONS
NUJOL MULL

A

2,5-Dinitro-9-fluorenone, 97%
M.W. 270.2 m.p. 232-234° Beil. 7(2),410

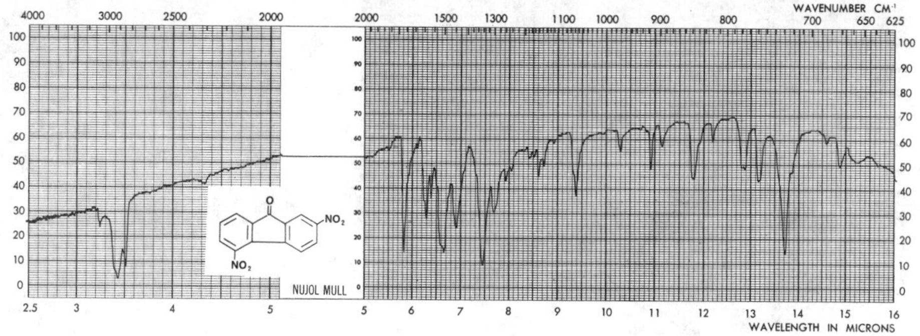

NUJOL MULL

B

T8080-2 2,4,7-Trinitro-9-fluorenone
M.W. 315.20 m.p. 175°

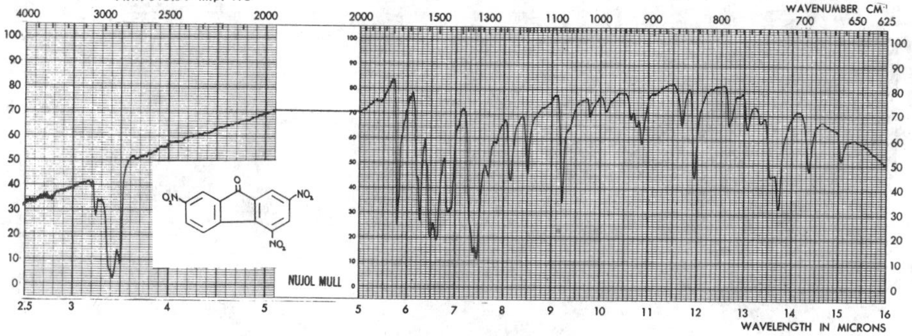

NUJOL MULL

C

12,783-3 2,4,5,7-Tetranitro-9-fluorenone
M.W. 360.20 m.p. 251-253°

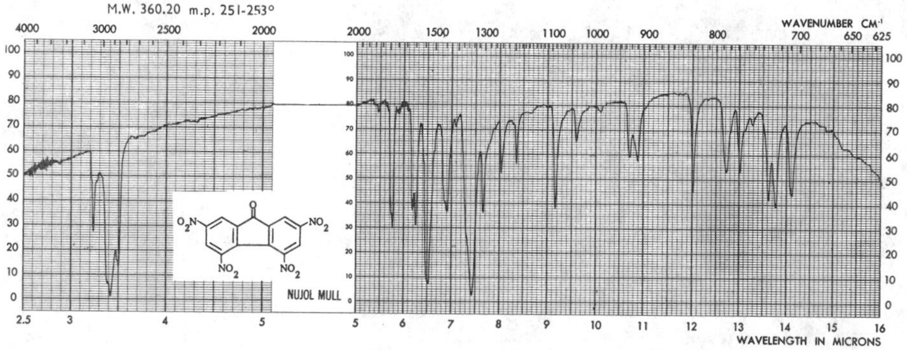

NUJOL MULL

D

11,287-9 2,5-Diphenyl-1,4-benzoquinone
$(C_6H_5)_2C_6H_2(:O)_2$ M.W. 260.29
m.p. 209-211°

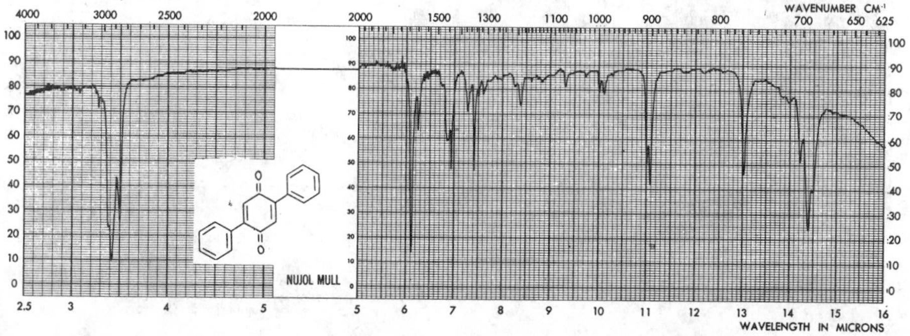

NUJOL MULL

E

G30-7 Galvinoxyl [2,6-di-tert.-butyl-α-(3,5-di-tert.-butyl-4-oxo-2,5-cyclohexadien-1-ylidene)-p-tolyloxy], free radical
M.W. 421.65 m.p. 158-161°

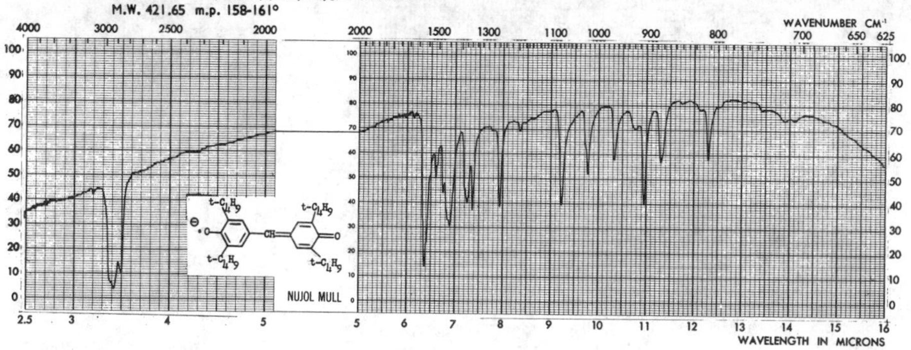

NUJOL MULL

F

16,107-1
1,2-Naphthoquinone
M.W. 158.16 m.p. 134-136° (dec.) Beil. 7,709
Fieser 1,713

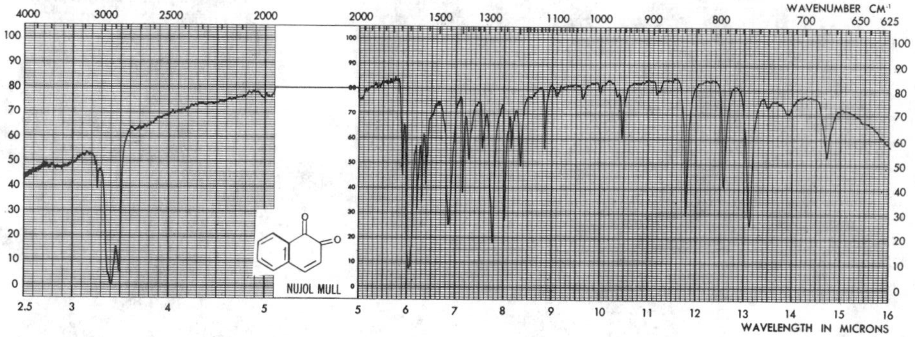

NUJOL MULL

G

15,275-7 1,4-Naphthoquinone, tech.,
M.W. 158.16 m.p. 121-122°

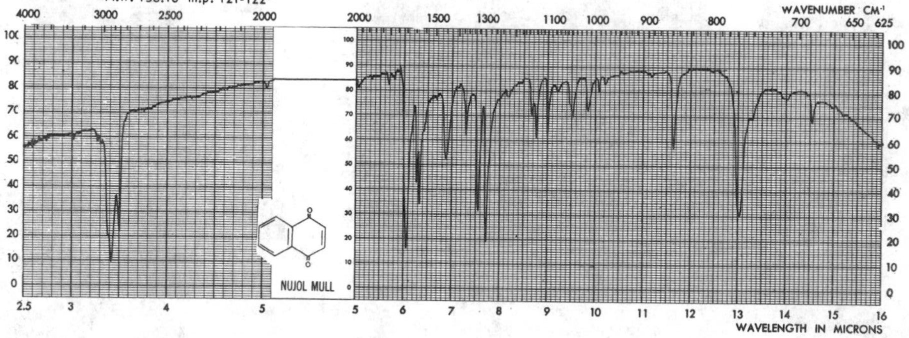

NUJOL MULL

H

M5740-5 2-Methyl-1,4-naphthoquinone
M.W. 172.18 m.p. 107°

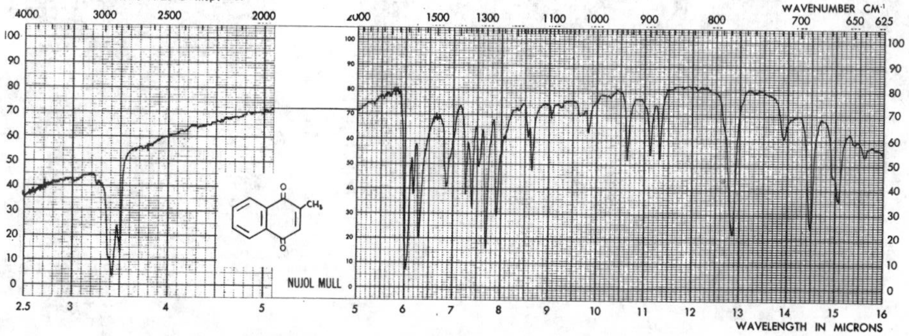

NUJOL MULL

AROMATIC KETONES

ALDRICH ®

A

18,409-8 **2-Hydroxy-1,4-naphthoquinone**, tech. (lawsone)
M.W. 174.16 m.p. 191 - 194° (dec.) *Beil.* 8,300
Fieser 1,484 *Merck Index* 8,611 Disp. C
Contains *ca.* 20% lawsone-3,3'-dimer

NUJOL MULL

B

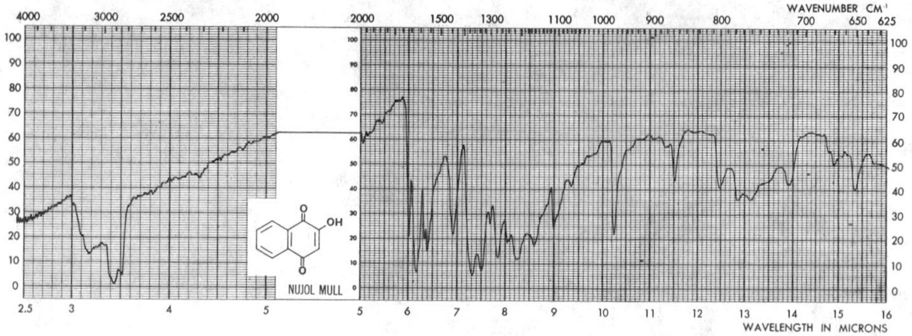

18,916-2
2-Methoxy-1,4-naphthoquinone, 98+%
FW 188.18 mp 180-182° *Beil.* 8,302 Disp. C

NUJOL MULL

C

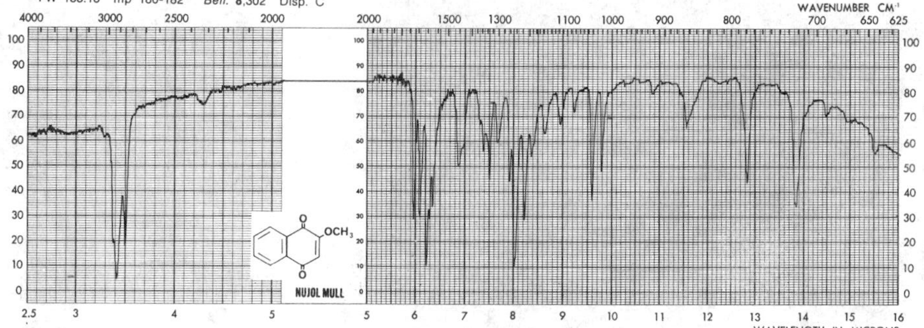

H4,700-3
5-Hydroxy-1,4-naphthoquinone (juglone)
M.W. 174.16 m.p. 161-163° Beil. 8,308

NUJOL MULL

D

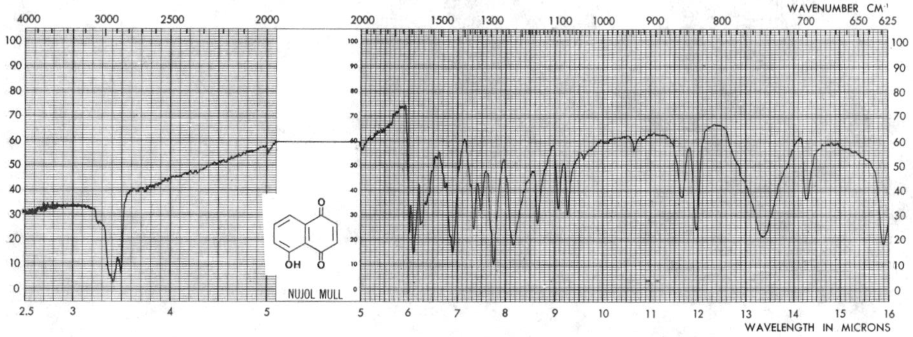

P5590-2 **Purpurogallin, tech.**
M.W. 220.18
m.p. 270-275° (dec.)

NUJOL MULL

E

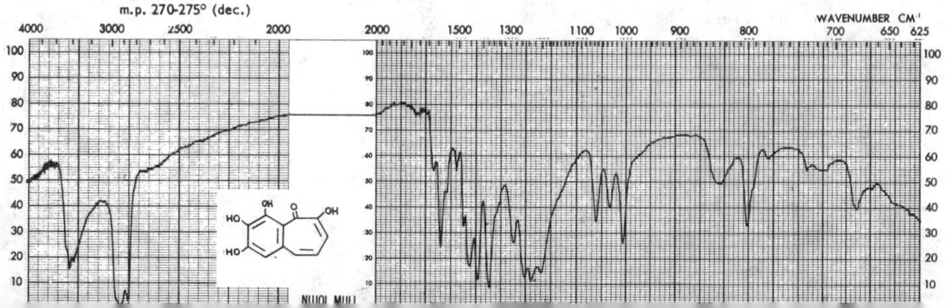

D6720-0 **2,3-Dichloro-1,4-naphthoquinone, tech.**
M.W. 227.05 m.p. 195-197°

NUJOL MULL

F

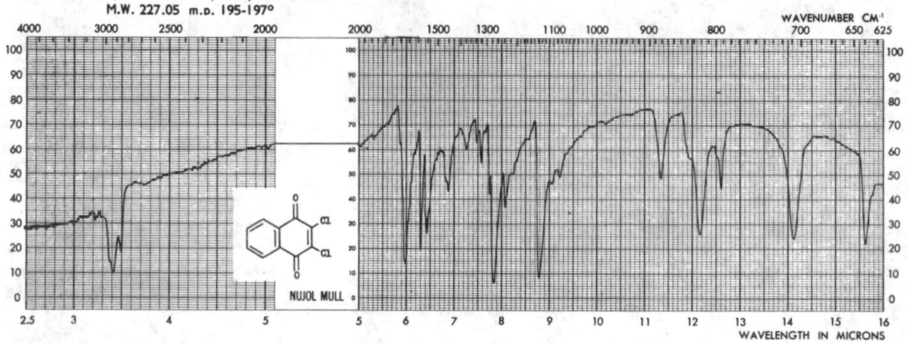

14,290-5
Lapachol [2-hydroxy-3-(3-methyl-2-butenyl)-1,4-naphthoquinone]

NUJOL MULL

G

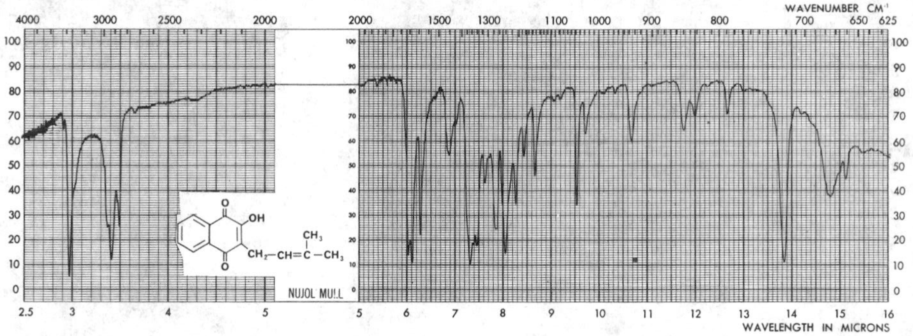

A20-1 **Acenaphthenequinone**
M.W. 182.18
m.p. 255-258° (dec.) .....

NUJOL MULL

H

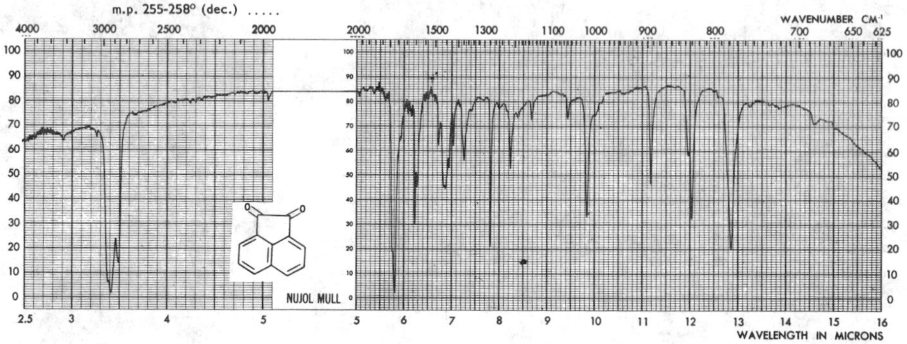

15,650-7
Phenanthrenequinone, free of anthraquinone
M.W. 208.22 m.p. 209-211° Beil. 7,796

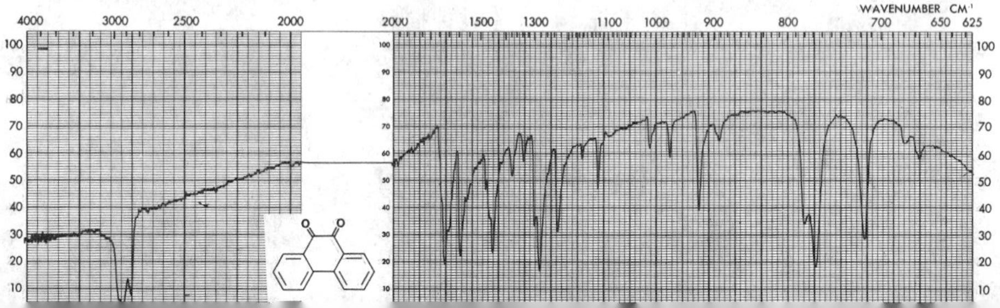

A

[illegible]
M.W. 270.33 m.p. 173-175°

NUJOL MULL

B

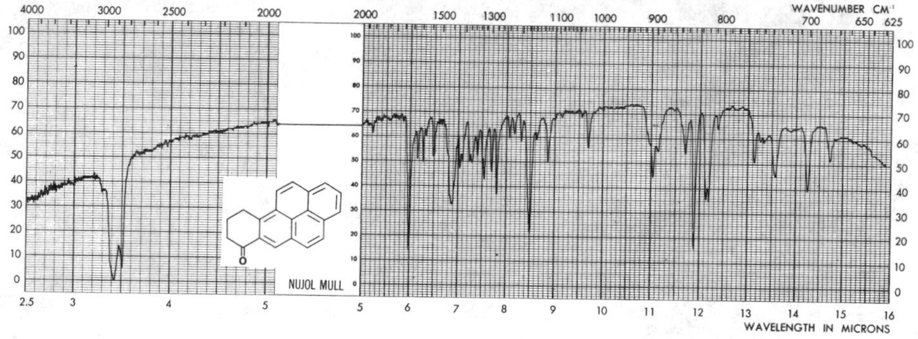

A9000-4 Anthraquinone
M.W. 208.22 m.p. 283.5-285°

NUJOL MULL

C

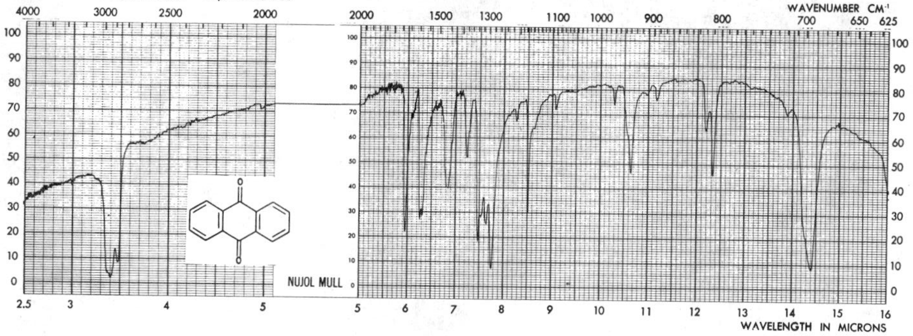

19,877-3
5,12-Naphthacenequinone
FW 258.28 mp 282-286° (dec.) Disp. C

NUJOL MULL

D

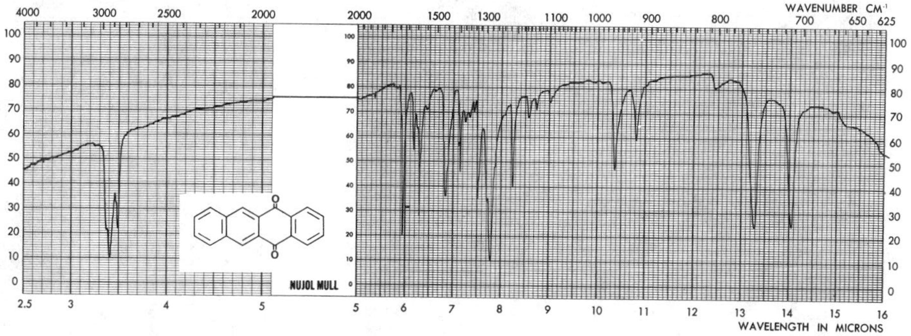

22,221-6
Benz[*a*]anthracene-7,12-dione, 99%
FW 258.28 mp 170-171° *Beil.* 7,826 Disp. C

NUJOL MULL

E

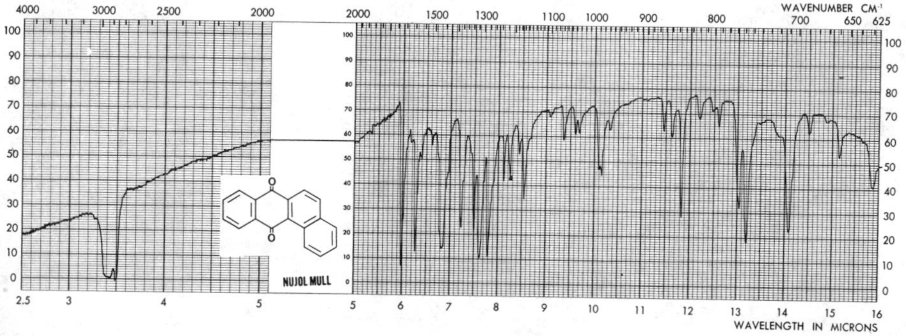

B3340-4 Bianthrone
M.W. 384.43 m.p. > 300°

NUJOL MULL

F

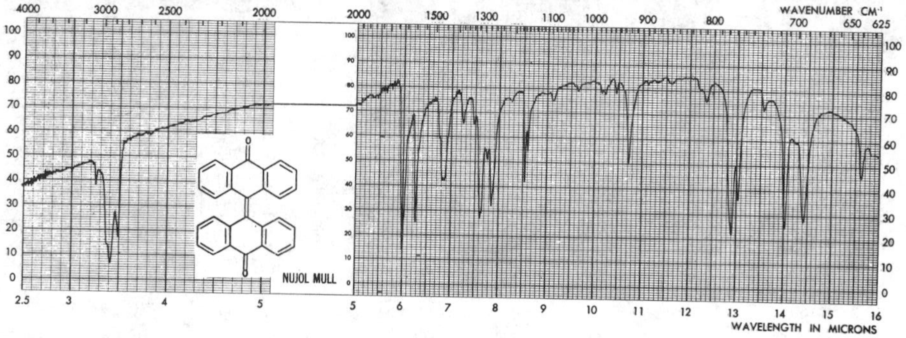

B3360-9 Bianthronyl
M.W. 386.45 m.p. 247-249° (dec.)

NUJOL MULL

G

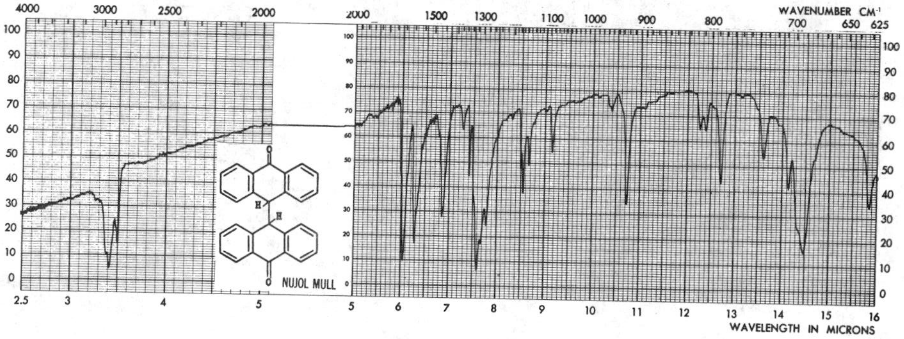

D15,080 2,2'-Dimethylbianthrone

NUJOL MULL

H

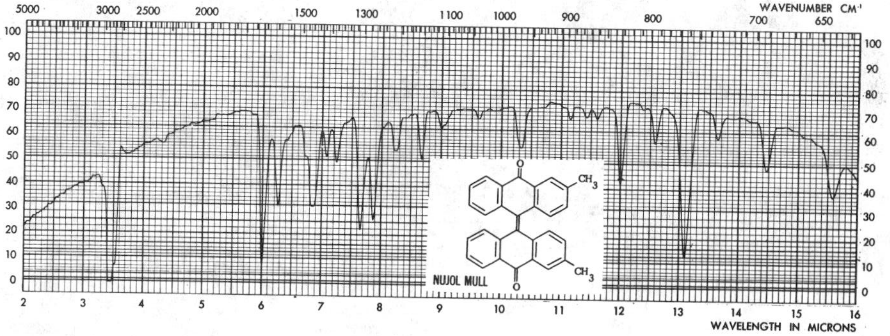

12,197-5 2,2'-Dimethyl-1,1'-bianthraquinone
M.W. 442.48 m.p. > 300°

NUJOL MULL

ALDRICH

AROMATIC KETONES

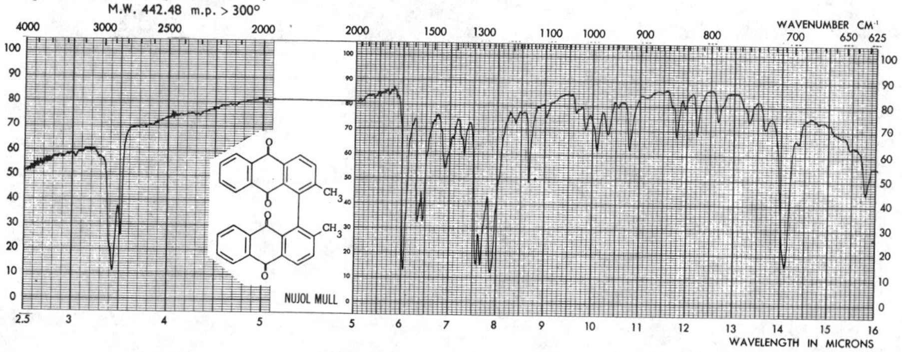

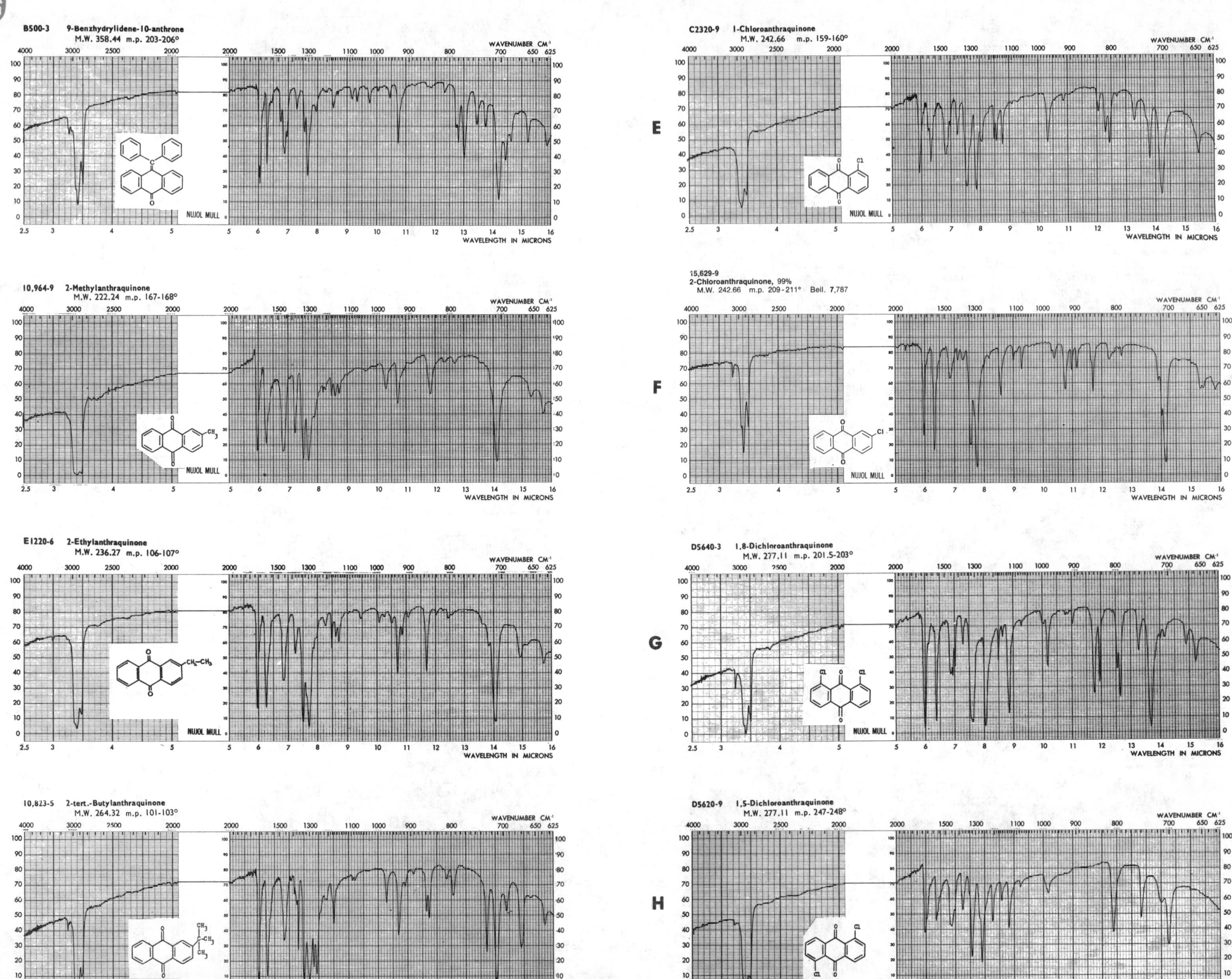
ALDRICH
A
B500-3 9-Benzhydrylidene-10-anthrone
M.W. 358.44 m.p. 203-206°
B
10,964-9 2-Methylanthraquinone
M.W. 222.24 m.p. 167-168°
C
E1220-6 2-Ethylanthraquinone
M.W. 236.27 m.p. 106-107°
D
10,823-5 2-tert.-Butylanthraquinone
M.W. 264.32 m.p. 101-103°
E
C2320-9 1-Chloroanthraquinone
M.W. 242.66 m.p. 159-160°
F
15,629-9
2-Chloroanthraquinone, 99%
M.W. 242.66 m.p. 209-211° Beil. 7,787
G
D5640-3 1,8-Dichloroanthraquinone
M.W. 277.11 m.p. 201.5-203°
H
D5620-9 1,5-Dichloroanthraquinone
M.W. 277.11 m.p. 247-248°
NUJOL MULL
WAVENUMBER CM⁻¹
WAVELENGTH IN MICRONS

A

M975-0 1-Methoxyanthraquinone
M.W. 238.23 m.p. 167-168°

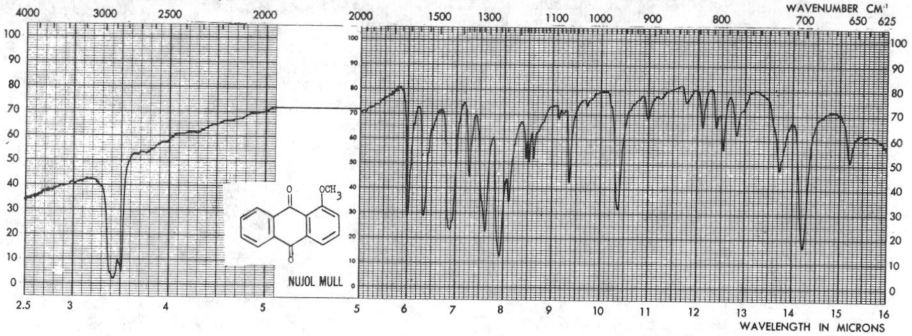

NUJOL MULL

B

12,277-7 Alizarin (1,2-dihydroxyanthraquinone)
M.W. 240.21 m.p. 287-289°

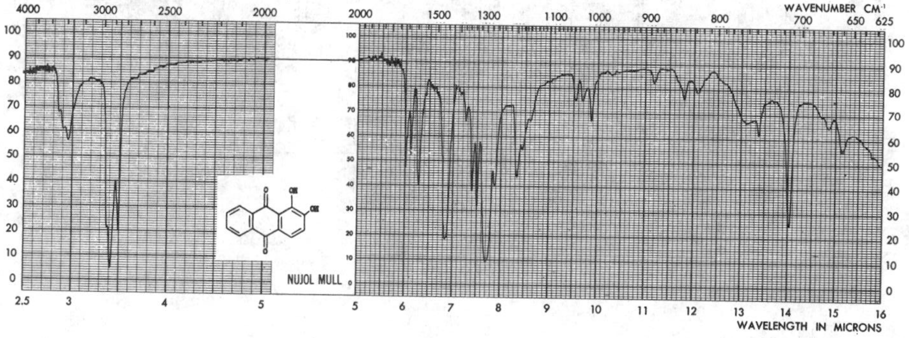

NUJOL MULL

C

Q90-6 Quinizarin (1,4-dihydroxyanthraquinone)
M.W. 240.21 m.p. 191-195°

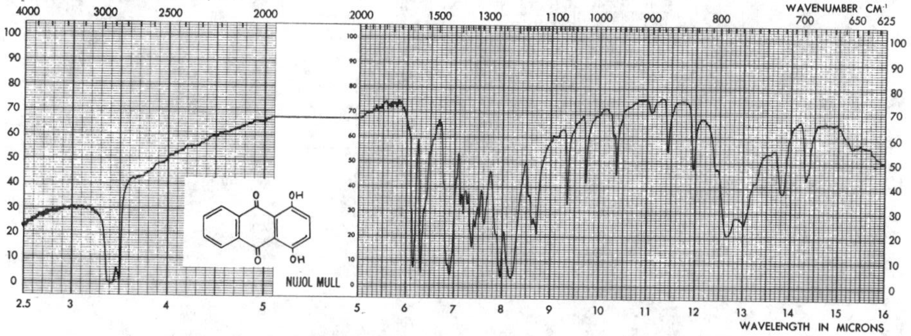

NUJOL MULL

D

D10,810-3 1,8-Dihydroxyanthraquinone
M.W. 240.21 m.p. 187°

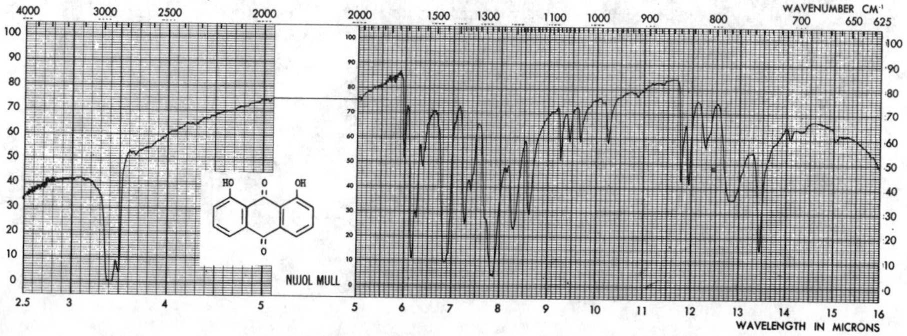

NUJOL MULL

E

A8950-2 Anthraflavic acid (2,6-dihydroxyanthraquinone)
M.W. 240.22 m.p. > 320°

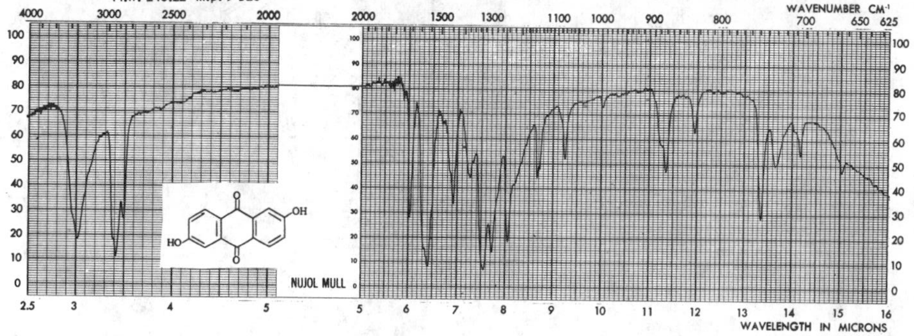

NUJOL MULL

F

E70-3 Emodin (6-methyl-1,3,8-trihydroxyanthraquinone), tech.
M.W. 270.23 m.p. 253° (dec.)

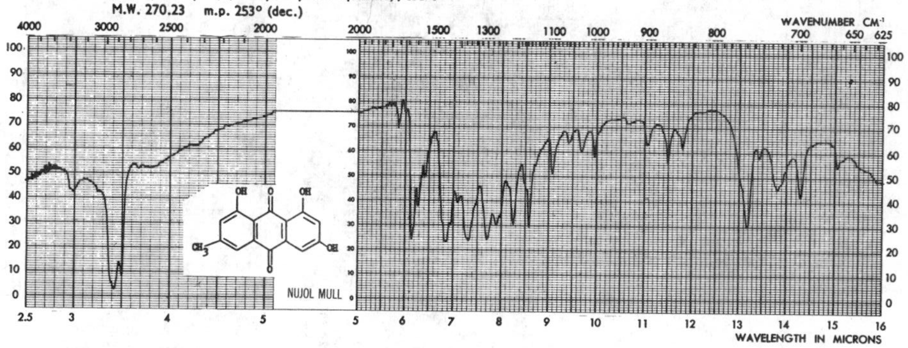

NUJOL MULL

G

13,677-8 Quinalizarin (1,2,5,8-tetrahydroxyanthraquinone)
M.W. 272.22 m.p. > 300°

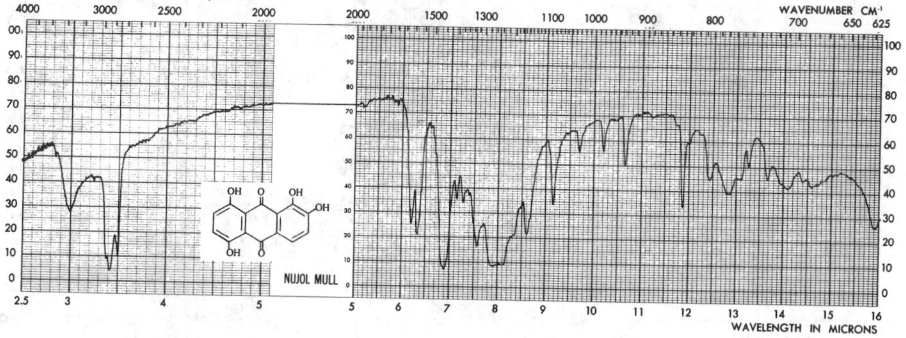

NUJOL MULL

H

T6500-5 1,2,4-Trihydroxyanthraquinone (purpurin)
M.W. 256.21 m.p. 251-256°

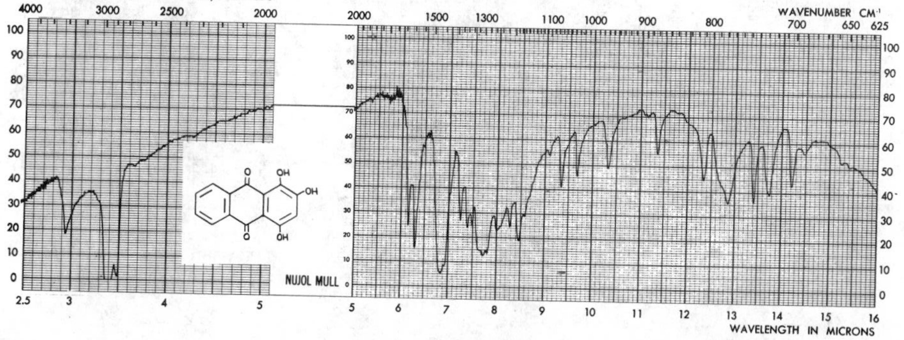

NUJOL MULL

ALDRICH

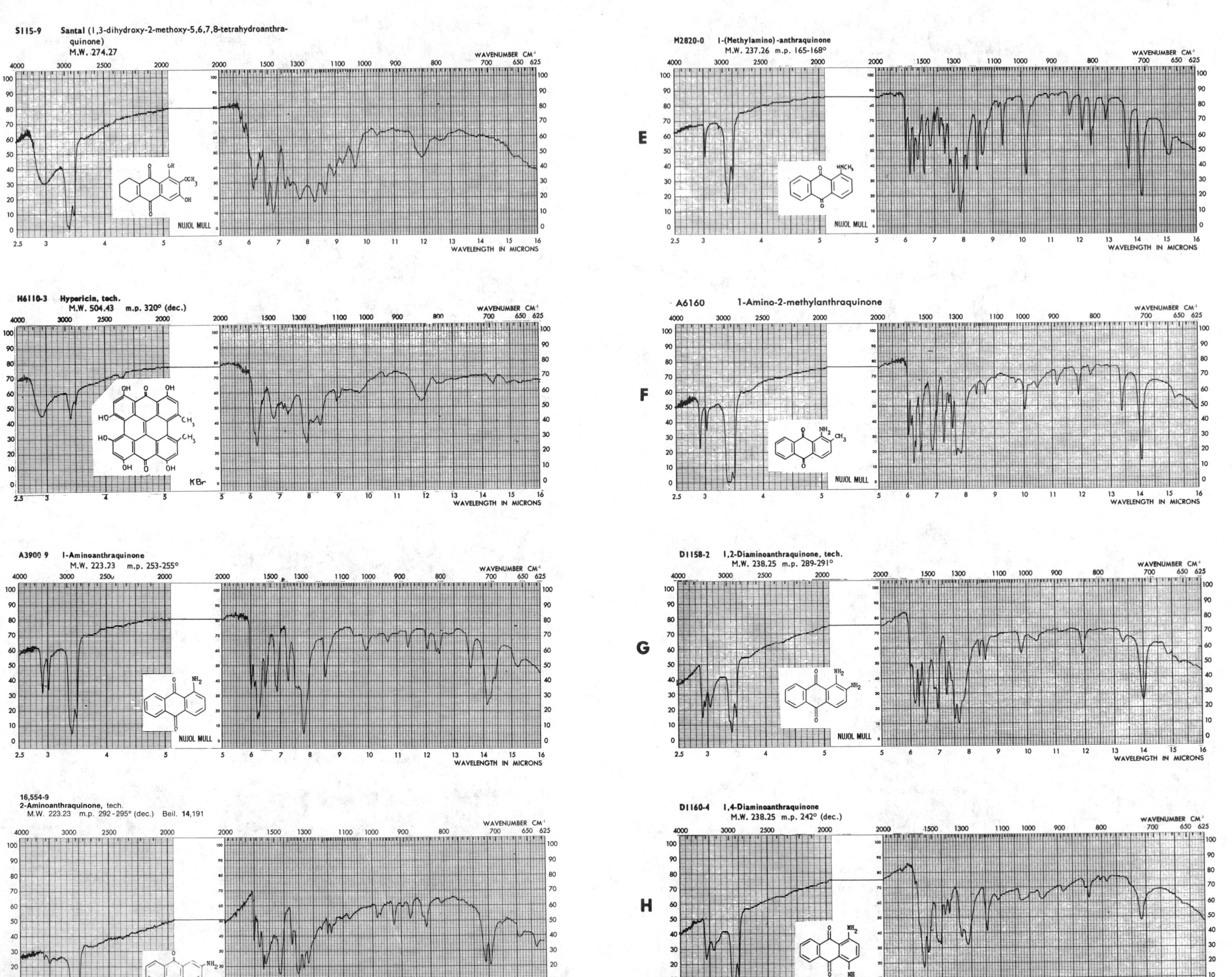
ALDRICH
A
S115-9 Santal (1,3-dihydroxy-2-methoxy-5,6,7,8-tetrahydroanthraquinone)
M.W. 274.27
NUJOL MULL
B
H6110-3 Hypericin, tech.
M.W. 504.43 m.p. 320° (dec.)
KBr
C
A3900 9 1-Aminoanthraquinone
M.W. 223.23 m.p. 253-255°
NUJOL MULL
D
16,554-9
2-Aminoanthraquinone, tech.
M.W. 223.23 m.p. 292-295° (dec.) Beil. 14,191
E
M2820-0 1-(Methylamino)-anthraquinone
M.W. 237.26 m.p. 165-168°
NUJOL MULL
F
A6160 1-Amino-2-methylanthraquinone
NUJOL MULL
G
D1158-2 1,2-Diaminoanthraquinone, tech.
M.W. 238.25 m.p. 289-291°
NUJOL MULL
H
D1160-4 1,4-Diaminoanthraquinone
M.W. 238.25 m.p. 242° (dec.)
WAVENUMBER CM⁻¹
WAVELENGTH IN MICRONS

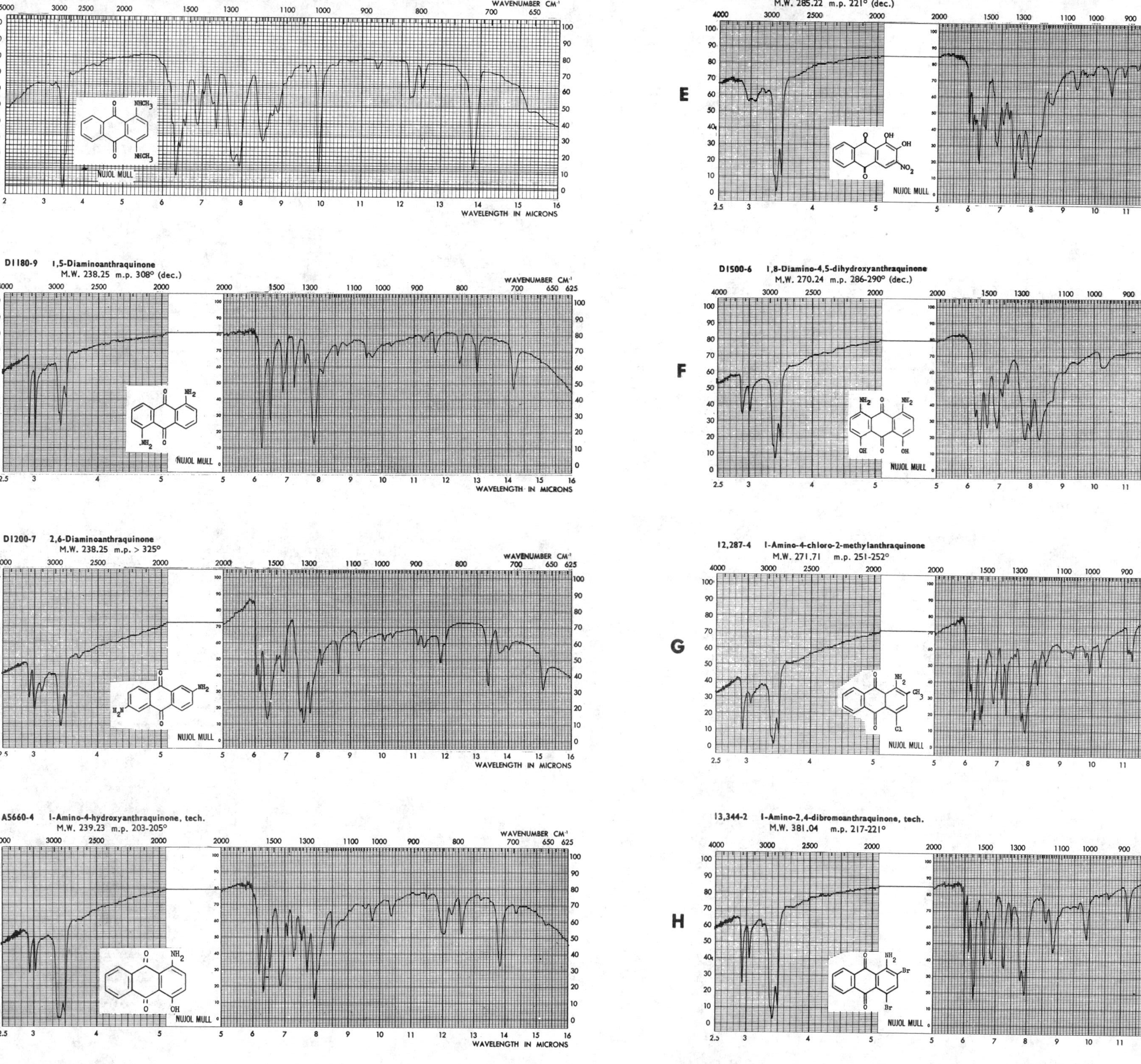
A
B4,725 1,4-Bis-(methylamino)-anthraquinone, tech.
M.W. 265.10 m.p. 217°
NUJOL MULL
B
D1180-9 1,5-Diaminoanthraquinone
M.W. 238.25 m.p. 308° (dec.)
NUJOL MULL
C
D1200-7 2,6-Diaminoanthraquinone
M.W. 238.25 m.p. > 325°
NUJOL MULL
D
A5660-4 1-Amino-4-hydroxyanthraquinone, tech.
M.W. 239.23 m.p. 203-205°
NUJOL MULL
E
12,733-7 Alizarin orange (1,2-dihydroxy-3-nitroanthraquinone)
M.W. 285.22 m.p. 221° (dec.)
NUJOL MULL
F
D1500-6 1,8-Diamino-4,5-dihydroxyanthraquinone
M.W. 270.24 m.p. 286-290° (dec.)
NUJOL MULL
G
12,287-4 1-Amino-4-chloro-2-methylanthraquinone
M.W. 271.71 m.p. 251-252°
NUJOL MULL
H
13,344-2 1-Amino-2,4-dibromoanthraquinone, tech.
M.W. 381.04 m.p. 217-221°
NUJOL MULL
WAVENUMBER CM⁻¹
WAVELENGTH IN MICRONS
ALDRICH

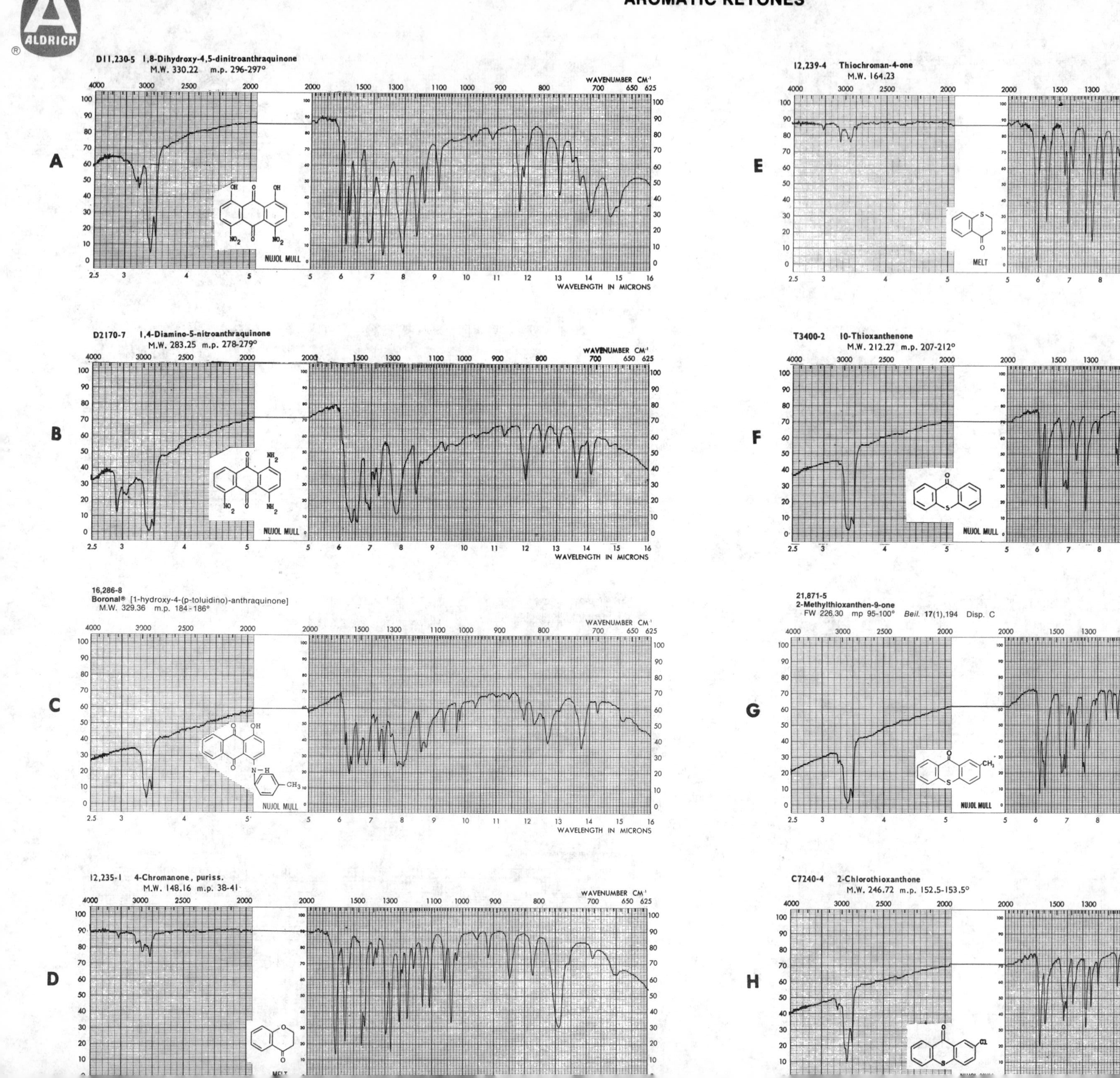
ALDRICH
A
D11,230-5 1,8-Dihydroxy-4,5-dinitroanthraquinone
M.W. 330.22 m.p. 296-297°
NUJOL MULL
B
D2170-7 1,4-Diamino-5-nitroanthraquinone
M.W. 283.25 m.p. 278-279°
NUJOL MULL
C
16,286-8
Boronal® [1-hydroxy-4-(p-toluidino)-anthraquinone]
M.W. 329.36 m.p. 184-186°
NUJOL MULL
D
12,235-1 4-Chromanone, puriss.
M.W. 148.16 m.p. 38-41
MELT
E
12,239-4 Thiochroman-4-one
M.W. 164.23
MELT
F
T3400-2 10-Thioxanthenone
M.W. 212.27 m.p. 207-212°
NUJOL MULL
G
21,871-5
2-Methylthioxanthen-9-one
FW 226.30 mp 95-100° Beil. 17(1),194 Disp. C
NUJOL MULL
H
C7240-4 2-Chlorothioxanthone
M.W. 246.72 m.p. 152.5-153.5°
WAVENUMBER CM⁻¹
WAVELENGTH IN MICRONS

A X60-0 **Xanthone** (9-xanthenone)
M.W. 196.21 m.p. 170-173°
NUJOL MULL

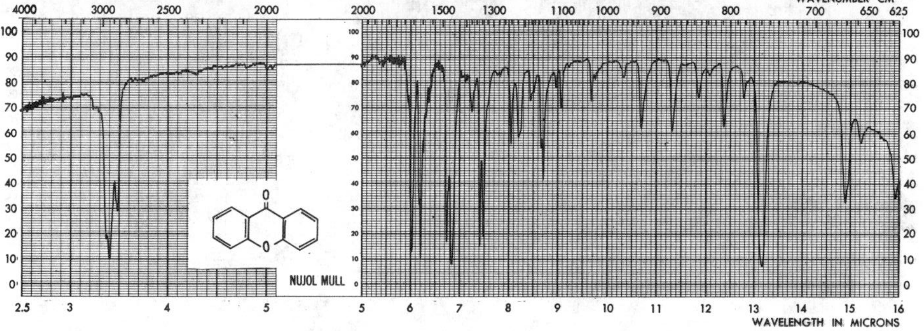

B 15,021-5 **9(10H)-Acridone** (9-acridanone)
M.W. 195.22 m.p. >300°
NUJOL MULL

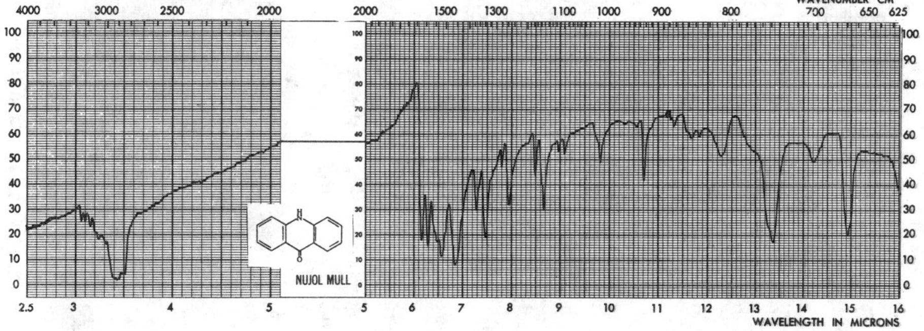

C 19,250-3
10-Methyl-9(10*H*)-acridone, 98%
FW 209.25 mp 204-207° Disp. C
NUJOL MULL

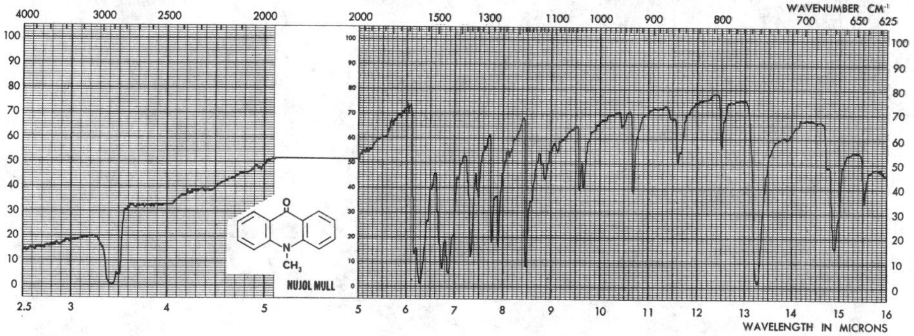

D 12,496-6 **3-Chloro-9-acridone**
M.W. 229.67 m.p. >325°
NUJOL MULL

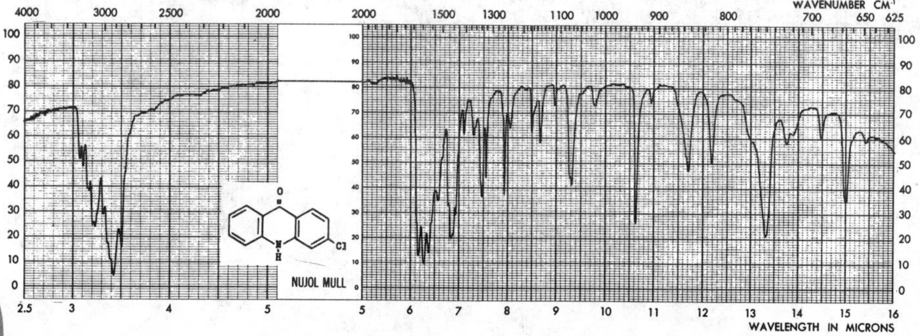

E 19,922-2
Chromone, 97% [1-benzopyran-4(4*H*)-one]
FW 146.15 mp 55-57° *Beil.* **17**,327 Disp. C
MELT

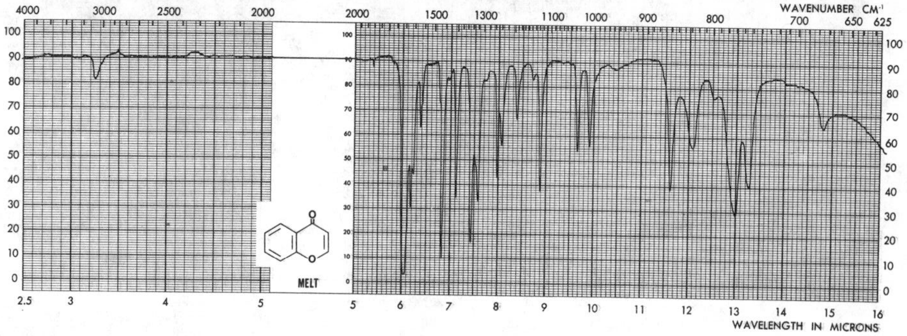

F 12,977-1 **3-Methylchromone**
M.W. 160.17 m.p. 67-70°
MELT

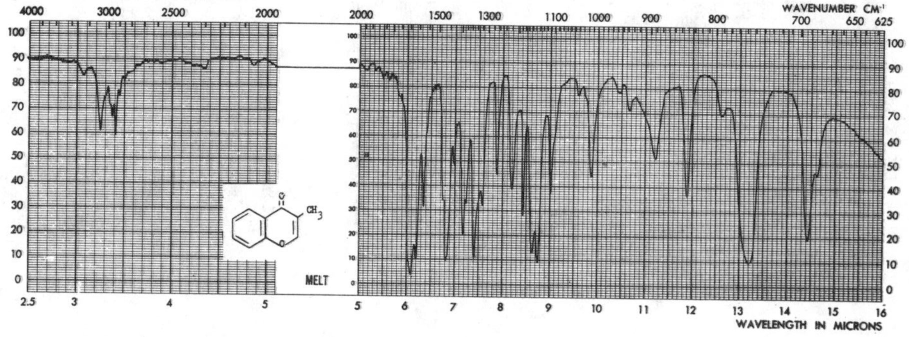

G 12,977-1 **3-Methylchromone**
M.W. 160.17 m.p. 67-70°
NUJOL MULL

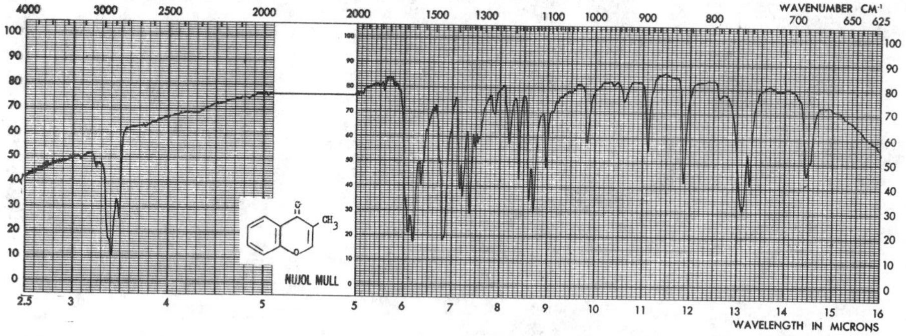

H 15,672-8
6-Methyl-4-chromanone
M.W. 162.19 m.p. 33-35°
b.p. 141-143°/13.5mm. d 1.071 Beil. **17**(1),163
MELT

ALDRICH ®

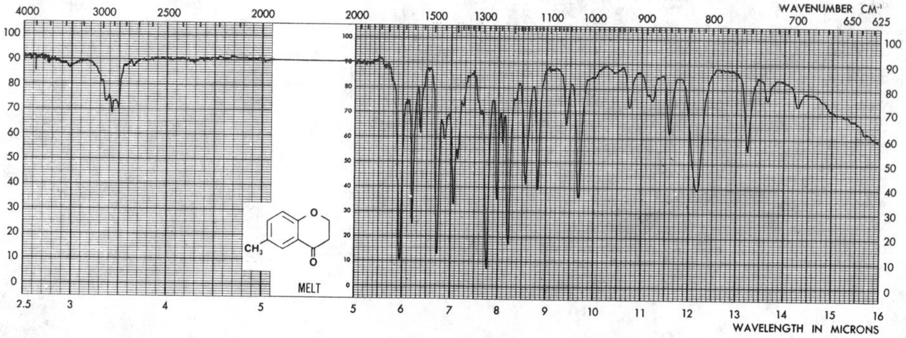

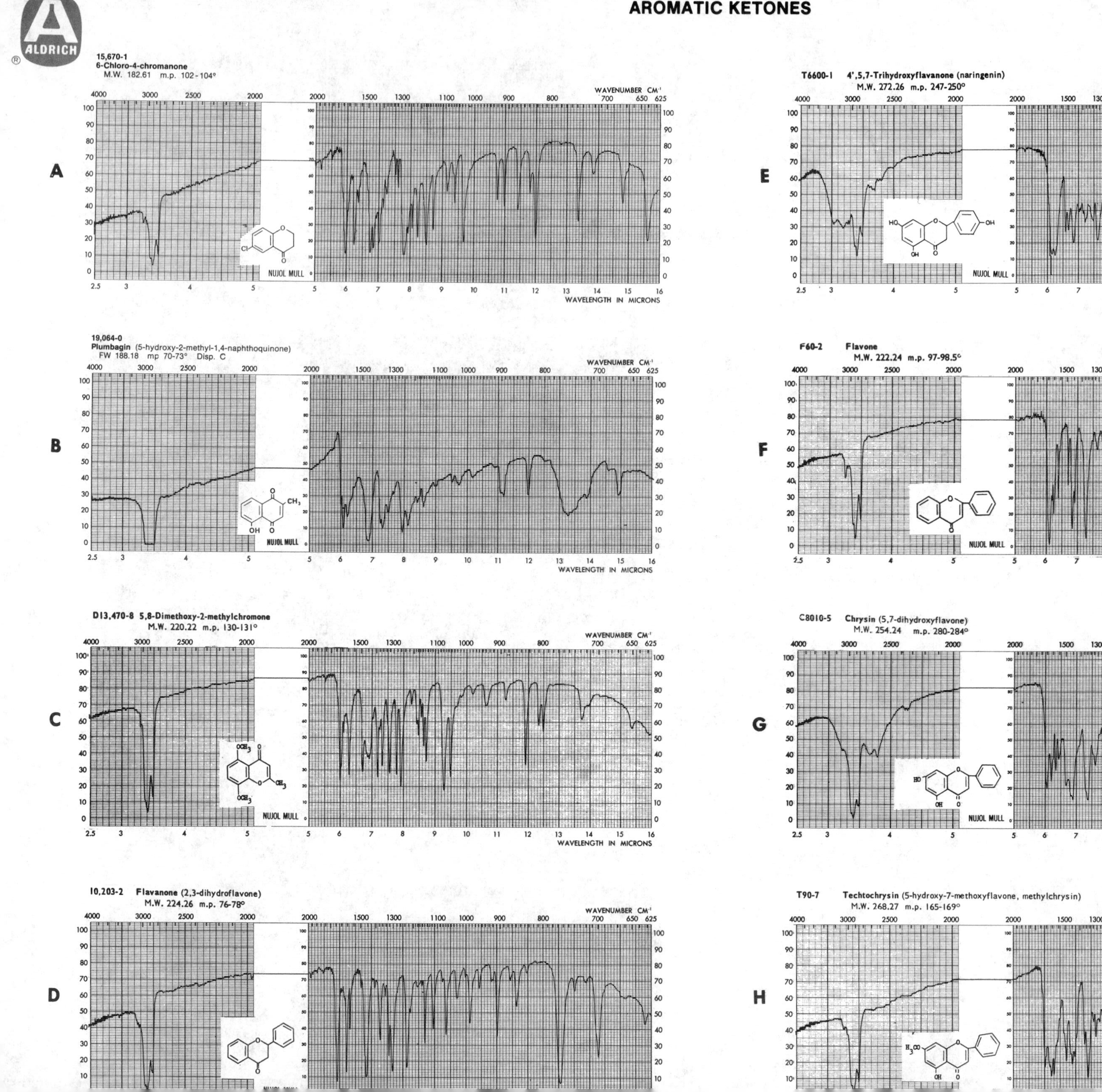
ALDRICH
A
15,670-1
6-Chloro-4-chromanone
M.W. 182.61 m.p. 102-104°
NUJOL MULL
B
19,064-0
Plumbagin (5-hydroxy-2-methyl-1,4-naphthoquinone)
FW 188.18 mp 70-73° Disp. C
NUJOL MULL
C
D13,470-8 5,8-Dimethoxy-2-methylchromone
M.W. 220.22 m.p. 130-131°
NUJOL MULL
D
10,203-2 Flavanone (2,3-dihydroflavone)
M.W. 224.26 m.p. 76-78°
E
T6600-1 4',5,7-Trihydroxyflavanone (naringenin)
M.W. 272.26 m.p. 247-250°
NUJOL MULL
F
F60-2 Flavone
M.W. 222.24 m.p. 97-98.5°
NUJOL MULL
G
C8010-5 Chrysin (5,7-dihydroxyflavone)
M.W. 254.24 m.p. 280-284°
NUJOL MULL
H
T90-7 Techtochrysin (5-hydroxy-7-methoxyflavone, methylchrysin)
M.W. 268.27 m.p. 165-169°
WAVENUMBER CM⁻¹
WAVELENGTH IN MICRONS

A

M.W. 270.24 m.p. 360°

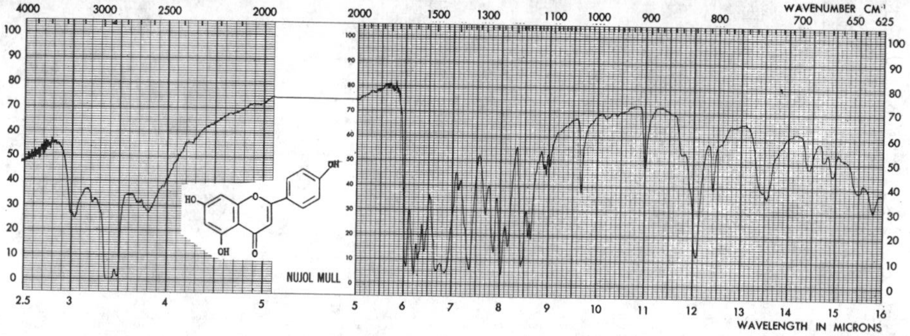

NUJOL MULL

B

14,563-7 Biochanin A (5,7-dihydroxy-4'-methoxyisoflavone)
M.W. 284.27

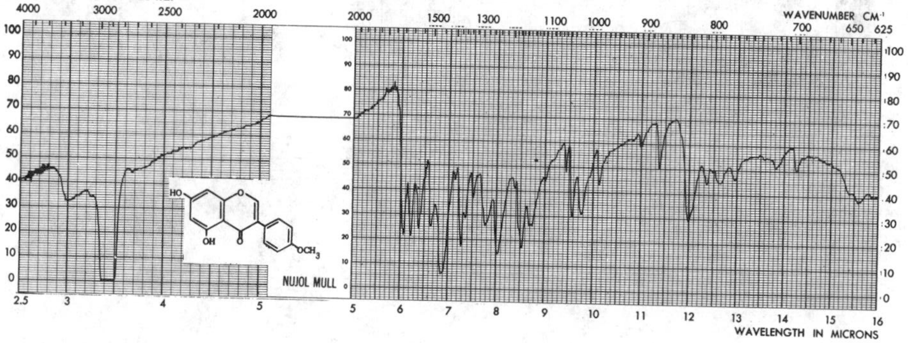

NUJOL MULL

C

A5-9 Acacetin (5,7-dihydroxy-4'-methoxyflavone)
M.W. 284.27 m.p. 266-267°

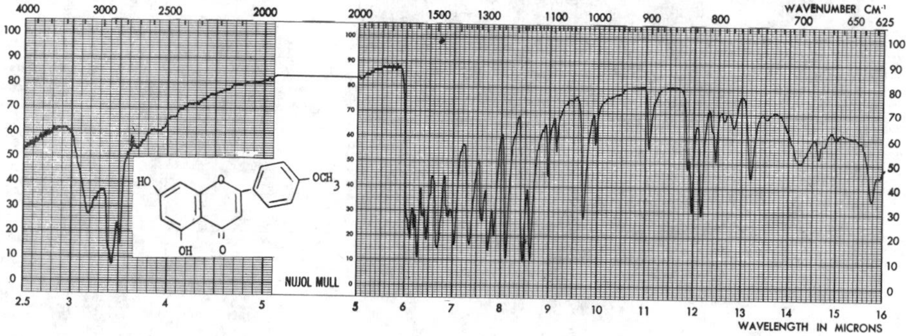

NUJOL MULL

D

M2600-3 4'-Methoxy-3',5,7-trihydroxyflavanone
M.W. 302.28 m.p. 223-225°

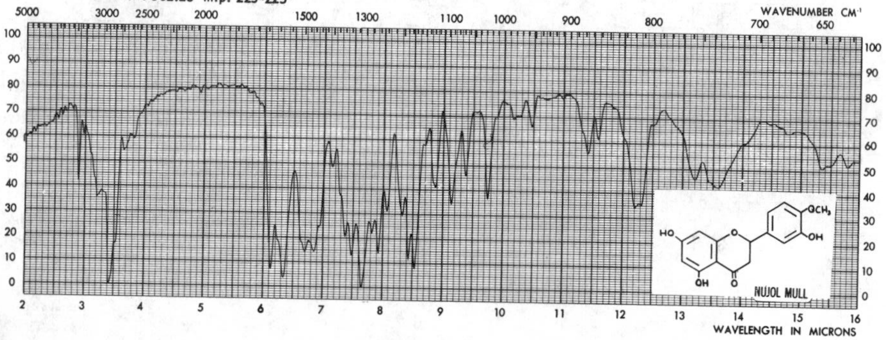

NUJOL MULL

E

F50-5 Fisetin (3,3',4',7-tetrahydroxyflavone), tech.
M.W. 286.24

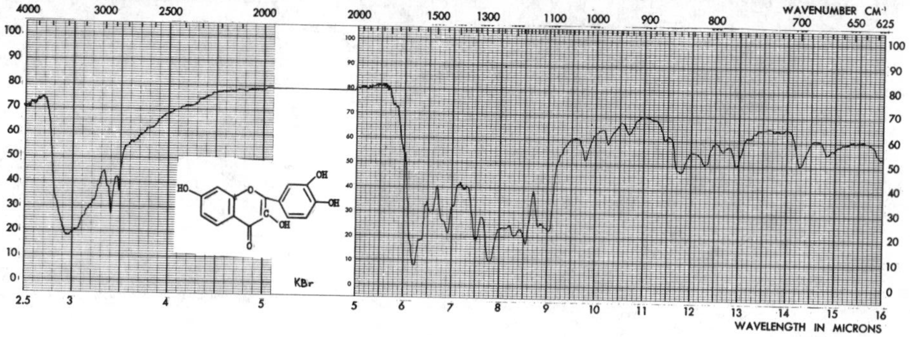

KBr

F

17,196-4
Quercetin dihydrate (3,3',4',5,7-pentahydroxyflavone)
M.W. 338.26 m.p. >300° Beil. 18,242

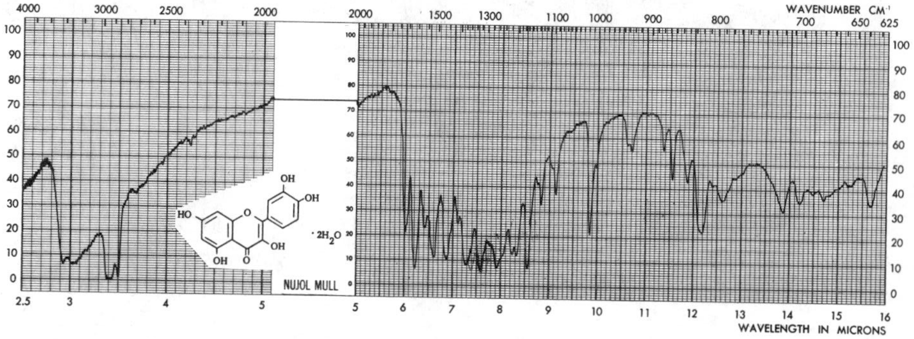

$\cdot 2H_2O$

NUJOL MULL

G

M8763-0 Morin (2',3,4',5,7-pentahydroxyflavone) dihydrate
M.W. 338.26 m.p. 299° (dec.)

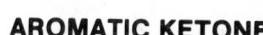

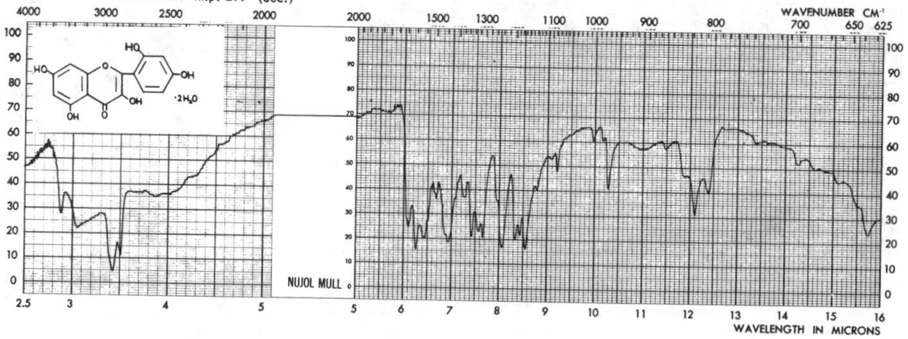

$\cdot 2H_2O$

NUJOL MULL

H

R230-3 Rutin
M.W. 610.51 m.p. 195°

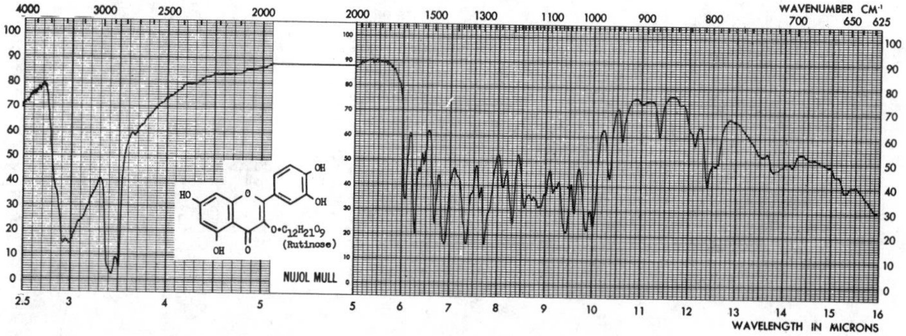

$O\text{-}C_{12}H_{21}O_9$ (Rutinose)

NUJOL MULL

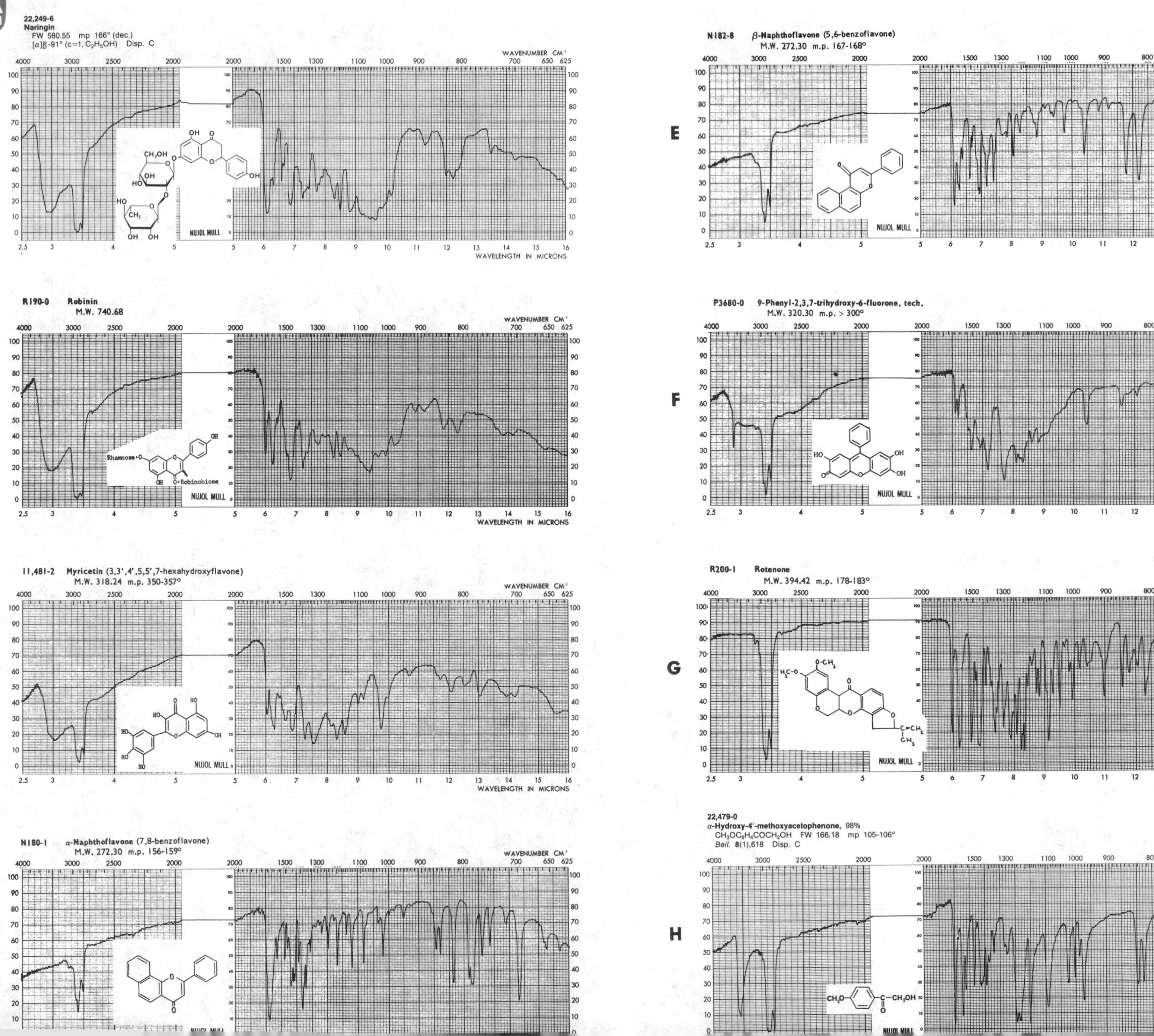
A
22,249-6
Naringin
FW 580.55 mp 166° (dec.)
[α]D -91° (c=1, C2H5OH) Disp. C
NUJOL MULL
B
R190-0 Robinin
M.W. 740.68
Rhamnose-O
O-Robinobiose
NUJOL MULL
C
11,481-2 Myricetin (3,3',4',5,5',7-hexahydroxyflavone)
M.W. 318.24 m.p. 350-357°
NUJOL MULL
D
N180-1 α-Naphthoflavone (7,8-benzoflavone)
M.W. 272.30 m.p. 156-159°
E
N182-8 β-Naphthoflavone (5,6-benzoflavone)
M.W. 272.30 m.p. 167-168°
NUJOL MULL
F
P3680-0 9-Phenyl-2,3,7-trihydroxy-6-fluorone, tech.
M.W. 320.30 m.p. > 300°
NUJOL MULL
G
R200-1 Rotenone
M.W. 394.42 m.p. 178-183°
NUJOL MULL
H
22,479-0
α-Hydroxy-4'-methoxyacetophenone, 98%
CH3OC6H4COCH2OH FW 166.18 mp 105-106°
Beil. 8(1),618 Disp. C
NUJOL MULL
WAVENUMBER CM-1
WAVELENGTH IN MICRONS

AROMATIC ALDEHYDES

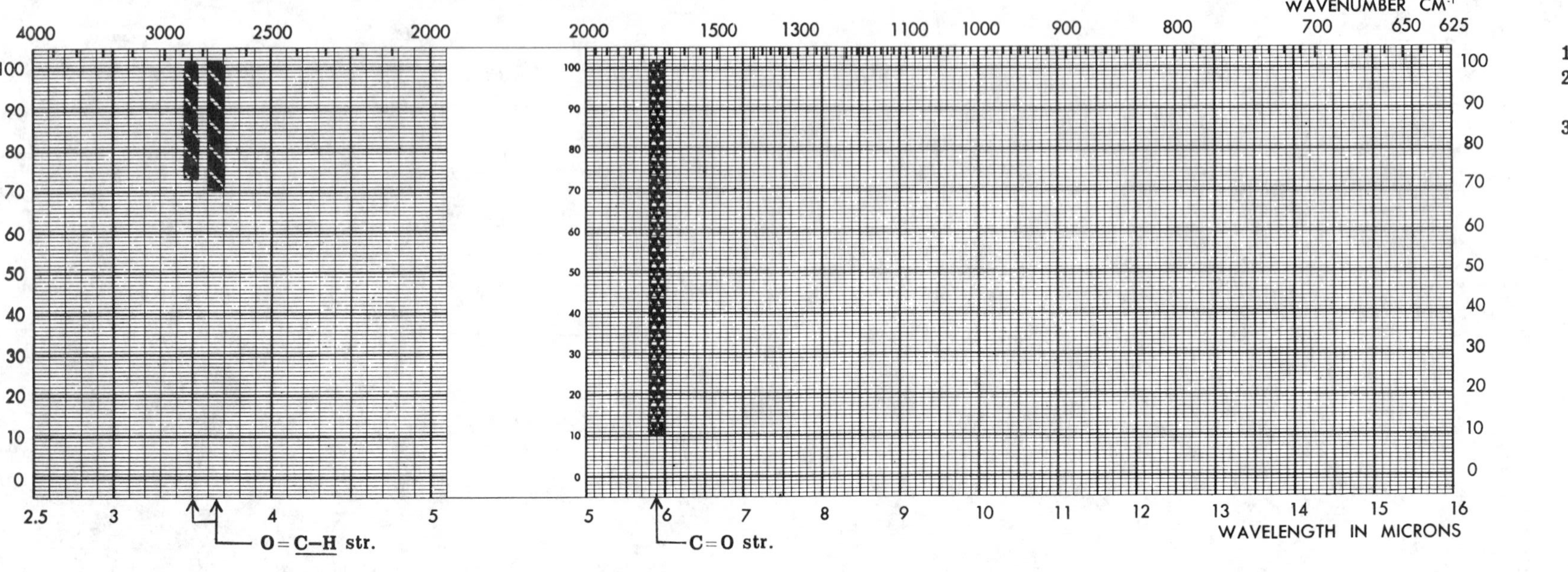

The effect of conjugation on the position of the carbonyl band at 5.8 μ (1725 cm^{-1}) is similar to that seen in the aromatic ketone section in shifting it to 5.9 – 6 μ (1695 – 1665 cm^{-1}). The exact position of this band is influenced to a certain extent by other substituents on the ring. For instance, the hydroxybenzaldehydes absorb near 6 μ (1665 cm^{-1}) (see spectra 912E 913G and 915D) while meta-nitrobenzaldehyde (spectrum 913H) absorbs near 5.85 μ (1710 cm^{-1}).

The CH of the aldehyde function absorbs at 3.65 μ (2740 cm^{-1}) and 3.5 μ (2855 cm^{-1}).

The aldehyde carbonyl attached directly to the aromatic ring alters the substitution bands between 11 and 15 μ (910 – 665 cm^{-1}) but not as much as the keto or nitro groups.

M.W. 120.15 m.p. -10° b.p. 195° n_D^{20} 1.5293
d 1.027 Beil. 7,292

A

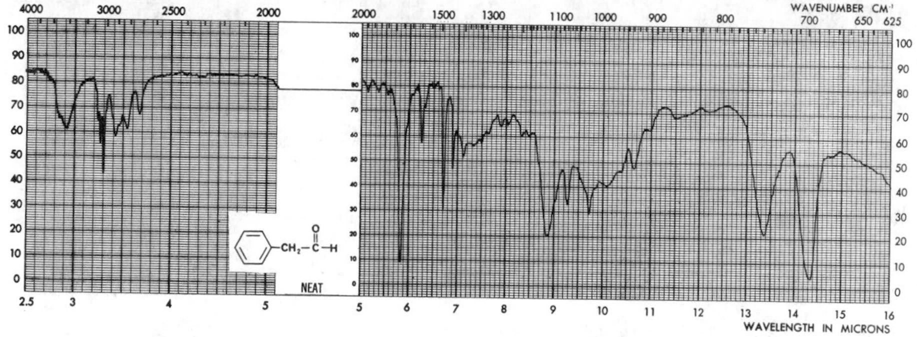

P3160-4 2-Phenylpropionaldehyde, tech.
$CH_3CH(C_6H_5)CHO$ M.W. 134.18 n_D^{20} 1.5201
b.p. 82-84°/10 mm

B

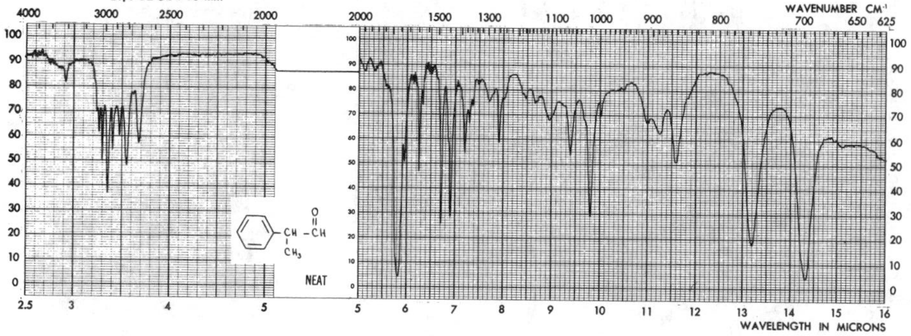

D20,425-0 Diphenylacetaldehyde
$(C_6H_5)_2CHCHO$ M.W. 196.25 n_D^{20} 1.5893

C

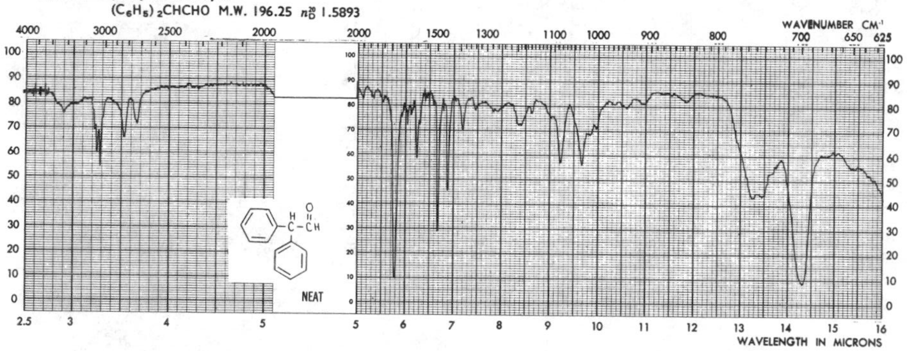

11,536-3 Bis-(o-chlorophenyl)-acetaldehyde
$(ClC_6H_4)_2CHCHO$ M.W. 265.14 m.p. 85-87°

D

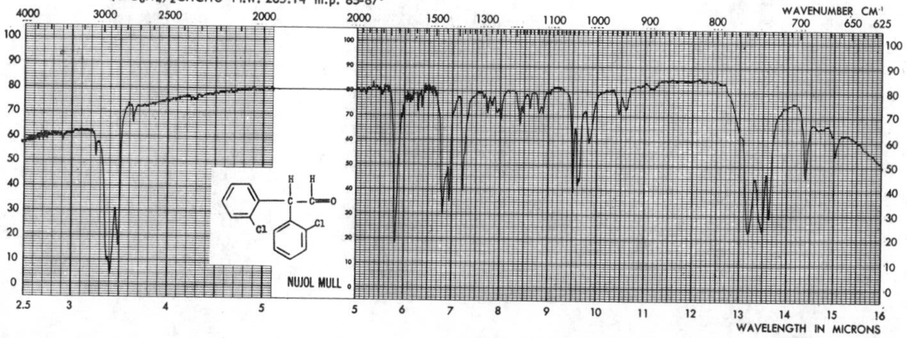

C8068-7 *trans*-Cinnamaldehyde
$C_6H_5CH{:}CHCHO$ M.W. 132.16 n_D^{20} 1.6219

E

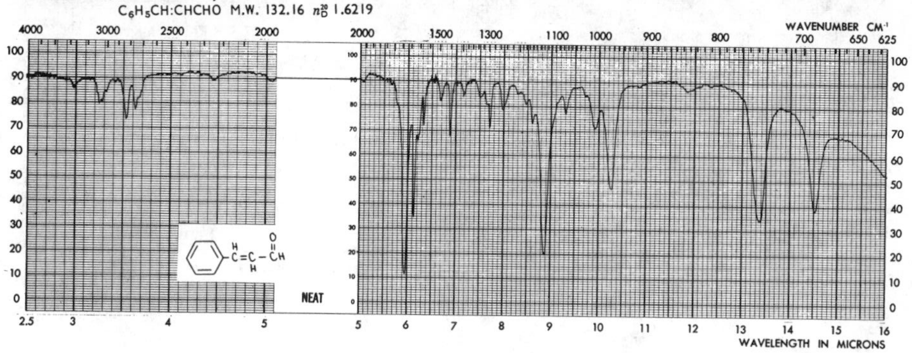

11,227-5 α-Methylcinnamaldehyde
$C_6H_5CH{:}C(CH_3)CHO$ M.W. 146.19 n_D^{20} 1.6045
b.p. 113-117°/8 mm.

F

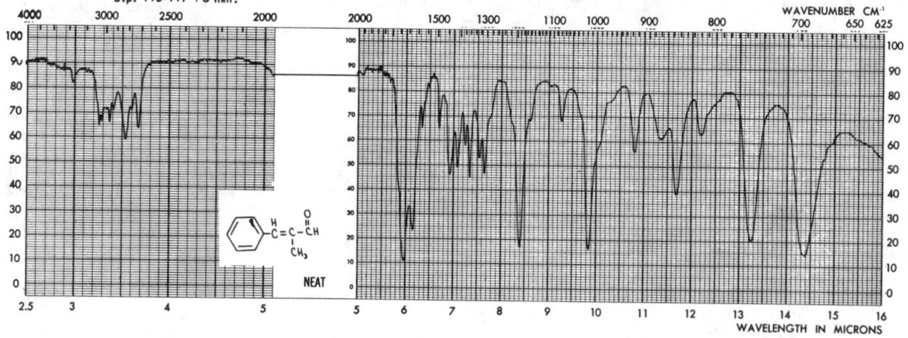

16,141-1
α-Chlorocinnamaldehyde, 95%
$C_6H_5CH{=}C(Cl)CHO$
M.W. 166.61 m.p. 32-33° Beil. 7,357
LACHRYMATOR

G

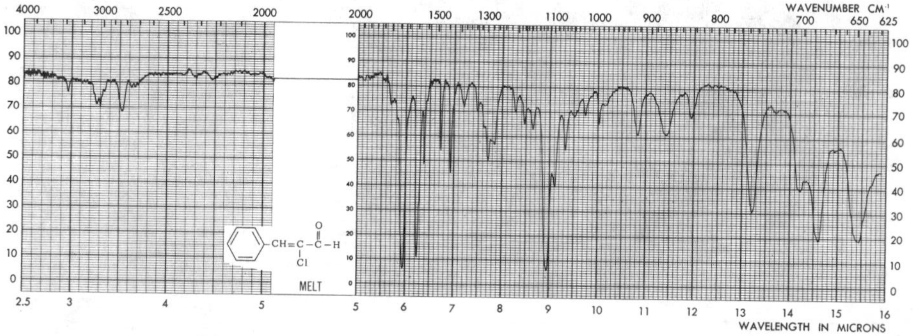

16,116-0
α-Bromocinnamaldehyde, 98%
$C_6H_5CH{=}C(Br)CHO$
M.W. 211.06 m.p. 66-68° Beil. 7,358 *IRRITANT*

H

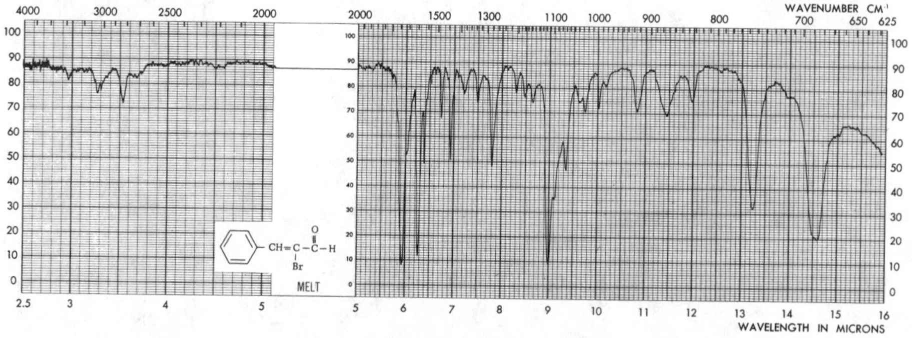

ALDRICH®

A

P2195-1 β-Phenylcinnamaldehyde (3,3-diphenylacrolein)
$(C_6H_5)_2C{:}CHCHO$ M.W. 208.26 m.p. 39-41°

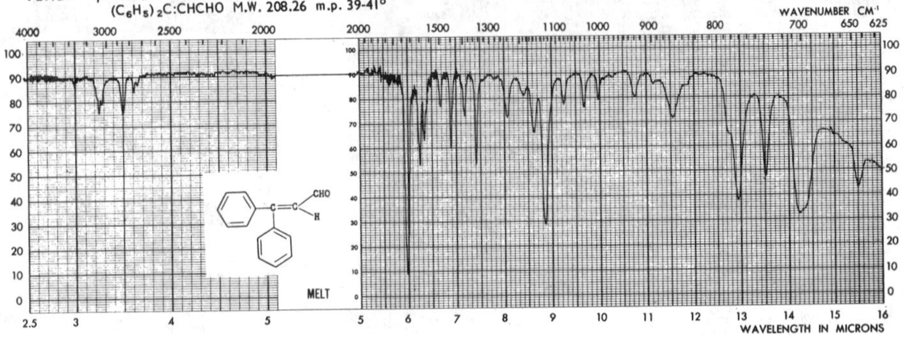

MELT

B

D14,040-6 4-Dimethylaminocinnamaldehyde
$(CH_3)_2NC_6H_4CH{:}CHCHO$ M.W. 175.23
m.p. 132-136°

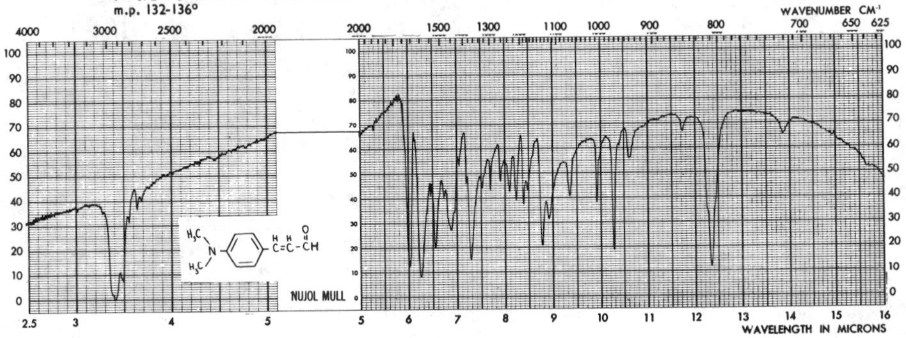

NUJOL MULL

C

N1620-7 o-Nitrocinnamaldehyde
$O_2NC_6H_4CH{:}CHCHO$ M.W. 177.16 m.p. 127-129°

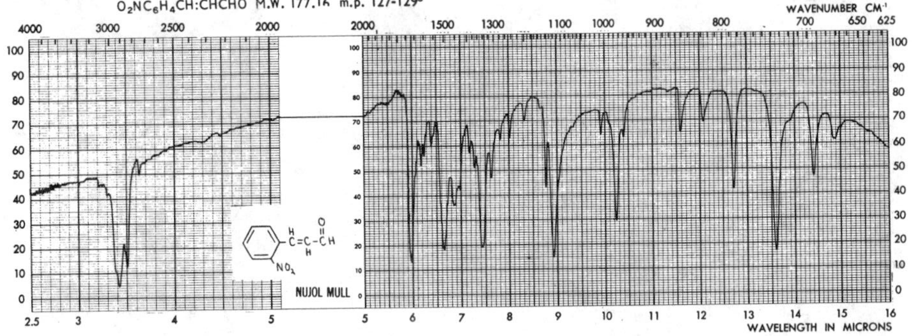

NUJOL MULL

D

14,243-3
Phenylglyoxal monohydrate, 97%
$C_6H_5COCHO{\cdot}H_2O$
M.W. 152.15 m.p. 74-76° b.p. 142°/125mm.
Beil. 7,670

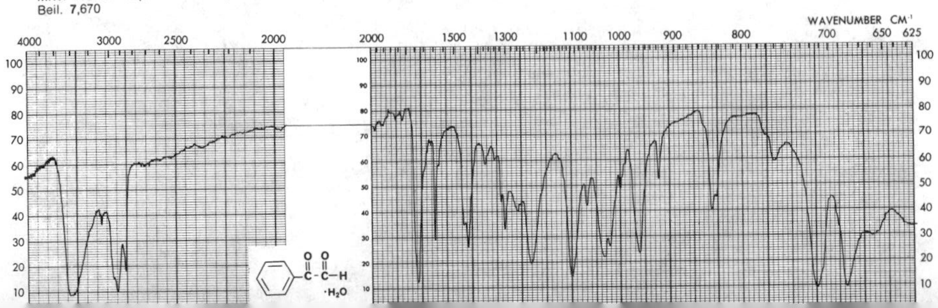

E

B133-4 Benzaldehyde
C_6H_5CHO M.W. 106.12 n_D^{20} 1.5454

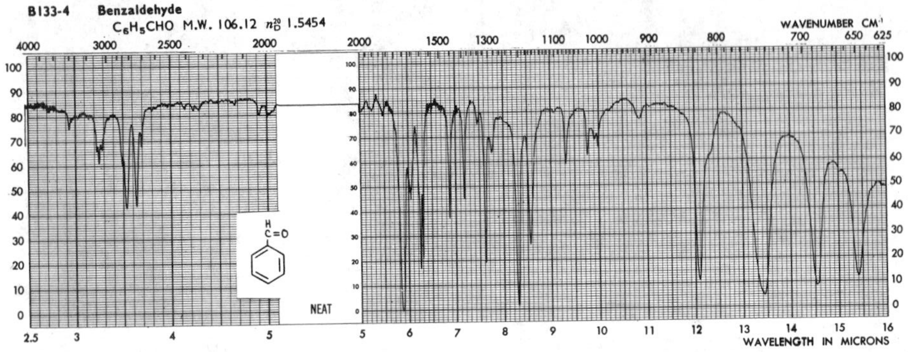

NEAT

F

11,755-2 o-Tolualdehyde
$CH_3C_6H_4CHO$ M.W. 120.15 n_D^{20} 1.5472
b.p. 85-87°/14 mm.

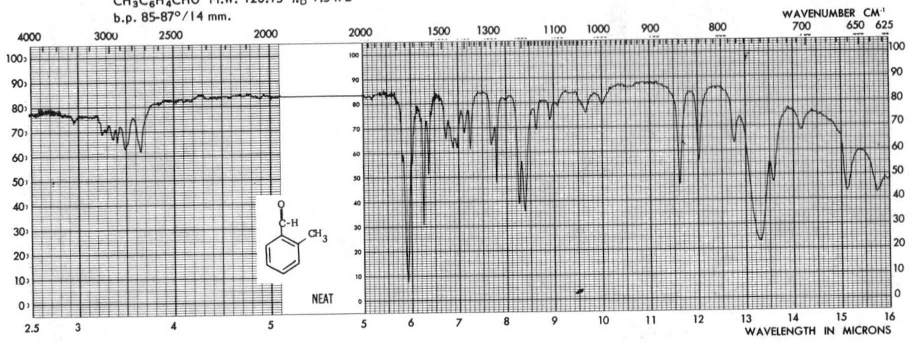

NEAT

G

13,238-1 o-(2-Chloroethyl)-benzaldehyde tech.
$ClCH_2CH_2C_6H_4CHO$ M.W. 168.62 n_D^{20} 1.5641
b.p. 101-105°/3 mm

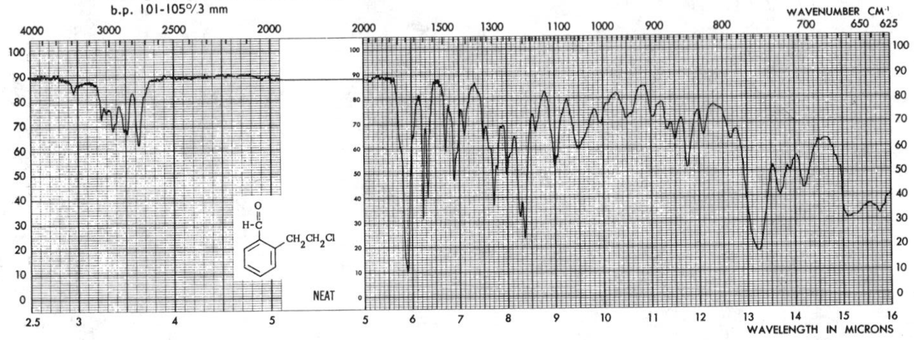

NEAT

H

F480-7 o-Fluorobenzaldehyde
FC_6H_4CHO M.W. 124.11 n_D^{20} 1.5234

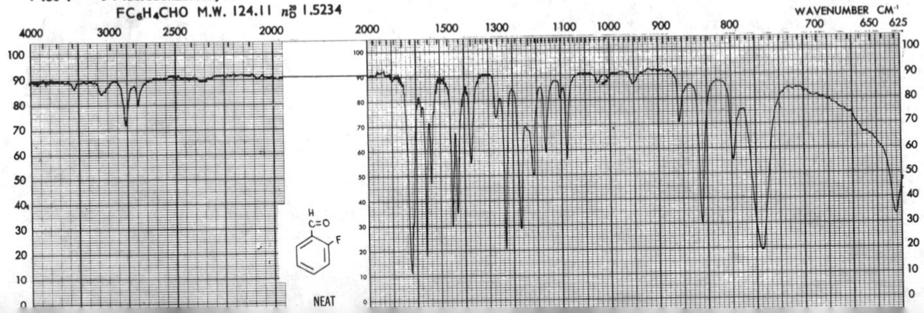

NEAT

A 12,497-4 2-Chlorobenzaldehyde
ClC_6H_4CHO M.W. 140.57 n_D^{20} 1.5658 m.p. 10-11.5°
NEAT

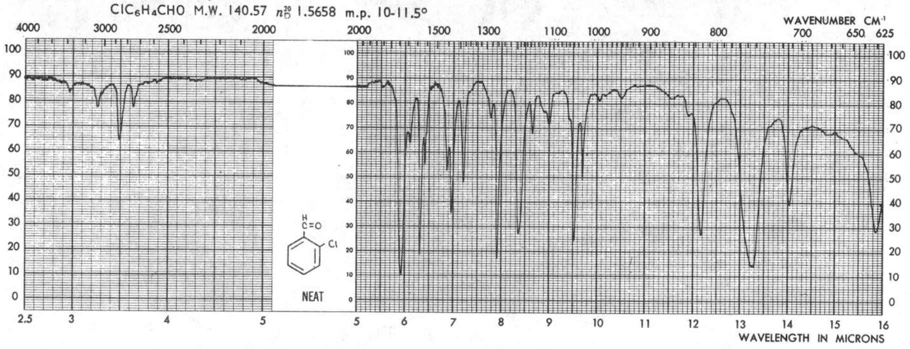

B B5700-1 2-Bromobenzaldehyde
BrC_6H_4CHO M.W. 185.03 n_D^{20} 1.5928
NEAT

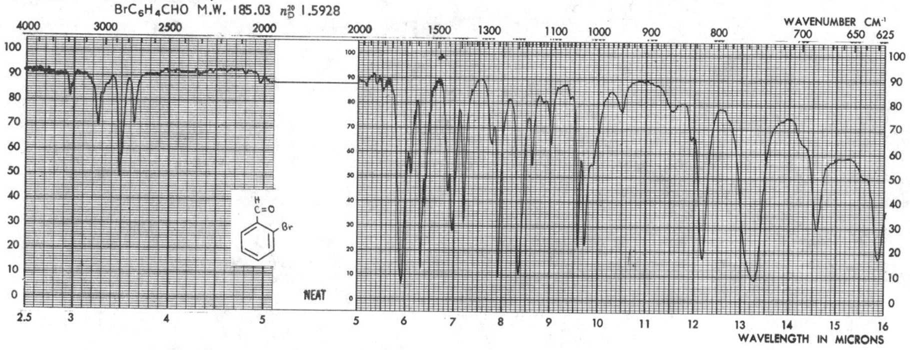

C 10,962-2 o-Anisaldehyde (o-methoxybenzaldehyde)
$CH_3OC_6H_4CHO$ M.W. 136.15 m.p. 37-39°
MELT

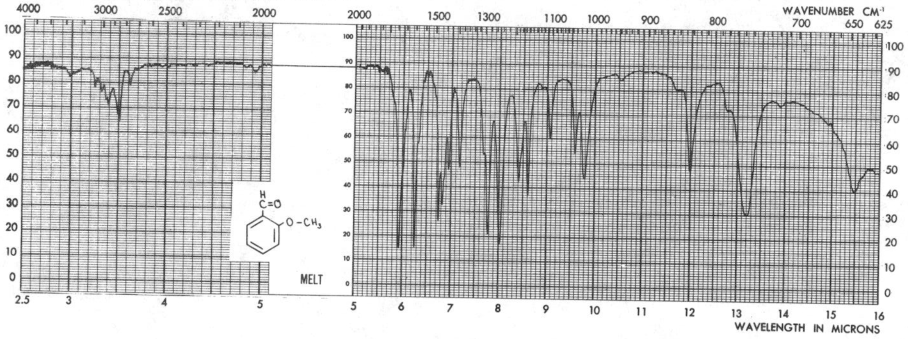

D 15,372-9 o-Ethoxybenzaldehyde
$C_2H_5OC_6H_4CHO$ M.W. 150.18
NEAT

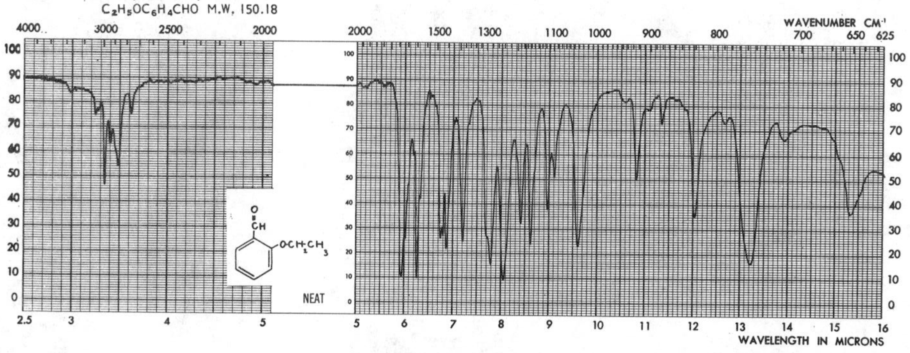

E S35-6 Salicylaldehyde
2-(HO)C_6H_4CHO M.W. 122.12 n_D^{20} 1.5719
b.p. 196.8°
NEAT

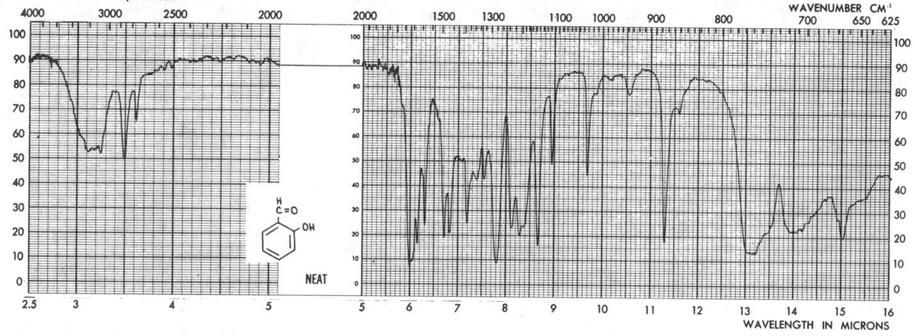

F 85,167-1
Helicin, 99% (salicylaldehyde β-D-glucoside)
M.W. 284.26 m.p. 178° $[\alpha]^{25}$ -57.1° (c=1.5, H_2O)
Beil. 31,223
NUJOL MULL

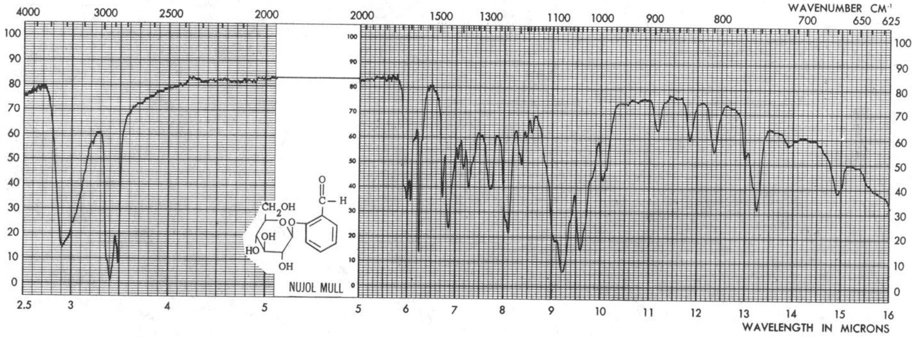

G N1080-2 o-Nitrobenzaldehyde, puriss.
$O_2NC_6H_4CHO$ M.W. 151.12
m.p. 43-46°
MELT

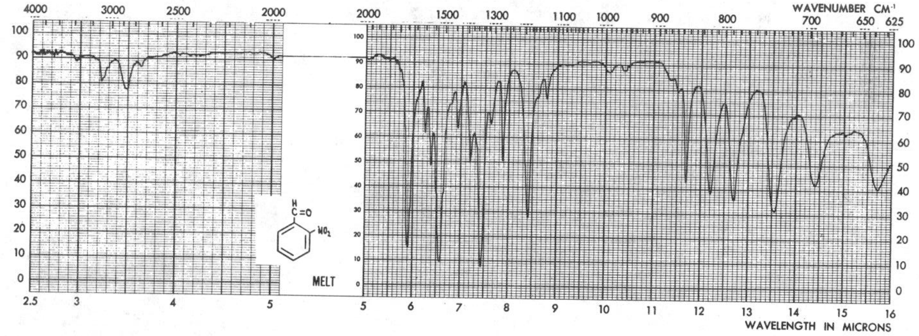

H P3940-0 o-Phthalicdicarboxaldehyde (phthalaldehyde)
$C_6H_4(CHO)_2$ M.W. 134.13
m.p. 55-58°
MELT

ALDRICH

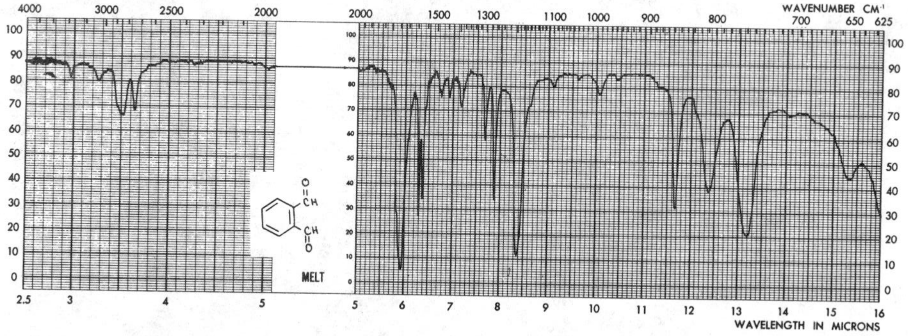

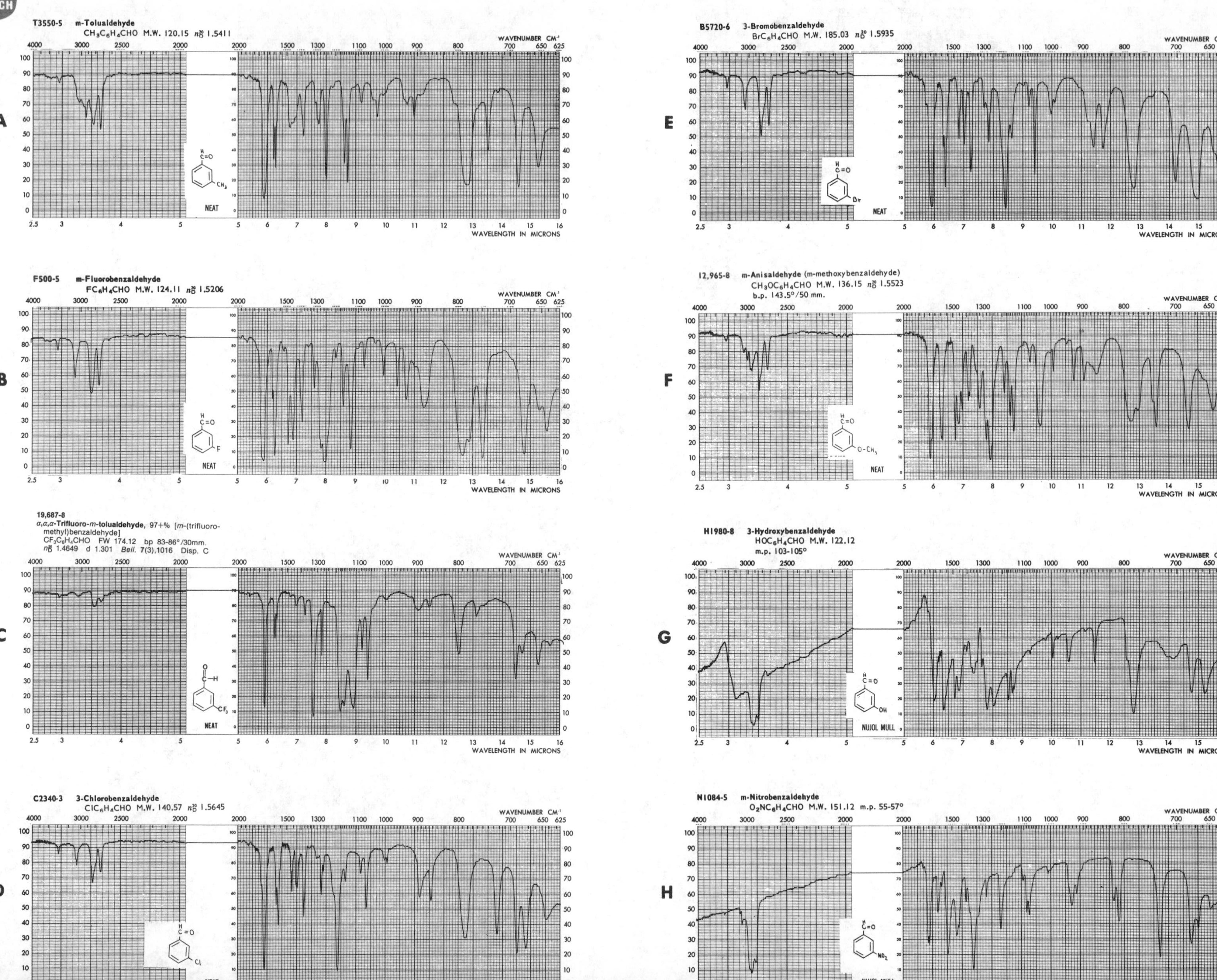
ALDRICH
A
T3550-5 m-Tolualdehyde
$CH_3C_6H_4CHO$ M.W. 120.15 n_D^{20} 1.5411
NEAT
B
F500-5 m-Fluorobenzaldehyde
FC_6H_4CHO M.W. 124.11 n_D^{20} 1.5206
NEAT
C
19,687-8
α,α,α-Trifluoro-m-tolualdehyde, 97+% [m-(trifluoromethyl)benzaldehyde]
$CF_3C_6H_4CHO$ FW 174.12 bp 83-86°/30mm.
n_D^{20} 1.4649 d 1.301 Beil. 7(3),1016 Disp. C
NEAT
D
C2340-3 3-Chlorobenzaldehyde
ClC_6H_4CHO M.W. 140.57 n_D^{20} 1.5645
E
B5720-6 3-Bromobenzaldehyde
BrC_6H_4CHO M.W. 185.03 n_D^{20} 1.5935
NEAT
F
12,965-8 m-Anisaldehyde (m-methoxybenzaldehyde)
$CH_3OC_6H_4CHO$ M.W. 136.15 n_D^{20} 1.5523
b.p. 143.5°/50 mm.
NEAT
G
H1980-8 3-Hydroxybenzaldehyde
HOC_6H_4CHO M.W. 122.12
m.p. 103-105°
NUJOL MULL
H
N1084-5 m-Nitrobenzaldehyde
$O_2NC_6H_4CHO$ M.W. 151.12 m.p. 55-57°
WAVENUMBER CM⁻¹
WAVELENGTH IN MICRONS

A

11,528-2 **Isophthalaldehyde**
C_6H_4-1,3-$(CHO)_2$ M.W. 134.13 m.p. 88-90°

NUJOL MULL

B

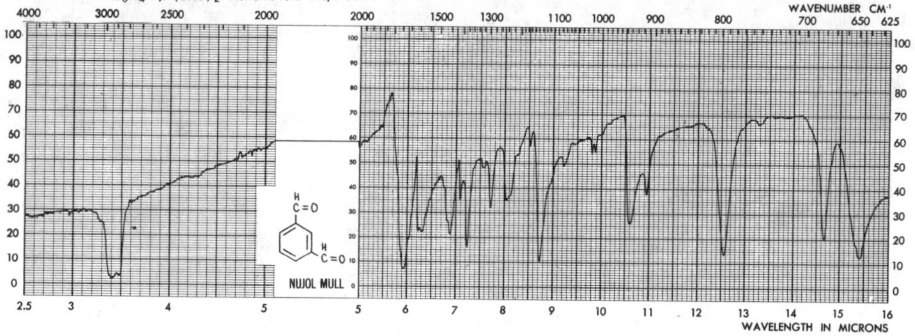

T3560-2 **p-Tolualdehyde**
$CH_3C_6H_4CHO$ M.W. 120.15 n_D^{20} 1.5447
b.p. 204-205°

NEAT

C

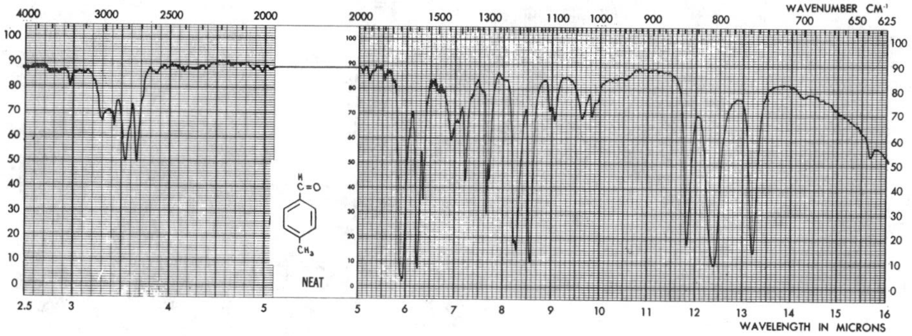

13,517-8 **p-Isopropylbenzaldehyde**
$(CH_3)_2CHC_6H_4CHO$ M.W. 148.21 n_D^{20} 1.5308
b.p. 98-100°/9 mm.

NEAT

D

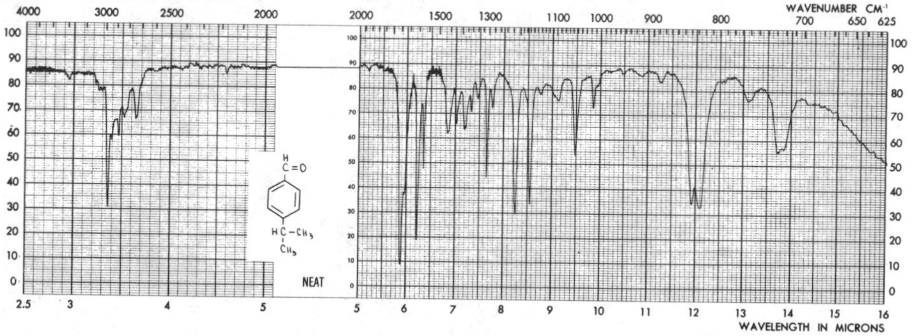

12,837-6 **p-Fluorobenzaldehyde**
FC_6H_4CHO M.W. 124.11 n_D^{20} 1.5195

NEAT

E

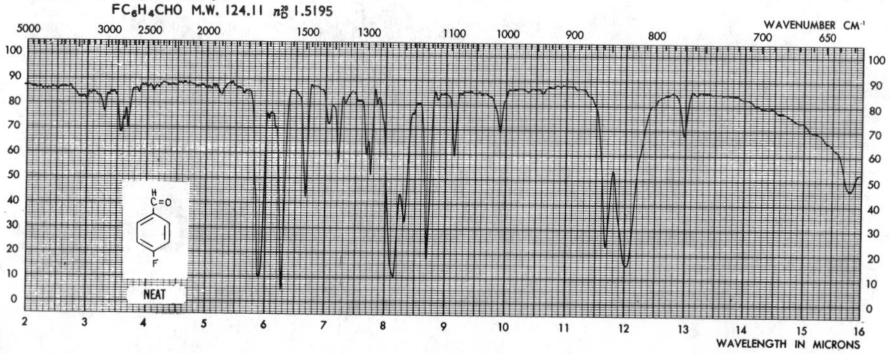

11,221-6 **4-Chlorobenzaldehyde**
ClC_6H_4CHO M.W. 140.57 m.p. 46-48°

MELT

F

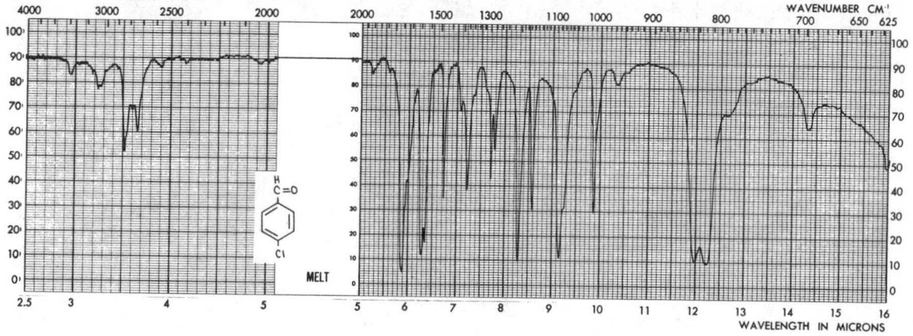

B5740-0 **4-Bromobenzaldehyde**
BrC_6H_4CHO M.W. 185.03 m.p. 58-61°

MELT

G

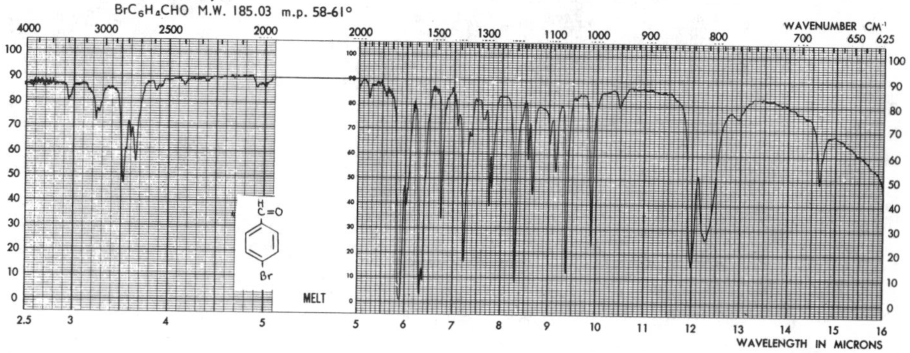

22,277-1
p-(Methylthio)benzaldehyde, 98%
$CH_3SC_6H_4CHO$ FW 152.22 bp 86-90°/1mm.
n_D^{20} 1.6452 d 1.144 *Beil.* **8**(1),533 Disp. C

NEAT

H

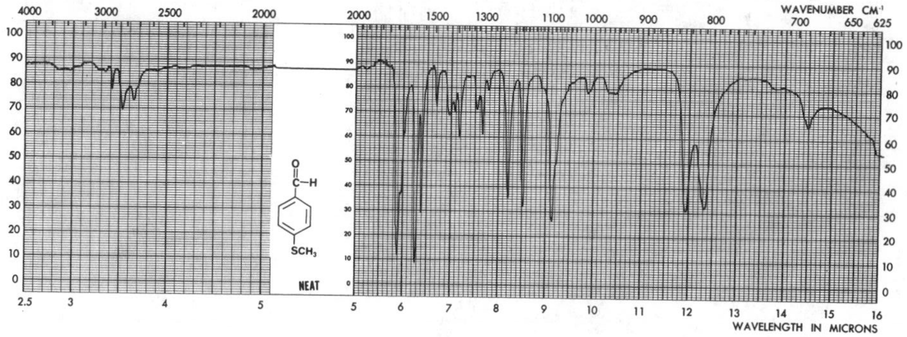

A8810-7 **p-Anisaldehyde** (p-methoxybenzaldehyde)
$CH_3OC_6H_4CHO$ M.W. 136.15 n_D^{20} 1.5713
m.p. 0-1°

NEAT

WAVENUMBER CM⁻¹ — WAVELENGTH IN MICRONS

AROMATIC ALDEHYDES

ALDRICH ®

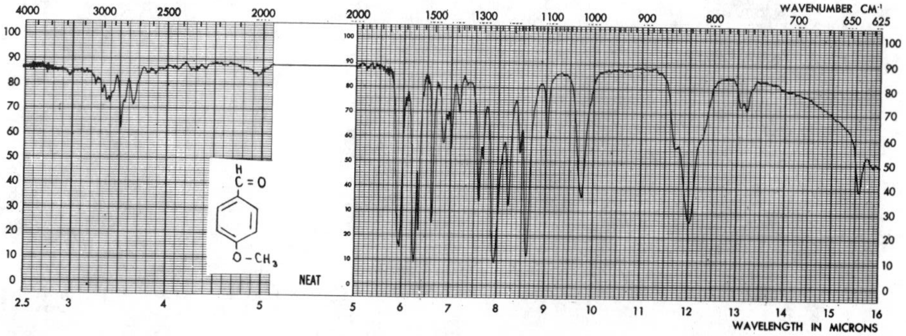

A — 17,360-6
p-Ethoxybenzaldehyde, 99%
$C_2H_5OC_6H_4CHO$
M.W. 150.18 m.p. 13-14° b.p. 255° n_D^{20} 1.5584
d 1.08 Beil. 8,73

B — 10,095-1 **p-(2-Bromoethoxy)-benzaldehyde**
$BrCH_2CH_2OC_6H_4CHO$ M.W. 229.08 m.p. 52-54°

C — D8680-9 **4-[β-(Diethylamino)-ethoxy]-benzaldehyde**
$(C_2H_5)_2NCH_2CH_2OC_6H_4CHO$ M.W. 221.30
n_D^{20} 1.5364

D — 14,408-8 **4-Hydroxybenzaldehyde**
HOC_6H_4CHO M.W. 122.12 m.p. 117-119°

E — 15,647-7
p-Dimethylaminobenzaldehyde, 99+%, GOLD LABEL
$(CH_3)_2NC_6H_4CHO$
M.W. 149.19 m.p. 73-75° Beil. 14,31
Fieser 1,273 2,146

F — D8625-6 **4-(Diethylamino)-benzaldehyde**
$(C_2H_5)_2NC_6H_4CHO$ M.W. 177.25 m.p. 39-41°

G — 12,387-0 **p-N,N-Bis-(2-chloroethyl)-aminobenzaldehyde**
$(ClCH_2CH_2)_2NC_6H_4CHO$ M.W. 246.14 m.p. 87-89°

H — 13,017-6 **p-Nitrobenzaldehyde**
$O_2NC_6H_4CHO$ M.W. 151.12 m.p. 105-108°

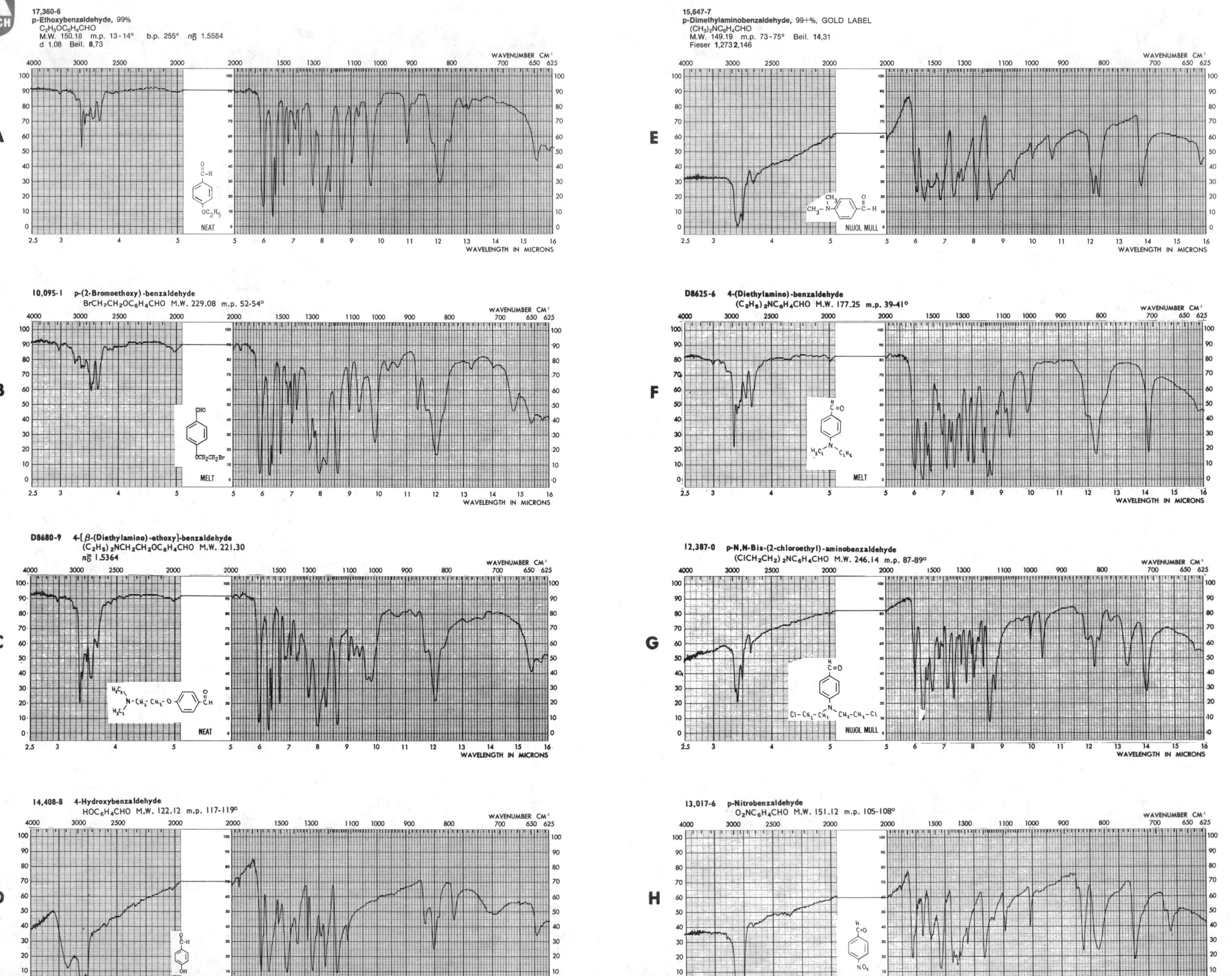

A

T220-7 Terephthaldicarboxaldehyde (terephthalaldehyde)
C_6H_4-1,4-$(CHO)_2$ M.W. 134.13
m.p. 115-116°

NUJOL MULL

B

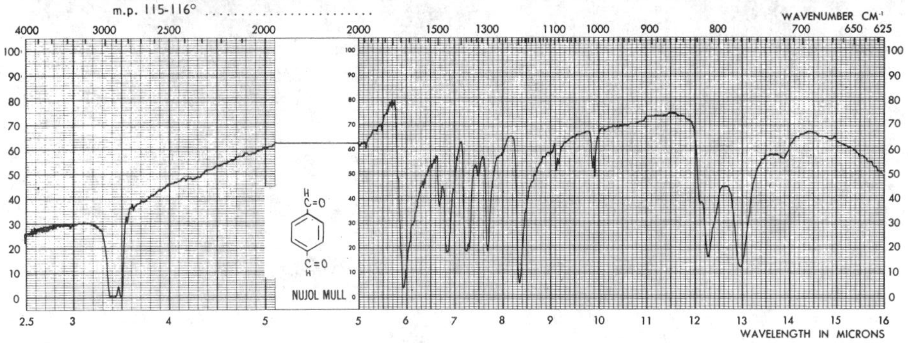

14,124-0 2-Chloro-6-fluorobenzaldehyde
$ClC_6H_3(F)CHO$ M.W. 158.56

MELT

C

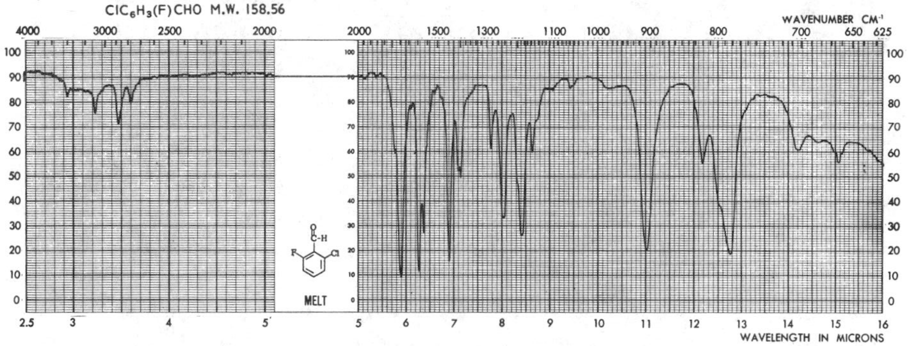

D5650-0 2,6-Dichlorobenzaldehyde
$Cl_2C_6H_3CHO$ M.W. 175.01 m.p. 70-71°

MELT

D

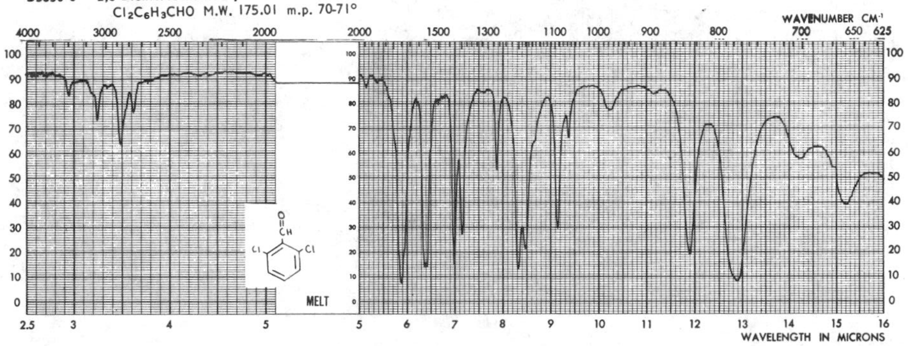

D13,020-6 2,3-Dimethoxybenzaldehyde
$(CH_3O)_2C_6H_3CHO$ M.W. 166.18
m.p. 48-52°

MELT

E

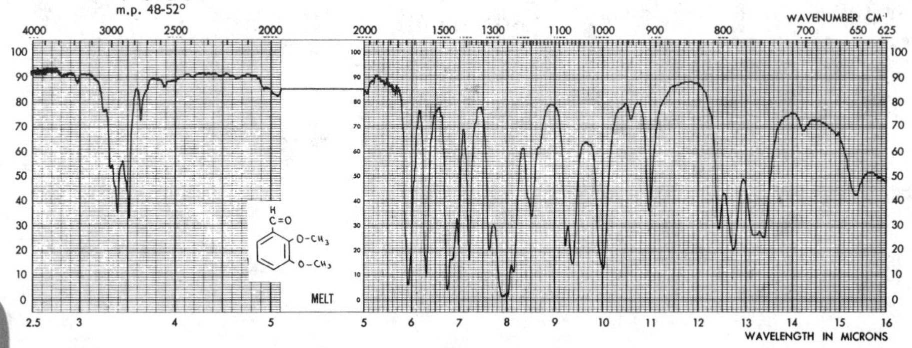

E540-9 2-Ethoxy-3-methoxybenzaldehyde (2-ethoxy-m-anisaldehyde)
$C_2H_5OC_6H_3(OCH_3)CHO$ M.W. 180.20 n_D^{20} 1.5333
b.p. 142-144°/11 mm.

NEAT

F

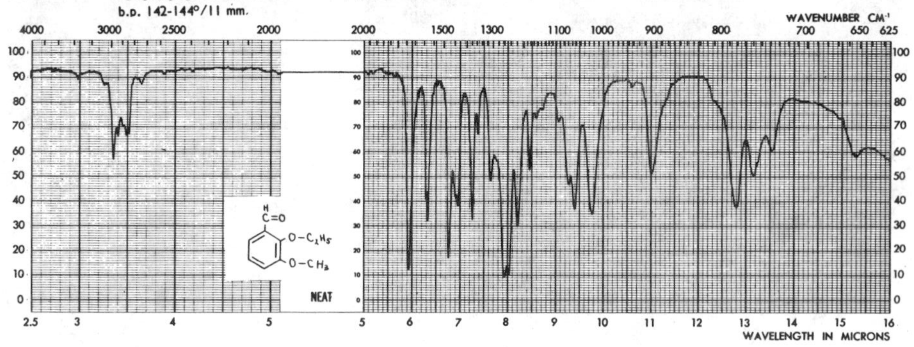

12,080-4 o-Vanillin (3-methoxysalicylaldehyde), tech.
$CH_3OC_6H_3$-2-(OH)CHO M.W. 152.15
m.p. 40-42°

MELT

G

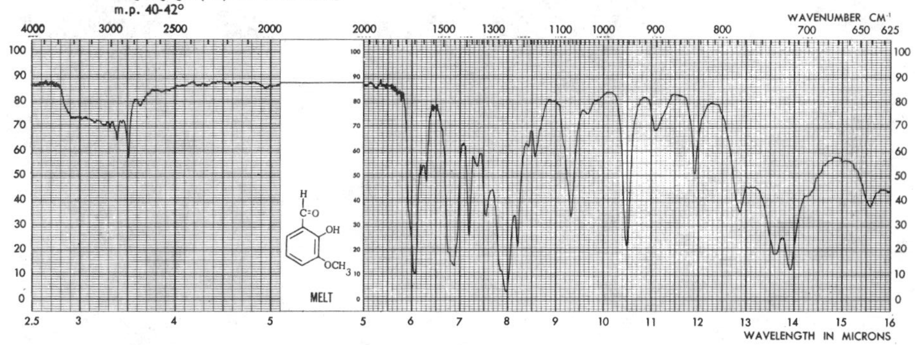

16,098-9
3-Ethoxysalicylaldehyde
$C_2H_5OC_6H_3$-2-(OH)CHO
M.W. 166.18 m.p. 66-68° b.p. 263-264°
Beil. 8(2),267

NUJOL MULL

H

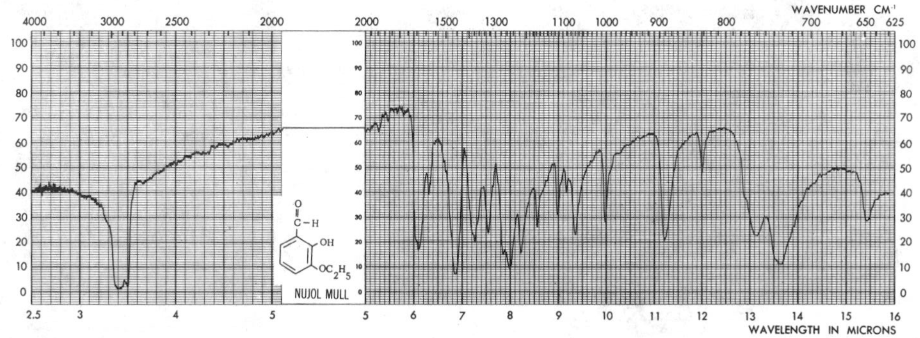

18,983-9
2,3-Dihydroxybenzaldehyde, 97%
$(HO)_2C_6H_3CHO$ FW 138.12 mp 108-110°
Beil. 8,240 Disp. B

NUJOL MULL

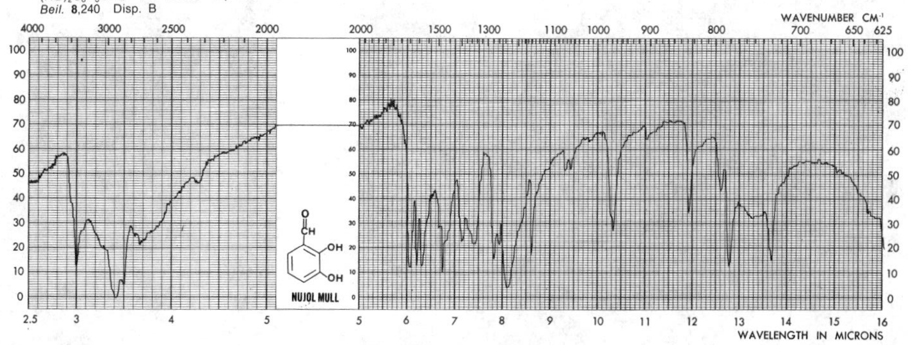

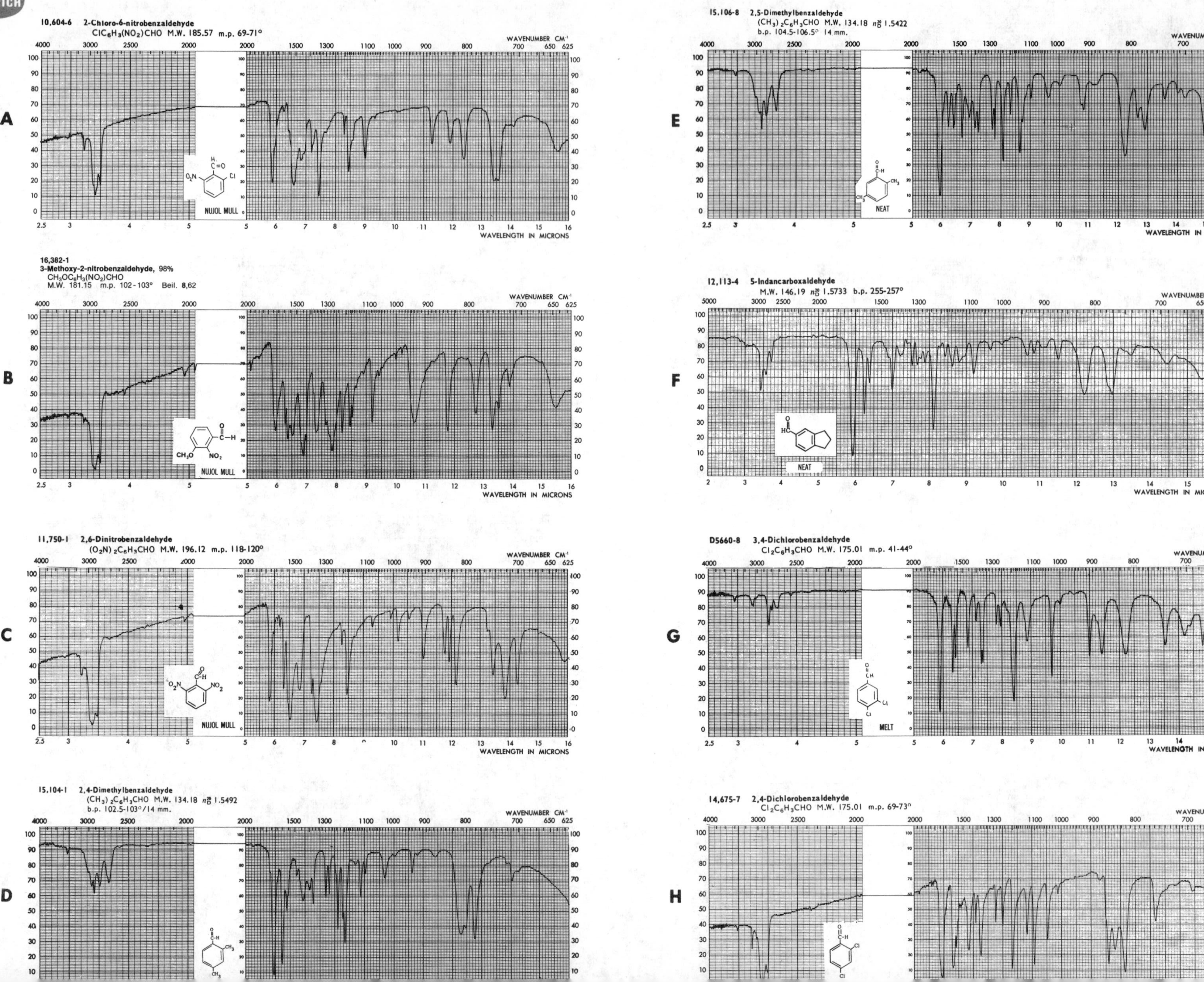
ALDRICH
A
10,604-6 2-Chloro-6-nitrobenzaldehyde
$ClC_6H_3(NO_2)CHO$ M.W. 185.57 m.p. 69-71°
NUJOL MULL
B
16,382-1
3-Methoxy-2-nitrobenzaldehyde, 98%
$CH_3OC_6H_3(NO_2)CHO$
M.W. 181.15 m.p. 102-103° Beil. 8,62
NUJOL MULL
C
11,750-1 2,6-Dinitrobenzaldehyde
$(O_2N)_2C_6H_3CHO$ M.W. 196.12 m.p. 118-120°
NUJOL MULL
D
15,104-1 2,4-Dimethylbenzaldehyde
$(CH_3)_2C_6H_3CHO$ M.W. 134.18 n_D^{20} 1.5492
b.p. 102.5-103°/14 mm.
E
15,106-8 2,5-Dimethylbenzaldehyde
$(CH_3)_2C_6H_3CHO$ M.W. 134.18 n_D^{20} 1.5422
b.p. 104.5-106.5° 14 mm.
NEAT
F
12,113-4 5-Indancarboxaldehyde
M.W. 146.19 n_D^{20} 1.5733 b.p. 255-257°
NEAT
G
D5660-8 3,4-Dichlorobenzaldehyde
$Cl_2C_6H_3CHO$ M.W. 175.01 m.p. 41-44°
MELT
H
14,675-7 2,4-Dichlorobenzaldehyde
$Cl_2C_6H_3CHO$ M.W. 175.01 m.p. 69-73°
WAVENUMBER CM⁻¹
WAVELENGTH IN MICRONS

A

M.W. 154.14 m.p. 34-35° IR 680G

MELT

B

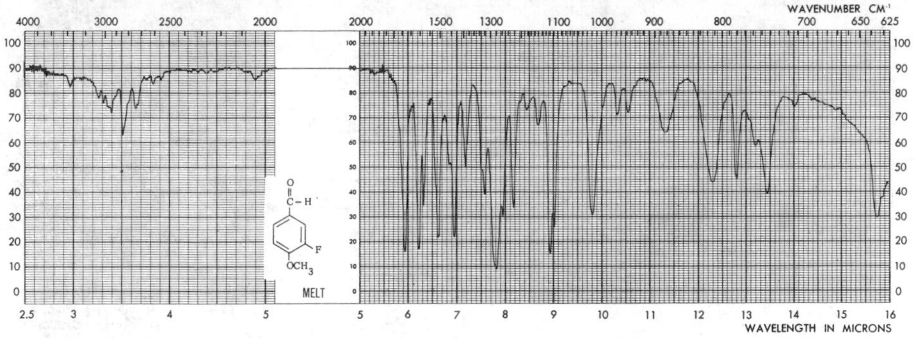

15,429-6 **5-Bromo-o-anisaldehyde** (5-bromo-2-methoxybenzaldehyde)
$BrC_6H_3(OCH_3)CHO$ M.W. 215.06
m.p. 116-119°

NUJOL MULL

C

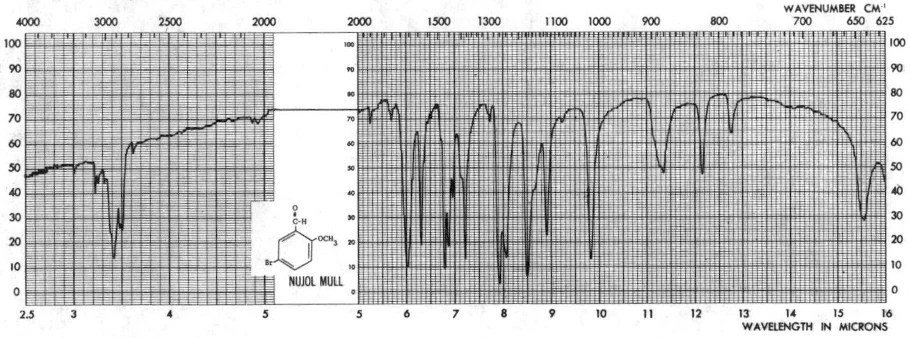

15,247-1 **2-Methyl-p-anisaldehyde** (4-methoxy-2-methylbenzaldehyde)
$CH_3C_6H_3(OCH_3)CHO$ M.W. 150.18 n_D^{20} 1.5653
b.p. 98-100°/2 mm.

NEAT

D

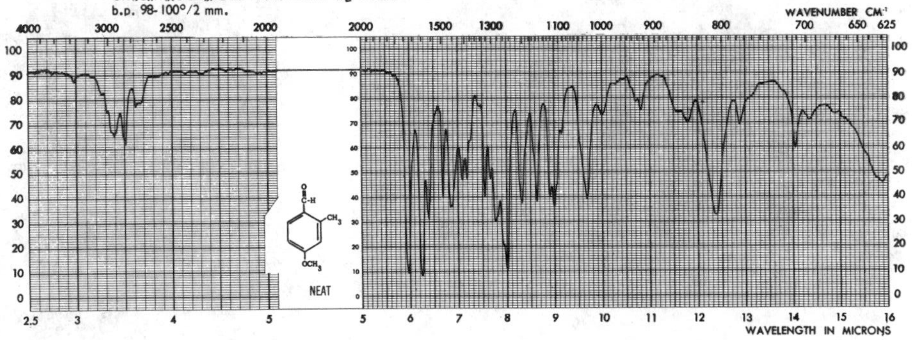

15,212-9 **3-Methyl-p-anisaldehyde** (4-methoxy-3-methylbenzaldehyde)
$CH_3C_6H_3(OCH_3)CHO$ M.W. 150.18 n_D^{20} 1.5670 b.p. 80-85°/1 mm.

NEAT

E

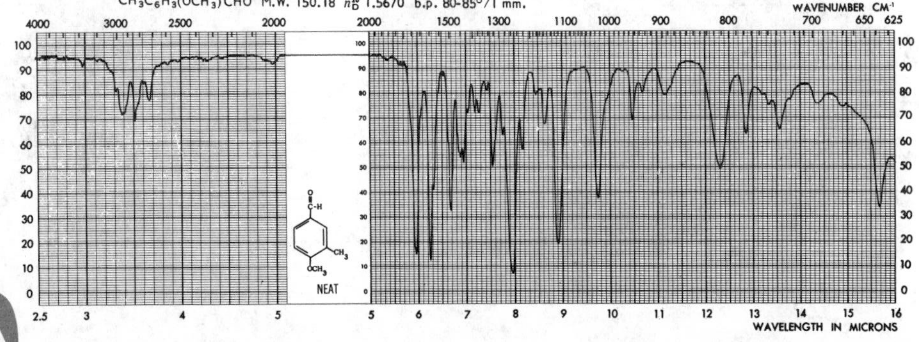

D13,040-0 **2,4-Dimethoxybenzaldehyde**
$(CH_3O)_2C_6H_3CHO$ M.W. 166.18 m.p. 69-72°

NUJOL MULL

F

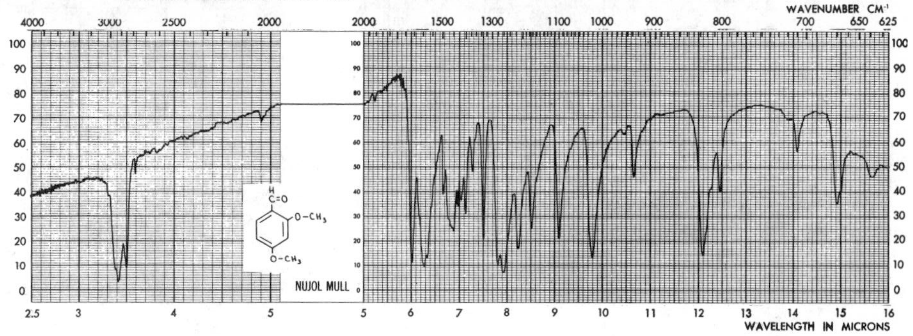

D13,060-5 **2,5-Dimethoxybenzaldehyde, tech.**
$(CH_3O)_2C_6H_3CHO$ M.W. 166.18 m.p. 49-52°

NUJOL MULL

G

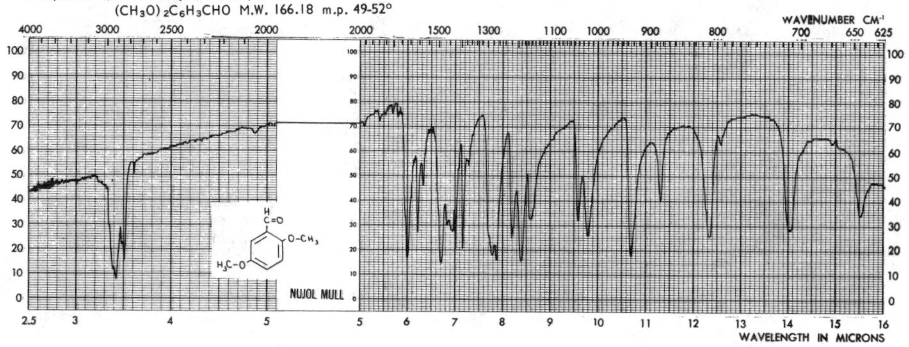

14,375-8 **3,4-Dimethoxybenzaldehyde** (veratraldehyde)
$(CH_3O)_2C_6H_3CHO$ M.W. 166.18 m.p. 42-45°

MELT

H

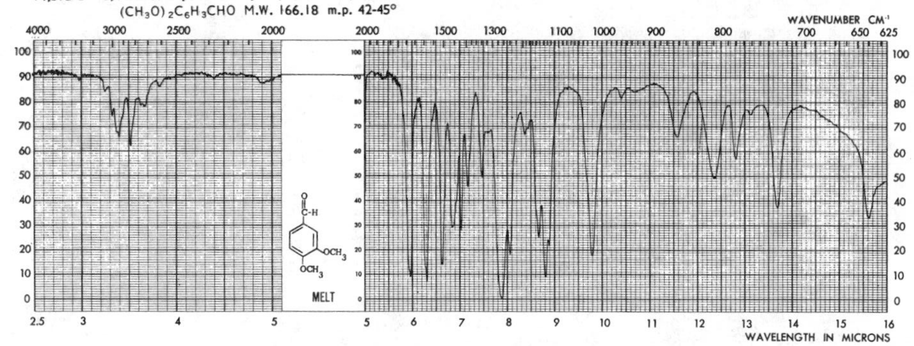

E560-3 **4-Ethoxy-3-methoxybenzaldehyde (4-ethoxy-m-anisaldehyde)**
$C_2H_5OC_6H_3(OCH_3)CHO$ M.W. 180.20 m.p. 59-60° ....

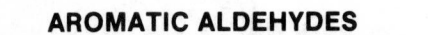

MELT

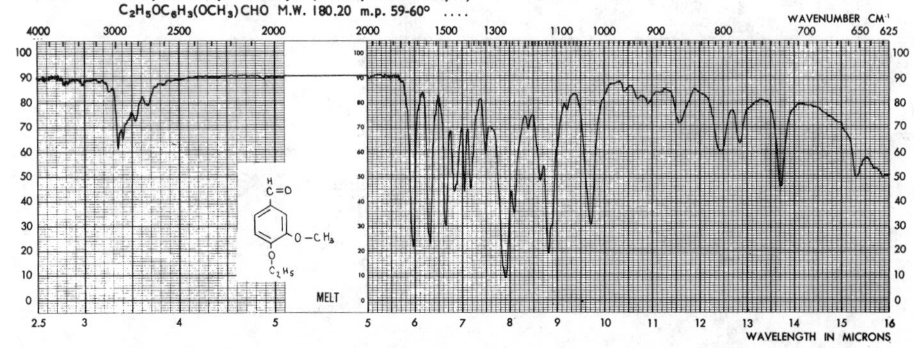

A

P4910-4 **Piperonal**
M.W. 150.13 m.p. 35-37.5°
MELT

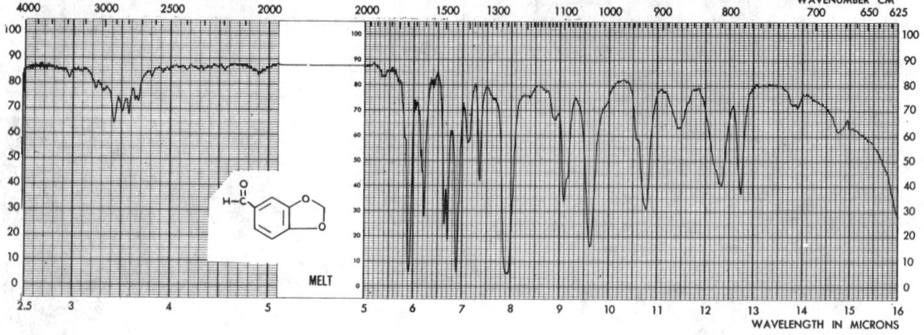

B

13,728-6 **5-Bromosalicylaldehyde**
BrC_6H_3-2-(OH)CHO M.W. 201.02
m.p. 105-108°
NUJOL MULL

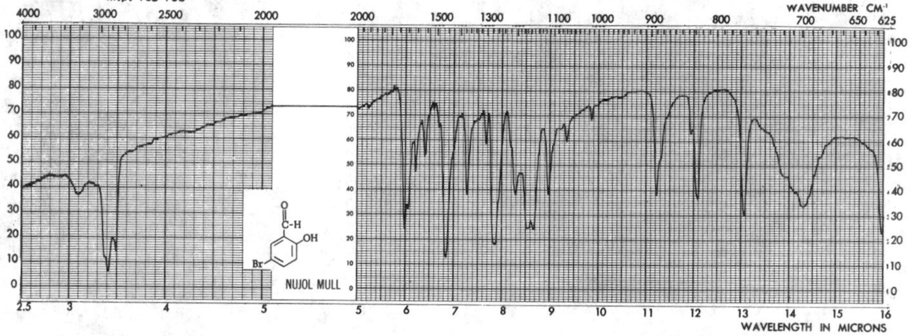

C

14,686-2 **2-Hydroxy-5-methoxybenzaldehyde** (5-methoxysalicylaldehyde)
$HOC_6H_3(OCH_3)CHO$ M.W. 152.15 n_D^{20} 1.5784
b.p. 103°/2.5 mm.
NEAT

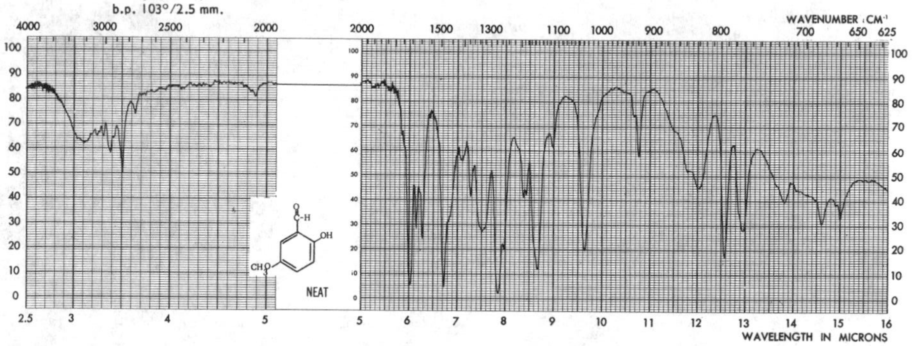

D

16,069-5
2-Hydroxy-4-methoxybenzaldehyde, 99%
$HOC_6H_3(OCH_3)CHO$
M.W. 152.15 m.p. 41-43° Beil. 8,242

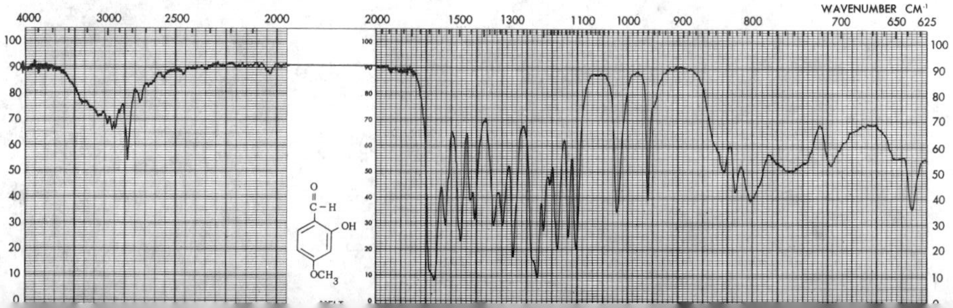

E

14,368-5 **3-Hydroxy-p-anisaldehyde** (isovanillin)
$HOC_6H_3(OCH_3)CHO$ M.W. 152.15
m.p. 113-115°
NUJOL MULL

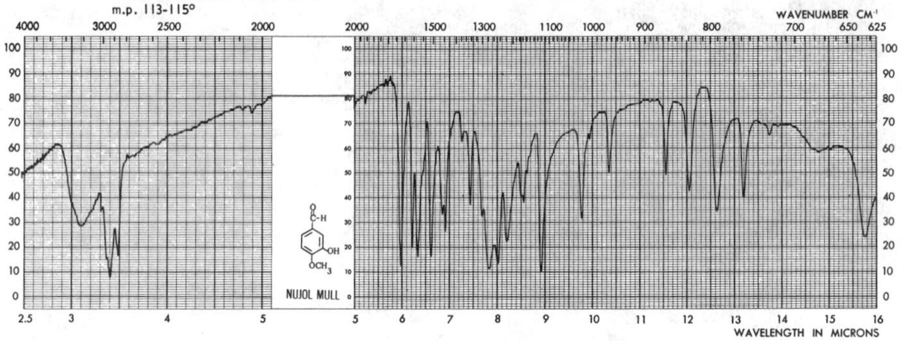

F

19,074-8
4-Ethoxy-3-hydroxybenzaldehyde
$C_2H_5OC_6H_3(OH)CHO$ FW 166.18 mp 126-128°
Beil. 8(2),282 Disp. C
NUJOL MULL

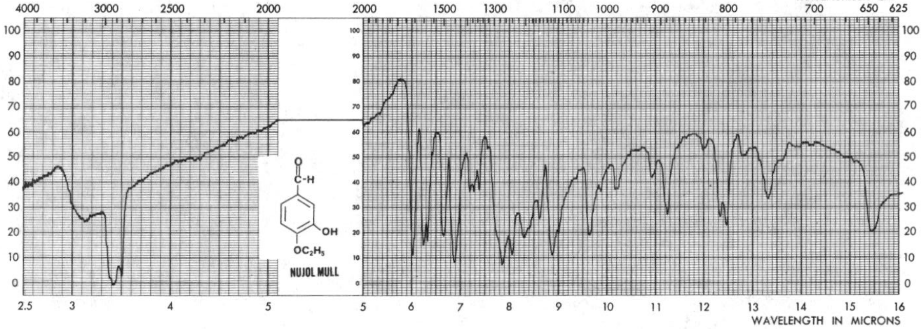

G

V110-4 **Vanillin**
4-(HO)C_6H_3-3-(OCH_3)CHO M.W. 152.15
m.p. 83-84.5°
NUJOL MULL

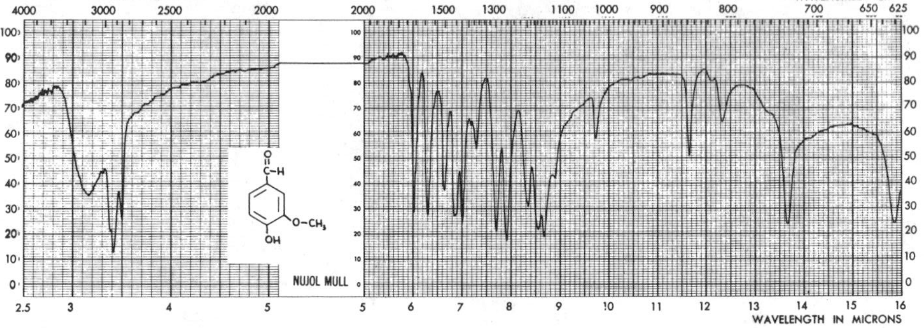

H

12,809-0 **3-Ethoxy-4-hydroxybenzaldehyde**
$C_2H_5OC_6H_3(OH)CHO$ M.W. 166.18 m.p. 76-77°
NUJOL MULL

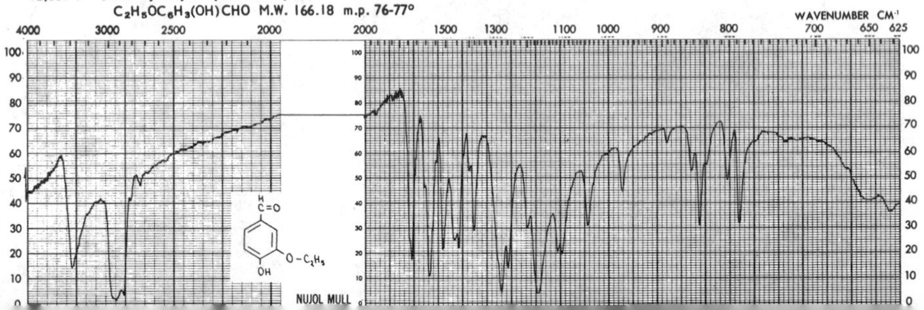

A D10,840-5 **3,4-Dihydroxybenzaldehyde (protocatechualdehyde), tech.**
$(HO)_2C_6H_3CHO$ M.W. 138.12 m.p. 150-153°

B D10,820-0 **2,5-Dihydroxybenzaldehyde (gentisaldehyde)**
$(HO)_2C_6H_3CHO$ M.W. 138.12 m.p. 96-98°

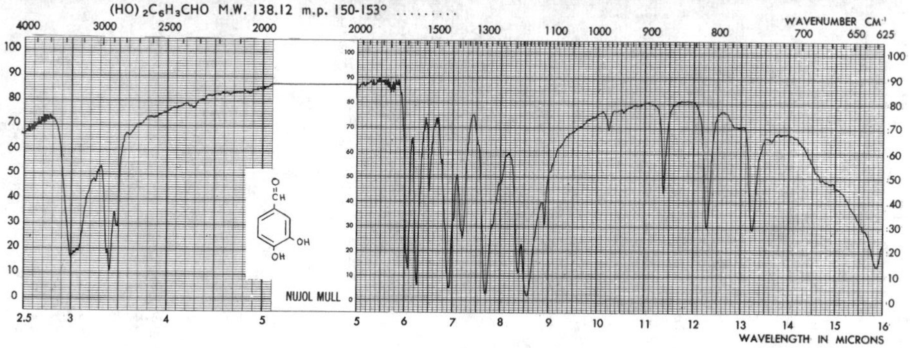

C 16,863-7
2,4-Dihydroxybenzaldehyde, 98%
(β-resorcylaldehyde)
$(HO)_2C_6H_3CHO$ FW 138.12 mp 135-137°
bp 220-228°/22mm. *Beil.* 8,241 Disp. B

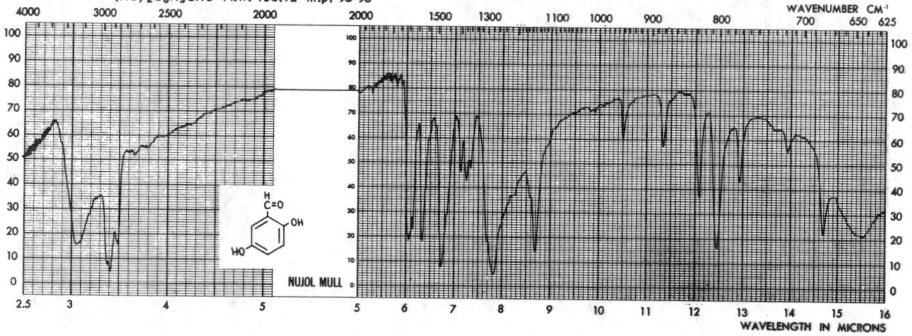

D 12,502-4 **2-Chloro-4-dimethylaminobenzaldehyde, tech.**
$(CH_3)_2NC_6H_3(Cl)CHO$ M.W. 183.64 m.p. 77-79°

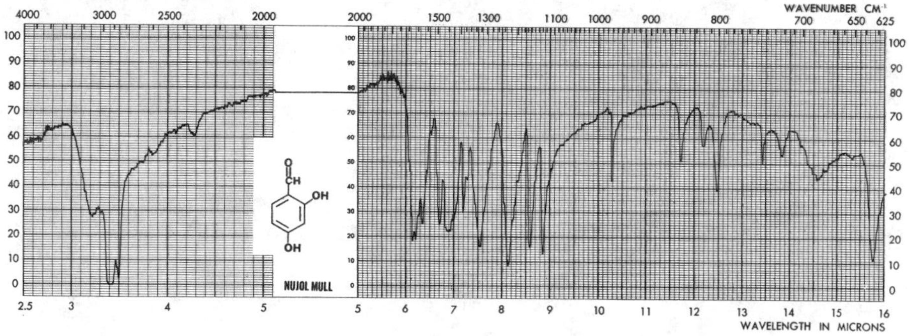

E 10,278-4 **4-Fluoro-2-nitrobenzaldehyde**
$FC_6H_3(NO_2)CHO$ M.W. 169.11 m.p. 35-36°

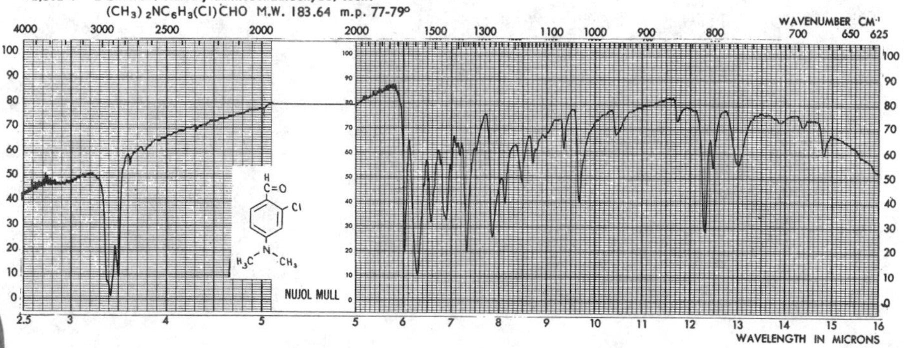

F C5880-0 **5-Chloro-2-nitrobenzaldehyde**
$ClC_6H_3(NO_2)CHO$ M.W. 185.57 m.p. 65°

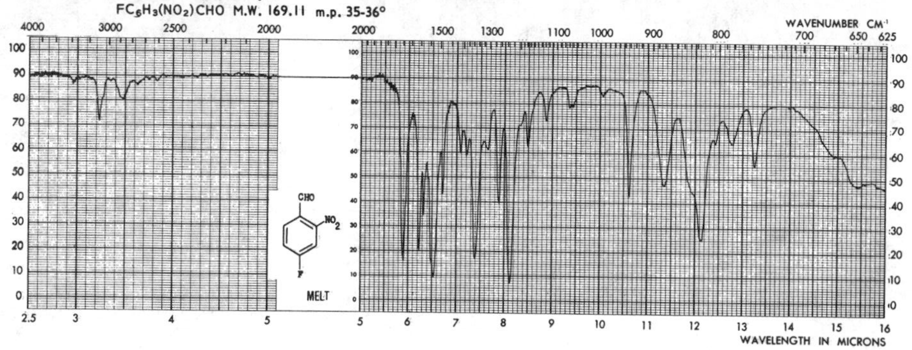

G 22,407-3
4-Chloro-2-nitrobenzaldehyde, 98%
$ClC_6H_3(NO_2)CHO$ FW 185.57 mp 66-68°
Beil. 7,261 Disp. C

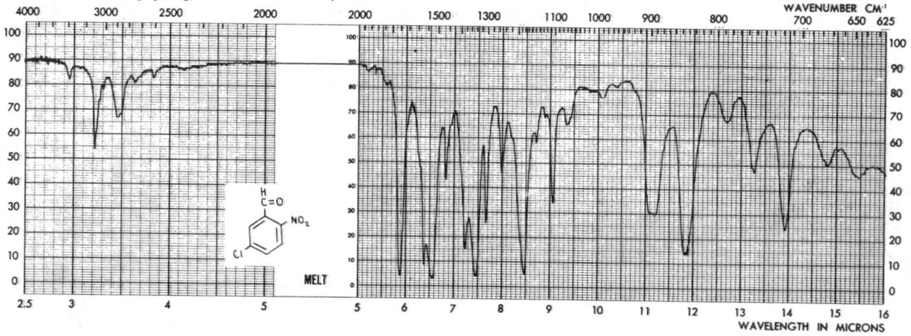

H 13,903-3 **2-Chloro-5-nitrobenzaldehyde**
$ClC_6H_3(NO_2)CHO$ M.W. 185.57 m.p. 71-75°

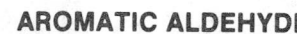

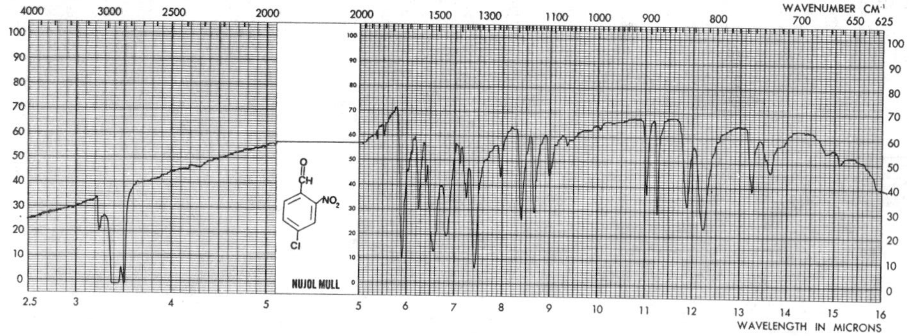

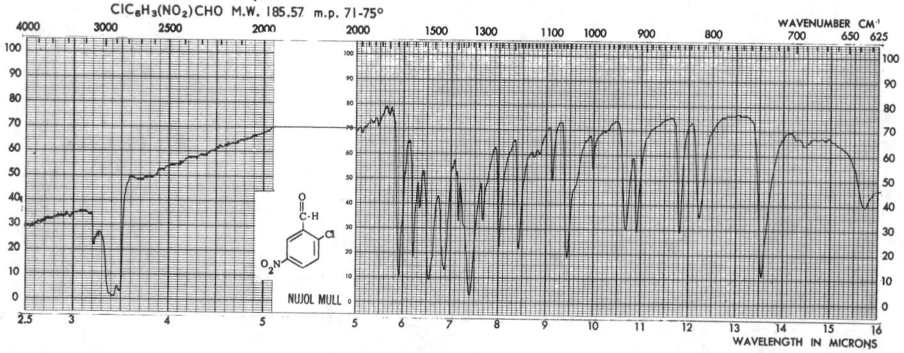

A C5870-3 **4-Chloro-3-nitrobenzaldehyde**
$ClC_6H_3(NO_2)CHO$ M.W. 185.57 m.p. 63-65°
NUJOL MULL

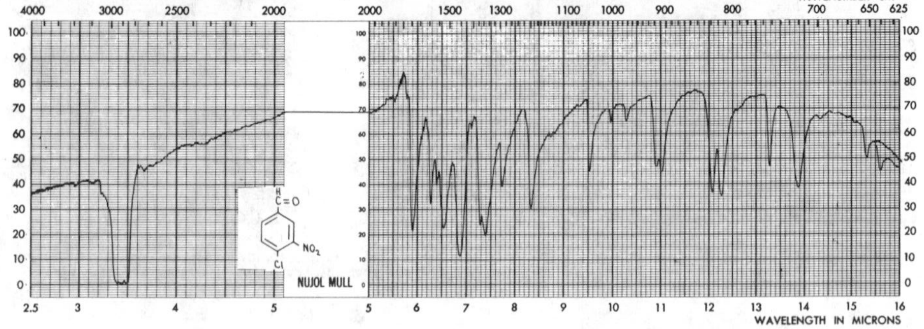

B 13,983-1 **4-Methoxy-2-nitrobenzaldehyde**
$CH_3OC_6H_3(NO_2)CHO$ M.W. 181.15
m.p. 88-92°
NUJOL MULL

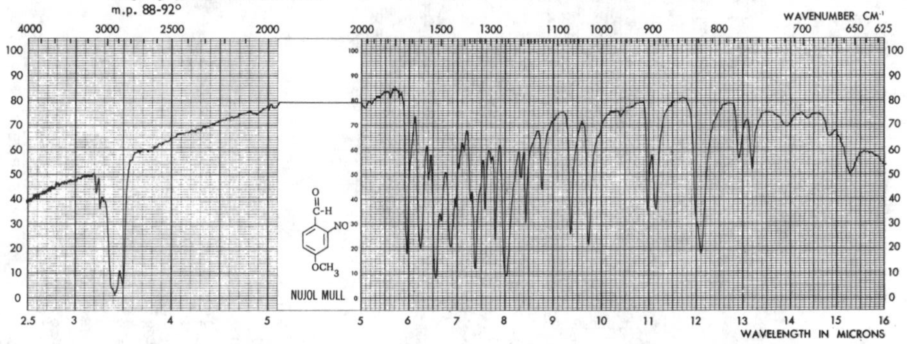

C 14,432-0 **4-Hydroxy-3-nitrobenzaldehyde**
$HOC_6H_3(NO_2)CHO$ M.W. 167.12
m.p. 138-143°
NUJOL MULL

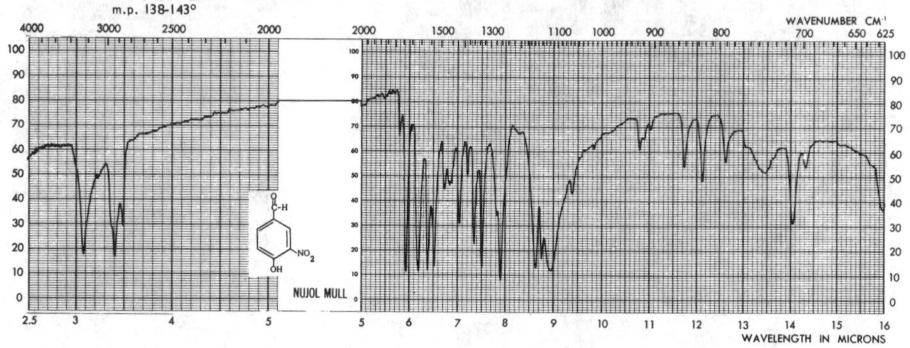

D 15,616-7
3-Hydroxy-4-nitrobenzaldehyde
$HOC_6H_3(NO_2)CHO$
M.W. 167.12 m.p. 129-131° Beil. 8,62

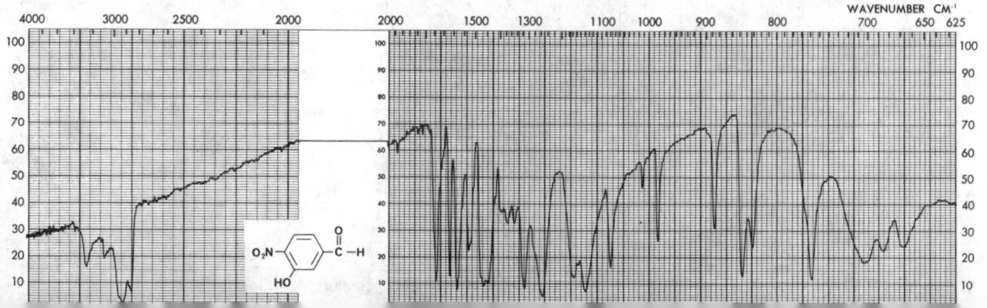

E D19,360-7 **2,4-Dinitrobenzaldehyde**
$(O_2N)_2C_6H_3CHO$ M.W. 196.12 m.p. 68-71°
NUJOL MULL

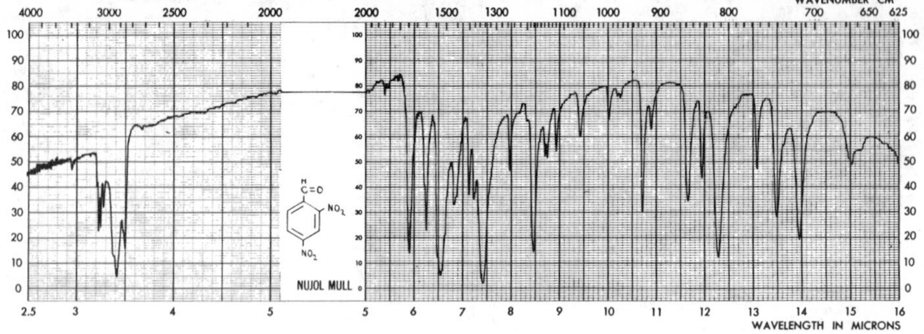

F 13,940-8 **3,5-Dichlorobenzaldehyde**
$Cl_2C_6H_3CHO$ M.W. 175.01 m.p. 63.5-65.5°
NUJOL MULL

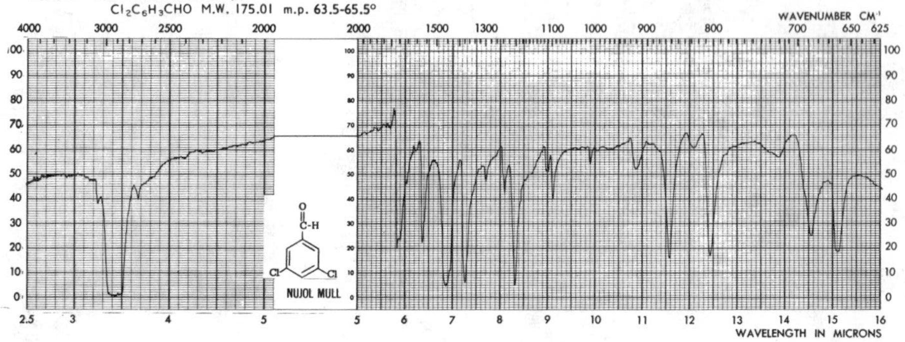

G 12,629-2 **3,5-Dimethoxybenzaldehyde**
$(CH_3O)_2C_6H_3CHO$ M.W. 166.18 m.p. 41-44°
MELT

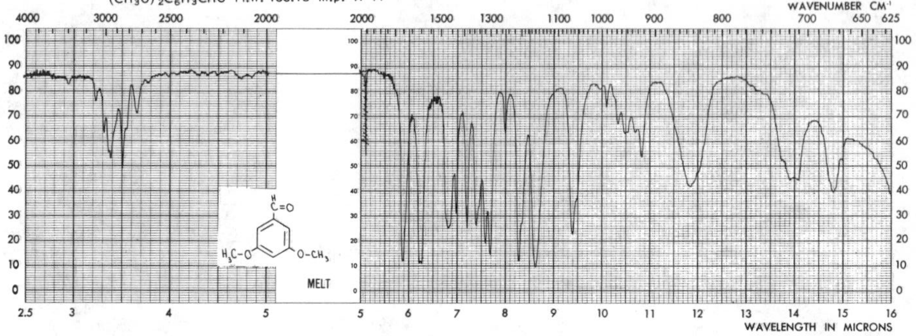

H M680-8 **Mesitaldehyde (2,4,6-trimethylbenzaldehyde)**
$(CH_3)_3C_6H_2CHO$ M.W. 148.21 n_D^{20} 1.5522
b.p. 237°

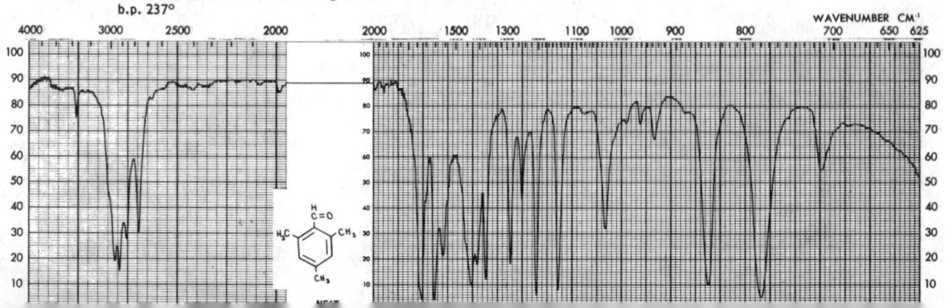

WAVENUMBER CM^{-1}
WAVELENGTH IN MICRONS

m.p. 63-64°

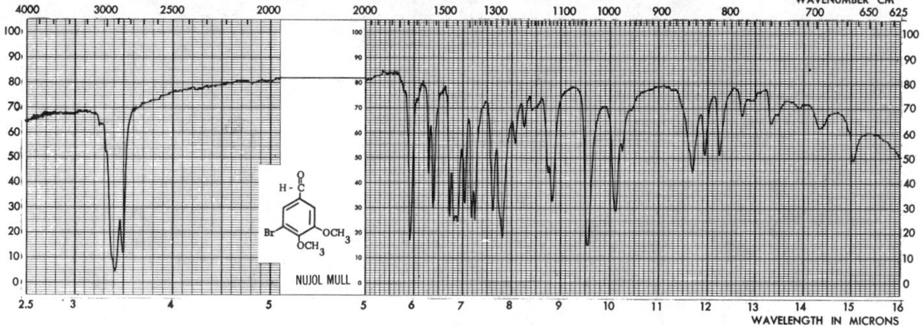

A NUJOL MULL

13,871-1 2,4,6-Trimethoxybenzaldehyde
$(CH_3O)_3C_6H_2CHO$ M.W. 196.20
m.p. 118-120°

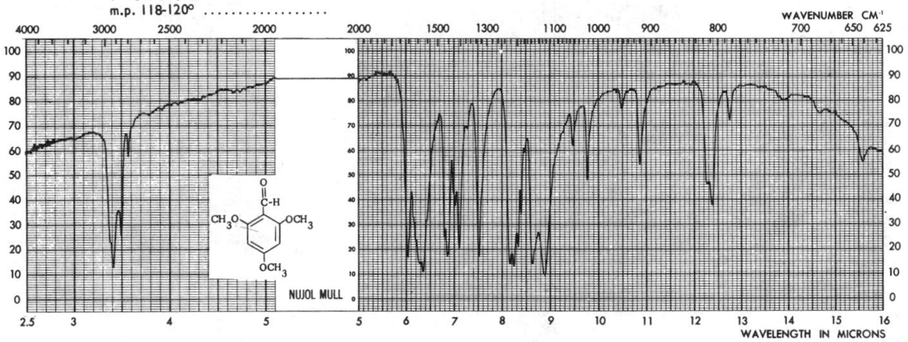

B NUJOL MULL

15,832-1
2,4,6-Triethoxybenzaldehyde, 98%
$(C_2H_5O)_3C_6H_2CHO$
M.W. 238.28 m.p. 96-98°

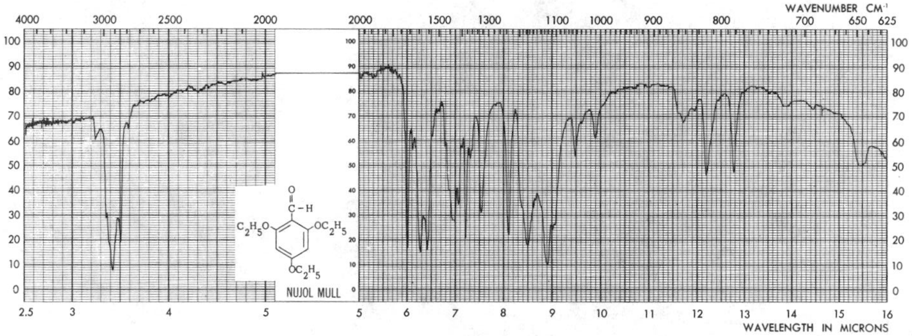

C NUJOL MULL

T6840-3 3,4,5-Trimethoxybenzaldehyde
$(CH_3O)_3C_6H_2CHO$ M.W. 196.20 m.p. 73-75°

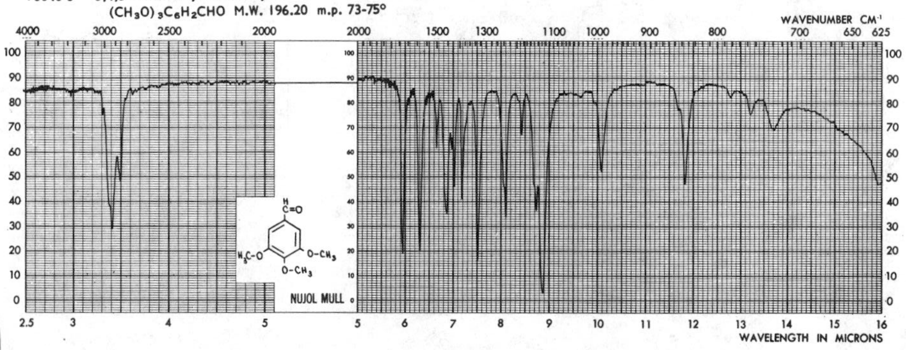

D NUJOL MULL

m.p. 113.5-115.5°

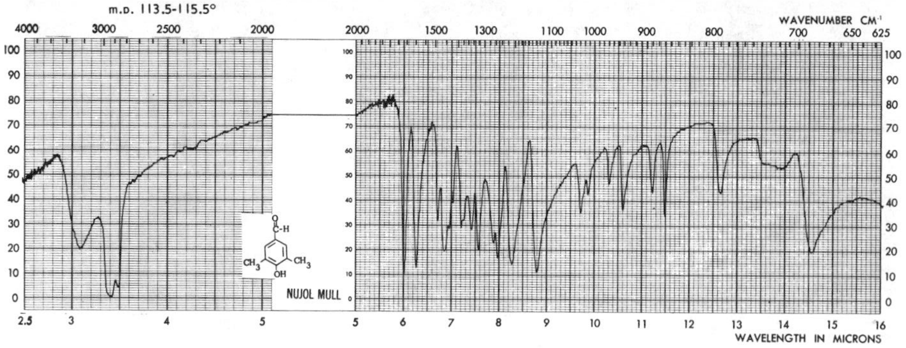

E NUJOL MULL

14,040-6 3,5-Di-tert.-butyl-4-hydroxybenzaldehyde
$HOC_6H_2[C(CH_3)_3]_2CHO$ M.W. 234.34
m.p. 187-189°

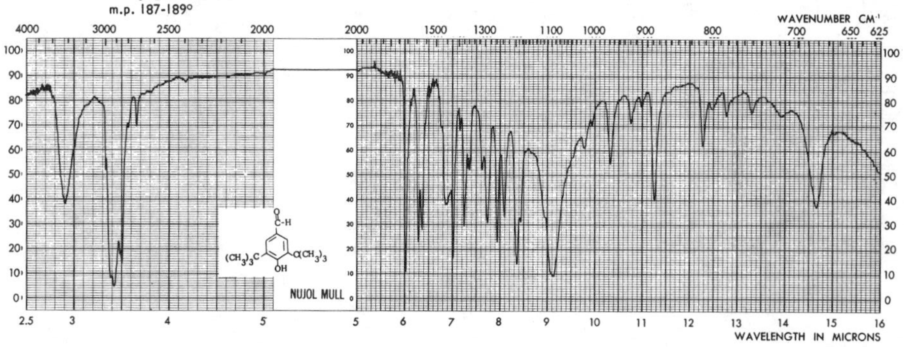

F NUJOL MULL

14,041-4 3,5-Di-tert.-butyl-2-hydroxybenzaldehyde
$HOC_6H_2[C(CH_3)_3]_2CHO$ M.W. 234.34
m.p. 58-60.5°

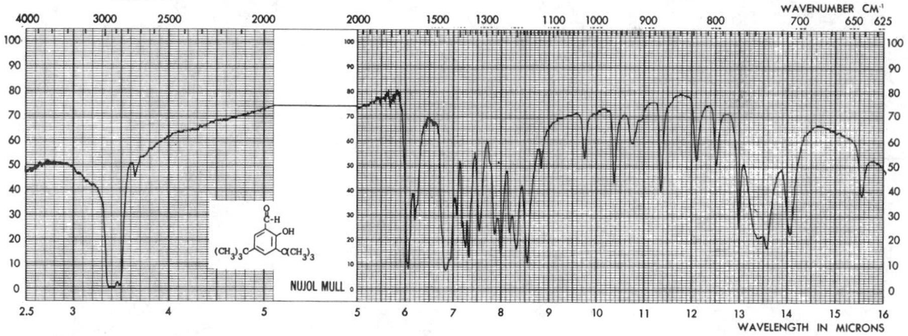

G NUJOL MULL

12,213-0 3,5-Dibromosalicylaldehyde
$Br_2C_6H_2\text{-}2\text{-}(OH)CHO$ M.W. 279.93
m.p. 82-83.5°

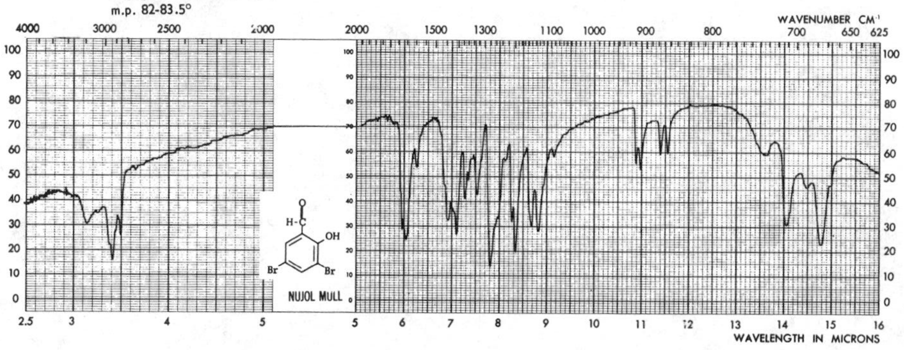

H NUJOL MULL

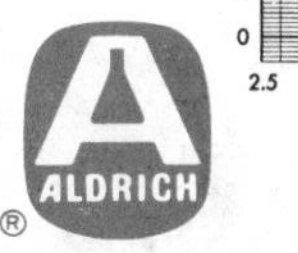

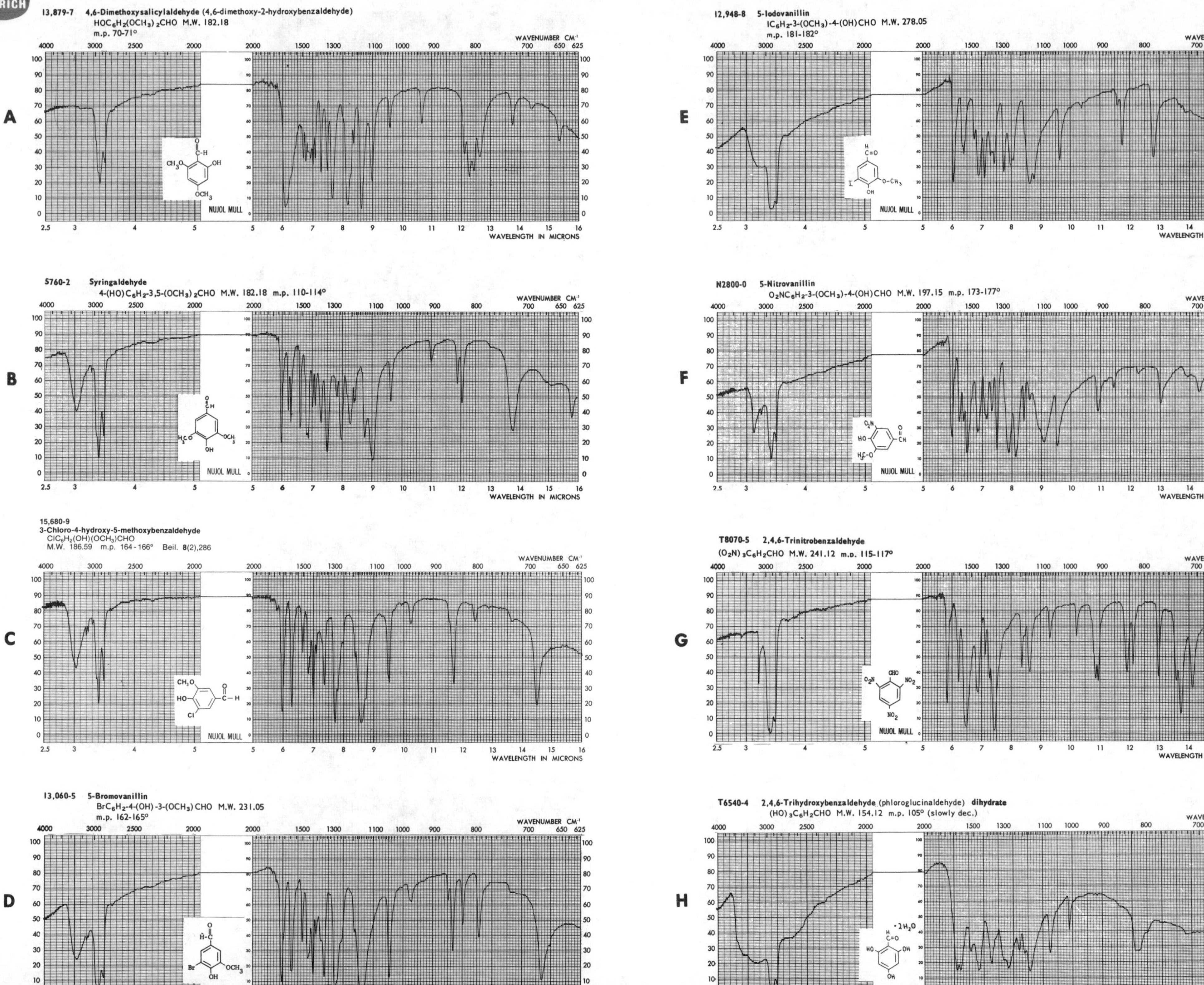
ALDRICH
A
13,879-7 4,6-Dimethoxysalicylaldehyde (4,6-dimethoxy-2-hydroxybenzaldehyde)
$HOC_6H_2(OCH_3)_2CHO$ M.W. 182.18
m.p. 70-71°
B
5760-2 Syringaldehyde
$4-(HO)C_6H_2-3,5-(OCH_3)_2CHO$ M.W. 182.18 m.p. 110-114°
C
15,680-9
3-Chloro-4-hydroxy-5-methoxybenzaldehyde
$ClC_6H_2(OH)(OCH_3)CHO$
M.W. 186.59 m.p. 164-166° Beil. 8(2),286
D
13,060-5 5-Bromovanillin
$BrC_6H_2-4-(OH)-3-(OCH_3)CHO$ M.W. 231.05
m.p. 162-165°
E
12,948-8 5-Iodovanillin
$IC_6H_2-3-(OCH_3)-4-(OH)CHO$ M.W. 278.05
m.p. 181-182°
F
N2800-0 5-Nitrovanillin
$O_2NC_6H_2-3-(OCH_3)-4-(OH)CHO$ M.W. 197.15 m.p. 173-177°
G
T8070-5 2,4,6-Trinitrobenzaldehyde
$(O_2N)_3C_6H_2CHO$ M.W. 241.12 m.p. 115-117°
H
T6540-4 2,4,6-Trihydroxybenzaldehyde (phloroglucinaldehyde) dihydrate
$(HO)_3C_6H_2CHO$ M.W. 154.12 m.p. 105° (slowly dec.)
NUJOL MULL
WAVENUMBER CM⁻¹
WAVELENGTH IN MICRONS

A

$CH_3OC_6H_2(CH_3)_2CHO$ M.W. 164.20 m.p. 31-35°

MELT

B

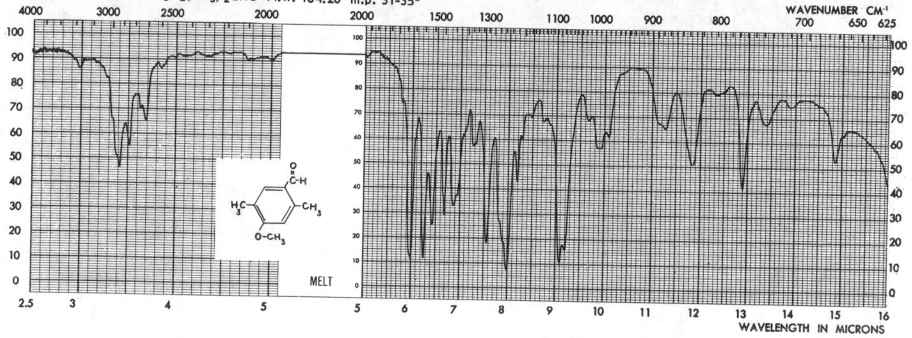

15,557-8 6-Bromoveratraldehyde
BrC_6H_2-3,4-$(OCH_3)_2CHO$ M.W. 245.08
m.p. 150-151°

NUJOL MULL

C

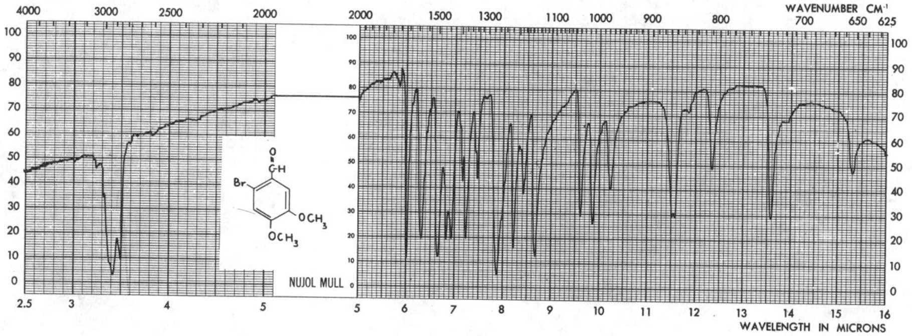

13,215-2 2,4,5-Trimethoxybenzaldehyde
$(CH_3O)_3C_6H_2CHO$ M.W. 196.20
m.p. 113-115°

NUJOL MULL

D

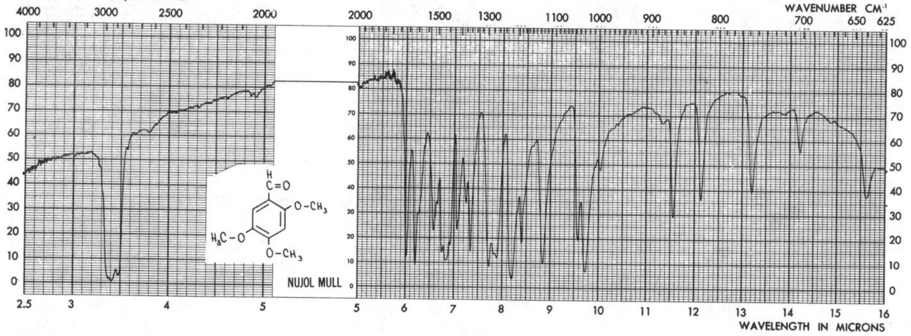

13,880-0 2,4,5-Triethoxybenzaldehyde
$(C_2H_5O)_3C_6H_2CHO$ M.W. 238.29
m.p. 92.5-94.5°

NUJOL MULL

E

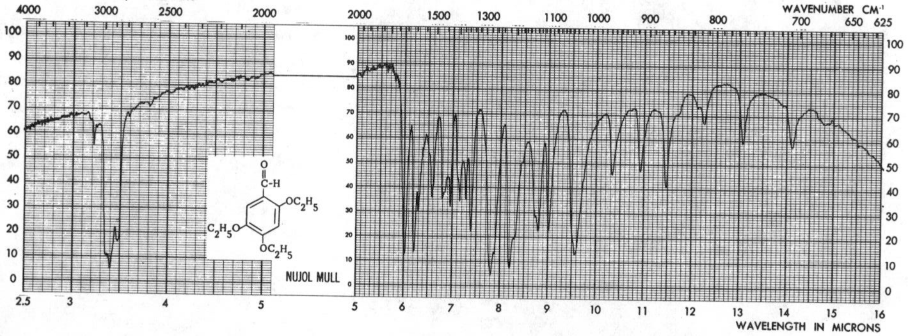

N2820-5 6-Nitroveratraldehyde
$O_2NC_6H_2$-3,4-$(OCH_3)_2CHO$ M.W. 211.17 m.p. 131-133°

NUJOL MULL

F

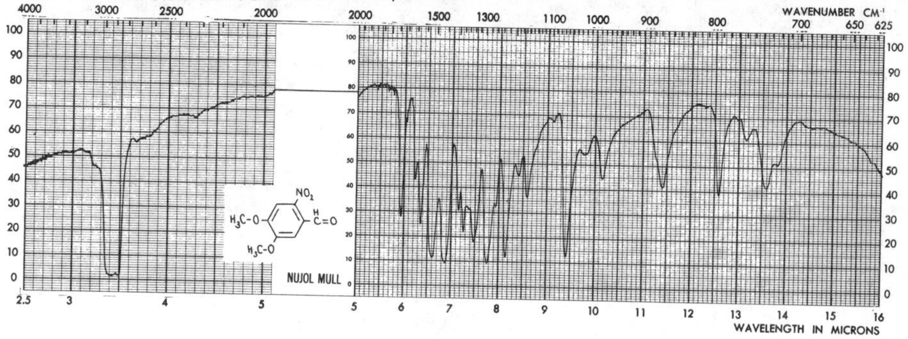

13,765-0 6-Nitropiperonal
M.W. 195.13 m.p. 91-93°

NUJOL MULL

G

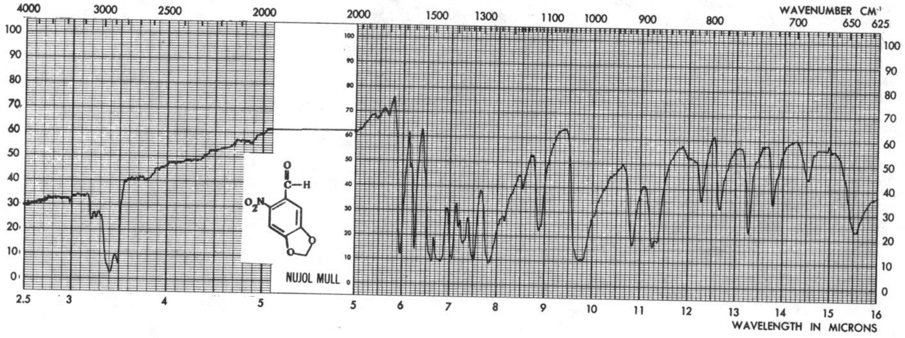

15,201-3 2,3-Dimethyl-p-anisaldehyde (2,3-dimethyl-4-methoxybenzaldehyde)
$CH_3OC_6H_2(CH_3)_2CHO$ M.W. 164.20 m.p. 48.5-52°

MELT

H

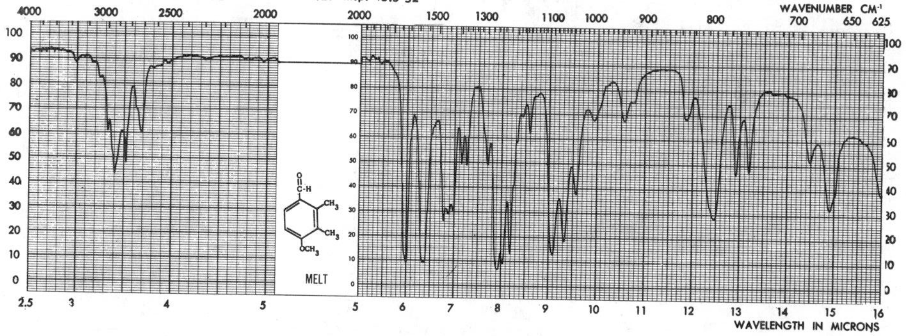

15,209-9 2,3,4-Trimethoxybenzaldehyde
$(CH_3O)_3C_6H_2CHO$ M.W. 196.20 n_D^{20} 1.5547 b.p. 120-125°/0.5 mm.

NEAT

AROMATIC ALDEHYDES

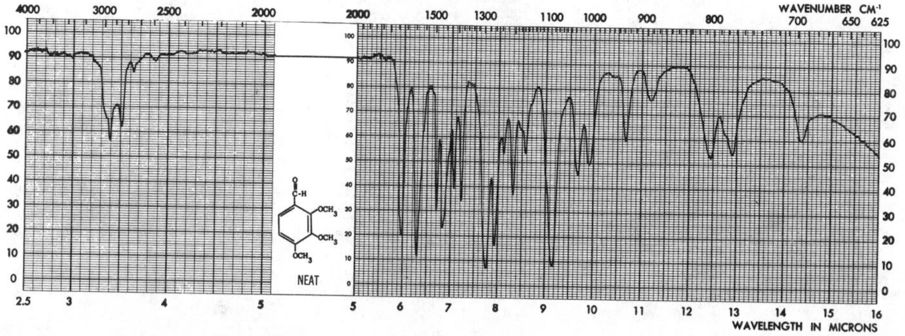

A 15,012-6 **2,4-Dimethoxy-3-hydroxybenzaldehyde** $HOC_6H_2(OCH_3)_2CHO$ M.W. 182.18 m.p. 101-104°

B 10,374-8 **Pentafluorobenzaldehyde** C_6F_5CHO M.W. 196.07 n_D^{20} 1.4506

C 14,141-0 **2,3,5,6-Tetrachloroterephthalaldehyde, tech.** $C_6Cl_4(CHO)_2$ M.W. 271.92

D B3468-0 **4-Biphenylcarboxaldehyde** (p-phenylbenzaldehyde) $C_6H_5C_6H_4CHO$ M.W. 182.22 m.p. 63-64°

E B2700-5 **3-Benzyloxybenzaldehyde** $C_6H_5CH_2OC_6H_4CHO$ M.W. 212.25 m.p. 56-58°

F 19,175-2 ***m*-Phenoxybenzaldehyde,** 95+% $C_6H_5OC_6H_4CHO$ FW 198.22 bp 140°/0.100mm. n_D^{20} 1.5954 d 1.147 Disp. C

G 19,540-5 ***m*-(*p*-Methylphenoxy)benzaldehyde,** 97% [*m*-(*p*-tolyloxy)benzaldehyde] $CH_3C_6H_4OC_6H_4CHO$ FW 212.25 bp 140°/2mm. n_D^{20} 1.5902 d 1.102 Disp. C

H 19,592-8 ***m*-(*p*-*tert*-Butylphenoxy)benzaldehyde,** 99% $(CH_3)_3CC_6H_4OC_6H_4CHO$ FW 254.33 bp 152°/0.400mm. n_D^{20} 1.5702 d 0.984 Disp. C

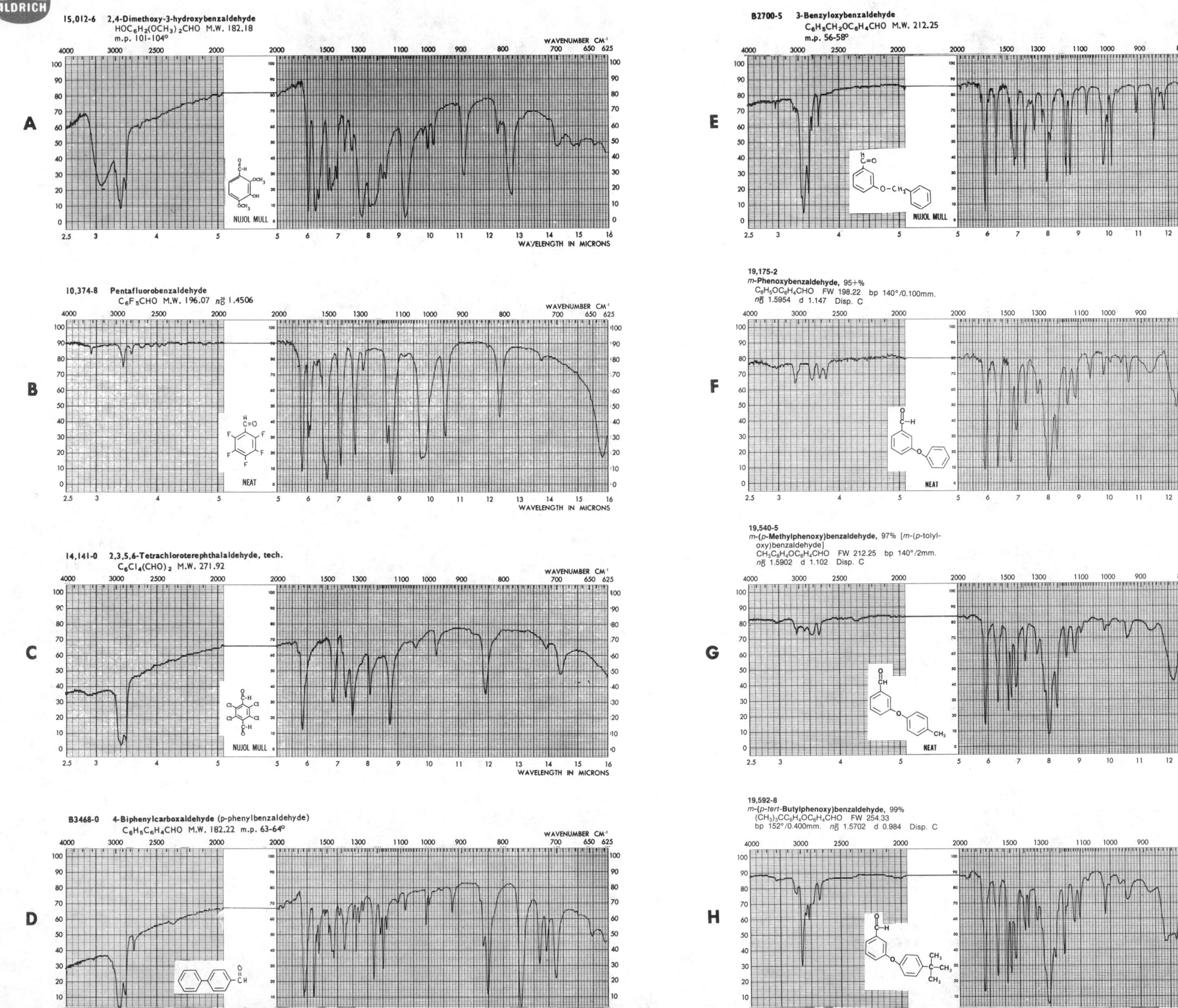

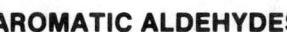

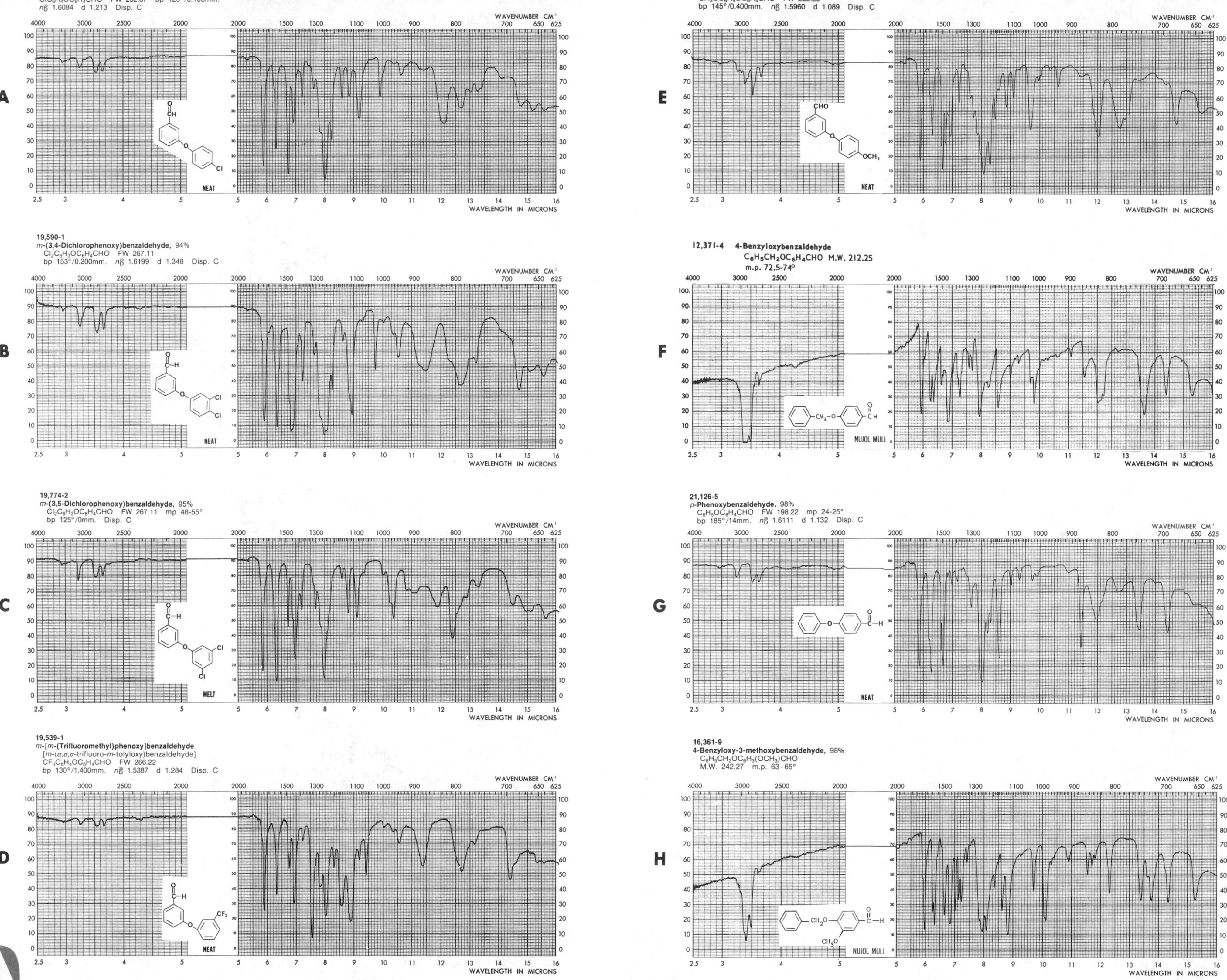
A
$ClC_6H_4OC_6H_4CHO$ FW 232.67 bp 125°/0.100mm.
n_D^{20} 1.6084 d 1.213 Disp. C
NEAT
B
19,590-1
m-(3,4-Dichlorophenoxy)benzaldehyde, 94%
$Cl_2C_6H_3OC_6H_4CHO$ FW 267.11
bp 153°/0.200mm. n_D^{20} 1.6199 d 1.348 Disp. C
NEAT
C
19,774-2
m-(3,5-Dichlorophenoxy)benzaldehyde, 95%
$Cl_2C_6H_3OC_6H_4CHO$ FW 267.11 mp 48-55°
bp 125°/0mm. Disp. C
MELT
D
19,539-1
m-[m-(Trifluoromethyl)phenoxy]benzaldehyde
[m-(α,α,α-trifluoro-m-tolyloxy)benzaldehyde]
$CF_3C_6H_4OC_6H_4CHO$ FW 266.22
bp 130°/1.400mm. n_D^{20} 1.5387 d 1.284 Disp. C
NEAT
E
$CH_3OC_6H_4OC_6H_4CHO$ FW 228.25
bp 145°/0.400mm. n_D^{20} 1.5960 d 1.089 Disp. C
NEAT
F
12,371-4 4-Benzyloxybenzaldehyde
$C_6H_5CH_2OC_6H_4CHO$ M.W. 212.25
m.p. 72.5-74°
NUJOL MULL
G
21,126-5
p-Phenoxybenzaldehyde, 98%
$C_6H_5OC_6H_4CHO$ FW 198.22 mp 24-25°
bp 185°/14mm. n_D^{20} 1.6111 d 1.132 Disp. C
NEAT
H
16,361-9
4-Benzyloxy-3-methoxybenzaldehyde, 98%
$C_6H_5CH_2OC_6H_3(OCH_3)CHO$
M.W. 242.27 m.p. 63-65°
NUJOL MULL
WAVENUMBER CM⁻¹
WAVELENGTH IN MICRONS
ALDRICH

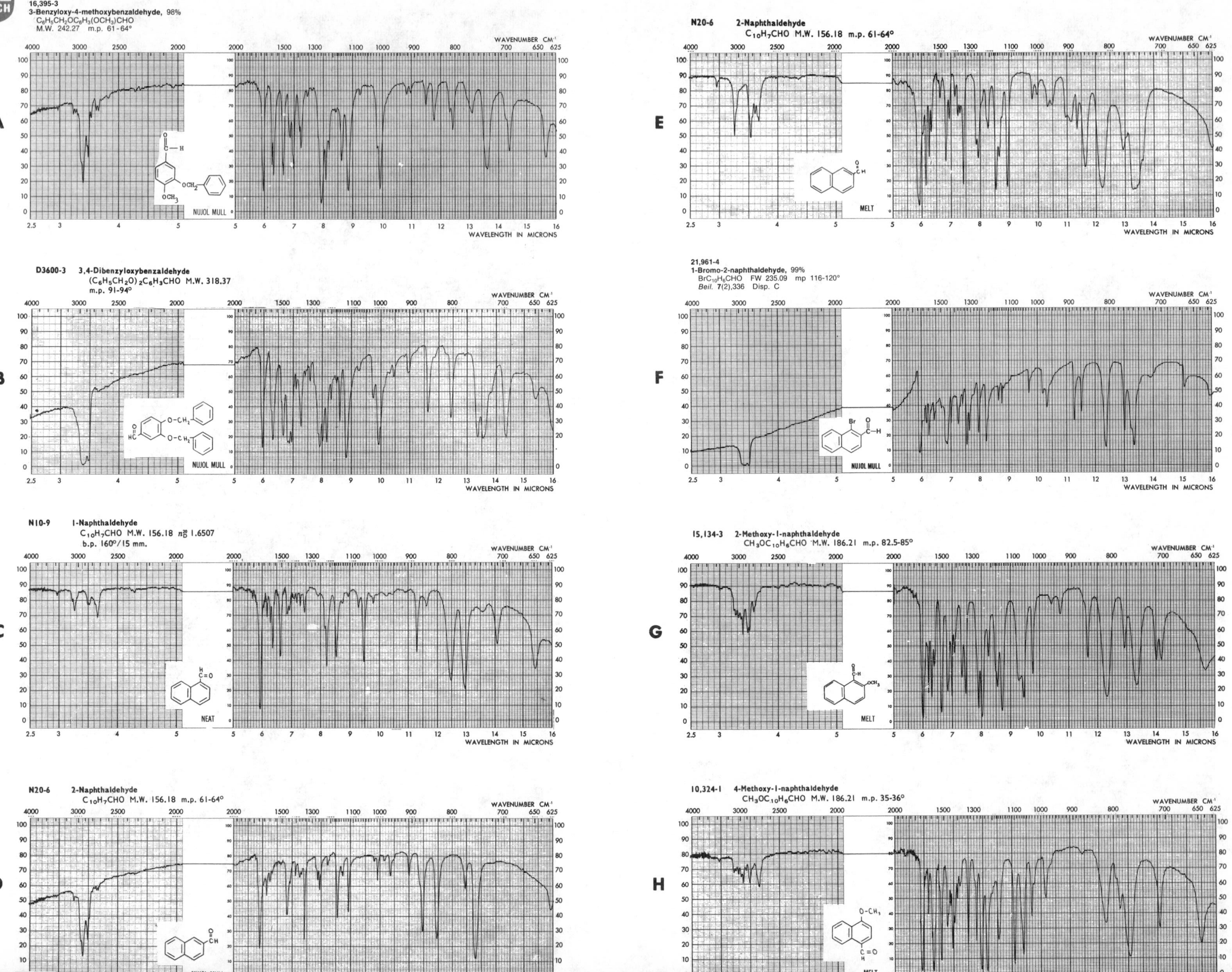
ALDRICH
A
16,395-3
3-Benzyloxy-4-methoxybenzaldehyde, 98%
$C_6H_5CH_2OC_6H_3(OCH_3)CHO$
M.W. 242.27 m.p. 61-64°
NUJOL MULL
B
D3600-3 3,4-Dibenzyloxybenzaldehyde
$(C_6H_5CH_2O)_2C_6H_3CHO$ M.W. 318.37
m.p. 91-94°
NUJOL MULL
C
N10-9 1-Naphthaldehyde
$C_{10}H_7CHO$ M.W. 156.18 n_D^{20} 1.6507
b.p. 160°/15 mm.
NEAT
D
N20-6 2-Naphthaldehyde
$C_{10}H_7CHO$ M.W. 156.18 m.p. 61-64°
E
N20-6 2-Naphthaldehyde
$C_{10}H_7CHO$ M.W. 156.18 m.p. 61-64°
MELT
F
21,961-4
1-Bromo-2-naphthaldehyde, 99%
$BrC_{10}H_6CHO$ FW 235.09 mp 116-120°
Beil. 7(2),336 Disp. C
NUJOL MULL
G
15,134-3 2-Methoxy-1-naphthaldehyde
$CH_3OC_{10}H_6CHO$ M.W. 186.21 m.p. 82.5-85°
MELT
H
10,324-1 4-Methoxy-1-naphthaldehyde
$CH_3OC_{10}H_6CHO$ M.W. 186.21 m.p. 35-36°
WAVENUMBER CM⁻¹
WAVELENGTH IN MICRONS

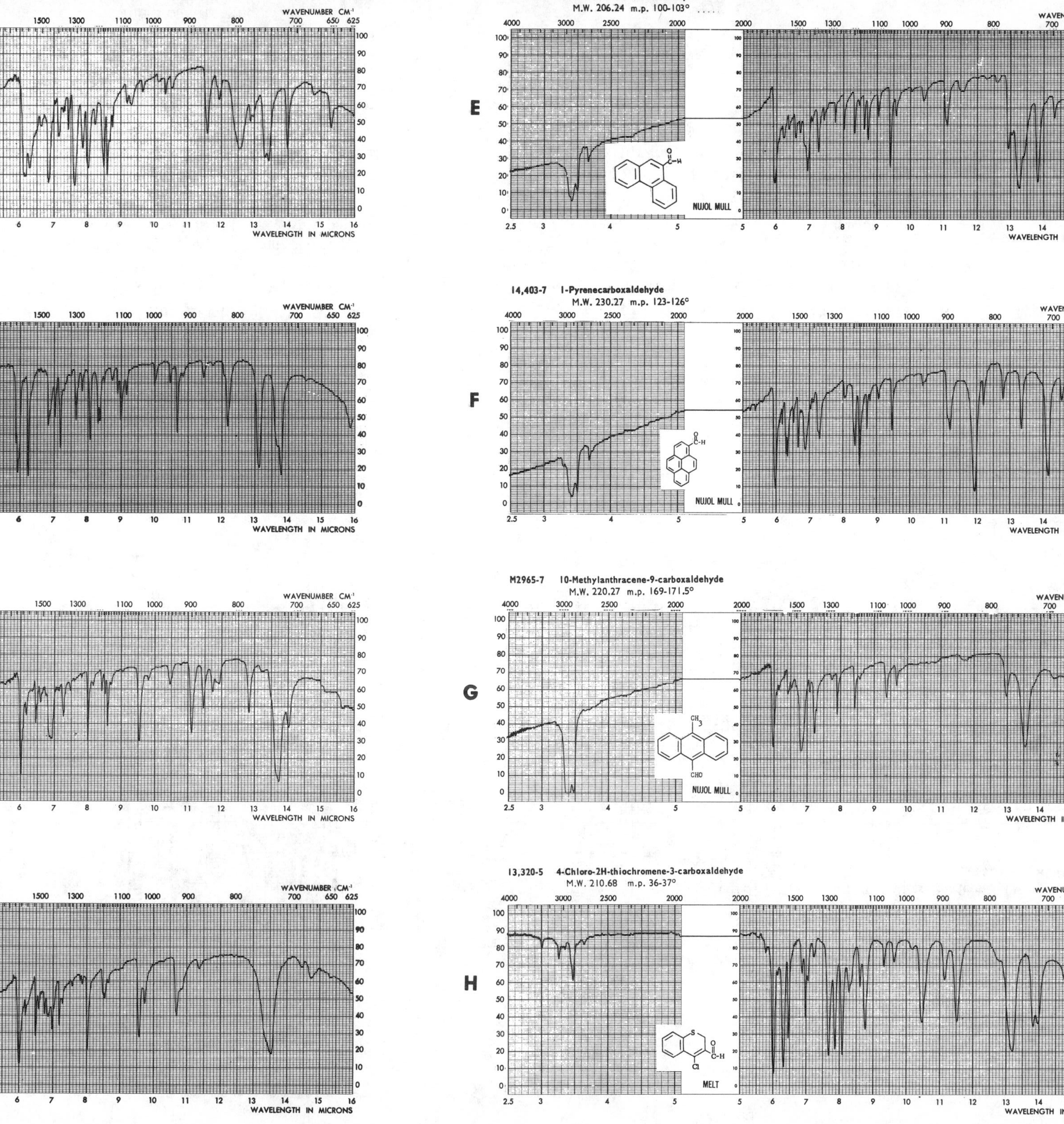

A — $HOC_{10}H_6CHO$ M.W. 172.18 m.p. 82-85°

B — 15,014-2 2-Fluorenecarboxaldehyde M.W. 194.23 m.p. 85-86°

C — 12,323-4 9-Anthraldehyde M.W. 206.24 m.p. 103-105°

D — 15,211-0 10-Chloro-9-anthraldehyde M.W. 240.69 m.p. 215-218°

E — P1160-3 Phenanthrene-9-carboxaldehyde M.W. 206.24 m.p. 100-103°

F — 14,403-7 1-Pyrenecarboxaldehyde M.W. 230.27 m.p. 123-126°

G — M2965-7 10-Methylanthracene-9-carboxaldehyde M.W. 220.27 m.p. 169-171.5°

H — 13,320-5 4-Chloro-2H-thiochromene-3-carboxaldehyde M.W. 210.68 m.p. 36-37°

AROMATIC CARBOXYLIC ACIDS

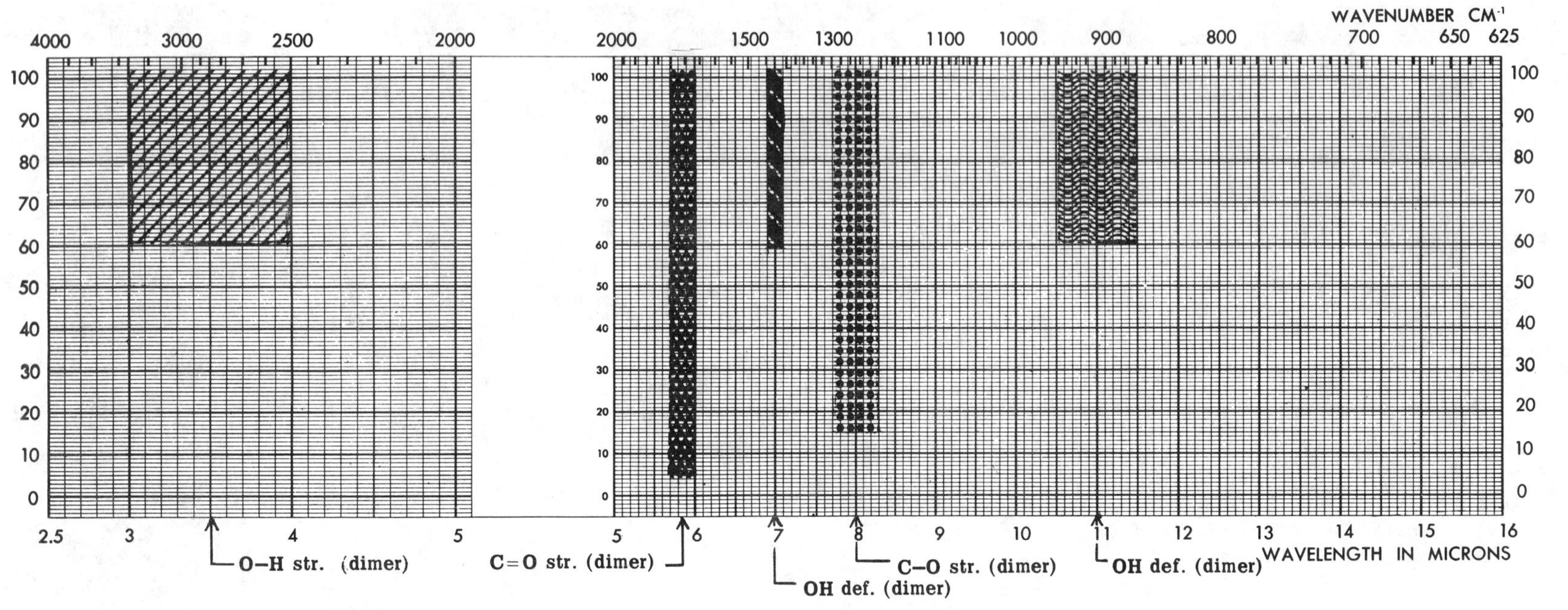

Once again the effect of conjugation of the carboxylic acid carbonyl with the aromatic ring shifts the position of the carbonyl band to 5.9 – 6 μ (1695 – 1665 cm^{-1}). The other bands of the carboxylic acid dimer seen in the non-aromatic section remain essentially unaltered; the strongly bonded OH stretch absorption between 3 and 4 μ (3335 – 2500 cm^{-1}); the OH deformation band near 7 μ (1430 cm^{-1}); the single bonded carbon-oxygen stretch absorption near 8 μ (1250 cm^{-1}) and the other OH deformation band at 10.5 – 11.5 μ (950 – 870 cm^{-1}). In spectrum 957F, the compound exists primarily in the monomeric form with the OH stretch absorption appearing as a more definite band near 3.05 μ (3280 cm^{-1}) along with a small amount of the dimer OH stretch extending out to 4 μ (2500 cm^{-1}). The carbonyl appears at 5.8 μ (1725 cm^{-1}) with the shoulder at 5.95 μ (1680 cm^{-1}) being that of the dimeric structure. The compounds of spectra 958F and 958G may also be in the monomeric form, or in their crystalline form may exist as phthalides.

It is again interesting to note the carbonyl position as it is affected by other substituents on the aromatic ring.

Prediction as to band position in the 11 – 15 μ (910 – 665 cm^{-1}) region for any of the various substitution positions is extremely difficult. Bands may appear in the general vicinity of the expected positions; however, numerous other bands accompany them.

The S–H group of a thiol-carboxylic acid absorbs at 3.9 – 4 μ (2565 – 2500 cm^{-1}), with the C=O group absorbing at 6.1 – 6.2 μ (1640 – 1615 cm^{-1}) and another band appearing near 8.2 μ (1220 cm^{-1}). (See spectra 956F and 963G).

The basic strength of an amine group attached directly to an aromatic ring is not strong enough to form a zwitter ion as does an aliphatic amino acid. In spectra 958B, 962B, 966A, etc., the normal bands for the carboxylic acid appear along with two sharp N–H stretch bands near 2.8 to 3.0 μ (3570 – 3335 cm^{-1}).

A P1662-1 Phenylacetic acid
$C_6H_5CH_2CO_2H$ M.W. 136.15 m.p. 77-78.5°
NUJOL MULL

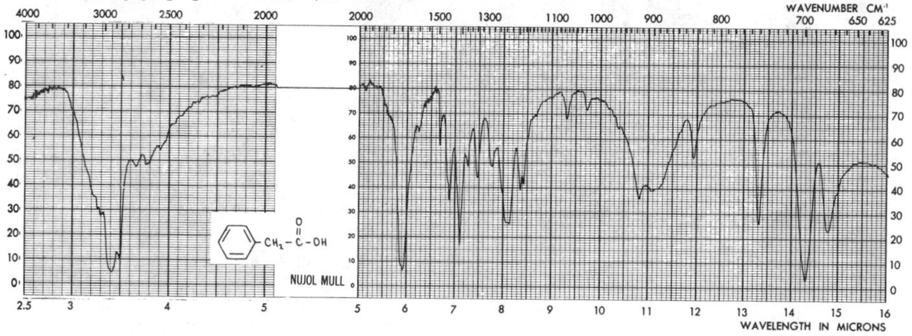

B P3170-1 2-Phenylpropionic acid
$CH_3CH(C_6H_5)CO_2H$ M.W. 150.18 n_D^{20} 1.5237
b.p. 145-147°/12 mm.
NEAT

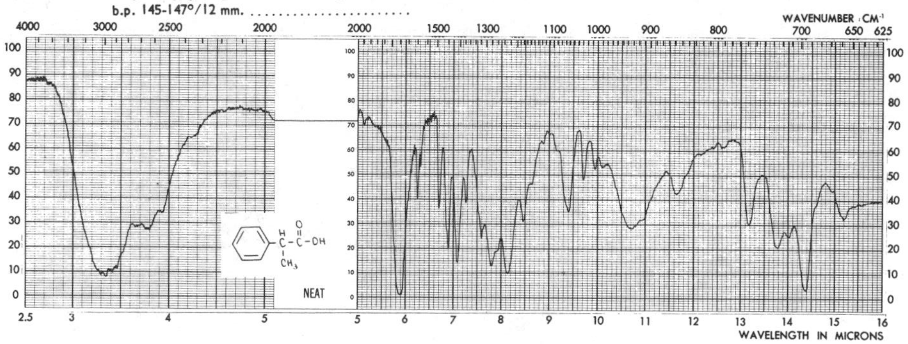

C 16,007-5
1-Phenyl-1-cyclopropanecarboxylic acid, 97%
$C_6H_5C_3H_4CO_2H$
M.W. 162.19 m.p. 85-87°
NUJOL MULL

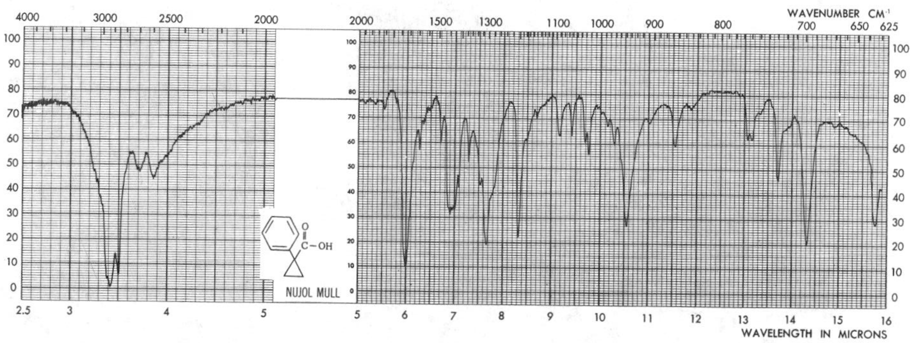

D P2235-4 *trans*-2-Phenylcyclopropane-1-carboxylic acid
$C_6H_5C_3H_4CO_2H$ M.W. 162.19 m.p. 89-90°
NUJOL MULL

E 12,572-5 1-Phenylcyclobutanecarboxylic acid
$C_6H_5C_4H_6CO_2H$ M.W. 176.22
m.p. 105-108°
NUJOL MULL

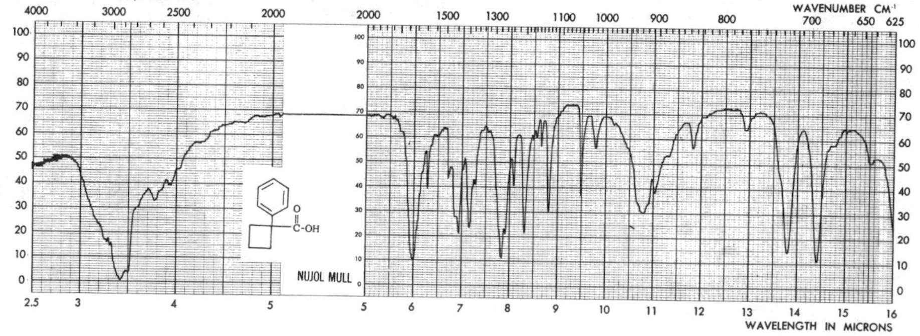

F 14,020-1 1-Phenylcyclopentanecarboxylic acid
$C_6H_5C_5H_8CO_2H$ M.W. 190.25
m.p. 159-161°
NUJOL MULL

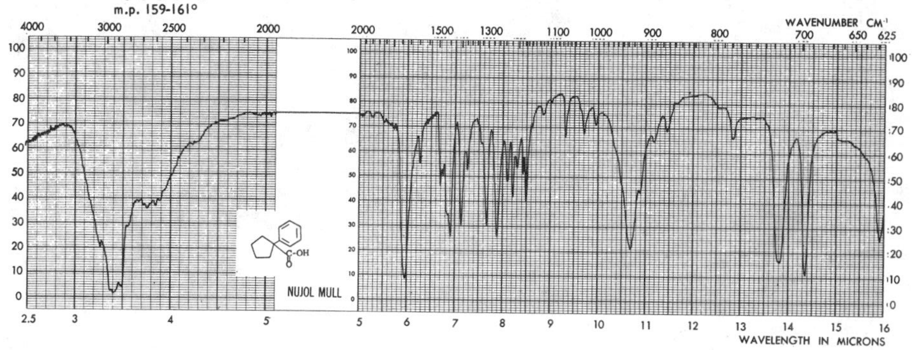

G 18,994-4
α-Phenylcyclopentaneacetic acid, 98%
$C_5H_9CH(C_6H_5)CO_2H$ FW 204.27 mp 98-100°
Disp. C
NUJOL MULL

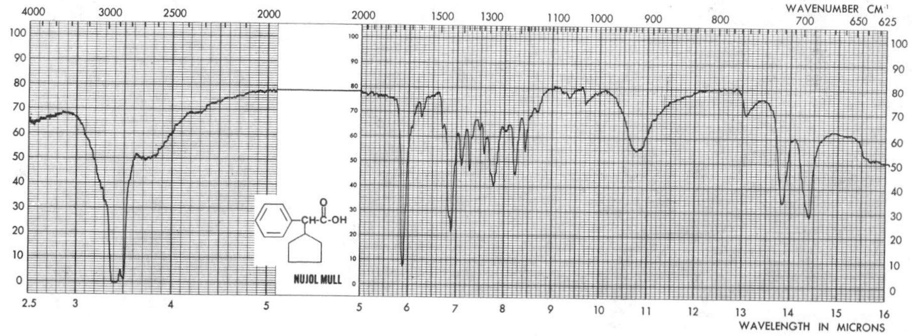

H 16,016-4
1-Phenyl-1-cyclohexanecarboxylic acid, 95%
$C_6H_5C_6H_{10}CO_2H$
M.W. 204.27 m.p. 121-123°
NUJOL MULL

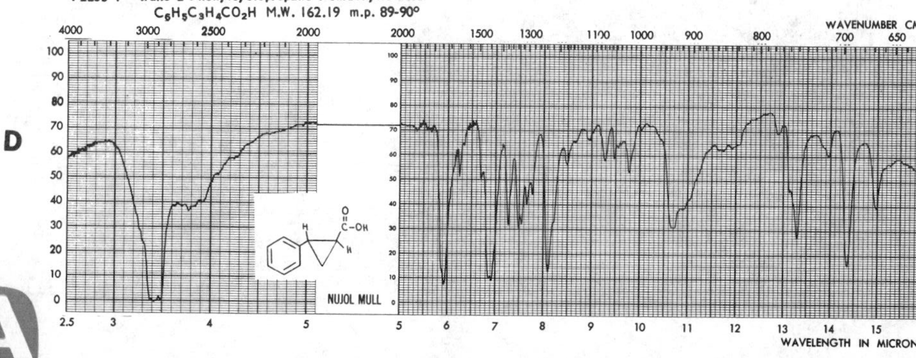

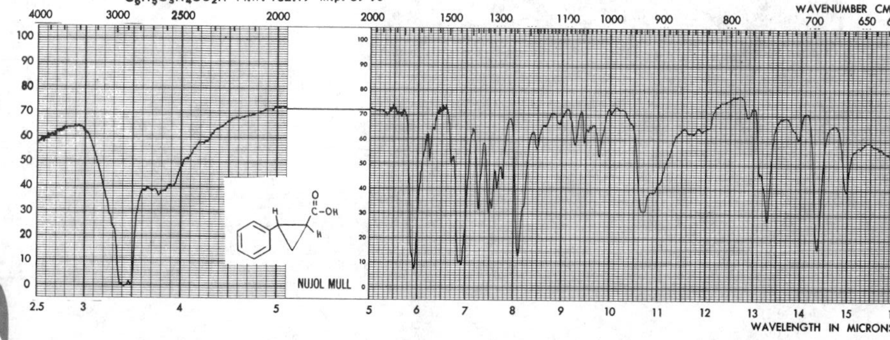

ALDRICH ®

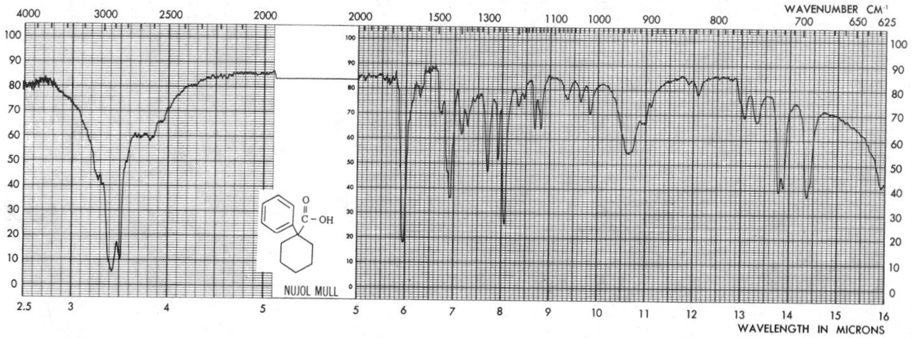

A

C10,760-3 **Cyclohexylphenylacetic acid** (α-phenylcyclohexaneacetic acid)
$C_6H_{11}CH(C_6H_5)CO_2H$ M.W. 218.30 m.p. 151.5-153° ....

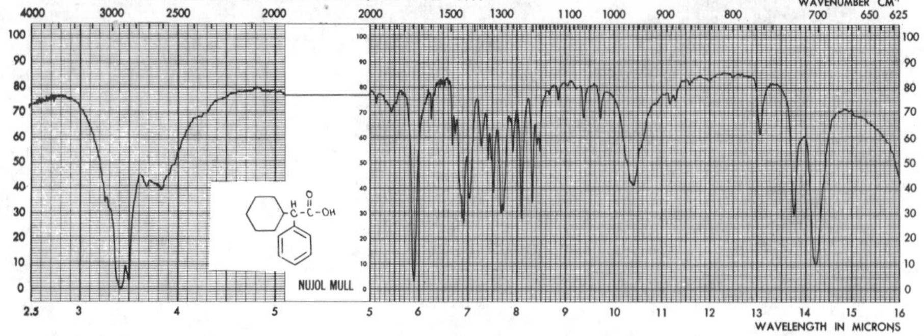

NUJOL MULL

B

D20,430-7 **Diphenylacetic acid, puriss.**
$(C_6H_5)_2CHCO_2H$ M.W. 212.25
m.p. 148° ....

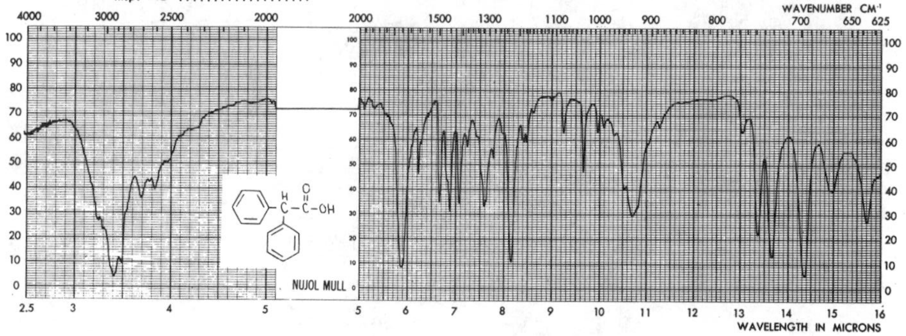

NUJOL MULL

C

T8120-5 **Triphenylacetic acid**
$(C_6H_5)_3CCO_2H$ M.W. 288.35 m.p. 267-271°

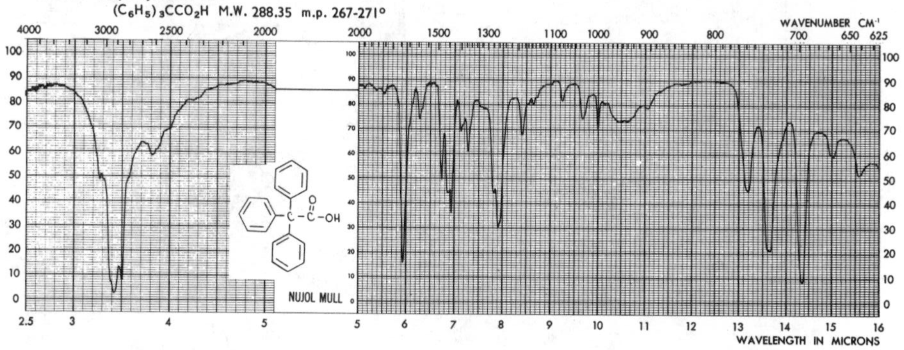

NUJOL MULL

D

13,523-2 **Hydrocinnamic acid**
$C_6H_5CH_2CH_2CO_2H$ M.W. 150.18
m.p. 47-49°

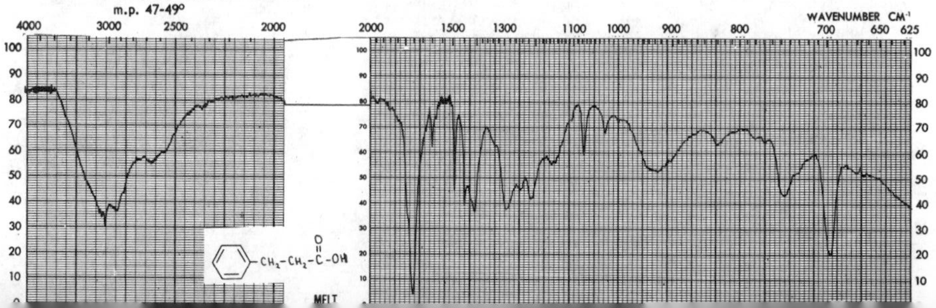

MELT

E

D21,160-5 **2,2-Diphenylpropionic acid**
$CH_3C(C_6H_5)_2CO_2H$ M.W. 226.28 m.p. 175-177°

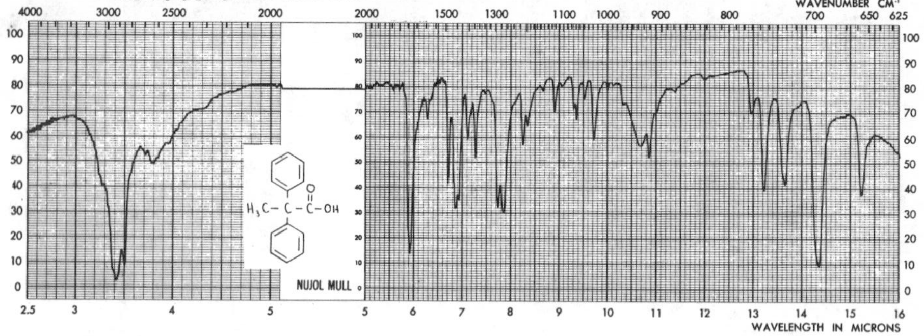

NUJOL MULL

F

D21,165-6 **3,3-Diphenylpropionic acid**
$(C_6H_5)_2CHCH_2CO_2H$ M.W. 226.28
m.p. 155-157°

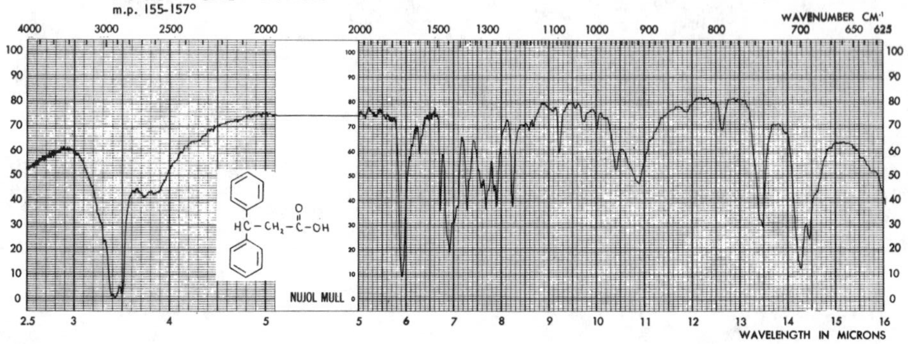

NUJOL MULL

G

P2095-5 **2-Phenylbutyric acid**
$C_2H_5CH(C_6H_5)CO_2H$ M.W. 164.20 m.p. 42-44°

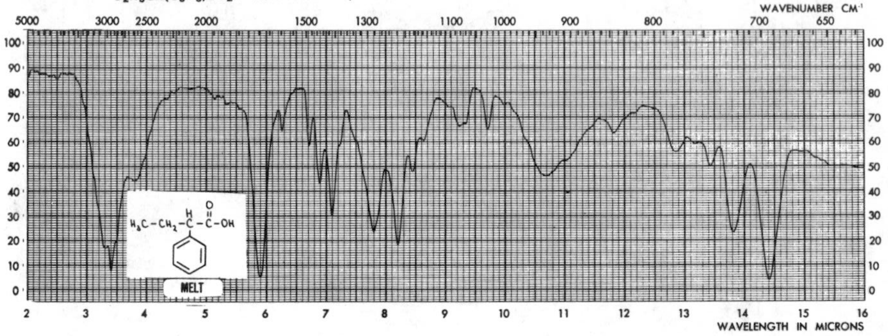

MELT

H

11,680-7 **3-Phenylbutyric acid**
$CH_3CH(C_6H_5)CH_2CO_2H$ M.W. 164.20
m.p. 40-42°

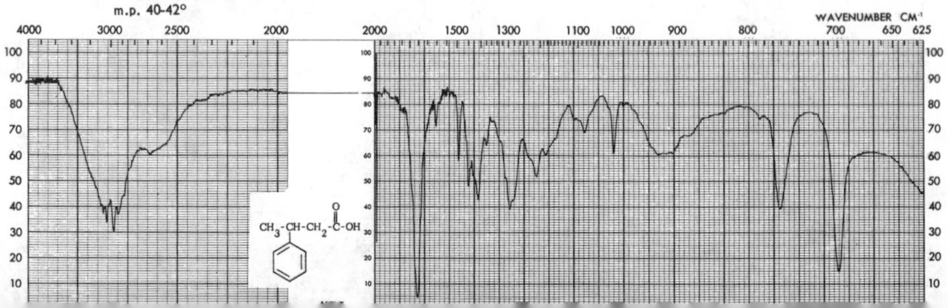

WAVENUMBER CM⁻¹ / WAVELENGTH IN MICRONS

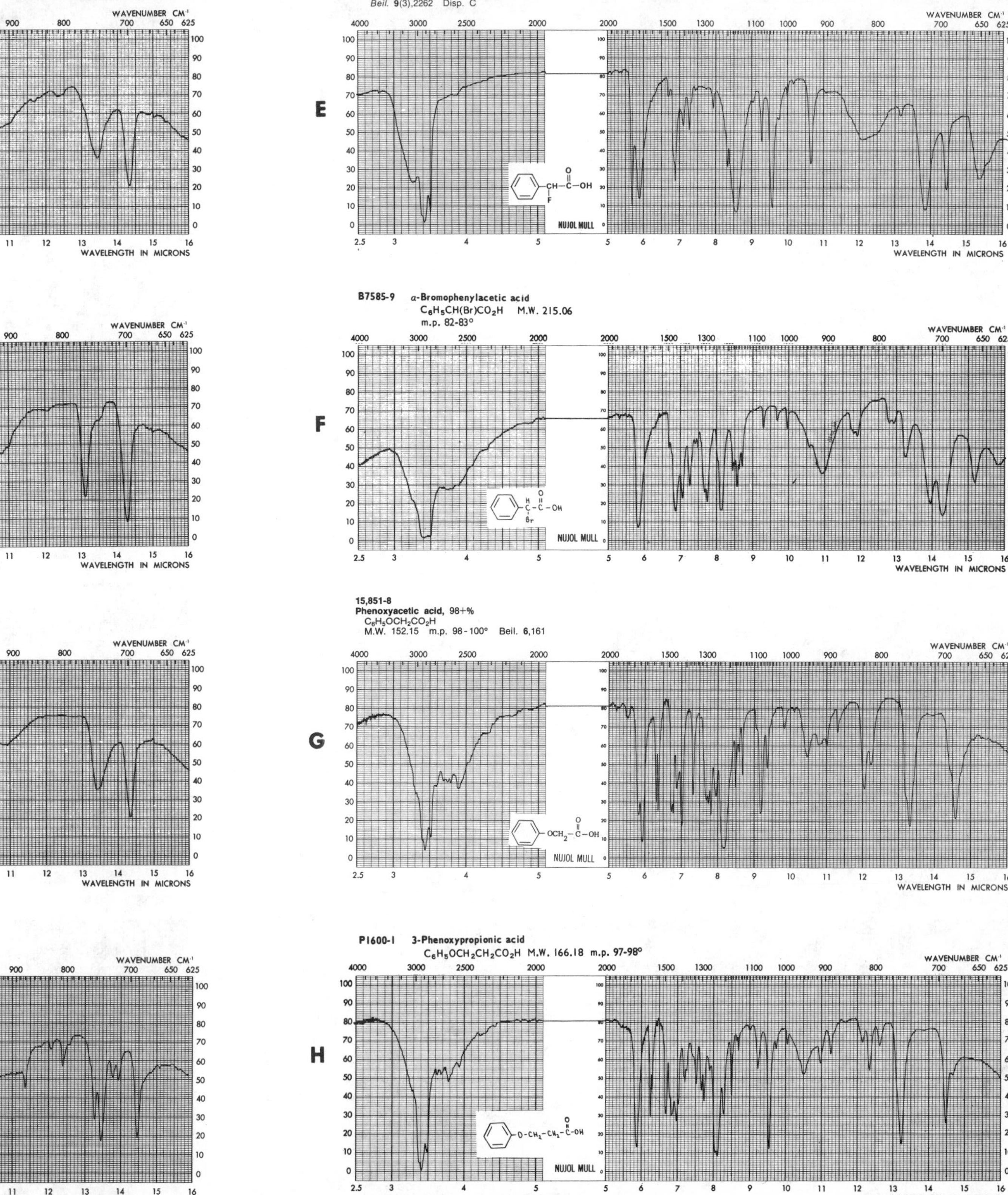

A $C_6H_5(CH_2)_3CO_2H$ M.W. 164.20
m.p. 50-52°
MELT

B P3740-8 4-Phenylvaleric acid
$CH_3CH(C_6H_5)CH_2CH_2CO_2H$ M.W. 178.23 n_D^{20} 1.5144
NEAT

C P3760-2 5-Phenylvaleric acid
$C_6H_5(CH_2)_4CO_2H$ M.W. 178.23 m.p. 54-57°
MELT

D 16,079-2
11-Phenoxyundecanoic acid, 99%
$C_6H_5O(CH_2)_{10}CO_2H$
M.W. 278.39 m.p. 75-77° b.p. 217-222°/3mm
NUJOL MULL

E $C_6H_5CH(F)CO_2H$ FW 154.14 mp 79-83°
Beil. 9(3),2262 Disp. C
NUJOL MULL

F B7585-9 α-Bromophenylacetic acid
$C_6H_5CH(Br)CO_2H$ M.W. 215.06
m.p. 82-83°
NUJOL MULL

G 15,851-8
Phenoxyacetic acid, 98+%
$C_6H_5OCH_2CO_2H$
M.W. 152.15 m.p. 98-100° Beil. 6,161
NUJOL MULL

H P1600-1 3-Phenoxypropionic acid
$C_6H_5OCH_2CH_2CO_2H$ M.W. 166.18 m.p. 97-98°
NUJOL MULL

ALDRICH

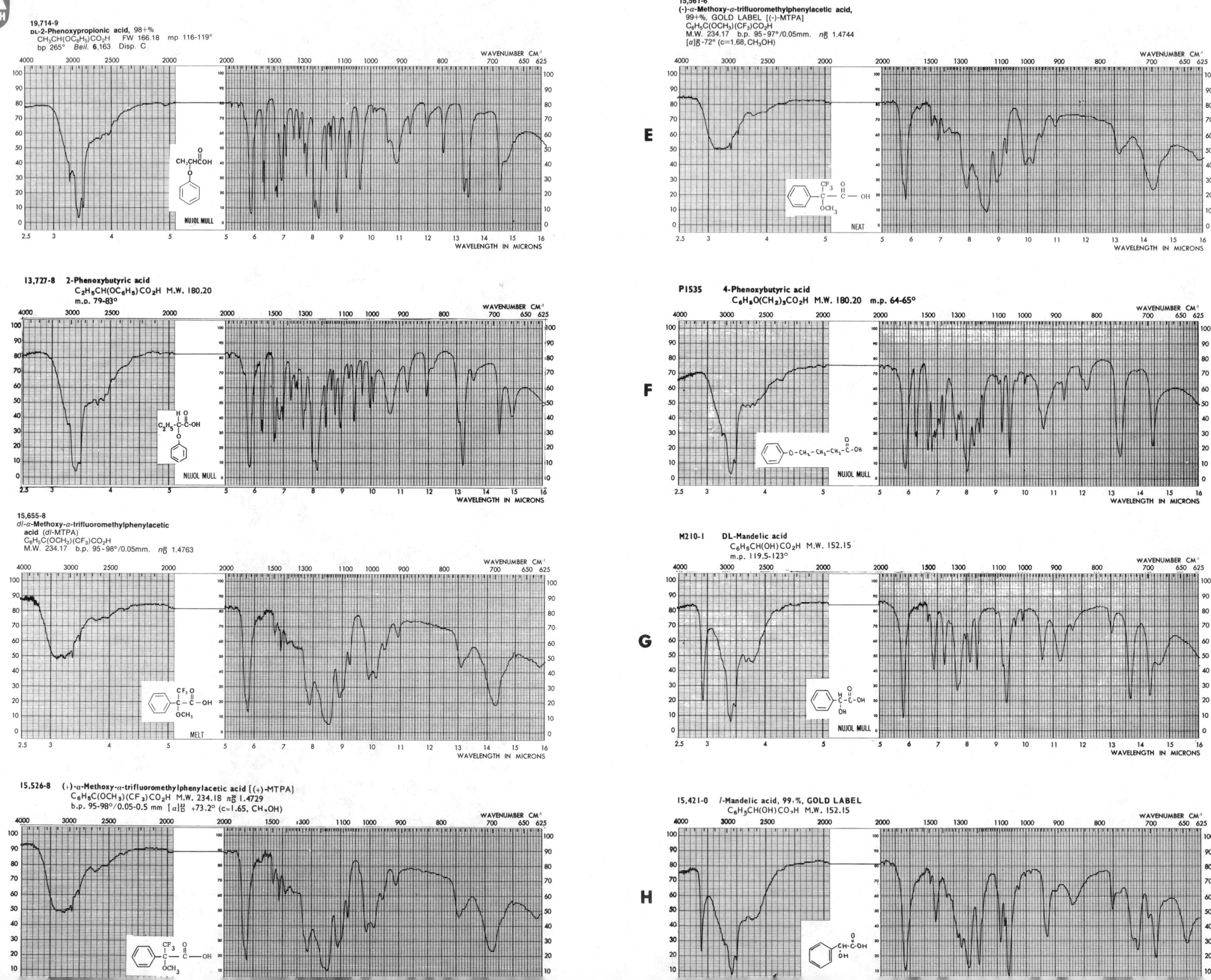

A 19,714-9
DL-2-Phenoxypropionic acid, 98+%
$CH_3CH(OC_6H_5)CO_2H$ FW 166.18 mp 116-119°
bp 265° *Beil.* 6,163 Disp. C
NUJOL MULL

B 13,727-8 2-Phenoxybutyric acid
$C_2H_5CH(OC_6H_5)CO_2H$ M.W. 180.20
m.p. 79-83°
NUJOL MULL

C 15,655-8
dl-α-Methoxy-α-trifluoromethylphenylacetic acid (*dl*-MTPA)
$C_6H_5C(OCH_3)(CF_3)CO_2H$
M.W. 234.17 b.p. 95-98°/0.05mm. n_D^{20} 1.4763
MELT

D 15,526-8 (+)-α-Methoxy-α-trifluoromethylphenylacetic acid [(+)-MTPA]
$C_6H_5C(OCH_3)(CF_3)CO_2H$ M.W. 234.18 n_D^{20} 1.4729
b.p. 95-98°/0.05-0.5 mm $[\alpha]_D^{22}$ +73.2° (c=1.65, CH_3OH)

E 15,561-6
(-)-α-Methoxy-α-trifluoromethylphenylacetic acid, 99+%, GOLD LABEL [(-)-MTPA]
$C_6H_5C(OCH_3)(CF_3)CO_2H$
M.W. 234.17 b.p. 95-97°/0.05mm. n_D^{20} 1.4744
$[\alpha]_D^{20}$ -72° (c=1.68, CH_3OH)
NEAT

F P1535 4-Phenoxybutyric acid
$C_6H_5O(CH_2)_3CO_2H$ M.W. 180.20 m.p. 64-65°
NUJOL MULL

G M210-1 DL-Mandelic acid
$C_6H_5CH(OH)CO_2H$ M.W. 152.15
m.p. 119.5-123°
NUJOL MULL

H 15,421-0 *l*-Mandelic acid, 99+%, GOLD LABEL
$C_6H_5CH(OH)CO_2H$ M.W. 152.15

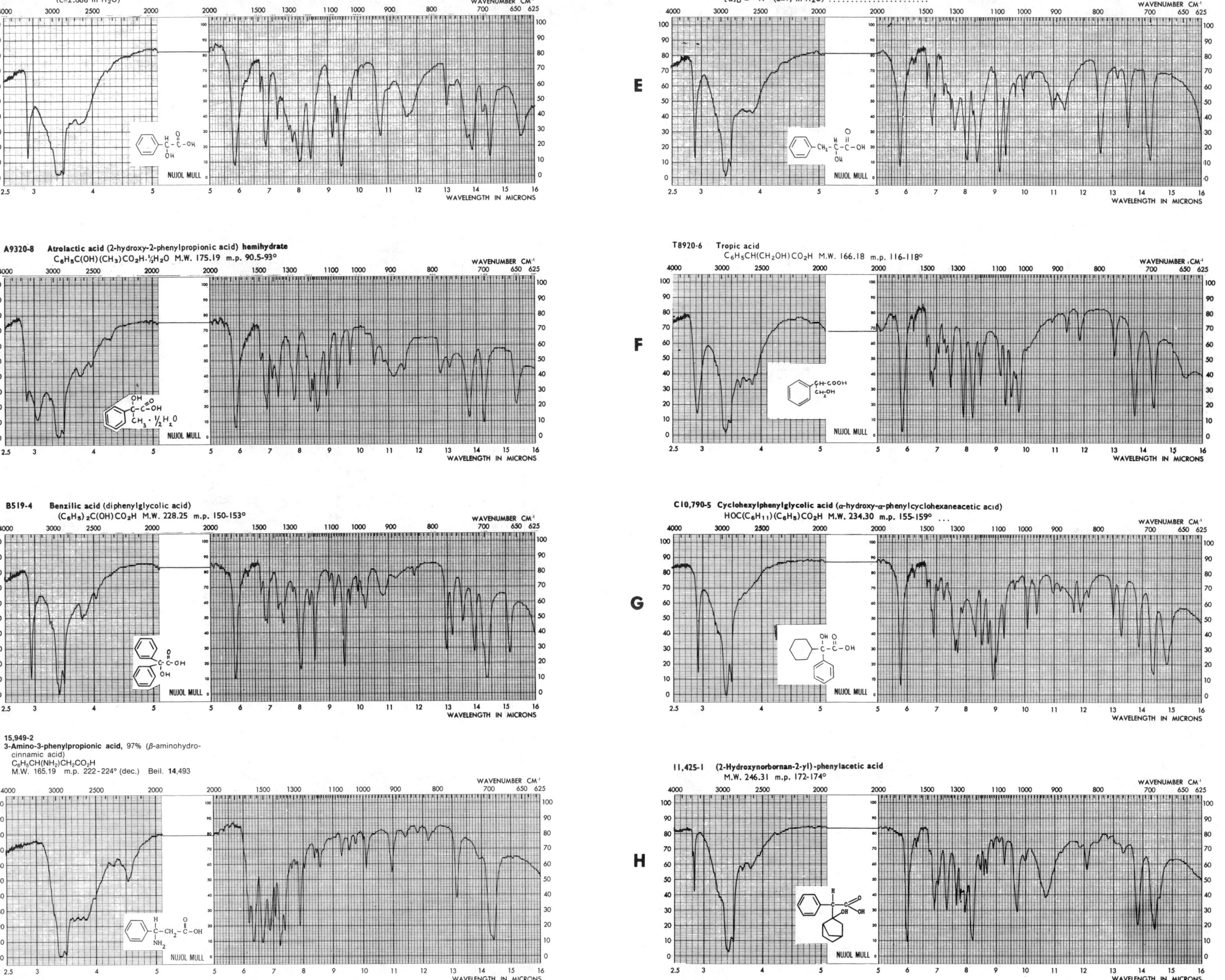

A
$[\alpha]_D$ + 156.8 (c=2.886 in H_2O)

B
A9320-8 **Atrolactic acid (2-hydroxy-2-phenylpropionic acid) hemihydrate**
$C_6H_5C(OH)(CH_3)CO_2H \cdot \frac{1}{2}H_2O$ M.W. 175.19 m.p. 90.5-93°

C
B519-4 **Benzilic acid (diphenylglycolic acid)**
$(C_6H_5)_2C(OH)CO_2H$ M.W. 228.25 m.p. 150-153°

D
15,949-2
3-Amino-3-phenylpropionic acid, 97% (β-aminohydrocinnamic acid)
$C_6H_5CH(NH_2)CH_2CO_2H$
M.W. 165.19 m.p. 222-224° (dec.) Beil. **14**,493

E
$[\alpha]_D^{22}$ = - 17° (c=1, in H_2O) . . . .

F
T8920-6 **Tropic acid**
$C_6H_5CH(CH_2OH)CO_2H$ M.W. 166.18 m.p. 116-118°

G
C10,790-5 **Cyclohexylphenylglycolic acid (α-hydroxy-α-phenylcyclohexaneacetic acid)**
$HOC(C_6H_{11})(C_6H_5)CO_2H$ M.W. 234.30 m.p. 155-159° . . .

H
11,425-1 **(2-Hydroxynorbornan-2-yl)-phenylacetic acid**
M.W. 246.31 m.p. 172-174°

A

T3300-6 **Thiophenoxyacetic acid [(phenylthio)-acetic acid], puriss.**
$C_6H_5SCH_2CO_2H$ M.W. 168.71 m.p. 64-65°

NUJOL MULL

B

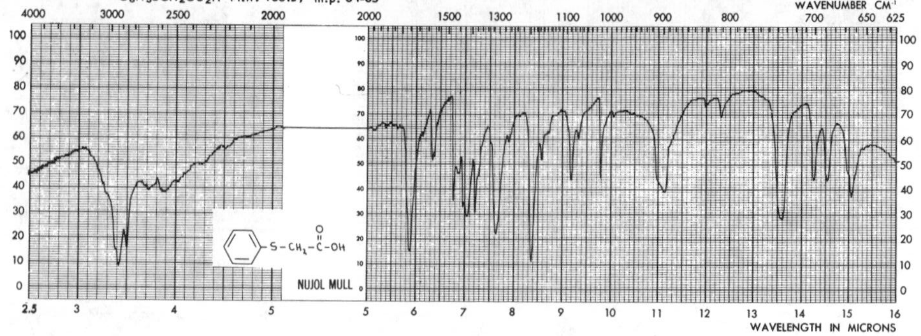

B3220-3 **S-Benzylthioglycolic acid** [benzylmercaptoacetic acid, (benzylthio)-acetic acid]
$C_6H_5CH_2SCH_2CO_2H$ M.W. 182.24
m.p. 59-63°

NUJOL MULL

C

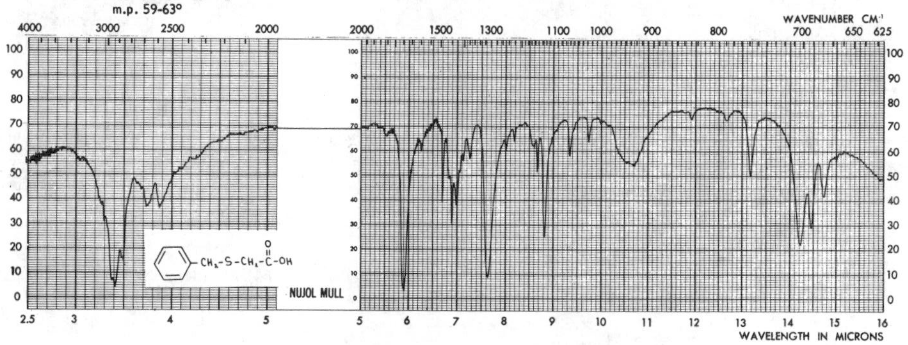

B1305-5 **Benzoylformic acid** (phenylglyoxylic acid)
$C_6H_5COCO_2H$ M.W. 150.13 m.p. 67-69°

MELT

D

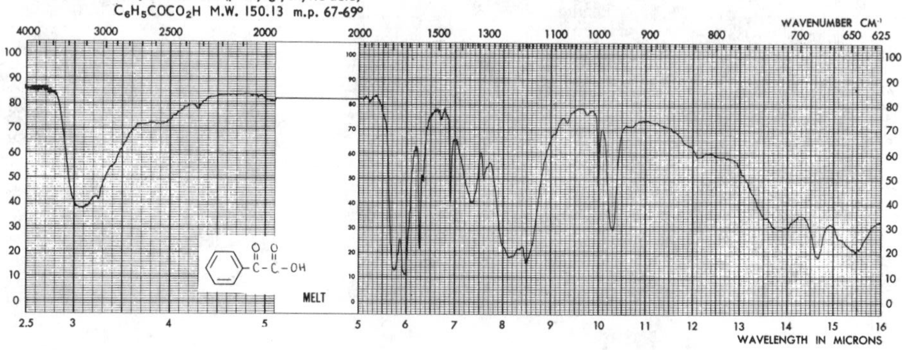

B1380-2 **3-Benzoylpropionic acid**
$C_6H_5COCH_2CH_2CO_2H$ M.W. 178.19
m.p. 115-118°

E

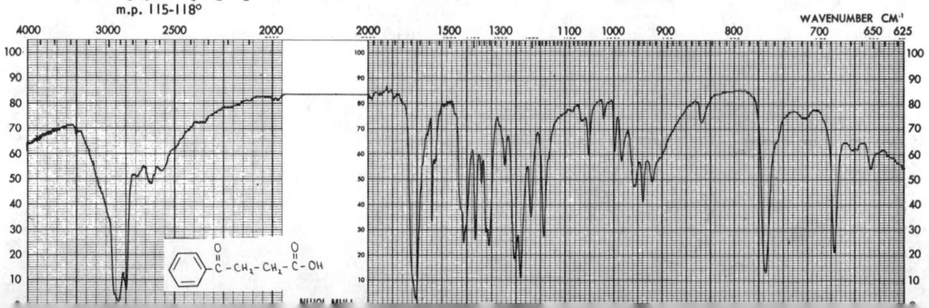

B1268-7 **4-Benzoylbutyric acid**
$C_6H_5CO(CH_2)_3CO_2H$ M.W. 192.21
m.p. 126.5-128°

NUJOL MULL

F

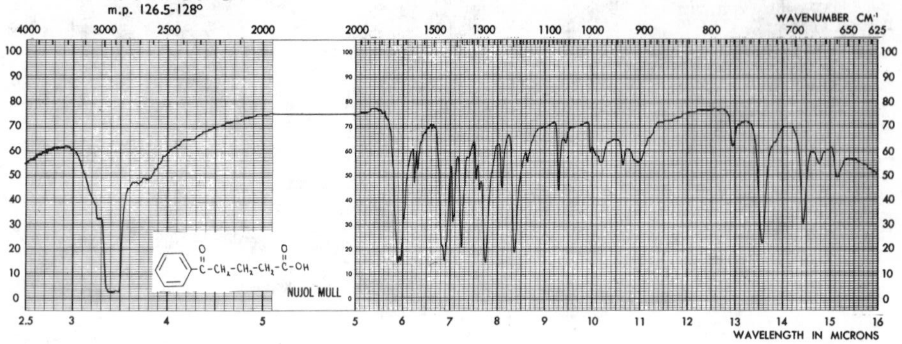

B1,520-1
5-Benzoylvaleric acid, 99%
$C_6H_5CO(CH_2)_4CO_2H$
M.W. 206.24 m.p. 78-80° d 1.088 Beil. **10**,716

NUJOL MULL

G

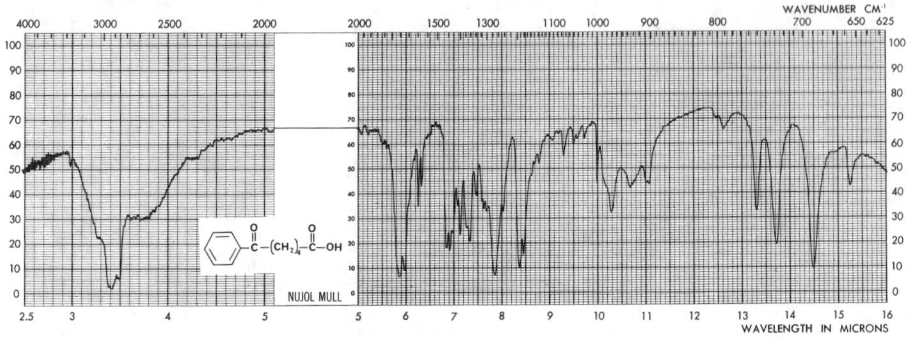

16,036-9
Phenylmalonic acid, 97%
$C_6H_5CH(CO_2H)_2$
M.W. 180.16 m.p. 153-155° (dec.)

NUJOL MULL

H

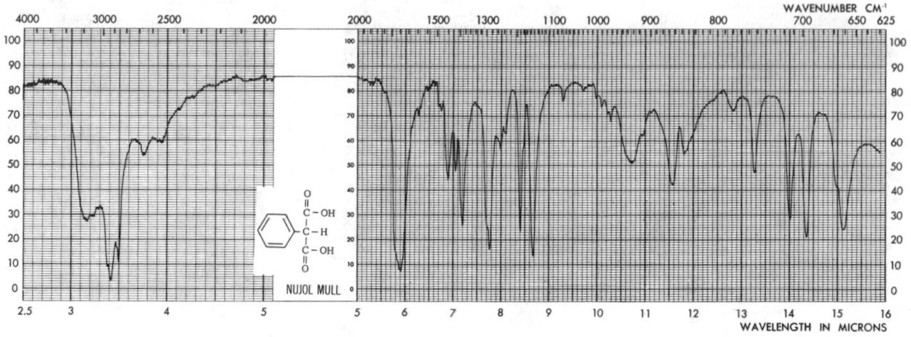

P2680-5 **2-Phenyllevulinic acid**
$CH_3COCH_2CH(C_6H_5)CO_2H$ M.W. 192.22
m.p. 126°

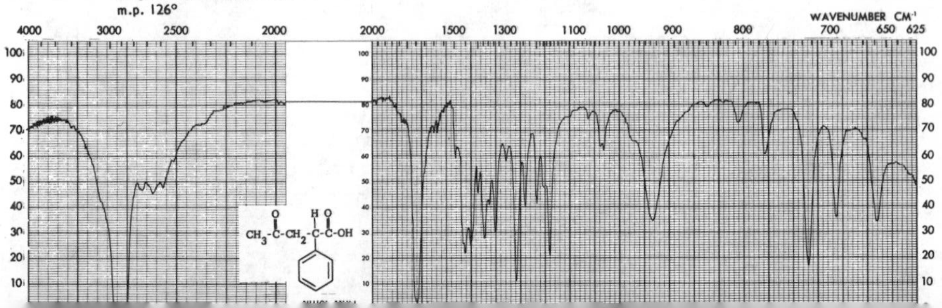

A

$HO_2CCH(CH_2C_6H_5)CO_2H$ M.W. 194.19
m.p. 120-122°

NUJOL MULL

B

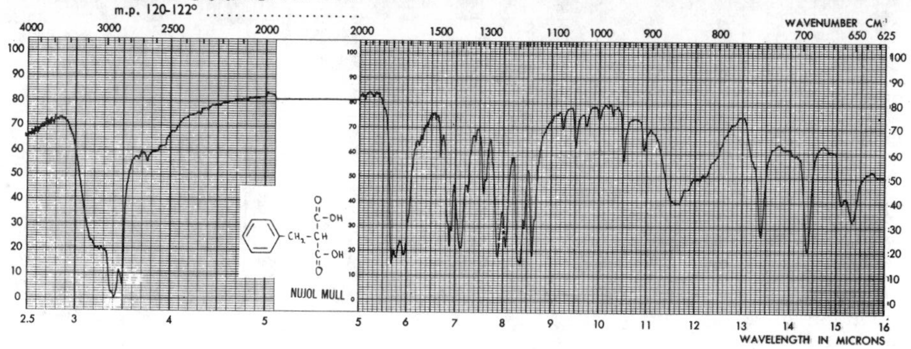

P3520-0 Phenylsuccinic acid
$HO_2CCH_2CH(C_6H_5)CO_2H$ M.W. 194.19
m.p. 168-171°

NUJOL MULL

C

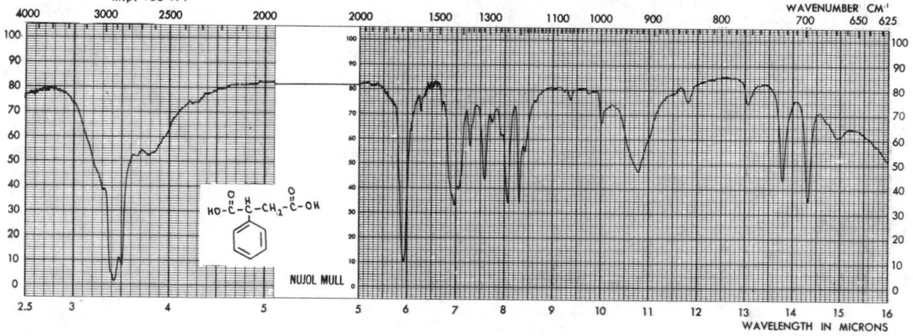

D21,400-0 *meso*-2,3-Diphenylsuccinic acid
$HO_2CCH(C_6H_5)CH(C_6H_5)CO_2H$ M.W. 270.28
m.p. 244° (dec.)

NUJOL MULL

D

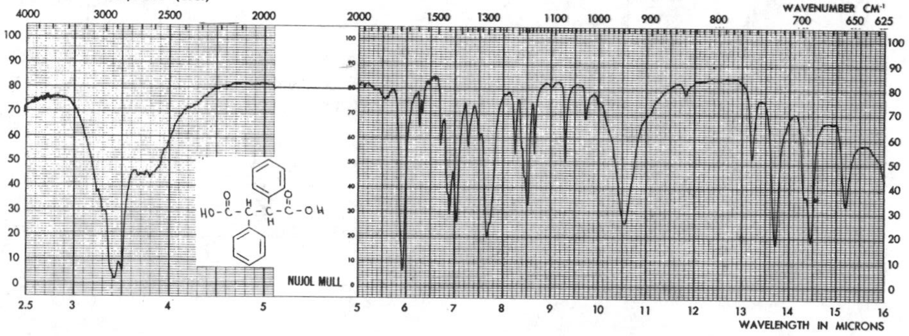

19,126-4
3-Phenylglutaric acid
$C_6H_5CH(CH_2CO_2H)_2$ FW 208.21 mp 140-143°
Beil. 9,878 Disp. C

NUJOL MULL

E

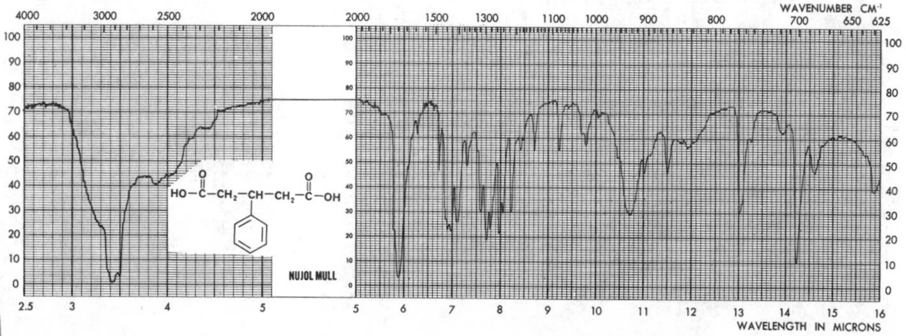

13,358-2 1-Benzyl-4-carboxy-4-phenylpiperidine (1-benzyl-4-phenyl-4-piperidine-carboxylic acid)
M.W. 295.38 m.p. 292-294°

NUJOL MULL

F

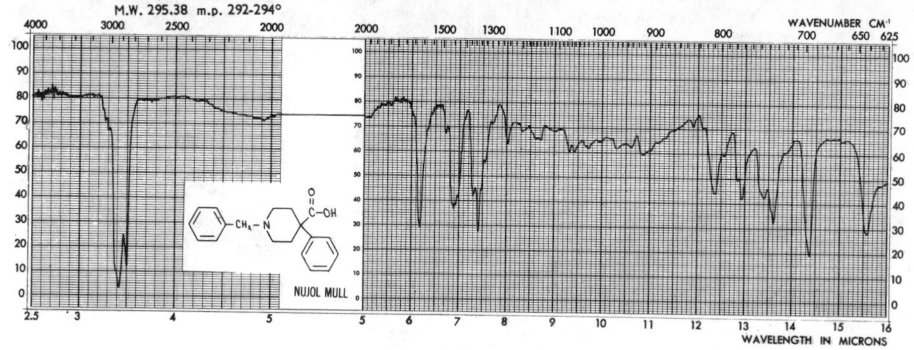

A8684 4-Anilino-1-benzylisonipecotic acid hydrochloride
M.W. 346.87 m.p. 266-270°

NUJOL MULL

G

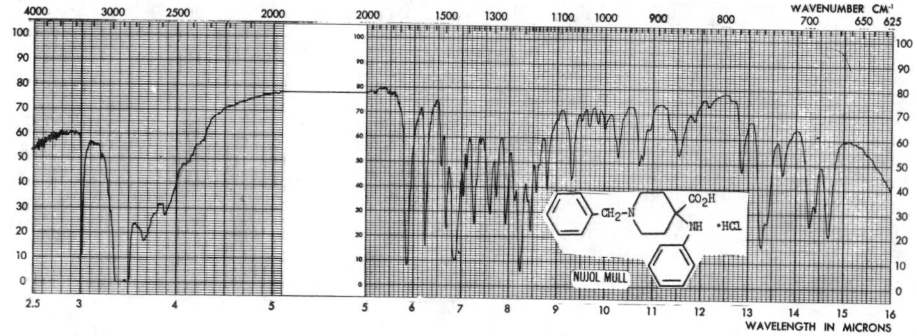

21,493-0
1,2,3,4-Tetrahydro-3-isoquinolinecarboxylic acid hydrochloride, 98%
FW 213.66 mp >300° *Beil.* **22**(1),506 Disp. C

NUJOL MULL

H

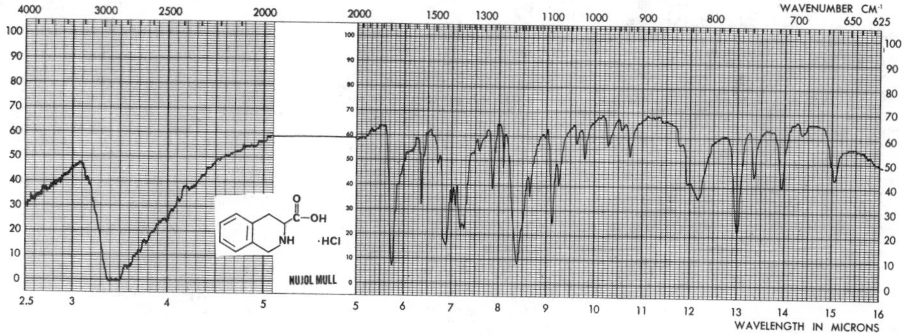

T3808-3 o-Tolylacetic acid
$CH_3C_6H_4CH_2CO_2H$ M.W. 150.18 m.p. 88-90°

NUJOL MULL

ALDRICH

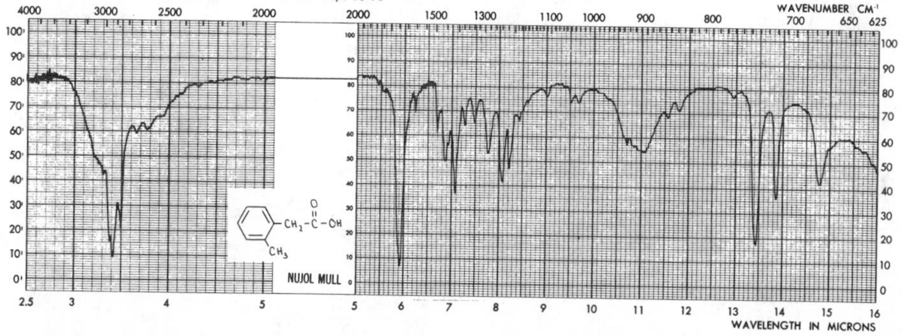

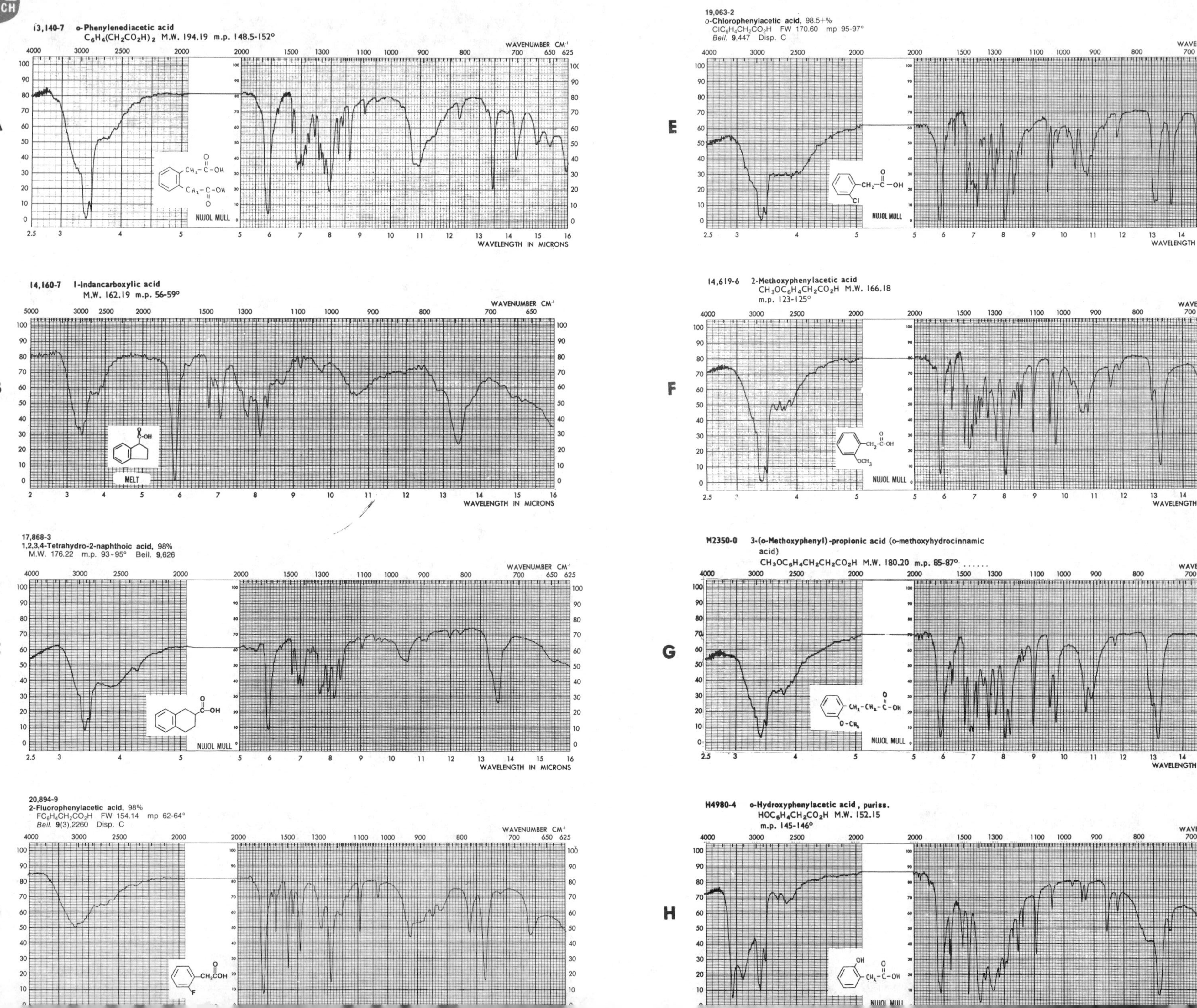

A
13,140-7 o-Phenylenediacetic acid
$C_6H_4(CH_2CO_2H)_2$ M.W. 194.19 m.p. 148.5-152°
NUJOL MULL
B
14,160-7 1-Indancarboxylic acid
M.W. 162.19 m.p. 56-59°
MELT
C
17,868-3
1,2,3,4-Tetrahydro-2-naphthoic acid, 98%
M.W. 176.22 m.p. 93-95° Beil. 9,626
NUJOL MULL
D
20,894-9
2-Fluorophenylacetic acid, 98%
$FC_6H_4CH_2CO_2H$ FW 154.14 mp 62-64°
Beil. 9(3),2260 Disp. C
E
19,063-2
o-Chlorophenylacetic acid, 98.5+%
$ClC_6H_4CH_2CO_2H$ FW 170.60 mp 95-97°
Beil. 9,447 Disp. C
NUJOL MULL
F
14,619-6 2-Methoxyphenylacetic acid
$CH_3OC_6H_4CH_2CO_2H$ M.W. 166.18
m.p. 123-125°
NUJOL MULL
G
M2350-0 3-(o-Methoxyphenyl)-propionic acid (o-methoxyhydrocinnamic acid)
$CH_3OC_6H_4CH_2CH_2CO_2H$ M.W. 180.20 m.p. 85-87°
NUJOL MULL
H
H4980-4 o-Hydroxyphenylacetic acid, puriss.
$HOC_6H_4CH_2CO_2H$ M.W. 152.15
m.p. 145-146°
WAVENUMBER CM⁻¹
WAVELENGTH IN MICRONS

A m.p. 139-142°

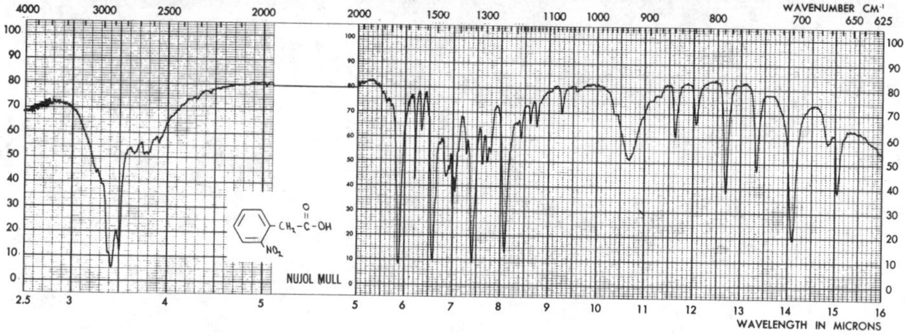

NUJOL MULL

B N1985-0 o-Nitrophenoxyacetic acid
$O_2NC_6H_4OCH_2CO_2H$ M.W. 197.15 m.p. 155-160°

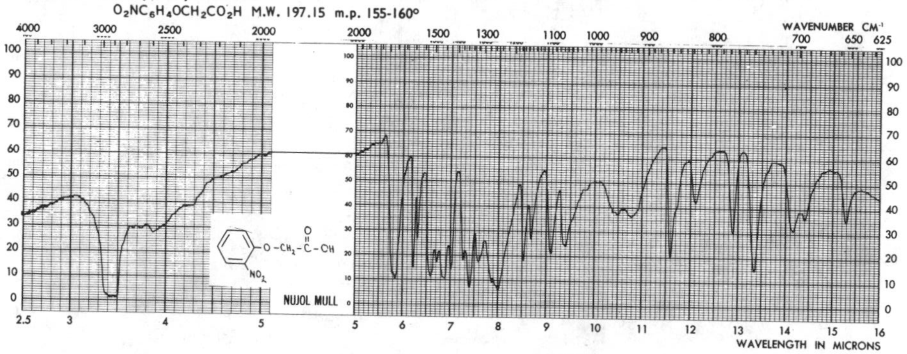

NUJOL MULL

C N2240-1 o-Nitrophenylpyruvic acid
$O_2NC_6H_4CH_2COCO_2H$ M.W. 209.16 m.p. 119-120° ......

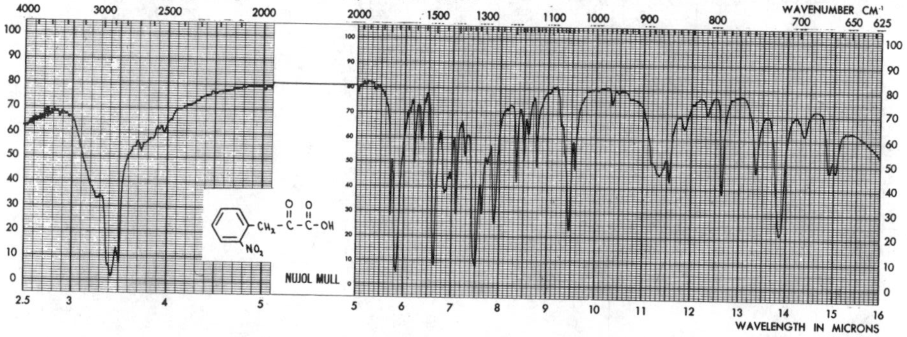

NUJOL MULL

D 11,537-1 3,3-Bis-(o-chlorophenyl)-glycidic acid
M.W. 309.15 m.p. 128° (dec.)

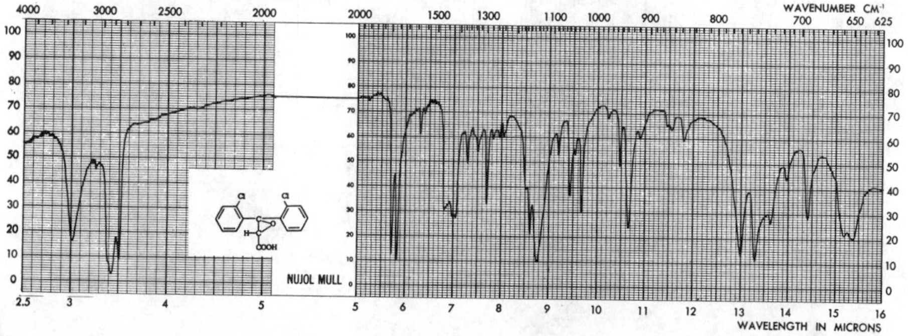

NUJOL MULL

E 15,215-3 o-Formylphenoxyacetic acid
$HCOC_6H_4OCH_2CO_2H$ M.W. 180.16 m.p. 129.5-132°

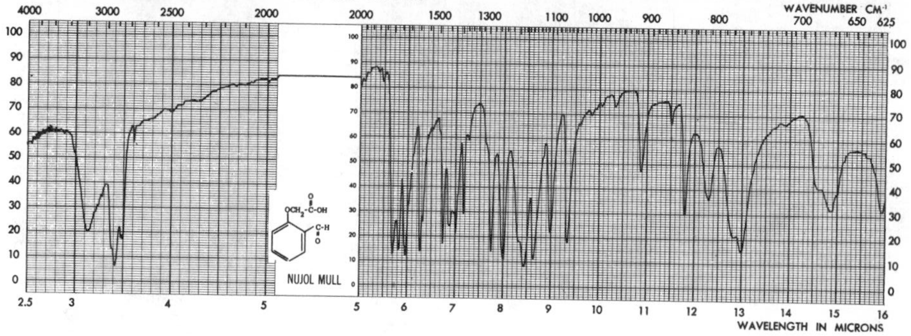

NUJOL MULL

F H1620-5 Homophthalic acid (α-carboxy-o-toluic acid)
$HO_2CCH_2C_6H_4CO_2H$ M.W. 180.16
m.p. 185-187°

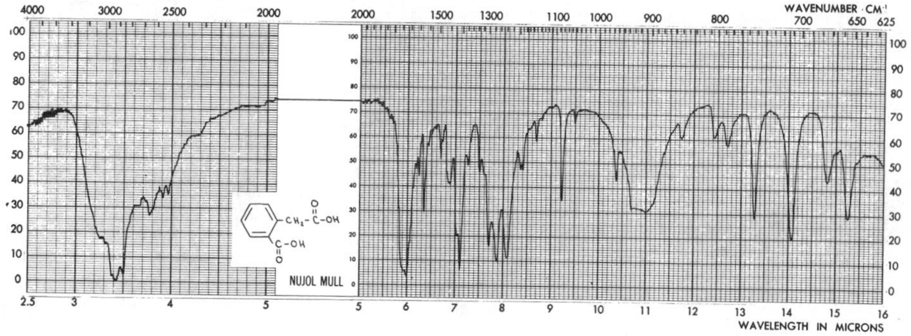

NUJOL MULL

G T3809-1 m-Tolylacetic acid
$CH_3C_6H_4CH_2CO_2H$ M.W. 150.18 m.p. 62-64°

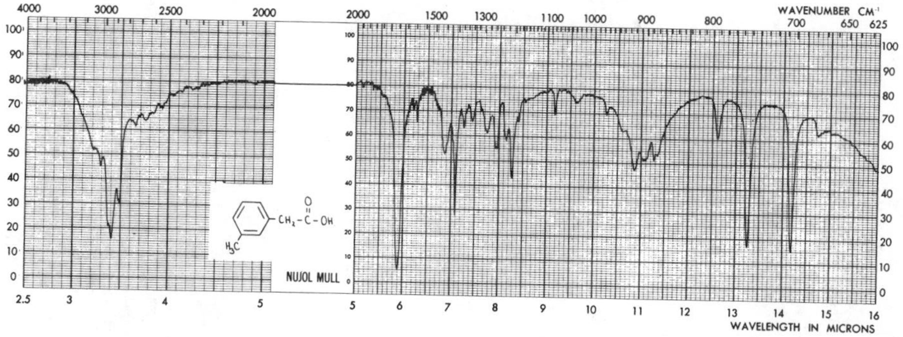

NUJOL MULL

H P2335-0 m-Phenylenediacetic acid
$C_6H_4(CH_2CO_2H)_2$ M.W. 194.19 m.p. 173-175°

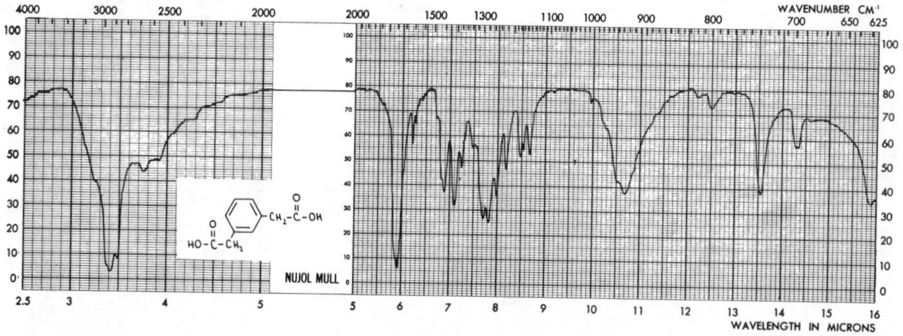

NUJOL MULL

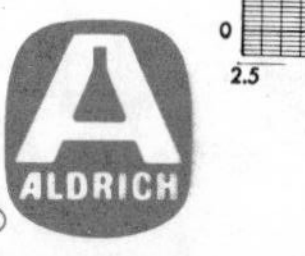

ALDRICH

A 14,268-9 1-m-Tolylcyclopentanecarboxylic acid
$CH_3C_6H_4C_5H_8CO_2H$ M.W. 204.27
m.p. 156-158°

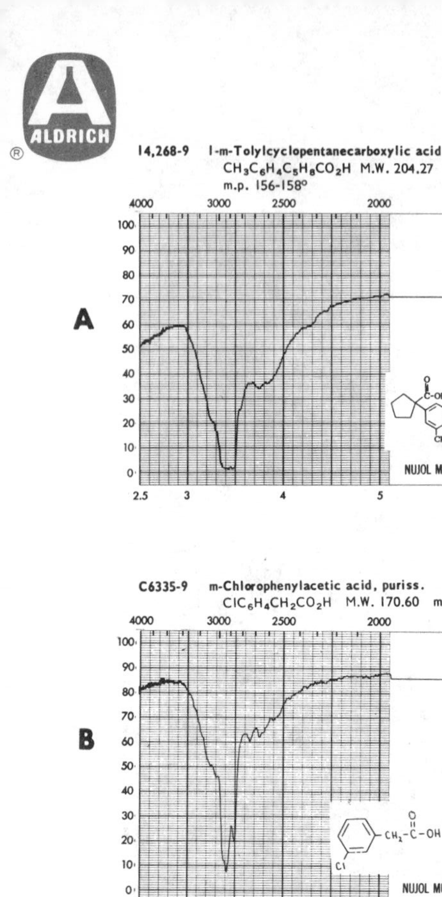

B C6335-9 m-Chlorophenylacetic acid, puriss.
$ClC_6H_4CH_2CO_2H$ M.W. 170.60 m.p. 78-79.5°

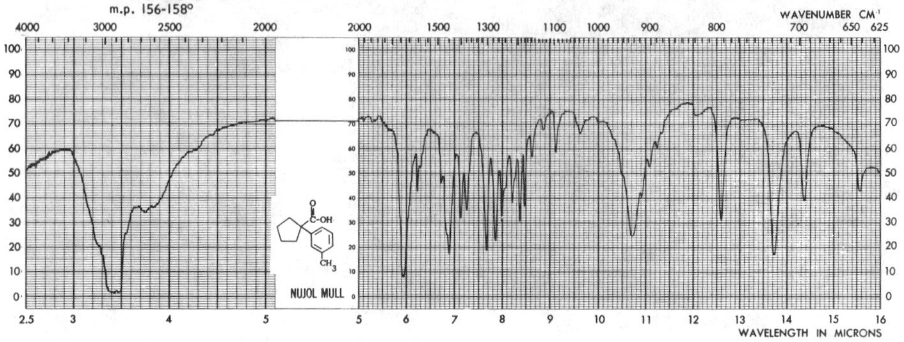

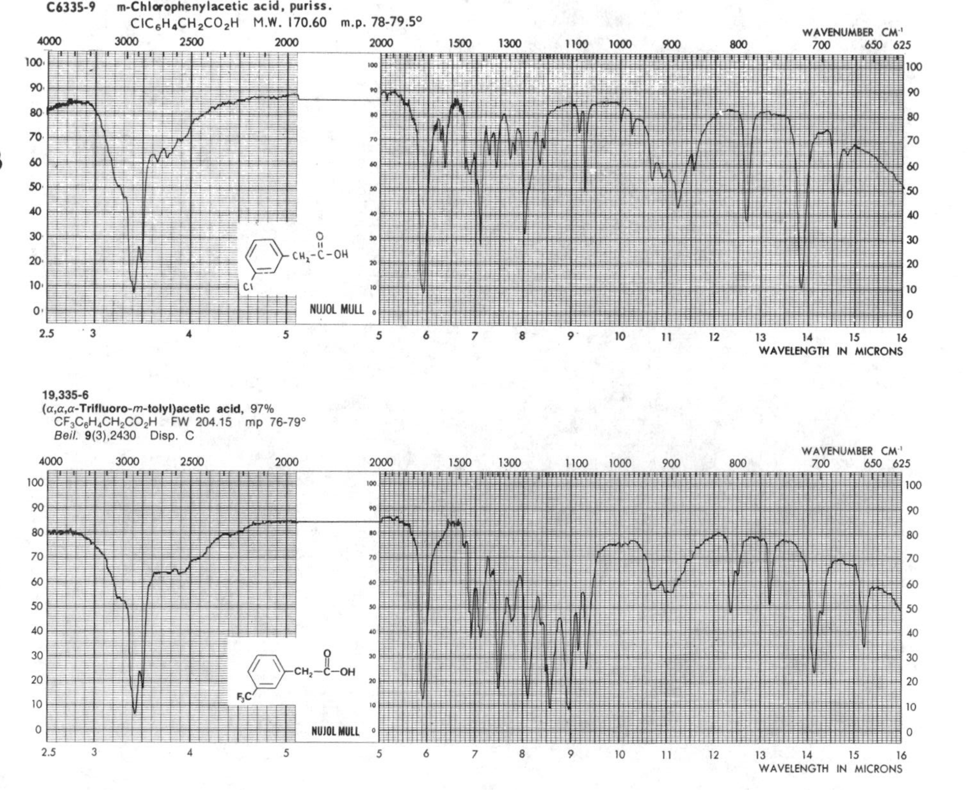

C 19,335-6
(α,α,α-Trifluoro-*m*-tolyl)acetic acid, 97%
$CF_3C_6H_4CH_2CO_2H$ FW 204.15 mp 76-79°
Beil. **9**(3),2430 Disp. C

D M1900-7 3-Methoxyphenylacetic acid
$CH_3OC_6H_4CH_2CO_2H$ M.W. 166.18
m.p. 71-73°

E H4990-1 m-Hydroxyphenylacetic acid, puriss.
$HOC_6H_4CH_2CO_2H$ M.W. 152.15
m.p. 131-134°

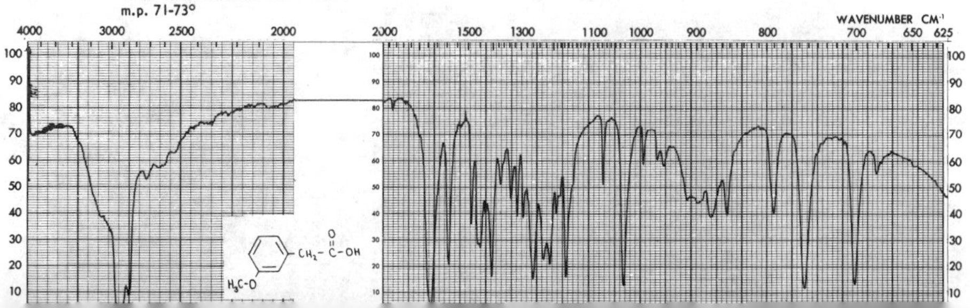

F 12,568-7 m-Hydroxymandelic acid
$HOC_6H_4CH(OH)CO_2H$ M.W. 168.15
m.p. 130-132°

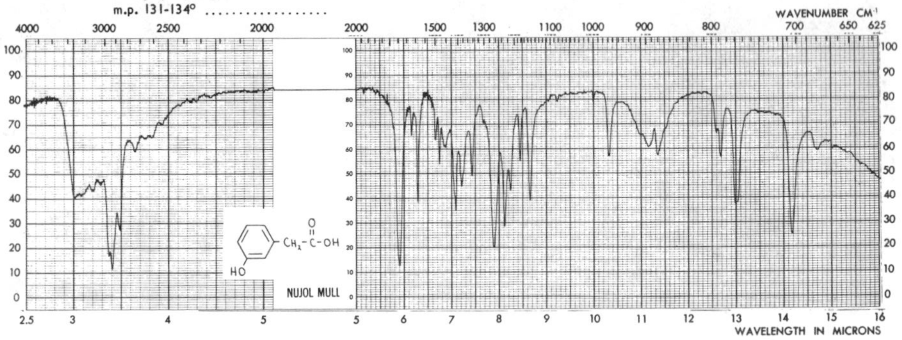

G 10,360-8 m-Nitrophenylacetic acid
$O_2NC_6H_4CH_2CO_2H$ M.W. 181.15
m.p. 120-122°

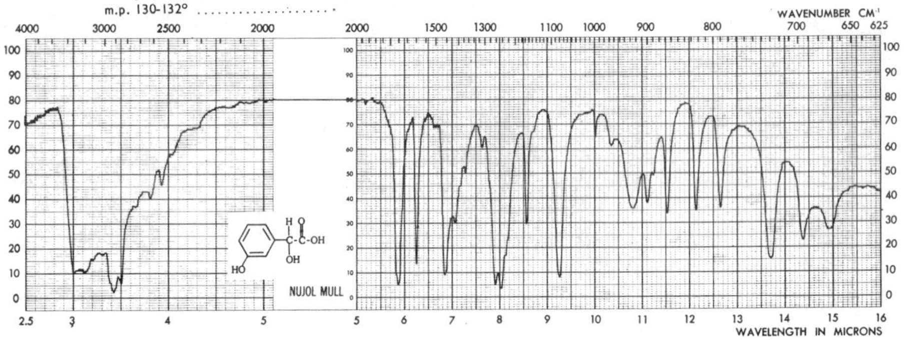

H T3810-5 p-Tolylacetic acid
$CH_3C_6H_4CH_2CO_2H$ M.W. 150.18 m.p. 90-93°

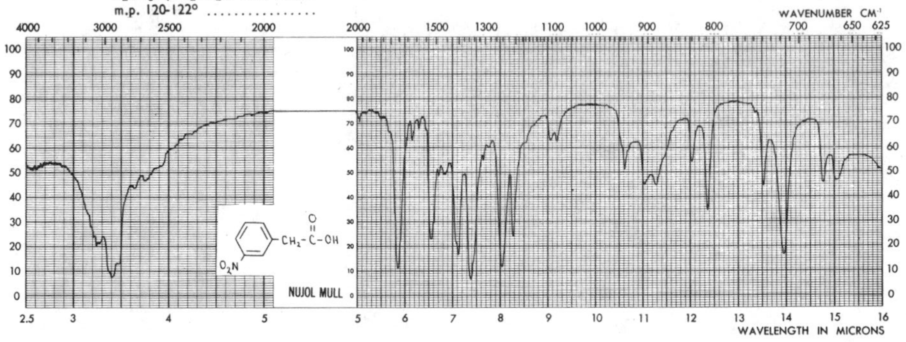

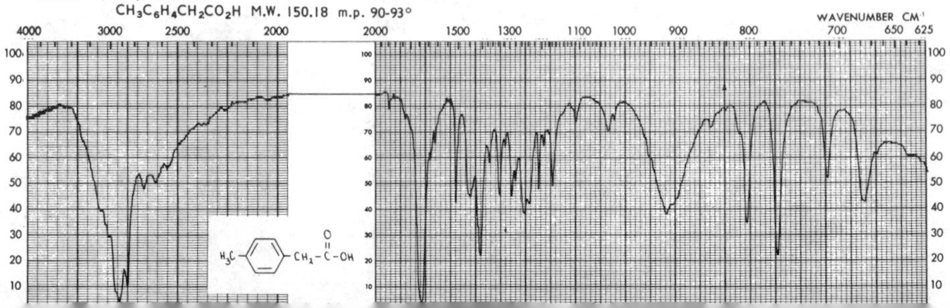

A

$(CH_3C_6H_4)_2CHCO_2H$ M.W. 240.31
m.p. 142-144°

NUJOL MULL

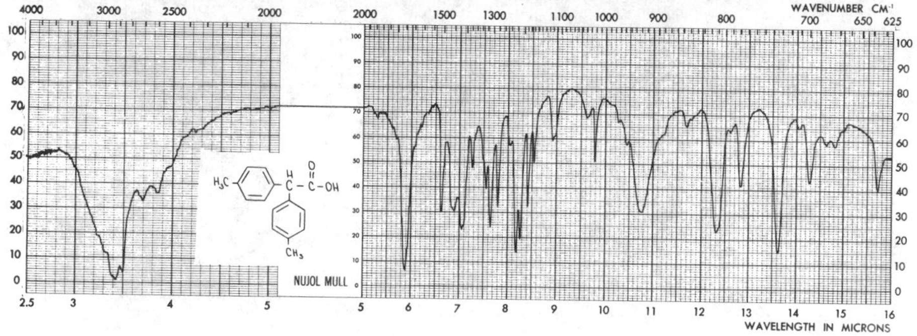

18,662-7
p-Carboxyphenoxyacetic acid, tech., 94%
(α-carboxy-p-anisic acid)
$HO_2CC_6H_4OCH_2CO_2H$
M.W. 196.16 Beil. **10**,158

B

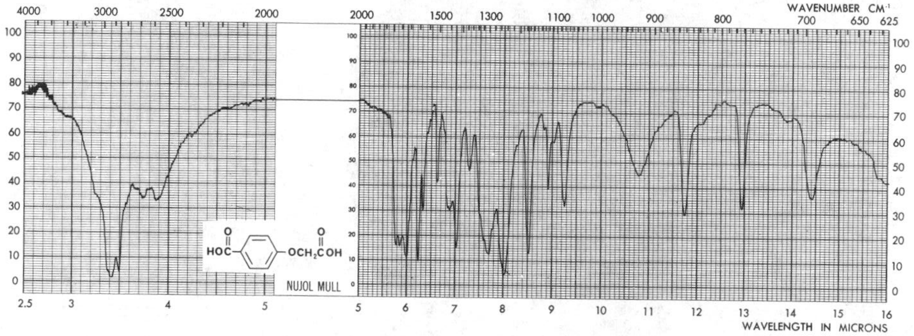

NUJOL MULL

P2340-7 **p-Phenylenediacetic acid**
$C_6H_4(CH_2CO_2H)_2$ M.W. 194.19
m.p. 254-256°

C

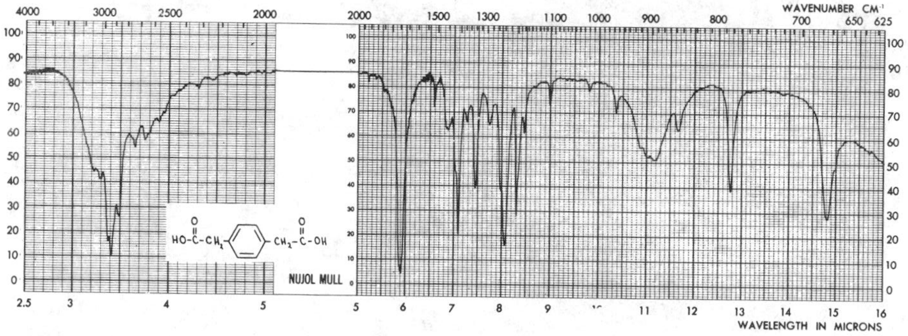

NUJOL MULL

18,365-2
5-Bromo-N-(carboxymethyl)anthranilic acid, 97%
[N-(4-bromo-2-carboxyphenyl)glycine]
BrC_6H_3-2-$(NHCH_2CO_2H)CO_2H$
M.W. 274.08 m.p. 215-218° (dec.) Beil. **14**,371

D

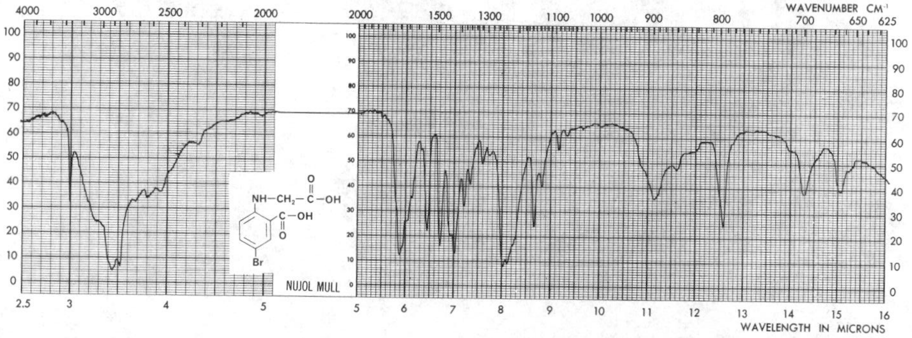

NUJOL MULL

E

4-Fluorophenylacetic acid
$FC_6H_4CH_2CO_2H$ M.W. 154.14
m.p. 80.5-82°

NUJOL MULL

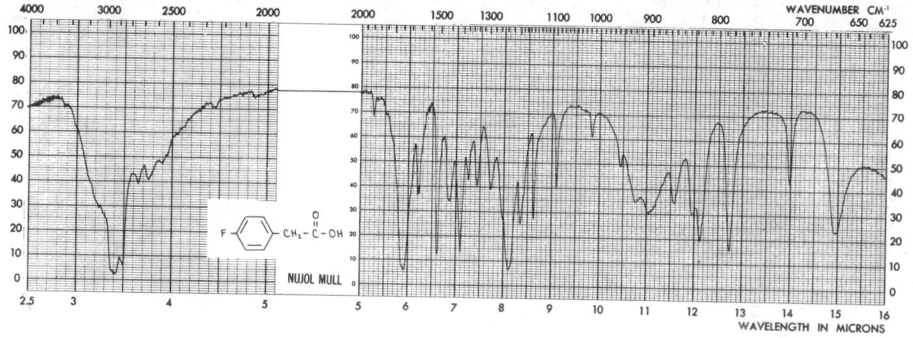

17,647-8
3-(p-Fluorobenzoyl)-propionic acid, 99%
$FC_6H_4COCH_2CH_2CO_2H$
M.W. 196.18 m.p. 100-102°

F

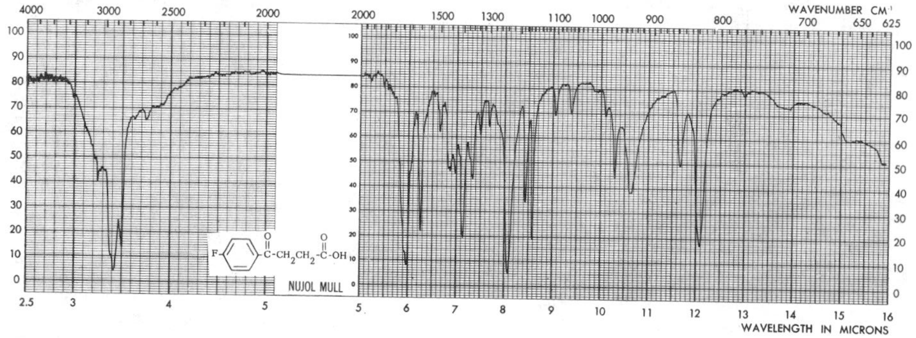

NUJOL MULL

13,926-2 **p-Chlorophenylacetic acid**
$ClC_6H_4CH_2CO_2H$ M.W. 170.60
m.p. 103-105°

G

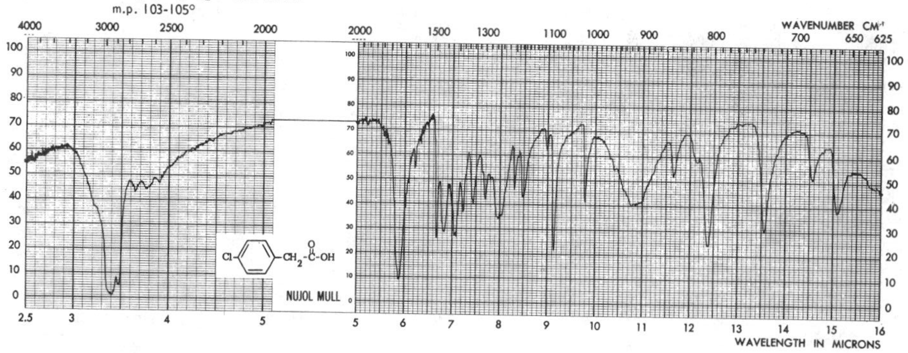

NUJOL MULL

15,410-5 **p-Chloro-α-methylphenylacetic acid**
$ClC_6H_4CH(CH_3)CO_2H$ M.W. 184.62
m.p. 56-58°

H

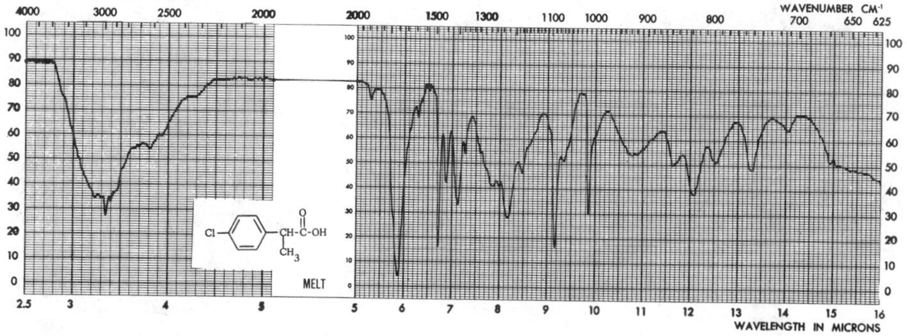

MELT

AROMATIC CARBOXYLIC ACIDS

A 15,409-1
p-Fluoro-α-methylphenylacetic acid, 98%
$FC_6H_4CH(CH_3)CO_2H$
M.W. 168.17 m.p. 51-53°

B 10,087-0 Bis-(p-chlorophenyl)-acetic acid
$(ClC_6H_4)_2CHCO_2H$ M.W. 281.14 m.p. 167-170°

C 13,867-3 p-Bromophenylacetic acid
$BrC_6H_4CH_2CO_2H$ M.W. 215.06 m.p. 117-119°

D 16,009-1
1-(p-Tolyl)-1-cyclopropanecarboxylic acid, tech.
$CH_3C_6H_4C_3H_4CO_2H$
M.W. 176.22 m.p. 109-111°

E 16,008-3
1-(p-Chlorophenyl)-1-cyclopropane-carboxylic acid, 99%
$ClC_6H_4C_3H_4CO_2H$
M.W. 196.63 m.p. 150-152°

F 16,011-3
1-(p-Chlorophenyl)-1-cyclobutane-carboxylic acid, 94%
$ClC_6H_4C_4H_6CO_2H$
M.W. 210.66 m.p. 80-82°

G 16,014-8
1-(p-Tolyl)-1-cyclopentanecarboxylic acid, 98%
$CH_3C_6H_4C_5H_8CO_2H$
M.W. 204.27 m.p. 182-183°

H 14,156-9 1-(p-Chlorophenyl)-1-cyclopentanecarboxylic acid
$ClC_6H_4C_5H_8CO_2H$ M.W. 224.69
m.p. 162-164°

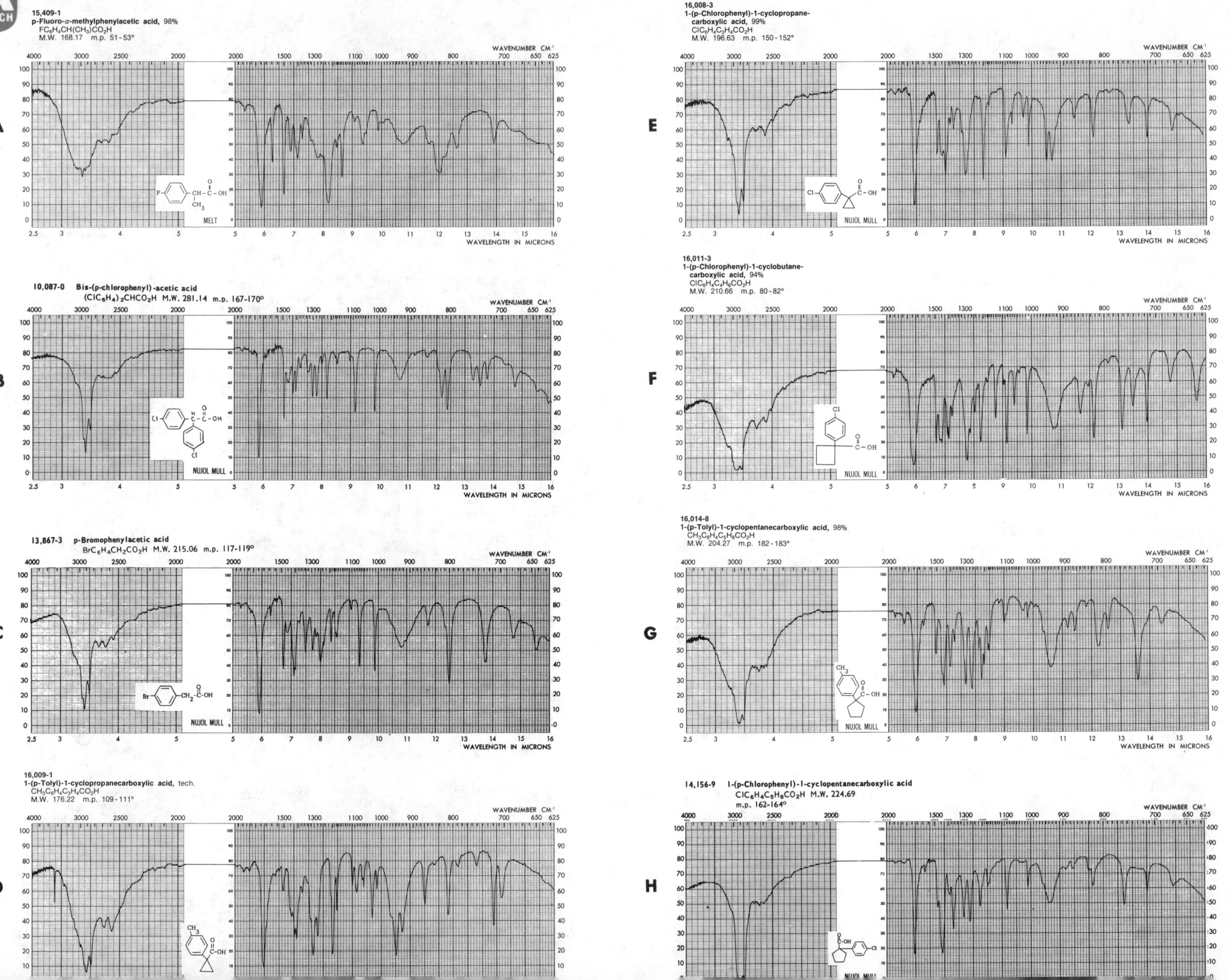

[illegible] acid, 98%
$ClC_6H_4COCH_2CH_2CO_2H$ FW 212.63 mp 128-130°
Disp. C

A

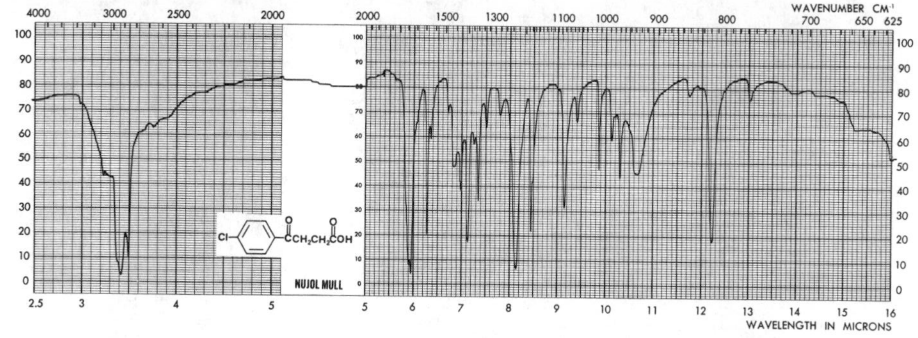

16,010-5
1-(p-Methoxyphenyl)-1-cyclopropane-carboxylic acid, 97%
$CH_3OC_6H_4C_3H_4CO_2H$
M.W. 192.21 m.p. 124-126°

B

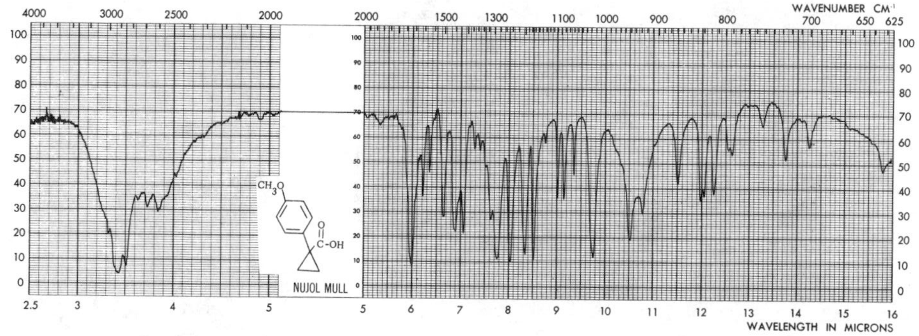

16,015-6
1-(p-Methoxyphenyl)-1-cyclopentanecarboxylic acid
$CH_3OC_6H_4C_5H_8CO_2H$
M.W. 220.27 m.p. 151-153°

C

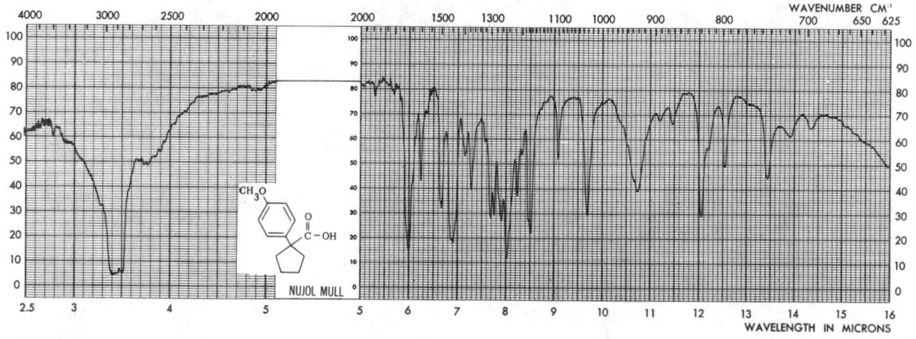

16,017-2
1-(p-Chlorophenyl)-1-cyclohexane-carboxylic acid, 97%
$ClC_6H_4C_6H_{10}CO_2H$
M.W. 238.71 m.p. 153-155°

D

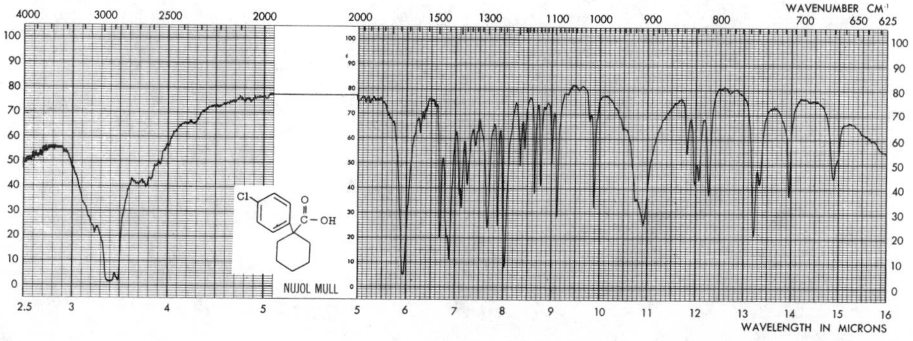

carboxylic acid, 97%
$CH_3OC_6H_4C_6H_{10}CO_2H$
M.W. 234.3 m.p. 173-175°

E

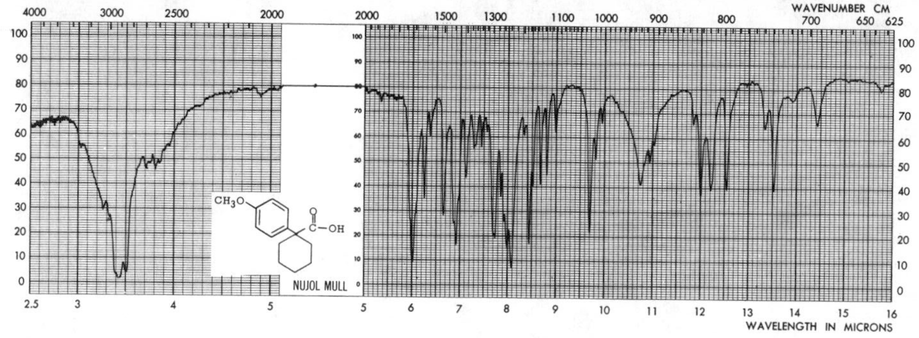

16,018-0
1-(p-Tolyl)-1-cyclohexanecarboxylic acid, 97%
$CH_3C_6H_4C_6H_{10}CO_2H$
M.W. 218.3 m.p. 168-170°

F

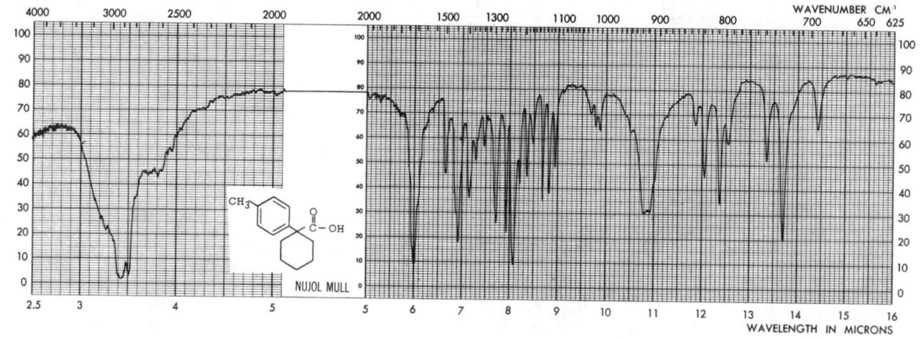

M1920-1 4-Methoxyphenylacetic acid
$CH_3OC_6H_4CH_2CO_2H$ M.W. 166.18 m.p. 86-88.5°

G

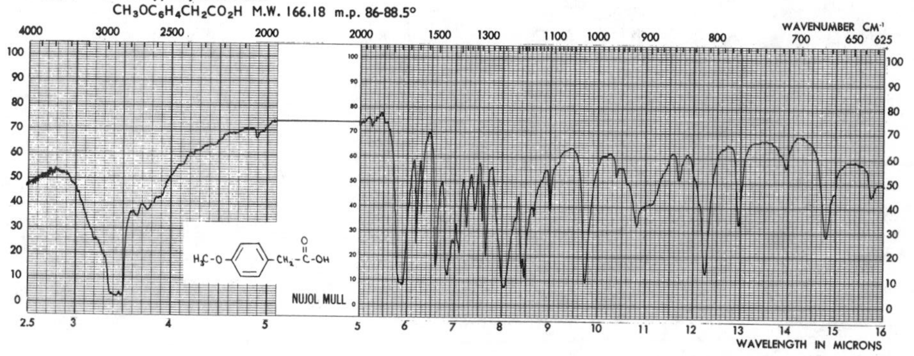

12,811-2 p-Ethoxyphenylacetic acid
$C_2H_5OC_6H_4CH_2CO_2H$ M.W. 180.20 m.p. 87-90°

H

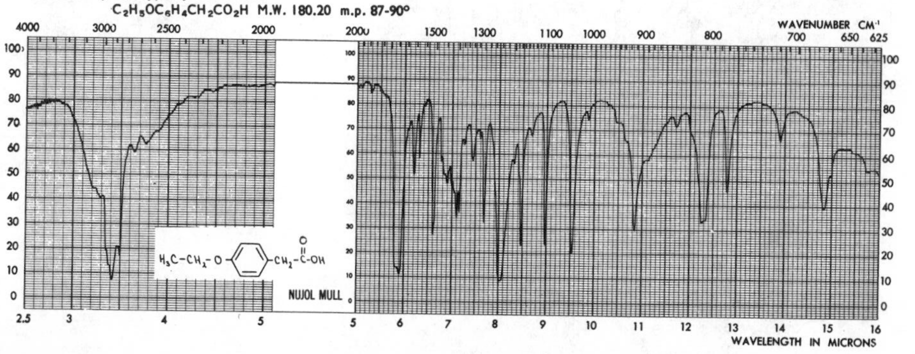

ALDRICH ®

AROMATIC CARBOXYLIC ACIDS

A

M2352-7 3-(p-Methoxyphenyl)-propionic acid (p-methoxyhydrocinnamic acid)
$CH_3OC_6H_4CH_2CH_2CO_2H$ M.W. 180.20
m.p. 98-100°

NUJOL MULL

B

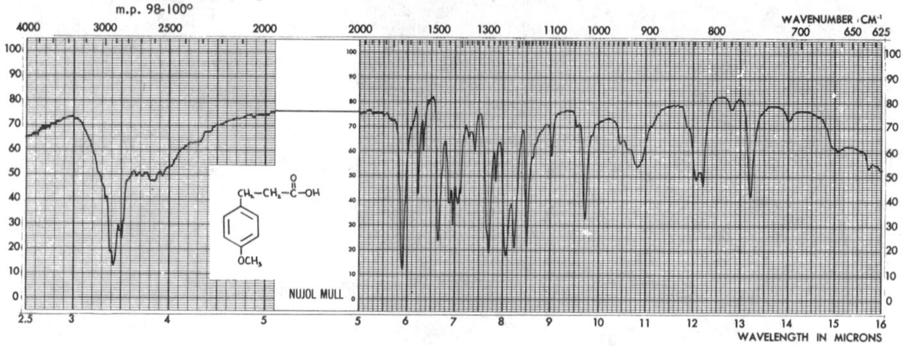

16,338-4
4-(p-Methoxyphenyl)-butyric acid, 97%
$CH_3OC_6H_4(CH_2)_3CO_2H$
M.W. 194.23 m.p. 56-59° Beil. **10**(2),164

NUJOL MULL

C

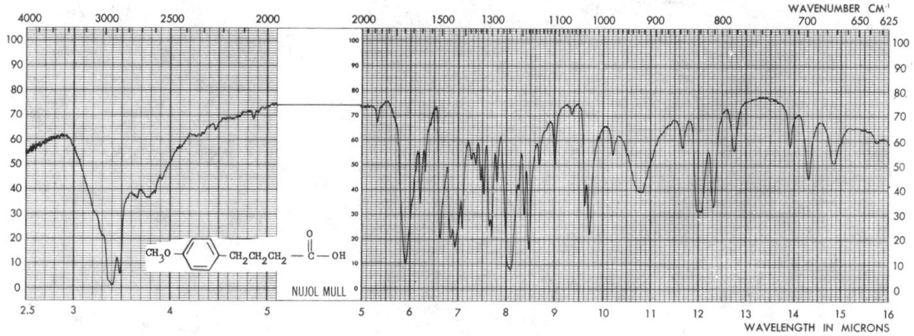

H5000-4 p-Hydroxyphenylacetic acid, puriss.
$HOC_6H_4CH_2CO_2H$ M.W. 152.15
m.p. 149-151° . . . .

NUJOL MULL

D

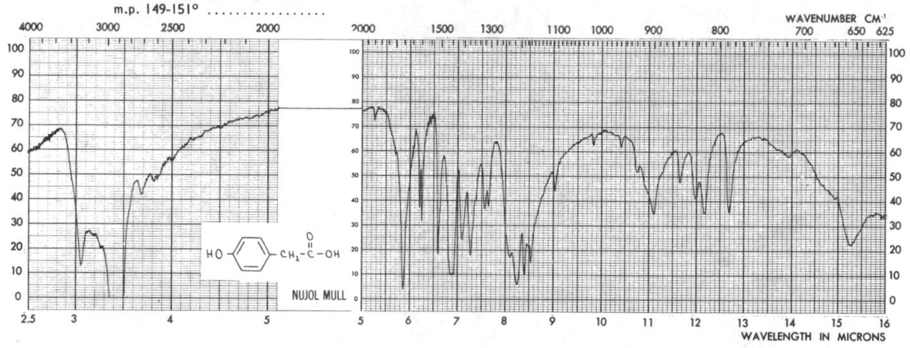

H5240-6 3-(p-Hydroxyphenyl)-propionic acid
$HOC_6H_4CH_2CH_2CO_2H$ M.W. 166.18 m.p. 129-131°

NUJOL MULL

E

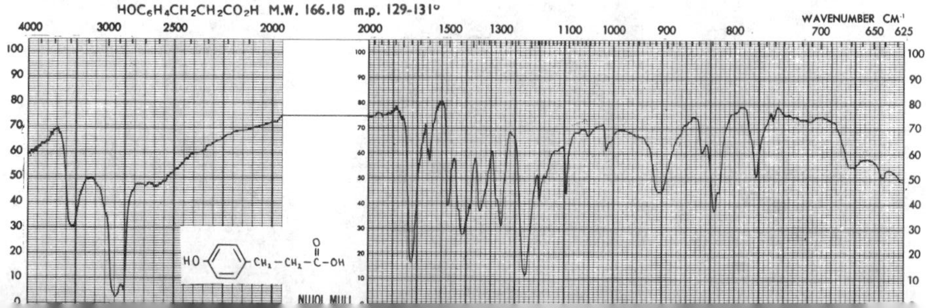

16,832-7
DL-p-Hydroxymandelic acid, 95%
$HOC_6H_4CH(OH)CO_2H$ FW 168.15 mp 103-106°
Beil. **10**,410 Disp. I

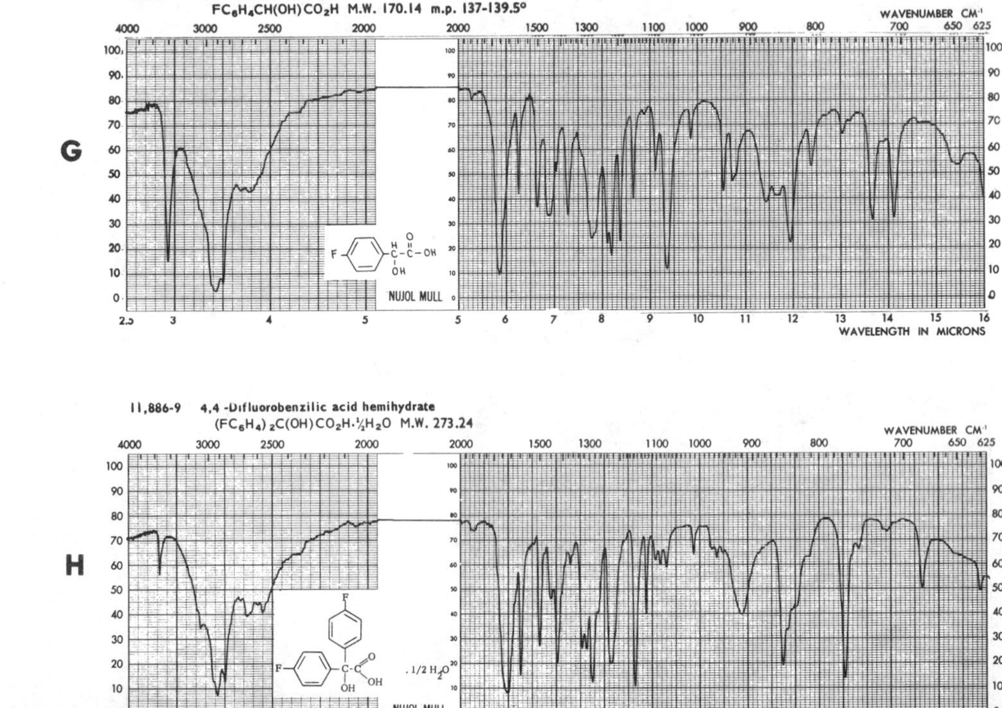

NUJOL MULL

F

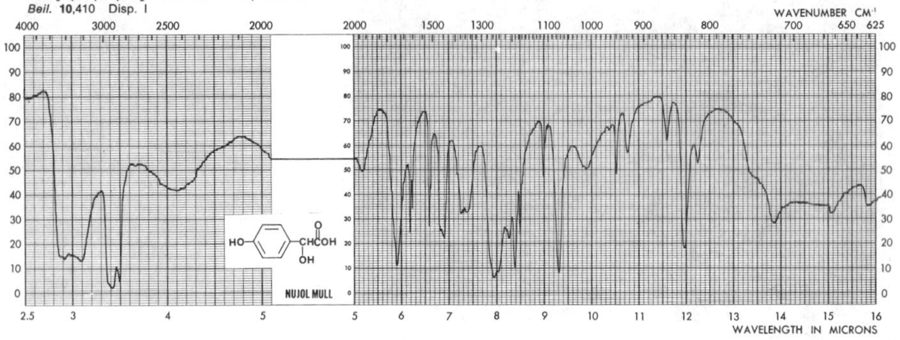

13,670-0 3-(p-Hydroxyphenyl)-lactic acid monohydrate
$HOC_6H_4CH_2CH(OH)CO_2H \cdot H_2O$ M.W. 200.19

NUJOL MULL

G

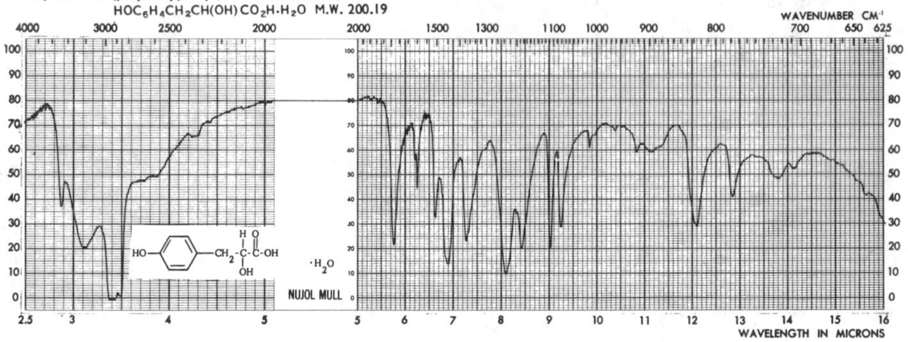

F950-7 4-Fluoromandelic acid
$FC_6H_4CH(OH)CO_2H$ M.W. 170.14 m.p. 137-139.5°

NUJOL MULL

H

11,886-9 4,4'-Difluorobenzilic acid hemihydrate
$(FC_6H_4)_2C(OH)CO_2H \cdot \frac{1}{2}H_2O$ M.W. 273.24

NUJOL MULL

A $ClC_6H_4OCH_2CO_2H$ M.W. 186.59
m.p. 157-159°

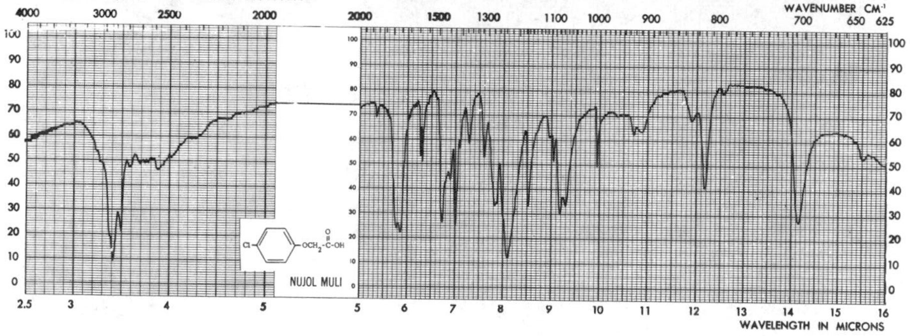

NUJOL MULL

B 15,515-2 Bis-(p-chlorophenoxy)-acetic acid
$(ClC_6H_4O)_2CHCO_2H$ M.W. 313.14
m.p. 140-142

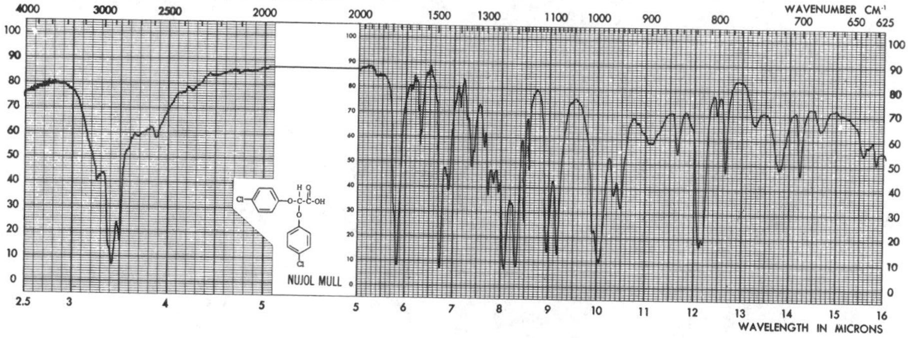

NUJOL MULL

C C4920-8 **4-Chloromandelic acid**
$ClC_6H_4CH(OH)CO_2H$ M.W. 186.59
m.p. 119-120°

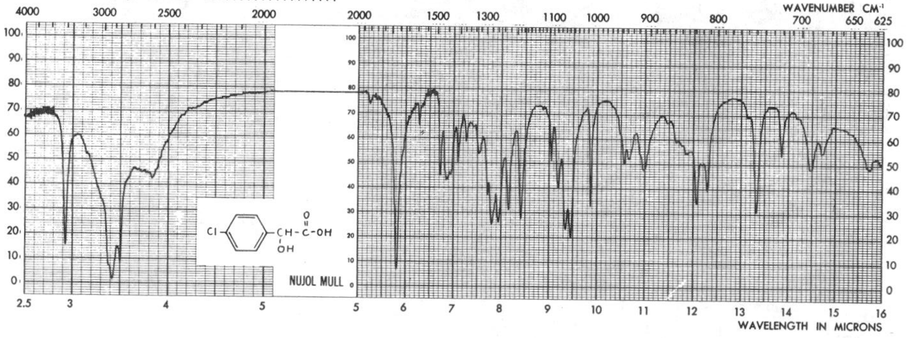

NUJOL MULL

D B7120-9 **p-Bromomandelic acid**
$BrC_6H_4CH(OH)CO_2H$ M.W. 231.05 m.p. 118-120°

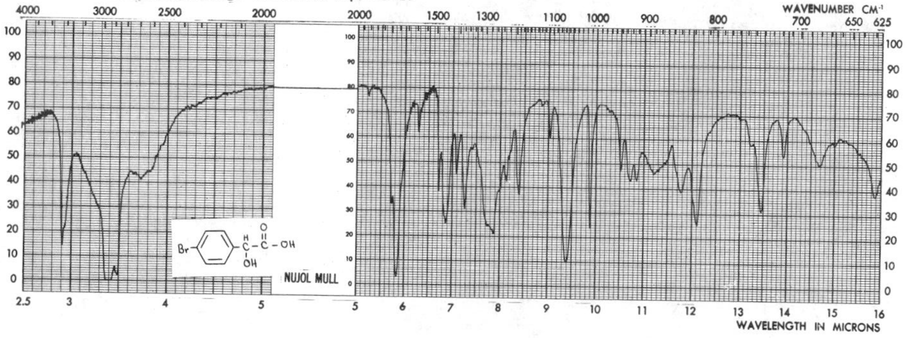

NUJOL MULL

E A7135-2 **p-Aminophenylacetic acid**
$H_2NC_6H_4CH_2CO_2H$ M.W. 151.17 m.p. 201°

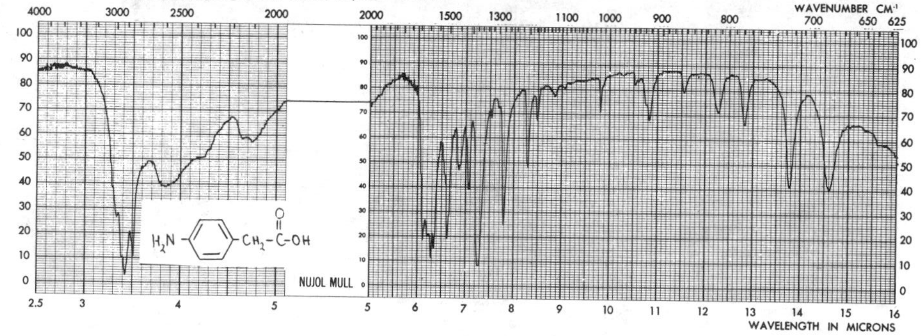

NUJOL MULL

F 12,314-5 **p-Aminothiophenoxyacetic acid** [p-aminophenylmercaptoacetic acid, (p-aminophenylthio)acetic acid]
$H_2NC_6H_4SCH_2CO_2H$ M.W. 183.23 m.p. 200-201° (dec.)

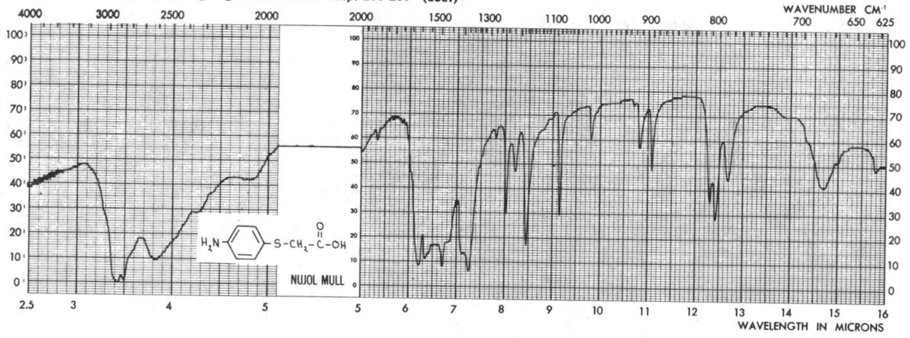

NUJOL MULL

G N2020-4 **p-Nitrophenylacetic acid**
$O_2NC_6H_4CH_2CO_2H$ M.W. 181.15
m.p. 154-155°

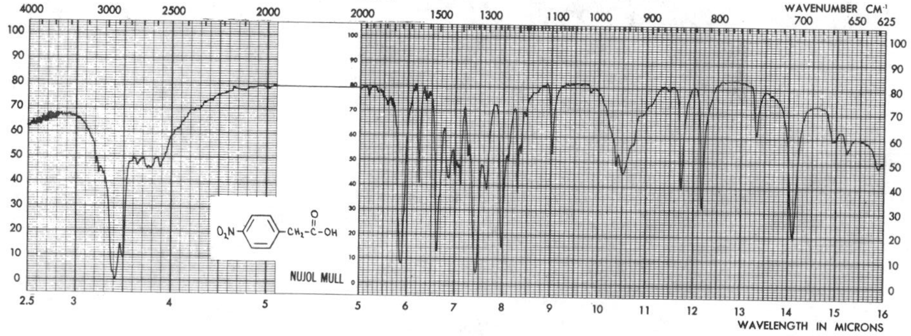

NUJOL MULL

H N2050-6 **4-(p-Nitrophenyl)-butyric acid**
$O_2NC_6H_4(CH_2)_3CO_2H$ M.W. 209.20
m.p. 92-93.5°

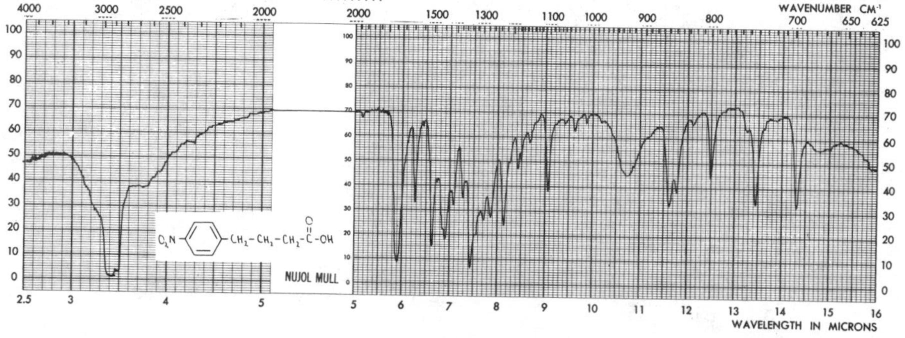

NUJOL MULL

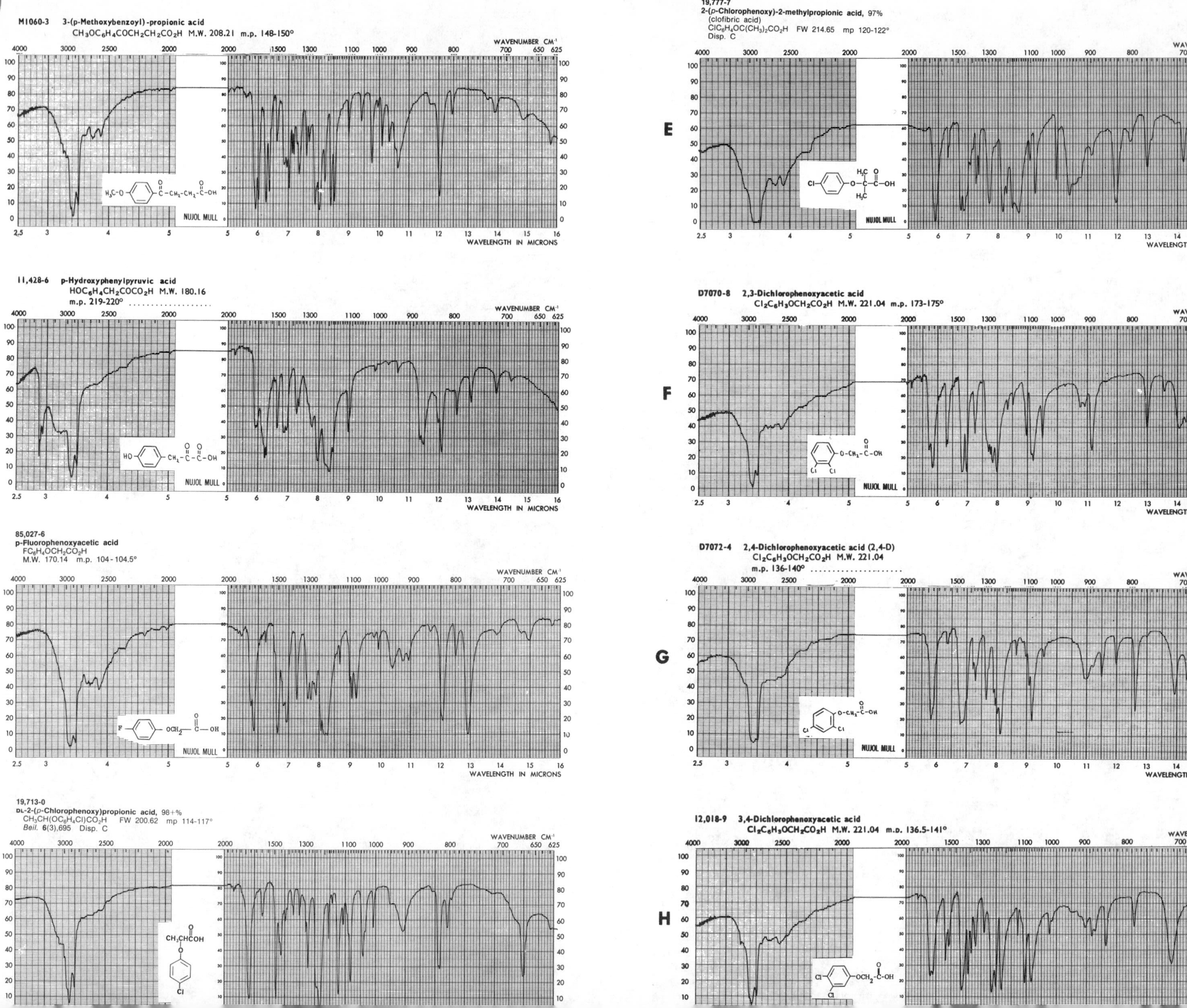

A M1060-3 3-(p-Methoxybenzoyl)-propionic acid
$CH_3OC_6H_4COCH_2CH_2CO_2H$ M.W. 208.21 m.p. 148-150°

B 11,428-6 p-Hydroxyphenylpyruvic acid
$HOC_6H_4CH_2COCO_2H$ M.W. 180.16
m.p. 219-220°

C 85,027-6
p-Fluorophenoxyacetic acid
$FC_6H_4OCH_2CO_2H$
M.W. 170.14 m.p. 104-104.5°

D 19,713-0
DL-2-(p-Chlorophenoxy)propionic acid, 98+%
$CH_3CH(OC_6H_4Cl)CO_2H$ FW 200.62 mp 114-117°
Beil. **6**(3),695 Disp. C

E 19,777-7
2-(p-Chlorophenoxy)-2-methylpropionic acid, 97%
(clofibric acid)
$ClC_6H_4OC(CH_3)_2CO_2H$ FW 214.65 mp 120-122°
Disp. C

F D7070-8 2,3-Dichlorophenoxyacetic acid
$Cl_2C_6H_3OCH_2CO_2H$ M.W. 221.04 m.p. 173-175°

G D7072-4 2,4-Dichlorophenoxyacetic acid (2,4-D)
$Cl_2C_6H_3OCH_2CO_2H$ M.W. 221.04
m.p. 136-140°

H 12,018-9 3,4-Dichlorophenoxyacetic acid
$Cl_2C_6H_3OCH_2CO_2H$ M.W. 221.04 m.p. 136.5-141°

A C5560 α-(4-Chloro-2-methylphenoxy)-propionic acid
$CH_3CH[OC_6H_3(CH_3)Cl]CO_2H$ M.W. 214.65 m.p. 90-93°
NUJOL MULL

B 19,712-2
2,4,5-Trichlorophenoxyacetic acid, 98% (2,4,5-T)
$Cl_3C_6H_2OCH_2CO_2H$ FW 255.49 mp 150-159°
Beil. 6(3),720 Disp. C
NUJOL MULL

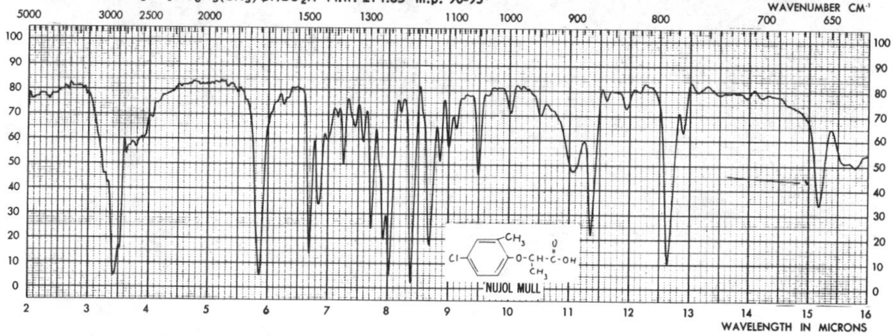

C 16,186-1
2-(2,4,5-Trichlorophenoxy)-propionic acid, 97%
$CH_3CH(OC_6H_2Cl_3)CO_2H$
M.W. 269.51 m.p. 175-177°
NUJOL MULL

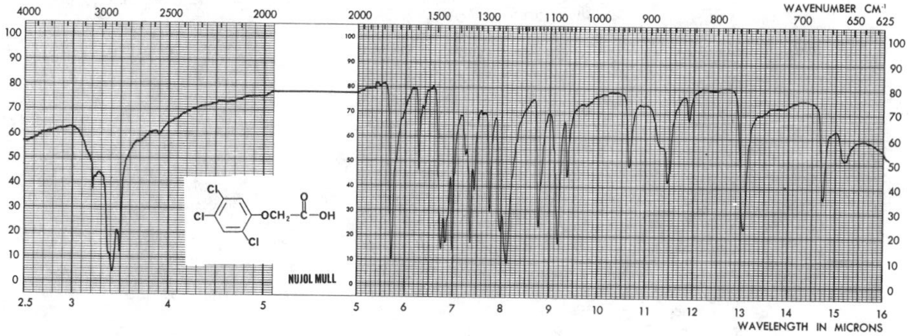

D E580-8 4-Ethoxy-3-methoxyphenylacetic acid
$C_2H_5OC_6H_3(OCH_3)CH_2CO_2H$ M.W. 210.23 m.p. 122-124°
NUJOL MULL

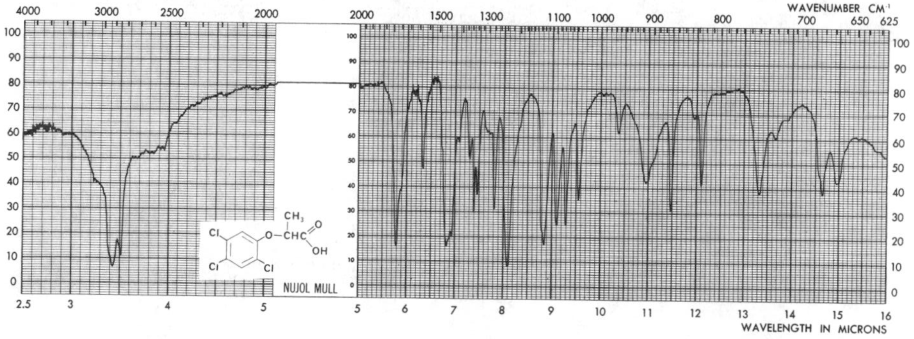

E D13,590-9 (3,4-Dimethoxyphenyl)-acetic acid (homoveratric acid)
$(CH_3O)_2C_6H_3CH_2CO_2H$ M.W. 196.20 m.p. 96-98°
NUJOL MULL

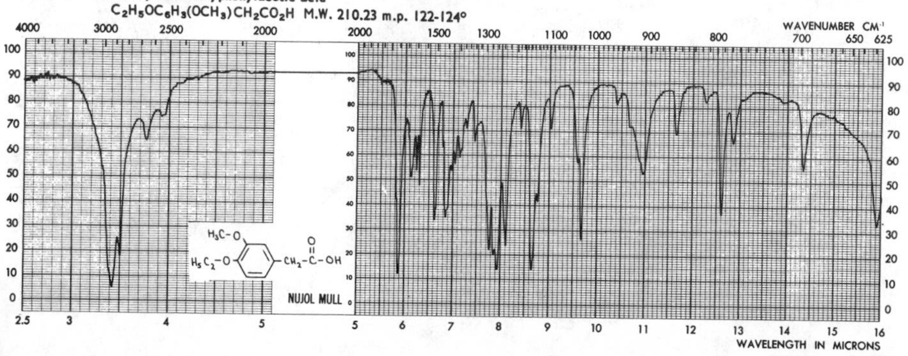

F 17,901-9
1,4-Benzodioxan-6-acetic acid
FW 194.19 mp 73-75° *NMR* 6,129A Disp. C
NUJOL MULL

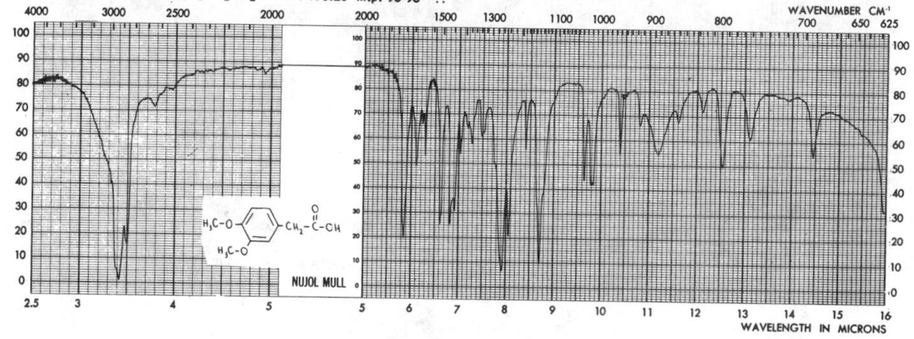

G 15,705-8
2-Benzoxazolinone
M.W. 135.12 m.p. 137-139°
NUJOL MULL

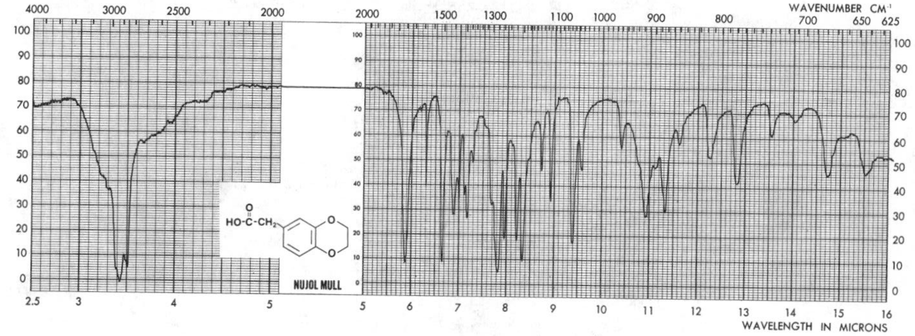

H 16,234-5
3-(3,4-Dimethoxyphenyl)-propionic acid
(3,4-dimethoxyhydrocinnamic acid)
$(CH_3O)_2C_6H_3CH_2CH_2CO_2H$
M.W. 210.23 m.p. 96-97° Beil. 10,424
NUJOL MULL

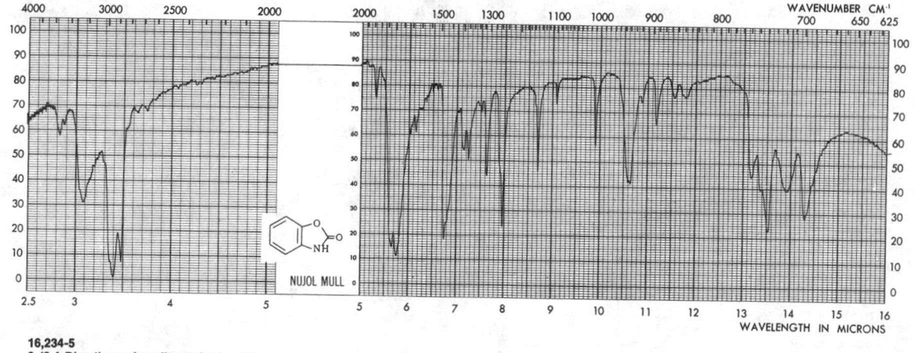

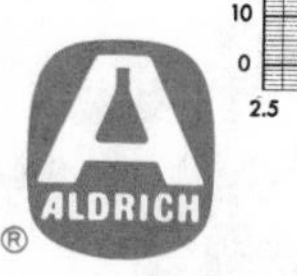

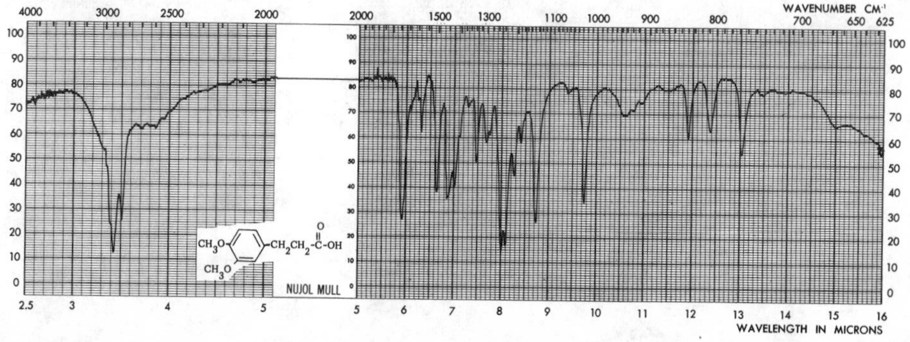

A

D13,580-1 **(2,5-Dimethoxyphenyl)-acetic acid**
$(CH_3O)_2C_6H_3CH_2CO_2H$ M.W. 196.20
m.p. 123-125°

NUJOL MULL

B

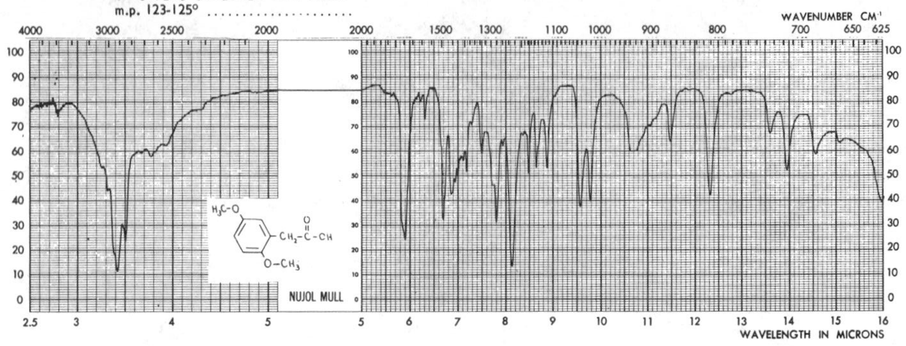

14,364-2 **Homovanillic acid (4-hydroxy-3-methoxyphenylacetic acid)**
$HOC_6H_3(OCH_3)CH_2CO_2H$ M.W. 182.18
m.p. 142-145°

NUJOL MULL

C

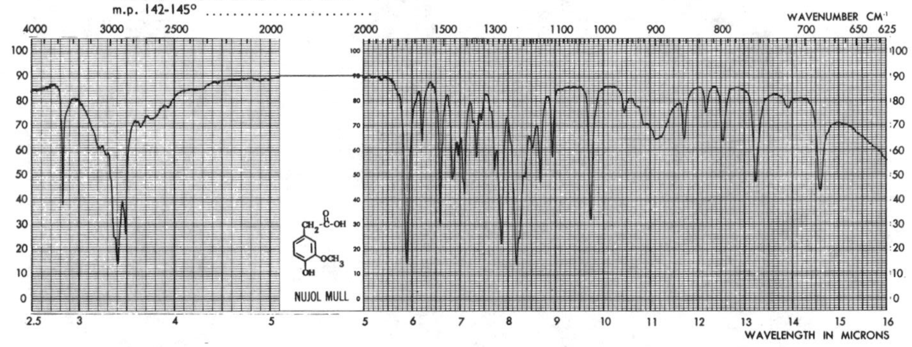

16,033-4
3,4-Dichloro-α-methylmandelic acid
(3,4-dichloroatrolactic acid)
$Cl_2C_6H_3C(CH_3)(OH)CO_2H$
M.W. 235.07 m.p. 108-110°

NUJOL MULL

D

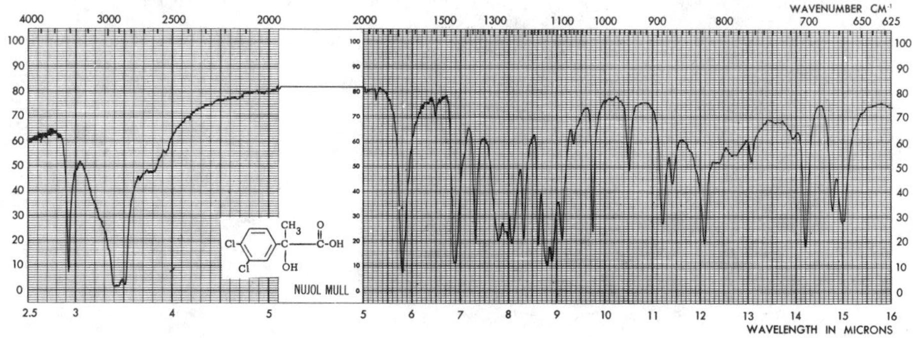

14,880-6 VMA (DL-vanillomandelic acid, DL-4-hydroxy-3-methoxymandelic acid)
$HOC_6H_3(OCH_3)CH(OH)CO_2H$ M.W. 198.17
m.p. 132-134° (dec.)

E

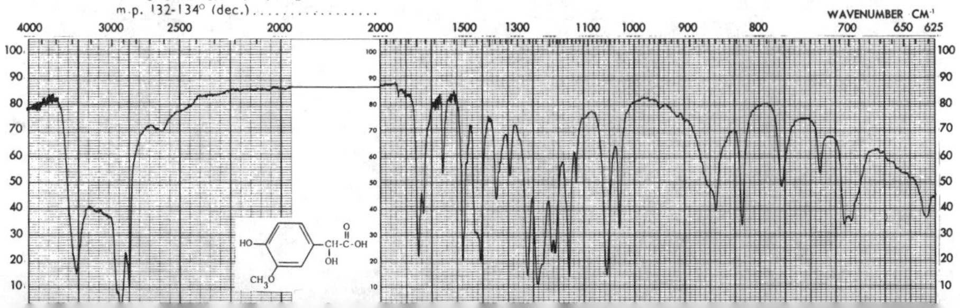

15,161-0 **DL-3,4-Dihydroxymandelic acid**
$(HO)_2C_6H_3CH(OH)CO_2H$ M.W. 184.15
m.p. 136-137° (dec.)

NUJOL MULL

F

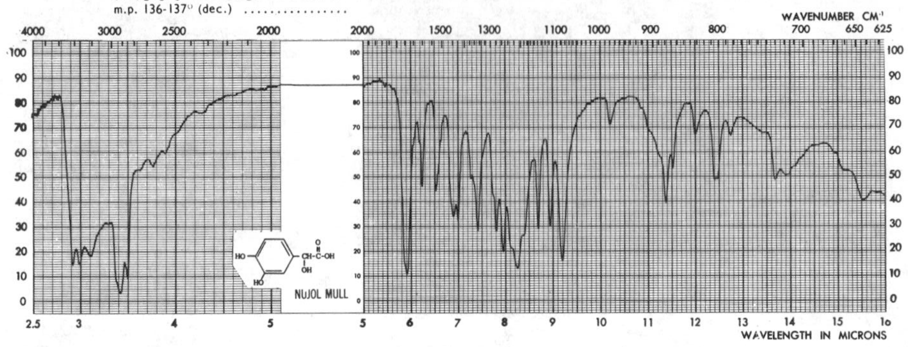

22,453-7
3-Bromo-4-hydroxyphenylacetic acid, 98%
$BrC_6H_3(OH)CH_2CO_2H$ FW 231.05 mp 108-110°
Beil. **10**(3),441 Disp. C

NUJOL MULL

G

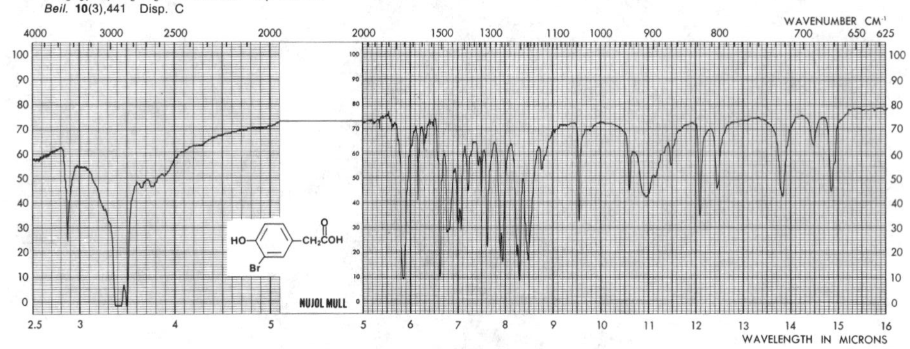

85,021-7
3,4-Dihydroxyphenylacetic acid
$(HO)_2C_6H_3CH_2CO_2H$
M.W. 168.15 m.p. 127-130°

NUJOL MULL

H

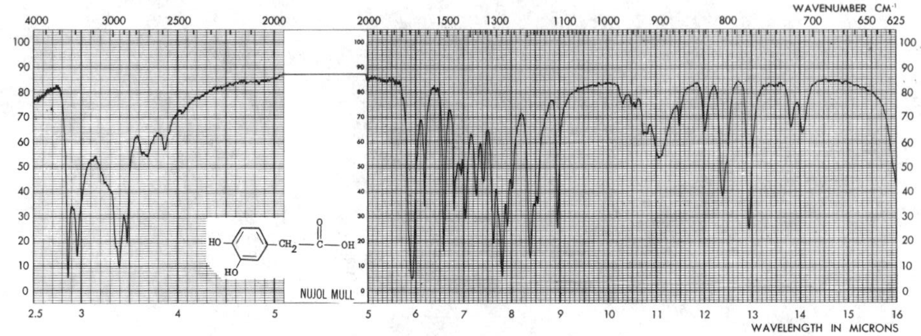

10,260-1 **3,4-Dihydroxyhydrocinnamic acid (hydrocaffeic acid)**
$(HO)_2C_6H_3CH_2CH_2CO_2H$ M.W. 182.18
m.p. 137-138°

WAVENUMBER CM^{-1} — WAVELENGTH IN MICRONS

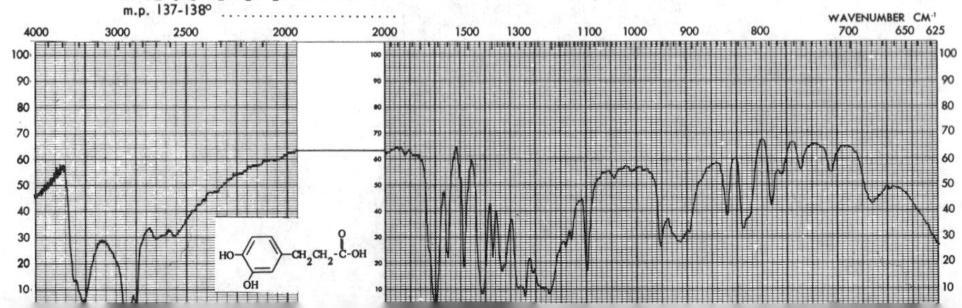

A

$HOC_6H_3(NO_2)CH_2CO_2H$ FW 197.15 mp 146-148°
Disp. C

NUJOL MULL

B

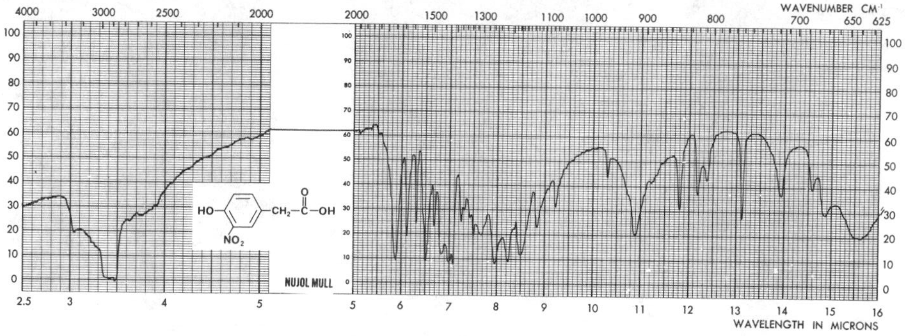

12,393-5 **4,4-Bis-(4-hydroxy-3-nitrophenyl)-valeric acid**
$CH_3C[C_6H_3(NO_2)OH]_2CH_2CH_2CO_2H$ M.W. 376.32
m.p. 124-130°

NUJOL MULL

C

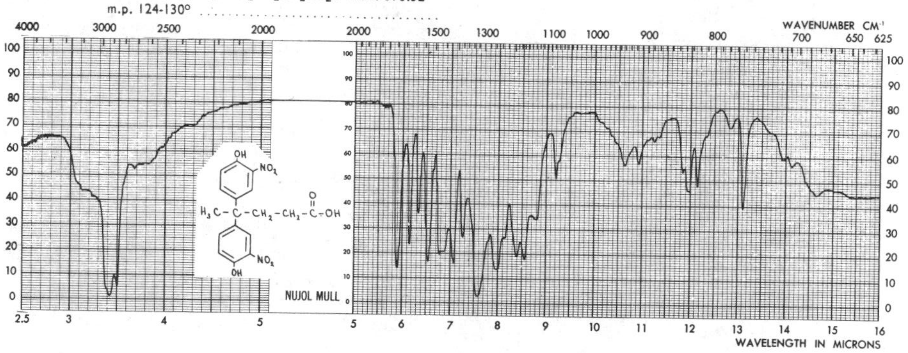

20,956-2
2,4-Dinitrophenylacetic acid, tech.
$(O_2N)_2C_6H_3CH_2CO_2H$ FW 226.15 mp 169-175°
Beil. 9,459 Disp. C

NUJOL MULL

D

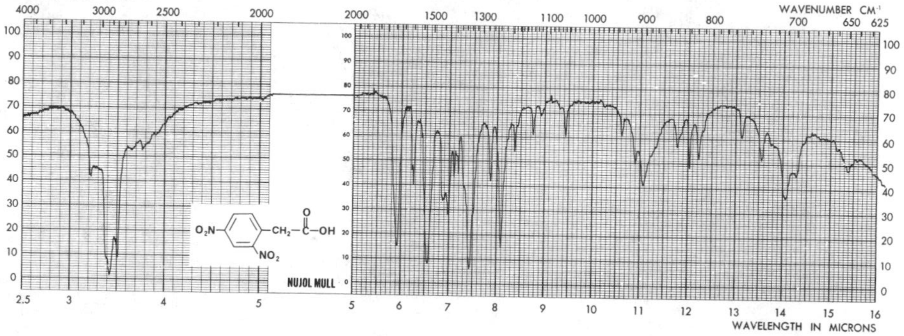

11,979-2 **Podocarpic acid** (1,4a-dimethyl-6-hydroxy-1,2,3,4,4a,9,10,10a-octahydro-1-phenanthrenecarboxylic acid)
M.W. 274.36 m.p. 193-196°

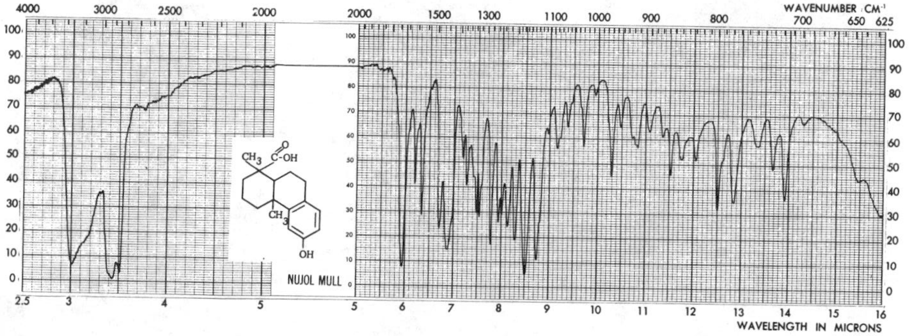

NUJOL MULL

E

2,5-Dihydroxy-p-benzenediacetic acid
$(HO)_2C_6H_2(CH_2CO_2H)_2$ M.W. 226.18
m.p. 234-236°

NUJOL MULL

F

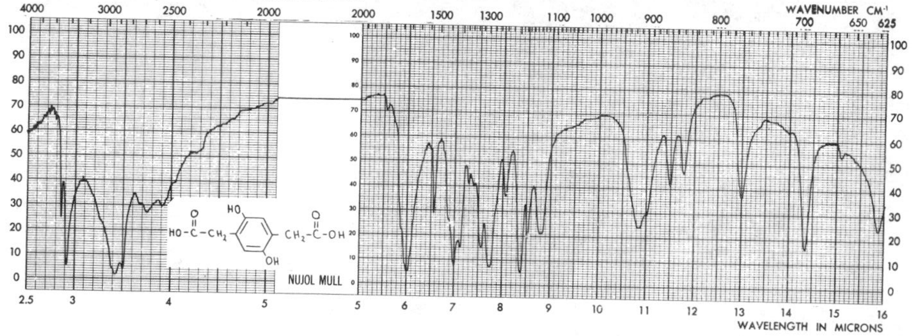

T7060-2 **3,4,5-Trimethoxyphenylacetic acid**
$(CH_3O)_3C_6H_2CH_2CO_2H$ M.W. 226.23
m.p. 118-120°

NUJOL MULL

G

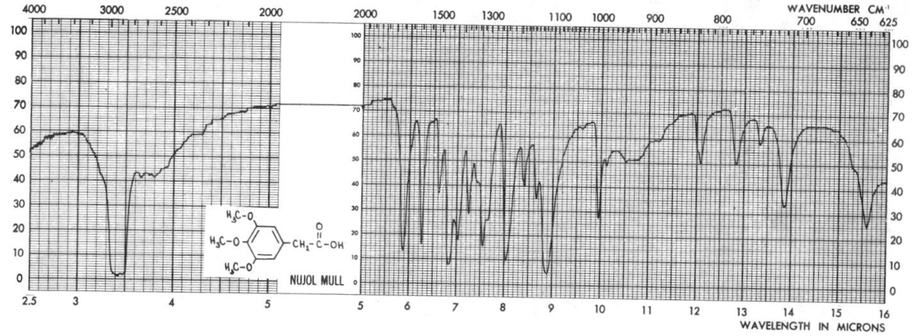

19,787-4
3-(3,4,5-Trimethoxyphenyl)propionic acid, 98+%
(3,4,5-trimethoxyhydrocinnamic acid)
$(CH_3O)_3C_6H_2CH_2CH_2CO_2H$ FW 240.26
mp 100-104° *Beil.* **10**(3),2120 Disp. C

NUJOL MULL

H

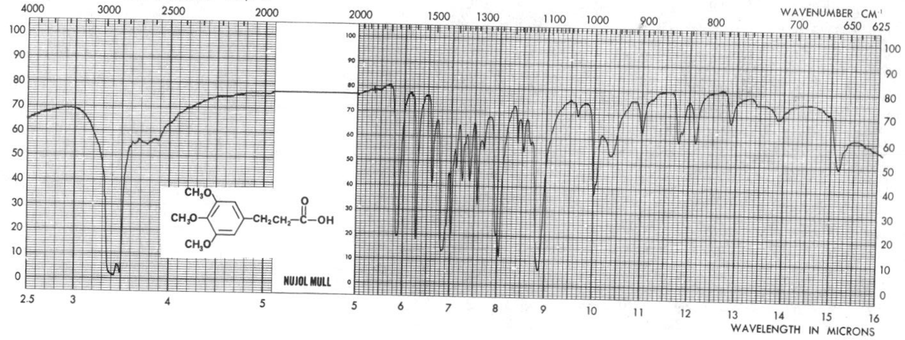

19,786-6
3-(2,3,4-Trimethoxyphenyl)propionic acid, 98+%
(2,3,4-trimethoxyhydrocinnamic acid)
$(CH_3O)_3C_6H_2CH_2CH_2CO_2H$ FW 240.26 mp 70-73°
Beil. **10**(3),2118 Disp. C

NUJOL MULL

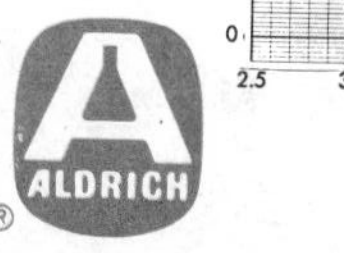

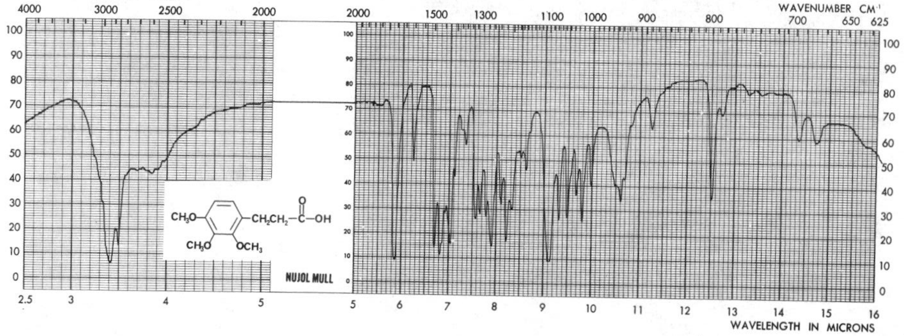

A 10,394-2 **3-(Pentafluorophenyl)-propionic acid** (2,3,4,5,6-pentafluorohydrocinnamic acid)
$C_6F_5CH_2CH_2CO_2H$ M.W. 240.13 m.p. 96-99° .....
NUJOL MULL

B 11,887-7 **3-(o-Chlorophenyl)-3-(m-chlorophenyl)-glycidic acid**
M.W. 309.15 m.p. 98.5° (dec.) ....
NUJOL MULL

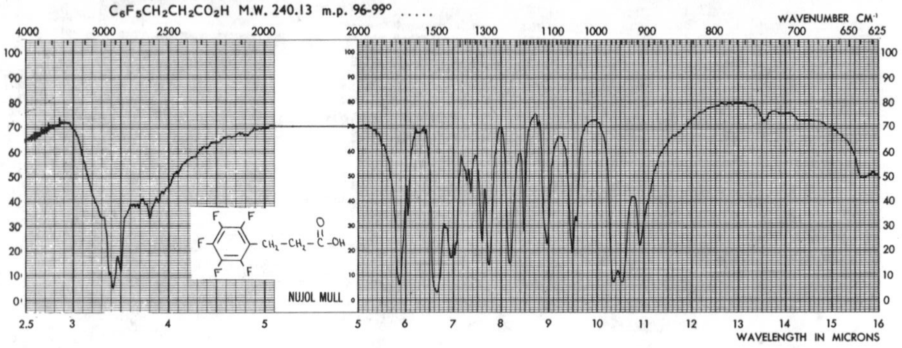

C 12,053-7 **α-Phenyl-α-(2,4,6-triiodophenoxy)-acetic acid**
$I_3C_6H_2OCH(C_6H_5)CO_2H$ M.W. 605.94 m.p. 189-192°
NUJOL MULL

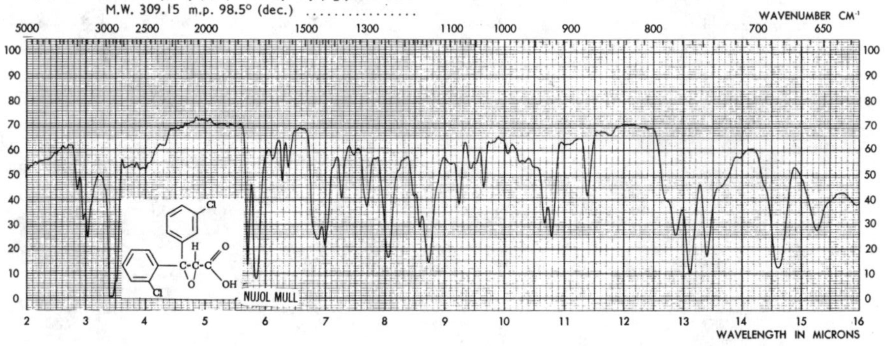

D 19,648-7
4-Biphenylacetic acid, 98%
$C_6H_5C_6H_4CH_2CO_2H$ FW 212.25 mp 159-162°
Beil. 9(1),284 Disp. C

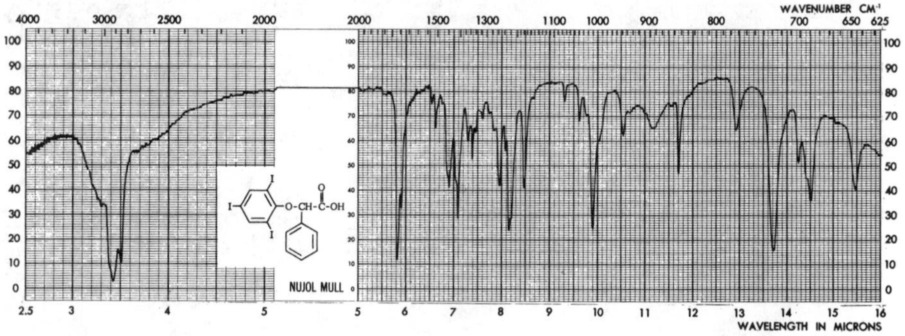

E N380-4 **1-Naphthylacetic acid** (1-naphthaleneacetic acid)
$C_{10}H_7CH_2CO_2H$ M.W. 186.21
m.p. 129-131.5° ....
NUJOL MULL

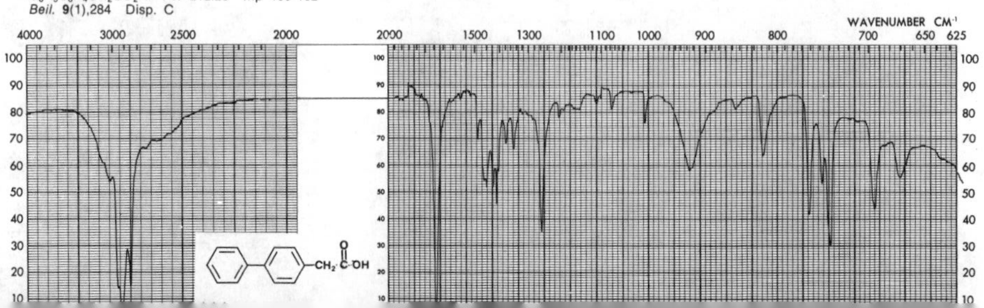

F N400-2 **2-Naphthylacetic acid** (2-naphthaleneacetic acid)
$C_{10}H_7CH_2CO_2H$ M.W. 186.21 m.p. 141-143° ...
NUJOL MULL

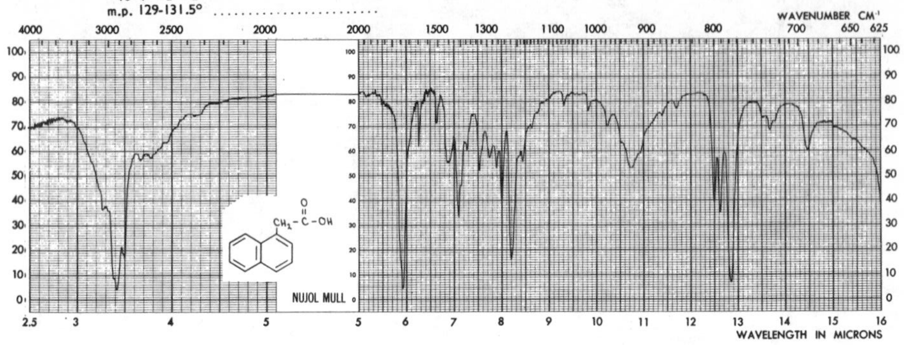

G N340-5 **(2-Naphthoxy)-acetic acid**
$C_{10}H_7OCH_2CO_2H$ M.W. 202.21 m.p. 150.5-154°
NUJOL MULL

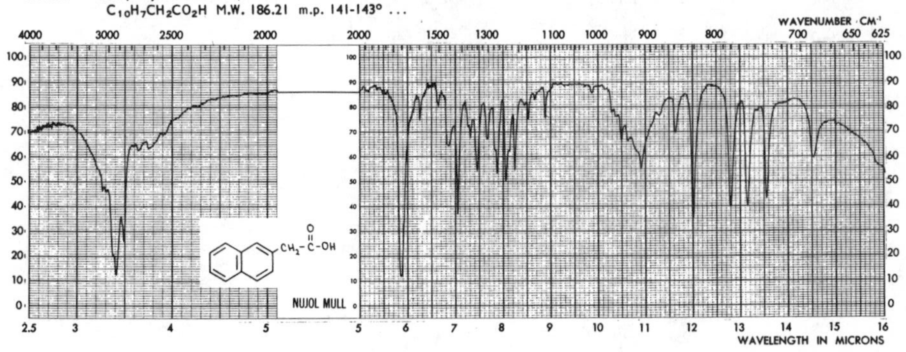

H 15,532-2 **Styrylacetic acid** (4-phenyl-3-butenoic acid)
$C_6H_5CH{:}CHCH_2CO_2H$ M.W. 162.19 .....

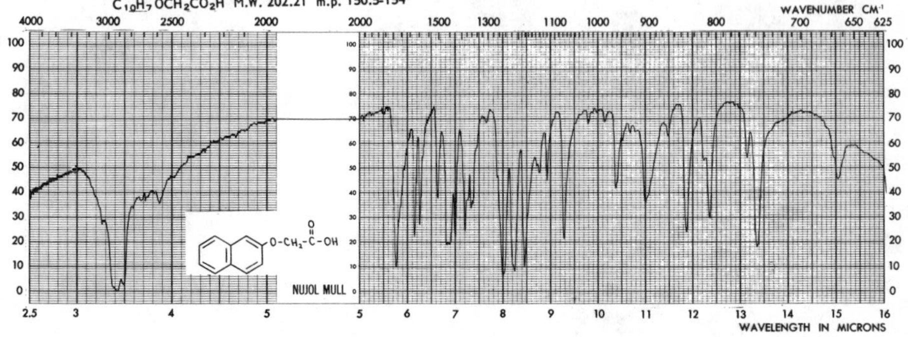

WAVENUMBER CM^{-1} — WAVELENGTH IN MICRONS

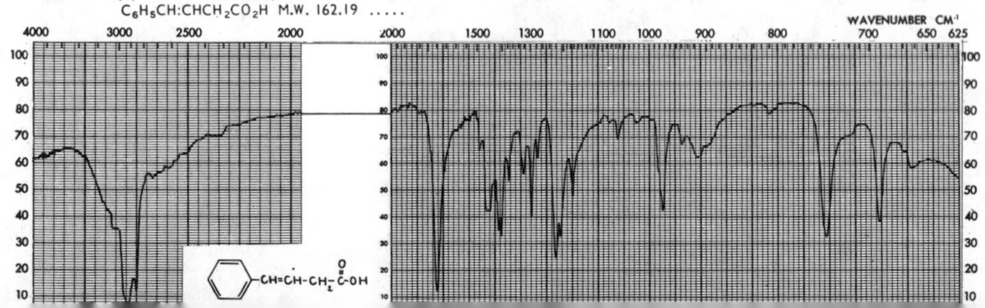

A

trans-Cinnamic acid, puriss.
$C_6H_5CH{:}CHCO_2H$ M.W. 148.16 m.p. 133-134°

NUJOL MULL

B

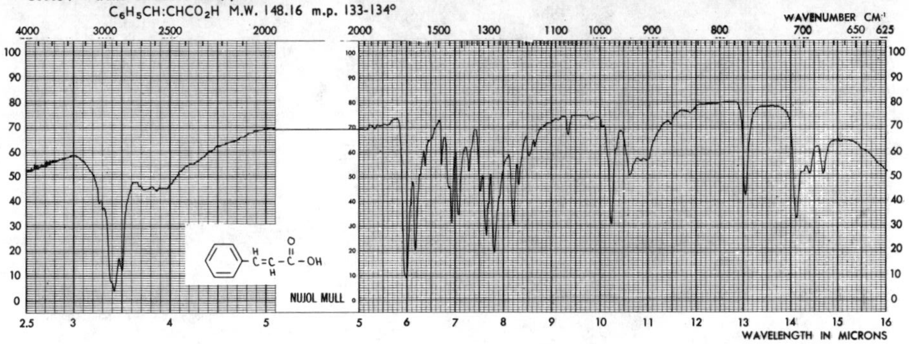

M3560-6 α-Methylcinnamic acid
$C_6H_5CH{:}C(CH_3)CO_2H$ M.W. 162.19
m.p. 79-81°

NUJOL MULL

C

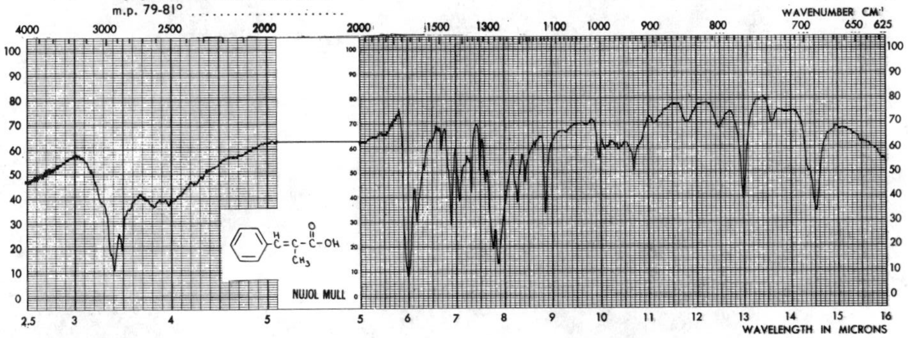

16,384-8
α-Fluorocinnamic acid, 98%
$C_6H_5CH{=}C(F)CO_2H$
M.W. 166.15 m.p. 156-159° b.p. 290°
Beil. 9(1),237

NUJOL MULL

D

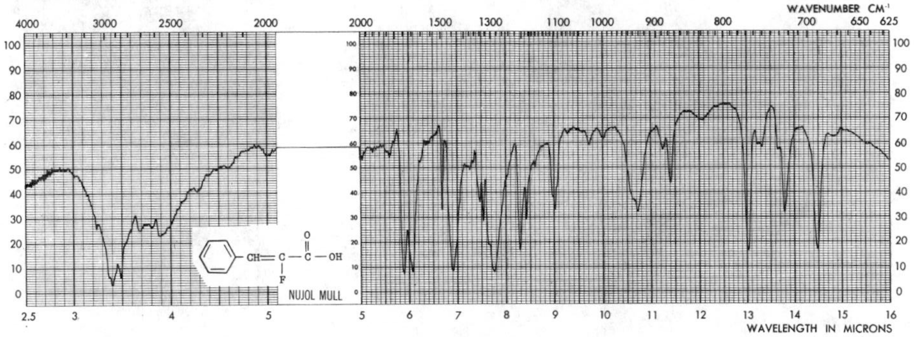

P2200-1 α-Phenylcinnamic acid
$C_6H_5CH{:}C(C_6H_5)CO_2H$ M.W. 224.26
m.p. 170-172°

NUJOL MULL

E

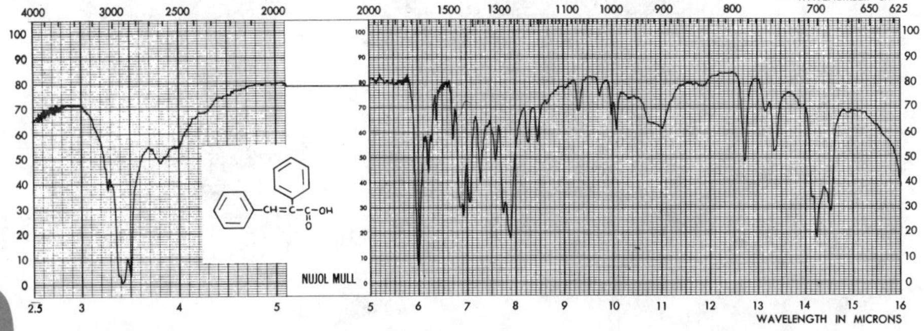

$C_6H_5CH{:}CHCH{:}C(CO_2H)_2$ M.W. 218.21
m.p. 219° (dec.)

NUJOL MULL

F

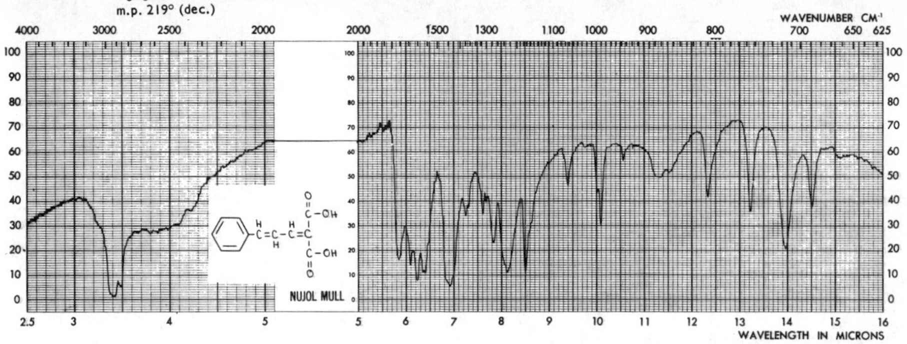

22,271-2
2-Fluorocinnamic acid, 98%
$FC_6H_4CH{=}CHCO_2H$

NUJOL MULL

G

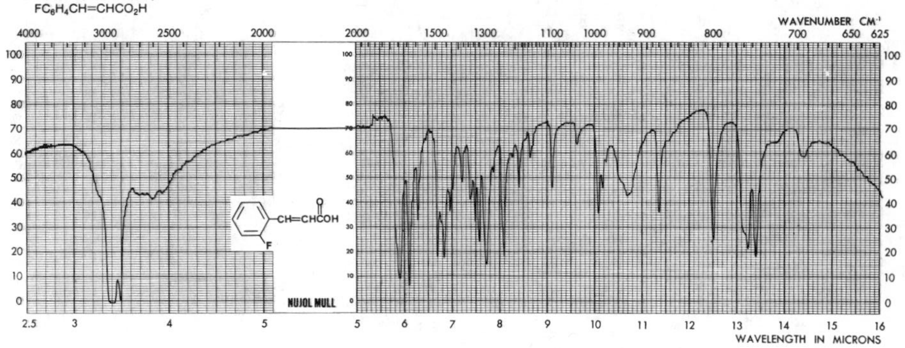

C3139-2 o-Chlorocinnamic acid
$ClC_6H_4CH{:}CHCO_2H$ M.W. 182.61 m.p. 203-205°

NUJOL MULL

H

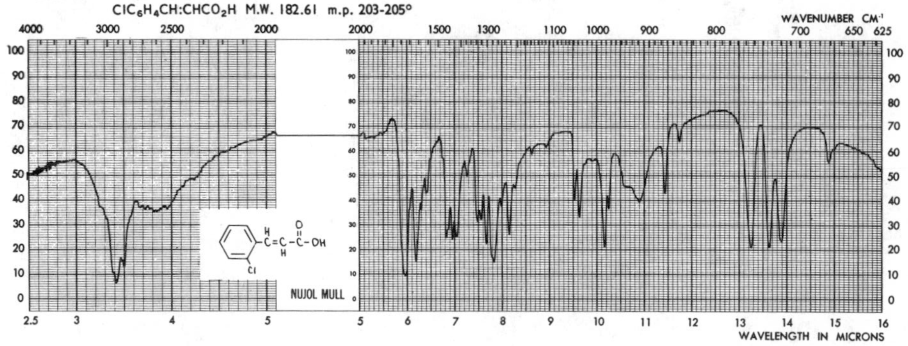

M1340-8 o-Methoxycinnamic acid
$CH_3OC_6H_4CH{:}CHCO_2H$ M.W. 178.19 m.p. 183-186°

NUJOL MULL

WAVENUMBER CM⁻¹ — WAVELENGTH IN MICRONS

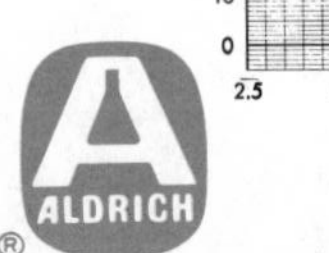

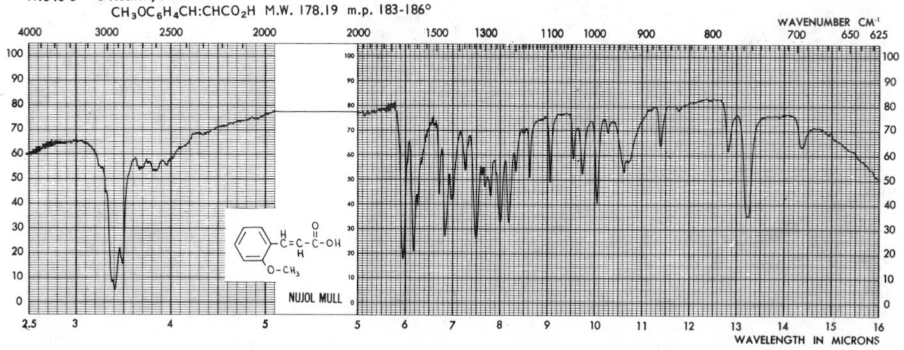

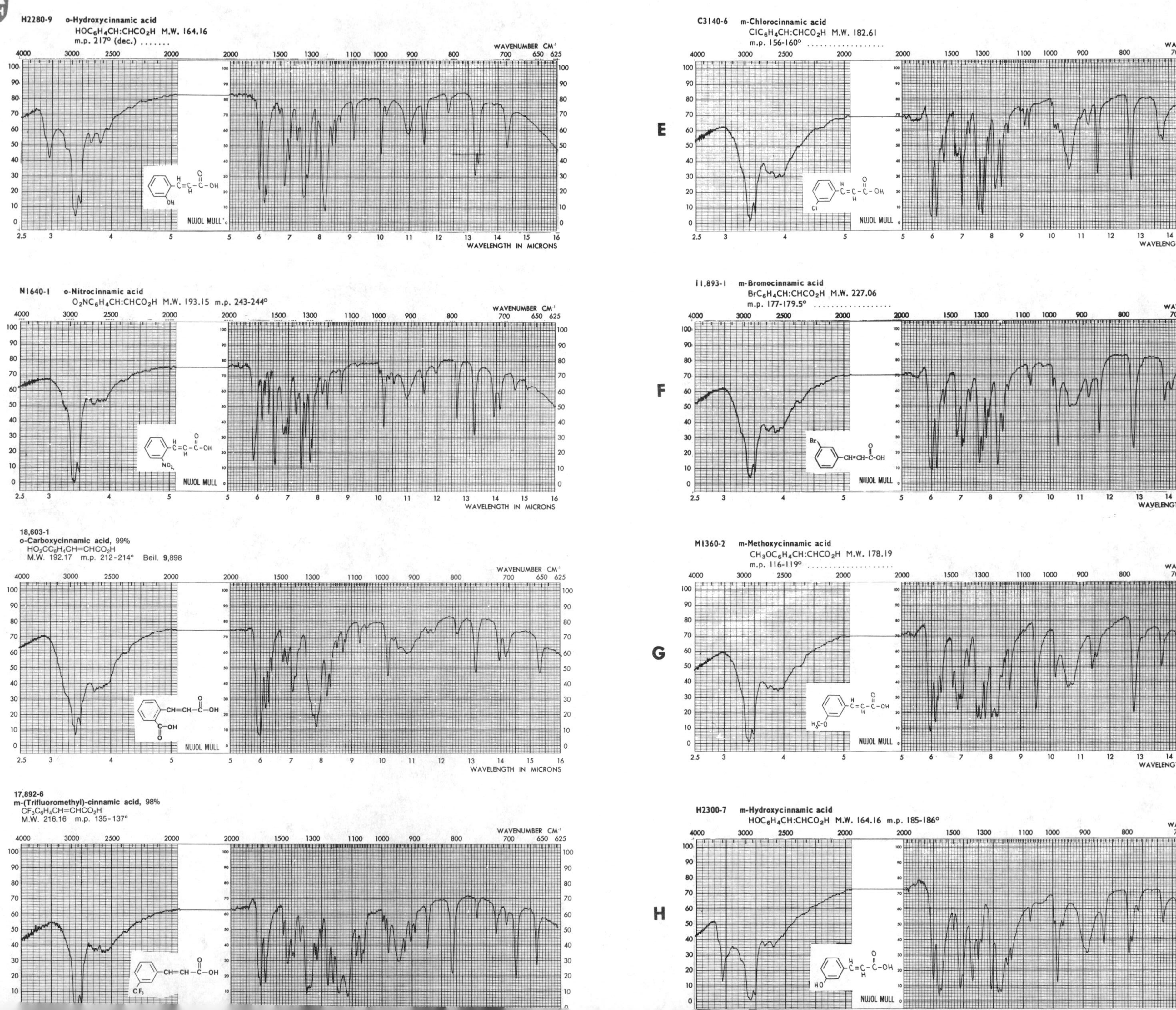

A — H2280-9 **o-Hydroxycinnamic acid**
$HOC_6H_4CH{:}CHCO_2H$ M.W. 164.16
m.p. 217° (dec.)

B — N1640-1 **o-Nitrocinnamic acid**
$O_2NC_6H_4CH{:}CHCO_2H$ M.W. 193.15 m.p. 243-244°

C — 18,603-1
o-Carboxycinnamic acid, 99%
$HO_2CC_6H_4CH{=}CHCO_2H$
M.W. 192.17 m.p. 212-214° Beil. 9,898

D — 17,892-6
m-(Trifluoromethyl)-cinnamic acid, 98%
$CF_3C_6H_4CH{=}CHCO_2H$
M.W. 216.16 m.p. 135-137°

E — C3140-6 **m-Chlorocinnamic acid**
$ClC_6H_4CH{:}CHCO_2H$ M.W. 182.61
m.p. 156-160°

F — 11,893-1 **m-Bromocinnamic acid**
$BrC_6H_4CH{:}CHCO_2H$ M.W. 227.06
m.p. 177-179.5°

G — M1360-2 **m-Methoxycinnamic acid**
$CH_3OC_6H_4CH{:}CHCO_2H$ M.W. 178.19
m.p. 116-119°

H — H2300-7 **m-Hydroxycinnamic acid**
$HOC_6H_4CH{:}CHCO_2H$ M.W. 164.16 m.p. 185-186°

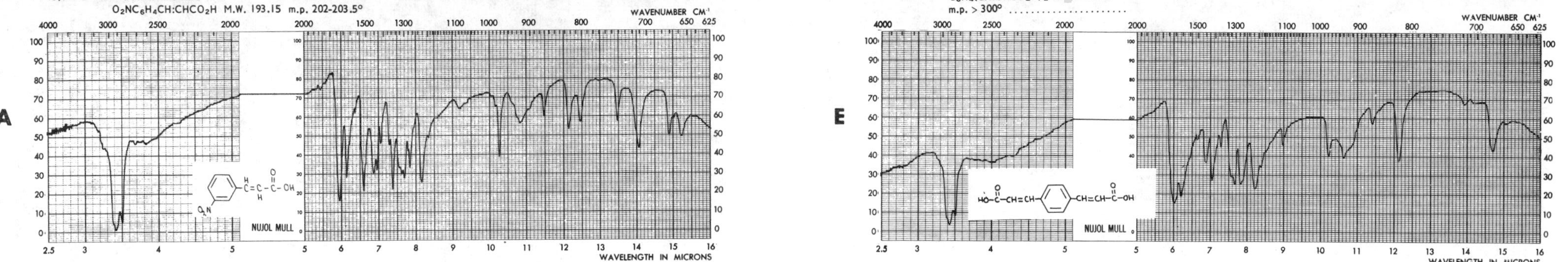

A

$O_2NC_6H_4CH{:}CHCO_2H$ M.W. 193.15 m.p. 202-203.5°

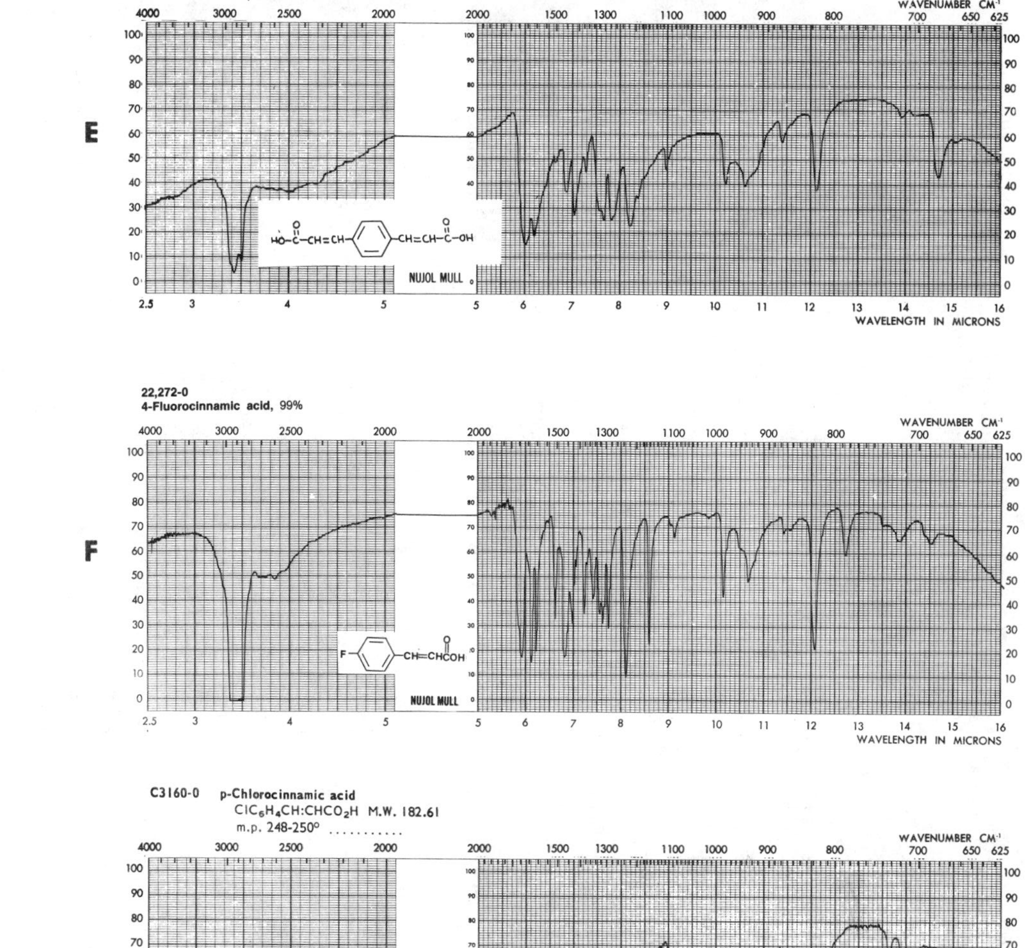

B

17,538-2
m-Phenylenediacrylic acid
$C_6H_4(CH{=}CHCO_2H)_2$
M.W. 218.21 m.p. 279-280° (dec.)

C

M3580-0 **p-Methylcinnamic acid**
$CH_3C_6H_4CH{:}CHCO_2H$ M.W. 162.19
m.p. 196-198°

D

14,466-5 **p-Isopropylcinnamic acid**
$(CH_3)_2CHC_6H_4CH{:}CHCO_2H$ M.W. 190.25
m.p. 157-159°

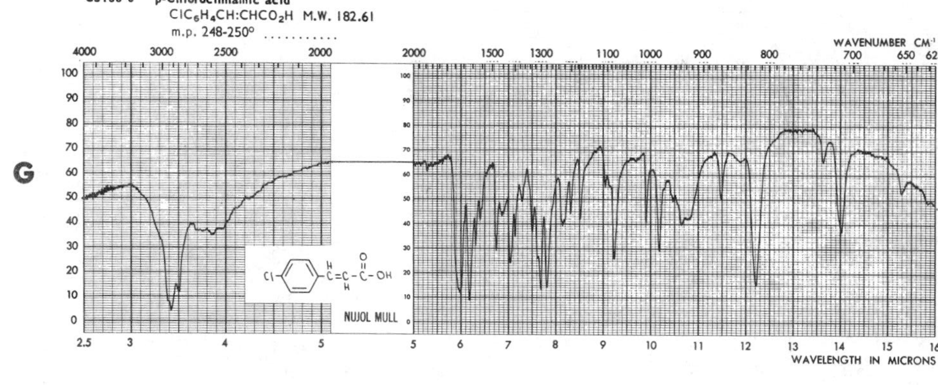

E

m.p. > 300°

F

22,272-0
4-Fluorocinnamic acid, 99%

G

C3160-0 **p-Chlorocinnamic acid**
$ClC_6H_4CH{:}CHCO_2H$ M.W. 182.61
m.p. 248-250°

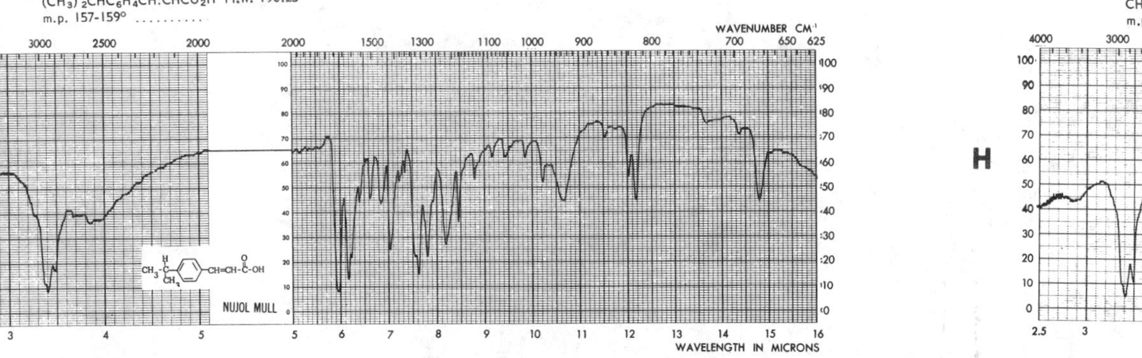

H

M1380-7 **p-Methoxycinnamic acid**
$CH_3OC_6H_4CH{:}CHCO_2H$ M.W. 178.19
m.p. 172-175°

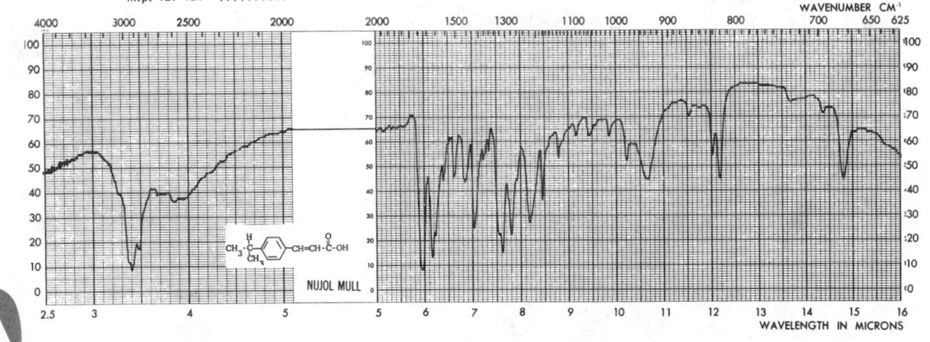

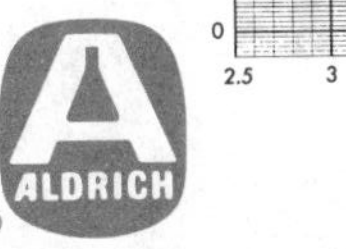

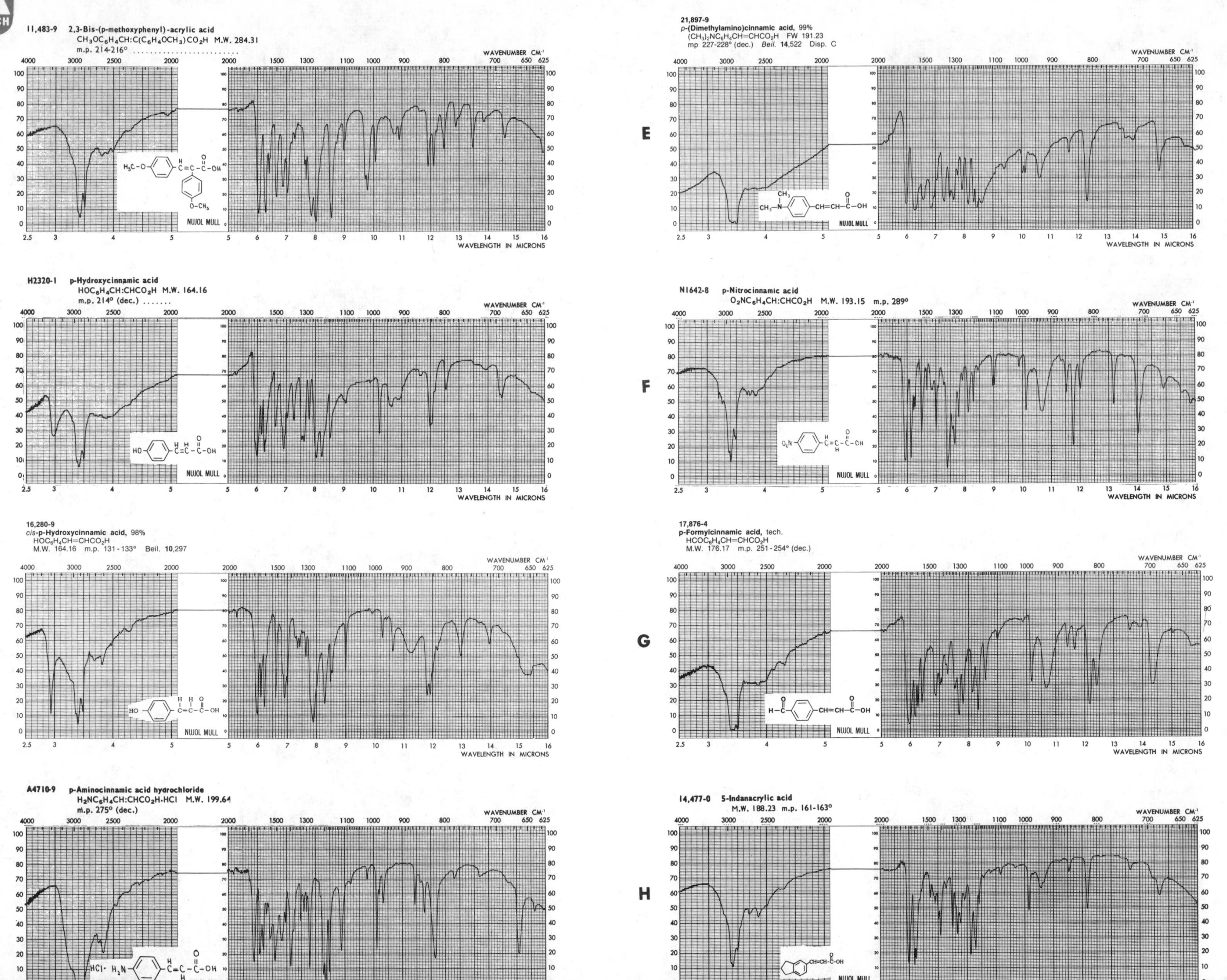
ALDRICH
A
11,483-9 2,3-Bis-(p-methoxyphenyl)-acrylic acid
$CH_3OC_6H_4CH:C(C_6H_4OCH_3)CO_2H$ M.W. 284.31
m.p. 214-216°
B
H2320-1 p-Hydroxycinnamic acid
$HOC_6H_4CH:CHCO_2H$ M.W. 164.16
m.p. 214° (dec.)
C
16,280-9
cis-p-Hydroxycinnamic acid, 98%
$HOC_6H_4CH{=}CHCO_2H$
M.W. 164.16 m.p. 131-133° Beil. 10,297
D
A4710-9 p-Aminocinnamic acid hydrochloride
$H_2NC_6H_4CH:CHCO_2H{\cdot}HCl$ M.W. 199.64
m.p. 275° (dec.)
E
21,897-9
p-(Dimethylamino)cinnamic acid, 99%
$(CH_3)_2NC_6H_4CH{=}CHCO_2H$ FW 191.23
mp 227-228° (dec.) Beil. 14,522 Disp. C
F
N1642-8 p-Nitrocinnamic acid
$O_2NC_6H_4CH:CHCO_2H$ M.W. 193.15 m.p. 289°
G
17,876-4
p-Formylcinnamic acid, tech.
$HCOC_6H_4CH{=}CHCO_2H$
M.W. 176.17 m.p. 251-254° (dec.)
H
14,477-0 5-Indanacrylic acid
M.W. 188.23 m.p. 161-163°
NUJOL MULL
WAVENUMBER CM⁻¹
WAVELENGTH IN MICRONS

A

m.p. 194-196°

NUJOL MULL

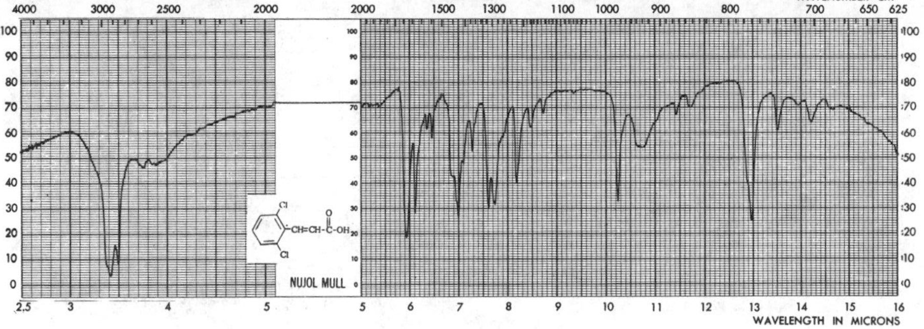

14,462-2 2,4-Dichlorocinnamic acid
$Cl_2C_6H_3CH{:}CHCO_2H$ M.W. 217.05
m.p. 233-235°

B

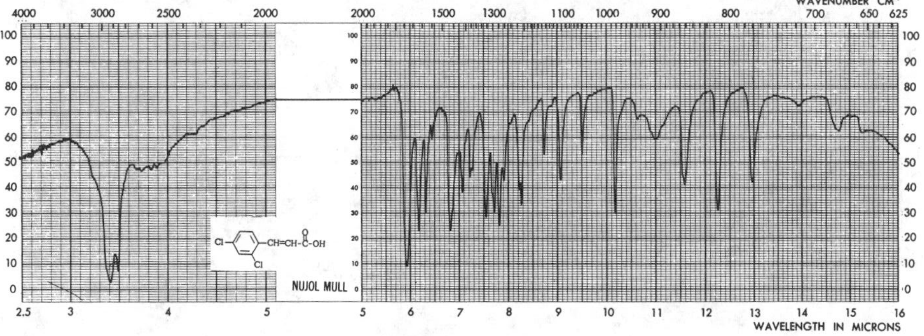

NUJOL MULL

14,470-3 3,4-Dichlorocinnamic acid
$Cl_2C_6H_3CH{:}CHCO_2H$ M.W. 217.05
m.p. 217-218°

C

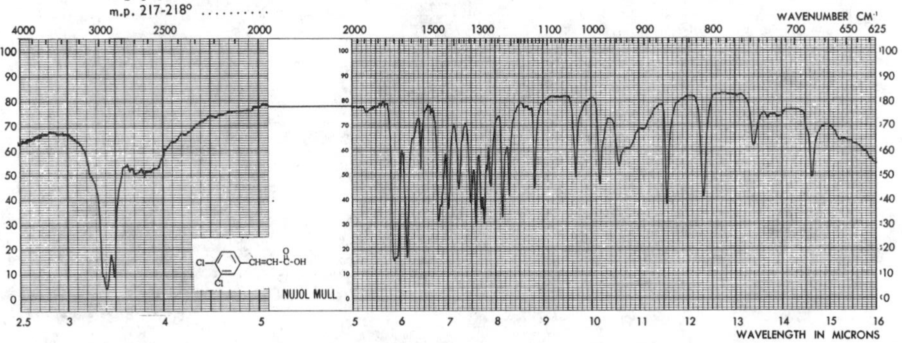

NUJOL MULL

D13,360-4 2,4-Dimethoxycinnamic acid
$(CH_3O)_2C_6H_3CH{:}CHCO_2H$ M.W. 208.21 m.p. 187.5-189°

D

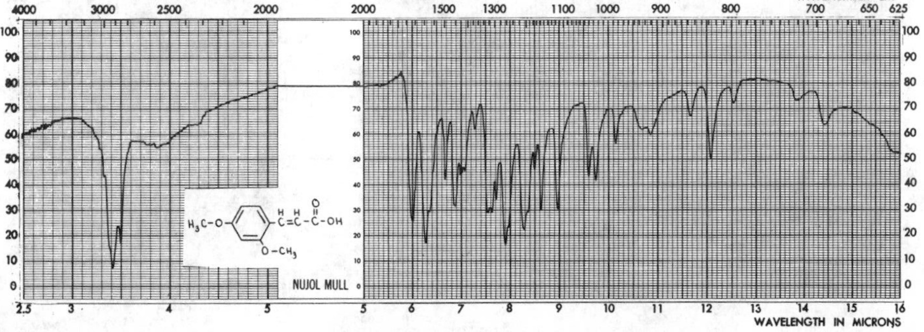

NUJOL MULL

E

m.p. 148-150°

NUJOL MULL

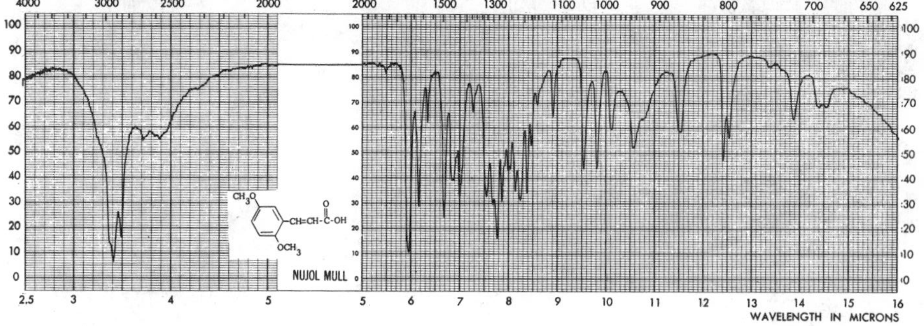

D13,380-9 3,4-Dimethoxycinnamic acid
$(CH_3O)_2C_6H_3CH{:}CHCO_2H$ M.W. 208.21
m.p. 181-183°

F

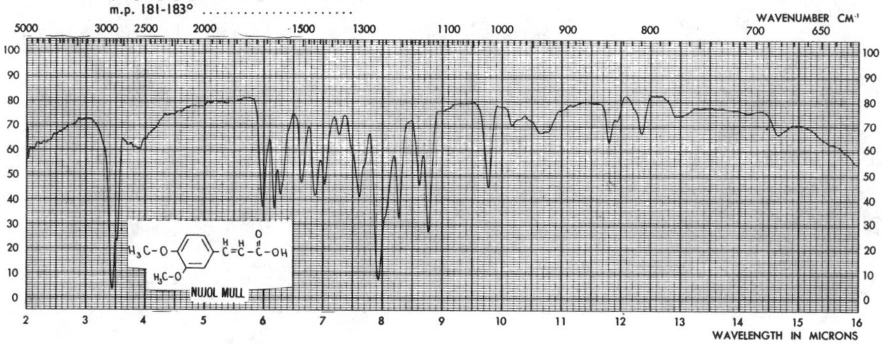

NUJOL MULL

14,474-6 4-Ethoxy-3-methoxycinnamic acid
$C_2H_5OC_6H_3(OCH_3)CH{:}CHCO_2H$ M.W. 222.24
m.p. 194-200°

G

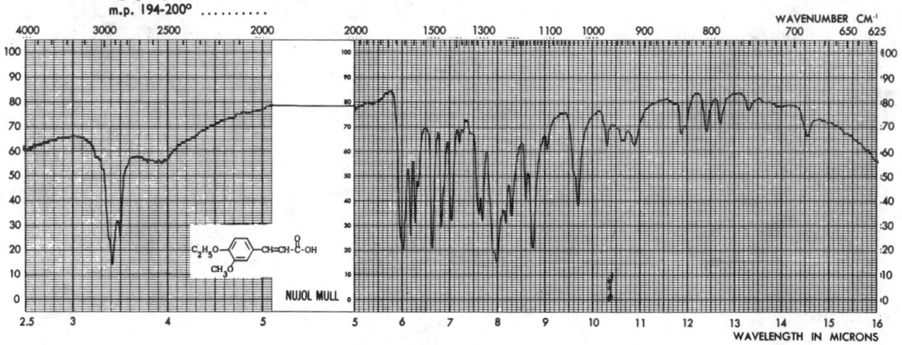

NUJOL MULL

14,624-2 3,4-Methylenedioxycinnamic acid
M.W. 192.17 m.p. 242-244° (dec.)

H

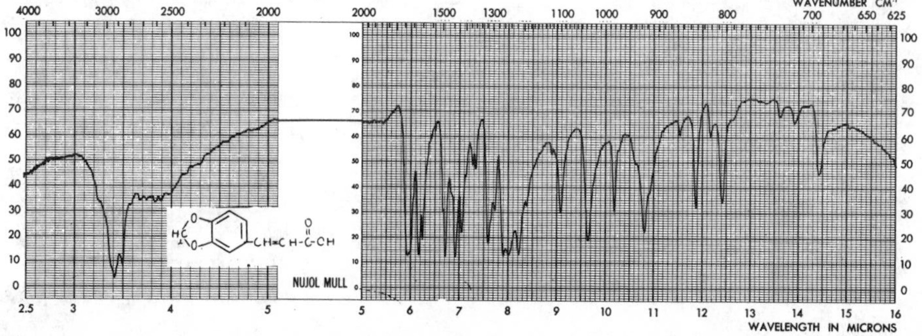

NUJOL MULL

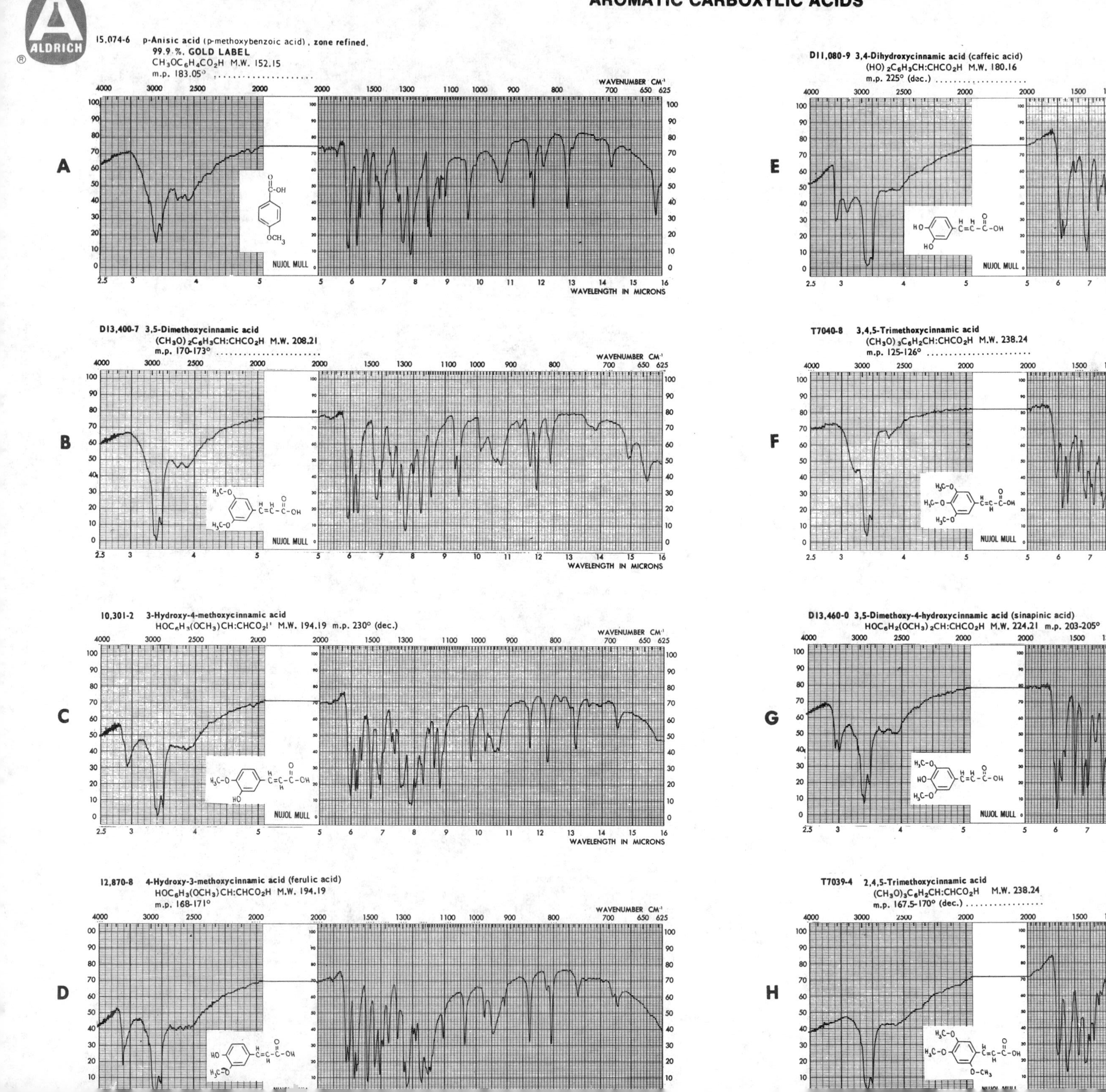

ALDRICH
A
15,074-6 p-Anisic acid (p-methoxybenzoic acid), zone refined, 99.9 %, GOLD LABEL
$CH_3OC_6H_4CO_2H$ M.W. 152.15
m.p. 183.05°
B
D13,400-7 3,5-Dimethoxycinnamic acid
$(CH_3O)_2C_6H_3CH:CHCO_2H$ M.W. 208.21
m.p. 170-173°
C
10,301-2 3-Hydroxy-4-methoxycinnamic acid
$HOC_6H_3(OCH_3)CH:CHCO_2H$ M.W. 194.19 m.p. 230° (dec.)
D
12,870-8 4-Hydroxy-3-methoxycinnamic acid (ferulic acid)
$HOC_6H_3(OCH_3)CH:CHCO_2H$ M.W. 194.19
m.p. 168-171°
E
D11,080-9 3,4-Dihydroxycinnamic acid (caffeic acid)
$(HO)_2C_6H_3CH:CHCO_2H$ M.W. 180.16
m.p. 225° (dec.)
F
T7040-8 3,4,5-Trimethoxycinnamic acid
$(CH_3O)_3C_6H_2CH:CHCO_2H$ M.W. 238.24
m.p. 125-126°
G
D13,460-0 3,5-Dimethoxy-4-hydroxycinnamic acid (sinapinic acid)
$HOC_6H_2(OCH_3)_2CH:CHCO_2H$ M.W. 224.21 m.p. 203-205°
H
T7039-4 2,4,5-Trimethoxycinnamic acid
$(CH_3O)_3C_6H_2CH:CHCO_2H$ M.W. 238.24
m.p. 167.5-170° (dec.)
WAVENUMBER CM⁻¹
WAVELENGTH IN MICRONS
NUJOL MULL

A

(CH₃O)₃C₆H₂CH=CHCO₂H FW 238.24
mp 172-174° *Beil.* 10(3),2197 Disp. C

NUJOL MULL

B

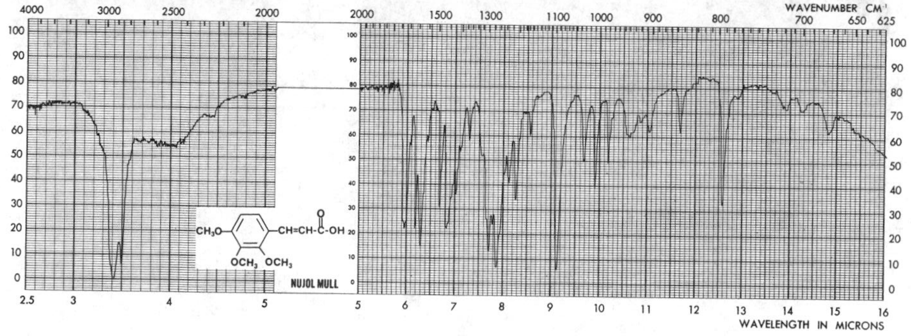

19,883-8
3,4-Dihydro-5,6,7-trimethoxy-2-naphthoic acid, 95+%
FW 264.28 mp 156-159° Disp. C

NUJOL MULL

C

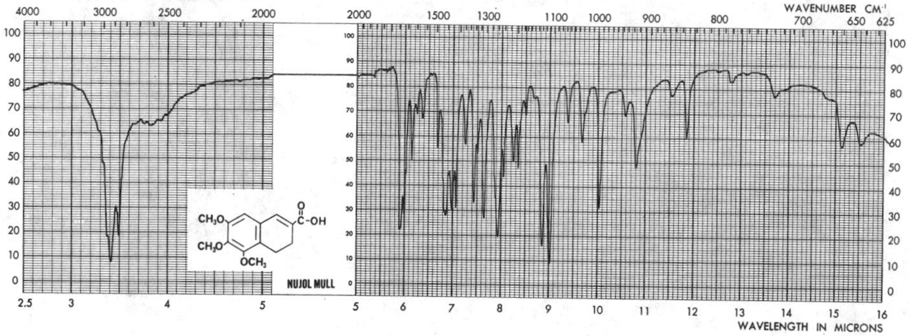

18,842-5
3-Methylindene-2-carboxylic acid, 97%
FW 174.20 mp 201-203° *Beil.* 9,644 Disp. C

NUJOL MULL

D

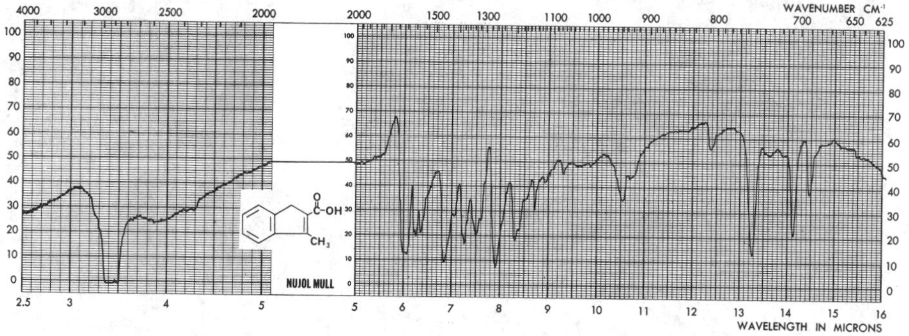

B3500-8 Biphenyleneacrylic acid (fluoren-9-ylideneacetic acid)
M.W. 222.24 m.p. 231-233° (dec.)

NUJOL MULL

E

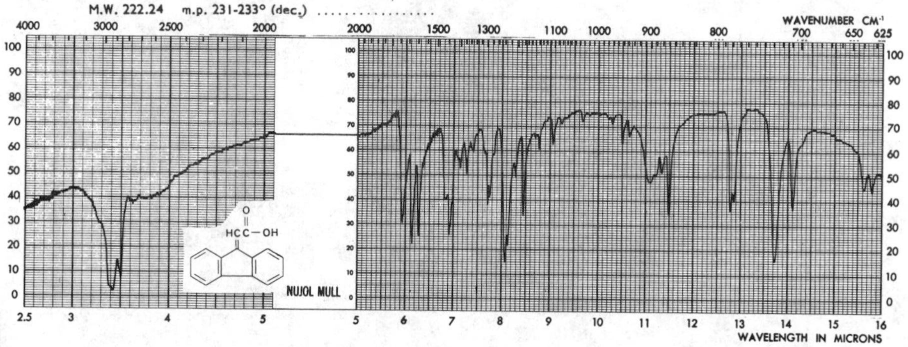

10,420-5 Benzoic acid, zone refined
$C_6H_5CO_2H$ M.W. 122.12 m.p. 122.39°

NUJOL MULL

F

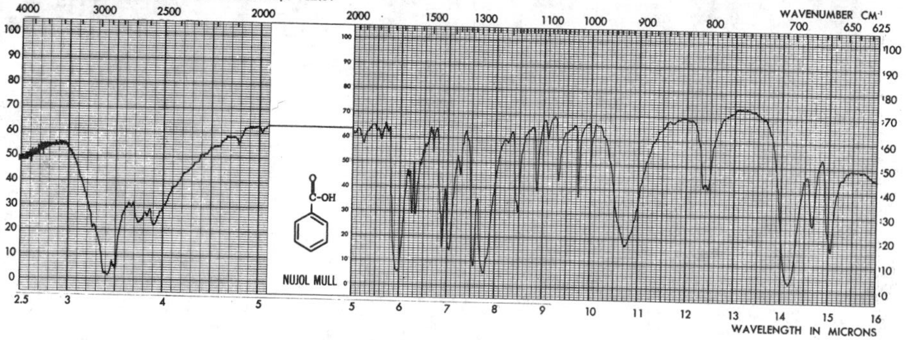

T2820-7 Thiobenzoic acid
C_6H_5COSH M.W. 138.19 n_D^{20} 1.6040
m.p. 15-18°

NEAT

G

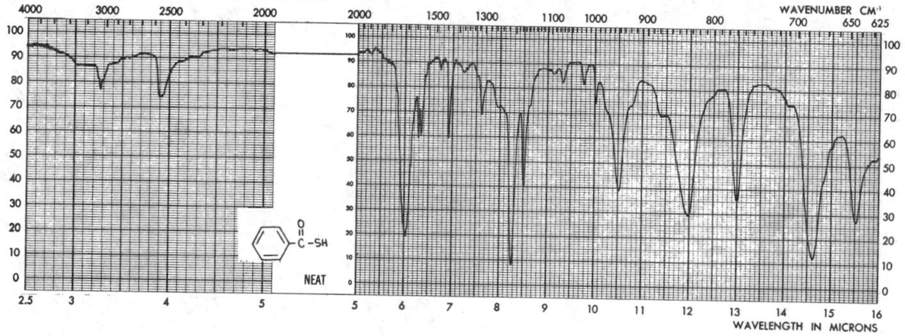

15,092-4
o-Toluic acid, zone refined, 99.9+%, GOLD LABEL
$CH_3C_6H_4CO_2H$
M.W. 136.15 m.p. 104.08° b.p. 258-260°
d 1.062 Beil. 9,462

NUJOL MULL

H

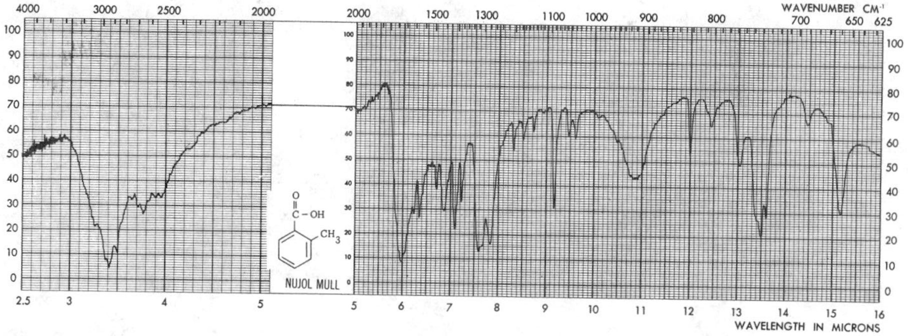

F640-0 o-Fluorobenzoic acid, puriss.
$FC_6H_4CO_2H$ M.W. 140.11 m.p. 124°

NUJOL MULL

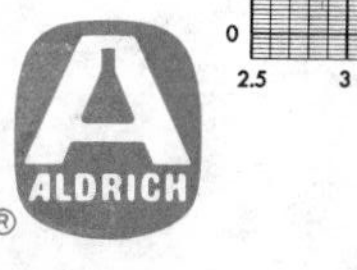

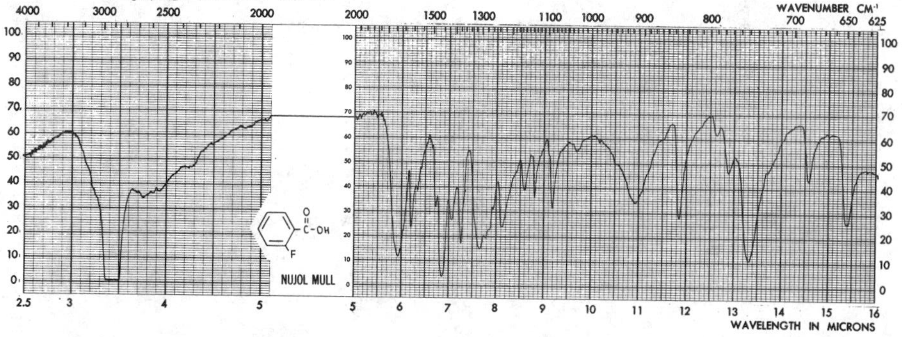

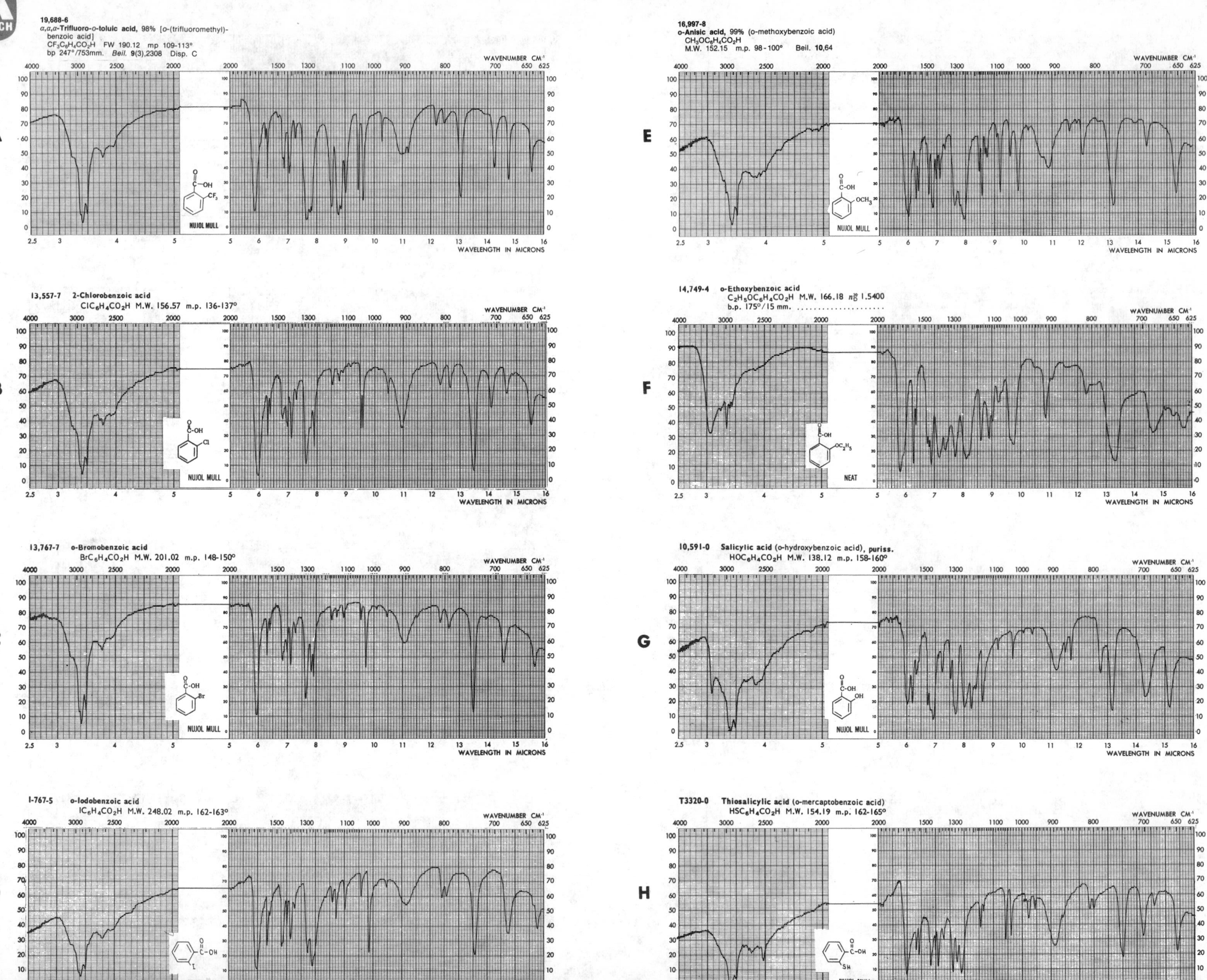
ALDRICH
A
19,688-6
α,α,α-Trifluoro-o-toluic acid, 98% [o-(trifluoromethyl)-benzoic acid]
$CF_3C_6H_4CO_2H$ FW 190.12 mp 109-113°
bp 247°/753mm. Beil. 9(3),2308 Disp. C
NUJOL MULL
B
13,557-7 2-Chlorobenzoic acid
$ClC_6H_4CO_2H$ M.W. 156.57 m.p. 136-137°
NUJOL MULL
C
13,767-7 o-Bromobenzoic acid
$BrC_6H_4CO_2H$ M.W. 201.02 m.p. 148-150°
NUJOL MULL
D
I-767-5 o-Iodobenzoic acid
$IC_6H_4CO_2H$ M.W. 248.02 m.p. 162-163°
E
16,997-8
o-Anisic acid, 99% (o-methoxybenzoic acid)
$CH_3OC_6H_4CO_2H$
M.W. 152.15 m.p. 98-100° Beil. 10,64
NUJOL MULL
F
14,749-4 o-Ethoxybenzoic acid
$C_2H_5OC_6H_4CO_2H$ M.W. 166.18 n_D^{20} 1.5400
b.p. 175°/15 mm.
NEAT
G
10,591-0 Salicylic acid (o-hydroxybenzoic acid), puriss.
$HOC_6H_4CO_2H$ M.W. 138.12 m.p. 158-160°
NUJOL MULL
H
T3320-0 Thiosalicylic acid (o-mercaptobenzoic acid)
$HSC_6H_4CO_2H$ M.W. 154.19 m.p. 162-165°
WAVENUMBER CM⁻¹
WAVELENGTH IN MICRONS

A

$CH_3(CH_2)_{15}SC_6H_4CO_2H$ M.W. 378.62
m.p. 95-98°

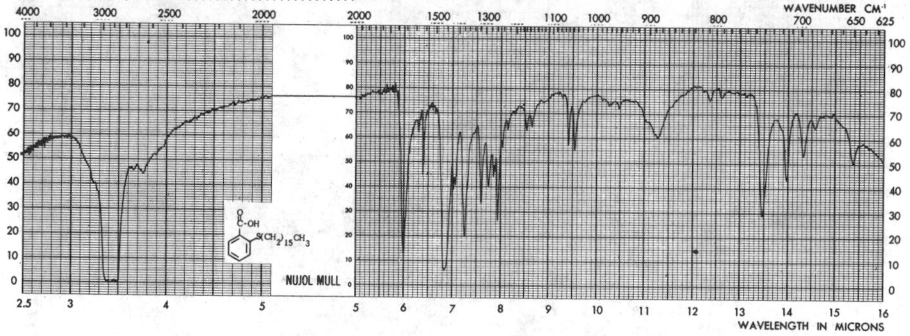

NUJOL MULL

B

A8985-5 **Anthranilic acid** (o-aminobenzoic acid)
$2\text{-}(H_2N)C_6H_4CO_2H$ M.W. 137.14
m.p. 144-148°

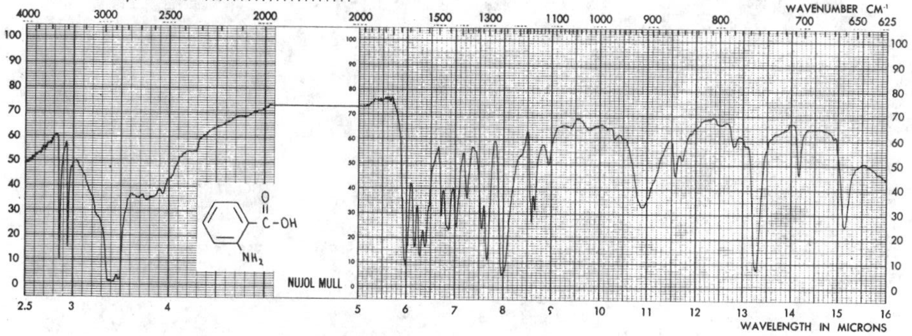

NUJOL MULL

C

13,706-5 **N-Methylanthranilic acid**
$2\text{-}(CH_3NH)C_6H_4CO_2H$ M.W. 151.17
m.p. 170-172° (dec.)

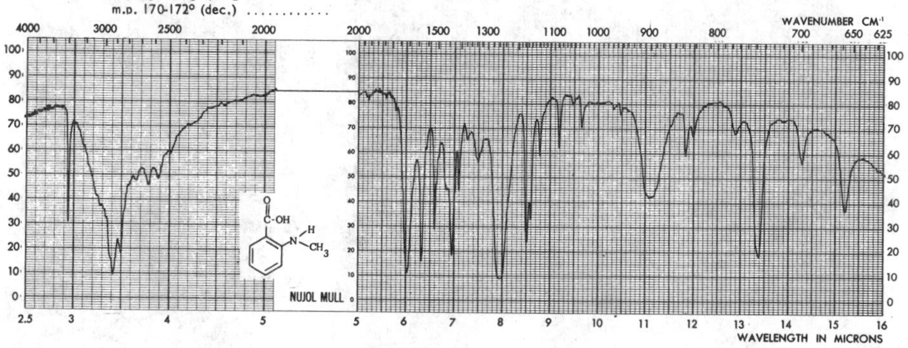

NUJOL MULL

D

10,951-7 **2-Dimethylaminobenzoic acid hydrochloride**
$(CH_3)_2NC_6H_4CO_2H{\cdot}HCl$ M.W. 201.65 m.p. 202° (dec.)

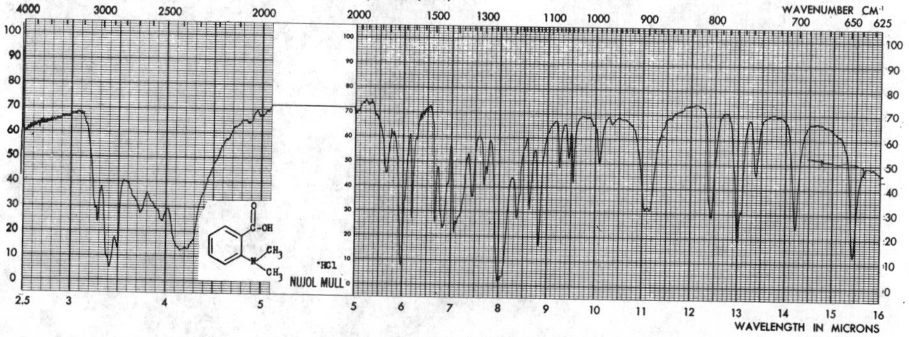

NUJOL MULL

E

12,769-8 **o-Nitrobenzoic acid**
$O_2NC_6H_4CO_2H$ M.W. 167.12 m.p. 146-148°

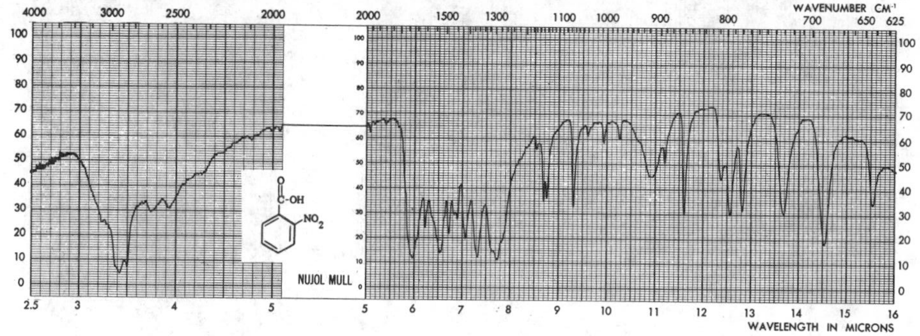

NUJOL MULL

F

A1280-1 **2-Acetylbenzoic acid** (3-hydroxy-3-methylphthalide)
M.W. 164.16 m.p. 111-114°

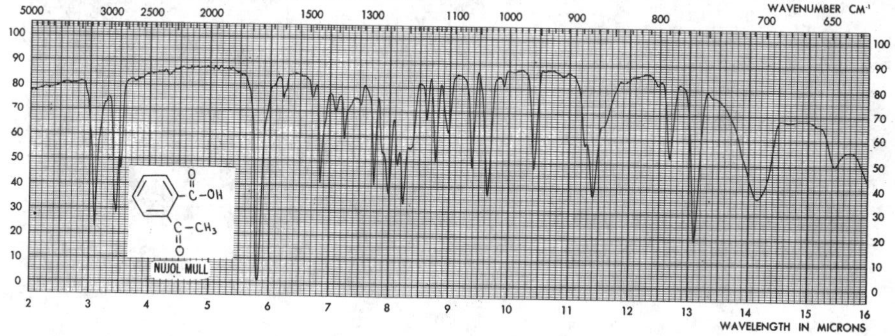

NUJOL MULL

G

11,601-7 **2-Carboxybenzaldehyde** (phthalaldehydic acid, 3-hydroxyphthalide)
M.W. 150.14 m.p. 95-98°

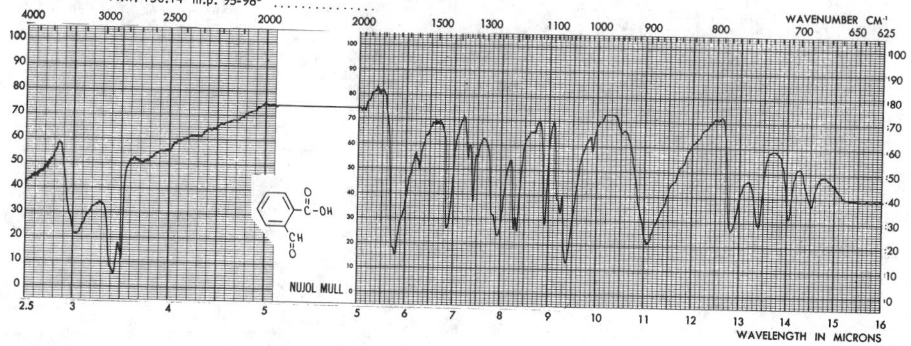

NUJOL MULL

H

T3660-9 **m-Toluic acid**
$CH_3C_6H_4CO_2H$ M.W. 136.15 m.p. 108-110°

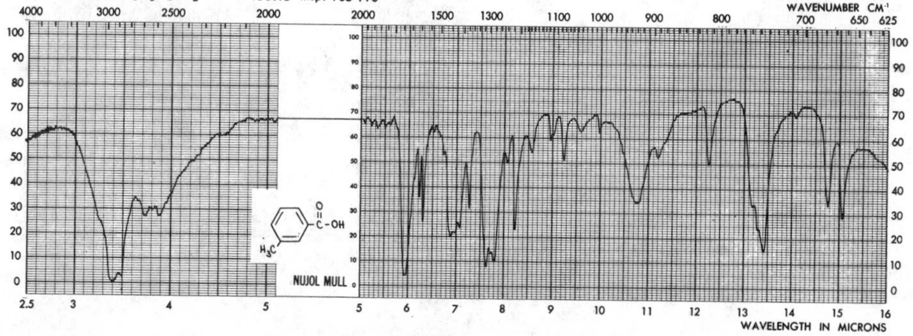

NUJOL MULL

ALDRICH ®

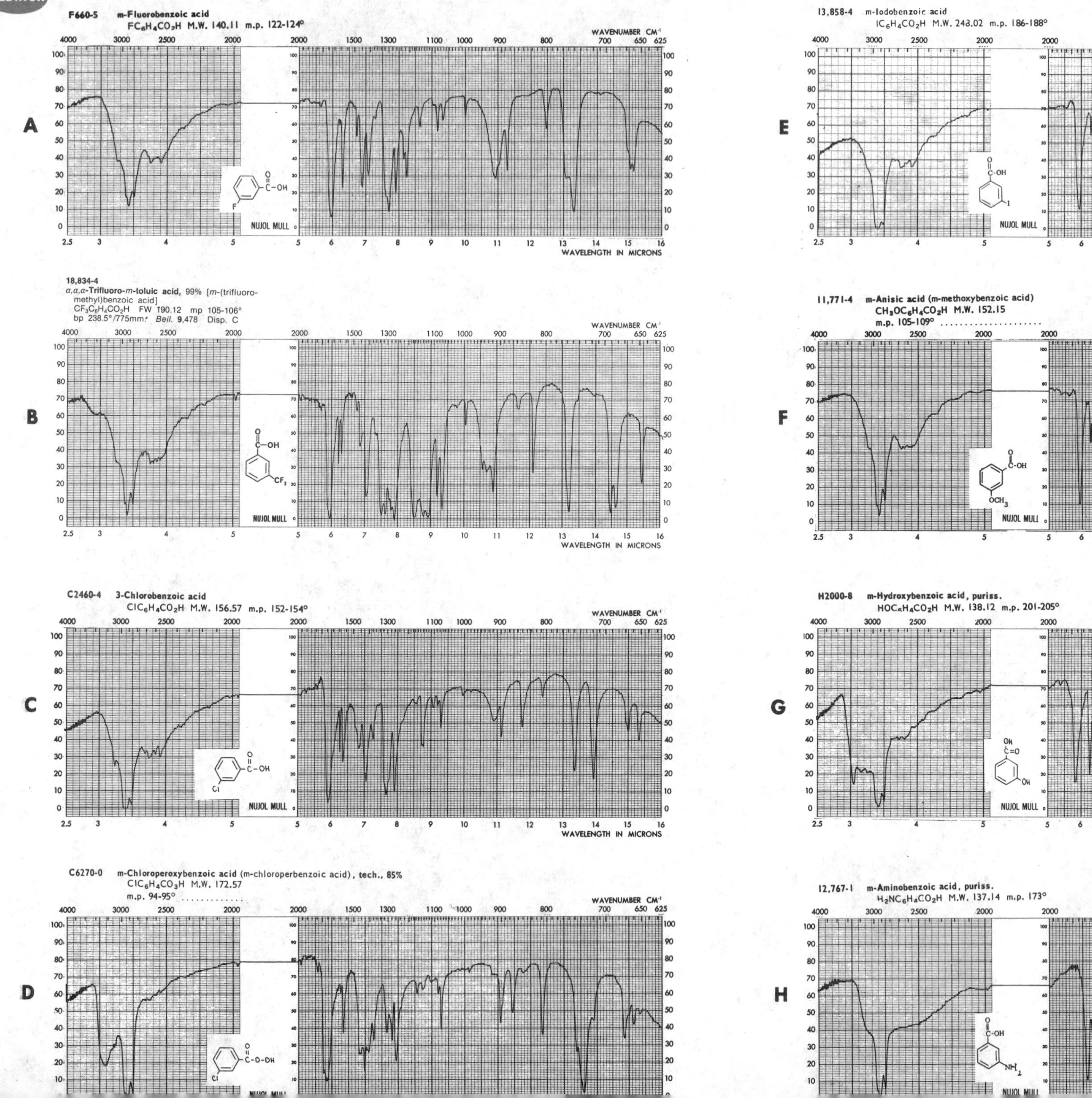
ALDRICH
A
F660-5 m-Fluorobenzoic acid
$FC_6H_4CO_2H$ M.W. 140.11 m.p. 122-124°
NUJOL MULL
B
18,834-4
α,α,α-Trifluoro-m-toluic acid, 99% [m-(trifluoromethyl)benzoic acid]
$CF_3C_6H_4CO_2H$ FW 190.12 mp 105-106°
bp 238.5°/775mm; Beil. 9,478 Disp. C
NUJOL MULL
C
C2460-4 3-Chlorobenzoic acid
$ClC_6H_4CO_2H$ M.W. 156.57 m.p. 152-154°
NUJOL MULL
D
C6270-0 m-Chloroperoxybenzoic acid (m-chloroperbenzoic acid), tech., 85%
$ClC_6H_4CO_3H$ M.W. 172.57
m.p. 94-95°
E
13,858-4 m-Iodobenzoic acid
$IC_6H_4CO_2H$ M.W. 243.02 m.p. 186-188°
NUJOL MULL
F
11,771-4 m-Anisic acid (m-methoxybenzoic acid)
$CH_3OC_6H_4CO_2H$ M.W. 152.15
m.p. 105-109°
NUJOL MULL
G
H2000-8 m-Hydroxybenzoic acid, puriss.
$HOC_6H_4CO_2H$ M.W. 138.12 m.p. 201-205°
NUJOL MULL
H
12,767-1 m-Aminobenzoic acid, puriss.
$H_2NC_6H_4CO_2H$ M.W. 137.14 m.p. 173°
WAVENUMBER CM⁻¹
WAVELENGTH IN MICRONS

A D13,940-8 3-Dimethylaminobenzoic acid
$(CH_3)_2NC_6H_4CO_2H$ M.W. 165.19 m.p. 154-155°
NUJOL MULL

B N1178-7 m-Nitrobenzoic acid
$O_2NC_6H_4CO_2H$ M.W. 167.12 m.p. 138-142°
NUJOL MULL

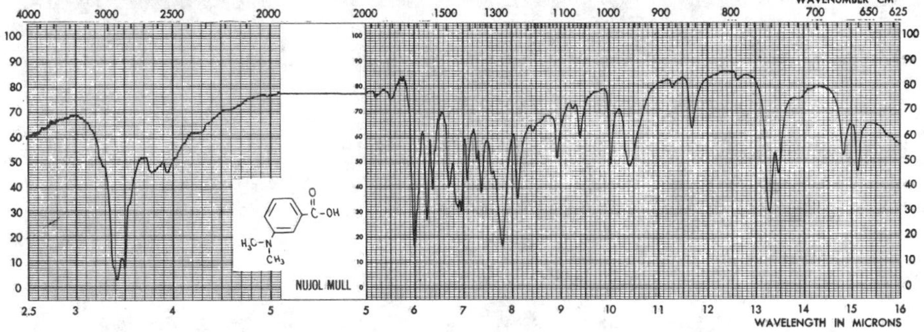

C T3680-3 p-Toluic acid
$CH_3C_6H_4CO_2H$ M.W. 136.15 m.p. 180-182°
NUJOL MULL

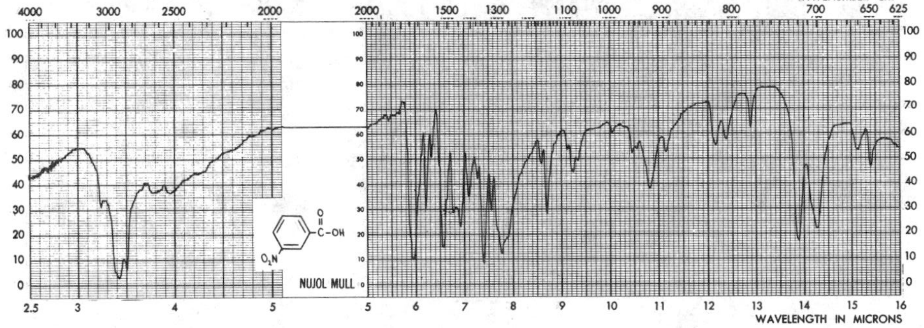

D 19,128-0
p-Ethylbenzoic acid, 99%
$C_2H_5C_6H_4CO_2H$ FW 150.18 mp 112-113°
Beil. 9,529 Disp. C
NUJOL MULL

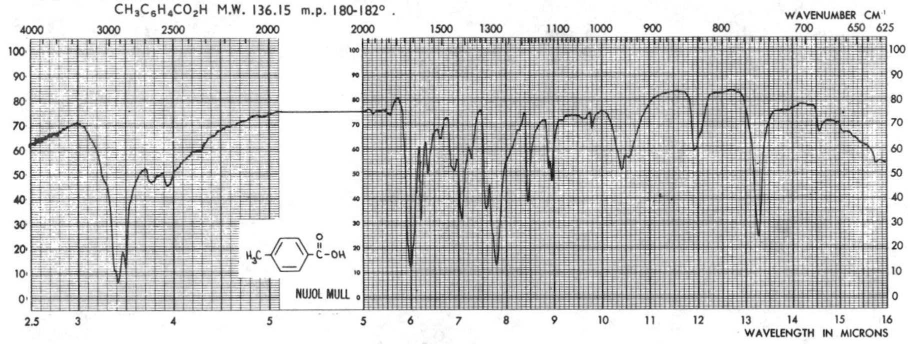

E $(CH_3)_3CC_6H_4CO_2H$ M.W. 178.23
m.p. 165-167°
NUJOL MULL

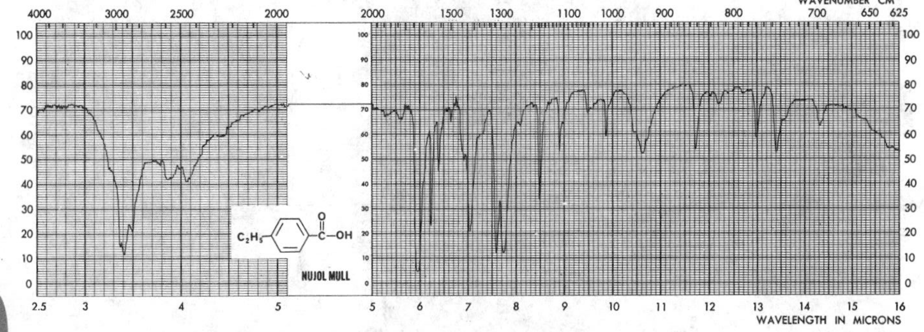

F 12,838-4 p-Fluorobenzoic acid
$FC_6H_4CO_2H$ M.W. 140.11 m.p. 182-184°
NUJOL MULL

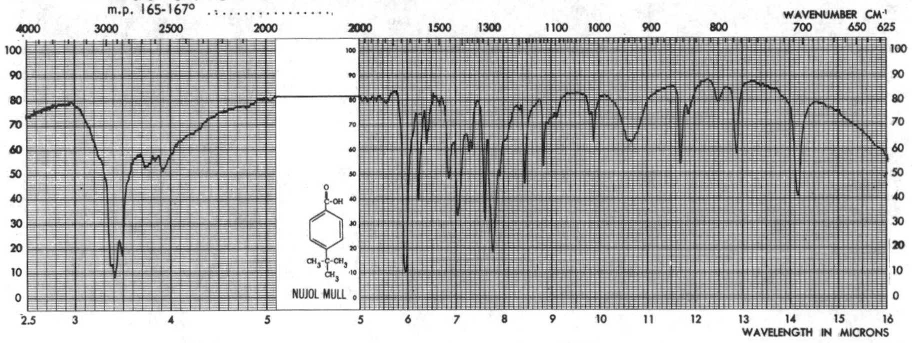

G 13,558-5 4-Chlorobenzoic acid
$ClC_6H_4CO_2H$ M.W. 156.57 m.p. 239-241°
NUJOL MULL

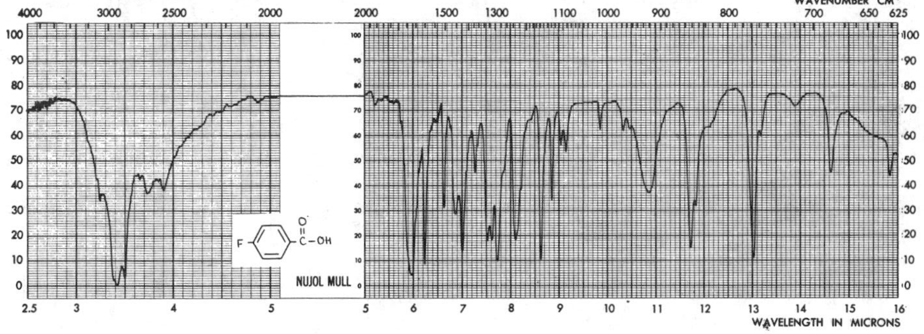

H 10,851-0 p-Bromobenzoic acid, puriss.
$BrC_6H_4CO_2H$ M.W. 201.02 m.p. 252-254°
NUJOL MULL

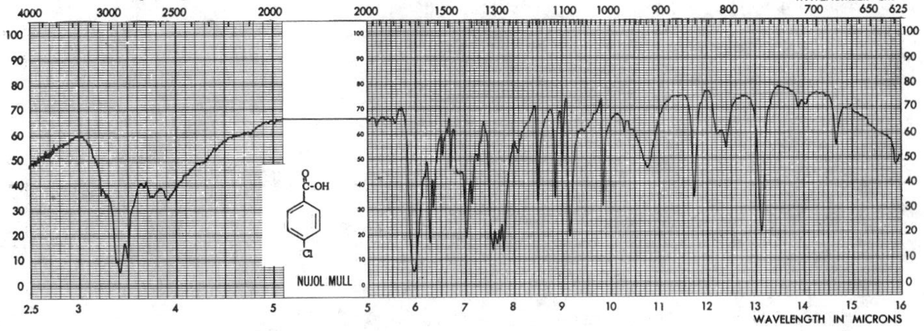

ALDRICH ®

AROMATIC CARBOXYLIC ACIDS

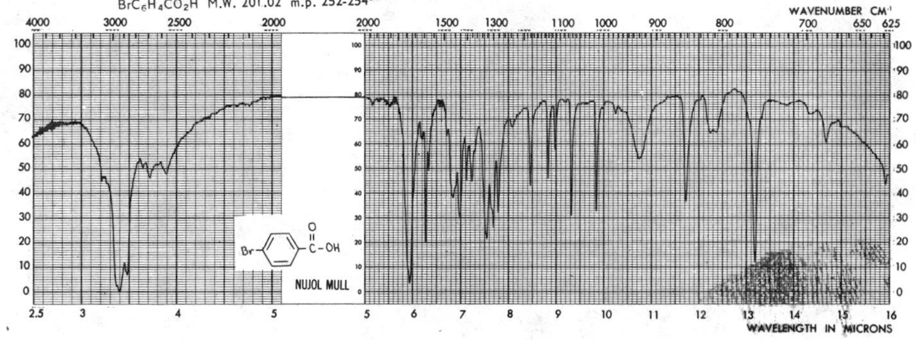

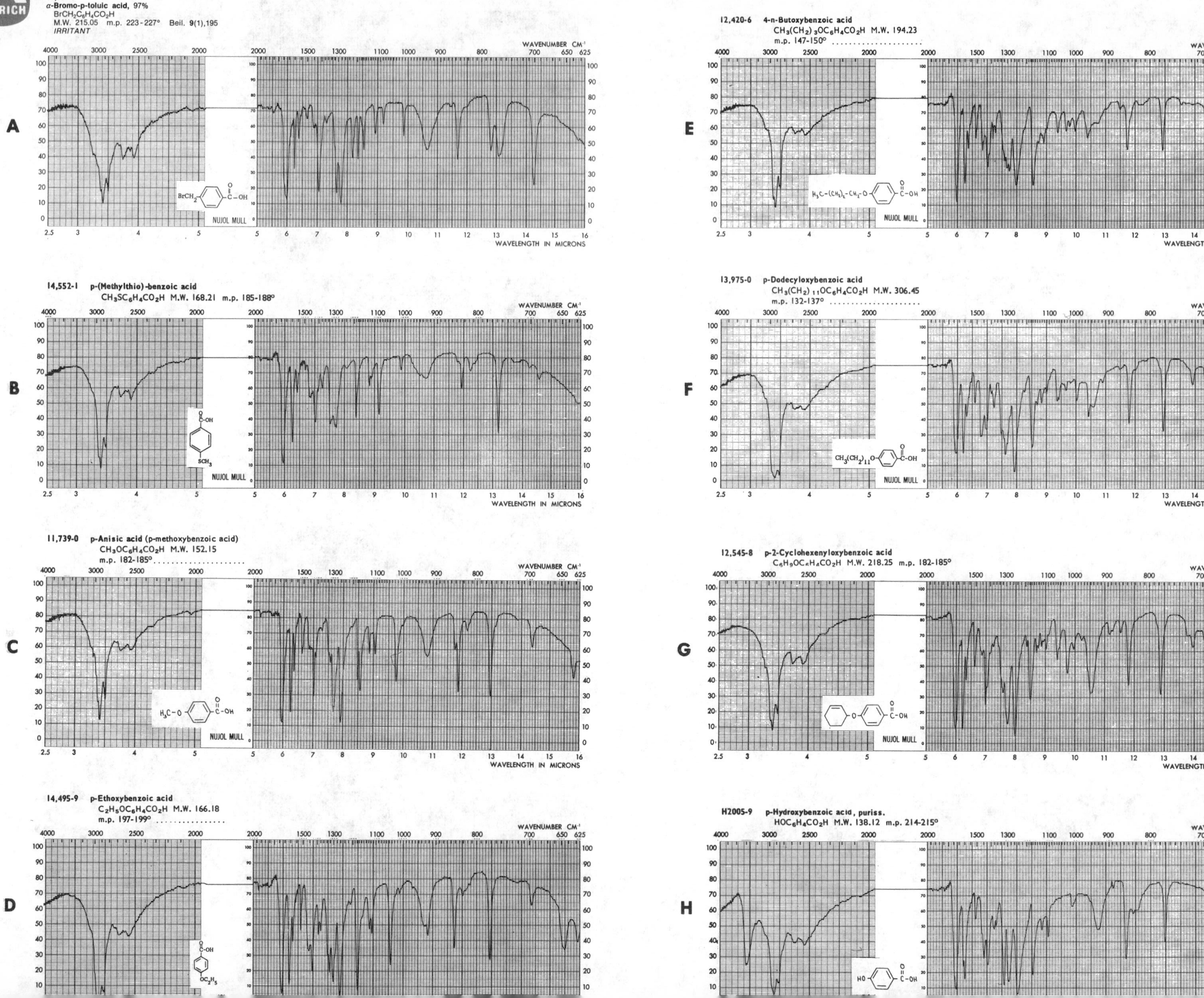
ALDRICH

A
15,954-9
α-Bromo-p-toluic acid, 97%
$BrCH_2C_6H_4CO_2H$
M.W. 215.05 m.p. 223-227° Beil. 9(1),195
IRRITANT

B
14,552-1 p-(Methylthio)-benzoic acid
$CH_3SC_6H_4CO_2H$ M.W. 168.21 m.p. 185-188°

C
11,739-0 p-Anisic acid (p-methoxybenzoic acid)
$CH_3OC_6H_4CO_2H$ M.W. 152.15
m.p. 182-185°

D
14,495-9 p-Ethoxybenzoic acid
$C_2H_5OC_6H_4CO_2H$ M.W. 166.18
m.p. 197-199°

E
12,420-6 4-n-Butoxybenzoic acid
$CH_3(CH_2)_3OC_6H_4CO_2H$ M.W. 194.23
m.p. 147-150°

F
13,975-0 p-Dodecyloxybenzoic acid
$CH_3(CH_2)_{11}OC_6H_4CO_2H$ M.W. 306.45
m.p. 132-137°

G
12,545-8 p-2-Cyclohexenyloxybenzoic acid
$C_6H_9OC_6H_4CO_2H$ M.W. 218.25 m.p. 182-185°

H
H2005-9 p-Hydroxybenzoic acid, puriss.
$HOC_6H_4CO_2H$ M.W. 138.12 m.p. 214-215°

NUJOL MULL
WAVENUMBER CM⁻¹
WAVELENGTH IN MICRONS

A $C_2H_5SC_6H_4CO_2H$ FW 182.24 mp 145-147°
Beil. **10**,185 Disp. S

NUJOL MULL

E N1179-5 **p-Nitrobenzoic acid, puriss.**
$O_2NC_6H_4CO_2H$ M.W. 167.12 m.p. 239-241°

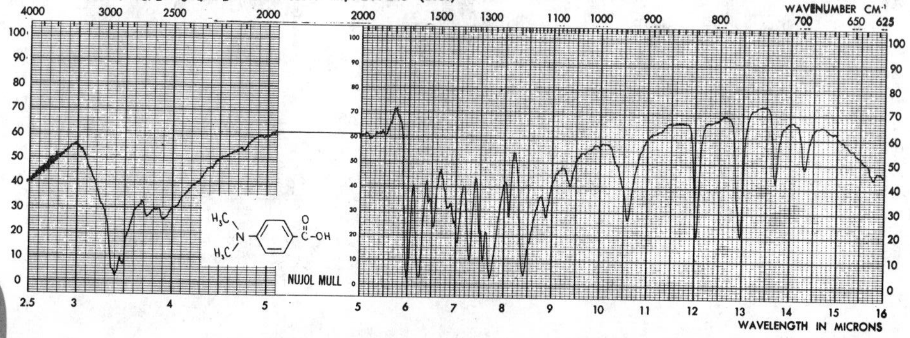

NUJOL MULL

B 10,053-6 **p-Aminobenzoic acid**
$H_2NC_6H_4CO_2H$ M.W. 137.14 m.p. 188-189°

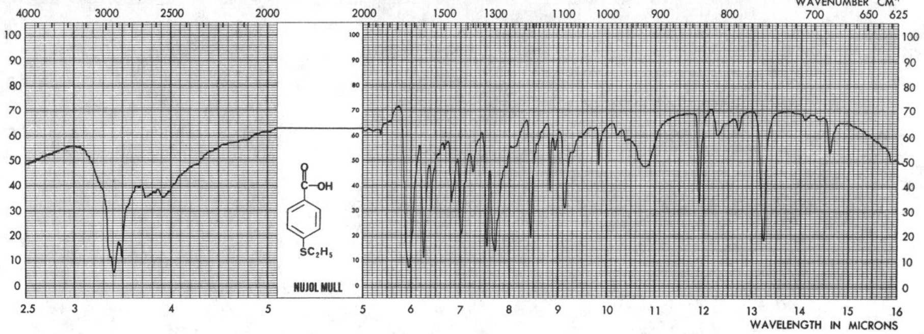

NUJOL MULL

F 18,044-0
p-Nitroperoxybenzoic acid, tech., 85% (p-nitro-perbenzoic acid)
$O_2NC_6H_4CO_3H$
M.W. 183.12 m.p. 144° (dec.)

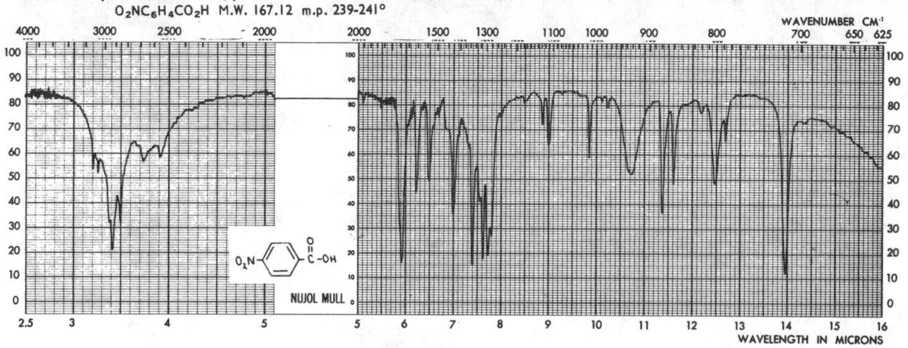

NUJOL MULL

C 11,969-5 **p-(Methylamino)-benzoic acid**
$CH_3NHC_6H_4CO_2H$ M.W. 151.17
m.p. 158-159° ....

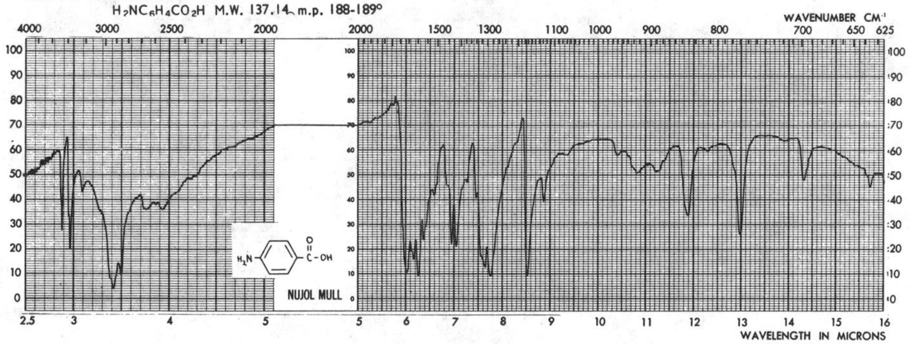

NUJOL MULL

G 17,745-8
4-Acetylbenzoic acid
$CH_3COC_6H_4CO_2H$
M.W. 164.16 m.p. 208-210°

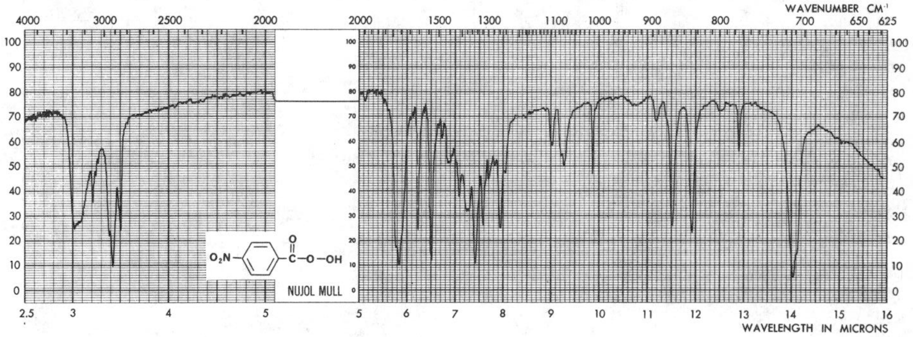

NUJOL MULL

D D13,945-9 **4-Dimethylaminobenzoic acid**
$(CH_3)_2NC_6H_4CO_2H$ M.W. 165.19 m.p. 244-246° (dec.)

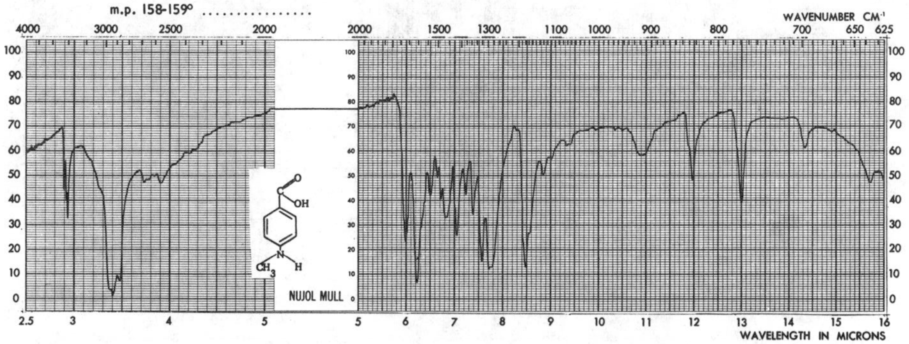

NUJOL MULL

H 12,491-5 **4-Carboxybenzaldehyde** (terephthalaldehydic acid)
$HO_2CC_6H_4CHO$ M.W. 150.13
Titration 97% ....

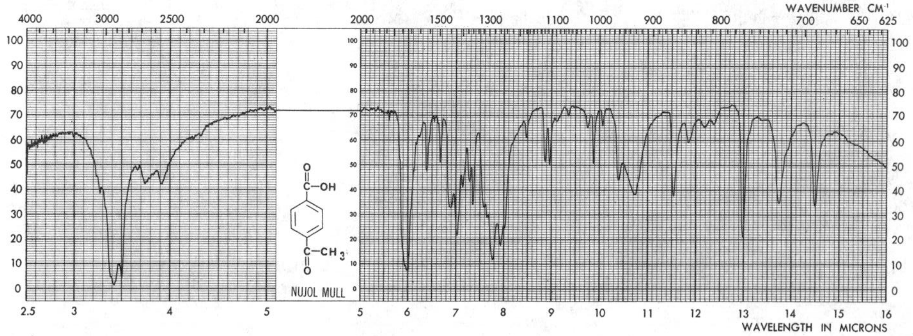

NUJOL MULL

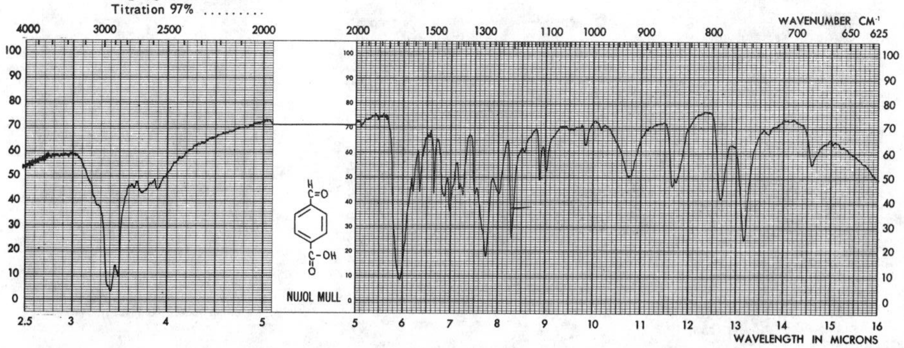

10,947-9 Benzoic acid, U.S.P.
$C_6H_5CO_2H$ M.W. 122.12 m.p. 122-123°

P3930-3 Phthalic acid
C_6H_4-1,2-$(CO_2H)_2$ M.W. 166.13
m.p. 210-211° (dec.)

18,629-5
m-Bromobenzoic acid, 99%
$BrC_6H_4CO_2H$
M.W. 201.02 m.p. 155-158° Beil. 9,349

I-1920-9 Isophthalic acid
C_6H_4-1,3-$(CO_2H)_2$ M.W. 166.13 m.p. 341-343°

B420-1
1,2,3-Benzenetricarboxylic acid dihydrate
(hemimellitic acid)
$C_6H_3(CO_2H)_3 \cdot 2H_2O$
M.W. 246.18 m.p. 190-192° (dec.) Beil. 9,976

T230-4 Terephthalic acid
C_6H_4-1,4-$(CO_2H)_2$ M.W. 166.13
m.p. > 320°

D21,950-9 Dithioterephthalic acid
C_6H_4-1,4-$(COSH)_2$ M.W. 198.26 m.p. 130-132°

B458-9 1,2,4-Benzenetricarboxylic acid (trimellitic acid), puriss.
$C_6H_3(CO_2H)_3$ M.W. 210.14 m.p. 239° (dec.)

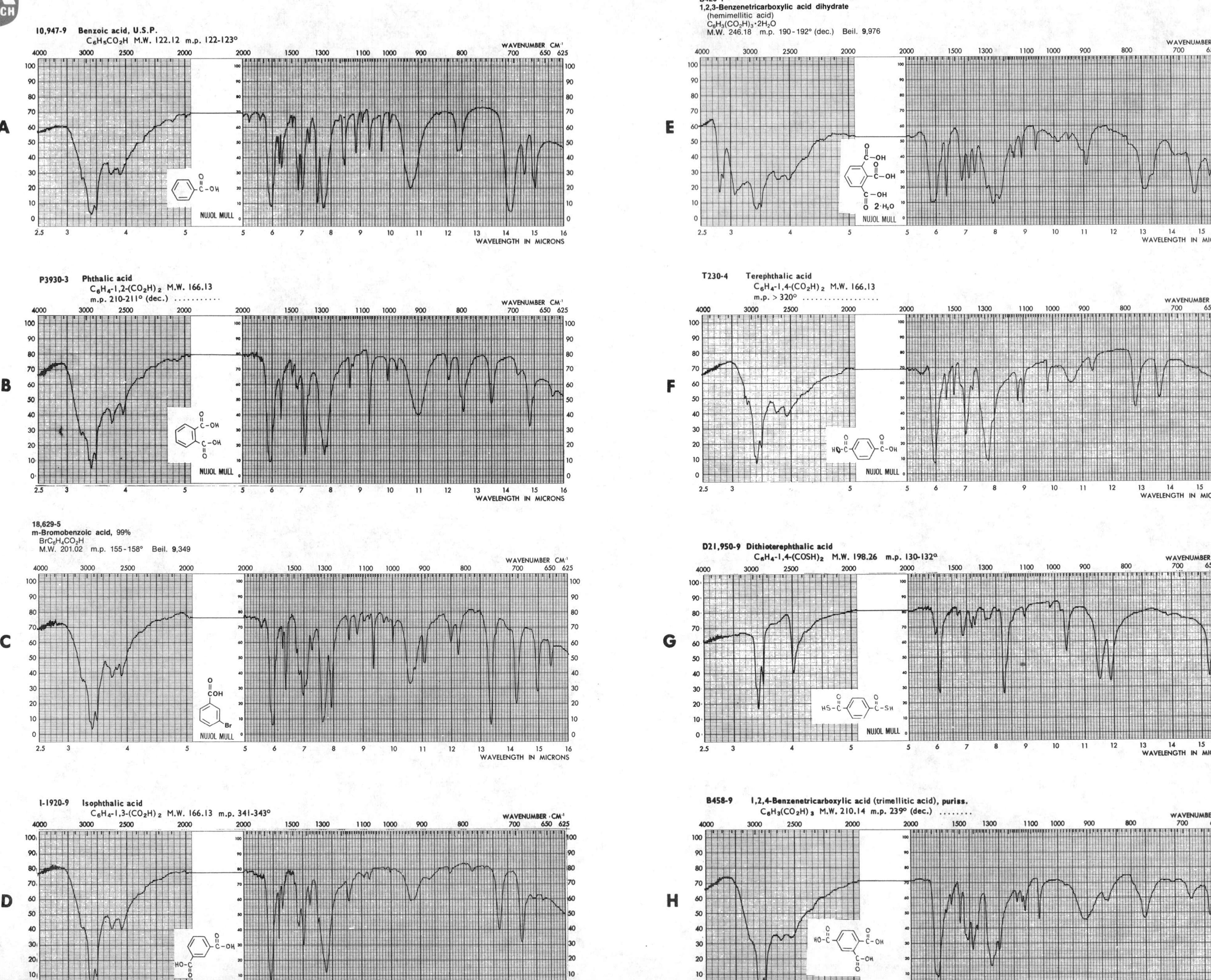

1,3,5-Benzenetricarboxylic acid (trimesic acid), puriss.
$C_6H_3(CO_2H)_3$ M.W. 210.14 m.p. > 330° ....

(CH$_3$)$_2$C$_6$H$_3$CO$_2$H M.W. 150.18
m.p. 144.5-146.5° ....

B400-7 1,2,4,5-Benzenetetracarboxylic acid (pyromellitic acid)
$C_6H_2(CO_2H)_4$ M.W. 254.15
m.p. 281-284.5° ....

15,690-6
2,6-Dimethylbenzoic acid, 97%
$(CH_3)_2C_6H_3CO_2H$
M.W. 150.18 m.p. 114-116° Beil. **9**,531

10,042-0 Benzenepentacarboxylic acid, puriss.
$C_6H(CO_2H)_5$ M.W. 298.16 m.p. 237°

19,003-9
2,6-Difluorobenzoic acid, 95+%
$F_2C_6H_3CO_2H$ FW 158.11 mp 158-160° Disp. C

M270-5 Mellitic acid
$C_6(CO_2H)_6$ M.W. 342.17
m.p. > 300° (dec.); 288° (dec.) (sealed tube)

17,803-9
2-Chloro-6-fluorobenzoic acid, 98%
$ClC_6H_3(F)CO_2H$
M.W. 174.56 m.p. 159-161°

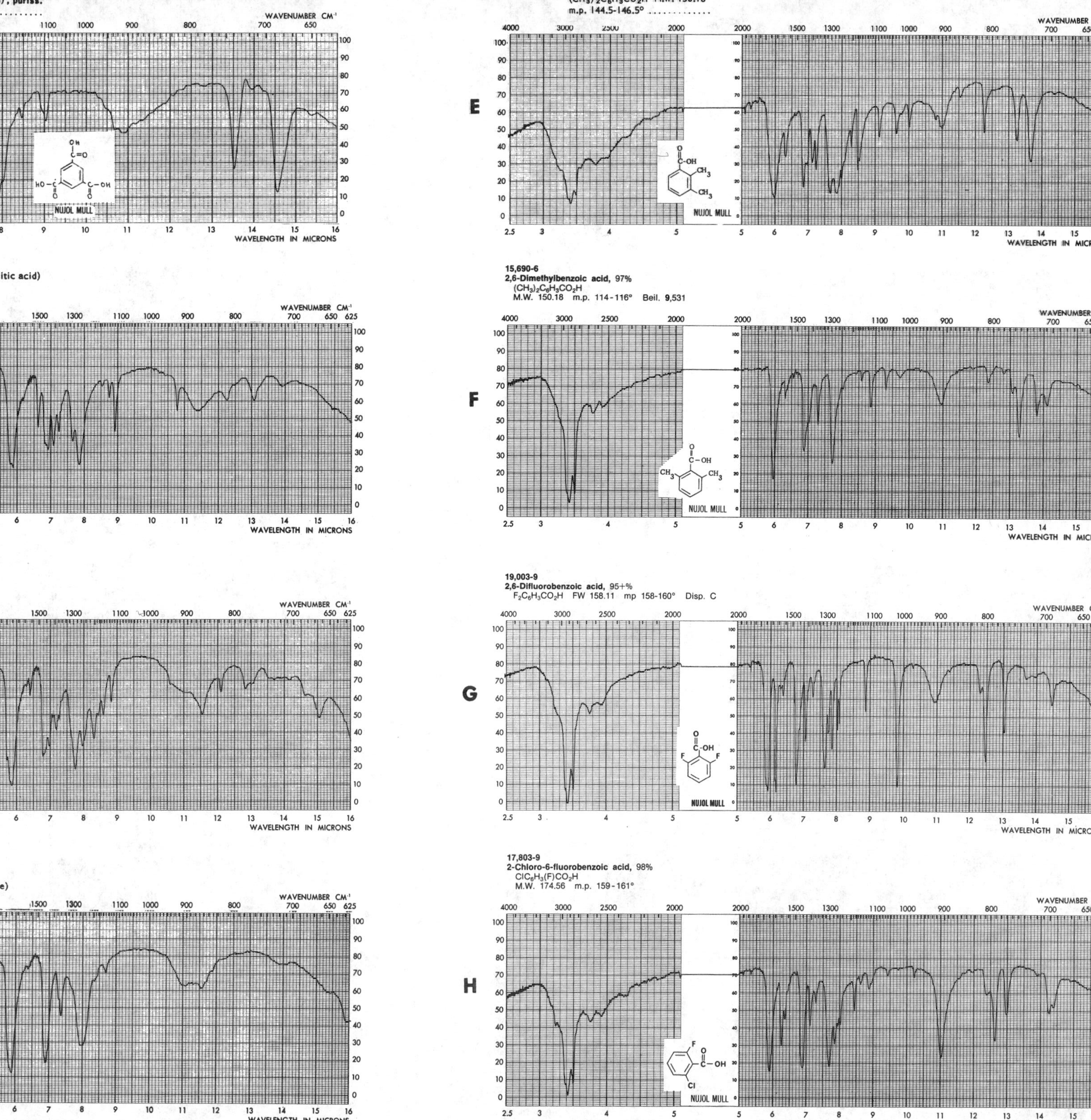

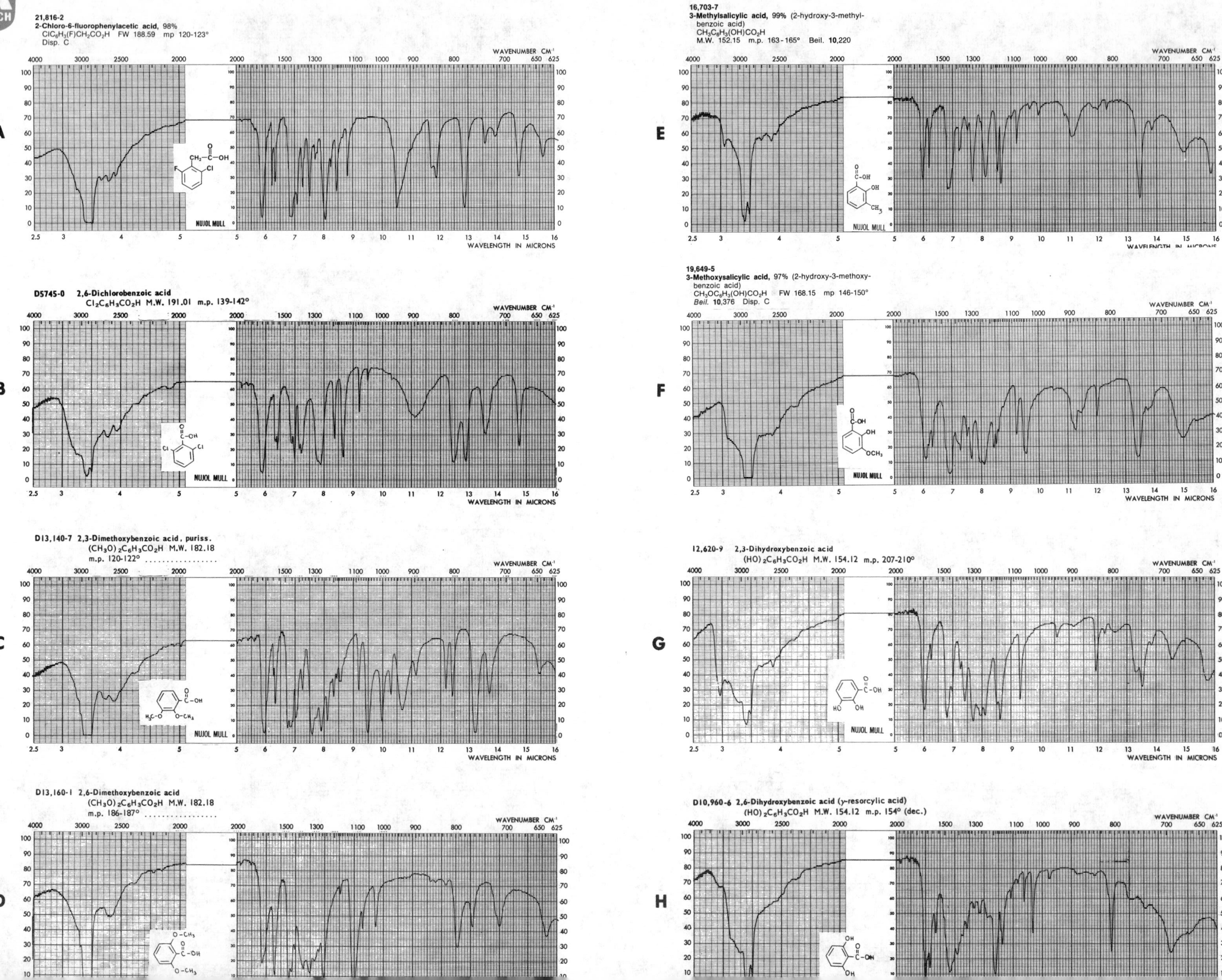

A
21,816-2
2-Chloro-6-fluorophenylacetic acid, 98%
$ClC_6H_3(F)CH_2CO_2H$ FW 188.59 mp 120-123°
Disp. C

B
D5745-0 2,6-Dichlorobenzoic acid
$Cl_2C_6H_3CO_2H$ M.W. 191.01 m.p. 139-142°

C
D13,140-7 2,3-Dimethoxybenzoic acid, puriss.
$(CH_3O)_2C_6H_3CO_2H$ M.W. 182.18
m.p. 120-122°

D
D13,160-1 2,6-Dimethoxybenzoic acid
$(CH_3O)_2C_6H_3CO_2H$ M.W. 182.18
m.p. 186-187°

E
16,703-7
3-Methylsalicylic acid, 99% (2-hydroxy-3-methylbenzoic acid)
$CH_3C_6H_3(OH)CO_2H$
M.W. 152.15 m.p. 163-165° Beil. 10,220

F
19,649-5
3-Methoxysalicylic acid, 97% (2-hydroxy-3-methoxybenzoic acid)
$CH_3OC_6H_3(OH)CO_2H$ FW 168.15 mp 146-150°
Beil. 10,376 Disp. C

G
12,620-9 2,3-Dihydroxybenzoic acid
$(HO)_2C_6H_3CO_2H$ M.W. 154.12 m.p. 207-210°

H
D10,960-6 2,6-Dihydroxybenzoic acid (γ-resorcylic acid)
$(HO)_2C_6H_3CO_2H$ M.W. 154.12 m.p. 154° (dec.)

m.p. 156-162°

$CH_3C_6H_3(NO_2)CO_2H$ M.W. 181.15 m.p. 222-225°

14,877-6 **3-Hydroxyanthranilic acid**
HOC_6H_3-2-$(NH_2)CO_2H$ M.W. 153.14
m.p. 240° (dec.)

13,784-7 **2-Methyl-3-nitrobenzoic acid**
$CH_3C_6H_3(NO_2)CO_2H$ M.W. 181.15
m.p. 182-184°

16,557-3
3-Aminophthalic acid hydrochloride
$H_2NC_6H_3$-1,2-$(CO_2H)_2\cdot HCl$ FW 217.61
mp 182° (dec.) *Beil.* 14,552 Disp. C

11,521-5 **3-Chloro-2-nitrobenzoic acid**
$ClC_6H_3(NO_2)CO_2H$ M.W. 201.57
m.p. 237-239°

15,139-4 **2-Methyl-6-nitrobenzoic acid** (6-nitro-o-toluic acid)
$CH_3C_6H_3(NO_2)CO_2H$ M.W. 181.15 m.p. 154-156.5°

14,120-8 **2-Chloro-3-nitrobenzoic acid**
$ClC_6H_3(NO_2)CO_2H$ M.W. 201.57
m.p. 181-184°

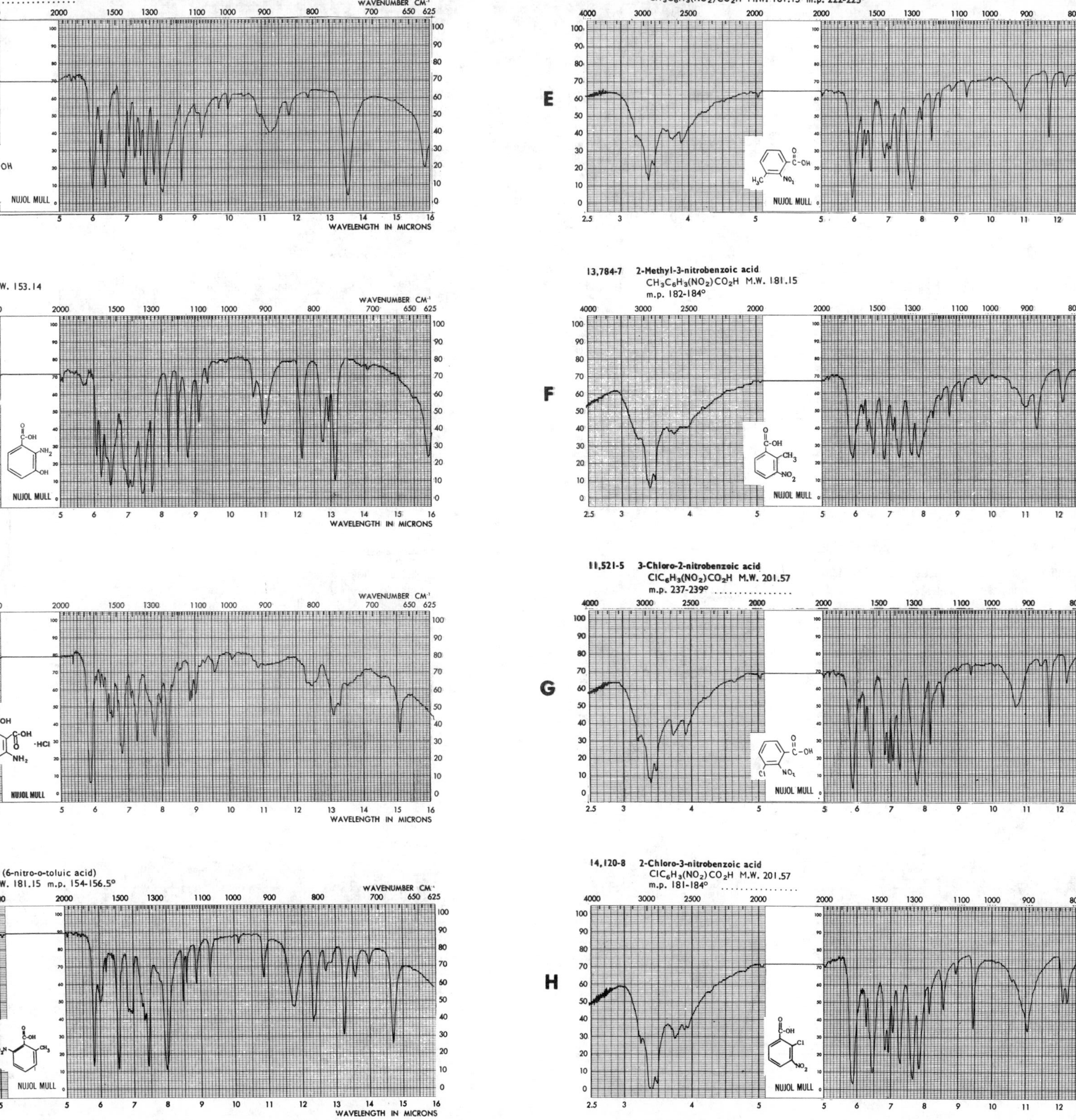

A
M1780-2 3-Methoxy-2-nitrobenzoic acid
$CH_3OC_6H_3(NO_2)CO_2H$ M.W. 197.15 m.p. 250-253°
NUJOL MULL

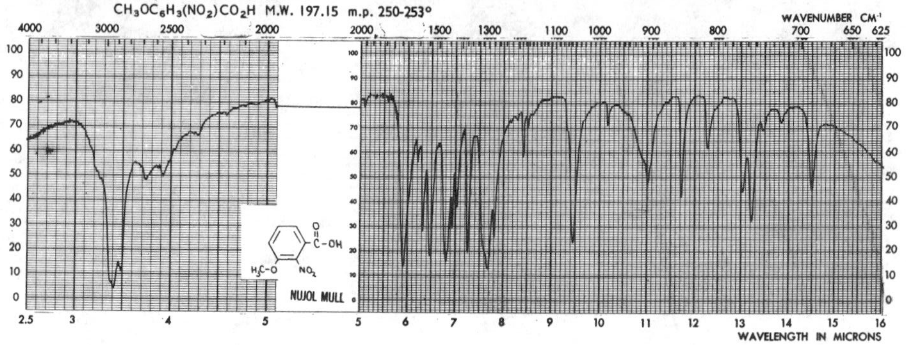

B
12,753-1 3-Nitroanthranilic acid, tech.
$O_2NC_6H_3$-2-$(NH_2)CO_2H$ M.W. 182.14
m.p. 195-198° (dec.)
NUJOL MULL

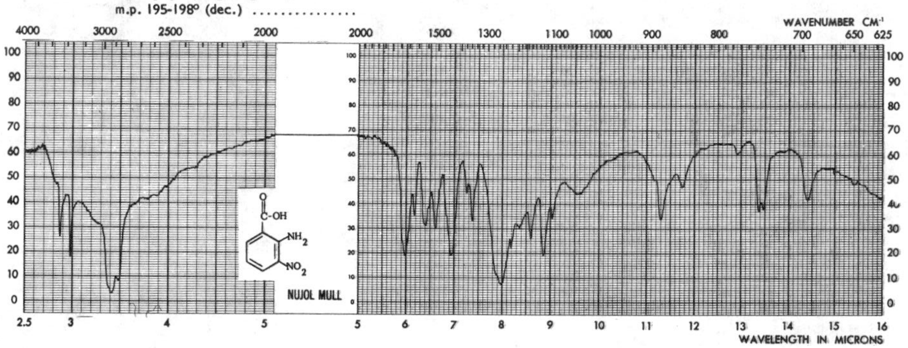

C
13,792-8 2,3-Dinitrobenzoic acid, puriss.
$(O_2N)_2C_6H_3CO_2H$ M.W. 212.12
m.p. 202.5-205.5°
NUJOL MULL

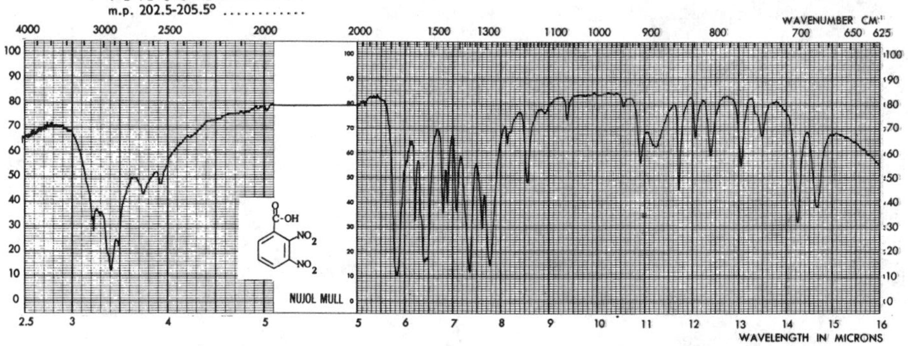

D
15,141-6 2,6-Dinitrobenzoic acid
$(O_2N)_2C_6H_3CO_2H$ M.W. 212.12
m.p. 205-208°

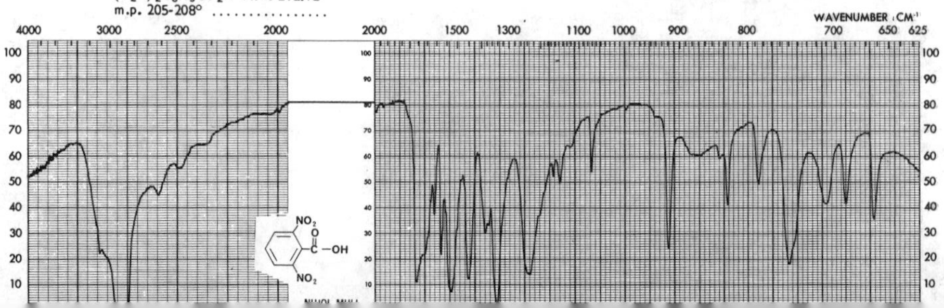

E
13,780-4 2-Nitroisophthalic acid
$O_2NC_6H_3$-1,3-$(CO_2H)_2$ M.W. 211.13
m.p. 317-320° (dec.)
NUJOL MULL

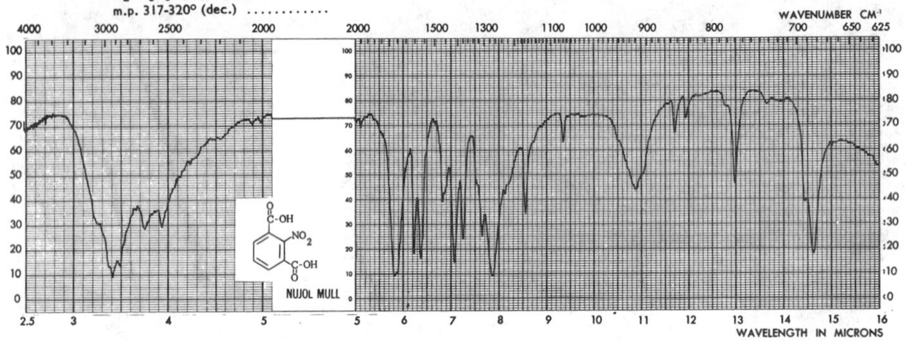

F
13,782-0 3-Nitrophthalic acid
$O_2NC_6H_3$-1,2-$(CO_2H)_2$ M.W. 211.13
m.p. 213-216° (dec.)
NUJOL MULL

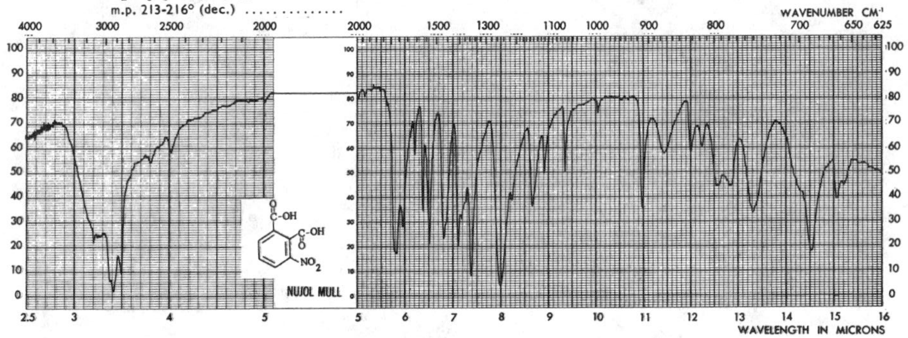

G
D14,940-3 3,4-Dimethylbenzoic acid
$(CH_3)_2C_6H_3CO_2H$ M.W. 150.18
m.p. 162-166°
NUJOL MULL

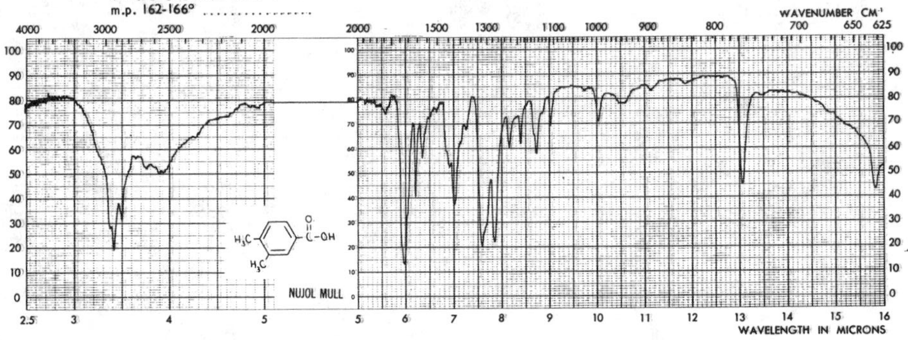

H
13,816-9 2,4-Dimethylbenzoic acid
$(CH_3)_2C_6H_3CO_2H$ M.W. 150.18
m.p. 122-124°

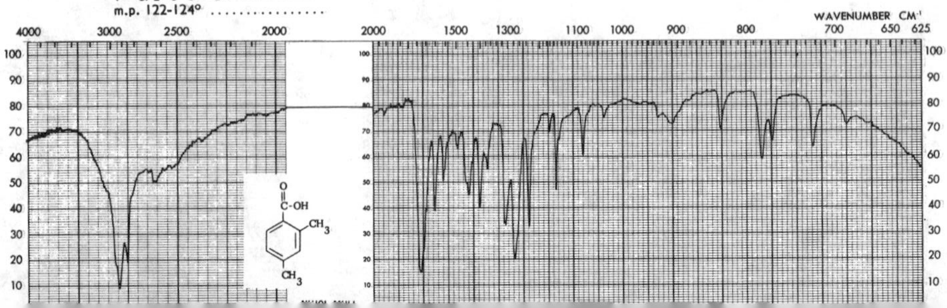

A

m.p. 132.5-134.5° ....

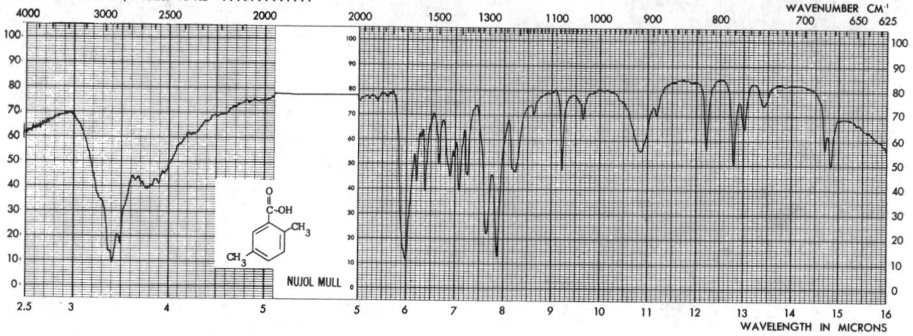

NUJOL MULL

B

F1060-7 3-Fluoro-4-methylbenzoic acid
$FC_6H_3(CH_3)CO_2H$ M.W. 154.14 m.p. 169-171°

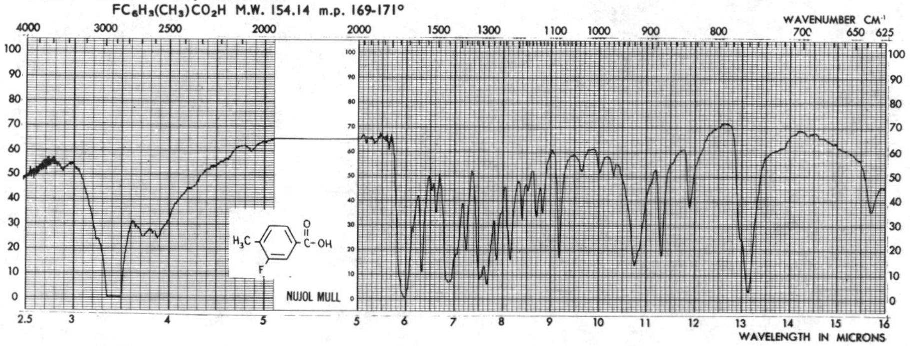

NUJOL MULL

C

13,957-2 2,4-Dichlorobenzoic acid
$Cl_2C_6H_3CO_2H$ M.W. 191.01 m.p. 157-160°

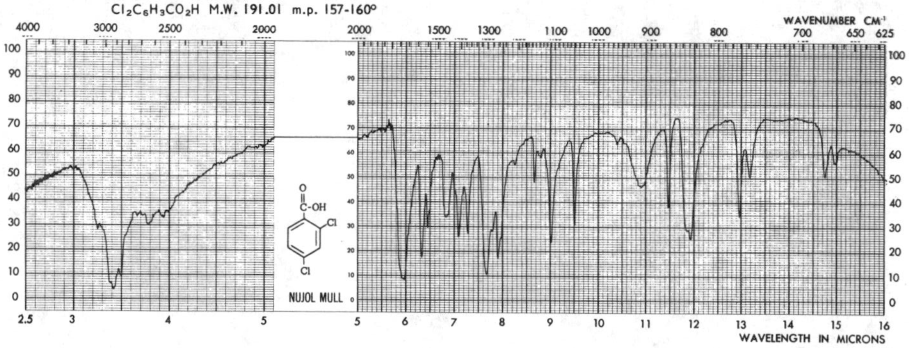

NUJOL MULL

D

20,631-8
4-Chlorophthalic acid, 99+%
ClC_6H_3-1,2-$(CO_2H)_2$ FW 200.58 mp 145-148°
Beil. 9,816 Disp. C

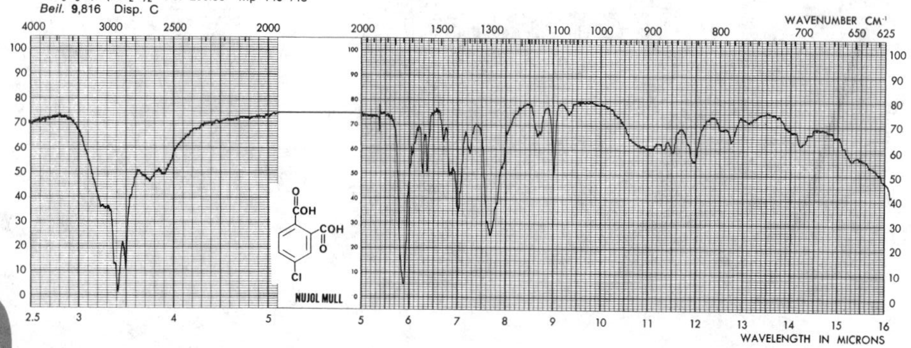

NUJOL MULL

E

14,493-2 3,4-Dichlorobenzoic acid, puriss.
$Cl_2C_6H_3CO_2H$ M.W. 191.01 m.p. 207-209°

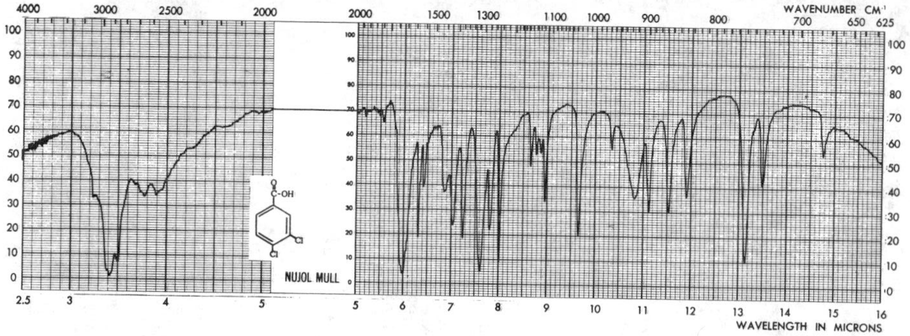

NUJOL MULL

F

14,494-0 2,5-Dichlorobenzoic acid, puriss.
$Cl_2C_6H_3CO_2H$ M.W. 191.01
m.p. 151-154° ....

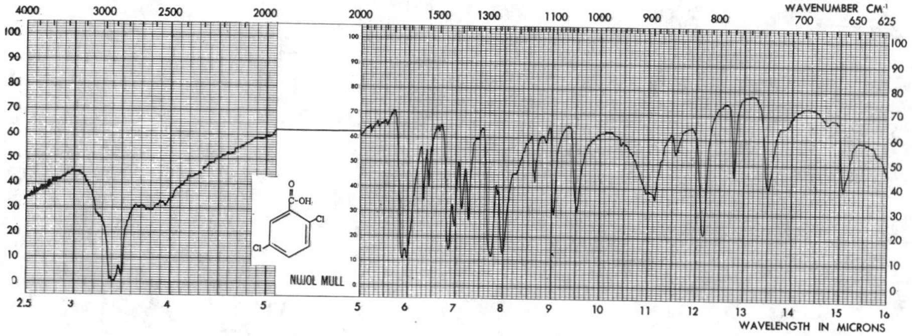

NUJOL MULL

G

17,554-4
5-Bromo-2-chlorobenzoic acid, 98%
$BrC_6H_3(Cl)CO_2H$
M.W. 235.47 m.p. 154-156° Beil. 9,356

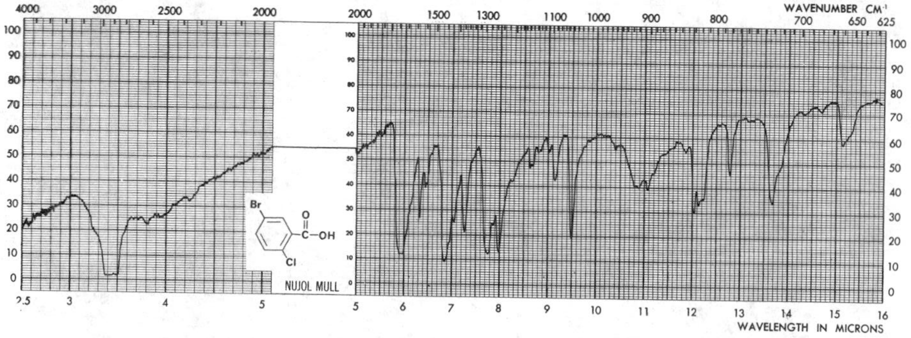

NUJOL MULL

H

M1505-2 3-Methoxy-4-methylbenzoic acid (4-methyl-m-anisic acid, 3-methoxy-p-toluic acid)
$CH_3OC_6H_3(CH_3)CO_2H$ M.W. 166.18
m.p. 157-159° ....

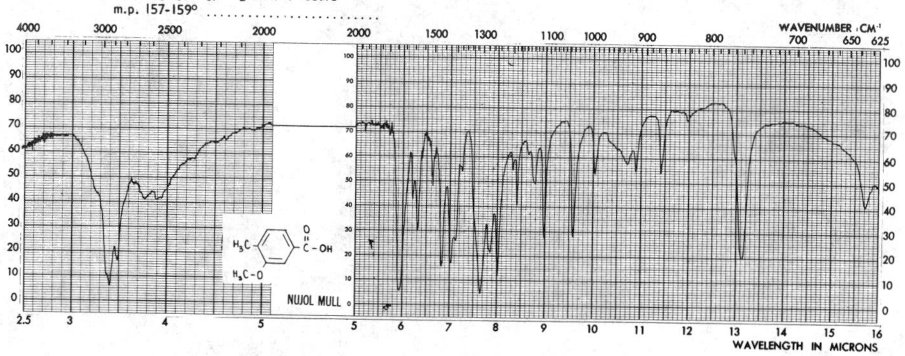

NUJOL MULL

ALDRICH

A 14,579-3 **4-Chloro-o-anisic acid** (4-chloro-2-methoxybenzoic acid)
$ClC_6H_3(OCH_3)CO_2H$ M.W. 186.59
m.p. 146-148°
NUJOL MULL

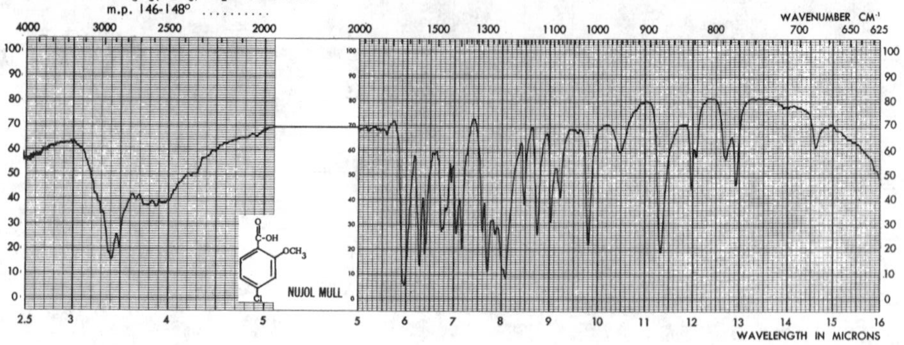

B D13,150-4 **2,4-Dimethoxybenzoic acid**
$(CH_3O)_2C_6H_3CO_2H$ M.W. 182.18
m.p. 108-110°
NUJOL MULL

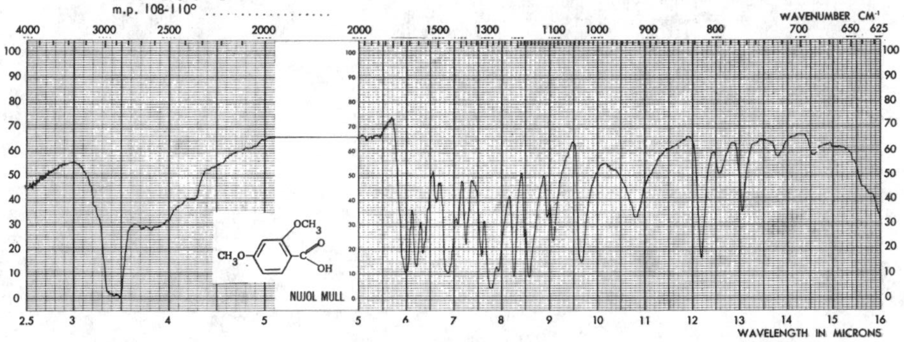

C D13,180-6 **3,4-Dimethoxybenzoic acid** (veratric acid), **puriss.**
$(CH_3O)_2C_6H_3CO_2H$ M.W. 182.18
m.p. 179-182°
NUJOL MULL

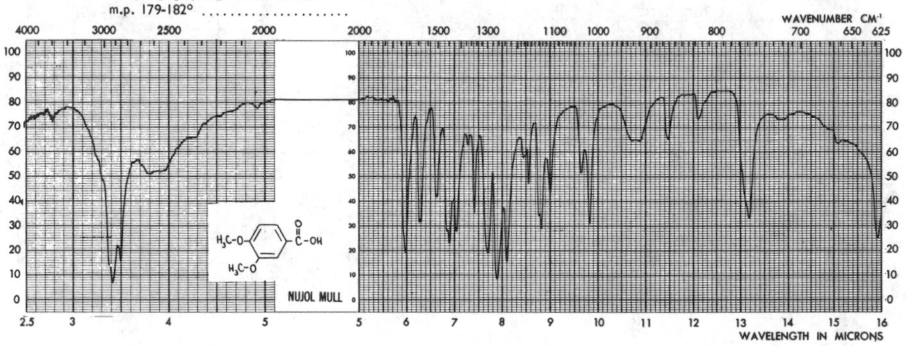

D 22,159-7
3,4-Diethoxybenzoic acid, 99%
$(C_2H_5O)_2C_6H_3CO_2H$ FW 210.23 mp 167-169°
Beil. **10**,395 Disp. C

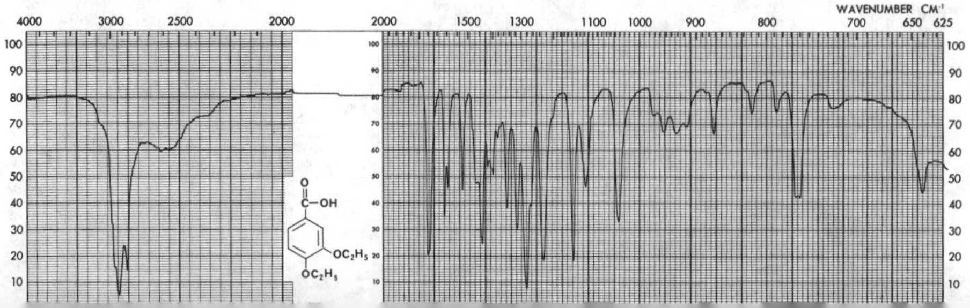

E P4980-5 **Piperonylic acid**
M.W. 166.13 m.p. 229-231°
NUJOL MULL

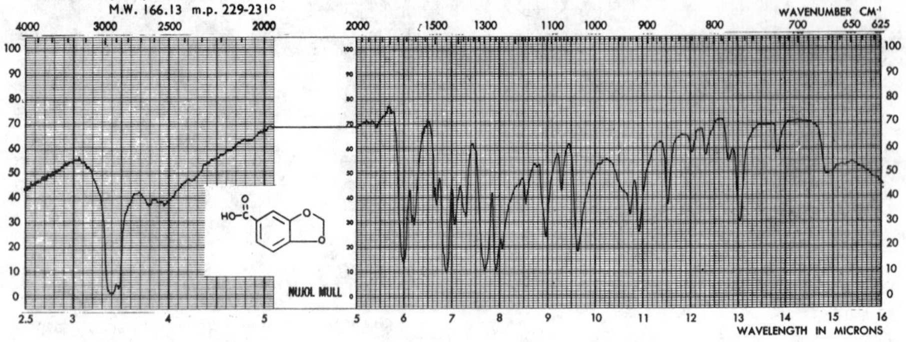

F H3,850-0
3-Hydroxy-4-methylbenzoic acid, 99%
$HOC_6H_3(CH_3)CO_2H$
M.W. 152.15 m.p. 207-209° Beil. **10**,237
NUJOL MULL

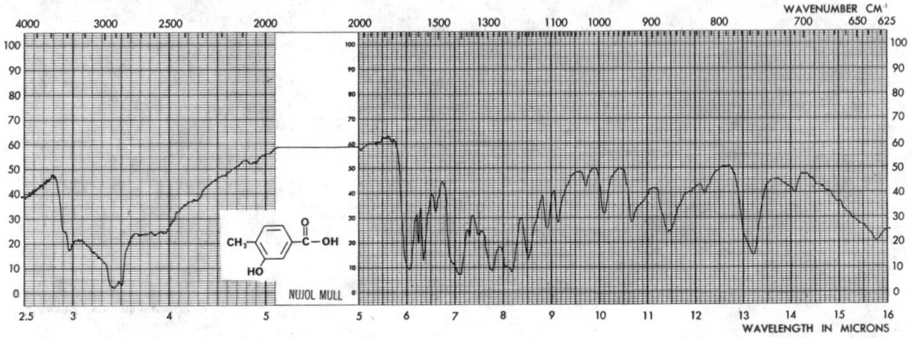

G 14,616-1 **5-Methylsalicylic acid** (2-hydroxy-5-methylbenzoic acid)
$CH_3C_6H_3(OH)CO_2H$
M.W. 152.15
NUJOL MULL

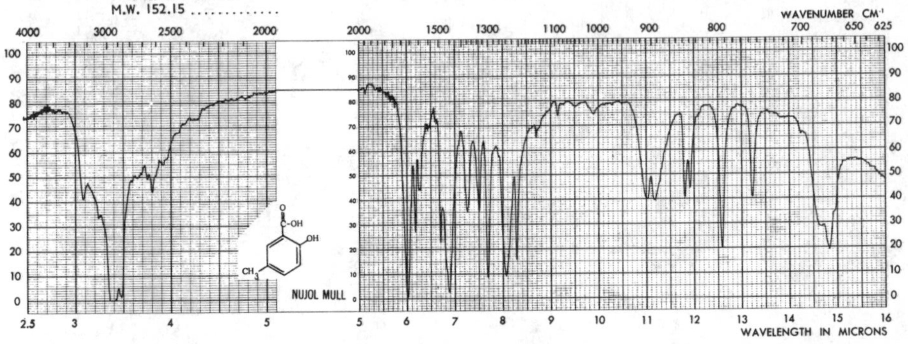

H 14,903-9 **5-tert.-Octylsalicylic acid** [5-(1,1,3,3-tetramethylbutyl)-salicylic acid]
$(CH_3)_3CCH_2C(CH_3)_2C_6H_3$-2-$(OH)CO_2H$ M.W. 250.34
m.p. 155-157°

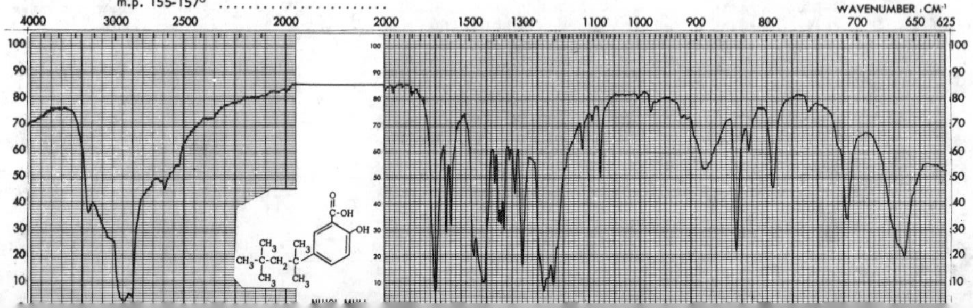

WAVENUMBER CM^{-1} / WAVELENGTH IN MICRONS

A

m.p. 177-179°

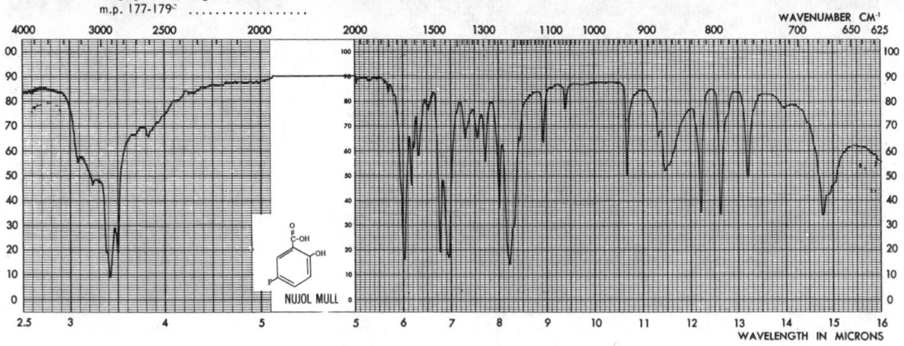

NUJOL MULL

B

C7090-8 5-Chlorosalicylic acid
ClC_6H_3-2-(OH)CO_2H M.W. 172.57
m.p. 171.5-172°

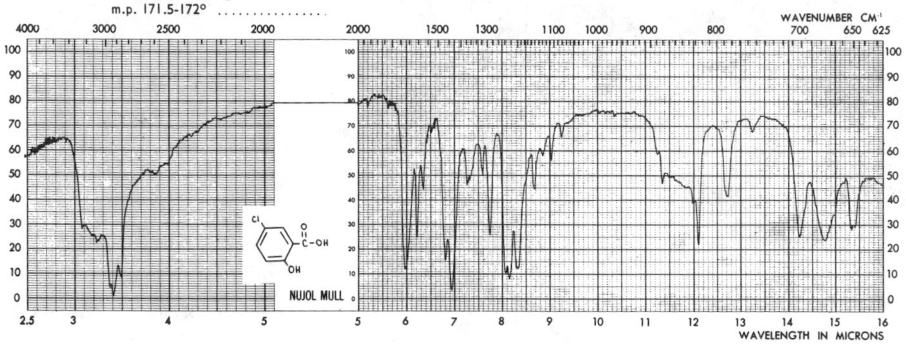

NUJOL MULL

C

18,378-4
4-Chlorosalicylic acid, 98%
ClC_6H_3-2-(OH)CO_2H FW 172.57 mp 210-212°
Beil. **10**,101 Disp. C

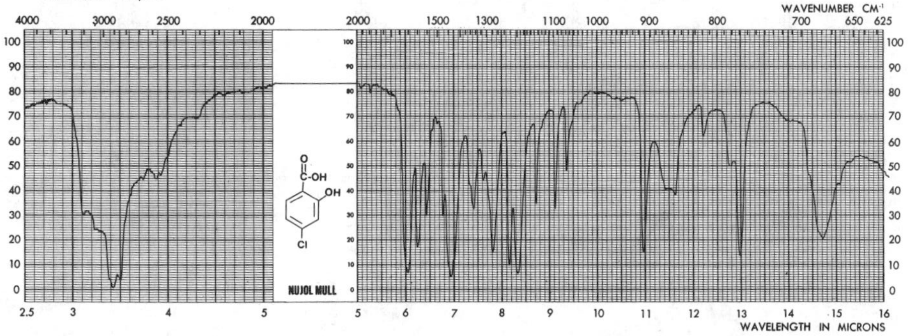

NUJOL MULL

D

C4460-5 3-Chloro-4-hydroxybenzoic acid, puriss.
$ClC_6H_3(OH)CO_2H$ M.W. 172.57
m.p. 170-172°

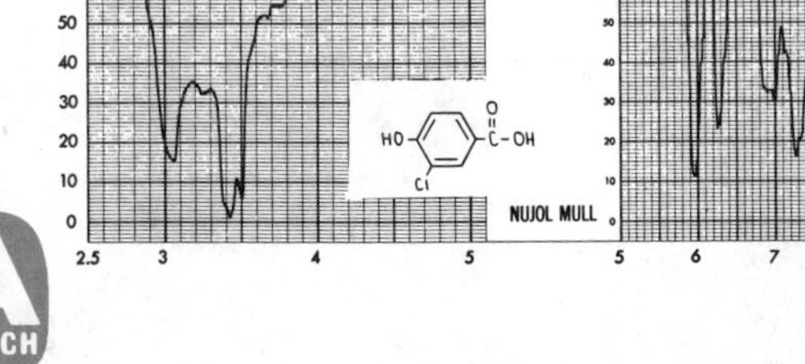

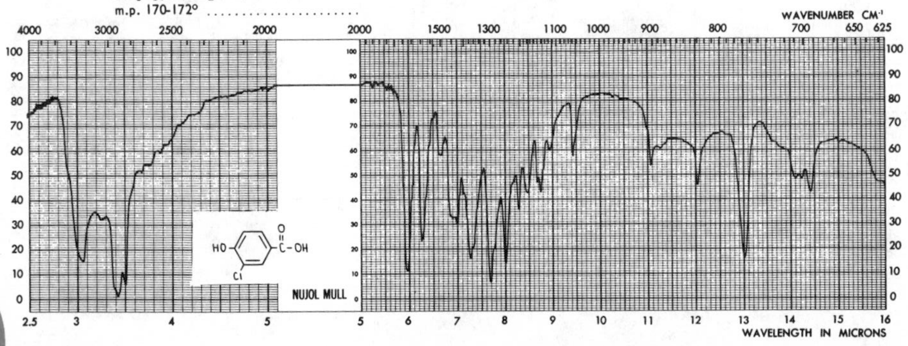

NUJOL MULL

E

BrC_6H_3-2-(OH)CO_2H M.W. 217.03
m.p. 164-166°

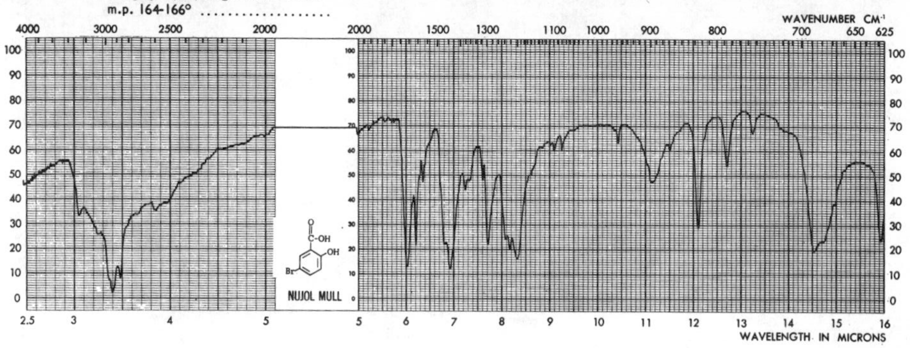

NUJOL MULL

F

I-1060-0 5-Iodosalicylic acid, tech.
IC_6H_3-2-(OH)CO_2H M.W. 264.02

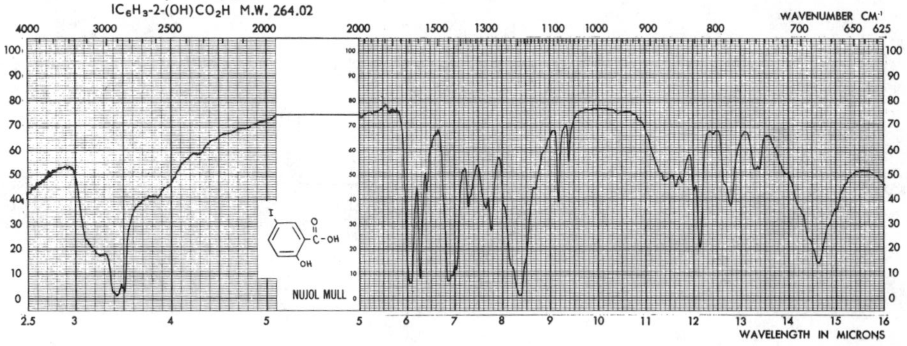

NUJOL MULL

G

15,452-0 5-(Methylthio)-salicylic acid
$CH_3SC_6H_3$-2-(OH)CO_2H M.W. 184.21
m.p. 123-124°

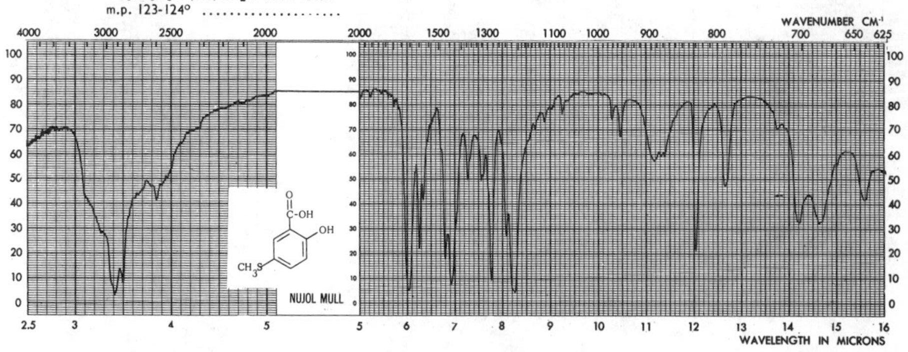

NUJOL MULL

H

14,618-8 5-Methoxysalicylic acid (2-hydroxy-5-methoxybenzoic acid)
$CH_3OC_6H_3(OH)CO_2H$ M.W. 168.15
m.p. 141-143°

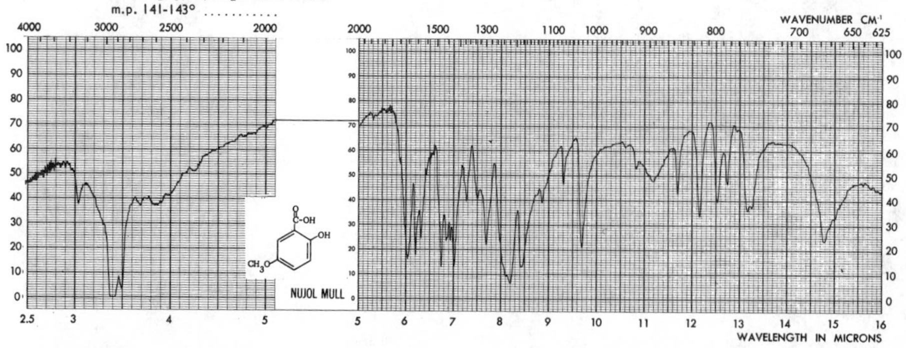

NUJOL MULL

ALDRICH

A

17,347-9
4-Methoxysalicylic acid, 99% (2-hydroxy-4-methoxybenzoic acid)
$CH_3OC_6H_3(OH)CO_2H$ FW 168.15 mp 158-159°
Beil. **10**,379 Disp. C

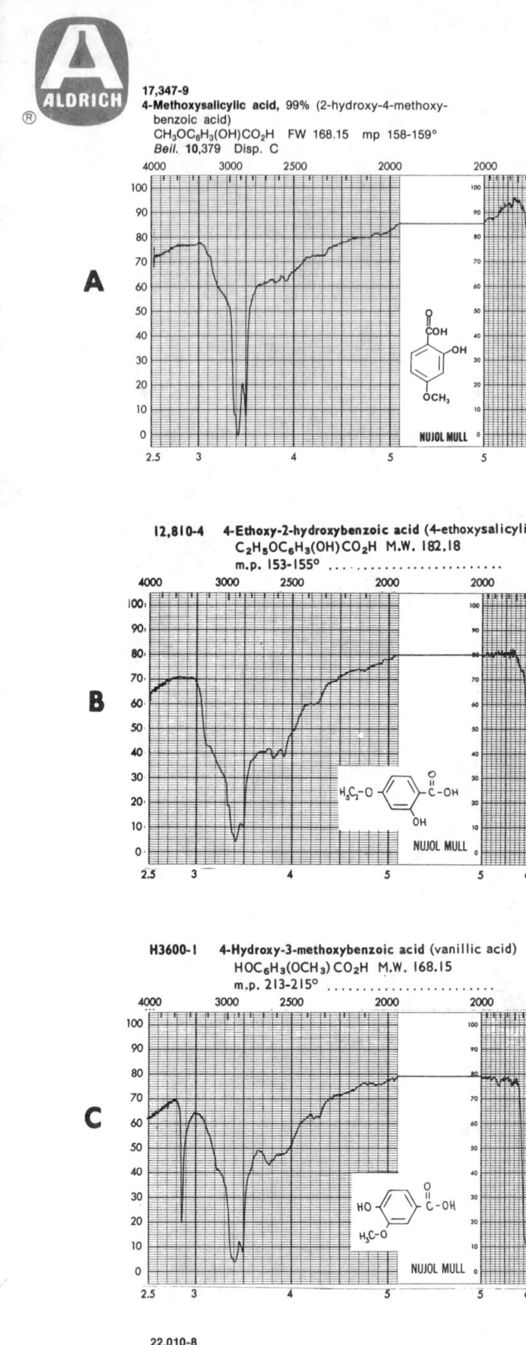

B

12,810-4 **4-Ethoxy-2-hydroxybenzoic acid** (4-ethoxysalicylic acid)
$C_2H_5OC_6H_3(OH)CO_2H$ M.W. 182.18
m.p. 153-155°

C

H3600-1 **4-Hydroxy-3-methoxybenzoic acid** (vanillic acid)
$HOC_6H_3(OCH_3)CO_2H$ M.W. 168.15
m.p. 213-215°

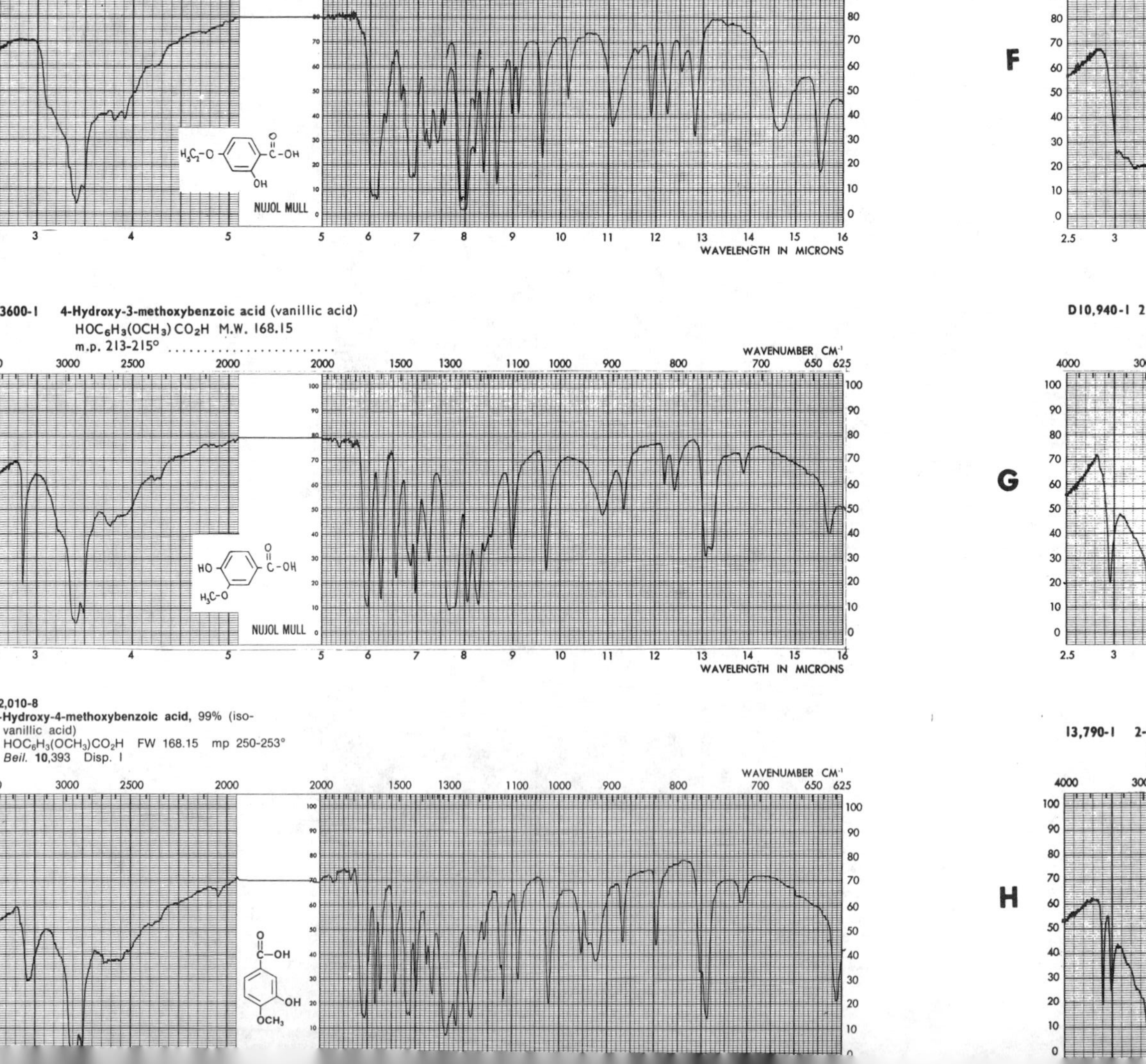

D

22,010-8
3-Hydroxy-4-methoxybenzoic acid, 99% (isovanillic acid)
$HOC_6H_3(OCH_3)CO_2H$ FW 168.15 mp 250-253°
Beil. **10**,393 Disp. I

E

D10,980-0 **3,4-Dihydroxybenzoic acid** (protocatechuic acid)
$(HO)_2C_6H_3CO_2H$ M.W. 154.12 m.p. 200-202°

F

14,935-7 **2,5-Dihydroxybenzoic acid** (gentisic acid)
$(HO)_2C_6H_3CO_2H$ M.W. 154.12
m.p. 205° (dec.)

G

D10,940-1 **2,4-Dihydroxybenzoic acid** (β-resorcylic acid)
$(HO)_2C_6H_3CO_2H$ M.W. 154.12
m.p. 225-227°

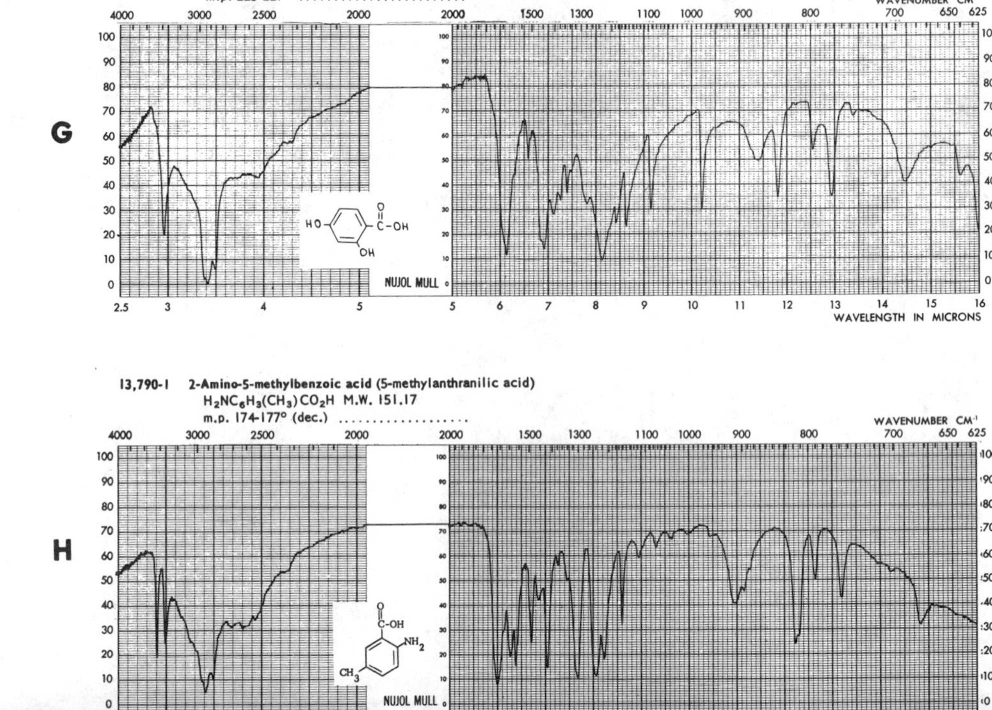

H

13,790-1 **2-Amino-5-methylbenzoic acid (5-methylanthranilic acid)**
$H_2NC_6H_3(CH_3)CO_2H$ M.W. 151.17
m.p. 174-177° (dec.)

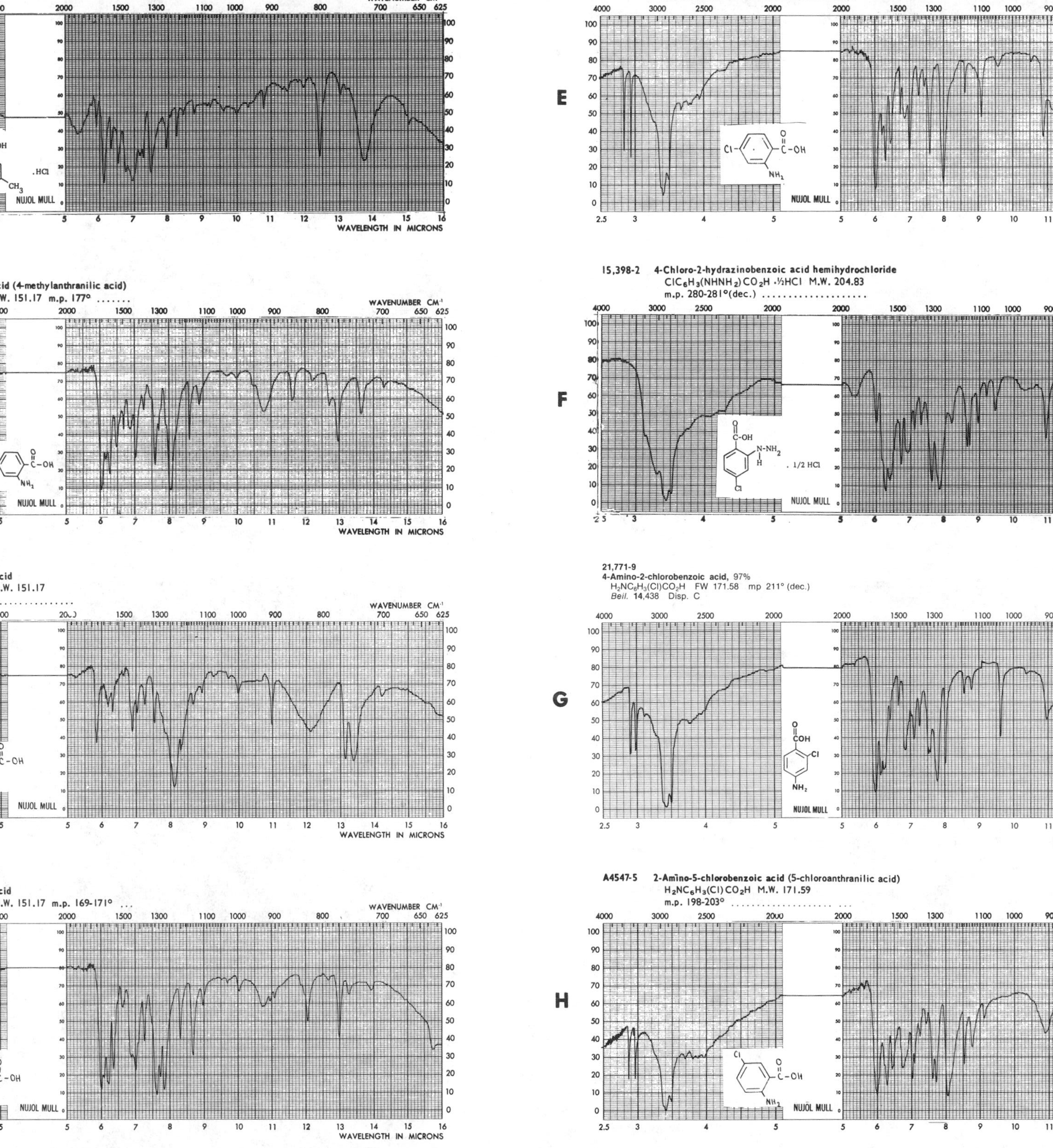

A
m.p. 215° (dec.)

B
12,299-8 2-Amino-4-methylbenzoic acid (4-methylanthranilic acid)
$H_2NC_6H_3(CH_3)CO_2H$ M.W. 151.17 m.p. 177°

C
A6280-9 3-Amino-4-methylbenzoic acid
$H_2NC_6H_3(CH_3)CO_2H$ M.W. 151.17
m.p. 163-165°

D
A6300-7 4-Amino-3-methylbenzoic acid
$H_2NC_6H_3(CH_3)CO_2H$ M.W. 151.17 m.p. 169-171°

E
m.p. 238-239°

F
15,398-2 4-Chloro-2-hydrazinobenzoic acid hemihydrochloride
$ClC_6H_3(NHNH_2)CO_2H \cdot ½HCl$ M.W. 204.83
m.p. 280-281°(dec.)

G
21,771-9
4-Amino-2-chlorobenzoic acid, 97%
$H_2NC_6H_3(Cl)CO_2H$ FW 171.58 mp 211° (dec.)
Beil. 14,438 Disp. C

H
A4547-5 2-Amino-5-chlorobenzoic acid (5-chloroanthranilic acid)
$H_2NC_6H_3(Cl)CO_2H$ M.W. 171.59
m.p. 198-203°

A A5960-3 **2-Amino-5-iodobenzoic acid** (5-iodoanthranilic acid)
$H_2NC_6H_3(I)CO_2H$ M.W. 263.03
m.p. 219-221° (dec.)

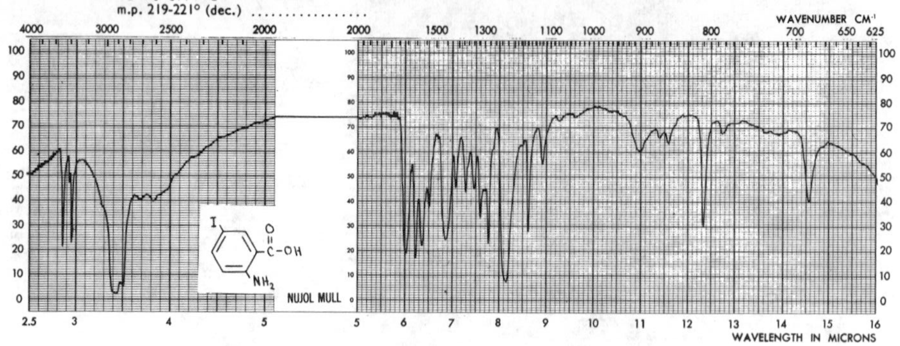

NUJOL MULL

B 12,286-6 **5-Amino-2-chlorobenzoic acid sulfate, tech.**
$H_2NC_6H_3(Cl)CO_2H{\cdot}H_2SO_4$ M.W. 269.66
m.p. 230-232°

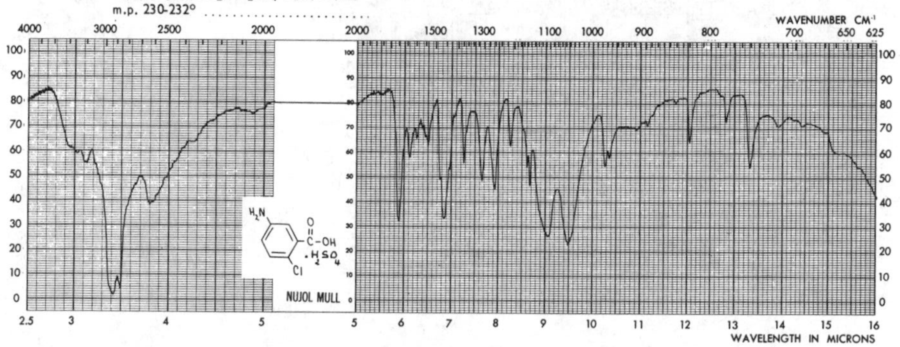

NUJOL MULL

C A7980-9 **5-Aminosalicylic acid, tech.**
$H_2NC_6H_3$-2-(OH)CO_2H M.W. 153.14 m.p. 290°

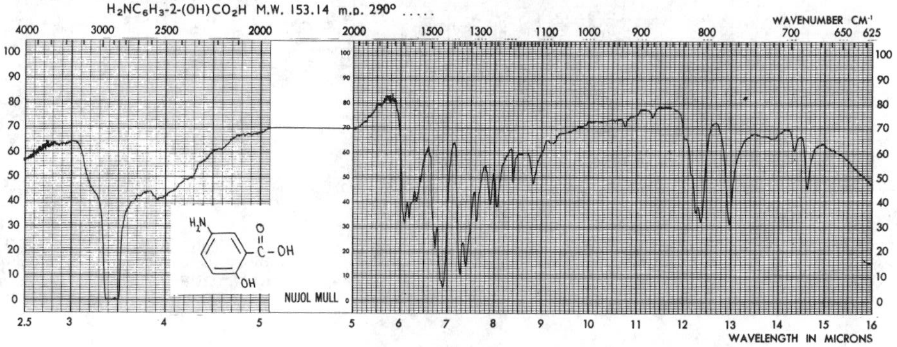

NUJOL MULL

D A7960-4 **4-Aminosalicylic acid**
$H_2NC_6H_3$-2-(OH)CO_2H M.W. 153.14
m.p. 147°

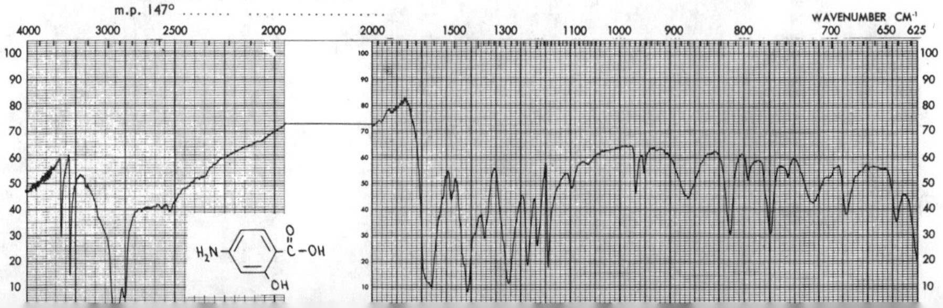

E 14,653-6 **4-Dimethylaminosalicylic acid**
$(CH_3)_2NC_6H_3$-2-(OH)CO_2H M.W. 181.19
m.p. 142° (dec.)

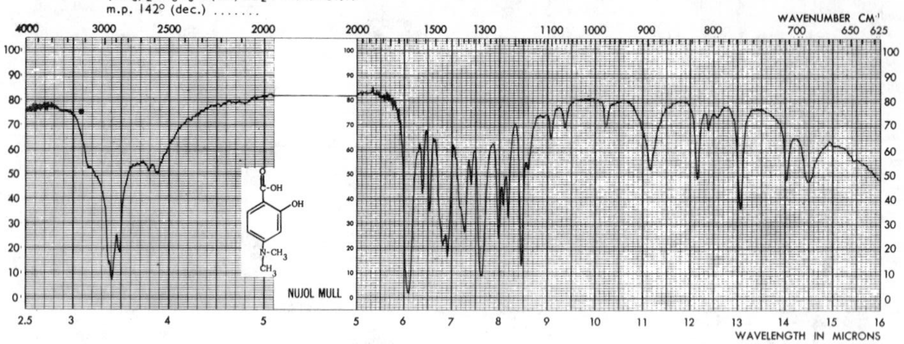

NUJOL MULL

F 14,639-0 **4-Diethylaminosalicylic acid**
$(C_2H_5)_2NC_6H_3$-2-(OH)CO_2H M.W. 209.25
m.p. 137° (dec.)

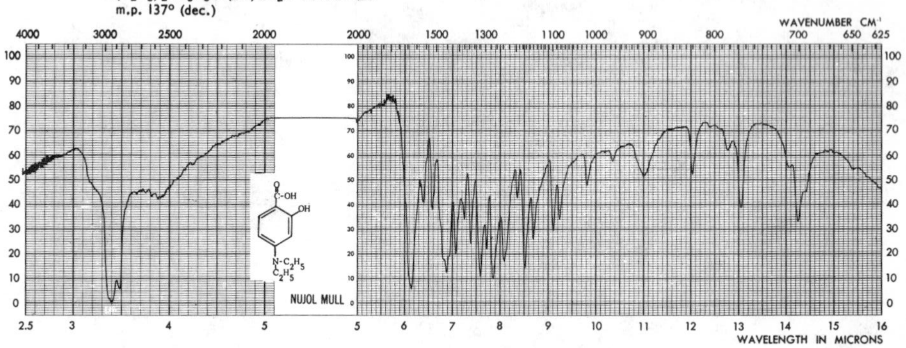

NUJOL MULL

G 18,606-6
3-Amino-4-methoxybenzoic acid, 98+%
$H_2NC_6H_3(OCH_3)CO_2H$ FW 167.16 mp 239-241°
Beil. 14(1),657 Disp. C

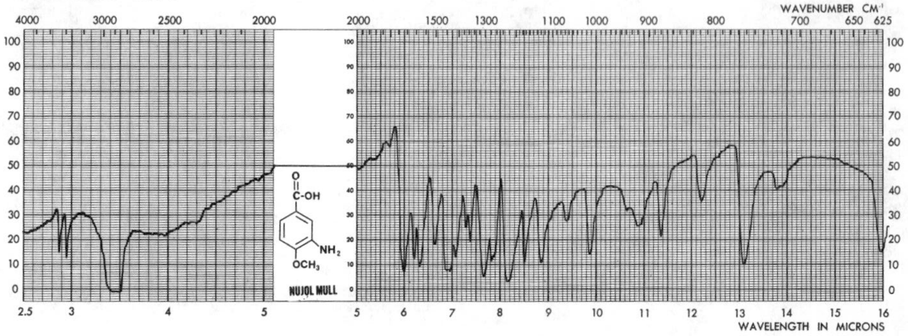

NUJOL MULL

H A6850-5 **5-Amino-2-nitrobenzoic acid, moist, 70%**
$H_2NC_6H_3(NO_2)CO_2H$ M.W. 182.14 (dry)
m.p. 230° (dec.)

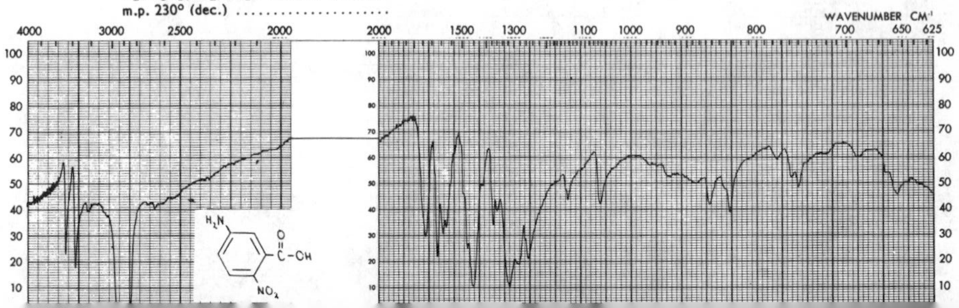

$(H_2N)_2C_6H_3CO_2H$ M.W. 152.15
m.p. 215-218° (dec.)

11,340-9 **3-Methyl-6-nitrobenzoic acid**
$CH_3C_6H_3(NO_2)CO_2H$ M.W. 181.15 m.p. 134-136°

15,140-8 **4-Methyl-3-nitrobenzoic acid** (3-nitro-p-toluic acid)
$CH_3C_6H_3(NO_2)CO_2H$ M.W. 181.15 m.p. 187-190.5°

M6060-0 **3-Methyl-4-nitrobenzoic acid**
$CH_3C_6H_3(NO_2)CO_2H$ M.W. 181.15
m.p. 216-218°

$CH_3C_6H_3(NO_2)CO_2H$
M.W. 181.15 m.p. 178-180° Beil. 9,471

11,545-2 **4-Fluoro-2-nitrobenzoic acid**
$FC_6H_3(NO_2)CO_2H$ M.W. 185.11
m.p. 146-147°

C5980-7 **4-Chloro-2-nitrobenzoic acid**
$ClC_6H_3(NO_2)CO_2H$ M.W. 201.57
m.p. 140-143°

C5960-2 **2-Chloro-4-nitrobenzoic acid**
$ClC_6H_3(NO_2)CO_2H$ M.W. 201.57 m.p. 136-140°

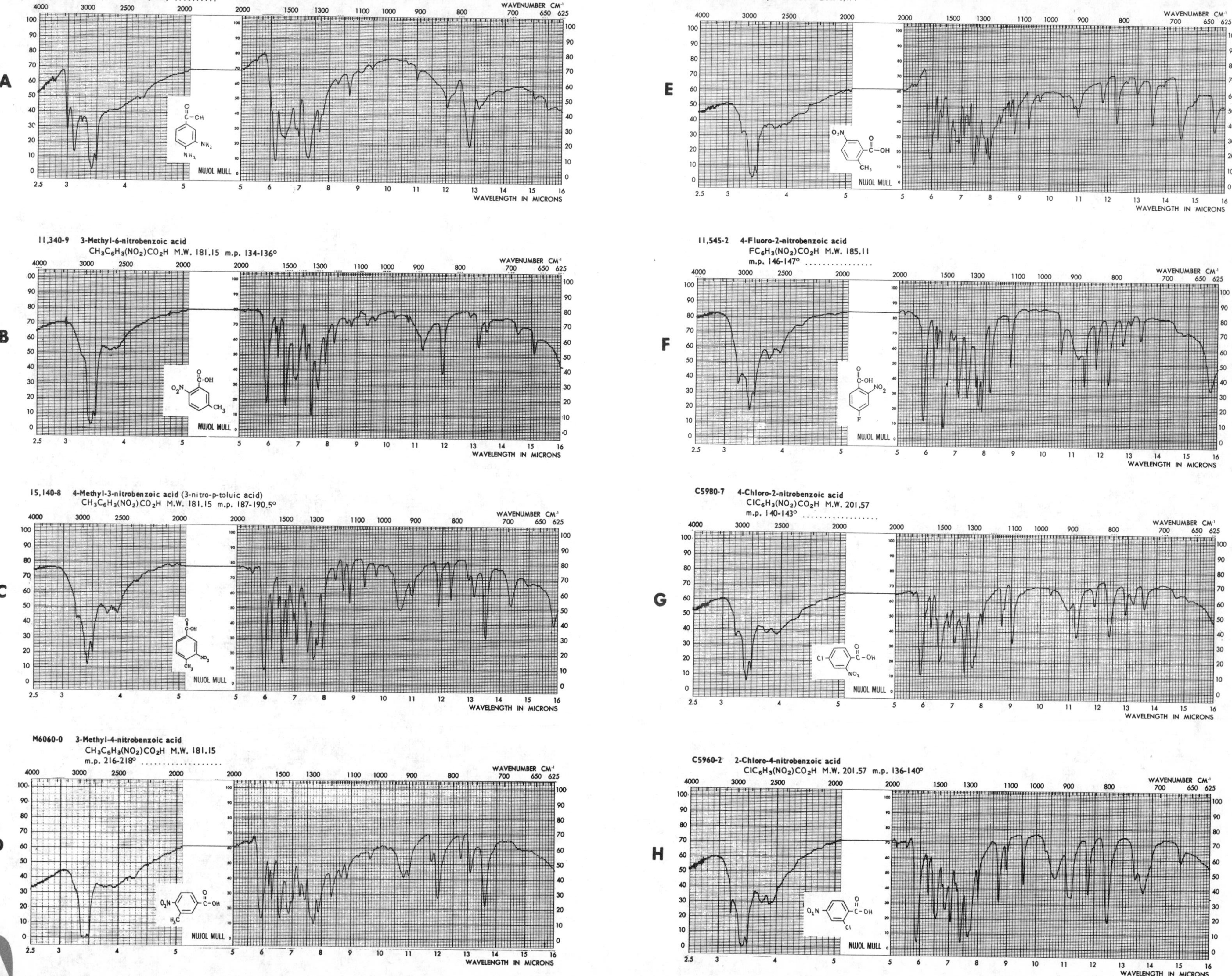

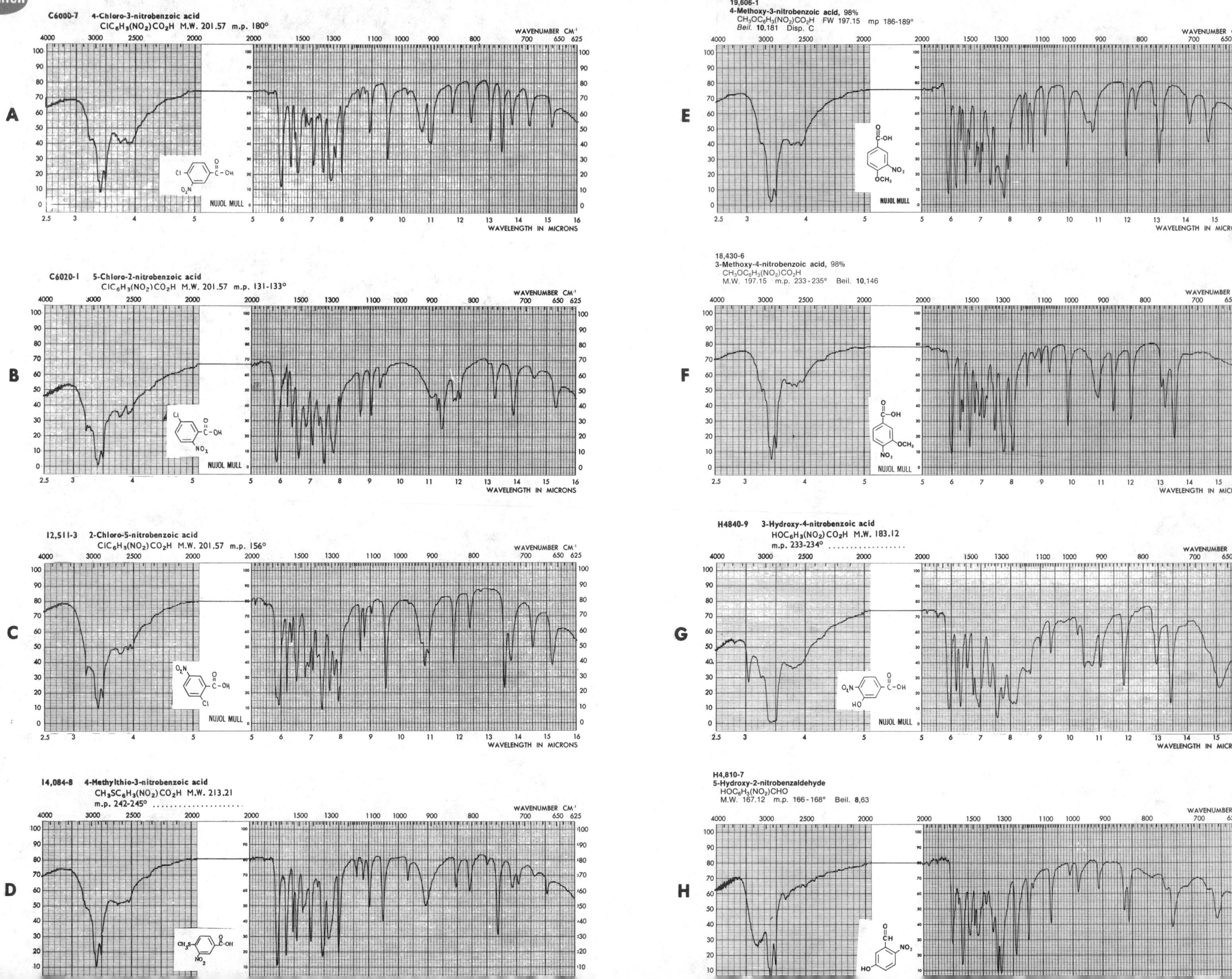

A — C6000-7 4-Chloro-3-nitrobenzoic acid
$ClC_6H_3(NO_2)CO_2H$ M.W. 201.57 m.p. 180°
NUJOL MULL

B — C6020-1 5-Chloro-2-nitrobenzoic acid
$ClC_6H_3(NO_2)CO_2H$ M.W. 201.57 m.p. 131-133°
NUJOL MULL

C — 12,511-3 2-Chloro-5-nitrobenzoic acid
$ClC_6H_3(NO_2)CO_2H$ M.W. 201.57 m.p. 156°
NUJOL MULL

D — 14,084-8 4-Methylthio-3-nitrobenzoic acid
$CH_3SC_6H_3(NO_2)CO_2H$ M.W. 213.21
m.p. 242-245°

E — 19,606-1
4-Methoxy-3-nitrobenzoic acid, 98%
$CH_3OC_6H_3(NO_2)CO_2H$ FW 197.15 mp 186-189°
Beil. 10,181 Disp. C
NUJOL MULL

F — 18,430-6
3-Methoxy-4-nitrobenzoic acid, 98%
$CH_3OC_6H_3(NO_2)CO_2H$
M.W. 197.15 m.p. 233-235° Beil. 10,146
NUJOL MULL

G — H4840-9 3-Hydroxy-4-nitrobenzoic acid
$HOC_6H_3(NO_2)CO_2H$ M.W. 183.12
m.p. 233-234°
NUJOL MULL

H — H4,810-7
5-Hydroxy-2-nitrobenzaldehyde
$HOC_6H_3(NO_2)CHO$
M.W. 167.12 m.p. 166-168° Beil. 8,63

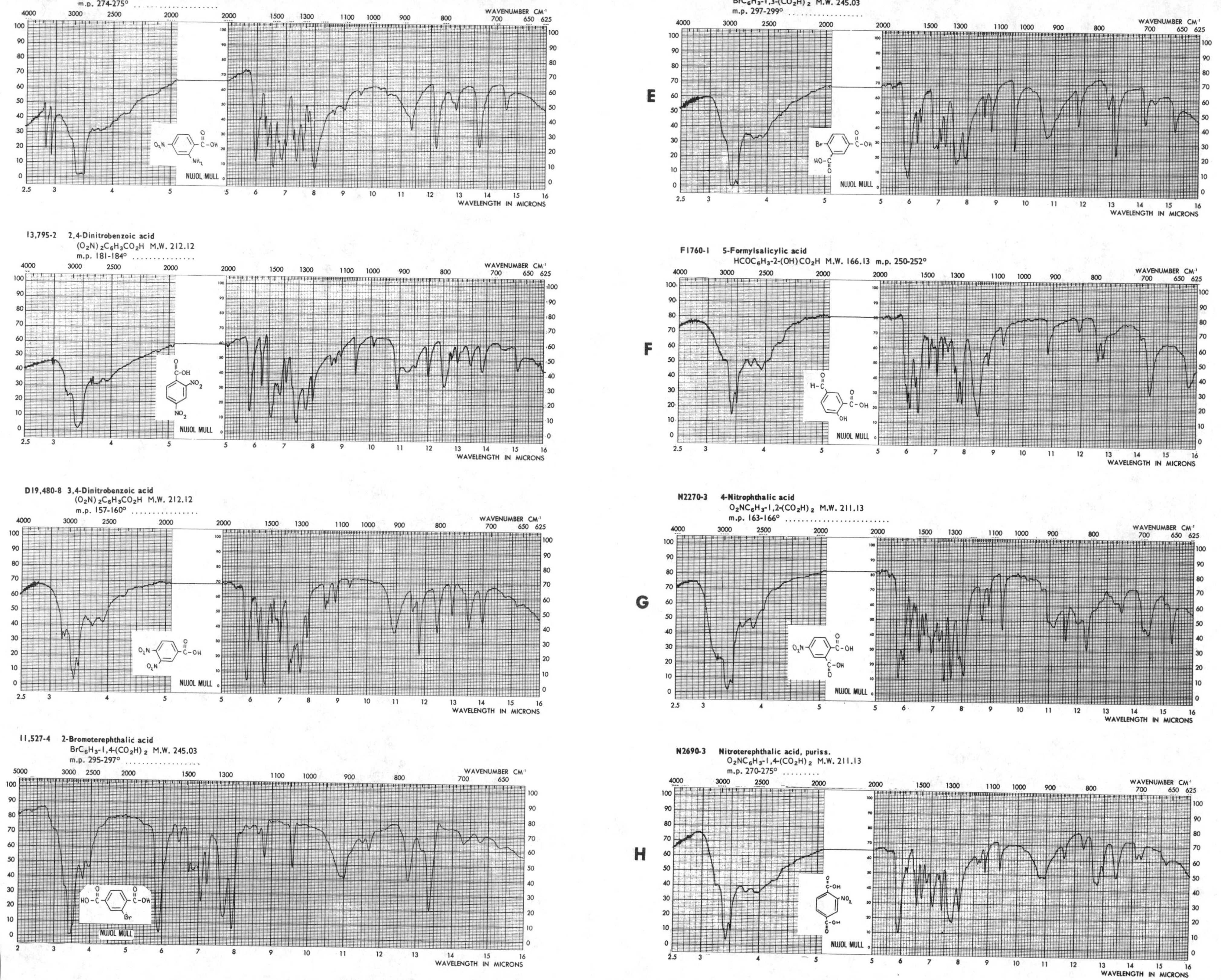

A
$O_2NC_6H_3$-2-$(NH_2)CO_2H$ M.W. 182.14
m.p. 274-275°
NUJOL MULL
B
13,795-2 2,4-Dinitrobenzoic acid
$(O_2N)_2C_6H_3CO_2H$ M.W. 212.12
m.p. 181-184°
NUJOL MULL
C
D19,480-8 3,4-Dinitrobenzoic acid
$(O_2N)_2C_6H_3CO_2H$ M.W. 212.12
m.p. 157-160°
NUJOL MULL
D
11,527-4 2-Bromoterephthalic acid
BrC_6H_3-1,4-$(CO_2H)_2$ M.W. 245.03
m.p. 295-297°
NUJOL MULL
E
4-Bromoisophthalic acid
BrC_6H_3-1,3-$(CO_2H)_2$ M.W. 245.03
m.p. 297-299°
NUJOL MULL
F
F1760-1 5-Formylsalicylic acid
$HCOC_6H_3$-2-$(OH)CO_2H$ M.W. 166.13 m.p. 250-252°
NUJOL MULL
G
N2270-3 4-Nitrophthalic acid
$O_2NC_6H_3$-1,2-$(CO_2H)_2$ M.W. 211.13
m.p. 163-166°
NUJOL MULL
H
N2690-3 Nitroterephthalic acid, puriss.
$O_2NC_6H_3$-1,4-$(CO_2H)_2$ M.W. 211.13
m.p. 270-275°
NUJOL MULL
WAVENUMBER CM⁻¹
WAVELENGTH IN MICRONS
ALDRICH

A — 18,376-8 p-Phenylenedipropionic acid, 98%
$C_6H_4(CH_2CH_2CO_2H)_2$ M.W. 222.24 m.p. 231-234°

B — D14,960-8 3,5-Dimethylbenzoic acid
$(CH_3)_2C_6H_3CO_2H$ M.W. 150.18 m.p. 168-171°

C — D5750-7 3,5-Dichlorobenzoic acid
$Cl_2C_6H_3CO_2H$ M.W. 191.01 m.p. 180-184°

D — D13,200-4 3,5-Dimethoxybenzoic acid
$(CH_3O)_2C_6H_3CO_2H$ M.W. 182.18
m.p. 182-184°

E — D11,000-0 3,5-Dihydroxybenzoic acid (α-resorcylic acid)
$(HO)_2C_6H_3CO_2H$ M.W. 154.12 m.p. 236-238°

F — D1280-5 3,5-Diaminobenzoic acid
$(H_2N)_2C_6H_3CO_2H$ M.W. 152.15
m.p. 235-238°

G — 11,383-2 3,5-Diaminobenzoic acid dihydrochloride, puriss. (for the analysis of DNA and sialic acid)
$(H_2N)_2C_6H_3CO_2H{\cdot}2HCl$ M.W. 225.08
m.p. > 300°

H — 12,125-8 3,5-Dinitrobenzoic acid
$(O_2N)_2C_6H_3CO_2H$ M.W. 212.12
m.p. 202.5-206°

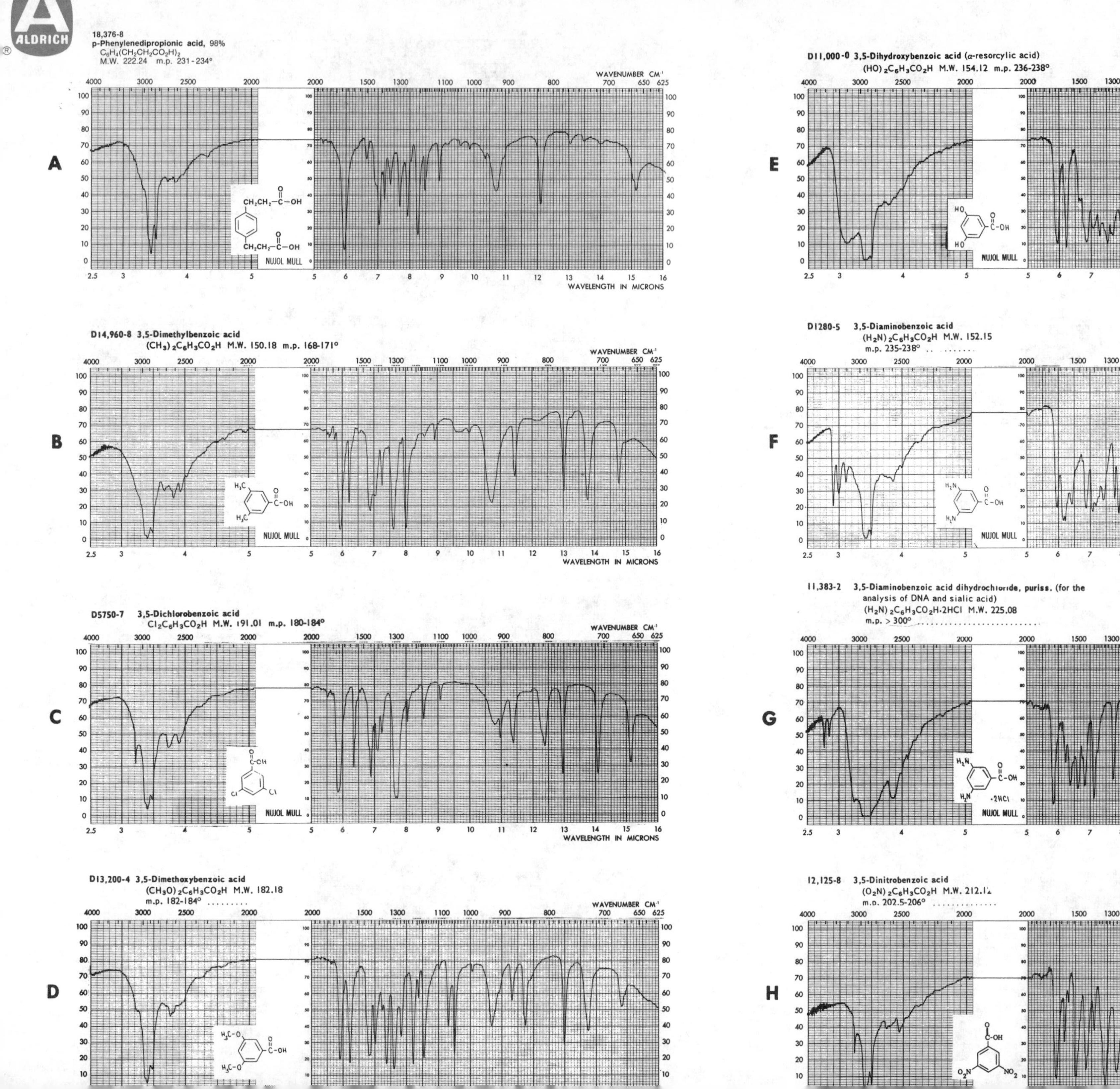

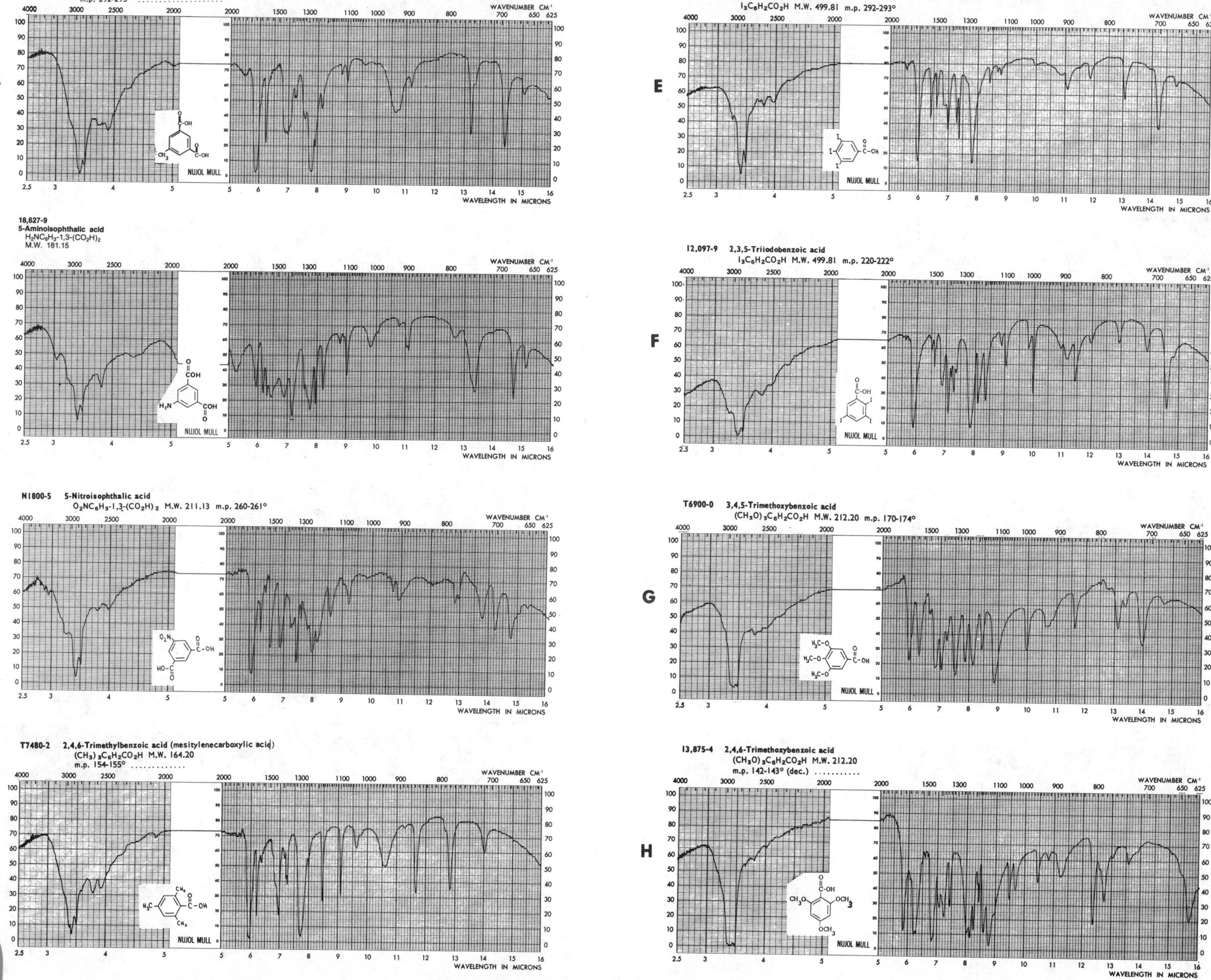

A
CH3C6H3-1,3-(CO2H)2 M.W. 180.16
m.p. 292-295°
B
18,627-9
5-Aminoisophthalic acid
H2NC6H3-1,3-(CO2H)2
M.W. 181.15
C
N1800-5 5-Nitroisophthalic acid
O2NC6H3-1,3-(CO2H)2 M.W. 211.13 m.p. 260-261°
D
T7480-2 2,4,6-Trimethylbenzoic acid (mesitylenecarboxylic acid)
(CH3)3C6H2CO2H M.W. 164.20
m.p. 154-155°
E
T6700-8 3,4,5-Triiodobenzoic acid
I3C6H2CO2H M.W. 499.81 m.p. 292-293°
F
12,097-9 2,3,5-Triiodobenzoic acid
I3C6H2CO2H M.W. 499.81 m.p. 220-222°
G
T6900-0 3,4,5-Trimethoxybenzoic acid
(CH3O)3C6H2CO2H M.W. 212.20 m.p. 170-174°
H
13,875-4 2,4,6-Trimethoxybenzoic acid
(CH3O)3C6H2CO2H M.W. 212.20
m.p. 142-143° (dec.)
NUJOL MULL
WAVENUMBER CM⁻¹
WAVELENGTH IN MICRONS
ALDRICH

AROMATIC CARBOXYLIC ACIDS

A

14,914-4 3-tert.-Butyl-5-methylsalicylic acid
$(CH_3)_3CC_6H_2(CH_3)$-2-(OH)CO_2H M.W. 208.26
m.p. 197-199°

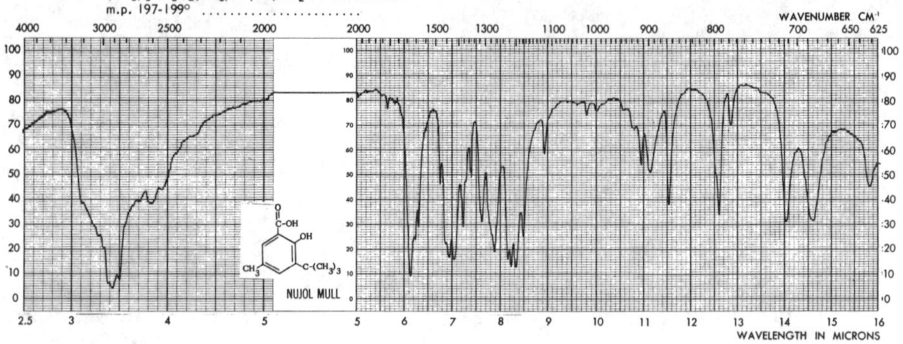

NUJOL MULL

B

14,640-4
3-*tert*.-Butyl-6-methylsalicylic acid, 98%
$(CH_3)_3CC_6H_2(CH_3)$-2-(OH)CO_2H
M.W. 208.26 m.p. 179-181°

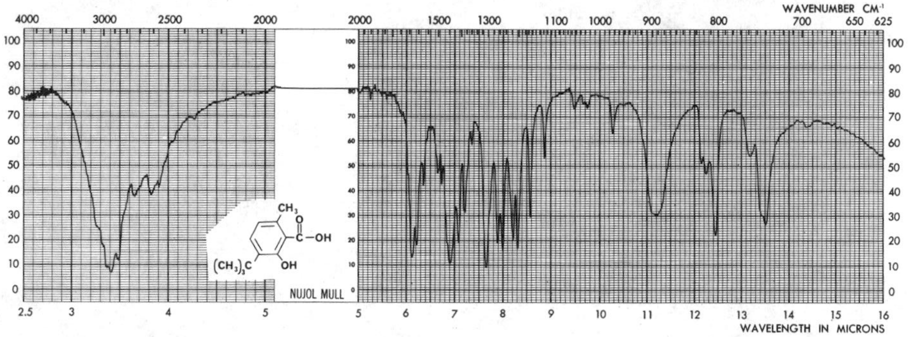

NUJOL MULL

C

13,569-0 3,5-Diisopropylsalicylic acid
$[(CH_3)_2CH]_2C_6H_2$-2-(OH)CO_2H M.W. 222.29
m.p. 117-119°

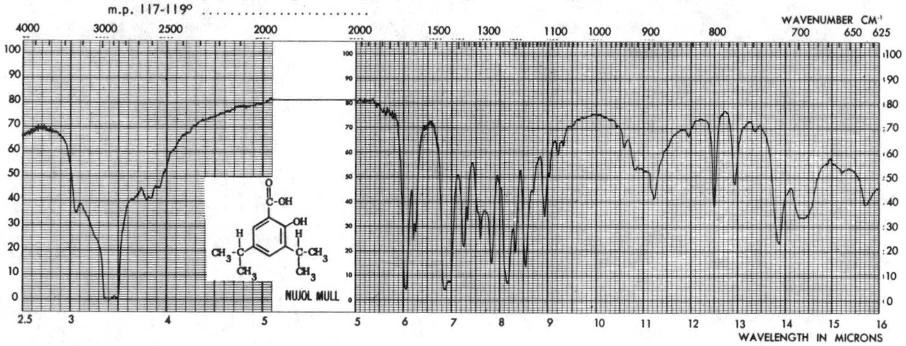

NUJOL MULL

D

14,913-6 3,5-Di-tert.-butylsalicylic acid
$[(CH_3)_3C]_2C_6H_2$-2-(OH)CO_2H M.W. 250.34
m.p. 161-164°

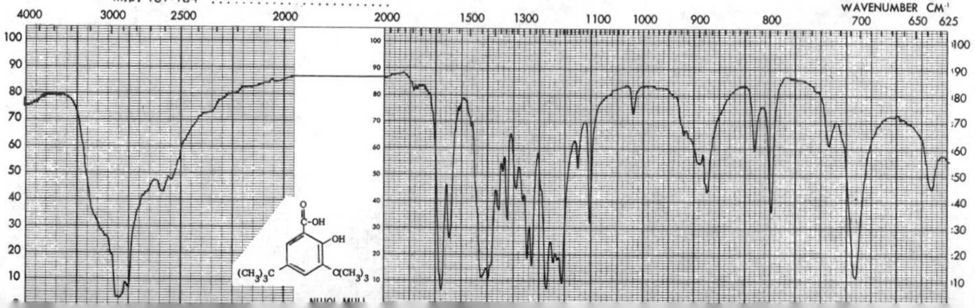

NUJOL MULL

E

14,547-5 3,5-Dimethyl-4-hydroxybenzoic acid
$HOC_6H_2(CH_3)_2CO_2H$ M.W. 166.18
m.p. 221-223°

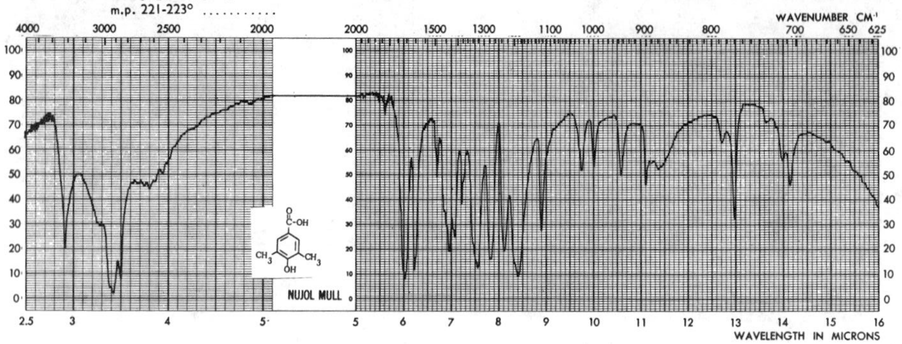

NUJOL MULL

F

14,347-2 3,5-Di-tert.-butyl-4-hydroxybenzoic acid
$[(CH_3)_3C]_2C_6H_2(OH)CO_2H$ M.W. 250.34
m.p. 214-216°

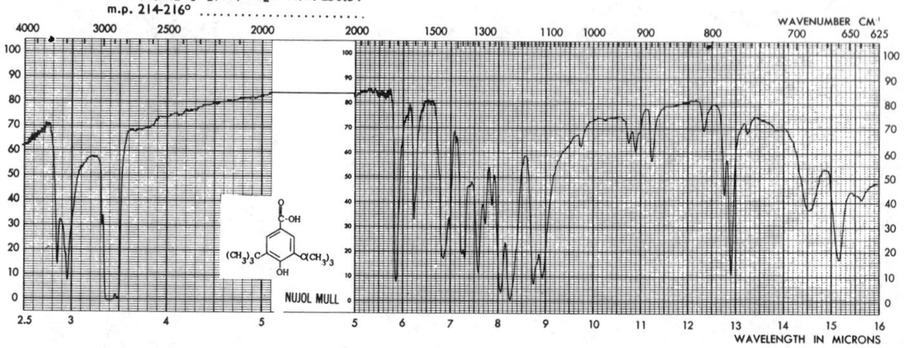

NUJOL MULL

G

15,723-6
4-Bromo-3,5-dihydroxybenzoic acid
monohydrate, 97%
$BrC_6H_2(OH)_2CO_2H \cdot H_2O$
M.W. 251.05 m.p. 271-273° Beil. 10,406

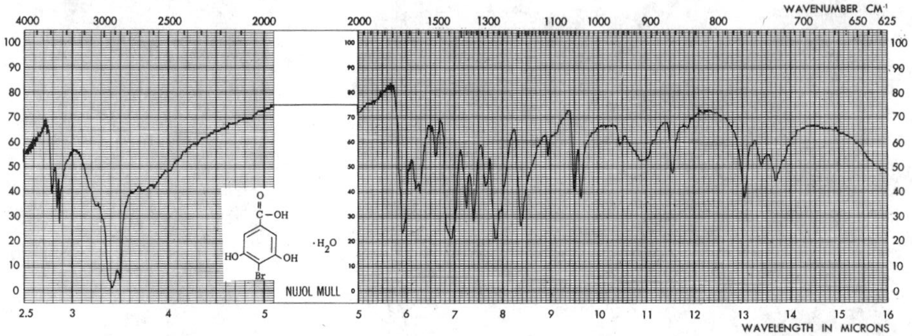

NUJOL MULL

H

D6400-7 3,5-Dichloro-4-hydroxybenzoic acid
$Cl_2C_6H_2(OH)CO_2H$ M.W. 207.01
m.p. 264-266°

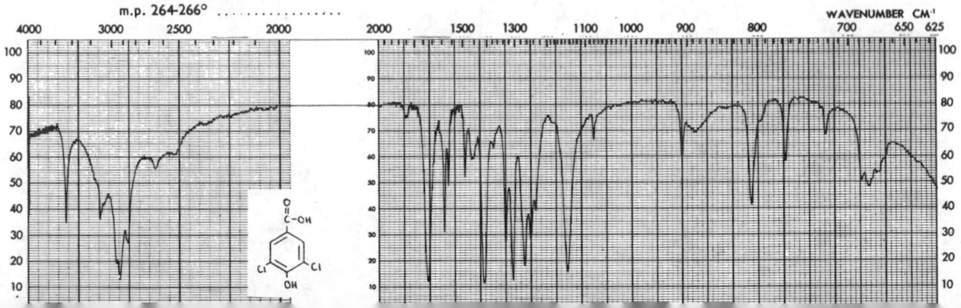

A D4360-3 **3,5-Dibromosalicylic acid**
$Br_2C_6H_2$-2-(OH)CO_2H M.W. 295.92 m.p. 226-228°
NUJOL MULL

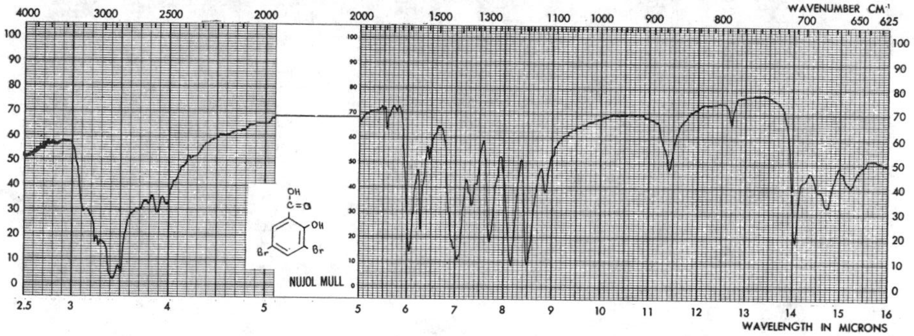

B D12,400-1 **3,5-Diiodosalicylic acid** (2-hydroxy-3,5-diiodobenzoic acid)
$I_2C_6H_2(OH)CO_2H$ M.W. 389.91 m.p. 232-234°
NUJOL MULL

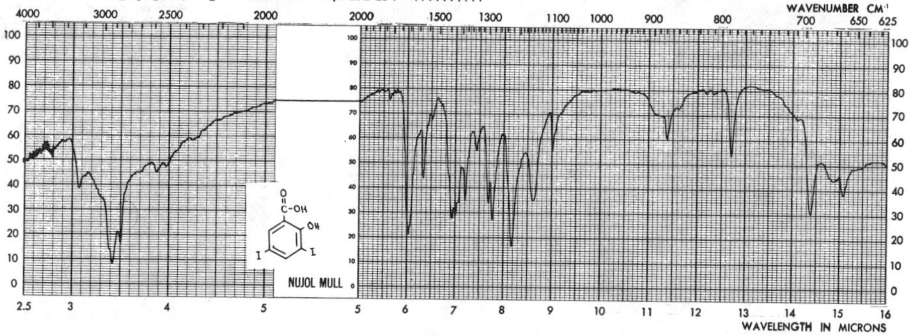

C T6560-9 **2,4,6-Trihydroxybenzoic acid monohydrate**
$(HO)_3C_6H_2CO_2H \cdot H_2O$ M.W. 188.14 m.p. 100° (dec.)
NUJOL MULL

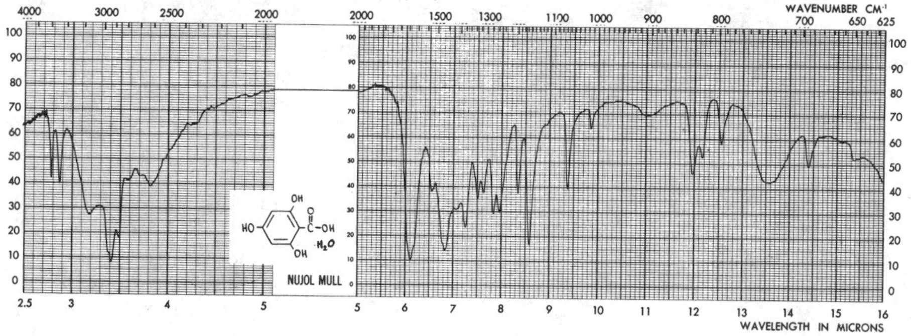

D 14,791-5 **Gallic acid** (3,4,5-trihydroxybenzoic acid) **monohydrate, N.F.**
$(HO)_3C_6H_2CO_2H \cdot H_2O$ M.W. 188.14
m.p. 251° (dec.)
NUJOL MULL

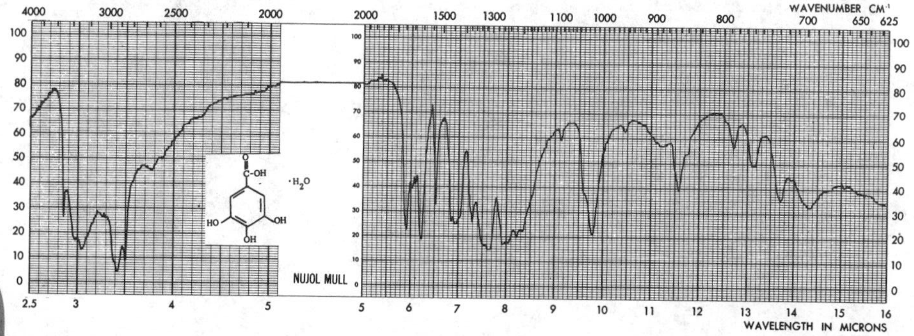

E S800-5 **Syringic acid**
4-(HO)C_6H_2-3,5-$(OCH_3)_2CO_2H$ M.W. 198.17
m.p. 207.5-209°
NUJOL MULL

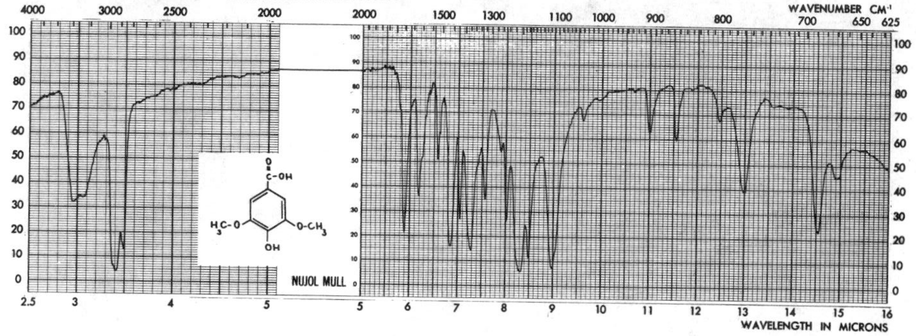

F 19,504-9
3,5-Dimethyl-*p*-anisic acid, 98% (3,5-dimethyl-4-methoxybenzoic acid)
$CH_3OC_6H_2(CH_3)_2CO_2H$ FW 180.20 mp 189-192°
Disp. C
NUJOL MULL

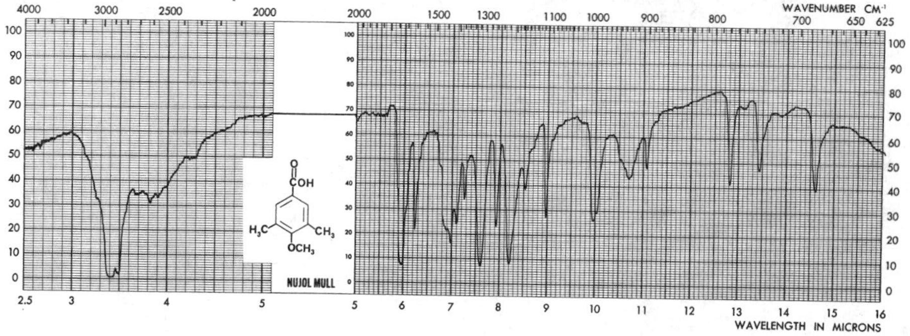

G A5130-0 **4-Amino-3,5-dimethylbenzoic acid**
$H_2NC_6H_2(CH_3)_2CO_2H$ M.W. 165.19 m.p. 253-254.5°
NUJOL MULL

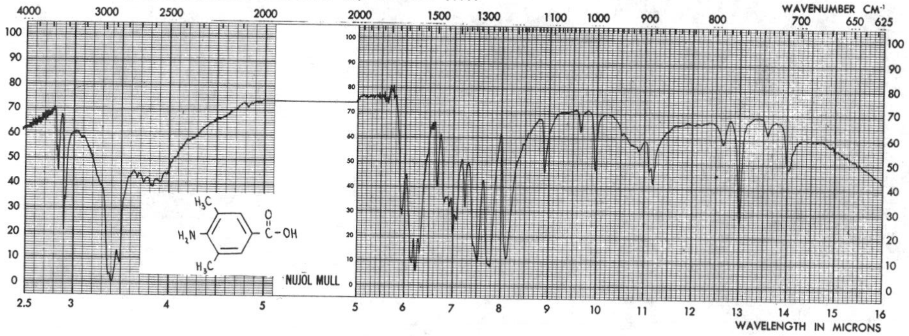

H D14,680 **3,5-Dimethylanthranilic acid**
NUJOL MULL

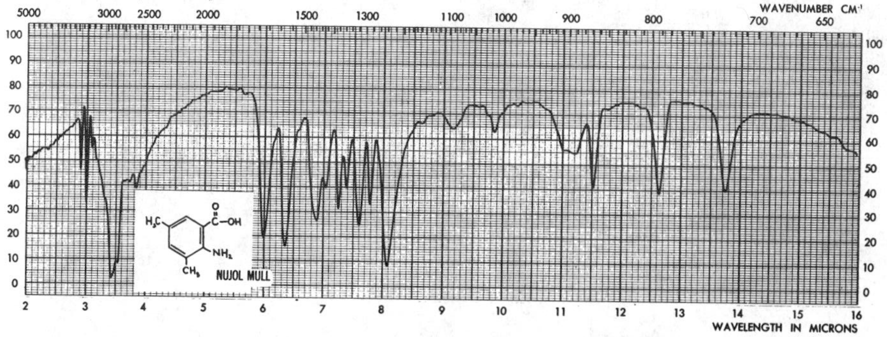

AROMATIC CARBOXYLIC ACIDS

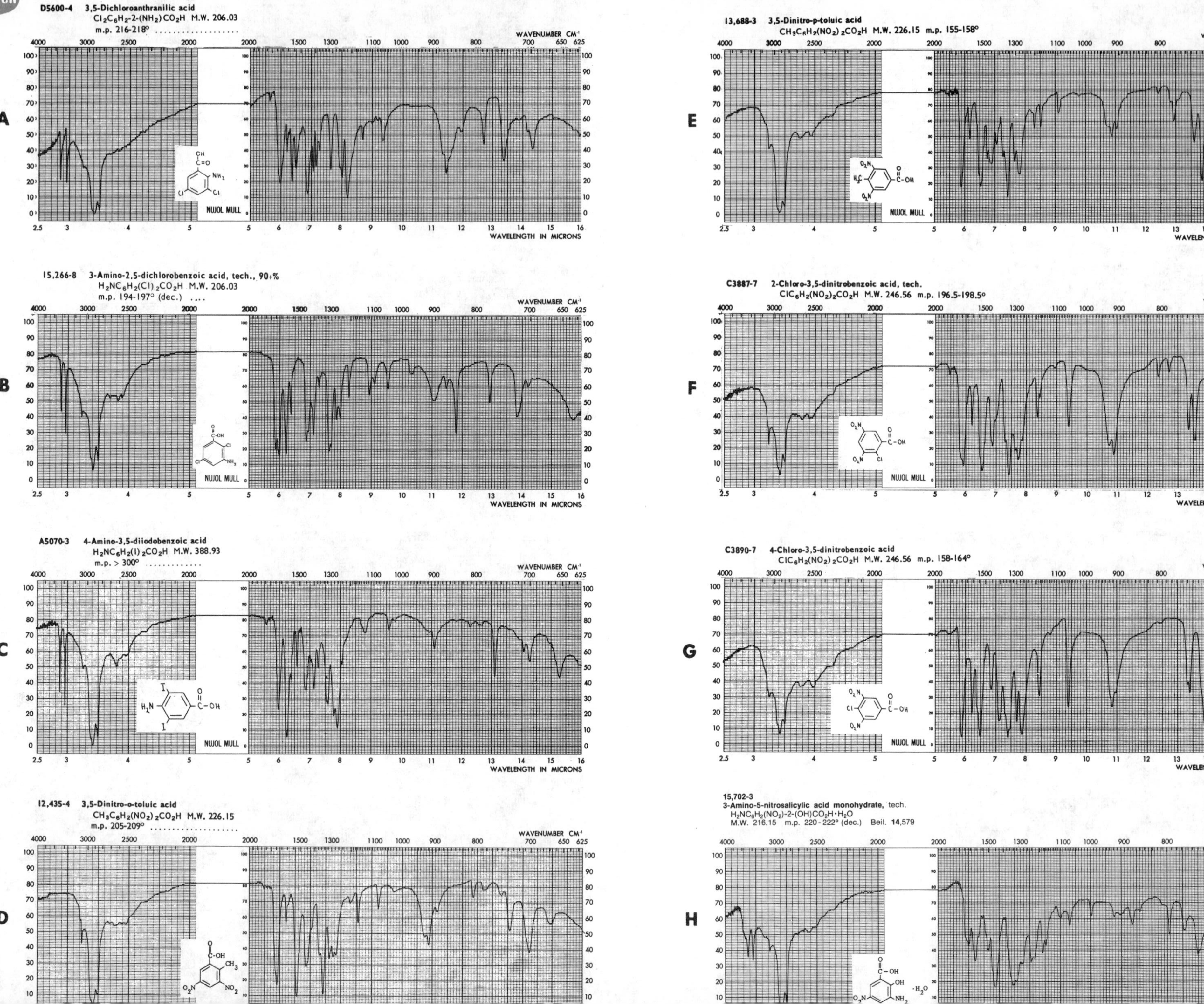
ALDRICH
A
D5600-4 3,5-Dichloroanthranilic acid
$Cl_2C_6H_2$-2-$(NH_2)CO_2H$ M.W. 206.03
m.p. 216-218°
NUJOL MULL
B
15,266-8 3-Amino-2,5-dichlorobenzoic acid, tech., 90+%
$H_2NC_6H_2(Cl)_2CO_2H$ M.W. 206.03
m.p. 194-197° (dec.)
NUJOL MULL
C
A5070-3 4-Amino-3,5-diiodobenzoic acid
$H_2NC_6H_2(I)_2CO_2H$ M.W. 388.93
m.p. > 300°
NUJOL MULL
D
12,435-4 3,5-Dinitro-o-toluic acid
$CH_3C_6H_2(NO_2)_2CO_2H$ M.W. 226.15
m.p. 205-209°
E
13,688-3 3,5-Dinitro-p-toluic acid
$CH_3C_6H_2(NO_2)_2CO_2H$ M.W. 226.15 m.p. 155-158°
NUJOL MULL
F
C3887-7 2-Chloro-3,5-dinitrobenzoic acid, tech.
$ClC_6H_2(NO_2)_2CO_2H$ M.W. 246.56 m.p. 196.5-198.5°
NUJOL MULL
G
C3890-7 4-Chloro-3,5-dinitrobenzoic acid
$ClC_6H_2(NO_2)_2CO_2H$ M.W. 246.56 m.p. 158-164°
NUJOL MULL
H
15,702-3
3-Amino-5-nitrosalicylic acid monohydrate, tech.
$H_2NC_6H_2(NO_2)$-2-$(OH)CO_2H \cdot H_2O$
M.W. 216.15 m.p. 220-222° (dec.) Beil. 14,579
WAVENUMBER CM⁻¹
WAVELENGTH IN MICRONS

A

$(CH_3)_2NC_6H_2(NO_2)_2CO_2H$ M.W. 255.19
m.p. 248-251° (dec.)

NUJOL MULL

B

12,884-8 3,5-Dinitrosalicylic acid monohydrate
$(O_2N)_2C_6H_2$-2-(OH)$CO_2H \cdot H_2O$ M.W. 246.13
m.p. 172-173.5°

NUJOL MULL

C

14,640-4 3-tert.-Butyl-6-methylsalicylic acid
$(CH_3)_3CC_6H_2(CH_3)$-2-(OH)CO_2H M.W. 208.26
m.p. 179-181°

NUJOL MULL

D

H4145-5 3-Hydroxy-4-methyl-2-nitrobenzoic acid
$HOC_6H_2(CH_3)(NO_2)CO_2H$ M.W. 197.15 m.p. 186-188°

NUJOL MULL

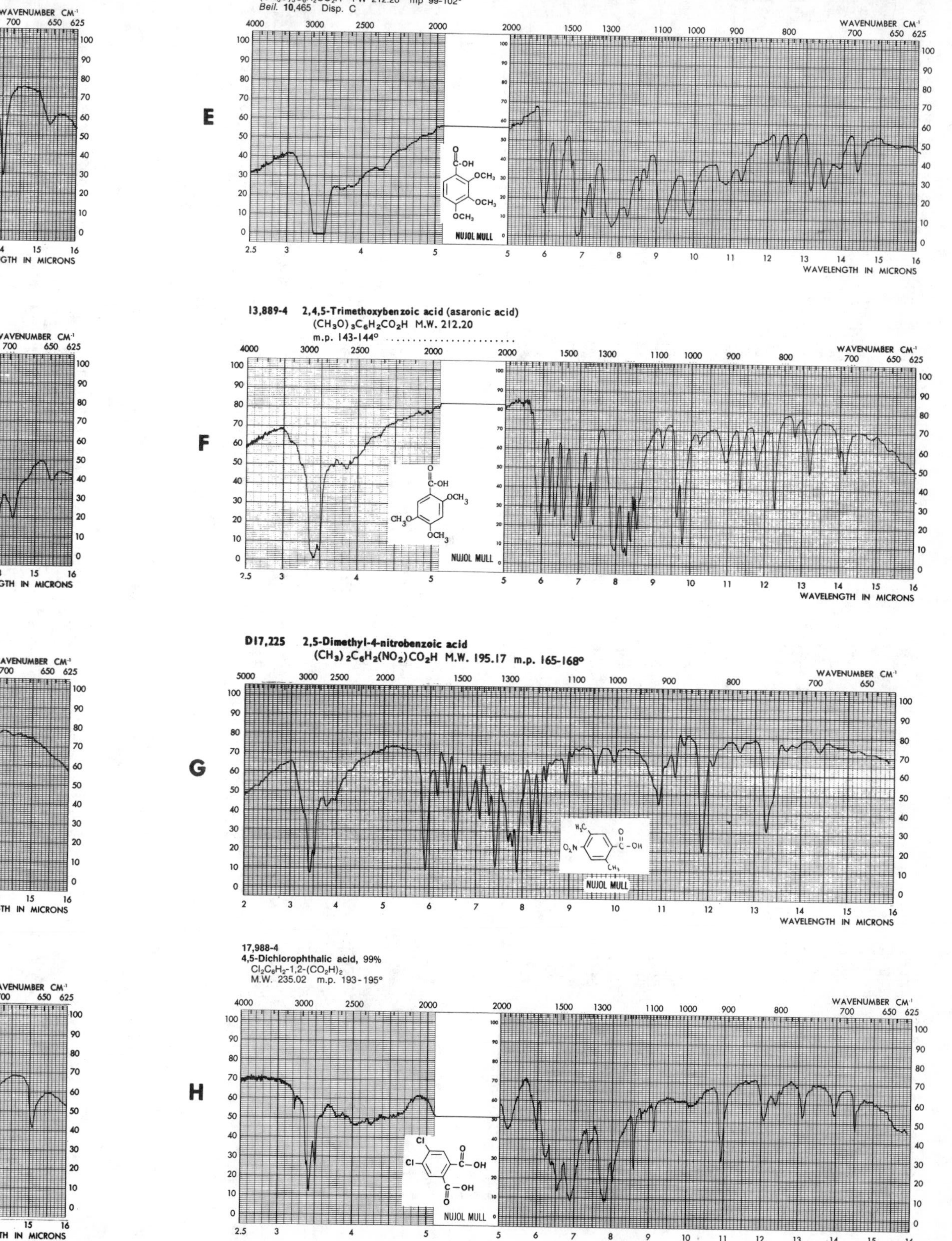

E

2,3,4-Trimethoxybenzoic acid, 98+%
$(CH_3O)_3C_6H_2CO_2H$ FW 212.20 mp 99-102°
Beil. 10,465 Disp. C

NUJOL MULL

F

13,889-4 2,4,5-Trimethoxybenzoic acid (asaronic acid)
$(CH_3O)_3C_6H_2CO_2H$ M.W. 212.20
m.p. 143-144°

NUJOL MULL

G

D17,225 2,5-Dimethyl-4-nitrobenzoic acid
$(CH_3)_2C_6H_2(NO_2)CO_2H$ M.W. 195.17 m.p. 165-168°

NUJOL MULL

H

17,988-4
4,5-Dichlorophthalic acid, 99%
$Cl_2C_6H_2$-1,2-$(CO_2H)_2$
M.W. 235.02 m.p. 193-195°

NUJOL MULL

A 10,233-4 **2,5-Dimethylterephthalic acid**
$(CH_3)_2C_6H_2$-1,4-$(CO_2H)_2$ M.W. 194.19
m.p. > 300°

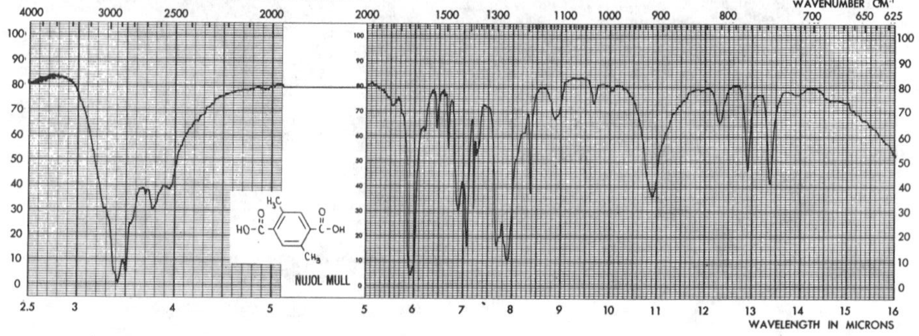

NUJOL MULL

B 10,204-0 **2,5-Dichloroterephthalic acid, puriss.**
$Cl_2C_6H_2$-1,4-$(CO_2H)_2$ M.W. 235.02 m.p. 305-308°

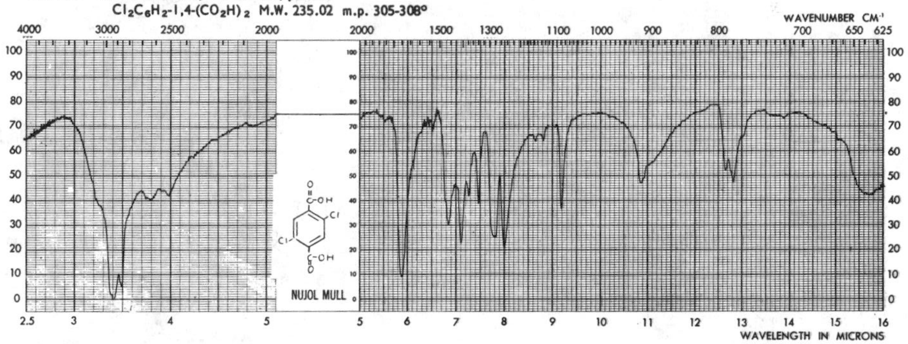

NUJOL MULL

C 14,673-0 **3,5-Di-tert.-butyl-2,6-dihydroxybenzoic acid (3,5-di-tert.-butyl-γ-resorcylic acid)**
$[(CH_3)_3C]_2C_6H(OH)_2CO_2H$ M.W. 266.34
m.p. 174° (dec.)

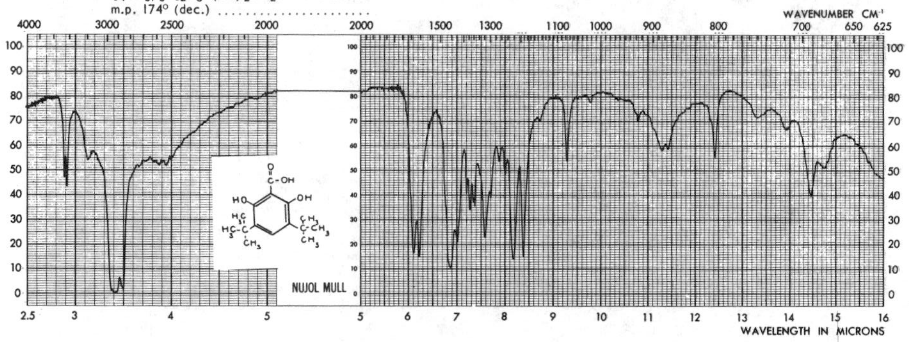

NUJOL MULL

D H5935-4 **3-Hydroxy-2,4,6-triiodobenzoic acid**
$HOC_6H(I)_3CO_2H$ M.W. 515.81 m.p. 210° (dec.)

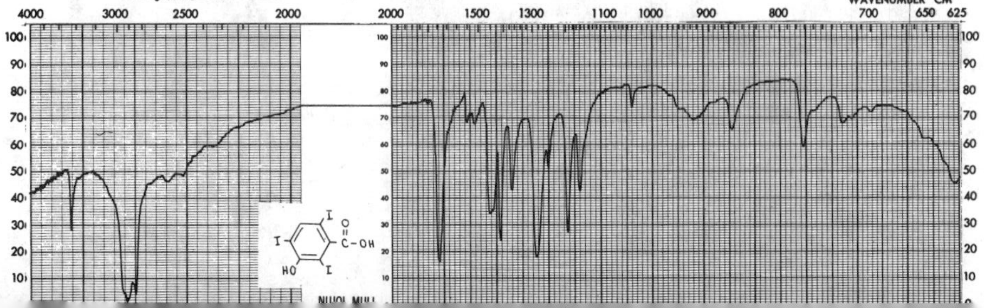

NUJOL MULL

E D6085-0 **2,4-Dichloro-3,5-dinitrobenzoic acid**
$Cl_2C_6H(NO_2)_2CO_2H$ M.W. 281.01 m.p. 212-213°

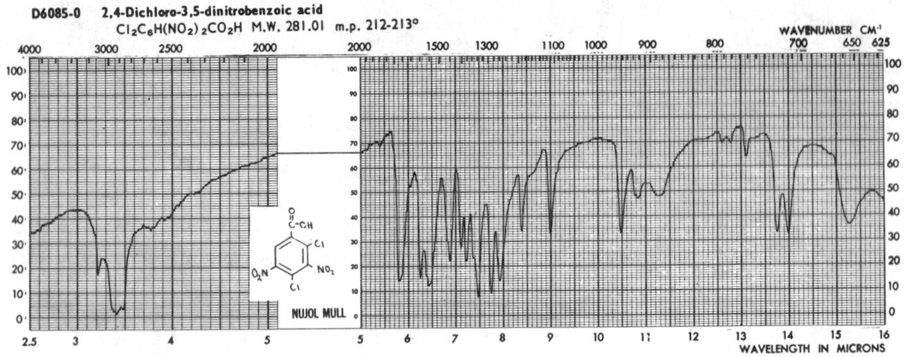

NUJOL MULL

F P536-0 **Pentafluorobenzoic acid**
$C_6F_5CO_2H$ M.W. 212.07 m.p. 101-105°

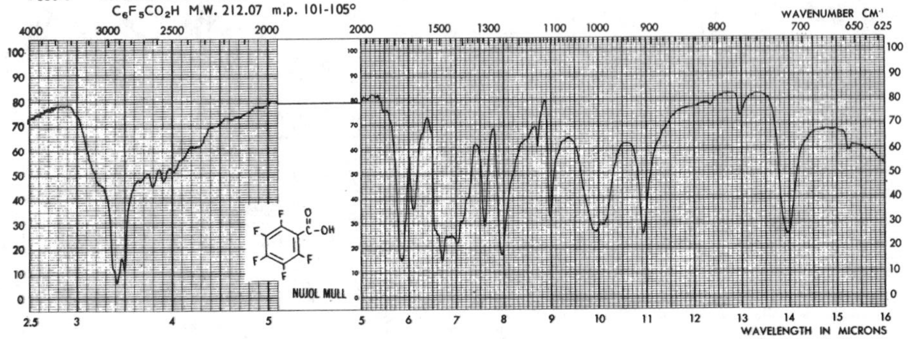

NUJOL MULL

G 10,441-8 **Tetrafluoroterephthalic acid**
C_6F_4-1,4-$(CO_2H)_2$ M.W. 238.09 m.p. 276-278°

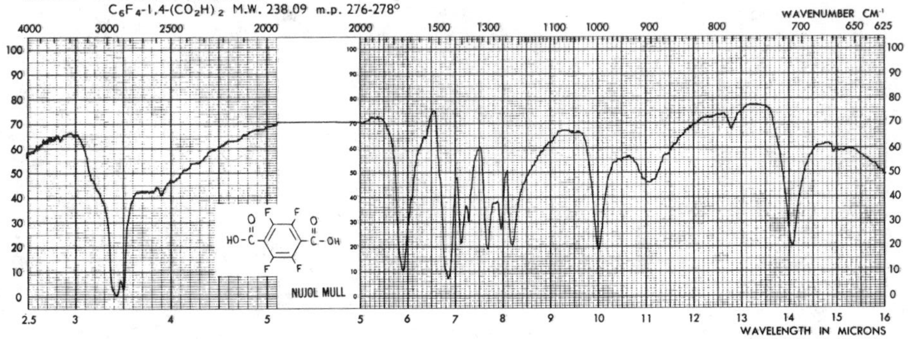

NUJOL MULL

H 10,444-2 **Tetramethylterephthalic acid, puriss.**
$(CH_3)_4C_6$-1,4-$(CO_2H)_2$ M.W. 222.24 m.p. > 330°

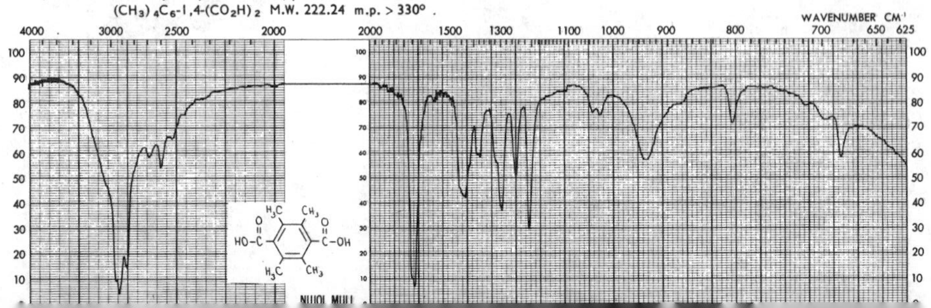

NUJOL MULL

A — B3470-2 2-Biphenylcarboxylic acid (o-phenylbenzoic acid)
$C_6H_5C_6H_4CO_2H$ M.W. 198.22 m.p. 112-114°

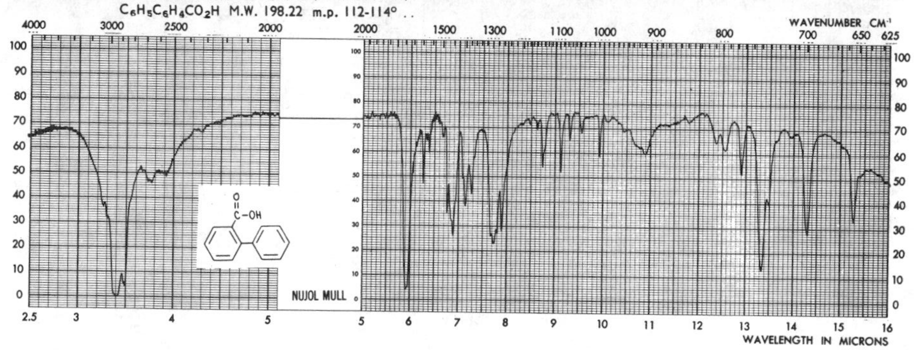

NUJOL MULL

B — B3472-9 4-Biphenylcarboxylic acid (p-phenylbenzoic acid)
$C_6H_5C_6H_4CO_2H$ M.W. 198.22 m.p. 225-226°

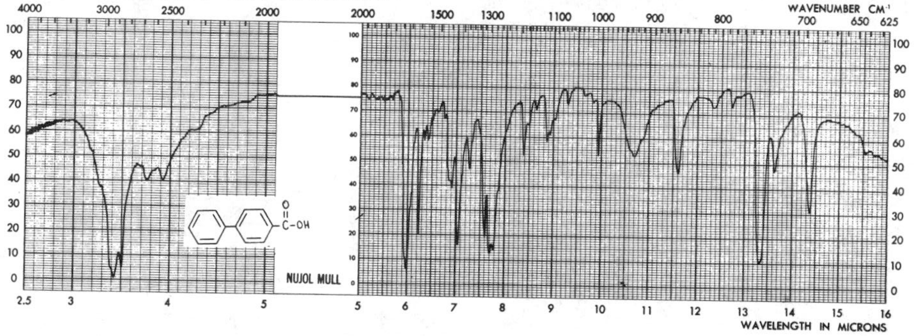

NUJOL MULL

C — 12,669-1 Diphenic acid
2-$(HO_2C)C_6H_4C_6H_4$-2-(CO_2H) M.W. 242.23
m.p. 229-231°

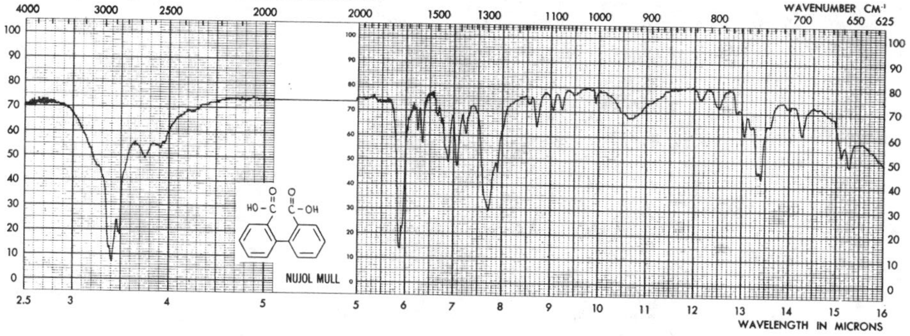

NUJOL MULL

D — 12,218-1 3-Phenylsalicylic acid
$C_6H_5C_6H_3$-2-$(OH)CO_2H$ M.W. 214.22
m.p. 188-189°

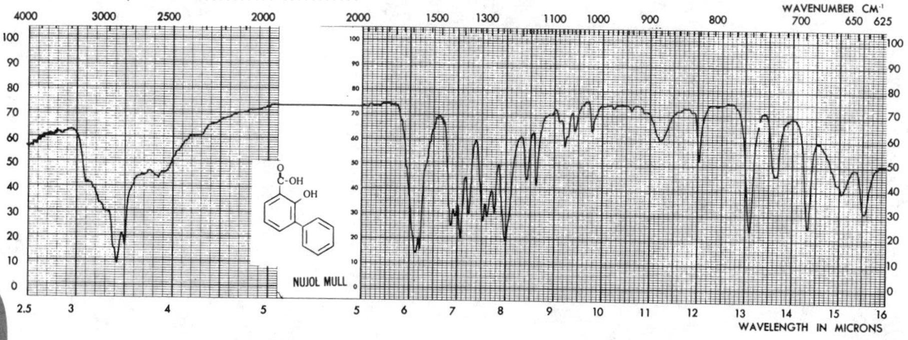

NUJOL MULL

E — P3665-7 α-Phenyl-o-toluic acid (2-benzylbenzoic acid)
$C_6H_5CH_2C_6H_4CO_2H$ M.W. 212.25 m.p. 110-113°

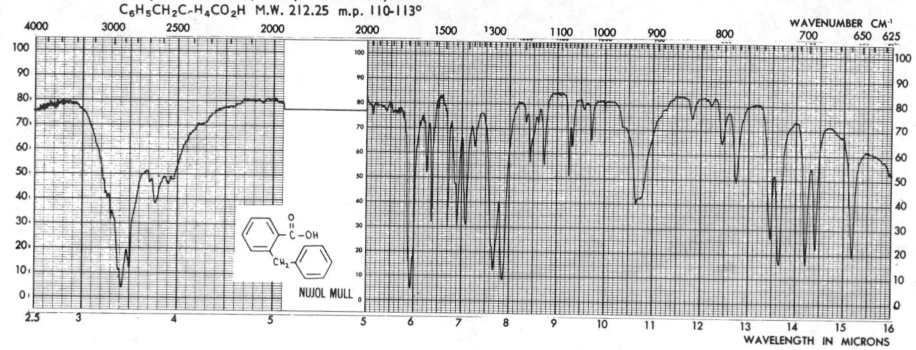

NUJOL MULL

F — 15,151-3 2-Bibenzylcarboxylic acid (o-phenethylbenzoic acid)
$C_6H_5CH_2CH_2C_6H_4CO_2H$ M.W. 226.28
m.p. 128-131

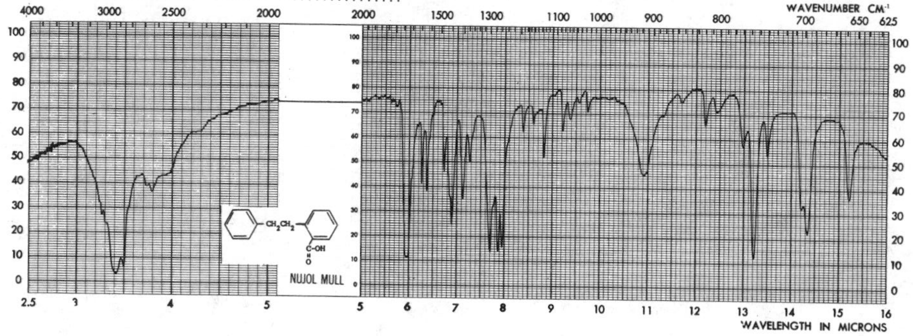

NUJOL MULL

G — 14,909-8 5-(α,α-Dimethyl-p-hydroxybenzyl)-salicylic acid
(carboxybisphenol A), tech.
$HOC_6H_4C(CH_3)_2C_6H_3$-2-$(OH)CO_2H$
M.W. 272.30

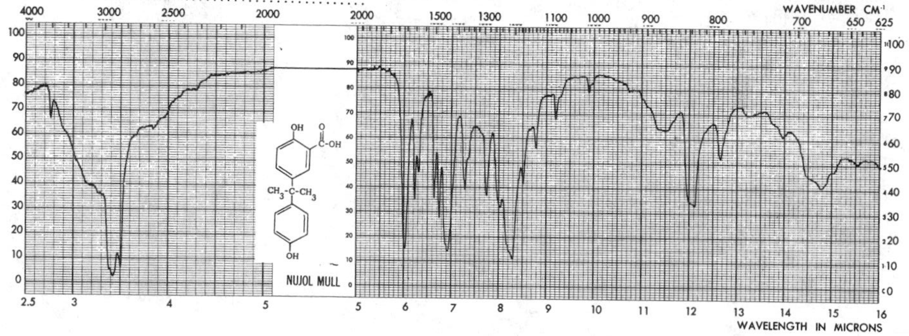

NUJOL MULL

H — 12,326-9 Aurintricarboxylic acid
M.W. 422.35 m.p. > 320°

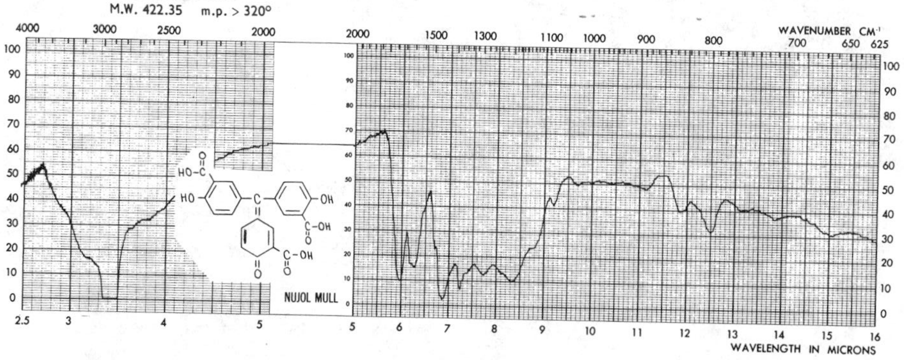

NUJOL MULL

AROMATIC CARBOXYLIC ACIDS

ALDRICH

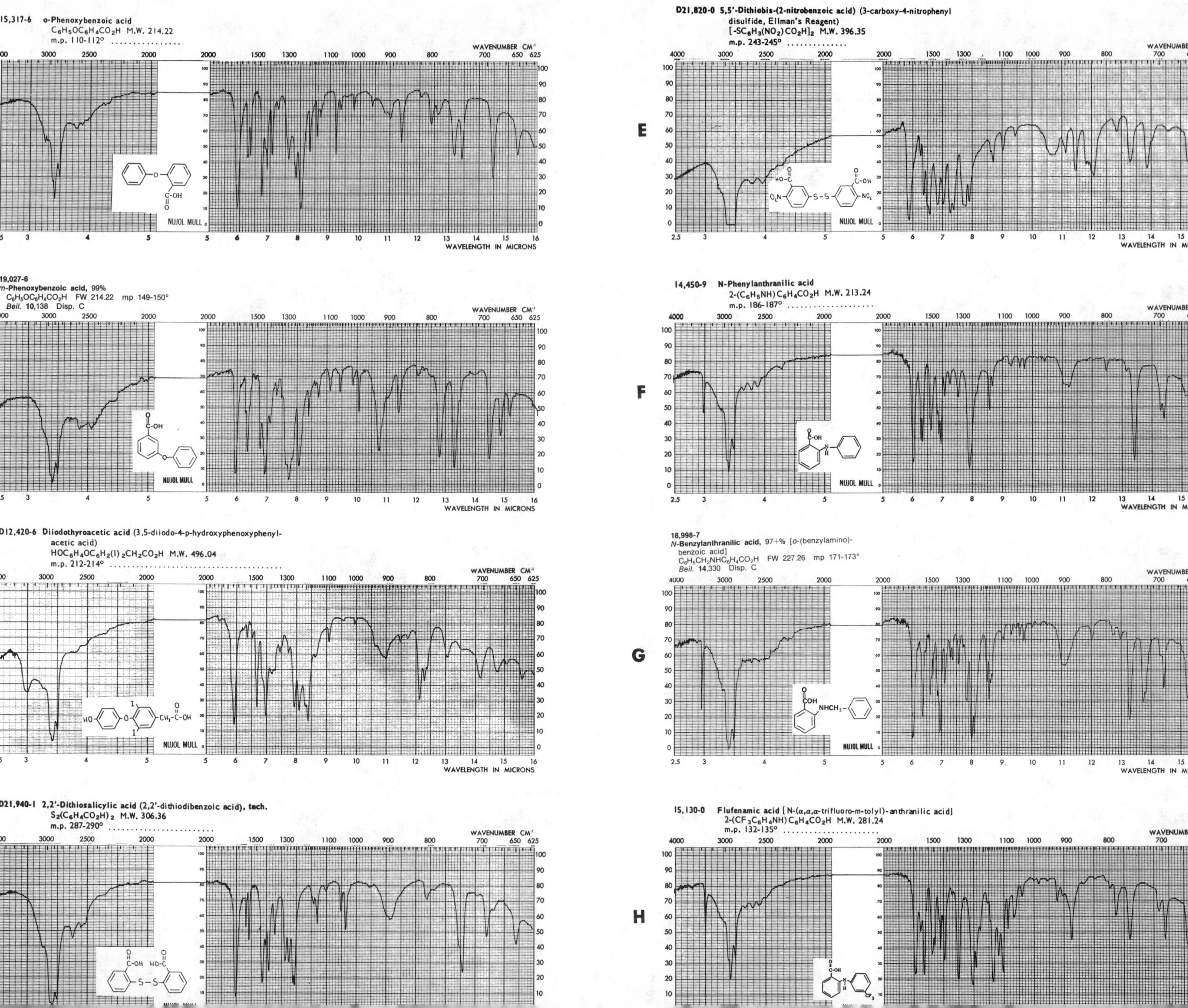

ALDRICH
A
15,317-6 o-Phenoxybenzoic acid
$C_6H_5OC_6H_4CO_2H$ M.W. 214.22
m.p. 110-112°
NUJOL MULL
B
19,027-6
m-Phenoxybenzoic acid, 99%
$C_6H_5OC_6H_4CO_2H$ FW 214.22 mp 149-150°
Beil. 10,138 Disp. C
NUJOL MULL
C
D12,420-6 Diiodothyroacetic acid (3,5-diiodo-4-p-hydroxyphenoxyphenyl-acetic acid)
$HOC_6H_4OC_6H_2(I)_2CH_2CO_2H$ M.W. 496.04
m.p. 212-214°
NUJOL MULL
D
D21,940-1 2,2'-Dithiosalicylic acid (2,2'-dithiodibenzoic acid), tech.
$S_2(C_6H_4CO_2H)_2$ M.W. 306.36
m.p. 287-290°
E
D21,820-0 5,5'-Dithiobis-(2-nitrobenzoic acid) (3-carboxy-4-nitrophenyl disulfide, Ellman's Reagent)
$[-SC_6H_3(NO_2)CO_2H]_2$ M.W. 396.35
m.p. 243-245°
NUJOL MULL
F
14,450-9 N-Phenylanthranilic acid
$2-(C_6H_5NH)C_6H_4CO_2H$ M.W. 213.24
m.p. 186-187°
NUJOL MULL
G
18,998-7
N-Benzylanthranilic acid, 97+% [o-(benzylamino)-benzoic acid]
$C_6H_5CH_2NHC_6H_4CO_2H$ FW 227.26 mp 171-173°
Beil. 14,330 Disp. C
NUJOL MULL
H
15,130-0 Flufenamic acid [N-(α,α,α-trifluoro-m-tolyl)-anthranilic acid]
$2-(CF_3C_6H_4NH)C_6H_4CO_2H$ M.W. 281.24
m.p. 132-135°
WAVENUMBER CM⁻¹
WAVELENGTH IN MICRONS

A

m.p. 202-204°

NUJOL MULL

B

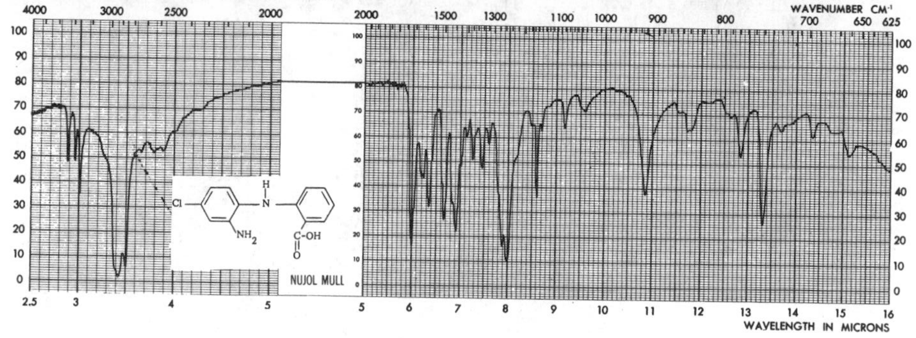

13,853-3 N-(2,4-Dinitrophenyl)-anthranilic acid
$2\text{-}[(O_2N)_2C_6H_3NH]C_6H_4CO_2H$ M.W. 303.23
m.p. 258-262°

NUJOL MULL

C

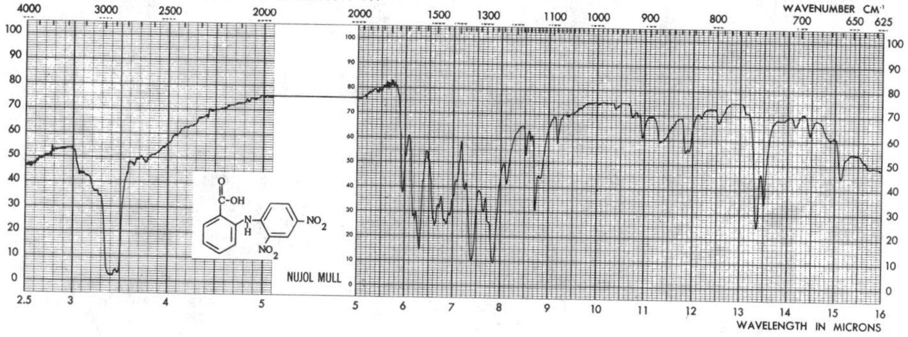

B1240-7 4-Benzoylbenzoic acid
$C_6H_5COC_6H_4CO_2H$ M.W. 226.23
m.p. 198-200°

NUJOL MULL

D

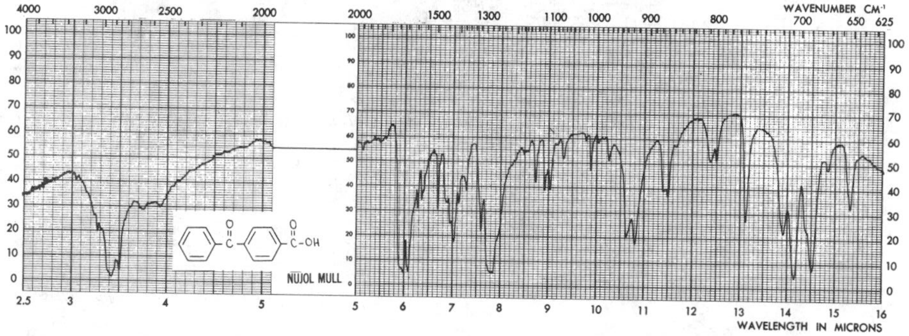

B1238-5 2-Benzoylbenzoic acid
$C_6H_5COC_6H_4CO_2H$ M.W. 226.23
m.p. 127-129°

NUJOL MULL

E

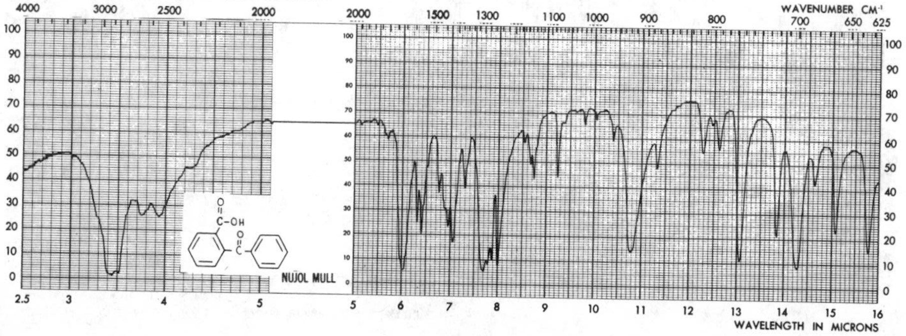

$FC_6H_4COC_6H_4CO_2H$ M.W. 244.22
m.p. 135-136°

NUJOL MULL

F

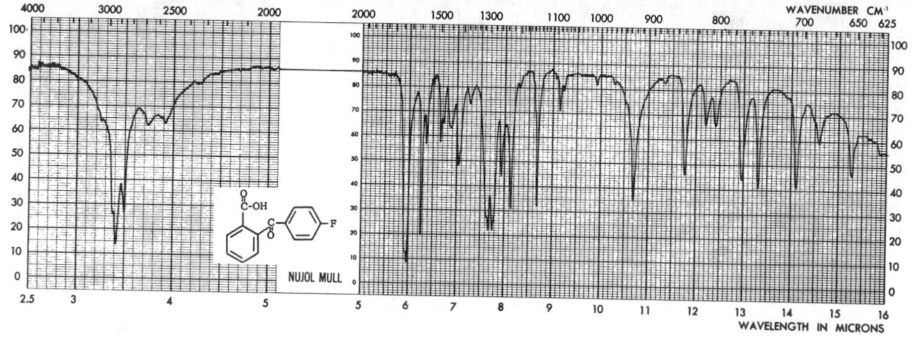

C2660-7 o-(p-Chlorobenzoyl)-benzoic acid
$ClC_6H_4COC_6H_4CO_2H$ M.W. 260.68 m.p. 149.5-151°

NUJOL MULL

G

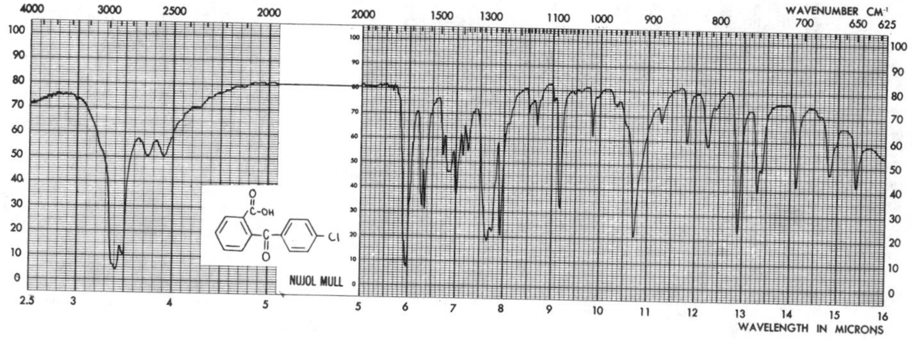

B5910-1 2-(p-Bromobenzoyl)-benzoic acid
$BrC_6H_4COC_6H_4CO_2H$ M.W. 305.14
m.p. 170-171°

NUJOL MULL

H

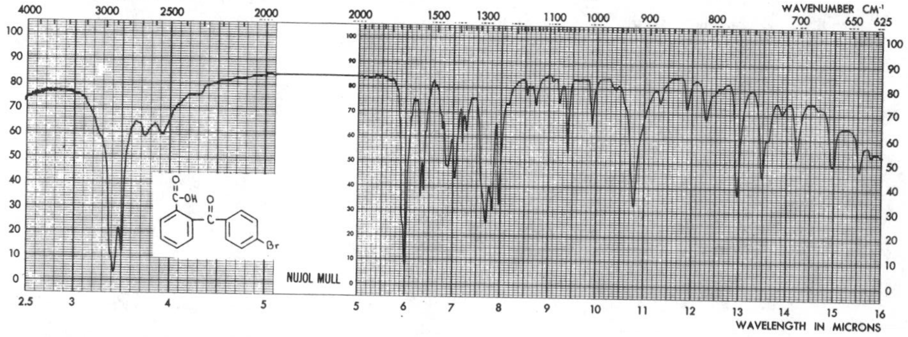

H2040-7 2-(p-Hydroxybenzoyl)-benzoic acid
$HOC_6H_4COC_6H_4CO_2H$ M.W. 242.23 m.p. 215-217°

NUJOL MULL

AROMATIC CARBOXYLIC ACIDS

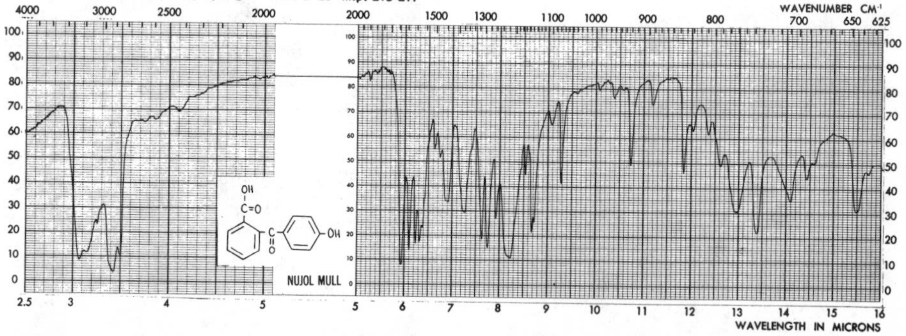

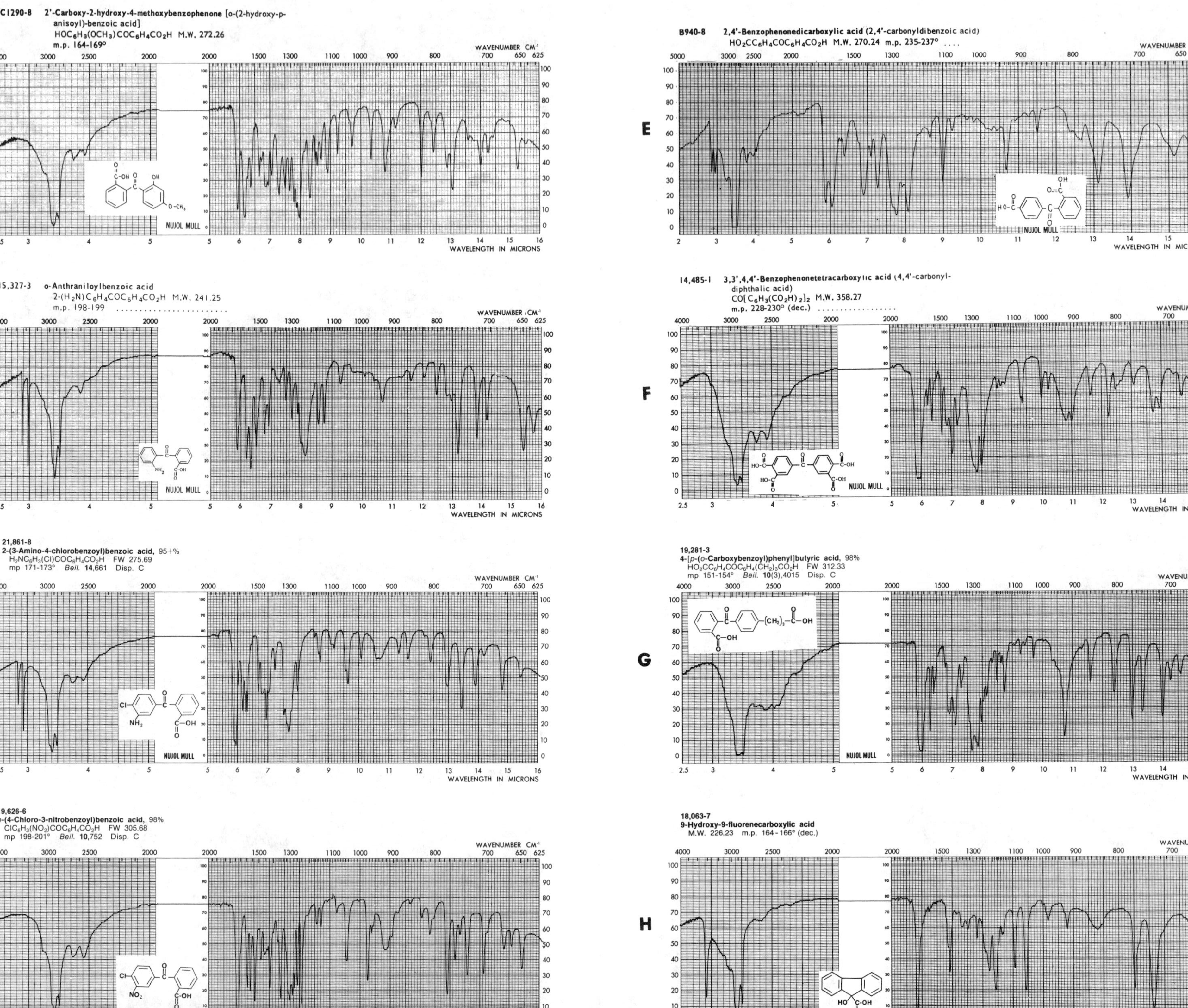

A C1290-8 **2'-Carboxy-2-hydroxy-4-methoxybenzophenone** [o-(2-hydroxy-p-anisoyl)-benzoic acid]
$HOC_6H_3(OCH_3)COC_6H_4CO_2H$ M.W. 272.26
m.p. 164-169°

B 15,327-3 o-Anthraniloylbenzoic acid
$2\text{-}(H_2N)C_6H_4COC_6H_4CO_2H$ M.W. 241.25
m.p. 198-199

C 21,861-8
2-(3-Amino-4-chlorobenzoyl)benzoic acid, 95+%
$H_2NC_6H_3(Cl)COC_6H_4CO_2H$ FW 275.69
mp 171-173° *Beil.* **14**,661 Disp. C

D 19,626-6
o-(4-Chloro-3-nitrobenzoyl)benzoic acid, 98%
$ClC_6H_3(NO_2)COC_6H_4CO_2H$ FW 305.68
mp 198-201° *Beil.* **10**,752 Disp. C

E B940-8 **2,4'-Benzophenonedicarboxylic acid** (2,4'-carbonyldibenzoic acid)
$HO_2CC_6H_4COC_6H_4CO_2H$ M.W. 270.24 m.p. 235-237°

F 14,485-1 **3,3',4,4'-Benzophenonetetracarboxylic acid** (4,4'-carbonyl-diphthalic acid)
$CO[C_6H_3(CO_2H)_2]_2$ M.W. 358.27
m.p. 228-230° (dec.)

G 19,281-3
4-[p-(o-Carboxybenzoyl)phenyl]butyric acid, 98%
$HO_2CC_6H_4COC_6H_4(CH_2)_3CO_2H$ FW 312.33
mp 151-154° *Beil.* **10**(3),4015 Disp. C

H 18,063-7
9-Hydroxy-9-fluorenecarboxylic acid
M.W. 226.23 m.p. 164-166° (dec.)

M.W. 324.38 m.p. 290-292.5° ....

A

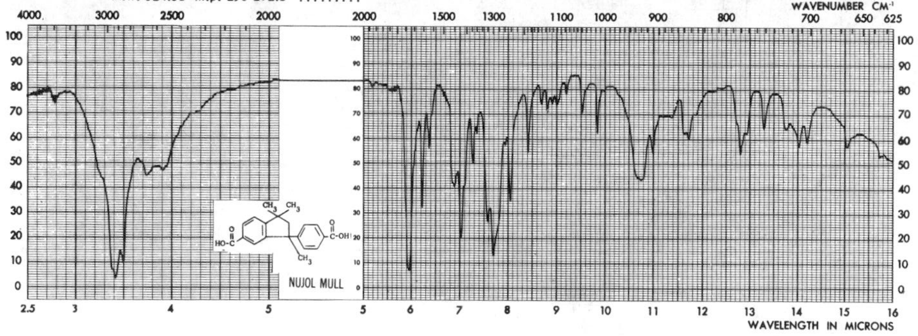

Beil. 9(2),455 Disp. C

E

15,968-9
1-Methylindene-2-carboxylic acid, 97%
M.W. 174.2 m.p. 201-203° Beil. 9,644

B

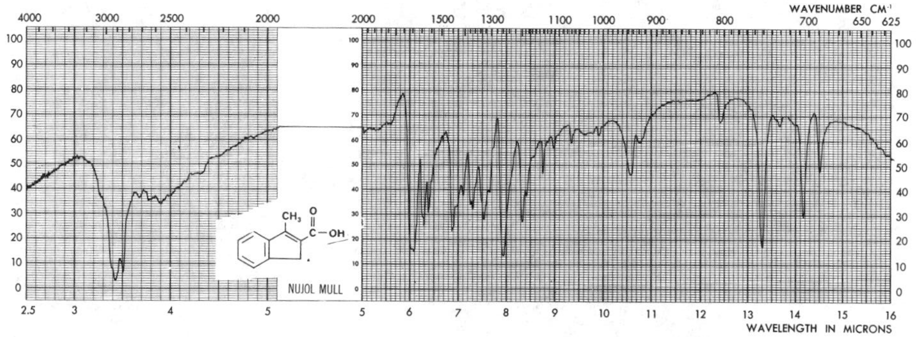

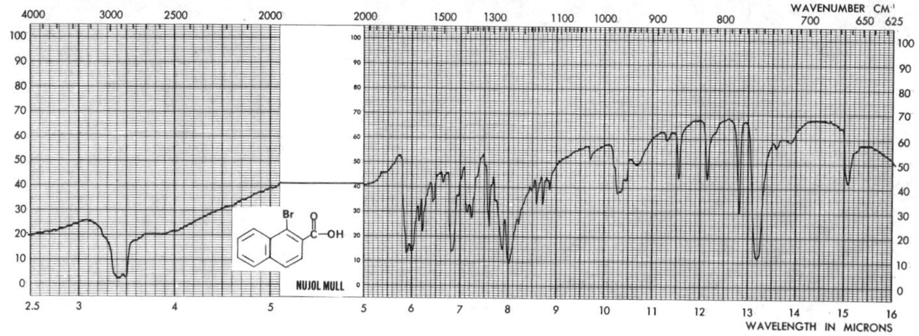

10,963-0 **1-Hydroxy-2-naphthoic acid**
$HOC_{10}H_6CO_2H$ M.W. 188.18 m.p. 205° (dec.)

F

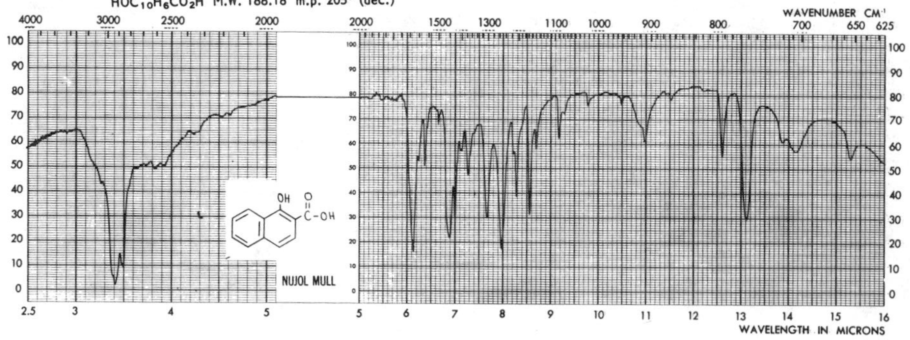

N190-9 **1-Naphthoic acid**
$C_{10}H_7CO_2H$ M.W. 172.18 m.p. 157-161°

C

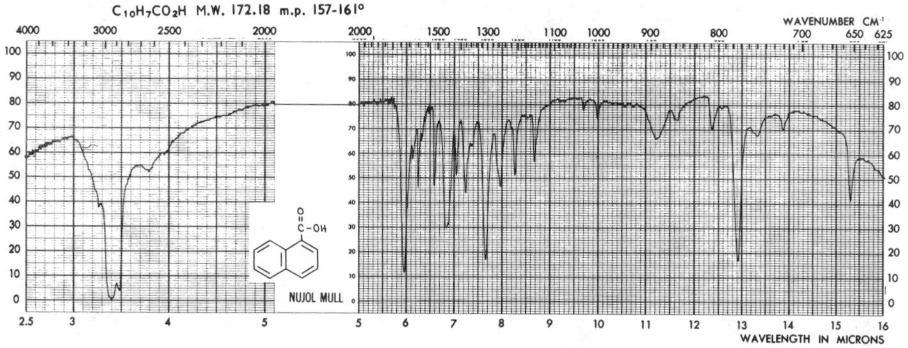

H4580-9 **2-Hydroxy-1-naphthoic acid**
$HOC_{10}H_6CO_2H$ M.W. 188.18 m.p. 157-158°

G

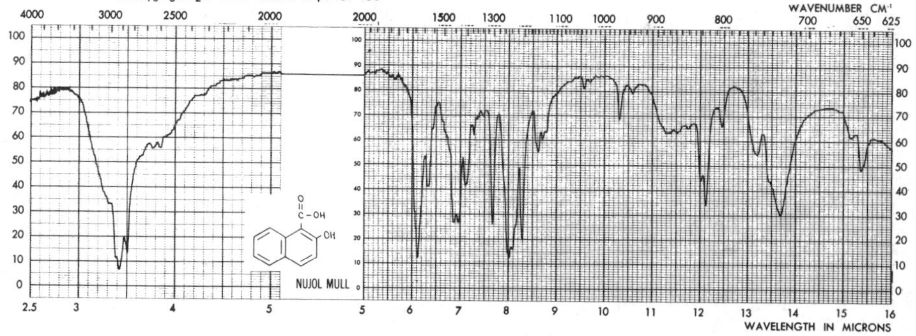

18,024-6
2-Naphthoic acid, 99%
$C_{10}H_7CO_2H$
M.W. 172.18 m.p. 185-187° Beil. 9,656

D

H4600-7 **3-Hydroxy-2-naphthoic acid, tech.**
$HOC_{10}H_6CO_2H$ M.W. 188.18 m.p. 218-221°

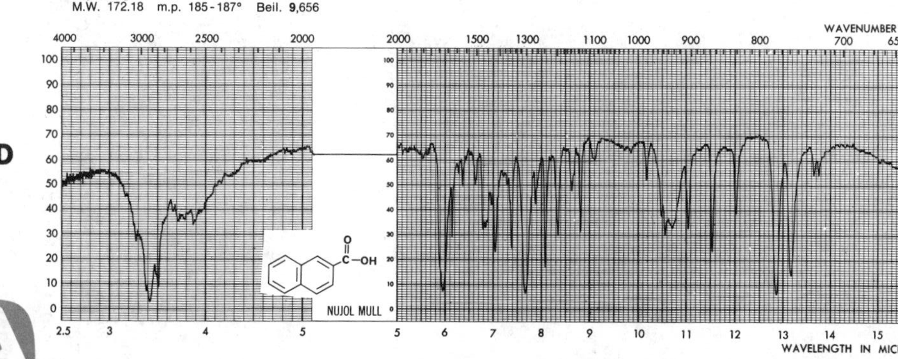

H

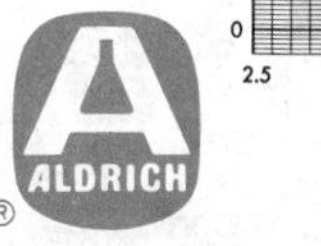

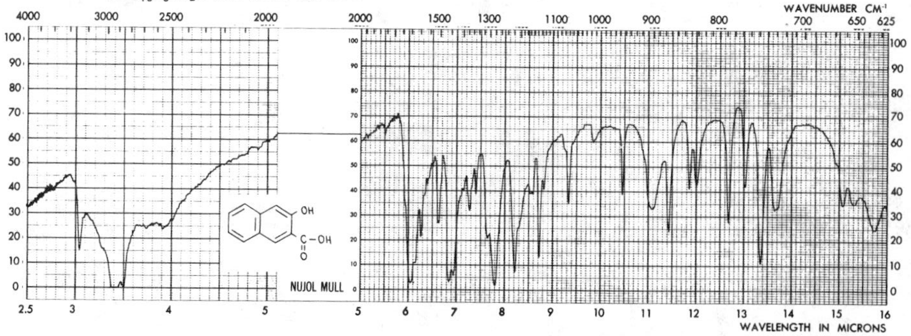

AROMATIC CARBOXYLIC ACIDS

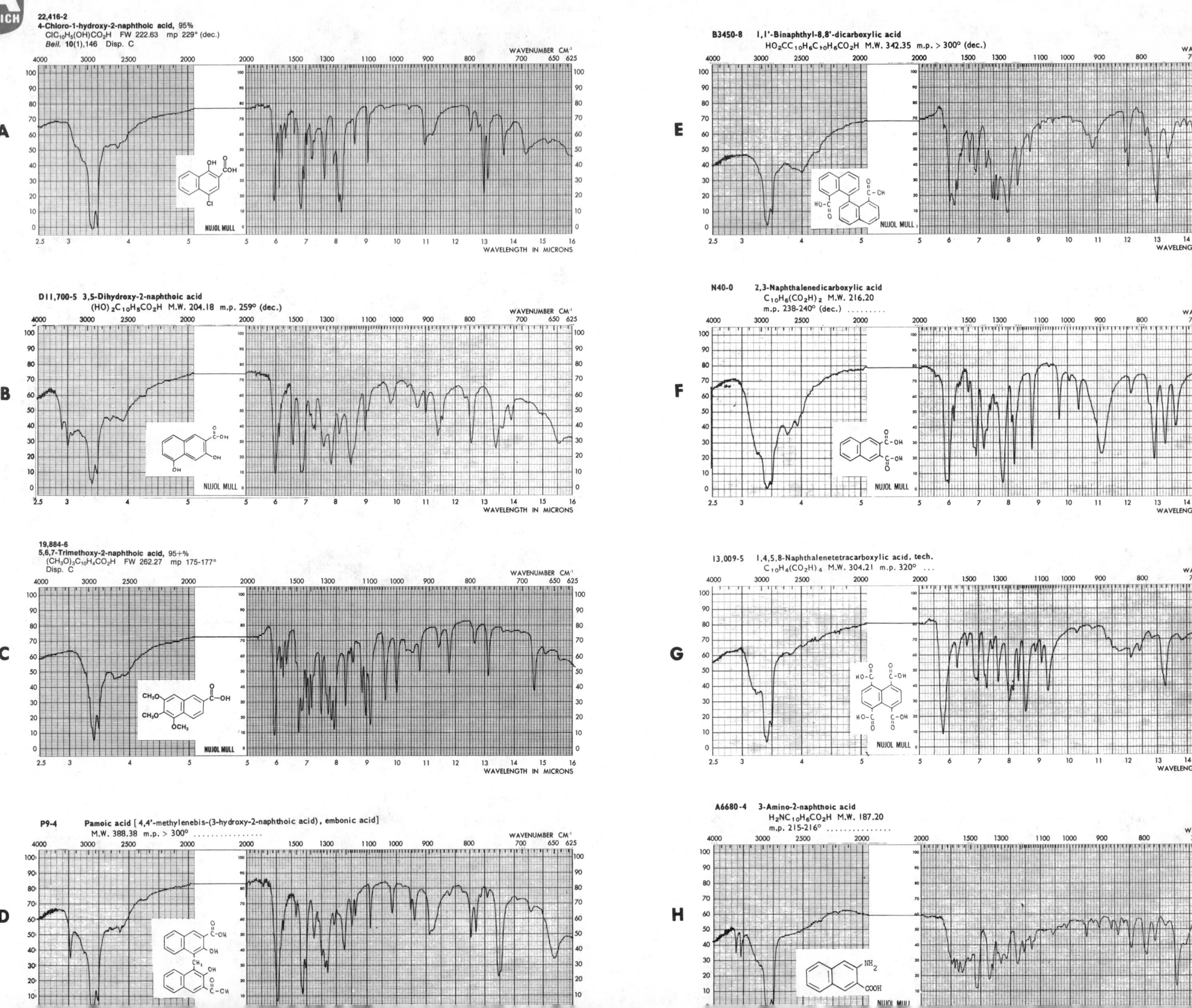
ALDRICH
A
22,416-2
4-Chloro-1-hydroxy-2-naphthoic acid, 95%
ClC10H5(OH)CO2H FW 222.63 mp 229° (dec.)
Beil. 10(1),146 Disp. C
NUJOL MULL
B
D11,700-5 3,5-Dihydroxy-2-naphthoic acid
(HO)2C10H5CO2H M.W. 204.18 m.p. 259° (dec.)
NUJOL MULL
C
19,884-6
5,6,7-Trimethoxy-2-naphthoic acid, 95+%
(CH3O)3C10H4CO2H FW 262.27 mp 175-177°
Disp. C
NUJOL MULL
D
P9-4 Pamoic acid [4,4'-methylenebis-(3-hydroxy-2-naphthoic acid), embonic acid]
M.W. 388.38 m.p. > 300°
E
B3450-8 1,1'-Binaphthyl-8,8'-dicarboxylic acid
HO2CC10H6C10H6CO2H M.W. 342.35 m.p. > 300° (dec.)
NUJOL MULL
F
N40-0 2,3-Naphthalenedicarboxylic acid
C10H6(CO2H)2 M.W. 216.20
m.p. 238-240° (dec.)
NUJOL MULL
G
13,009-5 1,4,5,8-Naphthalenetetracarboxylic acid, tech.
C10H4(CO2H)4 M.W. 304.21 m.p. 320°
NUJOL MULL
H
A6680-4 3-Amino-2-naphthoic acid
H2NC10H6CO2H M.W. 187.20
m.p. 215-216°
WAVENUMBER CM⁻¹
WAVELENGTH IN MICRONS

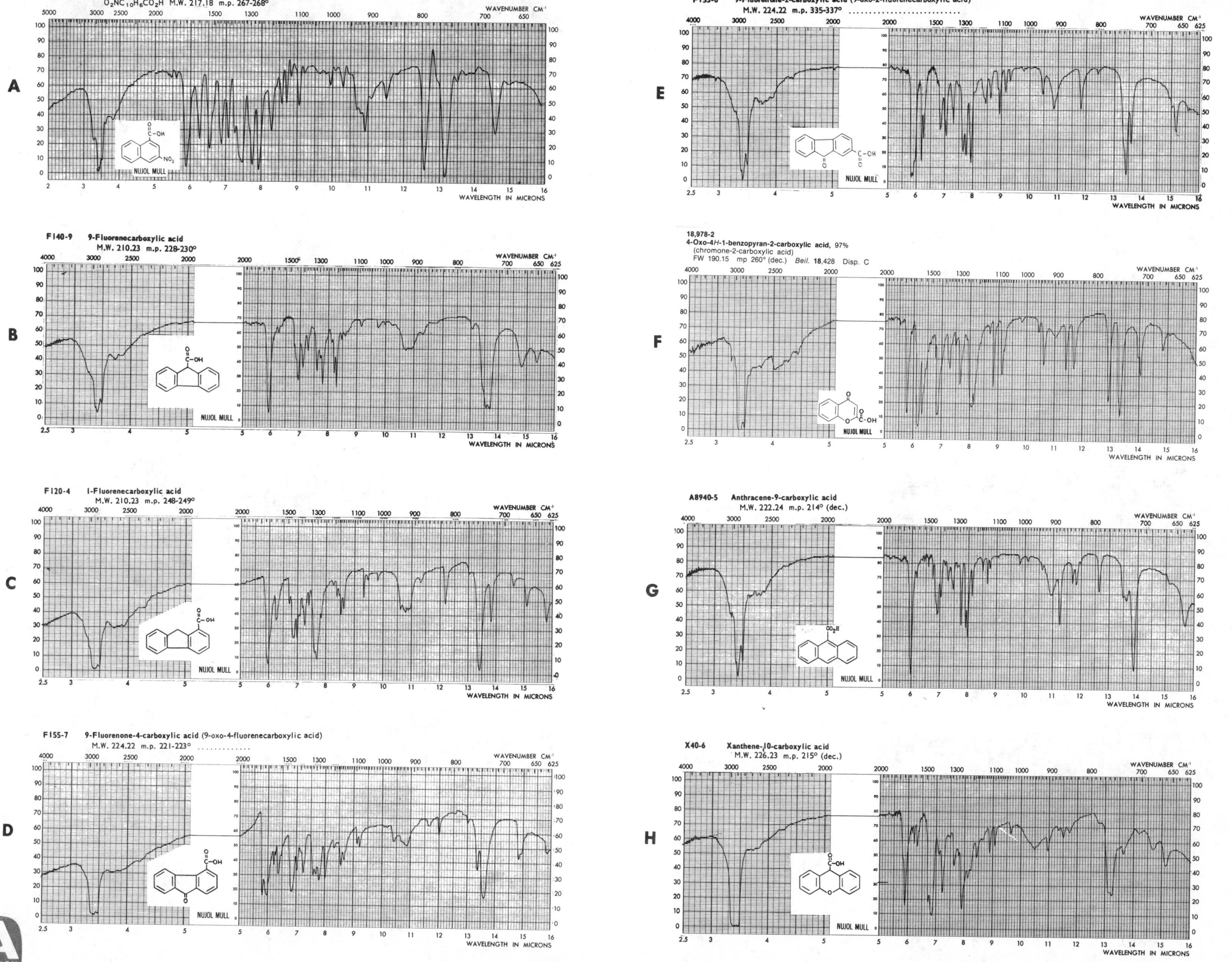
A
N1920-6 3-Nitro-1-naphthoic acid
$O_2NC_{10}H_6CO_2H$ M.W. 217.18 m.p. 267-268°
NUJOL MULL
B
F140-9 9-Fluorenecarboxylic acid
M.W. 210.23 m.p. 228-230°
NUJOL MULL
C
F120-4 1-Fluorenecarboxylic acid
M.W. 210.23 m.p. 248-249°
NUJOL MULL
D
F155-7 9-Fluorenone-4-carboxylic acid (9-oxo-4-fluorenecarboxylic acid)
M.W. 224.22 m.p. 221-223°
NUJOL MULL
E
F153-0 9-Fluorenone-2-carboxylic acid (9-oxo-2-fluorenecarboxylic acid)
M.W. 224.22 m.p. 335-337°
NUJOL MULL
F
18,978-2
4-Oxo-4H-1-benzopyran-2-carboxylic acid, 97%
(chromone-2-carboxylic acid)
FW 190.15 mp 260° (dec.) Beil. 18,428 Disp. C
NUJOL MULL
G
A8940-5 Anthracene-9-carboxylic acid
M.W. 222.24 m.p. 214° (dec.)
NUJOL MULL
H
X40-6 Xanthene-10-carboxylic acid
M.W. 226.23 m.p. 215° (dec.)
NUJOL MULL
WAVENUMBER CM⁻¹
WAVELENGTH IN MICRONS
ALDRICH

AROMATIC CARBOXYLIC ACIDS

A

85,179-5
Aristolochic acid
M.W. 341.28 m.p. 269-270° (dec.)

B

12,765-5 **Alizarin complexone** [(3,4-dihydroxy-2-anthraquinonyl)-methyl-iminodiacetic acid] **dihydrate**
M.W. 421.36 m.p. 147° (dec.)

C

18,384-9
Narceine hydrochloride
M.W. 481.93 m.p. 197° (dec.) Beil. **19**,370

D

22,598-3
3-Chloro-4-hydroxymandelic acid, 98%
$ClC_6H_3(OH)CH(OH)CO_2H$ FW 202.60
mp 145-147° Disp. C

E

22,419-7
4-Hexadecyloxybenzoic acid, 98%
$CH_3(CH_2)_{15}OC_6H_4CO_2H$ FW 362.56 mp 132°
Beil. **10**(3),286 Disp. C

F

22,004-3 **o-Iodosobenzoic acid, 97%**
$OIC_6H_4CO_2H$ FW 273.02 mp (dec.) 223-225°

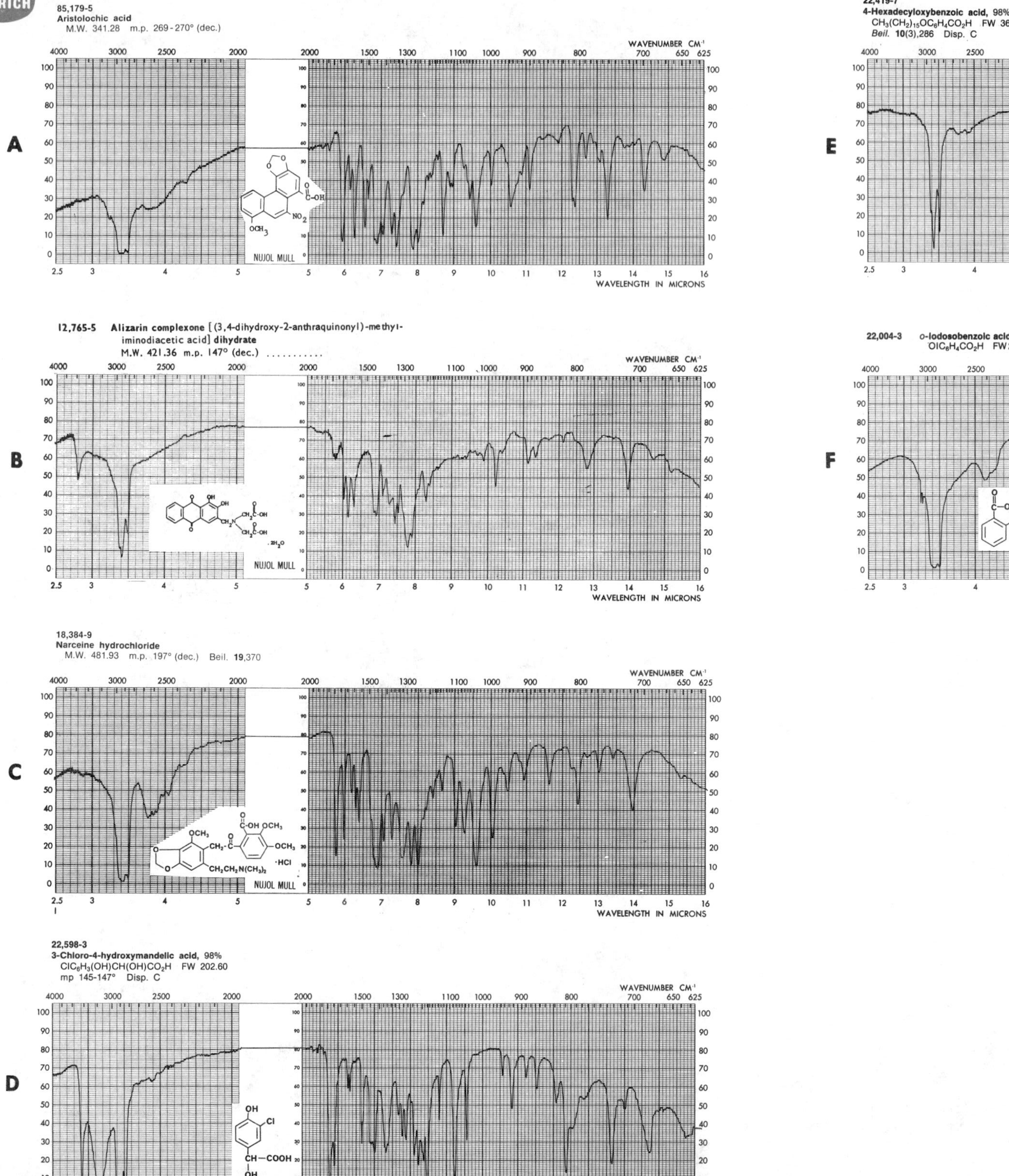

ALDRICH

ALDRICH

AROMATIC AMINO ACIDS AND ACID SALTS

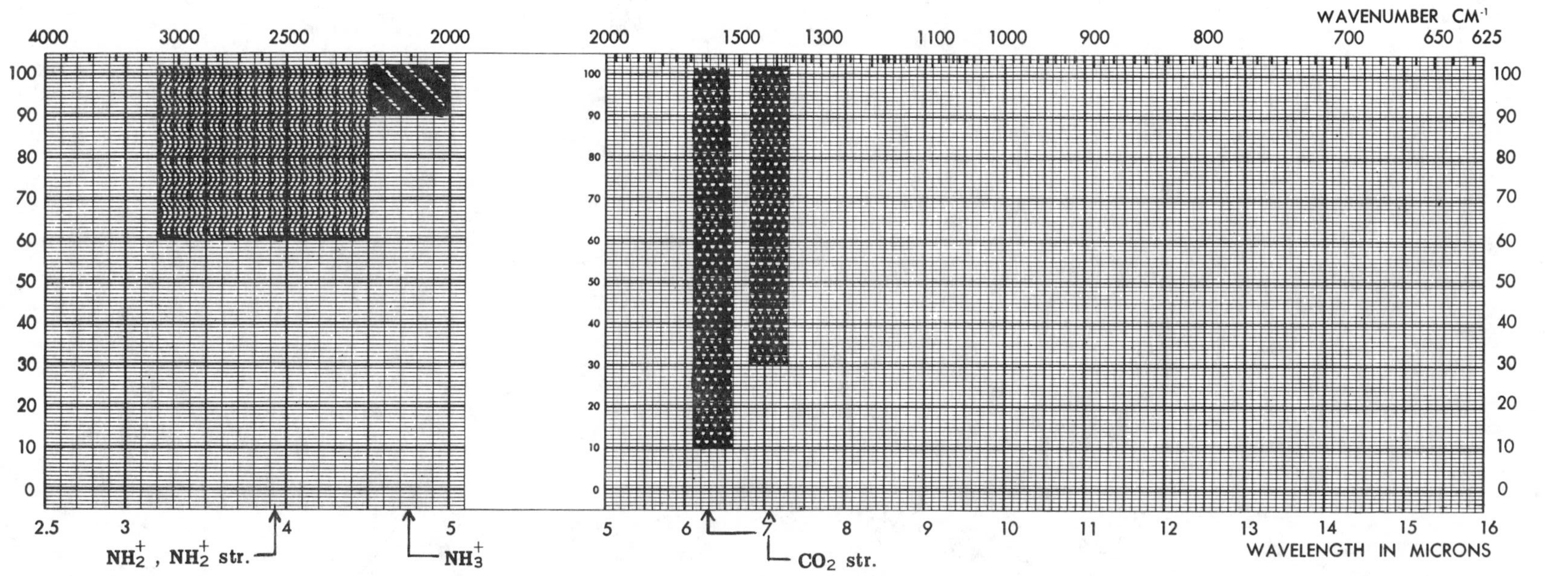

The aromatic amino acids absorb between 3.2 and 4.5 μ (3125 – 2220 cm^{-1}), protonated N–H stretch, and near 6.2 μ (1615 cm^{-1}), carboxylate stretch. When the aromatic ring is not conjugated with the carboxylate group, the normal positions of the substitution bands between 11 and 15 μ (910 – 665 cm^{-1}) are maintained.

In spectra 1000F—1012C, the amine function is blocked as an amide, thereby allowing the acid ($\overset{O}{\overset{\|}{C}}$–OH) absorptions to retain their regular positions.

The carboxylic acid salts display their carboxylate bands between 6.1 and 6.5 μ (1640 – 1540 cm^{-1}).

The sulfur linkage of the thioacetate of spectrum 1013B absorbs at 6.1 μ (1640 cm^{-1}) whereas the acetate counterpart (spectrum 1013A) absorbs strongly near 6.5 μ (1540 cm^{-1}).

Considerable interference from the ring conjugated carbonyl is again encountered in the 11 – 15 μ (910 – 665 cm^{-1}) aromatic substitution patterns.

A

$C_6H_5CH(NH_2)CO_2H$ M.W. 151.17
m.p. 290° (slowly sublimes)

NUJOL MULL

B

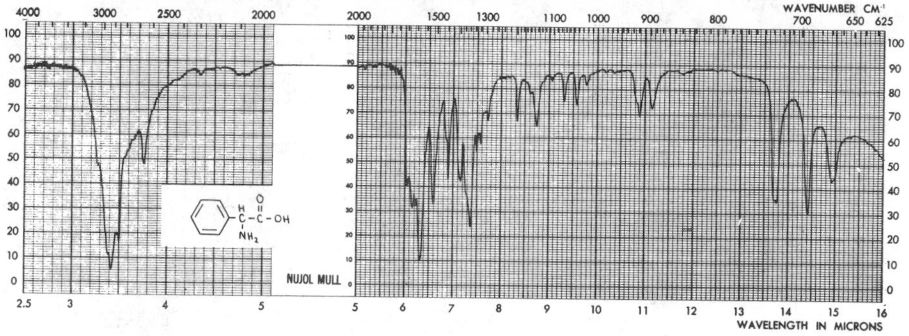

P2548-5 D-(-)-α-Phenylglycine [D-(-)-α-aminophenylacetic acid]
$C_6H_5CH(NH_2)CO_2H$ M.W. 151.17 m.p. 302°
$[\alpha]_D^{20}$ - 154.5° (c=1 in 1N HCl)

NUJOL MULL

C

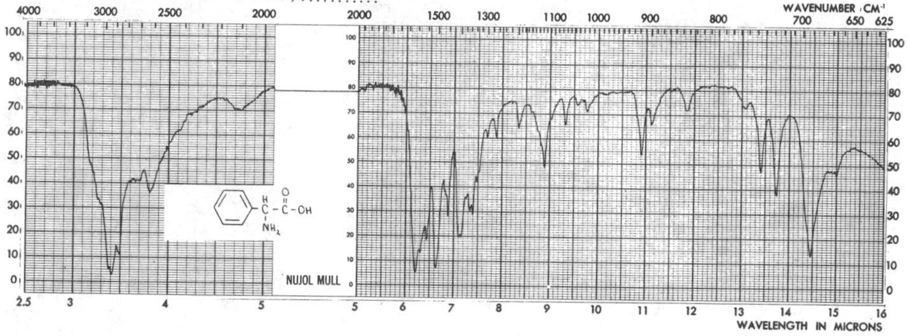

16,191-8
α,α-Diphenylglycine, 98%
$H_2NC(C_6H_5)_2CO_2H$
M.W. 227.26 m.p. 245-247° (dec.) Beil. 14(1),625

NUJOL MULL

D

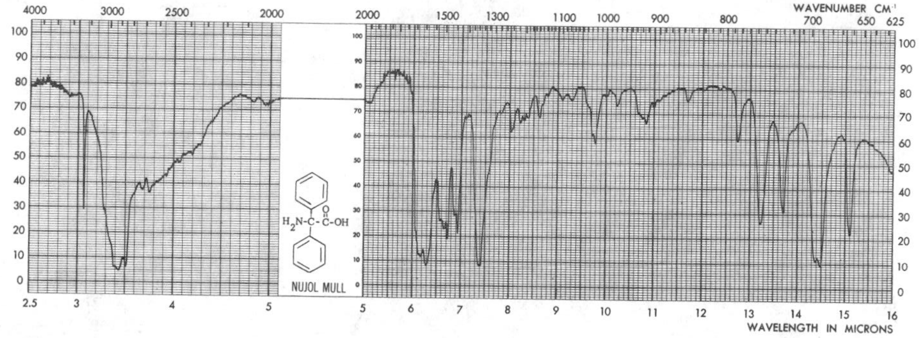

B2475-8 N-Benzyliminodiacetic acid
$C_6H_5CH_2N(CH_2CO_2H)_2$ M.W. 223.23 m.p. 202° (dec.)

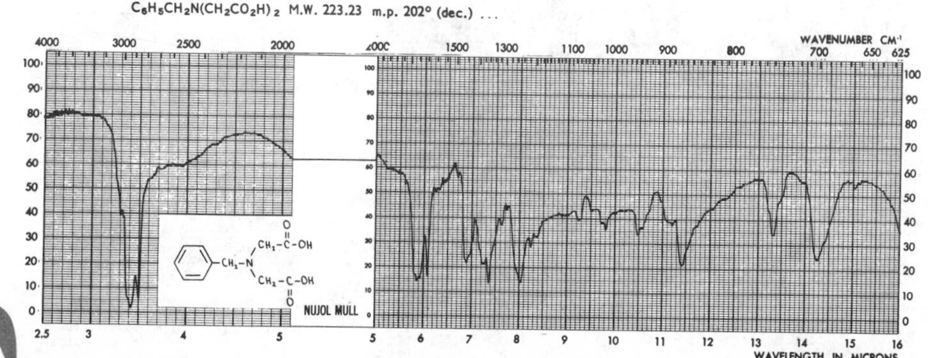

NUJOL MULL

E

11,308-5 2-Cyclopropyl-2-phenylglycine
$H_2NC(C_3H_5)(C_6H_5)CO_2H$ M.W. 191.23
m.p. 247° (dec.)

NUJOL MULL

F

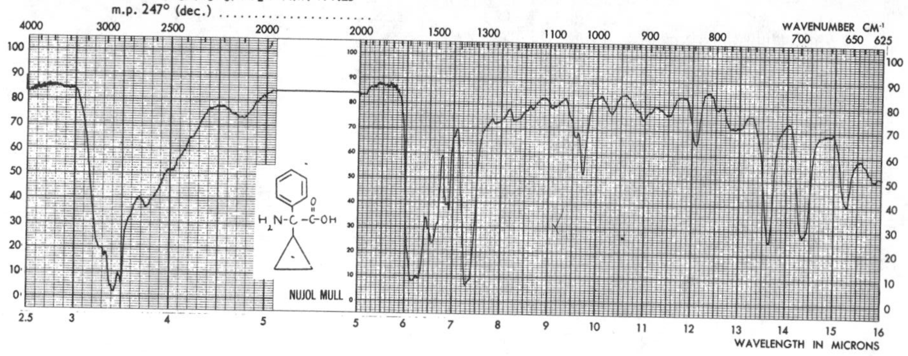

11,307-7 2-Cyclobutyl-2-phenylglycine
m.p. 294-296°
$H_2NC(C_4H_7)(C_6H_5)CO_2H$ M.W. 205.26

NUJOL MULL

G

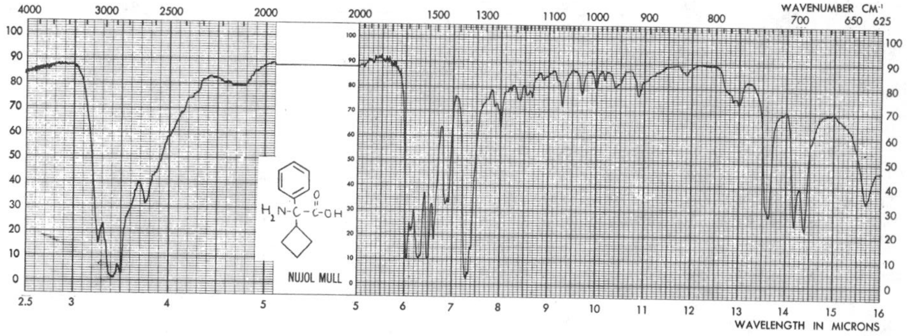

H5150-7 N-(p-Hydroxyphenyl)-glycine (glycin)
$HOC_6H_4NHCH_2CO_2H$ M.W. 167.16
m.p. 190° (dec.)

NUJOL MULL

H

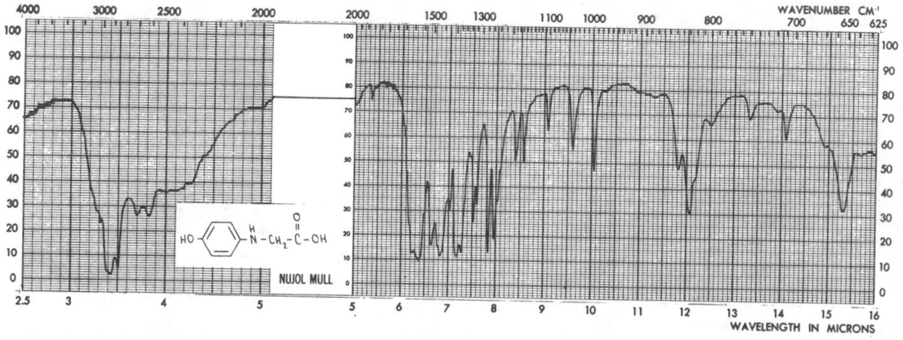

14,796-6 DL-Phenylalanine
$C_6H_5CH_2CH(NH_2)CO_2H$ M.W. 165.19
m.p. 266-267° (dec.)

NUJOL MULL

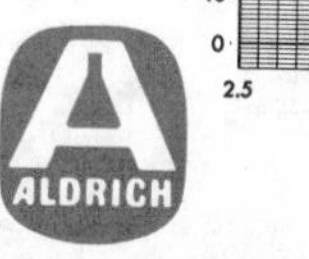

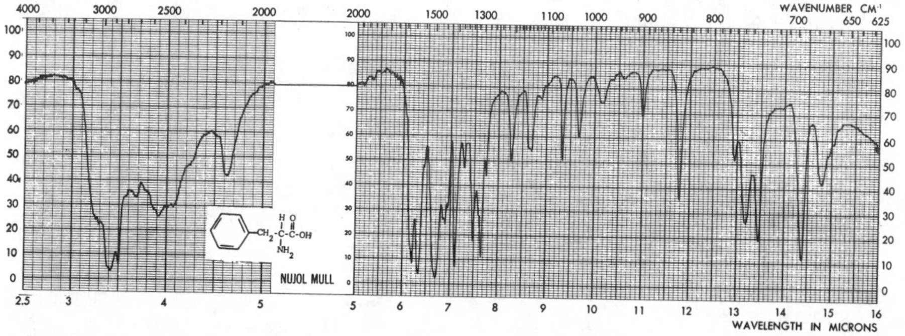

A

16,261-2
D-Phenylalanine, 99+%, GOLD LABEL
$C_6H_5CH_2CH(NH_2)CO_2H$
M.W. 165.19 m.p. 273-276° $[\alpha]^{23}$ +35° (c=2, H_2O)
Beil. **14**,494

NUJOL MULL

B

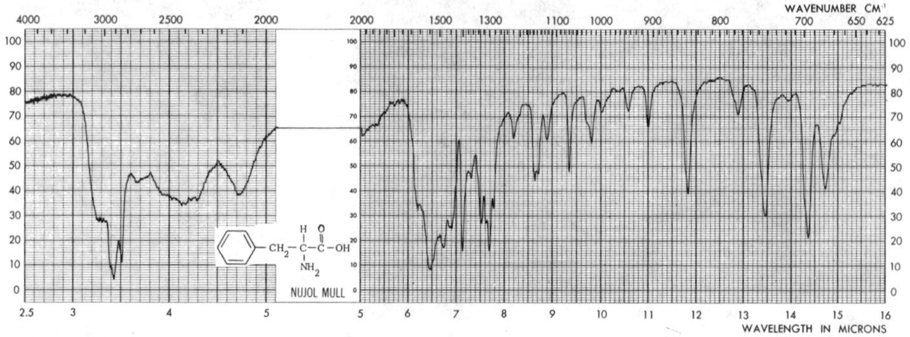

P1700-8 **L-Phenylalanine**
$C_6H_5CH_2CH(NH_2)CO_2H$ M.W. 165.19 m.p. 279-283°
$[\alpha]_D^{20}$ - 33° to - 34.6° (c=2 in H_2O)

NUJOL MULL

C

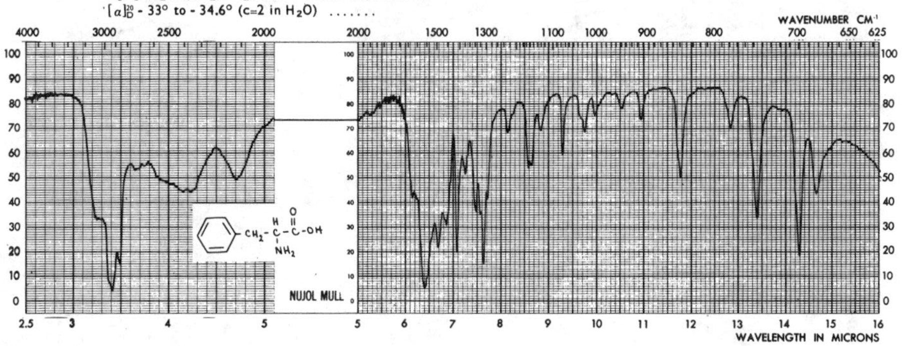

21,703-4
β-Methyl-DL-phenylalanine hydrochloride
$C_6H_5CH(CH_3)CH(NH_2)CO_2H \cdot HCl$ FW 215.68
mp 210° (dec.) *Beil.* **14**,512 Disp. D

NUJOL MULL

D

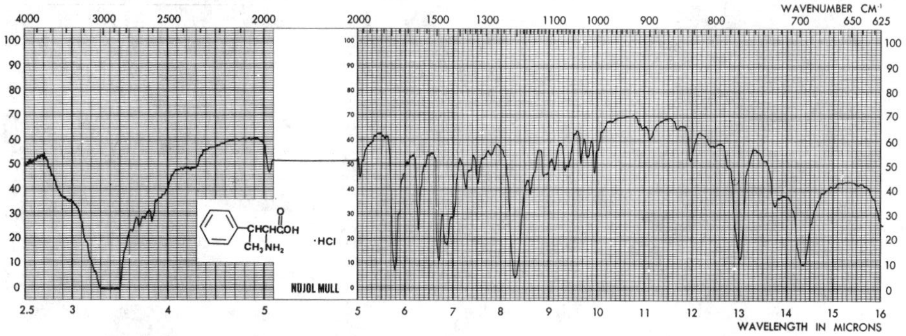

A7360-6 **DL-3-Amino-3-phenylpropionic acid** (DL-β-phenyl-β-alanine)
$C_6H_5CH(NH_2)CH_2CO_2H$ M.W. 165.19
m.p. 217°

E

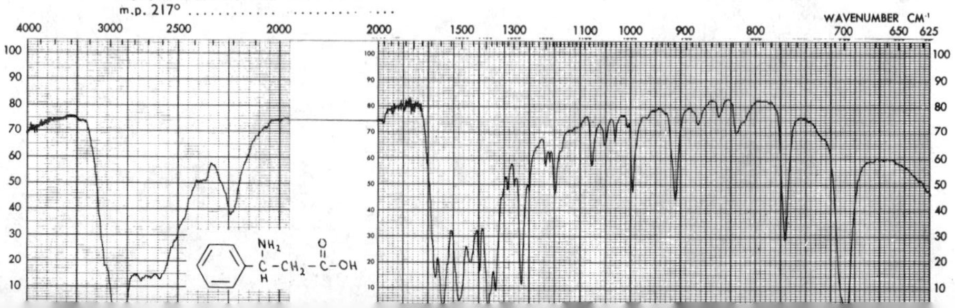

P3500 **β-Phenylserine**

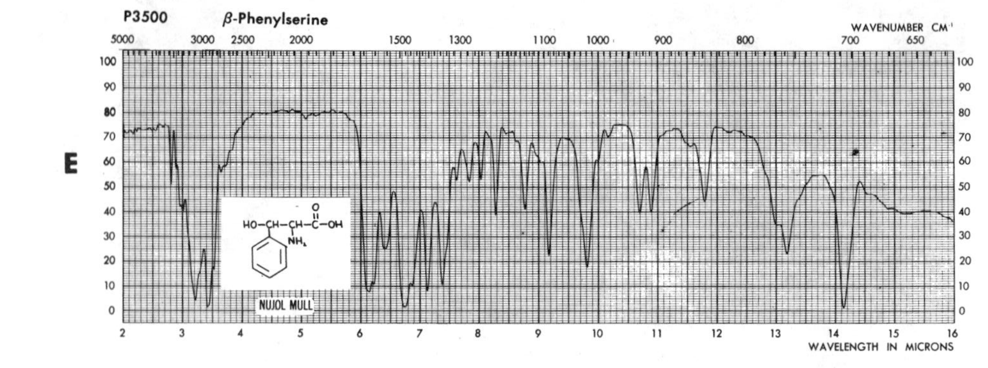

F

B1980-0 **S-Benzyl-L-cysteine**
$C_6H_5CH_2SCH_2CH(NH_2)CO_2H$ M.W. 211.28 m.p. 214° (dec.

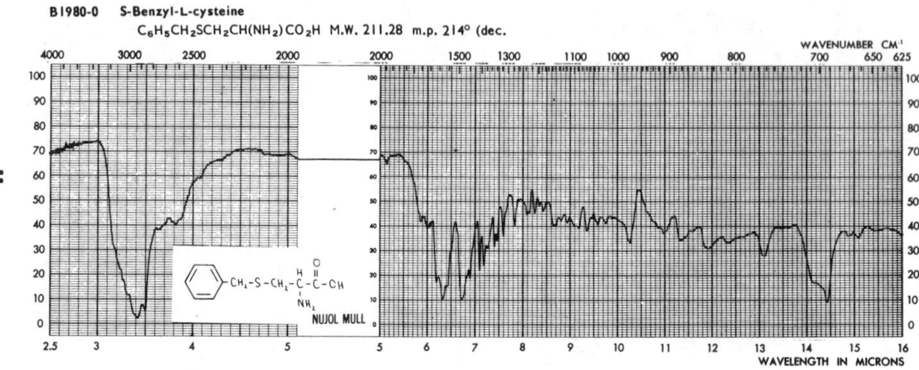

G

12,674-8 **S-Diphenylmethyl-L-cysteine** [3-(diphenylmethylthio)-alanine]
$(C_6H_5)_2CHSCH_2CH(NH_2)CO_2H$ M.W. 287.38
m.p. 204-206°

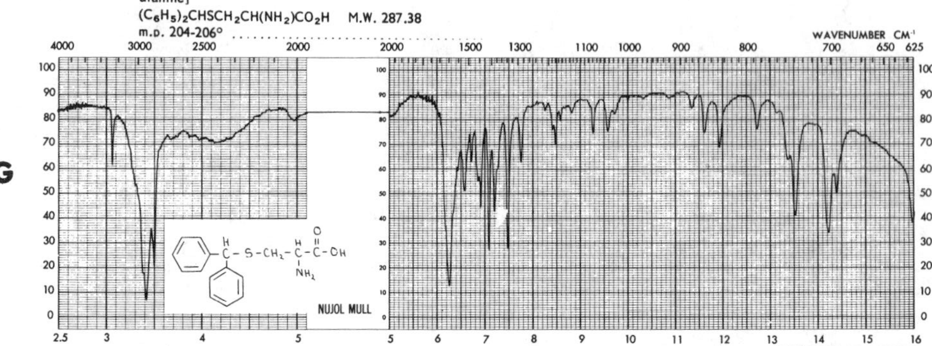

H

16,473-9
S-Trityl-L-cysteine, 97%
$(C_6H_5)_3CSCH_2CH(NH_2)CO_2H$
M.W. 363.48 m.p. 182-183° (dec.)
Protecting group in peptide synthesis.

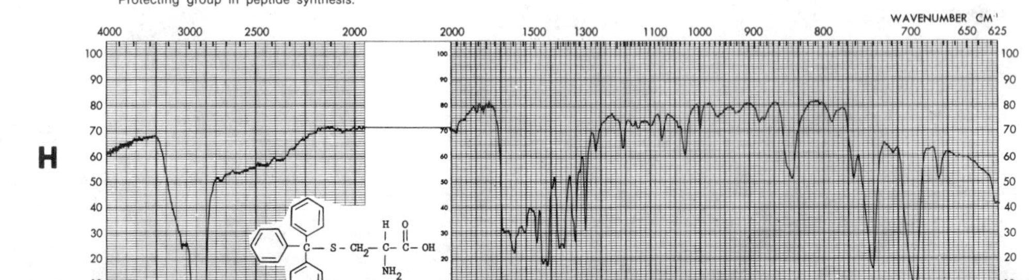

$FC_6H_4CH(NH_2)CO_2H$ FW 169.16
mp 290° (sublimes) Disp. C

A

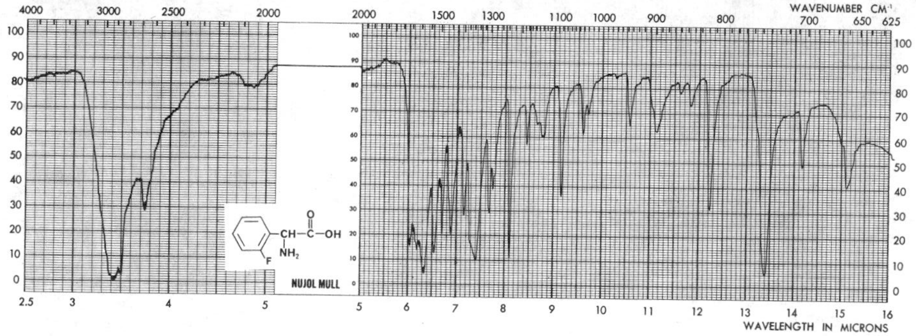

21,944-4
DL-o-Fluorophenylalanine, 99%
$FC_6H_4CH_2CH(NH_2)CO_2H$ FW 183.18
mp 243-246° *Beil.* **14**(3),1268 Disp. C

B

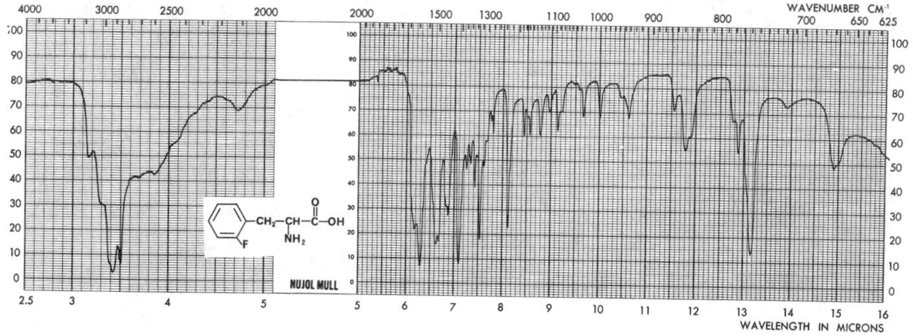

21,943-6
DL-m-Fluorophenylalanine, 95%
$FC_6H_4CH_2CH(NH_2)CO_2H$ FW 183.18
mp 240-250° *Beil.* **14**(3),1268 Disp. C

C

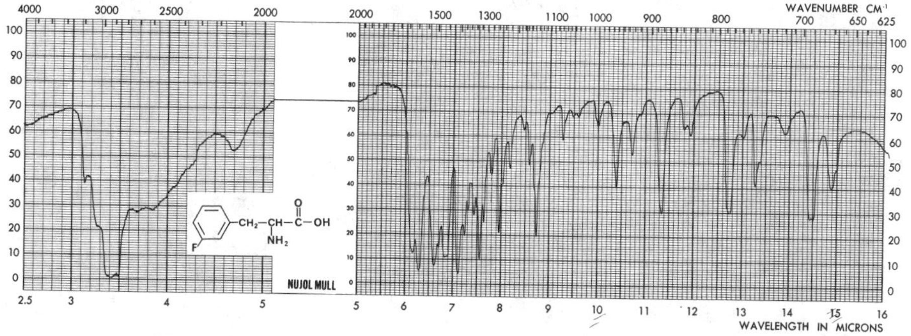

F1380-0 **DL-p-Fluorophenylalanine**
$FC_6H_4CH_2CH(NH_2)CO_2H$ M.W. 183.18 m.p. 261-263°

D

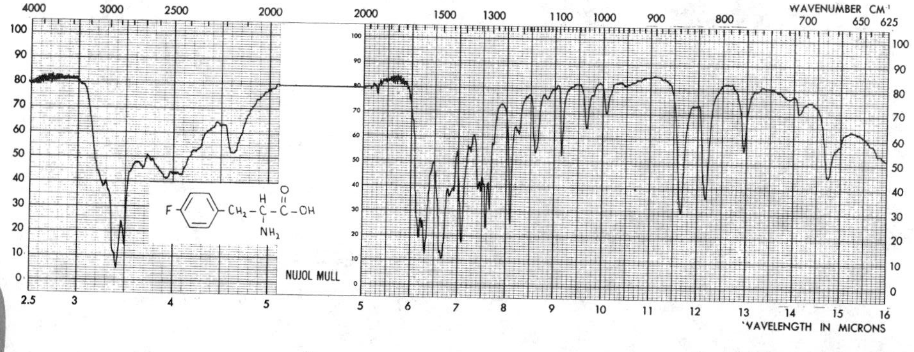

p-Chlorophenylalanine
$ClC_6H_4CH_2CH(NH_2)CO_2H$ M.W. 199.64
m.p. 258° (dec.)

E

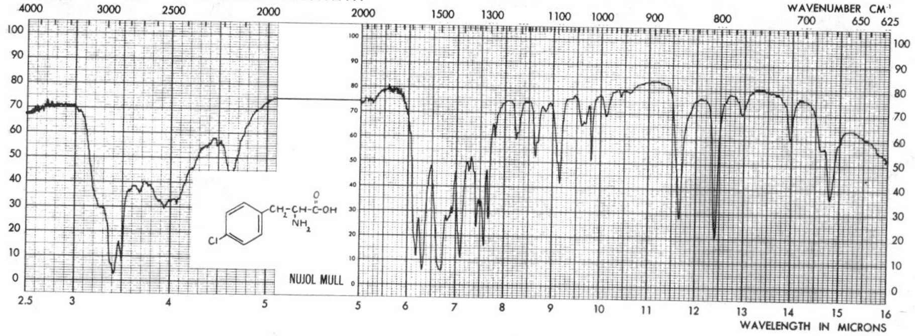

85,724-6
p-Bromo-DL-phenylalanine, 98+%
$BrC_6H_4CH_2CH(NH_2)CO_2H$
M.W. 244.09 m.p. 262-263° (dec.)

F

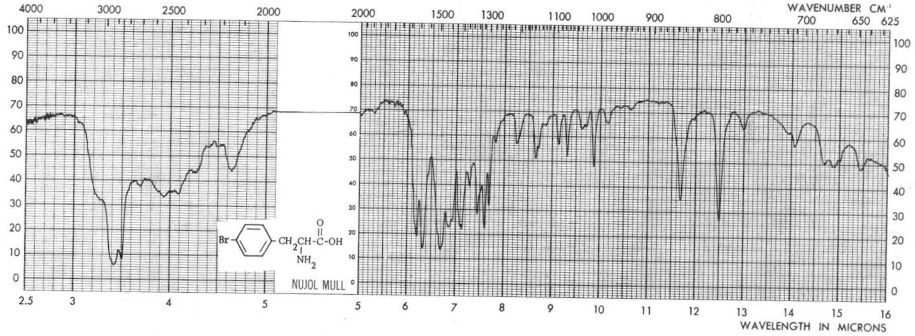

D12,430-3 **3,5-Diiodo-D-thyronine**
$4\text{-}[4\text{-}(HO)C_6H_4O]C_6H_2(I)_2CH_2CH(NH_2)CO_2H$ M.W. 525.08
$[\alpha]_D^{20}$ - 27° (c=1 in 1N HCl)

G

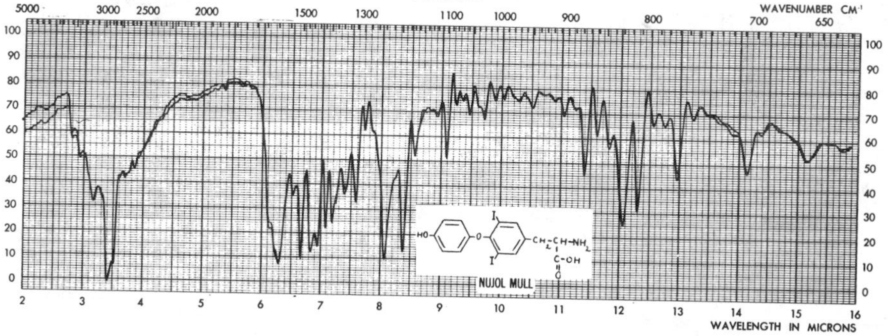

12,803-1 **3,5-Diiodo-L-thyronine**
$4\text{-}[4\text{-}(HO)C_6H_4O]C_6H_2(I)_2CH_2CH(NH_2)CO_2H$ M.W. 525.08
m.p. 260° (dec.) $[\alpha]_D^{20}$ + 27° (c=1 in 1N HCl)

H

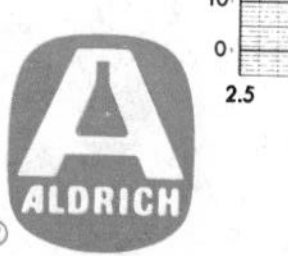

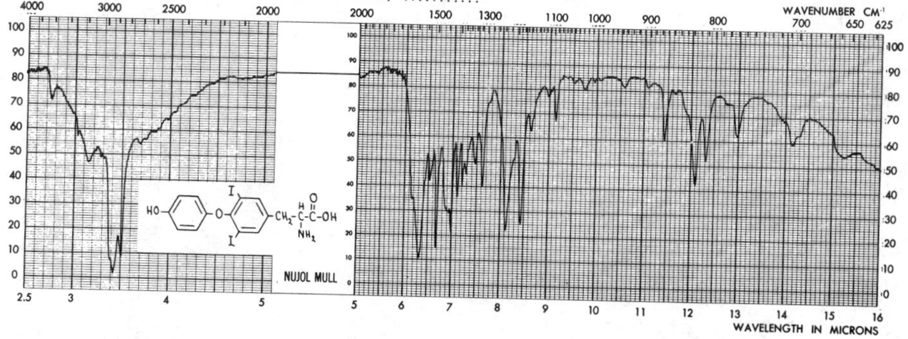

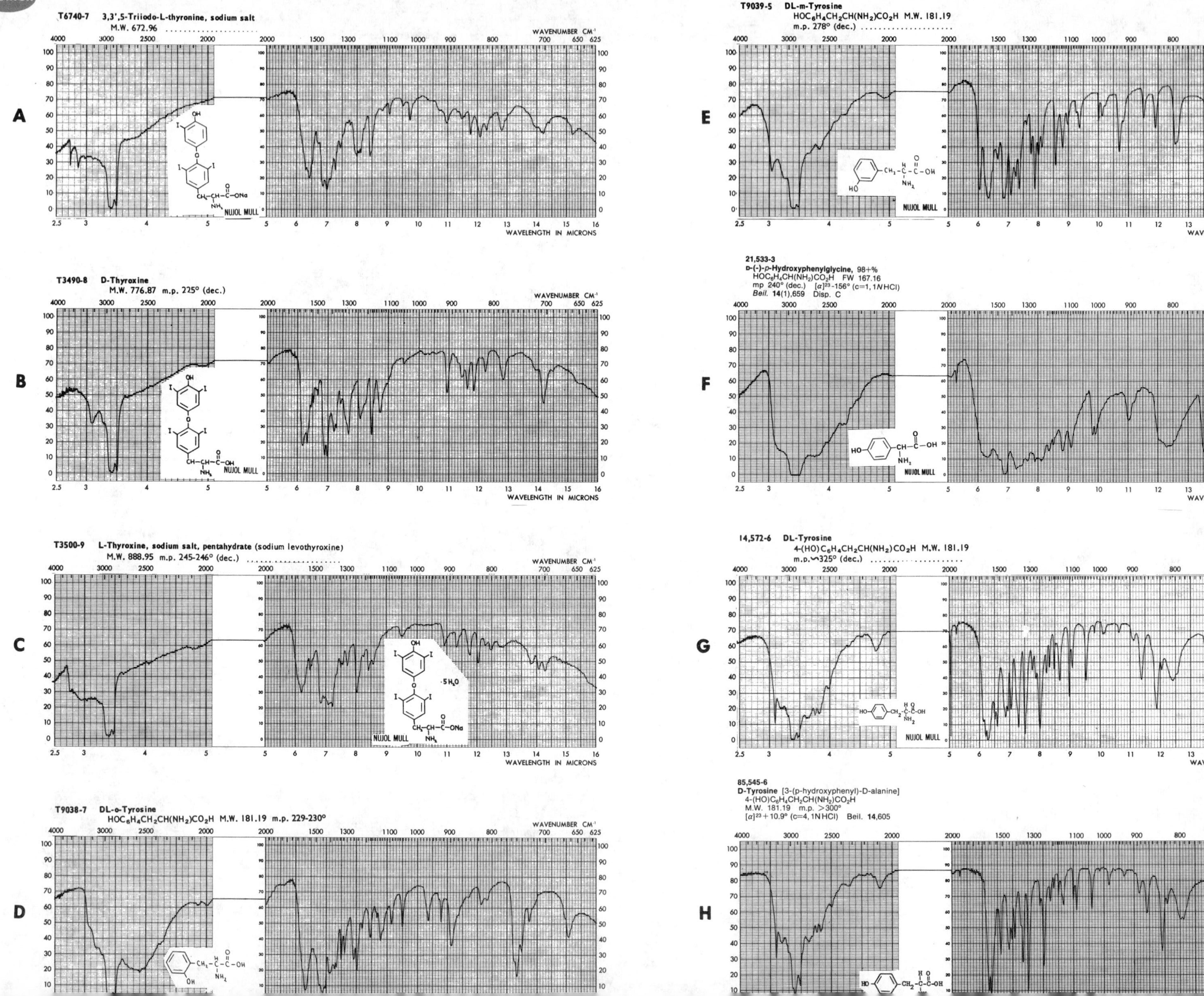

A T6740-7 3,3',5-Triiodo-L-thyronine, sodium salt
M.W. 672.96

B T3490-8 D-Thyroxine
M.W. 776.87 m.p. 225° (dec.)

C T3500-9 L-Thyroxine, sodium salt, pentahydrate (sodium levothyroxine)
M.W. 888.95 m.p. 245-246° (dec.)

D T9038-7 DL-o-Tyrosine
$HOC_6H_4CH_2CH(NH_2)CO_2H$ M.W. 181.19 m.p. 229-230°

E T9039-5 DL-m-Tyrosine
$HOC_6H_4CH_2CH(NH_2)CO_2H$ M.W. 181.19
m.p. 278° (dec.)

F 21,533-3
D-(-)-p-Hydroxyphenylglycine, 98+%
$HOC_6H_4CH(NH_2)CO_2H$ FW 167.16
mp 240° (dec.) $[\alpha]^{23}$ -156° (c=1, 1NHCl)
Beil. 14(1),659 Disp. C

G 14,572-6 DL-Tyrosine
$4\text{-}(HO)C_6H_4CH_2CH(NH_2)CO_2H$ M.W. 181.19
m.p. ~325° (dec.)

H 85,545-6
D-Tyrosine [3-(p-hydroxyphenyl)-D-alanine]
$4\text{-}(HO)C_6H_4CH_2CH(NH_2)CO_2H$
M.W. 181.19 m.p. >300°
$[\alpha]^{23}$ +10.9° (c=4, 1NHCl) Beil. 14,605

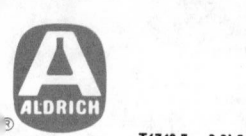

$[\alpha]_D^{18}$ - 10.2° (4% in IN HCl) ....

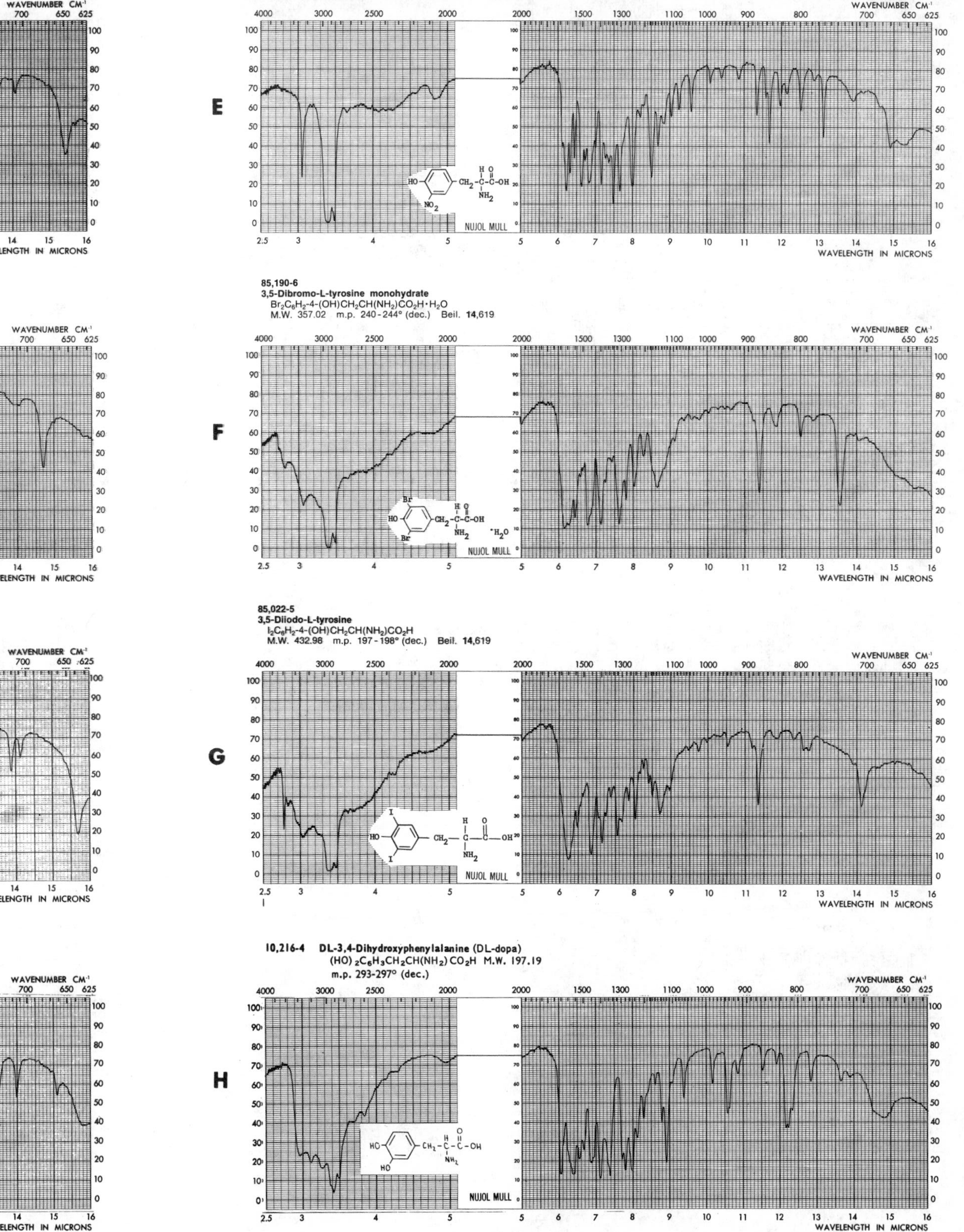

15,825-9
O-Methyl-L-tyrosine (p-methoxy-L-phenylalanine)
$CH_3OC_6H_4CH_2CH(NH_2)CO_2H$
M.W. 195.22 m.p. 259-261° (dec.)
$[\alpha]^{25}$ -7° (c=0.5, IN HCl) Beil. **14**(1),668

13,840-1 **m-Fluoro-DL-tyrosine**
FC_6H_3-4-(OH)$CH_2CH(NH_2)CO_2H$ M.W. 199.18
m.p. 268-270° (dec.) ....

I-1180-1 **3-Iodo-L-tyrosine, puriss.**
IC_6H_3-4-(OH)$CH_2CH(NH_2)CO_2H$ M.W. 307.09
m.p. 211° (dec.)

M.W. 226.19 m.p. 233-235° (dec.) Beil. **14**(2),379

85,190-6
3,5-Dibromo-L-tyrosine monohydrate
$Br_2C_6H_2$-4-(OH)$CH_2CH(NH_2)CO_2H \cdot H_2O$
M.W. 357.02 m.p. 240-244° (dec.) Beil. **14**,619

85,022-5
3,5-Diiodo-L-tyrosine
$I_2C_6H_2$-4-(OH)$CH_2CH(NH_2)CO_2H$
M.W. 432.98 m.p. 197-198° (dec.) Beil. **14**,619

10,216-4 **DL-3,4-Dihydroxyphenylalanine** (DL-dopa)
$(HO)_2C_6H_3CH_2CH(NH_2)CO_2H$ M.W. 197.19
m.p. 293-297° (dec.)

A 15,431-8 **L-DOPA** [3-(3,4-dihydroxyphenyl)-L-alanine]
$(HO)_2C_6H_3CH_2CH(NH_2)CO_2H$ M.W. 197.19
m.p. 295° (dec.) $[\alpha]_D^{25}$ -11.7° (c=5.3, 1N HCl)

NUJOL MULL

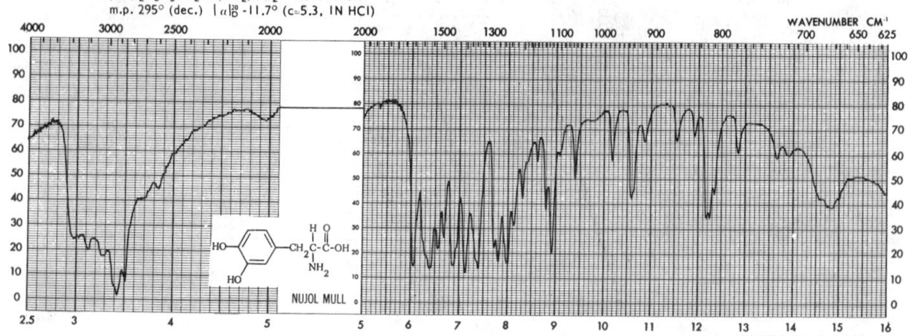

B 13,549-6
3-Amino-L-tyrosine dihydrochloride monohydrate
$H_2NC_6H_3$-4-$(OH)CH_2CH(NH_2)CO_2H \cdot 2HCl \cdot H_2O$
M.W. 285.13 m.p. 158-160° (dec.) Beil. **14**,622

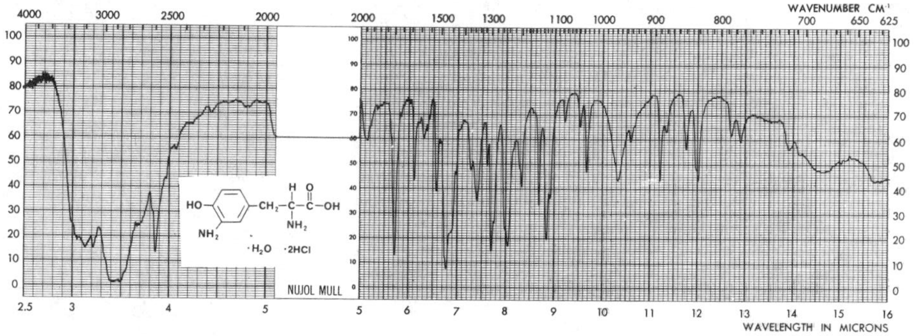

NUJOL MULL

C 85,870-6
p-Amino-DL-phenylalanine hydrate, 97%
$H_2NC_6H_4CH_2CH(NH_2)CO_2H \cdot xH_2O$
M.W. 180.21 m.p. 255-258° (dec.)

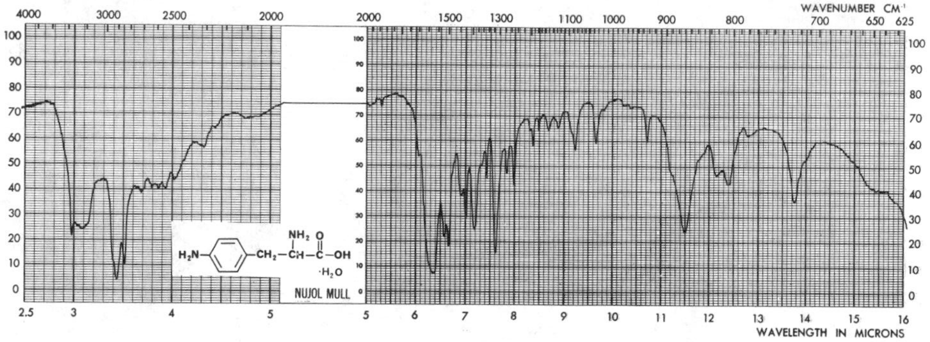

NUJOL MULL

D 85,129-9
p-Nitro-DL-phenylalanine
$O_2NC_6H_4CH_2CH(NH_2)CO_2H$
M.W. 210.19 m.p. 236-237° (dec.) Beil. **14**,506

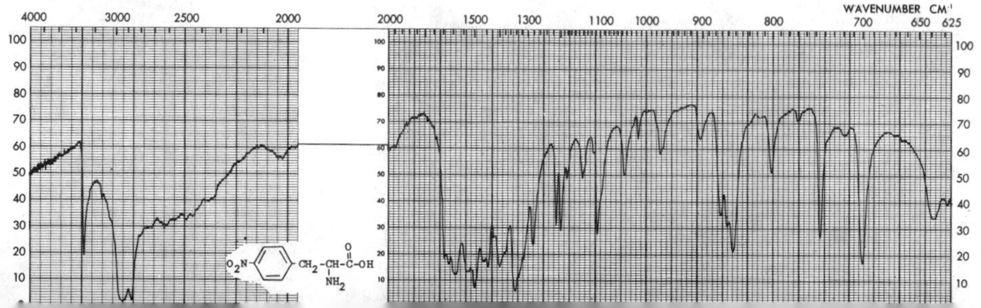

E 12,069-3 **DL-α-Methyltyrosine**
(send for data sheet)
$4\text{-}(HO)C_6H_4CH_2C(CH_3)(NH_2)CO_2H$ M.W. 195.22
m.p. > 300° ....

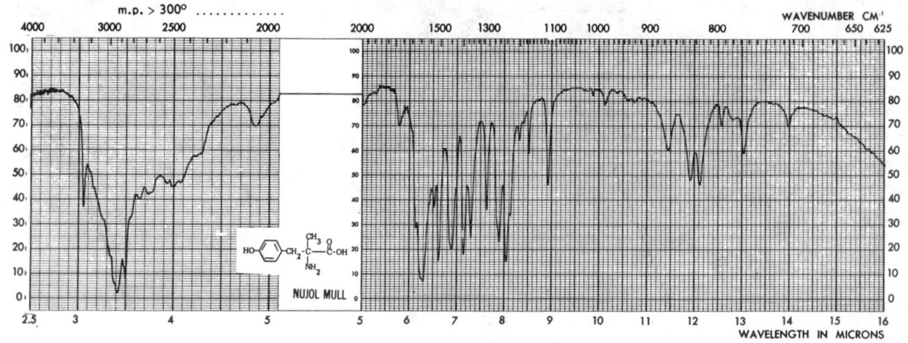

NUJOL MULL

F 85,583-9
O-Benzyl-L-tyrosine (p-benzyloxy-L-phenylalanine)
$C_6H_5CH_2OC_6H_4CH_2CH(NH_2)CO_2H$
M.W. 271.32 m.p. 259° (dec.)

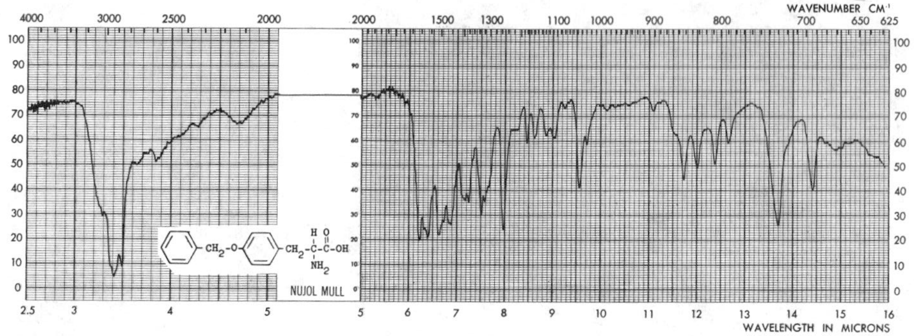

NUJOL MULL

G 14,882-2 **α-MMT** (DL-α-methyl-m-tyrosine) **monohydrate**
$HOC_6H_4CH_2C(CH_3)(NH_2)CO_2H \cdot H_2O$ M.W. 213.24
m.p. 290° (dec.)

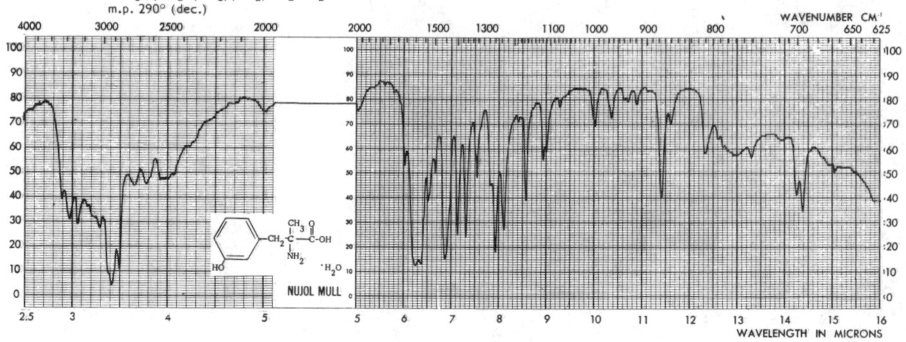

NUJOL MULL

H 85,742-4
3-(3,4-Dihydroxyphenyl)-2-methyl-DL-alanine, 99+%,
GOLD LABEL (α-methyl-DL-DOPA)
$(HO)_2C_6H_3CH_2C(CH_3)(NH_2)CO_2H$
M.W. 211.22 m.p. >300°

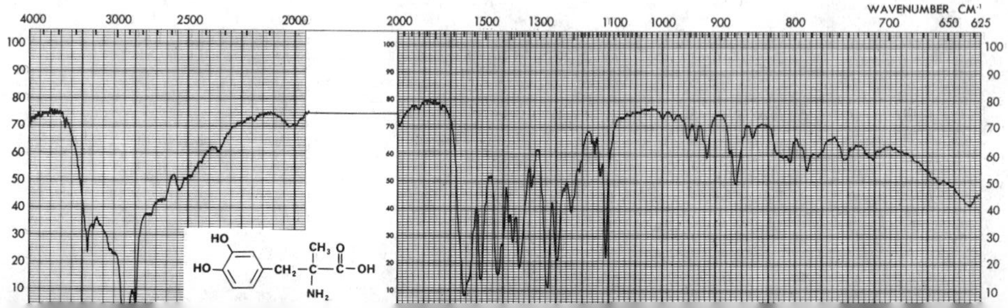

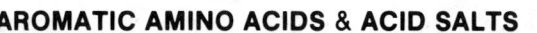

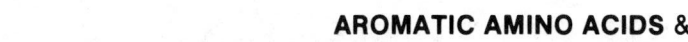

M.W. 229.24 m.p. >300°

A

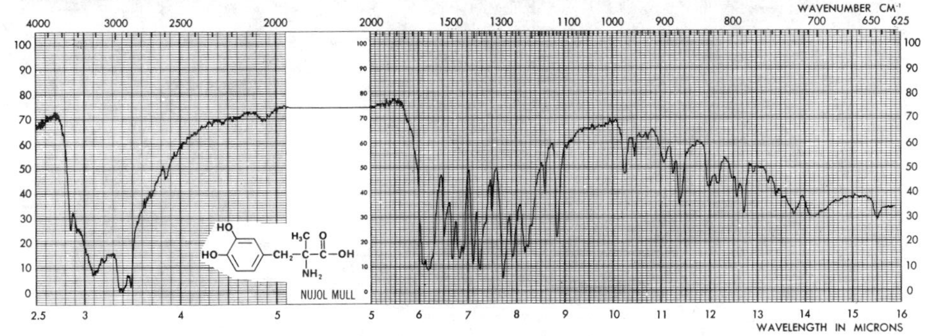

14,885-7 DL-α,3-Dimethyltyrosine
$CH_3C_6H_3$-4-(OH) $CH_2C(CH_3)(NH_2)CO_2H$
M.W. 209.25 m.p. >300°

B

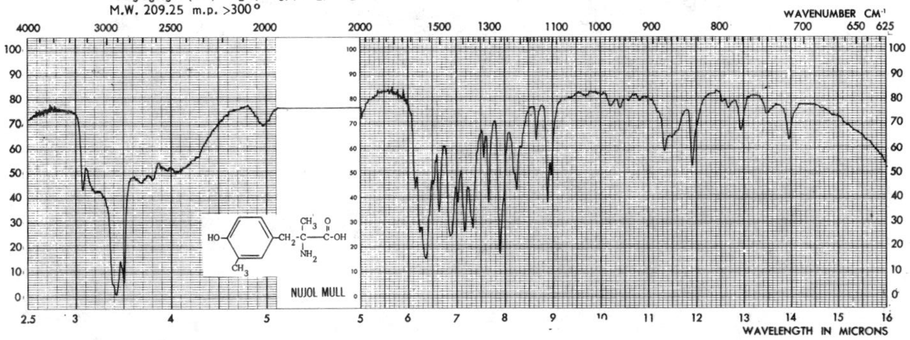

17,160-3
DL-3-Phenylserine hydrate
$C_6H_5CH(OH)CH(NH_2)CO_2H \cdot xH_2O$
M.W. 181.19 m.p. 186° (dec.) Beil. **14**,623

C

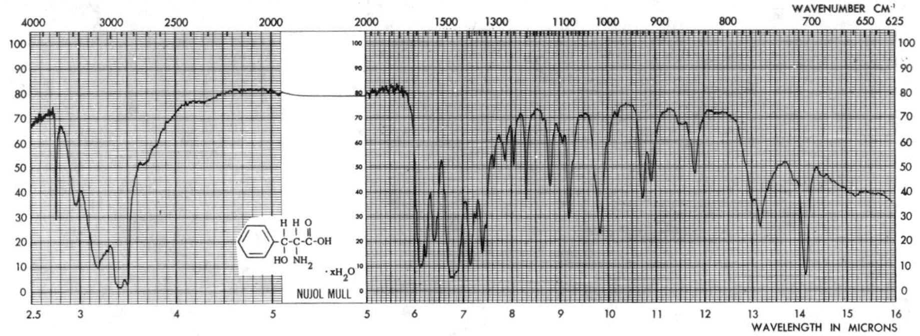

14,884-9 DL-DOPS (DL-*threo*-3,4-dihydroxyphenylserine)
$(HO)_2C_6H_3CH(OH)CH(NH_2)CO_2H$ M.W. 213.19
m.p. 210° (dec.) ....

D

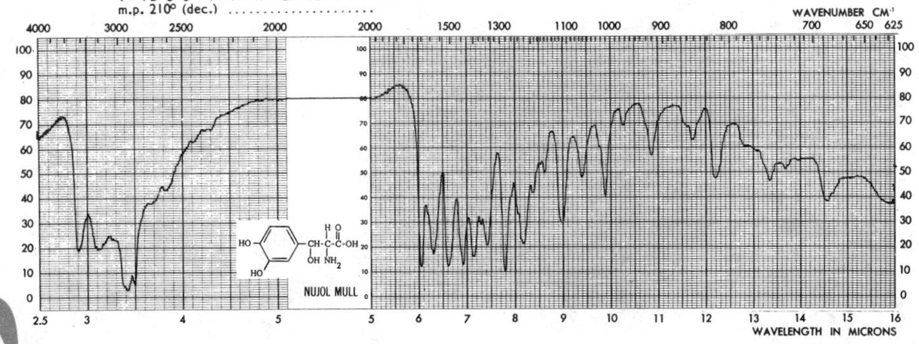

m.p. 221° (dec.) ....

E

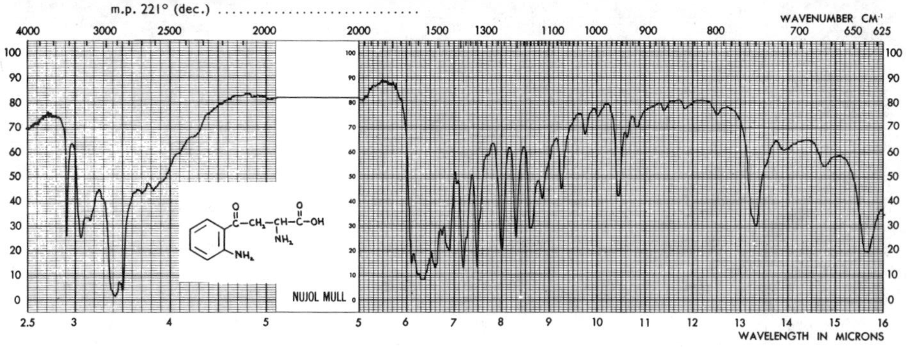

85,710-6
N-Benzoyl-L-alanine, 99%
$CH_3CH(NHCOC_6H_5)CO_2H$
M.W. 193.2 m.p. 143-145° $[\alpha]^{25}_{D}$ -3.3° (c=1, H_2O)

F

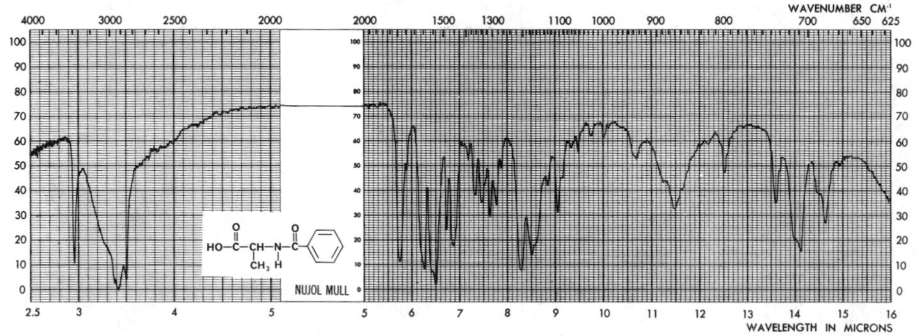

85,296-1
N-Benzoyl-L-tyrosinamide
4-(HO)$C_6H_4CH_2CH(NHCOC_6H_5)CONH_2$
M.W. 284.32 m.p. 205-208°

G

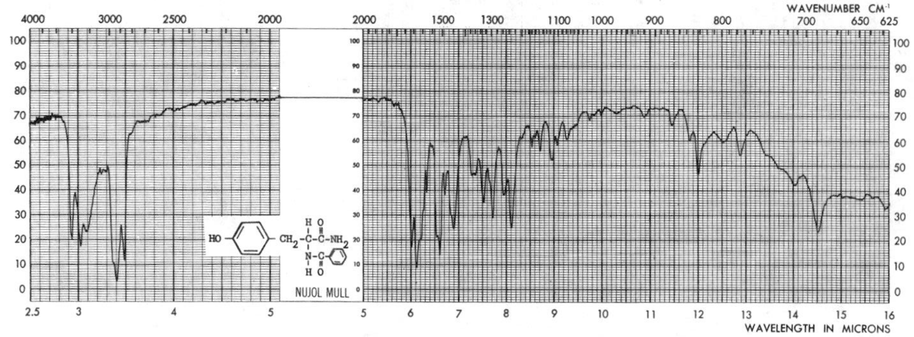

85,871-4
N-Benzoyl-DL-methionine, 99%
$CH_3SCH_2CH_2CH(NHCOC_6H_5)CO_2H$
M.W. 253.32 m.p. 154-156°

H

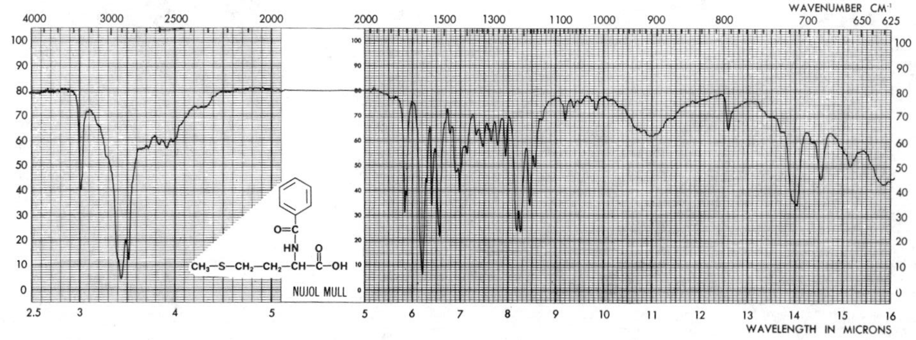

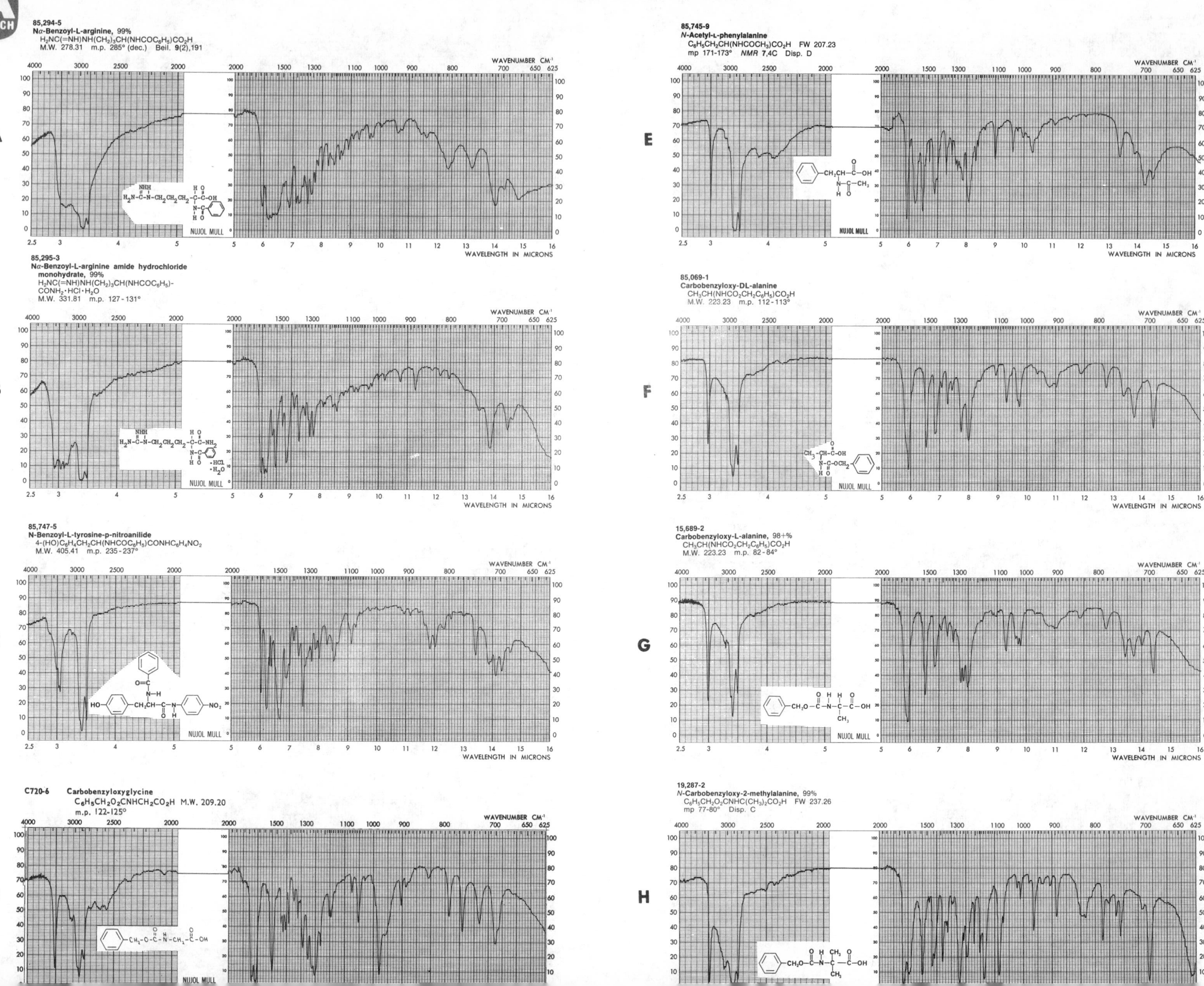
ALDRICH
A
85,294-5
Nα-Benzoyl-L-arginine, 99%
H₂NC(=NH)NH(CH₂)₃CH(NHCOC₆H₅)CO₂H
M.W. 278.31 m.p. 285° (dec.) Beil. 9(2),191
B
85,295-3
Nα-Benzoyl-L-arginine amide hydrochloride monohydrate, 99%
H₂NC(=NH)NH(CH₂)₃CH(NHCOC₆H₅)-CONH₂·HCl·H₂O
M.W. 331.81 m.p. 127-131°
C
85,747-5
N-Benzoyl-L-tyrosine-p-nitroanilide
4-(HO)C₆H₄CH₂CH(NHCOC₆H₅)CONHC₆H₄NO₂
M.W. 405.41 m.p. 235-237°
D
C720-6 Carbobenzyloxyglycine
C₆H₅CH₂O₂CNHCH₂CO₂H M.W. 209.20
m.p. 122-125°
E
85,745-9
N-Acetyl-L-phenylalanine
C₆H₅CH₂CH(NHCOCH₃)CO₂H FW 207.23
mp 171-173° NMR 7,4C Disp. D
F
85,069-1
Carbobenzyloxy-DL-alanine
CH₃CH(NHCO₂CH₂C₆H₅)CO₂H
M.W. 223.23 m.p. 112-113°
G
15,689-2
Carbobenzyloxy-L-alanine, 98+%
CH₃CH(NHCO₂CH₂C₆H₅)CO₂H
M.W. 223.23 m.p. 82-84°
H
19,287-2
N-Carbobenzyloxy-2-methylalanine, 99%
C₆H₅CH₂O₂CNHC(CH₃)₂CO₂H FW 237.26
mp 77-80° Disp. C
NUJOL MULL
WAVENUMBER CM⁻¹
WAVELENGTH IN MICRONS

m.p. 124-126°

A

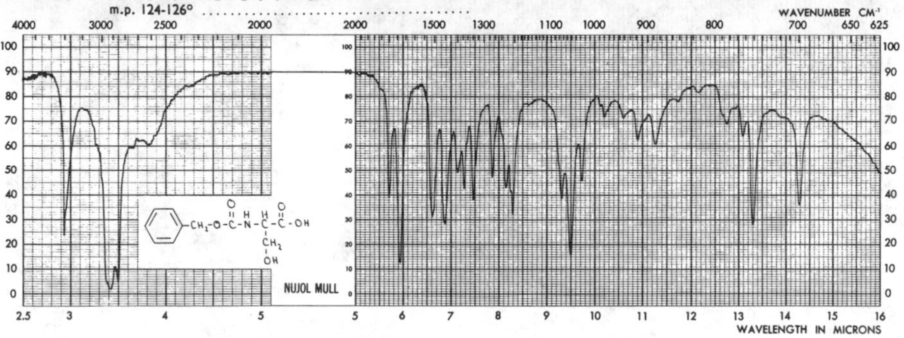

NUJOL MULL

86,070-0
Carbobenzyloxy-L-serine, 99+%
$HOCH_2CH(NHCO_2CH_2C_6H_5)CO_2H$ FW 239.23
mp 117-119° $[\alpha]_D^{25}$ +5.8°±0.5° (c=2.7, CH_3CO_2H)
Disp. D

B

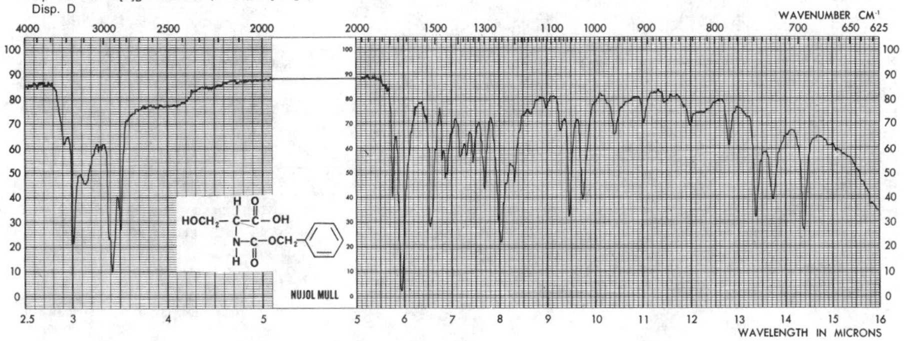

NUJOL MULL

C860-1 **Carbobenzyloxy-L-proline**
M.W. 249.27 n_D^{20} 1.5338

C

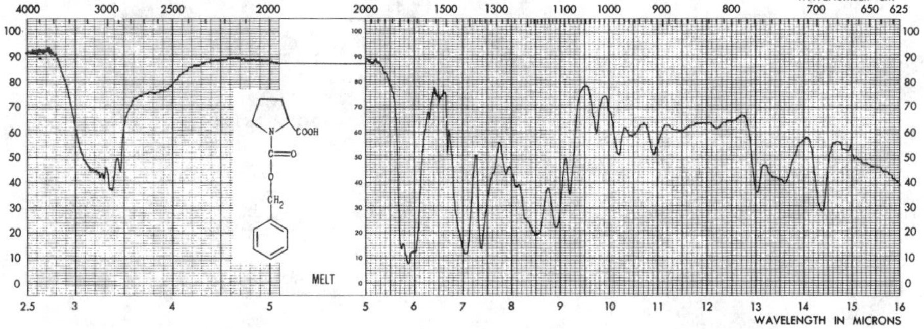

MELT

85,831-5
Carbobenzyloxy-DL-norvaline
$CH_3CH_2CH_2CH(NHCO_2CH_2C_6H_5)CO_2H$
M.W. 251.28 m.p. 85-87°

D

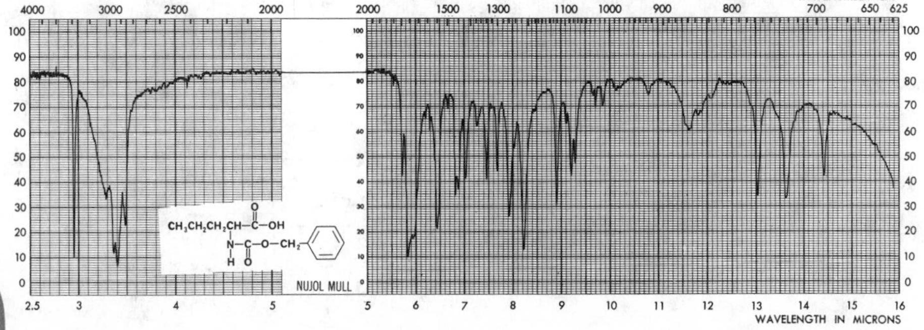

NUJOL MULL

m.p. 249° (dec.)

E

NUJOL MULL

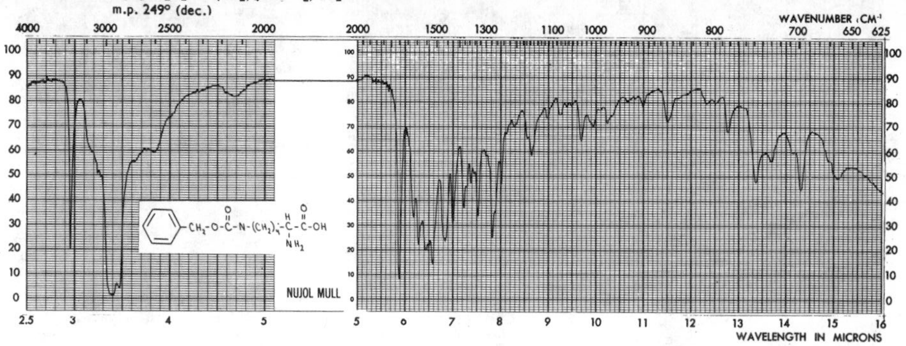

86,057-3
Nα-Carbobenzyloxy-L-lysine *p*-nitrophenyl ester hydrochloride
$H_2N(CH_2)_4CH(NHCO_2CH_2C_6H_5)CO_2C_6H_4NO_2 \cdot HCl$
FW 437.88 mp 150-152° (dec.)
$[\alpha]^{25}$ -25.0° (c=1, CH_3CO_2H) Disp. C

F

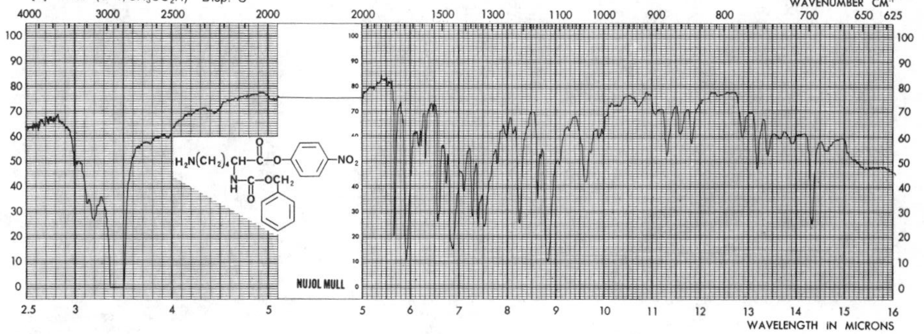

NUJOL MULL

16,262-0
N-Carbobenzyloxy-L-aspartic acid
$HO_2CCH_2CH(NHCO_2CH_2C_6H_5)CO_2H$
M.W. 267.24 m.p. 117-119°
$[\alpha]^{23}$ +8.6° (c=7, CH_3CO_2H)

G

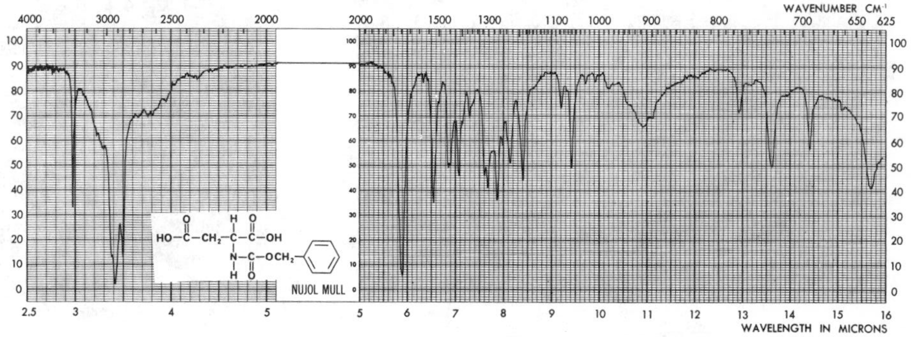

NUJOL MULL

C640-4 **Carbobenzyloxy-L-asparagine**
$H_2NCOCH_2CH(NHCO_2CH_2C_6H_5)CO_2H$ M.W. 266.25
m.p. 158-160°

H

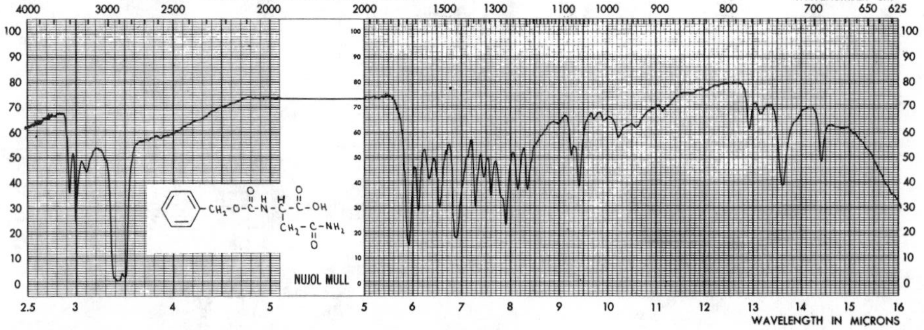

NUJOL MULL

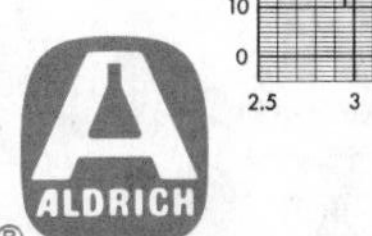

A

85,902-8
L-γ-Glutamyl-p-nitroanilide
$O_2NC_6H_4NHCOCH_2CH_2CH(NH_2)CO_2H$
M.W. 267.24 m.p. 192-193°

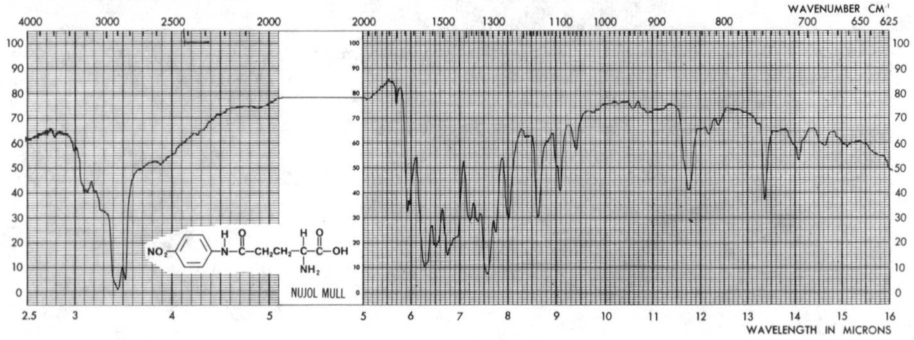

NUJOL MULL

B

22,110-4
N-(p-Nitrobenzoyl)-L-glutamic acid diethyl ester, 98%
$C_2H_5O_2CCH_2CH_2CH(NHCOC_6H_4NO_2)CO_2C_2H_5$
$[\alpha]^{24}$ +20.5° (c=2, $CHCl_3$)

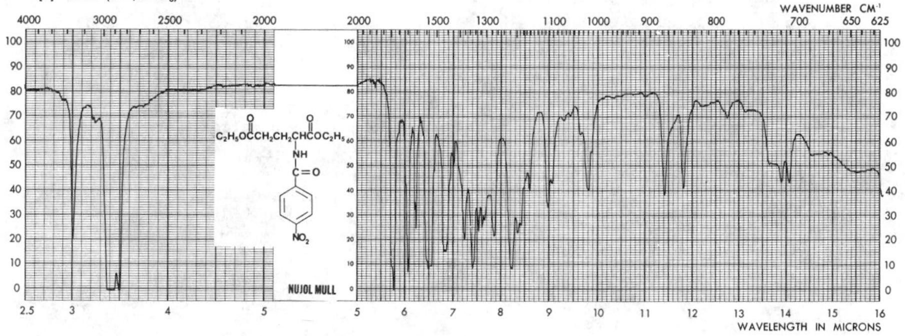

NUJOL MULL

C

85,906-0
N-Benzyloxycarbonyl-L-glutamic acid
$HO_2CCH_2CH_2CH(NHCO_2CH_2C_6H_5)CO_2H$
FW 281.26 mp 118-120°
$[\alpha]^{22}$ -7.4° (c=10, CH_3CO_2H) Disp. C

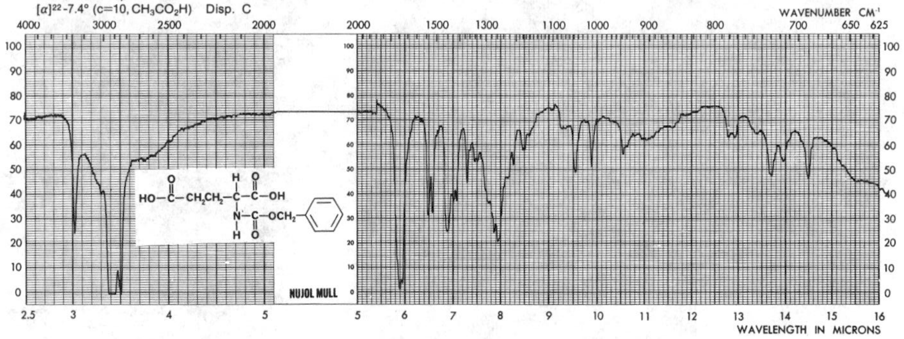

NUJOL MULL

D

C660-9 **Carbobenzyloxy-L-glutamic acid**
$HO_2CCH_2CH_2CH(NHCO_2CH_2C_6H_5)CO_2H$ M.W. 281.26
m.p. 120-122°

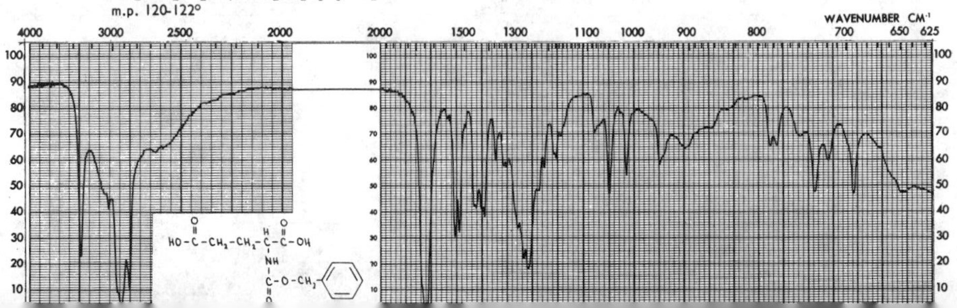

E

22,111-2
N-(p-Nitrobenzoyl)-L-glutamic acid hemihydrate, 98%
$HO_2CCH_2CH_2CH(NHCOC_6H_4NO_2)CO_2H \cdot 1/2H_2O$
$[\alpha]^{24}$ +15.1° (c=2, 1N NaOH)

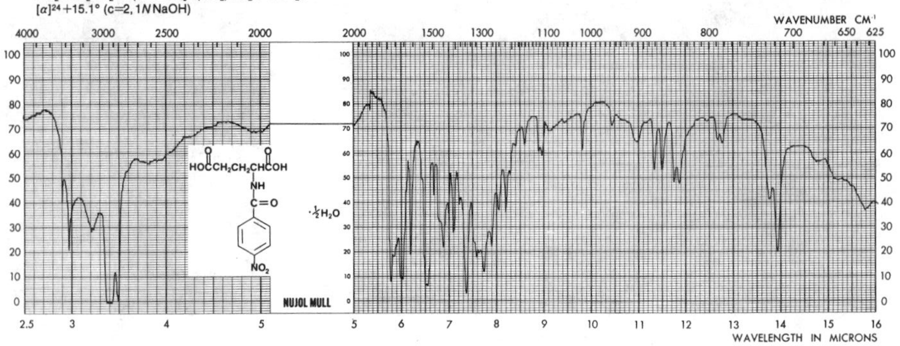

NUJOL MULL

F

22,112-0
N-(p-Aminobenzoyl)-L-glutamic acid diethyl ester, 99%
$C_2H_5O_2CCH_2CH_2CH(NHCOC_6H_4NH_2)CO_2C_2H_5$
FW 322.36 mp 139-142°
$[\alpha]^{21}$ +17.9° (c=5, $CHCl_3$) Disp. C

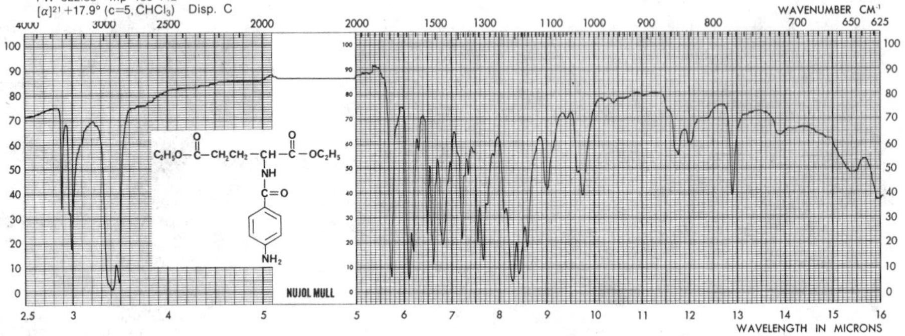

NUJOL MULL

G

16,264-7
Carbobenzyloxy-L-glutamine
$H_2NCOCH_2CH_2CH(NHCO_2CH_2C_6H_5)CO_2H$
M.W. 280.28 m.p. 135-137°
$[\alpha]^{23}$ -7.3° (c=2, C_2H_5OH)

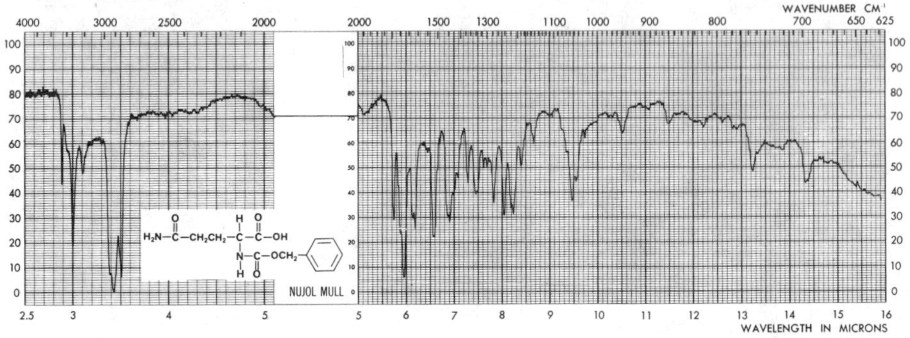

NUJOL MULL

H

86,020-4
N-(γ-L-Glutamyl)phenylalanine
$C_6H_5CH_2CH(CO_2H)NHCOCH_2CH_2CH(NH_2)CO_2H$
FW 294.31 mp 180-183° $[\alpha]^{24}$ +17.4° (c=4, H_2O)
Disp. L

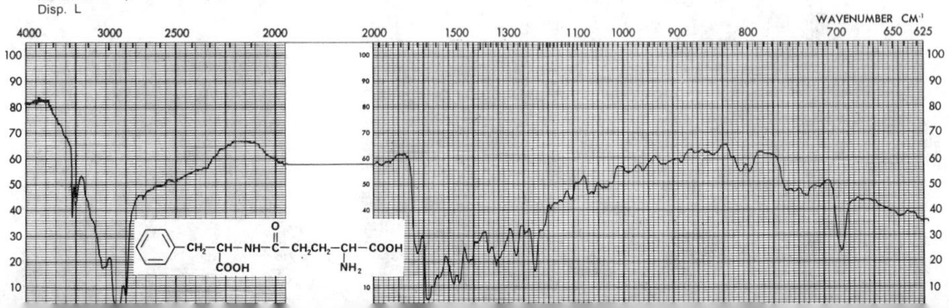

WAVENUMBER CM^{-1} — WAVELENGTH IN MICRONS

m.p. 94-96.5°

A

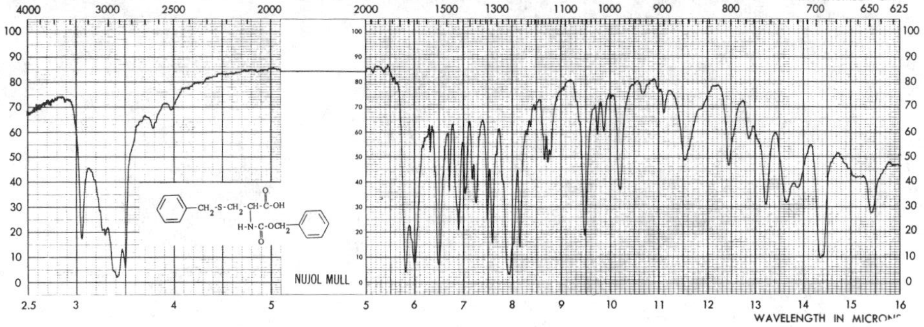

16,263-9
N^2-Carbobenzyloxy-L-arginine
$H_2NC(=NH)NH(CH_2)_3CH(NHCO_2CH_2C_6H_5)CO_2H$
M.W. 308.34 m.p. 173-175°
$[\alpha]^{23}$ -9.3° (c=5.3, 0.2N HCl)

B

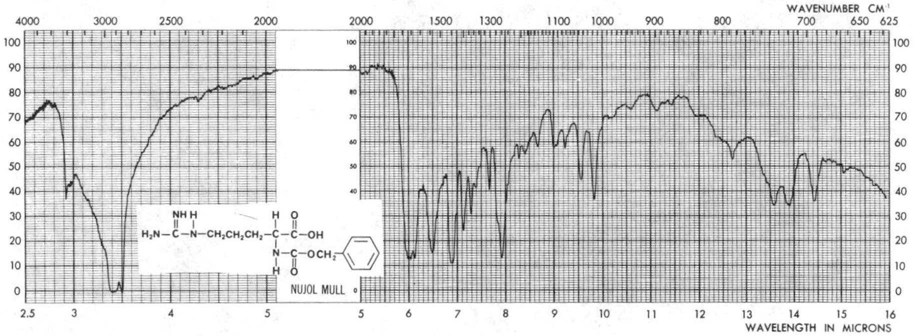

11,535-5 **N,N'-Dicarbobenzyloxy-L-lysine**
$C_6H_5CH_2O_2CNH(CH_2)_4CH(NHCO_2CH_2C_6H_5)CO_2H$
M.W. 414.46 m.p. 70-76° $[\alpha]^{25}_D$ - 3.9°
(c=2 in CH_3OH)

C

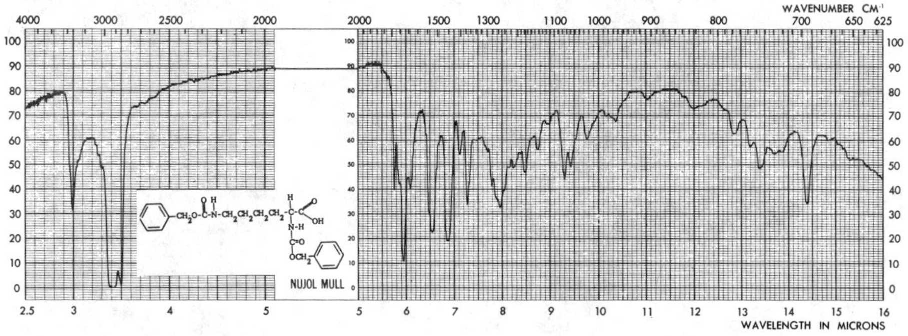

11,534-7 **N,N'-Dicarbobenzyloxy-L-ornithine**
$C_6H_5CH_2O_2CNH(CH_2)_3CH(NHCO_2CH_2C_6H_5)CO_2H$
M.W. 400.43 m.p. 112-114°

D

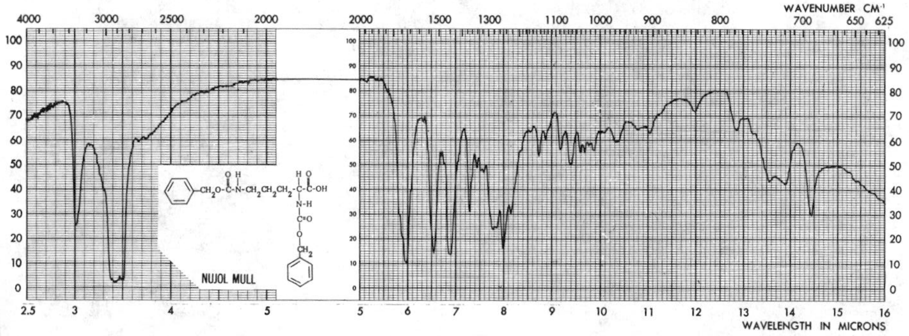

$C_6H_5CH_2CH[NHCO_2C(CH_3)_3]CO_2H$ M.W. 265.31
m.p. 77-80°

E

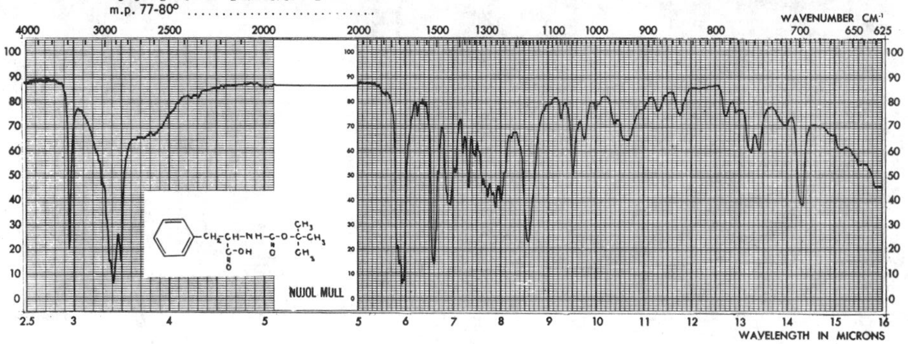

86,079-4
***N*-Carbobenzyloxy-L-phenylalanyl chloromethyl ketone, 98% (ZPCK)**
$C_6H_5CH_2CH(NHCO_2CH_2C_6H_5)COCH_2Cl$ FW 331.80
mp 107-108° $[\alpha]^{23}$ +30.1° (c=1, $CHCl_3$) Disp. C

F

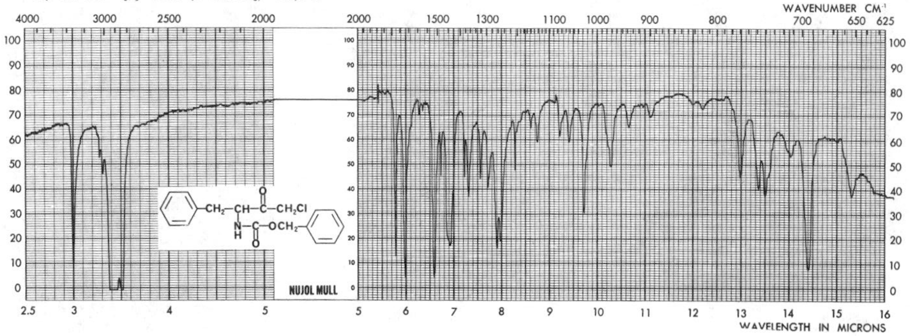

B1225-3 **Nα-Benzoyl-L-arginine ethyl ester hydrochloride**
$H_2NC(:NH)NH(CH_2)_3CH(NHCOC_6H_5)CO_2C_2H_5 \cdot HCl$
M.W. 342.84 m.p. 127-131°

G

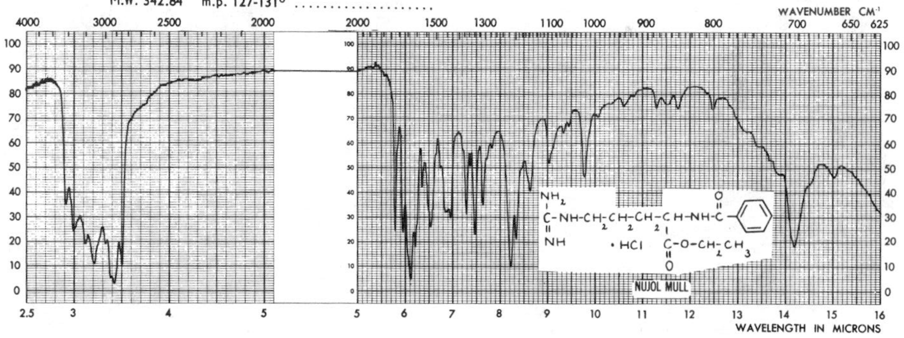

D830 **N,O-Diacetyl-3,5-diiodo-L-tyrosine**

H

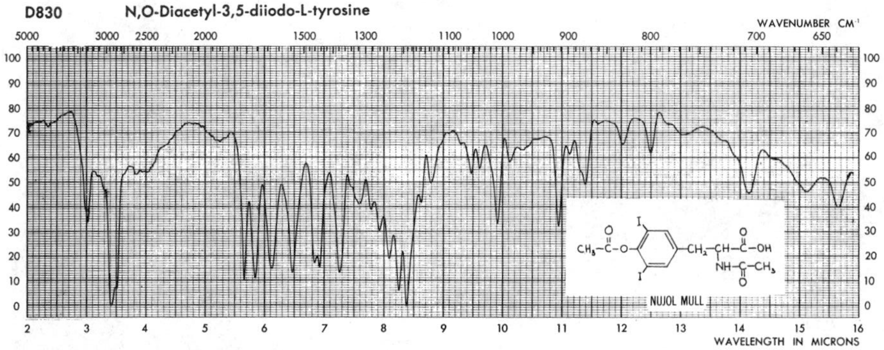

AROMATIC AMINO ACIDS & ACID SALTS

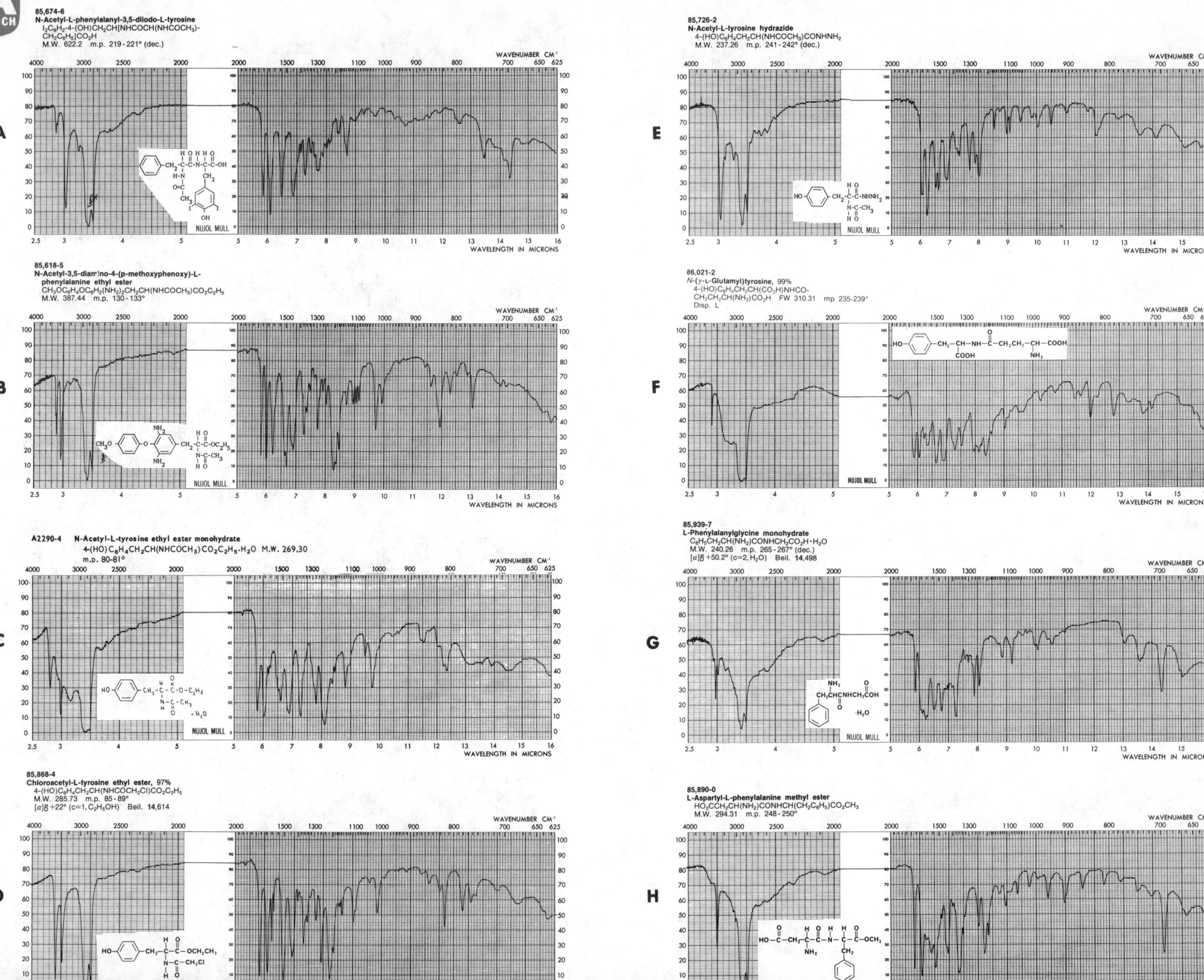
ALDRICH
A
85,674-6
N-Acetyl-L-phenylalanyl-3,5-diiodo-L-tyrosine
$I_2C_6H_2$-4-(OH)$CH_2CH[NHCOCH(NHCOCH_3)$-$CH_2C_6H_5]CO_2H$
M.W. 622.2 m.p. 219-221° (dec.)
NUJOL MULL
B
85,618-5
N-Acetyl-3,5-diamino-4-(p-methoxyphenoxy)-L-phenylalanine ethyl ester
$CH_3OC_6H_4OC_6H_2(NH_2)_2CH_2CH(NHCOCH_3)CO_2C_2H_5$
M.W. 387.44 m.p. 130-133°
NUJOL MULL
C
A2290-4 N-Acetyl-L-tyrosine ethyl ester monohydrate
4-(HO)$C_6H_4CH_2CH(NHCOCH_3)CO_2C_2H_5 \cdot H_2O$ M.W. 269.30
m.p. 80-81°
NUJOL MULL
D
85,868-4
Chloroacetyl-L-tyrosine ethyl ester, 97%
4-(HO)$C_6H_4CH_2CH(NHCOCH_2Cl)CO_2C_2H_5$
M.W. 285.73 m.p. 85-89°
$[\alpha]^{20}_D$ +22° (c=1, C_2H_5OH) Beil. 14,614
E
85,726-2
N-Acetyl-L-tyrosine hydrazide
4-(HO)$C_6H_4CH_2CH(NHCOCH_3)CONHNH_2$
M.W. 237.26 m.p. 241-242° (dec.)
NUJOL MULL
F
86,021-2
N-(γ-L-Glutamyl)tyrosine, 99%
4-(HO)$C_6H_4CH_2CH(CO_2H)NHCO$-$CH_2CH_2CH(NH_2)CO_2H$ FW 310.31 mp 235-239°
Disp. L
NUJOL MULL
G
85,939-7
L-Phenylalanylglycine monohydrate
$C_6H_5CH_2CH(NH_2)CONHCH_2CO_2H \cdot H_2O$
M.W. 240.26 m.p. 265-267° (dec.)
$[\alpha]^{20}_D$ +50.2° (c=2, H_2O) Beil. 14,498
NUJOL MULL
H
85,890-0
L-Aspartyl-L-phenylalanine methyl ester
$HO_2CCH_2CH(NH_2)CONHCH(CH_2C_6H_5)CO_2CH_3$
M.W. 294.31 m.p. 248-250°
WAVENUMBER CM⁻¹
WAVELENGTH IN MICRONS

M.W. 235.28 m.p. 89-92° (sublimes)
$[\alpha]^{22}$ +13.3° (c=2, C_2H_5OH) Beil. **14**(2),303

A

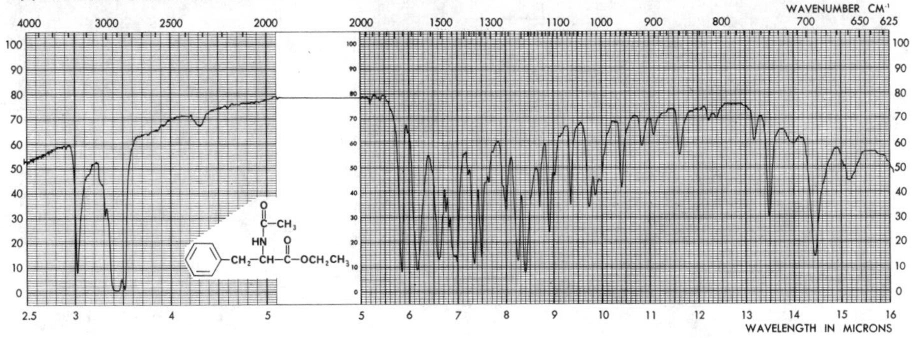

85,941-9
L-Phenylalanyl-L-proline
M.W. 262.31 m.p. 108-111° (dec.)

B

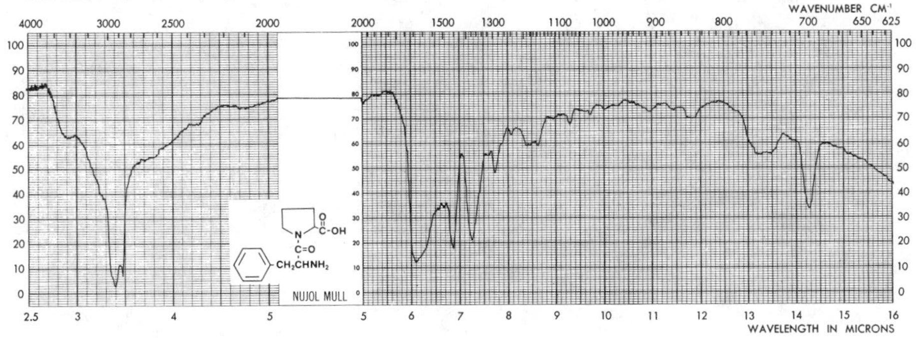

85,658-4
N-Benzoyl-L-tyrosine ethyl ester (BTEE)
4-(HO)$C_6H_4CH_2CH(NHCOC_6H_5)CO_2C_2H_5$
M.W. 313.36 m.p. 118-121° Beil. **14**(1),669

C

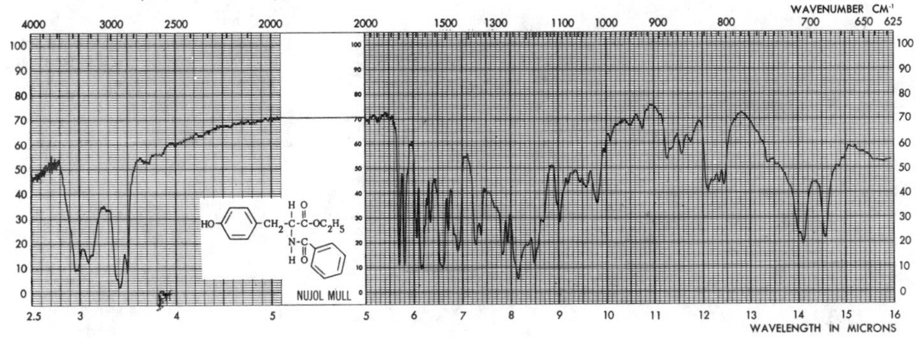

13,458-9 **N-(Carbobenzyloxy)-L-phenylalanine 2,4,5-trichlorophenyl ester**
$C_6H_5CH_2CH(NHCO_2CH_2C_6H_5)CO_2C_6H_2Cl_3$ M.W. 478.76
m.p. 139-141°

D

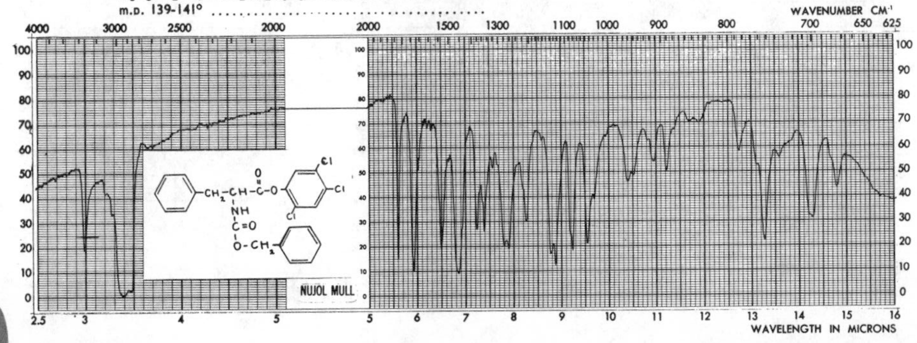

thiolcarbonate
M.W. 304.37 m.p. 59-62°

E

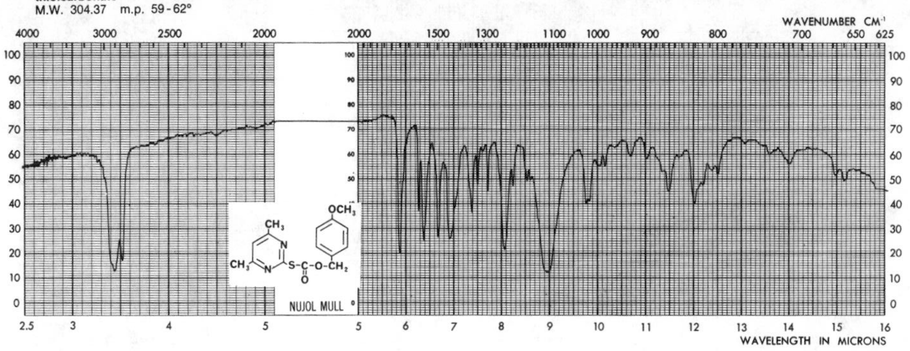

85,725-4
L-1-p-Tosylamino-2-phenylethyl chloromethyl ketone,
99+%, GOLD LABEL (TPCK)
$C_6H_5CH_2CH(NHSO_2C_6H_4CH_3)COCH_2Cl$
M.W. 351.85 m.p. 106-108°

F

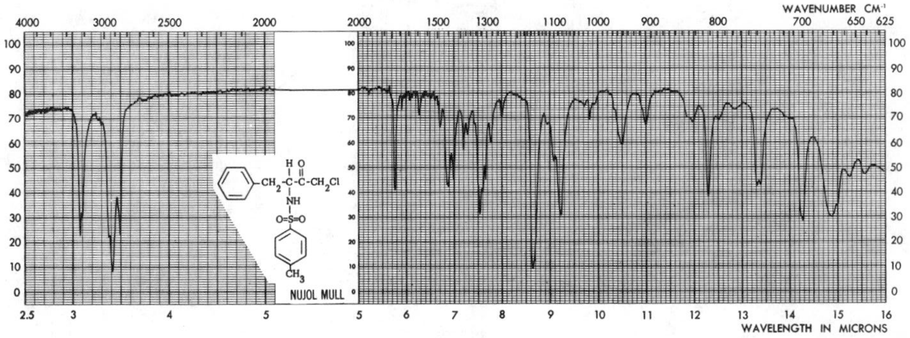

85,830-7
Carbobenzyloxy-DL-methionine
$CH_3SCH_2CH_2CH(NHCO_2CH_2C_6H_5)CO_2H$
M.W. 283.35 m.p. 112-114°

G

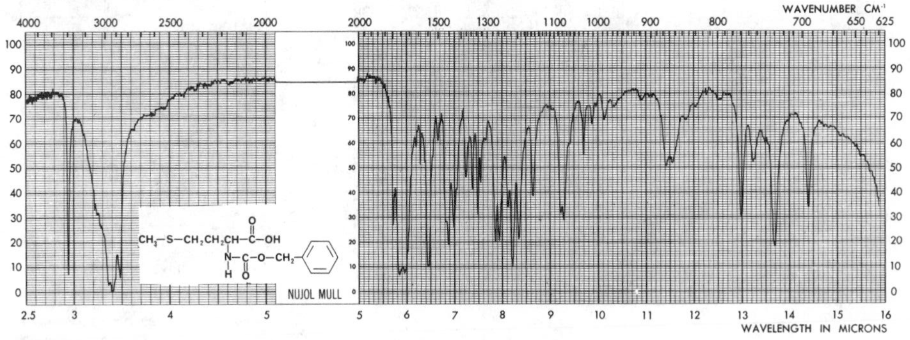

85,829-3
N,N'-Dicarbobenzyloxy-DL-lysine
$C_6H_5CH_2O_2CNH(CH_2)_4CH(NHCO_2CH_2C_6H_5)CO_2H$
M.W. 414.46 m.p. 103-105°

H

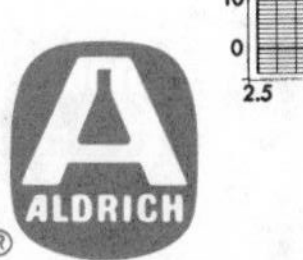

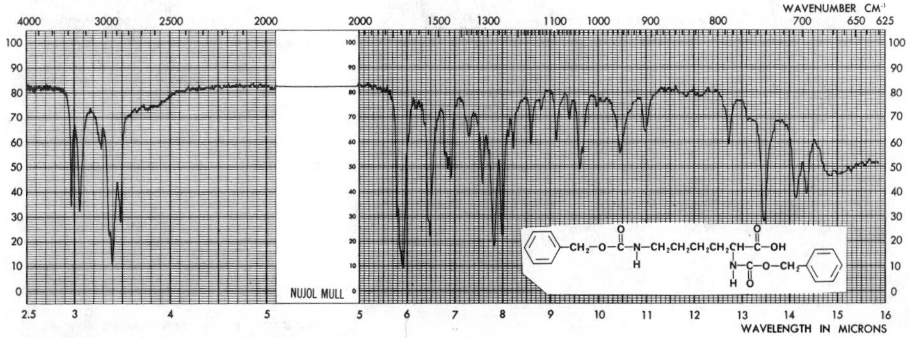

ALDRICH

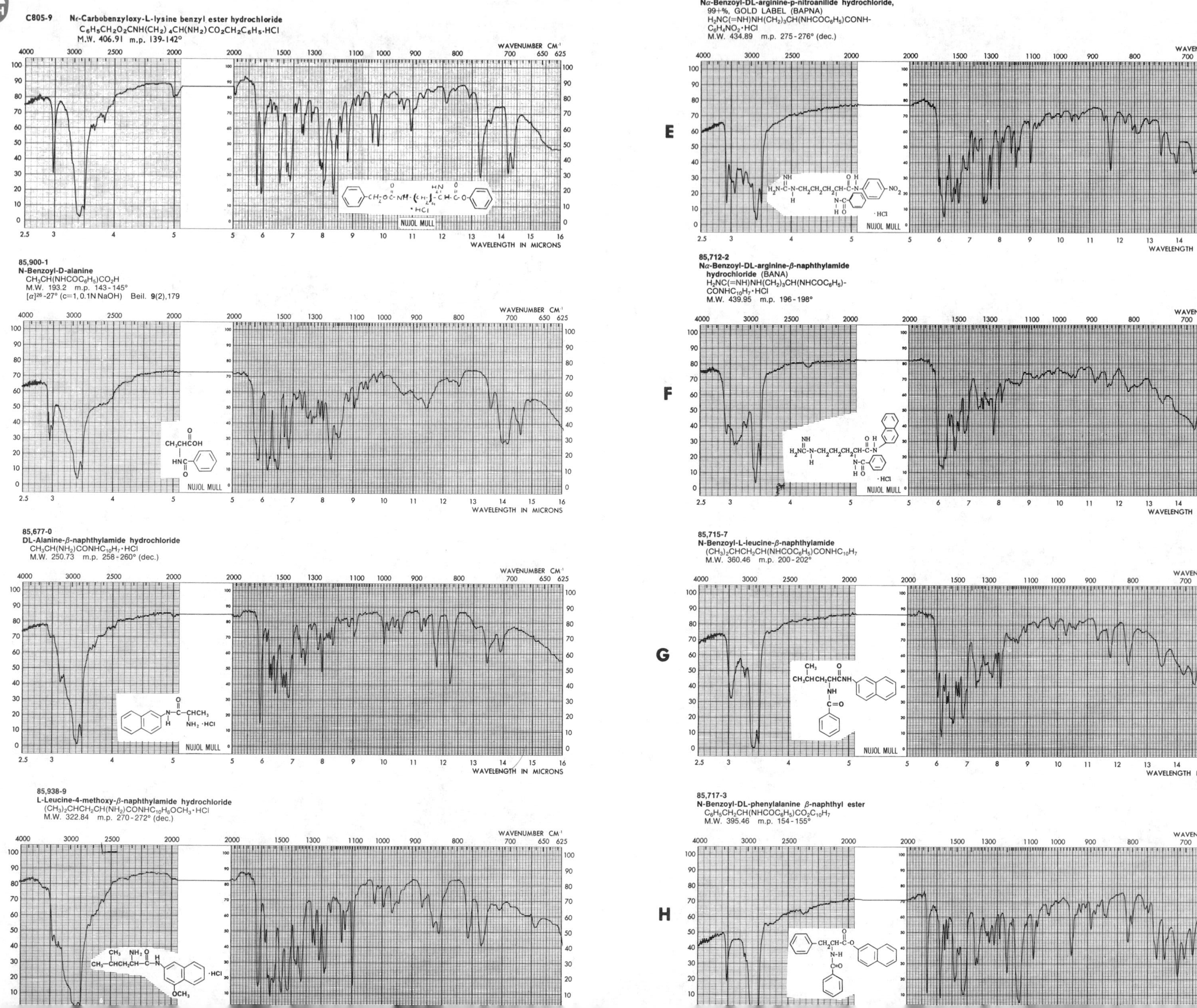

A
C805-9 Nε-Carbobenzyloxy-L-lysine benzyl ester hydrochloride
$C_6H_5CH_2O_2CNH(CH_2)_4CH(NH_2)CO_2CH_2C_6H_5 \cdot HCl$
M.W. 406.91 m.p. 139-142°

B
85,900-1
N-Benzoyl-D-alanine
$CH_3CH(NHCOC_6H_5)CO_2H$
M.W. 193.2 m.p. 143-145°
$[\alpha]^{26}$ -27° (c=1, 0.1N NaOH) Beil. **9**(2),179

C
85,677-0
DL-Alanine-β-naphthylamide hydrochloride
$CH_3CH(NH_2)CONHC_{10}H_7 \cdot HCl$
M.W. 250.73 m.p. 258-260° (dec.)

D
85,938-9
L-Leucine-4-methoxy-β-naphthylamide hydrochloride
$(CH_3)_2CHCH_2CH(NH_2)CONHC_{10}H_6OCH_3 \cdot HCl$
M.W. 322.84 m.p. 270-272° (dec.)

E
85,711-4
Nα-Benzoyl-DL-arginine-p-nitroanilide hydrochloride, 99+%, GOLD LABEL (BAPNA)
$H_2NC(=NH)NH(CH_2)_3CH(NHCOC_6H_5)CONH$-$C_6H_4NO_2 \cdot HCl$
M.W. 434.89 m.p. 275-276° (dec.)

F
85,712-2
Nα-Benzoyl-DL-arginine-β-naphthylamide hydrochloride (BANA)
$H_2NC(=NH)NH(CH_2)_3CH(NHCOC_6H_5)$-$CONHC_{10}H_7 \cdot HCl$
M.W. 439.95 m.p. 196-198°

G
85,715-7
N-Benzoyl-L-leucine-β-naphthylamide
$(CH_3)_2CHCH_2CH(NHCOC_6H_5)CONHC_{10}H_7$
M.W. 360.46 m.p. 200-202°

H
85,717-3
N-Benzoyl-DL-phenylalanine β-naphthyl ester
$C_6H_5CH_2CH(NHCOC_6H_5)CO_2C_{10}H_7$
M.W. 395.46 m.p. 154-155°

A

M.W. 336.46 m.p. 94-95°

NUJOL MULL

B

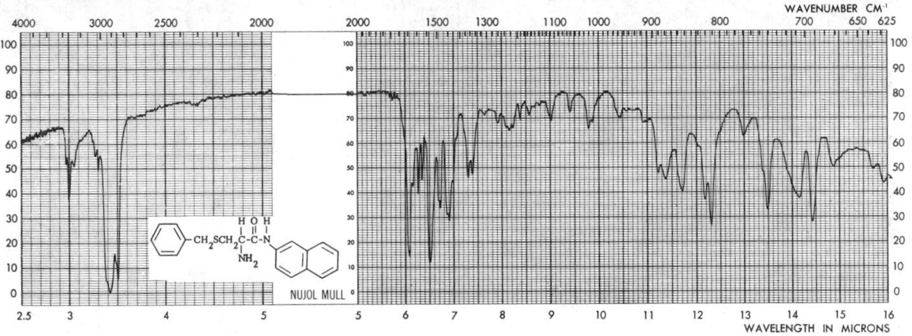

85,752-1
N-γ-L-Glutamyl-α-naphthylamide monohydrate
$C_{10}H_7NHCOCH_2CH_2CH(NH_2)CO_2H \cdot H_2O$
M.W. 290.32 m.p. 181-183° (dec.)

KBr

C

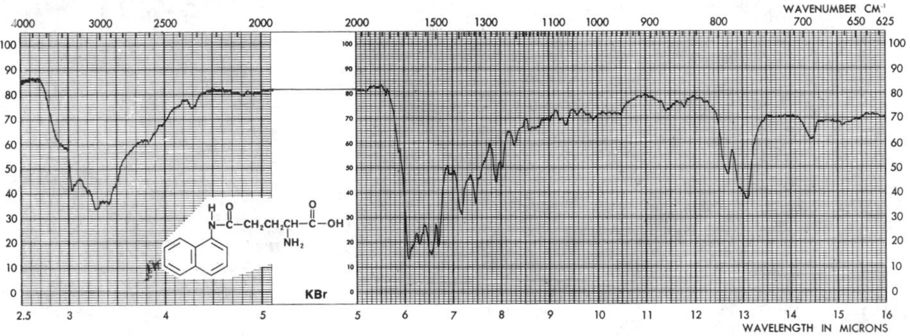

85,678-9
L-Alanine-β-naphthylamide
$CH_3CH(NH_2)CONHC_{10}H_7$
M.W. 214.27 m.p. 100-101°

NUJOL MULL

D

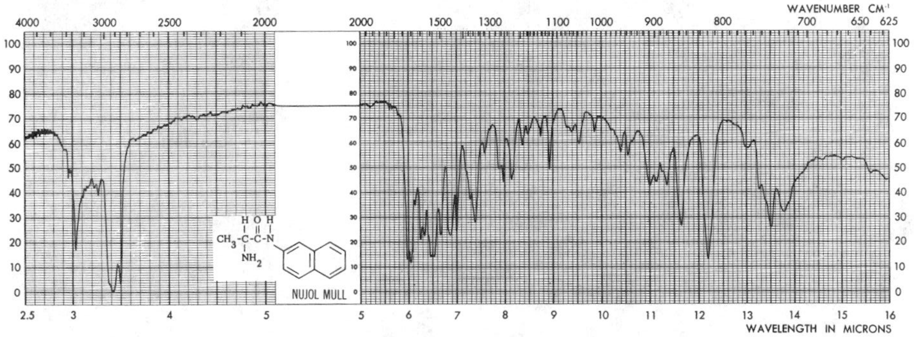

85,899-4
DL-Alanine-β-naphthylamide
$CH_3CH(NH_2)CONHC_{10}H_7$
M.W. 214.27 m.p. 205° (dec.)

NUJOL MULL

E

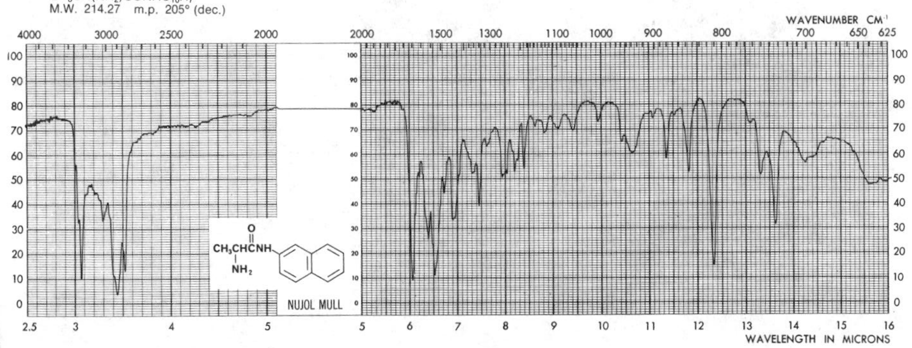

M.W. 272.3 m.p. 209° (dec.)

NUJOL MULL

F

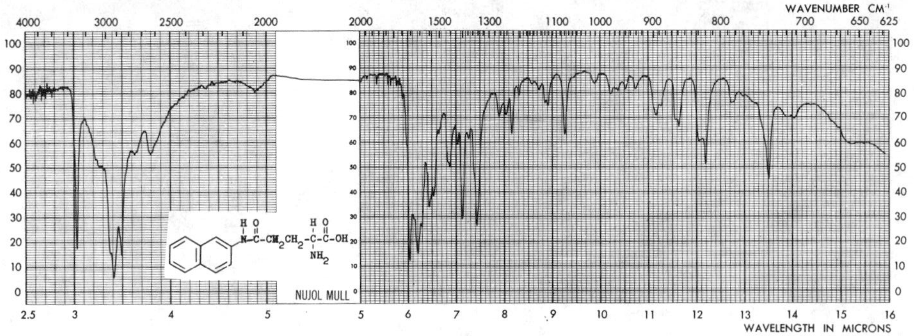

85,897-8
L-Phenylalanine-β-naphthylamide
$C_6H_5CH_2CH(NH_2)CONHC_{10}H_7$
M.W. 290.37 m.p. 129-131°

NUJOL MULL

G

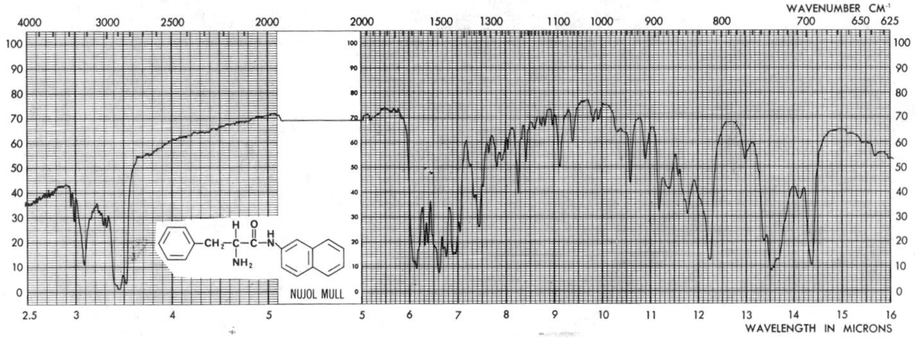

85,933-8
Glycyl-L-phenylalanine-β-naphthylamide
$C_6H_5CH_2CH(NHCOCH_2NH_2)CONHC_{10}H_7$
M.W. 347.42

NUJOL MULL

H

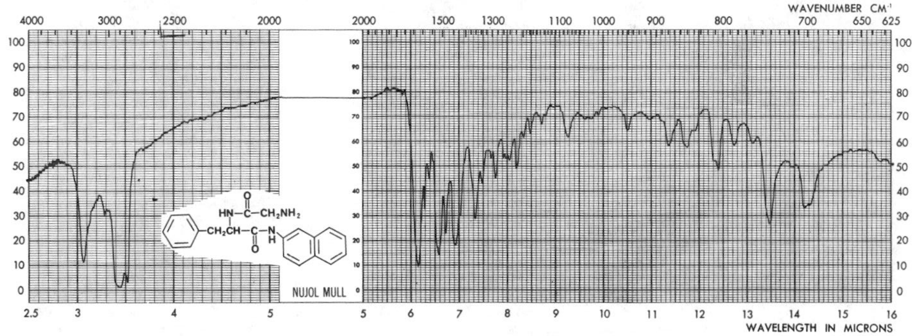

85,714-9
N-Benzoyl-DL-leucine-β-naphthylamide
$(CH_3)_2CHCH_2CH(NHCOC_6H_5)CONHC_{10}H_7$
M.W. 360.46 m.p. 201-203°

NUJOL MULL

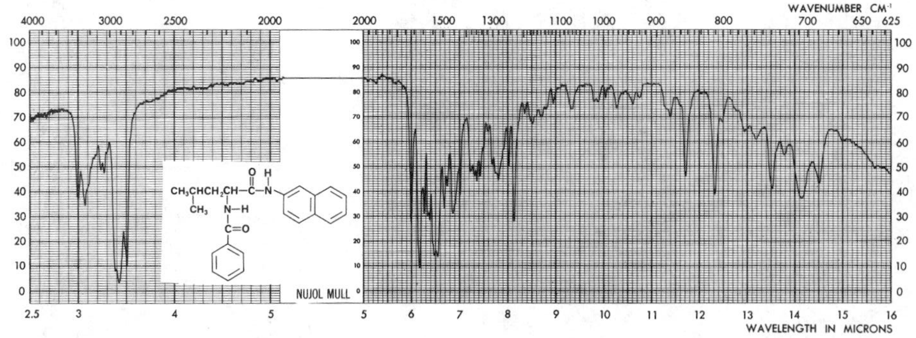

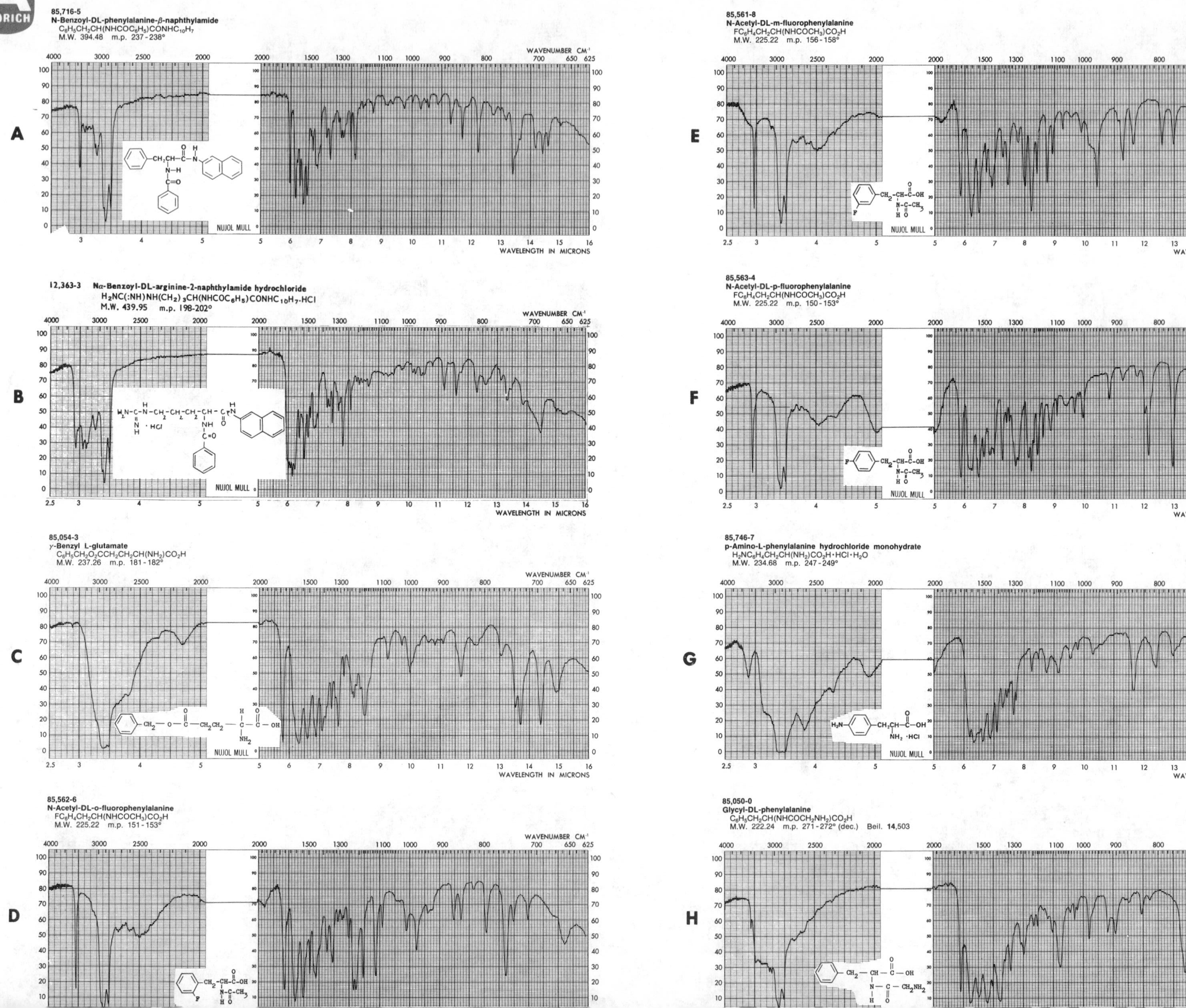
A
85,716-5
N-Benzoyl-DL-phenylalanine-β-naphthylamide
$C_6H_5CH_2CH(NHCOC_6H_5)CONHC_{10}H_7$
M.W. 394.48 m.p. 237-238°
NUJOL MULL
B
12,363-3 Nα-Benzoyl-DL-arginine-2-naphthylamide hydrochloride
$H_2NC(:NH)NH(CH_2)_3CH(NHCOC_6H_5)CONHC_{10}H_7 \cdot HCl$
M.W. 439.95 m.p. 198-202°
NUJOL MULL
C
85,054-3
γ-Benzyl L-glutamate
$C_6H_5CH_2O_2CCH_2CH_2CH(NH_2)CO_2H$
M.W. 237.26 m.p. 181-182°
NUJOL MULL
D
85,562-6
N-Acetyl-DL-o-fluorophenylalanine
$FC_6H_4CH_2CH(NHCOCH_3)CO_2H$
M.W. 225.22 m.p. 151-153°
E
85,561-8
N-Acetyl-DL-m-fluorophenylalanine
$FC_6H_4CH_2CH(NHCOCH_3)CO_2H$
M.W. 225.22 m.p. 156-158°
NUJOL MULL
F
85,563-4
N-Acetyl-DL-p-fluorophenylalanine
$FC_6H_4CH_2CH(NHCOCH_3)CO_2H$
M.W. 225.22 m.p. 150-153°
NUJOL MULL
G
85,746-7
p-Amino-L-phenylalanine hydrochloride monohydrate
$H_2NC_6H_4CH_2CH(NH_2)CO_2H \cdot HCl \cdot H_2O$
M.W. 234.68 m.p. 247-249°
NUJOL MULL
H
85,050-0
Glycyl-DL-phenylalanine
$C_6H_5CH_2CH(NHCOCH_2NH_2)CO_2H$
M.W. 222.24 m.p. 271-272° (dec.) Beil. 14,503
WAVENUMBER CM⁻¹
WAVELENGTH IN MICRONS

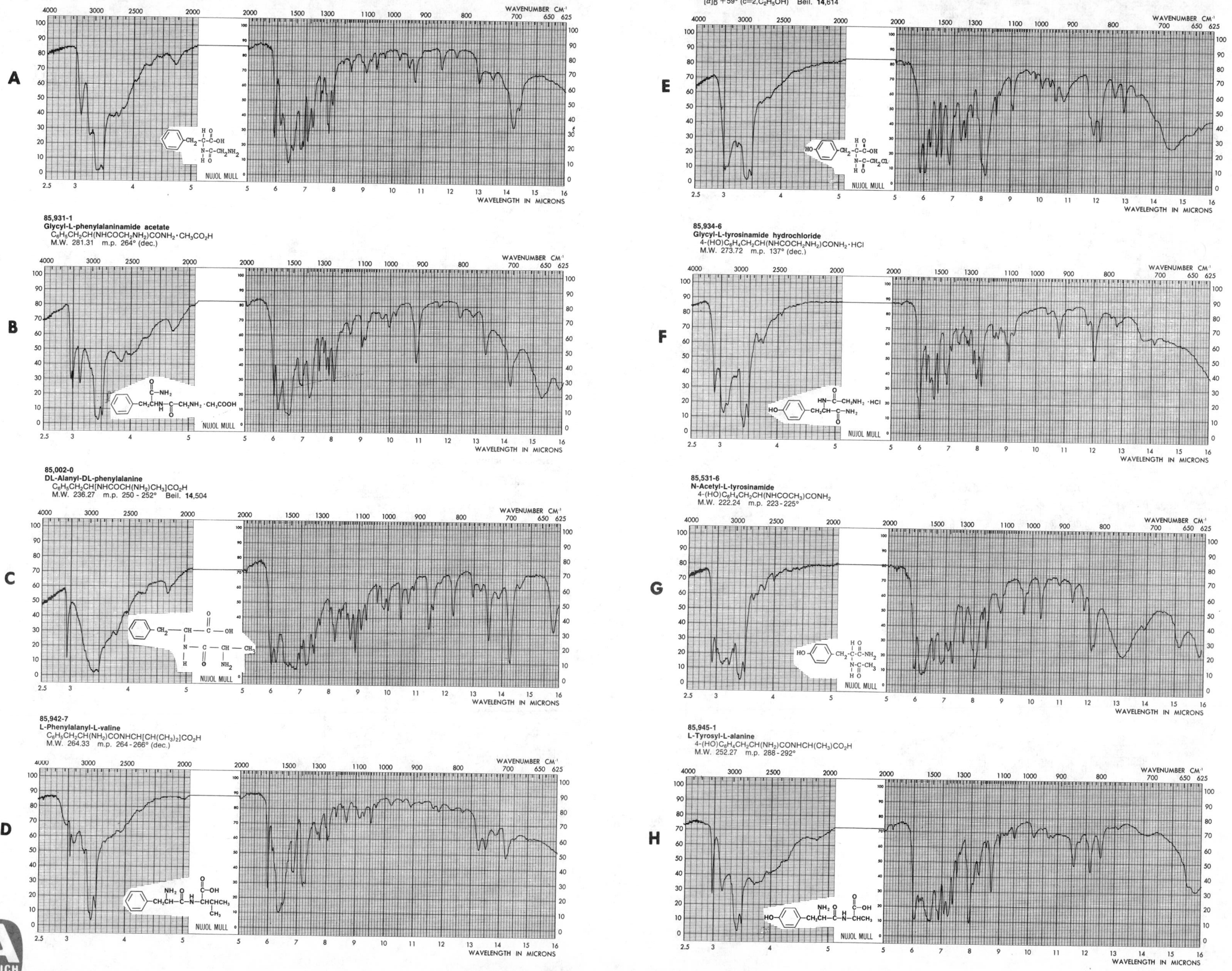

A

$C_6H_5CH_2CH(NHCOCH_2NH_2)CO_2H$
M.W. 222.24 m.p. 260 - 262° Beil. **14**,498

B

85,931-1
Glycyl-L-phenylalaninamide acetate
$C_6H_5CH_2CH(NHCOCH_2NH_2)CONH_2 \cdot CH_3CO_2H$
M.W. 281.31 m.p. 264° (dec.)

C

85,002-0
DL-Alanyl-DL-phenylalanine
$C_6H_5CH_2CH[NHCOCH(NH_2)CH_3]CO_2H$
M.W. 236.27 m.p. 250 - 252° Beil. **14**,504

D

85,942-7
L-Phenylalanyl-L-valine
$C_6H_5CH_2CH(NH_2)CONHCH[CH(CH_3)_2]CO_2H$
M.W. 264.33 m.p. 264 - 266° (dec.)

E

4-(HO)$C_6H_4CH_2CH(NHCOCH_2Cl)CO_2H$
M.W. 257.67 m.p. 153 - 154°
$[\alpha]_D^{25}$ +59° (c=2,C_2H_5OH) Beil. **14**,614

F

85,934-6
Glycyl-L-tyrosinamide hydrochloride
4-(HO)$C_6H_4CH_2CH(NHCOCH_2NH_2)CONH_2 \cdot HCl$
M.W. 273.72 m.p. 137° (dec.)

G

85,531-6
N-Acetyl-L-tyrosinamide
4-(HO)$C_6H_4CH_2CH(NHCOCH_3)CONH_2$
M.W. 222.24 m.p. 223 - 225°

H

85,945-1
L-Tyrosyl-L-alanine
4-(HO)$C_6H_4CH_2CH(NH_2)CONHCH(CH_3)CO_2H$
M.W. 252.27 m.p. 288 - 292°

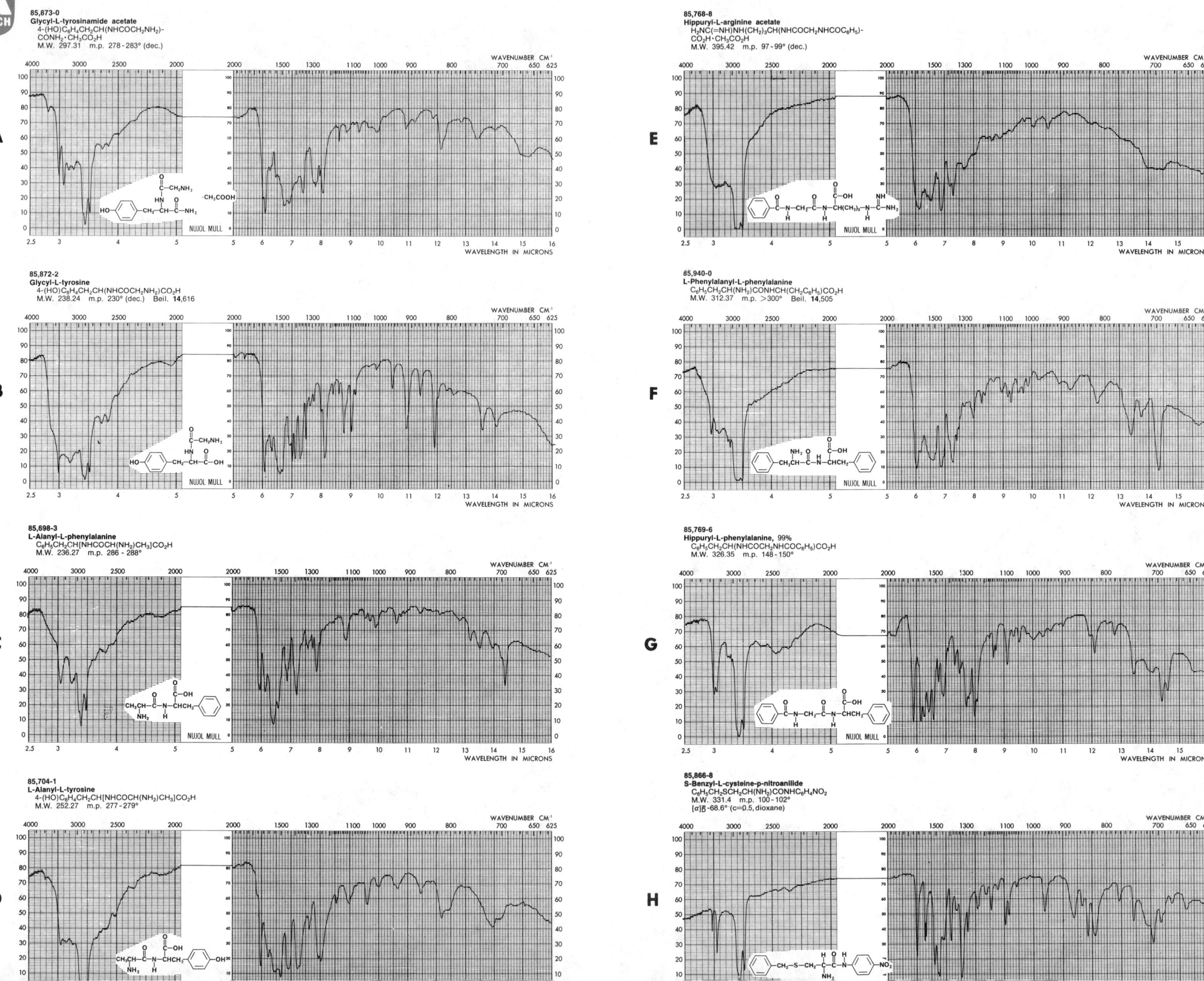

A — 85,873-0
Glycyl-L-tyrosinamide acetate
4-(HO)$C_6H_4CH_2CH(NHCOCH_2NH_2)$-$CONH_2 \cdot CH_3CO_2H$
M.W. 297.31 m.p. 278-283° (dec.)

B — 85,872-2
Glycyl-L-tyrosine
4-(HO)$C_6H_4CH_2CH(NHCOCH_2NH_2)CO_2H$
M.W. 238.24 m.p. 230° (dec.) Beil. **14**,616

C — 85,698-3
L-Alanyl-L-phenylalanine
$C_6H_5CH_2CH[NHCOCH(NH_2)CH_3]CO_2H$
M.W. 236.27 m.p. 286 - 288°

D — 85,704-1
L-Alanyl-L-tyrosine
4-(HO)$C_6H_4CH_2CH[NHCOCH(NH_2)CH_3]CO_2H$
M.W. 252.27 m.p. 277-279°

E — 85,768-8
Hippuryl-L-arginine acetate
$H_2NC(=NH)NH(CH_2)_3CH(NHCOCH_2NHCOC_6H_5)$-$CO_2H \cdot CH_3CO_2H$
M.W. 395.42 m.p. 97-99° (dec.)

F — 85,940-0
L-Phenylalanyl-L-phenylalanine
$C_6H_5CH_2CH(NH_2)CONHCH(CH_2C_6H_5)CO_2H$
M.W. 312.37 m.p. >300° Beil. **14**,505

G — 85,769-6
Hippuryl-L-phenylalanine, 99%
$C_6H_5CH_2CH(NHCOCH_2NHCOC_6H_5)CO_2H$
M.W. 326.35 m.p. 148-150°

H — 85,866-8
S-Benzyl-L-cysteine-p-nitroanilide
$C_6H_5CH_2SCH_2CH(NH_2)CONHC_6H_4NO_2$
M.W. 331.4 m.p. 100-102°
$[\alpha]^{20}_{D}$ -68.6° (c=0.5, dioxane)

M.W. 327.34 m.p. 264-267° (dec.)

A

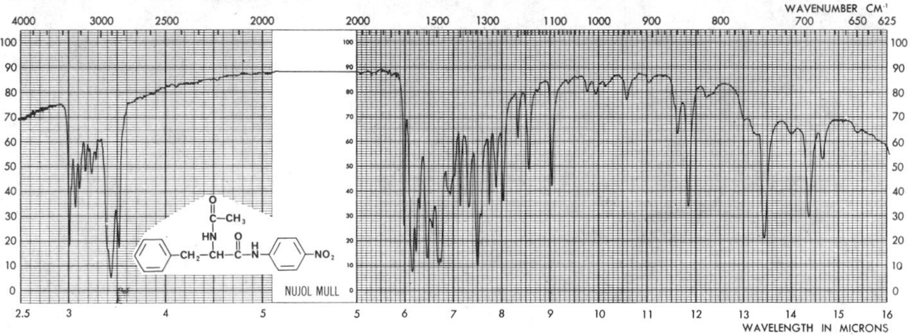

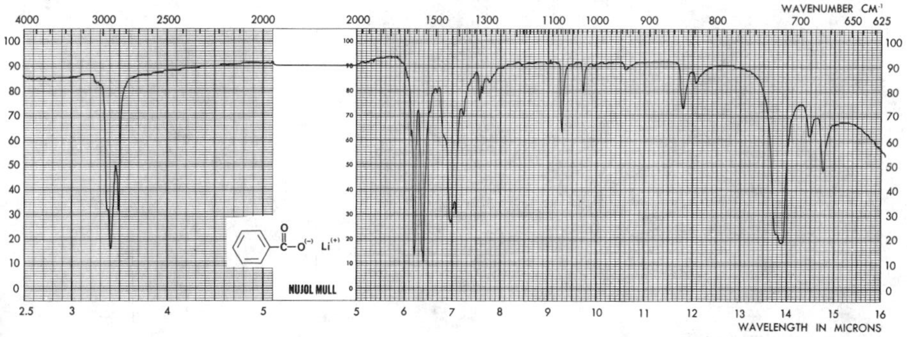

10,916-9 **Benzoic acid, sodium salt (sodium benzoate), U.S.P.**
$C_6H_5CO_2Na$ M.W. 144.11 m.p. > 300°

E

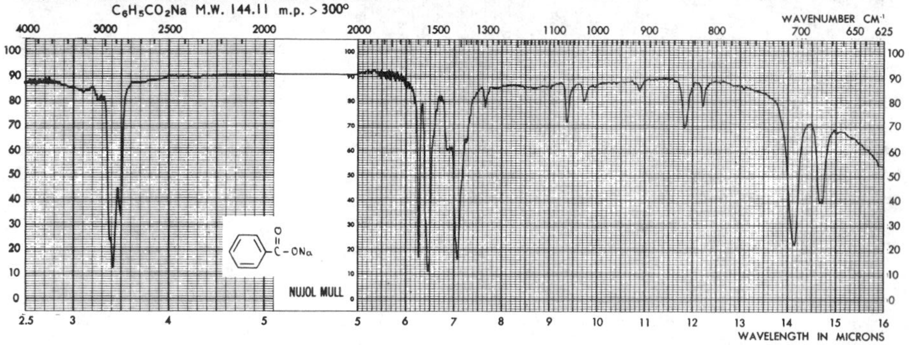

85,091-8
N-Phthaloyl-DL-methionine
M.W. 279.31 m.p. 108-110°

B

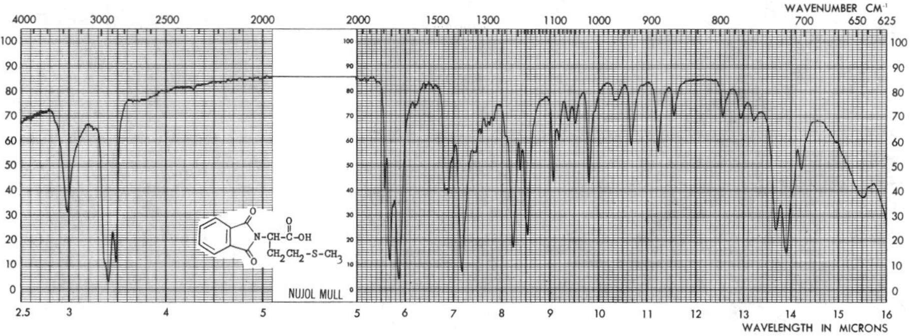

18,333-4
Benzoic acid, ammonium salt, 98%
(ammonium benzoate)
$C_6H_5CO_2NH_4$
M.W. 139.15 m.p. 192-198° (dec.) Beil. **9**,107

F

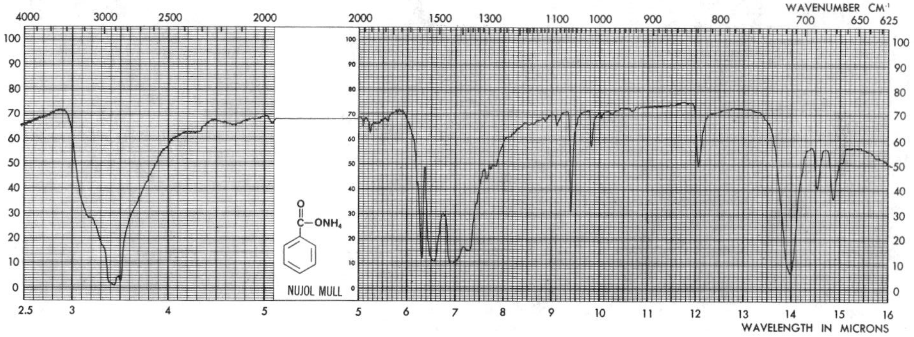

85,132-9
N-Phthalylglycylglycine
M.W. 262.22 m.p. 227-230° Beil. **21**(2),358

C

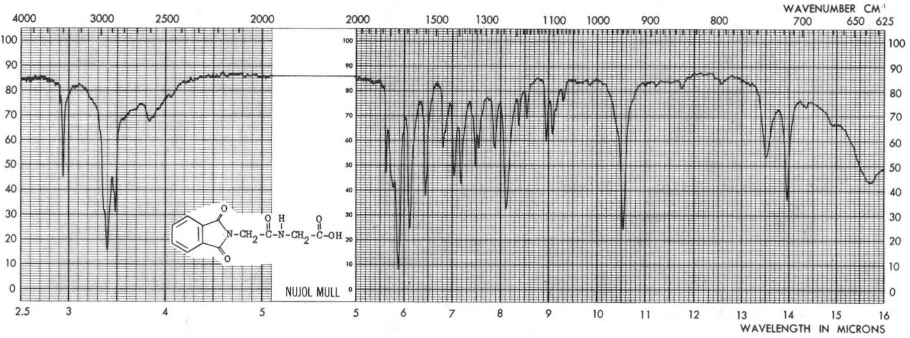

P2712-7 **Phenylmercuric acetate**
$CH_3CO_2HgC_6H_5$ M.W. 336.74
m.p. 150-160°

G

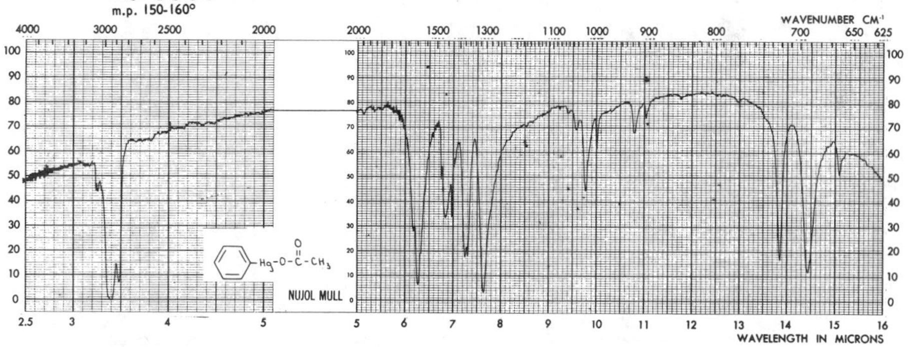

20,116-2
Lithium benzoate, 98+% (benzoic acid, lithium salt)
$C_6H_5CO_2Li$ FW 128.06 mp >300° *Beil.* **9**,107
Disp. L

D

11,923-7 Diphenylplumbylene diacetate (contains acetic acid of crystallization)
$(CH_3CO_2)_2Pb(C_6H_5)_2 \cdot CH_3CO_2H$ M.W. 539.54
m.p. 210-213.5°

H

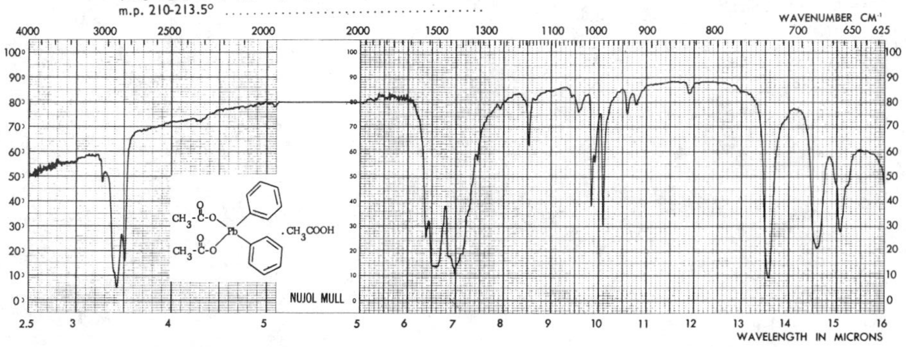

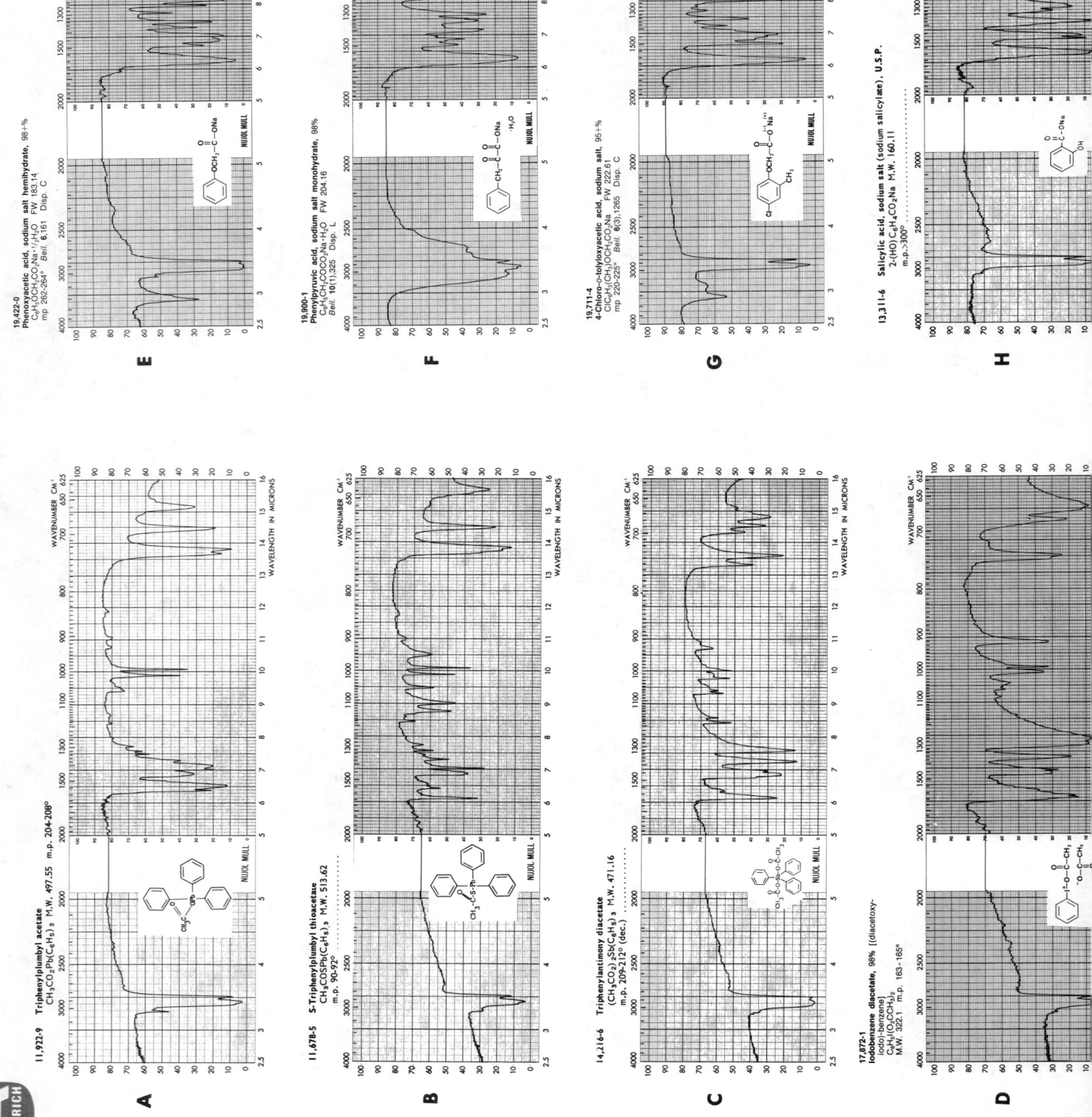

A 11,922-9 **Triphenylplumbyl acetate**
$CH_3CO_2Pb(C_6H_5)_3$ M.W. 497.55 m.p. 204-208°
NUJOL MULL

B 11,678-5 **S-Triphenylplumbyl thioacetate**
$CH_3COSPb(C_6H_5)_3$ M.W. 513.62
m.p. 90-92°
NUJOL MULL

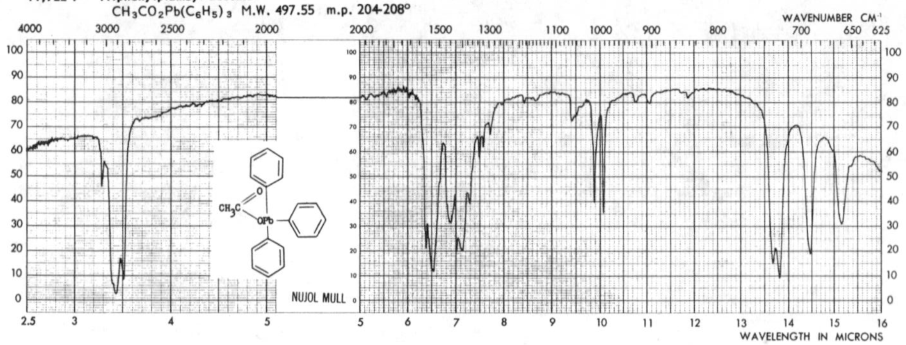

C 14,216-6 **Triphenylantimony diacetate**
$(CH_3CO_2)_2Sb(C_6H_5)_3$ M.W. 471.16
m.p. 209-212° (dec.)
NUJOL MULL

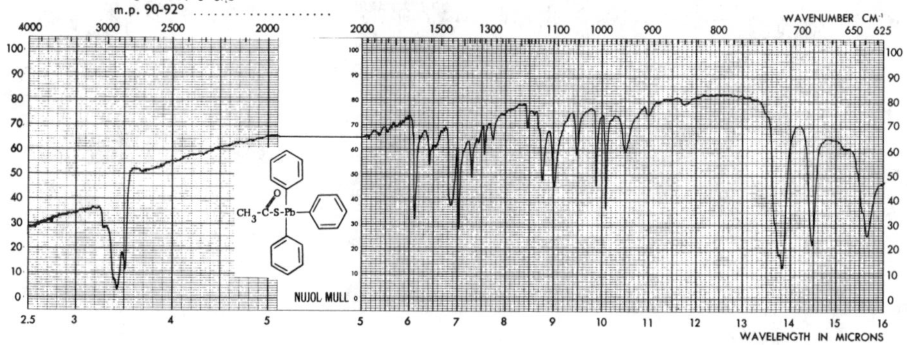

D 17,872-1
Iodobenzene diacetate, 98% [(diacetoxy-iodo)-benzene]
$C_6H_5I(O_2CCH_3)_2$
M.W. 322.1 m.p. 163-165°

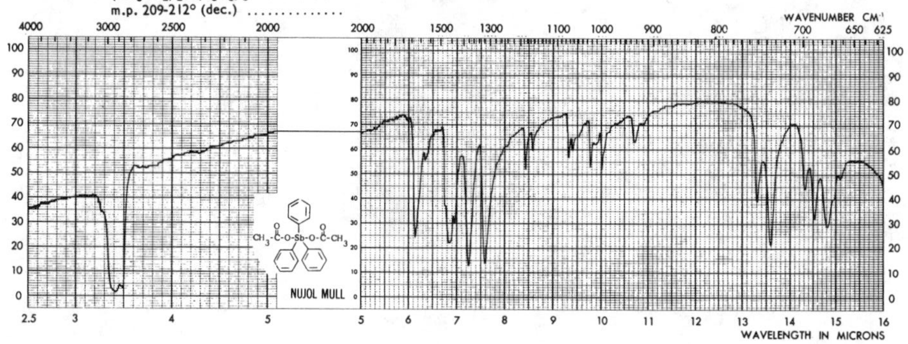

E 19,422-0
Phenoxyacetic acid, sodium salt hemihydrate, 98+%
$C_6H_5OCH_2CO_2Na \cdot 1/2H_2O$ FW 183.14
mp 262-264° *Beil.* **6**,161 Disp. C
NUJOL MULL

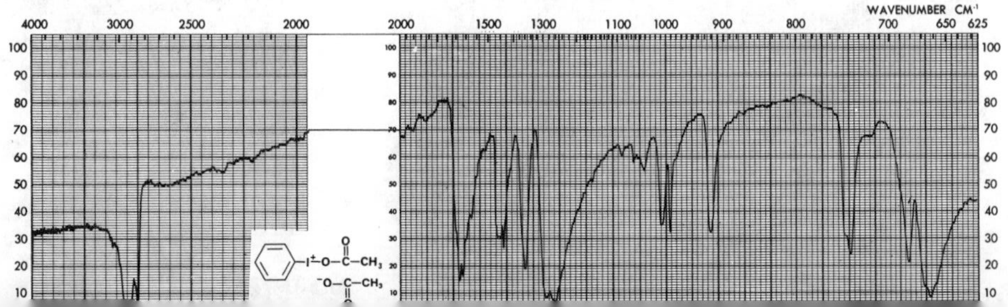

F 19,900-1
Phenylpyruvic acid, sodium salt monohydrate, 98%
$C_6H_5CH_2COCO_2Na \cdot H_2O$ FW 204.16
Beil. **10**(1),325 Disp. L
NUJOL MULL

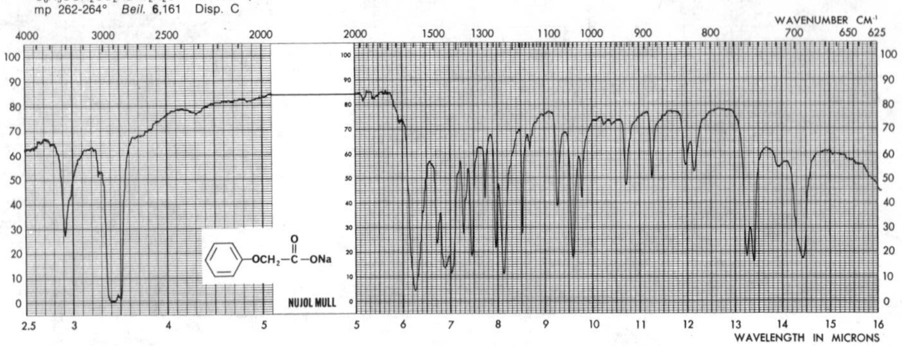

G 19,711-4
4-Chloro-*o*-tolyloxyacetic acid, sodium salt, 95+%
$ClC_6H_3(CH_3)OCH_2CO_2Na$ FW 222.61
mp 220-225° *Beil.* **6**(3),1265 Disp. C
NUJOL MULL

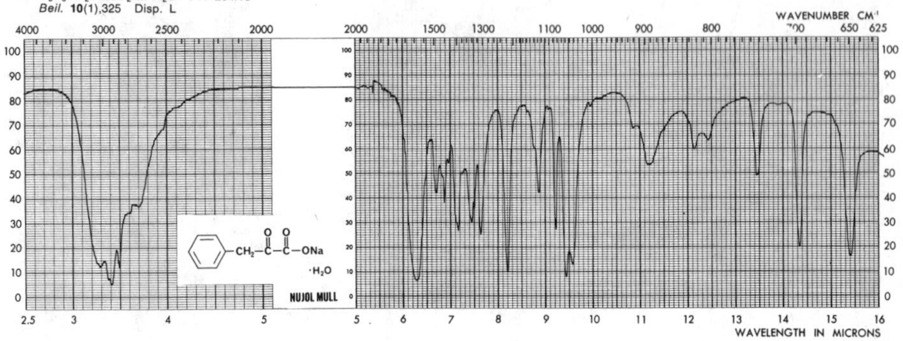

H 13,311-6 **Salicylic acid, sodium salt** (sodium salicylate), **U.S.P.**
2-(HO)$C_6H_4CO_2Na$ M.W. 160.11
m.p.>300°

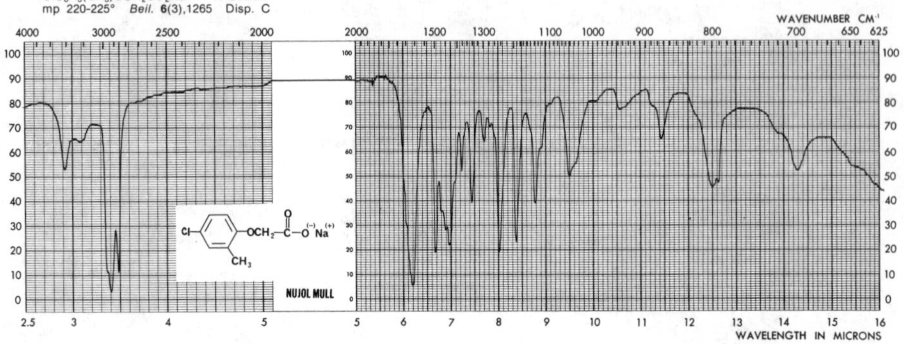

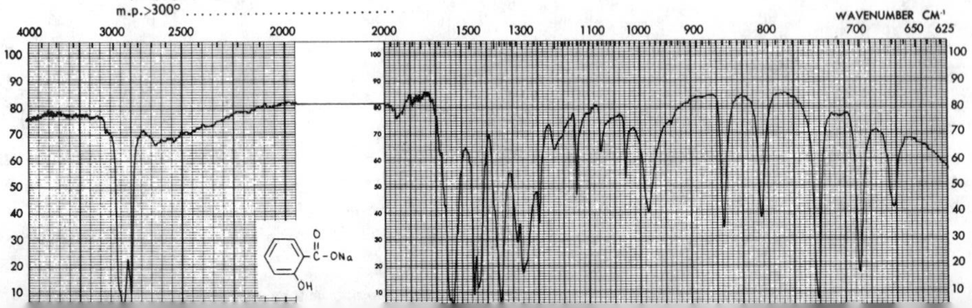

A

m.p. 232-235° (dec.)...................

NUJOL MULL

B

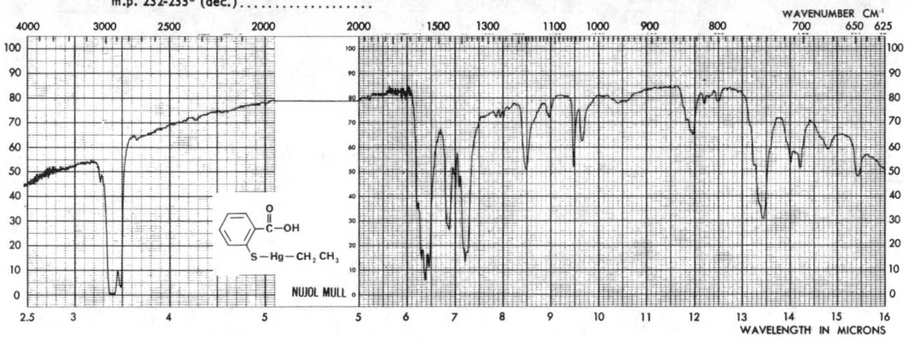

17,992-2
Potassium hydrogen phthalate, A.C.S. reagent
2-$(HO_2C)C_6H_4CO_2K$
M.W. 204.23 m.p. 295-300° (dec.) Beil. **9**,791

NUJOL MULL

C

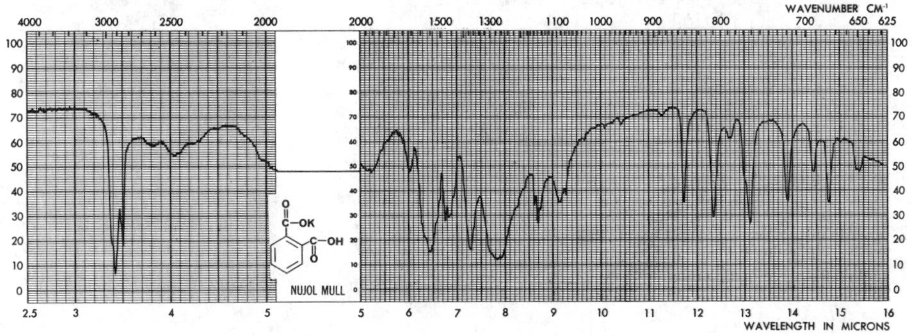

12,770-1 m-Nitrobenzoic acid, sodium salt
$O_2NC_6H_4CO_2Na$ M.W. 189.11 m.p. > 300°

NUJOL MULL

D

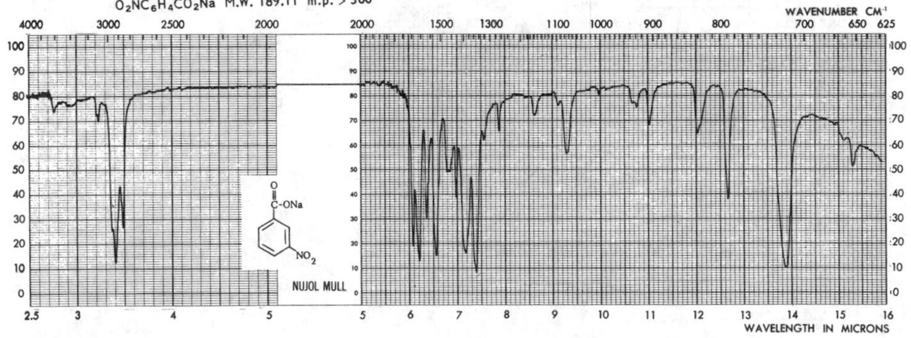

85,291-0
p-Aminobenzoic acid, sodium salt
$H_2NC_6H_4CO_2Na$
M.W. 159.12 m.p. >300° Beil. **14**,418

NUJOL MULL

E

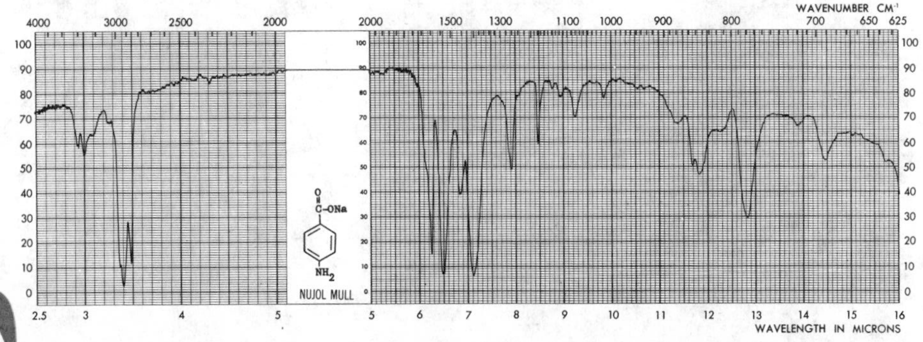

m.p. 163-165°

NUJOL MULL

F

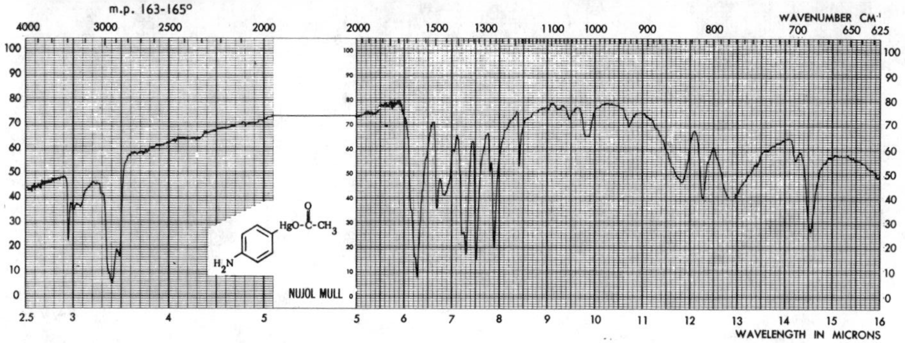

85,654-1
4-Aminosalicylic acid, sodium salt dihydrate
$H_2NC_6H_3$-2-$(OH)CO_2Na \cdot 2H_2O$
M.W. 211.15 m.p. 250-254° (dec.)

NUJOL MULL

G

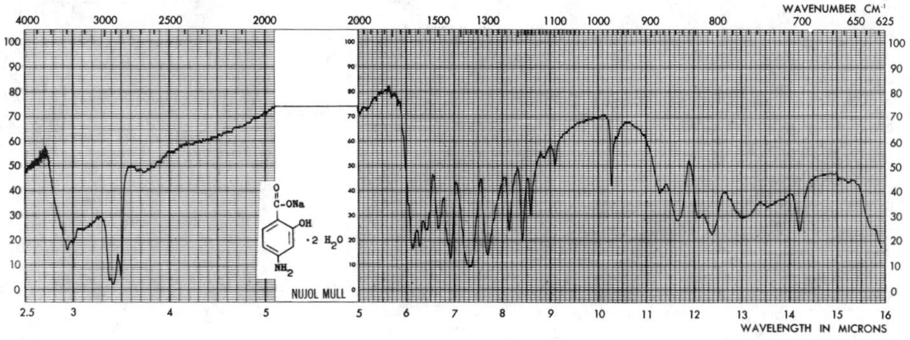

15,267-6 3-Amino-2,5-dichlorobenzoic acid, sodium salt, tech., 90+%
$H_2NC_6H_2(Cl)_2CO_2Na$ M.W. 228.01
m.p. 250-253° (dec.) ....

NUJOL MULL

H

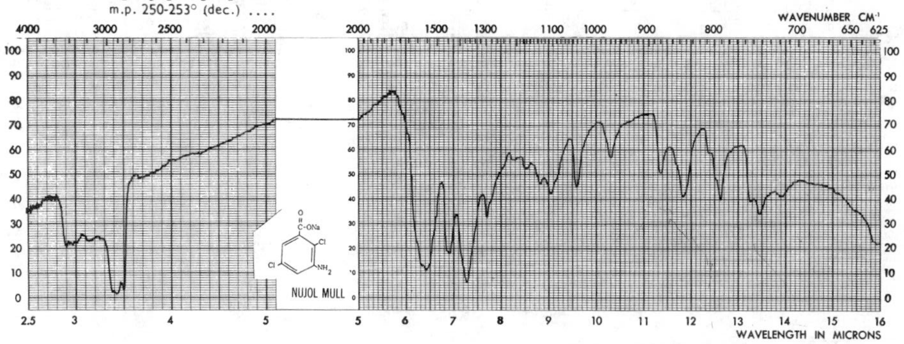

15,387-7 Ethyl benzoylacetate, thallium(I) salt
$(C_6H_5COCHCO_2C_2H_5)Tl$ M.W. 395.58 ..

NUJOL MULL

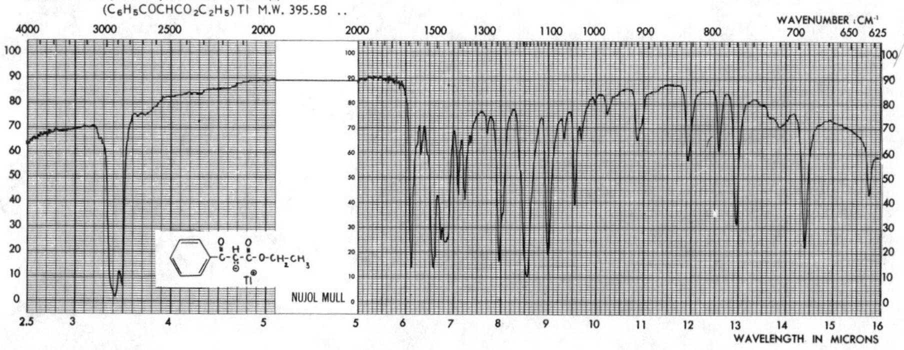

A

14,978-0 **Diphenyliodonium 2-carboxylate monohydrate**
$C_6H_5IC_6H_4CO_2{\cdot}H_2O$ M.W. 342.13
m.p. 226° (dec.)

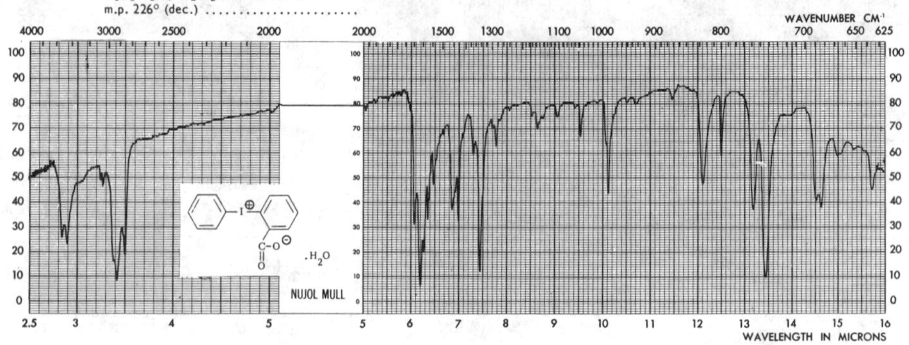

NUJOL MULL

B

12,003-0 **p-Benzamidosalicylic acid, calcium salt**
M.W. 552.55 m.p. > 360°

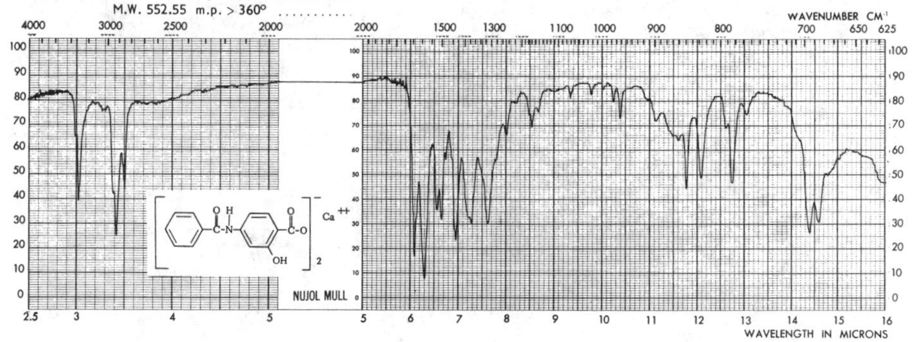

NUJOL MULL

C

T6720-2 **3,3',5-Triiodothyroacetic acid, diethanolamine salt**
M.W. 727.07 m.p. 156-158°

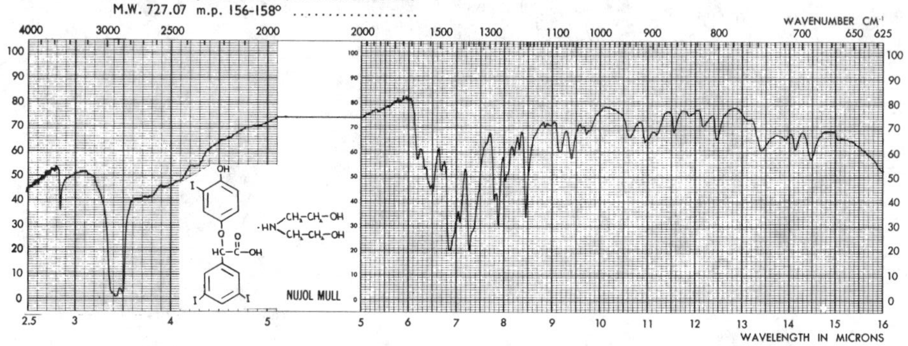

NUJOL MULL

D

D12,160-6 **Dihydroxytartaric acid osazone, disodium salt**
$NaO_2CC(:NNHC_6H_5)C(:NNHC_6H_5)CO_2Na$ M.W. 370.28
m.p. 238° (dec.)

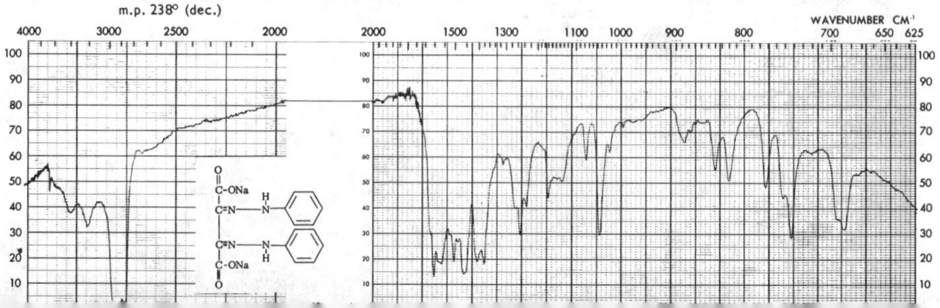

E

A3688-3 **Aluminon** (aurintricarboxylic acid, triammonium salt)
M.W. 473.44
m.p. 252° (dec.)

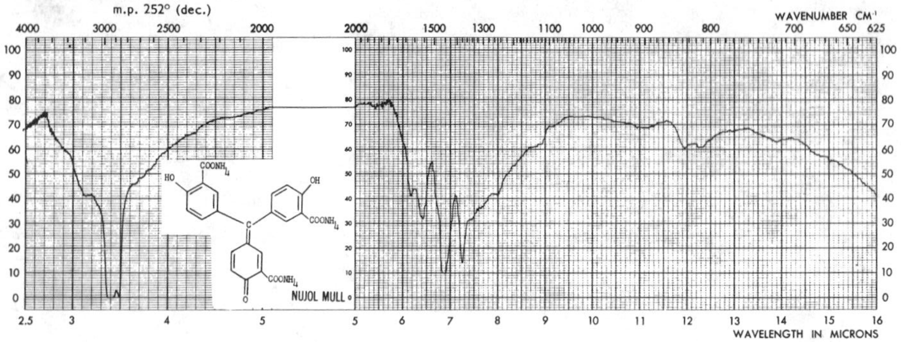

NUJOL MULL

F

12,488-5 Pamoic acid [4,4'-methylenebis-(3-hydroxy-2-naphthoic acid), embonic acid],
disodium salt
M.W. 432.34 m.p. > 300°

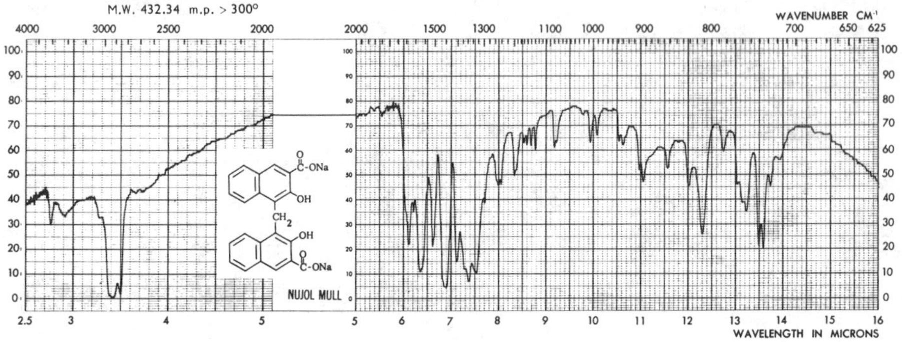

NUJOL MULL

G

P10-1 **Pamoic acid [4,4'-methylenebis-(3-hydroxy-2-naphthoic acid), embonic acid],**
monopotassium salt
M.W. 426.47 m.p. 315°

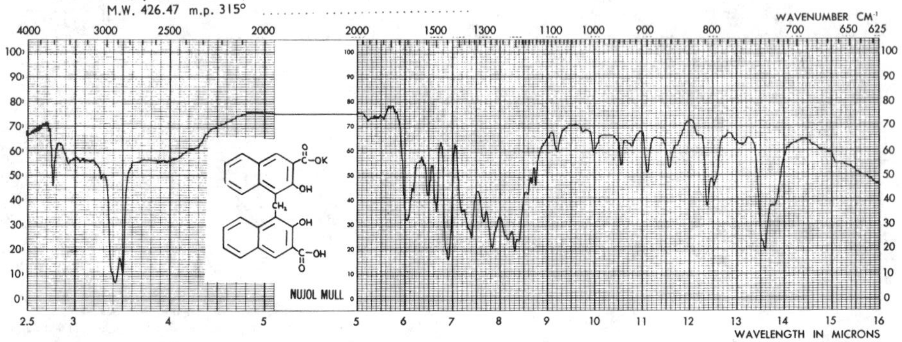

NUJOL MULL

H

18,497-7
3-Nitro-2-naphthoic acid, magnesium salt-bis(hexa-chlorocyclopentadiene) adduct, tech.
M.W. 1547.76 m.p. 231° (dec.)

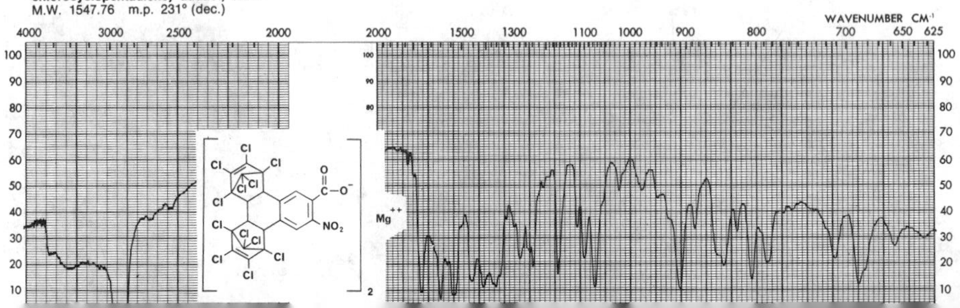

$[\alpha]^{23}$ -30° (c=1, CH_3OH) Disp. L

A

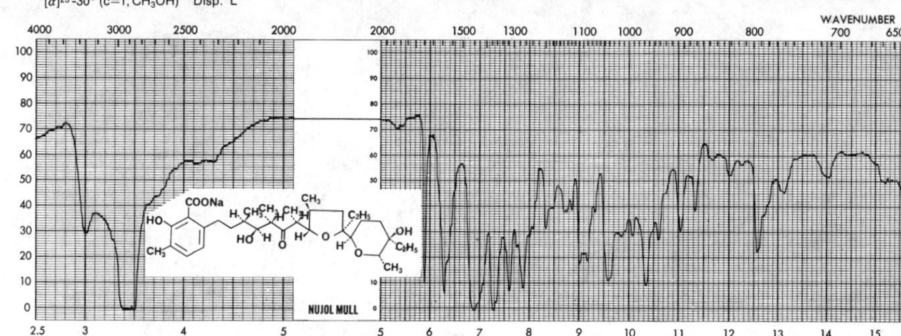

AROMATIC ESTERS AND LACTONES

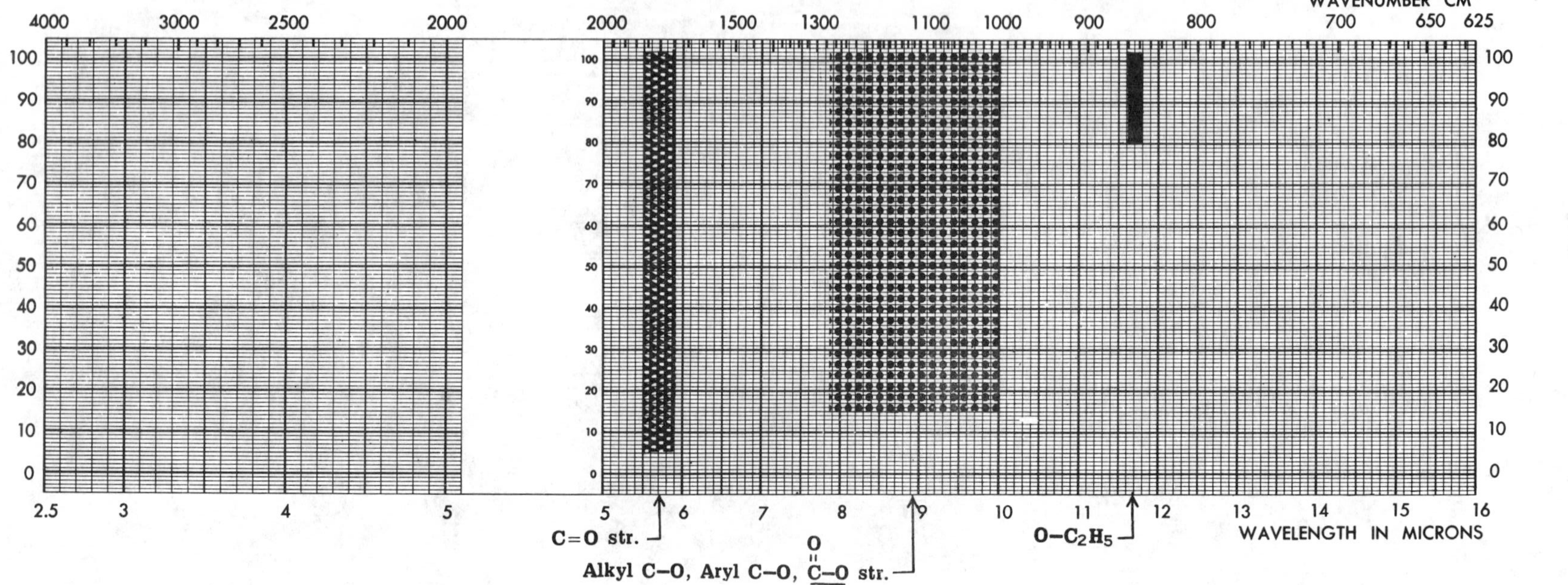

The conjugated carbonyl of the aromatic ester is shifted from its position at 5.75 μ (1740 cm^{-1}) in aliphatic esters to 5.8 – 5.9 μ (1725 – 1695 cm^{-1}). When there is amino or hydroxy substitution on the aromatic ring, this absorption shifts to a higher wavelength. (See spectra 1029C—1033F). The carbon-oxygen stretch vibrations appear as several bands between 7.7 and 10 μ (1300 – 1000 cm^{-1}).

The phenolic esters such as those seen in spectra 1038C—1040H have their carbonyl absorptions shifted to 5.7 μ (1755 cm^{-1}). The carbonates (spectra 1041B—1041G) also absorb near 5.7 μ (1755 cm^{-1}).

A trifluoromethyl group attached to the carbonyl shifts the band to 5.55 μ (1800 cm^{-1}). (See spectrum 1043B).

The ring conjugated lactone carbonyl (spectra 1043B) absorbs at approximately the same wavelength as the corresponding non-aromatic lactones, 5.6 – 5.7 μ (1785 – 1755 cm^{-1}). However, when the carbonyl is conjugated as in the coumarin spectra (1044B—1046G), the band is shifted to near 5.9 μ (1695 cm^{-1}).

Notice the carbonyl band in spectrum 1042H where the carbonyl is both nonconjugated and joined through the oxygen to the aromatic ring (β,γ-unsaturated five-membered lactone).

The ester carbonyl conjugated to the aromatic ring again disturbs the substitution pattern between 11 and 15 μ (910 – 665 cm^{-1}). Note the medium to strong absorption at 13 μ (770 cm^{-1}) in many of the para-and 1,2,4-substituted aromatic esters. This band is usually indicative of 3 or 4 adjacent aromatic hydrogens, and therefore, can be misleading.

A $HCO_2CH_2C_6H_5$ M.W. 136.15 b.p. 202-203°/747 mm.

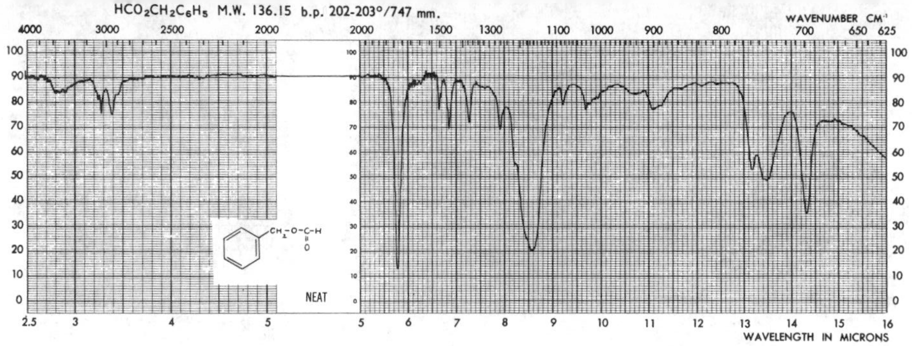

NEAT

12,528-8 Cinnamyl formate
$HCO_2CH_2CH{:}CHC_6H_5$ M.W. 162.19 n_D^{20} 1.5516

B NEAT

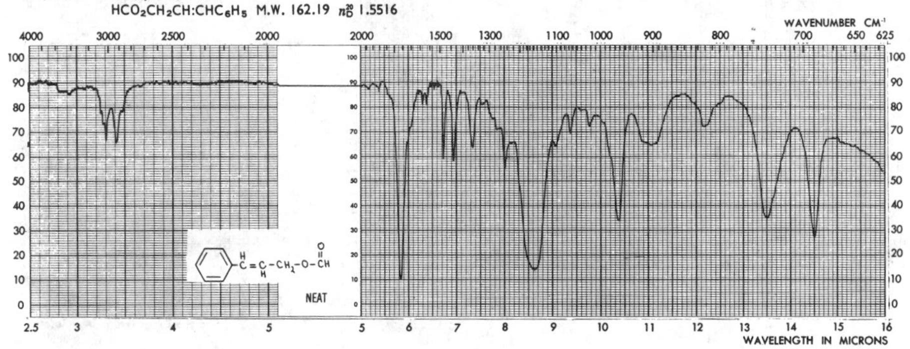

B1,580-5
Benzyl acetate, 99+%
$CH_3CO_2CH_2C_6H_5$
M.W. 150.18 b.p. 206° n_D^{20} 1.5006 d 1.04
Beil. 6,435

C NEAT

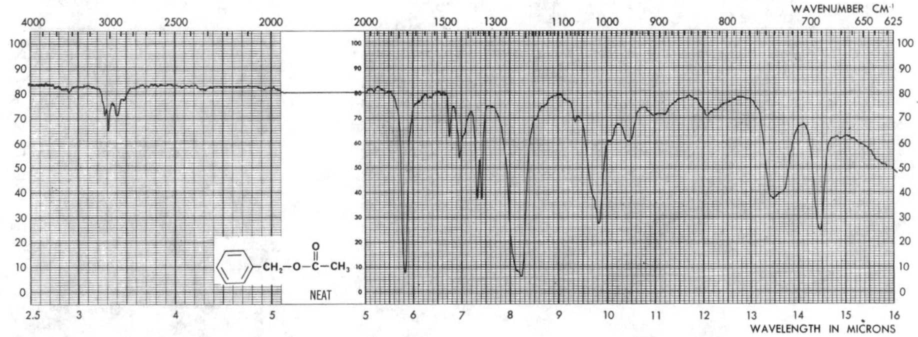

19,550-2
4-Phenyl-2-butyl acetate, 98+% (1-methyl-3-phenylpropyl acetate)
$CH_3CO_2CH(CH_3)CH_2CH_2C_6H_5$ FW 192.26
bp 72-74°/0mm. d 0.991 *Beil.* 6(1),258 Disp. C

D NEAT

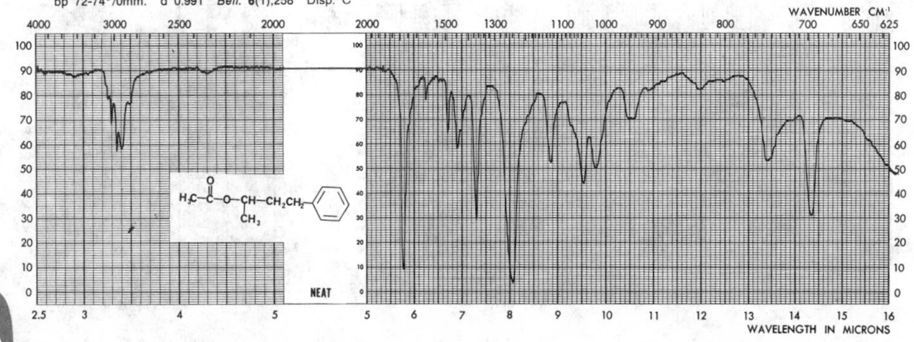

n_D^{20} 1.4855 Disp. C

E NEAT

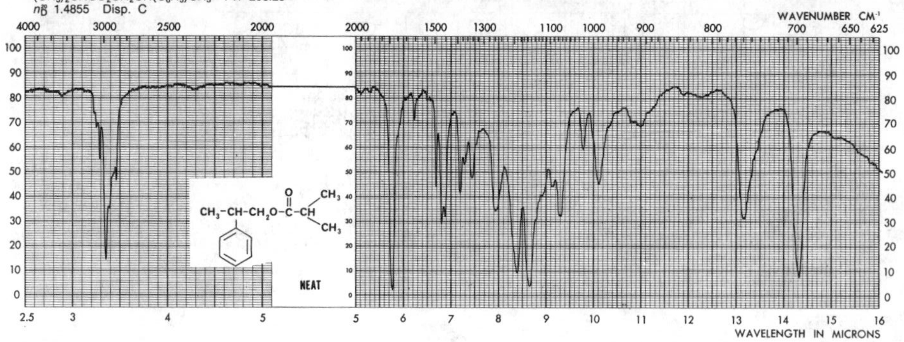

19,045-4
2-Phenylpropyl butyrate, 98%
$CH_3CH_2CH_2CO_2CH_2CH(C_6H_5)CH_3$ FW 206.29
n_D^{20} 1.4885 Disp. C

F NEAT

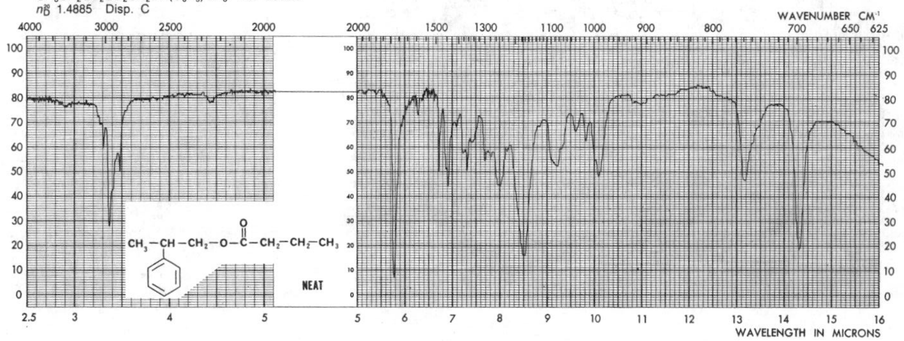

11,239-9 Benzyl butyrate
$CH_3CH_2CH_2CO_2CH_2C_6H_5$ M.W. 178.23 n_D^{20} 1.4902
b.p. 108-110°/9 mm.

G NEAT

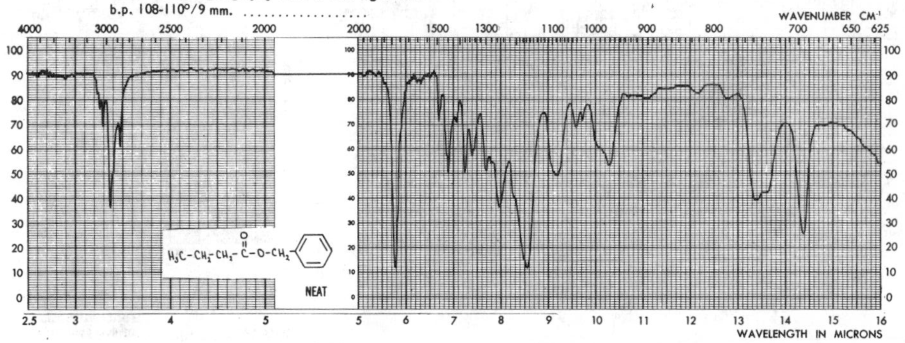

19,332-1
Piperonyl isobutyrate, 99%
FW 222.24 bp 91-92°/0mm. n_D^{20} 1.5115 d 1.154
Disp. C

H NEAT

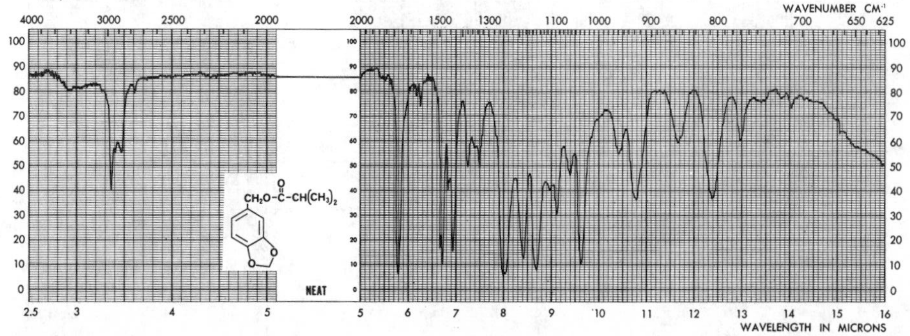

A

10,805-7 **Methyl phenylacetate, puriss.**
$C_6H_5CH_2CO_2CH_3$ M.W. 150.18 n_D^{20} 1.5075
b.p. 218°

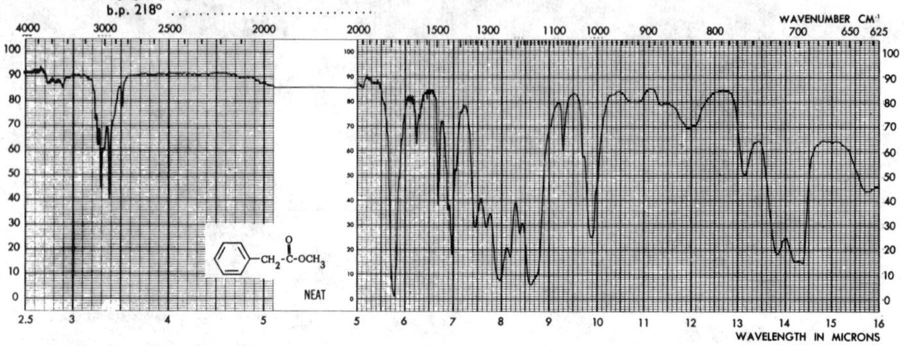

B

10,804-9 **Ethyl phenylacetate**
$C_6H_5CH_2CO_2C_2H_5$ M.W. 164.20 n_D^{20} 1.4980
b.p. 229°

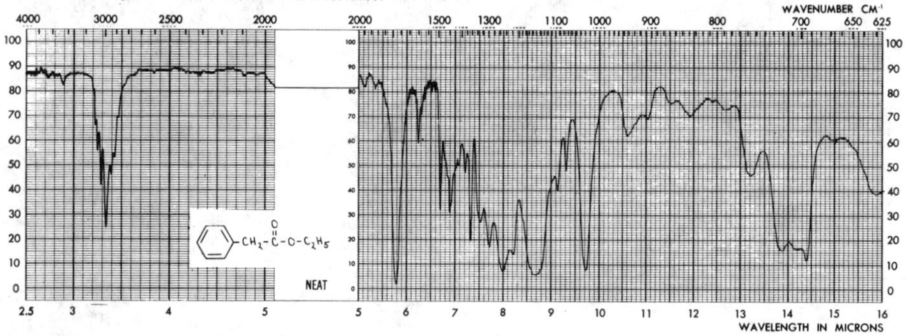

C

19,920-6
Methyl 4-methoxyphenylacetate, 97+%
$CH_3OC_6H_4CH_2CO_2CH_3$ FW 180.20
bp 158°/19mm. n_D^{20} 1.5165 d 1.135 *Beil.* **10**,191
Disp. C

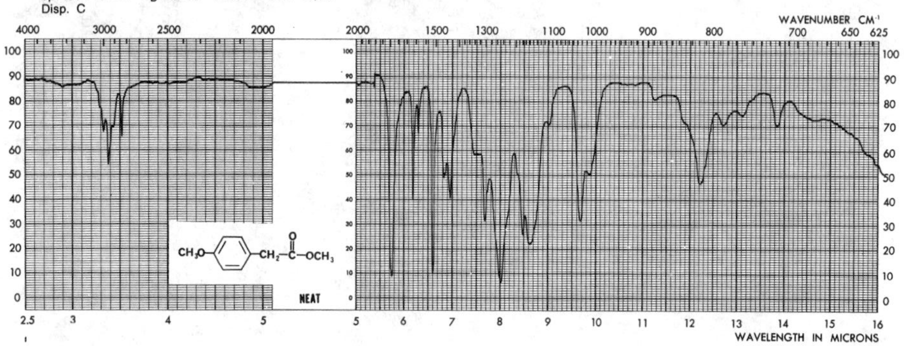

D

19,921-4
Ethyl 4-methoxyphenylacetate, 97+%
$CH_3OC_6H_4CH_2CO_2C_2H_5$ FW 194.23
bp 138-140°/7mm. n_D^{20} 1.5075 d 1.097
Beil. **10**(1),83 Disp. C

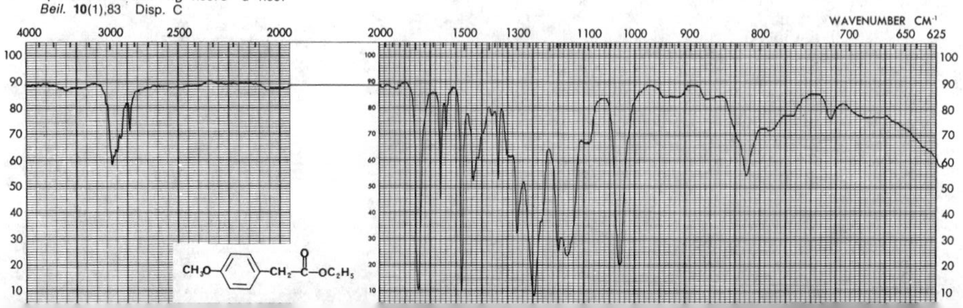

E

22,450-2
Methyl 4-hydroxyphenylacetate, 99%
$HOC_6H_4CH_2CO_2CH_3$ FW 166.18 mp 57-60°
bp 162-163°/5mm. *Beil.* **10**,191 Disp. C

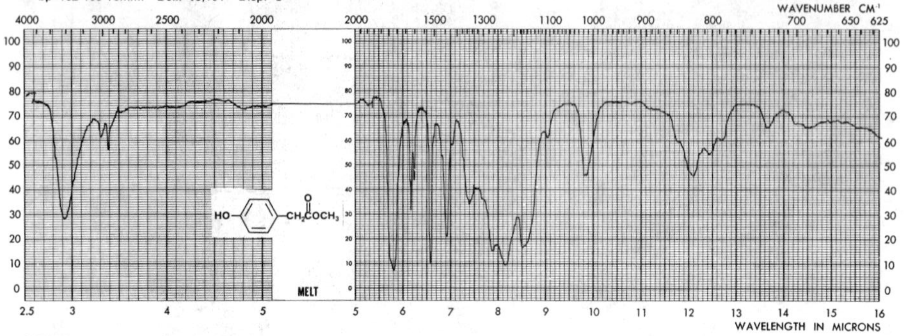

F

19,797-1
Ethyl homovanillate, 98+% (ethyl 4-hydroxy-3-methoxyphenylacetate)
$HOC_6H_3(OCH_3)CH_2CO_2C_2H_5$ FW 210.23
mp 44-47° bp 180-185°/14mm. *Beil.* **10**(1),198
Disp. C

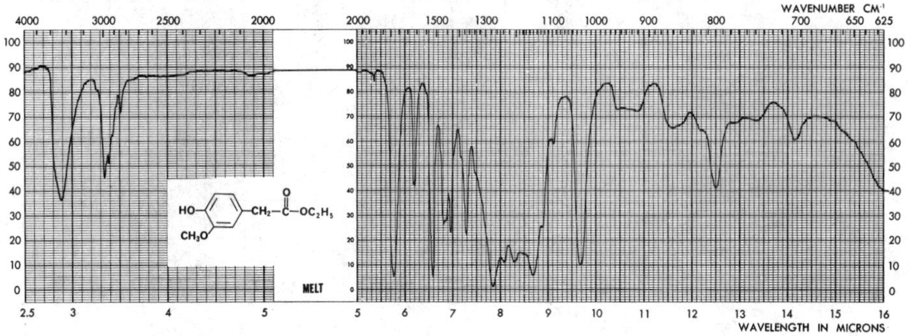

G

10,658-5 **Methyl 5-phenylvalerate**
$C_6H_5(CH_2)_4CO_2CH_3$ M.W. 192.26 n_D^{20} 1.4968
b.p. 87.5-88°/0.1 mm.

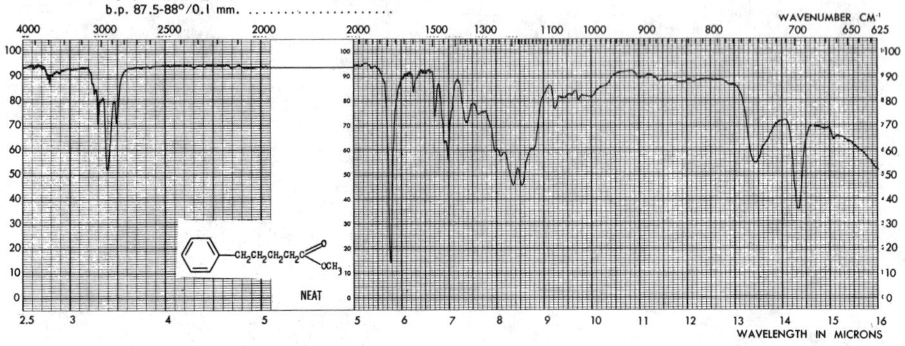

H

C538 ***trans*-1-Carbethoxy-2-phenylcyclopropane**
$C_6H_5C_3H_4CO_2C_2H_5$ M.W. 190.24 n_D^{20} 1.5048

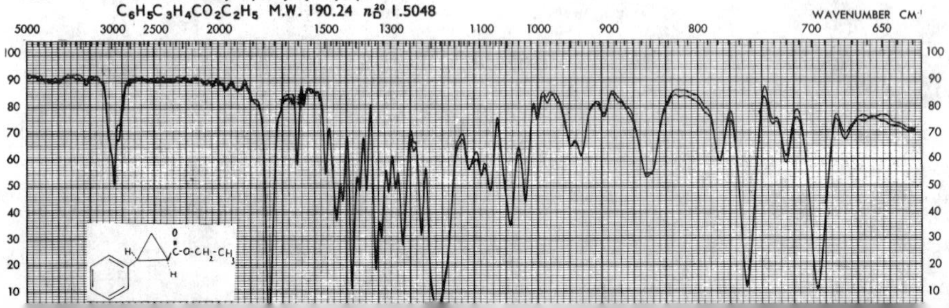

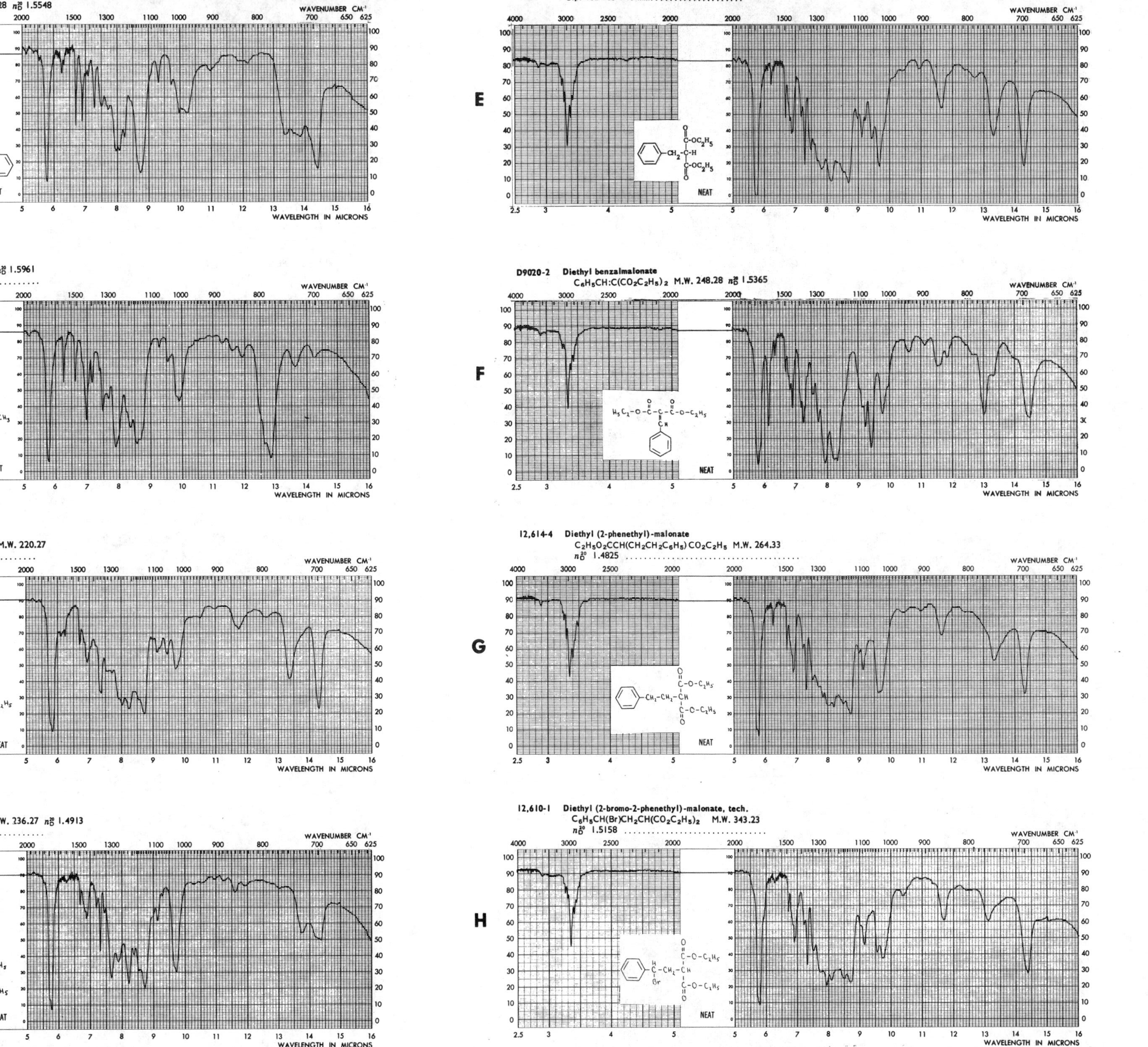

A
$C_6H_5CH_2CO_2CH_2C_6H_5$ M.W. 226.28 n_D^{20} 1.5548
NEAT
B
11,271-2 Methyl 1-naphthaleneacetate, 99+%
$C_{10}H_7CH_2CO_2CH_3$ M.W. 200.24 n_D^{20} 1.5961
b.p. 160-162°/5 mm.
NEAT
C
E1320-2 Ethyl 2-benzylacetoacetate
$CH_3COCH(CH_2C_6H_5)CO_2C_2H_5$ M.W. 220.27
n_D^{20} 1.4996
NEAT
D
11,199-6 Diethyl phenylmalonate
$C_2H_5O_2CCH(C_6H_5)CO_2C_2H_5$ M.W. 236.27 n_D^{20} 1.4913
b.p. 158-162°/10 mm.
NEAT
E
b.p. 162-163°/10 mm.
NEAT
F
D9020-2 Diethyl benzalmalonate
$C_6H_5CH{:}C(CO_2C_2H_5)_2$ M.W. 248.28 n_D^{20} 1.5365
NEAT
G
12,614-4 Diethyl (2-phenethyl)-malonate
$C_2H_5O_2CCH(CH_2CH_2C_6H_5)CO_2C_2H_5$ M.W. 264.33
n_D^{20} 1.4825
NEAT
H
12,610-1 Diethyl (2-bromo-2-phenethyl)-malonate, tech.
$C_6H_5CH(Br)CH_2CH(CO_2C_2H_5)_2$ M.W. 343.23
n_D^{20} 1.5158
NEAT
WAVENUMBER CM⁻¹
WAVELENGTH IN MICRONS
ALDRICH

A

D9918-8 Diethyl 2-phenylcyclopropane-1,1-dicarboxylate
$C_6H_5C_3H_3(CO_2C_2H_5)_2$ M.W. 262.31
n_D^{20} 1.4938

NEAT

B

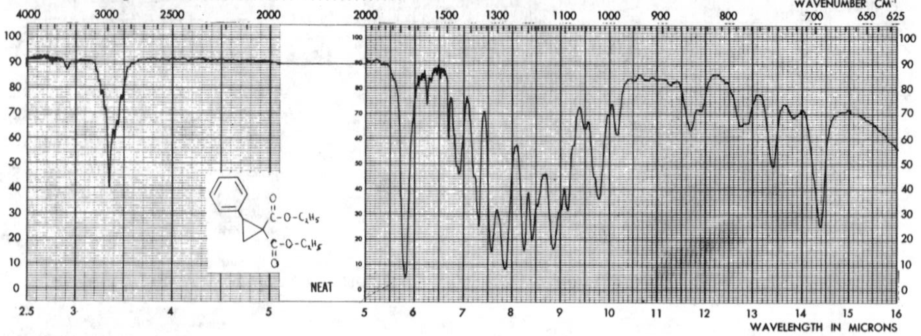

19,554-5
Diethyl 2-ethyl-2-(p-tolyl)malonate, 99%
$CH_3C_6H_4C(C_2H_5)(CO_2C_2H_5)_2$ FW 278.35
bp 116-117°/0.500mm. n_D^{20} 1.4915 d 1.041
Beil. 9(3),4320 Disp. C

NEAT

C

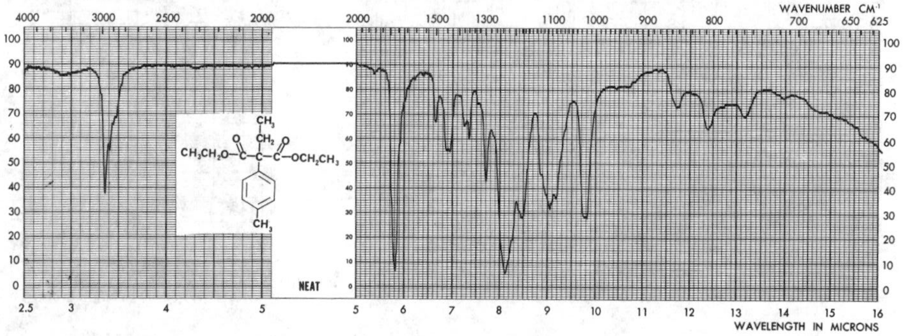

16,040-7
Dibenzyl malonate
$CH_2(CO_2CH_2C_6H_5)_2$
M.W. 284.31 b.p. 188°/0.2mm. n_D^{20} 1.5447
d 1.137 Beil. 6,436 Fieser 1,198

NEAT

D

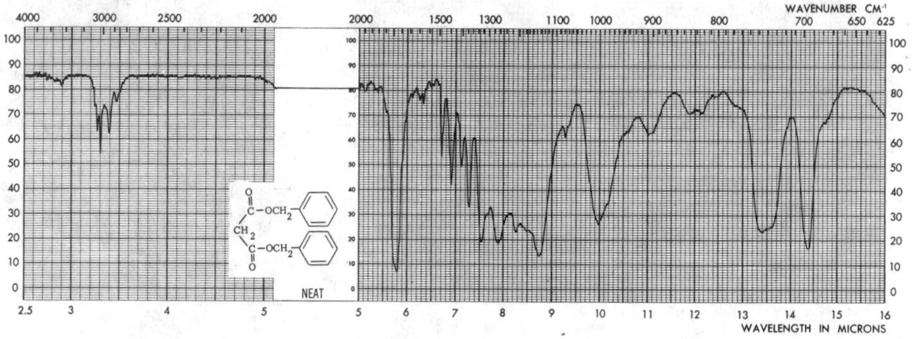

13,937-8 Dibenzyl succinate
$C_6H_5CH_2O_2CCH_2CH_2CO_2CH_2C_6H_5$ M.W. 298.34
m.p. 44.5-46.5°

E

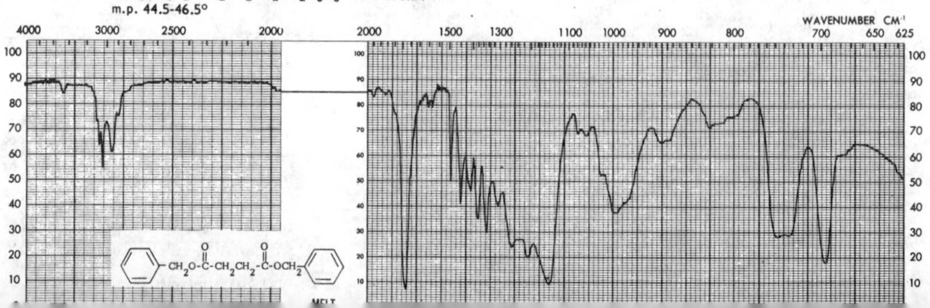

M5410-4 Methyl mandelate
$C_6H_5CH(OH)CO_2CH_3$ M.W. 166.18 m.p. 51-54°

NUJOL MULL

F

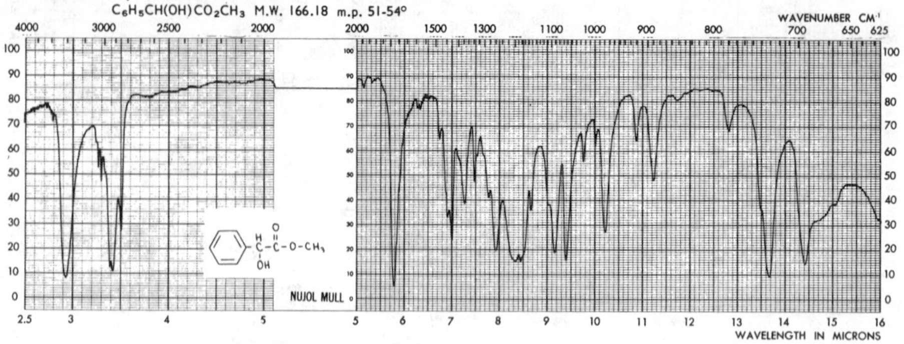

M6885-7 Methyl α-phenylcyclopentaneglycolate
$HOC(C_5H_9)(C_6H_5)CO_2CH_3$ M.W. 234.30 n_D^{20} 1.5219

NEAT

G

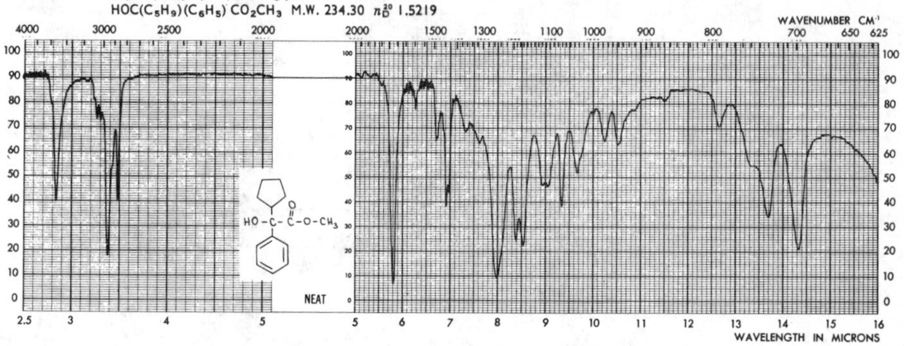

10,788-3 Methyl benzilate
$(C_6H_5)_2C(OH)CO_2CH_3$ M.W. 242.27
m.p. 74-76°

NUJOL MULL

H

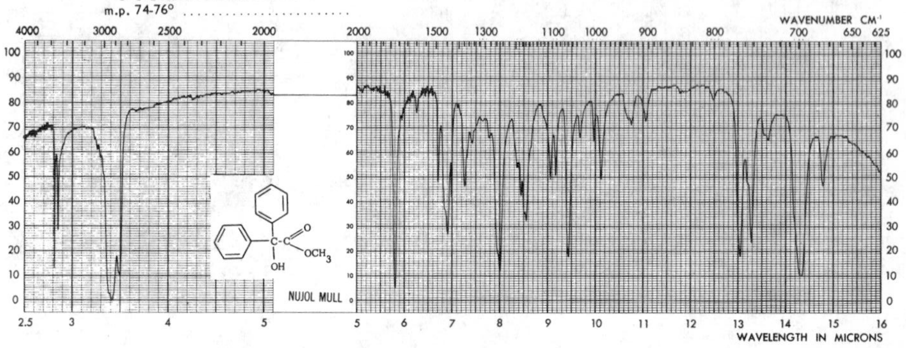

E1260-5 Ethyl benzilate
$(C_6H_5)_2C(OH)CO_2C_2H_5$ M.W. 256.30 n_D^{20} 1.5629
b.p. 188-190°/15 mm.

WAVENUMBER CM⁻¹ — WAVELENGTH IN MICRONS

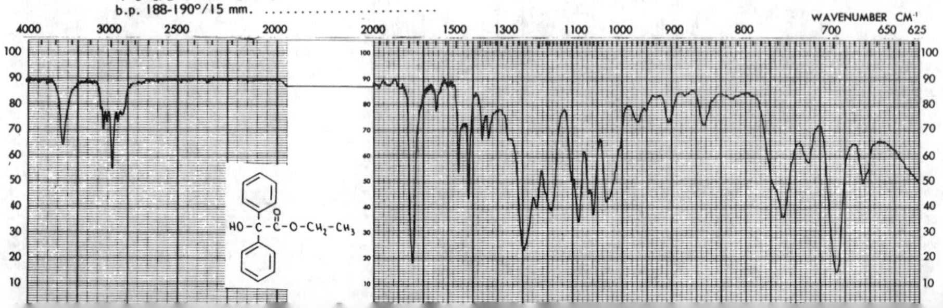

A

$HOC_6H_4CH(OH)CO_2C_2H_5$ M.W. 196.20
m.p. 127-129°

NUJOL MULL

B

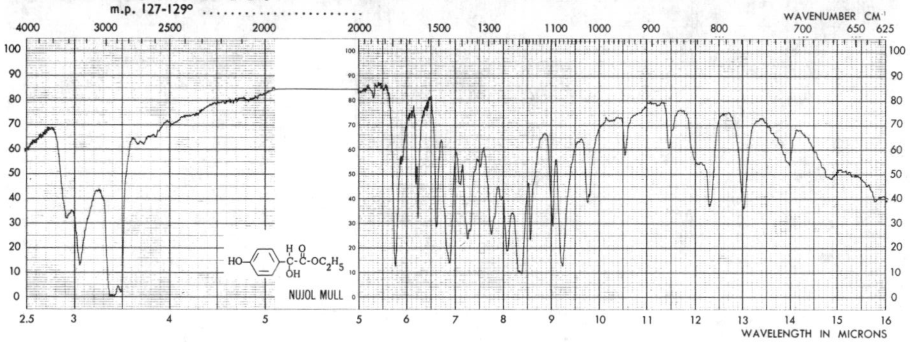

B70-4 **Benactyzine (2-diethylaminoethyl benzilate) hydrochloride**
$(C_6H_5)_2C(OH)CO_2CH_2CH_2N(C_2H_5)_2\cdot HCl$ M.W. 363.89
m.p. 180-182°

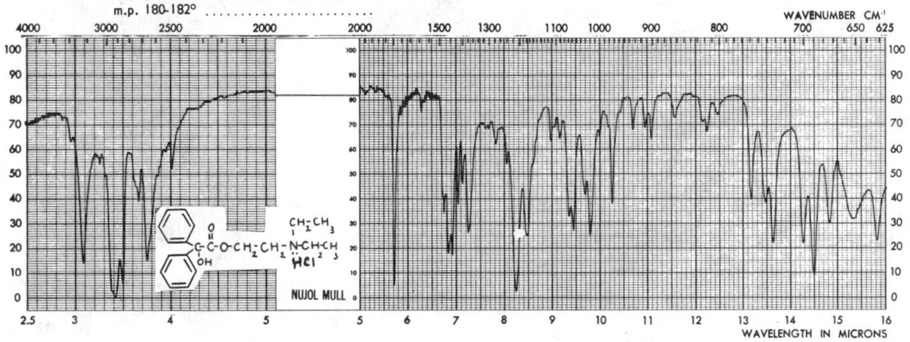

NUJOL MULL

C

P1720-2 **L-Phenylalanine methyl ester hydrochloride**
$C_6H_5CH_2CH(NH_2)CO_2CH_3\cdot HCl$ M.W. 215.68 m.p. 158-162°

NUJOL MULL

D

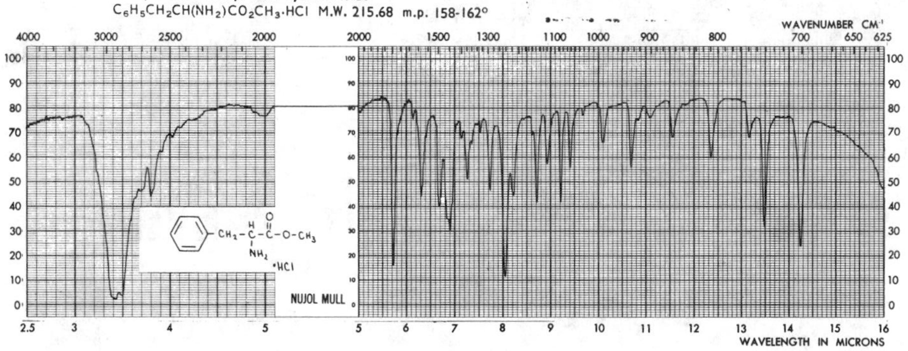

22,070-1
L-Phenylalanine ethyl ester hydrochloride, 99%
$C_6H_5CH_2CH(NH_2)CO_2C_2H_5\cdot HCl$ FW 229.71
mp 155-156° $[\alpha]^{21}$ +33.2° (c=5, C_2H_5OH)
Beil. 14,497 Disp. D

NUJOL MULL

E

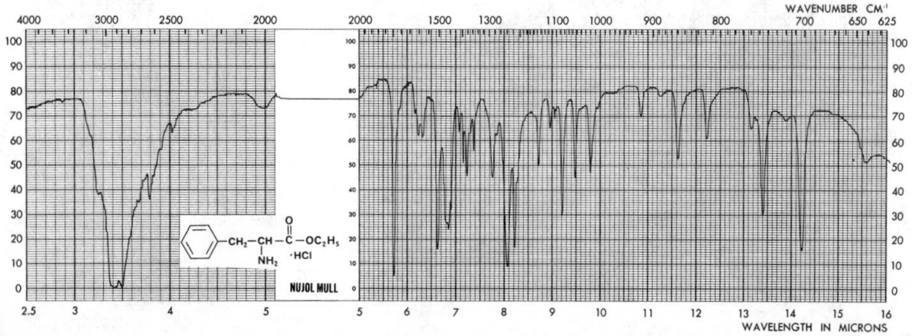

$C_6H_5CH_2NHCH_2CO_2C_2H_5$ M.W. 193.25
n_D^{20} 1.5071

NEAT

F

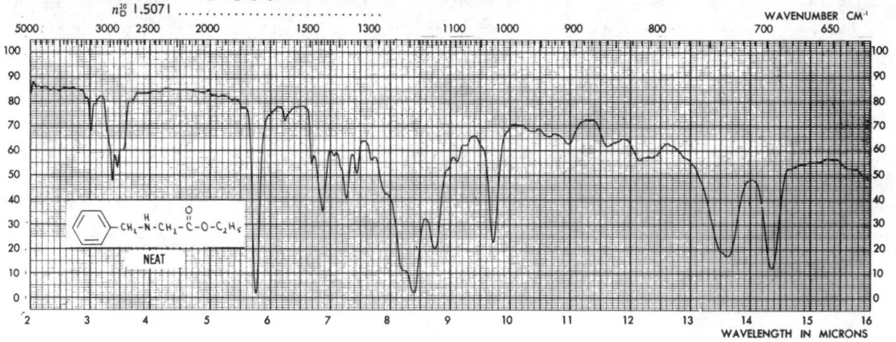

17,841-1
N-(α-Methylbenzyl)-glycine methyl ester, 95%
$C_6H_5CH(CH_3)NHCH_2CO_2CH_3$
M.W. 193.25 n_D^{20} 1.5090

NEAT

G

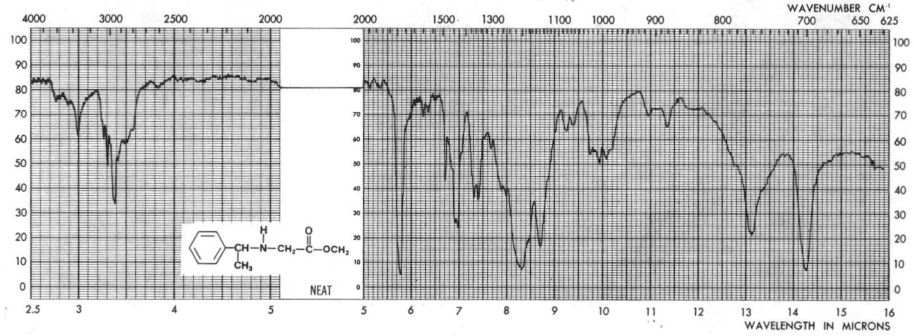

85,892-7
N-Benzoyl-L-alanine methyl ester
$CH_3CH(NHCOC_6H_5)CO_2CH_3$
M.W. 207.23 m.p. 60-62° Beil. 9,248

NUJOL MULL

H

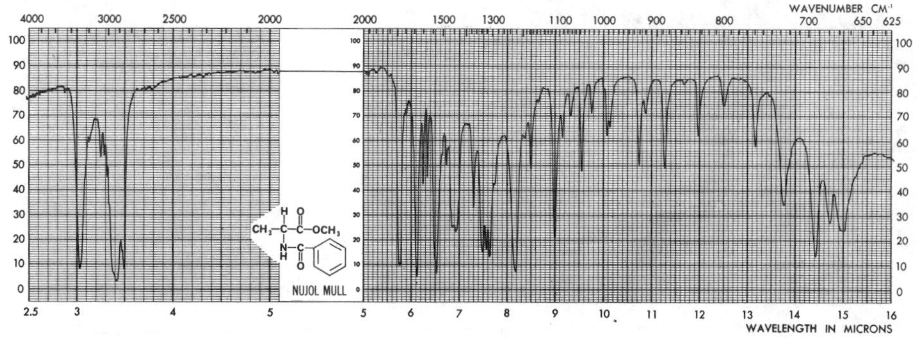

14,881-4 **α-MMT** (DL-α-methyl-m-tyrosine) **methyl ester hydrochloride**
$HOC_6H_4CH_2C(CH_3)(NH_2)CO_2CH_3\cdot HCl$ M.W. 245.71
m.p. 135° (dec.)

NUJOL MULL

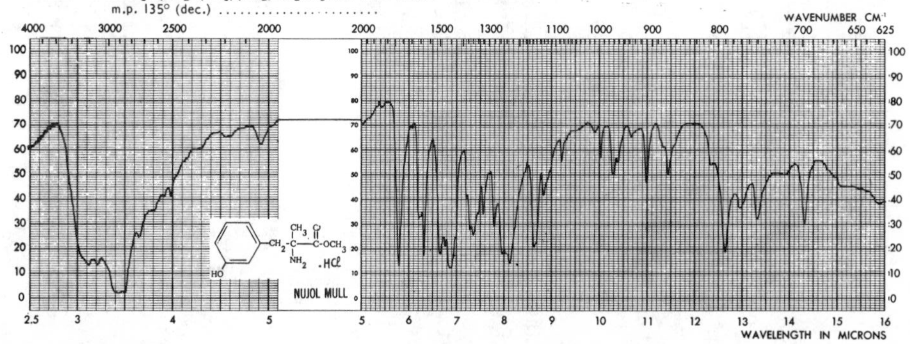

A

T9080-8 **L-Tyrosine methyl ester**
$4\text{-(HO)}C_6H_4CH_2CH(NH_2)CO_2CH_3$ M.W. 195.22
m.p. 136-137°

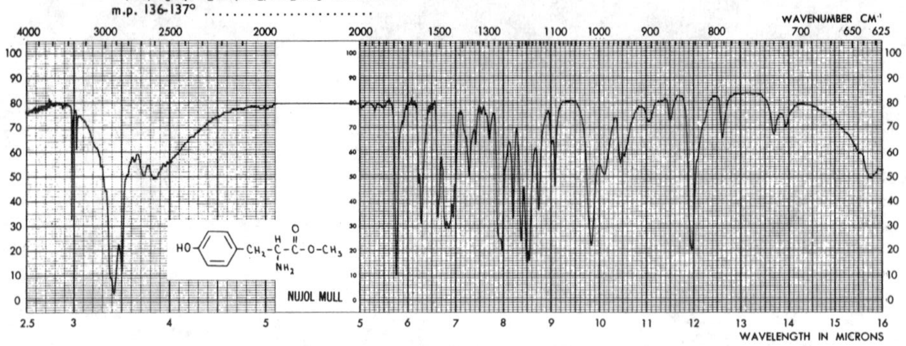

NUJOL MULL

B

85,095-0
DL-Tyrosine methyl ester hydrochloride
$4\text{-(HO)}C_6H_4CH_2CH(NH_2)CO_2CH_3 \cdot HCl$
M.W. 231.68 m.p. 192-193° (dec.) Beil. 14,612

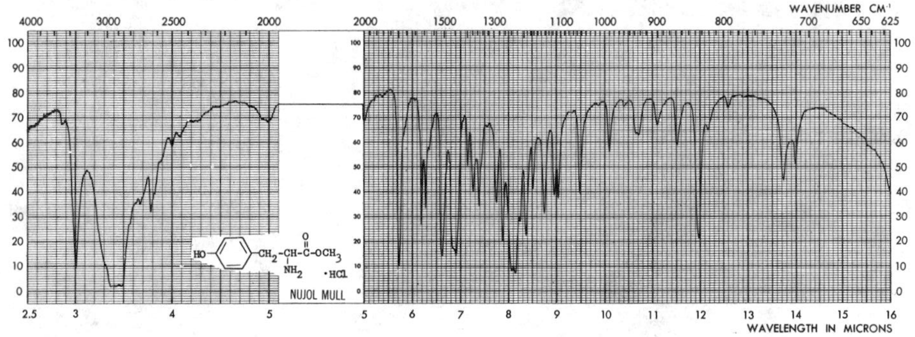

NUJOL MULL

C

85,048-9
L-Tyrosine methyl ester hydrochloride
$4\text{-(HO)}C_6H_4CH_2CH(NH_2)CO_2CH_3 \cdot HCl$
M.W. 231.68 m.p. 193-194° (dec.)
$[\alpha]^{22}$ -5.2° (c=2.4, H_2O) Beil. 14,612

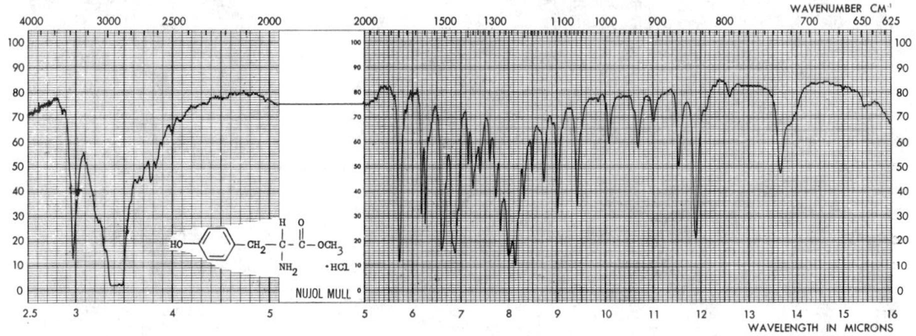

NUJOL MULL

D

14,888-1 **DL-α-Methyltyrosine-(α-MT) methyl ester hydrochloride**
$4\text{-(HO)}C_6H_4CH_2C(CH_3)(NH_2)CO_2CH_3 \cdot HCl$
m.p. 189-191° (dec.)

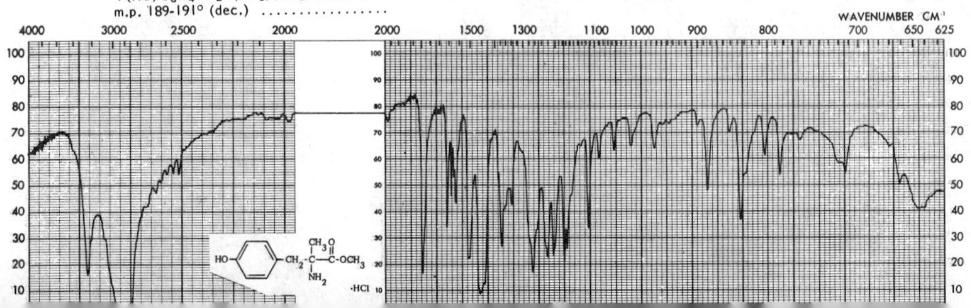

E

13,814-2 **L-Tyrosine ethyl ester hydrochloride**
$4\text{-(HO)}C_6H_4CH_2CH(NH_2)CO_2C_2H_5 \cdot HCl$ M.W. 245.71
m.p. 168-170° (dec.)

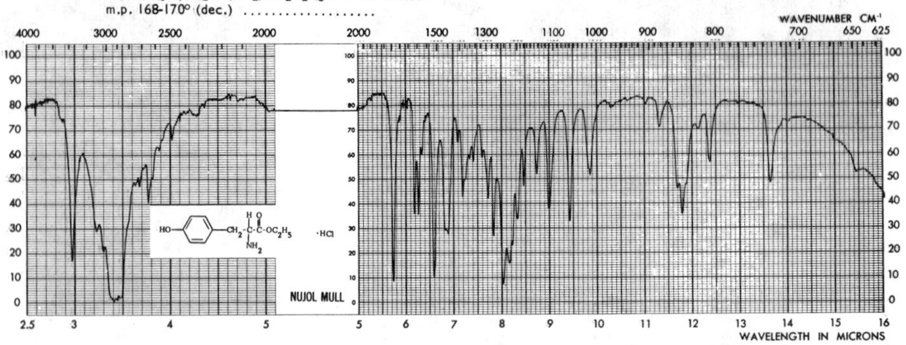

NUJOL MULL

F

15,678-7
p-Chlorophenylalanine ethyl ester hydrochloride
$ClC_6H_4CH_2CH(NH_2)CO_2C_2H_5 \cdot HCl$
M.W. 264.16 m.p. 166-168°

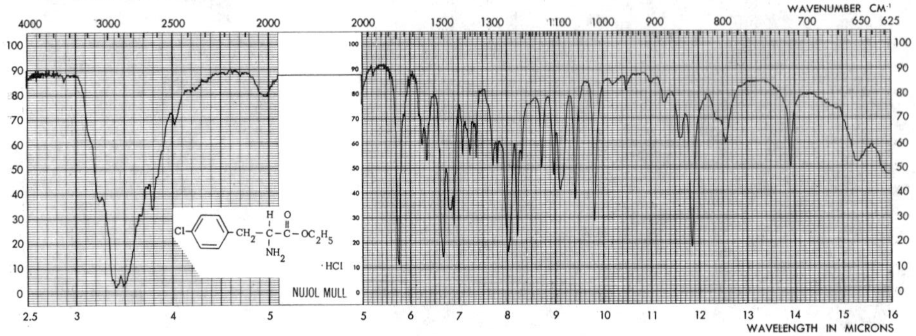

NUJOL MULL

G

14,886-5 **DL-α,3-Dimethyltyrosine methyl ester hydrochloride**
$CH_3C_6H_3\text{-4-(OH)}CH_2C(CH_3)(NH_2)CO_2CH_3 \cdot HCl$
m.p. 217.5° (dec.)

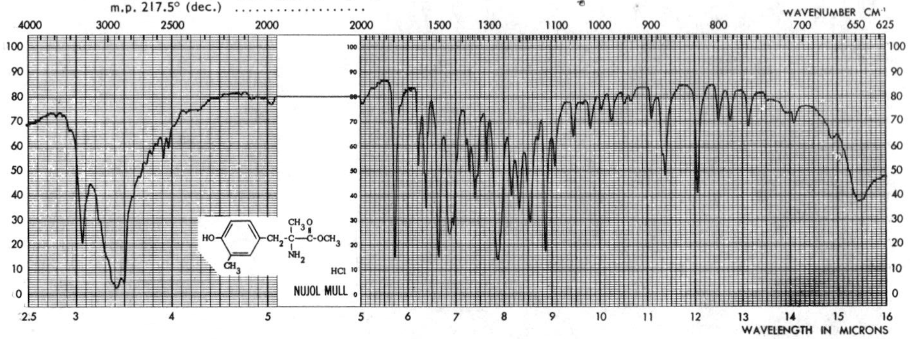

NUJOL MULL

H

12,040-5 **Ethyl α-(p-benzyloxyanilino)-phenylacetate**
$C_6H_5CH_2OC_6H_4NHCH(C_6H_5)CO_2C_2H_5$ M.W. 361.44
m.p. 82-83°

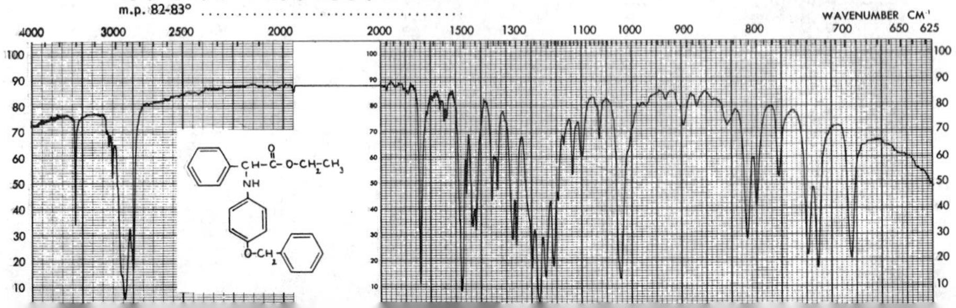

A

M.W. 328.33 m.p. 160-162°

NUJOL MULL

B

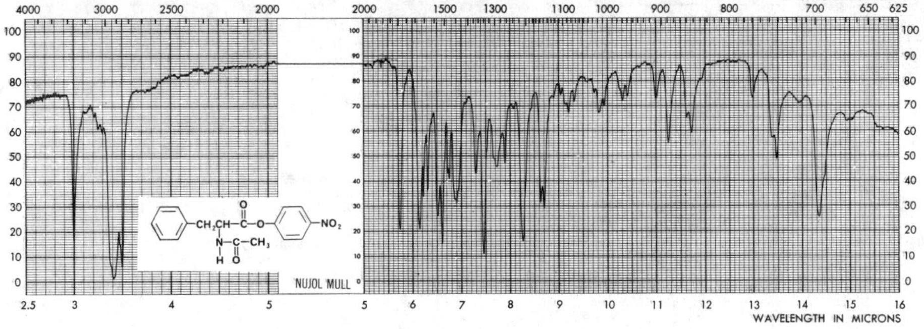

14,191-7 Tropacocaine hydrochloride
M.W. 281.79 m.p. 282-286° (dec.)

NUJOL MULL

C

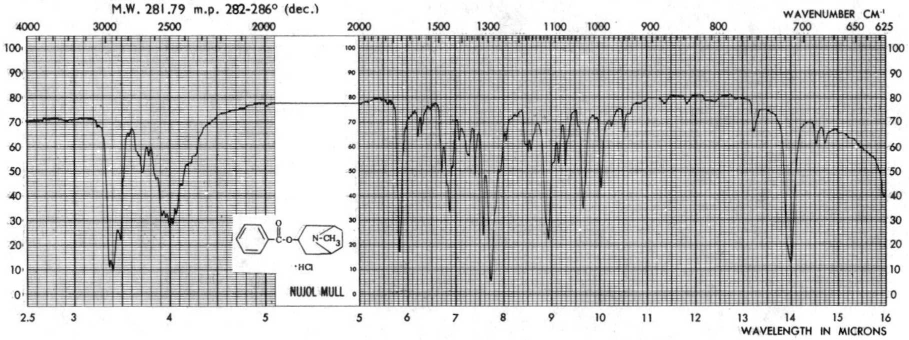

14,185-2 Homatropine hydrobromide
M.W. 356.27 m.p. 212-214°

NUJOL MULL

D

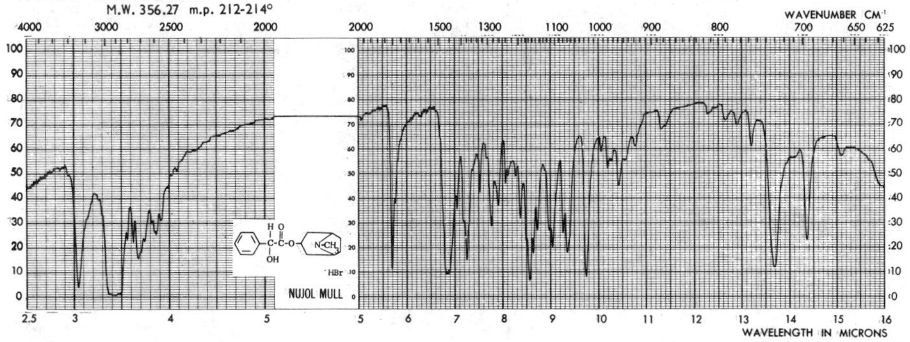

85,063-2
Homatropine-N-oxide hydrobromide
M.W. 372.26 m.p. 227° (dec.) Beil. **21**(2),21

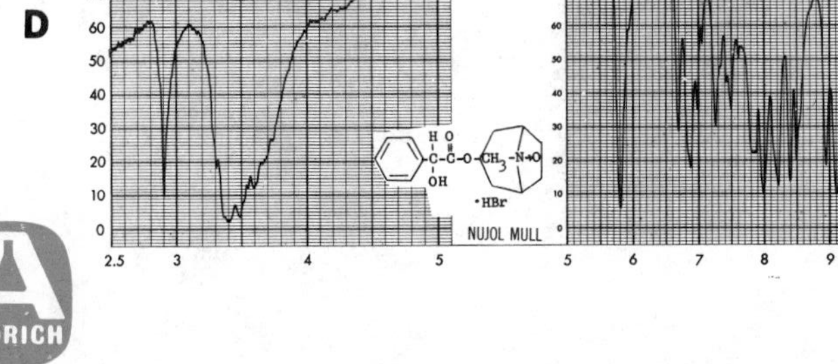

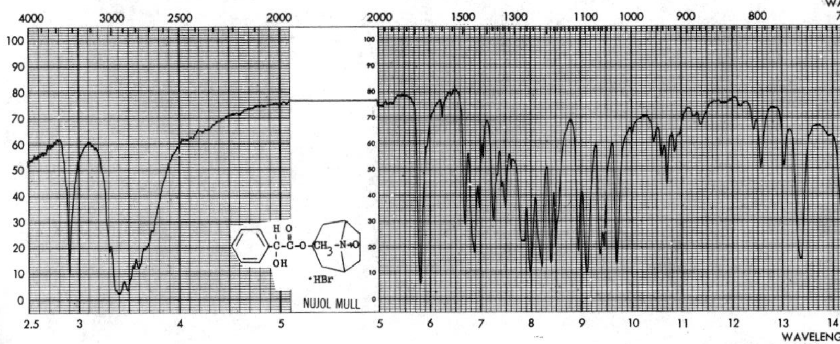

NUJOL MULL

E

A9340-2 Atropine (*dl*-hyoscyamine), puriss.
M.W. 289.38 m.p. 116-119° . . . .

NUJOL MULL

F

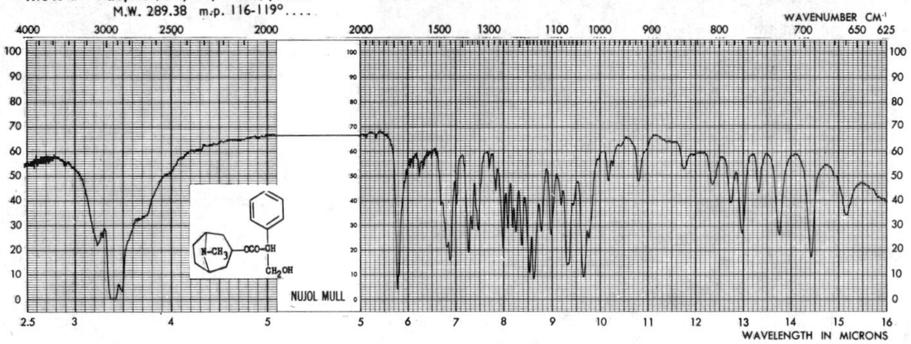

85,299-6
Atropine sulfate monohydrate
M.W. 694.86 m.p. 189-192° (anhydrous)
Beil. **21**,27

NUJOL MULL

G

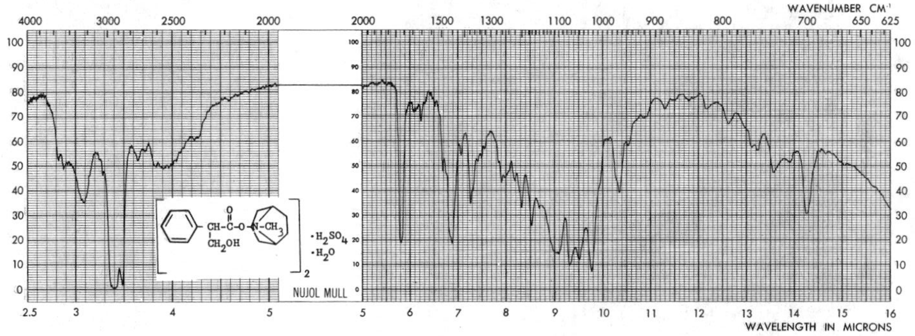

S160-4 Scopolamine (hyoscine)
M.W. 303.36 n_D^{20} 1.5425 $[\alpha]_D^{20}$ - 28° (c=2.7)

NEAT

H

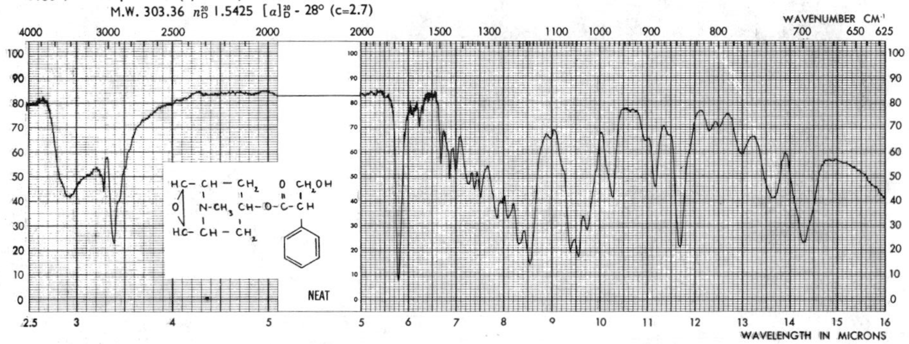

14,199-2 Scopolamine (hyoscine) hydrobromide trihydrate
M.W. 438.33 m.p. 191-194° (anhydrous) $[\alpha]_D^{20}$ -24° to - 26°
(c=2.5, H_2O) . . . .

NUJOL MULL

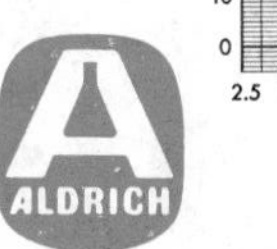

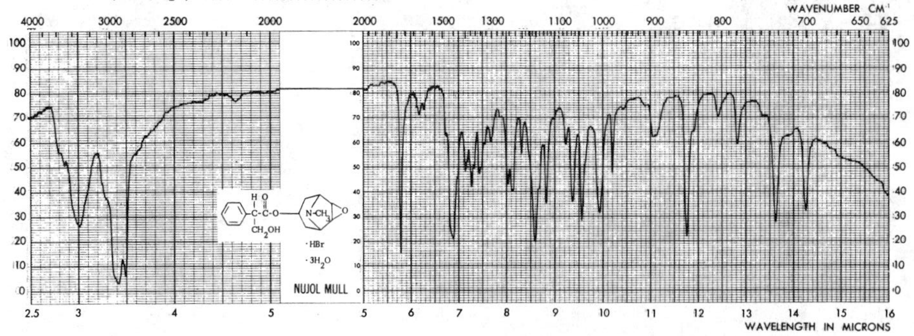

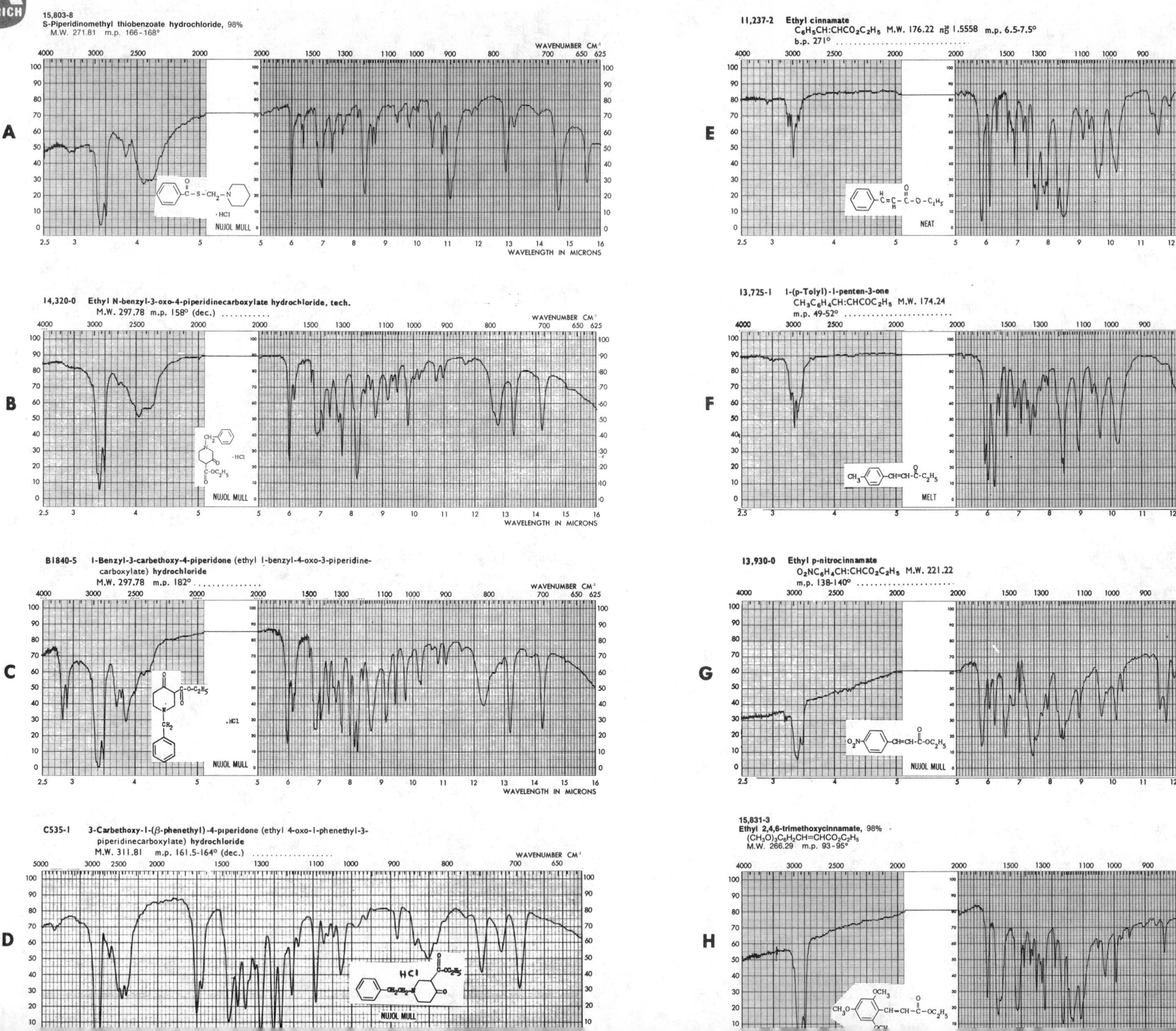

ALDRICH
A
15,803-8 S-Piperidinomethyl thiobenzoate hydrochloride, 98%
M.W. 271.81 m.p. 166-168°
NUJOL MULL
B
14,320-0 Ethyl N-benzyl-3-oxo-4-piperidinecarboxylate hydrochloride, tech.
M.W. 297.78 m.p. 158° (dec.)
NUJOL MULL
C
B1840-5 1-Benzyl-3-carbethoxy-4-piperidone (ethyl 1-benzyl-4-oxo-3-piperidinecarboxylate) hydrochloride
M.W. 297.78 m.p. 182°
NUJOL MULL
D
C535-1 3-Carbethoxy-1-(β-phenethyl)-4-piperidone (ethyl 4-oxo-1-phenethyl-3-piperidinecarboxylate) hydrochloride
M.W. 311.81 m.p. 161.5-164° (dec.)
NUJOL MULL
E
11,237-2 Ethyl cinnamate
C6H5CH:CHCO2C2H5 M.W. 176.22 n20D 1.5558 m.p. 6.5-7.5°
b.p. 271°
NEAT
F
13,725-1 1-(p-Tolyl)-1-penten-3-one
CH3C6H4CH:CHCOC2H5 M.W. 174.24
m.p. 49-52°
MELT
G
13,930-0 Ethyl p-nitrocinnamate
O2NC6H4CH:CHCO2C2H5 M.W. 221.22
m.p. 138-140°
NUJOL MULL
H
15,831-3 Ethyl 2,4,6-trimethoxycinnamate, 98%
(CH3O)3C6H2CH=CHCO2C2H5
M.W. 266.29 m.p. 93-95°
WAVENUMBER CM⁻¹
WAVELENGTH IN MICRONS

A

C4420-6 **Chlorogenic acid**
M.W. 354.31 m.p. 207-209°

NUJOL MULL

B

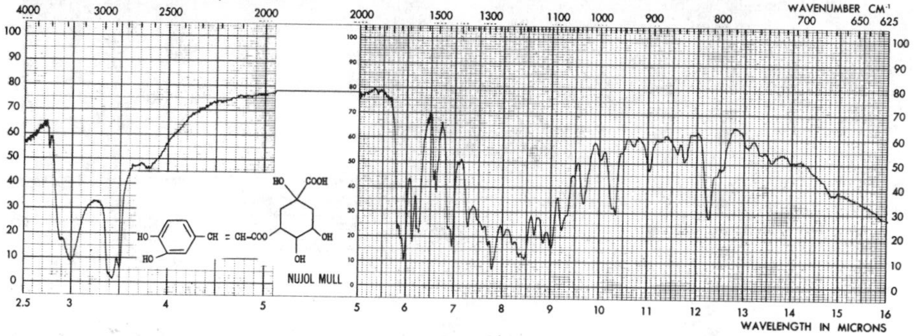

21,419-1
1-Methyl-4-piperidinyl bis(4-chlorophenoxy)-acetate, 97%
FW 410.30 mp 96-100° Disp. C

NUJOL MULL

C

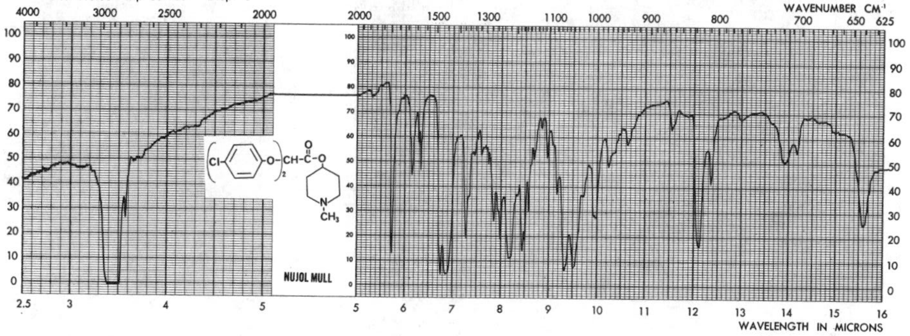

C12,147-9 **Cynarine [1-carboxy-3,5-dihydroxy-1,4-cyclohexylene bis-(3,4-dihydroxy-cinnamate)] hydrate**
M.W. 534.47 m.p. 223-224°

NUJOL MULL

D

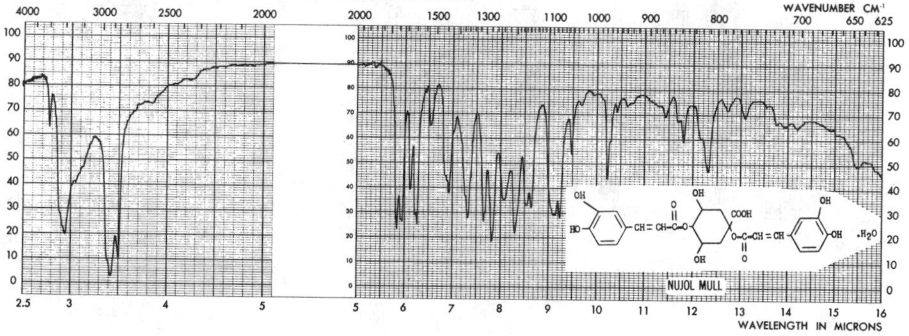

M3050-7 **Methyl benzoylformate** (methyl phenylglyoxylate)
$C_6H_5COCO_2CH_3$ M.W. 164.16 n_D^{20} 1.5268 b.p. 88-90°/2 mm.

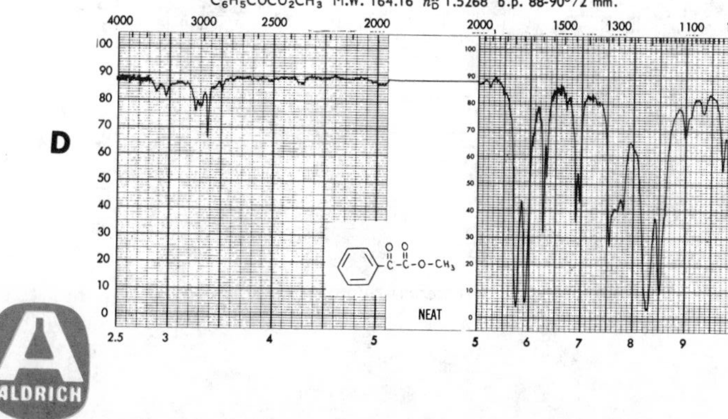

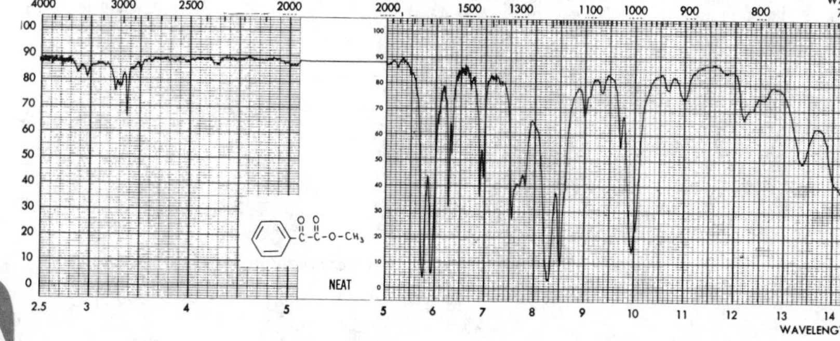

NEAT

E

13,047-8 **Ethyl benzoylacetate**
$C_6H_5COCH_2CO_2C_2H_5$ M.W. 192.22 n_D^{20} 1.5270
b.p. 125-131°/4 mm.

NEAT

F

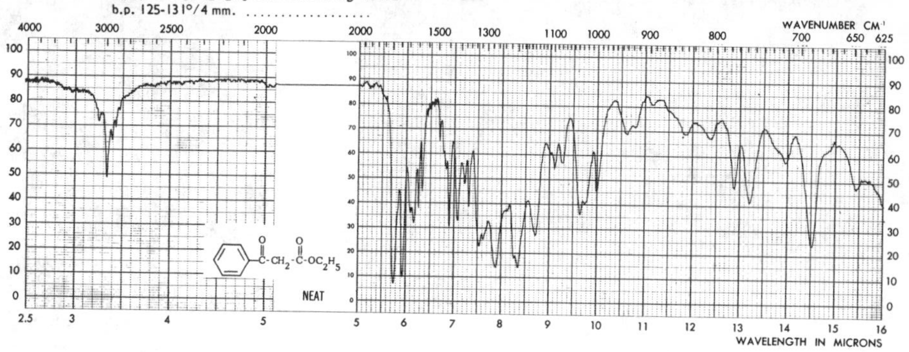

21,505-8
Ethyl 2-benzylbenzoylacetate
$C_6H_5COCH(CH_2C_6H_5)CO_2C_2H_5$ FW 282.34
bp 265-270°/80mm. n_D^{20} 1.5567 d 1.110
Beil. **10**,764 Disp. C

NEAT

G

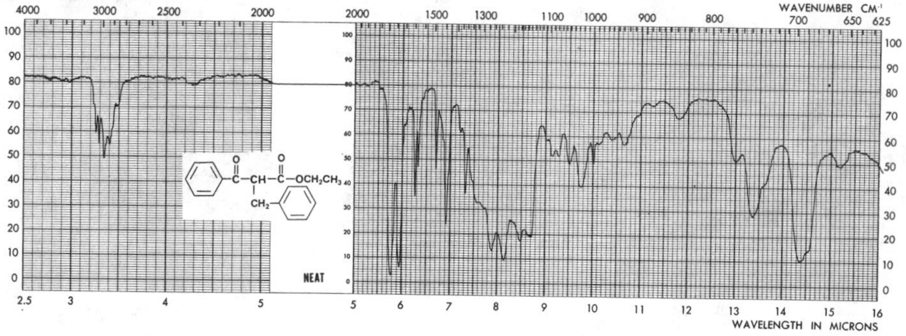

21,306-3
Methyl *p*-fluorobenzoylacetate, 99%
$FC_6H_4COCH_2CO_2CH_3$ FW 196.18 n_D^{20} 1.5228
d 1.228 Disp. C

NEAT

H

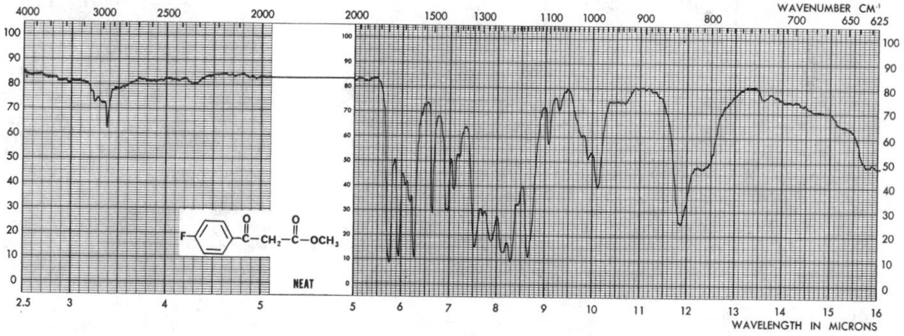

14,629-3 **Ethyl p-fluorobenzoylacetate**
$FC_6H_4COCH_2CO_2C_2H_5$ M.W. 210.21 n_D^{20} 1.5068
b.p. 145°/6 mm.

NEAT

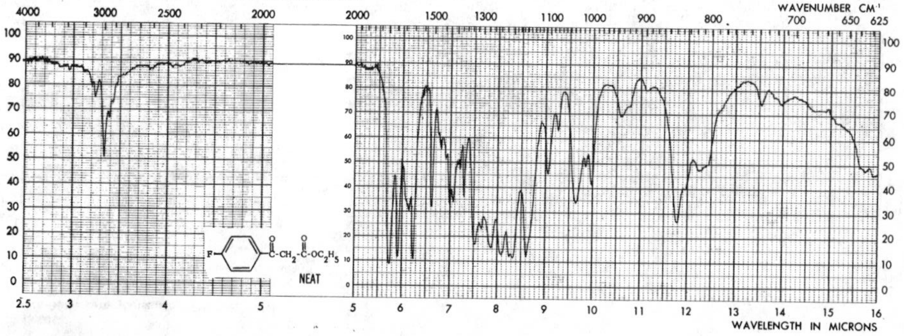

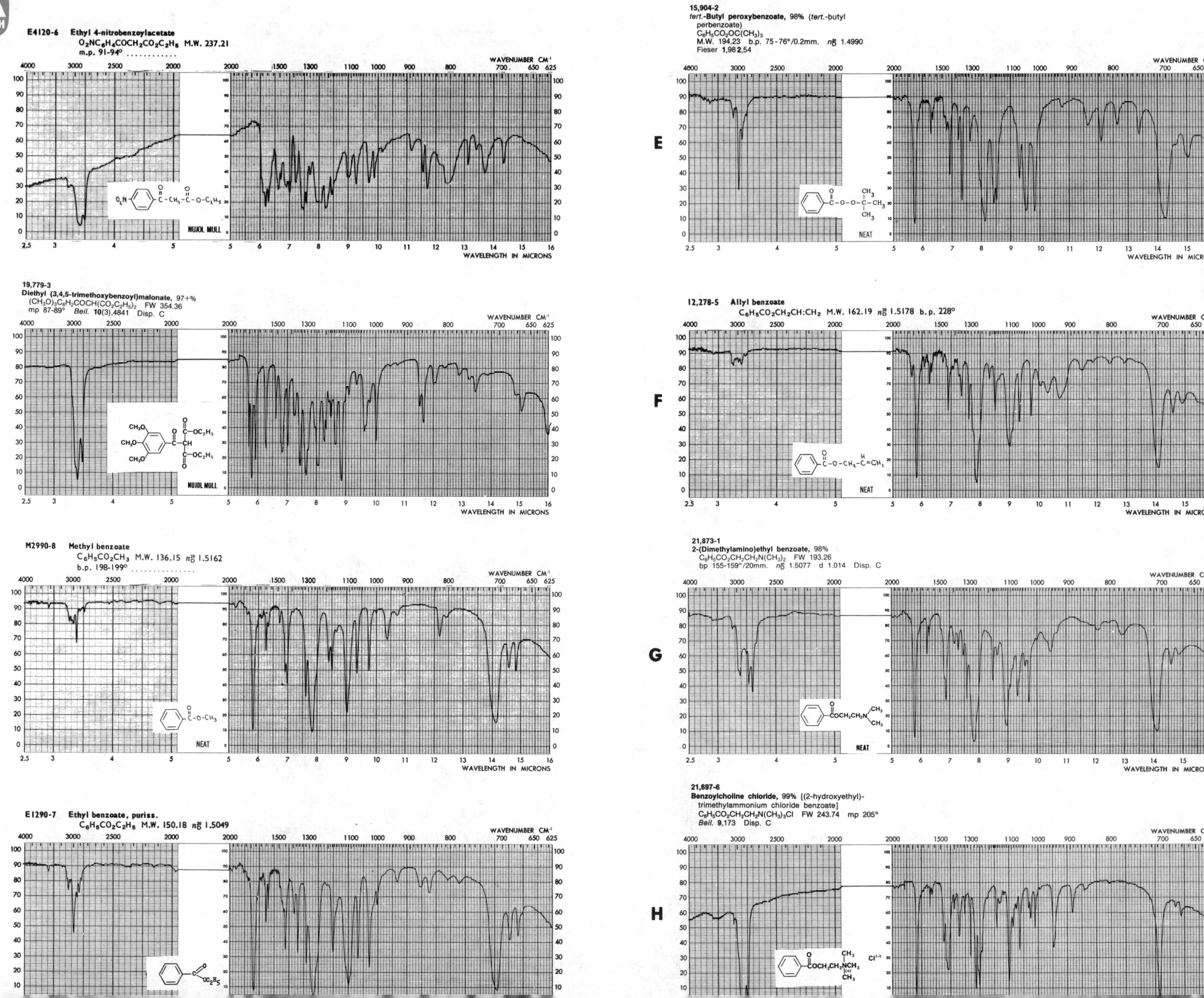

ALDRICH
A
E4120-6 Ethyl 4-nitrobenzoylacetate
$O_2NC_6H_4COCH_2CO_2C_2H_5$ M.W. 237.21
m.p. 91-94°
NUJOL MULL
B
19,779-3
Diethyl (3,4,5-trimethoxybenzoyl)malonate, 97+%
$(CH_3O)_3C_6H_2COCH(CO_2C_2H_5)_2$ FW 354.36
mp 87-89° Beil. 10(3),4841 Disp. C
NUJOL MULL
C
M2990-8 Methyl benzoate
$C_6H_5CO_2CH_3$ M.W. 136.15 n_D^{20} 1.5162
b.p. 198-199°
NEAT
D
E1290-7 Ethyl benzoate, puriss.
$C_6H_5CO_2C_2H_5$ M.W. 150.18 n_D^{20} 1.5049
E
15,904-2
tert.-Butyl peroxybenzoate, 98% (tert.-butyl perbenzoate)
$C_6H_5CO_2OC(CH_3)_3$
M.W. 194.23 b.p. 75-76°/0.2mm. n_D^{20} 1.4990
Fieser 1,98 2,54
NEAT
F
12,278-5 Allyl benzoate
$C_6H_5CO_2CH_2CH{:}CH_2$ M.W. 162.19 n_D^{20} 1.5178 b.p. 228°
NEAT
G
21,873-1
2-(Dimethylamino)ethyl benzoate, 98%
$C_6H_5CO_2CH_2CH_2N(CH_3)_2$ FW 193.26
bp 155-159°/20mm. n_D^{20} 1.5077 d 1.014 Disp. C
NEAT
H
21,697-6
Benzoylcholine chloride, 99% [(2-hydroxyethyl)-trimethylammonium chloride benzoate]
$C_6H_5CO_2CH_2CH_2N(CH_3)_3Cl$ FW 243.74 mp 205°
Beil. 9,173 Disp. C
WAVENUMBER CM⁻¹
WAVELENGTH IN MICRONS

$C_6H_5CO_2C_6H_5$ M.W. 198.22
m.p. 68-70° ....

B1770-0 **Benzyl benzoate, puriss.**
$C_6H_5CO_2CH_2C_6H_5$ M.W. 212.25 n_D^{20} 1.5680 m.p. 18-20°

11,489-8 **S-Benzoylcysteamine (S-2-aminoethyl thiobenzoate) hydrochloride**
$C_6H_5COSCH_2CH_2NH_2 \cdot HCl$ M.W. 217.72
m.p. 180-182° ....

15,788-0
S-(Thiobenzoyl)-thioglycolic acid, 97% [(thiobenzoyl-thio)-acetic acid]
$C_6H_5CS_2CH_2CO_2H$
M.W. 212.29 m.p. 125-127°

$(CH_3)_3CC_6H_4CO_2CH_3$ FW 192.26
bp 122-124°/9mm. n_D^{20} 1.5100 d 0.995
Beil. 9,560 Disp. C

10,334-9 **Methyl o-fluorobenzoate**
$FC_6H_4CO_2CH_3$ M.W. 154.14 b.p. 207°

12,070-7 **Methyl p-fluorobenzoate**
$FC_6H_4CO_2CH_3$ M.W. 154.14 n_D^{20} 1.4921
b.p. 90-92°/20 mm.

10,264-4 **Ethyl p-fluorobenzoate**
$FC_6H_4CO_2C_2H_5$ M.W. 168.17 n_D^{20} 1.4863
b.p. 210° ....

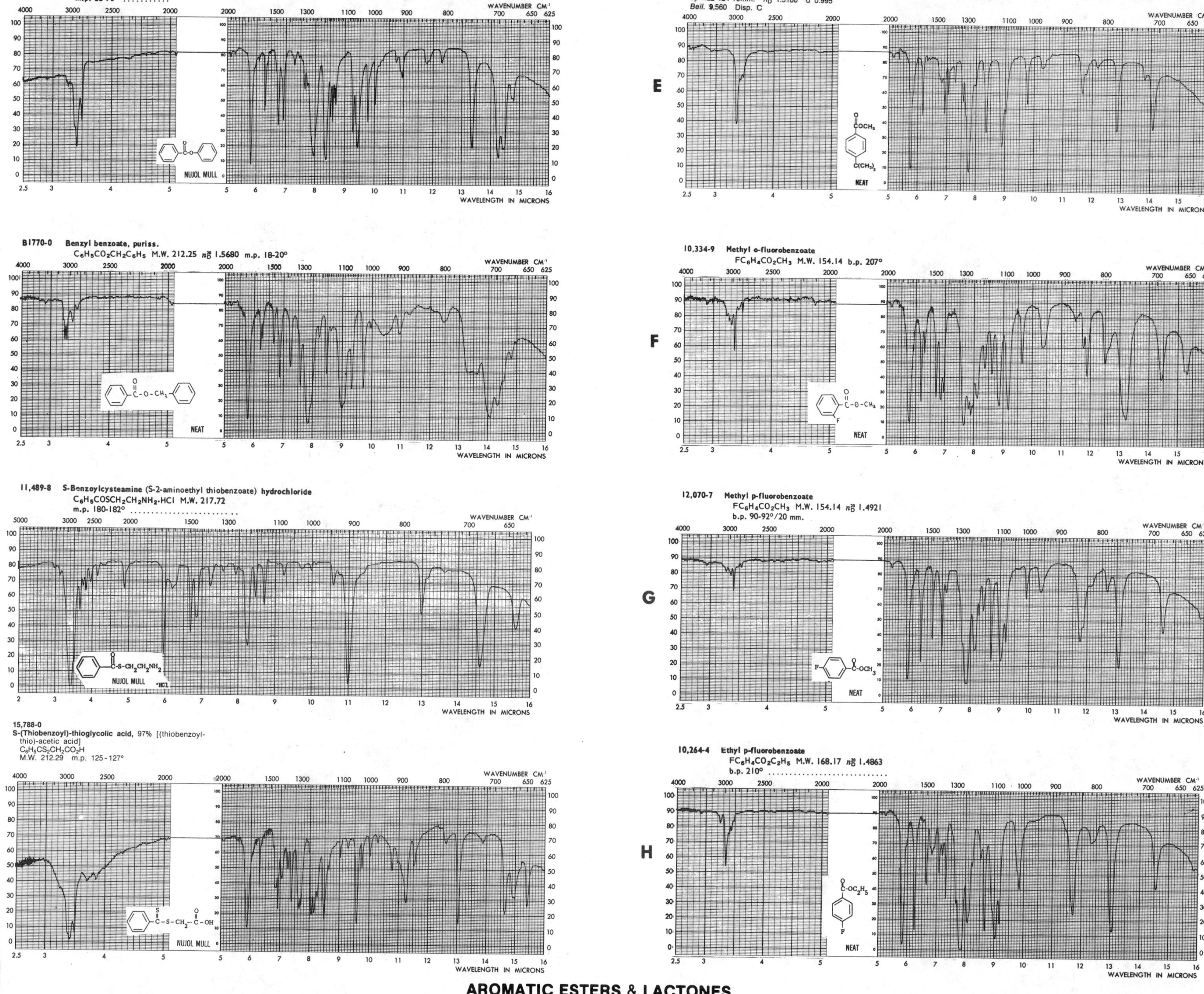

AROMATIC ESTERS & LACTONES

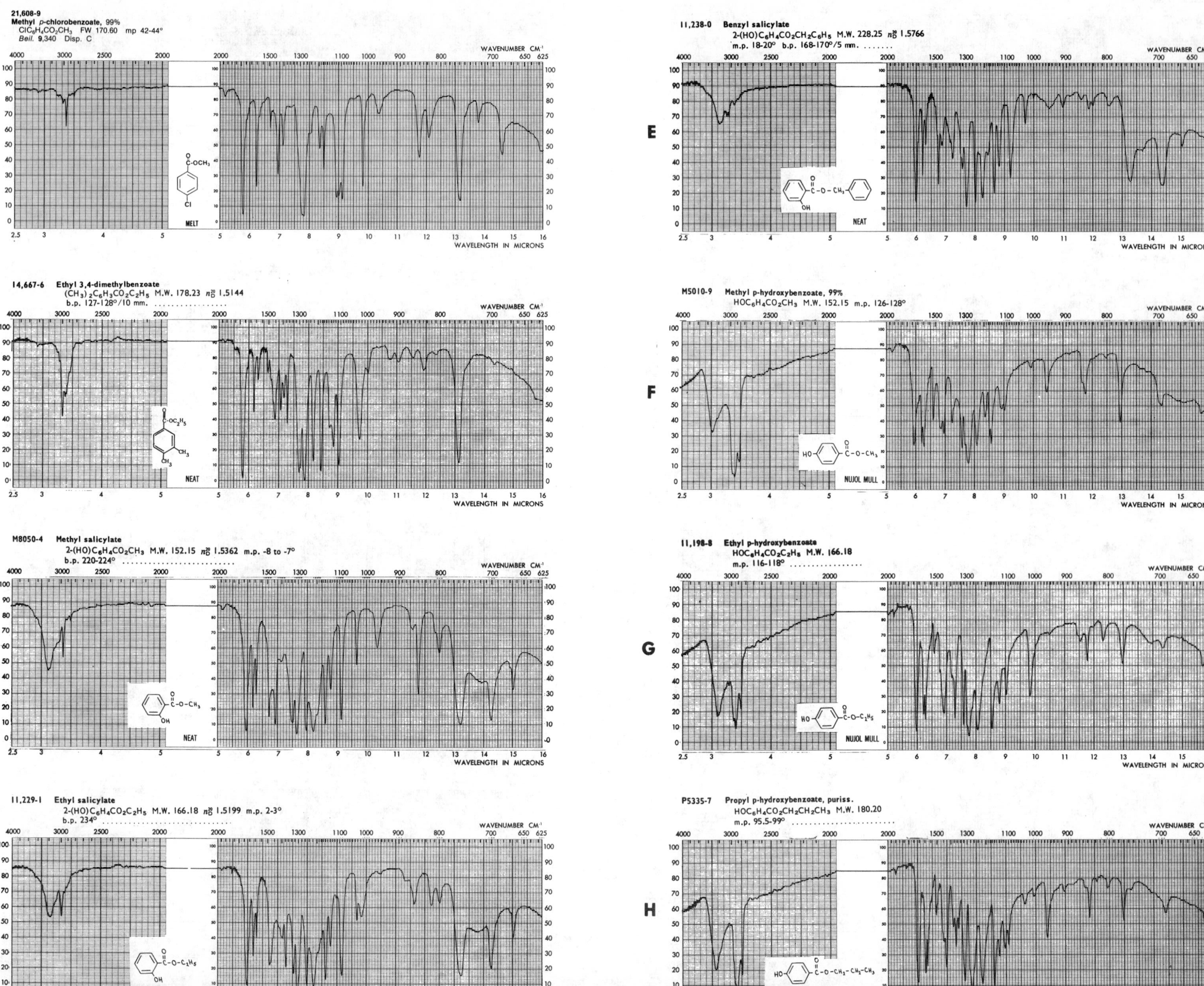

A 21,608-9 **Methyl *p*-chlorobenzoate, 99%**
$ClC_6H_4CO_2CH_3$ FW 170.60 mp 42-44°
Beil. 9,340 Disp. C
MELT

B 14,667-6 **Ethyl 3,4-dimethylbenzoate**
$(CH_3)_2C_6H_3CO_2C_2H_5$ M.W. 178.23 n_D^{20} 1.5144
b.p. 127-128°/10 mm.
NEAT

C M8050-4 **Methyl salicylate**
$2\text{-}(HO)C_6H_4CO_2CH_3$ M.W. 152.15 n_D^{20} 1.5362 m.p. -8 to -7°
b.p. 220-224°
NEAT

D 11,229-1 **Ethyl salicylate**
$2\text{-}(HO)C_6H_4CO_2C_2H_5$ M.W. 166.18 n_D^{20} 1.5199 m.p. 2-3°
b.p. 234°

E 11,238-0 **Benzyl salicylate**
$2\text{-}(HO)C_6H_4CO_2CH_2C_6H_5$ M.W. 228.25 n_D^{20} 1.5766
m.p. 18-20° b.p. 168-170°/5 mm.
NEAT

F M5010-9 **Methyl p-hydroxybenzoate, 99%**
$HOC_6H_4CO_2CH_3$ M.W. 152.15 m.p. 126-128°
NUJOL MULL

G 11,198-8 **Ethyl p-hydroxybenzoate**
$HOC_6H_4CO_2C_2H_5$ M.W. 166.18
m.p. 116-118°
NUJOL MULL

H P5335-7 **Propyl p-hydroxybenzoate, puriss.**
$HOC_6H_4CO_2CH_2CH_2CH_3$ M.W. 180.20
m.p. 95.5-99°

A

NEAT

16,673-1
Methyl 2,5-dichlorobenzoate
$Cl_2C_6H_3CO_2CH_3$ FW 205.04 mp 37-40° Disp. C

B

MELT

12,462-1 Methyl 5-bromosalicylate
BrC_6H_3-2-(OH)CO_2CH_3 M.W. 231.05
m.p. 59-61°

C

NUJOL MULL

E2790-4 Ethyl p-ethoxybenzoate
$C_2H_5OC_6H_4CO_2C_2H_5$ M.W. 194.23
n_D^{20} 1.5181

D

NEAT

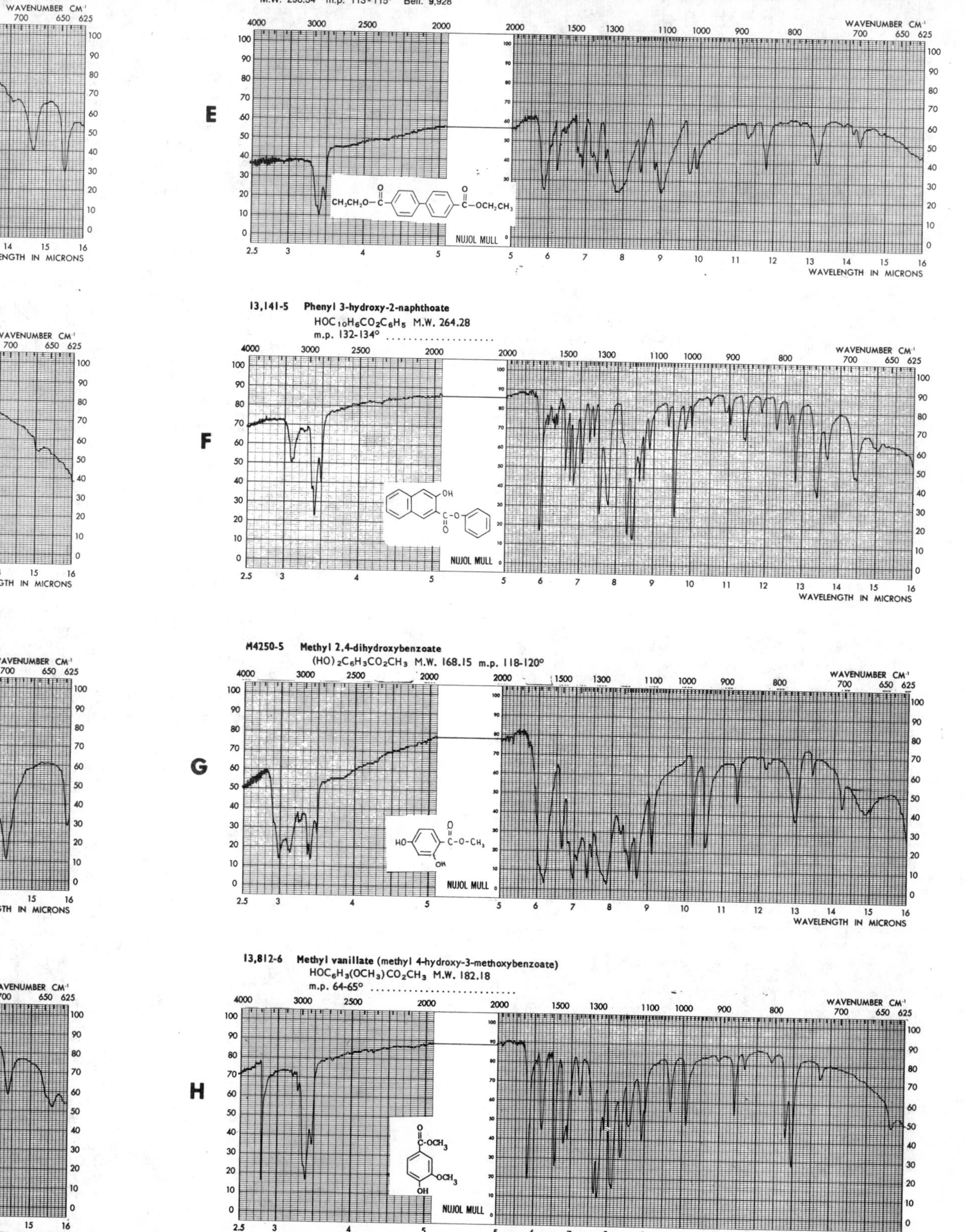

ALDRICH

ALDRICH

A
19,795-5
Methyl 3,4-dimethoxybenzoate, 98+% (methyl veratrate)
$(CH_3O)_2C_6H_3CO_2CH_3$ FW 196.20 mp 57-60°
bp 283° *Beil.* 10,396 Disp. C

B
13,811-8 **Ethyl vanillate (ethyl 4-hydroxy-3-methoxybenzoate)**
$HOC_6H_3(OCH_3)CO_2C_2H_5$ M.W. 196.20
m.p. 45-47°

C
17,368-1
Methyl 4-methoxysalicylate, 98% (methyl 2-hydroxy-4-methoxybenzoate)
$CH_3OC_6H_3(OH)CO_2CH_3$ FW 182.18 mp 47-49°
Beil. 10,381 Disp. C

D
16,406-2
Methyl 4-benzyloxy-3-methoxybenzoate, 98%
$C_6H_5CH_2OC_6H_3(OCH_3)CO_2CH_3$
M.W. 272.3 m.p. 85-88°

E
E2485-9 **Ethyl 3,4-dihydroxybenzoate (ethyl protocatechuate)**
$(HO)_2C_6H_3CO_2C_2H_5$ M.W. 182.17 m.p. 131-132°

F
15,960-3
Methyl 3,5-dihydroxybenzoate, 97%
$(HO)_2C_6H_3CO_2CH_3$
M.W. 168.15 m.p. 164-166° Beil. 10,405

G
16,879-3
Methyl 3,5-dimethoxybenzoate
$(CH_3O)_2C_6H_3CO_2CH_3$ FW 196.20 mp 42-43°
bp 298° *Beil.* 10,405 Disp. C

H
13,874-6 **Methyl 2,4,6-trihydroxybenzoate**
$(HO)_3C_6H_2CO_2CH_3$ M.W. 184.15
m.p. 179-180°

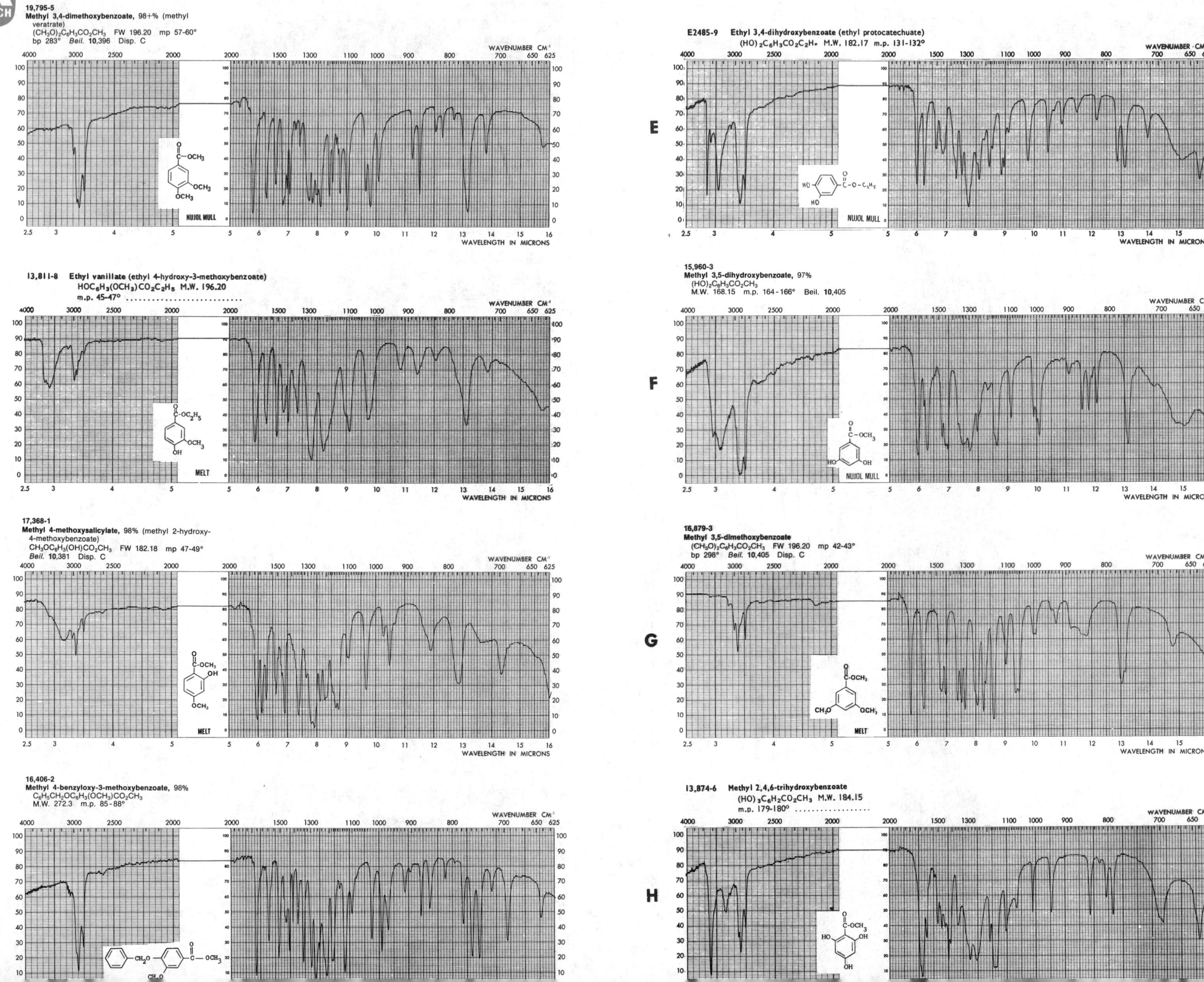

A

m.p. 187-189° ....

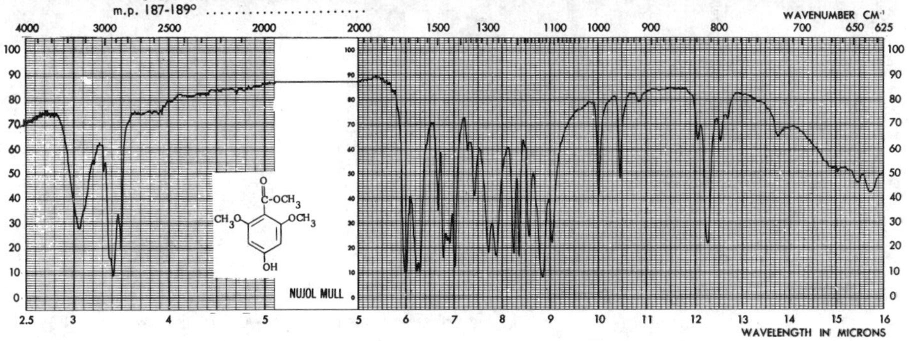

B

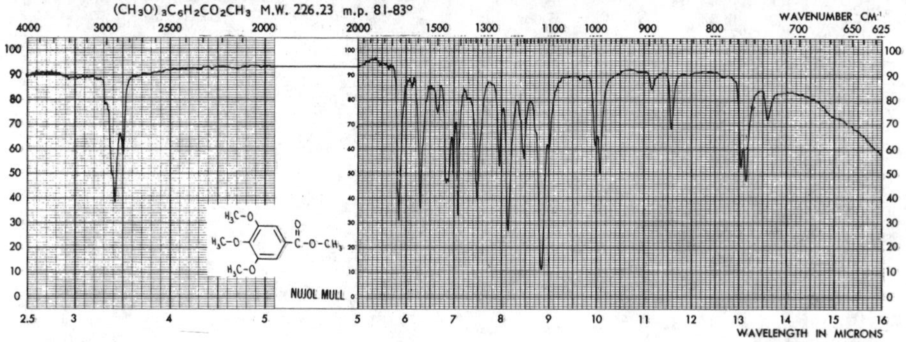

13,876-2 **Methyl 2,4,6-trimethoxybenzoate**
$(CH_3O)_3C_6H_2CO_2CH_3$ M.W. 226.23
m.p. 68-70° ....

C

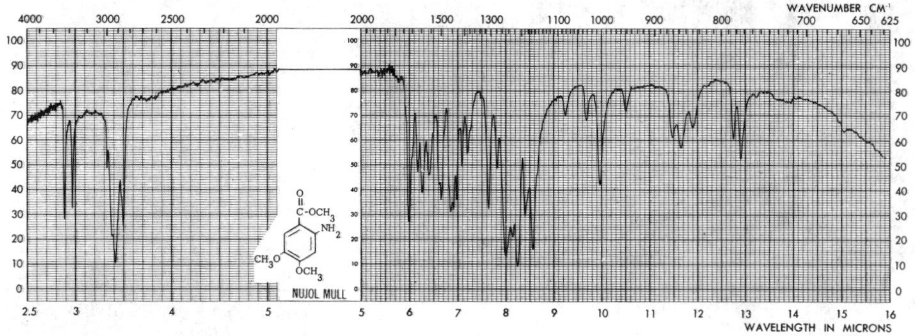

14,989-6 **Methyl 3,5-di-tert.-butyl-4-hydroxybenzoate**
$HOC_6H_2[C(CH_3)_3]_2CO_2CH_3$ M.W. 264.37
m.p. 163-165° ....

D

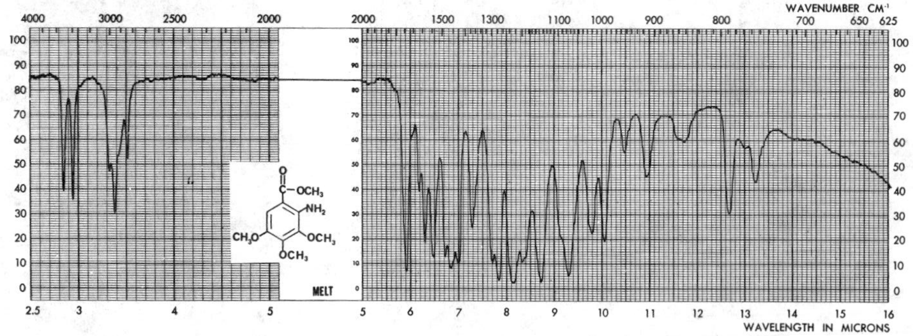

P5330-6 **Propyl gallate**
3,4,5-$(HO)_3C_6H_2CO_2CH_2CH_2CH_3$ M.W. 212.20
m.p. 146-148° ....

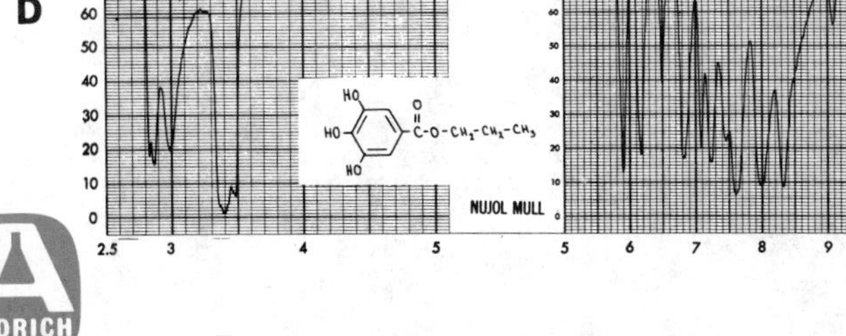

E

$(CH_3O)_3C_6H_2CO_2CH_3$ M.W. 226.23 m.p. 81-83°

F

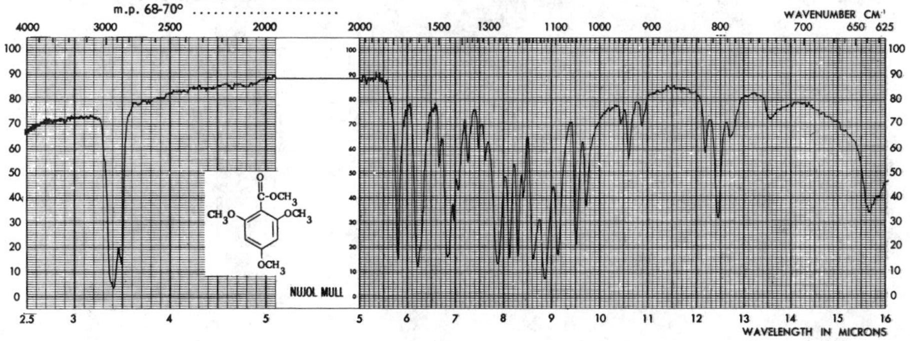

17,529-3
Methyl 4,5-dimethoxyanthranilate, tech.
$(CH_3O)_2C_6H_2$-2-$(NH_2)CO_2CH_3$
M.W. 211.22 m.p. 125-127° Beil. **14**,635

G

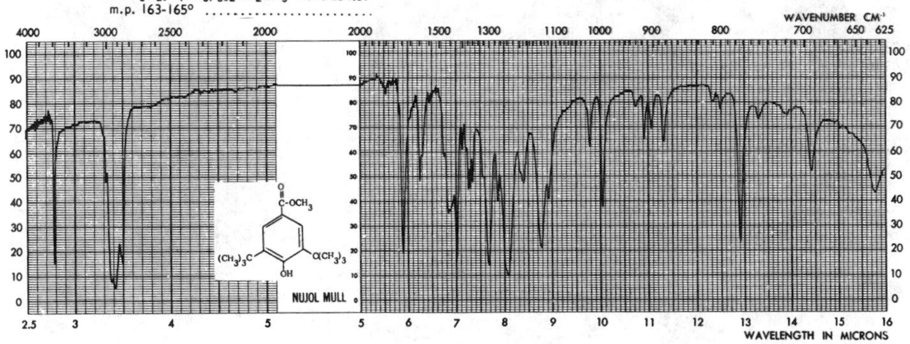

21,595-3
Methyl 3,4,5-trimethoxyanthranilate, 99%
$(CH_3O)_3C_6H$-2-$(NH_2)CO_2CH_3$ FW 241.25
mp 44-45° bp 127-140°/0.100mm. *Beil.* **14**,639
Disp. C

H

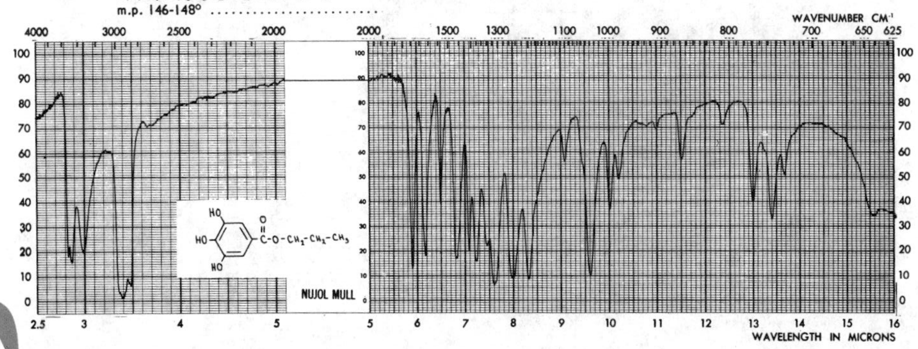

M2970-3 **Methyl anthranilate**
2-$(H_2N)C_6H_4CO_2CH_3$ M.W. 151.17
m.p. 24° ... .

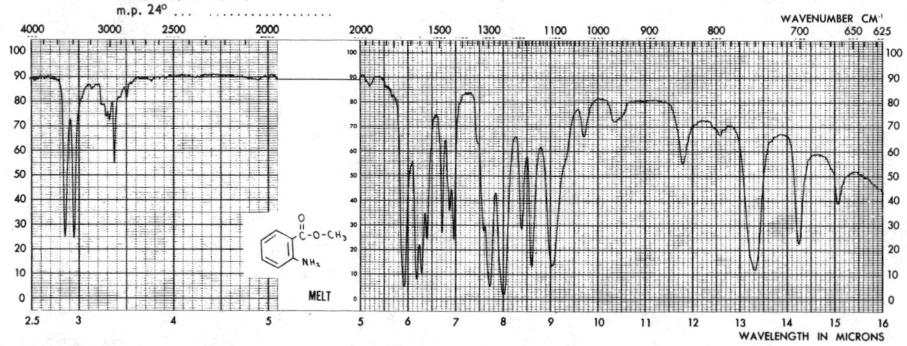

A

10,837-5 **Methyl o-dimethylaminobenzoate**
$(CH_3)_2NC_6H_4CO_2CH_3$ M.W. 179.21
n_D^{20} 1.5552 b.p. 120°/8 mm.

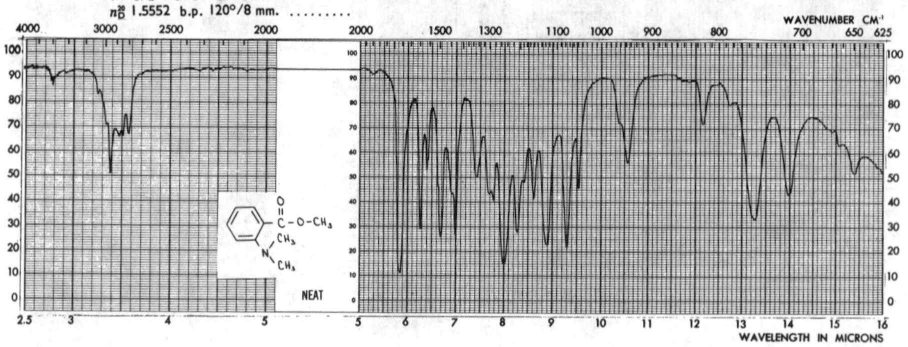

NEAT

B

21,872-3
Ethyl o-dimethylaminobenzoate, tech., 75%
$(CH_3)_2NC_6H_4CO_2C_2H_5$ FW 193.25 n_D^{20} 1.5425
d 1.061 Disp. C

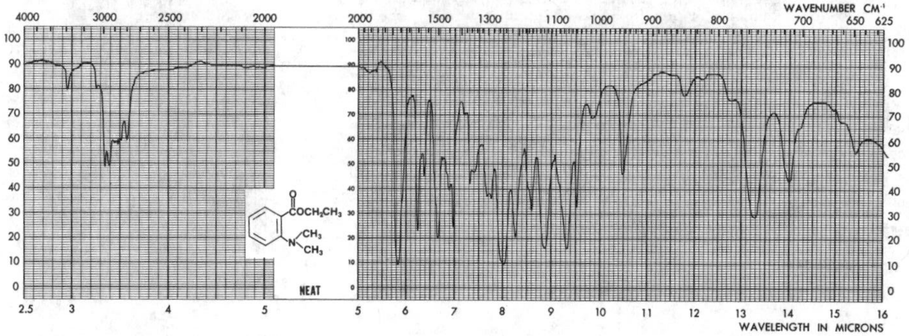

NEAT

C

E1050-5 **Ethyl m-aminobenzoate, puriss.**
$H_2NC_6H_4CO_2C_2H_5$ M.W. 165.19 n_D^{20} 1.5608

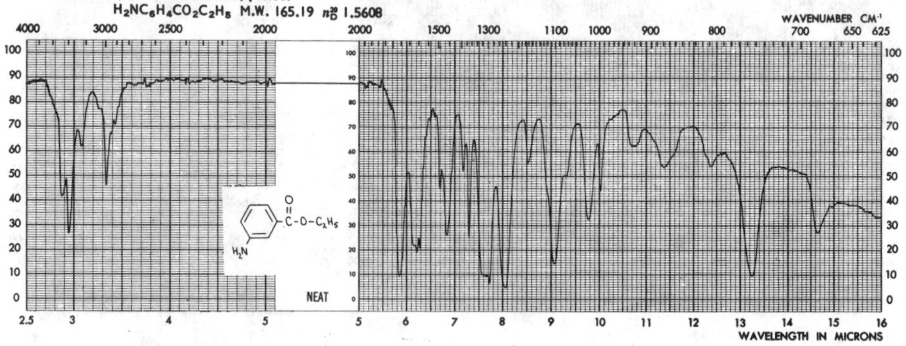

NEAT

D

E1052-1 **Ethyl m-aminobenzoate, methanesulfonic acid salt (tricaine methanesulfonate)**
$H_2NC_6H_4CO_2C_2H_5 \cdot CH_3SO_3H$ M.W. 261.30
m.p. 149-151°

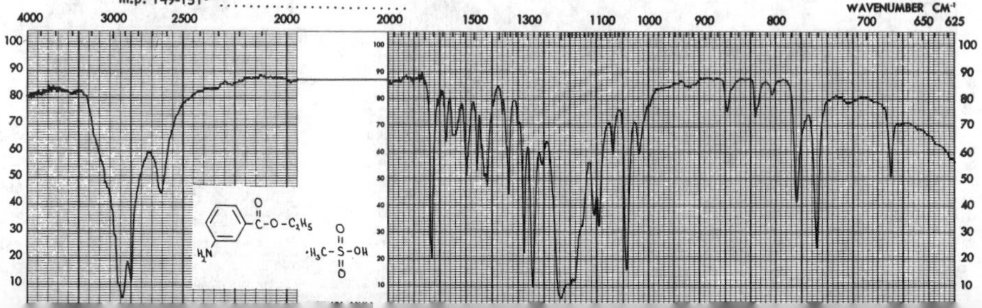

E

11,290-9 **Ethyl p-aminobenzoate**
$H_2NC_6H_4CO_2C_2H_5$ M.W. 165.19 m.p. 90-93°

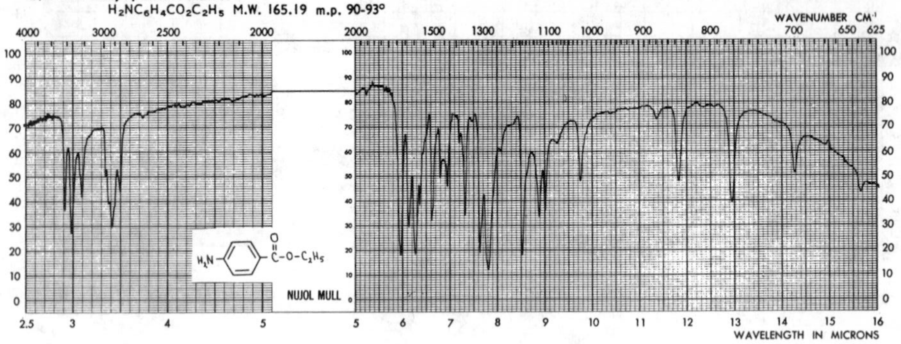

NUJOL MULL

F

E2490-5 **Ethyl p-dimethylaminobenzoate, puriss.**
$(CH_3)_2NC_6H_4CO_2C_2H_5$ M.W. 193.25 m.p. 63.5-65.5°

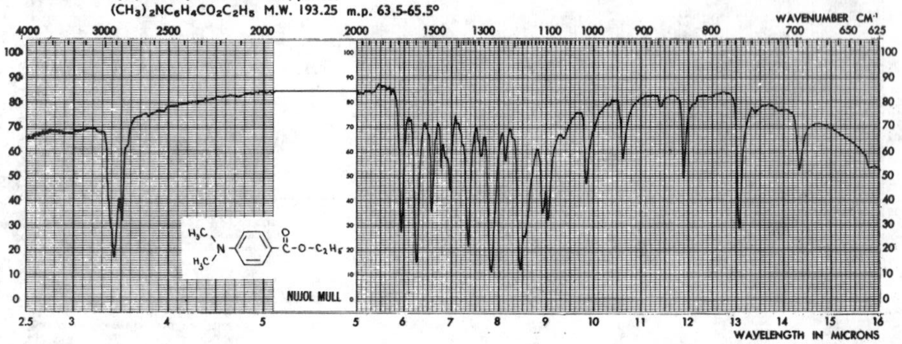

NUJOL MULL

G

22,297-6
Procaine hydrochloride, 99% [2-(diethylamino)ethyl 4-aminobenzoate]
$H_2NC_6H_4CO_2CH_2CH_2N(C_2H_5)_2 \cdot HCl$ FW 272.78
mp 155-156° *Beil.* 14,424 Disp. C

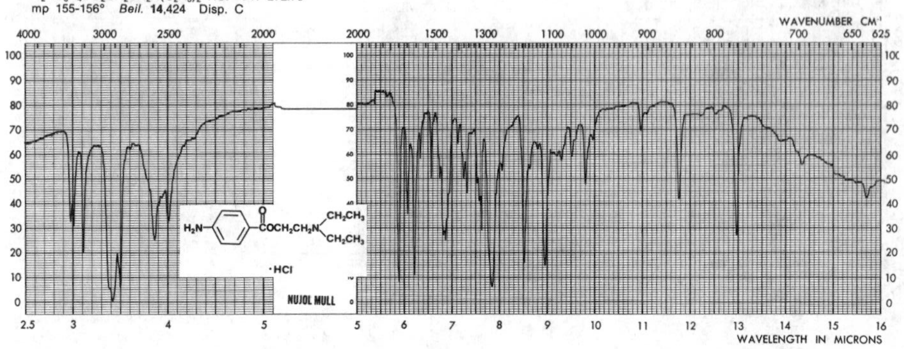

NUJOL MULL

H

19,263-5
Methyl 4-amino-3-methoxybenzoate, 98%
$H_2NC_6H_3(OCH_3)CO_2CH_3$ FW 181.19 mp 126-127°
Disp. C

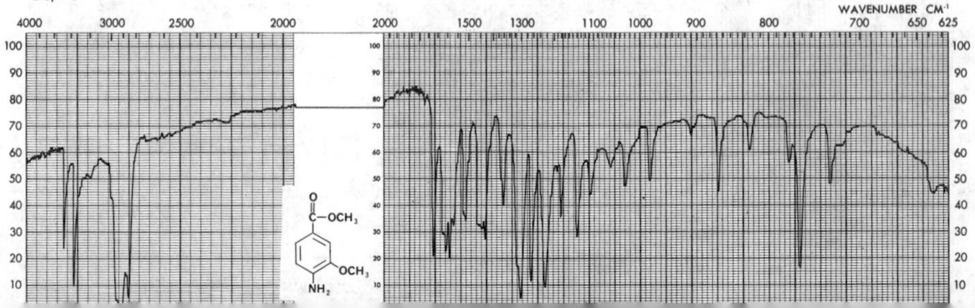

A

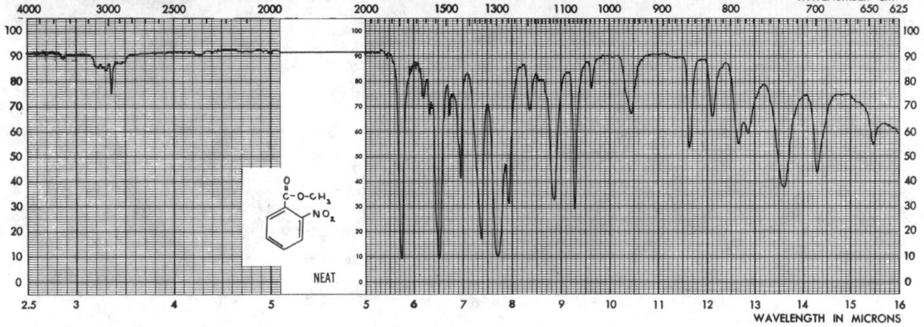

NEAT

B

15,594-2 Ethyl o-nitrobenzoate
$O_2NC_6H_4CO_2C_2H_5$ M.W. 195.18

MELT

C

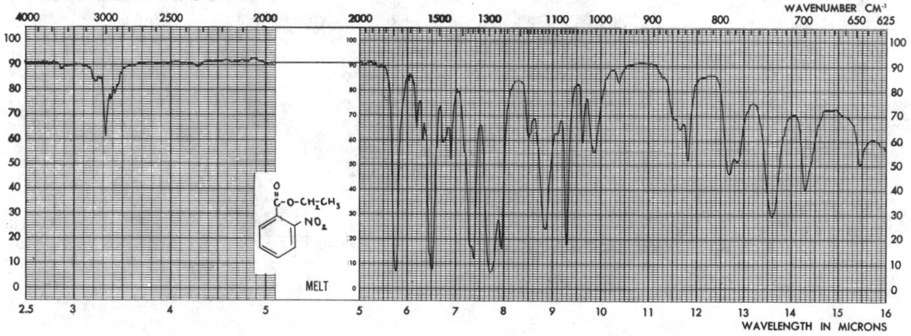

15,597-7 Methyl m-nitrobenzoate
$O_2NC_6H_4CO_2CH_3$ M.W. 181.15

NUJOL MULL

D

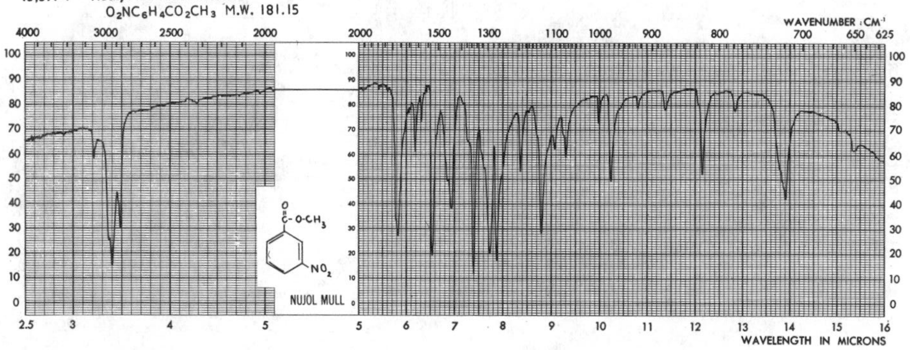

15,662-0
Ethyl p-nitrosobenzoate
$ONC_6H_4CO_2C_2H_5$
M.W. 179.18 m.p. 79-81° Beil. 9,369

NUJOL MULL

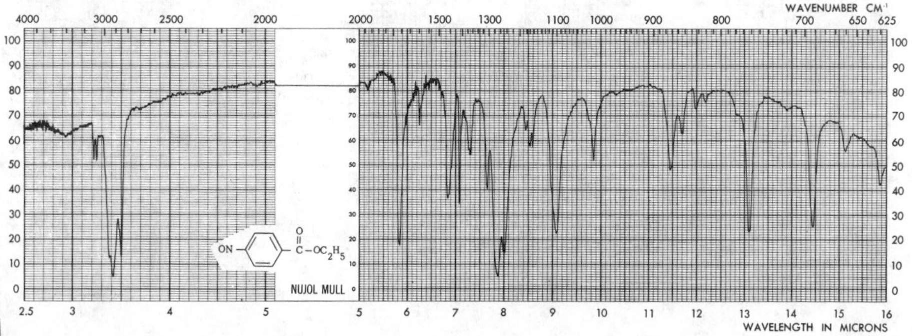

E

NUJOL MULL

F

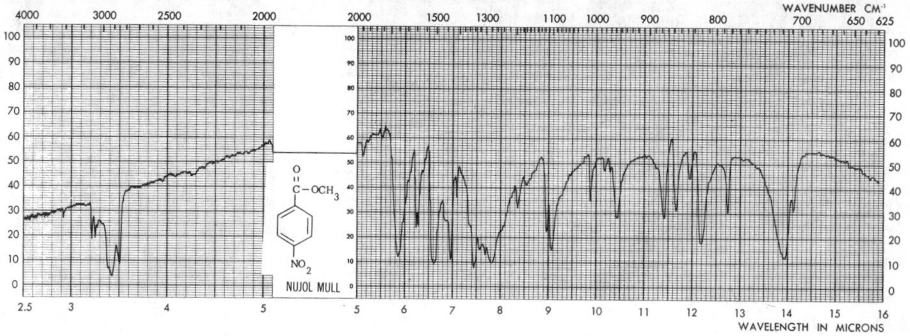

15,595-0
Ethyl p-nitrobenzoate, 99%
$O_2NC_6H_4CO_2C_2H_5$
M.W. 195.17 m.p. 56-58° Beil. 9,390

NEAT

G

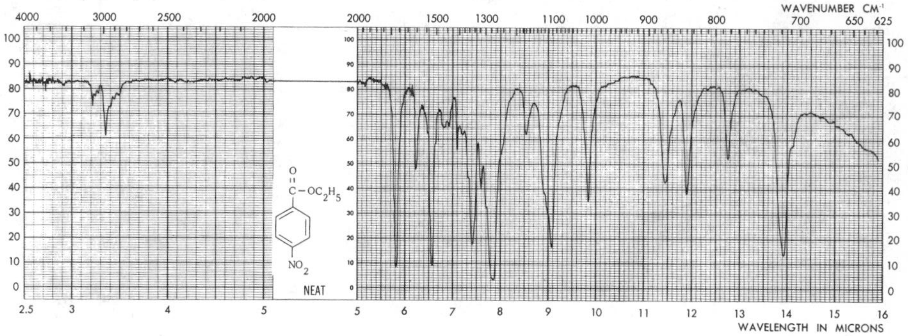

17,947-7
Methyl 2-chloro-4-nitrobenzoate, 99%
$ClC_6H_3(NO_2)CO_2CH_3$
M.W. 215.59 m.p. 76-78° Beil. 9,404

NUJOL MULL

H

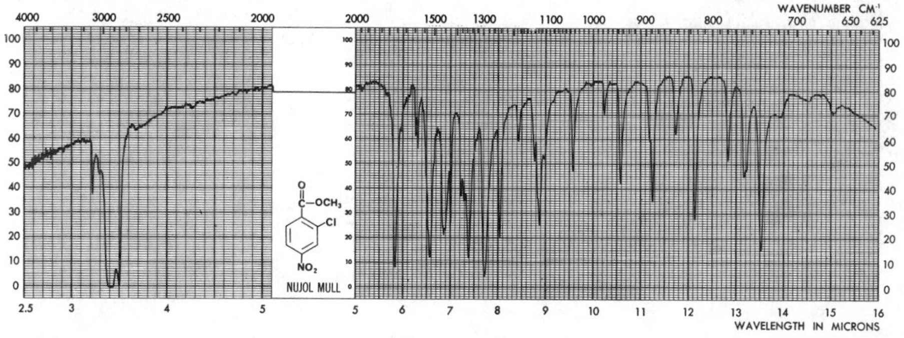

21,735-2
Methyl 4-chloro-2-nitrobenzoate, 99%
$ClC_6H_3(NO_2)CO_2CH_3$ FW 215.60 mp 43-45°
Disp. C

MELT

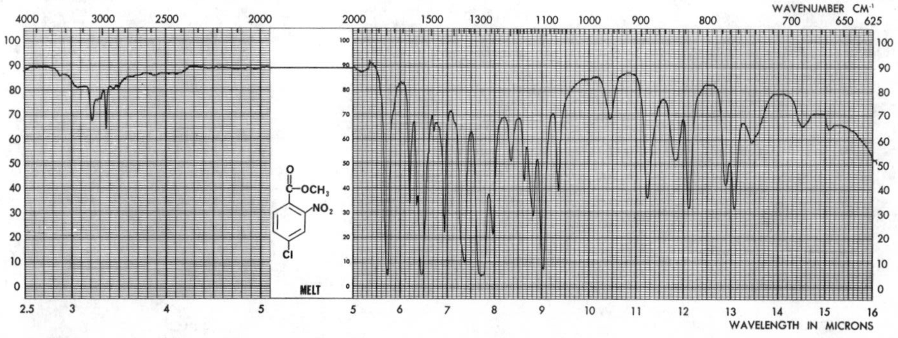

A

19,927-3 **Methyl 5-acetyl-2-methoxybenzoate,** 98%
[39971-36-3]

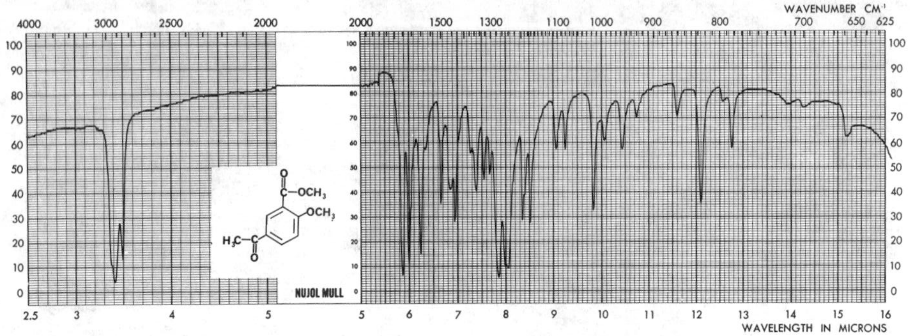

NUJOL MULL

B

19,604-5
Ethyl 5-acetyl-2-benzyloxybenzoate, 98+%
$CH_3COC_6H_3(OCH_2C_6H_5)CO_2C_2H_5$ FW 298.34
mp 78-80° Disp. C

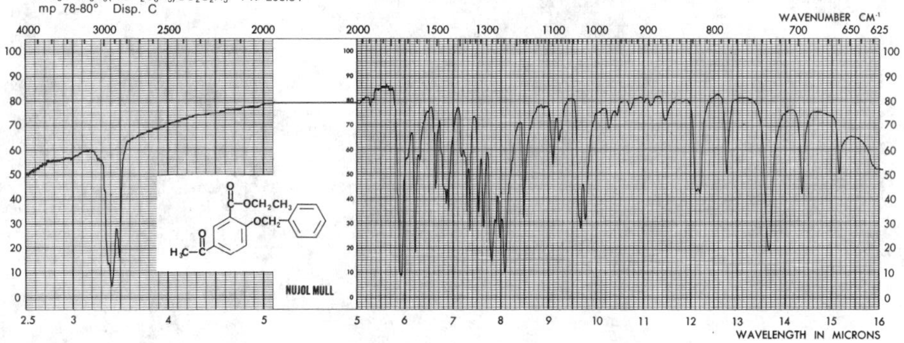

NUJOL MULL

C

D17,898-5 **Dimethyl phthalate**
C_6H_4-1,2-$(CO_2CH_3)_2$ M.W. 194.19
n_D^{20} 1.5135 m.p. 0-2°

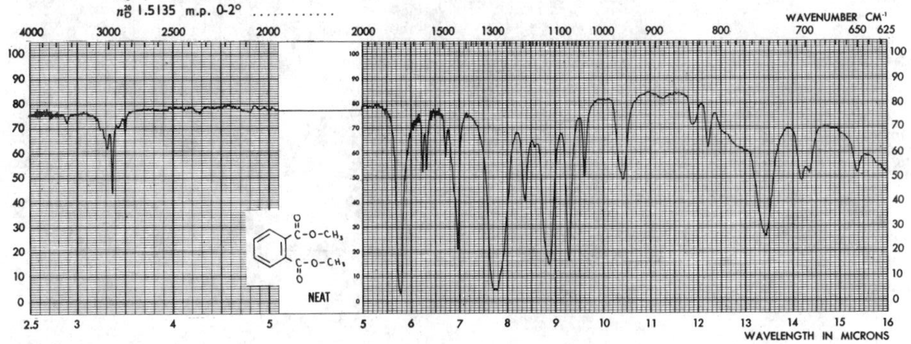

NEAT

D

D9962-5 **Diethyl phthalate**
C_6H_4-1,2-$(CO_2C_2H_5)_2$ M.W. 222.24 n_D^{20} 1.5000

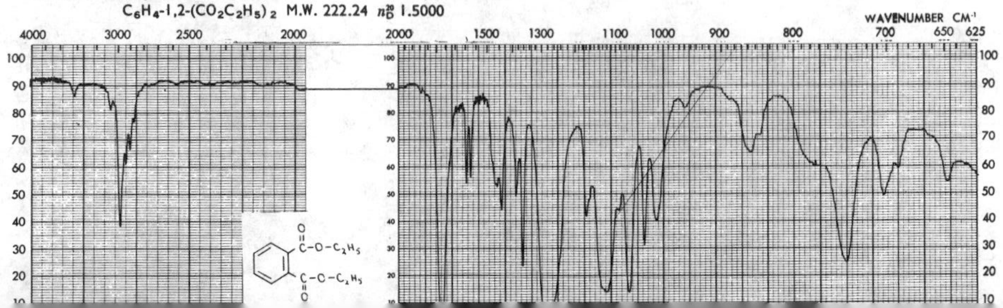

E

15,243-9 **Dibutyl phthalate**
C_6H_4-1,2-$[CO_2(CH_2)_3CH_3]_2$ M.W. 278.35 n_D^{20} 1.4910
b.p. 340°

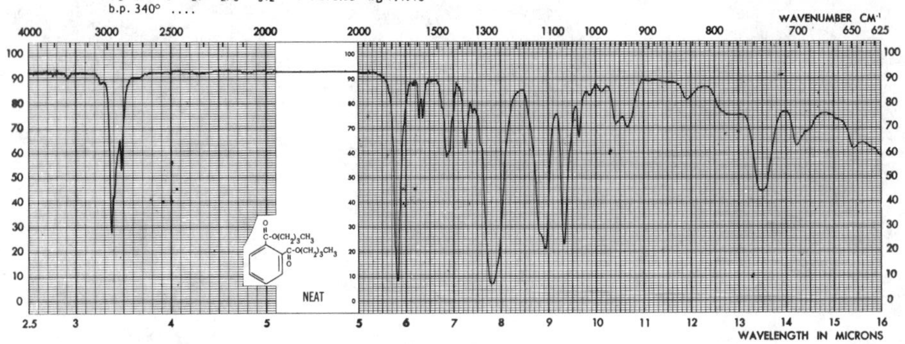

NEAT

F

15,264-1 **Diisobutyl phthalate**
C_6H_4-1,2-$[CO_2CH_2CH(CH_3)_2]_2$ M.W. 278.35
n_D^{20} 1.4888 b.p. 327°

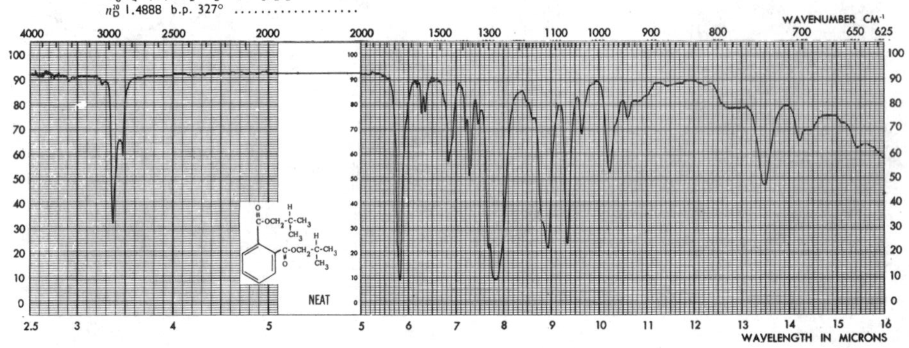

NEAT

G

D20,115-4 **Dioctyl phthalate**
n_D^{20} 1.4853

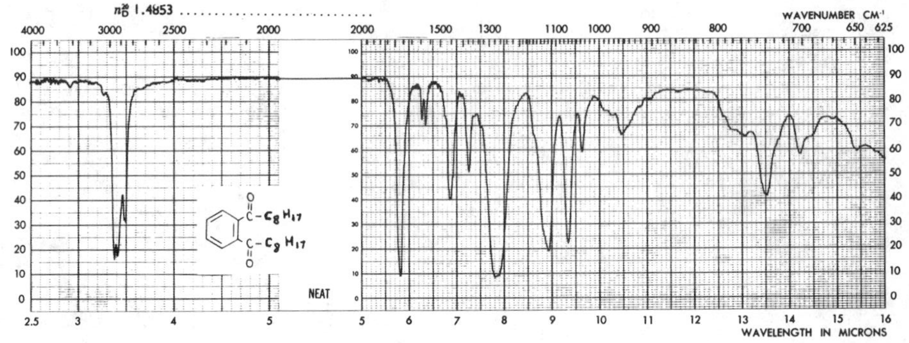

NEAT

H

13,381-7 **Didecyl phthalate, puriss.**
C_6H_4-1,2-$[CO_2(CH_2)_9CH_3]_2$ M.W. 446.67 n_D^{20} 1.4837

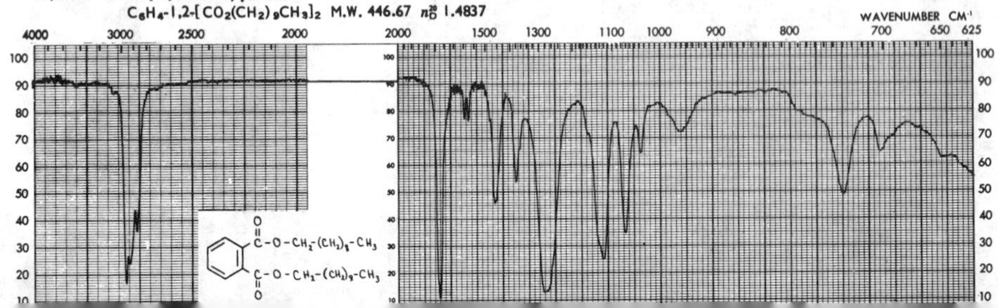

WAVENUMBER CM⁻¹

WAVELENGTH IN MICRONS

A

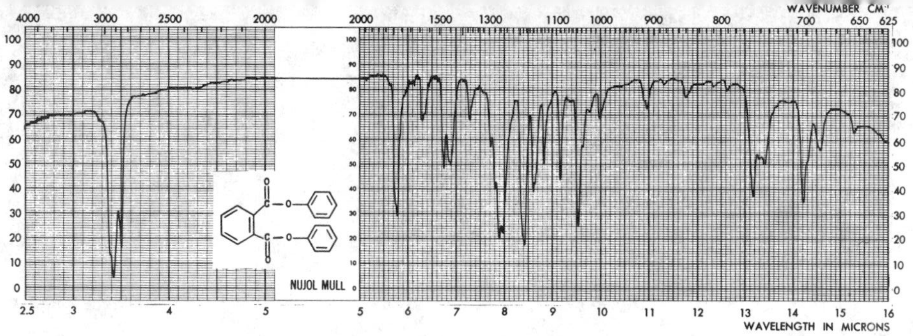

19,423-9
Dimethyl isophthalate, 99%
C_6H_4-1,3-$(CO_2CH_3)_2$ FW 194.19 Disp. C

B

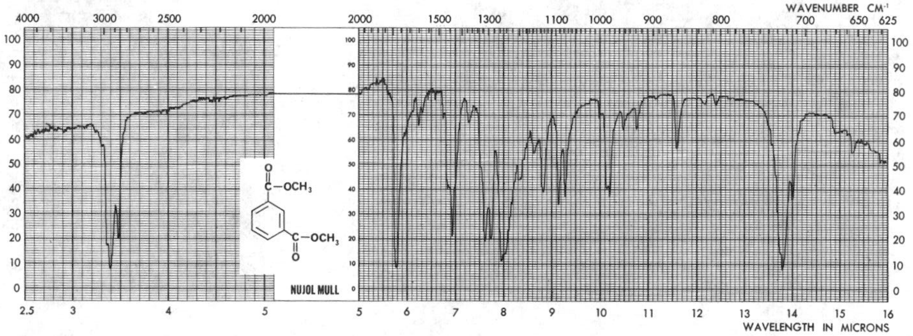

11,389-1 **Dimethyl terephthalate, zone refined**
C_6H_4-1,4-$(CO_2CH_3)_2$ M.W. 194.19
m.p. 139.63° ....

C

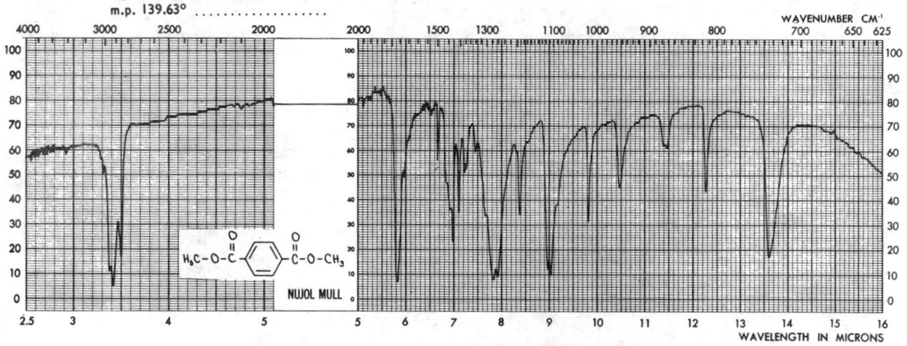

19,776-9
3,5-Dimethoxy-4-(ethoxycarbonyl)benzoic acid, 95%
$C_2H_5O_2CC_6H_2(OCH_3)_2CO_2H$ FW 254.24
mp 179-183° Disp. C

D

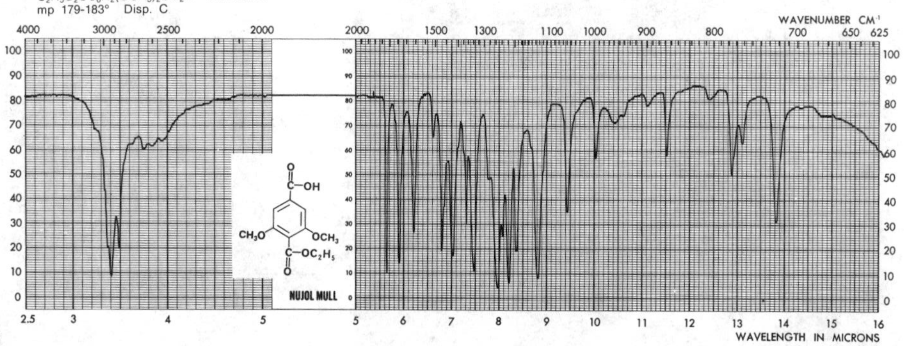

E

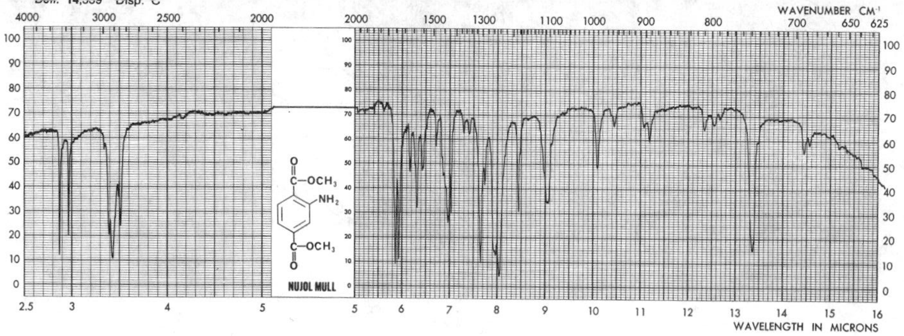

20,536-2
Dimethyl nitroterephthalate, 99%
$O_2NC_6H_3$-1,4-$(CO_2CH_3)_2$ FW 239.19 mp 72-75°
Beil. 9,826 Disp. C

F

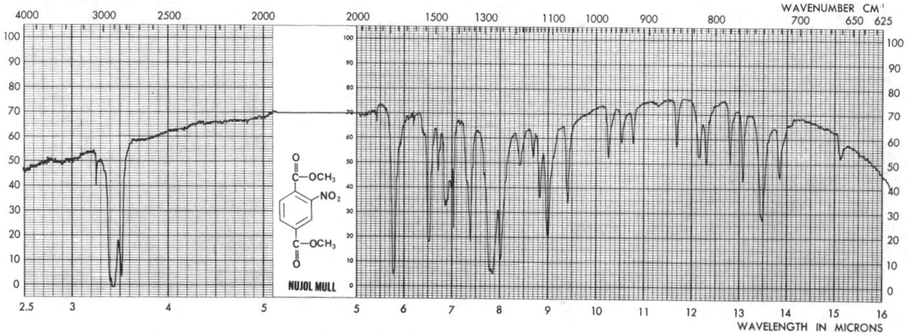

D18,700 Dimethyl 2,3,5,6-tetrachloroterephthalate

G

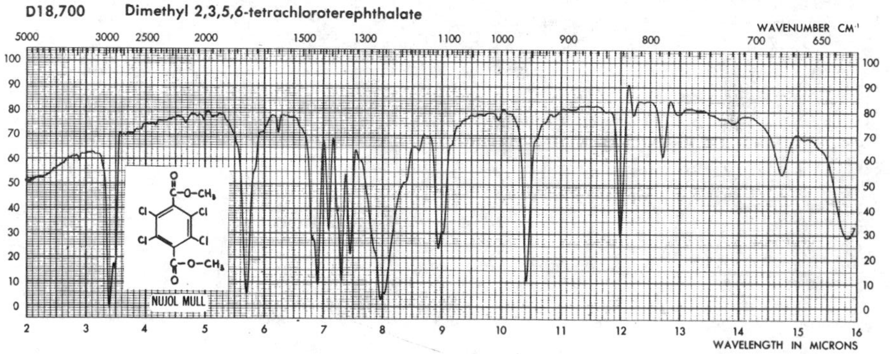

D17,130-1 **Dimethyl 2,6-naphthalenedicarboxylate**
$C_{10}H_6(CO_2CH_3)_2$ M.W. 244.24 m.p. 190-192°

H

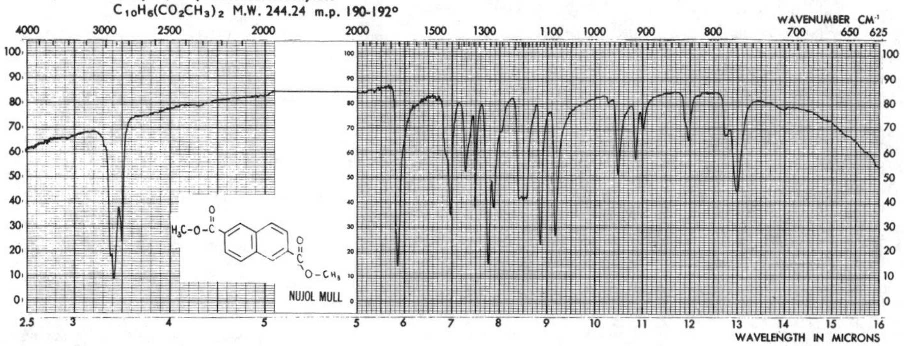

A

11,598-3 **Trimethyl 1,3,5-benzenetricarboxylate**
$C_6H_3(CO_2CH_3)_3$ M.W. 252.23 m.p. 145-146°

B

22,553-3
Triallyl 1,3,5-benzenetricarboxylate, 98% (triallyl trimesate)
$C_6H_3(CO_2CH_2CH{=}CH_2)_3$ FW 330.34 mp 27-31°
bp 175-190°/0.100mm. Disp. C

C

12,373-0 **mono-Benzyl phthalate**
$2\text{-}(HO_2C)C_6H_4CO_2CH_2C_6H_5$ M.W. 256.26 m.p. 105-106.5°

D

13,803-7 **Dibenzoyl-*d*-tartaric acid monohydrate**
$[C_6H_5CO_2CH(CO_2H\text{-}]_2 \cdot H_2O$ M.W. 276.32
$[\alpha]_D^{20}$ - 105° (c=1.5, C_2H_5OH) ....

E

16,344-9
Dibenzoyl-*l*-tartaric acid monohydrate, made from unnatural tartaric acid
$[C_6H_5CO_2CH(CO_2H)\text{-}]_2 \cdot H_2O$
M.W. 376.34 m.p. 89-92°
$[\alpha]^{24}$ +111.7° (c=9, C_2H_5OH) Beil. 9,170

F

D21,960-6 **Di-p-toluoyl-*d*-tartaric acid** (made from natural tartaric acid)
$[CH_3C_6H_4CO_2CH(CO_2H)\text{-}]_2$ M.W. 386.36 m.p. 169-173°
$[\alpha]_D^{20}$ - 135° (c=1 in C_2H_5OH) ....

G

10,808-1 **Di-p-toluoyl-*l*-tartaric acid** (made from unnatural tartaric acid)
$[CH_3C_6H_4CO_2CH(CO_2H)\text{-}]_2$ M.W. 386.36 m.p. 178-180°
$[\alpha]_D^{20}$ + 132° (c=1 in C_2H_5OH) ....

H

15,901-8
β-D-Ribofuranose 1-acetate 2,3,5-tribenzoate
M.W. 504.49 m.p. 128-130°
$[\alpha]_D^{20}$ +24.3° (c=1, pyridine)

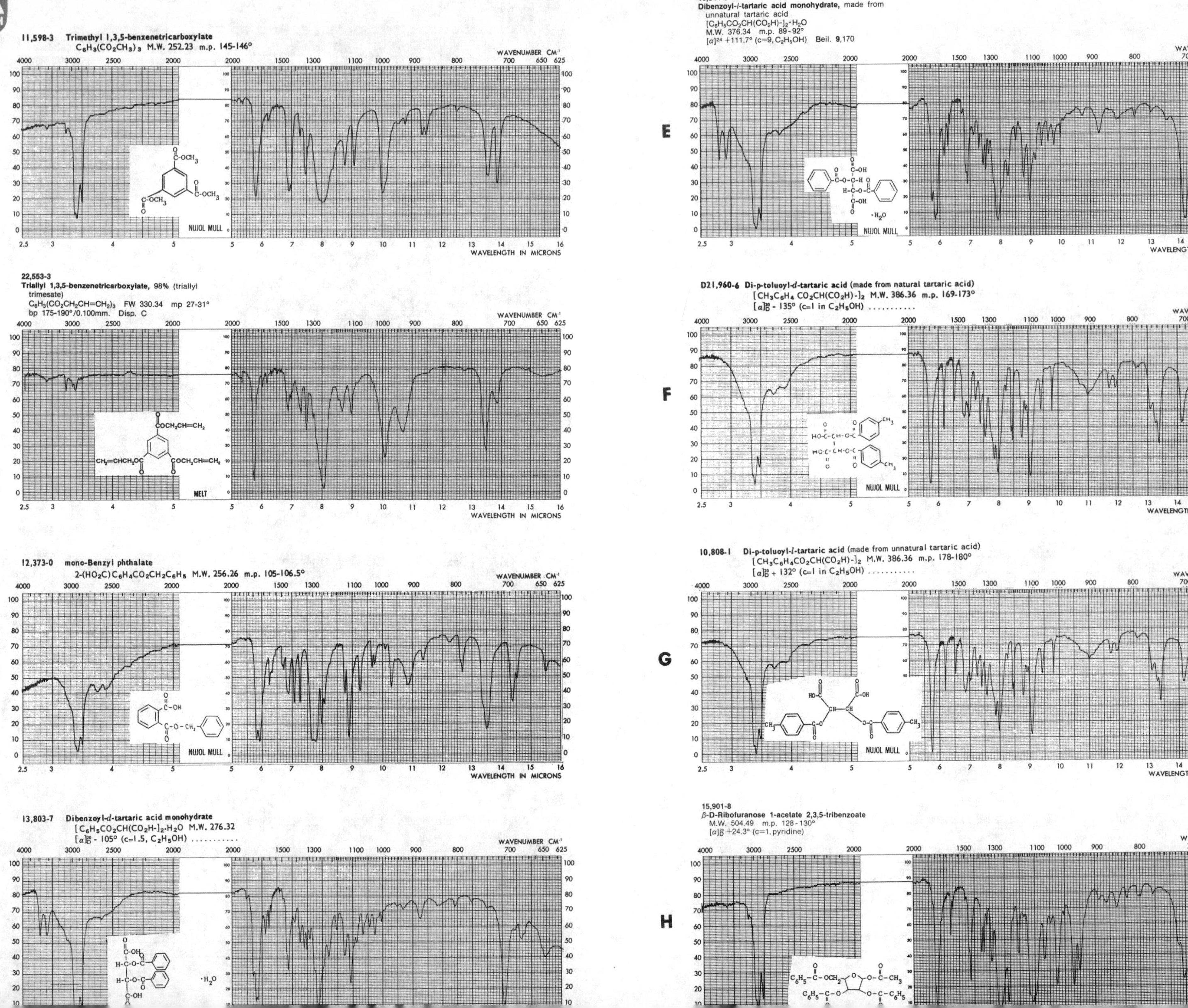

A

$[\alpha]^{23}$ +69.2° (c=1, benzene)

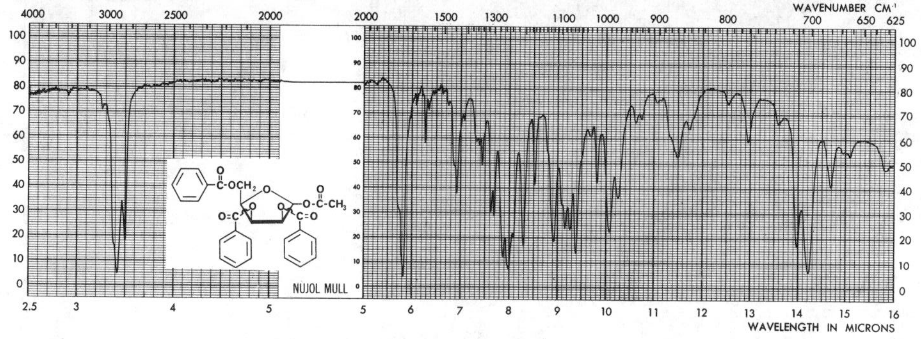

NUJOL MULL

B

C330-8 **2-Carbethoxy-5,7-dihydroxy-4'-methoxyisoflavone** {ethyl 5,7-dihydroxy-3-(p-methoxyphenyl)-4-oxo-4H-benzo[b]pyran-2-carboxylate}
M.W. 356.33 m.p. 190-193°

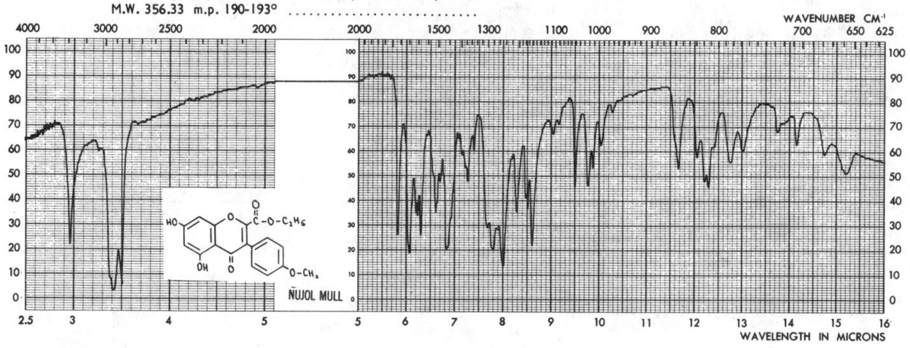

NUJOL MULL

C

10,872-3 **Phenyl acetate**
$CH_3CO_2C_6H_5$ M.W. 136.15 n_D^{20} 1.5051
b.p. 196°

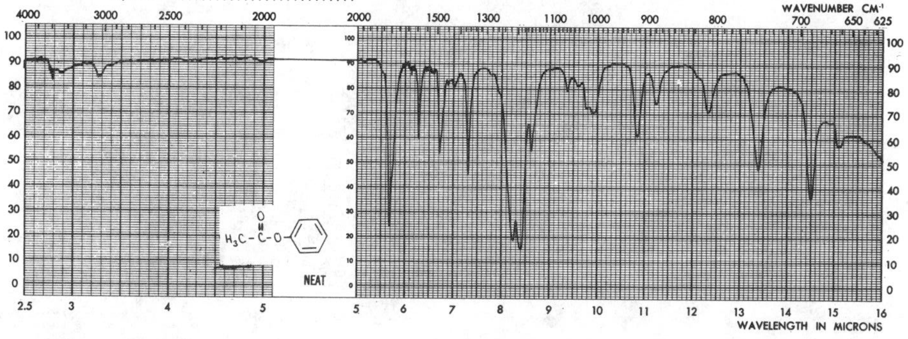

NEAT

D

18,317-2
S-Phenyl thioacetate, 98%
$CH_3COSC_6H_5$
M.W. 152.22 b.p. 99-100°/6mm. n_D^{20} 1.5720

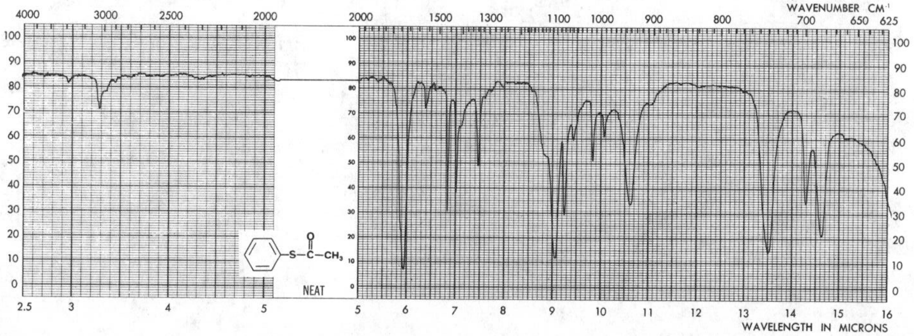

NEAT

E

13,203-9 **1,2,4-Triacetoxybenzene** (1,2,4-phenenyl triacetate)
$(CH_3CO_2)_3C_6H_3$ M.W. 252.22 m.p. 98-100°

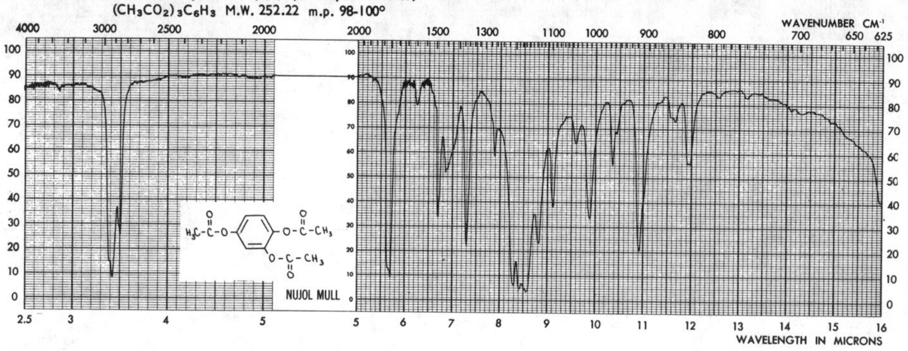

NUJOL MULL

F

N1990-7 **4-Nitrophenyl acetate**
$CH_3CO_2C_6H_4NO_2$ M.W. 181.15 m.p. 77-7

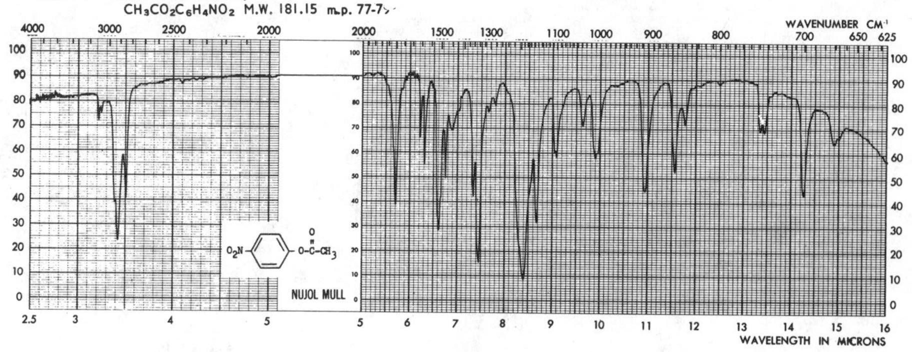

NUJOL MULL

G

13,504-6 **p-Nitrophenyl trimethylacetate** (p-nitrophenyl pivalate)
$(CH_3)_3CCO_2C_6H_4NO_2$ M.W. 223.23
m.p. 92-95°

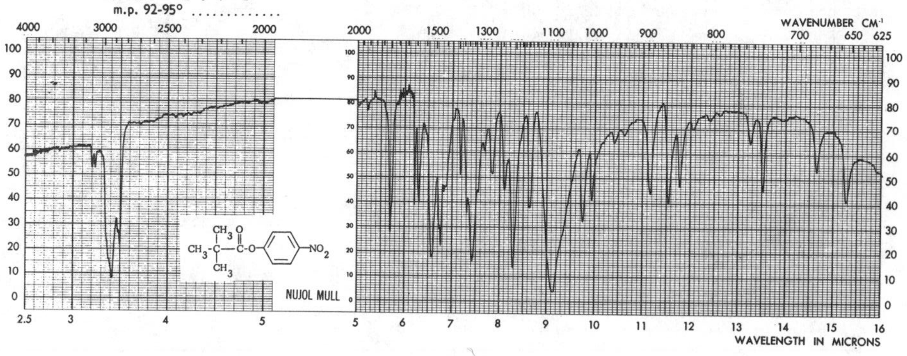

NUJOL MULL

H

N2265-7 **p-Nitrophenyl trifluoroacetate**
$CF_3CO_2C_6H_4NO_2$ M.W. 235.12
m.p. 38-40°

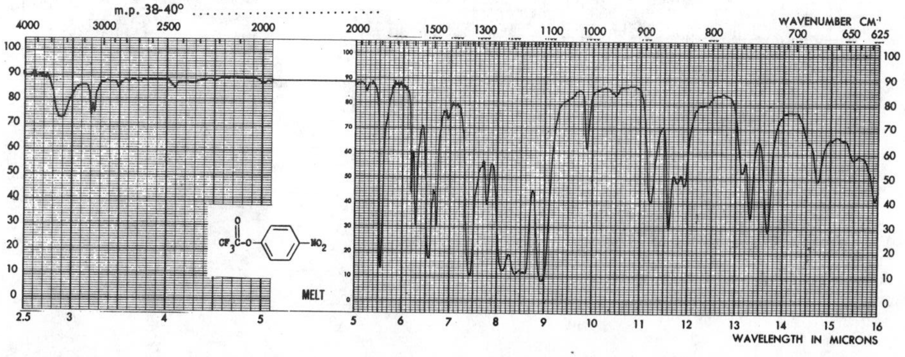

MELT

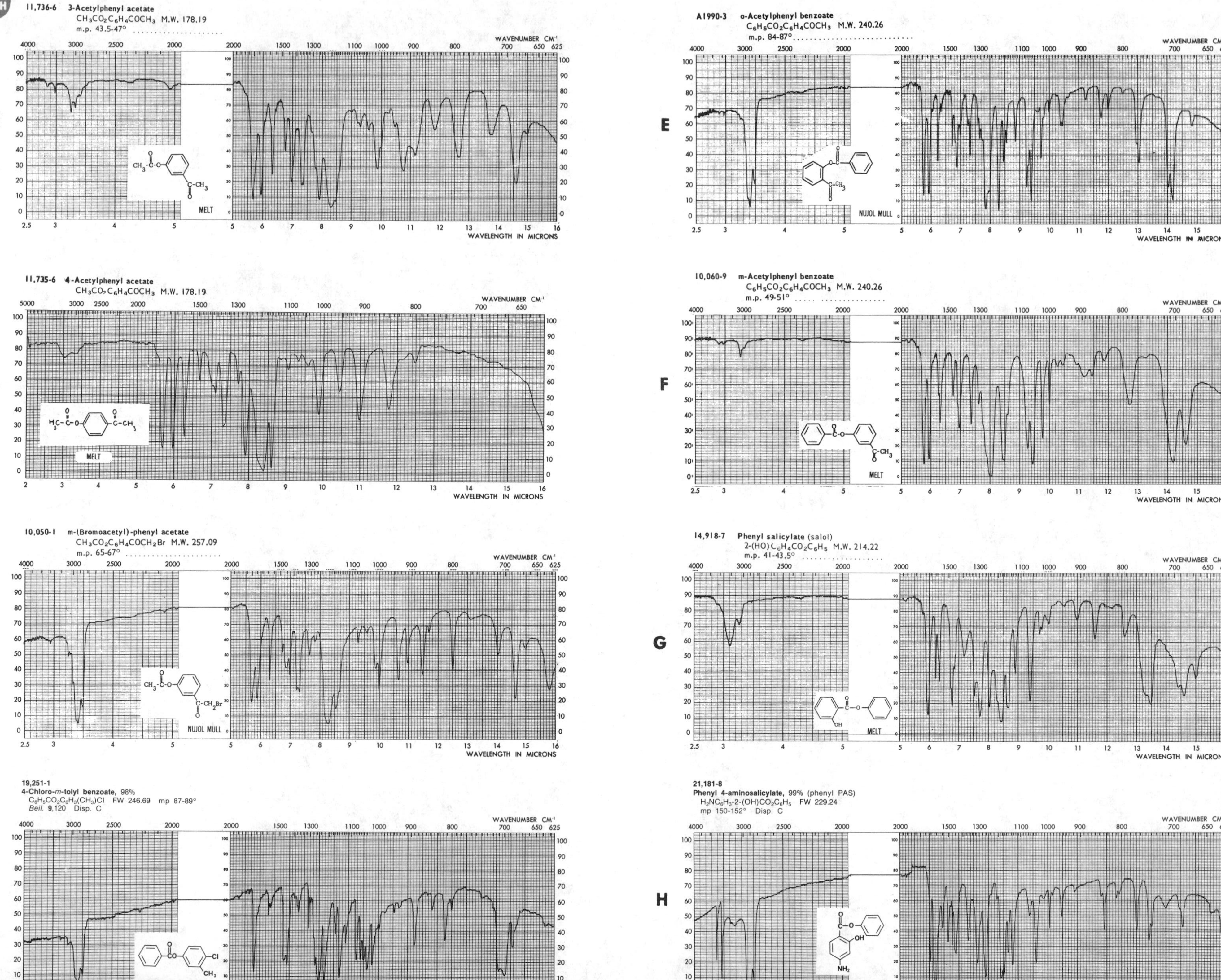
ALDRICH
A
11,736-6 3-Acetylphenyl acetate
CH3CO2C6H4COCH3 M.W. 178.19
m.p. 43.5-47°
MELT
B
11,735-6 4-Acetylphenyl acetate
CH3CO2C6H4COCH3 M.W. 178.19
MELT
C
10,050-1 m-(Bromoacetyl)-phenyl acetate
CH3CO2C6H4COCH2Br M.W. 257.09
m.p. 65-67°
NUJOL MULL
D
19,251-1
4-Chloro-m-tolyl benzoate, 98%
C6H5CO2C6H3(CH3)Cl FW 246.69 mp 87-89°
Beil. 9,120 Disp. C
E
A1990-3 o-Acetylphenyl benzoate
C6H5CO2C6H4COCH3 M.W. 240.26
m.p. 84-87°
NUJOL MULL
F
10,060-9 m-Acetylphenyl benzoate
C6H5CO2C6H4COCH3 M.W. 240.26
m.p. 49-51°
MELT
G
14,918-7 Phenyl salicylate (salol)
2-(HO)C6H4CO2C6H5 M.W. 214.22
m.p. 41-43.5°
MELT
H
21,181-8
Phenyl 4-aminosalicylate, 99% (phenyl PAS)
H2NC6H3-2-(OH)CO2C6H5 FW 229.24
mp 150-152° Disp. C
WAVENUMBER CM⁻¹
WAVELENGTH IN MICRONS

m.p. 133-135°

A (NUJOL MULL)

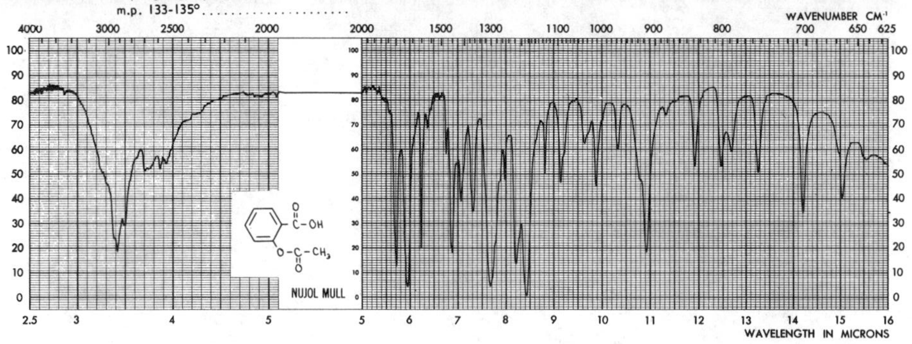

12,793-0 **Methyl acetylsalicylate**
2-$(CH_3CO_2)C_6H_4CO_2CH_3$ M.W. 194.19
m.p. 45.5-47°

B (NUJOL MULL)

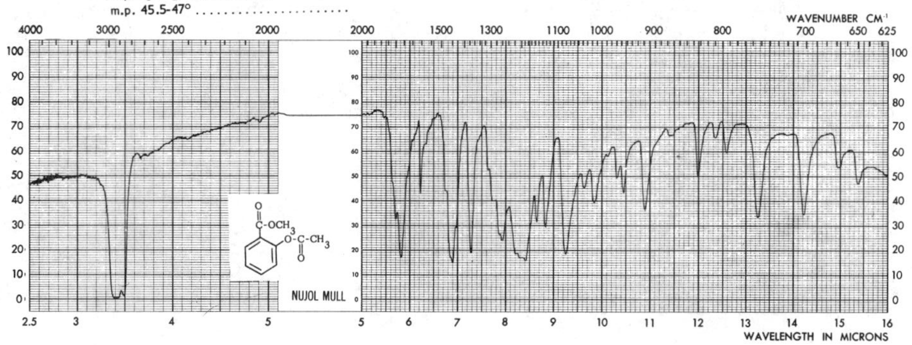

11,738-2 **3',5'-Diacetoxyacetophenone**
$(CH_3CO_2)_2C_6H_3COCH_3$ M.W. 236.23
m.p. 91-94°

C (NUJOL MULL)

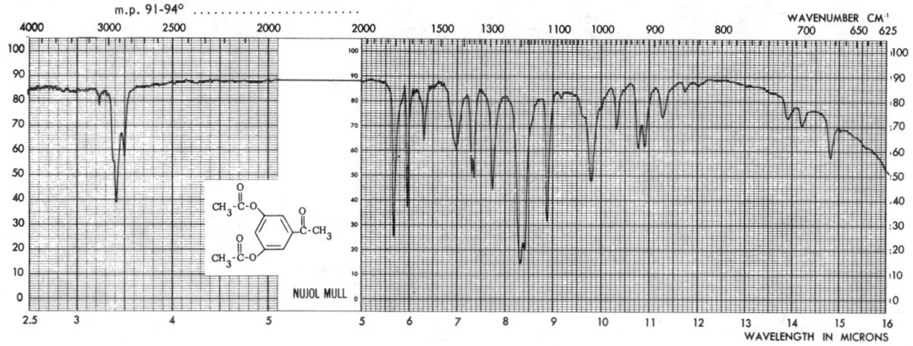

A9315 **Atranorin** (usnarin, parmelin, atranoric acid)
M.W. 374.33 m.p. 197-200°

D (NUJOL MULL)

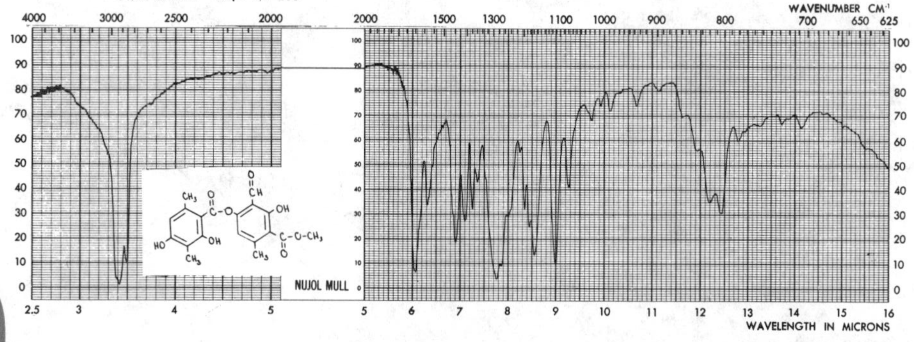

bp 190-193°/2mm. n_D^{20} 1.4950 d 1.032
Beil. **12**(2),597 Disp. C

E (NEAT)

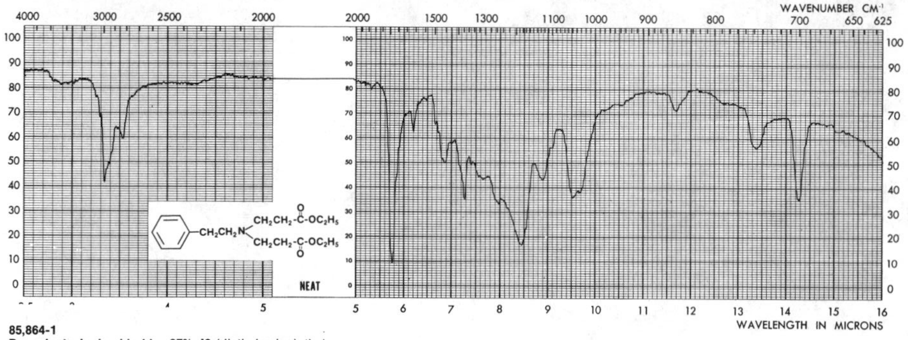

85,864-1
Benoxinate hydrochloride, 97% [2-(diethylamino)ethyl 4-amino-3-butoxybenzoate]
$CH_3(CH_2)_3OC_6H_3(NH_2)CO_2CH_2CH_2N(C_2H_5)_2\cdot HCl$
M.W. 344.89 m.p. 159-161°
Local anesthetic. *Arzneim.-Forsch.*, **21**, 2074 (1971).

F (NUJOL MULL)

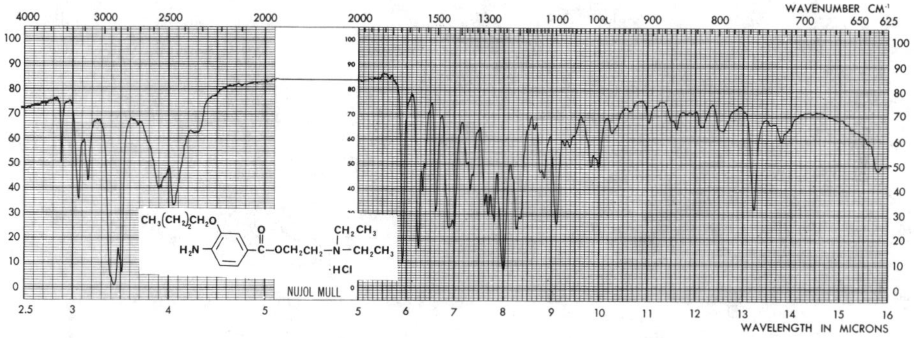

15,632-9
Bisphenol A dimethacrylate (4,4'-isopropylidenediphenol dimethacrylate)
$[H_2C{=}C(CH_3)CO_2C_6H_4]_2C(CH_3)_2$
M.W. 364.44 m.p. 72-74°

G (NUJOL MULL)

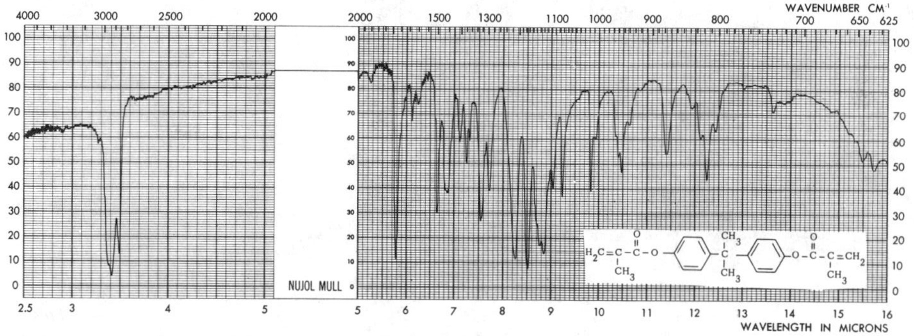

85,603-7
1-Naphthyl acetate
$CH_3CO_2C_{10}H_7$
M.W. 186.21 m.p. 43-46° Beil. **6**,608

H (MELT)

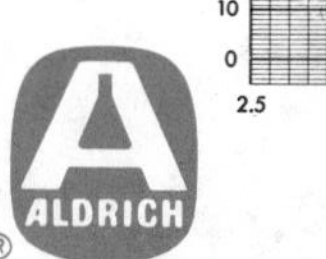

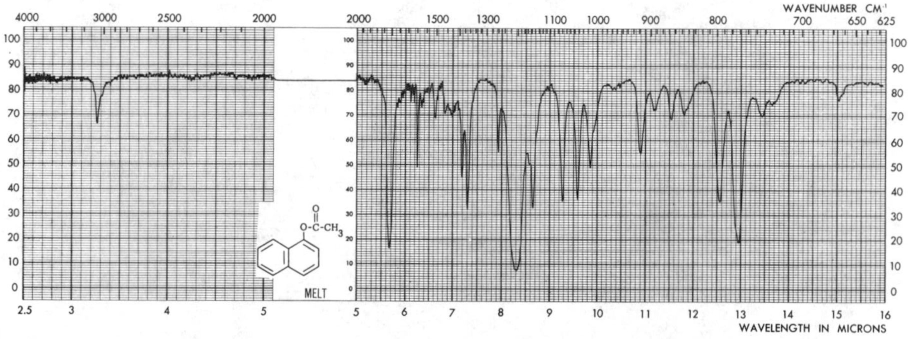

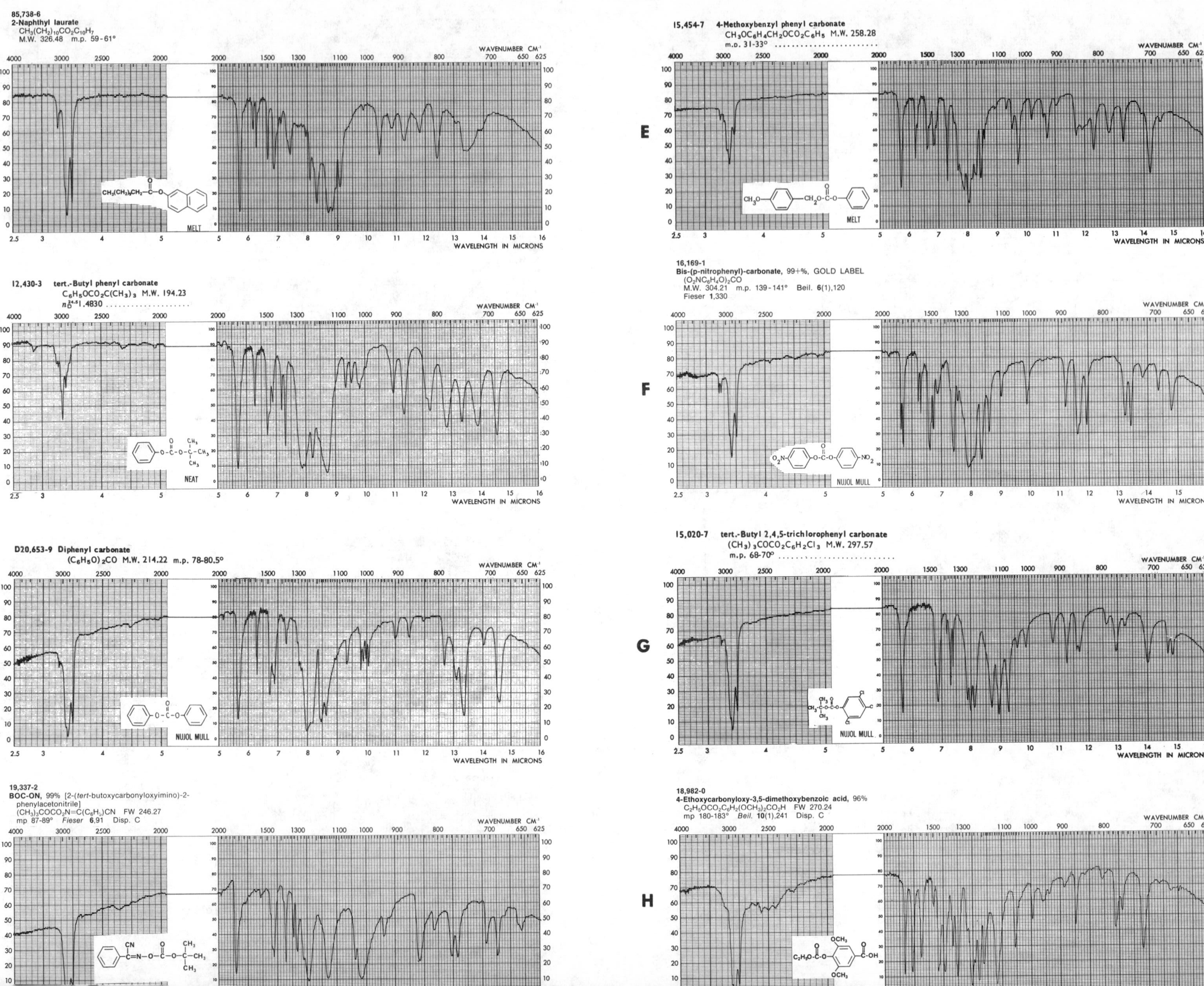

A 85,738-6
2-Naphthyl laurate
$CH_3(CH_2)_{10}CO_2C_{10}H_7$
M.W. 326.48 m.p. 59-61°

B 12,430-3 **tert.-Butyl phenyl carbonate**
$C_6H_5OCO_2C(CH_3)_3$ M.W. 194.23
$n_D^{24.5}$ 1.4830

C D20,653-9 **Diphenyl carbonate**
$(C_6H_5O)_2CO$ M.W. 214.22 m.p. 78-80.5°

D 19,337-2
BOC-ON, 99% [2-(*tert*-butoxycarbonyloxyimino)-2-phenylacetonitrile]
$(CH_3)_3COCO_2N{=}C(C_6H_5)CN$ FW 246.27
mp 87-89° *Fieser* **6**,91 Disp. C

E 15,454-7 **4-Methoxybenzyl phenyl carbonate**
$CH_3OC_6H_4CH_2OCO_2C_6H_5$ M.W. 258.28
m.p. 31-33°

F 16,169-1
Bis-(p-nitrophenyl)-carbonate, 99+%, GOLD LABEL
$(O_2NC_6H_4O)_2CO$
M.W. 304.21 m.p. 139-141° Beil. **6**(1),120
Fieser **1**,330

G 15,020-7 **tert.-Butyl 2,4,5-trichlorophenyl carbonate**
$(CH_3)_3COCO_2C_6H_2Cl_3$ M.W. 297.57
m.p. 68-70°

H 18,982-0
4-Ethoxycarbonyloxy-3,5-dimethoxybenzoic acid, 96%
$C_2H_5OCO_2C_6H_2(OCH_3)_2CO_2H$ FW 270.24
mp 180-183° *Beil.* **10**(1),241 Disp. C

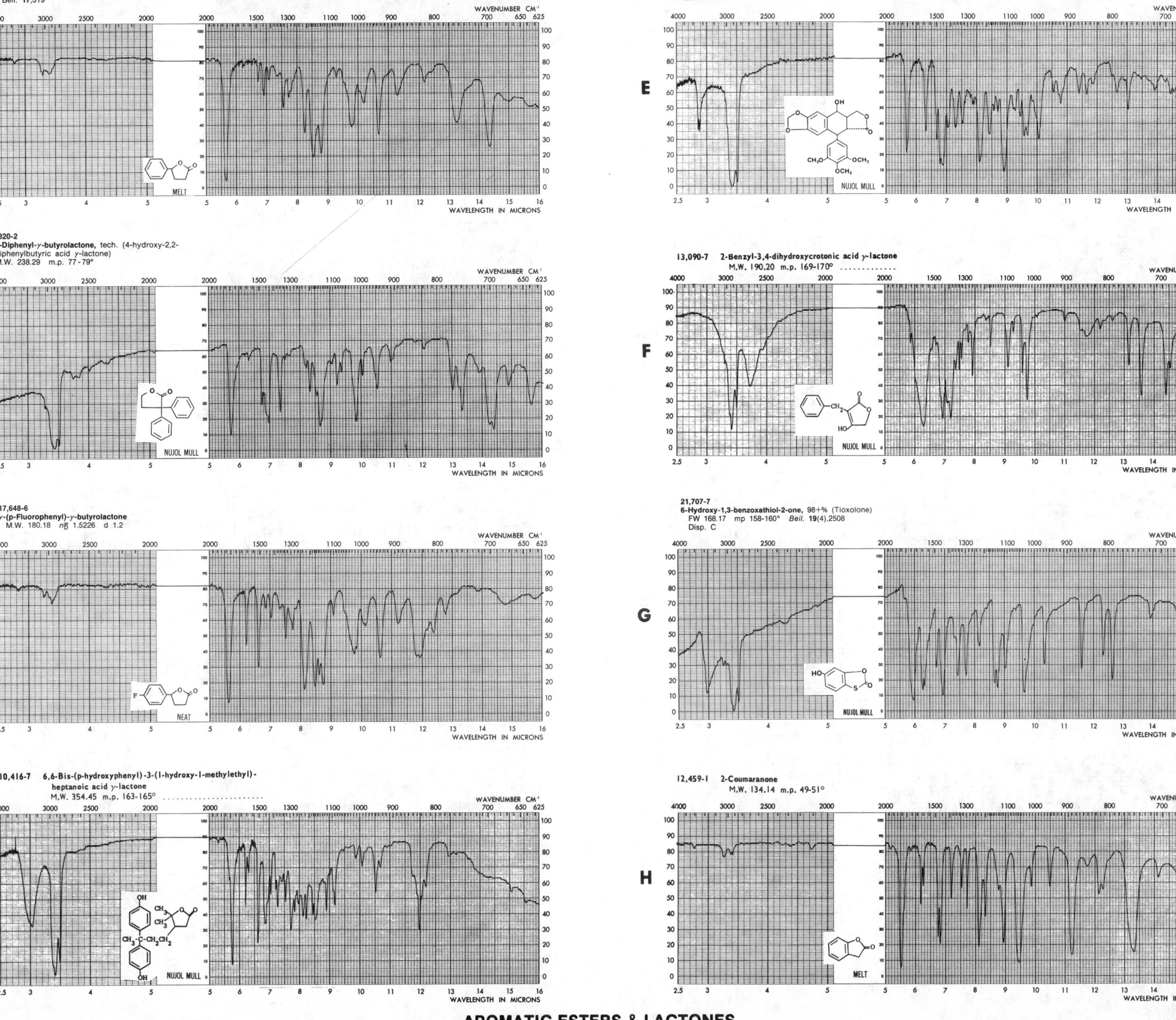

A
M.W. 162.19 m.p. 36-37° b.p. 306° d 1.155
Beil. **17**,319

B
18,320-2
α,α-**Diphenyl-*γ*-butyrolactone,** tech. (4-hydroxy-2,2-diphenylbutyric acid *γ*-lactone)
M.W. 238.29 m.p. 77-79°

C
17,648-6
γ-**(p-Fluorophenyl)-*γ*-butyrolactone**
M.W. 180.18 n_D^{20} 1.5226 d 1.2

D
10,416-7 **6,6-Bis-(p-hydroxyphenyl)-3-(1-hydroxy-1-methylethyl)-heptanoic acid *γ*-lactone**
M.W. 354.45 m.p. 163-165°

E
Podophyllotoxin
M.W. 414.41

F
13,090-7 **2-Benzyl-3,4-dihydroxycrotonic acid *γ*-lactone**
M.W. 190.20 m.p. 169-170°

G
21,707-7
6-Hydroxy-1,3-benzoxathiol-2-one, 98+% (Tioxolone)
FW 168.17 mp 158-160° *Beil.* **19**(4),2508
Disp. C

H
12,459-1 **2-Coumaranone**
M.W. 134.14 m.p. 49-51°

AROMATIC ESTERS & LACTONES

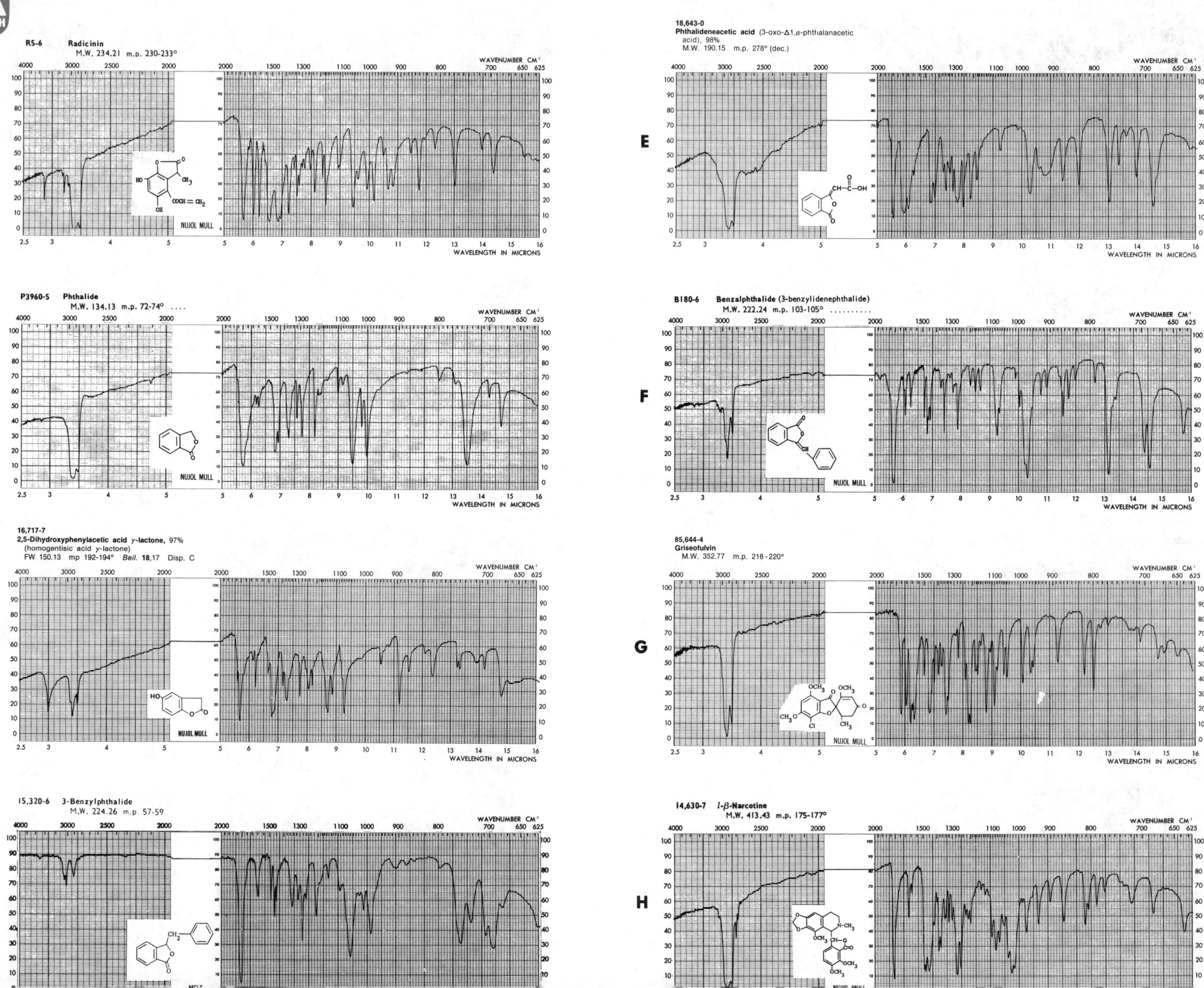
ALDRICH
A
R5-6 Radicinin
M.W. 234.21 m.p. 230-233°
NUJOL MULL
B
P3960-5 Phthalide
M.W. 134.13 m.p. 72-74°
NUJOL MULL
C
16,717-7
2,5-Dihydroxyphenylacetic acid γ-lactone, 97%
(homogentisic acid γ-lactone)
FW 150.13 mp 192-194° Beil. 18,17 Disp. C
NUJOL MULL
D
15,320-6 3-Benzylphthalide
M.W. 224.26 m.p. 57-59
E
18,643-0
Phthalideneacetic acid (3-oxo-Δ1,α-phthalanacetic acid), 98%
M.W. 190.15 m.p. 278° (dec.)
F
B180-6 Benzalphthalide (3-benzylidenephthalide)
M.W. 222.24 m.p. 103-105°
NUJOL MULL
G
85,644-4
Griseofulvin
M.W. 352.77 m.p. 218-220°
NUJOL MULL
H
14,630-7 l-β-Narcotine
M.W. 413.43 m.p. 175-177°
WAVENUMBER CM⁻¹
WAVELENGTH IN MICRONS

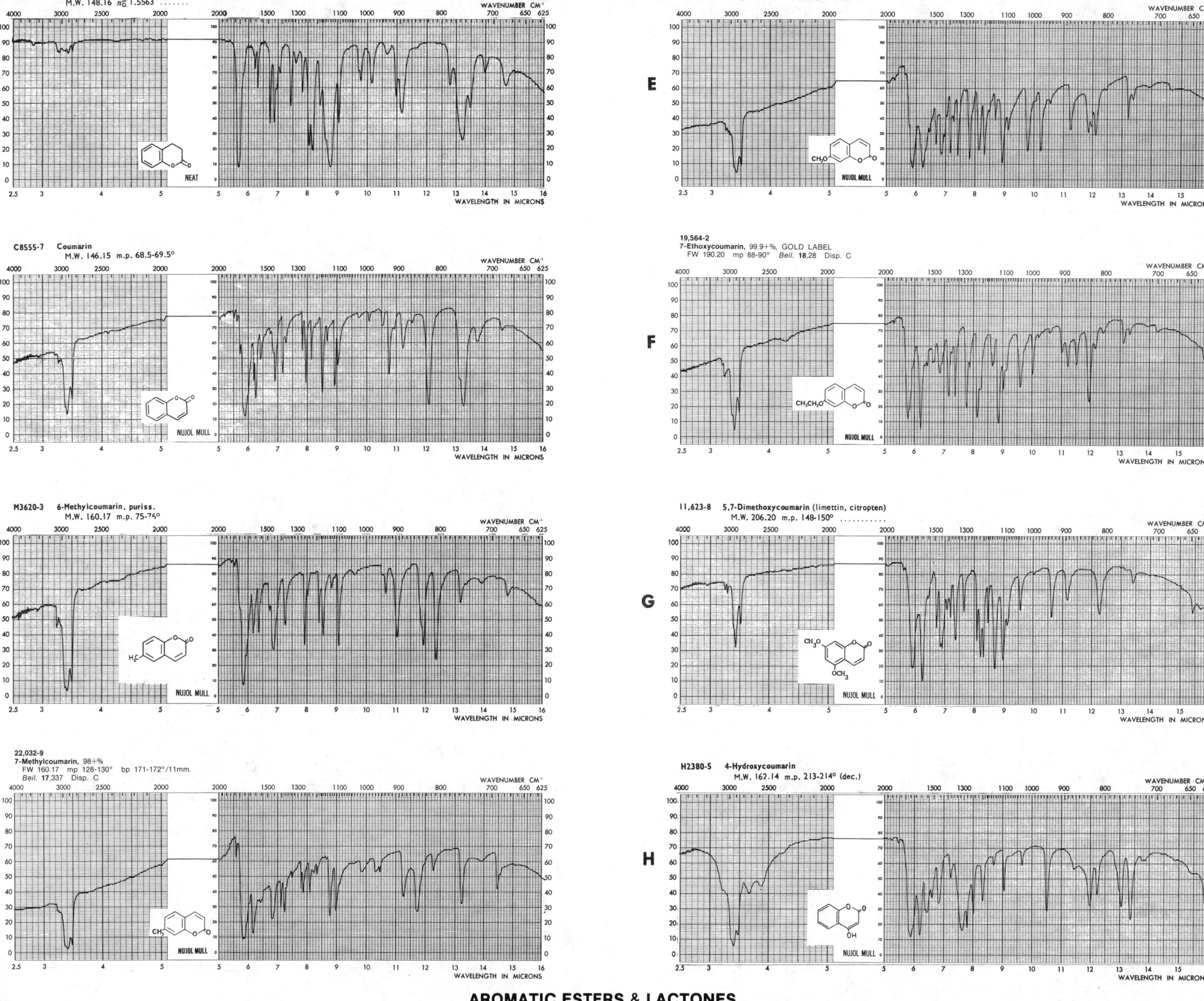

A
D10,480-9 Dihydrocoumarin (hydrocoumarin)
M.W. 148.16 n_D^{20} 1.5563
NEAT
B
C8555-7 Coumarin
M.W. 146.15 m.p. 68.5-69.5°
NUJOL MULL
C
M3620-3 6-Methylcoumarin, puriss.
M.W. 160.17 m.p. 75-76°
NUJOL MULL
D
22,032-9
7-Methylcoumarin, 98+%
FW 160.17 mp 128-130° bp 171-172°/11mm.
Beil. 17,337 Disp. C
NUJOL MULL
E
7-Methoxycoumarin, 98+%
FW 176.17 mp 118-120° Beil. 18,27 Disp. C
NUJOL MULL
F
19,564-2
7-Ethoxycoumarin, 99.9+%, GOLD LABEL
FW 190.20 mp 88-90° Beil. 18,28 Disp. C
NUJOL MULL
G
11,623-8 5,7-Dimethoxycoumarin (limettin, citropten)
M.W. 206.20 m.p. 148-150°
NUJOL MULL
H
H2380-5 4-Hydroxycoumarin
M.W. 162.14 m.p. 213-214° (dec.)
NUJOL MULL
WAVENUMBER CM⁻¹
WAVELENGTH IN MICRONS
ALDRICH

AROMATIC ESTERS & LACTONES

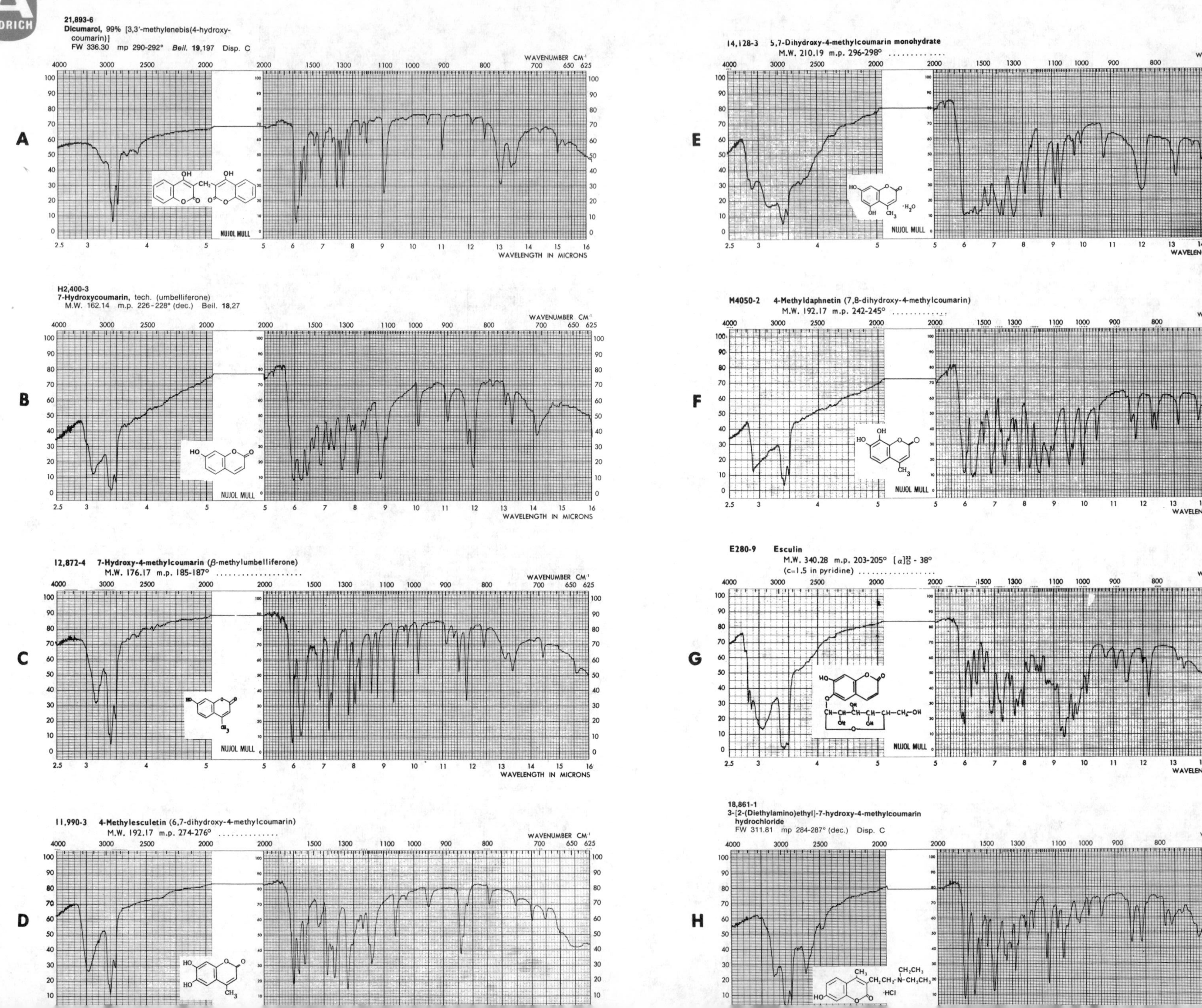

A — 21,893-6 **Dicumarol**, 99% [3,3'-methylenebis(4-hydroxycoumarin)] FW 336.30 mp 290-292° *Beil.* **19**,197 Disp. C

B — H2,400-3 **7-Hydroxycoumarin**, tech. (umbelliferone) M.W. 162.14 m.p. 226-228° (dec.) Beil. **18**,27

C — 12,872-4 **7-Hydroxy-4-methylcoumarin** (β-methylumbelliferone) M.W. 176.17 m.p. 185-187°

D — 11,990-3 **4-Methylesculetin** (6,7-dihydroxy-4-methylcoumarin) M.W. 192.17 m.p. 274-276°

E — 14,128-3 **5,7-Dihydroxy-4-methylcoumarin monohydrate** M.W. 210.19 m.p. 296-298°

F — M4050-2 **4-Methyldaphnetin** (7,8-dihydroxy-4-methylcoumarin) M.W. 192.17 m.p. 242-245°

G — E280-9 **Esculin** M.W. 340.28 m.p. 203-205° $[\alpha]_D^{22}$ - 38° (c=1.5 in pyridine)

H — 18,861-1 **3-[2-(Diethylamino)ethyl]-7-hydroxy-4-methylcoumarin hydrochloride** FW 311.81 mp 284-287° (dec.) Disp. C

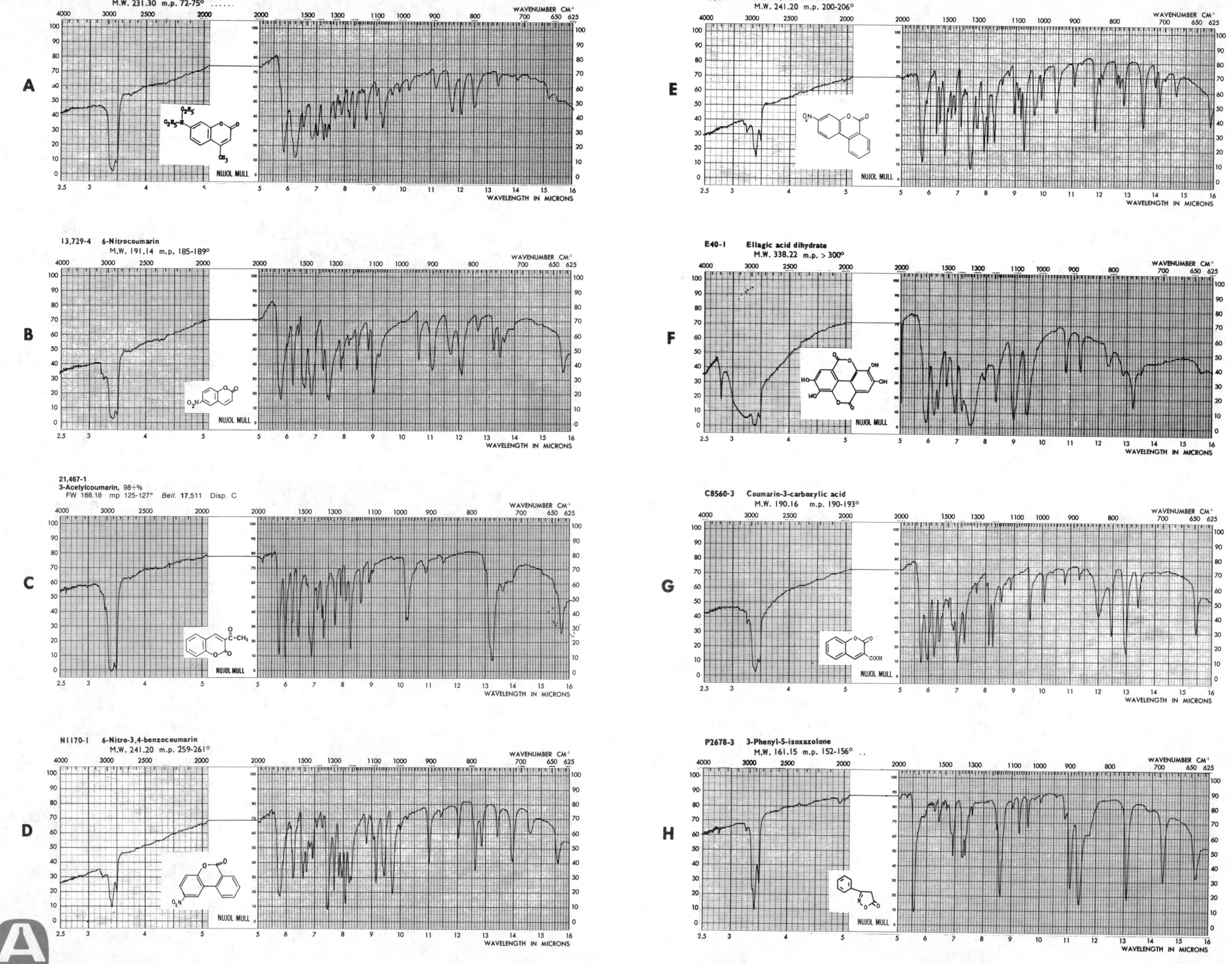
A
D8775-9 7-Diethylamino-4-methylcoumarin
M.W. 231.30 m.p. 72-75°
NUJOL MULL
B
13,729-4 6-Nitrocoumarin
M.W. 191.14 m.p. 185-189°
NUJOL MULL
C
21,467-1
3-Acetylcoumarin, 98+%
FW 188.18 mp 125-127° Beil. 17,511 Disp. C
NUJOL MULL
D
N1170-1 6-Nitro-3,4-benzocoumarin
M.W. 241.20 m.p. 259-261°
NUJOL MULL
E
13,018-4 7-Nitro-3,4-benzocoumarin
M.W. 241.20 m.p. 200-206°
NUJOL MULL
F
E40-1 Ellagic acid dihydrate
M.W. 338.22 m.p. > 300°
NUJOL MULL
G
C8560-3 Coumarin-3-carboxylic acid
M.W. 190.16 m.p. 190-193°
NUJOL MULL
H
P2678-3 3-Phenyl-5-isoxazolone
M.W. 161.15 m.p. 152-156°
NUJOL MULL
WAVENUMBER CM⁻¹
WAVELENGTH IN MICRONS
ALDRICH

AROMATIC ESTERS & LACTONES

A

14,025-2 **4-Ethoxymethylene-2-phenyl-2-oxazolin-5-one**
M.W. 217.23 m.p. 93.5-94.5°

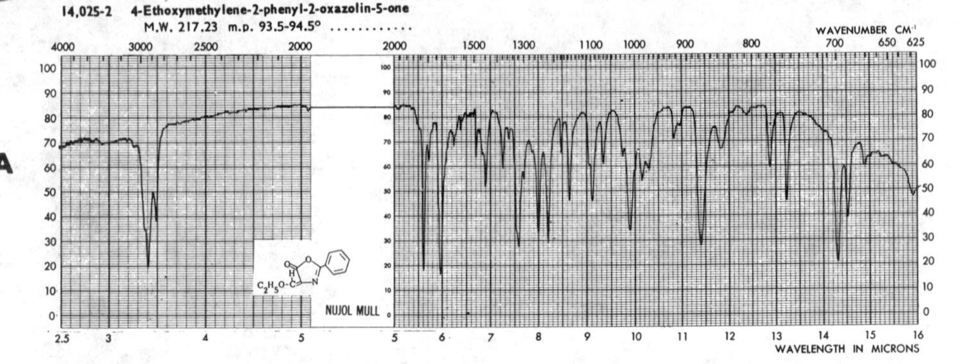

B

22,513-4
Ethyl o-fluorobenzoylacetate
$FC_6H_4COCH_2CO_2C_2H_5$ FW 210.20 n_D^{20} 1.5180
d 1.164 Disp. C

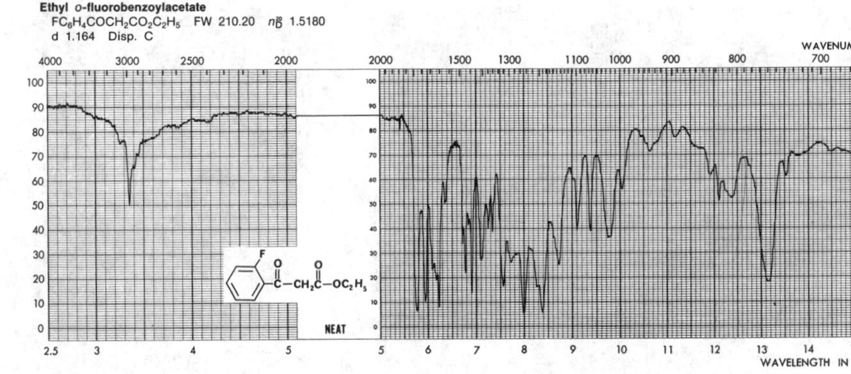

C

85,612-6
Methyl O-methylpodocarpate
M.W. 302.41 m.p. 129-131°

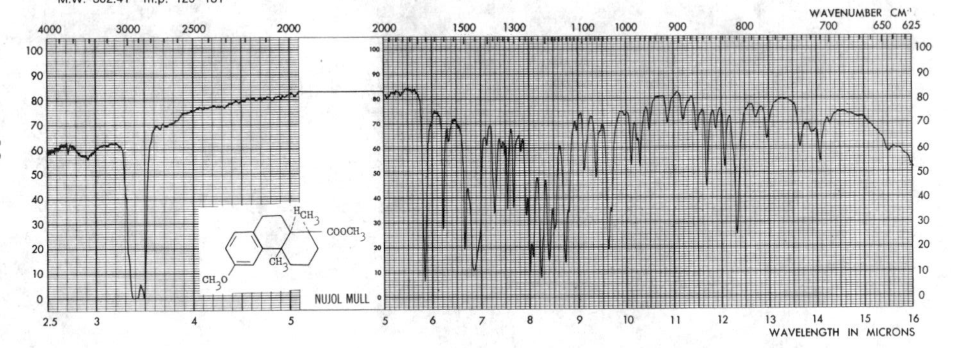

AROMATIC ANHYDRIDES

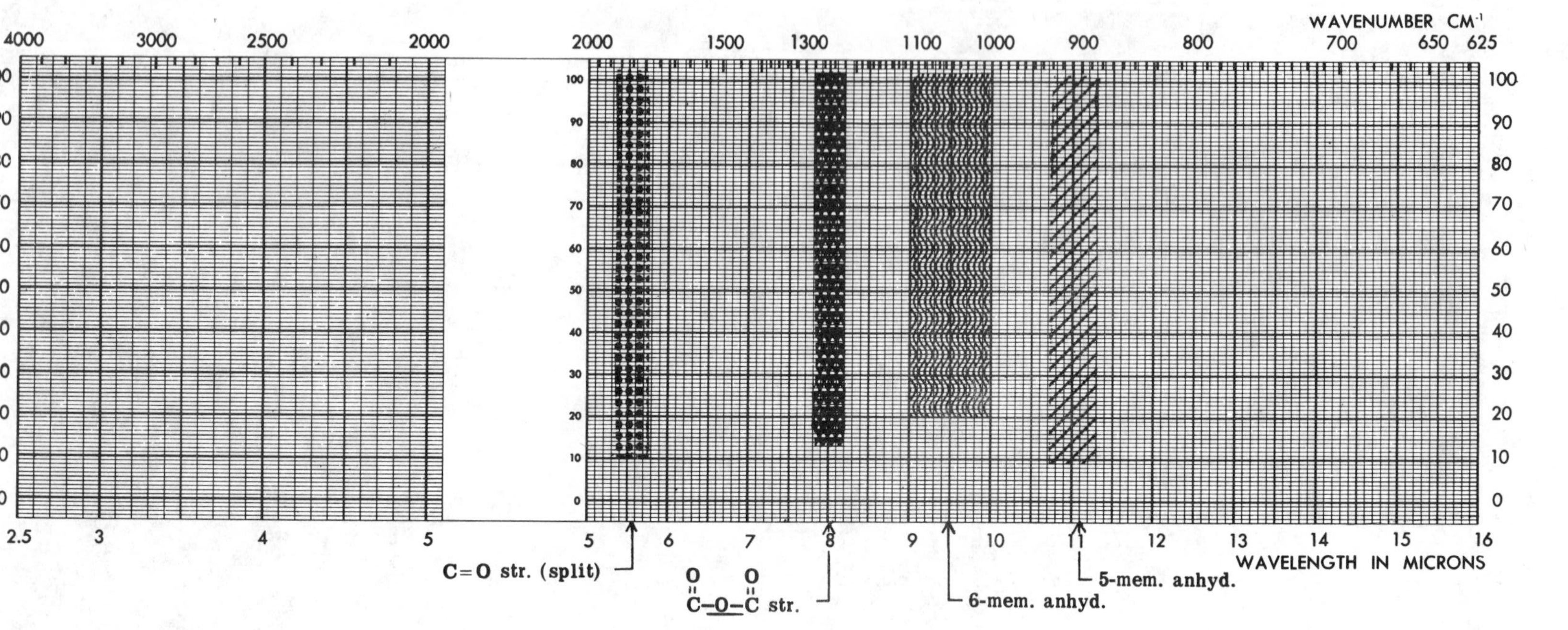

The unique split of the anhydride carbonyl absorptions in the vicinity 5.3 to 5.8 μ (1885 – 1725 cm^{-1}) is retained in the aromatic anhydrides. The split is not always well pronounced, however, as can be seen in spectra 1050F, 1051B, F and G.

Similar to the non-aromatic anhydrides, there is a strong absorption for five-membered anhydrides at 11 μ (910 cm^{-1}) while the larger ring cyclic anhydrides usually have this absorption split and shifted to between 9 and 10 μ (1110 – 1000 cm^{-1}).

The carbonyl attached directly to the aromatic ring completely upsets the substitution pattern between 11 and 15 μ (910 – 665 cm^{-1}). In spectrum 1052D, where there are no ring hydrogens, this region still has numerous bands.

m.p. 39-40° ....

M.W. 263.25 m.p. 99-101° ....

17,998-1
Benzoyl peroxide (dibenzoyl peroxide)
$(C_6H_5CO)_2O_2$
M.W. 242.23 m.p. 104-106° (dec.)

12,858-9 **Homophthalic anhydride** (1,3-isochromandione)
M.W. 162.14 m.p. 140-142° ....

B1280 **Benzoyl disulfide**
$(C_6H_5CO)_2S_2$ M.W. 274.36 m.p. 125-129°

I-1280-8 **Isatoic anhydride**
M.W. 163.13 m.p. 233° (dec.)

P2520-5 **2-Phenylglutaric anhydride**
M.W. 190.20 m.p. 95-99° .....

12,988-7 **N-Methylisatoic anhydride**
M.W. 177.16 m.p. 165-173°

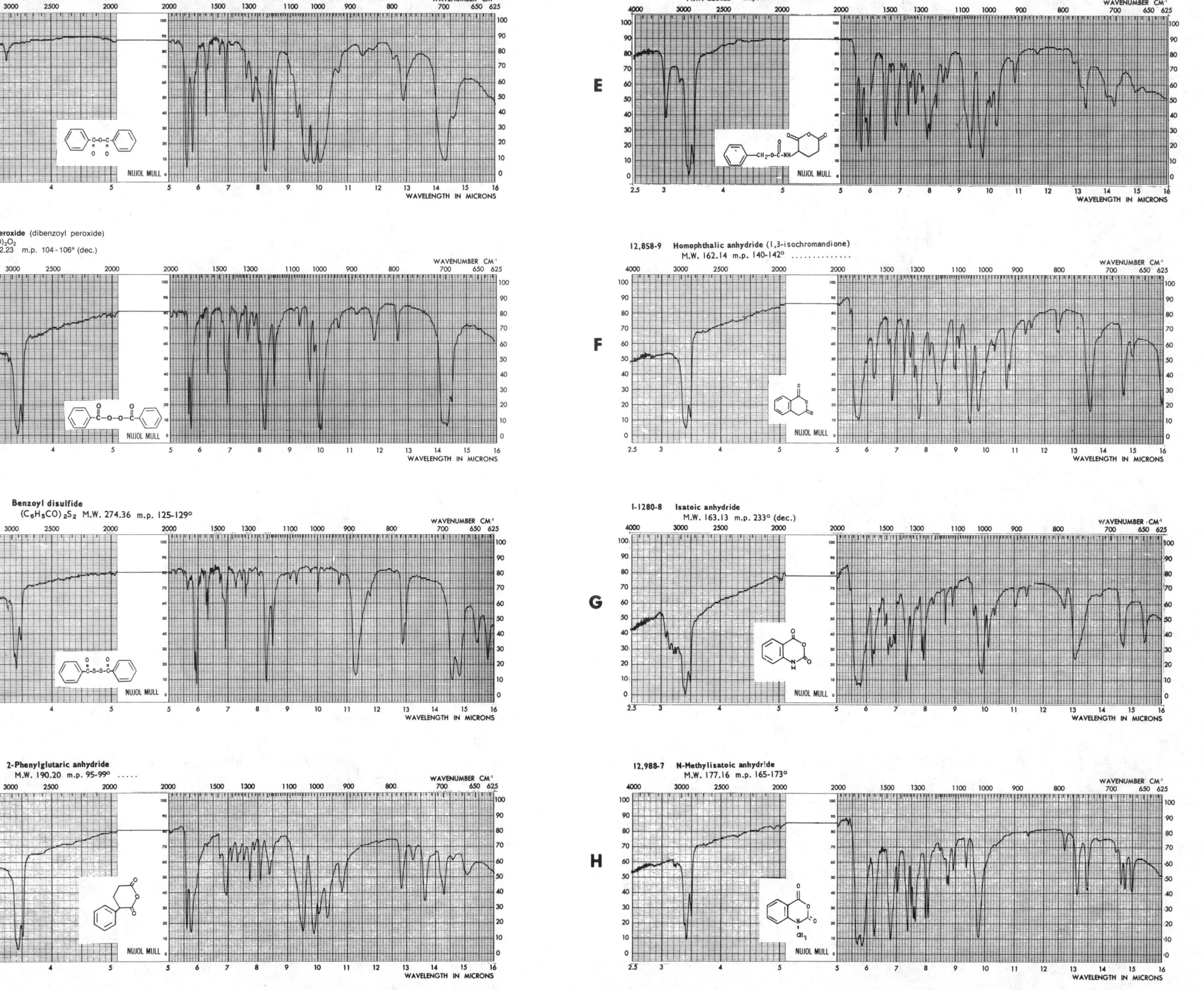

A

C4810-4 **5-Chloroisatoic anhydride** (6-chloro-1,2-dihydro-4H-3,1-benzoxazine-2,4-dione)
M.W. 197.58 m.p. 272-280° (dec.)

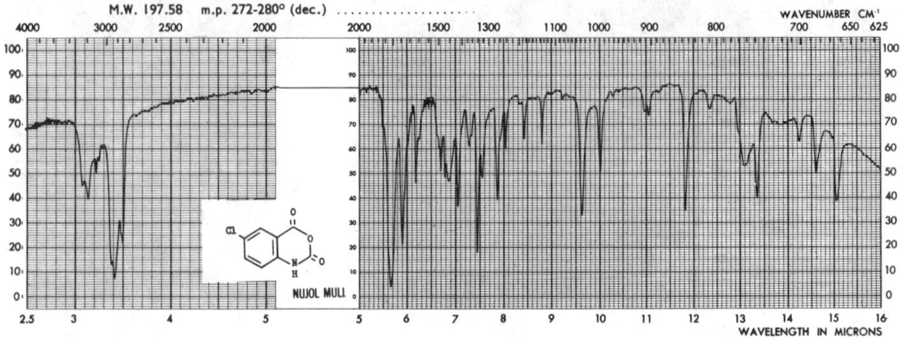

NUJOL MULL

B

N1790-4 **5-Nitroisatoic anhydride**
M.W. 208.13 m.p. 268° (dec.)

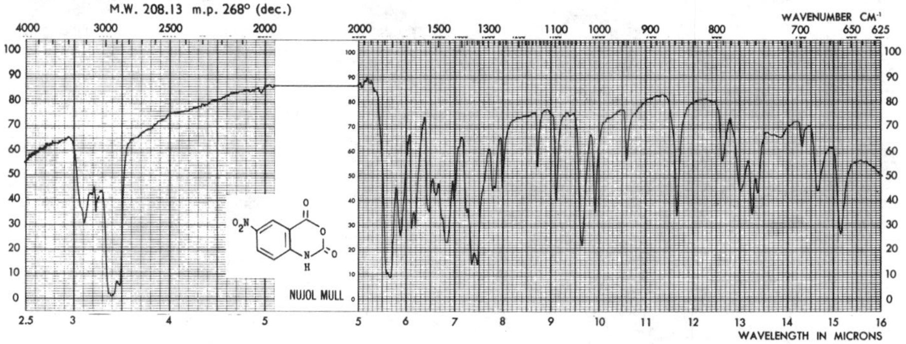

NUJOL MULL

C

12,573-3 **Phthalic anhydride, 99+%**
M.W. 148.12 m.p. 130.5-132°

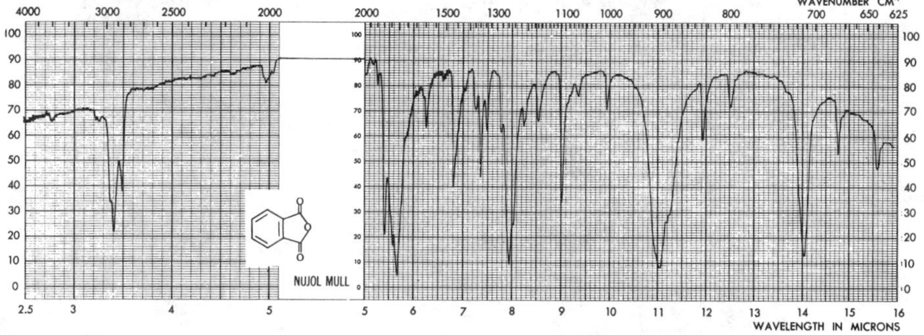

NUJOL MULL

D

19,169-8
o-Sulfobenzoic acid cyclic anhydride, tech.
FW 184.17 bp 184-186°/18mm. *Beil.* **19**,110
Disp. C

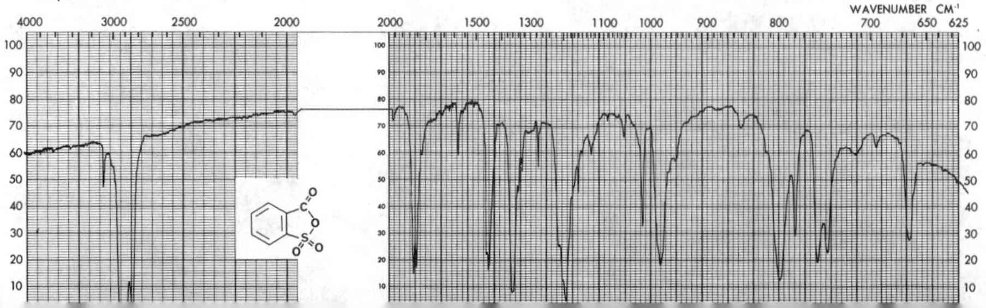

E

B975-0 **3,3',4,4'-Benzophenonetetracarboxylic dianhydride** (4,4'-carbonyldiphthalic anhydride)
M.W. 322.23 m.p. 223-225°

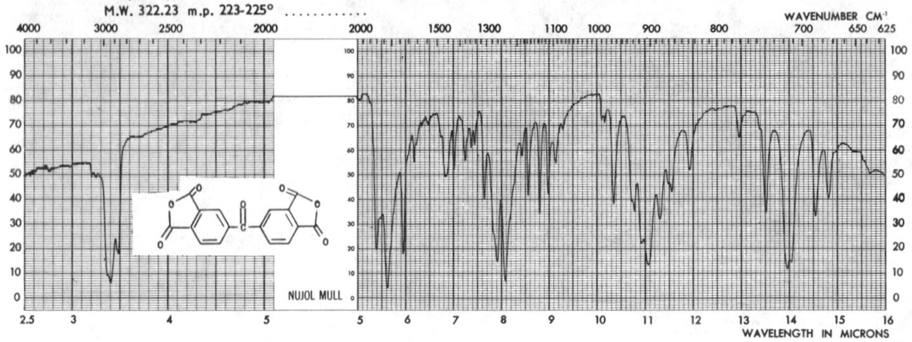

NUJOL MULL

F

13,186-5 **Tetrachlorophthalic anhydride**
M.W. 285.90 m.p. 254-258°

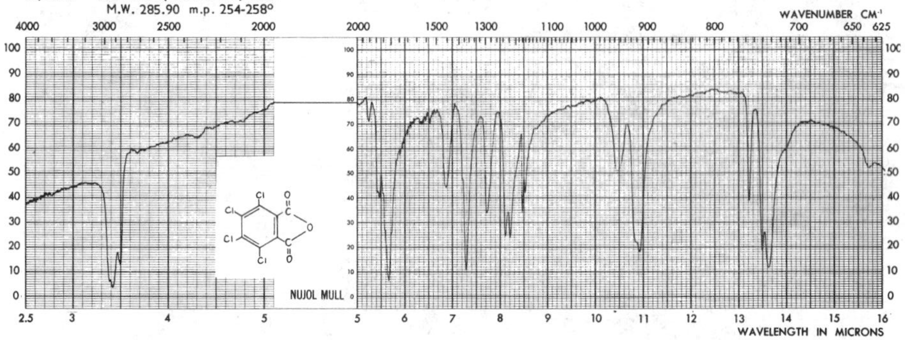

NUJOL MULL

G

T520-6 **Tetrabromophthalic anhydride**
M.W. 463.72 m.p. 271-274°

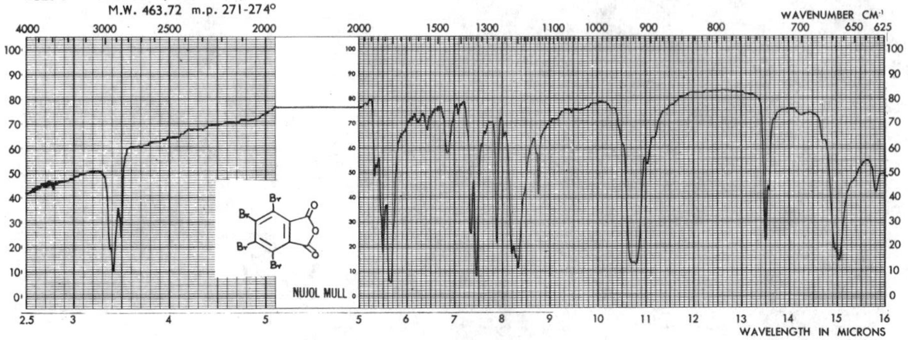

NUJOL MULL

H

B460-0 **1,2,4-Benzenetricarboxylic anhydride** (trimellitic anhydride)
M.W. 192.13 m.p. 167-169°

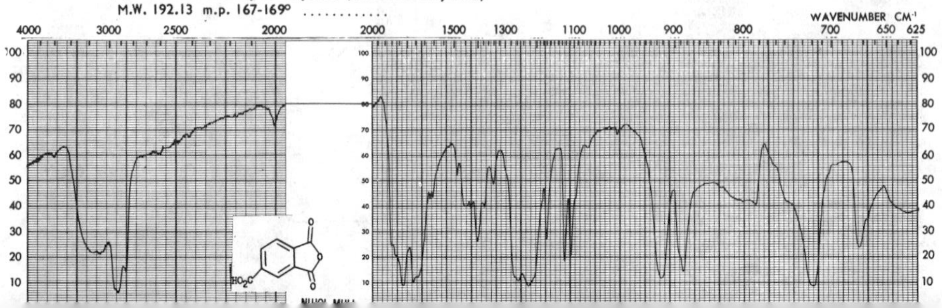

M.W. 193.11 m.p. 163-165° Beil. 17,486

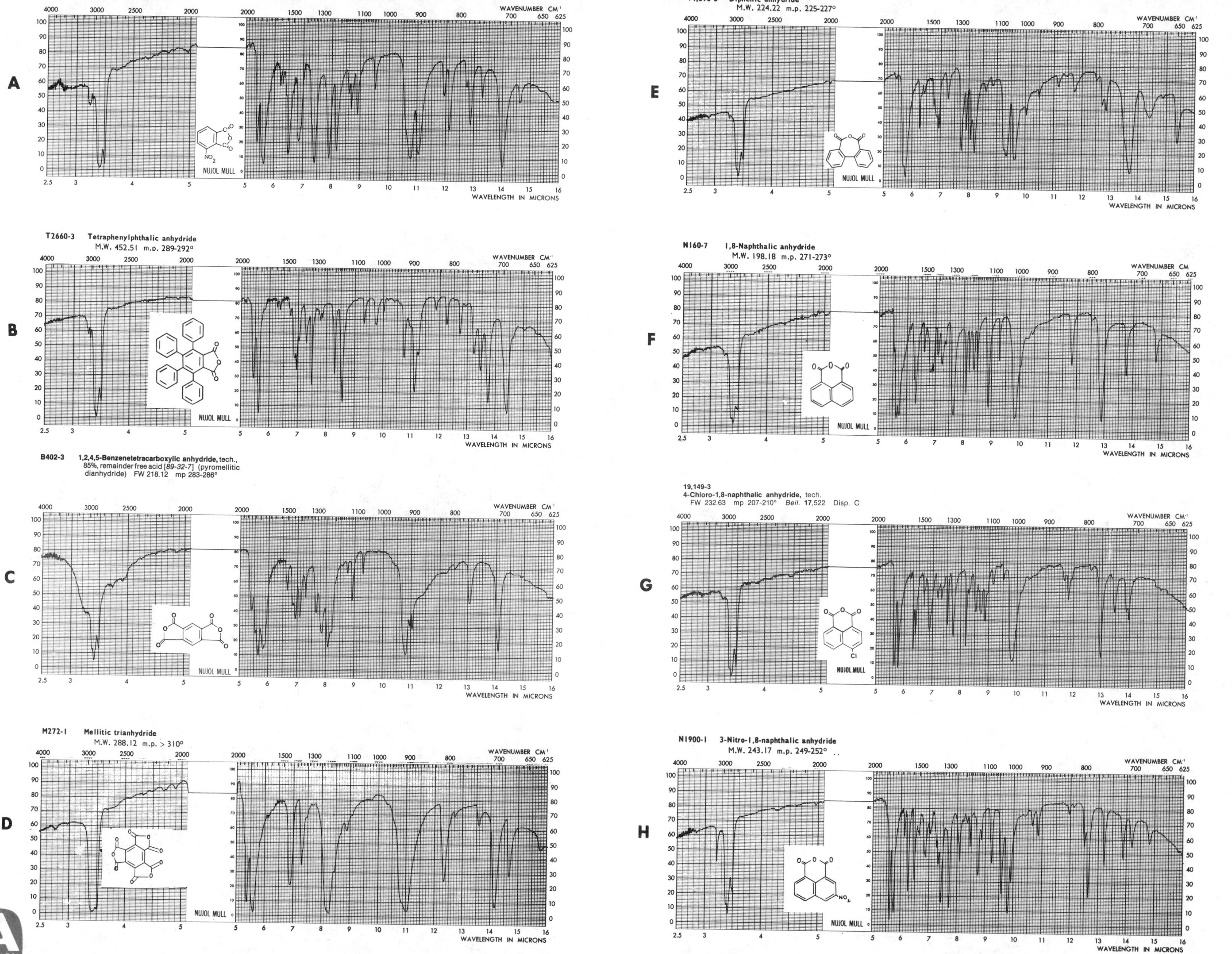
A
B
C
D
E
F
G
H
T2660-3 Tetraphenylphthalic anhydride
M.W. 452.51 m.p. 289-292°
B402-3 1,2,4,5-Benzenetetracarboxylic anhydride, tech., 85%, remainder free acid [89-32-7] (pyromellitic dianhydride) FW 218.12 mp 283-286°
M272-1 Mellitic trianhydride
M.W. 288.12 m.p. > 310°
14,890-3 Diphenic anhydride
M.W. 224.22 m.p. 225-227°
N160-7 1,8-Naphthalic anhydride
M.W. 198.18 m.p. 271-273°
19,149-3
4-Chloro-1,8-naphthalic anhydride, tech.
FW 232.63 mp 207-210° Beil. 17,522 Disp. C
N1900-1 3-Nitro-1,8-naphthalic anhydride
M.W. 243.17 m.p. 249-252°
NUJOL MULL
WAVENUMBER CM⁻¹
WAVELENGTH IN MICRONS
ALDRICH

AROMATIC ANHYDRIDES

ALDRICH

A

N81-8 1,4,5,8-Naphthalenetetracarboxylic dianhydride
M.W. 268.17 m.p. > 320°

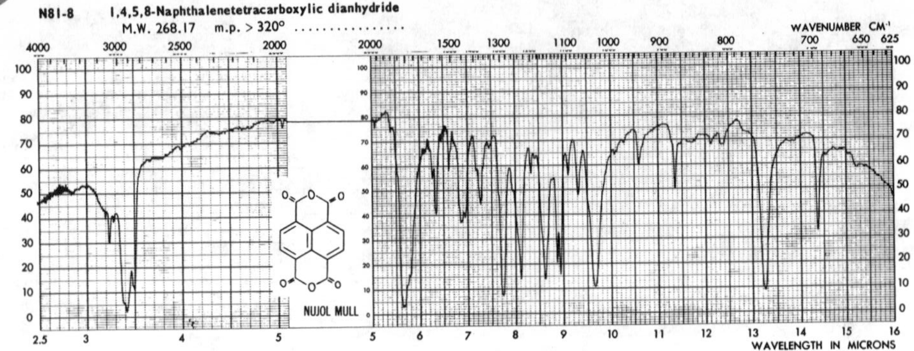

B

P1125-5 3,4,9,10-Perylenetetracarboxylic dianhydride
M.W. 392.30 m.p. > 360°

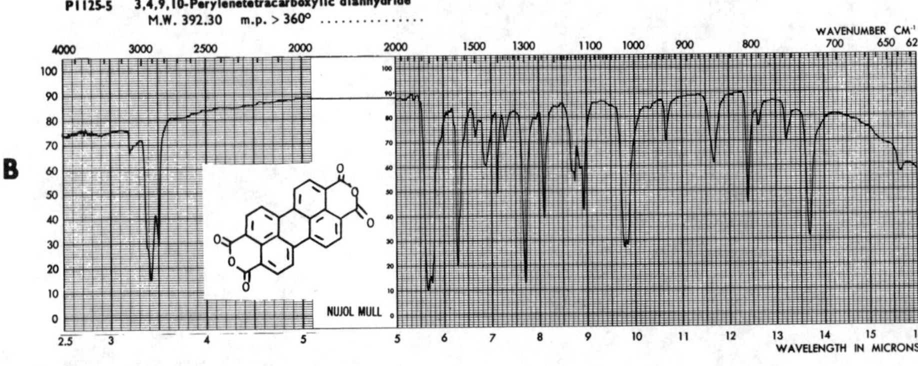

C

17,787-3
3,4-Coronenedicarboxylic anhydride
M.W. 370.37 m.p. >300°

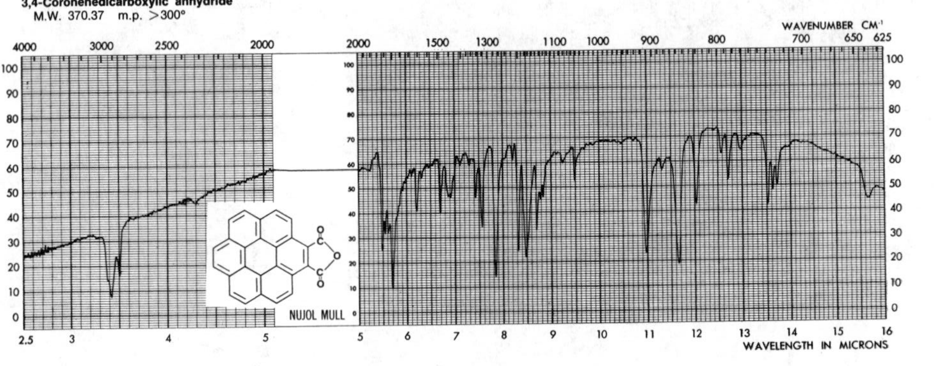

AROMATIC ACID HALIDES

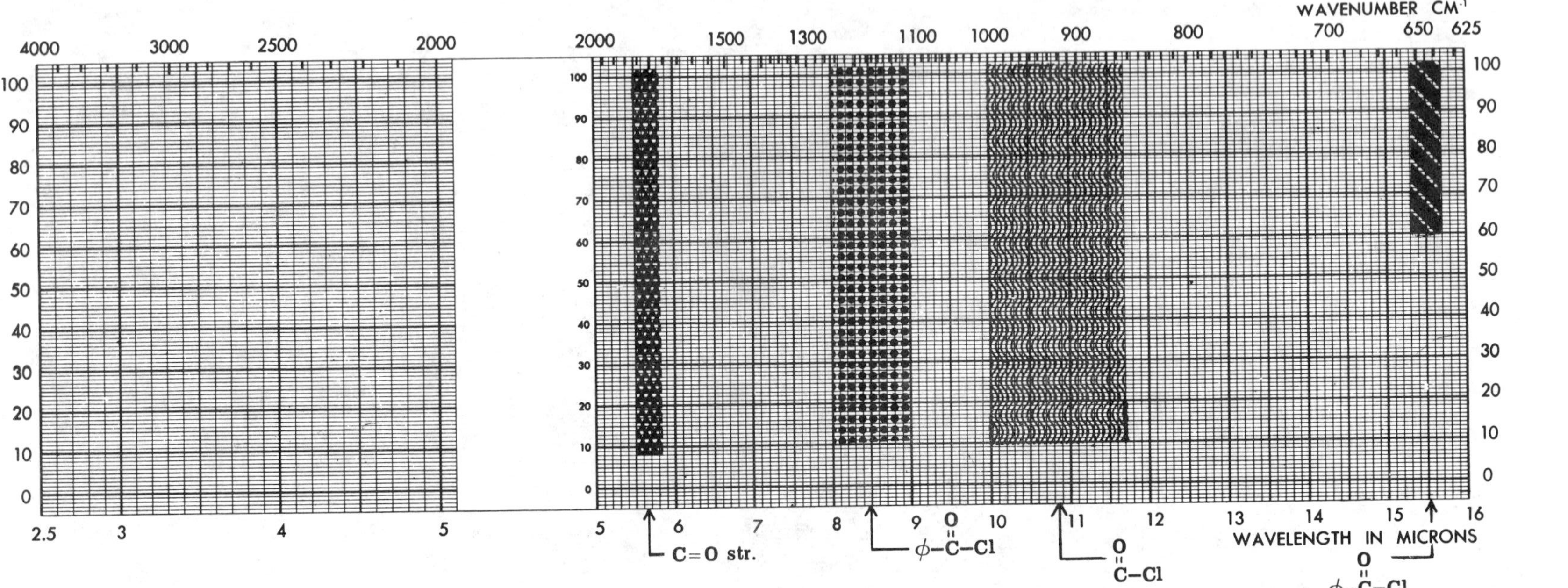

Conjugation of the acid halide carbonyl with the aromatic ring again shifts the carbonyl band to a higher wavelength, in this case to near 5.65 μ (1770 cm^{-1}). This band is often split. In spectrum 1060A, the band has the appearance of an anhydride carbonyl.

The carbonyl band is accompanied by several strong sharp bands between 8 and 9 μ (1250 – 1110 cm^{-1}).

The strong and broad band near 11.5 μ (870 cm^{-1}) in the ortho and para examples is shifted to a lower wavelength position in spectra 1058E-1059A , where the ring is meta substituted.

The ring conjugated acid chlorides also have a very strong absorption near 15.5 μ (645 cm^{-1}).

The usual interference by the carbonyl conjugated with the ring can be seen in the patterns between 11 and 15 μ (910 – 665 cm^{-1}).

A

b.p. 94-95°/12 mm.

NEAT

B

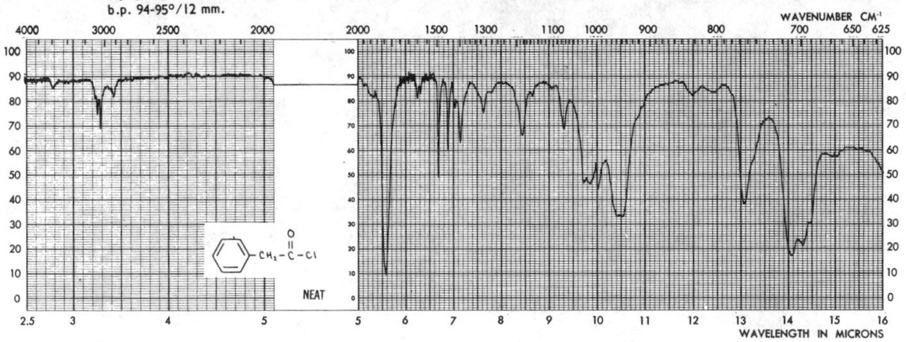

P2135-8 2-Phenylbutyryl chloride
$C_2H_5CH(C_6H_5)COCl$ M.W. 182.65 n_D^{20} 1.5169

NEAT

C

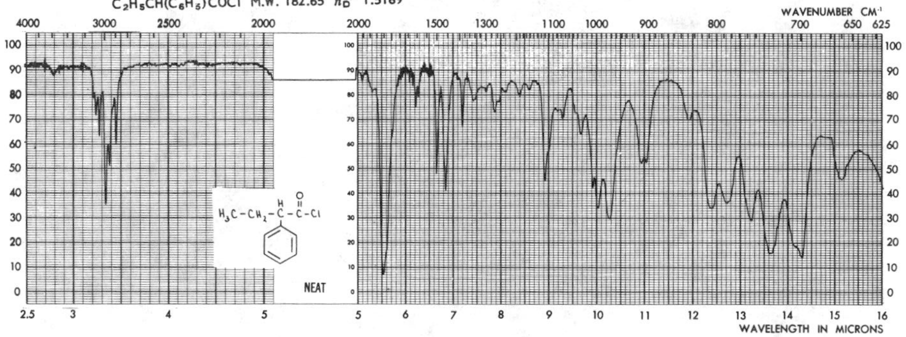

13,430-9 *trans*-2-Phenylcyclopropane-1-carboxylic acid chloride
$C_6H_5C_3H_4COCl$ M.W. 180.64 n_D^{20} 1.5560 b.p. 120°/9 mm.

NEAT

D

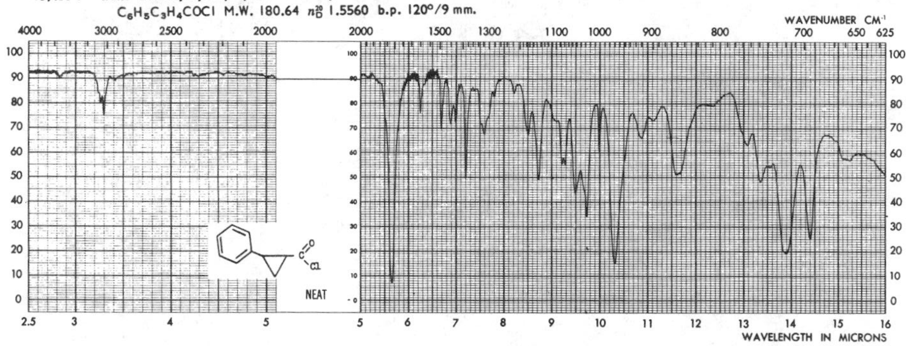

13,096-6
α-Chlorophenylacetyl chloride, 97%
$C_6H_5CH(Cl)COCl$ FW 189.04 bp 120°/23mm.
n_D^{20} 1.5440 d 1.196 *Beil.* **9**,449 *NMR* **7**,61D
Disp. C

NEAT

E

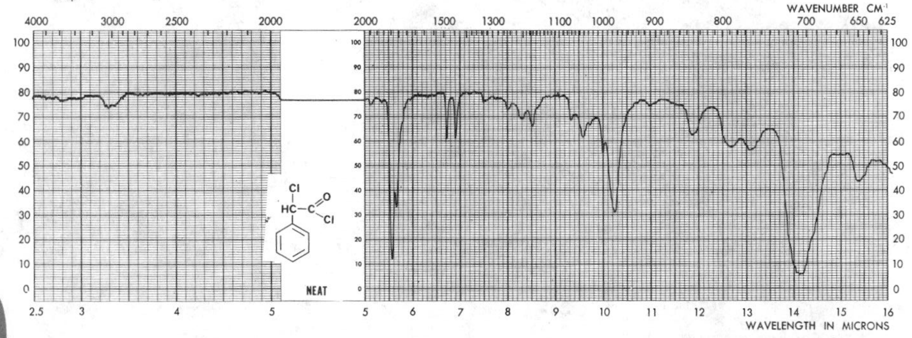

m.p. 48-50°

NUJOL MULL

F

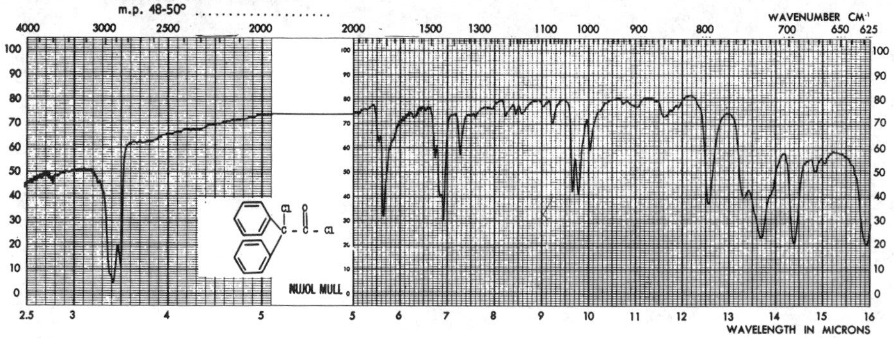

16,446-1
2-Bromo-2,2-diphenylacetyl bromide
$BrC(C_6H_5)_2COBr$
M.W. 354.05 m.p. 63-65° Beil. **9**(1),283
IRRITANT

MELT

G

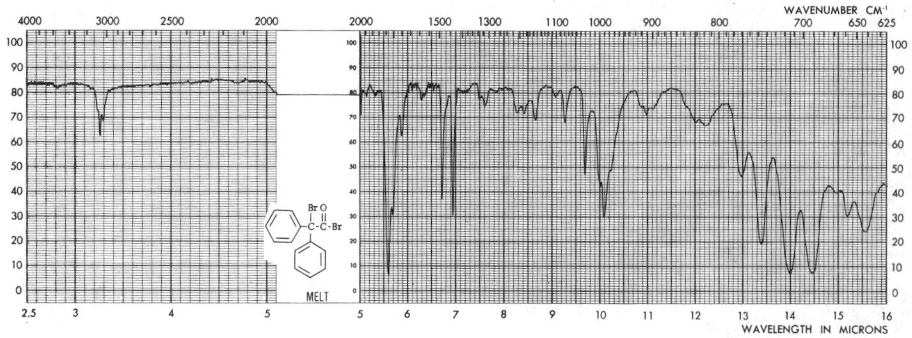

15,862-3
Phenoxyacetyl chloride, tech.
$C_6H_5OCH_2COCl$
M.W. 170.6 b.p. 225-226° n_D^{20} 1.5322
Beil. **6**,162 *CORROSIVE*

NEAT

H

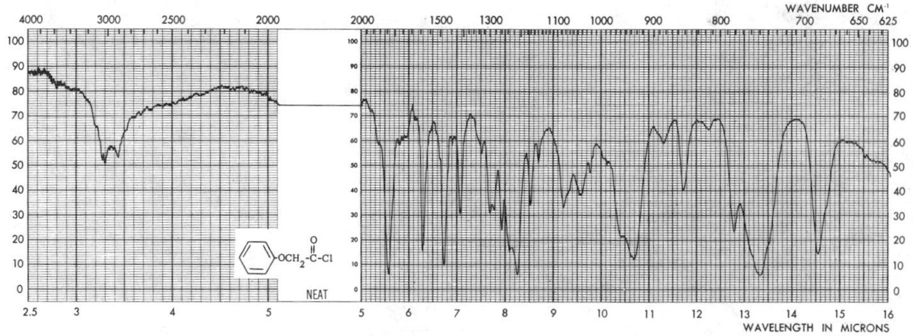

A1740-4 O-Acetylmandelic acid chloride (2-acetoxy-2-phenylacetyl chloride), **puriss.**
$CH_3CO_2CH(C_6H_5)COCl$ M.W. 212.63 n_D^{20} 1.5140
b.p. 125-130°/10 mm.

NEAT

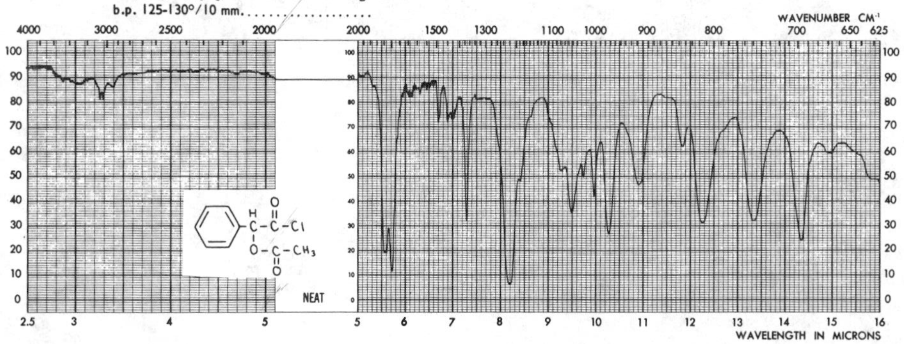

A

19,394-1
p-Chlorophenoxyacetyl chloride
$ClC_6H_4OCH_2COCl$ FW 205.04 mp 18.80°
bp 142°/17mm. n_D^{20} 1.5486 d 1.314
Beil. **6**(2),177 Disp. C

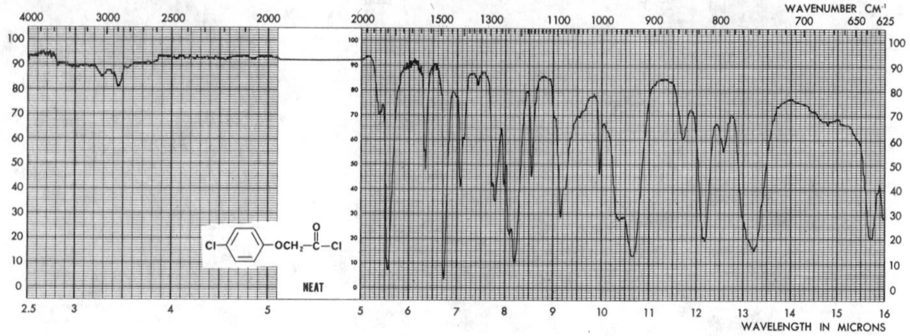

NEAT

B

16,051-2
9-Fluorenylmethyl chloroformate, 97%
M.W. 258.7 m.p. 62-64° Fieser **3**,145

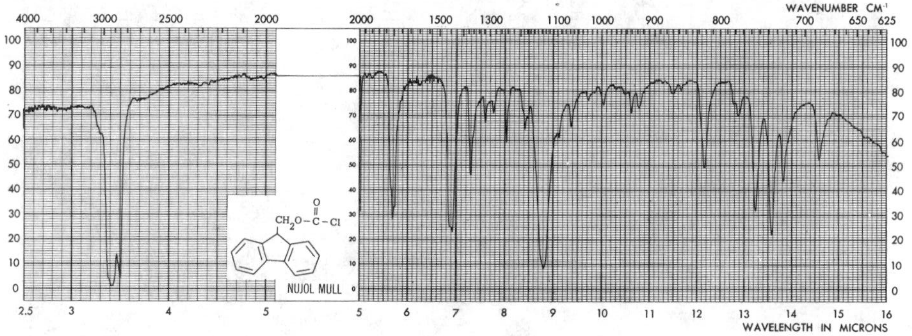

NUJOL MULL

C

10,384-5 **Pentafluorophenylacetyl chloride**
$C_6F_5CH_2COCl$ M.W. 244.55 n_D^{20} 1.4530

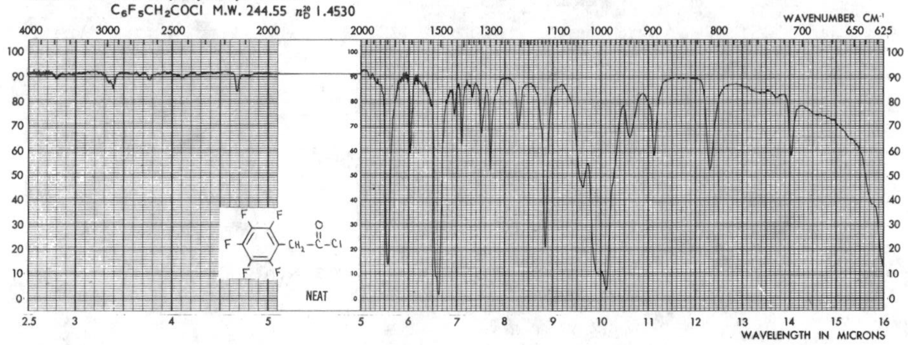

NEAT

D

C8110-1 **Cinnamoyl chloride**
$C_6H_5CH{:}CHCOCl$ M.W. 166.61 m.p. 37-38°

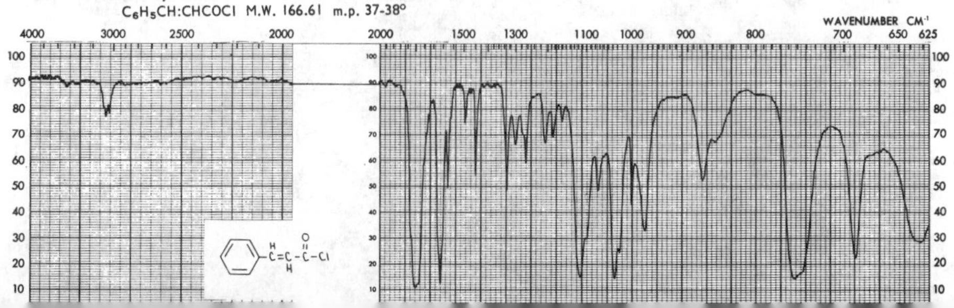

E

14,074-0 **Benzoyl fluoride**
C_6H_5COF M.W. 124.11 n_D^{20} 1.5048
b.p. 159-161°

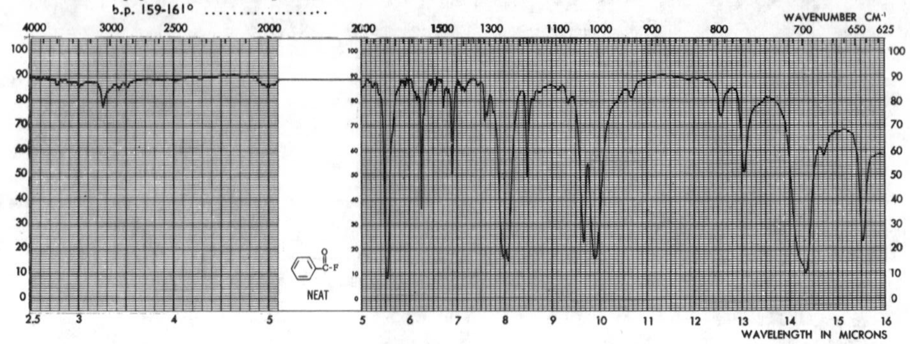

NEAT

F

B1269-5 **Benzoyl chloride**
C_6H_5COCl M.W. 140.57 n_D^{20} 1.5493 m.p. -0.5 to +0.5°

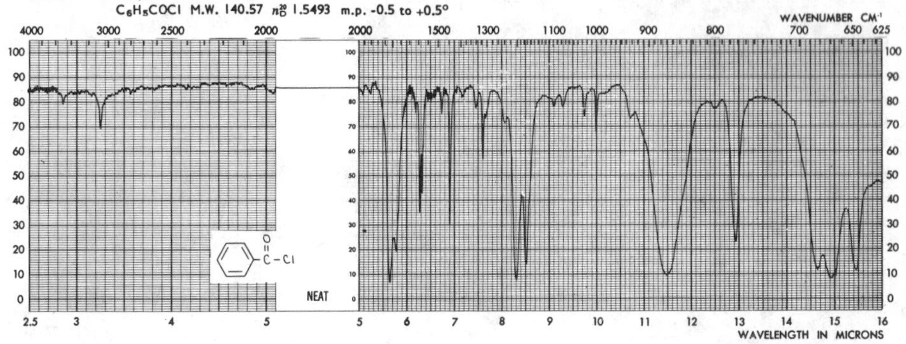

NEAT

G

13,972-6
Benzoyl bromide, 97%
C_6H_5COBr
M.W. 185.03 b.p. 218-219° n_D^{20} 1.5883 d 1.57
Beil. **9**,195 *LACHRYMATOR*

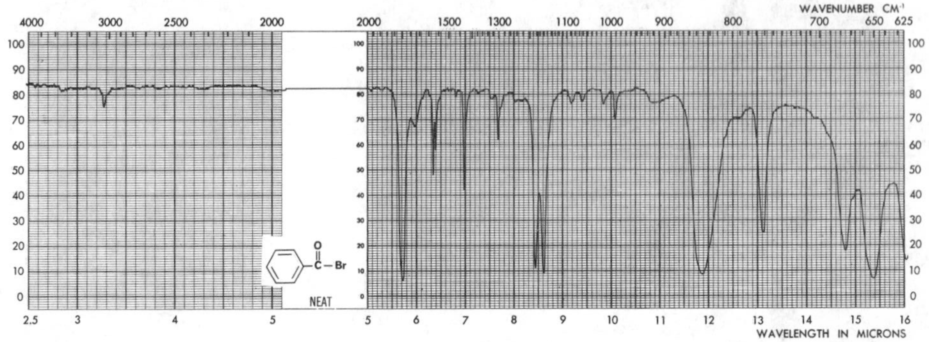

NEAT

H

12,201-7 **o-Toluoyl chloride**
$CH_3C_6H_4COCl$ M.W. 154.60 n_D^{20} 1.5549
b.p. 88-90°/12 mm.

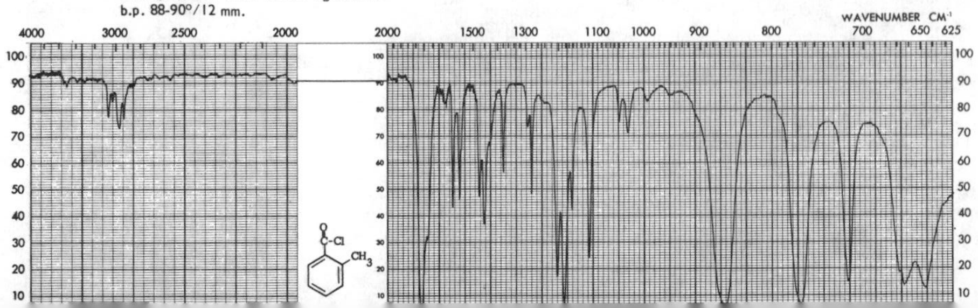

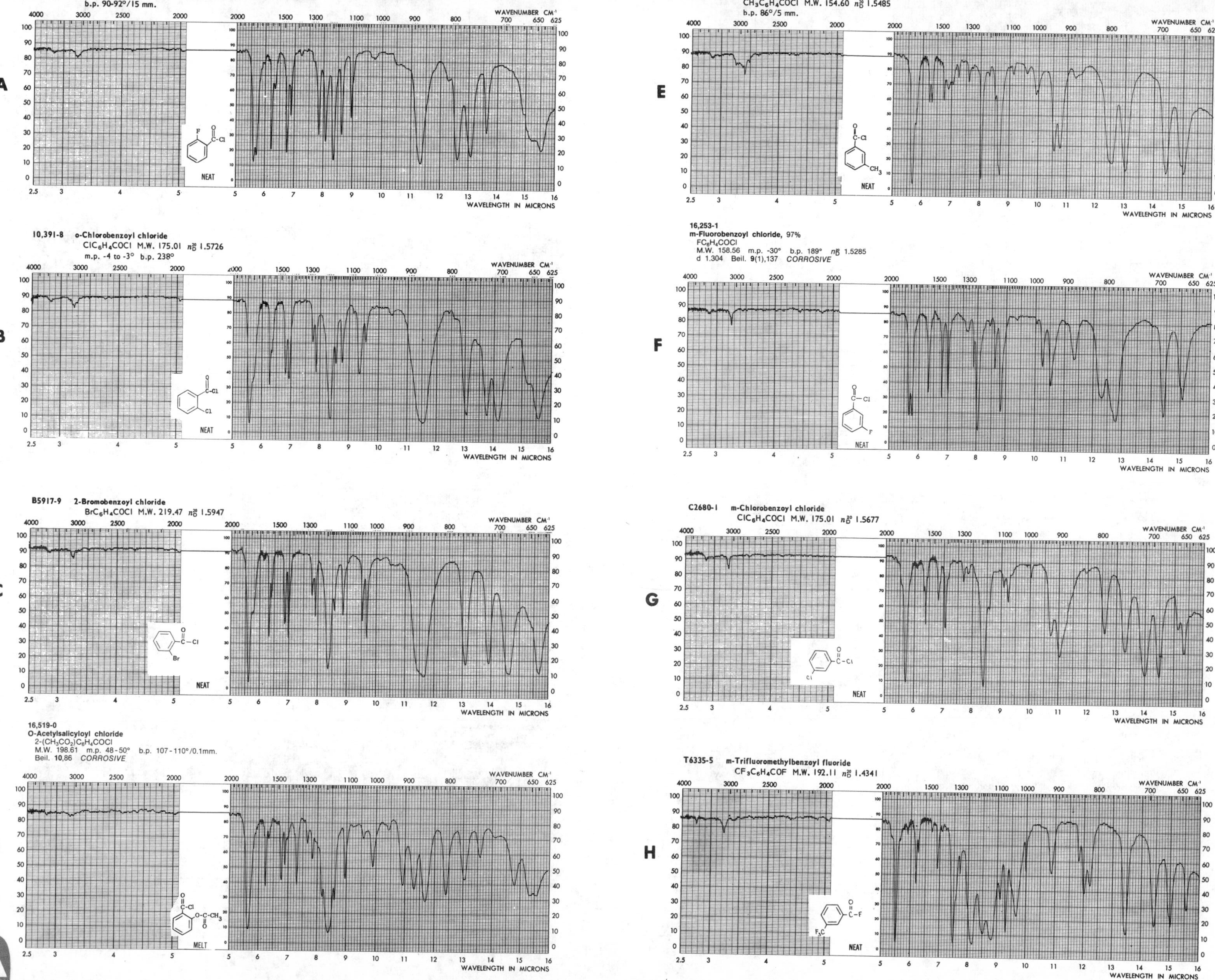
A
FC$_6$H$_4$COCl M.W. 158.56 n_D^{20} 1.5365
b.p. 90-92°/15 mm.
NEAT
B
10,391-8 o-Chlorobenzoyl chloride
ClC$_6$H$_4$COCl M.W. 175.01 n_D^{20} 1.5726
m.p. -4 to -3° b.p. 238°
NEAT
C
B5917-9 2-Bromobenzoyl chloride
BrC$_6$H$_4$COCl M.W. 219.47 n_D^{20} 1.5947
NEAT
D
16,519-0
O-Acetylsalicyloyl chloride
2-(CH$_3$CO$_2$)C$_6$H$_4$COCl
M.W. 198.61 m.p. 48-50° b.p. 107-110°/0.1mm.
Beil. 10,86 CORROSIVE
MELT
E
12,225-4 m-Toluoyl chloride
CH$_3$C$_6$H$_4$COCl M.W. 154.60 n_D^{20} 1.5485
b.p. 86°/5 mm.
NEAT
F
16,253-1
m-Fluorobenzoyl chloride, 97%
FC$_6$H$_4$COCl
M.W. 158.56 m.p. -30° b.p. 189° n_D^{20} 1.5285
d 1.304 Beil. 9(1),137 CORROSIVE
NEAT
G
C2680-1 m-Chlorobenzoyl chloride
ClC$_6$H$_4$COCl M.W. 175.01 n_D^{20} 1.5677
NEAT
H
T6335-5 m-Trifluoromethylbenzoyl fluoride
CF$_3$C$_6$H$_4$COF M.W. 192.11 n_D^{20} 1.4341
NEAT
WAVENUMBER CM^{-1}
WAVELENGTH IN MICRONS
ALDRICH

A

12,766-3 **m-Nitrobenzoyl chloride**
$O_2NC_6H_4COCl$ M.W. 185.57 m.p. 32.5-33.5°

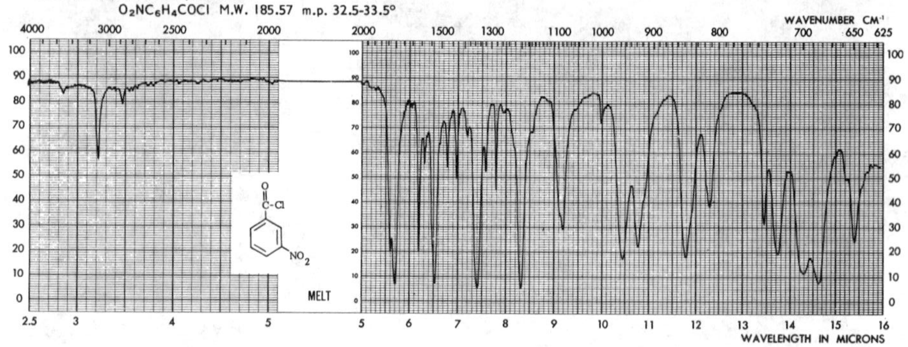

MELT

B

10,663-1 **p-Toluoyl chloride**
$CH_3C_6H_4COCl$ M.W. 154.60 n_D^{20} 1.5547
b.p. 225-227°

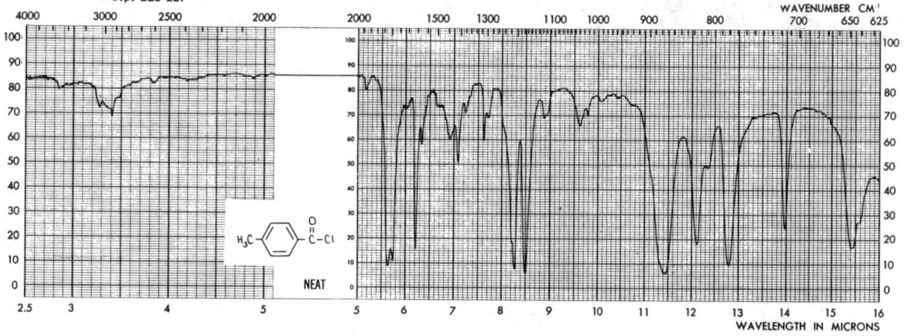

NEAT

C

15,712-0
p-*tert*.-Butylbenzoyl chloride, 98%
$(CH_3)_3CC_6H_4COCl$
M.W. 196.68 b.p. 135°/20mm. n_D^{20} 1.5364
CORROSIVE

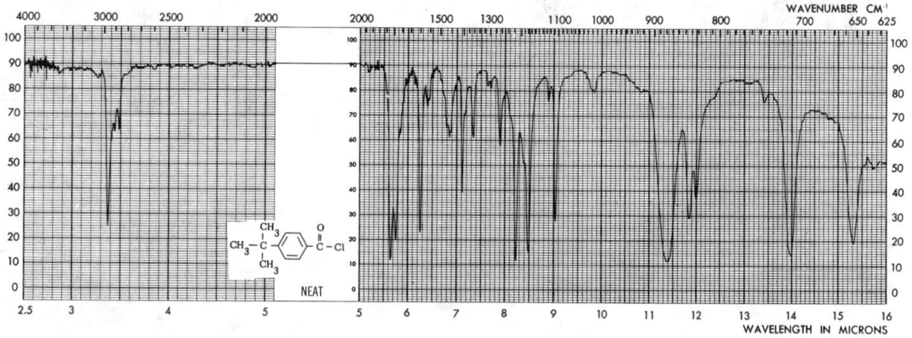

NEAT

D

22,203-8
4-Butylbenzoyl chloride, 99%
$CH_3(CH_2)_3C_6H_4COCl$ FW 196.68
bp 155-156°/22mm. n_D^{20} 1.5351 d 1.051
Beil. **9**(3),2520 Disp. S

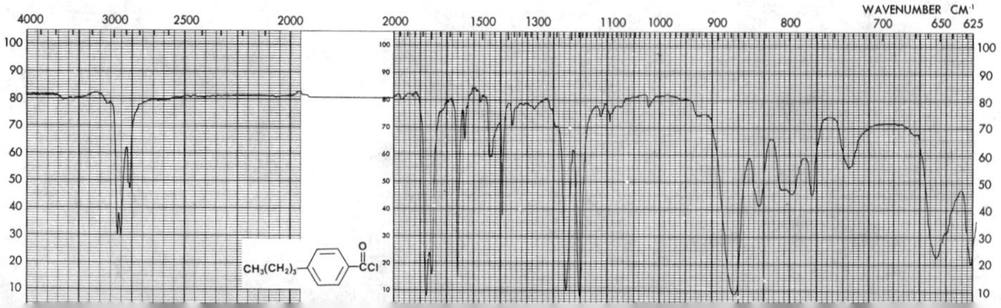

E

22,214-3
4-Pentylbenzoyl chloride, 99%
$CH_3(CH_2)_4C_6H_4COCl$ FW 210.71 n_D^{20} 1.5300
d 1.036 Disp. S

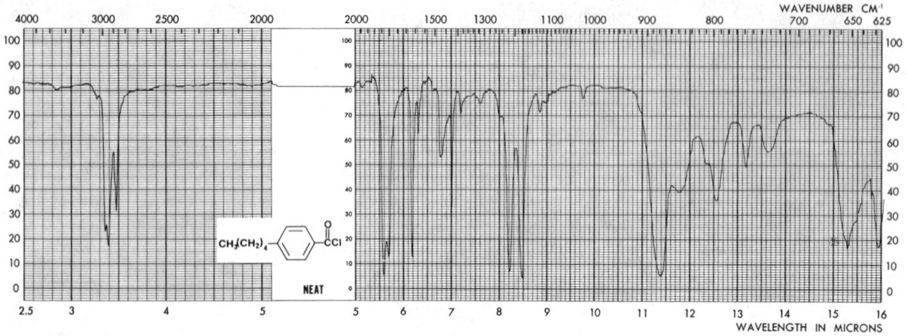

NEAT

F

22,209-7
4-Hexylbenzoyl chloride, 99%
$CH_3(CH_2)_5C_6H_4COCl$ FW 224.73 n_D^{20} 1.5256
d 1.029 Disp. S

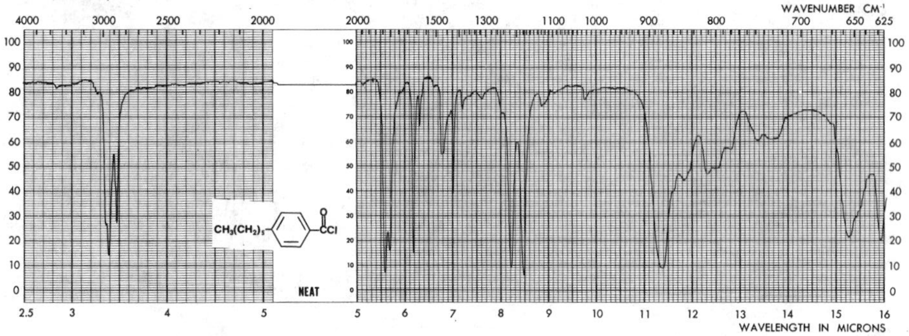

NEAT

G

22,205-4
4-Heptylbenzoyl chloride, 99%
$CH_3(CH_2)_6C_6H_4COCl$ FW 238.76 n_D^{20} 1.5218
d 1.002 Disp. S

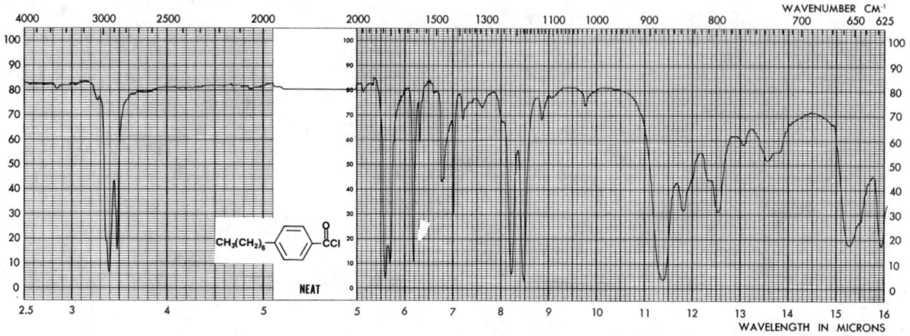

NEAT

H

11,994-6 **p-Fluorobenzoyl chloride**
FC_6H_4COCl M.W. 158.56 n_D^{20} 1.5296
b.p. 82°/20 mm.

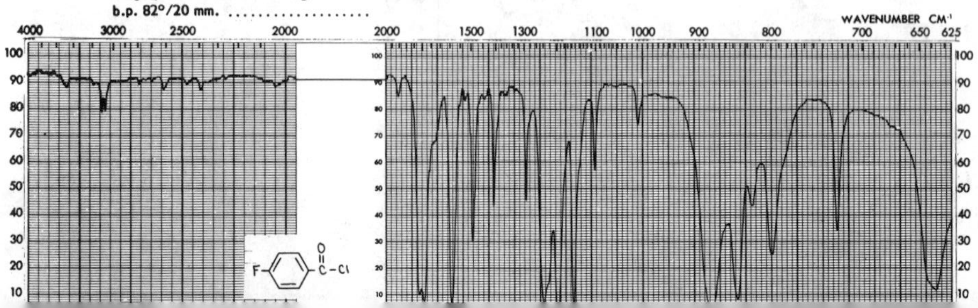

ClC$_6$H$_4$COCl M.W. 175.01 n_D^{20} 1.5756
m.p. 12-14° b.p. 222° ....

B5920-9 **4-Bromobenzoyl chloride**
BrC$_6$H$_4$COCl M.W. 219.47 m.p. 39-40.5°

A8847-6 **p-Anisoyl chloride (p-methoxybenzoyl chloride)**
CH$_3$OC$_6$H$_4$COCl M.W. 170.60 m.p. 23-25° ...

22,204-6
4-Butoxybenzoyl chloride, 99%
CH$_3$(CH$_2$)$_3$OC$_6$H$_4$COCl FW 212.68 bp 160°/8mm.
n_D^{20} 1.5495 d 1.122 *Beil.* **10**(3),338 Disp. S

bp 198-200°/30mm. n_D^{20} 1.5434 d 1.087
Beil. **10**(3),338 Disp. S

22,211-9
4-Hexyloxybenzoyl chloride, 98%
CH$_3$(CH$_2$)$_5$OC$_6$H$_4$COCl FW 240.73
bp 213-214°/30mm. n_D^{20} 1.5383 d 1.081
Beil. **10**(3),338 Disp. S

22,206-2
4-Heptyloxybenzoyl chloride, 99%
CH$_3$(CH$_2$)$_6$OC$_6$H$_4$COCl FW 254.76
bp 226-227°/30mm. n_D^{20} 1.5330 d 1.061
Beil. **10**(3),338 Disp. S

11,220-8 **p-Nitrobenzoyl chloride**
O$_2$NC$_6$H$_4$COCl M.W. 185.57 m.p. 72-74°

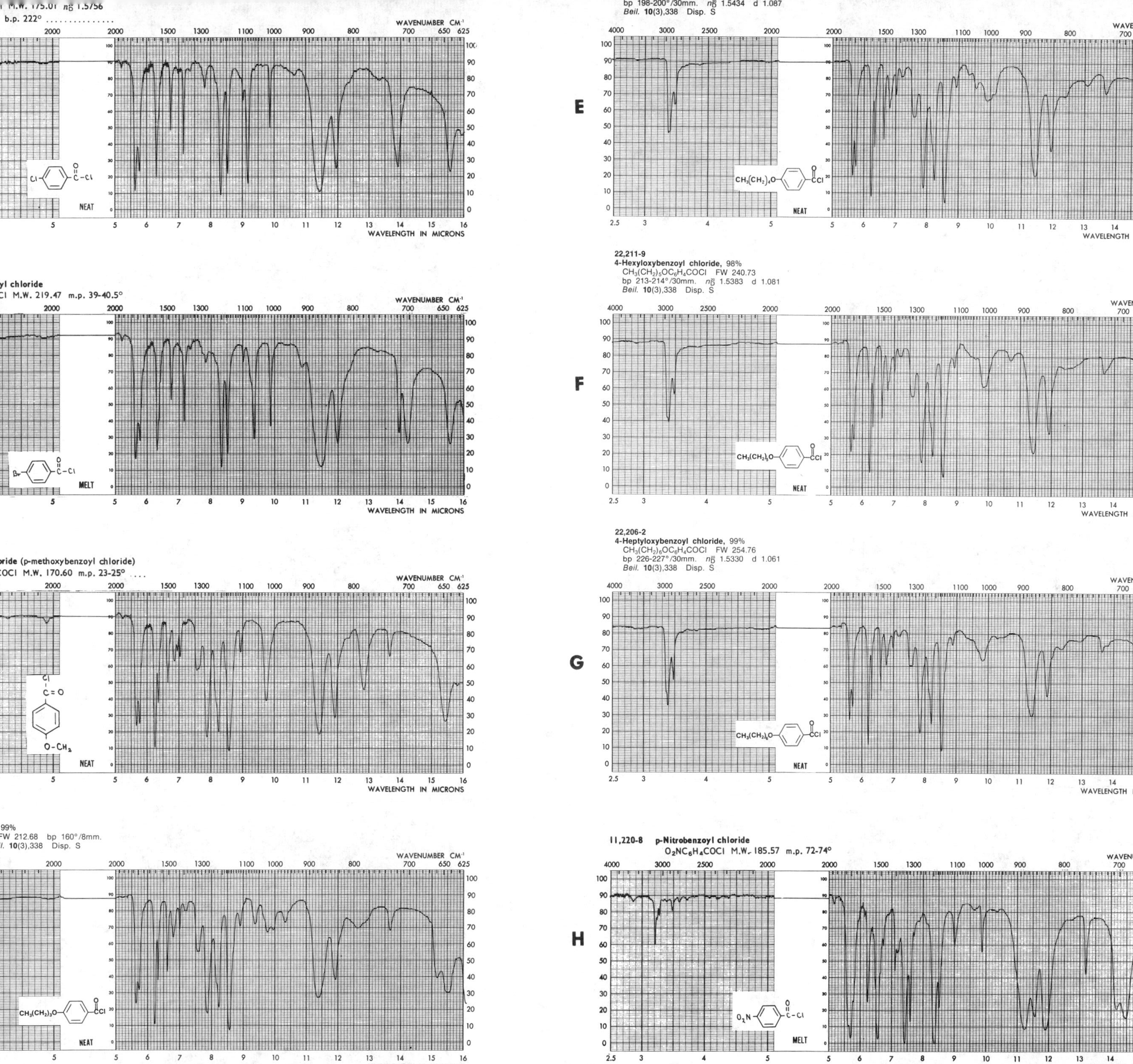

A

16,404-6
p-(Chloroformyl)-phenyl methyl carbonate, tech.
$ClCOC_6H_4OCO_2CH_3$
M.W. 214.6 m.p. 77-79° *CORROSIVE*

NUJOL MULL

B

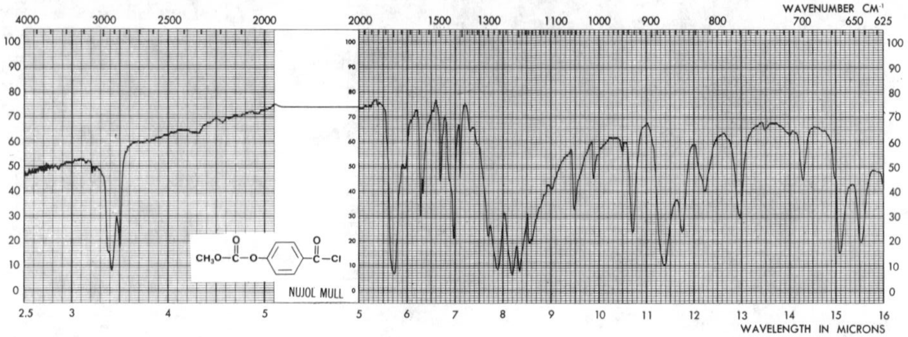

12,482-6 **4-Cyanobenzoyl chloride**
NCC_6H_4COCl M.W. 165.58 m.p. 70-71°

MELT

C

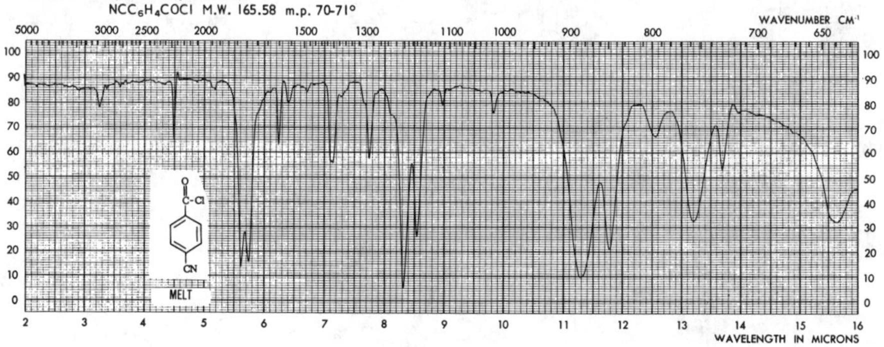

18,751-8
2,6-Dichlorobenzoyl chloride, 99%
$Cl_2C_6H_3COCl$ FW 209.46 bp 142-143°/21mm.
n_D^{20} 1.5608 *Beil.* 9,343 Disp. I

NEAT

D

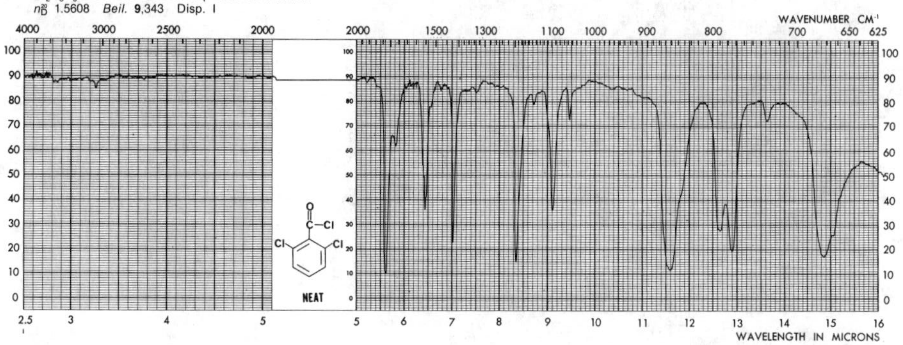

11,194-5 **3,4-Dichlorobenzoyl chloride**
$Cl_2C_6H_3COCl$ M.W. 209.46 m.p. 24-26°

E

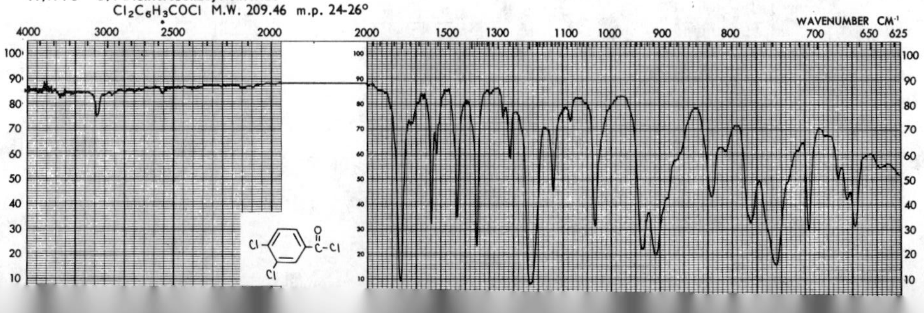

11,193-7 **2,4-Dichlorobenzoyl chloride**
$Cl_2C_6H_3COCl$ M.W. 209.46 n_D^{20} 1.5895
m.p. 15-18°

NEAT

F

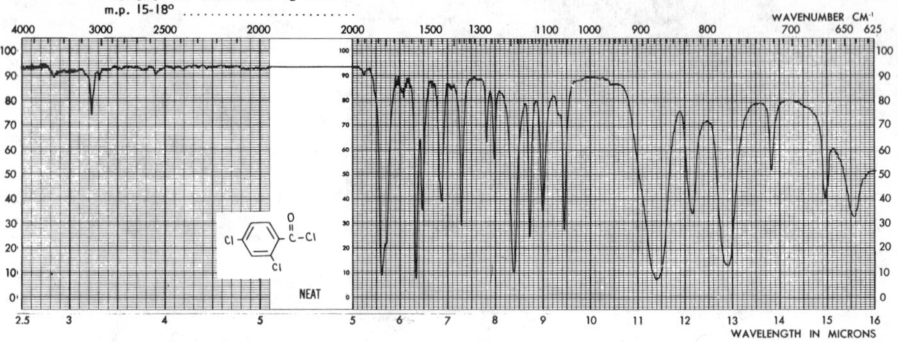

16,171-3
3,5-Dimethoxybenzoyl chloride, 97%
$(CH_3O)_2C_6H_3COCl$
M.W. 200.62 m.p. 26-27° b.p. 157

NEAT

G

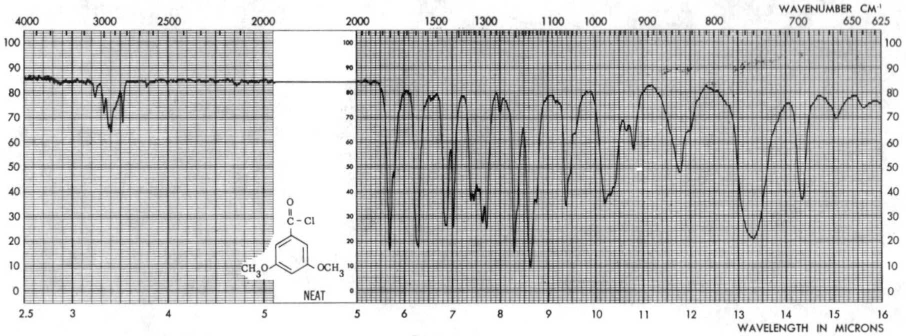

T6980-9 **3,4,5-Trimethoxybenzoyl chloride**
$(CH_3O)_3C_6H_2COCl$ M.W. 230.65
m.p. 80-81°

NUJOL MULL

H

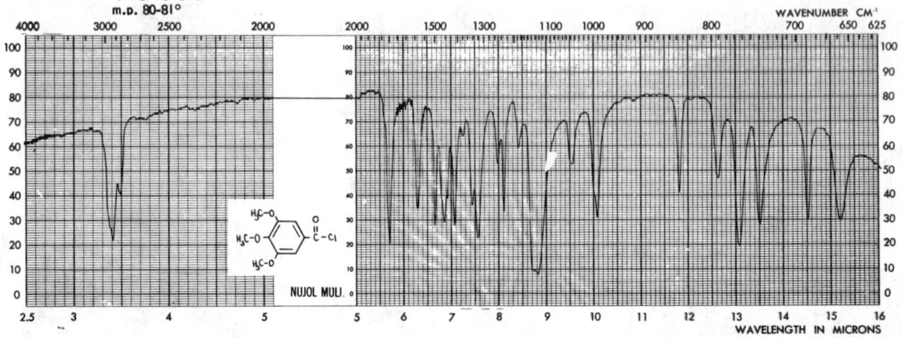

15,627-2
3,5-Dinitrobenzoyl chloride, 98+%
$(O_2N)_2C_6H_3COCl$
M.W. 230.56 m.p. 69-71° b.p. 196°/11mm.
Beil. 9,414 Fieser 1,320 *LACHRYMATOR*

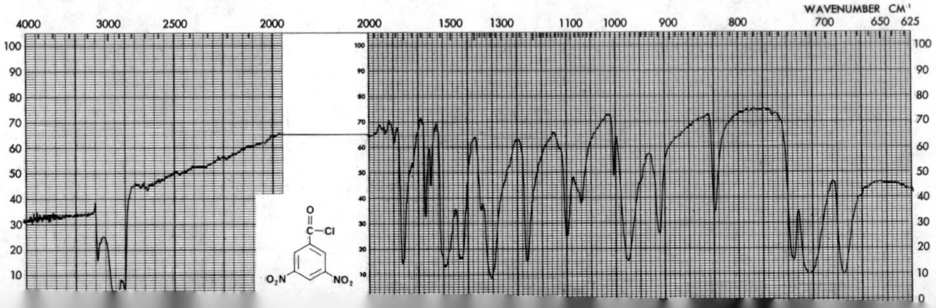

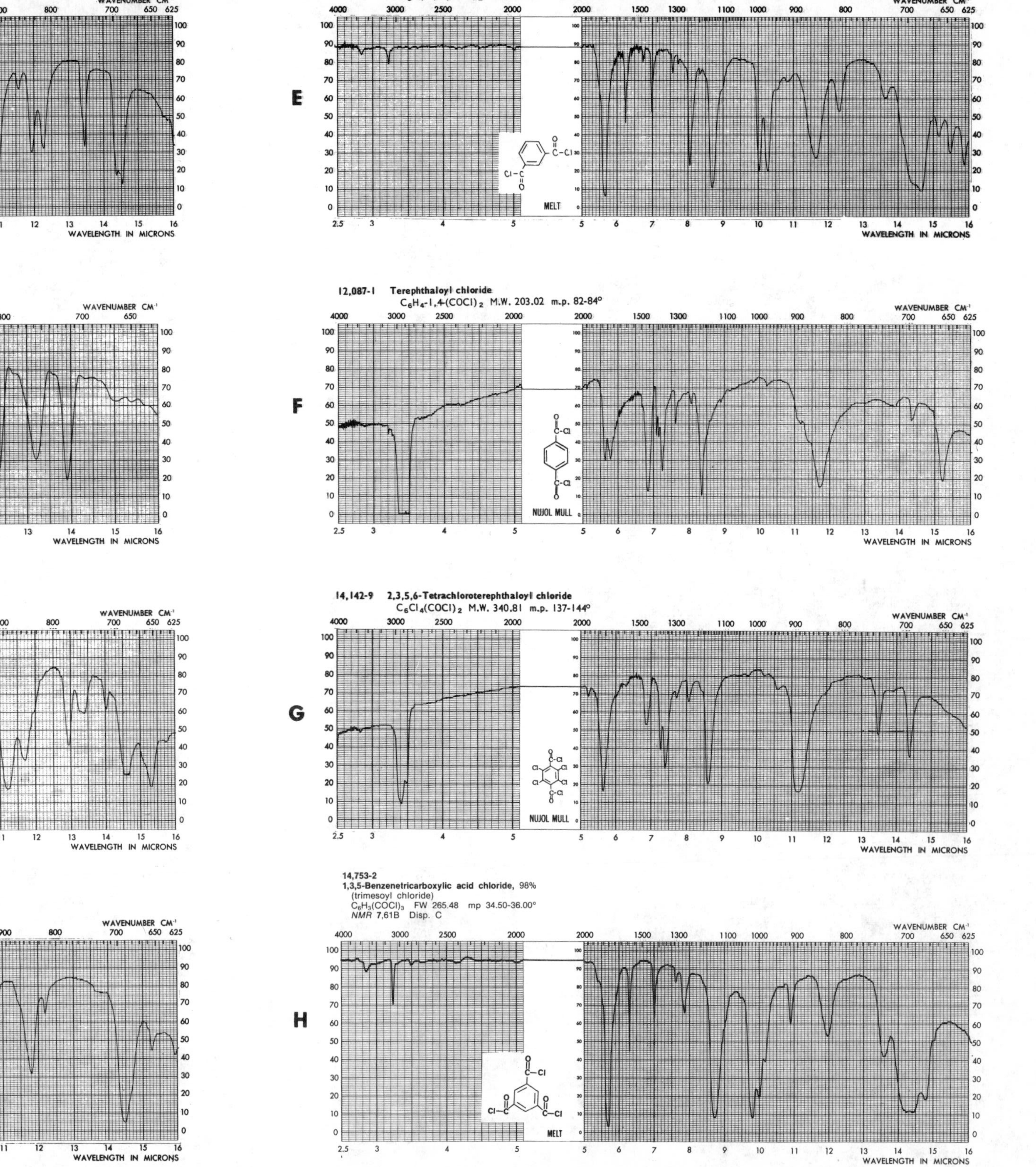
A
M.W. 210.58 m.p. 65-70°
NUJOL MULL
B
10,377-2 Pentafluorobenzoyl chloride
C_6F_5COCl M.W. 230.52 n_D^{20} 1.4536
NEAT
C
P4040-9 o-Phthaloyl dichloride (phthaloyl chloride)
$C_6H_4(COCl)_2$ M.W. 203.02 n_D^{20} 1.5684 b.p. 269-271°
NEAT
D
I-1940-3 Isophthaloyl dichloride
C_6H_4-1,3-$(COCl)_2$ M.W. 203.02 m.p. 43-44°
NUJOL MULL
E
C_6H_4-1,3-$(COCl)_2$ M.W. 203.02 m.p. 43-44°
MELT
F
12,087-1 Terephthaloyl chloride
C_6H_4-1,4-$(COCl)_2$ M.W. 203.02 m.p. 82-84°
NUJOL MULL
G
14,142-9 2,3,5,6-Tetrachloroterephthaloyl chloride
$C_6Cl_4(COCl)_2$ M.W. 340.81 m.p. 137-144°
NUJOL MULL
H
14,753-2
1,3,5-Benzenetricarboxylic acid chloride, 98%
(trimesoyl chloride)
$C_6H_3(COCl)_3$ FW 265.48 mp 34.50-36.00°
NMR 7,61B Disp. C
MELT
WAVENUMBER CM⁻¹
WAVELENGTH IN MICRONS

ALDRICH

AROMATIC ACID HALIDES

A

16,114-4
4-Biphenylcarbonyl chloride, 97%
$C_6H_5C_6H_4COCl$
M.W. 216.67 m.p. 110-112° Beil. **9**(1),280

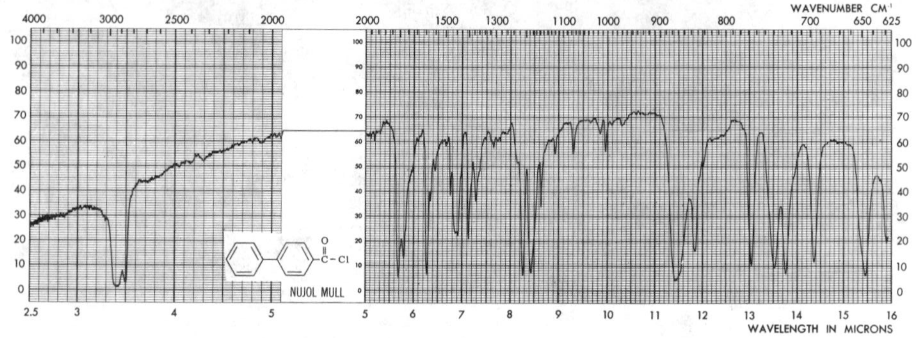

NUJOL MULL

B

11,993-8 **Benzyl chloroformate** (carbobenzoxy chloride), **tech.**
$ClCO_2CH_2C_6H_5$ M.W. 170.60
n_D^{20} 1.5160

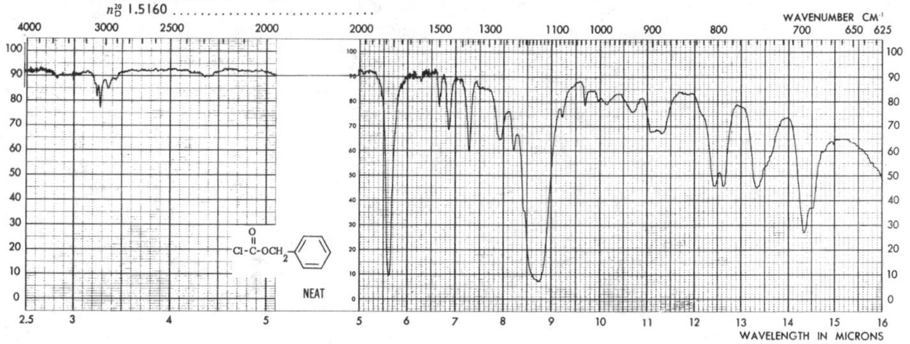

NEAT

C

19,562-6
2,4,5-Trichlorophenyl chloroformate
$ClCO_2C_6H_2Cl_3$ FW 259.91 mp 62-65° Disp. C

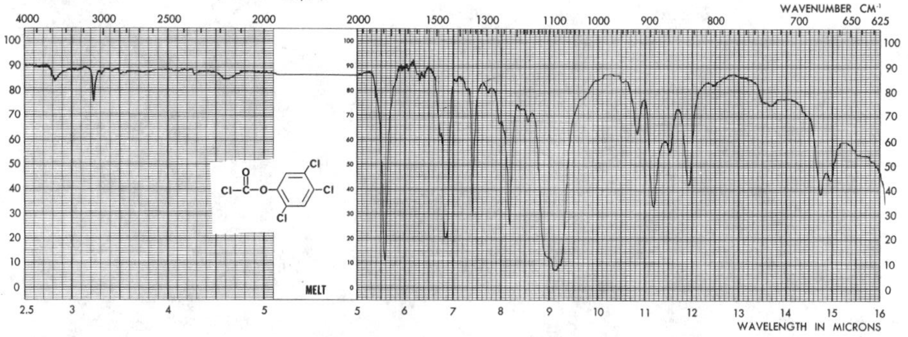

MELT

D

16,021-0
p-Nitrophenyl chloroformate, 97%
$ClCO_2C_6H_4NO_2$
M.W. 201.57 m.p. 77-79° b.p. 159-162°/19mm.
Beil. **6**(1),120 Fieser **2**,297 *IRRITANT*

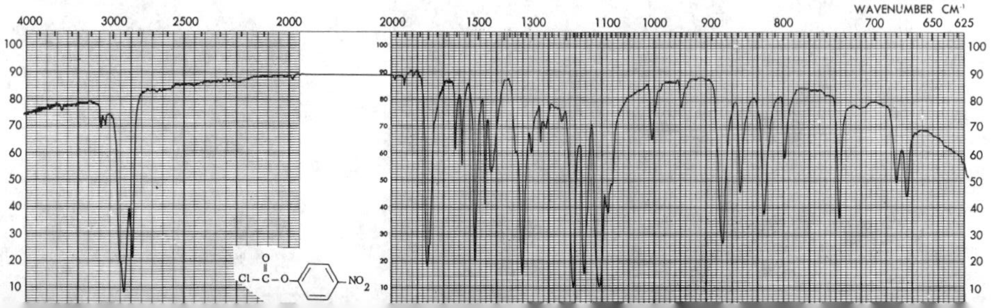

E

22,280-1
***p*-Nitrobenzyl chloroformate**
$ClCO_2CH_2C_6H_4NO_2$ FW 215.60 mp 32-34°
Beil. **6**,452 Disp. S

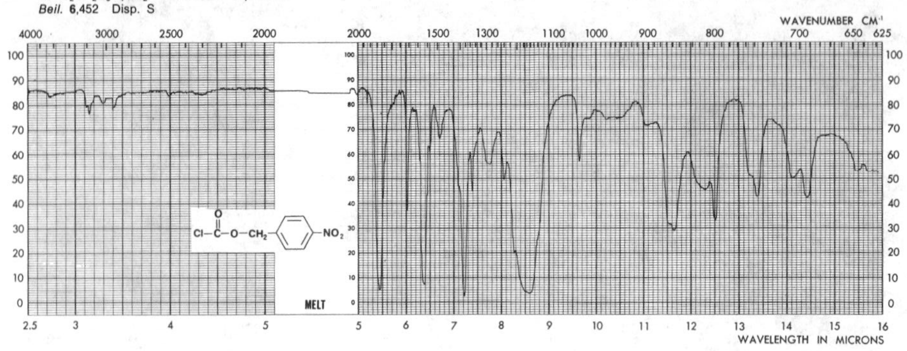

MELT

F

15,359-1 **Diphenylcarbamyl chloride** (diphenylcarbamoyl chloride)
$(C_6H_5)_2NCOCl$ M.W. 231.68 m.p. 82-84°

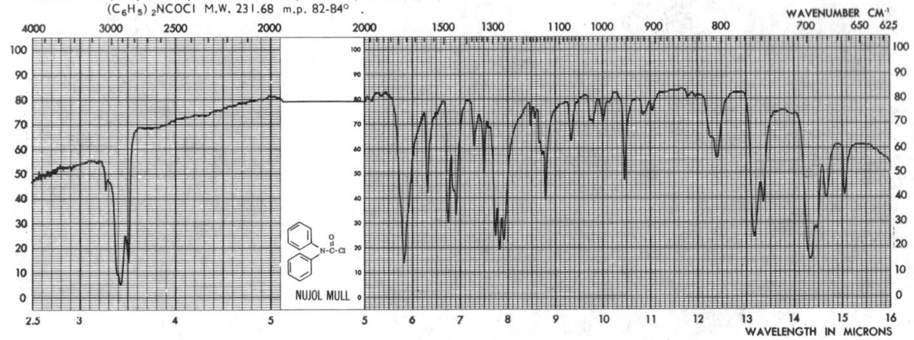

NUJOL MULL

G

15,368-0 **Phenothiazine-10-carbonyl chloride**
M.W. 261.73 m.p. 168-170°

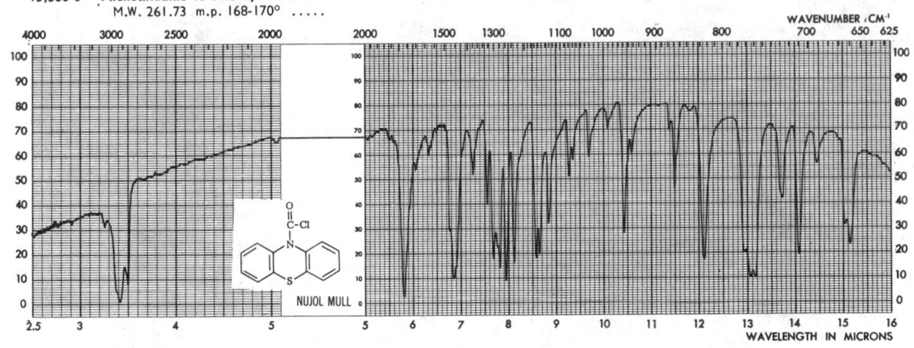

NUJOL MULL

ALDRICH

AROMATIC AMIDES

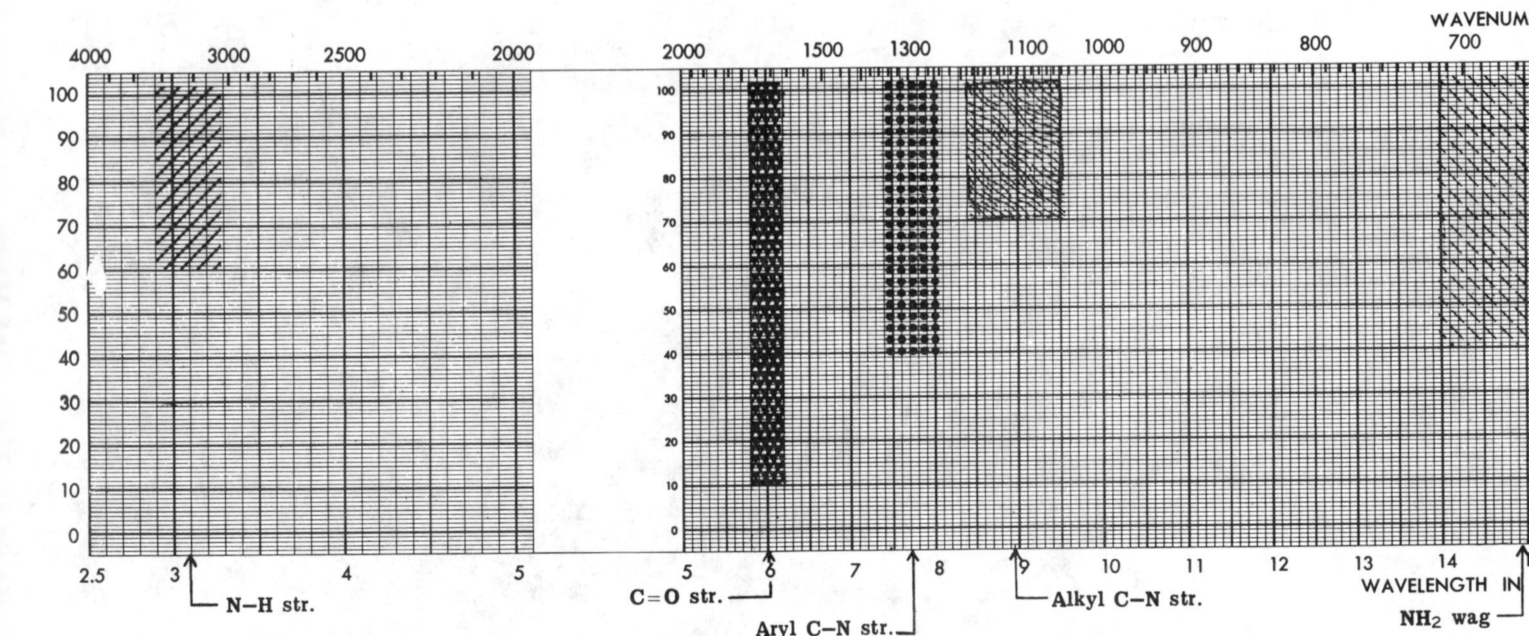

The amide absorptions described in the non-aromatic amide section remain essentially unaltered in the aromatic amides. The effect of conjugation on the position of the amide carbonyl is negligible. With the substitution of an aromatic ring directly onto the nitrogen of the amide, an absorption between 7.5 and 8 μ (1335 – 1250 cm^{-1}) can be seen and is due to the aromatic carbon-nitrogen stretch vibration.

Unlike β-diketones and β-keto esters, the β-keto-amides (1074H—1076E) are mainly in the keto form.

The substitution patterns between 11 and 15 μ (910 – 665 cm^{-1}) are not as prone to disruption by the amide carbonyl as they are by other carbonyls.

A

HCONHC$_6$H$_5$ M.W. 121.14 m.p. 46-48°

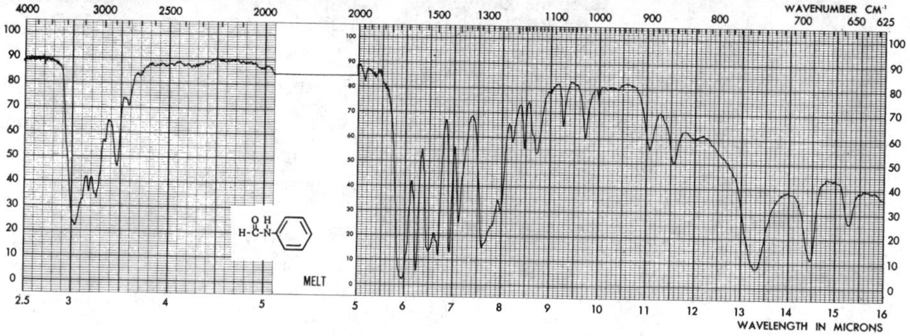

MELT

B

15,284-6 **N-Benzylformamide**

HCONHCH$_2$C$_6$H$_5$ M.W. 135.17 m.p. 60-61°

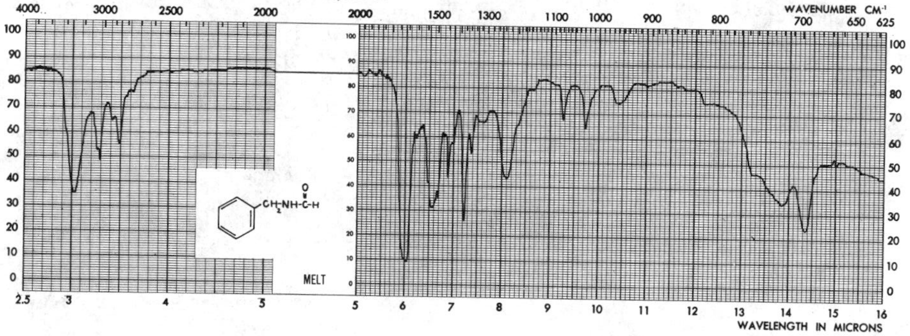

MELT

C

M4680-2 **N-Methylformanilide**

HCON(CH$_3$)C$_6$H$_5$ M.W. 135.17 n_D^{20} 1.5593

m.p. 14-15° b.p. 243-244°

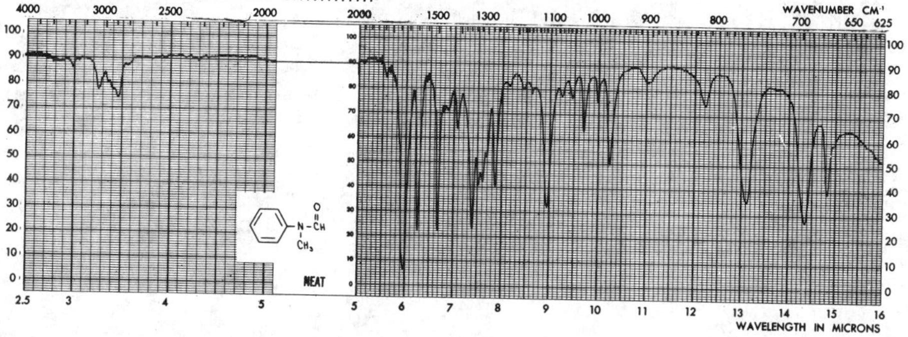

NEAT

D

D20,760-8 **N,N-Diphenylformamide**

HCON(C$_6$H$_5$)$_2$ M.W. 197.24 m.p. 71-72°

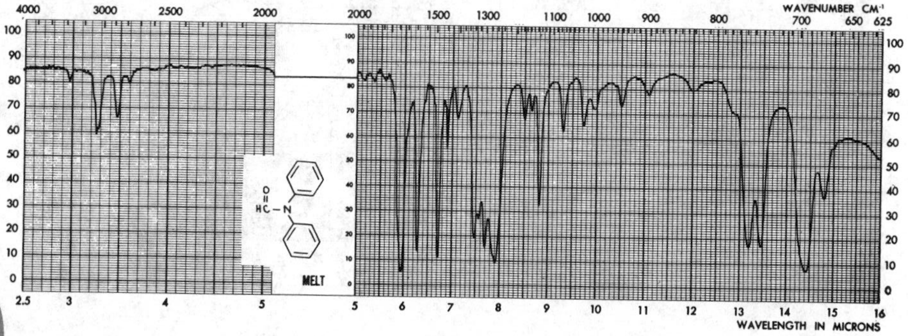

MELT

E

11,432-4 **Acetanilide, zone refined**

CH$_3$CONHC$_6$H$_5$ M.W. 135.17 m.p. 114.29°

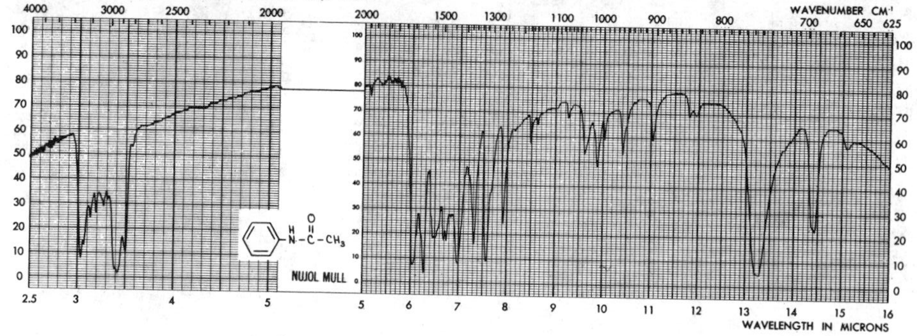

NUJOL MULL

F

C1961-9 **α-Chloroacetanilide**

ClCH$_2$CONHC$_6$H$_5$ M.W. 169.61 m.p. 134-136°

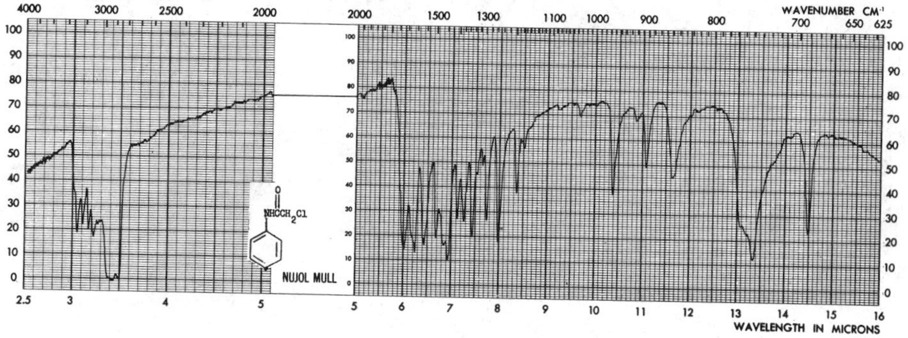

NUJOL MULL

G

13,762-6 **N-Ethylacetanilide**

CH$_3$CON(C$_2$H$_5$)C$_6$H$_5$ M.W. 163.22

m.p. 53-55°

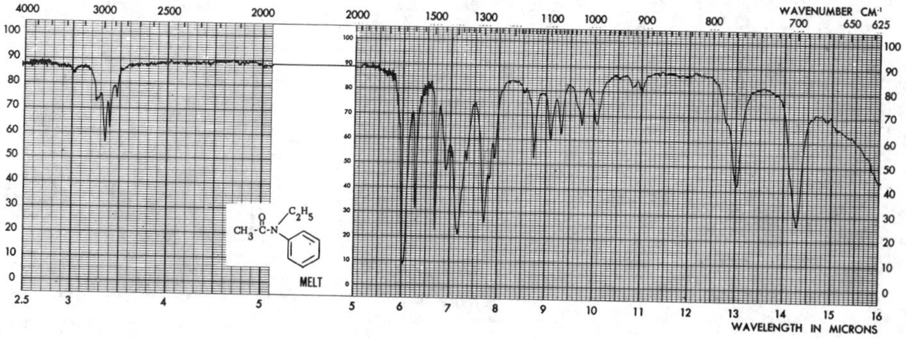

MELT

H

12,271-8 **4-(N-Acetylanilino)-piperidine [N-(4-piperidyl)-acetanilide]**

M.W. 218.30 m.p. 128-130°

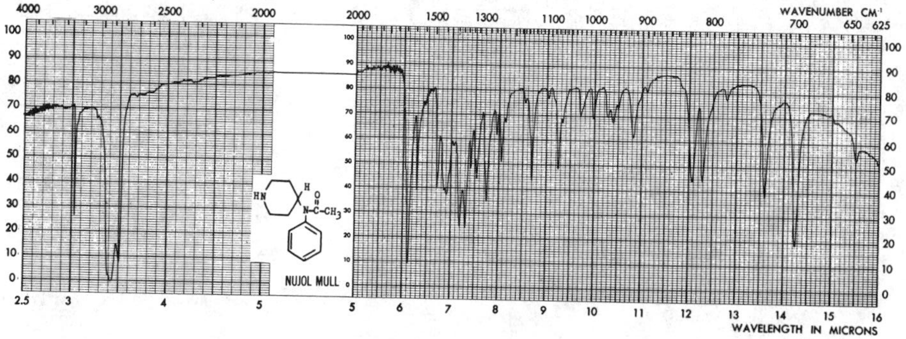

NUJOL MULL

AROMATIC AMIDES

A

P5150-8 **4-(N-Propionylanilino)-piperidine** (N-4-piperidylpropionanilide)
M.W. 232.33 m.p. 88-91°

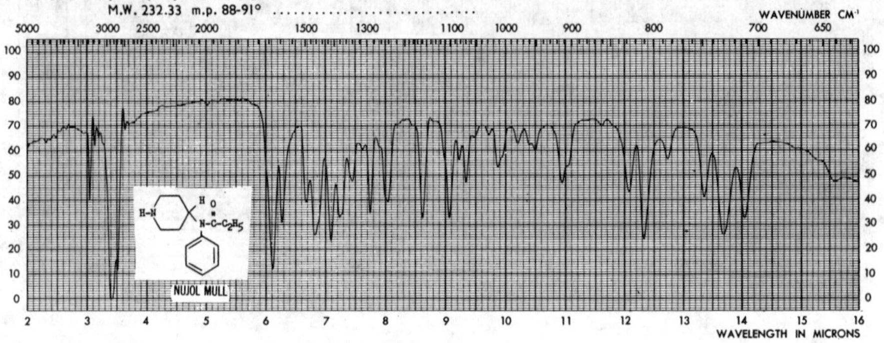

NUJOL MULL

B

15,059-2 **N-(Triphenylmethyl)-formamide** (N-tritylformamide)
$HCONHC(C_6H_5)_3$ M.W. 287.36 m.p. 202-204°

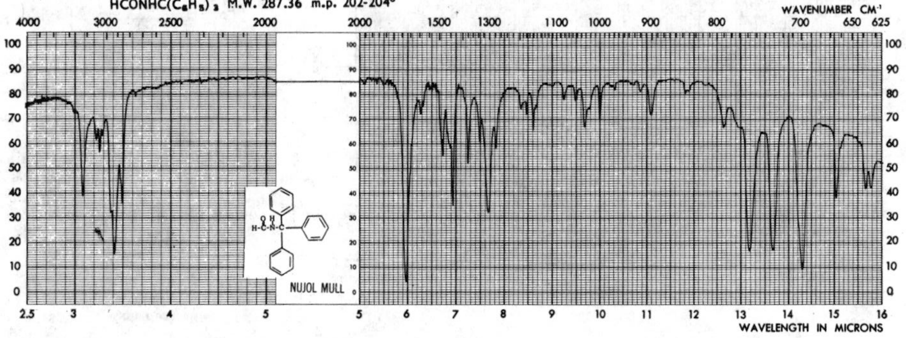

NUJOL MULL

C

A700-0 **2-Acetamidophenol** (o-hydroxyacetanilide)
$CH_3CONHC_6H_4OH$ M.W. 151.17
m.p. 203-204°

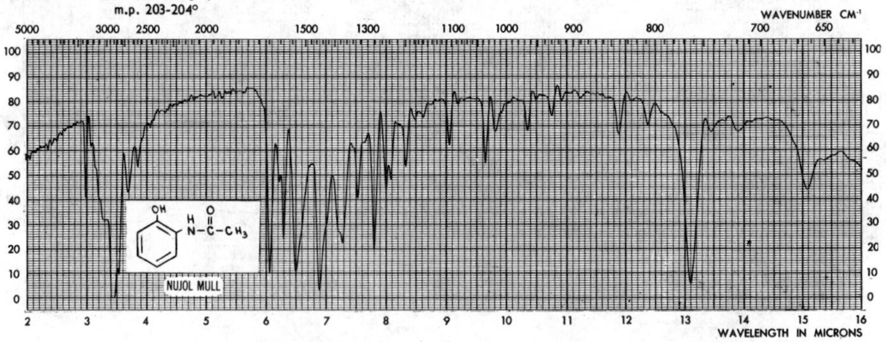

NUJOL MULL

D

11,806-0 **2-Chloro-2'-nitroacetanilide**
$ClCH_2CONHC_6H_4NO_2$ M.W. 214.61
m.p. 85-88.5°

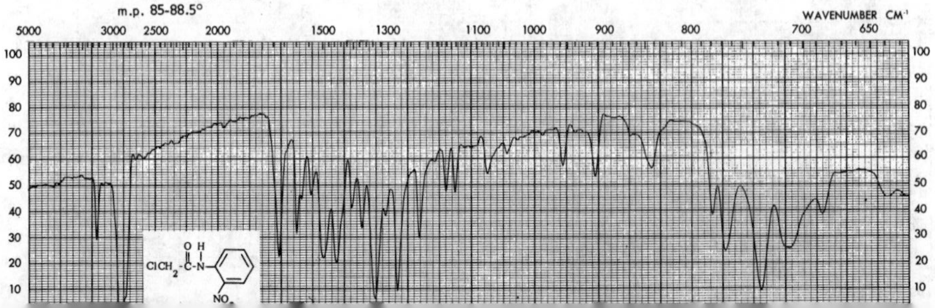

E

A1265-8 **N-Acetylanthranilic acid** (o-acetamidobenzoic acid)
$2\text{-}(CH_3CONH)C_6H_4CO_2H$ M.W. 179.18
m.p. 184.5-187°

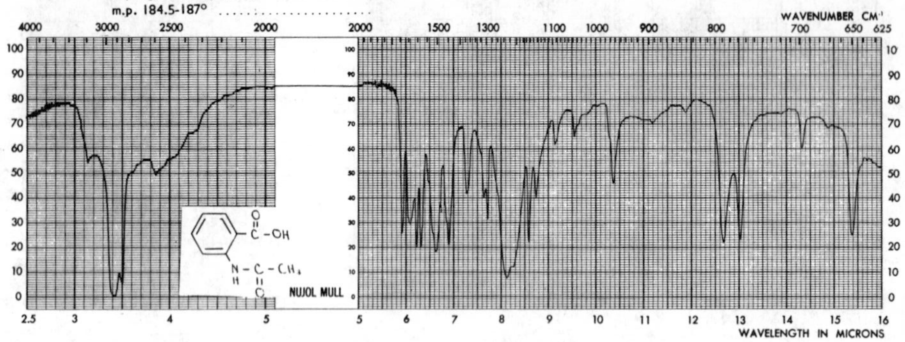

NUJOL MULL

F

A220-3 **3-Acetamidobenzotrifluoride** (α,α,α-trifluoro-m-acetotoluidide)
$CH_3CONHC_6H_4CF_3$ M.W. 203.16 m.p. 103-106°

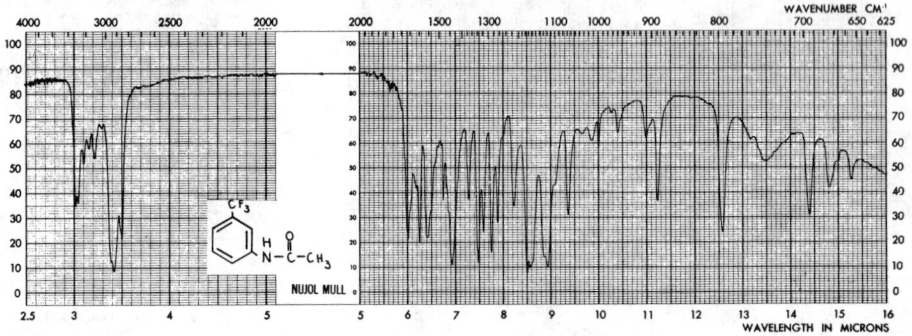

NUJOL MULL

G

A720-5
3-Acetamidophenol (m-hydroxyacetanilide)
$CH_3CONHC_6H_4OH$
M.W. 151.17 m.p. 146 - 149° Beil. **13**,415

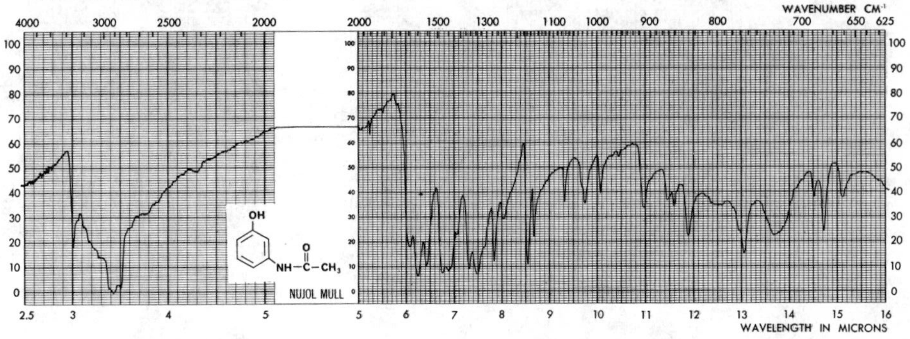

NUJOL MULL

H

13,976-9 **3'-Nitropalmitanilide, tech.**
$CH_3(CH_2)_{14}CONHC_6H_4NO_2$ M.W. 376.54
m.p. 70-73°

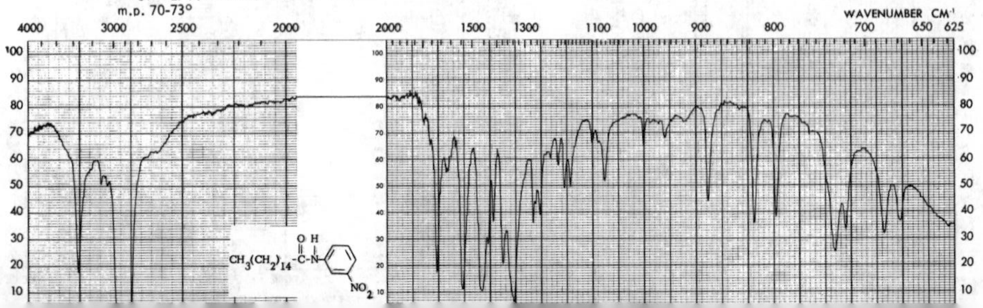

WAVENUMBER CM⁻¹

WAVELENGTH IN MICRONS

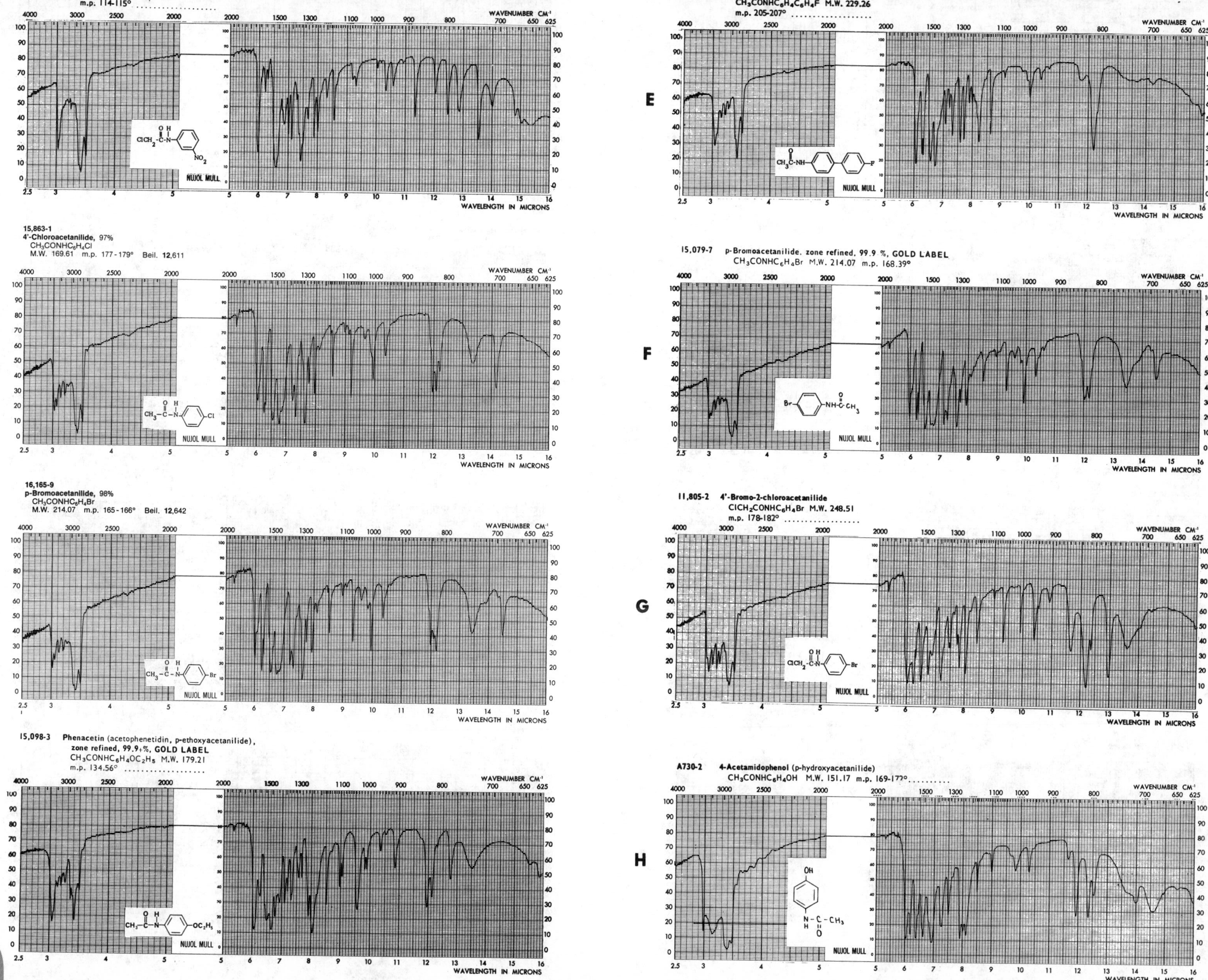

A
$ClCH_2CONHC_6H_4NO_2$ M.W. 214.61
m.p. 114-115°

15,863-1
B
4'-Chloroacetanilide, 97%
$CH_3CONHC_6H_4Cl$
M.W. 169.61 m.p. 177-179° Beil. 12,611

16,165-9
C
p-Bromoacetanilide, 98%
$CH_3CONHC_6H_4Br$
M.W. 214.07 m.p. 165-166° Beil. 12,642

15,098-3
D
Phenacetin (acetophenetidin, p-ethoxyacetanilide), zone refined, 99.9+%, GOLD LABEL
$CH_3CONHC_6H_4OC_2H_5$ M.W. 179.21
m.p. 134.56°

E
4'-(p-Fluorophenyl)-acetanilide
$CH_3CONHC_6H_4C_6H_4F$ M.W. 229.26
m.p. 205-207°

15,079-7
F
p-Bromoacetanilide, zone refined, 99.9 %, GOLD LABEL
$CH_3CONHC_6H_4Br$ M.W. 214.07 m.p. 168.39°

11,805-2
G
4'-Bromo-2-chloroacetanilide
$ClCH_2CONHC_6H_4Br$ M.W. 248.51
m.p. 178-182°

A730-2
H
4-Acetamidophenol (p-hydroxyacetanilide)
$CH_3CONHC_6H_4OH$ M.W. 151.17 m.p. 169-172°

AROMATIC AMIDES

A

A820-1 **4-Acetamidothiophenol** (p-mercaptoacetanilide)
$CH_3CONHC_6H_4SH$ M.W. 167.23 m.p. 150-153°

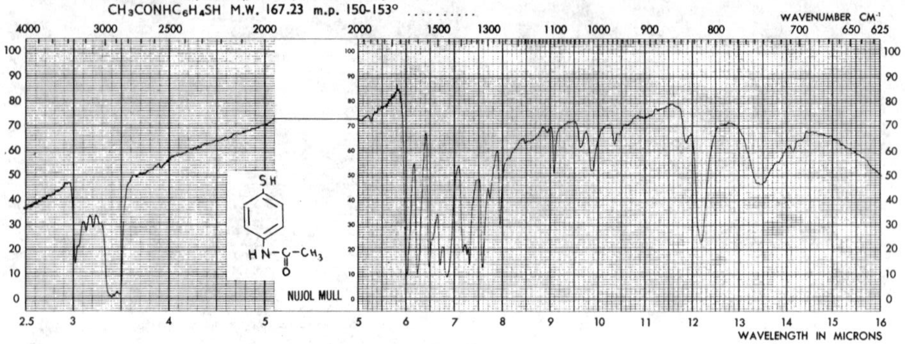

NUJOL MULL

B

10,052-8 **p-Aminoacetanilide, tech.**
$CH_3CONHC_6H_4NH_2$ M.W. 150.18
m.p. 165-168°

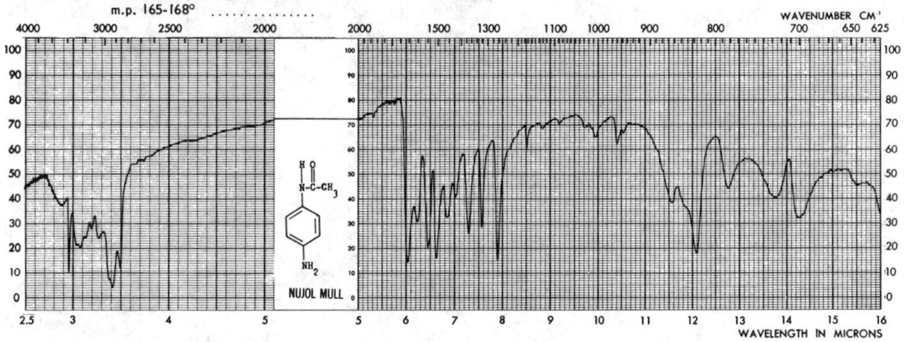

NUJOL MULL

C

21,688-7
4'-Aminooxanilic acid, 99%
$H_2NC_6H_4NHCOCO_2H$ FW 180.16 mp 270°
Beil. **13**,99 Disp. C

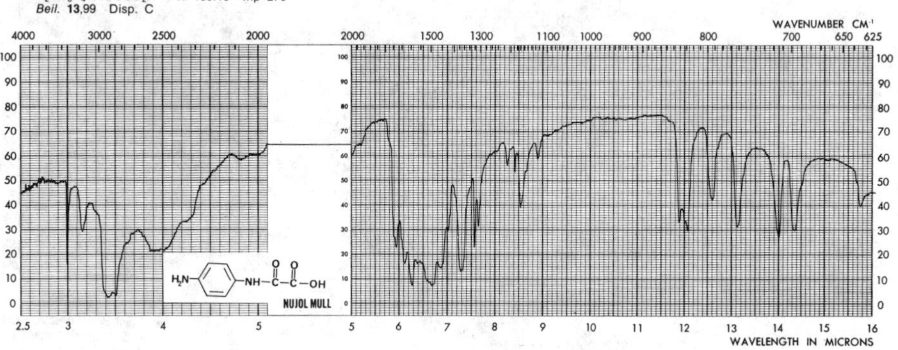

NUJOL MULL

D

13,890-8 **4'-Diethylaminoacetanilide**
$CH_3CONHC_6H_4N(C_2H_5)_2$ M.W. 206.28
m.p. 104-106°

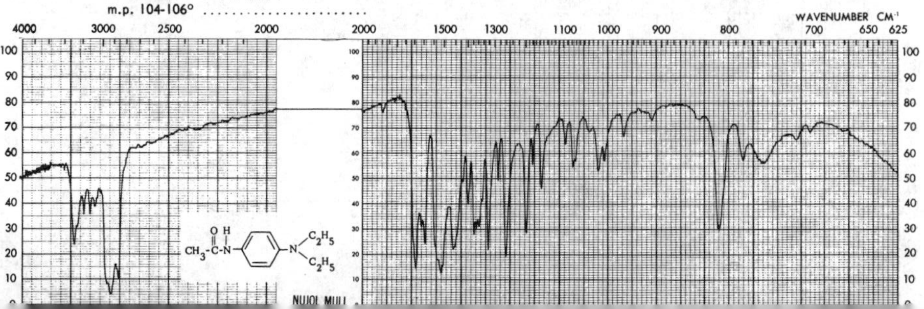

NUJOL MULL

E

19,492-1
2-Chloro-2',6'-acetoxylidide, 99%
$ClCH_2CONHC_6H_3(CH_3)_2$ FW 197.67 mp 150-151°
Beil. **12**(3),2464 Disp. C

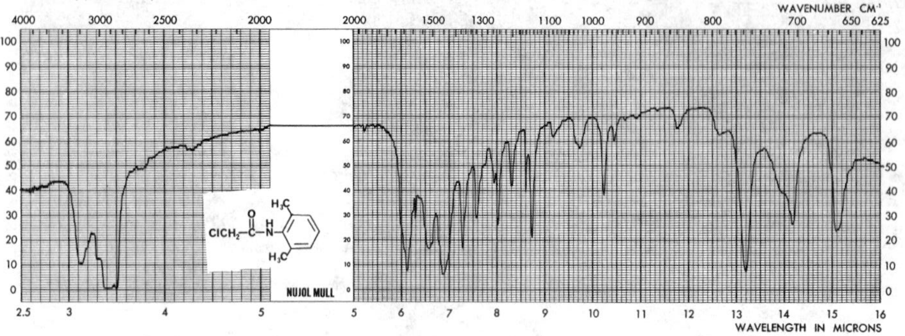

NUJOL MULL

F

12,635-7 **2',6'-Dimethylacetanilide** (2',6'-acetoxylidide)
$CH_3CONHC_6H_3(CH_3)_2$ M.W. 163.22 m.p. 178-181°

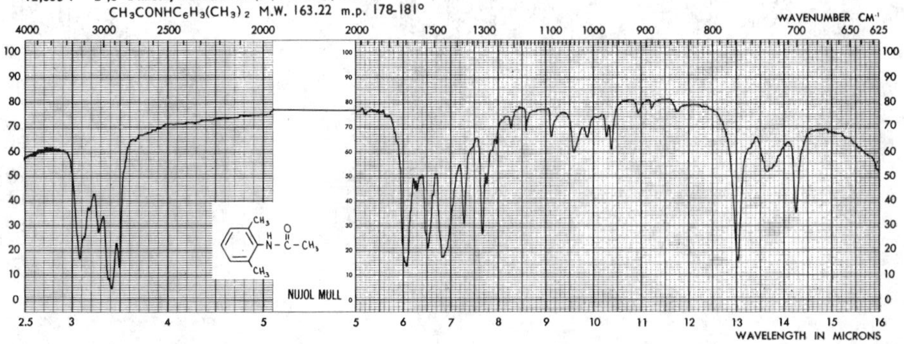

NUJOL MULL

G

13,534-8 **6'-Chloro-2-(2-diethylaminoethoxy)-o-acetotoluidide hydrochloride**
$(C_2H_5)_2NCH_2CH_2OCH_2CONHC_6H_3(CH_3)Cl{\cdot}HCl$ M.W. 335.28
m.p. 129-131°

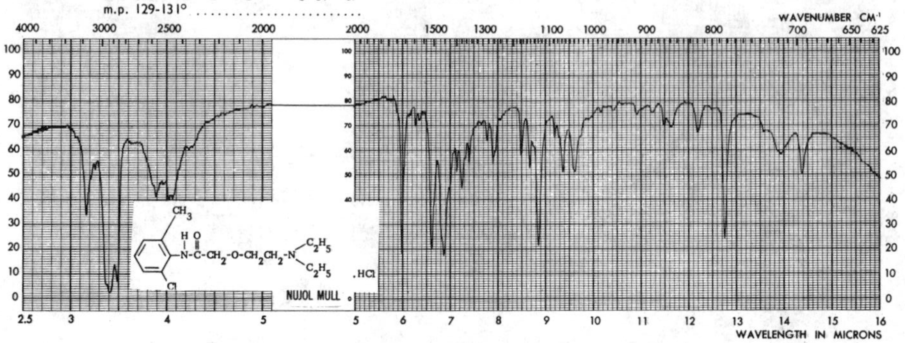

NUJOL MULL

H

B7180-2 **2'-Bromo-4'-methylacetanilide**
$BrC_6H_3(CH_3)NHCOCH_3$ M.W. 228.09 m.p. 111.5-114°

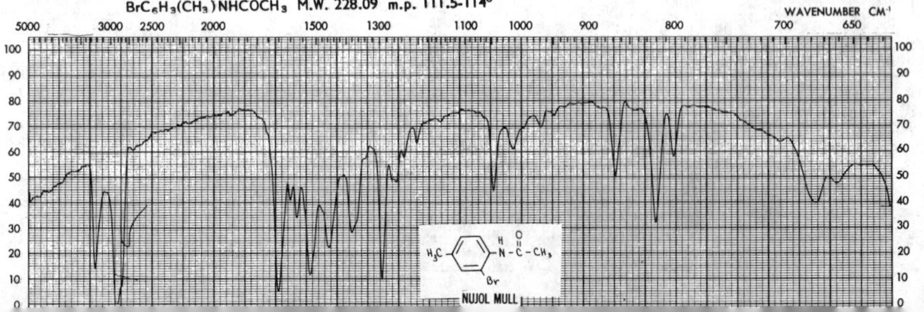

NUJOL MULL

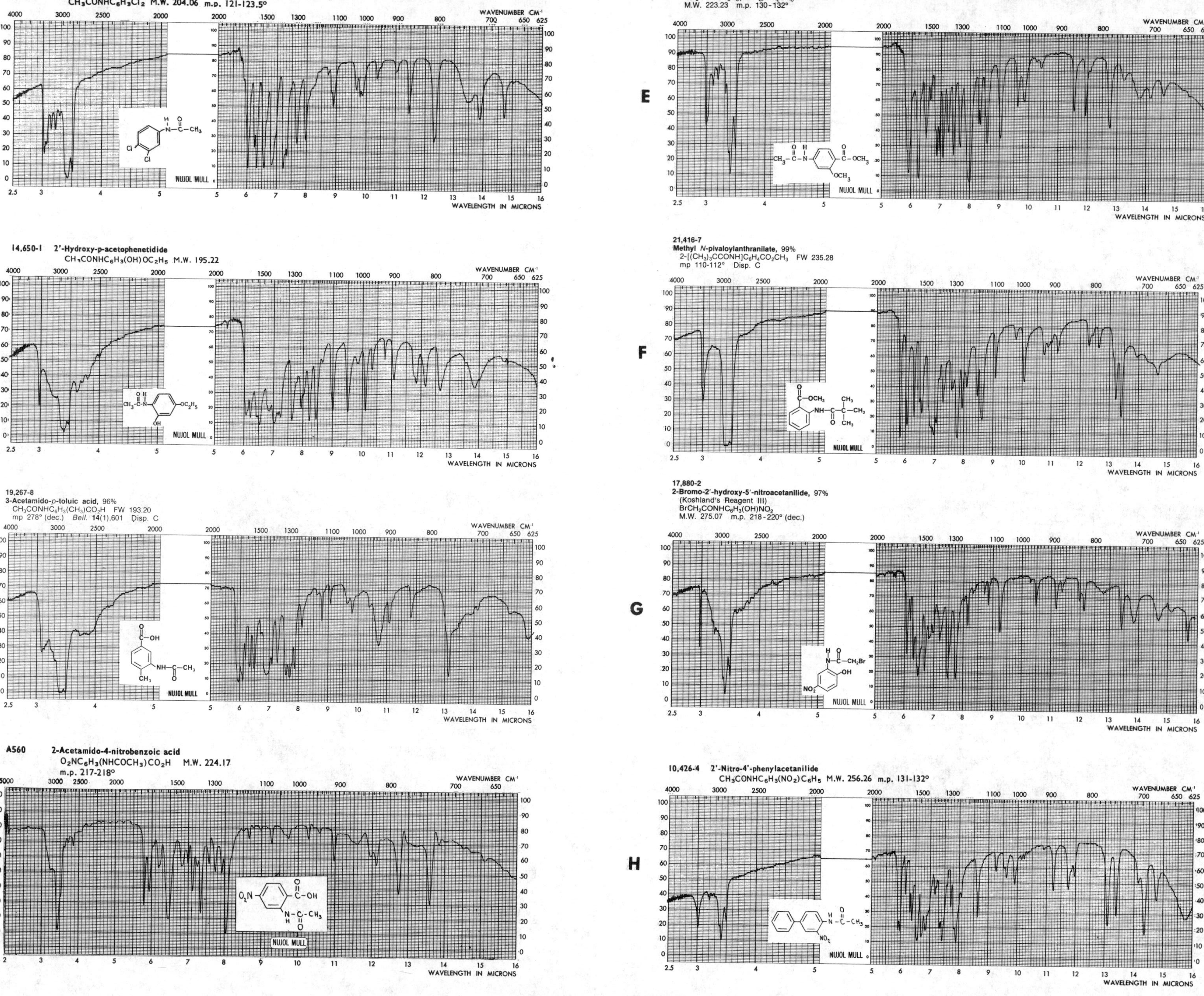
D5460 3',4'-Dichloroacetanilide
$CH_3CONHC_6H_3Cl_2$ M.W. 204.06 m.p. 121-123.5°
14,650-1 2'-Hydroxy-p-acetophenetidide
$CH_3CONHC_6H_3(OH)OC_2H_5$ M.W. 195.22
19,267-8
3-Acetamido-p-toluic acid, 96%
$CH_3CONHC_6H_3(CH_3)CO_2H$ FW 193.20
mp 278° (dec.) Beil. 14(1),601 Disp. C
A560 2-Acetamido-4-nitrobenzoic acid
$O_2NC_6H_3(NHCOCH_3)CO_2H$ M.W. 224.17
m.p. 217-218°
Methyl 4-acetamido-2-methoxybenzoate, 99%
$CH_3CONHC_6H_3(OCH_3)CO_2CH_3$
M.W. 223.23 m.p. 130-132°
21,416-7
Methyl N-pivaloylanthranilate, 99%
$2-[(CH_3)_3CCONH]C_6H_4CO_2CH_3$ FW 235.28
mp 110-112° Disp. C
17,880-2
2-Bromo-2'-hydroxy-5'-nitroacetanilide, 97%
(Koshland's Reagent III)
$BrCH_2CONHC_6H_3(OH)NO_2$
M.W. 275.07 m.p. 218-220° (dec.)
10,426-4 2'-Nitro-4'-phenylacetanilide
$CH_3CONHC_6H_3(NO_2)C_6H_5$ M.W. 256.26 m.p. 131-132°
A
B
C
D
E
F
G
H
WAVENUMBER CM⁻¹
WAVELENGTH IN MICRONS
NUJOL MULL
ALDRICH

A

A495-8
2-Acetamidonaphthalene [N-(2-naphthyl)-acetamide]
$CH_3CONHC_{10}H_7$
M.W. 185.23 m.p. 130-133° Beil. **12**,1284
CARCINOGEN

NUJOL MULL

B

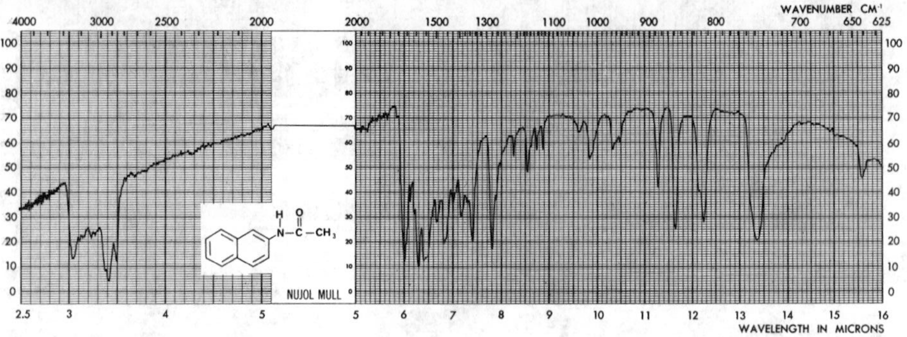

A410-9
2-Acetamidofluorene CAS 53-96-3 [N-(2-fluorenyl)-acetamide]
M.W. 223.28 m.p. 192-196° Beil. **12**,1331
CARCINOGEN

NUJOL MULL

C

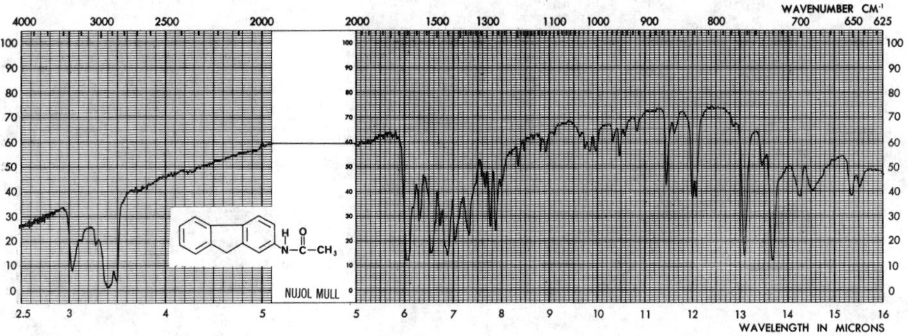

15,562-4 **2'-(o-Chlorobenzoyl)-2,4'-dichloroacetanilide**
$ClCH_2CONHC_6H_3(Cl)COC_6H_4Cl$ M.W. 342.61
m.p. 159-160°

NUJOL MULL

D

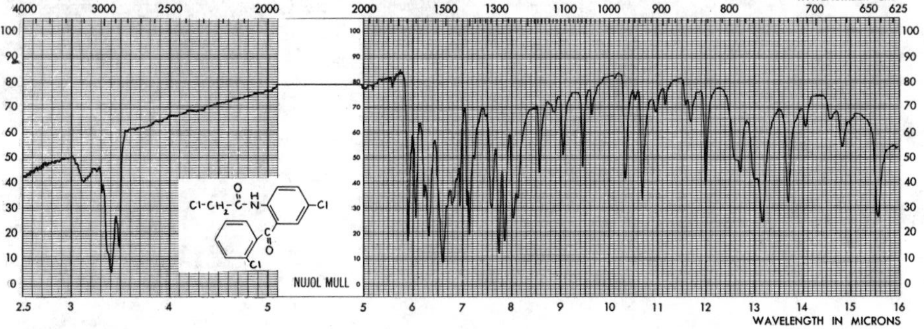

13,064-8 **p-Nitroacetanilide**
$CH_3CONHC_6H_4NO_2$ M.W. 180.16
m.p. 212.5-214.5°

E

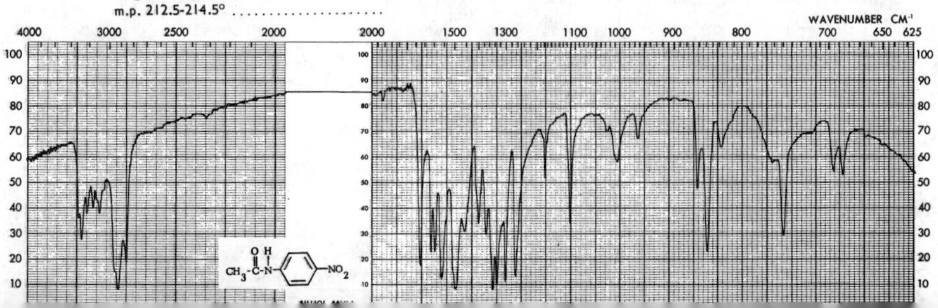

A180-0 **p-Acetamidobenzaldehyde**
$CH_3CONHC_6H_4CHO$ M.W. 163.18
m.p. 154-156°

NUJOL MULL

F

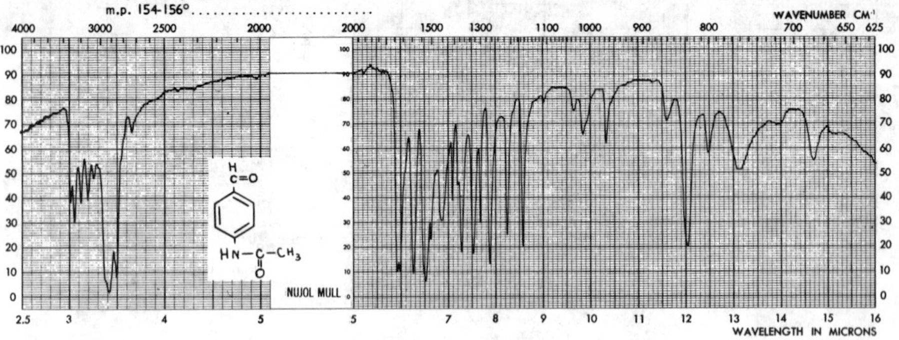

13,333-7 **p-Acetamidobenzoic acid**
$CH_3CONHC_6H_4CO_2H$ M.W. 179.18
m.p. 259-262° (dec.)

NUJOL MULL

G

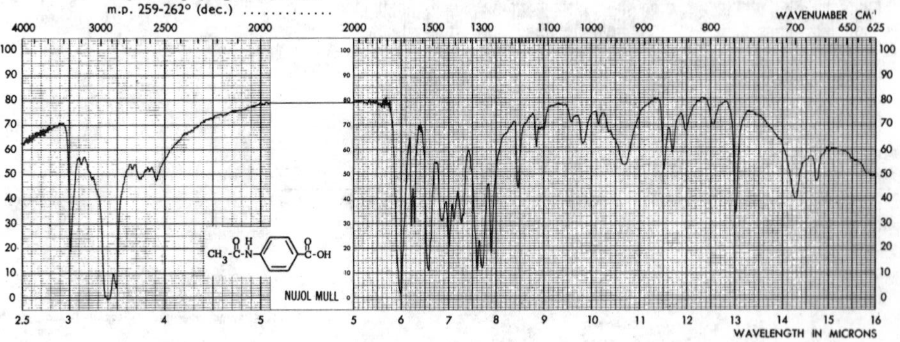

A310-2 **p-Acetamidocinnamic acid**
$CH_3CONHC_6H_4CH{:}CHCO_2H$ M.W. 205.21
m.p. 264° (dec.)

NUJOL MULL

H

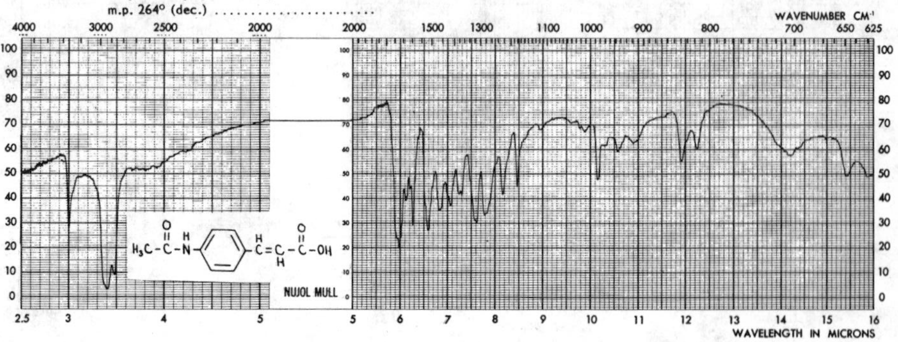

12,266-1 **p-Acetamidophenylmercuric acetate**
$CH_3CO_2HgC_6H_4NHCOCH_3$ M.W. 393.79
m.p. 219-220°

(Each spectrum: WAVENUMBER CM⁻¹ 4000–625; WAVELENGTH IN MICRONS 2.5–16; % transmittance 0–100)

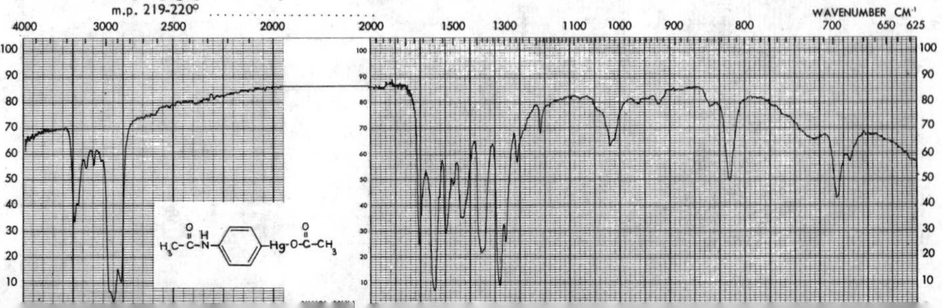

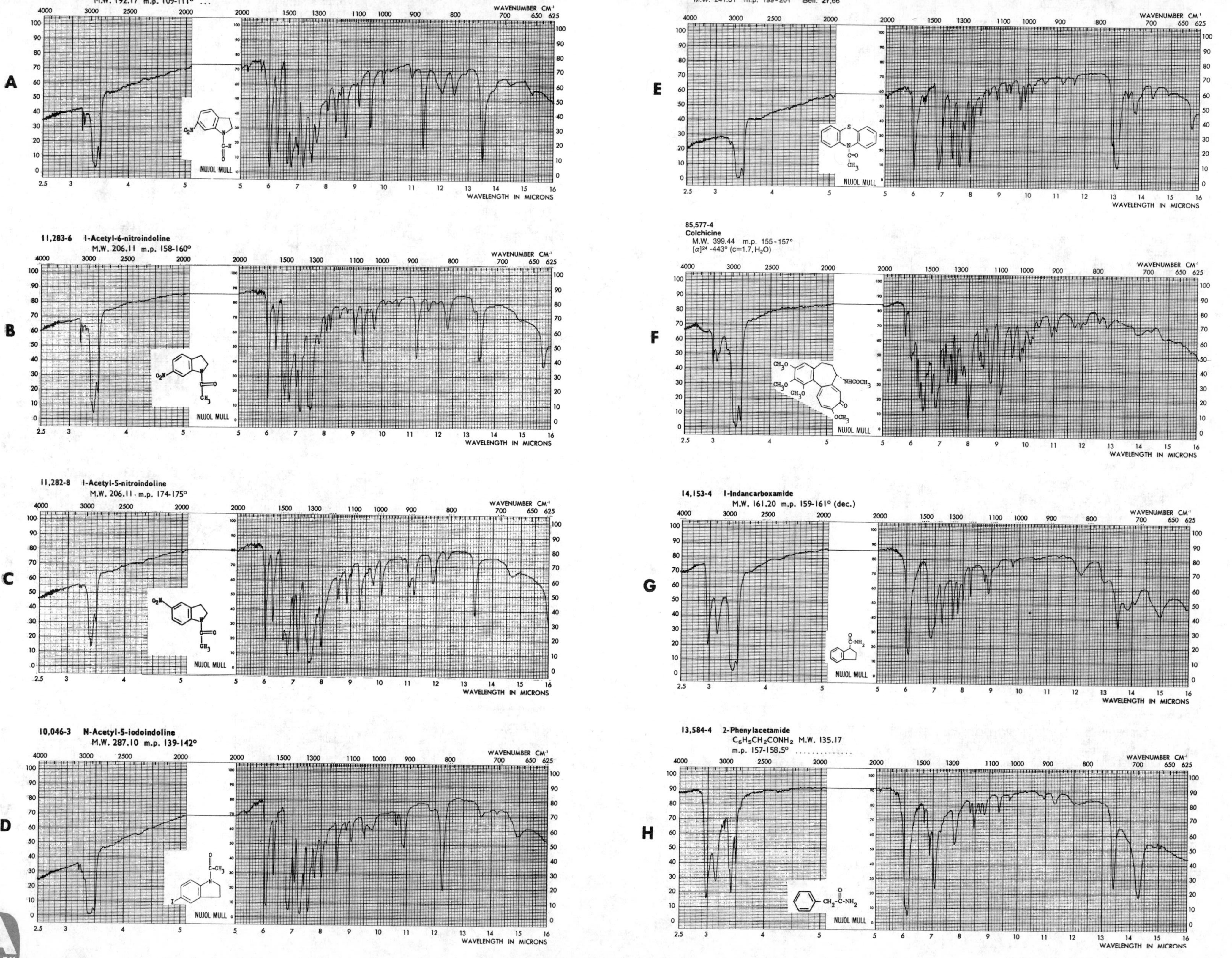

A
10,243-1 6-Nitro-1-indolinecarboxaldehyde
M.W. 192.17 m.p. 109-111° ...
NUJOL MULL
B
11,283-6 1-Acetyl-6-nitroindoline
M.W. 206.11 m.p. 158-160°
NUJOL MULL
C
11,282-8 1-Acetyl-5-nitroindoline
M.W. 206.11 m.p. 174-175°
NUJOL MULL
D
10,046-3 N-Acetyl-5-iodoindoline
M.W. 287.10 m.p. 139-142°
NUJOL MULL
E
10-Acetylphenothiazine, 98%
M.W. 241.31 m.p. 199-201° Beil. 27,66
NUJOL MULL
F
85,577-4
Colchicine
M.W. 399.44 m.p. 155-157°
[α]24 -443° (c=1.7, H2O)
NUJOL MULL
G
14,153-4 1-Indancarboxamide
M.W. 161.20 m.p. 159-161° (dec.)
NUJOL MULL
H
13,584-4 2-Phenylacetamide
C6H5CH2CONH2 M.W. 135.17
m.p. 157-158.5°
NUJOL MULL
WAVENUMBER CM-1
WAVELENGTH IN MICRONS
ALDRICH

AROMATIC AMIDES

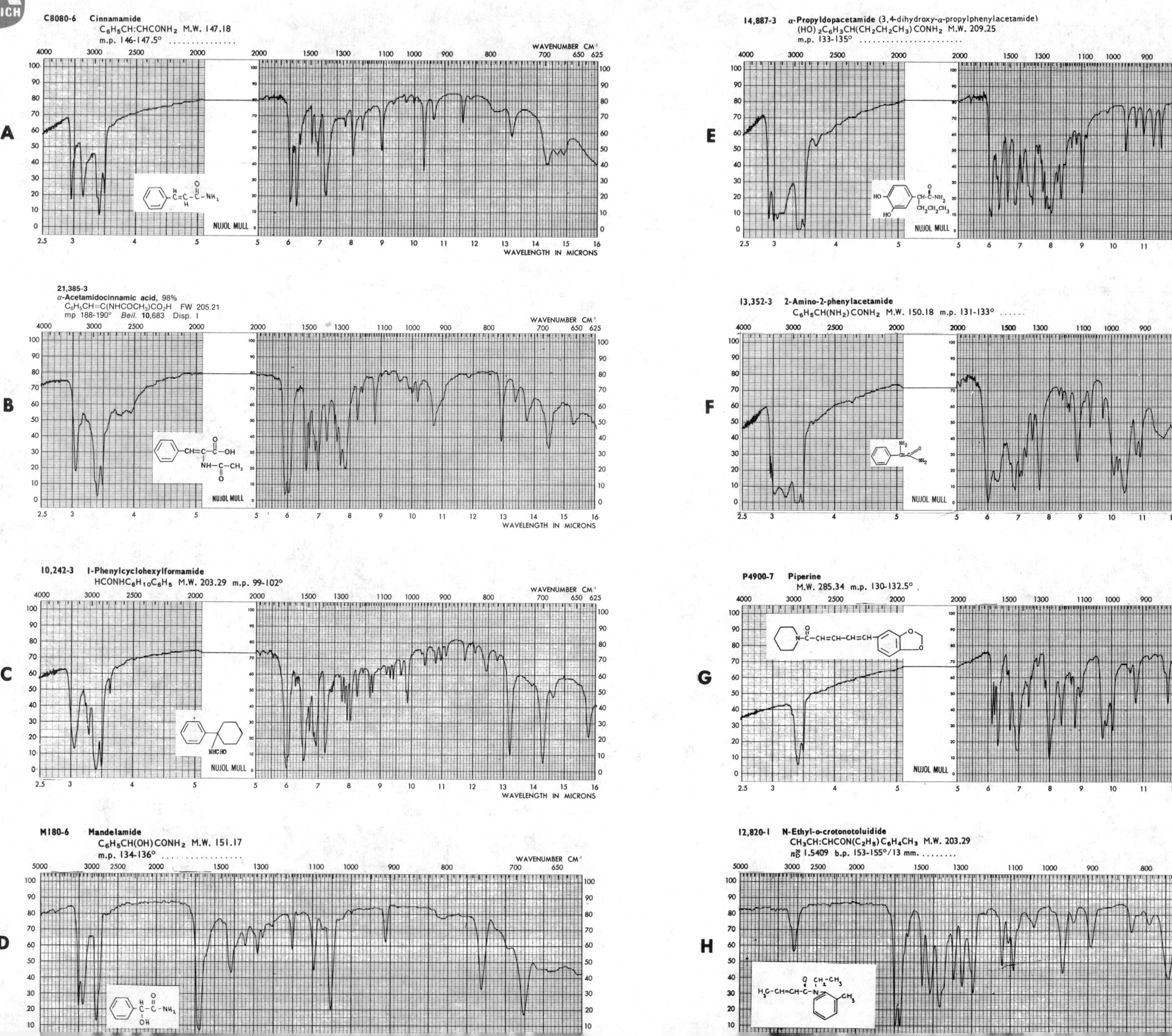
A
C8080-6 Cinnamamide
$C_6H_5CH{:}CHCONH_2$ M.W. 147.18
m.p. 146-147.5°
NUJOL MULL
B
21,385-3
α-Acetamidocinnamic acid, 98%
$C_6H_5CH{=}C(NHCOCH_3)CO_2H$ FW 205.21
mp 188-190° Beil. 10,683 Disp. I
NUJOL MULL
C
10,242-3 1-Phenylcyclohexylformamide
$HCONHC_6H_{10}C_6H_5$ M.W. 203.29 m.p. 99-102°
NUJOL MULL
D
M180-6 Mandelamide
$C_6H_5CH(OH)CONH_2$ M.W. 151.17
m.p. 134-136°
E
14,887-3 α-Propyldopacetamide (3,4-dihydroxy-α-propylphenylacetamide)
$(HO)_2C_6H_3CH(CH_2CH_2CH_3)CONH_2$ M.W. 209.25
m.p. 133-135°
NUJOL MULL
F
13,352-3 2-Amino-2-phenylacetamide
$C_6H_5CH(NH_2)CONH_2$ M.W. 150.18 m.p. 131-133°
NUJOL MULL
G
P4900-7 Piperine
M.W. 285.34 m.p. 130-132.5°
NUJOL MULL
H
12,820-1 N-Ethyl-o-crotonotoluidide
$CH_3CH{:}CHCON(C_2H_5)C_6H_4CH_3$ M.W. 203.29
n_D^{20} 1.5409 b.p. 153-155°/13 mm.
WAVENUMBER CM⁻¹
WAVELENGTH IN MICRONS

A

M.W. 323.13 m.p. 148-150°
$[\alpha]^{24}$ +19° (c=4.9, C_2H_5OH)

NUJOL MULL

B

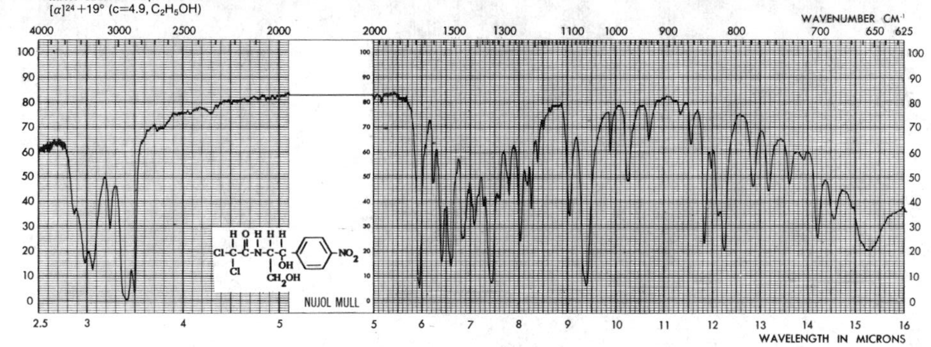

12,011-1 6'-Chloro-o-crotonotoluidide
$CH_3CH{:}CHCONHC_6H_3(CH_3)Cl$ M.W. 209.68 m.p. 172-174°

NUJOL MULL

C

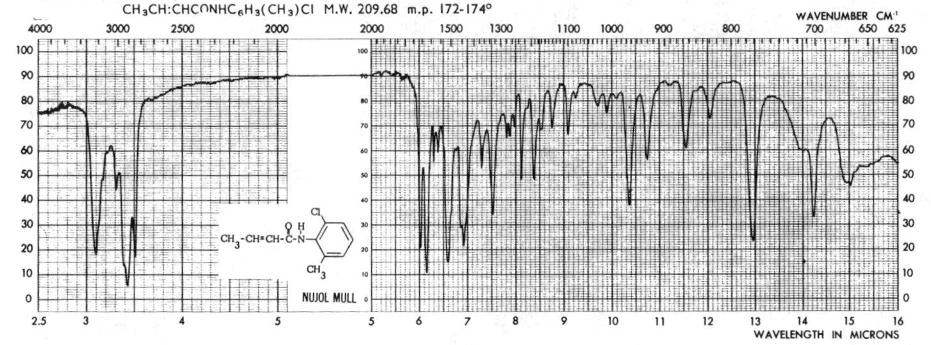

12,265-3 α-Acetamidocinnamic acid dihydrate
$C_6H_5CH{:}C(NHCOCH_3)CO_2H \cdot 2H_2O$

NUJOL MULL

D

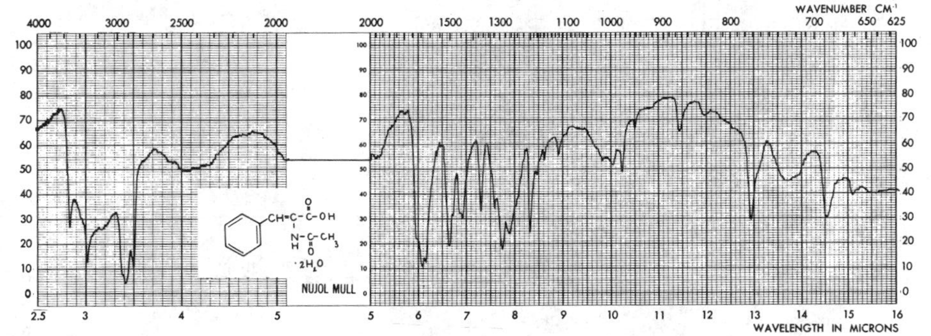

12,390-0 N-[1,1-Bis-(p-chlorophenyl)-2,2,2-trifluoroethyl]-acetamide
$CH_3CONHC(C_6H_4Cl)_2CF_3$ M.W. 362.18 m.p. 212-214°

NUJOL MULL

E

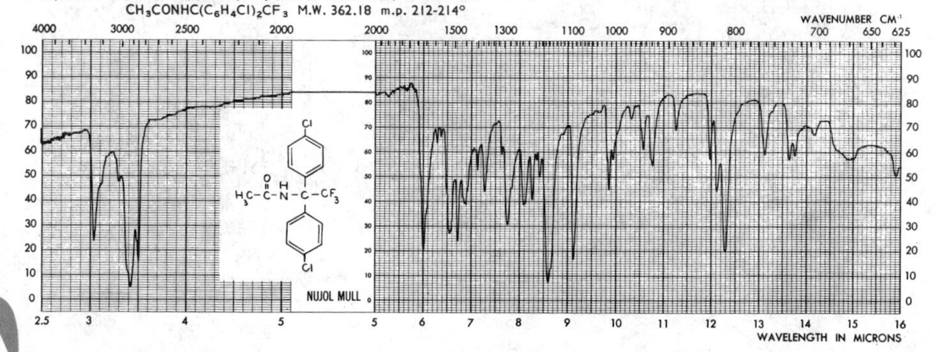

B3990-9 N-[1,1-Bis-(p-chlorophenyl)-2,2,2-trichloroethyl]-acetamide
$CH_3CONHC(C_6H_4Cl)_2CCl_3$ M.W. 411.55 m.p. 210-214°

NUJOL MULL

F

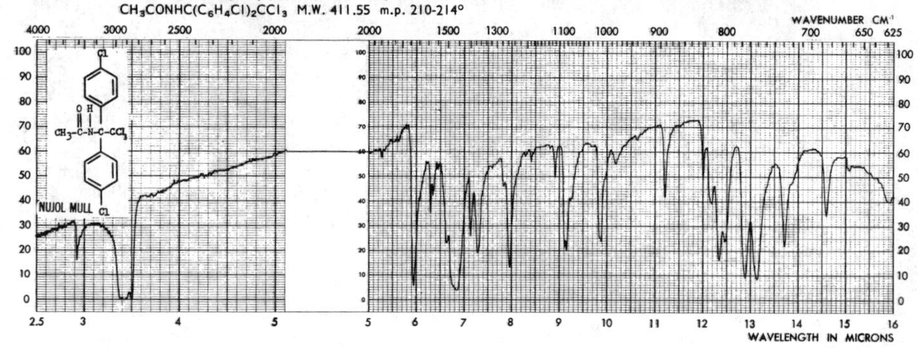

A8682-1 4-Anilino-1-benzyl-4-carbamylpiperidine (4-anilino-1-benzyl-4-piperidine-carboxamide)
M.W. 309.41 m.p. 188-190°

NUJOL MULL

G

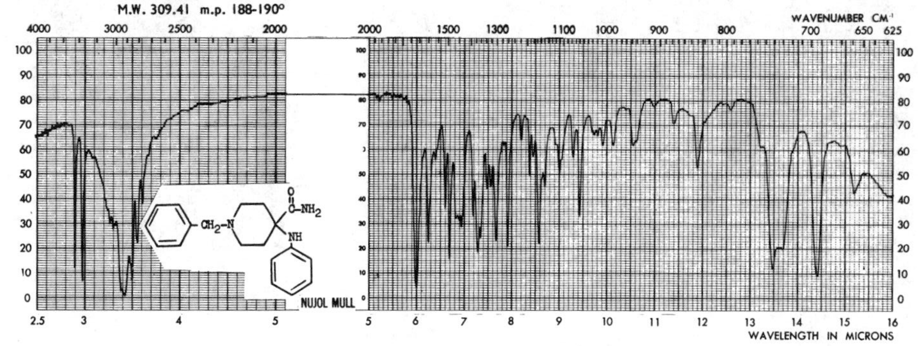

P3430-1 4-Phenyl-4-pyrrolidinamidopiperidine (N,N-tetramethylene-4-phenyl-4-piperidinecarboxamide) hydrochloride
M.W. 294.83 m.p. 234.5-237°

NUJOL MULL

H

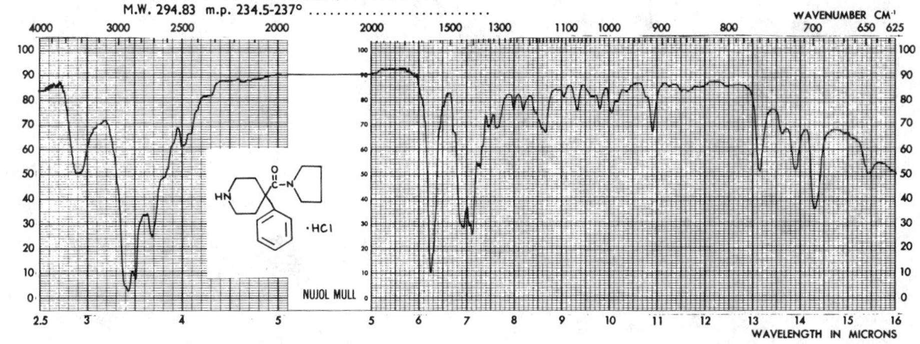

A873-2 Acetoacetanilide
$CH_3COCH_2CONHC_6H_5$ M.W. 177.21 m.p. 85-86°

NUJOL MULL

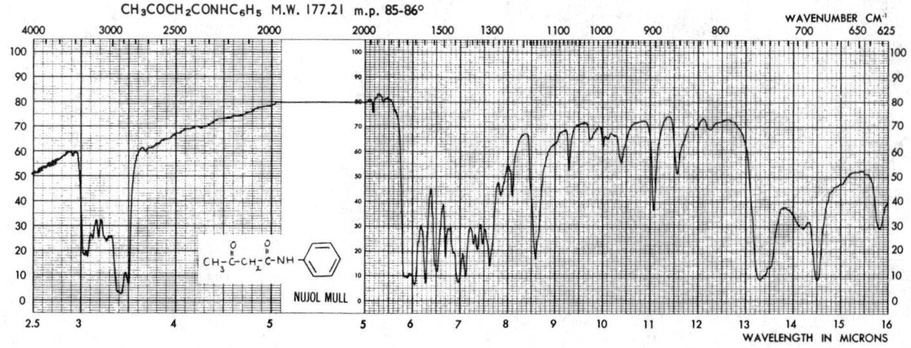

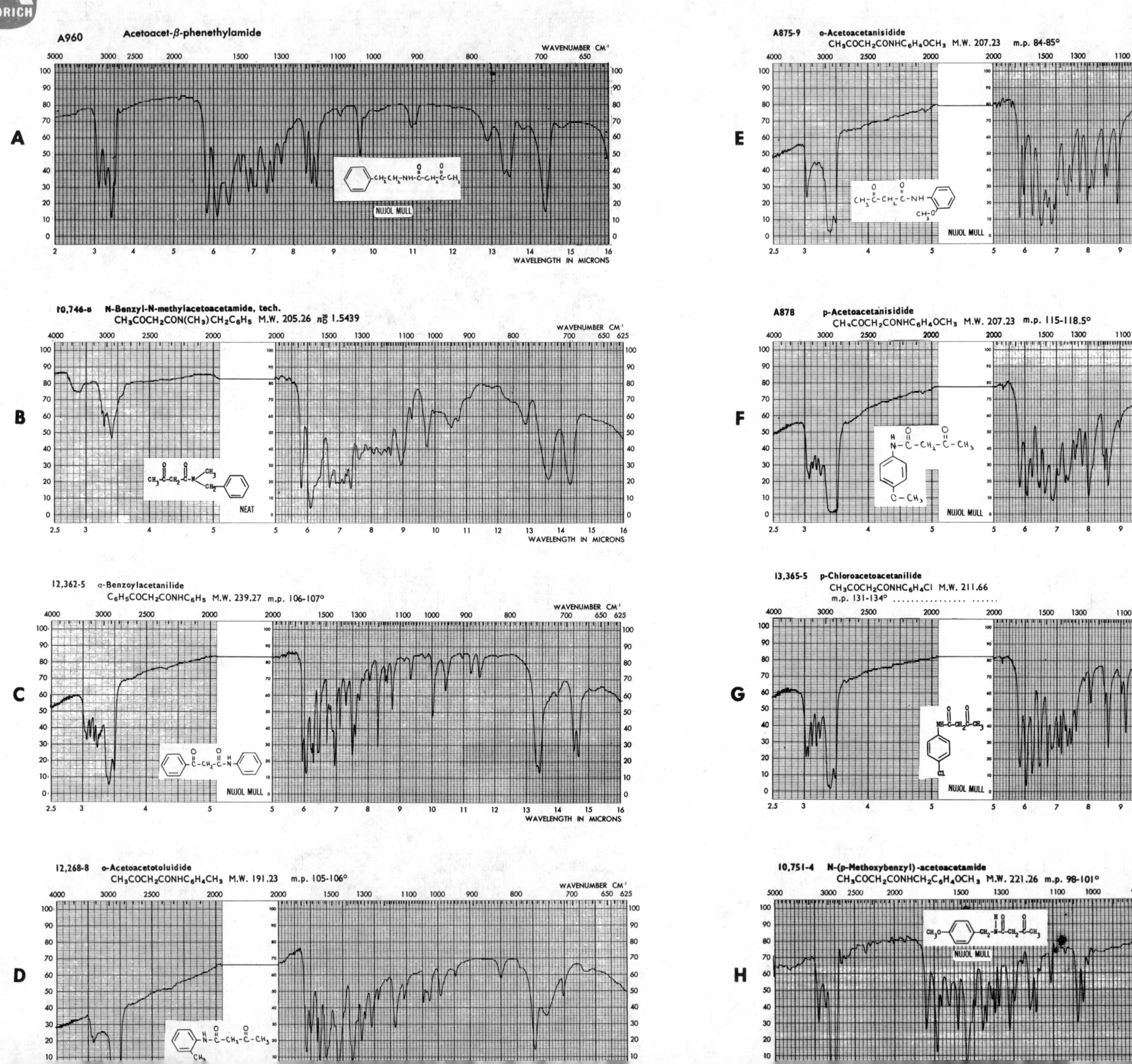

A
A960 Acetoacet-β-phenethylamide
NUJOL MULL
B
10,746-8 N-Benzyl-N-methylacetoacetamide, tech.
CH3COCH2CON(CH3)CH2C6H5 M.W. 205.26 n20D 1.5439
NEAT
C
12,362-5 α-Benzoylacetanilide
C6H5COCH2CONHC6H5 M.W. 239.27 m.p. 106-107°
NUJOL MULL
D
12,268-8 o-Acetoacetotoluidide
CH3COCH2CONHC6H4CH3 M.W. 191.23 m.p. 105-106°
E
A875-9 o-Acetoacetanisidide
CH3COCH2CONHC6H4OCH3 M.W. 207.23 m.p. 84-85°
NUJOL MULL
F
A878 p-Acetoacetanisidide
CH3COCH2CONHC6H4OCH3 M.W. 207.23 m.p. 115-118.5°
NUJOL MULL
G
13,365-5 p-Chloroacetoacetanilide
CH3COCH2CONHC6H4Cl M.W. 211.66
m.p. 131-134°
NUJOL MULL
H
10,751-4 N-(p-Methoxybenzyl)-acetoacetamide
CH3COCH2CONHCH2C6H4OCH3 M.W. 221.26 m.p. 98-101°
NUJOL MULL
WAVENUMBER CM-1
WAVELENGTH IN MICRONS

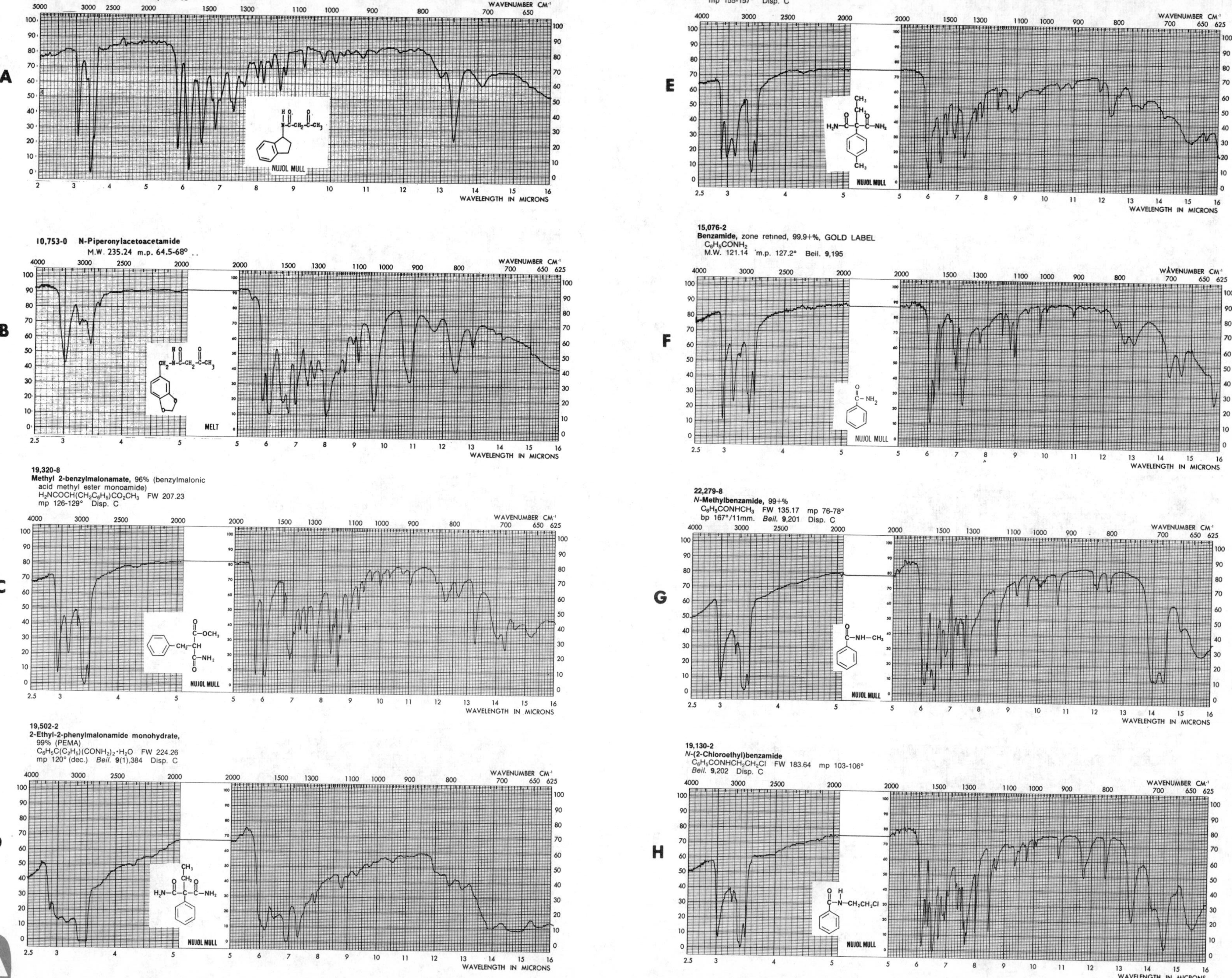
A
M.W. 217.27 m.p. 82-85°
NUJOL MULL
B
10,753-0 N-Piperonylacetoacetamide
M.W. 235.24 m.p. 64.5-68°
MELT
C
19,320-8
Methyl 2-benzylmalonamate, 96% (benzylmalonic acid methyl ester monoamide)
$H_2NCOCH(CH_2C_6H_5)CO_2CH_3$ FW 207.23
mp 126-129° Disp. C
NUJOL MULL
D
19,502-2
2-Ethyl-2-phenylmalonamide monohydrate, 99% (PEMA)
$C_6H_5C(C_2H_5)(CONH_2)_2 \cdot H_2O$ FW 224.26
mp 120° (dec.) Beil. 9(1),384 Disp. C
NUJOL MULL
E
$CH_3C_6H_4C(C_2H_5)(CONH_2)_2$ FW 220.27
mp 155-157° Disp. C
NUJOL MULL
F
15,076-2
Benzamide, zone refined, 99.9+%, GOLD LABEL
$C_6H_5CONH_2$
M.W. 121.14 m.p. 127.2° Beil. 9,195
NUJOL MULL
G
22,279-8
N-Methylbenzamide, 99+%
$C_6H_5CONHCH_3$ FW 135.17 mp 76-78°
bp 167°/11mm. Beil. 9,201 Disp. C
NUJOL MULL
H
19,130-2
N-(2-Chloroethyl)benzamide
$C_6H_5CONHCH_2CH_2Cl$ FW 183.64 mp 103-106°
Beil. 9,202 Disp. C
NUJOL MULL
WAVENUMBER CM⁻¹
WAVELENGTH IN MICRONS
ALDRICH

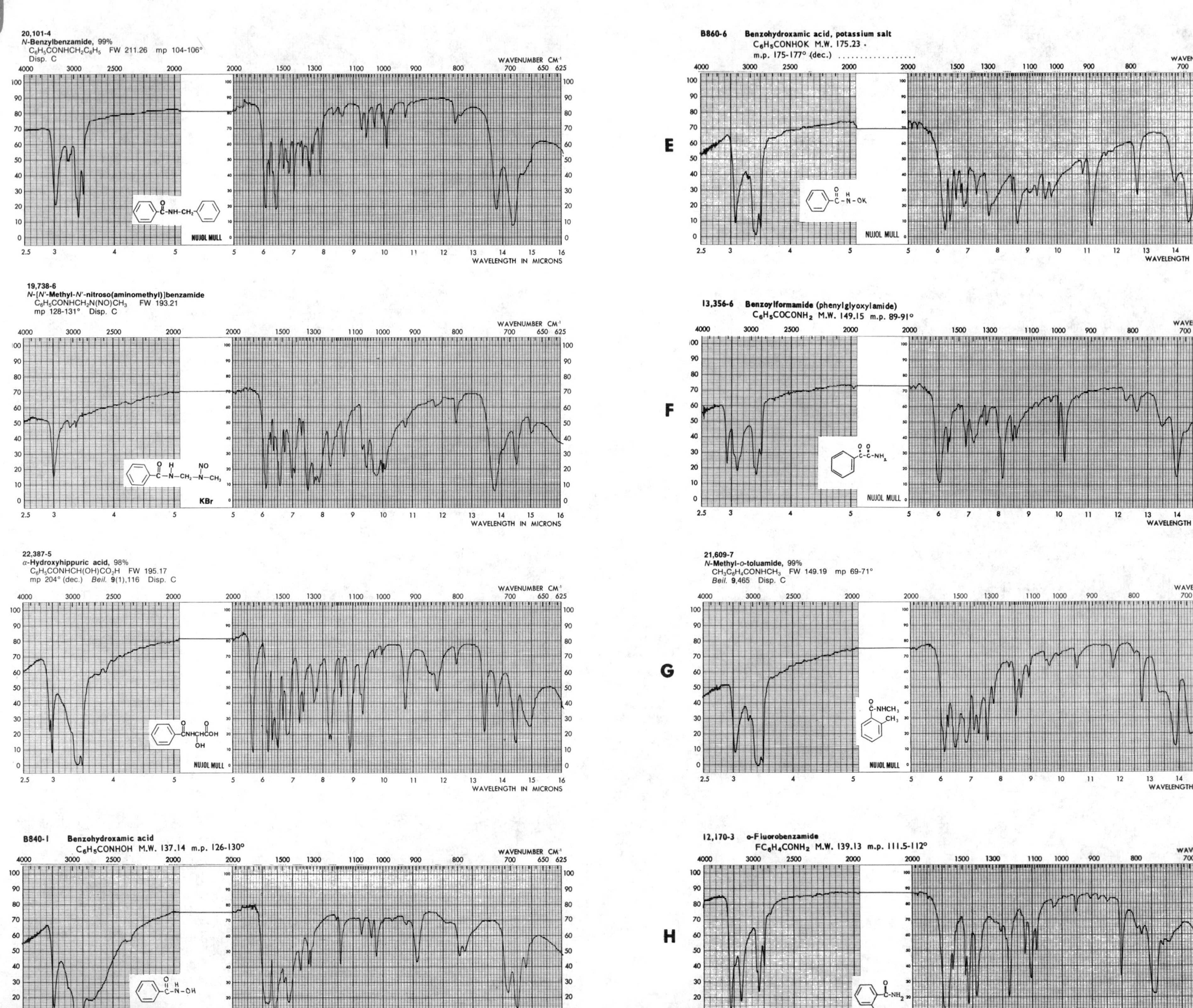

ALDRICH
A
20,101-4
N-Benzylbenzamide, 99%
C6H5CONHCH2C6H5 FW 211.26 mp 104-106°
Disp. C
NUJOL MULL
B
19,738-6
N-[N'-Methyl-N'-nitroso(aminomethyl)]benzamide
C6H5CONHCH2N(NO)CH3 FW 193.21
mp 128-131° Disp. C
KBr
C
22,387-5
α-Hydroxyhippuric acid, 98%
C6H5CONHCH(OH)CO2H FW 195.17
mp 204° (dec.) Beil. 9(1),116 Disp. C
NUJOL MULL
D
B840-1 Benzohydroxamic acid
C6H5CONHOH M.W. 137.14 m.p. 126-130°
E
B860-6 Benzohydroxamic acid, potassium salt
C6H5CONHOK M.W. 175.23
m.p. 175-177° (dec.)
NUJOL MULL
F
13,356-6 Benzoylformamide (phenylglyoxylamide)
C6H5COCONH2 M.W. 149.15 m.p. 89-91°
NUJOL MULL
G
21,609-7
N-Methyl-o-toluamide, 99%
CH3C6H4CONHCH3 FW 149.19 mp 69-71°
Beil. 9,465 Disp. C
NUJOL MULL
H
12,170-3 o-Fluorobenzamide
FC6H4CONH2 M.W. 139.13 m.p. 111.5-112°
WAVENUMBER CM⁻¹
WAVELENGTH IN MICRONS

A

Beil. 9,348 Disp. C

NUJOL MULL

B

86,041-7
Salicylamide, 99% (o-hydroxybenzamide)
$HOC_6H_4CONH_2$ FW 137.14 mp 140-144°
Beil. **10**,87 Disp. C

NUJOL MULL

C

M1004-2 o-Methoxybenzamide (o-anisamide)
$CH_3OC_6H_4CONH_2$ M.W. 151.17 m.p. 127-128°

NUJOL MULL

D

E440-2 2-Ethoxybenzamide
$C_2H_5OC_6H_4CONH_2$ M.W. 165.19 m.p. 132-133°

NUJOL MULL

E

$(H_2N)C_6H_4CONH_2$ M.W. 136.15
m.p. 108-110°

NUJOL MULL

F

19,142-6
o-Nitrobenzamide, 98%
$O_2NC_6H_4CONH_2$ FW 166.14 mp 174-178°
bp 317° *Beil.* 9,373 Disp. C

NUJOL MULL

G

D10,095-1 N,N-Diethyl-m-toluamide
$CH_3C_6H_4CON(C_2H_5)_2$ M.W. 191.28
n_D^{20} 1.5212

NEAT

H

19,069-1
m-Fluorobenzamide, 99%
$FC_6H_4CONH_2$ FW 139.13 mp 129-132°
Beil. 9(1),137 Disp. C

NUJOL MULL

AROMATIC AMIDES

A

M1005-0 **m-Methoxybenzamide** (m-anisamide)
$CH_3OC_6H_4CONH_2$ M.W. 151.17 m.p. 132.5-135.5°

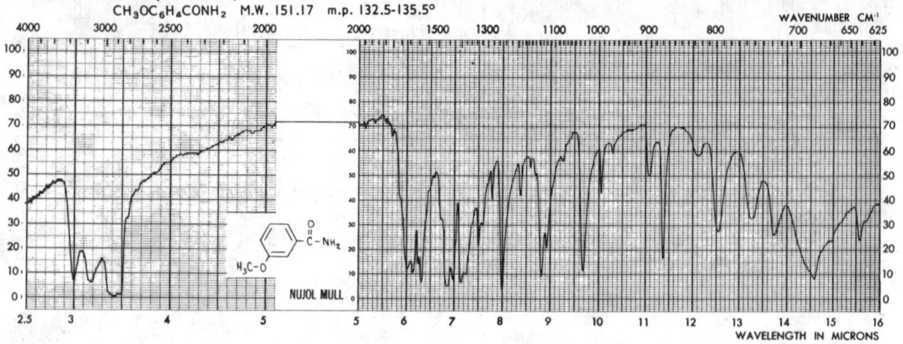

NUJOL MULL

B

18,975-8
***m*-Nitrobenzamide**, 98%
$O_2NC_6H_4CONH_2$ FW 166.14 mp 140-143°
Beil. 9,381 Disp. C

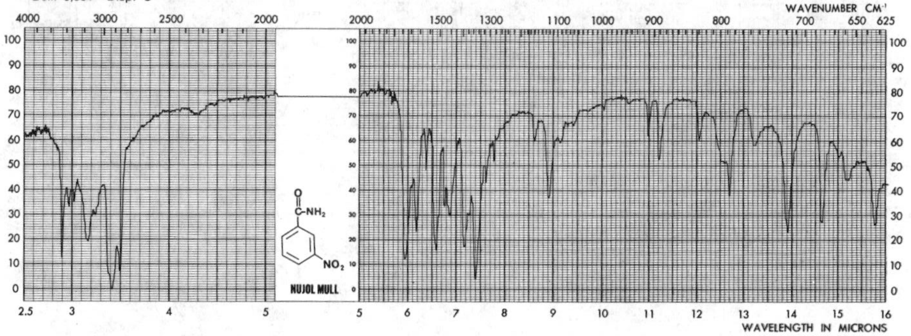

NUJOL MULL

C

12,159-2 **p-Fluorobenzamide**
$FC_6H_4CONH_2$ M.W. 139.13 m.p. 154-156.5°

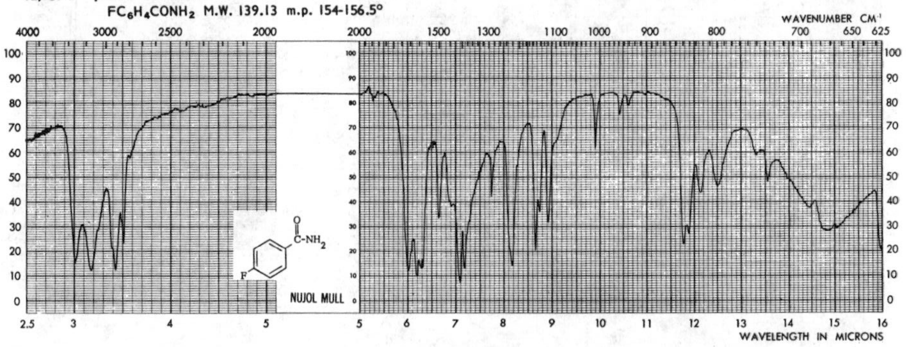

NUJOL MULL

D

C2380-2 **4-Chlorobenzamide**
$ClC_6H_4CONH_2$ M.W. 155.58 m.p. 172-176°

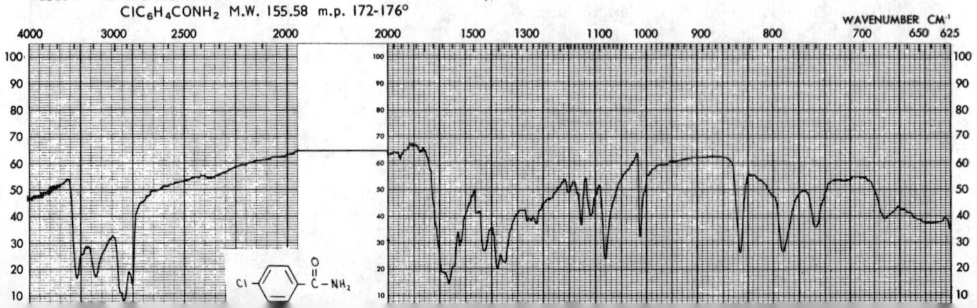

E

19,077-2
***p*-Bromobenzamide**, 97%
$BrC_6H_4CONH_2$ FW 200.04 mp 190-193°
Beil. 9,353 Disp. C

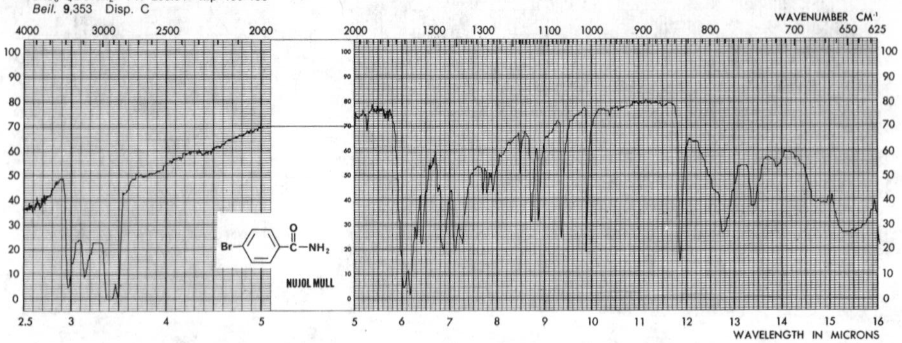

NUJOL MULL

F

20,185-5
***N*-(2-Aminoethyl)-*p*-hydroxybenzamide hydrochloride**, 99%
$HOC_6H_4CONHCH_2CH_2NH_2 \cdot HCl$ FW 216.67
mp 235-237° Disp. C

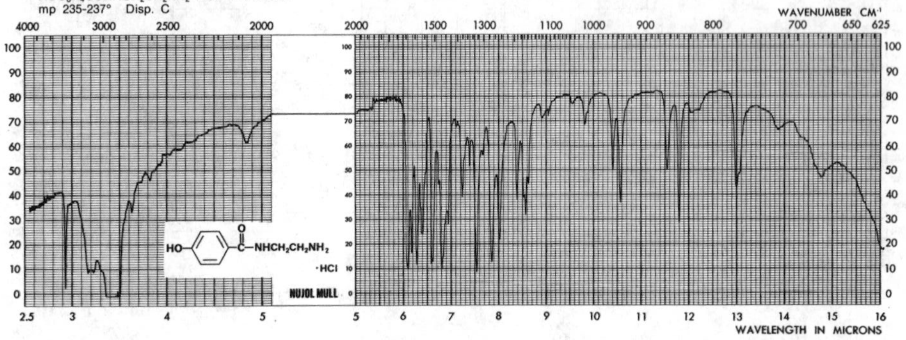

NUJOL MULL

G

M1006-9 **p-Methoxybenzamide** (p-anisamide)
$CH_3OC_6H_4CONH_2$ M.W. 151.17 m.p. 159-164°

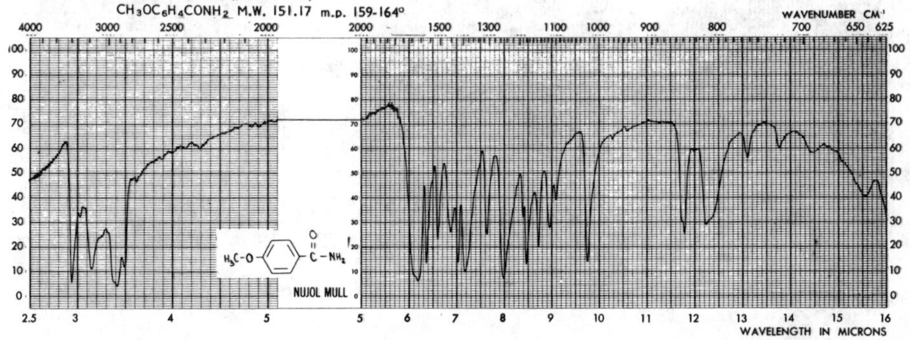

NUJOL MULL

H

18,928-6
***p*-Nitrobenzamide**, 98%
$O_2NC_6H_4CONH_2$ FW 166.14 mp 200-201°
Beil. 9,394 Disp. C

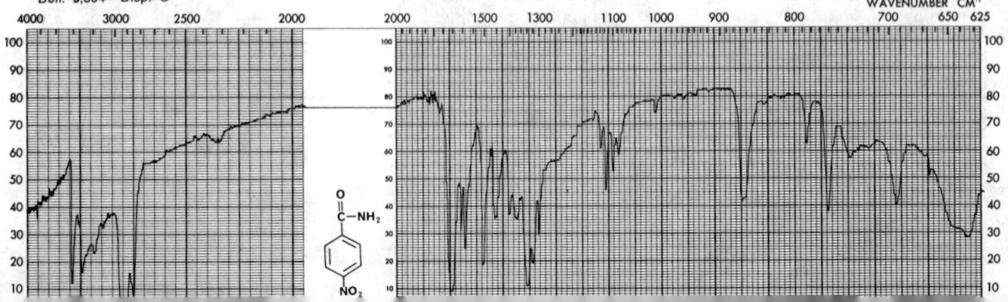

A

$C_2H_5OC_6H_4CONH(CH_2)_3N(C_2H_5)_2 \cdot HCl$ FW 314.86
mp 140-143° Disp. C

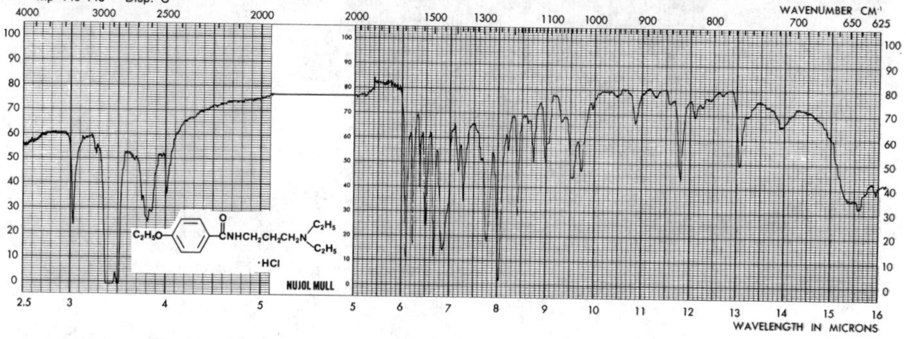

NUJOL MULL

20,775-6
***N*-(2-Diethylaminoethyl)-*p*-ethoxybenzamide hydrochloride**, 99%
$C_2H_5OC_6H_4CONHCH_2CH_2N(C_2H_5)_2 \cdot HCl$ FW 300.83
mp 153-155° Disp. C

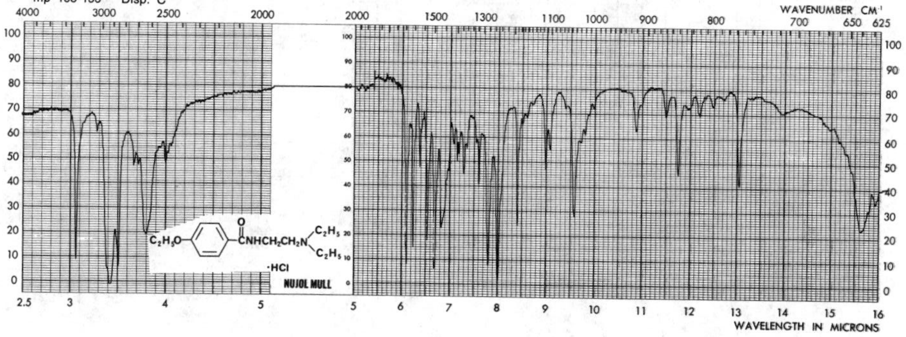

B

NUJOL MULL

D15,558-6 N,N'-Dimethyl-N,N'-dinitrosoterephthalamide, 70% in mineral oil
C_6H_4-1,4-$[CON(CH_3)NO]_2$
M.W. 250.21 (dry)

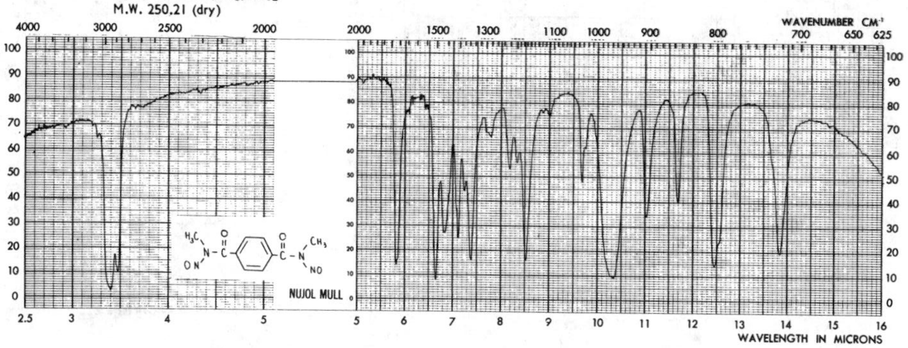

C

NUJOL MULL

22,296-8
Procainamide hydrochloride, 99% [4-amino-*N*-(diethylaminoethyl)benzamide]
$H_2NC_6H_4CONHCH_2CH_2N(C_2H_5)_2 \cdot HCl$ FW 271.79
mp 167-169° *Beil.* **14**(3),1077 Disp. C

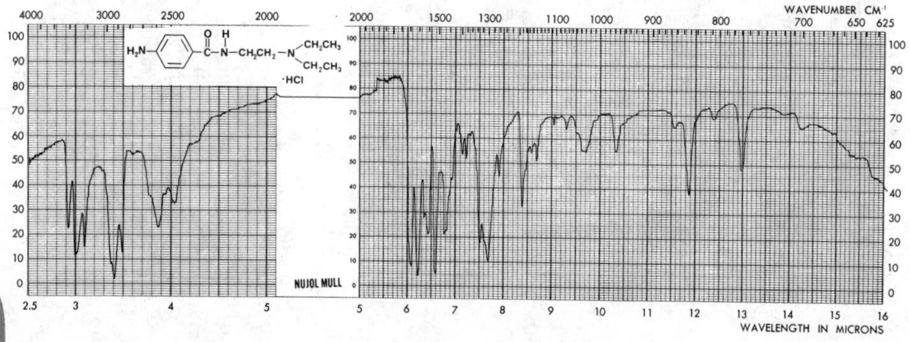

D

NUJOL MULL

***N*-Acetylprocainamide hydrochloride**, 99%
4-$(CH_3CONH)C_6H_4CONHCH_2CH_2N(C_2H_5)_2 \cdot HCl$
FW 313.83 mp 184-186° Disp. L

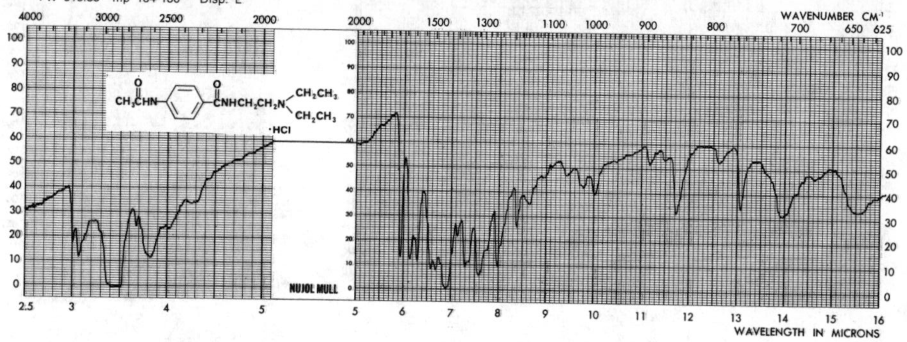

E

NUJOL MULL

20,841-8
***N*-Propionylprocainamide hydrochloride**, 98%
$C_2H_5CONHC_6H_4CONHCH_2CH_2N(C_2H_5)_2 \cdot HCl$
FW 327.86 mp 140-143° Disp. C

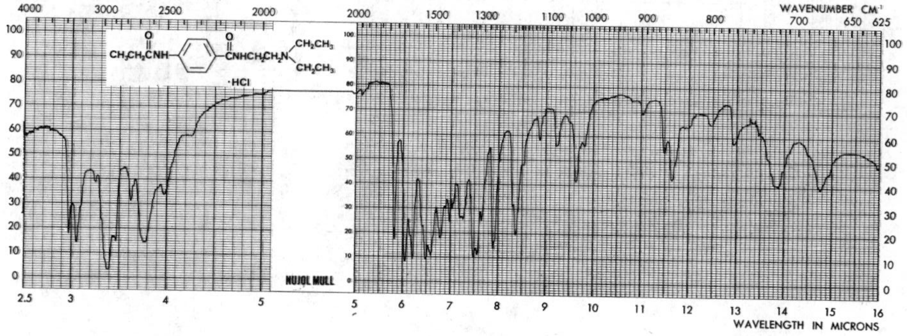

F

NUJOL MULL

14,183-6 2,6-Dichlorobenzamide
$Cl_2C_6H_3CONH_2$ M.W. 190.03 m.p. 198-200°

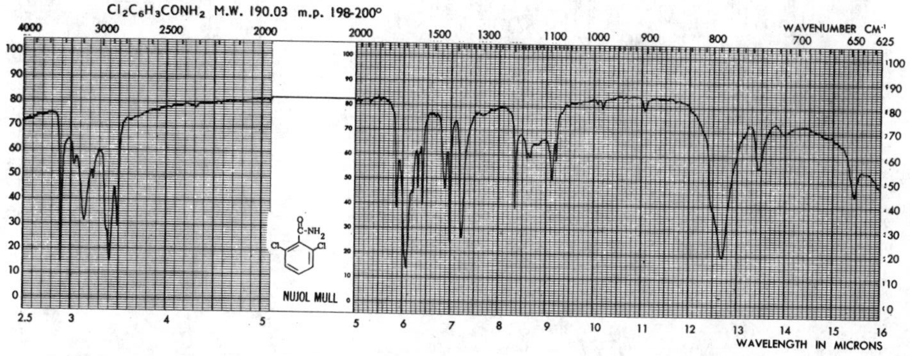

G

NUJOL MULL

22,090-6
2,4-Dichlorobenzamide, 98%
$Cl_2C_6H_3CONH_2$ FW 190.03 mp 191-194°
Beil. **9**(3),1376 Disp. C

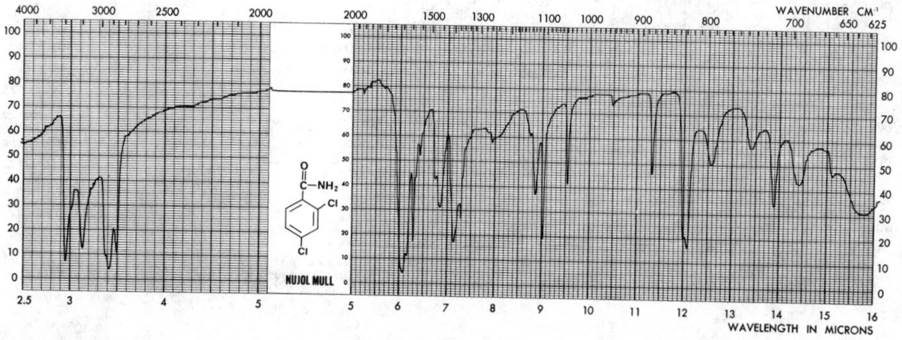

H

NUJOL MULL

A

12,619-5 2,4-Dihydroxybenzamide
$(HO)_2C_6H_3CONH_2$ M.W. 153.14
m.p. 229° (dec.)

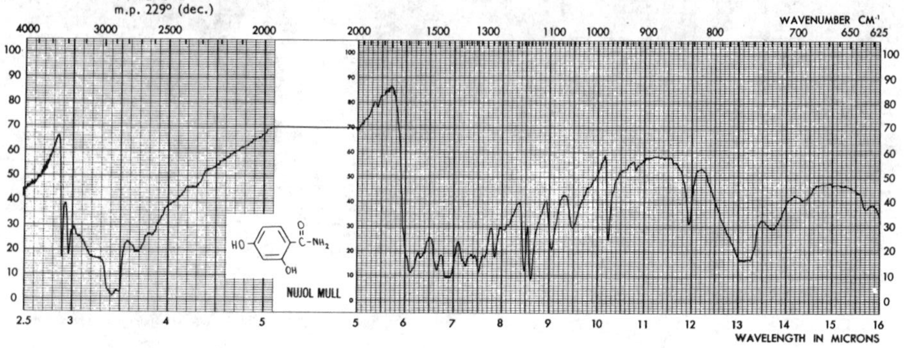

NUJOL MULL

B

D13,120-2 3,5-Dimethoxybenzamide
$(CH_3O)_2C_6H_3CONH_2$ M.W. 181.19
m.p. 145-148°

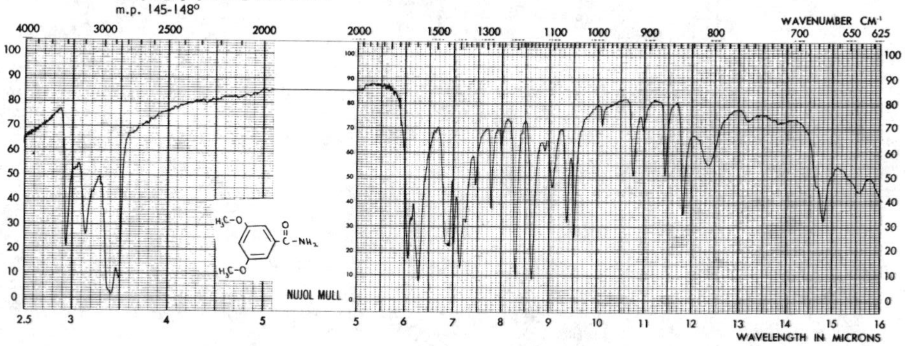

NUJOL MULL

C

D19,380-1 3,5-Dinitrobenzamide
$(O_2N)_2C_6H_3CONH_2$ M.W. 211.13
m.p. 183-185°

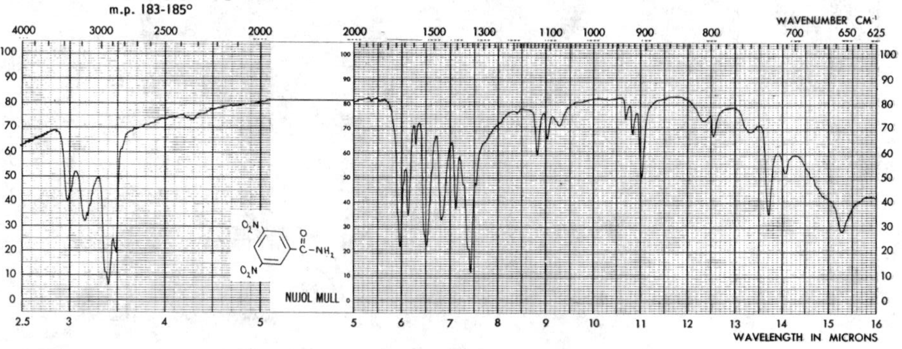

NUJOL MULL

D

T6860-8 3,4,5-Trimethoxybenzamide
$(CH_3O)_3C_6H_2CONH_2$ M.W. 211.22 m.p. 180.5-183°

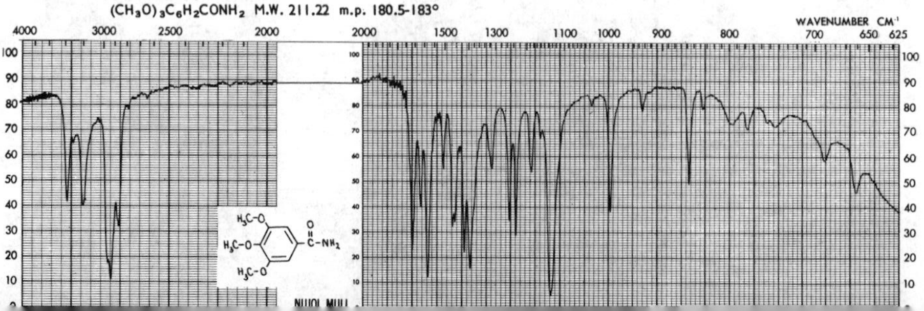

NUJOL MULL

E

A4815-6 4-Amino-N-cyclopropyl-3,5-dichlorobenzamide
$H_2NC_6H_2(Cl)_2CONHC_3H_5$ M.W. 245.11 m.p. 173-177° ...

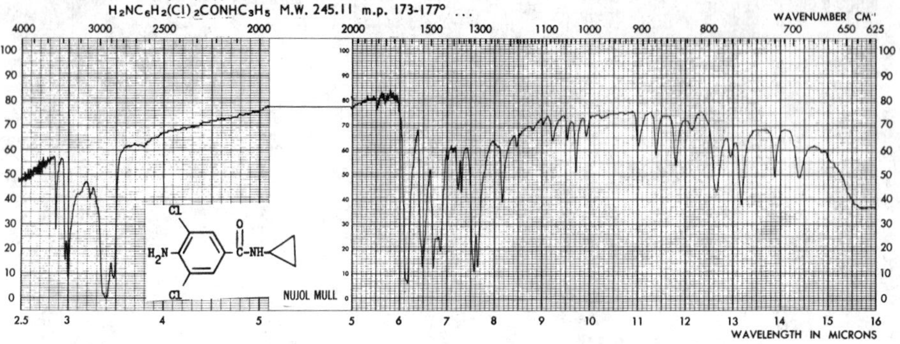

NUJOL MULL

F

10,375-6
2,3,4,5,6-Pentafluorobenzamide, 99%
$C_6F_5CONH_2$ FW 211.09 mp 146-149° Disp. C

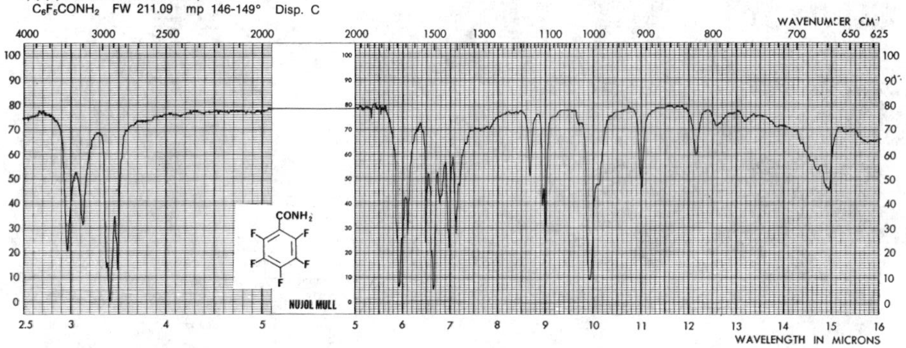

NUJOL MULL

G

10,061-7 4-Amino-2,3,5,6-tetrafluorobenzamide
$H_2NC_6F_4CONH_2$ M.W. 208.11 m.p. 180-182°

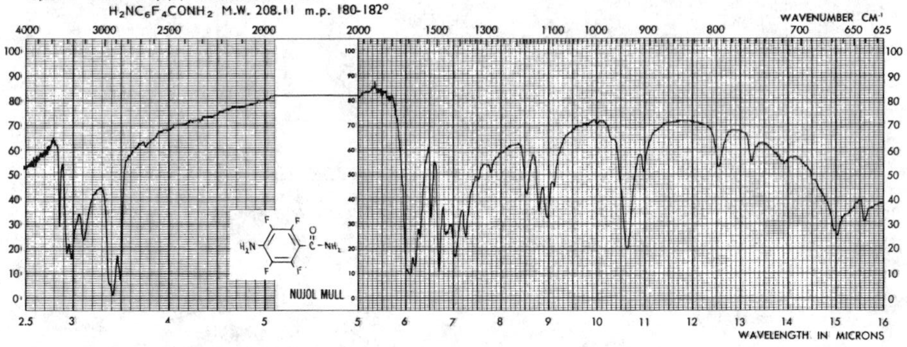

NUJOL MULL

H

10,822-7 Benzanilide
$C_6H_5CONHC_6H_5$ M.W. 197.24
m.p. 163-165°

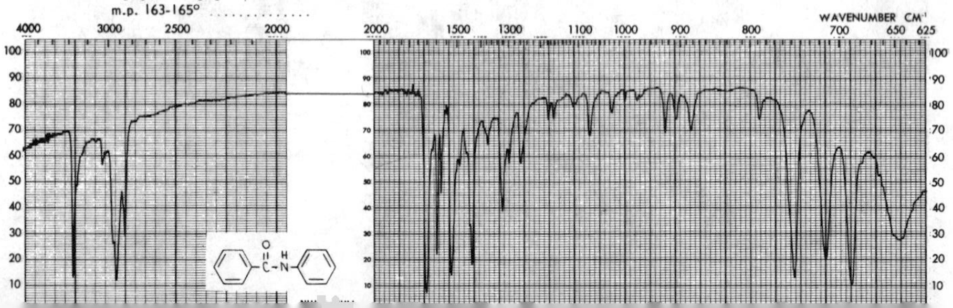

A

m.p. 136-138°

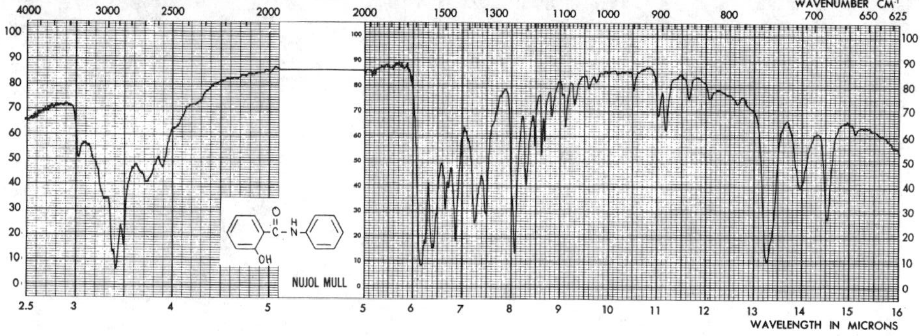

NUJOL MULL

B

H5890 4'-Hydroxysalicylanilide
2-$HOC_6H_4CONHC_6H_4OH$ M.W. 229.24 m.p. 162-163°

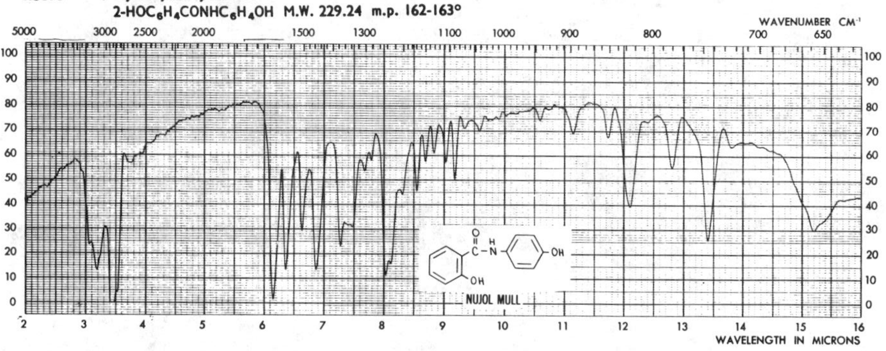

NUJOL MULL

C

10,732-8 N-Benzoyl-4-piperidone, tech.
M.W. 203.24 m.p. 55-59°

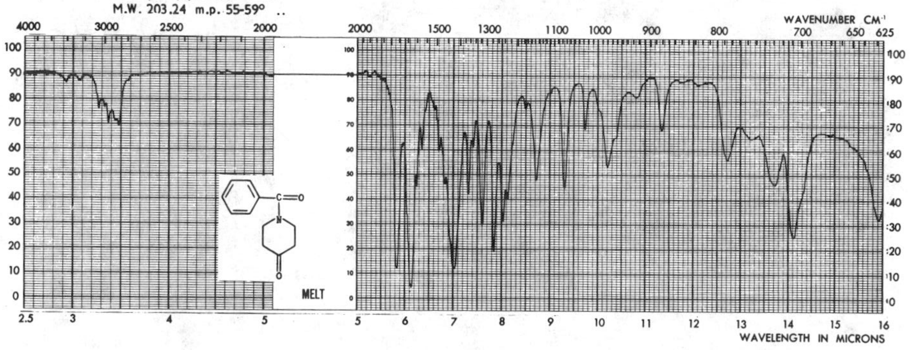

MELT

D

11,995-4 Algol red (1,5-dibenzamido-4-hydroxyanthraquinone)
M.W. 462.47 m.p. > 300°

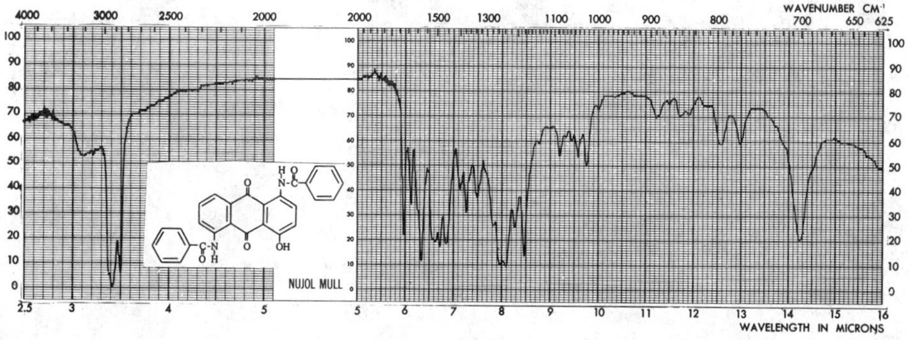

NUJOL MULL

E

$C_6H_5CONHCH_2COC_6H_5$ M.W. 239.28
m.p. 124-126°

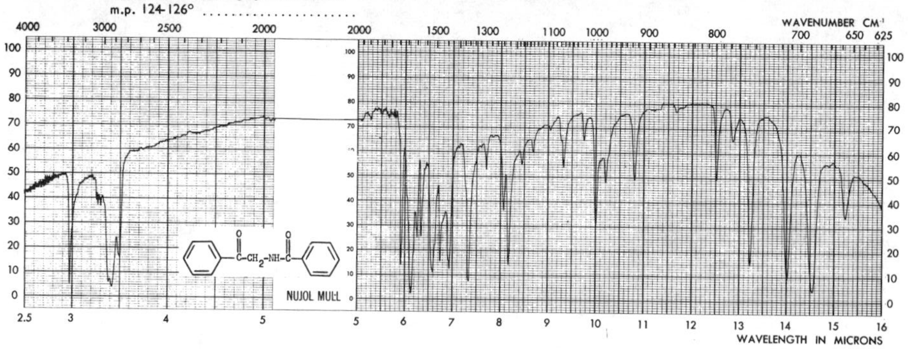

NUJOL MULL

F

11,382-4 N-(2-Benzylideneamino-1,2-diphenylethyl)-benzamide
$C_6H_5CONHCH(C_6H_5)CH(C_6H_5)N{:}CHC_6H_5$ M.W. 404.52
m.p. 254-256°
Leucomalachite green

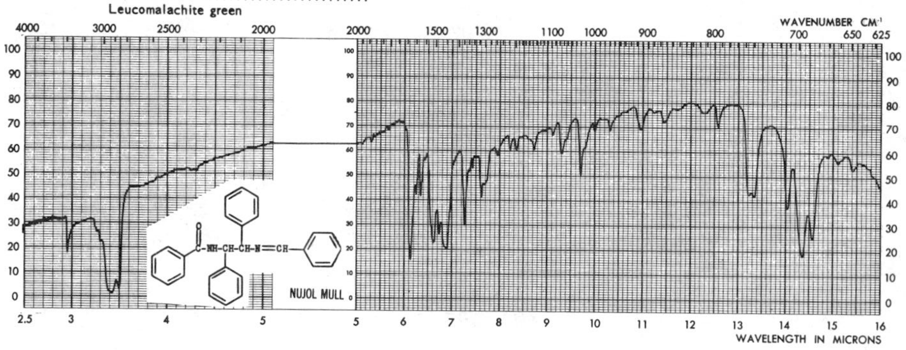

NUJOL MULL

G

11,200-3 Hippuric acid
$C_6H_5CONHCH_2CO_2H$ M.W. 179.18
m.p. 190-193°

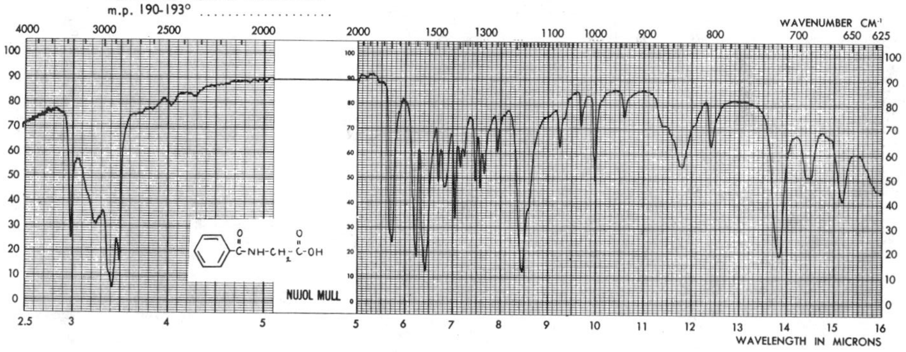

NUJOL MULL

H

85,074-8
5-Benzamidovaleric acid
$C_6H_5CONH(CH_2)_4CO_2H$
M.W. 221.26 m.p. 94-95° Beil. 9,252

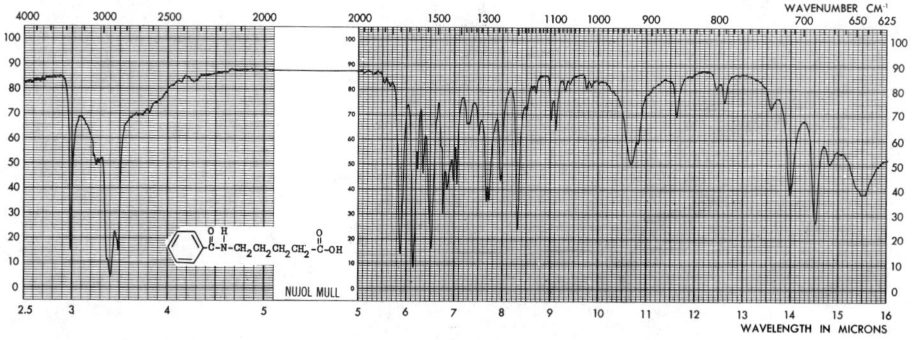

NUJOL MULL

A

10,403-5 p-Phenylhippuric acid
$C_6H_5C_6H_4CONHCH_2CO_2H$ M.W. 255.27 m.p. 222-224° ...

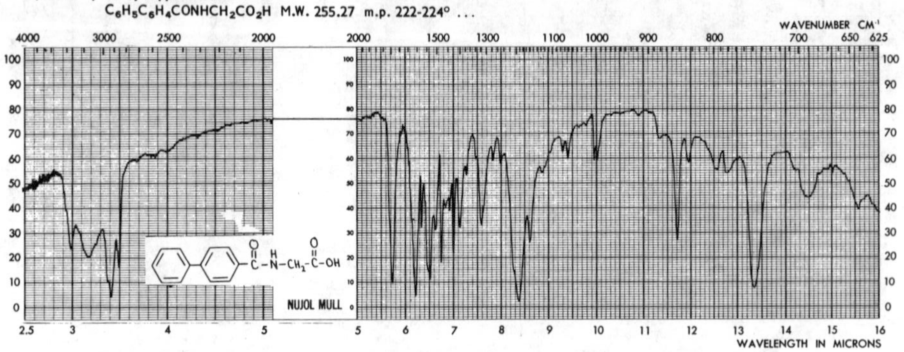

NUJOL MULL

B

10,657-7 o-Iodohippuric acid
$IC_6H_4CONHCH_2CO_2H$ M.W. 305.07 m.p. 163-165° ....

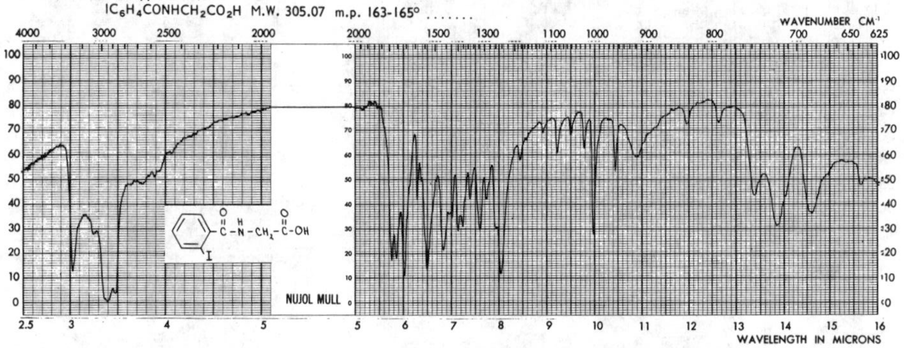

NUJOL MULL

C

13,406-6 o-Hydroxyhippuric acid
$HOC_6H_4CONHCH_2CO_2H$ M.W. 195.18 m.p. 170-171.5°

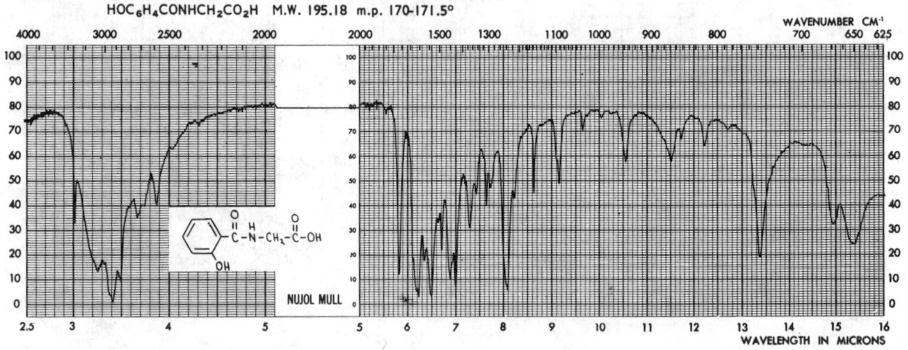

NUJOL MULL

D

16,508-5
p-Acetoacetanisidide, 98%
$CH_3COCH_2CONHC_6H_4OCH_3$
M.W. 207.23 m.p. 115-117° Beil. 13(1),177

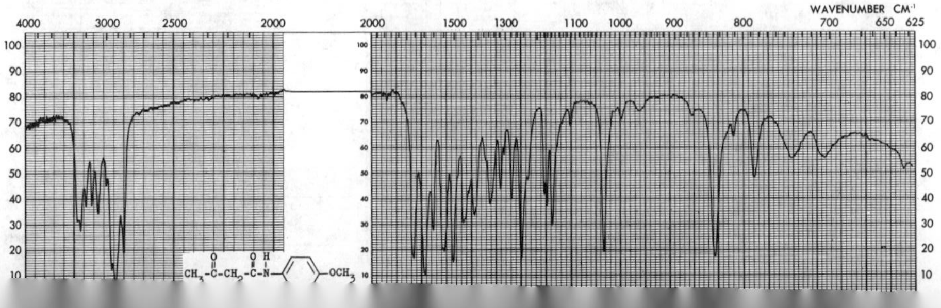

E

15,661-2
(+)-4-Chlorotartranilic acid, 97%
$ClC_6H_4NHCO[CH(OH)]_2CO_2H$
M.W. 259.65 m.p. 202-204° (dec.)
$[\alpha]^{24}$ + 107.2° (c=5, CH_3OH)

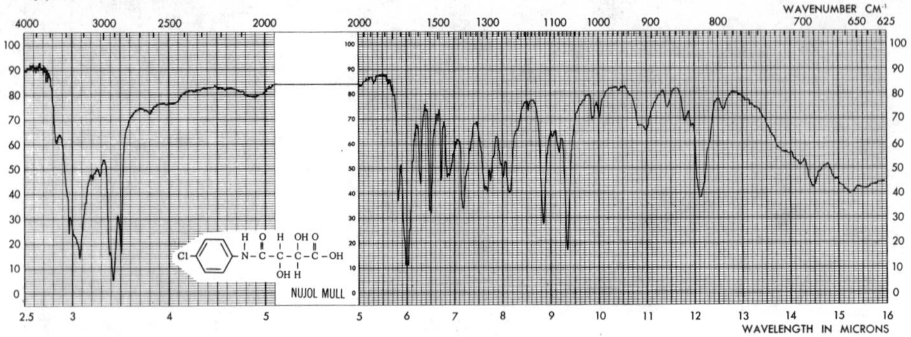

NUJOL MULL

F

12,295-5 p-Aminohippuric acid
$H_2NC_6H_4CONHCH_2CO_2H$ M.W. 194.19 m.p. 199-200° (dec.)

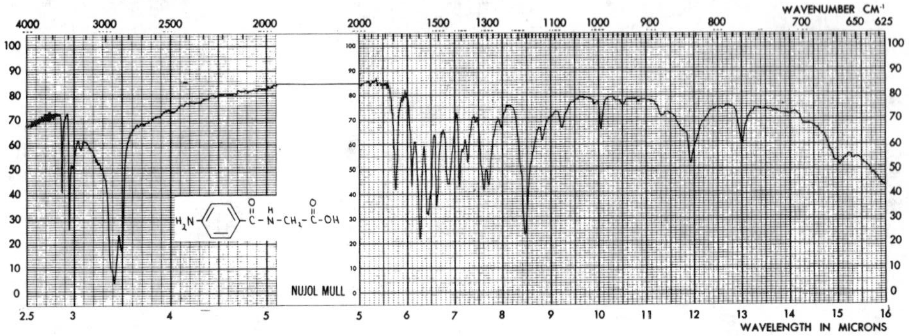

NUJOL MULL

G

21,778-6
p-Aminohippuric acid, sodium salt, 98%
$H_2NC_6H_4CONHCH_2CO_2Na$ FW 216.17
mp 123-125° Disp. C

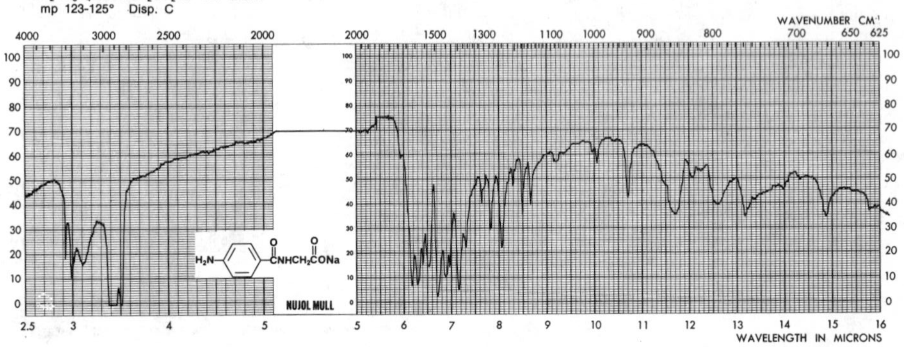

NUJOL MULL

H

12,051-0 p-Nitrohippuric acid
$O_2NC_6H_4CONHCH_2CO_2H$ M.W. 224.17 m.p. 128-131° ...

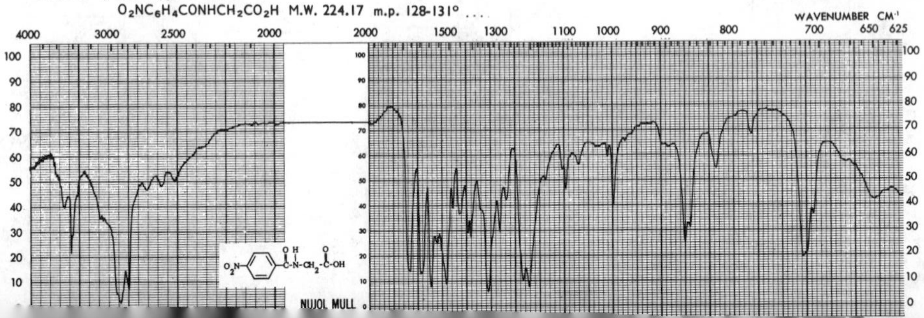

NUJOL MULL

A

m.p. 40-41.5°

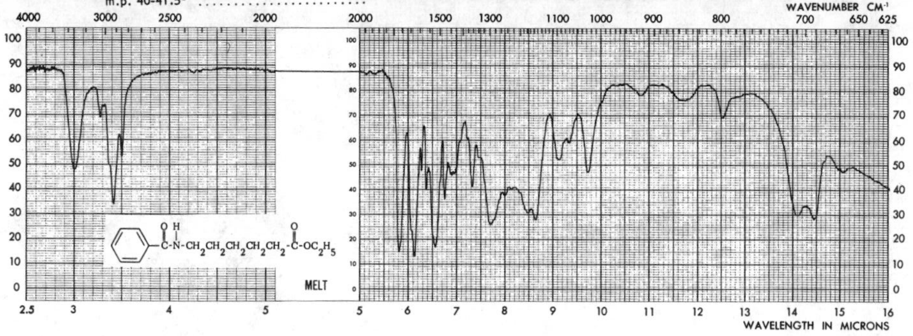

12,775-2 **1-Naphthaleneacetamide**
$C_{10}H_7CH_2CONH_2$ M.W. 185.23
m.p. 182-183.5°

B

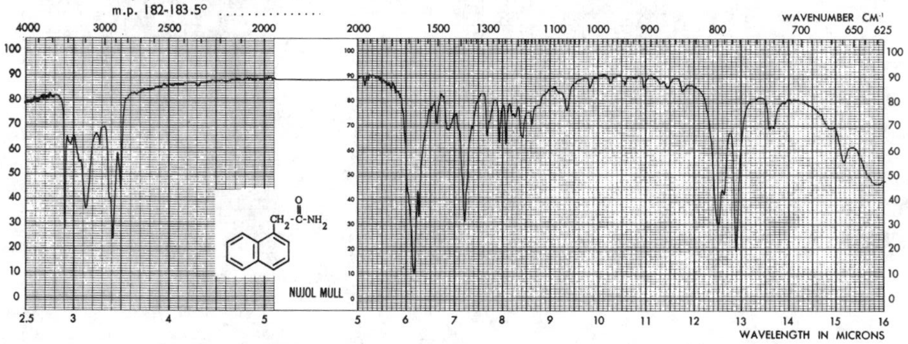

A5510 **N-(2-Aminoethyl)-1-naphthylacetamide hydrochloride**
$C_{10}H_7CH_2CONH(CH_2)_2NH_2 \cdot HCl$ M.W. 264.75
m.p. 169-171°

C

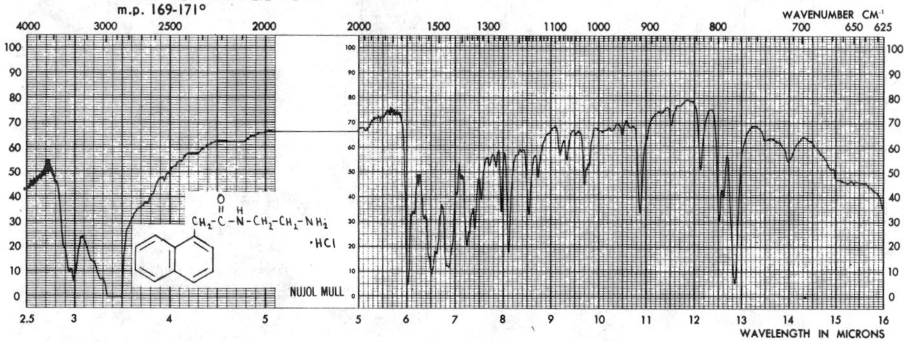

86,003-4
Naphthol AS BI, indicator grade (7-bromo-3-hydroxy-2-naphth-o-anisidide, C.I. 37566)
$BrC_{10}H_5(OH)CONHC_6H_4OCH_3$ FW 372.23
mp 180-183° Disp. C

D

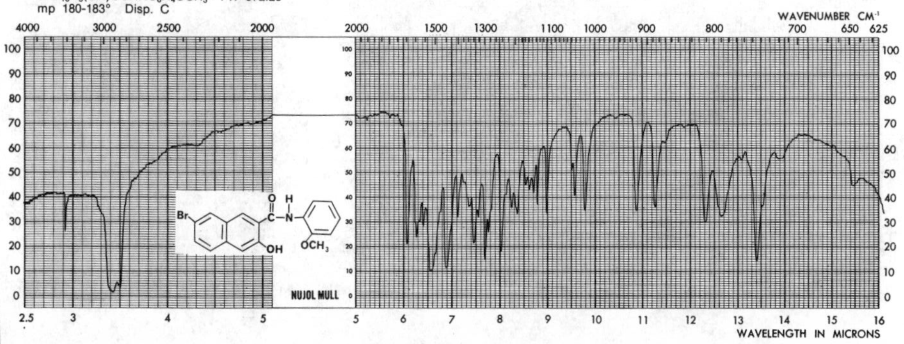

E

M.W. 211.27 m.p. 189-190°

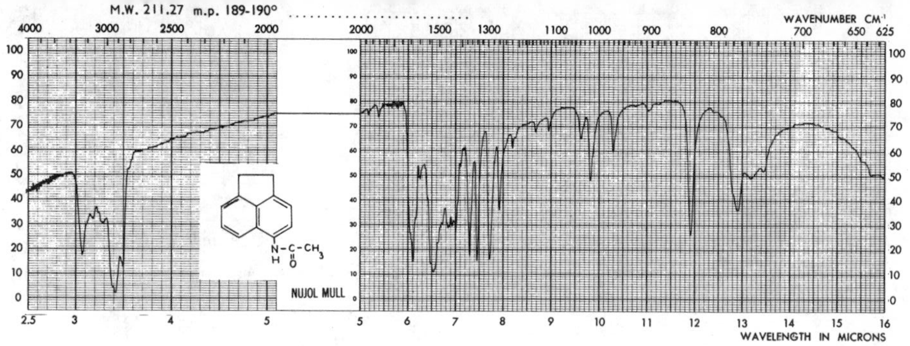

D785-6 **2-Diacetylaminofluorene** (N-2-fluorenyldiacetamide)
M.W. 265.31 m.p. 132-134.5°

F

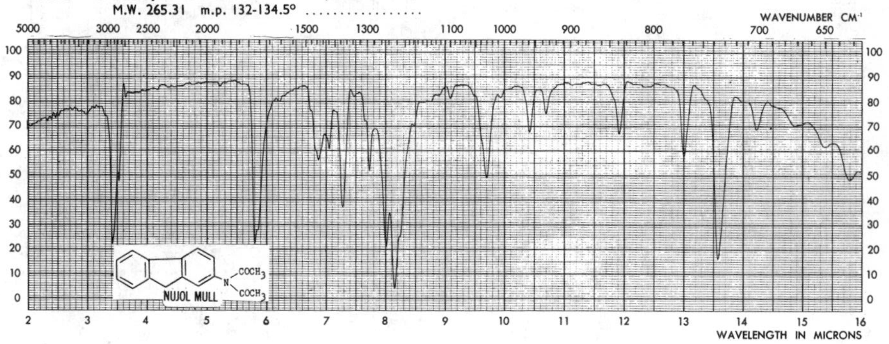

D700-7 **2,7-Diacetamidofluorene** (N,N'-fluoren-2,7-ylenebisacetamide)
M.W. 280.33 m.p. 285-289°

G

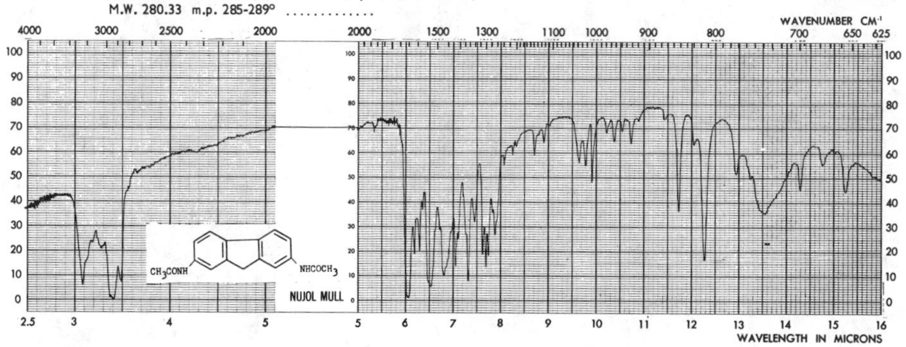

11,661-0 **N-(2-Fluorenyl)-p-toluamide**
M.W. 299.38 m.p. 216-218°

H

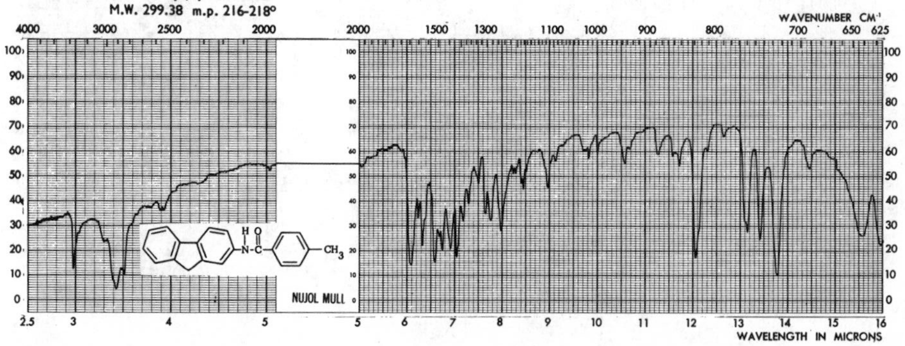

A

A750 **1-Acetamidopyrene** (N-1-pyrenylacetamide)
M.W. 259.31 m.p. 260-261°

NUJOL MULL

B

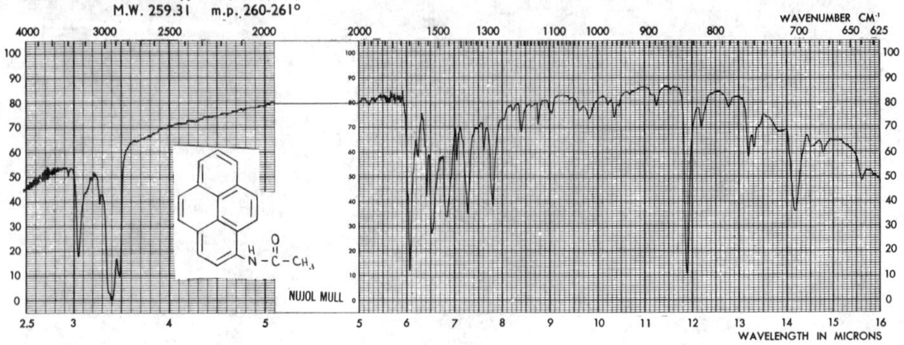

B1307-1 **Benzoylhydrazine** (benzhydrazide, benzoic acid hydrazide)
$C_6H_5CONHNH_2$ M.W. 136.15 m.p. 113-117°

NUJOL MULL

C

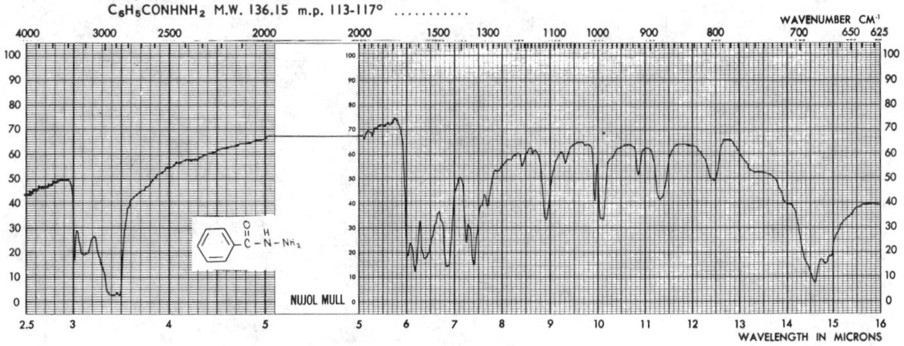

P1665-6 **Phenylacetic acid hydrazide**
$C_6H_5CH_2CONHNH_2$ M.W. 150.18 m.p. 115-116°

NUJOL MULL

D

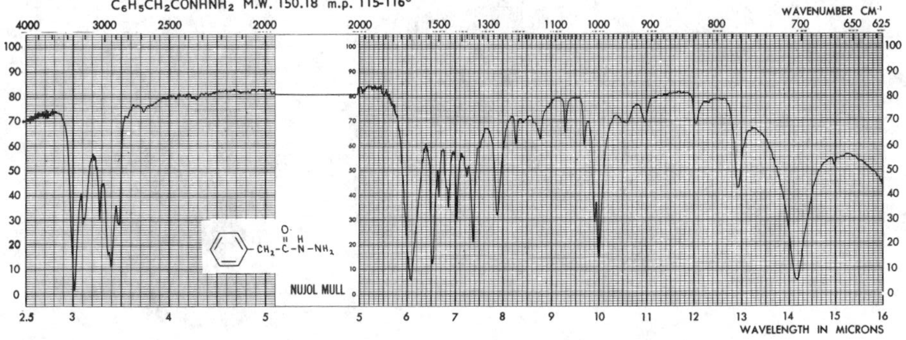

13,011-7 **1-Naphthylacetic acid hydrazide**
$C_{10}H_7CH_2CONHNH_2$ M.W. 200.24
m.p. 163-165°

E

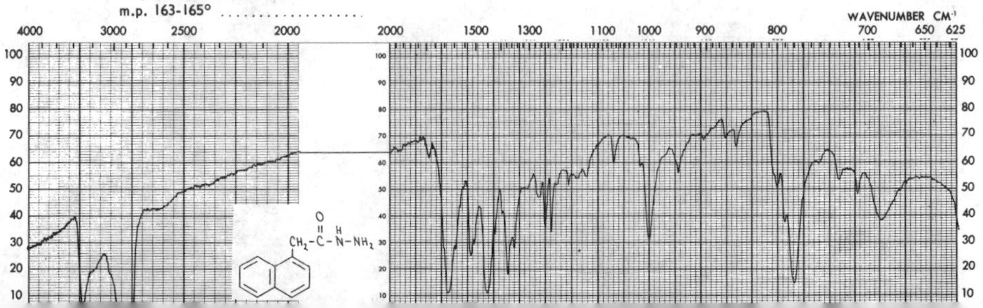

T3700-1 **p-Toluic acid hydrazide**
$CH_3C_6H_4CONHNH_2$ M.W. 150.18 m.p. 115-116°

NUJOL MULL

F

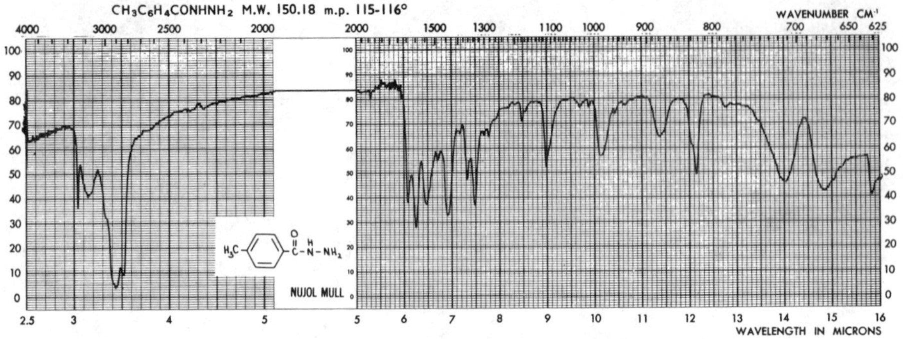

H2010-5 **p-Hydroxybenzoic acid hydrazide**
$HOC_6H_4CONHNH_2$ M.W. 152.15 m.p. 268-271°

NUJOL MULL

G

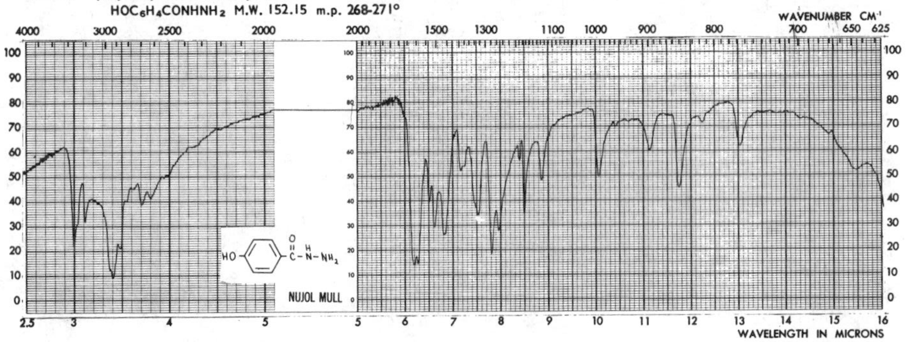

A4190-9 **p-Aminobenzoyl hydrazide** (p-aminobenzoic acid hydrazide)
$H_2NC_6H_4CONHNH_2$ M.W. 151.17
m.p. 225-227.5°

NUJOL MULL

H

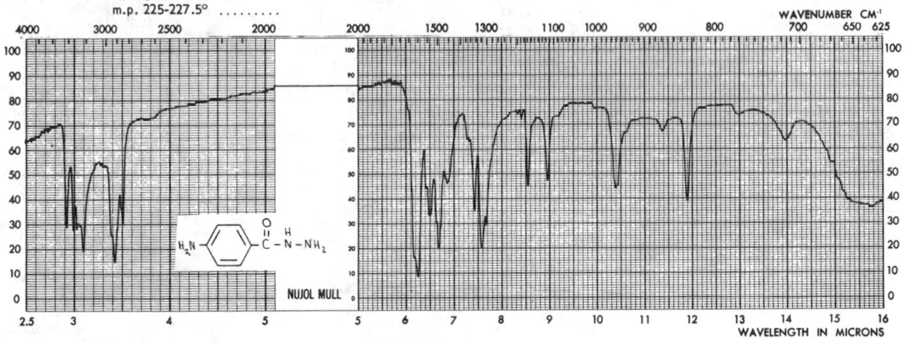

14,071-6 **Formic acid phenylhydrazide**
$HCONHNHC_6H_5$ M.W. 136.15 m.p. 143-145°

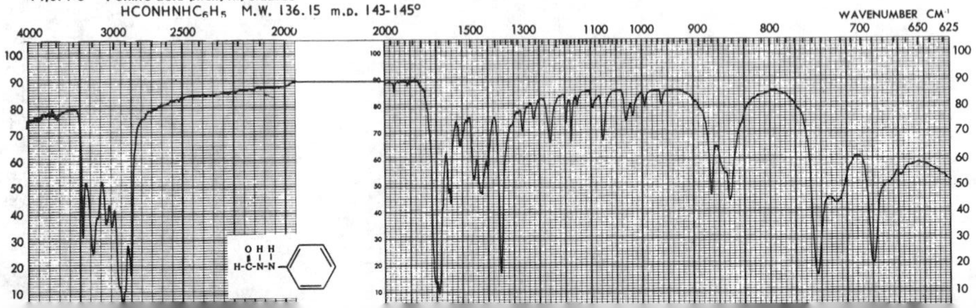

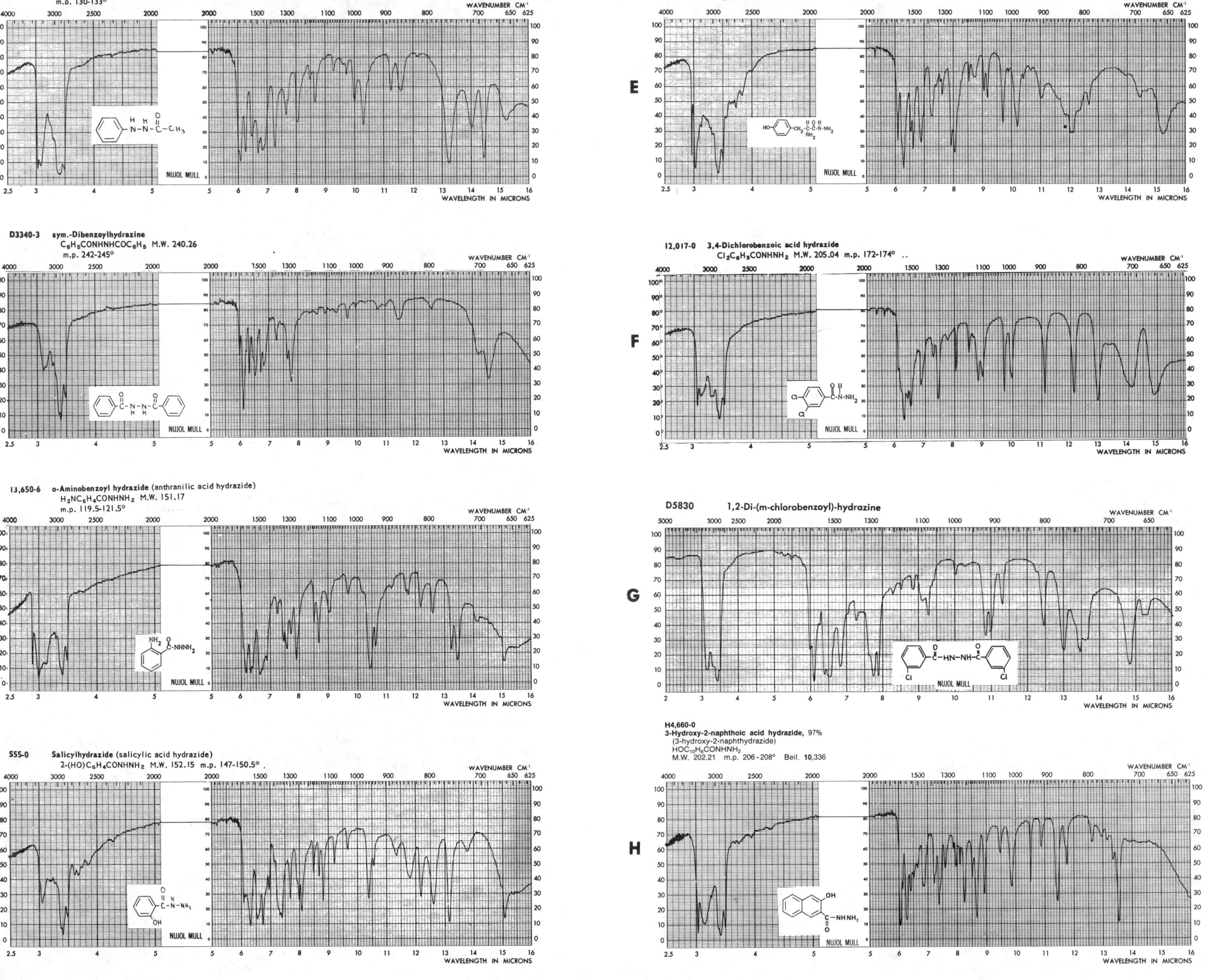

A — $C_6H_5NHNHCOCH_3$ M.W. 150.18
m.p. 130-133°

B — D3340-3 sym.-Dibenzoylhydrazine
$C_6H_5CONHNHCOC_6H_5$ M.W. 240.26
m.p. 242-245°

C — 13,650-6 o-Aminobenzoyl hydrazide (anthranilic acid hydrazide)
$H_2NC_6H_4CONHNH_2$ M.W. 151.17
m.p. 119.5-121.5°

D — S55-0 Salicylhydrazide (salicylic acid hydrazide)
2-(HO)$C_6H_4CONHNH_2$ M.W. 152.15 m.p. 147-150.5°

E — m.p. 196-198°

F — 12,017-0 3,4-Dichlorobenzoic acid hydrazide
$Cl_2C_6H_3CONHNH_2$ M.W. 205.04 m.p. 172-174°

G — D5830 1,2-Di-(m-chlorobenzoyl)-hydrazine

H — H4,660-0
3-Hydroxy-2-naphthoic acid hydrazide, 97%
(3-hydroxy-2-naphthydrazide)
$HOC_{10}H_6CONHNH_2$
M.W. 202.21 m.p. 206-208° Beil. 10,336

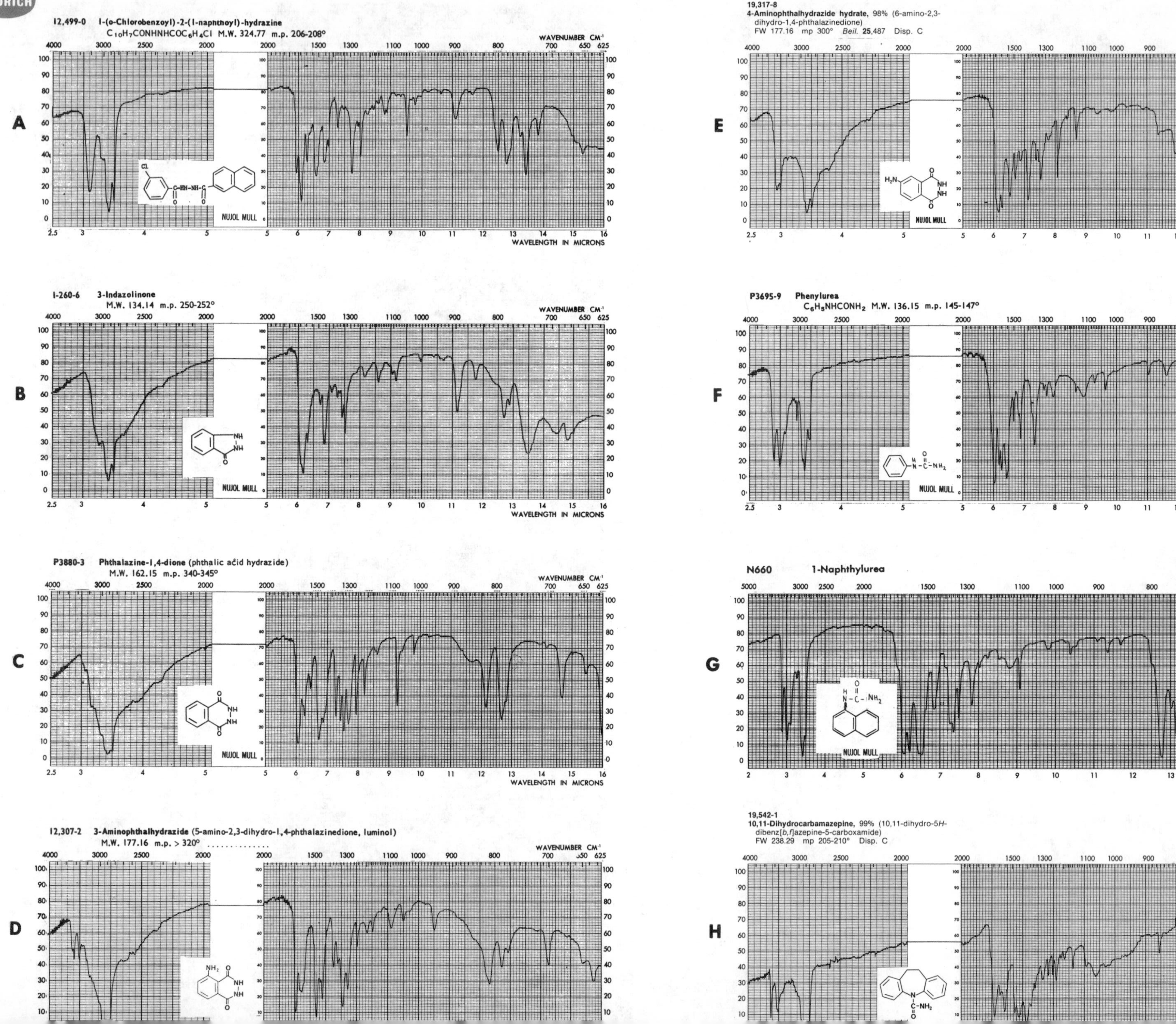
A
12,499-0 1-(o-Chlorobenzoyl)-2-(1-naphthoyl)-hydrazine
$C_{10}H_7CONHNHCOC_6H_4Cl$ M.W. 324.77 m.p. 206-208°
NUJOL MULL
B
1-260-6 3-Indazolinone
M.W. 134.14 m.p. 250-252°
NUJOL MULL
C
P3880-3 Phthalazine-1,4-dione (phthalic acid hydrazide)
M.W. 162.15 m.p. 340-345°
NUJOL MULL
D
12,307-2 3-Aminophthalhydrazide (5-amino-2,3-dihydro-1,4-phthalazinedione, luminol)
M.W. 177.16 m.p. > 320°
E
19,317-8
4-Aminophthalhydrazide hydrate, 98% (6-amino-2,3-dihydro-1,4-phthalazinedione)
FW 177.16 mp 300° Beil. 25,487 Disp. C
NUJOL MULL
F
P3695-9 Phenylurea
$C_6H_5NHCONH_2$ M.W. 136.15 m.p. 145-147°
NUJOL MULL
G
N660 1-Naphthylurea
NUJOL MULL
H
19,542-1
10,11-Dihydrocarbamazepine, 99% (10,11-dihydro-5H-dibenz[b,f]azepine-5-carboxamide)
FW 238.29 mp 205-210° Disp. C
WAVENUMBER CM⁻¹
WAVELENGTH IN MICRONS
ALDRICH

A B2872-9 **Benzyloxyurea**
$C_6H_5CH_2ONHCONH_2$ M.W. 166.18 m.p. 139-143°

B P3480-8 **4-Phenylsemicarbazide**
$C_6H_5NHCONHNH_2$ M.W. 151.17 m.p. 122-125°

C 22,160-0
4-Phenylsemicarbazide hydrochloride, 99%
$C_6H_5NHCONHNH_2 \cdot HCl$ FW 187.63 mp 215-217°
Beil. 12,378 Disp. C

D 14,215-8 **Carbanilide** (sym.-diphenylurea)
$C_6H_5NHCONHC_6H_5$ M.W. 212.25
m.p. 235-238°

E 13,472-4 **sym.-Diphenylcarbazide (1,5-diphenylcarbohydrazide), tech.**
$C_6H_5NHNHCONHNHC_6H_5$ M.W. 242.28
m.p. 166-168°

F 12,453-2 **Phenylazoformic acid 2-phenylhydrazide** (diphenylcarbazone)
$C_6H_5N{:}NCONHNHC_6H_5$ M.W. 240.27
m.p. 156° (dec.)

G 12,035-9 **N,N-Diphenyl-N'-methylurea**
$(C_6H_5)_2NCONHCH_3$ M.W. 226.28 m.p. 170-174°

H 21,410-8
N,N'-Bis[3-(4,5-dihydro-1*H*-imidazol-2-yl)phenyl]urea dipropanoate, 99%
FW 496.57 mp 205° (dec.) Disp. C

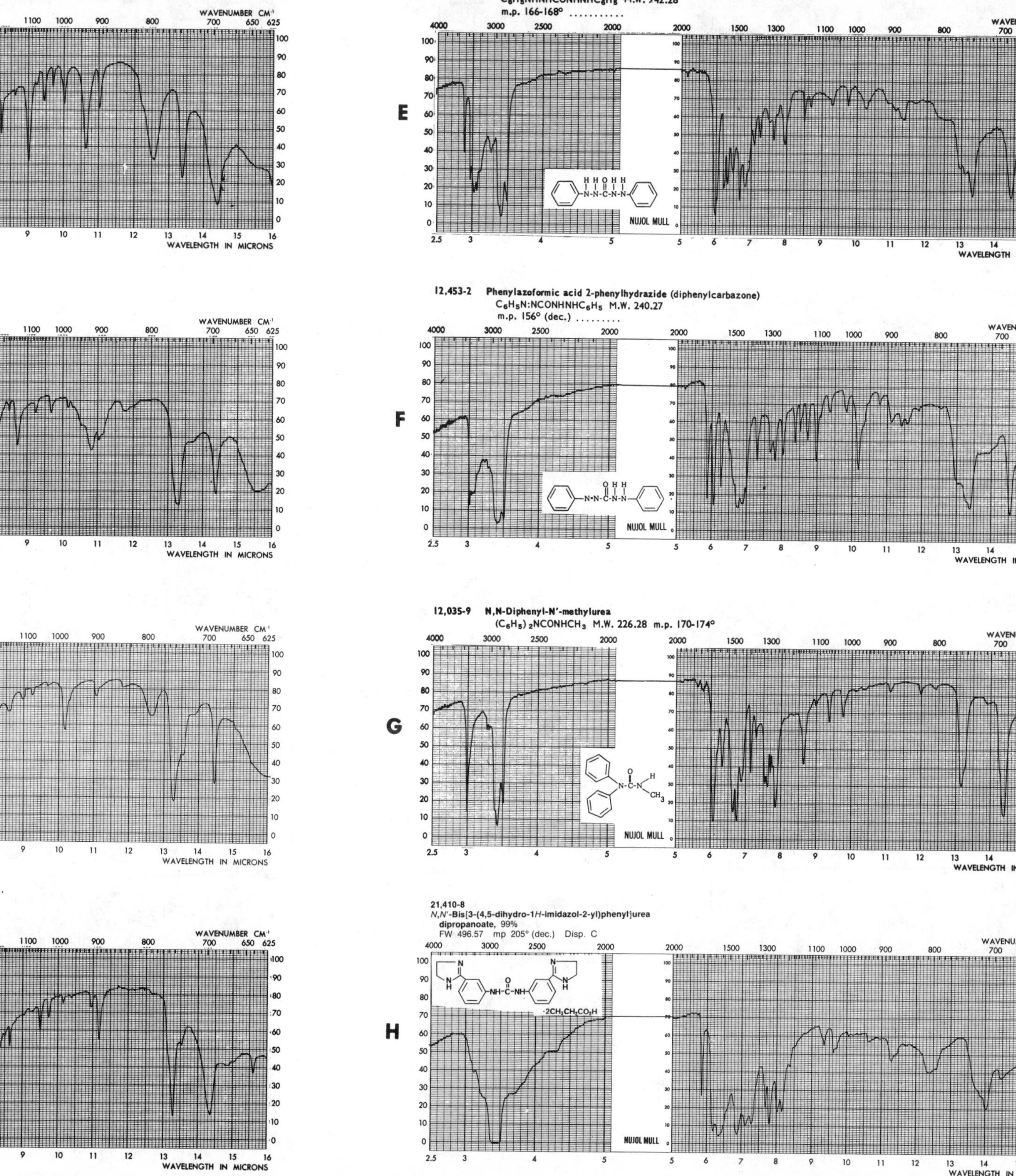

ALDRICH

A

B1,500-7
Benzoylurea
$C_6H_5CONHCONH_2$
M.W. 164.16 m.p. 211-213° Beil. 9,215

NUJOL MULL

B

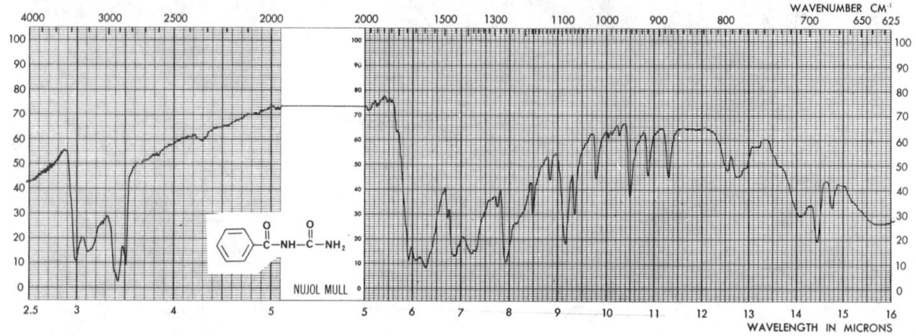

11,814-1 **Phenylacetylurea**
$C_6H_5CH_2CONHCONH_2$ M.W. 178.19
m.p. 214-216°

NUJOL MULL

C

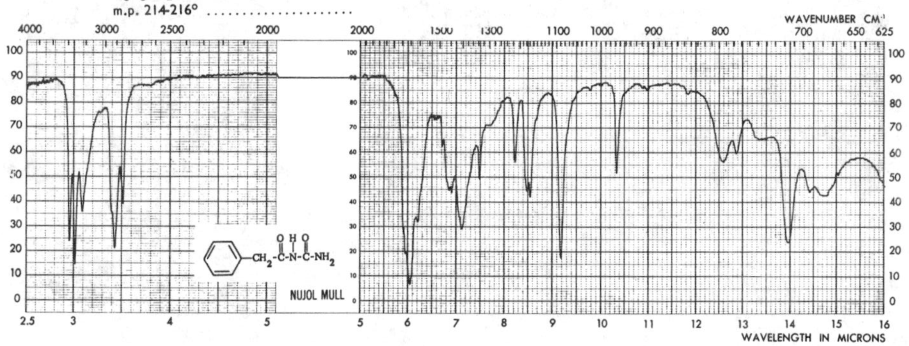

12,794-9 **1-Benzoylsemicarbazide**
$C_6H_5CONHNHCONH_2$ M.W. 179.18
m.p. 218° (dec.)

NUJOL MULL

D

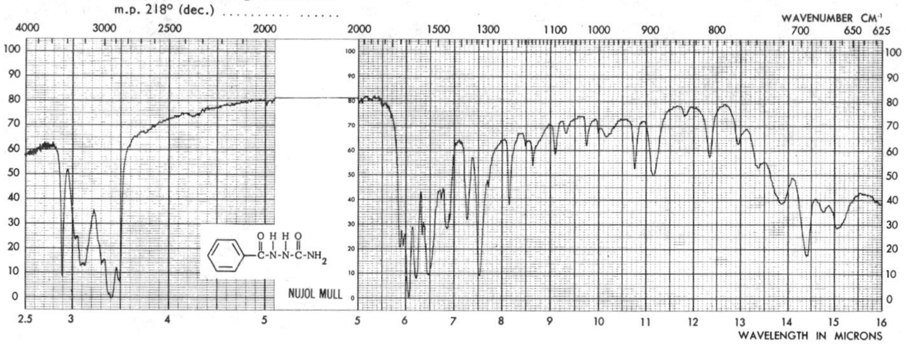

11,726-9 **α-Chloro-α-phenylacetylurea**
$C_6H_5CH(Cl)CONHCONH_2$ M.W. 212.64
m.p. 190-191.5°

E

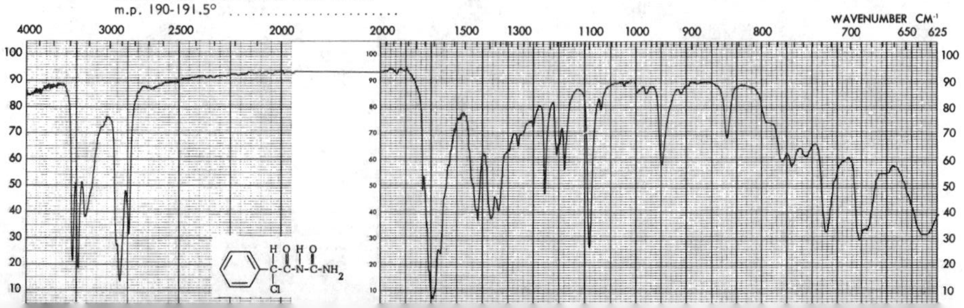

17,821-7
Ethyl oxanilate, 98%
$C_6H_5NHCOCO_2C_2H_5$
M.W. 193.2 m.p. 67-69°

NUJOL MULL

F

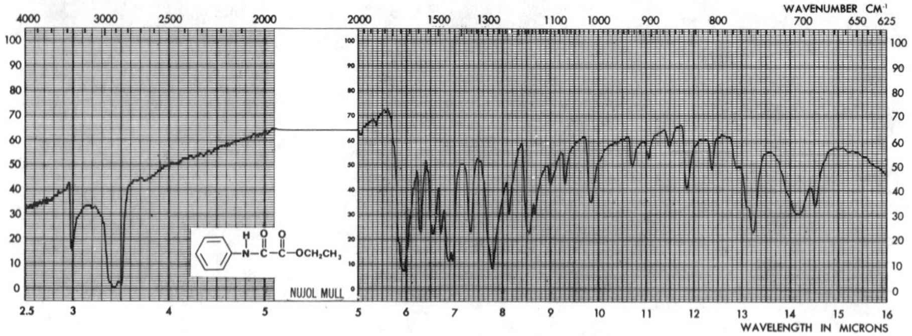

17,743-1
Ethyl 4'-methyloxanilate, 97%
$CH_3C_6H_4NHCOCO_2C_2H_5$
M.W. 207.23 m.p. 67-68° Beil. 12,930

NUJOL MULL

G

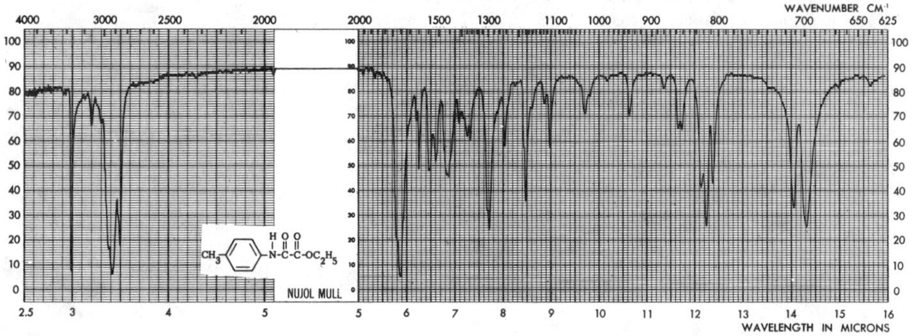

17,741-5
Ethyl 4'-chlorooxanilate, 97%
$ClC_6H_4NHCOCO_2C_2H_5$
M.W. 227.65 m.p. 151-153° Beil. 12,614

NUJOL MULL

H

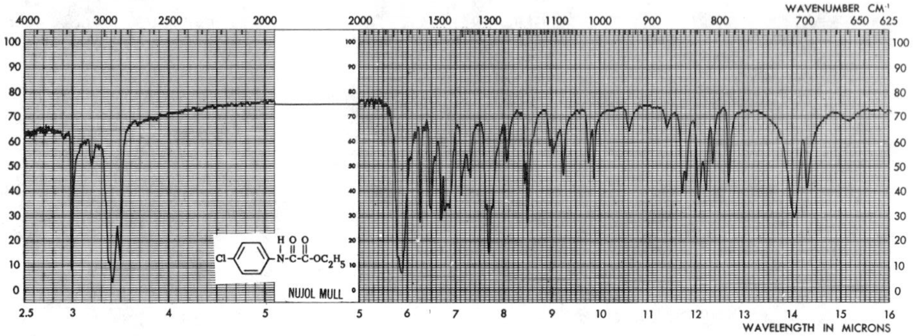

17,742-3
Ethyl 4'-phenyloxanilate, 98%
$C_6H_5C_6H_4NHCOCO_2C_2H_5$
M.W. 269.3 m.p. 129-132°

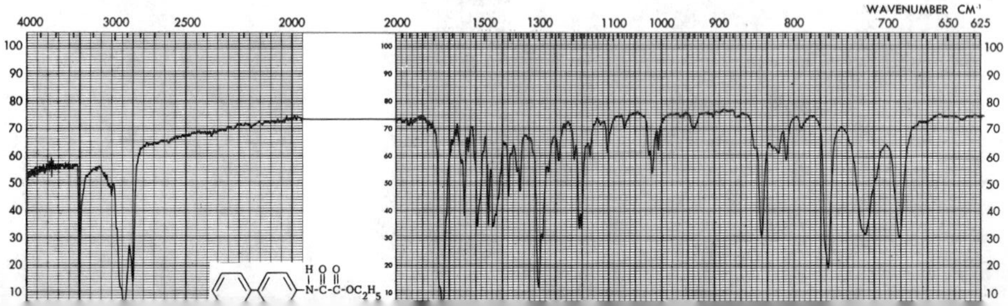

A

$CH_3C_6H_4NHCONH_2$ M.W. 150.18
m.p. 187-188°

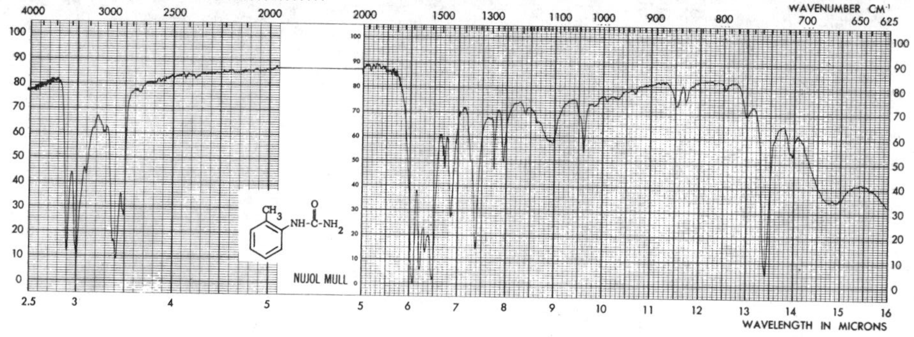

NUJOL MULL

B

14,919-5 p-Chlorophenylurea
$ClC_6H_4NHCONH_2$ M.W. 170.60 m.p. 203-205°

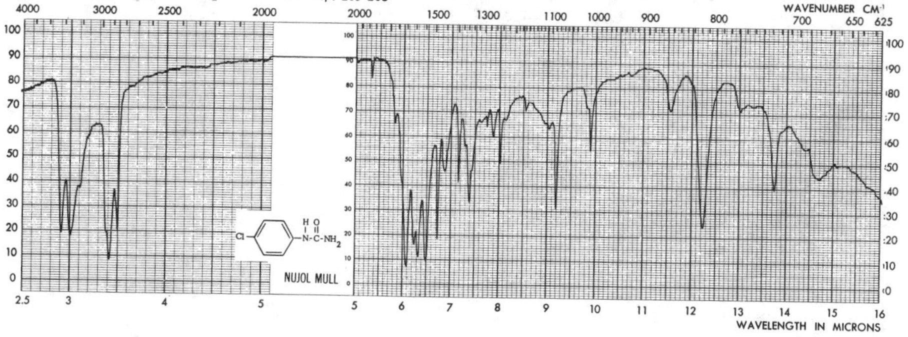

NUJOL MULL

C

12,671-3 3a,6a-Diphenylglycoluril
M.W. 294.32 m.p. > 300°

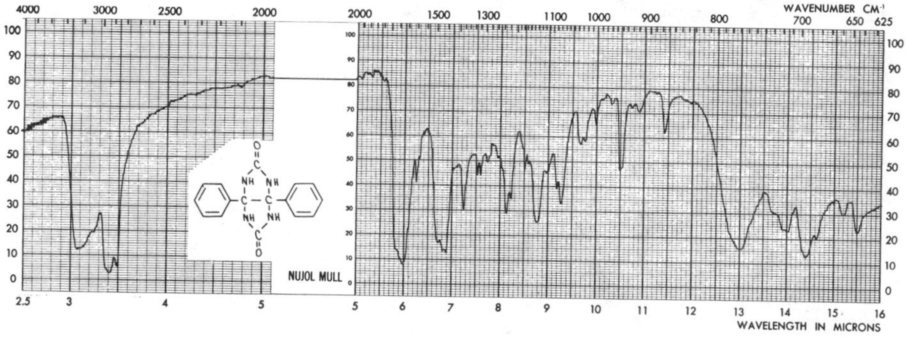

NUJOL MULL

D

12,955-0 4-(2-Keto-1-benzimidazolinyl)-piperidine
M.W. 217.27 m.p. 180-185°

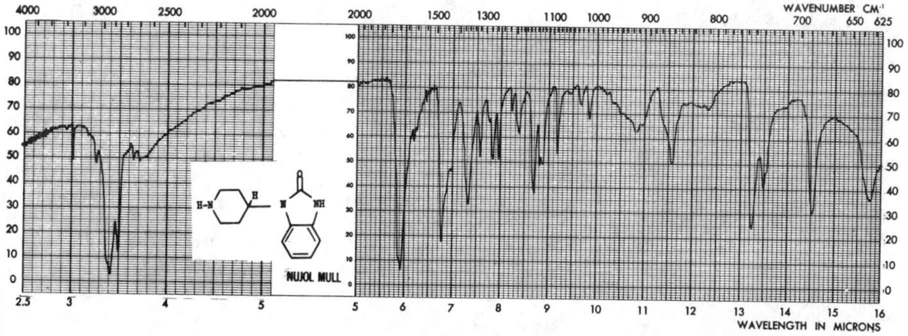

NUJOL MULL

E

K15-0 4-(2-Keto-1-benzimidazolinyl)-1,2,3,6-tetrahydropyridine
M.W. 215.26 m.p. 193-198°

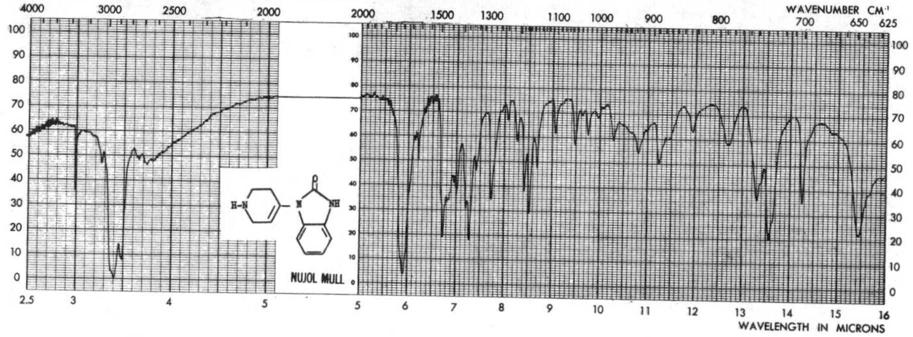

NUJOL MULL

F

B2536-3 1-Benzyl-4-(2-keto-1-benzimidazolinyl)-1,2,3,6-tetrahydropyridine [1-(1-benzyl-1,2,3,6-tetrahydropyrid-4-yl)-benzimidazolin-2-one)
M.W. 305.38 m.p. 164-166°

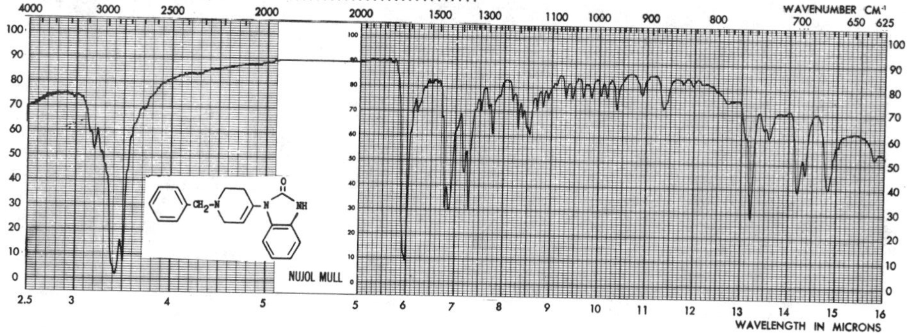

NUJOL MULL

G

86,165-0
d-Biotin *p*-nitrophenyl ester, 99%
FW 365.40 mp 166-167°
$[\alpha]^{25}$ +47° (c=2, DMF/1% C_2H_5OH) Disp. C

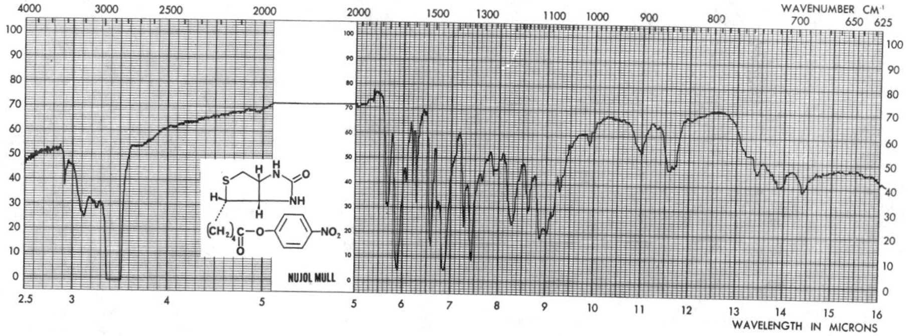

NUJOL MULL

H

P2140-4 Phenyl carbamate
$H_2NCO_2C_6H_5$ M.W. 137.14 m.p. 149-152°

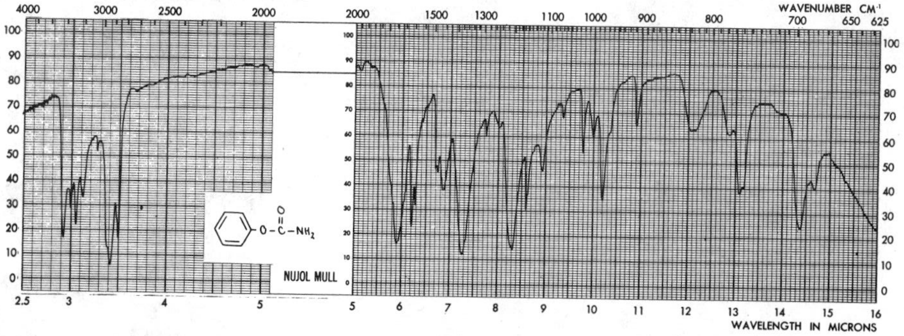

NUJOL MULL

ALDRICH

A

B1820-0 **Benzyl carbamate**
$H_2NCO_2CH_2C_6H_5$ M.W. 151.17 m.p. 87-89°
NUJOL MULL

B

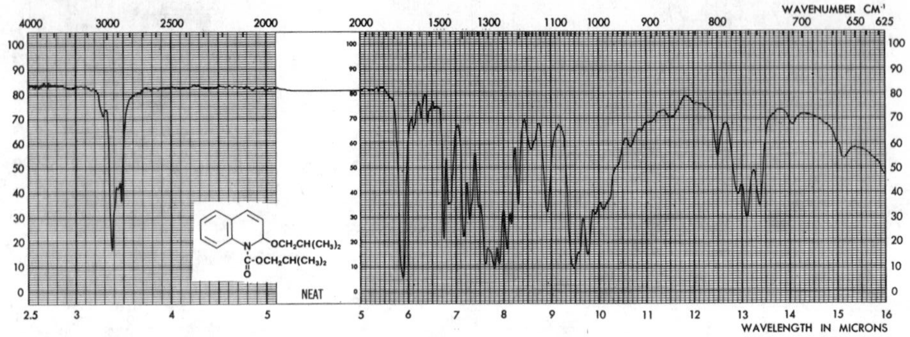

15,239-0 **Ethyl N-benzyl-N-cyclopropylcarbamate**
$C_6H_5CH_2N(C_3H_5)CO_2C_2H_5$ M.W. 219.29
n_D^{20} 1.5104
NEAT

C

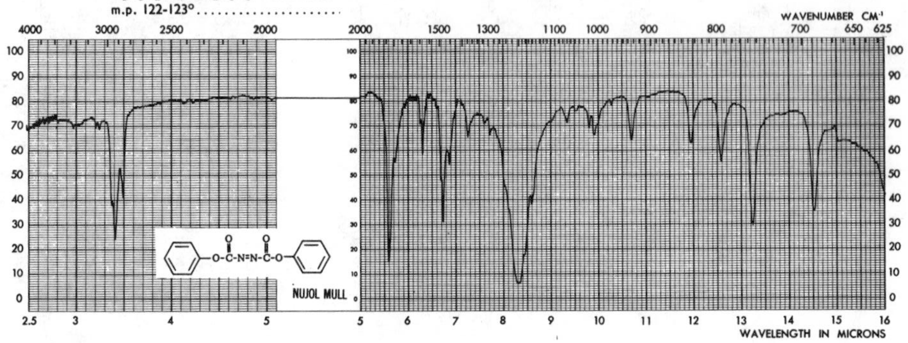

15,250-1 **p-Methoxybenzyl hydrazinocarboxylate** (p-methoxybenzyl carbazate)
$H_2NNHCO_2CH_2C_6H_4OCH_3$ M.W. 196.21
m.p. 75-76°
NUJOL MULL

D

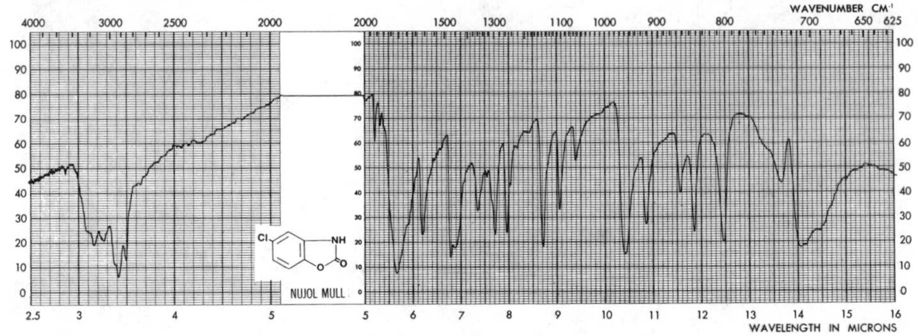

14,983-7 **EEDQ** (N-ethoxycarbonyl-2-ethoxy-1,2-dihydroquinoline, ethyl 1,2-dihydro-2-ethoxy-1-quinolinecarboxylate), **puriss., 99+%**
M.W. 247.30 m.p. 66-67°

E

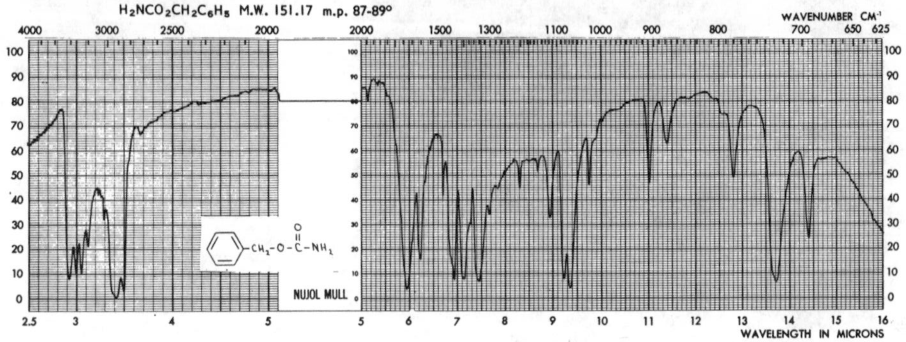

17,824-1
IIDQ (2-isobutoxy-1-isobutoxycarbonyl-1,2-dihydroquinoline, isobutyl 1,2-dihydro-2-isobutoxy-1-quinolinecarboxylate)
M.W. 303.4 b.p. 140-142°/0.2mm. n_D^{20} 1.5230
d 1.022
NEAT

F

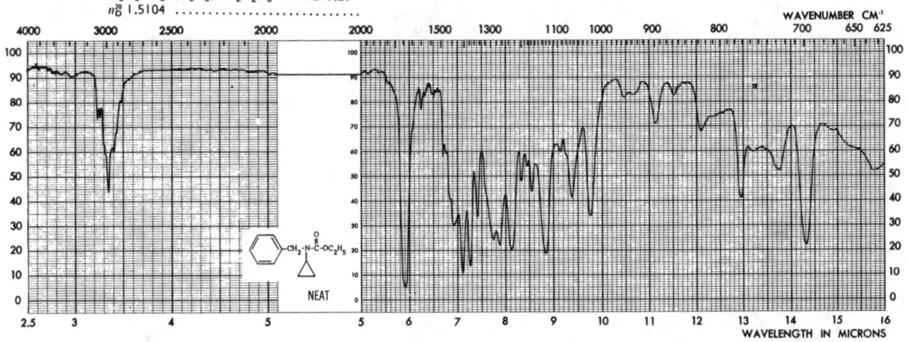

13,341-8 **Diphenyl azodicarboxylate**
$C_6H_5O_2CN{:}NCO_2C_6H_5$ M.W. 270.25
m.p. 122-123°
NUJOL MULL

G

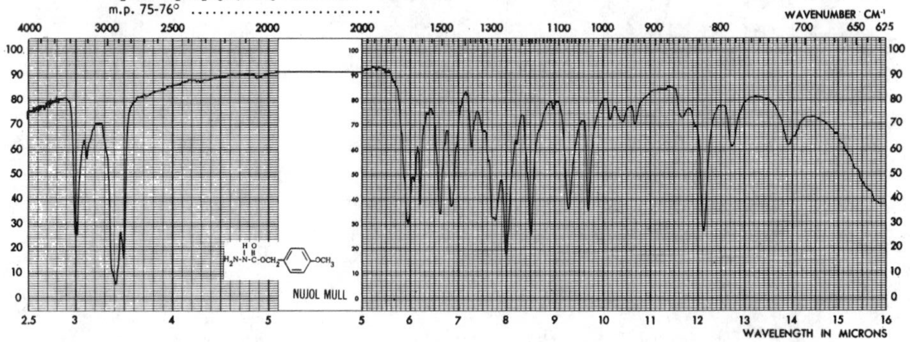

85,974-5
Chlorzoxazone (5-chloro-2-benzoxazolone), 98%
M.W. 169.57 m.p. 191-192° Beil. **27**,179
NUJOL MULL

H

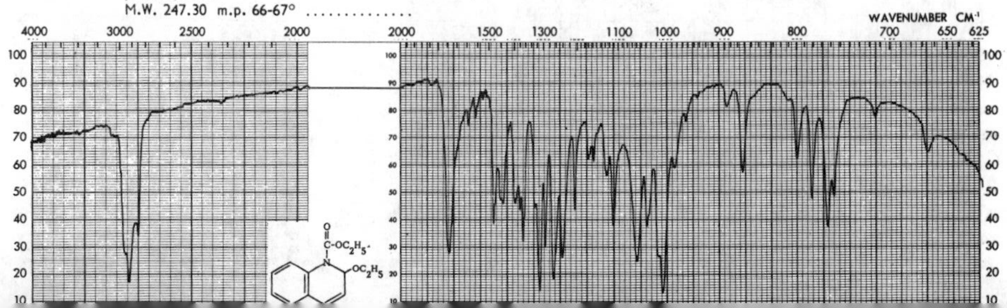

12,375-7 **1-Benzyl-2-pyrrolidone**
M.W. 175.23 n_D^{20} 1.5491

WAVENUMBER CM⁻¹ / WAVELENGTH IN MICRONS

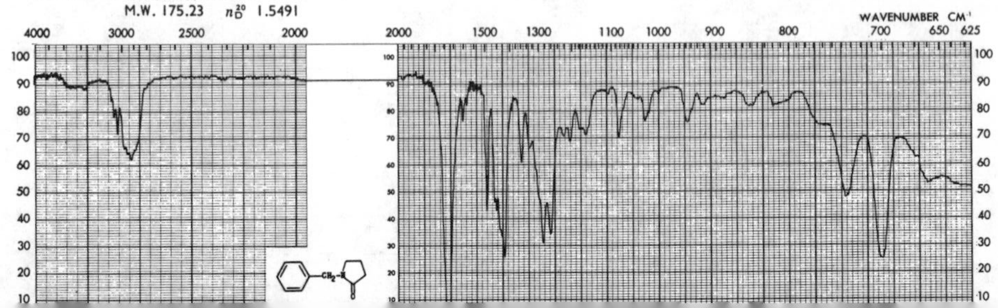

A O-980-8 **Oxindole**
M.W. 133.15 m.p. 125-127°
NUJOL MULL

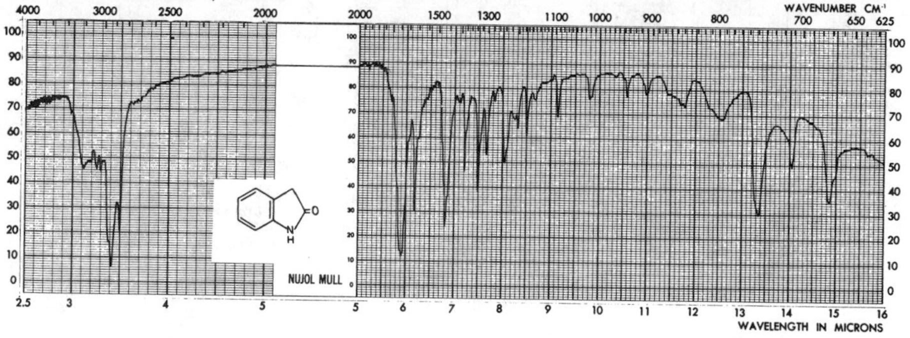

B 11,406-5 **N-Phenylphthalimidine**
M.W. 209.25 m.p. 159-160°
NUJOL MULL

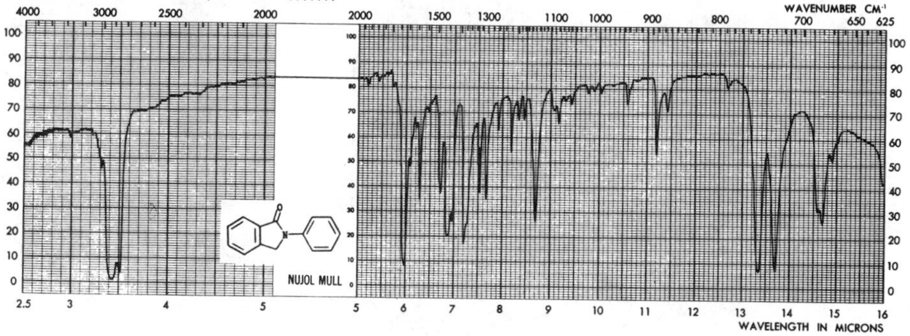

C 18,367-9
Methyl 1-benzyl-5-oxo-3-pyrrolidinecarboxylate, 98%
M.W. 233.27 m.p. 63-66°
MELT

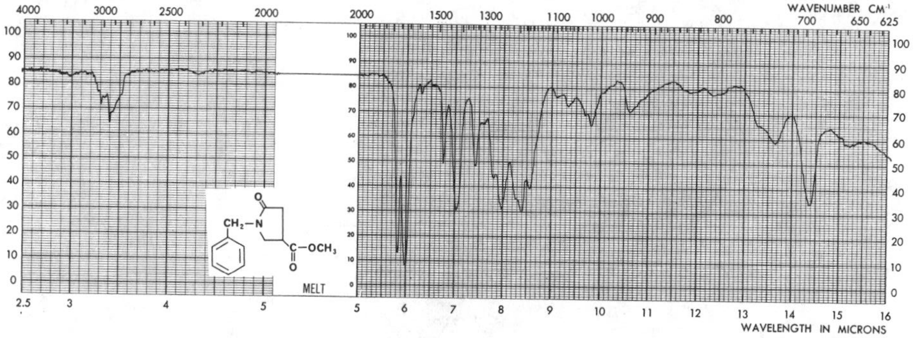

D 12,748-5 **5-Chlorooxindole**
M.W. 167.60 m.p. 197-199°
NUJOL MULL

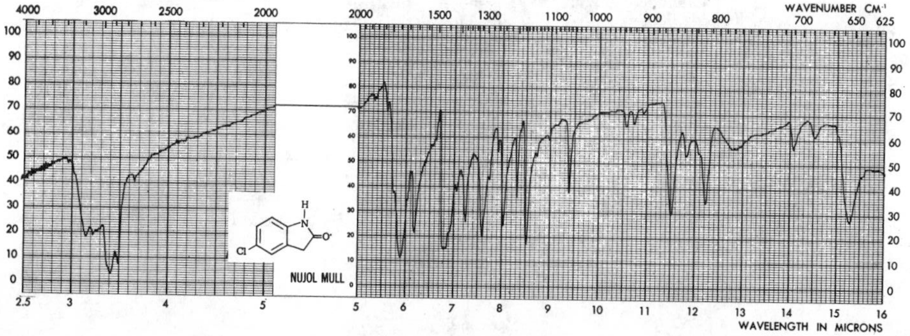

E 12,249-1 **5-Hydroxyoxindole**
M.W. 149.15 m.p. 272-274° (dec.)
NUJOL MULL

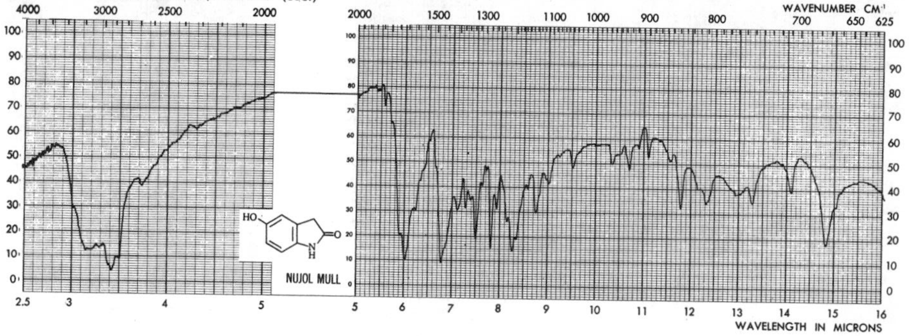

F 85,012-8
1-Acetyl-5-nitroindoline
FW 206.20 mp 175-176° *NMR* 7,91A Disp. C
NUJOL MULL

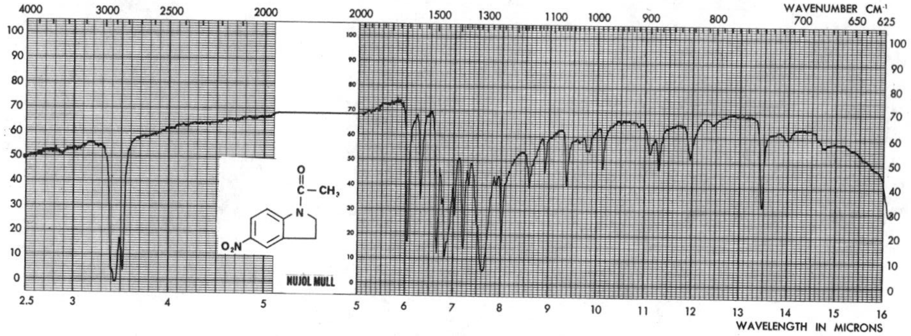

G B4720-0 **3,3-Bis-(4-hydroxyphenyl)-oxindole [3,3-bis-(p-hydroxyphenyl)-2-indolinol**
M.W. 317.34 m.p. 259-261°
NUJOL MULL

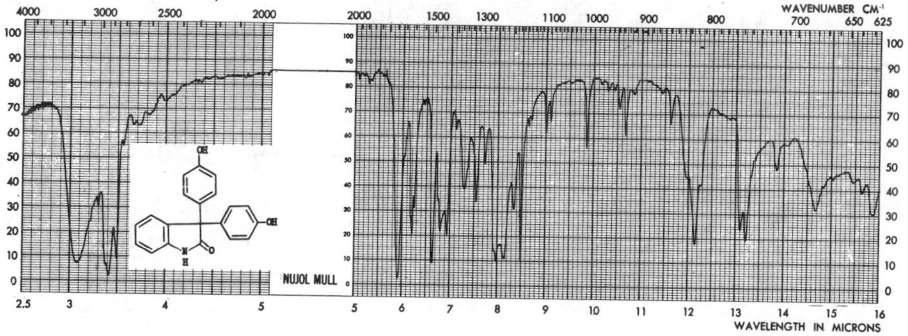

H 14,366-9 **1-Benzyl-3-benzyloxy-2(1H)-pyridone**
M.W. 291.35 m.p. 113-116°
NUJOL MULL

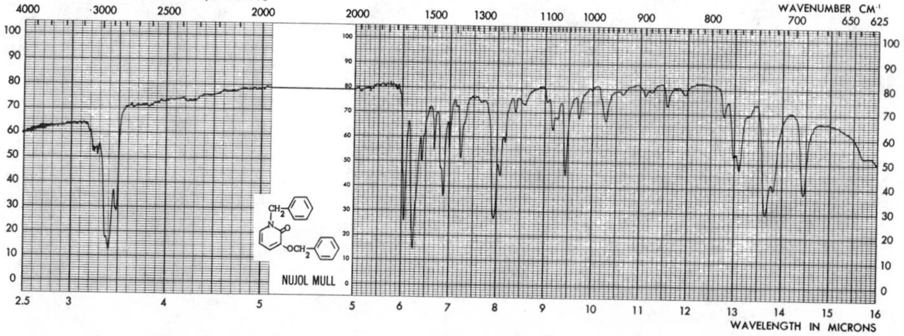

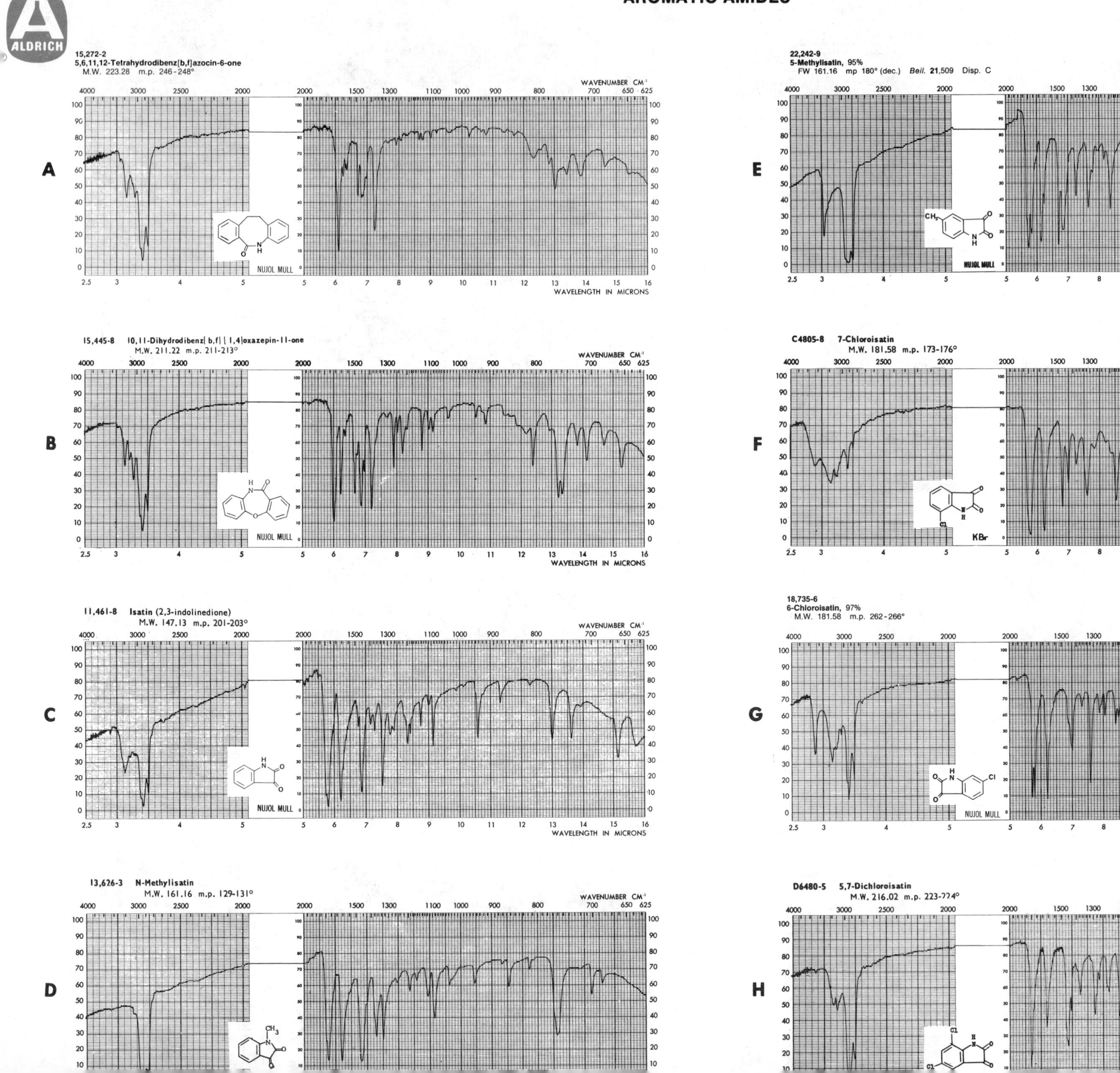
ALDRICH
A
15,272-2
5,6,11,12-Tetrahydrodibenz[b,f]azocin-6-one
M.W. 223.28 m.p. 246-248°
NUJOL MULL
B
15,445-8 10,11-Dihydrodibenz[b,f][1,4]oxazepin-11-one
M.W. 211.22 m.p. 211-213°
NUJOL MULL
C
11,461-8 Isatin (2,3-indolinedione)
M.W. 147.13 m.p. 201-203°
NUJOL MULL
D
13,626-3 N-Methylisatin
M.W. 161.16 m.p. 129-131°
E
22,242-9
5-Methylisatin, 95%
FW 161.16 mp 180° (dec.) Beil. 21,509 Disp. C
NUJOL MULL
F
C4805-8 7-Chloroisatin
M.W. 181.58 m.p. 173-176°
KBr
G
18,735-6
6-Chloroisatin, 97%
M.W. 181.58 m.p. 262-266°
NUJOL MULL
H
D6480-5 5,7-Dichloroisatin
M.W. 216.02 m.p. 223-224°
WAVENUMBER CM⁻¹
WAVELENGTH IN MICRONS

A

12,407-9 5-Bromoisatin
M.W. 226.03 m.p. 251-253°

NUJOL MULL

B

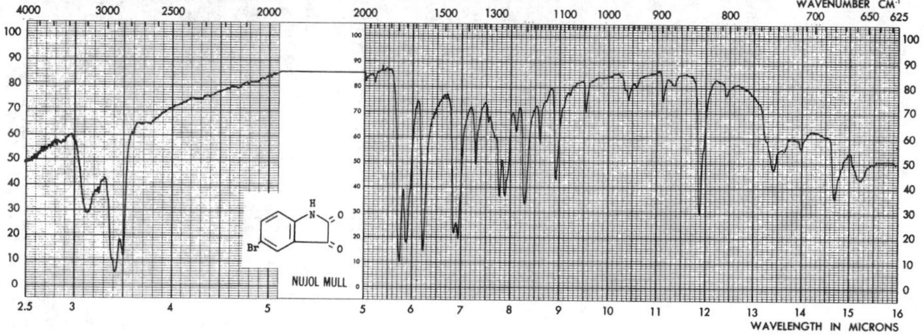

10,462-0 4-(Trifluoromethyl)-isatin [4-(trifluoromethyl)-2,3-indolinedione]
M.W. 215.13 m.p. 225-228°

NUJOL MULL

C

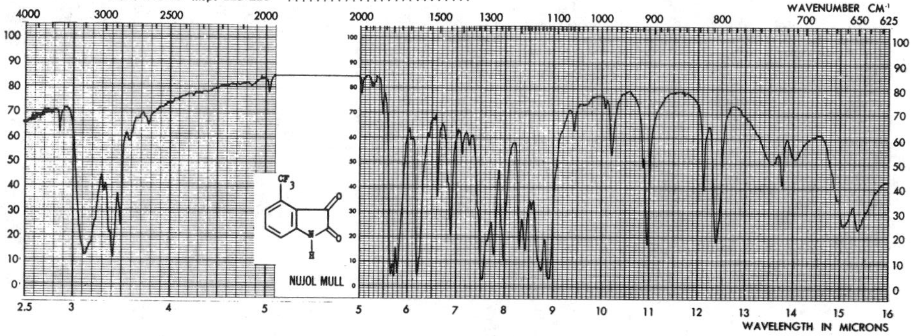

N1780-7 5-Nitroisatin
M.W. 192.13 m.p. 251° (dec.)

NUJOL MULL

D

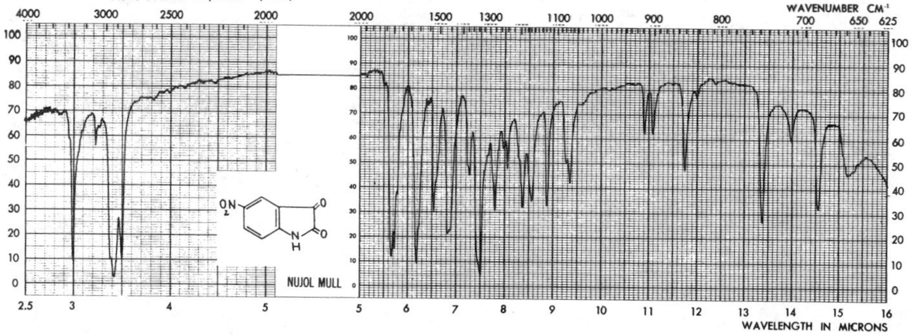

10,541-4 4-Methyl-1-phenyl-3-pyrazolidinone
M.W. 176.22 m.p. 102-105°

NUJOL MULL

E

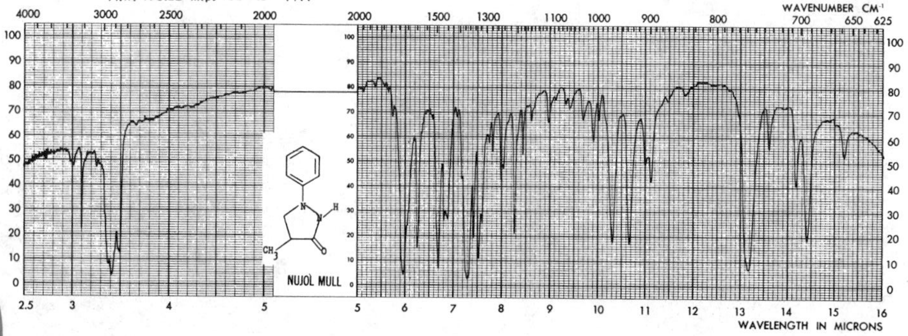

12,791-4 1-Phenyl-3-pyrazolidinone
M.W. 162.20 m.p. 122-123°

NUJOL MULL

F

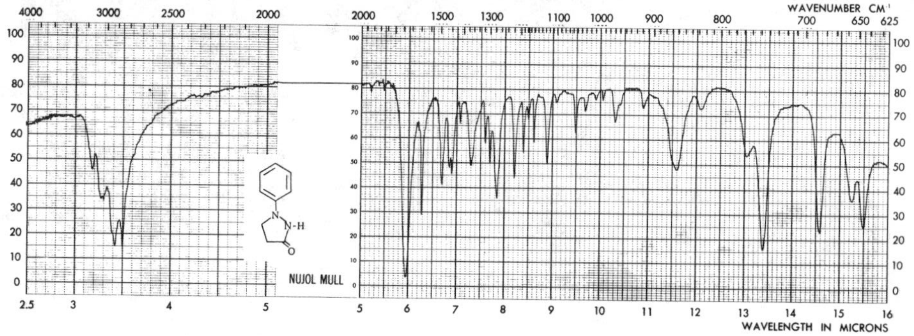

D21,240-7 1,3-Diphenyl-5-pyrazolone
M.W. 236.27 m.p. 135-137°

NUJOL MULL

G

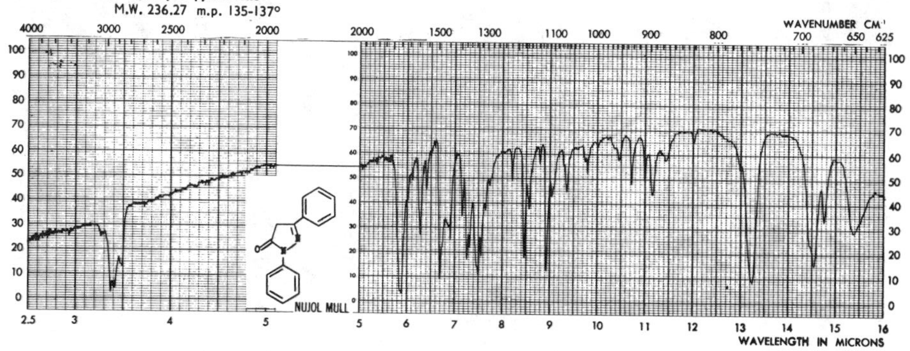

12,782-5 4,5-Dihydro-6-methyl-2-phenyl-3(2H)-pyridazinone
M.W. 188.23 m.p. 105.5-108°

NUJOL MULL

H

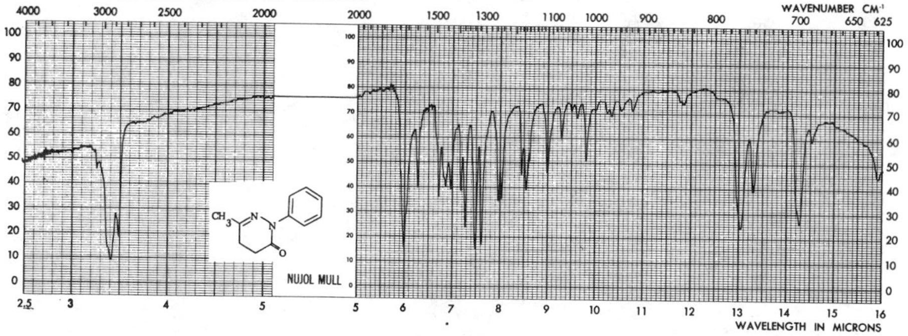

17,684-2
1-Phenyl-4,5-dichloro-6-pyridazone, 99+%,
GOLD LABEL
M.W. 241.08 m.p. 164-166°

NUJOL MULL

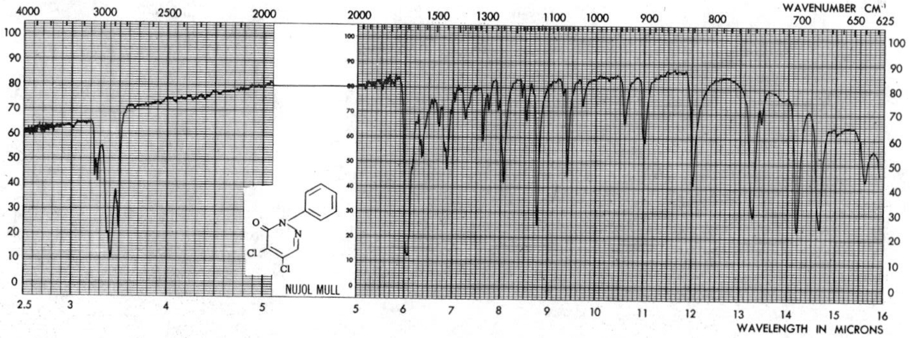

A A9135-3 **Antipyrine** (2,3-dimethyl-1-phenyl-3-pyrazolin-5-one, phenazone)
M.W. 188.23 m.p. 111.5-114°
NUJOL MULL

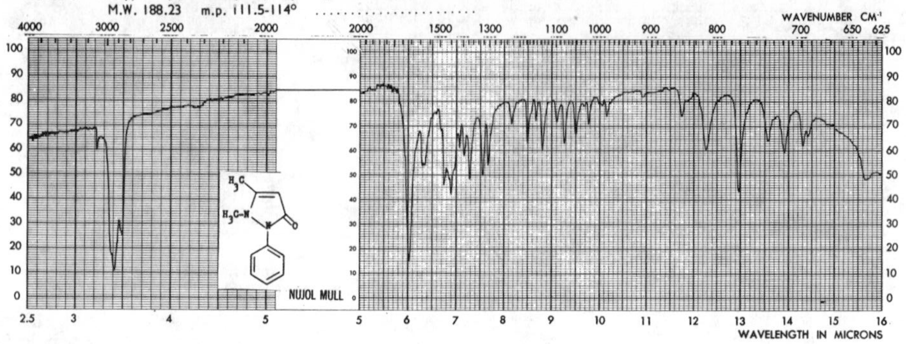

B 21,405-1
2,3-Dimethyl-1-(4-methylphenyl)-3-pyrazolin-5-one,
99+% (4'-methylphenazone)
FW 202.26 mp 134-137° *Beil.* **24**,39 Disp. C
NUJOL MULL

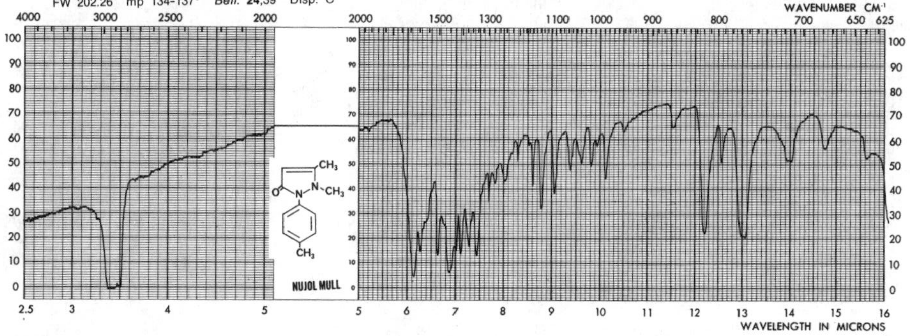

C D2760-8 **4,4'-Diantipyrylmethane** (trichachnine) **monohydrate**
M.W. 406.49 m.p. 151-158°
NUJOL MULL

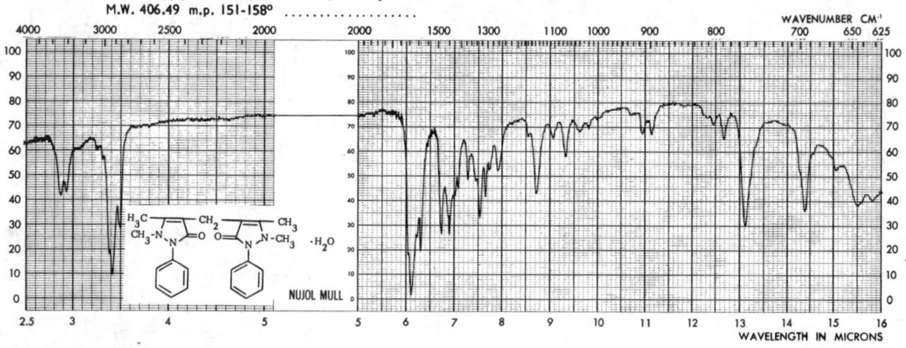

D 10,942-8 **4-Hydroxyantipyrine**
M.W. 204.23 m.p. 184-186°

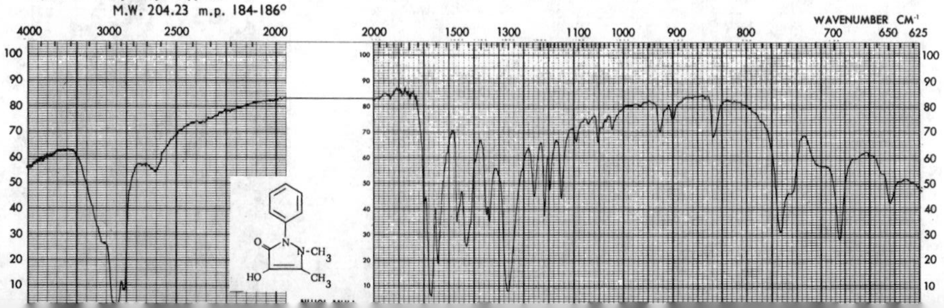

E A3930-0 **4-Aminoantipyrine** (4-aminophenazone)
M.W. 203.25 m.p. 107.5-109°
NUJOL MULL

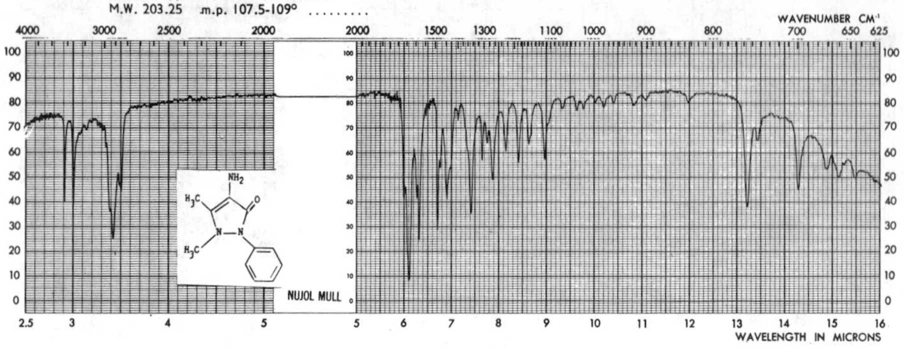

F D13,910-6 **4-Dimethylaminoantipyrine** (aminopyrine)
M.W. 231.30 m.p. 105-107°
NUJOL MULL

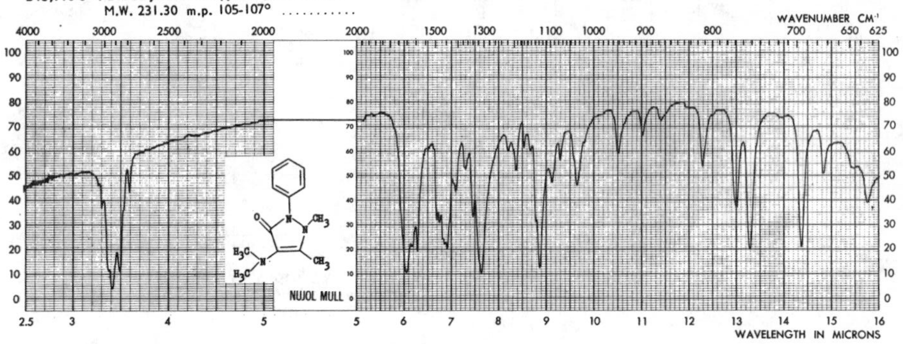

G A160-6 **4-Acetamidoantipyrine**
M.W. 245.28 m.p. 200-203°
NUJOL MULL

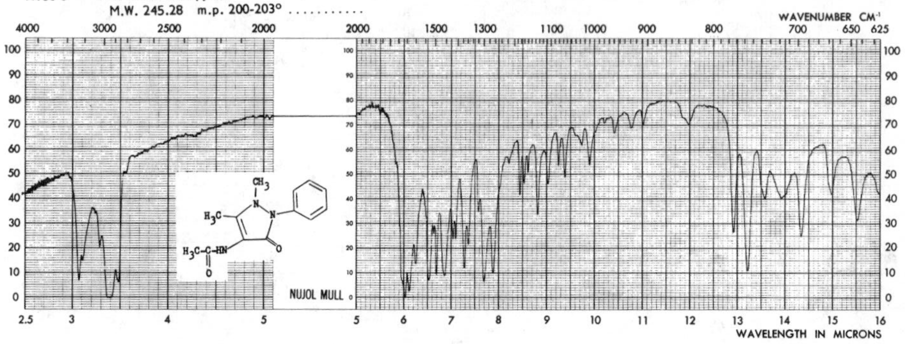

H 13,151-2 **Picrolonic acid**
M.W. 264.20 m.p. 115° (dec.)

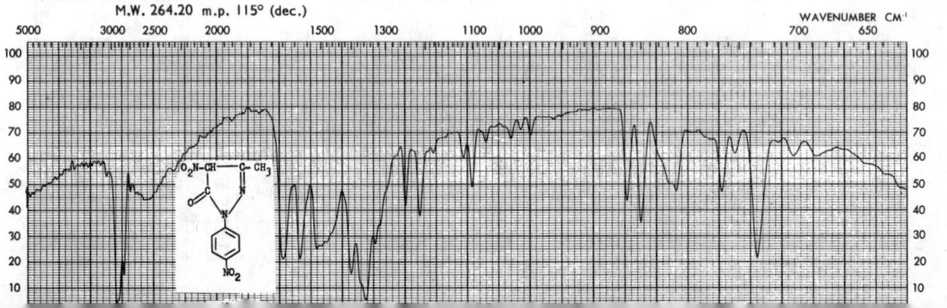

A

4-Phenylurazole, 95%
FW 177.16 mp 207-209° *Beil.* **26**,195 Disp. C

NUJOL MULL

B

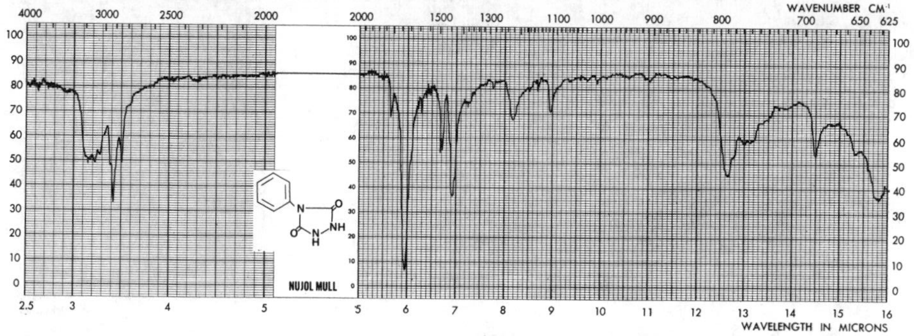

18,082-3
5-Methyl-5-phenylhydantoin, 99%
M.W. 190.2 m.p. 199-201° Beil. **24**(1),347

NUJOL MULL

C

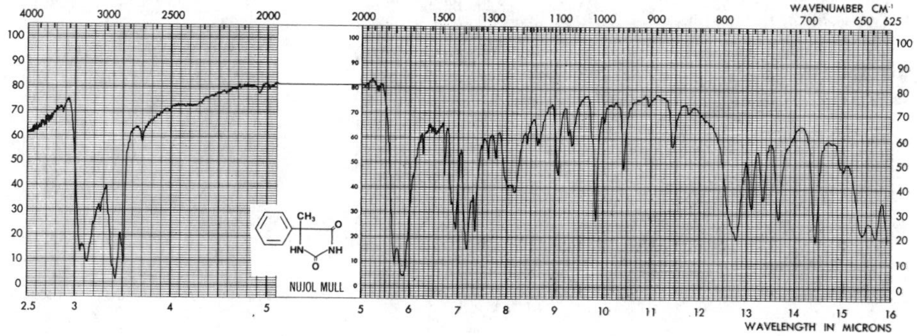

18,083-1
5-Ethyl-5-phenylhydantoin, 99%
M.W. 204.23 m.p. 201-203°

NUJOL MULL

D

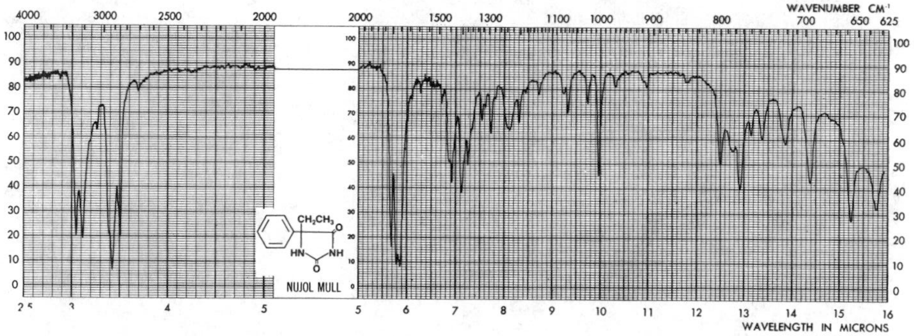

11,310-7 **5-Cyclopropyl-5-phenylhydantoin**
M.W. 216.24 m.p. 210-215°

NUJOL MULL

E

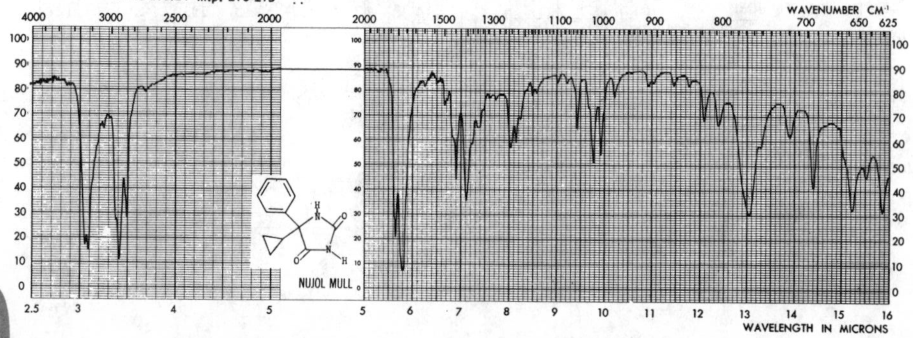

11,309-3 **5-Cyclobutyl-5-phenylhydantoin**
M.W. 230.27 m.p. 236-237°

NUJOL MULL

F

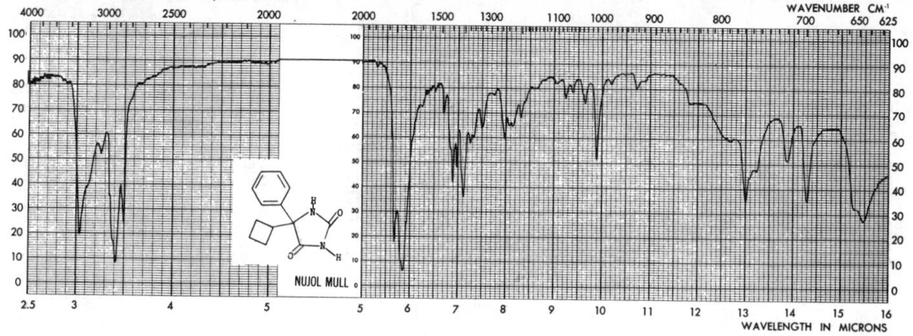

16,192-6
5,5-Diphenylhydantoin, 99+%, GOLD LABEL
M.W. 252.27 m.p. 293.5-295° Beil. **24**,410

NUJOL MULL

G

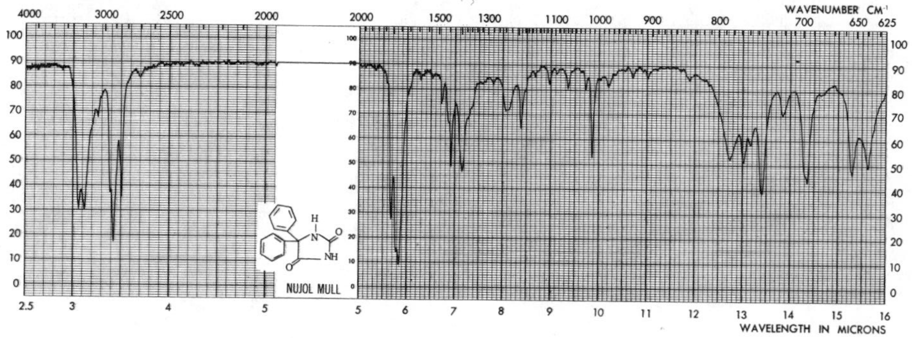

16,145-4
5-(p-Methylphenyl)-5-phenylhydantoin, 99+%, GOLD LABEL [MPPH, 5-phenyl-5-(p-tolyl)-hydantoin]
M.W. 266.3 m.p. 225-226°

NUJOL MULL

H

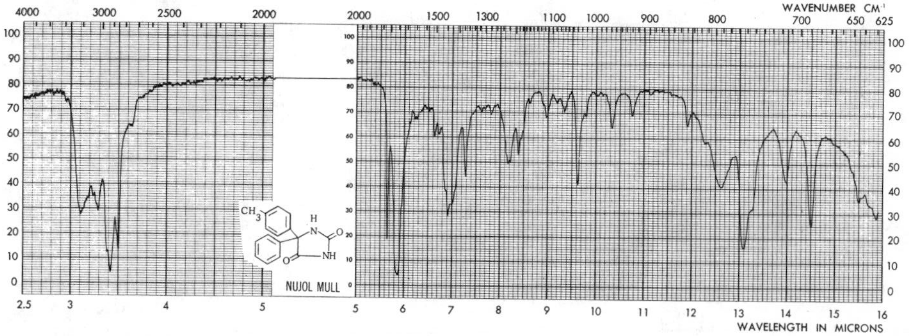

22,158-9
5-(*m*-Hydroxyphenyl)-5-phenylhydantoin, 99+%, GOLD LABEL (*m*-HPPH)
FW 268.27 mp 215-217° Disp. C

NUJOL MULL

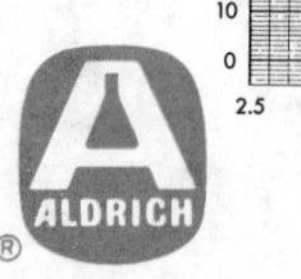

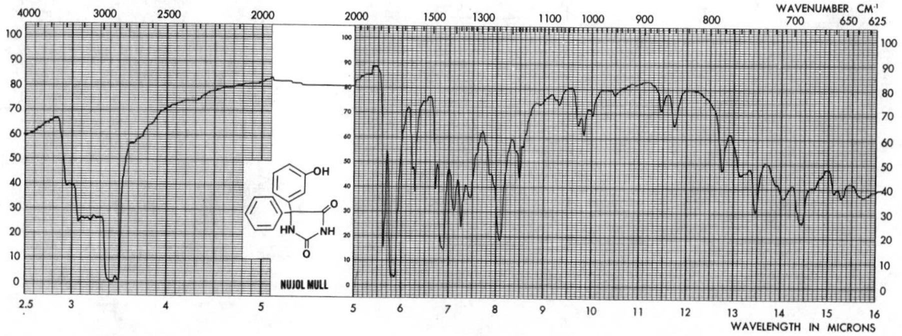

ALDRICH

A

16,154-3
5-(p-Hydroxyphenyl)-5-phenylhydantoin, 99+%, GOLD LABEL
M.W. 268.27 m.p. >300°

B

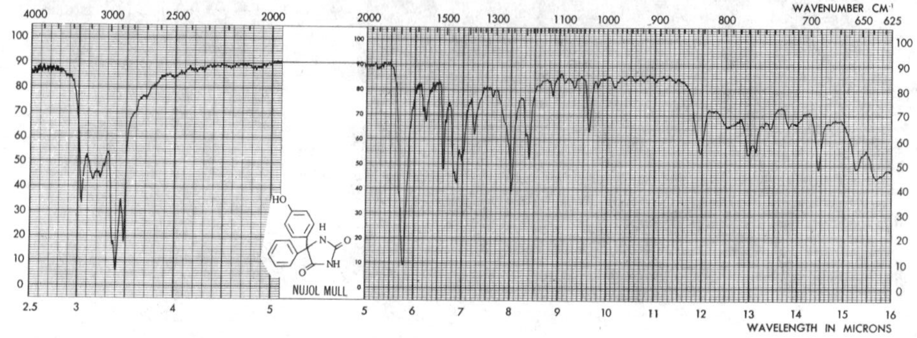

22,083-3
5-(p-Hydroxyphenyl)-5-(p-tolyl)hydantoin, 99%
FW 282.30 mp >300° Disp. C

C

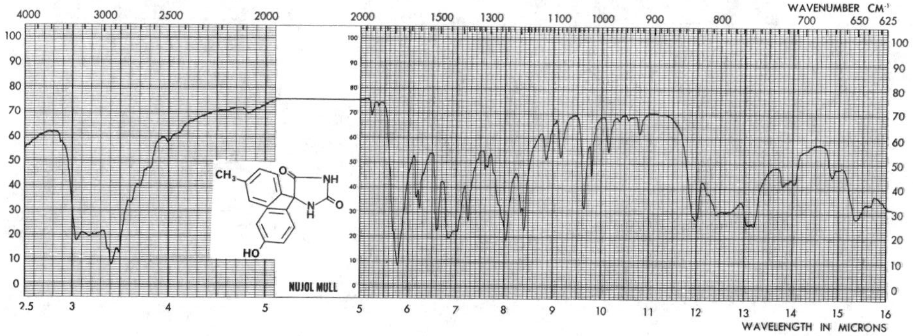

B635-2 **7,8-Benzo-1,3-diazaspiro[4.5]decane-2,4-dione** (β-tetralone-hydantoin)
M.W. 216.24 m.p. 268-270°

D

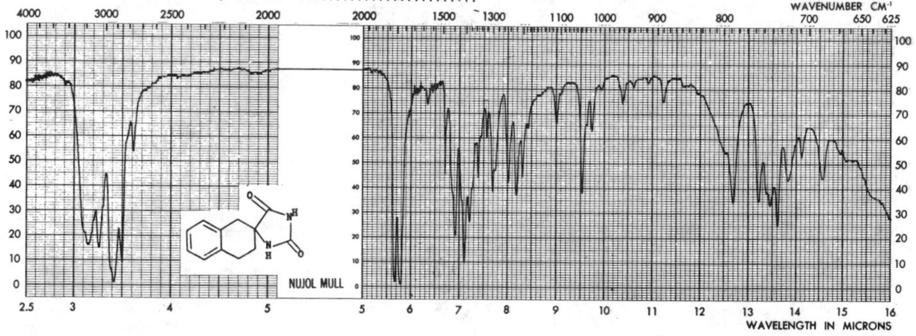

16,049-0
1-Phenyl-1,3,8-triazaspiro[4.5]decan-4-one, 92%, remainder solvent
M.W. 231.3 m.p. 183-185°

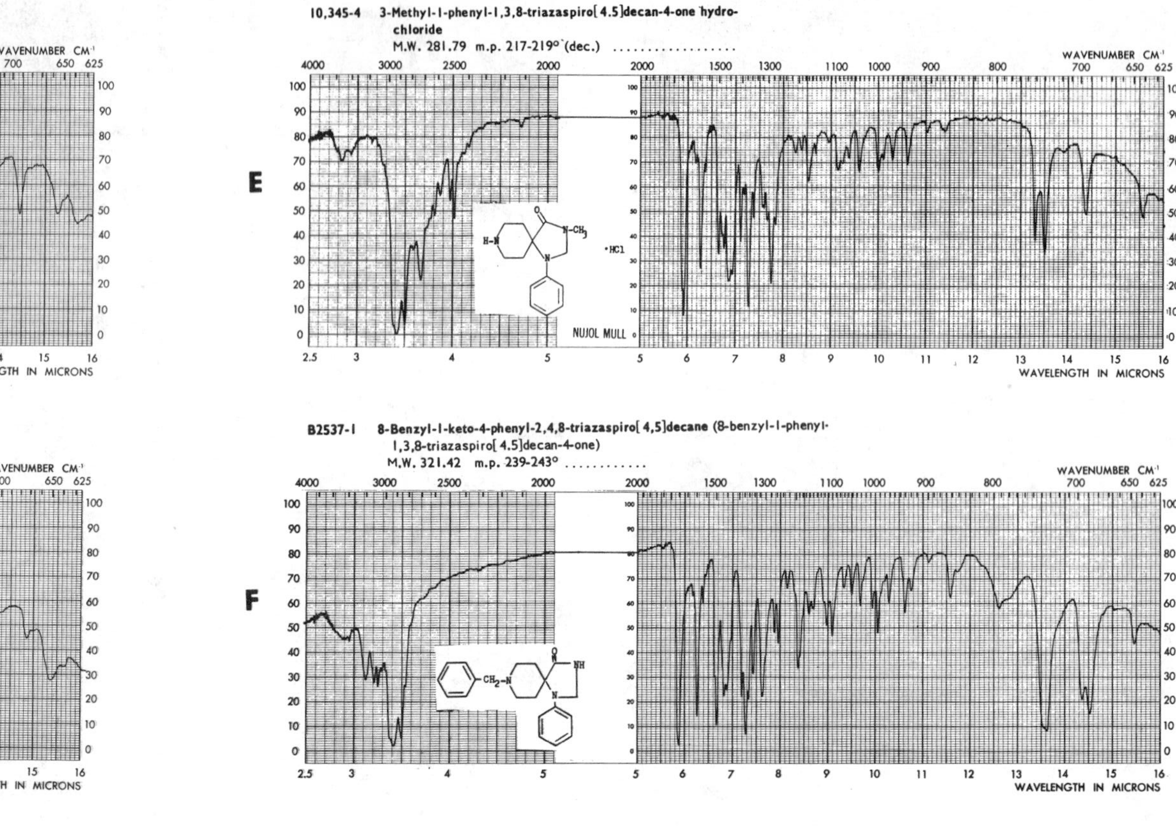

E

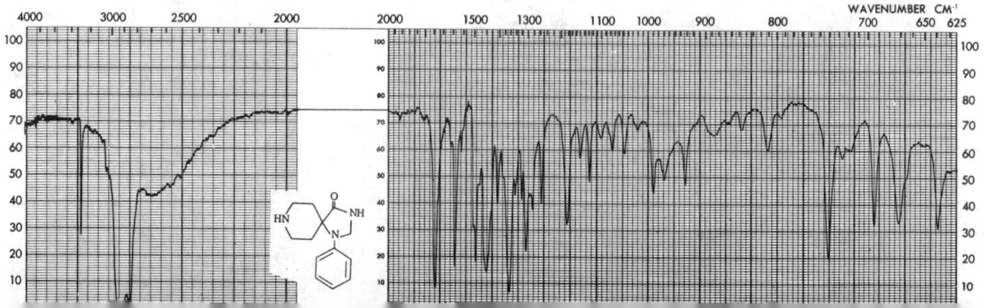

10,345-4 **3-Methyl-1-phenyl-1,3,8-triazaspiro[4.5]decan-4-one hydrochloride**
M.W. 281.79 m.p. 217-219° (dec.)

F

B2537-1 **8-Benzyl-1-keto-4-phenyl-2,4,8-triazaspiro[4.5]decane** (8-benzyl-1-phenyl-1,3,8-triazaspiro[4.5]decan-4-one)
M.W. 321.42 m.p. 239-243°

G

E210-8 **Ergotamine tartrate**
M.W. 1313.46 m.p. 195° (dec.)

H

85,755-6
4-Ethoxymethylene-2-phenyl-2-oxazolin-5-one
FW 217.22 mp 93-94° *NMR* 6,5B Disp. C

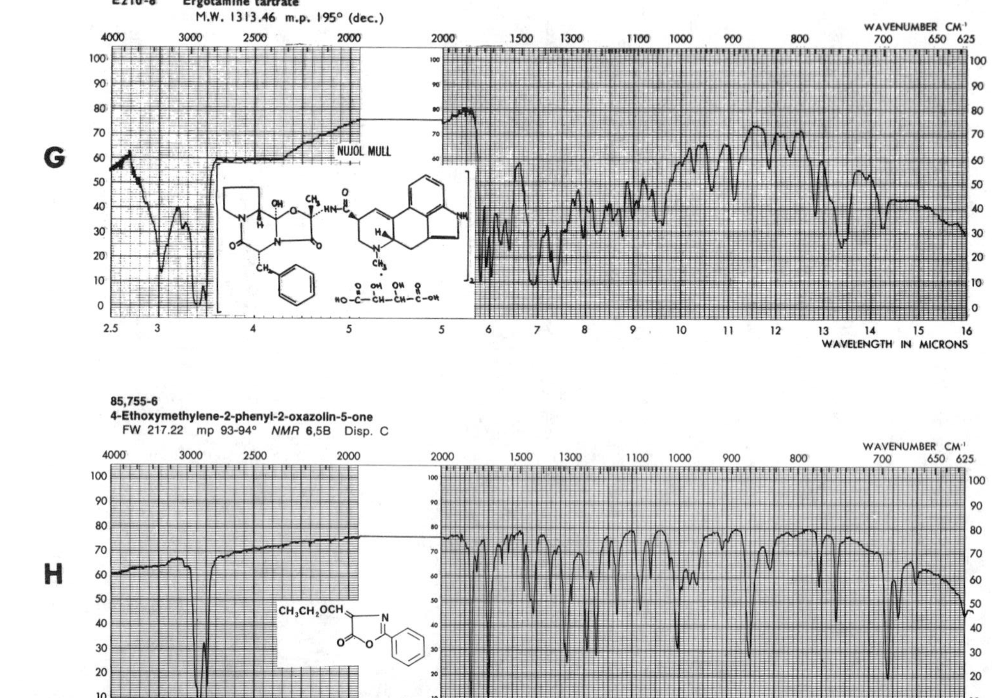

A

FW 308.38 mp 106-108° Disp. C

NUJOL MULL

B

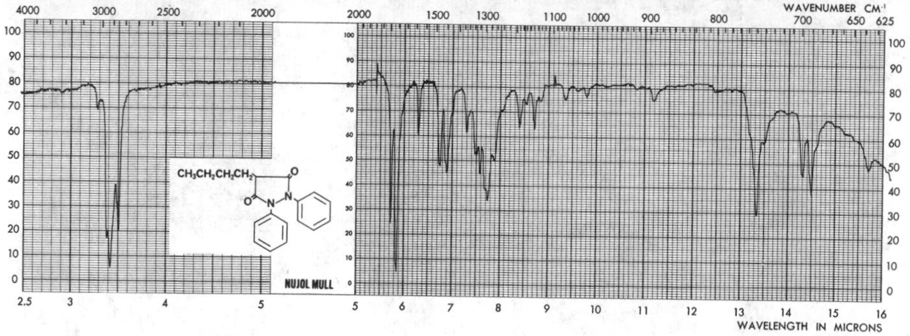

21,415-9
1-(*p*-Fluorobenzyl)-1,2-dihydro-2-(methylamino)-quinazolin-4(3*H*)-one, 99%
FW 285.32 mp 252-255° Disp. C

NUJOL MULL

C

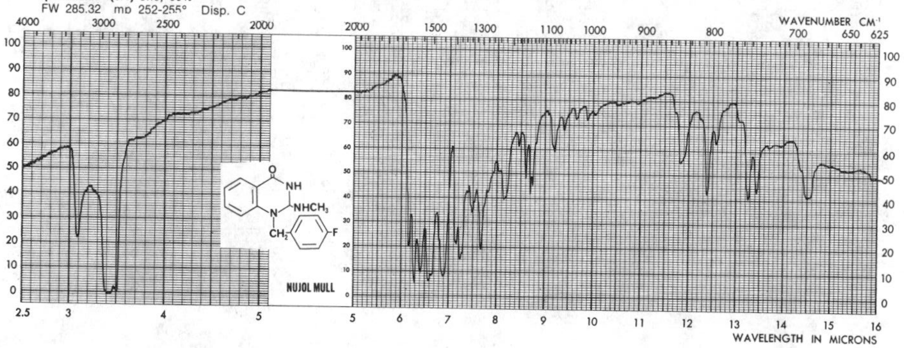

19,924-9
3a,4,5,6-Tetrahydrosuccinimido[3,4-*b*]acenaphthen-10-one, 99% [7,8-dihydro-2-oxo-1,8a(6*H*)-acenaphthenedicarboximide]
FW 241.25 mp 250-254° Disp. C

NUJOL MULL

D

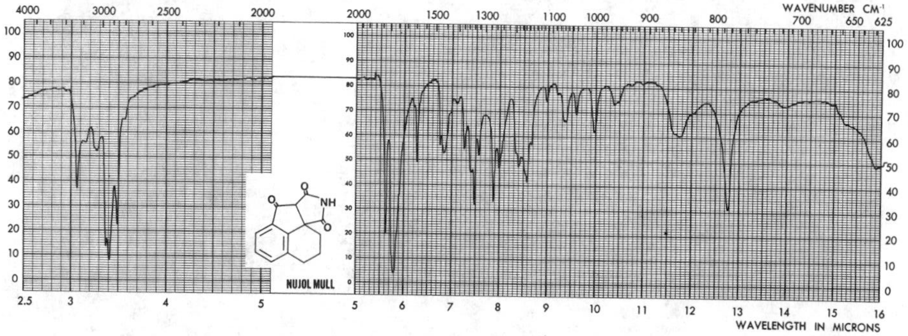

21,409-4
10-(*p*-Fluorobenzyl)-2,10-dihydroimidazo[2,1-*b*]-quinazolin-5(3*H*)-one hydrochloride, 97%
FW 331.78 mp 239° (dec.) Disp. C

NUJOL MULL

E

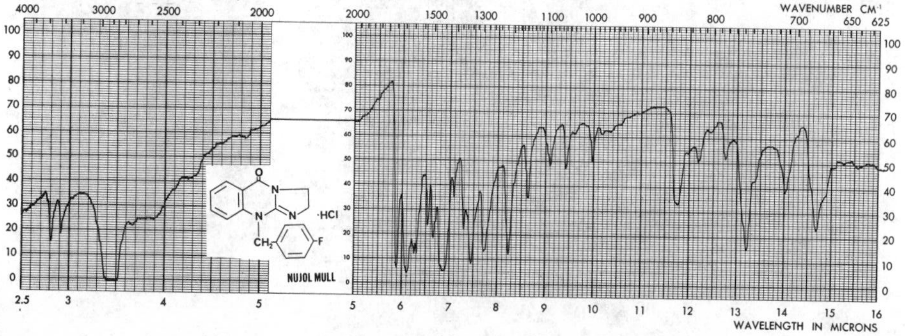

10,11-Dihydro-2'-methylspiro(5*H*-dibenzo[*a,d*]-cycloheptene-5,1'-[1*H*]isoindol)-3'(2'*H*)-one
FW 325.41 mp 188-190° Disp. C

NUJOL MULL

F

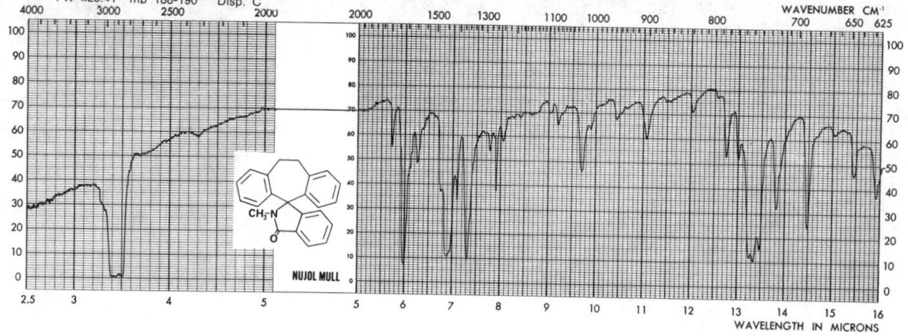

85,880-3
(2-Naphthoxy)acetic acid, N-hydroxysuccinimide ester
M.W. 299.29 m.p. 150-152°

NUJOL MULL

G

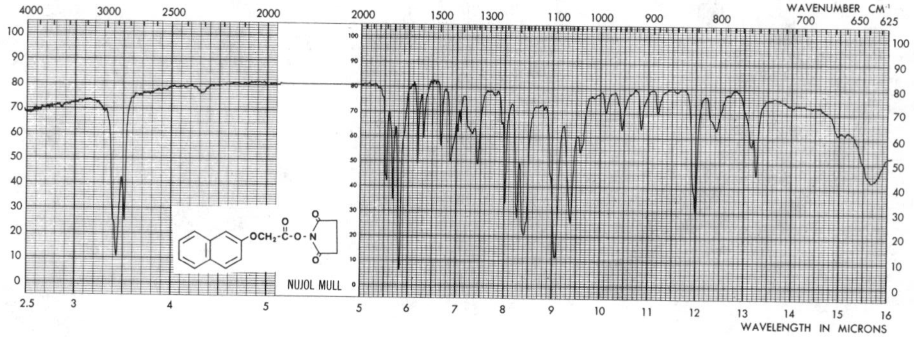

86,015-8
3-(*p*-Hydroxyphenyl)propionic acid *N*-hydroxysuccinimide ester, 99+% [*N*-[(*p*-hydroxyhydrocinnamoyl)oxy]succinimide]
FW 263.25 mp 133-135° Disp. C

NUJOL MULL

H

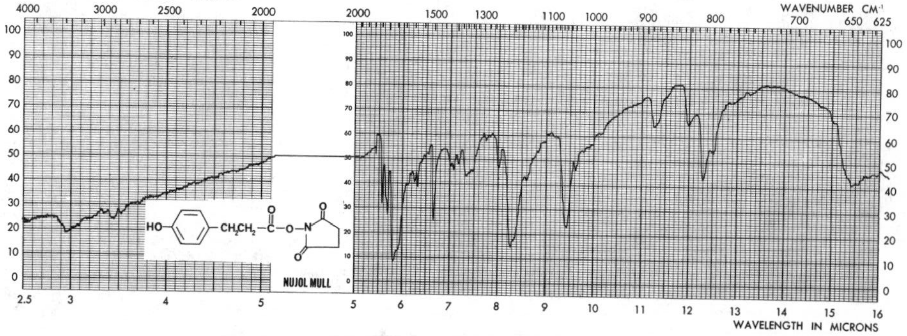

20,891-4
N-Benzyloxycarbonyloxy-5-norbornene-2,3-dicarboximide, 99%
FW 313.32 mp 125° (dec.) Disp. C

NUJOL MULL

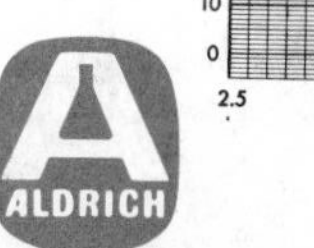

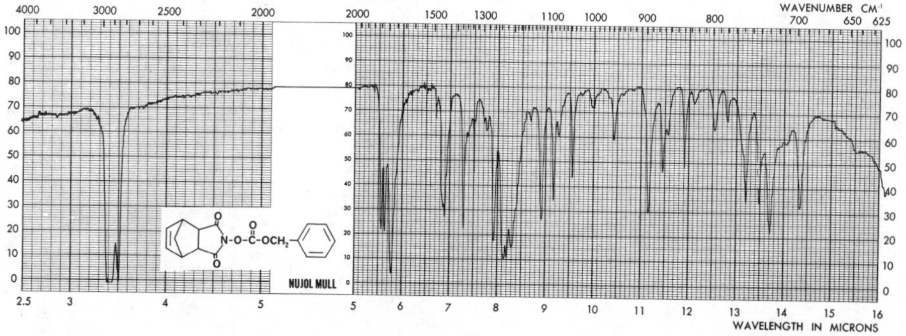

A 86,058-1
α-Methyl-α-phenylsuccinimide, 99%
FW 189.21 mp 83-85° Disp. C

B P2710-0 **N-Phenylmaleimide**
M.W. 173.17 m.p. 81-82°

C 10,459-0 **N,N'-o-Phenylenedimaleimide**
M.W. 268.23 m.p. > 300°

D P2398-9 **N,N'-p-Phenylenedimaleimide**
M.W. 268.23 m.p. > 330°

E P1860-8 **p-Phenylazomaleinanil**
M.W. 277.28 m.p. 161-162°

F D14,080-5 **N-(4-Dimethylamino-3,5-dinitrophenyl)-maleimide** (Tuppy's maleimide)
M.W. 306.23 m.p. 177-181°

G 17,763-6
2-Ethyl-2-phenylglutarimide, 99% (glutethimide)
M.W. 217.27 m.p. 88-90°

H N165-8 **1,8-Naphthalimide**
M.W. 197.20 m.p. 296-300°

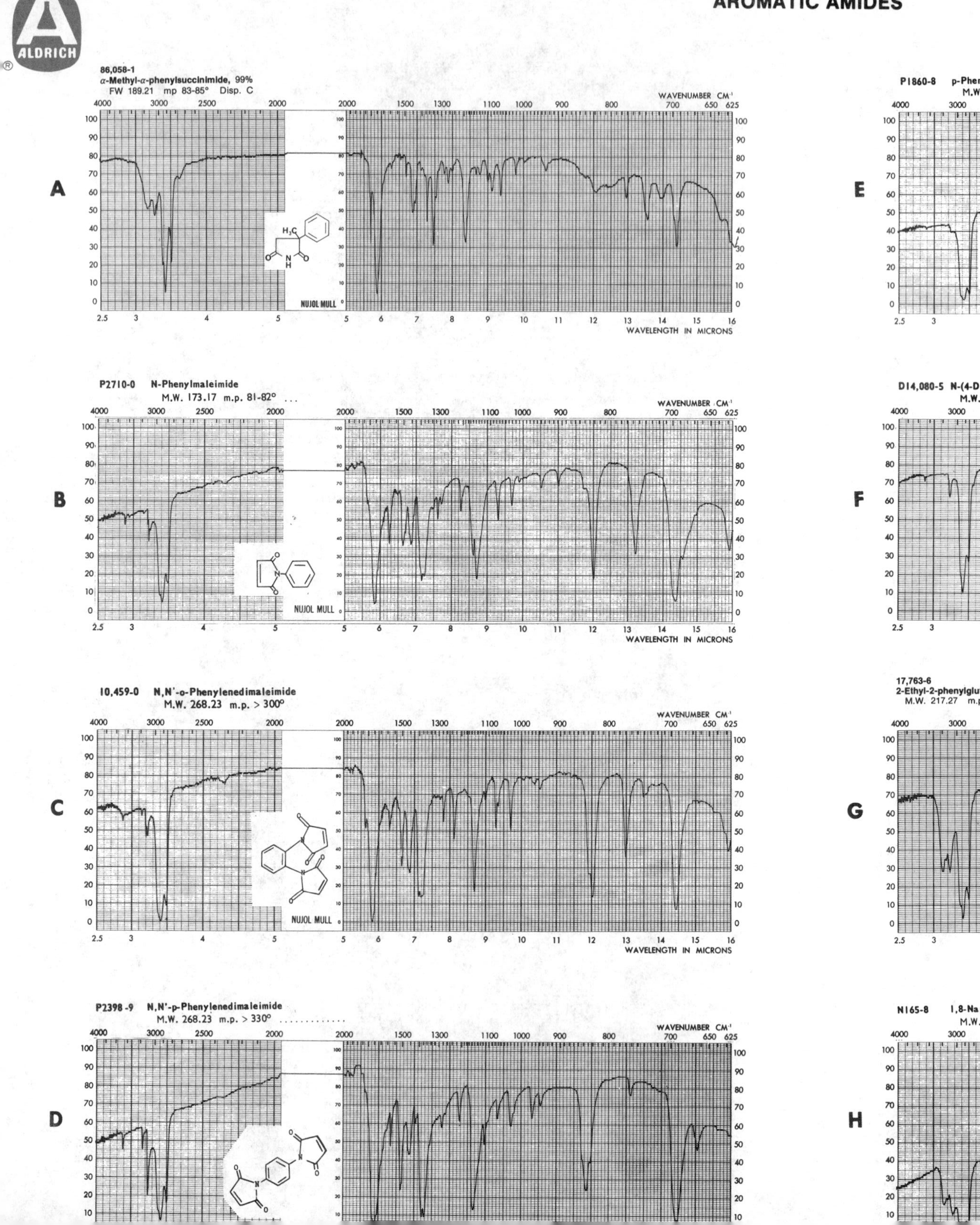

A — 1,4,5,8-Naphthalenetetracarboxylic diimide
M.W. 246.20 m.p. > 300°

B — 12,184-3 N-Hydroxynaphthalimide (naphthalhydroxamic acid), sodium salt
M.W. 235.18 (dry) m.p. > 300°

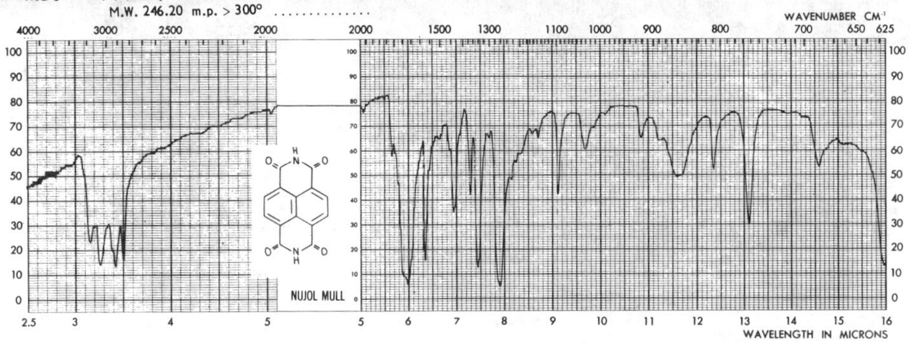

C — 12,184-3 N-Hydroxynaphthalimide (naphthalhydroxamic acid), sodium salt, moist
M.W. 235.18 (dry) m.p. > 300°

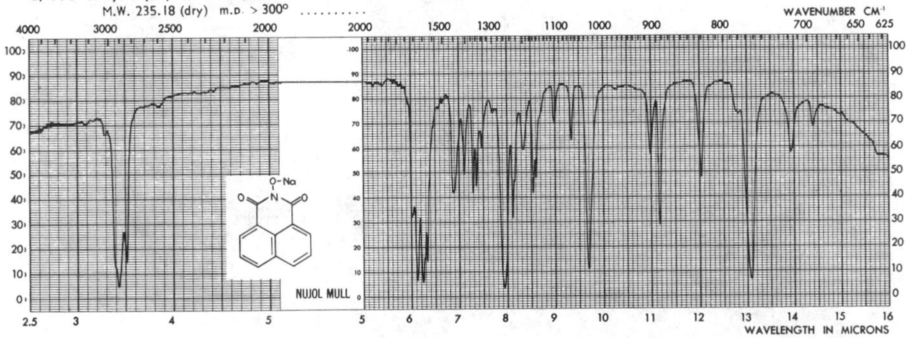

D — A6670-7 4-Amino-1,8-naphthalimide
M.W. 212.21 m.p. > 360°

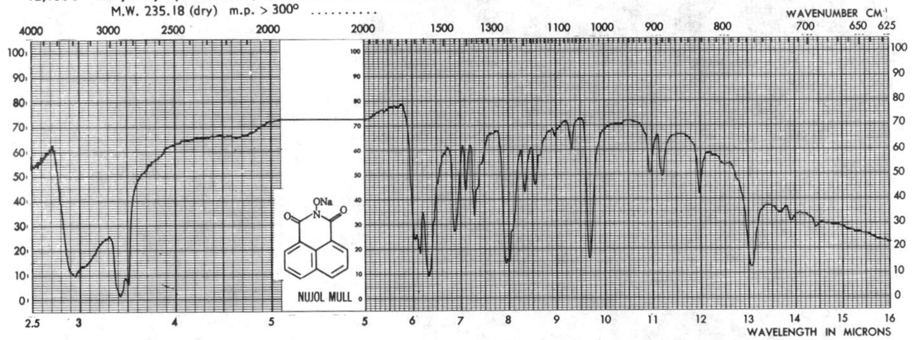

E — 2H-1,4-Benzothiazin-3(4H)-one, 97%
M.W. 165.21 m.p. 176-178° Beil. 27,192

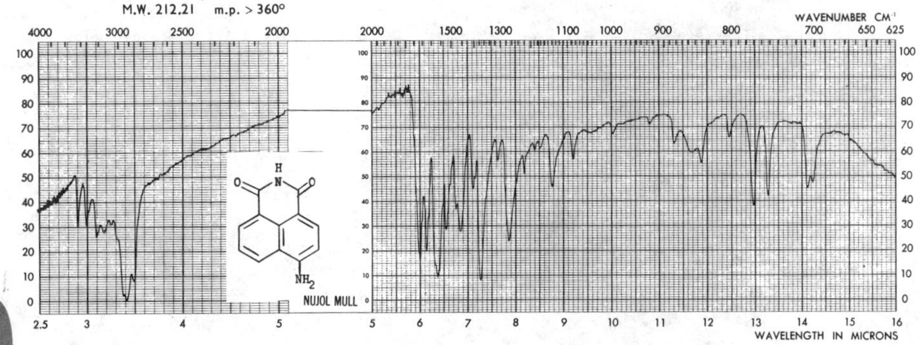

F — P3970-2 Phthalimide
M.W. 147.13 m.p. 233.5-235°

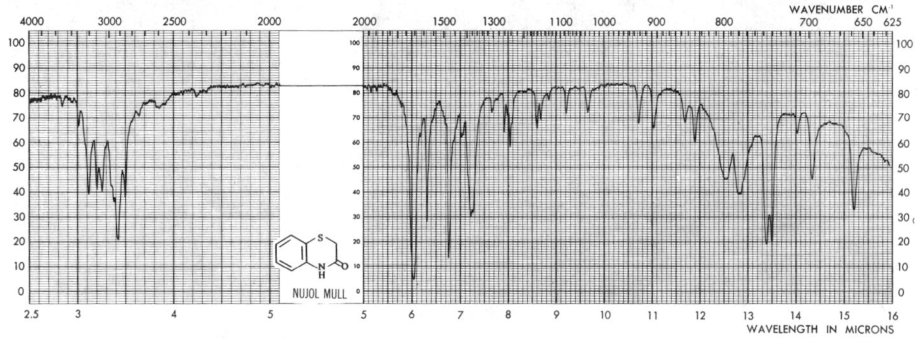

G — 16,038-5
Phthalimide, potassium derivative, 98% (potassium phthalimide)
M.W. 185.23 m.p. >300° *IRRITANT*

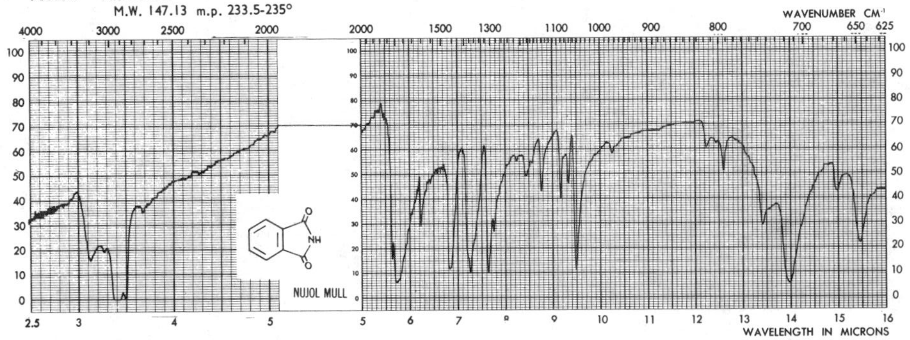

H — C6850-4 N-Chlorophthalimide
M.W. 181.58 m.p. 181-184°

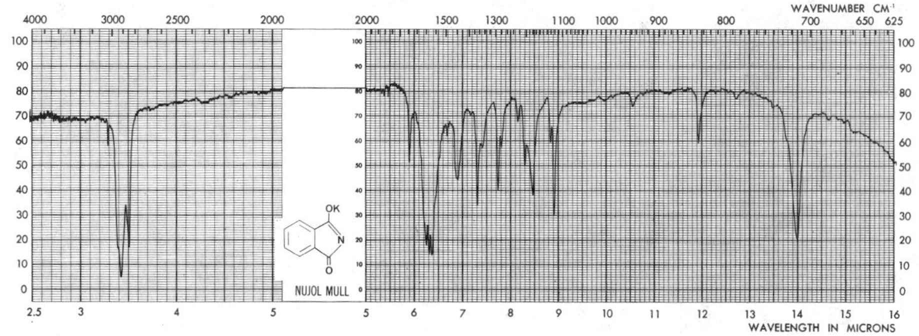

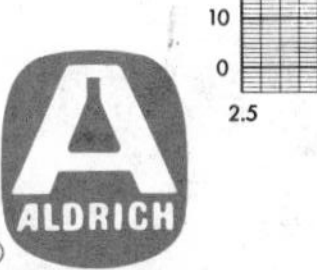

AROMATIC AMIDES

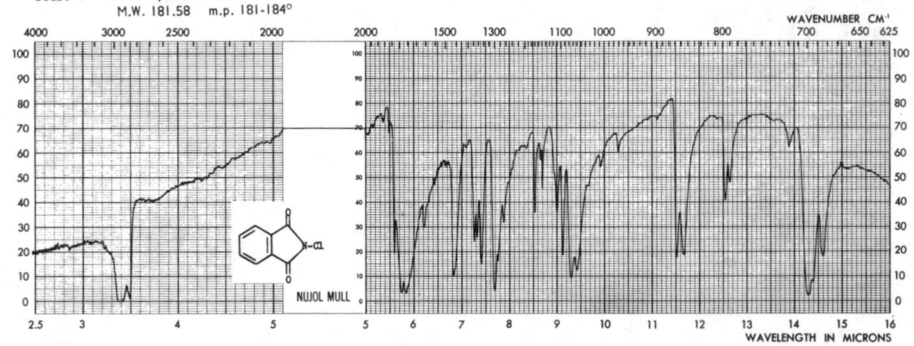

A B6630-2 N-(2-Bromoethyl)-phthalimide
M.W. 254.09 m.p. 81-84°
NUJOL MULL

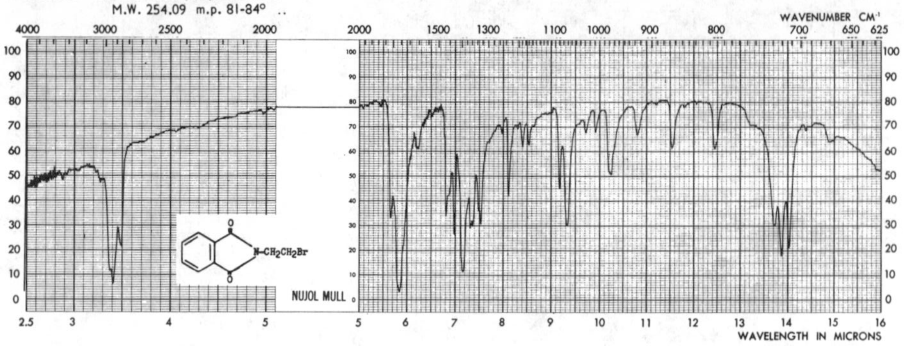

B B8000-3 N-(3-Bromopropyl)-phthalimide
M.W. 268.12 m.p. 74-75°
MELT

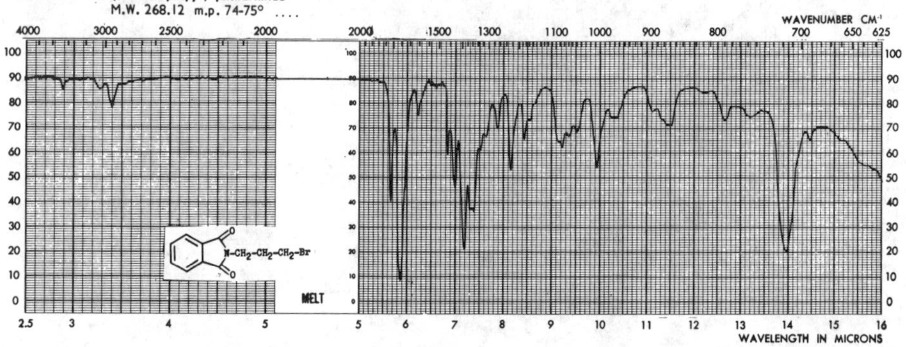

C 10,091-9 N-(4-Bromobutyl)-phthalimide
M.W. 282.14 m.p. 76-78°
NUJOL MULL

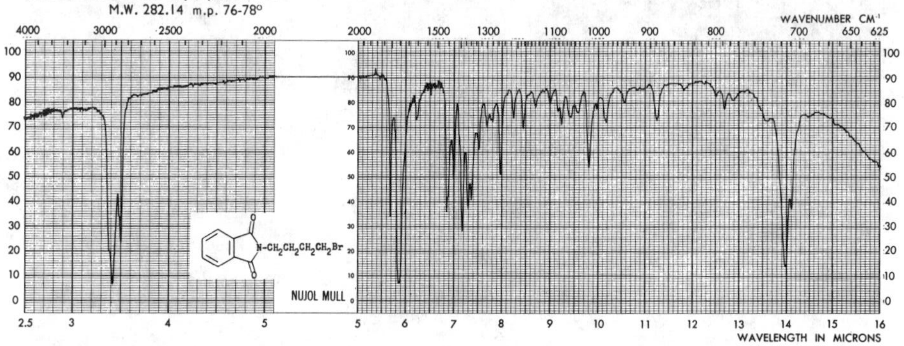

D H5370-4 N-Hydroxyphthalimide
M.W. 163.13 m.p. 231-233°

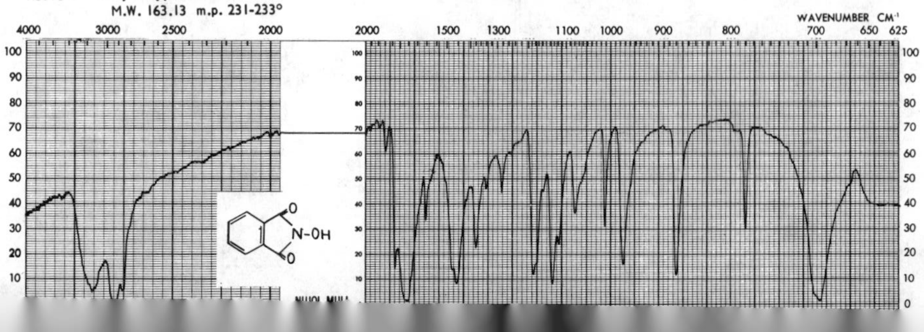

E 17,831-4 N-Aminophthalimide, 98%
M.W. 162.15 m.p. 200-202° Fieser 1,38
NUJOL MULL

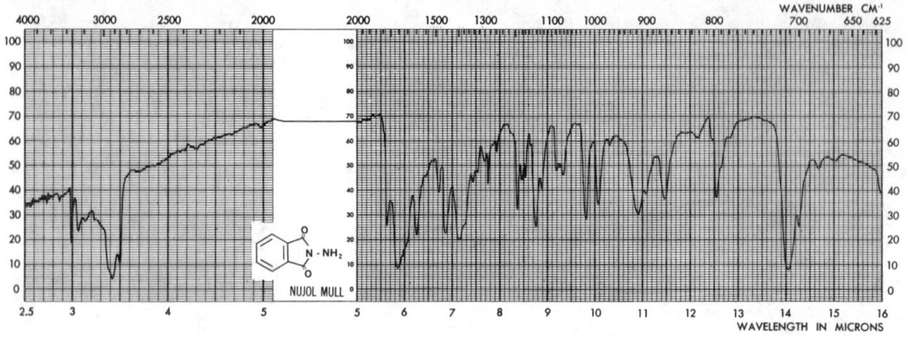

F H4180-3 N-(Hydroxymethyl)-phthalimide
M.W. 177.16 m.p. 147°
NUJOL MULL

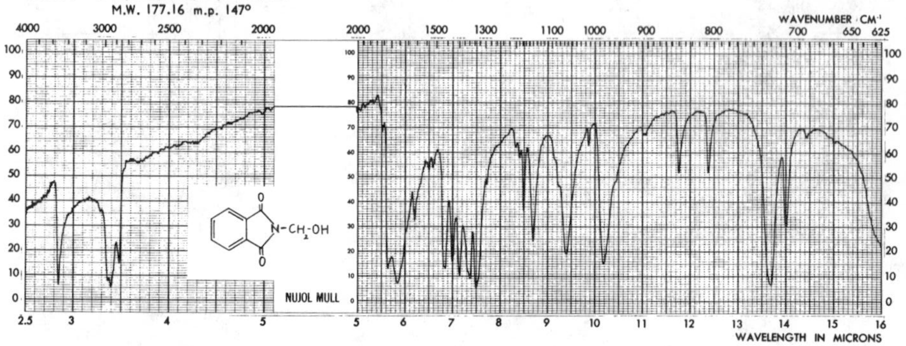

G 13,833-9 N-(2-Hydroxyethyl)-phthalimide
M.W. 191.19 m.p. 123-127°
NUJOL MULL

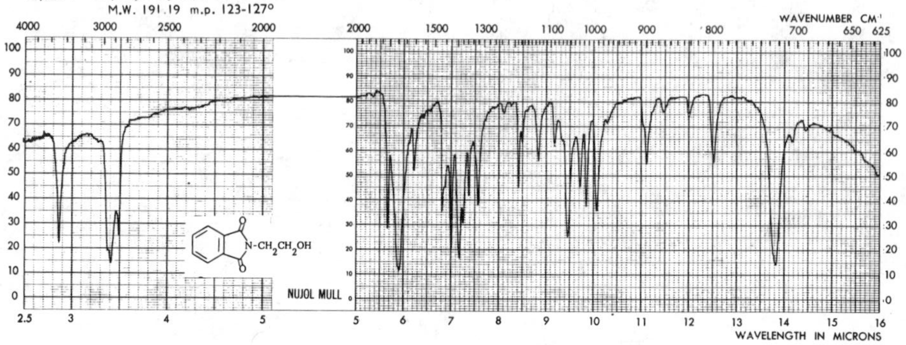

H 10,306-3 N-(3-Hydroxypropyl)-phthalimide
M.W. 205.21 m.p. 74-76°
NUJOL MULL

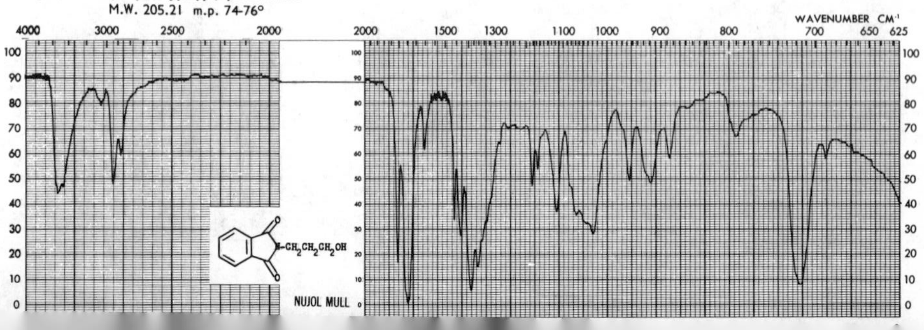

M.W. 203.2 m.p. 98-100°

A

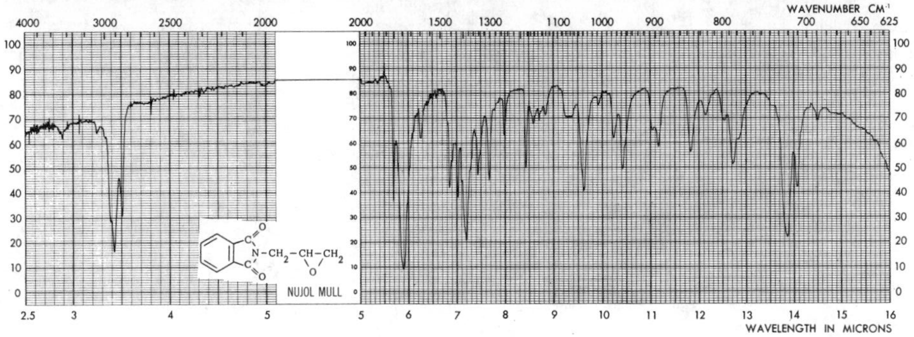

NUJOL MULL

18,856-5
Phthalimidoacetaldehyde dimethyl acetal, 98%
[*N*-(2,2-dimethoxyethyl)phthalimide]
FW 235.24 mp 102-105° Disp. C

B

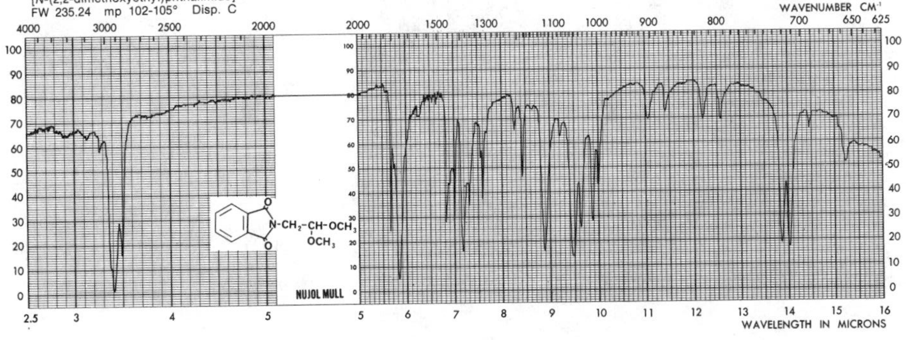

NUJOL MULL

P7,300-5 **Pyromellitic diimide,** 97%
M.W. 216.15 m.p. > 320° *Beil.* **24**(1),449

C

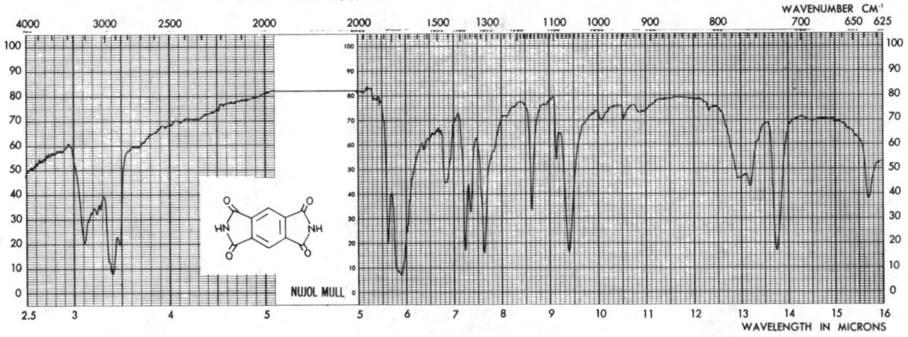

NUJOL MULL

13,555-0 **3,4,5,6-Tetrachlorophthalimide** (4,5,6,7-tetrachloroisoindoie-1,3-dione)
M.W. 284.92 m.p. > 300°

D

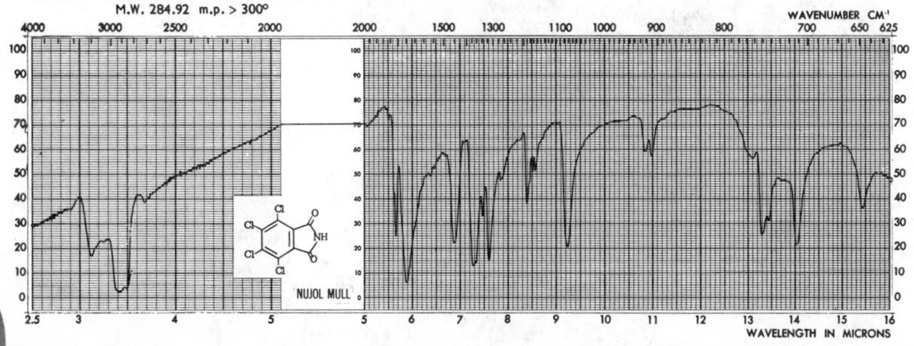

NUJOL MULL

1,3-dione)
M.W. 462.74 m.p. > 330°

E

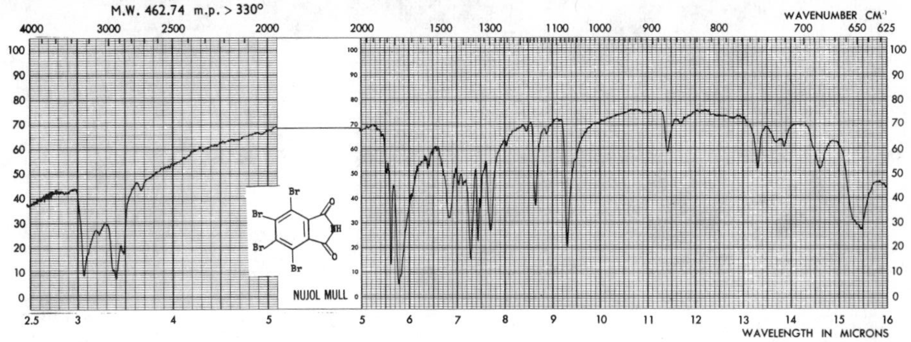

NUJOL MULL

P4050-6 **N-Phthaloylglycine** (1,3-dioxo-2-isoindolineacetic acid)
M.W. 205.17 m.p. 193-196°

F

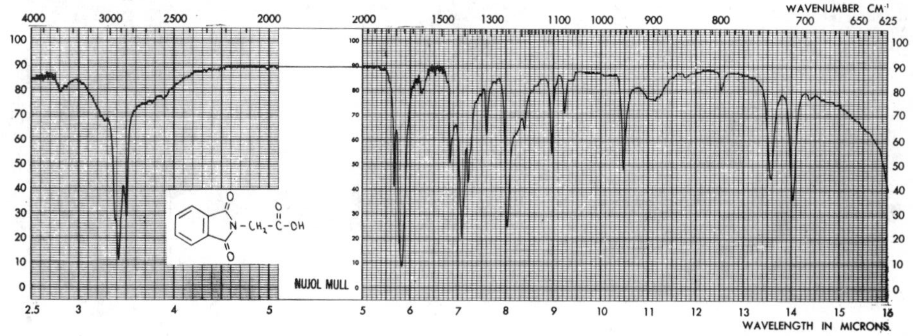

NUJOL MULL

20,872-8
***N*-(4-Amino-2-methylphenyl)-4-chlorophthalimide,** 99%
FW 286.72 mp 208-210° Disp. C

G

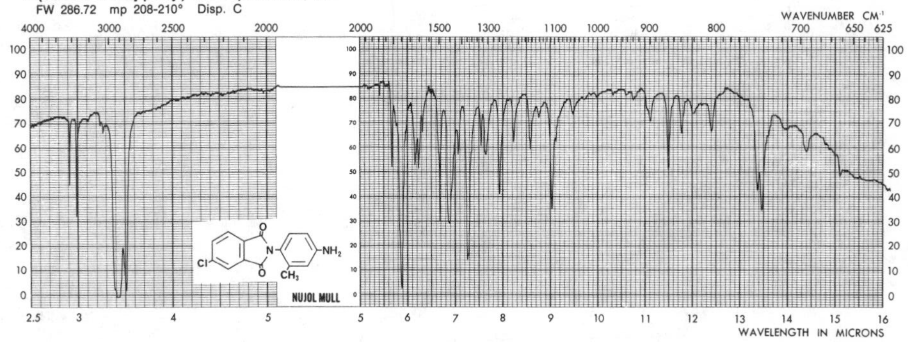

NUJOL MULL

13,766-9 **o-Phthalimidobenzoic acid**
M.W. 267.23 m.p. 220-222°

H

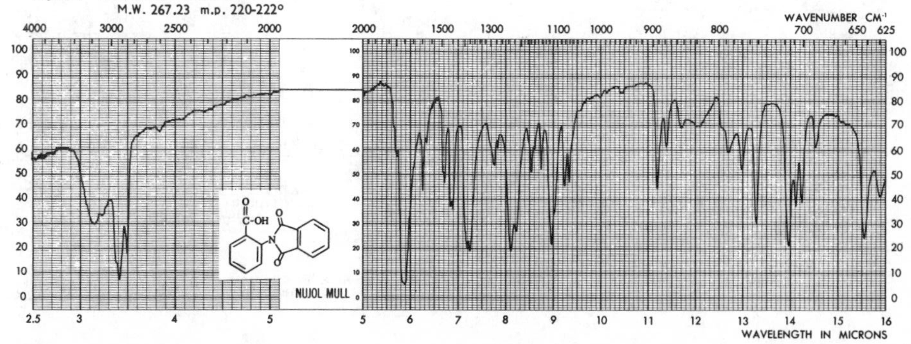

NUJOL MULL

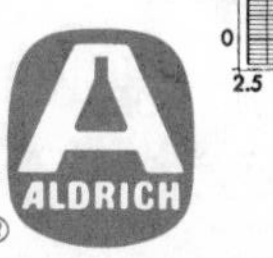

A

C545-9 **N-Carbethoxyphthalimide** (ethyl 1,3-dioxo-2-isoindolinecarboxylate)
M.W. 219.20 m.p. 90-91°

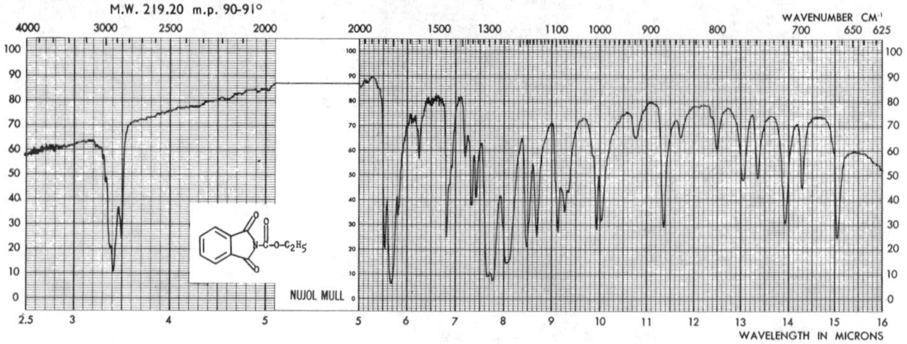

NUJOL MULL

B

14,924-1 **N-(tert.-Butoxycarbonyloxy)-phthalimide**
M.W. 263.25 m.p. 118° (dec.)

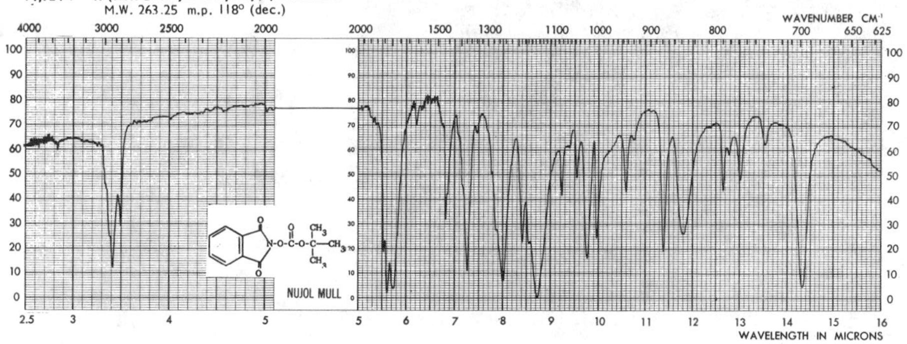

NUJOL MULL

C

14,912-8 **N-(Benzyloxycarbonyloxy)-phthalimide**
M.W. 297.27 m.p. 98-100°

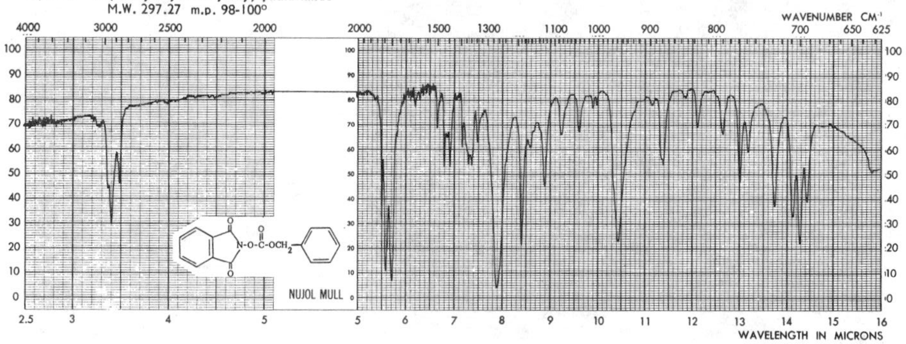

NUJOL MULL

D

P4180-4 **Phthalylglycyl-DL-phenylalanine**
M.W. 352.35 m.p. 199-203°

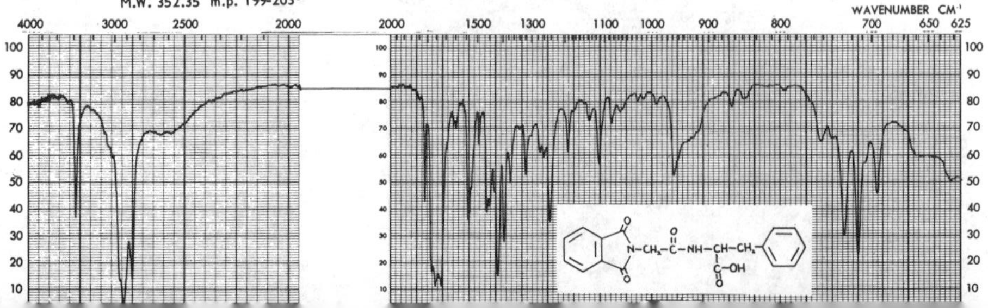

E

11,759-5 **3-Phenyl-2,4(1H,3H)-quinazolinedione**
$C_{14}H_{10}N_2O_2$ M.W. 238.25 m.p. 279-282°

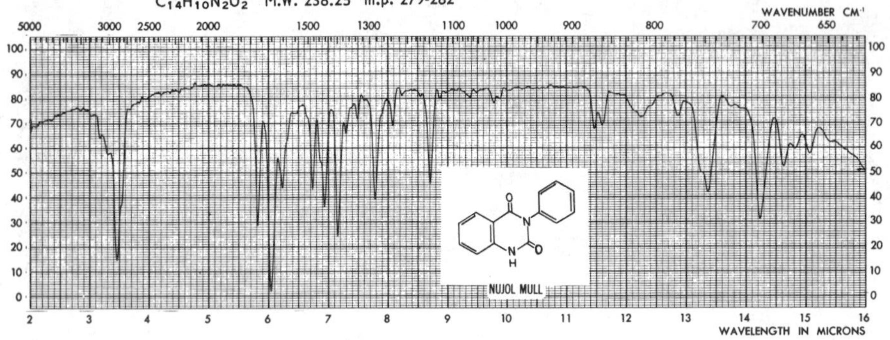

NUJOL MULL

F

22,354-9
Dihydro-5-phenyl-5-propyl-4,6-(1*H*,5*H*)pyrimidine-dione, 99+%
FW 232.28 Disp. C

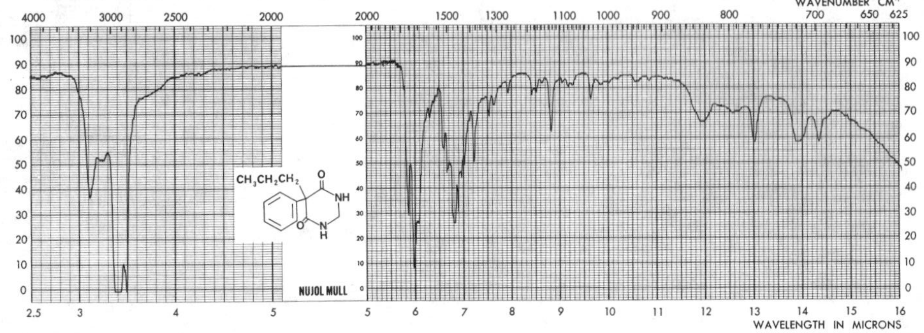

NUJOL MULL

G

21,754-9
5-Ethyl-5-(*p*-tolyl)-2-thiobarbituric acid, 99%
FW 262.33 mp 220-223° Disp. C

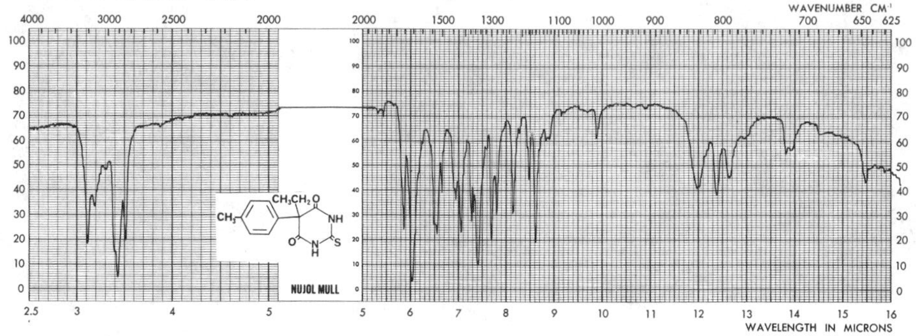

NUJOL MULL

H

22,477-4
Chlorthenoxazin, 98% [2-(2-Chloroethyl)-2,3-dihydro-4*H*-1,3-benzoxazin-4-one]
FW 211.65 mp 144-145° Disp. C

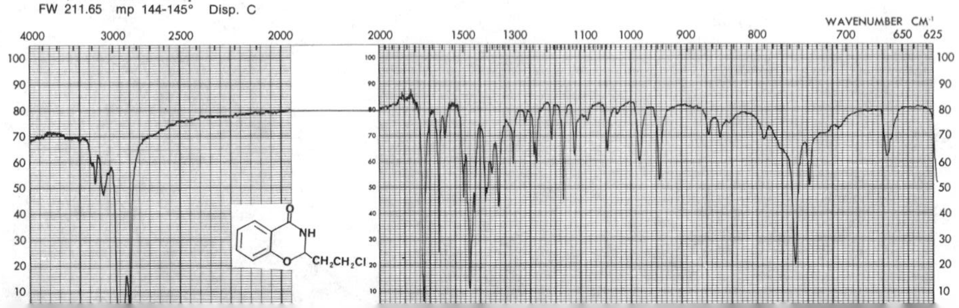

M.W. 303.84 m.p. >250° (dec.) CARCINOGEN

A

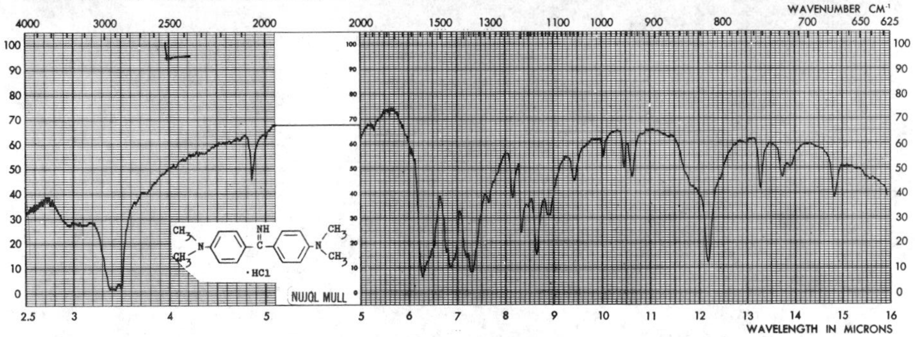

B200-4 **Benzamidine hydrochloride hydrate**
$C_6H_5C(:NH)NH_2 \cdot HCl \cdot xH_2O$
M.W. 156.61 (anhydrous)

B

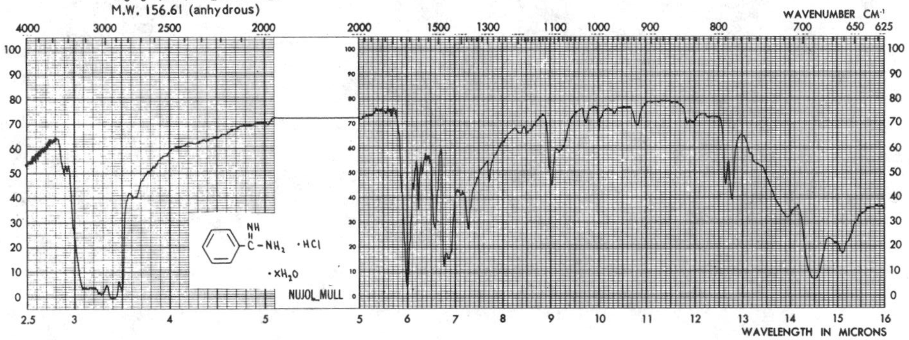

15,964-6
N,N'-Diphenylformamidine, 98%
$HC(=NC_6H_5)NHC_6H_5$
M.W. 196.25 m.p. 138-141° Beil. **12**,236
Fieser **1**,339

C

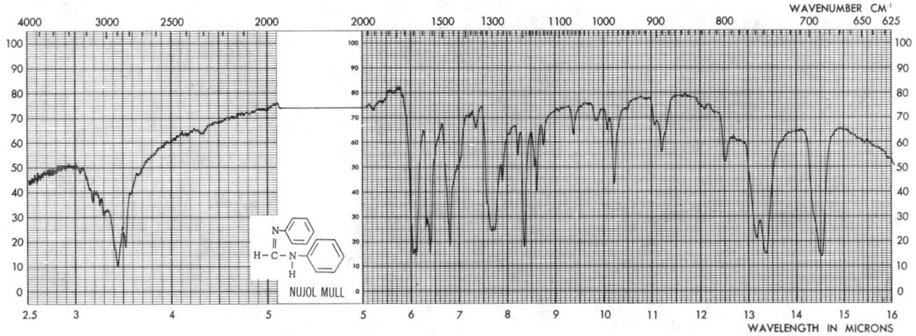

16,423-2
Phenylguanidine bicarbonate, 98%
$C_6H_5NHC(=NH)NH_2 \cdot H_2CO_3$
M.W. 197.19 m.p. 148° (dec.) Beil. **12**,369

D

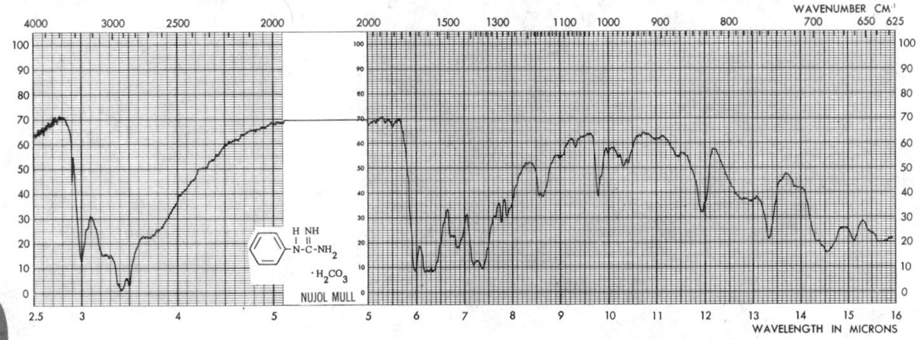

m.p. 148-150°

E

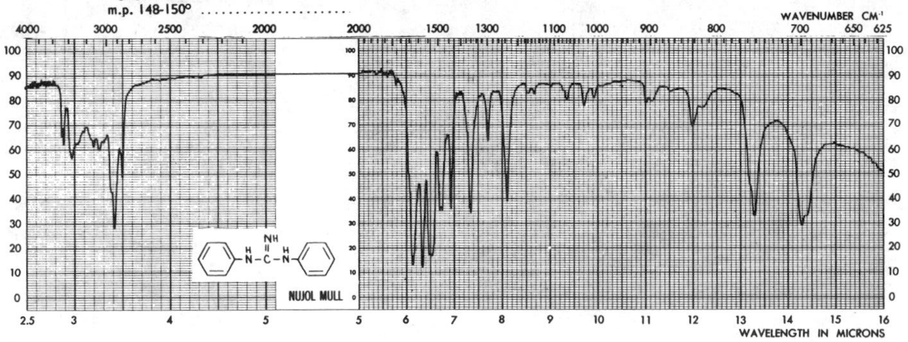

10,977-0 **1,2,3-Triphenylguanidine**
$C_6H_5NHC(:NC_6H_5)NHC_6H_5$ M.W. 287.37
m.p. 146-147°

F

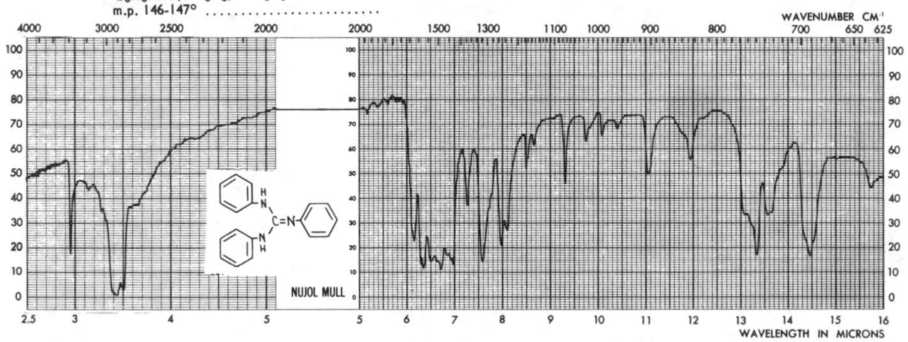

11,265-8 **1,3-Di-o-tolylguanidine**
$CH_3C_6H_4NHC(:NH)NHC_6H_4CH_3$ M.W. 239.32
m.p. 175-177°

G

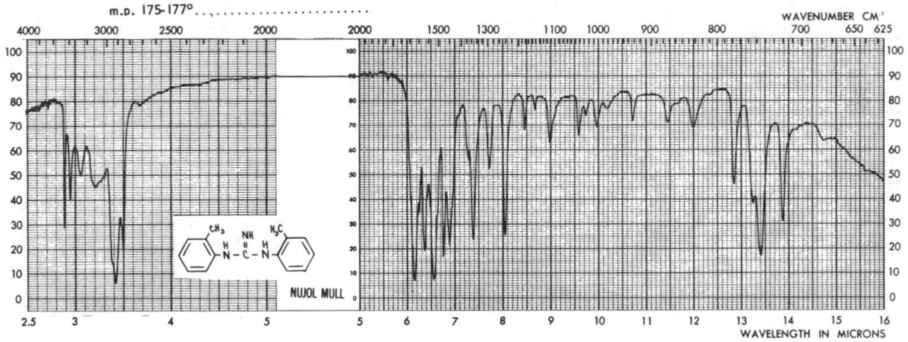

85,773-4
m-Aminobenzamidine dihydrochloride monohydrate
$H_2NC_6H_4C(=NH)NH_2 \cdot 2HCl \cdot H_2O$
M.W. 226.11 m.p. 262-264°

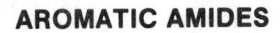

H

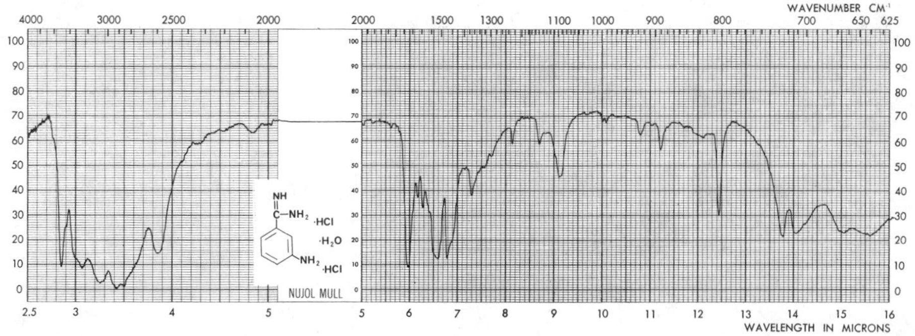

A

85,766-1
p-**Aminobenzamidine dihydrochloride**
$H_2NC_6H_4C(=NH)NH_2 \cdot 2HCl$ FW 208.09
mp >300° Disp. C

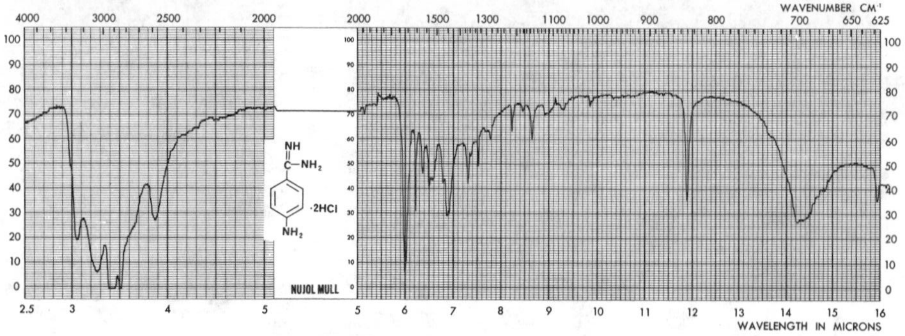

NUJOL MULL

B

13,932-7 **m-Nitrobenzamidine hydrochloride**
$O_2NC_6H_4C(:NH)NH_2 \cdot HCl$ M.W. 201.61
m.p. 245-248°

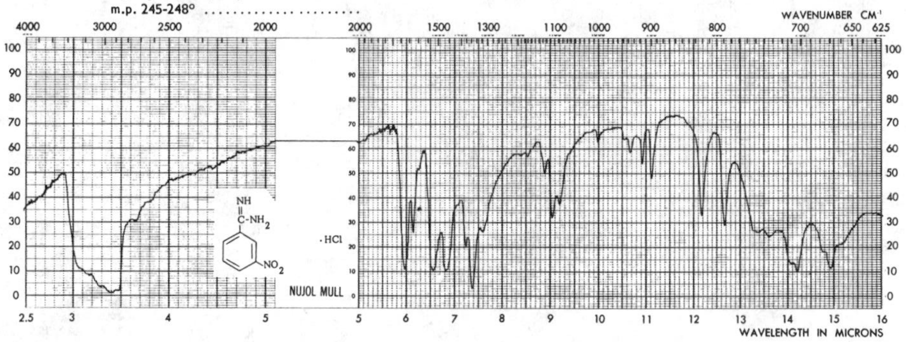

NUJOL MULL

C

22,161-9
1-(3-Phenylpropylamino)guanidine hydrochloride, 98%
$C_6H_5(CH_2)_3NHNHC(=NH)NH_2 \cdot HCl$ FW 228.73
mp 122-125° Disp. D

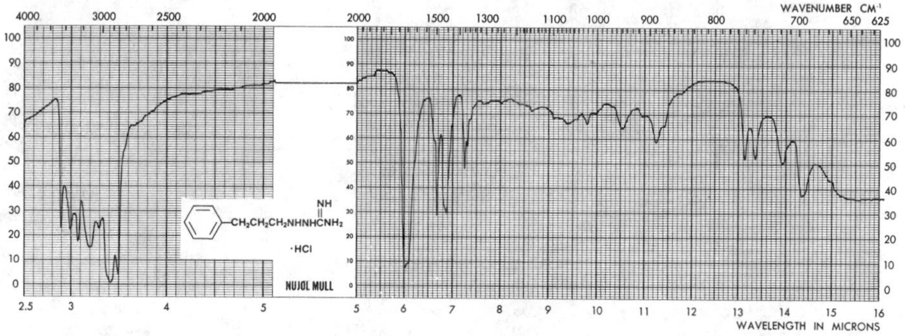

NUJOL MULL

D

16,421-6
1-Phenylbiguanide, 97%
$C_6H_5NHC(=NH)NHC(=NH)NH_2$
M.W. 177.21 m.p. 144-146°

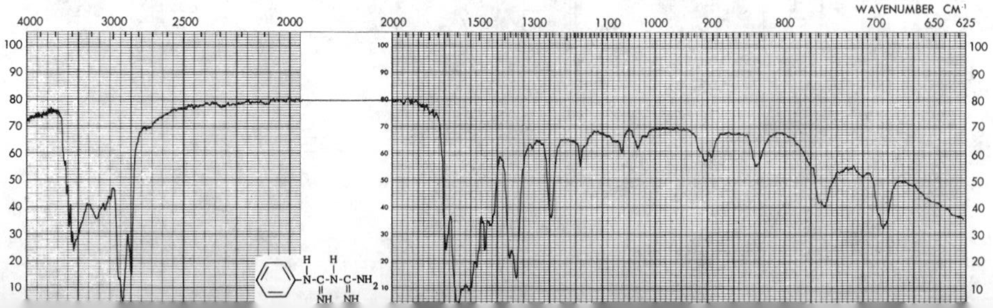

E

P1990-6 **1-Phenylbiguanide hydrochloride**
$C_6H_5NHC(:NH)NHC(:NH)NH_2 \cdot HCl$ M.W. 213.67
m.p. 260° (dec.)

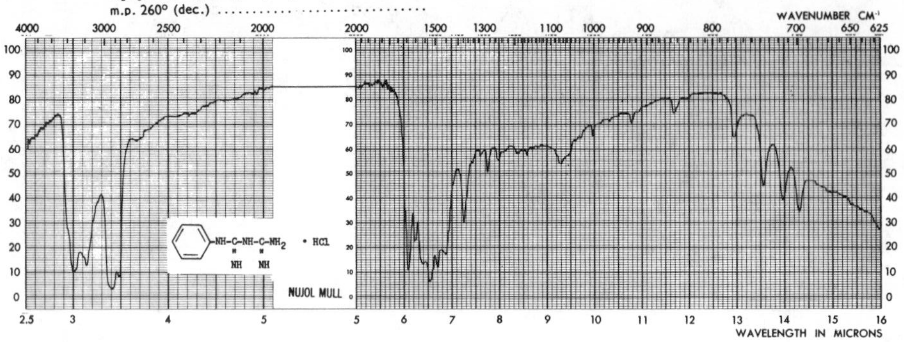

NUJOL MULL

F

P1420-3 **N[1]-β-Phenethylbiguanide hydrochloride**
$C_6H_5CH_2CH_2NHC(:NH)NHC(:NH)NH_2 \cdot HCl$ M.W. 241.73
m.p. 177-178° (dec.)

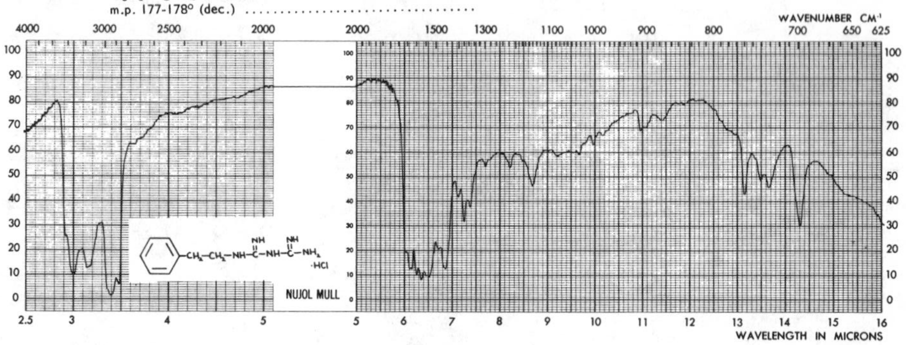

NUJOL MULL

G

12,516-4 **p-Chlorophenylbiguanide hydrate, tech.**
$ClC_6H_4NHC(:NH)NHC(:NH)NH_2 \cdot xH_2O$
M.W. 211.66 (dry basis)

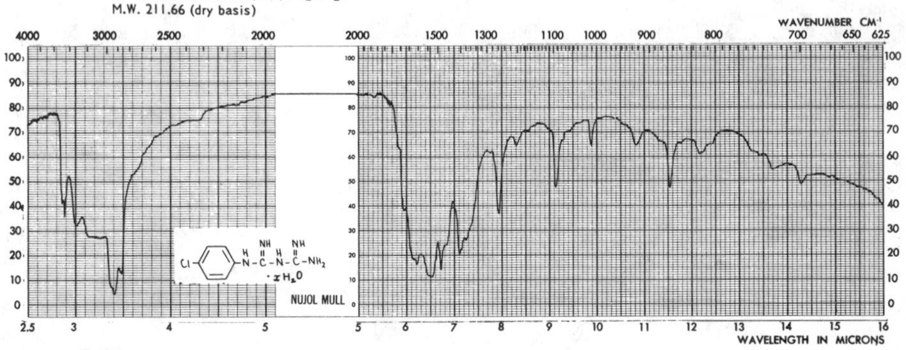

NUJOL MULL

H

13,742-1 **2,2'-(4,5-Dimethyl-o-xylylene)-bis-(2-thiopseudourea) dihydrochloride**
M.W. 355.35 m.p. 232° (dec.)

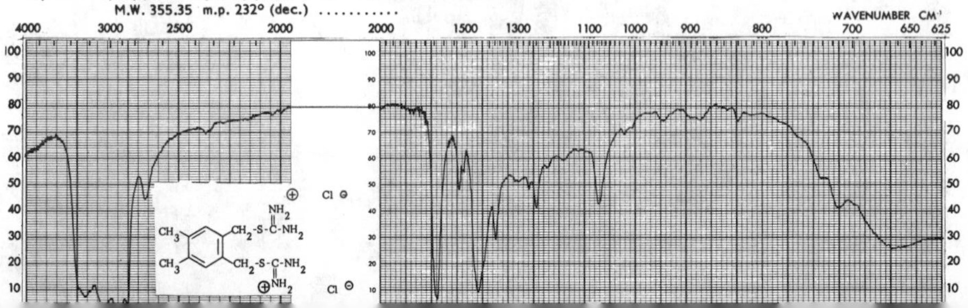

WAVENUMBER CM⁻¹

WAVELENGTH IN MICRONS

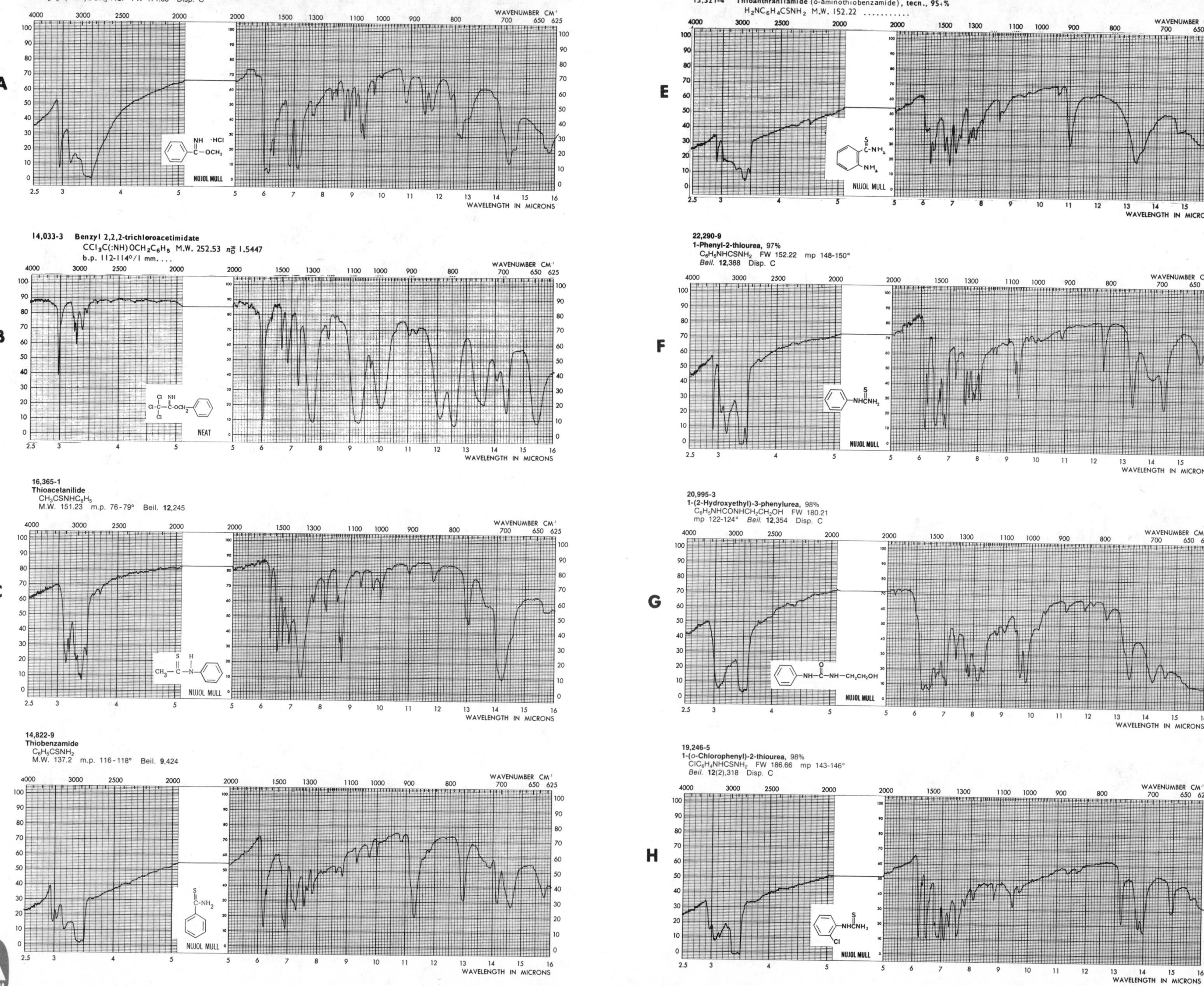

carboximidate)
C6H5C(=NH)OCH3·HCl FW 171.63 Disp. C
A
NUJOL MULL
14,033-3 Benzyl 2,2,2-trichloroacetimidate
CCl3C(:NH)OCH2C6H5 M.W. 252.53 n20D 1.5447
b.p. 112-114°/1 mm. . . .
B
NEAT
16,365-1
Thioacetanilide
CH3CSNHC6H5
M.W. 151.23 m.p. 76-79° Beil. 12,245
C
NUJOL MULL
14,822-9
Thiobenzamide
C6H5CSNH2
M.W. 137.2 m.p. 116-118° Beil. 9,424
D
NUJOL MULL
15,321-4 Thioanthranilamide (o-aminothiobenzamide), tecn., 95+%
H2NC6H4CSNH2 M.W. 152.22 . . . .
E
NUJOL MULL
22,290-9
1-Phenyl-2-thiourea, 97%
C6H5NHCSNH2 FW 152.22 mp 148-150°
Beil. 12,388 Disp. C
F
NUJOL MULL
20,995-3
1-(2-Hydroxyethyl)-3-phenylurea, 98%
C6H5NHCONHCH2CH2OH FW 180.21
mp 122-124° Beil. 12,354 Disp. C
G
NUJOL MULL
19,246-5
1-(o-Chlorophenyl)-2-thiourea, 98%
ClC6H4NHCSNH2 FW 186.66 mp 143-146°
Beil. 12(2),318 Disp. C
H
NUJOL MULL
WAVENUMBER CM⁻¹
WAVELENGTH IN MICRONS
ALDRICH

A

19,727-0
1-(3,4-Dichlorophenyl)-2-thiourea, tech.
$Cl_2C_6H_3NHCSNH_2$ FW 221.11 mp 183-191°
Beil. **12**(2),337 Disp. C

NUJOL MULL

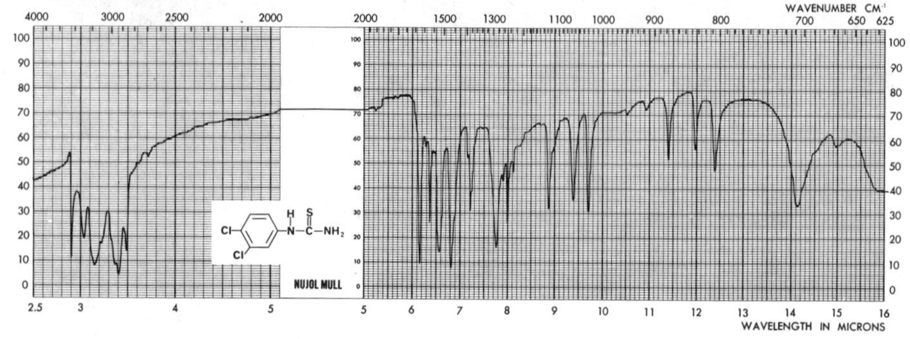

B

21,610-0
1-Isopropyl-1-(*m*-tolyl)urea, tech.
$CH_3C_6H_4N[CH(CH_3)_2]CONH_2$ FW 192.26
mp 81-84° Disp. C

NUJOL MULL

C

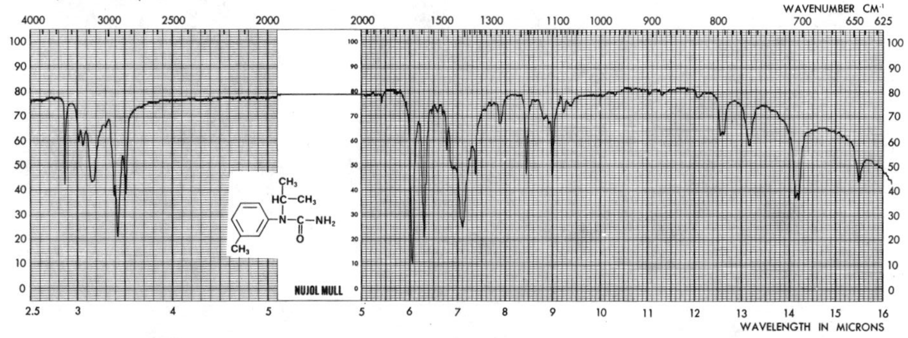

19,936-2
1-(*p*-Methoxyphenyl)-2-thiourea, 98%
$CH_3OC_6H_4NHCSNH_2$ FW 182.25 mp 212° (dec.)
Beil. **13**(2),253 Disp. C

NUJOL MULL

D

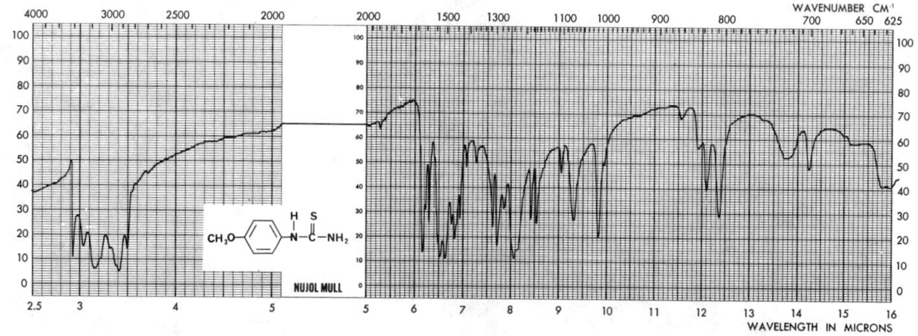

19,935-4
1-[*p*-(Dimethylamino)phenyl]-2-thiourea, 98%
$(CH_3)_2NC_6H_4NHCSNH_2$ FW 195.29 mp 202-204°
Beil. **13**,102 Disp. C

E

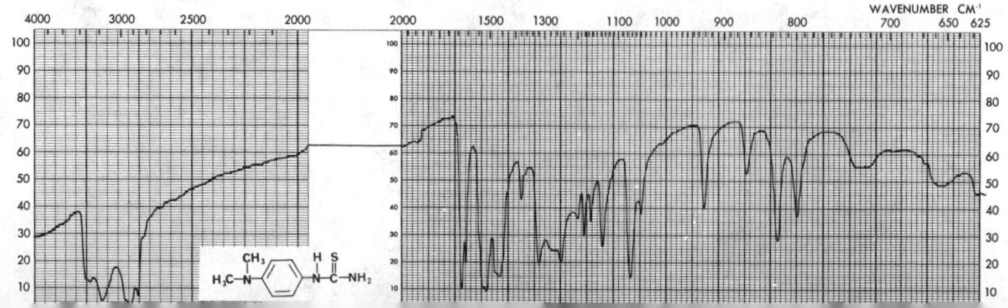

19,937-0
1-(*p*-Nitrophenyl)-2-thiourea, 98%
$O_2NC_6H_4NHCSNH_2$ FW 197.22 mp 206° (dec.)
Beil. **12**(2),393 Disp. C

NUJOL MULL

F

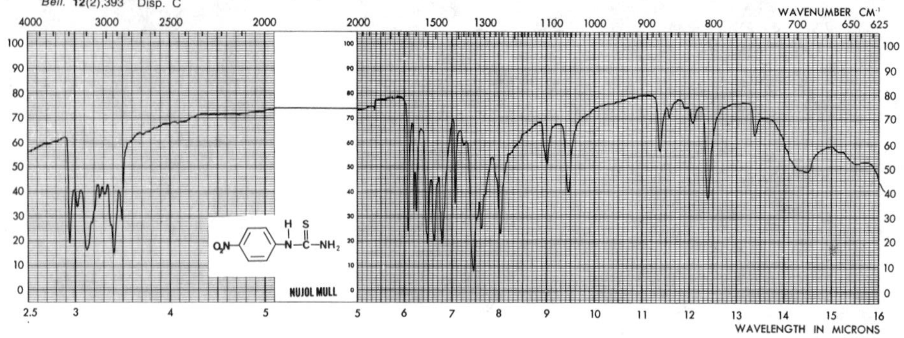

21,417-5
***N*-Isopropyl-*N*-[(3,4-methylenedioxy)phenyl]urea**, 98%
[*N*-(1,3-benzodioxol-5-yl)-*N*-(1-methylethyl)urea]
FW 222.24 mp 121-123° Disp. C

NUJOL MULL

G

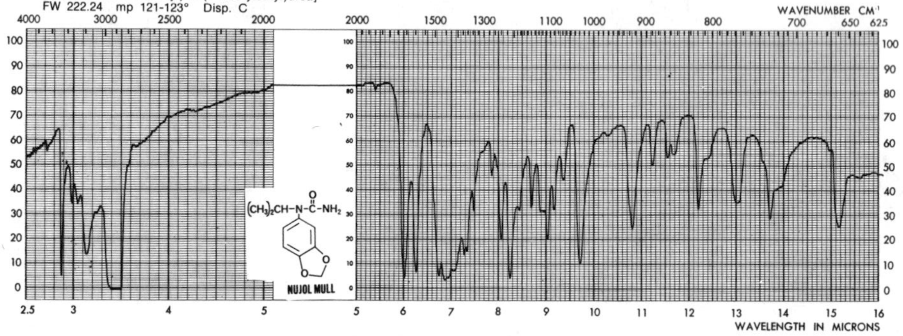

10,349-7 **N-(1-Naphthyl)-thioacetamide**
$CH_3CSNHC_{10}H_7$ M.W. 201.29 m.p. 108-110°

NUJOL MULL

H

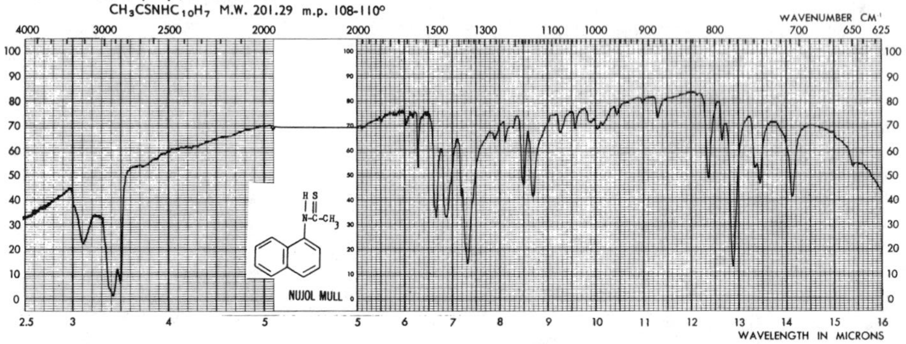

15,527-6
1-(1-Naphthyl)-2-thiourea, tech.
$C_{10}H_7NHCSNH_2$
M.W. 202.28 m.p. 190-192° Beil. **12**,1241

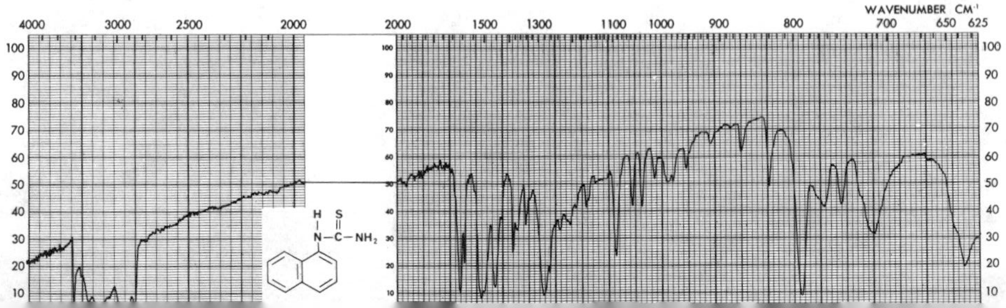

A

m.p. 149-151.5°

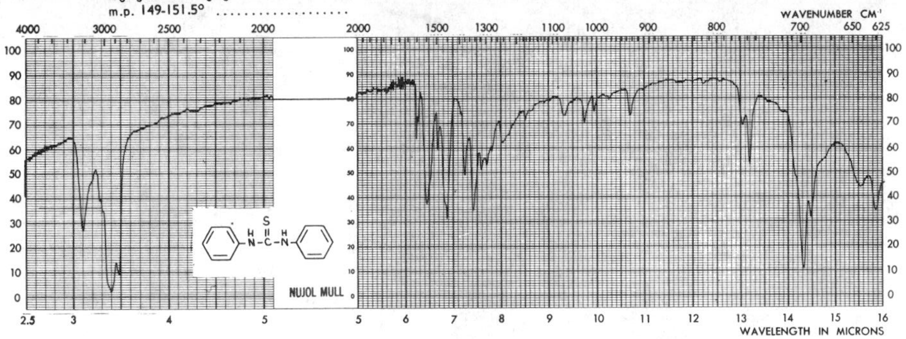

13,148-2 4-Phenyl-3-thiosemicarbazide
$C_6H_5NHCSNHNH_2$ M.W. 167.23
m.p. 137-138°

B

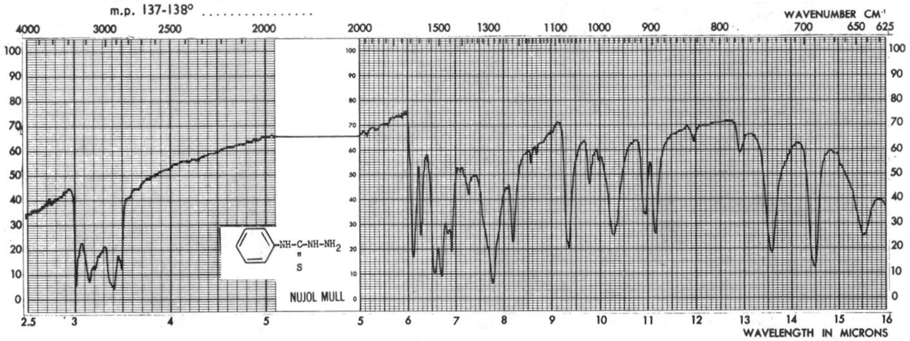

D3675-5 1,3-Dibenzylthiourea
$C_6H_5CH_2NHCSNHCH_2C_6H_5$ M.W. 256.37 m.p. 149-151°

C

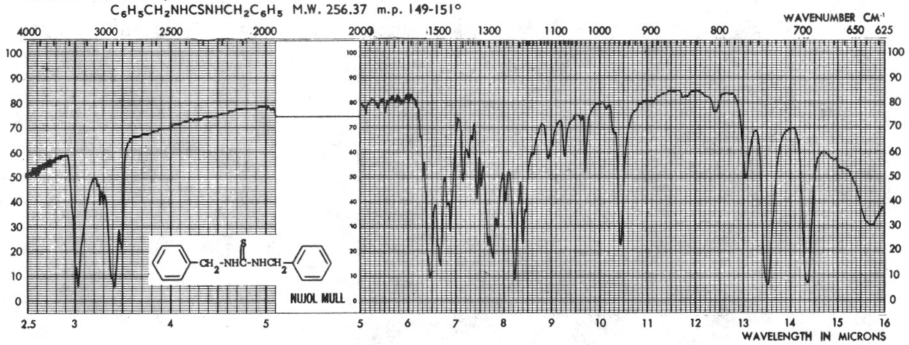

14,710-9 N,N'-Di-o-tolylthiourea (2,2'-dimethylthiocarbanilide)
$CH_3C_6H_4NHCSNHC_6H_4CH_3$ M.W. 256.37
m.p. 150-153.5°

D

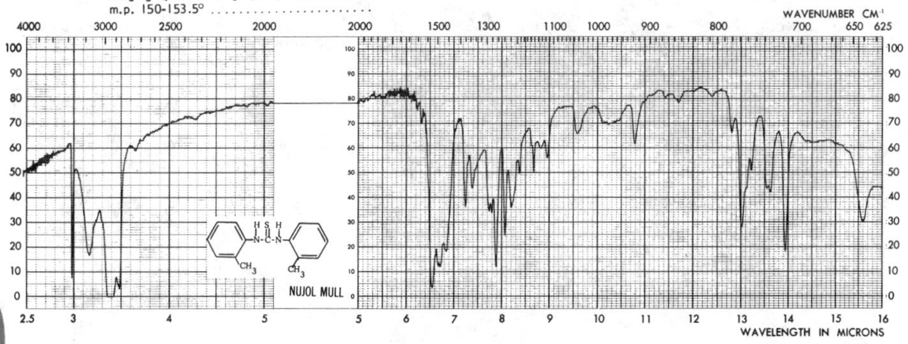

E

m.p. 180-181°

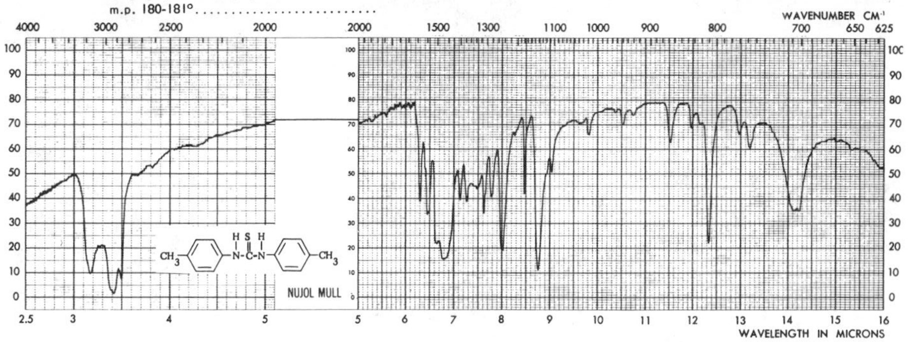

14,048-1 N-(o-Hydroxyphenyl)-N'-phenylthiourea (2'-hydroxythiocarbanilide)
$HOC_6H_4NHCSNHC_6H_5$ M.W. 244.32
m.p. 141-143°

F

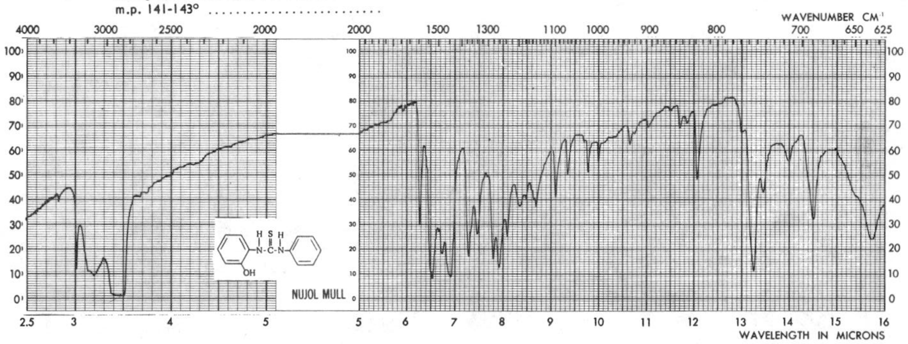

A4040 4-Aminobenzaldehyde thiosemicarbazone
$H_2NC_6H_4CH{:}NNHCSNH_2$ M.W. 194.26 m.p. 192° (dec.)

G

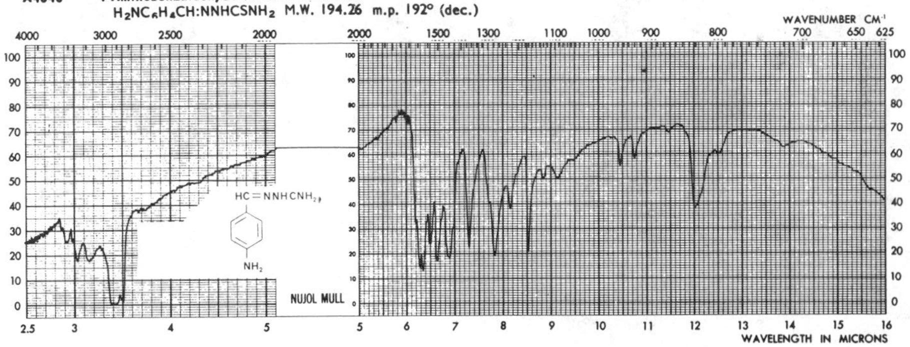

12,441-9 Thiacetazone (4'-formylacetanilide thiosemicarbazone)
$CH_3CONHC_6H_4CH{:}NNHCSNH_2$ M.W. 236.30
m.p. 231.5° (dec.)

H

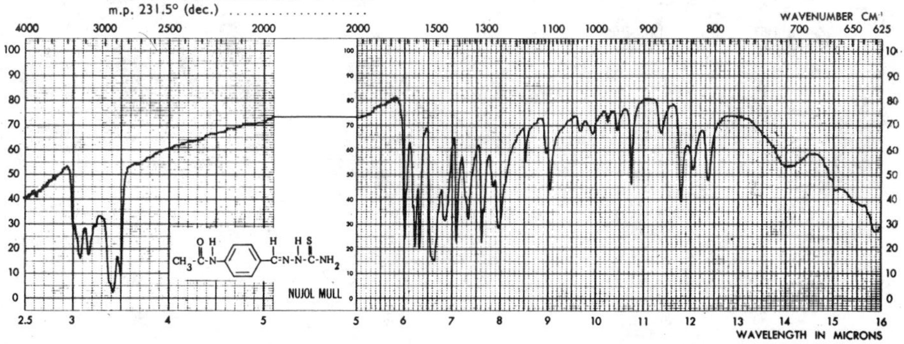

A

19,483-2
Diphenylthiocarbazone (dithizone)
$C_6H_5N{=}NCSNHNHC_6H_5$ FW 256.33
mp 168° (dec.) *Beil.* **16**,26 Disp. C

NUJOL MULL

B

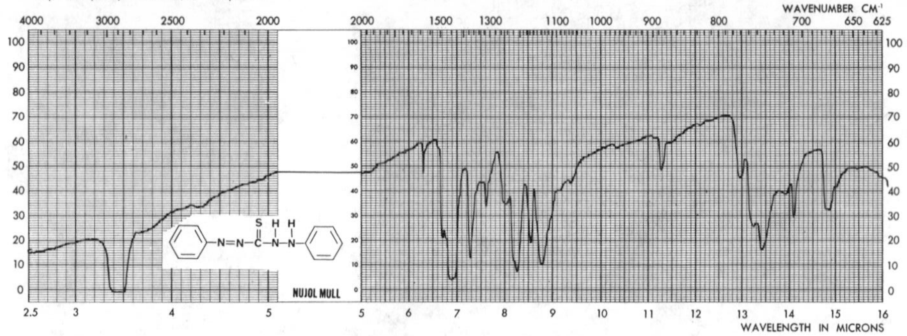

10,235-0 **1,3-Bis-(2-naphthylimino)-2-thiourea monohydrate, puriss.**
$(C_{10}H_7N{:}N)_2CS{\cdot}H_2O$ M.W. 372.45 ....

NUJOL MULL

C

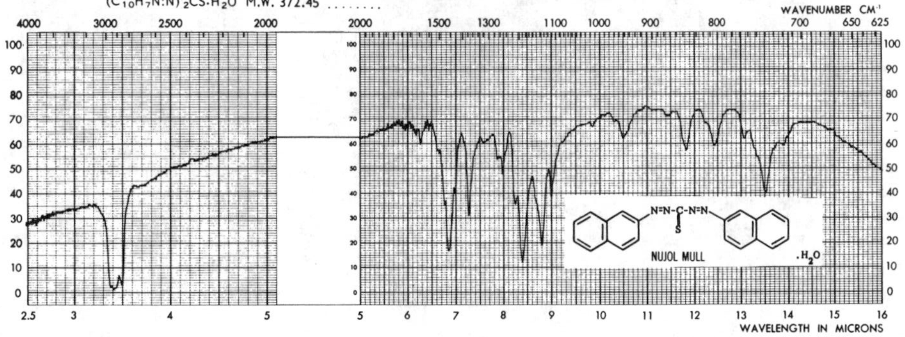

M5285-3 **N-Methylisatin 3-(thiosemicarbazone)**
M.W. 234.29 m.p. 241-244° (dec.)

NUJOL MULL

D

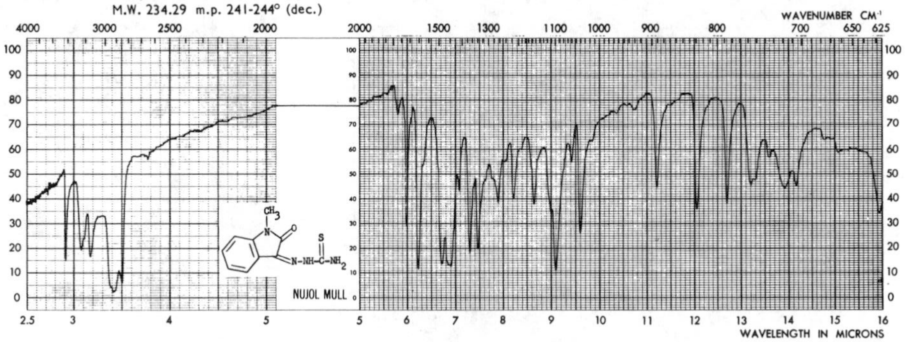

14,050-3 **3-Phenyl-1-thiocarbamoyl-5-pyrazolone** (5-oxo-3-phenyl-2-pyrazoline-1-thiocarboxamide)
M.W. 219.27 m.p. 152-154° (dec.) ......

E

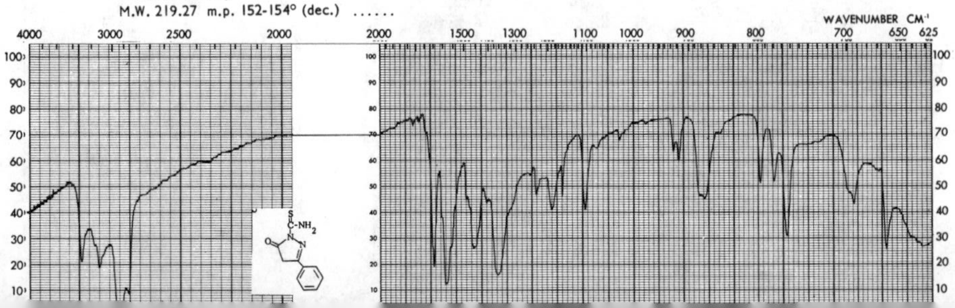

14,340-5 **4,5-Diphenyl-4-oxazoline-2-thione**
M.W. 253.33 m.p. 258-262° ....

NUJOL MULL

F

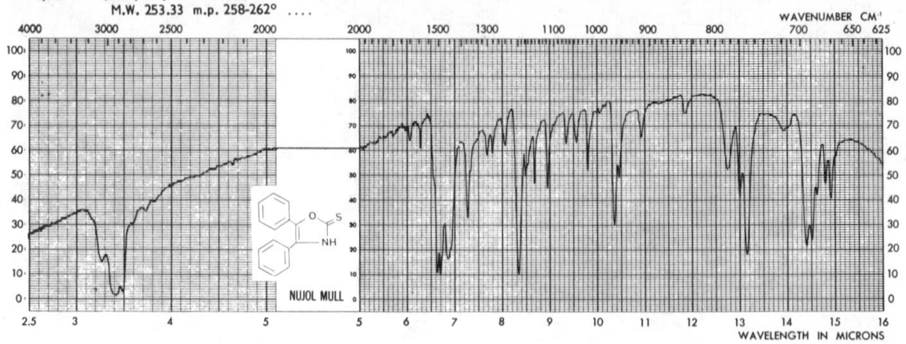

D21,425-6 **5,5-Diphenyl-2-thiohydantoin**
M.W. 268.33 m.p. 235-237°

NUJOL MULL

G

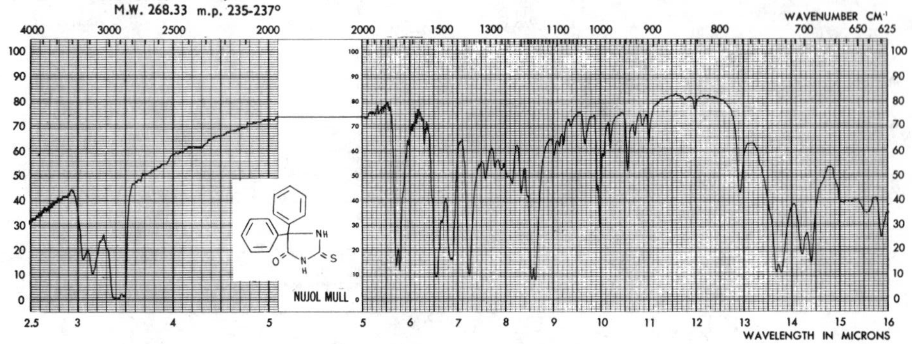

12,321-8 **N-Anilinorhodanine**
M.W. 224.30 m.p. 133-137°

NUJOL MULL

H

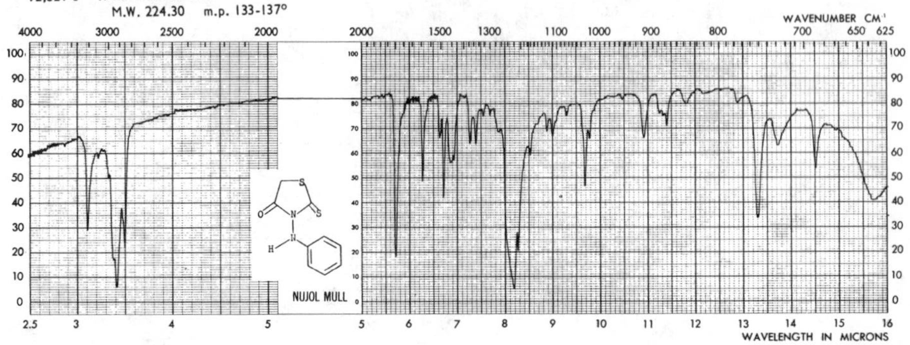

M540-2 **5-Mercapto-3-phenyl-1,3,4-thiadiazole-2-thione, potassium salt**
(bismuthiol II)
M.W. 264.44
m.p. 250-255° (dec.) .....

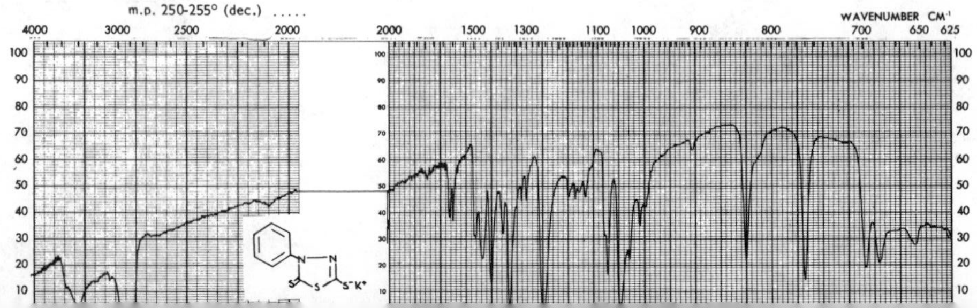

M.W. 264.37 m.p. 285-288°

A

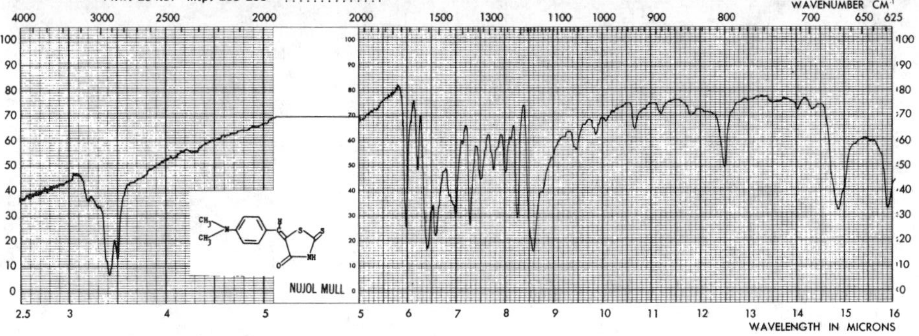

M3000-0 N-Methylbenzothiazole-2-thione
M.W. 181.28 m.p. 87.5-89°

B

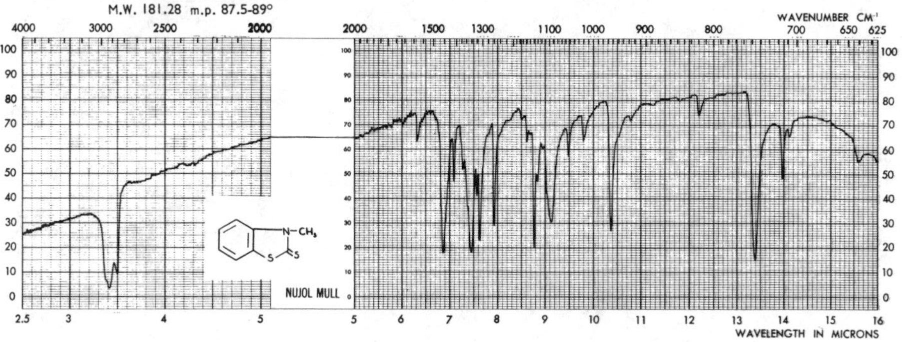

14,206-9
2-Methyl-5H-1,5-benzothiazepin-4-one, 99%
M.W. 191.25 m.p. 117-121°

C

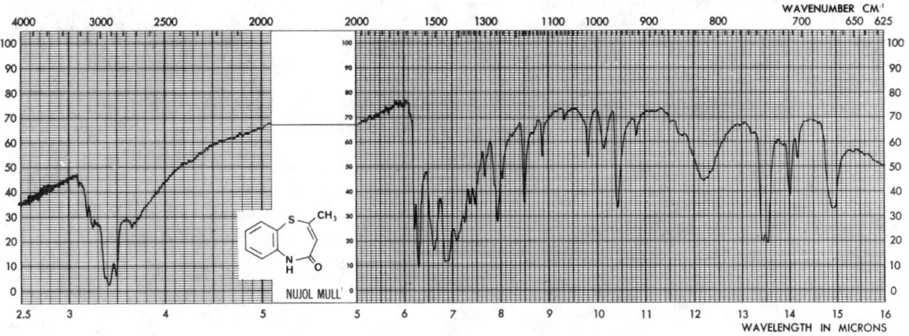

11,565-7 S-(p-Chlorobenzyl)-thiuronium chloride [2-(p-chlorobenzyl)-2-thio-pseudourea hydrochloride], **puriss.**
$ClC_6H_4CH_2S{:}C(NH_2)_2Cl$ M.W. 237.15
m.p. 205-207°

D

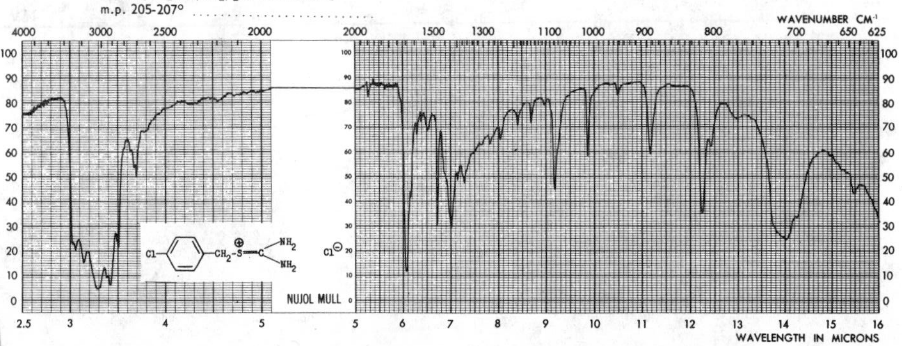

$[\alpha]^{22}$ +217.1° (c=0.47, H_2O) Disp. L

E

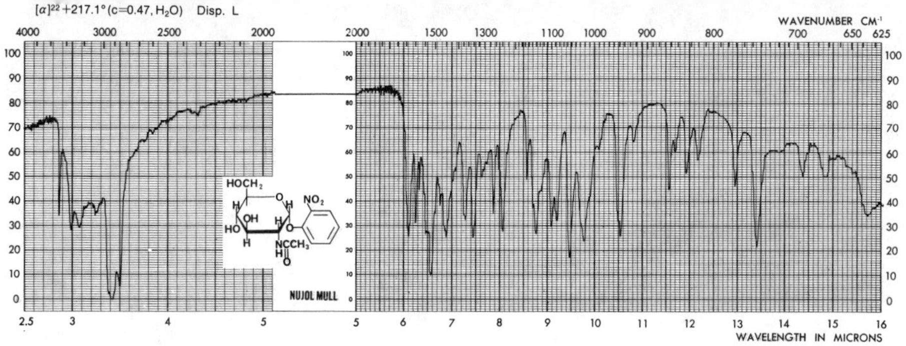

86,047-6
***p*-Nitrophenyl-2-acetamido-2-deoxy-α-D-glucopyranoside, 99%** (*p*-nitrophenyl-*N*-acetyl-α-D-glucosaminide)
FW 342.31 mp 264-266° (dec.)
$[\alpha]^{22}$ +280.3° (c=0.5, CH_3OH) Disp. L

F

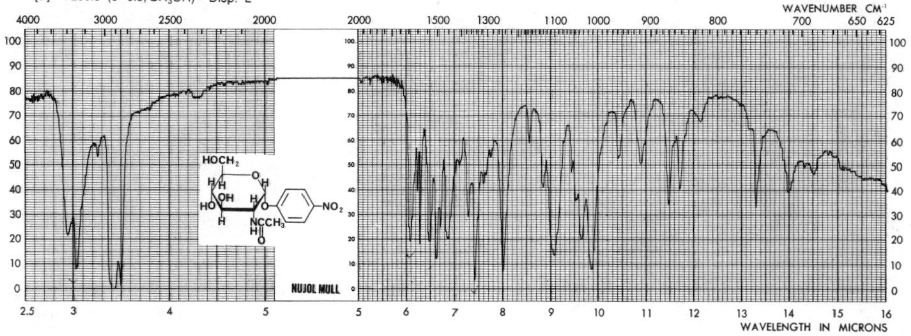

86,048-4
***p*-Nitrophenyl-2-acetamido-2-deoxy-β-D-glucopyranoside** (*p*-nitrophenyl-*N*-acetyl-β-D-glucosaminide)
FW 342.31 mp 210-212° Disp. L

G

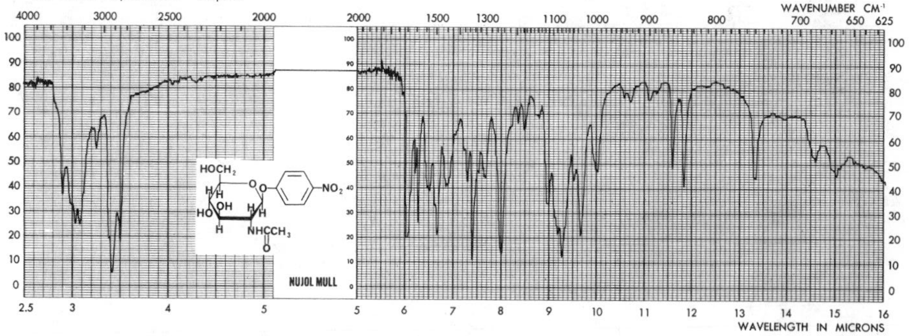

86,002-6
***N*-Carbobenzyloxy-D-glucosamine**
FW 313.31 mp 214° (dec.)
$[\alpha]^{22}$ +46.3° (c=1, DMF) Disp. C

H

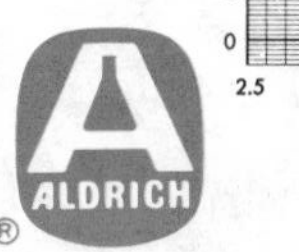

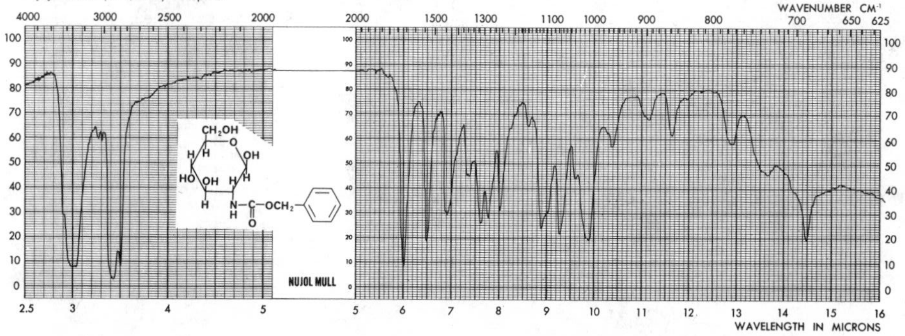

A

86,050-6
Metrizamide [2-[3-acetamido-5-(*N*-methylacetamido)-2,4,6-triiodobenzamido]-2-deoxy-D-glucose]
FW 789.10 mp 222-224° (dec.)
$[\alpha]^{24}$ +18.8° (c=5, H_2O) Disp. C
NUJOL MULL

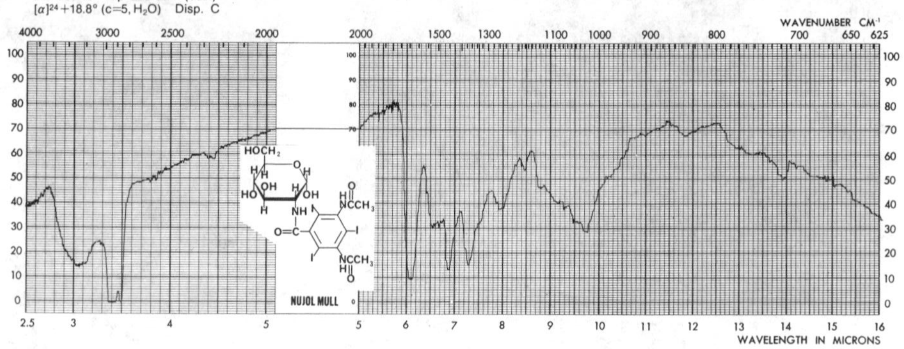

B

85,779-3
Cytochalasin A
FW 477.61 mp 193-195°
$[\alpha]^{21}$ +83.7° (c=1, CH_3OH) Disp. C
KBr

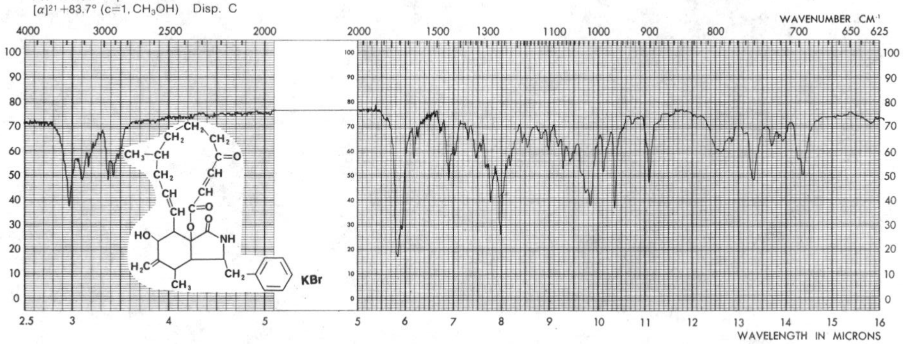

C

85,777-7
Cytochalasin B
FW 479.62 mp 221-223°
$[\alpha]^{21}$ +86.7° (c=0.9, CH_3OH) Disp. C
KBr

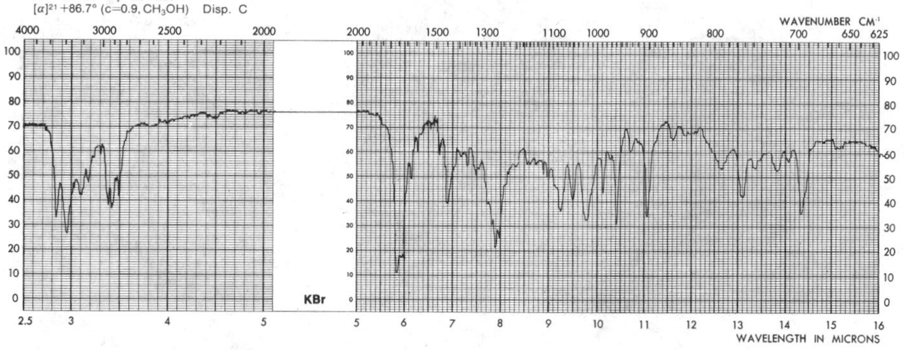

D

85,993-1
Cytochalasin C
FW 507.63 mp 260-266° (dec.)
$[\alpha]^{28}$ -14.7° (c=0.8, dioxane) Disp. C

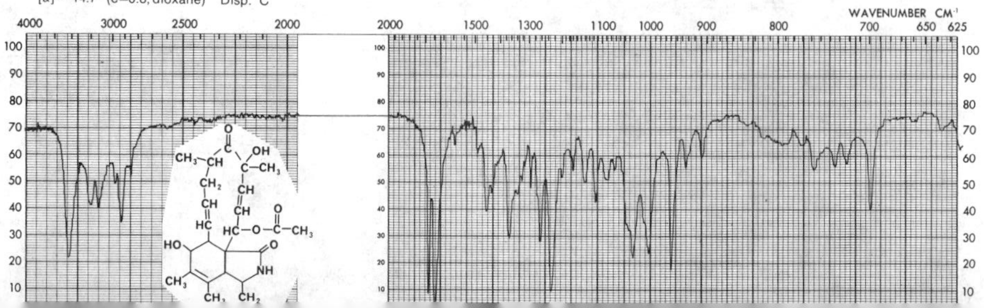

E

85,995-8
Cytochalasin D
FW 507.63 mp 255-260° (dec.)
$[\alpha]^{25}$ -7.5° (c=0.55, dioxane) Disp. C
KBr

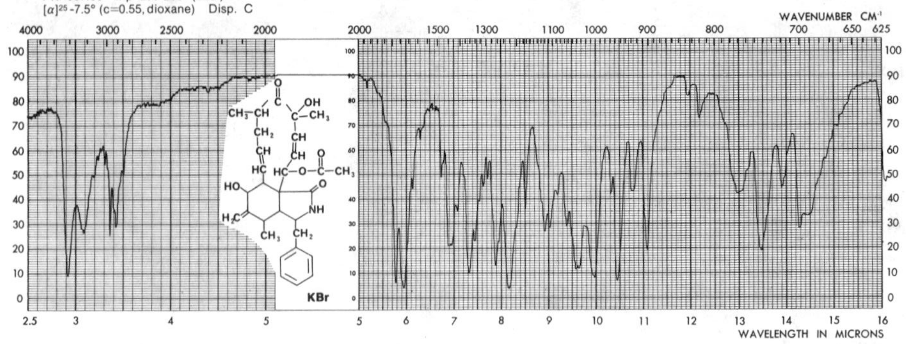

F

85,783-1
Cytochalasin E
FW 495.58 mp 206° (dec.)
$[\alpha]^{21}$ +22.7° (c=0.85, CH_3OH) Disp. C
KBr

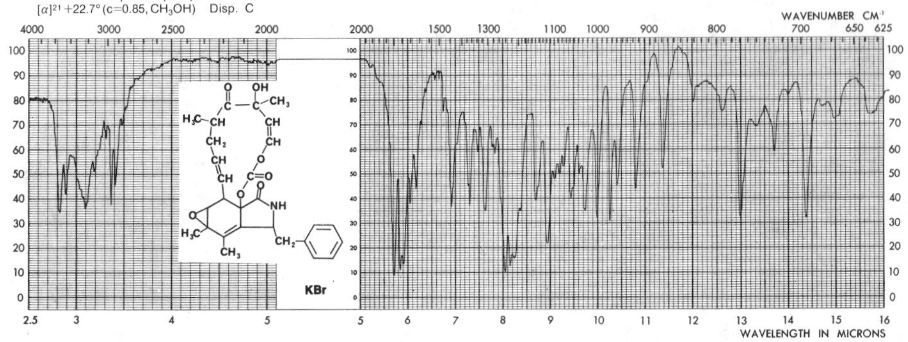

G

22,560-6
***N,N*-Dimethyl-2,2-diphenylacetamide, 95%**
(diphenamid)
$(C_6H_5)_2CHCON(CH_3)_2$ FW 239.32 mp 132-136°
Disp. C
NUJOL MULL

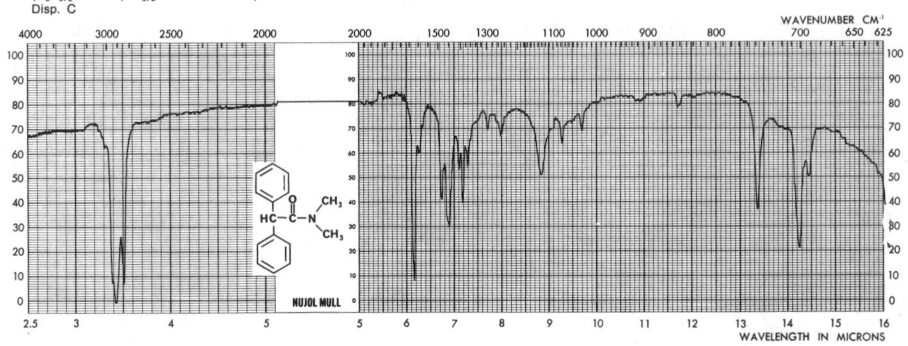

ALDRICH

AROMATIC NITRILES AND CUMULATED DOUBLE BONDS

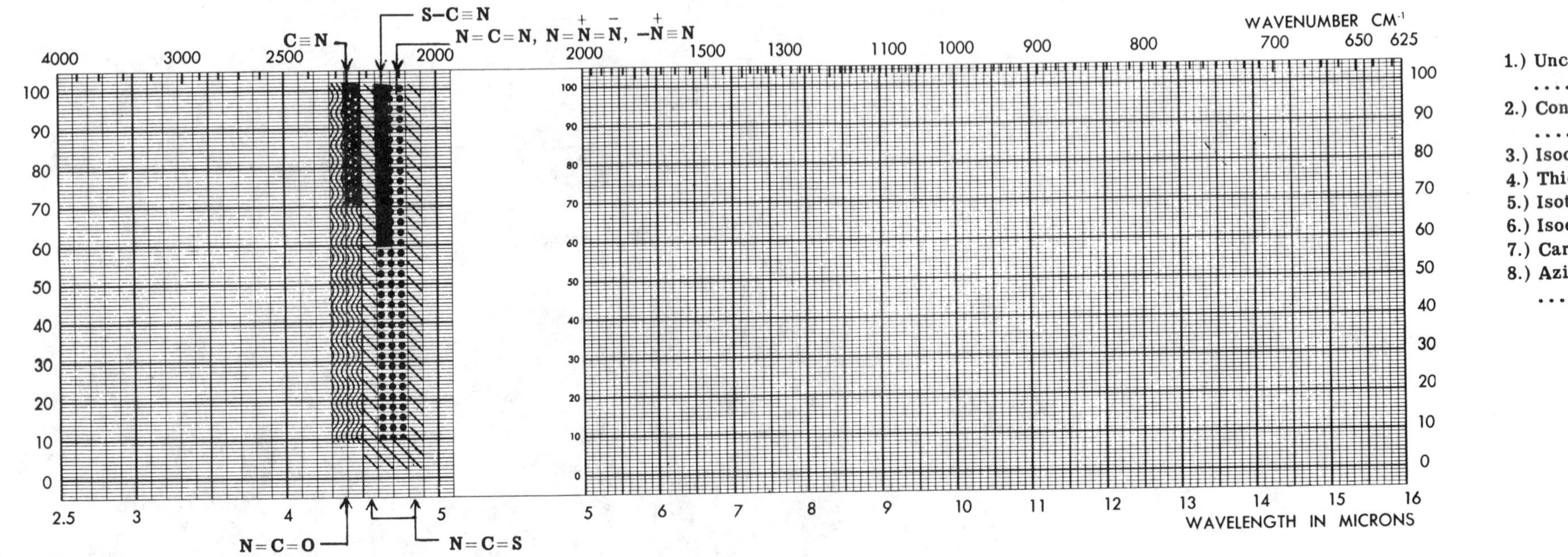

The nitrile absorption is shifted from its aliphatic position near 4.45 μ (2245 cm^{-1}) to a slightly higher wavelength. Its exact position is influenced by other groups and their positions on the aromatic ring.

The thiocyanates, isothiocyanates, isocyanates, carbodiimides and azides retain their aliphatic positions [thiocyanates, 4.6 to 4.7 μ (2175 – 2130 cm^{-1}); isothiocyanates, 4.5 to 4.9 μ (2220 – 2040 cm^{-1}); isocyanates, 4.4 μ (2275 cm^{-1}); carbodiimides and azides, near 4.7 μ (2130 cm^{-1})].

The diazonium group ($N{\equiv}\overset{+}{N}-$) absorbs very strongly near 4.6 μ (2175 cm^{-1}). (See spectra 1145C and E).

The substitution patterns between 11 and 15 μ (910 – 665 cm^{-1}) are not disturbed by any of the groups mentioned above.

$C_6H_5CH_2CN$ M.W. 117.15 n_D 1.5230

A — NEAT

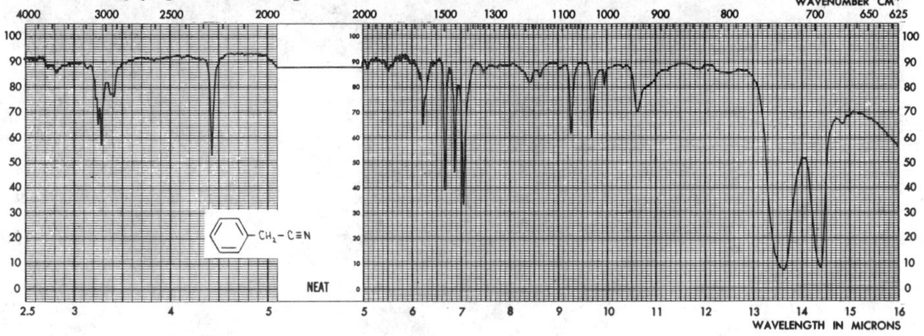

M3150-3 **α-Methylbenzyl cyanide** (α-methylphenylacetonitrile), **tech.**
$C_6H_5CH(CH_3)CN$ M.W. 131.18 n_D^{20} 1.5106

B — NEAT

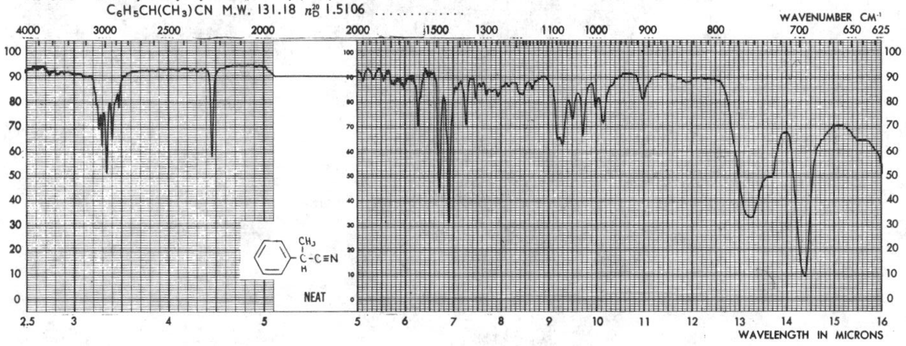

22,273-9
DL-2-Phenylbutyronitrile, 95%
$C_2H_5CH(C_6H_5)CN$ FW 145.21 bp 114-115°/15mm.
n_D^{20} 1.5086 d 0.974 *Beil.* 9,541 Disp. C

C — NEAT

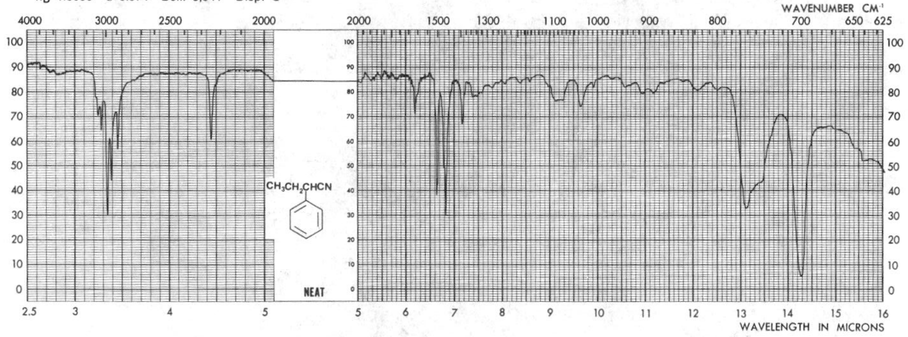

11,212-7 **Diphenylacetonitrile**
$(C_6H_5)_2CHCN$ M.W. 193.25 m.p. 71-73°

D — NUJOL MULL

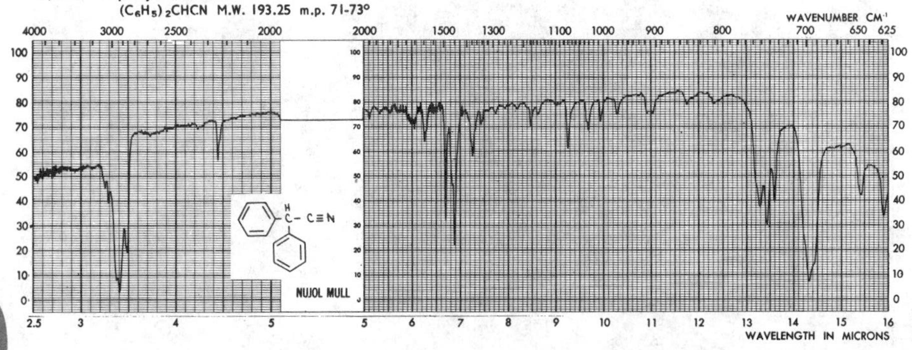

m.p. 89-92°

E — NUJOL MULL

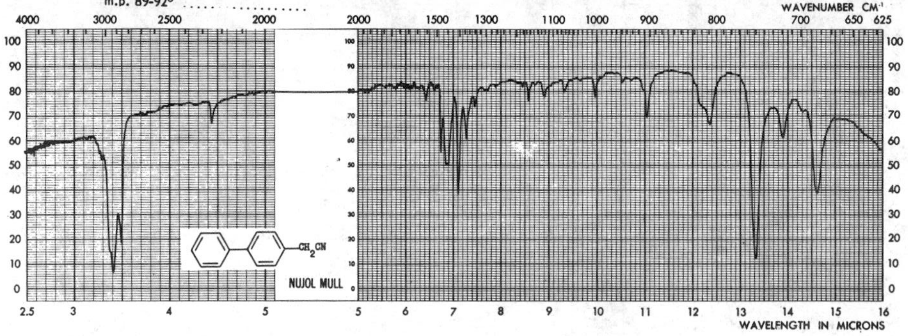

D7750-8 ***meso*-1,2-Dicyano-1,2-diphenylethane** (*meso*-α,β-diphenylsuccinonitrile)
NCCH(C_6H_5)CH(C_6H_5)CN M.W. 232.29 m.p. 211-212°

F — NUJOL MULL

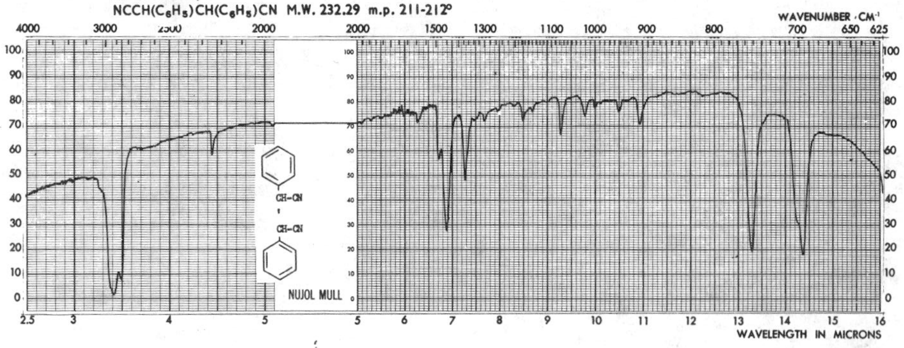

16,276-0
2-Naphthylacetonitrile (2-naphthaleneacetonitrile)
$C_{10}H_7CH_2CN$
M.W. 167.21 m.p. 82-84° b.p. 303° d 1.092
Beil. 9,659

G — NUJOL MULL

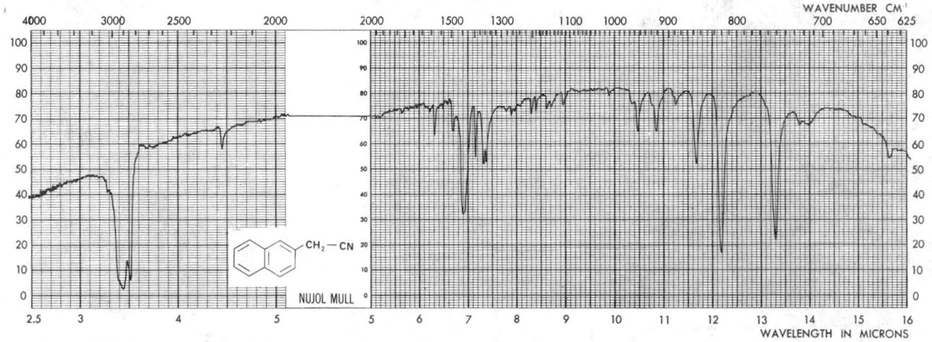

17,157-3
Hydrocinnamonitrile (3-phenylpropionitrile)
$C_6H_5CH_2CH_2CN$ FW 131.18 mp -2 to 1°
bp 113°/9mm. n_D^{20} 1.5210 d 1.001 *Beil.* 9,512
IR 2,970G Disp. J

H — NEAT

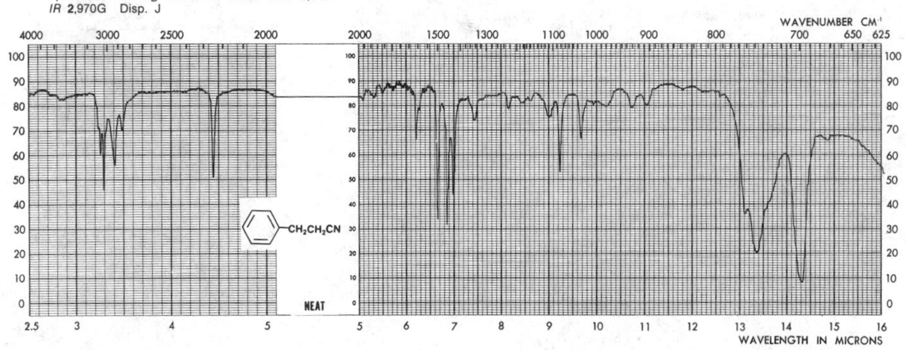

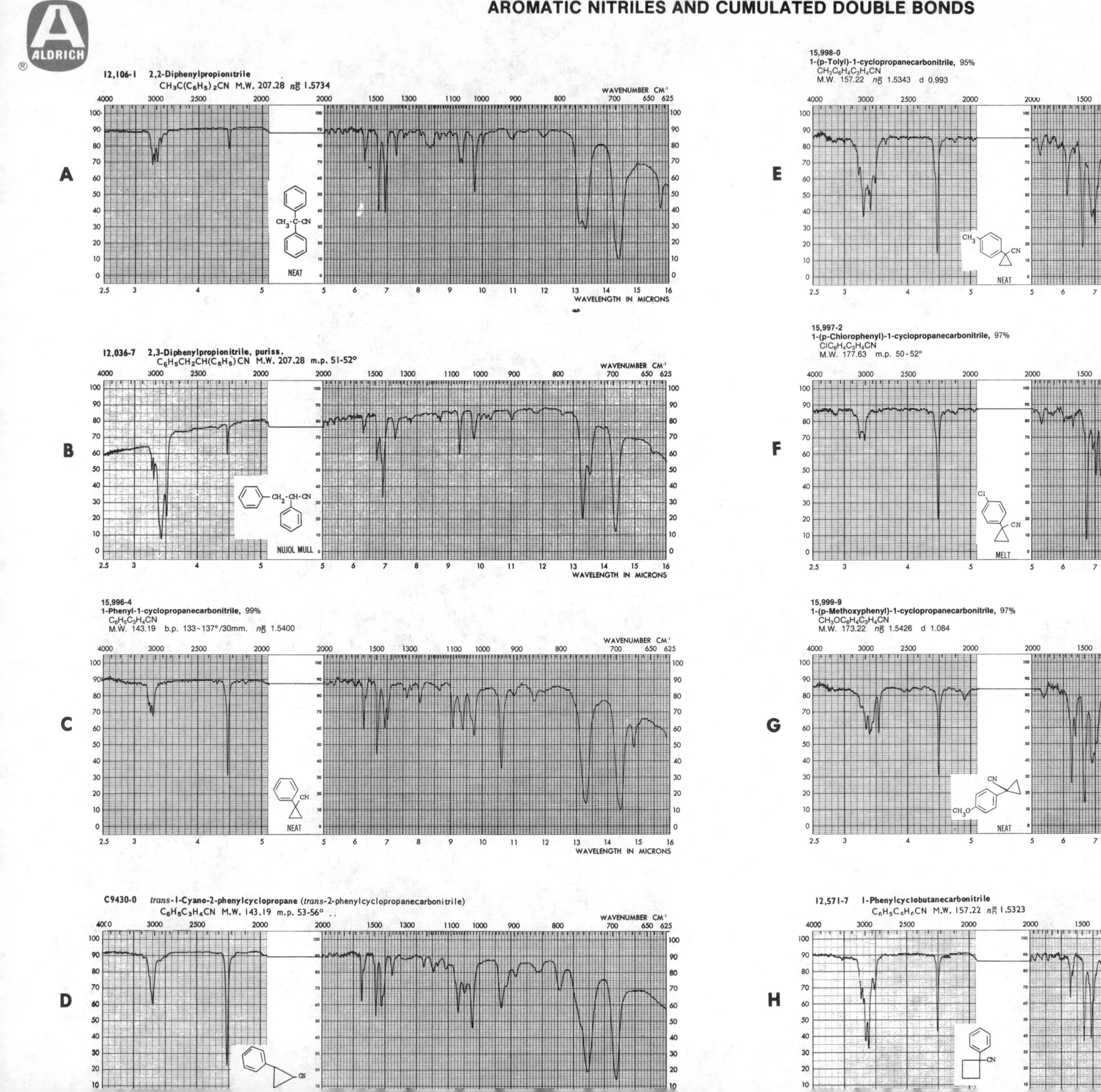

A 12,106-1 2,2-Diphenylpropionitrile
$CH_3C(C_6H_5)_2CN$ M.W. 207.28 n_D^{20} 1.5734
NEAT

B 12,036-7 2,3-Diphenylpropionitrile, puriss.
$C_6H_5CH_2CH(C_6H_5)CN$ M.W. 207.28 m.p. 51-52°
NUJOL MULL

C 15,996-4
1-Phenyl-1-cyclopropanecarbonitrile, 99%
$C_6H_5C_3H_4CN$
M.W. 143.19 b.p. 133-137°/30mm. n_D^{20} 1.5400
NEAT

D C9430-0 *trans*-1-Cyano-2-phenylcyclopropane (*trans*-2-phenylcyclopropanecarbonitrile)
$C_6H_5C_3H_4CN$ M.W. 143.19 m.p. 53-56°

E 15,998-0
1-(p-Tolyl)-1-cyclopropanecarbonitrile, 95%
$CH_3C_6H_4C_3H_4CN$
M.W. 157.22 n_D^{20} 1.5343 d 0.993
NEAT

F 15,997-2
1-(p-Chlorophenyl)-1-cyclopropanecarbonitrile, 97%
$ClC_6H_4C_3H_4CN$
M.W. 177.63 m.p. 50-52°
MELT

G 15,999-9
1-(p-Methoxyphenyl)-1-cyclopropanecarbonitrile, 97%
$CH_3OC_6H_4C_3H_4CN$
M.W. 173.22 n_D^{20} 1.5426 d 1.084
NEAT

H 12,571-7 1-Phenylcyclobutanecarbonitrile
$C_6H_5C_4H_6CN$ M.W. 157.22 n_D^{20} 1.5323

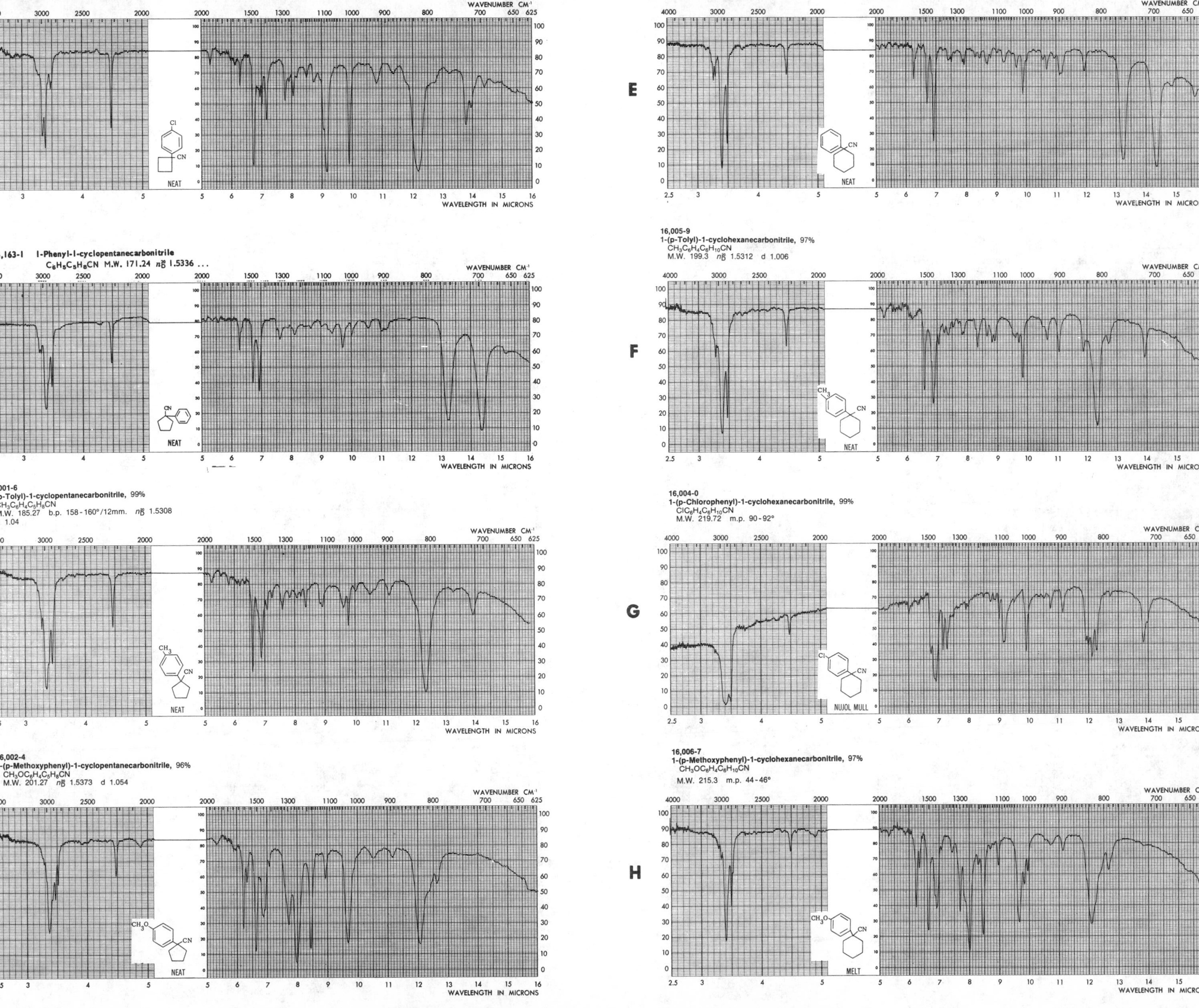

M.W. 191.66 n_D^{20} 1.5473 d 1.137

14,163-1 1-Phenyl-1-cyclopentanecarbonitrile
$C_6H_5C_5H_8CN$ M.W. 171.24 n_D^{20} 1.5336 ...

16,001-6
1-(p-Tolyl)-1-cyclopentanecarbonitrile, 99%
$CH_3C_6H_4C_5H_8CN$
M.W. 185.27 b.p. 158-160°/12mm. n_D^{20} 1.5308
d 1.04

16,002-4
1-(p-Methoxyphenyl)-1-cyclopentanecarbonitrile, 96%
$CH_3OC_6H_4C_5H_8CN$
M.W. 201.27 n_D^{20} 1.5373 d 1.054

M.W. 185.27 n_D^{20} 1.5334 d 1.017

16,005-9
1-(p-Tolyl)-1-cyclohexanecarbonitrile, 97%
$CH_3C_6H_4C_6H_{10}CN$
M.W. 199.3 n_D^{20} 1.5312 d 1.006

16,004-0
1-(p-Chlorophenyl)-1-cyclohexanecarbonitrile, 99%
$ClC_6H_4C_6H_{10}CN$
M.W. 219.72 m.p. 90-92°

16,006-7
1-(p-Methoxyphenyl)-1-cyclohexanecarbonitrile, 97%
$CH_3OC_6H_4C_6H_{10}CN$
M.W. 215.3 m.p. 44-46°

A

C10,780-8 Cyclohexylphenylacetonitrile (α-phenylcyclohexaneacetonitrile)
$C_6H_{11}CH(C_6H_5)CN$ M.W. 199.30

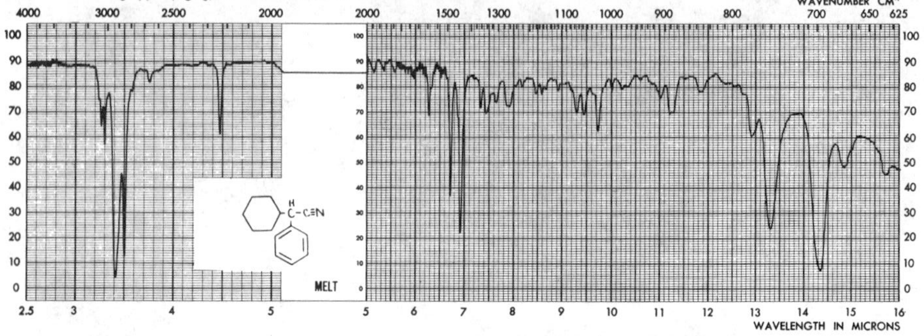

MELT

B

B6500-4 4-Bromo-2,2-diphenylbutyronitrile
$BrCH_2CH_2C(C_6H_5)_2CN$ M.W. 300.20
m.p. 70-71°

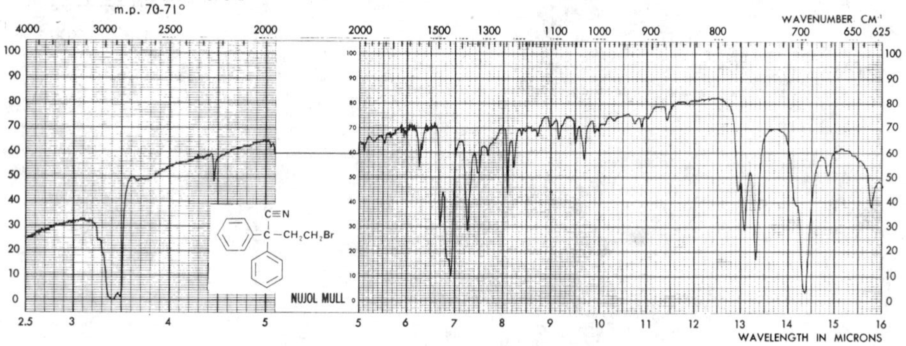

NUJOL MULL

C

11,602-5 Mandelonitrile, tech.
$C_6H_5CH(OH)CN$ M.W. 133.15 n_D^{20} 1.5201
b.p. 170° (dec.)

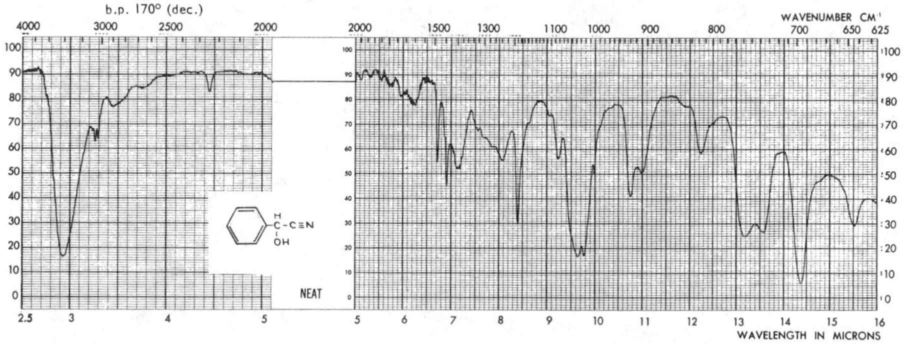

NEAT

D

19,286-4
α-Methoxy-α-(trifluoromethyl)phenylacetonitrile, 98%
$C_6H_5C(OCH_3)(CF_3)CN$ FW 215.18
bp 76-82°/12mm. n_D^{20} 1.4440 d 1.152
Fieser **7**,400 Disp. C

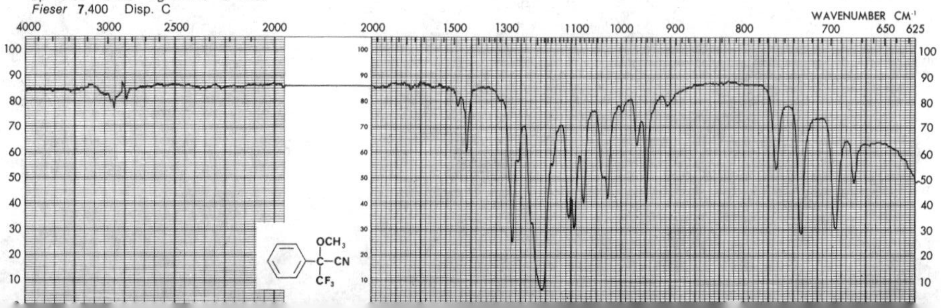

E

A8320-2 Amygdalin
M.W. 457.43 m.p. 223-226°

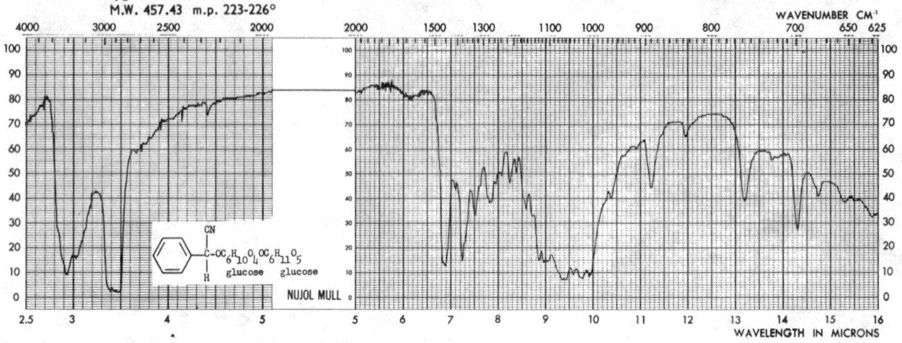

NUJOL MULL

F

P2555-8 2-Phenylglycinonitrile (α-aminobenzyl cyanide) **hydrochloride, tech.**
$C_6H_5CH(NH_2)CN{\cdot}HCl$ M.W. 168.63 m.p. 164-165° (dec.)

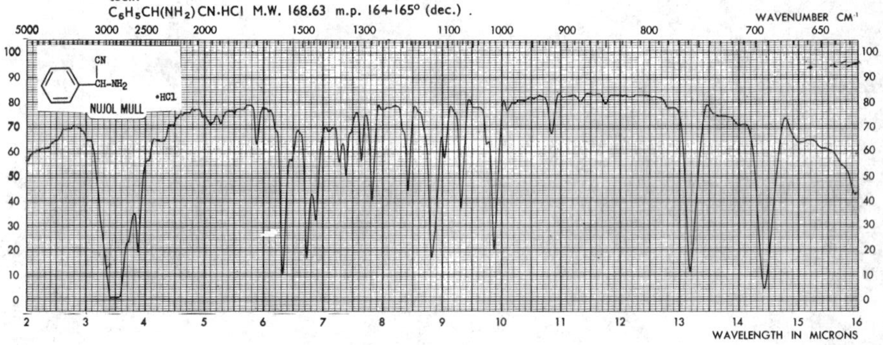

NUJOL MULL

G

A8775-5 3-Anilinopropionitrile
$C_6H_5NHCH_2CH_2CN$ M.W. 146.19
m.p. 52-53°

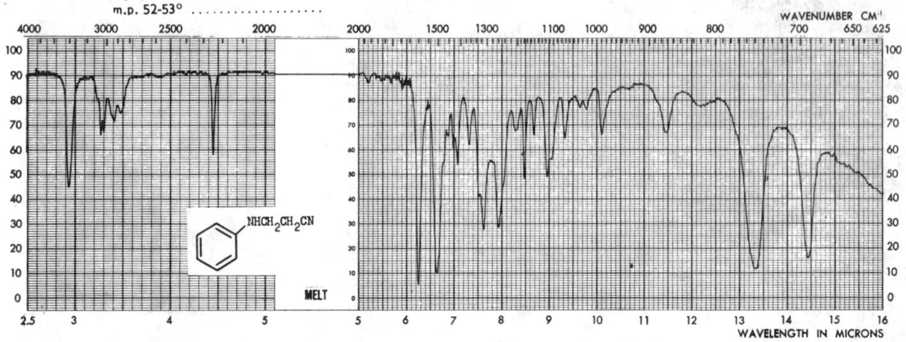

MELT

H

18,516-7
3-(Benzylamino)propionitrile, 97%
$C_6H_5CH_2NHCH_2CH_2CN$
M.W. 160.22 n_D^{20} 1.5308

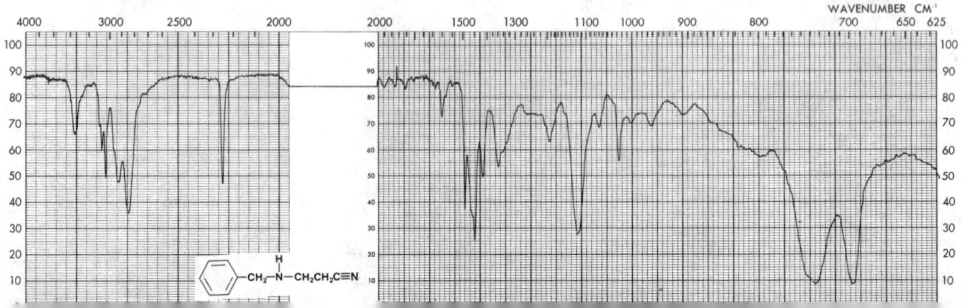

A

$C_6H_5N(C_2H_5)CH_2CH_2CN$ M.W. 174.24
n_D^{20} 1.5530

NEAT

B

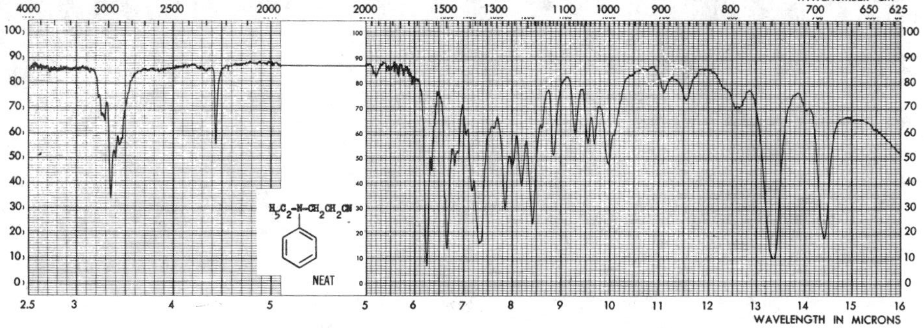

C9440-8 4-Cyano-4-phenylpiperidine (4-phenyl-4-piperidinecarbonitrile) hydrochloride
M.W. 222.72 m.p. 208-210°

NUJOL MULL

C

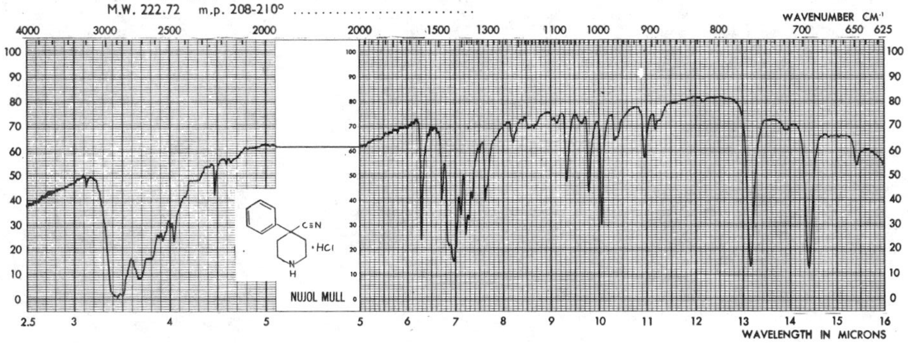

C8990-0 4-(α-Cyanobenzyl)-piperidine hydrochloride
M.W. 236.75 m.p. 248-250°

NUJOL MULL

D

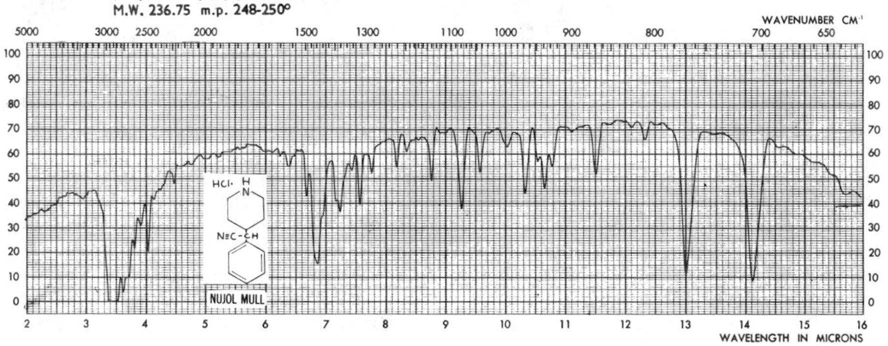

12,319-6 4-Anilino-1-benzyl-4-cyanopiperidine (4-anilino-1-benzyl-4-piperidinecarbonitrile)
M.W. 291.40 m.p. 145-147°

NUJOL MULL

E

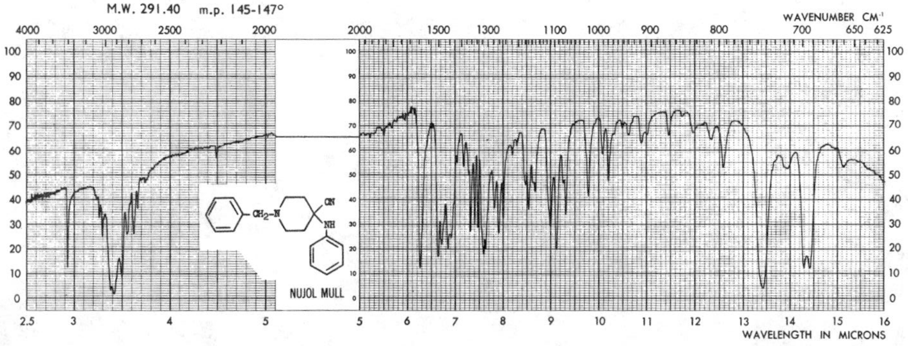

M.W. 325.84 m.p. 126-128°

NUJOL MULL

F

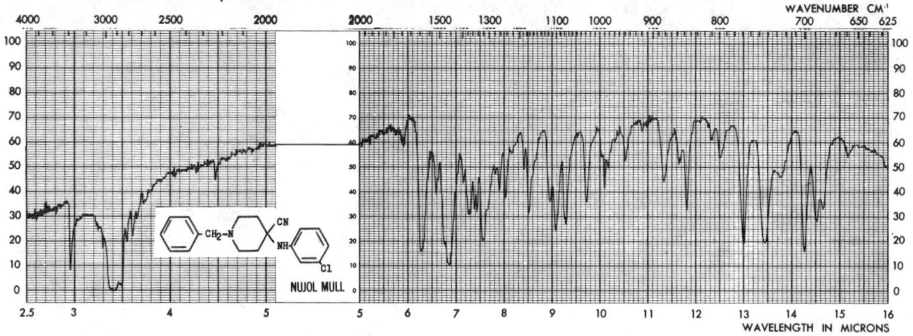

11,595-9 Benzoyl cyanide (phenylglyoxylonitrile)
C_6H_5COCN M.W. 131.13 m.p. 32-34°

MELT

G

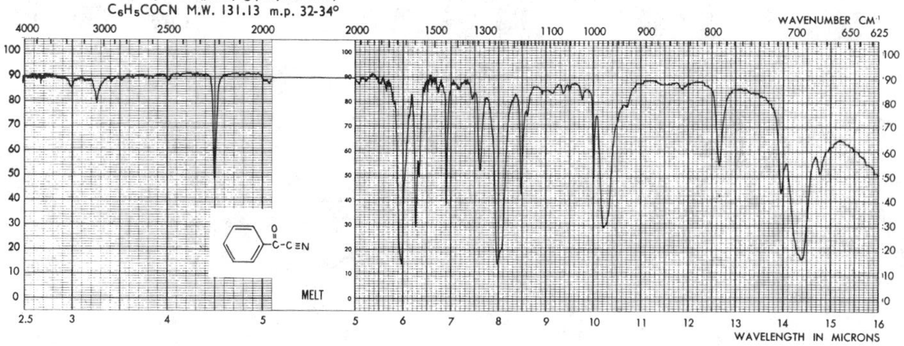

12,366-8 2-Benzoylpropionitrile
$CH_3CH(COC_6H_5)CN$ M.W. 159.19 n_D^{20} 1.5390

NEAT

H

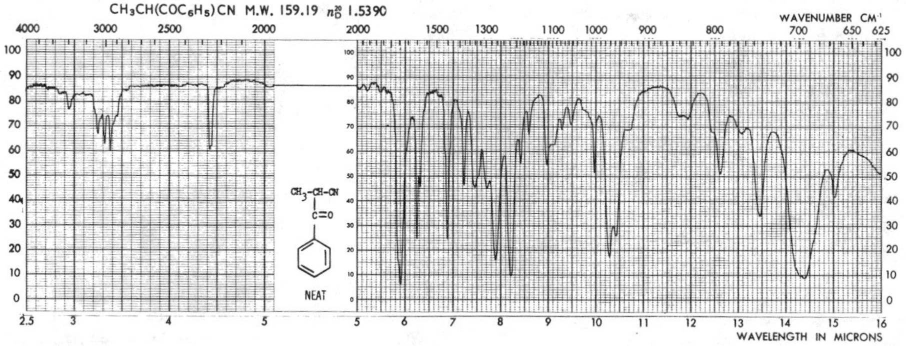

19,065-9
α-Acetylphenylacetonitrile, 98% (2-phenylacetoacetonitrile)
$C_6H_5CH(COCH_3)CN$ FW 159.19 mp 89-92°
Beil. 10,699 Disp. C

NUJOL MULL

AROMATIC NITRILES AND CUMULATED DOUBLE BONDS

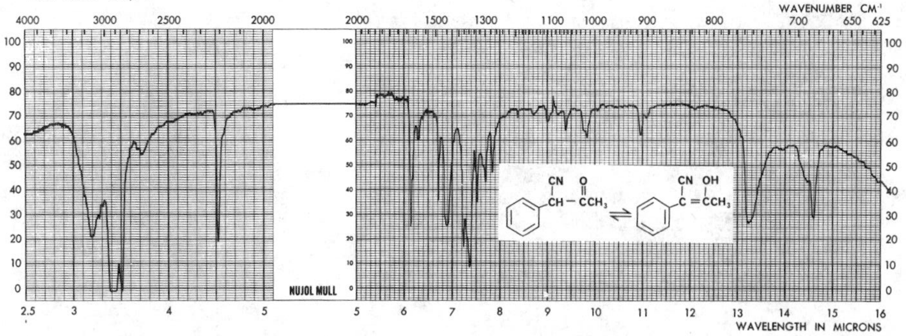

A 12,786-8 **β-Iminohydrocinnamonitrile** (3-imino-3-phenylpropionitrile)
$C_6H_5C(:NH)CH_2CN$ M.W. 144.18
m.p. 84-87.5°
NUJOL MULL

B B1350-0 **3-Benzoyl-2-phenylpropionitrile**
$C_6H_5COCH_2CH(C_6H_5)CN$ M.W. 235.29
m.p. 123-126°
NUJOL MULL

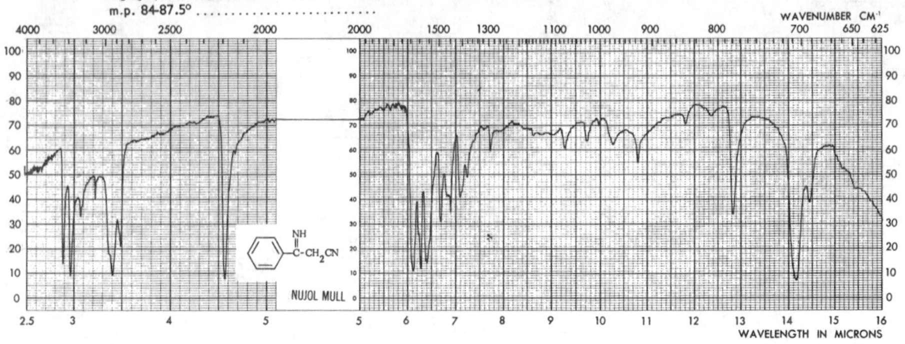

C 12,004-9 **2-Benzyl-3-oxo-2-phenylbutyronitrile** (2-benzyl-2-phenylacetoacetonitrile)
$CH_3COC(CH_2C_6H_5)(C_6H_5)CN$ M.W. 249.31 m.p. 79-81°
NUJOL MULL

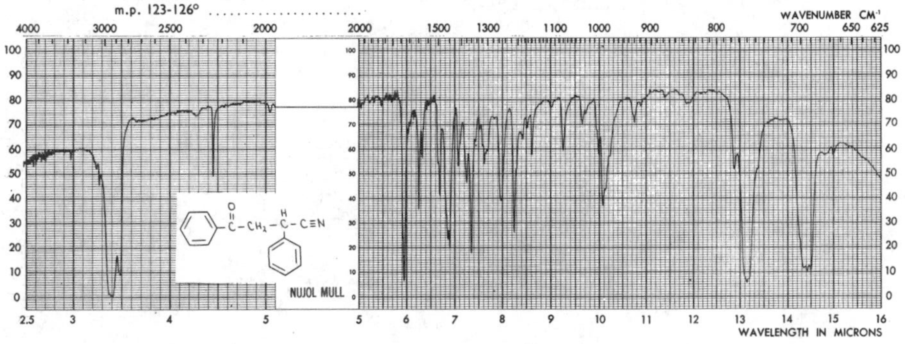

D E4520-1 **Ethyl phenylcyanoacetate**
$C_6H_5CH(CN)CO_2C_2H_5$ M.W. 189.21 n_D^{20} 1.5053

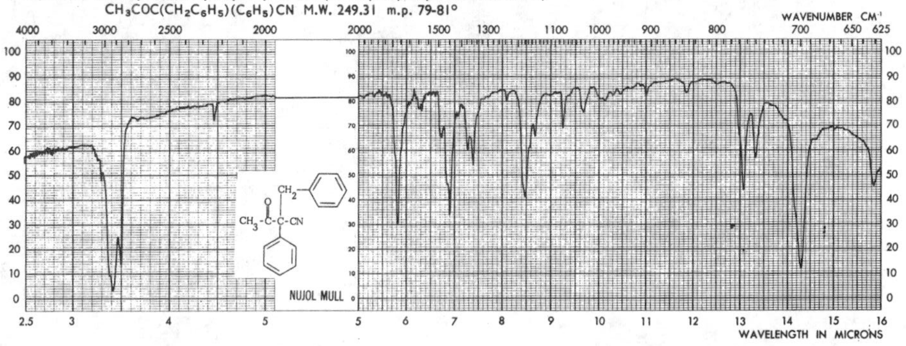

E 15,126-2 **Ethyl 3-cyano-3-phenylpyruvate**
$C_6H_5CH(CN)COCO_2C_2H_5$ M.W. 217.23 m.p. 125-128°
NUJOL MULL

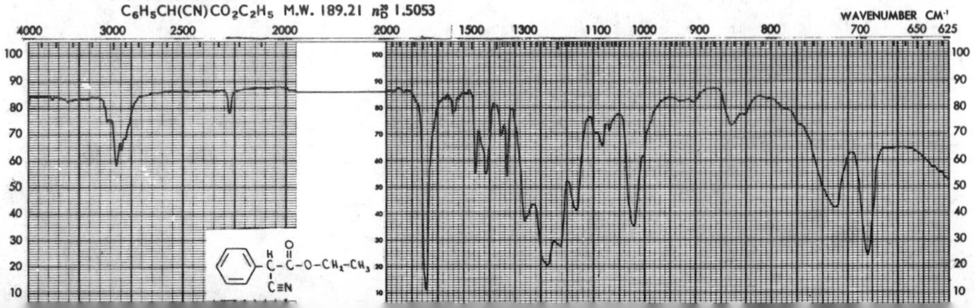

F M3155-4 **2-Methylbenzyl cyanide** (o-methylphenylacetonitrile)
$CH_3C_6H_4CH_2CN$ M.W. 131.18 n_D^{20} 1.5274 b.p. 212°
NEAT

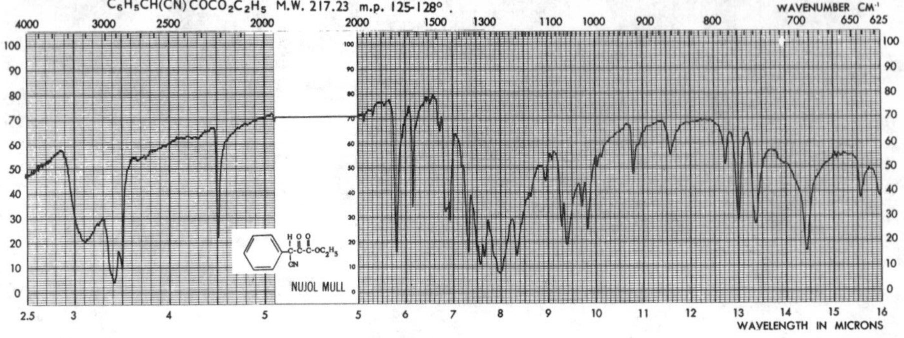

G 19,934-6
o-Fluorophenylacetonitrile, 97% (2-fluorobenzyl cyanide)
$FC_6H_4CH_2CN$ FW 135.14 bp 114-117°
n_D^{20} 1.5009 d 1.059 *Beil.* **9**(3),2260 Disp. C
NEAT

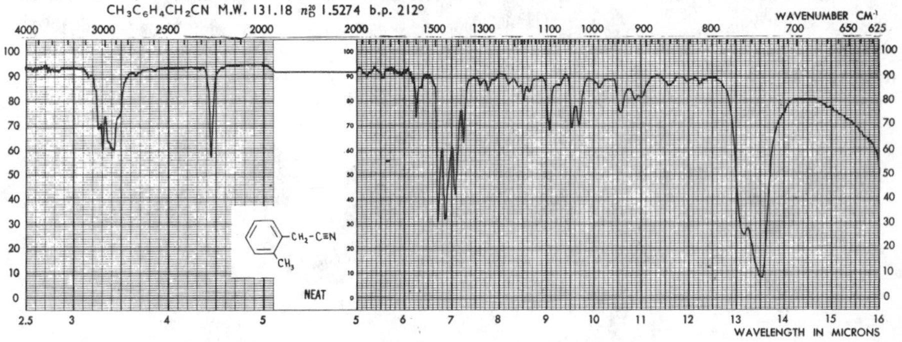

H 18,849-2
2-Chlorobenzyl cyanide, 97% [(o-chlorophenyl)-acetonitrile]
$ClC_6H_4CH_2CN$ FW 151.60 mp 24° bp 240-242°
n_D^{20} 1.5440 *Beil.* **9**,448 Disp. C

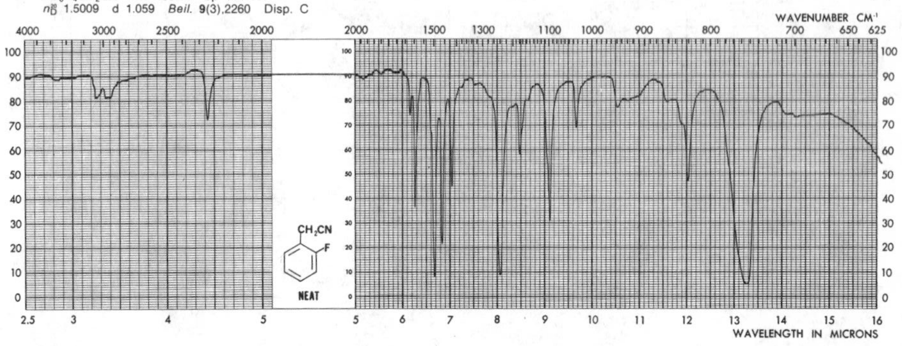

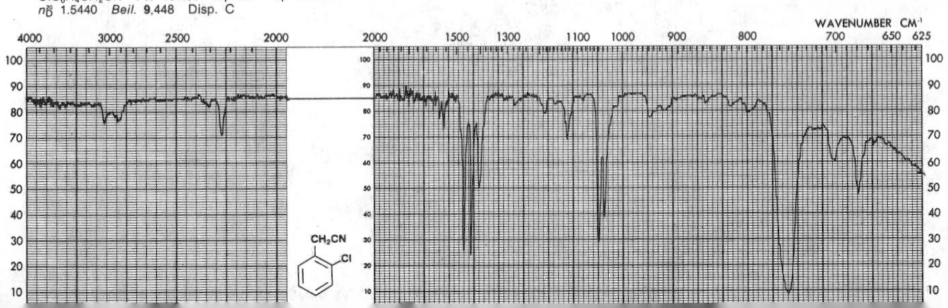

Beil. 10,130

A

$CH_2C{\equiv}N$, OCH_3 — NUJOL MULL

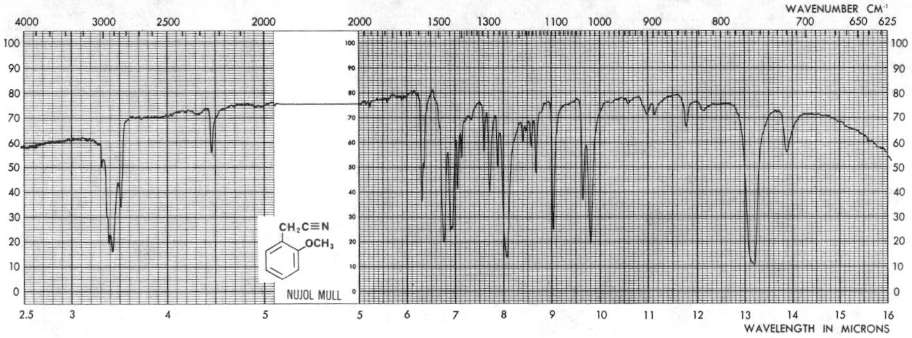

16,334-1
o-Nitrophenylacetonitrile
$O_2NC_6H_4CH_2CN$
M.W. 162.15 m.p. 82-85° Beil. 9,455

B

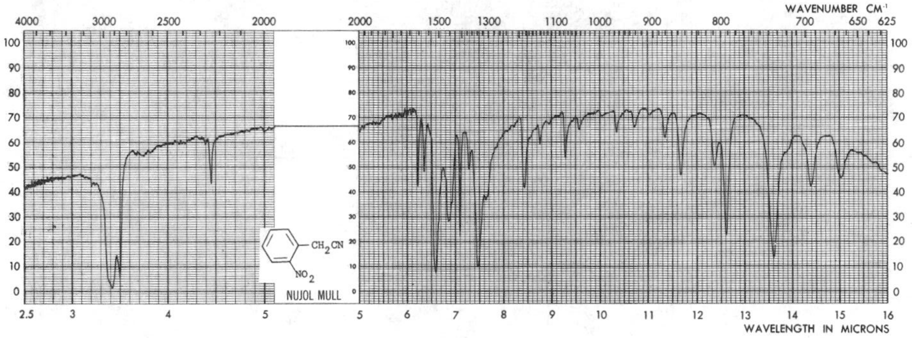

CH_2CN, NO_2 — NUJOL MULL

11,813-3 **α-Cyano-o-tolunitrile** (homophthalonitrile), **tech.**
$NCCH_2C_6H_4CN$ M.W. 142.16 ....

C

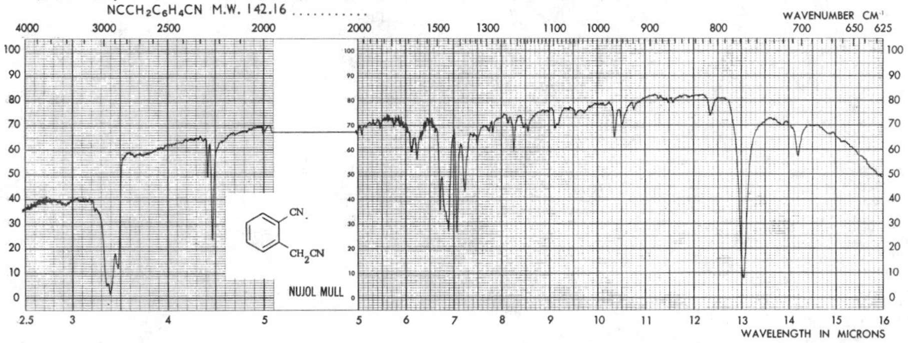

CN, CH_2CN — NUJOL MULL

P2360-1 **o-Phenylenediacetonitrile**
$C_6H_4(CH_2CN)_2$ M.W. 156.19 m.p. 58-61°

D

$CH_2-C{\equiv}N$, $CH_2-C{\equiv}N$ — MELT

M.W. 189.17 m.p. 139-141° ....

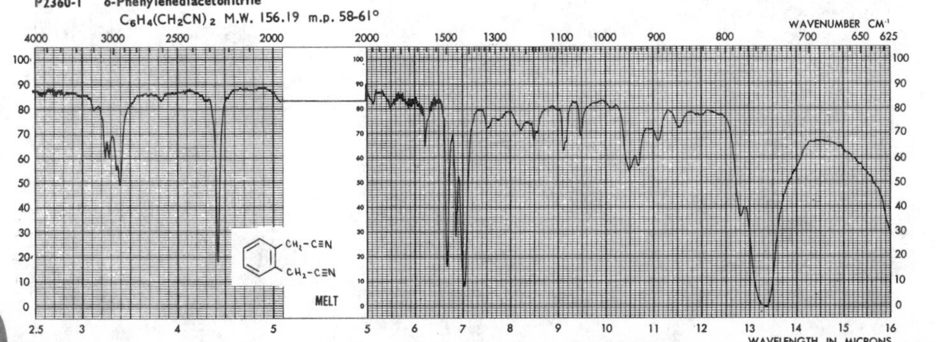

E

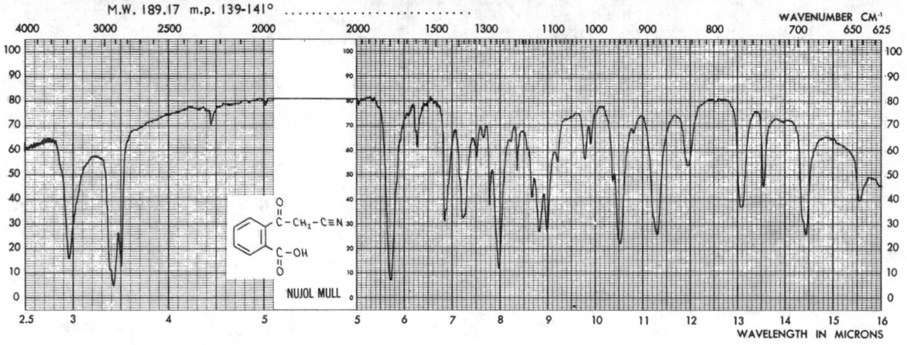

$C(=O)-CH_2-C{\equiv}N$, $C(=O)-OH$ — NUJOL MULL

19,634-7
2-(m-Benzoylphenyl)propionitrile, 95%
$CH_3CH(C_6H_4COC_6H_5)CN$ FW 235.29 mp 47-53°
Disp. C

F

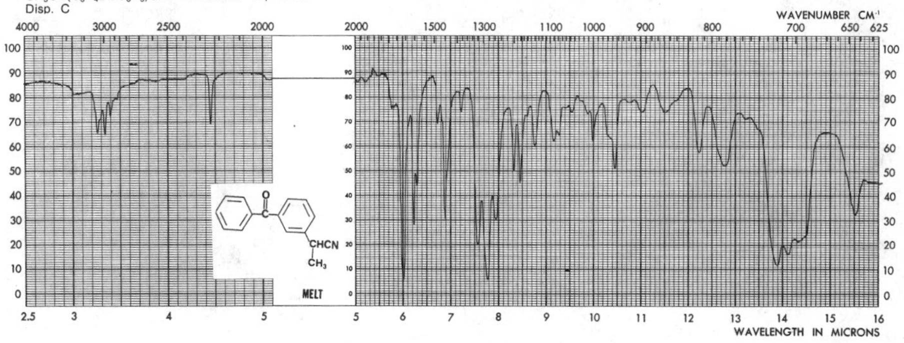

CHCN, CH_3 — MELT

M3160-0 **3-Methylbenzyl cyanide (m-methylphenylacetonitrile)**
$CH_3C_6H_4CH_2CN$ M.W. 131.18 n_D^{25} 1.5233 ....

G

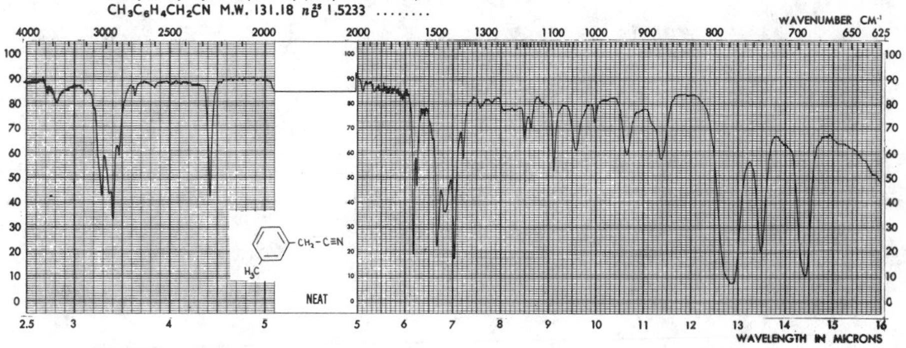

$CH_2-C{\equiv}N$, H_3C — NEAT

F1335-5 **m-Fluorophenylacetonitrile** (3-fluorobenzyl cyanide)
$FC_6H_4CH_2CN$ M.W. 135.14 n_D^{20} 1.5020
b.p. 113-114°/18 mm.

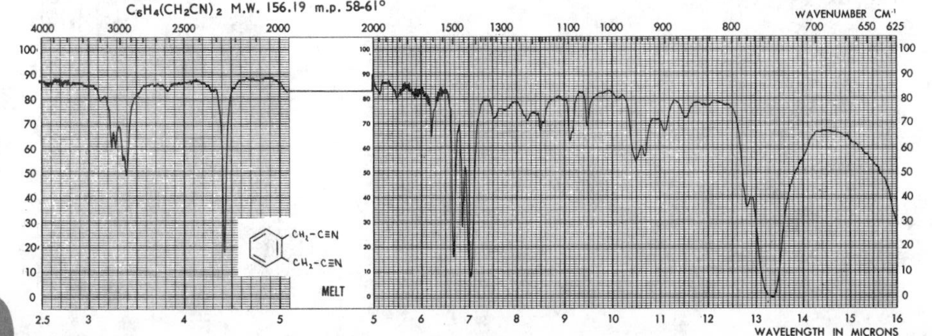

H

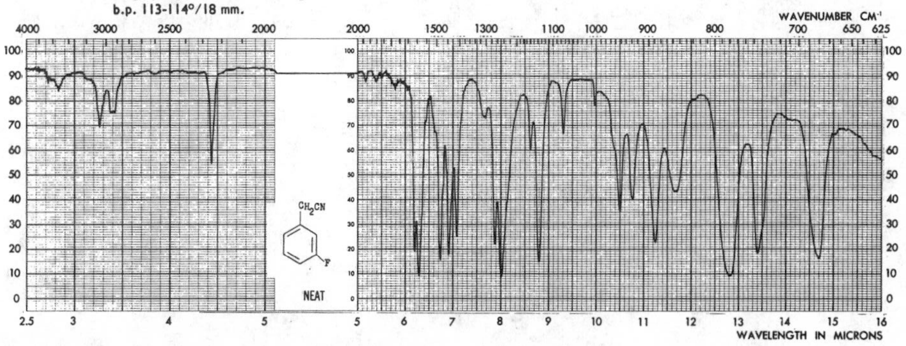

CH_2CN, F — NEAT

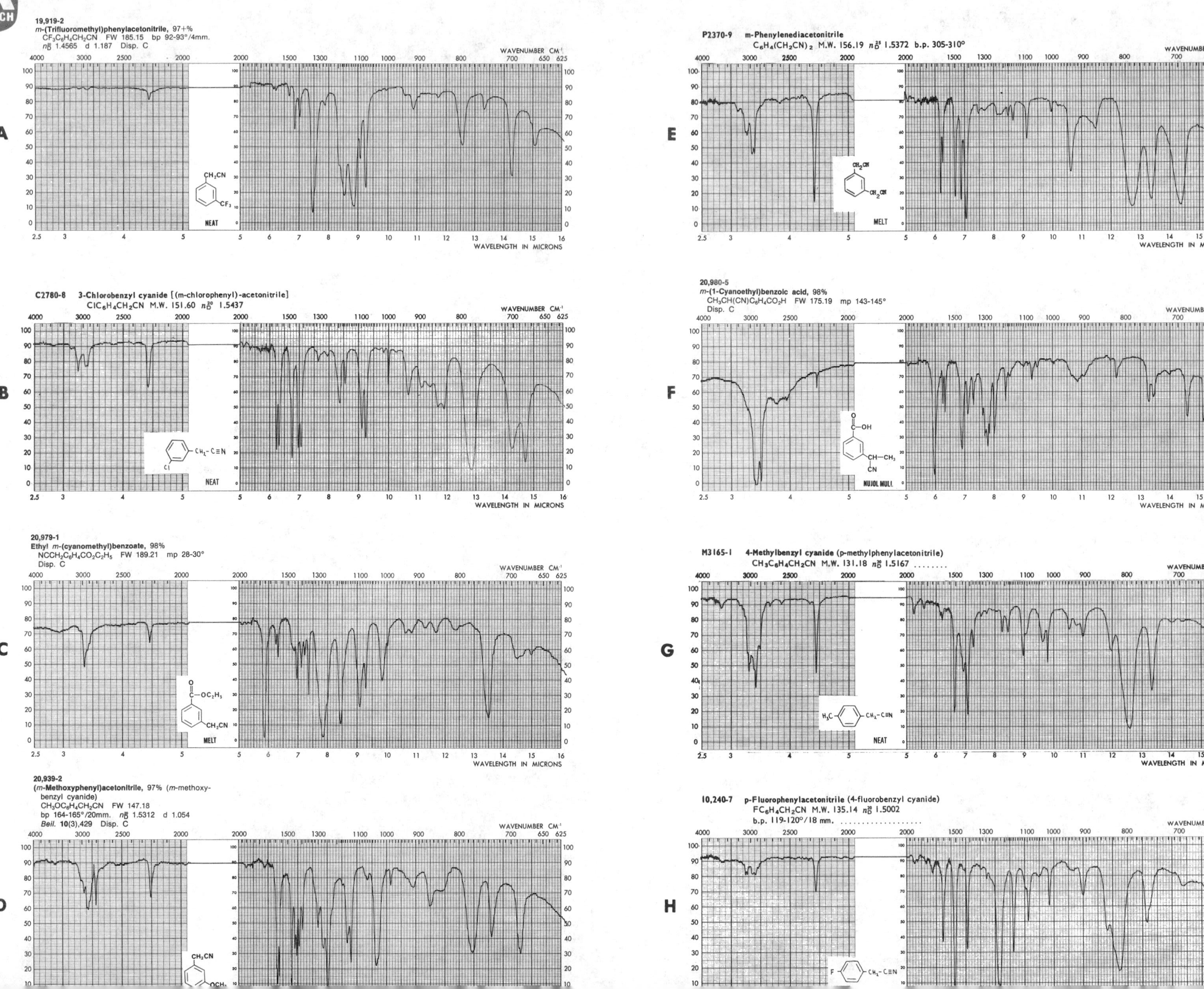

A 19,919-2
m-(Trifluoromethyl)phenylacetonitrile, 97+%
$CF_3C_6H_4CH_2CN$ FW 185.15 bp 92-93°/4mm.
n_D^{20} 1.4565 d 1.187 Disp. C
NEAT

B C2780-8 3-Chlorobenzyl cyanide [(m-chlorophenyl)-acetonitrile]
$ClC_6H_4CH_2CN$ M.W. 151.60 n_D^{20} 1.5437
NEAT

C 20,979-1
Ethyl *m*-(cyanomethyl)benzoate, 98%
$NCCH_2C_6H_4CO_2C_2H_5$ FW 189.21 mp 28-30°
Disp. C
MELT

D 20,939-2
(*m*-Methoxyphenyl)acetonitrile, 97% (*m*-methoxybenzyl cyanide)
$CH_3OC_6H_4CH_2CN$ FW 147.18
bp 164-165°/20mm. n_D^{20} 1.5312 d 1.054
Beil. 10(3),429 Disp. C

E P2370-9 m-Phenylenediacetonitrile
$C_6H_4(CH_2CN)_2$ M.W. 156.19 n_D^{25} 1.5372 b.p. 305-310°
MELT

F 20,980-5
m-(1-Cyanoethyl)benzoic acid, 98%
$CH_3CH(CN)C_6H_4CO_2H$ FW 175.19 mp 143-145°
Disp. C
NUJOL MULL

G M3165-1 4-Methylbenzyl cyanide (p-methylphenylacetonitrile)
$CH_3C_6H_4CH_2CN$ M.W. 131.18 n_D^{20} 1.5167
NEAT

H 10,240-7 p-Fluorophenylacetonitrile (4-fluorobenzyl cyanide)
$FC_6H_4CH_2CN$ M.W. 135.14 n_D^{20} 1.5002
b.p. 119-120°/18 mm.

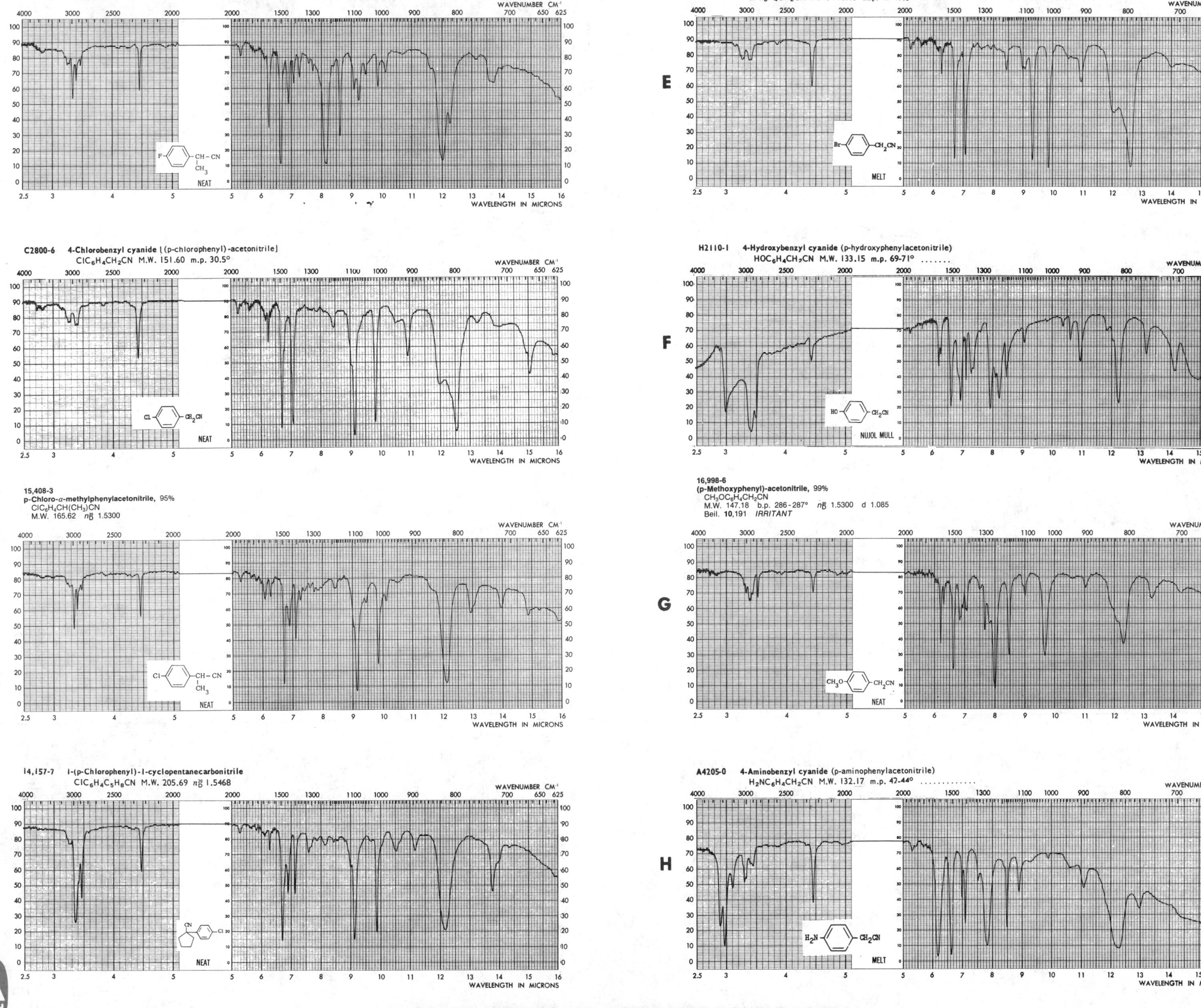

A
$FC_6H_4CH(CH_3)CN$
M.W. 149.17 n_D^{20} 1.4931 *IRRITANT*

B
C2800-6 **4-Chlorobenzyl cyanide** [(p-chlorophenyl)-acetonitrile]
$ClC_6H_4CH_2CN$ M.W. 151.60 m.p. 30.5°

C
15,408-3
p-Chloro-α-methylphenylacetonitrile, 95%
$ClC_6H_4CH(CH_3)CN$
M.W. 165.62 n_D^{20} 1.5300

D
14,157-7 **1-(p-Chlorophenyl)-1-cyclopentanecarbonitrile**
$ClC_6H_4C_5H_8CN$ M.W. 205.69 n_D^{20} 1.5468

E
12,466-4 **p-Bromophenylacetonitrile** (p-bromobenzyl cyanide,
$BrC_6H_4CH_2CN$ M.W. 196.05 m.p. 47-49.5°

F
H2110-1 **4-Hydroxybenzyl cyanide** (p-hydroxyphenylacetonitrile)
$HOC_6H_4CH_2CN$ M.W. 133.15 m.p. 69-71° ....

G
16,998-6
(p-Methoxyphenyl)-acetonitrile, 99%
$CH_3OC_6H_4CH_2CN$
M.W. 147.18 b.p. 286-287° n_D^{20} 1.5300 d 1.085
Beil. **10**,191 *IRRITANT*

H
A4205-0 **4-Aminobenzyl cyanide** (p-aminophenylacetonitrile)
$H_2NC_6H_4CH_2CN$ M.W. 132.17 m.p. 42-44° ....

A 15,157-2 p-Nitrophenylacetonitrile
$O_2NC_6H_4CH_2CN$ M.W. 162.15
m.p. 115-116°

B P2380-6 p-Phenylenediacetonitrile
$C_6H_4(CH_2CN)_2$ M.W. 156.19

C 17,707-5
2-Chloro-3-(3-chloro-o-tolyl)-propionitrile, 99%
$ClC_6H_3(CH_3)CH_2CH(Cl)CN$
M.W. 214.1 b.p. 110-112°/0.5mm. n_D^{20} 1.5538

D 21,814-6
2-Chloro-6-fluorophenylacetonitrile, 98%
$ClC_6H_3(F)CH_2CN$ FW 169.59 mp 41-42°
Fieser 7,40 Disp. J

E 12,601-2 2,6-Dichlorophenylacetonitrile (2,6-dichlorobenzyl cyanide)
$Cl_2C_6H_3CH_2CN$ M.W. 186.04 m.p. 76-79°

F 17,846-2
2,4-Dichlorophenylacetonitrile, 98%
$Cl_2C_6H_3CH_2CN$
M.W. 186.04 m.p. 61-62°

G 11,544-4 5-Fluoro-2-nitrophenylacetonitrile
$FC_6H_3(NO_2)CH_2CN$ M.W. 180.14
m.p. 68-69°

H 22,374-3
4-Hydroxy-3-methoxyphenylacetonitrile, 99%
(homovanillonitrile)
$HOC_6H_3(OCH_3)CH_2CN$ FW 163.18 mp 56-57°
bp 135-145°/2mm. Disp. J

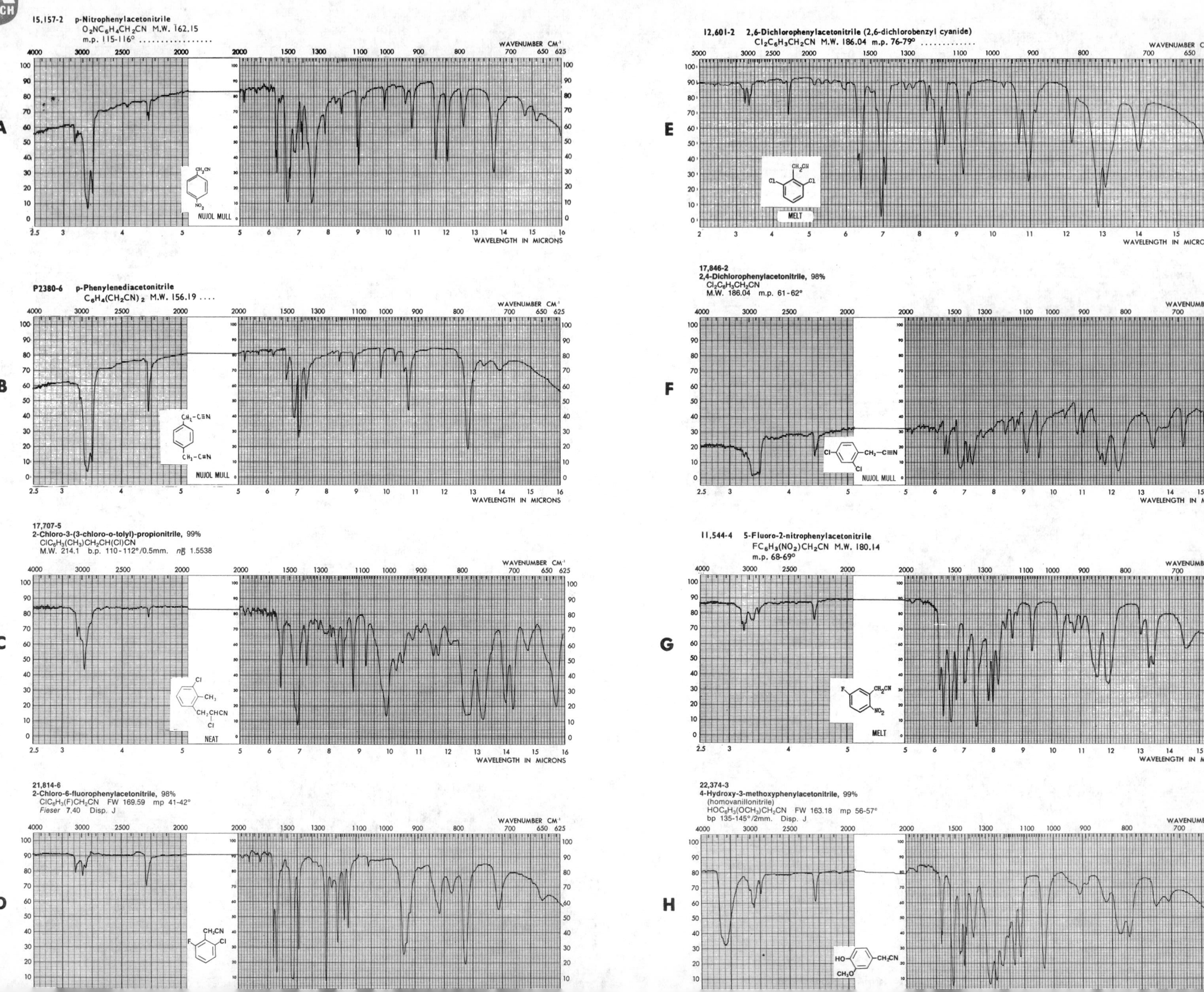

A

$(CH_3O)_2C_6H_3CH_2CN$ M.W. 177.20
m.p. 62-63.5°

MELT

B

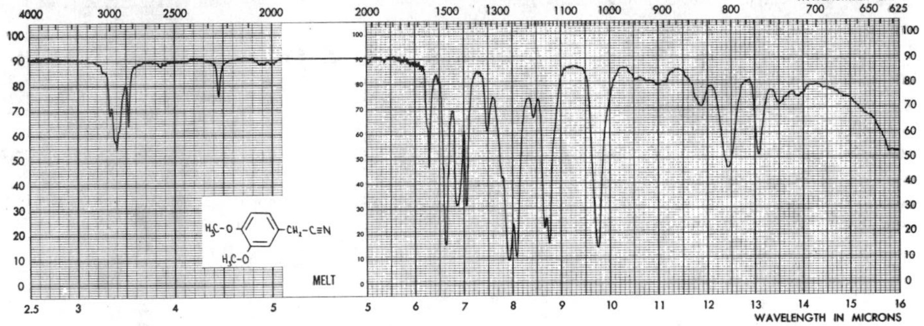

14,530-0 **3,4-Methylenedioxyphenylacetonitrile**
M.W. 161.16 m.p. 43-45°

MELT

C

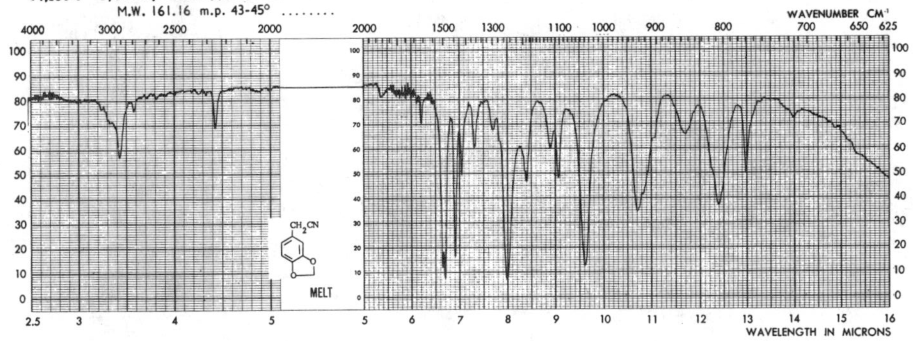

11,336-0 3,4,5-Trimethoxyphenylacetonitrile (3,4,5-trimethoxybenzyl cyanide)
$(CH_3O)_3C_6H_2CH_2CN$ M.W. 207.23
m.p. 74-76°

NUJOL MULL

D

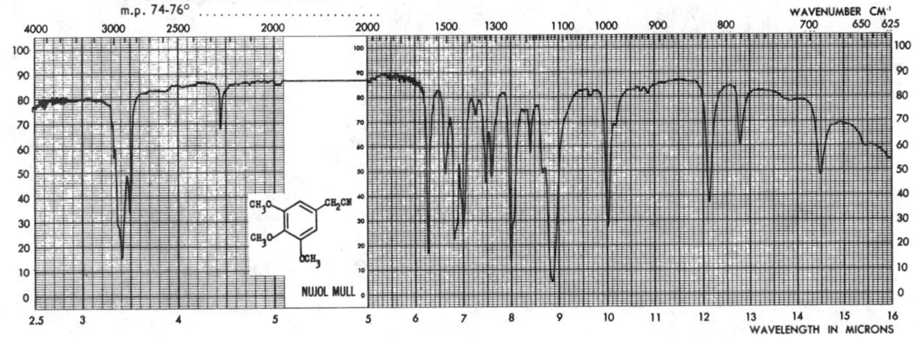

11,646-7 **(p-Aminophenyl)-(phenyl)-acetonitrile** [α-(4-aminophenyl)-benzyl cyanide] **hydrochloride**
$H_2NC_6H_4CH(C_6H_5)CN{\cdot}HCl$ M.W. 244.73
m.p. 234-237°

NUJOL MULL

E

...tolyl)-... cyanide] hydrochloride
$H_2NC_6H_4CH(C_6H_4CH_3)CN{\cdot}HCl$ M.W. 259.75
m.p. 230-232°

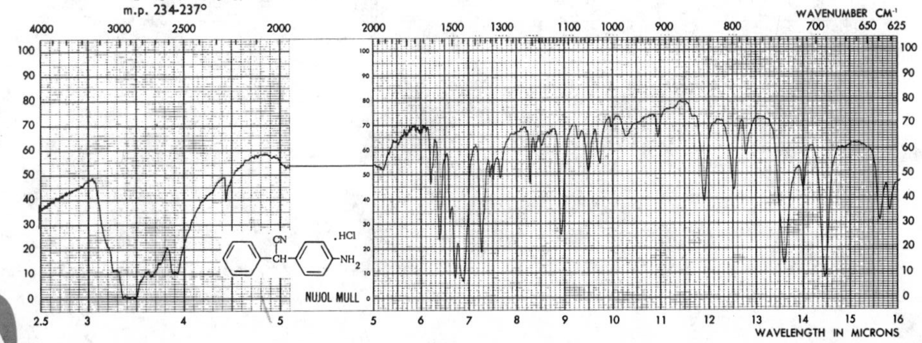

NUJOL MULL

F

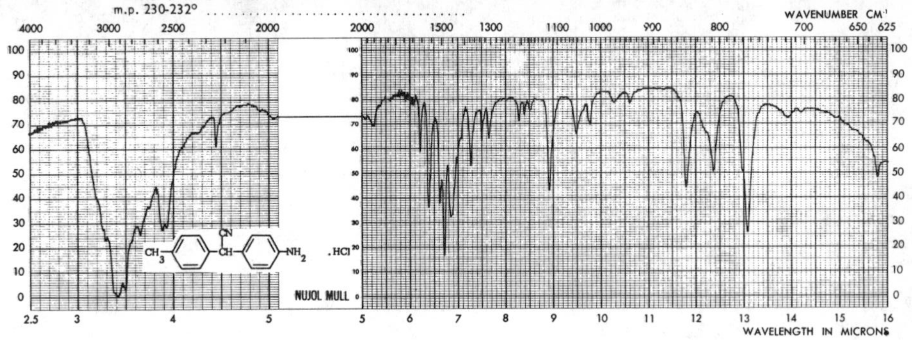

11,644-0 **(p-Aminophenyl)-(m-tolyl)-acetonitrile** [α-(4-aminophenyl)-3-methylbenzyl cyanide] **hydrochloride**
$H_2NC_6H_4CH(C_6H_4CH_3)CN{\cdot}HCl$ M.W. 258.75
m.p. 210-212°

NUJOL MULL

G

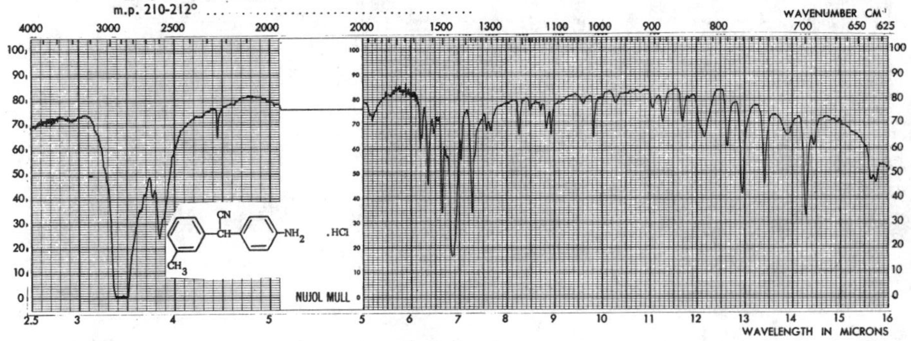

11,642-4 **(p-Aminophenyl)-(p-fluorophenyl)-acetonitrile** [α-(4-aminophenyl)-4-fluorobenzyl cyanide] **hydrochloride, puriss.**
$H_2NC_6H_4CH(C_6H_4F)CN{\cdot}HCl$ M.W. 262.72 m.p. 236-238°

NUJOL MULL

H

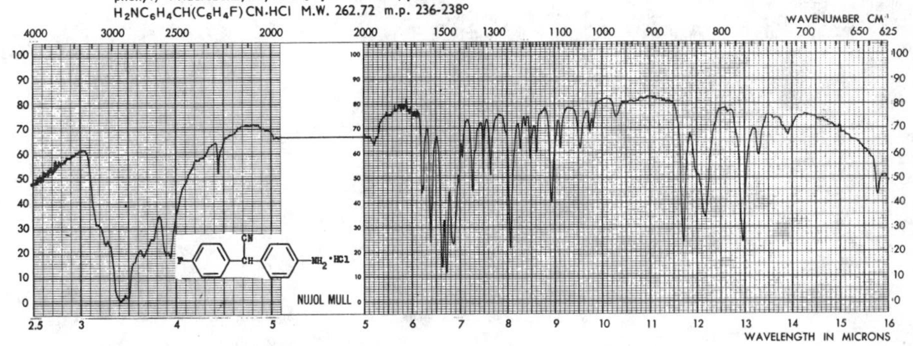

11,643-2 **(p-Aminophenyl)-(p-anisyl)-acetonitrile** [α-(4-aminophenyl)-4-methoxybenzyl cyanide] **hydrochloride**
$H_2NC_6H_4CH(C_6H_4OCH_3)CN{\cdot}HCl$ M.W. 274.75
m.p. 225-227°

NUJOL MULL

WAVENUMBER CM⁻¹ / WAVELENGTH IN MICRONS

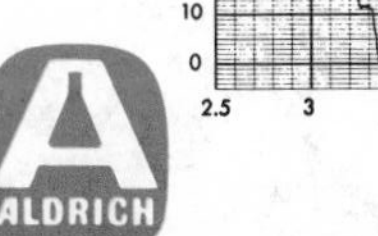

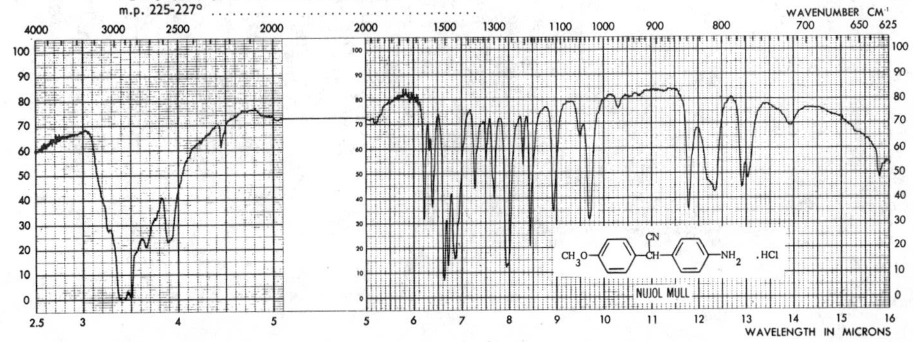

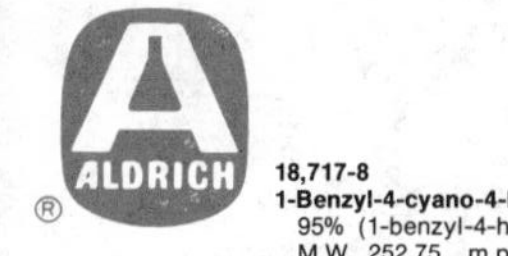

A

18,717-8
1-Benzyl-4-cyano-4-hydroxypiperidine hydrochloride, 95% (1-benzyl-4-hydroxyisonipecotonitrile)
M.W. 252.75 m.p. 175-177° (dec.)
NUJOL MULL

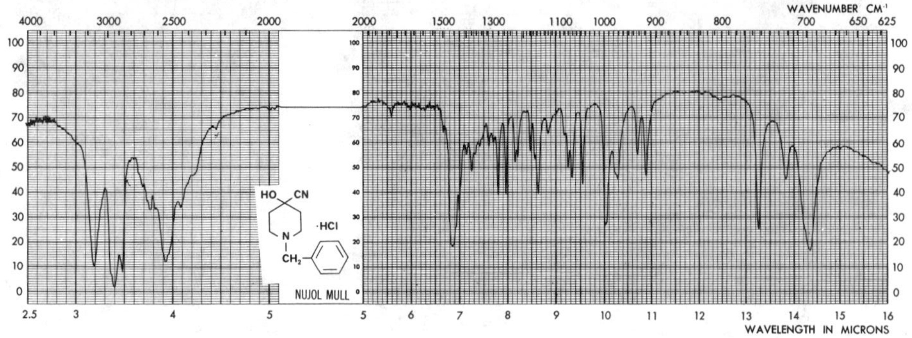

B

18,890-5
α-Benzoyloxy-α-phenylmalononitrile, 98%
(α,α-dicyanobenzyl benzoate)
$C_6H_5CO_2C(CN)_2C_6H_5$ FW 262.27 mp 96-98°
Disp. C
NUJOL MULL

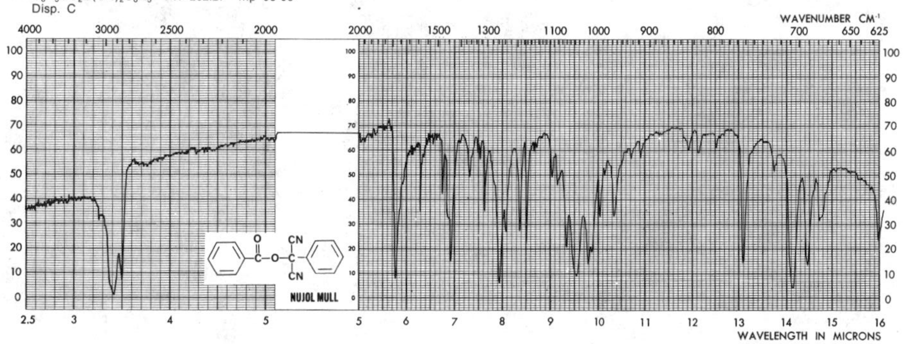

C

C8100-4 **Cinnamonitrile**
$C_6H_5CH{:}CHCN$ M.W. 129.16 n_D^{20} 1.6013
m.p. 18-20°
NEAT

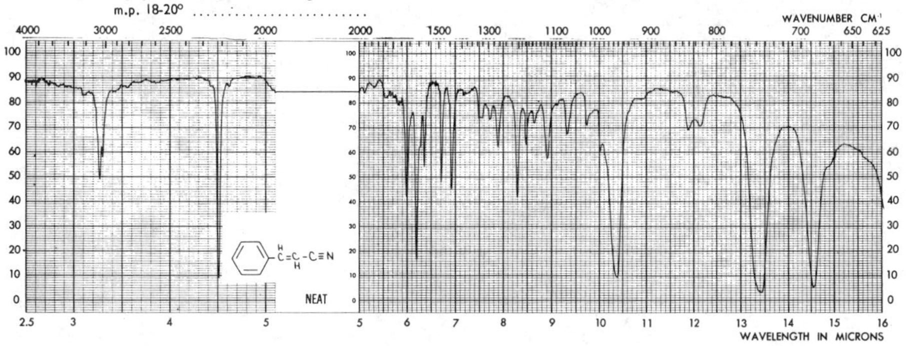

D

14,733-8 **Benzylidenemalononitrile**
$C_6H_5CH{:}C(CN)_2$ M.W. 154.17
m.p. 83-85°

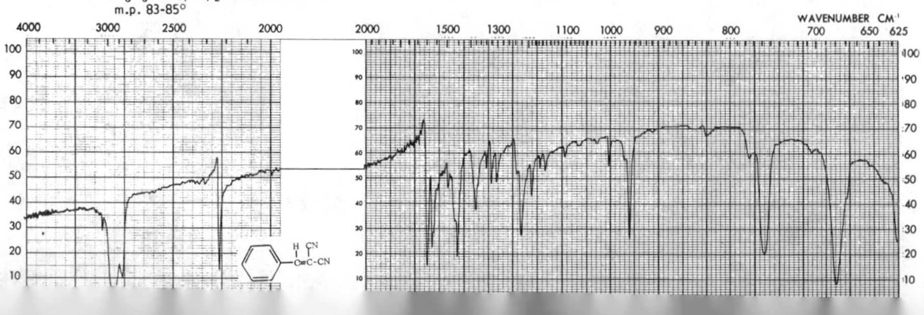

E

15,403-2 **β-Phenylcinnamonitrile** (3,3-diphenylacrylonitrile)
$(C_6H_5)_2C{:}CHCN$ M.W. 205.26 n_D^{20} 1.6352
b.p. 125-128°/0.15 mm
NEAT

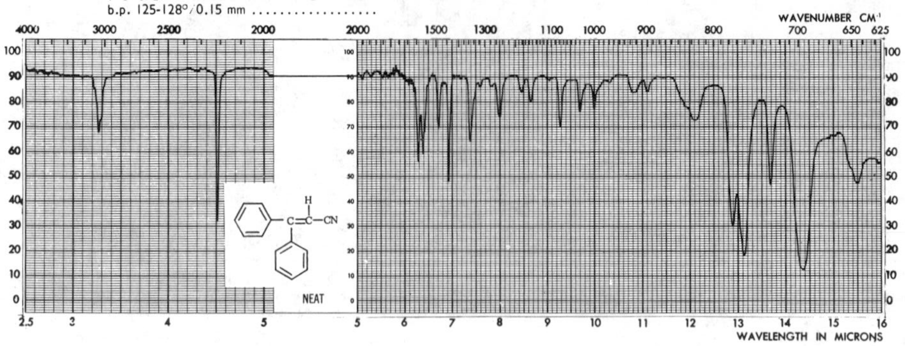

F

11,571-1 **Diphenylmethylenemalononitrile** (1,1-dicyano-2,2-diphenylethylene)
$(C_6H_5)_2C{:}C(CN)_2$ M.W. 230.27
m.p. 139.5-141°
NUJOL MULL

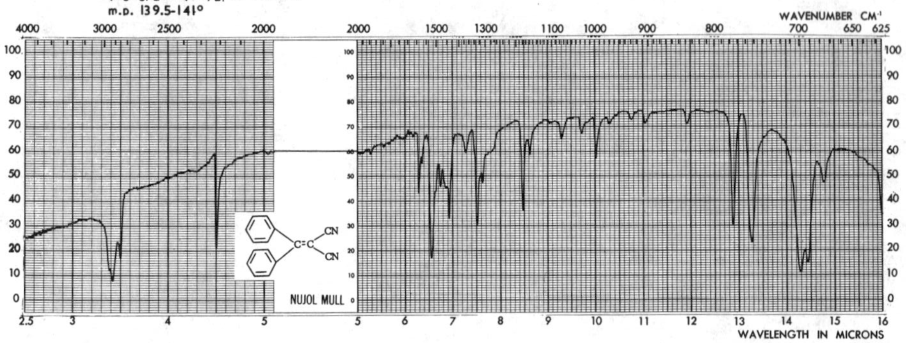

G

12,114-2 **Triphenylacrylonitrile**
$(C_6H_5)_2C{:}C(C_6H_5)CN$ M.W. 281.36
m.p. 164.5-167°
NUJOL MULL

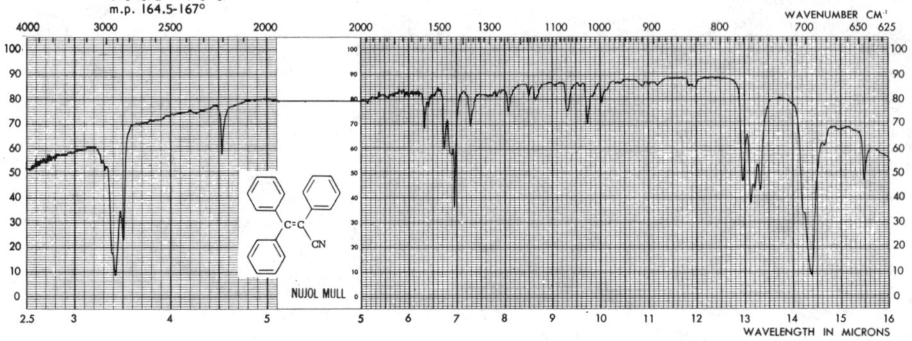

H

22,447-2
Citronitrile, 97%, mixture of *cis* and *trans* (3-methyl-5-phenyl-2-pentenenitrile)
$C_6H_5CH_2CH_2C(CH_3){=}CHCN$ FW 171.24
n_D^{20} 1.5345 d 0.968 Disp. C

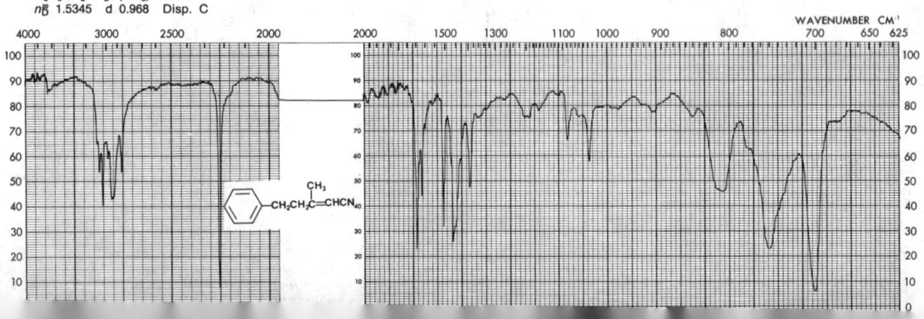

A

$CH_3C_6H_4CH{:}CHCN$ M.W. 143.19 ....

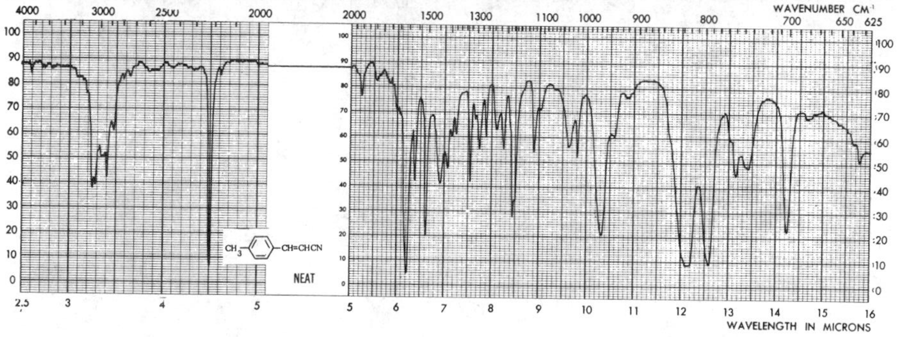

NEAT

B

14,737-0 p-Methylbenzylidenemalononitrile
$CH_3C_6H_4CH{:}C(CN)_2$ M.W. 168.20
m.p. 135-137° ....

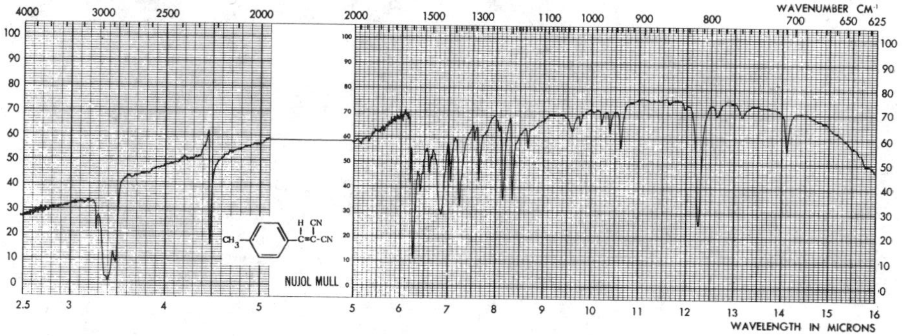

NUJOL MULL

C

14,535-1 4-Isopropylcinnamonitrile (mixture of *cis* and *trans*)
$(CH_3)_2CHC_6H_4CH{:}CHCN$ M.W. 171.24 n_D^{20} 1.5733
b.p. 95-120°/0.5 mm. ....

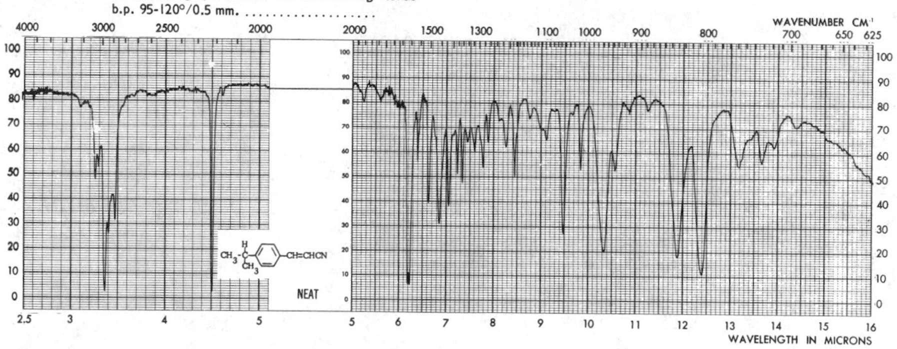

NEAT

D

14,461-4 p-Chlorocinnamonitrile (mixture of *cis* and *trans*)
$ClC_6H_4CH{:}CHCN$ M.W. 163.61 ....

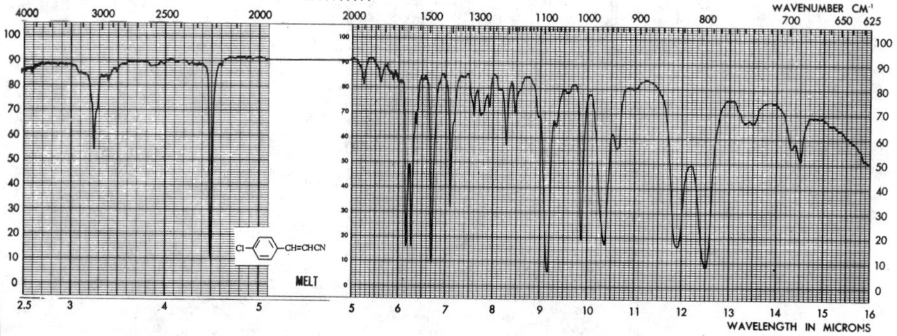

MELT

E

14,559-9 o-Chlorocinnamonitrile (mixture of *cis* and *trans*)
$ClC_6H_4CH{:}CHCN$ M.W. 163.61 ....

NEAT

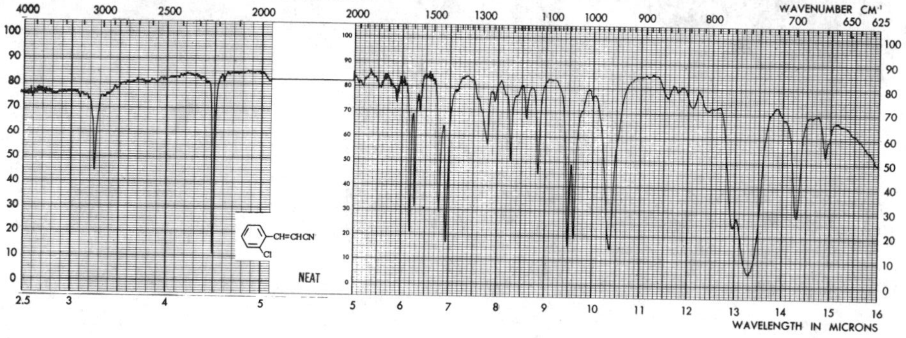

F

17,399-1
trans-o-Chlorocinnamonitrile, 99%
$ClC_6H_4CH{=}CHCN$
M.W. 163.61 m.p. 40-42° Beil. 9(1),238

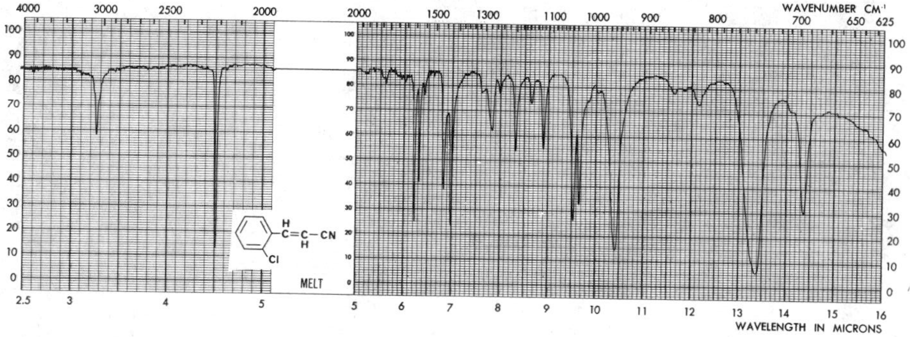

MELT

G

C2865-0 o-Chlorobenzylidenemalononitrile
$ClC_6H_4CH{:}C(CN)_2$ M.W. 188.62 m.p. 94-96°

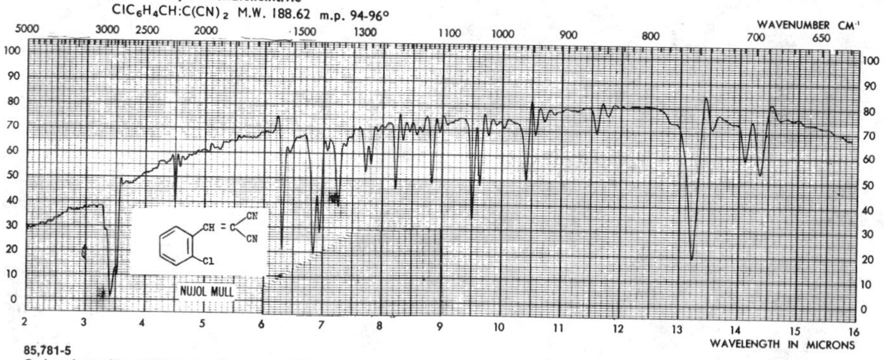

NUJOL MULL

H

85,781-5
Carbonyl cyanide m-chlorophenylhydrazone, 99+%,
GOLD LABEL [mesoxalonitrile (m-chlorophenyl)-hydrazone]
$ClC_6H_4NHN{=}C(CN)_2$
M.W. 204.62 m.p. 175-177° (dec.)

NUJOL MULL

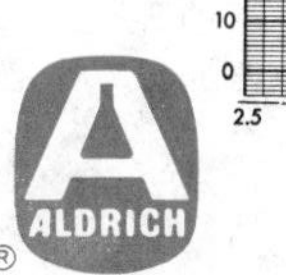

AROMATIC NITRILES AND CUMULATED DOUBLE BONDS

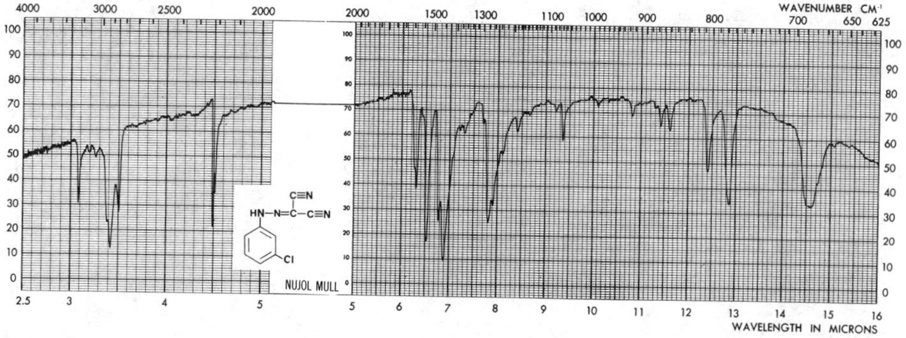

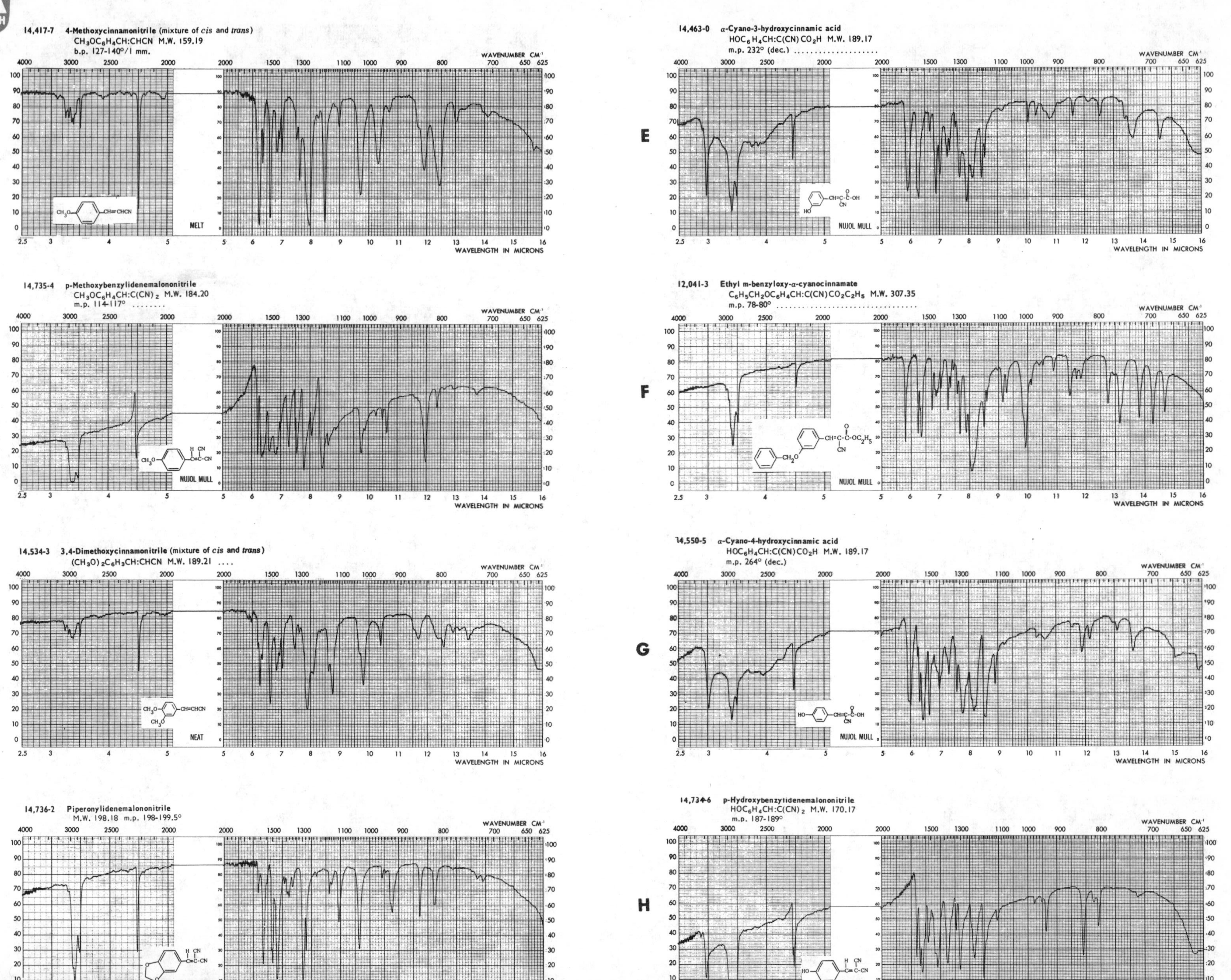
ALDRICH
A
14,417-7 4-Methoxycinnamonitrile (mixture of cis and trans)
CH3OC6H4CH:CHCN M.W. 159.19
b.p. 127-140°/1 mm.
MELT
B
14,735-4 p-Methoxybenzylidenemalononitrile
CH3OC6H4CH:C(CN)2 M.W. 184.20
m.p. 114-117°
NUJOL MULL
C
14,534-3 3,4-Dimethoxycinnamonitrile (mixture of cis and trans)
(CH3O)2C6H3CH:CHCN M.W. 189.21
NEAT
D
14,736-2 Piperonylidenemalononitrile
M.W. 198.18 m.p. 198-199.5°
E
14,463-0 α-Cyano-3-hydroxycinnamic acid
HOC6H4CH:C(CN)CO2H M.W. 189.17
m.p. 232° (dec.)
NUJOL MULL
F
12,041-3 Ethyl m-benzyloxy-α-cyanocinnamate
C6H5CH2OC6H4CH:C(CN)CO2C2H5 M.W. 307.35
m.p. 78-80°
NUJOL MULL
G
14,550-5 α-Cyano-4-hydroxycinnamic acid
HOC6H4CH:C(CN)CO2H M.W. 189.17
m.p. 264° (dec.)
NUJOL MULL
H
14,734-6 p-Hydroxybenzylidenemalononitrile
HOC6H4CH:C(CN)2 M.W. 170.17
m.p. 187-189°
WAVENUMBER CM⁻¹
WAVELENGTH IN MICRONS

A

$(CH_3)_2NC_6H_4CH{:}CHCN$ M.W. 172.23
m.p. 165-168°

NUJOL MULL

B

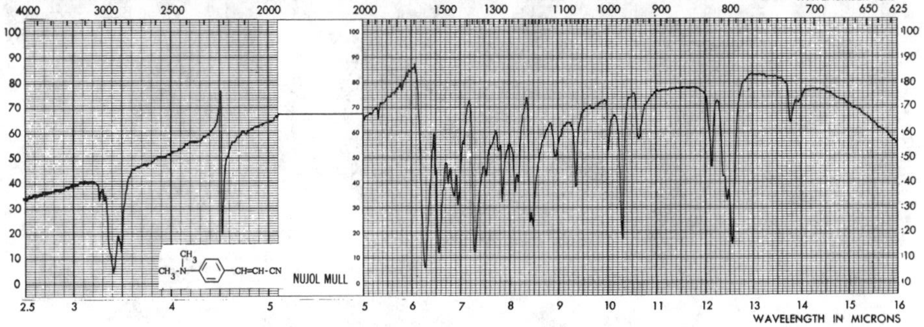

12,746-9 (2,4,7-Trinitro-9-fluorenylidene)-malononitrile
M.W. 363.25 m.p. 265-267°

NUJOL MULL

C

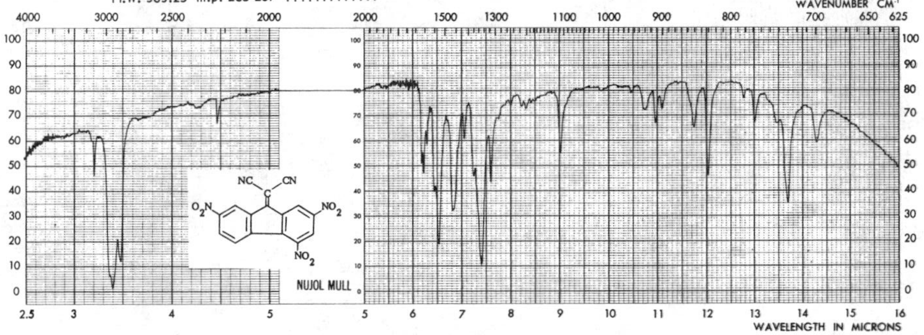

B895-9 Benzonitrile
C_6H_5CN M.W. 103.12 n_D^{20} 1.5271

NEAT

D

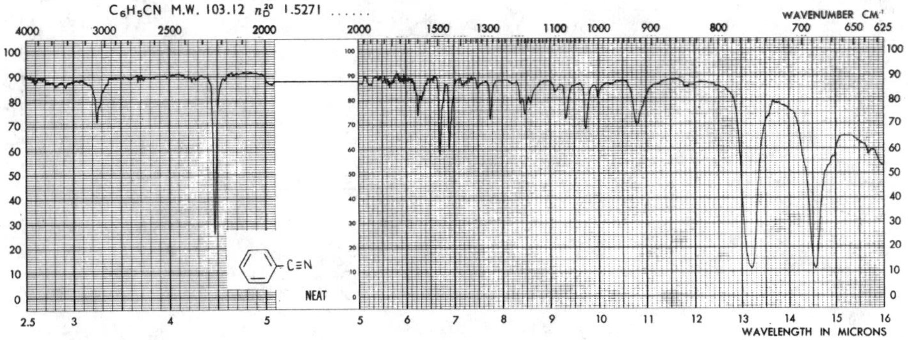

11,977-6 o-Tolunitrile
$CH_3C_6H_4CN$ M.W. 117.15 n_D^{20} 1.5279 b.p. 205°

NEAT

E

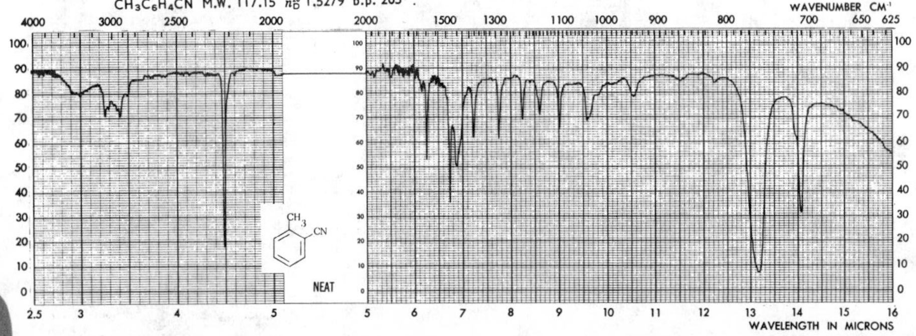

M.W. 196.05 m.p. 67-72° Beil. 9,470 *IRRITANT*

NUJOL MULL

F

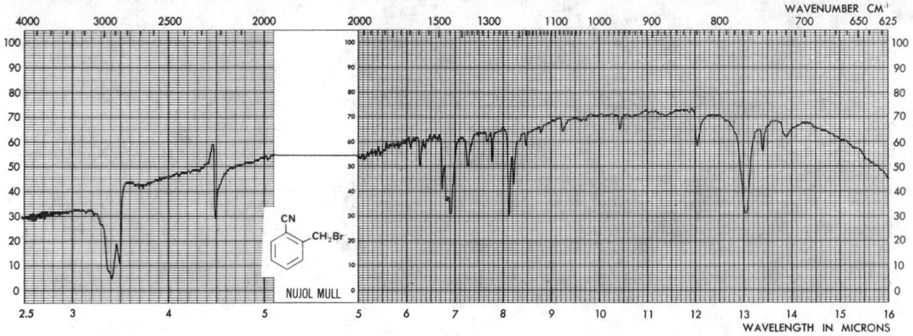

19,664-9
o-Fluorobenzonitrile, 99%
FC_6H_4CN FW 121.11 bp 90°/21mm. n_D^{20} 1.5083
d 1.116 *Beil.* 9(3),1326 Disp. C

NEAT

G

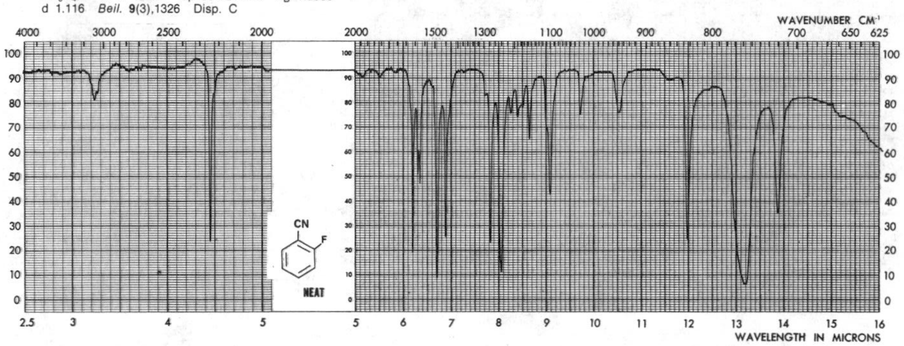

C2479-5 2-Chlorobenzonitrile
ClC_6H_4CN M.W. 137.57 m.p. 43-46°

MELT

H

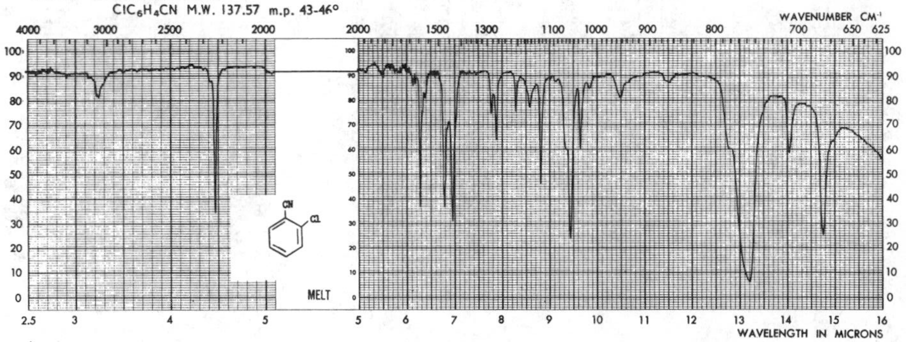

B5800-8 2-Bromobenzonitrile
BrC_6H_4CN M.W. 182.03 m.p. 53-57°

MELT

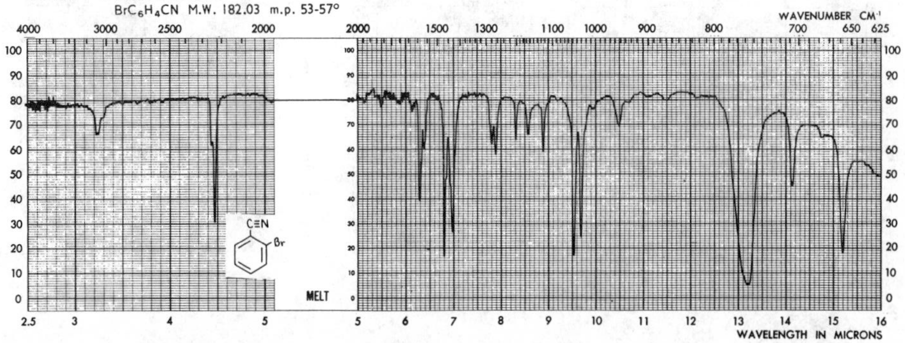

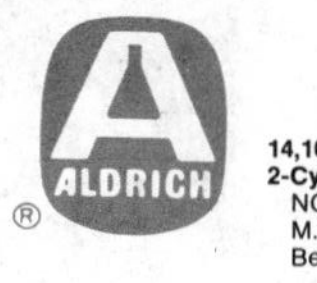

A

14,103-8
2-Cyanophenol, 99% (o-hydroxybenzonitrile)
NCC_6H_4OH
M.W. 119.12 m.p. 92-95° b.p. 149°/14mm.
Beil. 10,96

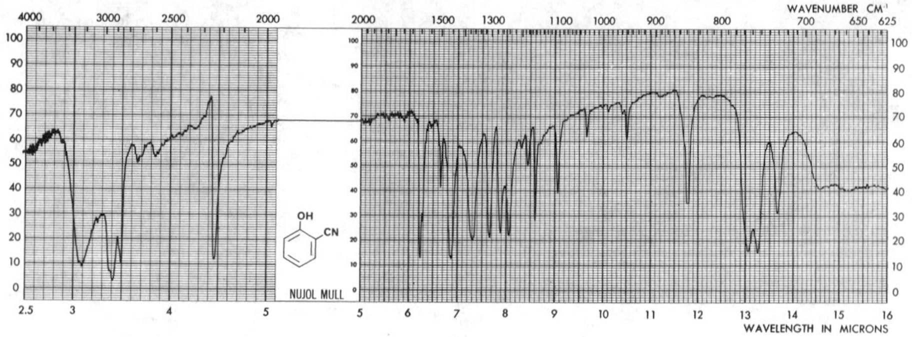

NUJOL MULL

B

A8990-1 **Anthranilonitrile** (o-aminobenzonitrile)
$H_2NC_6H_4CN$ M.W. 118.14 m.p. 48-52°

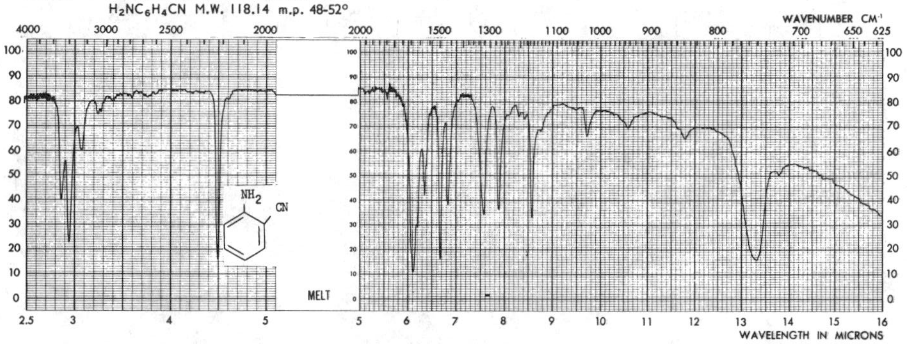

MELT

C

N1180-9 **o-Nitrobenzonitrile**
$O_2NC_6H_4CN$ M.W. 148.12
m.p. 104-106°

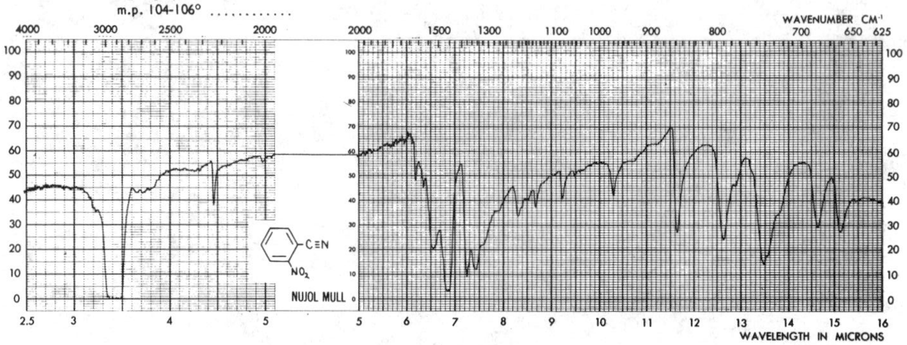

NUJOL MULL

D

15,440-7 **Methyl 2-cyanobenzoate**
$NCC_6H_4CO_2CH_3$ M.W. 161.16 m.p. 49-51°

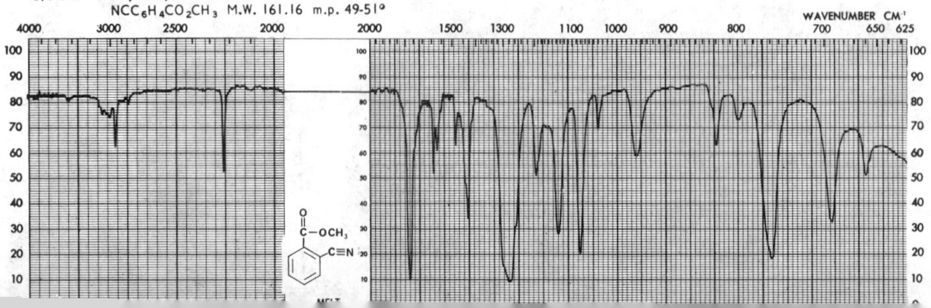

E

17,171-9
1,2-Dicyanobenzene, 98% (phthalonitrile)
$C_6H_4(CN)_2$
M.W. 128.13 m.p. 139-141° Beil. 9,815

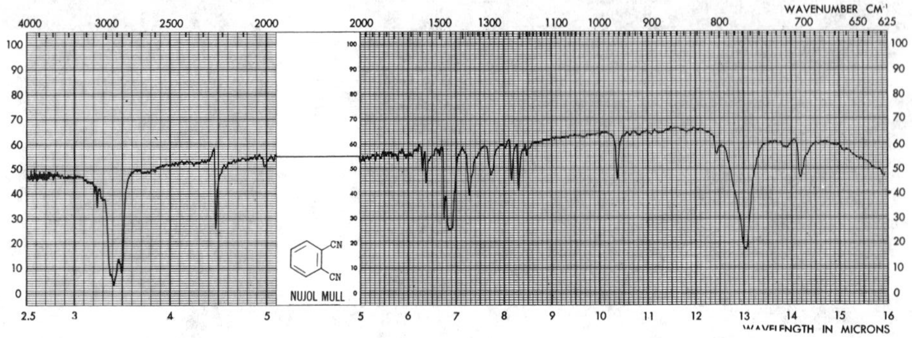

NUJOL MULL

F

13,232-2 **m-Tolunitrile**
$CH_3C_6H_4CN$ M.W. 117.15 n_D^{20} 1.5256
b.p. 99-101°/20 mm.

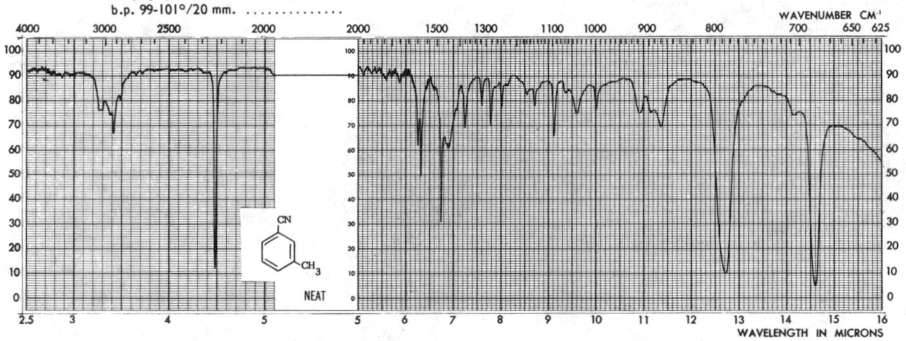

NEAT

G

C2480-9 **3-Chlorobenzonitrile**
ClC_6H_4CN M.W. 137.57 m.p. 39-42°

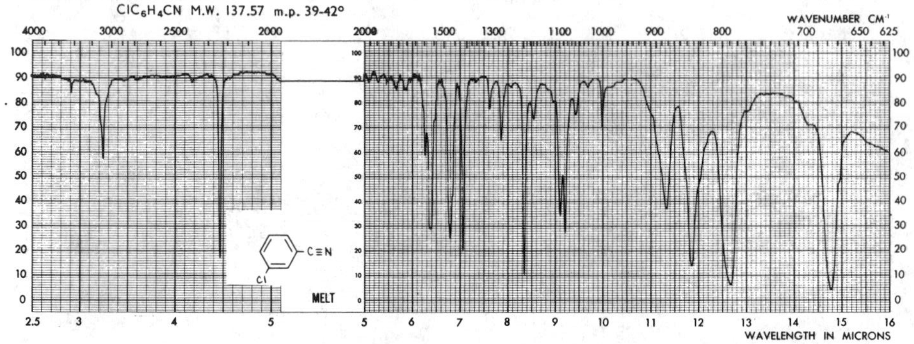

MELT

H

B5820-2 **3-Bromobenzonitrile**
BrC_6H_4CN M.W. 182.03 m.p. 38-40°

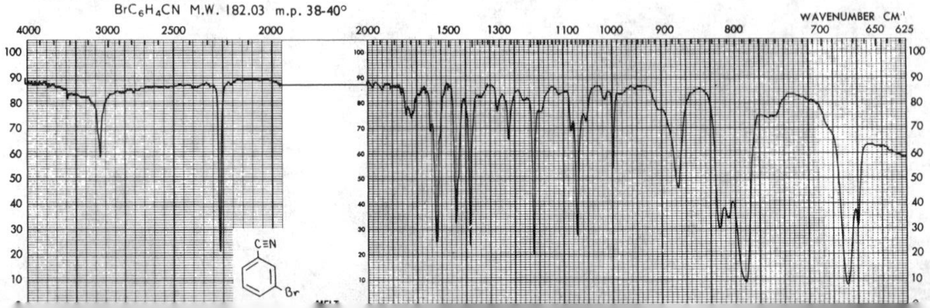

WAVENUMBER CM^{-1} / WAVELENGTH IN MICRONS

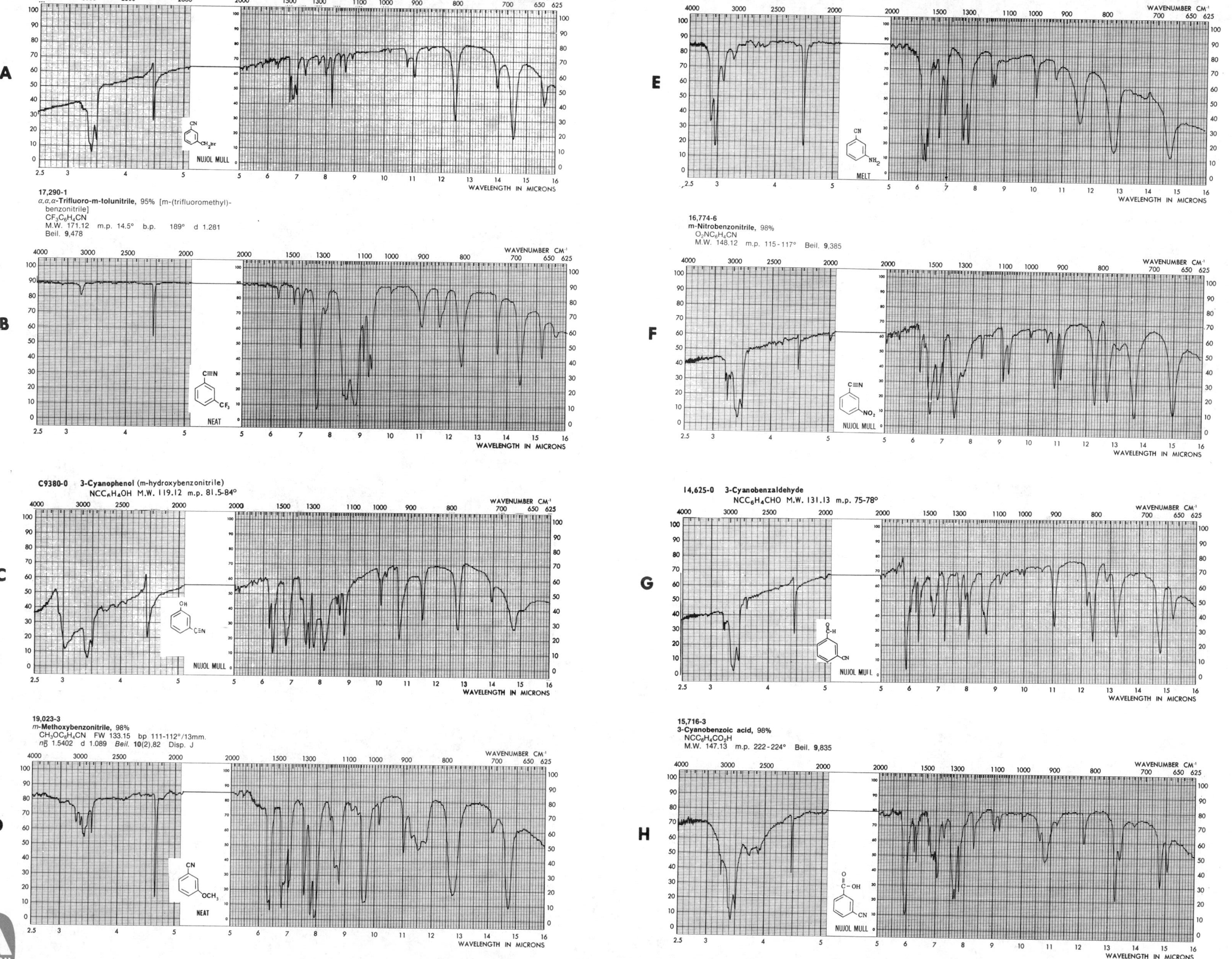

A

$BrCH_2C_6H_4CN$ M.W. 196.05 m.p. 93-96°

NUJOL MULL

B

17,290-1
α,α,α-**Trifluoro-m-tolunitrile**, 95% [m-(trifluoromethyl)-benzonitrile]
$CF_3C_6H_4CN$
M.W. 171.12 m.p. 14.5° b.p. 189° d 1.281
Beil. **9**,478

NEAT

C

C9380-0 **3-Cyanophenol** (m-hydroxybenzonitrile)
NCC_6H_4OH M.W. 119.12 m.p. 81.5-84°

NUJOL MULL

D

19,023-3
m-**Methoxybenzonitrile**, 98%
$CH_3OC_6H_4CN$ FW 133.15 bp 111-112°/13mm.
n_D^{20} 1.5402 d 1.089 *Beil.* **10**(2),82 Disp. J

NEAT

E

M.W. 118.14 m.p. 51-53° Beil. **14**,391

MELT

F

16,774-6
m-Nitrobenzonitrile, 98%
$O_2NC_6H_4CN$
M.W. 148.12 m.p. 115-117° Beil. 9,385

NUJOL MULL

G

14,625-0 **3-Cyanobenzaldehyde**
NCC_6H_4CHO M.W. 131.13 m.p. 75-78°

NUJOL MULL

H

15,716-3
3-Cyanobenzoic acid, 98%
$NCC_6H_4CO_2H$
M.W. 147.13 m.p. 222-224° Beil. **9**,835

NUJOL MULL

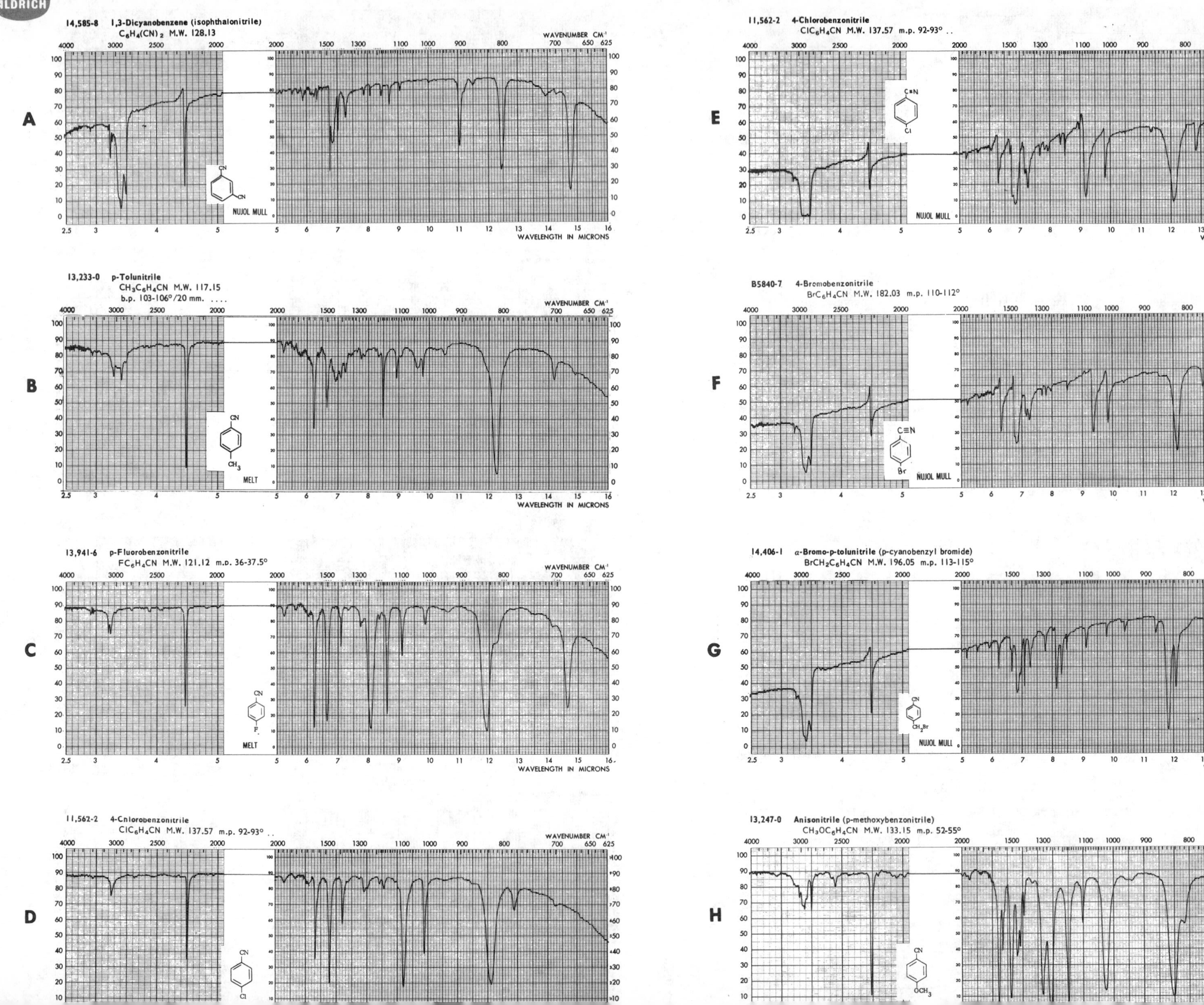
ALDRICH
A
14,585-8 1,3-Dicyanobenzene (isophthalonitrile)
$C_6H_4(CN)_2$ M.W. 128.13
NUJOL MULL
B
13,233-0 p-Tolunitrile
$CH_3C_6H_4CN$ M.W. 117.15
b.p. 103-106°/20 mm.
MELT
C
13,941-6 p-Fluorobenzonitrile
FC_6H_4CN M.W. 121.12 m.p. 36-37.5°
MELT
D
11,562-2 4-Chlorobenzonitrile
ClC_6H_4CN M.W. 137.57 m.p. 92-93°
E
11,562-2 4-Chlorobenzonitrile
ClC_6H_4CN M.W. 137.57 m.p. 92-93°
NUJOL MULL
F
B5840-7 4-Bromobenzonitrile
BrC_6H_4CN M.W. 182.03 m.p. 110-112°
NUJOL MULL
G
14,406-1 α-Bromo-p-tolunitrile (p-cyanobenzyl bromide)
$BrCH_2C_6H_4CN$ M.W. 196.05 m.p. 113-115°
NUJOL MULL
H
13,247-0 Anisonitrile (p-methoxybenzonitrile)
$CH_3OC_6H_4CN$ M.W. 133.15 m.p. 52-55°
WAVENUMBER CM⁻¹
WAVELENGTH IN MICRONS

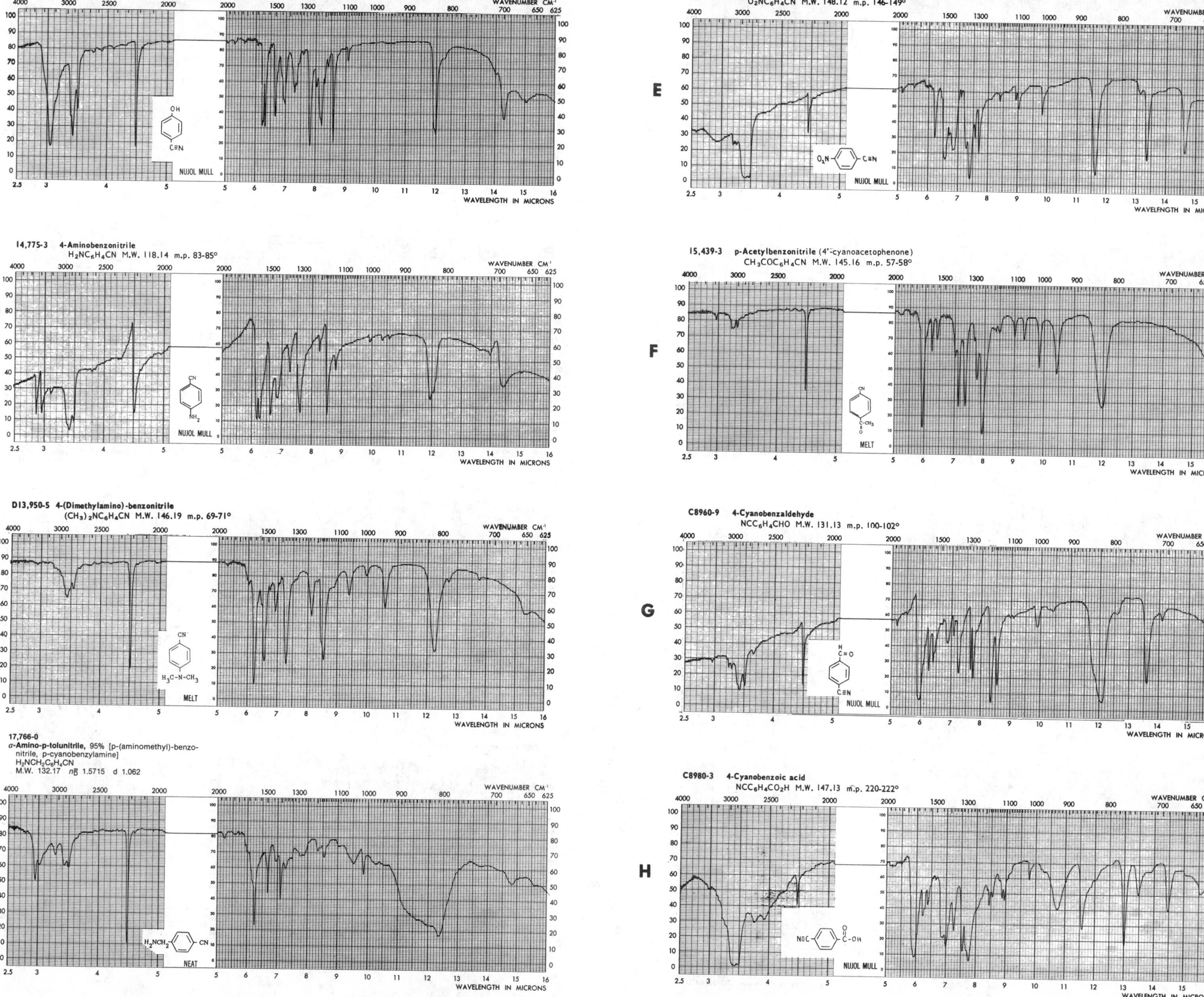
A
NCC$_6$H$_4$OH M.W. 119.12 m.p. 110-113°
NUJOL MULL
B
14,775-3 4-Aminobenzonitrile
H$_2$NC$_6$H$_4$CN M.W. 118.14 m.p. 83-85°
NUJOL MULL
C
D13,950-5 4-(Dimethylamino)-benzonitrile
(CH$_3$)$_2$NC$_6$H$_4$CN M.W. 146.19 m.p. 69-71°
MELT
D
17,766-0
α-Amino-p-tolunitrile, 95% [p-(aminomethyl)-benzonitrile, p-cyanobenzylamine]
H$_2$NCH$_2$C$_6$H$_4$CN
M.W. 132.17 n_D^{20} 1.5715 d 1.062
NEAT
E
N1200-7 p-Nitrobenzonitrile
O$_2$NC$_6$H$_4$CN M.W. 148.12 m.p. 146-149°
NUJOL MULL
F
15,439-3 p-Acetylbenzonitrile (4'-cyanoacetophenone)
CH$_3$COC$_6$H$_4$CN M.W. 145.16 m.p. 57-58°
MELT
G
C8960-9 4-Cyanobenzaldehyde
NCC$_6$H$_4$CHO M.W. 131.13 m.p. 100-102°
NUJOL MULL
H
C8980-3 4-Cyanobenzoic acid
NCC$_6$H$_4$CO$_2$H M.W. 147.13 m.p. 220-222°
NUJOL MULL
WAVENUMBER CM⁻¹
WAVELENGTH IN MICRONS
ALDRICH

A E1860-3 Ethyl 4-cyanobenzoate
$NCC_6H_4CO_2C_2H_5$ M.W. 175.19
m.p. 52-54°

B E1860 Ethyl 4-cyanobenzoate
$NCC_6H_4CO_2C_2H_5$ M.W. 175.19
m.p. 52-54°

C 18,032-7
p-Cyanophenyl p-butylbenzoate, 99+%,
GOLD LABEL
$CH_3(CH_2)_3C_6H_4CO_2C_6H_4CN$
M.W. 279.34 m.p. 67-69°

D C8940-4 N-(p-Cyanobenzal)-p-anisidine [α-(4-methoxyphenylimino)-p-tolunitrile]
$NCC_6H_4CH{:}NC_6H_4OCH_3$ M.W. 236.27 m.p. 114° and 125°

E 18,031-9
p-Cyanophenyl p-heptylbenzoate, 99+%,
GOLD LABEL
$CH_3(CH_2)_6C_6H_4CO_2C_6H_4CN$
M.W. 321.42 m.p. 44-45°

F 12,534-2 p-(4-Cyanobenzalamino)-cinnamic acid active amyl ester [2-methylbutyl p-(4-cyanobenzylideneamino)-cinnamate], puriss.
$NCC_6H_4CH{:}NC_6H_4CH{:}CHCO_2CH_2CH(CH_3)C_2H_5$
M.W. 346.43 m.p. 96° and 106°

G D7672-2 1,4-Dicyanobenzene (terephthalonitrile)
$C_6H_4(CN)_2$ M.W. 128.13
m.p. 226-227°

H 13,234-9 2,3-Dimethylbenzonitrile
$(CH_3)_2C_6H_3CN$ M.W. 131.18 n_D^{20} 1.5340
b.p. 118-120°/20 mm.

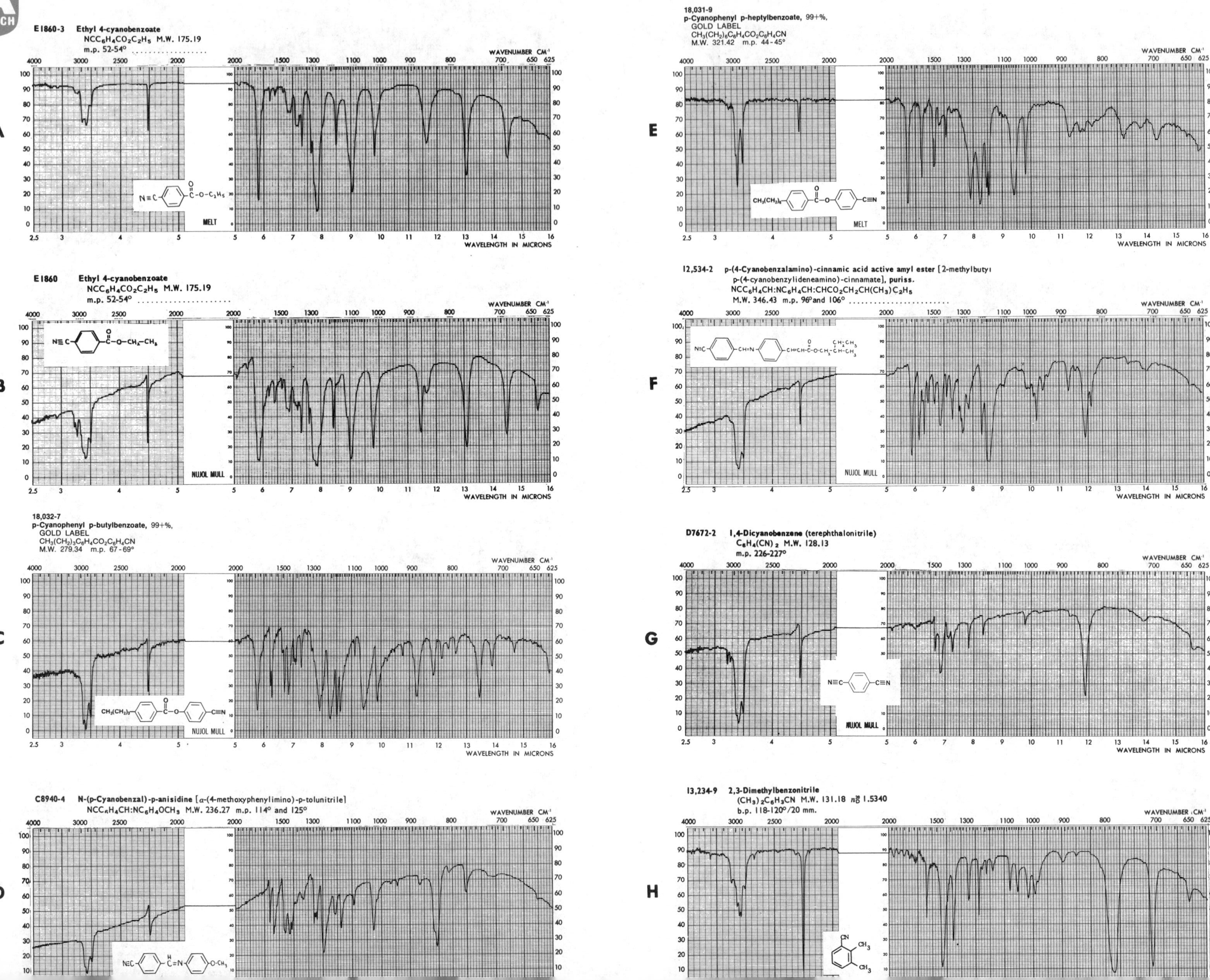

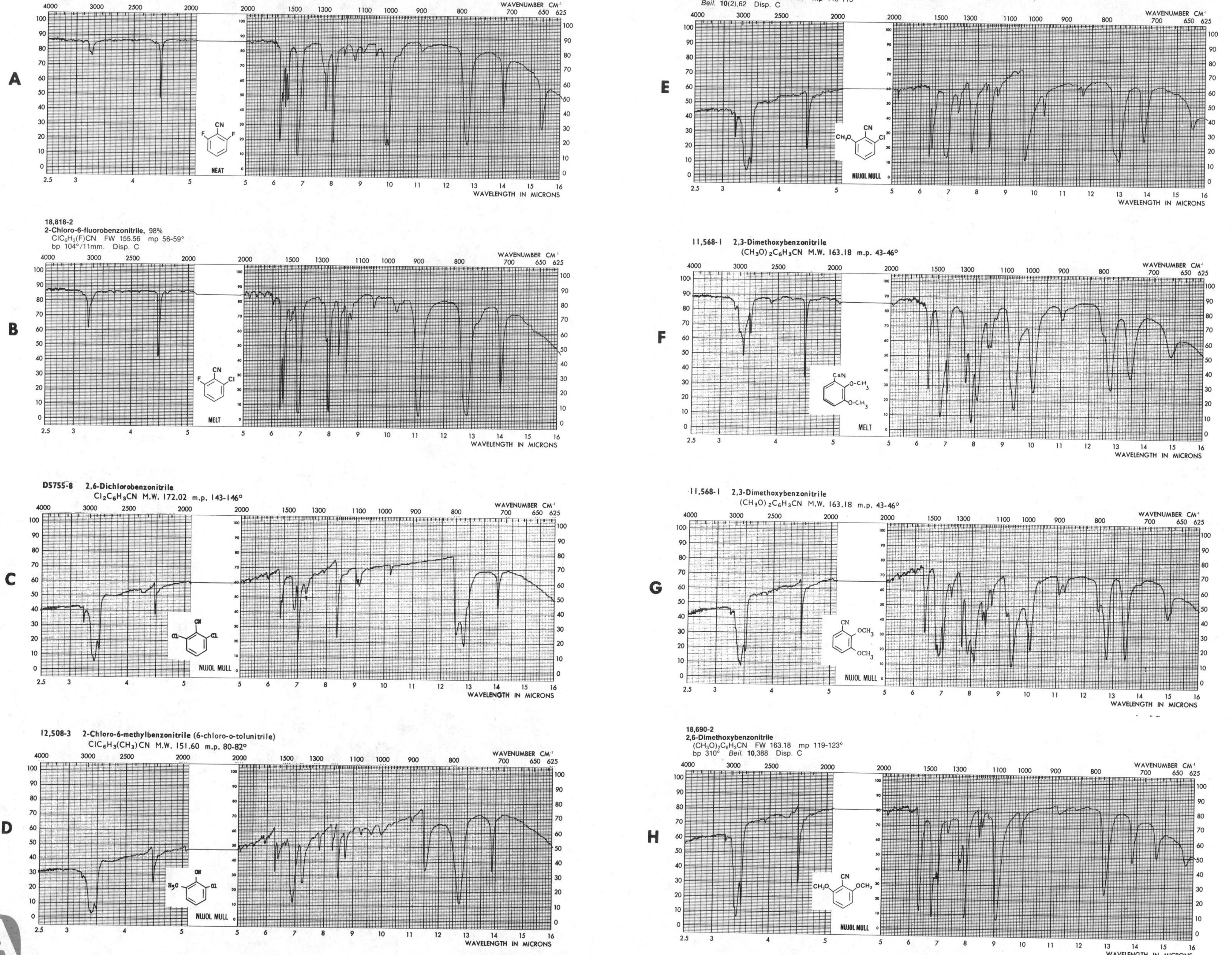

A

2,6-Difluorobenzonitrile, 97%
$F_2C_6H_3CN$ FW 139.11 n_D^{20} 1.4875 Disp. C

NEAT

B

18,818-2
2-Chloro-6-fluorobenzonitrile, 98%
$ClC_6H_3(F)CN$ FW 155.56 mp 56-59°
bp 104°/11mm. Disp. C

MELT

C

D5755-8 2,6-Dichlorobenzonitrile
$Cl_2C_6H_3CN$ M.W. 172.02 m.p. 143-146°

NUJOL MULL

D

12,508-3 2-Chloro-6-methylbenzonitrile (6-chloro-o-tolunitrile)
$ClC_6H_3(CH_3)CN$ M.W. 151.60 m.p. 80-82°

NUJOL MULL

E

2-Chloro-6-methoxybenzonitrile, 97%
$ClC_6H_3(OCH_3)CN$ FW 167.60 mp 113-115°
Beil. **10**(2),62 Disp. C

NUJOL MULL

F

11,568-1 2,3-Dimethoxybenzonitrile
$(CH_3O)_2C_6H_3CN$ M.W. 163.18 m.p. 43-46°

MELT

G

11,568-1 2,3-Dimethoxybenzonitrile
$(CH_3O)_2C_6H_3CN$ M.W. 163.18 m.p. 43-46°

NUJOL MULL

H

18,690-2
2,6-Dimethoxybenzonitrile
$(CH_3O)_2C_6H_3CN$ FW 163.18 mp 119-123°
bp 310° *Beil.* **10**,388 Disp. C

NUJOL MULL

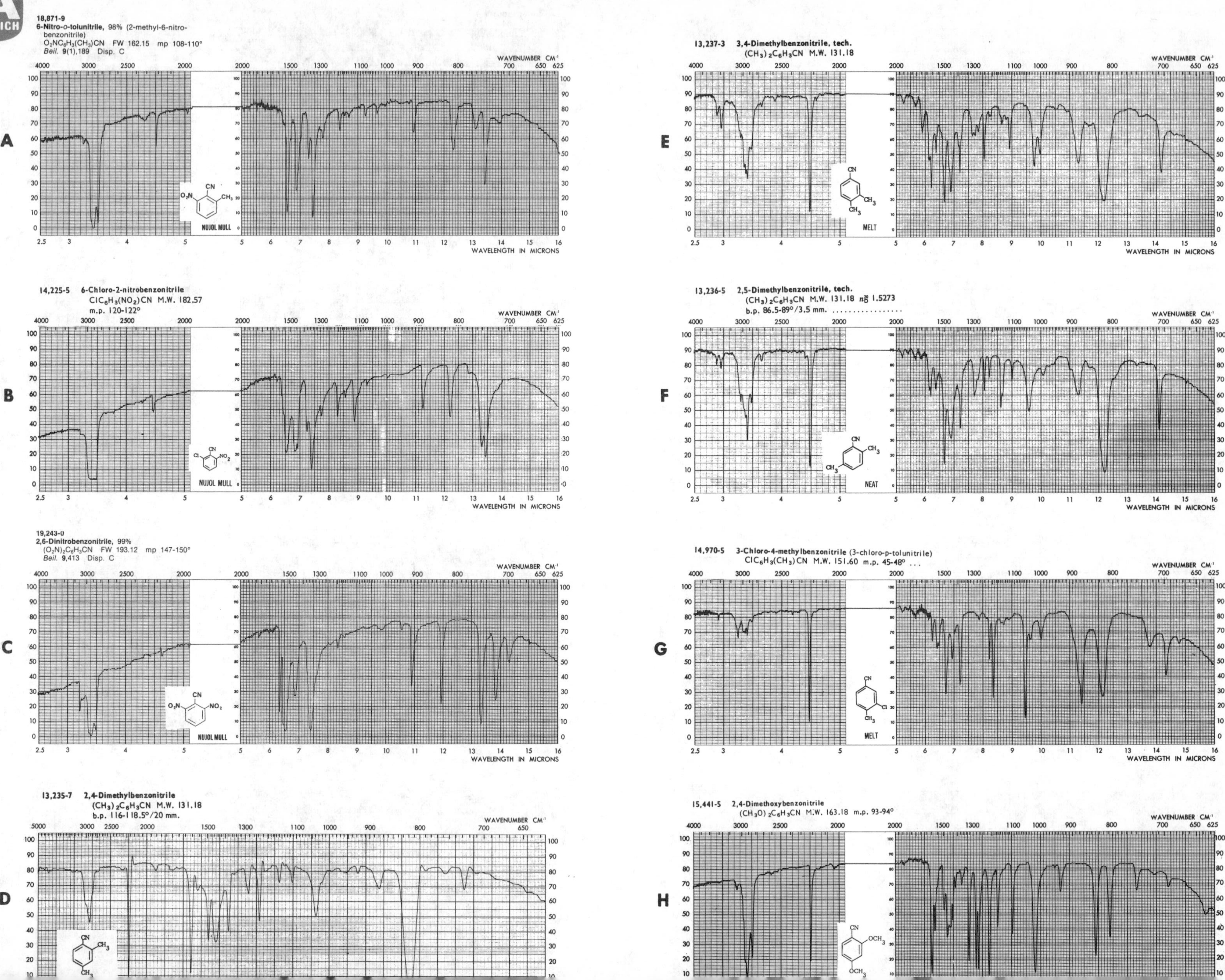
ALDRICH
A
18,871-9
6-Nitro-o-tolunitrile, 98% (2-methyl-6-nitrobenzonitrile)
$O_2NC_6H_3(CH_3)CN$ FW 162.15 mp 108-110°
Beil. 9(1),189 Disp. C
NUJOL MULL
B
14,225-5 6-Chloro-2-nitrobenzonitrile
$ClC_6H_3(NO_2)CN$ M.W. 182.57
m.p. 120-122°
NUJOL MULL
C
19,243-0
2,6-Dinitrobenzonitrile, 99%
$(O_2N)_2C_6H_3CN$ FW 193.12 mp 147-150°
Beil. 9,413 Disp. C
NUJOL MULL
D
13,235-7 2,4-Dimethylbenzonitrile
$(CH_3)_2C_6H_3CN$ M.W. 131.18
b.p. 116-118.5°/20 mm.
E
13,237-3 3,4-Dimethylbenzonitrile, tech.
$(CH_3)_2C_6H_3CN$ M.W. 131.18
MELT
F
13,236-5 2,5-Dimethylbenzonitrile, tech.
$(CH_3)_2C_6H_3CN$ M.W. 131.18 n_D^{20} 1.5273
b.p. 86.5-89°/3.5 mm.
NEAT
G
14,970-5 3-Chloro-4-methylbenzonitrile (3-chloro-p-tolunitrile)
$ClC_6H_3(CH_3)CN$ M.W. 151.60 m.p. 45-48°
MELT
H
15,441-5 2,4-Dimethoxybenzonitrile
$(CH_3O)_2C_6H_3CN$ M.W. 163.18 m.p. 93-94°
WAVENUMBER CM⁻¹
WAVELENGTH IN MICRONS

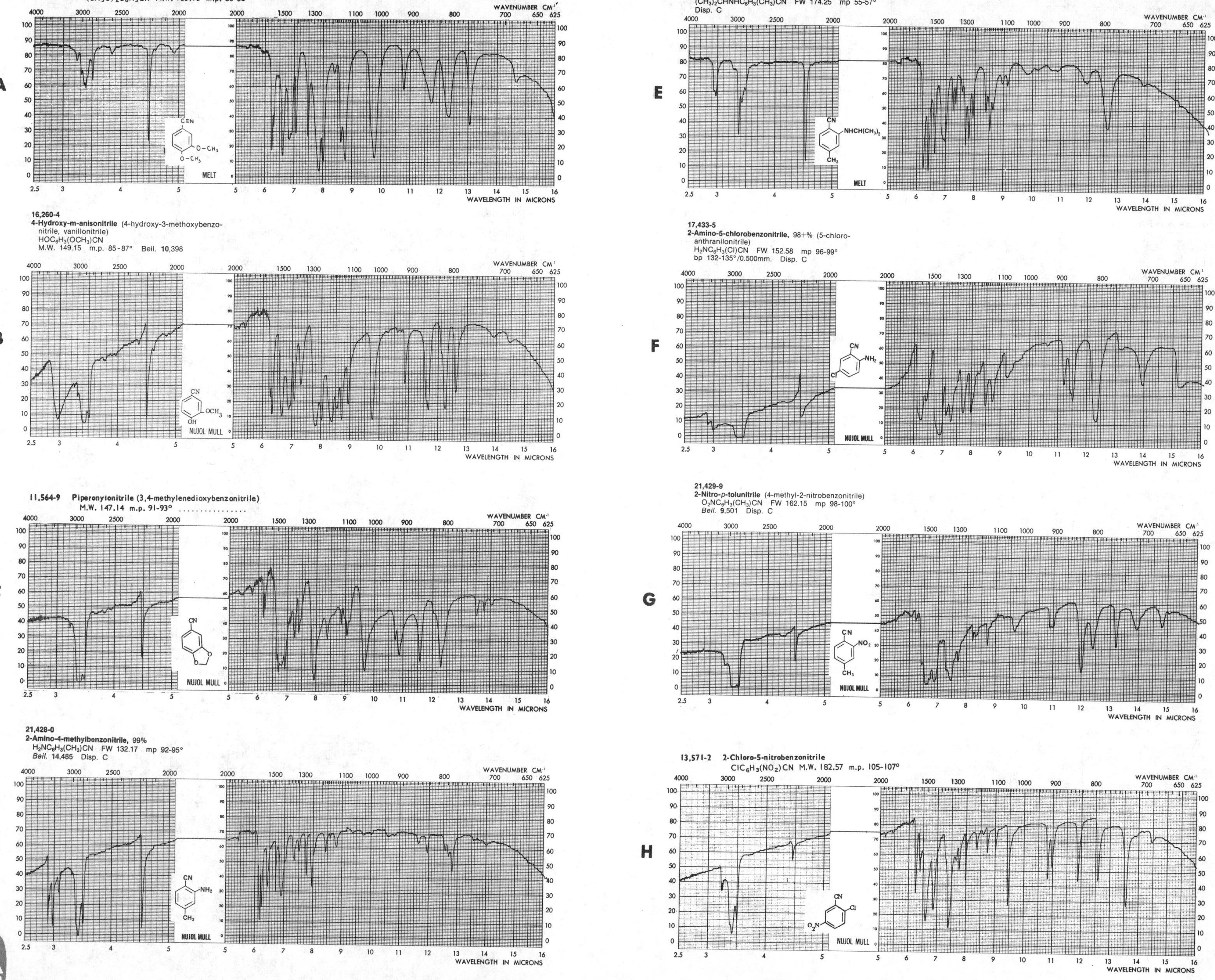

A
3,4-Dimethoxybenzonitrile
$(CH_3O)_2C_6H_3CN$ M.W. 163.18 m.p. 66-68°
MELT
B
16,260-4
4-Hydroxy-m-anisonitrile (4-hydroxy-3-methoxybenzonitrile, vanillonitrile)
$HOC_6H_3(OCH_3)CN$
M.W. 149.15 m.p. 85-87° Beil. 10,398
NUJOL MULL
C
11,564-9 Piperonylonitrile (3,4-methylenedioxybenzonitrile)
M.W. 147.14 m.p. 91-93°
NUJOL MULL
D
21,428-0
2-Amino-4-methylbenzonitrile, 99%
$H_2NC_6H_3(CH_3)CN$ FW 132.17 mp 92-95°
Beil. 14,485 Disp. C
NUJOL MULL
E
2-Isopropylamino-4-methylbenzonitrile, 97%
$(CH_3)_2CHNHC_6H_3(CH_3)CN$ FW 174.25 mp 55-57°
Disp. C
MELT
F
17,433-5
2-Amino-5-chlorobenzonitrile, 98+% (5-chloroanthranilonitrile)
$H_2NC_6H_3(Cl)CN$ FW 152.58 mp 96-99°
bp 132-135°/0.500mm. Disp. C
NUJOL MULL
G
21,429-9
2-Nitro-p-tolunitrile (4-methyl-2-nitrobenzonitrile)
$O_2NC_6H_3(CH_3)CN$ FW 162.15 mp 98-100°
Beil. 9,501 Disp. C
NUJOL MULL
H
13,571-2 2-Chloro-5-nitrobenzonitrile
$ClC_6H_3(NO_2)CN$ M.W. 182.57 m.p. 105-107°
NUJOL MULL
WAVENUMBER CM⁻¹
WAVELENGTH IN MICRONS
ALDRICH

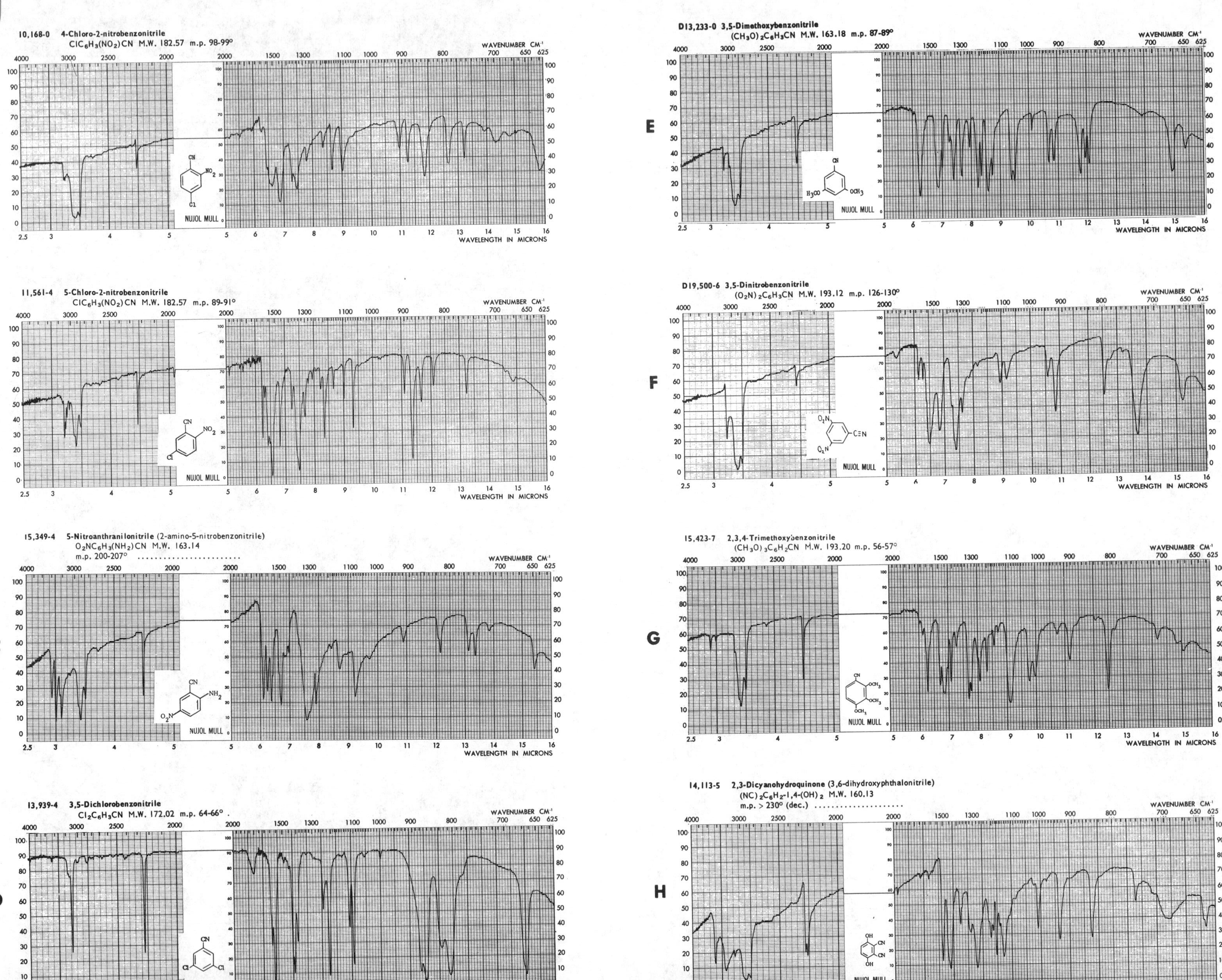

A
10,168-0 4-Chloro-2-nitrobenzonitrile
$ClC_6H_3(NO_2)CN$ M.W. 182.57 m.p. 98-99°
B
11,561-4 5-Chloro-2-nitrobenzonitrile
$ClC_6H_3(NO_2)CN$ M.W. 182.57 m.p. 89-91°
C
15,349-4 5-Nitroanthranilonitrile (2-amino-5-nitrobenzonitrile)
$O_2NC_6H_3(NH_2)CN$ M.W. 163.14
m.p. 200-207°
D
13,939-4 3,5-Dichlorobenzonitrile
$Cl_2C_6H_3CN$ M.W. 172.02 m.p. 64-66°
E
D13,233-0 3,5-Dimethoxybenzonitrile
$(CH_3O)_2C_6H_3CN$ M.W. 163.18 m.p. 87-89°
F
D19,500-6 3,5-Dinitrobenzonitrile
$(O_2N)_2C_6H_3CN$ M.W. 193.12 m.p. 126-130°
G
15,423-7 2,3,4-Trimethoxybenzonitrile
$(CH_3O)_3C_6H_2CN$ M.W. 193.20 m.p. 56-57°
H
14,113-5 2,3-Dicyanohydroquinone (3,6-dihydroxyphthalonitrile)
$(NC)_2C_6H_2$-1,4-$(OH)_2$ M.W. 160.13
m.p. > 230° (dec.)
NUJOL MULL
WAVENUMBER CM⁻¹
WAVELENGTH IN MICRONS

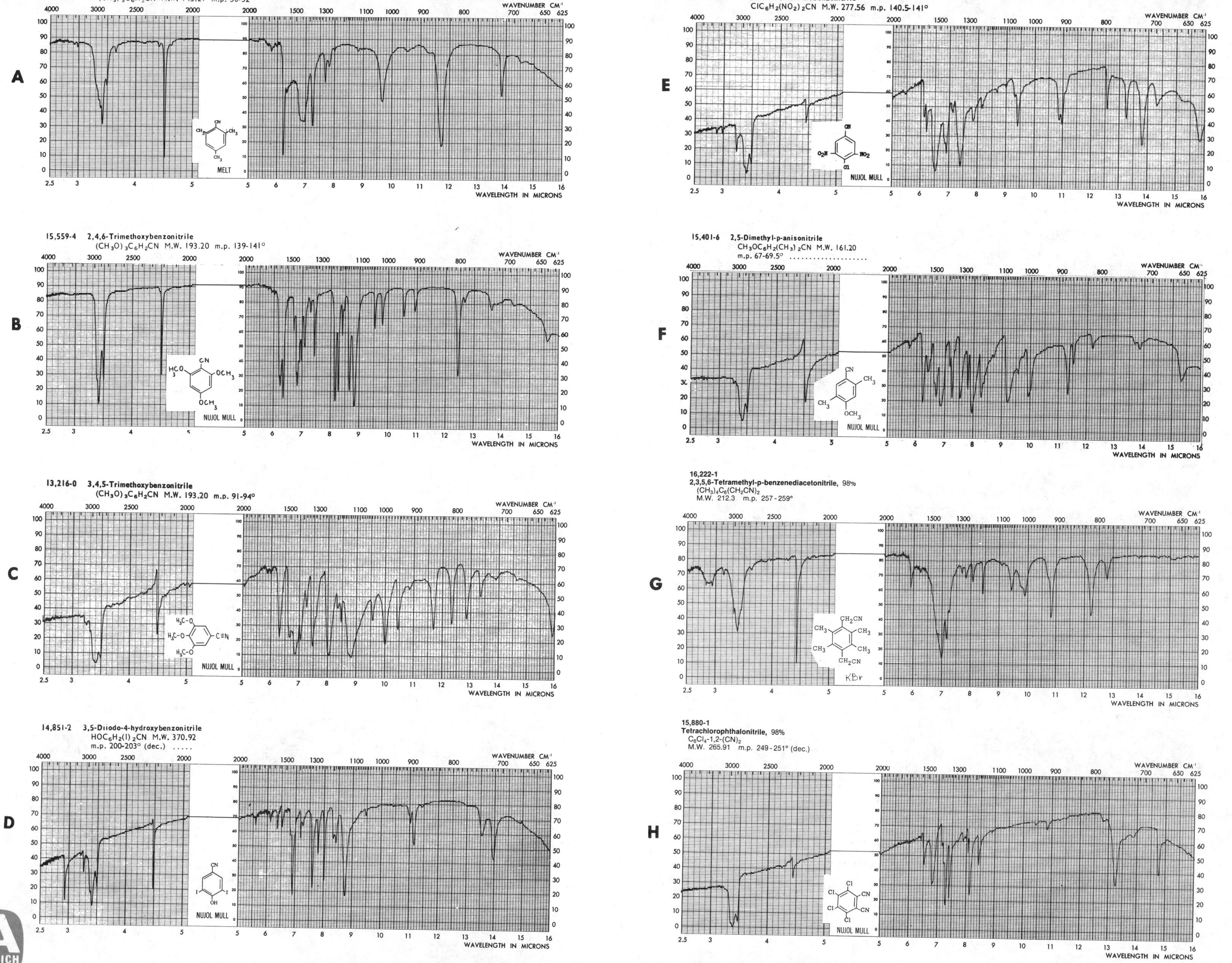
A
15,442-3 2,4,6-Trimethylbenzonitrile
$(CH_3)_3C_6H_2CN$ M.W. 145.21 m.p. 50-52°
MELT
B
15,559-4 2,4,6-Trimethoxybenzonitrile
$(CH_3O)_3C_6H_2CN$ M.W. 193.20 m.p. 139-141°
NUJOL MULL
C
13,216-0 3,4,5-Trimethoxybenzonitrile
$(CH_3O)_3C_6H_2CN$ M.W. 193.20 m.p. 91-94°
NUJOL MULL
D
14,851-2 3,5-Diiodo-4-hydroxybenzonitrile
$HOC_6H_2(I)_2CN$ M.W. 370.92
m.p. 200-203° (dec.)
NUJOL MULL
E
C3895-8 4-Chloro-3,5-dinitrobenzonitrile
$ClC_6H_2(NO_2)_2CN$ M.W. 277.56 m.p. 140.5-141°
NUJOL MULL
F
15,401-6 2,5-Dimethyl-p-anisonitrile
$CH_3OC_6H_2(CH_3)_2CN$ M.W. 161.20
m.p. 67-69.5°
NUJOL MULL
G
16,222-1
2,3,5,6-Tetramethyl-p-benzenediacetonitrile, 98%
$(CH_3)_4C_6(CH_2CN)_2$
M.W. 212.3 m.p. 257-259°
KBr
H
15,880-1
Tetrachlorophthalonitrile, 98%
C_6Cl_4-1,2-$(CN)_2$
M.W. 265.91 m.p. 249-251° (dec.)
NUJOL MULL
WAVENUMBER CM⁻¹
WAVELENGTH IN MICRONS
ALDRICH

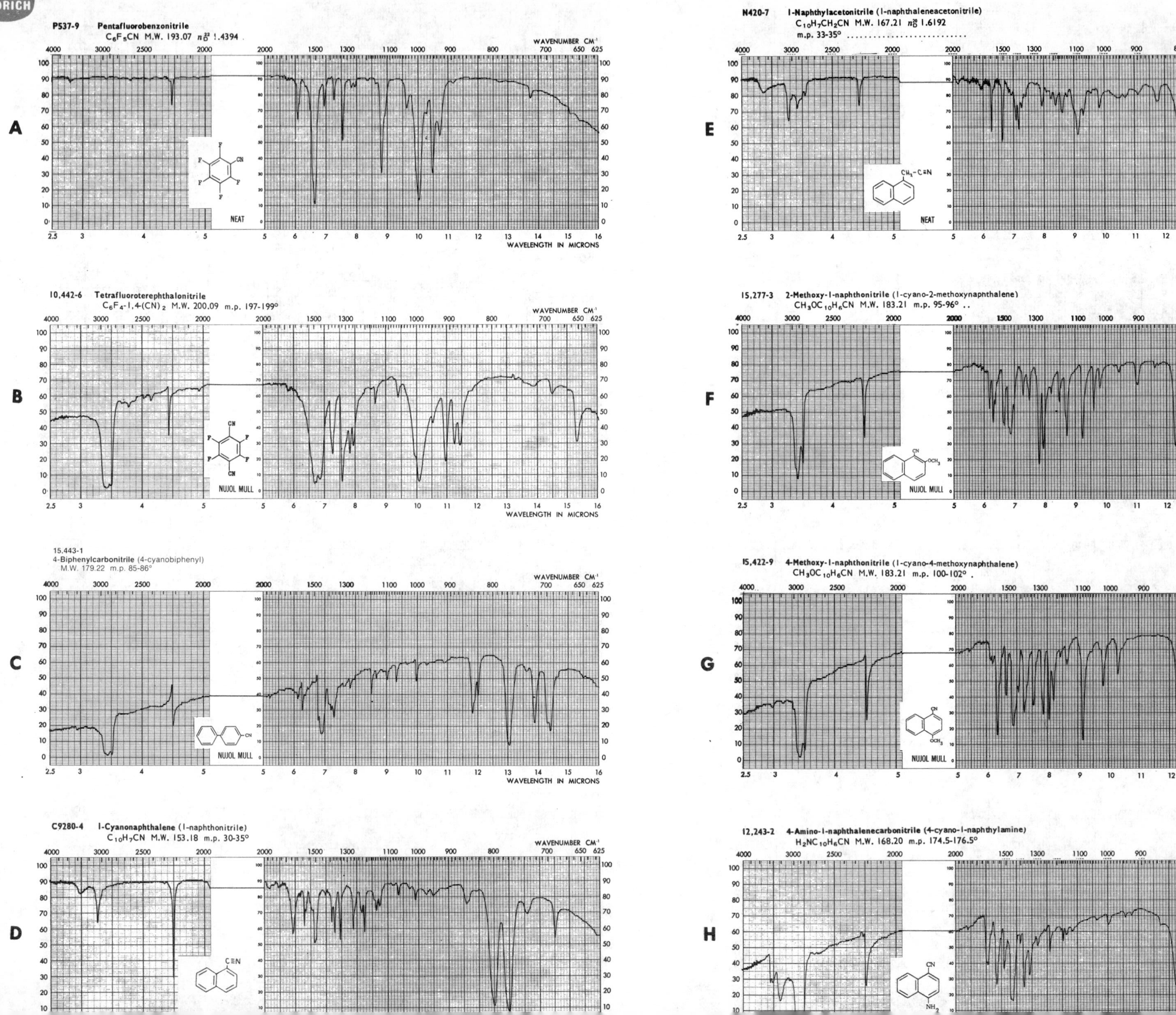
ALDRICH
A
P537-9 Pentafluorobenzonitrile
C_6F_5CN M.W. 193.07 n_D^{23} 1.4394
NEAT
B
10,442-6 Tetrafluoroterephthalonitrile
C_6F_4-1,4-$(CN)_2$ M.W. 200.09 m.p. 197-199°
NUJOL MULL
C
15,443-1
4-Biphenylcarbonitrile (4-cyanobiphenyl)
M.W. 179.22 m.p. 85-86°
NUJOL MULL
D
C9280-4 1-Cyanonaphthalene (1-naphthonitrile)
$C_{10}H_7CN$ M.W. 153.18 m.p. 30-35°
E
N420-7 1-Naphthylacetonitrile (1-naphthaleneacetonitrile)
$C_{10}H_7CH_2CN$ M.W. 167.21 n_D^{20} 1.6192
m.p. 33-35°
NEAT
F
15,277-3 2-Methoxy-1-naphthonitrile (1-cyano-2-methoxynapnthalene)
$CH_3OC_{10}H_6CN$ M.W. 183.21 m.p. 95-96°
NUJOL MULL
G
15,422-9 4-Methoxy-1-naphthonitrile (1-cyano-4-methoxynaphthalene)
$CH_3OC_{10}H_6CN$ M.W. 183.21 m.p. 100-102°
NUJOL MULL
H
12,243-2 4-Amino-1-naphthalenecarbonitrile (4-cyano-1-naphthylamine)
$H_2NC_{10}H_6CN$ M.W. 168.20 m.p. 174.5-176.5°
WAVENUMBER CM⁻¹
WAVELENGTH IN MICRONS

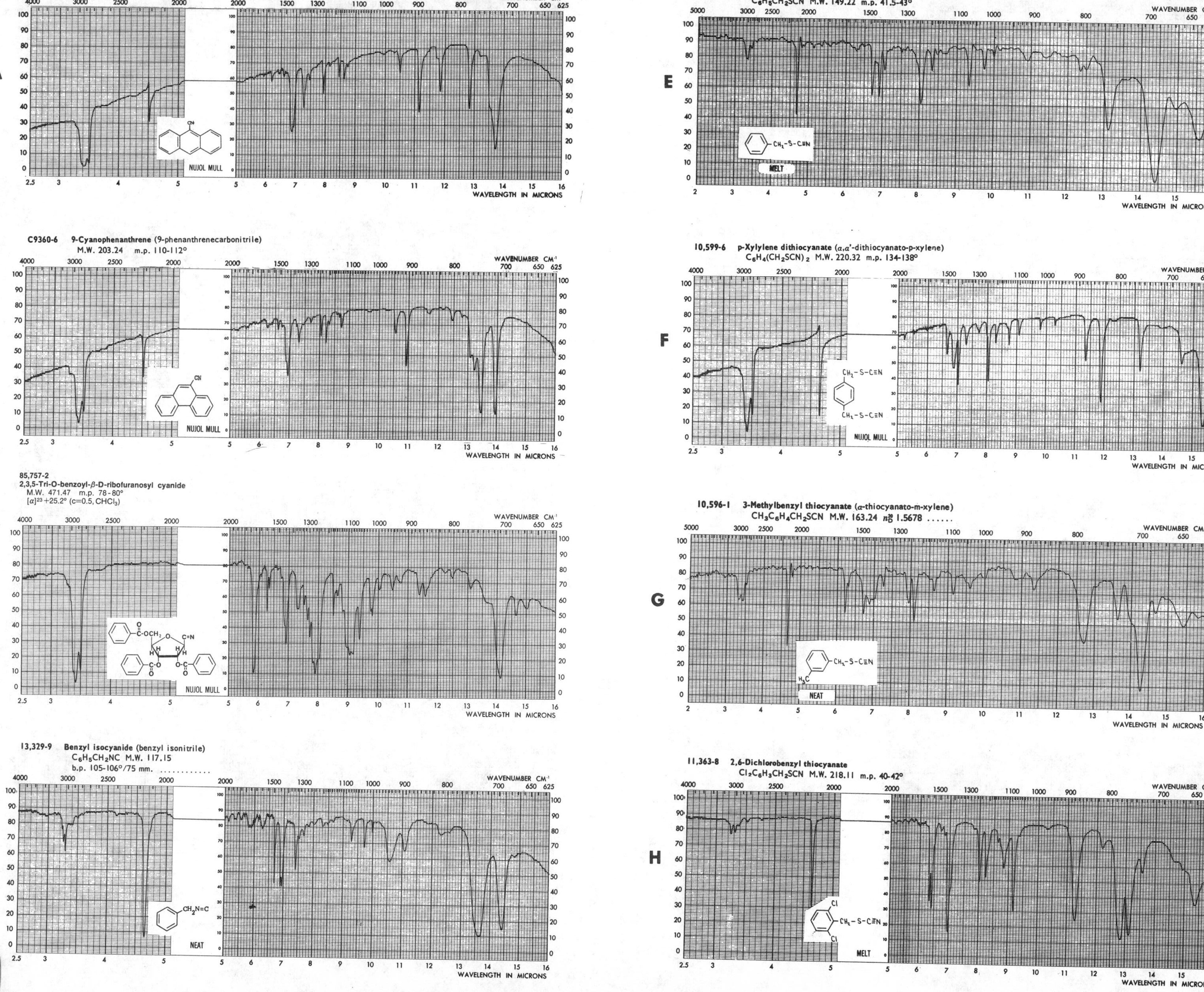

A
15,276-5 9-Anthracenecarbonitrile (9-cyanoanthracene)
M.W. 203.25 m.p. 173-177°
NUJOL MULL
B
C9360-6 9-Cyanophenanthrene (9-phenanthrenecarbonitrile)
M.W. 203.24 m.p. 110-112°
NUJOL MULL
C
85,757-2
2,3,5-Tri-O-benzoyl-β-D-ribofuranosyl cyanide
M.W. 471.47 m.p. 78-80°
[α]²³ +25.2° (c=0.5, CHCl₃)
NUJOL MULL
D
13,329-9 Benzyl isocyanide (benzyl isonitrile)
C₆H₅CH₂NC M.W. 117.15
b.p. 105-106°/75 mm.
NEAT
E
B3200-9 Benzyl thiocyanate
C₆H₅CH₂SCN M.W. 149.22 m.p. 41.5-43°
MELT
F
10,599-6 p-Xylylene dithiocyanate (α,α'-dithiocyanato-p-xylene)
C₆H₄(CH₂SCN)₂ M.W. 220.32 m.p. 134-138°
NUJOL MULL
G
10,596-1 3-Methylbenzyl thiocyanate (α-thiocyanato-m-xylene)
CH₃C₆H₄CH₂SCN M.W. 163.24 n²⁰D 1.5678
NEAT
H
11,363-8 2,6-Dichlorobenzyl thiocyanate
Cl₂C₆H₃CH₂SCN M.W. 218.11 m.p. 40-42°
MELT
WAVENUMBER CM⁻¹
WAVELENGTH IN MICRONS
ALDRICH

AROMATIC NITRILES AND CUMULATED DOUBLE BONDS

A 14,936-5 4-Hydroxyphenyl thiocyanate
HOC_6H_4SCN M.W. 151.18 m.p. 58-60°
NUJOL MULL

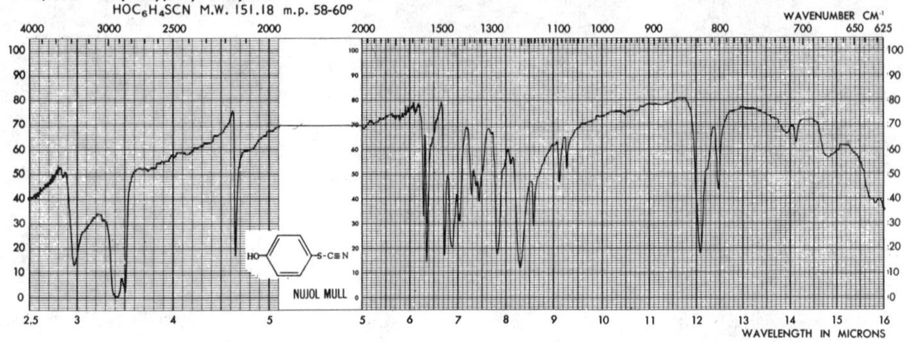

B 11,754-4 p-Nitrobenzyl thiocyanate
$O_2NC_6H_4CH_2SCN$ M.W. 194.21 m.p. 84-86°
NUJOL MULL

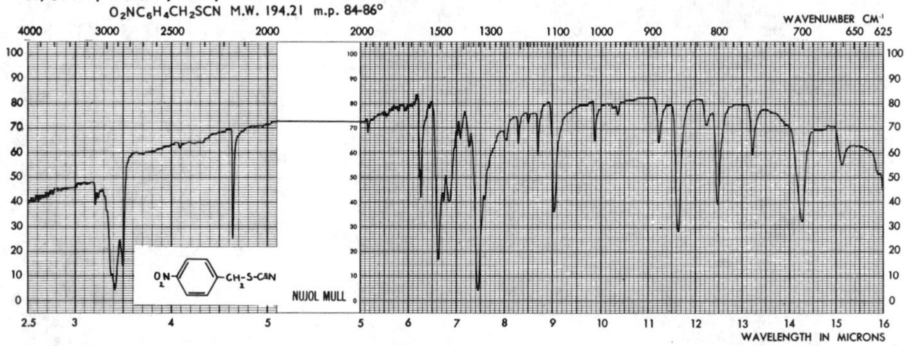

C 12,449-4 2,4-Dinitrophenyl thiocyanate
$(O_2N)_2C_6H_3SCN$ M.W. 225.18
m.p. 137-139.5°
NUJOL MULL

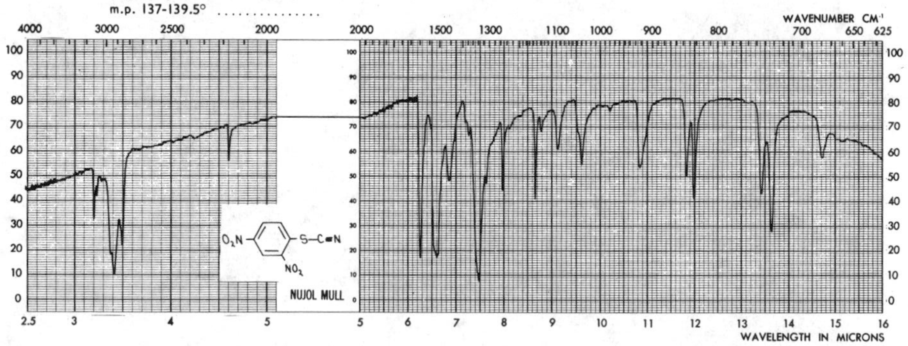

D 11,354-9 p-Chlorobenzoylmethyl thiocyanate
$ClC_6H_4COCH_2SCN$ M.W. 211.67 m.p. 135-137°
NUJOL MULL

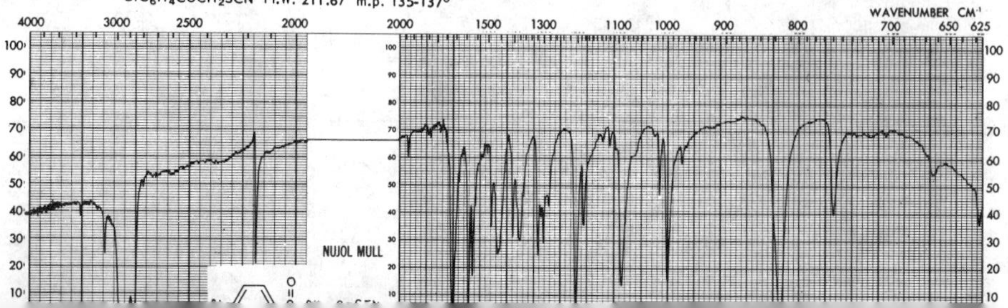

E 11,360-3 2-Naphthoylmethyl thiocyanate
$C_{10}H_7COCH_2SCN$ M.W. 227.29 m.p. 105-107°
NUJOL MULL

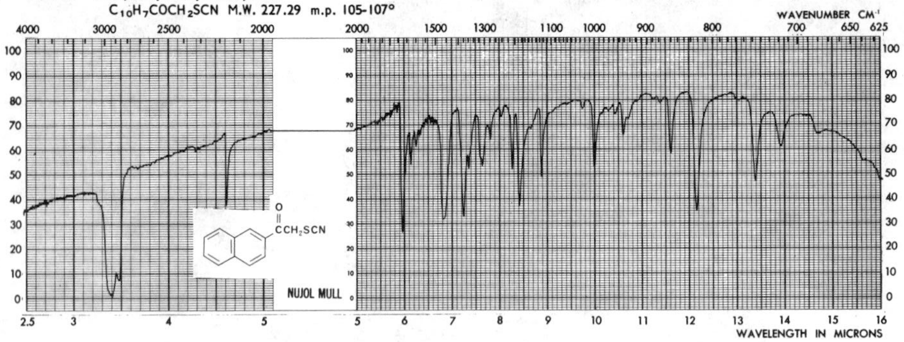

F 13,974-2 Phenyl isothiocyanate (phenyl mustard oil)
C_6H_5NCS M.W. 135.19 n_D^{20} 1.6497
b.p. 221°
NEAT

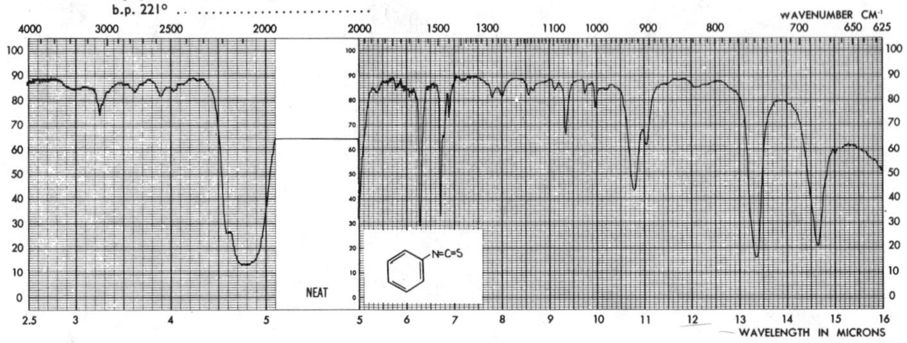

G F1435-1 3-Fluorophenyl isothiocyanate
FC_6H_4NCS M.W. 153.18 n_D^{20} 1.6186
b.p. 226.7°
NEAT

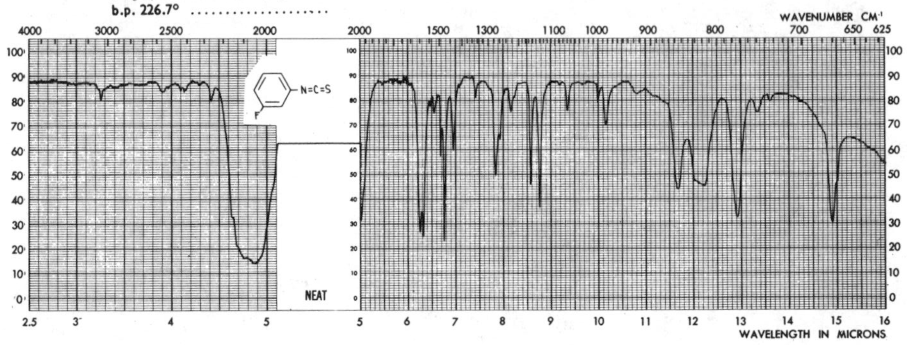

H 12,840-6 4-Fluorophenyl isothiocyanate
FC_6H_4NCS M.W. 153.18 m.p. 26-28°

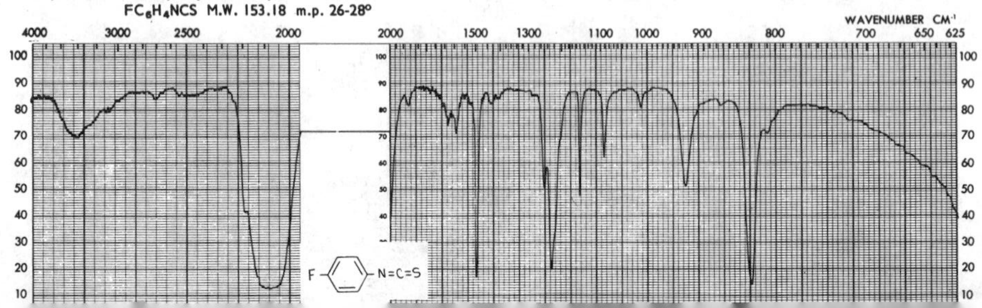

A

ClC_6H_4NCS M.W. 169.63 n_D^{20} 1.6580
b.p. 90°/1 mm.

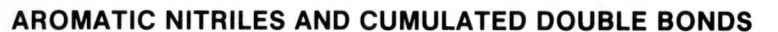

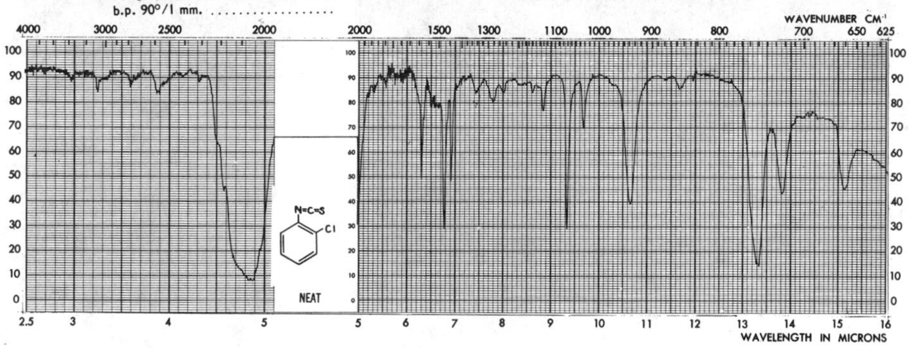

NEAT

B

N452-5 **1-Naphthyl isothiocyanate**
$C_{10}H_7NCS$ M.W. 185.25 m.p. 55.5-57°

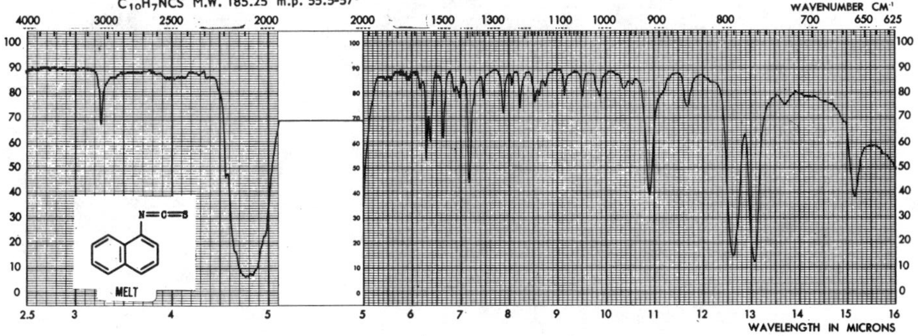

MELT

C

10,348-9 **2-Naphthyl isothiocyanate**
$C_{10}H_7NCS$ M.W. 185.25 m.p. 59-61.5°

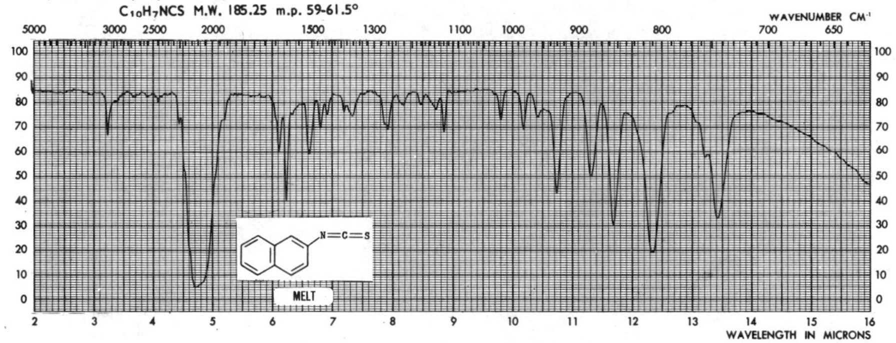

MELT

D

F250-2 **Fluorescein isothiocyanate**
M.W. 389.39 m.p. > 360°

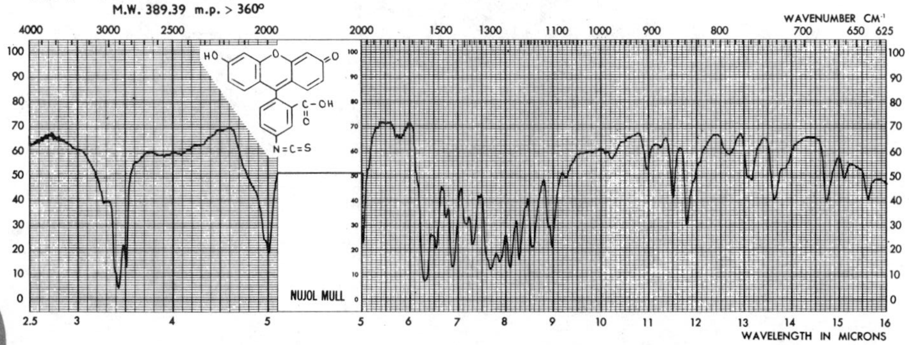

NUJOL MULL

E

C_6H_5NCO M.W. 119.12 n_D^{20} 1.5350
b.p. 165°

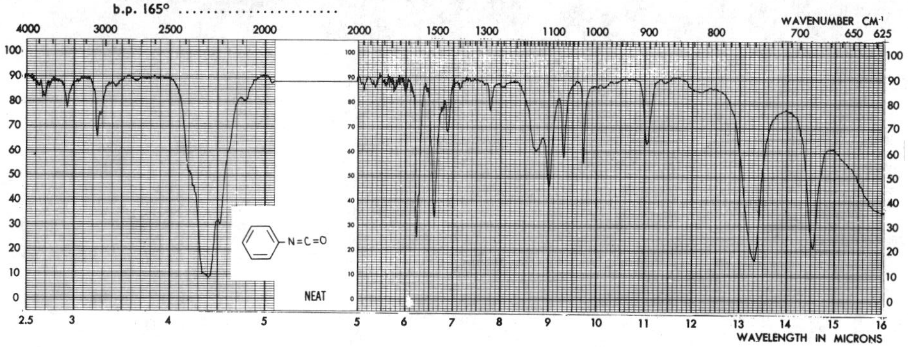

NEAT

F

22,057-4
S-(+)-α-Methylbenzyl isocyanate, 95%
$C_6H_5CH(CH_3)NCO$ FW 147.18
bp 55-56°/2.500mm. n_D^{20} 1.5124 $[\alpha]^{19}$ +9.6° (neat)
Fieser 7,20 Disp. C

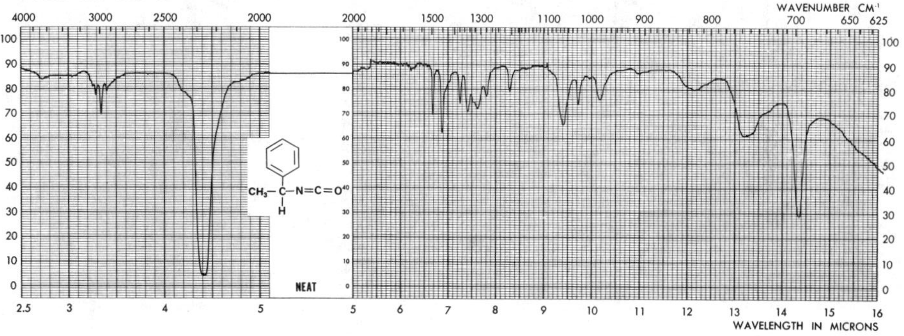

NEAT

G

22,056-6
R-(-)-α-Methylbenzyl isocyanate, 95%
$C_6H_5CH(CH_3)NCO$ FW 147.18
bp 55-56°/2.500mm. n_D^{20} 1.5145 $[\alpha]_D^{20}$ -9.2° (neat)
Disp. C

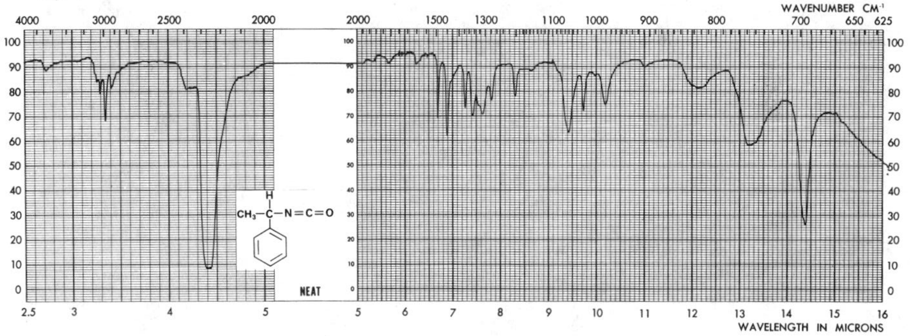

NEAT

H

14,362-6 **m-Tolyl isocyanate**
$CH_3C_6H_4NCO$ M.W. 133.15 n_D^{20} 1.5305
b.p. 75-76°/12 mm.

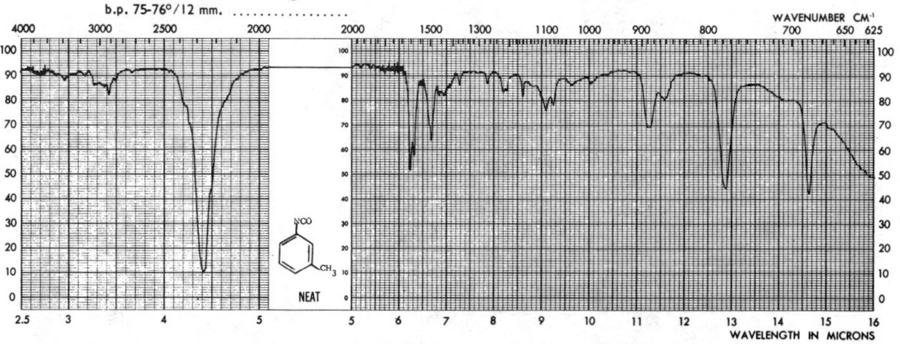

NEAT

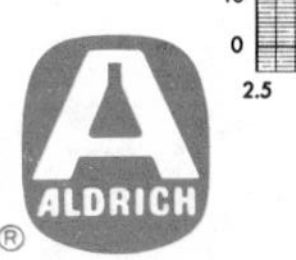

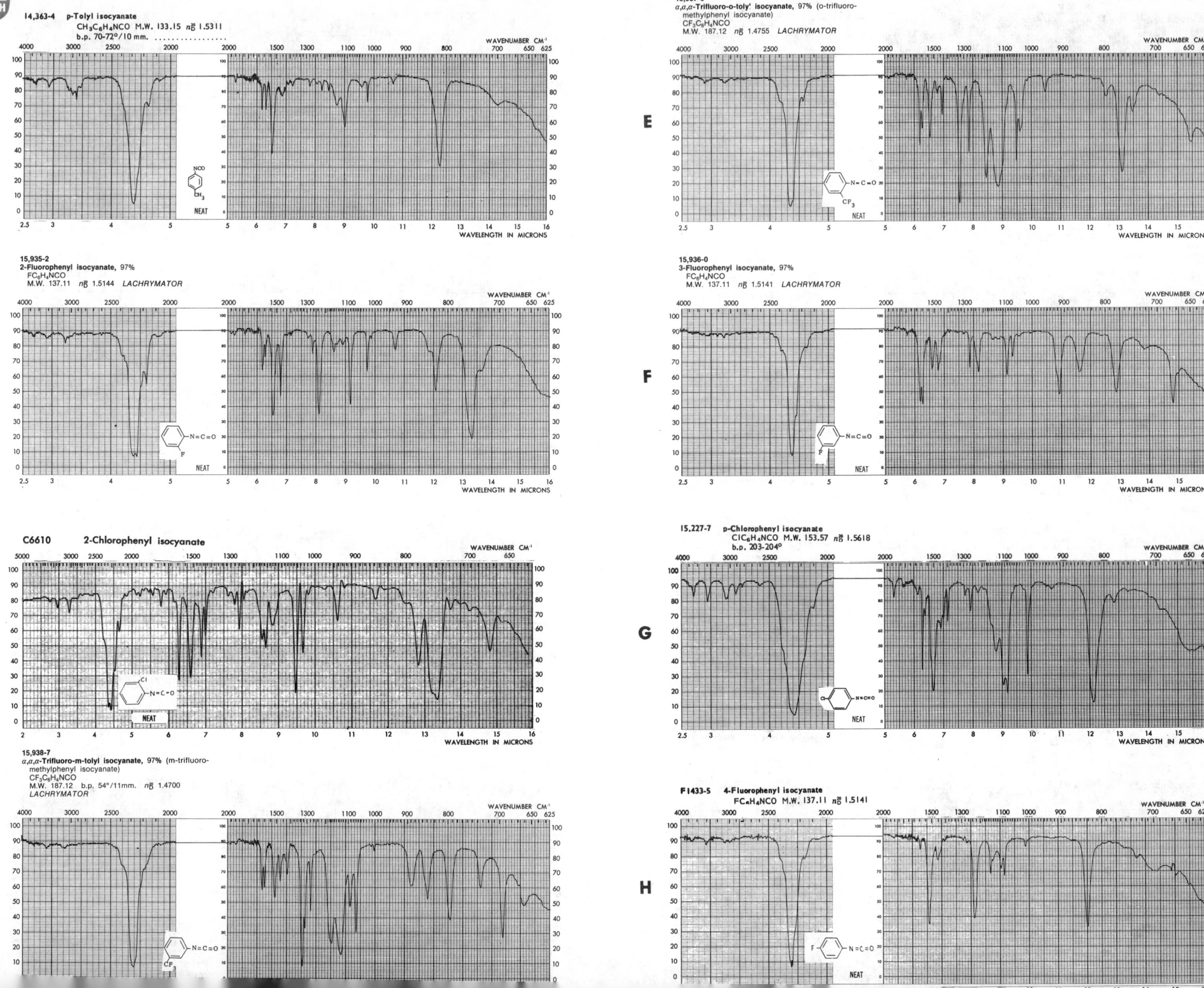

A 14,363-4 **p-Tolyl isocyanate**
$CH_3C_6H_4NCO$ M.W. 133.15 n_D^{20} 1.5311
b.p. 70-72°/10 mm.

B 15,935-2
2-Fluorophenyl isocyanate, 97%
FC_6H_4NCO
M.W. 137.11 n_D^{20} 1.5144 *LACHRYMATOR*

C C6610 **2-Chlorophenyl isocyanate**

D 15,938-7
α,α,α-Trifluoro-m-tolyl isocyanate, 97% (m-trifluoromethylphenyl isocyanate)
$CF_3C_6H_4NCO$
M.W. 187.12 b.p. 54°/11mm. n_D^{20} 1.4700
LACHRYMATOR

E 15,937-9
α,α,α-Trifluoro-o-tolyl isocyanate, 97% (o-trifluoromethylphenyl isocyanate)
$CF_3C_6H_4NCO$
M.W. 187.12 n_D^{20} 1.4755 *LACHRYMATOR*

F 15,936-0
3-Fluorophenyl isocyanate, 97%
FC_6H_4NCO
M.W. 137.11 n_D^{20} 1.5141 *LACHRYMATOR*

G 15,227-7 **p-Chlorophenyl isocyanate**
ClC_6H_4NCO M.W. 153.57 n_D^{20} 1.5618
b.p. 203-204°

H F1433-5 **4-Fluorophenyl isocyanate**
FC_6H_4NCO M.W. 137.11 n_D^{20} 1.5141

M.W. 191.19 m.p. 27-29 LACHRYMATOR

A

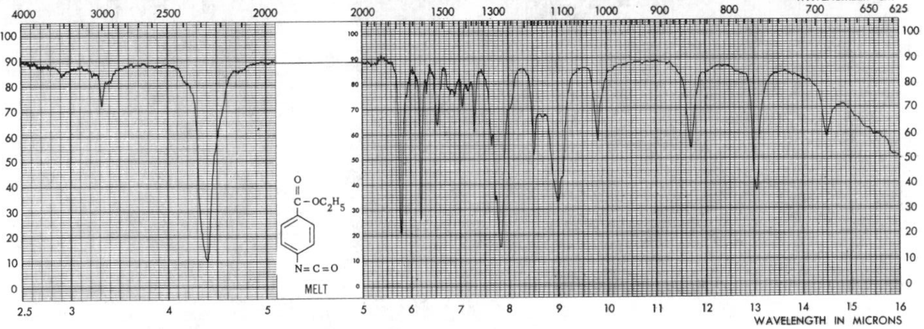

E

n_D^{20} 1.6248 b.p. 140°/0.9 mm.

T3985-3 Tolylene-2,4-diisocyanate (4-methyl-m-phenylene diisocyanate)
$CH_3C_6H_3(NCO)_2$ M.W. 174.16 n_D^{20} 1.5669 m.p. 17-20°
b.p. 120°/10 mm.

B

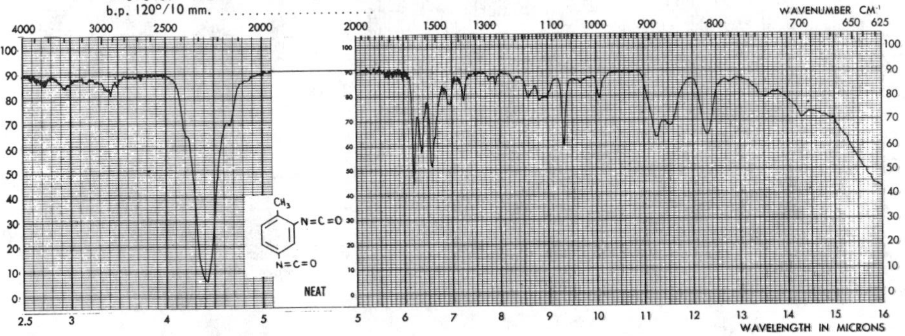

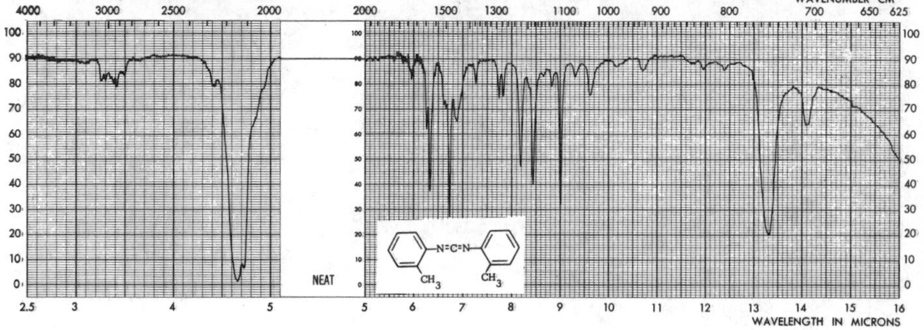

D21,980-0 N,N'-Di-p-tolylcarbodiimide
$CH_3C_6H_4N{:}C{:}NC_6H_4CH_3$ M.W. 222.29 m.p. 56-58°

F

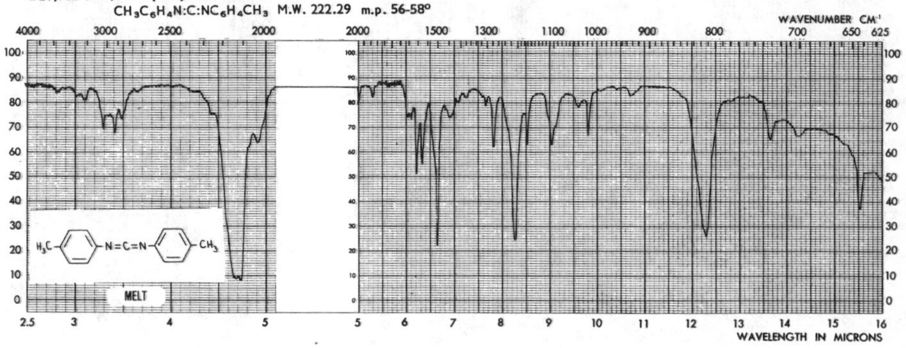

22,386-7
Tolylene-2,6-diisocyanate, 97% (2-methyl-*m*-phenylene diisocyanate)
$CH_3C_6H_3(NCO)_2$ FW 174.16 bp 129-133°/18mm.
n_D^{20} 1.5708 d 1.225 *Beil.* 13(3),291 Disp. C

C

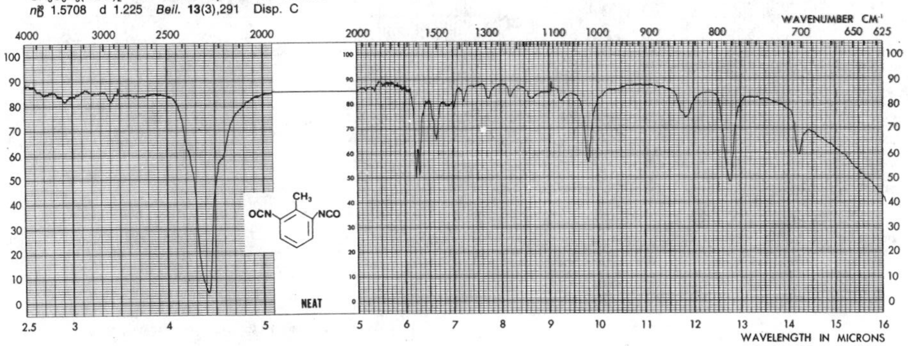

11,908-3 N,N'-Bis-(2,6-diethylphenyl)-carbodiimide
$(C_2H_5)_2C_6H_3N{:}C{:}NC_6H_3(C_2H_5)_2$ M.W. 306.45
n_D^{20} 1.5910 b.p. 192-194°/0.4 mm.

G

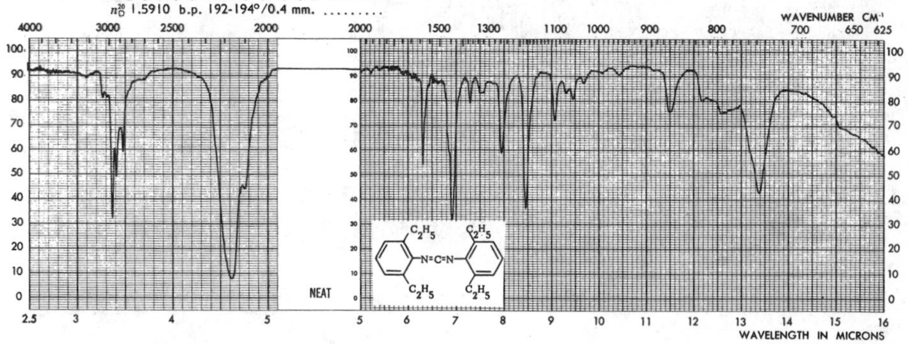

13,431-7 *trans*-2-Phenylcyclopropyl isocyanate
$C_6H_5C_3H_4NCO$ M.W. 159.19 n_D^{20} 1.5363
b.p. 75-76°/0.5 mm.

D

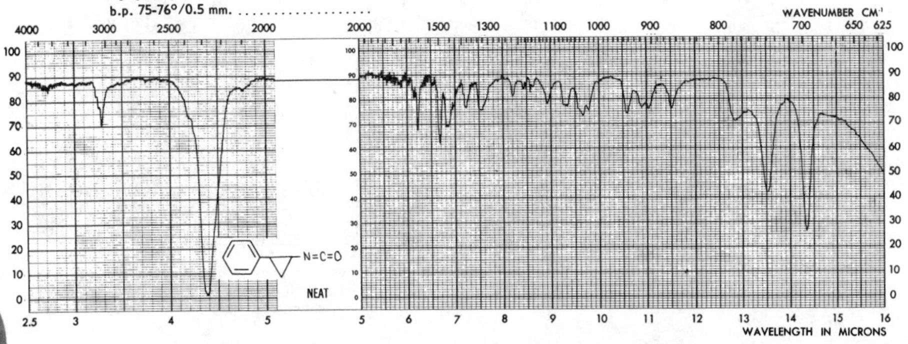

13,530-5 N-tert.-Butyl-N'-(triphenylmethyl)-carbodiimide
$(C_6H_5)_3CN{:}C{:}NC(CH_3)_3$ M.W. 340.47
m.p. 71-73°

H

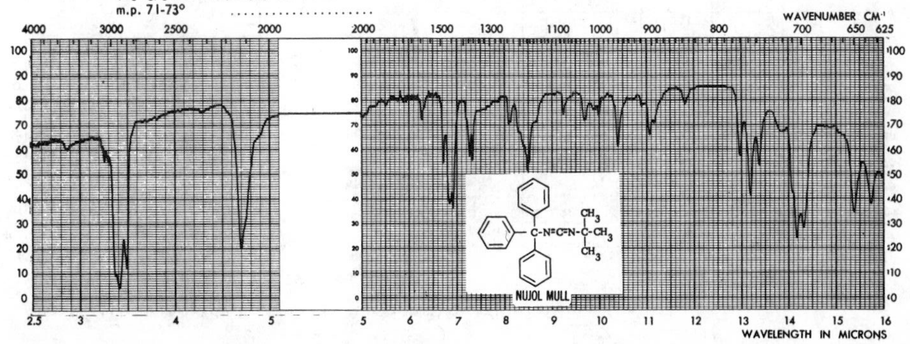

A

15,310-9 **N,N'-Bis-(4-nitrophenyl)-carbodiimide**
$O_2NC_6H_4N{:}C{:}NC_6H_4NO_2$ M.W. 284.23
m.p. 166-168°

NUJOL MULL

B

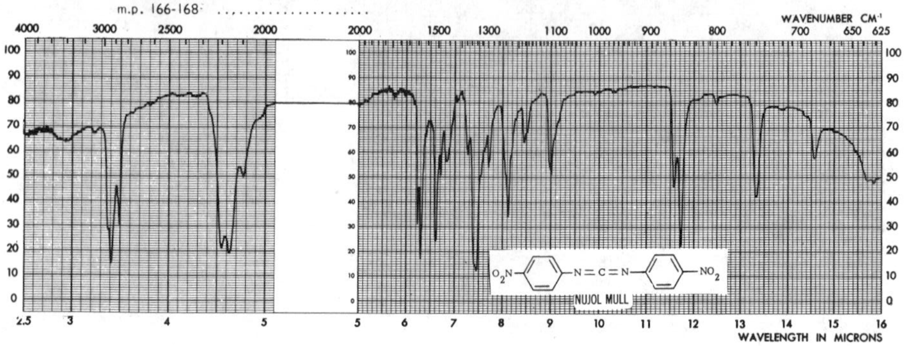

15,285-4 **4-Methoxybenzyloxycarbonyl azide (4-methoxybenzyl azidoformate)**
$N_3CO_2CH_2C_6H_4OCH_3$ M.W. 207.19
m.p. 30-32°

MELT

C

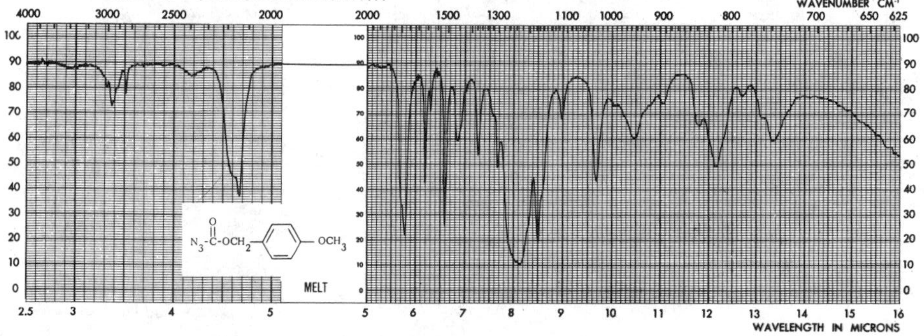

M1680-6 **2-Methoxy-4-morpholinobenzenediazonium chloride, zinc chloride double salt**
M.W. 356.53 m.p. 131° (dec.)

NUJOL MULL

D

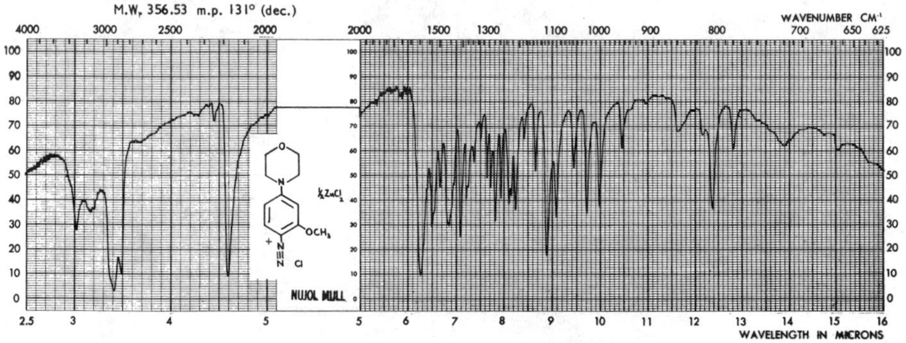

21,774-3
p-(4-Aminoanilino)benzenediazonium sulfate
$H_2NC_6H_4NHC_6H_4N_2HSO_4$ FW 308.32
mp 270-272° Disp. F

E

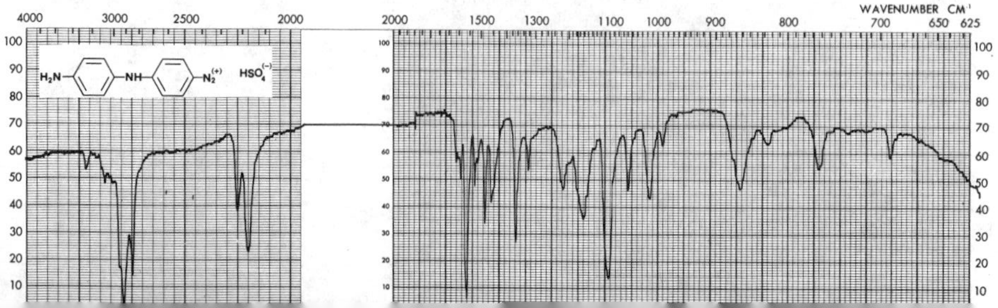

D2820-5 **4-Diazo-N,N-diethylaniline fluoroborate (4-diethylaminobenzenediazonium tetrafluoroborate)**
$(C_2H_5)_2NC_6H_4N_2BF_4$ M.W. 263.05 m.p. 111-113°

NUJOL MULL

F

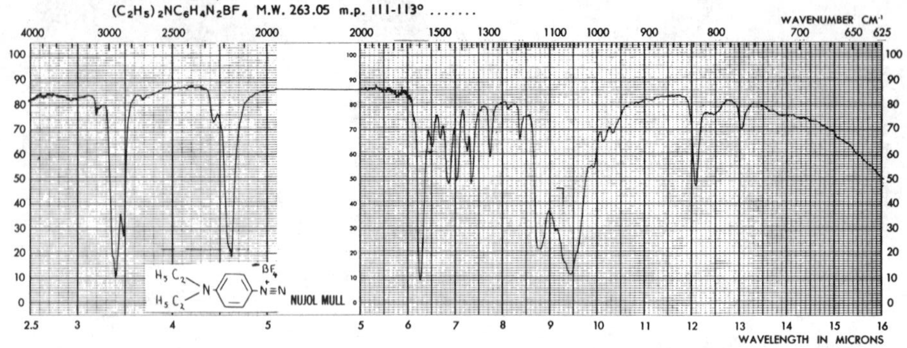

22,502-9
4-Biphenylcarbonitrile, 99% (p-phenylbenzonitrile)
$C_6H_5C_6H_4CN$ FW 179.22 mp 85-87° *Beil.* 9,672
IR 2,992B Disp. C

NUJOL MULL

G

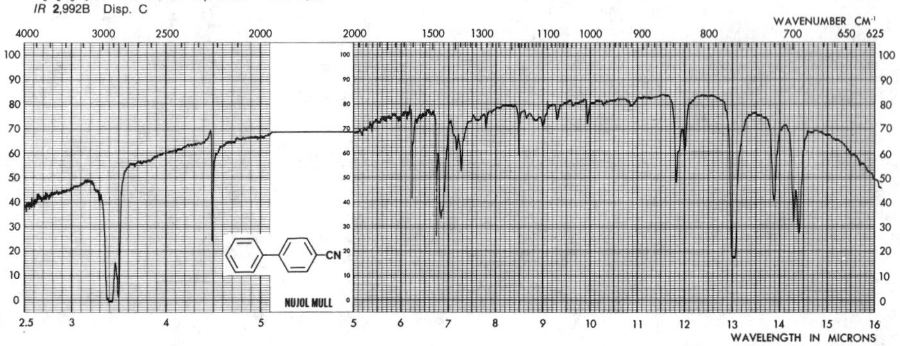

22,561-4
3,5-Dichloro-4-hydroxybenzonitrile, 95%
$Cl_2C_6H_2(OH)CN$ FW 188.01 mp 134-137°
Beil. 10,177 Disp. C

NUJOL MULL

H

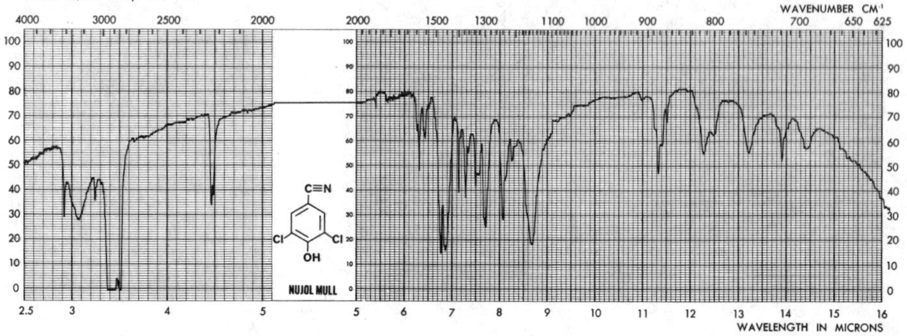

22,627-0
4-Dimethylamino-1-naphthyl isothiocyanate, 98%
$(CH_3)_2NC_{10}H_6NCS$ FW 228.32 mp 67-69°
Disp. C

WAVENUMBER CM⁻¹ — WAVELENGTH IN MICRONS

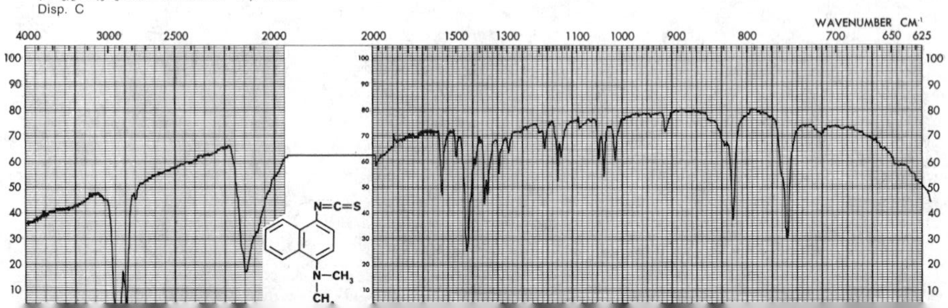

AROMATIC SULFUR OXYGEN COMPOUNDS

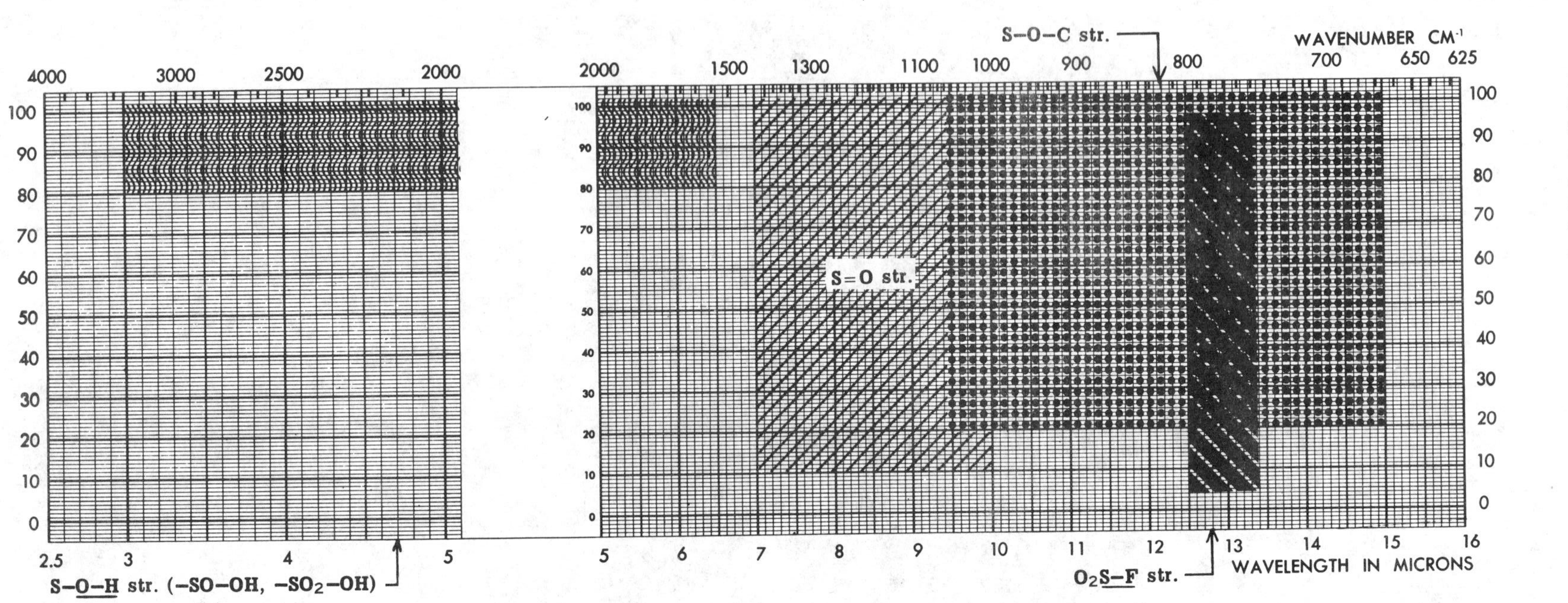

The positions and intensities of various sulfur-oxygen group combinations described in the non-aromatic sulfur-oxygen section are applicable to the aromatic analogues.

A group not represented in the non-aromatic series is the sulfonyl fluoride function. The asymmetric and symmetric SO_2 stretch bands are shifted to lower wavelength positions [7.1 and 8.2 μ (1410 and 1220 cm^{-1})] than the corresponding sulfonyl chlorides [7.5 and 8.5 μ (1335 and 1175 cm^{-1})]. The sulfur-fluorine stretch can also be seen absorbing very strongly between 12.5 and 13.3 μ (800 – 750 cm^{-1}).

The relative intensities of bands from various functional groups combined in the same molecule should be noted. For instance, the aromatic sulfur-oxygen combination presents a very uniform spectrum. The spectra appear crowded with many absorptions appearing between 6 and 16 μ (1665 – 625 cm^{-1}).

The aromatic substitution bands between 11 and 15 μ (910 – 665 cm^{-1}) are also disturbed significantly by the presence of the SO_2 group attached directly to the aromatic ring.

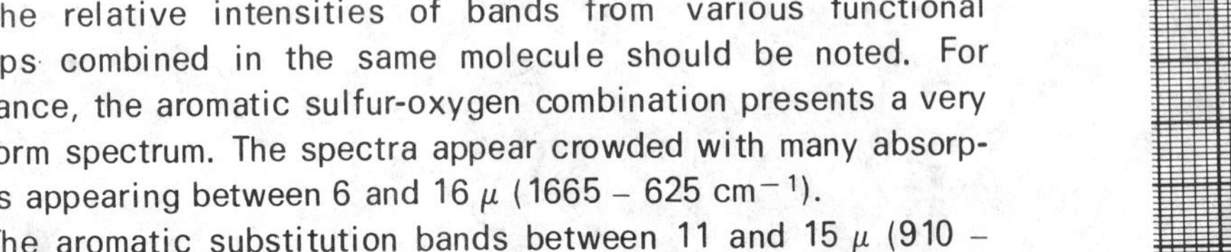

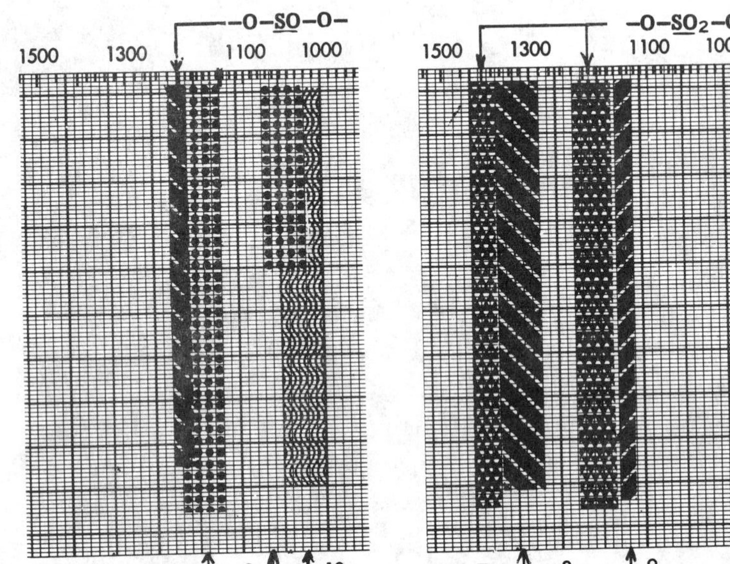

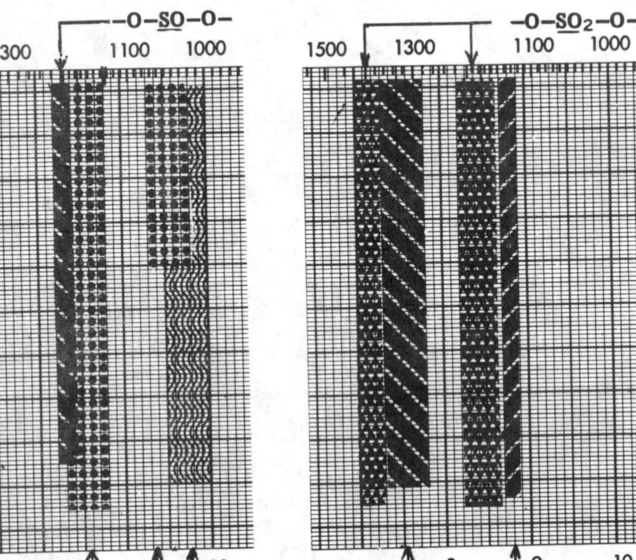

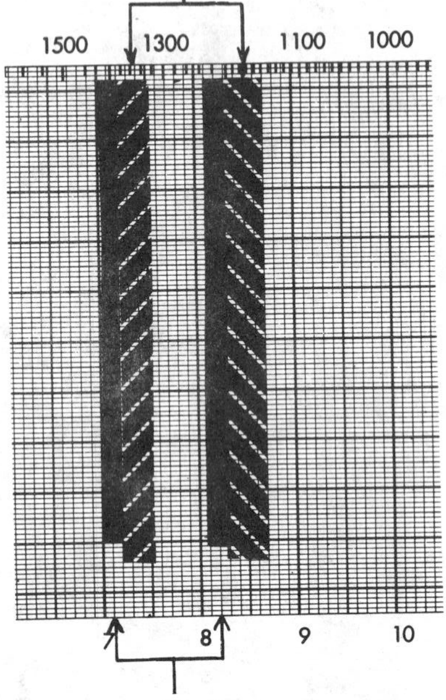

A m.p. 69-71° ....

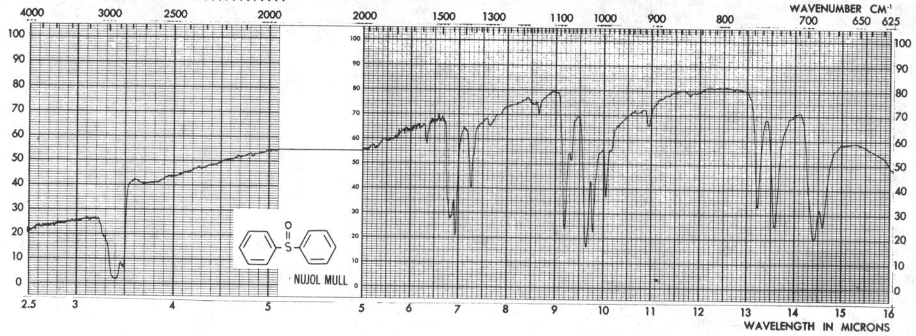

NUJOL MULL

B B3160-6 **Benzyl sulfoxide**
$(C_6H_5CH_2)_2SO$ M.W. 230.33 m.p. 133-135°

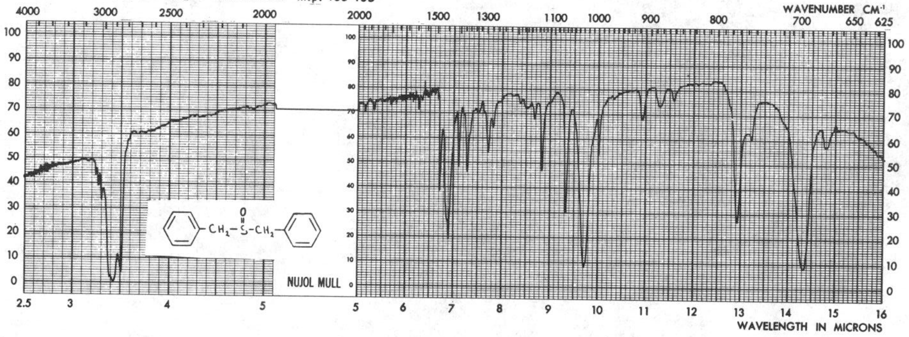

NUJOL MULL

C T4280-3 **p-Tolyl sulfoxide**
$(CH_3C_6H_4)_2SO$ M.W. 230.33 m.p. 93-95°

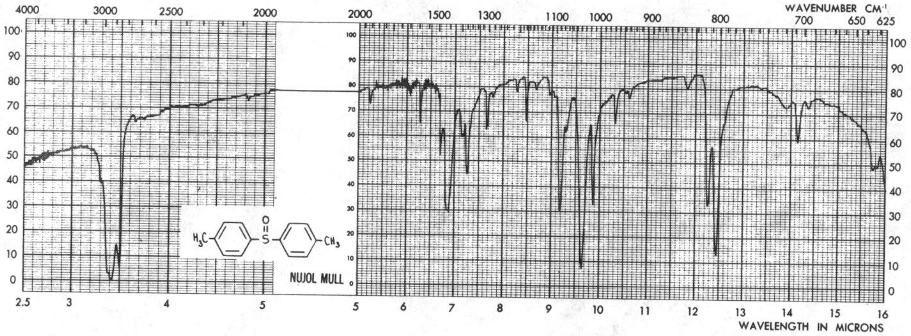

NUJOL MULL

D 18,418-7
4,4'-Sulfonyldibenzyl alcohol, 98%
$O_2S(C_6H_4CH_2OH)_2$
M.W. 278.33 m.p. 140-144° Beil. **6**,901

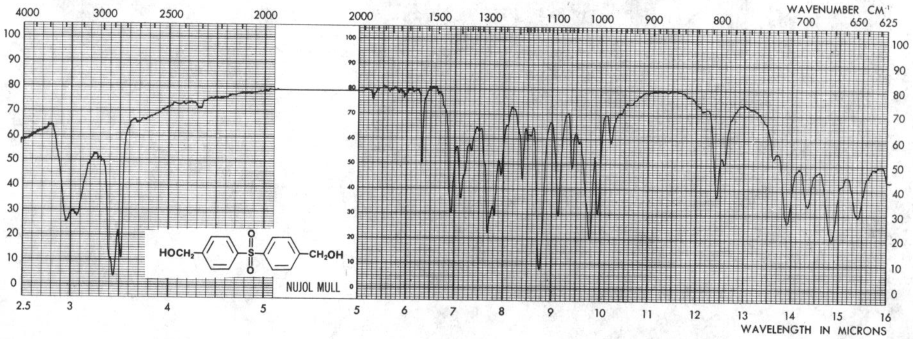

NUJOL MULL

E 12,104-5 **4-Chlorophenyl sulfoxide** [bis-(p-chlorophenyl) sulfoxide]
$(ClC_6H_4)_2SO$ M.W. 271.17 m.p. 143-145.5°

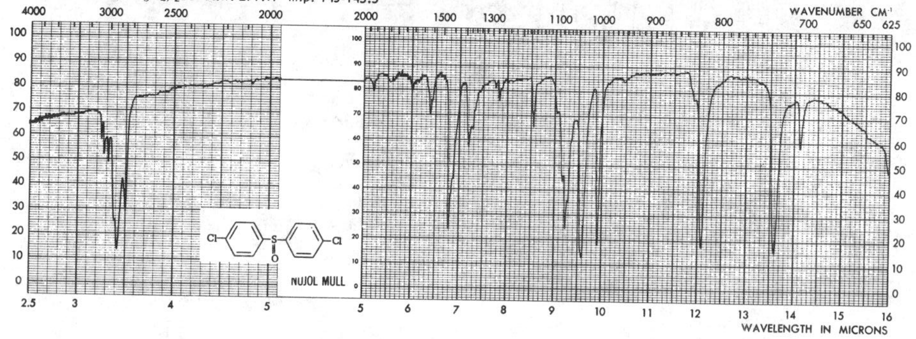

NUJOL MULL

F M7115-7 **Methyl phenyl sulfone**
$C_6H_5SO_2CH_3$ M.W. 156.20 m.p. 87-89°

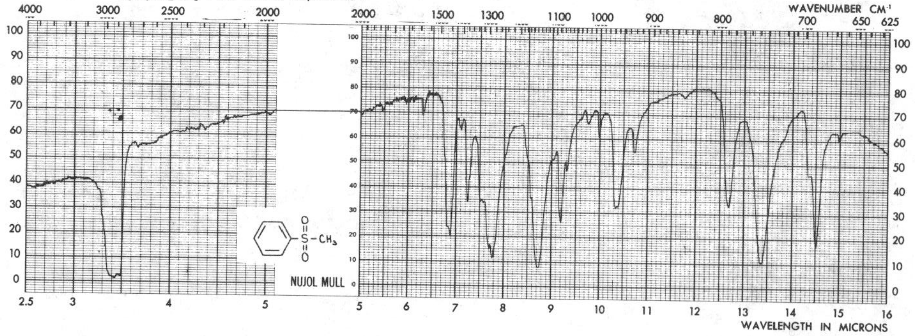

NUJOL MULL

G 10,536-8 **Benzyl tert.-butyl sulfone**
$C_6H_5CH_2SO_2C(CH_3)_3$ M.W. 212.31 m.p. 124-125°

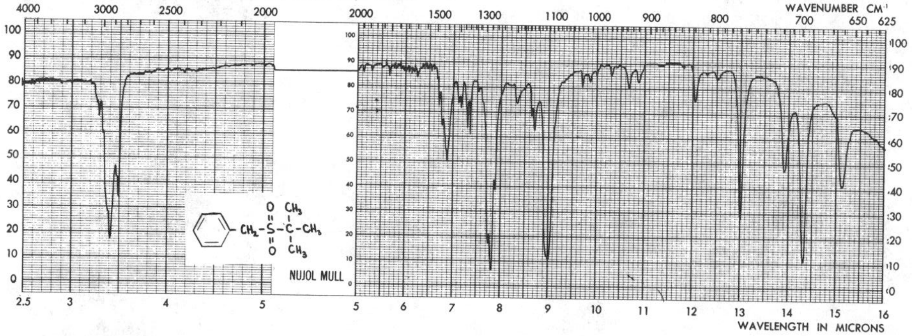

NUJOL MULL

H 21,330-6
Phenyl vinyl sulfoxide
$C_6H_5SOCH{=}CH_2$ FW 152.22 bp 93-95°/0.200mm.
n_D^{20} 1.5865 d 1.139 *Beil.* **6**(3),987 *Fieser* **6**,468
Disp. C

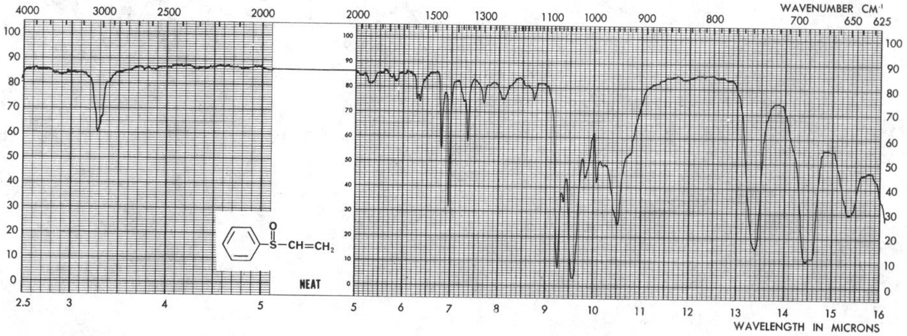

NEAT

AROMATIC SULFUR-OXYGEN

A

18,435-7
(Phenylsulfonyl)acetonitrile, 98%
$C_6H_5SO_2CH_2CN$
M.W. 181.22 m.p. 112-114° Beil. 6,316

NUJOL MULL

B

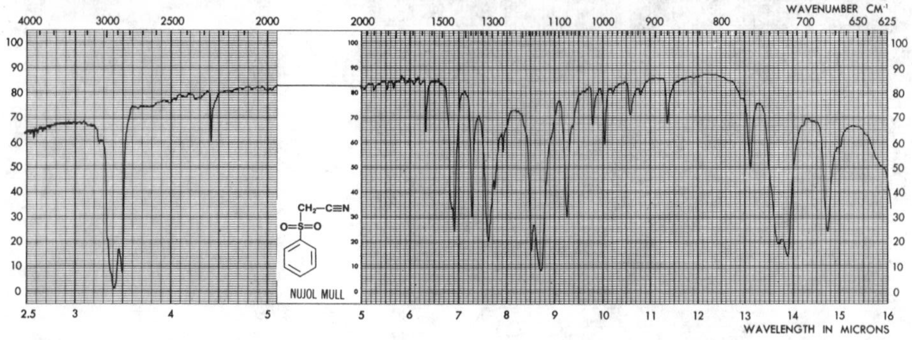

M8515-8 **Methyl p-tolyl sulfone**
$CH_3C_6H_4SO_2CH_3$ M.W. 170.23 m.p. 87-88°

NUJOL MULL

C

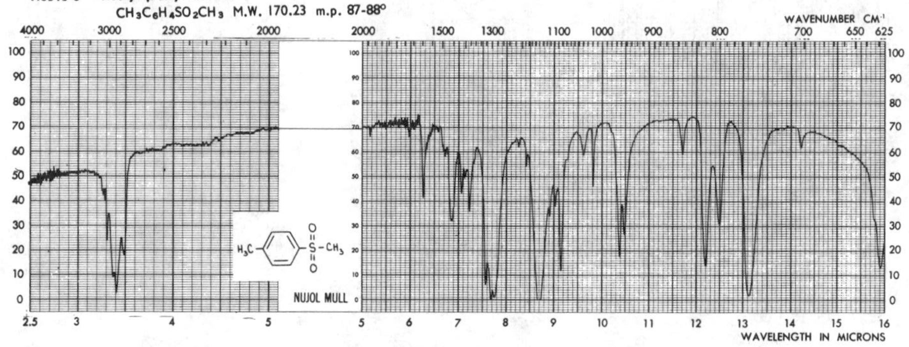

18,432-2
p-Methoxyphenyl methyl sulfone, 95%
$CH_3OC_6H_4SO_2CH_3$
M.W. 186.23 m.p. 116-119°

NUJOL MULL

D

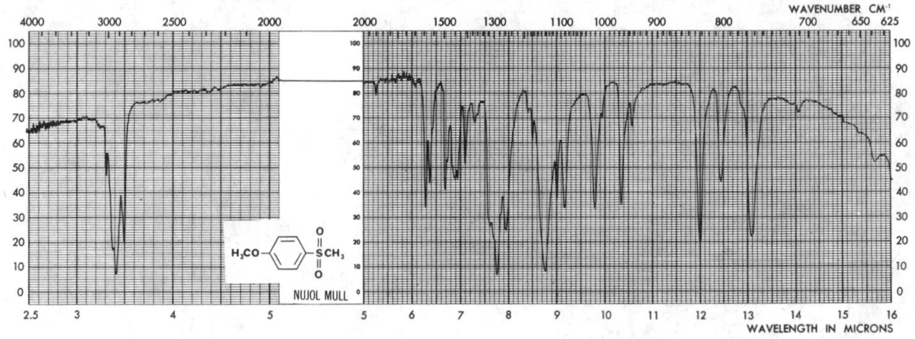

13,961-0 **(Methylsulfonyl)(p-toluenesulfonyl)methane**
$CH_3C_6H_4SO_2CH_2SO_2CH_3$ M.W. 248.32 m.p. 160-163° ....

E

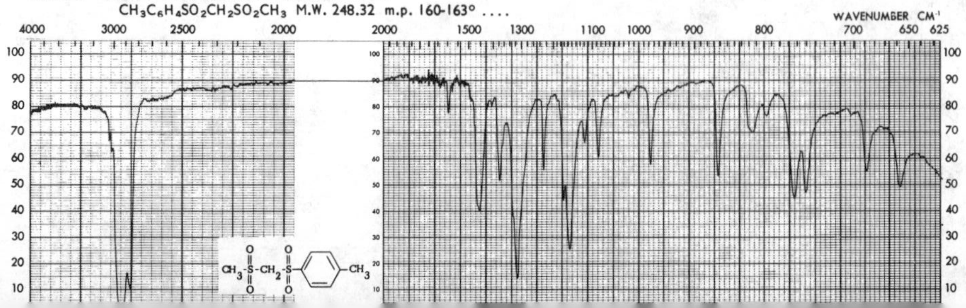

18,438-1
1-(p-Tolylsulfonyl)-2-propanone, 98%
$CH_3C_6H_4SO_2CH_2COCH_3$
M.W. 212.27 m.p. 52-54° Beil. 6,421

MELT

F

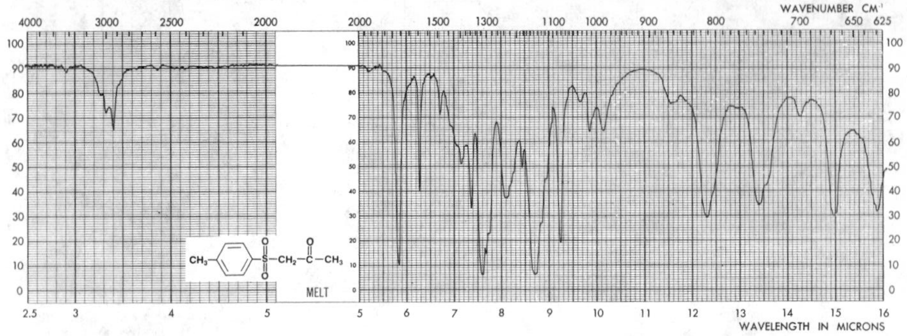

18,433-0
p-Fluorophenyl methyl sulfone, 98%
$FC_6H_4SO_2CH_3$
M.W. 174.19 m.p. 76-79°

NUJOL MULL

G

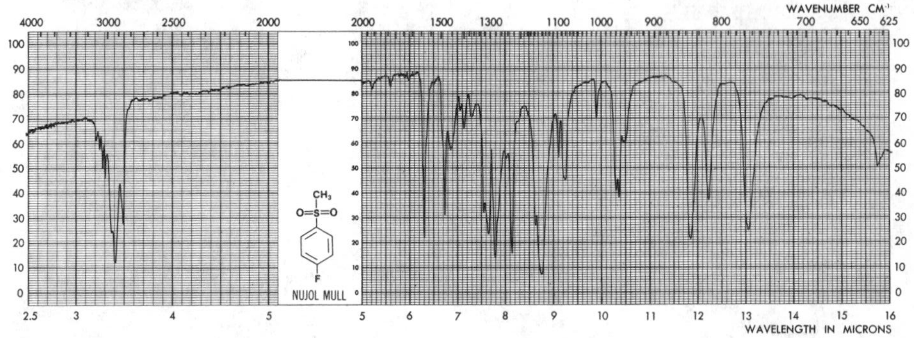

14,338-3 **p-Hexadecylsulfonylaniline**
$CH_3(CH_2)_{15}SO_2C_6H_4NH_2$ M.W. 381.63
m.p. 115-117° ....

NUJOL MULL

H

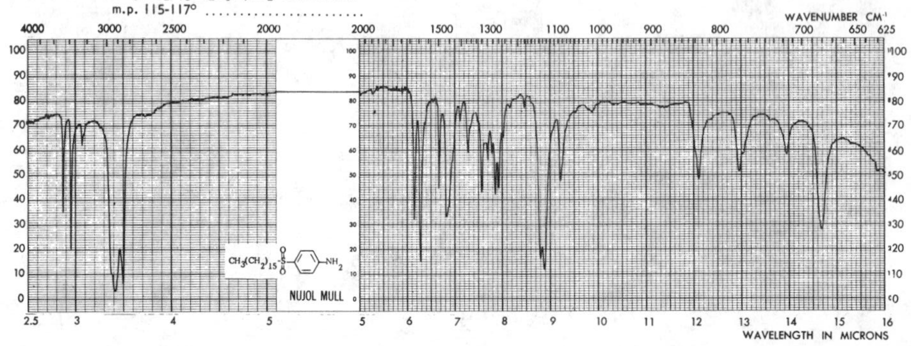

13,038-9 **4-(Methylsulfonyl)-phenylhydrazine**
$CH_3SO_2C_6H_4NHNH_2$ M.W. 186.23
m.p. 134-135.5° ....

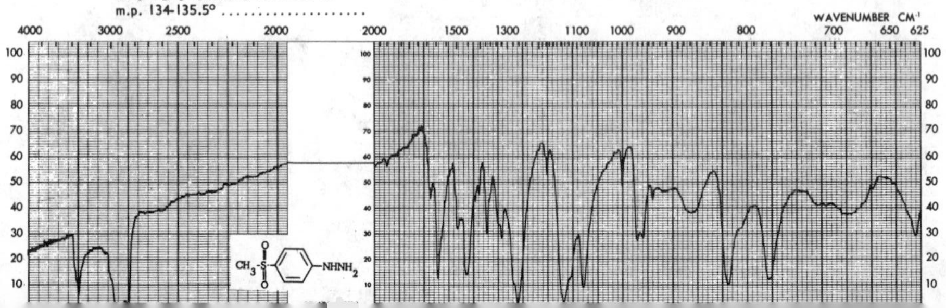

A

$F_2CHSO_2C_6H_4NHNH_2$ M.W. 222.22
m.p. 75-77°

B

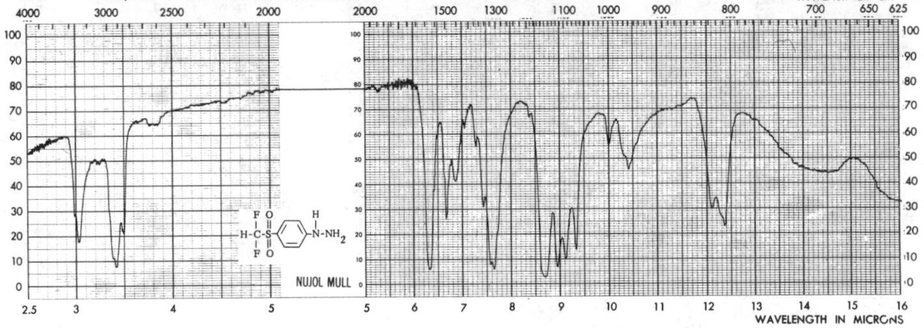

13,823-1 **p-Chlorophenyl 2-chloro-1,1,2-trifluoroethyl sulfone**
$ClC_6H_4SO_2CF_2CH(F)Cl$ M.W. 293.09
m.p. 55-57°

C

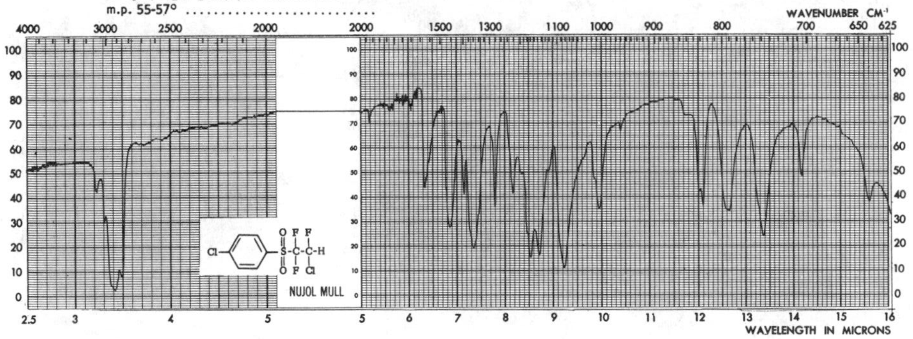

18,820-4
Tosylmethyl isocyanide [(*p*-tolylsulfonyl)methyl isocyanide, TosMIC]
$CH_3C_6H_4SO_2CH_2NC$ FW 195.24 mp 114-115°
Fieser 4,514 5,684 6,600 7,377 Disp. C

D

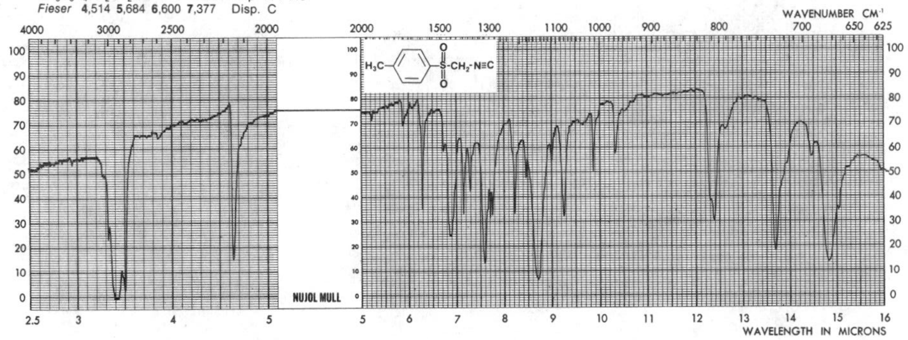

12,465-6 **p-Toluenesulfonyl isocyanate**
$CH_3C_6H_4SO_2NCO$ M.W. 197.21 n_D^{20} 1.5357
b.p. 144°/10 mm.

E

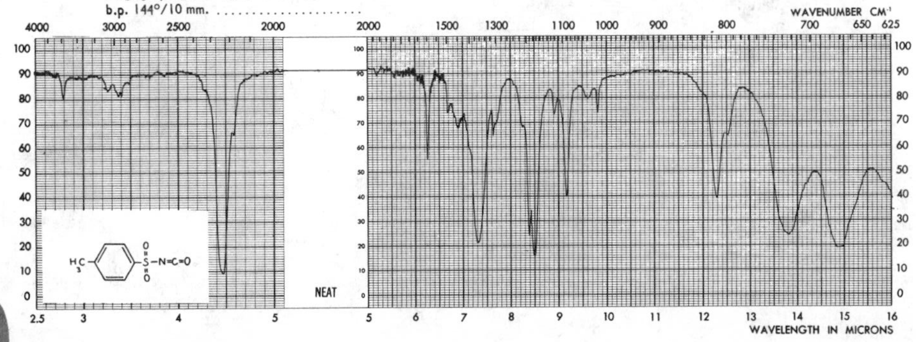

m.p. 268-271°

F

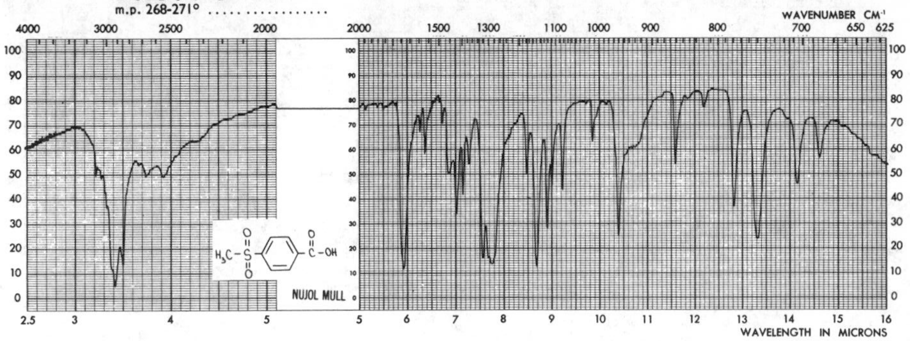

17,987-6
2-Chloro-4-(methylsulfonyl)-aniline
$ClC_6H_3(SO_2CH_3)NH_2$
M.W. 205.66 m.p. 195-197°

G

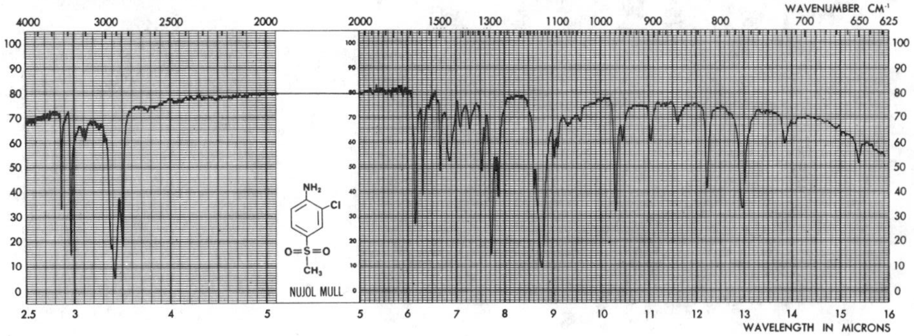

14,082-1 **5-Chloro-2-(n-hexadecylsulfonyl)-aniline**
$CH_3(CH_2)_{15}SO_2C_6H_3(Cl)NH_2$ M.W. 416.07

H

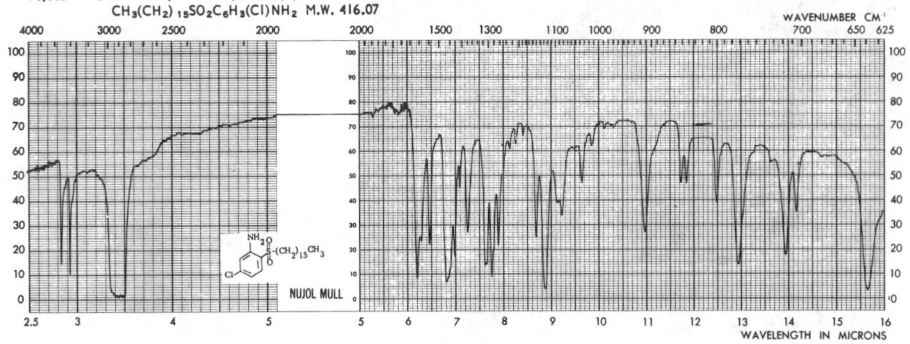

14,081-3 **4-Methylsulfonyl-3-nitrobenzoic acid**
$CH_3SO_2C_6H_3(NO_2)CO_2H$ M.W. 245.21
m.p. 274° (dec.)

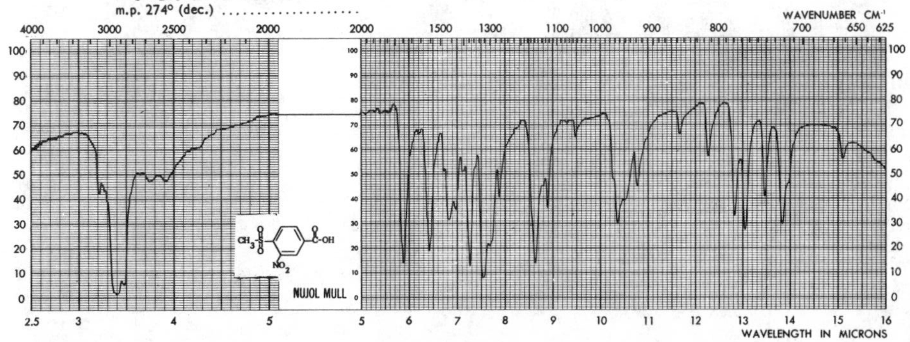

A

14,430-4 **2,4-Bis-(methylsulfonyl)-1-chlorobenzene**
$(CH_3SO_2)_2C_6H_3Cl$ M.W. 268.74 m.p. 178-180°

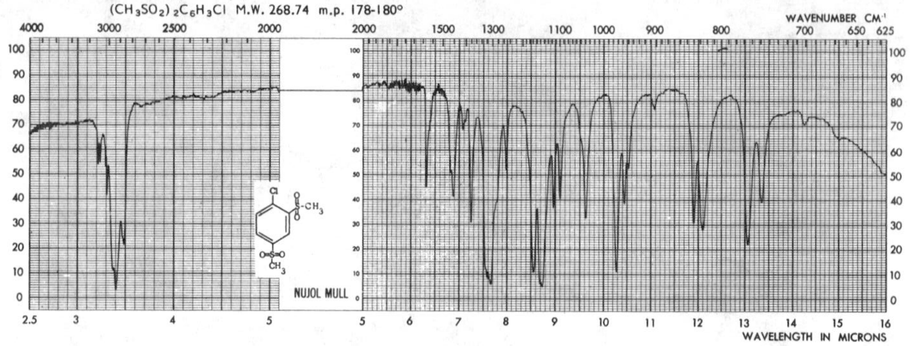

NUJOL MULL

B

14,431-2 **2,4-Bis-(methylsulfonyl)-phenylhydrazine**
$(CH_3SO_2)_2C_6H_3NHNH_2$ M.W. 264.32
m.p. 180-183°

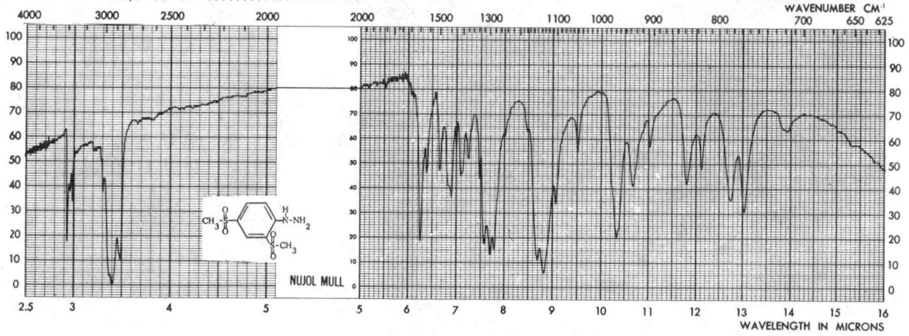

NUJOL MULL

C

19,728-9
2,6-Dichloro-4-(methylsulfonyl)aniline, 98%
$Cl_2C_6H_2(SO_2CH_3)NH_2$ FW 240.11 mp 155-160°
Disp. C

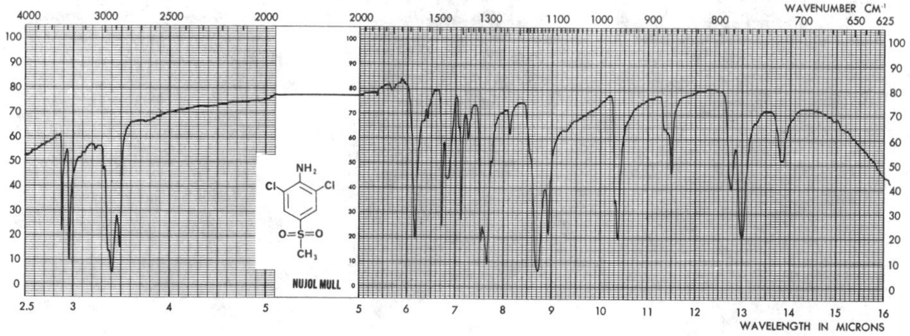

NUJOL MULL

D

P3535-9 **Phenyl sulfone**
$(C_6H_5)_2SO_2$ M.W. 218.27 m.p. 124-127°

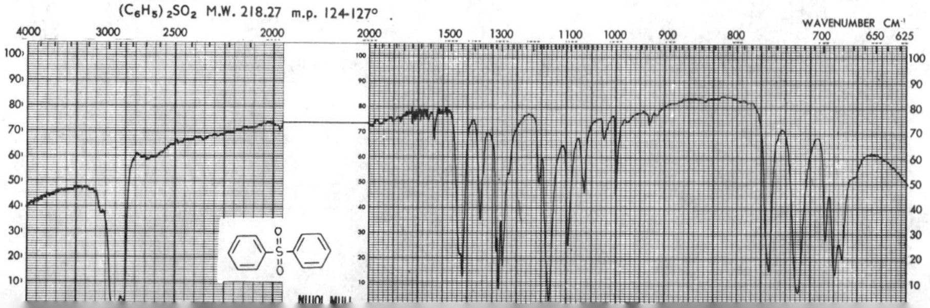

NUJOL MULL

E

16,184-5
Phenyl p-tolyl sulfone, 98%
$CH_3C_6H_4SO_2C_6H_5$
M.W. 232.3 m.p. 127-129° Beil. 6,418

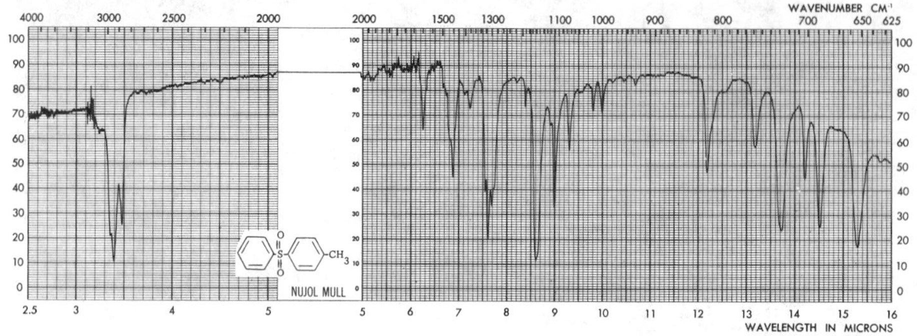

NUJOL MULL

F

12,444-3 **p-Fluorophenyl phenyl sulfone**
$FC_6H_4SO_2C_6H_5$ M.W. 236.27
m.p. 110-112°

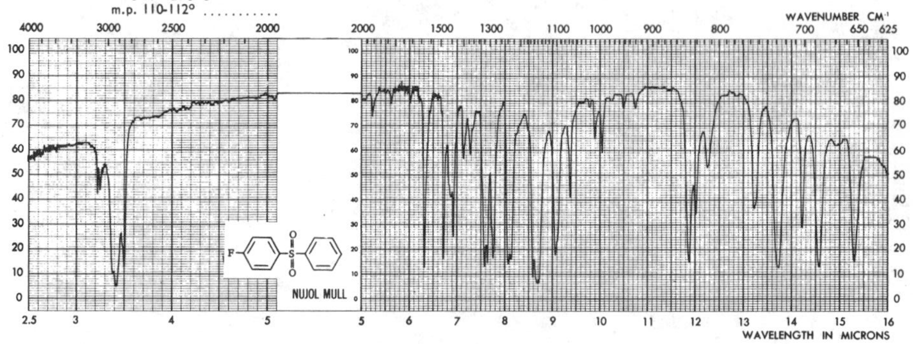

NUJOL MULL

G

19,411-5
p-**Chlorophenyl phenyl sulfone,** 97+%
$ClC_6H_4SO_2C_6H_5$ FW 252.72 mp 90-94°
Beil. 6(1),149 Disp. C

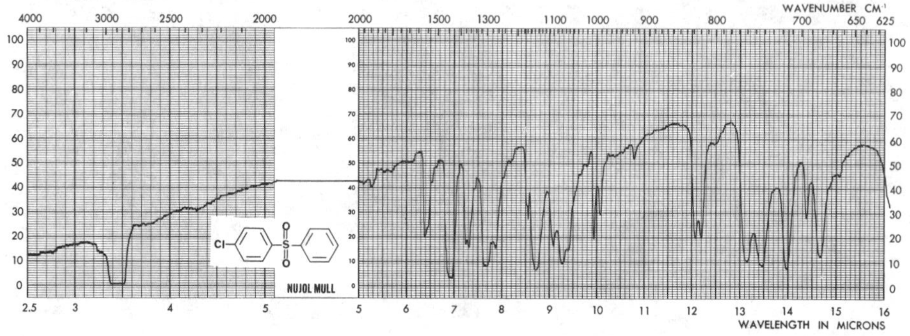

NUJOL MULL

H

F1514-5 **4-Fluorophenyl sulfone** [bis-(p-fluorophenyl) sulfone]
$(FC_6H_4)_2SO_2$ M.W. 254.26 m.p. 98-99°

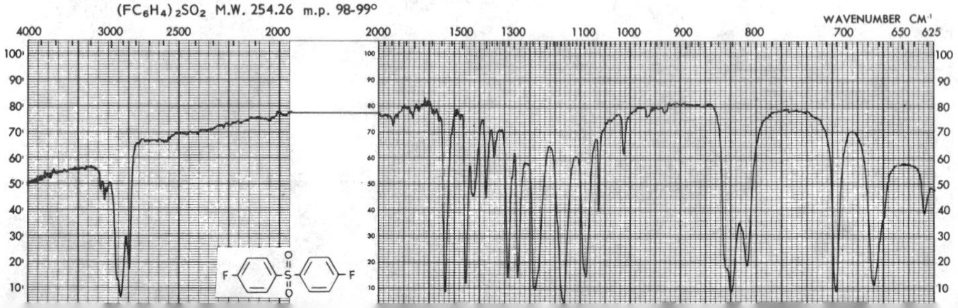

WAVENUMBER CM⁻¹ — WAVELENGTH IN MICRONS

A

$FC_6H_4SO_2C_6H_4CH_3$ M.W. 250.29
m.p. 92-96°

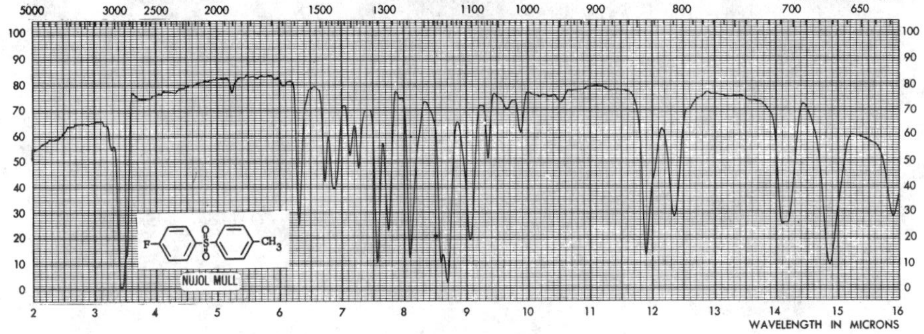

NUJOL MULL

B

13,594-1 p-Chlorophenyl p-fluorophenyl sulfone
$ClC_6H_4SO_2C_6H_4F$ M.W. 270.71
m.p. 109-112°

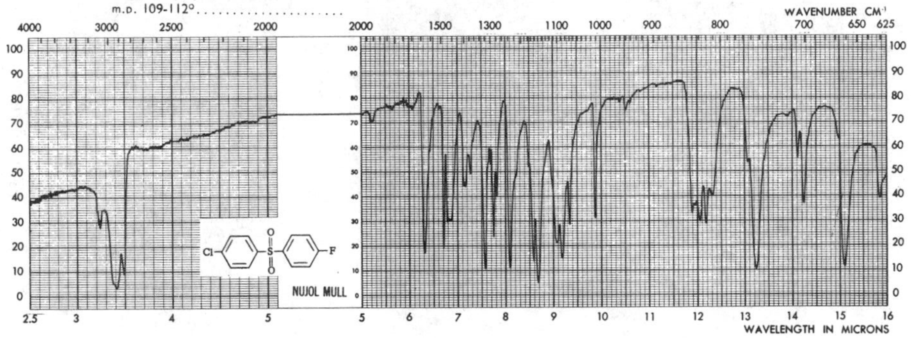

NUJOL MULL

C

13,819-3 p-Chlorophenyl p-tolyl sulfone
$ClC_6H_4SO_2C_6H_4CH_3$ M.W. 266.75
m.p. 122-124°

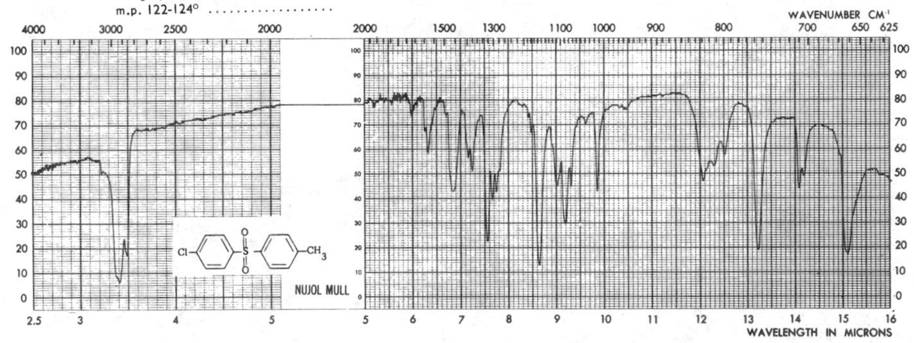

NUJOL MULL

D

15,137-8 4-Chlorophenyl sulfone [bis-(p-chlorophenyl) sulfone]
$(ClC_6H_4)_2SO_2$ M.W. 287.17
m.p. 145.5-148.5°

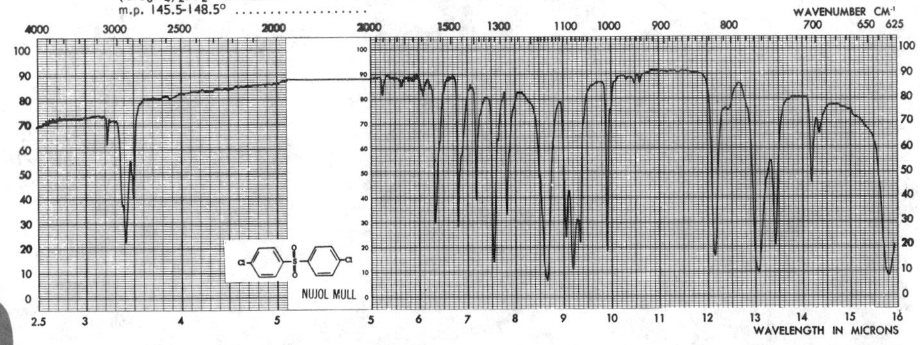

NUJOL MULL

E

$CH_3OC_6H_4SO_2C_6H_4F$ M.W. 266.29
m.p. 96-98.5°

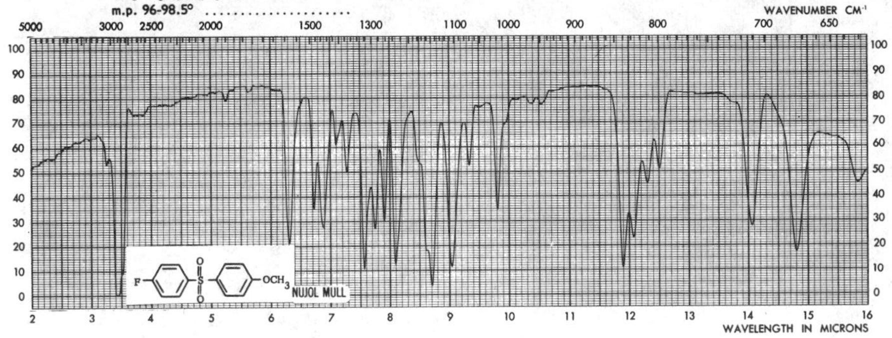

NUJOL MULL

F

10,303-9 4,4'-Sulfonyldiphenol
$O_2S(C_6H_4OH)_2$ M.W. 250.27 m.p. 243-247°

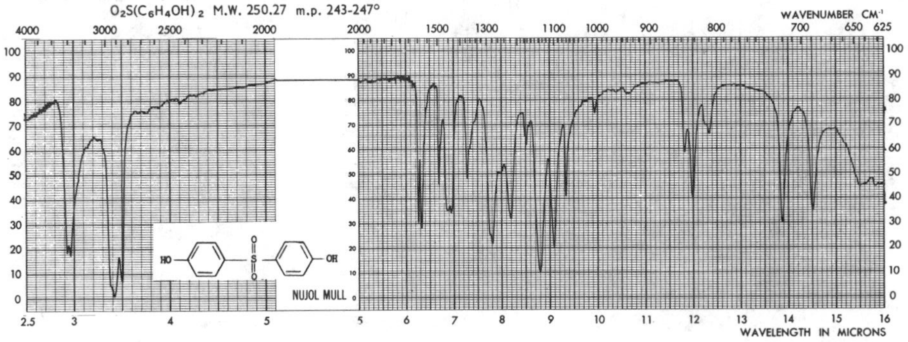

NUJOL MULL

G

19,441-7
4,4'-Sulfonylbis(2,6-dibromophenol), 98%
$O_2S[C_6H_2(Br)_2OH]_2$ FW 565.88 mp 289-292°
Beil. 6,865 Disp. C

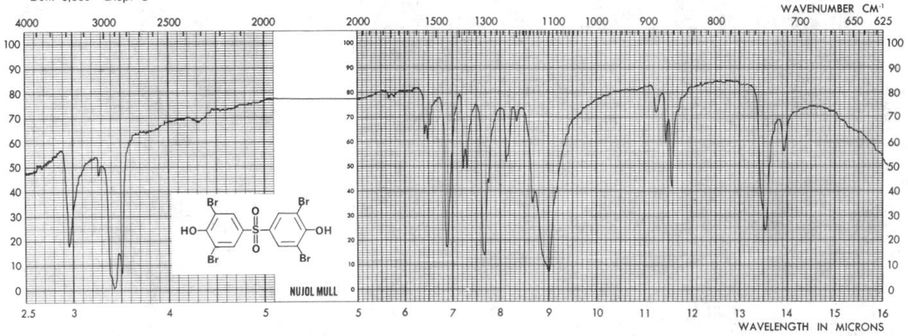

NUJOL MULL

H

13,820-7 4-(p-Chlorophenylsulfonyl)-benzoic acid
$ClC_6H_4SO_2C_6H_4CO_2H$ M.W. 296.73
m.p. 273-278°

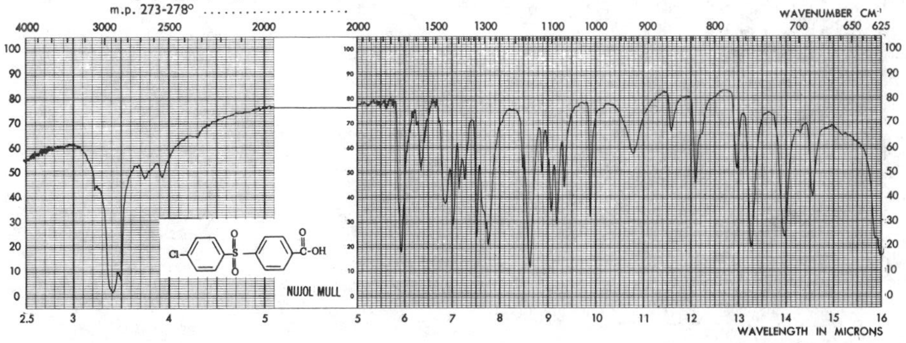

NUJOL MULL

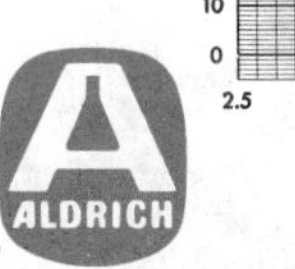

A

16,329-5
4,4'-Sulfonyldibenzoic acid, 98% (diphenyl sulfone 4,4'-dicarboxylic acid)
$O_2S(C_6H_4CO_2H)_2$
M.W. 306.29 m.p. >305° Beil. 10,186

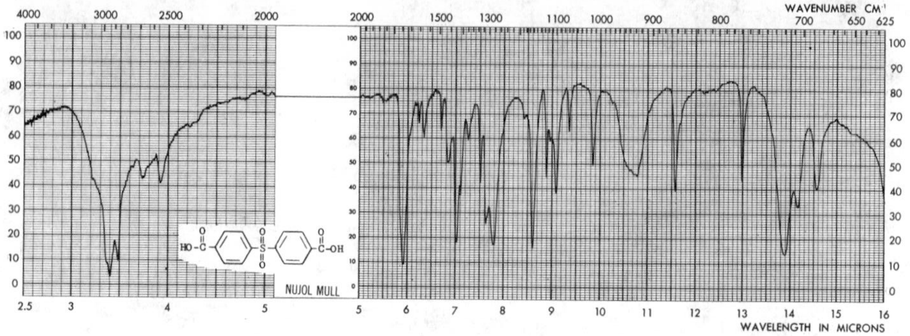

NUJOL MULL

B

12,014-6 **N-[4-(p-Chlorophenylsulfonyl)-phenyl]-glycine**
$ClC_6H_4SO_2C_6H_4NHCH_2CO_2H$ M.W. 325.77 m.p. 223-226°

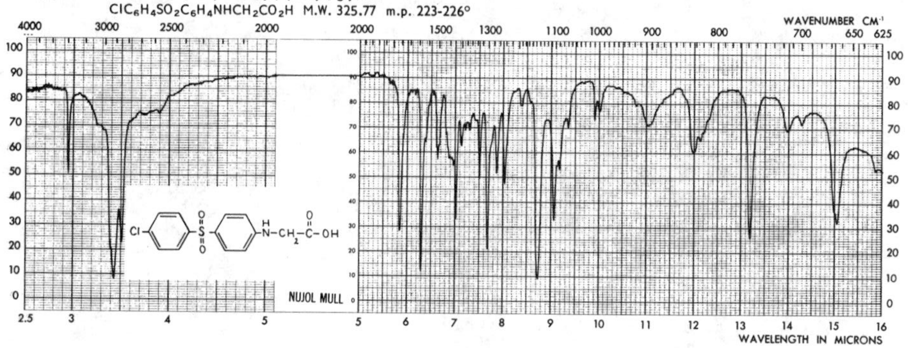

NUJOL MULL

C

A7480-7 **p-Aminophenyl sulfone** (dapsone, DDS, 4,4'-sulfonyldianiline)
$(H_2NC_6H_4)_2SO_2$ M.W. 248.31
m.p. 175-177°

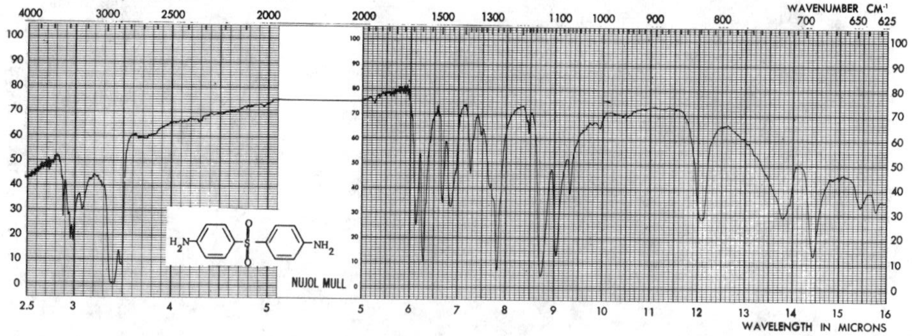

NUJOL MULL

D

A7460-2 **m-Aminophenyl sulfone** (3,3'-sulfonyldianiline)
$(H_2NC_6H_4)_2SO_2$ M.W. 248.31
m.p. 150-153°

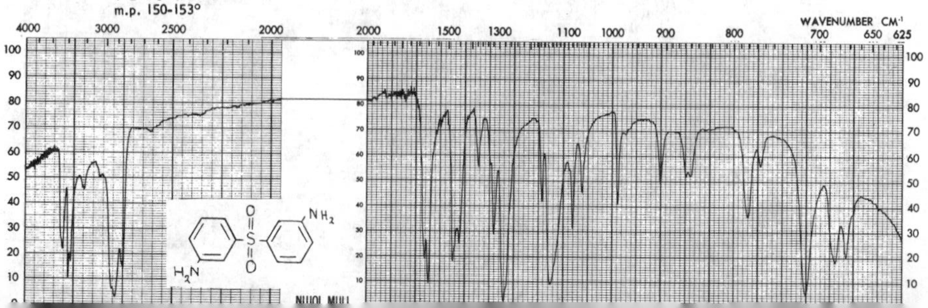

NUJOL MULL

E

14,177-1 **2,4,4',5-Tetrachlorodiphenyl sulfone**
$Cl_3C_6H_2SO_2C_6H_4Cl$ M.W. 356.06
m.p. 142-145°

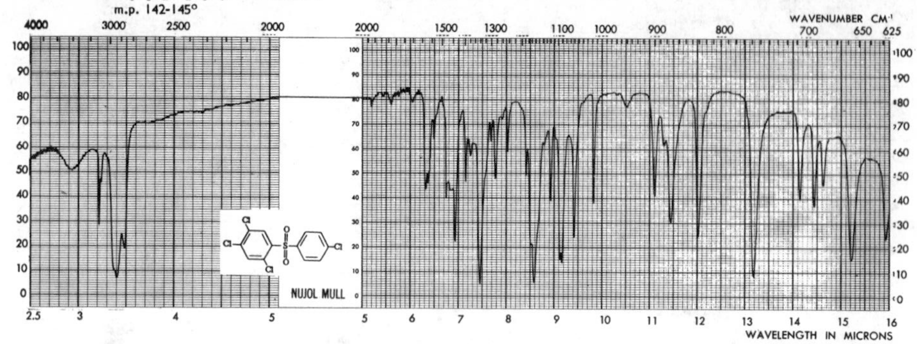

NUJOL MULL

F

14,000-7 **4-Fluoro-3-nitrophenyl 3-nitrophenyl sulfone**
$FC_6H_3(NO_2)SO_2C_6H_4NO_2$ M.W. 326.26
m.p. 163-165°

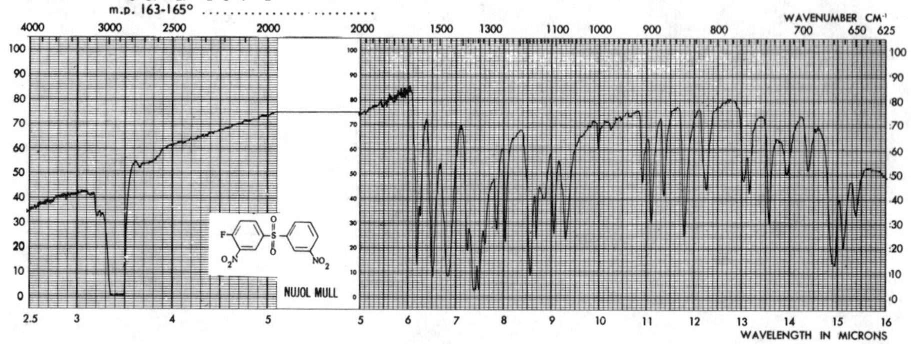

NUJOL MULL

G

F1170-0 **4-Fluoro-3-nitrophenyl sulfone** [bis-(4-fluoro-3-nitrophenyl) sulfone]
$[FC_6H_3(NO_2)]_2SO_2$ M.W. 344.25
m.p. 193-194°

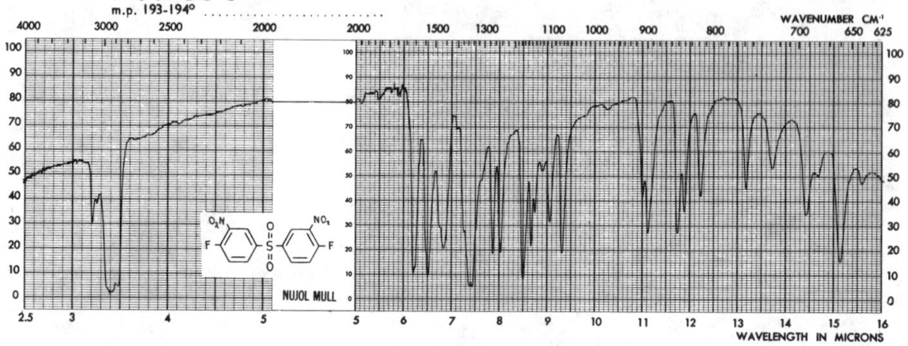

NUJOL MULL

H

C6155-0 **4-Chloro-3-nitrophenyl sulfone** [bis-(4-chloro-3-nitrophenyl) sulfone]
$[ClC_6H_3(NO_2)]_2SO_2$ M.W. 377.18
m.p. 199-202°

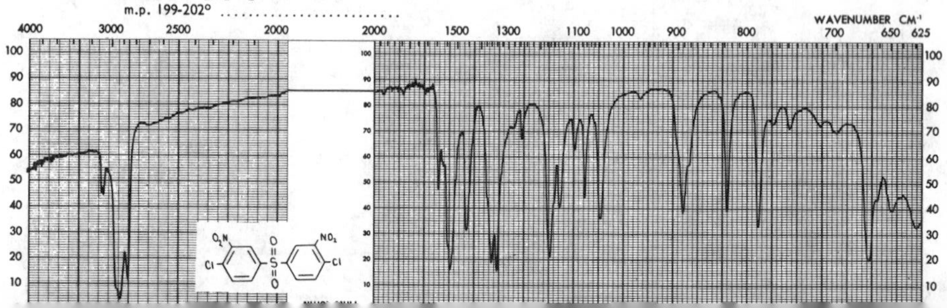

A

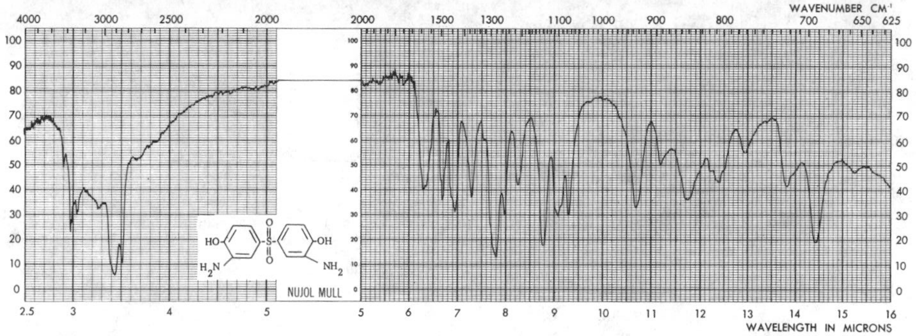

16,330-9
4,4'-Sulfonylbis-(methyl benzoate), 99% (dimethyl diphenyl sulfone 4,4'-dicarboxylate)
$O_2S(C_6H_4CO_2CH_3)_2$
M.W. 334.35 m.p. 240-243° (dec.) Beil. **10**(2),109

B

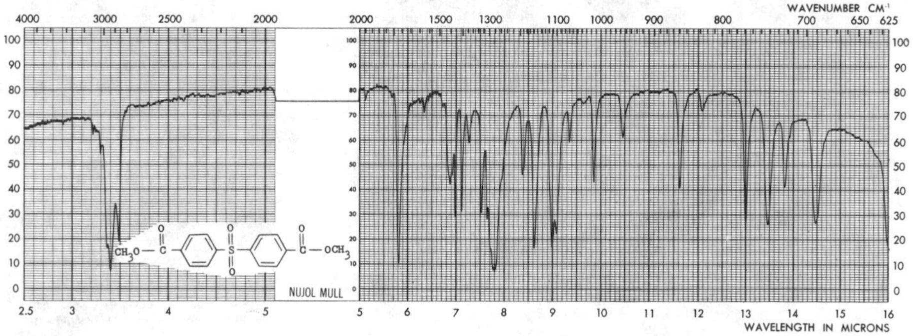

A200-9 4-Acetamidobenzenesulfinic acid
$CH_3CONHC_6H_4SO_2H$ M.W. 199.23
m.p. 145° (dec.)

C

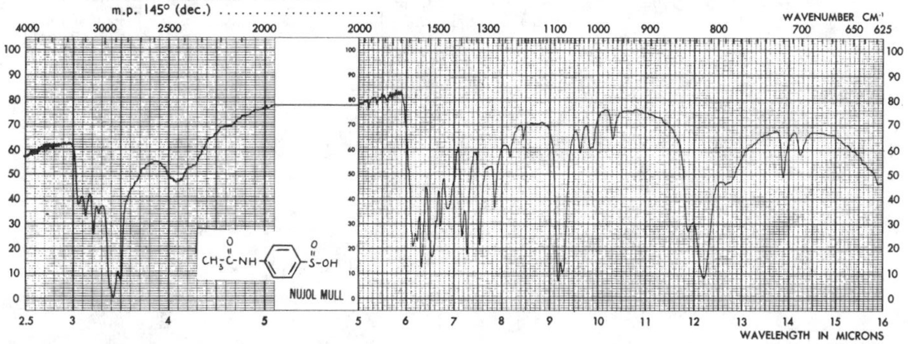

15,809-7
3-Acetamido-4-methoxybenzenesulfinic acid hydrate, 97%
$CH_3CONHC_6H_3(OCH_3)SO_2H \cdot xH_2O$
M.W. 229.25 m.p. 116 - 118° (dec.)

D

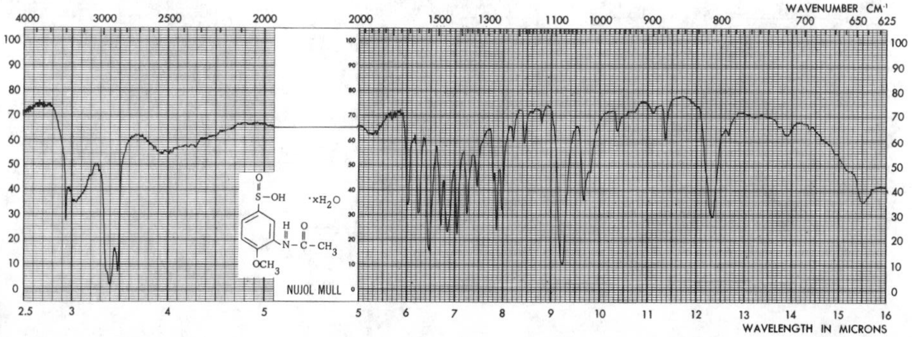

m.p. > 345° (dec.)

E

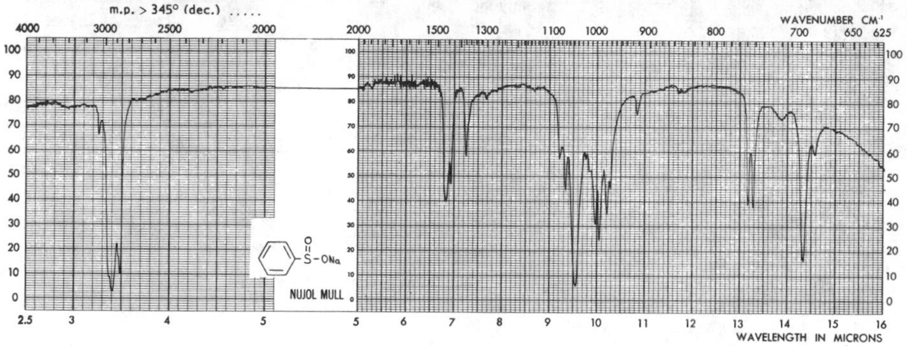

T3580-7 p-Toluenesulfinic acid, sodium salt
$CH_3C_6H_4SO_2Na$ M.W. 214.22
m.p. > 300°

F

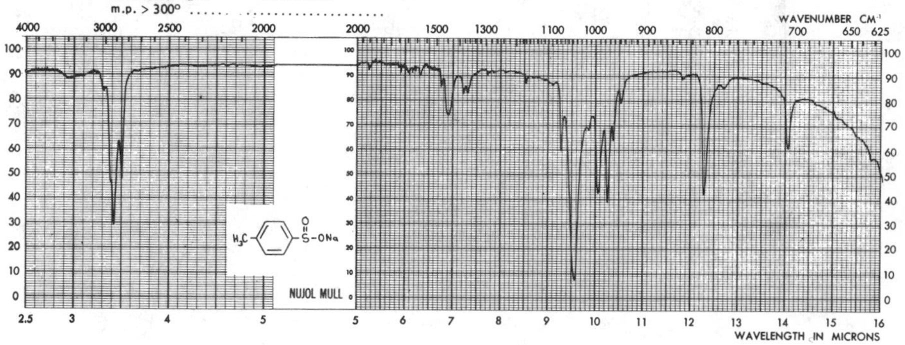

13,507-0 Benzenesulfonic acid, tech., 90%
$C_6H_5SO_3H$ M.W. 158.18

G

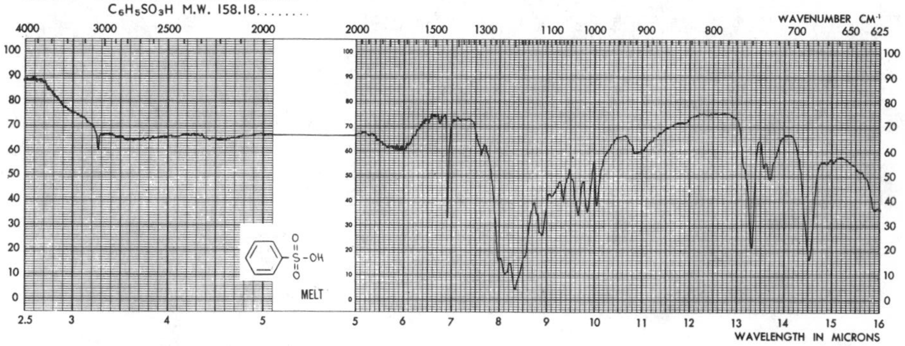

21,300-4
Benzeneseleninic acid, 99%
$C_6H_5Se(O)OH$ FW 189.07 mp 121-124°
Disp. BB

H

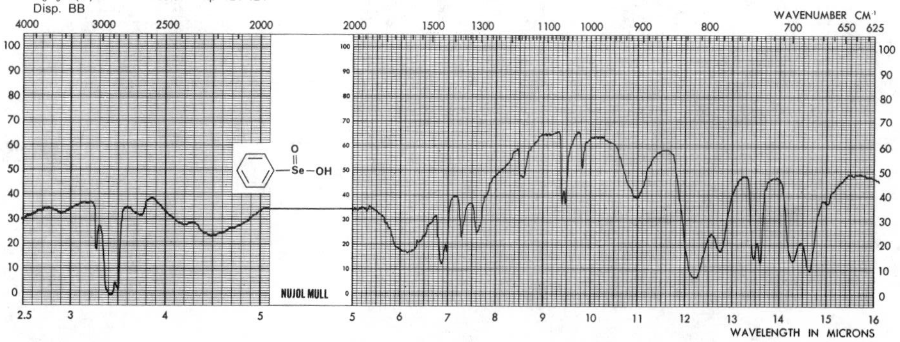

A

T3592-0 p-Toluenesulfonic acid
$CH_3C_6H_4SO_3H$
m.p. 103-106°

B

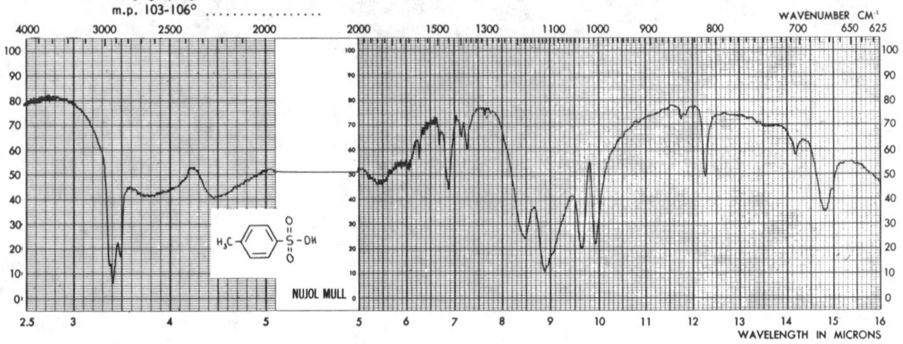

11,273-9 Sulfanilic acid
$4\text{-}(H_2N)C_6H_4SO_3H$ M.W. 173.19 m.p. > 360°

C

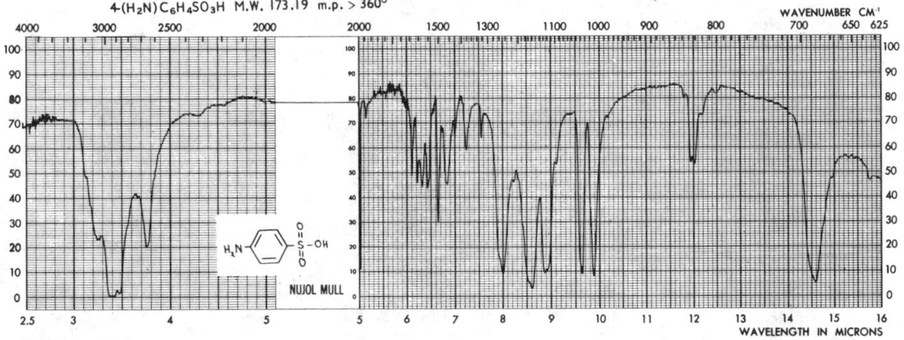

21,150-8
p-(Dimethylamino)benzenesulfonic acid, sodium salt,
tech., 90+% (N,N-dimethylsulfanilic acid, sodium salt)
$(CH_3)_2NC_6H_4SO_3Na$ FW 223.23 mp >300°
Beil. 14(3),2023 Disp. D

D

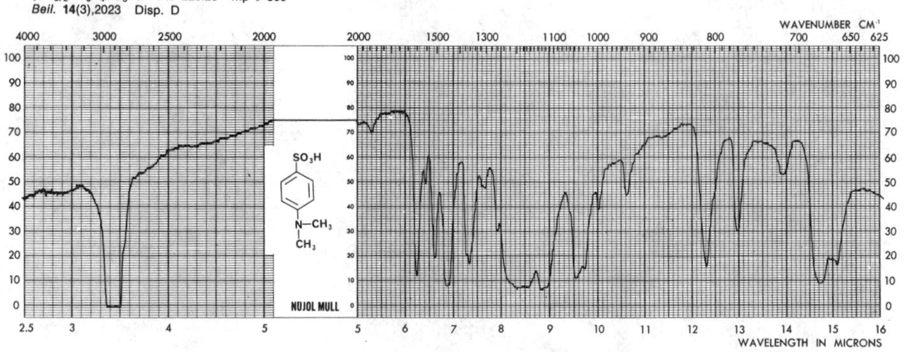

A8680-5 Aniline-2-sulfonic acid (o-aminobenzenesulfonic acid), **tech.**
$H_2NC_6H_4SO_3H$ M.W. 173.19 m.p. > 320°

E

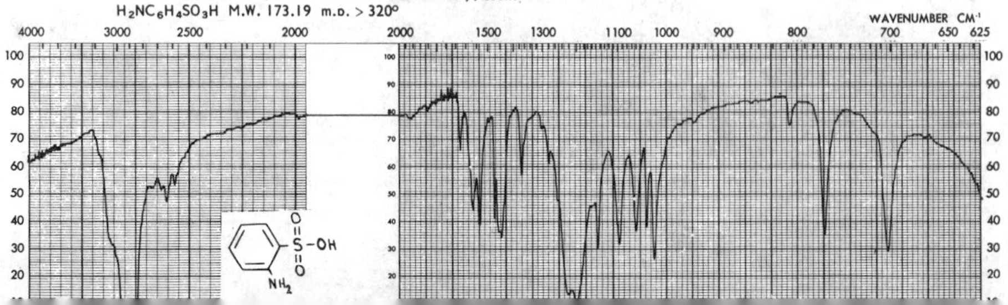

21,876-6
6-Amino-m-toluenesulfonic acid, 99%
$H_2NC_6H_3(CH_3)SO_3H$ FW 187.22 mp >300°
Beil. 14,723 Disp. C

F

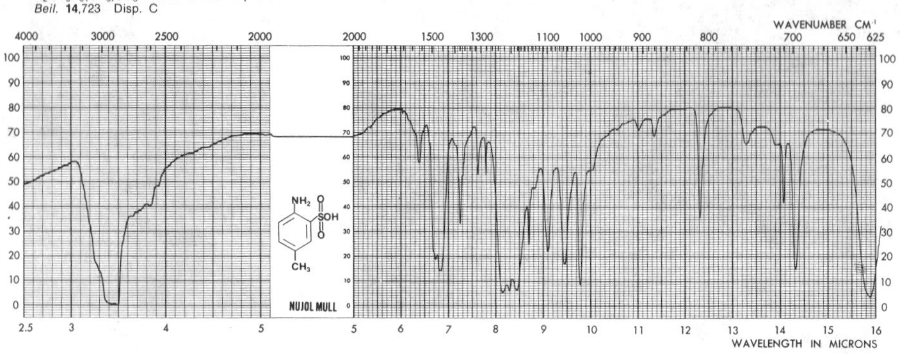

10,255-5 4-Amino-m-toluenesulfonic acid (3-methylsulfanilic acid), **tech.**
$H_2NC_6H_3(CH_3)SO_3H$ M.W. 187.22
m.p. > 320°

G

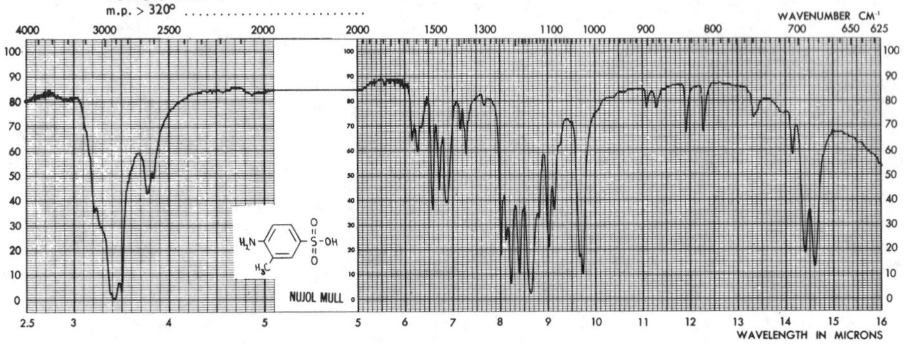

12,651-9 N,4-Dimethylmetanilic acid [3-(methylamino)-p-toluenesulfonic acid], **tech.**
$CH_3C_6H_3(NHCH_3)SO_3H$ M.W. 201.25
m.p. > 350°

H

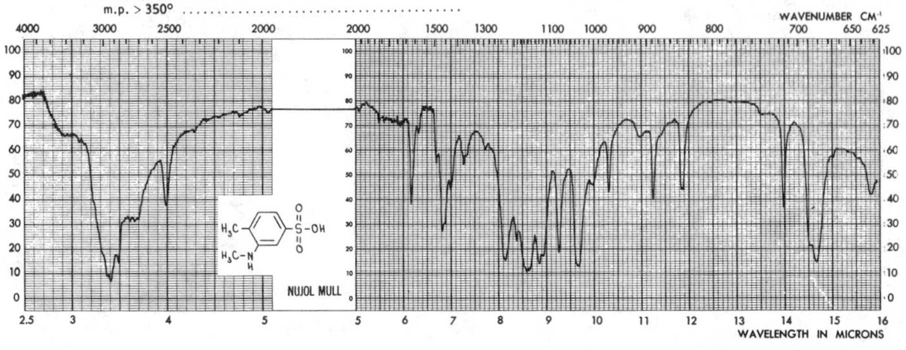

C2280-6 2-Chloroaniline-5-sulfonic acid (4-chlorometanilic acid), **tech.**
$ClC_6H_3(NH_2)SO_3H$ M.W. 207.64 m.p. > 300°

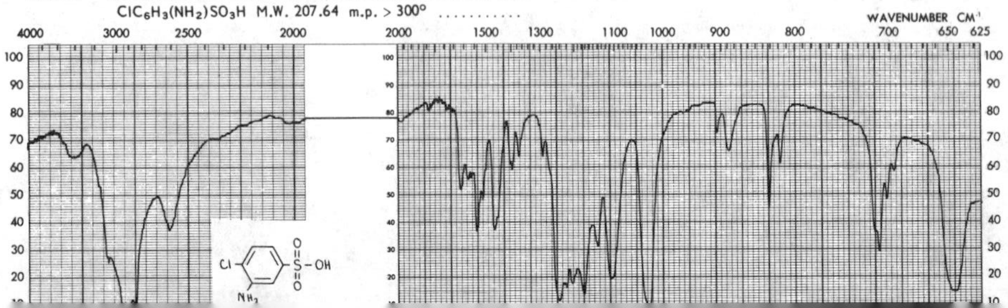

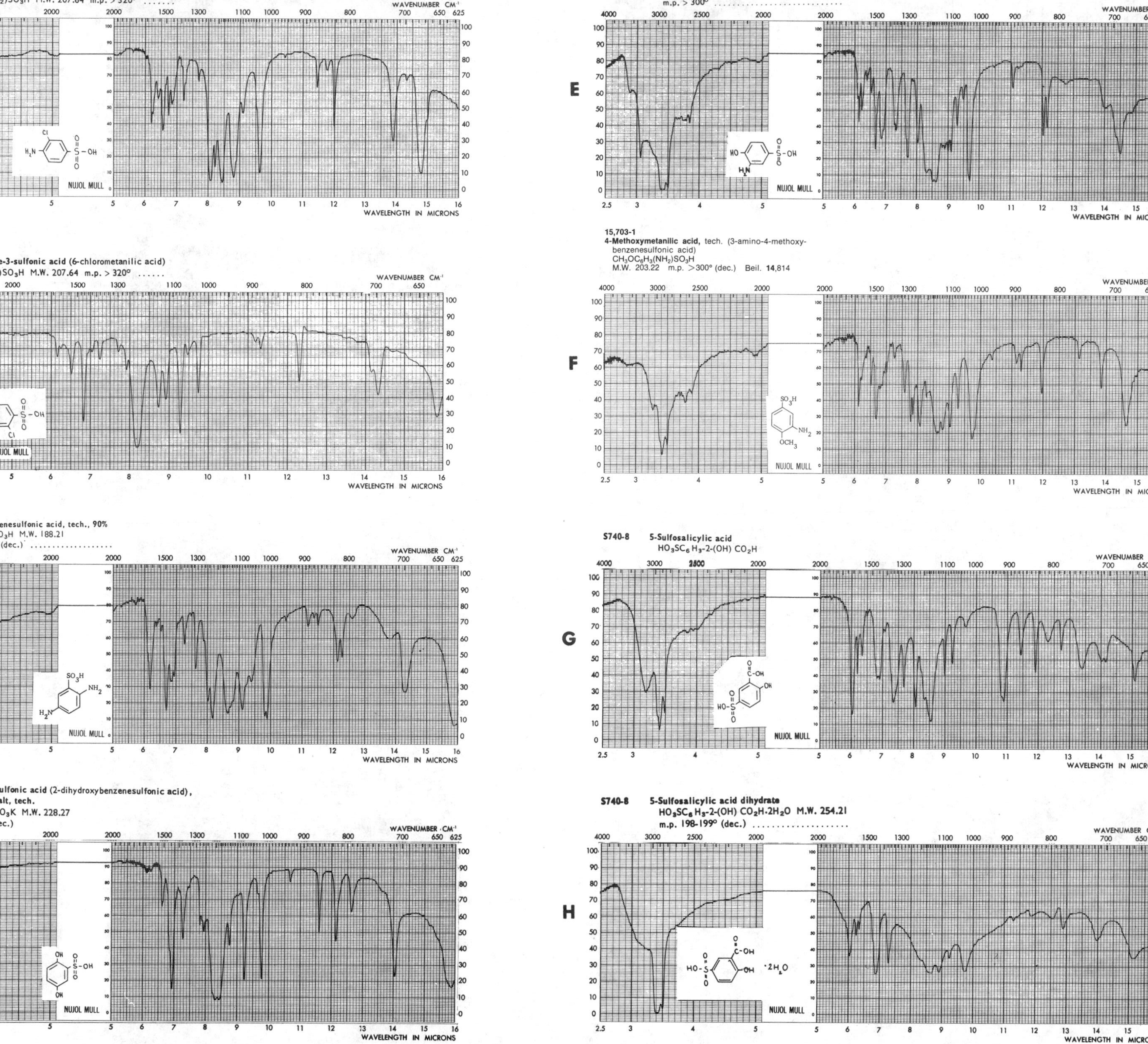

$ClC_6H_3(NH_2)SO_3H$ M.W. 207.64 m.p. > 320°
A
NUJOL MULL
C2300-4 4-Chloroaniline-3-sulfonic acid (6-chlorometanilic acid)
$ClC_6H_3(NH_2)SO_3H$ M.W. 207.64 m.p. > 320°
B
NUJOL MULL
15,350-8 2,5-Diaminobenzenesulfonic acid, tech., 90%
$(H_2N)_2C_6H_3SO_3H$ M.W. 188.21
m.p. 298-300° (dec.)
C
NUJOL MULL
H1840-2 Hydroquinonesulfonic acid (2-dihydroxybenzenesulfonic acid), potassium salt, tech.
$(HO)_2C_6H_3SO_3K$ M.W. 228.27
m.p. 251° (dec.)
D
NUJOL MULL
m.p. > 300°
E
NUJOL MULL
15,703-1
4-Methoxymetanilic acid, tech. (3-amino-4-methoxybenzenesulfonic acid)
$CH_3OC_6H_3(NH_2)SO_3H$
M.W. 203.22 m.p. >300° (dec.) Beil. 14,814
F
NUJOL MULL
S740-8 5-Sulfosalicylic acid
$HO_3SC_6H_3$-2-(OH) CO_2H
G
NUJOL MULL
S740-8 5-Sulfosalicylic acid dihydrate
$HO_3SC_6H_3$-2-(OH) $CO_2H \cdot 2H_2O$ M.W. 254.21
m.p. 198-199° (dec.)
H
NUJOL MULL
WAVENUMBER CM⁻¹
WAVELENGTH IN MICRONS
ALDRICH

A

12,963-1 **2-Mesitylenesulfonic acid** (2,4,6-trimethylbenzenesulfonic acid) **dihydrate**
$(CH_3)_3C_6H_2SO_3H \cdot 2H_2O$ M.W. 236.29 m.p. 70-72° ....

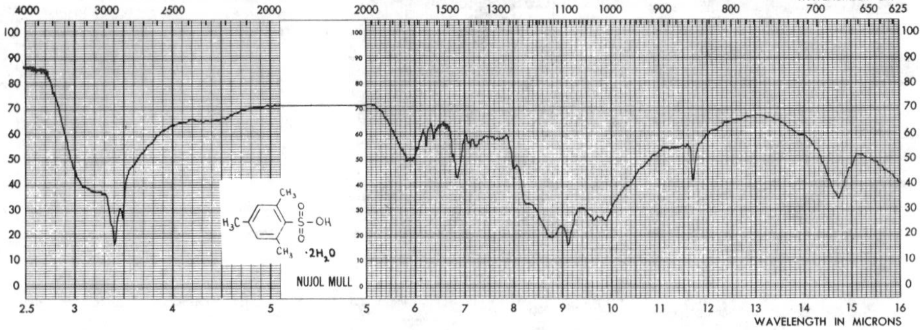

NUJOL MULL

B

11,729-3 **6-Amino-4-chloro-m-toluenesulfonic acid**
$H_2NC_6H_2(Cl)(CH_3)SO_3H$ M.W. 221.66
m.p. > 300° ....

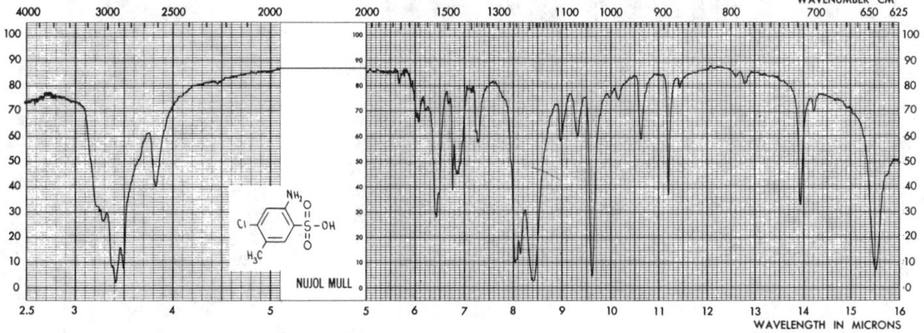

NUJOL MULL

C

13,685-9 **2-Amino-5-chloro-p-toluenesulfonic acid**
$H_2NC_6H_2(Cl)(CH_3)SO_3H$ M.W. 221.66 m.p. > 320°

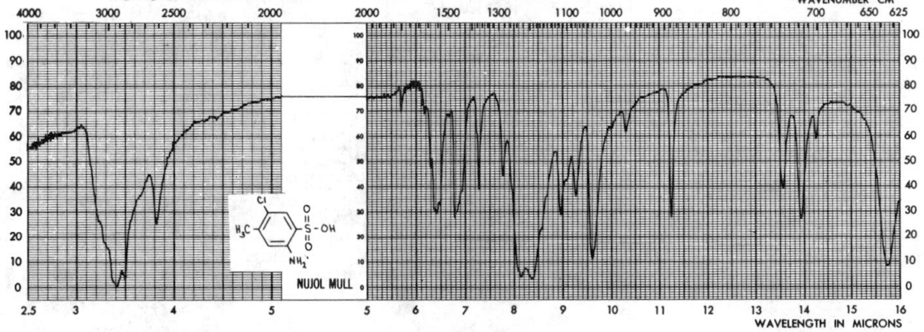

NUJOL MULL

D

17,299-5
Picrylsulfonic acid dihydrate, 97%
(2,4,6-trinitrobenzenesulfonic acid)
$(O_2N)_3C_6H_2SO_3H \cdot 2H_2O$ FW 329.20
mp 190° (dec.) *Beil.* **11**,80 Disp. C

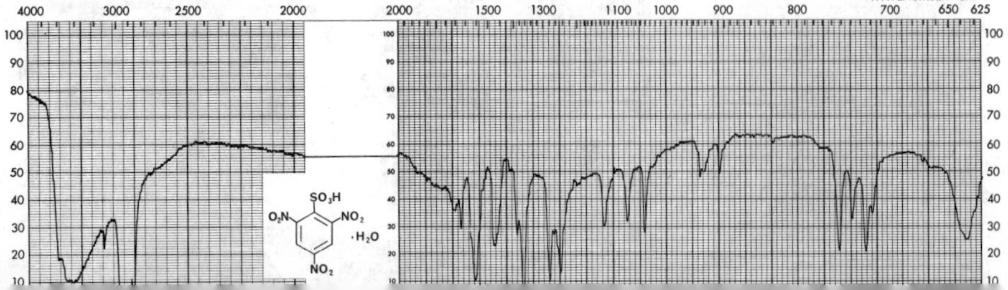

E

H3638-9 **2-Hydroxy-4-methoxybenzophenone-5-sulfonic acid** (5-benzoyl-4-hydroxy-2-methoxybenzenesulfonic acid)
$HOC_6H_2(OCH_3)(COC_6H_5)SO_3H$ M.W. 308.31 m.p. 121-123°

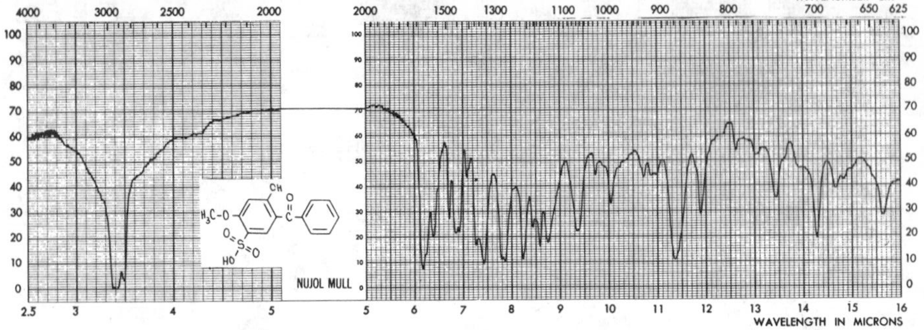

NUJOL MULL

F

16,179-9
4-Biphenylsulfonic acid, 96%
$C_6H_5C_6H_4SO_3H$
M.W. 234.27 m.p. 128° (dry) Beil. **11**,192
HYGROSCOPIC

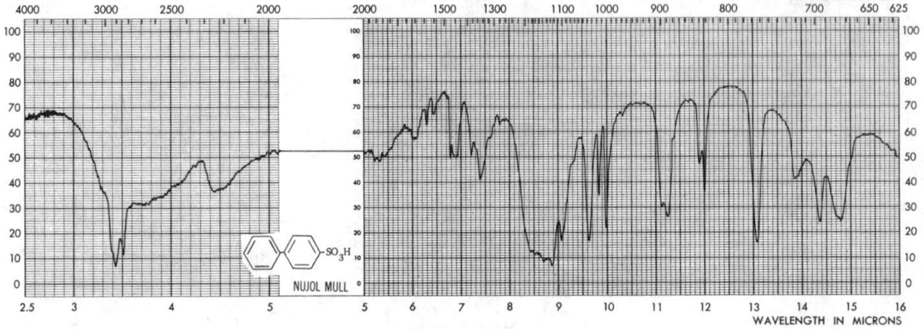

NUJOL MULL

G

18,634-1
1-Naphthalenesulfonic acid, 97%
$C_{10}H_7SO_3H$
M.W. 208.24 m.p. 77-79° Beil. **14**,936

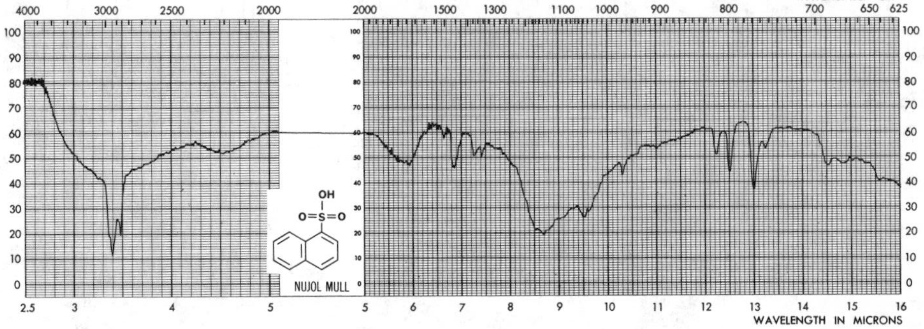

NUJOL MULL

H

10,058-7 **1-Amino-2-naphthalenesulfonic acid** (o-naphthionic acid)
$H_2NC_{10}H_6SO_3H$ M.W. 223.25 m.p. 275° (dec.) ......

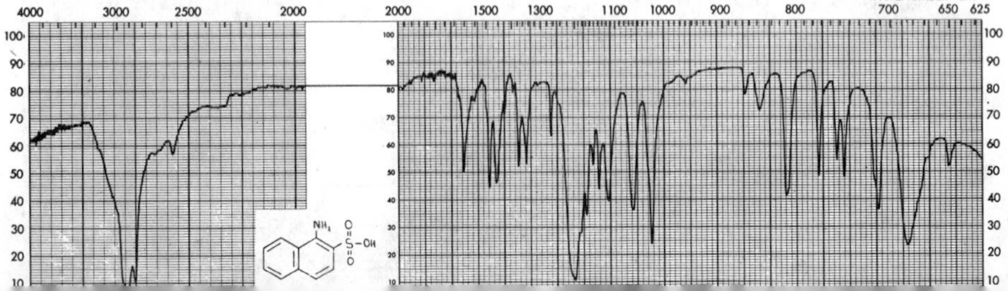

A

$H_2NC_{10}H_6SO_3H$ M.W. 223.25 m.p. > 330°

B

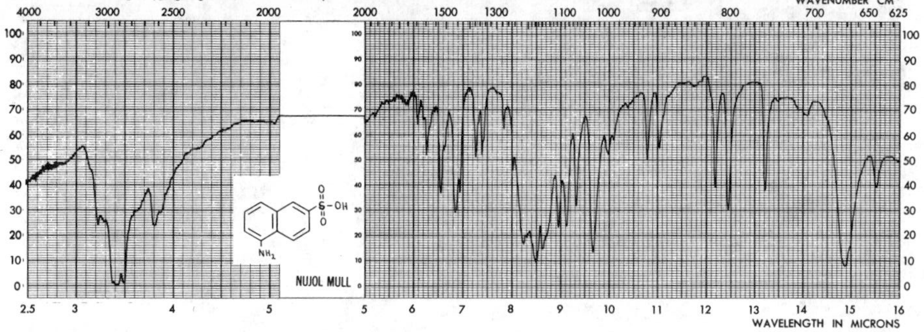

19,434-4
5-Dimethylamino-1-naphthalenesulfonic acid hydrate,
99+% (DNS)
$(CH_3)_2NC_{10}H_6SO_3H \cdot xH_2O$ FW 251.31
mp 320° (dec.) *Beil.* **14**,746 Disp. I

C

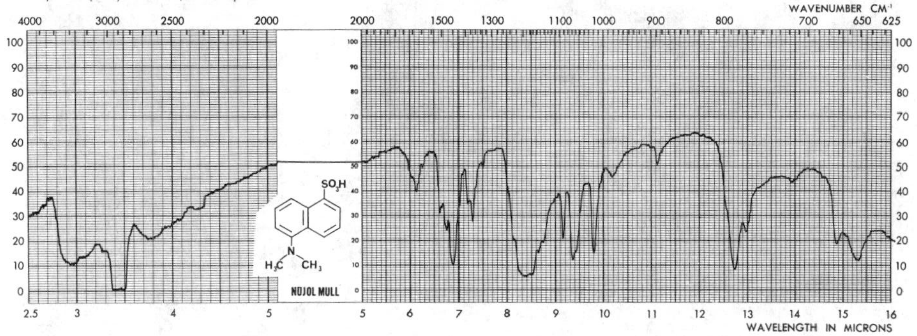

19,387-9
5-(2-Aminoethylamino)-1-naphthalenesulfonic acid,
99% (1,5-EDANS)
$H_2NCH_2CH_2NHC_{10}H_6SO_3H$ FW 266.32 mp >300°
Disp. C

D

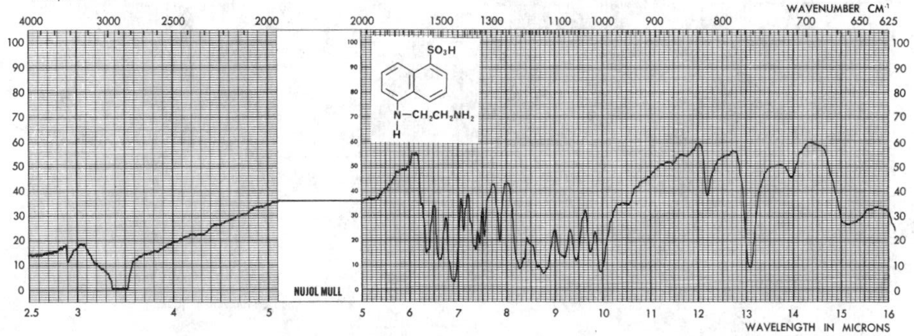

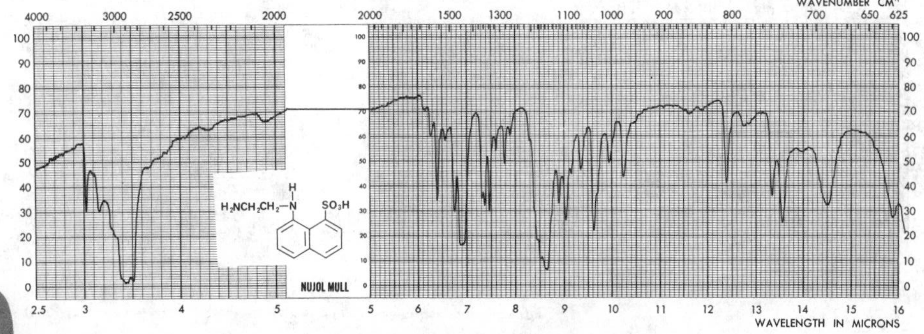

19,388-7
8-(2-Aminoethylamino)-1-naphthalenesulfonic acid,
99% (1,8-EDANS)
$H_2NCH_2CH_2NHC_{10}H_6SO_3H$ FW 266.32 mp >300°
Disp. C

E

$ICH_2CONHCH_2CH_2NHC_{10}H_6SO_3H$ FW 434.26
mp 226° (dec.) Disp. C

F

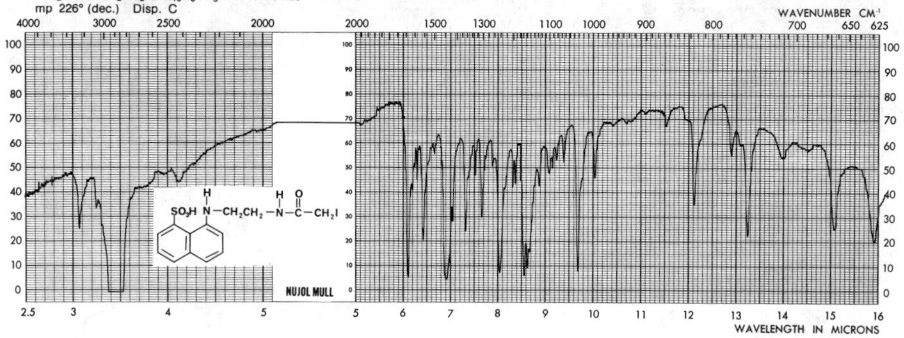

85,861-7
***N*-Iodoacetyl-*N'*-(5-sulfo-1-naphthyl)ethylenediamine**
[1,5-I-AEDANS, 5-[2-(2-iodoacetamido)ethylamino]-1-naphthalenesulfonic acid]
$ICH_2CONHCH_2CH_2NHC_{10}H_6SO_3H$ FW 434.26
mp >300° Disp. C

G

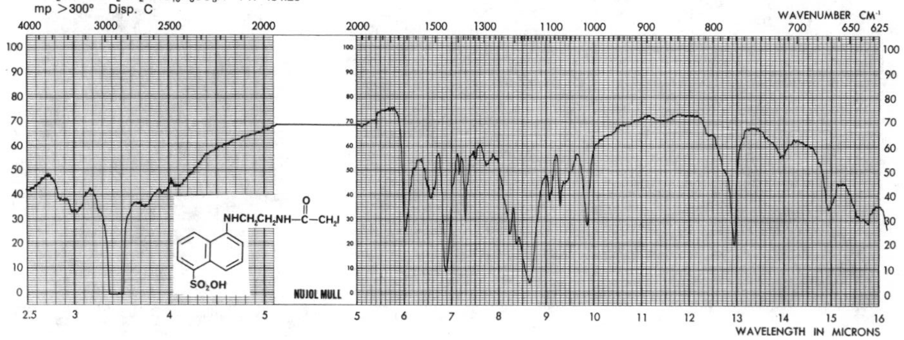

13,992-0 **8-Anilino-1-naphthalenesulfonic acid**
$C_6H_5NHC_{10}H_6SO_3H$ M.W. 299.35
m.p. 215-217° (dec.)

H

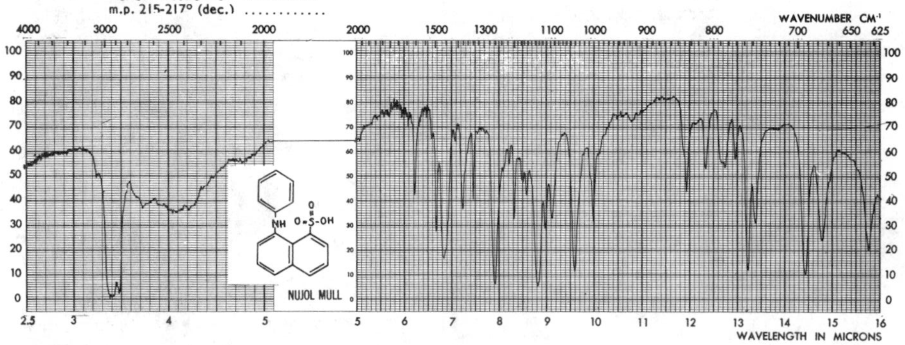

16,182-9
6-Dimethylamino-4-hydroxy-2-naphthalenesulfonic acid, tech.
$(CH_3)_2NC_{10}H_5(OH)SO_3H$
M.W. 267.3 m.p. 251-252° (dec.)

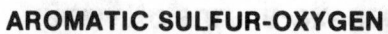

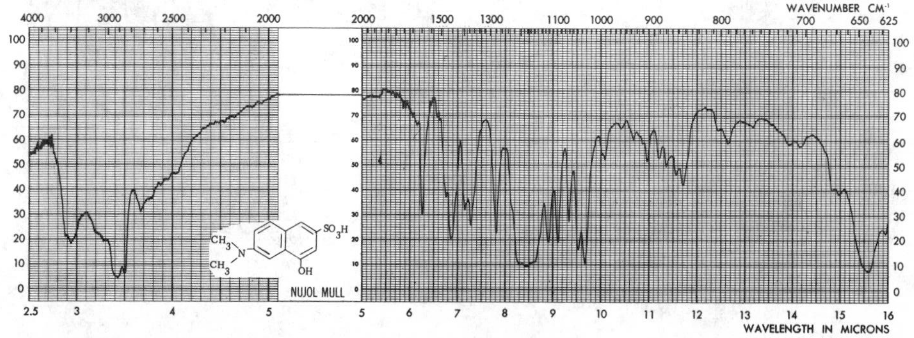

A

10,457-4 **1-Amino-2-naphthol-4-sulfonic acid (4-amino-3-hydroxy-1-naphthalene-sulfonic acid) hemihydrate, 97+%**
$H_2NC_{10}H_5(OH)SO_3H \cdot \frac{1}{2}H_2O$ M.W. 248.26
m.p. 298° (dec.)

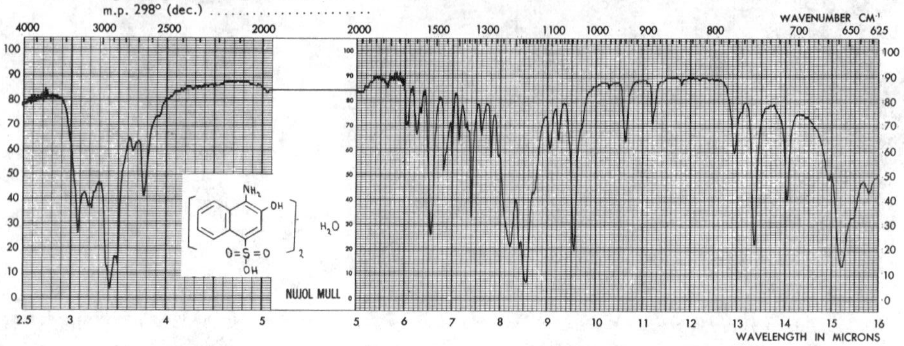

B

21,686-0
4-Amino-5-hydroxy-1-naphthalenesulfonic acid, tech., 80%
$H_2NC_{10}H_5(OH)SO_3H$ FW 239.25 *Beil.* **14**,835
Disp. C

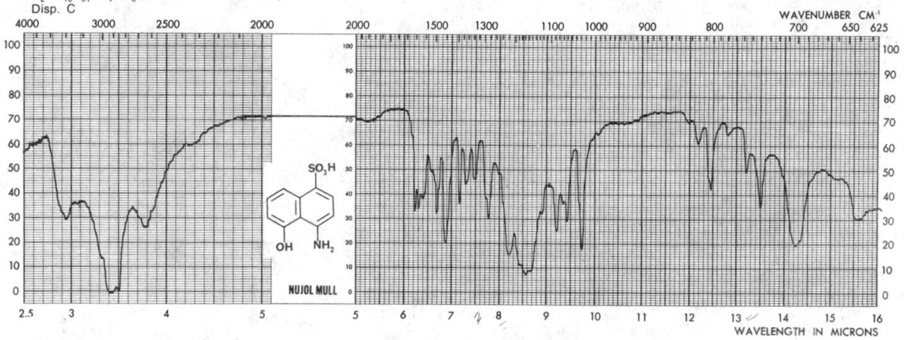

C

17,989-2
6-Amino-7-hydroxy-2-naphthalenesulfonic acid, tech.
$H_2NC_{10}H_5(OH)SO_3H$
M.W. 239.25 m.p. >300° Beil. **14**,849

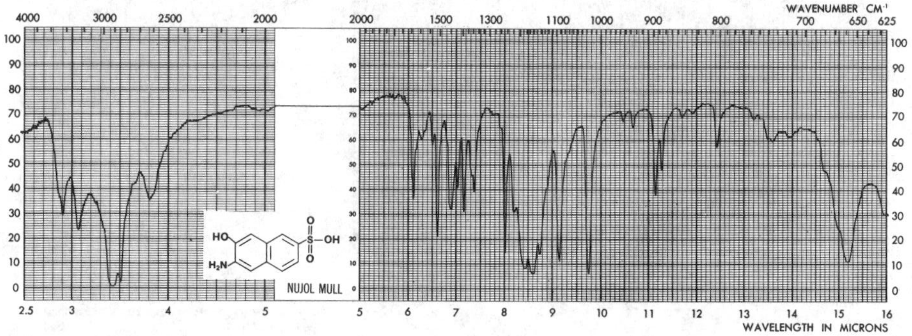

D

12,909-7 **4-Hydroxy-3-nitroso-1-naphthalenesulfonic acid**
$HOC_{10}H_5(NO)SO_3H$ M.W. 253.24
m.p. 136-138°

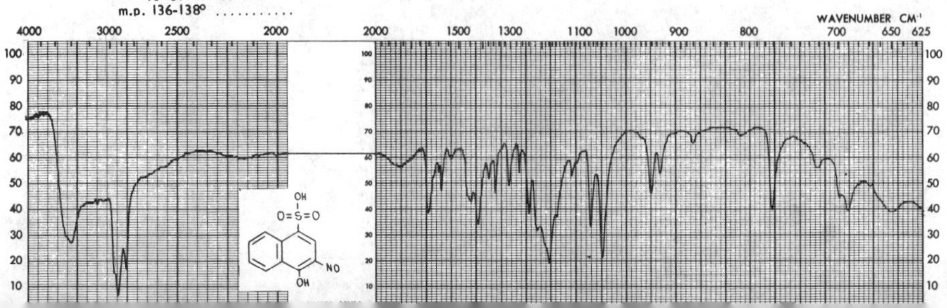

E

22,501-0
Flavianic acid hydrate (8-Hydroxy-5,7-dinitro-2-naphthalenesulfonic acid)
FW 314.23 mp 148-151° *Beil.* **11**,275 Disp. C,D

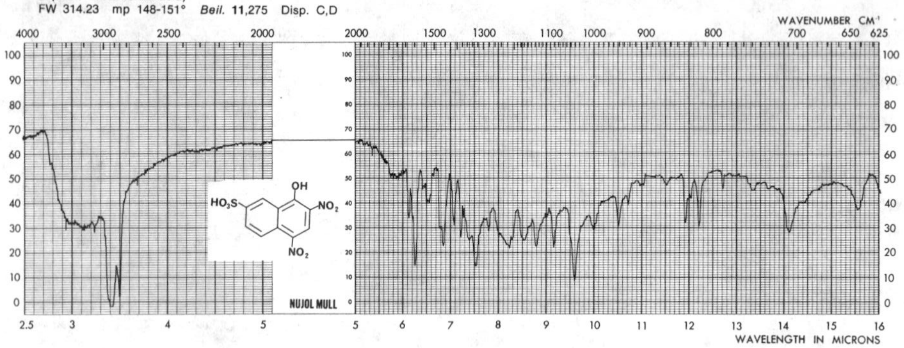

F

N2538-9 **1-Nitroso-2-naphthol-3,6-disulfonic acid, disodium salt** (nitroso-R-salt)
$HOC_{10}H_4(NO)(SO_3Na)_2$ M.W. 377.26
m.p. > 320°

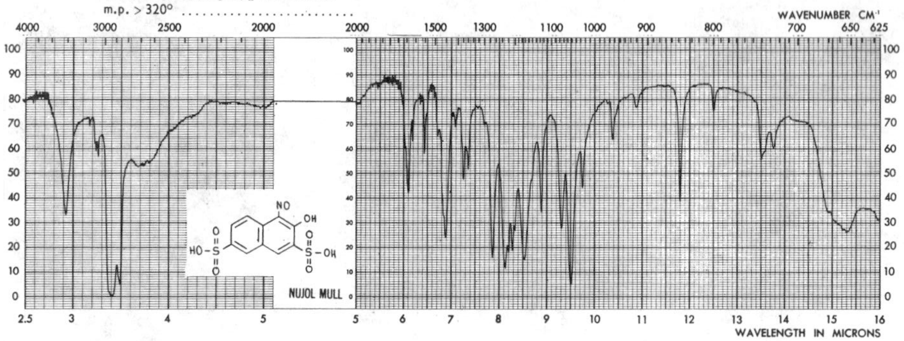

G

14,644-7 **7-Amino-1,3-naphthalenedisulfonic acid, tech.** (contains approx. 30% moisture)
$H_2NC_{10}H_5(SO_3H)_2$ M.W. 303.31
m.p. >300°

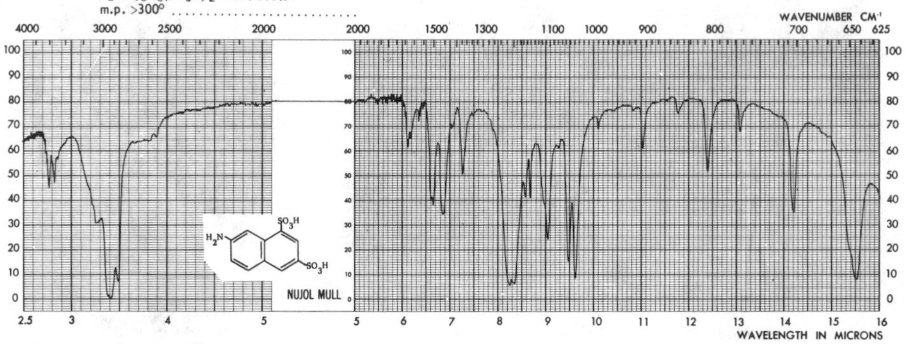

H

12,300-5 **2-Amino-1,5-naphthalenedisulfonic acid, tech.**
$H_2NC_{10}H_5(SO_3H)_2$ M.W. 303.31
m.p. > 300°

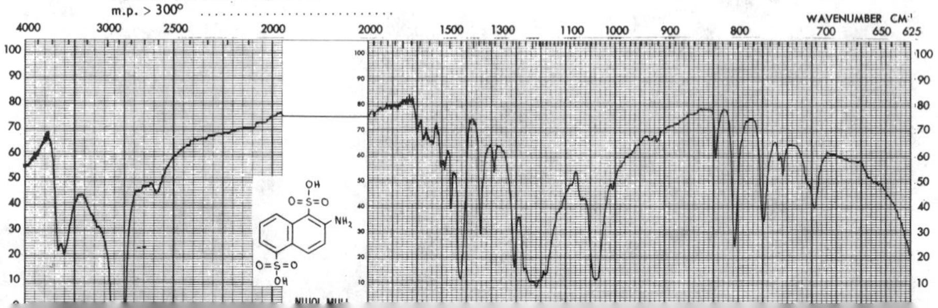

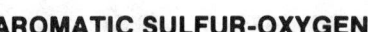

A

m.p. > 300°

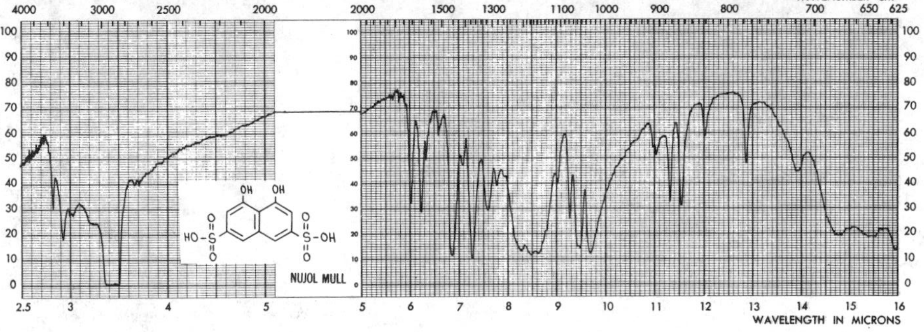

NUJOL MULL

B

13,172-5 Quinizarin-2-sulfonic acid
M.W. 320.28 m.p. 145-145.5°

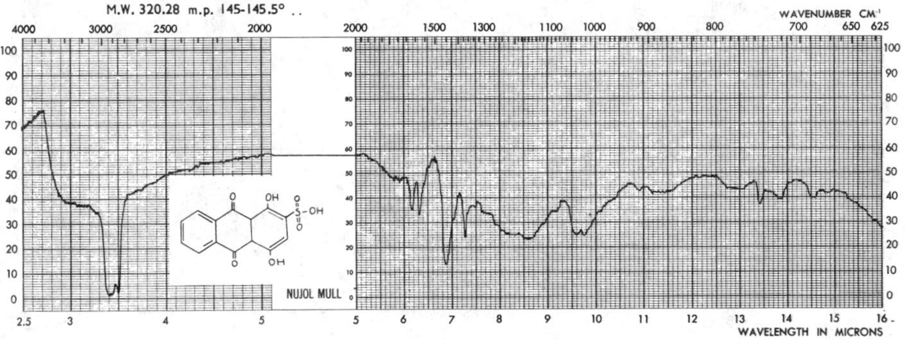

NUJOL MULL

C

14,728-1 Benzenesulfonic acid, sodium salt, 95+%
$C_6H_5SO_3Na$ M.W. 180.16
m.p. >300°

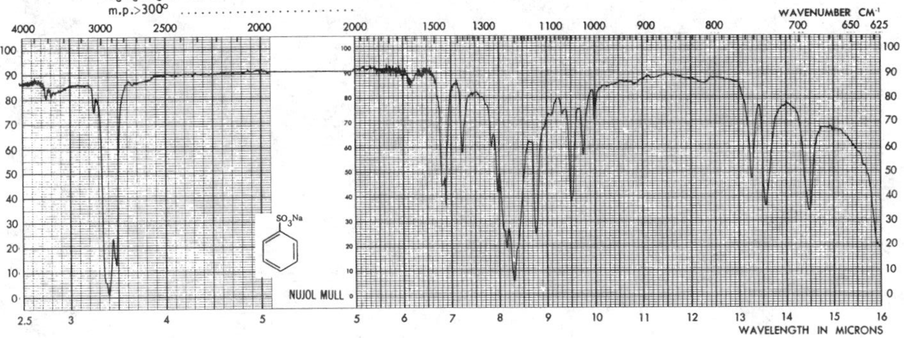

NUJOL MULL

D

15,253-6 p-Toluenesulfonic acid, sodium salt
$CH_3C_6H_4SO_3Na$ M.W. 194.19
m.p. >300°

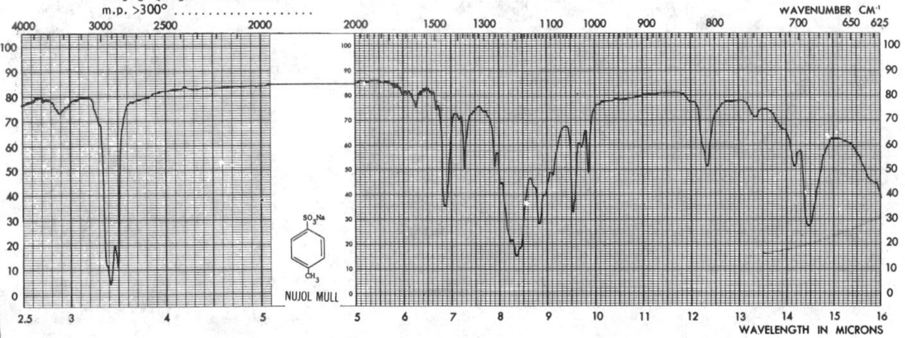

NUJOL MULL

E

NUJOL MULL

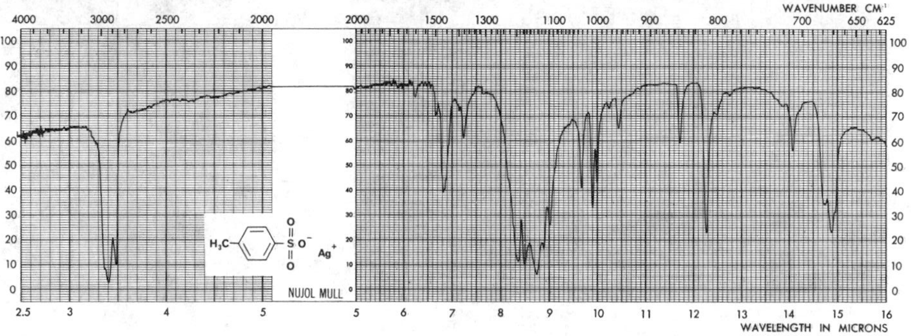

F

13,447-3 Tetraethylammonium p-toluenesulfonate
$(C_2H_5)_4N(O_3SC_6H_4CH_3)$ M.W. 301.45
m.p. 105-108°

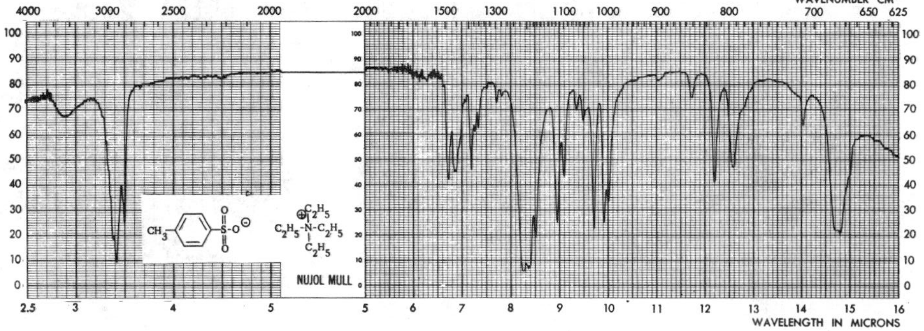

NUJOL MULL

G

22,114-7
Aminomalononitrile *p*-toluenesulfonate, 98%
$H_2NCH(CN)_2 \cdot CH_3C_6H_4SO_3H$ FW 253.28
mp 174° (dec.) Disp. C

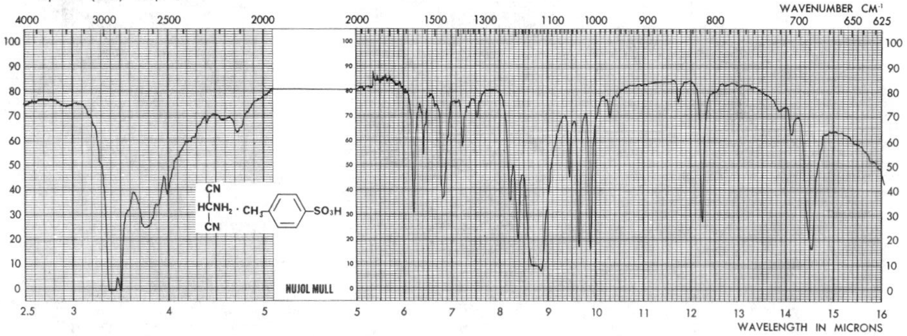

NUJOL MULL

H

19,981-8
N,N-Diisopropylethylamine *p*-toluenesulfonate, 97%
(*N*-ethyldiisopropylamine)
$[(CH_3)_2CH]_2NC_2H_5 \cdot CH_3C_6H_4SO_3H$ FW 301.45
mp 84-86° Disp. C

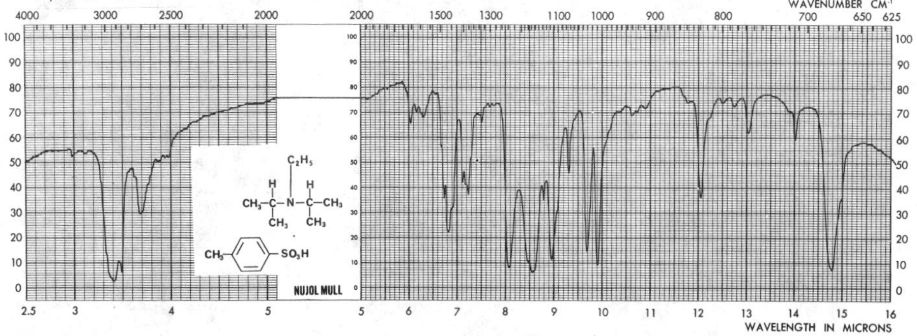

NUJOL MULL

ALDRICH

A
85,649-5
p-Nitrophenyl sulfate, potassium salt monohydrate,
99+%, GOLD LABEL
$O_2NC_6H_4OSO_3K \cdot H_2O$
M.W. 275.28 m.p. 246-250° Beil. **6**(2),225

B
22,519-3
***m*-Nitrobenzenesulfonic acid, sodium salt,** 99%
$O_2NC_6H_4SO_3Na$ FW 225.16 *Beil.* **11**,68 Disp. C

C
15,892-5
p-Acetylbenzenesulfonic acid, sodium salt, 98%
$CH_3COC_6H_4SO_3Na$
M.W. 222.2 m.p. >300° Beil. **11**(2),186

D
85,782-3
p-Sulfophenyl isothiocyanate, sodium salt monohydrate (p-isothiocyanatobenzenesulfonic acid)
$NaO_3SC_6H_4NCS \cdot H_2O$
M.W. 255.25 m.p. >300°

E
14,940-3 **p-Diphenylaminesulfonic acid** (N-phenylsulfanilic acid), **barium salt**
$(C_6H_5NHC_6H_4SO_3)_2Ba$ M.W. 633.90
m.p. >300°

F
10,831-6 **Metanilic acid, sodium salt, tech.**
$3-(H_2N)C_6H_4SO_3Na$ M.W. 195.17
m.p. 302-304°

G
B315-9 **o-Benzenedisulfonic acid, dipotassium salt**
$C_6H_4(SO_3K)_2$ M.W. 314.42 m.p. > 350°

H
H1841-0 **Hydroquinonesulfonic acid** (2,5-dihydroxybenzenesulfonic acid) **sodium salt**
$(HO)_2C_6H_3SO_3Na$ M.W. 212.16 m.p. > 330°

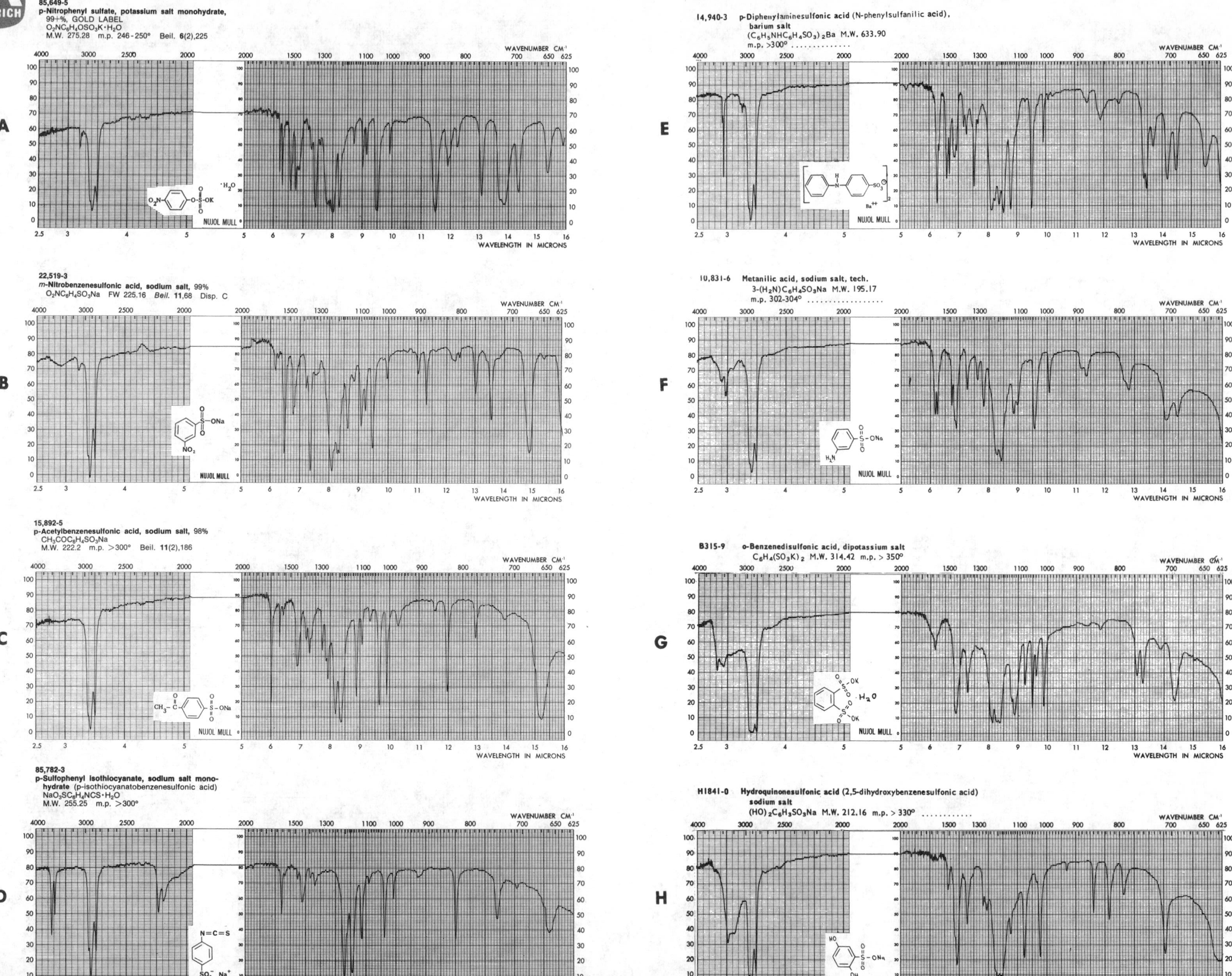

M.W. 346.43 m.p. >300° Beil. 11,300

A

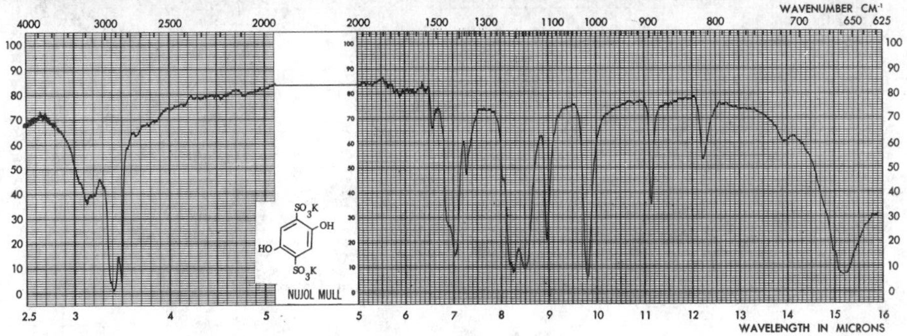

85,650-9
4-Nitrocatechol sulfate, dipotassium salt dihydrate
(2-hydroxy-5-nitrophenyl sulfate)
$O_2NC_6H_3(OK)OSO_3K \cdot 2H_2O$
M.W. 347.39 m.p. >300°

B

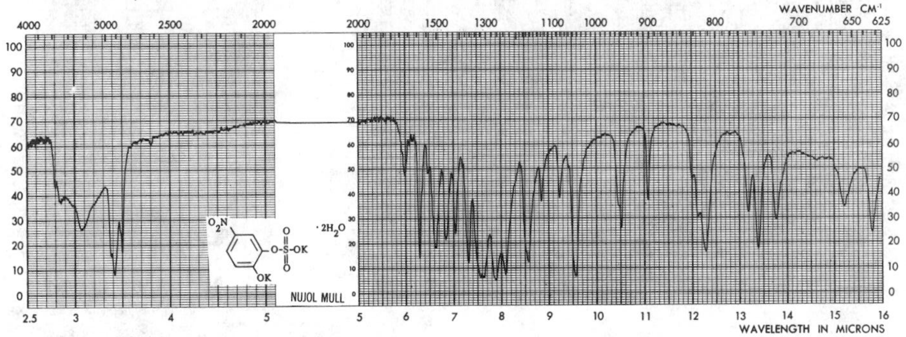

14,279-4 **5-Sulfoisophthalic acid, monosodium salt**
$NaO_3SC_6H_3$-1,3-$(CO_2H)_2$ M.W. 268.18
m.p. > 310°

C

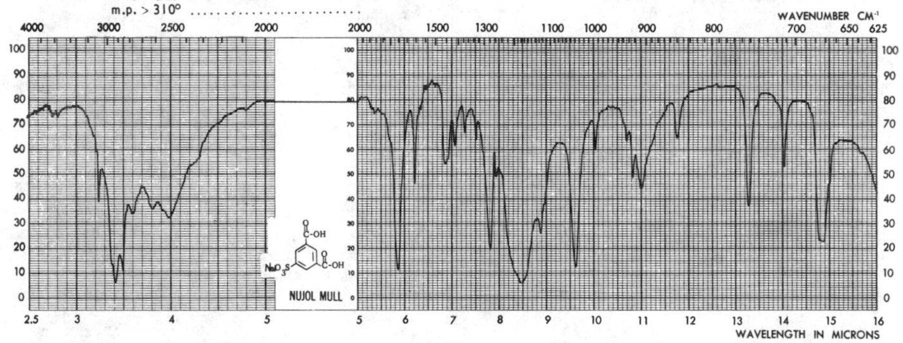

15,001-0 **Dimethyl 5-sulfoisophthalate, sodium salt**
$NaO_3SC_6H_3$-1,3-$(CO_2CH_3)_2$ M.W. 296.23
m.p. >300°

D

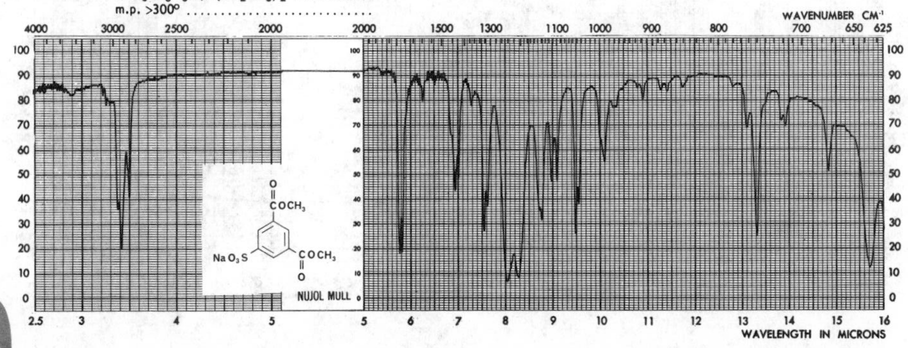

$(O_2N)_3C_6H_2SO_3Na$ M.W. 315.15 m.p. > 300°

E

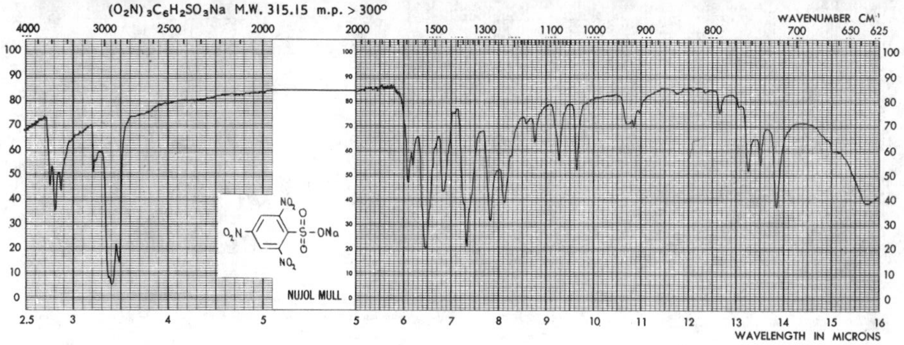

12,666-7 **2,4-Dinitro-4'-hydroxydiphenylamine-3'-sulfonic acid** [5-(2,4-dinitroanilino)-2-hydroxybenzenesulfonic acid], **sodium salt, tech.**
$(O_2N)_2C_6H_3NHC_6H_3(OH)SO_3Na$ M.W. 377.26
m.p. 288° (dec.)

F

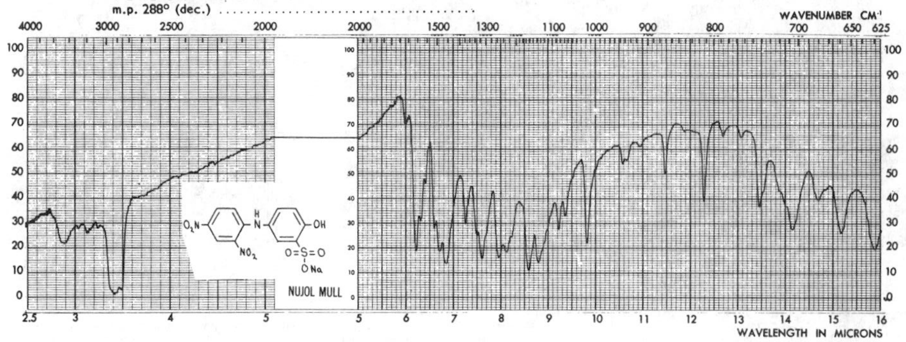

14,933-0 **5-Isatinsulfonic acid** (2,3-dioxo-5-indolinesulfonic acid)
sodium salt
M.W. 249.18 m.p. >300°

G

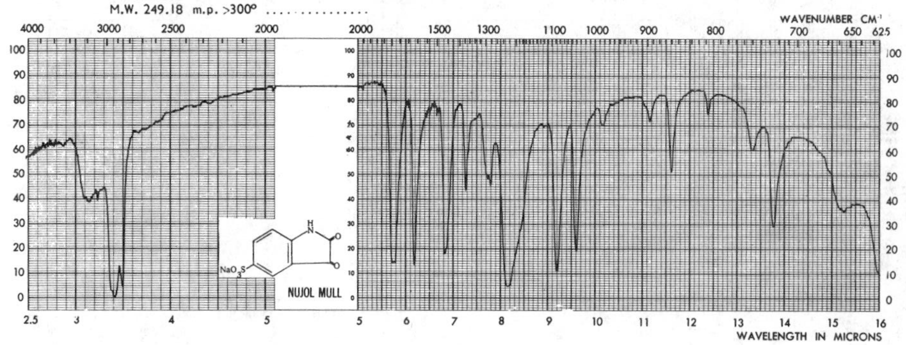

I-320-3 **Indigotetrasulfonic acid, potassium salt**
M.W. 734.89 m.p. > 310°

H

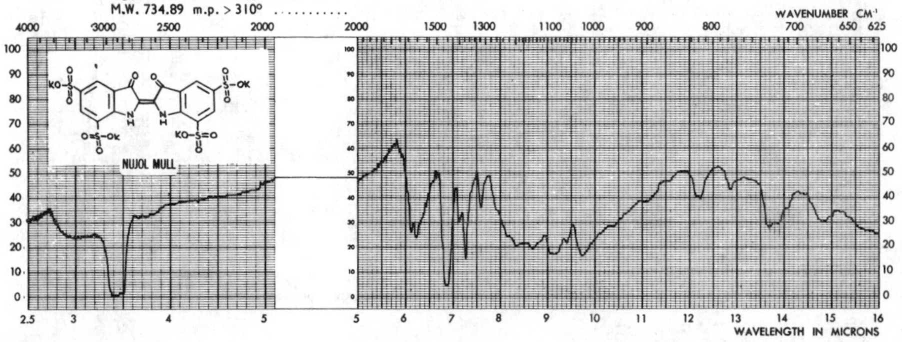

A

10,967-3 **2-Naphthalenesulfonic acid, sodium salt**
$C_{10}H_7SO_3Na$ M.W. 230.22 m.p. > 300° ...

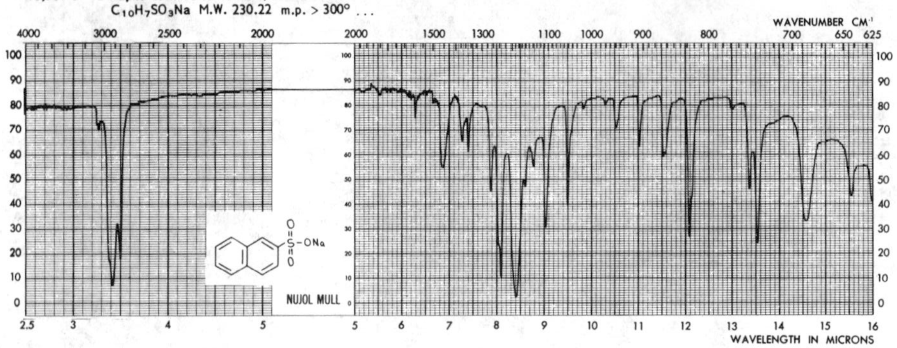

NUJOL MULL

B

10,256-3 **4-Amino-1-naphthalenesulfonic acid, sodium salt, tech.**
$H_2NC_{10}H_6SO_3Na$ M.W. 245.23 m.p. 280° (dec.) ....

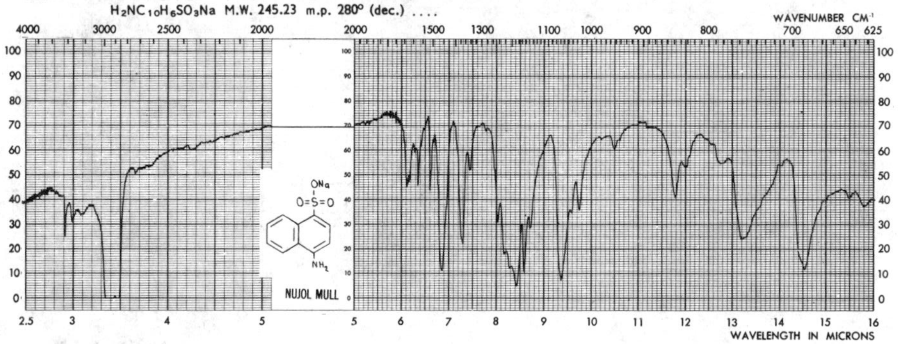

NUJOL MULL

C

18,314-8
5-Amino-1-naphthalenesulfonic acid, sodium salt
$H_2NC_{10}H_6SO_3Na$
M.W. 245.23 m.p. >300° Beil. **14**,744

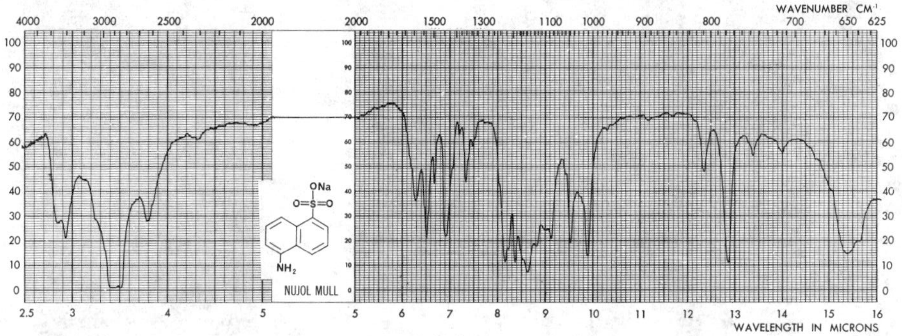

NUJOL MULL

D

10,971-1 **6-Amino-2-naphthalenesulfonic acid, sodium salt, tech., 80%**
$H_2NC_{10}H_6SO_3Na$ M.W. 245.23 ....

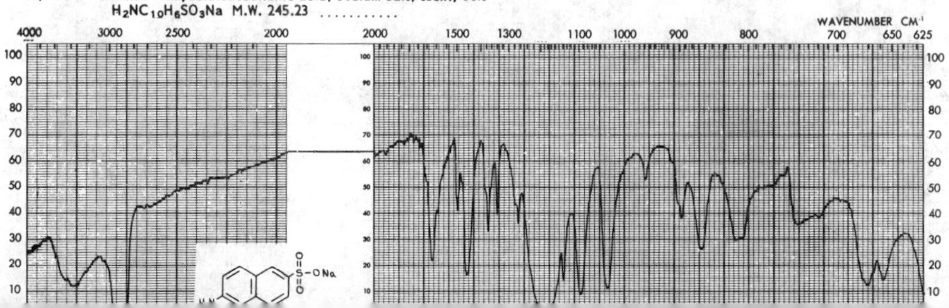

E

11,262-3 **8-Amino-2-naphthalenesulfonic acid, sodium salt, tech., 65%**
$H_2NC_{10}H_6SO_3Na$ M.W. 245.23 ....

NUJOL MULL

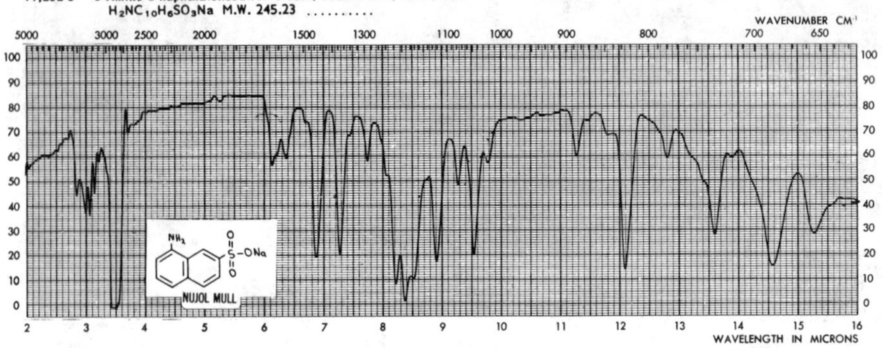

F

21,690-9
8-Anilino-1-naphthalenesulfonic acid, ammonium salt
$C_6H_5NHC_{10}H_6SO_3NH_4$ FW 316.38 mp 242-244°
Disp. C,D

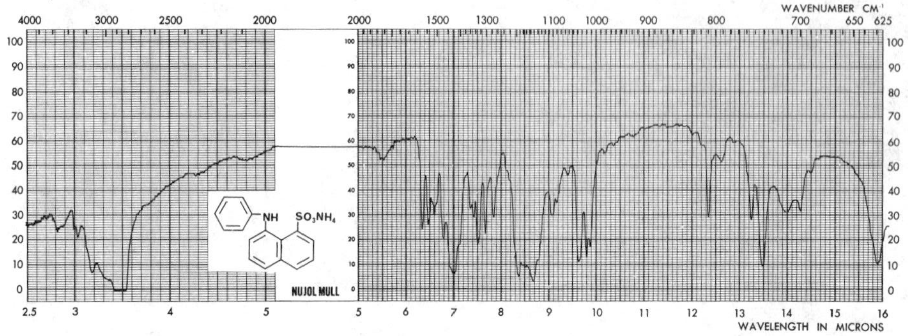

NUJOL MULL

G

19,426-3
6-(*p*-Toluidino)-2-naphthalenesulfonic acid, potassium salt (TNS)
$CH_3C_6H_4NHC_{10}H_6SO_3K$ FW 351.47 mp >300°
Beil. **14**,762 Disp. C

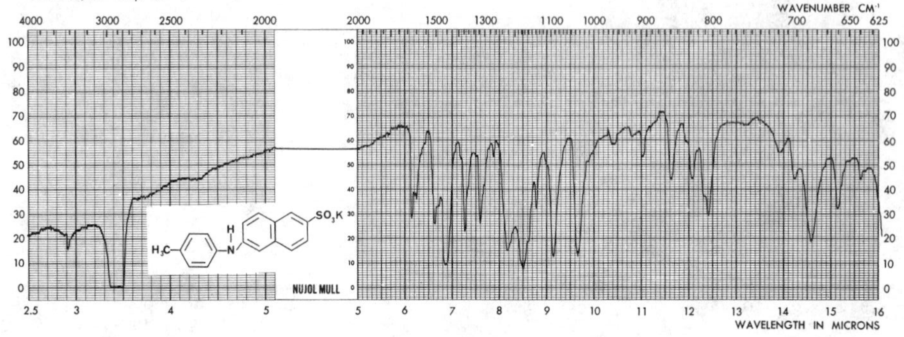

NUJOL MULL

H

14,250-6 **4-Methoxy-1-naphthalenesulfonic acid, sodium salt hydrate**
$CH_3OC_{10}H_6SO_3Na{\cdot}xH_2O$ M.W. 260.24 (anhydrous)
m.p. > 300° ....

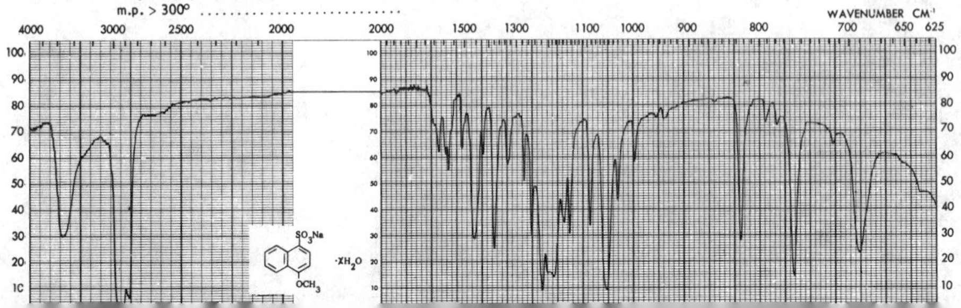

A

sulfonic acid), sodium salt
$(HO)_2C_{10}H_5SO_3Na$ M.W. 262.22 m.p. > 300° ....

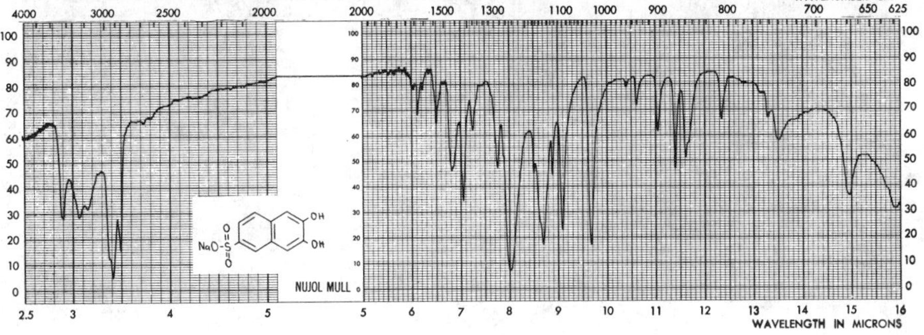

NUJOL MULL

B

D3030-7 1-Diazo-2-naphthol-4-sulfonic acid, sodium salt
M.W. 272.22 m.p. 168° ....

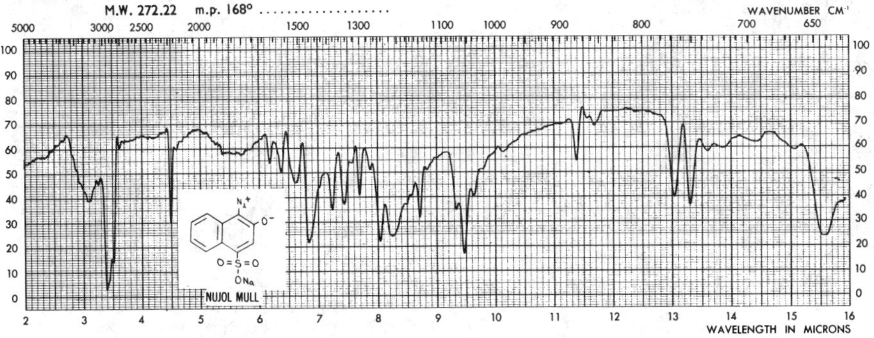

NUJOL MULL

C

11,464-2 1,2-Naphthoquinone-4-sulfonic acid, sodium salt
M.W. 260.20 m.p. 287° (dec.)

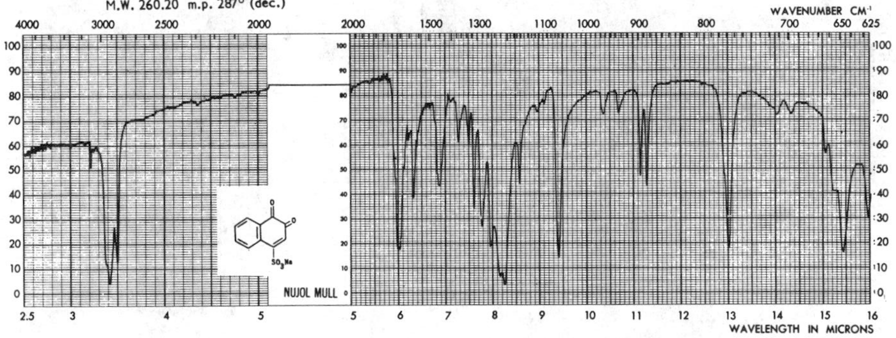

NUJOL MULL

D

18,918-9
1,2-Naphthoquinone-4-sulfonic acid, potassium salt,
tech., 90%
FW 276.31 mp 286-288° *Beil.* 11(1),80 Disp. C

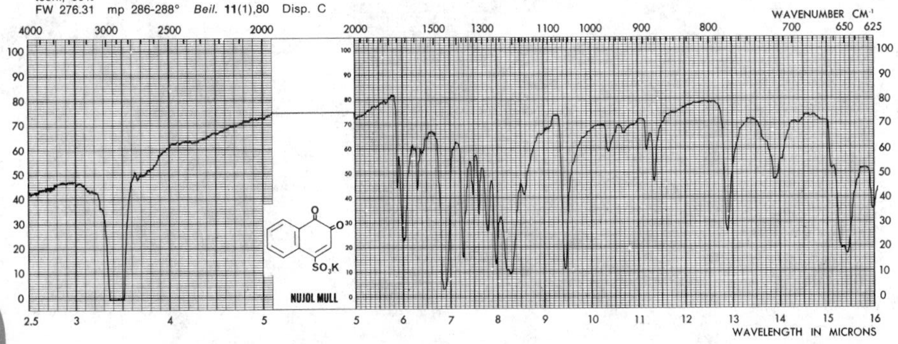

NUJOL MULL

E

$C_{10}H_6(SO_3Na)_2$ M.W. 332.26 m.p. > 335°

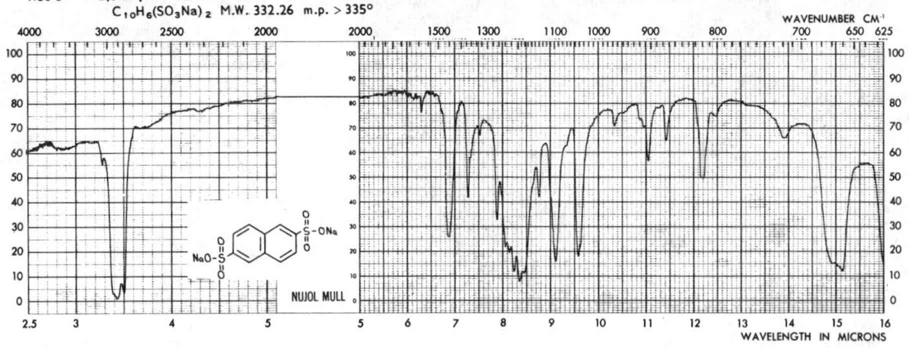

NUJOL MULL

F

10,973-8 4-Amino-1,5-naphthalenedisulfonic acid, monosodium salt
$H_2NC_{10}H_5(SO_3Na)SO_3H$ M.W. 325.30
m.p. > 300° ....

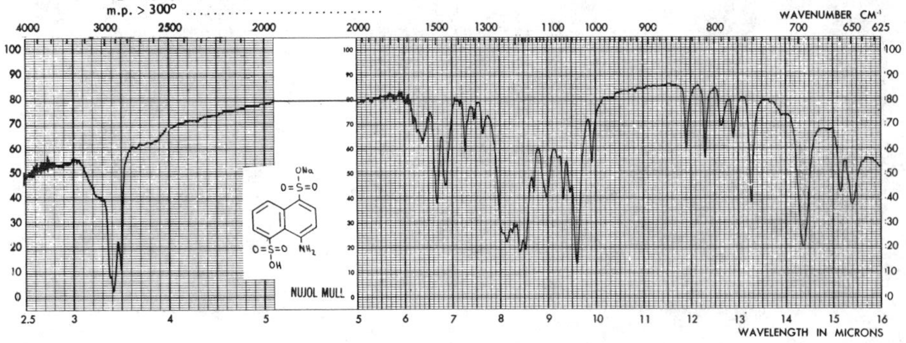

NUJOL MULL

G

21,281-4
1-Naphthol-3,6-disulfonic acid, disodium salt, tech.
(4-hydroxy-2,7-naphthalenedisulfonic acid)
$HOC_{10}H_5(SO_3Na)_2$ FW 348.26 mp >300°
Beil. 11,227 Disp. C

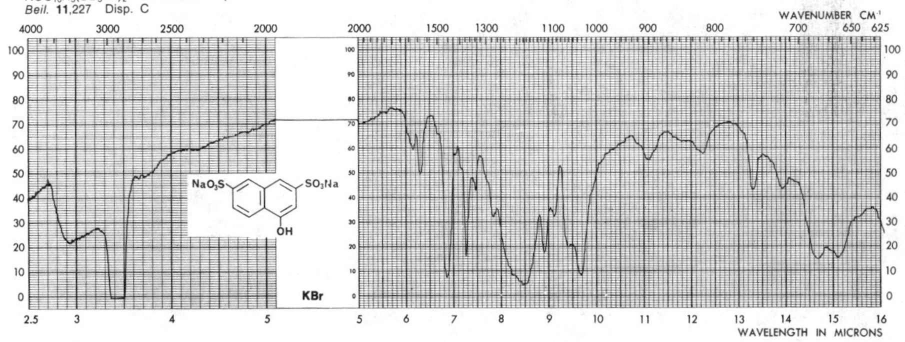

KBr

H

D11,660-2 2,7-Dihydroxynaphthalene-3,6-disulfonic acid, disodium salt
$(HO)_2C_{10}H_4(SO_3Na)_2$ M.W. 364.26 m.p. > 300° ....

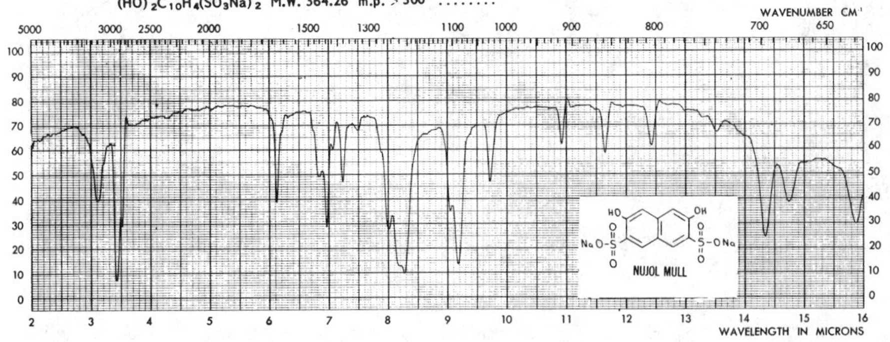

NUJOL MULL

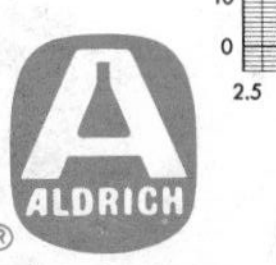

A

N100-3 **1,3,6-Naphthalenetrisulfonic acid, trisodium salt trihydrate**
$C_{10}H_5(SO_3Na)_3 \cdot 3H_2O$ M.W. 488.35
m.p. > 300°

NUJOL MULL

B

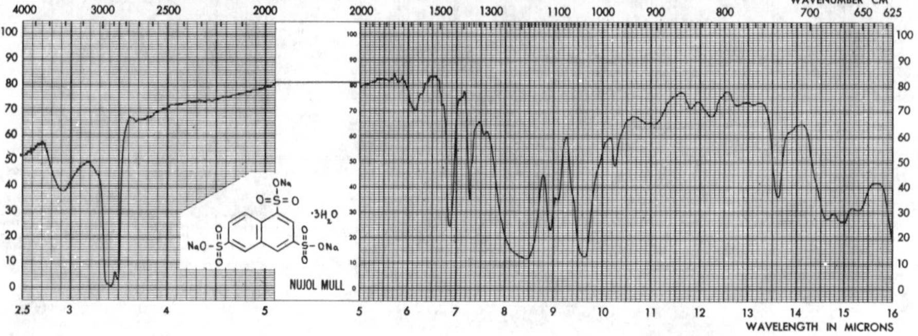

85,651-7
Naphthol AS sulfate, potassium salt
3-$(C_6H_5NHCO)C_{10}H_6$-2-(OSO_3K)
M.W. 381.45 m.p. 244-249°

NUJOL MULL

C

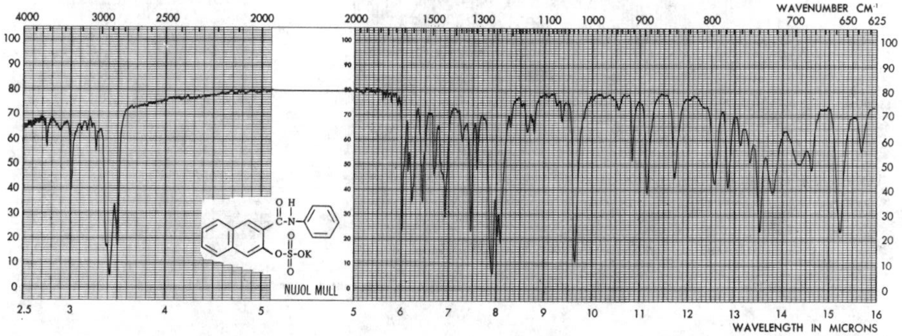

11,475-8 **2-(p-Sulfophenylazo)-1,8-dihydroxy-3,6-naphthalenedisulfonic acid, trisodium salt (SPADNS)**
$NaO_3SC_6H_4N{:}NC_{10}H_3(OH)_2(SO_3Na)_2$ M.W. 570.41
m.p. > 300°

NUJOL MULL

D

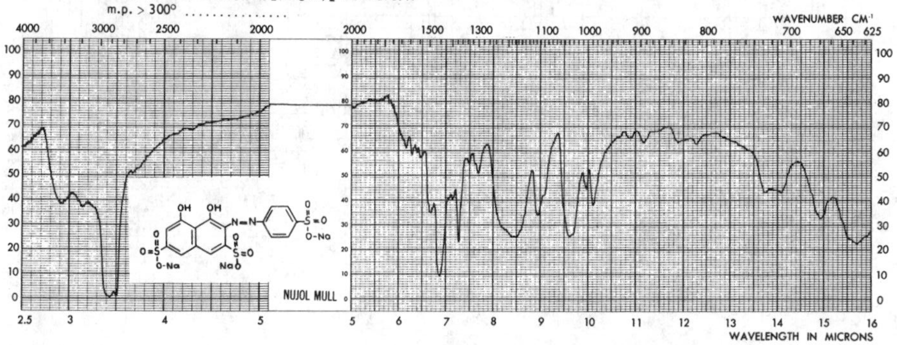

C8445-3 **Congo red**
M.W. 696.67 m.p. > 360°

NUJOL MULL

E

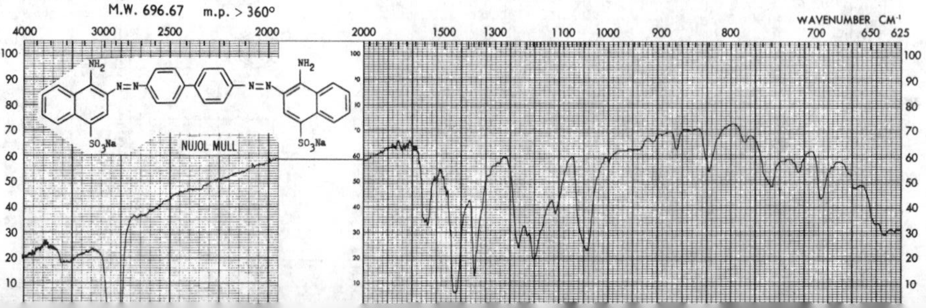

A30 **Acenaphthene-5-sulfonic acid, potassium salt**
$C_{12}H_9SO_3K$ M.W. 272.37 m.p. 310° (dec.)

NUJOL MULL

F

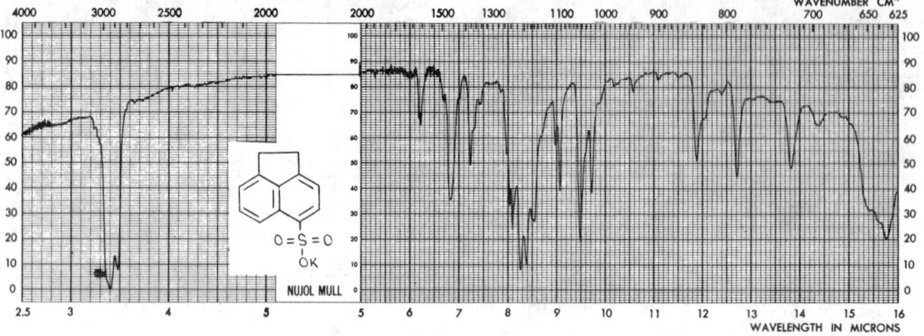

12,324-2 **Anthraquinone-2-sulfonic acid, sodium salt**
M.W. 310.26 m.p. > 320°

NUJOL MULL

G

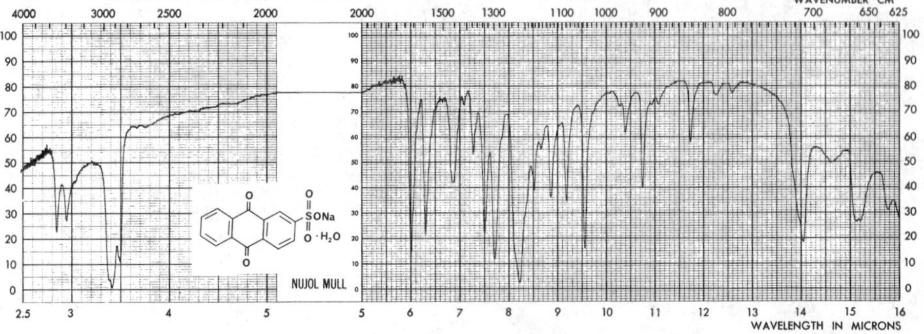

11,996-2 **Alizarin red S (3,4-dihydroxy-9,10-dioxo-2-anthracenesulfonic acid, sodium salt) monohydrate**
M.W. 360.28 m.p. > 300°

NUJOL MULL

H

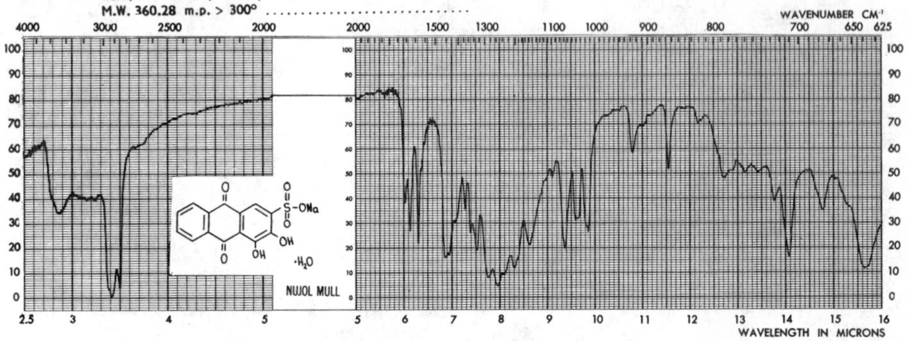

A9040-3 **Anthraquinone-1,5-disulfonic acid, disodium salt**
M.W. 412.31 m.p. > 300°

WAVENUMBER CM⁻¹ — WAVELENGTH IN MICRONS

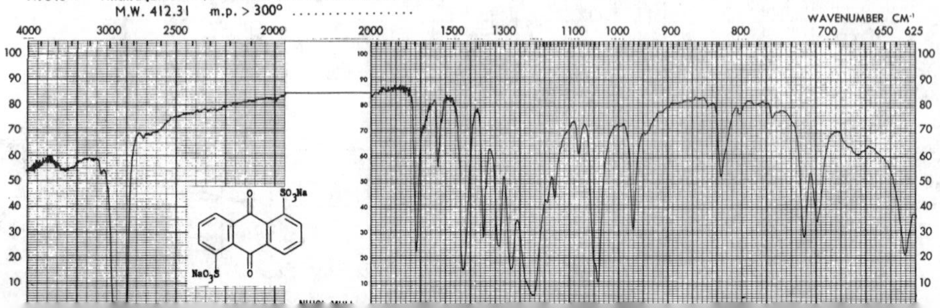

A

A9060-8 **Anthraquinone-2,6-disulfonic acid, disodium salt**
M.W. 412.31 m.p. > 325°

NUJOL MULL

B

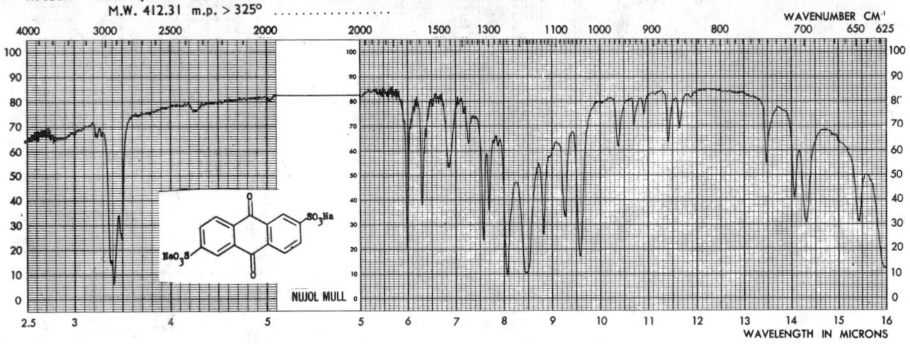

18,495-0
3-Sulfo-2-naphthoic acid, magnesium salt-bis(hexachlorocyclopentadiene) adduct, tech., moist
M.W. 820.09 m.p. >300° (dec.)

NUJOL MULL

C

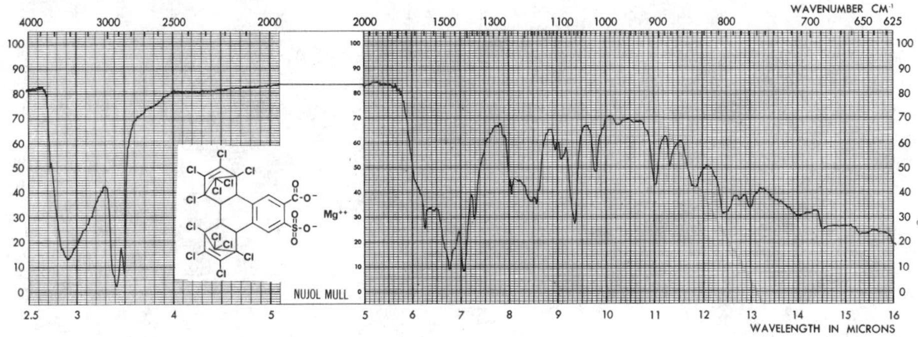

10,425-6 **Ethyl p-toluenesulfonate, tech.**
$CH_3C_6H_4SO_3C_2H_5$ M.W. 200.26

NEAT

D

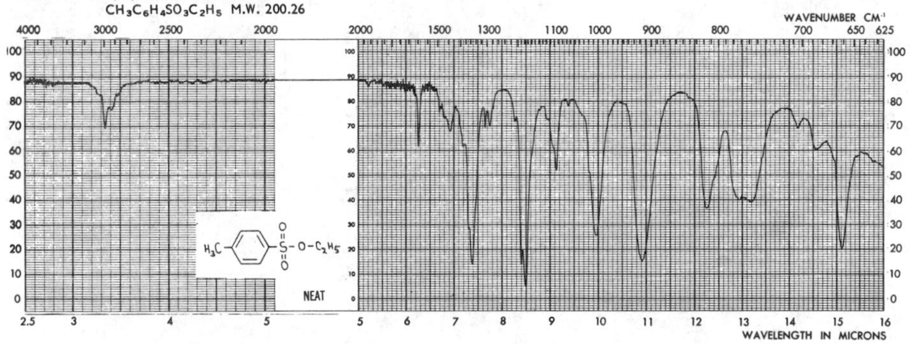

10,799-9 **2-Chloroethyl p-toluenesulfonate**
$CH_3C_6H_4SO_3CH_2CH_2Cl$ M.W. 234.70 n_D^{20} 1.5279
b.p. 153°/0.3 mm.

NEAT

E

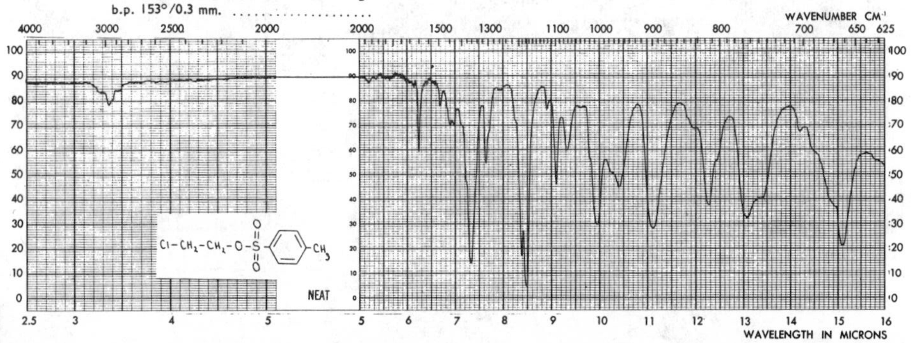

11,485-5 **3-Quinuclidyl p-toluenesulfonate hydrochloride**
M.W. 317.84 m.p. 200-201°

NUJOL MULL

F

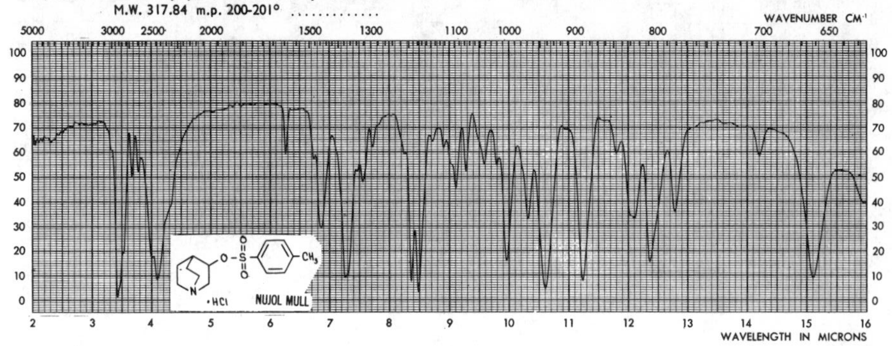

20,660-1
1,6-Anhydro-3,4-O-isopropylidene-2-tosyl-D-galactose
FW 356.40 mp 118-122°
$[\alpha]^{23}$ -60° (c=0.92, $CHCl_3$) Disp. C

NUJOL MULL

G

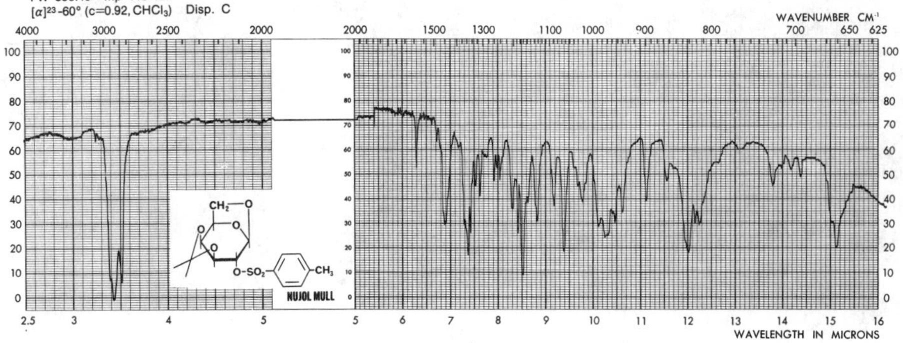

14,460-6 **Cyanomethyl benzenesulfonate**
$C_6H_5SO_3CH_2CN$ M.W. 197.21 n_D^{20} 1.5231
b.p. 142-146°/1 mm.

MELT

H

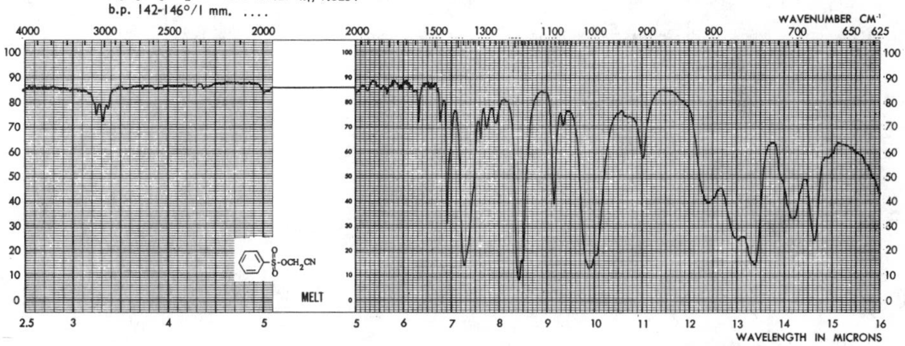

15,899-2
Methyl p-toluenesulfonate, 97%
$CH_3C_6H_4SO_3CH_3$
M.W. 186.23 m.p. 27.5° Beil. 11,99

NEAT

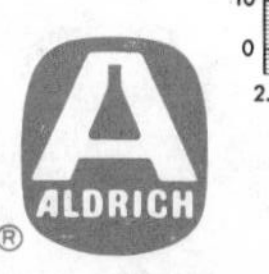

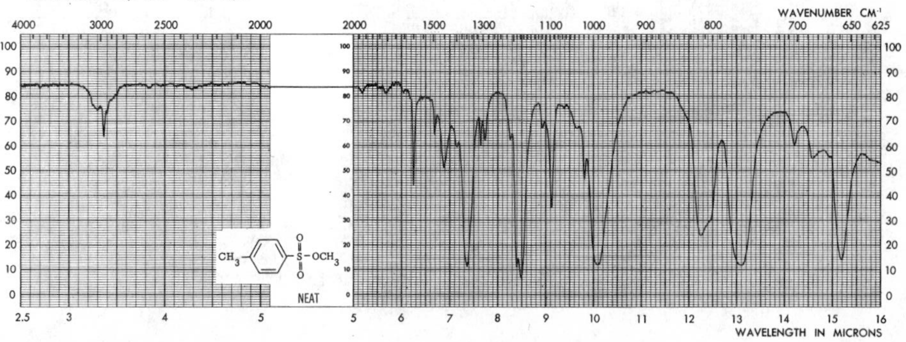

A

17,782-2
2,2,2-Trifluoroethyl p-toluenesulfonate
$CH_3C_6H_4SO_3CH_2CF_3$
M.W. 254.23 m.p. 36-38° b.p. 87-92°/0.1mm.

MELT

B

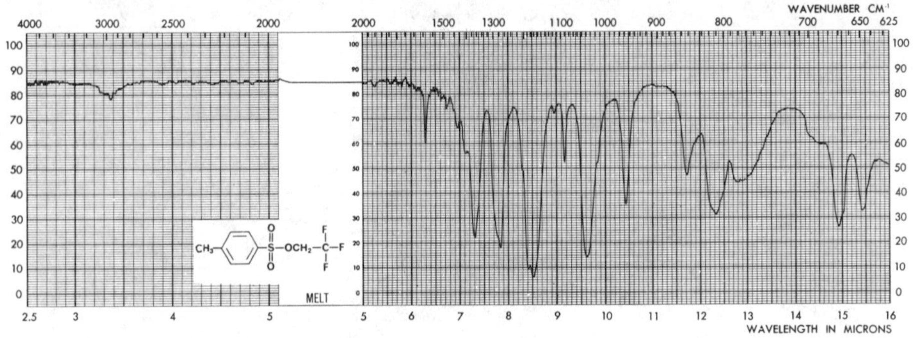

14,467-3 **Cyanomethyl p-toluenesulfonate**
(send for data sheet)
$CH_3C_6H_4SO_3CH_2CN$ M.W. 211.24
m.p. 47-49° . . . .

MELT

C

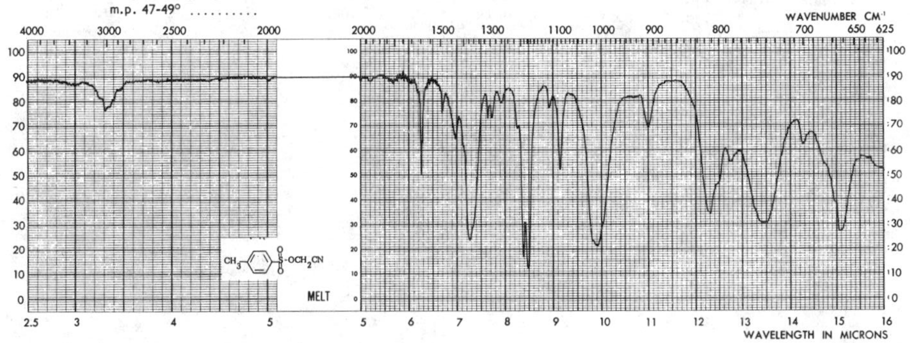

22,223-2
(O-p-Tosylisonitroso)malononitrile, 98%
$CH_3C_6H_4SO_2ON{=}C(CN)_2$ FW 249.25
mp 115-117° Disp. J

NUJOL MULL

D

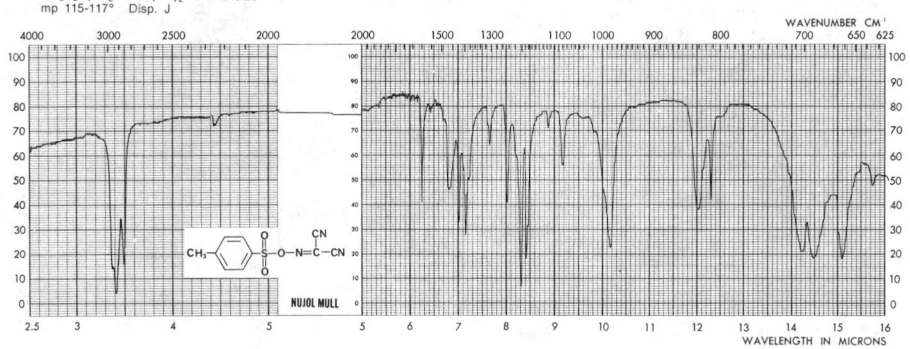

12,907-0 **α-Hydroxy-o-toluenesulfonic acid γ-sultone**
M.W. 170.19 m.p. 110-114° . . . .

E

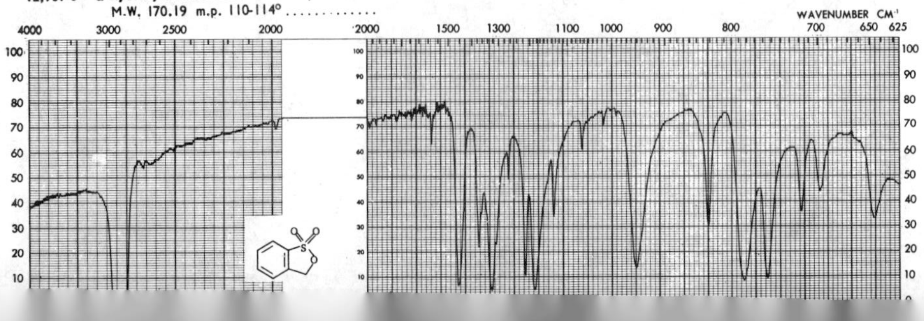

12,906-2 **α-Chloro-α-hydroxy-o-toluenesulfonic acid γ-sultone**
M.W. 204.63 m.p. 114-116° . . . .

NUJOL MULL

F

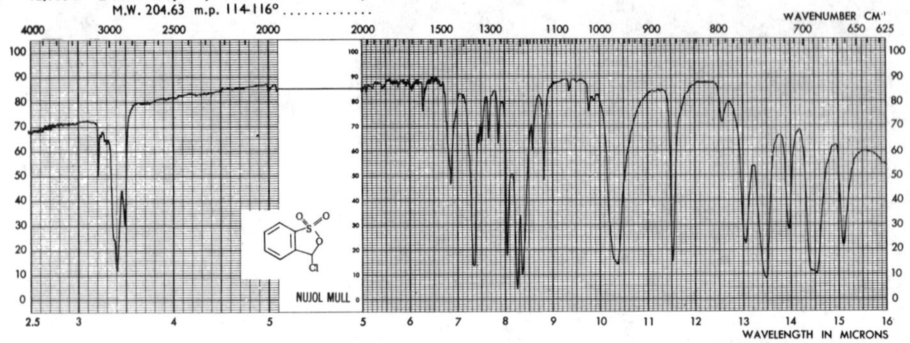

10,813-8 **Benzenesulfonyl chloride, 99+%**
$C_6H_5SO_2Cl$ M.W. 176.62 n_D^{20} 1.5518
m.p. 15-17° b.p. 251° . . . .

NEAT

G

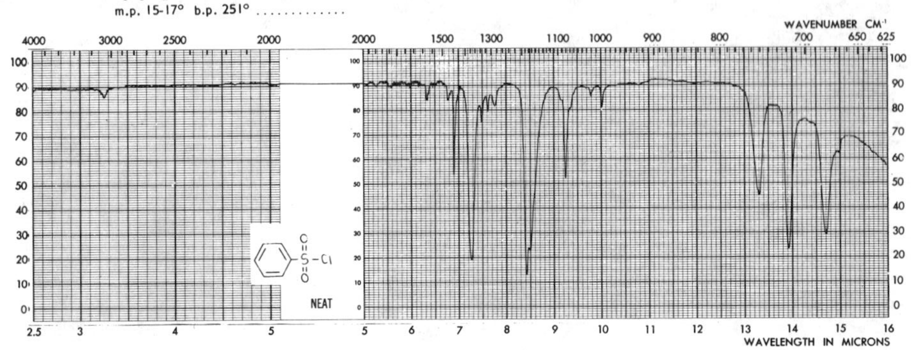

15,971-9
α-Toluenesulfonyl chloride, 98%
$C_6H_5CH_2SO_2Cl$
M.W. 190.65 m.p. 92-94° Beil. **11**,116
IRRITANT

NUJOL MULL

H

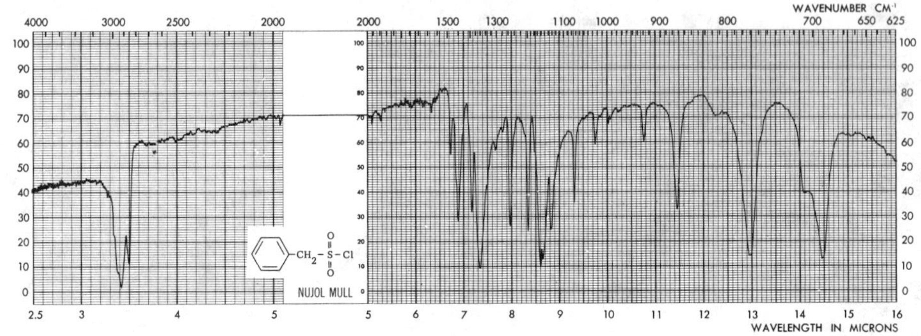

15,052-5 **β-Styrenesulfonyl chloride**
$C_6H_5CH{:}CHSO_2Cl$ M.W. 202.66
m.p. 84-87° . . . .

NUJOL MULL

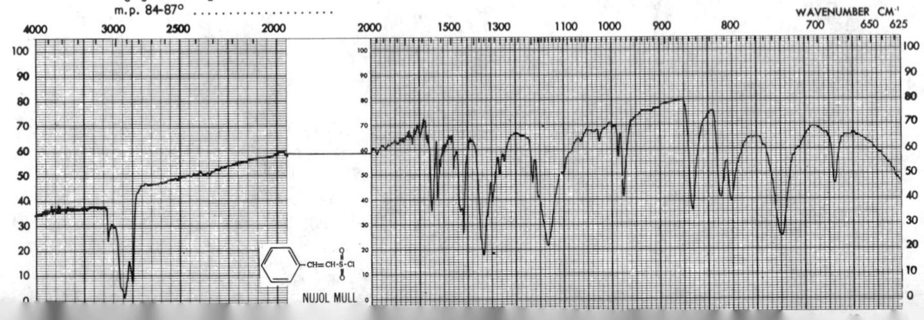

A 13,635-2 o-Aminobenzenesulfonyl fluoride
$H_2NC_6H_4SO_2F$ M.W. 175.18 m.p. 64-65°
NUJOL MULL

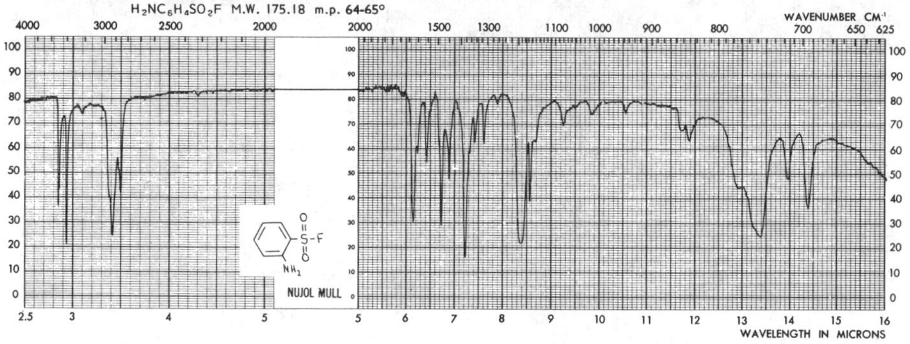

B N1150-7 o-Nitrobenzenesulfonyl chloride
$O_2NC_6H_4SO_2Cl$ M.W. 221.62 m.p. 65-67°
NUJOL MULL

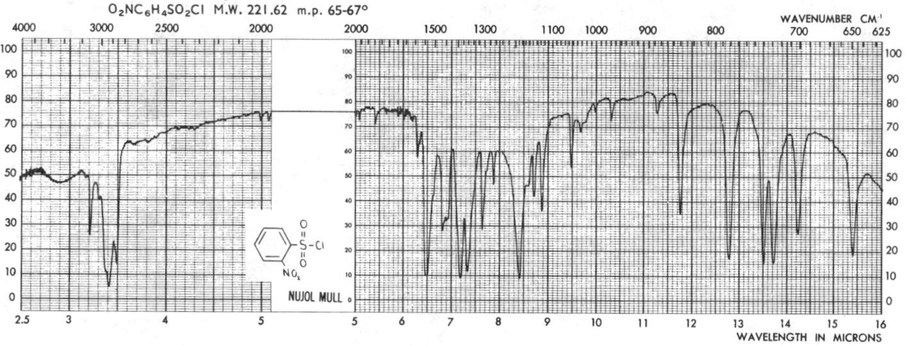

C 14,296-4 o-Nitrobenzenesulfonyl fluoride
$O_2NC_6H_4SO_2F$ M.W. 205.17 m.p. 55-58°
NUJOL MULL

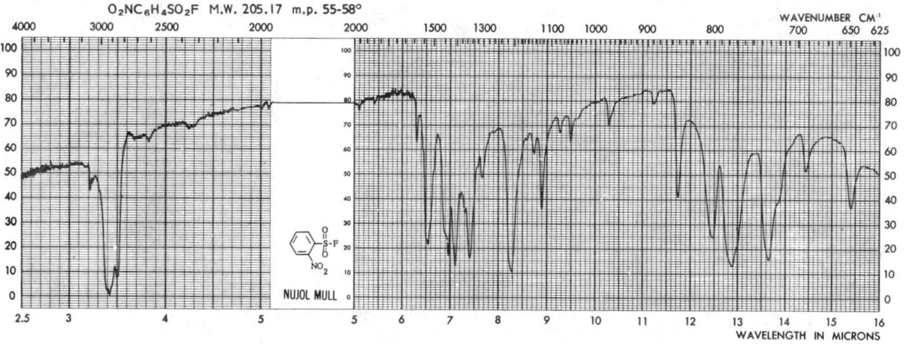

D 13,636-0 o-Fluorosulfonylbenzenesulfonyl chloride
$FSO_2C_6H_4SO_2Cl$ M.W. 258.68 m.p. 87-89°
NUJOL MULL

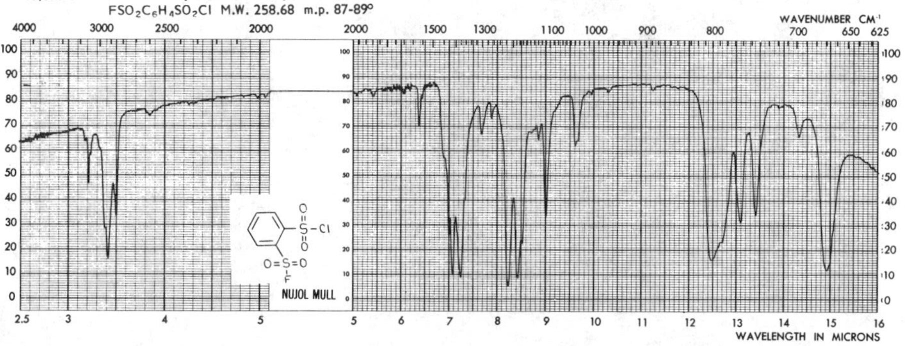

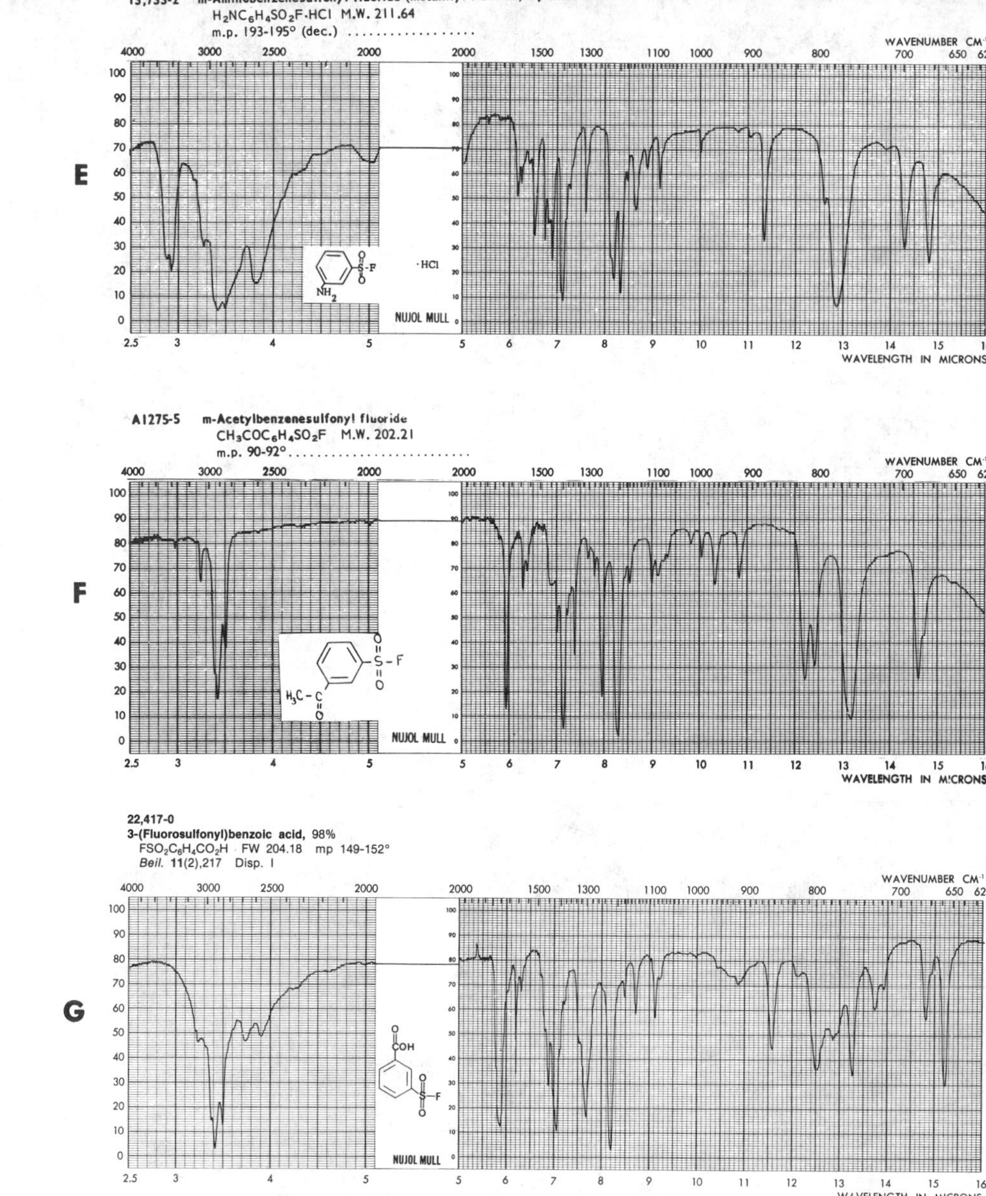

E 13,733-2 m-Aminobenzenesulfonyl fluoride (metanilyl fluoride) hydrochloride, tech.
$H_2NC_6H_4SO_2F \cdot HCl$ M.W. 211.64
m.p. 193-195° (dec.)
NUJOL MULL

F A1275-5 m-Acetylbenzenesulfonyl fluoride
$CH_3COC_6H_4SO_2F$ M.W. 202.21
m.p. 90-92°
NUJOL MULL

G 22,417-0
3-(Fluorosulfonyl)benzoic acid, 98%
$FSO_2C_6H_4CO_2H$ FW 204.18 mp 149-152°
Beil. 11(2),217 Disp. I
NUJOL MULL

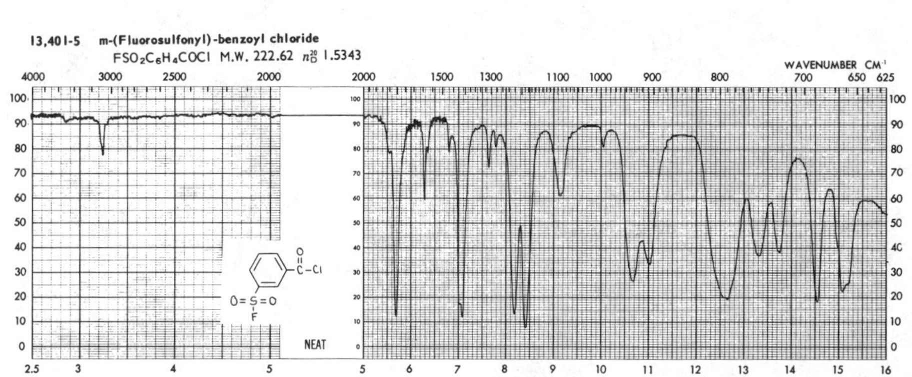

H 13,401-5 m-(Fluorosulfonyl)-benzoyl chloride
$FSO_2C_6H_4COCl$ M.W. 222.62 n_D^{20} 1.5343
NEAT

A 10,780-8 **m-Fluorosulfonylphenyl isocyanate**
$FSO_2C_6H_4NCO$ M.W. 201.18 n_D^{20} 1.5351
m.p. 27-30° (supercooled)

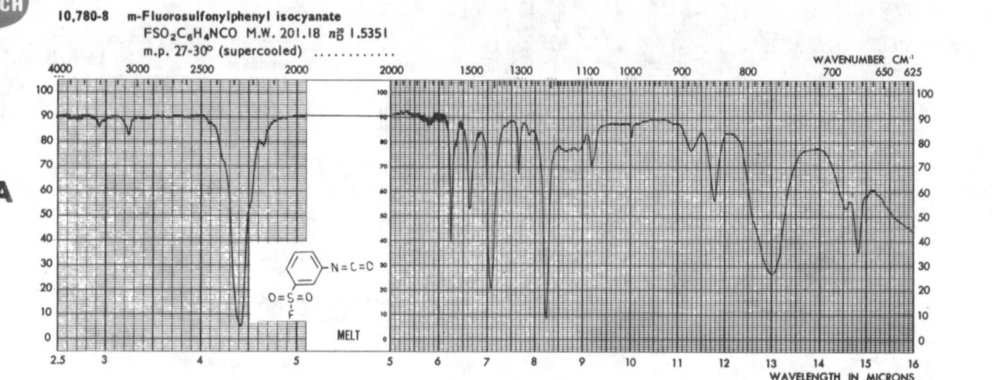

B 10,778-6
m-Fluorosulfonylbenzenesulfonyl chloride
$FSO_2C_6H_4SO_2Cl$
M.W. 258.67 b.p. 156-158°/5mm. n_D^{20} 1.5372
CORROSIVE

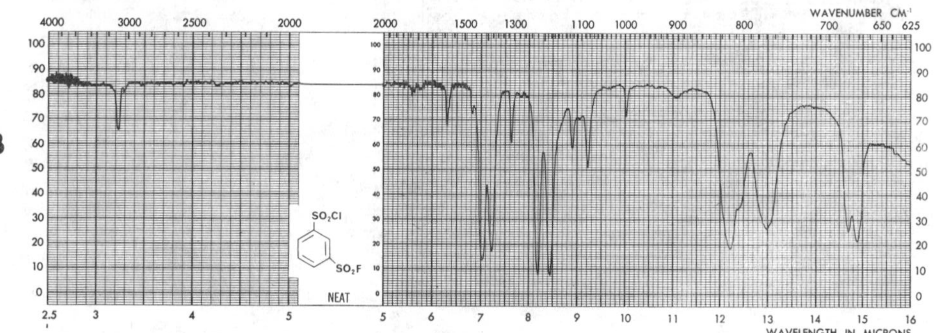

C 11,745-5 **p-Toluenesulfonyl fluoride**
$CH_3C_6H_4SO_2F$ M.W. 174.20 m.p. 41-42°

D T3595-5 **p-Toluenesulfonyl chloride** (tosyl chloride), **98%**
$CH_3C_6H_4SO_2Cl$ M.W. 190.65 m.p. 67-68°

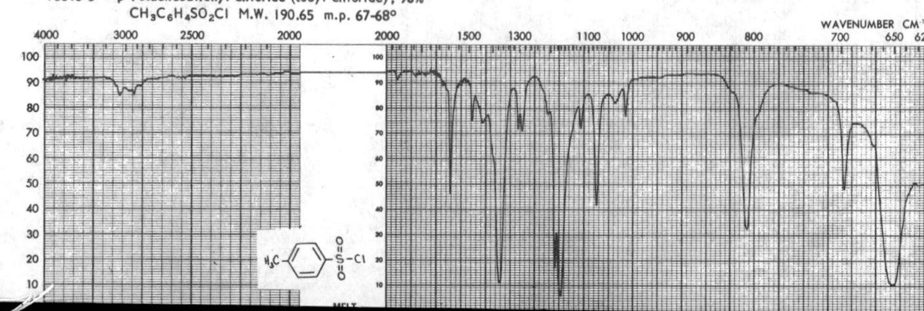

E F620-6 **4-Fluorobenzenesulfonyl chloride**
$FC_6H_4SO_2Cl$ M.W. 194.61 m.p. 34-36°

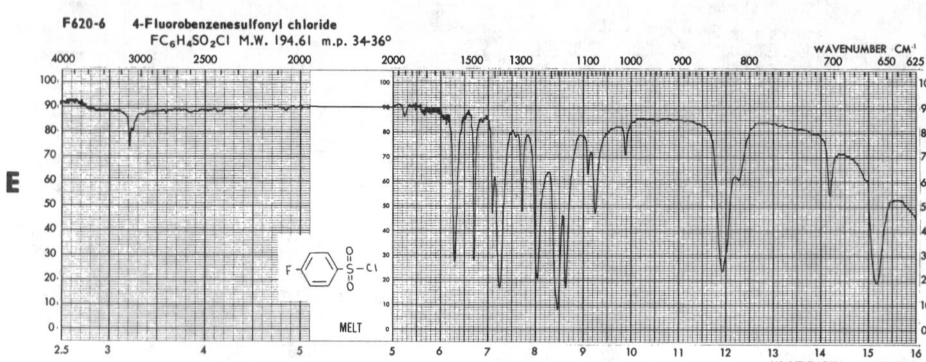

F 13,369-8 **4-Chlorobenzenesulfonyl chloride**
$ClC_6H_4SO_2Cl$ M.W. 211.08 m.p. 50-52°

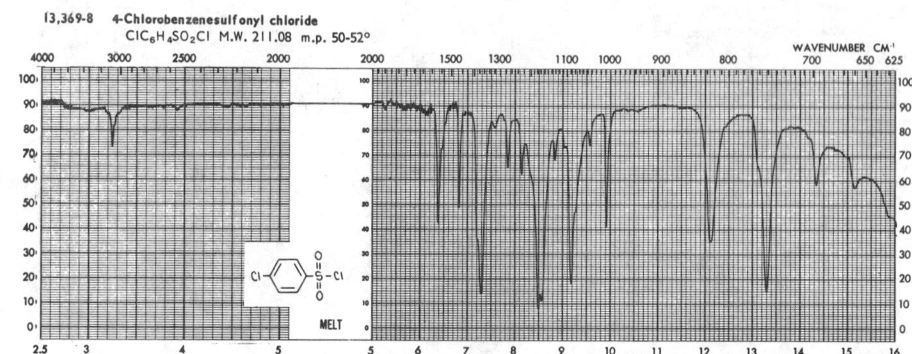

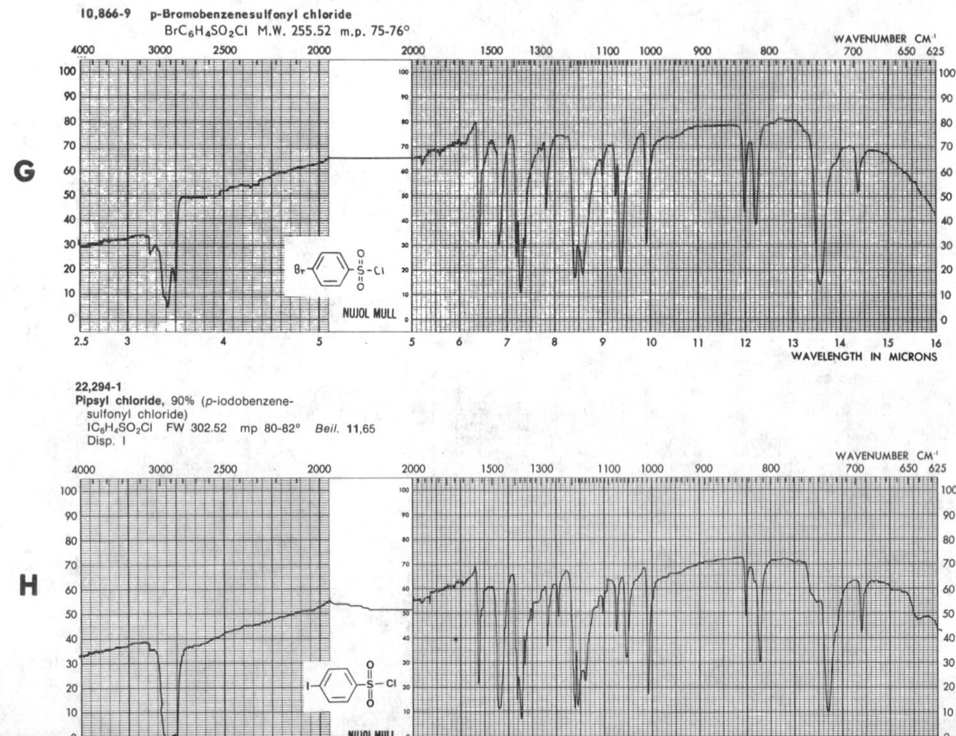

G 10,866-9 **p-Bromobenzenesulfonyl chloride**
$BrC_6H_4SO_2Cl$ M.W. 255.52 m.p. 75-76°

H 22,294-1
Pipsyl chloride, 90% (*p*-iodobenzenesulfonyl chloride)
$IC_6H_4SO_2Cl$ FW 302.52 mp 80-82° *Beil.* 11,65
Disp. I

A 11020-4 **4-Methoxybenzenesulfonyl chloride, tech.**
$CH_3OC_6H_4SO_2Cl$ M.W. 206.65 m.p. 40-43°
MELT

B 10,782-4 **Sulfanilyl fluoride**
$4\text{-}H_2NC_6H_4SO_2F$ M.W. 175.18 m.p. 70-72°
MELT

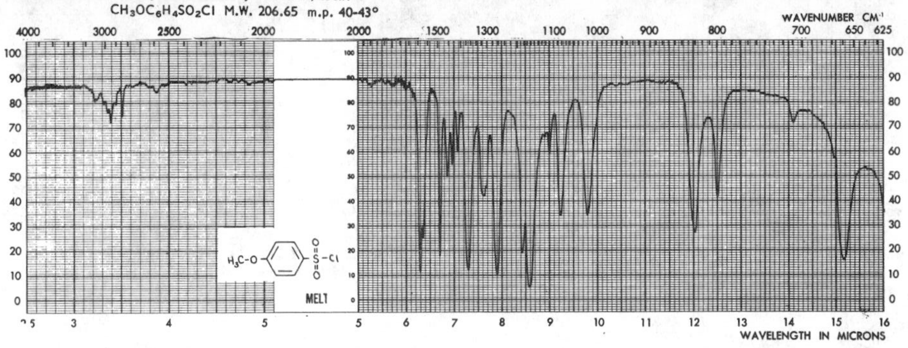

C 10,782-4 **Sulfanilyl fluoride**
$4\text{-}(H_2N)C_6H_4SO_2F$ M.W. 175.18 m.p. 70-72°
NUJOL MULL

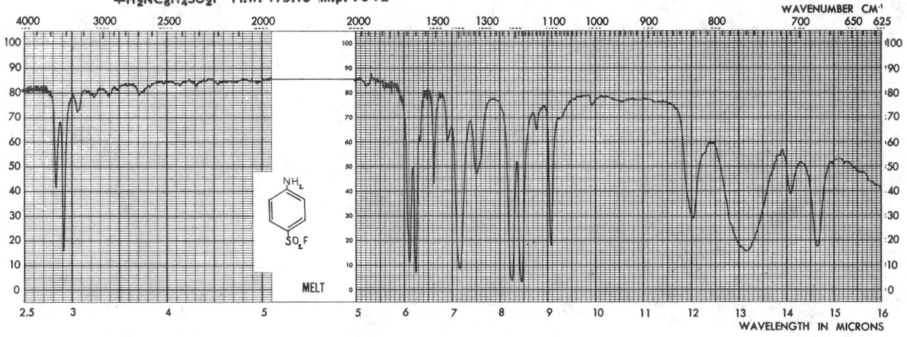

D 17,092-5
p-Nitrobenzenesulfonyl chloride, tech., 75%
$O_2NC_6H_4SO_2Cl$
M.W. 221.62 m.p. 66-70° Beil. 11,72
NUJOL MULL

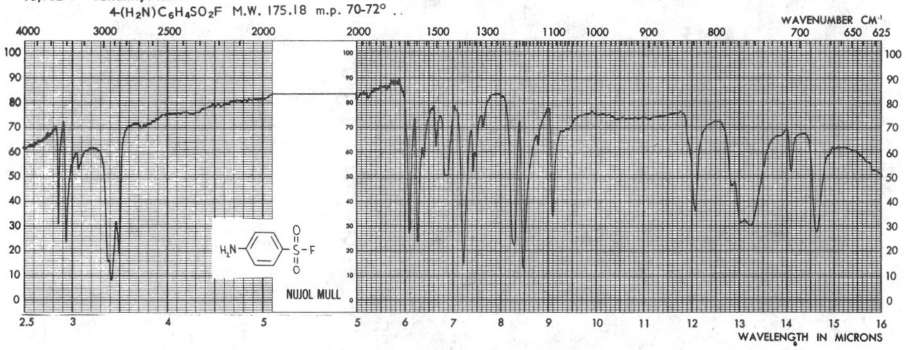

E 10,783-2 **N-Acetylsulfanilyl fluoride** (p-acetamidobenzenesulfonyl fluoride)
$4\text{-}(CH_3CONH)C_6H_4SO_2F$ M.W. 217.22
m.p. 174-176°
NUJOL MULL

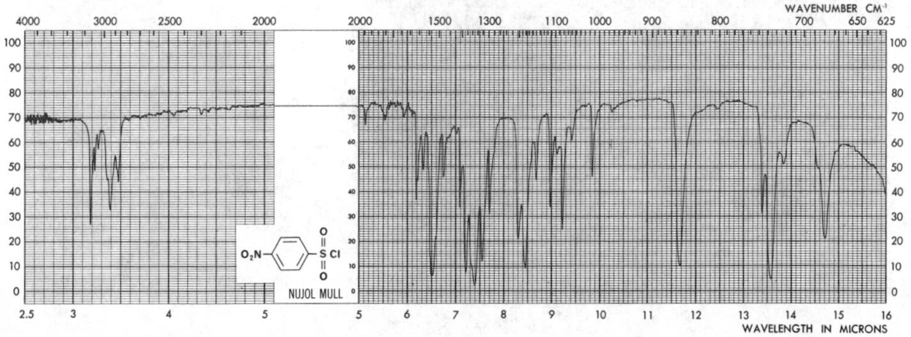

F 11,274-7 **N-Acetylsulfanilyl chloride** (p-acetamidobenzenesulfonyl chloride)
$4\text{-}(CH_3CONH)C_6H_4SO_2Cl$ M.W. 233.67
m.p. 140-143° (dec.)
NUJOL MULL

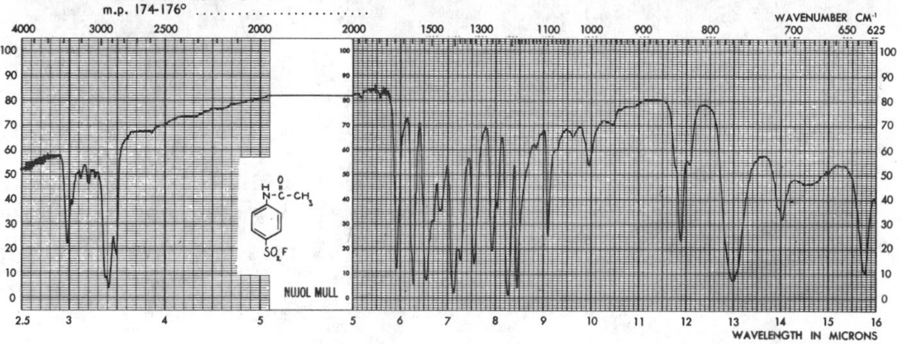

G 13,637-9 **p-(Fluorosulfonyl)-benzoic acid**
$FSO_2C_6H_4CO_2H$ M.W. 204.18
m.p. 271-273°
NUJOL MULL

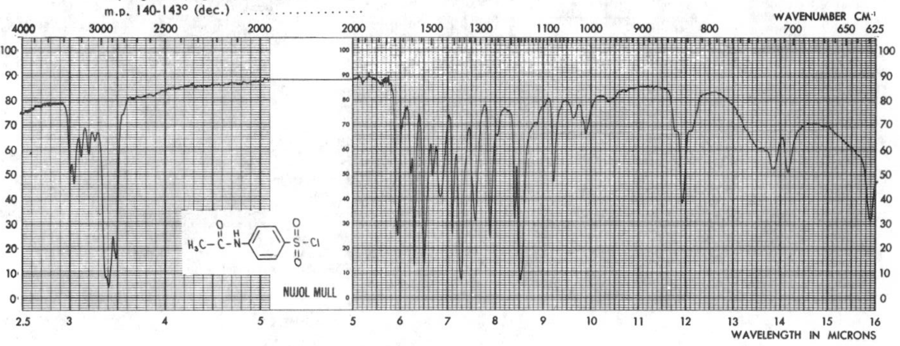

H 13,638-7 **p-(Fluorosulfonyl)-benzoyl chloride, tech.**
$FSO_2C_6H_4COCl$ M.W. 222.62
MELT

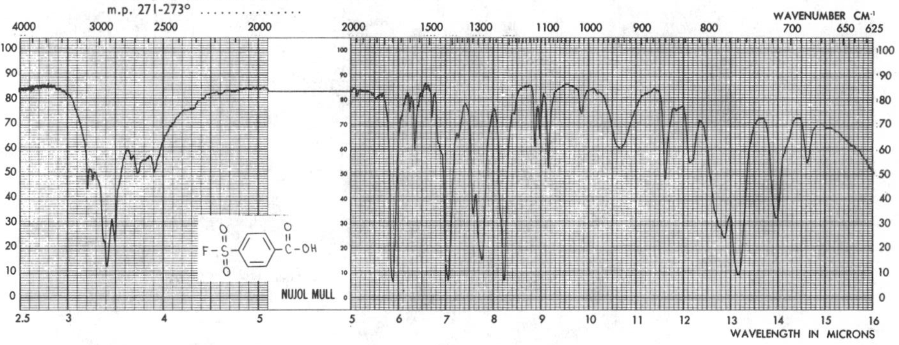

WAVENUMBER CM⁻¹ — WAVELENGTH IN MICRONS

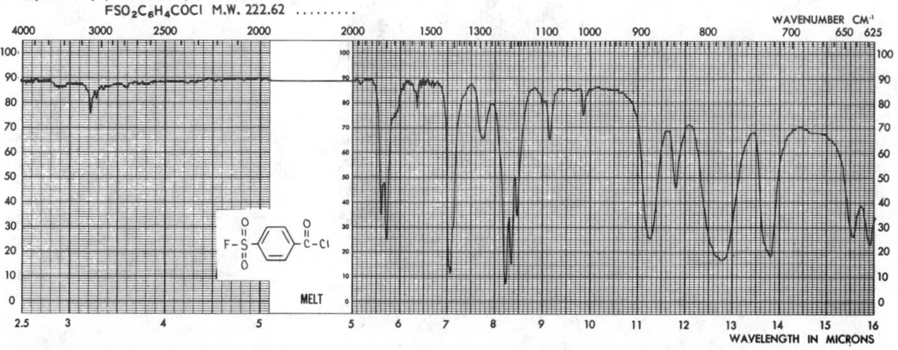

A 11,746-3 p-Fluorosulfonylbenzenesulfonyl chloride
$FSO_2C_6H_4SO_2Cl$ M.W. 258.68
m.p. 110-112.5°
NUJOL MULL

B 12,481-8 4,4'-Biphenyldisulfonyl chloride
$ClSO_2C_6H_4C_6H_4SO_2Cl$ M.W. 351.23
m.p. 205-209°
NUJOL MULL

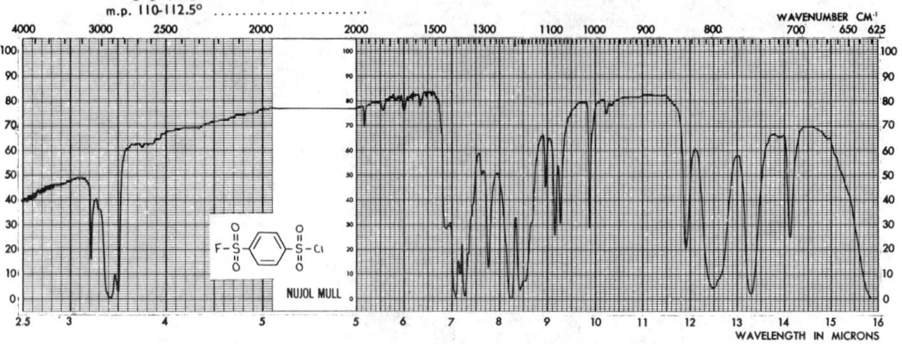

C 17,754-7
2,5-Dichlorobenzenesulfonyl chloride, 98%
$Cl_2C_6H_3SO_2Cl$
M.W. 245.51 m.p. 36-37° Beil. 11(1),15
IRRITANT
MELT

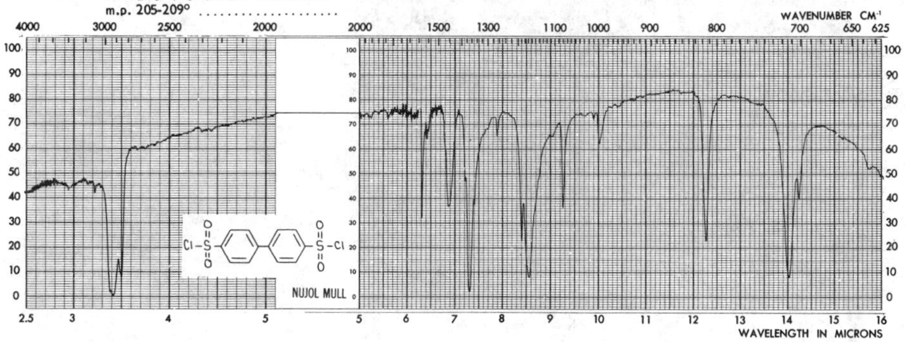

D 14,297-2 3-Amino-4-chlorobenzenesulfonyl fluoride
$H_2NC_6H_3(Cl)SO_2F$ M.W. 209.63 m.p. 62-64°

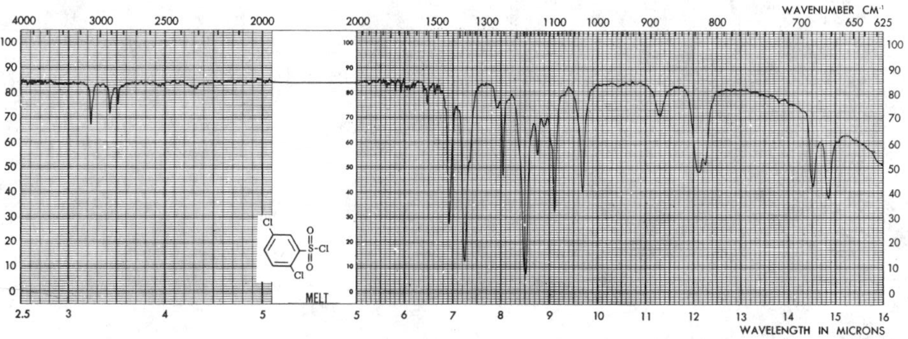

E 10,781-6 4-Methoxymetanilyl fluoride
$CH_3OC_6H_3$-3-$(NH_2)SO_2F$ M.W. 205.21 m.p. 62-65°
MELT

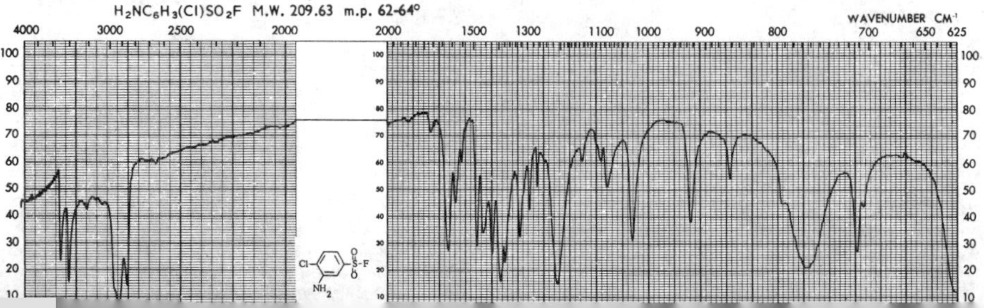

F 13,642-5 4-Amino-3-nitrobenzenesulfonyl fluoride
$H_2NC_6H_3(NO_2)SO_2F$ M.W. 220.18
m.p. 145-148°
NUJOL MULL

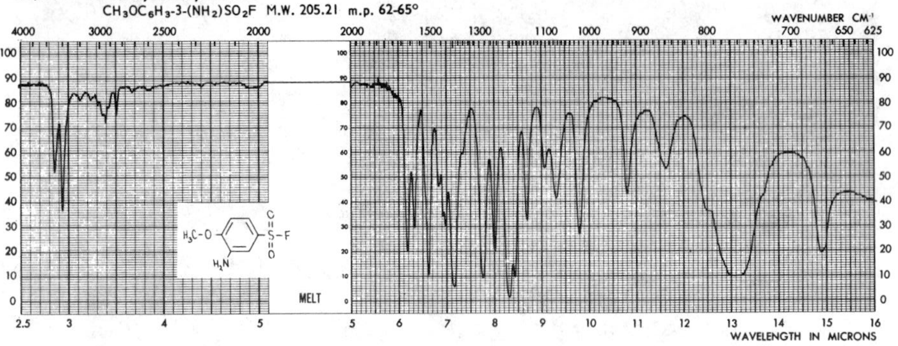

G C5940-8 4-Chloro-3-nitrobenzenesulfonyl chloride
$ClC_6H_3(NO_2)SO_2Cl$ M.W. 256.06 m.p. 59-60°
MELT

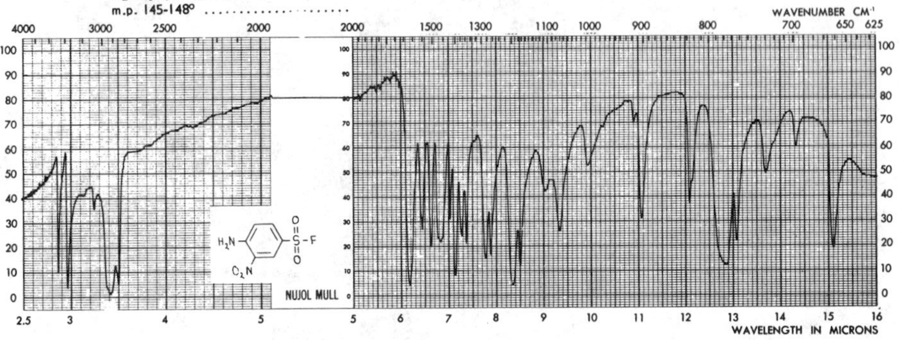

H C5935-1 4-Chloro-2-nitrobenzenesulfonyl chloride
$ClC_6H_3(NO_2)SO_2Cl$ M.W. 256.06 m.p. 59-60°

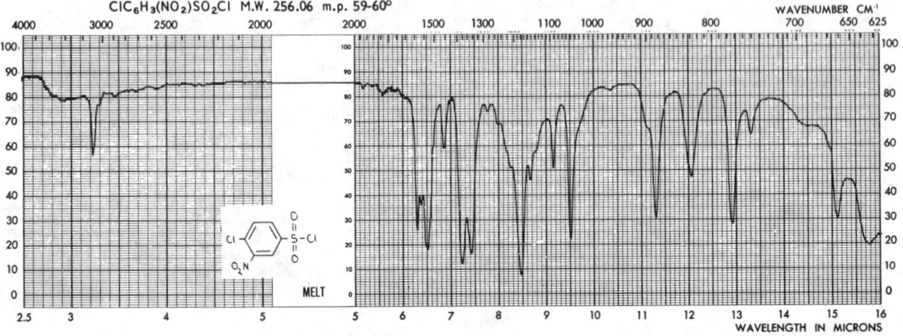

WAVENUMBER CM⁻¹
WAVELENGTH IN MICRONS

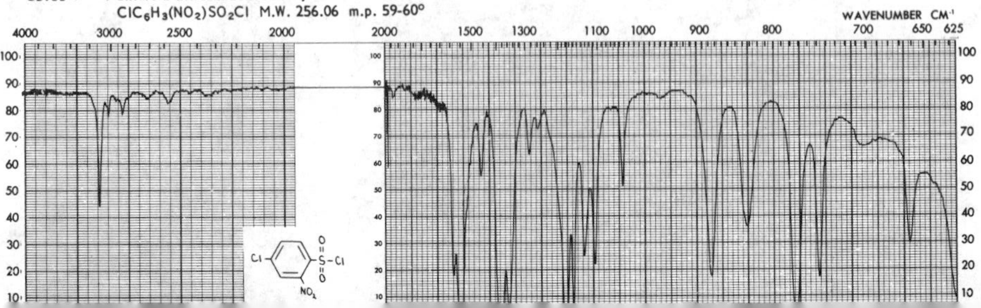

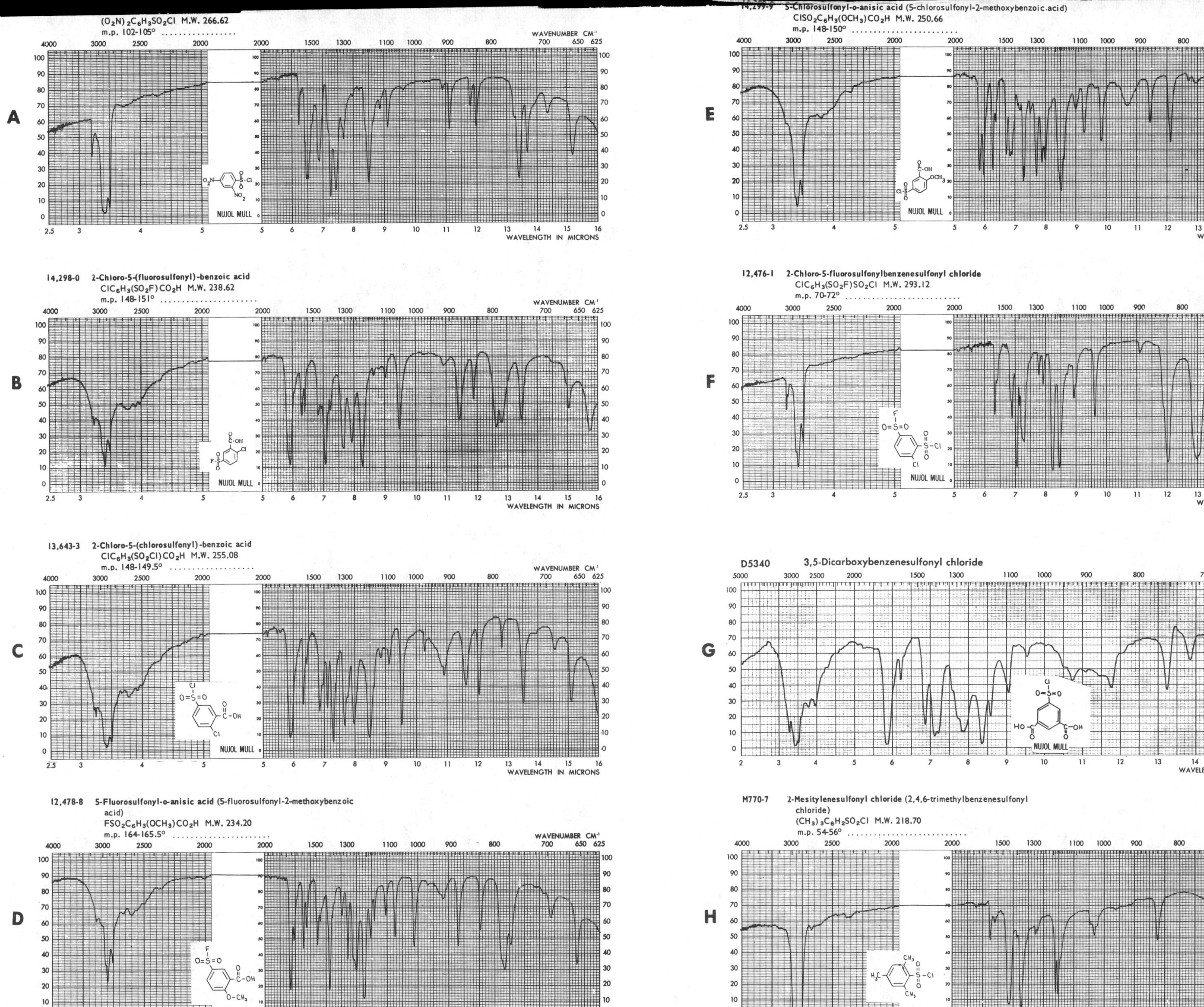
A
$(O_2N)_2C_6H_3SO_2Cl$ M.W. 266.62
m.p. 102-105°
B
14,298-0 2-Chloro-5-(fluorosulfonyl)-benzoic acid
$ClC_6H_3(SO_2F)CO_2H$ M.W. 238.62
m.p. 148-151°
C
13,643-3 2-Chloro-5-(chlorosulfonyl)-benzoic acid
$ClC_6H_3(SO_2Cl)CO_2H$ M.W. 255.08
m.p. 148-149.5°
D
12,478-8 5-Fluorosulfonyl-o-anisic acid (5-fluorosulfonyl-2-methoxybenzoic acid)
$FSO_2C_6H_3(OCH_3)CO_2H$ M.W. 234.20
m.p. 164-165.5°
E
5-Chlorosulfonyl-o-anisic acid (5-chlorosulfonyl-2-methoxybenzoic acid)
$ClSO_2C_6H_3(OCH_3)CO_2H$ M.W. 250.66
m.p. 148-150°
F
12,476-1 2-Chloro-5-fluorosulfonylbenzenesulfonyl chloride
$ClC_6H_3(SO_2F)SO_2Cl$ M.W. 293.12
m.p. 70-72°
G
D5340 3,5-Dicarboxybenzenesulfonyl chloride
H
M770-7 2-Mesitylenesulfonyl chloride (2,4,6-trimethylbenzenesulfonyl chloride)
$(CH_3)_3C_6H_2SO_2Cl$ M.W. 218.70
m.p. 54-56°
NUJOL MULL
WAVENUMBER CM⁻¹
WAVELENGTH IN MICRONS
ALDRICH

A 11,949-0 **2,4,6-Triisopropylbenzenesulfonyl chloride**
$[(CH_3)_2CH]_3C_6H_2SO_2Cl$ M.W. 302.86
m.p. 90-94°

NUJOL MULL

B 11,523-1 **2,3,4-Trichlorobenzenesulfonyl chloride**
$Cl_3C_6H_2SO_2Cl$ M.W. 279.96 m.p. 62-64°

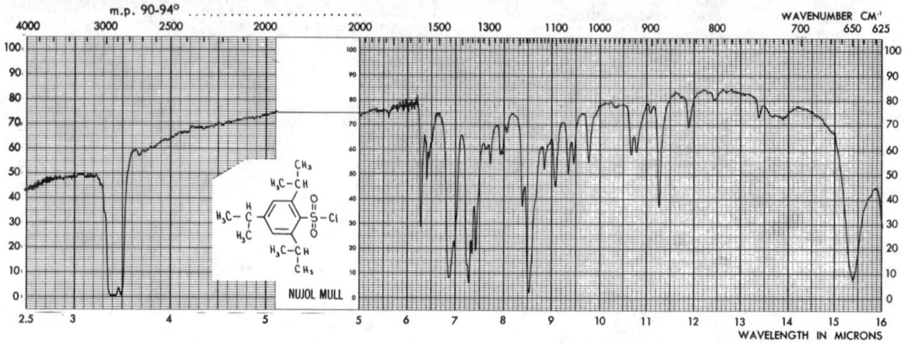

MELT

C T5465-8 **2,4,5-Trichlorobenzenesulfonyl chloride**
$Cl_3C_6H_2SO_2Cl$ M.W. 279.96
m.p. 68-70°

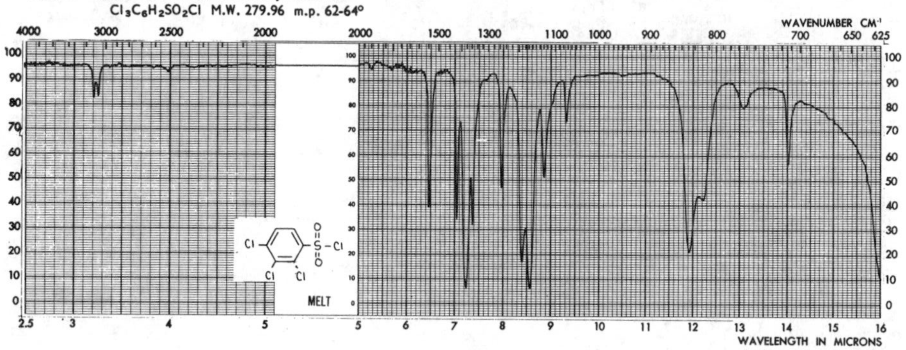

NUJOL MULL

D 14,611-0 **3,5-Dichloro-2-hydroxybenzenesulfonyl chloride** (2,4-dichlorophenol-6-sulfonyl chloride)
$Cl_2C_6H_2(OH)SO_2Cl$ M.W. 261.51
m.p. 80-83°

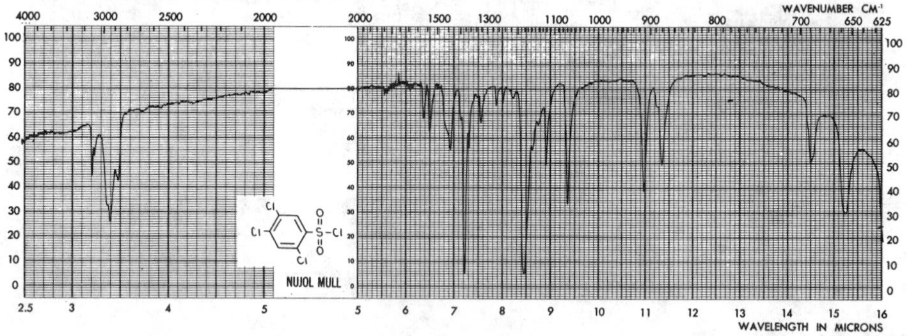

E 10,376-4 **Pentafluorobenzenesulfonyl chloride**
$C_6F_5SO_2Cl$ M.W. 266.57 n_D^{20} 1.4789

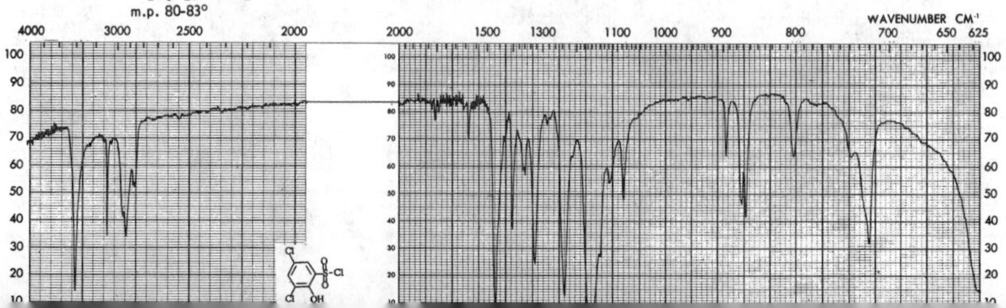

NEAT

F 10,049-8 **Sinalbin hydrate**
M.W. 734.79 (anhydrous) m.p. 100-102°
$[\alpha]_D$ - 8.23° (in H_2O)

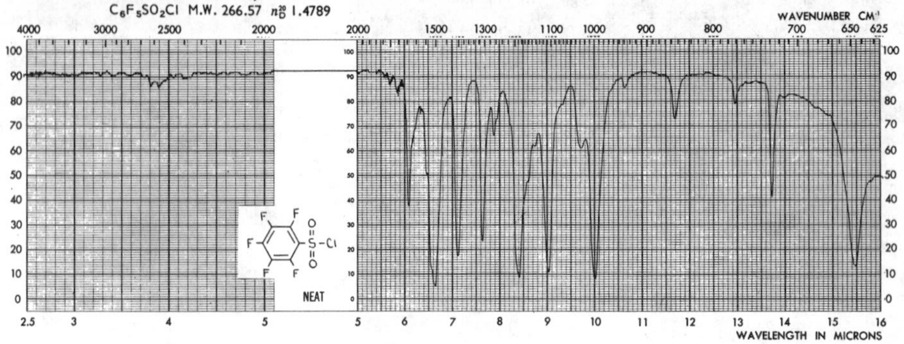

G 13,336-1 **2-Naphthalenesulfonyl chloride**
$C_{10}H_7SO_2Cl$ M.W. 226.68
m.p. 76-78°

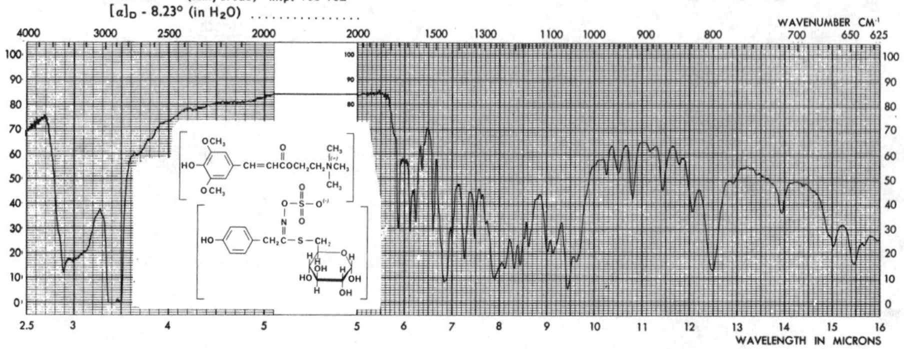

NUJOL MULL

H D14,335-9 **5-Dimethylamino-1-naphthalenesulfonyl chloride** (dansyl chloride)
$(CH_3)_2NC_{10}H_6SO_2Cl$ M.W. 269.75 m.p. 69-71°

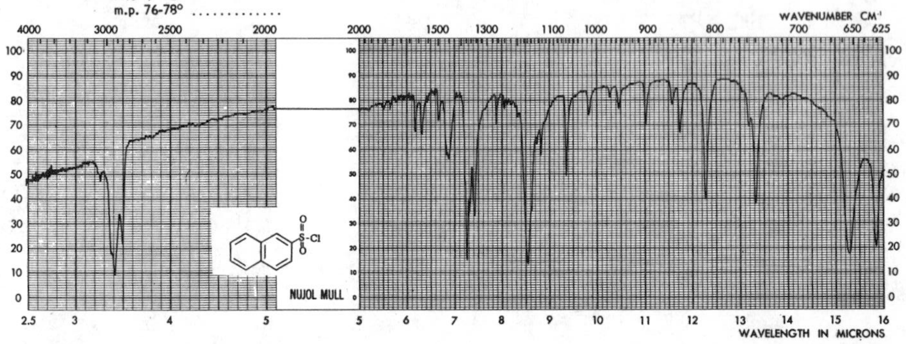

WAVENUMBER CM⁻¹ / WAVELENGTH IN MICRONS

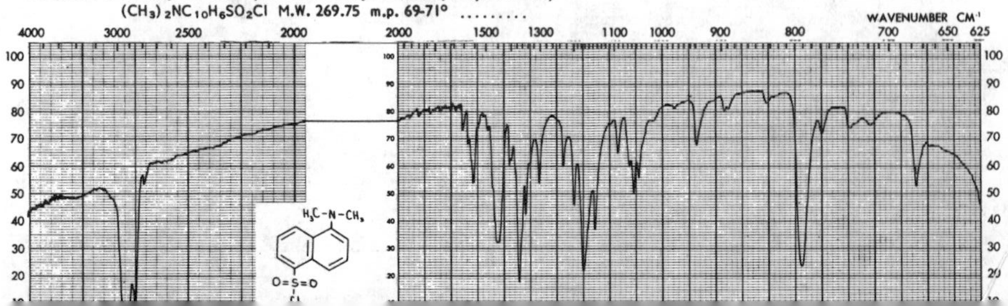

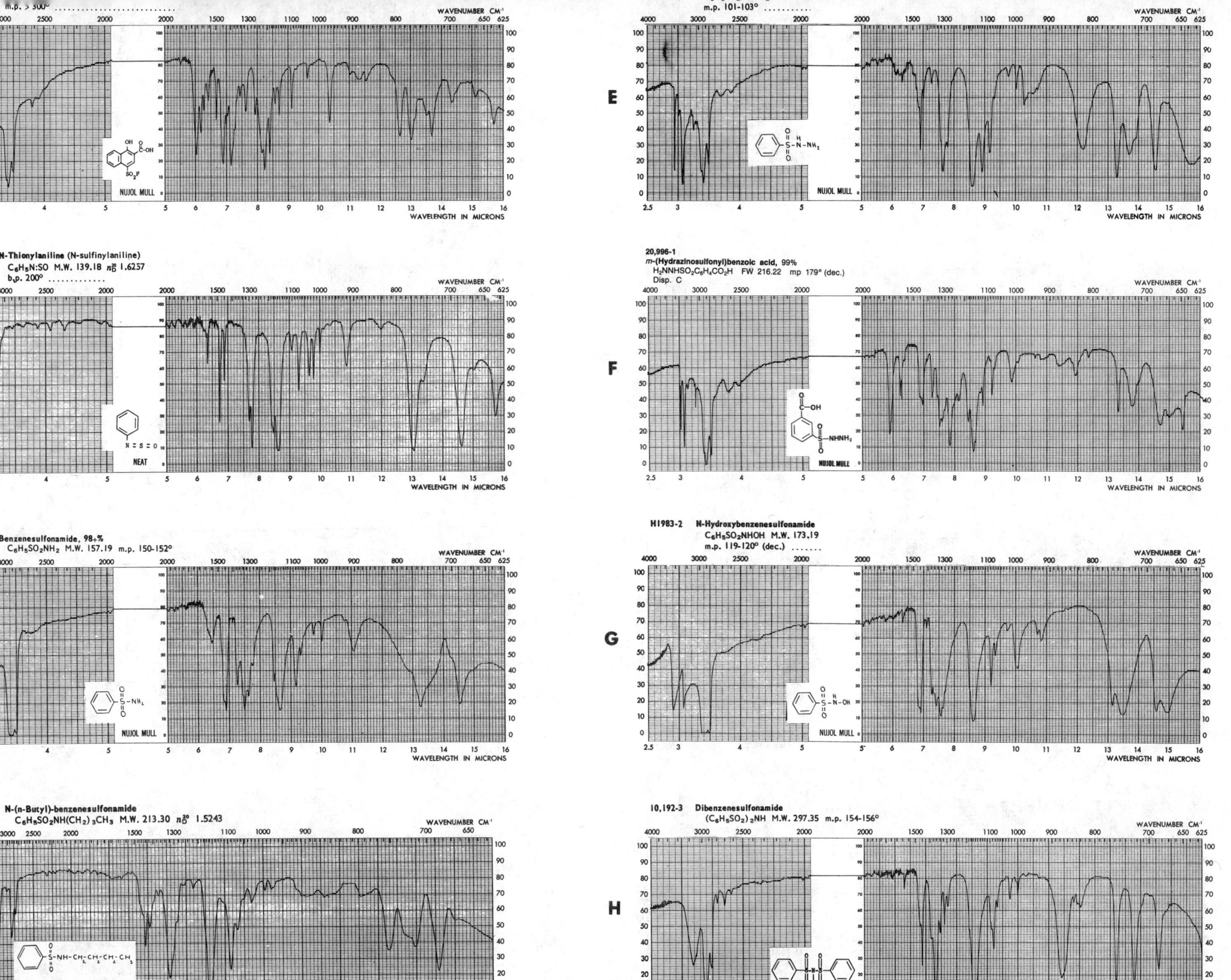

A — m.p. > 300° (NUJOL MULL)

T3170-4 **N-Thionylaniline (N-sulfinylaniline)**
$C_6H_5N{:}SO$ M.W. 139.18 n_D^{20} 1.6257
b.p. 200° (NEAT)

10,814-6 **Benzenesulfonamide, 98+%**
$C_6H_5SO_2NH_2$ M.W. 157.19 m.p. 150-152° (NUJOL MULL)

B9065 **N-(n-Butyl)-benzenesulfonamide**
$C_6H_5SO_2NH(CH_2)_3CH_3$ M.W. 213.30 n_D^{20} 1.5243 (NEAT)

E — $C_6H_5SO_2NHNH_2$ M.W. 172.21
m.p. 101-103° (NUJOL MULL)

20,996-1
m-(Hydrazinosulfonyl)benzoic acid, 99%
$H_2NNHSO_2C_6H_4CO_2H$ FW 216.22 mp 179° (dec.)
Disp. C (NUJOL MULL)

H1983-2 **N-Hydroxybenzenesulfonamide**
$C_6H_5SO_2NHOH$ M.W. 173.19
m.p. 119-120° (dec.) (NUJOL MULL)

10,192-3 **Dibenzenesulfonamide**
$(C_6H_5SO_2)_2NH$ M.W. 297.35 m.p. 154-156° (NUJOL MULL)

A

14,815-6 **N,N'-Diacetylsulfanilamide**
$4\text{-}(CH_3CONH)C_6H_4SO_2NHCOCH_3$ M.W. 256.28
m.p. 267° (dec.)

NUJOL MULL

B

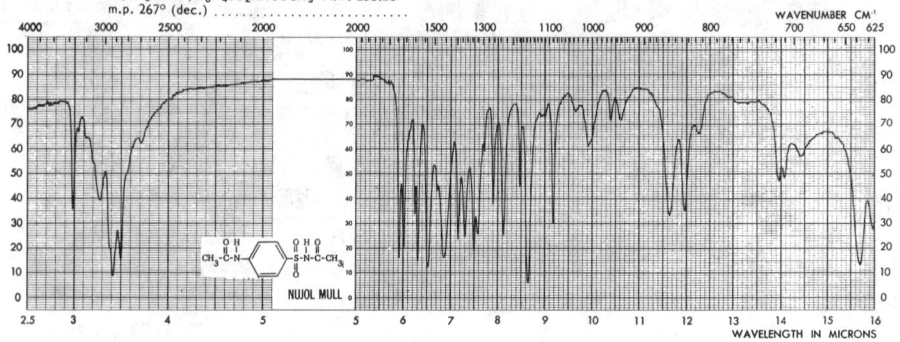

10,590-2 **p-Toluenesulfonamide**
$CH_3C_6H_4SO_2NH_2$ M.W. 171.22 m.p. 137-140°

NUJOL MULL

C

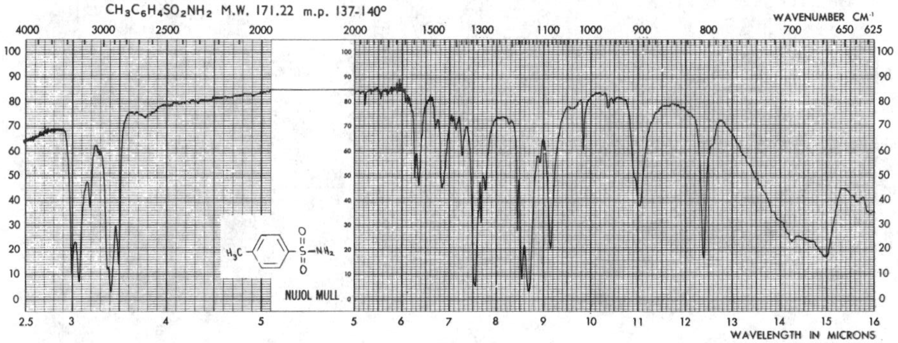

85,731-9
Chloramine-T (N-chloro-p-toluenesulfonamide, sodium salt trihydrate)
$CH_3C_6H_4SO_2N(Cl)Na\cdot 3H_2O$
M.W. 281.69 m.p. 167-170° (dec.)

NUJOL MULL

D

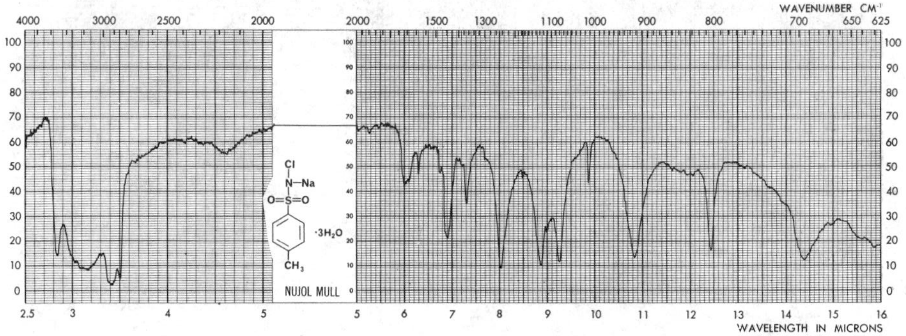

14,860-1 **N-Methyl-p-toluenesulfonamide**
$CH_3C_6H_4SO_2NHCH_3$ M.W. 185.25
m.p. 76-79°

E

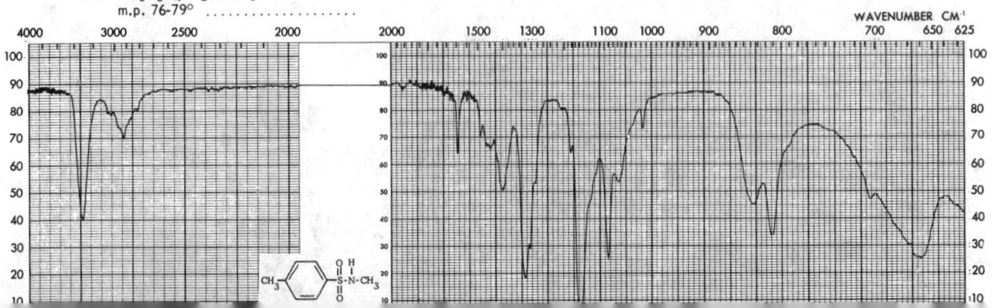

11,288-7 **N-(tert.-Butyl)-p-toluenesulfonamide**
$CH_3C_6H_4SO_2NHC(CH_3)_3$ M.W. 227.33 m.p. 113-114°

NUJOL MULL

F

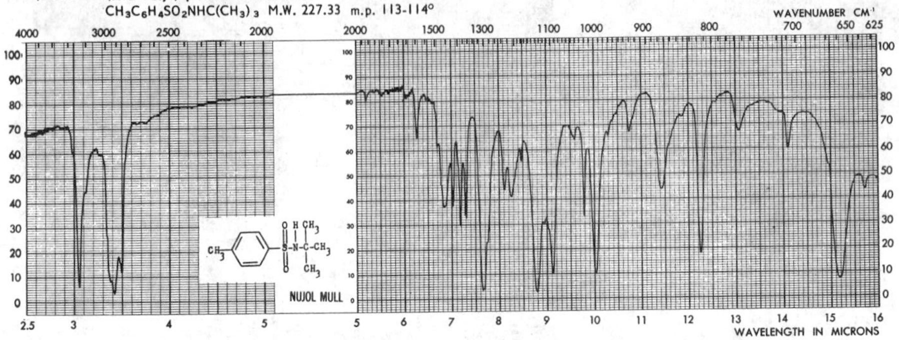

13,200-4 **p-Toluenesulfonhydrazide**
$CH_3C_6H_4SO_2NHNH_2$ M.W. 186.23
m.p. 108-110° (dec.)

NUJOL MULL

G

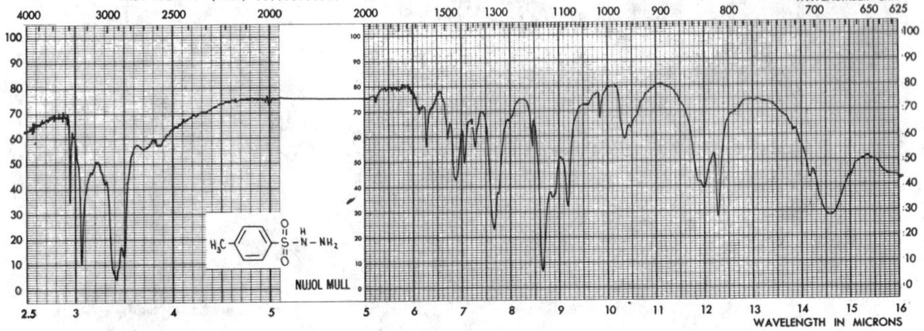

D2800-0 **Diazald®** (N-methyl-N-nitroso-p-toluenesulfonamide)
(send for data sheet)
$CH_3C_6H_4SO_2N(CH_3)NO$ M.W. 214.24
m.p. 59-61°

NUJOL MULL

H

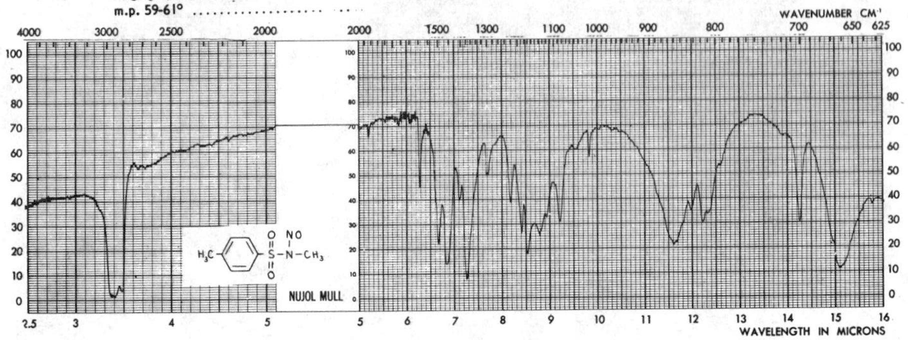

12,103-7 **N,N-Bis-(2-hydroxyethyl)-p-toluenesulfonamide**
$CH_3C_6H_4SO_2N(CH_2CH_2OH)_2$ M.W. 254.33
m.p. 96-99°

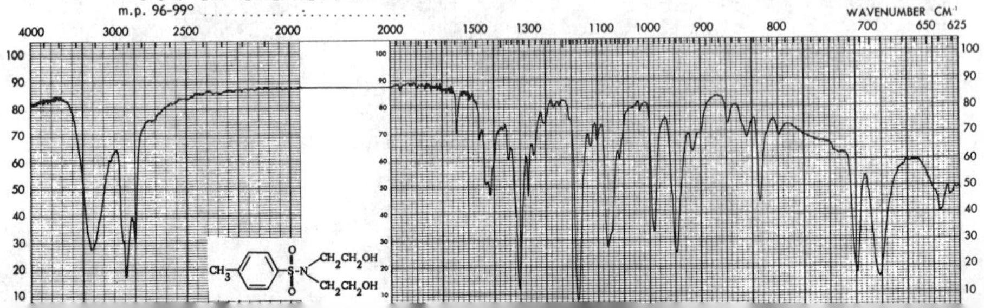

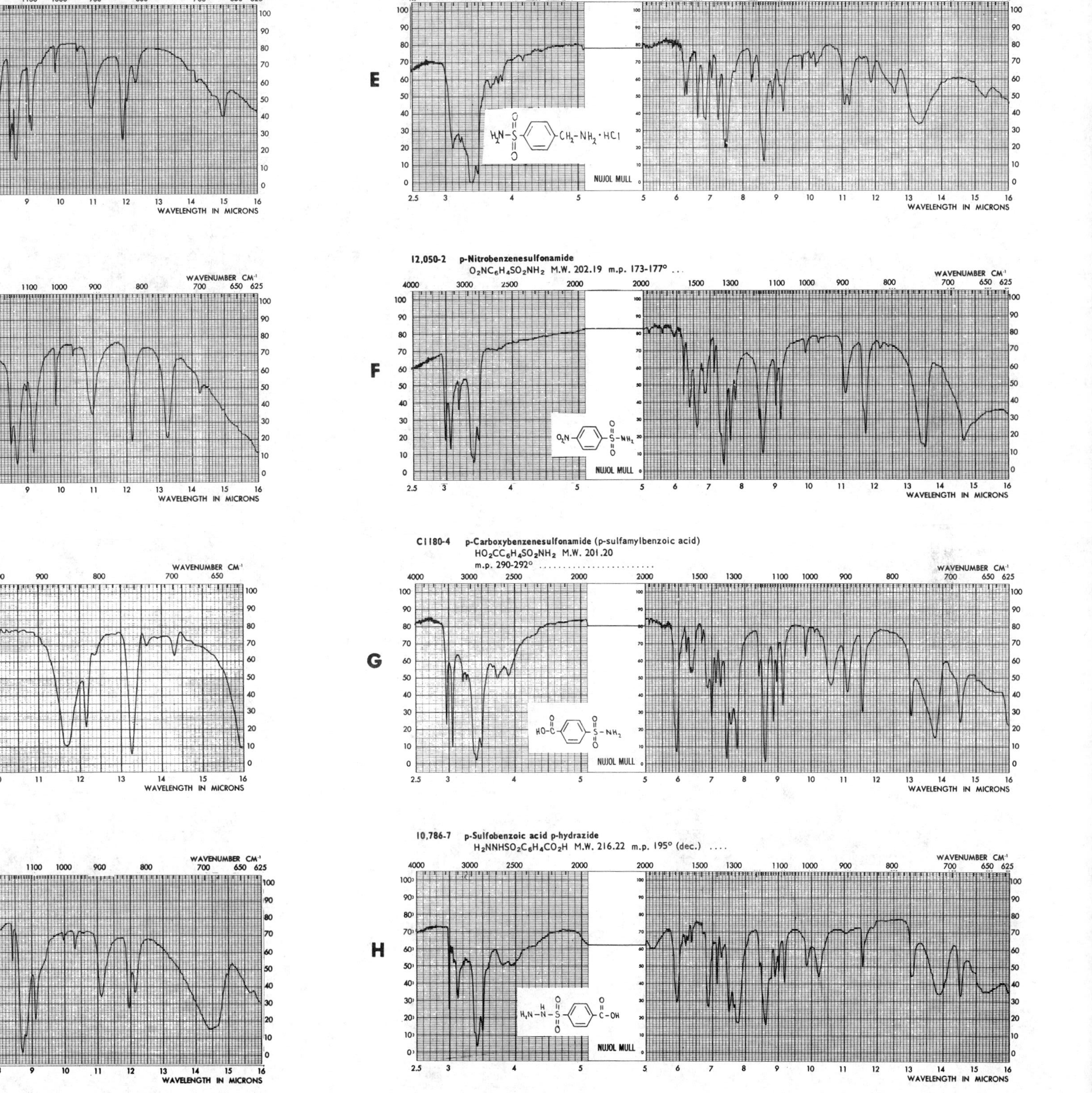

A $FC_6H_4SO_2NH_2$ M.W. 175.18 m.p. 122-124°

B C2419-1 4-Chlorobenzenesulfonamide
$ClC_6H_4SO_2NH_2$ M.W. 191.65
m.p. 145-146.5°

C D6120 4,4'-Dichlorodiphenyldisulfimide

D S652-5 Sulfanilamide
4-$(H_2N)C_6H_4SO_2NH_2$ M.W. 172.21 m.p. 164-166°

E m.p. 281-284

F 12,050-2 p-Nitrobenzenesulfonamide
$O_2NC_6H_4SO_2NH_2$ M.W. 202.19 m.p. 173-177°

G C1180-4 p-Carboxybenzenesulfonamide (p-sulfamylbenzoic acid)
$HO_2CC_6H_4SO_2NH_2$ M.W. 201.20
m.p. 290-292°

H 10,786-7 p-Sulfobenzoic acid p-hydrazide
$H_2NNHSO_2C_6H_4CO_2H$ M.W. 216.22 m.p. 195° (dec.)

ALDRICH®

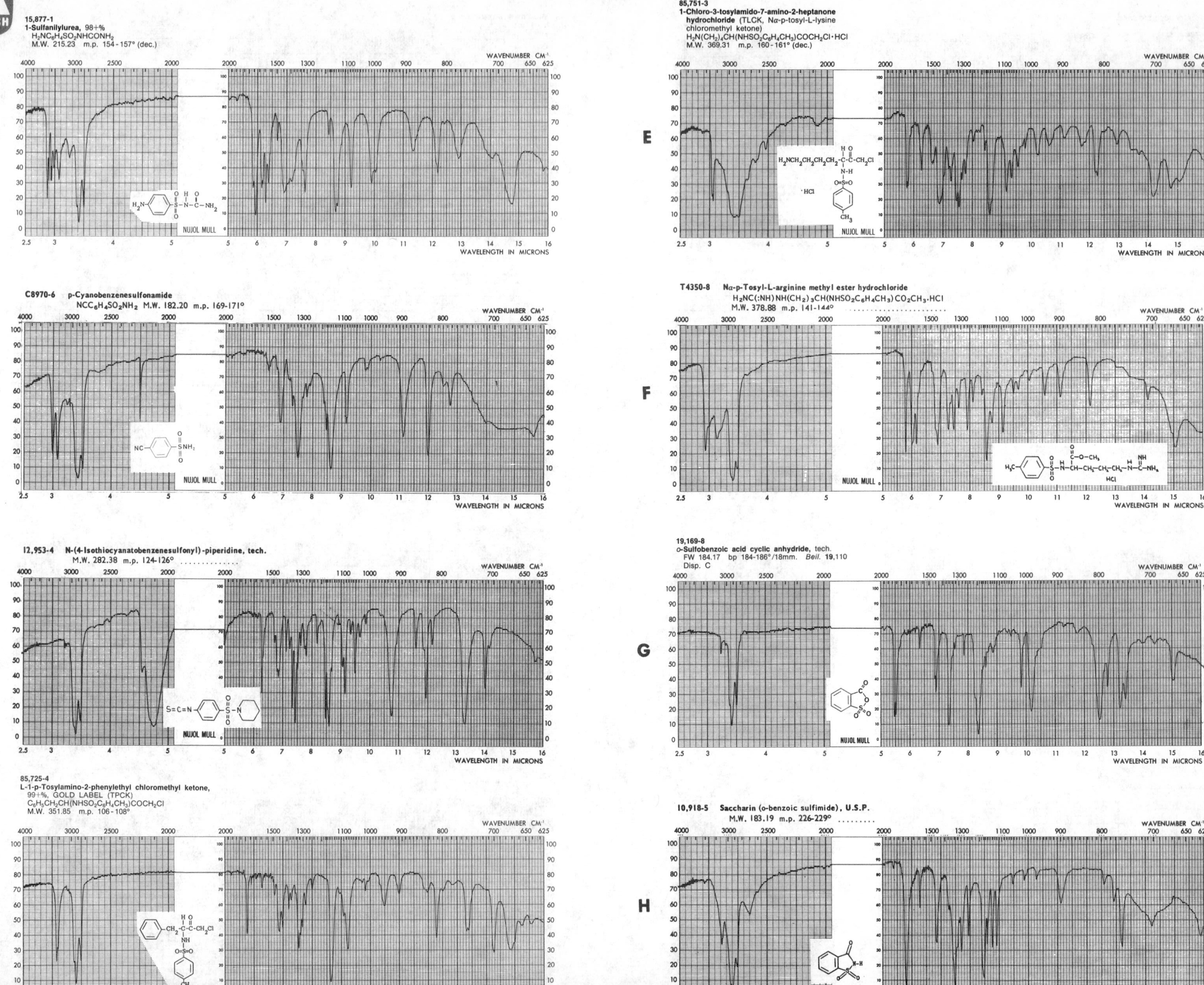

A 15,877-1
1-Sulfanilylurea, 98+%
$H_2NC_6H_4SO_2NHCONH_2$
M.W. 215.23 m.p. 154-157° (dec.)
NUJOL MULL

B C8970-6 **p-Cyanobenzenesulfonamide**
$NCC_6H_4SO_2NH_2$ M.W. 182.20 m.p. 169-171°
NUJOL MULL

C 12,953-4 **N-(4-Isothiocyanatobenzenesulfonyl)-piperidine, tech.**
M.W. 282.38 m.p. 124-126°
NUJOL MULL

D 85,725-4
L-1-p-Tosylamino-2-phenylethyl chloromethyl ketone,
99+%, GOLD LABEL (TPCK)
$C_6H_5CH_2CH(NHSO_2C_6H_4CH_3)COCH_2Cl$
M.W. 351.85 m.p. 106-108°

E 85,751-3
1-Chloro-3-tosylamido-7-amino-2-heptanone hydrochloride (TLCK, Nα-p-tosyl-L-lysine chloromethyl ketone)
$H_2N(CH_2)_4CH(NHSO_2C_6H_4CH_3)COCH_2Cl \cdot HCl$
M.W. 369.31 m.p. 160-161° (dec.)
NUJOL MULL

F T4350-8 **Nα-p-Tosyl-L-arginine methyl ester hydrochloride**
$H_2NC(:NH)NH(CH_2)_3CH(NHSO_2C_6H_4CH_3)CO_2CH_3 \cdot HCl$
M.W. 378.88 m.p. 141-144°
NUJOL MULL

G 19,169-8
o-Sulfobenzoic acid cyclic anhydride, tech.
FW 184.17 bp 184-186°/18mm. *Beil.* 19,110
Disp. C
NUJOL MULL

H 10,918-5 **Saccharin (o-benzoic sulfimide), U.S.P.**
M.W. 183.19 m.p. 226-229°

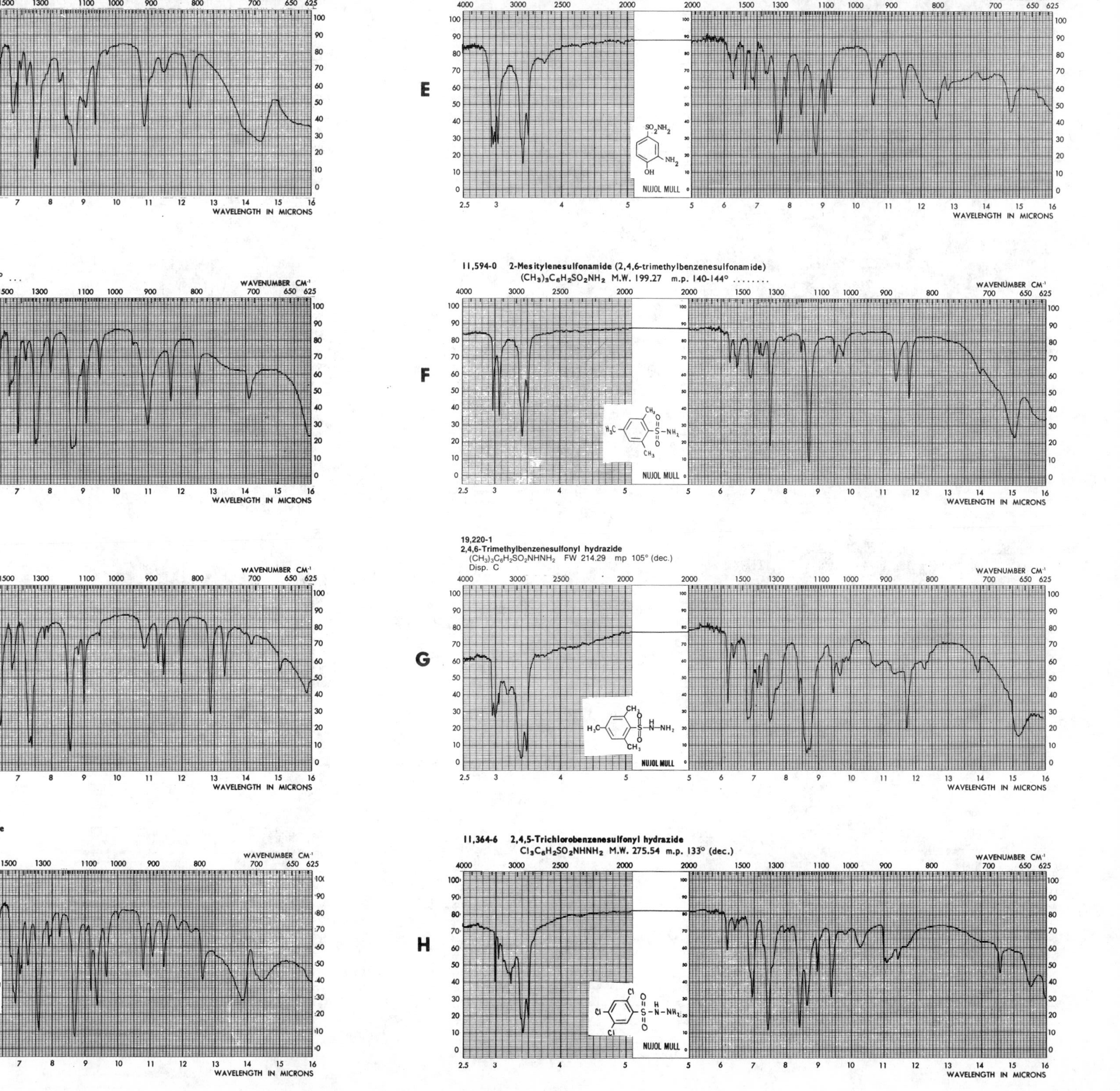

A

A4543-2 2-Amino-4-chlorobenzenesulfonamide
$H_2NC_6H_3(Cl)SO_2NH_2$ M.W. 206.65 m.p. 141.5-145° ...

B

C5930-0 4-Chloro-2-nitrobenzenesulfonamide
$ClC_6H_3(NO_2)SO_2NH_2$ M.W. 236.63 m.p. 164-165°

C

14,554-8 3-Amino-4-chloro-N-(2-cyanoethyl)-benzenesulfonamide
$H_2NC_6H_3(Cl)SO_2NHCH_2CH_2CN$ M.W. 259.72
m.p. 95-97° ....

D

E

11,594-0 2-Mesitylenesulfonamide (2,4,6-trimethylbenzenesulfonamide)
$(CH_3)_3C_6H_2SO_2NH_2$ M.W. 199.27 m.p. 140-144° ....

F

19,220-1
2,4,6-Trimethylbenzenesulfonyl hydrazide
$(CH_3)_3C_6H_2SO_2NHNH_2$ FW 214.29 mp 105° (dec.)
Disp. C

G

11,364-6 2,4,5-Trichlorobenzenesulfonyl hydrazide
$Cl_3C_6H_2SO_2NHNH_2$ M.W. 275.54 m.p. 133° (dec.)

H

ALDRICH

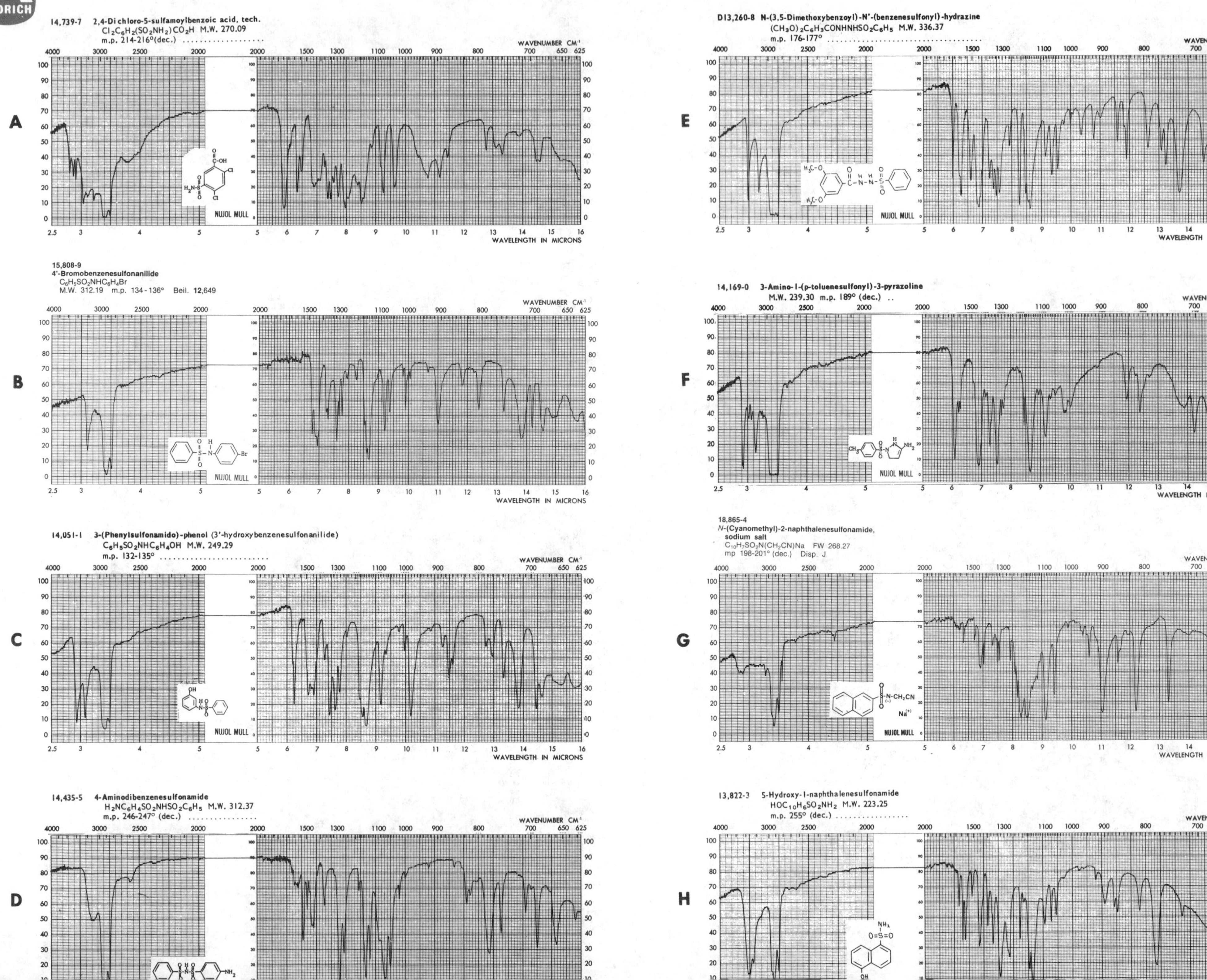
ALDRICH
A
14,739-7 2,4-Dichloro-5-sulfamoylbenzoic acid, tech.
$Cl_2C_6H_2(SO_2NH_2)CO_2H$ M.W. 270.09
m.p. 214-216°(dec.)
NUJOL MULL
B
15,808-9
4'-Bromobenzenesulfonanilide
$C_6H_5SO_2NHC_6H_4Br$
M.W. 312.19 m.p. 134-136° Beil. 12,649
NUJOL MULL
C
14,051-1 3-(Phenylsulfonamido)-phenol (3'-hydroxybenzenesulfonanilide)
$C_6H_5SO_2NHC_6H_4OH$ M.W. 249.29
m.p. 132-135°
NUJOL MULL
D
14,435-5 4-Aminodibenzenesulfonamide
$H_2NC_6H_4SO_2NHSO_2C_6H_5$ M.W. 312.37
m.p. 246-247° (dec.)
E
D13,260-8 N-(3,5-Dimethoxybenzoyl)-N'-(benzenesulfonyl)-hydrazine
$(CH_3O)_2C_6H_3CONHNHSO_2C_6H_5$ M.W. 336.37
m.p. 176-177°
NUJOL MULL
F
14,169-0 3-Amino-1-(p-toluenesulfonyl)-3-pyrazoline
M.W. 239.30 m.p. 189° (dec.)
NUJOL MULL
G
18,865-4
N-(Cyanomethyl)-2-naphthalenesulfonamide, sodium salt
$C_{10}H_7SO_2N(CH_2CN)Na$ FW 268.27
mp 198-201° (dec.) Disp. J
NUJOL MULL
H
13,822-3 5-Hydroxy-1-naphthalenesulfonamide
$HOC_{10}H_6SO_2NH_2$ M.W. 223.25
m.p. 255° (dec.)
WAVENUMBER CM⁻¹
WAVELENGTH IN MICRONS

Disp. C

A

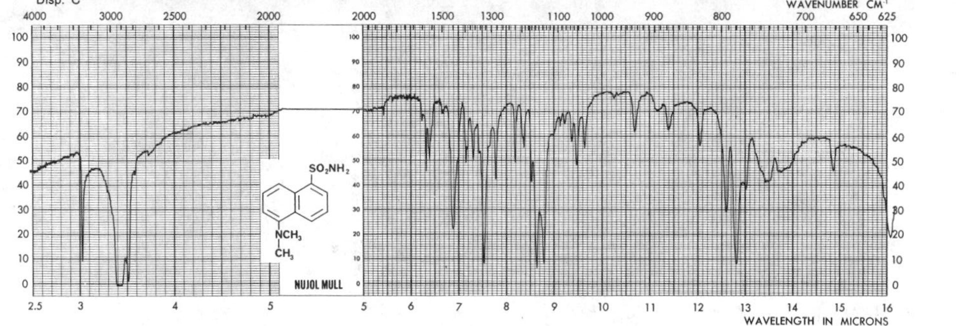

14,353-7 **4-Aminosulfonyl-1-hydroxy-2-naphthoic acid**
$H_2NSO_2C_{10}H_5(OH)CO_2H$ M.W. 267.26
m.p. 222° (dec.)

B

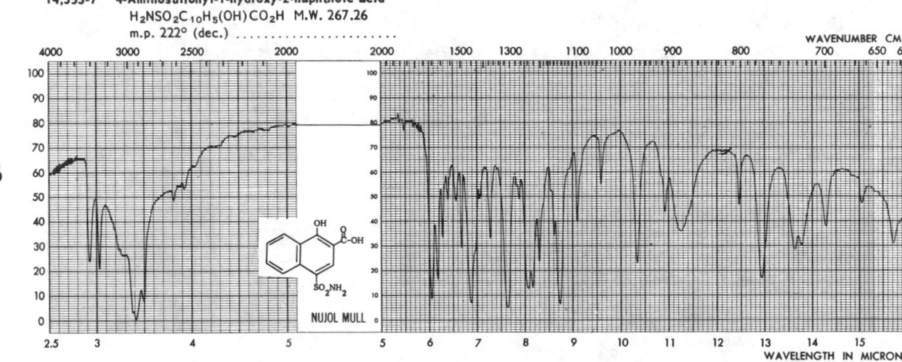

18,927-8
***p*-Toluenesulfonyl isocyanate**, 96+% (tosyl isocyanate)
$CH_3C_6H_4SO_2NCO$ FW 197.21 bp 144°/10mm.
n_D^{20} 1.5344 *Fieser* **7**,377 Disp. C

C

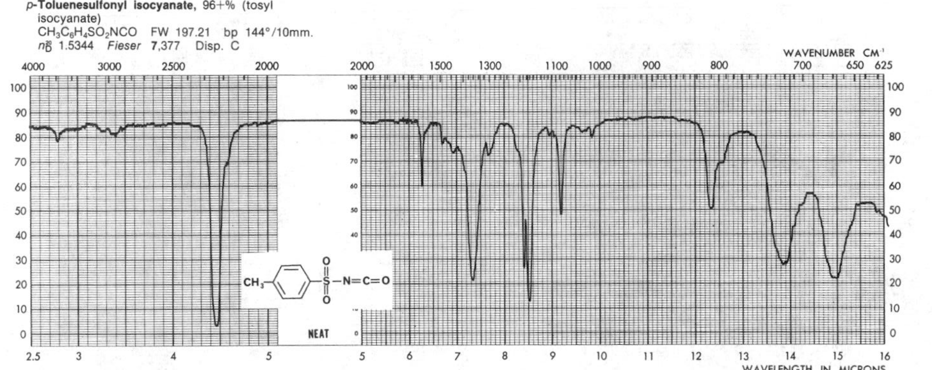

22,417-0
3-(Fluorosulfonyl)benzoic acid, 98%
$FSO_2C_6H_4CO_2H$ FW 204.18 mp 149-152°
Beil. **11**(2),217 Disp. I

D

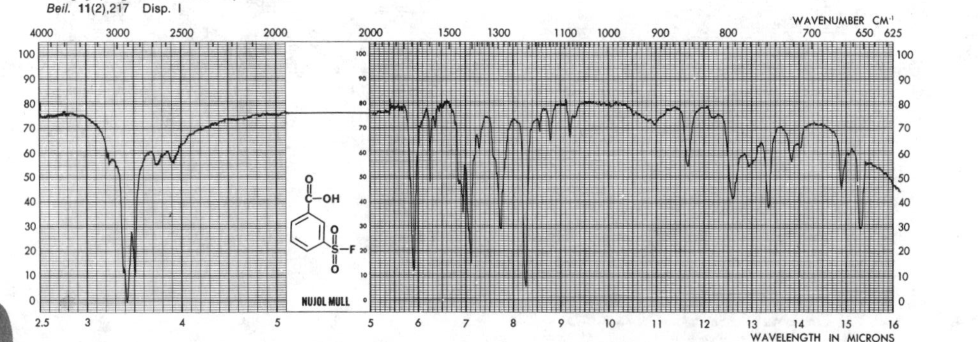

AROMATIC PHOSPHORUS COMPOUNDS

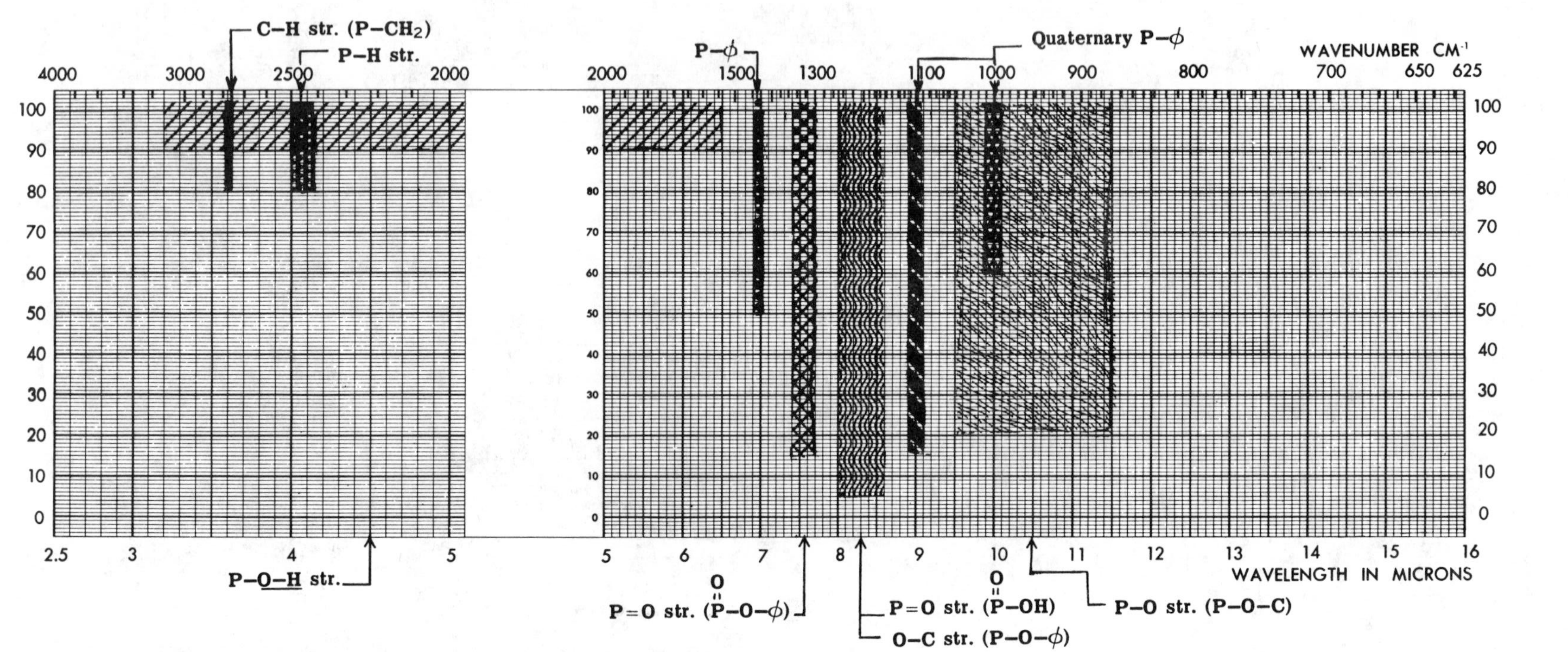

The phenyl ring attached directly to the phosphorus atom (spectra 1182A—D) displays an unusually sharp and relatively strong aromatic band at 7.0 μ (1430 cm^{-1}). The quaternary phosphorus compounds (spectra 1182E—1186B) display a very strong band at 9 μ (1110 cm^{-1}) with a medium band appearing at 10 μ (1000 cm^{-1}). A weak but sharp band at 3.6 μ (2780 cm^{-1}) is apparently due to the shift of the CH_2 carbon-hydrogen stretch caused by its attachment to the phosphorus atom. The substitution pattern between 13 and 15 μ (770 – 665 cm^{-1}) is broken up into a number of strong absorptions. The sharp aromatic bands at 7, 9 and 10 μ (1430, 1110 and 1000 cm^{-1}) can best be seen in the phosphine and quaternary phosphorus compounds due to the lack of interference from other bands where P=O and P–O groups are present.

The P–O–ϕ group absorbs strongly at 8 – 8.6 μ (1250 – 1165 cm^{-1}) due to the C–O linkage and between 9.5 and 11.5 μ (1055–870 cm^{-1}) due to the P–O stretch vibration. The P=O attached to the aromatic ring through an oxygen atom absorbs between 7.4 and 7.7 μ (1350 – 1300 cm^{-1}) except when OH groups are attached to phosphorus. The band is then shifted to 8 – 8.5 μ (1250 – 1175 cm^{-1}).

The substitution patterns between 11 and 15 μ (910 – 665 cm^{-1}) are disrupted somewhat by the attachment of the P or P=O group to the ring.

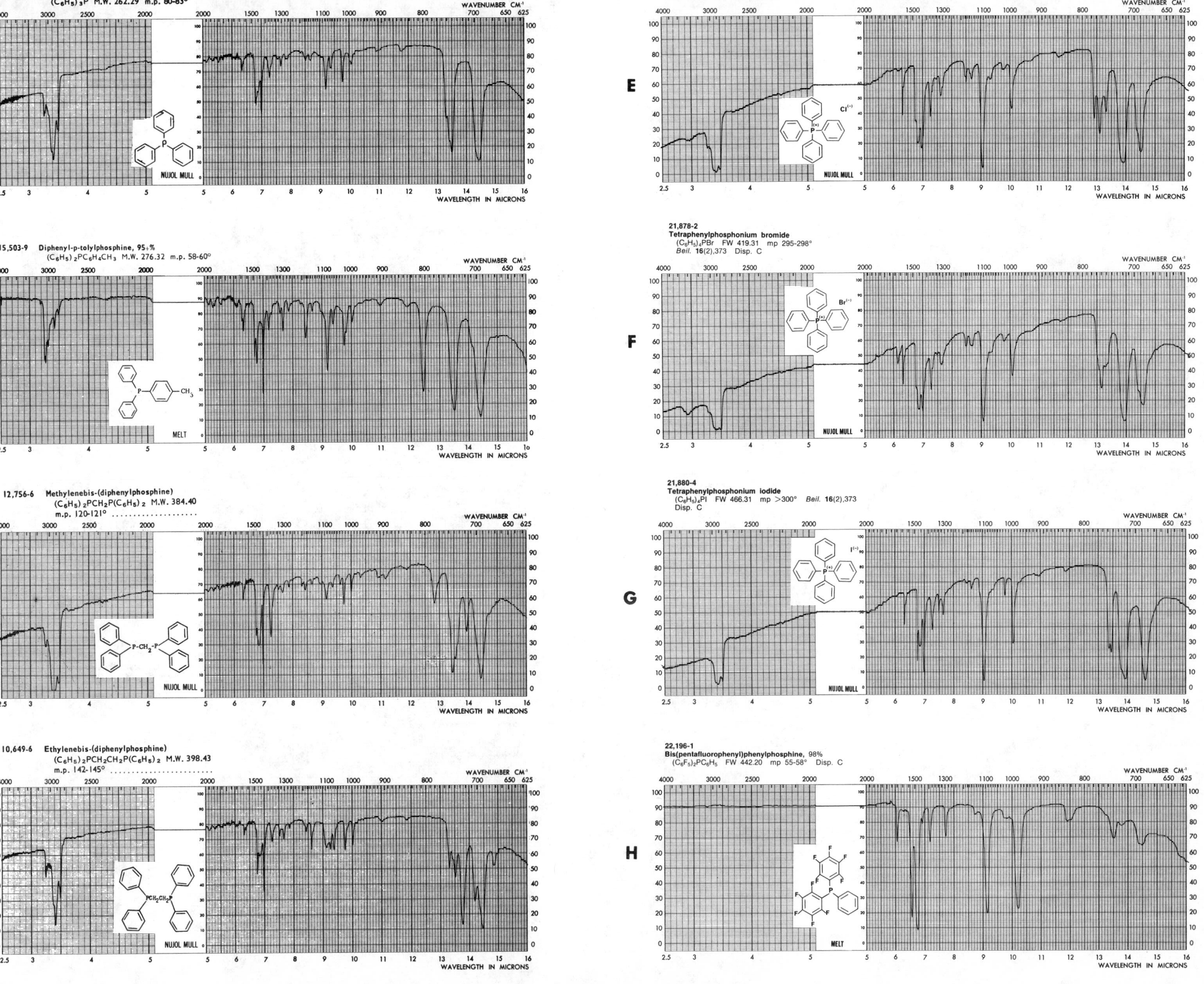
A
18440-9 Triphenylphosphine
$(C_6H_5)_3P$ M.W. 262.29 m.p. 80-83°
NUJOL MULL
B
15,503-9 Diphenyl-p-tolylphosphine, 95+%
$(C_6H_5)_2PC_6H_4CH_3$ M.W. 276.32 m.p. 58-60°
MELT
C
12,756-6 Methylenebis-(diphenylphosphine)
$(C_6H_5)_2PCH_2P(C_6H_5)_2$ M.W. 384.40
m.p. 120-121°
NUJOL MULL
D
10,649-6 Ethylenebis-(diphenylphosphine)
$(C_6H_5)_2PCH_2CH_2P(C_6H_5)_2$ M.W. 398.43
m.p. 142-145°
NUJOL MULL
E
Beil. 16(2),373 Disp. C
NUJOL MULL
F
21,878-2
Tetraphenylphosphonium bromide
$(C_6H_5)_4PBr$ FW 419.31 mp 295-298°
Beil. 16(2),373 Disp. C
NUJOL MULL
G
21,880-4
Tetraphenylphosphonium iodide
$(C_6H_5)_4PI$ FW 466.31 mp >300° Beil. 16(2),373
Disp. C
NUJOL MULL
H
22,196-1
Bis(pentafluorophenyl)phenylphosphine, 98%
$(C_6F_5)_2PC_6H_5$ FW 442.20 mp 55-58° Disp. C
MELT
WAVENUMBER CM⁻¹
WAVELENGTH IN MICRONS

A

13,007-9 (Methyl)-triphenylphosphonium bromide
$CH_3P(C_6H_5)_3Br$ M.W. 357.24
m.p. 230-233° ....

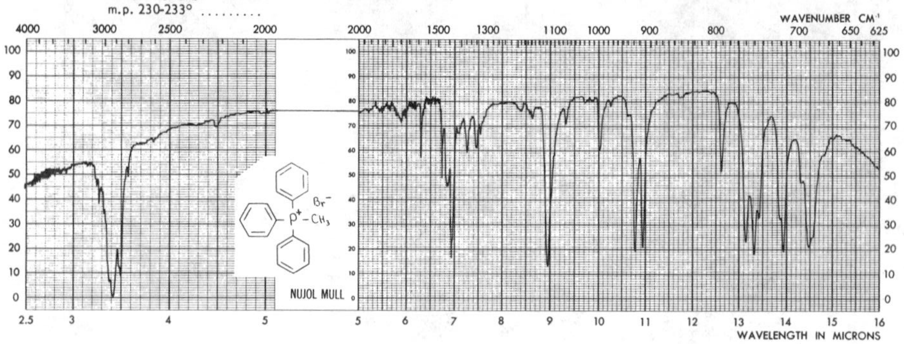

NUJOL MULL

B

E5060-4 (Ethyl)-triphenylphosphonium bromide
$C_2H_5P(C_6H_5)_3Br$ M.W. 371.26 m.p. 206-208°

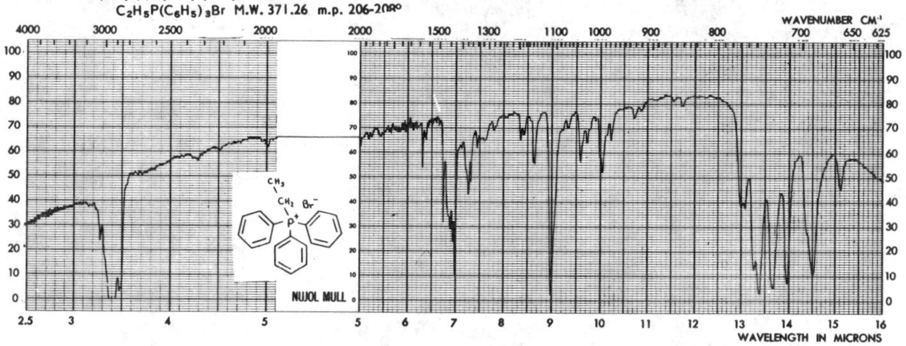

NUJOL MULL

C

13,156-3 (n-Propyl)-triphenylphosphonium bromide
$CH_3CH_2CH_2P(C_6H_5)_3Br$ M.W. 385.29 m.p. 232-237.5° ...

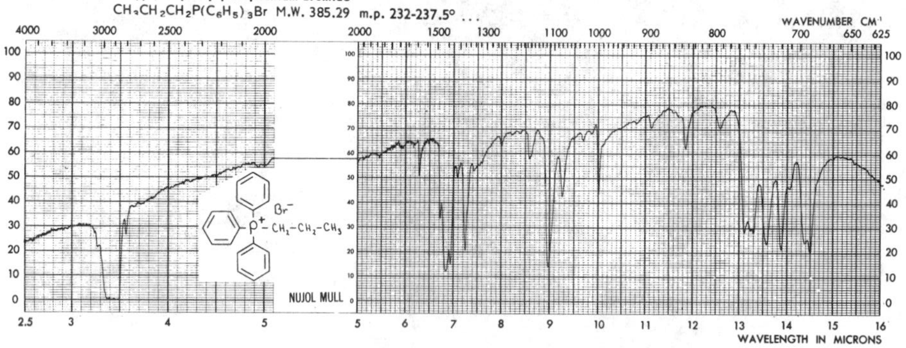

NUJOL MULL

D

B10,280-6 (n-Butyl)-triphenylphosphonium bromide
$CH_3(CH_2)_3P(C_6H_5)_3Br$ M.W. 399.32 m.p. 241-243°

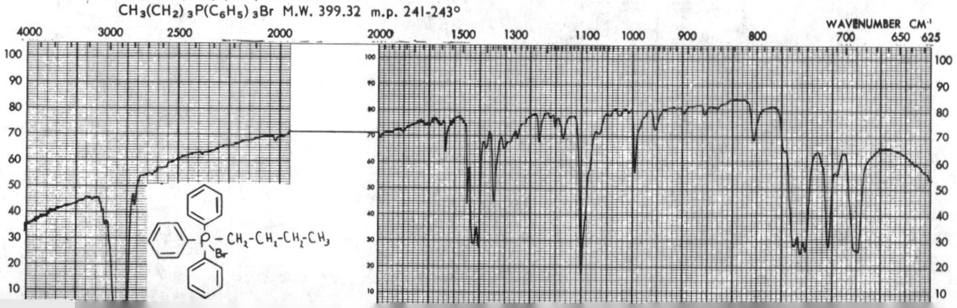

E

17,262-6
Dodecyltriphenylphosphonium bromide
$CH_3(CH_2)_{11}P(C_6H_5)_3Br$ FW 511.53 mp 86-88°
Disp. C

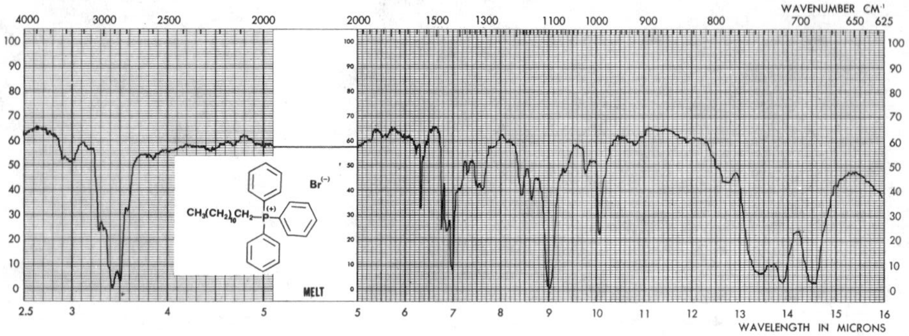

MELT

F

15,019-3
Vinyl triphenylphosphonium bromide, 97% (triphenylvinylphosphonium bromide)
$H_2C{=}CHP(C_6H_5)_3Br$
M.W. 369.25 m.p. 176-178° Fieser 1,1274 2,456
(send for data sheet)

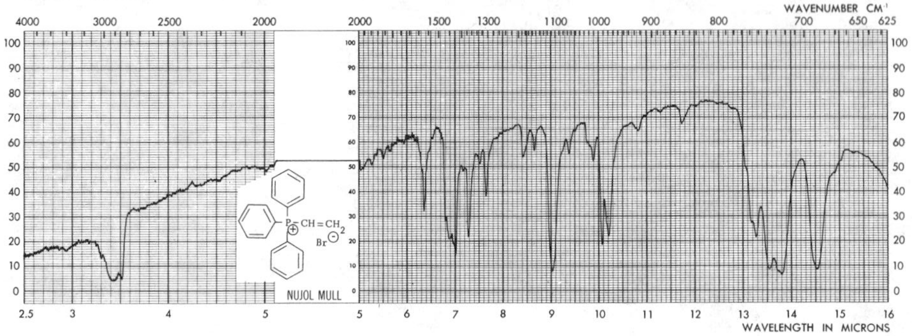

NUJOL MULL

G

A3660-3 (Allyl)-triphenylphosphonium bromide
$H_2C{:}CHCH_2P(C_6H_5)_3Br$ M.W. 383.27 m.p. 229-232° .....

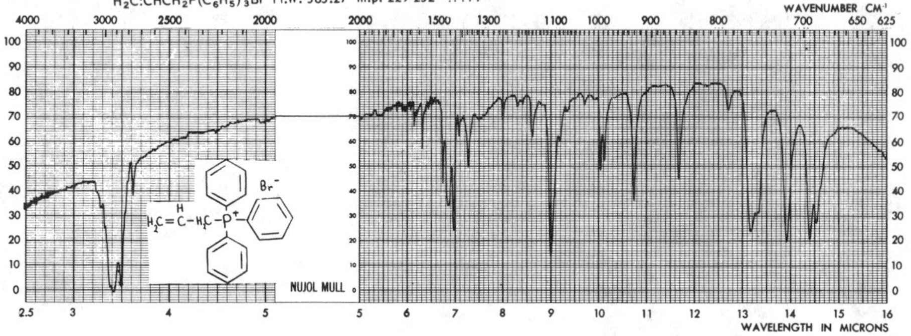

NUJOL MULL

H

C5762-6 (Chloromethyl)-triphenylphosphonium chloride, tech.
$ClCH_2P(C_6H_5)_3Cl$ M.W. 347.23 ....

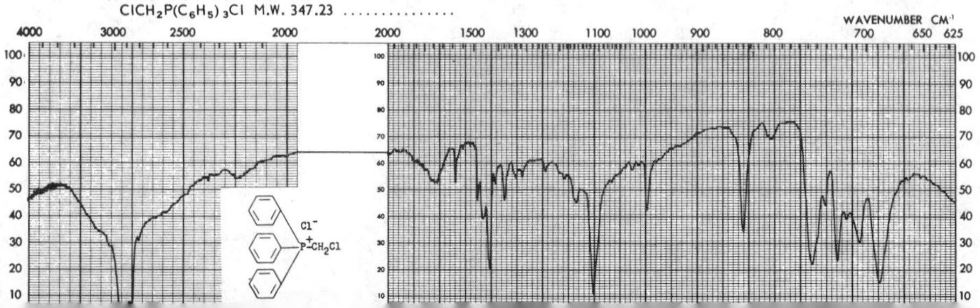

A

$Br(CH_2)_3P(C_6H_5)_3Br$ M.W. 464.19
m.p. 230-231°

NUJOL MULL

B

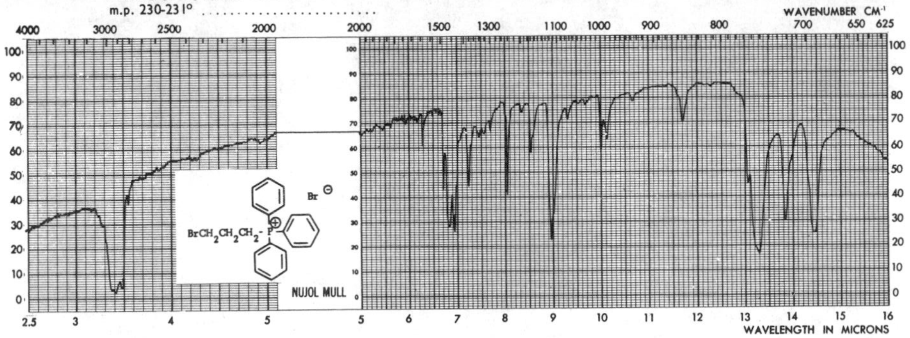

14,761-3 (4-Bromobutyl)triphenylphosphonium bromide
$Br(CH_2)_4P(C_6H_5)_3Br$ M.W. 478.22
m.p. 214-216°

NUJOL MULL

C

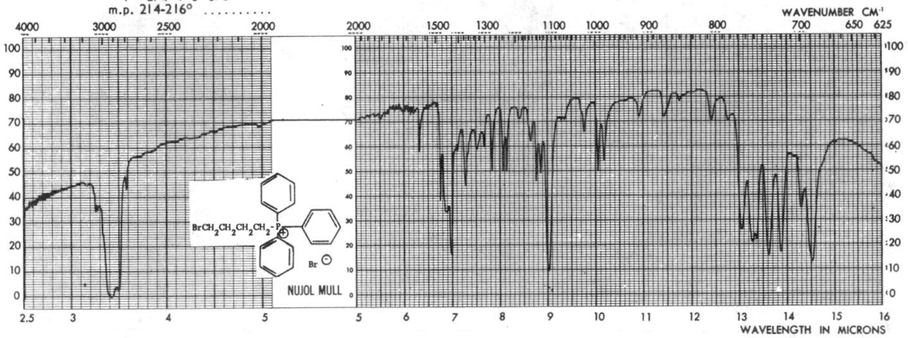

21,544-9
(2-Dimethylaminoethyl)triphenylphosphonium bromide, 97%
$(CH_3)_2NCH_2CH_2P(C_6H_5)_3Br$ FW 414.33
mp 201° (dec.) Disp. C

NUJOL MULL

D

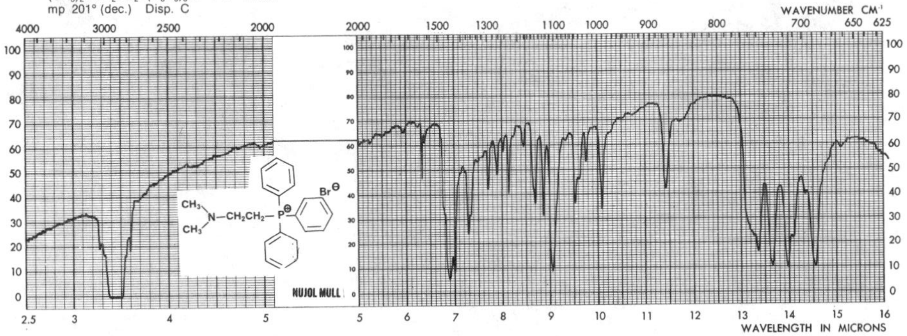

10,000-5 (Methoxymethyl)-triphenylphosphonium chloride
$CH_3OCH_2P(C_6H_5)_3Cl$ M.W. 342.61
m.p. 195-197°

NUJOL MULL

E

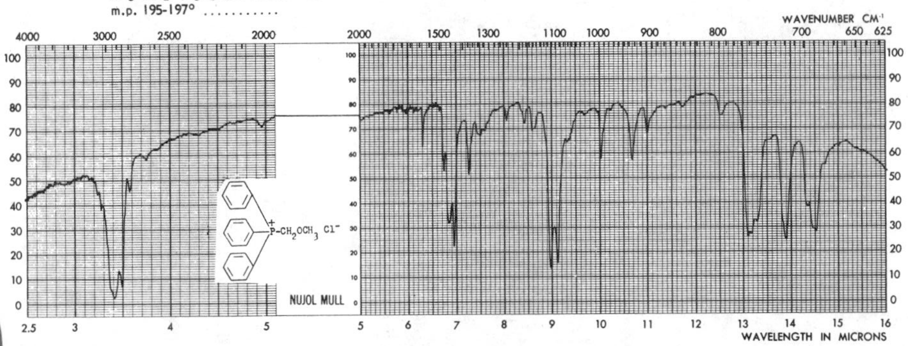

FW 429.30 mp 193-195° *Fieser* 5,269 Disp. C

NUJOL MULL

F

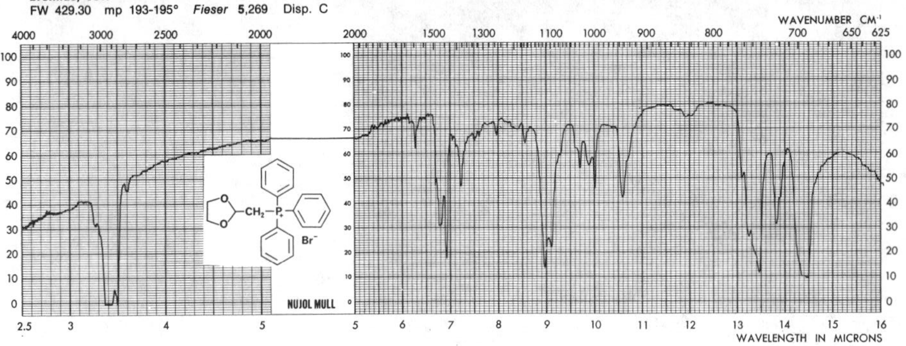

21,959-2
[2-(1,3-Dioxan-2-yl)ethyl]triphenylphosphonium bromide, 98%
FW 357.36 mp 193-195° Disp. C

NUJOL MULL

G

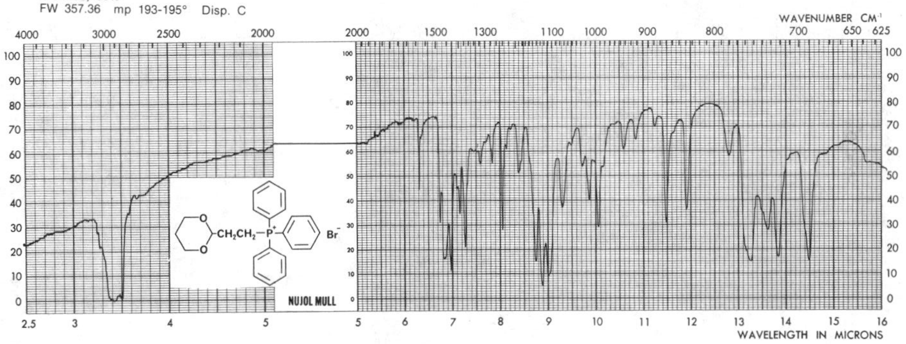

B3280-7 (Benzyl)-triphenylphosphonium chloride
$C_6H_5CH_2P(C_6H_5)_3Cl$ M.W. 388.88
m.p. > 300°

NUJOL MULL

H

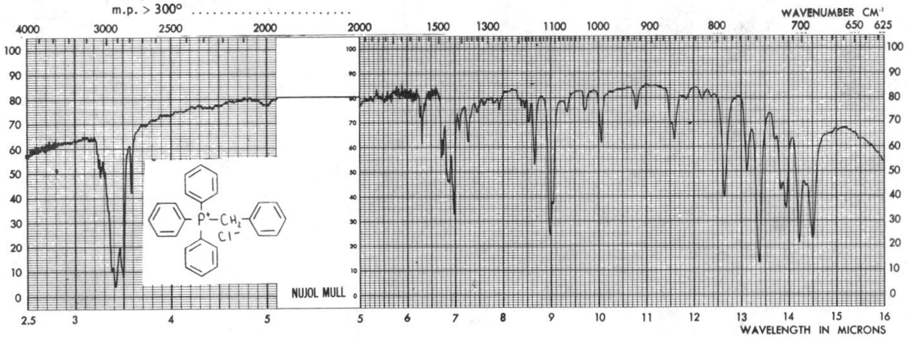

15,908-5
(p-Chlorophenoxymethyl)-triphenylphosphonium chloride, 98%
$ClC_6H_4OCH_2P(C_6H_5)_3Cl$
M.W. 439.32 m.p. 219-221°

NUJOL MULL

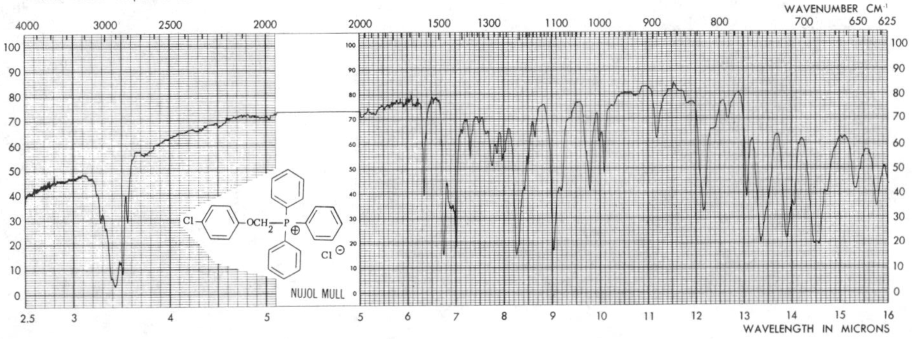

A

21,629-1
(o-Hydroxybenzyl)triphenylphosphonium bromide, 98%
$HOC_6H_4CH_2P(C_6H_5)_3Br$ FW 449.34 mp 242-245°
Disp. C

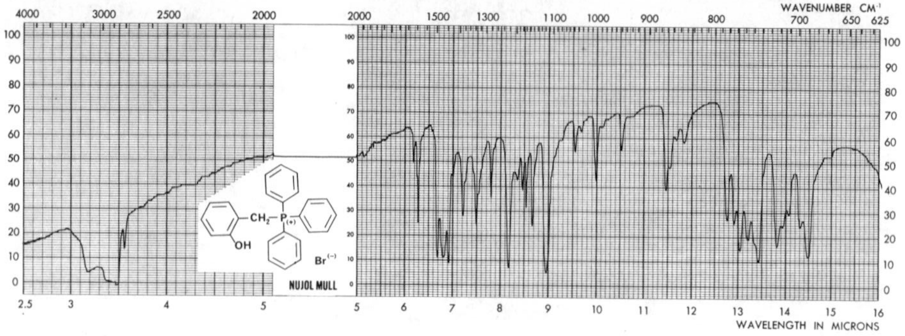

NUJOL MULL

B

C8205 **(Cinnamyl)-triphenylphosphonium bromide**
$C_6H_5CH{:}CHCH_2P(C_6H_5)_3Br$

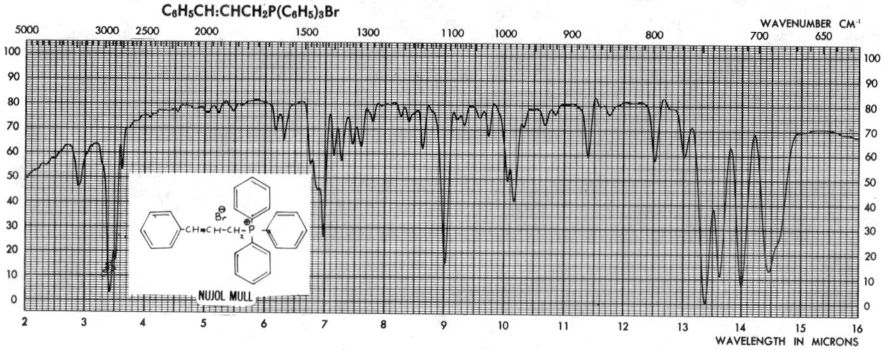

NUJOL MULL

C

B7230-2 **o-(Bromomethyl)-benzyltriphenylphosphonium bromide**
$BrCH_2C_6H_4CH_2P(C_6H_5)_3Br$ M.W. 526.28
m.p. 243-245°

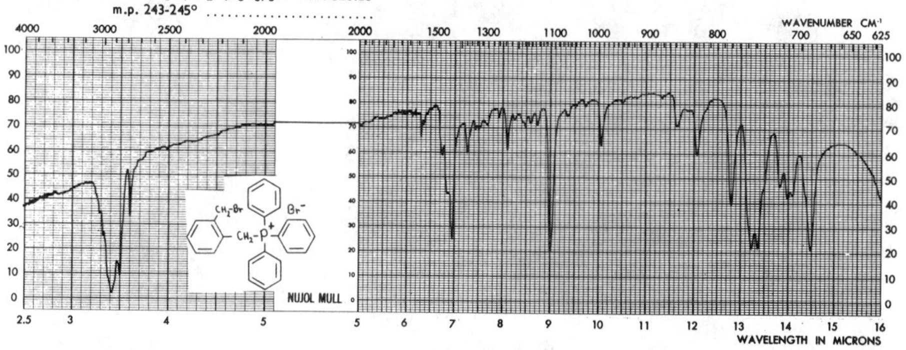

NUJOL MULL

D

X110-5 **o-Xylylenebis-(triphenylphosphonium bromide)**
$C_6H_4[CH_2P(C_6H_5)_3Br]_2$ M.W. 788.55
m.p. 320-324°

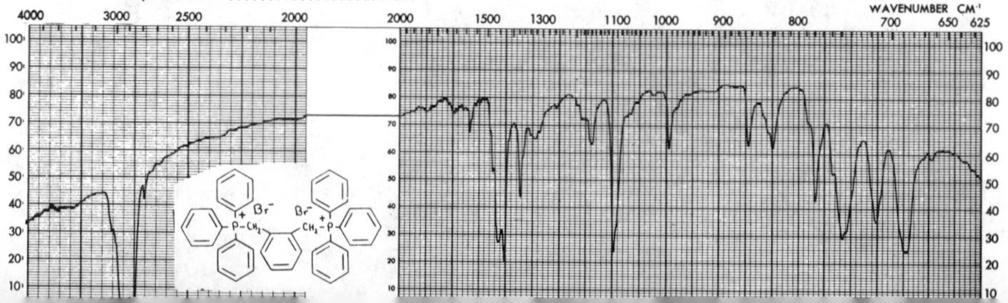

E

X112-1 **p-Xylylenebis-(triphenylphosphonium bromide)**
$C_6H_4[CH_2P(C_6H_5)_3Br]_2$ M.W. 788.55
m.p. > 340°

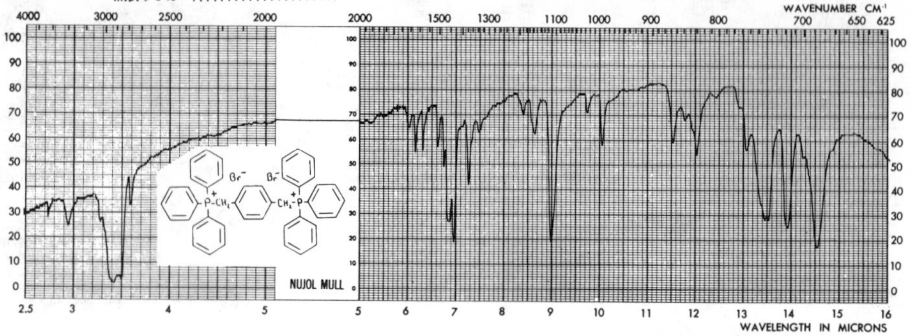

NUJOL MULL

F

14,778-8 **Decarbon** [chlorotris(triphenylphosphine)rhodium (I)]
$[(C_6H_5)_3P]_3RhCl$ M.W. 925.24

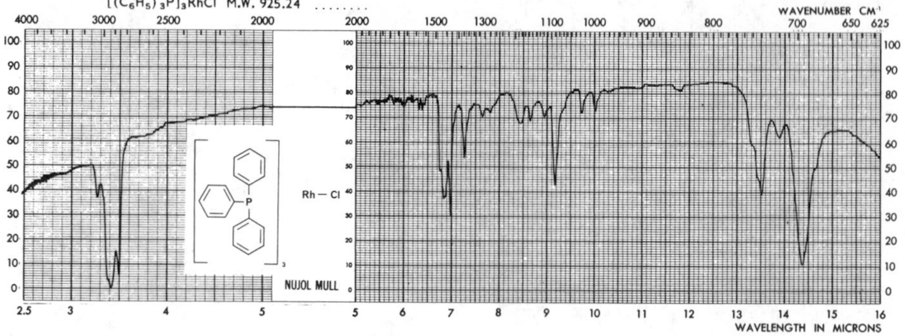

NUJOL MULL

G

15,794-5
(4-Carboxybutyl)triphenylphosphonium bromide, 98%
$HO_2C(CH_2)_4P(C_6H_5)_3Br$
M.W. 443.33 m.p. 205-207° *HYGROSCOPIC*

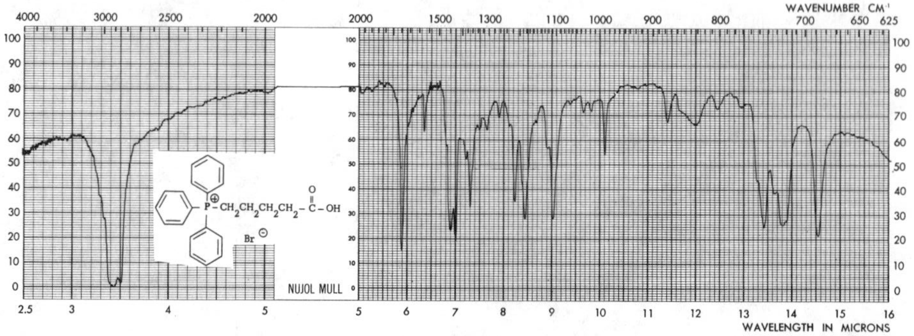

NUJOL MULL

H

C530-0 **(Carbethoxymethyl)-triphenylphosphonium bromide**
$C_2H_5O_2CCH_2P(C_6H_5)_3Br$ M.W. 429.30
m.p. 158° (dec.)

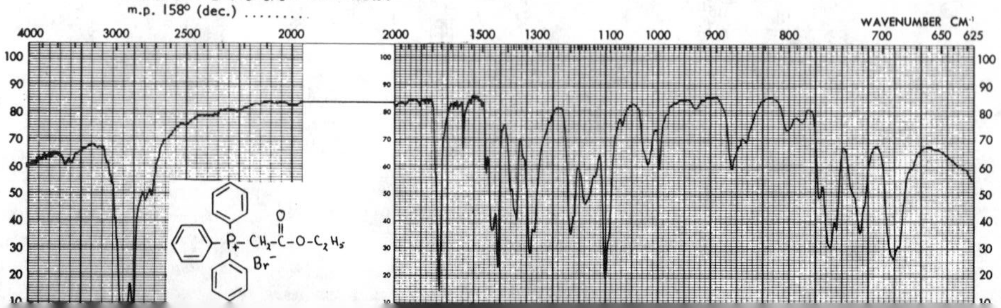

M.W. 334.82 m.p. 240-243° HYGROSCOPIC

A

NUJOL MULL

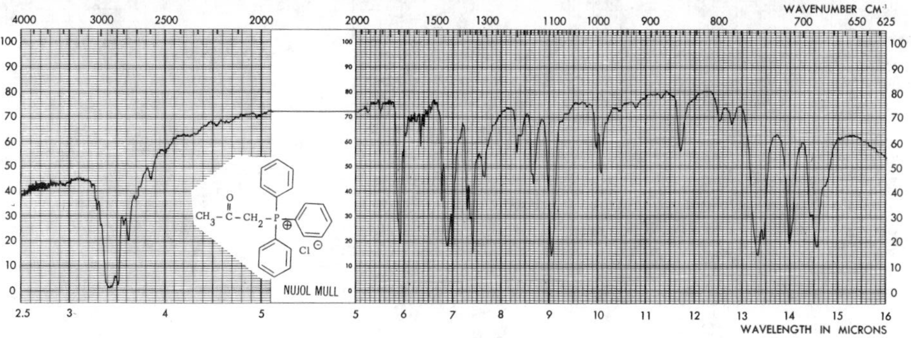

15,133-5 **Phenacyltriphenylphosphonium bromide**
$C_6H_5COCH_2P(C_6H_5)_3Br$ M.W. 461.35
m.p. 265-268° (dec.) ....

B

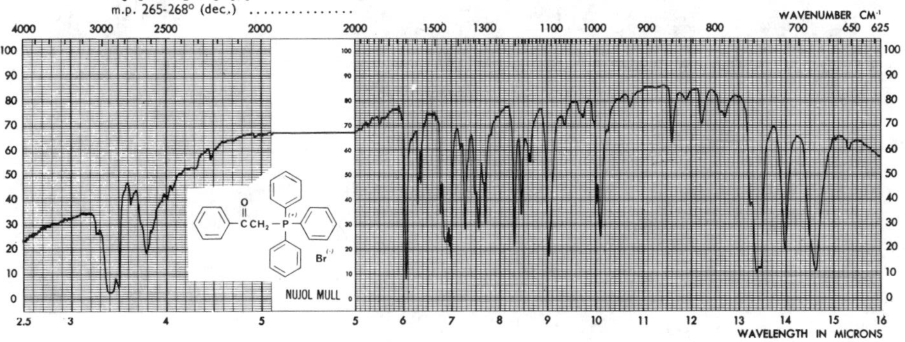

NUJOL MULL

T8470-0 **Triphenylphosphonium cyclopentadienylide** [(cyclopentadienylidene)-triphenylphosphorane]
M.W. 326.38 m.p. 245-247° ....

C

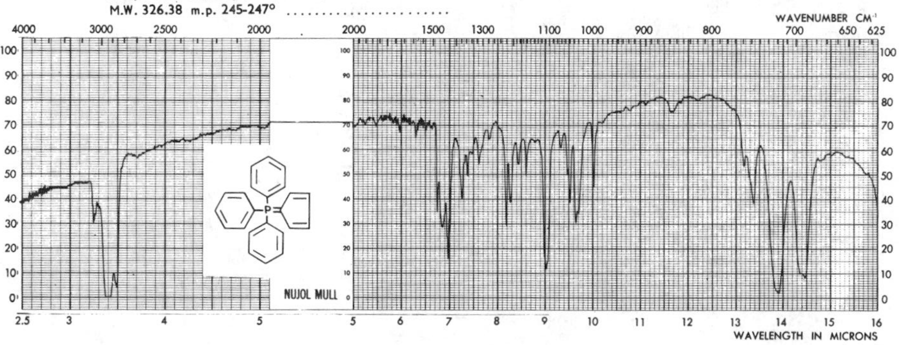

NUJOL MULL

11,391-3 **9-Fluorenylidenetriphenylphosphorane**
M.W. 426.50 m.p. 269-272° ......

D

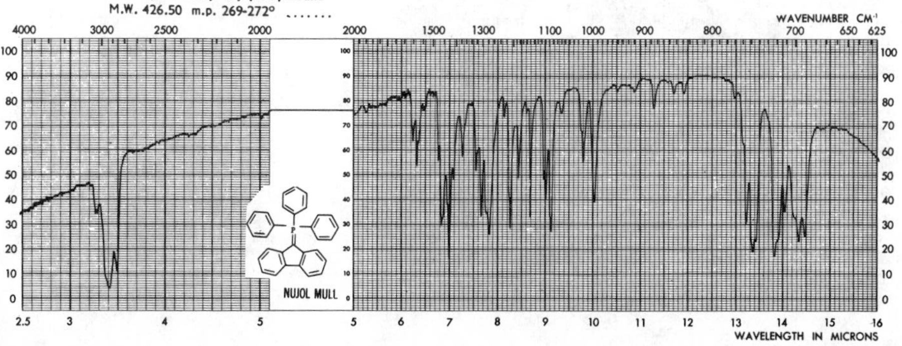

NUJOL MULL

M.W. 318.36 m.p. 203-205°

E

NUJOL MULL

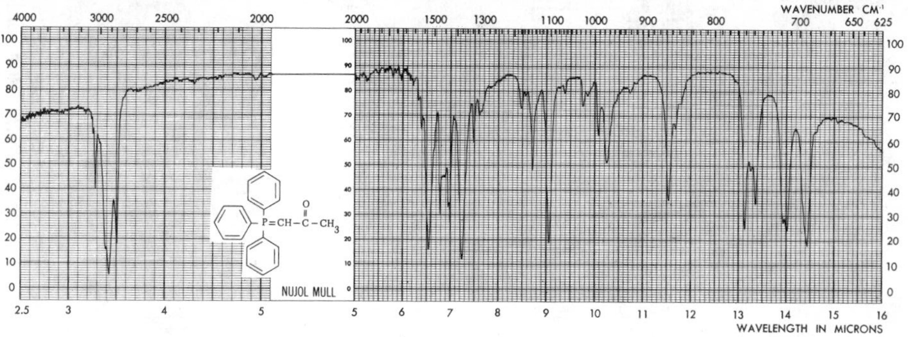

15,792-9
Methyl (triphenylphosphoranylidene)-acetate, 98%
$(C_6H_5)_3P{=}CHCO_2CH_3$
M.W. 334.36 m.p. 164-167° Fieser 1,112

F

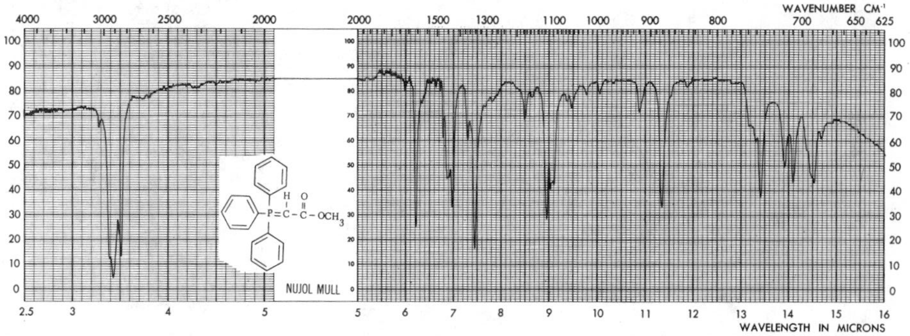

NUJOL MULL

C510-6 **(Carbethoxymethylene)-triphenylphosphorane** [ethyl (triphenylphosphoranylidene)-acetate]
$(C_6H_5)_3P{:}CHCO_2C_2H_5$ M.W. 348.38
m.p. 126-127° ....

G

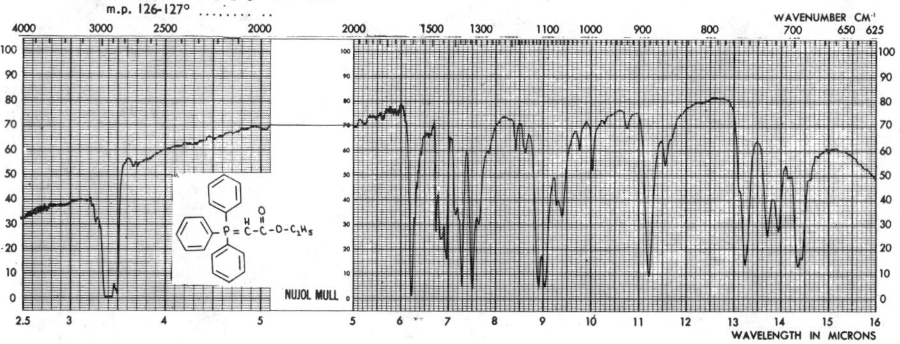

NUJOL MULL

10,019-6 **(Carbethoxyethylidene)-triphenylphosphorane** [ethyl 2-(triphenylphosphoranylidene)-propionate]
$CH_3C[{:}P(C_6H_5)_3]CO_2C_2H_5$ M.W. 362.41 m.p. 162-166° ..

H

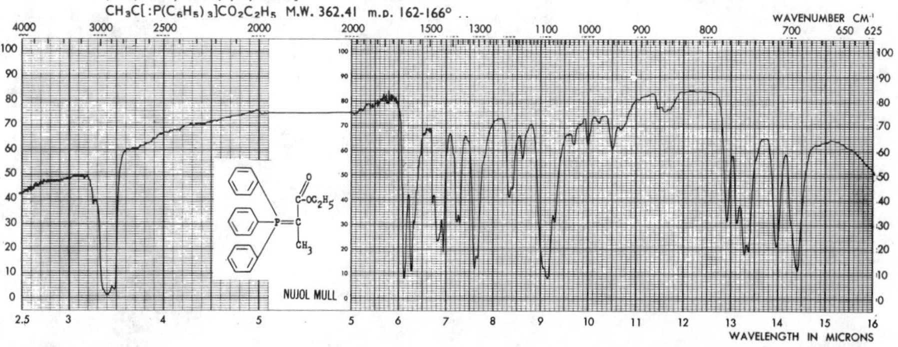

NUJOL MULL

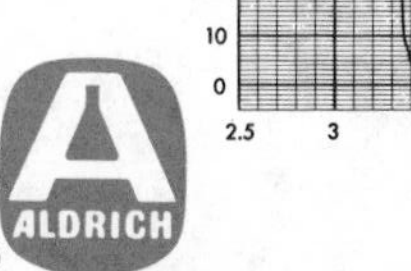

A

11,478-2 **2-(Triphenylphosphoranylidene)-γ-butyrolactone**
M.W. 346.37 m.p. 237° (dec.)

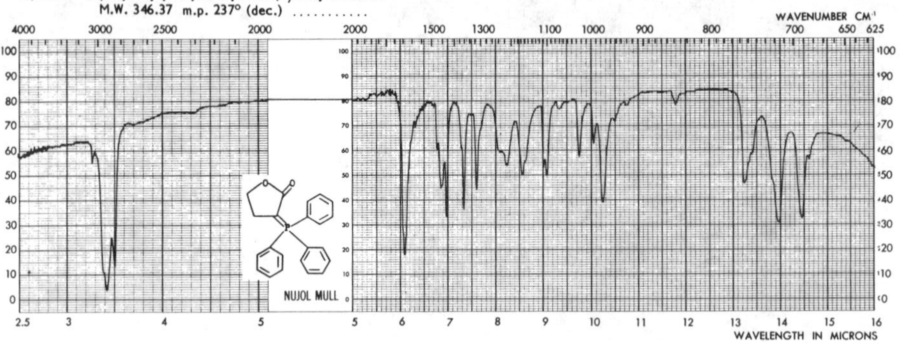

NUJOL MULL

B

D21,090-0 **Diphenylphosphonimidotriphenylphosphorane**
$(C_6H_5)_2P(O)N{:}P(C_6H_5)_3$ M.W. 477.48 m.p. 169-172°

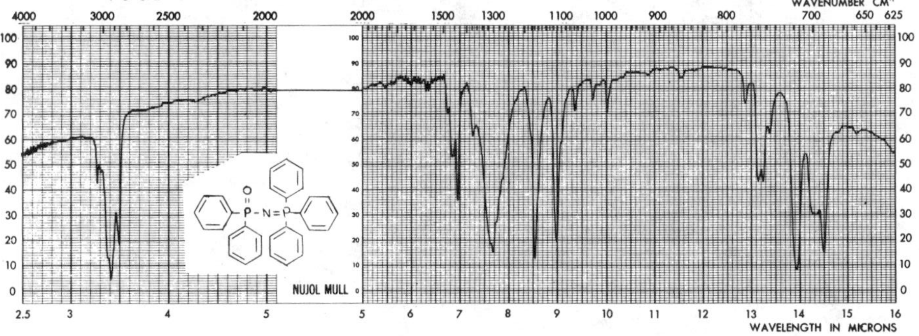

NUJOL MULL

C

22,383-2
Bis(triphenylphosphoranylidene)ammonium chloride, 99%
$[(C_6H_5)_3P{=}]_2NCl$ FW 574.05 mp 271-273°
Disp. C

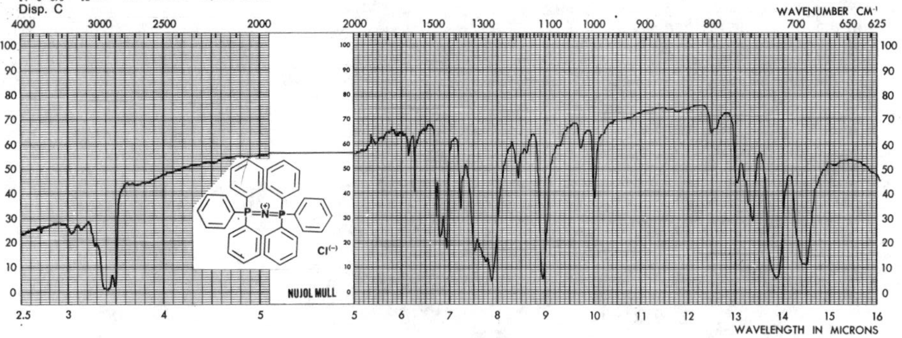

NUJOL MULL

D

D21,080-3 **Diphenyl phosphite**
$(C_6H_5O)_2P(O)H$ M.W. 234.19 n_D^{20} 1.5575

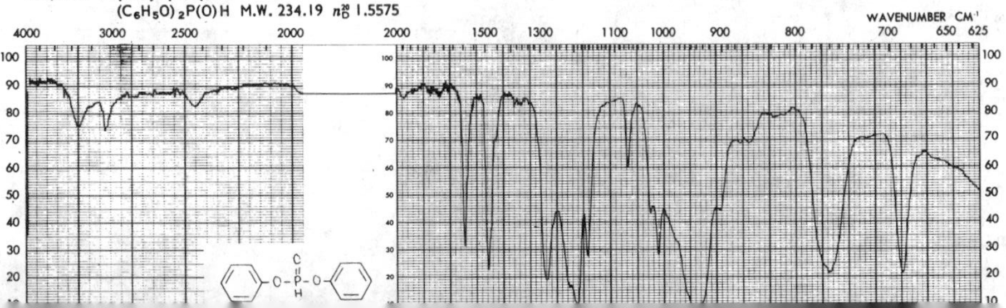

E

D3660-7 **Dibenzyl phosphite** (dibenzyl phosphonate)
$(C_6H_5CH_2O)_2POH$ M.W. 262.25
n_D^{20} 1.5505

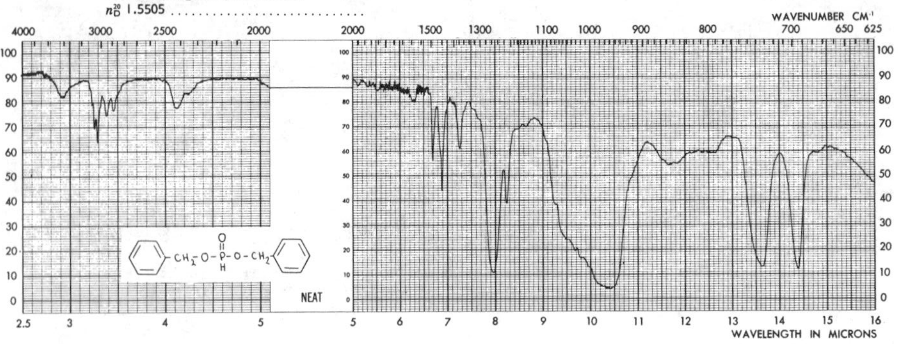

NEAT

F

11,249-6 **Dimethyl benzylphosphonate**
$(CH_3O)_2P(O)CH_2C_6H_5$ M.W. 200.17 n_D^{20} 1.5152
b.p. 114°/0.75 mm.

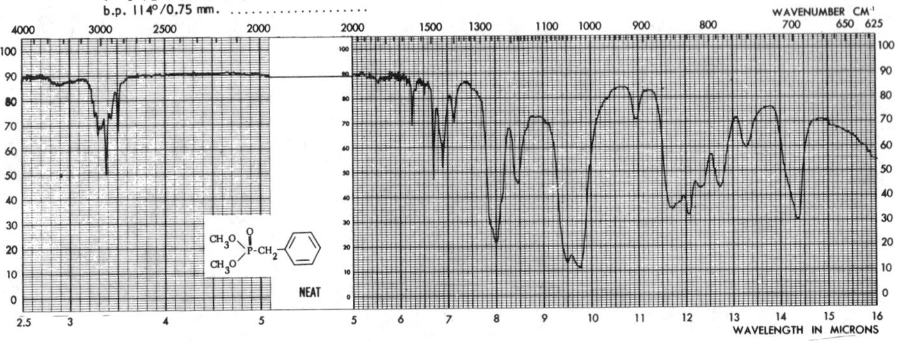

NEAT

G

T8465-4 **Triphenyl phosphite**
$(C_6H_5O)_3P$ M.W. 310.29 m.p. 22-24°

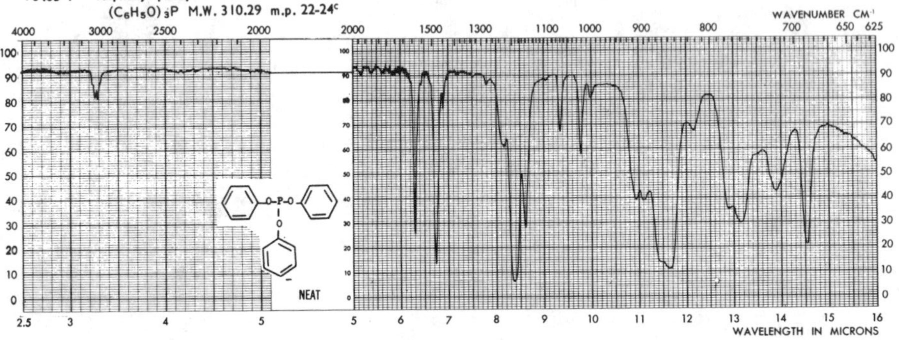

NEAT

H

15,504-7 **Dibutyl phenylphosphonite** (dibutoxyphenylphosphine), 95 %
$C_6H_5P[O(CH_2)_3CH_3]_2$ M.W. 254.31 n_D^{20} 1.4990
b.p. 171-172° 28 mm.

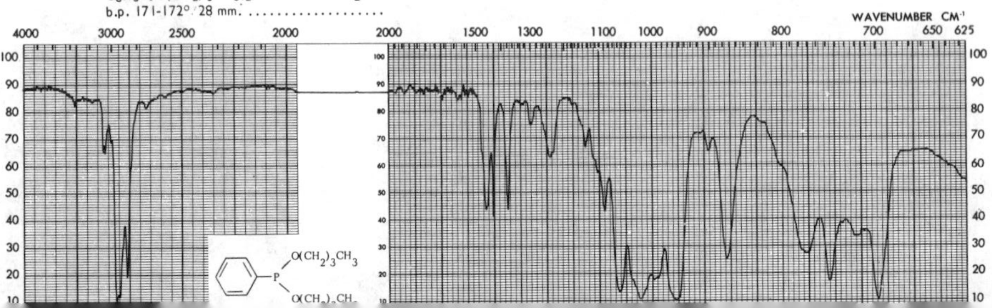

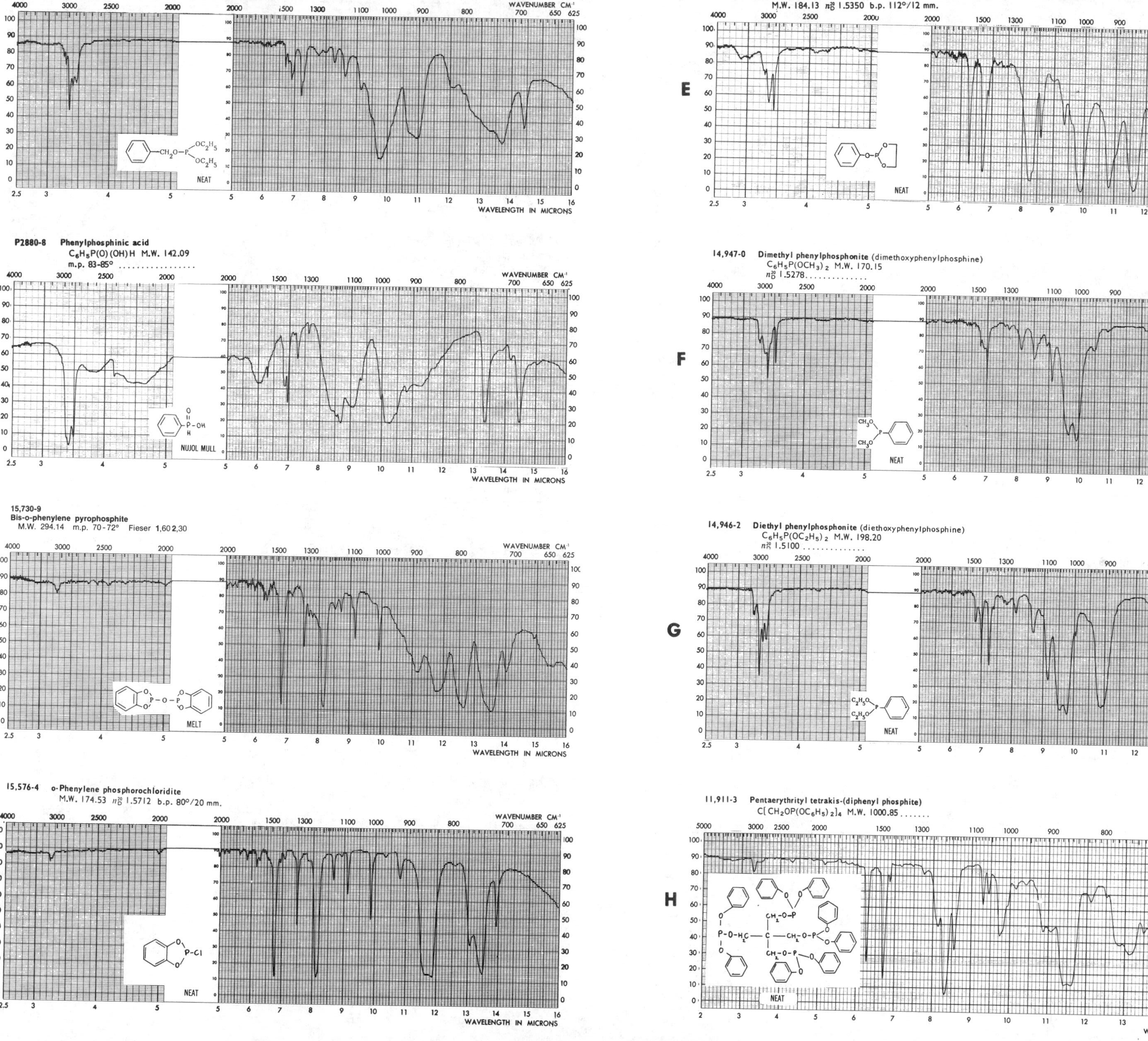

$C_6H_5CH_2OP(OC_2H_5)_2$ M.W. 228.23 n_D^{20} 1.4930
b.p. 110° 2 mm.
A
NEAT
P2880-8 Phenylphosphinic acid
$C_6H_5P(O)(OH)H$ M.W. 142.09
m.p. 83-85°
B
NUJOL MULL
15,730-9
Bis-o-phenylene pyrophosphite
M.W. 294.14 m.p. 70-72° Fieser 1,60 2,30
C
MELT
15,576-4 o-Phenylene phosphorochloridite
M.W. 174.53 n_D^{20} 1.5712 b.p. 80°/20 mm.
D
NEAT
P2420-9 Phenyl ethylene phosphite
M.W. 184.13 n_D^{20} 1.5350 b.p. 112°/12 mm.
E
NEAT
14,947-0 Dimethyl phenylphosphonite (dimethoxyphenylphosphine)
$C_6H_5P(OCH_3)_2$ M.W. 170.15
n_D^{20} 1.5278
F
NEAT
14,946-2 Diethyl phenylphosphonite (diethoxyphenylphosphine)
$C_6H_5P(OC_2H_5)_2$ M.W. 198.20
n_D^{20} 1.5100
G
NEAT
11,911-3 Pentaerythrityl tetrakis-(diphenyl phosphite)
$C[CH_2OP(OC_6H_5)_2]_4$ M.W. 1000.85
H
NEAT
WAVENUMBER CM⁻¹
WAVELENGTH IN MICRONS
ALDRICH

ALDRICH

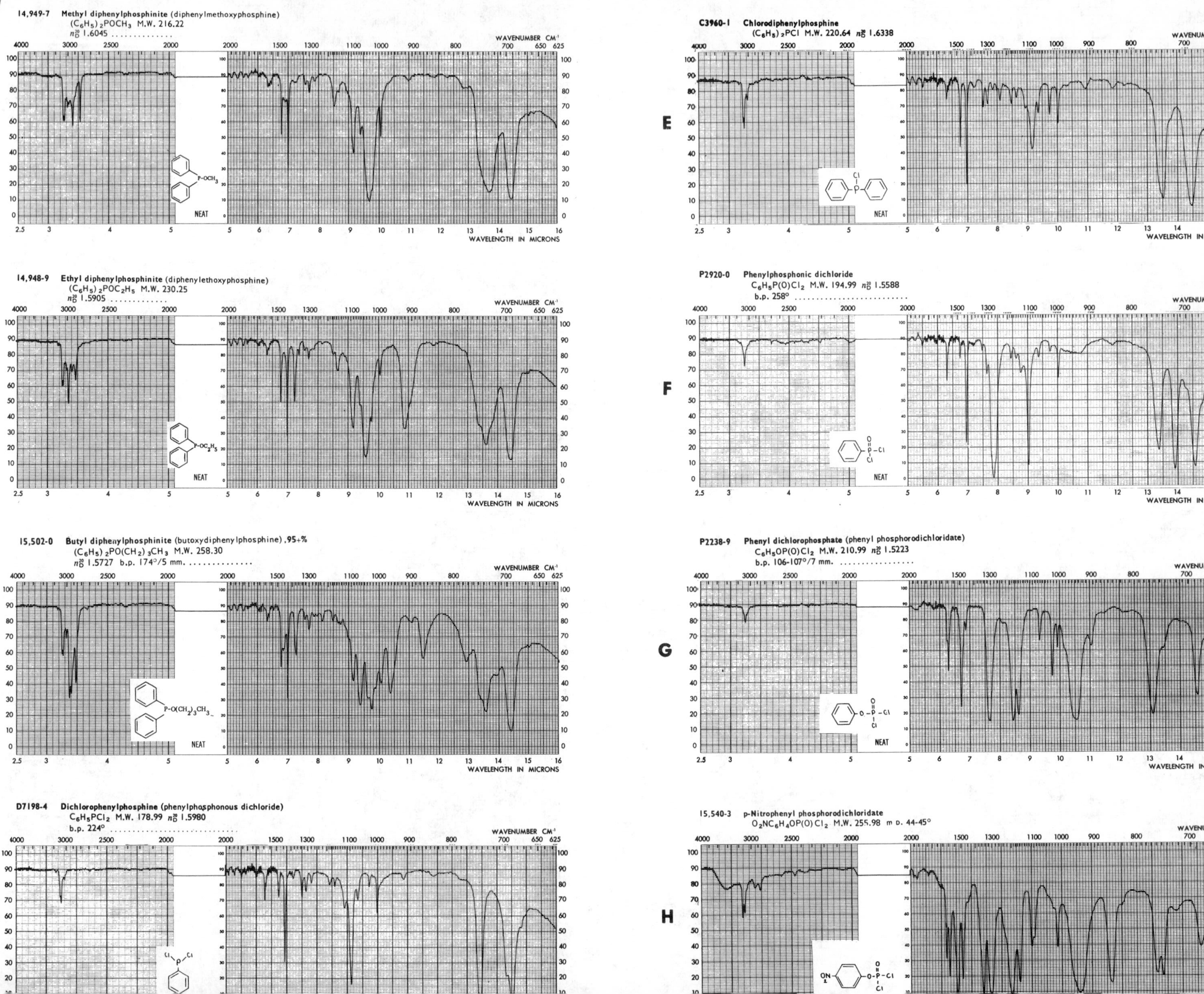

A
14,949-7 Methyl diphenylphosphinite (diphenylmethoxyphosphine)
$(C_6H_5)_2POCH_3$ M.W. 216.22
n_D^{20} 1.6045
NEAT
B
14,948-9 Ethyl diphenylphosphinite (diphenylethoxyphosphine)
$(C_6H_5)_2POC_2H_5$ M.W. 230.25
n_D^{20} 1.5905
NEAT
C
15,502-0 Butyl diphenylphosphinite (butoxydiphenylphosphine), 95+%
$(C_6H_5)_2PO(CH_2)_3CH_3$ M.W. 258.30
n_D^{20} 1.5727 b.p. 174°/5 mm.
NEAT
D
D7198-4 Dichlorophenylphosphine (phenylphosphonous dichloride)
$C_6H_5PCl_2$ M.W. 178.99 n_D^{20} 1.5980
b.p. 224°
E
C3960-1 Chlorodiphenylphosphine
$(C_6H_5)_2PCl$ M.W. 220.64 n_D^{20} 1.6338
NEAT
F
P2920-0 Phenylphosphonic dichloride
$C_6H_5P(O)Cl_2$ M.W. 194.99 n_D^{20} 1.5588
b.p. 258°
NEAT
G
P2238-9 Phenyl dichlorophosphate (phenyl phosphorodichloridate)
$C_6H_5OP(O)Cl_2$ M.W. 210.99 n_D^{20} 1.5223
b.p. 106-107°/7 mm.
NEAT
H
15,540-3 p-Nitrophenyl phosphorodichloridate
$O_2NC_6H_4OP(O)Cl_2$ M.W. 255.98 m.p. 44-45°
WAVENUMBER CM⁻¹
WAVELENGTH IN MICRONS

n_D^{20} 1.5500 ....

A

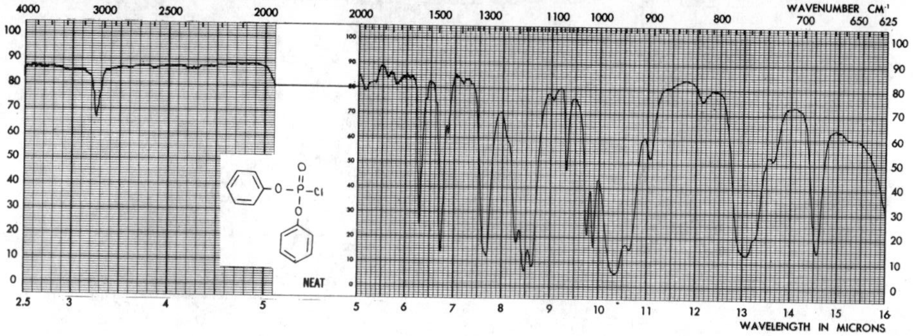

NEAT

17,460-2
Phenyl *N*-phenylphosphoramidochloridate, 99+%
$C_6H_5NHP(O)(Cl)OC_6H_5$ FW 267.66 mp 132-134°
Beil. 12,588 *Fieser* 7,286 Disp. C

B

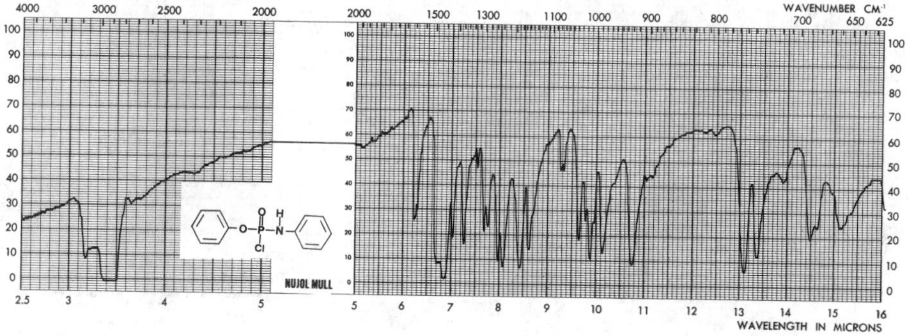

NUJOL MULL

12,678-0 **Di-p-tolyl chlorophosphate** (di-p-tolyl phosphorochloridate)
$(CH_3C_6H_4O)_2P(O)Cl$ M.W. 296.69 n_D^{20} 1.5406 ....

C

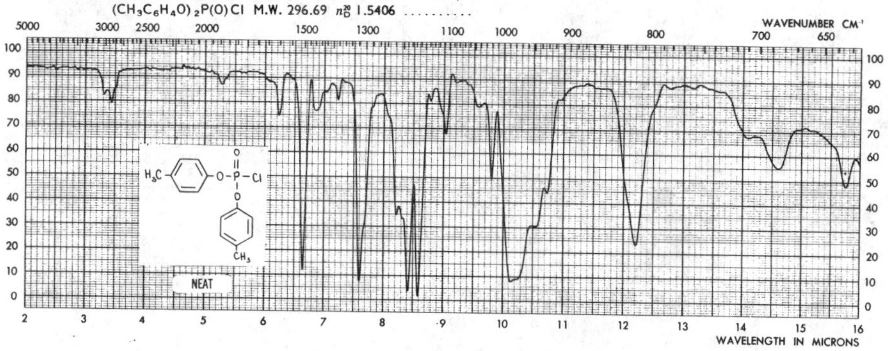

NEAT

15,614-0
***o*-Phenylene phosphorochloridate,** tech.
FW 190.52 bp 120°/9mm. *Beil.* 27,809
Fieser 1,837 2,321 3,223 Disp. C

D

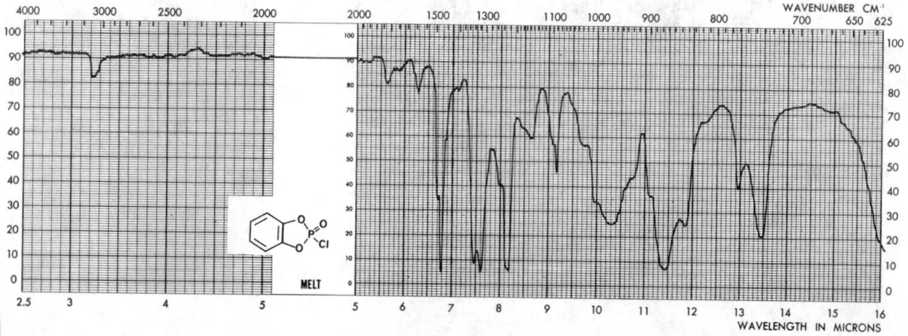

MELT

benzodioxaphosphole)
M.W. 245.43 m.p. 51-53° ....

E

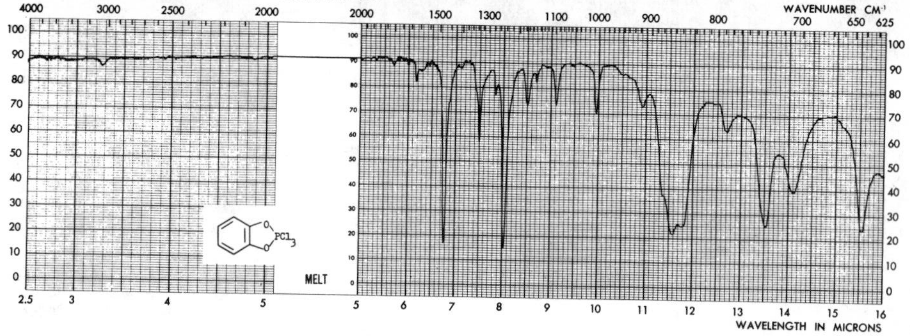

MELT

P2940-5 **Phenylphosphonothioic dichloride**
$C_6H_5P(S)Cl_2$ M.W. 211.05 n_D^{20} 1.6235
b.p. 205°/130 mm. ....

F

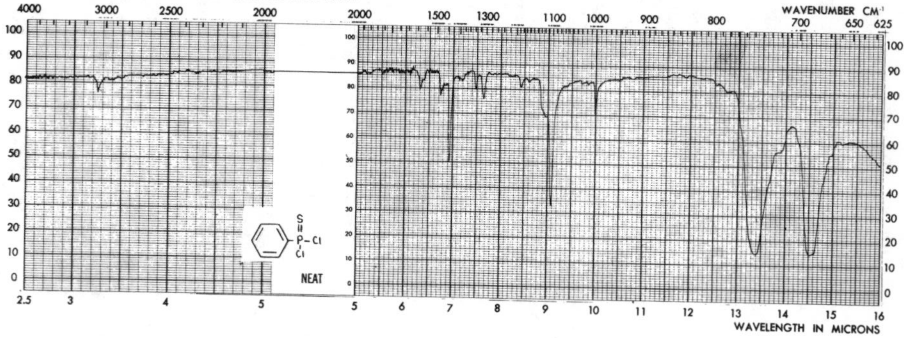

NEAT

11,430-8 **Diphenyldithiophosphinic acid (diphenylphosphinodithioic acid)**
$(C_6H_5)_2P(S)SH$ M.W. 250.32 m.p. 50-54°

G

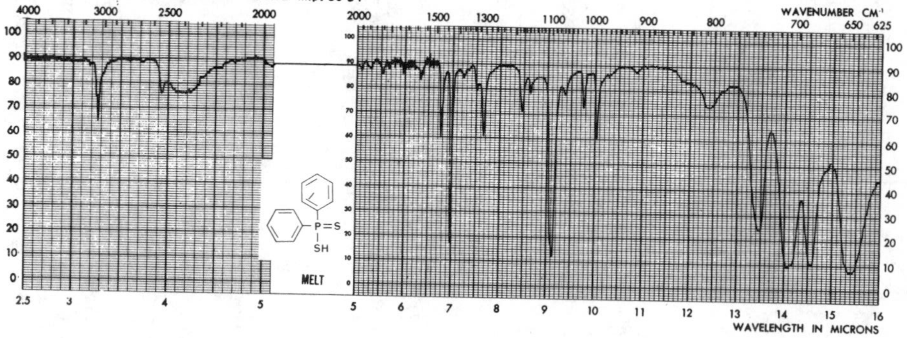

MELT

13,510-0 **Triphenylphosphine sulfide**
$(C_6H_5)_3P(S)$ M.W. 294.36 m.p. 162-164°

H

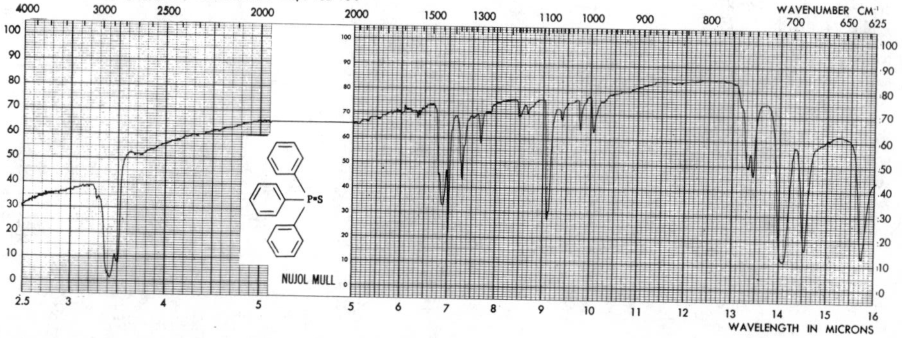

NUJOL MULL

ALDRICH

AROMATIC PHOSPHORUS

A 18,013-0 Triphenylphosphine selenide, 98%
$(C_6H_5)_3P(Se)$
M.W. 341.25 m.p. 187-189°
NUJOL MULL

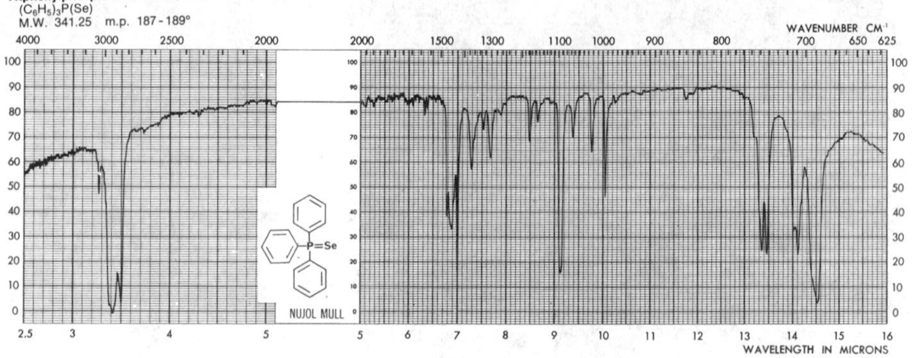

B 10,852-9 Diphenylphosphinic acid
$(C_6H_5)_2P(O)OH$ M.W. 218.19 m.p. 193-195°
NUJOL MULL

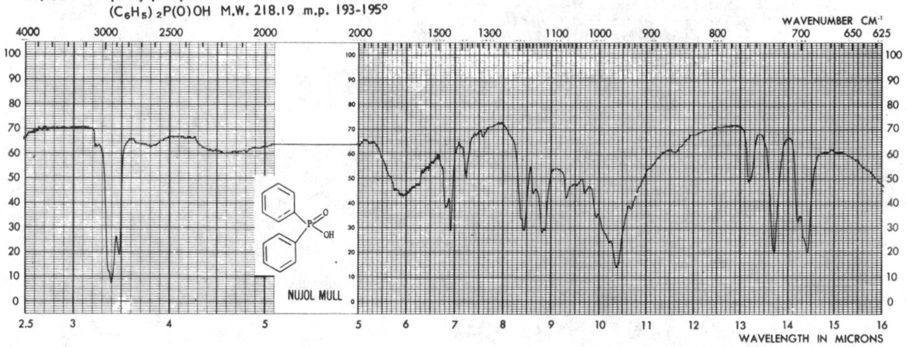

C 11,249-6 Dimethyl benzylphosphonate
$(CH_3O)_2P(O)CH_2C_6H_5$ M.W. 200.17 n_D^{20} 1.5152
b.p. 114°/0.75 mm.
NEAT

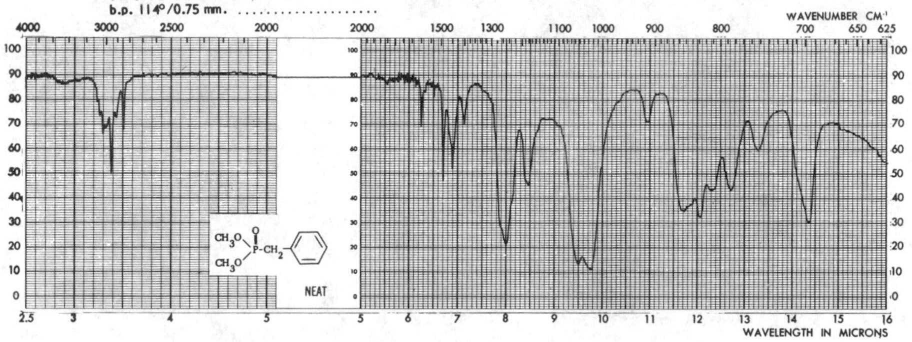

D D9107-1 Diethyl benzylphosphonate
$(C_2H_5O)_2P(O)CH_2C_6H_5$ M.W. 228.23
n_D^{20} 1.4944

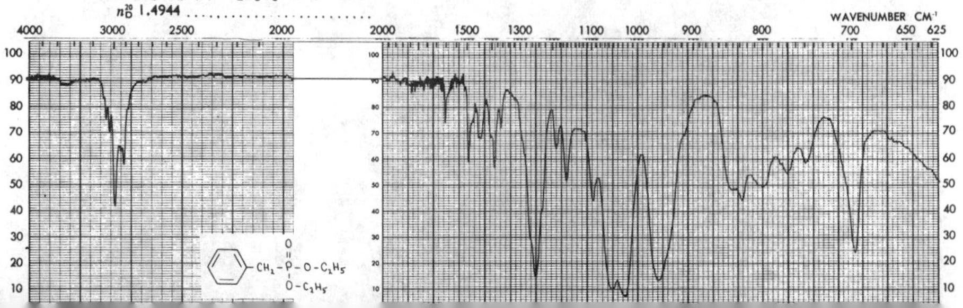

E D8635-3 Diethyl p-aminobenzylphosphonate
$(C_2H_5O)_2P(O)CH_2C_6H_4NH_2$ M.W. 243.24
m.p. 91-94°
NUJOL MULL

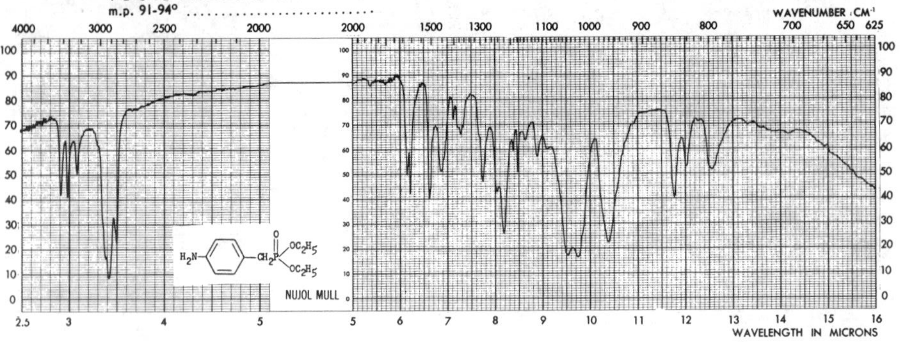

F P2900-6 Phenylphosphonic acid
$C_6H_5P(O)(OH)_2$ M.W. 158.09 m.p. 163-166°
NUJOL MULL

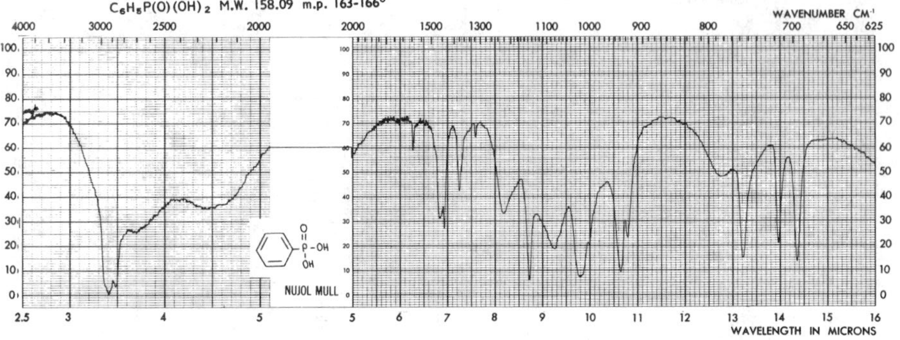

G T8460-3 Triphenylphosphine oxide
$(C_6H_5)_3P(O)$ M.W. 278.29
m.p. 154-157°
NUJOL MULL

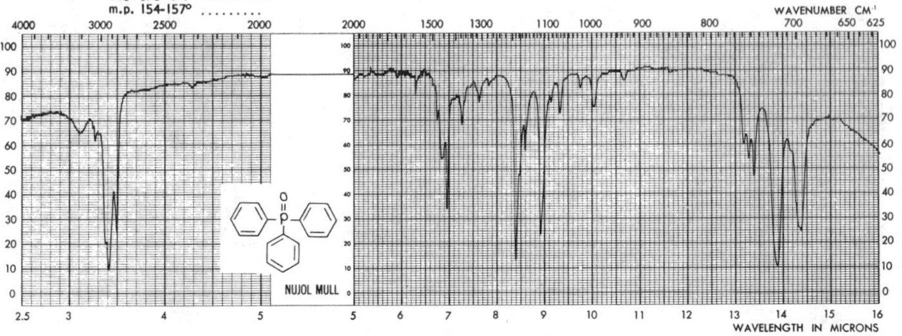

H 85,060-8
Diphenyl phosphate
$(C_6H_5O)_2P(O)OH$
M.W. 250.19 m.p. 63-64° Beil. 6,178

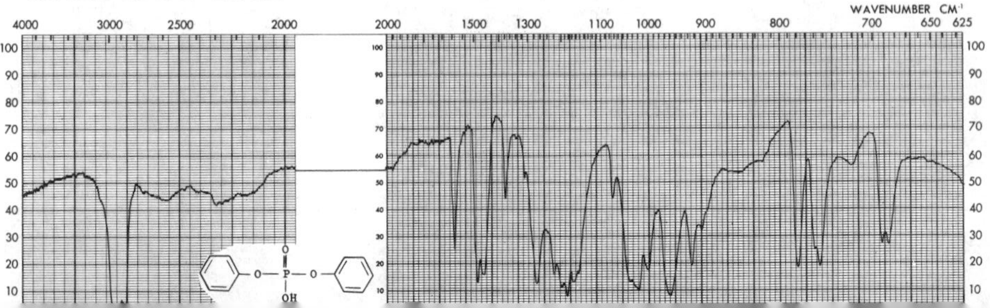

A

$(C_6H_5O)_3P(O)$ M.W. 326.29 m.p. 49-51°

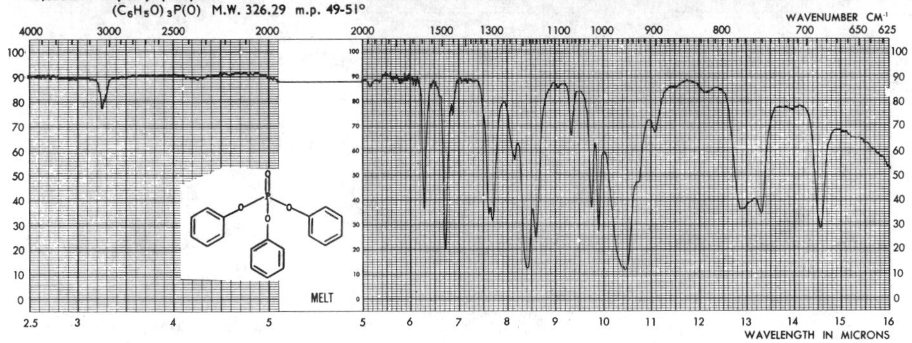

MELT

B

21,293-8
Methyltriphenoxyphosphonium trifluoromethanesulfonate, 95%
$CH_3P(OC_6H_5)_3(CF_3SO_3)$ FW 474.40 mp 90-95°
Disp. C

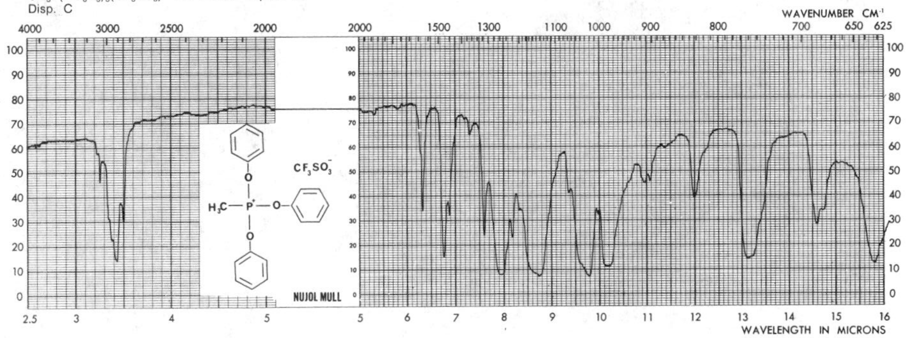

NUJOL MULL

C

10,587-2 **Diphenyl methyl phosphate**
$(C_6H_5O)_2P(O)OCH_3$ M.W. 264.22 n_D^{20} 1.5370

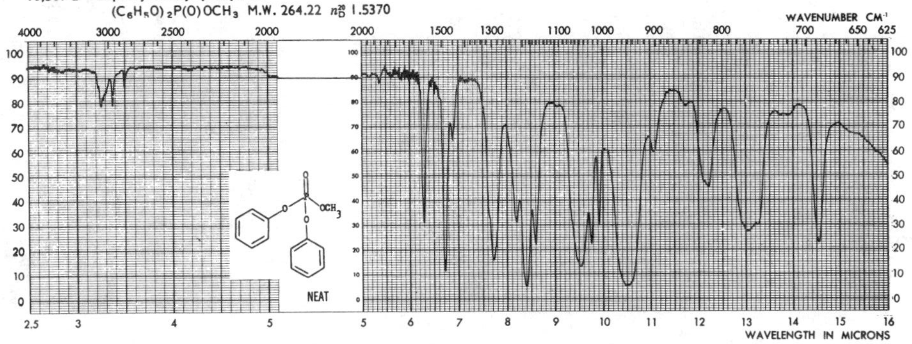

NEAT

D

11,714-5 **Tris-(o-chlorophenyl) phosphate, tech.**
$(ClC_6H_4O)_3P(O)$ M.W. 429.63 n_D^{20} 1.5856

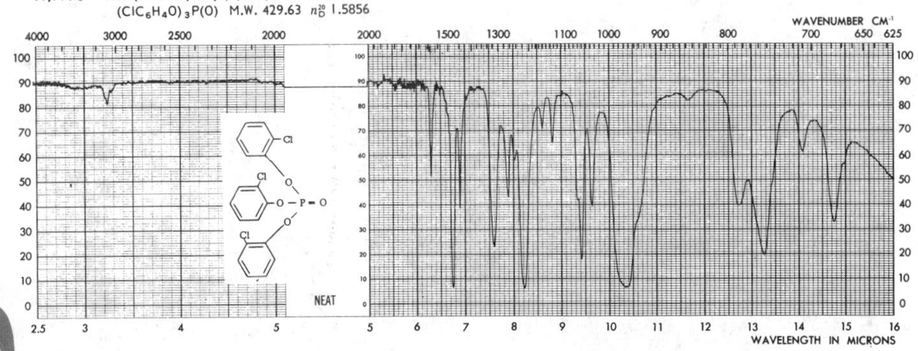

NEAT

E

Disp. C

NUJOL MULL

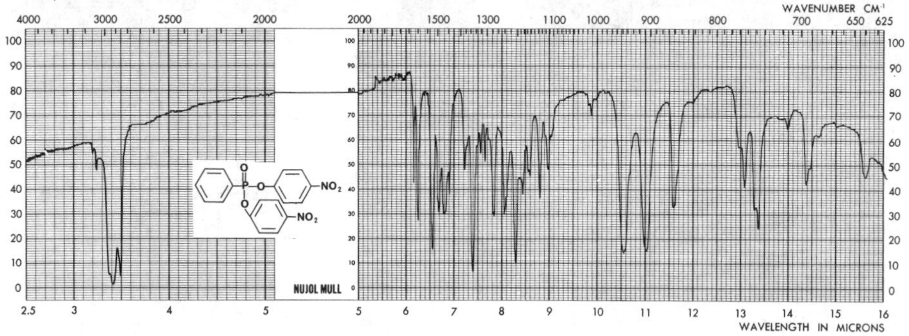

F

85,758-0
4-Nitrophenyl phosphate, bis-(cyclohexylammonium) salt, 99+%, GOLD LABEL
$O_2NC_6H_4OP(O)(ONH_3C_6H_{11})_2$
M.W. 417.45 m.p. 199-200°

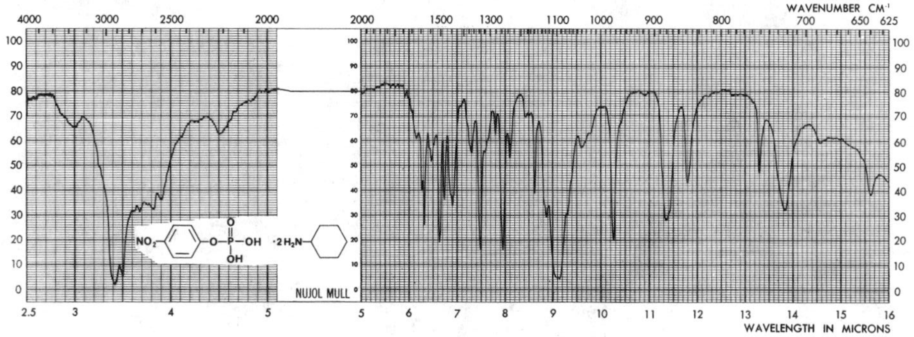

NUJOL MULL

G

12,394-3 **Bis-(p-nitrophenyl)-phosphate** (di-p-nitrophenyl hydrogen phosphate)
$(O_2NC_6H_4O)_2P(O)OH$ M.W. 340.18 m.p. 172-175°

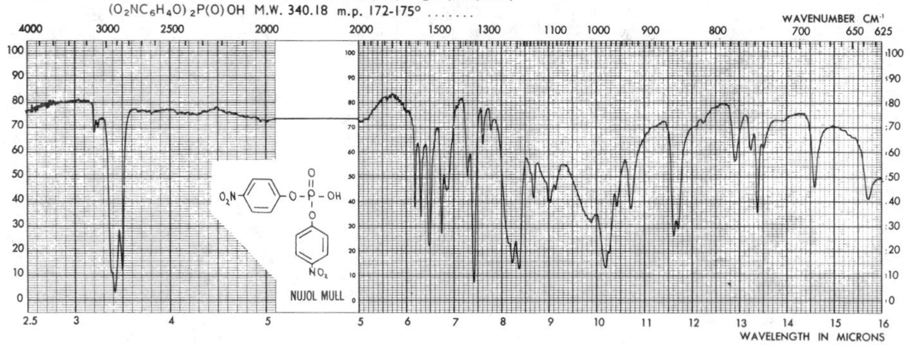

NUJOL MULL

H

D3655-0 **Dibenzyl phosphate**
$(C_6H_5CH_2O)_2P(O)OH$ M.W. 278.24
m.p. 79-80°

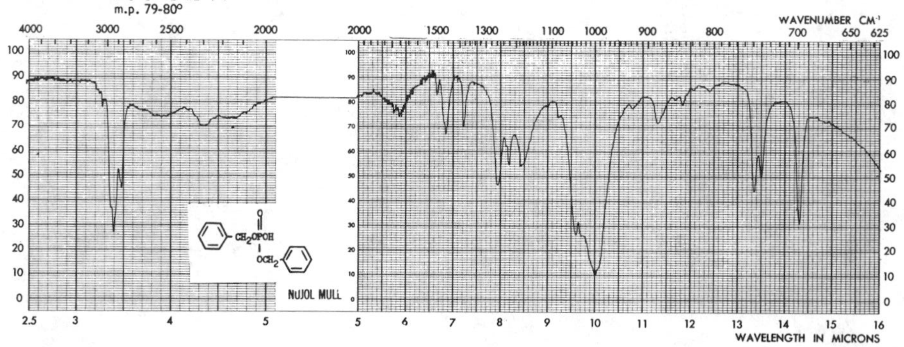

NUJOL MULL

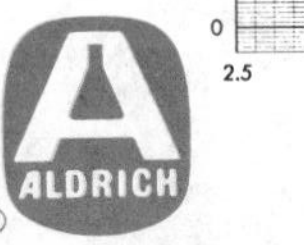

A

N600-5 **2-Naphthyl phosphate, disodium salt dihydrate**
$C_{10}H_7OP(O)(ONa)_2 \cdot 2H_2O$ M.W. 304.15 m.p. > 320°

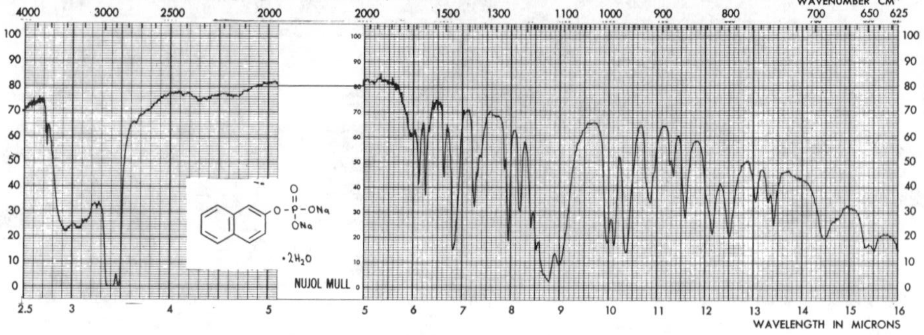

NUJOL MULL

B

N560-2 **1-Naphthyl phosphate**
$C_{10}H_7OP(O)(OH)_2$ M.W. 224.15 m.p. 157-159°

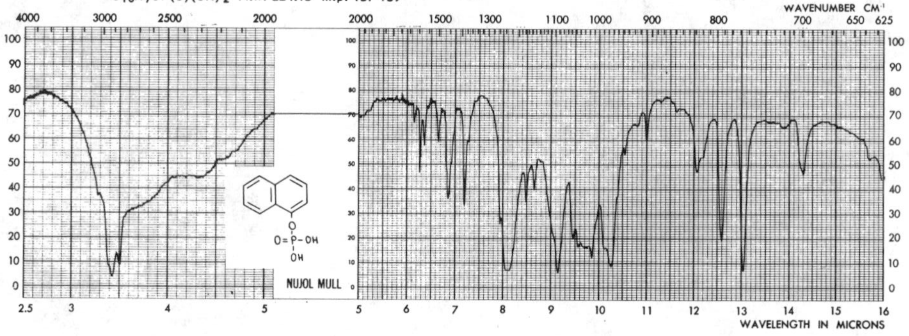

NUJOL MULL

C

85,314-3
o-Carboxyphenyl phosphate
$HO_2CC_6H_4OP(O)(OH)_2$
M.W. 218.1 m.p. 165-167° Beil. **10**,69

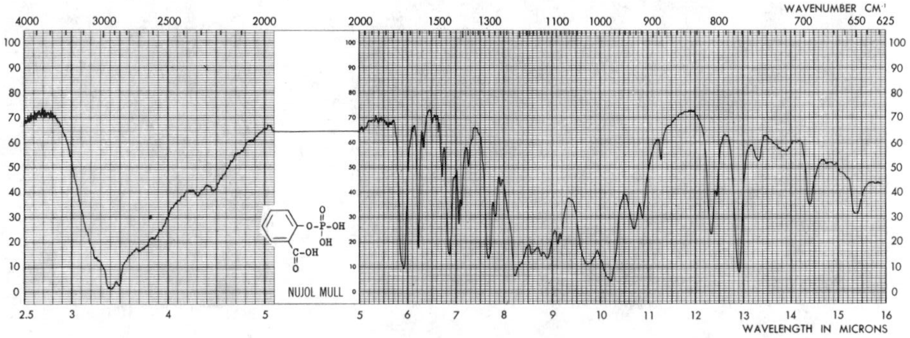

NUJOL MULL

D

85,541-3
1-Naphthyl phosphate, monosodium salt monohydrate
$C_{10}H_7OP(O)(OH)ONa \cdot H_2O$
M.W. 264.16 m.p. 189-191°

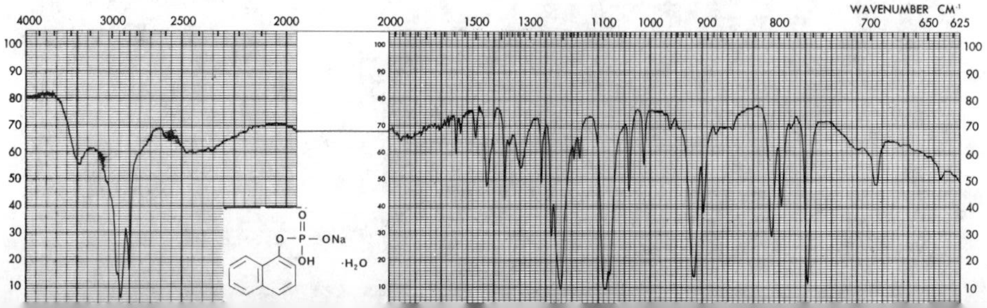

E

N2200-2 **4-Nitrophenyl phosphate, disodium salt, hydrate**
$O_2NC_6H_4OP(O)(ONa)_2 \cdot xH_2O$ M.W. 263.05 (anhydrous)

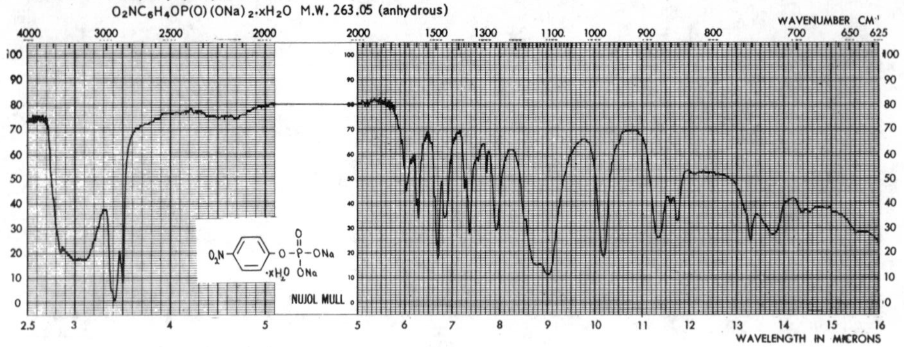

NUJOL MULL

F

13,221-7 **Tris-(p-nitrophenyl) phosphate**
$(O_2NC_6H_4O)_3P(O)$ M.W. 461.28 m.p. 148-153°

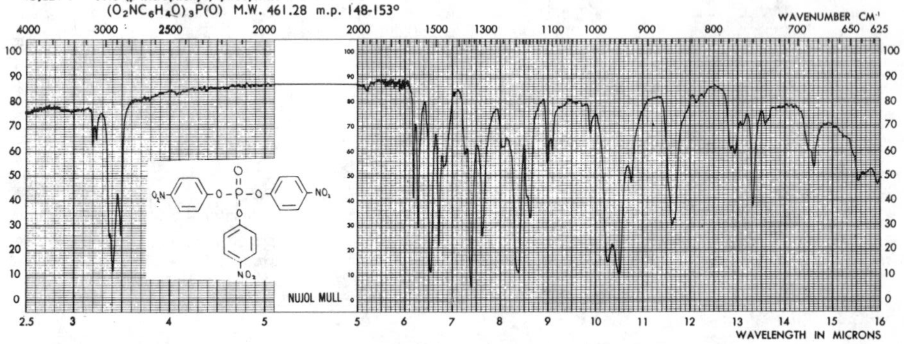

NUJOL MULL

G

11,626-2 **Diethyl phenylamidophosphate** (diethyl phenylphosphoramidate)
$(C_2H_5O)_2P(O)NHC_6H_5$ M.W. 229.22
m.p. 91-93°

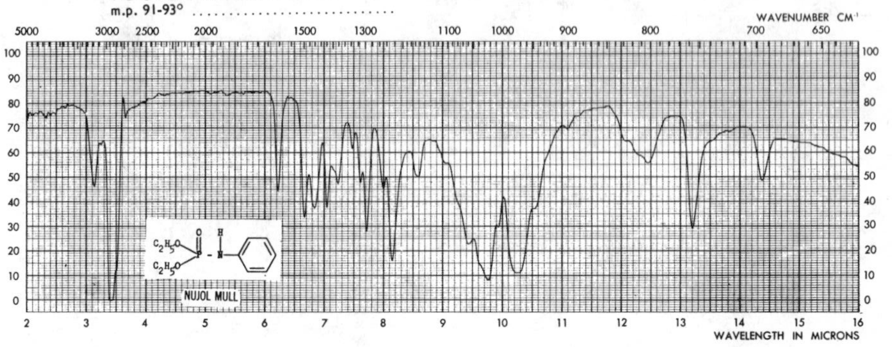

NUJOL MULL

H

10,159-1 **Diethyl phenethylamidophosphate** (diethyl phenethylphosphoramidate)
$(C_2H_5O)_2P(O)NHCH_2CH_2C_6H_5$ M.W. 257.27
n_D^{20} 1.4881 b.p. 158-160°/0.5 mm.

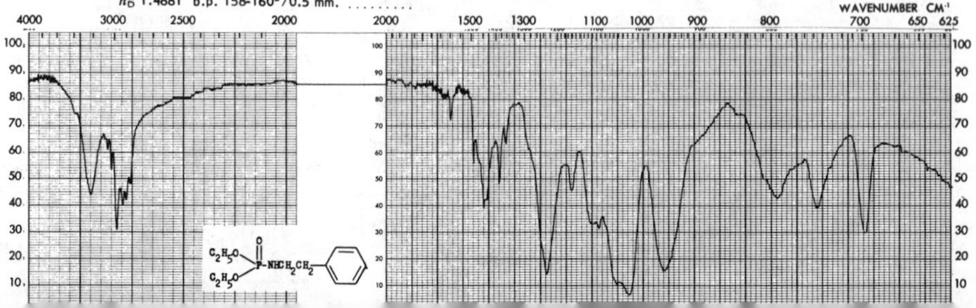

m.p. 118-120° . . . .

A

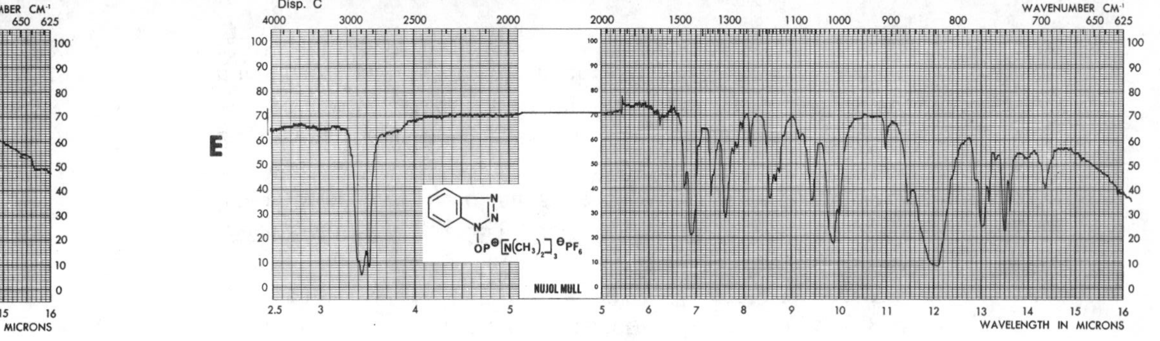

11,629-7 **Diethyl p-fluorophenylamidophosphate** (diethyl p-fluorophenylphosphoramidate)
$(C_2H_5O)_2P(O)NHC_6H_4F$ M.W. 247.21 n_D^{20} 1.4850
b.p. 138-140°/0.2 mm. . . . .

B

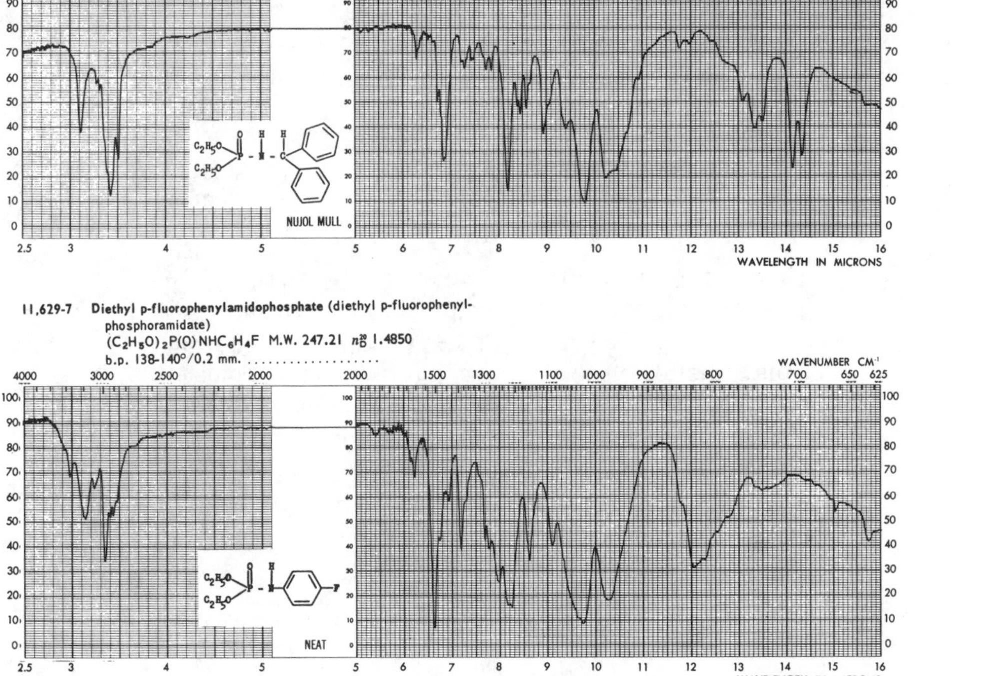

D21,070-6 **Diphenylphosphinyl azide**
$(C_6H_5)_2P(O)N_3$ M.W. 243.21 b.p. 137/0.5 mm.

C

17,875-6
Diphenylphosphoryl azide, 98%
$(C_6H_5O)_2P(O)N_3$
M.W. 275.2 b.p. 157°/0.17mm. n_D^{20} 1.5518
d 1.277

D

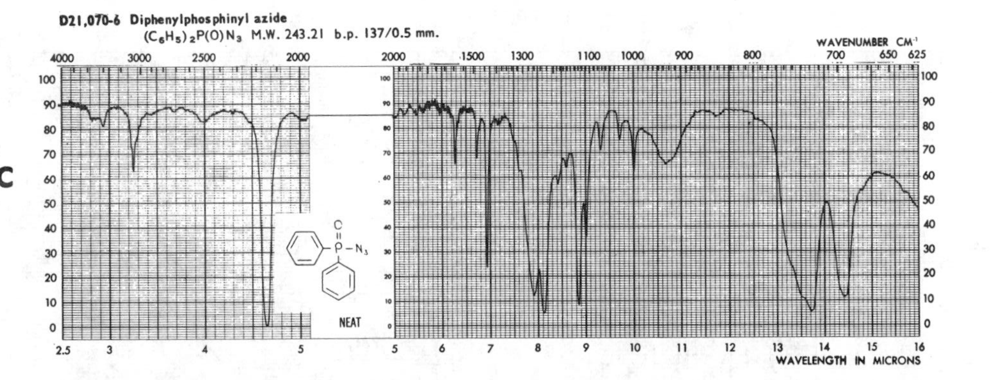

Disp. C

E

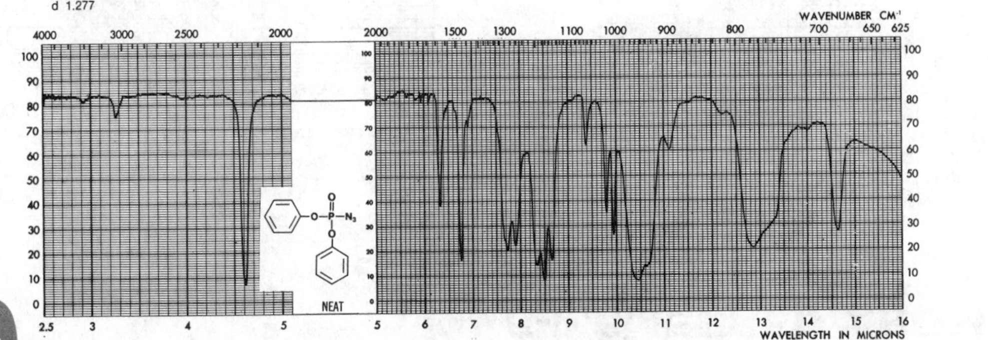

5-MEMBERED AROMATIC HETEROCYCLES

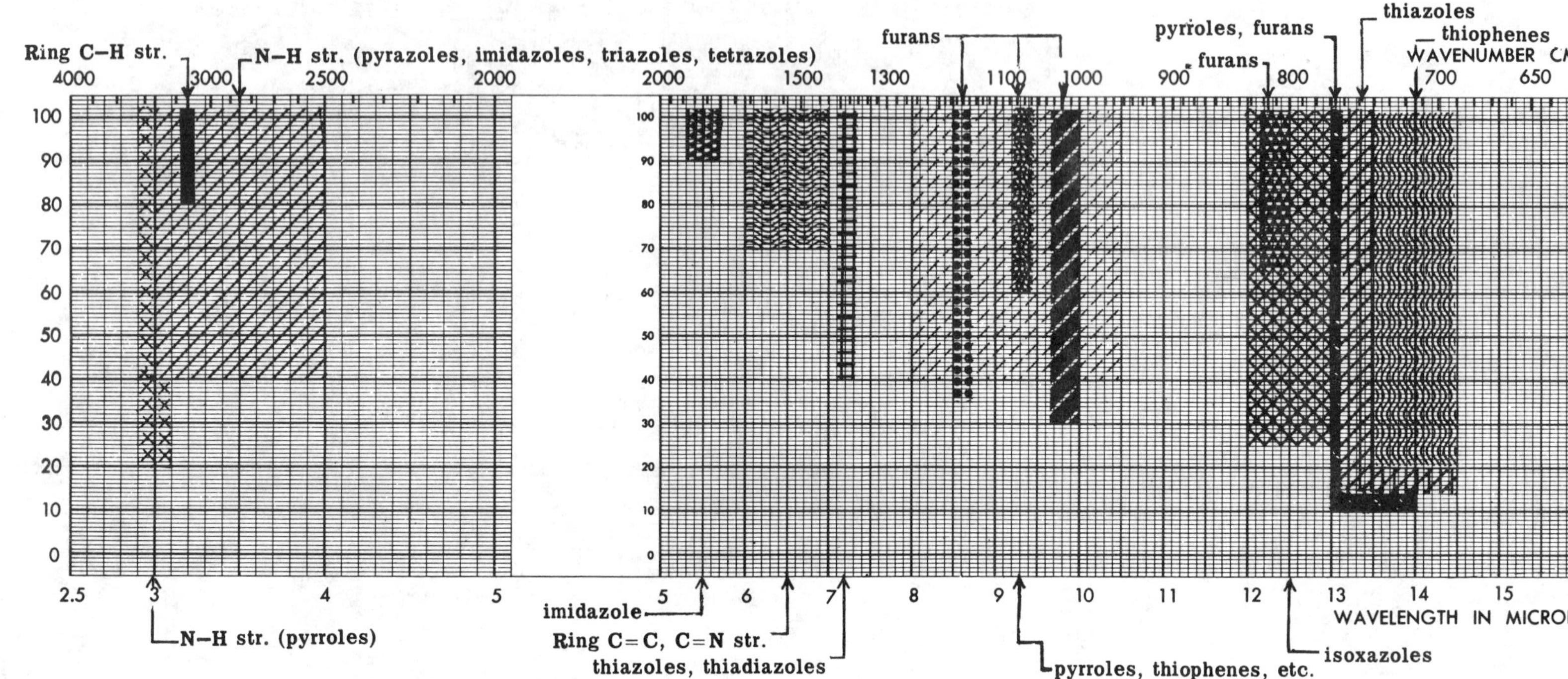

Pyrroles

The pyrrole ring C–H stretch bands appear near 3.2 μ (3125 cm^{-1}). The C=C ring stretch bands absorb between 6 and 7 μ (1665 – 1430 cm^{-1}) and are variable in intensity. There are also several bands between 8.5 and 10.5 μ (1175 – 950 cm^{-1}) (medium intensity) and a highly characteristic, strong, broad band between 13 and 14 μ (770 – 715 cm^{-1}), which is absent in the tetrasubstituted pyrroles (spectra 1198D, 1199B and D).

The NH stretch absorbs very strongly near 2.9 to 3.1 μ (3450 – 3225 cm^{-1}).

Furans

Furans also have their C–H stretch absorptions near 3.2 μ (3125 cm^{-1}). The ring C=C stretch absorbs between 6 and 7 μ (1665 – 1430 cm^{-1}) with more definite bands appearing near 6.2 μ (1615 cm^{-1}) and 6.5 to 6.7 μ (1540 – 1495 cm^{-1}) than in the case of the pyrroles. Medium to strong intensity bands also appear near 8.6, 9.3 and 9.7 – 9.9 μ (1165, 1075 and 1030 – 1010 cm^{-1}). The furan ring also displays a strong band between 13 and 14 μ (770 – 715 cm^{-1}) which weakens as the number of substituents on the ring increases. It is accompanied by a weaker band near 12.4 μ (805 cm^{-1}) in many of the spectra. (See spectra 1205A and C).

Thiophenes

The thiophene C–H absorbs near 3.2 μ (3125 cm^{-1}). The C=C stretch bands are quite weak near 6.3 and 6.5 to 6.7 μ (1585 and 1540 – 1495 cm^{-1}). The bands are extremely variable in intensity. The extremes are illustrated in spectrum 1206G where only slight bands are observed and spectra 1207D–08C where the absorptions are medium to strong. Several weak to medium bands appear between 8 and 10.5 μ (1250 – 950 cm^{-1}) and vary in position and intensity as the type of substituents vary. A strong absorption between 13.5 and 14.5 μ (740 – 690 cm^{-1}) is also noted. In the 2,5-disubstituted thiophenes, this absorption appears near 12.5 to 13 μ (800 – 770 cm^{-1}). With the 3 position substituted, the thiophenes absorb strongly near 13.2 μ (755 cm^{-1}). (See spectra 1206H and 1207F)

Pyrazoles, Imidazoles, Triazoles and Tetrazoles

Band positions and intensities throughout this series are exceptionally variable. The positioning of a hydroxyl, amino (NH_2 or NH) or mercapto group on the carbon adjacent to the nitrogen on the ring permits the formation of the keto, imine or thione tautomer. Disruption of the ring absorptions in the higher wavelength region [12 – 15 μ (835 – 665 cm^{-1})] results. The C–H stretch absorbs near 3.2 μ (3125 cm^{-1}). The double bonds of the ring absorb with several bands between 6 and 7 μ (1665 – 1430 cm^{-1}) when the pyrazole, imidazole, triazole or tetrazole ring is not substituted so as to allow the formation of the tautomers. The NH group absorbs strongly between 3 and 4 μ (3335 – 2500 cm^{-1}), and in many cases is very similar in shape to the OH stretch of the carboxylic acid dimer. In the imidazoles, this band is accompanied by a weak band near 5.5 μ (1820 cm^{-1}). This is also true of tetrazole, spectrum 1226F.

Isoxazoles and Oxazoles

The C=N and C=C absorptions of isoxazoles occur between 6 and 7 μ (1665 – 1430 cm^{-1}). A very strong band appears near 6.2 to 6.3 μ (1615 – 1585 cm^{-1}) in spectra 1228F-29A. The C–H stretch absorbs near 3.2 μ (3125 cm^{-1}). A strong absorption is also noted between 12 and 13 μ (835 – 770 cm^{-1}). In spectrum 901 D, this band appears weak compared to the very strong ClO_4^{-1} absorption at 9.2 μ (1085 cm^{-1}).

Thiazoles, Thiadiazoles

As with the other 5-membered rings, the CH stretch band in these sulfur-containing heterocycles appears near 3.2 μ (3125 cm^{-1}). The C=C and C=N stretch does not absorb significantly in the 6 to 6.5 μ (1665 – 1540 cm^{-1}) region. However, a 6.5 – 6.8 μ (1540 – 1470 cm^{-1}) band and a 7.2 μ (1390 cm^{-1}) band are characteristic. Many of the molecules of this type have groups whose absorptions obscure the typical bands seen in the simpler compounds (1231H—1232G).

The presence of an amino group in the 2-position of thiazole results in the imino tautomer. The C=N stretch absorbs near 6.1 to 6.2 μ (1640 – 1615 cm^{-1}) and the N–H stretch between 2.5 and 3.5 μ (4000 – 2855 cm^{-1}). Thiazoles display several absorptions in the 11 to 15 μ (910 – 665 cm^{-1}) region with a frequently observed band near 13 – 14.5 μ (770 – 690 cm^{-1}). The position of this band, however, is disturbed considerably by various substituents on the ring.

The thiadiazoles are not at all consistent with respect to absorption between 11 and 15 μ (910 – 665 cm^{-1}).

A

13,170-9 Pyrrole
M.W. 67.09 n_D^{20} 1.5082 b.p. 131°

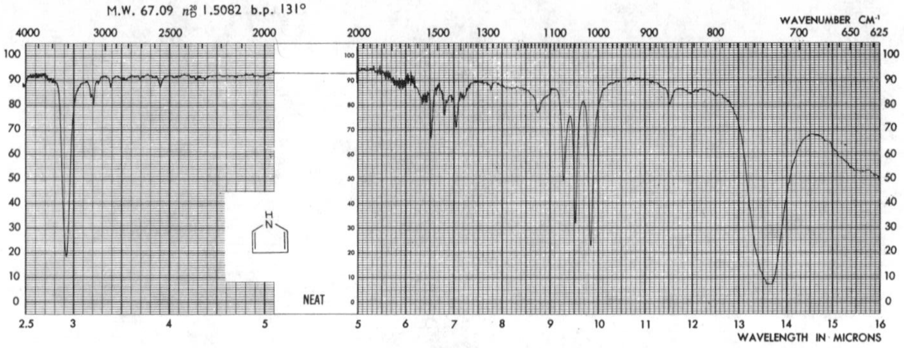

NEAT

B

15,108-4 Pyrrole, potassium derivative, tech.
M.W. 105.19 m.p. 200-205° (dec.)

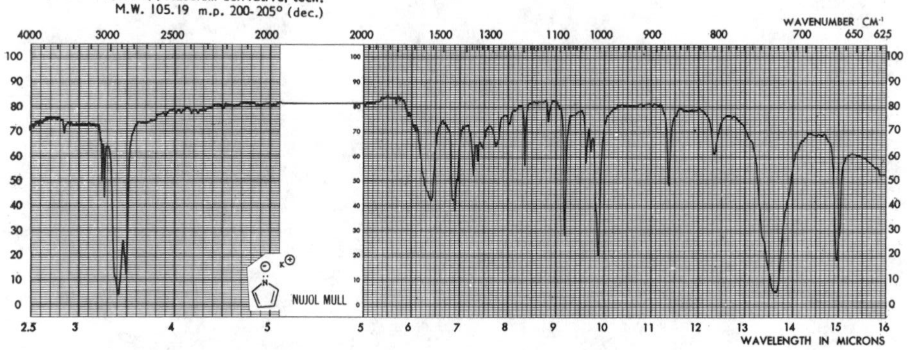

NUJOL MULL

C

M7880-1 N-Methylpyrrole
M.W. 81.12 n_D^{20} 1.4875 b.p. 112-113°

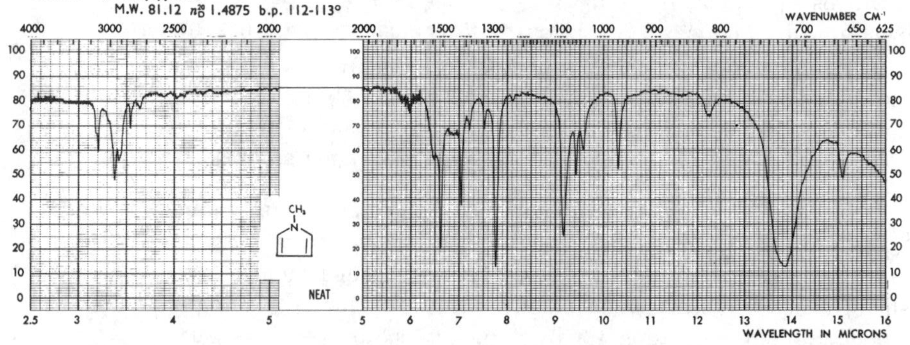

NEAT

D

D18,360-1 2,5-Dimethylpyrrole
M.W. 95.15

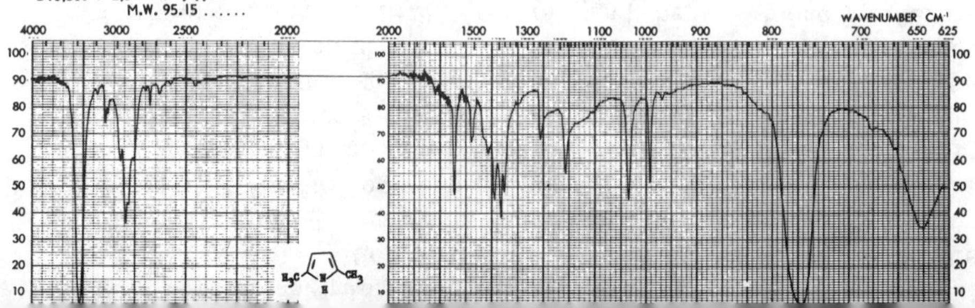

E

T8030-6 1,2,5-Trimethylpyrrole
M.W. 109.17 n_D^{20} 1.4969
b.p. 166-168°/745 mm.

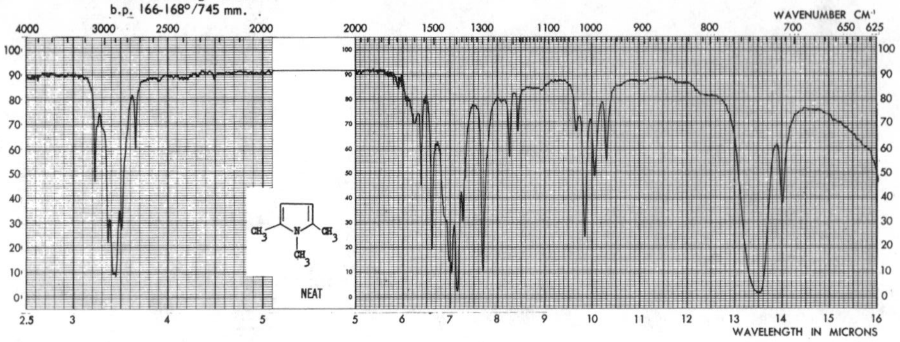

NEAT

F

D15,840-2 2,4-Dimethyl-3-ethylpyrrole (kryptopyrrole), puriss.
M.W. 123.20 n_D^{20} 1.4961

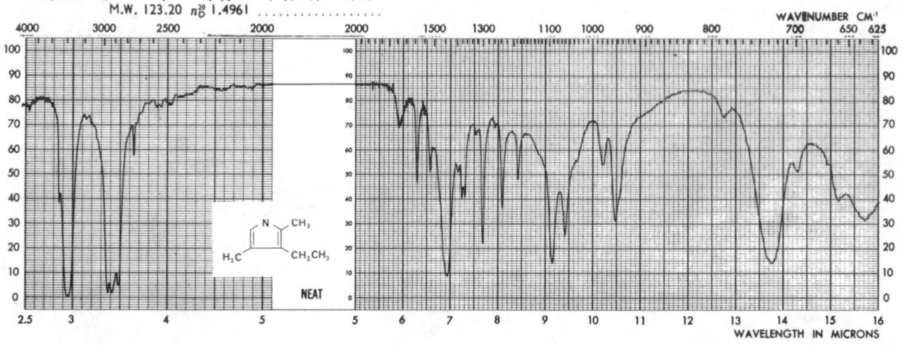

NEAT

G

13,147-4 1-Phenylpyrrole
M.W. 143.19 m.p. 59-61°

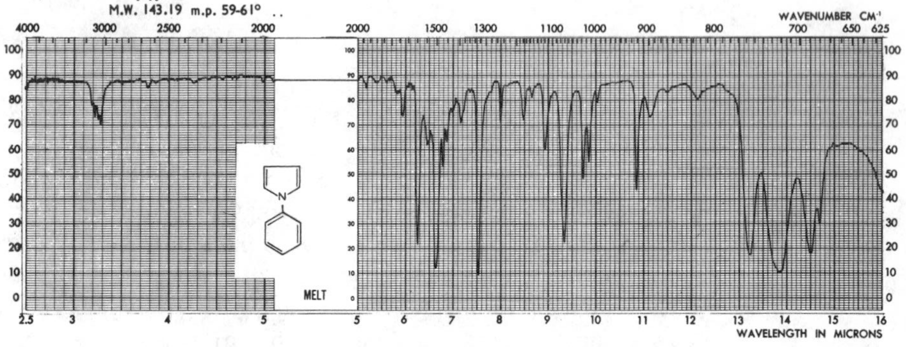

MELT

H

19,694-0
1-(*o*-Aminophenyl)pyrrole, 98+%
FW 158.20 mp 96-98° Disp. C

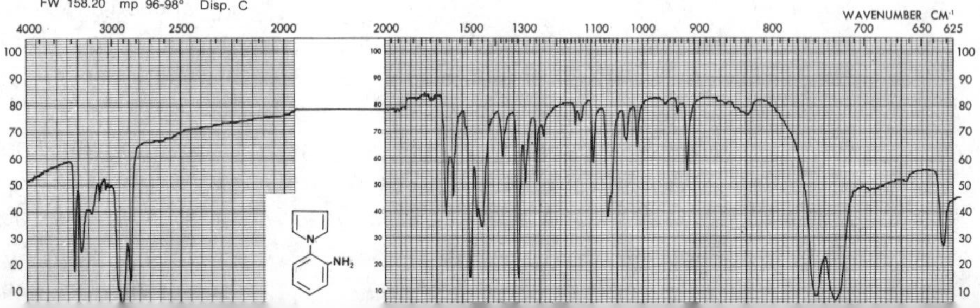

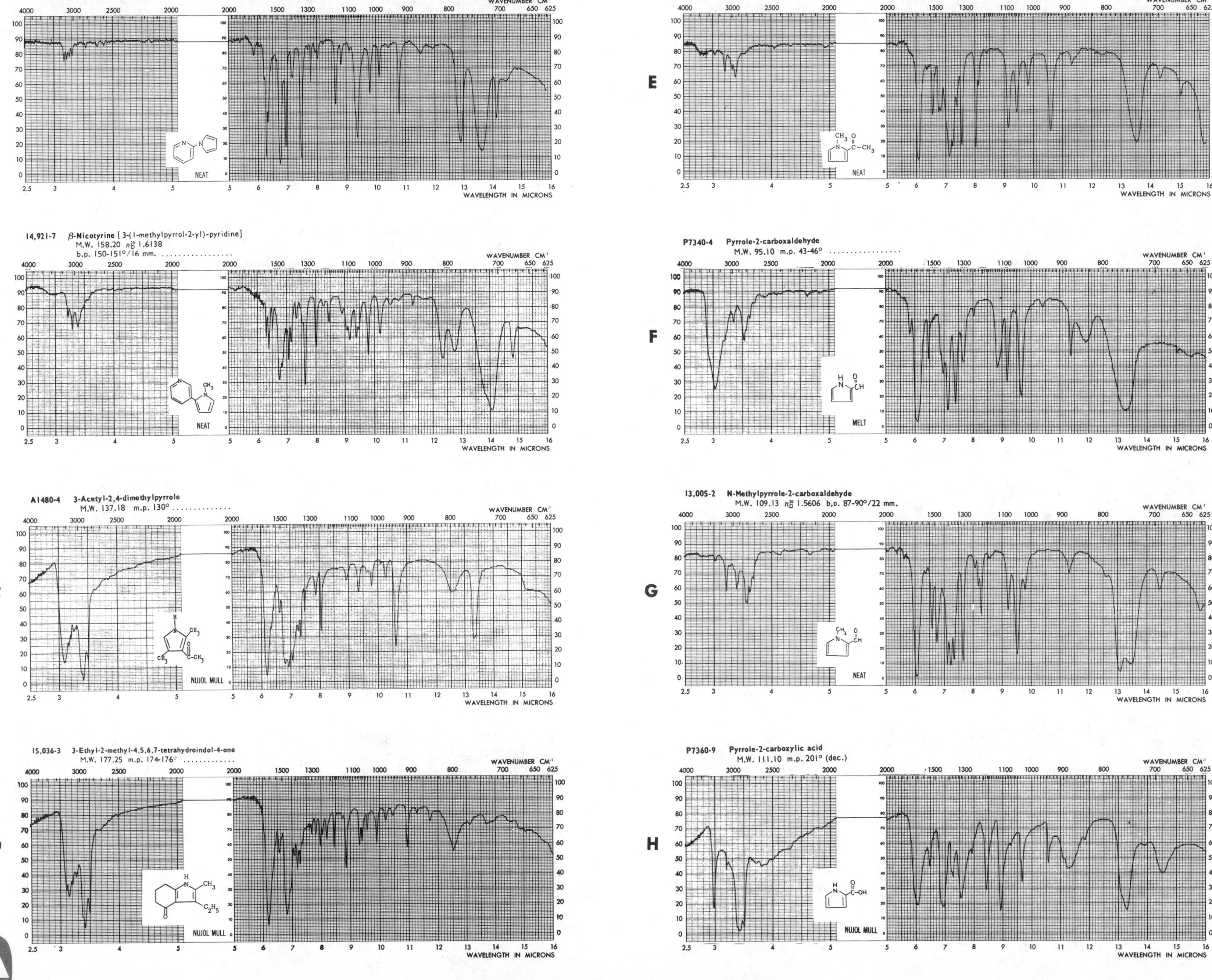
A
M.W. 144.18 n_D^{20} 1.6127 d 1.091 Beil. **22**(2),327
NEAT
B
14,921-7 β-Nicotyrine [3-(1-methylpyrrol-2-yl)-pyridine]
M.W. 158.20 n_D^{20} 1.6138
b.p. 150-151°/16 mm.
NEAT
C
A1480-4 3-Acetyl-2,4-dimethylpyrrole
M.W. 137.18 m.p. 130°
NUJOL MULL
D
15,036-3 3-Ethyl-2-methyl-4,5,6,7-tetrahydroindol-4-one
M.W. 177.25 m.p. 174-176°
NUJOL MULL
E
Beil. 21,272
NEAT
F
P7340-4 Pyrrole-2-carboxaldehyde
M.W. 95.10 m.p. 43-46°
MELT
G
13,005-2 N-Methylpyrrole-2-carboxaldehyde
M.W. 109.13 n_D^{20} 1.5606 b.p. 87-90°/22 mm.
NEAT
H
P7360-9 Pyrrole-2-carboxylic acid
M.W. 111.10 m.p. 201° (dec.)
NUJOL MULL
WAVENUMBER CM⁻¹
WAVELENGTH IN MICRONS
ALDRICH

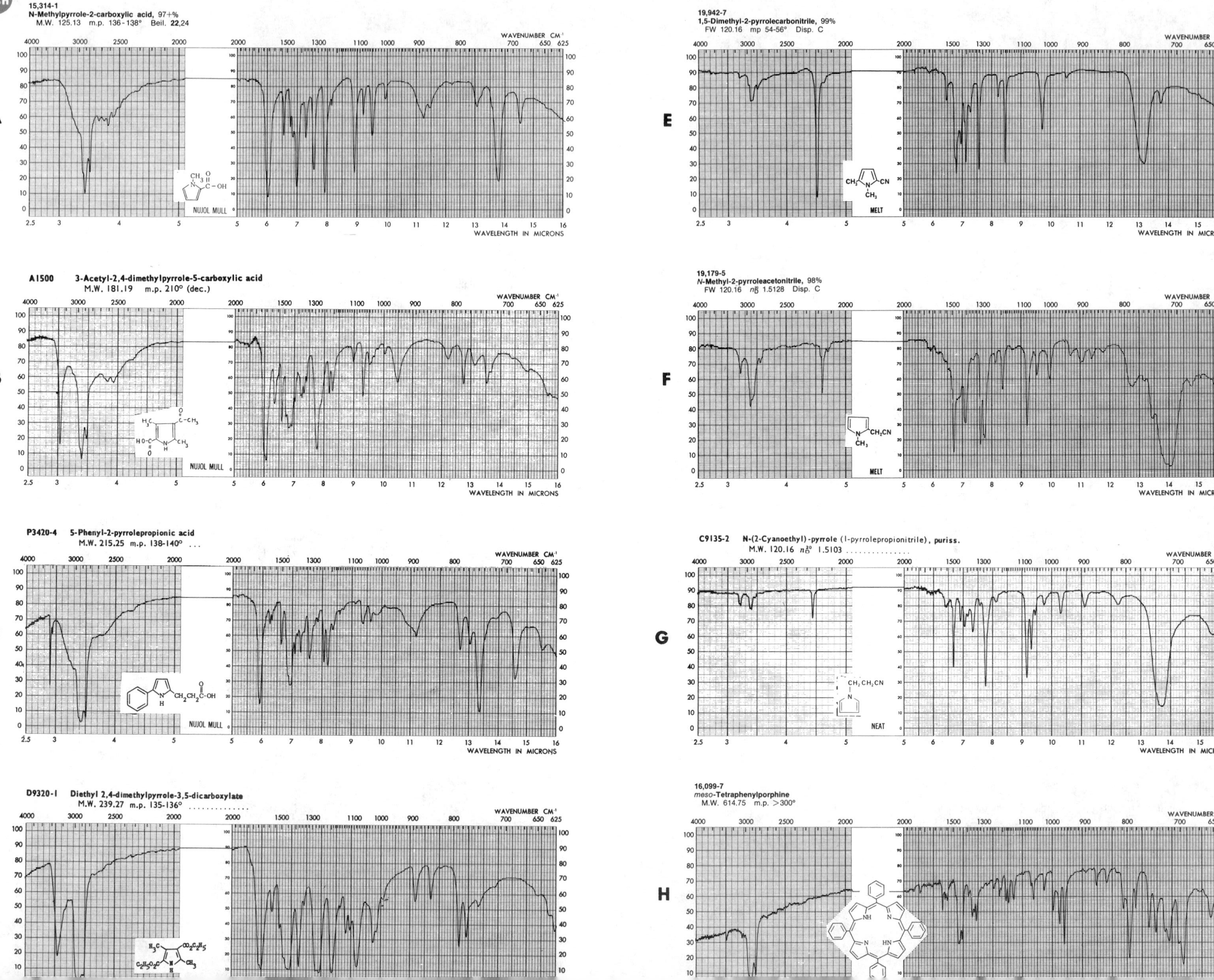
A
15,314-1
N-Methylpyrrole-2-carboxylic acid, 97+%
M.W. 125.13 m.p. 136-138° Beil. 22,24
NUJOL MULL
B
A1500 3-Acetyl-2,4-dimethylpyrrole-5-carboxylic acid
M.W. 181.19 m.p. 210° (dec.)
NUJOL MULL
C
P3420-4 5-Phenyl-2-pyrrolepropionic acid
M.W. 215.25 m.p. 138-140°
NUJOL MULL
D
D9320-1 Diethyl 2,4-dimethylpyrrole-3,5-dicarboxylate
M.W. 239.27 m.p. 135-136°
E
19,942-7
1,5-Dimethyl-2-pyrrolecarbonitrile, 99%
FW 120.16 mp 54-56° Disp. C
MELT
F
19,179-5
N-Methyl-2-pyrroleacetonitrile, 98%
FW 120.16 n_D^{20} 1.5128 Disp. C
MELT
G
C9135-2 N-(2-Cyanoethyl)-pyrrole (1-pyrrolepropionitrile), puriss.
M.W. 120.16 n_D^{20} 1.5103
NEAT
H
16,099-7
meso-Tetraphenylporphine
M.W. 614.75 m.p. >300°
WAVENUMBER CM⁻¹
WAVELENGTH IN MICRONS

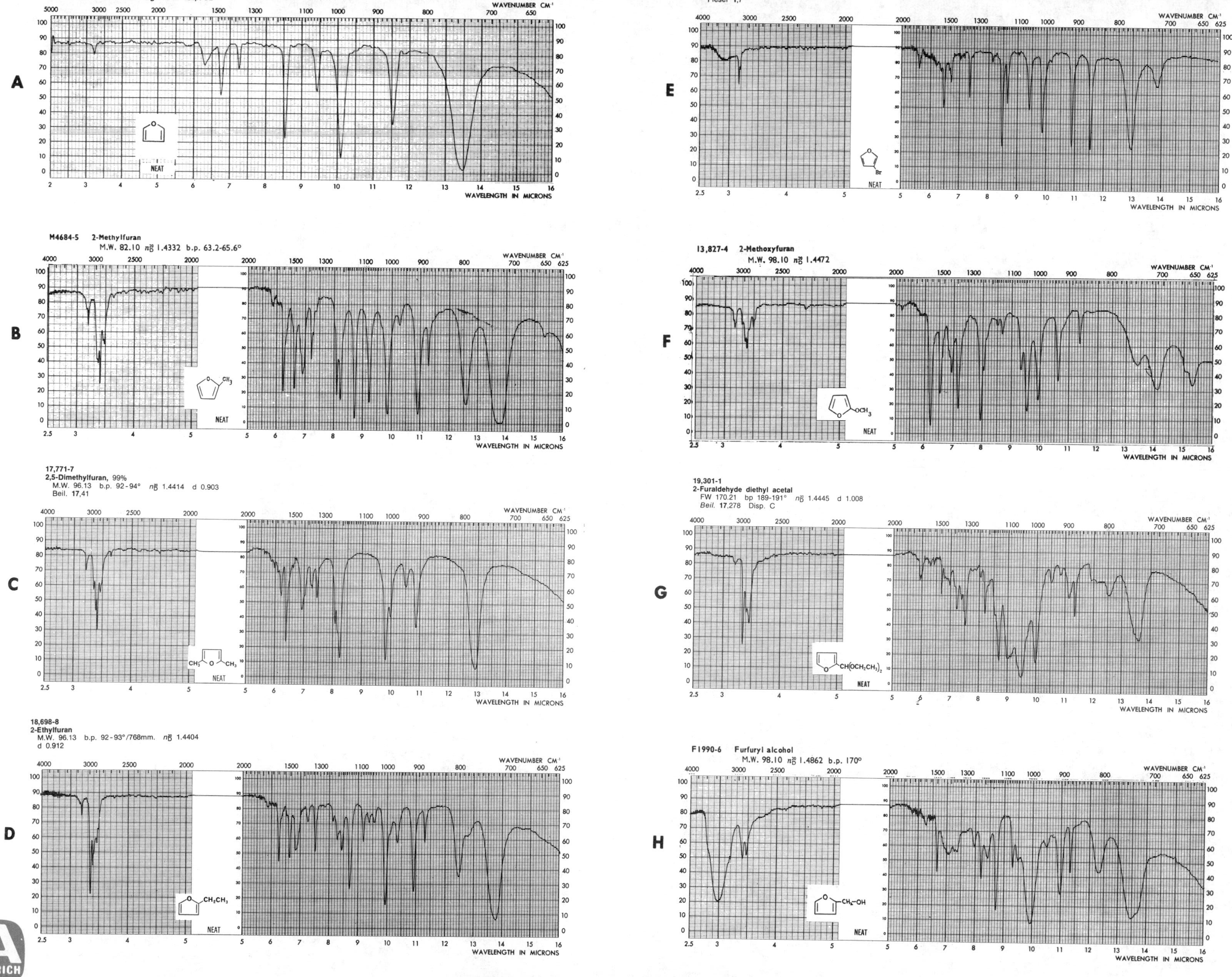
A
M.W. 68.08 n_D^{20} 1.4207 b.p. 32°
NEAT
E
M.W. 146.98 b.p. 103° n_D^{20} 1.4498 d 1.635
Fieser 1,7
NEAT
B
M4684-5 2-Methylfuran
M.W. 82.10 n_D^{20} 1.4332 b.p. 63.2-65.6°
NEAT
F
13,827-4 2-Methoxyfuran
M.W. 98.10 n_D^{20} 1.4472
NEAT
C
17,771-7
2,5-Dimethylfuran, 99%
M.W. 96.13 b.p. 92-94° n_D^{20} 1.4414 d 0.903
Beil. 17,41
NEAT
G
19,301-1
2-Furaldehyde diethyl acetal
FW 170.21 bp 189-191° n_D^{20} 1.4445 d 1.008
Beil. 17,278 Disp. C
NEAT
D
18,698-8
2-Ethylfuran
M.W. 96.13 b.p. 92-93°/768mm. n_D^{20} 1.4404
d 0.912
NEAT
H
F1990-6 Furfuryl alcohol
M.W. 98.10 n_D^{20} 1.4862 b.p. 170°
NEAT
WAVENUMBER CM⁻¹
WAVELENGTH IN MICRONS
ALDRICH

5 MEMBERED AROMATIC HETEROCYCLES

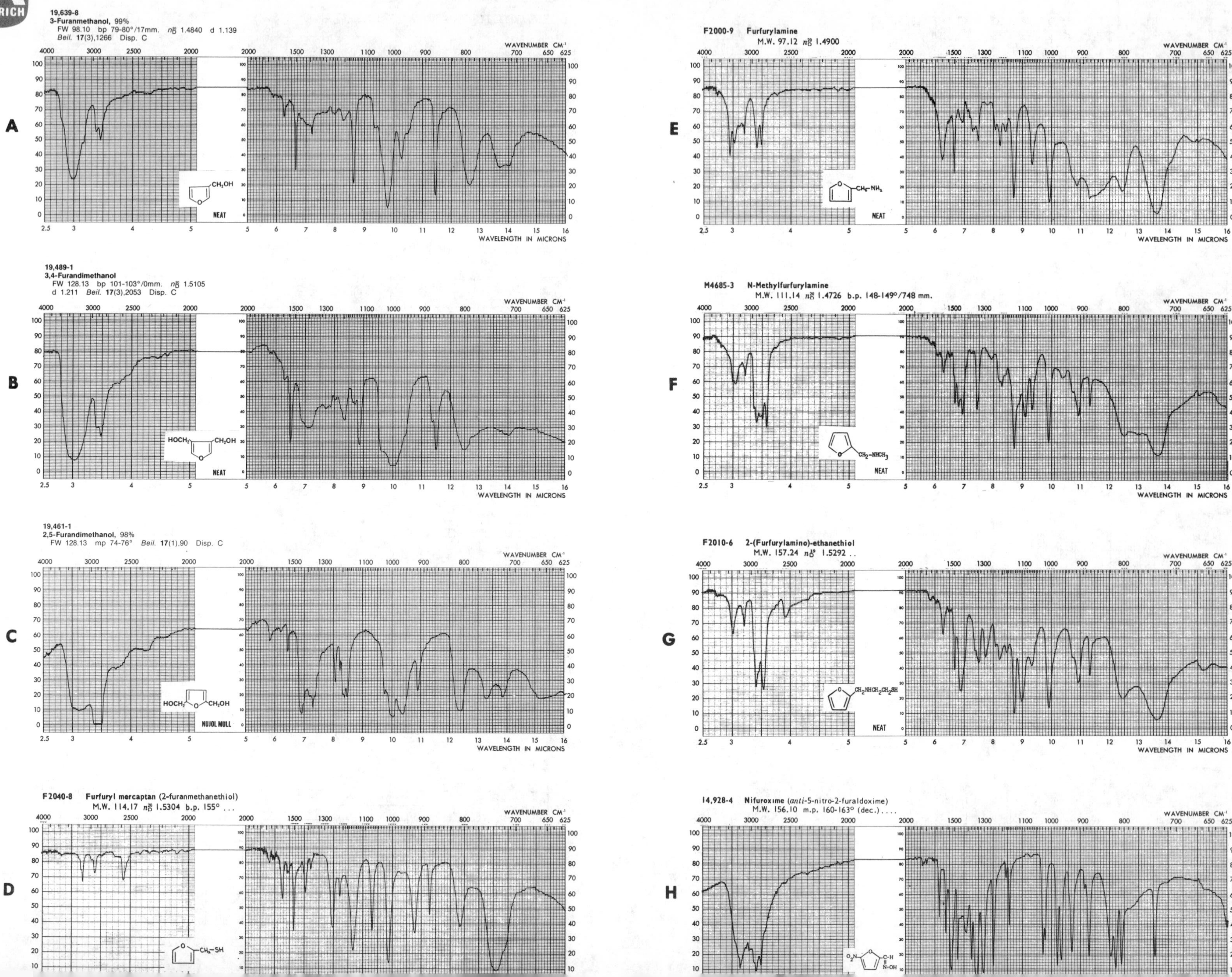
ALDRICH
A
19,639-8
3-Furanmethanol, 99%
FW 98.10 bp 79-80°/17mm. n_D^{20} 1.4840 d 1.139
Beil. 17(3),1266 Disp. C
NEAT
B
19,489-1
3,4-Furandimethanol
FW 128.13 bp 101-103°/0mm. n_D^{20} 1.5105
d 1.211 *Beil.* 17(3),2053 Disp. C
NEAT
C
19,461-1
2,5-Furandimethanol, 98%
FW 128.13 mp 74-76° *Beil.* 17(1),90 Disp. C
NUJOL MULL
D
F2040-8 Furfuryl mercaptan (2-furanmethanethiol)
M.W. 114.17 n_D^{20} 1.5304 b.p. 155° . . .
E
F2000-9 Furfurylamine
M.W. 97.12 n_D^{20} 1.4900
NEAT
F
M4685-3 N-Methylfurfurylamine
M.W. 111.14 n_D^{20} 1.4726 b.p. 148-149°/748 mm.
NEAT
G
F2010-6 2-(Furfurylamino)-ethanethiol
M.W. 157.24 n_D^{19} 1.5292 . .
NEAT
H
14,928-4 Nifuroxime (*anti*-5-nitro-2-furaldoxime)
M.W. 156.10 m.p. 160-163° (dec.) . . . .
WAVENUMBER CM⁻¹
WAVELENGTH IN MICRONS

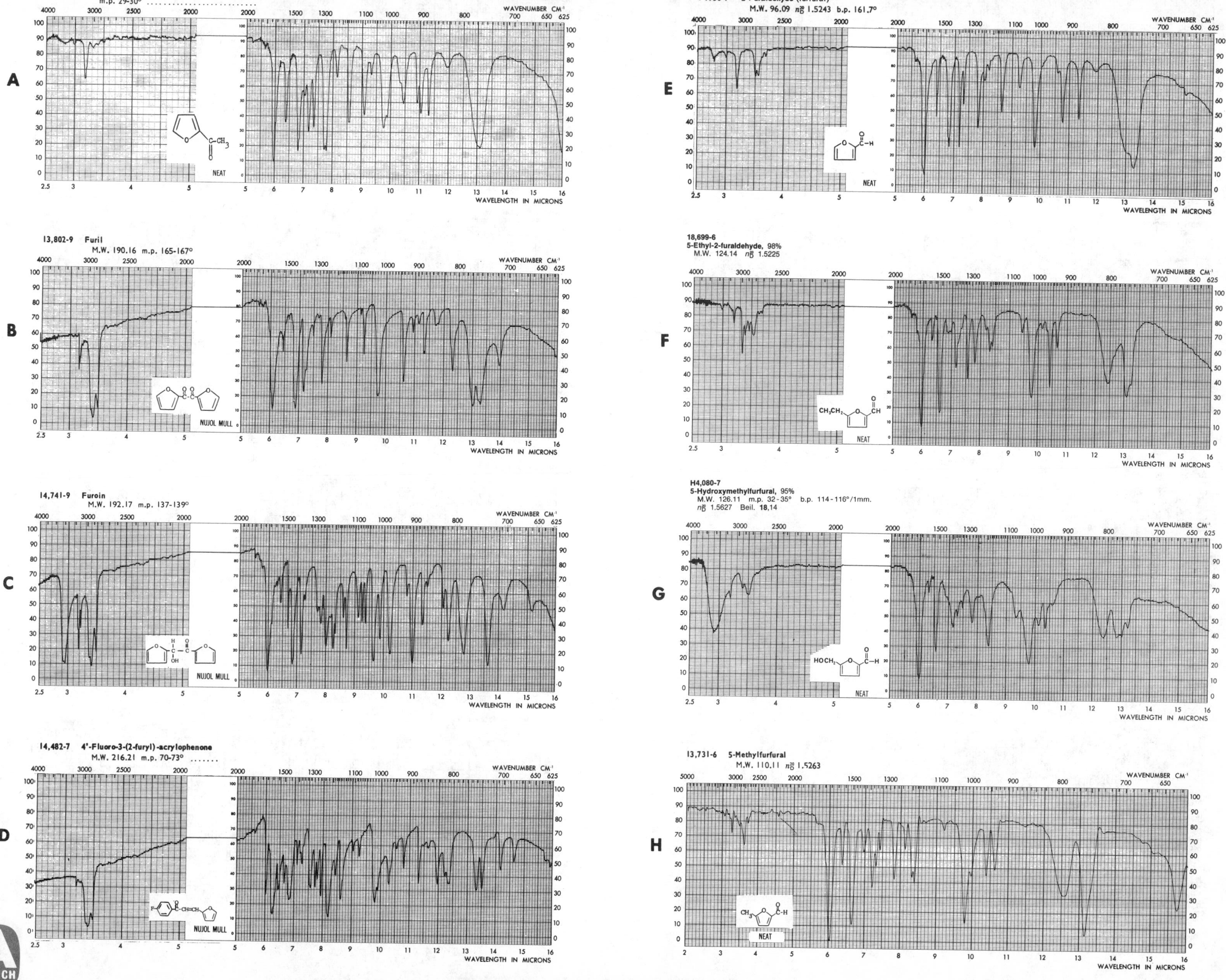

A
M.W. 110.11 n_D^{20} 1.4999 (supercooled)
m.p. 29-30°
NEAT
B
13,802-9 Furil
M.W. 190.16 m.p. 165-167°
NUJOL MULL
C
14,741-9 Furoin
M.W. 192.17 m.p. 137-139°
NUJOL MULL
D
14,482-7 4'-Fluoro-3-(2-furyl)-acrylophenone
M.W. 216.21 m.p. 70-73°
NUJOL MULL
E
F1950-7 2-Furaldehyde (furfural)
M.W. 96.09 n_D^{20} 1.5243 b.p. 161.7°
NEAT
F
18,699-6
5-Ethyl-2-furaldehyde, 98%
M.W. 124.14 n_D^{20} 1.5225
NEAT
G
H4,080-7
5-Hydroxymethylfurfural, 95%
M.W. 126.11 m.p. 32-35° b.p. 114-116°/1mm.
n_D^{20} 1.5627 Beil. 18,14
NEAT
H
13,731-6 5-Methylfurfural
M.W. 110.11 n_D^{20} 1.5263
NEAT
WAVENUMBER CM⁻¹
WAVELENGTH IN MICRONS

5 MEMBERED AROMATIC HETEROCYCLES

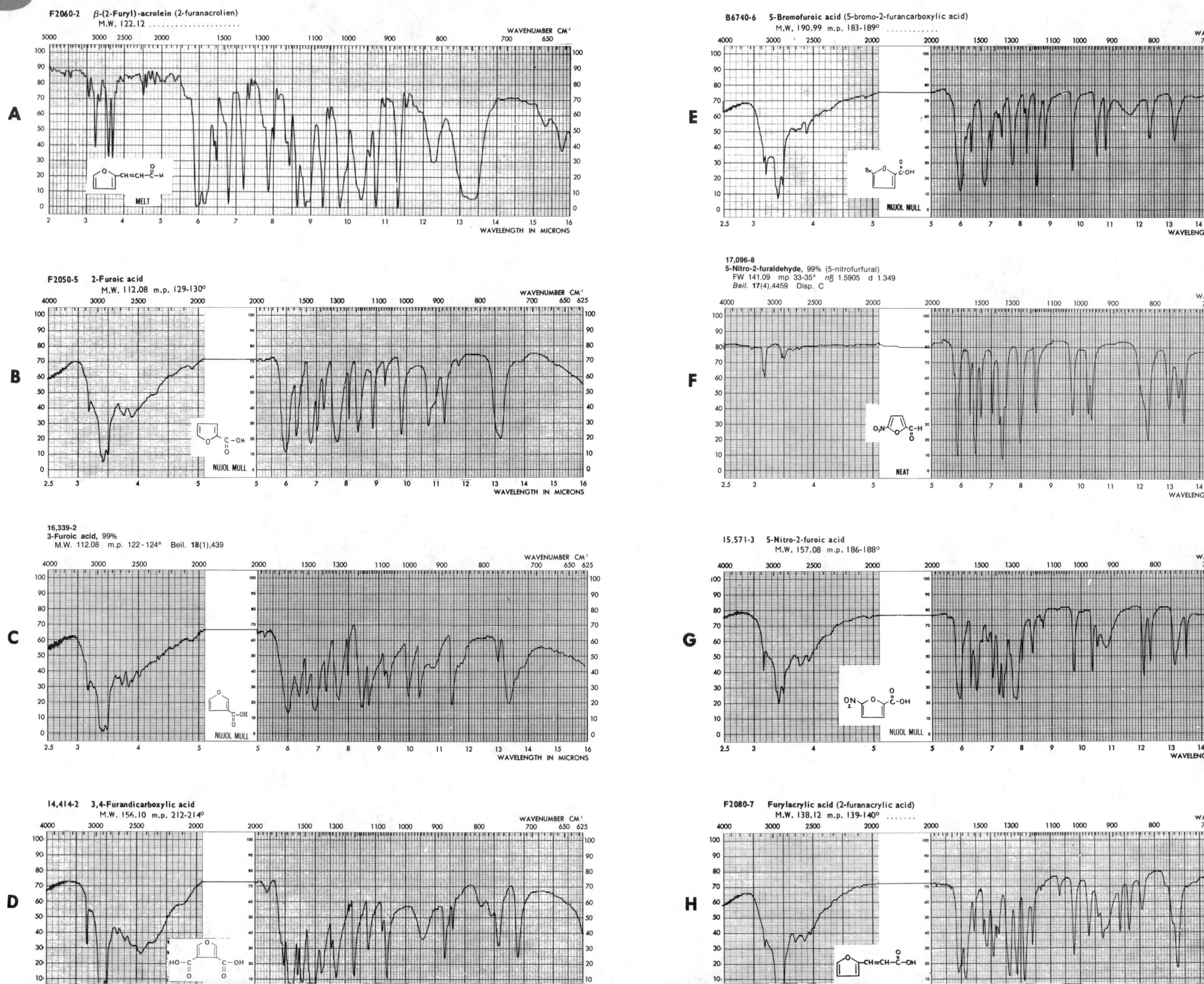
ALDRICH
A
F2060-2 β-(2-Furyl)-acrolein (2-furanacrolien)
M.W. 122.12
MELT
B
F2050-5 2-Furoic acid
M.W. 112.08 m.p. 129-130°
NUJOL MULL
C
16,339-2
3-Furoic acid, 99%
M.W. 112.08 m.p. 122-124° Beil. 18(1),439
NUJOL MULL
D
14,414-2 3,4-Furandicarboxylic acid
M.W. 156.10 m.p. 212-214°
E
B6740-6 5-Bromofuroic acid (5-bromo-2-furancarboxylic acid)
M.W. 190.99 m.p. 183-189°
NUJOL MULL
F
17,096-8
5-Nitro-2-furaldehyde, 99% (5-nitrofurfural)
FW 141.09 mp 33-35° n_D^{20} 1.5905 d 1.349
Beil. 17(4),4459 Disp. C
NEAT
G
15,571-3 5-Nitro-2-furoic acid
M.W. 157.08 m.p. 186-188°
NUJOL MULL
H
F2080-7 Furylacrylic acid (2-furanacrylic acid)
M.W. 138.12 m.p. 139-140°
WAVENUMBER CM⁻¹
WAVELENGTH IN MICRONS

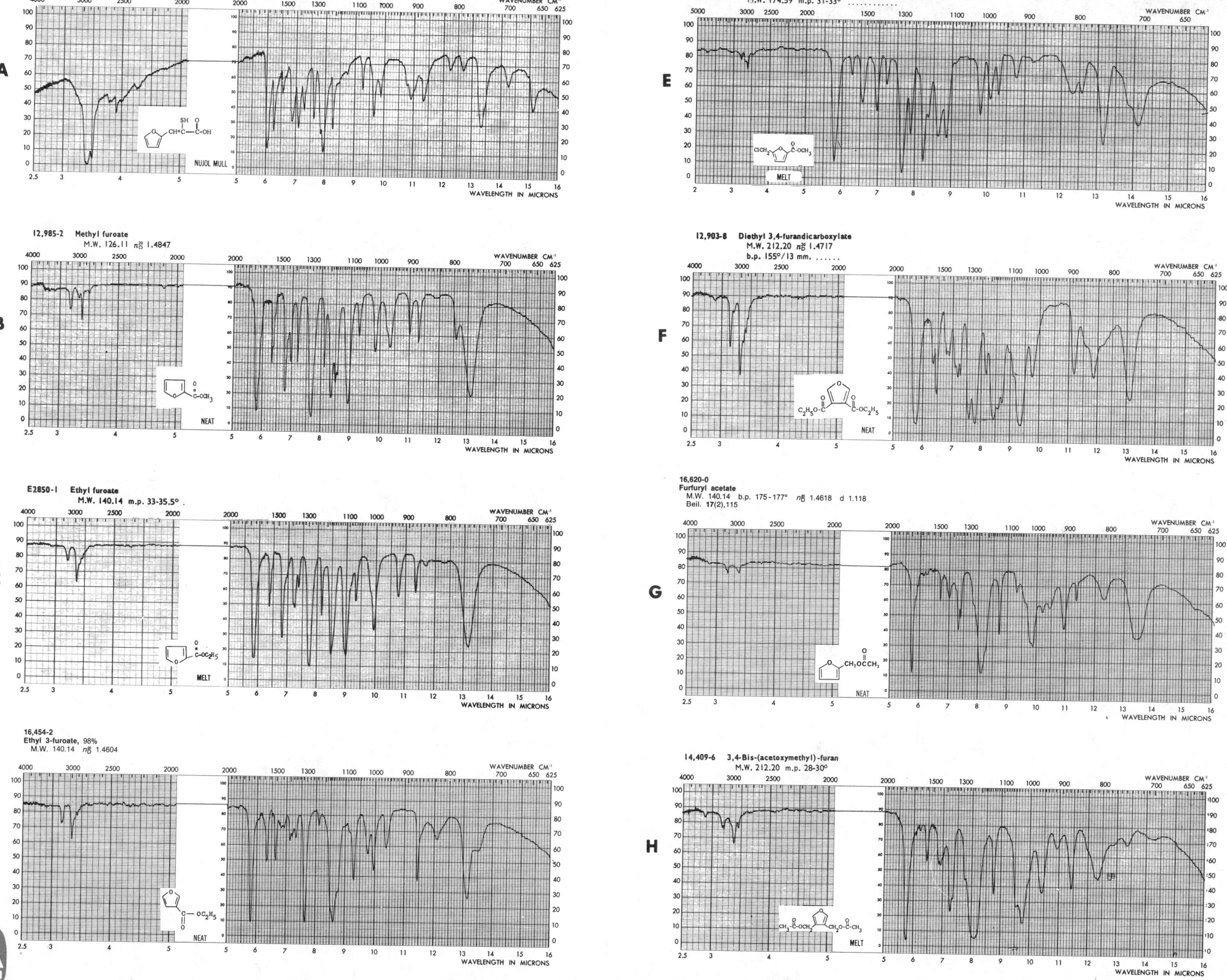
A
M.W. 170.19 m.p. 109-114°
NUJOL MULL
B
12,985-2 Methyl furoate
M.W. 126.11 n_D^{20} 1.4847
NEAT
C
E2850-1 Ethyl furoate
M.W. 140.14 m.p. 33-35.5°
MELT
D
16,454-2
Ethyl 3-furoate, 98%
M.W. 140.14 n_D^{20} 1.4604
NEAT
E
14,280-8 Methyl 5-chloromethyl-2-furancarboxylate
M.W. 174.59 m.p. 31-33°
MELT
F
12,903-8 Diethyl 3,4-furandicarboxylate
M.W. 212.20 n_D^{20} 1.4717
b.p. 155°/13 mm.
NEAT
G
16,620-0
Furfuryl acetate
M.W. 140.14 b.p. 175-177° n_D^{20} 1.4618 d 1.118
Beil. 17(2),115
NEAT
H
14,409-6 3,4-Bis-(acetoxymethyl)-furan
M.W. 212.20 m.p. 28-30°
MELT
WAVENUMBER CM⁻¹
WAVELENGTH IN MICRONS
ALDRICH

5 MEMBERED AROMATIC HETEROCYCLES

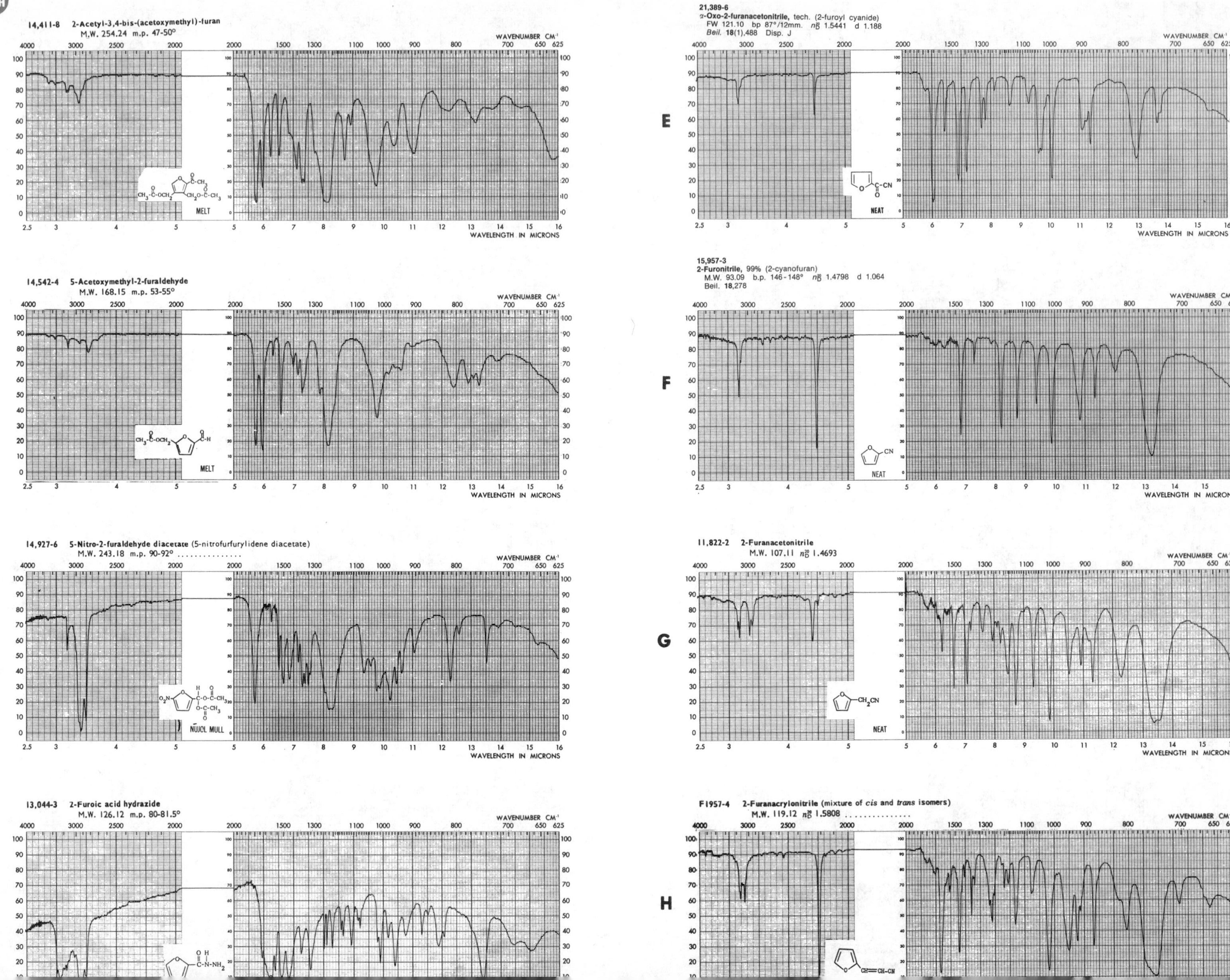
ALDRICH
A
14,411-8 2-Acetyl-3,4-bis-(acetoxymethyl)-furan
M.W. 254.24 m.p. 47-50°
MELT
B
14,542-4 5-Acetoxymethyl-2-furaldehyde
M.W. 168.15 m.p. 53-55°
MELT
C
14,927-6 5-Nitro-2-furaldehyde diacetate (5-nitrofurfurylidene diacetate)
M.W. 243.18 m.p. 90-92°
NUJOL MULL
D
13,044-3 2-Furoic acid hydrazide
M.W. 126.12 m.p. 80-81.5°
E
21,389-6
α-Oxo-2-furanacetonitrile, tech. (2-furoyl cyanide)
FW 121.10 bp 87°/12mm. n_D^{20} 1.5441 d 1.188
Beil. 18(1),488 Disp. J
NEAT
F
15,957-3
2-Furonitrile, 99% (2-cyanofuran)
M.W. 93.09 b.p. 146-148° n_D^{20} 1.4798 d 1.064
Beil. 18,278
NEAT
G
11,822-2 2-Furanacetonitrile
M.W. 107.11 n_D^{20} 1.4693
NEAT
H
F1957-4 2-Furanacrylonitrile (mixture of cis and trans isomers)
M.W. 119.12 n_D^{20} 1.5808
WAVENUMBER CM⁻¹
WAVELENGTH IN MICRONS

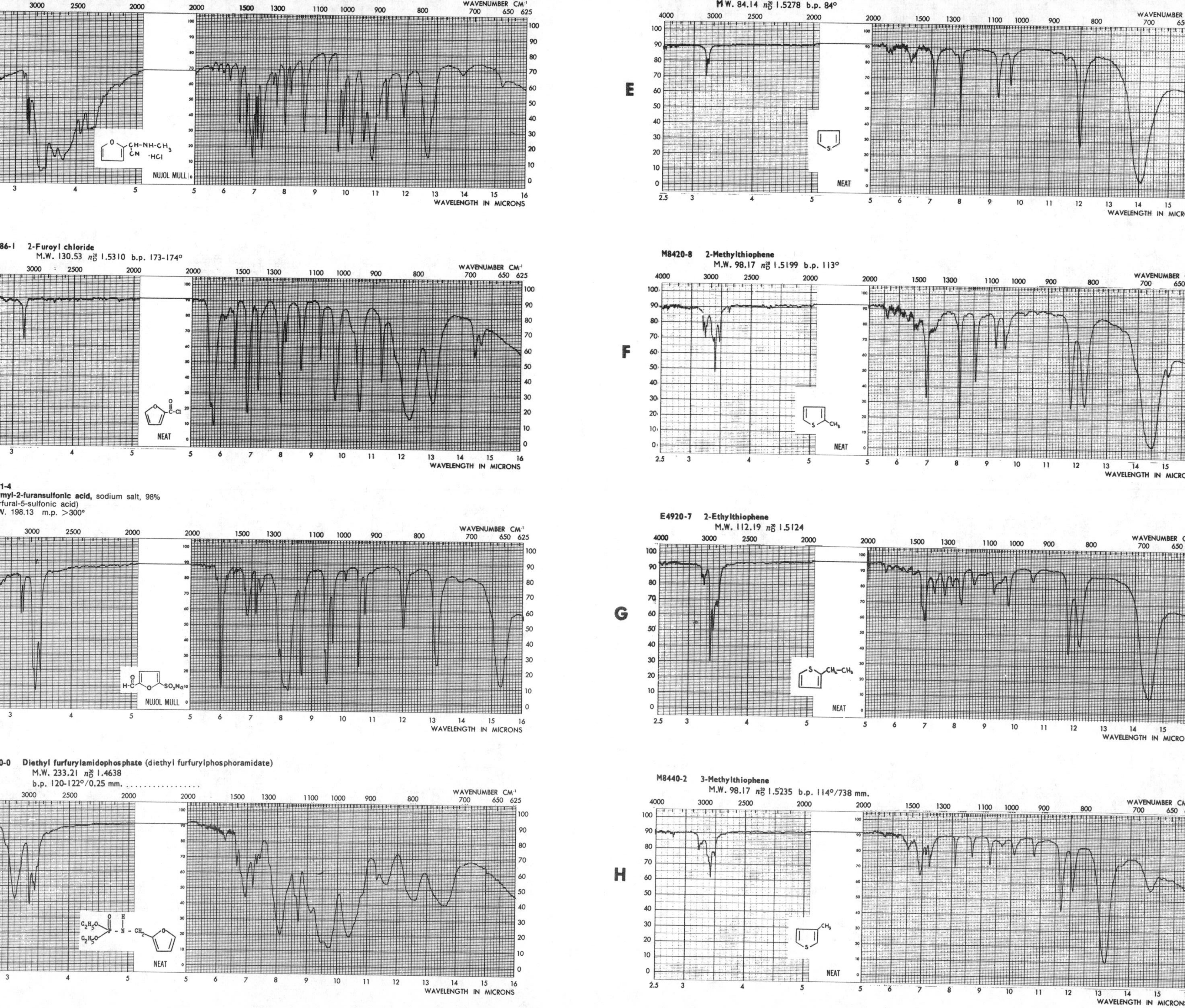

A — M.W. 172.62

14,986-1 2-Furoyl chloride
M.W. 130.53 n_D^{20} 1.5310 b.p. 173-174°

18,381-4
5-Formyl-2-furansulfonic acid, sodium salt, 98%
(furfural-5-sulfonic acid)
M.W. 198.13 m.p. >300°

11,630-0 Diethyl furfurylamidophosphate (diethyl furfurylphosphoramidate)
M.W. 233.21 n_D^{20} 1.4638
b.p. 120-122°/0.25 mm.

T3180-1 Thiophene, puriss.
M.W. 84.14 n_D^{20} 1.5278 b.p. 84°

M8420-8 2-Methylthiophene
M.W. 98.17 n_D^{20} 1.5199 b.p. 113°

E4920-7 2-Ethylthiophene
M.W. 112.19 n_D^{20} 1.5124

M8440-2 3-Methylthiophene
M.W. 98.17 n_D^{20} 1.5235 b.p. 114°/738 mm.

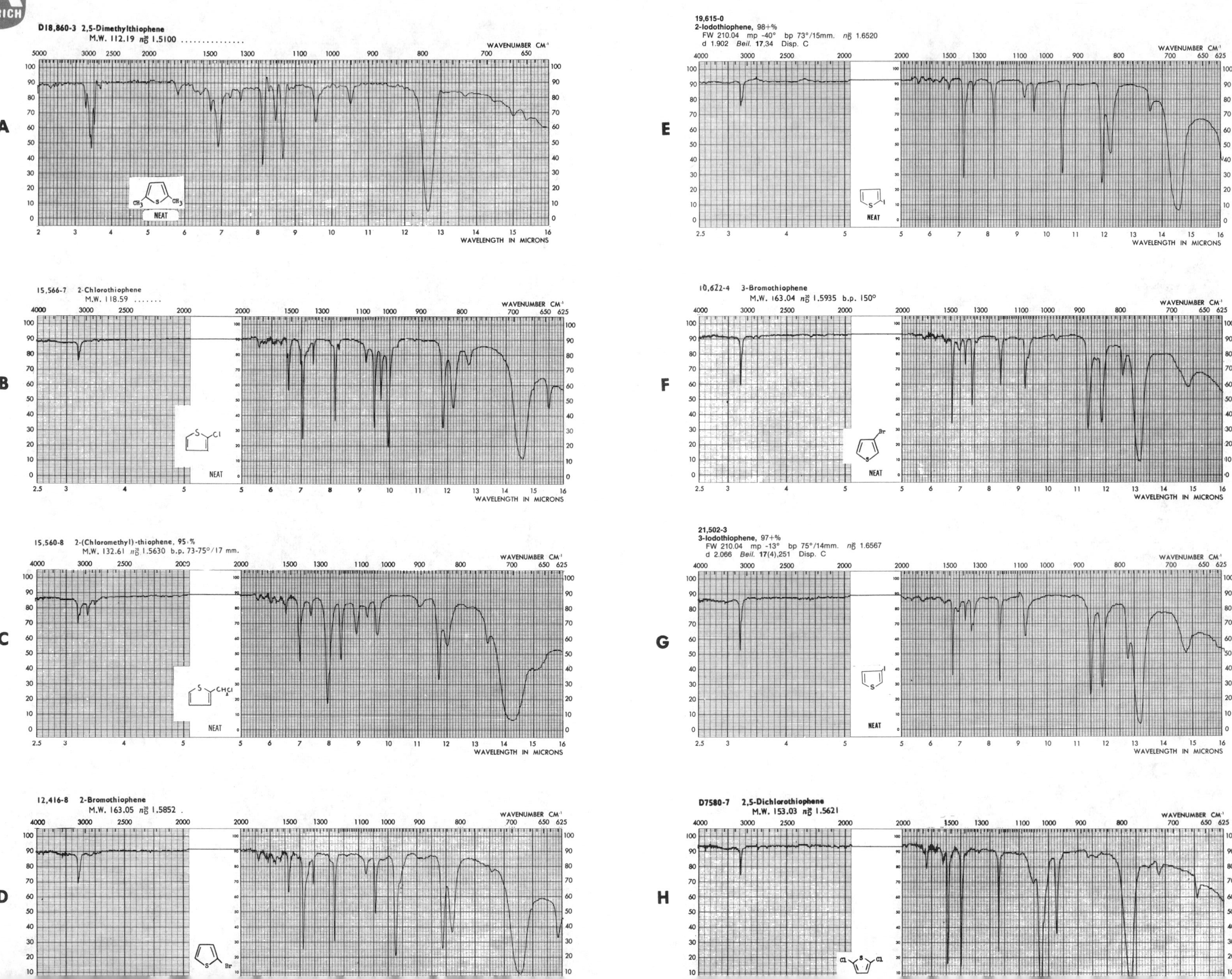

ALDRICH
A
D18,860-3 2,5-Dimethylthiophene
M.W. 112.19 n_D^{20} 1.5100
NEAT
B
15,566-7 2-Chlorothiophene
M.W. 118.59
NEAT
C
15,560-8 2-(Chloromethyl)-thiophene, 95%
M.W. 132.61 n_D^{20} 1.5630 b.p. 73-75°/17 mm.
NEAT
D
12,416-8 2-Bromothiophene
M.W. 163.05 n_D^{20} 1.5852
E
19,615-0
2-Iodothiophene, 98+%
FW 210.04 mp -40° bp 73°/15mm. n_D^{20} 1.6520
d 1.902 Beil. 17,34 Disp. C
NEAT
F
10,622-4 3-Bromothiophene
M.W. 163.04 n_D^{20} 1.5935 b.p. 150°
NEAT
G
21,502-3
3-Iodothiophene, 97+%
FW 210.04 mp -13° bp 75°/14mm. n_D^{20} 1.6567
d 2.066 Beil. 17(4),251 Disp. C
NEAT
H
D7580-7 2,5-Dichlorothiophene
M.W. 153.03 n_D^{20} 1.5621
WAVENUMBER CM⁻¹
WAVELENGTH IN MICRONS

A

M.W. 241.94 n_D^{20} 1.6269 b.p. 211°

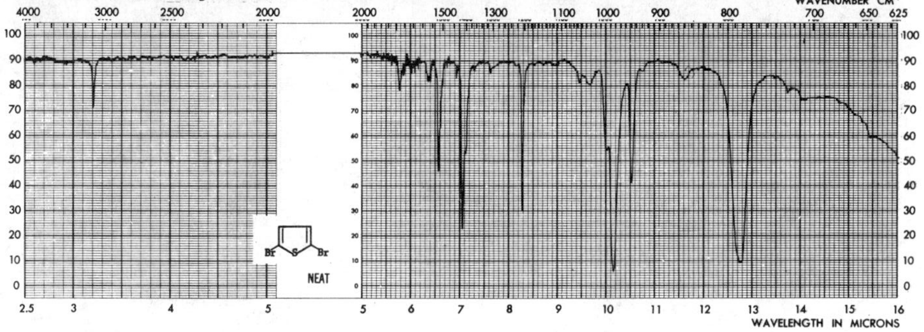

NEAT

B

D4390 **2,3-Dibromothiophene**
M.W. 241.94 n_D^{20} 1.6305

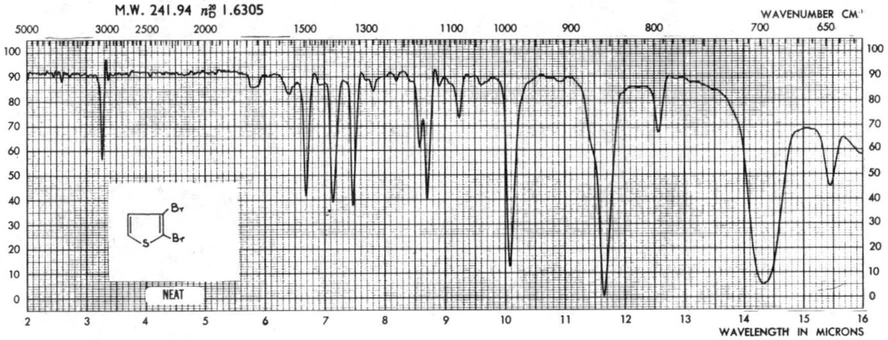

NEAT

C

13,187-3 **Tetrachlorothiophene**
M.W. 221.92 m.p. 30-31°

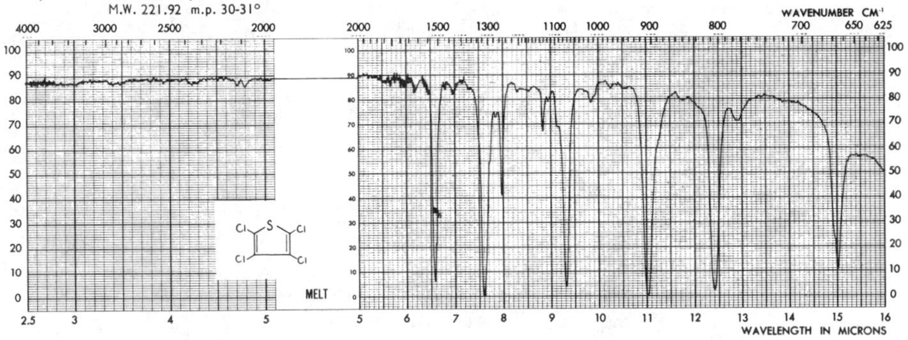

MELT

D

T540-0 **Tetrabromothiophene, puriss.**
M.W. 399.74 m.p. 113-116°

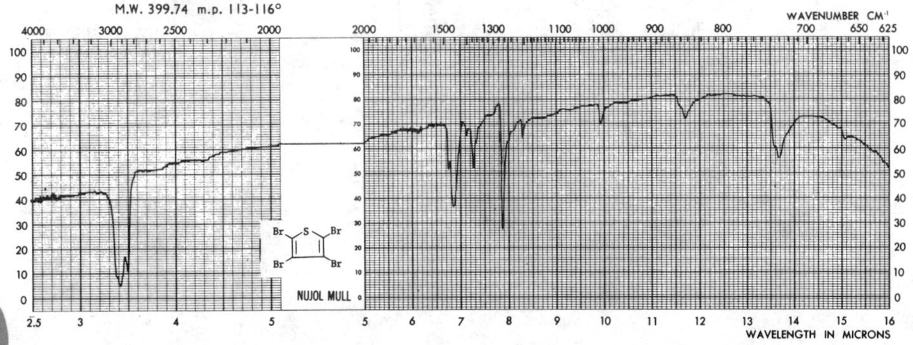

NUJOL MULL

E

T3265-4 **2-Thiophenemethanol**
M.W. 114.17 n_D^{20} 1.5696

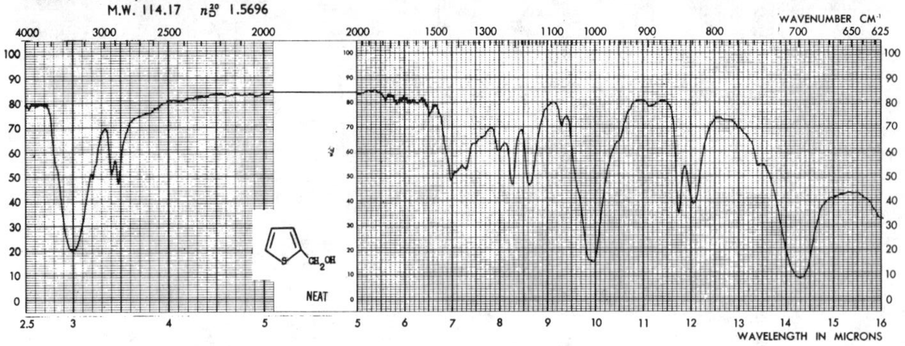

NEAT

F

T2785-5 **2-(2-Thienyl)-ethanol** (2-thiopheneethanol)
M.W. 128.19 n_D^{20} 1.5479 b.p. 108-109°/13 mm.

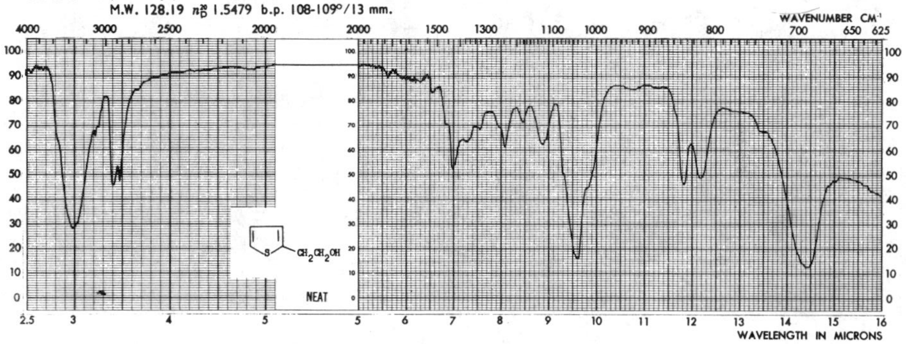

NEAT

G

C12,100-2 **Cyclopropyl 2-thienyl carbinol** (α-cyclopropyl-2-thiophene-methanol)
M.W. 154.23 n_D^{20} 1.5532

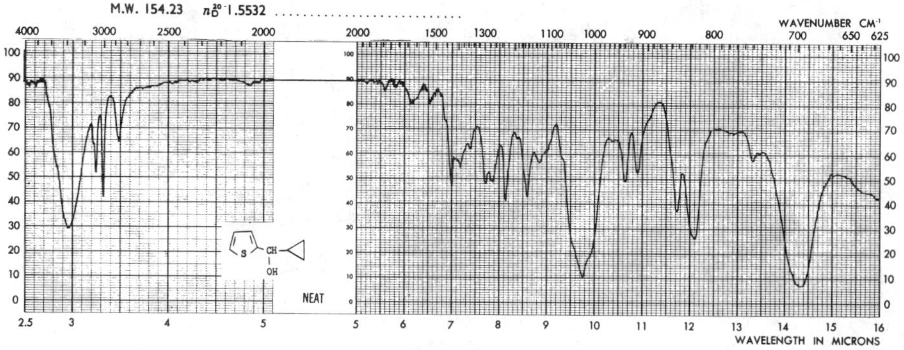

NEAT

H

22,088-4
2-Thiophenemethylamine, 96%
(2-aminomethylthiophene)
FW 113.19 bp 95-99°/28mm. n_D^{20} 1.5669 d 1.103
Beil. 18(4),7096 Disp. C

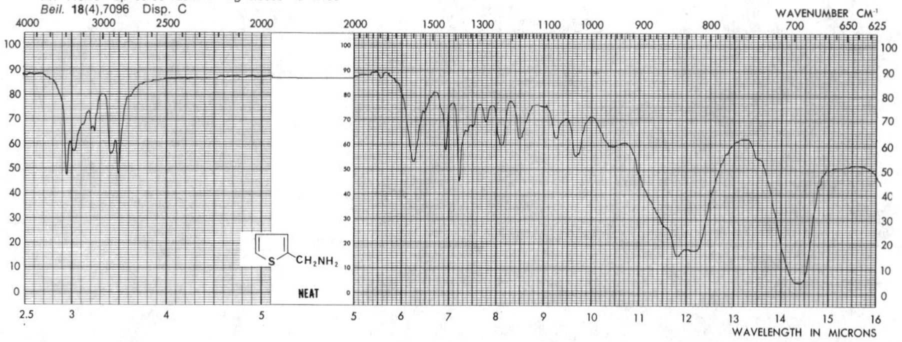

NEAT

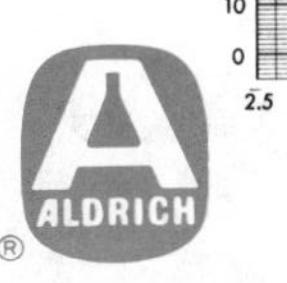

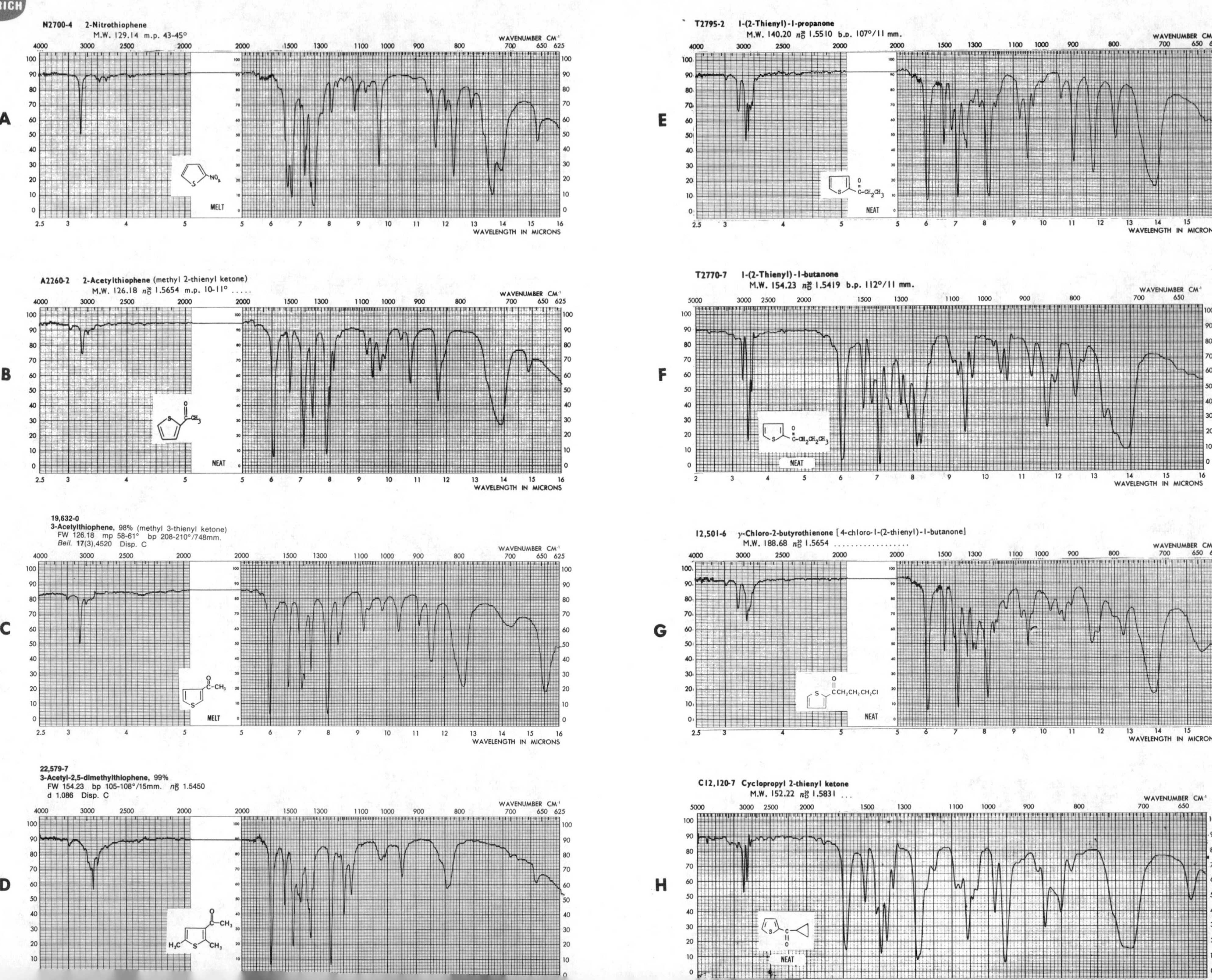
ALDRICH
A
N2700-4 2-Nitrothiophene
M.W. 129.14 m.p. 43-45°
MELT
B
A2260-2 2-Acetylthiophene (methyl 2-thienyl ketone)
M.W. 126.18 n_D^{20} 1.5654 m.p. 10-11°
NEAT
C
19,632-0
3-Acetylthiophene, 98% (methyl 3-thienyl ketone)
FW 126.18 mp 58-61° bp 208-210°/748mm.
Beil. 17(3),4520 Disp. C
MELT
D
22,579-7
3-Acetyl-2,5-dimethylthiophene, 99%
FW 154.23 bp 105-108°/15mm. n_D^{20} 1.5450
d 1.086 Disp. C
E
T2795-2 1-(2-Thienyl)-1-propanone
M.W. 140.20 n_D^{20} 1.5510 b.p. 107°/11 mm.
NEAT
F
T2770-7 1-(2-Thienyl)-1-butanone
M.W. 154.23 n_D^{20} 1.5419 b.p. 112°/11 mm.
NEAT
G
12,501-6 γ-Chloro-2-butyrothienone [4-chloro-1-(2-thienyl)-1-butanone]
M.W. 188.68 n_D^{20} 1.5654
NEAT
H
C12,120-7 Cyclopropyl 2-thienyl ketone
M.W. 152.22 n_D^{20} 1.5831
NEAT
WAVENUMBER CM⁻¹
WAVELENGTH IN MICRONS

A

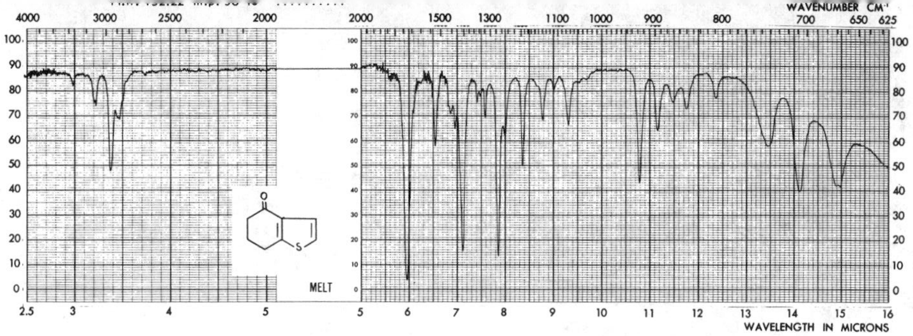

MELT

T2700-6 Thenoyltrifluoroacetone [4,4,4-trifluoro-1-(2-thienyl)-1,3-butanedione]
M.W. 222.18 m.p. 40-44°

B

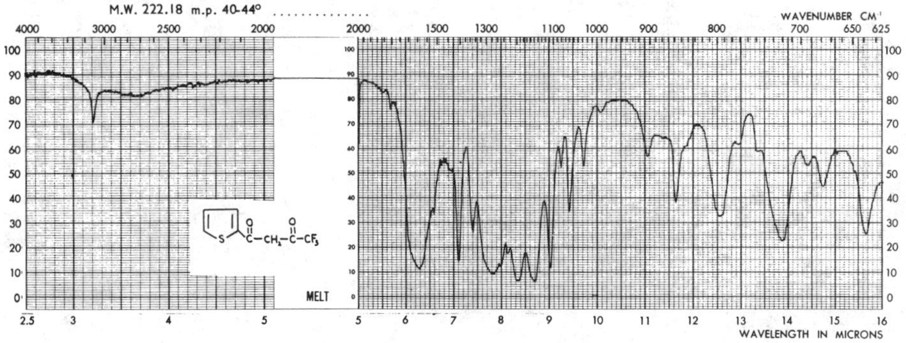

MELT

B1480-9 2-Benzoylthiophene
M.W. 188.25 m.p. 53.5-56°

C

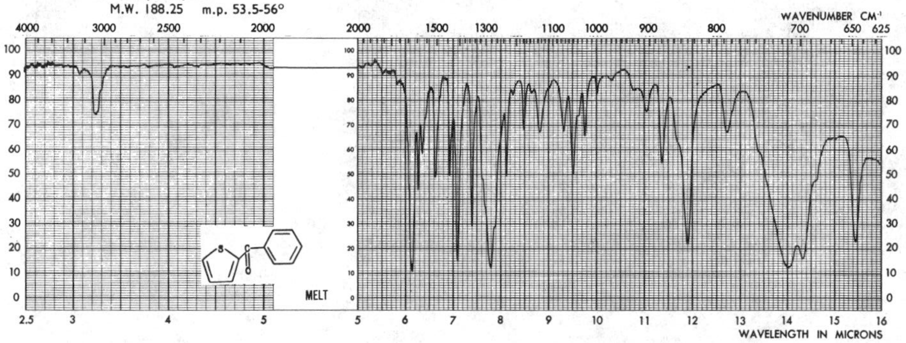

MELT

18,833-6
2-(*p*-Methoxybenzoyl)thiophene, 97%
FW 218.27 mp 74-75° Disp. C

D

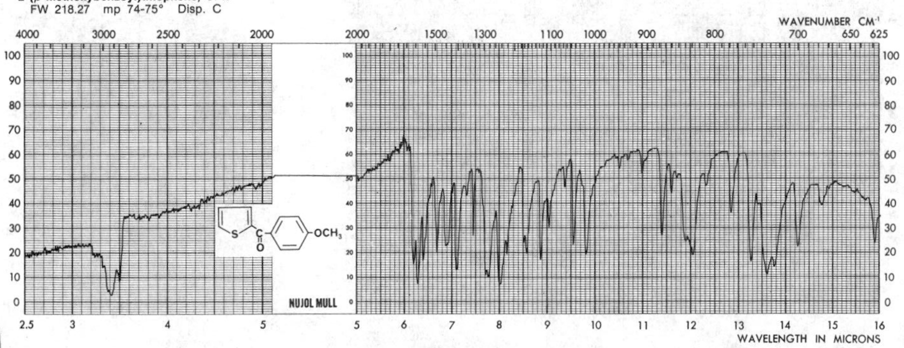

NUJOL MULL

E

NEAT

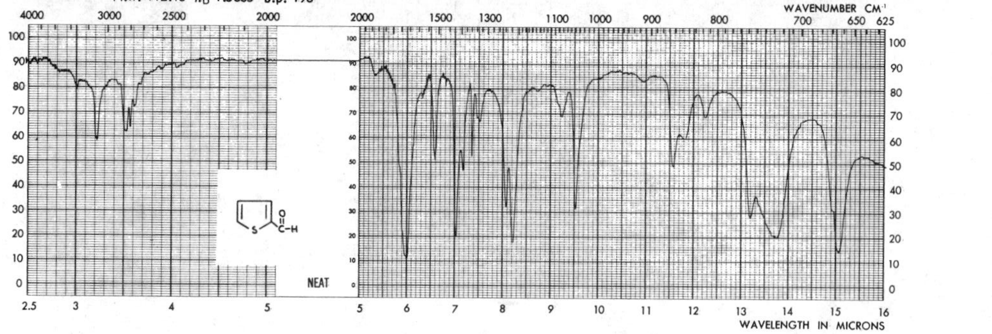

19,628-2
3-Thiophenecarboxaldehyde, 98%
FW 112.15 bp 86-87°/20mm. n_D^{20} 1.5850 d 1.280
Beil. **17**(3),4497 Disp. C

F

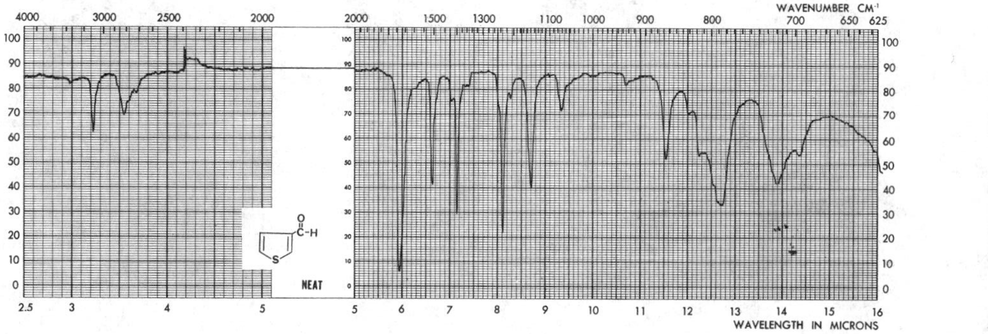

NEAT

M8441-0 5-Methyl-2-thiophenecarboxaldehyde
M.W. 126.18 n_D^{20} 1.5810

G

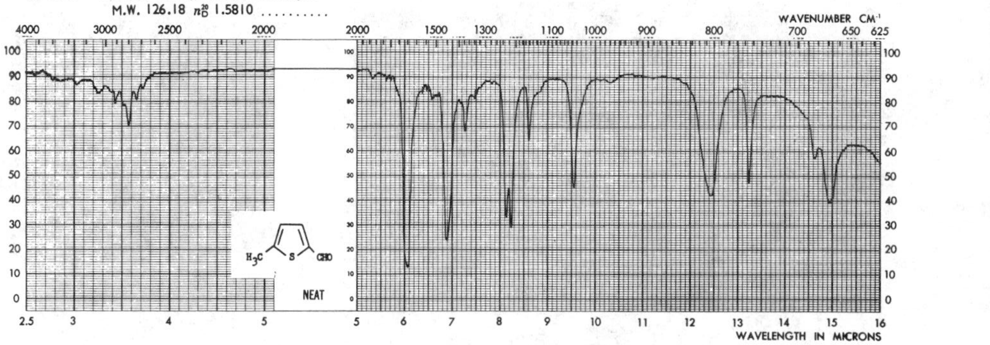

NEAT

16,413-5
3-Methyl-2-thiophenecarboxaldehyde, tech.
M.W. 126.18 n_D^{20} 1.5862

H

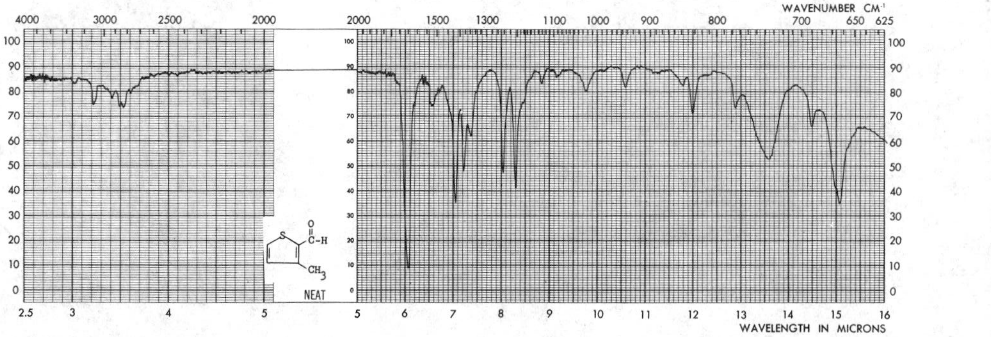

NEAT

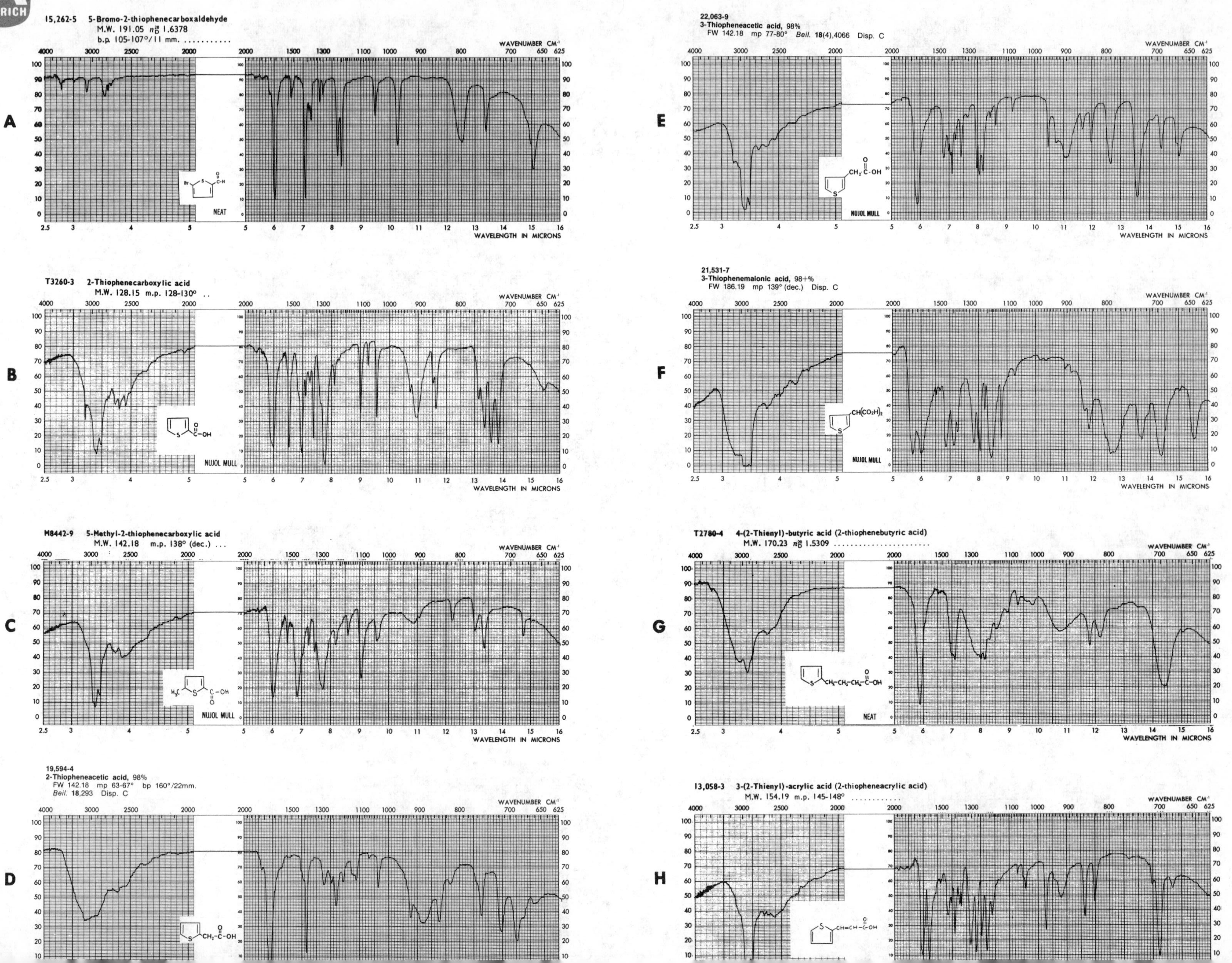
ALDRICH
A
15,262-5 5-Bromo-2-thiophenecarboxaldehyde
M.W. 191.05 n_D^{20} 1.6378
b.p. 105-107°/11 mm.
NEAT
B
T3260-3 2-Thiophenecarboxylic acid
M.W. 128.15 m.p. 128-130°
NUJOL MULL
C
M8442-9 5-Methyl-2-thiophenecarboxylic acid
M.W. 142.18 m.p. 138° (dec.)
NUJOL MULL
D
19,594-4
2-Thiopheneacetic acid, 98%
FW 142.18 mp 63-67° bp 160°/22mm.
Beil. 18,293 Disp. C
E
22,063-9
3-Thiopheneacetic acid, 98%
FW 142.18 mp 77-80° Beil. 18(4),4066 Disp. C
NUJOL MULL
F
21,531-7
3-Thiophenemalonic acid, 98+%
FW 186.19 mp 139° (dec.) Disp. C
NUJOL MULL
G
T2780-4 4-(2-Thienyl)-butyric acid (2-thiophenebutyric acid)
M.W. 170.23 n_D^{20} 1.5309
NEAT
H
13,058-3 3-(2-Thienyl)-acrylic acid (2-thiopheneacrylic acid)
M.W. 154.19 m.p. 145-148°
WAVENUMBER CM⁻¹
WAVELENGTH IN MICRONS

A

FW 156.16 mp 88-91° *Beil.* 18,407 Disp. C

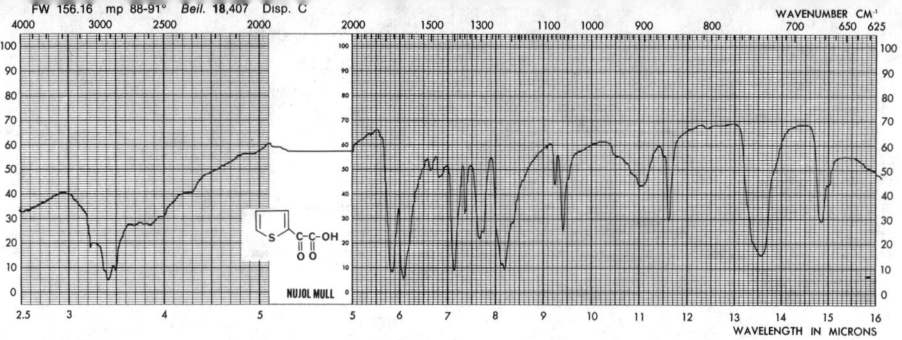

NUJOL MULL

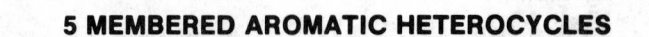

B

T2680-8 3-(2-Thenoyl)-propionic acid
M.W. 184.21 m.p. 120-121.5°

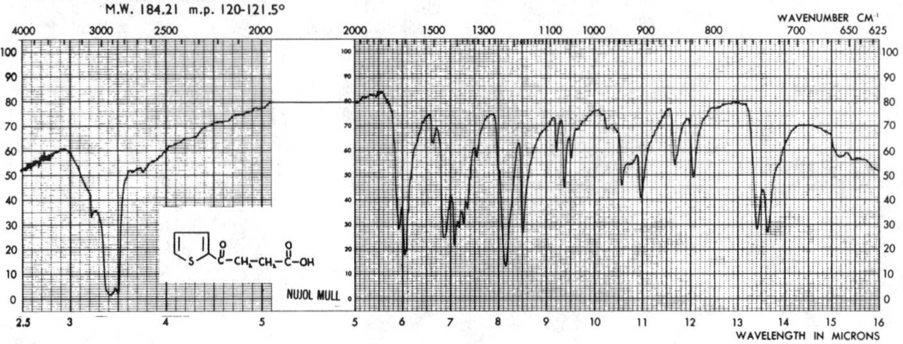

NUJOL MULL

C

E4925-8 Ethyl 2-thiophenecarboxylate
M.W. 156.21 n_D^{20} 1.5262 . . .

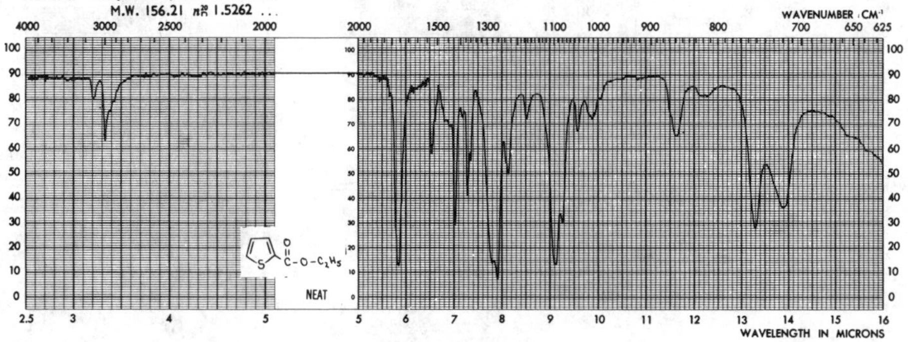

NEAT

D

18,880-8
DL-α-Amino-2-thiopheneacetic acid, 98%
FW 157.19 mp 208-210° *Beil.* 18,631 Disp. C

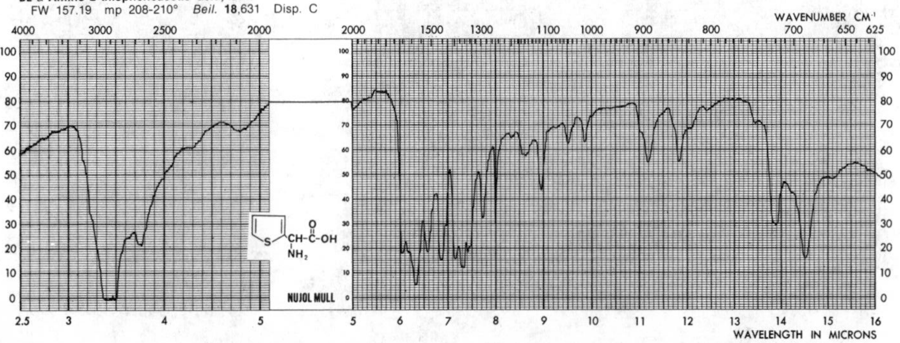

NUJOL MULL

E

M.W. 205.24 . . . .

NUJOL MULL

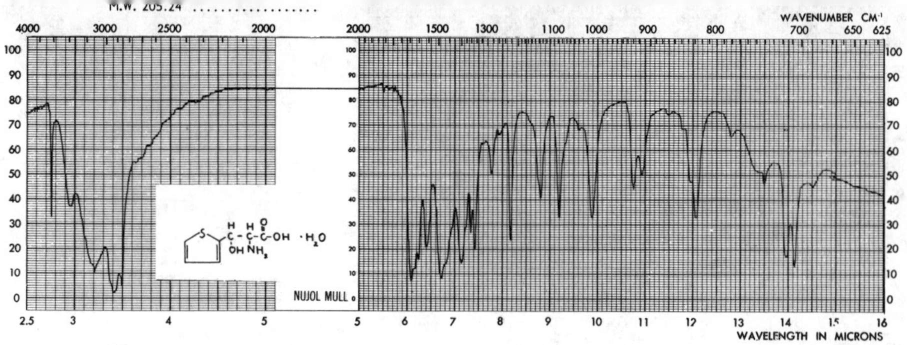

F

T2798-7 2-(2-Thienyl)-L-thiazolidine-4-carboxylic acid
M.W. 215.29 m.p. 145° . . . .

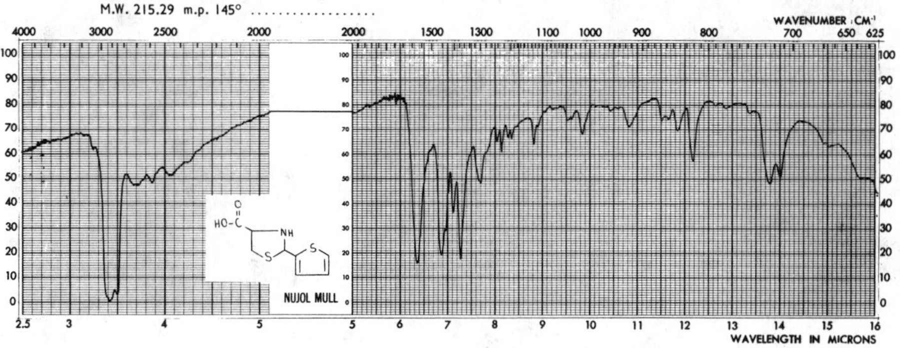

NUJOL MULL

G

13,639-5 Ethyl (2-thenoyl)-acetate
M.W. 198.24 n_D^{20} 1.5414
b.p. 114-116°/0.7 mm. . .

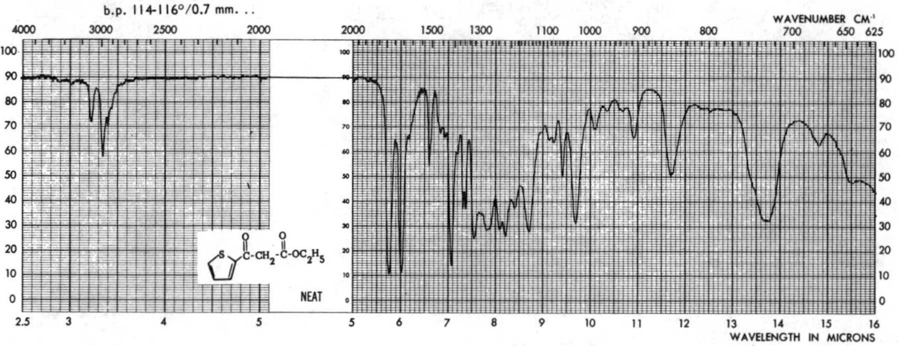

NEAT

H

15,918-2
Ethyl 2-amino-4,5,6,7-tetrahydrobenzo[b]thiophene-3-carboxylate, 97%
M.W. 225.31 m.p. 114-116°

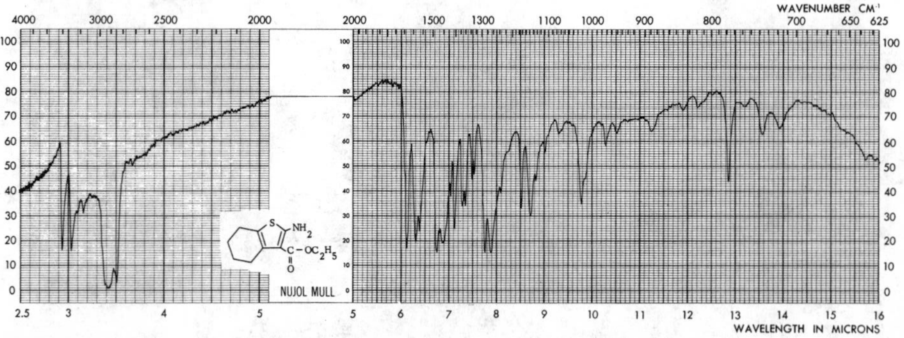

NUJOL MULL

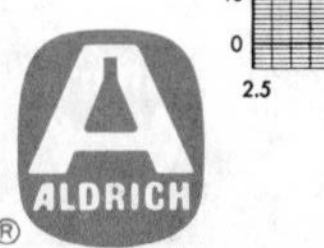

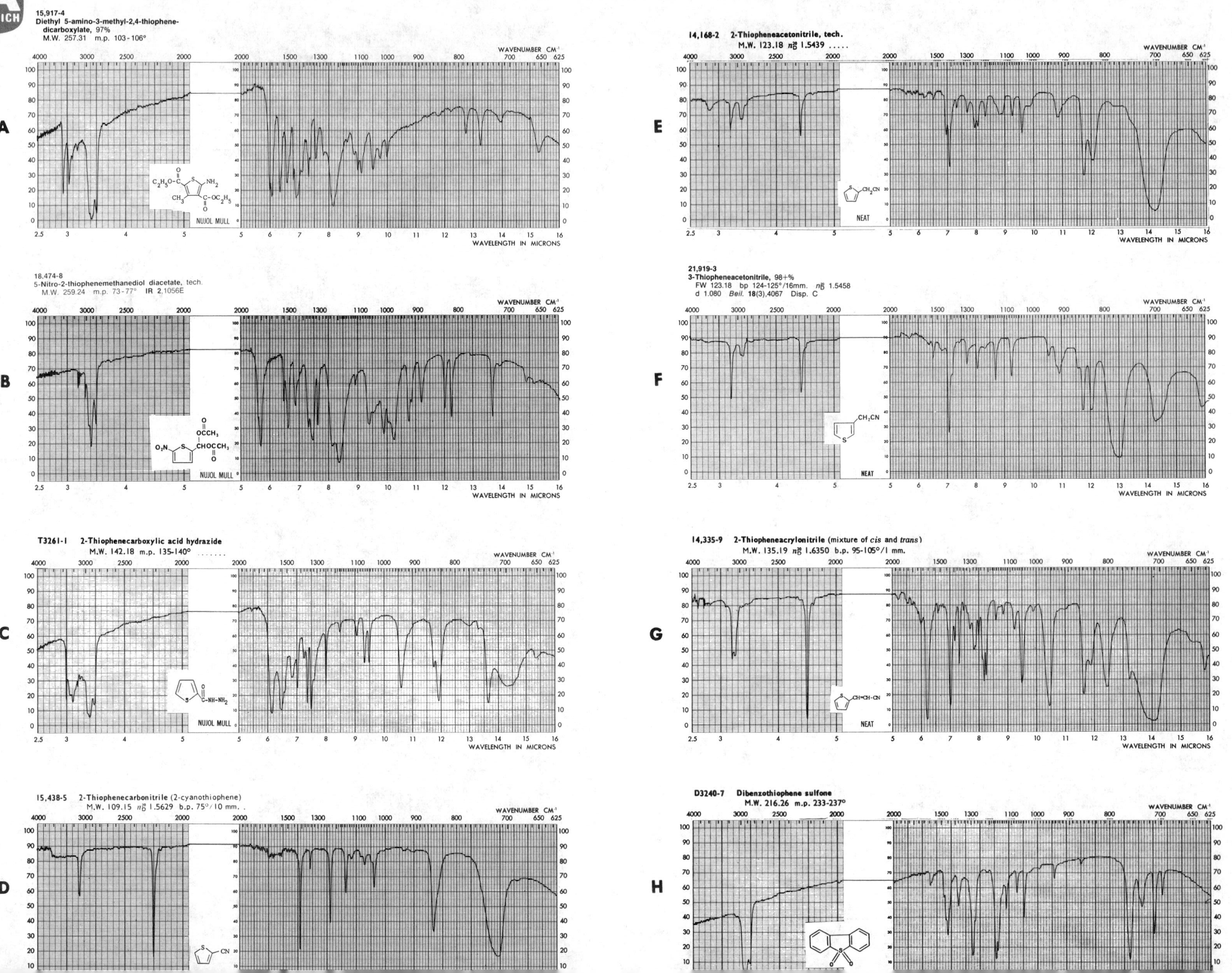
ALDRICH
A
15,917-4
Diethyl 5-amino-3-methyl-2,4-thiophenedicarboxylate, 97%
M.W. 257.31 m.p. 103-106°
NUJOL MULL
B
18,474-8
5-Nitro-2-thiophenemethanediol diacetate, tech.
M.W. 259.24 m.p. 73-77° IR 2,1056E
NUJOL MULL
C
T3261-1 2-Thiophenecarboxylic acid hydrazide
M.W. 142.18 m.p. 135-140°
NUJOL MULL
D
15,438-5 2-Thiophenecarbonitrile (2-cyanothiophene)
M.W. 109.15 n20/D 1.5629 b.p. 75°/10 mm.
E
14,168-2 2-Thiopheneacetonitrile, tech.
M.W. 123.18 n20/D 1.5439
NEAT
F
21,919-3
3-Thiopheneacetonitrile, 98+%
FW 123.18 bp 124-125°/16mm. n20/D 1.5458
d 1.080 Beil. 18(3),4067 Disp. C
NEAT
G
14,335-9 2-Thiopheneacrylonitrile (mixture of cis and trans)
M.W. 135.19 n20/D 1.6350 b.p. 95-105°/1 mm.
NEAT
H
D3240-7 Dibenzothiophene sulfone
M.W. 216.26 m.p. 233-237°
WAVENUMBER CM⁻¹
WAVELENGTH IN MICRONS

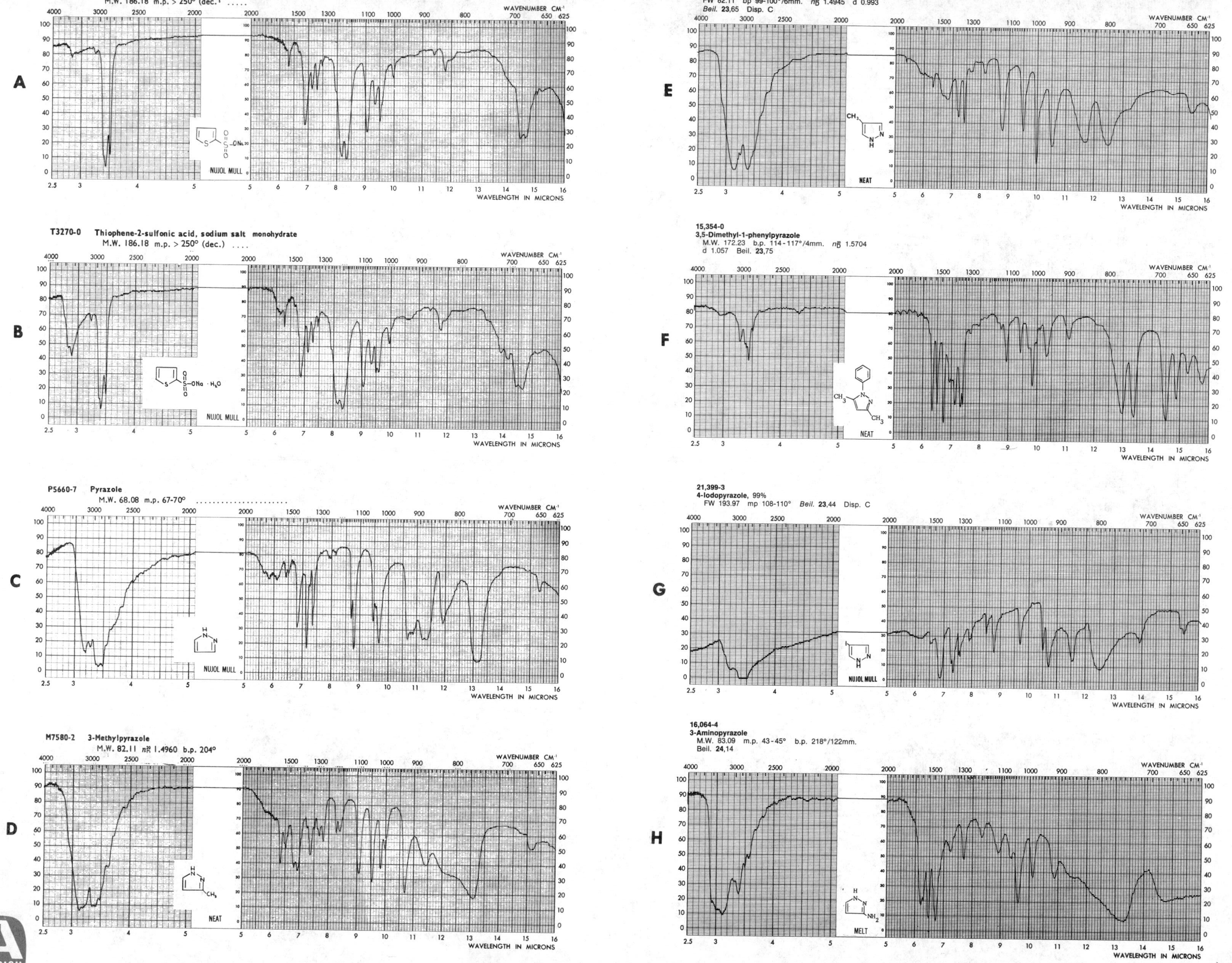

A
T3270-0 Thiophene-2-sulfonic acid, sodium salt
M.W. 186.18 m.p. > 250° (dec.)
NUJOL MULL
B
T3270-0 Thiophene-2-sulfonic acid, sodium salt monohydrate
M.W. 186.18 m.p. > 250° (dec.)
NUJOL MULL
C
P5660-7 Pyrazole
M.W. 68.08 m.p. 67-70°
NUJOL MULL
D
M7580-2 3-Methylpyrazole
M.W. 82.11 n20D 1.4960 b.p. 204°
NEAT
E
4-Methylpyrazole, 99%
FW 82.11 bp 99-100°/6mm. n20D 1.4945 d 0.993
Beil. 23,65 Disp. C
NEAT
F
15,354-0
3,5-Dimethyl-1-phenylpyrazole
M.W. 172.23 b.p. 114-117°/4mm. n20D 1.5704
d 1.057 Beil. 23,75
NEAT
G
21,399-3
4-Iodopyrazole, 99%
FW 193.97 mp 108-110° Beil. 23,44 Disp. C
NUJOL MULL
H
16,064-4
3-Aminopyrazole
M.W. 83.09 m.p. 43-45° b.p. 218°/122mm.
Beil. 24,14
MELT
WAVENUMBER CM⁻¹
WAVELENGTH IN MICRONS
ALDRICH

5 MEMBERED AROMATIC HETEROCYCLES

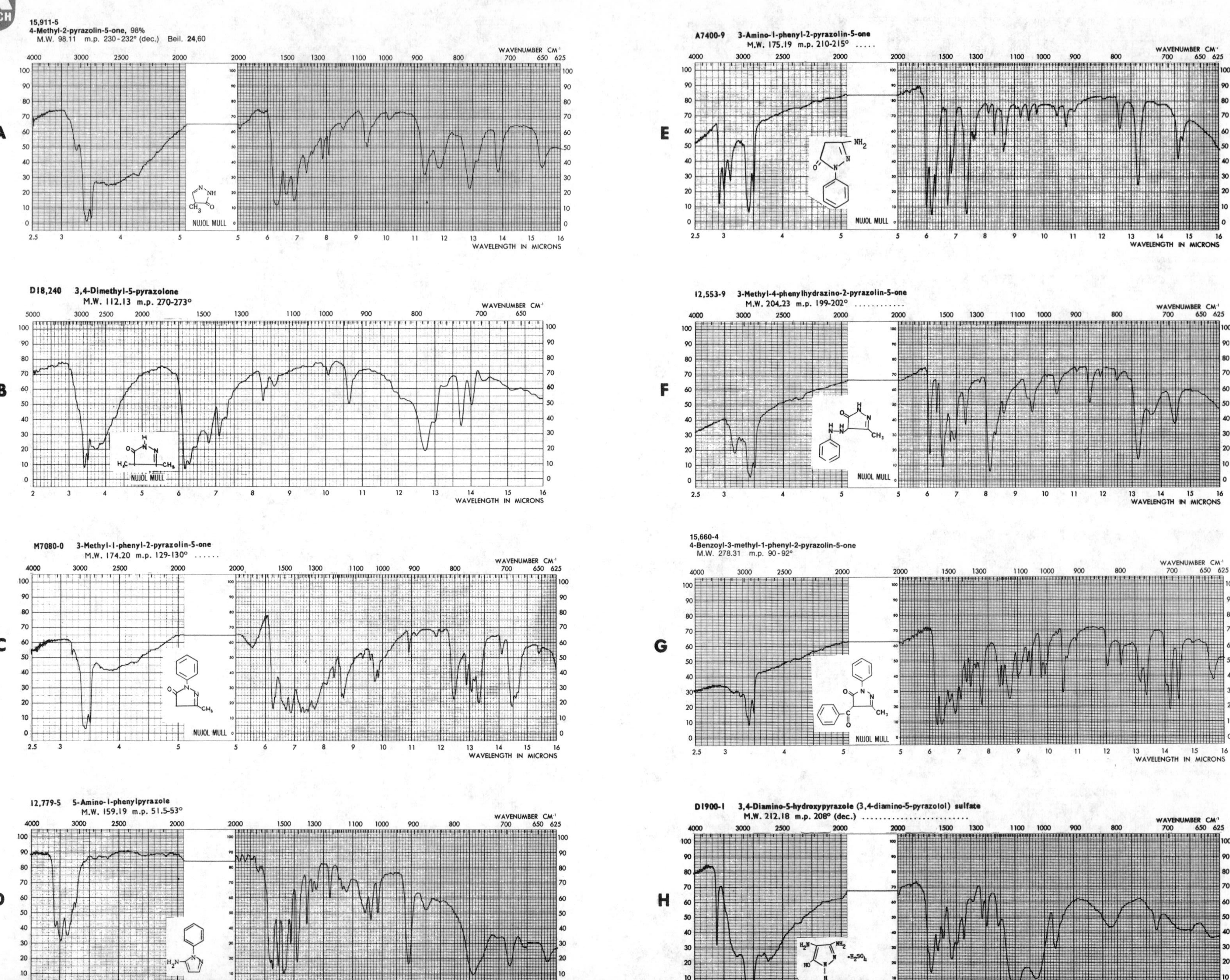
ALDRICH
A
15,911-5
4-Methyl-2-pyrazolin-5-one, 98%
M.W. 98.11 m.p. 230-232° (dec.) Beil. 24,60
B
D18,240 3,4-Dimethyl-5-pyrazolone
M.W. 112.13 m.p. 270-273°
C
M7080-0 3-Methyl-1-phenyl-2-pyrazolin-5-one
M.W. 174.20 m.p. 129-130° .....
D
12,779-5 5-Amino-1-phenylpyrazole
M.W. 159.19 m.p. 51.5-53°
E
A7400-9 3-Amino-1-phenyl-2-pyrazolin-5-one
M.W. 175.19 m.p. 210-215° .....
F
12,553-9 3-Methyl-4-phenylhydrazino-2-pyrazolin-5-one
M.W. 204.23 m.p. 199-202° ....
G
15,660-4
4-Benzoyl-3-methyl-1-phenyl-2-pyrazolin-5-one
M.W. 278.31 m.p. 90-92°
H
D1900-1 3,4-Diamino-5-hydroxypyrazole (3,4-diamino-5-pyrazolol) sulfate
M.W. 212.18 m.p. 208° (dec.) ....
NUJOL MULL
WAVENUMBER CM⁻¹
WAVELENGTH IN MICRONS

A

M.W. 156.10 m.p. 303° (dec.) . . . .

NUJOL MULL

B

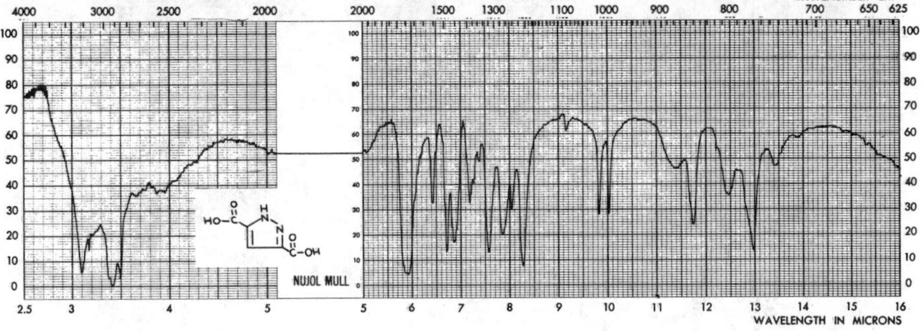

A7740-7 3-Aminopyrazole-4-carboxylic acid, puriss.
M.W. 127.10 m.p. 120-122° (dec.) . . . . . .

NUJOL MULL

C

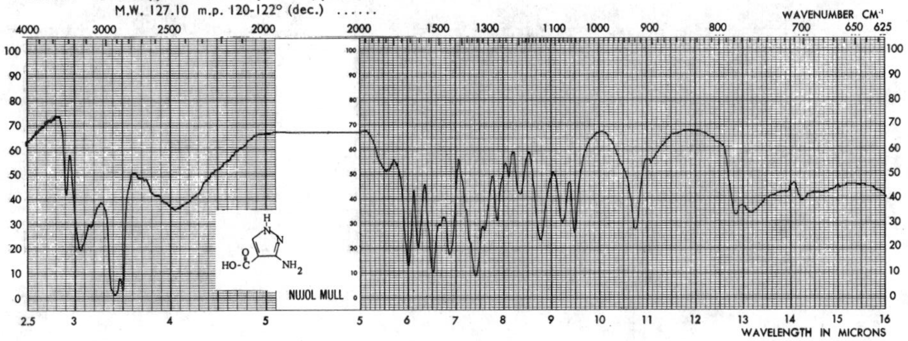

19,755-6
***p*-(3-Methyl-5-oxo-2-pyrazolin-1-yl)benzoic acid, 98+%**
FW 218.21 mp 285° (dec.) *Beil.* **24**(1),209
Disp. C

NUJOL MULL

D

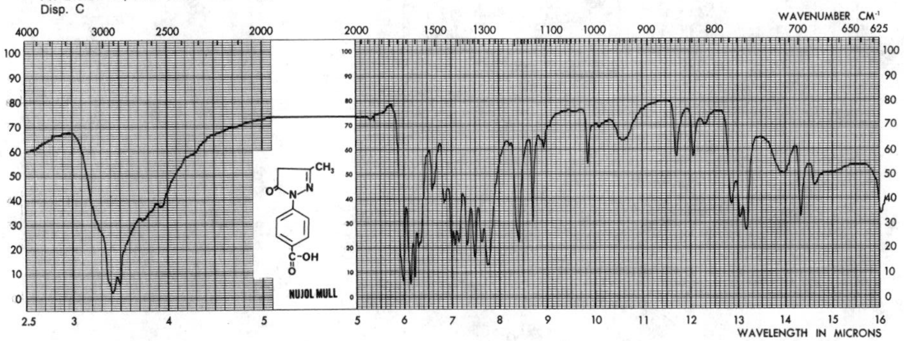

11,962-8 1-Pyrazole-DL-alanine, puriss.
M.W. 155.16 m.p. 242-243.5° (dec.)

NUJOL MULL

E

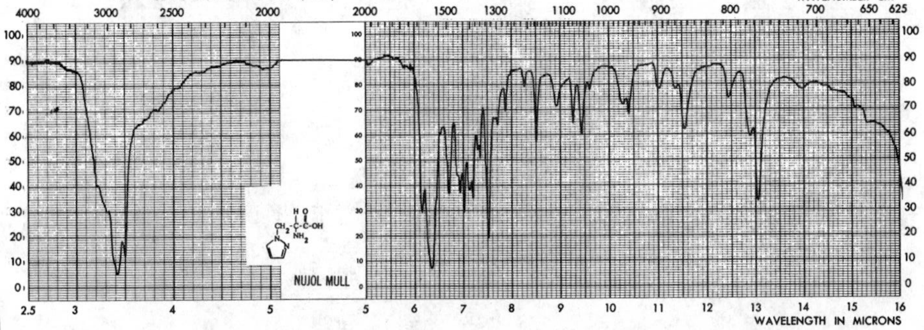

M.W. 155.16 m.p. 105-106° . . . .

NUJOL MULL

F

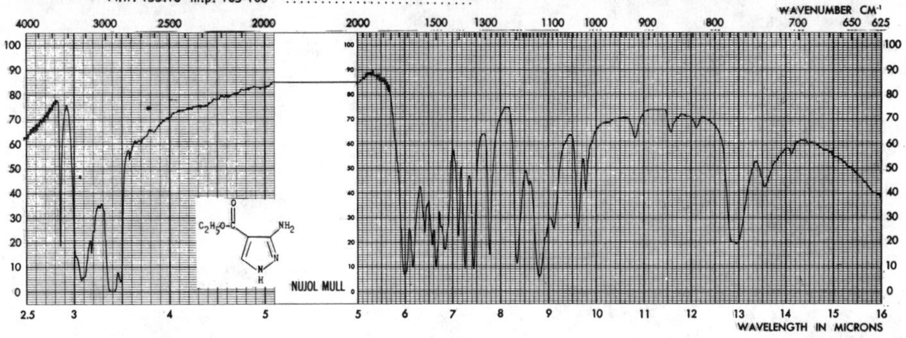

A7380-0 5-Amino-1-phenylpyrazole-4-carboxamide
M.W. 202.27 m.p. 167-170° . . . .

NUJOL MULL

G

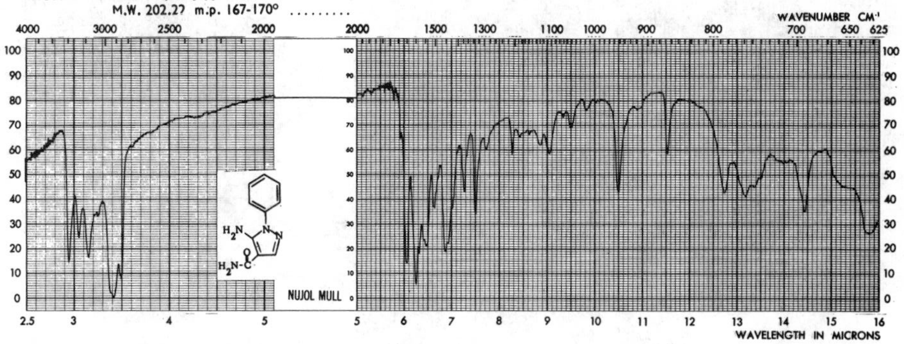

D18,220-6 3,5-Dimethylpyrazole-1-carboxamide
M.W. 139.16 m.p. 112-114° . . . . . .

NUJOL MULL

H

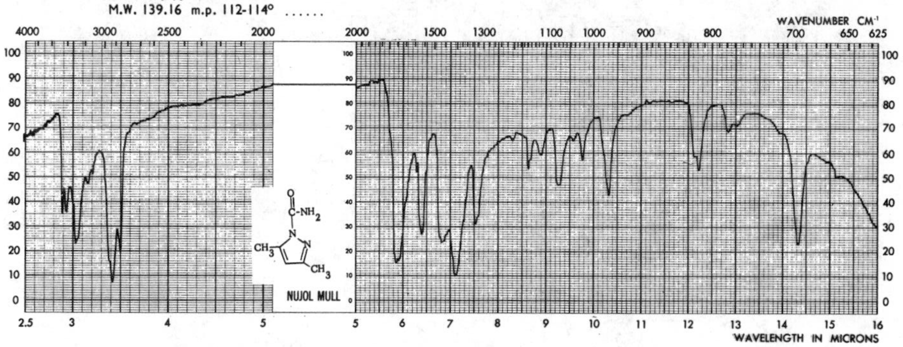

D18,225-7 3,5-Dimethylpyrazole-1-carboxamidine nitrate
M.W. 201.19 m.p. 167-168° (dec.) . . . .

NUJOL MULL

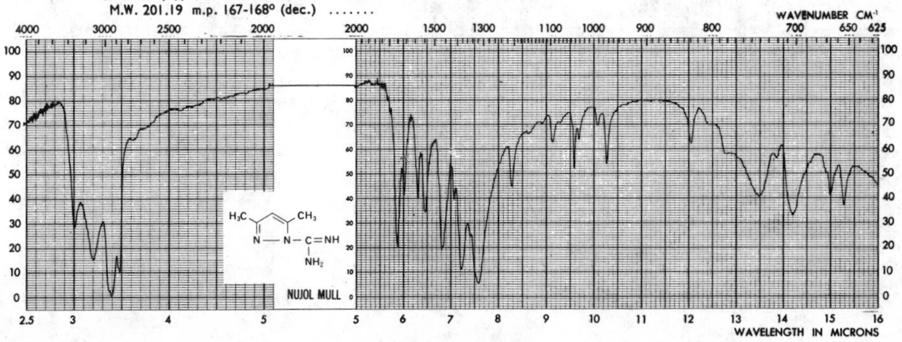

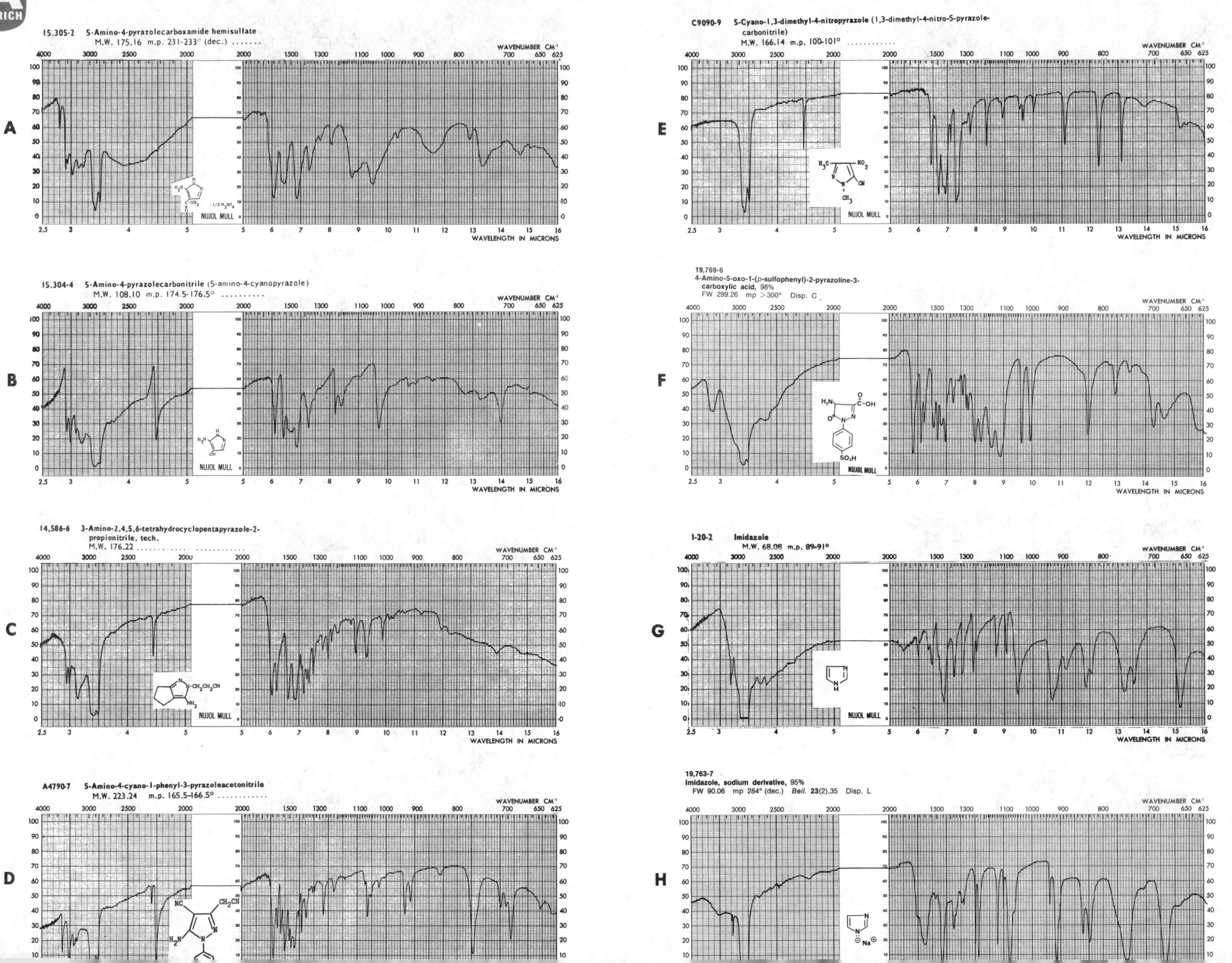
ALDRICH
A
15,305-2 5-Amino-4-pyrazolecarboxamide hemisulfate
M.W. 175.16 m.p. 231-233° (dec.)
NUJOL MULL
B
15,304-4 5-Amino-4-pyrazolecarbonitrile (5-amino-4-cyanopyrazole)
M.W. 108.10 m.p. 174.5-176.5°
NUJOL MULL
C
14,586-6 3-Amino-2,4,5,6-tetrahydrocyclopentapyrazole-2-propionitrile, tech.
M.W. 176.22
NUJOL MULL
D
A4790-7 5-Amino-4-cyano-1-phenyl-3-pyrazoleacetonitrile
M.W. 223.24 m.p. 165.5-166.5°
E
C9090-9 5-Cyano-1,3-dimethyl-4-nitropyrazole (1,3-dimethyl-4-nitro-5-pyrazolecarbonitrile)
M.W. 166.14 m.p. 100-101°
NUJOL MULL
F
19,769-6
4-Amino-5-oxo-1-(p-sulfophenyl)-2-pyrazoline-3-carboxylic acid, 98%
FW 299.26 mp >300° Disp. C
NUJOL MULL
G
I-20-2 Imidazole
M.W. 68.08 m.p. 89-91°
NUJOL MULL
H
19,763-7
Imidazole, sodium derivative, 95%
FW 90.06 mp 284° (dec.) Beil. 23(2),35 Disp. L
WAVENUMBER CM⁻¹
WAVELENGTH IN MICRONS

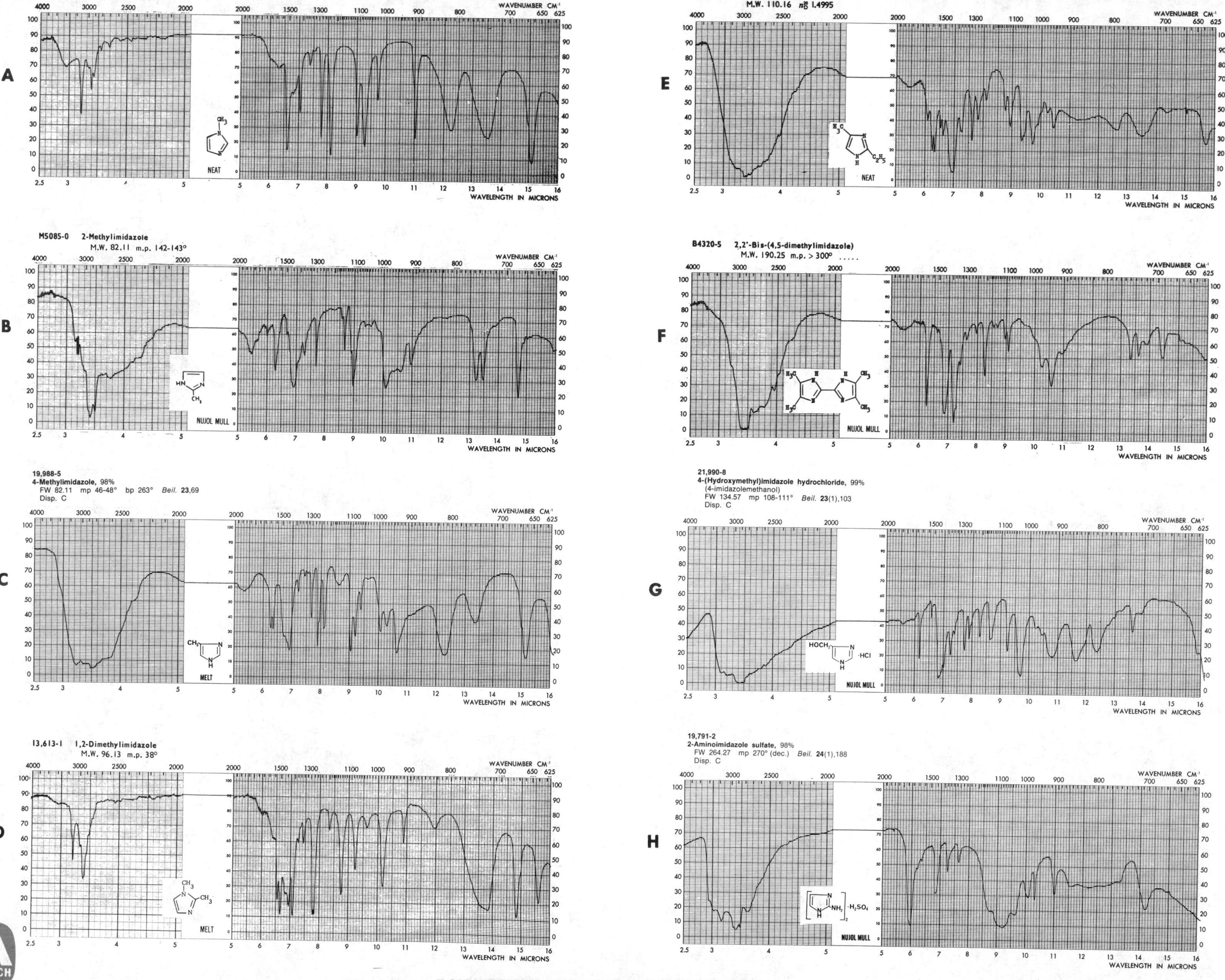
A
M5083-4 1-Methylimidazole
M.W. 82.11 n_D^{20} 1.6970
NEAT
B
M5085-0 2-Methylimidazole
M.W. 82.11 m.p. 142-143°
NUJOL MULL
C
19,988-5
4-Methylimidazole, 98%
FW 82.11 mp 46-48° bp 263° Beil. 23,69
Disp. C
MELT
D
13,613-1 1,2-Dimethylimidazole
M.W. 96.13 m.p. 38°
MELT
E
E3665-2 2-Ethyl-4-methylimidazole
M.W. 110.16 n_D^{20} 1.4995
NEAT
F
B4320-5 2,2'-Bis-(4,5-dimethylimidazole)
M.W. 190.25 m.p. > 300°
NUJOL MULL
G
21,990-8
4-(Hydroxymethyl)imidazole hydrochloride, 99%
(4-imidazolemethanol)
FW 134.57 mp 108-111° Beil. 23(1),103
Disp. C
NUJOL MULL
H
19,791-2
2-Aminoimidazole sulfate, 98%
FW 264.27 mp 270° (dec.) Beil. 24(1),188
Disp. C
NUJOL MULL
WAVENUMBER CM⁻¹
WAVELENGTH IN MICRONS
ALDRICH

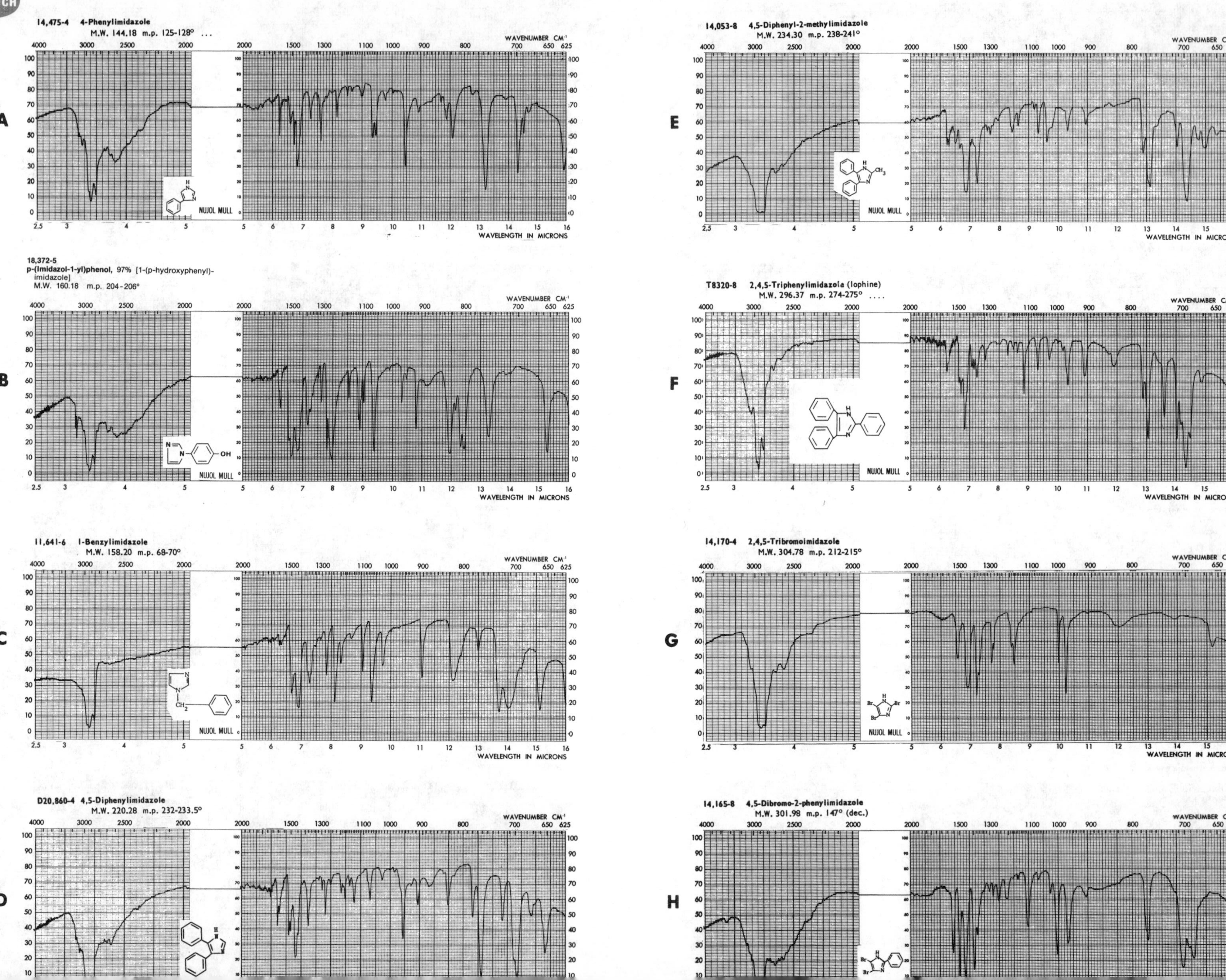

A
14,475-4 4-Phenylimidazole
M.W. 144.18 m.p. 125-128° ...
B
18,372-5
p-(Imidazol-1-yl)phenol, 97% [1-(p-hydroxyphenyl)-imidazole]
M.W. 160.18 m.p. 204-206°
C
11,641-6 1-Benzylimidazole
M.W. 158.20 m.p. 68-70°
D
D20,860-4 4,5-Diphenylimidazole
M.W. 220.28 m.p. 232-233.5°
E
14,053-8 4,5-Diphenyl-2-methylimidazole
M.W. 234.30 m.p. 238-241°
F
T8320-8 2,4,5-Triphenylimidazole (lophine)
M.W. 296.37 m.p. 274-275° ....
G
14,170-4 2,4,5-Tribromoimidazole
M.W. 304.78 m.p. 212-215°
H
14,165-8 4,5-Dibromo-2-phenylimidazole
M.W. 301.98 m.p. 147° (dec.)
NUJOL MULL
WAVENUMBER CM⁻¹
WAVELENGTH IN MICRONS

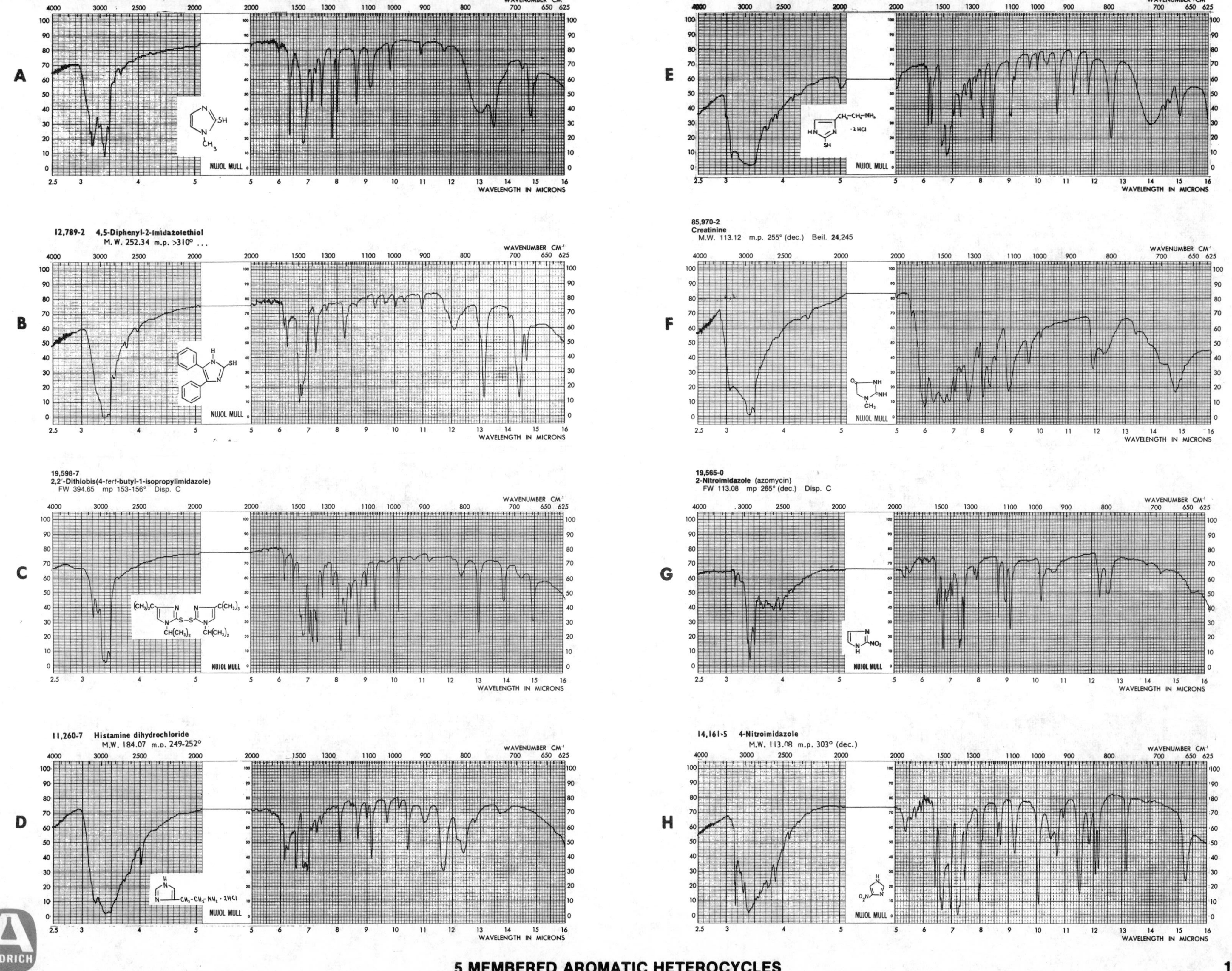
A
M.W. 114.17 m.p. 144-147°
NUJOL MULL
B
12,789-2 4,5-Diphenyl-2-imidazolethiol
M.W. 252.34 m.p. >310° ...
NUJOL MULL
C
19,598-7
2,2'-Dithiobis(4-tert-butyl-1-isopropylimidazole)
FW 394.65 mp 153-156° Disp. C
NUJOL MULL
D
11,260-7 Histamine dihydrochloride
M.W. 184.07 m.p. 249-252°
NUJOL MULL
E
M.W. 216.13 m.p. 250-252° ......
NUJOL MULL
F
85,970-2
Creatinine
M.W. 113.12 m.p. 255° (dec.) Beil. 24,245
NUJOL MULL
G
19,565-0
2-Nitroimidazole (azomycin)
FW 113.08 mp 265° (dec.) Disp. C
NUJOL MULL
H
14,161-5 4-Nitroimidazole
M.W. 113.08 m.p. 303° (dec.)
NUJOL MULL
WAVENUMBER CM⁻¹
WAVELENGTH IN MICRONS
ALDRICH

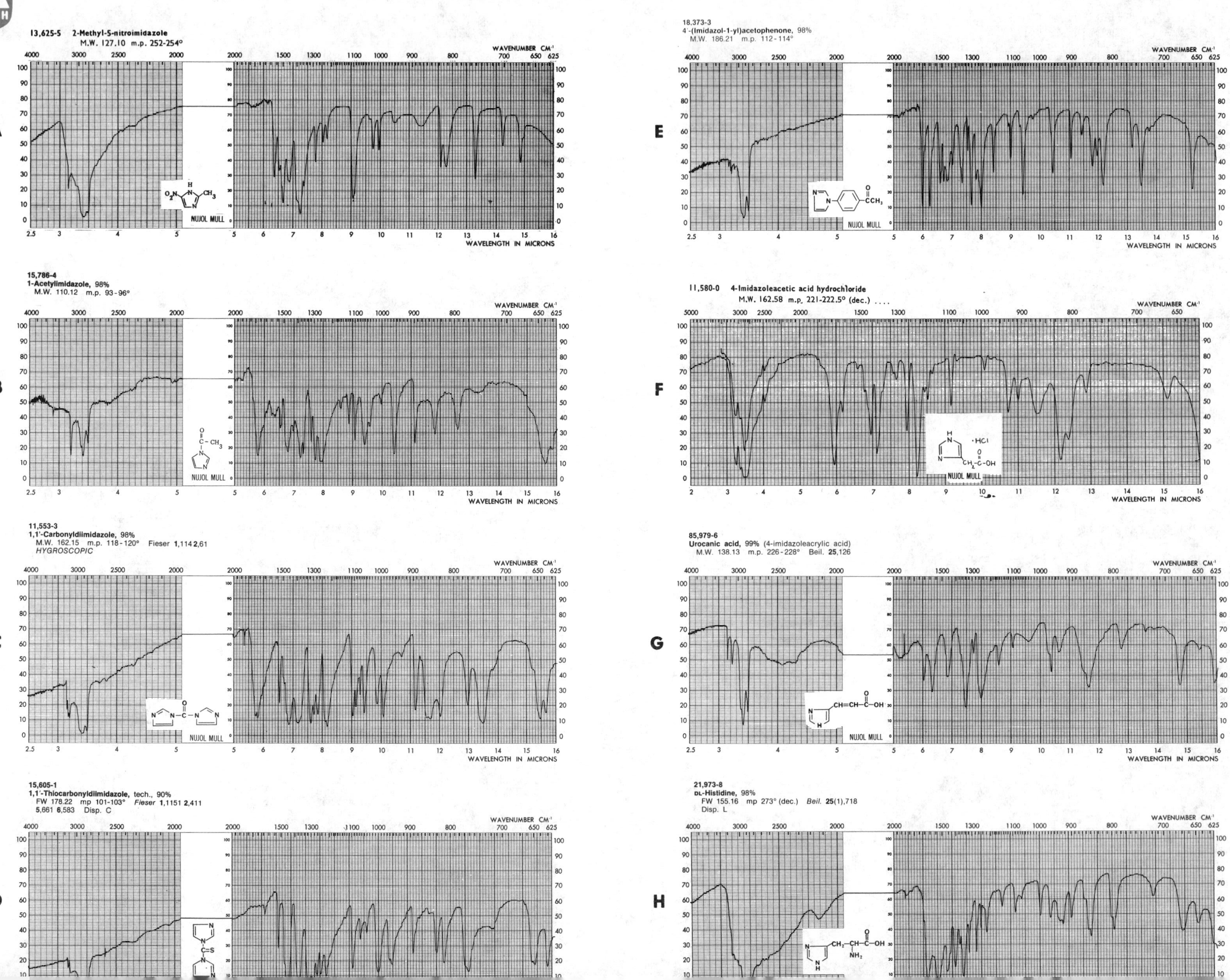
ALDRICH
A
13,625-5 2-Methyl-5-nitroimidazole
M.W. 127.10 m.p. 252-254°
NUJOL MULL
B
15,786-4
1-Acetylimidazole, 98%
M.W. 110.12 m.p. 93-96°
NUJOL MULL
C
11,553-3
1,1'-Carbonyldiimidazole, 98%
M.W. 162.15 m.p. 118-120° Fieser 1,114 2,61
HYGROSCOPIC
NUJOL MULL
D
15,605-1
1,1'-Thiocarbonyldiimidazole, tech., 90%
FW 178.22 mp 101-103° Fieser 1,1151 2,411
5,661 6,583 Disp. C
E
18,373-3
4'-(Imidazol-1-yl)acetophenone, 98%
M.W. 186.21 m.p. 112-114°
NUJOL MULL
F
11,580-0 4-Imidazoleacetic acid hydrochloride
M.W. 162.58 m.p. 221-222.5° (dec.)
NUJOL MULL
G
85,979-6
Urocanic acid, 99% (4-imidazoleacrylic acid)
M.W. 138.13 m.p. 226-228° Beil. 25,126
NUJOL MULL
H
21,973-8
DL-Histidine, 98%
FW 155.16 mp 273° (dec.) Beil. 25(1),718
Disp. L
WAVENUMBER CM⁻¹
WAVELENGTH IN MICRONS

$[\alpha]^{20}$ -15° (c=2,5N HCl) *Beil.* **25**(1),713 Disp. L

A

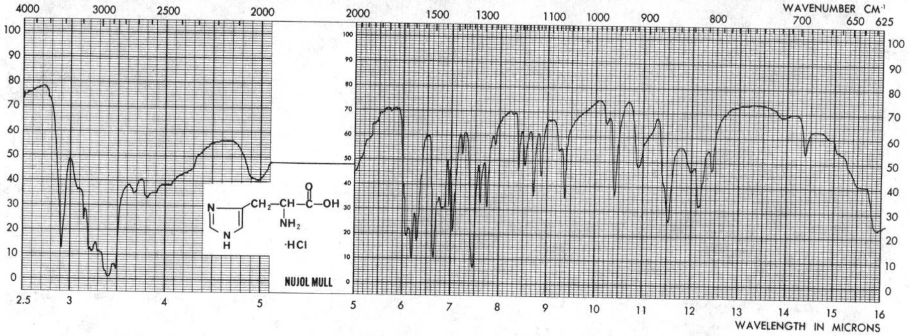

15,168-8 L-Histidine
M.W. 155.16 m.p. 282° (dec.) $[\alpha]^{25}_{D}$ -38.4° (c=3, H_2O)

B

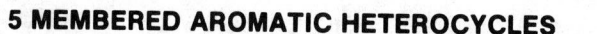

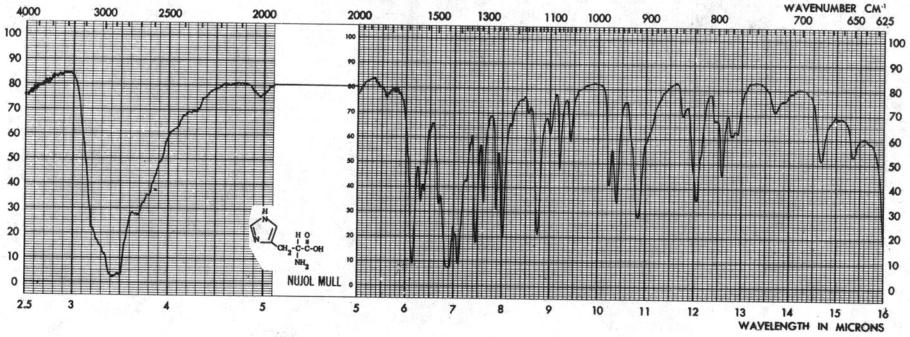

22,401-4
L-Carnosine, 98% (*N*-β-alanyl-L-histidine)
FW 226.24 mp 253° (dec.) $[\alpha]^{25}_{D}$ +20.7° (c=2, H_2O)
Beil. **25**,516 Disp. C

C

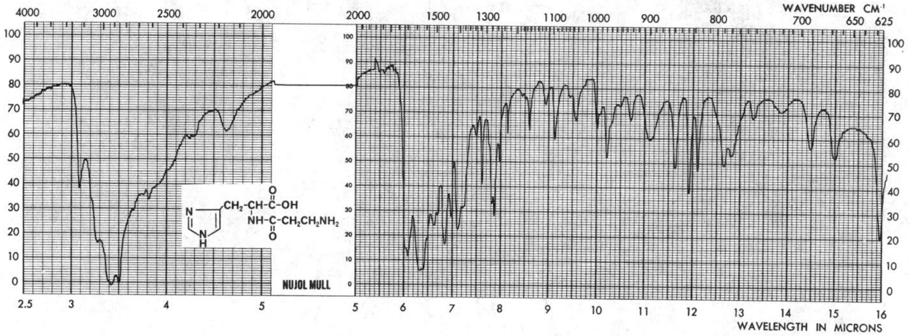

13,910-6 L-(+)-Homocarnosine sulfate
M.W. 338.34 m.p. 236-238° (dec.)

D

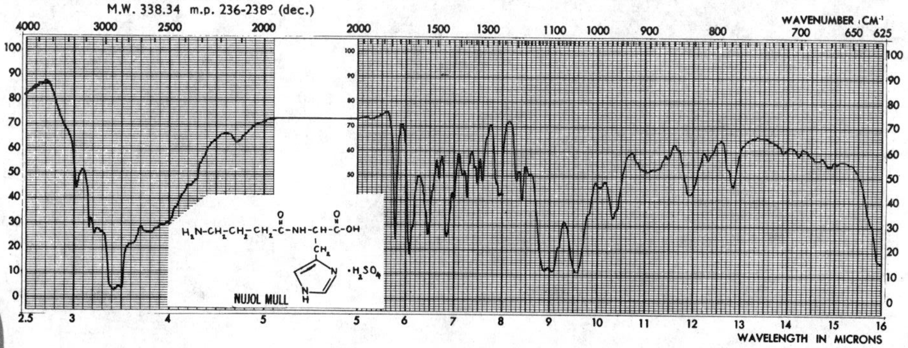

M.W. 214.1 m.p. 198-201° (dec.)

E

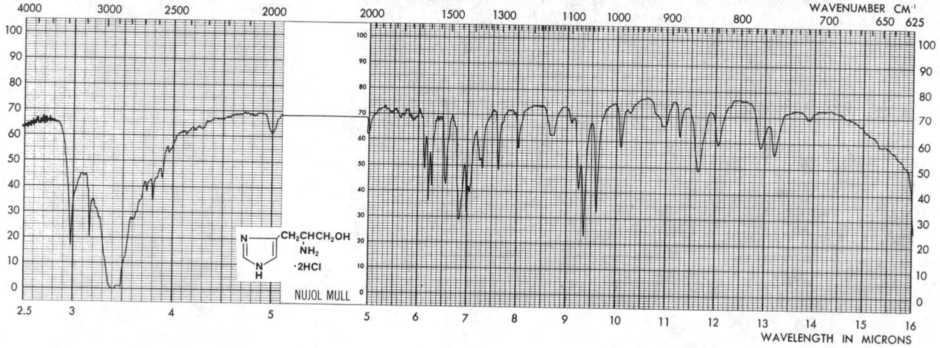

H1,520-9
L-(+)-Histidine hydrochloride monohydrate, 98%
M.W. 209.63 m.p. 254° (dec.)
$[\alpha]^{26}$ +8.0° (c=2, 3N HCl) Beil. **25**,513

F

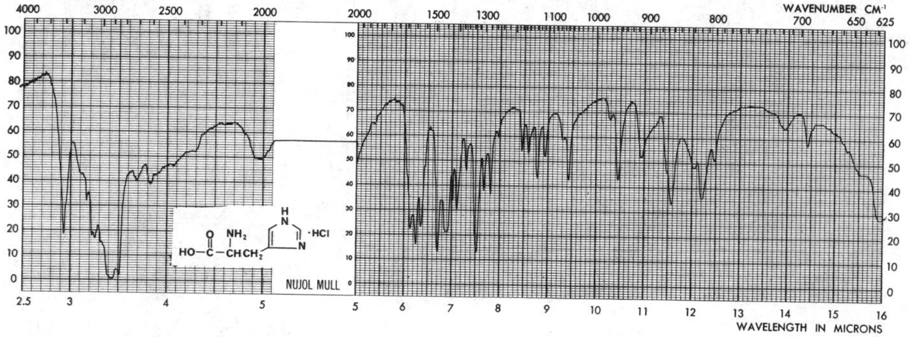

H1540-3 L-Histidine methyl ester dihydrochloride
M.W. 242.11 m.p. 218-219° (dec.)

G

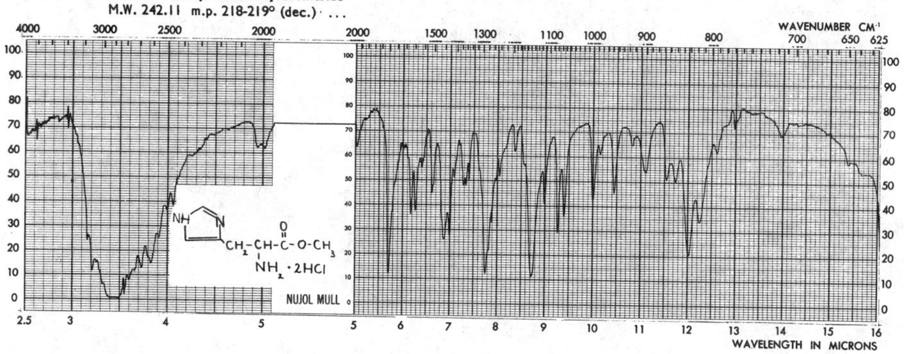

85,889-7
Nω-Acetylhistamine, 98%
M.W. 153.19 m.p. 147-149° Beil. **25**(2),304

H

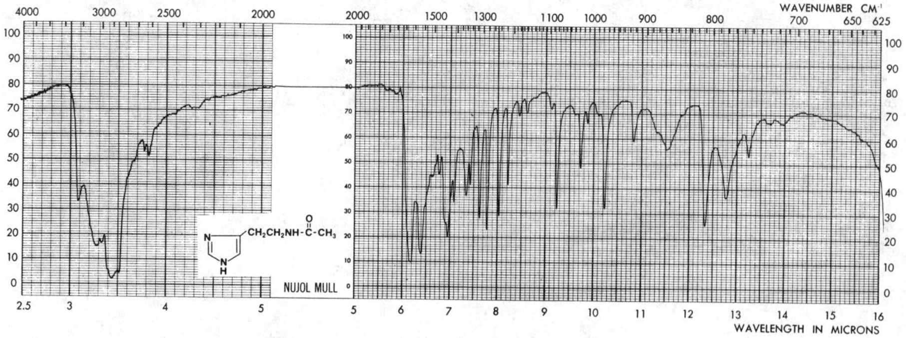

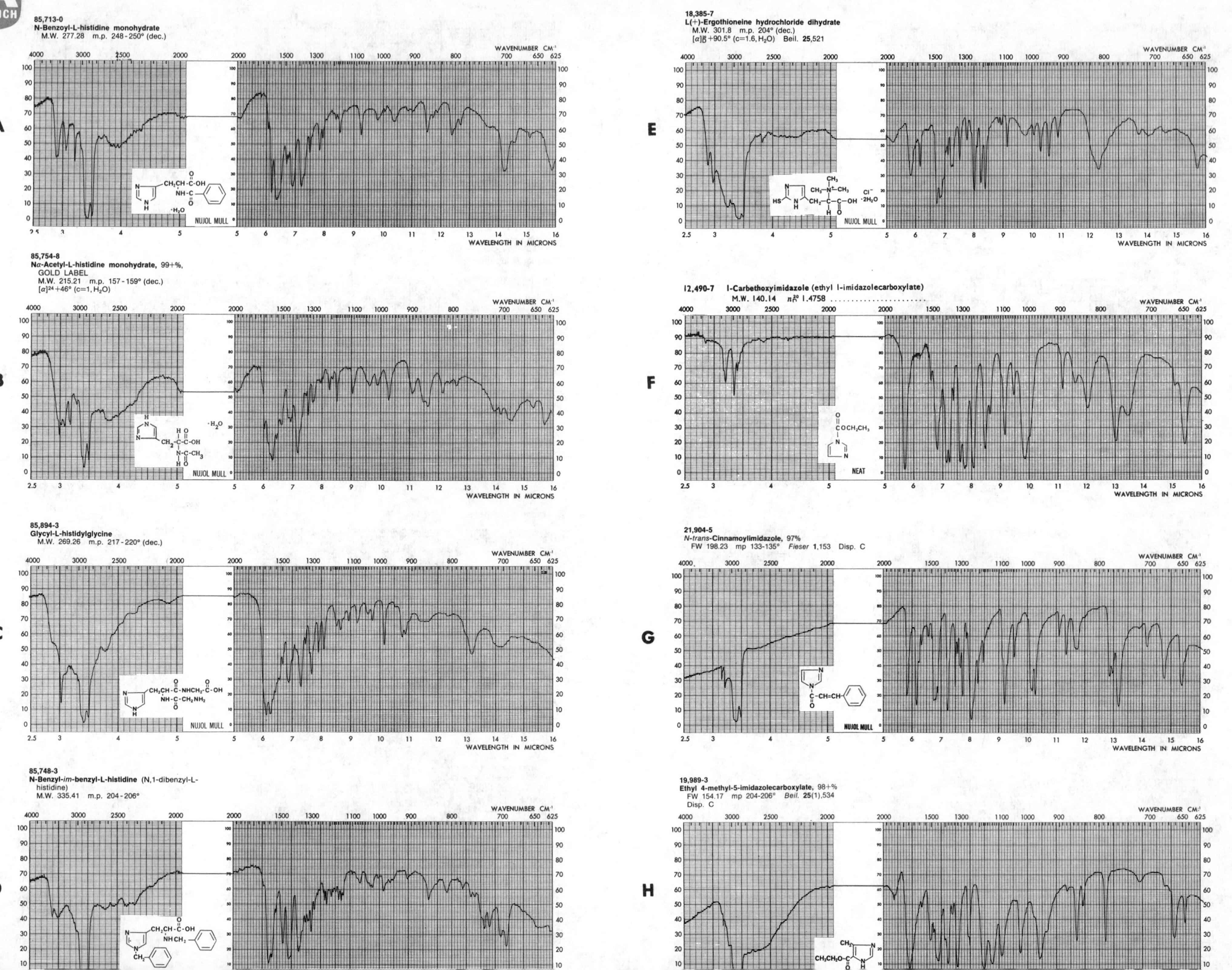
ALDRICH
A
85,713-0
N-Benzoyl-L-histidine monohydrate
M.W. 277.28 m.p. 248-250° (dec.)
NUJOL MULL
B
85,754-8
Nα-Acetyl-L-histidine monohydrate, 99+%,
GOLD LABEL
M.W. 215.21 m.p. 157-159° (dec.)
[α]²⁴ +46° (c=1, H₂O)
NUJOL MULL
C
85,894-3
Glycyl-L-histidylglycine
M.W. 269.26 m.p. 217-220° (dec.)
NUJOL MULL
D
85,748-3
N-Benzyl-im-benzyl-L-histidine (N,1-dibenzyl-L-histidine)
M.W. 335.41 m.p. 204-206°
E
18,385-7
L(+)-Ergothioneine hydrochloride dihydrate
M.W. 301.8 m.p. 204° (dec.)
[α]D +90.5° (c=1.6, H₂O) Beil. 25,521
NUJOL MULL
F
12,490-7 1-Carbethoxyimidazole (ethyl 1-imidazolecarboxylate)
M.W. 140.14 n20 1.4758
NEAT
G
21,904-5
N-trans-Cinnamoylimidazole, 97%
FW 198.23 mp 133-135° Fieser 1,153 Disp. C
NUJOL MULL
H
19,989-3
Ethyl 4-methyl-5-imidazolecarboxylate, 98+%
FW 154.17 mp 204-206° Beil. 25(1),534
Disp. C
WAVENUMBER CM⁻¹
WAVELENGTH IN MICRONS

A

M.W. 155.16 m.p. 180-183°

NUJOL MULL

B

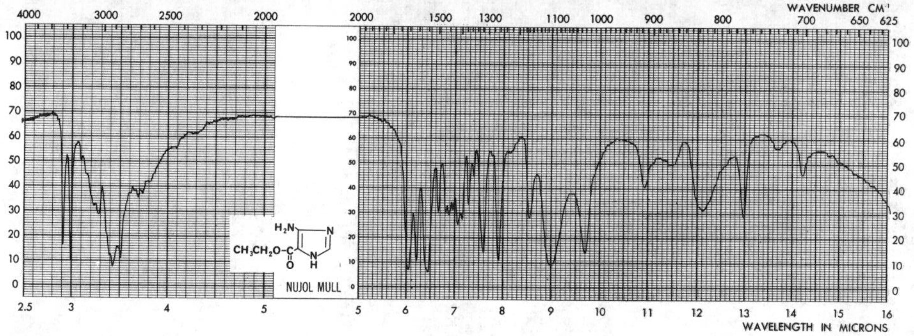

22,082-5
Propyl *dl*-1-(1-phenylethyl)imidazole-5-carboxylate hydrochloride, 99% (Propoxate, R 7464)
FW 294.78 mp 153-155° Disp. C

NUJOL MULL

C

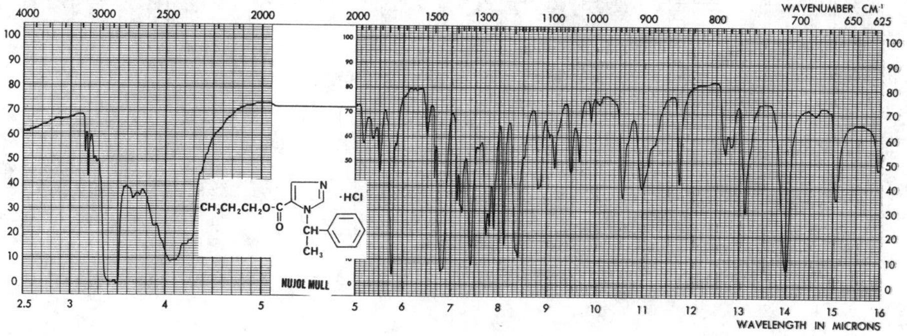

14,188-7 **Pilocarpine hydrochloride**
M.W. 244.72 m.p. 202-205°

NUJOL MULL

D

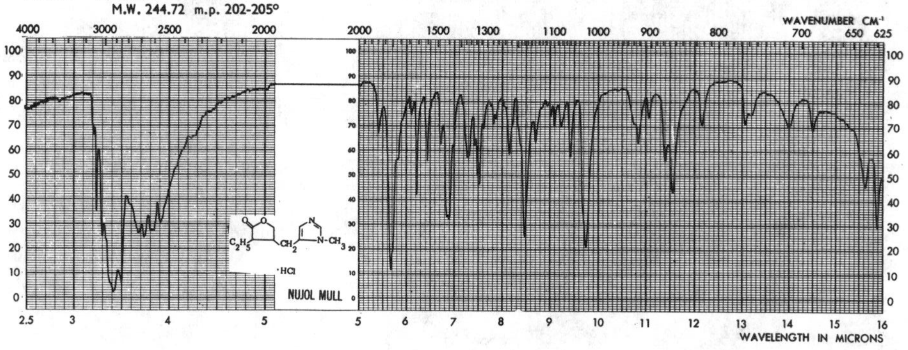

14,545-9 **Isopilocarpine nitrate**
M.W. 271.28 m.p. 157° (dec.)

NUJOL MULL

E

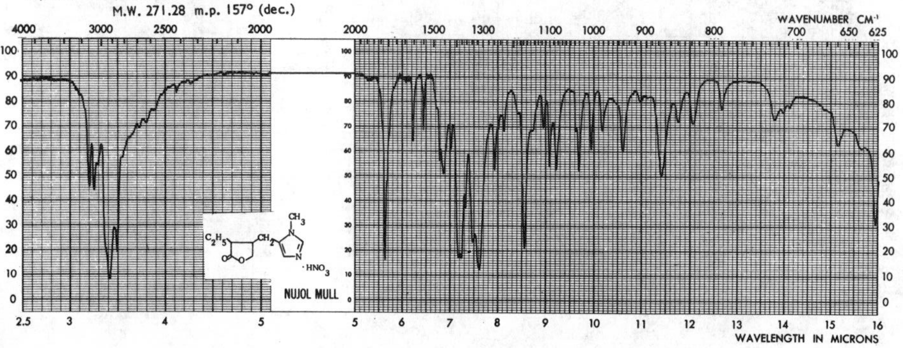

4-Amino-5-imidazolecarboxamide hydrochloride, 98%
M.W. 162.58 m.p. 250-252° (dec.) Beil. **25**(2),221

NUJOL MULL

F

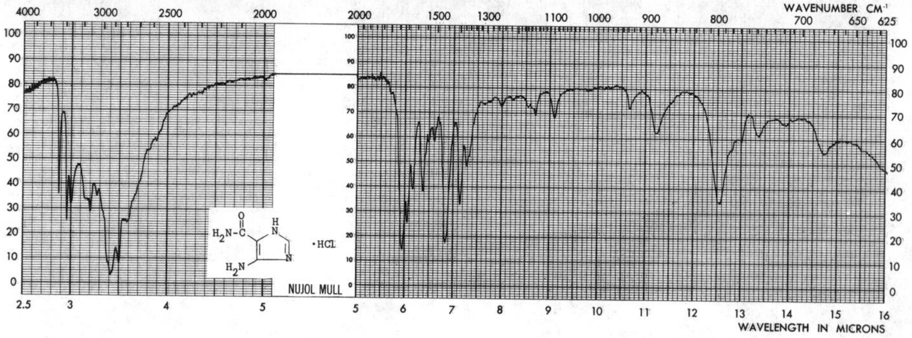

16,289-2
Purpald®, 99+%, GOLD LABEL (4-amino-3-hydrazino-5-mercapto-1,2,4-triazole, 4-amino-5-hydrazino-4H-1,2,4-triazole-3-thiol)
M.W. 146.18 m.p. 230-231° (dec.) Beil. **26**,217

NUJOL MULL

G

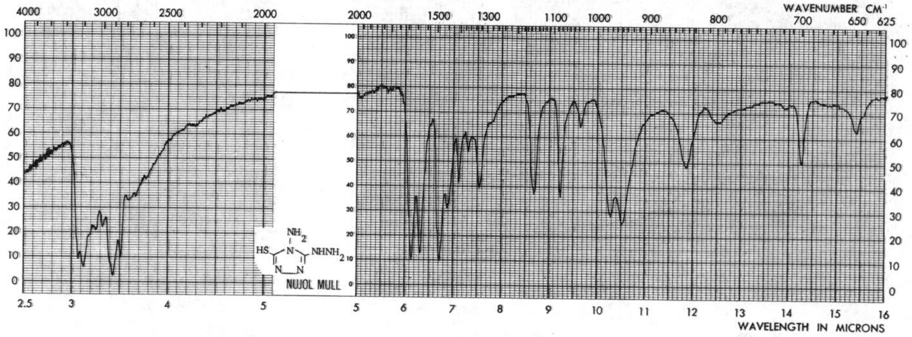

T4610-8 **1,2,4-Triazole**
M.W. 69.07 m.p. 119-121°

NUJOL MULL

H

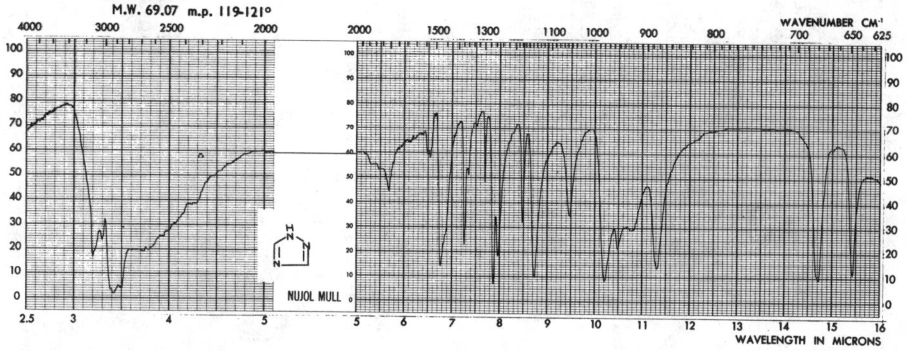

19,764-5
1,2,4-Triazole, sodium derivative, 98%
FW 91.05 mp 295° (dec.) *Beil.* **26**(2),7 Disp. L

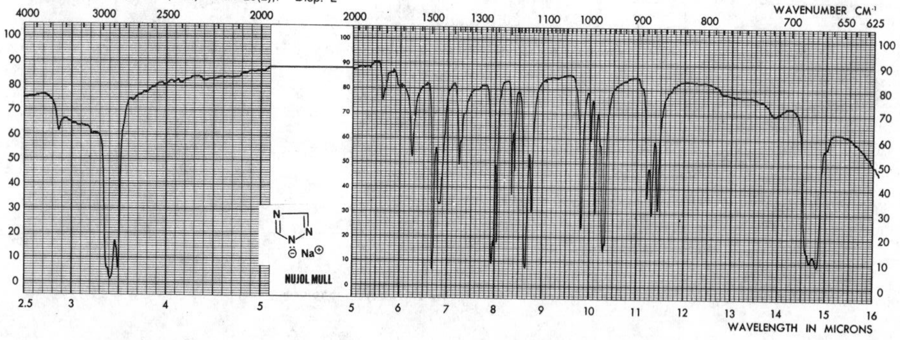

NUJOL MULL

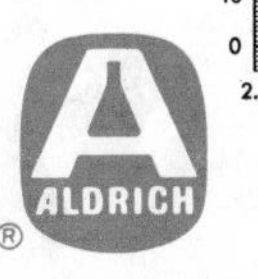

ALDRICH

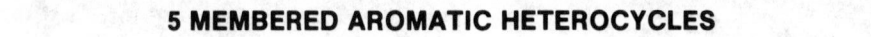

A

10,455-8 **1H-1,2,4-Triazole-3-thiol** (3-mercapto-1H-1,2,4-triazole)
M.W. 101.13 m.p. 221-224°

NUJOL MULL

B

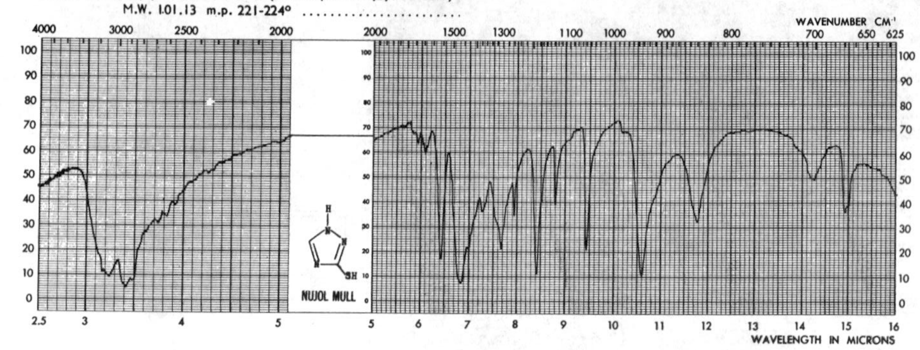

A8160-9 **3-Amino-1,2,4-triazole**
M.W. 84.08 m.p. 153-156°

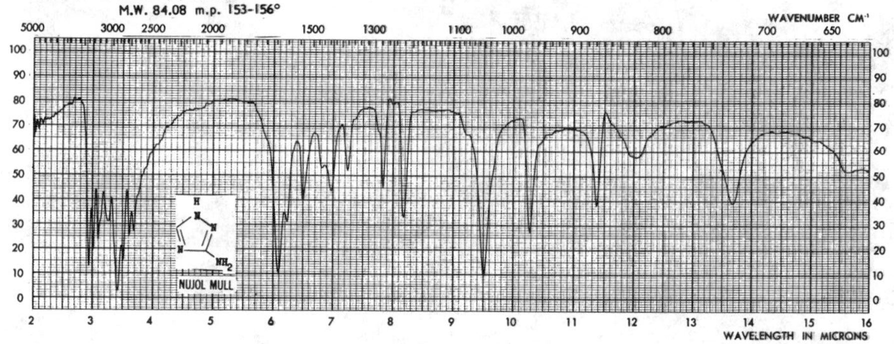

NUJOL MULL

C

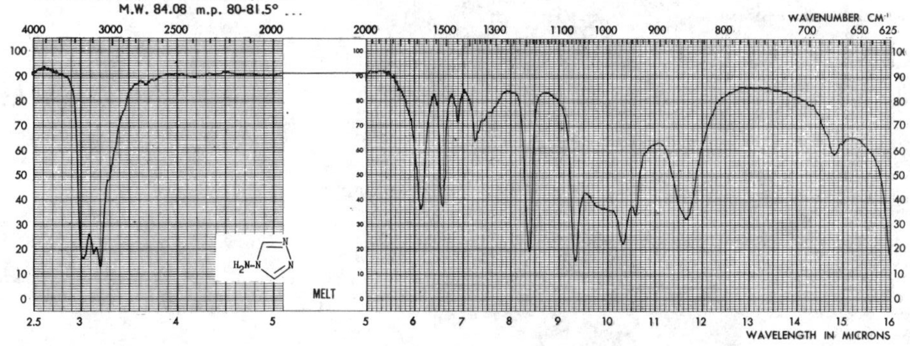

A8180-3 **4-Amino-1,2,4-triazole, puriss.**
M.W. 84.08 m.p. 80-81.5°

MELT

D

A8180-3 **4-Amino-1,2,4-triazole, puriss.**
M.W. 84.08 m.p. 80-81.5°

E

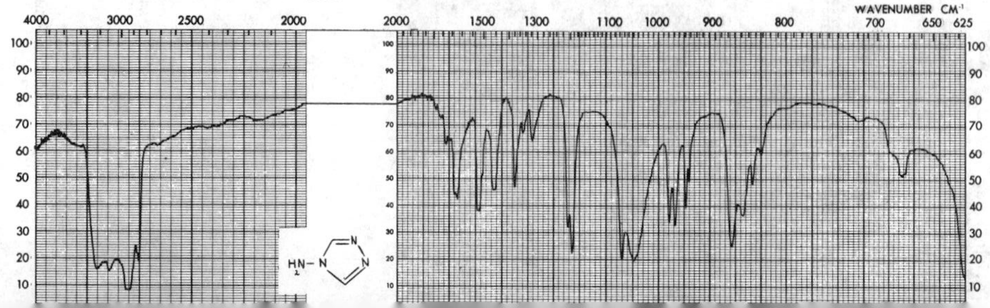

D2620-2 **3,5-Diamino-1,2,4-triazole (guanazole), tech.** (contains approx. 15% sodium chloride)
M.W. 99.10 m.p. 200-206°

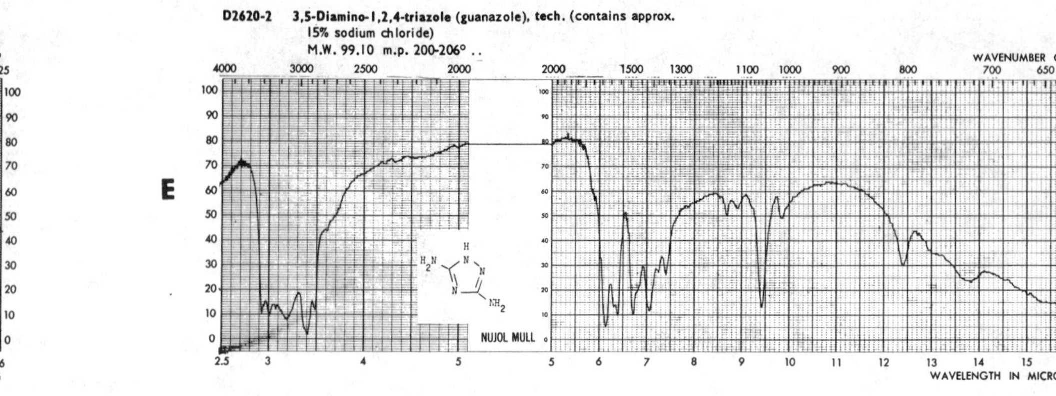

F

14,026-0 **3-Amino-5-mercapto-1,2,4-triazole** (3-amino-1,2,4-triazole-5-thiol)
M.W. 116.15 m.p. > 300°

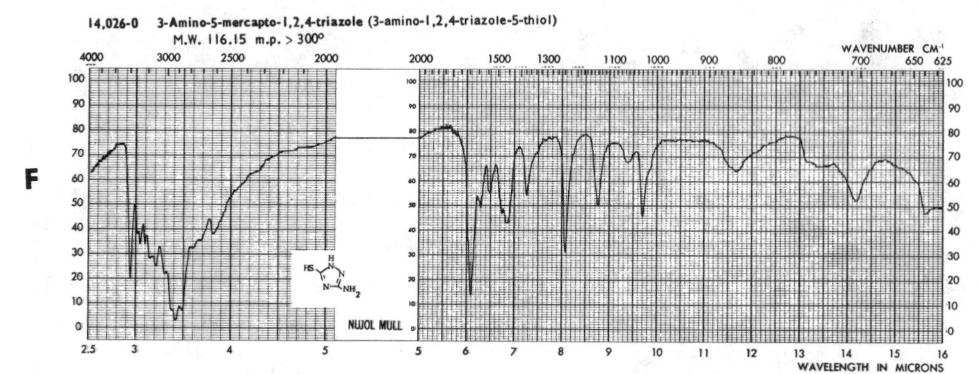

G

22,066-3
5-(Trifluoromethyl)-4H-1,2,4-triazole-3(2H)-thione, 97%
FW 169.13 mp 161-164° Disp. C

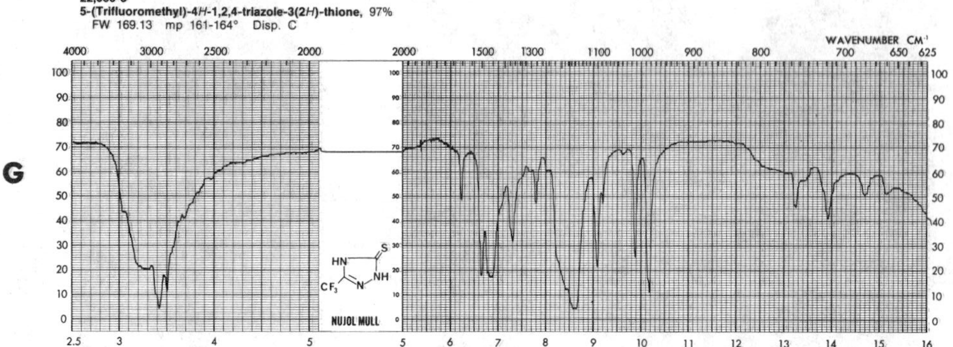

H

21,355-1
4-Methyl-5-trifluoromethyl-4H-1,2,4-triazolin-3(2H)-thione, 98%
FW 183.16 mp 116-118° Disp. C

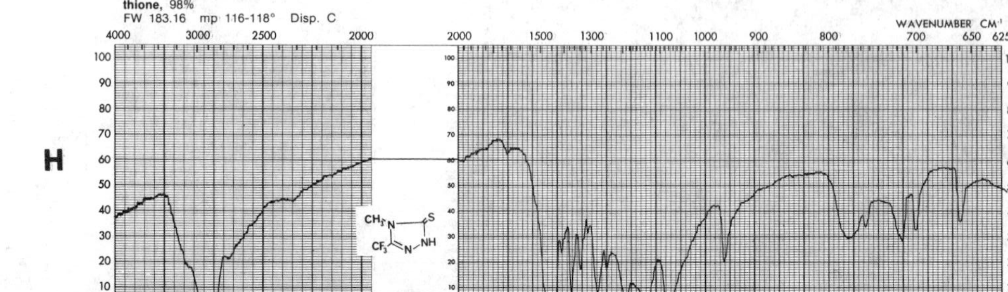

A

FW 130.17 mp 130-133° Disp. C

B

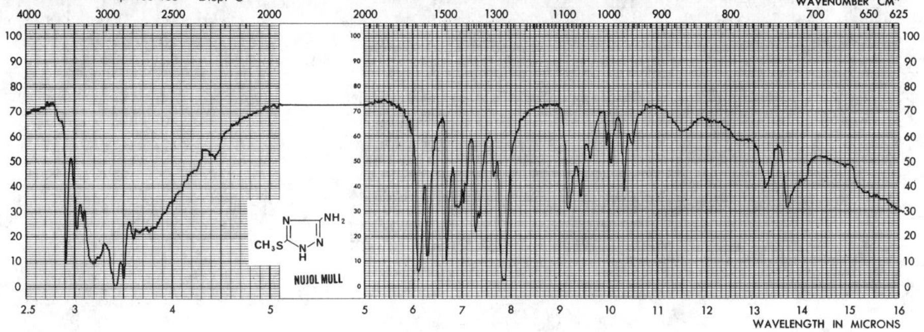

19,405-0
p-(1*H*-1,2,4-Triazol-1-yl)phenol
FW 161.16 mp 254-257° Disp. C

C

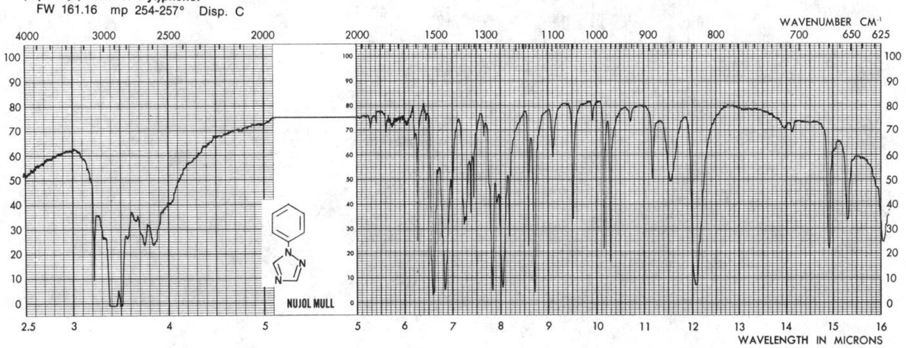

10,554-6 3-Amino-5-phenyl-1H-1,2,4-triazole
M.W. 160.18 m.p. 186-190° .....

D

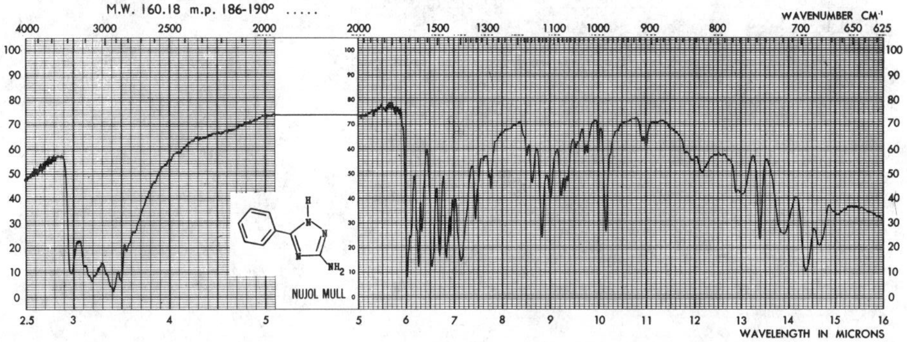

P4190-1 N-Phthalyl-DL-histidine
M.W. 285.26 m.p. 300° (dec.)

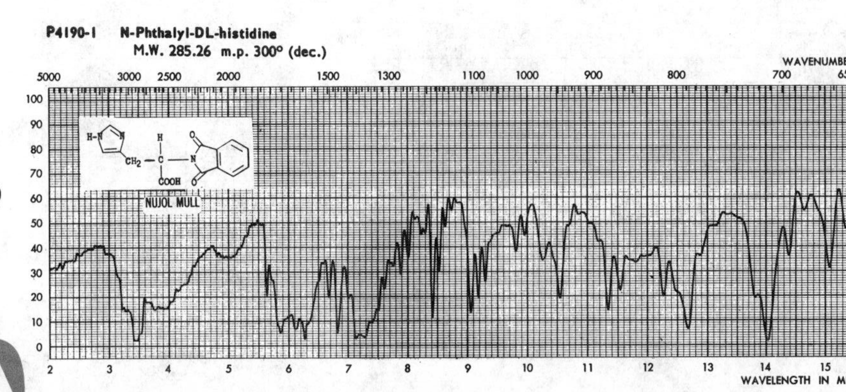

E

M.W. 164.13 m.p. 280° (dec.) ...

F

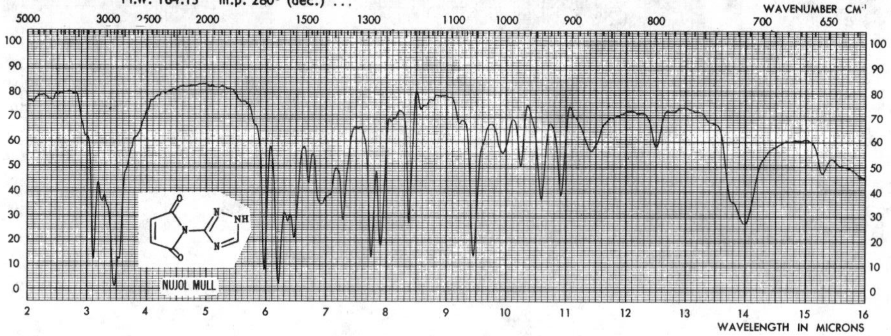

15,569-1 1H-Tetrazole
M.W. 70.05

G

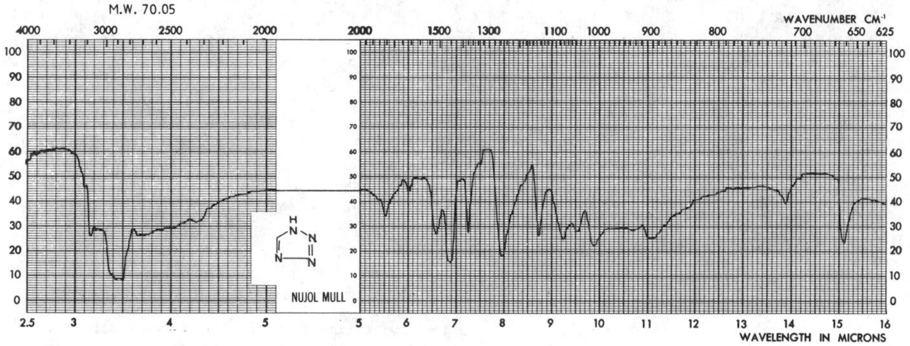

19,918-4
1,5-Dimethyltetrazole, 97+%
FW 98.11 mp 70-72° *Beil.* **26**(2),199 Disp. C

H

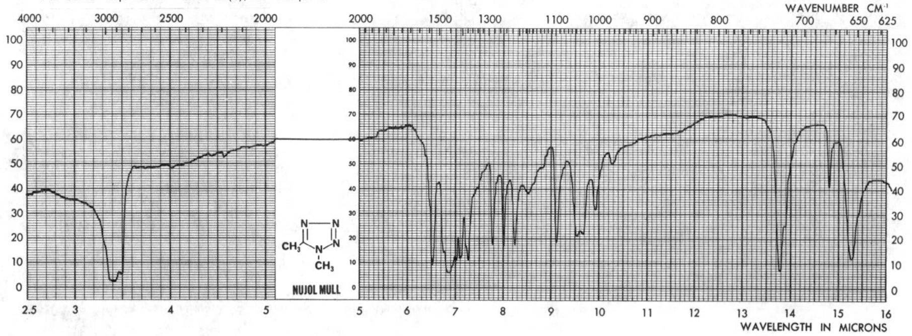

14,709-5 6,7-Dihydro-5H-pyrrolotetrazole (trimethylenetetrazole)
M.W. 110.10 m.p. 109-111° ....

5 MEMBERED AROMATIC HETEROCYCLES

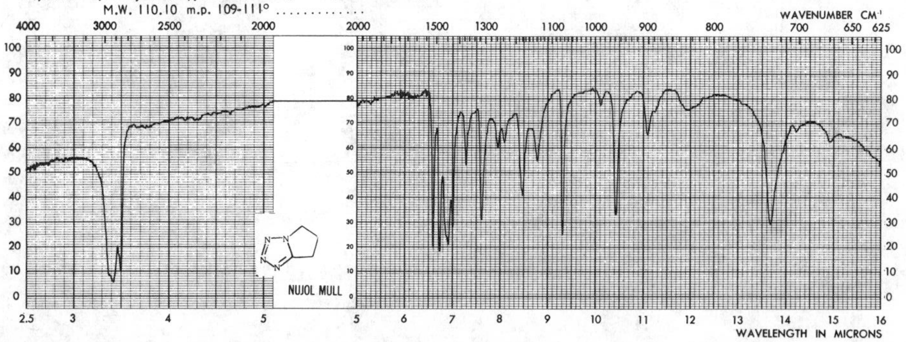

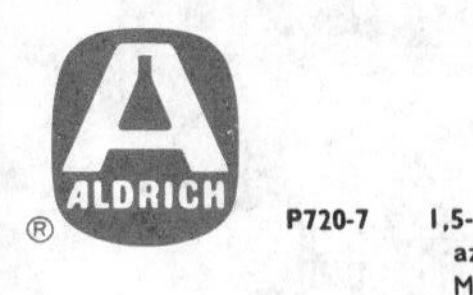

A P720-7 **1,5-Pentamethylenetetrazole** (6,7,8,9-tetrahydro-5H-tetrazolo-azepine)
M.W. 138.17 m.p. 60-62°
NUJOL MULL

B 16,989-7
1-Phenyl-1*H*-tetrazole-5-thiol
FW 178.22 mp 145° (dec.) *Beil.* **26**,409 Disp. C
NUJOL MULL

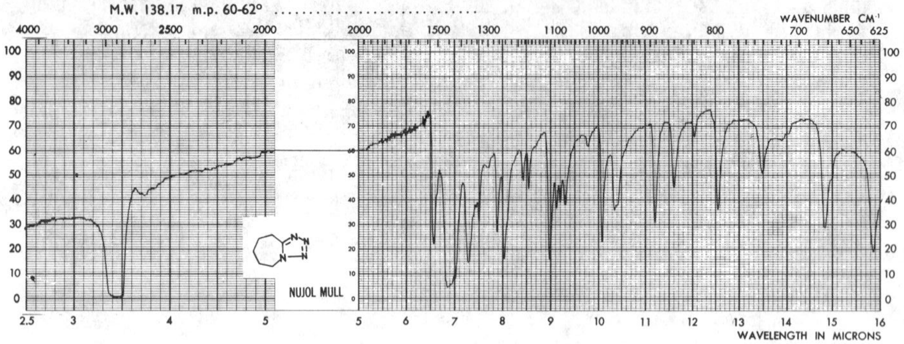

C T8485-9 **2,3,5-Triphenyl-2H-tetrazolium chloride**
M.W. 334.81
NUJOL MULL

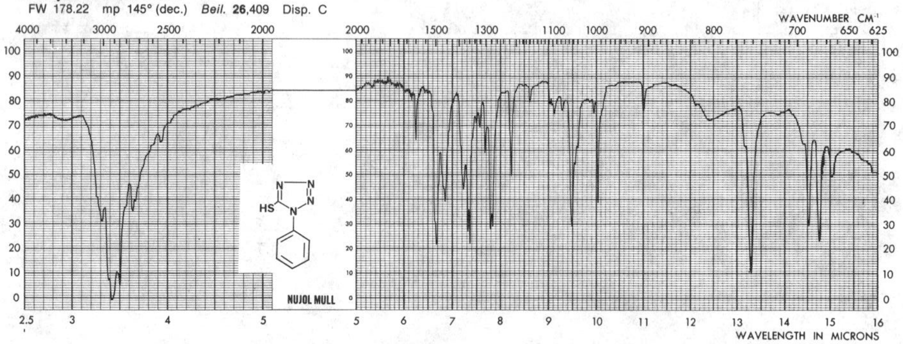

D 16,059-8
Tetrazolium violet [2,5-diphenyl-3-(1-naphthyl)-2H-tetrazolium chloride]
M.W. 384.87 m.p. 247-249° (dec.)

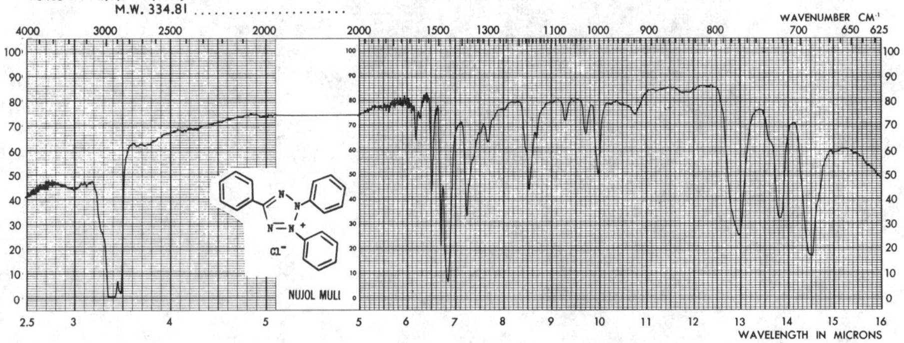

E B3510-5 **3,3'-(4,4'-Biphenylene)-bis-[2,5-diphenyl-2H-tetrazolium chloride]**
(neotetrazolium chloride)
M.W. 667.60 m.p. 170° (dec.)
NUJOL MULL

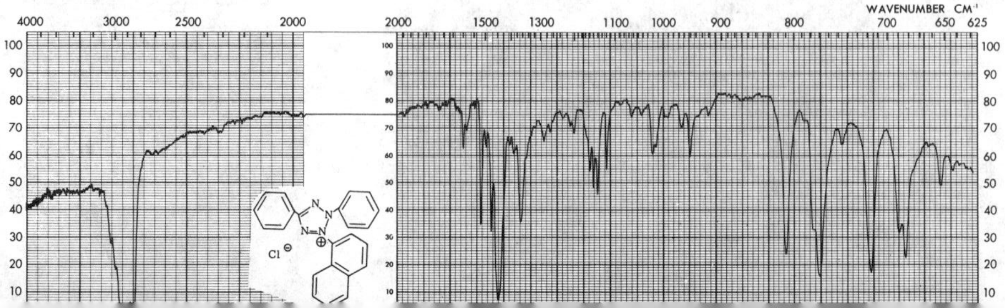

F B5480-0 **Blue tetrazolium** [3,3'-(3,3'-dimethoxy-4,4'-biphenylene)-bis-(2,5-diphenyl-2H-tetrazolium chloride)]
M.W. 727.66
m.p. 258-260° (dec.)
NUJOL MULL

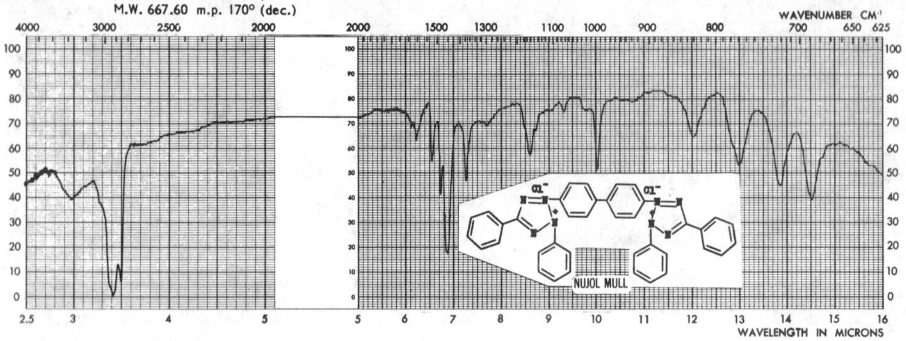

G 13,503-8 **MTT** [3-(4,5-dimethylthiazol-2-yl)-2,5-diphenyl-2H-tetrazolium bromide]
M.W. 414.34
m.p. 188-190° (dec.)
NUJOL MULL

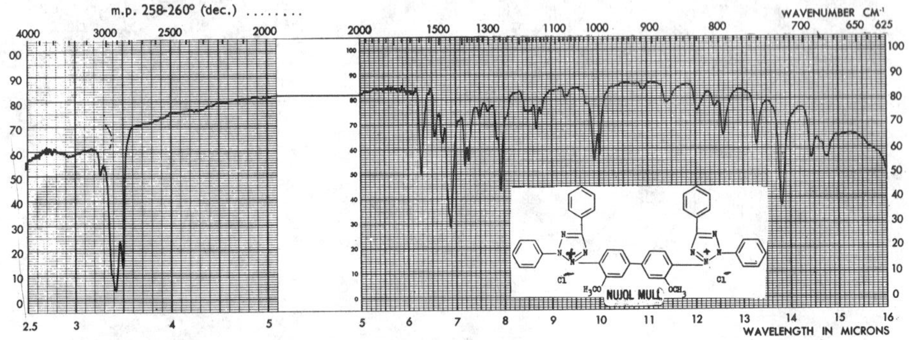

H 14,337-5 **5-Chloro-1-phenyl-1H-tetrazole**
M.W. 180.60 m.p. 115-116° (dec.)

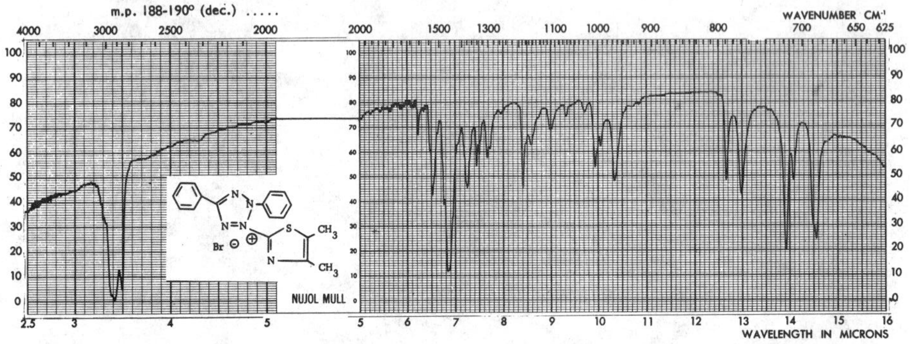

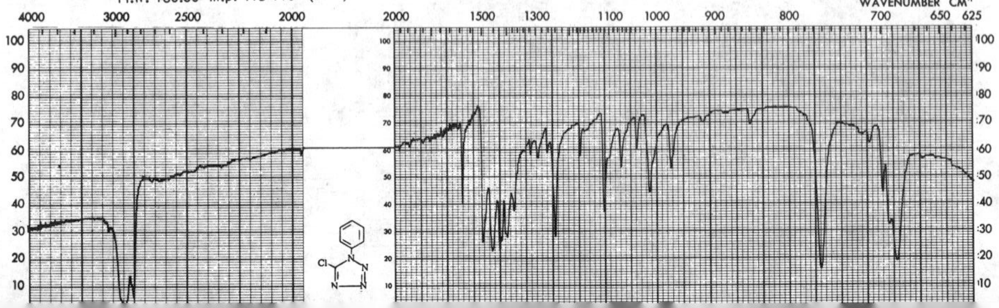

A

M.W. 103.08 m.p. 200-204° (dec.)

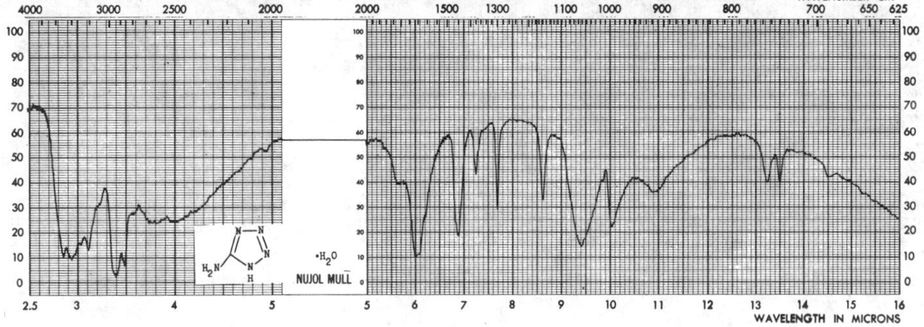

NUJOL MULL

B

I-1040-6 2-(p-Iodophenyl)-3-(p-nitrophenyl)-5-phenyltetrazolium chloride (INT)
M.W. 505.70
m.p. 231° (dec.) ....

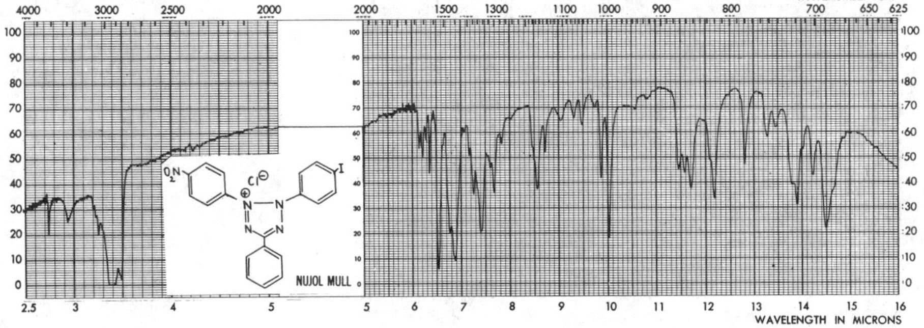

NUJOL MULL

C

N1540-5 Nitro blue tetrazolium chloride (with 10% ethanol of crystallization)
M.W. 817.65 (ethanol free compound) m.p. 205° (dec.)

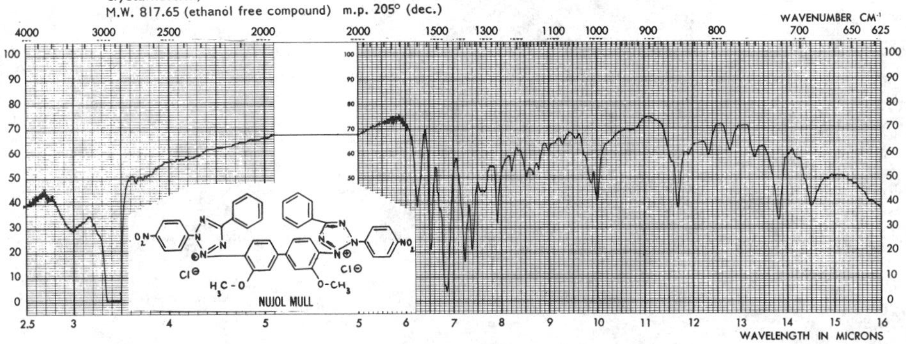

NUJOL MULL

D

13,316-7 Tetranitro blue tetrazolium chloride (contains ethanol of crystallization)
M.W. 907.65 (ethanol free compound)
m.p. 165° (dec.) ....

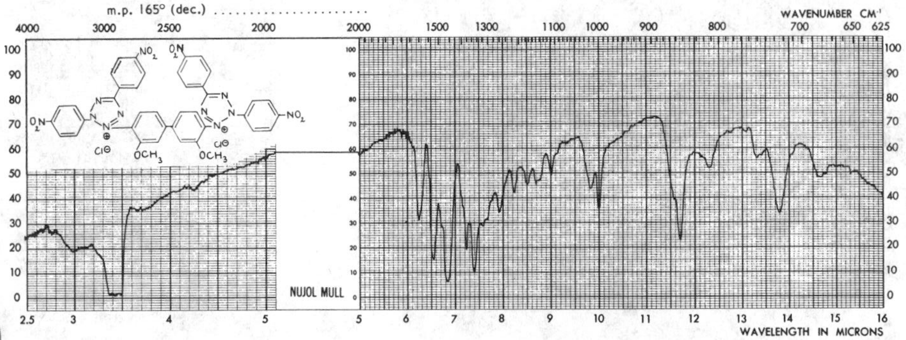

NUJOL MULL

E

15,163-7 Isoxazole
M.W. 69.06 n_D^{20} 1.4265 b.p. 93-95°

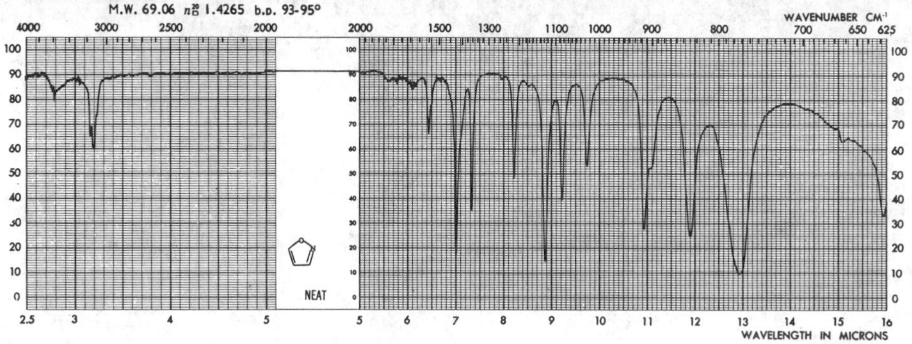

NEAT

F

15,370-2 5-Methylisoxazole
M.W. 83.09 n_D^{20} 1.4386 b.p. 122°

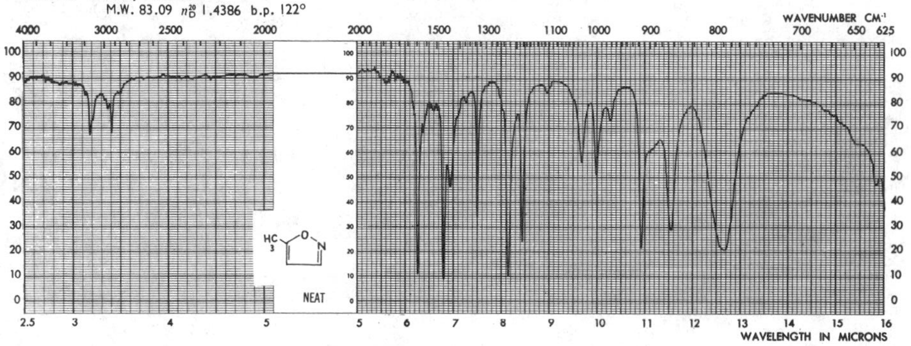

NEAT

G

15,369-9
3-Methylisoxazole, 98%
M.W. 83.09 b.p. 118° n_D^{20} 1.4365 d 1.015
Beil. 27,16

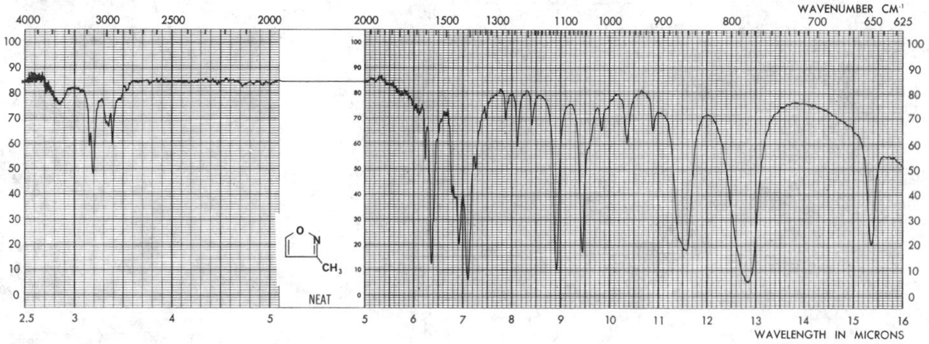

NEAT

H

D16,750-9 3,5-Dimethylisoxazole
M.W. 97.12 n_D^{20} 1.4421 b.p. 142-144°

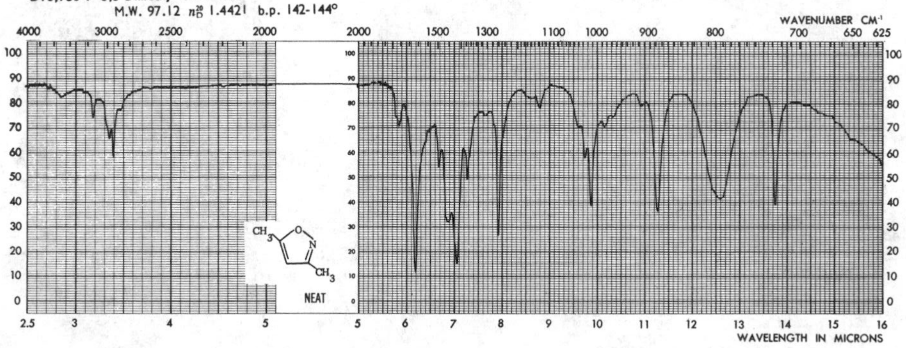

NEAT

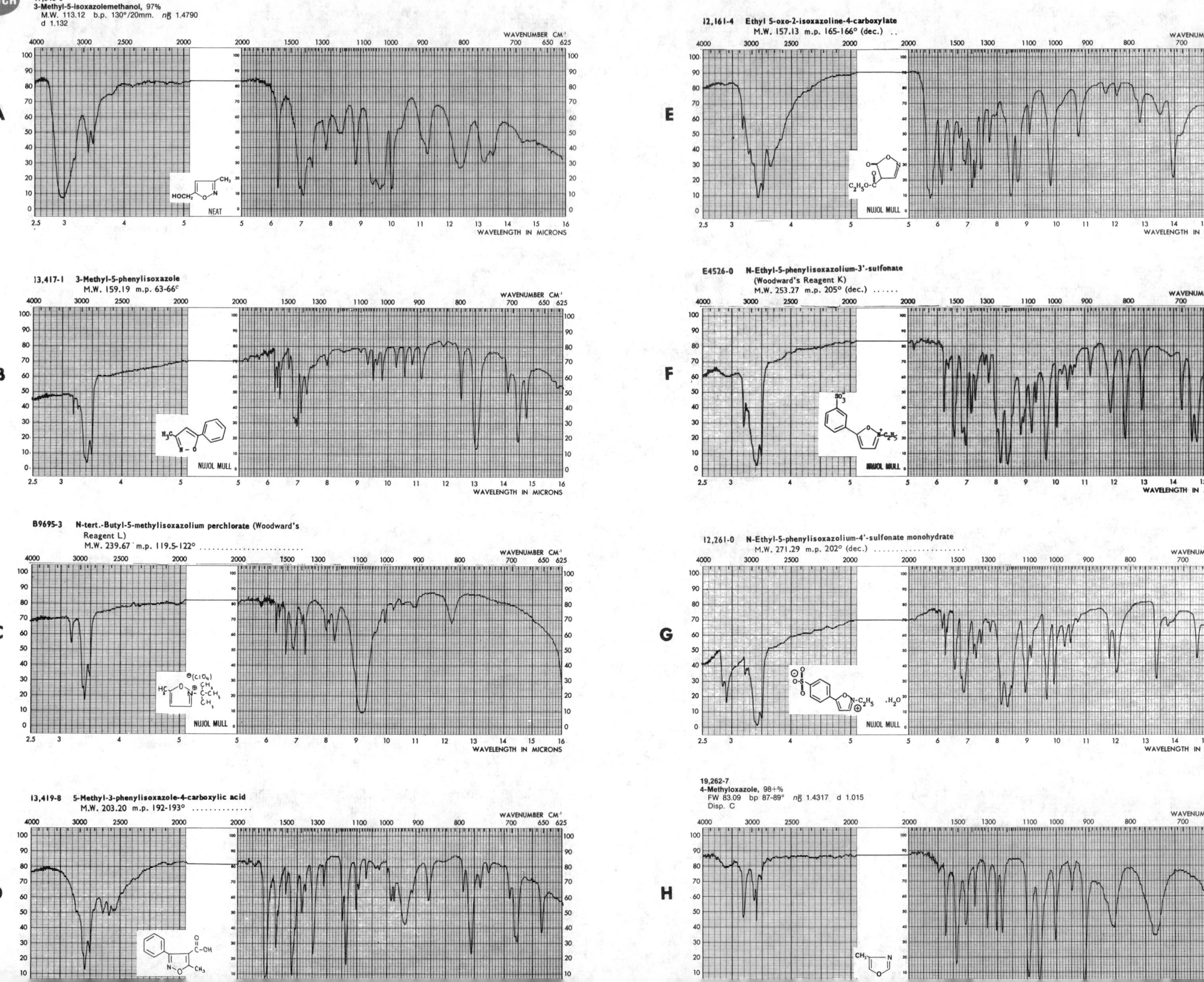
ALDRICH
A
17,945-0
3-Methyl-5-isoxazolemethanol, 97%
M.W. 113.12 b.p. 130°/20mm. n_D^{20} 1.4790
d 1.132
NEAT
B
13,417-1 3-Methyl-5-phenylisoxazole
M.W. 159.19 m.p. 63-66°
NUJOL MULL
C
B9695-3 N-tert.-Butyl-5-methylisoxazolium perchlorate (Woodward's Reagent L)
M.W. 239.67 m.p. 119.5-122°
NUJOL MULL
D
13,419-8 5-Methyl-3-phenylisoxazole-4-carboxylic acid
M.W. 203.20 m.p. 192-193°
E
12,161-4 Ethyl 5-oxo-2-isoxazoline-4-carboxylate
M.W. 157.13 m.p. 165-166° (dec.)
NUJOL MULL
F
E4526-0 N-Ethyl-5-phenylisoxazolium-3'-sulfonate (Woodward's Reagent K)
M.W. 253.27 m.p. 205° (dec.)
NUJOL MULL
G
12,261-0 N-Ethyl-5-phenylisoxazolium-4'-sulfonate monohydrate
M.W. 271.29 m.p. 202° (dec.)
NUJOL MULL
H
19,262-7
4-Methyloxazole, 98+%
FW 83.09 bp 87-89° n_D^{20} 1.4317 d 1.015
Disp. C
WAVENUMBER CM⁻¹
WAVELENGTH IN MICRONS

Disp. C

A

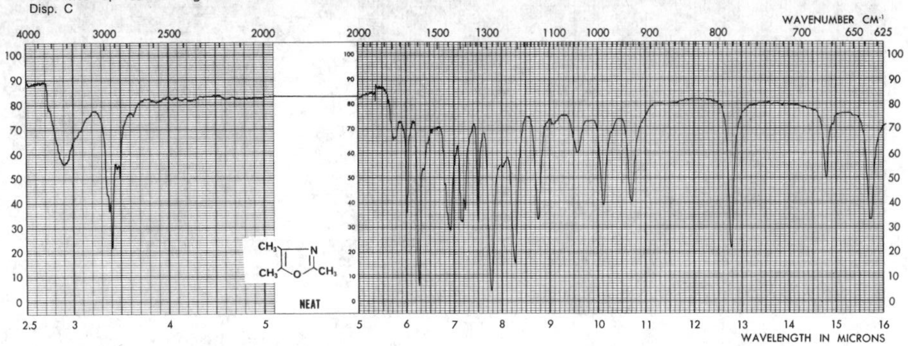

D21,040-4 2,5-Diphenyloxazole (PPO), **scintillation grade**
M.W. 221.26 m.p. 72-73°

B

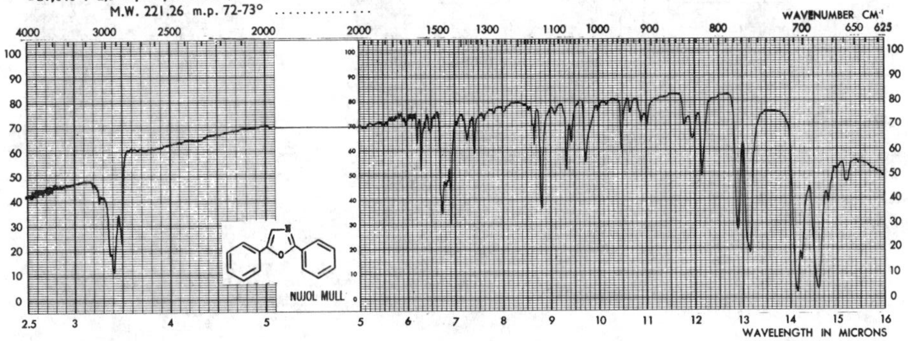

B5080-5 1,4-Bis-(5-phenyloxazol-2-yl)-benzene (POPOP), **scintillation grade**
M.W. 364.40 m.p. 243-244°

C

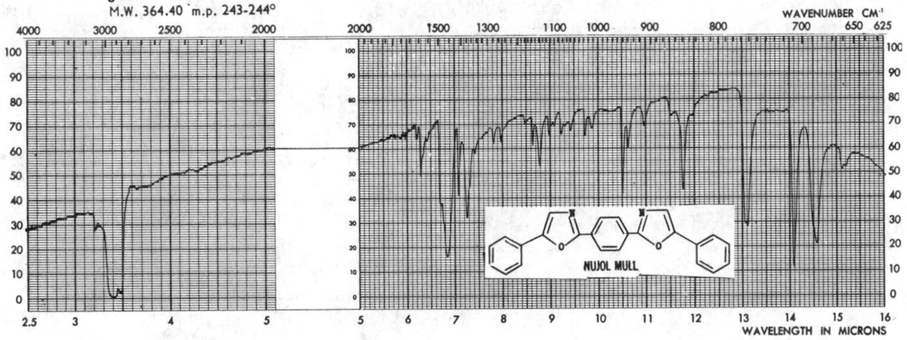

22,291-7
1,4-Bis(4-methyl-5-phenyloxazol-2-yl)benzene,
scintillation grade (dimethyl-POPOP)
FW 392.46 mp 233-235° Disp. C

D

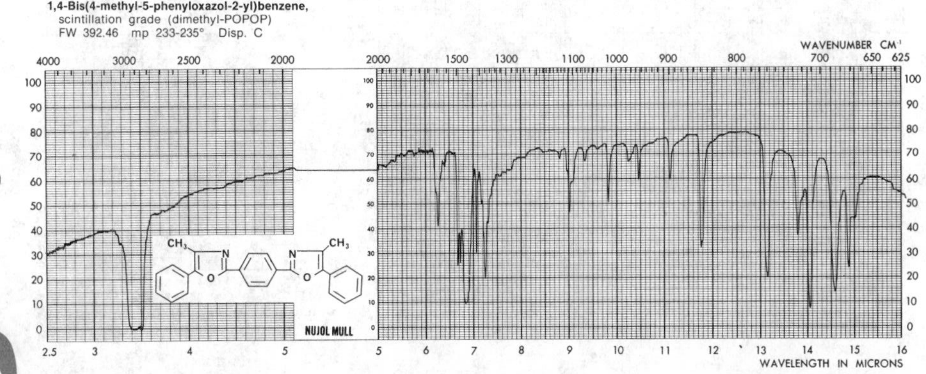

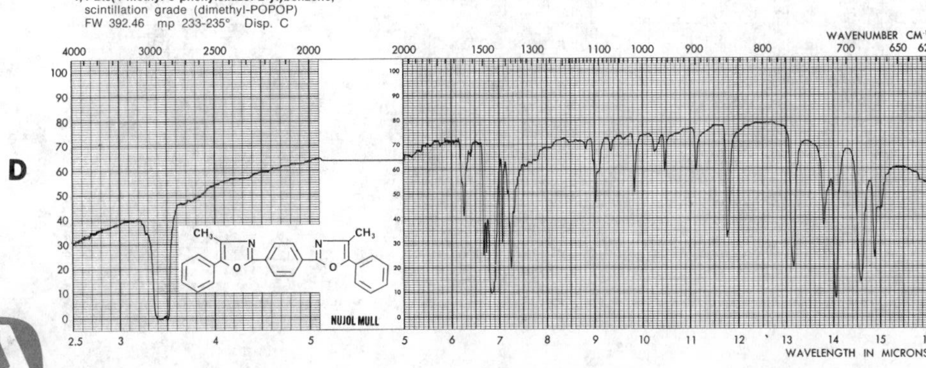

FW 297.36 mp 115-118° Disp. C

E

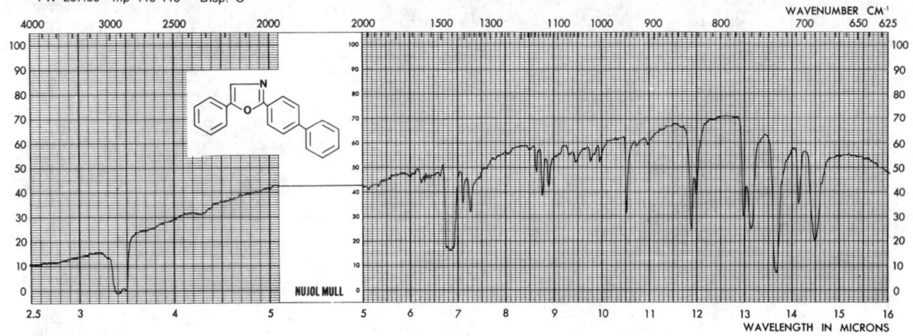

22,400-6
2-(4-Biphenylyl)-5-(4-*tert*-butylphenyl)-1,3,4-oxadiazole, 99+%, scintillation grade (butyl-PBD)
FW 354.46 mp 137-138° Disp. C

F

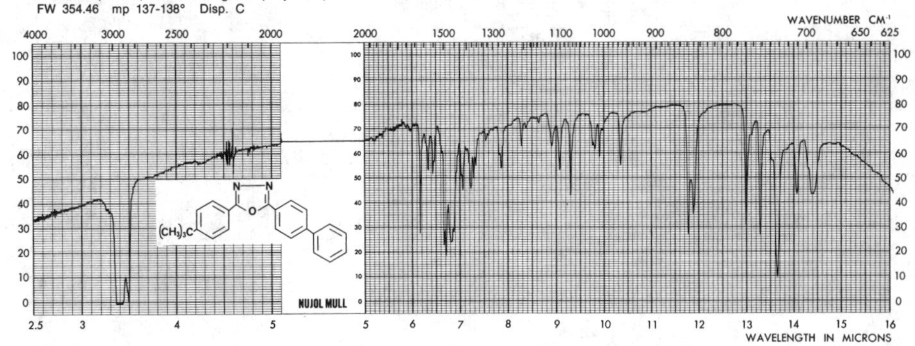

21,890-1
2,5-Bis(4-biphenylyl)oxazole, 99%, scintillation grade (BBO)
FW 373.46 mp 238-240° Disp. C

G

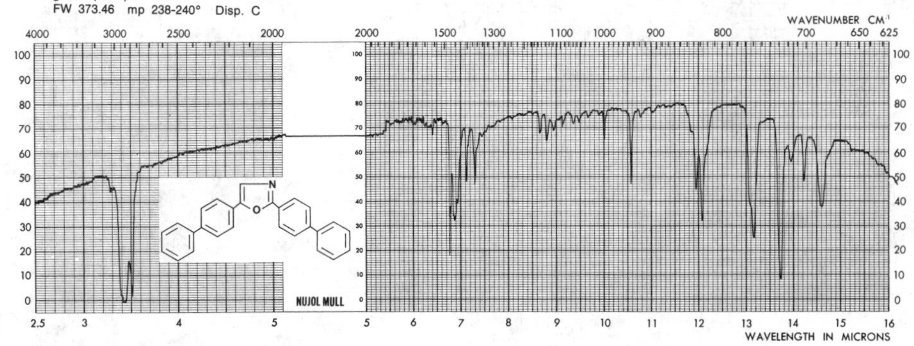

22,559-2
2-Methyl-4,5-diphenyloxazole, 99%
FW 235.29 mp 28° bp 214°/17mm. n_D^{20} 1.6280
d 1.116 *Beil.* **27**,79 Disp. C

H

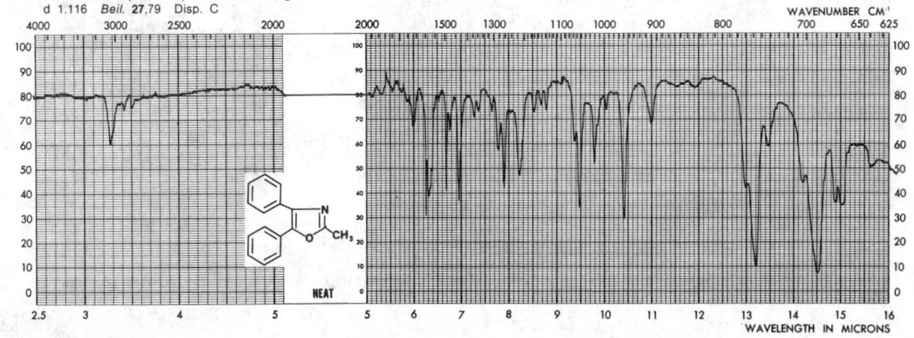

A 14,339-1 4,5-Diphenyl-2-(methylthio)-oxazole
M.W. 267.35 m.p. 64-67°

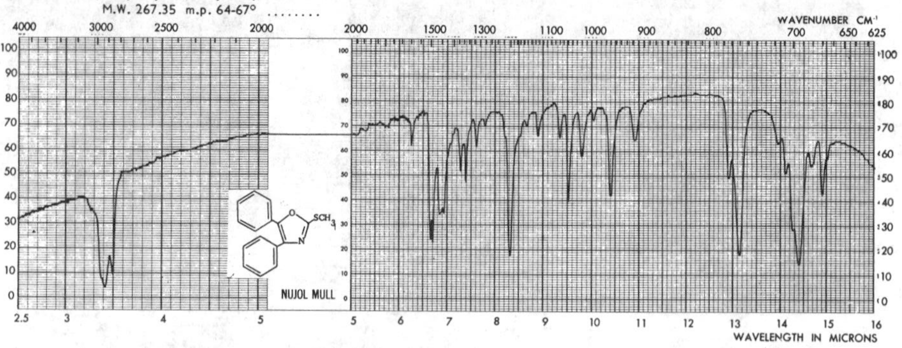

NUJOL MULL

B 21,432-9
9,10-Dihydro-2-methyl-4*H*-benzo[5,6]cyclohept[1,2-*d*]-oxazol-4-ol, 99%
FW 215.26 mp 136-138° Disp. C

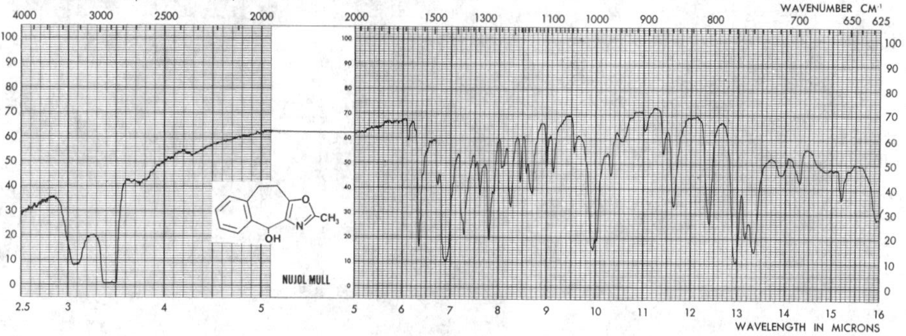

NUJOL MULL

C I-140-5 2-Imino-4-keto-5-phenyloxazolidine (5-phenylpseudohydantoin)
M.W. 176.18 m.p. 253-258°

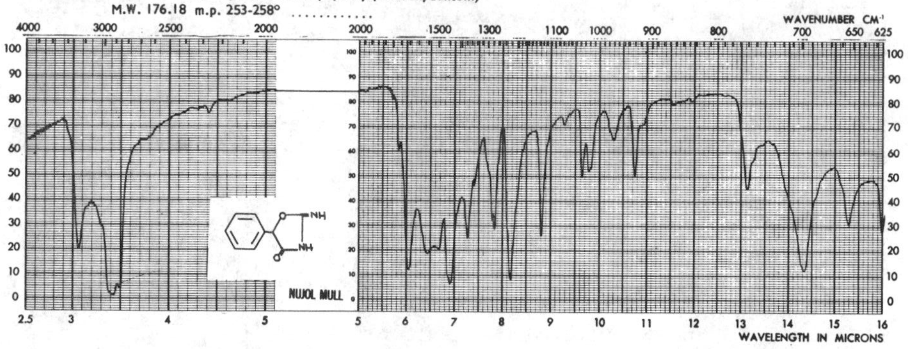

NUJOL MULL

D 13,989-0 N[1]-(4,5-Dimethyloxazol-2-yl)-sulfanilamide
M.W. 267.31 m.p. 185° (dec.)

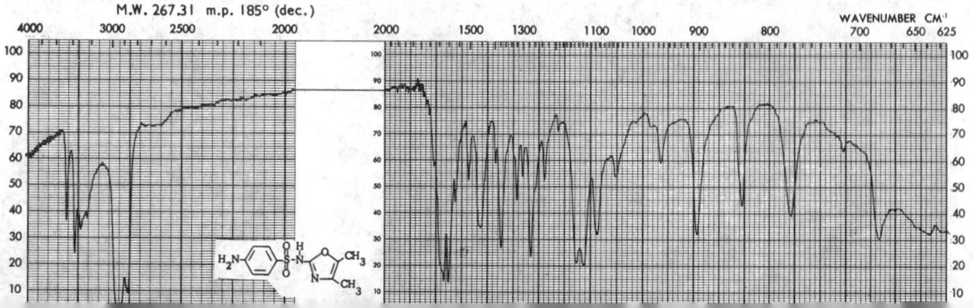

E 13,990-4 N[4]-Acetyl-N[1]-(4,5-dimethyloxazol-2-yl)-sulfanilamide, tech.
M.W. 309.35 m.p. 229-233° (dec.)

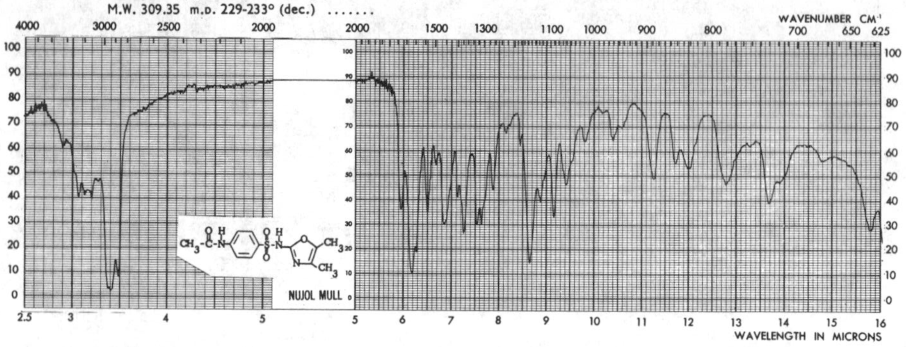

NUJOL MULL

F D15,860-7 3,4-Dimethylfurazan
M.W. 98.11 n_D^{20} 1.4237

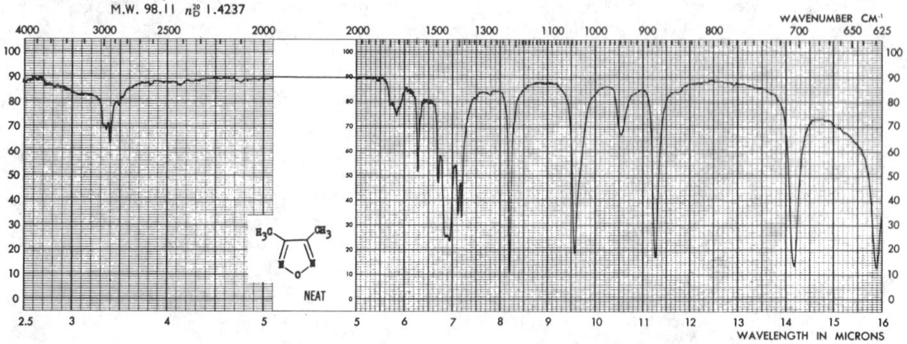

NEAT

G D21,021-8 2,5-Diphenyl-1,3,4-oxadiazole
M.W. 222.25 m.p. 140-141°

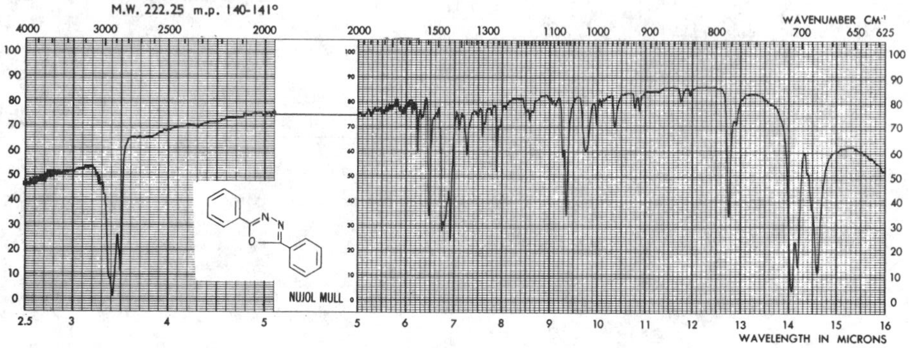

NUJOL MULL

H 15,567-5 Isothiazole
M.W. 85.13 n_D^{20} 1.5310

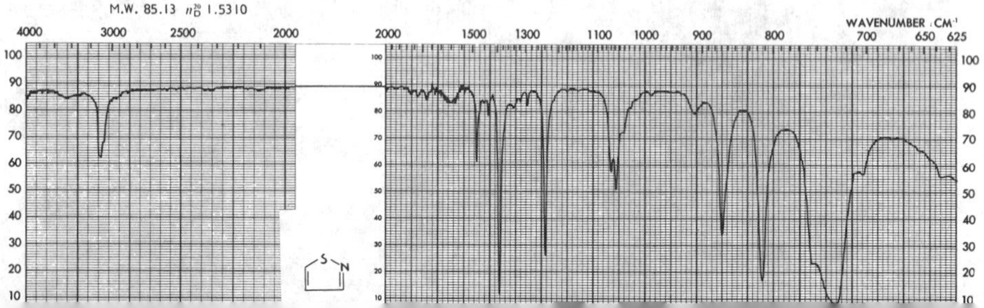

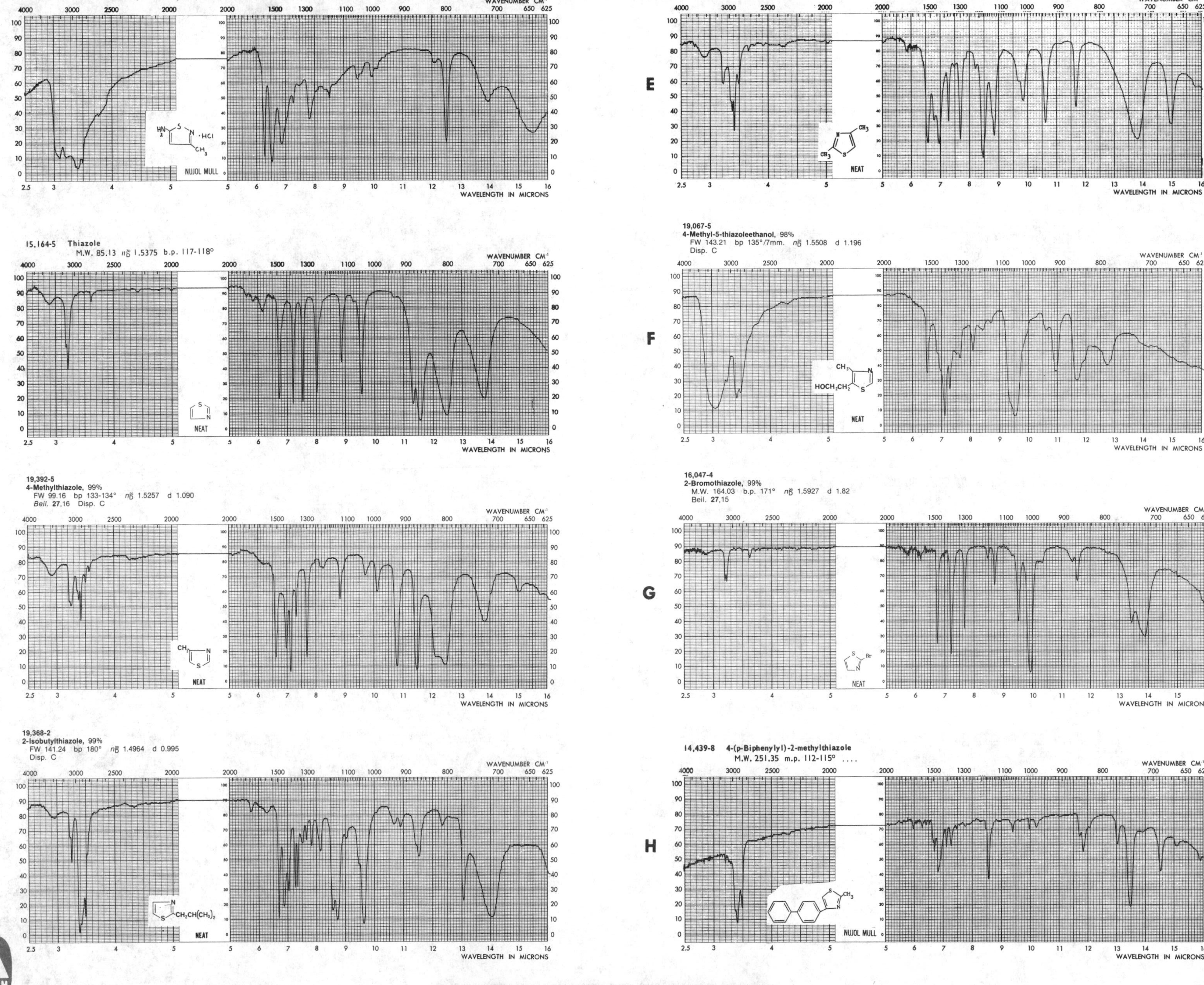
A
M.W. 150.63 m.p. 300° (dec.) ....
NUJOL MULL
B
15,164-5 Thiazole
M.W. 85.13 n_D^{20} 1.5375 b.p. 117-118°
NEAT
C
19,392-5
4-Methylthiazole, 99%
FW 99.16 bp 133-134° n_D^{20} 1.5257 d 1.090
Beil. 27,16 Disp. C
NEAT
D
19,368-2
2-Isobutylthiazole, 99%
FW 141.24 bp 180° n_D^{20} 1.4964 d 0.995
Disp. C
NEAT
E
M.W. 113.18 n_D^{20} 1.5091 ......
NEAT
F
19,067-5
4-Methyl-5-thiazoleethanol, 98%
FW 143.21 bp 135°/7mm. n_D^{20} 1.5508 d 1.196
Disp. C
NEAT
G
16,047-4
2-Bromothiazole, 99%
M.W. 164.03 b.p. 171° n_D^{20} 1.5927 d 1.82
Beil. 27,15
NEAT
H
14,439-8 4-(p-Biphenylyl)-2-methylthiazole
M.W. 251.35 m.p. 112-115° ....
NUJOL MULL
WAVENUMBER CM⁻¹
WAVELENGTH IN MICRONS
ALDRICH

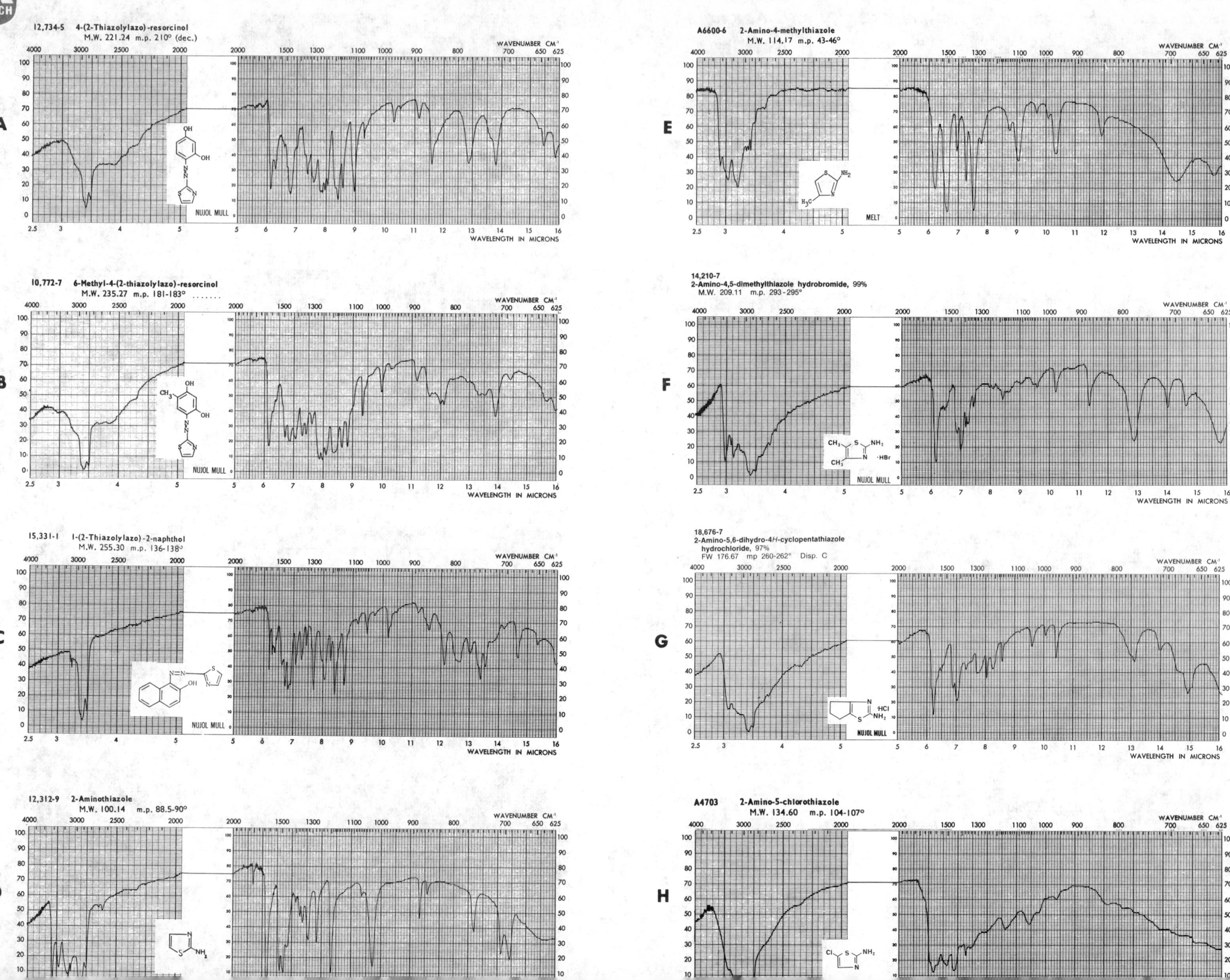
ALDRICH
A
12,734-5 4-(2-Thiazolylazo)-resorcinol
M.W. 221.24 m.p. 210° (dec.)
NUJOL MULL
B
10,772-7 6-Methyl-4-(2-thiazolylazo)-resorcinol
M.W. 235.27 m.p. 181-183°
NUJOL MULL
C
15,331-1 1-(2-Thiazolylazo)-2-naphthol
M.W. 255.30 m.p. 136-138°
NUJOL MULL
D
12,312-9 2-Aminothiazole
M.W. 100.14 m.p. 88.5-90°
E
A6600-6 2-Amino-4-methylthiazole
M.W. 114.17 m.p. 43-46°
MELT
F
14,210-7
2-Amino-4,5-dimethylthiazole hydrobromide, 99%
M.W. 209.11 m.p. 293-295°
NUJOL MULL
G
18,676-7
2-Amino-5,6-dihydro-4H-cyclopentathiazole
hydrochloride, 97%
FW 176.67 mp 260-262° Disp. C
NUJOL MULL
H
A4703 2-Amino-5-chlorothiazole
M.W. 134.60 m.p. 104-107°
WAVENUMBER CM⁻¹
WAVELENGTH IN MICRONS

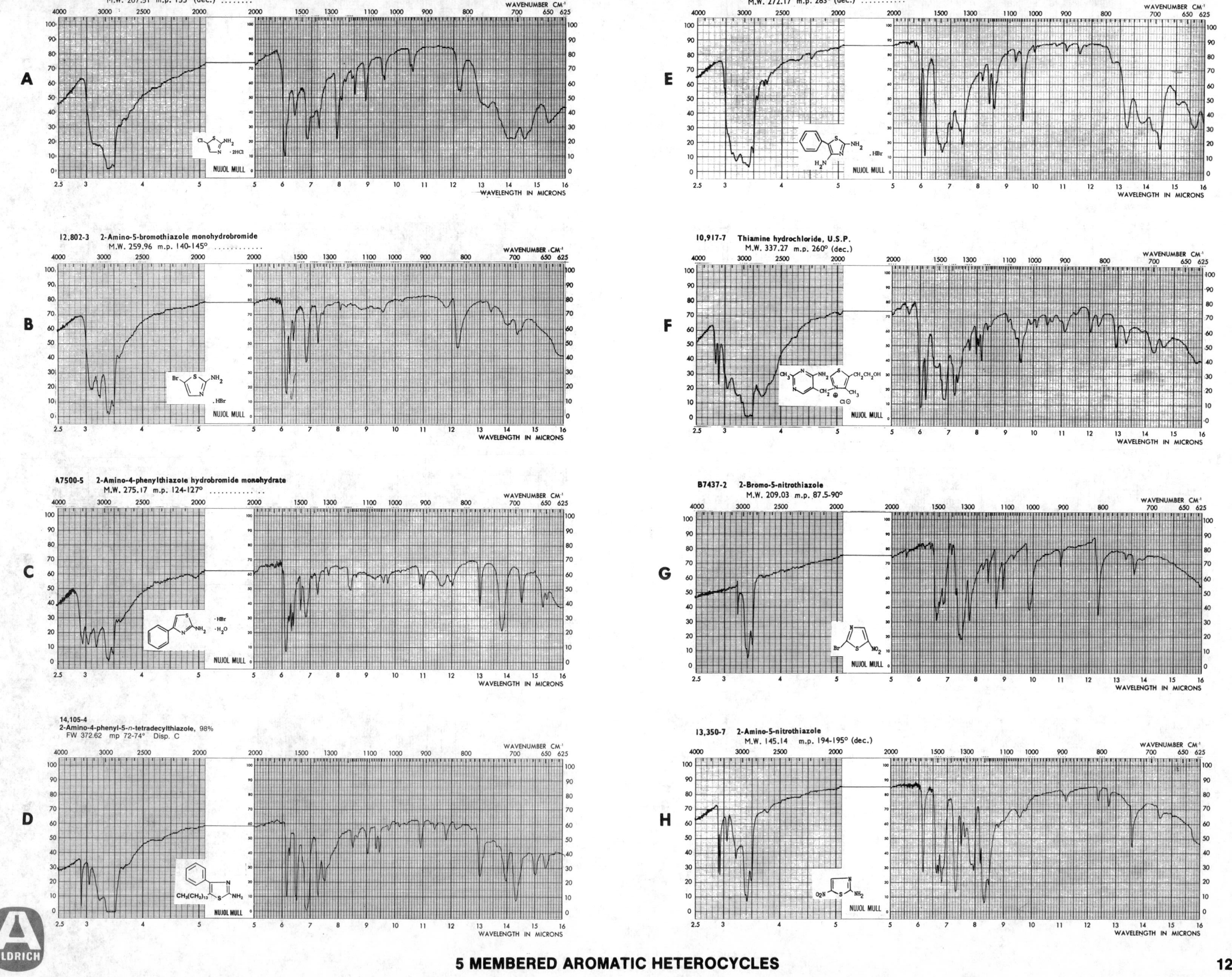
A
M.W. 207.51 m.p. 155° (dec.)
·2HCl
NUJOL MULL
B
12,802-3 2-Amino-5-bromothiazole monohydrobromide
M.W. 259.96 m.p. 140-145°
.HBr
NUJOL MULL
C
A7500-5 2-Amino-4-phenylthiazole hydrobromide monohydrate
M.W. 275.17 m.p. 124-127°
·HBr
·H2O
NUJOL MULL
D
14,105-4
2-Amino-4-phenyl-5-n-tetradecylthiazole, 98%
FW 372.62 mp 72-74° Disp. C
NUJOL MULL
E
M.W. 272.17 m.p. 283° (dec.)
.HBr
NUJOL MULL
F
10,917-7 Thiamine hydrochloride, U.S.P.
M.W. 337.27 m.p. 260° (dec.)
NUJOL MULL
G
B7437-2 2-Bromo-5-nitrothiazole
M.W. 209.03 m.p. 87.5-90°
NUJOL MULL
H
13,350-7 2-Amino-5-nitrothiazole
M.W. 145.14 m.p. 194-195° (dec.)
NUJOL MULL
WAVENUMBER CM⁻¹
WAVELENGTH IN MICRONS
ALDRICH

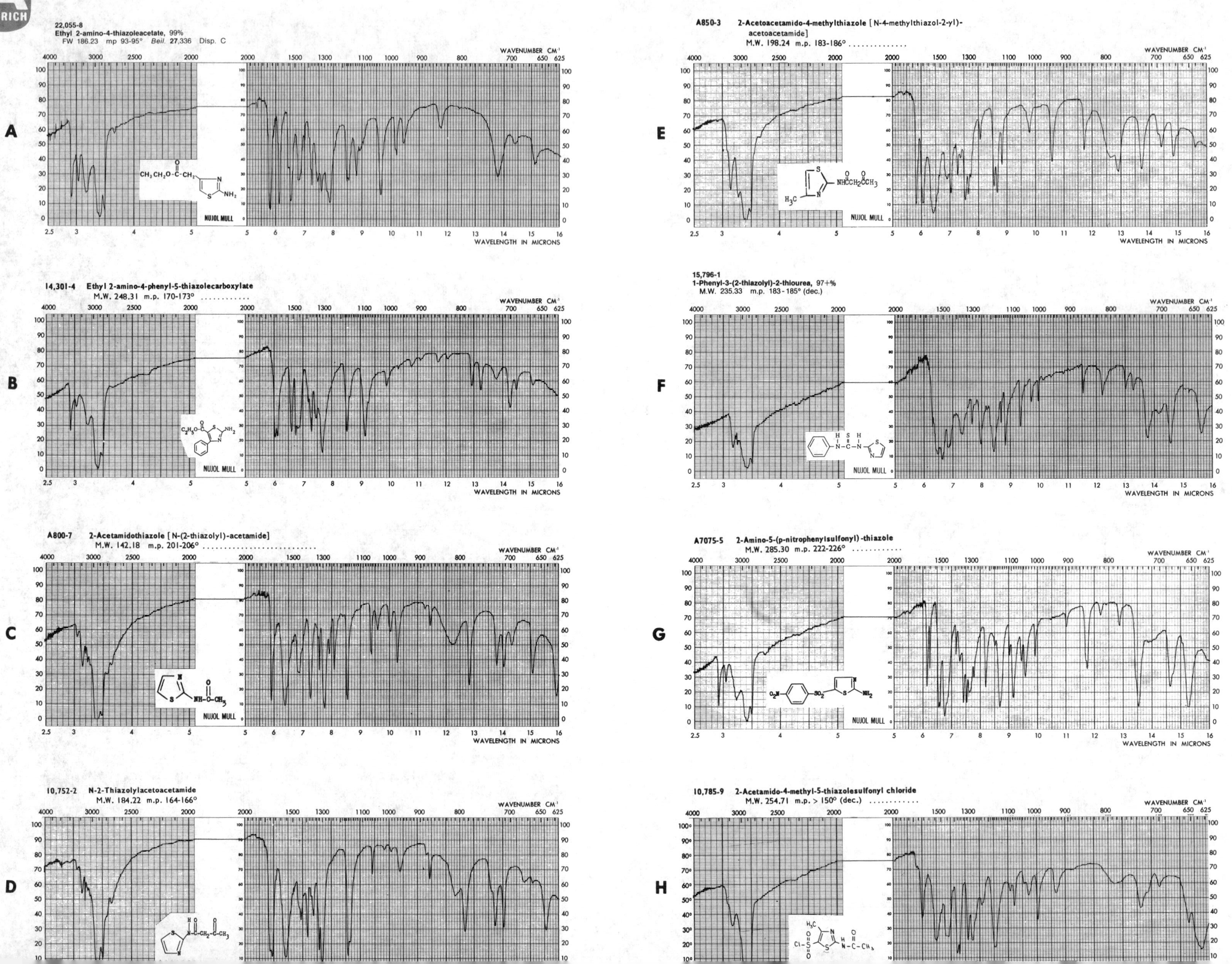
ALDRICH
A
22,055-8
Ethyl 2-amino-4-thiazoleacetate, 99%
FW 186.23 mp 93-95° Beil. 27,336 Disp. C
B
14,301-4 Ethyl 2-amino-4-phenyl-5-thiazolecarboxylate
M.W. 248.31 m.p. 170-173°
C
A800-7 2-Acetamidothiazole [N-(2-thiazolyl)-acetamide]
M.W. 142.18 m.p. 201-206°
D
10,752-2 N-2-Thiazolylacetoacetamide
M.W. 184.22 m.p. 164-166°
E
A850-3 2-Acetoacetamido-4-methylthiazole [N-4-methylthiazol-2-yl)-acetoacetamide]
M.W. 198.24 m.p. 183-186°
F
15,796-1
1-Phenyl-3-(2-thiazolyl)-2-thiourea, 97+%
M.W. 235.33 m.p. 183-185° (dec.)
G
A7075-5 2-Amino-5-(p-nitrophenylsulfonyl)-thiazole
M.W. 285.30 m.p. 222-226°
H
10,785-9 2-Acetamido-4-methyl-5-thiazolesulfonyl chloride
M.W. 254.71 m.p. > 150° (dec.)
NUJOL MULL
WAVENUMBER CM⁻¹
WAVELENGTH IN MICRONS

A

FW 403.44 mp 240° (dec.) Disp. C

NUJOL MULL

B

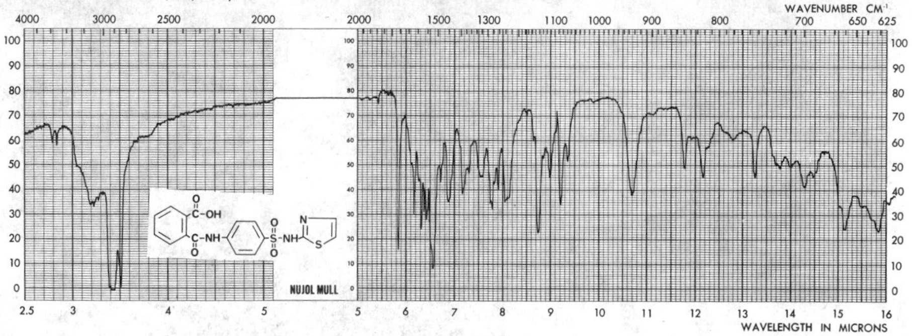

D18,775-5 2,5-Dimethyl-1,3,4-thiadiazole
M.W. 114.17 m.p. 63.5-67.5° .

MELT

C

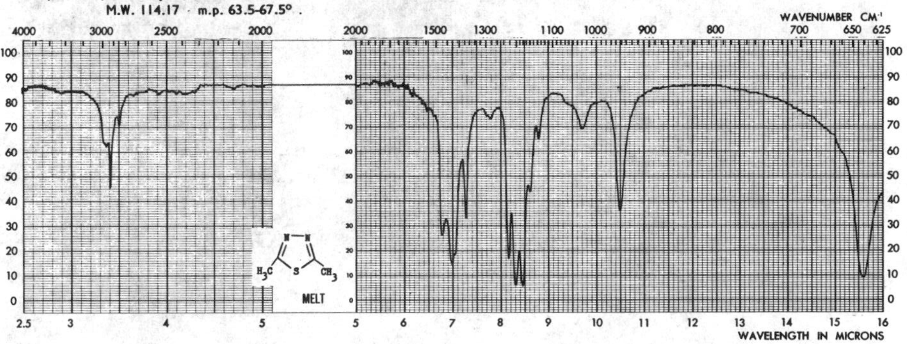

B5300-6 2,5-Bis-(4-pyridyl)-1,3,4-thiadiazole
M.W. 240.29 m.p. 239-240° ......

NUJOL MULL

D

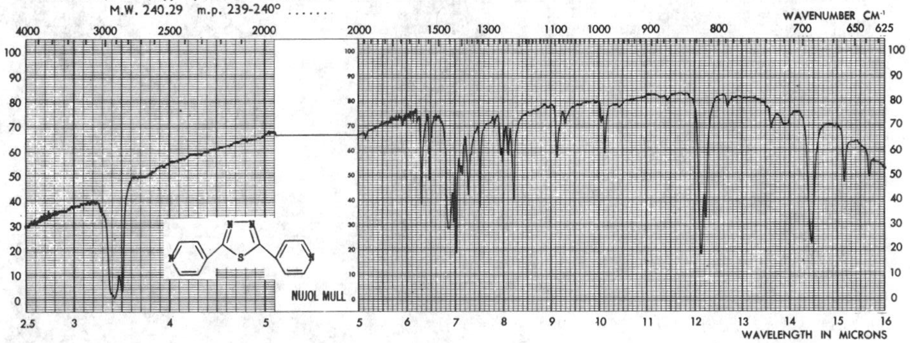

18,857-3
5-Methyl-1,3,4-thiadiazole-2-thiol, 97% (2-mercapto-5-methyl-1,3,4-thiadiazole)
FW 132.21 mp 188-189° Disp. C

NUJOL MULL

E

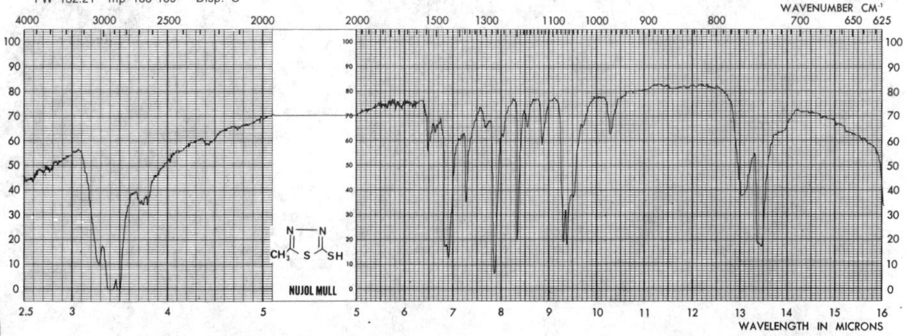

D12,900-3 2,5-Dimercapto-1,3,4-thiadiazole (bismuththiol I, 1,3,4-thiadiazole-2,5-dithiol)
M.W. 150.24 m.p. 162° ....

NUJOL MULL

F

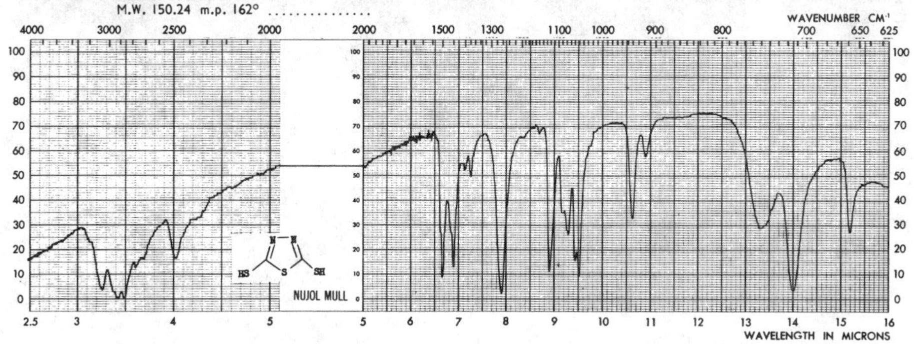

13,943-2 2,5-Dimercapto-1,3,4-thiadiazole (bismuththiol I, 1,3,4-thiadiazole-2,5-dithiol), dipotassium salt
M.W. 226.43
m.p. 274-276° (dec.) ....

NUJOL MULL

G

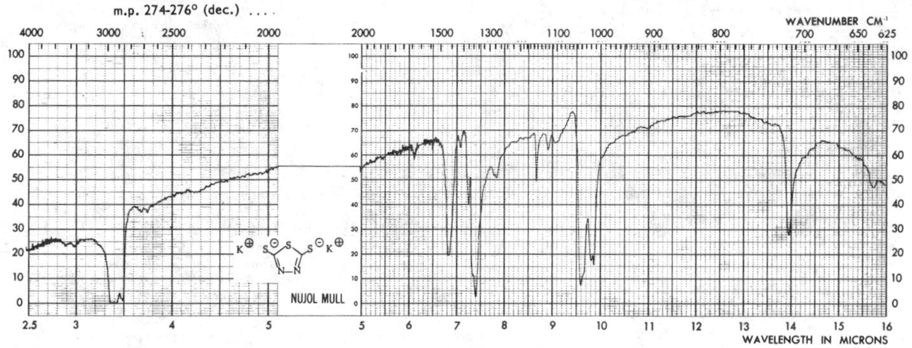

10,089-7 2,5-Bis-(methylthio)-1,3,4-thiadiazole, tech.
M.W. 178.30 n_D^{20} 1.6602 b.p. 200-202° ...

NEAT

H

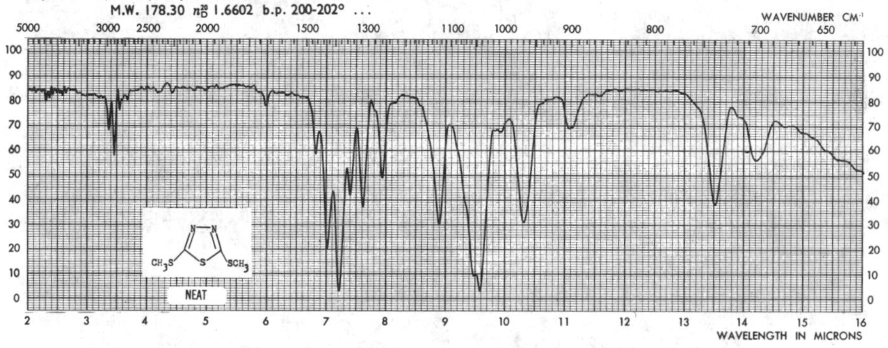

E1150-1 2-Ethylamino-1,3,4-thiadiazole hydrochloride
M.W. 165.66 m.p. 213-215.5° ....

NUJOL MULL

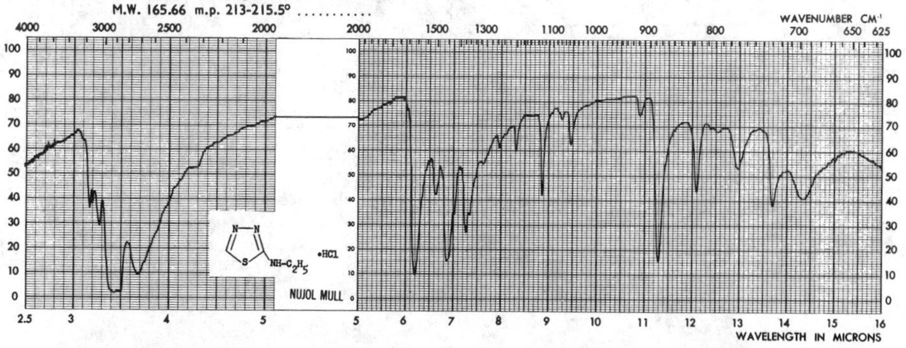

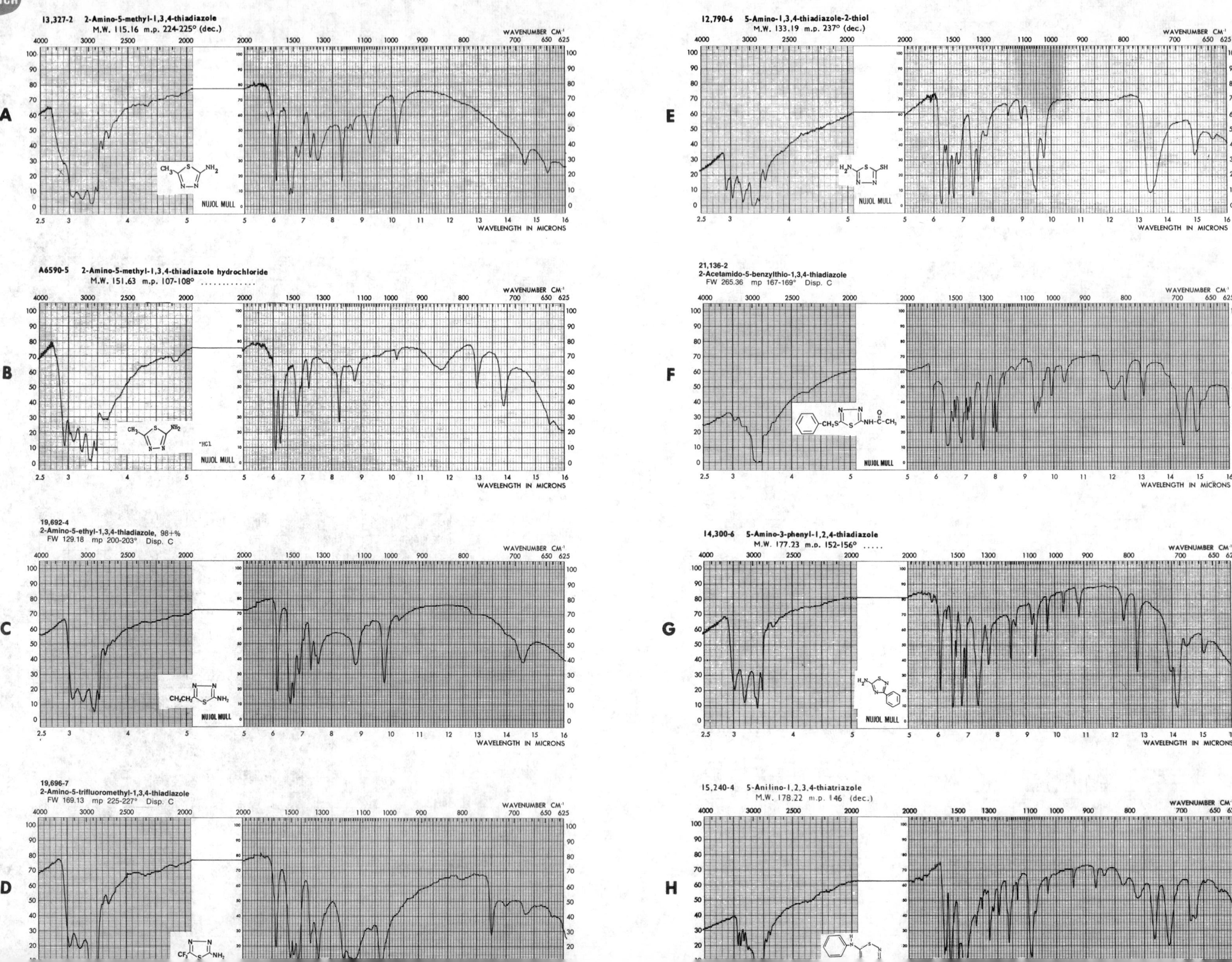
ALDRICH

A
13,327-2 2-Amino-5-methyl-1,3,4-thiadiazole
M.W. 115.16 m.p. 224-225° (dec.)
NUJOL MULL

B
A6590-5 2-Amino-5-methyl-1,3,4-thiadiazole hydrochloride
M.W. 151.63 m.p. 107-108°
·HCl
NUJOL MULL

C
19,692-4
2-Amino-5-ethyl-1,3,4-thiadiazole, 98+%
FW 129.18 mp 200-203° Disp. C
NUJOL MULL

D
19,696-7
2-Amino-5-trifluoromethyl-1,3,4-thiadiazole
FW 169.13 mp 225-227° Disp. C

E
12,790-6 5-Amino-1,3,4-thiadiazole-2-thiol
M.W. 133.19 m.p. 237° (dec.)
NUJOL MULL

F
21,136-2
2-Acetamido-5-benzylthio-1,3,4-thiadiazole
FW 265.36 mp 167-169° Disp. C
NUJOL MULL

G
14,300-6 5-Amino-3-phenyl-1,2,4-thiadiazole
M.W. 177.23 m.p. 152-156°
NUJOL MULL

H
15,240-4 5-Anilino-1,2,3,4-thiatriazole
M.W. 178.22 m.p. 146 (dec.)

WAVENUMBER CM⁻¹
WAVELENGTH IN MICRONS

A

[illegible]-ylamino)phenol
FW 194.22 mp 159° (dec.) Disp. C

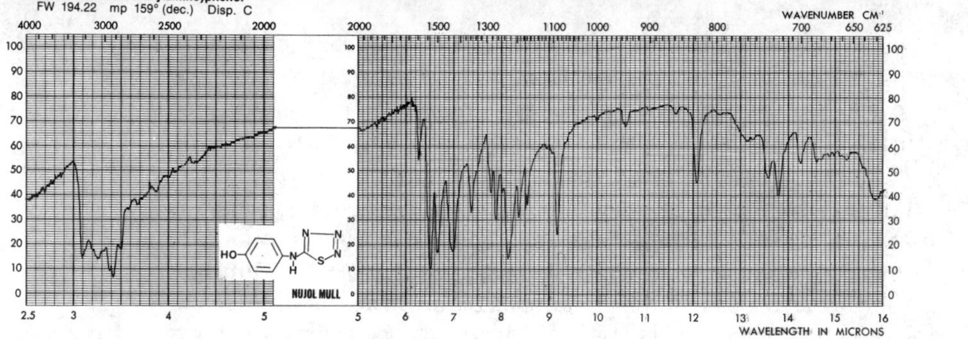

B

18,858-1
5-(1-Naphthylamino)-1,2,3,4-thiatriazole
FW 228.28 mp 134-136° (dec.) Disp. C

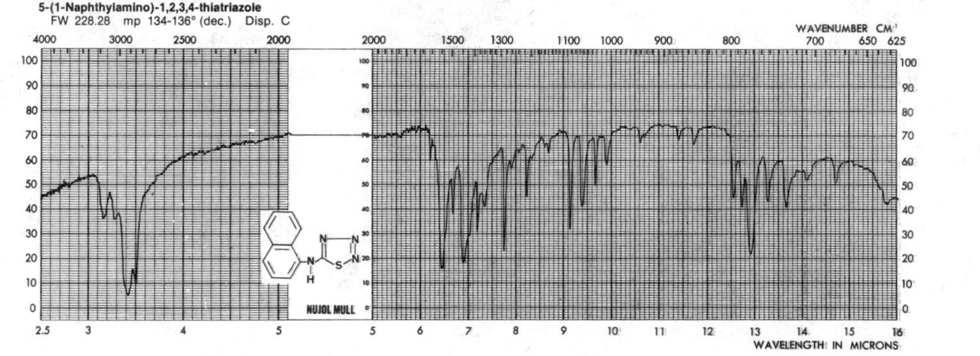

C

18,318-0
Tetrathiafulvalene, 97% (Δ2,2'-bi-1,3-dithiole, TTF)
FW 204.36 mp 120-123° Disp. C

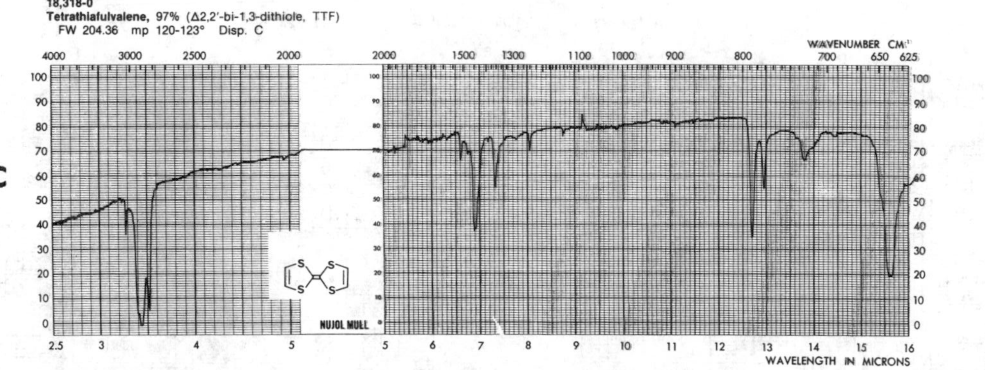

22,499-5
Methyl 2-methyl-3-furancarboxylate, 99%
FW 140.14 bp 75°/20mm. n_D^{20} 1.4730 d 1.116
Disp. C

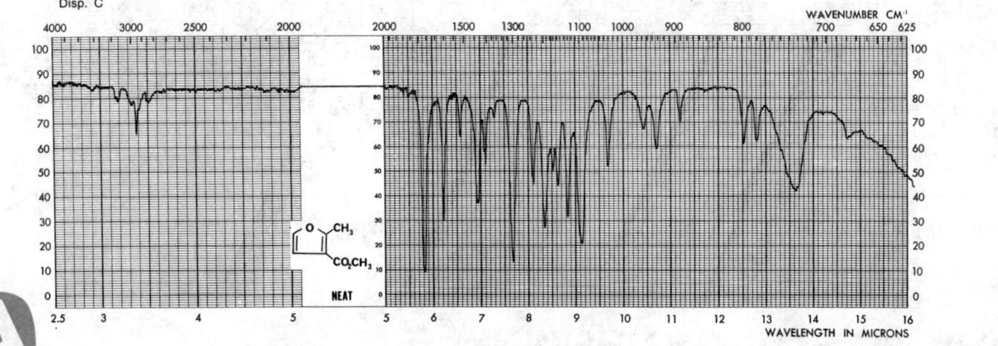

5-MEMBERED FUSED AROMATIC HETEROCYCLES

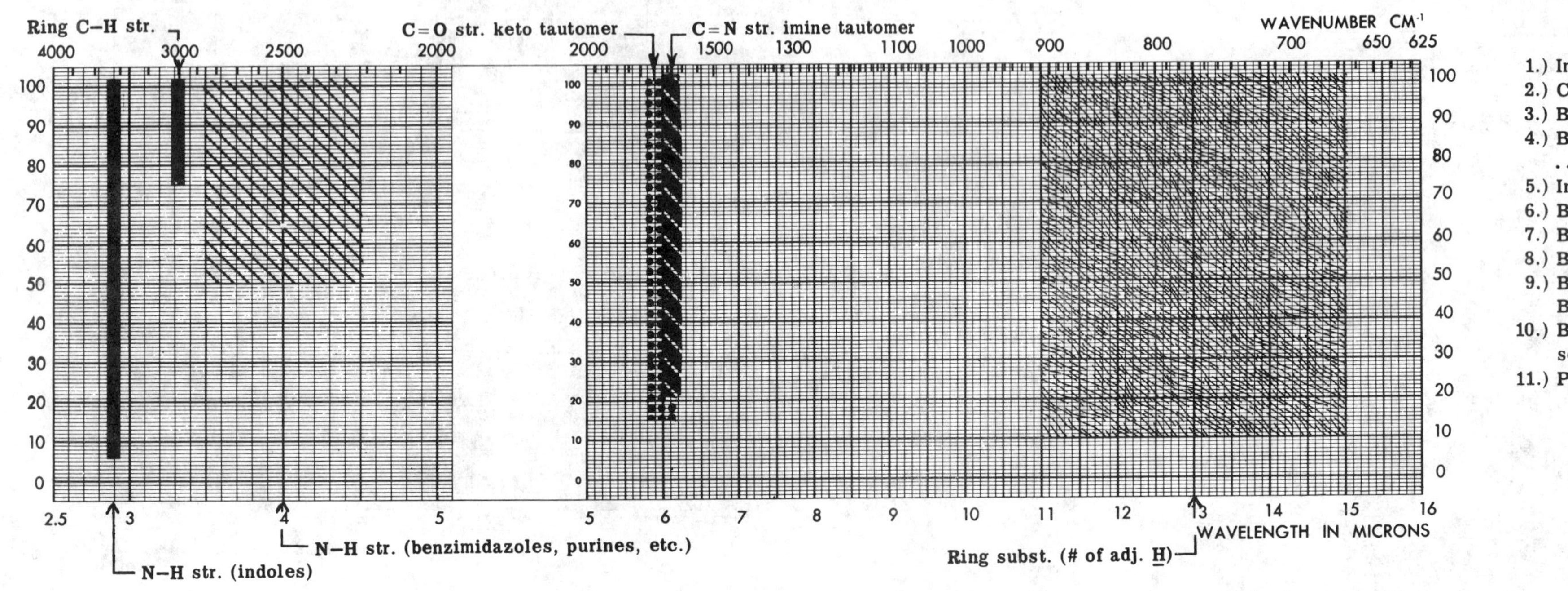

Fused aromatic heterocyclic rings retain, for the most part, their characteristic bands throughout the infrared spectrum. The substitution pattern between 11 and 15 μ (910 – 665 cm^{-1}) is subject to considerable disruption by the addition of a nitro or carbonyl group directly to the ring. A hydroxyl, amino or mercapto group on the carbon atom adjacent to a ring nitrogen atom results in the formation of the corresponding keto, imine or thione tautomer.

Indoles

The N–H stretch of the indole molecule is very strong near 2.9 μ (3450 cm^{-1}). The band is very similar in position and intensity to that seen in the spectra of various secondary anilines (spectra 714C—715A). The band is shifted and broadened considerably when an amino group is present in the molecule. (See spectra 1246F—1247C). When this amine is protonated (spectra 1247D, 1247F and 1248B), the NH absorbs near 3 μ (3335 cm^{-1}).

In two-ring fused heterocycles, the substitution pattern between 11 and 15 μ (910 – 665 cm^{-1}) reflects the presence of both ring systems. When the five-membered ring is unsubstituted, a band between 13.5 and 14 μ (740 – 715 cm^{-1}) is observed. The benzenoid portion of the molecule displays its characteristic absorptions for one, two, three or four consecutive hydrogen positions on the ring.

The infrared spectra of indoles are especially subject to variations due to crystalline modifications. Considerable shifts in band positions have been observed in different batches of the same indole. One such variation can be seen in spectra 1259E and F. In nujol comparison work, it is therefore necessary to prepare each specimen in the same way from the same solvent under identical conditions. Dissolving each sample in a volatile solvent followed by flash vaporization will usually produce the same crystalline form and subsequently, comparable spectra.

Benzofurans, Benzothiophenes

Benzofurans and benzothiophenes display the usual aromatic bands in the various regions of the infrared spectrum. In general, they follow the aromatic substitution patterns established in the aromatic carbocyclic sections. The carbon-oxygen band of the furan ring is not as outstanding as that of aromatic ethers.

Indazoles, Benzimidazoles, Benzotriazoles and Purines

In the indazole, benzimidazole, benzotriazole and purine spectra, where there are two or more nitrogen atoms, the hydrogen bonded N–H absorbs as a broad band between 3.5 and 4.5 μ (2855 – 2220 cm^{-1}). This NH stretch band is also present when tautomerism exists but is, of course, absent when the hydrogen is substituted (spectra 1268F and 1275C). Variations in this NH stretch absorption from compound to compound should be noted.

In the keto tautomeric form, the C=O stretch band is usually observed between 5.8 and 6.2 μ (1725 – 1615 cm^{-1}). The C=N stretch band occurs between 6 and 6.2 μ (1665 – 1615 cm^{-1}). The corresponding thione group, C=S, shows no significant bands

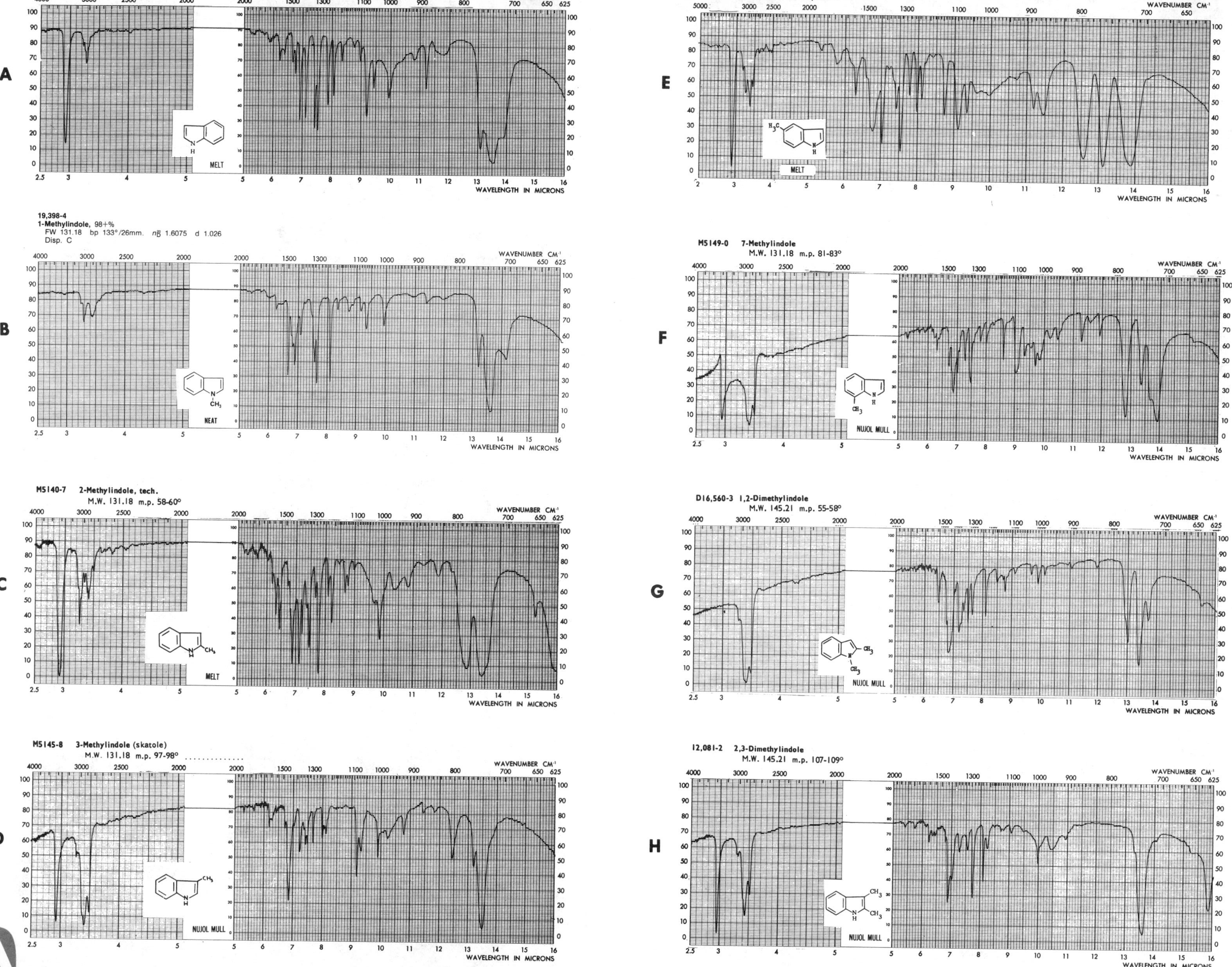
A
M.W. 117.15 m.p. 51.73°
MELT
19,398-4
1-Methylindole, 98+%
FW 131.18 bp 133°/26mm. n_D^{20} 1.6075 d 1.026
Disp. C
B
NEAT
M5140-7 2-Methylindole, tech.
M.W. 131.18 m.p. 58-60°
C
MELT
M5145-8 3-Methylindole (skatole)
M.W. 131.18 m.p. 97-98°
D
NUJOL MULL
M5147-4 5-Methylindole
M.W. 131.18 m.p. 59-60°
E
MELT
M5149-0 7-Methylindole
M.W. 131.18 m.p. 81-83°
F
NUJOL MULL
D16,560-3 1,2-Dimethylindole
M.W. 145.21 m.p. 55-58°
G
NUJOL MULL
12,081-2 2,3-Dimethylindole
M.W. 145.21 m.p. 107-109°
H
NUJOL MULL
WAVENUMBER CM⁻¹
WAVELENGTH IN MICRONS
ALDRICH

5 MEMBERED FUSED AROMATIC HETEROCYCLES

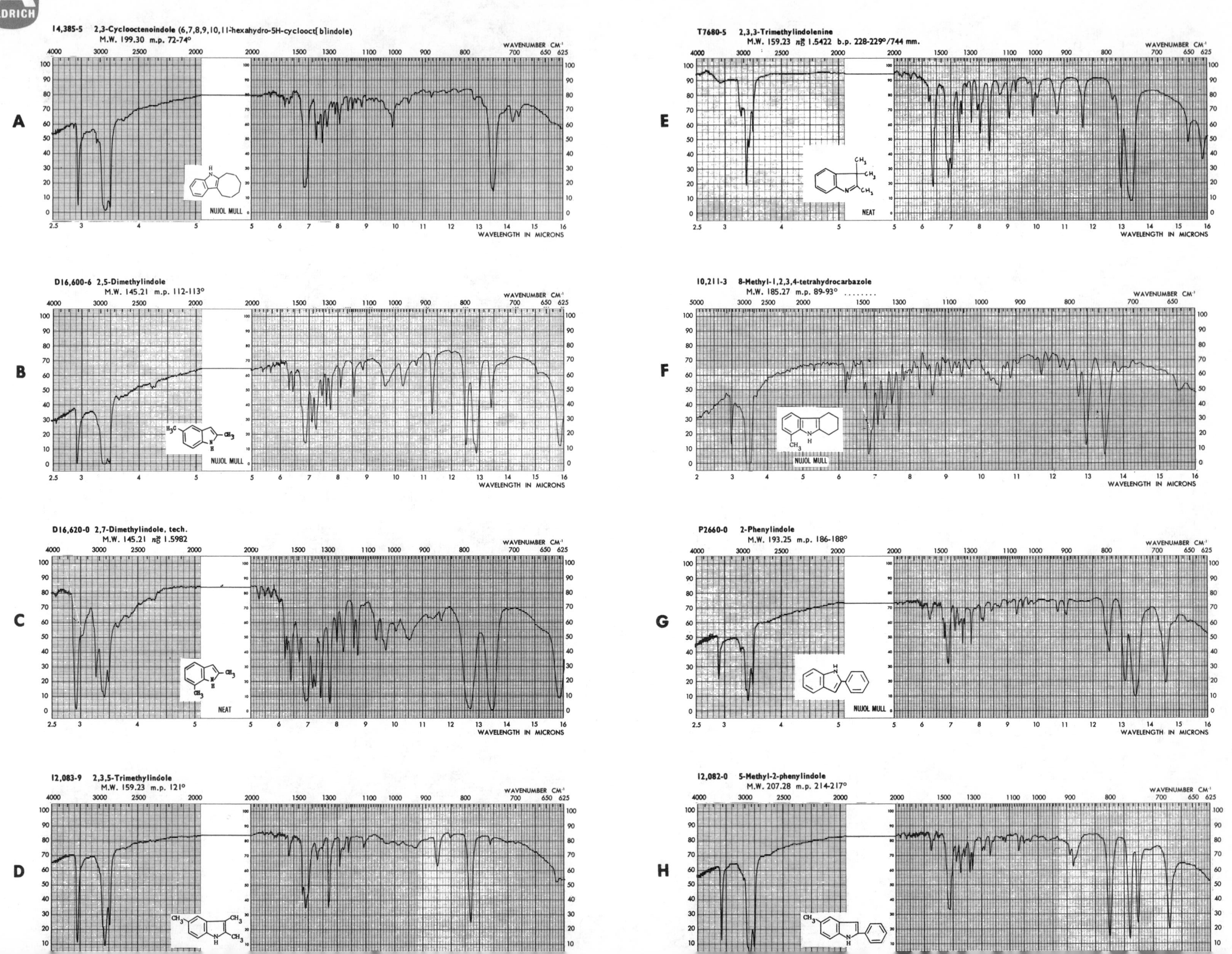
ALDRICH
A
14,385-5 2,3-Cyclooctenoindole (6,7,8,9,10,11-hexahydro-5H-cyclooct[b]indole)
M.W. 199.30 m.p. 72-74°
NUJOL MULL
B
D16,600-6 2,5-Dimethylindole
M.W. 145.21 m.p. 112-113°
NUJOL MULL
C
D16,620-0 2,7-Dimethylindole, tech.
M.W. 145.21 n_D^{20} 1.5982
NEAT
D
12,083-9 2,3,5-Trimethylindole
M.W. 159.23 m.p. 121°
E
T7680-5 2,3,3-Trimethylindolenine
M.W. 159.23 n_D^{20} 1.5422 b.p. 228-229°/744 mm.
NEAT
F
10,211-3 8-Methyl-1,2,3,4-tetrahydrocarbazole
M.W. 185.27 m.p. 89-93°
NUJOL MULL
G
P2660-0 2-Phenylindole
M.W. 193.25 m.p. 186-188°
NUJOL MULL
H
12,082-0 5-Methyl-2-phenylindole
M.W. 207.28 m.p. 214-217°
WAVENUMBER CM⁻¹
WAVELENGTH IN MICRONS

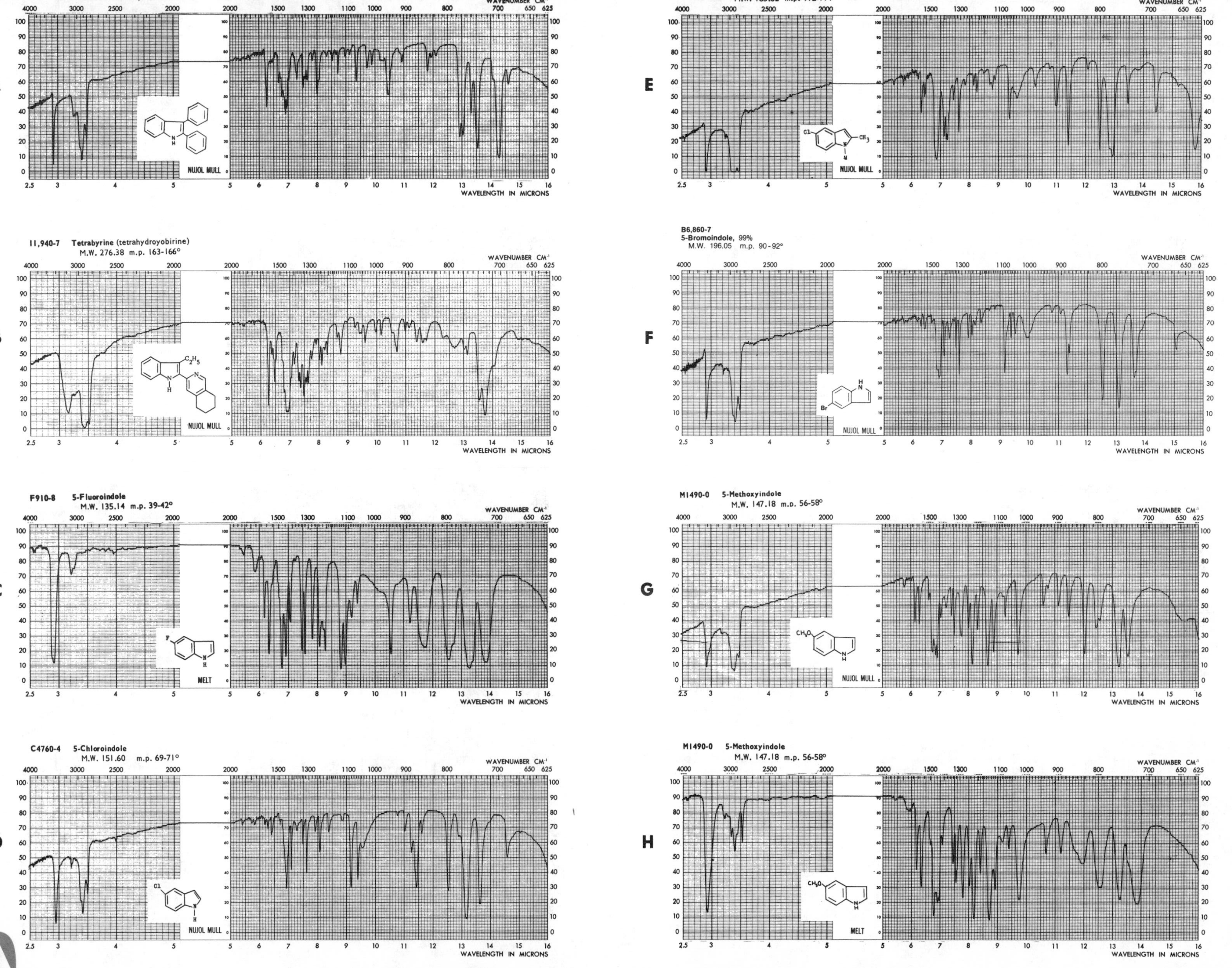

A
M.W. 269.35 m.p. 124-125°
NUJOL MULL
B
11,940-7 Tetrabyrine (tetrahydroyobirine)
M.W. 276.38 m.p. 163-166°
NUJOL MULL
C
F910-8 5-Fluoroindole
M.W. 135.14 m.p. 39-42°
MELT
D
C4760-4 5-Chloroindole
M.W. 151.60 m.p. 69-71°
NUJOL MULL
E
M.W. 165.62 m.p. 112-114°
NUJOL MULL
F
B6,860-7
5-Bromoindole, 99%
M.W. 196.05 m.p. 90-92°
NUJOL MULL
G
M1490-0 5-Methoxyindole
M.W. 147.18 m.p. 56-58°
NUJOL MULL
H
M1490-0 5-Methoxyindole
M.W. 147.18 m.p. 56-58°
MELT
WAVENUMBER CM⁻¹
WAVELENGTH IN MICRONS
ALDRICH

5 MEMBERED FUSED AROMATIC HETEROCYCLES

A 13,985-8 **6-Methoxyindole**
M.W. 147.18 m.p. 90-92°
NUJOL MULL

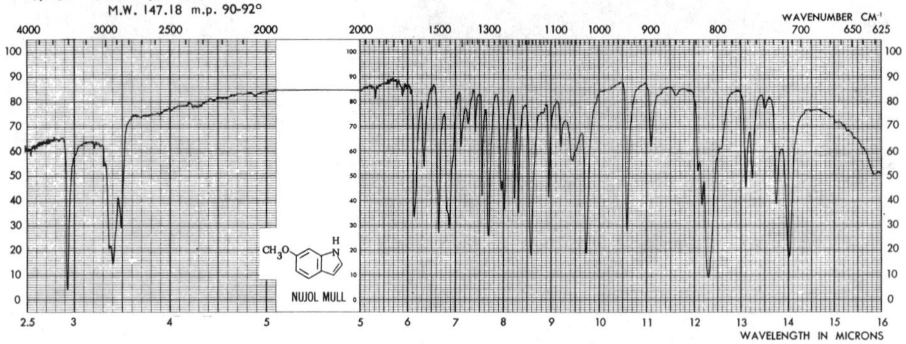

B 11,398-0 **7-Methoxyindole**
M.W. 147.18 n_D^{20} 1.6113
NEAT

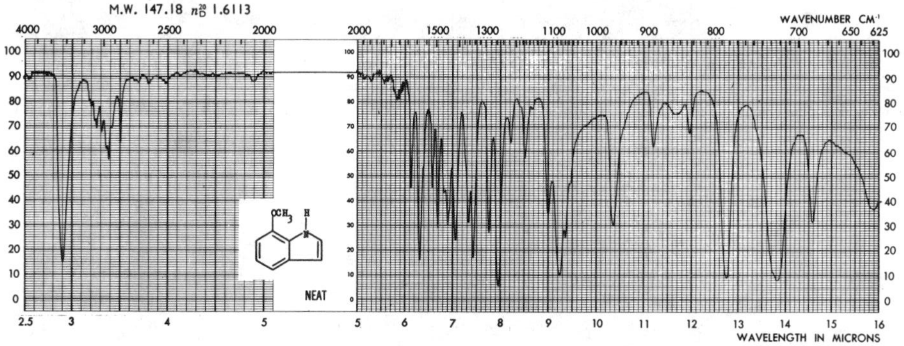

C M1545-1 **5-Methoxy-2-methylindole**
M.W. 161.20 m.p. 86-88°
NUJOL MULL

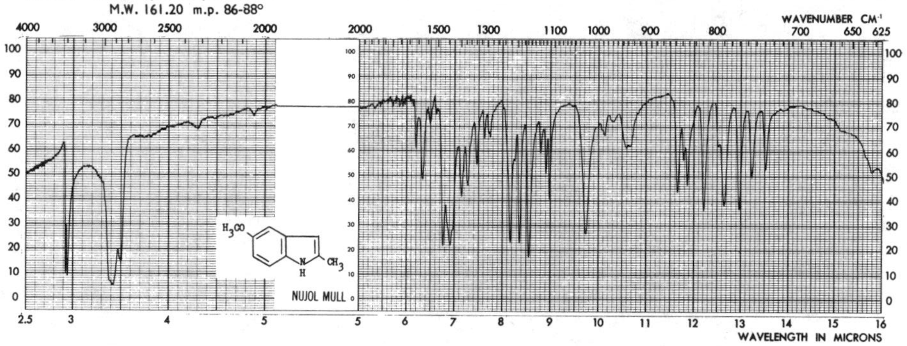

D 22,239-9
5,6-(Methylenedioxy)indole, 99%
FW 161.16 mp 109-110° Disp. C

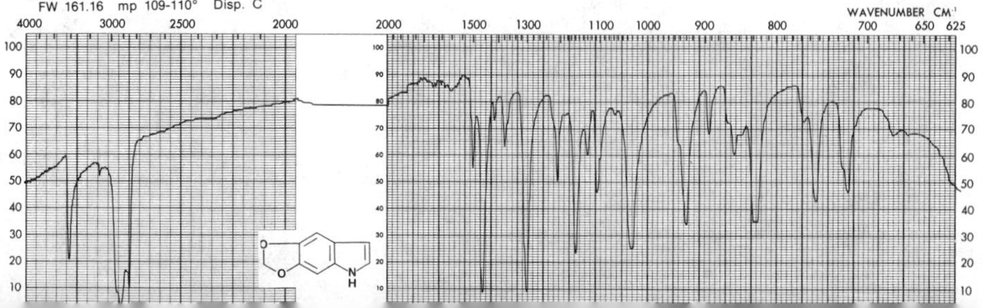

E B2780-3 **5-Benzyloxyindole**
M.W. 223.28 m.p. 108-111°
NUJOL MULL

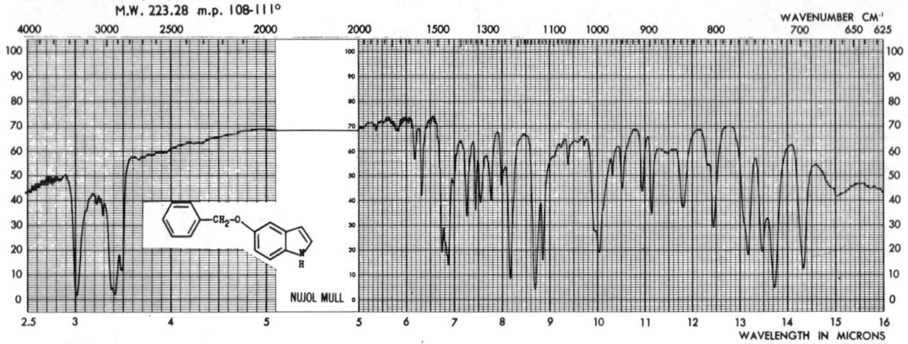

F 85,908-7
N-Acetyl-5-bromoindolyl-β-D-glucosaminide
(3-[(2-acetamido-2-deoxy-β-D-glucopyranosyl)oxy]-5-bromoindole)
M.W. 415.25 m.p. >300°
NUJOL MULL

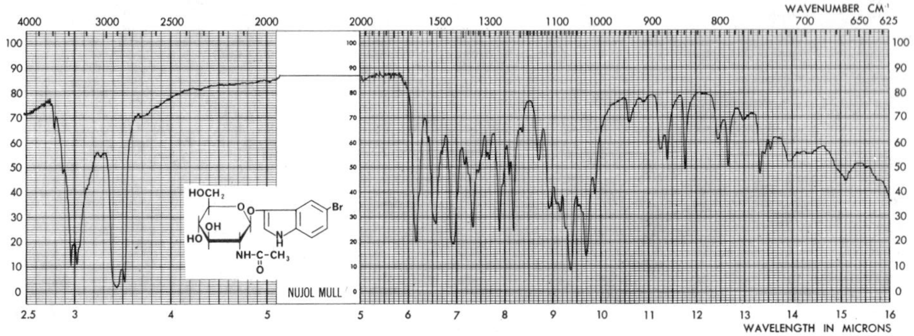

G 85,721-1
5-Bromo-4-chloro-3-indolyl-β-D-galactoside
M.W. 408.64 m.p. 230° (dec.)
NUJOL MULL

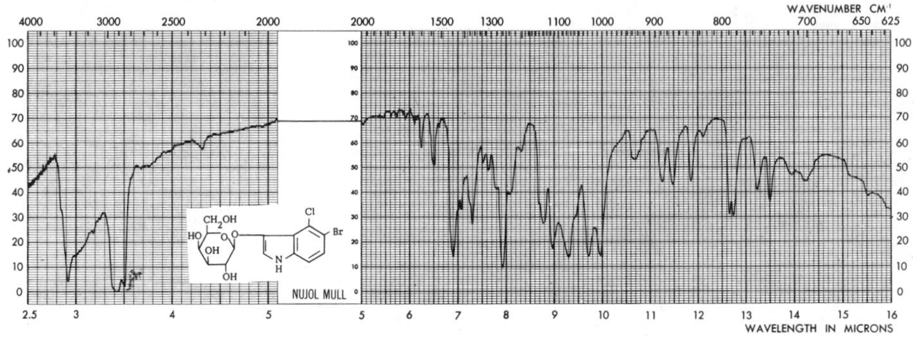

H I-400-5 **Indole-3-carbinol** (3-indolemethanol)
M.W. 147.18 m.p. 96-99°

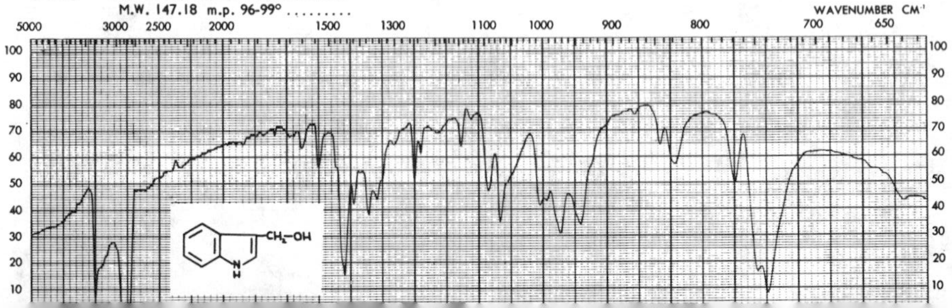

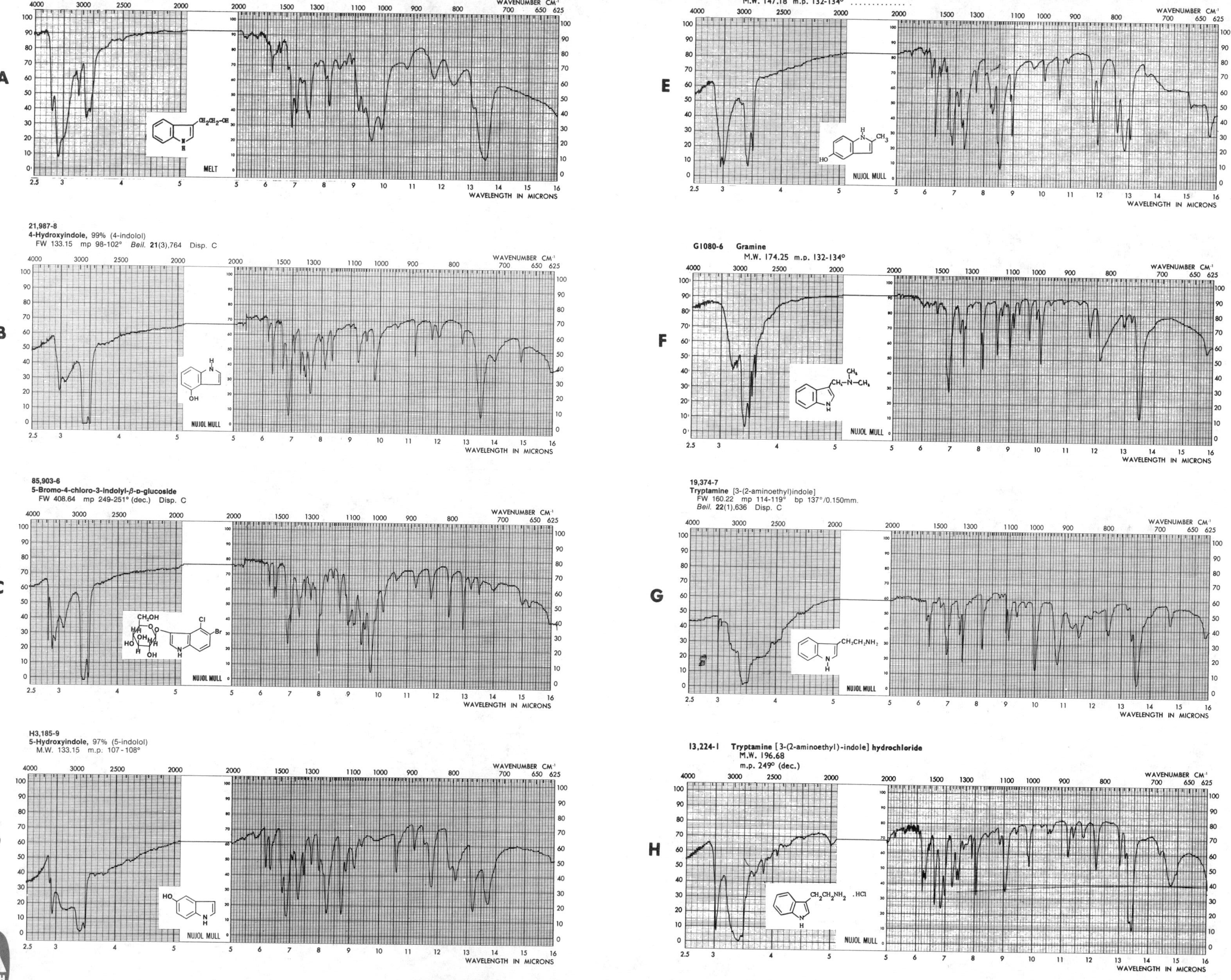
A
T9030-1 Tryptophol (β-3-indolylethanol)
M.W. 161.20 m.p. 57-60°
MELT
B
21,987-8
4-Hydroxyindole, 99% (4-indolol)
FW 133.15 mp 98-102° Beil. 21(3),764 Disp. C
NUJOL MULL
C
85,903-6
5-Bromo-4-chloro-3-indolyl-β-D-glucoside
FW 408.64 mp 249-251° (dec.) Disp. C
NUJOL MULL
D
H3,185-9
5-Hydroxyindole, 97% (5-indolol)
M.W. 133.15 m.p. 107-108°
NUJOL MULL
E
12,187-8 5-Hydroxy-2-methylindole (2-methyl-5-indolol)
M.W. 147.18 m.p. 132-134°
NUJOL MULL
F
G1080-6 Gramine
M.W. 174.25 m.p. 132-134°
NUJOL MULL
G
19,374-7
Tryptamine [3-(2-aminoethyl)indole]
FW 160.22 mp 114-119° bp 137°/0.150mm.
Beil. 22(1),636 Disp. C
NUJOL MULL
H
13,224-1 Tryptamine [3-(2-aminoethyl)-indole] hydrochloride
M.W. 196.68
m.p. 249° (dec.)
NUJOL MULL
WAVENUMBER CM⁻¹
WAVELENGTH IN MICRONS
ALDRICH

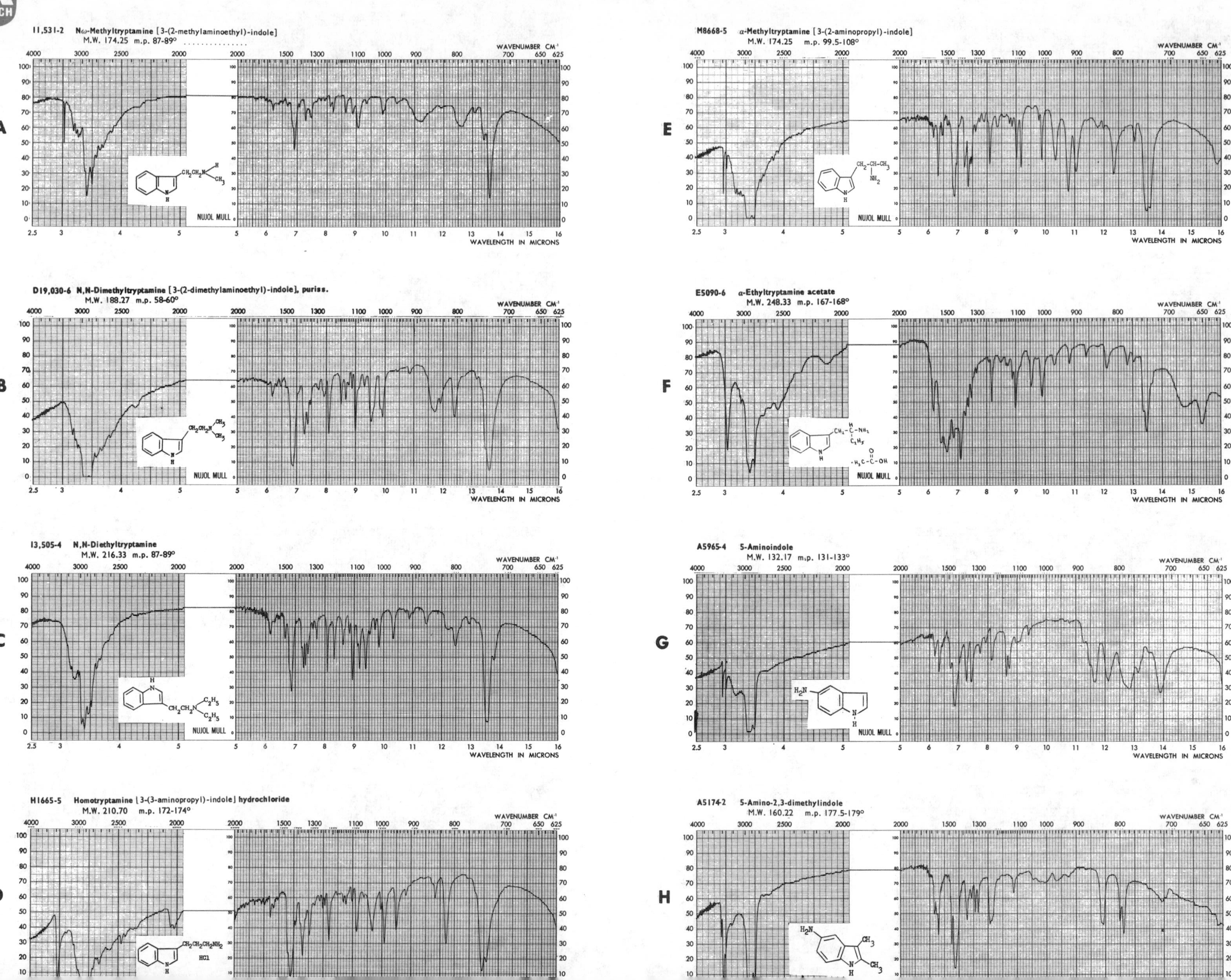
ALDRICH
A
11,531-2 Nω-Methyltryptamine [3-(2-methylaminoethyl)-indole]
M.W. 174.25 m.p. 87-89°
NUJOL MULL
B
D19,030-6 N,N-Dimethyltryptamine [3-(2-dimethylaminoethyl)-indole], puriss.
M.W. 188.27 m.p. 58-60°
NUJOL MULL
C
13,505-4 N,N-Diethyltryptamine
M.W. 216.33 m.p. 87-89°
NUJOL MULL
D
H1665-5 Homotryptamine [3-(3-aminopropyl)-indole] hydrochloride
M.W. 210.70 m.p. 172-174°
HCl
E
M8668-5 α-Methyltryptamine [3-(2-aminopropyl)-indole]
M.W. 174.25 m.p. 99.5-108°
NUJOL MULL
F
E5090-6 α-Ethyltryptamine acetate
M.W. 248.33 m.p. 167-168°
NUJOL MULL
G
A5965-4 5-Aminoindole
M.W. 132.17 m.p. 131-133°
NUJOL MULL
H
A5174-2 5-Amino-2,3-dimethylindole
M.W. 160.22 m.p. 177.5-179°
WAVENUMBER CM⁻¹
WAVELENGTH IN MICRONS

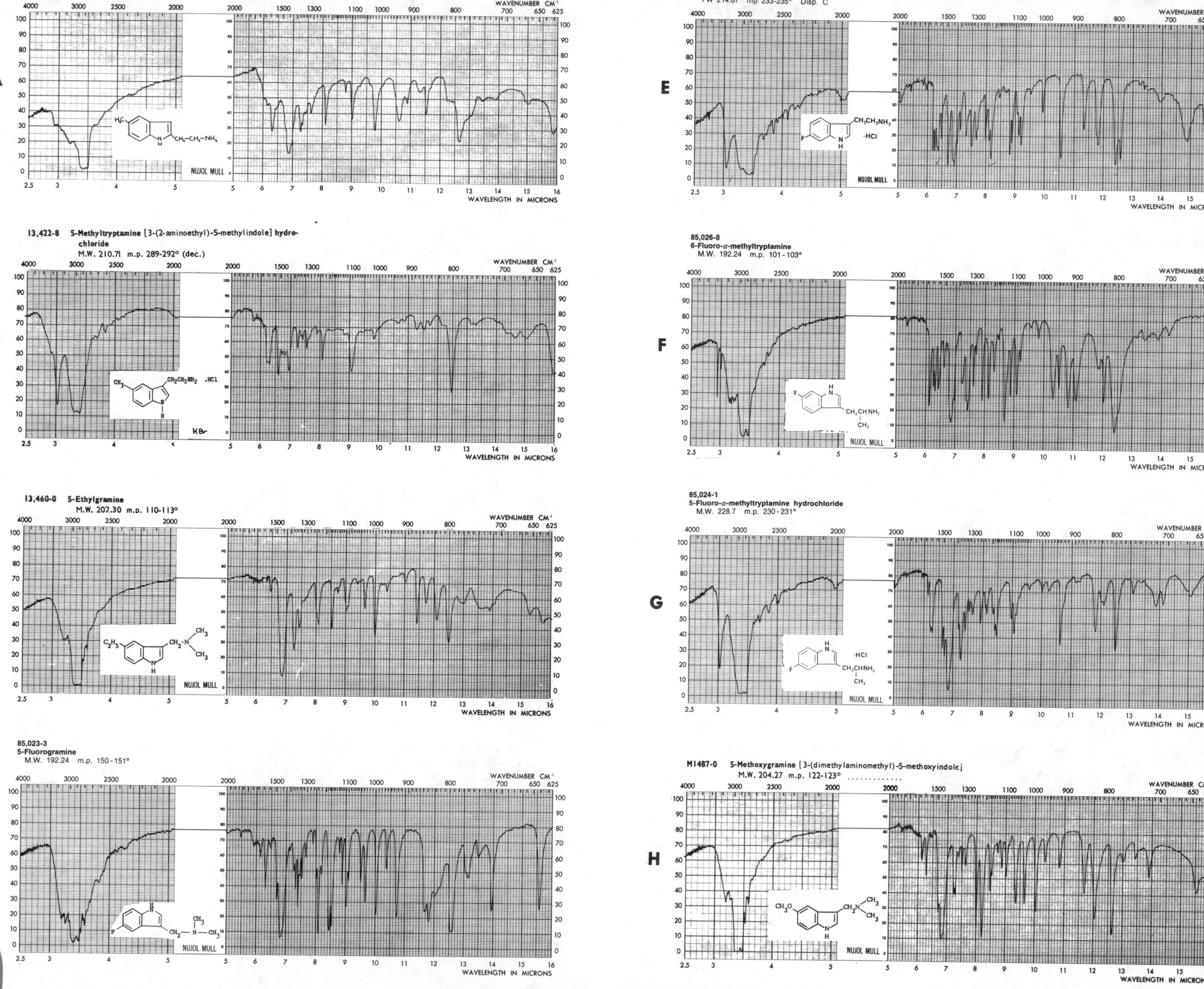
A
M8670-7 5-Methyltryptamine [3-(2-aminoethyl)-5-methylindole], tech.
M.W. 174.25
NUJOL MULL
B
13,422-8 5-Methyltryptamine [3-(2-aminoethyl)-5-methylindole] hydrochloride
M.W. 210.71 m.p. 289-292° (dec.)
KBr
C
13,460-0 5-Ethylgramine
M.W. 202.30 m.p. 110-113°
NUJOL MULL
D
85,023-3
5-Fluorogramine
M.W. 192.24 m.p. 150-151°
NUJOL MULL
E
6-Fluorotryptamine hydrochloride, 99%
FW 214.67 mp 233-235° Disp. C
NUJOL MULL
F
85,026-8
6-Fluoro-α-methyltryptamine
M.W. 192.24 m.p. 101-103°
NUJOL MULL
G
85,024-1
5-Fluoro-α-methyltryptamine hydrochloride
M.W. 228.7 m.p. 230-231°
NUJOL MULL
H
M1487-0 5-Methoxygramine [3-(dimethylaminomethyl)-5-methoxyindole]
M.W. 204.27 m.p. 122-123°
NUJOL MULL
WAVENUMBER CM⁻¹
WAVELENGTH IN MICRONS
ALDRICH

5 MEMBERED FUSED AROMATIC HETEROCYCLES

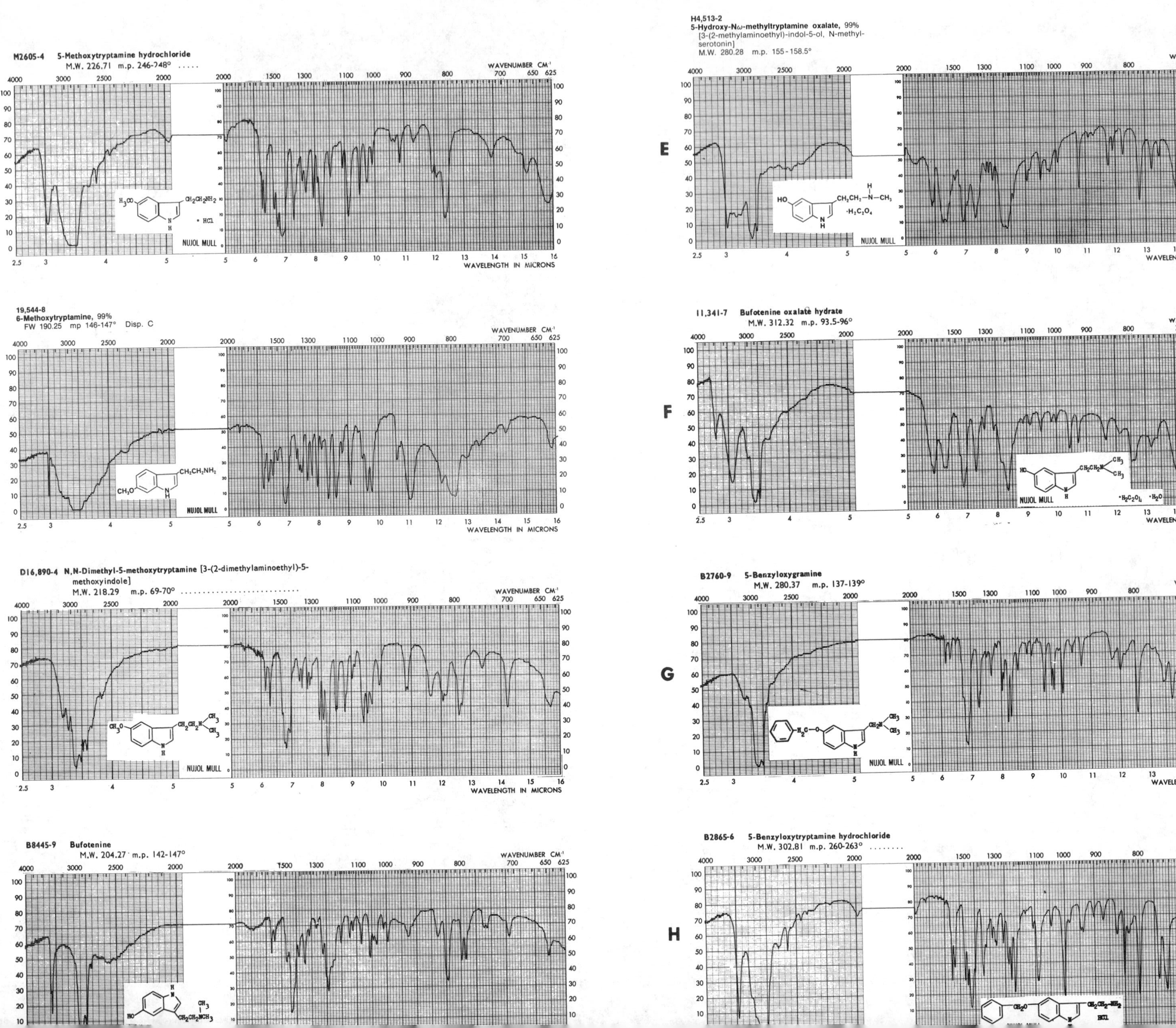
ALDRICH
A
M2605-4 5-Methoxytryptamine hydrochloride
M.W. 226.71 m.p. 246-248°
NUJOL MULL
B
19,544-8
6-Methoxytryptamine, 99%
FW 190.25 mp 146-147° Disp. C
NUJOL MULL
C
D16,890-4 N,N-Dimethyl-5-methoxytryptamine [3-(2-dimethylaminoethyl)-5-methoxyindole]
M.W. 218.29 m.p. 69-70°
NUJOL MULL
D
B8445-9 Bufotenine
M.W. 204.27 m.p. 142-147°
E
H4,513-2
5-Hydroxy-Nω-methyltryptamine oxalate, 99%
[3-(2-methylaminoethyl)-indol-5-ol, N-methylserotonin]
M.W. 280.28 m.p. 155-158.5°
NUJOL MULL
F
11,341-7 Bufotenine oxalate hydrate
M.W. 312.32 m.p. 93.5-96°
NUJOL MULL
G
B2760-9 5-Benzyloxygramine
M.W. 280.37 m.p. 137-139°
NUJOL MULL
H
B2865-6 5-Benzyloxytryptamine hydrochloride
M.W. 302.81 m.p. 260-263°
WAVENUMBER CM⁻¹
WAVELENGTH IN MICRONS

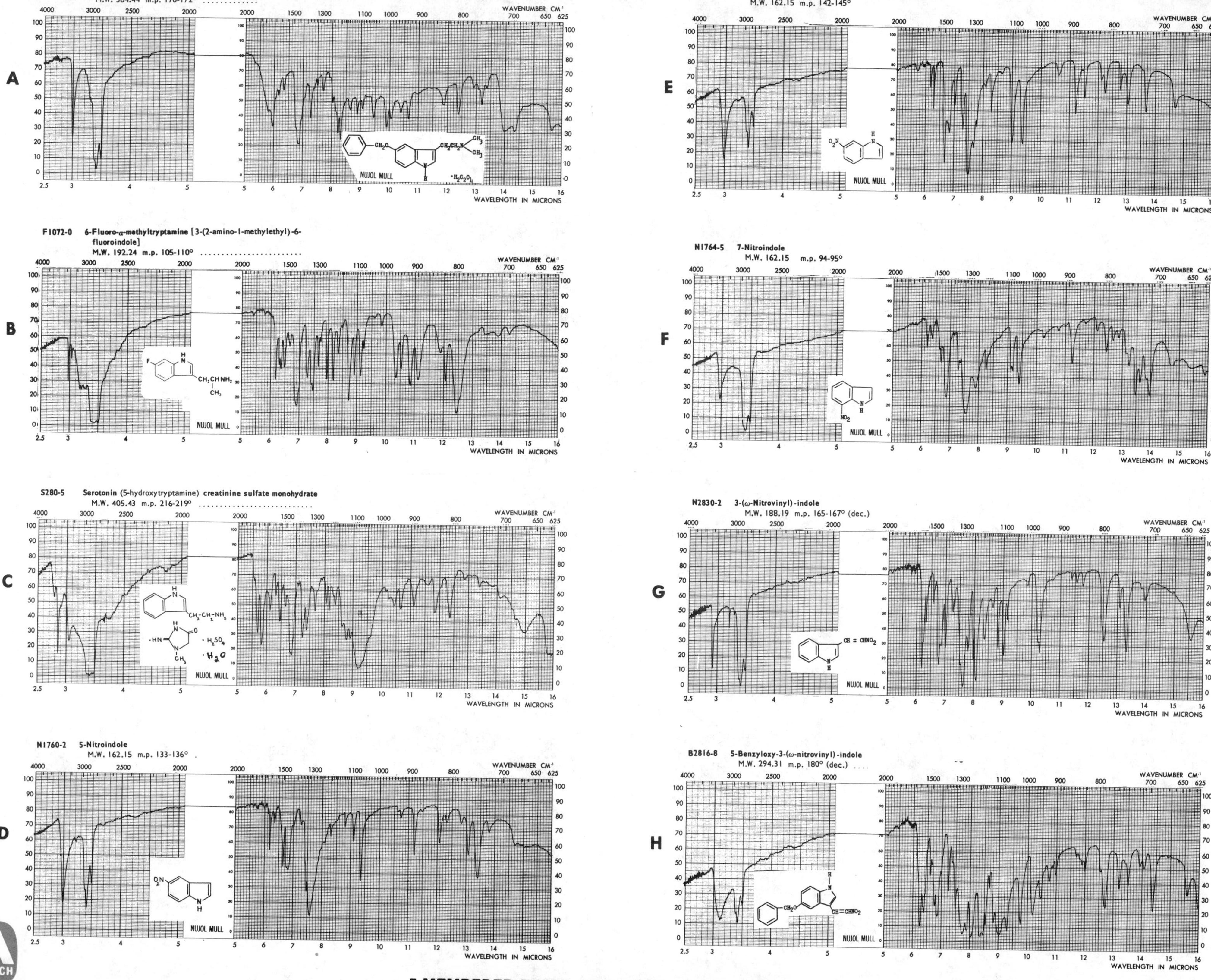

A 11,533-9 5-Benzyloxy-N,N-dimethyltryptamine oxalate
M.W. 384.44 m.p. 170-172°

B F1072-0 6-Fluoro-α-methyltryptamine [3-(2-amino-1-methylethyl)-6-fluoroindole]
M.W. 192.24 m.p. 105-110°

C S280-5 Serotonin (5-hydroxytryptamine) creatinine sulfate monohydrate
M.W. 405.43 m.p. 216-219°

D N1760-2 5-Nitroindole
M.W. 162.15 m.p. 133-136°

E N1763-7 6-Nitroindole
M.W. 162.15 m.p. 142-145°

F N1764-5 7-Nitroindole
M.W. 162.15 m.p. 94-95°

G N2830-2 3-(ω-Nitrovinyl)-indole
M.W. 188.19 m.p. 165-167° (dec.)

H B2816-8 5-Benzyloxy-3-(ω-nitrovinyl)-indole
M.W. 294.31 m.p. 180° (dec.)

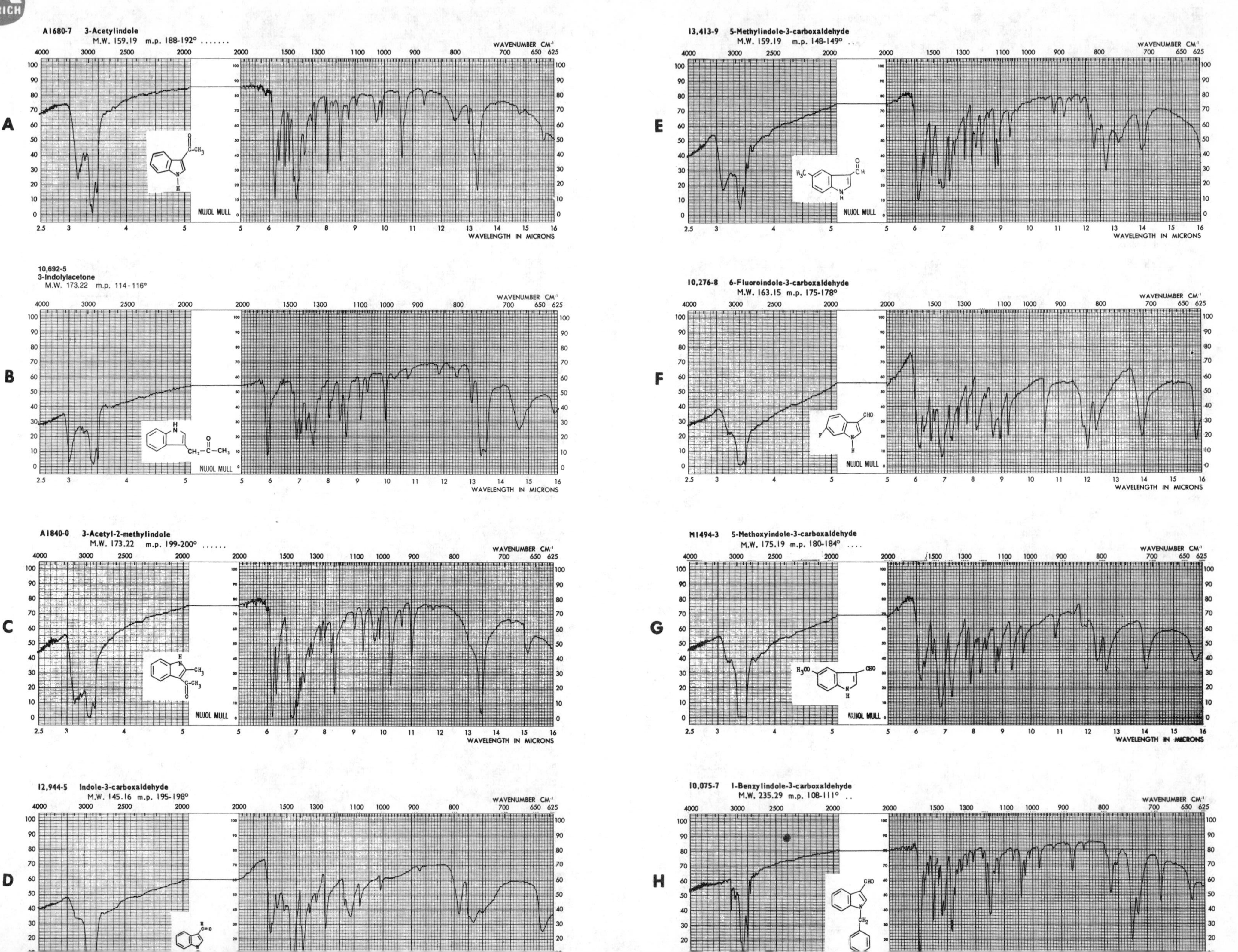
ALDRICH
A
A1680-7 3-Acetylindole
M.W. 159.19 m.p. 188-192°
B
10,692-5
3-Indolylacetone
M.W. 173.22 m.p. 114-116°
C
A1840-0 3-Acetyl-2-methylindole
M.W. 173.22 m.p. 199-200°
D
12,944-5 Indole-3-carboxaldehyde
M.W. 145.16 m.p. 195-198°
E
13,413-9 5-Methylindole-3-carboxaldehyde
M.W. 159.19 m.p. 148-149°
F
10,276-8 6-Fluoroindole-3-carboxaldehyde
M.W. 163.15 m.p. 175-178°
G
M1494-3 5-Methoxyindole-3-carboxaldehyde
M.W. 175.19 m.p. 180-184°
H
10,075-7 1-Benzylindole-3-carboxaldehyde
M.W. 235.29 m.p. 108-111°
NUJOL MULL
WAVENUMBER CM⁻¹
WAVELENGTH IN MICRONS

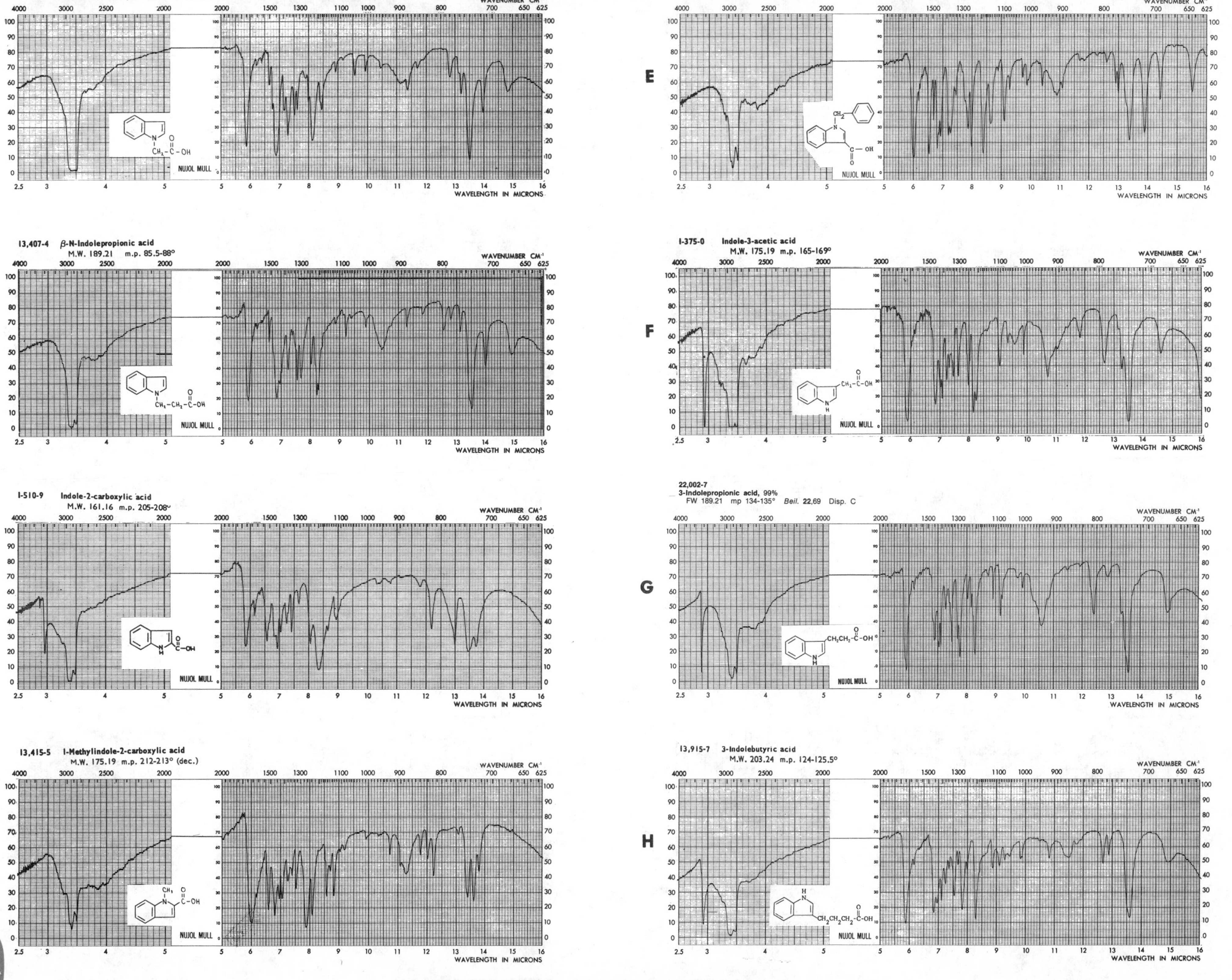
A
M.W. 175.19 m.p. 175-178°
B
13,407-4 β-N-Indolepropionic acid
M.W. 189.21 m.p. 85.5-88°
C
I-510-9 Indole-2-carboxylic acid
M.W. 161.16 m.p. 205-208°
D
13,415-5 1-Methylindole-2-carboxylic acid
M.W. 175.19 m.p. 212-213° (dec.)
E
F
I-375-0 Indole-3-acetic acid
M.W. 175.19 m.p. 165-169°
G
22,002-7
3-Indolepropionic acid, 99%
FW 189.21 mp 134-135° Beil. 22,69 Disp. C
H
13,915-7 3-Indolebutyric acid
M.W. 203.24 m.p. 124-125.5°
NUJOL MULL
WAVENUMBER CM⁻¹
WAVELENGTH IN MICRONS
ALDRICH

5 MEMBERED FUSED AROMATIC HETEROCYCLES

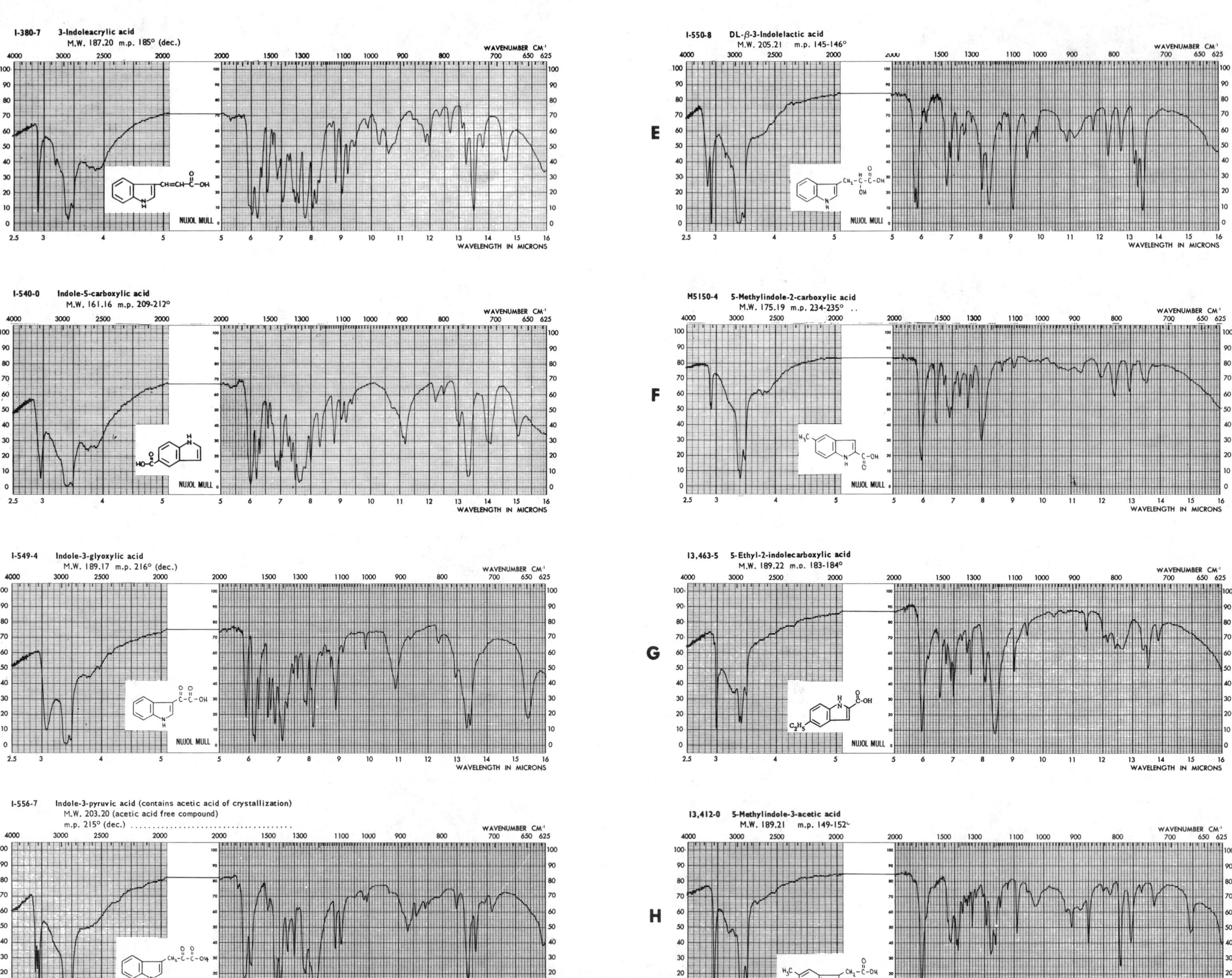
ALDRICH
A
I-380-7 3-Indoleacrylic acid
M.W. 187.20 m.p. 185° (dec.)
NUJOL MULL
B
I-540-0 Indole-5-carboxylic acid
M.W. 161.16 m.p. 209-212°
NUJOL MULL
C
I-549-4 Indole-3-glyoxylic acid
M.W. 189.17 m.p. 216° (dec.)
NUJOL MULL
D
I-556-7 Indole-3-pyruvic acid (contains acetic acid of crystallization)
M.W. 203.20 (acetic acid free compound)
m.p. 215° (dec.)
E
I-550-8 DL-β-3-Indolelactic acid
M.W. 205.21 m.p. 145-146°
NUJOL MULL
F
M5150-4 5-Methylindole-2-carboxylic acid
M.W. 175.19 m.p. 234-235°
NUJOL MULL
G
13,463-5 5-Ethyl-2-indolecarboxylic acid
M.W. 189.22 m.p. 183-184°
NUJOL MULL
H
13,412-0 5-Methylindole-3-acetic acid
M.W. 189.21 m.p. 149-152°
WAVENUMBER CM⁻¹
WAVELENGTH IN MICRONS

A

M.W. 203.24 m.p. 130-132°

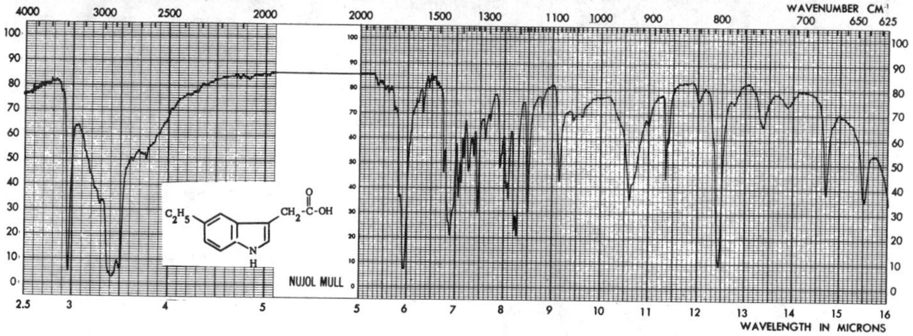

NUJOL MULL

B

F915-9 5-Fluoroindole-3-acetic acid
M.W. 193.17 m.p. 139-140°

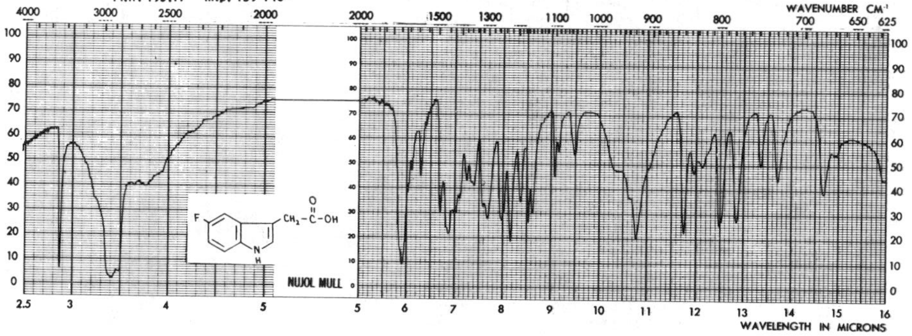

NUJOL MULL

C

13,461-9 5-Chloro-2-methyl-3-indoleacetic acid
M.W. 223.66 m.p. 192-194° ....

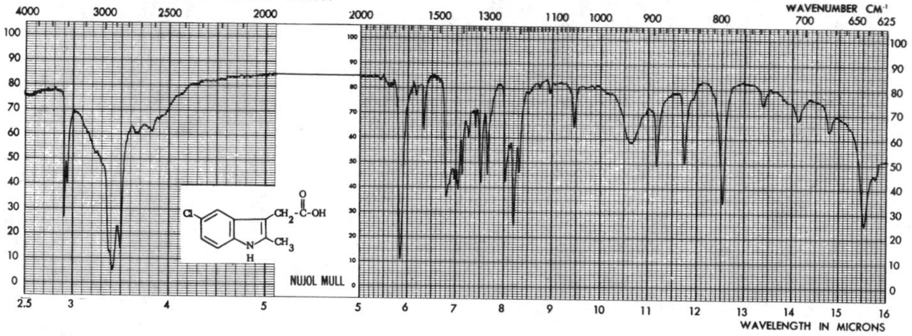

NUJOL MULL

D

C4780-9 5-Chloroindole-2-carboxylic acid, tech.
M.W. 195.61 m.p. 287° (dec.) .....

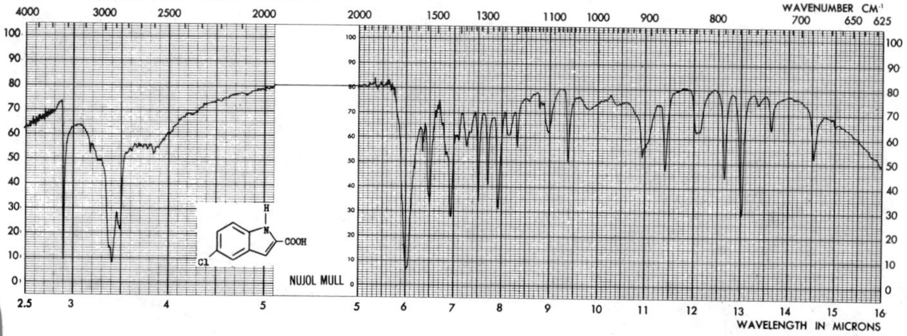

NUJOL MULL

E

B6885-2 5-Bromoindole-2-carboxylic acid
M.W. 240.06 m.p. 280-281° (dec.)

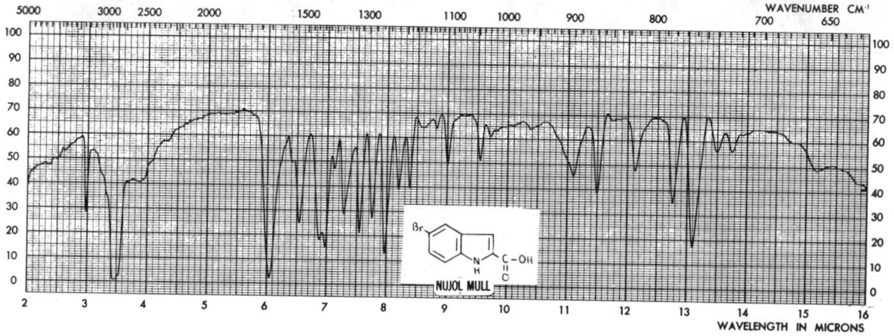

NUJOL MULL

F

B6872-0 5-Bromoindole-3-acetic acid
M.W. 254.10 m.p. 143-145°

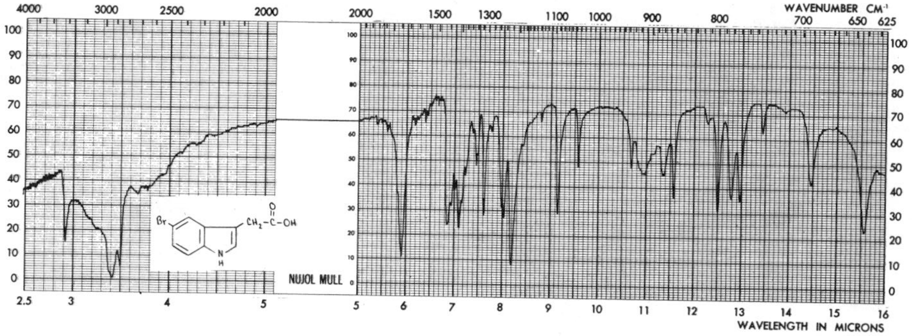

NUJOL MULL

G

M1495-1 5-Methoxyindole-2-carboxylic acid
M.W. 191.19 m.p. 196-198° ....

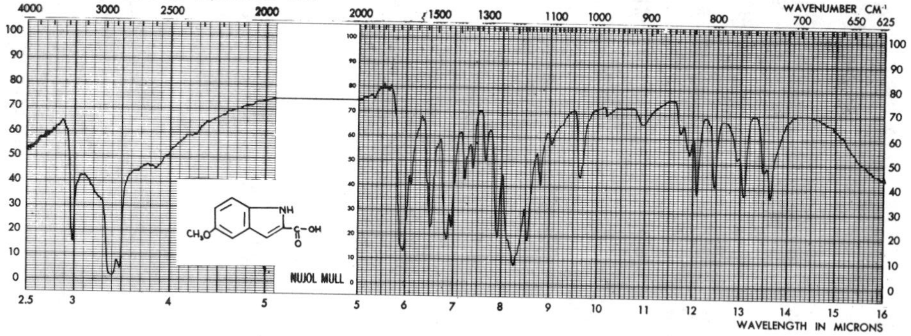

NUJOL MULL

H

M1493-5 5-Methoxyindole-3-acetic acid
M.W. 205.21 m.p. 148-151°

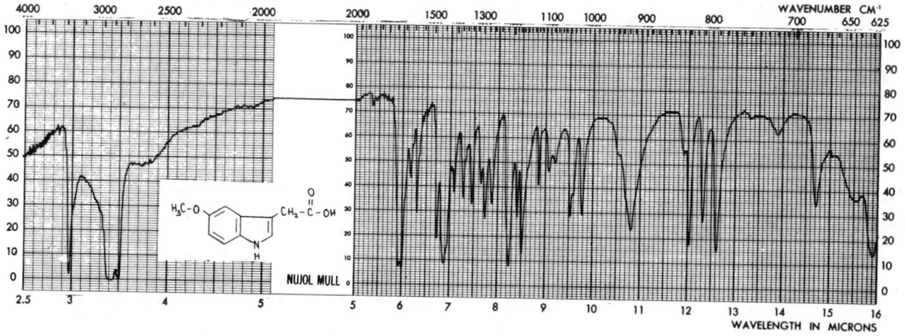

NUJOL MULL

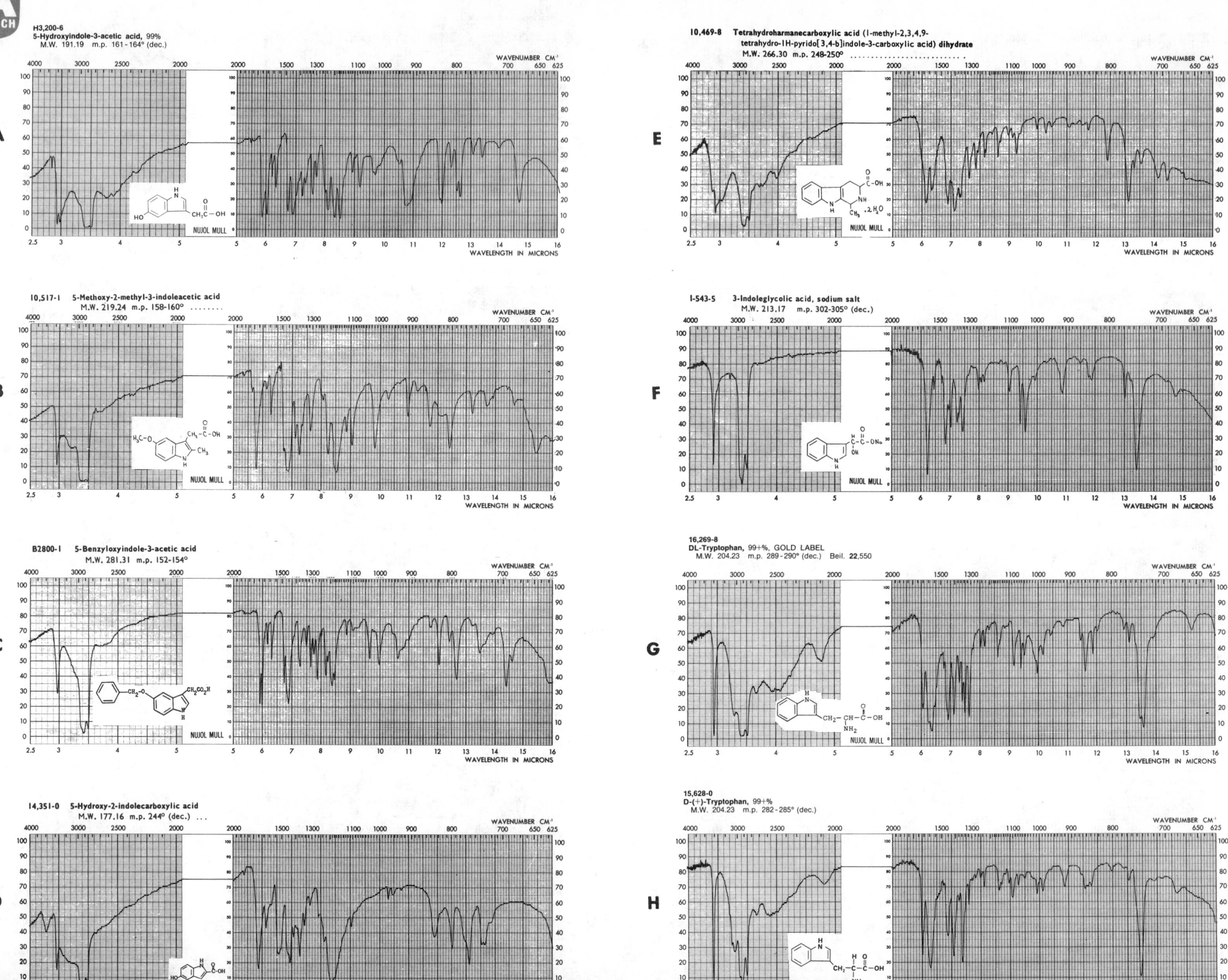
ALDRICH
A
H3,200-6
5-Hydroxyindole-3-acetic acid, 99%
M.W. 191.19 m.p. 161-164° (dec.)
B
10,517-1 5-Methoxy-2-methyl-3-indoleacetic acid
M.W. 219.24 m.p. 158-160°
C
B2800-1 5-Benzyloxyindole-3-acetic acid
M.W. 281.31 m.p. 152-154°
D
14,351-0 5-Hydroxy-2-indolecarboxylic acid
M.W. 177.16 m.p. 244° (dec.)
E
10,469-8 Tetrahydroharmanecarboxylic acid (1-methyl-2,3,4,9-tetrahydro-1H-pyrido[3,4-b]indole-3-carboxylic acid) dihydrate
M.W. 266.30 m.p. 248-250°
F
I-543-5 3-Indoleglycolic acid, sodium salt
M.W. 213.17 m.p. 302-305° (dec.)
G
16,269-8
DL-Tryptophan, 99+%, GOLD LABEL
M.W. 204.23 m.p. 289-290° (dec.) Beil. 22,550
H
15,628-0
D-(+)-Tryptophan, 99+%
M.W. 204.23 m.p. 282-285° (dec.)
NUJOL MULL
WAVENUMBER CM⁻¹
WAVELENGTH IN MICRONS

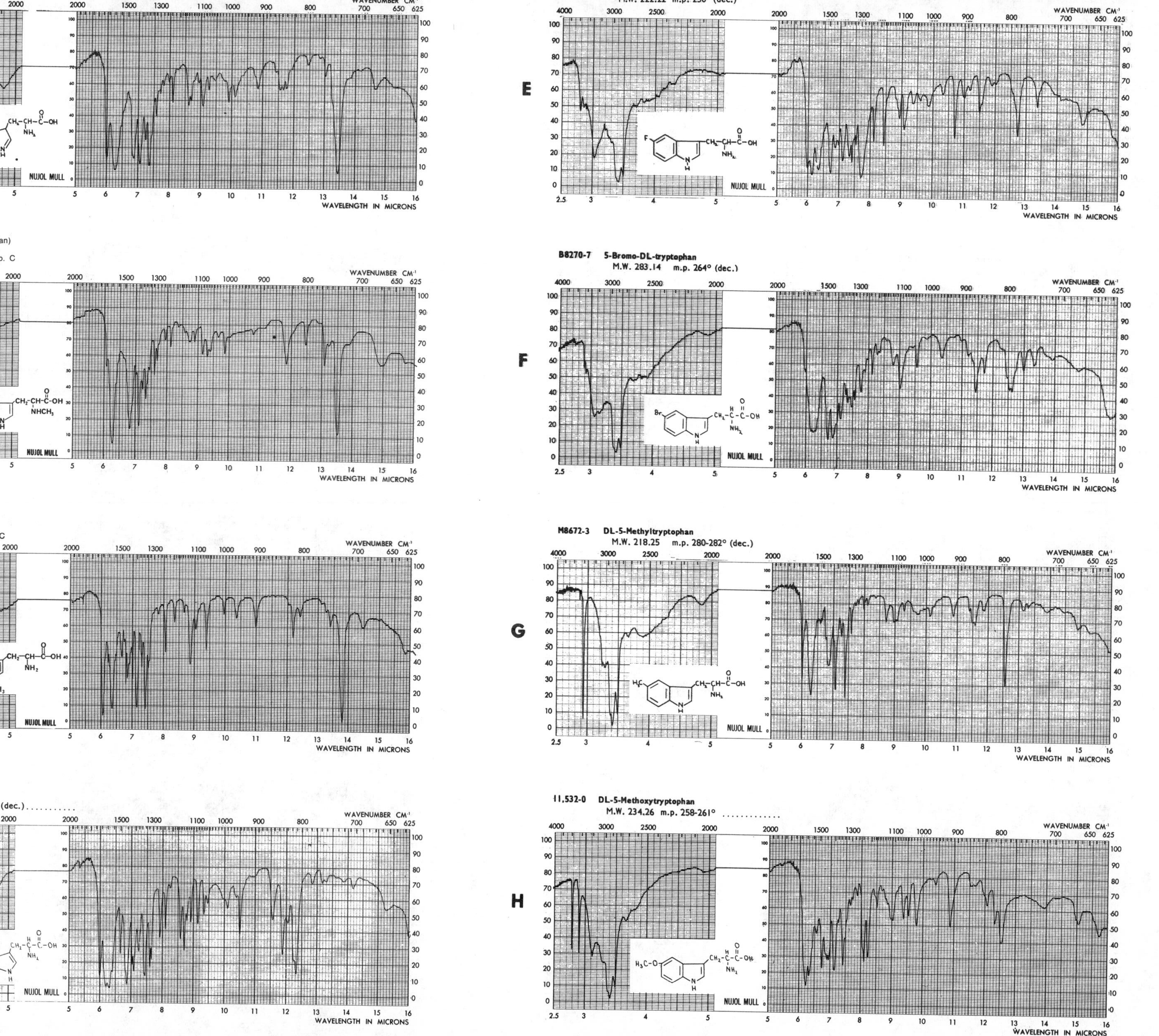
[α]$_D^{20}$ -31.5° (c=0.5 in H_2O) ....
A
B
21,902-9
L-Abrine, 99% (N-methyl-L-tryptophan)
FW 218.26 mp 295° (dec.)
[α]$_D^{20}$ +44.6° (c=2.8, 0.5N HCl) Disp. C
C
86,064-6
1-Methyl-DL-tryptophan, 97%
FW 218.26 mp 250° (dec.) Disp. C
D
10,245-8 6-Fluorotryptophan
M.W. 222.22 m.p. 279° (dec.) ....
E
F1535-8 5-Fluorotryptophan
M.W. 222.22 m.p. 250° (dec.)
F
B8270-7 5-Bromo-DL-tryptophan
M.W. 283.14 m.p. 264° (dec.)
G
M8672-3 DL-5-Methyltryptophan
M.W. 218.25 m.p. 280-282° (dec.)
H
11,532-0 DL-5-Methoxytryptophan
M.W. 234.26 m.p. 258-261° ....
NUJOL MULL
WAVENUMBER CM⁻¹
WAVELENGTH IN MICRONS

5 MEMBERED FUSED AROMATIC HETEROCYCLES

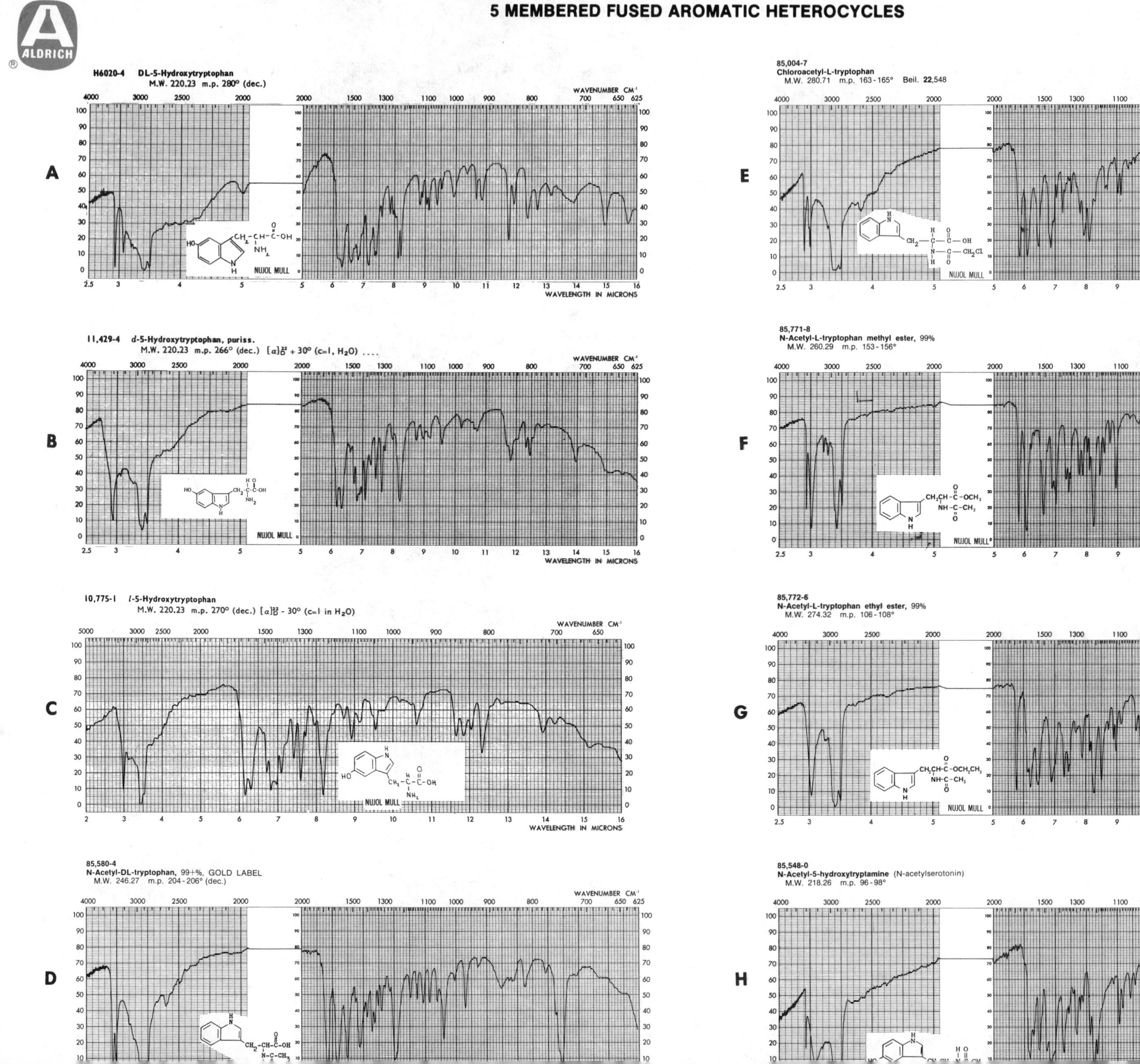
ALDRICH
A
H6020-4 DL-5-Hydroxytryptophan
M.W. 220.23 m.p. 280° (dec.)
NUJOL MULL
B
11,429-4 d-5-Hydroxytryptophan, puriss.
M.W. 220.23 m.p. 266° (dec.) [α]²²D + 30° (c=1, H₂O) ....
NUJOL MULL
C
10,775-1 l-5-Hydroxytryptophan
M.W. 220.23 m.p. 270° (dec.) [α]²²D - 30° (c=1 in H₂O)
NUJOL MULL
D
85,580-4
N-Acetyl-DL-tryptophan, 99+%, GOLD LABEL
M.W. 246.27 m.p. 204-206° (dec.)
E
85,004-7
Chloroacetyl-L-tryptophan
M.W. 280.71 m.p. 163-165° Beil. 22,548
NUJOL MULL
F
85,771-8
N-Acetyl-L-tryptophan methyl ester, 99%
M.W. 260.29 m.p. 153-156°
NUJOL MULL
G
85,772-6
N-Acetyl-L-tryptophan ethyl ester, 99%
M.W. 274.32 m.p. 106-108°
NUJOL MULL
H
85,548-0
N-Acetyl-5-hydroxytryptamine (N-acetylserotonin)
M.W. 218.26 m.p. 96-98°
WAVENUMBER CM⁻¹
WAVELENGTH IN MICRONS

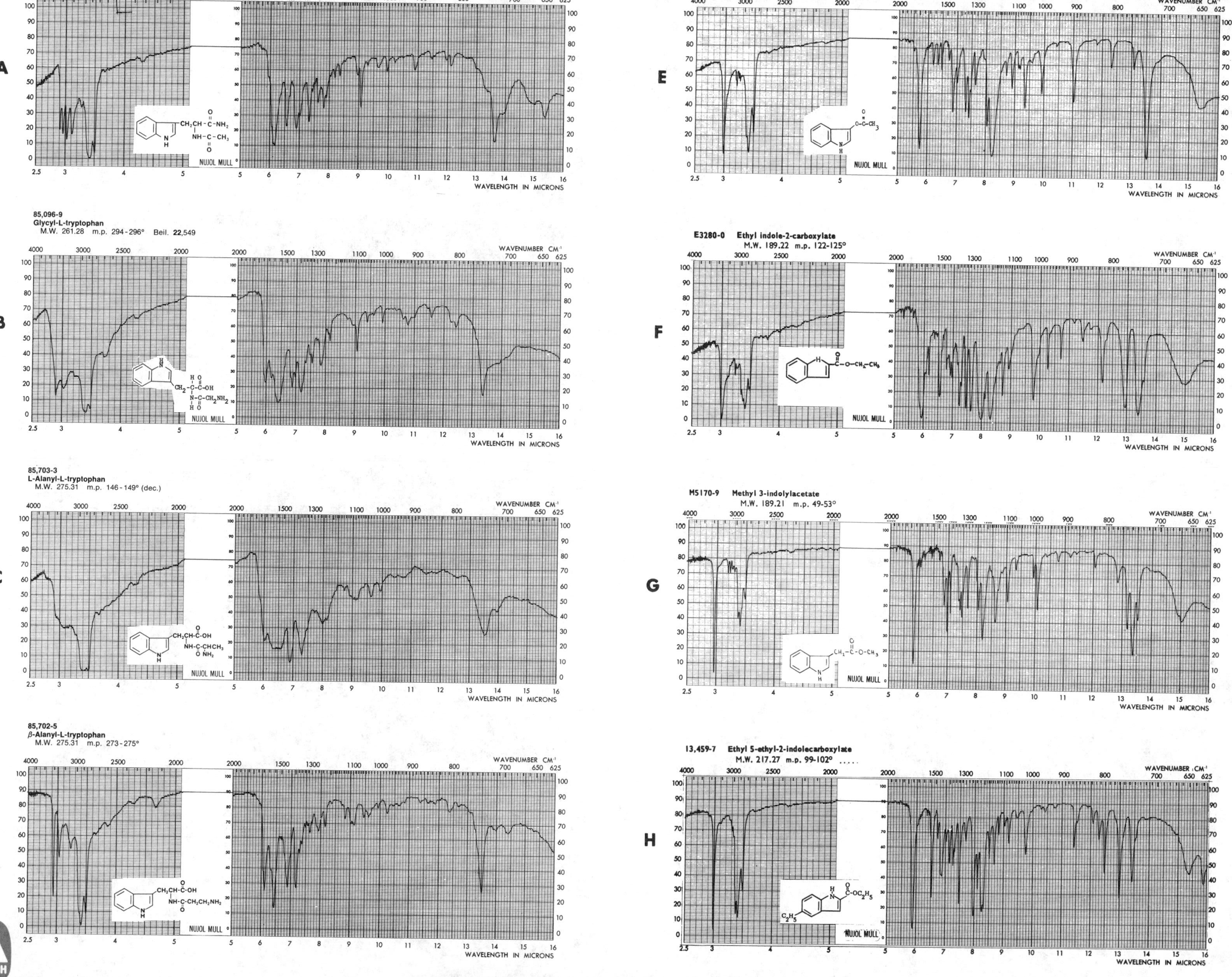
A
NUJOL MULL
85,096-9
Glycyl-L-tryptophan
M.W. 261.28 m.p. 294-296° Beil. 22,549
B
NUJOL MULL
85,703-3
L-Alanyl-L-tryptophan
M.W. 275.31 m.p. 146-149° (dec.)
C
NUJOL MULL
85,702-5
β-Alanyl-L-tryptophan
M.W. 275.31 m.p. 273-275°
D
NUJOL MULL
Indoxyl acetate (3-acetoxyindole)
M.W. 175.19 m.p. 127-130°
E
NUJOL MULL
E3280-0 Ethyl indole-2-carboxylate
M.W. 189.22 m.p. 122-125°
F
NUJOL MULL
M5170-9 Methyl 3-indolylacetate
M.W. 189.21 m.p. 49-53°
G
NUJOL MULL
13,459-7 Ethyl 5-ethyl-2-indolecarboxylate
M.W. 217.27 m.p. 99-102°
H
NUJOL MULL
WAVENUMBER CM⁻¹
WAVELENGTH IN MICRONS
ALDRICH

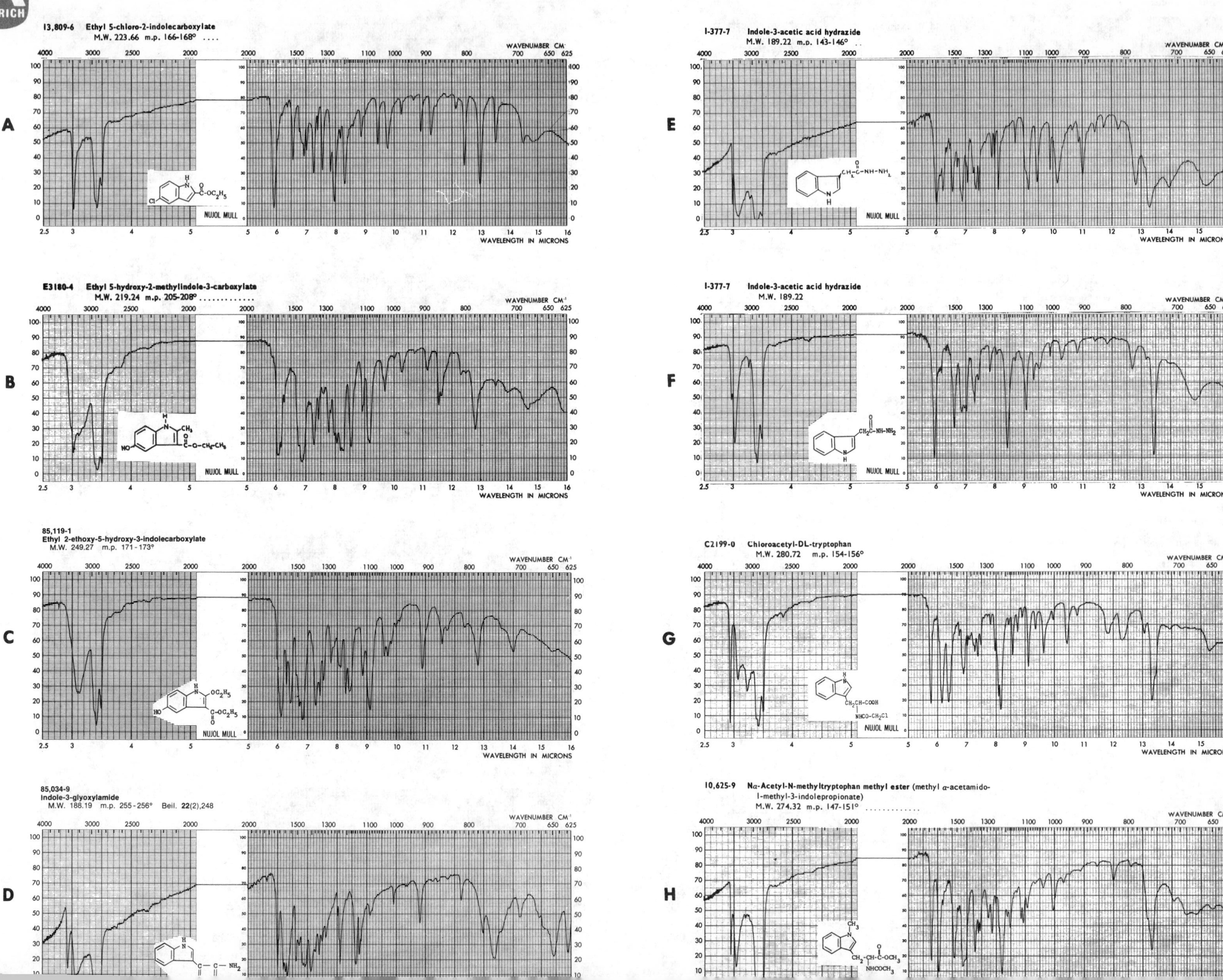
ALDRICH
A
13,809-6 Ethyl 5-chloro-2-indolecarboxylate
M.W. 223.66 m.p. 166-168°
B
E3180-4 Ethyl 5-hydroxy-2-methylindole-3-carboxylate
M.W. 219.24 m.p. 205-208°
C
85,119-1
Ethyl 2-ethoxy-5-hydroxy-3-indolecarboxylate
M.W. 249.27 m.p. 171-173°
D
85,034-9
Indole-3-glyoxylamide
M.W. 188.19 m.p. 255-256° Beil. 22(2),248
E
I-377-7 Indole-3-acetic acid hydrazide
M.W. 189.22 m.p. 143-146°
F
I-377-7 Indole-3-acetic acid hydrazide
M.W. 189.22
G
C2199-0 Chloroacetyl-DL-tryptophan
M.W. 280.72 m.p. 154-156°
H
10,625-9 Nα-Acetyl-N-methyltryptophan methyl ester (methyl α-acetamido-1-methyl-3-indolepropionate)
M.W. 274.32 m.p. 147-151°
WAVENUMBER CM⁻¹
WAVELENGTH IN MICRONS
NUJOL MULL

M.W. 232.29 m.p. 116.5-118°

A

B6870 5-Bromoindole-3-acetamide
M.W. 253.11 m.p. 177.5-179°

B

13,506-2 5-Bromoindoxyl diacetate

C

13,907-6 5-Bromo-4-chloroindoxyl diacetate

D

indol-1-one)
M.W. 186.22 m.p. 188-189.5°

E

12,485-0 8-Methyl-1-tetrahydronorharmanone (8-methyl-2,3,4,9-tetrahydro-1H-pyrido[3,4-b]indol-1-one), tech.
M.W. 200.24 m.p. 221-226°

F

12,763-9 6-Methyl-1-tetrahydronorharmanone (6-methyl-2,3,4,9-tetrahydro-1H-pyrido[3,4-b]indol-1-one)
M.W. 200.24 m.p. 208-209°

G

12,484-2 6-Fluoro-1-tetrahydronorharmanone (6-fluoro-2,3,4,9-tetrahydro-1H-pyrido[3,4-b]indol-1-one)
M.W. 204.21 m.p. 232-235°

H

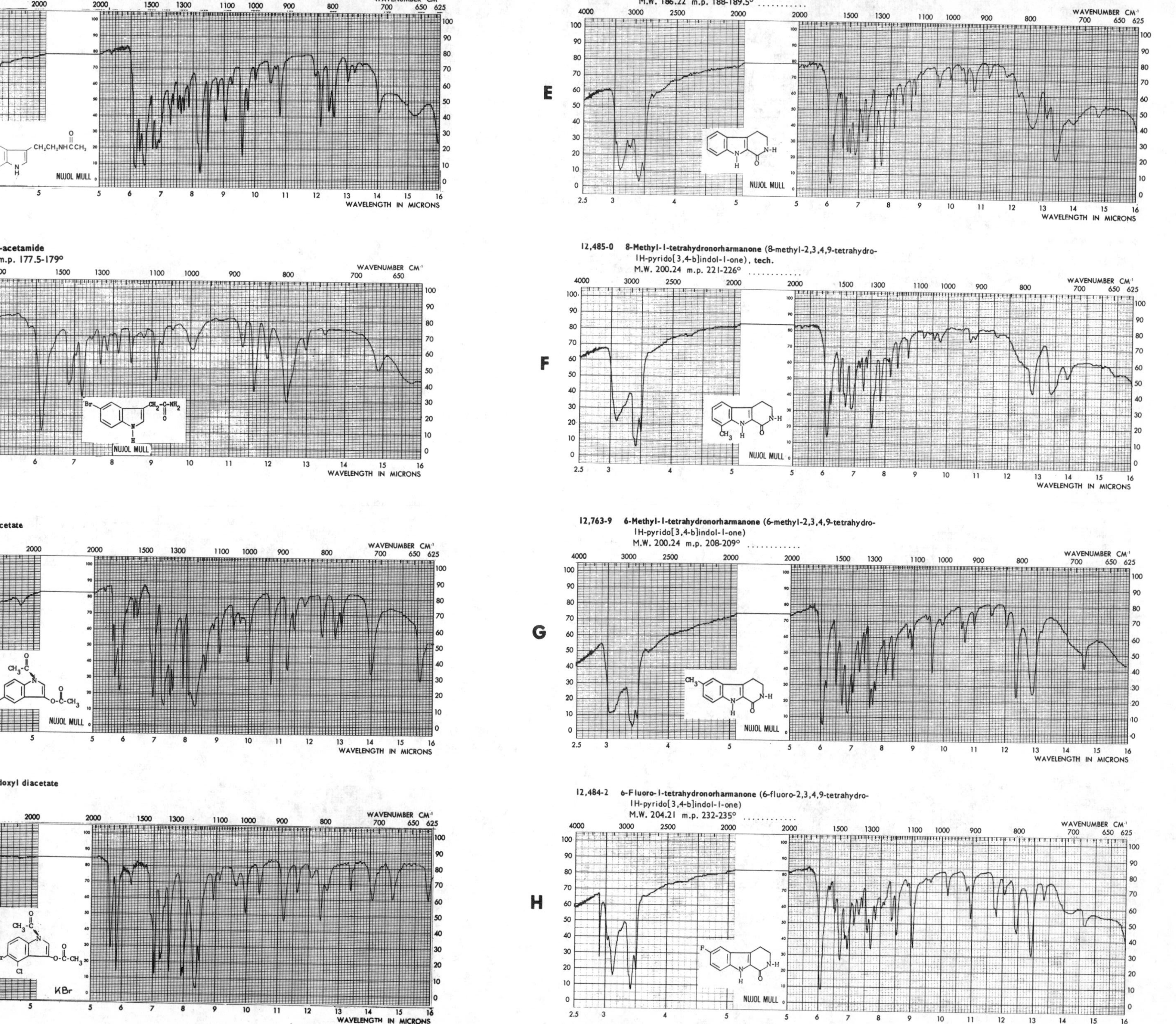

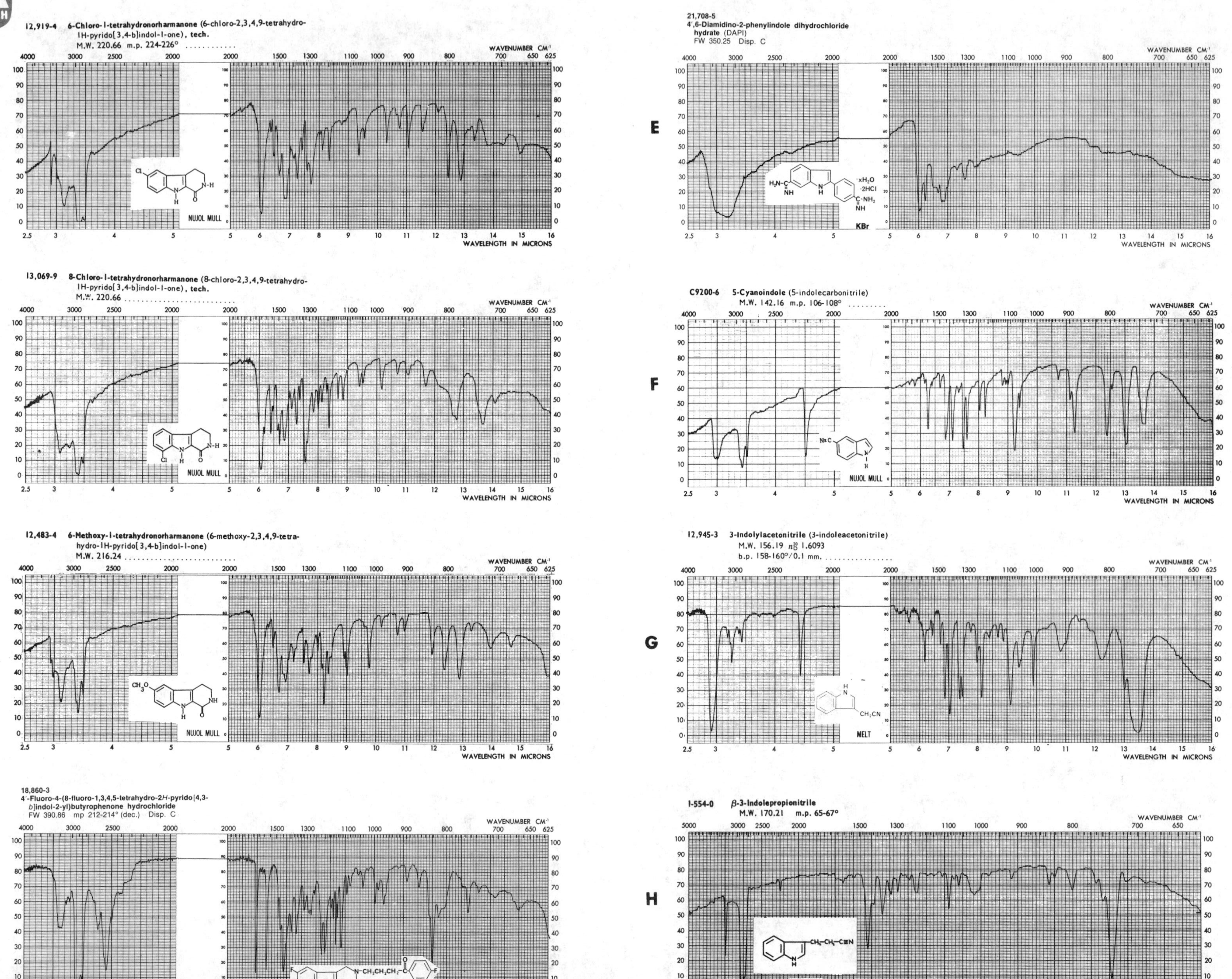
ALDRICH
A
12,919-4 6-Chloro-1-tetrahydronorharmanone (6-chloro-2,3,4,9-tetrahydro-1H-pyrido[3,4-b]indol-1-one), tech.
M.W. 220.66 m.p. 224-226°
NUJOL MULL
B
13,069-9 8-Chloro-1-tetrahydronorharmanone (8-chloro-2,3,4,9-tetrahydro-1H-pyrido[3,4-b]indol-1-one), tech.
M.W. 220.66
NUJOL MULL
C
12,483-4 6-Methoxy-1-tetrahydronorharmanone (6-methoxy-2,3,4,9-tetrahydro-1H-pyrido[3,4-b]indol-1-one)
M.W. 216.24
NUJOL MULL
D
18,860-3
4'-Fluoro-4-(8-fluoro-1,3,4,5-tetrahydro-2H-pyrido[4,3-b]indol-2-yl)butyrophenone hydrochloride
FW 390.86 mp 212-214° (dec.) Disp. C
E
21,708-5
4',6-Diamidino-2-phenylindole dihydrochloride hydrate (DAPI)
FW 350.25 Disp. C
KBr
F
C9200-6 5-Cyanoindole (5-indolecarbonitrile)
M.W. 142.16 m.p. 106-108°
NUJOL MULL
G
12,945-3 3-Indolylacetonitrile (3-indoleacetonitrile)
M.W. 156.19 n_D^{20} 1.6093
b.p. 158-160°/0.1 mm.
MELT
H
I-554-0 β-3-Indolepropionitrile
M.W. 170.21 m.p. 65-67°
WAVENUMBER CM⁻¹
WAVELENGTH IN MICRONS

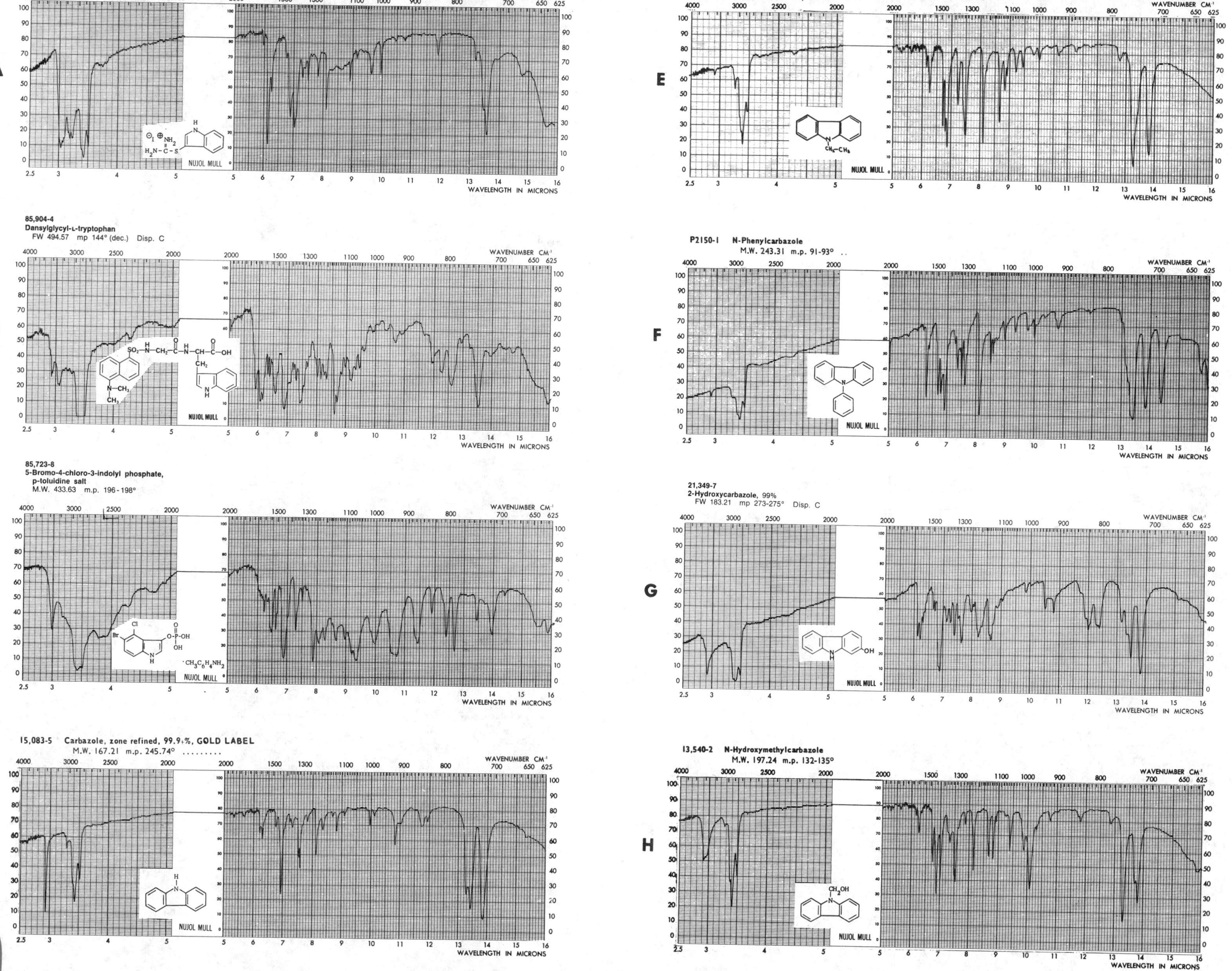
A
NUJOL MULL
85,904-4
Dansylglycyl-L-tryptophan
FW 494.57 mp 144° (dec.) Disp. C
B
NUJOL MULL
85,723-8
5-Bromo-4-chloro-3-indolyl phosphate, p-toluidine salt
M.W. 433.63 m.p. 196-198°
C
NUJOL MULL
15,083-5 Carbazole, zone refined, 99.9+%, GOLD LABEL
M.W. 167.21 m.p. 245.74°
D
NUJOL MULL
E1660-0 N-Ethylcarbazole
M.W. 195.27 m.p. 66-68°
E
NUJOL MULL
P2150-1 N-Phenylcarbazole
M.W. 243.31 m.p. 91-93°
F
NUJOL MULL
21,349-7
2-Hydroxycarbazole, 99%
FW 183.21 mp 273-275° Disp. C
G
NUJOL MULL
13,540-2 N-Hydroxymethylcarbazole
M.W. 197.24 m.p. 132-135°
H
NUJOL MULL
WAVENUMBER CM⁻¹
WAVELENGTH IN MICRONS
ALDRICH

5 MEMBERED FUSED AROMATIC HETEROCYCLES

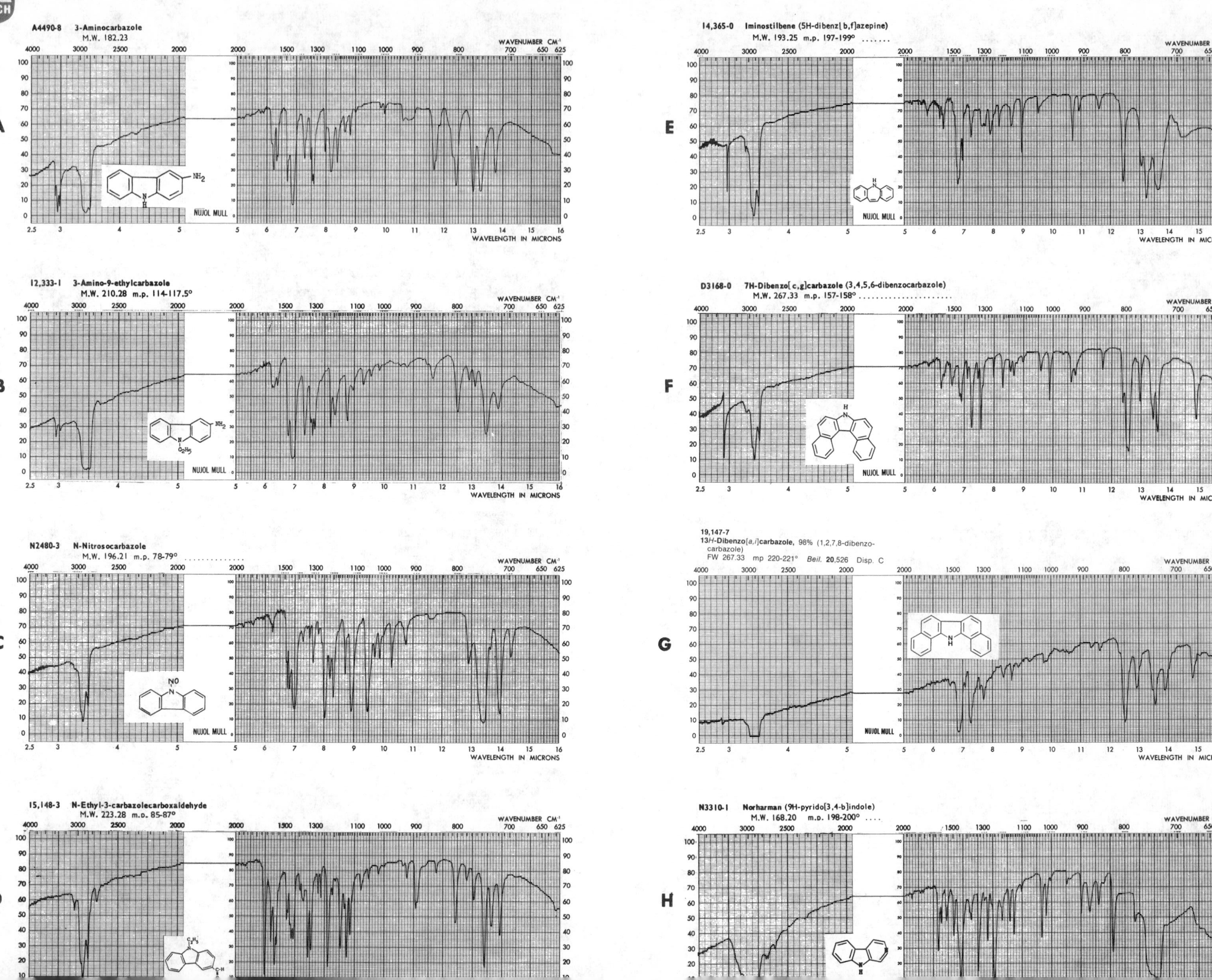
ALDRICH
A
A4490-8 3-Aminocarbazole
M.W. 182.23
NUJOL MULL
B
12,333-1 3-Amino-9-ethylcarbazole
M.W. 210.28 m.p. 114-117.5°
NUJOL MULL
C
N2480-3 N-Nitrosocarbazole
M.W. 196.21 m.p. 78-79°
NUJOL MULL
D
15,148-3 N-Ethyl-3-carbazolecarboxaldehyde
M.W. 223.28 m.p. 85-87°
E
14,365-0 Iminostilbene (5H-dibenz[b,f]azepine)
M.W. 193.25 m.p. 197-199°
NUJOL MULL
F
D3168-0 7H-Dibenzo[c,g]carbazole (3,4,5,6-dibenzocarbazole)
M.W. 267.33 m.p. 157-158°
NUJOL MULL
G
19,147-7
13H-Dibenzo[a,i]carbazole, 98% (1,2,7,8-dibenzocarbazole)
FW 267.33 mp 220-221° Beil. 20,526 Disp. C
NUJOL MULL
H
N3310-1 Norharman (9H-pyrido[3,4-b]indole)
M.W. 168.20 m.p. 198-200°
WAVENUMBER CM⁻¹
WAVELENGTH IN MICRONS

A

M.W. 182.23 m.p. 237-239°

NUJOL MULL

B

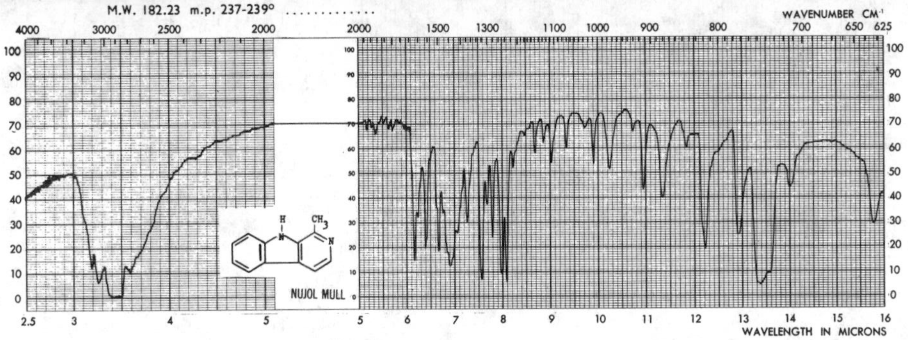

A9550-2 **7-Azaindole** (1H-pyrrolo[2,3-b]pyridine)
M.W. 118.14 m.p. 105-107°

NUJOL MULL

C

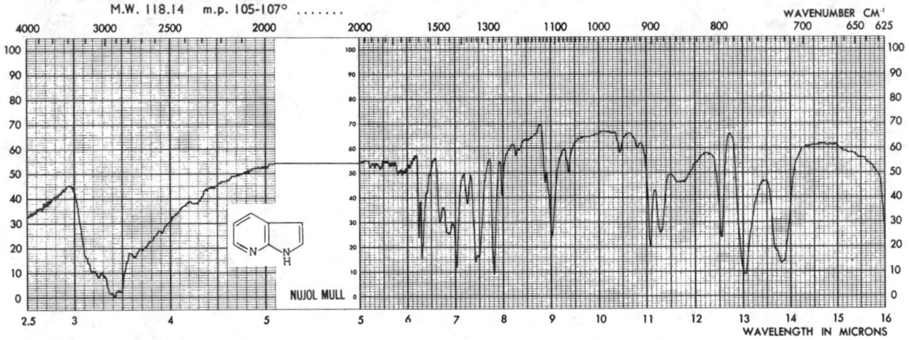

12,848-1 **Harmine hydrochloride hydrate**
M.W. 248.71 (anhydrous)

·HCl ·xH$_2$O

NUJOL MULL

D

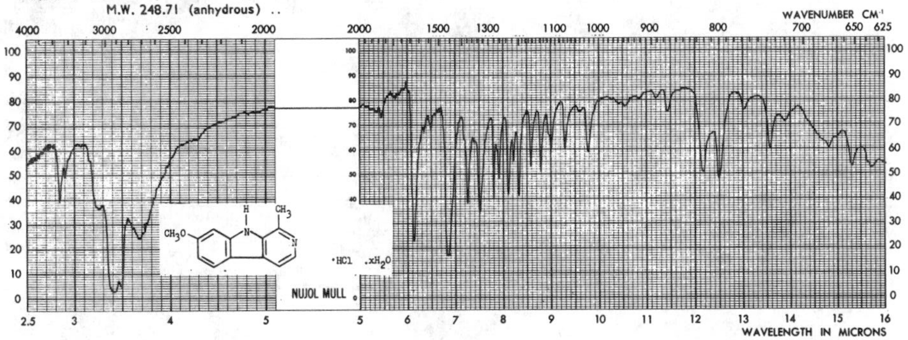

85,822-6
6-Bromoharmane hydrobromide dihydrate
M.W. 378.08 m.p. >300°

·HBr ·2H$_2$O

NUJOL MULL

E

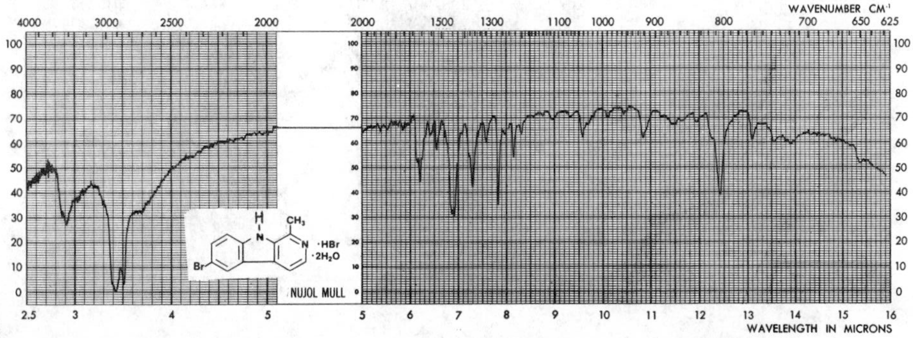

M.W. 372.07 m.p. > 300°

(?) Br .HBr

NUJOL MULL

F

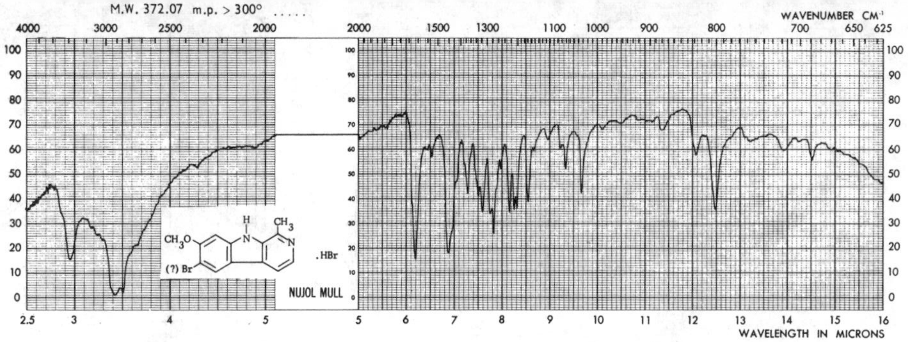

11,655-6 **Harmol** (1-methyl-9H-pyrido[3,4-b]indol-7-ol) **hydrochloride monohydrate**
M.W. 252.70

.HCl .H$_2$O

NUJOL MULL

G

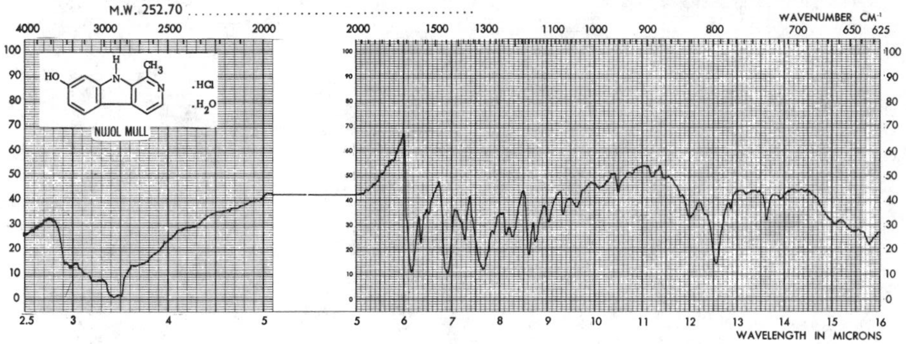

B800-2 **2,3-Benzofuran**
M.W. 118.14 n_D^{20} 1.5660

NEAT

H

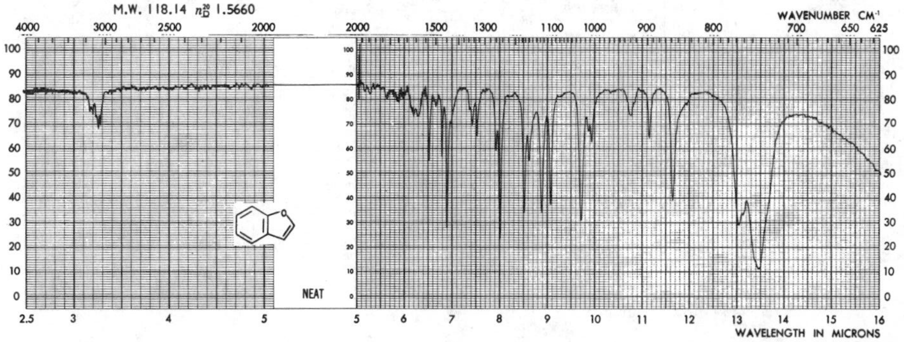

10,548-1 **1,3-Diphenylisobenzofuran** (2,5-diphenyl-3,4-benzofuran)
M.W. 270.33 m.p. 128-130°

NUJOL MULL

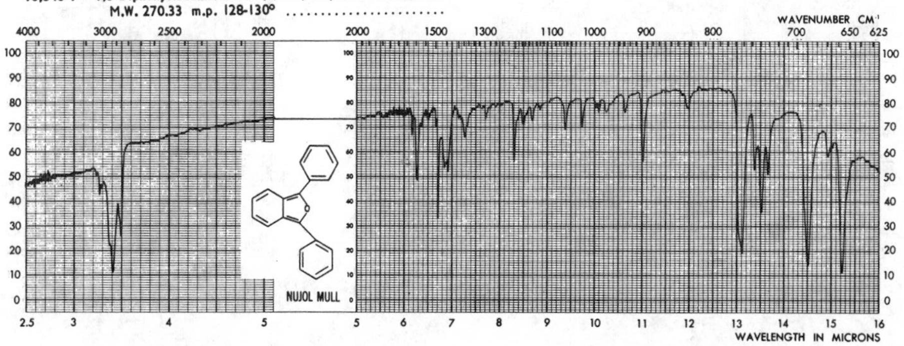

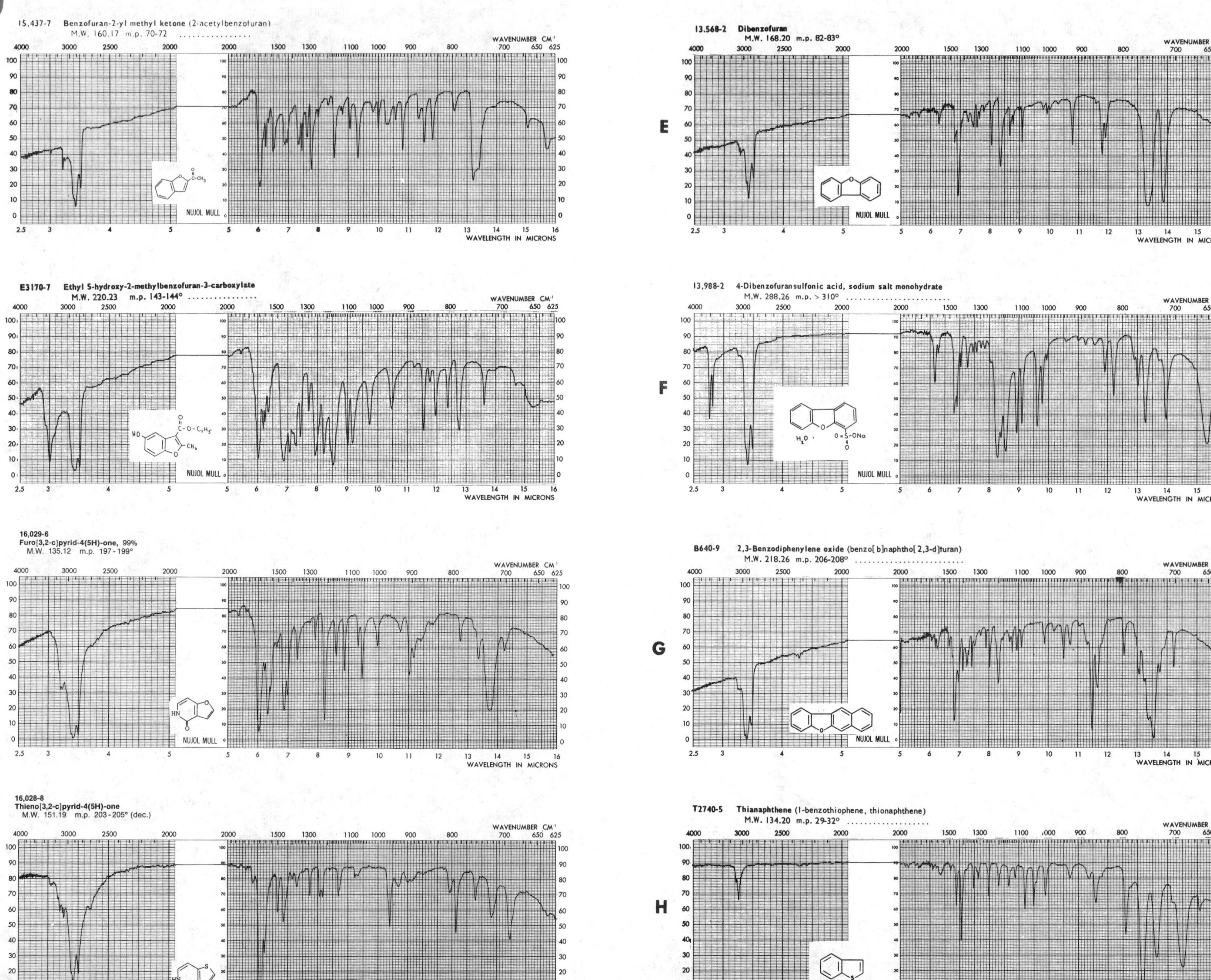
ALDRICH
A
15,437-7 Benzofuran-2-yl methyl ketone (2-acetylbenzofuran)
M.W. 160.17 m.p. 70-72
B
E3170-7 Ethyl 5-hydroxy-2-methylbenzofuran-3-carboxylate
M.W. 220.23 m.p. 143-144°
C
16,029-6
Furo[3,2-c]pyrid-4(5H)-one, 99%
M.W. 135.12 m.p. 197-199°
D
16,028-8
Thieno[3,2-c]pyrid-4(5H)-one
M.W. 151.19 m.p. 203-205° (dec.)
E
13,568-2 Dibenzofuran
M.W. 168.20 m.p. 82-83°
F
13,988-2 4-Dibenzofuransulfonic acid, sodium salt monohydrate
M.W. 288.26 m.p. > 310°
G
B640-9 2,3-Benzodiphenylene oxide (benzo[b]naphtho[2,3-d]furan)
M.W. 218.26 m.p. 206-208°
H
T2740-5 Thianaphthene (1-benzothiophene, thionaphthene)
M.W. 134.20 m.p. 29-32°
NUJOL MULL
WAVENUMBER CM⁻¹
WAVELENGTH IN MICRONS

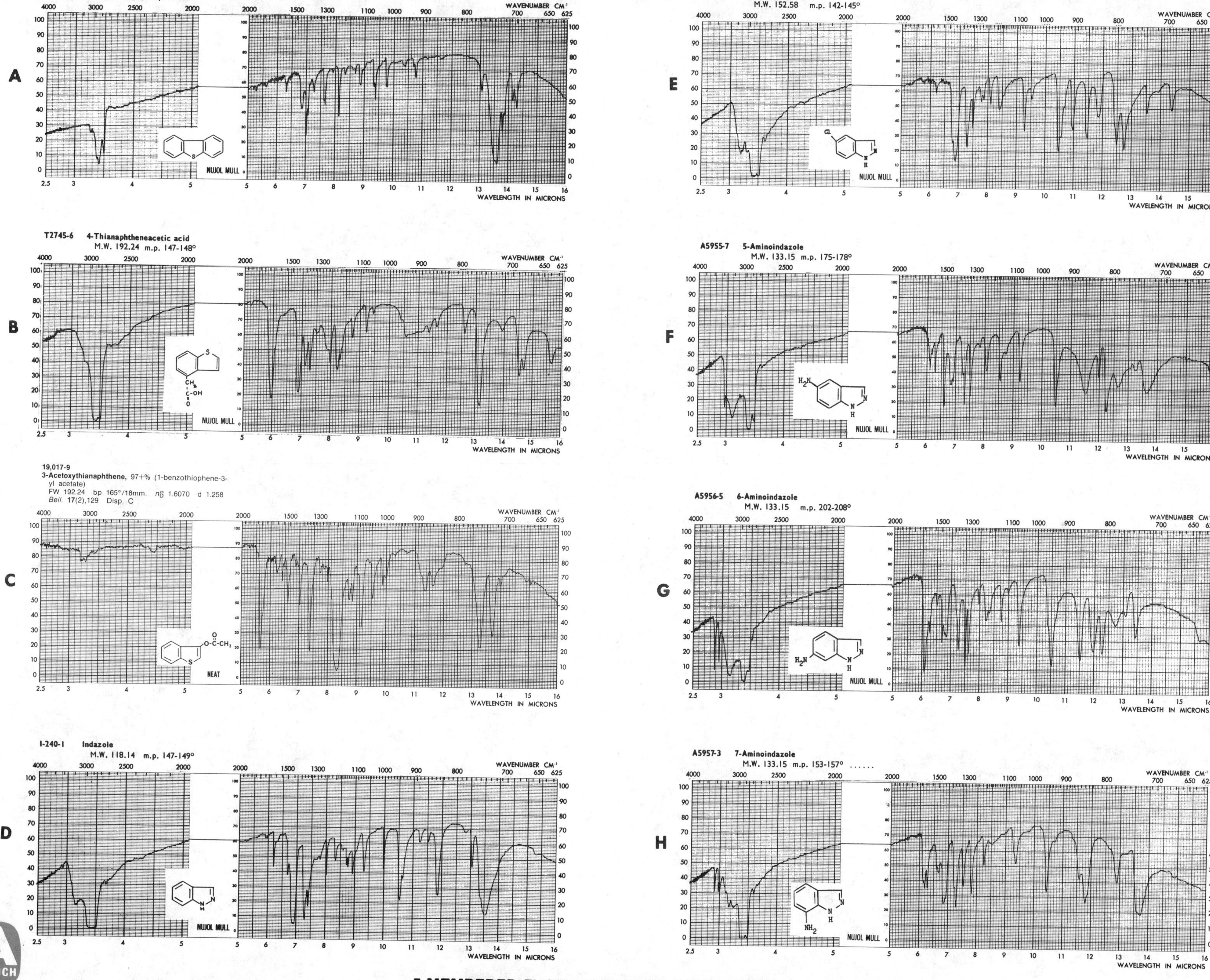
A
D3220-2 Dibenzothiophene
M.W. 184.26 m.p. 97-100°
NUJOL MULL
B
T2745-6 4-Thianaphtheneacetic acid
M.W. 192.24 m.p. 147-148°
NUJOL MULL
C
19,017-9
3-Acetoxythianaphthene, 97+% (1-benzothiophene-3-yl acetate)
FW 192.24 bp 165°/18mm. n_D^{20} 1.6070 d 1.258
Beil. 17(2),129 Disp. C
NEAT
D
I-240-1 Indazole
M.W. 118.14 m.p. 147-149°
NUJOL MULL
E
C4722-1 5-Chloroindazole
M.W. 152.58 m.p. 142-145°
NUJOL MULL
F
A5955-7 5-Aminoindazole
M.W. 133.15 m.p. 175-178°
NUJOL MULL
G
A5956-5 6-Aminoindazole
M.W. 133.15 m.p. 202-208°
NUJOL MULL
H
A5957-3 7-Aminoindazole
M.W. 133.15 m.p. 153-157°
NUJOL MULL
WAVENUMBER CM⁻¹
WAVELENGTH IN MICRONS
ALDRICH

5 MEMBERED FUSED AROMATIC HETEROCYCLES

A

11,707-2 **5,6-Diaminoindazole**
M.W. 148.17 m.p. 281-282° (dec.)

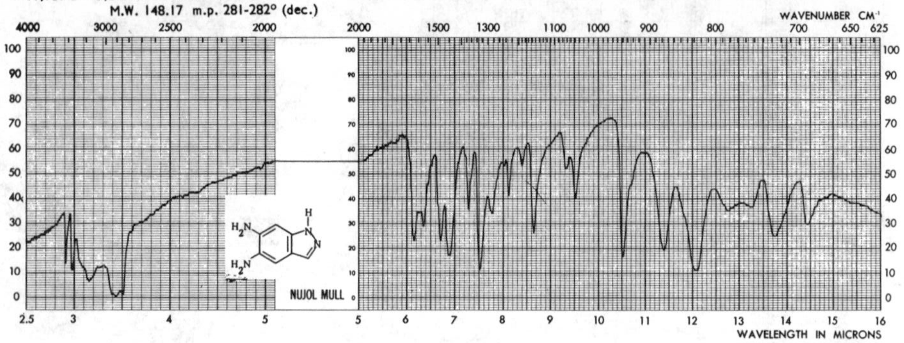

NUJOL MULL

B

22,415-4
6-Amino-3-indazolinone dihydrochloride, 98%
FW 222.08 mp 279° (dec.) Disp. C

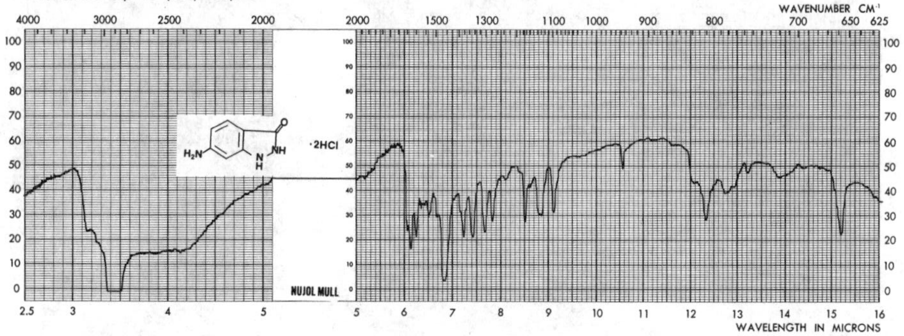

NUJOL MULL

C

N1750-5 **5-Nitroindazole**
M.W. 163.14 m.p. 207-208°

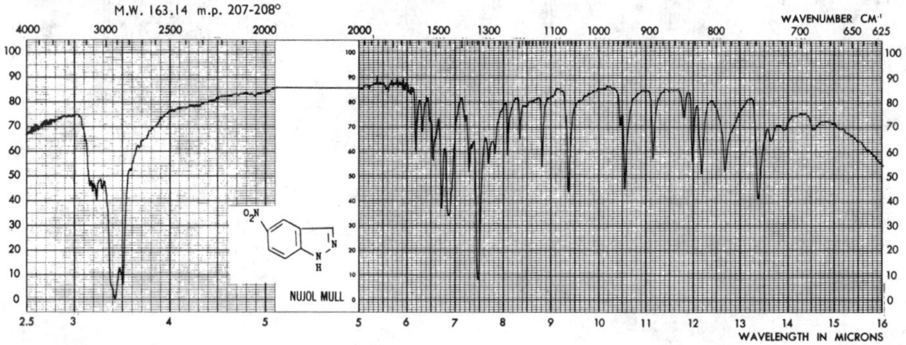

NUJOL MULL

D

N1751-3 **6-Nitroindazole**
M.W. 163.14 m.p. 176-180°

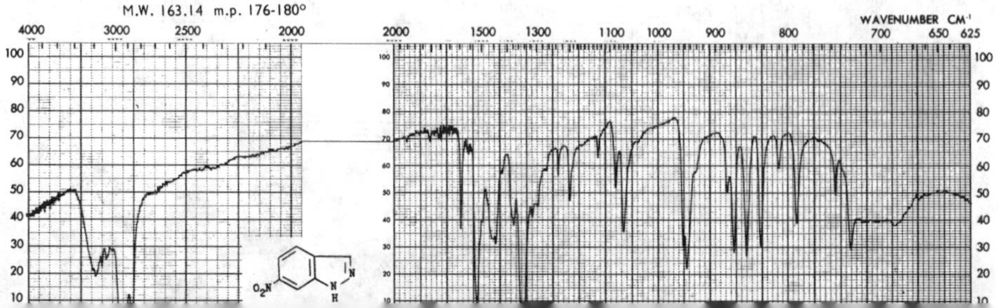

E

N1,752-1
7-Nitroindazole
M.W. 163.14 m.p. 186-188° Beil. 23,131

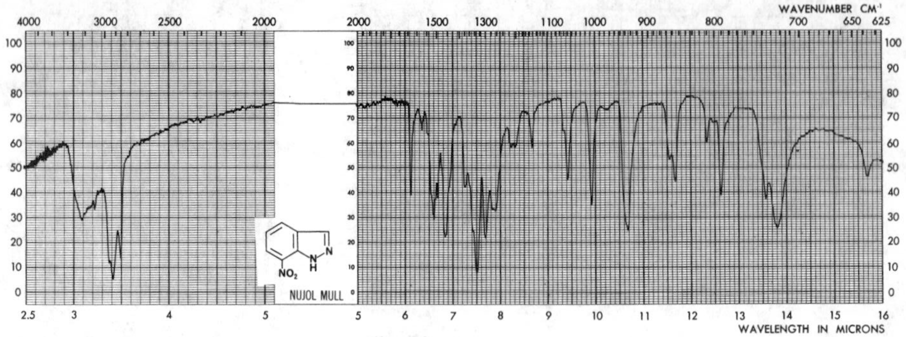

NUJOL MULL

F

14,464-9 **3-Chloro-5-nitroindazole**
M.W. 197.59 m.p. 208-213° (dec.)

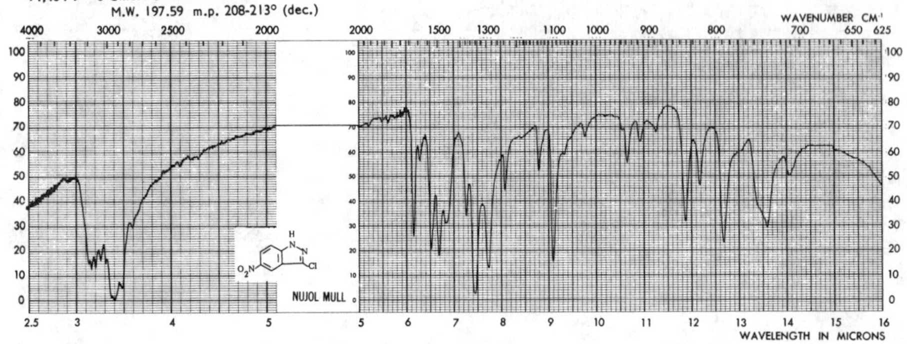

NUJOL MULL

G

C6095-3 **3-Chloro-6-nitroindazole**
M.W. 197.59 m.p. 200-201°

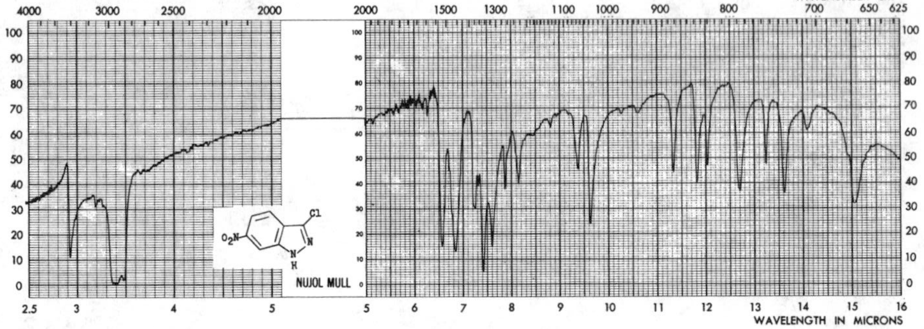

NUJOL MULL

H

11,706-4 **5,6-Dinitroindazole**
M.W. 208.14 m.p. 230-232°

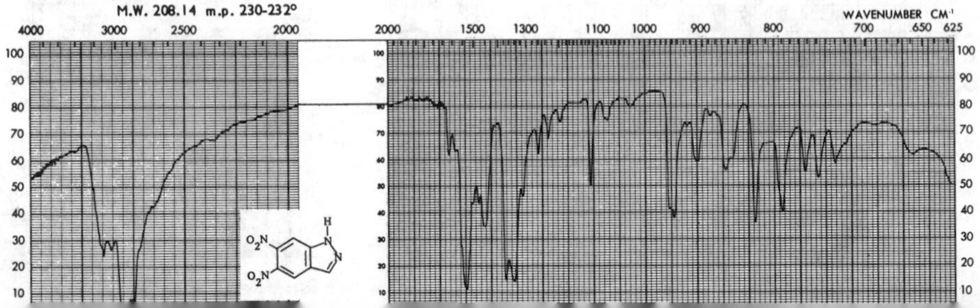

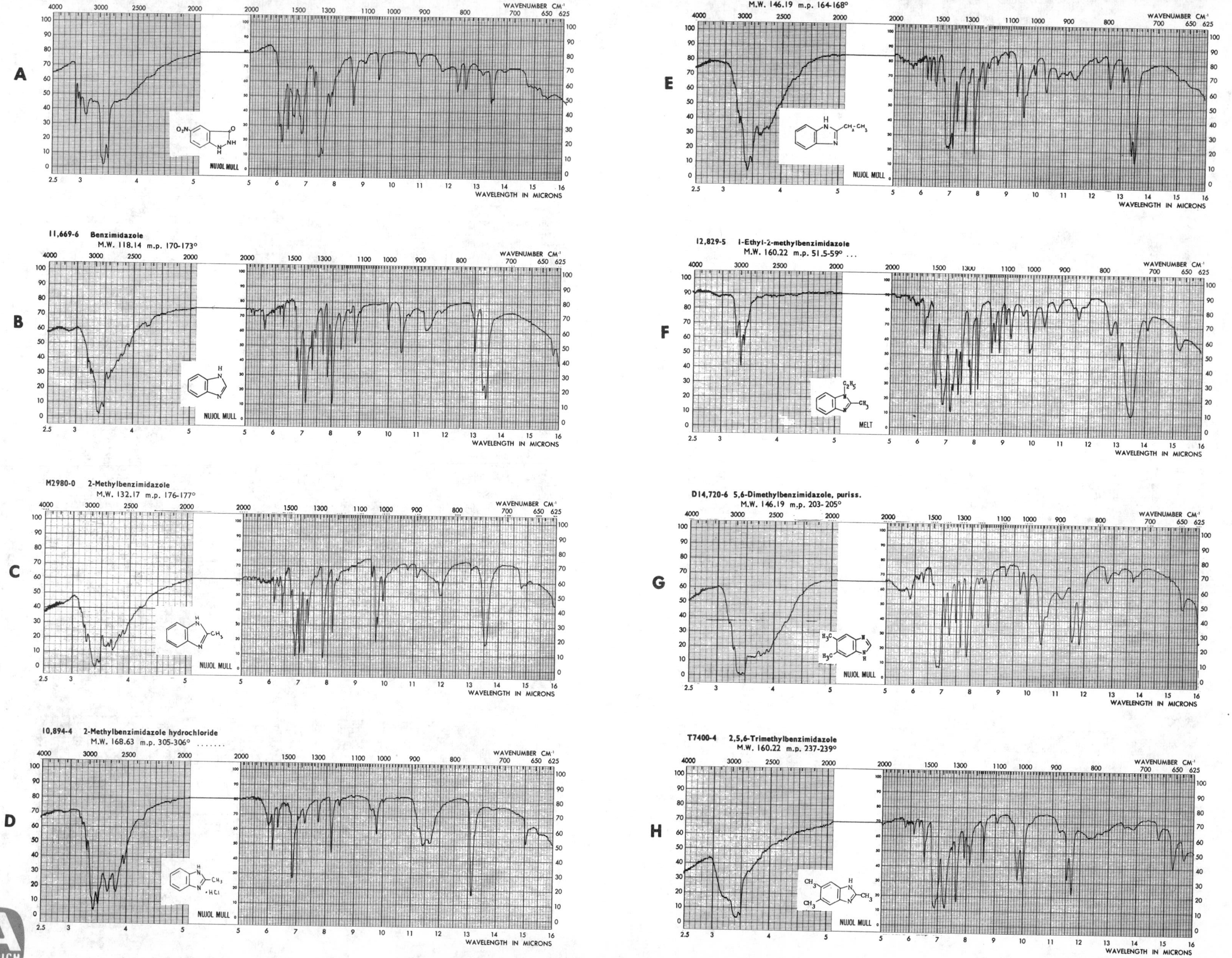

A
FW 179.14 mp 278° (dec.) Beil. 24(2),61
Disp. C
NUJOL MULL
B
11,669-6 Benzimidazole
M.W. 118.14 m.p. 170-173°
NUJOL MULL
C
M2980-0 2-Methylbenzimidazole
M.W. 132.17 m.p. 176-177°
NUJOL MULL
D
10,894-4 2-Methylbenzimidazole hydrochloride
M.W. 168.63 m.p. 305-306°
NUJOL MULL
E
12,814-7 2-Ethylbenzimidazole, tech.
M.W. 146.19 m.p. 164-168°
NUJOL MULL
F
12,829-5 1-Ethyl-2-methylbenzimidazole
M.W. 160.22 m.p. 51.5-59°
MELT
G
D14,720-6 5,6-Dimethylbenzimidazole, puriss.
M.W. 146.19 m.p. 203-205°
NUJOL MULL
H
T7400-4 2,5,6-Trimethylbenzimidazole
M.W. 160.22 m.p. 237-239°
NUJOL MULL
WAVENUMBER CM⁻¹
WAVELENGTH IN MICRONS
ALDRICH

5 MEMBERED FUSED AROMATIC HETEROCYCLES

A

P1980-9 2-Phenylbenzimidazole
M.W. 194.24 m.p. 290-293° (dec.)

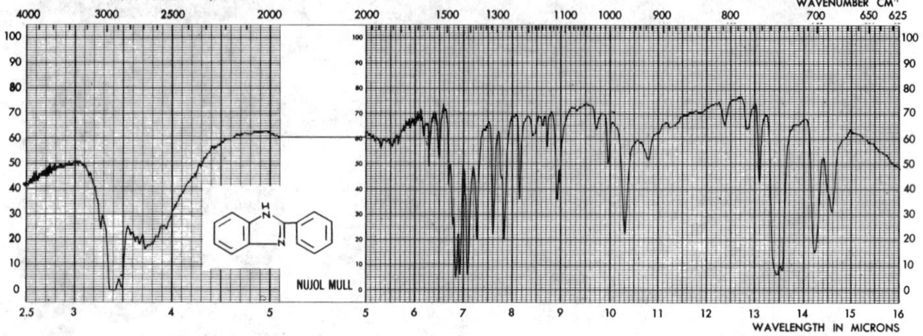

NUJOL MULL

B

22,261-5
1-Methyl-2-phenylbenzimidazole, 99+%
FW 208.26 mp 162-164° *Beil.* **23**,231 Disp. C

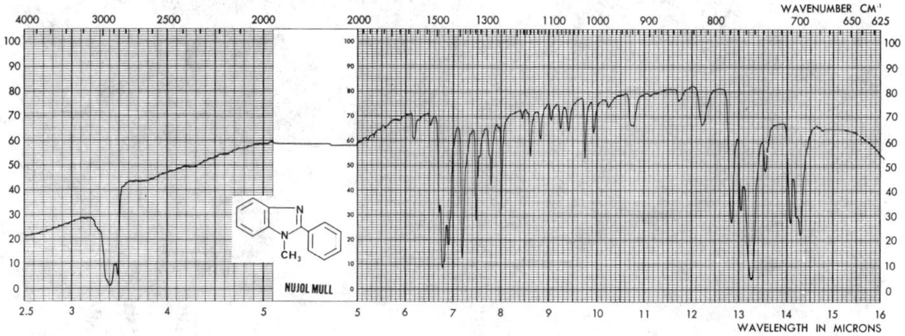

NUJOL MULL

C

15,510-1 2-(2-Pyridyl)-benzimidazole
M.W. 195.23 m.p. 218-220°

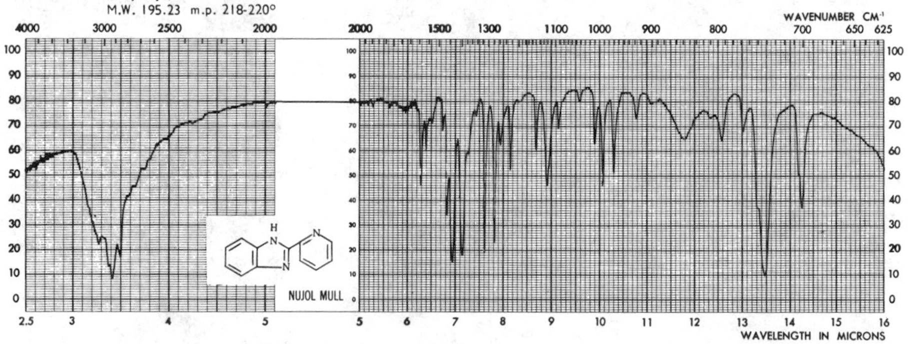

NUJOL MULL

D

12,358-7 12H-Benz[5,6]isoindolo[2,1-a]benzimidazole
M.W. 256.31 m.p. 187-189° ....

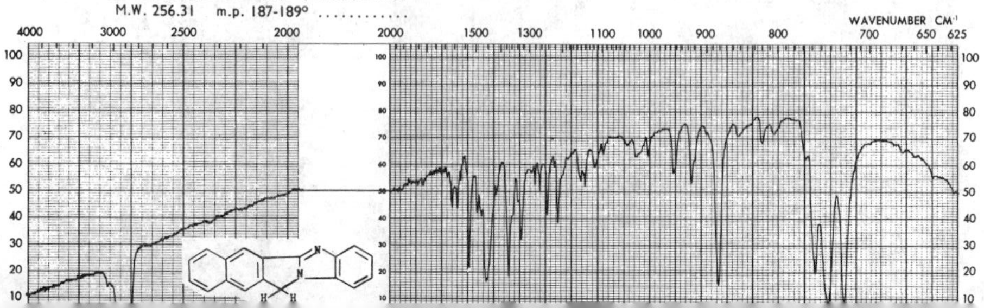

E

C5205-5 2-Chloromethylbenzimidazole
M.W. 166.61 m.p. 146-148°

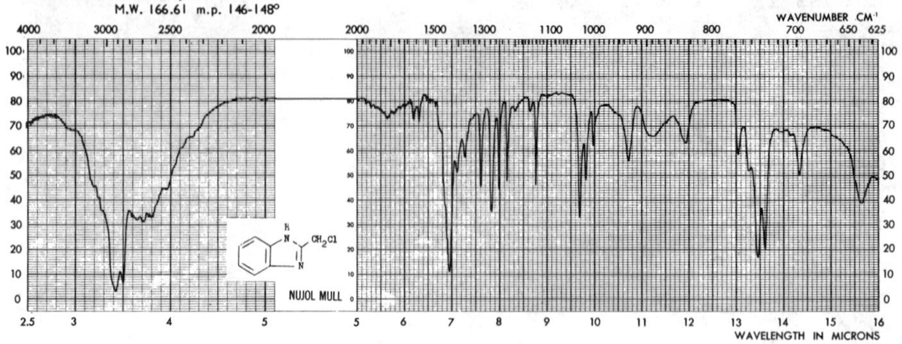

NUJOL MULL

F

C5200-4 5-Chloro-2-methylbenzimidazole
M.W. 166.61 m.p. 198-201° ...

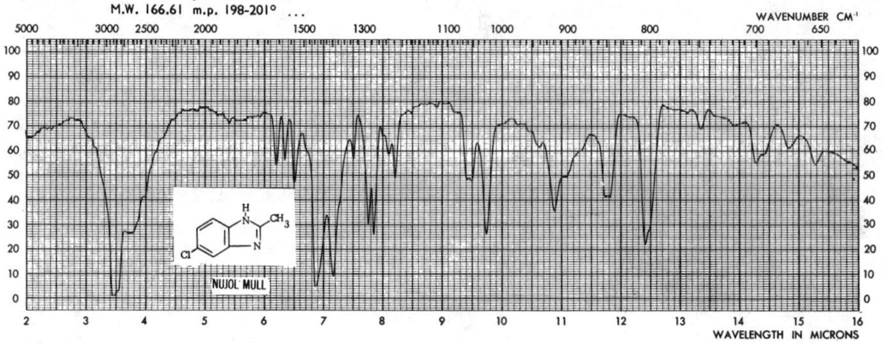

NUJOL MULL

G

22,544-4
2-Phenylbenzothiazole, 97%
FW 211.29 mp 111-113° *Beil.* **27**,74 Disp. C

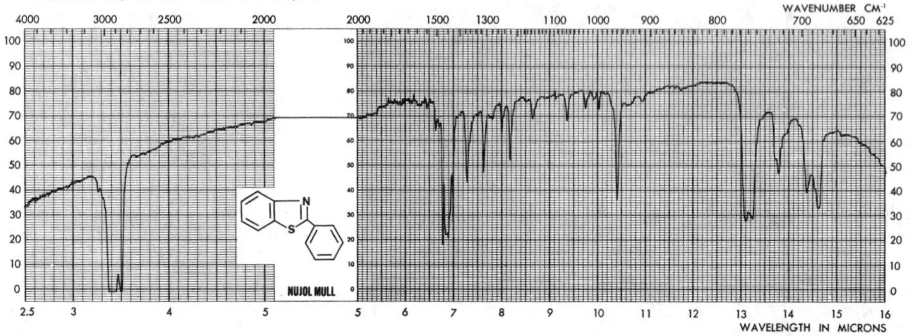

NUJOL MULL

H

D5720-5 5,6-Dichlorobenzimidazole
M.W. 187.03 m.p. 205-208°

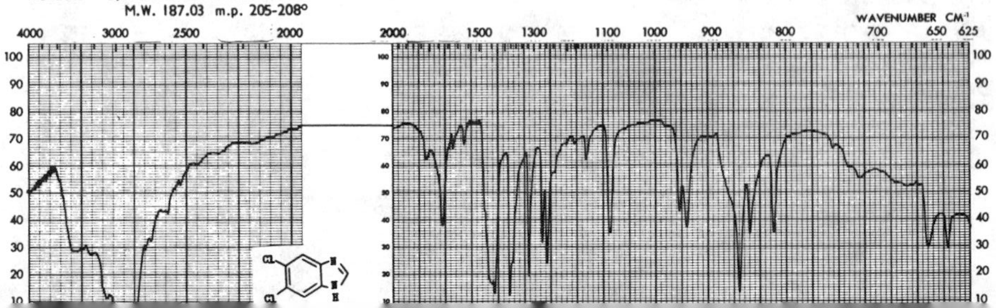

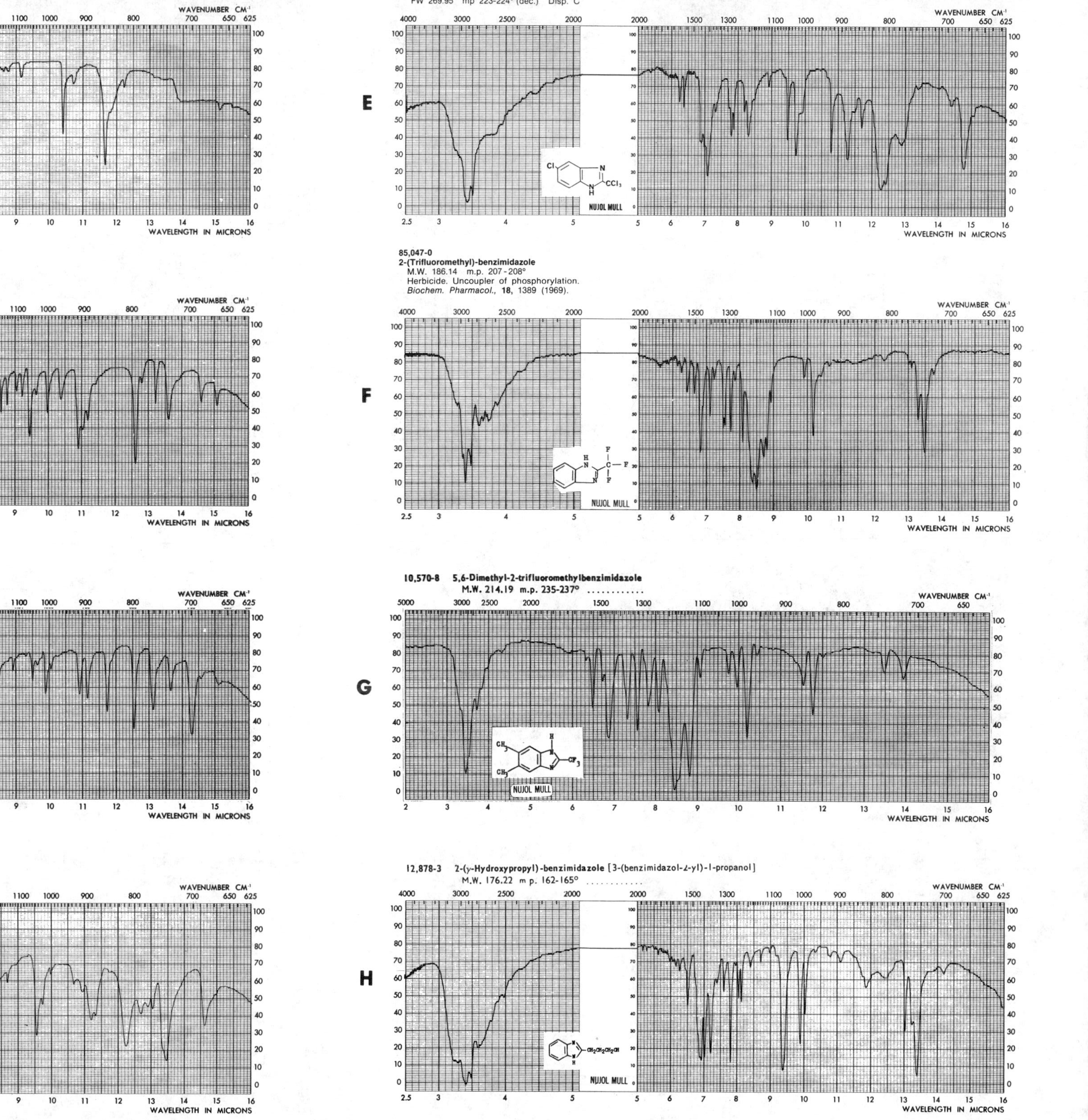

A

M.W. 223.49 m.p. > 300° ....

B

C4190-8 5-Chloro-1-ethyl-2-methylbenzimidazole
M.W. 194.67 m.p. 107.5-110.5° .....

C

C5590-9 5-Chloro-2-methyl-1-phenylbenzimidazole
M.W. 242.71 m.p. 120-122° ....

D

13,986-6 2-(Trichloromethyl)-benzimidazole
M.W. 235.50 m.p. 245° (dec.) ..

E

5-Chloro-2-(trichloromethyl)benzimidazole, 95%
FW 269.95 mp 223-224° (dec.) Disp. C

F

85,047-0
2-(Trifluoromethyl)-benzimidazole
M.W. 186.14 m.p. 207-208°
Herbicide. Uncoupler of phosphorylation.
Biochem. Pharmacol., **18**, 1389 (1969).

G

10,570-8 5,6-Dimethyl-2-trifluoromethylbenzimidazole
M.W. 214.19 m.p. 235-237° ....

H

12,878-3 2-(γ-Hydroxypropyl)-benzimidazole [3-(benzimidazol-2-yl)-1-propanol]
M.W. 176.22 m.p. 162-165° ....

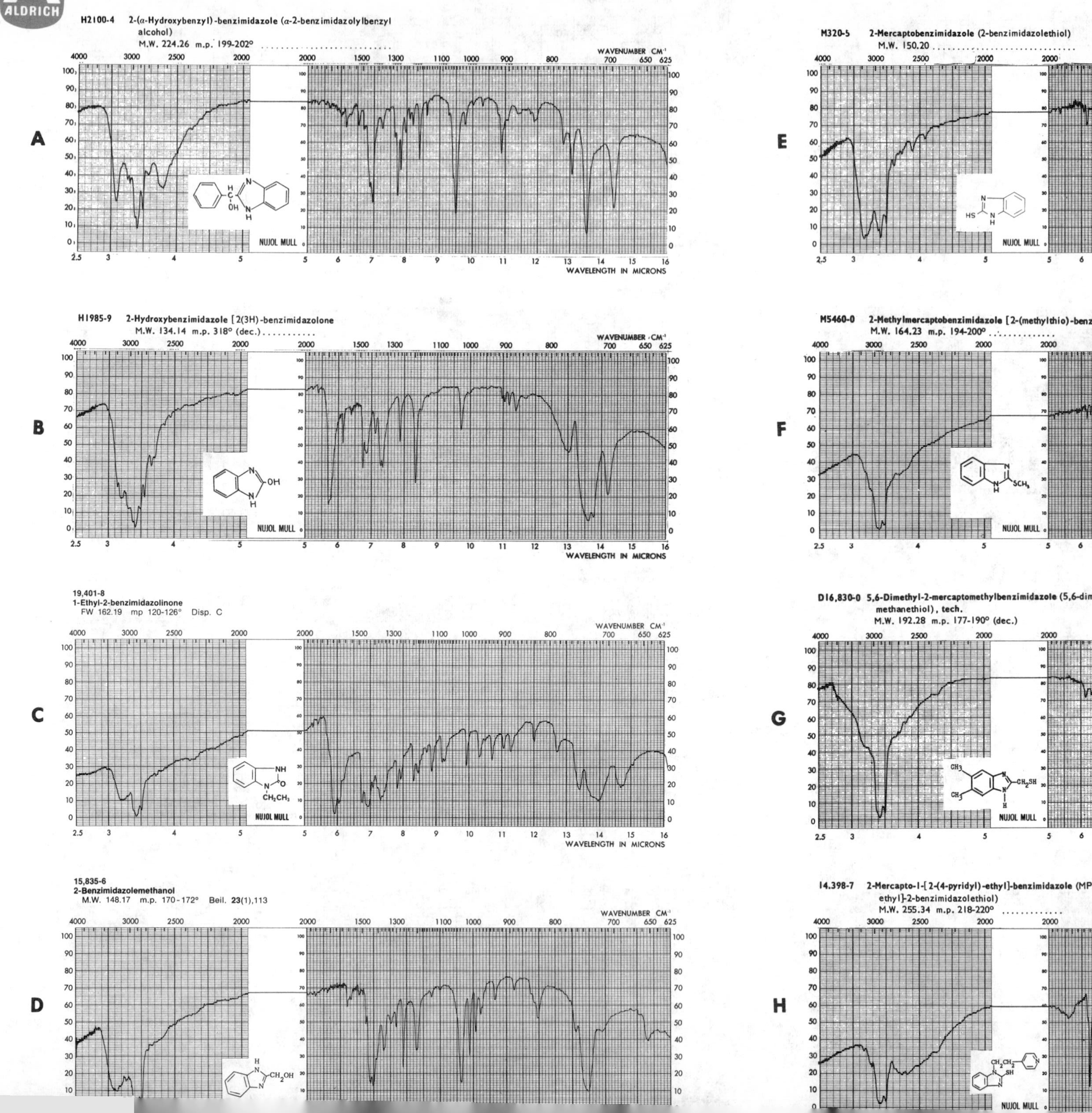
ALDRICH
A
H2100-4 2-(α-Hydroxybenzyl)-benzimidazole (α-2-benzimidazolylbenzyl alcohol)
M.W. 224.26 m.p. 199-202°
B
H1985-9 2-Hydroxybenzimidazole [2(3H)-benzimidazolone
M.W. 134.14 m.p. 318° (dec.)
C
19,401-8
1-Ethyl-2-benzimidazolinone
FW 162.19 mp 120-126° Disp. C
D
15,835-6
2-Benzimidazolemethanol
M.W. 148.17 m.p. 170-172° Beil. 23(1),113
E
M320-5 2-Mercaptobenzimidazole (2-benzimidazolethiol)
M.W. 150.20
F
M5460-0 2-Methylmercaptobenzimidazole [2-(methylthio)-benzimidazole]
M.W. 164.23 m.p. 194-200°
G
D16,830-0 5,6-Dimethyl-2-mercaptomethylbenzimidazole (5,6-dimethyl-2-benzimidazole-methanethiol), tech.
M.W. 192.28 m.p. 177-190° (dec.)
H
14,398-7 2-Mercapto-1-[2-(4-pyridyl)-ethyl]-benzimidazole (MPB, 1-[2-(4-pyridyl)-ethyl]-2-benzimidazolethiol)
M.W. 255.34 m.p. 218-220°
NUJOL MULL
WAVENUMBER CM⁻¹
WAVELENGTH IN MICRONS

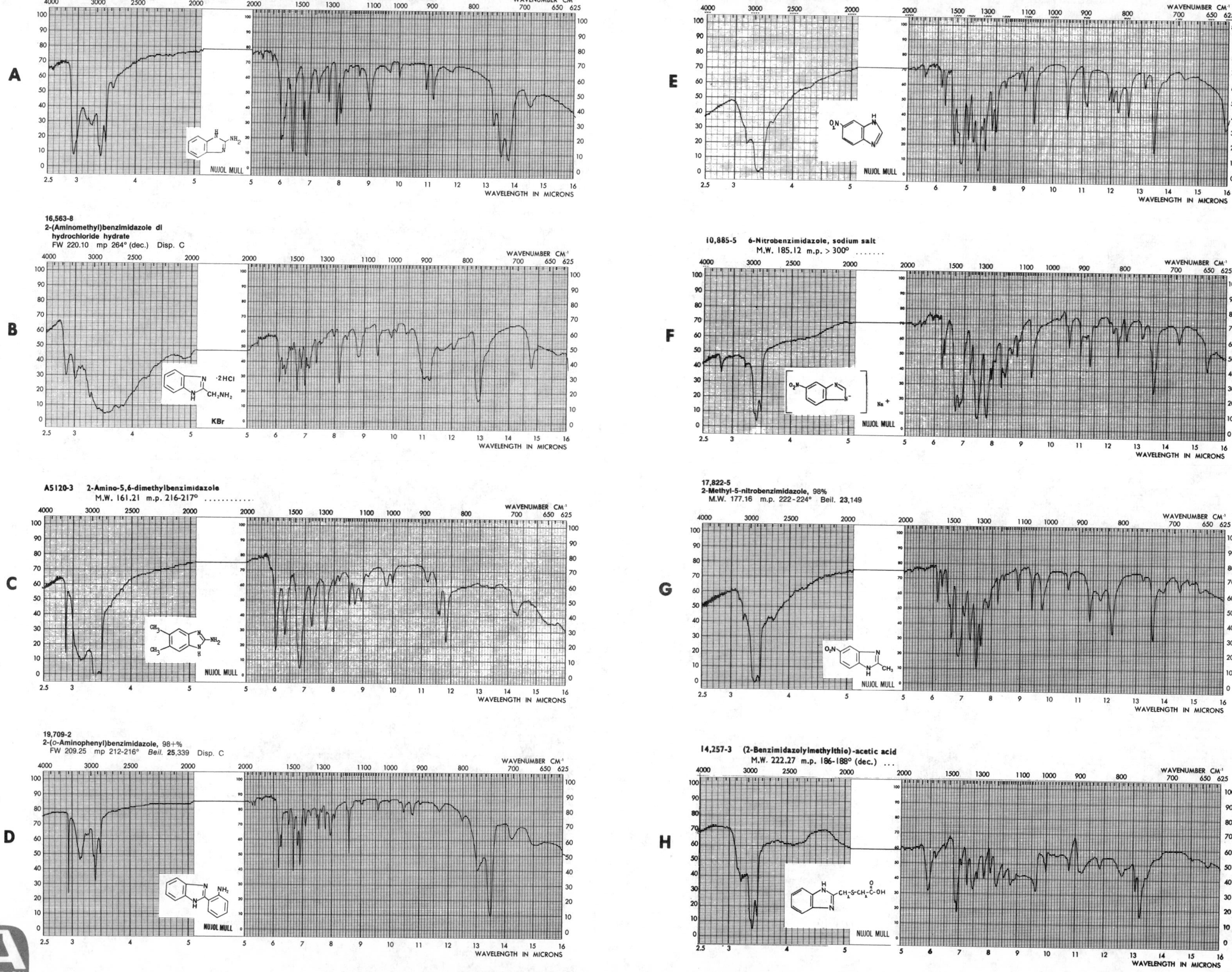
A
M.W. 133.15 m.p. 229-231° Beil. 24,116
NUJOL MULL
B
16,563-8
2-(Aminomethyl)benzimidazole di hydrochloride hydrate
FW 220.10 mp 264° (dec.) Disp. C
KBr
C
A5120-3 2-Amino-5,6-dimethylbenzimidazole
M.W. 161.21 m.p. 216-217°
NUJOL MULL
D
19,709-2
2-(o-Aminophenyl)benzimidazole, 98+%
FW 209.25 mp 212-216° Beil. 25,339 Disp. C
NUJOL MULL
E
N1160-4 6-Nitrobenzimidazole
M.W. 163.14 m.p. 209-210°
NUJOL MULL
F
10,885-5 6-Nitrobenzimidazole, sodium salt
M.W. 185.12 m.p. > 300°
NUJOL MULL
G
17,822-5
2-Methyl-5-nitrobenzimidazole, 98%
M.W. 177.16 m.p. 222-224° Beil. 23,149
NUJOL MULL
H
14,257-3 (2-Benzimidazolylmethylthio)-acetic acid
M.W. 222.27 m.p. 186-188° (dec.)
NUJOL MULL
WAVENUMBER CM⁻¹
WAVELENGTH IN MICRONS
ALDRICH

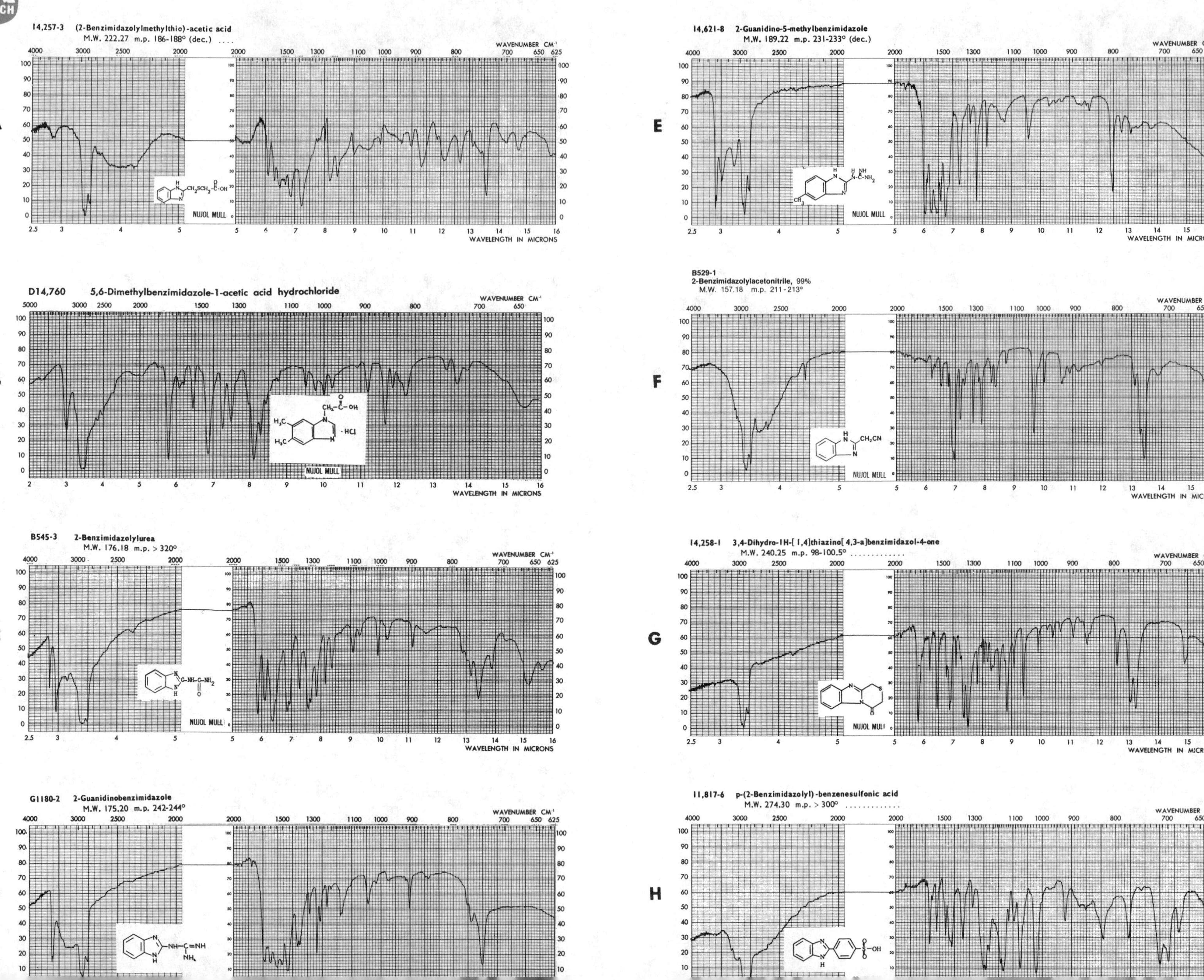
A
14,257-3 (2-Benzimidazolylmethylthio)-acetic acid
M.W. 222.27 m.p. 186-188° (dec.)
NUJOL MULL
B
D14,760 5,6-Dimethylbenzimidazole-1-acetic acid hydrochloride
NUJOL MULL
C
B545-3 2-Benzimidazolylurea
M.W. 176.18 m.p. > 320°
NUJOL MULL
D
G1180-2 2-Guanidinobenzimidazole
M.W. 175.20 m.p. 242-244°
E
14,621-8 2-Guanidino-5-methylbenzimidazole
M.W. 189.22 m.p. 231-233° (dec.)
NUJOL MULL
F
B529-1
2-Benzimidazolylacetonitrile, 99%
M.W. 157.18 m.p. 211-213°
NUJOL MULL
G
14,258-1 3,4-Dihydro-1H-[1,4]thiazino[4,3-a]benzimidazol-4-one
M.W. 240.25 m.p. 98-100.5°
NUJOL MULL
H
11,817-6 p-(2-Benzimidazolyl)-benzenesulfonic acid
M.W. 274.30 m.p. > 300°
WAVENUMBER CM⁻¹
WAVELENGTH IN MICRONS

A

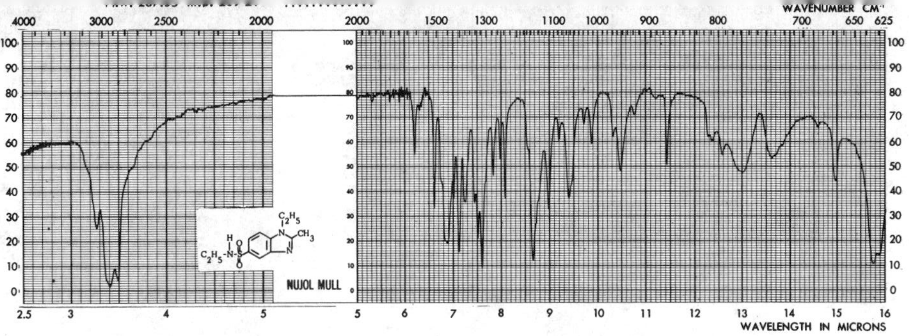

NUJOL MULL

19,429-8
Nocodazole, 99+%, GOLD LABEL [methyl [5-(2-thienylcarbonyl)-1*H*-benzimidazol-2-yl]-carbamate, R 17934]
FW 301.33 mp 299° (dec.) Disp. C

B

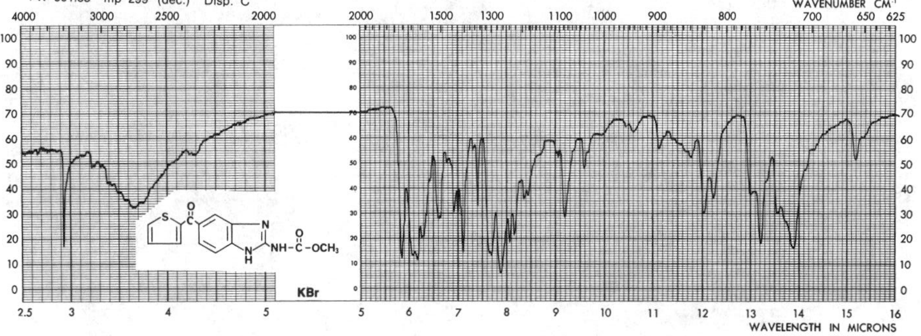

KBr

15,530-6 **N'-(6-Indazolyl)-sulfanilamide** (6-sulfanilamidoindazole)
M.W. 288.33

C

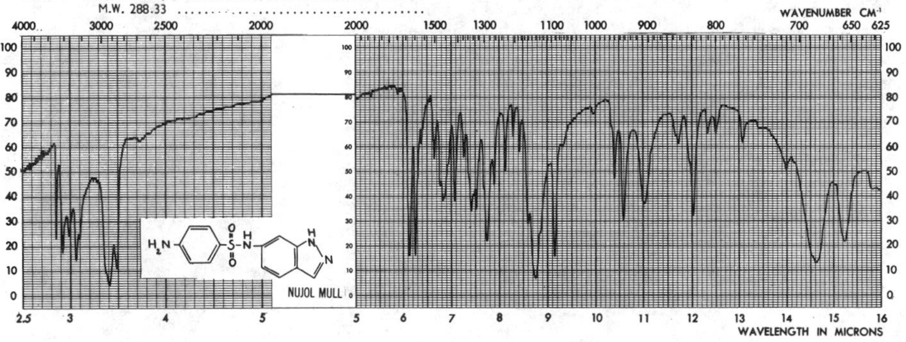

NUJOL MULL

13,896-7 **Pyrimidazole** (imidazo[1,2-a]pyridine)
M.W. 118.14 n_D^{20} 1.6189

D

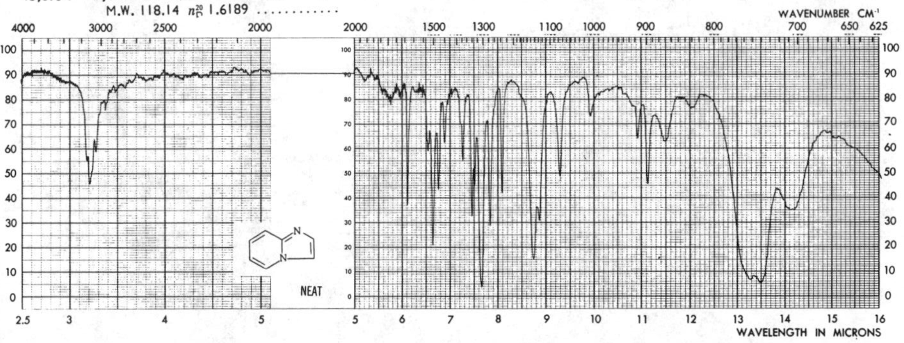

NEAT

M.W. 197.04 m.p. 92-93.5°

E

NUJOL MULL

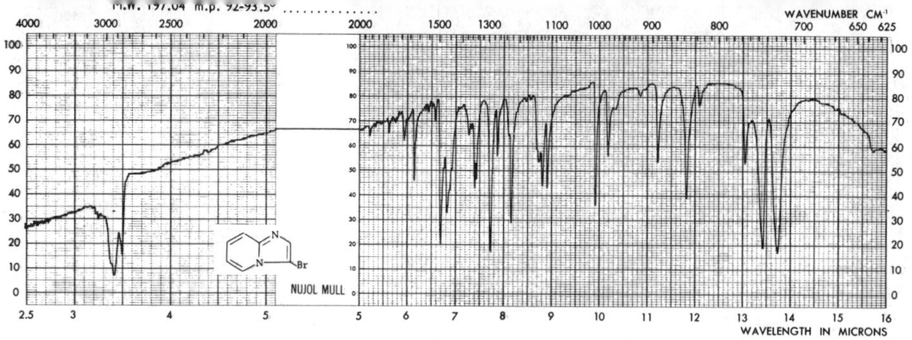

13,899-1 **3-Nitropyrimidazole** (3-nitroimidazo[1,2-a]pyridine)
M.W. 163.14 m.p. 204-206°

F

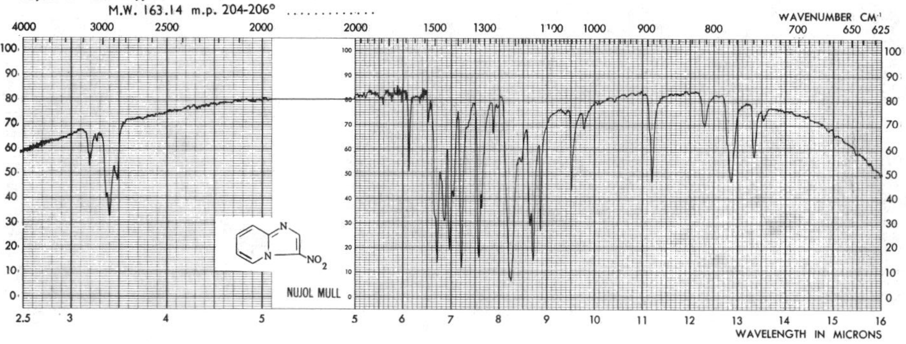

NUJOL MULL

B1140-0 **Benzotriazole, puriss.**
M.W. 119.13 m.p. 98-99°

G

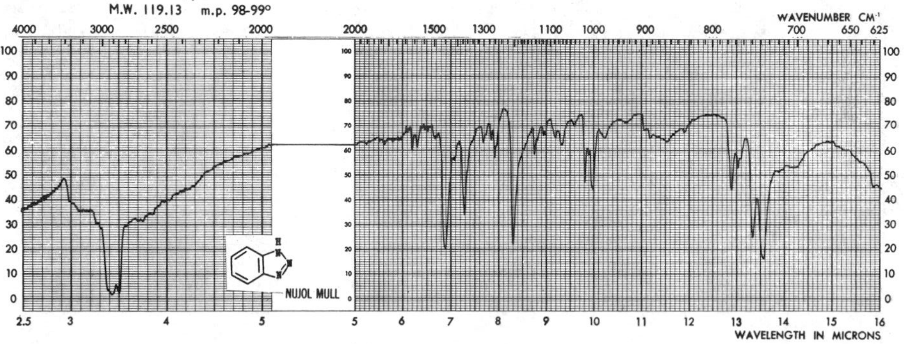

NUJOL MULL

19,630-4
6-Methylbenzotriazole, 98%
FW 133.15 mp 80-82° bp 210-212°/12mm.
Beil. **26**,58 Disp. D

H

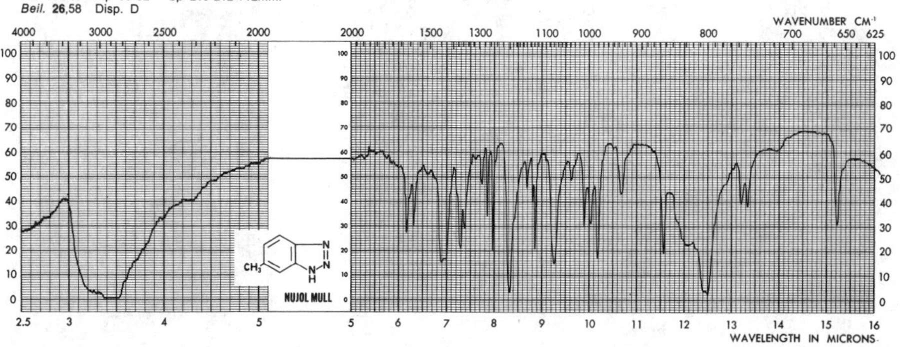

NUJOL MULL

5 MEMBERED FUSED AROMATIC HETEROCYCLES

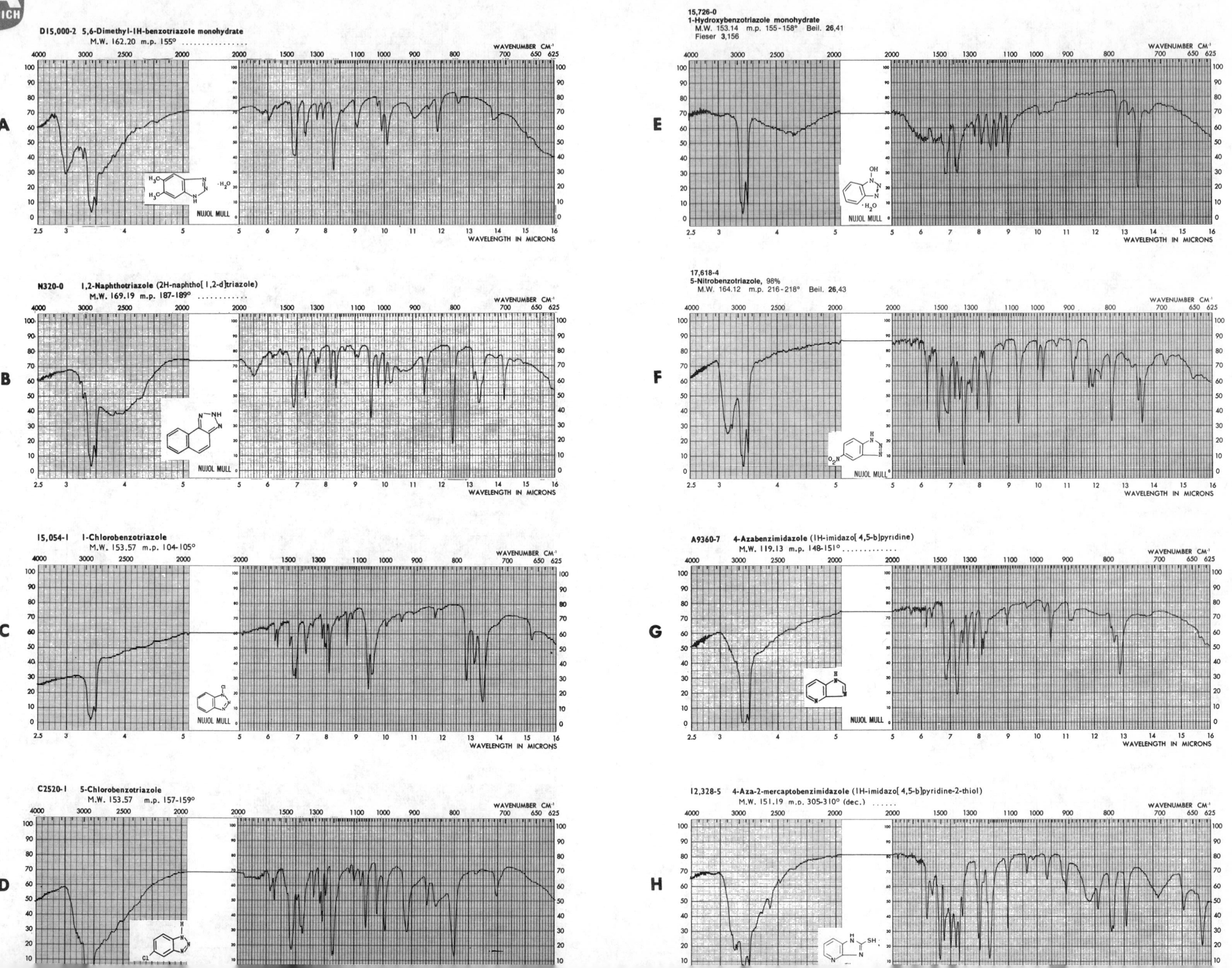

ALDRICH
A
D15,000-2 5,6-Dimethyl-1H-benzotriazole monohydrate
M.W. 162.20 m.p. 155°
B
N320-0 1,2-Naphthotriazole (2H-naphtho[1,2-d]triazole)
M.W. 169.19 m.p. 187-189°
C
15,054-1 1-Chlorobenzotriazole
M.W. 153.57 m.p. 104-105°
D
C2520-1 5-Chlorobenzotriazole
M.W. 153.57 m.p. 157-159°
E
15,726-0
1-Hydroxybenzotriazole monohydrate
M.W. 153.14 m.p. 155-158° Beil. 26,41
Fieser 3,156
F
17,618-4
5-Nitrobenzotriazole, 98%
M.W. 164.12 m.p. 216-218° Beil. 26,43
G
A9360-7 4-Azabenzimidazole (1H-imidazo[4,5-b]pyridine)
M.W. 119.13 m.p. 148-151°
H
12,328-5 4-Aza-2-mercaptobenzimidazole (1H-imidazo[4,5-b]pyridine-2-thiol)
M.W. 151.19 m.p. 305-310° (dec.)
NUJOL MULL
WAVENUMBER CM⁻¹
WAVELENGTH IN MICRONS

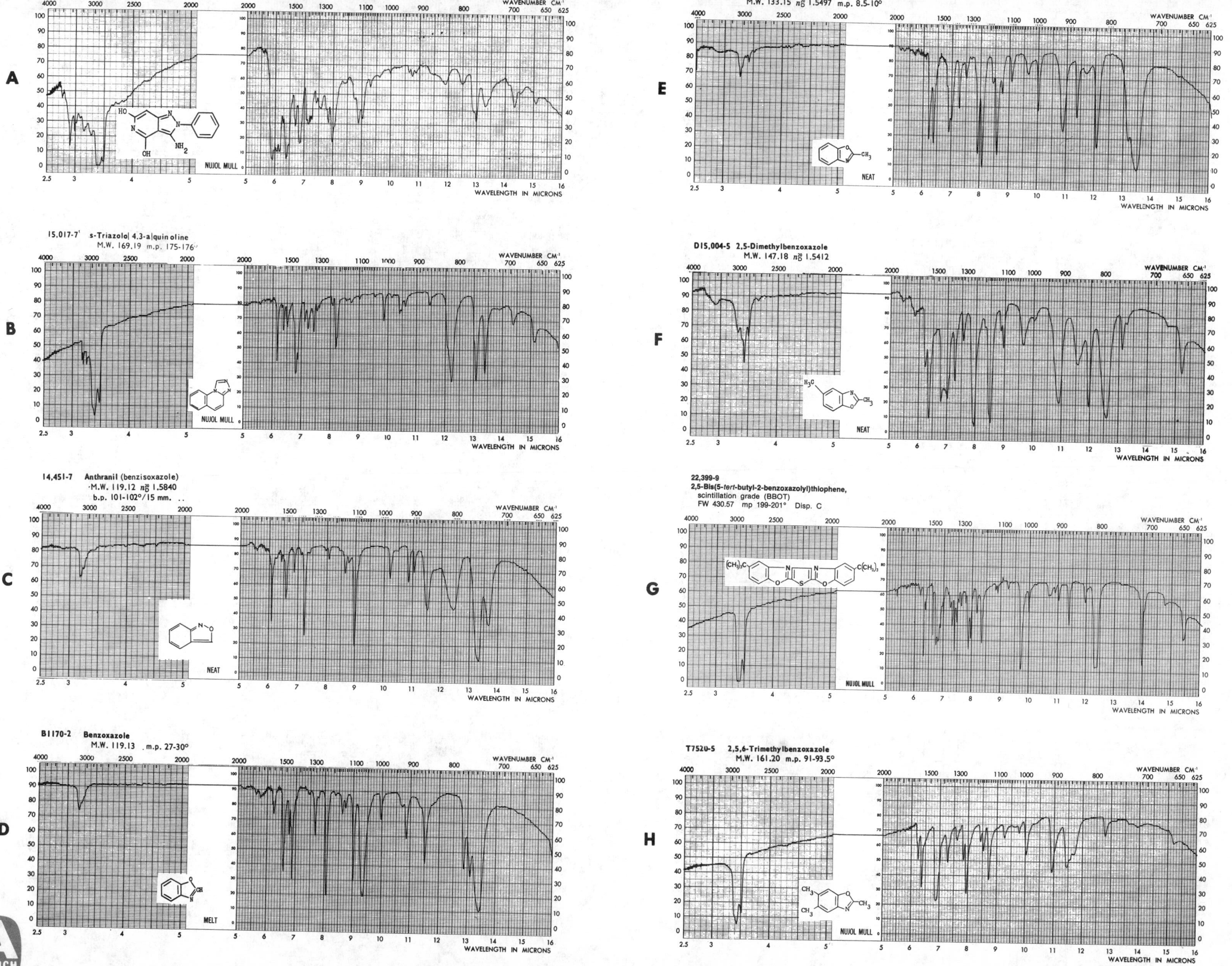
A
M.W. 242.24 m.p. 265-266°
NUJOL MULL
B
15,017-7 s-Triazolo[4,3-a]quinoline
M.W. 169.19 m.p. 175-176°
NUJOL MULL
C
14,451-7 Anthranil (benzisoxazole)
M.W. 119.12 n_D^{20} 1.5840
b.p. 101-102°/15 mm.
NEAT
D
B1170-2 Benzoxazole
M.W. 119.13 m.p. 27-30°
MELT
E
10,893-6 2-Methylbenzoxazole
M.W. 133.15 n_D^{20} 1.5497 m.p. 8.5-10°
NEAT
F
D15,004-5 2,5-Dimethylbenzoxazole
M.W. 147.18 n_D^{20} 1.5412
NEAT
G
22,399-9
2,5-Bis(5-tert-butyl-2-benzoxazolyl)thiophene,
scintillation grade (BBOT)
FW 430.57 mp 199-201° Disp. C
NUJOL MULL
H
T7520-5 2,5,6-Trimethylbenzoxazole
M.W. 161.20 m.p. 91-93.5°
NUJOL MULL
WAVENUMBER CM⁻¹
WAVELENGTH IN MICRONS
ALDRICH

5 MEMBERED FUSED AROMATIC HETEROCYCLES

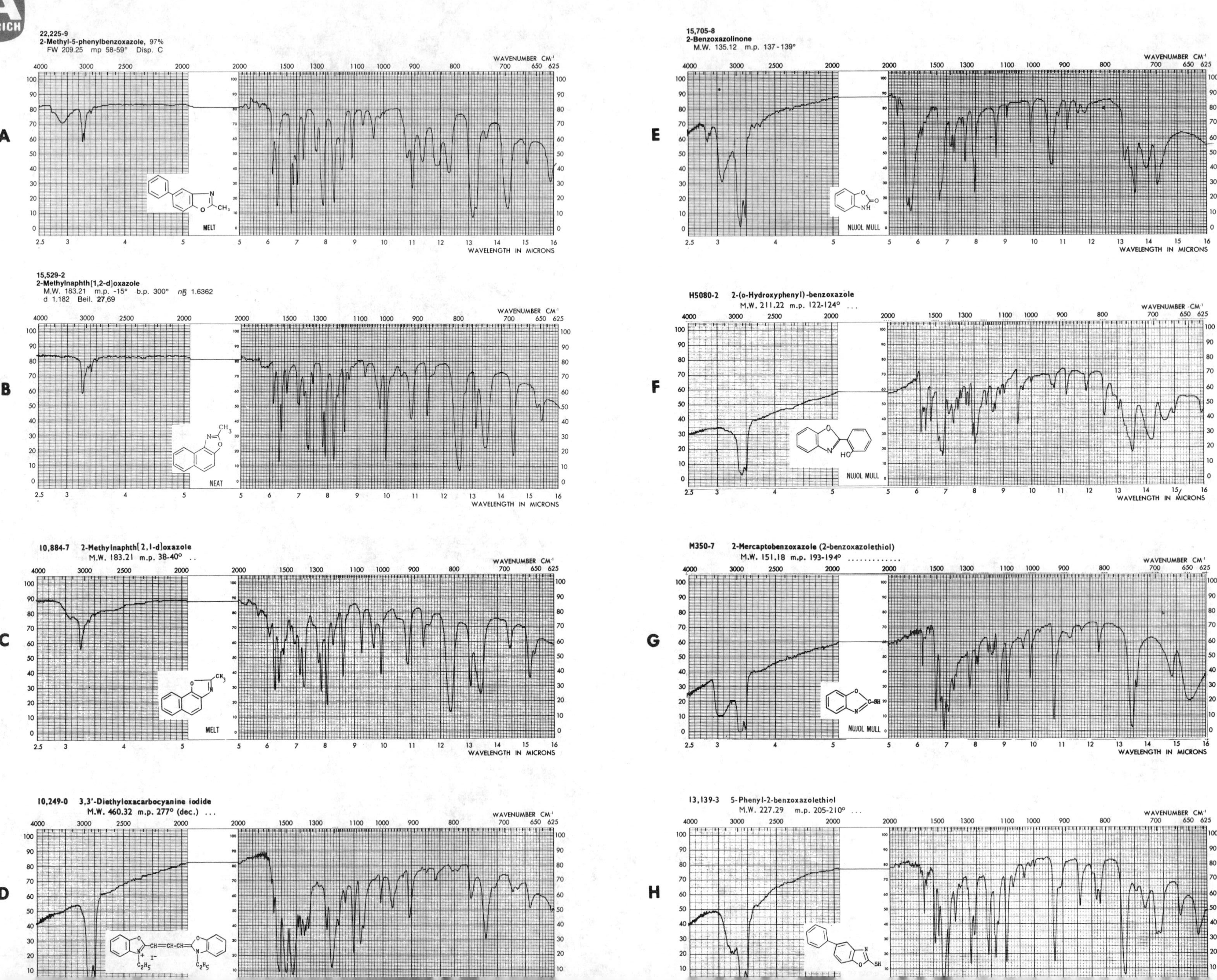
ALDRICH
A
22,225-9
2-Methyl-5-phenylbenzoxazole, 97%
FW 209.25 mp 58-59° Disp. C
MELT
B
15,529-2
2-Methylnaphth[1,2-d]oxazole
M.W. 183.21 m.p. -15° b.p. 300° n_D^{20} 1.6362
d 1.182 Beil. 27,69
NEAT
C
10,884-7 2-Methylnaphth[2,1-d]oxazole
M.W. 183.21 m.p. 38-40° ..
MELT
D
10,249-0 3,3'-Diethyloxacarbocyanine iodide
M.W. 460.32 m.p. 277° (dec.) ...
E
15,705-8
2-Benzoxazolinone
M.W. 135.12 m.p. 137-139°
NUJOL MULL
F
H5080-2 2-(o-Hydroxyphenyl)-benzoxazole
M.W. 211.22 m.p. 122-124° ...
NUJOL MULL
G
M350-7 2-Mercaptobenzoxazole (2-benzoxazolethiol)
M.W. 151.18 m.p. 193-194° ....
NUJOL MULL
H
13,139-3 5-Phenyl-2-benzoxazolethiol
M.W. 227.29 m.p. 205-210° ...
WAVENUMBER CM⁻¹
WAVELENGTH IN MICRONS

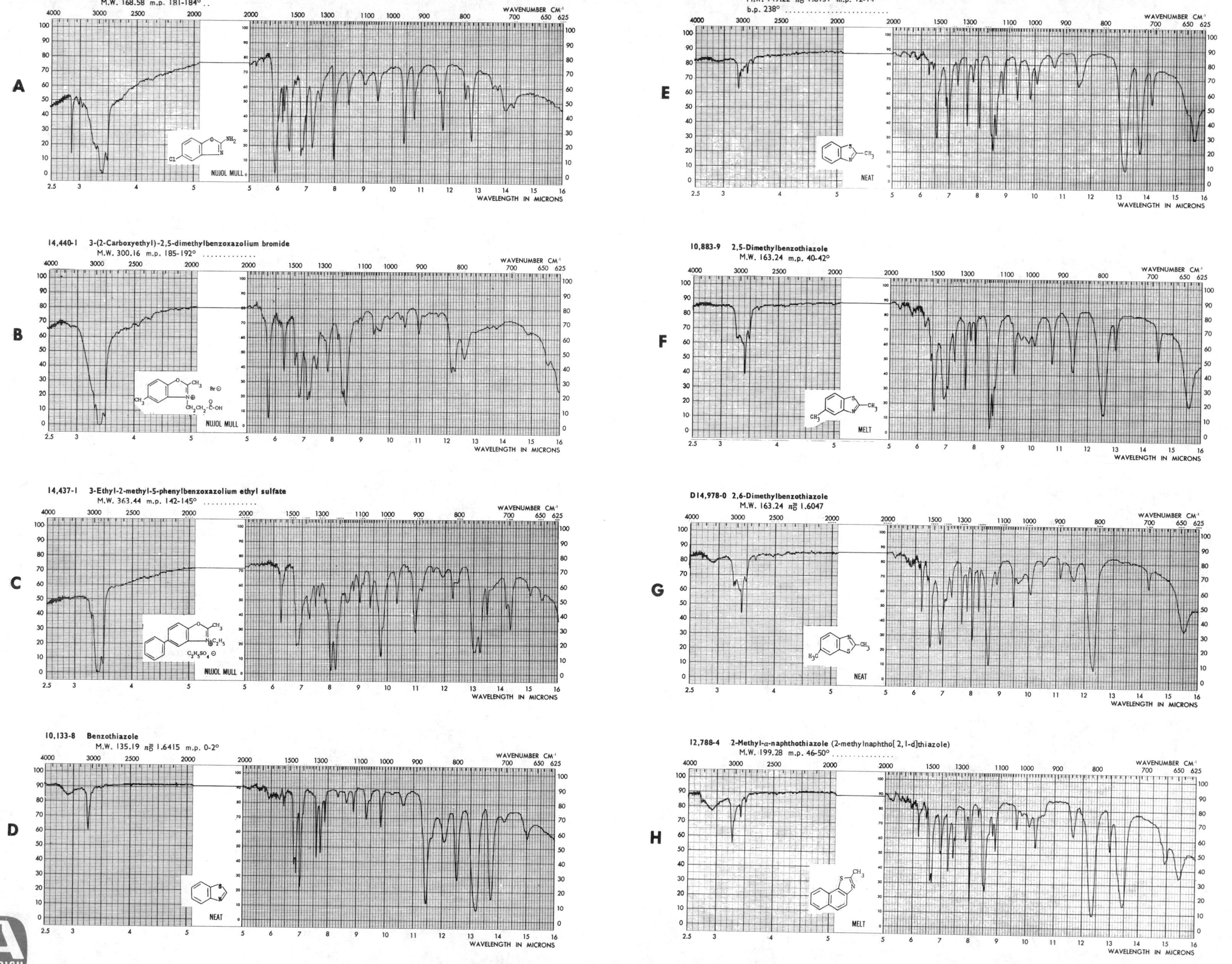

A
A4580-7 2-Amino-5-chlorobenzoxazole
M.W. 168.58 m.p. 181-184°
NUJOL MULL
B
14,440-1 3-(2-Carboxyethyl)-2,5-dimethylbenzoxazolium bromide
M.W. 300.16 m.p. 185-192°
NUJOL MULL
C
14,437-1 3-Ethyl-2-methyl-5-phenylbenzoxazolium ethyl sulfate
M.W. 363.44 m.p. 142-145°
NUJOL MULL
D
10,133-8 Benzothiazole
M.W. 135.19 n_D^{20} 1.6415 m.p. 0-2°
NEAT
E
M.W. 149.22 n_D^{20} 1.6131 m.p. 12-14°
b.p. 238°
NEAT
F
10,883-9 2,5-Dimethylbenzothiazole
M.W. 163.24 m.p. 40-42°
MELT
G
D14,978-0 2,6-Dimethylbenzothiazole
M.W. 163.24 n_D^{20} 1.6047
NEAT
H
12,788-4 2-Methyl-α-naphthothiazole (2-methylnaphtho[2,1-d]thiazole)
M.W. 199.28 m.p. 46-50°
MELT
WAVENUMBER CM⁻¹
WAVELENGTH IN MICRONS
ALDRICH

5 MEMBERED FUSED AROMATIC HETEROCYCLES

A

M5780-4 2-Methyl-β-naphthothiazole (2-methylnaphtho[1,2-d]thiazole)
M.W. 199.28 m.p. 95-97°

NUJOL MULL

B

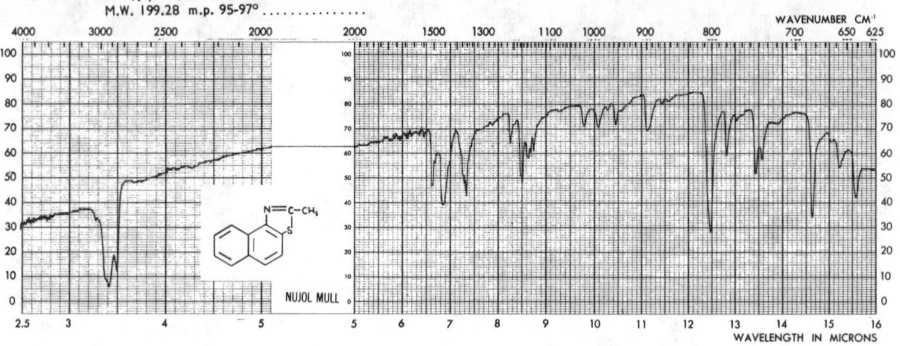

10,248-2 3,3'-Diethyl-9-methylthiacarbocyanine iodide
M.W. 506.47 m.p. 280-282°

NUJOL MULL

C

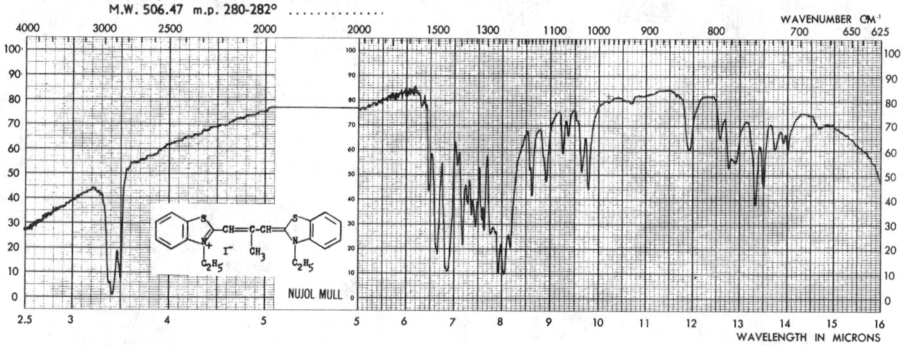

E2830-7 3-Ethyl-2-[5-(3-ethyl-2-benzothiazolinylidene)-1,3-pentadienyl]-benzothiazolium iodide
M.W. 518.48 m.p. 258-260°

NUJOL MULL

D

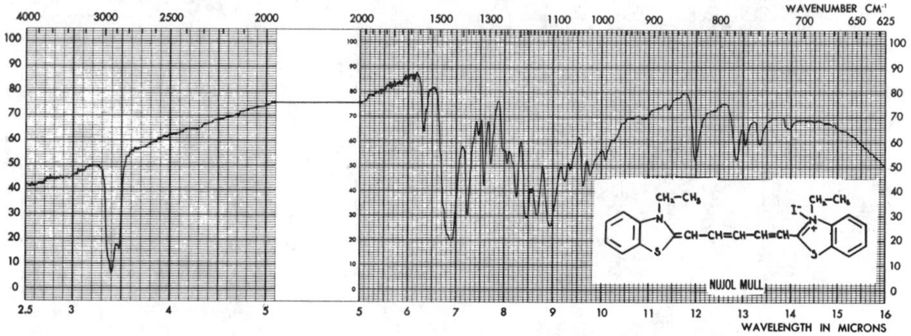

10,247-4 3,3'-Diallylthiacarbocyanine iodide
M.W. 516.47 m.p. 261° (dec.)

E

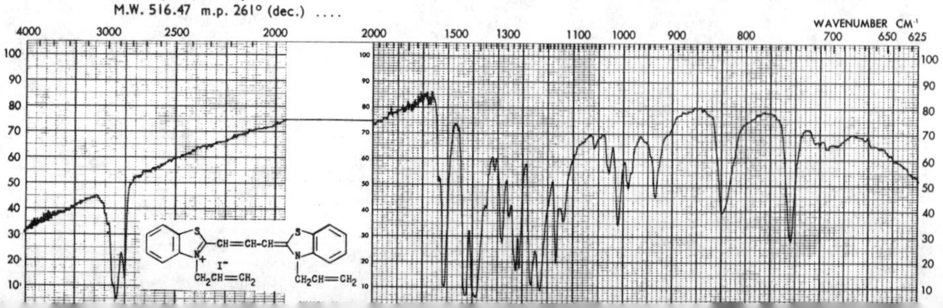

12,638-1 2,3-Dimethylbenzothiazolium iodide
M.W. 291.16 m.p. 219° (dec.)

NUJOL MULL

F

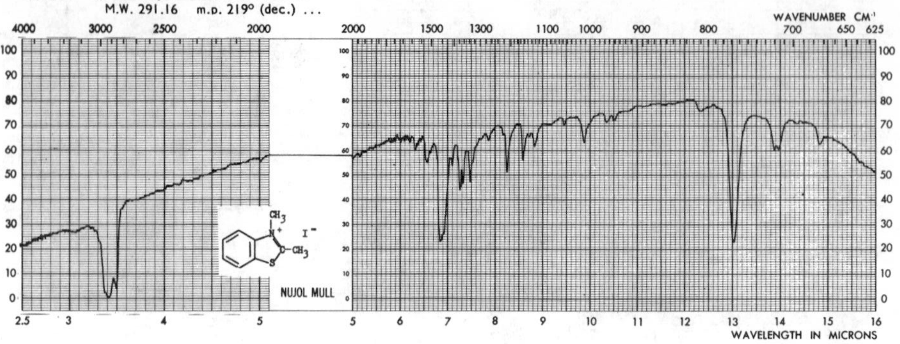

14,434-7 1,2-Dimethylnaphtho[1,2-d]thiazolium methyl sulfate
M.W. 325.41 m.p. 156° (dec.)

NUJOL MULL

G

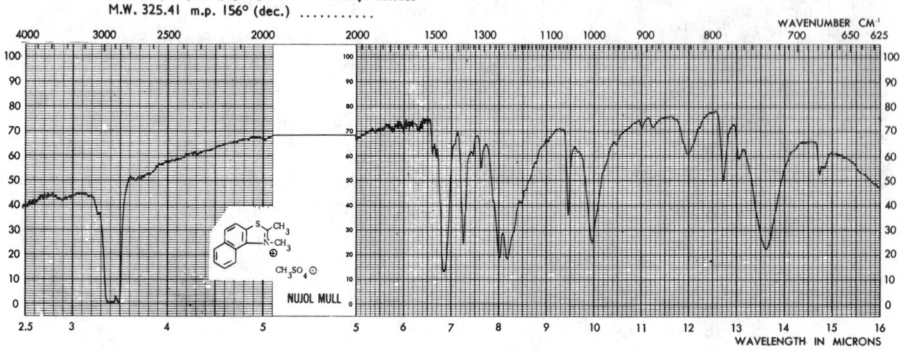

13,959-9 2-Trifluoromethylbenzothiazole
M.W. 203.19 b.p. 45-48°/0.1 mm.

NEAT

H

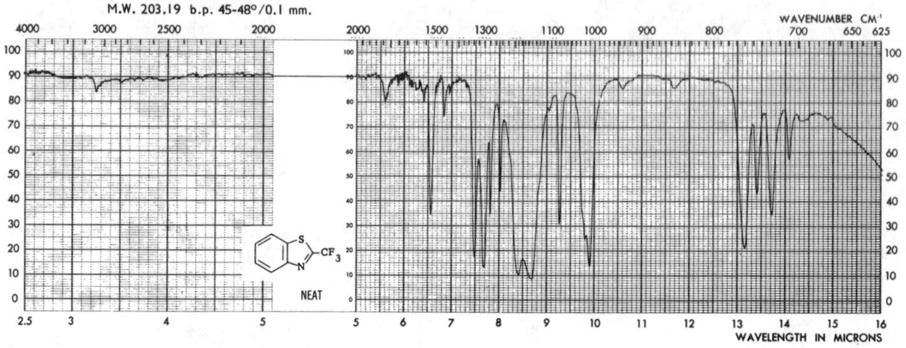

16,757-6
2-Chlorobenzothiazole, 99%
M.W. 169.63 m.p. 21-23° b.p. 141°/30mm.
n_D^{20} 1.6377 d 1.303 Beil. 27,44

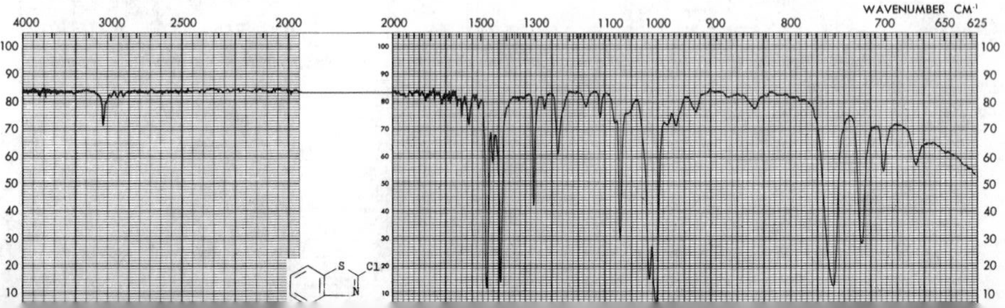

A

M.W. 179.24 n_D^{20} 1.6121 ......

NEAT

B

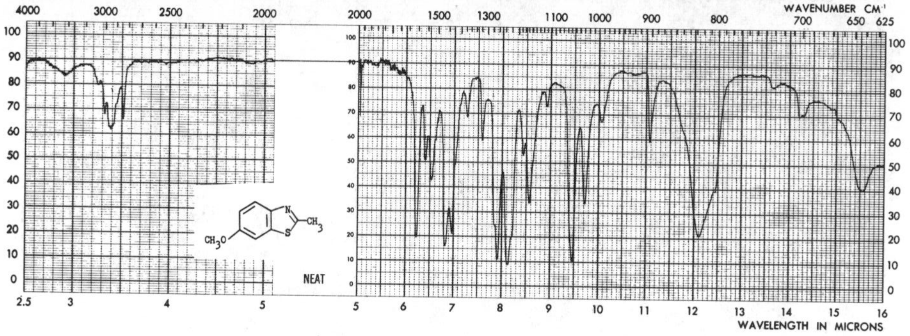

H5060-8 2-(o-Hydroxyphenyl)-benzothiazole
M.W. 227.29 m.p. 130-132° ....

NUJOL MULL

C

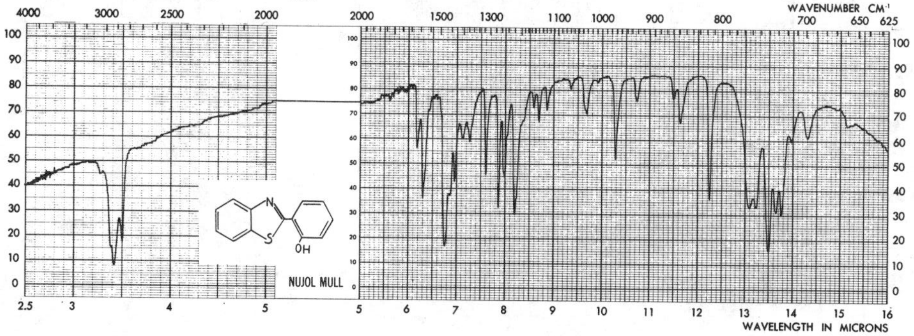

M330-2 2-Mercaptobenzothiazole (2-benzothiazolethiol)
M.W. 167.25 m.p. 177-181° ....

NUJOL MULL

D

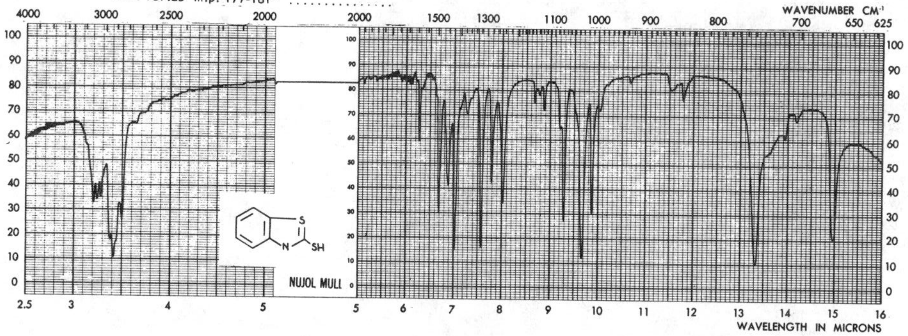

D21,815-4 2,2'-Dithiobis-(benzothiazole) (2-benzothiazolyl disulfide), tech.
M.W. 332.48 ....

NUJOL MULL

E

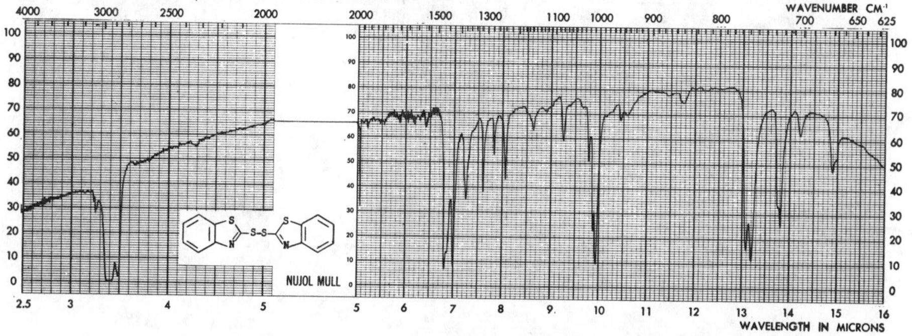

12,993-3 3-Methyl-2-(methylthio)-benzothiazolium p-toluenesulfonate
M.W. 367.51 m.p. 168-171° ....

NUJOL MULL

F

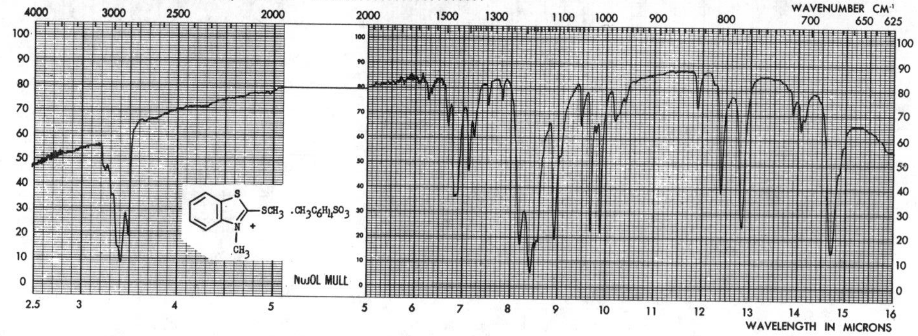

12,557-1 5-Chloro-2-mercaptobenzothiazole (5-chloro-2-benzothiazolethiol)
M.W. 201.70 m.p. 196-197.5° ....

NUJOL MULL

G

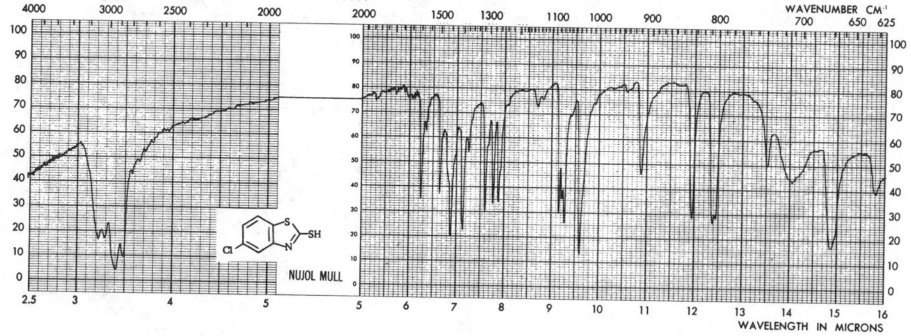

14,217-4 6-Ethoxy-2-mercaptobenzothiazole (6-ethoxy-2-benzothiazolethiol)
M.W. 211.31 m.p. 198-200°

NUJOL MULL

H

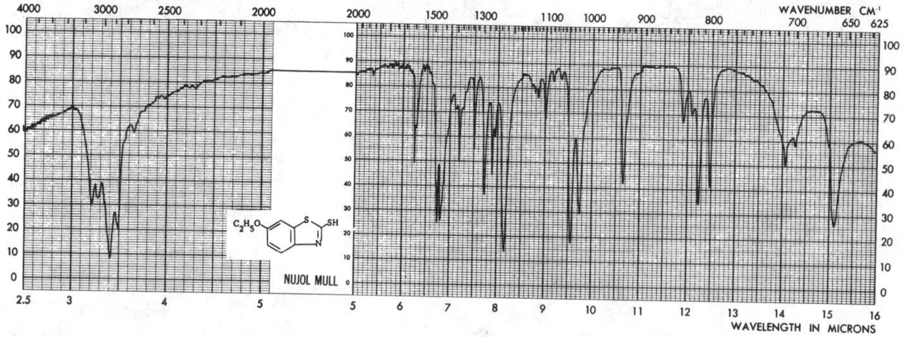

M5500-3 2-Methylmercaptobenzothiazole ethyl p-toluenesulfonate
M.W. 381.54 m.p. 150-152° ....

NUJOL MULL

5 MEMBERED FUSED AROMATIC HETEROCYCLES

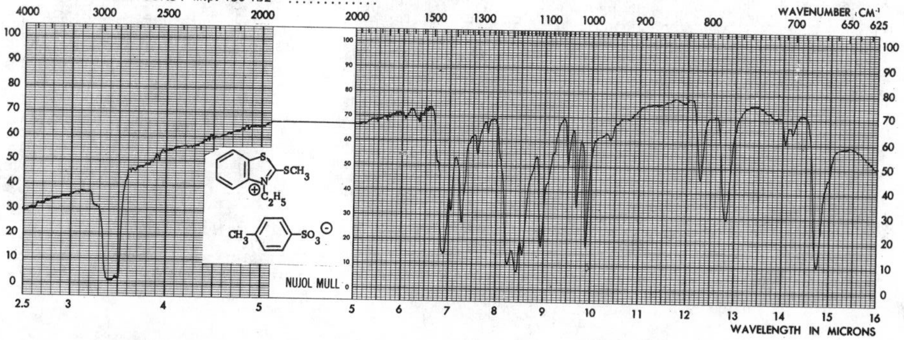

A 10,881-2 **2-Aminobenzothiazole**
M.W. 150.20 m.p. 126-129°
NUJOL MULL

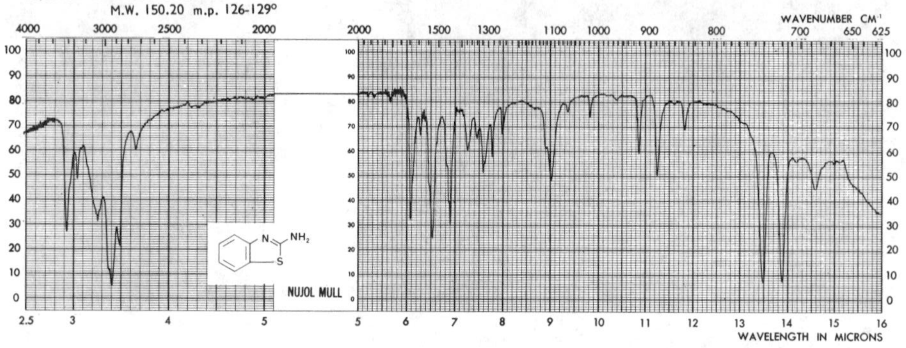

B 19,322-4
2-Amino-4-methylbenzothiazole
FW 164.23 mp 137-139° *Beil.* **27**,193 Disp. C
NUJOL MULL

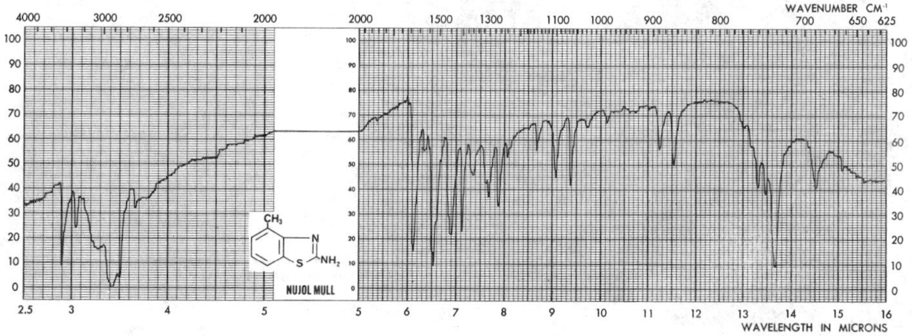

C 12,422-2 **N-tert.-Butyl-2-benzothiazolesulfenamide**
M.W. 238.37 m.p. 104-107°
NUJOL MULL

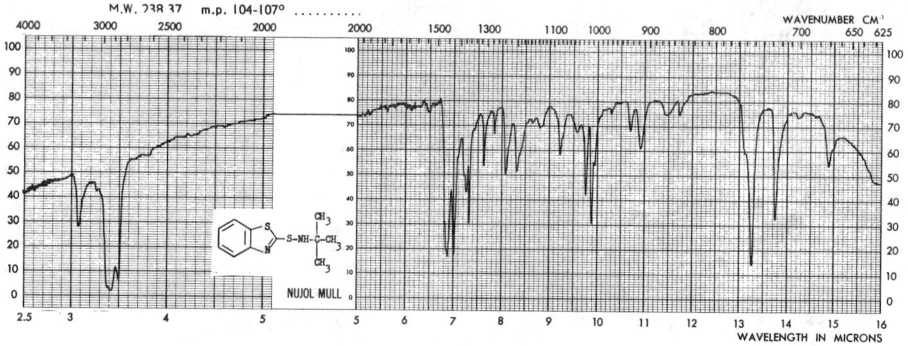

D A6330-9 **5-Amino-2-methylbenzothiazole dihydrochloride**
M.W. 237.15 m.p. 249° (dec.)

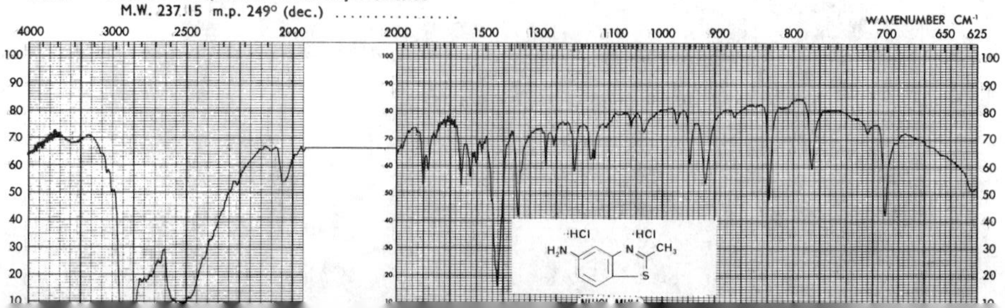

E A5140-8 **2-Amino-5,6-dimethylbenzothiazole**
M.W. 178.26 m.p. 185-189°
NUJOL MULL

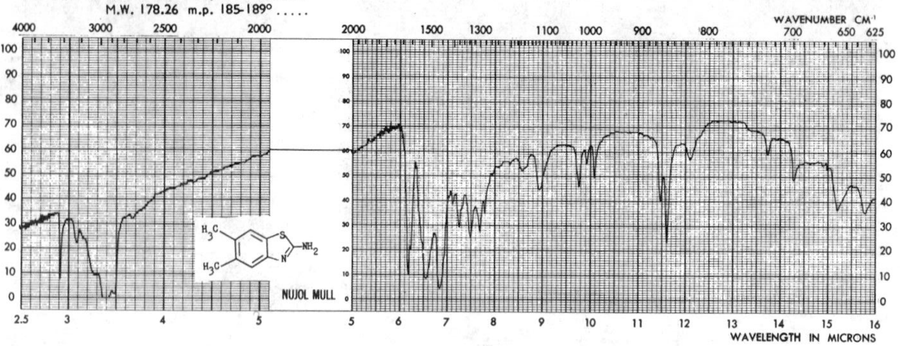

F 13,343-4 **2-Amino-4-chlorobenzothiazole**
M.W. 184.65 m.p. 203-205°
NUJOL MULL

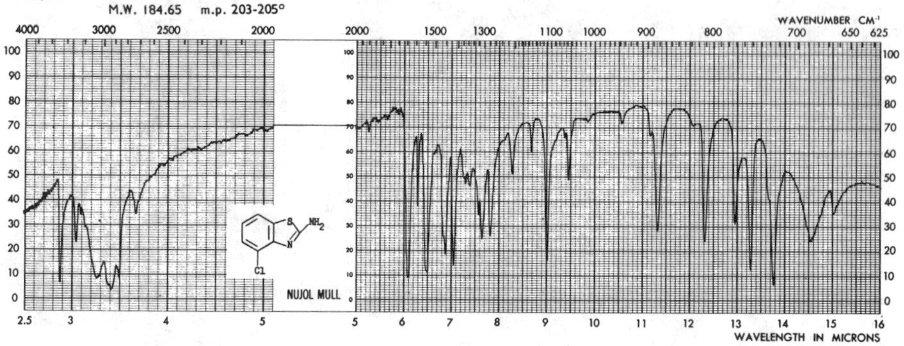

G A4558-0 **2-Amino-4-chlorobenzothiazole hydrobromide**
M.W. 265.57 m.p. 250-252°
NUJOL MULL

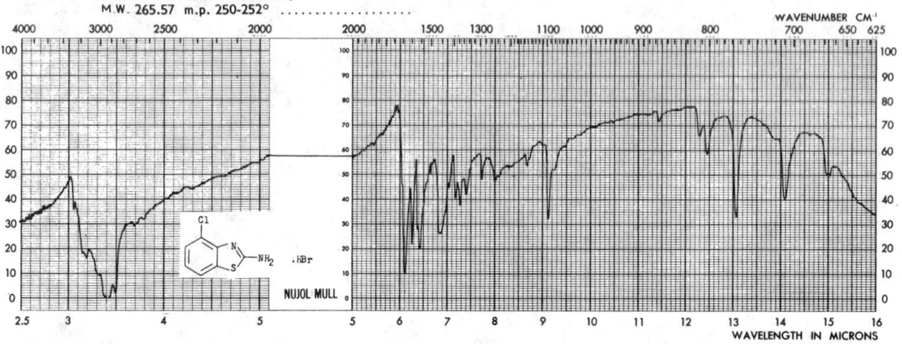

H 13,608-5 **2-Amino-6-chlorobenzothiazole**
M.W. 184.65 m.p. 199-201°

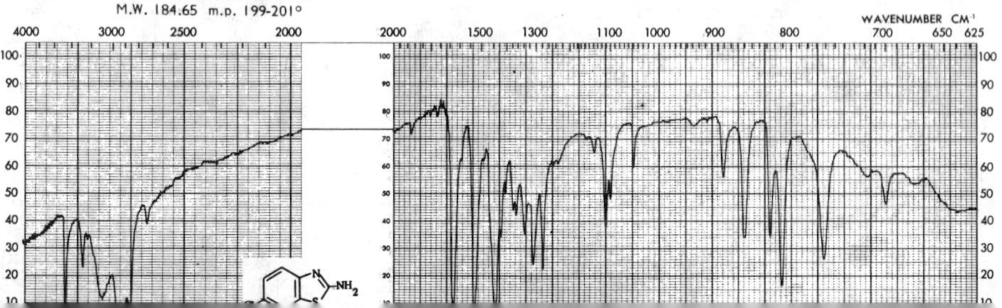

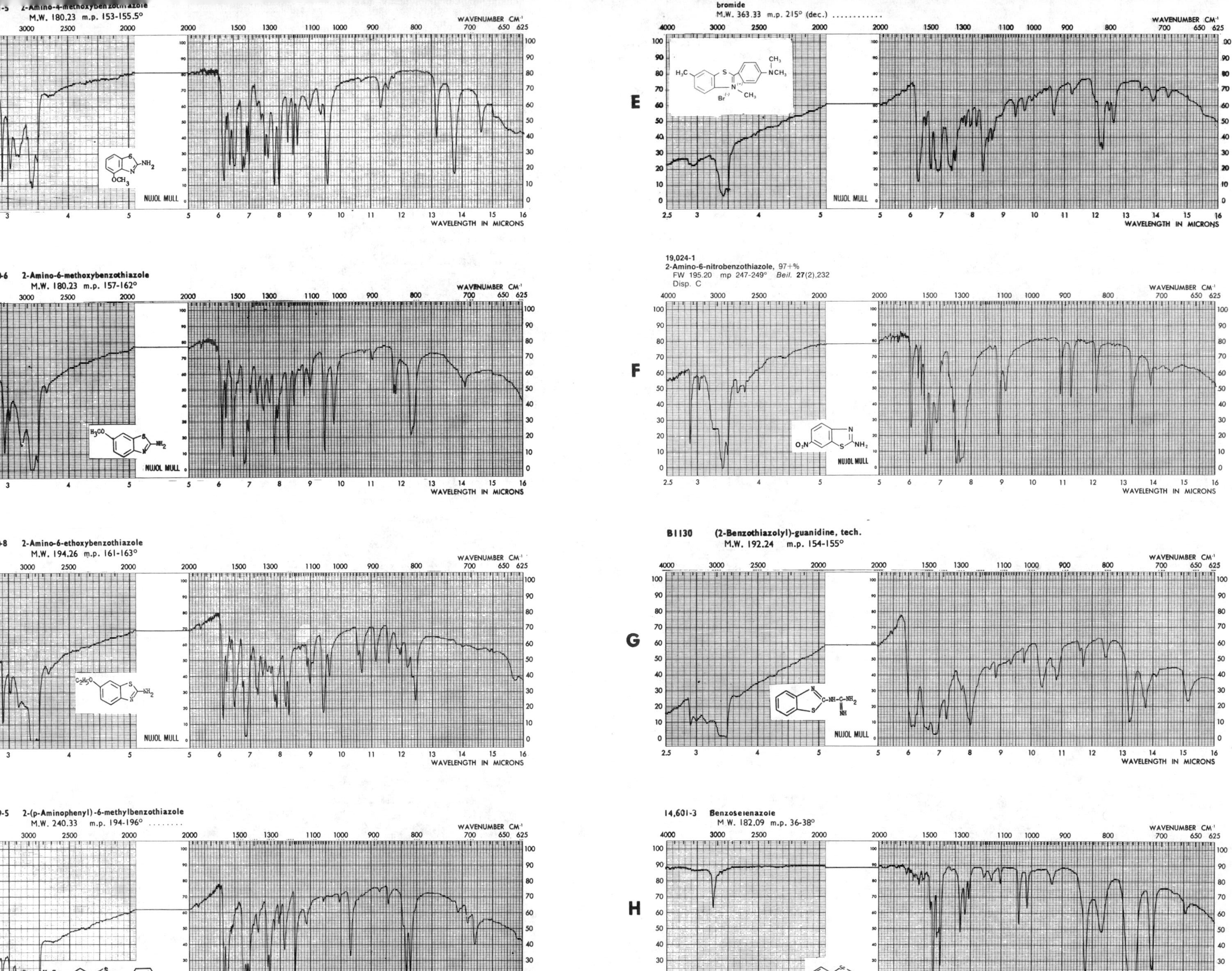

A
13,821-5 2-Amino-4-methoxybenzothiazole
M.W. 180.23 m.p. 153-155.5°
NUJOL MULL
B
A6080-6 2-Amino-6-methoxybenzothiazole
M.W. 180.23 m.p. 157-162°
NUJOL MULL
C
A5400-8 2-Amino-6-ethoxybenzothiazole
M.W. 194.26 m.p. 161-163°
NUJOL MULL
D
A7299-5 2-(p-Aminophenyl)-6-methylbenzothiazole
M.W. 240.33 m.p. 194-196°
NUJOL MULL
E
bromide
M.W. 363.33 m.p. 215° (dec.)
NUJOL MULL
F
19,024-1
2-Amino-6-nitrobenzothiazole, 97+%
FW 195.20 mp 247-249° Beil. 27(2),232
Disp. C
NUJOL MULL
G
B1130 (2-Benzothiazolyl)-guanidine, tech.
M.W. 192.24 m.p. 154-155°
NUJOL MULL
H
14,601-3 Benzoselenazole
M.W. 182.09 m.p. 36-38°
MELT
WAVENUMBER CM⁻¹
WAVELENGTH IN MICRONS
ALDRICH

5 MEMBERED FUSED AROMATIC HETEROCYCLES

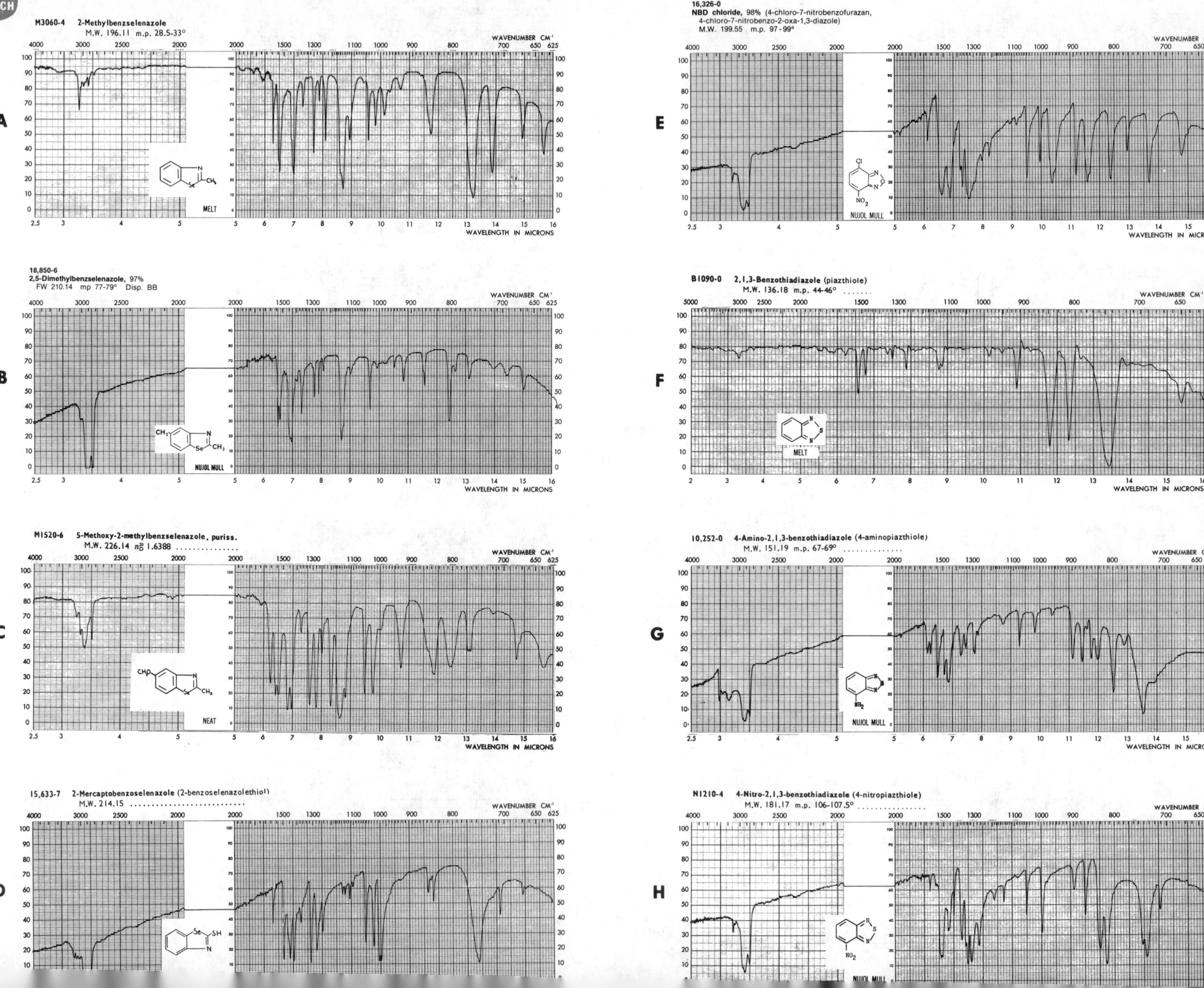
ALDRICH
A
M3060-4 2-Methylbenzselenazole
M.W. 196.11 m.p. 28.5-33°
MELT
B
18,850-6
2,5-Dimethylbenzselenazole, 97%
FW 210.14 mp 77-79° Disp. BB
NUJOL MULL
C
M1520-6 5-Methoxy-2-methylbenzselenazole, puriss.
M.W. 226.14 n_D^{20} 1.6388
NEAT
D
15,633-7 2-Mercaptobenzoselenazole (2-benzoselenazolethiol)
M.W. 214.15
E
16,326-0
NBD chloride, 98% (4-chloro-7-nitrobenzofurazan, 4-chloro-7-nitrobenzo-2-oxa-1,3-diazole)
M.W. 199.55 m.p. 97-99°
NUJOL MULL
F
B1090-0 2,1,3-Benzothiadiazole (piazthiole)
M.W. 136.18 m.p. 44-46°
MELT
G
10,252-0 4-Amino-2,1,3-benzothiadiazole (4-aminopiazthiole)
M.W. 151.19 m.p. 67-69°
NUJOL MULL
H
N1210-4 4-Nitro-2,1,3-benzothiadiazole (4-nitropiazthiole)
M.W. 181.17 m.p. 106-107.5°
NUJOL MULL
WAVENUMBER CM⁻¹
WAVELENGTH IN MICRONS

M.W. 183.07 m.p. 75-76°

FW 135.13 mp 231-233° Disp. C

M2998-3 5-Methyl-2,1,3-benzoselenadiazole (5-methylpiaselenole)
M.W. 197.10 m.p. 70-72°

A7780-6 4-Aminopyrazolo[3,4-d]pyrimidine
M.W. 135.13 m.p. > 325°

D14,975-6 5,6-Dimethyl-2,1,3-benzoselenadiazole
M.W. 211.13 m.p. 144-146°

A5880-1 4-Amino-6-hydroxypyrazolo[3,4-d]pyrimidine (4-aminopyrazolo[3,4-d]pyrimidin-6-ol)
M.W. 151.13 m.p. > 320°

17,767-9
5-Methyl-s-triazolo[1,5-a]pyrimidin-7-ol
M.W. 150.14 m.p. 281-283°

P5580-5 Purine
M.W. 120.12 m.p. 214-217°

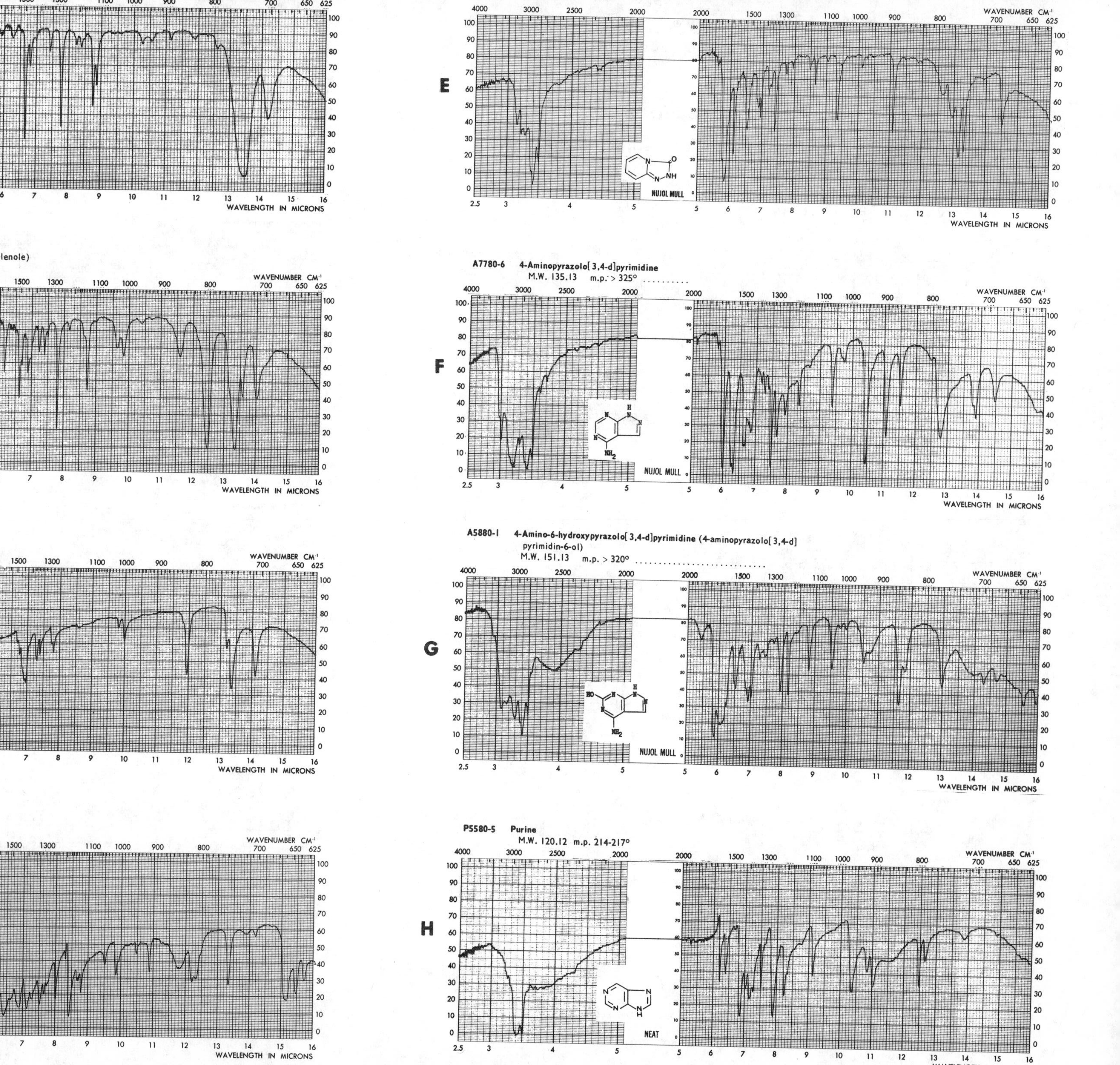

5 MEMBERED FUSED AROMATIC HETEROCYCLES

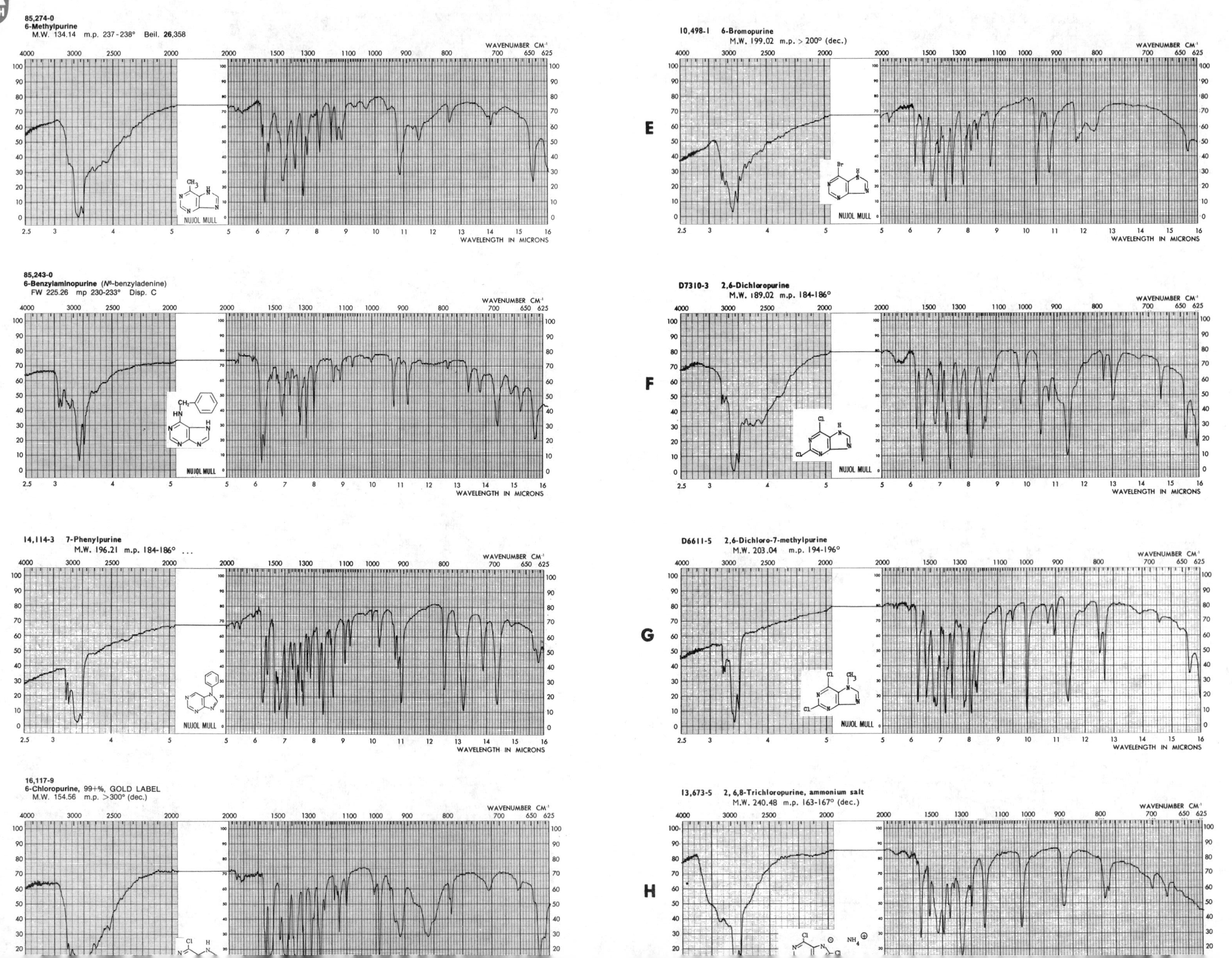
ALDRICH
A
85,274-0
6-Methylpurine
M.W. 134.14 m.p. 237-238° Beil. 26,358
NUJOL MULL
B
85,243-0
6-Benzylaminopurine (N⁶-benzyladenine)
FW 225.26 mp 230-233° Disp. C
NUJOL MULL
C
14,114-3 7-Phenylpurine
M.W. 196.21 m.p. 184-186° ...
NUJOL MULL
D
16,117-9
6-Chloropurine, 99+%, GOLD LABEL
M.W. 154.56 m.p. >300° (dec.)
E
10,498-1 6-Bromopurine
M.W. 199.02 m.p. > 200° (dec.)
NUJOL MULL
F
D7310-3 2,6-Dichloropurine
M.W. 189.02 m.p. 184-186°
NUJOL MULL
G
D6611-5 2,6-Dichloro-7-methylpurine
M.W. 203.04 m.p. 194-196°
NUJOL MULL
H
13,673-5 2,6,8-Trichloropurine, ammonium salt
M.W. 240.48 m.p. 163-167° (dec.)
WAVENUMBER CM⁻¹
WAVELENGTH IN MICRONS

A

M.W. 198.61 m.p. 112-115.5°

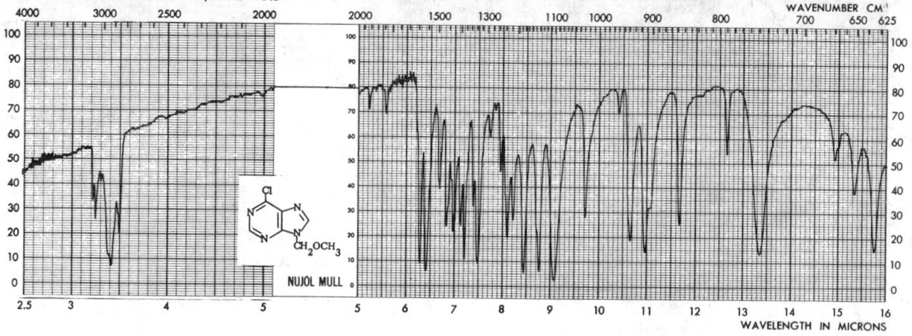

NUJOL MULL

B

85,805-6
6-Chloro-9-(tetrahydro-2-pyranyl)-purine
M.W. 238.68 m.p. 70-71°

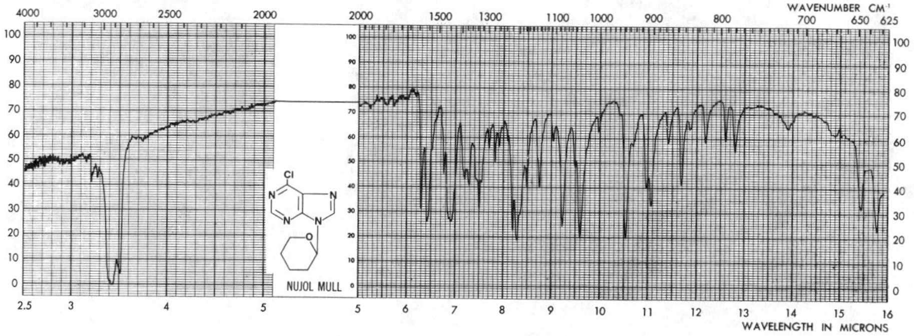

NUJOL MULL

C

H5660-6 4-Hydroxypyrazolo[3,4-d]pyrimidine (allopurinol)
M.W. 136.11 m.p. > 328°

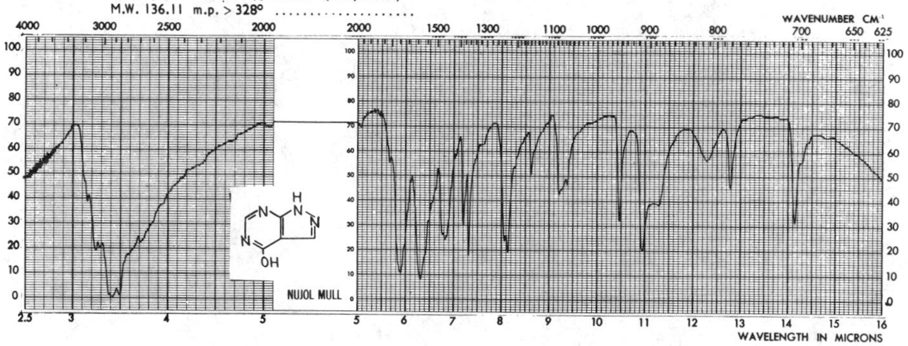

NUJOL MULL

D

13,520-8 2-Hydroxypurine (2-purinol) monohydrate
M.W. 154.13 m.p. > 300°

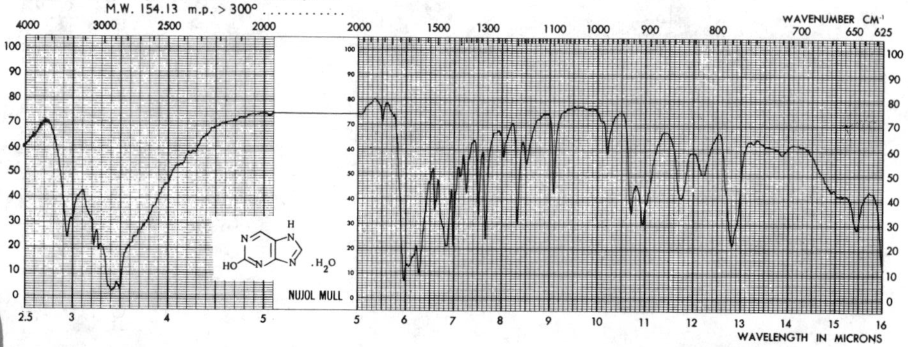

NUJOL MULL

E

Hypoxanthine
M.W. 136.11 m.p. > 320°

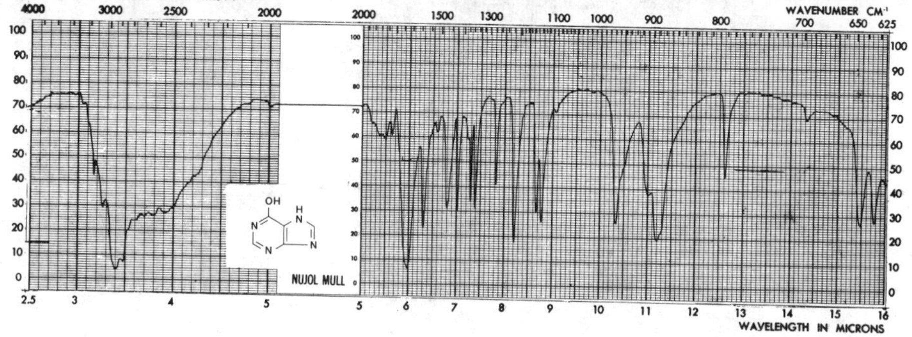

NUJOL MULL

F

85,270-8
6-Methoxypurine, 99+%
M.W. 150.14 m.p. 196-198°

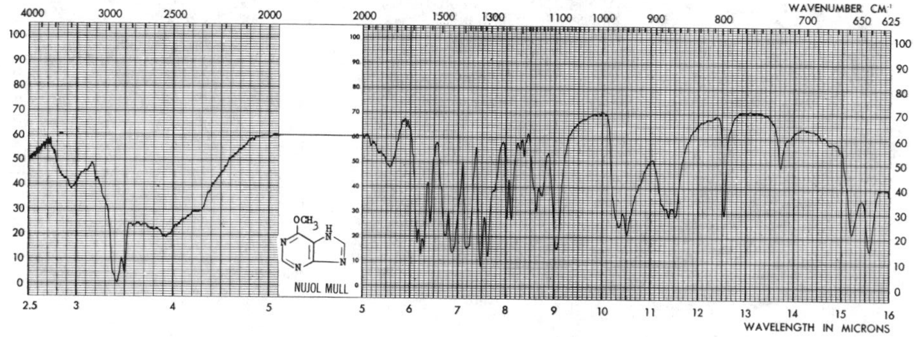

NUJOL MULL

G

85,059-4
6-Propoxypurine
M.W. 178.2 m.p. 181-182°

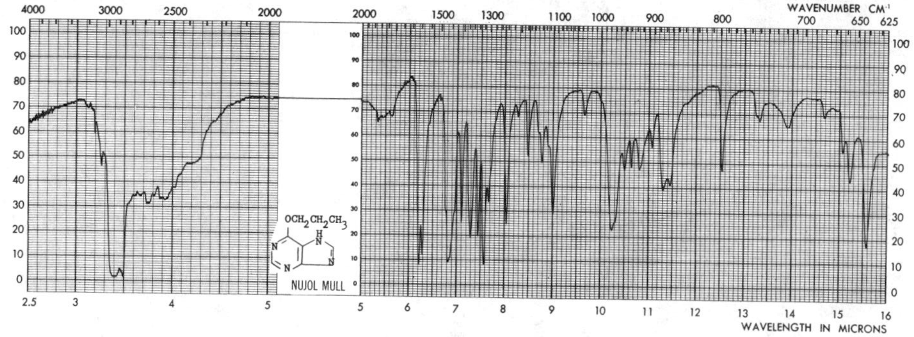

NUJOL MULL

H

10,954-1 Xanthine
M.W. 152.11 m.p. > 300°

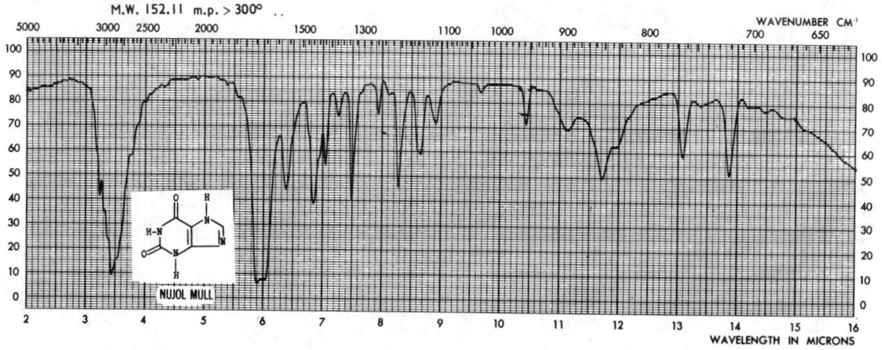

NUJOL MULL

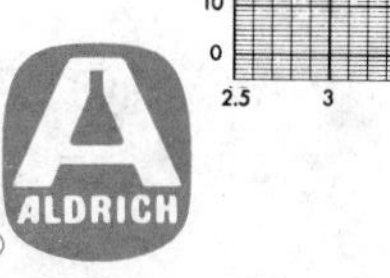

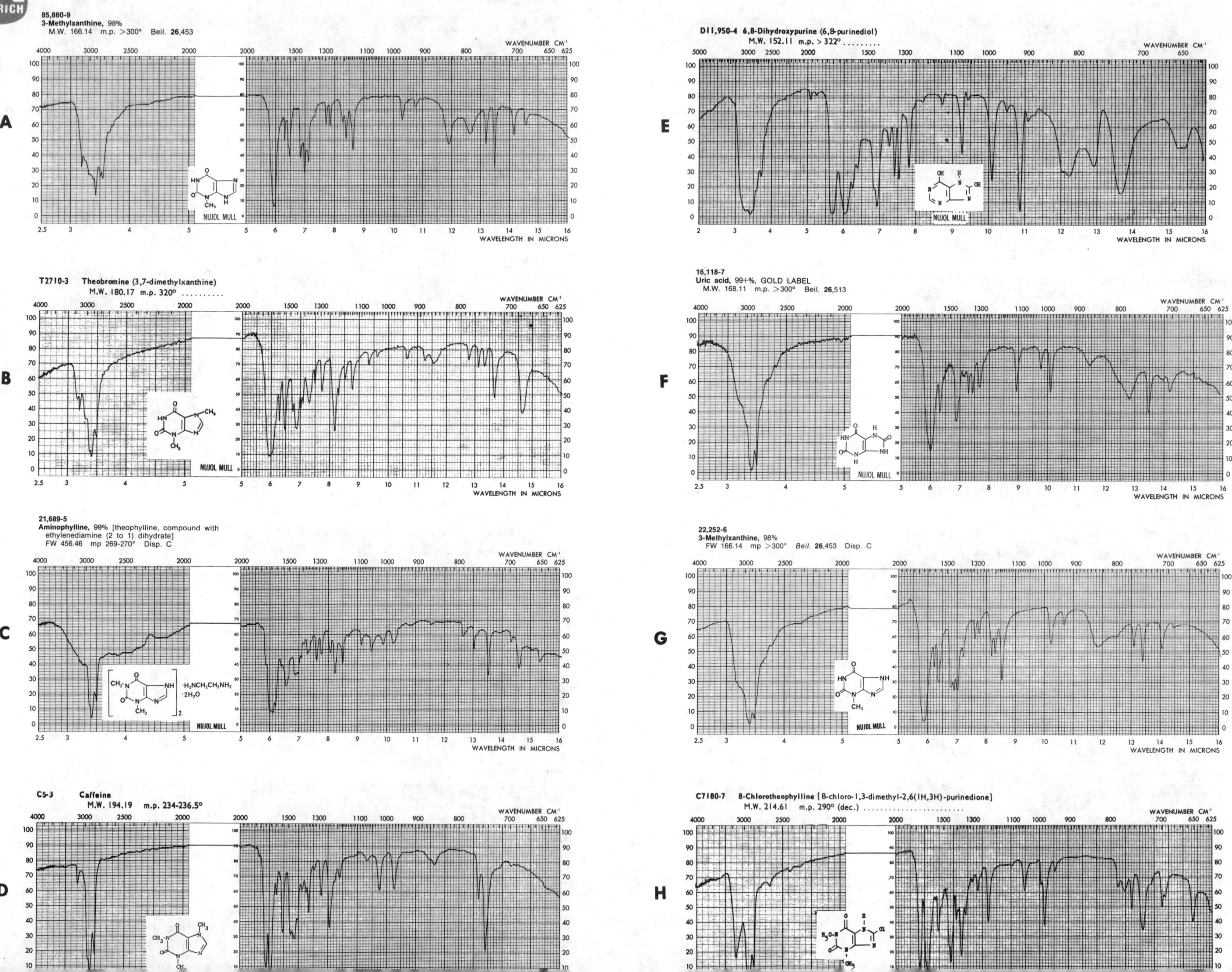
ALDRICH
A
85,860-9
3-Methylxanthine, 98%
M.W. 166.14 m.p. >300° Beil. 26,453
NUJOL MULL
E
D11,950-4 6,8-Dihydroxypurine (6,8-purinediol)
M.W. 152.11 m.p. > 322°
NUJOL MULL
B
T2710-3 Theobromine (3,7-dimethylxanthine)
M.W. 180.17 m.p. 320°
NUJOL MULL
F
16,118-7
Uric acid, 99+%, GOLD LABEL
M.W. 168.11 m.p. >300° Beil. 26,513
NUJOL MULL
C
21,689-5
Aminophylline, 99% [theophylline, compound with ethylenediamine (2 to 1) dihydrate]
FW 456.46 mp 269-270° Disp. C
NUJOL MULL
G
22,252-6
3-Methylxanthine, 98%
FW 166.14 mp >300° Beil. 26,453 Disp. C
NUJOL MULL
D
C5-3 Caffeine
M.W. 194.19 m.p. 234-236.5°
H
C7180-7 8-Chlorotheophylline [8-chloro-1,3-dimethyl-2,6(1H,3H)-purinedione]
M.W. 214.61 m.p. 290° (dec.)
WAVENUMBER CM⁻¹
WAVELENGTH IN MICRONS

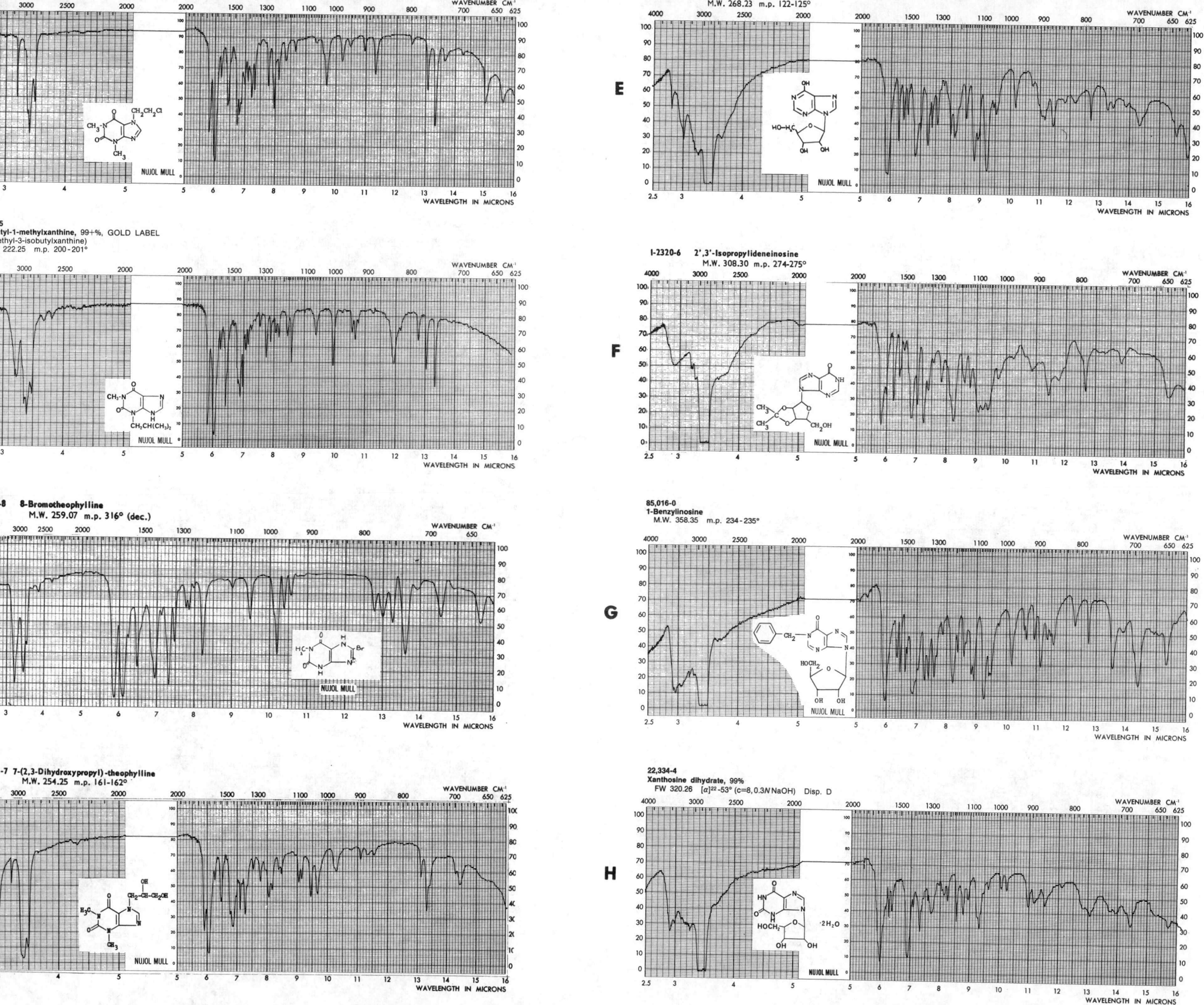
A
M.W. 242.67 m.p. 124-125°
NUJOL MULL
85,845-5
3-Isobutyl-1-methylxanthine, 99+%, GOLD LABEL
(1-methyl-3-isobutylxanthine)
M.W. 222.25 m.p. 200-201°
B
NUJOL MULL
B8180-8 8-Bromotheophylline
M.W. 259.07 m.p. 316° (dec.)
C
NUJOL MULL
D11,940-7 7-(2,3-Dihydroxypropyl)-theophylline
M.W. 254.25 m.p. 161-162°
D
NUJOL MULL
I-640-7 Inosine
M.W. 268.23 m.p. 122-125°
E
NUJOL MULL
I-2320-6 2',3'-Isopropylideneinosine
M.W. 308.30 m.p. 274-275°
F
NUJOL MULL
85,016-0
1-Benzylinosine
M.W. 358.35 m.p. 234-235°
G
NUJOL MULL
22,334-4
Xanthosine dihydrate, 99%
FW 320.26 [α]22 -53° (c=8,0.3N NaOH) Disp. D
H
NUJOL MULL
WAVENUMBER CM⁻¹
WAVELENGTH IN MICRONS
ALDRICH

5 MEMBERED FUSED AROMATIC HETEROCYCLES

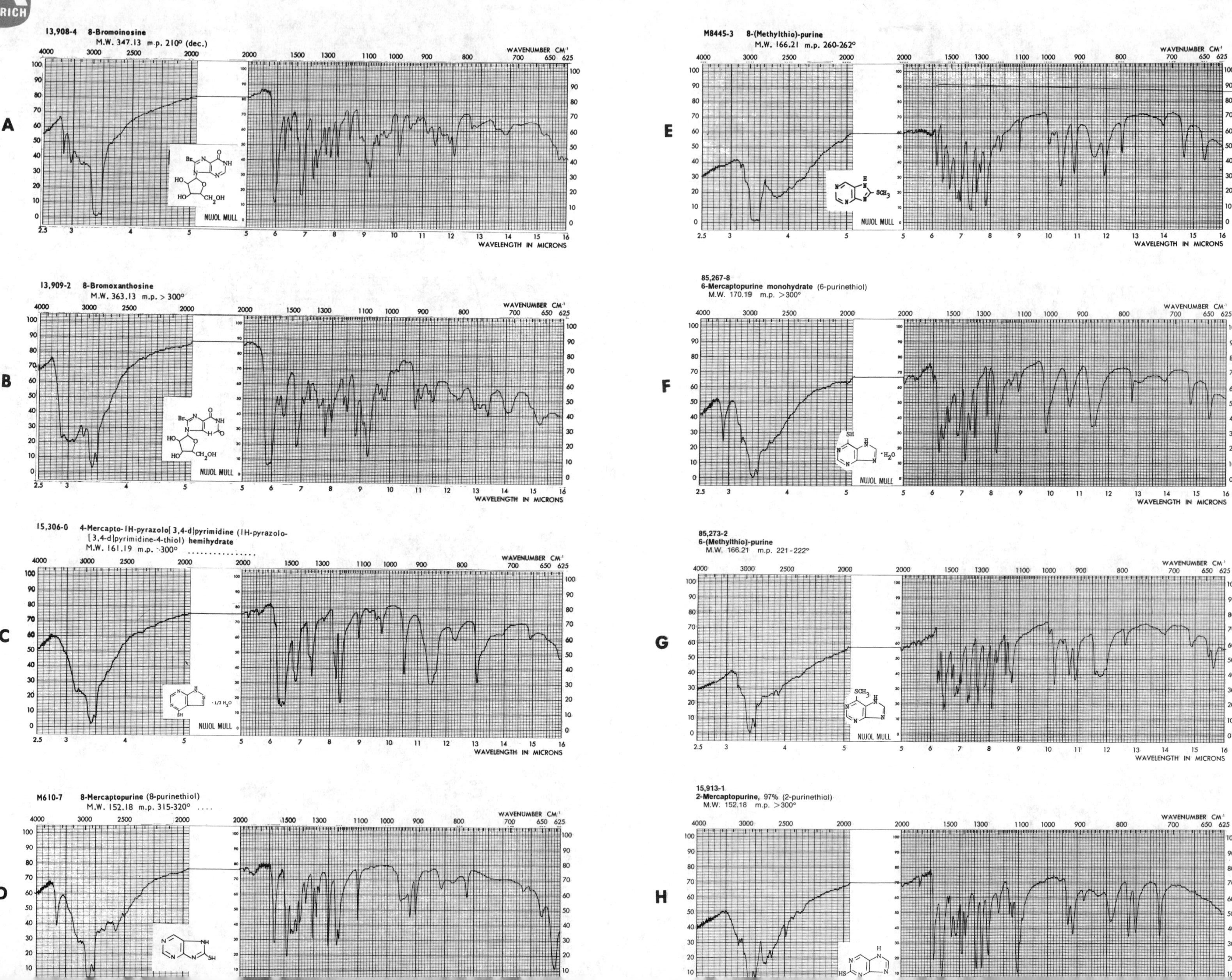
ALDRICH
A
13,908-4 8-Bromoinosine
M.W. 347.13 m.p. 210° (dec.)
NUJOL MULL
B
13,909-2 8-Bromoxanthosine
M.W. 363.13 m.p. > 300°
NUJOL MULL
C
15,306-0 4-Mercapto-1H-pyrazolo[3,4-d]pyrimidine (1H-pyrazolo-[3,4-d]pyrimidine-4-thiol) hemihydrate
M.W. 161.19 m.p. >300°
NUJOL MULL
D
M610-7 8-Mercaptopurine (8-purinethiol)
M.W. 152.18 m.p. 315-320°
E
M8445-3 8-(Methylthio)-purine
M.W. 166.21 m.p. 260-262°
NUJOL MULL
F
85,267-8
6-Mercaptopurine monohydrate (6-purinethiol)
M.W. 170.19 m.p. >300°
NUJOL MULL
G
85,273-2
6-(Methylthio)-purine
M.W. 166.21 m.p. 221-222°
NUJOL MULL
H
15,913-1
2-Mercaptopurine, 97% (2-purinethiol)
M.W. 152.18 m.p. >300°
WAVENUMBER CM⁻¹
WAVELENGTH IN MICRONS

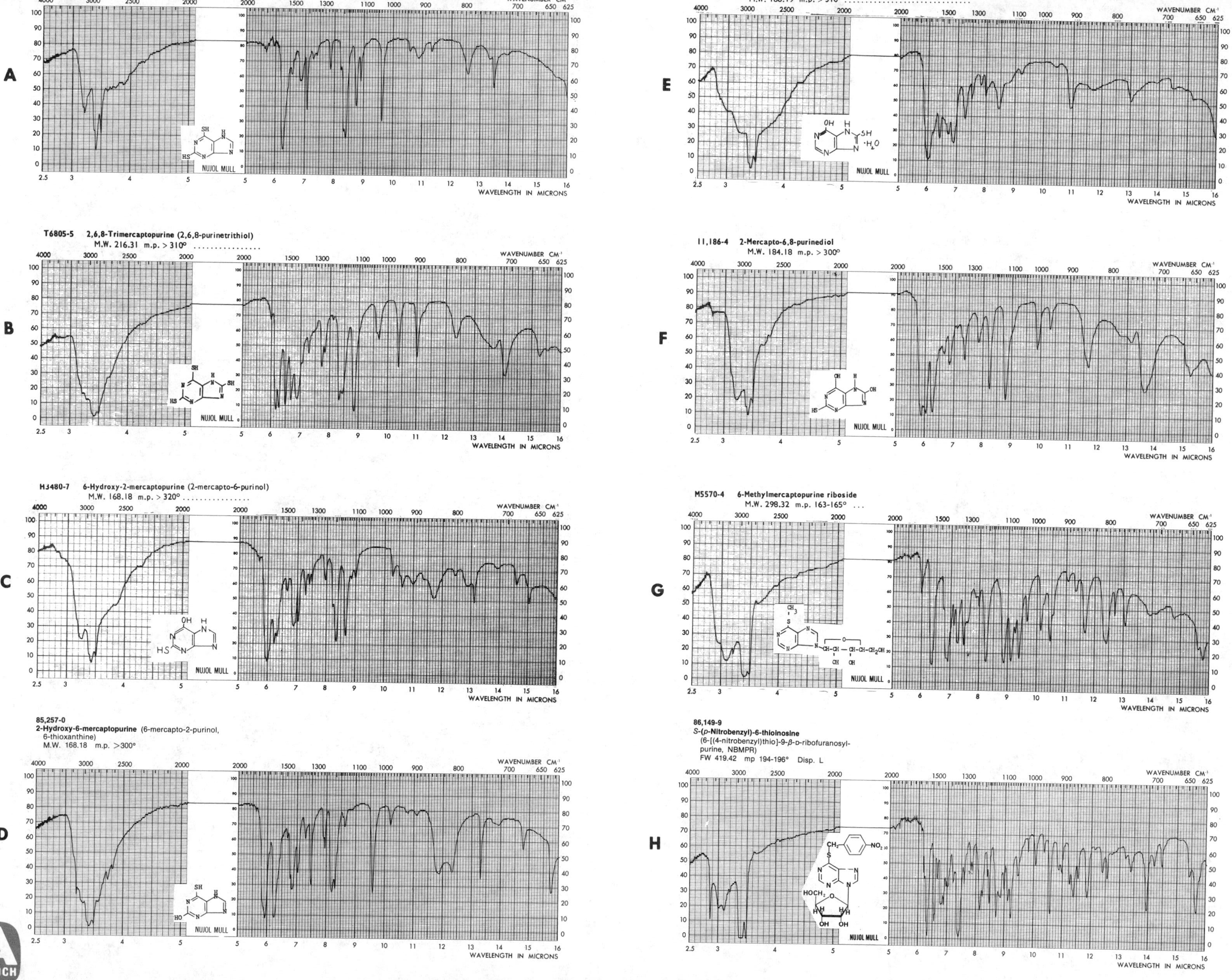

H3500-5 **6-Hydroxy-8-mercaptopurine** (8-mercapto-6-purinol) monohydrate
M.W. 186.19 m.p. > 310°

T6805-5 **2,6,8-Trimercaptopurine** (2,6,8-purinetrithiol)
M.W. 216.31 m.p. > 310°

11,186-4 **2-Mercapto-6,8-purinediol**
M.W. 184.18 m.p. > 300°

H3480-7 **6-Hydroxy-2-mercaptopurine** (2-mercapto-6-purinol)
M.W. 168.18 m.p. > 320°

M5570-4 **6-Methylmercaptopurine riboside**
M.W. 298.32 m.p. 163-165°

85,257-0
2-Hydroxy-6-mercaptopurine (6-mercapto-2-purinol, 6-thioxanthine)
M.W. 168.18 m.p. >300°

86,149-9
***S*-(*p*-Nitrobenzyl)-6-thioinosine**
(6-[(4-nitrobenzyl)thio]-9-β-D-ribofuranosylpurine, NBMPR)
FW 419.42 mp 194-196° Disp. L

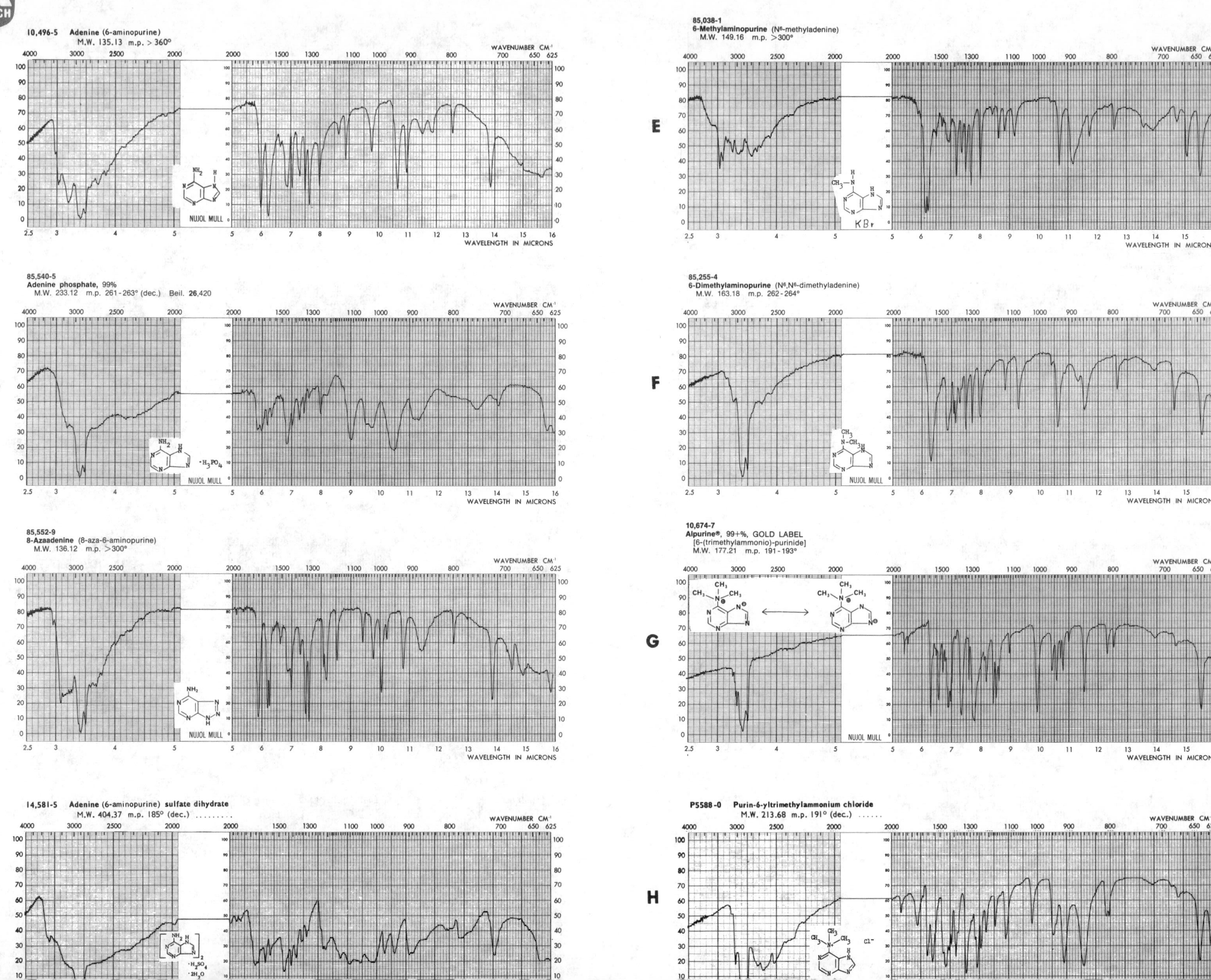
ALDRICH
A
10,496-5 Adenine (6-aminopurine)
M.W. 135.13 m.p. > 360°
NUJOL MULL
B
85,540-5
Adenine phosphate, 99%
M.W. 233.12 m.p. 261-263° (dec.) Beil. 26,420
NUJOL MULL
C
85,552-9
8-Azaadenine (8-aza-6-aminopurine)
M.W. 136.12 m.p. >300°
NUJOL MULL
D
14,581-5 Adenine (6-aminopurine) sulfate dihydrate
M.W. 404.37 m.p. 185° (dec.) ....
E
85,038-1
6-Methylaminopurine (N⁶-methyladenine)
M.W. 149.16 m.p. >300°
KBr
F
85,255-4
6-Dimethylaminopurine (N⁶,N⁶-dimethyladenine)
M.W. 163.18 m.p. 262-264°
NUJOL MULL
G
10,674-7
Alpurine®, 99+%, GOLD LABEL
[6-(trimethylammonio)-purinide]
M.W. 177.21 m.p. 191-193°
NUJOL MULL
H
P5588-0 Purin-6-yltrimethylammonium chloride
M.W. 213.68 m.p. 191° (dec.) ......
WAVENUMBER CM⁻¹
WAVELENGTH IN MICRONS

A

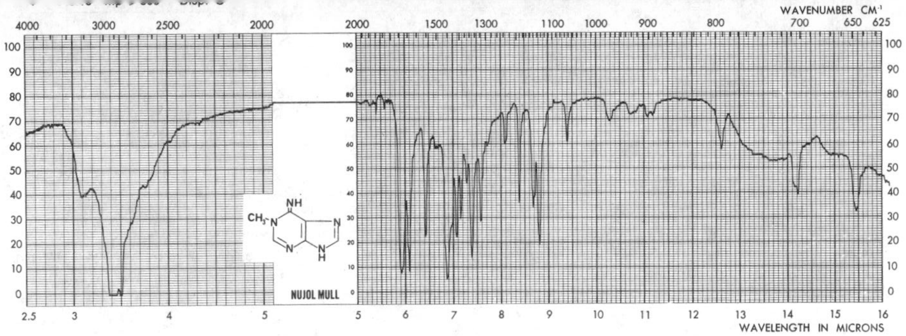

NUJOL MULL

B

85,996-6
1-Methyladenine hemihydrochloride monohydrate
M.W. 185.41 m.p. 275-280°

$\cdot\frac{1}{2}$HCl $\cdot H_2O$

NUJOL MULL

C

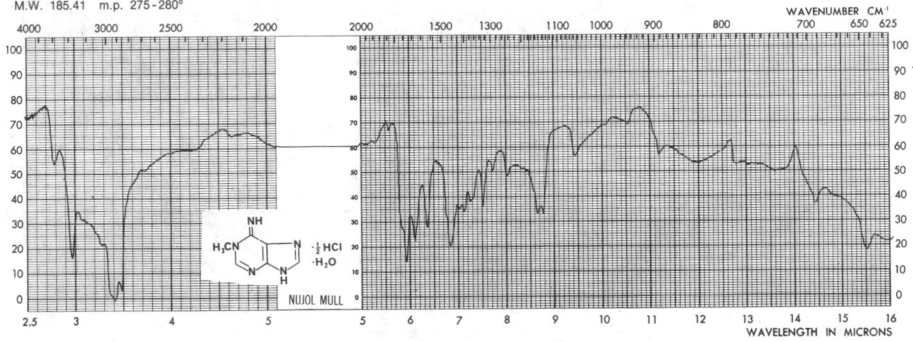

85,260-0
N⁶-(Δ_2-Isopentenyl)-adenine [6-(γ,γ-dimethylallyl-amino)-purine]
M.W. 203.25 m.p. 212-214°

NUJOL MULL

D

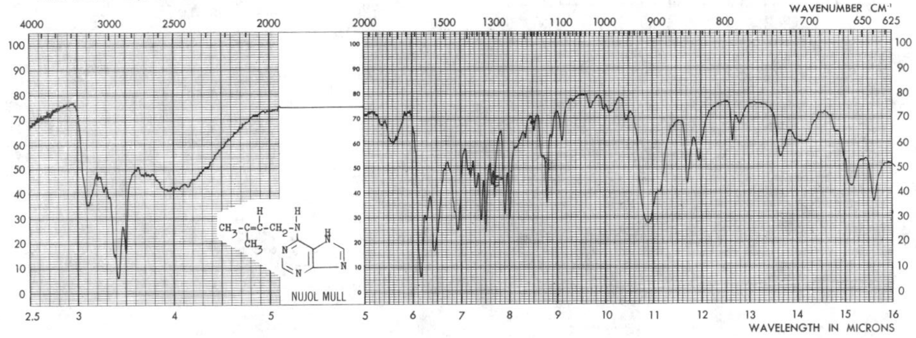

85,111-6
Triacanthine [3-(3-methyl-2-butenyl)-adenine]
M.W. 203.25 m.p. 228-231°

NUJOL MULL

E

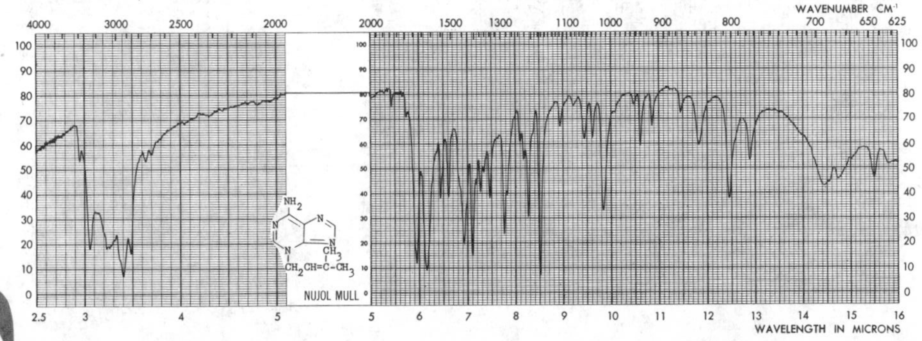

M.W. 179.18 m.p. 254-256°

NUJOL MULL

F

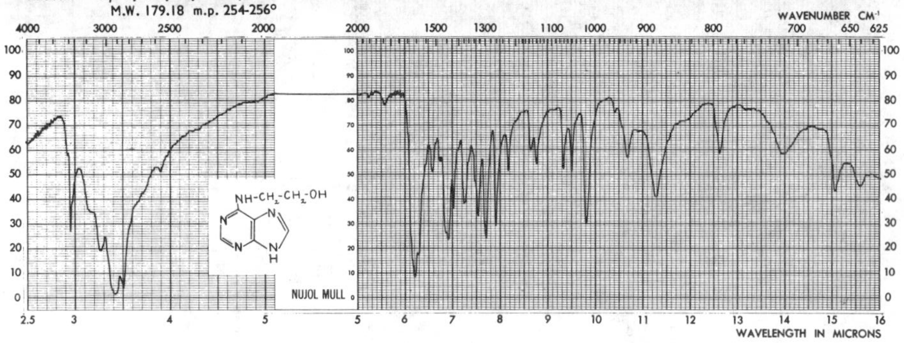

10,978-9 **2-Amino-6-chloropurine, puriss.**
M.W. 169.58 m.p. > 300°

NUJOL MULL

G

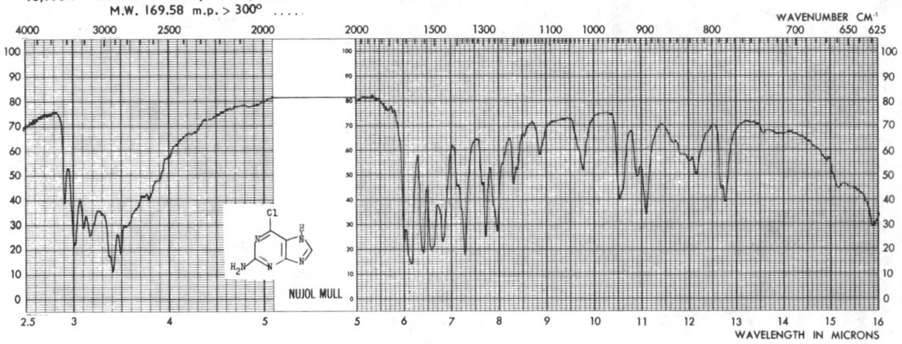

85,245-7
8-Bromoadenine
M.W. 214.03 m.p. >300° Beil. **26**,428

NUJOL MULL

H

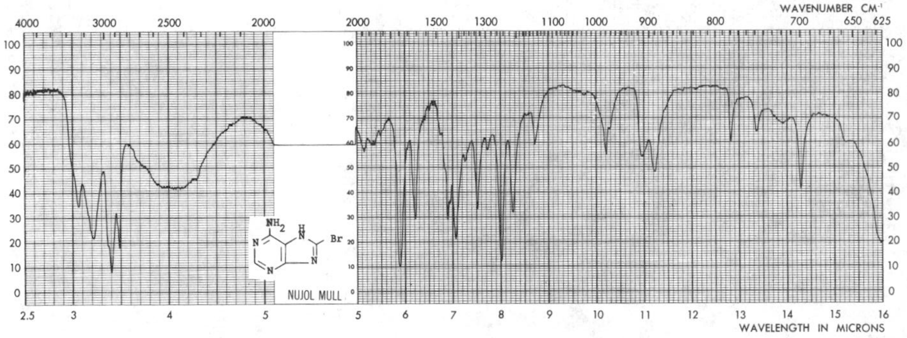

A7690-7 **2-Amino-6-purinethiol (6-thioguanine)**
M.W. 167.19 m.p. > 360°

NUJOL MULL

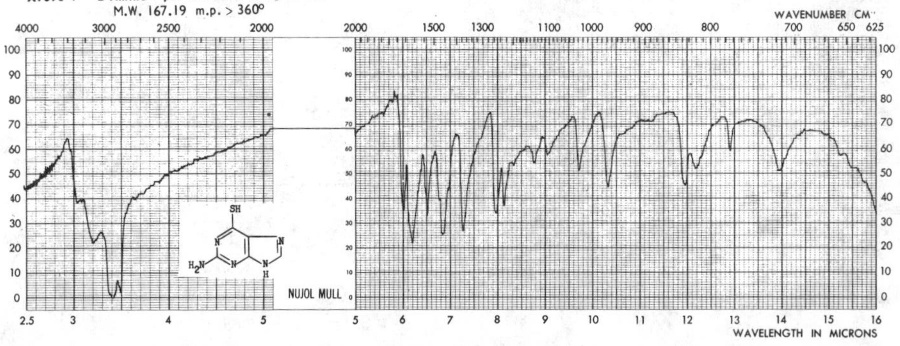

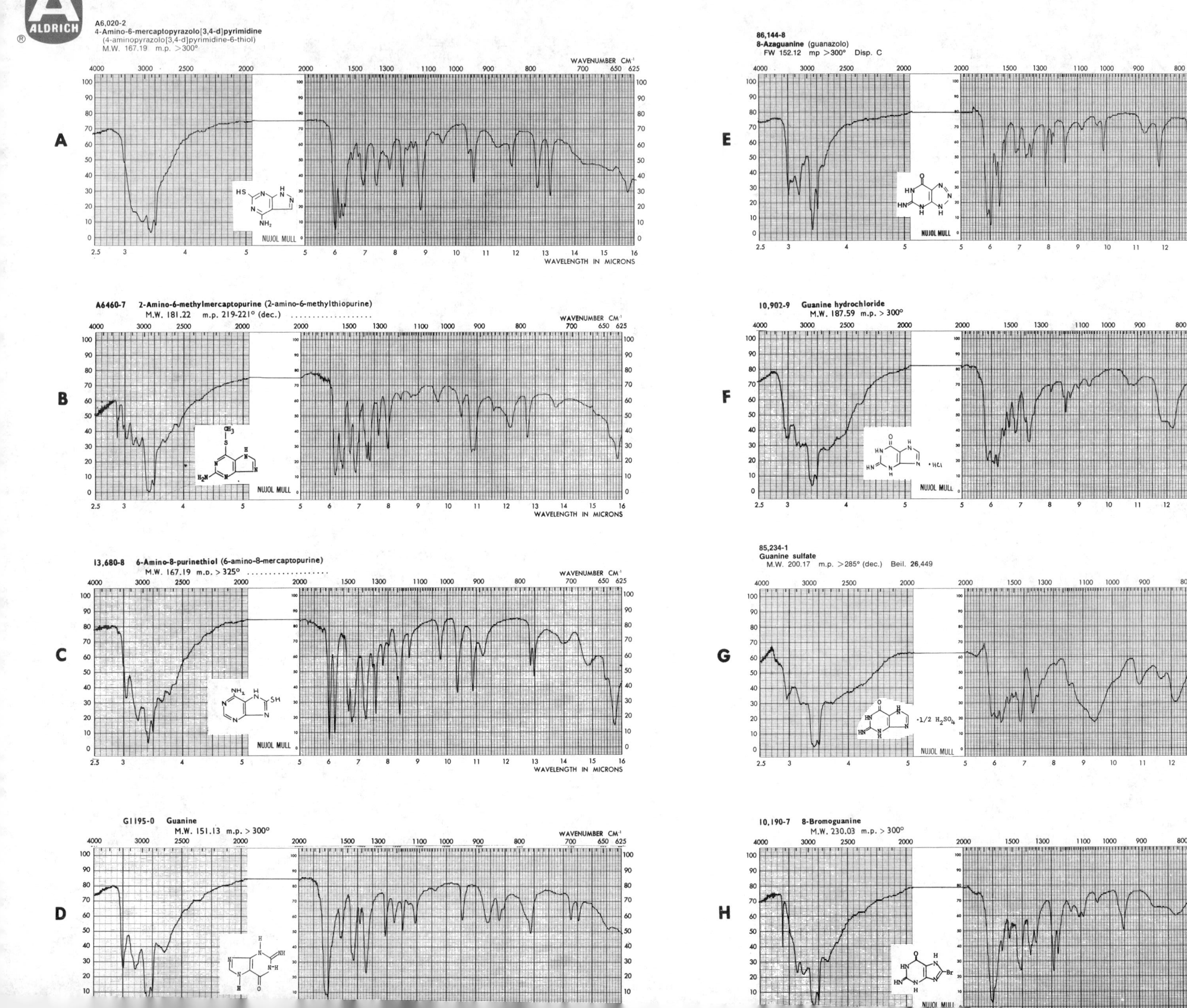

A — A6,020-2 4-Amino-6-mercaptopyrazolo[3,4-d]pyrimidine (4-aminopyrazolo[3,4-d]pyrimidine-6-thiol) M.W. 167.19 m.p. >300°

B — A6460-7 2-Amino-6-methylmercaptopurine (2-amino-6-methylthiopurine) M.W. 181.22 m.p. 219-221° (dec.)

C — 13,680-8 6-Amino-8-purinethiol (6-amino-8-mercaptopurine) M.W. 167.19 m.p. > 325°

D — G1195-0 Guanine M.W. 151.13 m.p. > 300°

E — 86,144-8 8-Azaguanine (guanazolo) FW 152.12 mp >300° Disp. C

F — 10,902-9 Guanine hydrochloride M.W. 187.59 m.p. > 300°

G — 85,234-1 Guanine sulfate M.W. 200.17 m.p. >285° (dec.) Beil. 26,449

H — 10,190-7 8-Bromoguanine M.W. 230.03 m.p. > 300°

A

M.W. 183.19 m.p. > 320° ....

NUJOL MULL

B

14,001-5 **2,8-Dihydroxyadenine**
M.W. 167.13 m.p. > 300°

NUJOL MULL

C

12,291-2 **2-Amino-6,8-dihydroxypurine** (2-amino-6,8-purinediol)
M.W. 167.13 m.p. > 320° ....

NUJOL MULL

D

11,187-2 **2,6-Diamino-8-purinol hemisulfate monohydrate**
M.W. 233.20 m.p. > 300° ....

NUJOL MULL

E

NUJOL MULL

F

85,275-9
6-Methylpurine riboside, 99+%, GOLD LABEL
M.W. 266.26 m.p. 206-208°

KBr

G

85,248-1
6-Chloropurine riboside
M.W. 286.68 m.p. 161-163° (dec.)

NUJOL MULL

H

85,271-6
6-Methoxypurine riboside, 99+%, GOLD LABEL
M.W. 282.26 m.p. 170-172°

NUJOL MULL

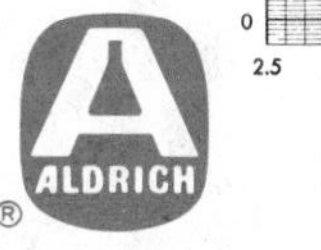

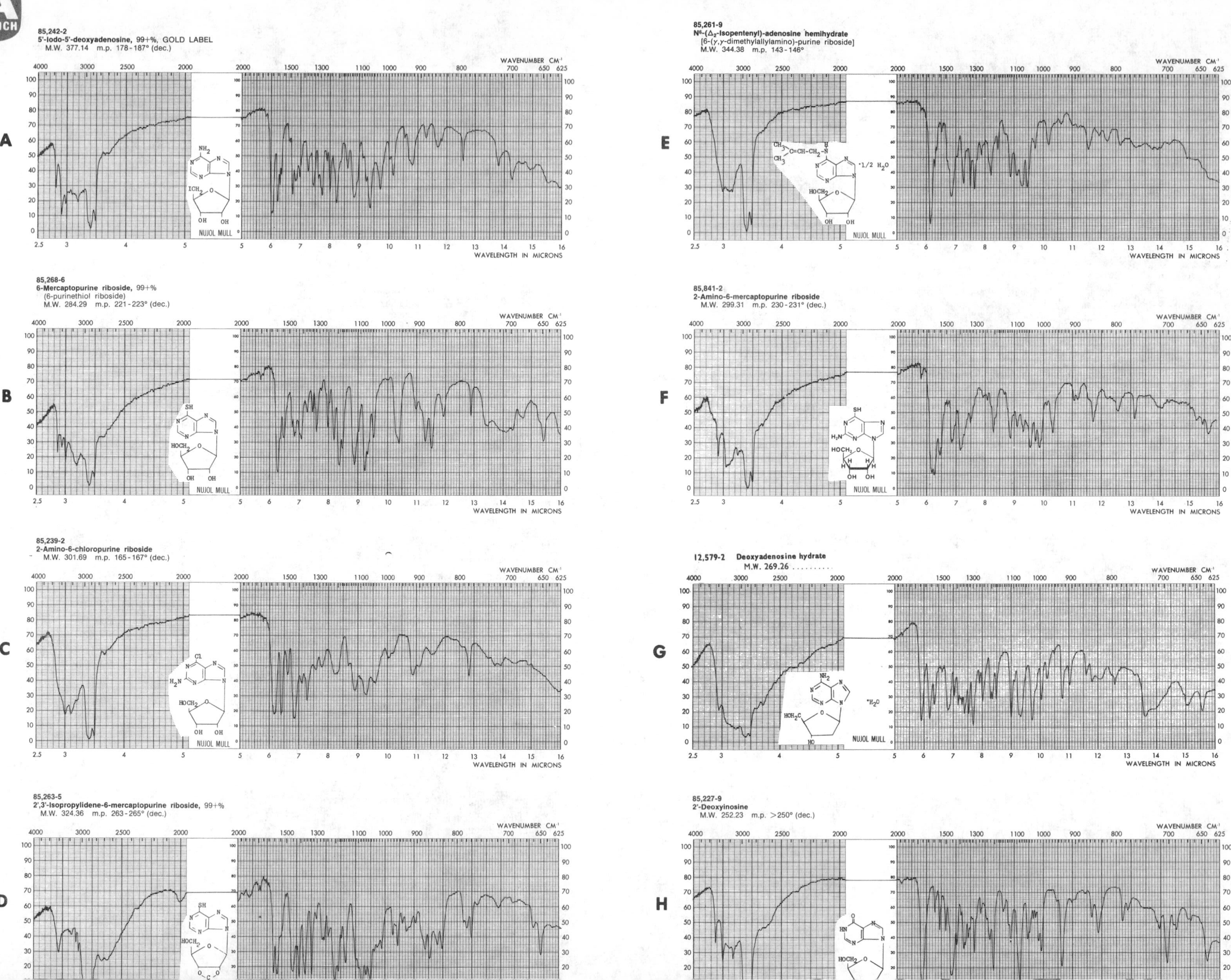
ALDRICH
A
85,242-2
5'-Iodo-5'-deoxyadenosine, 99+%, GOLD LABEL
M.W. 377.14 m.p. 178-187° (dec.)
B
85,268-6
6-Mercaptopurine riboside, 99+%
(6-purinethiol riboside)
M.W. 284.29 m.p. 221-223° (dec.)
C
85,239-2
2-Amino-6-chloropurine riboside
M.W. 301.69 m.p. 165-167° (dec.)
D
85,263-5
2',3'-Isopropylidene-6-mercaptopurine riboside, 99+%
M.W. 324.36 m.p. 263-265° (dec.)
E
85,261-9
N6-(Δ2-Isopentenyl)-adenosine hemihydrate
[6-(γ,γ-dimethylallylamino)-purine riboside]
M.W. 344.38 m.p. 143-146°
F
85,841-2
2-Amino-6-mercaptopurine riboside
M.W. 299.31 m.p. 230-231° (dec.)
G
12,579-2 Deoxyadenosine hydrate
M.W. 269.26
H
85,227-9
2'-Deoxyinosine
M.W. 252.23 m.p. >250° (dec.)
WAVENUMBER CM-1
WAVELENGTH IN MICRONS
NUJOL MULL

M.W. 281.27 m.p. 208-210°

A

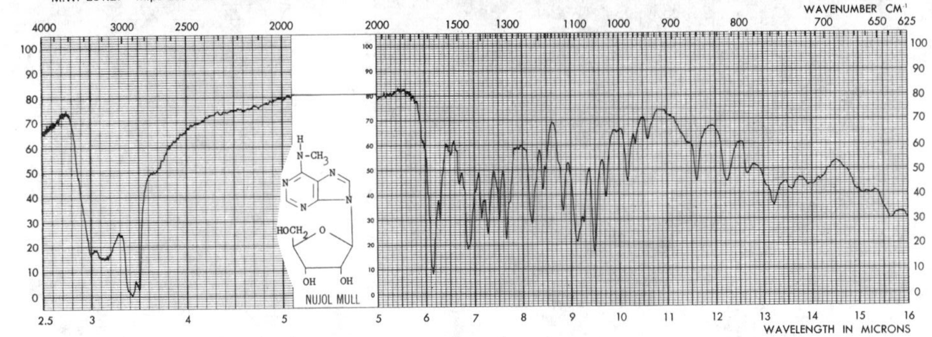

85,256-2
6-Dimethylaminopurine riboside, 99% (N⁶,N⁶-dimethyl-adenosine)
M.W. 295.3 m.p. 184-185°

B

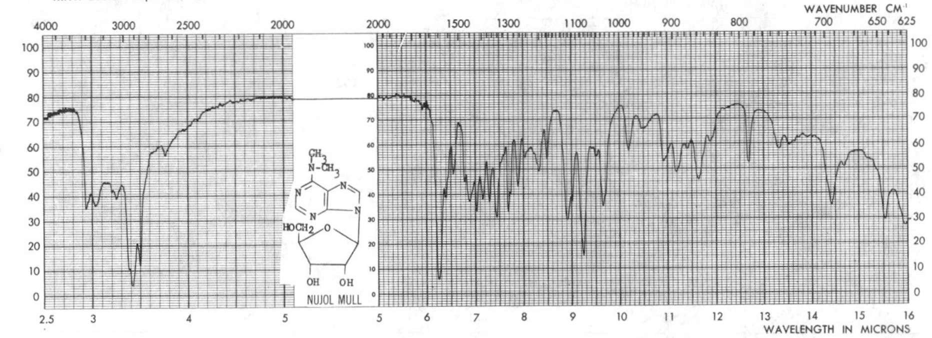

85,244-9
6-Benzylaminopurine riboside, 99+%, GOLD LABEL
(N⁶-benzyladenosine)
M.W. 357.37 m.p. 184-186°

C

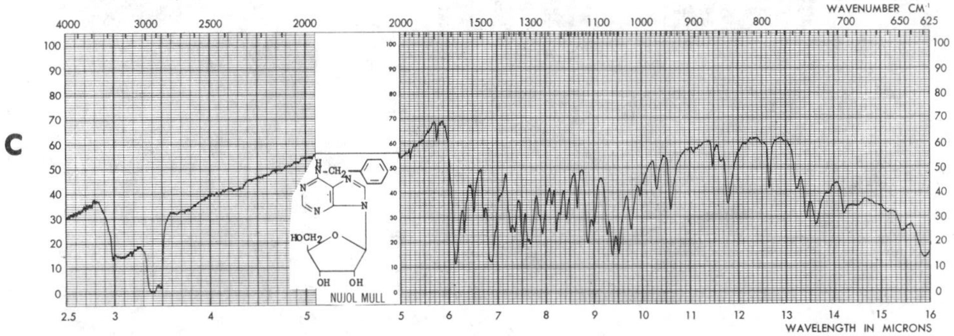

85,265-1
Kinetin riboside (N⁶-furfuryladenosine, 6-furfurylaminopurine riboside)
M.W. 347.33 m.p. 152-154°

D

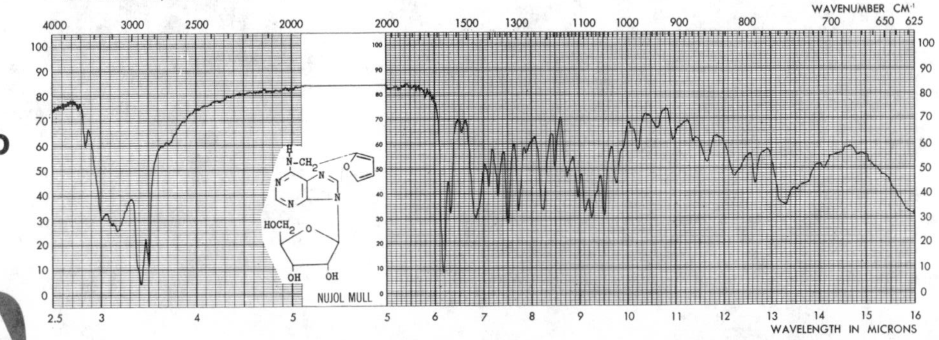

E

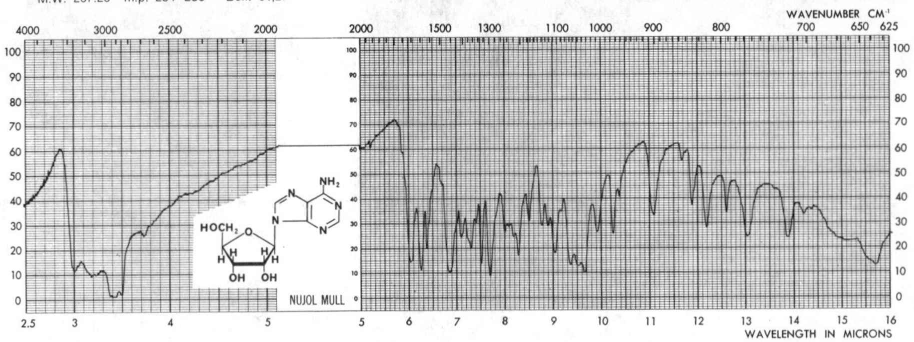

85,238-4
Adenosine-N¹-oxide monohydrate, 99+%
M.W. 301.26 m.p. 229-231° (dec.)

F

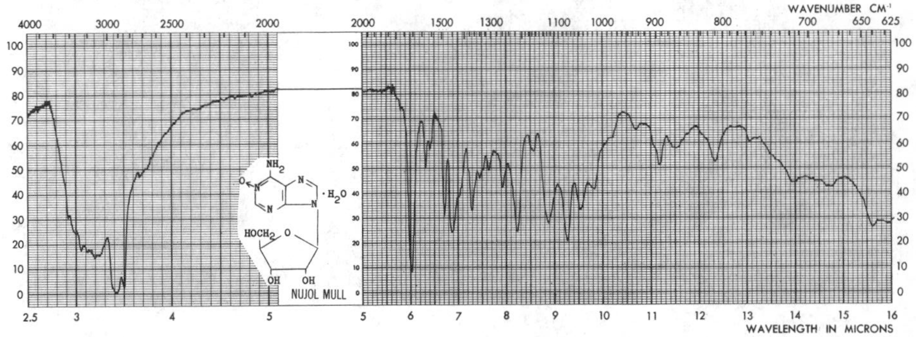

85,997-4
1-Methyladenosine
M.W. 281.27 m.p. 228-231°

G

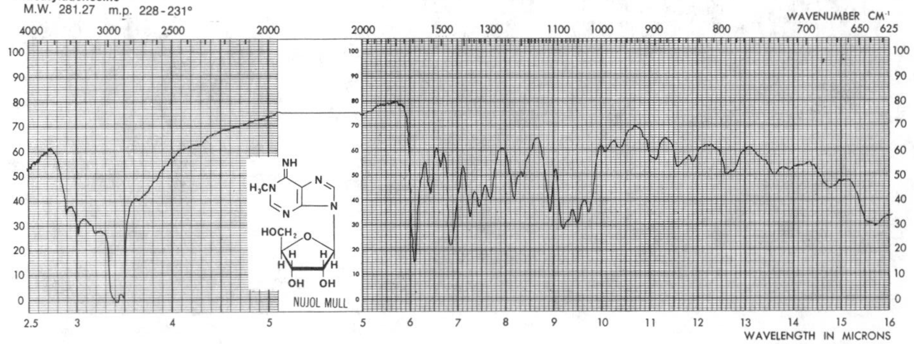

12,750-7 **8-Bromoadenosine**
M.W. 346.15 m.p. 230° (dec.)

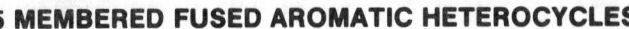

H

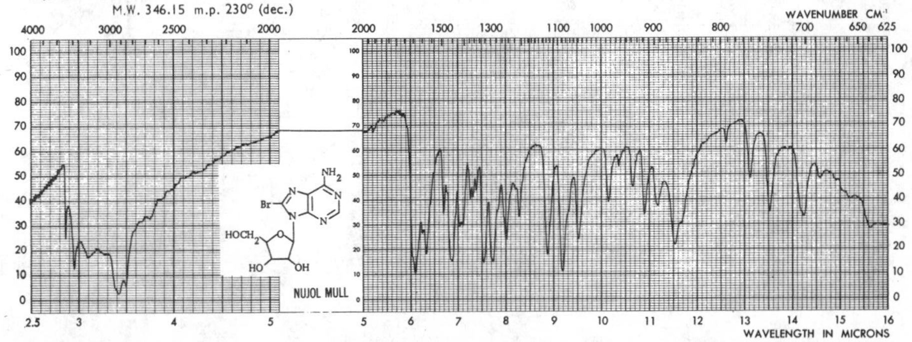

A

85,217-1
Xanthosine dihydrate
M.W. 320.26 m.p. >300° (dec.) Beil. **31**,28

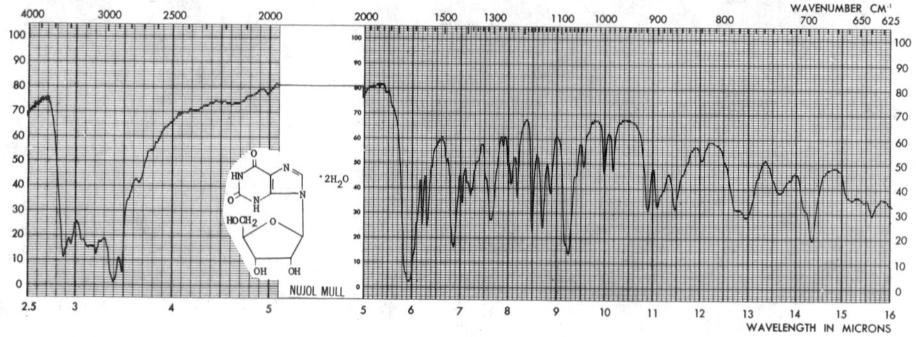

NUJOL MULL

B

85,499-9
2'-Deoxyguanosine hemihydrate, 99+%,
GOLD LABEL
M.W. 276.26 m.p. >300° (dec.)

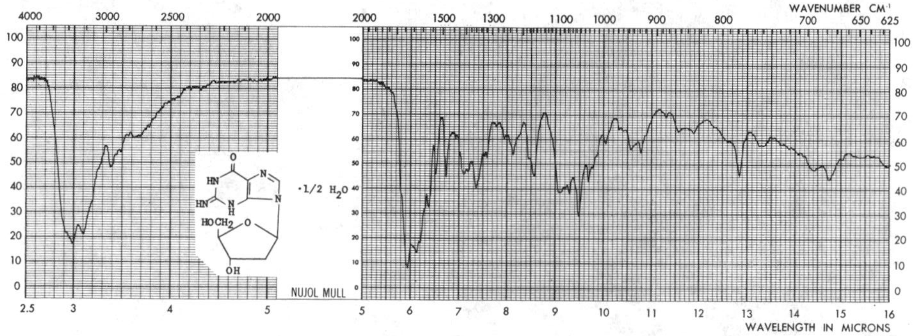

NUJOL MULL

C

G1200-0 **Guanosine**
M.W. 283.25 m.p. 250° (dec.)

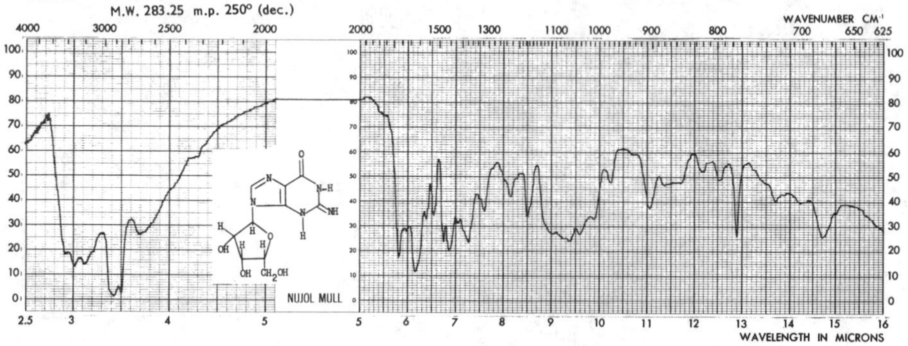

NUJOL MULL

D

85,017-9
8-Bromoguanosine
M.W. 362.15 m.p. >300°

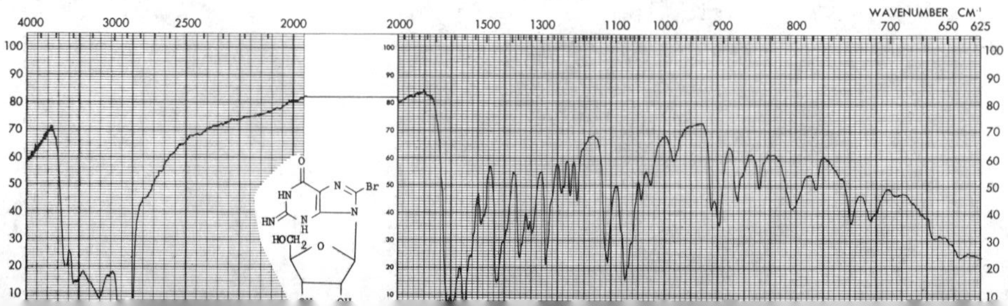

E

I-2240-4 **2',3'-Isopropylideneadenosine**
M.W. 307.31 m.p. 221-222°

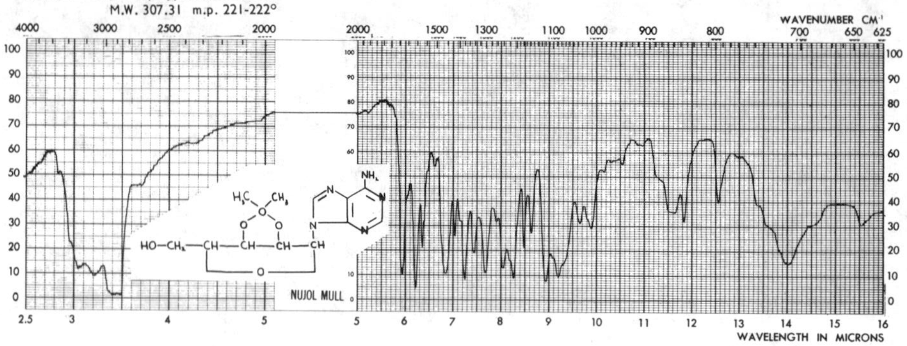

NUJOL MULL

F

I-2300-I **2',3'-Isopropylideneguanosine**
M.W. 323.31 m.p. 300-305° (dec.)

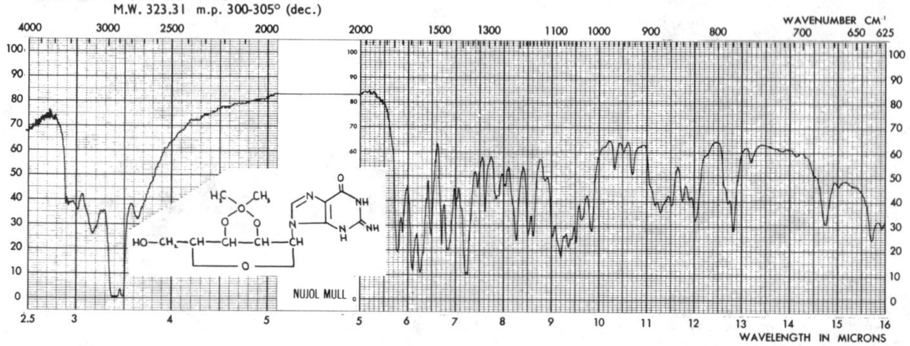

NUJOL MULL

G

14,421-5 **5'-(4-Methoxytrityl)-adenosine**
M.W. 539.60 m.p. 202-204° (dec.)

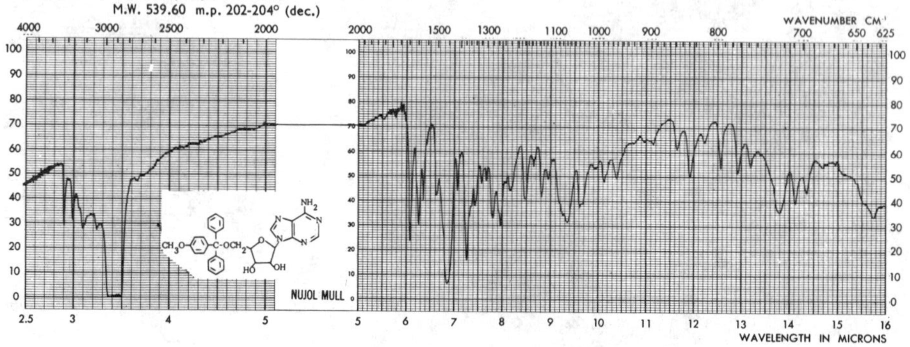

NUJOL MULL

H

85,804-8
6-(4-Carboxybutyl)-mercaptopurine (buthiopurine)
M.W. 252.3 m.p. 202-203°

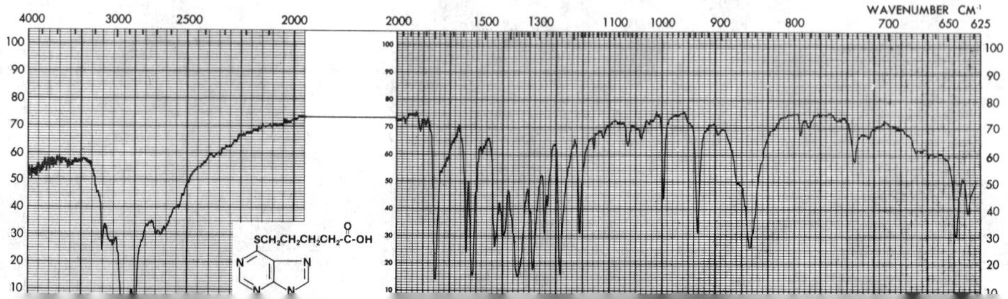

M.W. 202.18 m.p. > 300°

A

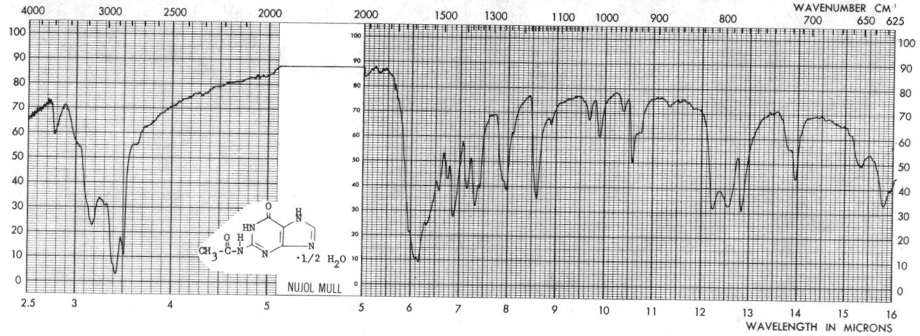

NUJOL MULL

85,250-3
6-Cyanopurine, 99+%, GOLD LABEL
(6-purinecarbonitrile)
M.W. 145.13 m.p. 186-189°

B

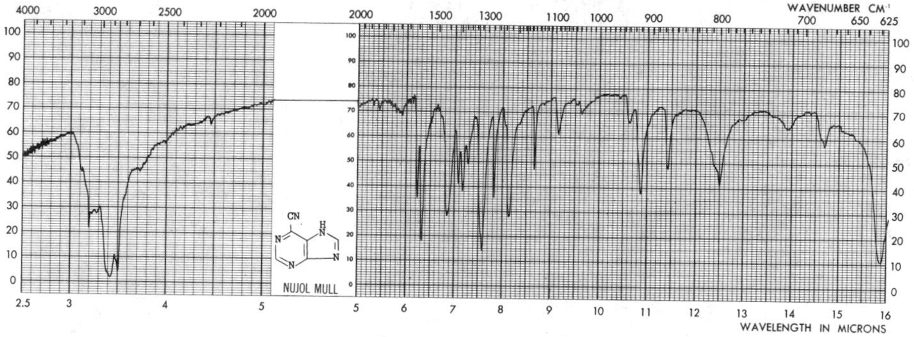

NUJOL MULL

14,151-8 **Ethyl 7-theophyllineacetate**
M.W. 266.26

C

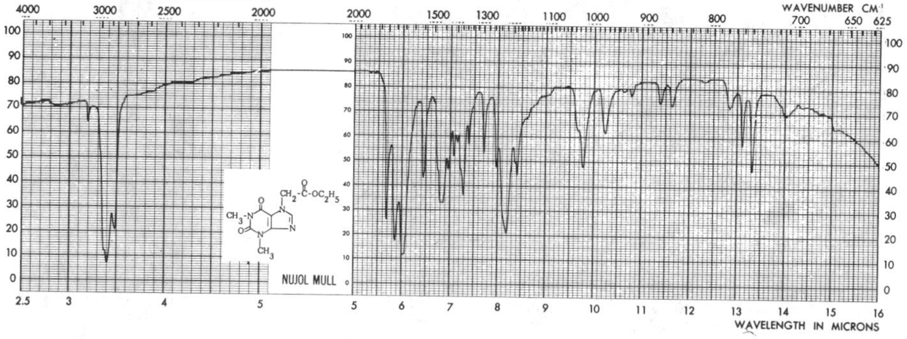

NUJOL MULL

85,801-3
5'-Acetyl-2',3'-isopropylideneadenosine
M.W. 349.35 m.p. 170-172°

D

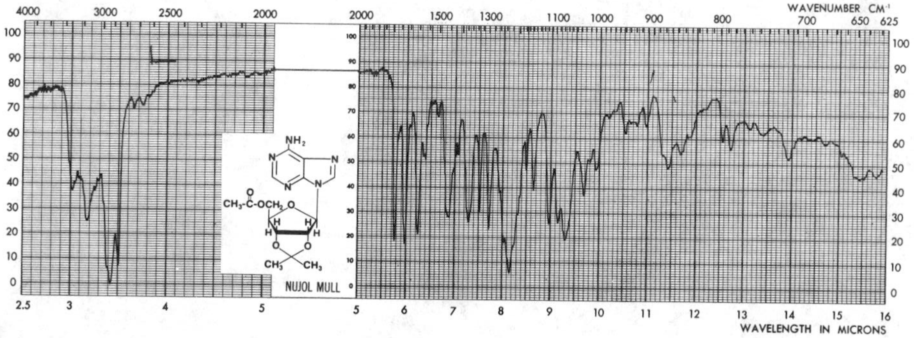

NUJOL MULL

(adenosine 2',3'-diacetate)
M.W. 351.32 m.p. 184-186°

E

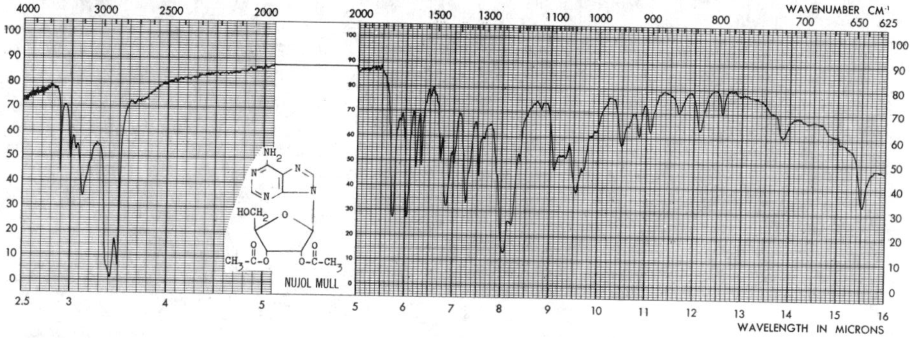

NUJOL MULL

85,279-1
2',3',5'-Triacetylinosine, 99+%, GOLD LABEL (inosine 2',3',5'-triacetate)
M.W. 394.34 m.p. 227° (dec.)

F

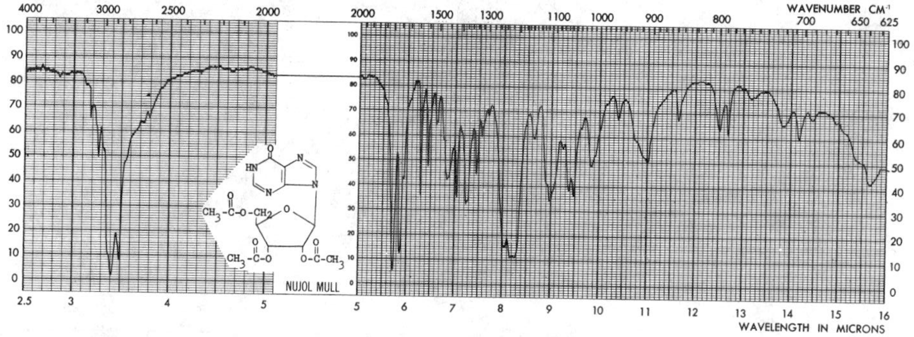

NUJOL MULL

85,092-6
2',3',5'-Triacetylguanosine (guanosine 2',3',5'-triacetate)
M.W. 409.36 m.p. 226-231°

G

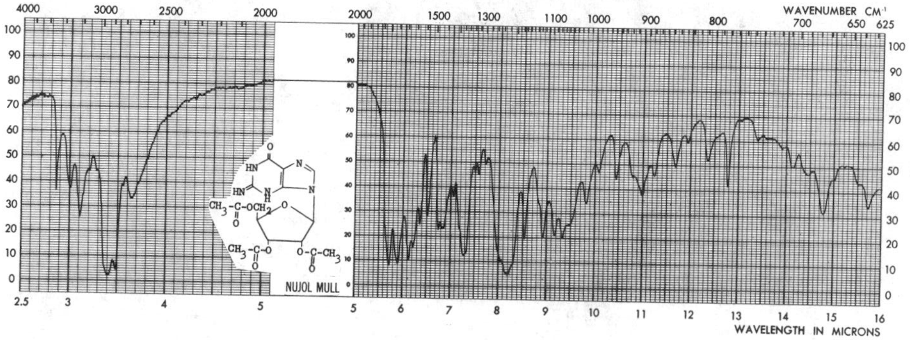

NUJOL MULL

85,269-4
6-Mercapto-2',3',5'-triacetylpurine riboside
(6-mercaptopurine riboside 2',3',5'-triacetate)
M.W. 410.41 m.p. 245° (dec.)

H

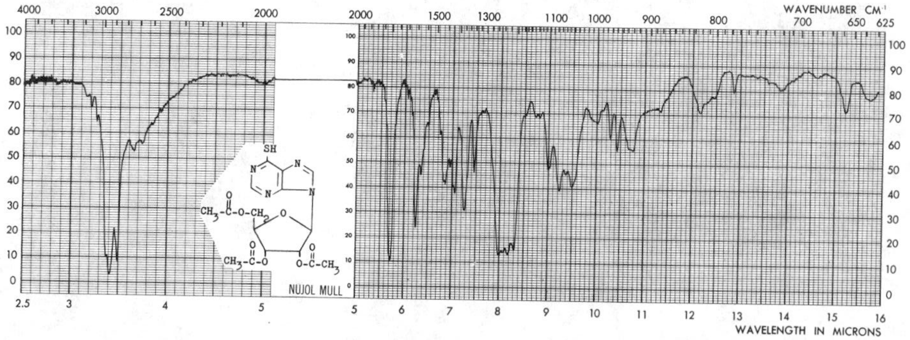

NUJOL MULL

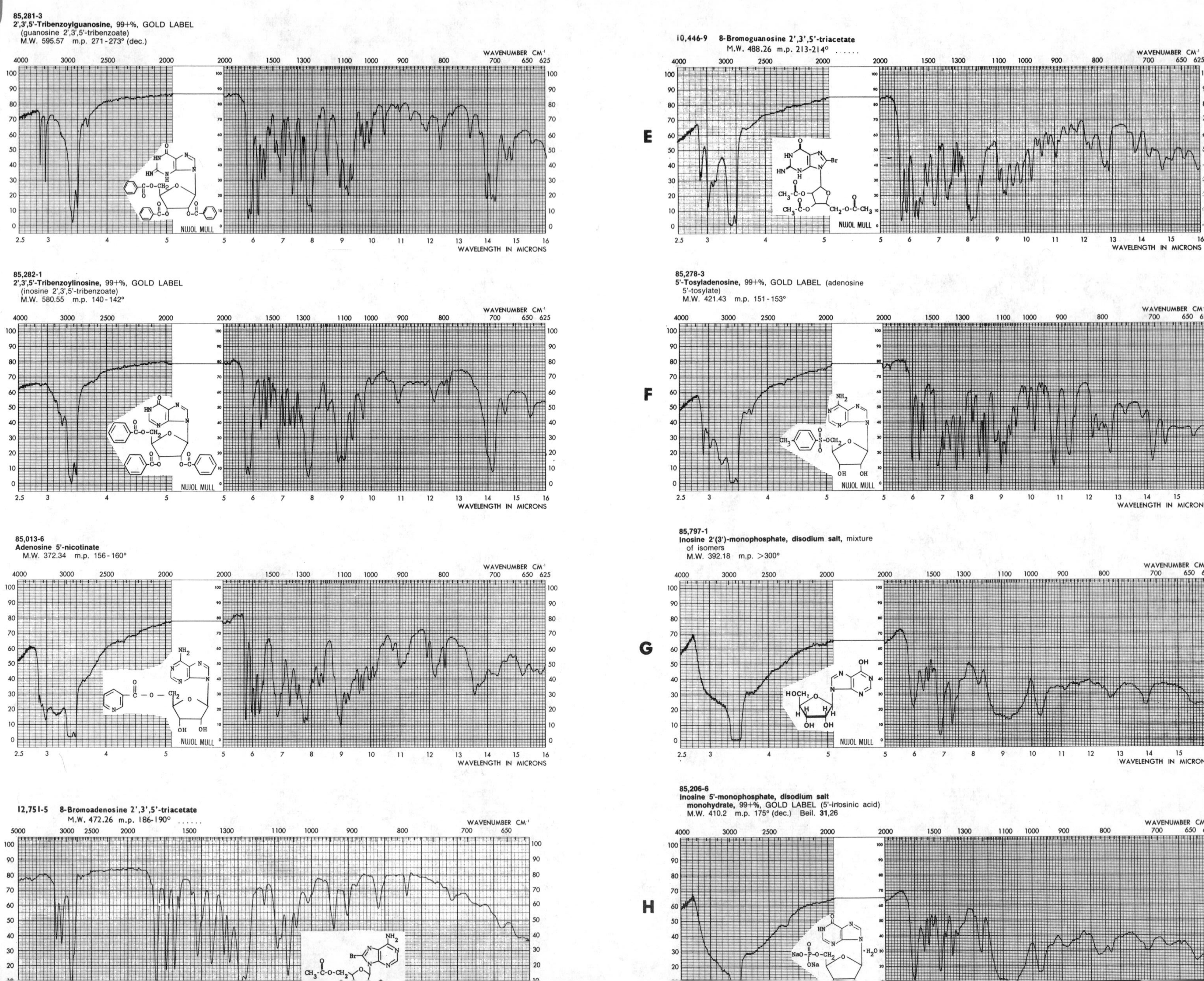

A

85,281-3
2',3',5'-Tribenzoylguanosine, 99+%, GOLD LABEL
(guanosine 2',3',5'-tribenzoate)
M.W. 595.57 m.p. 271-273° (dec.)

B

85,282-1
2',3',5'-Tribenzoylinosine, 99+%, GOLD LABEL
(inosine 2',3',5'-tribenzoate)
M.W. 580.55 m.p. 140-142°

C

85,013-6
Adenosine 5'-nicotinate
M.W. 372.34 m.p. 156-160°

D

12,751-5 **8-Bromoadenosine 2',3',5'-triacetate**
M.W. 472.26 m.p. 186-190°

E

10,446-9 **8-Bromoguanosine 2',3',5'-triacetate**
M.W. 488.26 m.p. 213-214°

F

85,278-3
5'-Tosyladenosine, 99+%, GOLD LABEL (adenosine 5'-tosylate)
M.W. 421.43 m.p. 151-153°

G

85,797-1
Inosine 2'(3')-monophosphate, disodium salt, mixture of isomers
M.W. 392.18 m.p. >300°

H

85,206-6
Inosine 5'-monophosphate, disodium salt monohydrate, 99+%, GOLD LABEL (5'-inosinic acid)
M.W. 410.2 m.p. 175° (dec.) Beil. 31,26

M.W. 412.21 m.p. >180° (dec.)

A

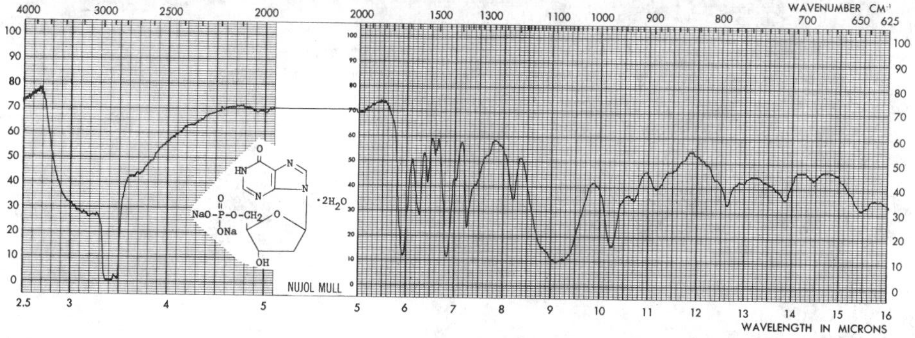

NUJOL MULL

85,214-7
Xanthosine 5'-monophosphate, disodium salt dihydrate
M.W. 444.21 m.p. >200° (dec.)

B

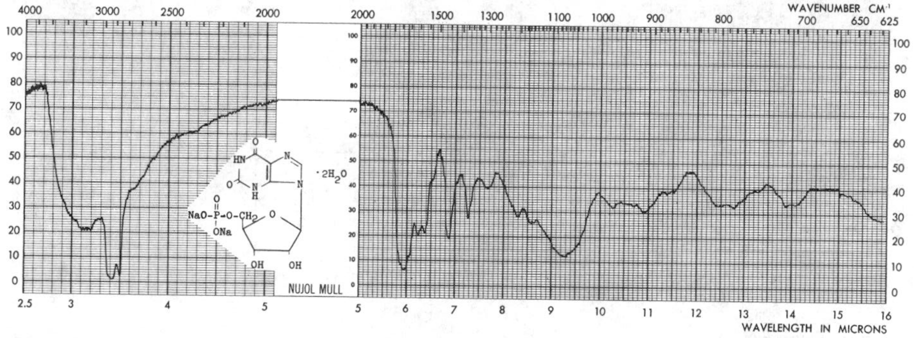

NUJOL MULL

85,796-3
Guanosine-5'-monophosphoric acid hydrate
M.W. 363.22 m.p. 91-93°

C

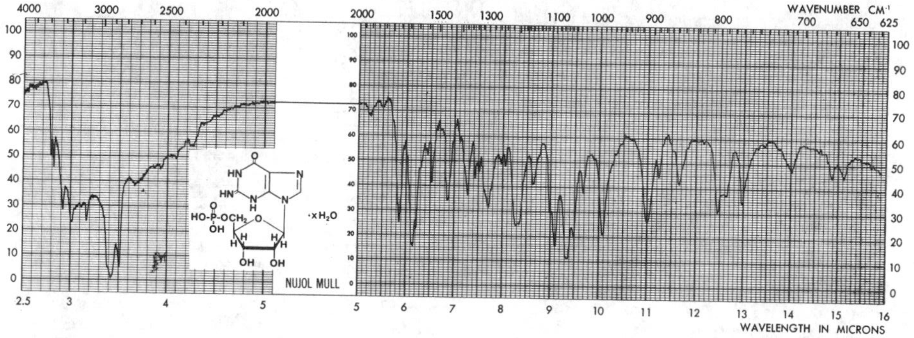

NUJOL MULL

85,222-8
2'-Deoxyguanosine 5'-monophosphate, disodium salt tetrahydrate
M.W. 463.25 m.p. >245° (dec.)

D

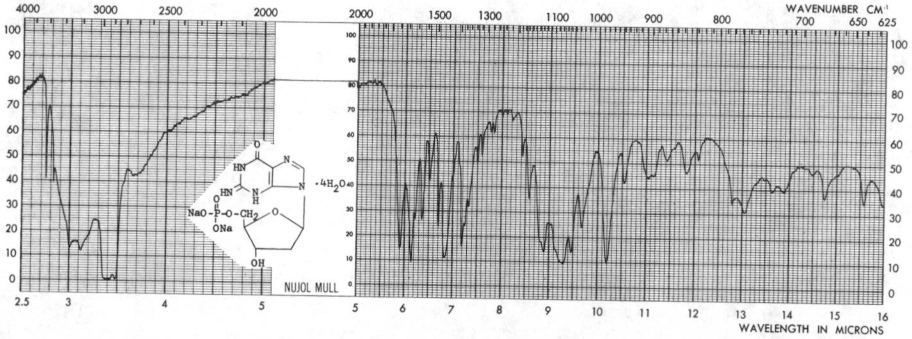

NUJOL MULL

hemihydrate (5'-guanylic acid)
M.W. 416.2 m.p. >300°

E

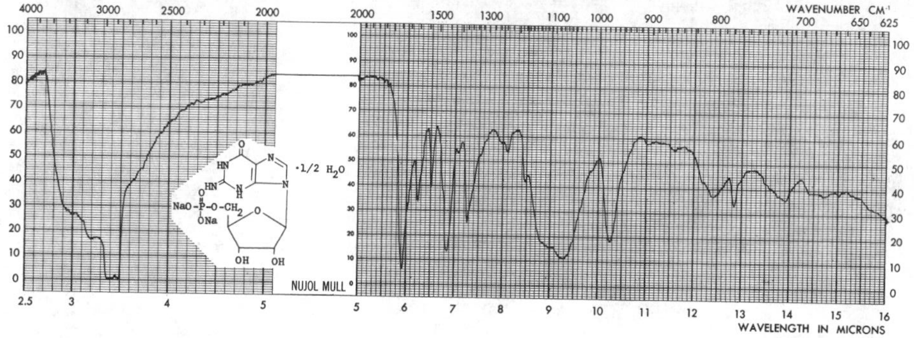

NUJOL MULL

85,202-3
Guanosine 2'(3')-monophosphate, disodium salt monohydrate, mixed isomers
M.W. 425.21 m.p. >300°

F

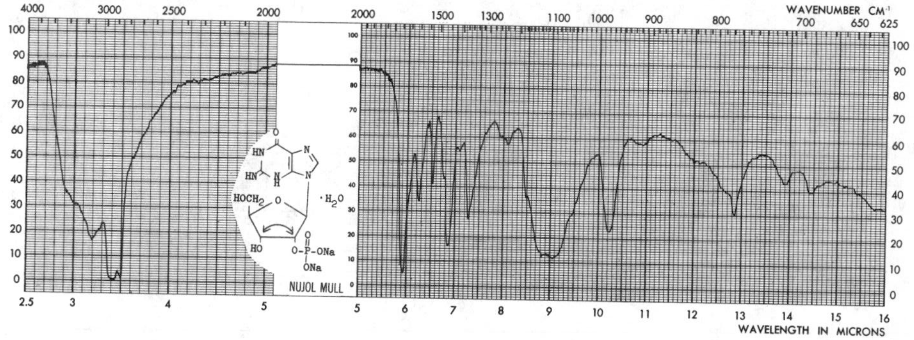

NUJOL MULL

A2500-8 **Adenosine monophosphate** (AMP, adenosine-5'-phosphoric acid)
M.W. 347.22 m.p. 205° (dec.)

G

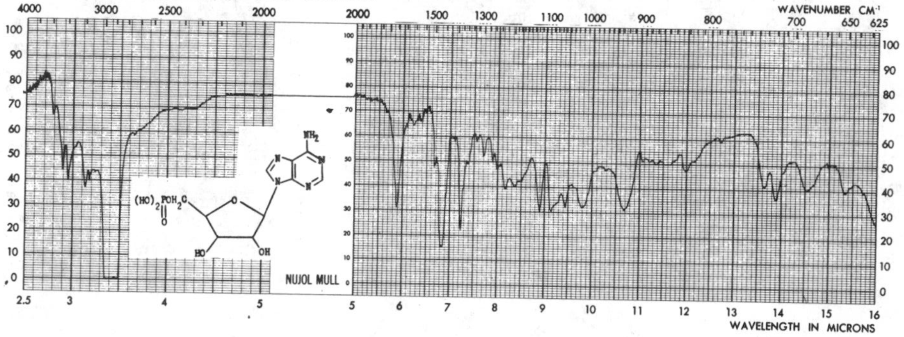

NUJOL MULL

85,195-7
Adenosine-2'(3')-monophosphoric acid, mixture of isomers
M.W. 347.22 m.p. 193° (dec.)

H

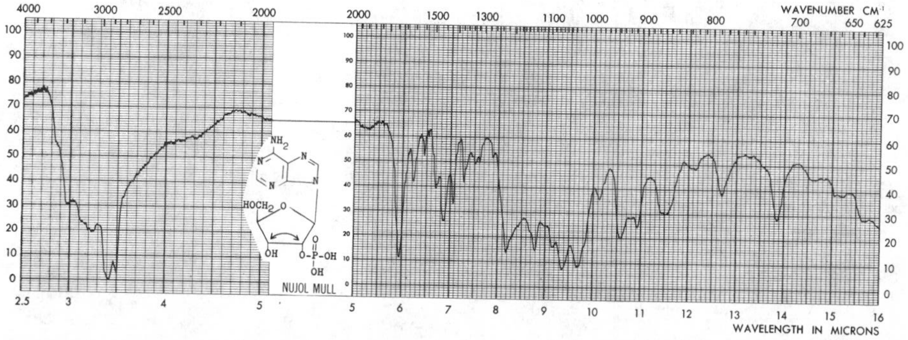

NUJOL MULL

ALDRICH

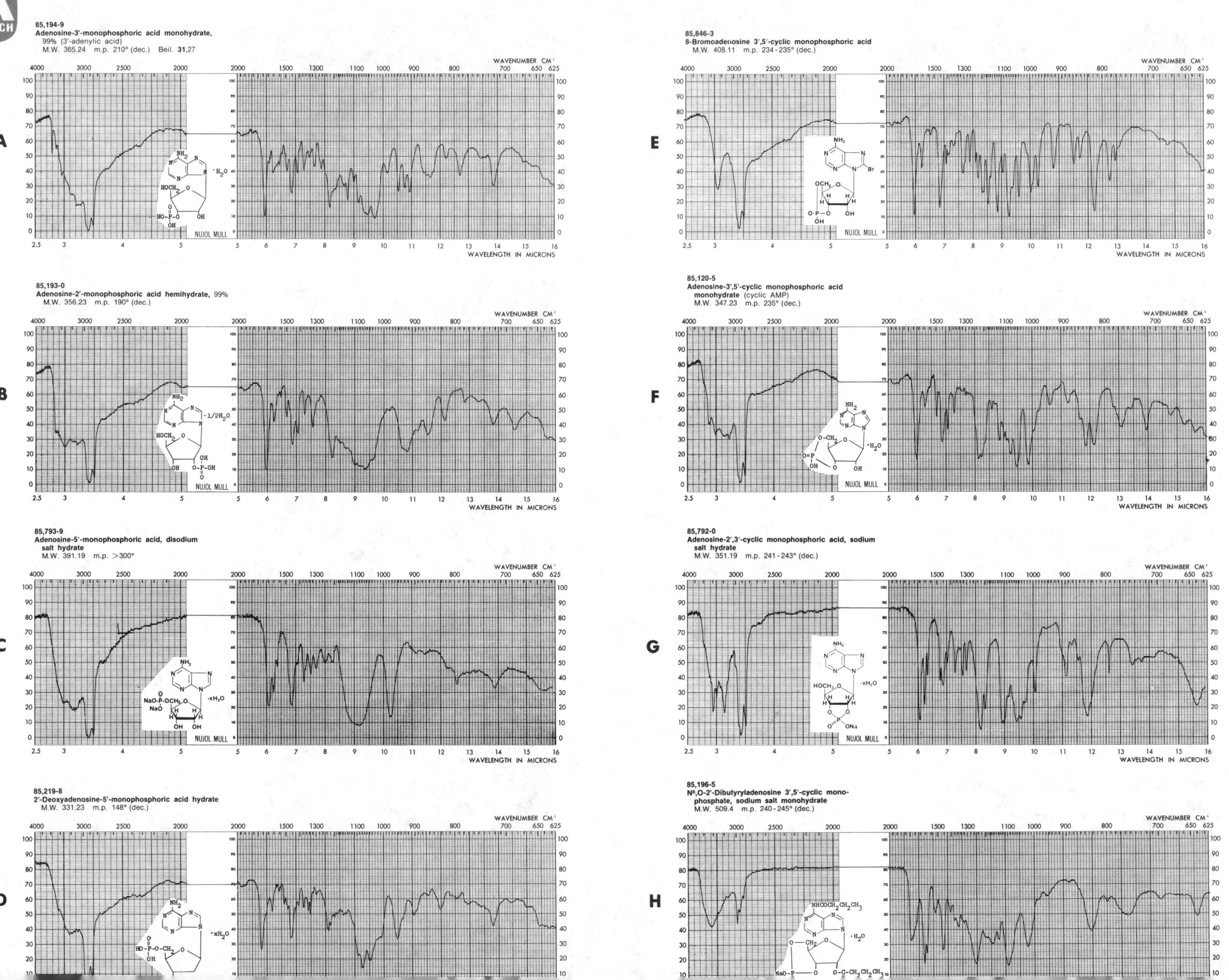

A

85,194-9
Adenosine-3'-monophosphoric acid monohydrate,
99% (3'-adenylic acid)
M.W. 365.24 m.p. 210° (dec.) Beil. **31**,27

E

85,846-3
8-Bromoadenosine 3',5'-cyclic monophosphoric acid
M.W. 408.11 m.p. 234-235° (dec.)

B

85,193-0
Adenosine-2'-monophosphoric acid hemihydrate, 99%
M.W. 356.23 m.p. 190° (dec.)

F

85,120-5
Adenosine-3',5'-cyclic monophosphoric acid monohydrate (cyclic AMP)
M.W. 347.23 m.p. 235° (dec.)

C

85,793-9
Adenosine-5'-monophosphoric acid, disodium salt hydrate
M.W. 391.19 m.p. >300°

G

85,792-0
Adenosine-2',3'-cyclic monophosphoric acid, sodium salt hydrate
M.W. 351.19 m.p. 241-243° (dec.)

D

85,219-8
2'-Deoxyadenosine-5'-monophosphoric acid hydrate
M.W. 331.23 m.p. 148° (dec.)

H

85,196-5
N⁶,O-2'-Dibutyryladenosine 3',5'-cyclic monophosphate, sodium salt monohydrate
M.W. 509.4 m.p. 240-245° (dec.)

A

M.W. 547.20

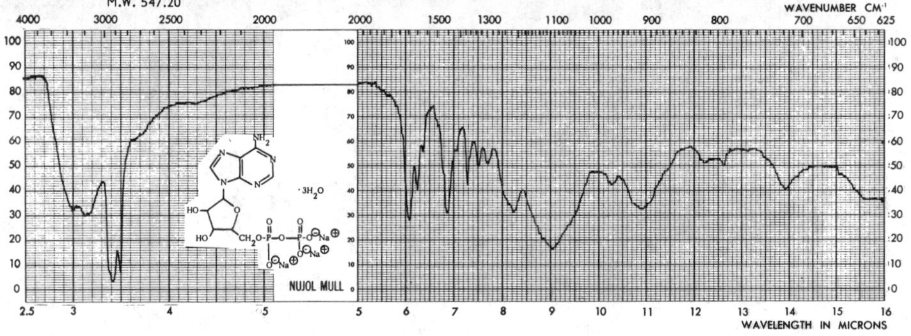

NUJOL MULL

B

85,207-4
Inosine 5'-diphosphate, trisodium salt hydrate
M.W. 494.14 m.p. 230-231° (dec.)

NUJOL MULL

C

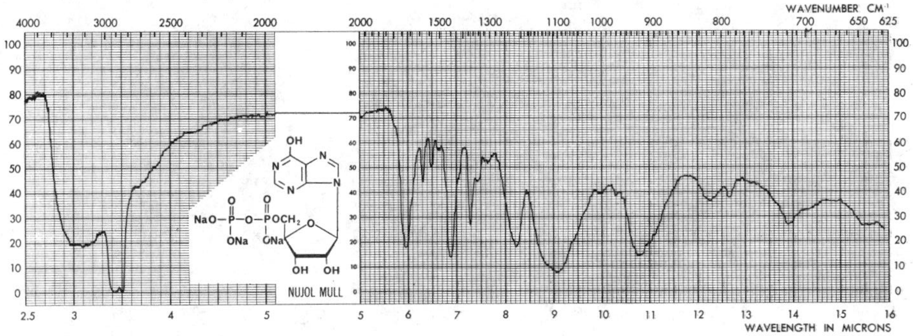

85,215-5
Xanthosine 5'-diphosphate, trisodium salt
M.W. 510.14 m.p. 260° (dec.)

NUJOL MULL

D

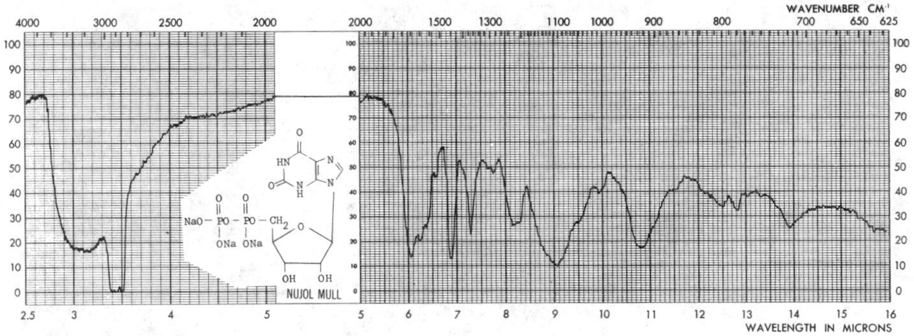

85,203-1
Guanosine 5'-diphosphate, trisodium salt hydrate
M.W. 509.15 m.p. >300°

NUJOL MULL

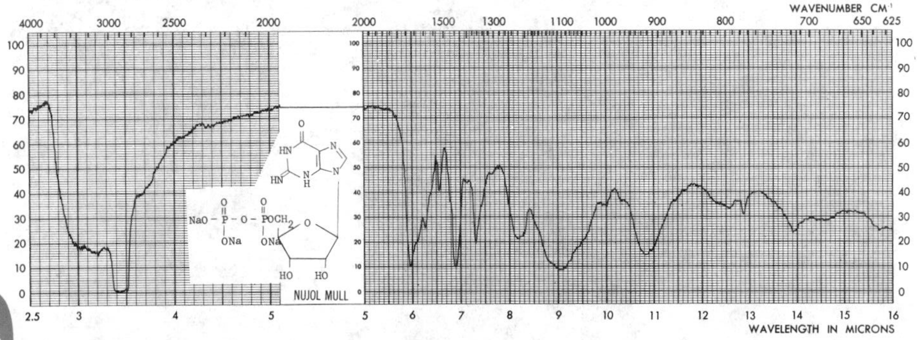

E

NUJOL MULL

F

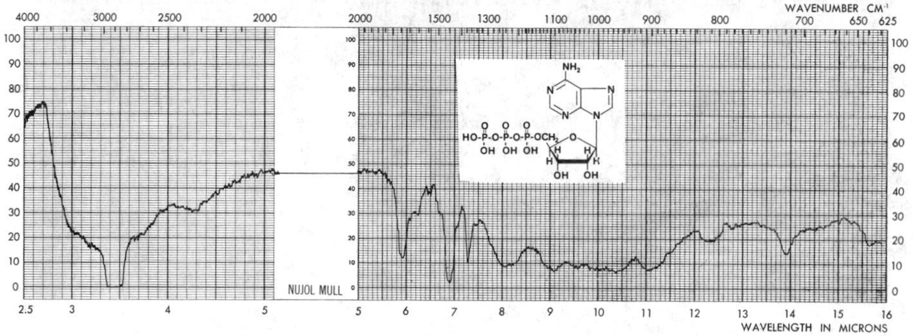

A2620-9 Adenosine triphosphate (ATP), disodium salt, crystalline
M.W. 551.15 m.p. > 170° (dec.)

NUJOL MULL

G

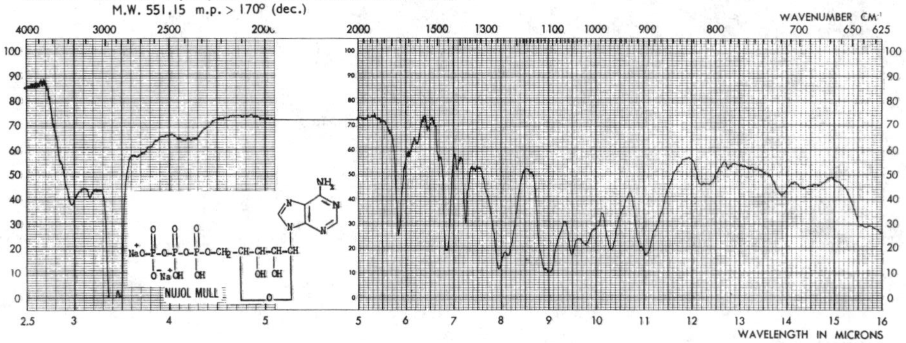

A2600-4 Adenosine triphosphate (ATP), dipotassium salt
M.W. 583.37

NUJOL MULL

H

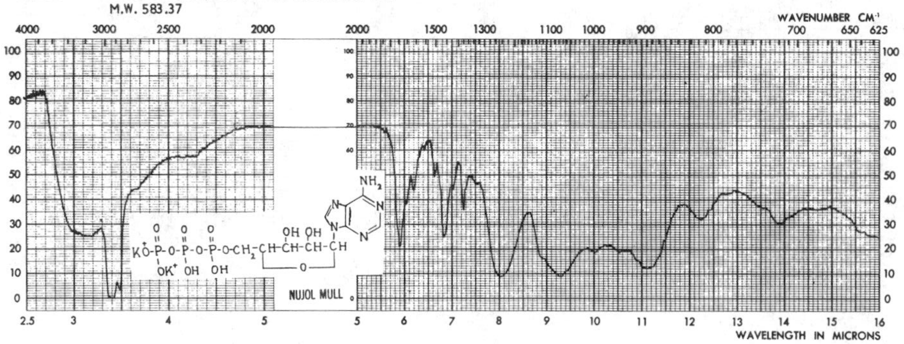

85,208-2
Inosine 5'-triphosphate, disodium salt dihydrate, 98%
M.W. 588.17 m.p. >160° (dec.)

NUJOL MULL

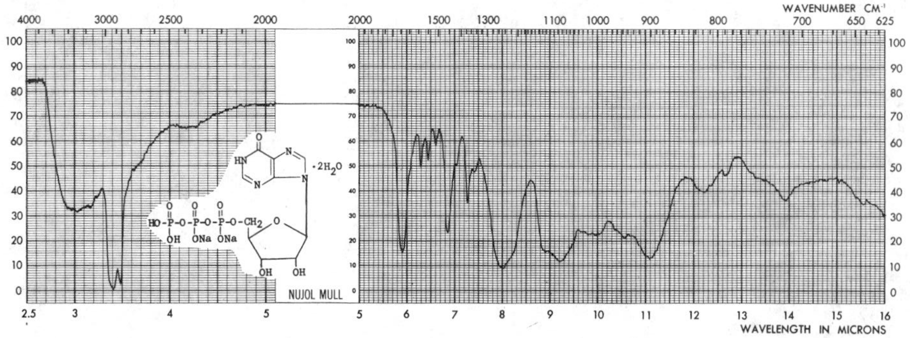

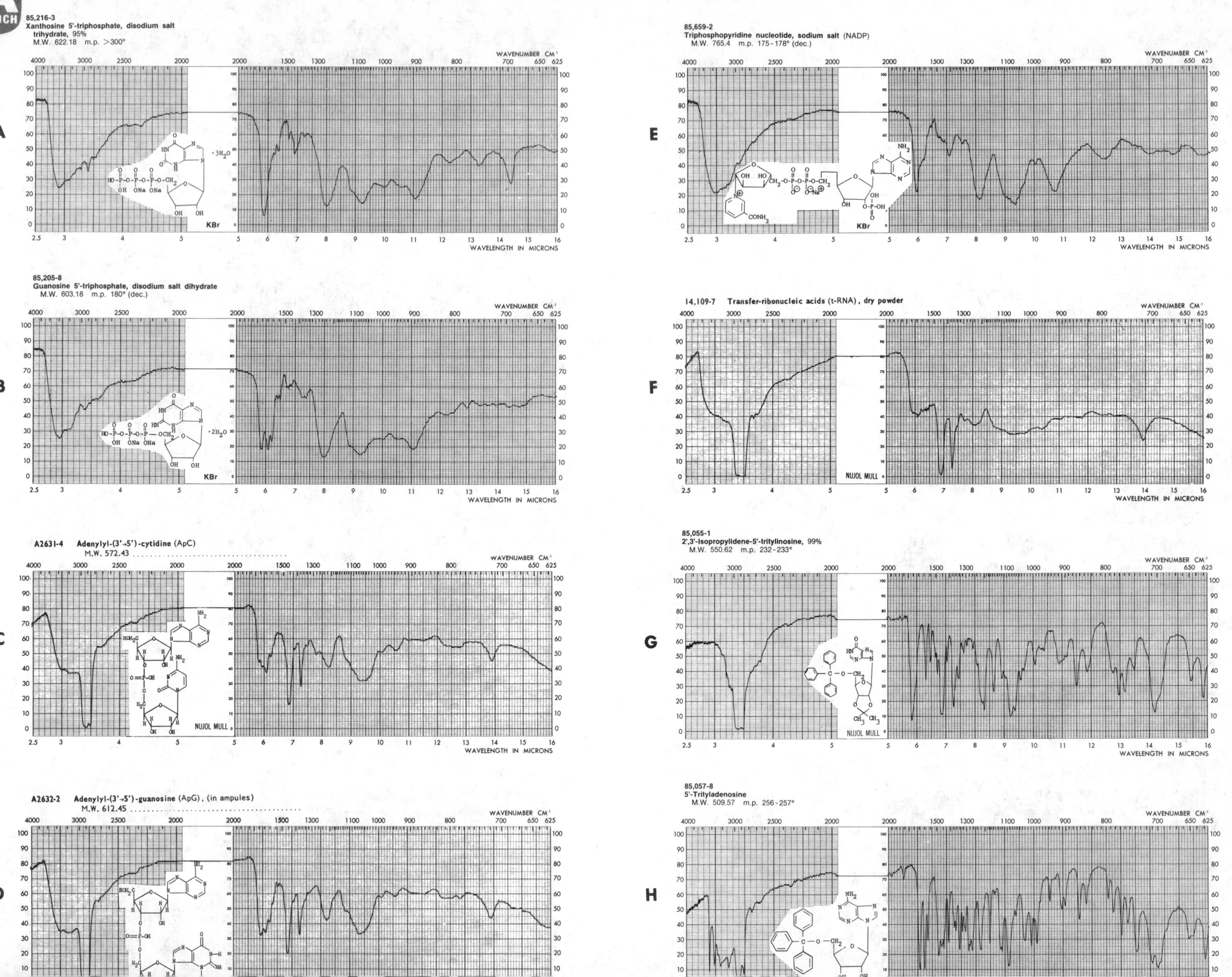
ALDRICH
A
85,216-3
Xanthosine 5'-triphosphate, disodium salt trihydrate, 95%
M.W. 622.18 m.p. >300°
KBr
B
85,205-8
Guanosine 5'-triphosphate, disodium salt dihydrate
M.W. 603.18 m.p. 180° (dec.)
KBr
C
A2631-4 Adenylyl-(3'→5')-cytidine (ApC)
M.W. 572.43
NUJOL MULL
D
A2632-2 Adenylyl-(3'→5')-guanosine (ApG), (in ampules)
M.W. 612.45
E
85,659-2
Triphosphopyridine nucleotide, sodium salt (NADP)
M.W. 765.4 m.p. 175-178° (dec.)
KBr
F
14,109-7 Transfer-ribonucleic acids (t-RNA), dry powder
NUJOL MULL
G
85,055-1
2',3'-Isopropylidene-5'-tritylinosine, 99%
M.W. 550.62 m.p. 232-233°
NUJOL MULL
H
85,057-8
5'-Trityladenosine
M.W. 509.57 m.p. 256-257°
WAVENUMBER CM⁻¹
WAVELENGTH IN MICRONS

A

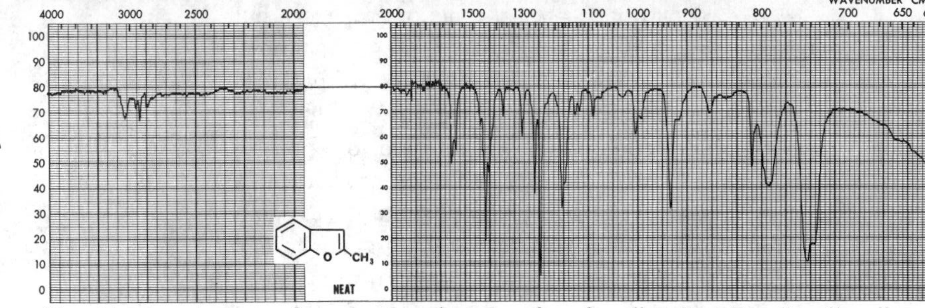

6-MEMBERED AROMATIC HETEROCYCLES

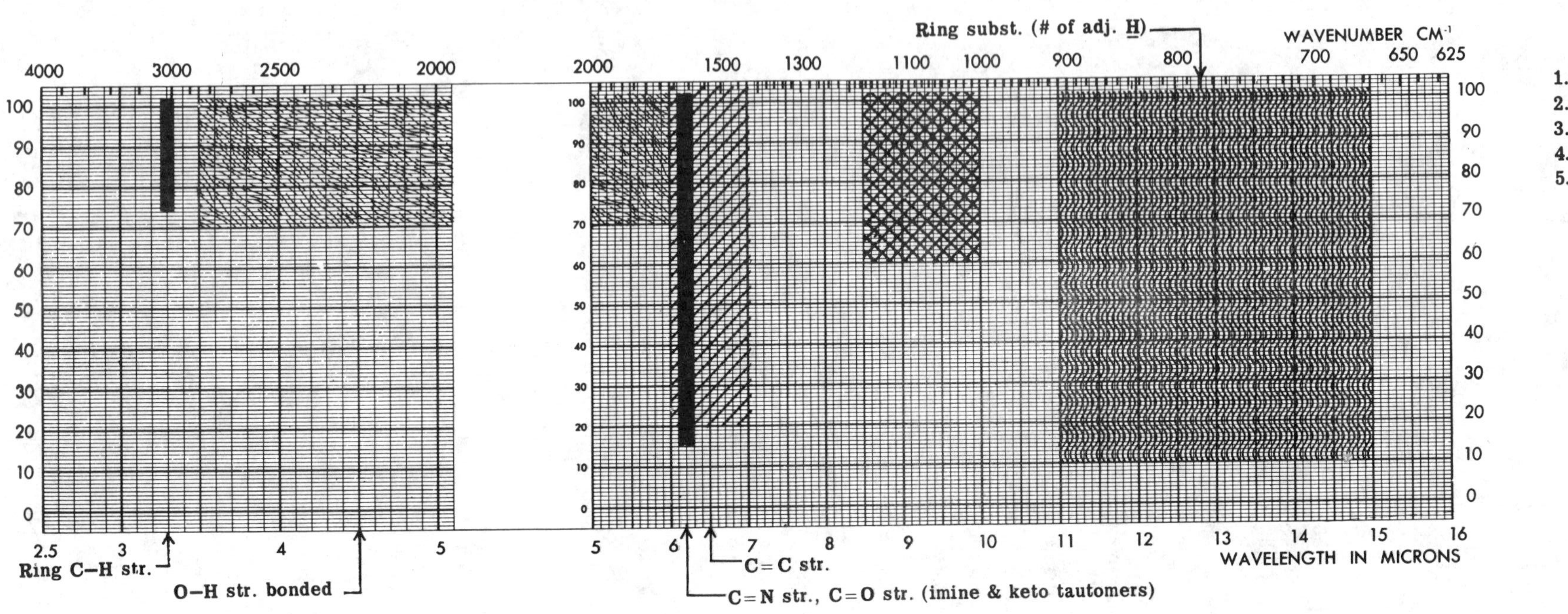

The six-membered heterocycles display bands very similar to the benzene ring with the CH stretch vibrations near 3.3 μ (3030 cm^{-1}), the ring stretching vibrations between 6 and 7 μ (1665 – 1430 cm^{-1}), the pattern of medium absorptions between 8.5 and 10 μ (1175 – 1000 cm^{-1}) and the substitution patterns between 11 and 15 μ (910 – 665 cm^{-1}).

A hydroxyl, amino or mercapto group on the carbon atom adjacent or para to a ring nitrogen atom results in the formation of the respective keto, imine or thione tautomer. With the formation of the keto form of 2-hydroxypyridine, the remaining four adjacent hydrogens still retain their substitution absorption at 12.8 μ (780 cm^{-1}) shifted only slightly from the normal ortho benzene position (see spectrum 1320F). In spectrum 1320H, which is also in the keto form, the three adjacent hydrogens absorb near 12.5 μ (800 cm^{-1}). The 1,2,4-substitution pattern (considering the ring nitrogen as a substituted position) displays its two adjacent hydrogens at 11.9 μ (840 cm^{-1}) with the single hydrogen appearing at 11 μ (910 cm^{-1}). (See spectrum 1321B).

When the OH group is in the 3 position of pyridine (where keto-enol tautomerism cannot occur), strong hydrogen bonding takes place between the phenolic type OH and the basic nitrogen. Broad bands are therefore observed between 3.5 and 6 μ (2855 – 1665 cm^{-1}). (See spectra 1322D—1323D).

The usual disruption from nitro and carbonyl substitution can be seen in the region between 11 and 15 μ (910 – 665 cm^{-1}).

The C=N stretch of the heterocyclic ring appears along with the C=C band near 6.2 μ (1615 cm^{-1}). The band is shifted to a lower wavelength near 6.15 μ (1625 cm^{-1}) in the quaternary (spectra 1306F and 1308C) or N-protonated forms (spectra 1309F and 1339F).

Pyridinecarboxylic acids display their strongly hydrogen bonded OH stretch absorption as broad bands between 3.5 and 6 μ (2855 – 1665 cm^{-1}). (See spectra 1339D—1342F). The carbonyl retains its 5.85 μ (1710 cm^{-1}) position except in spectrum 1341H.

A

M.W. 79.10 n_D 1.5073 b.p. 115.2

NEAT

B

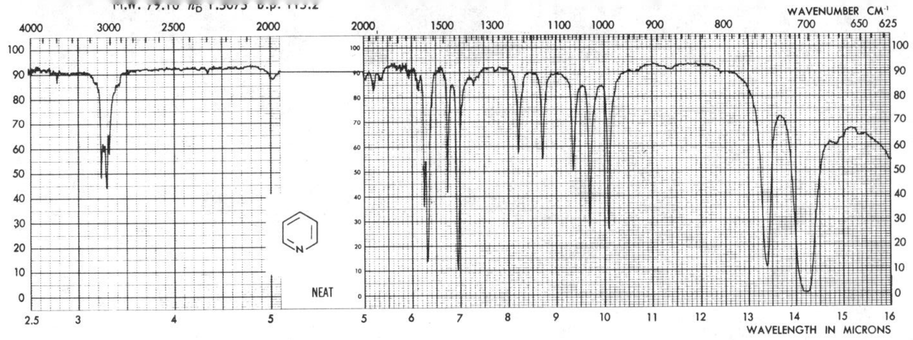

13,324-8 **Pyridinium bromide perbromide, tech.**
M.W. 319.84

$\cdot HBr$ $\cdot Br_2$ NUJOL MULL

C

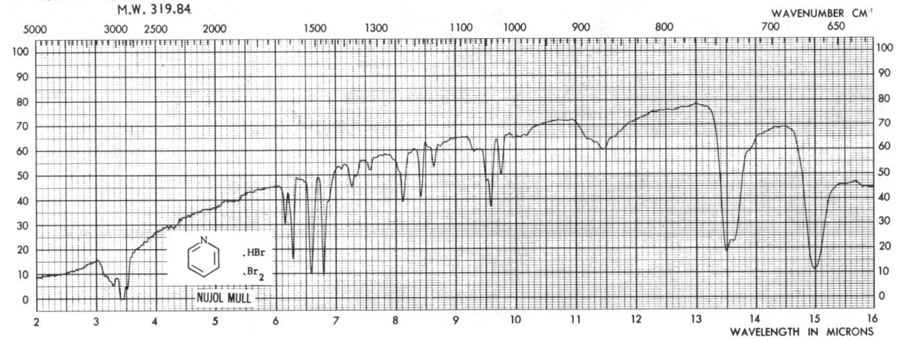

19,014-4
Pyridinium chlorochromate, 98%
FW 215.56 mp 205° (dec.) *Fieser* **6**,498 **7**,308
Disp. B

$CrO_3Cl^{\ominus}$ KBr

D

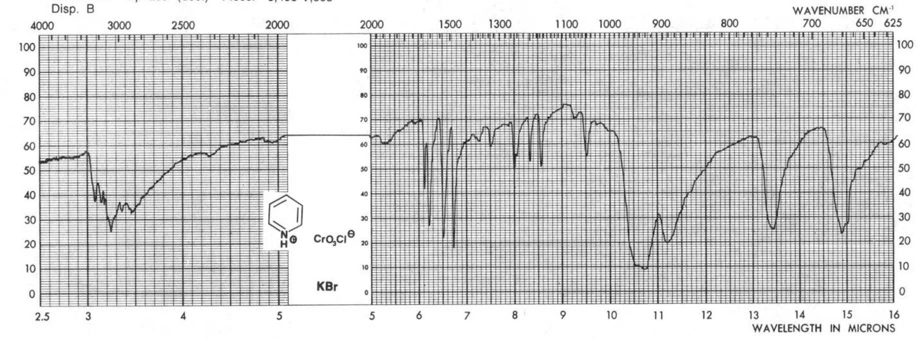

21,469-8
Pyridinium dichromate, 98%
FW 376.21 mp 152-153° Disp. B

$Cr_2O_7^{=}$ KBr

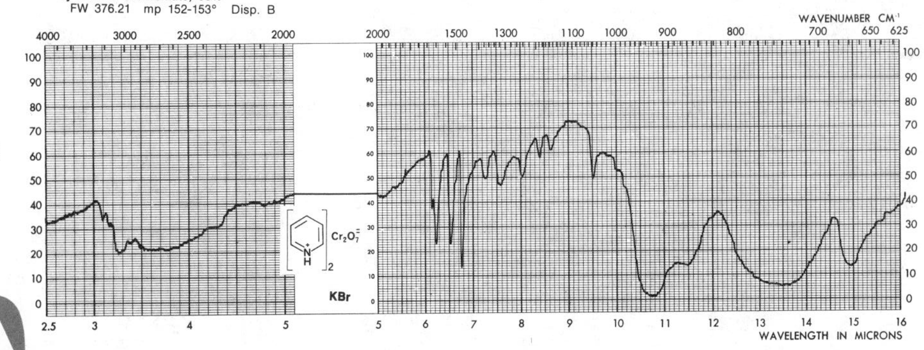

E

$CF_3CO_2^-$ NUJOL MULL

F

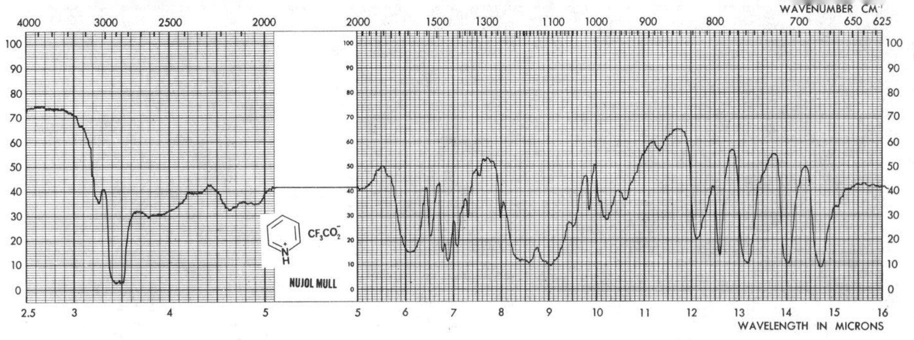

85,556-1
Cetylpyridinium chloride monohydrate
M.W. 358.01 m.p. 80-83°

$CH_2(CH_2)_{14}CH_3$ $Cl^{\ominus}$ $\cdot H_2O$ NUJOL MULL

G

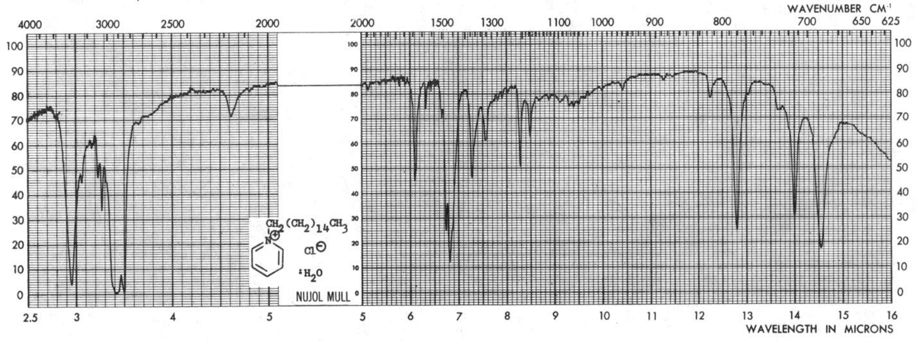

T2182-2 **N,N'-Tetramethylenebispyridinium dichloride**
M.W. 285.22 m.p. 258° (dec.)

$-CH_2CH_2CH_2CH_2-$ Cl^- Cl^- NUJOL MULL

H

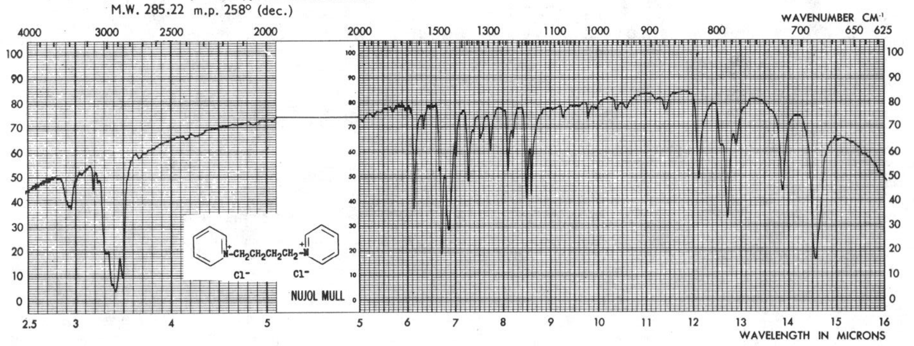

85,617-7
Methyl viologen hydrate (1,1'-dimethyl-4,4'-bipyridinium dichloride)
M.W. 257.17 m.p. >300°

$\cdot xH_2O$ KBr

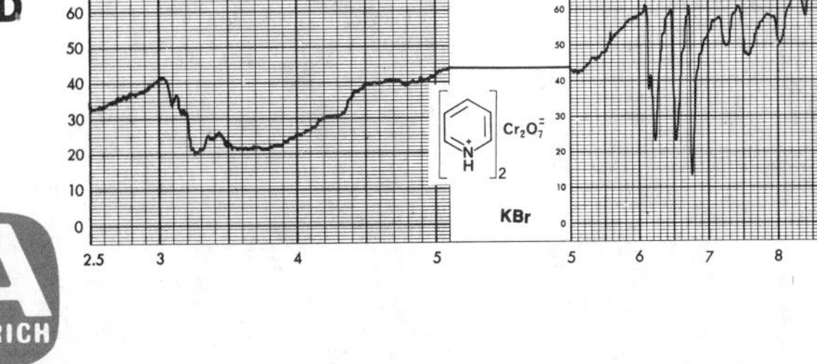

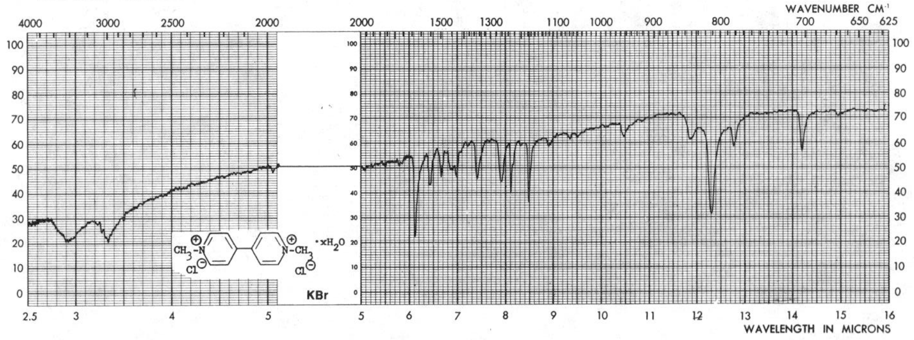

A 18,085-8
1,1'-Diheptyl-4,4'-bipyridinium dibromide
M.W. 514.4 m.p. 292-293° (dec.)
Viologen for electrochromic memory display. *Appl Phys. Letters*, **23**, 64 (1973).
NUJOL MULL

B D21,630-5 **2,2'-Dipyridyl** (2,2'-bipyridine)
M.W. 156.19 m.p. 70-73°
MELT

C 19,888-9
2,3'-Dipyridyl, 98% (2,3'-bipyridine)
FW 156.19 bp 295° n_D^{20} 1.6271 d 1.140
Beil. **23**,200 Disp. C
NEAT

D 19,889-7
2,4'-Dipyridyl, 97+% (2,4'-bipyridine)
FW 156.19 mp 60-62° bp 280-282° *Beil.* **23**,200
Disp. C

E 10,983-5 **2-Picoline**
M.W. 93.13 n_D^{20} 1.5000 b.p. 129°
NEAT

F 11,242-9 **2-Ethylpyridine**
M.W. 107.16 n_D^{20} 1.4964 b.p. 149°/752 mm.
NEAT

G 10,470-1 **Conyrine** (2-n-propylpyridine)
M.W. 121.18 n_D^{20} 1.4842 b.p. 166-167°
NEAT

H 13,229-2 **2-Vinylpyridine**
M.W. 105.14 n_D^{20} 1.5480 b.p. 79-82°/29 mm.

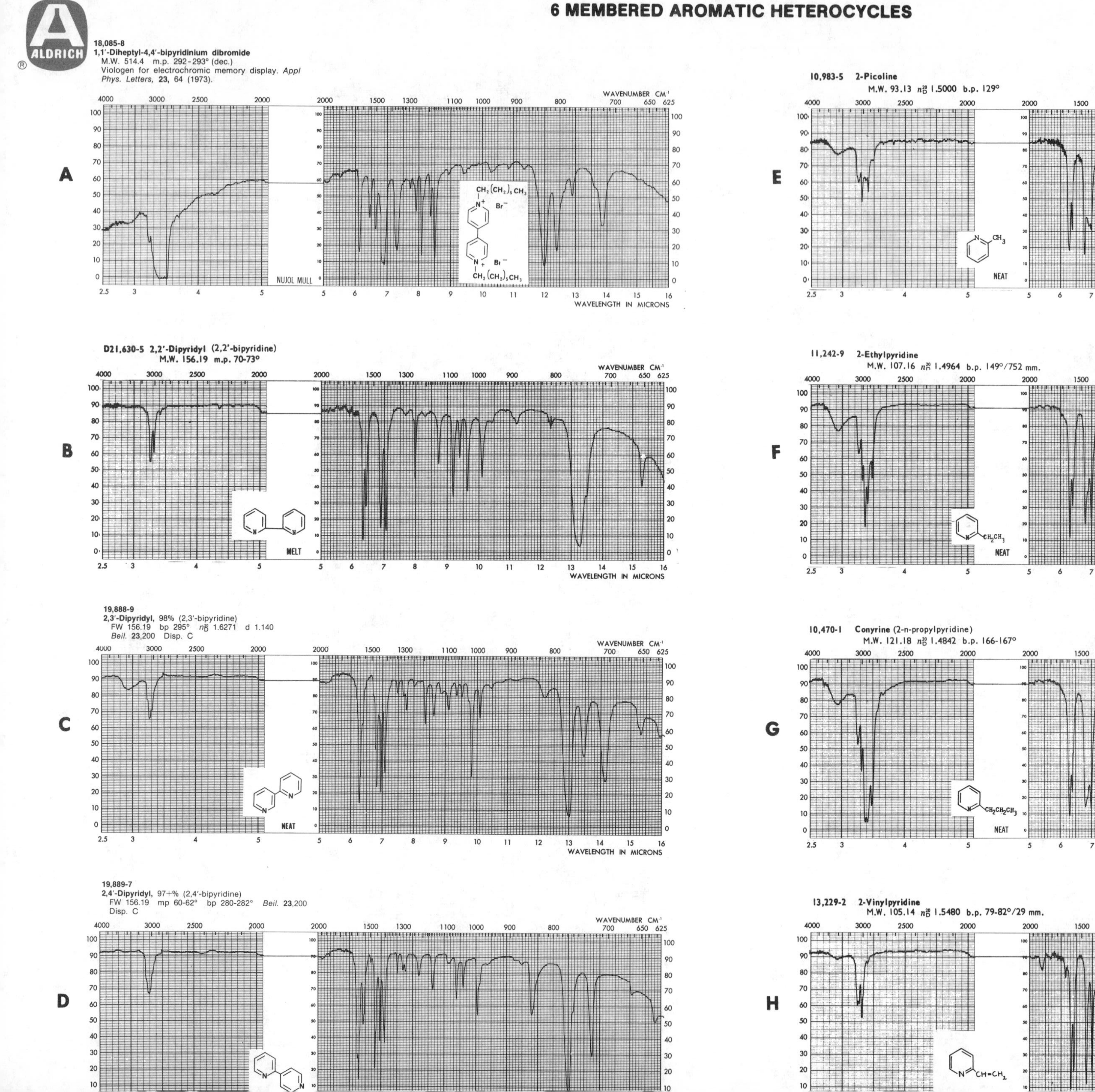

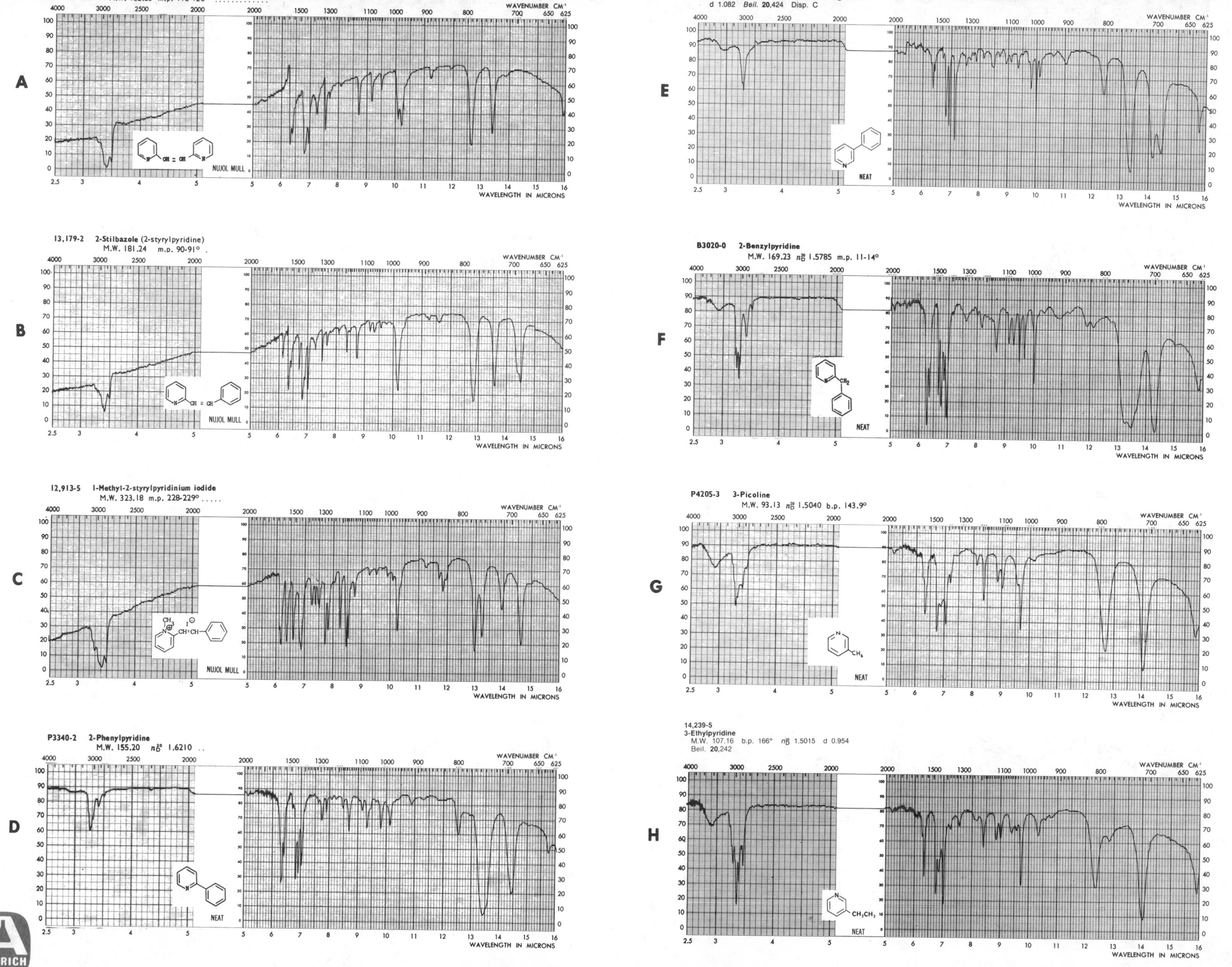

M.W. 182.23 m.p. 118-120°
A
NUJOL MULL
13,179-2 2-Stilbazole (2-styrylpyridine)
M.W. 181.24 m.p. 90-91°
B
NUJOL MULL
12,913-5 1-Methyl-2-styrylpyridinium iodide
M.W. 323.18 m.p. 228-229°
C
NUJOL MULL
P3340-2 2-Phenylpyridine
M.W. 155.20 n_D^{20} 1.6210
D
NEAT
FW 155.20 bp 269-270°/749mm. n_D^{20} 1.6155
d 1.082 Beil. 20,424 Disp. C
E
NEAT
B3020-0 2-Benzylpyridine
M.W. 169.23 n_D^{20} 1.5785 m.p. 11-14°
F
NEAT
P4205-3 3-Picoline
M.W. 93.13 n_D^{20} 1.5040 b.p. 143.9°
G
NEAT
14,239-5
3-Ethylpyridine
M.W. 107.16 b.p. 166° n_D^{20} 1.5015 d 0.954
Beil. 20,242
H
NEAT
WAVENUMBER CM⁻¹
WAVELENGTH IN MICRONS
ALDRICH

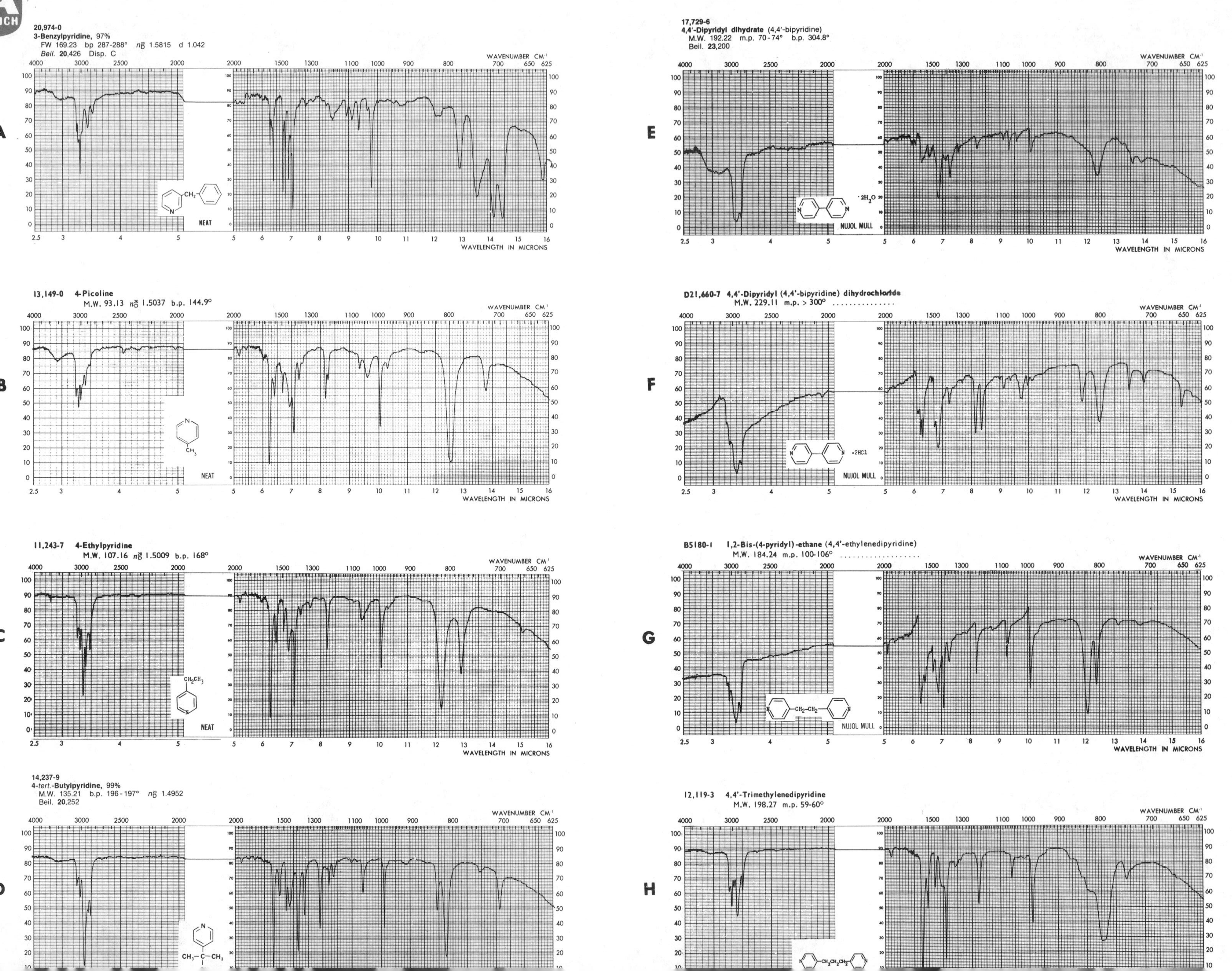
ALDRICH
A
20,974-0
3-Benzylpyridine, 97%
FW 169.23 bp 287-288° n_D^{20} 1.5815 d 1.042
Beil. 20,426 Disp. C
NEAT
B
13,149-0 4-Picoline
M.W. 93.13 n_D^{20} 1.5037 b.p. 144.9°
NEAT
C
11,243-7 4-Ethylpyridine
M.W. 107.16 n_D^{20} 1.5009 b.p. 168°
NEAT
D
14,237-9
4-*tert*.-Butylpyridine, 99%
M.W. 135.21 b.p. 196-197° n_D^{20} 1.4952
Beil. 20,252
E
17,729-6
4,4'-Dipyridyl dihydrate (4,4'-bipyridine)
M.W. 192.22 m.p. 70-74° b.p. 304.8°
Beil. 23,200
$\cdot 2H_2O$
NUJOL MULL
F
D21,660-7 4,4'-Dipyridyl (4,4'-bipyridine) dihydrochloride
M.W. 229.11 m.p. > 300°
$\cdot 2HCl$
NUJOL MULL
G
B5180-1 1,2-Bis-(4-pyridyl)-ethane (4,4'-ethylenedipyridine)
M.W. 184.24 m.p. 100-106°
NUJOL MULL
H
12,119-3 4,4'-Trimethylenedipyridine
M.W. 198.27 m.p. 59-60°
WAVENUMBER CM⁻¹
WAVELENGTH IN MICRONS

A

M.W. 198.27 m.p. 59-60°

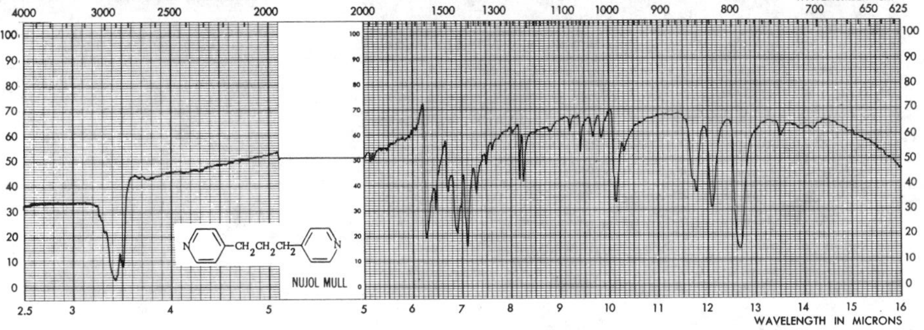

NUJOL MULL

B

P7150-9 N-(4-Pyridyl)-pyridinium chloride
M.W. 192.65

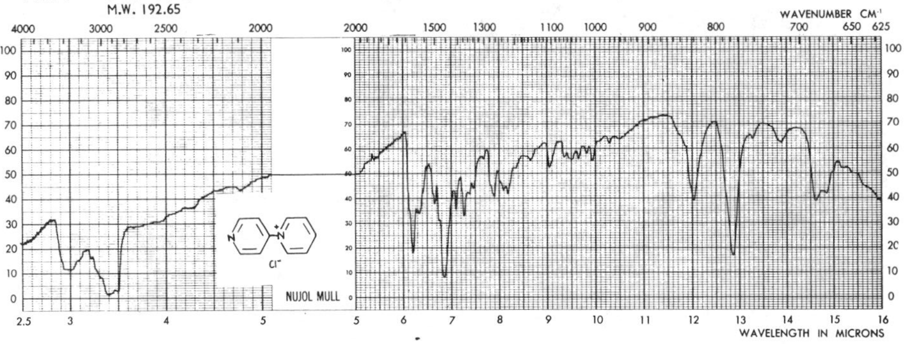

NUJOL MULL

C

P7151-7 N-(4-Pyridyl)-pyridinium chloride hydrochloride, tech.
M.W. 229.11 m.p. 145-150°

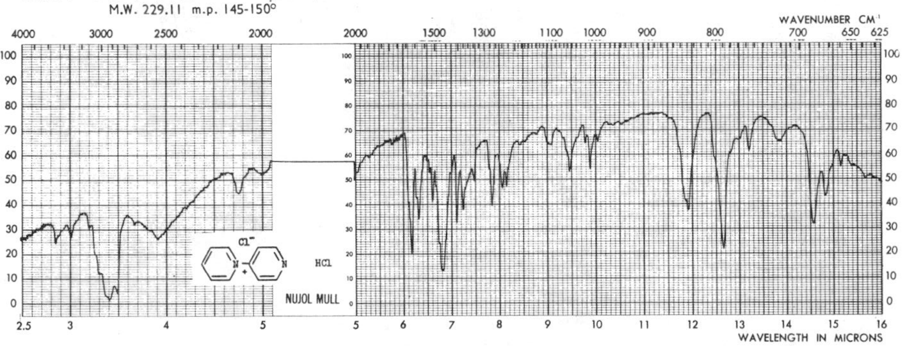

NUJOL MULL

D

B5280-8 1,2-Bis-(4-pyridyl)-ethylene (4,4'-vinylenedipyridine)
M.W. 182.23 m.p. 150-153°

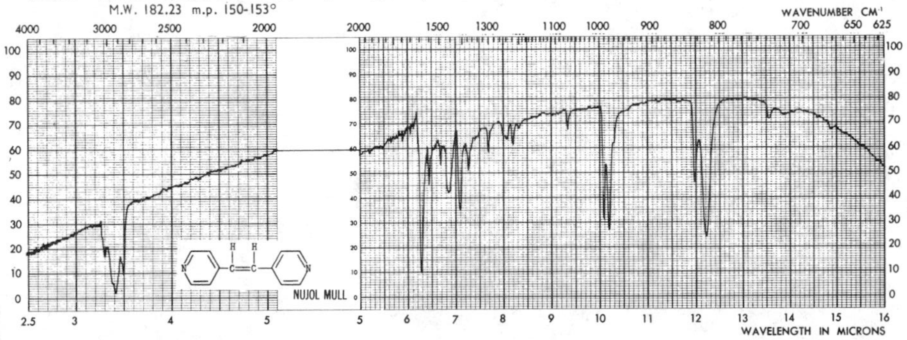

NUJOL MULL

E

M.W. 105.14 n_D^{20} 1.5500 b.p. 62-65°/15 mm.

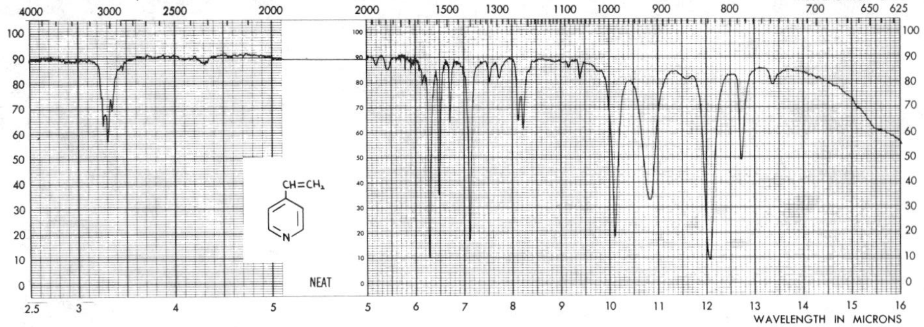

NEAT

F

19,745-9
trans-1-(2-Pyridyl)-2-(4-pyridyl)ethylene
FW 182.23 mp 70-72° Disp. C

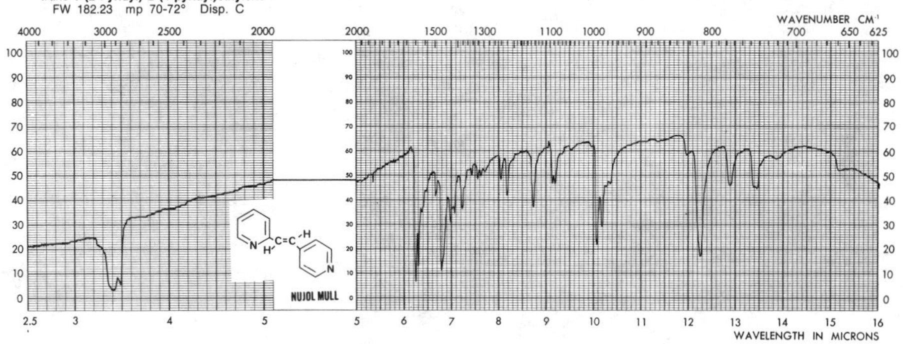

NUJOL MULL

G

P3342-9 4-Phenylpyridine
M.W. 155.20 m.p. 75.5-77°

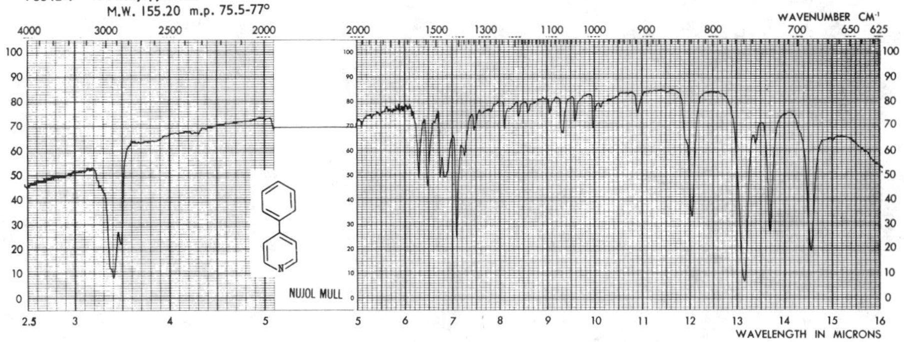

NUJOL MULL

H

19,887-0
2-(*p*-Tolyl)pyridine, 97+%
FW 169.23 bp 170-180°/20mm. n_D^{20} 1.6125
d 0.999 Disp. C

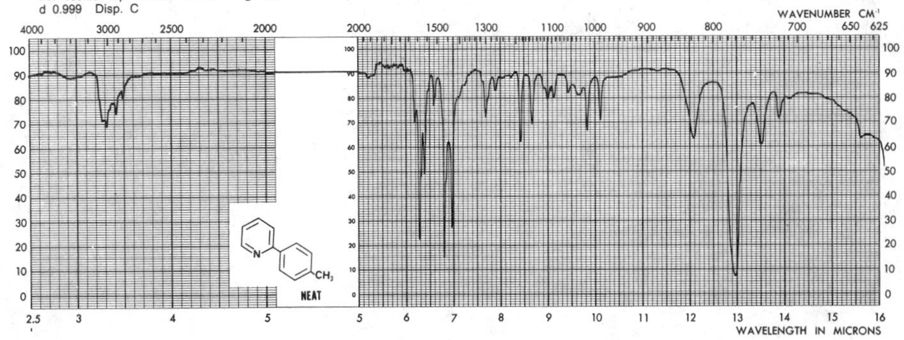

NEAT

6 MEMBERED AROMATIC HETEROCYCLES

ALDRICH ®

A

19,886-2
3-Methyl-2-phenylpyridine, 97+%
FW 169.23 bp 148-148°/16mm. n_D^{20} 1.6026
d 1.065 Disp. C

NEAT

B

19,892-7
2,6-Diphenylpyridine, 97+%
FW 231.30 mp 74-76° *Beil.* **20**,496 Disp. C

NUJOL MULL

C

19,893-5
2,6-Di-*p*-tolylpyridine, 97+%
FW 259.35 mp 163-165° *Beil.* **20**,503 Disp. C

NUJOL MULL

D

B3040-5 **4-Benzylpyridine, puriss.**
M.W. 169.23 n_D^{20} 1.5818

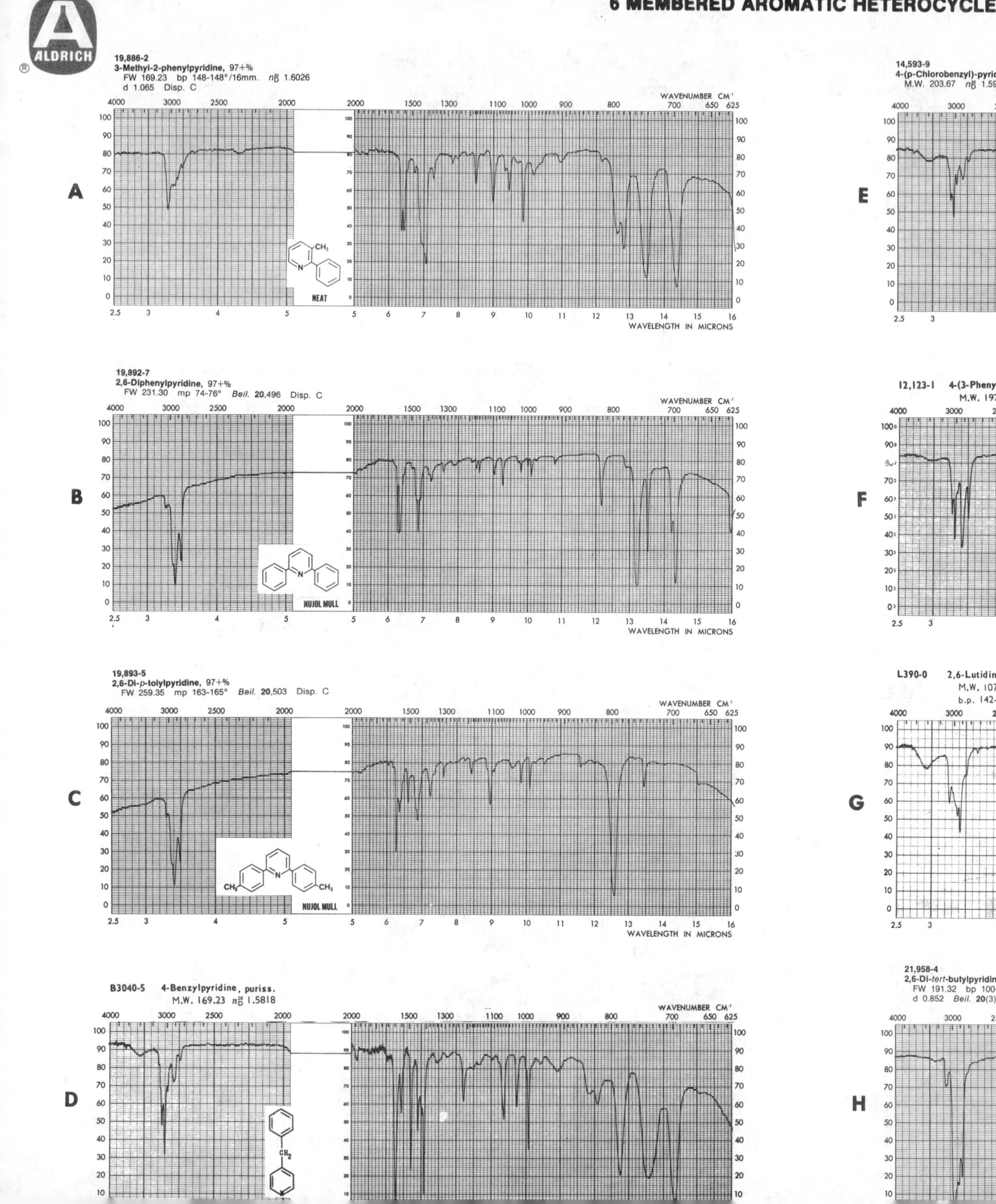

E

14,593-9
4-(p-Chlorobenzyl)-pyridine
M.W. 203.67 n_D^{20} 1.5900

NEAT

F

12,123-1 **4-(3-Phenylpropyl)-pyridine**
M.W. 197.28 n_D^{20} 1.5610 b.p. 322° . . .

NEAT

G

L390-0 **2,6-Lutidine** (2,6-dimethylpyridine)
M.W. 107.16 n_D^{20} 1.4976 m.p. - 9 to - 6°
b.p. 142-144°

NEAT

H

21,958-4
2,6-Di-*tert*-butylpyridine, 97%
FW 191.32 bp 100-101°/23mm. n_D^{20} 1.4739
d 0.852 *Beil.* **20**(3),2868 *Fieser* **1**,212 Disp. C

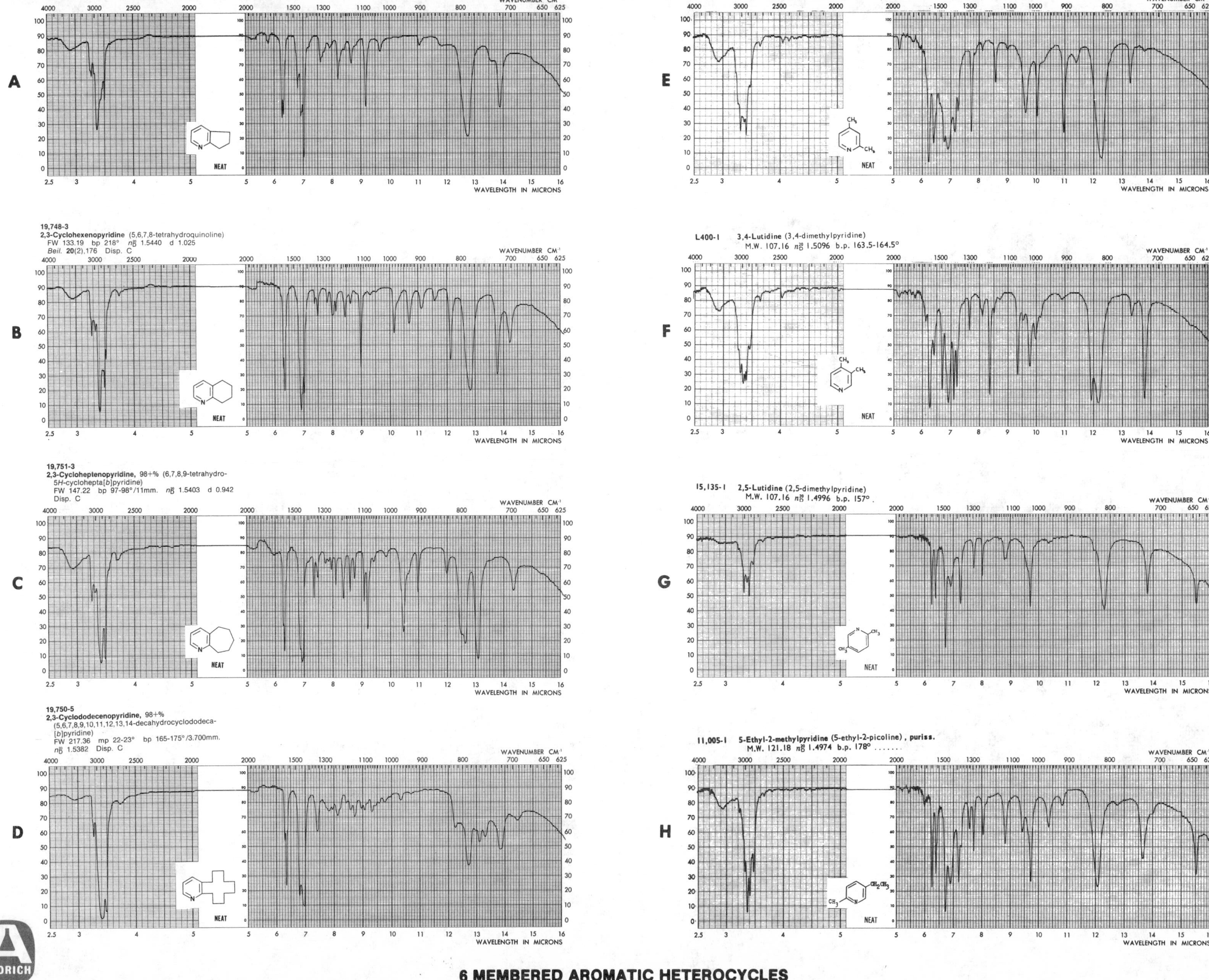

Disp. C
A
NEAT
19,748-3
2,3-Cyclohexenopyridine (5,6,7,8-tetrahydroquinoline)
FW 133.19 bp 218° n_D^{20} 1.5440 d 1.025
Beil. 20(2),176 Disp. C
B
NEAT
19,751-3
2,3-Cycloheptenopyridine, 98+% (6,7,8,9-tetrahydro-5H-cyclohepta[b]pyridine)
FW 147.22 bp 97-98°/11mm. n_D^{20} 1.5403 d 0.942
Disp. C
C
NEAT
19,750-5
2,3-Cyclododecenopyridine, 98+%
(5,6,7,8,9,10,11,12,13,14-decahydrocyclododeca-[b]pyridine)
FW 217.36 mp 22-23° bp 165-175°/3.700mm.
n_D^{20} 1.5382 Disp. C
D
NEAT
M.W. 107.16 n_D^{20} 1.4991 b.p. 158.5° ...
E
NEAT
L400-1 3,4-Lutidine (3,4-dimethylpyridine)
M.W. 107.16 n_D^{20} 1.5096 b.p. 163.5-164.5°
F
NEAT
15,135-1 2,5-Lutidine (2,5-dimethylpyridine)
M.W. 107.16 n_D^{20} 1.4996 b.p. 157°
G
NEAT
11,005-1 5-Ethyl-2-methylpyridine (5-ethyl-2-picoline), puriss.
M.W. 121.18 n_D^{20} 1.4974 b.p. 178° ......
H
NEAT
WAVENUMBER CM⁻¹
WAVELENGTH IN MICRONS
ALDRICH

A

12,773-6 **2-Methyl-5-vinylpyridine** (inhibited with tert.-butylcatechol)
M.W. 119.17 n_D^{20} 1.5437
b.p. 100°/50 mm.

NEAT

B

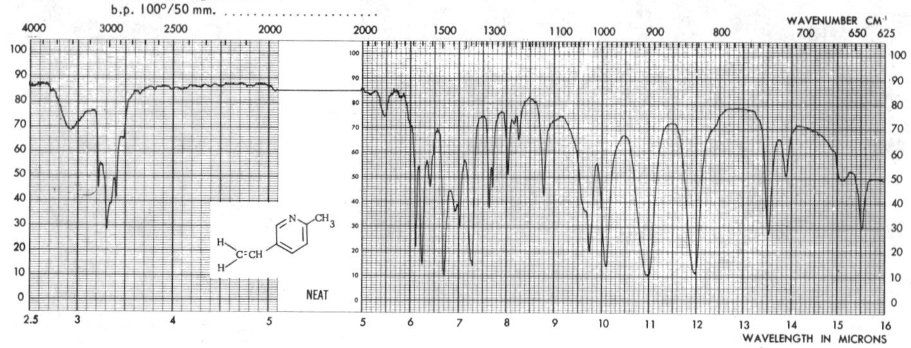

L420-6 **3,5-Lutidine** (3,5-dimethylpyridine)
M.W. 107.16 n_D^{20} 1.5043 b.p. 169-170°

NEAT

C

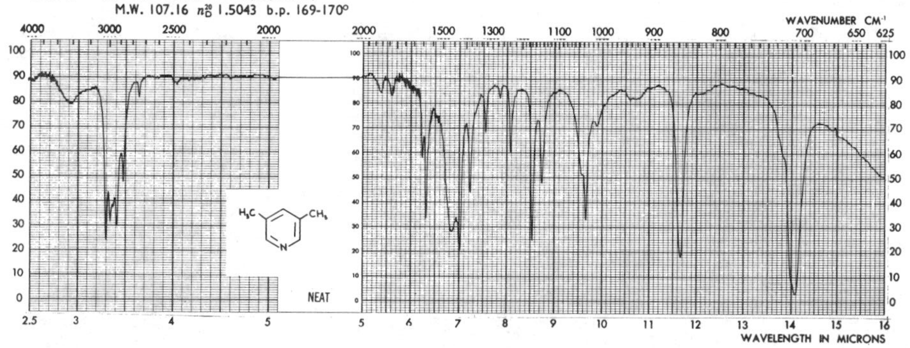

C8418-6 **2,3,6-Collidine** (2,3,6-trimethylpyridine)
M.W. 121.18 n_D^{20} 1.5053

NEAT

D

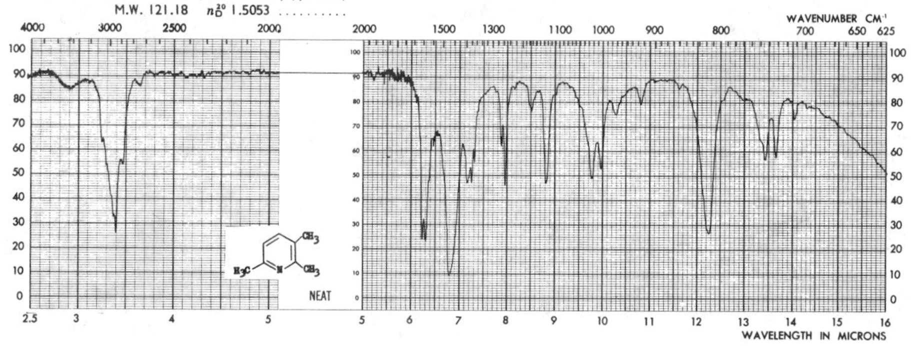

22,064-7
3-Methyl-5,6,7,8-tetrahydroquinoline, 99%
FW 147.22 bp 113-114°/9mm. n_D^{20} 1.5375
d 0.990 *Beil.* **20**(2),184 Disp. C

E

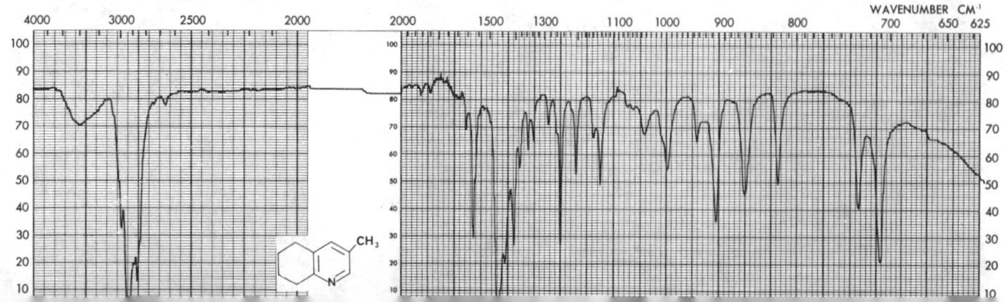

19,891-9
1,2,3,4,5,6,7,8-Octahydroacridine, 97+%
FW 187.29 mp 70-71° bp 175°/17mm.
Beil. **20**(2),219 Disp. C

MELT

F

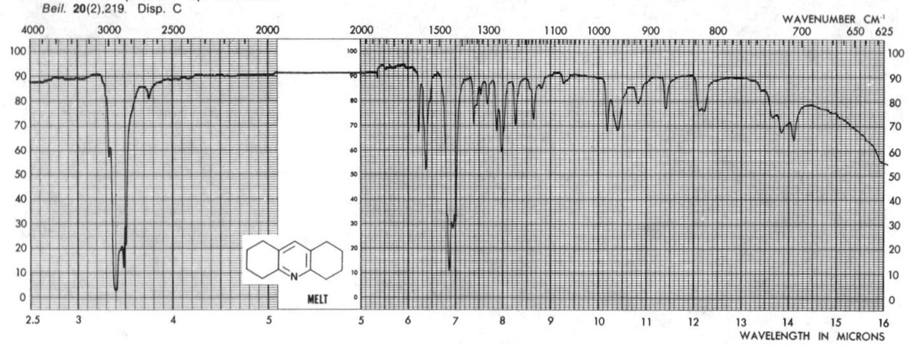

C8420-8 **Collidine** (trimethylpyridine) (for paper chromatography)
M.W. 121.18

NEAT

G

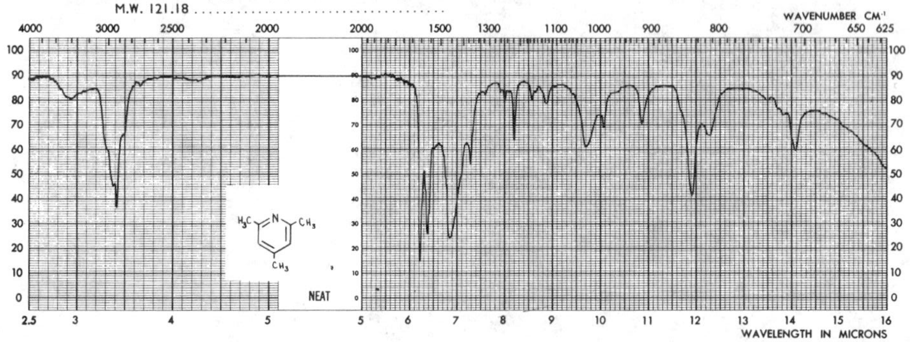

14,238-7
2,4,6-Collidine (2,4,6-trimethylpyridine)
M.W. 121.18 m.p. -43° b.p. 171-172°
n_D^{20} 1.4979 d 0.917 Beil. **20**,250 Fieser **1**,155
IRRITANT

NEAT

H

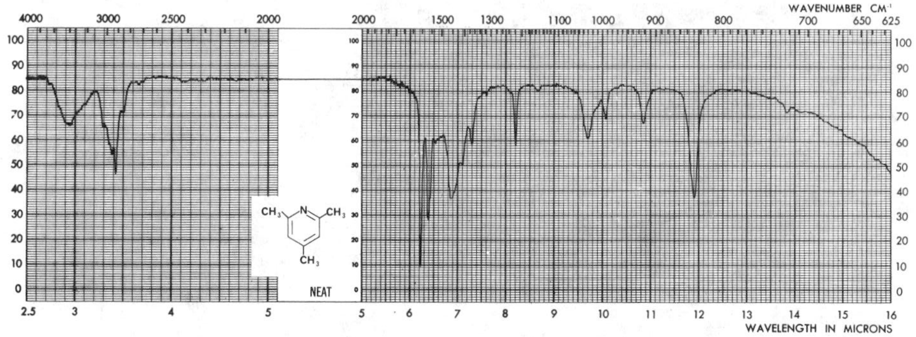

D21,280-6 **Diphenyl-2-pyridylmethane** (2-diphenylmethylpyridine), **puriss.**
M.W. 245.33 m.p. 55-58°

WAVENUMBER CM⁻¹ — WAVELENGTH IN MICRONS

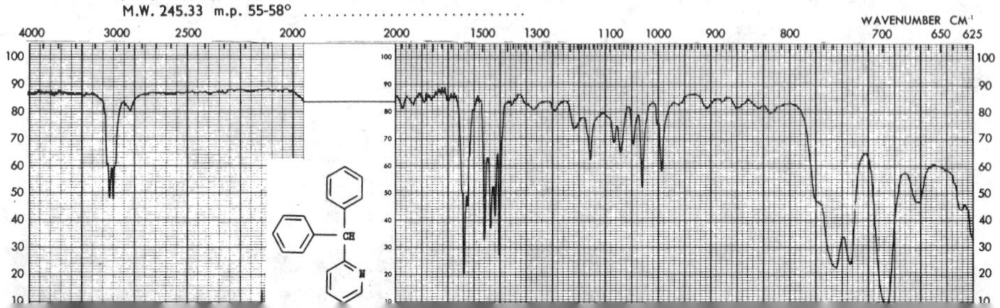

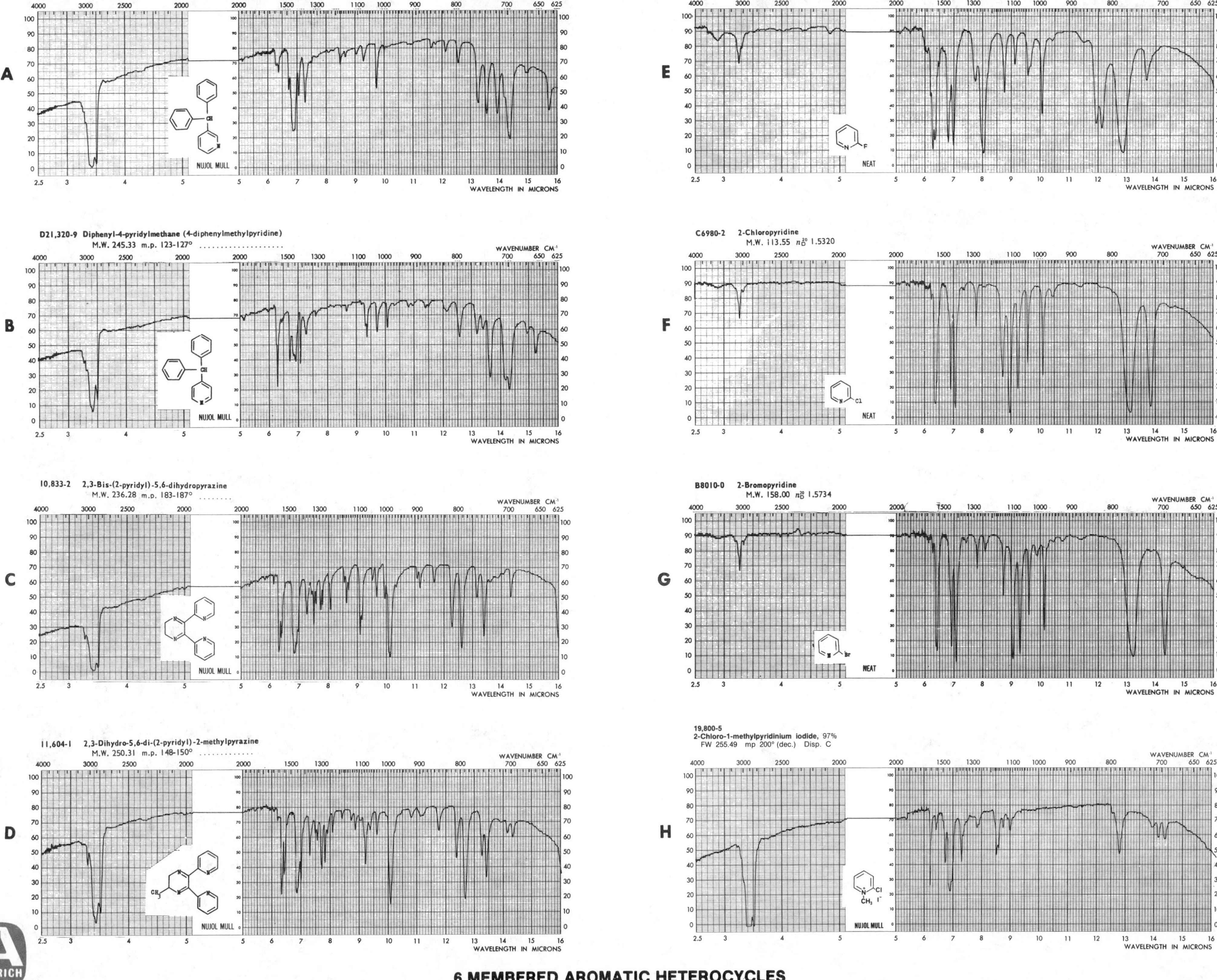
A
M.W. 245.33 m.p. 75-77°
NUJOL MULL
B
D21,320-9 Diphenyl-4-pyridylmethane (4-diphenylmethylpyridine)
M.W. 245.33 m.p. 123-127°
NUJOL MULL
C
10,833-2 2,3-Bis-(2-pyridyl)-5,6-dihydropyrazine
M.W. 236.28 m.p. 183-187°
NUJOL MULL
D
11,604-1 2,3-Dihydro-5,6-di-(2-pyridyl)-2-methylpyrazine
M.W. 250.31 m.p. 148-150°
NUJOL MULL
E
b.p. 126°/753 mm.
NEAT
F
C6980-2 2-Chloropyridine
M.W. 113.55 n_D^{20} 1.5320
NEAT
G
B8010-0 2-Bromopyridine
M.W. 158.00 n_D^{20} 1.5734
NEAT
H
19,800-5
2-Chloro-1-methylpyridinium iodide, 97%
FW 255.49 mp 200° (dec.) Disp. C
NUJOL MULL
WAVENUMBER CM⁻¹
WAVELENGTH IN MICRONS
ALDRICH

6 MEMBERED AROMATIC HETEROCYCLES

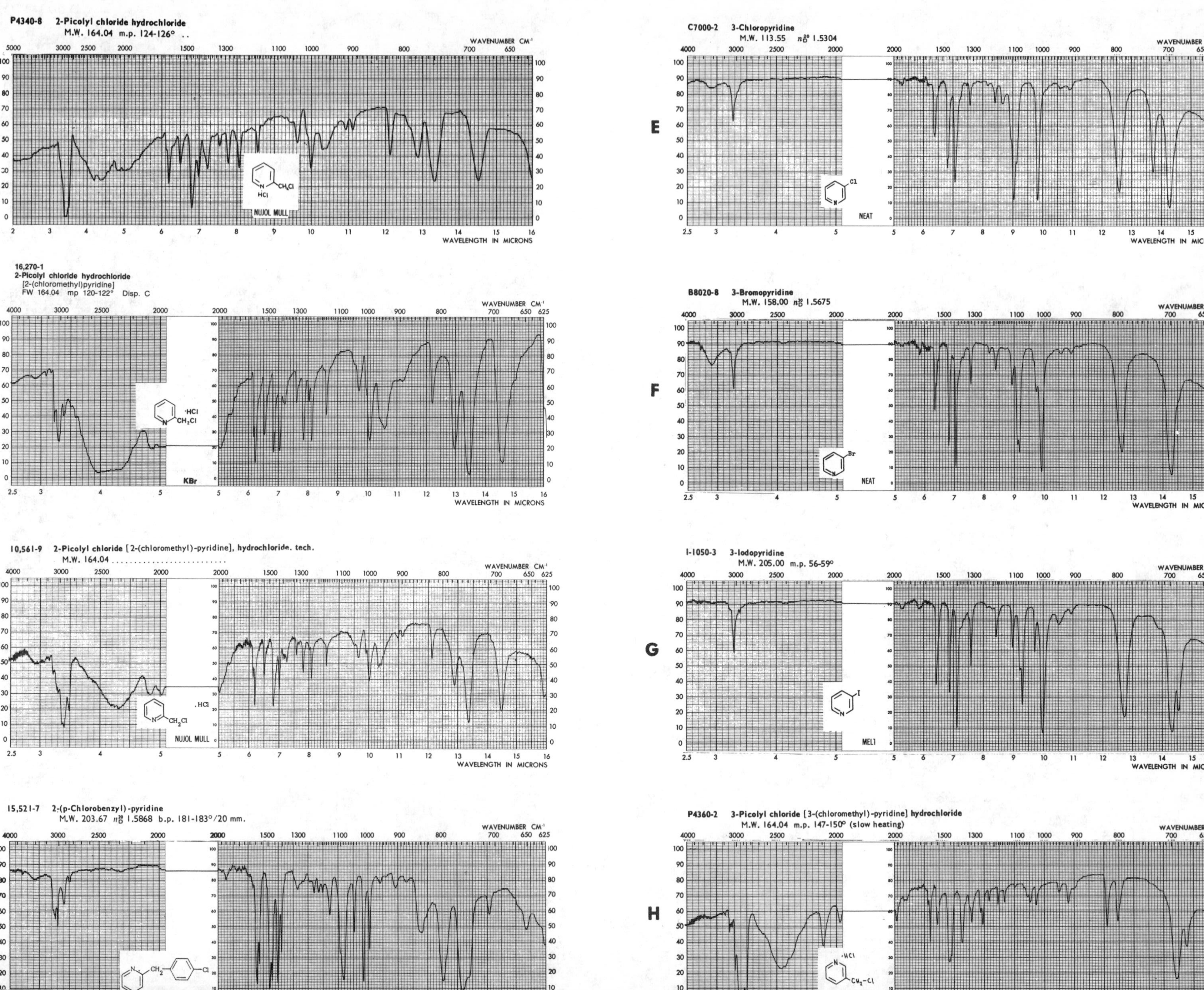
ALDRICH
A
P4340-8 2-Picolyl chloride hydrochloride
M.W. 164.04 m.p. 124-126°
NUJOL MULL
B
16,270-1
2-Picolyl chloride hydrochloride
[2-(chloromethyl)pyridine]
FW 164.04 mp 120-122° Disp. C
KBr
C
10,561-9 2-Picolyl chloride [2-(chloromethyl)-pyridine], hydrochloride, tech.
M.W. 164.04
NUJOL MULL
D
15,521-7 2-(p-Chlorobenzyl)-pyridine
M.W. 203.67 n_D^{20} 1.5868 b.p. 181-183°/20 mm.
E
C7000-2 3-Chloropyridine
M.W. 113.55 n_D^{20} 1.5304
NEAT
F
B8020-8 3-Bromopyridine
M.W. 158.00 n_D^{20} 1.5675
NEAT
G
I-1050-3 3-Iodopyridine
M.W. 205.00 m.p. 56-59°
MELT
H
P4360-2 3-Picolyl chloride [3-(chloromethyl)-pyridine] hydrochloride
M.W. 164.04 m.p. 147-150° (slow heating)
WAVENUMBER CM⁻¹
WAVELENGTH IN MICRONS

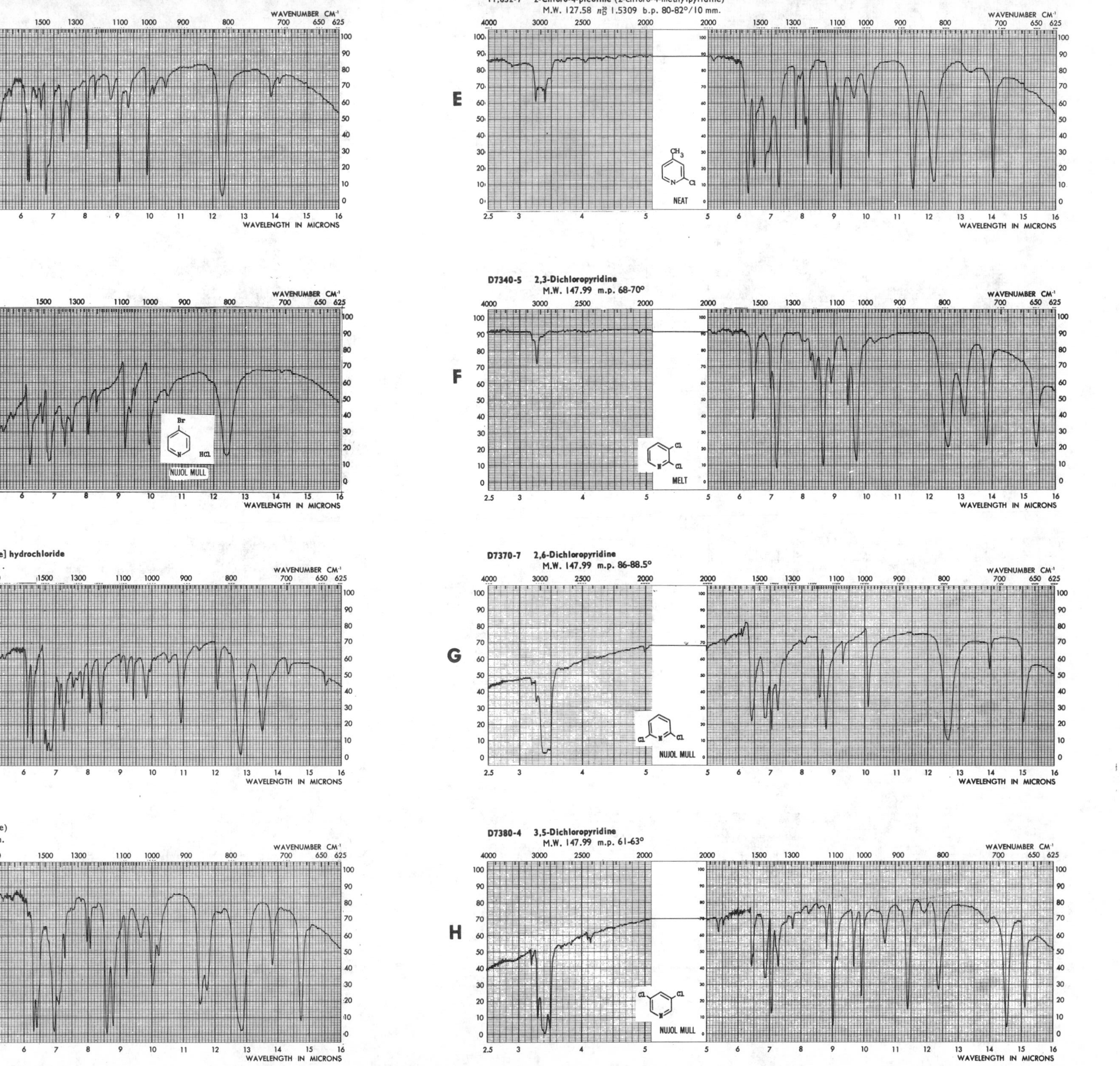

A
m.p. 240° (subl.) ......
NUJOL MULL
B
B8042-9 4-Bromopyridine hydrochloride
M.W. 194.46 m.p. 270° (dec.)
NUJOL MULL
C
P4380-7 4-Picolyl chloride [4-(chloromethyl)-pyridine] hydrochloride
M.W. 164.04 m.p. 167-172° ....
NUJOL MULL
D
11,633-5 6-Chloro-2-picoline (6-chloro-2-methylpyridine)
M.W. 127.58 n_D^{20} 1.5293 b.p. 64-68°/10 mm.
NEAT
E
11,632-7 2-Chloro-4-picoline (2-chloro-4-methylpyridine)
M.W. 127.58 n_D^{20} 1.5309 b.p. 80-82°/10 mm.
NEAT
F
D7340-5 2,3-Dichloropyridine
M.W. 147.99 m.p. 68-70°
MELT
G
D7370-7 2,6-Dichloropyridine
M.W. 147.99 m.p. 86-88.5°
NUJOL MULL
H
D7380-4 3,5-Dichloropyridine
M.W. 147.99 m.p. 61-63°
NUJOL MULL
WAVENUMBER CM⁻¹
WAVELENGTH IN MICRONS
ALDRICH

6 MEMBERED AROMATIC HETEROCYCLES

A

D4311-5 **2,6-Dibromopyridine**
M.W. 236.90 m.p. 117.5-118.5°

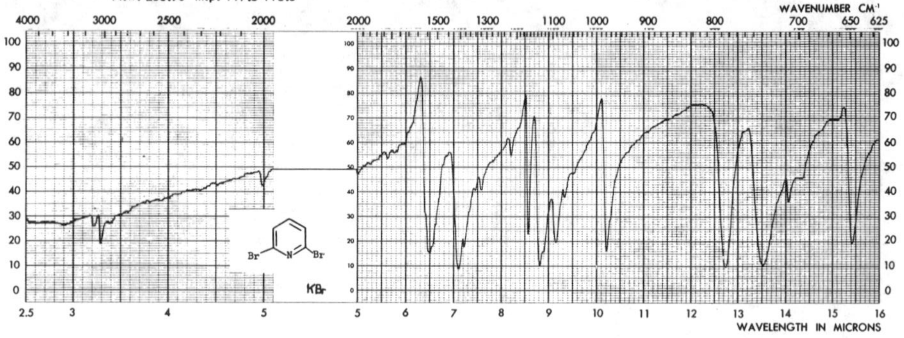

KBr

B

19,376-3
2,5-Dichloropyridine, 98%
FW 147.99 mp 59-62° *Beil.* **20**(1),80 Disp. C

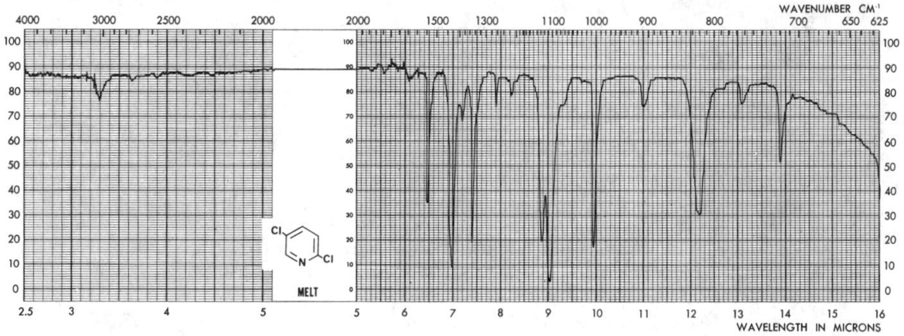

MELT

C

D4310-7 **2,5-Dibromopyridine**
M.W. 236.90 m.p. 93-94°

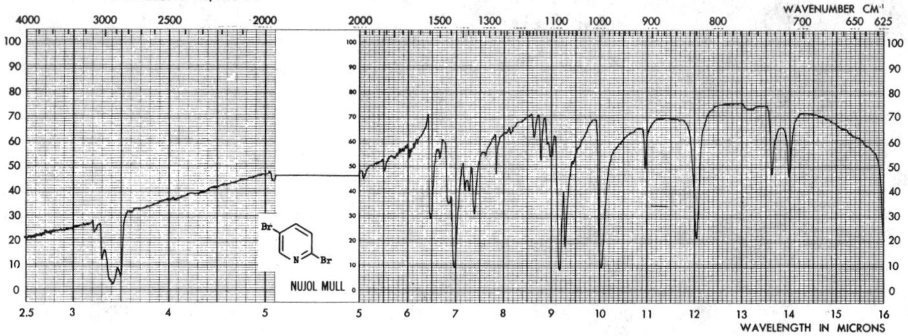

NUJOL MULL

D

12,016-2 **3,5-Dibromopyridine**
M.W. 236.90 m.p. 105-107.5°

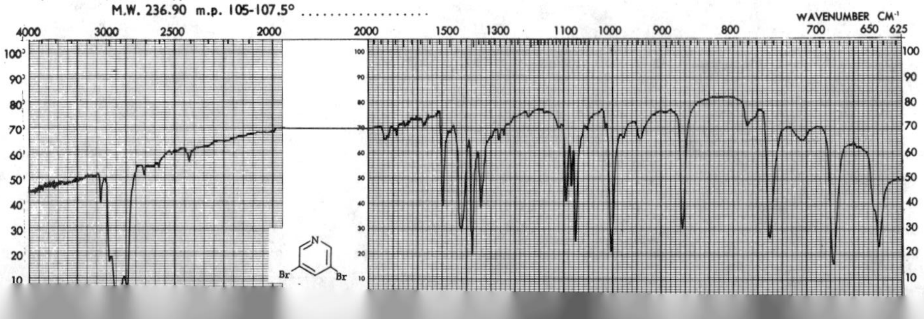

E

15,879-8
Pentafluoropyridine, 99+%, GOLD LABEL
M.W. 169.05 n_D^{20} 1.3860

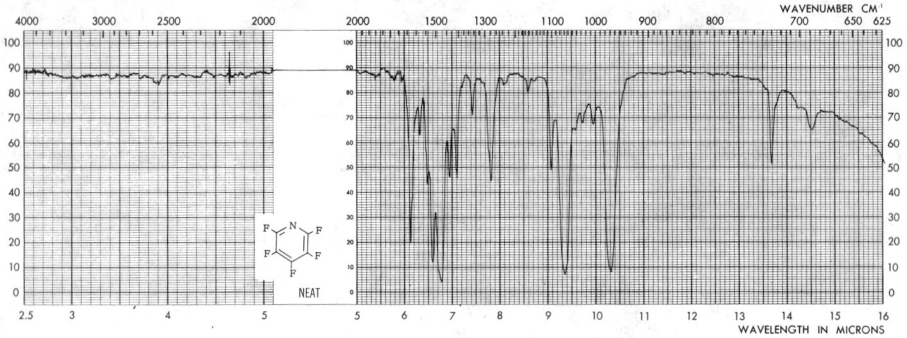

NEAT

F

18,703-8
3-Chloro-2,4,5,6-tetrafluoropyridine, 98%
FW 185.51 bp 117-118° d 1.435 Disp. C

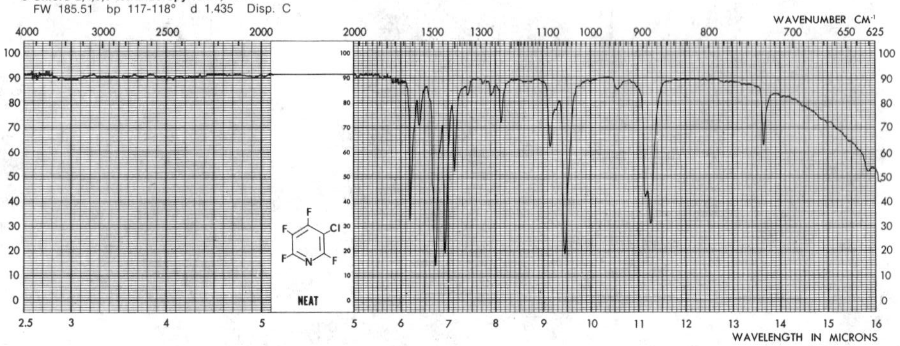

NEAT

G

13,800-2 **Pentachloropyridine, tech.**
M.W. 251.33

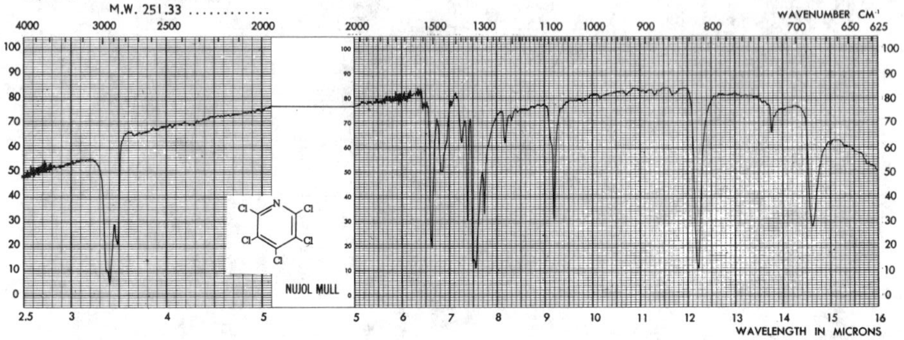

NUJOL MULL

H

M2540-6 **2-Methoxypyridine, puriss.**
M.W. 109.13 n_D^{20} 1.5029

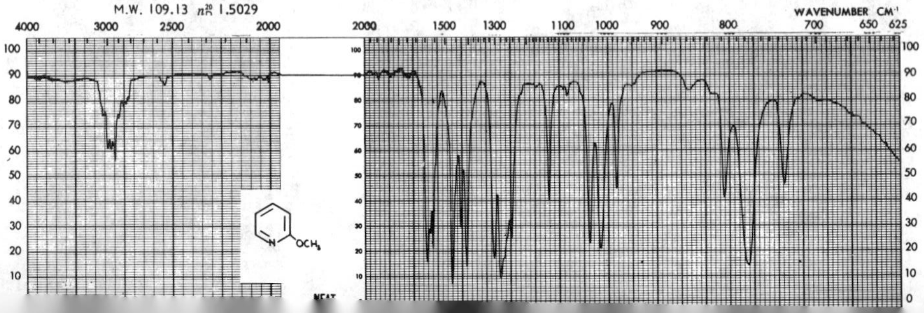

NEAT

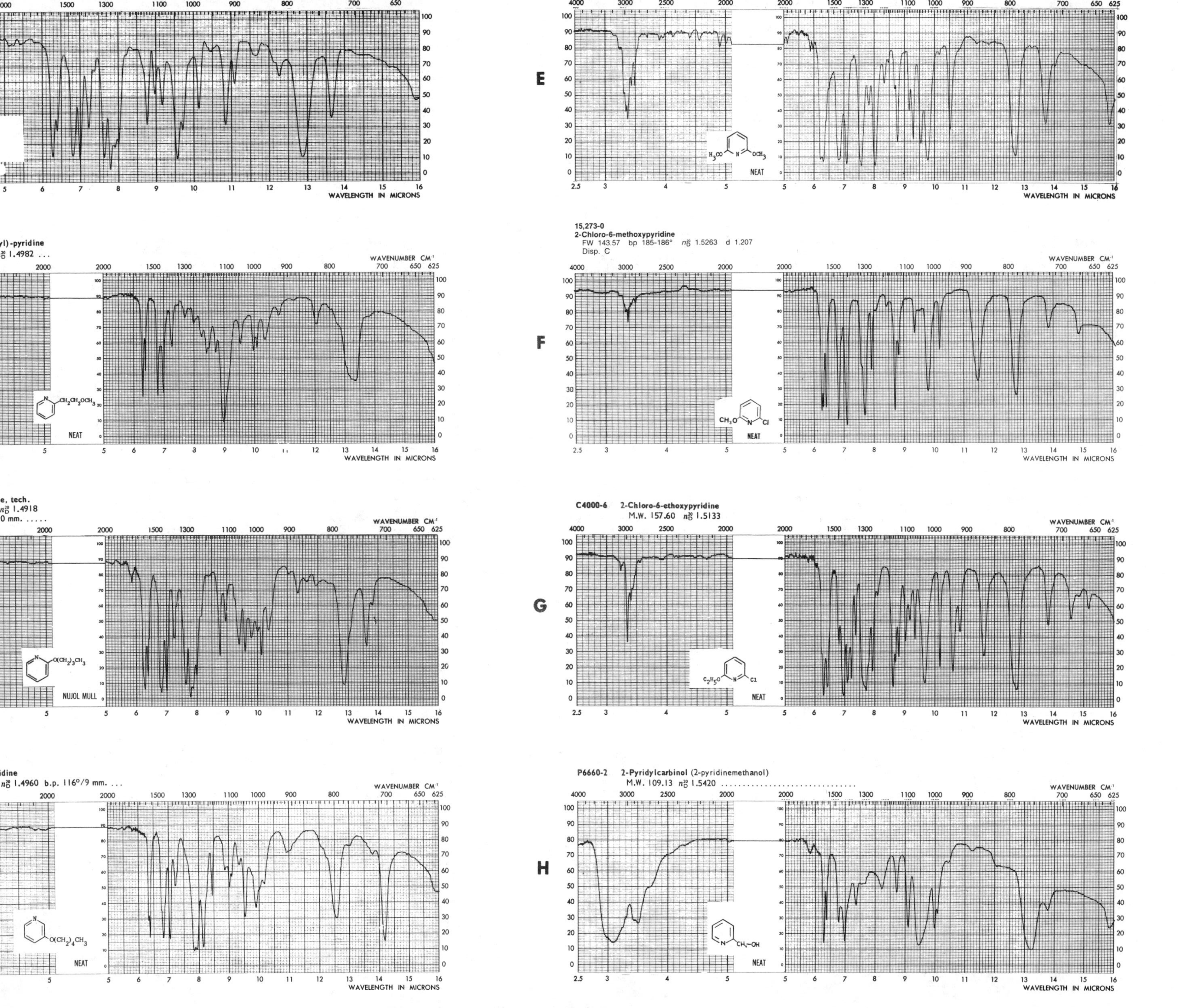
A
M.W. 123.16 n_D^{20} 1.4940
NEAT
14,249-2 2-(β-Methoxyethyl)-pyridine
M.W. 137.18 n_D^{20} 1.4982 . . .
B
NEAT
14,684-6 2-Butoxypyridine, tech.
M.W. 151.21 n_D^{20} 1.4918
b.p. 79-80°/10 mm. . . . . .
C
NUJOL MULL
11,916-4 3-Pentyloxypyridine
M.W. 165.24 n_D^{20} 1.4960 b.p. 116°/9 mm. . . .
D
NEAT
M.W. 139.15 n_D^{20} 1.5029
E
NEAT
15,273-0
2-Chloro-6-methoxypyridine
FW 143.57 bp 185-186° n_D^{20} 1.5263 d 1.207
Disp. C
F
NEAT
C4000-6 2-Chloro-6-ethoxypyridine
M.W. 157.60 n_D^{20} 1.5133
G
NEAT
P6660-2 2-Pyridylcarbinol (2-pyridinemethanol)
M.W. 109.13 n_D^{20} 1.5420 . . . .
H
NEAT
WAVENUMBER CM⁻¹
WAVELENGTH IN MICRONS
ALDRICH

6 MEMBERED AROMATIC HETEROCYCLES

A

12,864-3 **2-(β-Hydroxyethyl)-pyridine** (2-pyridineethanol)
M.W. 123.16 n_D^{20} 1.5368 b.p. 118-121°/15 mm.

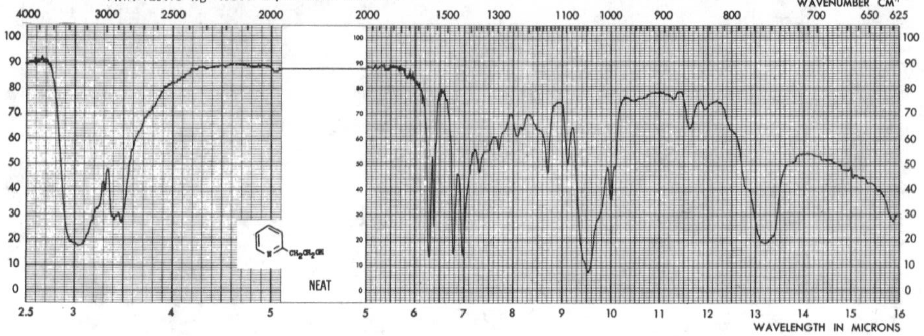

NEAT

B

P7100-2 **3-(2-Pyridyl)-1-propanol** (2-pyridinepropanol), **puriss.**
M.W. 137.18 n_D^{20} 1.5280

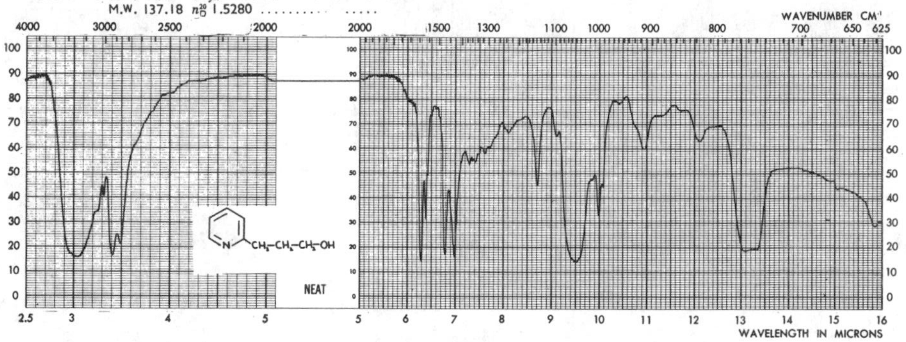

NEAT

C

P6770 **1-(2-Pyridyl)-1,2-ethanediol** [1-(2-pyridyl)-ethyleneglycol]
M.W. 139.16 m.p. 96-99°

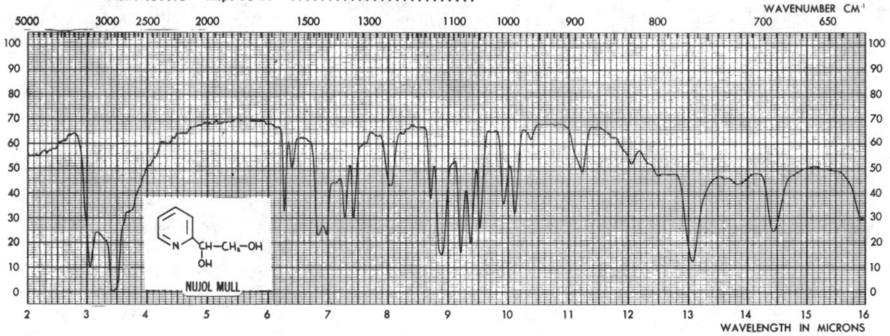

NUJOL MULL

D

13,813-4 **2-(2-Pyridyl)-1,3-propanediol**
M.W. 153.18 m.p. 80-83°

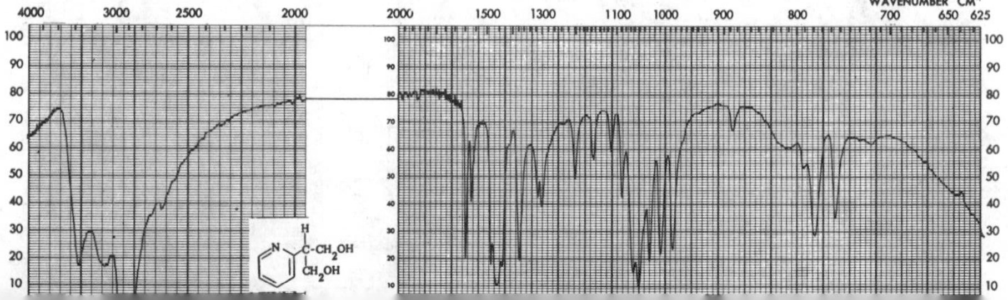

E

P6680-7 **3-Pyridylcarbinol** (3-pyridinemethanol)
M.W. 109.13 n_D^{20} 1.5425

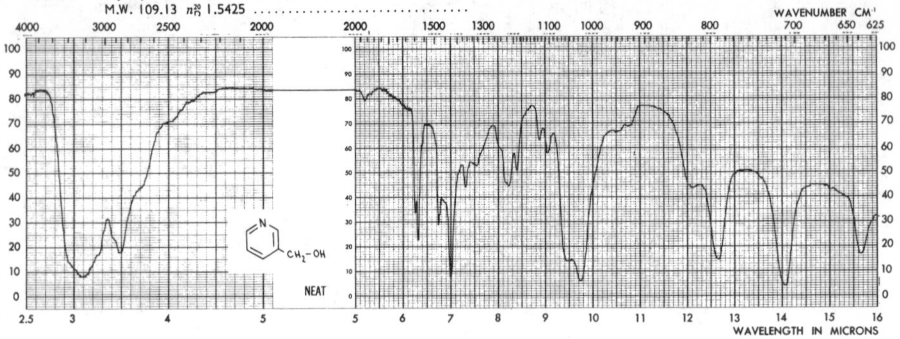

NEAT

F

P7120-7 **3-(3-Pyridyl)-1-propanol** (3-pyridinepropanol)
M.W. 137.18 n_D^{20} 1.5268

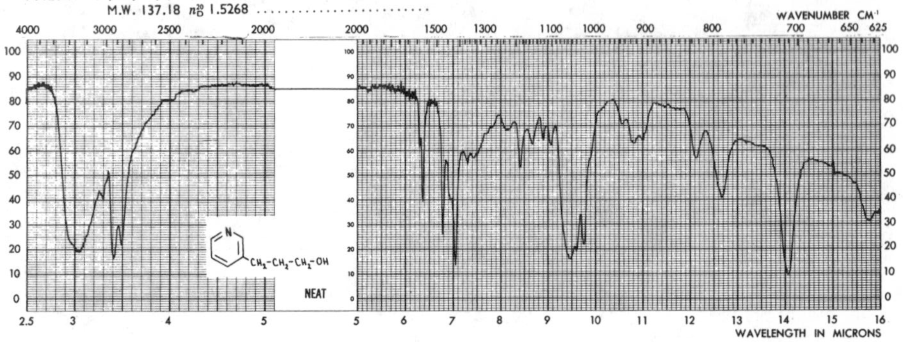

NEAT

G

15,162-9 **4-Pyridylcarbinol** (4-pyridinemethanol)
M.W. 109.13 m.p. 51-55°

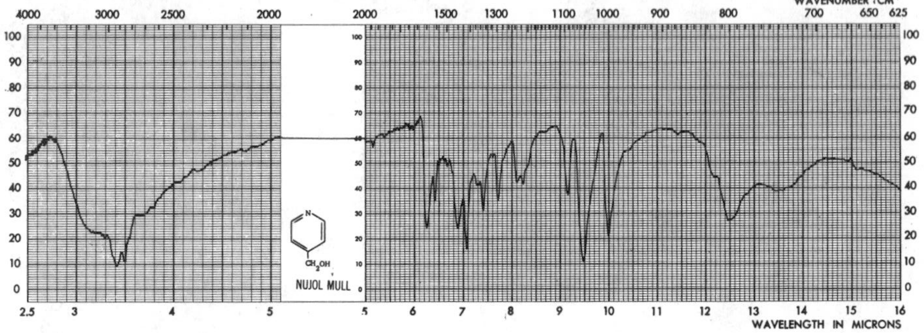

NUJOL MULL

H

P7140-1 **3-(4-Pyridyl)-1-propanol** (4-pyridinepropanol)
M.W. 137.18 m.p. 35-40°

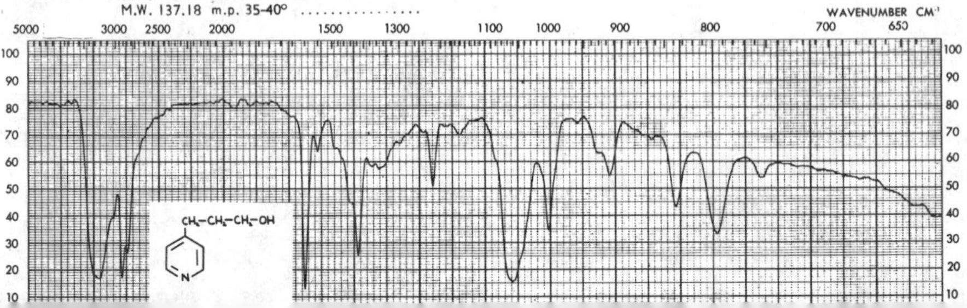

A

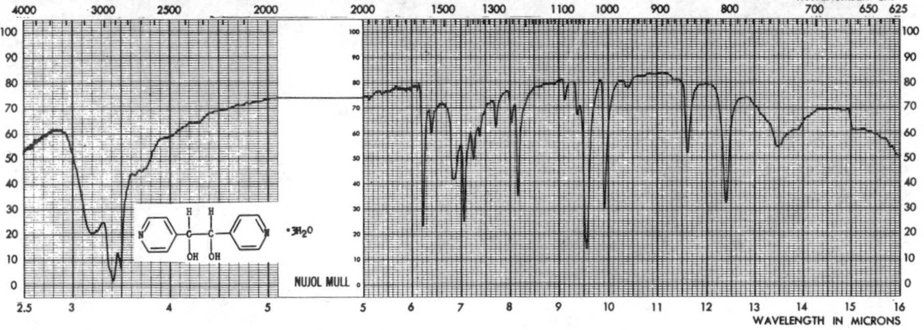

NUJOL MULL

16,077-6
dl-1,2-Bis-(4-pyridyl)-1,2-ethanediol monohydrate
M.W. 234.26 m.p. 205-207° (dec.)

B

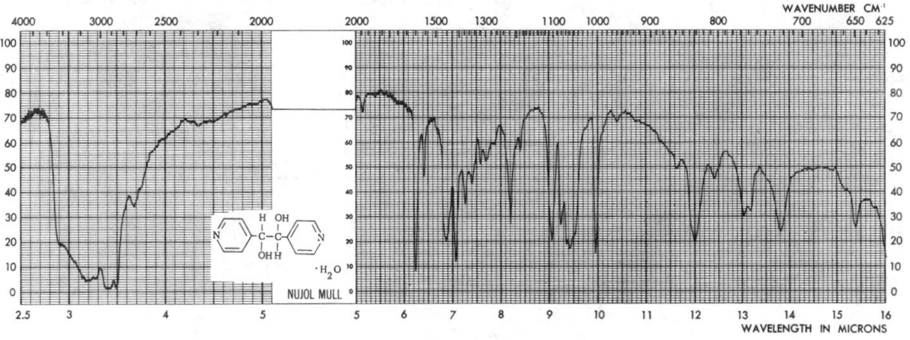

NUJOL MULL

12,198-3 α-4-Pyridylbenzhydrol, tech.
M.W. 261.33 m.p. 236-237.5°

C

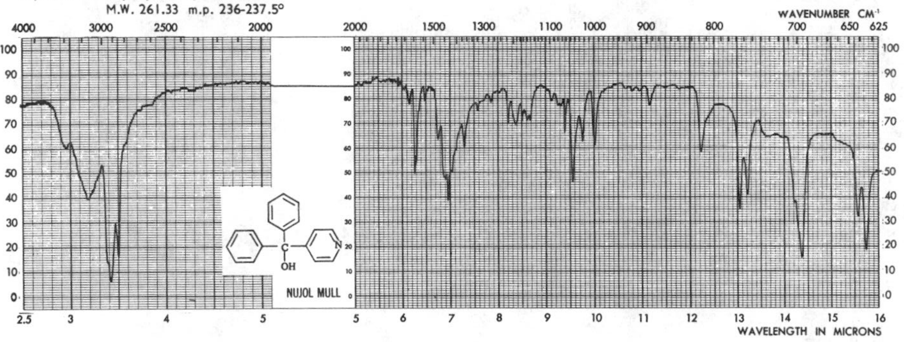

NUJOL MULL

12,914-3 2-(2-Hydroxystyryl)-1-methylpyridinium iodide
M.W. 339.18 m.p. 249-252°

D

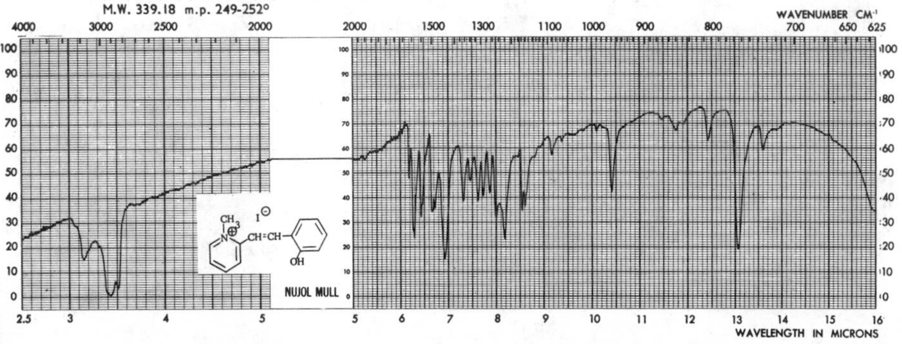

NUJOL MULL

E

NUJOL MULL

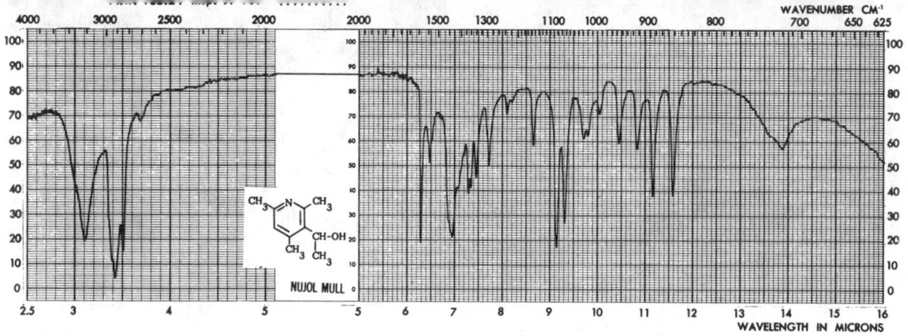

H5680-0 2-Hydroxypyridine (2-pyridinol)
M.W. 95.10 m.p. 105-107° ...

F

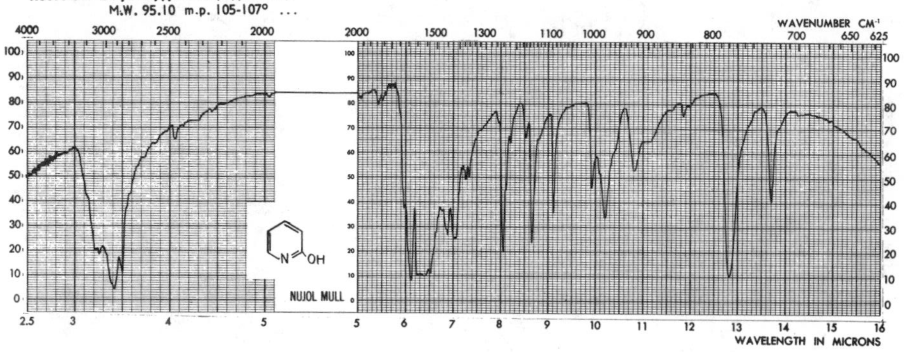

NUJOL MULL

15,229-3 2(1H)-Pyridone, thallium(I) salt
M.W. 298.46 m.p. 150-153° ....

G

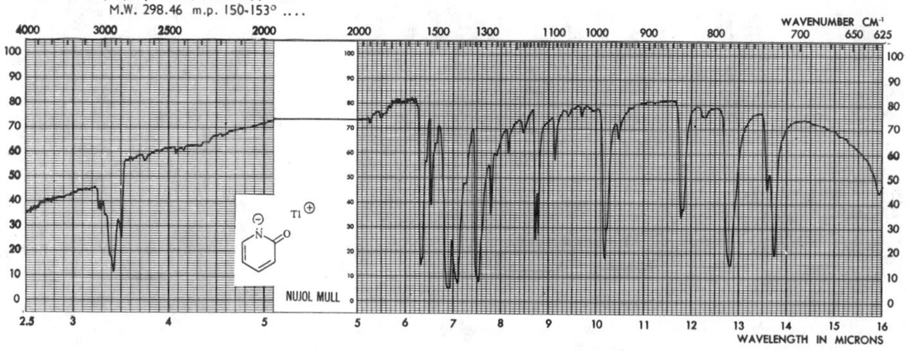

NUJOL MULL

12,874-0 2-Hydroxy-6-methylpyridine (6-methyl-2-pyridinol)
M.W. 109.13 m.p. 158-160° ....

H

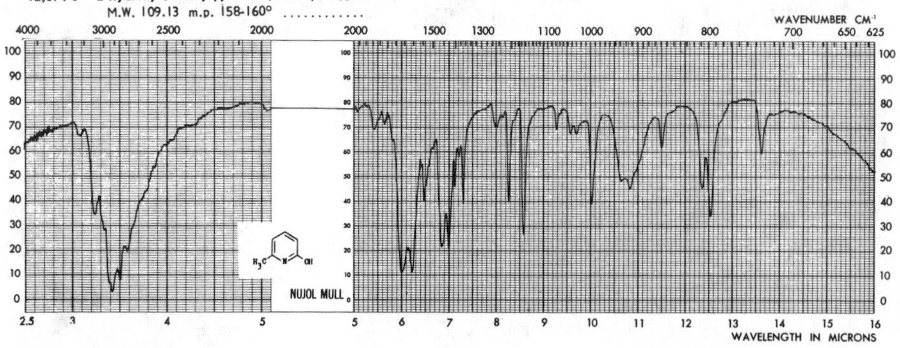

NUJOL MULL

A

13,678-6 6-Chloro-2-pyridinol
M.W. 129.55 m.p. 128-130°
NUJOL MULL

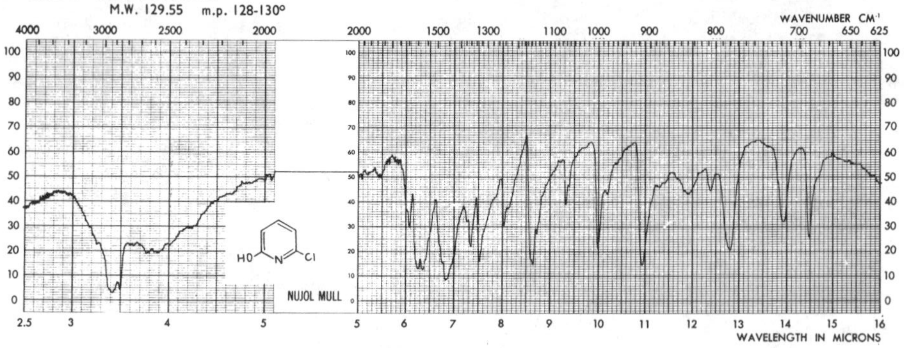

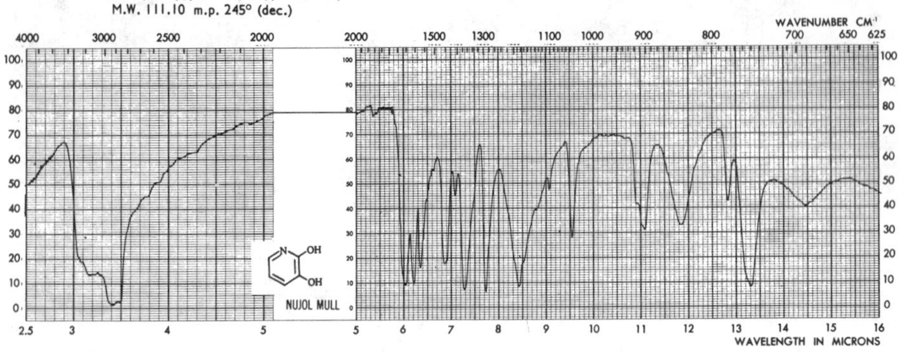

B

13,593-3 5-Chloro-2-pyridinol
M.W. 129.55 m.p. 163-165°
NUJOL MULL

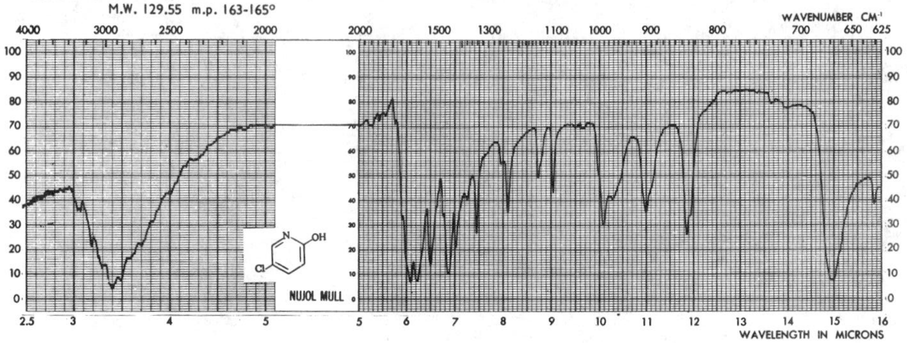

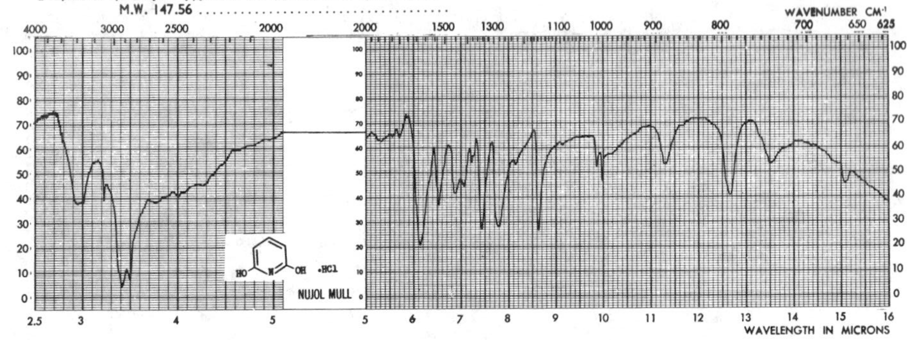

C

12,801-5 3,5-Dibromo-2-pyridone, sodium salt
M.W. 274.89 m.p. > 300°
NUJOL MULL

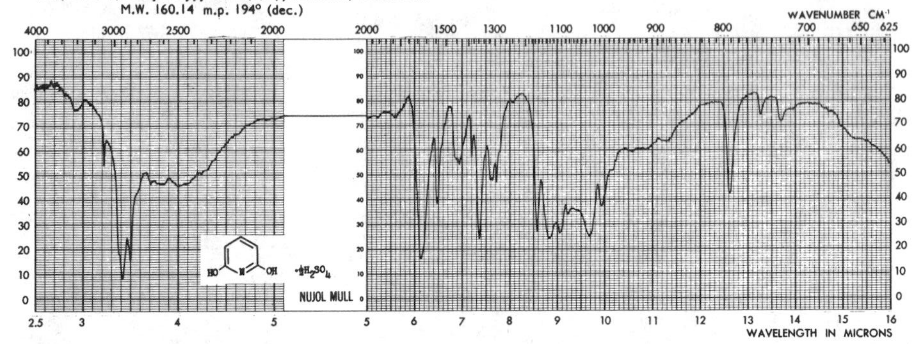

D

14,565-3 3-Methoxy-2(1H)-pyridone
M.W. 125.13 m.p. 109-112°

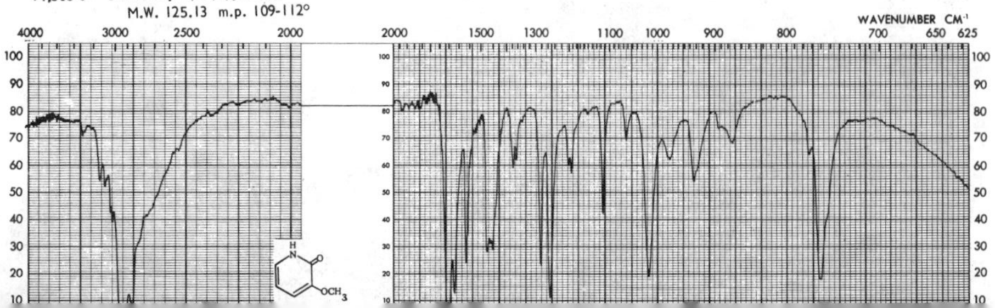

E

12,250-5 2,3-Dihydroxypyridine (2,3-pyridinediol)
M.W. 111.10 m.p. 245° (dec.)
NUJOL MULL

F

D12,000-6 2,6-Dihydroxypyridine (2,6-pyridinediol) hydrochloride
M.W. 147.56
NUJOL MULL

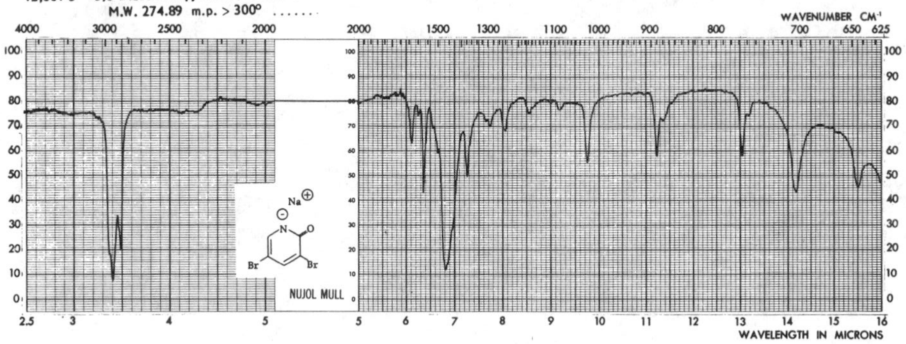

G

D12,002-2 2,6-Dihydroxypyridine (2,6-pyridinediol) hemisulfate
M.W. 160.14 m.p. 194° (dec.)
NUJOL MULL

H

13,107-5 5-Chloro-2,3-pyridinediol
M.W. 145.55 m.p. > 290° (dec.)

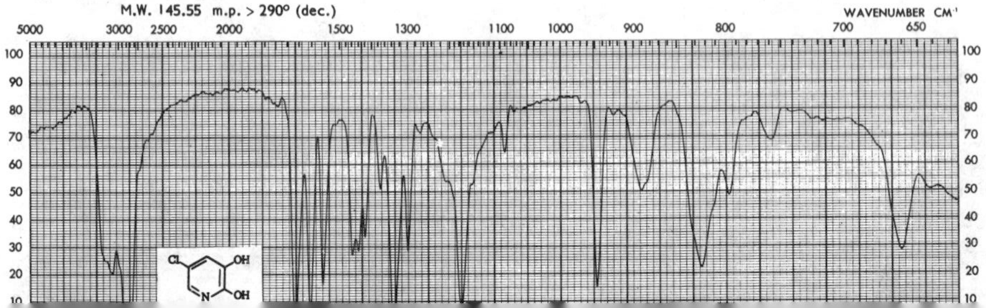

A

M.W. 95.10 ....

NUJOL MULL

B

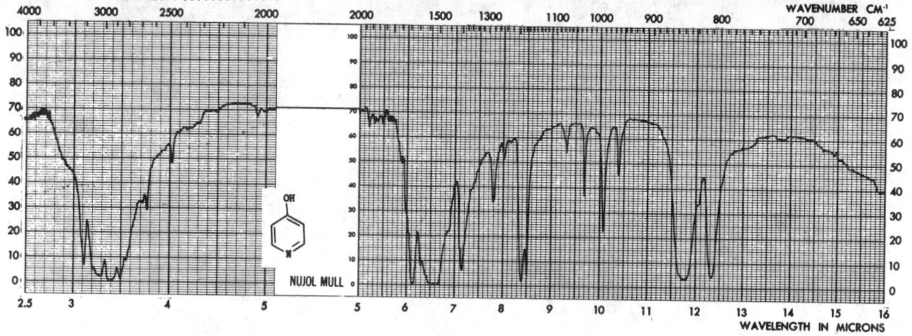

19,635-5
3,5-Dichloro-4-pyridinol, 95% (3,5-dichloro-4-hydroxypyridine)
FW 163.99 mp >300° Disp. C

NUJOL MULL

C

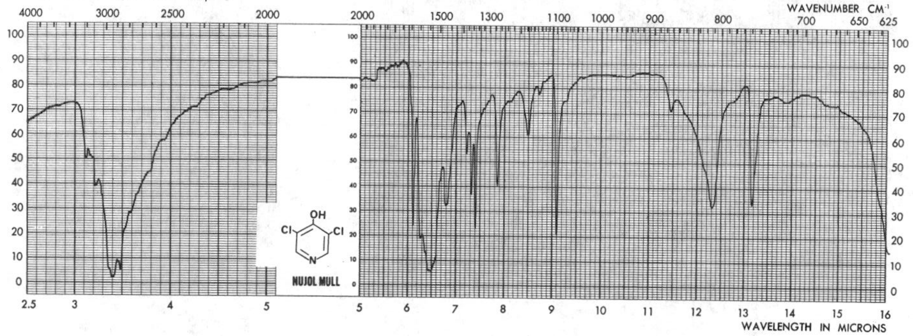

D12,340-4 **3,5-Diiodo-4-hydroxypyridine** (3,5-diiodo-4-pyridinol)
M.W. 346.89 m.p. > 300° ....

NUJOL MULL

D

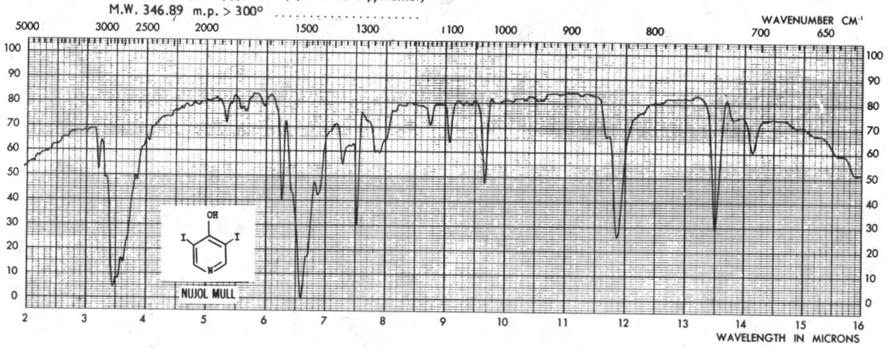

H5700-9 **3-Hydroxypyridine** (3-pyridinol)
(send for data sheet)
M.W. 95.10 m.p. 125-128° ...

NUJOL MULL

E

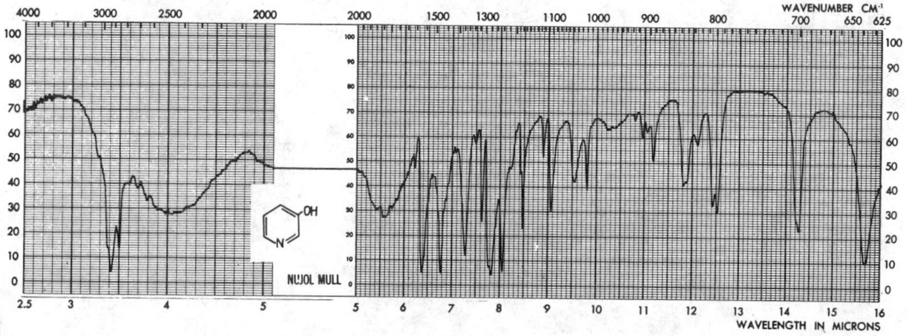

1-Ethyl-3-hydroxypyridinium bromide, 98%
FW 204.07 mp 104-108° *Fieser* 7,80 Disp. C

NUJOL MULL

F

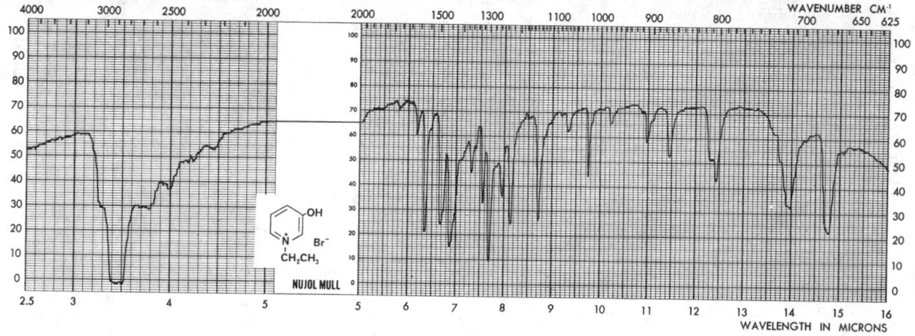

17,697-4
2,4-Dihydroxypyridine, 97% (4-hydroxy-2-pyridone, 2,4-pyridinediol)
M.W. 111.1 m.p. 278° (dec.) Beil. **21**,160

NUJOL MULL

G

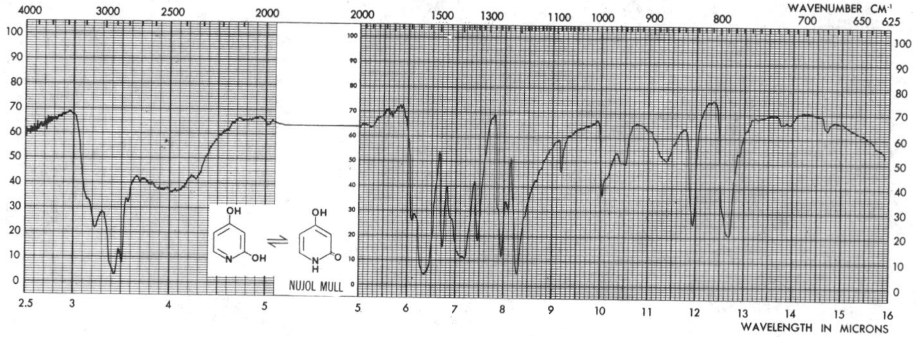

10,726-3 **3-Hydroxy-6-methylpyridine** (6-methyl-3-pyridinol)
M.W. 109.13 m.p. 168-170°

NUJOL MULL

H

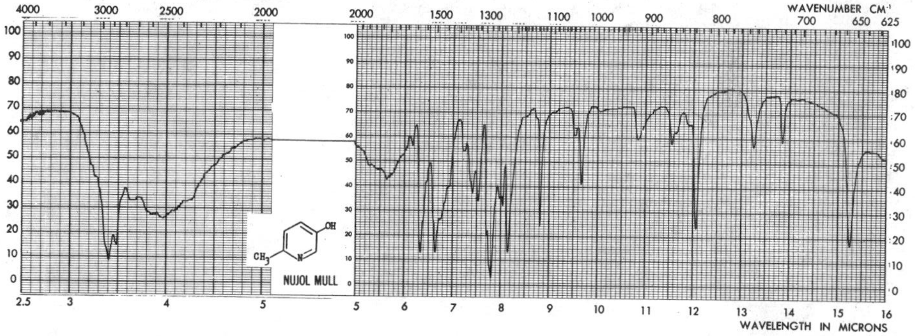

21,800-6
5-Chloro-3-pyridinol, 99%
FW 129.55 mp 160-162° Disp. C

NUJOL MULL

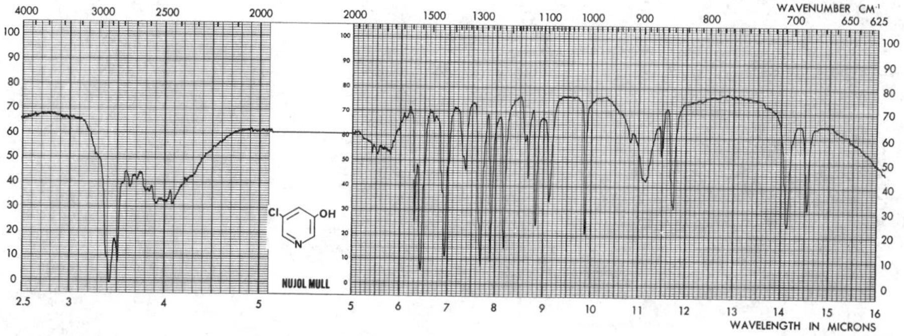

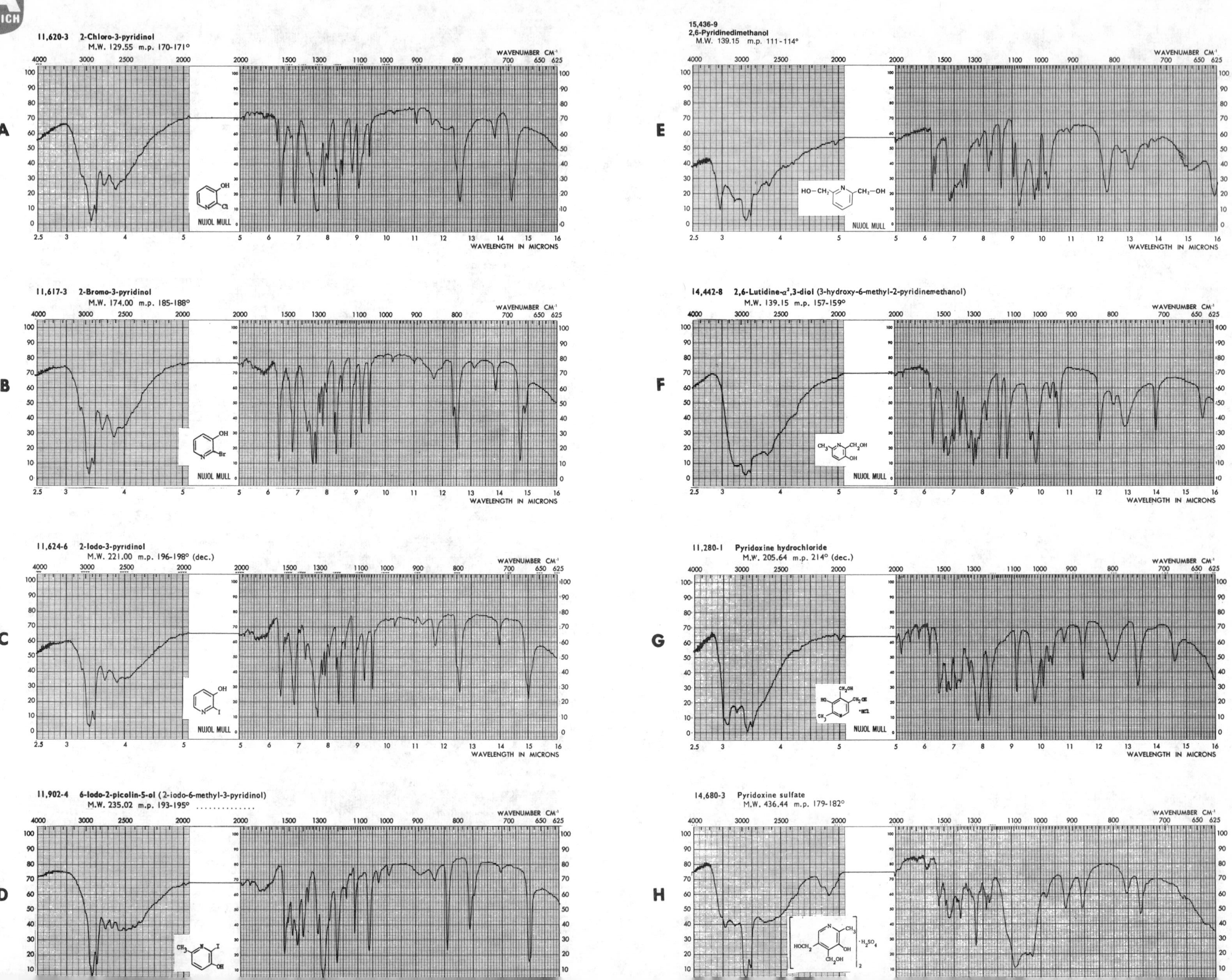
ALDRICH
A
11,620-3 2-Chloro-3-pyridinol
M.W. 129.55 m.p. 170-171°
NUJOL MULL
B
11,617-3 2-Bromo-3-pyridinol
M.W. 174.00 m.p. 185-188°
NUJOL MULL
C
11,624-6 2-Iodo-3-pyridinol
M.W. 221.00 m.p. 196-198° (dec.)
NUJOL MULL
D
11,902-4 6-Iodo-2-picolin-5-ol (2-iodo-6-methyl-3-pyridinol)
M.W. 235.02 m.p. 193-195°
E
15,436-9
2,6-Pyridinedimethanol
M.W. 139.15 m.p. 111-114°
NUJOL MULL
F
14,442-8 2,6-Lutidine-α²,3-diol (3-hydroxy-6-methyl-2-pyridinemethanol)
M.W. 139.15 m.p. 157-159°
NUJOL MULL
G
11,280-1 Pyridoxine hydrochloride
M.W. 205.64 m.p. 214° (dec.)
NUJOL MULL
H
14,680-3 Pyridoxine sulfate
M.W. 436.44 m.p. 179-182°
WAVENUMBER CM⁻¹
WAVELENGTH IN MICRONS

A

M.W. 111.17 m.p. 128-130° ......

NUJOL MULL

B

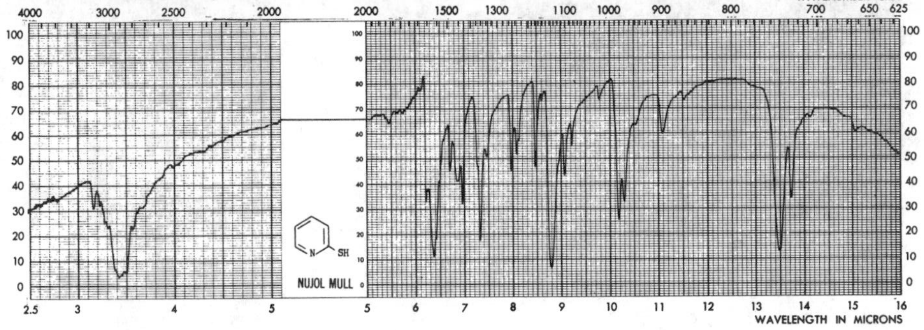

14,304-9 **Aldrithiol-2** (2,2'-dithiodipyridine)
(send for data sheet)
M.W. 220.32 m.p. 56-58°

MELT

C

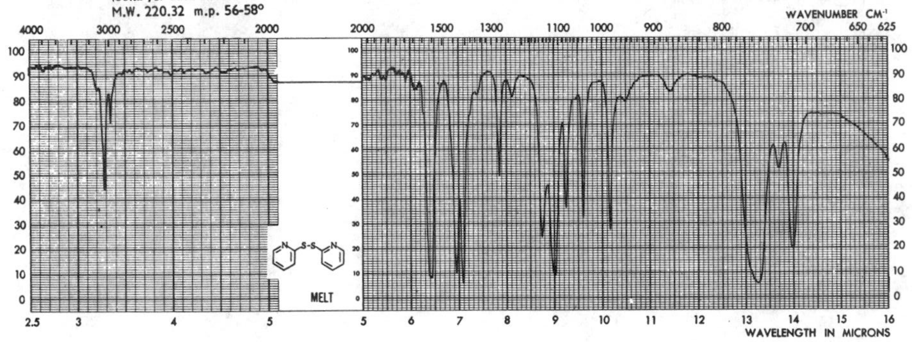

16,314-7
2-Mercapto-3-pyridinol, 97% (3-hydroxy-2-mercaptopyridine)
M.W. 127.17 m.p. 144-146°

NUJOL MULL

D

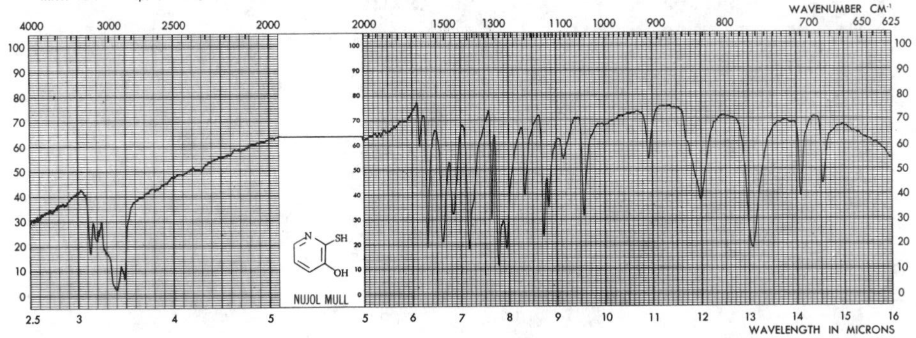

14,820-2 **4-Mercaptopyridine** (4-pyridinethiol)
M.W. 111.17 m.p. 181-183° ......

NUJOL MULL

E

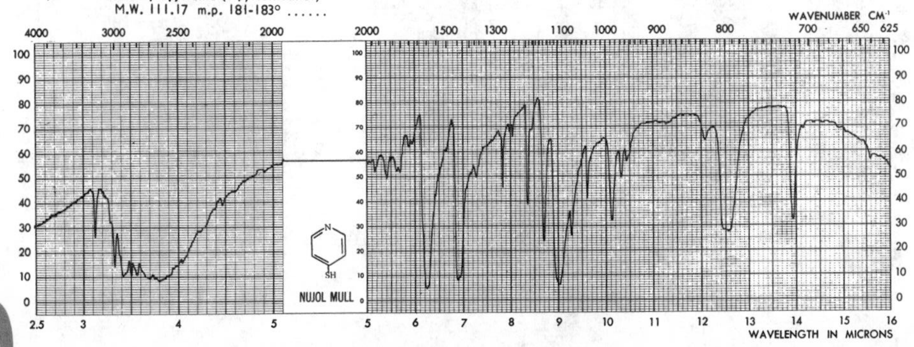

M.W. 220.32 m.p. 74-76° ......

MELT

F

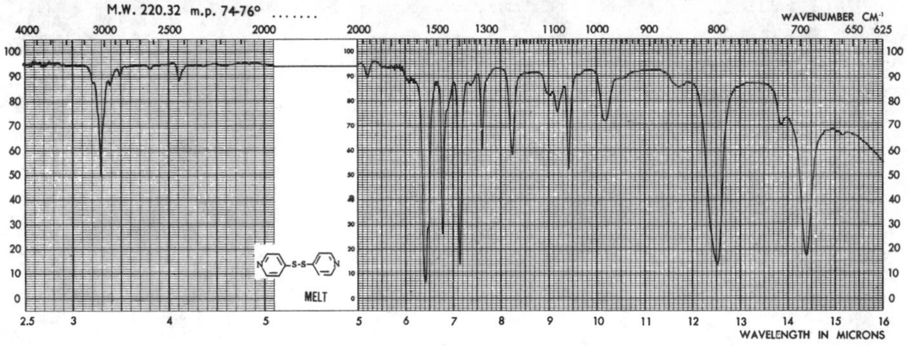

A7799-7 **2-Aminopyridine**
M.W. 94.12 m.p. 57-60°

MELT

G

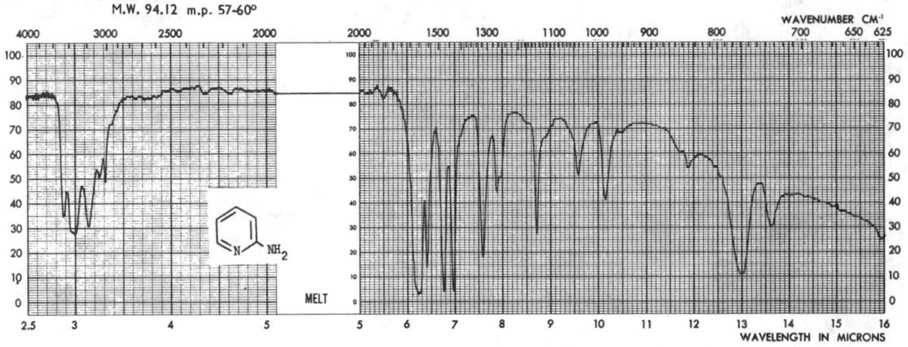

H1708-2 **2-Hydrazinopyridine**
M.W. 109.13 m.p. 44.5-46°

MELT

H

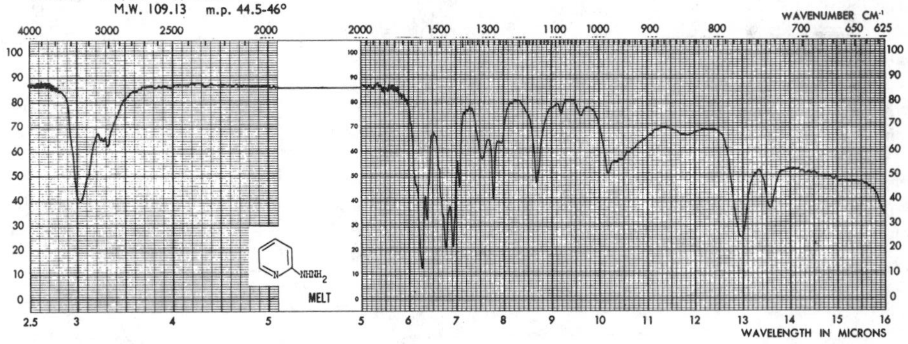

H1710-4 **2-Hydrazinopyridine hydrochloride**
M.W. 145.59 m.p. 212-213° (dec.)

NUJOL MULL

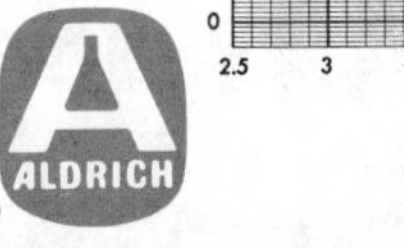

6 MEMBERED AROMATIC HETEROCYCLES

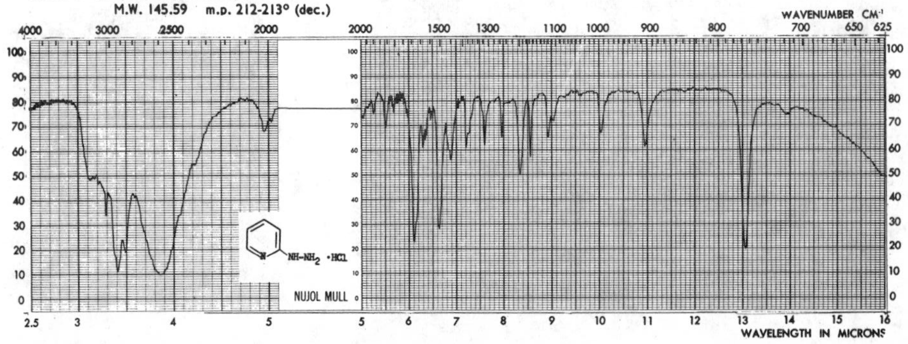

A

A8790-9 **2-Anilinopyridine**
M.W. 170.22 m.p. 107-110.5°
NUJOL MULL

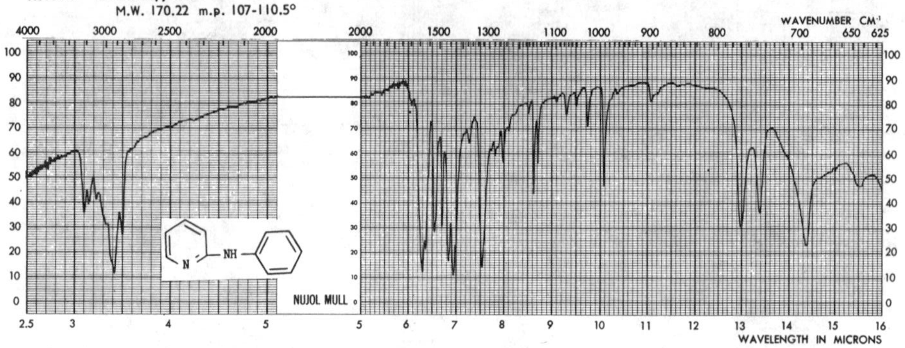

B

19,505-7
2-Benzylaminopyridine, 98%
FW 184.24 mp 95-97° bp 116-131°/0.600mm.
Disp. C
NUJOL MULL

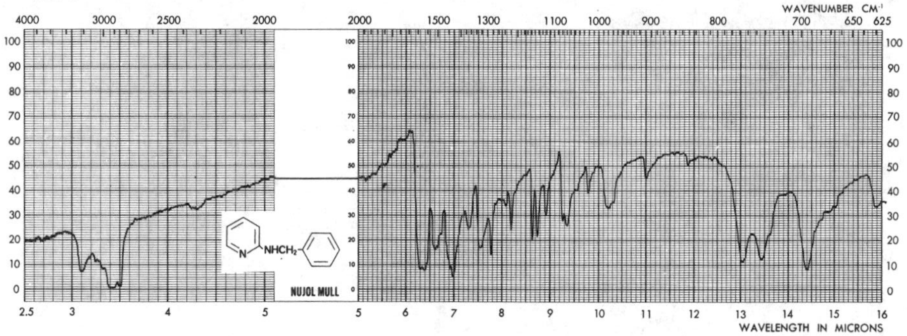

C

19,890-0
2-(2-Thienyl)pyridine, 97+%
FW 161.23 mp 61-63° Disp. C
MELT

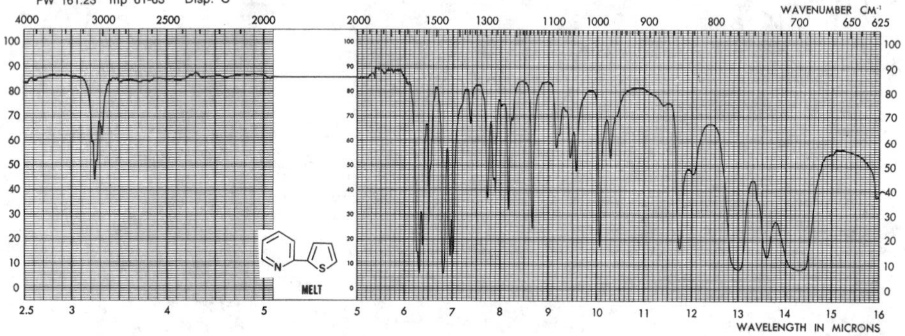

D

19,894-3
2-(3-Thienyl)pyridine, 97+%
FW 161.23 bp 93-95°/0.450mm. n_D^{20} 1.6517
d 1.166 Disp. C

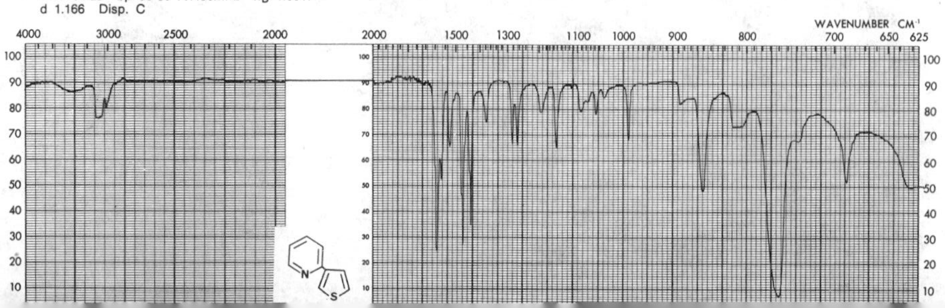

E

D21,640-2 **2,2'-Dipyridylamine**
M.W. 171.20 m.p. 94-97°
NUJOL MULL

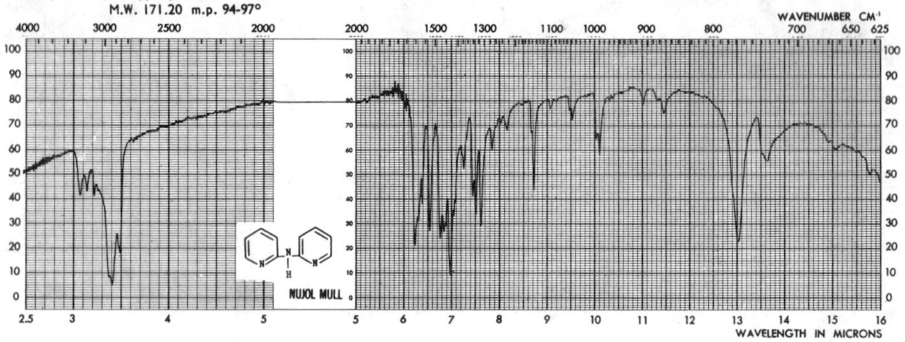

F

14,685-4 **2-(p-Methoxybenzylamino)-pyridine**
M W. 214.27 m.p. 122-124° ......
NUJOL MULL

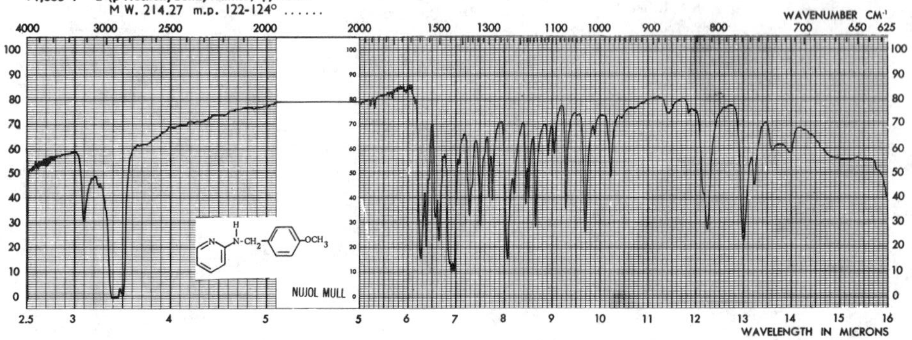

G

12,034-0 **2-(1,2-Diphenylethylamino)-pyridine**
M.W. 274.37 m.p. 69-71° ....
NUJOL MULL

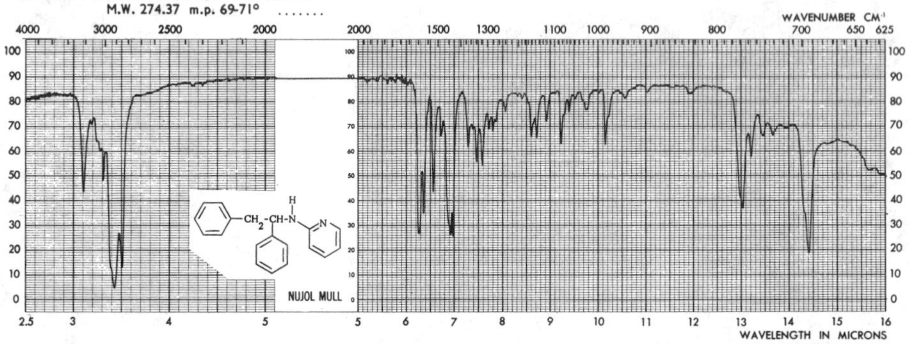

H

21,013-7
2-(Methylamino)pyridine, 98%
FW 108.14 mp 15° bp 200-201° n_D^{20} 1.5785
d 1.052 *Beil.* **22**(1),629 Disp. C

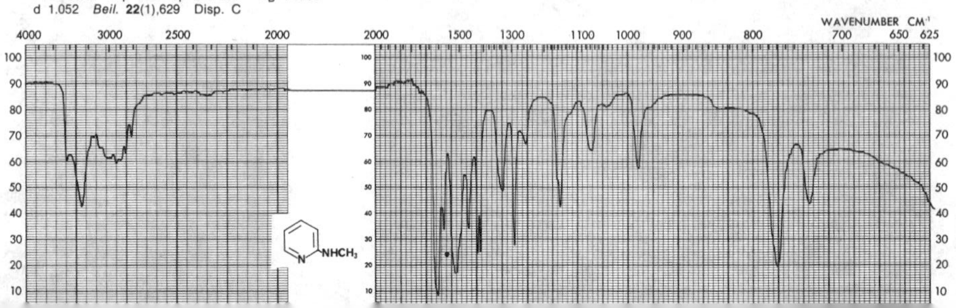

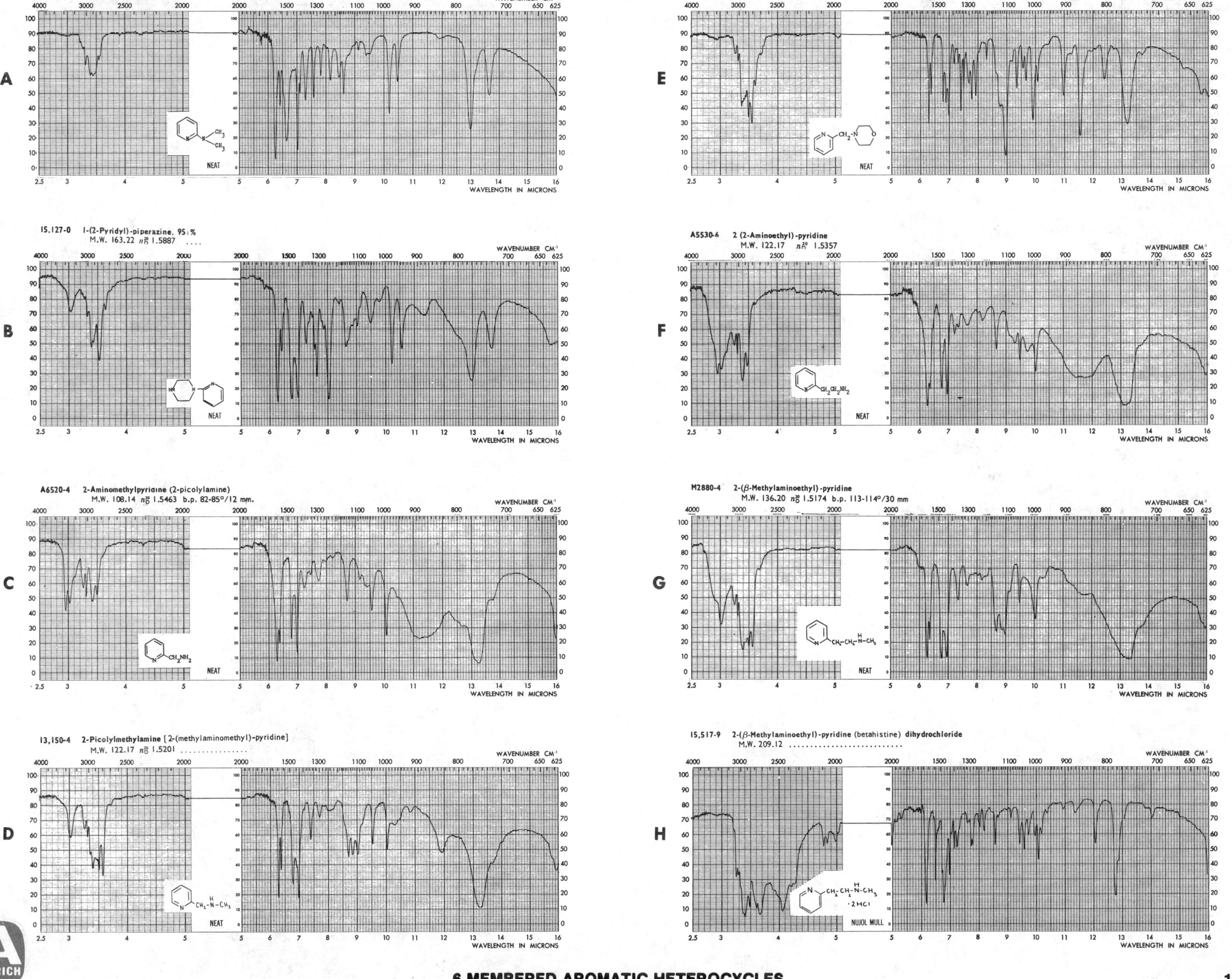

A
M.W. 122.17 n_D^{20} 1.5663
NEAT
15,127-0 1-(2-Pyridyl)-piperazine, 95 %
M.W. 163.22 n_D^{20} 1.5887
B
NEAT
A6520-4 2-Aminomethylpyridine (2-picolylamine)
M.W. 108.14 n_D^{20} 1.5463 b.p. 82-85°/12 mm.
C
NEAT
13,150-4 2-Picolylmethylamine [2-(methylaminomethyl)-pyridine]
M.W. 122.17 n_D^{20} 1.5201
D
NEAT
E
M.W. 178.24 n_D^{20} 1.5313
NEAT
A5530-6 2 (2-Aminoethyl)-pyridine
M.W. 122.17 n_D^{20} 1.5357
F
NEAT
M2880-4 2-(β-Methylaminoethyl)-pyridine
M.W. 136.20 n_D^{20} 1.5174 b.p. 113-114°/30 mm
G
NEAT
15,517-9 2-(β-Methylaminoethyl)-pyridine (betahistine) dihydrochloride
M.W. 209.12
H
·2HCl
NUJOL MULL
WAVENUMBER CM⁻¹
WAVELENGTH IN MICRONS
ALDRICH

ALDRICH ®

A 16,101-2 2-[2-(Dimethylamino)-ethyl]-pyridine, 97%
M.W. 150.23 n_D^{20} 1.5028 d 0.933

B 13,164-4 2-Pyridinecarboxaldehyde 2-pyridylhydrazone
M.W. 198.23 m.p. 181-182.5°

C P5760-3 2-Pyridinealdazine
M.W. 210.24 m.p. 146-148°

D 10,103-6 1-(2-Pyridylazo)-2-naphthol (PAN)
M.W. 249.27

E A7840-3 4-Aminopyridine
M.W. 94.12 m.p. 157-162°

F 10,770-0 4-Dimethylaminopyridine
M.W. 122.17 m.p. 108-110°

G A6560-3 4-Aminomethylpyridine (4-picolylamine)
M.W. 108.14 n_D^{20} 1.5480

H P4405-6 N-(4-Picolyl)-ethylenediamine [α-(2-aminoethylamino)-4-picoline]
M.W. 151.21 n_D^{20} 1.5432

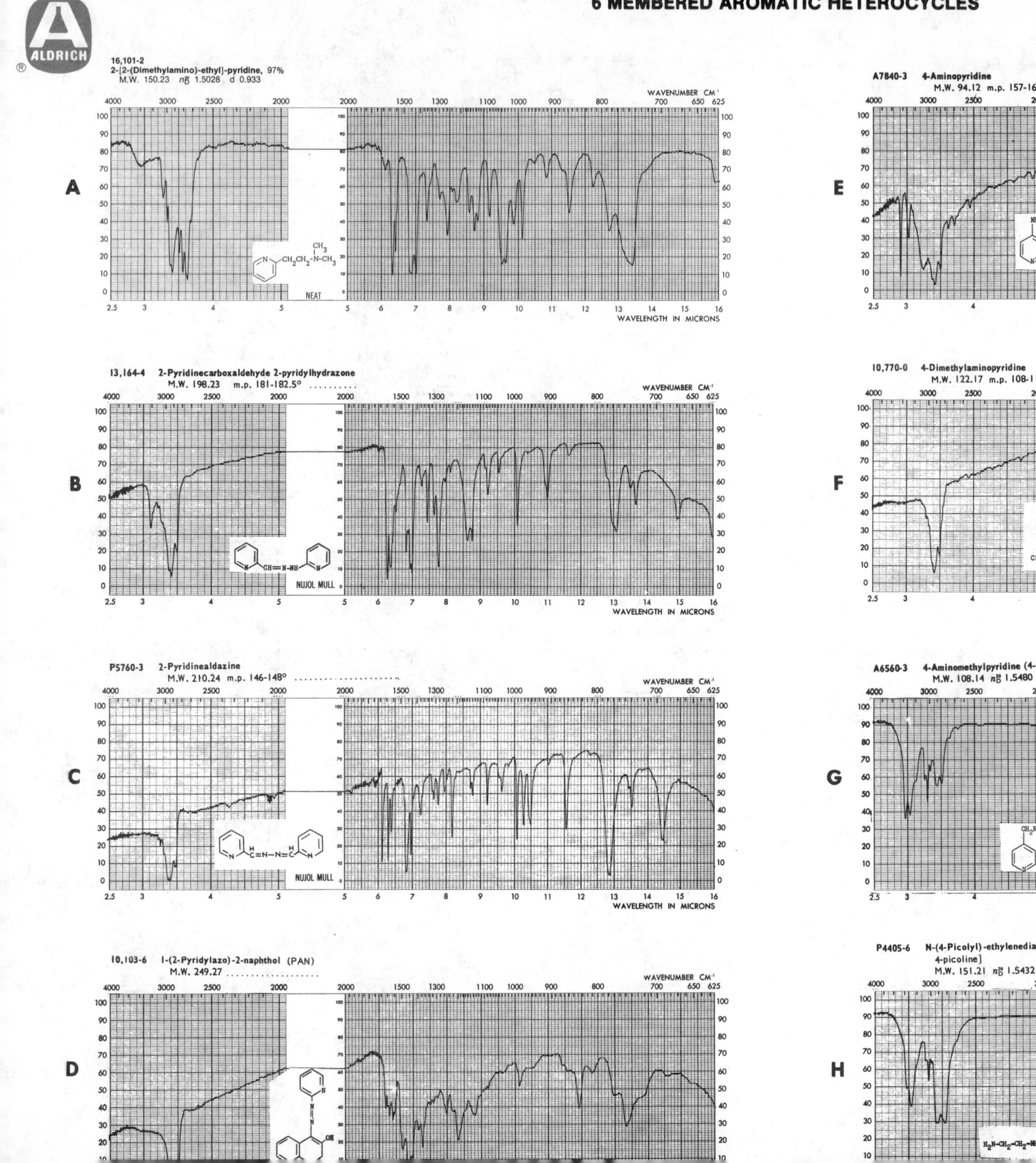

A

Disp. C

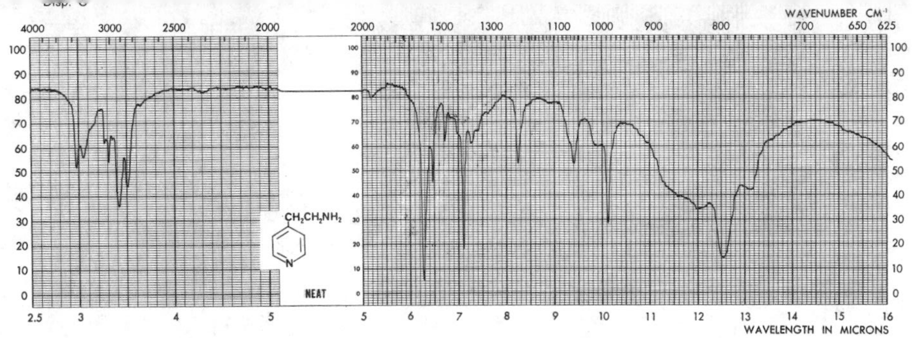

NEAT

B

21,337-3
4-Pyrrolidinopyridine, 98%
FW 148.21 mp 55-57° *Fieser* 4,416 Disp. C

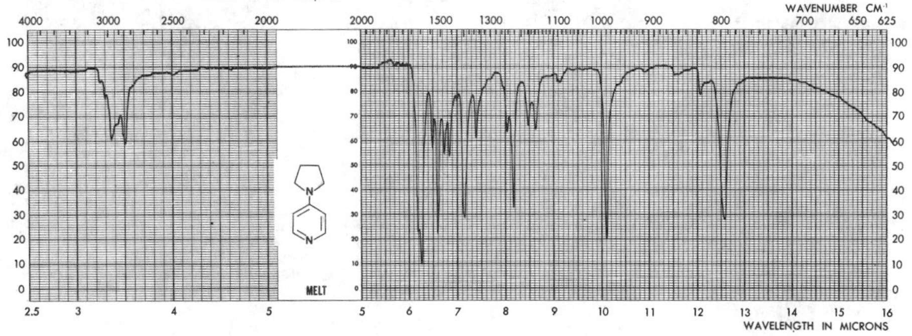

MELT

C

A7820-9 **3-Aminopyridine**
M.W. 94.12 m.p. 64-65°

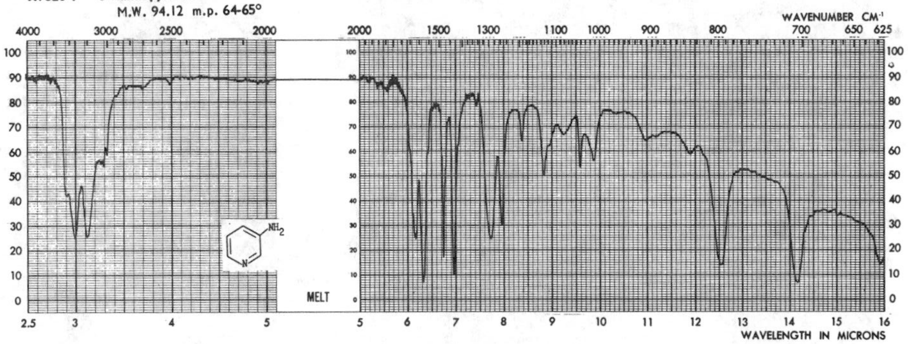

MELT

D

A6540-9 **3-Aminomethylpyridine** (3-picolylamine)
M.W. 108.14 n_D^{20} 1.5471

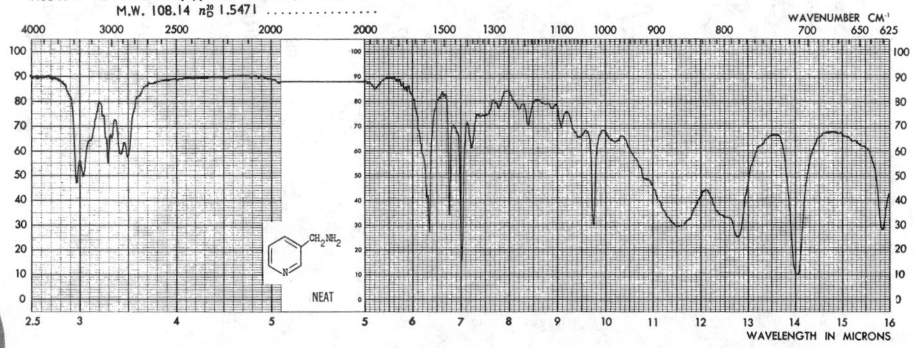

NEAT

E

Disp. C

NEAT

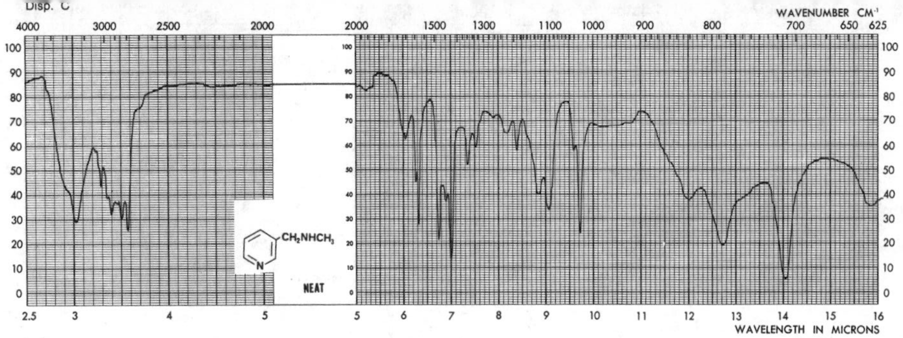

F

D21,465-5 **3,3'-Dipicolylamine** [3,3'-(iminodimethylene)-dipyridine]
M.W. 199.26 n_D^{20} 1.5822

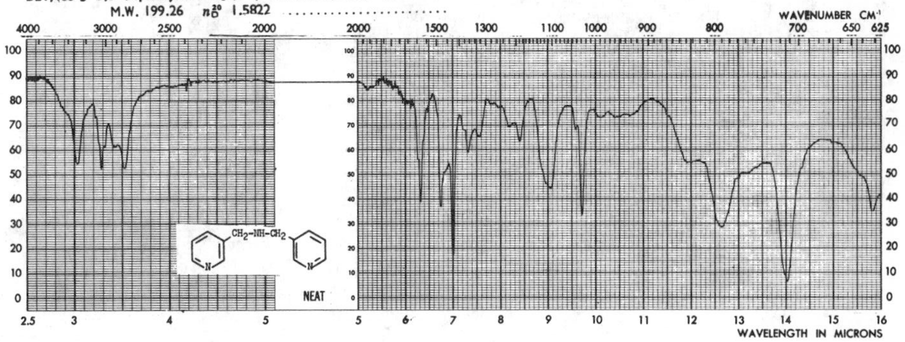

NEAT

G

18,637-6
Nicotine, 98%
FW 162.24 d 1.010 $[\alpha]^{22}$ -78° (c=5, H_2O)
Disp. C

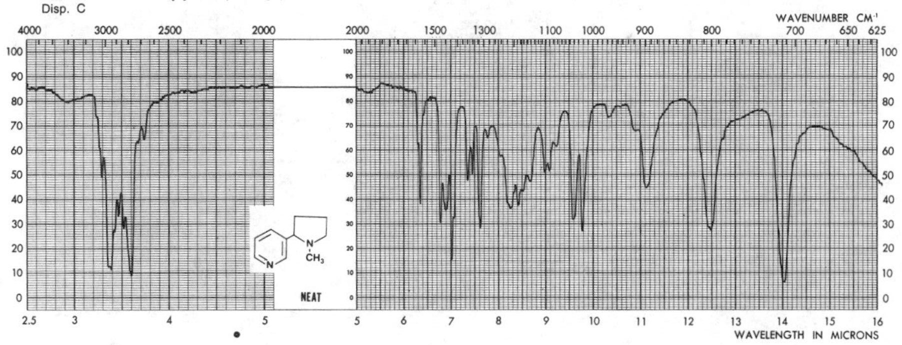

NEAT

H

A8560-4 **Anabasine** [(−)-2-(3-pyridyl)-piperidine]
M.W. 162.24 n_D^{20} 1.5363

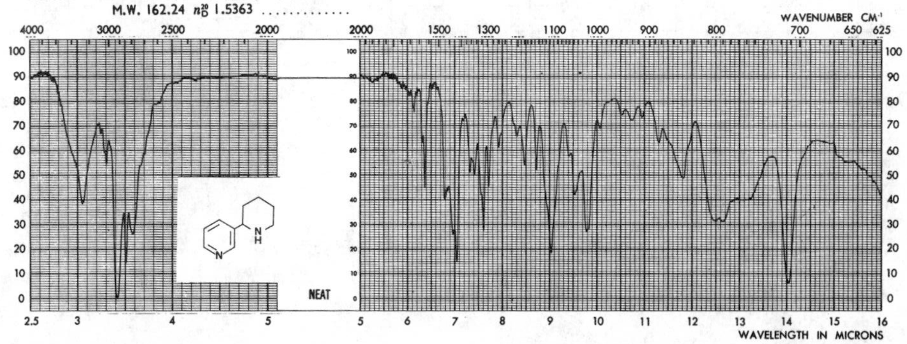

NEAT

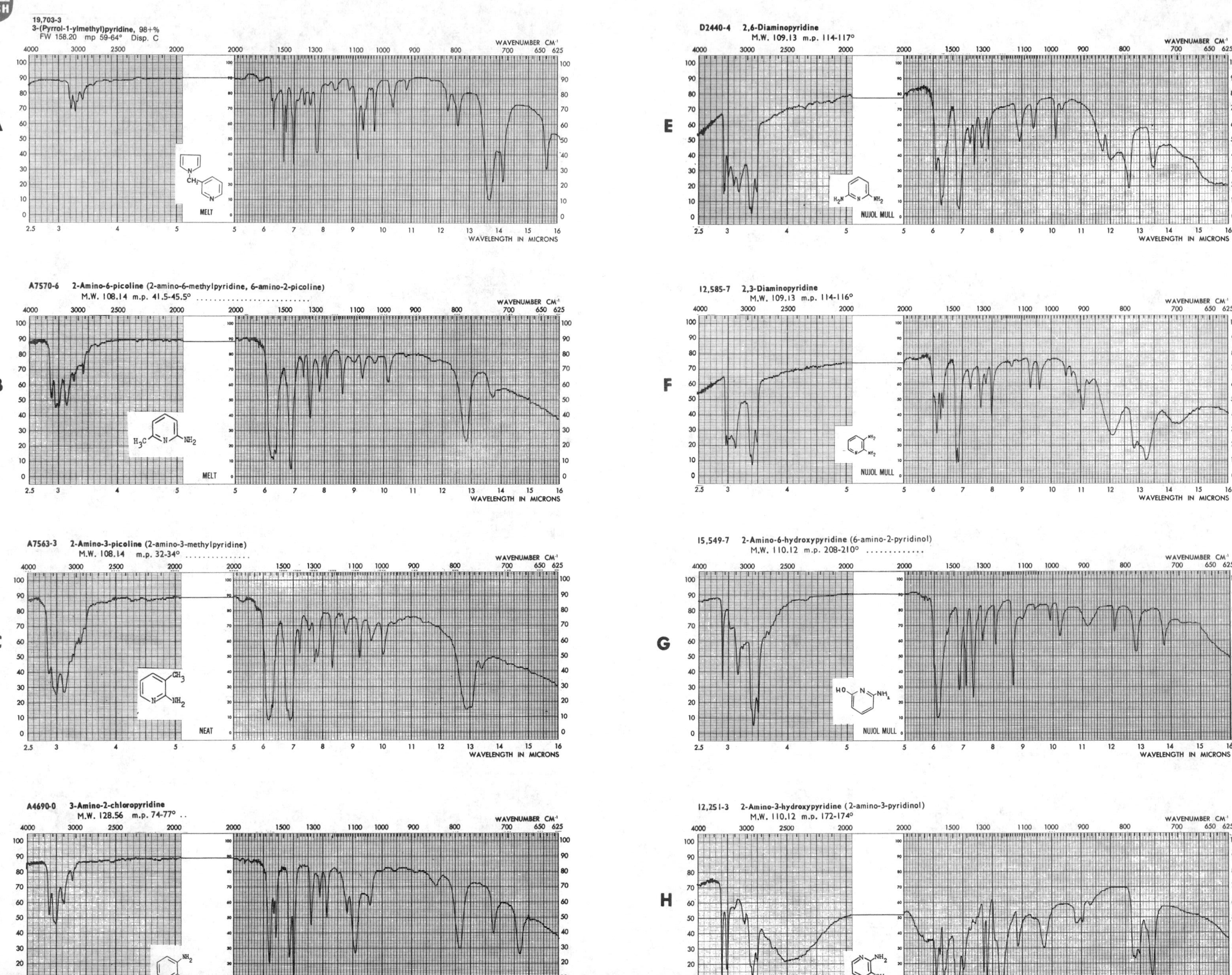
ALDRICH
A
19,703-3
3-(Pyrrol-1-ylmethyl)pyridine, 98+%
FW 158.20 mp 59-64° Disp. C
MELT
B
A7570-6 2-Amino-6-picoline (2-amino-6-methylpyridine, 6-amino-2-picoline)
M.W. 108.14 m.p. 41.5-45.5°
MELT
C
A7563-3 2-Amino-3-picoline (2-amino-3-methylpyridine)
M.W. 108.14 m.p. 32-34°
NEAT
D
A4690-0 3-Amino-2-chloropyridine
M.W. 128.56 m.p. 74-77°
E
D2440-4 2,6-Diaminopyridine
M.W. 109.13 m.p. 114-117°
NUJOL MULL
F
12,585-7 2,3-Diaminopyridine
M.W. 109.13 m.p. 114-116°
NUJOL MULL
G
15,549-7 2-Amino-6-hydroxypyridine (6-amino-2-pyridinol)
M.W. 110.12 m.p. 208-210°
NUJOL MULL
H
12,251-3 2-Amino-3-hydroxypyridine (2-amino-3-pyridinol)
M.W. 110.12 m.p. 172-174°
WAVENUMBER CM⁻¹
WAVELENGTH IN MICRONS

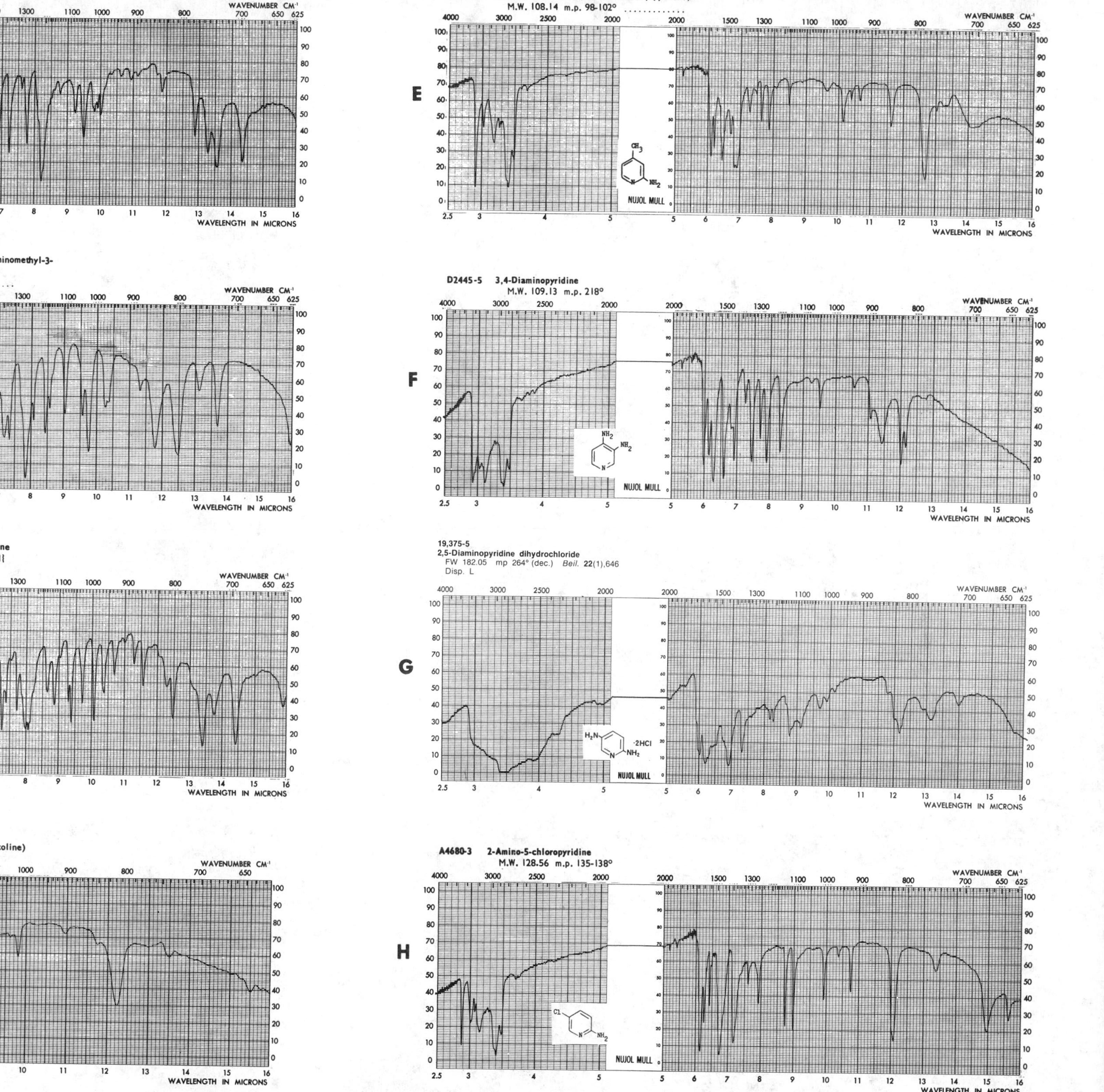

A 14,446-7 **2-Amino-3-benzyloxypyridine**
M.W. 200.24 m.p. 92-94°

B D14,270-0 **2-(Dimethylaminomethyl)-3-hydroxypyridine (2-dimethylaminomethyl-3-pyridinol)**
M.W. 152.20 m.p. 56-59°

C 12,370-6 **2-(N-Benzyl-N-β-hydroxyethylaminomethyl)-3-hydroxypyridine**
[2-[N-benzyl-N-(2-hydroxyethyl)-aminomethyl]-3-pyridinol]
M.W. 258.32 m.p. 127-130.5°

D A7568-4 **2-Amino-5-picoline (2-amino-5-methylpyridine, 6-amino-3-picoline)**
M.W. 108.14 m.p. 76-77°

E 12,308-0 **2-Amino-4-picoline (2-amino-4-methylpyridine)**
M.W. 108.14 m.p. 98-102°

F D2445-5 **3,4-Diaminopyridine**
M.W. 109.13 m.p. 218°

G 19,375-5
2,5-Diaminopyridine dihydrochloride
FW 182.05 mp 264° (dec.) *Beil.* **22**(1),646
Disp. L

H A4680-3 **2-Amino-5-chloropyridine**
M.W. 128.56 m.p. 135-138°

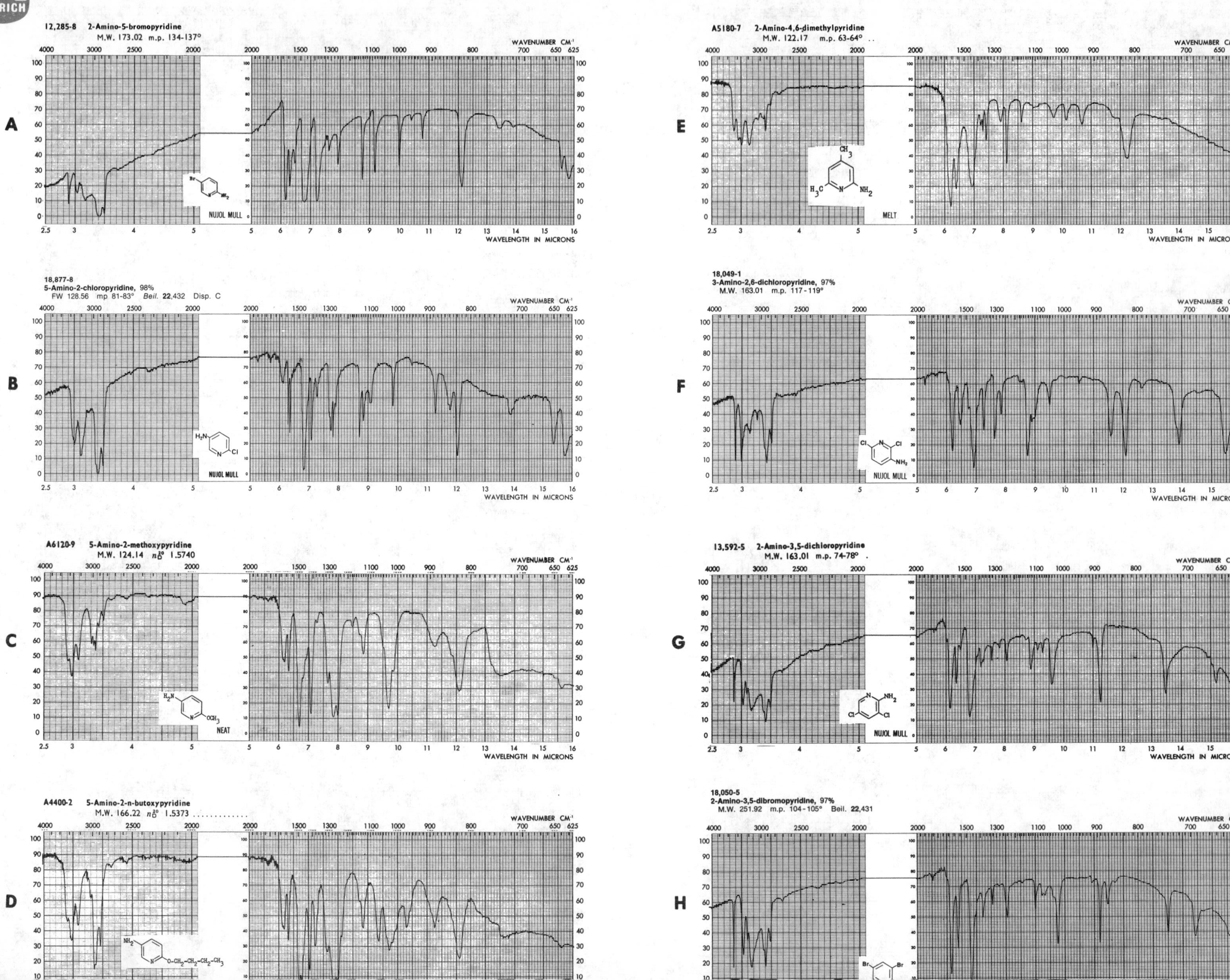
ALDRICH
A
12,285-8 2-Amino-5-bromopyridine
M.W. 173.02 m.p. 134-137°
NUJOL MULL
B
18,877-8
5-Amino-2-chloropyridine, 98%
FW 128.56 mp 81-83° Beil. 22,432 Disp. C
NUJOL MULL
C
A6120-9 5-Amino-2-methoxypyridine
M.W. 124.14 n20D 1.5740
NEAT
D
A4400-2 5-Amino-2-n-butoxypyridine
M.W. 166.22 n20D 1.5373
E
A5180-7 2-Amino-4,6-dimethylpyridine
M.W. 122.17 m.p. 63-64°
MELT
F
18,049-1
3-Amino-2,6-dichloropyridine, 97%
M.W. 163.01 m.p. 117-119°
NUJOL MULL
G
13,592-5 2-Amino-3,5-dichloropyridine
M.W. 163.01 m.p. 74-78°
NUJOL MULL
H
18,050-5
2-Amino-3,5-dibromopyridine, 97%
M.W. 251.92 m.p. 104-105° Beil. 22,431
WAVENUMBER CM⁻¹
WAVELENGTH IN MICRONS

A

M.W. 190.63 m.p. 212° (dec.)

NUJOL MULL

B

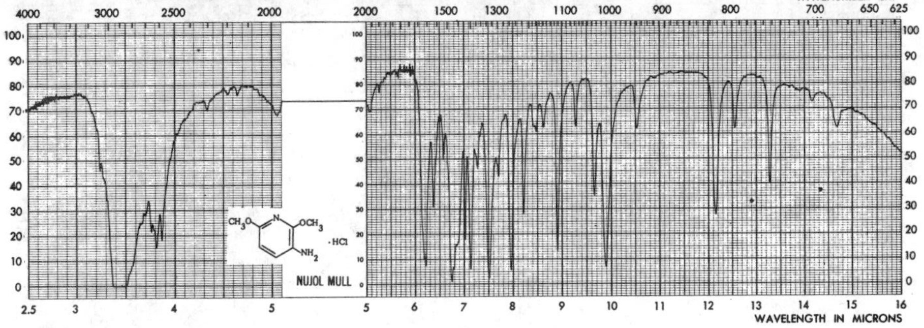

14,324-3 3,5-Diamino-2,6-dimethoxypyridine dihydrochloride
M.W. 242.11 m.p. >300°

NUJOL MULL

C

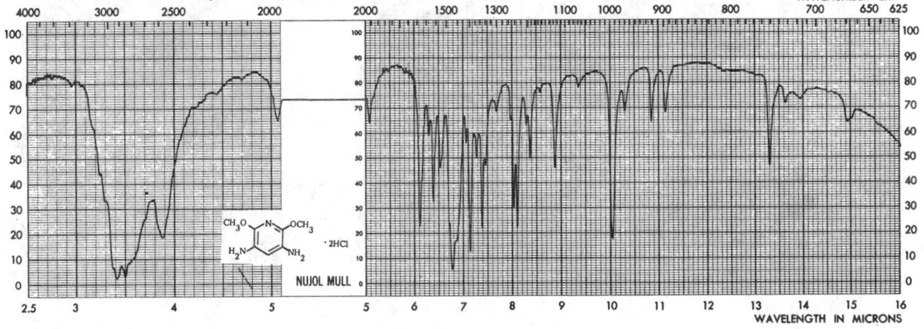

D2300-9 2,6-Diamino-3-phenylazopyridine (phenazopyridine) hydrochloride
M.W. 249.71 m.p. 246-248°

NUJOL MULL

D

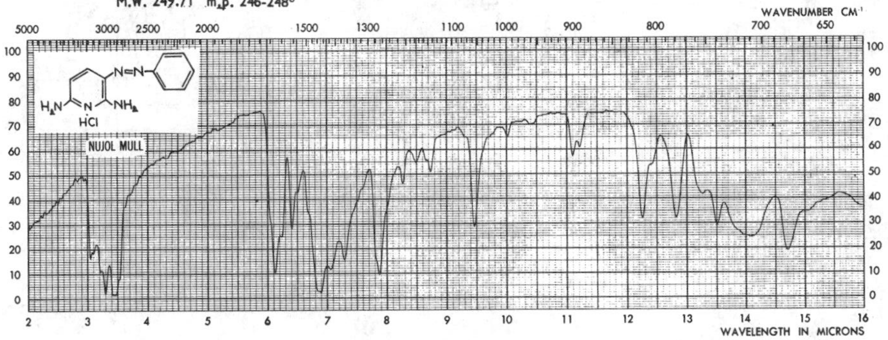

14,681-1 6'-Butoxy-2,6-diamino-3,3'-azodipyridine
M.W. 286.34 m.p. 129-130°

NUJOL MULL

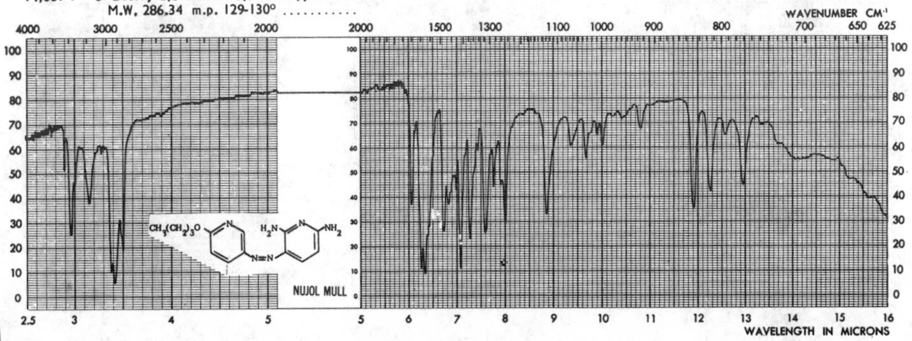

E

NUJOL MULL

F

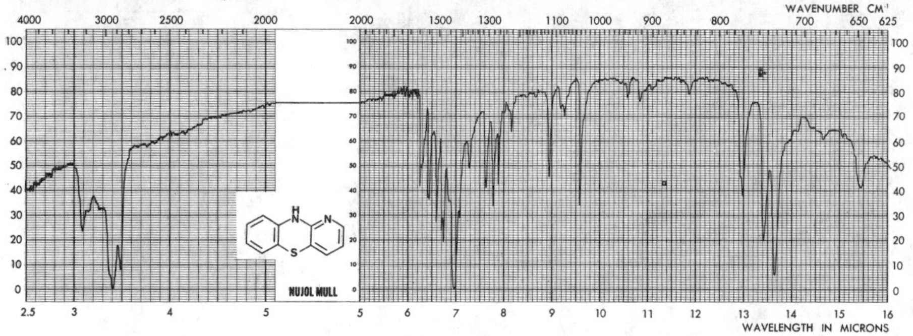

N1420-4 4-(p-Nitrobenzyl)-pyridine
M.W. 214.22 m.p. 70-72°

NUJOL MULL

G

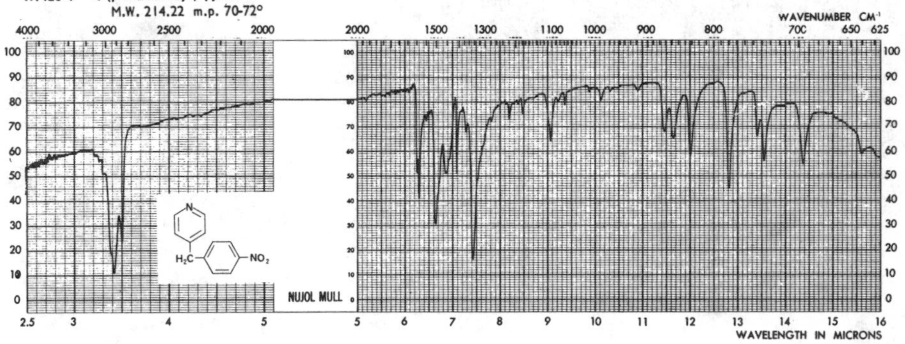

14,327-8 3-(2,4-Dinitrophenoxy)-pyridine
M.W. 261.20 m.p. 127-129°

NUJOL MULL

H

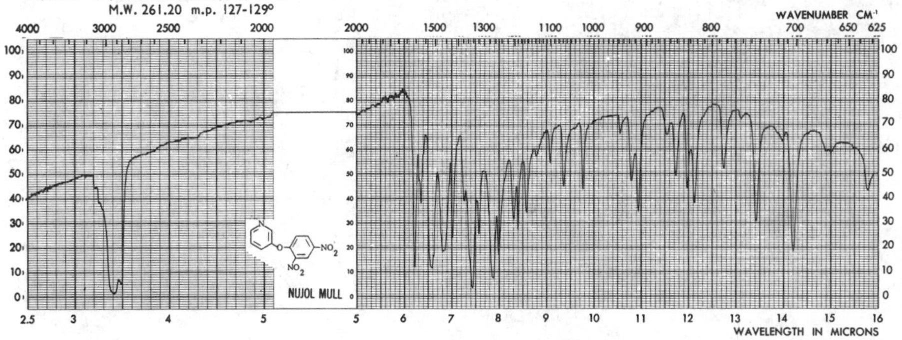

C6160-7 2-Chloro-3-nitropyridine
M.W. 158.54 m.p. 101-104°

NUJOL MULL

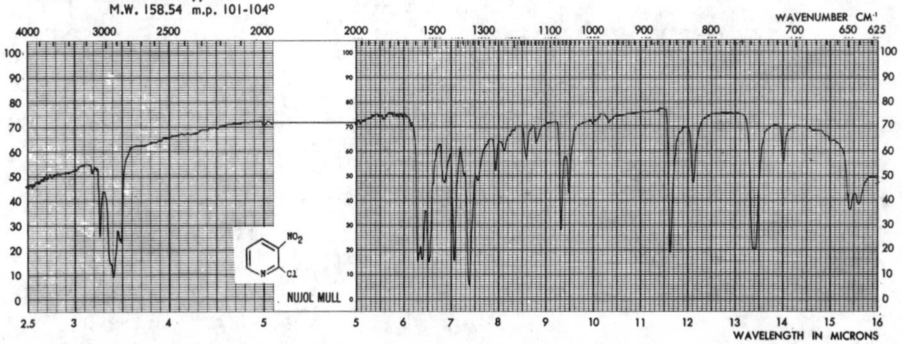

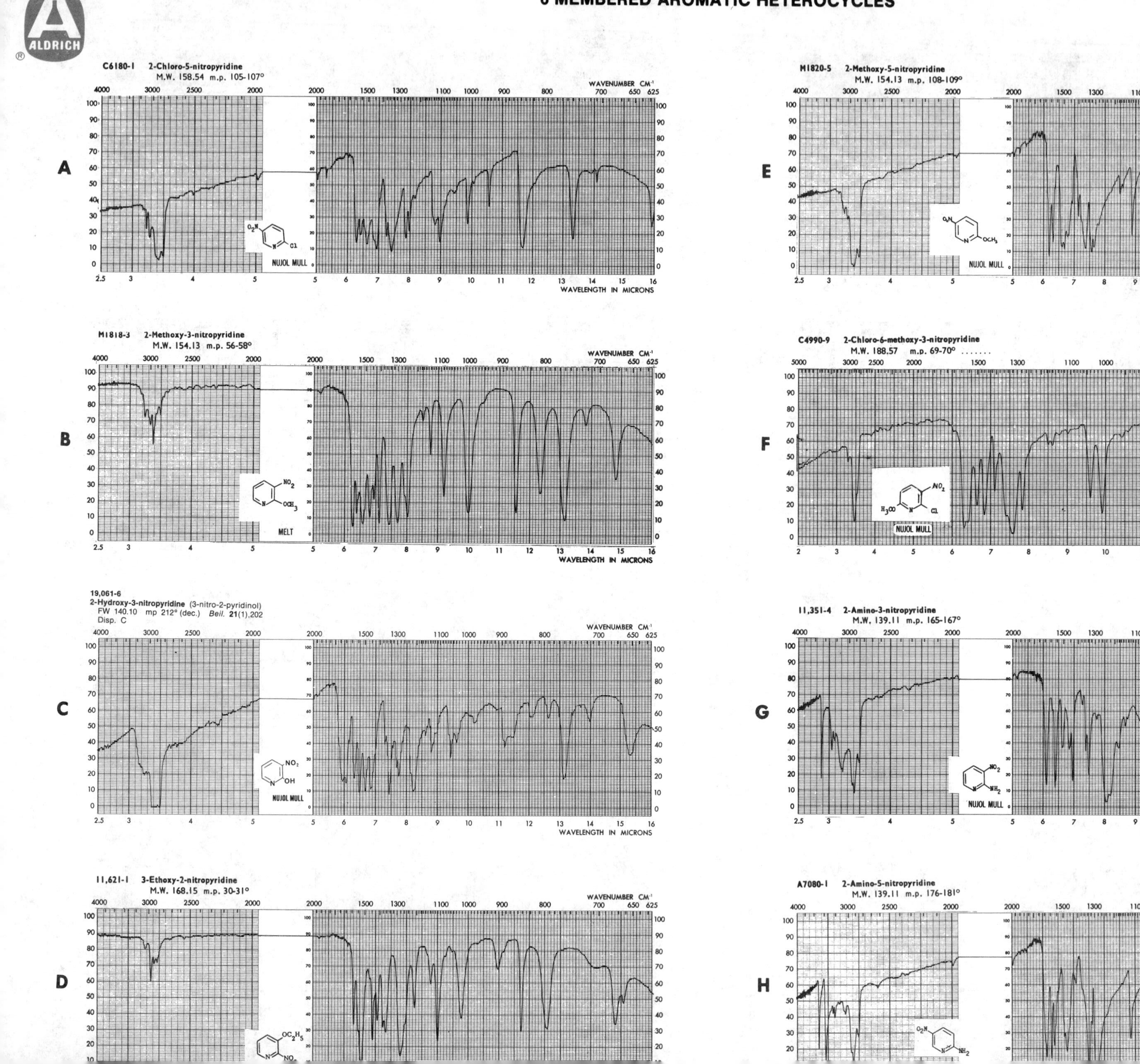
ALDRICH
A
C6180-1 2-Chloro-5-nitropyridine
M.W. 158.54 m.p. 105-107°
NUJOL MULL
B
M1818-3 2-Methoxy-3-nitropyridine
M.W. 154.13 m.p. 56-58°
MELT
C
19,061-6
2-Hydroxy-3-nitropyridine (3-nitro-2-pyridinol)
FW 140.10 mp 212° (dec.) Beil. 21(1),202
Disp. C
NUJOL MULL
D
11,621-1 3-Ethoxy-2-nitropyridine
M.W. 168.15 m.p. 30-31°
E
M1820-5 2-Methoxy-5-nitropyridine
M.W. 154.13 m.p. 108-109°
NUJOL MULL
F
C4990-9 2-Chloro-6-methoxy-3-nitropyridine
M.W. 188.57 m.p. 69-70°
NUJOL MULL
G
11,351-4 2-Amino-3-nitropyridine
M.W. 139.11 m.p. 165-167°
NUJOL MULL
H
A7080-1 2-Amino-5-nitropyridine
M.W. 139.11 m.p. 176-181°
WAVENUMBER CM⁻¹
WAVELENGTH IN MICRONS

A

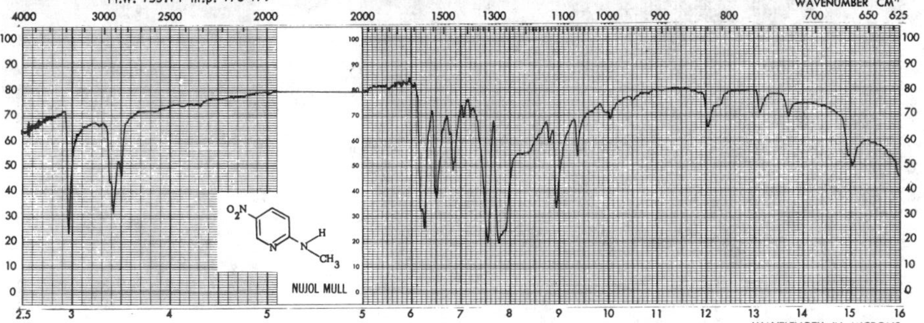

E

B 11,350-6 2-Ethylamino-5-nitropyridine
M.W. 167.17 m.p. 120-123°

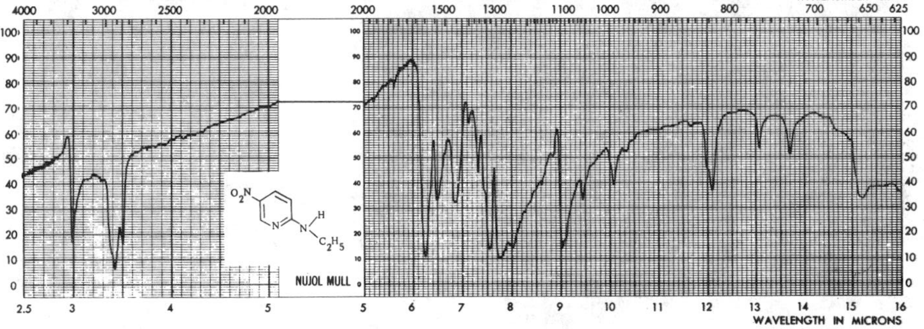

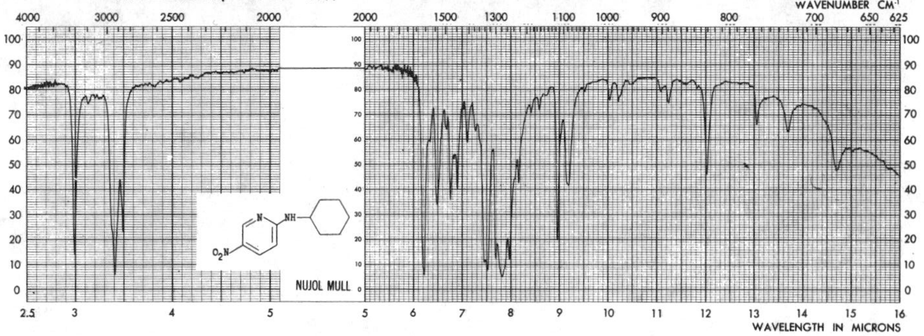

F 11,347-6 2-(3-Methoxypropylamino)-5-nitropyridine
M.W. 211.22 m.p. 72-73°

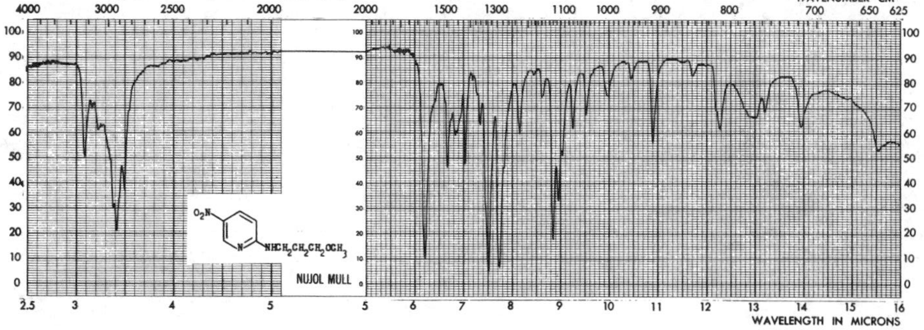

C 11,348-4 5-Nitro-2-n-propylaminopyridine
M.W. 181.20 m.p. 94-96°

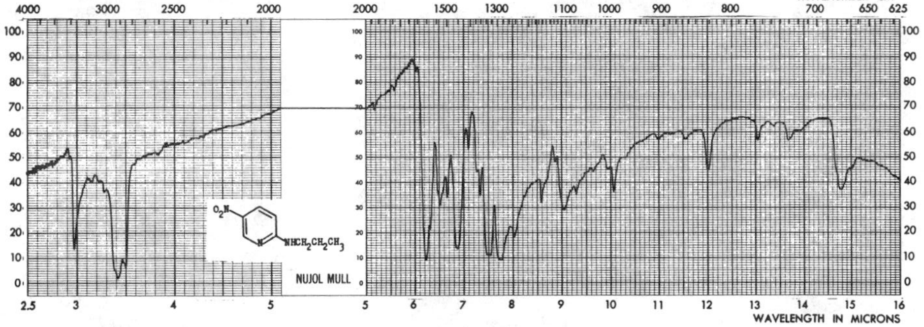

G 11,343-3 2-Anilino-5-nitropyridine
M.W. 215.21 m.p. 131-133°

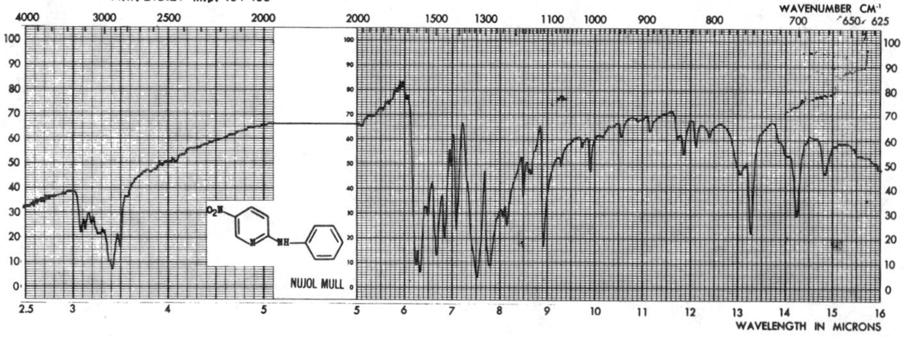

D 11,346-8 2-(2-Aminoethylamino)-5-nitropyridine
M.W. 182.18 m.p. 126-128°

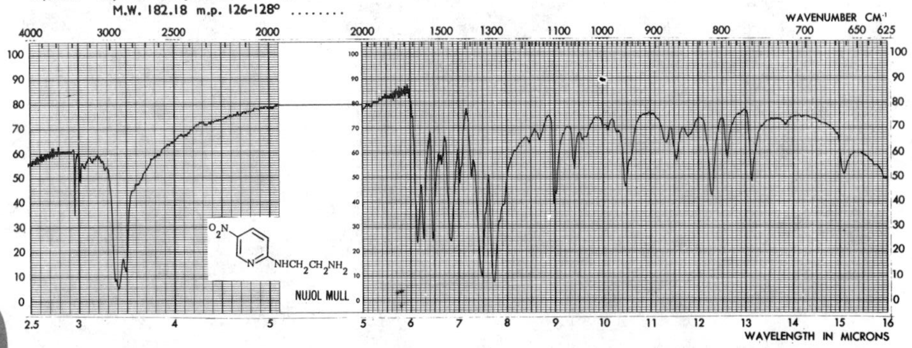

H 10,364-0 2-(5-Nitro-2-pyridylamino)-ethanol
M.W. 183.17 m.p. 127-129°

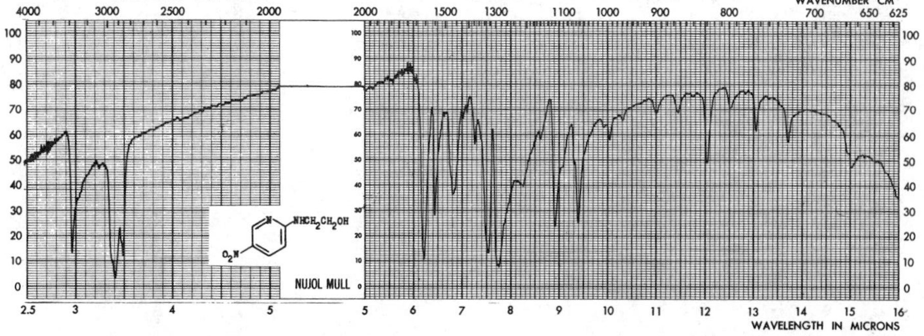

NUJOL MULL

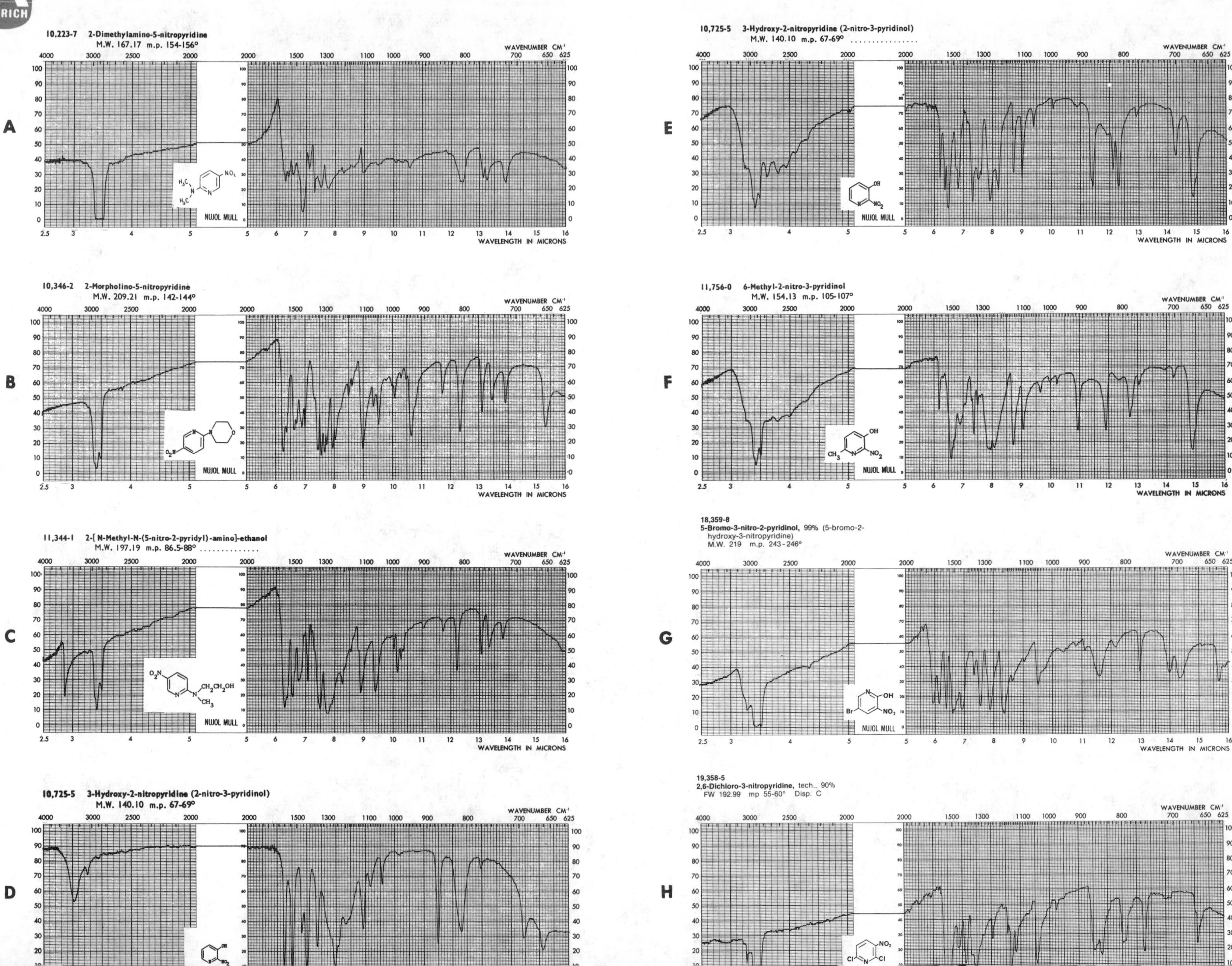

A
10,223-7 2-Dimethylamino-5-nitropyridine
M.W. 167.17 m.p. 154-156°
NUJOL MULL
B
10,346-2 2-Morpholino-5-nitropyridine
M.W. 209.21 m.p. 142-144°
NUJOL MULL
C
11,344-1 2-[N-Methyl-N-(5-nitro-2-pyridyl)-amino]-ethanol
M.W. 197.19 m.p. 86.5-88°
NUJOL MULL
D
10,725-5 3-Hydroxy-2-nitropyridine (2-nitro-3-pyridinol)
M.W. 140.10 m.p. 67-69°
E
10,725-5 3-Hydroxy-2-nitropyridine (2-nitro-3-pyridinol)
M.W. 140.10 m.p. 67-69°
NUJOL MULL
F
11,756-0 6-Methyl-2-nitro-3-pyridinol
M.W. 154.13 m.p. 105-107°
NUJOL MULL
G
18,359-8
5-Bromo-3-nitro-2-pyridinol, 99% (5-bromo-2-hydroxy-3-nitropyridine)
M.W. 219 m.p. 243-246°
NUJOL MULL
H
19,358-5
2,6-Dichloro-3-nitropyridine, tech., 90%
FW 192.99 mp 55-60° Disp. C
WAVENUMBER CM⁻¹
WAVELENGTH IN MICRONS

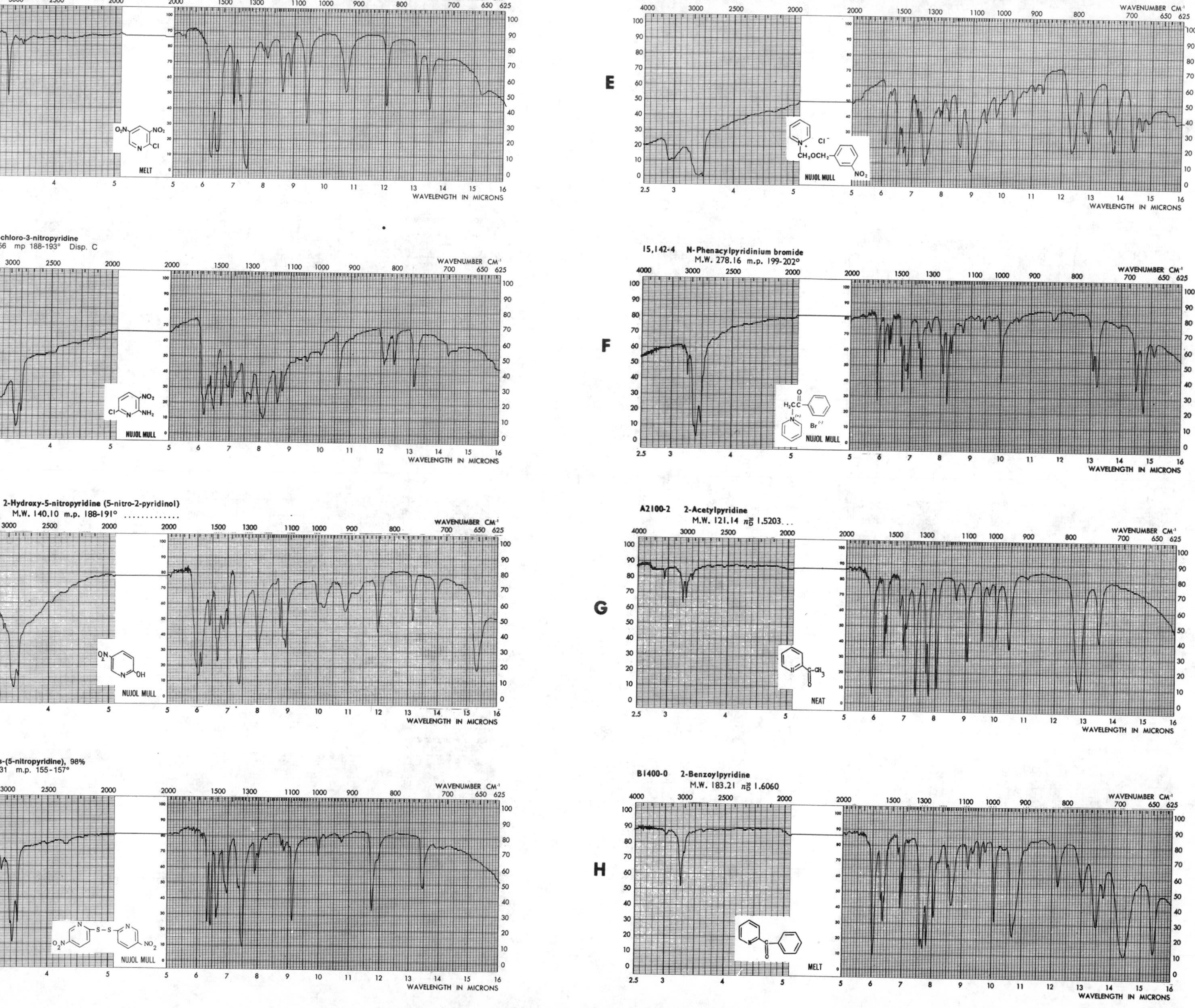

A mp 64-66° Beil. 20(3),2536 Disp. C

B 19,361-5
2-Amino-6-chloro-3-nitropyridine
FW 173.56 mp 188-193° Disp. C

C H4880-8 2-Hydroxy-5-nitropyridine (5-nitro-2-pyridinol)
M.W. 140.10 m.p. 188-191°

D 15,819-4
2,2'-Dithiobis-(5-nitropyridine), 98%
M.W. 310.31 m.p. 155-157°

E ...pyridinium chloride
FW 280.71 Disp. C

F 15,142-4 N-Phenacylpyridinium bromide
M.W. 278.16 m.p. 199-202°

G A2100-2 2-Acetylpyridine
M.W. 121.14 n_D^{20} 1.5203

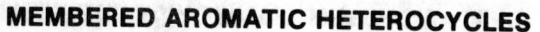

H B1400-0 2-Benzoylpyridine
M.W. 183.21 n_D^{20} 1.6060

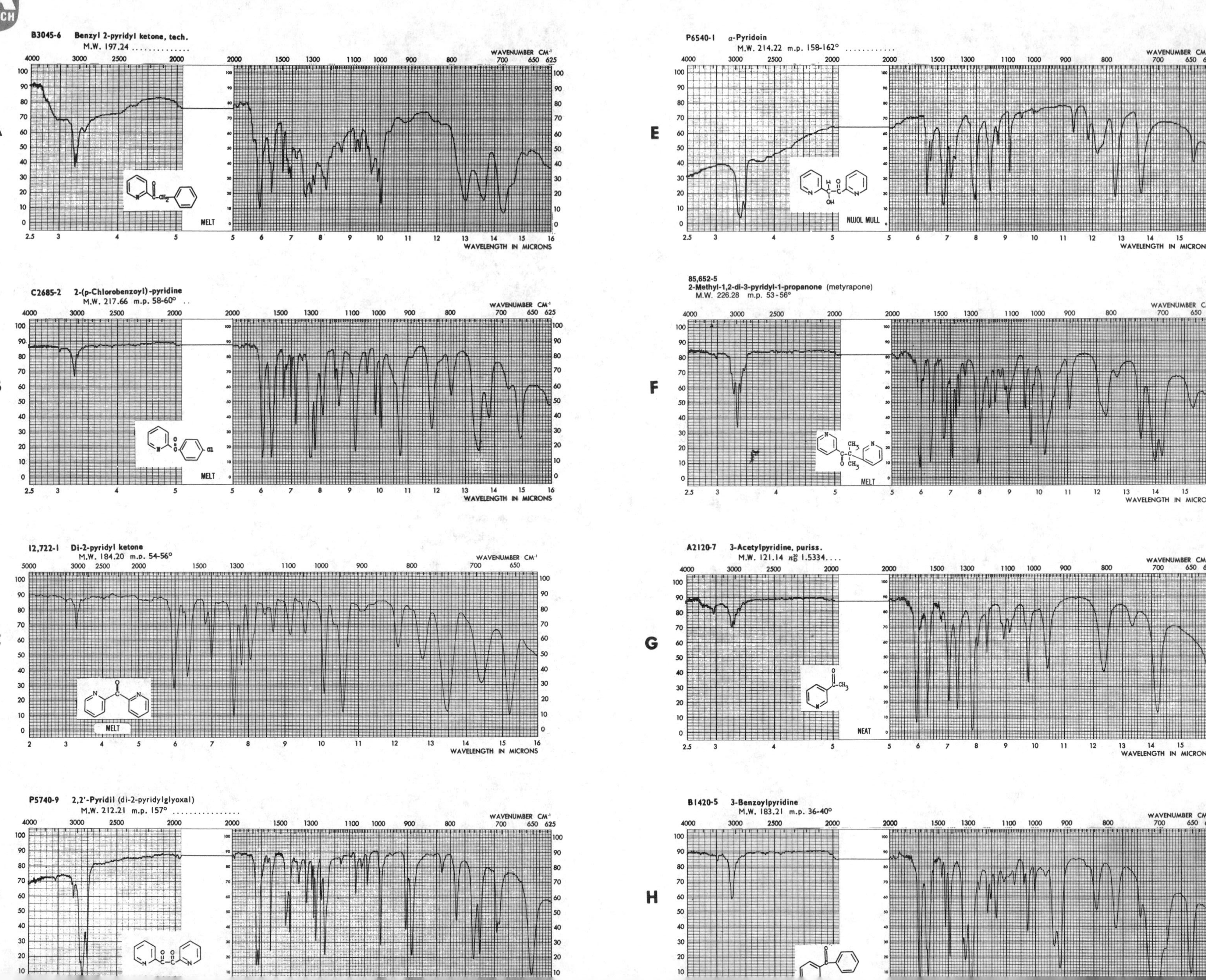
ALDRICH
A
B3045-6 Benzyl 2-pyridyl ketone, tech.
M.W. 197.24
MELT
B
C2685-2 2-(p-Chlorobenzoyl)-pyridine
M.W. 217.66 m.p. 58-60°
MELT
C
12,722-1 Di-2-pyridyl ketone
M.W. 184.20 m.p. 54-56°
MELT
D
P5740-9 2,2'-Pyridil (di-2-pyridylglyoxal)
M.W. 212.21 m.p. 157°
E
P6540-1 α-Pyridoin
M.W. 214.22 m.p. 158-162°
NUJOL MULL
F
85,652-5
2-Methyl-1,2-di-3-pyridyl-1-propanone (metyrapone)
M.W. 226.28 m.p. 53-56°
MELT
G
A2120-7 3-Acetylpyridine, puriss.
M.W. 121.14 n20/D 1.5334
NEAT
H
B1420-5 3-Benzoylpyridine
M.W. 183.21 m.p. 36-40°
WAVENUMBER CM⁻¹
WAVELENGTH IN MICRONS

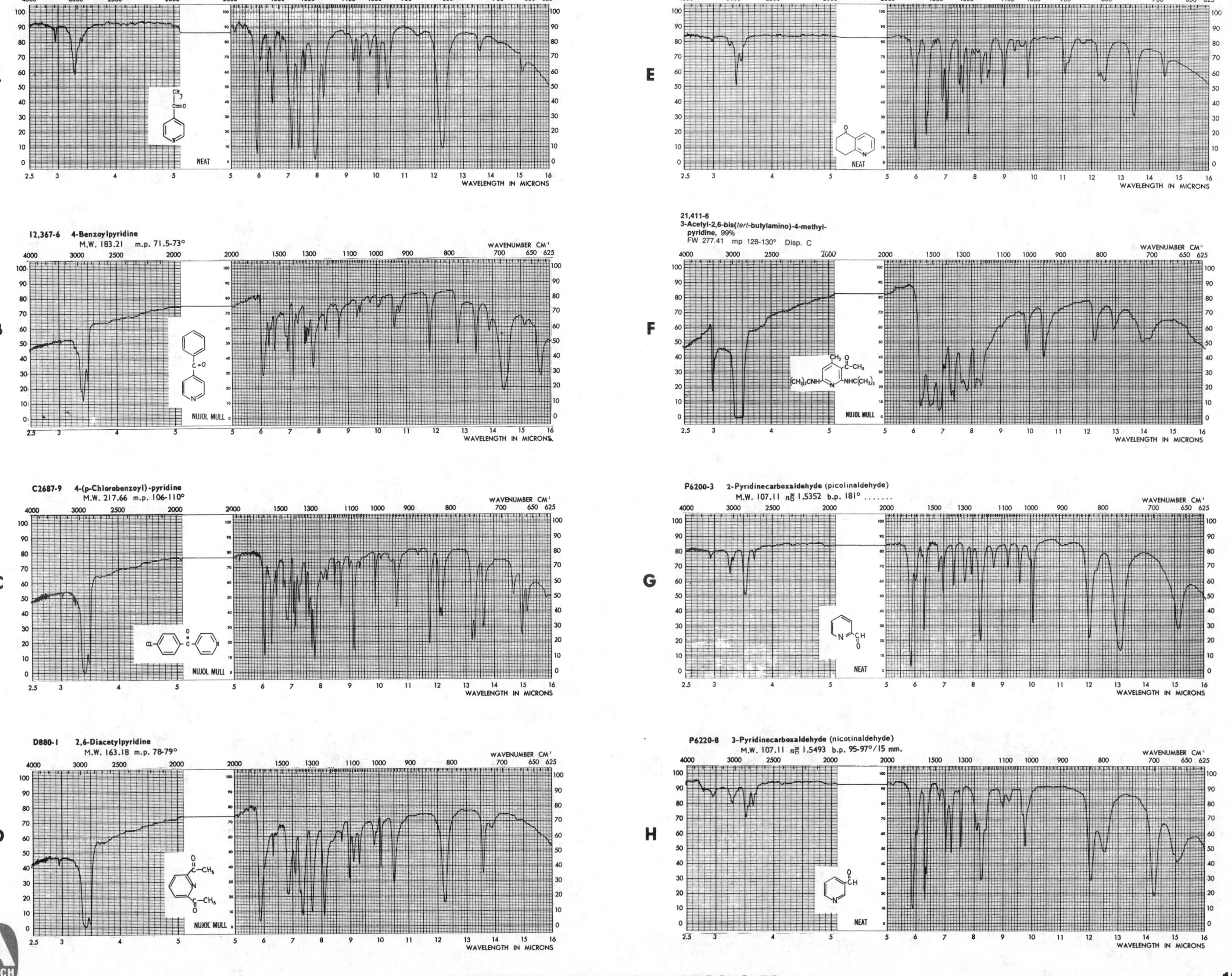

A
NEAT
B
12,367-6 4-Benzoylpyridine
M.W. 183.21 m.p. 71.5-73°
NUJOL MULL
C
C2687-9 4-(p-Chlorobenzoyl)-pyridine
M.W. 217.66 m.p. 106-110°
NUJOL MULL
D
D880-1 2,6-Diacetylpyridine
M.W. 163.18 m.p. 78-79°
NUJOL MULL
E
NEAT
F
21,411-6
3-Acetyl-2,6-bis(tert-butylamino)-4-methylpyridine, 99%
FW 277.41 mp 128-130° Disp. C
NUJOL MULL
G
P6200-3 2-Pyridinecarboxaldehyde (picolinaldehyde)
M.W. 107.11 n20D 1.5352 b.p. 181° ....
NEAT
H
P6220-8 3-Pyridinecarboxaldehyde (nicotinaldehyde)
M.W. 107.11 n20D 1.5493 b.p. 95-97°/15 mm.
NEAT
WAVENUMBER CM-1
WAVELENGTH IN MICRONS
ALDRICH

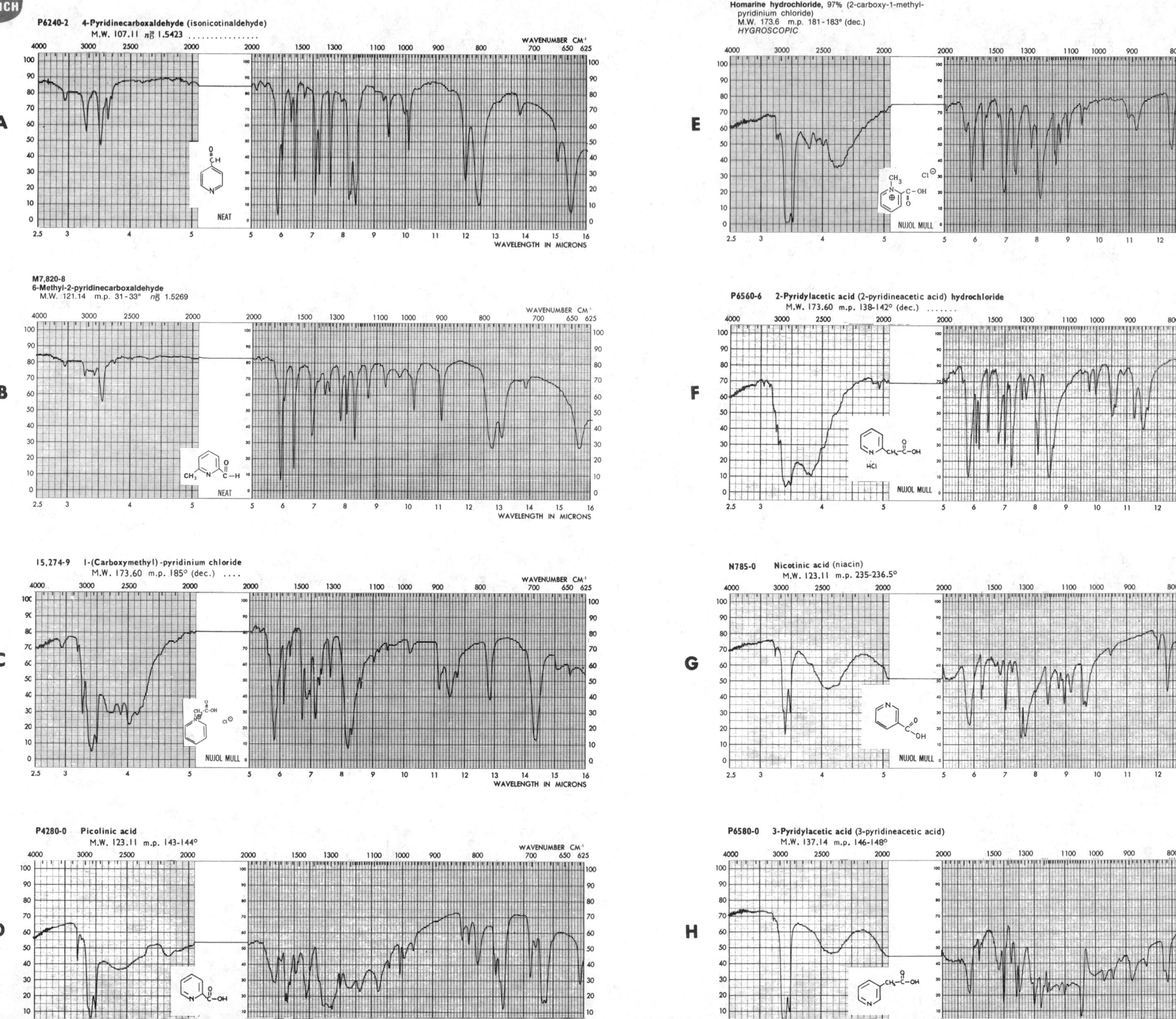
A
P6240-2 4-Pyridinecarboxaldehyde (isonicotinaldehyde)
M.W. 107.11 n_D^{20} 1.5423
NEAT
B
M7,820-8
6-Methyl-2-pyridinecarboxaldehyde
M.W. 121.14 m.p. 31-33° n_D^{20} 1.5269
NEAT
C
15,274-9 1-(Carboxymethyl)-pyridinium chloride
M.W. 173.60 m.p. 185° (dec.)
NUJOL MULL
D
P4280-0 Picolinic acid
M.W. 123.11 m.p. 143-144°
E
16,037-7
Homarine hydrochloride, 97% (2-carboxy-1-methyl-pyridinium chloride)
M.W. 173.6 m.p. 181-183° (dec.)
HYGROSCOPIC
NUJOL MULL
F
P6560-6 2-Pyridylacetic acid (2-pyridineacetic acid) hydrochloride
M.W. 173.60 m.p. 138-142° (dec.)
NUJOL MULL
G
N785-0 Nicotinic acid (niacin)
M.W. 123.11 m.p. 235-236.5°
NUJOL MULL
H
P6580-0 3-Pyridylacetic acid (3-pyridineacetic acid)
M.W. 137.14 m.p. 146-148°
WAVENUMBER CM⁻¹
WAVELENGTH IN MICRONS

A

M.W. 149.15 m.p. 232-235°

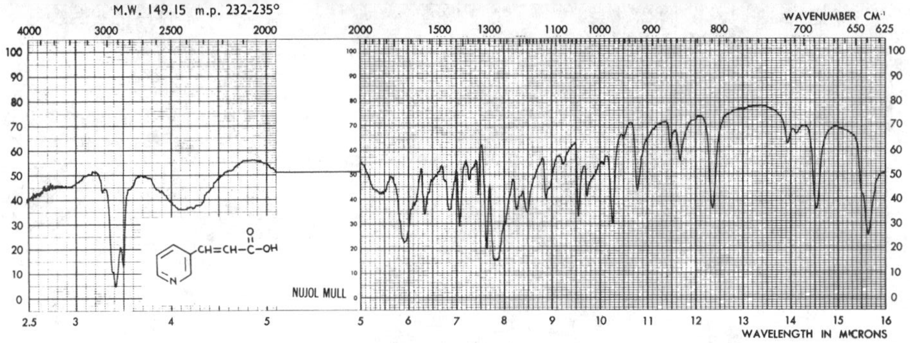

NUJOL MULL

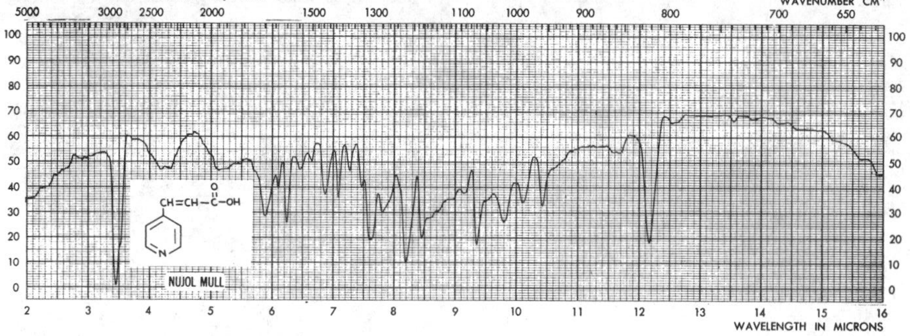

B

I-1750-8 **Isonicotinic acid**
M.W. 123.11
m.p. 310-315° (sublimes)

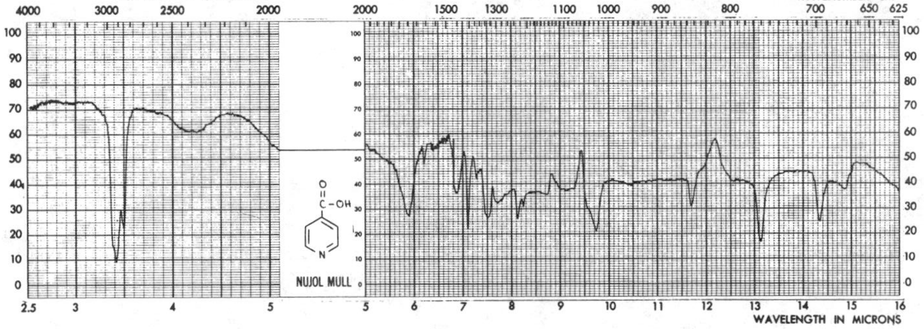

NUJOL MULL

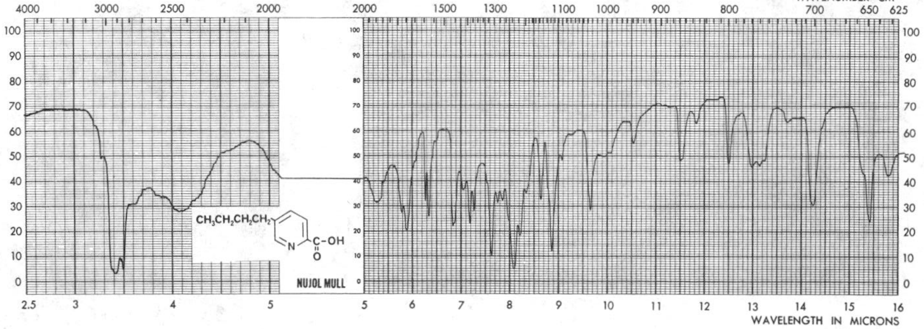

C

P6585-1 **4-Pyridylacetic acid (4-pyridineacetic acid) hydrochloride**
M.W. 173.60 m.p. 138-140°

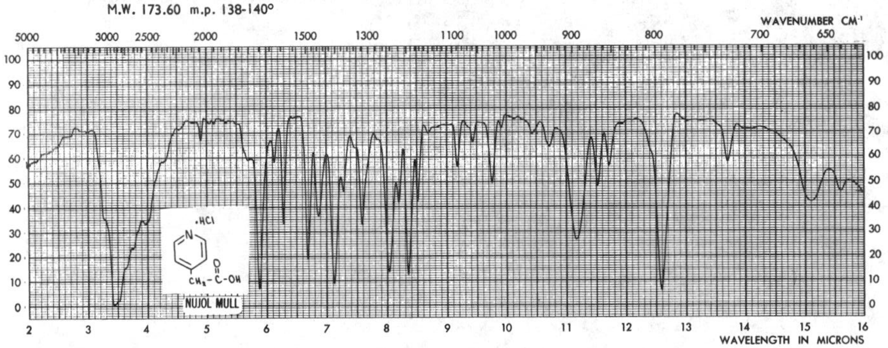

NUJOL MULL

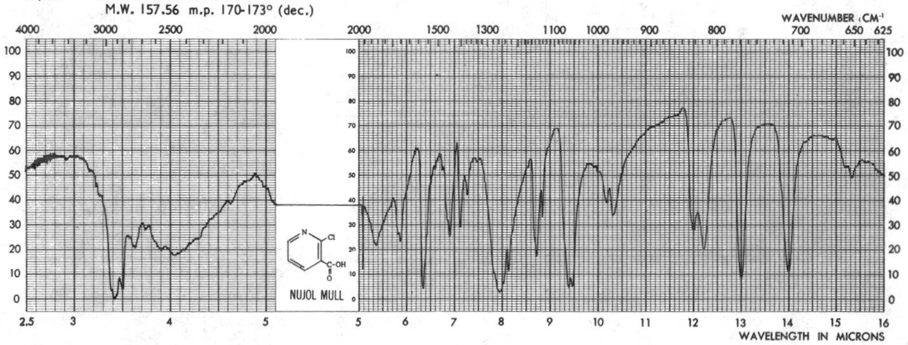

D

18,323-7
(4-Pyridylthio)acetic acid, 98%
M.W. 169.2 m.p. 251-255° (dec.)

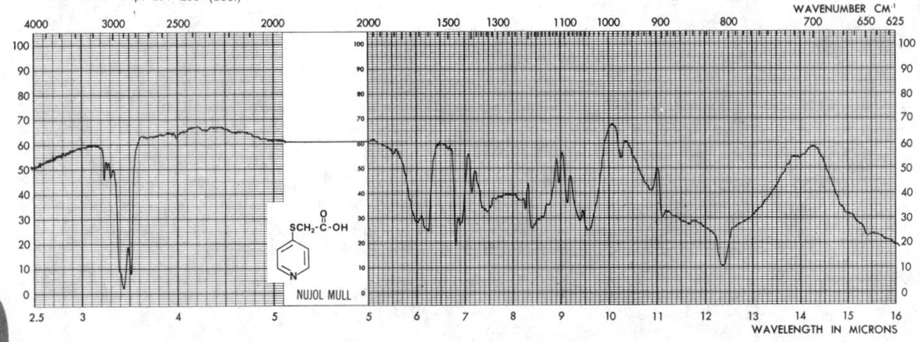

NUJOL MULL

E

M.W. 149.15 m.p. 294° (dec.)

NUJOL MULL

F

21,130-3
Fusaric acid, 99% (5-butylpicolinic acid)
FW 179.22 mp 95-98° Disp. C

NUJOL MULL

G

15,033-9 **2-Chloronicotinic acid**
M.W. 157.56 m.p. 170-173° (dec.)

NUJOL MULL

H

15,635-3
6-Chloronicotinic acid, 99%
M.W. 157.56 m.p. 198-200° (dec.) Beil. **22**,43

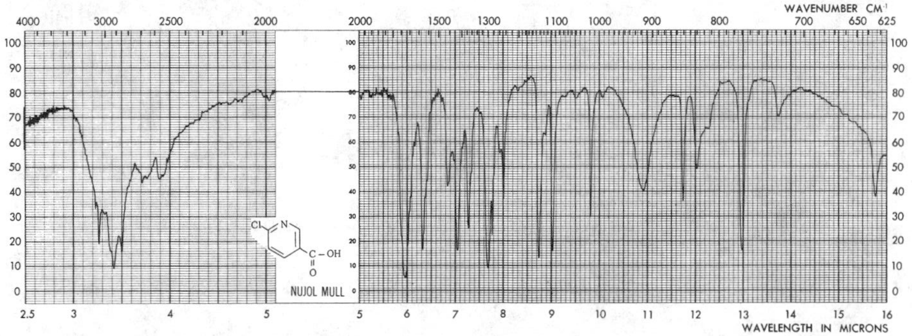

NUJOL MULL

A

12,875-9 **6-Hydroxynicotinic acid** (2-hydroxypyridine-5-carboxylic acid)
M.W. 139.11

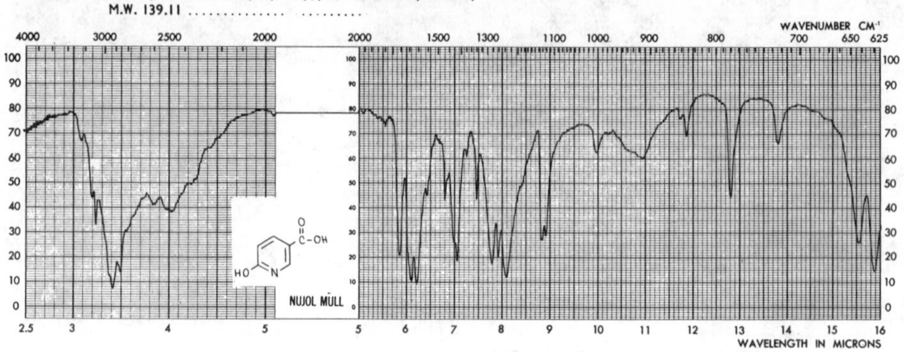

NUJOL MULL

B

15,230-7
3-Hydroxypicolinic acid
M.W. 139.11 m.p. 220-222° (dec.) Beil. **22**,212

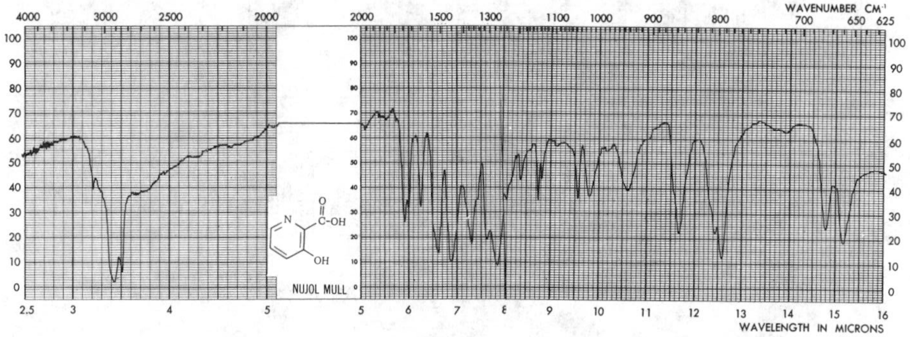

NUJOL MULL

C

H4300-8 **2-Hydroxy-6-methylpyridine-3-carboxylic acid**
M.W. 153.14 m.p. 233-235°

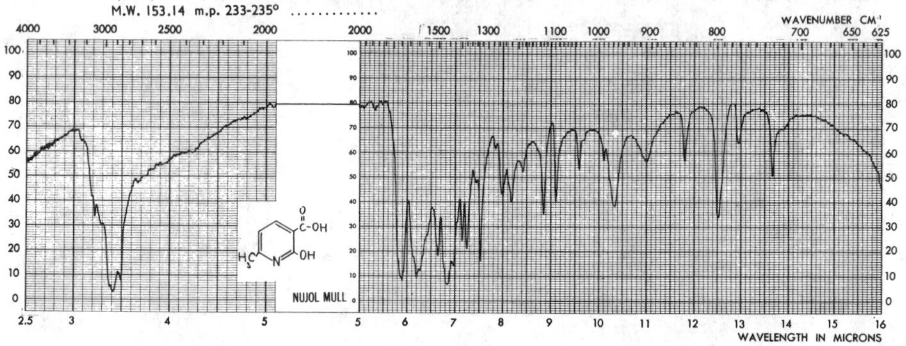

NUJOL MULL

D

15,820-8
6,6'-Dithiodinicotinic acid, 95%
M.W. 308.33 m.p. 247-249° (dec.)

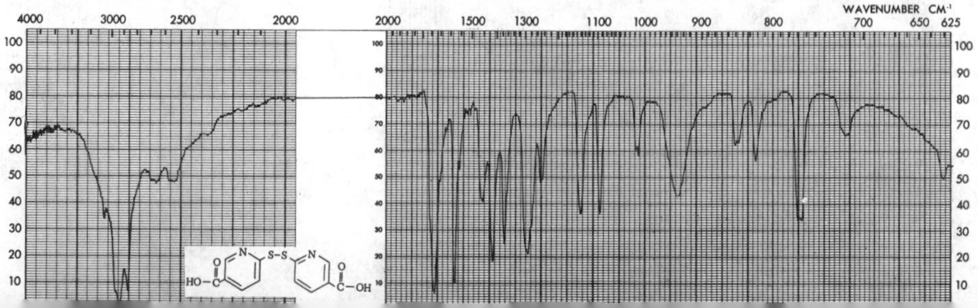

E

15,328-1
Citrazinic acid, 97+% (2,6-dihydroxyisonicotinic acid)
M.W. 155.11 m.p. >300° Beil. **22**,254

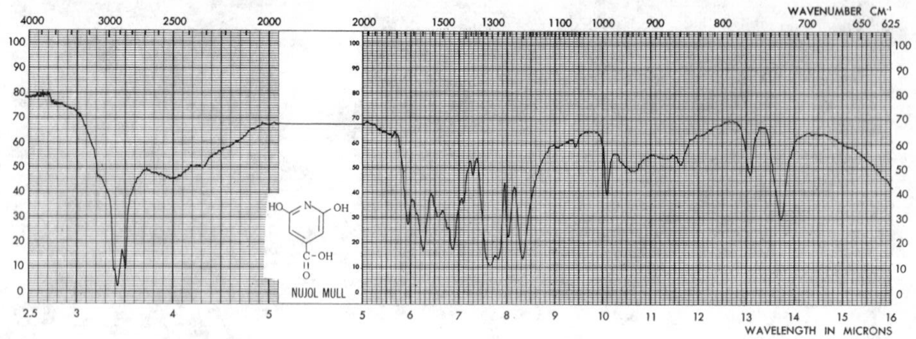

NUJOL MULL

F

A6830-0 **2-Aminonicotinic acid**
M.W. 138.13 m.p. 295-297°

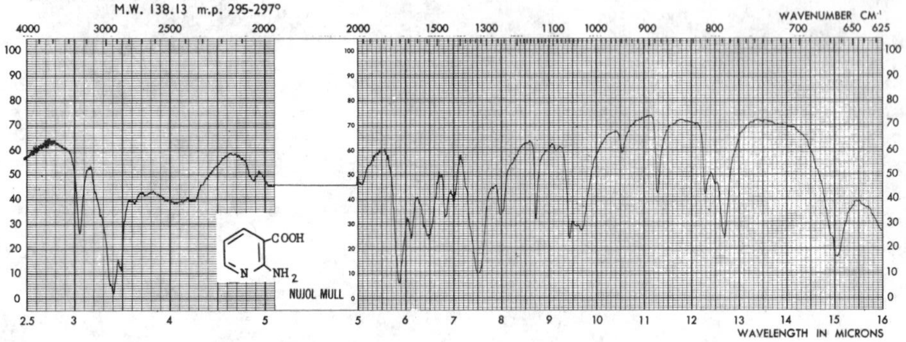

NUJOL MULL

G

21,687-9
6-Aminonicotinic acid, 98%
FW 138.13 mp >300° *Beil.* **22**,542 Disp. C

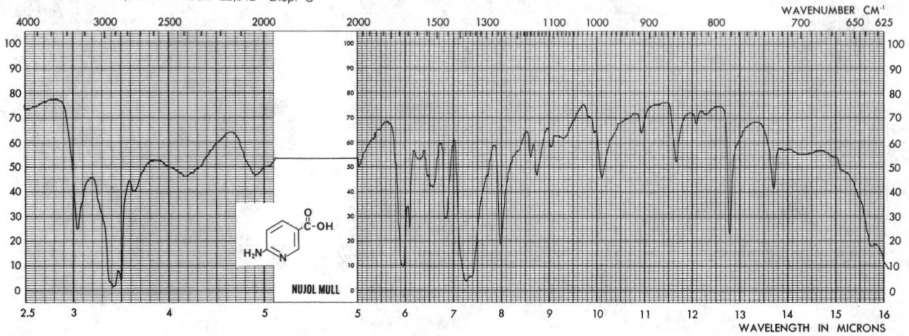

NUJOL MULL

H

P6320-4 **2,3-Pyridinedicarboxylic acid** (quinolinic acid)
M.W. 167.12 m.p. 188° (dec.)

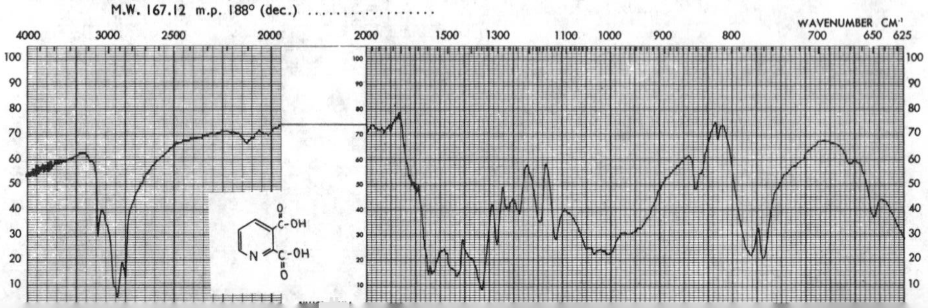

A

2,4-Pyridinedicarboxylic acid, puriss.
M.W. 167.12 m.p. 246°

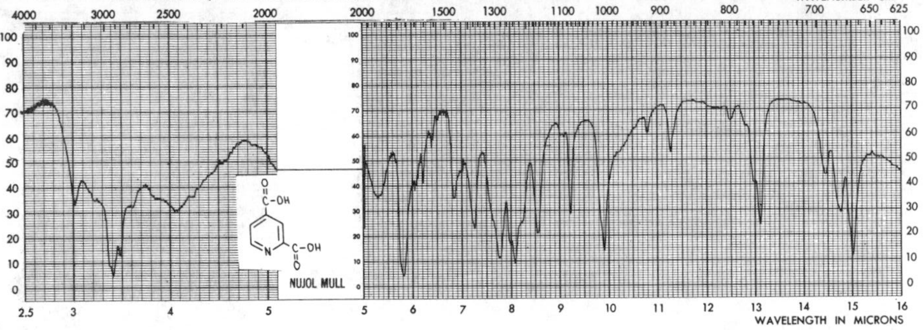

NUJOL MULL

B

P6400-6 3,4-Pyridinedicarboxylic acid (cinchomeronic acid)
M.W. 167.12 m.p. 262° (dec.)

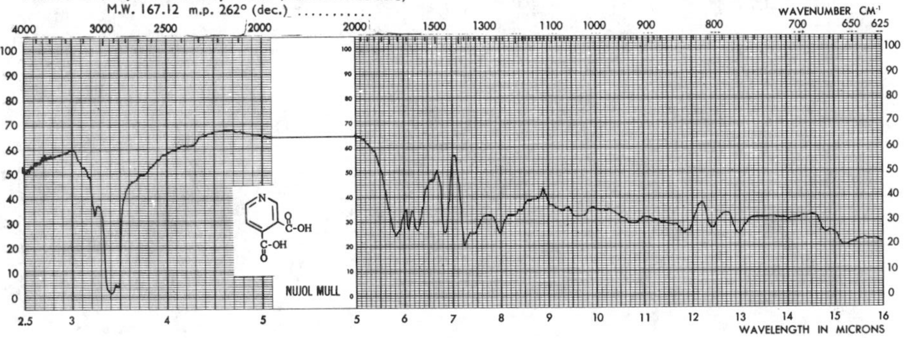

NUJOL MULL

C

P6360-3 2,5-Pyridinedicarboxylic acid (isocinchomeronic acid) **monohydrate**
M.W. 185.14 m.p. 256-258°

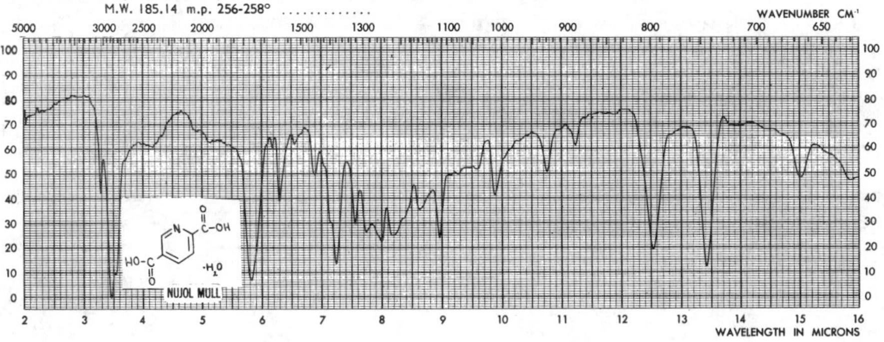

NUJOL MULL

D

P6420-0 3,5-Pyridinedicarboxylic acid
M.W. 167.12 m.p. 325° (dec.)

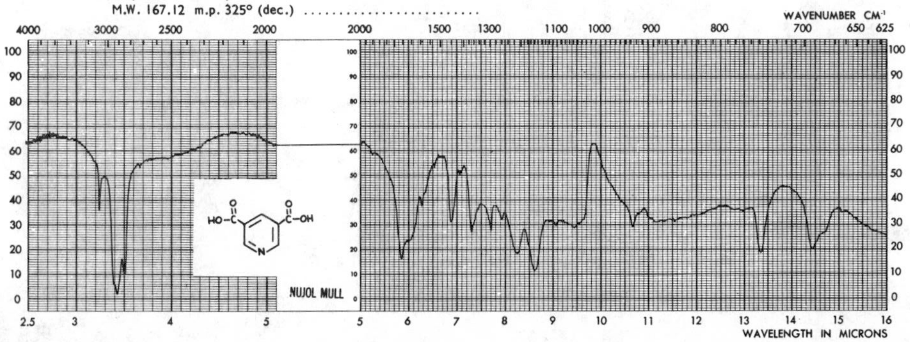

NUJOL MULL

E

P6380-8 2,6-Pyridinedicarboxylic acid (dipicolinic acid)
M.W. 167.12 m.p. 248° (dec.)

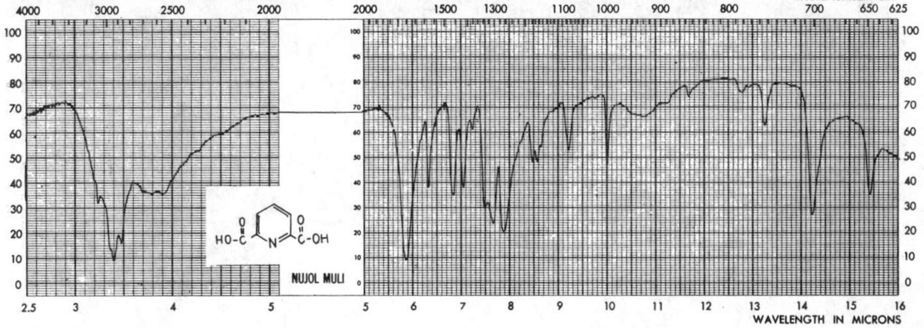

NUJOL MULL

F

C1820-5 Chelidamic acid (1,4-dihydro-4-oxo-2,6-pyridinedicarboxylic acid) **monohydrate**
M.W. 201.14 m.p. 267° (dec.)

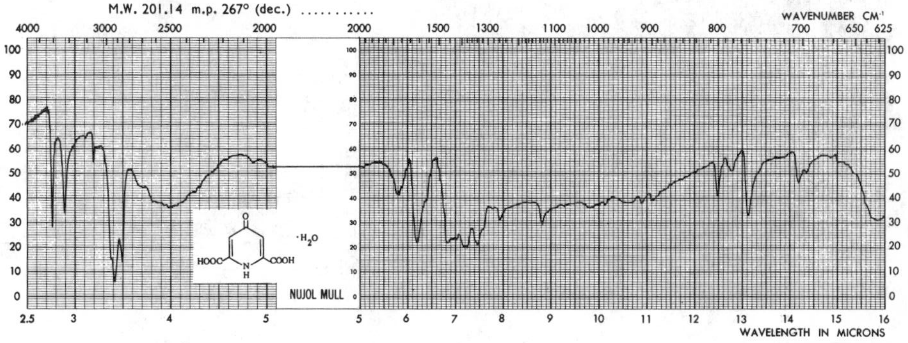

NUJOL MULL

G

P6,800-1
2-Pyridylglycolic acid, copper salt (2-pyridineglycolic acid)
M.W. 367.8 m.p. 125-127°

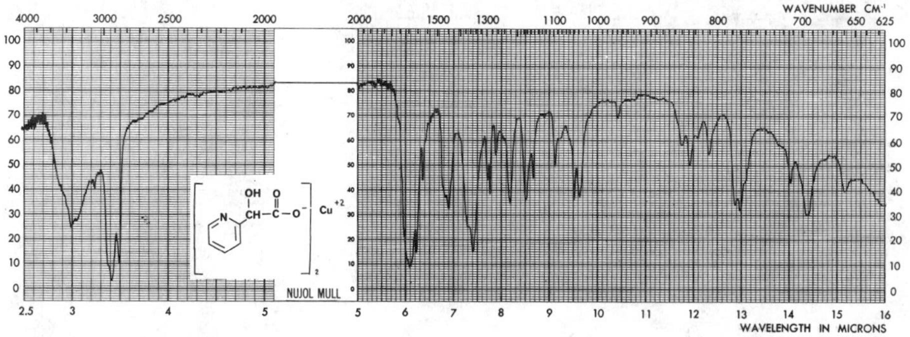

NUJOL MULL

H

E4541-4 Ethyl picolinate
M.W. 151.17 n_D^{20} 1.5088

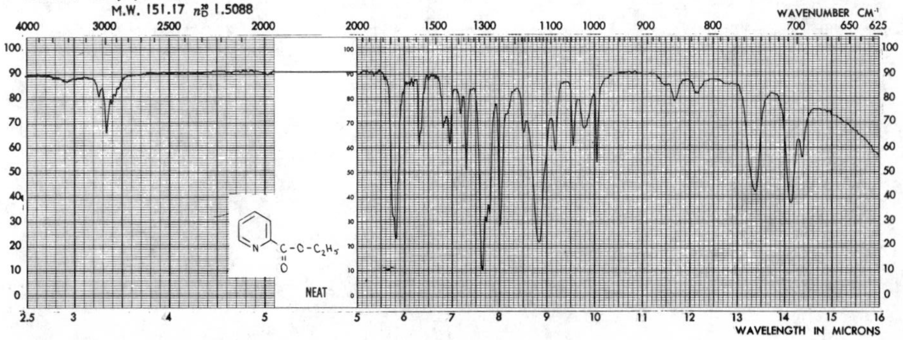

NEAT

ALDRICH

A 15,563-2 **Methyl iminopicolinate** (methyl picolinimidate)
M.W. 136.15 n_D^{20} 1.5311 — NEAT

B M7830-5 **Methyl 2-pyridylacetate**
M.W. 151.17 n_D^{20} 1.5063 — NEAT

C E4724-7 **Ethyl 2-pyridylacetate**
M.W. 165.19 n_D^{20} 1.4973 — NEAT

D 13,082-6 **3-Acetoxypyridine** (3-pyridyl acetate)
M.W. 137.14 n_D^{20} 1.5010

E 13,084-2 **3-Acetoxy-2(1H)-pyridone** (1,2-dihydro-2-oxo-3-pyridyl acetate)
M.W. 153.14 m.p. 151-153° — NUJOL MULL

F M5920-3 **Methyl nicotinate**
M.W. 137.14 m.p. 42-43° — MELT

G E4060-9 **Ethyl nicotinate**
M.W. 151.17 n_D^{20} 1.5019 m.p. 8-9.5° — NEAT

H P5350-0 **Propyl nicotinate**
M.W. 165.19 n_D^{20} 1.4970 — NEAT

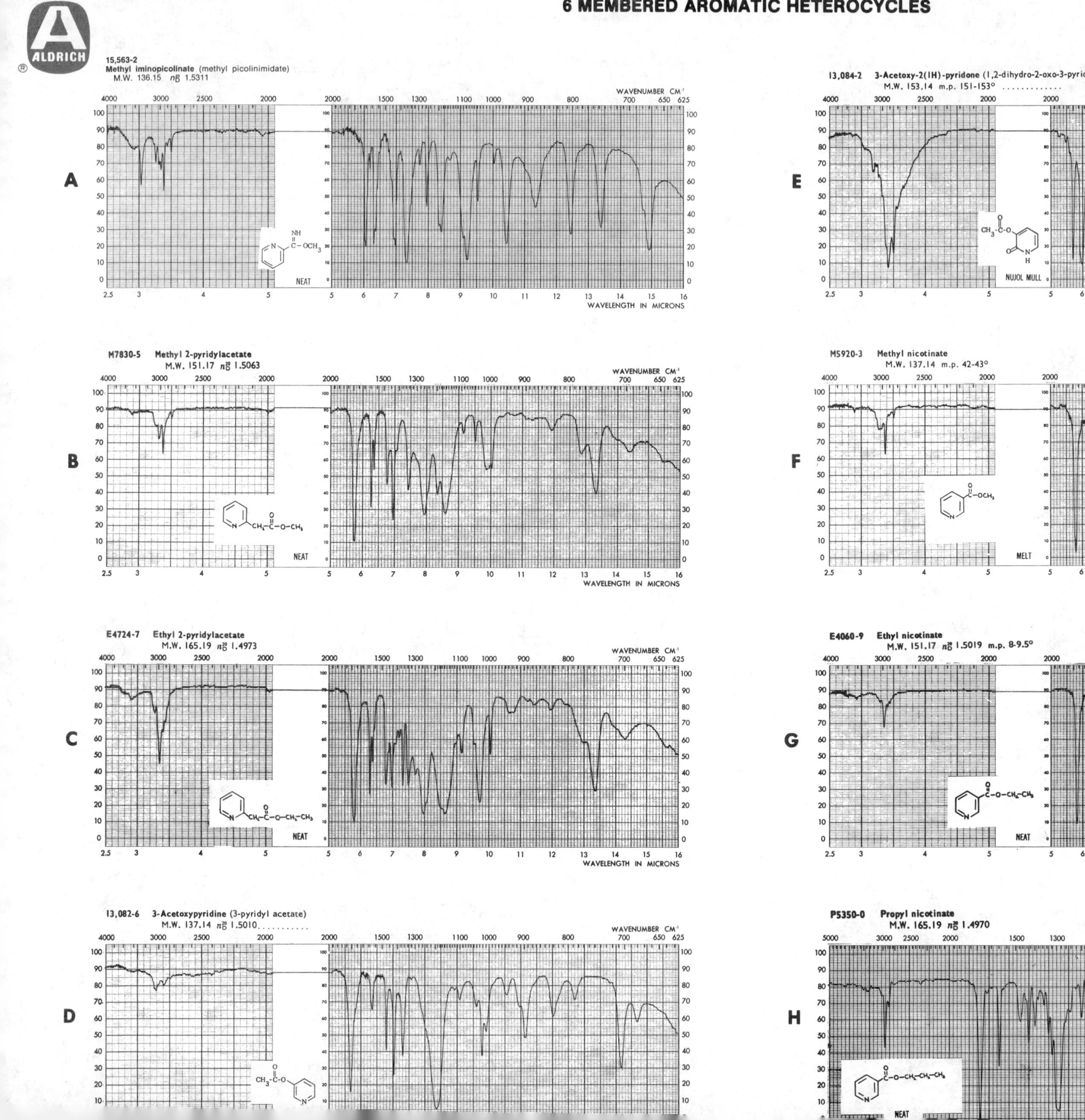

A

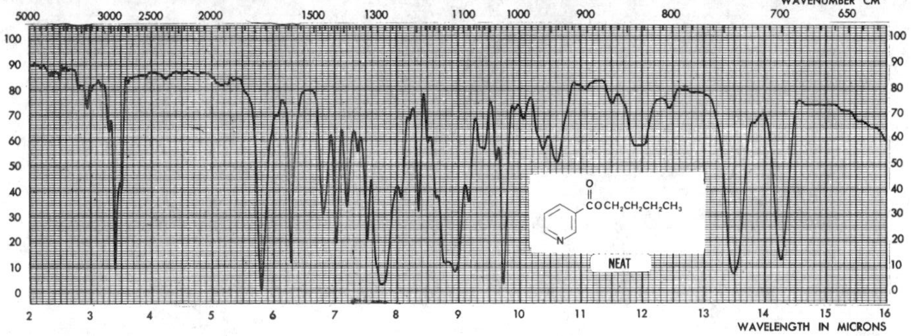

NEAT

E4725-5 Ethyl 3-pyridylacetate
M.W. 165.19 n_D^{20} 1.4992

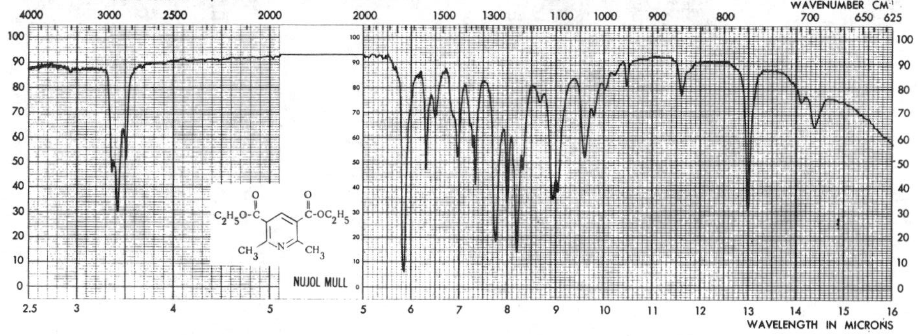

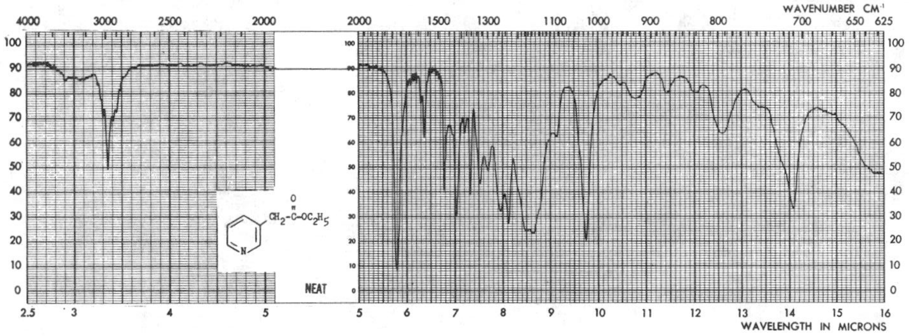

B

NEAT

14,423-1 Ethyl 6-methyl-3-pyridyloxyacetate
M.W. 195.22 n_D^{20} 1.5060 b.p. 110°/0.4 mm.

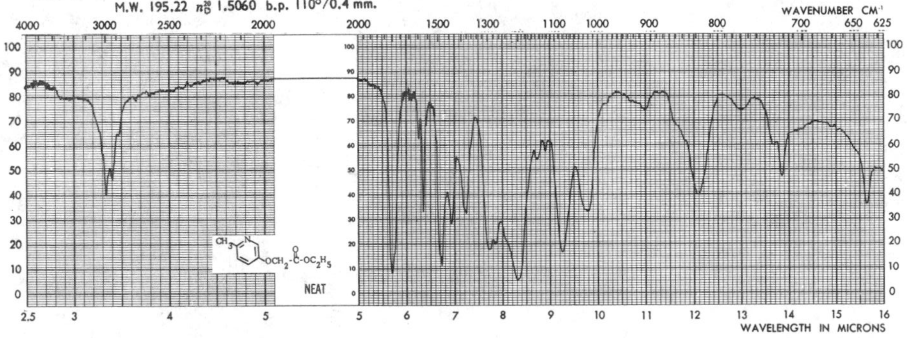

C

NEAT

12,045-6 Methyl 2,6-dichloroisonicotinate
M.W. 206.03 m.p. 80-83°

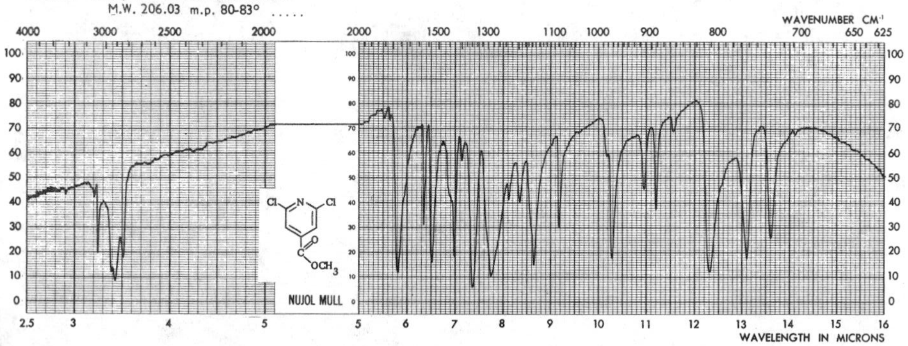

D

NUJOL MULL

M.W. 251.28 m.p. 70-72

E

NUJOL MULL

12,028-6 Diethyl 2,4,6-trimethyl-3,5-pyridinedicarboxylate
M.W. 265.31 n_D^{20} 1.4954 b.p. 152-153°/2 mm.

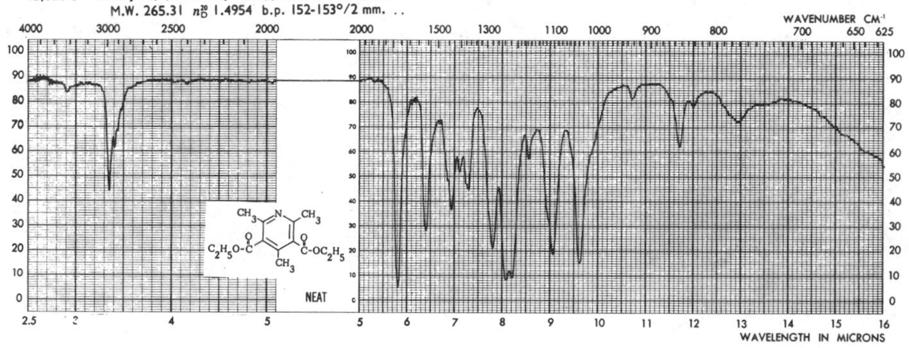

F

NEAT

M5295-0 Methyl isonicotinate
M.W. 137.14 n_D^{20} 1.5122

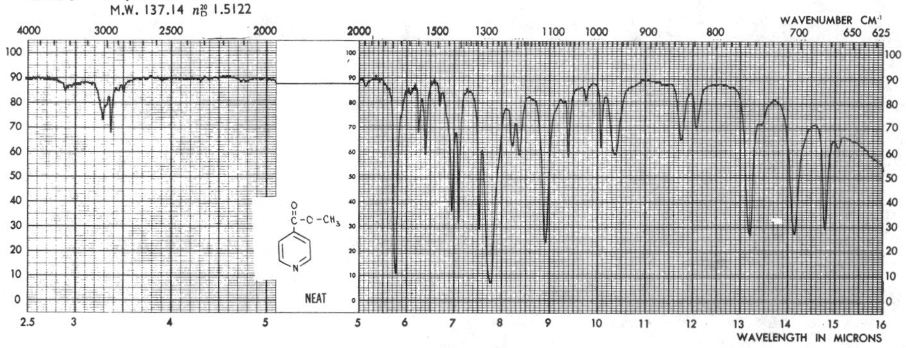

G

NEAT

10,473-6 Ethyl isonicotinate
M.W. 151.17 n_D^{20} 1.5009 b.p. 92°/8 mm.

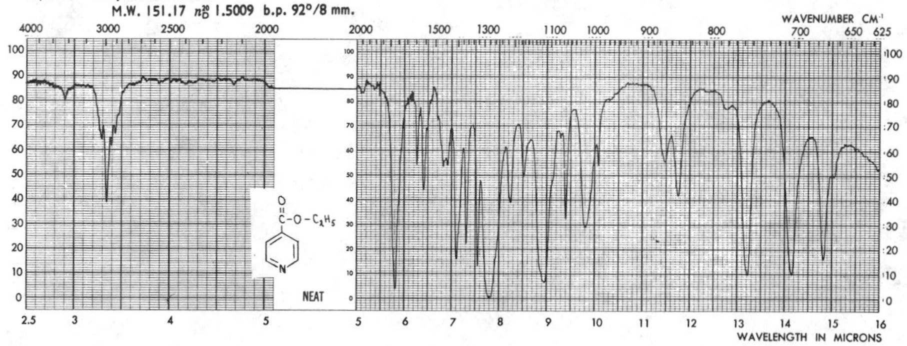

H

NEAT

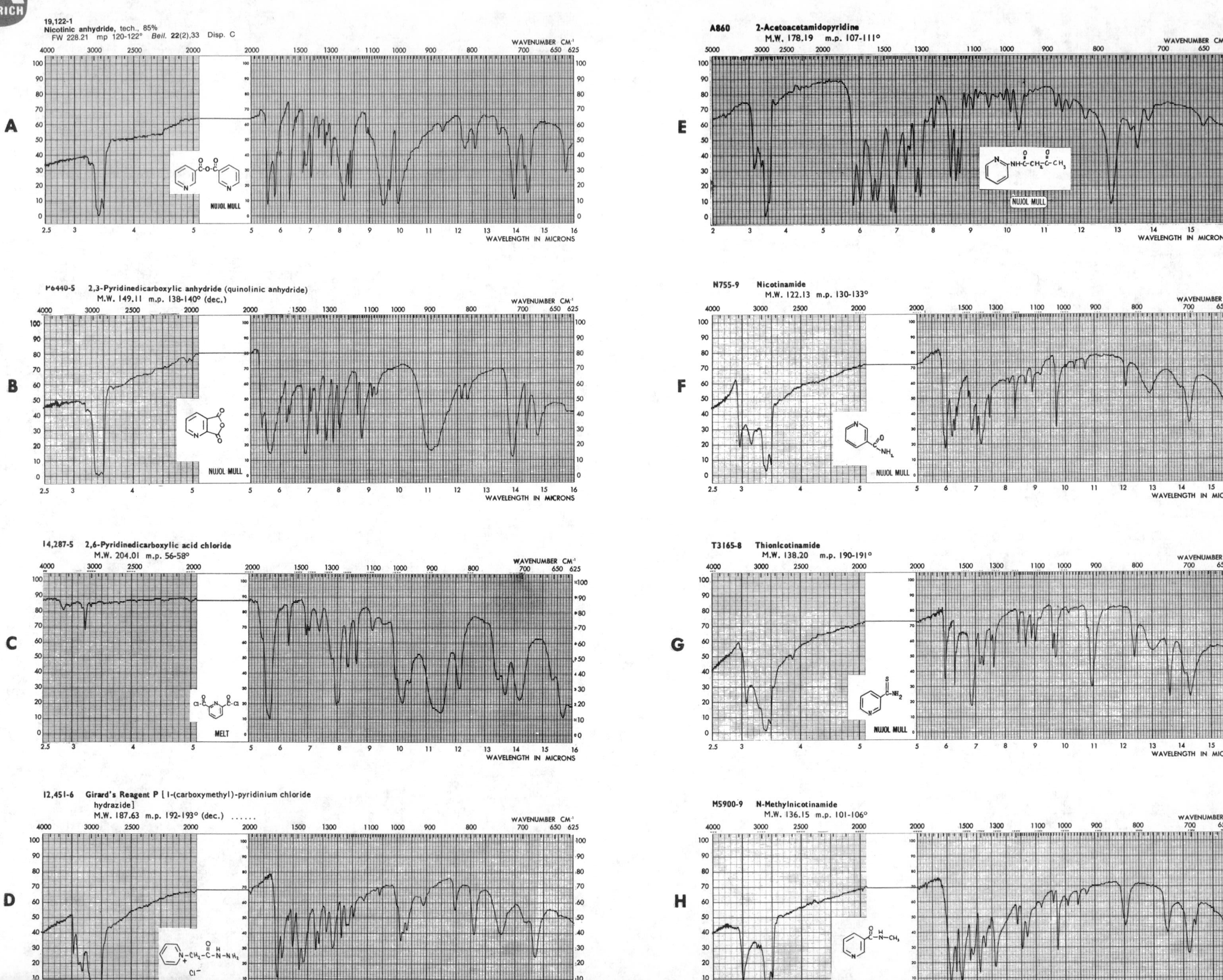
ALDRICH
A
19,122-1
Nicotinic anhydride, tech., 85%
FW 228.21 mp 120-122° Beil. 22(2),33 Disp. C
NUJOL MULL
B
P6440-5 2,3-Pyridinedicarboxylic anhydride (quinolinic anhydride)
M.W. 149.11 m.p. 138-140° (dec.)
NUJOL MULL
C
14,287-5 2,6-Pyridinedicarboxylic acid chloride
M.W. 204.01 m.p. 56-58°
MELT
D
12,451-6 Girard's Reagent P [1-(carboxymethyl)-pyridinium chloride hydrazide]
M.W. 187.63 m.p. 192-193° (dec.)
E
A860 2-Acetoacetamidopyridine
M.W. 178.19 m.p. 107-111°
NUJOL MULL
F
N755-9 Nicotinamide
M.W. 122.13 m.p. 130-133°
NUJOL MULL
G
T3165-8 Thionicotinamide
M.W. 138.20 m.p. 190-191°
NUJOL MULL
H
M5900-9 N-Methylnicotinamide
M.W. 136.15 m.p. 101-106°
WAVENUMBER CM⁻¹
WAVELENGTH IN MICRONS

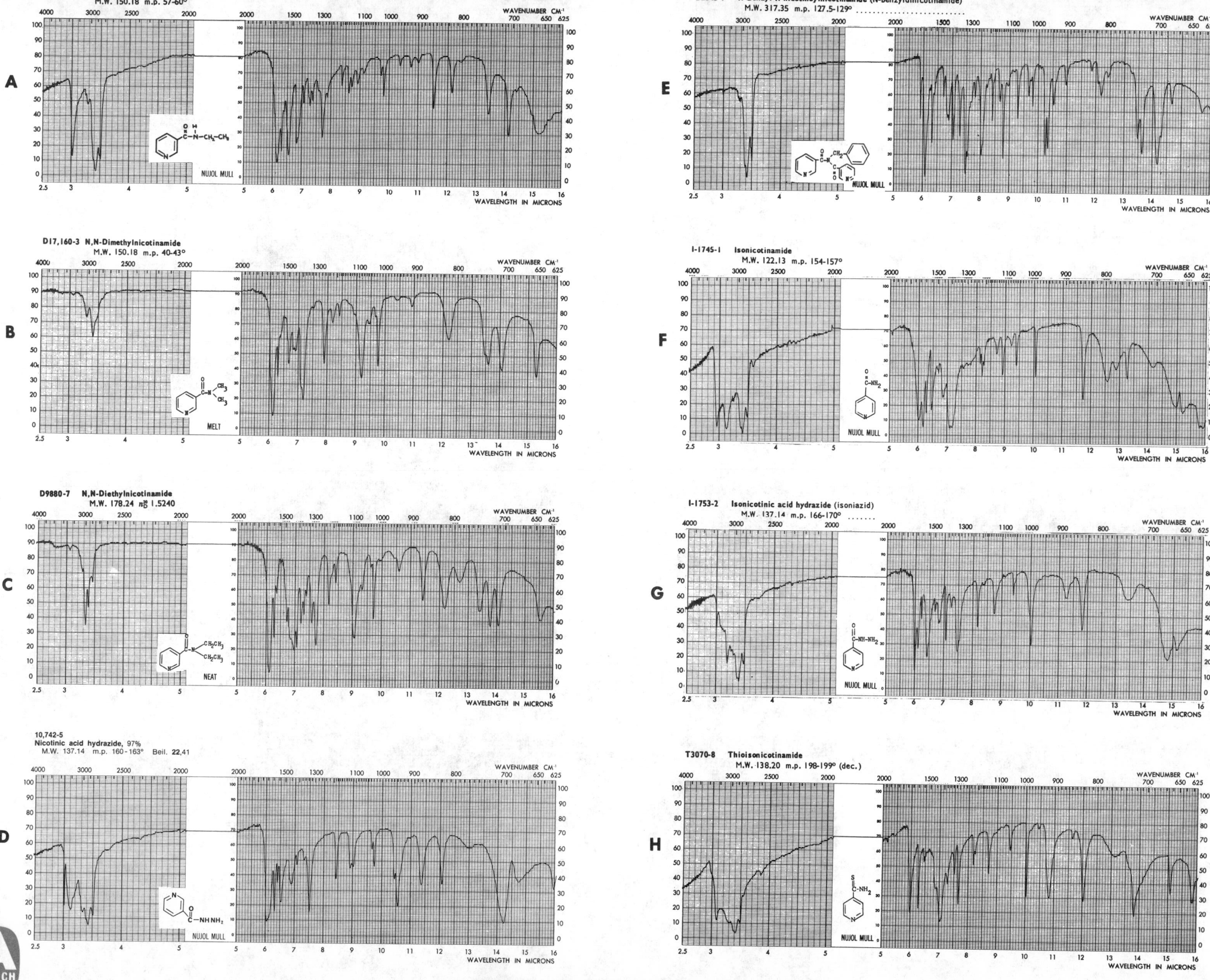
A
E4040-4 N-Ethylnicotinamide
M.W. 150.18 m.p. 57-60°
NUJOL MULL
B
D17,160-3 N,N-Dimethylnicotinamide
M.W. 150.18 m.p. 40-43°
MELT
C
D9880-7 N,N-Diethylnicotinamide
M.W. 178.24 n20D 1.5240
NEAT
D
10,742-5
Nicotinic acid hydrazide, 97%
M.W. 137.14 m.p. 160-163° Beil. 22,41
NUJOL MULL
E
B2645-9 N-Benzyl-N-nicotinoylnicotinamide (N-benzyldinicotinamide)
M.W. 317.35 m.p. 127.5-129°
NUJOL MULL
F
I-1745-1 Isonicotinamide
M.W. 122.13 m.p. 154-157°
NUJOL MULL
G
I-1753-2 Isonicotinic acid hydrazide (isoniazid)
M.W. 137.14 m.p. 166-170°
NUJOL MULL
H
T3070-8 Thioisonicotinamide
M.W. 138.20 m.p. 198-199° (dec.)
NUJOL MULL
WAVENUMBER CM-1
WAVELENGTH IN MICRONS
ALDRICH

6 MEMBERED AROMATIC HETEROCYCLES

A 85,065-9
N-(Hydroxymethyl)-isonicotinamide
M.W. 152.15 m.p. 154-155°
NUJOL MULL

B C5800-2 6-Chloronicotinamide, tech.
M.W. 156.57
NUJOL MULL

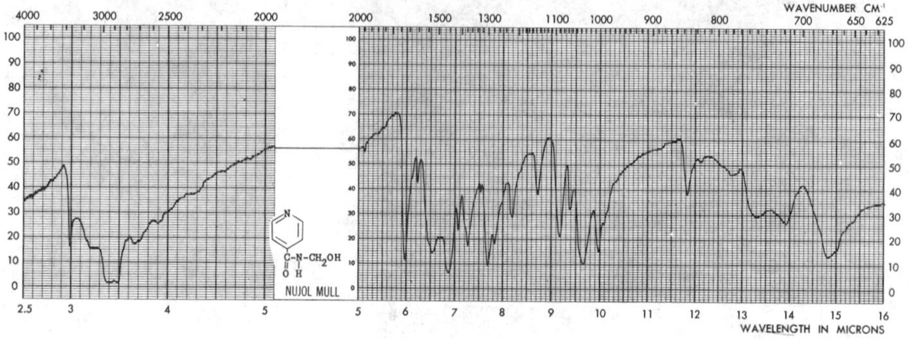

C 19,321-6
2-Chloronicotinamide, 98%
FW 156.57 mp 164-167° *Beil.* **22**(2),36 Disp. C
NUJOL MULL

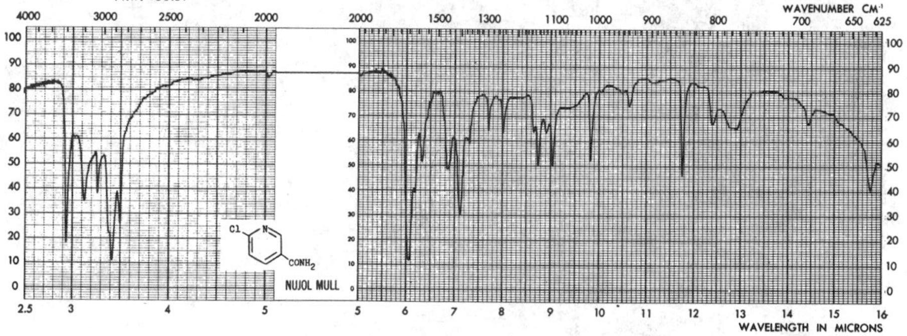

D 15,313-3 3-Hydroxypicolinamide
M.W. 138.13 m.p. 194-196°

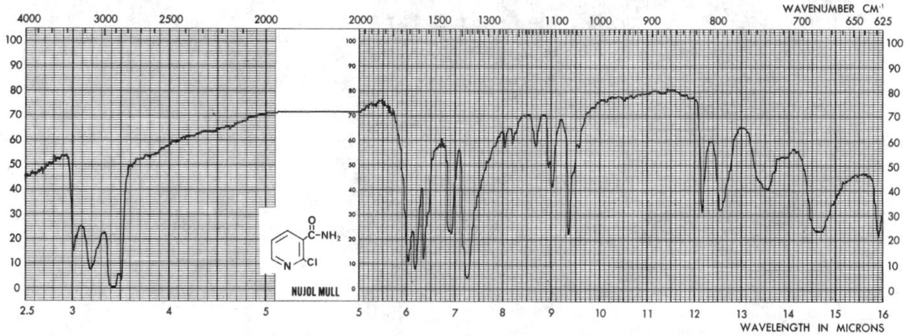

E A6820-3 6-Aminonicotinamide, puriss.
M.W. 137.14 m.p. 249-251°
NUJOL MULL

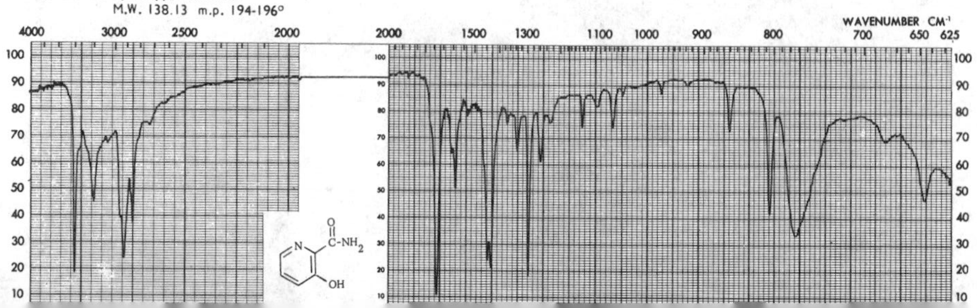

F 12,044-8 5-[(Hydroxymethyl)-carbamoyl]-nicotinic acid, sodium salt
M.W. 218.14 m.p. 288° (dec.)
NUJOL MULL

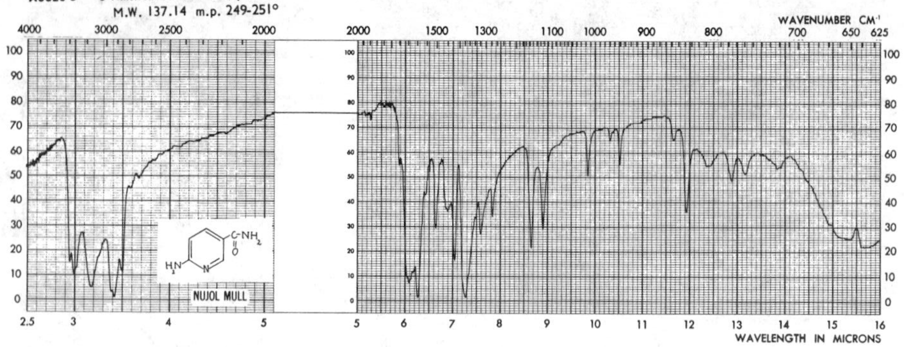

G 14,524-6 2H-Pyrido[3,2-b]-1,4-oxazin-3(4H)-one
M.W. 150.14 m.p. 204-206°
NUJOL MULL

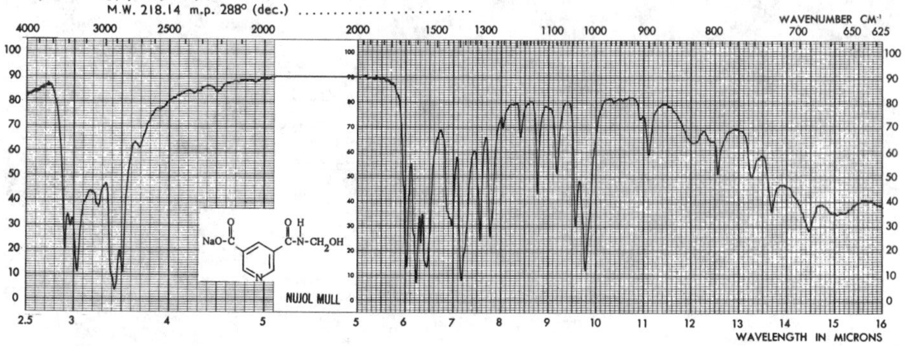

H C9460-2 2-Cyanopyridine (picolinonitrile)
M.W. 104.11

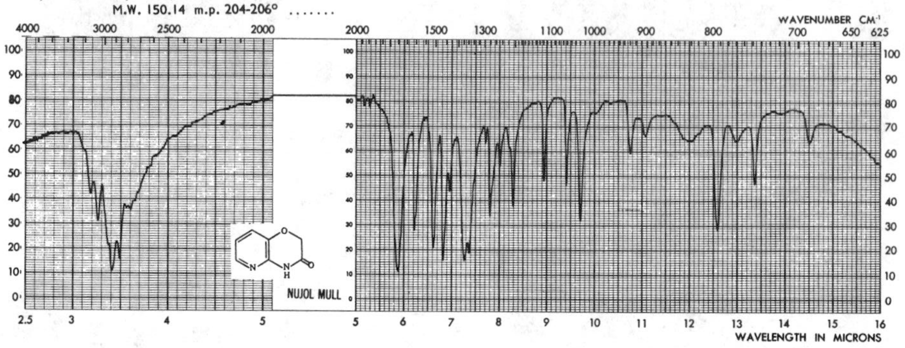

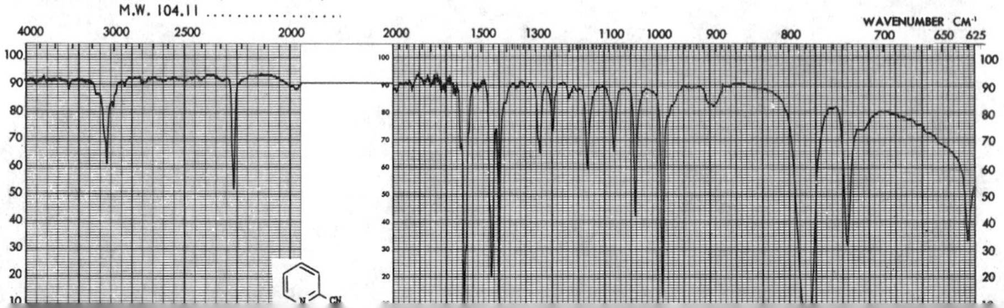

M.W. 104.11 m.p. 50-52° ......

M.W. 147.14 m.p. 281-284° ....

P6600-9 **3-Pyridylacetonitrile** (3-pyridineacetonitrile)
M.W. 118.14 n_D^{20} 1.5289 ....

17,949-3
1-Methyl-4-cyanoformylpyridinium oximate [CPO, 4-(cyanoformyl)-1-methylpyridinium hydroxide, oxime, inner salt]
M.W. 161.16 m.p. 248-250° (dec.)

C9500-5 **4-Cyanopyridine** (isonicotinonitrile)
M.W. 104.11 m.p. 78-80° ....

C9155-7 **4-[Cyano-(hydroximino)-methyl]-1-methylpyridinium iodide**
M.W. 289.08 m.p. 165° (dec.) ....

13,146-6 **Phenyl-2-pyridylacetonitrile**
M.W. 194.24 m.p. 87-90° ....

C9080-1 **3-Cyano-4,6-dimethyl-2-hydroxypyridine** (4,6-dimethyl-2-hydroxynicotinonitrile)
M.W. 148.17 m.p. 285-287° ....

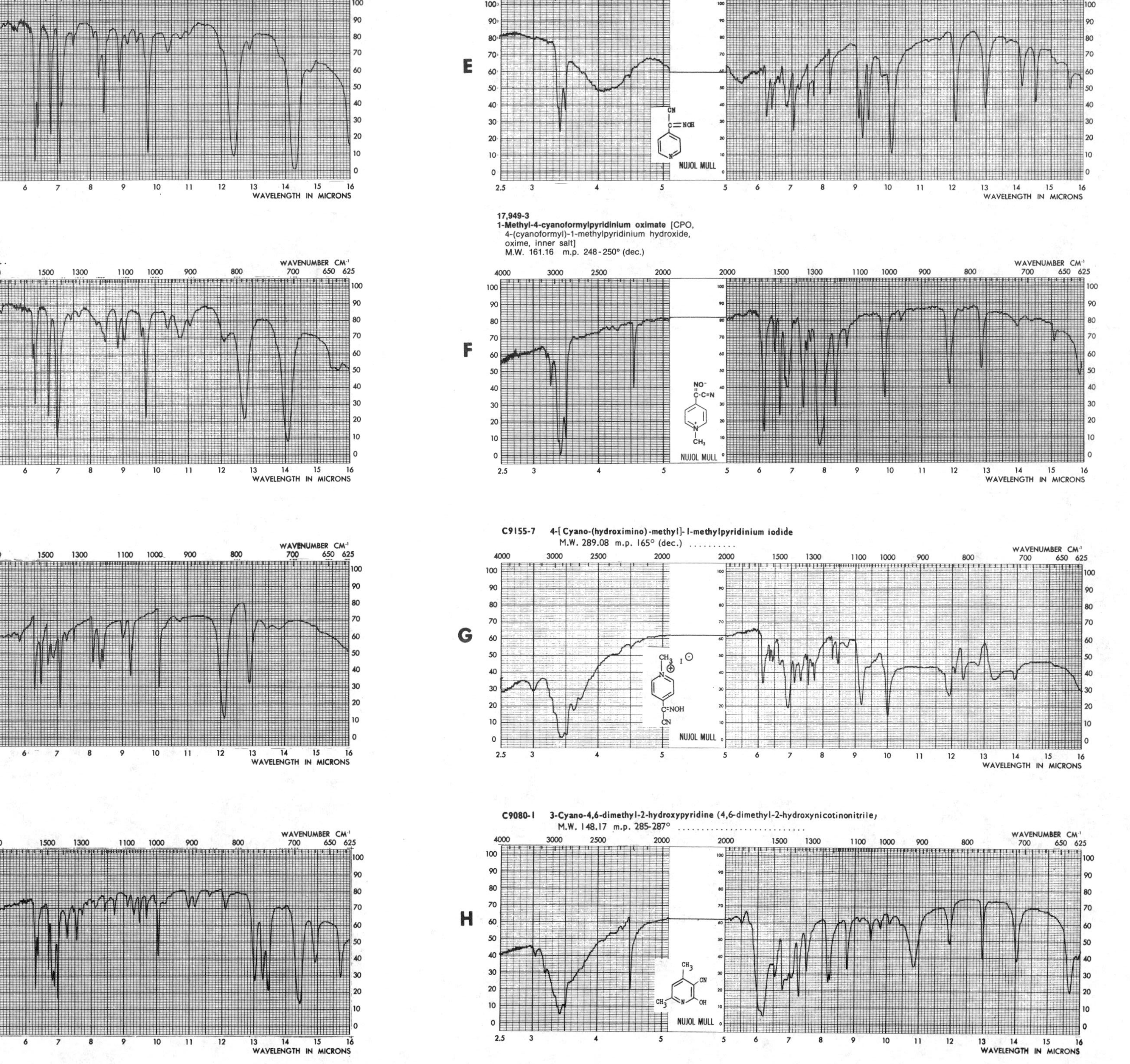

ALDRICH

A 12,168-1 2-Chloro-4-(methoxymethyl)-6-methyl-5-nitronicotinonitrile
M.W. 241.63 m.p. 72-75°

B 12,199-1 1,2-Dihydro-4-(methoxymethyl)-6-methyl-5-nitro-2-oxonicotinonitrile
M.W. 223.19 m.p. 215°

C 10,685-2 1,2-Dihydro-4,6-dimethyl-2-oxo-1-(salicylideneamino)-nicotinonitrile
M.W. 267.29 m.p. 235-237°

D S755-6 Sulfur trioxide pyridine complex (pyridine sulfur trioxide)
M.W. 159.16

E P6480-4 3-Pyridinesulfonic acid
M.W. 159.16 m.p. 340-345° (dec.)

F P6820-6 2-Pyridylhydroxymethanesulfonic acid (2-pyridinecarboxaldehyde bisulfite adduct), tech.
M.W. 189.19 m.p. 261-263° (dec.)

G 15,708-2 1-Methylpyridinium 3-sulfonate, 99%
M.W. 173.19 m.p. >300° *HYGROSCOPIC*

H 15,707-4 1-Allylpyridinium 3-sulfonate, 98%
M.W. 199.23 m.p. 178-180° *HYGROSCOPIC*

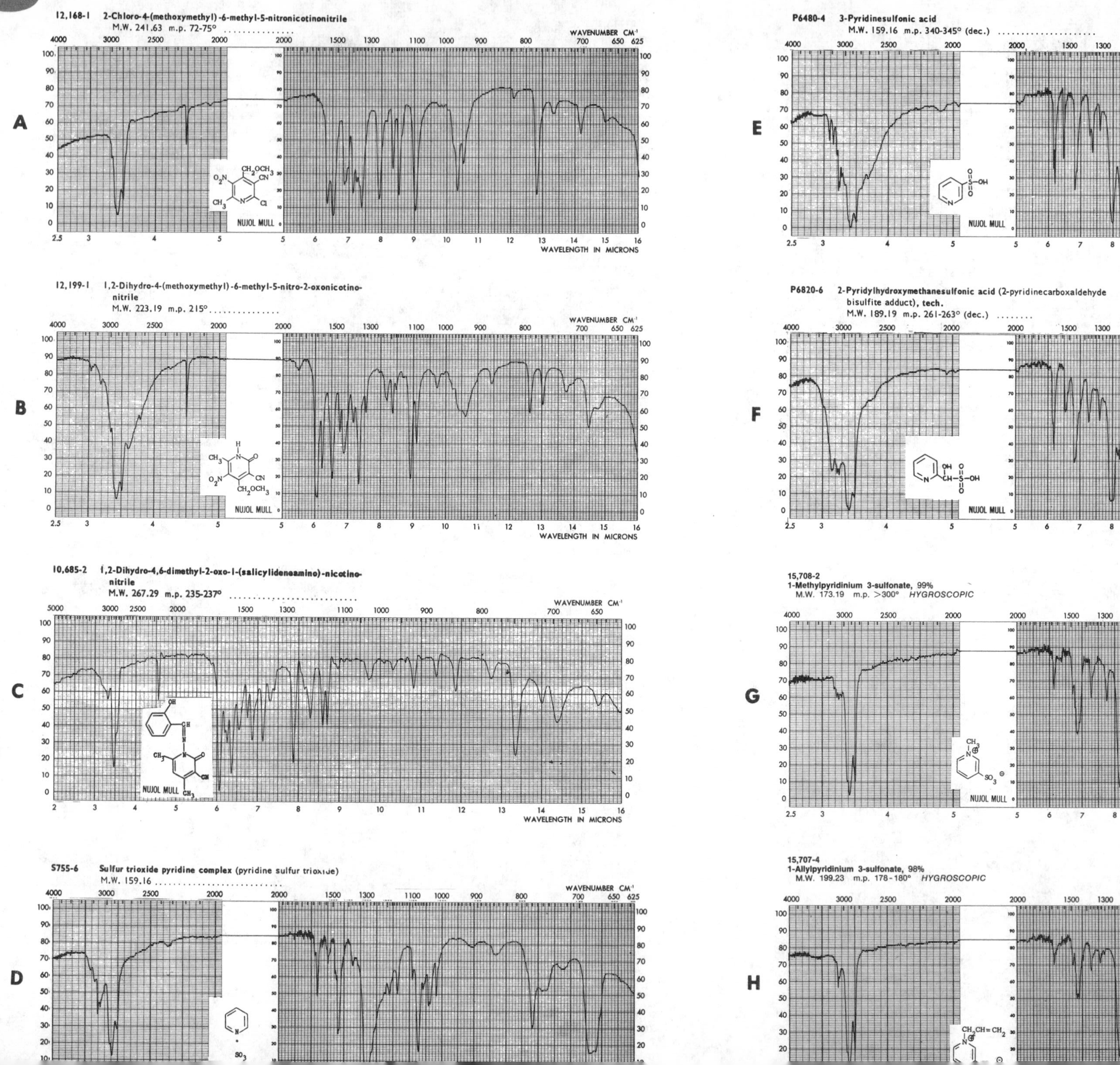

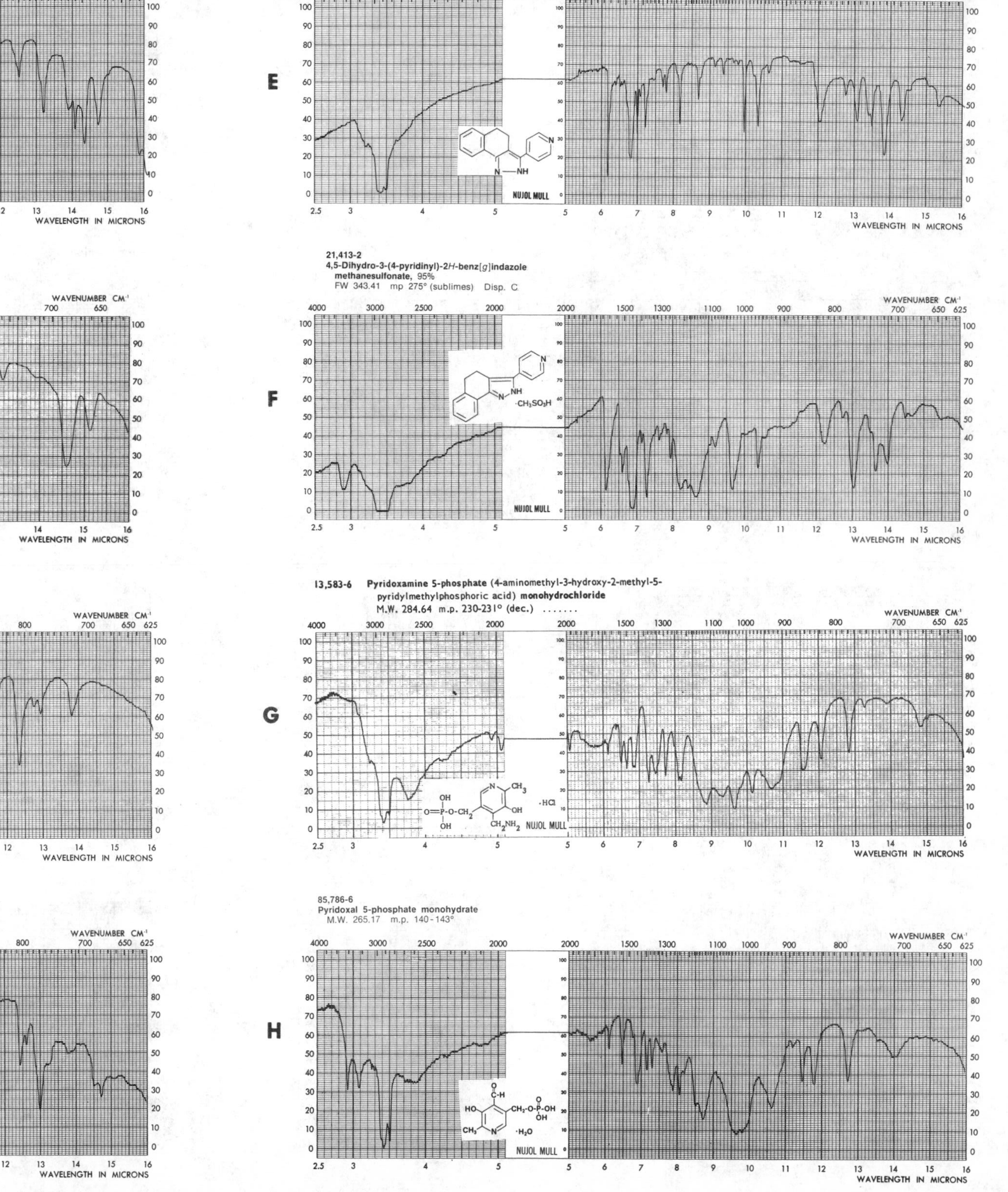

A
E
P6840-0 3-Pyridylhydroxymethanesulfonic acid (3-pyridinecarboxaldehyde bisulfite adduct)
M.W. 189.19 m.p. 140° (sublimes)
B
21,413-2
4,5-Dihydro-3-(4-pyridinyl)-2H-benz[g]indazole methanesulfonate, 95%
FW 343.41 mp 275° (sublimes) Disp. C
F
14,242-5
4-Pyridineethanesulfonic acid
M.W. 187.22 m.p. 295° (dec.)
C
13,583-6 Pyridoxamine 5-phosphate (4-aminomethyl-3-hydroxy-2-methyl-5-pyridylmethylphosphoric acid) monohydrochloride
M.W. 284.64 m.p. 230-231° (dec.)
G
19,318-6
2-(3-Sulfobenzoyl)pyridine 2-pyridylhydrazone
FW 354.39 mp 180° (dec.) Disp. C
D
85,786-6
Pyridoxal 5-phosphate monohydrate
M.W. 265.17 m.p. 140-143°
H
NUJOL MULL
WAVENUMBER CM⁻¹
WAVELENGTH IN MICRONS

ALDRICH

6 MEMBERED AROMATIC HETEROCYCLES

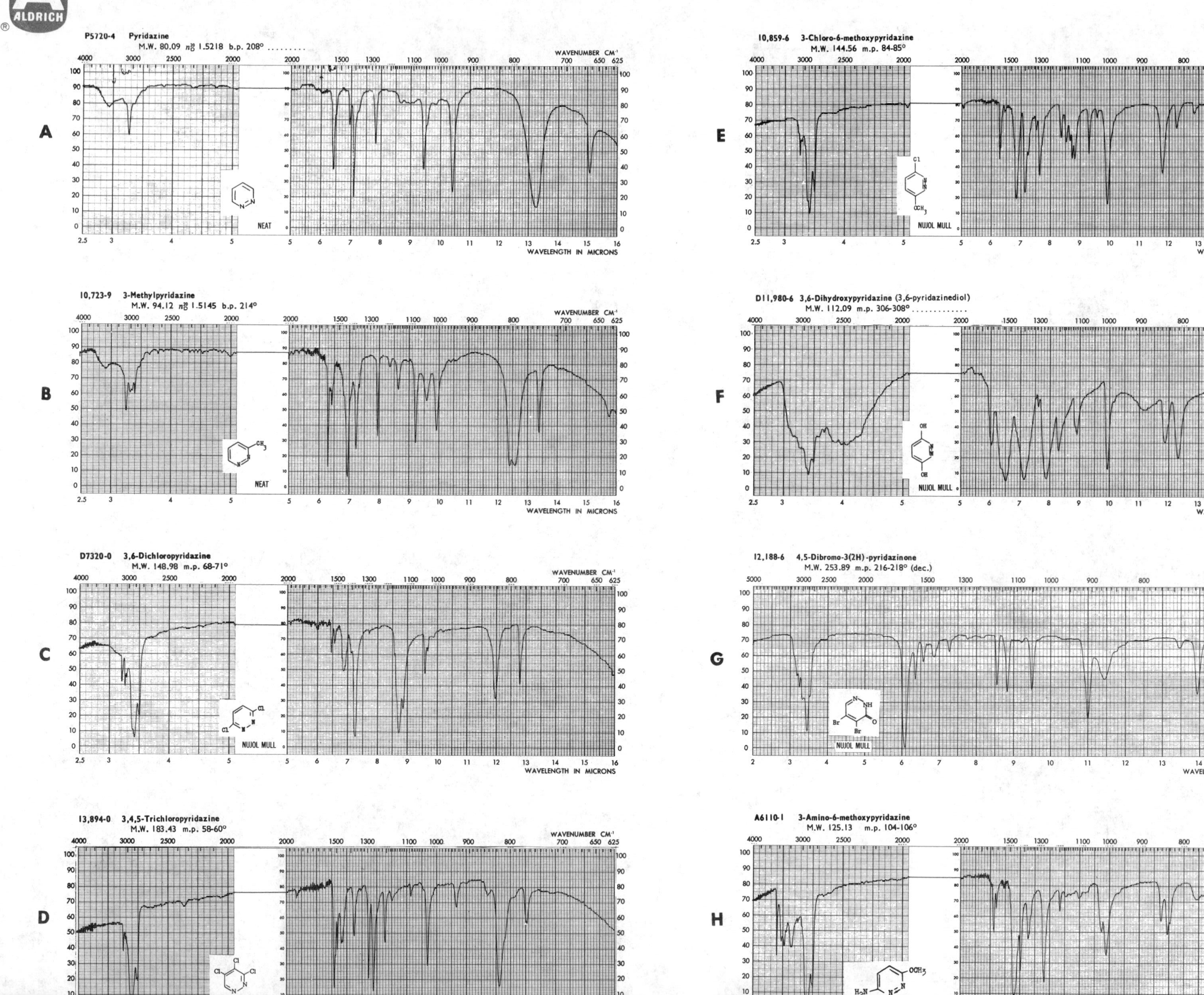
ALDRICH
A
P5720-4 Pyridazine
M.W. 80.09 n_D^{20} 1.5218 b.p. 208°
NEAT
B
10,723-9 3-Methylpyridazine
M.W. 94.12 n_D^{20} 1.5145 b.p. 214°
NEAT
C
D7320-0 3,6-Dichloropyridazine
M.W. 148.98 m.p. 68-71°
NUJOL MULL
D
13,894-0 3,4,5-Trichloropyridazine
M.W. 183.43 m.p. 58-60°
E
10,859-6 3-Chloro-6-methoxypyridazine
M.W. 144.56 m.p. 84-85°
NUJOL MULL
F
D11,980-6 3,6-Dihydroxypyridazine (3,6-pyridazinediol)
M.W. 112.09 m.p. 306-308°
NUJOL MULL
G
12,188-6 4,5-Dibromo-3(2H)-pyridazinone
M.W. 253.89 m.p. 216-218° (dec.)
NUJOL MULL
H
A6110-1 3-Amino-6-methoxypyridazine
M.W. 125.13 m.p. 104-106°
WAVENUMBER CM⁻¹
WAVELENGTH IN MICRONS

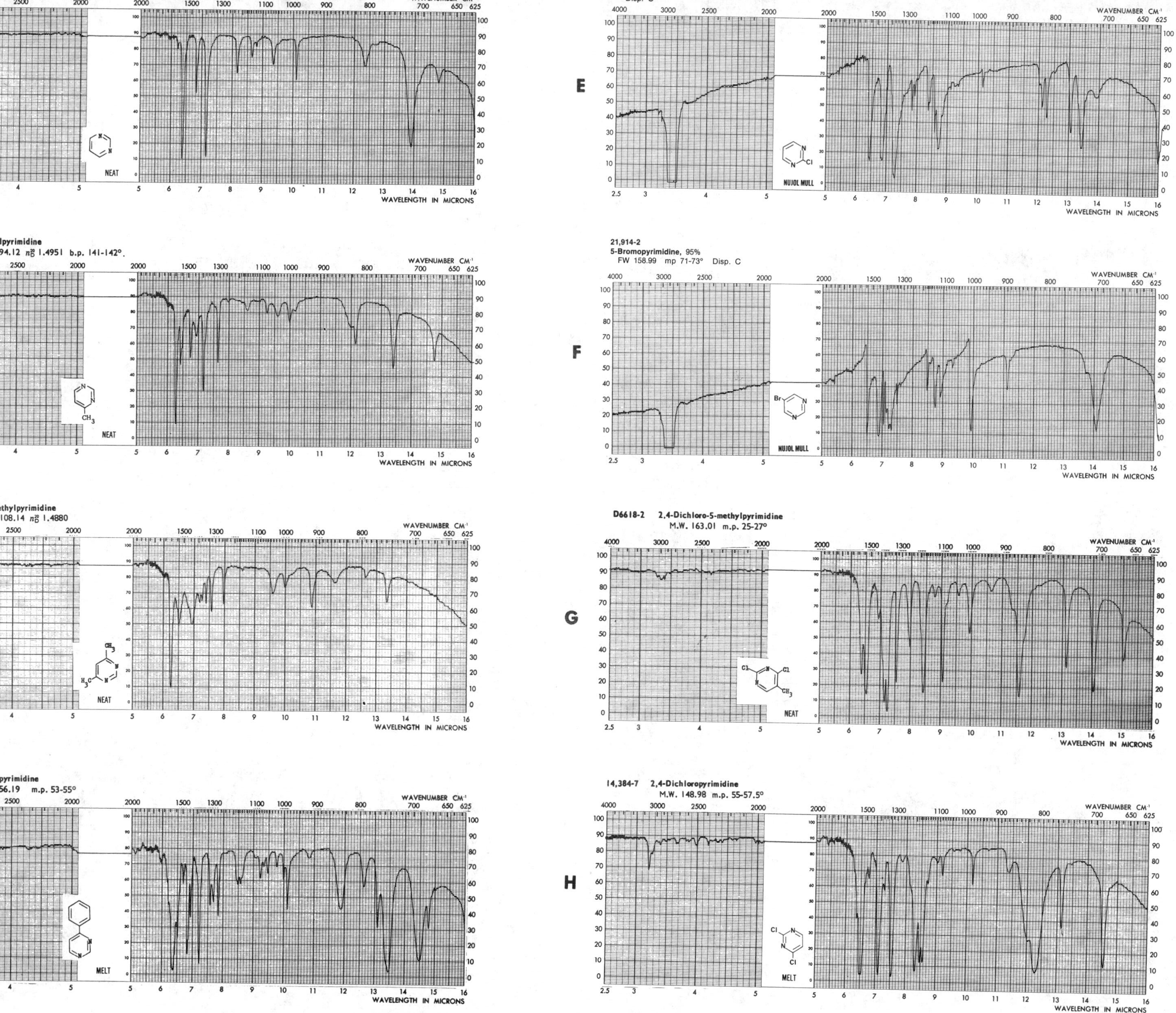

A
M.W. 80.09 n_D^{20} 1.4998 b.p. 123-124°
NEAT
B
12,749-3 4-Methylpyrimidine
M.W. 94.12 n_D^{20} 1.4951 b.p. 141-142°.
NEAT
C
D18,320-2 4,6-Dimethylpyrimidine
M.W. 108.14 n_D^{20} 1.4880
NEAT
D
P3380-1 4-Phenylpyrimidine
M.W. 156.19 m.p. 53-55°
MELT
E
FW 114.54 mp 66-68° bp 75-76°/10mm.
Disp. C
NUJOL MULL
F
21,914-2
5-Bromopyrimidine, 95%
FW 158.99 mp 71-73° Disp. C
NUJOL MULL
G
D6618-2 2,4-Dichloro-5-methylpyrimidine
M.W. 163.01 m.p. 25-27°
NEAT
H
14,384-7 2,4-Dichloropyrimidine
M.W. 148.98 m.p. 55-57.5°
MELT
WAVENUMBER CM⁻¹
WAVELENGTH IN MICRONS
ALDRICH

6 MEMBERED AROMATIC HETEROCYCLES

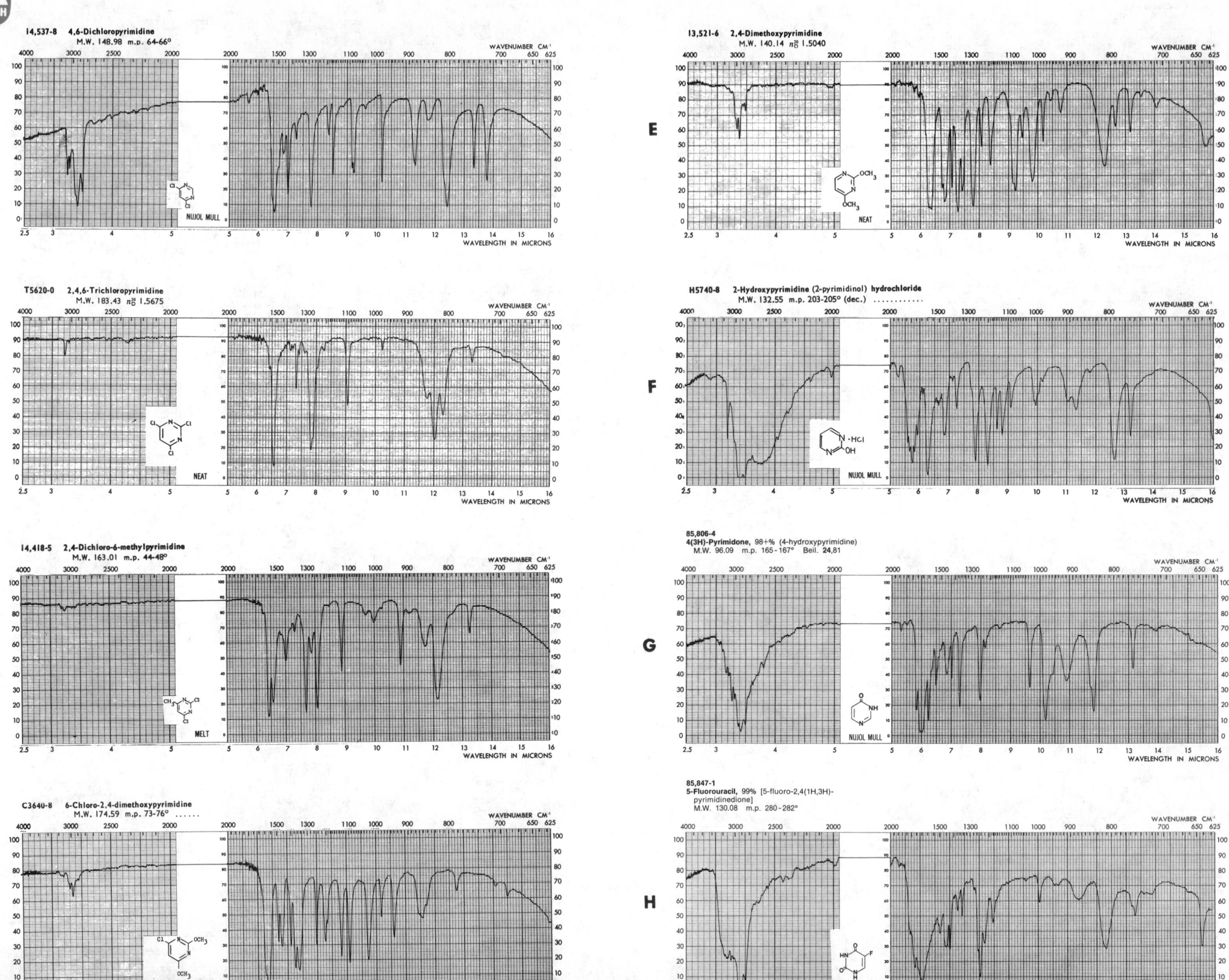
ALDRICH
A
14,537-8 4,6-Dichloropyrimidine
M.W. 148.98 m.p. 64-66°
NUJOL MULL
B
T5620-0 2,4,6-Trichloropyrimidine
M.W. 183.43 n_D^{20} 1.5675
NEAT
C
14,418-5 2,4-Dichloro-6-methylpyrimidine
M.W. 163.01 m.p. 44-48°
MELT
D
C3640-8 6-Chloro-2,4-dimethoxypyrimidine
M.W. 174.59 m.p. 73-76°
E
13,521-6 2,4-Dimethoxypyrimidine
M.W. 140.14 n_D^{20} 1.5040
NEAT
F
H5740-8 2-Hydroxypyrimidine (2-pyrimidinol) hydrochloride
M.W. 132.55 m.p. 203-205° (dec.)
NUJOL MULL
G
85,806-4
4(3H)-Pyrimidone, 98+% (4-hydroxypyrimidine)
M.W. 96.09 m.p. 165-167° Beil. 24,81
NUJOL MULL
H
85,847-1
5-Fluorouracil, 99% [5-fluoro-2,4(1H,3H)-pyrimidinedione]
M.W. 130.08 m.p. 280-282°
WAVENUMBER CM⁻¹
WAVELENGTH IN MICRONS

A

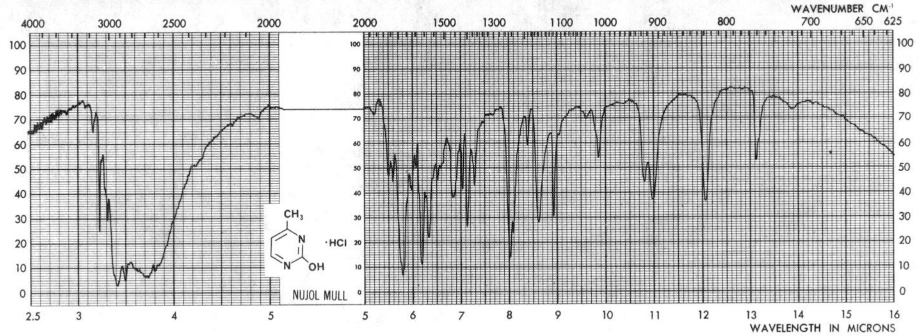

85,785-8
5-Iodouracil
M.W. 237.99 m.p. 274-276° (dec.)

B

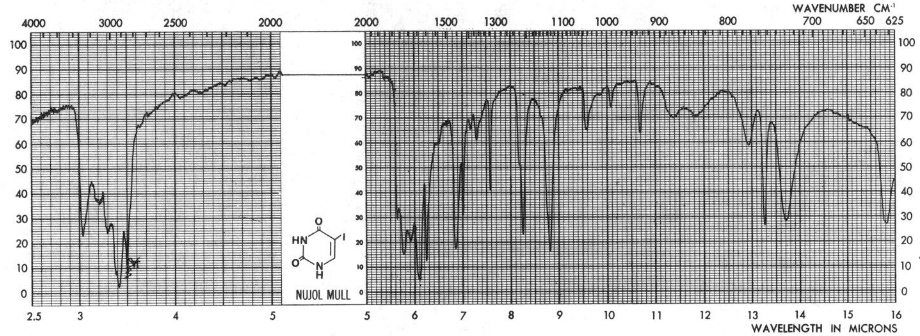

D16,515-8 2,4-Dimethyl-6-hydroxypyrimidine (2,6-dimethyl-4-pyrimidinol)
M.W. 124.14 m.p. 198.5-200° ....

C

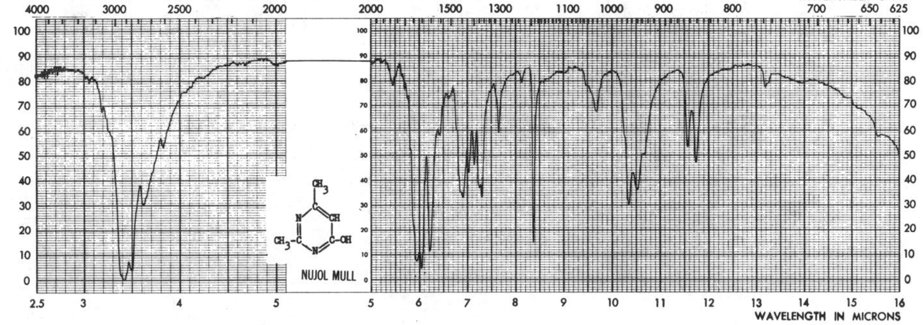

D12,040-5 4,6-Dihydroxypyrimidine (4,6-pyrimidinediol)
M.W. 112.09 m.p. > 250° ....

D

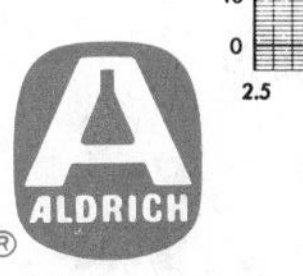

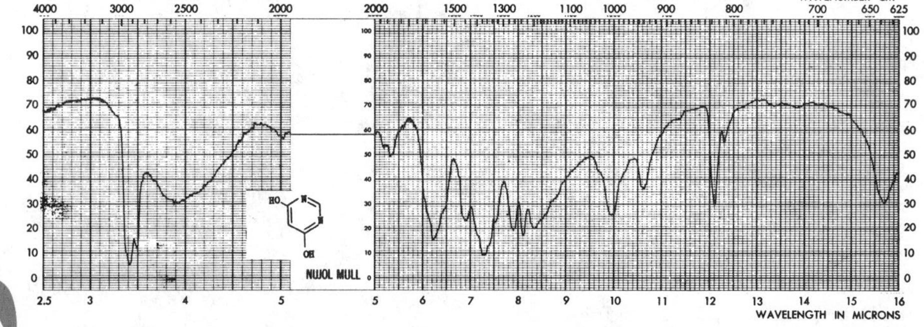

M.W. 112.09 m.p.>300° ....

E

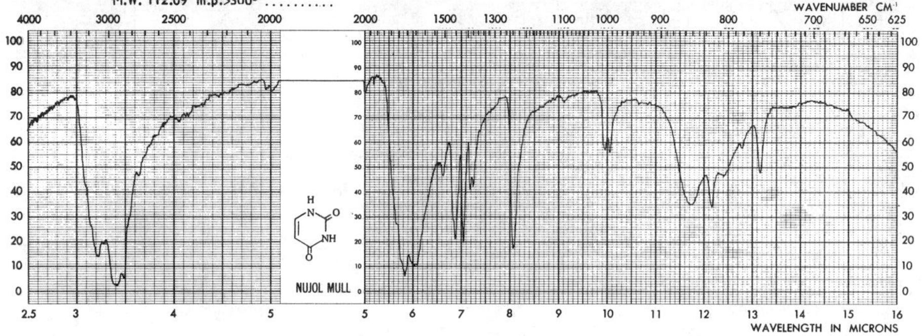

16,536-0
2,4-Dihydroxy-5,6-dimethylpyrimidine
(5,6-dimethyluracil)
FW 140.14 mp 297-300° (dec.) *Beil.* **24**,359
Disp. C

F

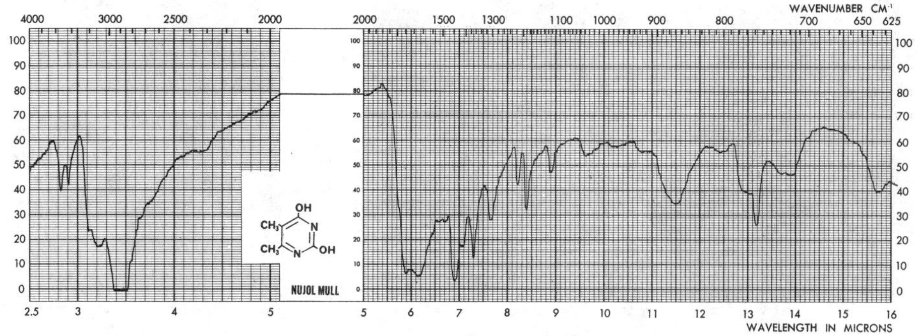

85,847-1
5-Fluorouracil, 99% [5-fluoro-2,4(1H,3H)-pyrimidinedione]
M.W. 130.08 m.p. 280-282°

G

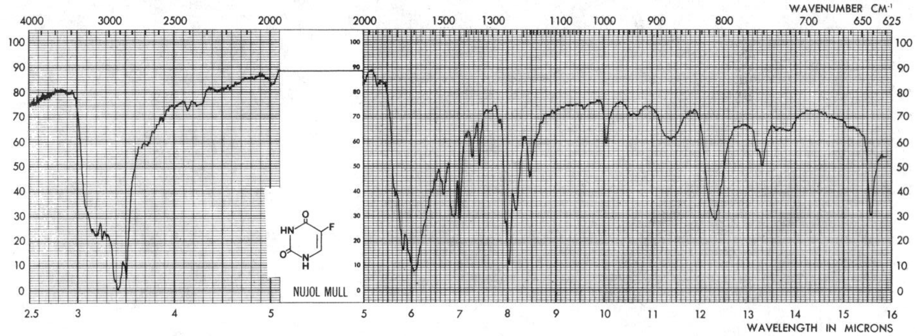

85,247-3
5-Bromouracil, 99+%
M.W. 190.99 m.p. >300° Beil. **24**,318

H

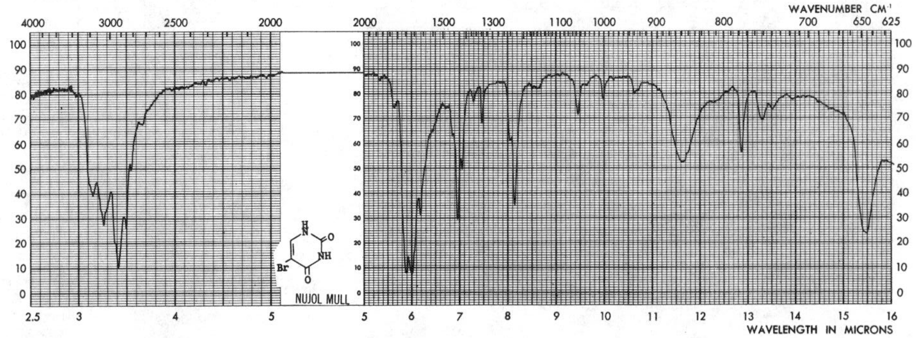

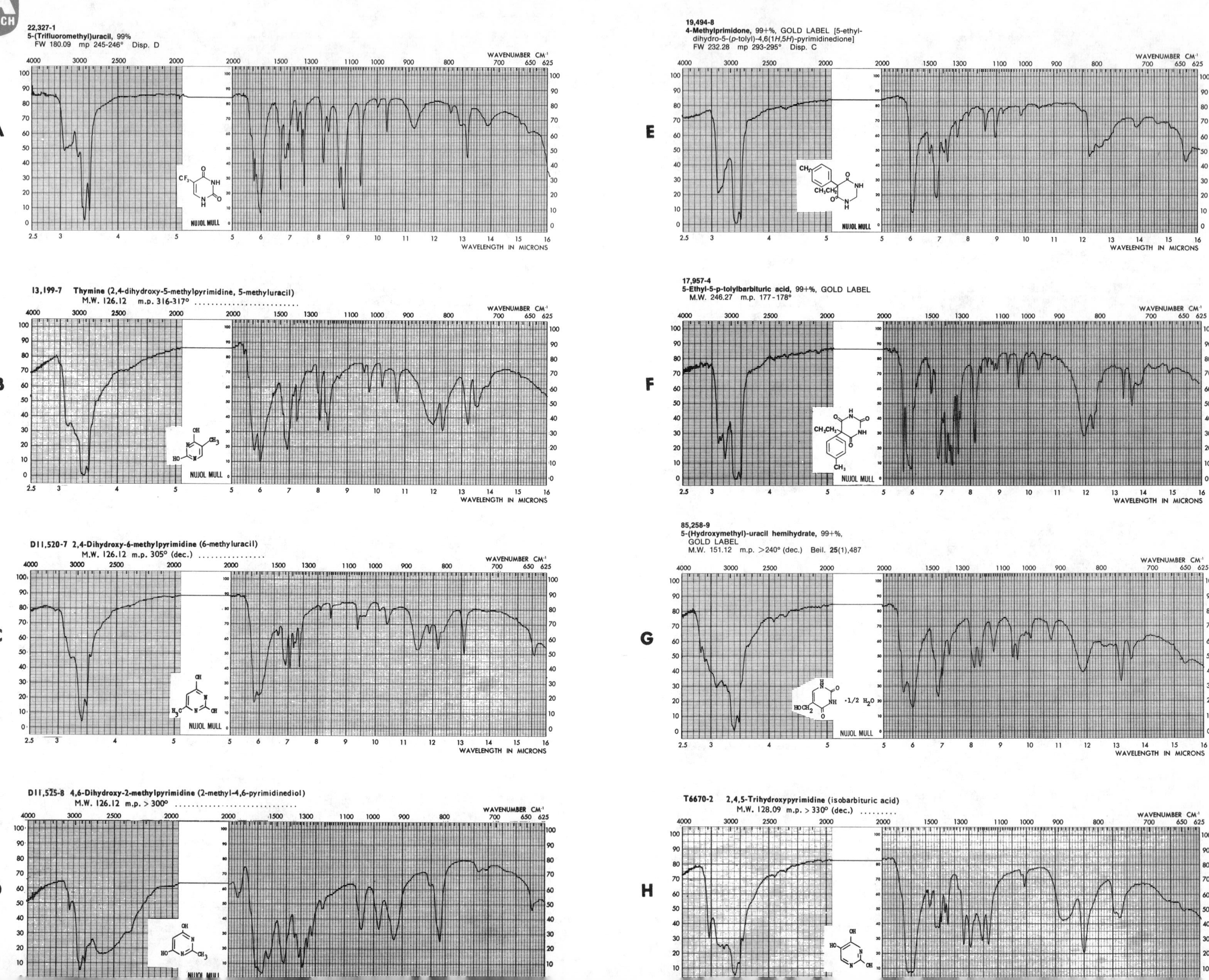
ALDRICH
A
22,327-1
5-(Trifluoromethyl)uracil, 99%
FW 180.09 mp 245-246° Disp. D
B
13,199-7 Thymine (2,4-dihydroxy-5-methylpyrimidine, 5-methyluracil)
M.W. 126.12 m.p. 316-317°
C
D11,520-7 2,4-Dihydroxy-6-methylpyrimidine (6-methyluracil)
M.W. 126.12 m.p. 305° (dec.)
D
D11,525-8 4,6-Dihydroxy-2-methylpyrimidine (2-methyl-4,6-pyrimidinediol)
M.W. 126.12 m.p. > 300°
E
19,494-8
4-Methylprimidone, 99+%, GOLD LABEL [5-ethyl-dihydro-5-(p-tolyl)-4,6(1H,5H)-pyrimidinedione]
FW 232.28 mp 293-295° Disp. C
F
17,957-4
5-Ethyl-5-p-tolylbarbituric acid, 99+%, GOLD LABEL
M.W. 246.27 m.p. 177-178°
G
85,258-9
5-(Hydroxymethyl)-uracil hemihydrate, 99+%, GOLD LABEL
M.W. 151.12 m.p. >240° (dec.) Beil. 25(1),487
H
T6670-2 2,4,5-Trihydroxypyrimidine (isobarbituric acid)
M.W. 128.09 m.p. > 330° (dec.)
NUJOL MULL
WAVENUMBER CM⁻¹
WAVELENGTH IN MICRONS

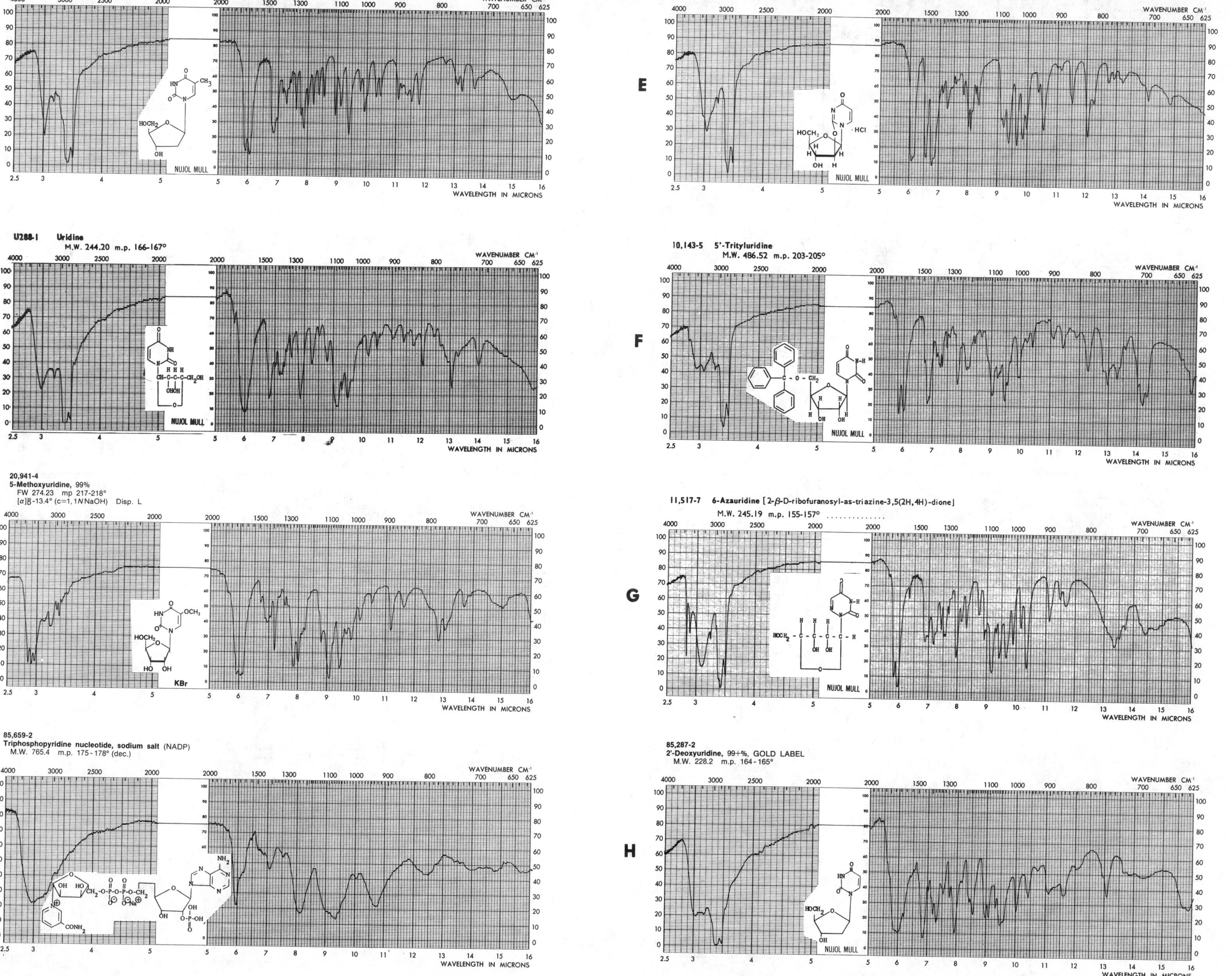
M.W. 262.65 m.p. 247-249° (dec.)
U288-1 Uridine
M.W. 244.20 m.p. 166-167°
20,941-4
5-Methoxyuridine, 99%
FW 274.23 mp 217-218°
$[\alpha]_D^{20}$ -13.4° (c=1, 1N NaOH) Disp. L
85,659-2
Triphosphopyridine nucleotide, sodium salt (NADP)
M.W. 765.4 m.p. 175-178° (dec.)
10,143-5 5'-Trityluridine
M.W. 486.52 m.p. 203-205°
11,517-7 6-Azauridine [2-β-D-ribofuranosyl-as-triazine-3,5(2H,4H)-dione]
M.W. 245.19 m.p. 155-157°
85,287-2
2'-Deoxyuridine, 99+%, GOLD LABEL
M.W. 228.2 m.p. 164-165°
A
B
C
D
E
F
G
H
NUJOL MULL
KBr
WAVENUMBER CM⁻¹
WAVELENGTH IN MICRONS
ALDRICH

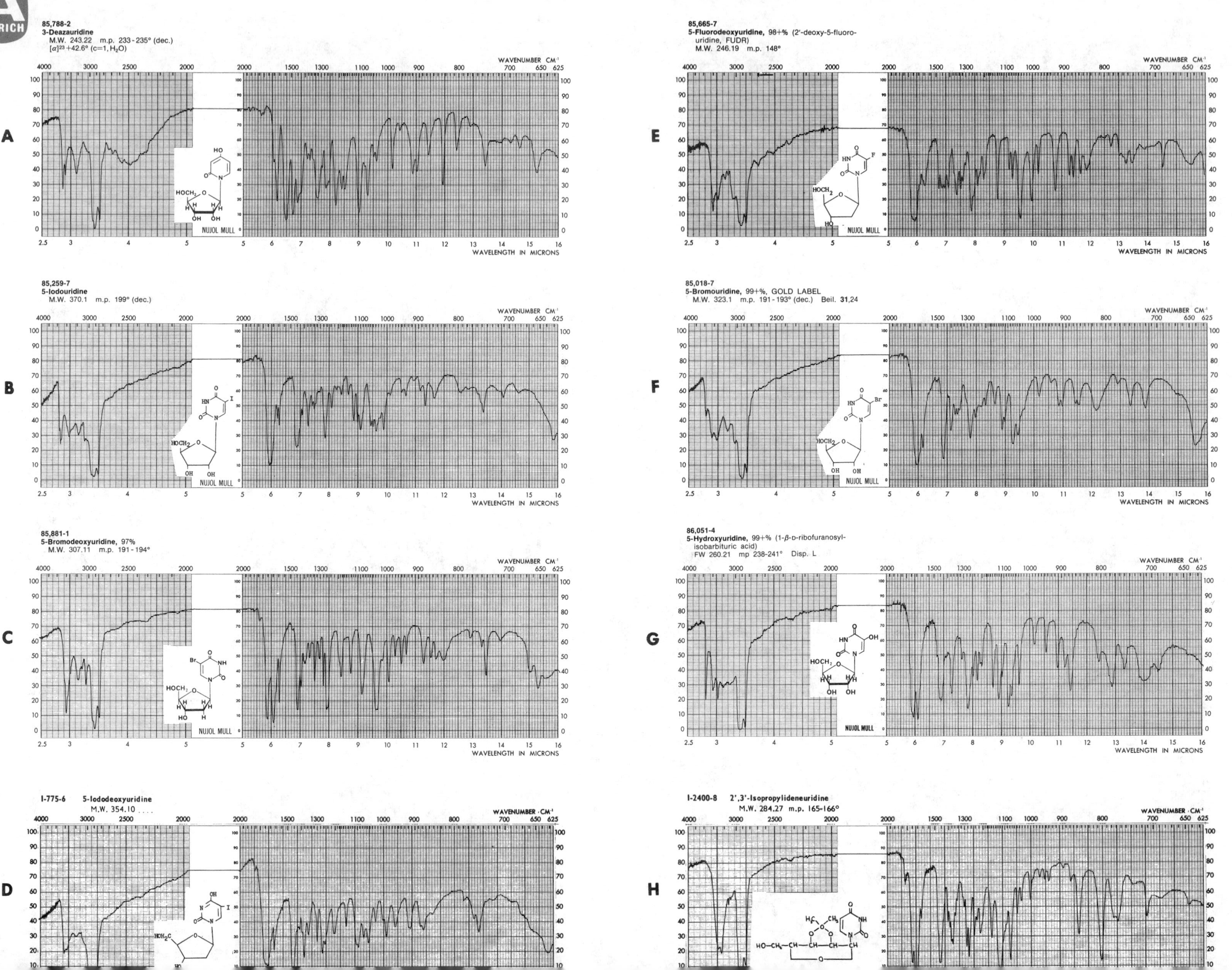
ALDRICH
A
85,788-2
3-Deazauridine
M.W. 243.22 m.p. 233-235° (dec.)
[α]23 +42.6° (c=1, H2O)
NUJOL MULL
B
85,259-7
5-Iodouridine
M.W. 370.1 m.p. 199° (dec.)
NUJOL MULL
C
85,881-1
5-Bromodeoxyuridine, 97%
M.W. 307.11 m.p. 191-194°
NUJOL MULL
D
I-775-6 5-Iododeoxyuridine
M.W. 354.10 . . . .
E
85,665-7
5-Fluorodeoxyuridine, 98+% (2'-deoxy-5-fluoro-uridine, FUDR)
M.W. 246.19 m.p. 148°
NUJOL MULL
F
85,018-7
5-Bromouridine, 99+%, GOLD LABEL
M.W. 323.1 m.p. 191-193° (dec.) Beil. 31,24
NUJOL MULL
G
86,051-4
5-Hydroxyuridine, 99+% (1-β-D-ribofuranosyl-isobarbituric acid)
FW 260.21 mp 238-241° Disp. L
NUJOL MULL
H
I-2400-8 2',3'-Isopropylideneuridine
M.W. 284.27 m.p. 165-166°
WAVENUMBER CM⁻¹
WAVELENGTH IN MICRONS

A

M.W. 363.17 m.p. 229-231°

B

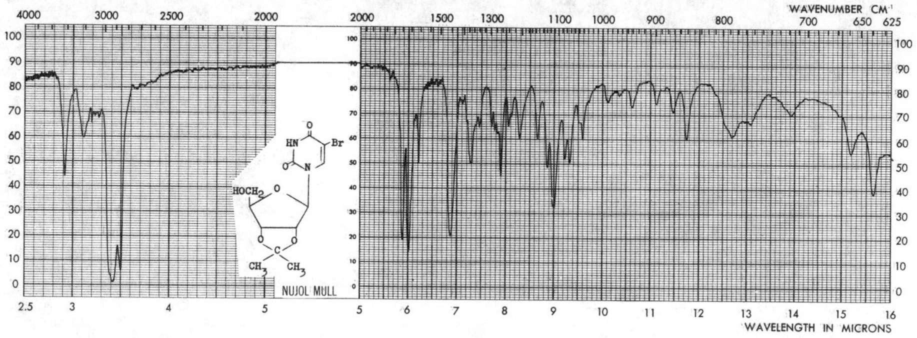

85,237-6
5'-Acetyl-2',3'-isopropylideneuridine, 99+%, GOLD LABEL
M.W. 326.31 m.p. 148-150°

C

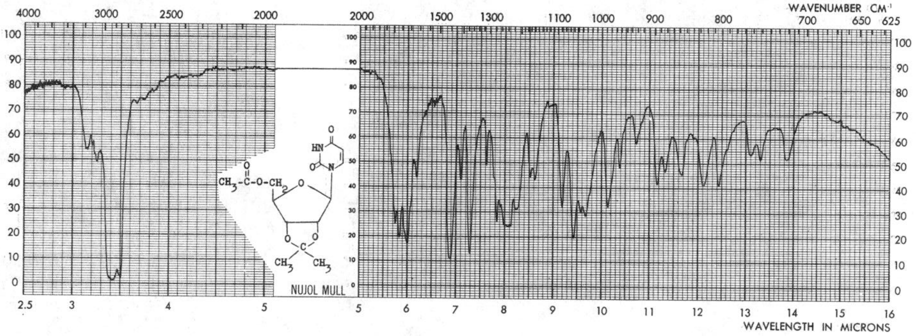

85,229-5
3',5'-Diacetylthymidine, 99+%, GOLD LABEL (thymidine 3',5'-diacetate)
M.W. 326.31 m.p. 126-128°

D

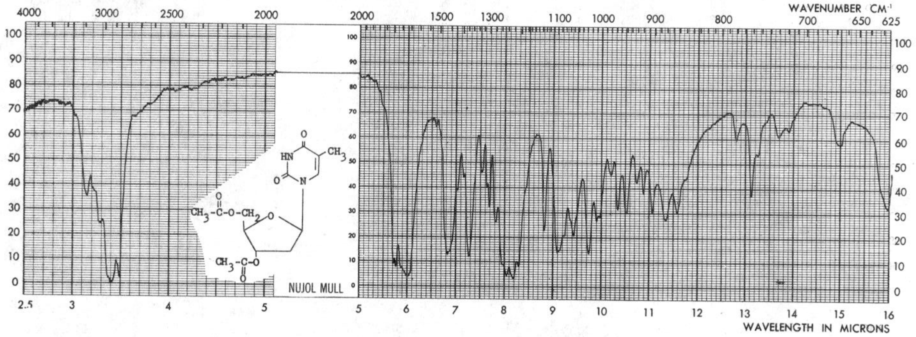

85,230-9
3',5'-Dibenzoylthymidine, 99% (thymidine 3',5'-dibenzoate)
M.W. 450.45 m.p. 195-197°

E

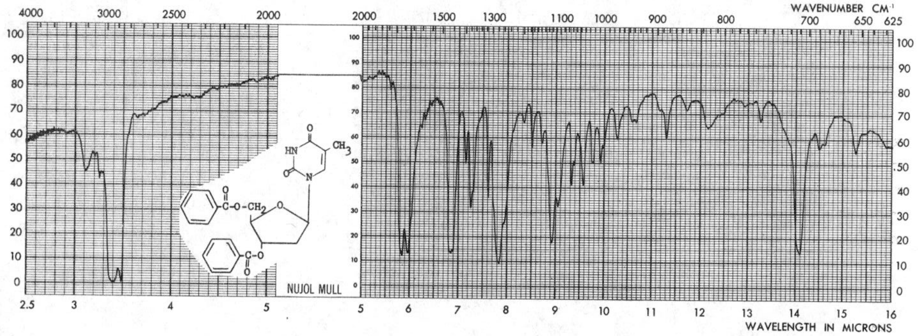

M.W. 466.51 m.p. 161-163°
$[\alpha]^{25}$ -52° (c=1, $CHCl_3$)

F

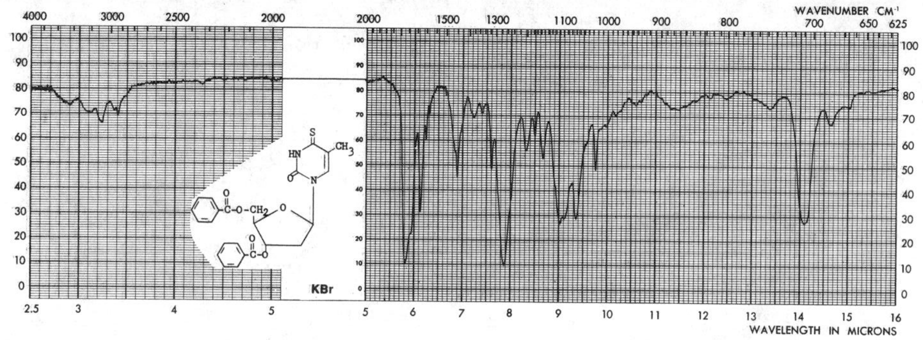

85,253-8
2',3'-Dibenzoyluridine (uridine 2',3'-dibenzoate)
M.W. 452.42 m.p. 194-196°

G

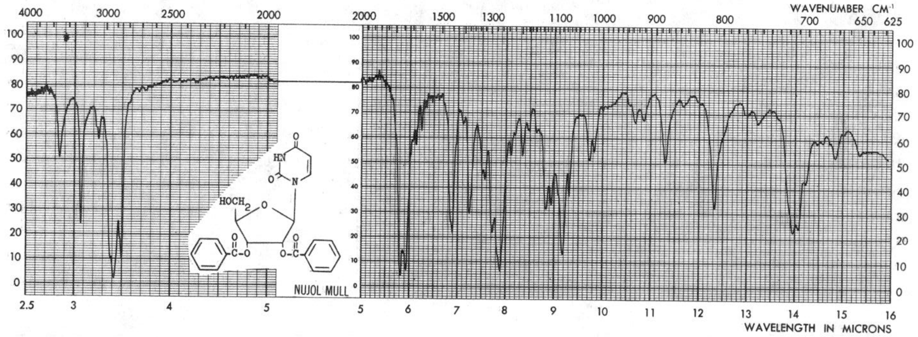

85,228-7
3',5'-Diacetyl-5-iodo-2'-deoxyuridine, 99+%, GOLD LABEL (5-iodo-2'-deoxyuridine 3',5'-diacetate)
M.W. 438.17 m.p. 161-163°

H

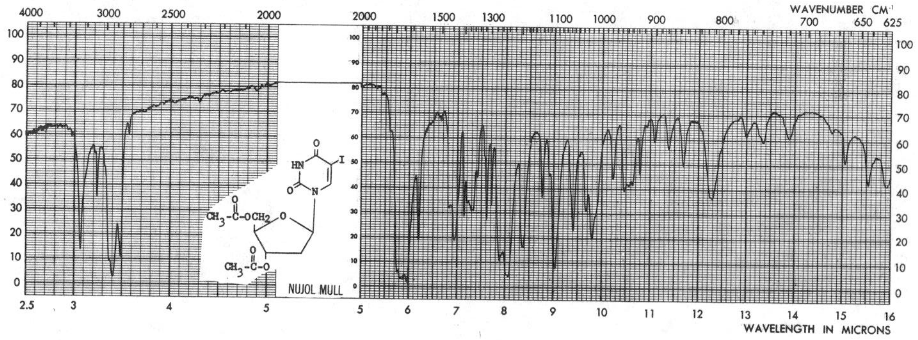

85,280-5
2',3',5'-Triacetyluridine, 99+%, GOLD LABEL (uridine 2',3',5'-triacetate)
M.W. 370.31 m.p. 130-134°

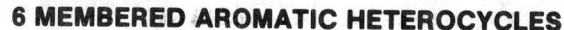

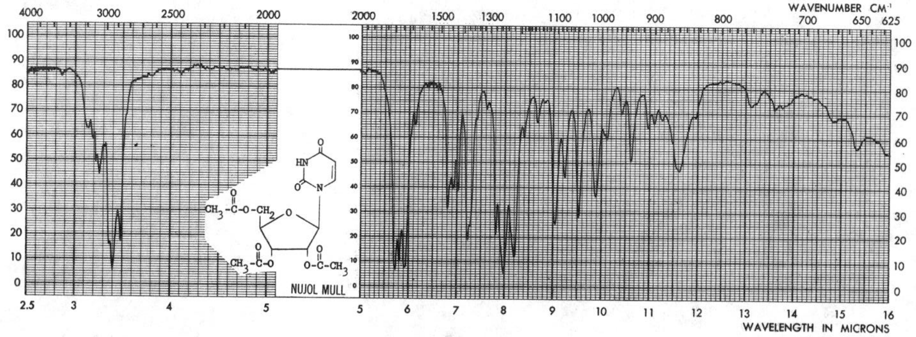

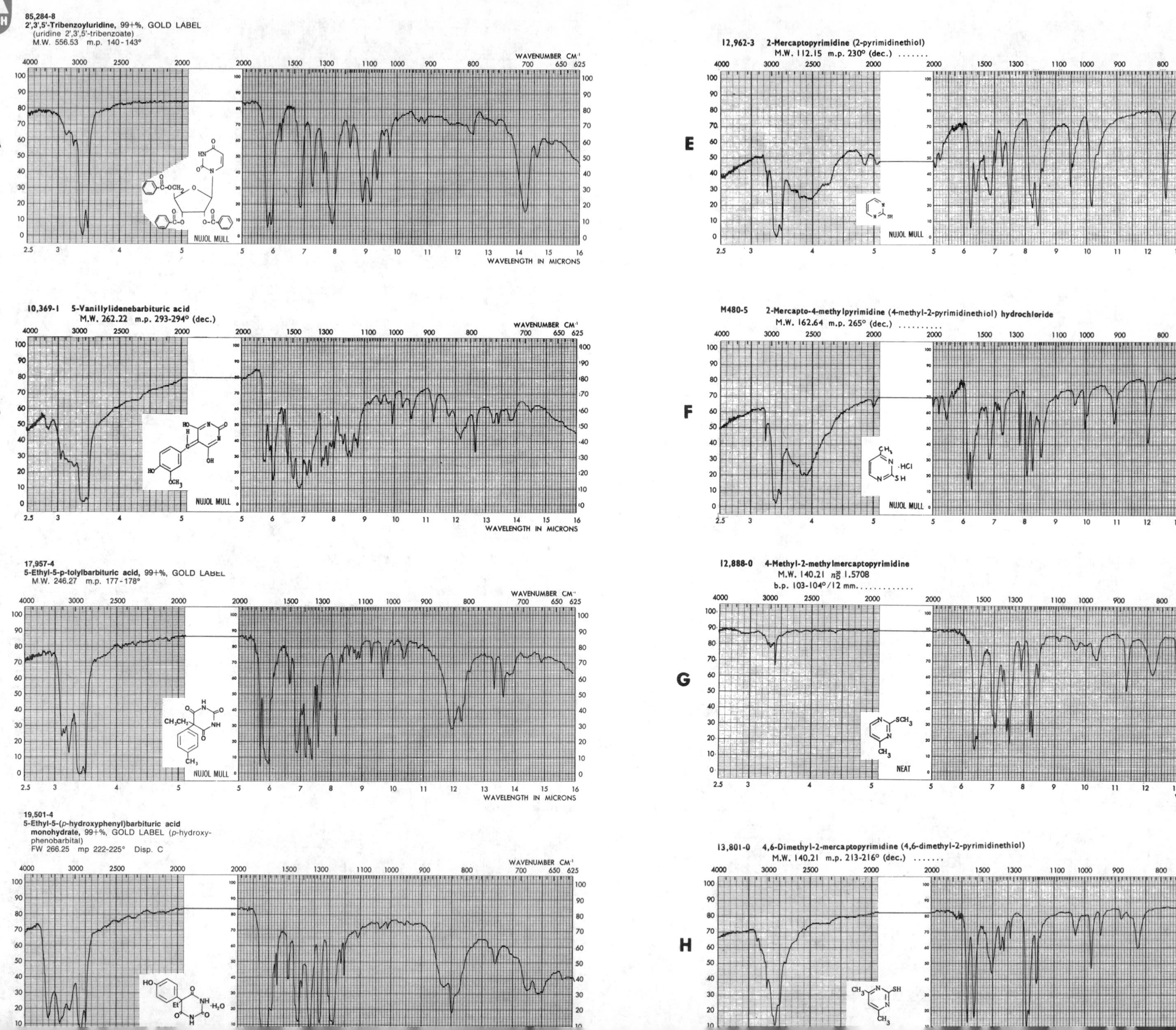

A 85,284-8
2',3',5'-Tribenzoyluridine, 99+%, GOLD LABEL
(uridine 2',3',5'-tribenzoate)
M.W. 556.53 m.p. 140-143°

B 10,369-1 **5-Vanillylidenebarbituric acid**
M.W. 262.22 m.p. 293-294° (dec.)

C 17,957-4
5-Ethyl-5-p-tolylbarbituric acid, 99+%, GOLD LABEL
M.W. 246.27 m.p. 177-178°

D 19,501-4
5-Ethyl-5-(p-hydroxyphenyl)barbituric acid monohydrate, 99+%, GOLD LABEL (p-hydroxy-phenobarbital)
FW 266.25 mp 222-225° Disp. C

E 12,962-3 **2-Mercaptopyrimidine** (2-pyrimidinethiol)
M.W. 112.15 m.p. 230° (dec.)

F M480-5 **2-Mercapto-4-methylpyrimidine** (4-methyl-2-pyrimidinethiol) **hydrochloride**
M.W. 162.64 m.p. 265° (dec.)

G 12,888-0 **4-Methyl-2-methylmercaptopyrimidine**
M.W. 140.21 n_D^{20} 1.5708
b.p. 103-104°/12 mm.

H 13,801-0 **4,6-Dimethyl-2-mercaptopyrimidine** (4,6-dimethyl-2-pyrimidinethiol)
M.W. 140.21 m.p. 213-216° (dec.)

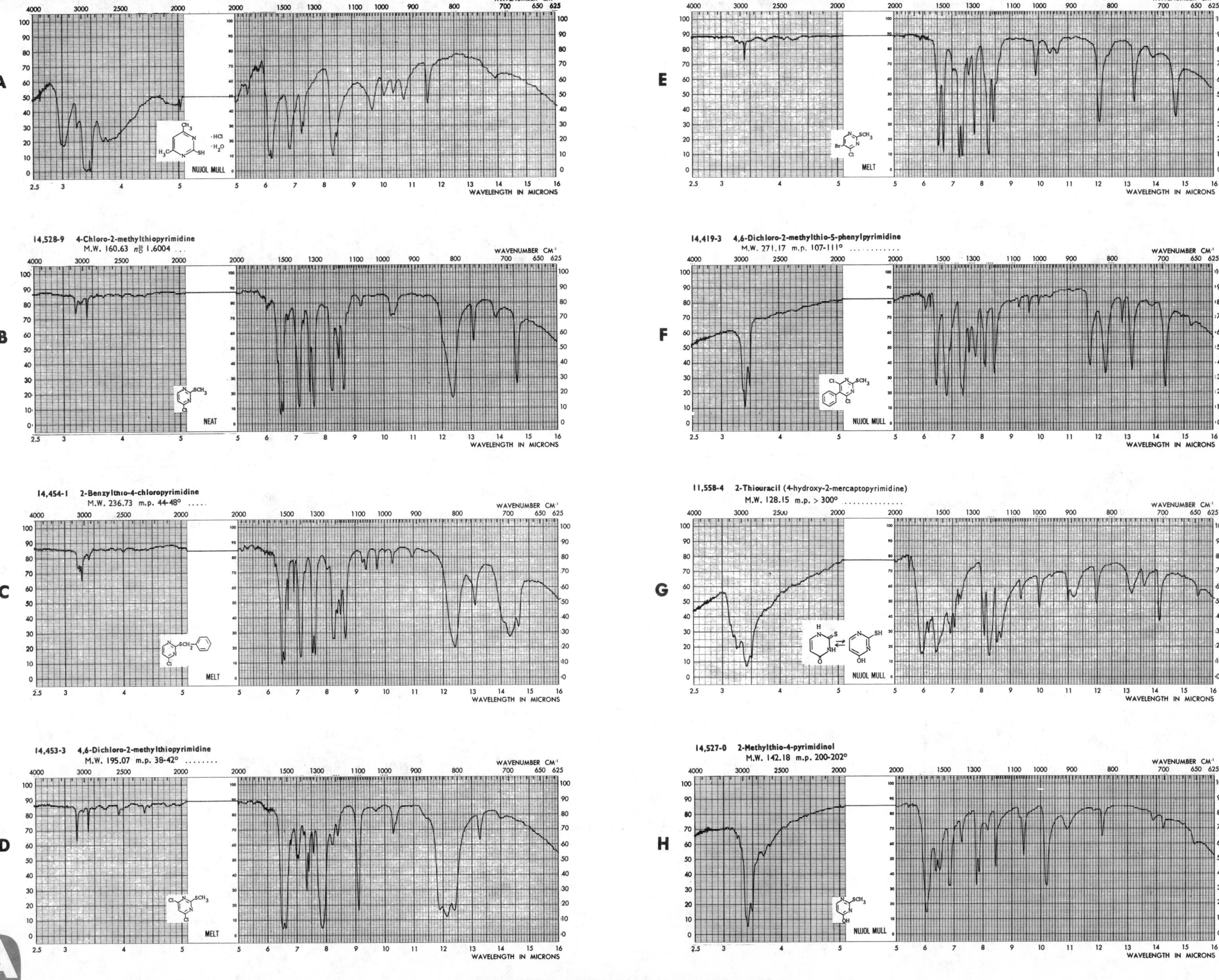

A
hydrochloride monohydrate
M.W. 194.68 m.p. 270° (dec.)
NUJOL MULL
B
14,528-9 4-Chloro-2-methylthiopyrimidine
M.W. 160.63 n_D^{20} 1.6004
NEAT
C
14,454-1 2-Benzylthio-4-chloropyrimidine
M.W. 236.73 m.p. 44-48°
MELT
D
14,453-3 4,6-Dichloro-2-methylthiopyrimidine
M.W. 195.07 m.p. 38-42°
MELT
E
M.W. 239.53 m.p. 39-43°
MELT
F
14,419-3 4,6-Dichloro-2-methylthio-5-phenylpyrimidine
M.W. 271.17 m.p. 107-111°
NUJOL MULL
G
11,558-4 2-Thiouracil (4-hydroxy-2-mercaptopyrimidine)
M.W. 128.15 m.p. > 300°
NUJOL MULL
H
14,527-0 2-Methylthio-4-pyrimidinol
M.W. 142.18 m.p. 200-202°
NUJOL MULL
WAVENUMBER CM⁻¹
WAVELENGTH IN MICRONS
ALDRICH

ALDRICH ®

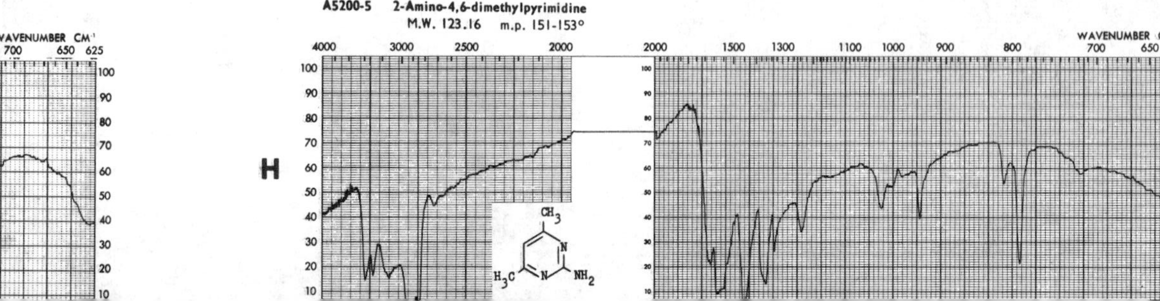

A

15,846-1
Dithiouracil, 95% [2,4(1H,3H)-pyrimidinedithione]
M.W. 144.22 m.p. 279-281° (dec.) Beil. **24**,323

NUJOL MULL

B

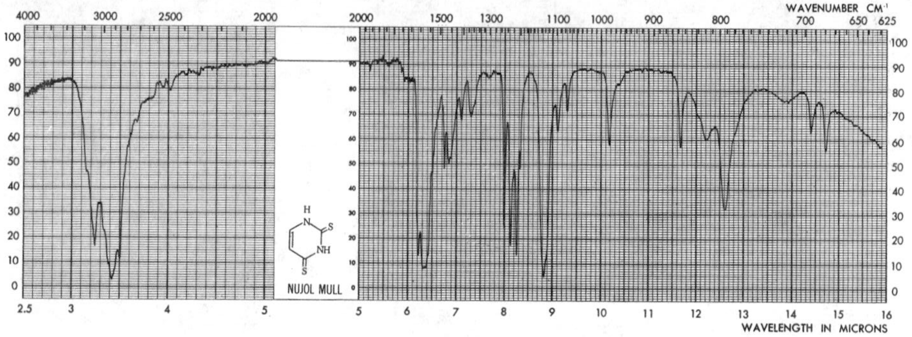

H3380-0 **4-Hydroxy-2-mercapto-6-methylpyrimidine** (6-methyl-2-thiouracil)
M.W. 142.18 m.p. > 320°

NUJOL MULL

C

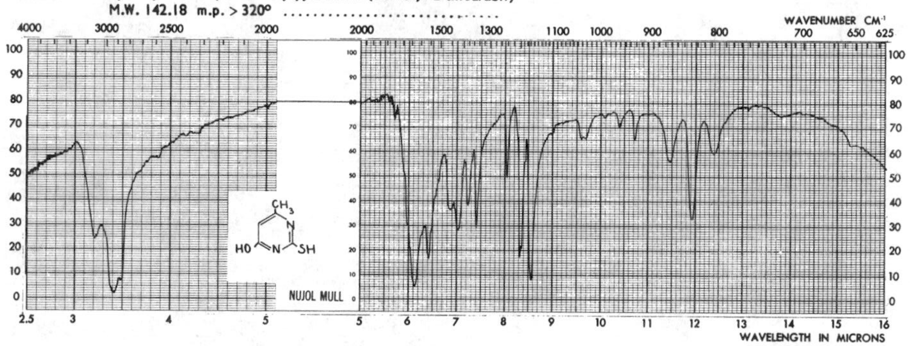

H3420-3 **4-Hydroxy-2-mercapto-6-propylpyrimidine** (6-propyl-2-thiouracil)
M.W. 170.23 m.p. 218-222°

NUJOL MULL

D

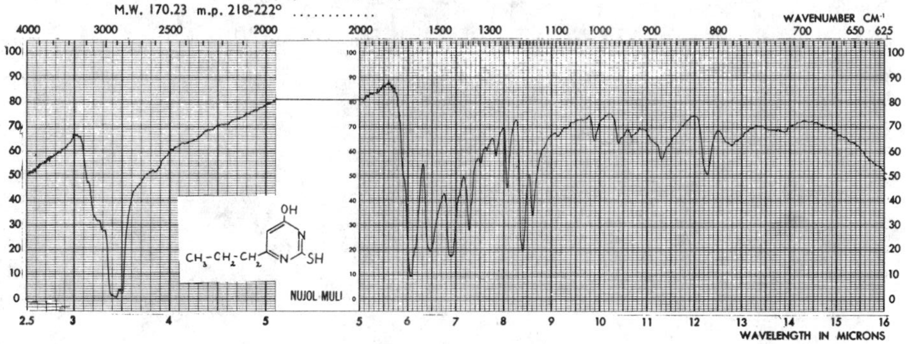

D11,350-6 **4,6-Dihydroxy-2-mercaptopyrimidine** (2-thiobarbituric acid)
M.W. 144.15 m.p. 244° (dec.)

E

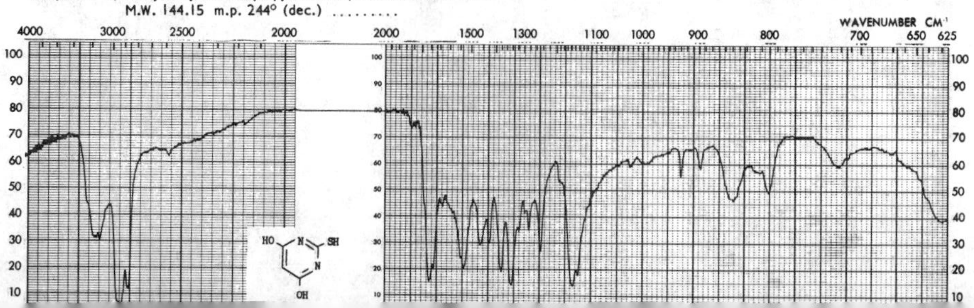

D11,480-4 **4,6-Dihydroxy-2-methylmercaptopyrimidine** (2-methylthio-4,6-pyrimidinediol)
M.W. 158.18 m.p. > 300°

NUJOL MULL

F

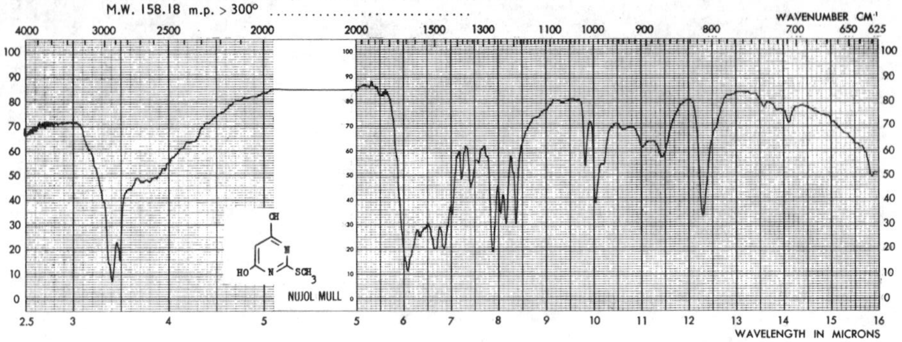

A7860-8 **2-Aminopyrimidine**
M.W. 95.11 m.p. 125-127°

NUJOL MULL

G

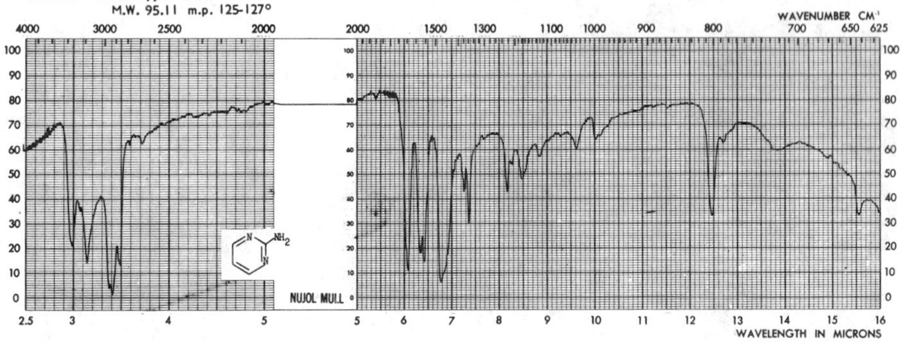

A6570-0 **2-Amino-4-methylpyrimidine**
M.W. 109.14 m.p. 154-158°

NUJOL MULL

H

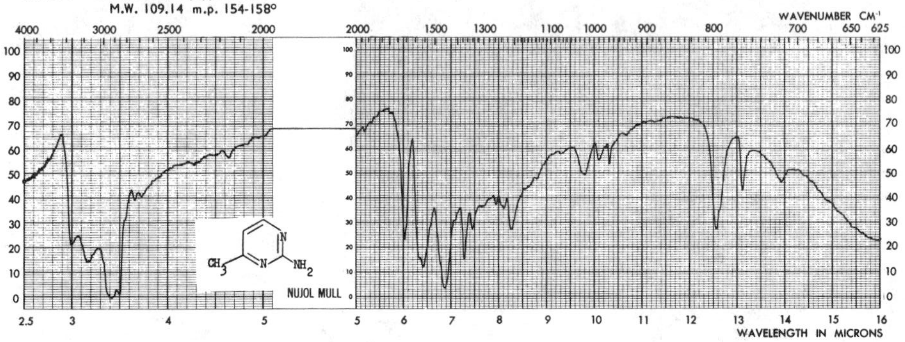

A5200-5 **2-Amino-4,6-dimethylpyrimidine**
M.W. 123.16 m.p. 151-153°

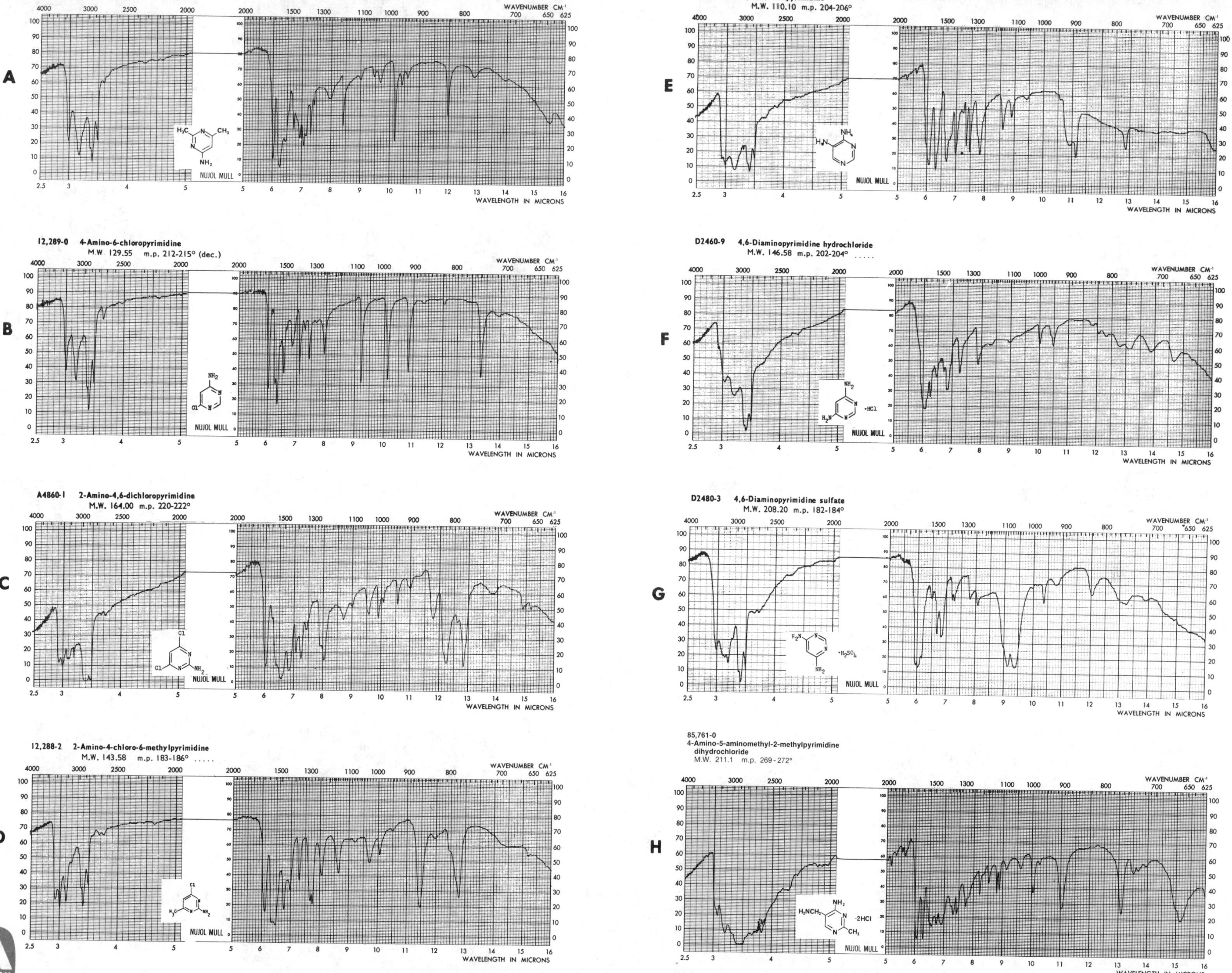
M.W. 123.16 m.p. 180-181 Beil. 24(2),45
A
NUJOL MULL
12,289-0 4-Amino-6-chloropyrimidine
M.W. 129.55 m.p. 212-215° (dec.)
B
NUJOL MULL
A4860-1 2-Amino-4,6-dichloropyrimidine
M.W. 164.00 m.p. 220-222°
C
NUJOL MULL
12,288-2 2-Amino-4-chloro-6-methylpyrimidine
M.W. 143.58 m.p. 183-186°
D
NUJOL MULL
D2450-1 4,5-Diaminopyrimidine
M.W. 110.10 m.p. 204-206°
E
NUJOL MULL
D2460-9 4,6-Diaminopyrimidine hydrochloride
M.W. 146.58 m.p. 202-204°
F
·HCl
NUJOL MULL
D2480-3 4,6-Diaminopyrimidine sulfate
M.W. 208.20 m.p. 182-184°
G
·H2SO4
NUJOL MULL
85,761-0
4-Amino-5-aminomethyl-2-methylpyrimidine
dihydrochloride
M.W. 211.1 m.p. 269-272°
H
·2HCl
NUJOL MULL
WAVENUMBER CM⁻¹
WAVELENGTH IN MICRONS
ALDRICH

ALDRICH

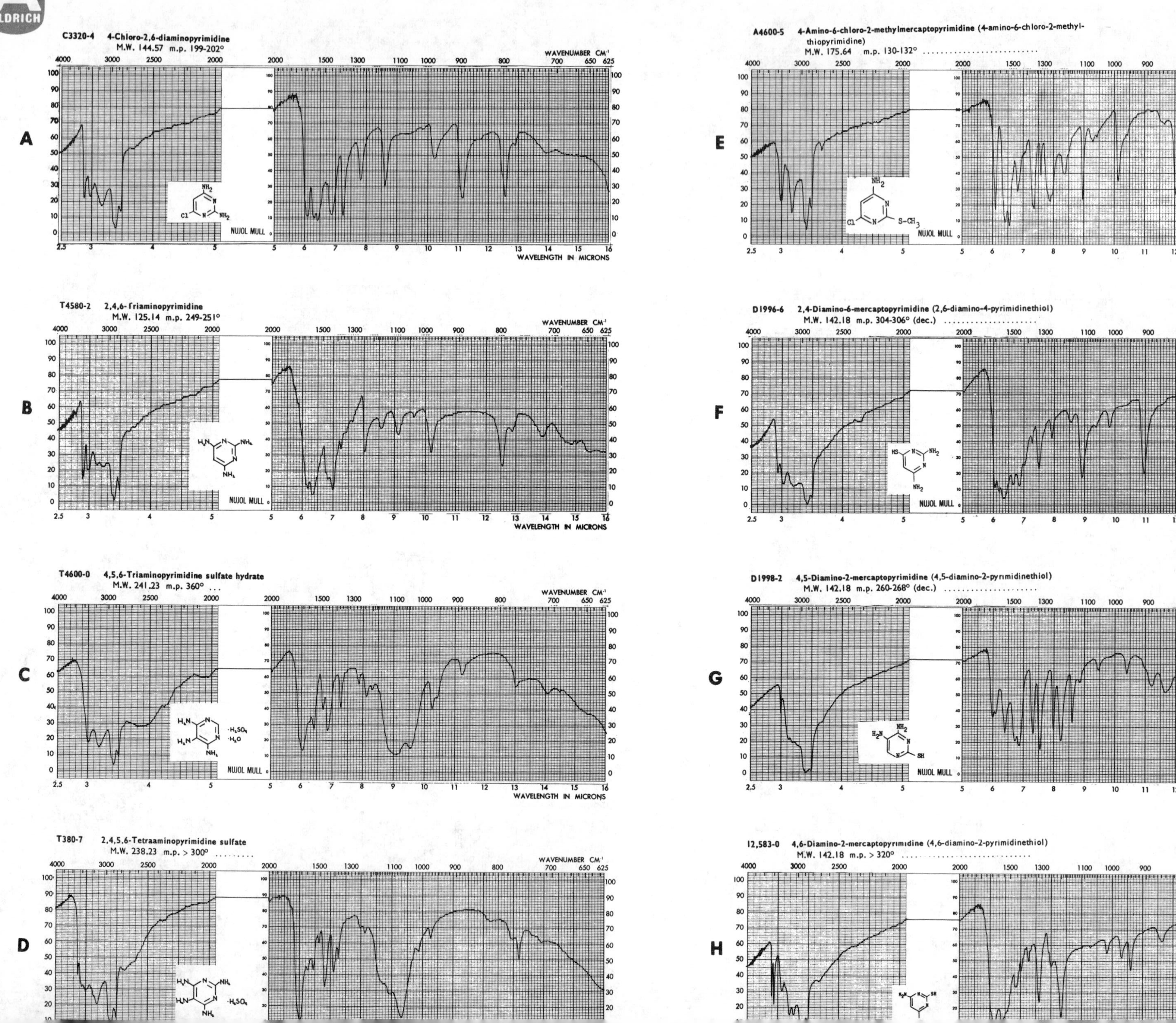

A C3320-4 4-Chloro-2,6-diaminopyrimidine
M.W. 144.57 m.p. 199-202°

B T4580-2 2,4,6-Triaminopyrimidine
M.W. 125.14 m.p. 249-251°

C T4600-0 4,5,6-Triaminopyrimidine sulfate hydrate
M.W. 241.23 m.p. 360° ...

D T380-7 2,4,5,6-Tetraaminopyrimidine sulfate
M.W. 238.23 m.p. > 300° ....

E A4600-5 4-Amino-6-chloro-2-methylmercaptopyrimidine (4-amino-6-chloro-2-methylthiopyrimidine)
M.W. 175.64 m.p. 130-132° ....

F D1996-6 2,4-Diamino-6-mercaptopyrimidine (2,6-diamino-4-pyrimidinethiol)
M.W. 142.18 m.p. 304-306° (dec.) ....

G D1998-2 4,5-Diamino-2-mercaptopyrimidine (4,5-diamino-2-pyrimidinethiol)
M.W. 142.18 m.p. 260-268° (dec.) ....

H 12,583-0 4,6-Diamino-2-mercaptopyrimidine (4,6-diamino-2-pyrimidinethiol)
M.W. 142.18 m.p. > 320° ....

NUJOL MULL

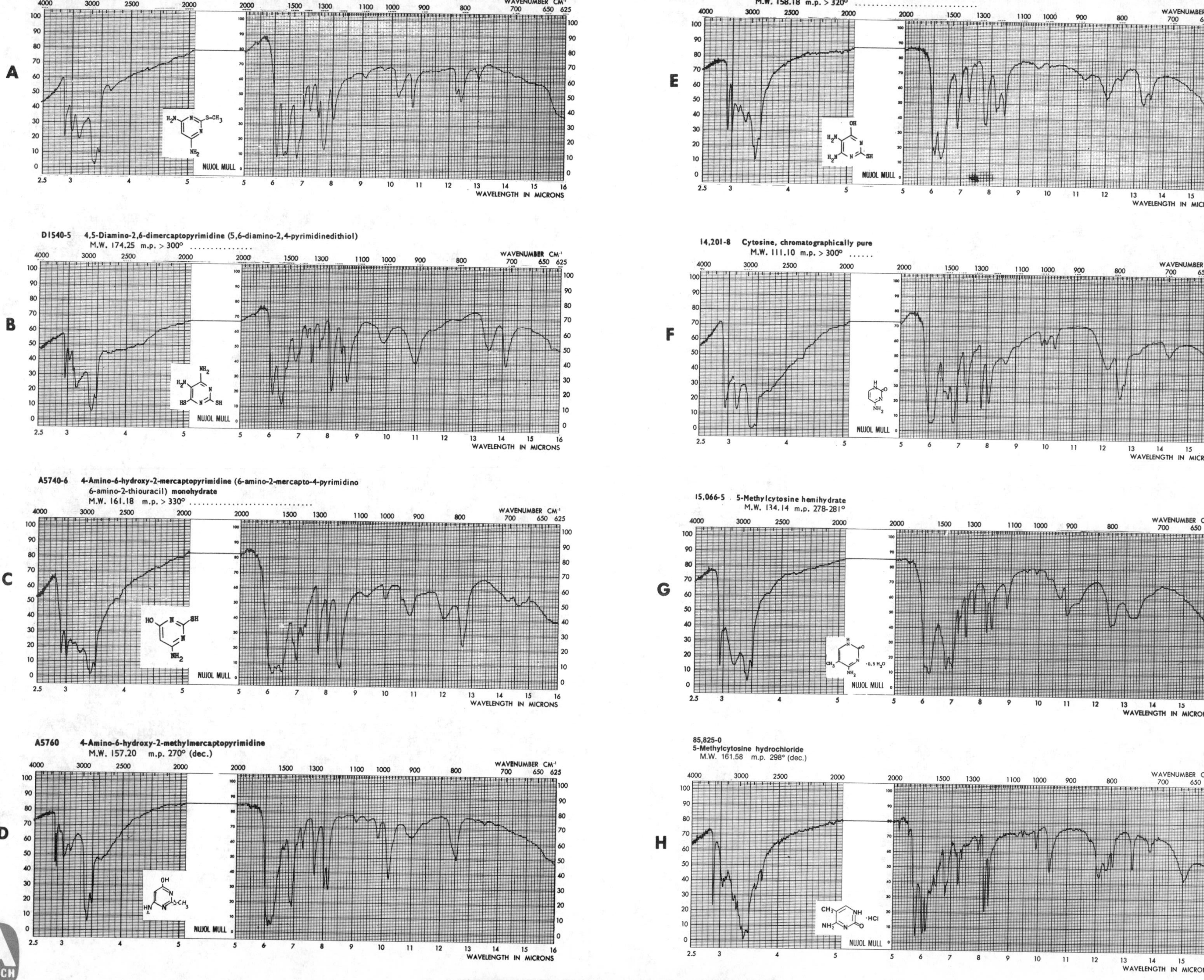
A
4,6-Diamino-2-methylmercaptopyrimidine
M.W. 156.21 m.p. 188-190°
NUJOL MULL
B
D1540-5 4,5-Diamino-2,6-dimercaptopyrimidine (5,6-diamino-2,4-pyrimidinedithiol)
M.W. 174.25 m.p. > 300°
NUJOL MULL
C
A5740-6 4-Amino-6-hydroxy-2-mercaptopyrimidine (6-amino-2-mercapto-4-pyrimidino
6-amino-2-thiouracil) monohydrate
M.W. 161.18 m.p. > 330°
NUJOL MULL
D
A5760 4-Amino-6-hydroxy-2-methylmercaptopyrimidine
M.W. 157.20 m.p. 270° (dec.)
NUJOL MULL
E
D1780-7 4,5-Diamino-6-hydroxy-2-mercaptopyrimidine (5,6-diamino-2-thiouracil)
M.W. 158.18 m.p. > 320°
NUJOL MULL
F
14,201-8 Cytosine, chromatographically pure
M.W. 111.10 m.p. > 300°
NUJOL MULL
G
15,066-5 5-Methylcytosine hemihydrate
M.W. 134.14 m.p. 278-281°
NUJOL MULL
H
85,825-0
5-Methylcytosine hydrochloride
M.W. 161.58 m.p. 298° (dec.)
NUJOL MULL
WAVENUMBER CM⁻¹
WAVELENGTH IN MICRONS
ALDRICH

6 MEMBERED AROMATIC HETEROCYCLES

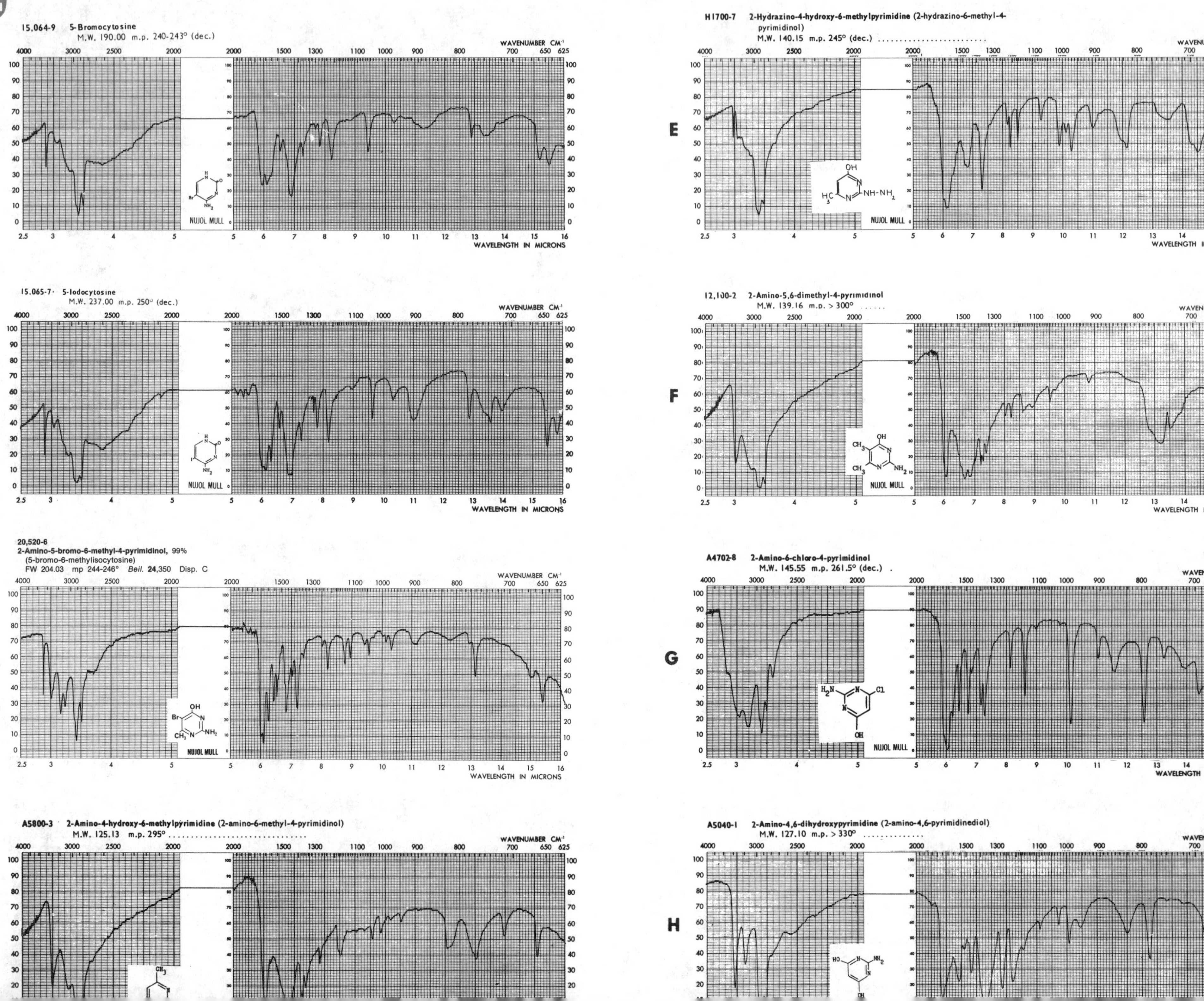

A — 15,064-9 5-Bromocytosine
M.W. 190.00 m.p. 240-243° (dec.)

B — 15,065-7 5-Iodocytosine
M.W. 237.00 m.p. 250° (dec.)

C — 20,520-6
2-Amino-5-bromo-6-methyl-4-pyrimidinol, 99%
(5-bromo-6-methylisocytosine)
FW 204.03 mp 244-246° *Beil.* **24**,350 Disp. C

D — A5800-3 2-Amino-4-hydroxy-6-methylpyrimidine (2-amino-6-methyl-4-pyrimidinol)
M.W. 125.13 m.p. 295°

E — H1700-7 2-Hydrazino-4-hydroxy-6-methylpyrimidine (2-hydrazino-6-methyl-4-pyrimidinol)
M.W. 140.15 m.p. 245° (dec.)

F — 12,100-2 2-Amino-5,6-dimethyl-4-pyrimidinol
M.W. 139.16 m.p. > 300°

G — A4702-8 2-Amino-6-chloro-4-pyrimidinol
M.W. 145.55 m.p. 261.5° (dec.)

H — A5040-1 2-Amino-4,6-dihydroxypyrimidine (2-amino-4,6-pyrimidinediol)
M.W. 127.10 m.p. > 330°

A

M.W. 127.10 m.p. > 360°

NUJOL MULL

B

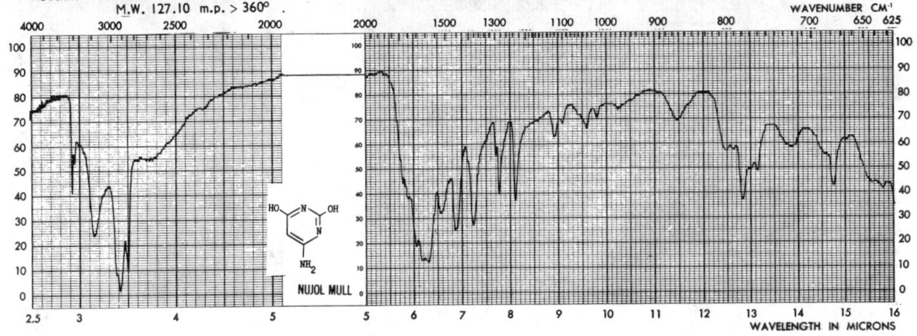

D1920-6 2,4-Diamino-6-hydroxypyrimidine (2,6-diamino-4-pyrimidinol) monohydrate
M.W. 144.13 m.p. 285-286° (dec.)

NUJOL MULL

C

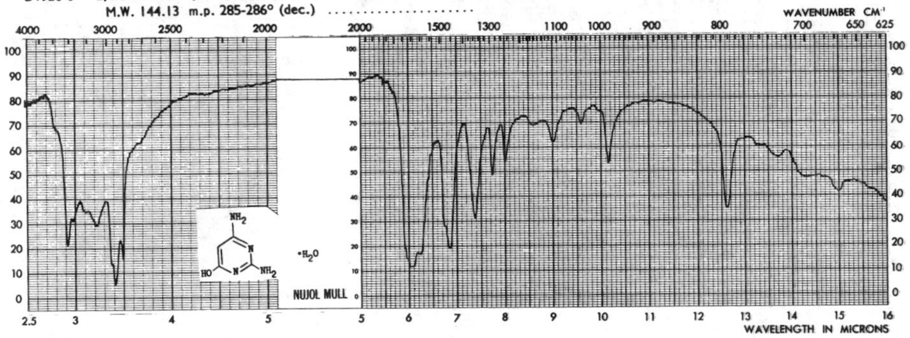

85,528-6
5-Aminouracil
M.W. 127.1 m.p. >300° Beil. 24,463

NUJOL MULL

D

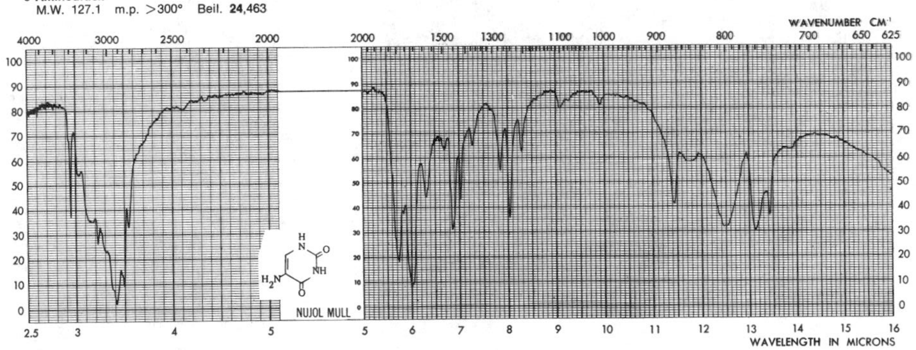

D1930-3 4,5-Diamino-6-hydroxypyrimidine (5,6-diamino-4-pyrimidinol) sulfate
M.W. 224.20 m.p. 270° (dec.)

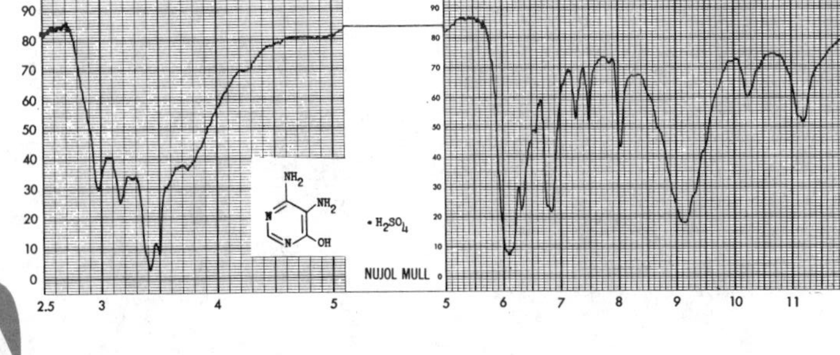

NUJOL MULL

E

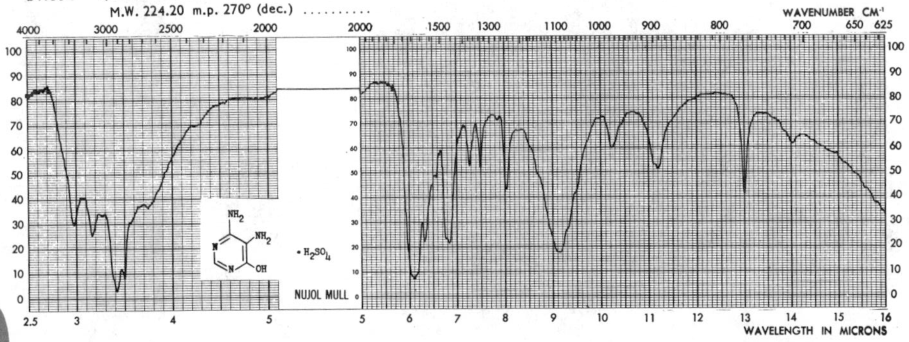

hydrochloride
M.W. 178.58

NUJOL MULL

F

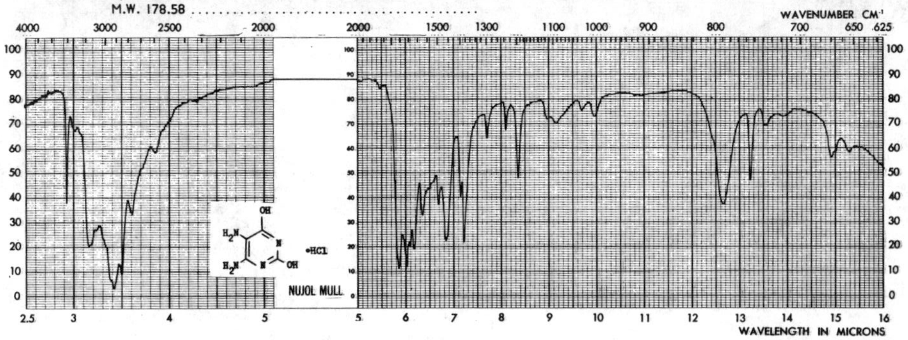

D1510-3 5,6-Diamino-2,4-dihydroxypyrimidine (5,6-diaminouracil) hemisulfate
M.W. 191.16 m.p. > 330°

NUJOL MULL

G

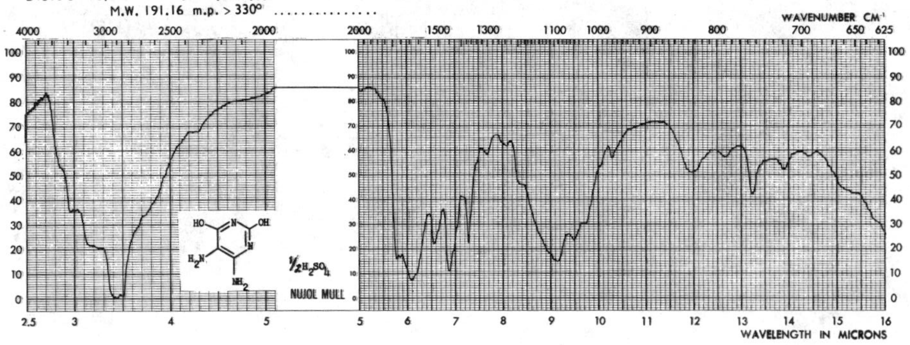

H5920-6 6-Hydroxy-2,4,5-triaminopyrimidine (2,5,6-triamino-4-pyrimidinol) sulfate
M.W. 239.21 m.p. 250° (dec.)

NUJOL MULL

H

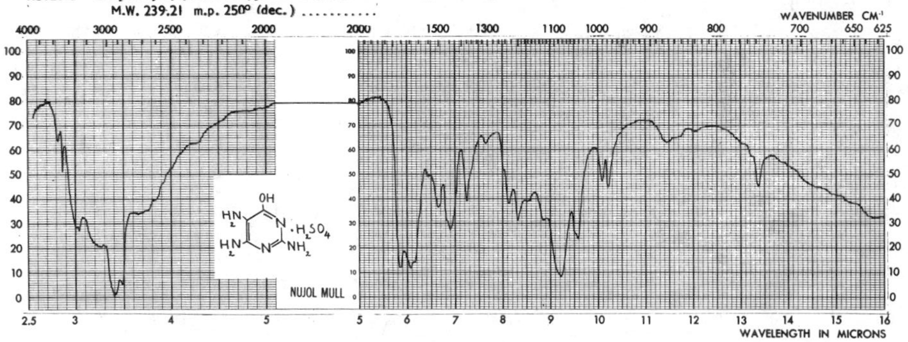

A5173-4 2-Amino-6,7-dimethyl-4-hydroxy-5,6,7,8-tetrahydropteridine
(2-amino-6,7-dimethyl-5,6,7,8-tetrahydro-4-pteridinol) hydrochloride
M.W. 231.69 m.p. 243-244°

NUJOL MULL

ALDRICH

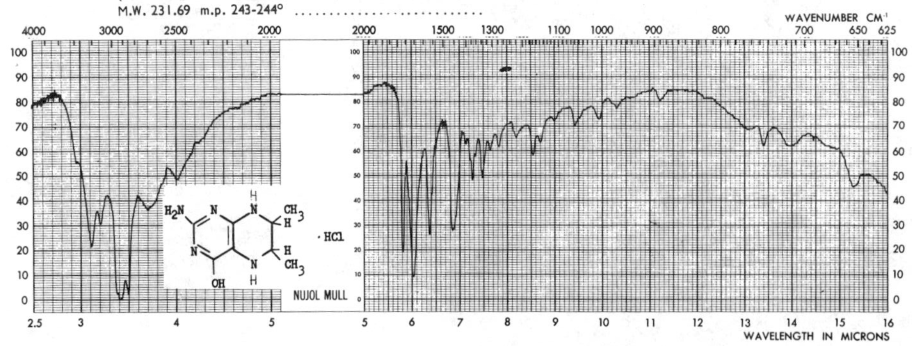

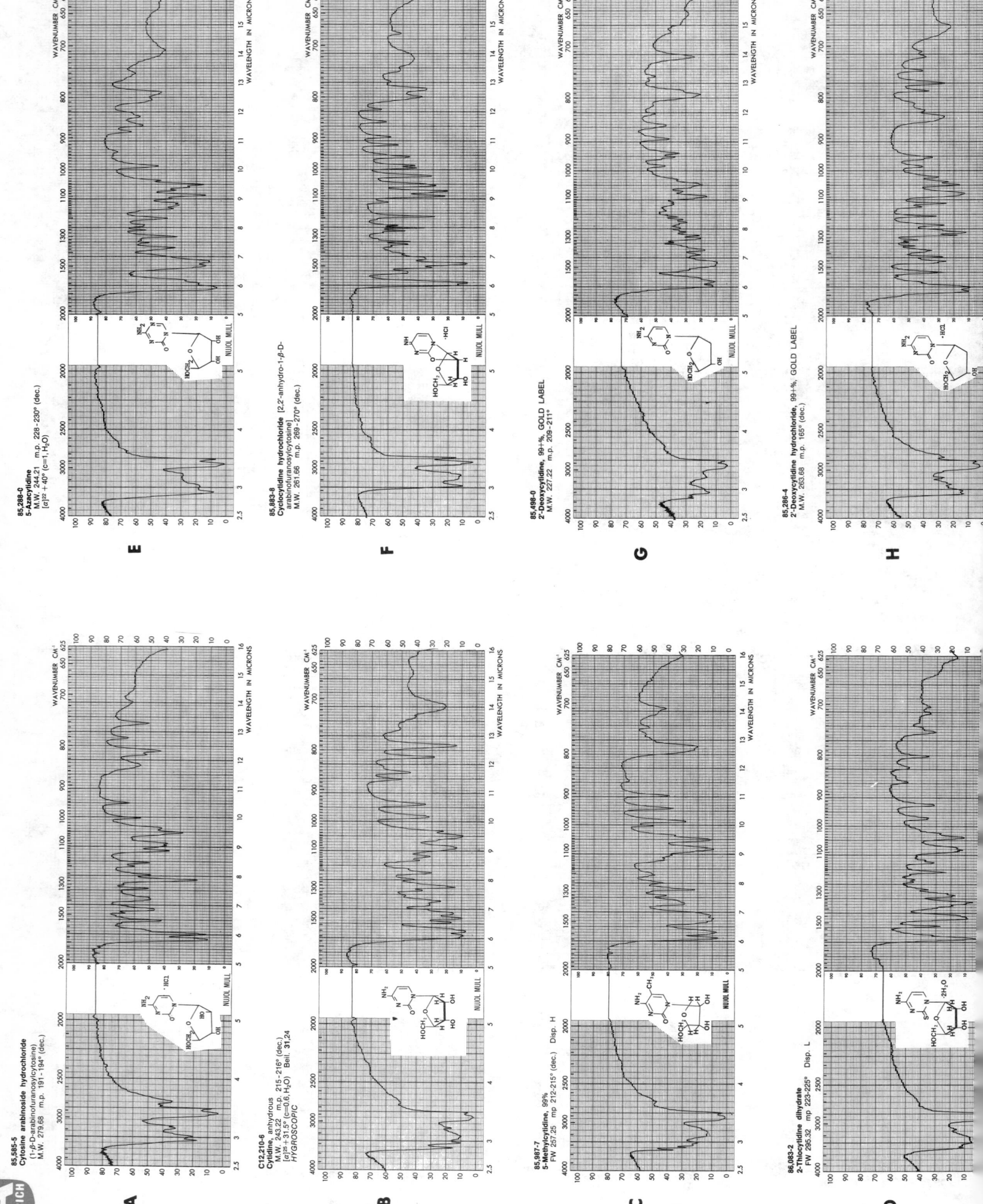

A — 85,585-5
Cytosine arabinoside hydrochloride
(1-β-D-arabinofuranosylcytosine)
M.W. 279.68 m.p. 191-194° (dec.)

B — C12,210-6
Cytidine, anhydrous
M.W. 243.22 m.p. 215-216° (dec.)
$[\alpha]^{25}$ +31.5° (c=0.6, H_2O) Beil. **31**,24
HYGROSCOPIC

C — 85,987-7
5-Methylcytidine, 99%
FW 257.25 mp 212-215° (dec.) Disp. H

D — 86,083-2
2-Thiocytidine dihydrate
FW 295.32 mp 223-225° Disp. L

E — 85,288-0
5-Azacytidine
M.W. 244.21 m.p. 228-230° (dec.)
$[\alpha]^{22}$ +40° (c=1, H_2O)

F — 85,883-8
Cyclocytidine hydrochloride [2,2'-anhydro-1-β-D-arabinofuranosylcytosine]
M.W. 261.66 m.p. 269-270° (dec.)

G — 85,498-0
2'-Deoxycytidine, 99+%, GOLD LABEL
M.W. 227.22 m.p. 209-211°

H — 85,286-4
2'-Deoxycytidine hydrochloride, 99+%, GOLD LABEL
M.W. 263.68 m.p. 165° (dec.)

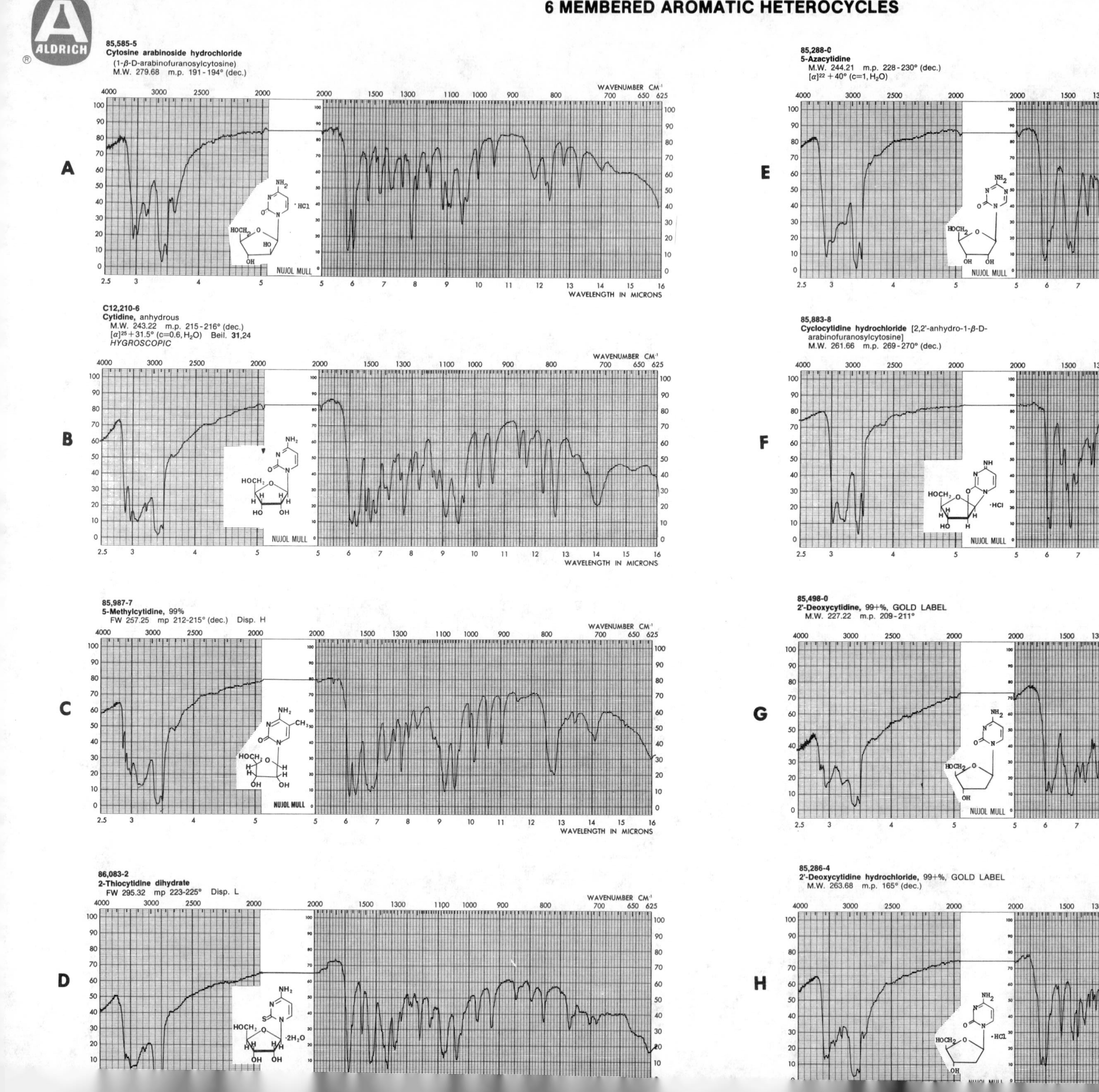

M.W. 283.28 m.p. 84° (dec.)

A

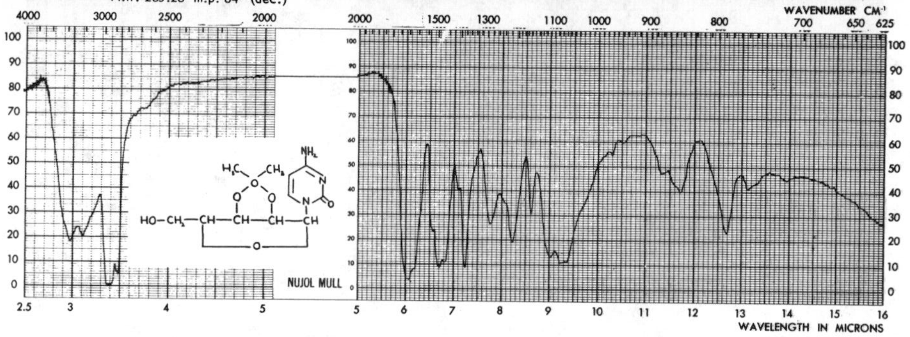

NUJOL MULL

I-2280-3 2',3'-Isopropylidenecytidine hydrochloride
M.W. 283.28 m.p. 84° (dec.)

B

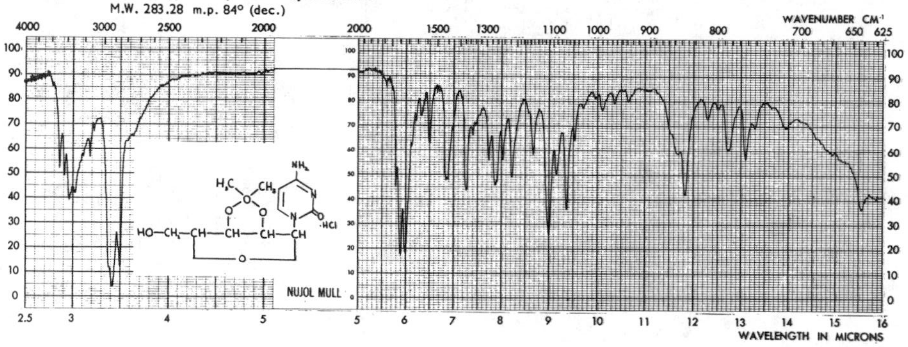

NUJOL MULL

85,232-5
5-Iodo-2'-deoxycytidine
M.W. 353.12 m.p. 187-189° (dec.)

C

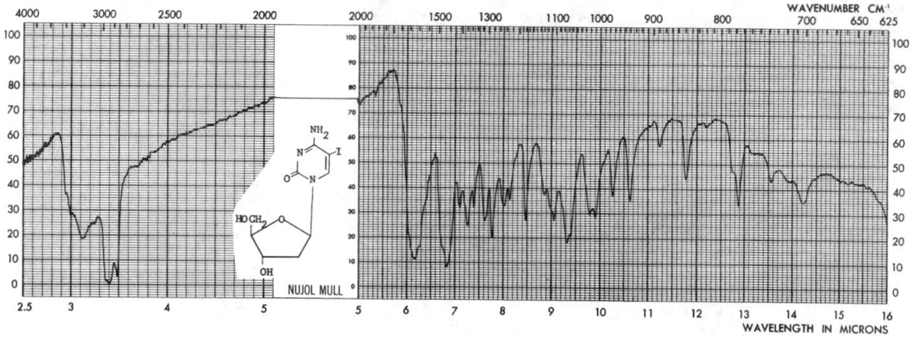

NUJOL MULL

86,082-4
N^4-Acetylcytidine
FW 285.26 mp 199° (dec.) Disp. L

D

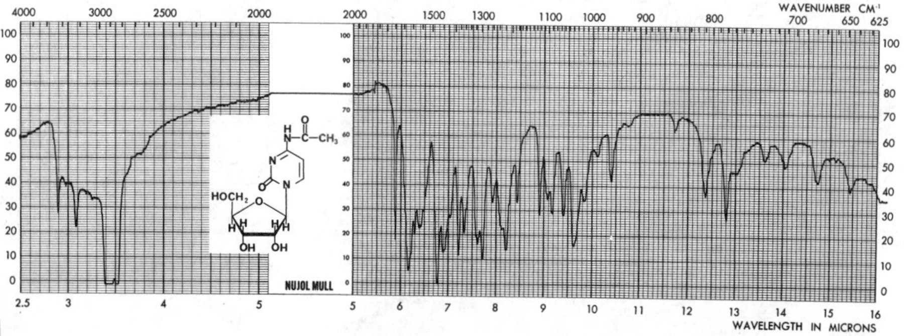

NUJOL MULL

FW 154.13 mp >300° Disp. C

E

KBr

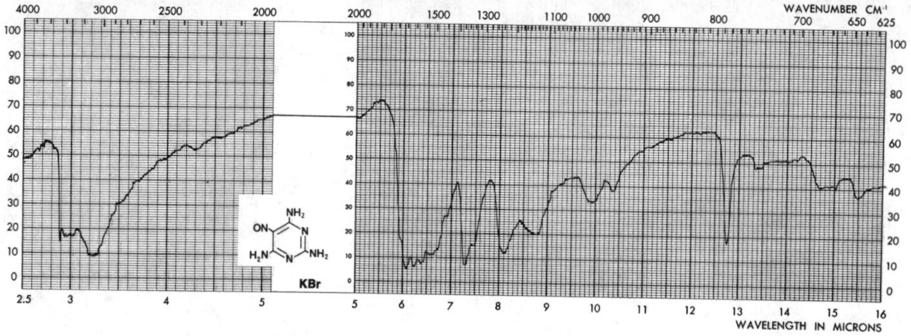

86,055-7
6-Amino-5-nitroso-2-thiouracil, 99% (4-amino-6-hydroxy-2-mercapto-5-nitrosopyrimidine)
FW 172.17 Disp. C

F

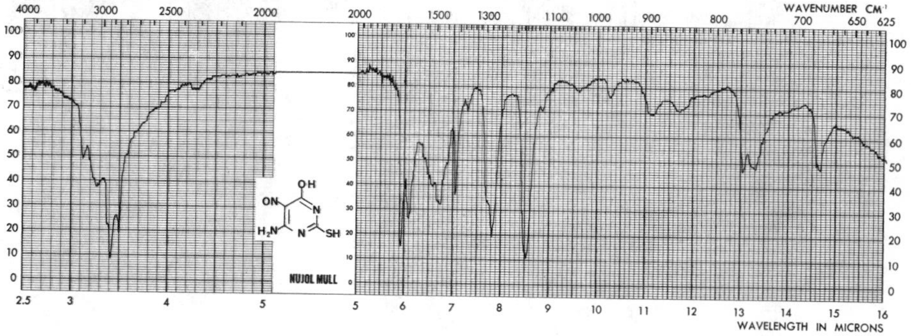

NUJOL MULL

D6930-0 4,6-Dichloro-5-nitropyrimidine
M.W. 193.98 m.p. 101-102.5°

G

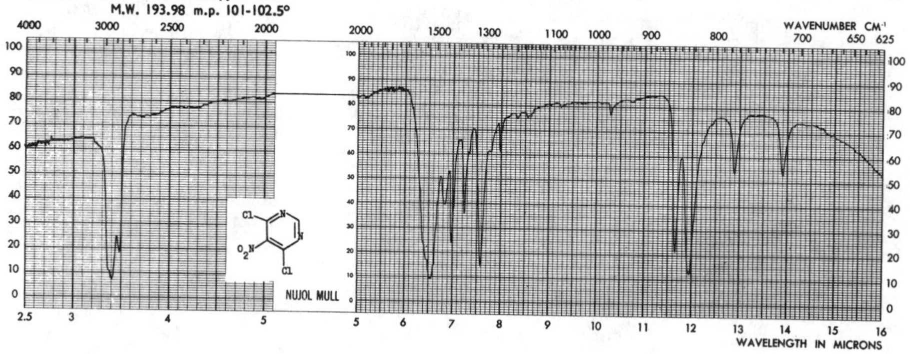

NUJOL MULL

12,623-3 4,6-Dihydroxy-5-nitropyrimidine (5-nitro-4,6-pyrimidinediol)
M.W. 157.09 m.p. > 320°

H

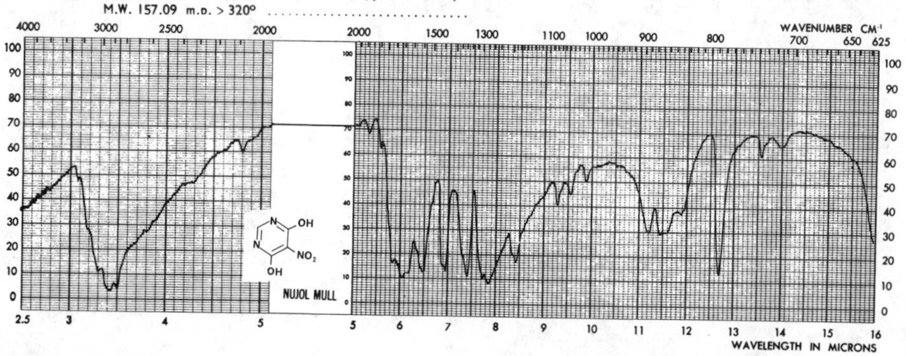

NUJOL MULL

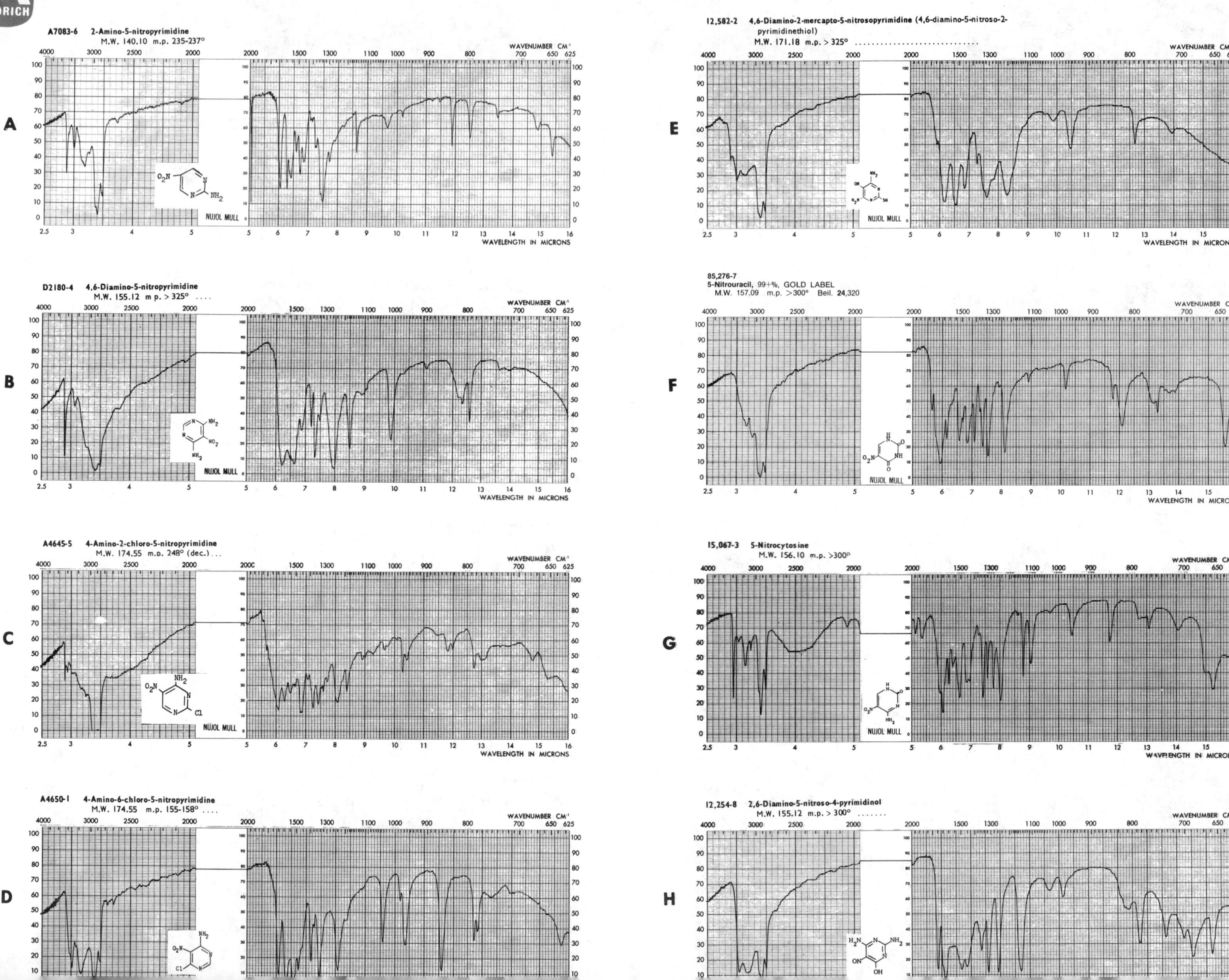
A
A7083-6 2-Amino-5-nitropyrimidine
M.W. 140.10 m.p. 235-237°
NUJOL MULL
B
D2180-4 4,6-Diamino-5-nitropyrimidine
M.W. 155.12 m.p. > 325° ....
NUJOL MULL
C
A4645-5 4-Amino-2-chloro-5-nitropyrimidine
M.W. 174.55 m.p. 248° (dec.)...
NUJOL MULL
D
A4650-1 4-Amino-6-chloro-5-nitropyrimidine
M.W. 174.55 m.p. 155-158° ....
E
12,582-2 4,6-Diamino-2-mercapto-5-nitrosopyrimidine (4,6-diamino-5-nitroso-2-pyrimidinethiol)
M.W. 171.18 m.p. > 325°
NUJOL MULL
F
85,276-7
5-Nitrouracil, 99+%, GOLD LABEL
M.W. 157.09 m.p. >300° Beil. 24,320
NUJOL MULL
G
15,067-3 5-Nitrocytosine
M.W. 156.10 m.p. >300°
NUJOL MULL
H
12,254-8 2,6-Diamino-5-nitroso-4-pyrimidinol
M.W. 155.12 m.p. > 300° ....
WAVENUMBER CM⁻¹
WAVELENGTH IN MICRONS

M.W. 156.10 m.p. > 330°

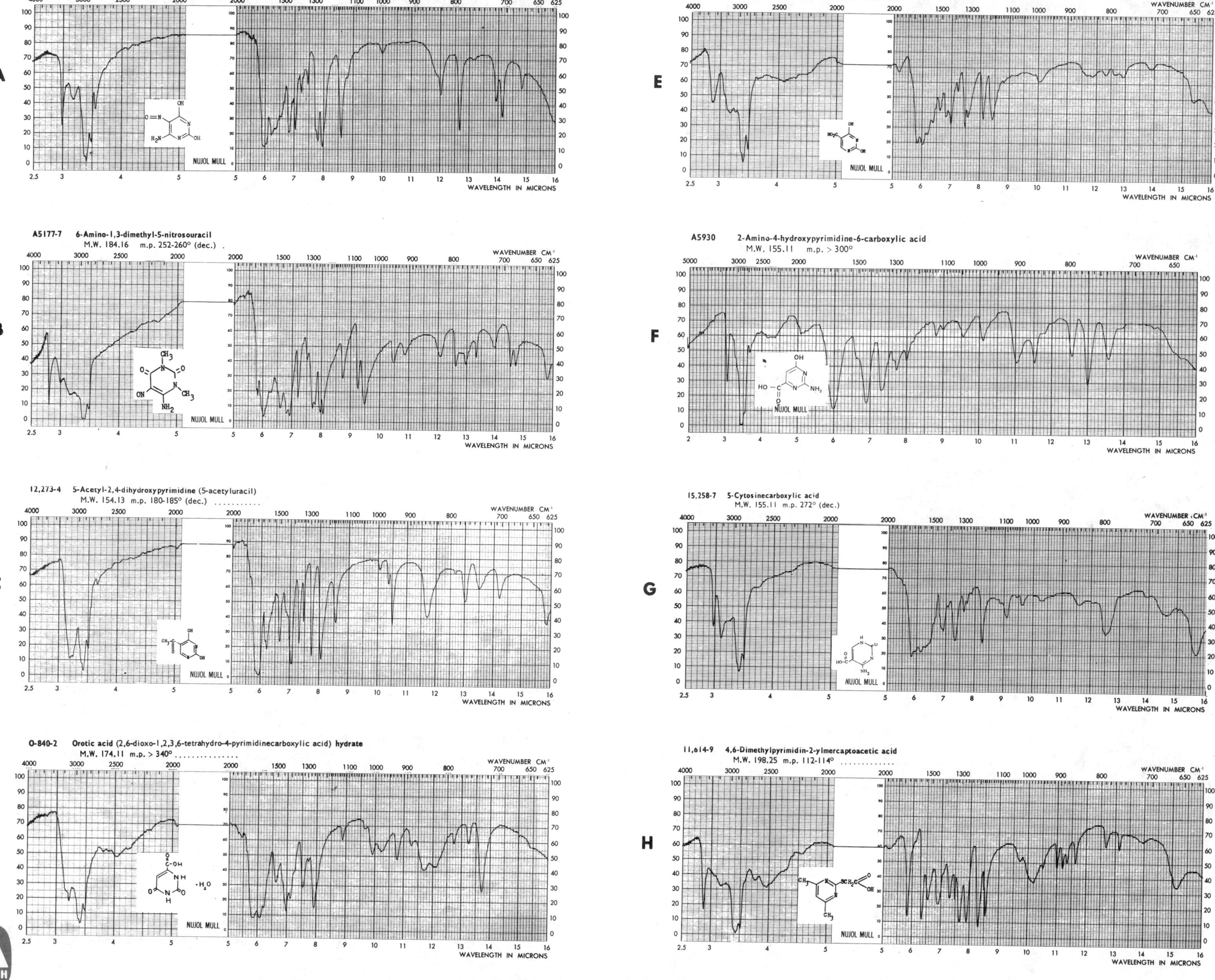

A

A5177-7 6-Amino-1,3-dimethyl-5-nitrosouracil
M.W. 184.16 m.p. 252-260° (dec.)

B

12,273-4 5-Acetyl-2,4-dihydroxypyrimidine (5-acetyluracil)
M.W. 154.13 m.p. 180-185° (dec.)

C

O-840-2 Orotic acid (2,6-dioxo-1,2,3,6-tetrahydro-4-pyrimidinecarboxylic acid) hydrate
M.W. 174.11 m.p. > 340°

D

acid)
M.W. 156.10 m.p. 283° (dec.)

E

A5930 2-Amino-4-hydroxypyrimidine-6-carboxylic acid
M.W. 155.11 m.p. > 300°

F

15,258-7 5-Cytosinecarboxylic acid
M.W. 155.11 m.p. 272° (dec.)

G

11,614-9 4,6-Dimethylpyrimidin-2-ylmercaptoacetic acid
M.W. 198.25 m.p. 112-114°

H

A

M500-3 **2-Mercaptoorotic acid** (6-hydroxy-2-mercaptopyrimidine-4-carboxylic acid)
M.W. 172.16 m.p. 296-297° (dec.)

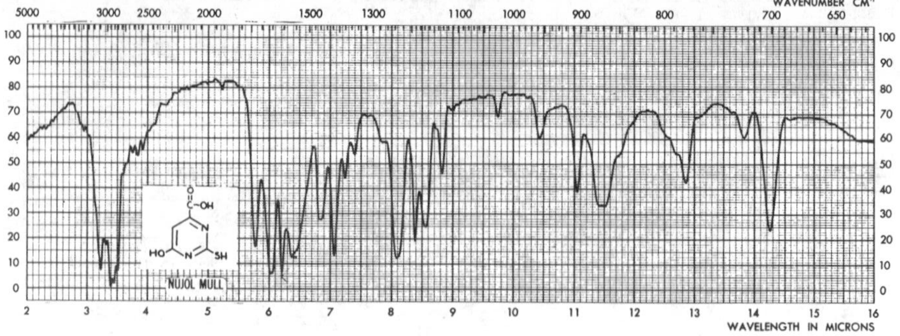

NUJOL MULL

B

13,054-0 **Orotic acid** (2,6-dioxo-1,2,3,6-tetrahydro-4-pyrimidinecarboxylic acid), **potassium salt**
M.W. 194.19 m.p. > 300°

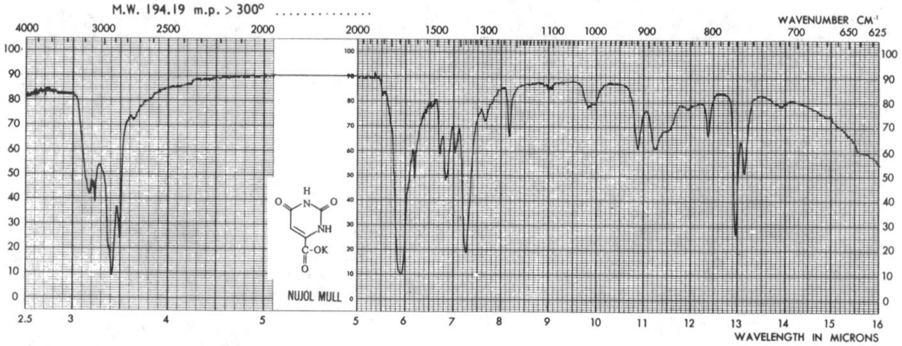

NUJOL MULL

C

22,478-2
Methyl orotate, 97% (orotic acid methyl ester)
FW 170.13 mp 244° (dec.) *Beil.* **25**,254 Disp. C

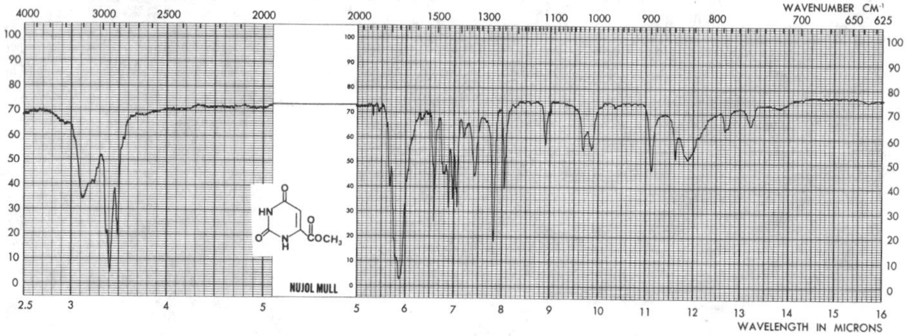

NUJOL MULL

D

22,456-1
2-Thioorotic acid, 97%
FW 172.16 mp >300° *IR* **2**,1194G Disp. D

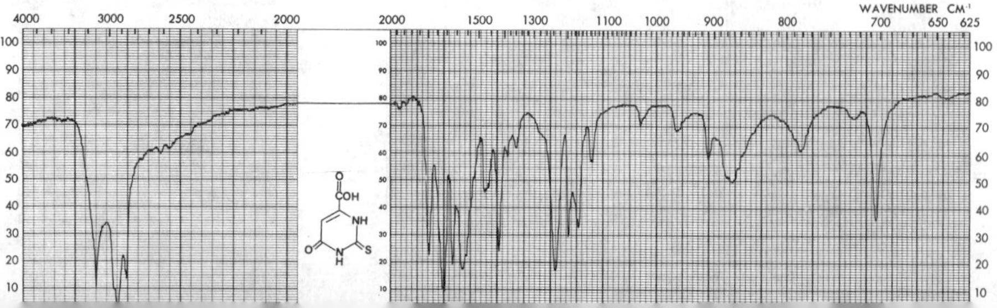

E

19,121-3
5-Aminoorotic acid, 99% (5-amino-2,6-dioxo-1,2,3,6-tetrahydro-4-pyrimidinecarboxylic acid)
FW 171.11 mp >300° *Beil.* **25**,264 Disp. C

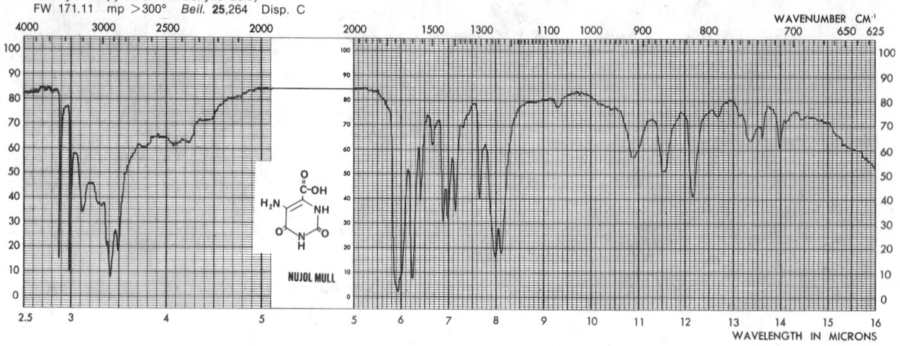

NUJOL MULL

F

18,528-0
5-Nitroorotic acid, potassium salt monohydrate, 98%
M.W. 257.21 m.p. >300° Beil. **25**,255

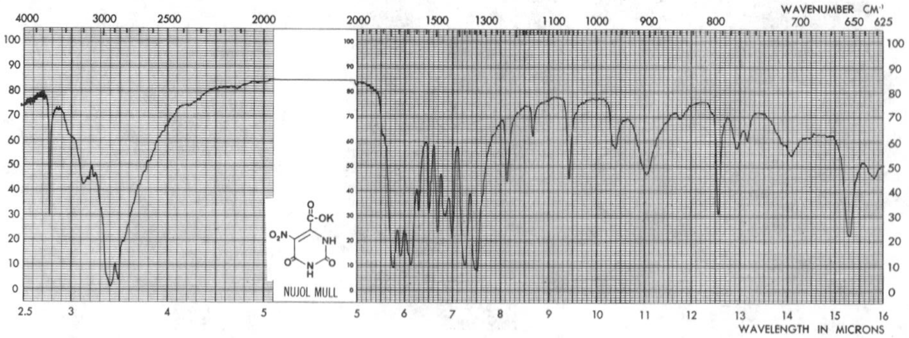

NUJOL MULL

G

85,525-1
5-Carbethoxy-2-thiouracil, 99% (ethyl 2-thiouracil-5-carboxylate)
FW 200.22 mp 249-255° (dec.) Disp. C

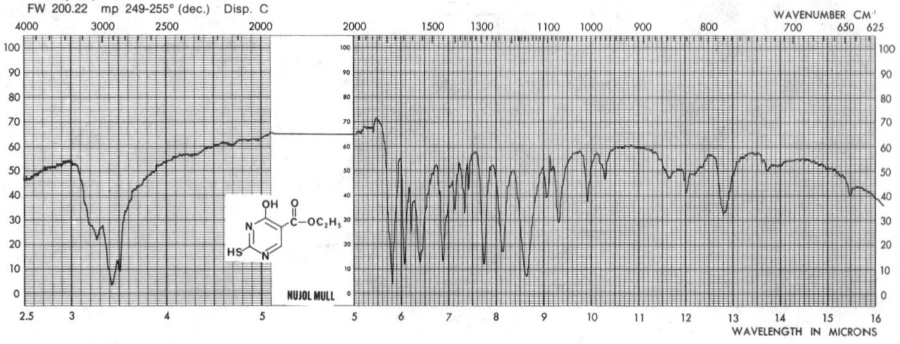

NUJOL MULL

H

14,596-3 **Ethyl 4-chloro-2-methylthio-5-pyrimidinecarboxylate**
M.W. 232.69 m.p. 60-63°

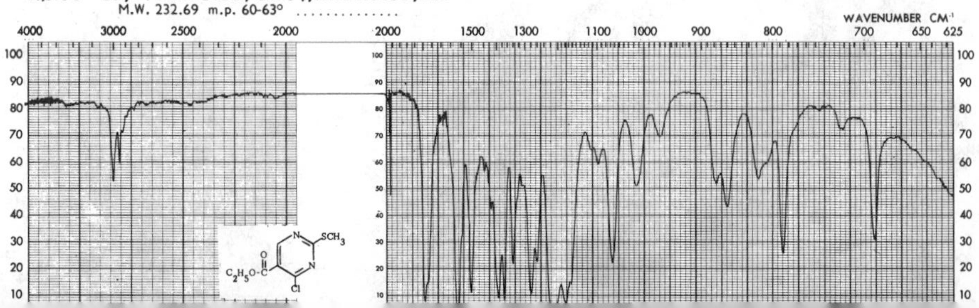

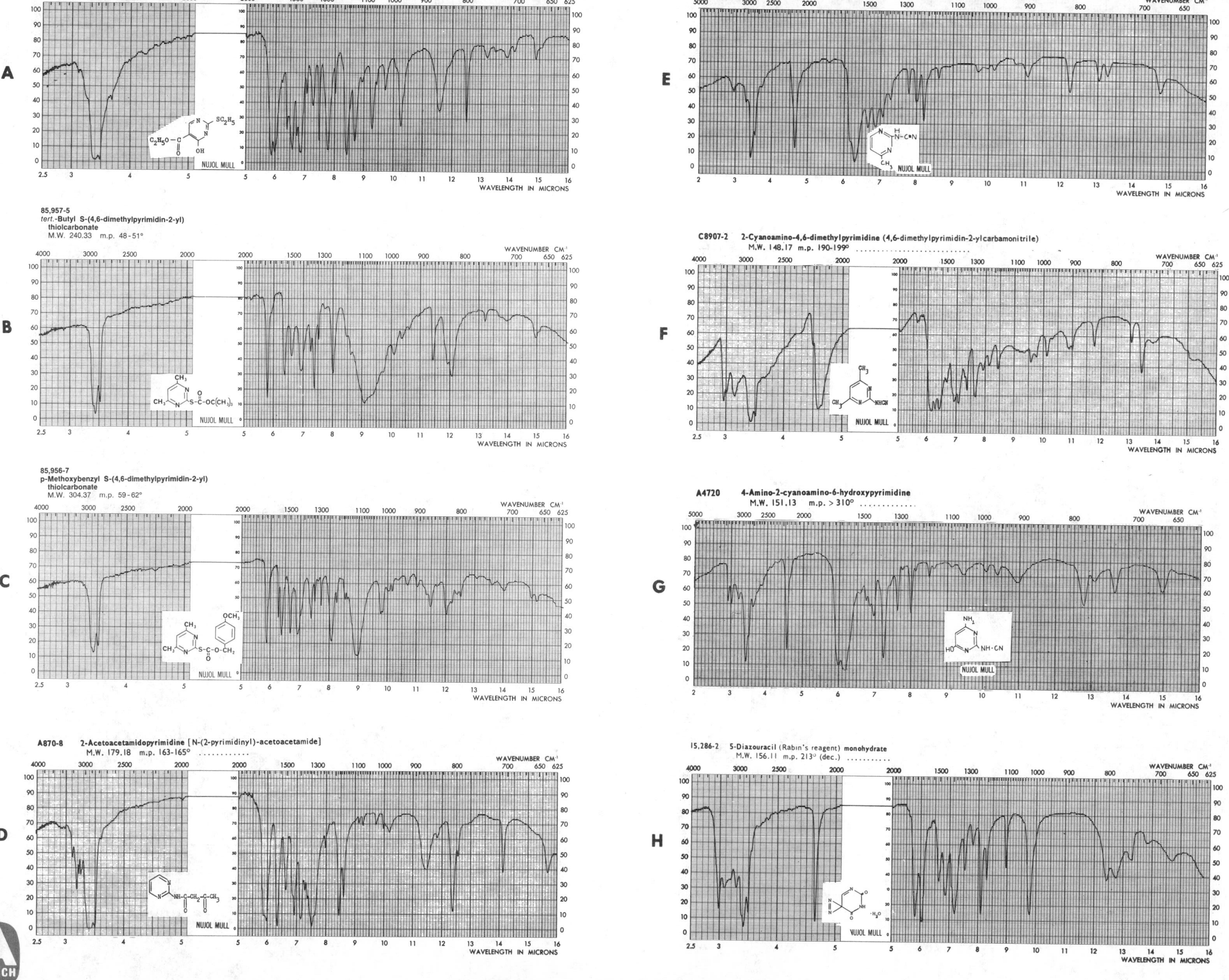

A

85,957-5
tert.-**Butyl S-(4,6-dimethylpyrimidin-2-yl) thiolcarbonate**
M.W. 240.33 m.p. 48-51°

B

85,956-7
p-Methoxybenzyl S-(4,6-dimethylpyrimidin-2-yl) thiolcarbonate
M.W. 304.37 m.p. 59-62°

C

A870-8 **2-Acetoacetamidopyrimidine** [N-(2-pyrimidinyl)-acetoacetamide]
M.W. 179.18 m.p. 163-165°

D

C8915-3 **2-Cyanoamino-4-methylpyrimidine**
M.W. 134.14 m.p. 155-160° (dec.)

E

C8907-2 **2-Cyanoamino-4,6-dimethylpyrimidine** (4,6-dimethylpyrimidin-2-ylcarbamonitrile)
M.W. 148.17 m.p. 190-199°

F

A4720 **4-Amino-2-cyanoamino-6-hydroxypyrimidine**
M.W. 151.13 m.p. > 310°

G

15,286-2 **5-Diazouracil** (Rabin's reagent) **monohydrate**
M.W. 156.11 m.p. 213° (dec.)

H

A 15,237-4 **N⁴-(2-Aminopyrimidin-4-yl)-sulfanilamide monohydrochloride**
M.W. 301.76 m.p. 281-285° (dec.)

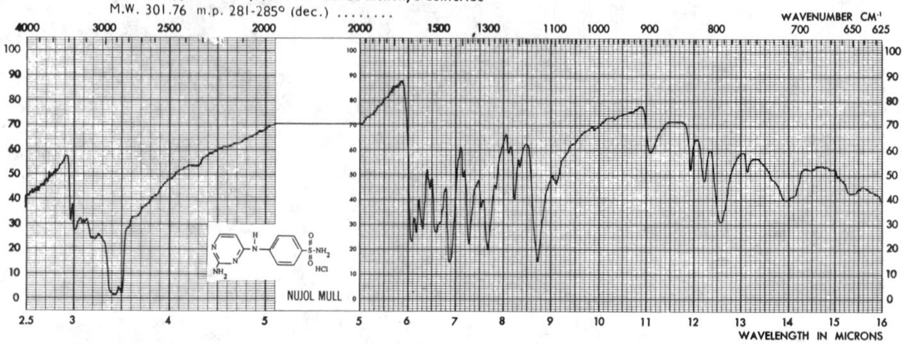

NUJOL MULL

B 15,241-2 **N⁴-(6-Aminopyrimidin-4-yl)-sulfanilamide monohydrochloride**
M.W. 301.76 m.p. 297-300° (dec.)

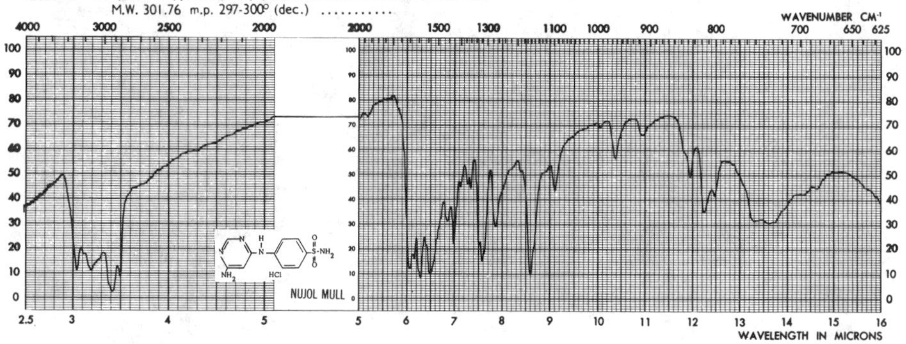

NUJOL MULL

C 21,185-0
Sulfamethazine, 99% [N^1-(4,6-dimethyl-2-pyrimidinyl)-sulfanilamide]
FW 278.34 mp 198-201° Disp. C

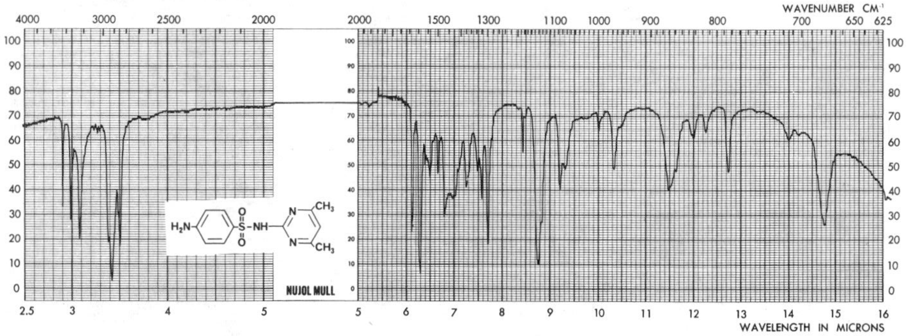

NUJOL MULL

D 12,032-4 **N-(4,6-Dimethyl-2-pyrimidinyl)-p-nitrobenzenesulfonamide [4,6-dimethyl-2-(p-nitrobenzenesulfonamido)-pyrimidine]**
M.W. 308.32 m.p. 219-220°

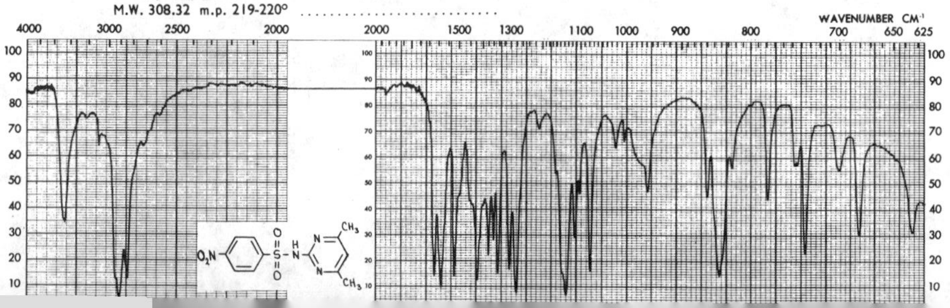

E 22,496-0
5-Methoxysulfadiazine, 99% [N^1-(5-methoxy-2-pyrimidinyl)sulfanilamide, sulfameter]
FW 280.31 mp 210-212° Disp. C

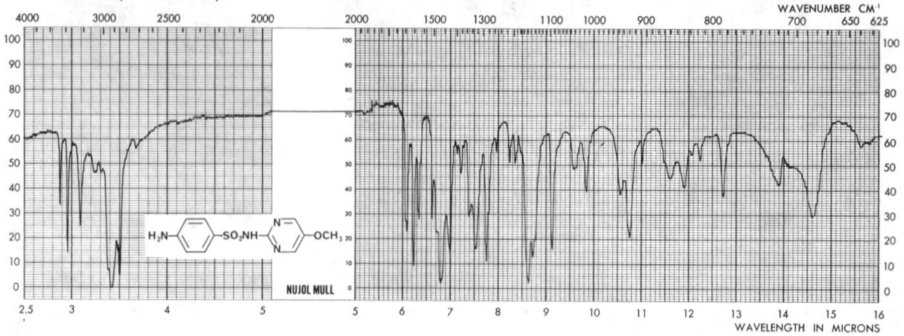

NUJOL MULL

F 85,225-2
Thymidine 5'-monophosphate, disodium salt dihydrate
M.W. 402.21 m.p. >300°

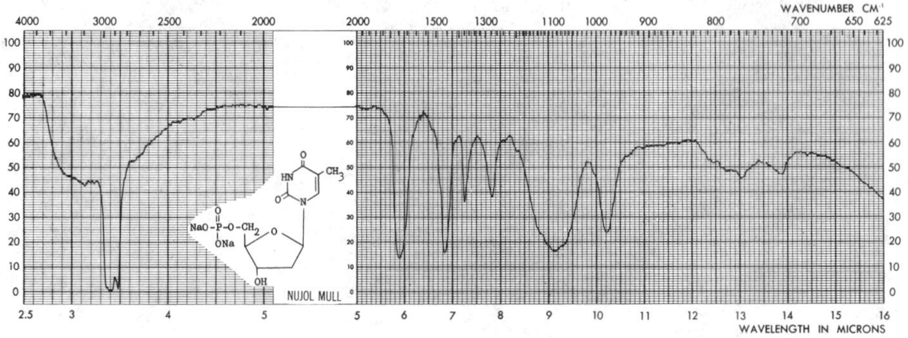

NUJOL MULL

G 85,209-0
Uridine 2',3'-cyclic monophosphate, sodium salt
M.W. 328.15 m.p. 166-170° (dec.)

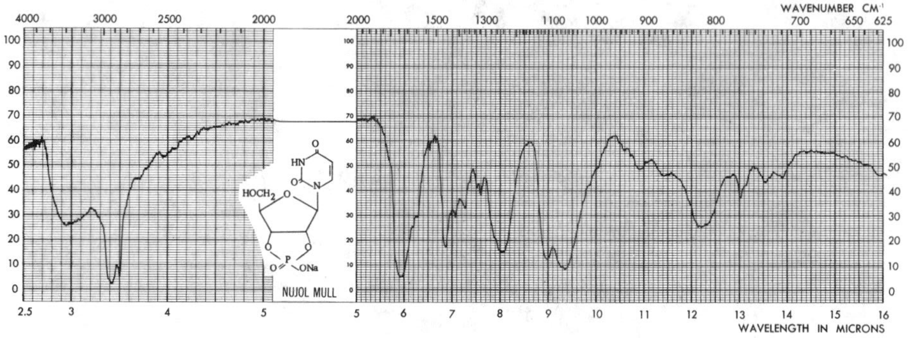

NUJOL MULL

H 85,799-8
Uridine 2'(3')-monophosphate, disodium salt, mixture of isomers
M.W. 368.15 m.p. 224° (dec.)

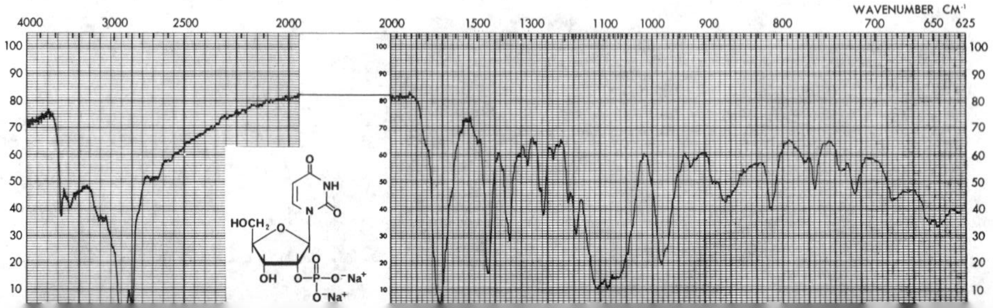

M.W. 388.15 m.p. 208-210° (dec.)

A

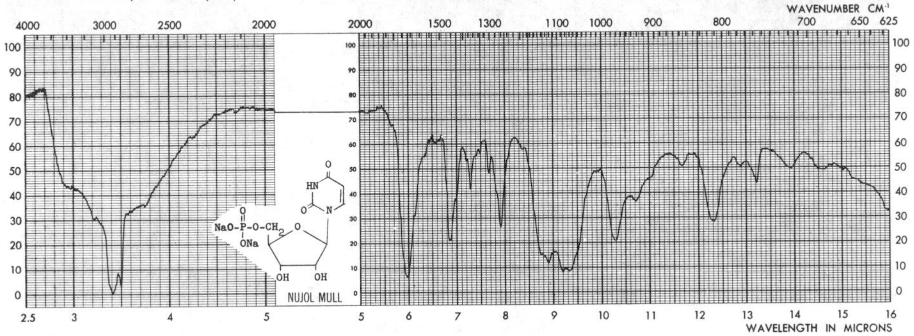

85,224-4
2'-Deoxyuridine 5'-monophosphate, disodium salt dihydrate
M.W. 388.18 m.p. >195° (dec.)

B

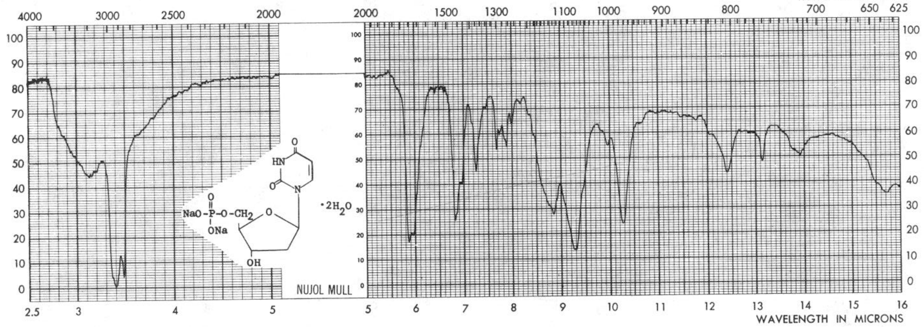

85,211-2
Uridine 5'-diphosphate, trisodium salt
M.W. 470.11 m.p. 195° (dec.)

C

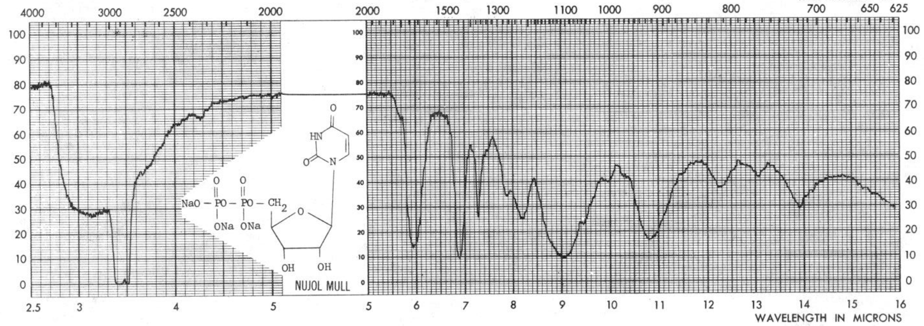

85,212-0
Uridine-5'-diphosphoglucose, disodium salt, 80% by enzymatic analysis (uridine diphosphate glucose)
M.W. 610.27 m.p. 170-190° (dec.)

D

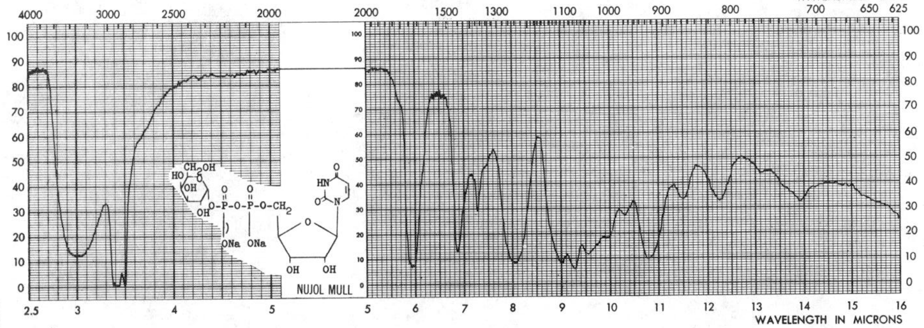

E

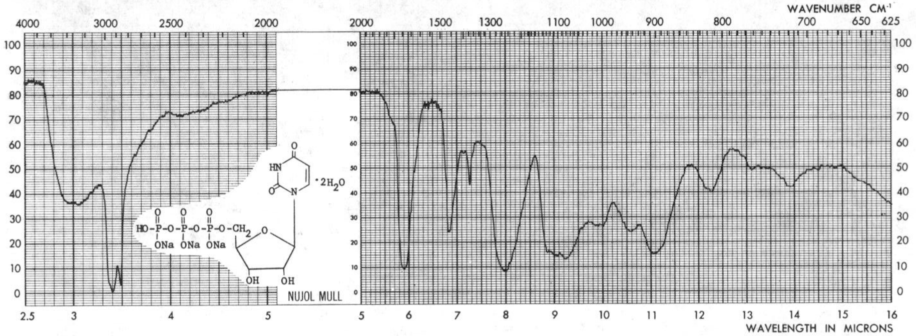

85,197-3
Cytidine-2'(3')-monophosphoric acid, 99+%, GOLD LABEL, mixture of isomers
M.W. 323.2 m.p. 239° (dec.)

F

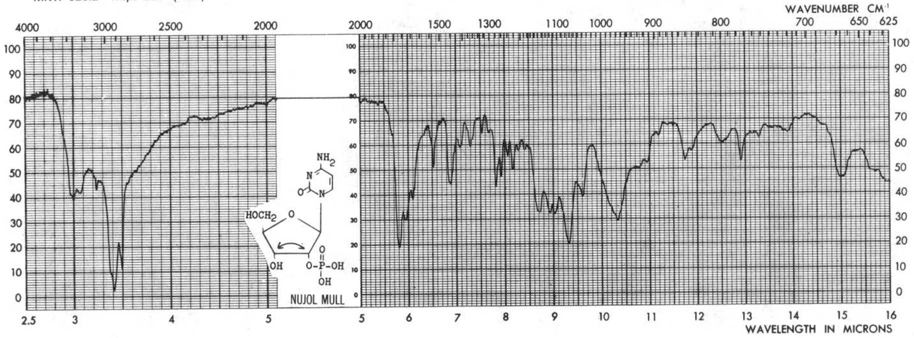

85,200-7
Cytidine-5'-monophosphoric acid, 99%
M.W. 323.2 m.p. 233° (dec.)

G

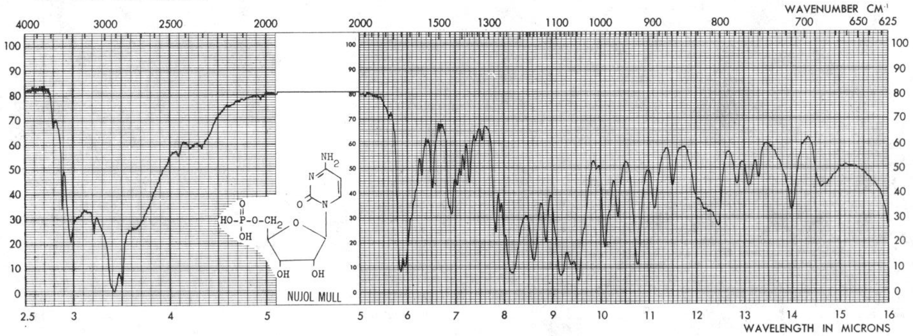

85,795-5
Cytidine 5'-monophosphate, disodium salt hydrate
M.W. 367.17 m.p. >300°

H

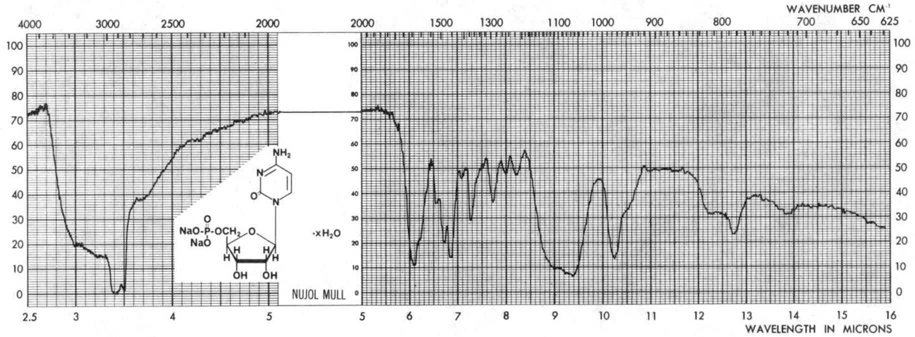

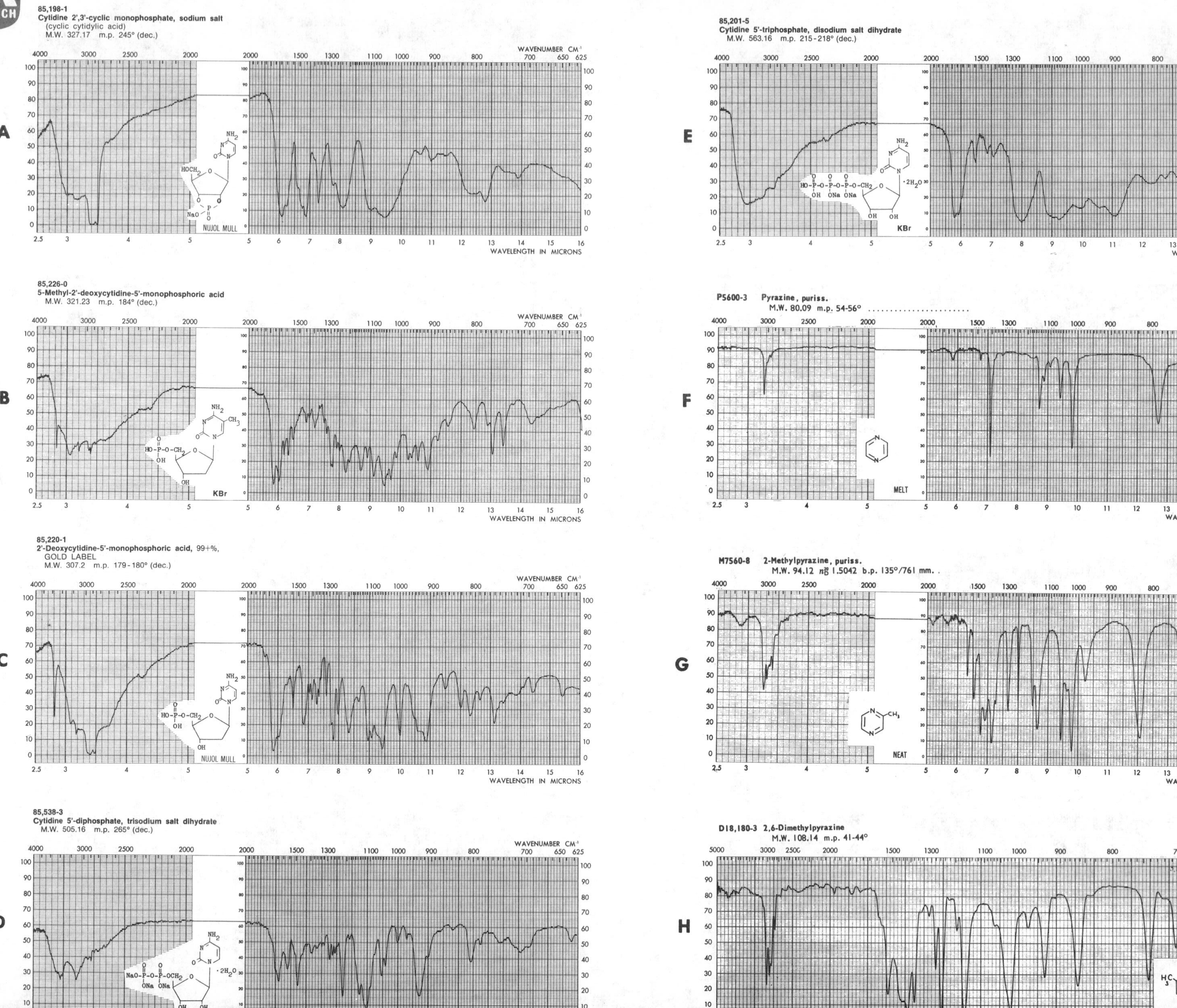
ALDRICH
A
85,198-1
Cytidine 2',3'-cyclic monophosphate, sodium salt
(cyclic cytidylic acid)
M.W. 327.17 m.p. 245° (dec.)
NUJOL MULL
B
85,226-0
5-Methyl-2'-deoxycytidine-5'-monophosphoric acid
M.W. 321.23 m.p. 184° (dec.)
KBr
C
85,220-1
2'-Deoxycytidine-5'-monophosphoric acid, 99+%,
GOLD LABEL
M.W. 307.2 m.p. 179-180° (dec.)
NUJOL MULL
D
85,538-3
Cytidine 5'-diphosphate, trisodium salt dihydrate
M.W. 505.16 m.p. 265° (dec.)
E
85,201-5
Cytidine 5'-triphosphate, disodium salt dihydrate
M.W. 563.16 m.p. 215-218° (dec.)
KBr
F
P5600-3 Pyrazine, puriss.
M.W. 80.09 m.p. 54-56°
MELT
G
M7560-8 2-Methylpyrazine, puriss.
M.W. 94.12 n_D^{20} 1.5042 b.p. 135°/761 mm.
NEAT
H
D18,180-3 2,6-Dimethylpyrazine
M.W. 108.14 m.p. 41-44°
WAVENUMBER CM⁻¹
WAVELENGTH IN MICRONS

A

Beil. 23,96 *HYGROSCOPIC*

NEAT

B

19,940-0
2,3-Dimethylpyrazine, 99%
FW 108.14 bp 156° n_D^{20} 1.5070 d 1.022
Beil. 23,95 Disp. C

NEAT

C

19,941-9
2,3,5-Trimethylpyrazine, 99%
FW 122.17 bp 171-172° n_D^{20} 1.5048 d 0.979
Beil. 23,97 Disp. C

NEAT

D

18,393-8
Tetramethylpyrazine, 98%
M.W. 136.2 m.p. 84-86° b.p. 190° Beil. 23,99

NUJOL MULL

E

13,248-9 **Chloropyrazine**
M.W. 114.54 n_D^{20} 1.5323

NEAT

F

13,249-7 **2,6-Dichloropyrazine, tech.**
M.W. 148.98 m.p. 55-57°

MELT

G

C5700-6 **2-Chloro-3-methylpyrazine, tech., 70%**
M.W. 128.56 n_D^{20} 1.5296 ....

NEAT

H

C3840-0 **3-Chloro-2,5-dimethylpyrazine**
M.W. 142.59 n_D^{20} 1.5240 ....

NEAT

A 13,253-5 Pyrazinol, sodium salt, tech.
M.W. 118.07 m.p.>300°

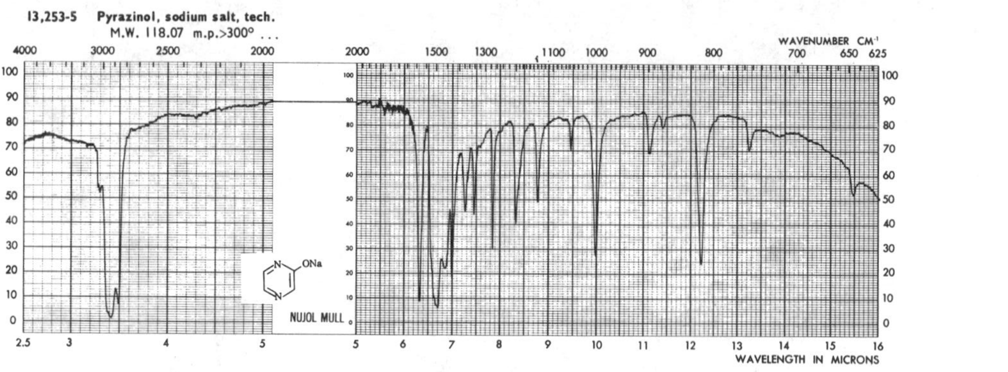

B 11,365-4 1,2-Dihydro-1-[2-(2-pyridyl)-ethyl]-3,6-pyridazinedione
M.W. 217.23 m.p. 217-219°

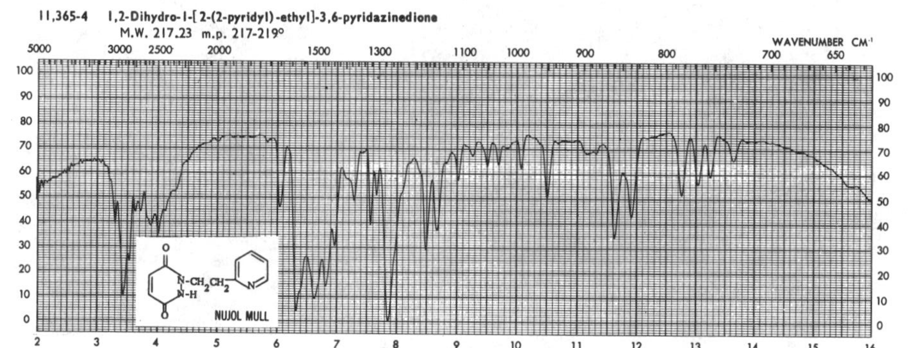

C A7695-8 Aminopyrazine, puriss.
M.W. 95.11 m.p. 119-120°

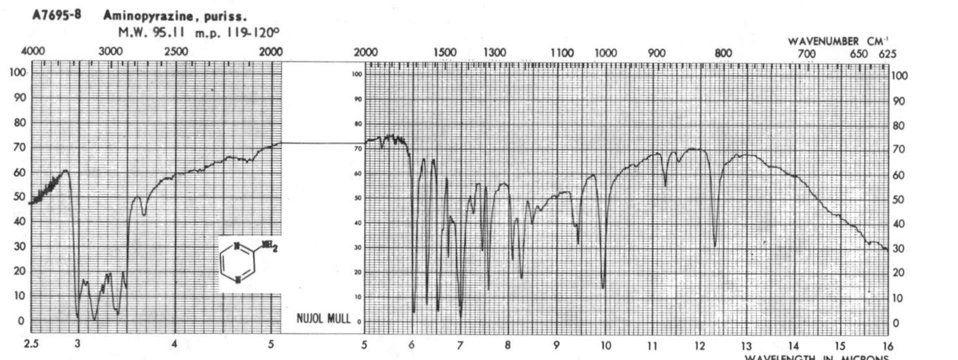

D 13,250-0 2-Amino-6-chloropyrazine
M.W. 129.55 m.p. 150-153°

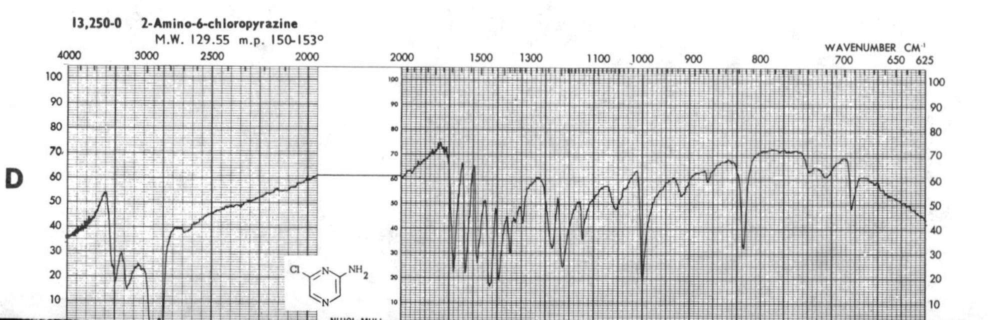

E A7698-2 3-Aminopyrazine-2-carboxylic acid, puriss.
M.W. 139.11 m.p. 210° (dec.)

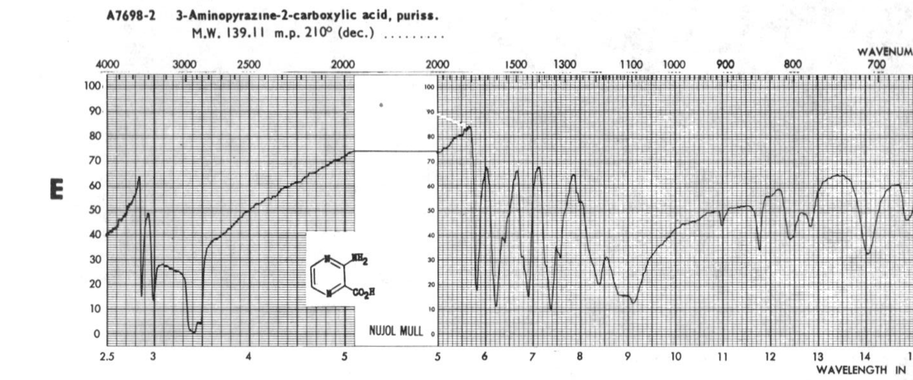

F P5610-0 2-Pyrazinecarboxylic acid
M.W. 124.10 m.p. 222-225°

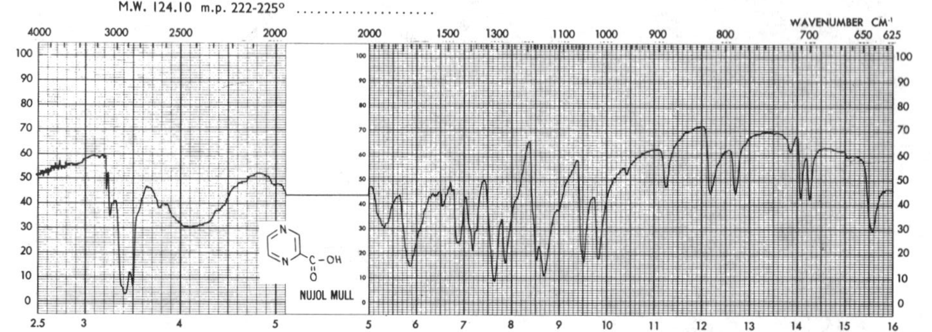

G P5620-8 2,3-Pyrazinedicarboxylic acid
M.W. 168.11 m.p. 188° (dec.)

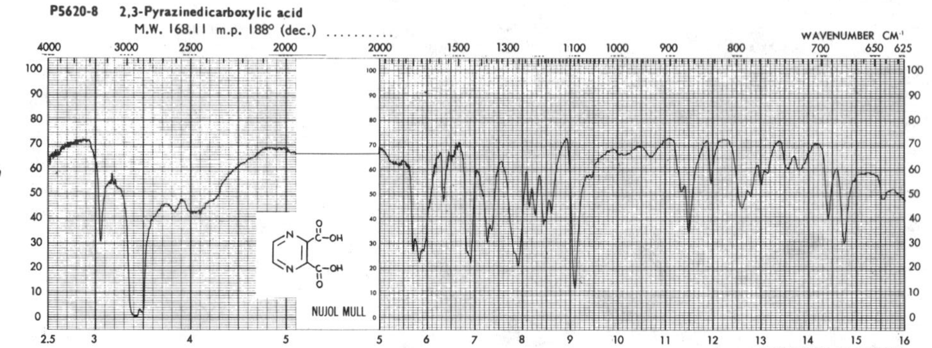

H P5622 2,5-Pyrazinedicarboxylic acid

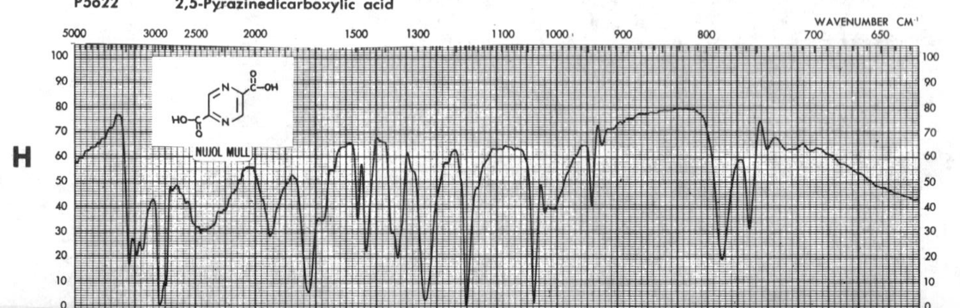

M.W. 123.12 m.p. 189-194°

A

P5615-1 2,3-Pyrazinedicarboxamide
M.W. 166.14 m.p. 248° (dec.) ....

B

86,162-6
5-Acetoxymethyl-2-amino-3-cyanopyrazine, 95%
(5-amino-6-cyano-2-pyrazinylmethyl acetate)
FW 192.18 mp 141-142° Disp. C

C

86,156-1
4-[N-(2-Amino-3-cyano-5-pyrazinylmethyl)-N-methylamino]benzoic acid, 98%
FW 283.29 mp 261° (dec.) Disp. C,O

D

benzoic acid, 98%
FW 269.27 mp 273° (dec.) Disp. C,O

E

10,677-1
2,3-Dihydro-5,6-diphenylpyrazine, 98%
M.W. 234.3 m.p. 160-163°

F

D20,850 5,6-Diphenyl-3-hydroxy-1,2,4-triazine
M.W. 249.27 m.p. 225° (dec.) ....

G

12,329-3 6-Azauracil [as-triazine-3,5(2H,4H)-dione]
M.W. 113.08 m.p. 274-275° ....

H

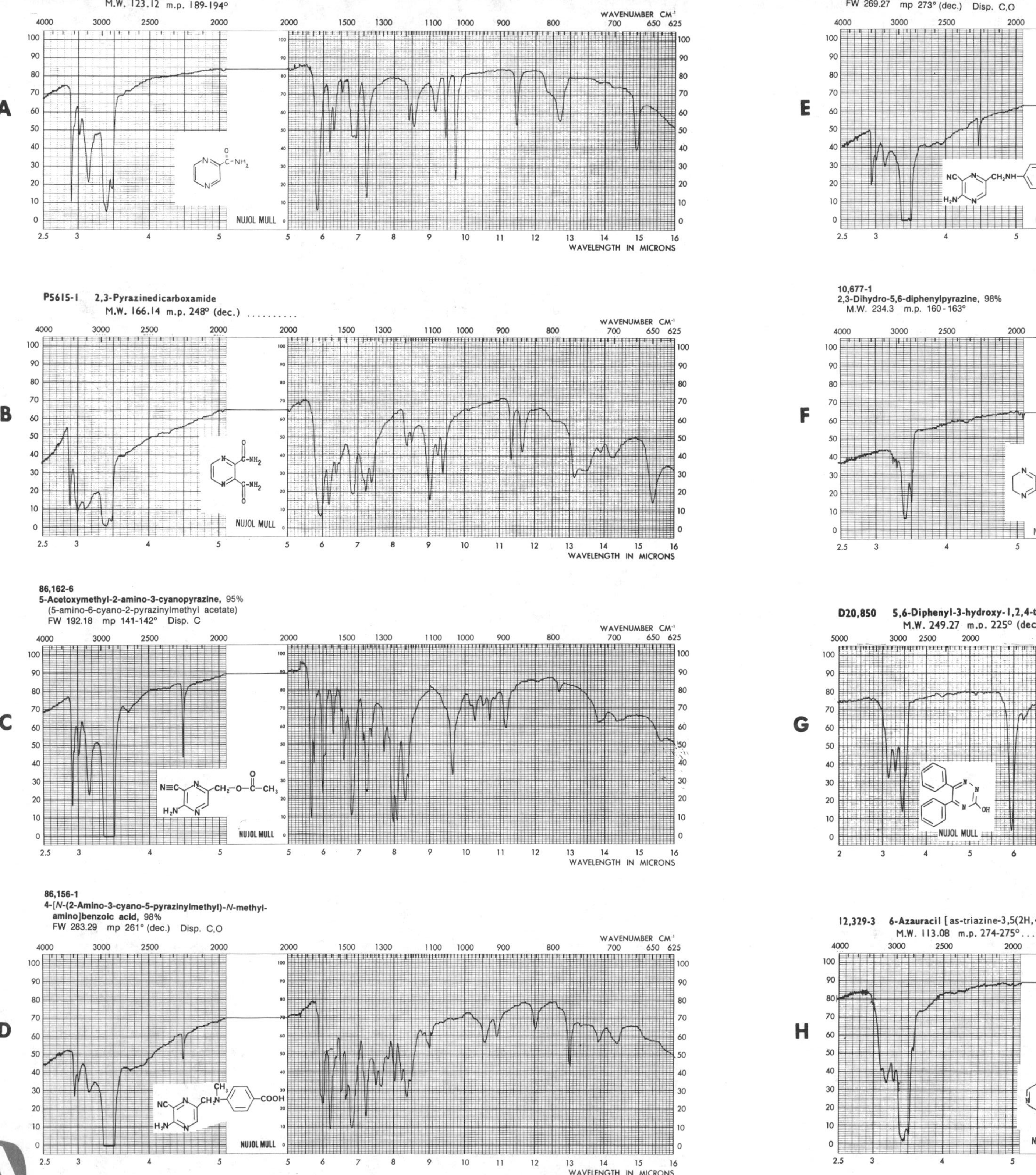

A

11,518-5 **6-Azauridine 2',3',5'-triacetate** [2-β-D-ribofuranosyl-as-triazine-3,5(2H,4H)-dione 2',3',5'-triacetate]
M.W. 371.30 m.p. 98-101°

NUJOL MULL

B

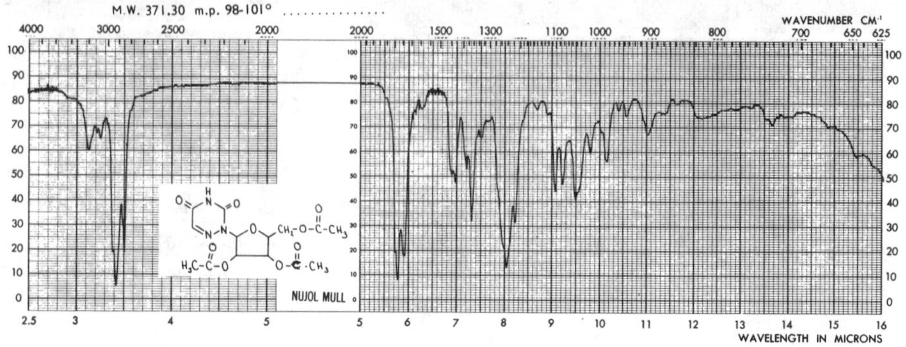

21,693-3
6-Azathymine, 98%
FW 127.10 mp 210-212° *Beil.* **26**,227 Disp. C

NUJOL MULL

C

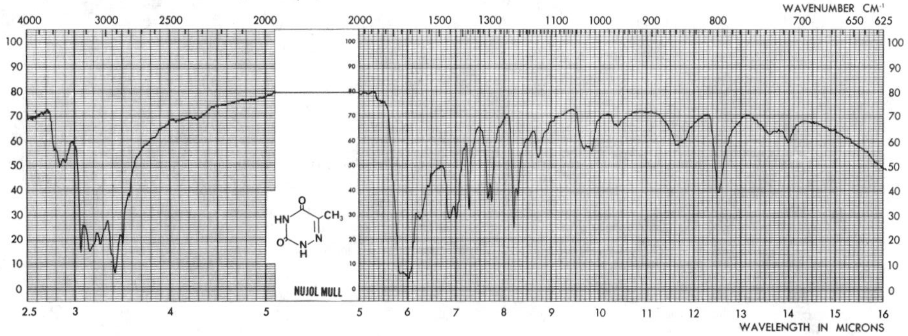

10,062-5 **3-Amino-1,2,4-triazine**
M.W. 96.09 m.p. 172-175°

NUJOL MULL

D

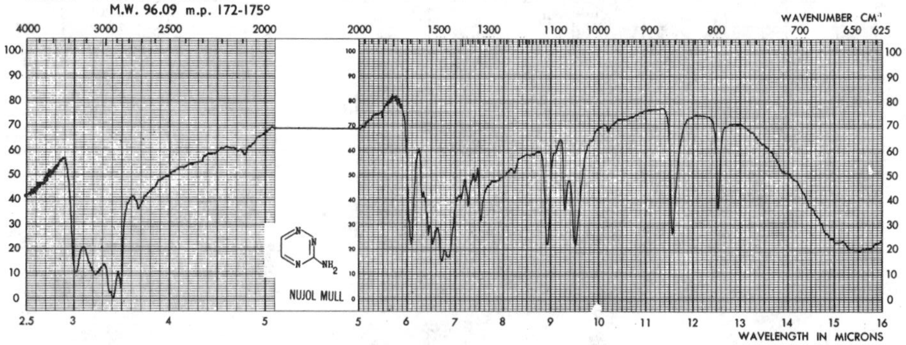

13,346-9 **3-Amino-5,6-dimethyl-1,2,4-triazine**
M.W. 124.15 m.p. 210-212°

E

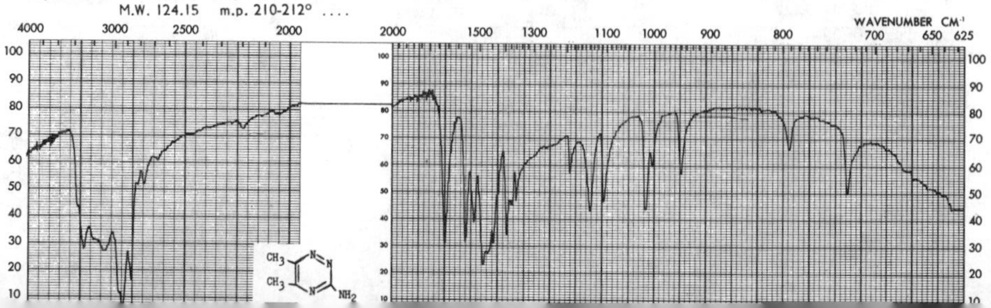

15,063-0 **6-Azacytosine**
M.W. 112.09 m.p. 300°

NUJOL MULL

F

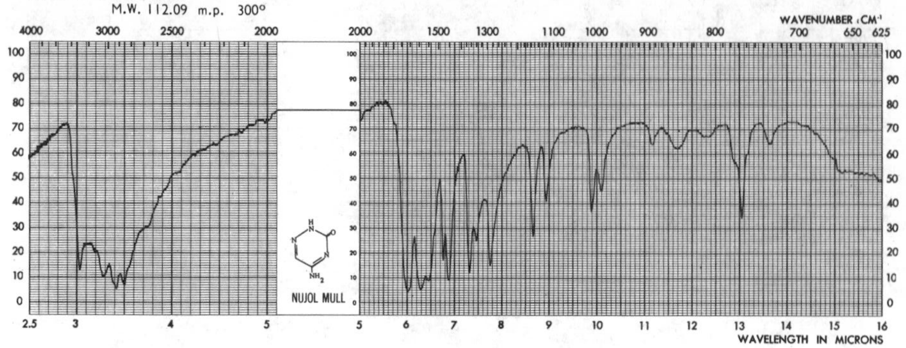

20,940-6
6-Aza-2-thiouridine, 99%
FW 261.26 mp 201-203° Disp. C

NUJOL MULL

G

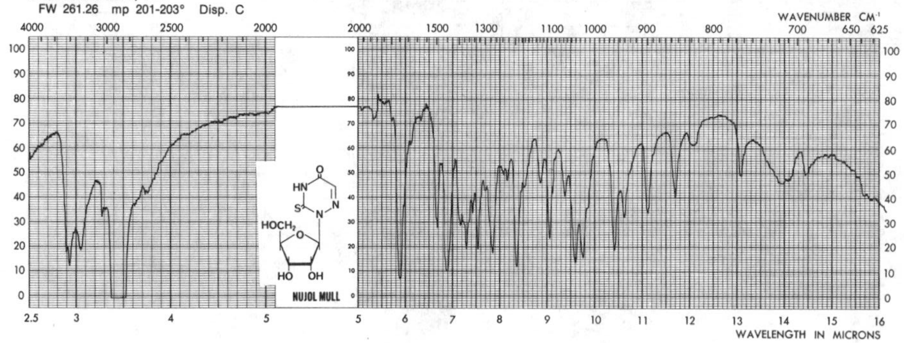

16,041-5
3-(2-Pyridyl)-5,6-diphenyl-1,2,4-triazine, 99+%, GOLD LABEL [5,6-diphenyl-3-(2-pyridyl)-1,2,4-triazine, PDT]
M.W. 310.36 m.p. 191-193°

NUJOL MULL

H

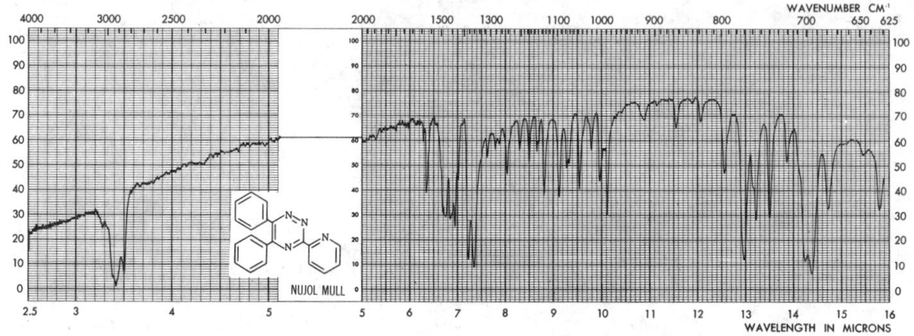

22,260-7
5,7-Dihydro-5,5,7,7-tetramethyl-3-(3-nitrophenyl)-furo[3,4-e]-1,2,4-triazine, 99%
FW 300.32 mp 167-168° Disp. C

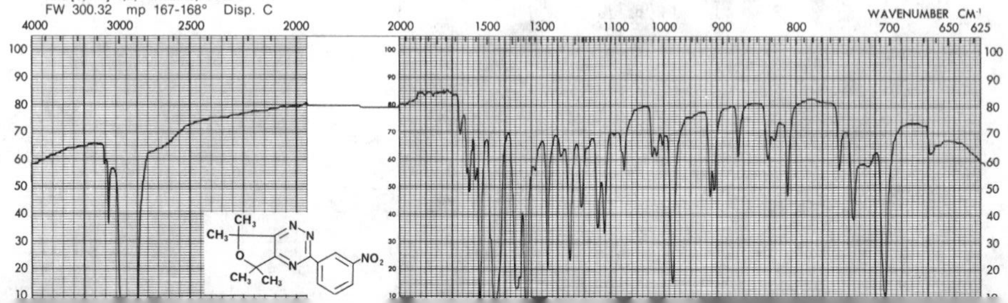

A

M.W. 568.5 m.p. >300

B

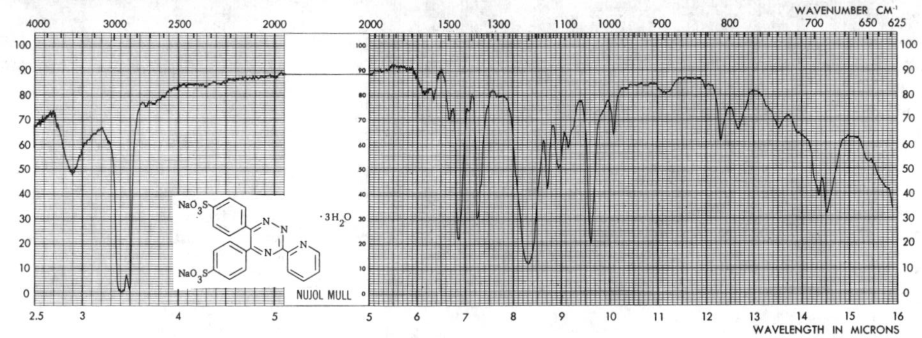

T4605-1 s-Triazine
M.W. 81.08 m.p. 77-79°

C

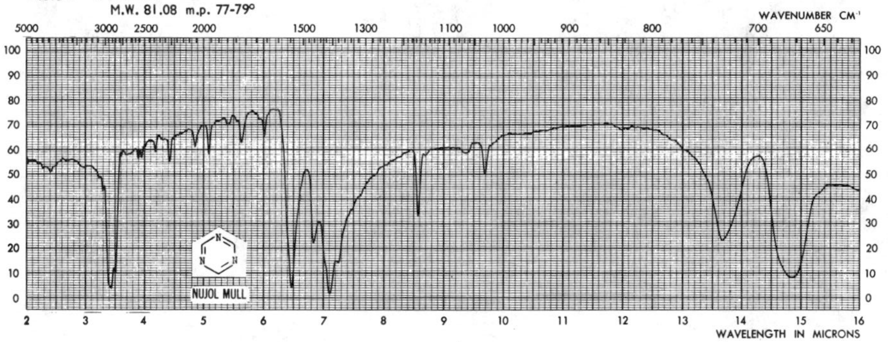

18,423-3
Cyanuric fluoride (2,4,6-trifluoro-1,3,5-triazine)
M.W. 135.05

D

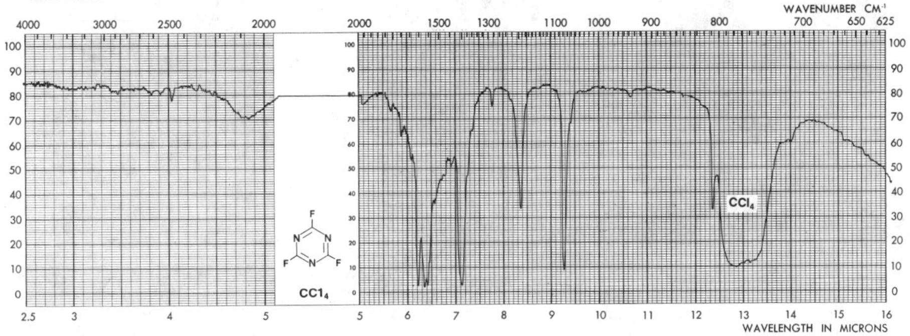

C9,550-1
Cyanuric chloride, 99% (2,4,6-trichloro-1,3,5-triazine)
M.W. 184.41 m.p. 145.5-148.5° b.p. 190°
Beil. **26**,35 Fieser **3**,72 *LACHRYMATOR*

E

2,4-Dichloro-6-methoxy-s-triazine, 95+%
FW 179.99 mp 86-88° bp 132-134°/49mm.
Disp. C

F

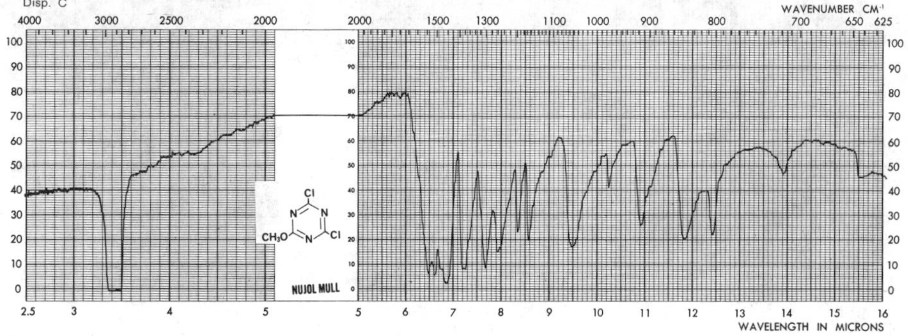

85,241-4
5-Azauracil
M.W. 113.08 m.p. 266-269° (dec.) Beil. **26**(2),120

G

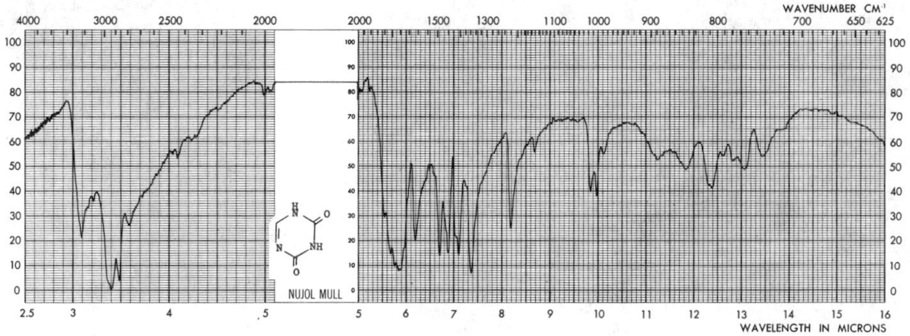

C9,545-5
Cyanuric acid (1,3,5-triazine-2,4,6-triol)
M.W. 129.08 m.p. >360° Beil. **26**,239

H

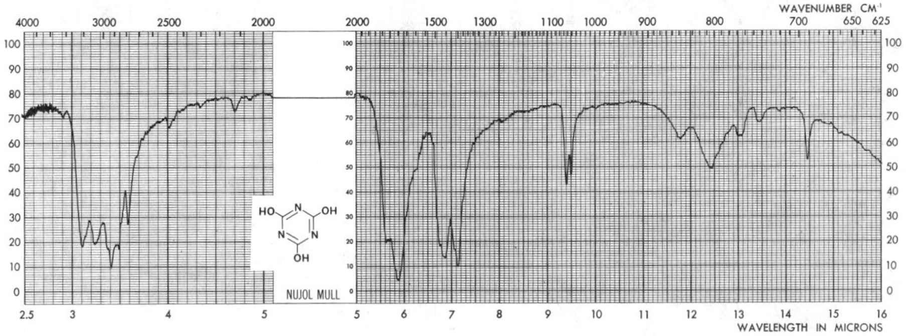

15,366-4 **2,4,6-Triphenoxy-s-triazine**
M.W. 357.37 m.p. 232-234°

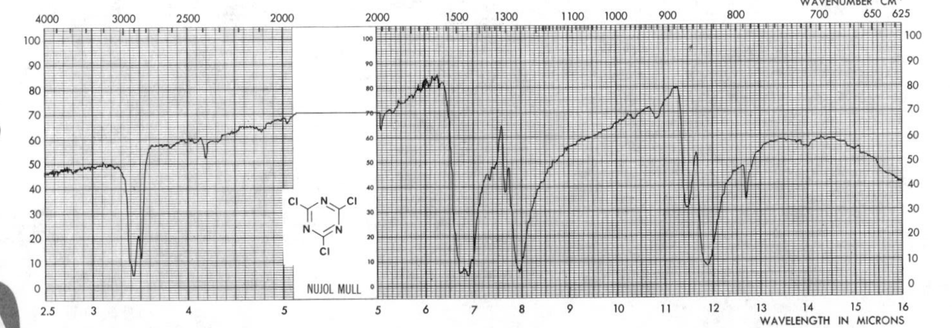

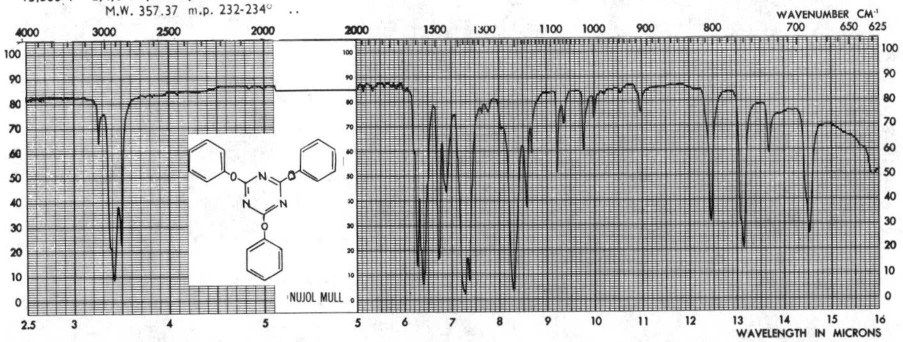

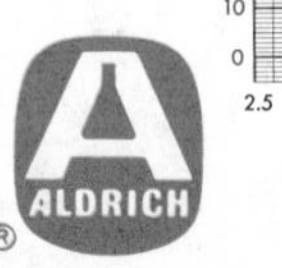

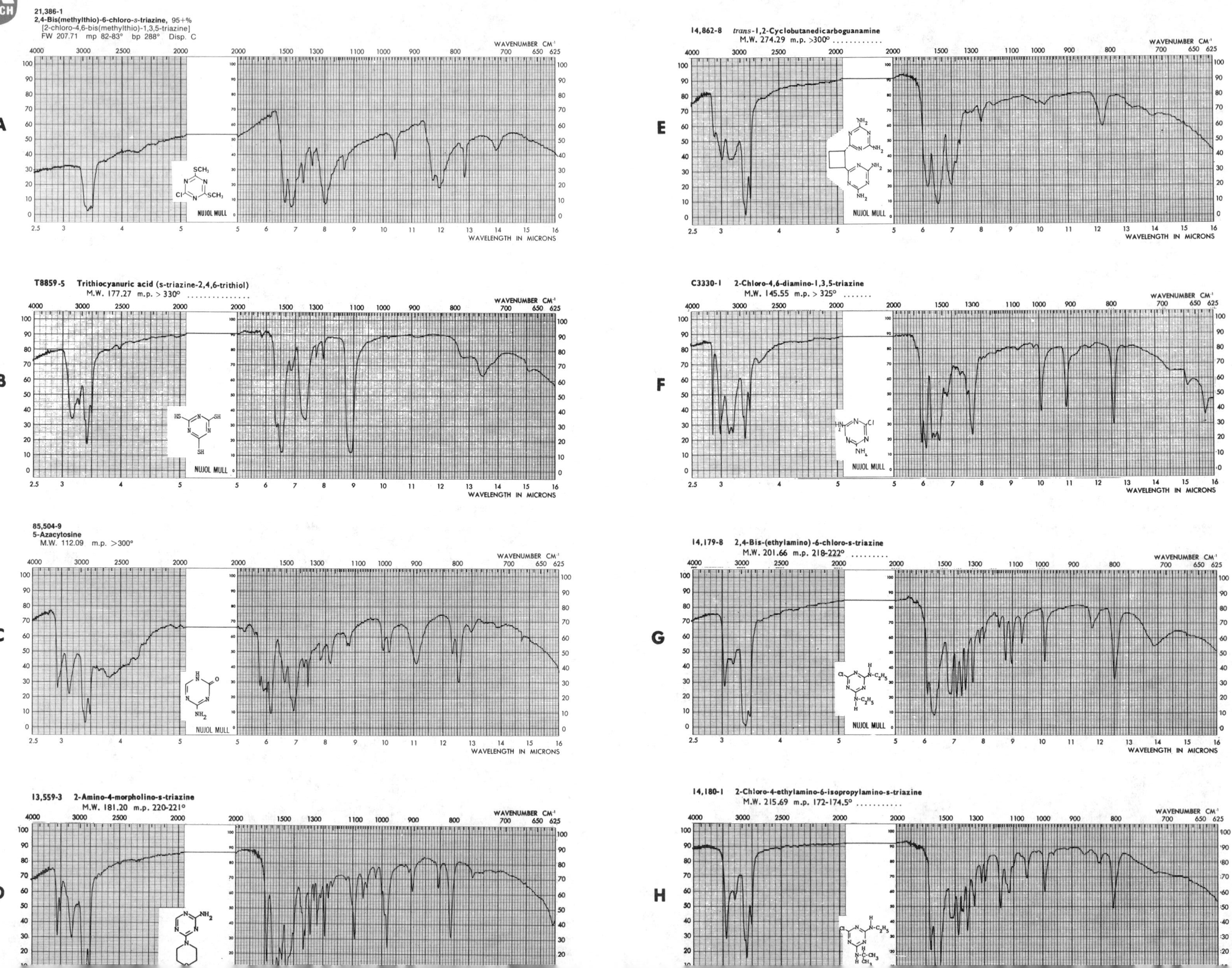
ALDRICH
A
21,386-1
2,4-Bis(methylthio)-6-chloro-s-triazine, 95+%
[2-chloro-4,6-bis(methylthio)-1,3,5-triazine]
FW 207.71 mp 82-83° bp 288° Disp. C
NUJOL MULL
B
T8859-5 Trithiocyanuric acid (s-triazine-2,4,6-trithiol)
M.W. 177.27 m.p. > 330°
NUJOL MULL
C
85,504-9
5-Azacytosine
M.W. 112.09 m.p. >300°
NUJOL MULL
D
13,559-3 2-Amino-4-morpholino-s-triazine
M.W. 181.20 m.p. 220-221°
E
14,862-8 trans-1,2-Cyclobutanedicarboguanamine
M.W. 274.29 m.p. >300°
NUJOL MULL
F
C3330-1 2-Chloro-4,6-diamino-1,3,5-triazine
M.W. 145.55 m.p. > 325°
NUJOL MULL
G
14,179-8 2,4-Bis-(ethylamino)-6-chloro-s-triazine
M.W. 201.66 m.p. 218-222°
NUJOL MULL
H
14,180-1 2-Chloro-4-ethylamino-6-isopropylamino-s-triazine
M.W. 215.69 m.p. 172-174.5°
WAVENUMBER CM⁻¹
WAVELENGTH IN MICRONS

A

M.W. 187.21 m.p. 226-228°

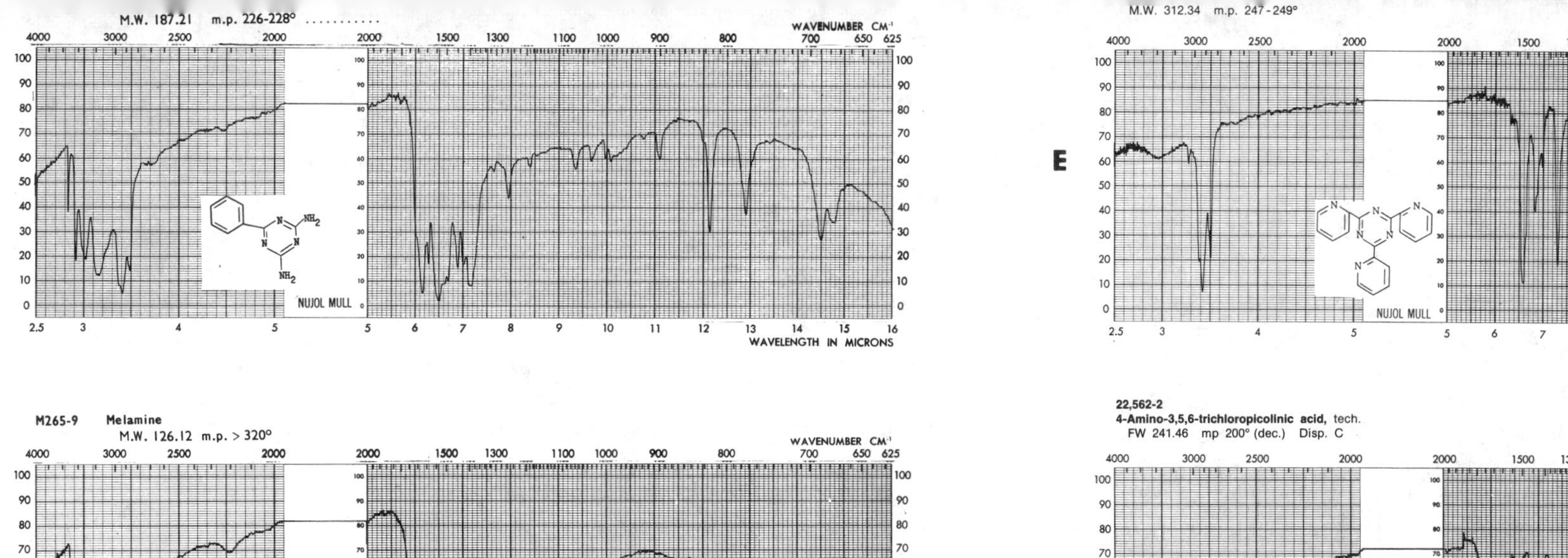

B

M265-9 Melamine
M.W. 126.12 m.p. > 320°

C

10,624-0 Trichloromelamine (N^2,N^4,N^6-trichloro-2,4,6-triamino-s-triazine)
M.W. 229.46 m.p. > 300°

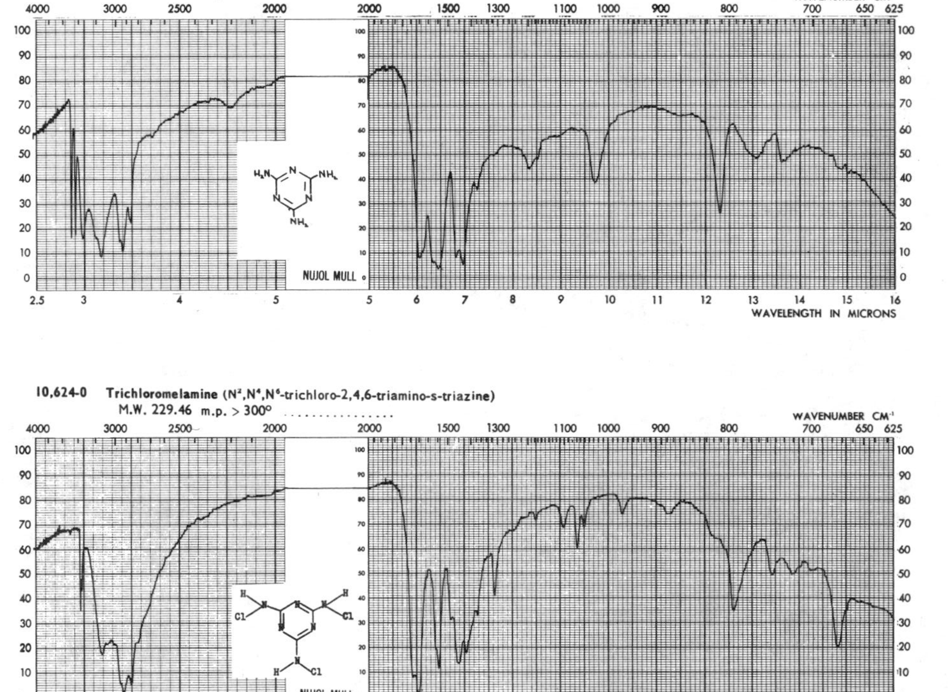

D

16,319-8
1-Ethoxy-4-(dichloro-s-triazinyl)-naphthalene
[2,4-dichloro-6-(4-ethoxy-1-naphth-
triazine, EDTN]
M.W. 320.18 m.p. 104-106°

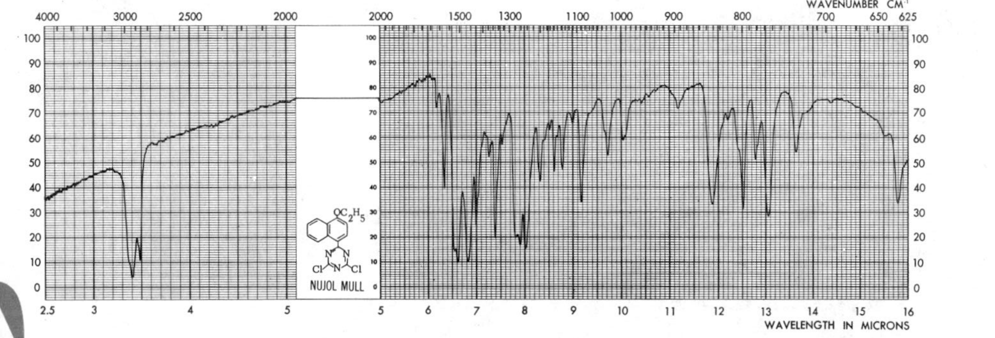

E

M.W. 312.34 m.p. 247-249°

22,562-2
4-Amino-3,5,6-trichloropicolinic acid, tech.
FW 241.46 mp 200° (dec.) Disp. C

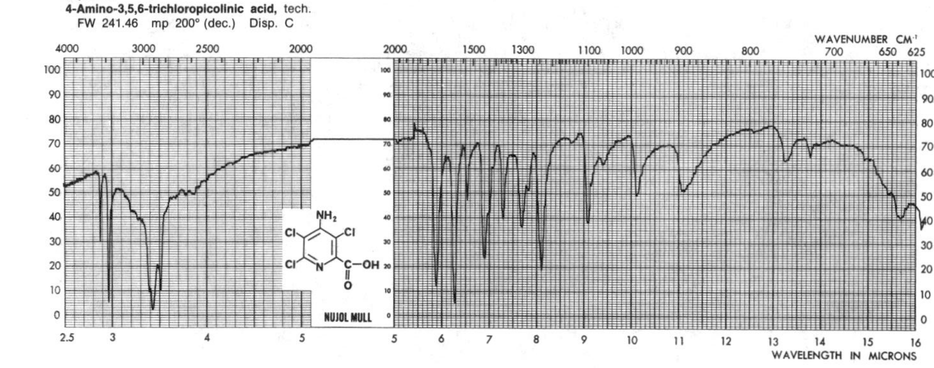

22,588-6
4,6-Dimethyl-2-hydroxypyrimidine dihydrate, 97%
FW 160.17 mp 190-193° *Beil.* **24**,93 Disp. C

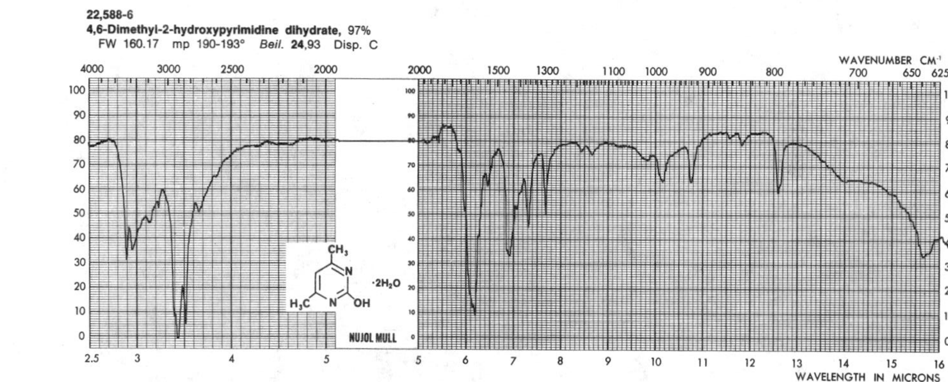

6-MEMBERED FUSED AROMATIC HETEROCYCLES

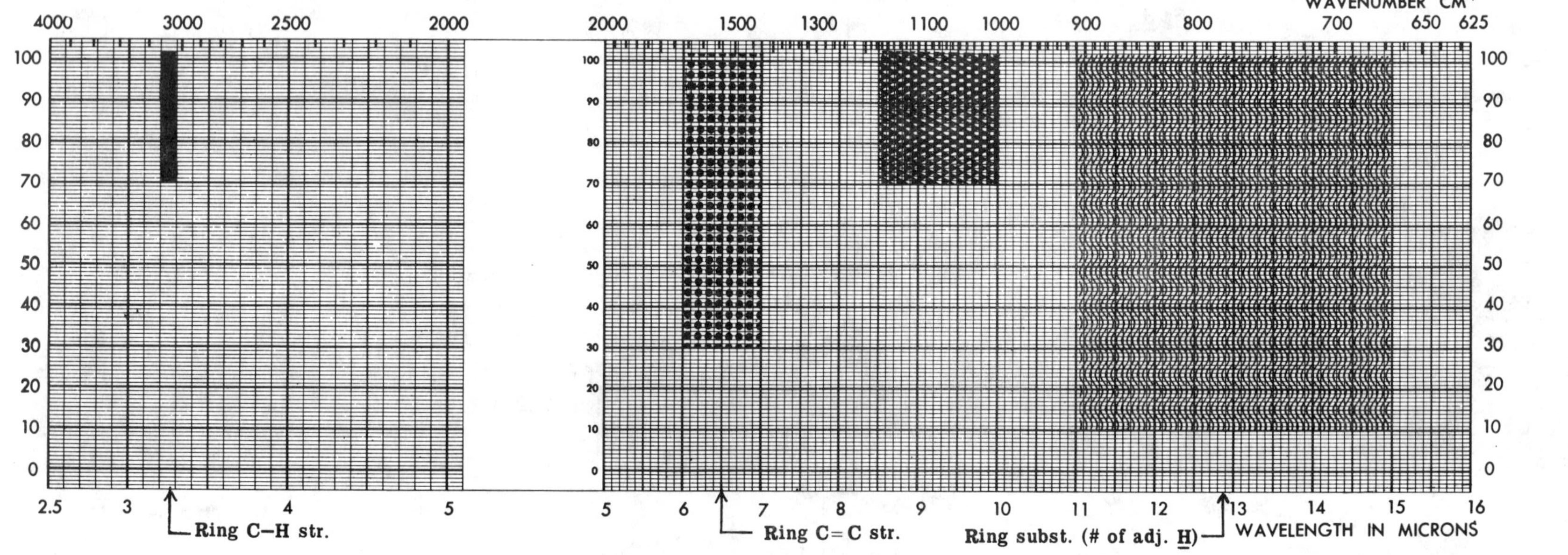

The heterocyclic ring fused to either another heterocyclic or carbocyclic aromatic ring displays bands very similar in position and intensity to those of the carbocyclic aromatics. The substitution patterns between 11 and 15 μ (910 – 665 cm^{-1}) remain quite useful in identifying the positions of substituents on the ring.

A hydroxyl, amino or mercapto group on the carbon atom adjacent or para to a ring nitrogen atom results in the formation of the corresponding keto, imine or thione tautomer.

Variations in the OH stretch region as a result of hydrogen bonding between the free carboxylic acid proton and the ring nitrogen atom can be observed in the quinolinecarboxylic acids. (See spectra 1394G—1396G). The carbonyl position also varies considerably.

A

M.W. 129.16 n_D^{20} 1.6230 b.p. 237°

NEAT

B

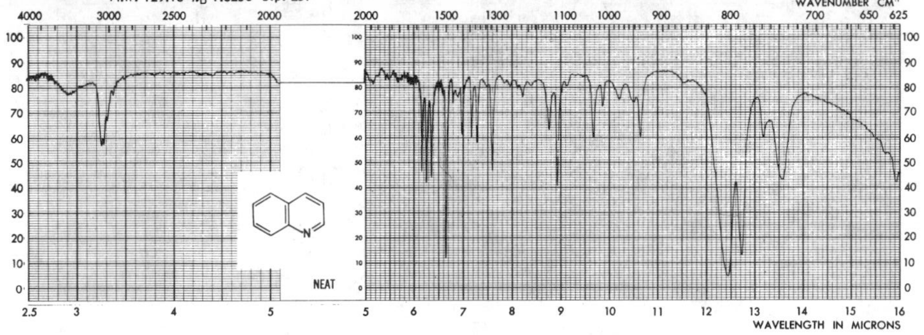

B3540-7 2,2'-Biquinoline
M.W. 256.31 m.p. 193-196°

NUJOL MULL

C

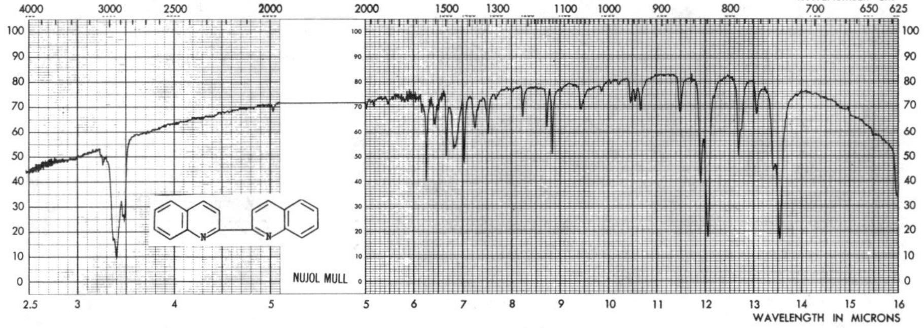

Q80-9 Quinaldine (2-methylquinoline), 98+%
M.W. 143.19 n_D^{20} 1.6108 b.p. 247.6° ...

NEAT

D

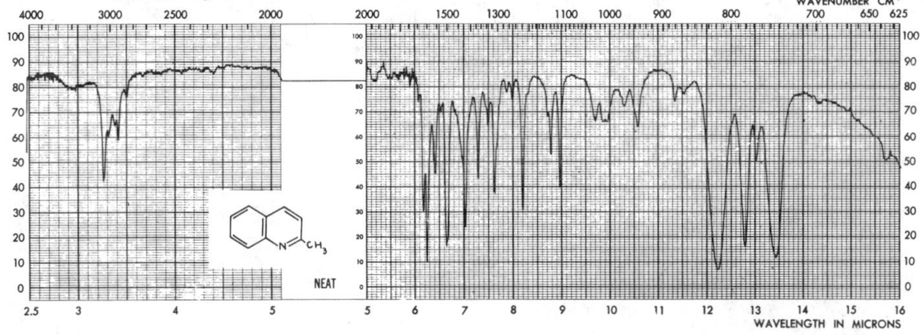

15,828-3
Lepidine, 99% (4-methylquinoline)
M.W. 143.19 m.p. 9-10° b.p. 261-263°
n_D^{20} 1.6200 d 1.083 Beil. **20**,395

NEAT

E

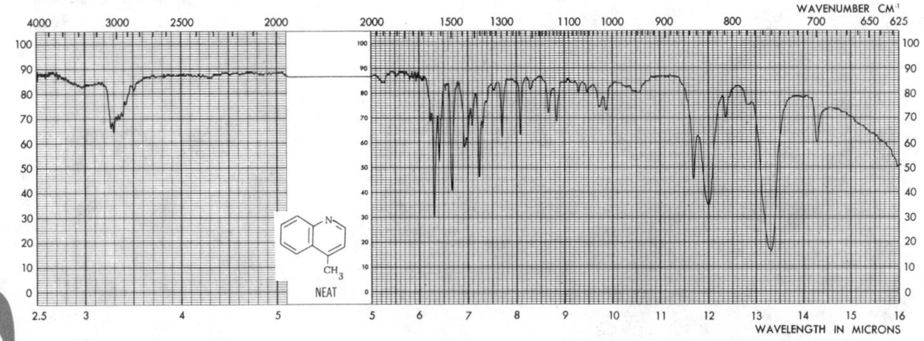

M.W. 157.22 n_D^{20} 1.6046

NEAT

F

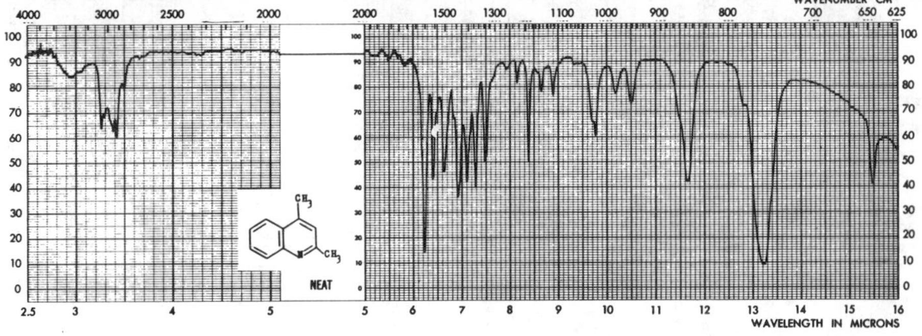

14,402-9 2,6-Dimethylquinoline
M.W. 157.22 m.p. 57-59°

MELT

G

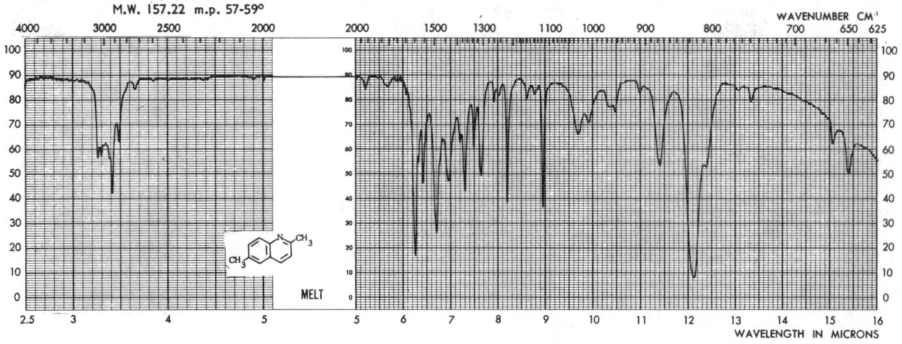

14,564-5 2,7-Dimethylquinoline
M.W. 157.22 m.p. 58-60°

MELT

H

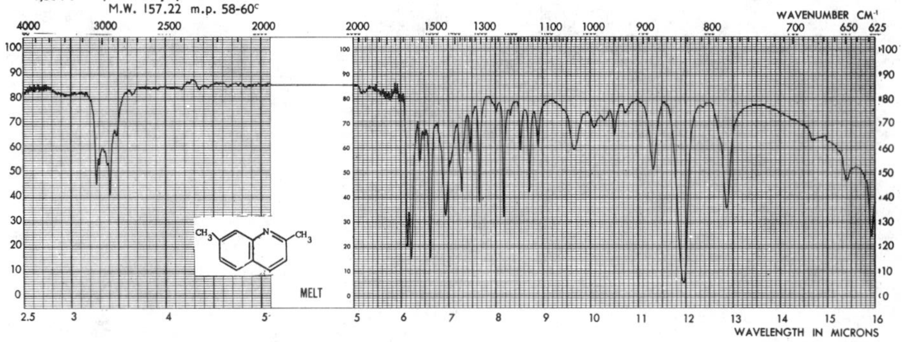

D9153-5 1,1'-Diethyl-4,4'-carbocyanine iodide (cryptocyanine, kryptocyanine)
M.W. 480.40 m.p. 250.5-253° ....

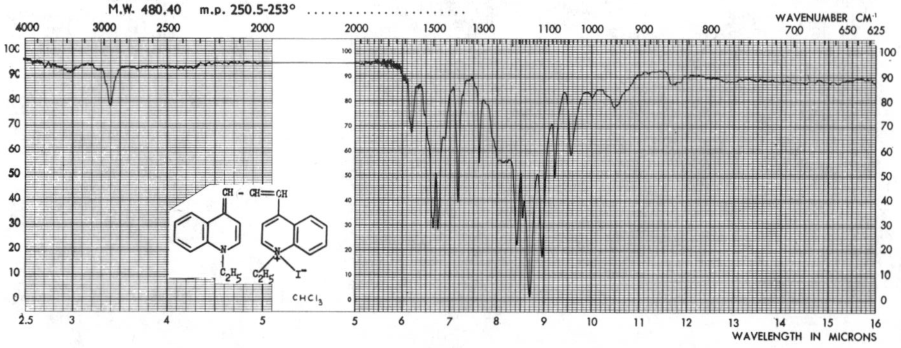

$CHCl_3$

A 10,251-2 1,1'-Diallyl-6,6'-dimethyl-2,2'-carbocyanine iodide
M.W. 532.47 m.p. 265-267°

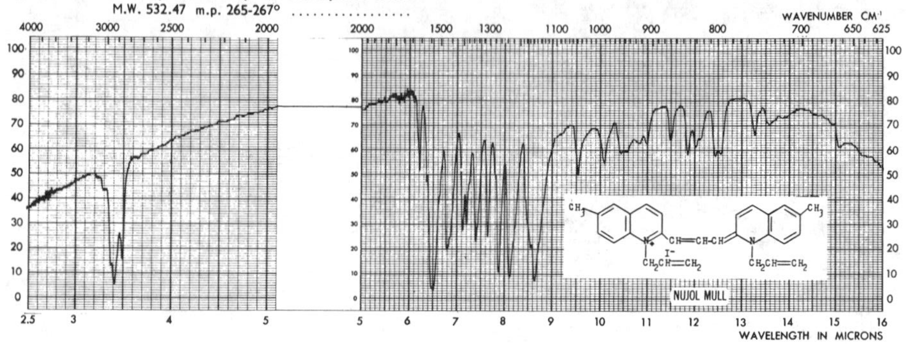

NUJOL MULL

B B1018-8 5,6-Benzoquinoline (benzo[f]quinoline), puriss.
M.W. 179.22 m.p. 90-93°

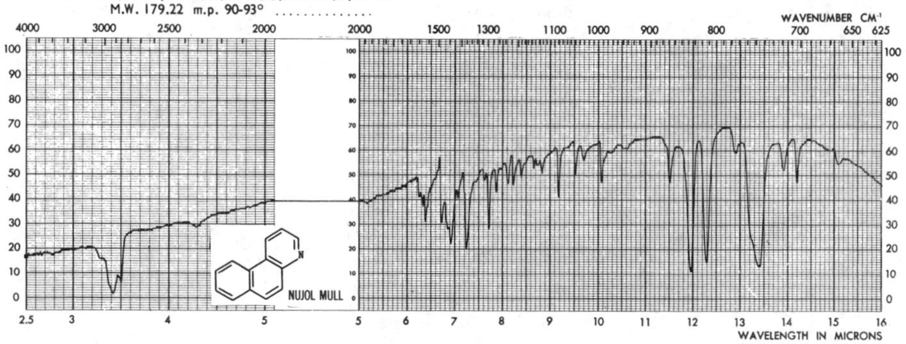

NUJOL MULL

C 12,361-7 7,8-Benzoquinoline (benzo[h]quinoline)
M.W. 179.22 m.p. 50-53°

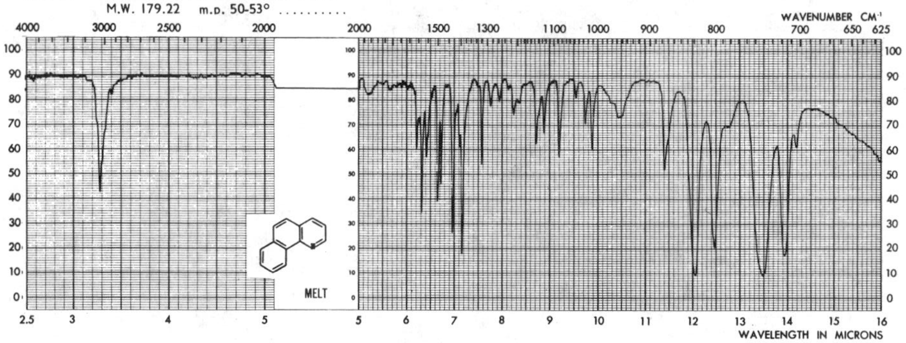

MELT

D P1200-6 Phenanthridine
M.W. 179.22 m.p. 106-107°

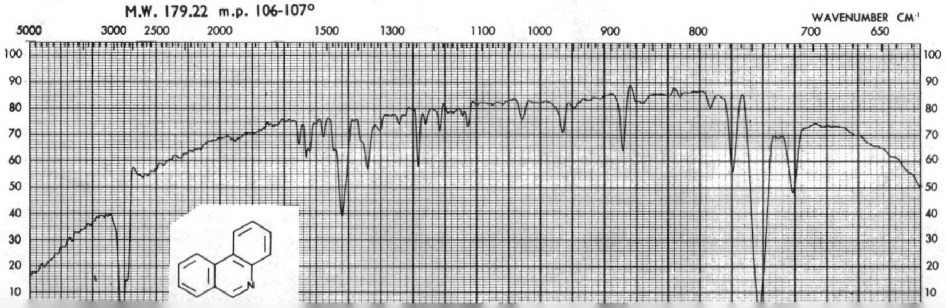

E 13,797-9 1,2,5,6-Dibenzacridine
M.W. 279.35 m.p. 218-222°

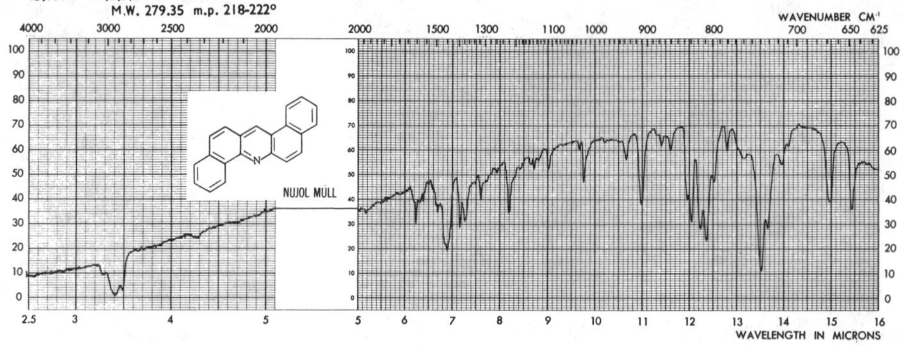

NUJOL MULL

F 13,798-7 1,2,7,8-Dibenzacridine
M.W. 279.35 m.p. 217-219°

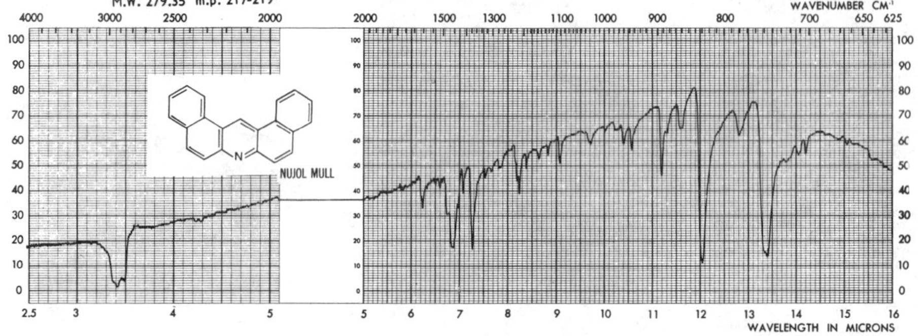

NUJOL MULL

G C7040-1 2-Chloroquinoline
M.W. 163.61 m.p. 34-37°

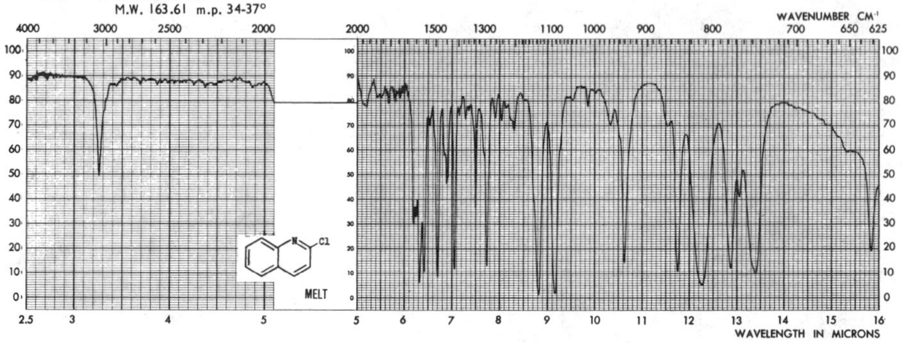

MELT

H C5710-3 2-Chloromethylquinoline (α-chloroquinaldine) hydrochloride
M.W. 214.10 m.p. 183-187°

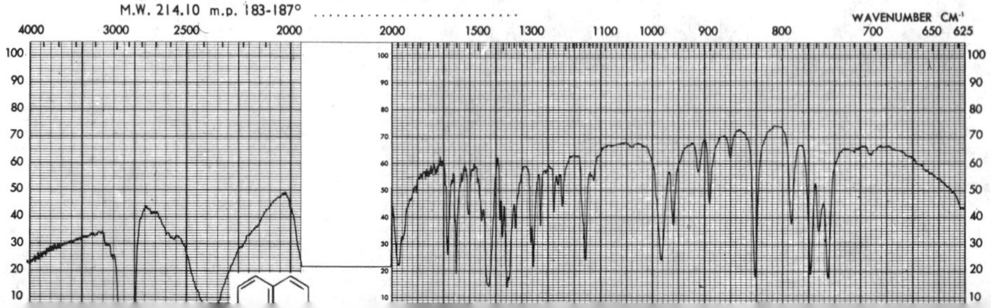

A

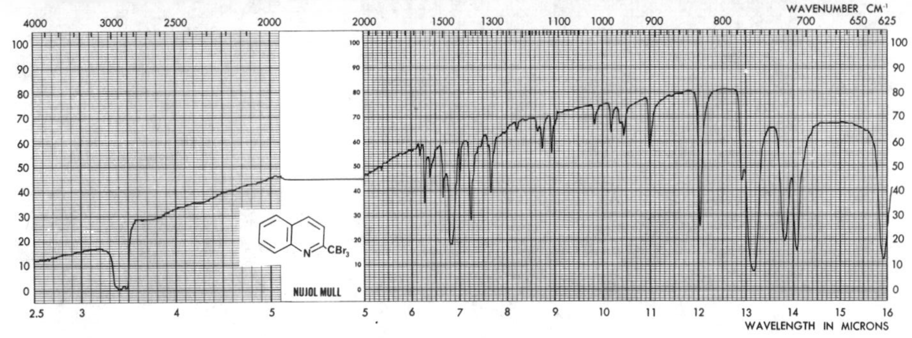

NUJOL MULL

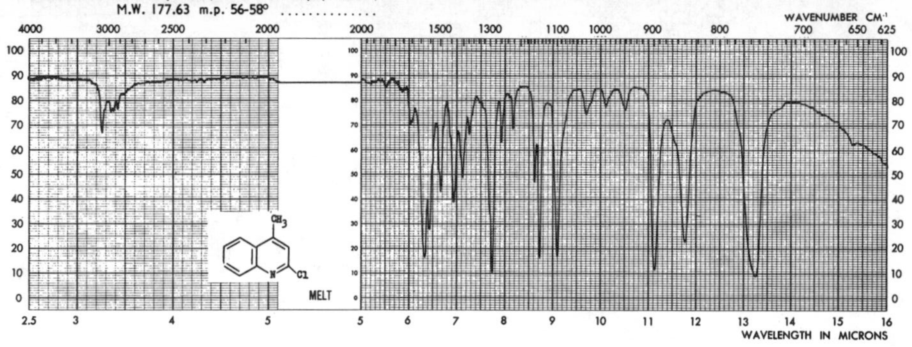

B

C7050-9 4-Chloroquinoline
M.W. 163.61 m.p. 29-31°

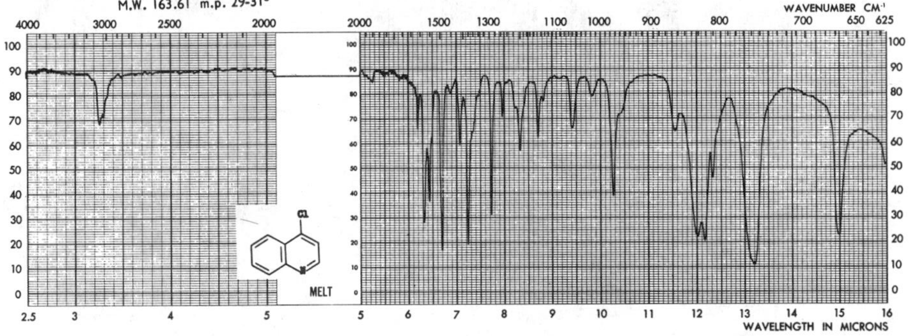

MELT

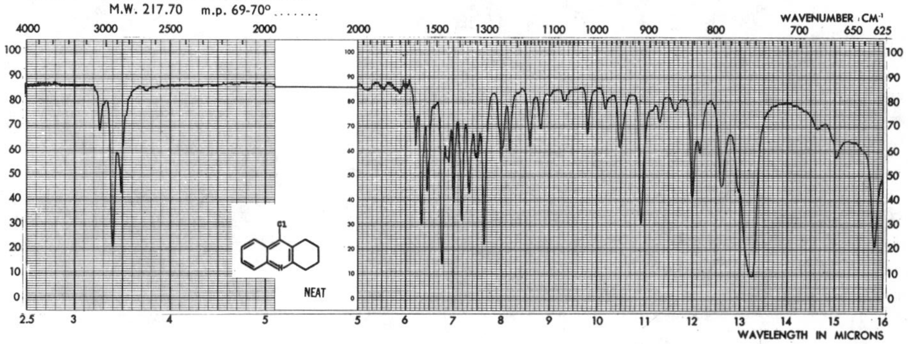

C

18,602-3
4-Chloro-7-(trifluoromethyl)quinoline, 98%
M.W. 231.61 m.p. 69-71°

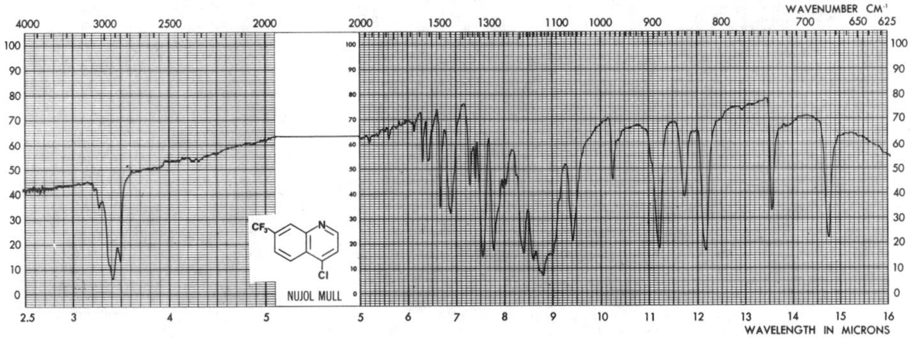

NUJOL MULL

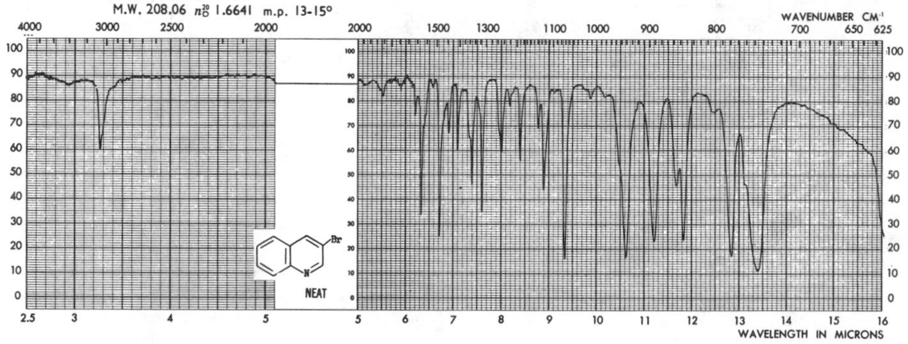

D

15,023-1 4-Chloroquinaldine, puriss.
M.W. 177.64 n_D^{20} 1.6224
b.p. 269-270° ....

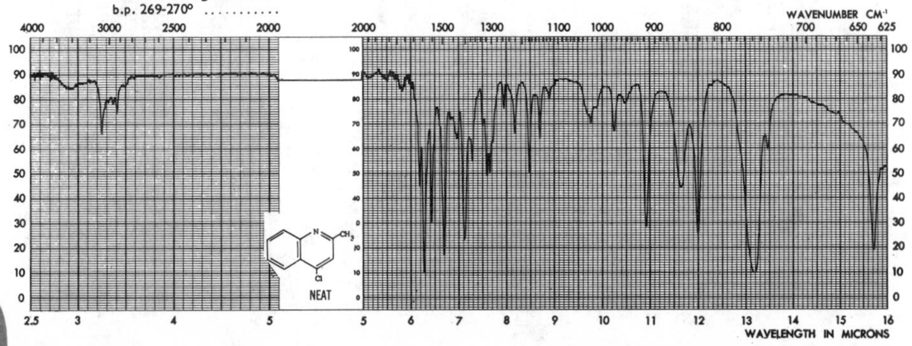

NEAT

E

M.W. 177.63 m.p. 56-58° ....

MELT

F

12,522-9 9-Chloro-1,2,3,4-tetrahydroacridine
M.W. 217.70 m.p. 69-70° ......

NEAT

G

12,413-3 3-Bromoquinoline
M.W. 208.06 n_D^{20} 1.6641 m.p. 13-15°

NEAT

H

14,143-7 4,7-Dichloroquinoline, puriss.
M.W. 198.05 m.p. 84-86° ..

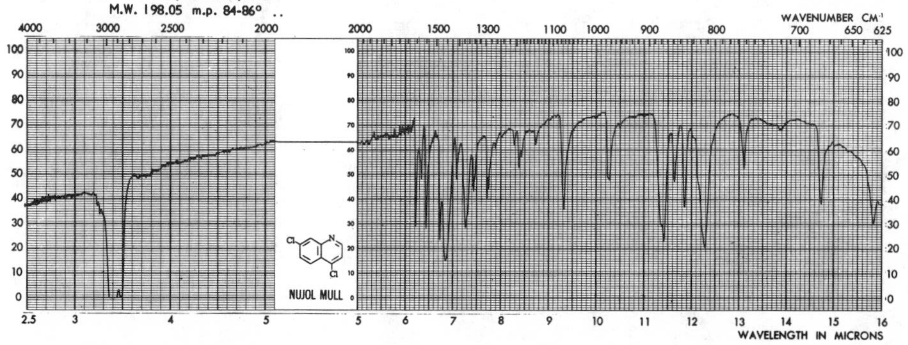

NUJOL MULL

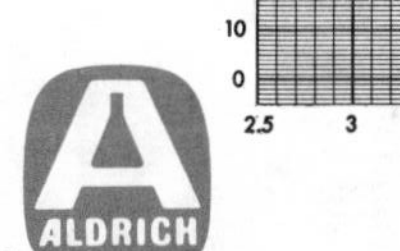

6 MEMBERED FUSED AROMATIC HETEROCYCLES

A

14,874-1 **4-Chloro-2-phenylquinoline**
M.W. 239.71 m.p. 64°

NUJOL MULL

B

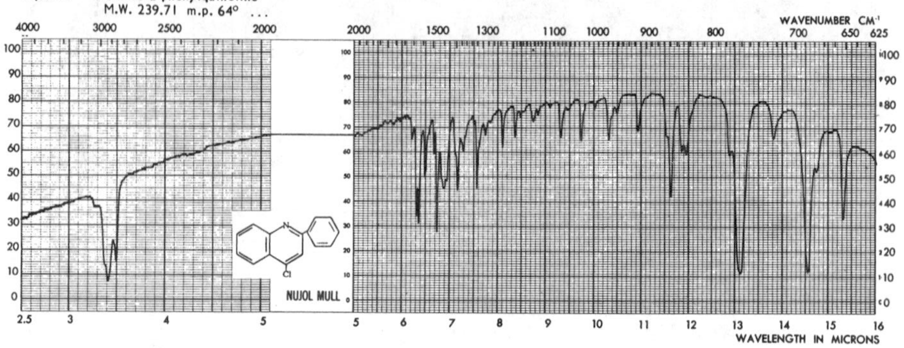

18,306-7
6-Methoxyquinoline, 98%
M.W. 159.19 m.p. 18-20° b.p. 193°/50mm.
d 1.154 Beil. **21**,85

NEAT

C

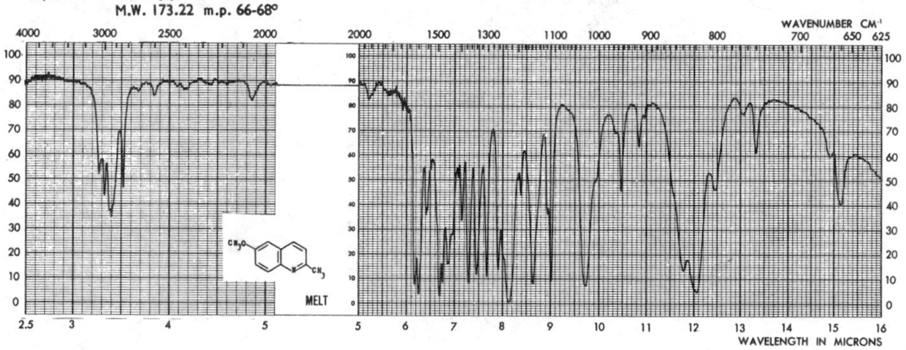

10,329-2 **6-Methoxyquinaldine**
M.W. 173.22 m.p. 66-68°

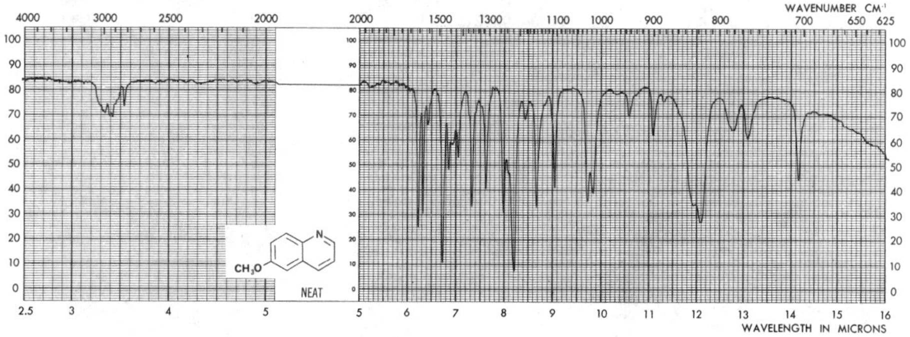

MELT

D

10,329-2 **6-Methoxyquinaldine**
M.W. 173.22 m.p. 66-68°

E

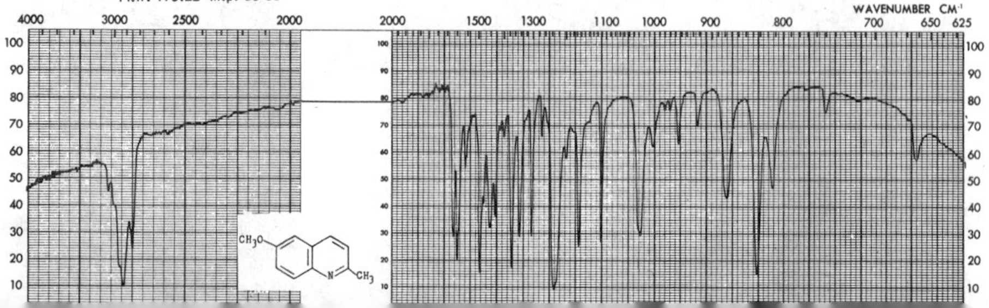

11,504-5 **2-(2-Hydroxyethyl)-quinoline** (2-quinolineethanol), **puriss.**
M.W. 173.22 m.p. 102-104°

NUJOL MULL

F

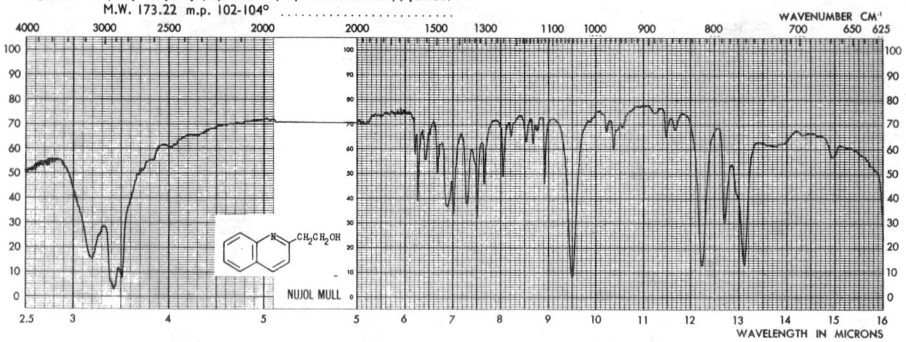

H4360-1 **2-Hydroxy-4-methylquinoline** (4-methylcarbostyril, 4-methyl-2-quinolinol)
M.W. 159.19 m.p. 221-223°

NUJOL MULL

G

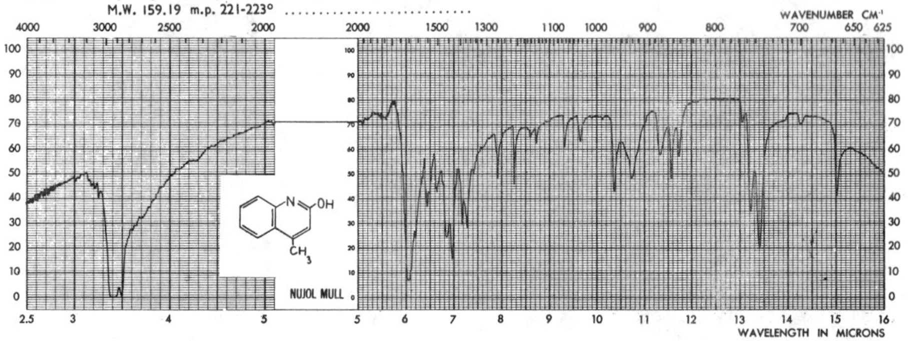

H5800-5 **4-Hydroxyquinoline** (4-quinolinol) **trihydrate**
M.W. 199.21 m.p. 200-202°

NUJOL MULL

H

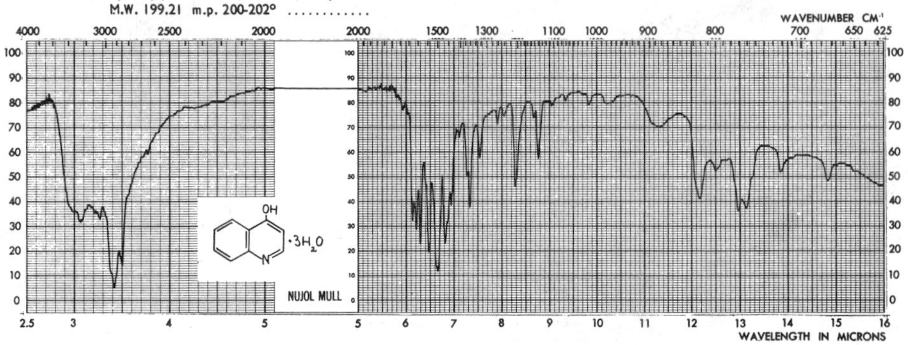

10,553-8 **7-Chloro-4-hydroxyquinoline**
M.W. 179.61 m.p. 232° (dec.)

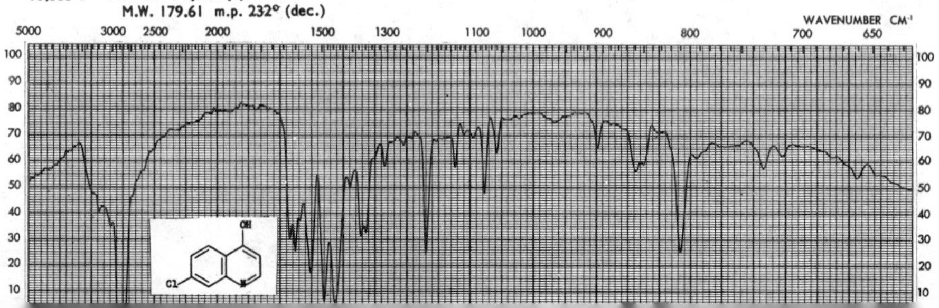

A

M.W. 175.19 m.p. 241-243°

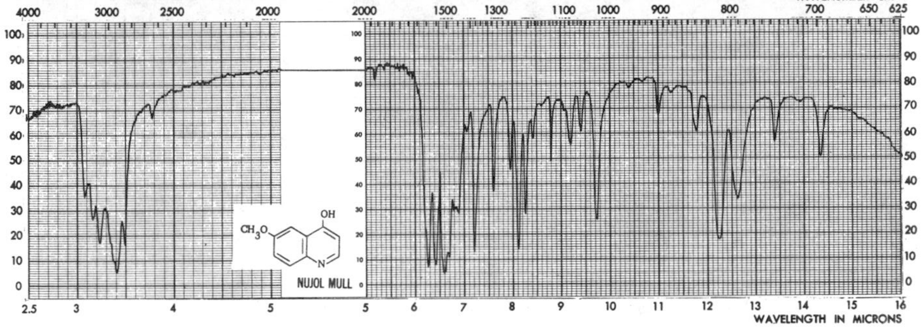

NUJOL MULL

B

Q133-6 **2,4-Quinolinediol**
M.W. 161.16 m.p. > 335°

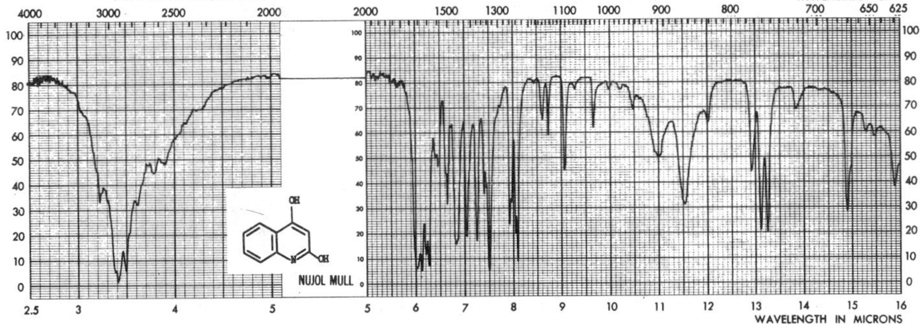

NUJOL MULL

C

12,879-1 **5-Hydroxyquinoline** (5-quinolinol)
M.W. 145.16 m.p. 227-229°

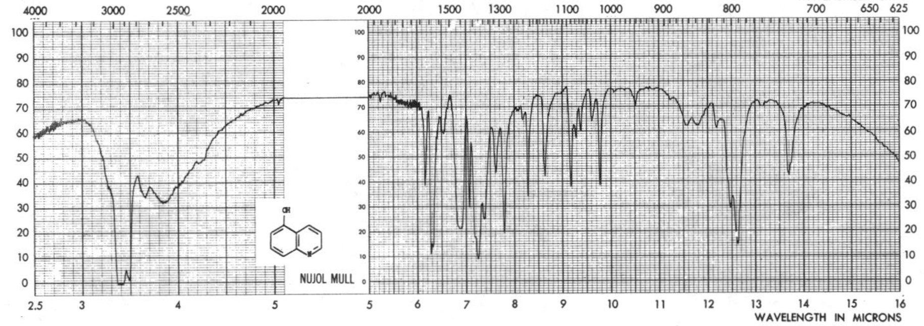

NUJOL MULL

D

15,090-8 **8-Hydroxyquinoline** (8-quinolinol), **zone refined, 99.9+%, GOLD LABEL**
M.W. 145.16 m.p. 72.97°

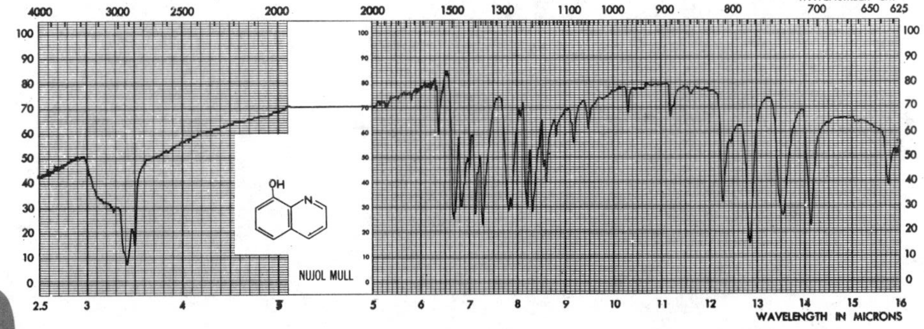

NUJOL MULL

E

10,807-3 **8-Hydroxyquinoline** (8-quinolinol) **sulfate**
M.W. 388.40 m.p. 176-179°

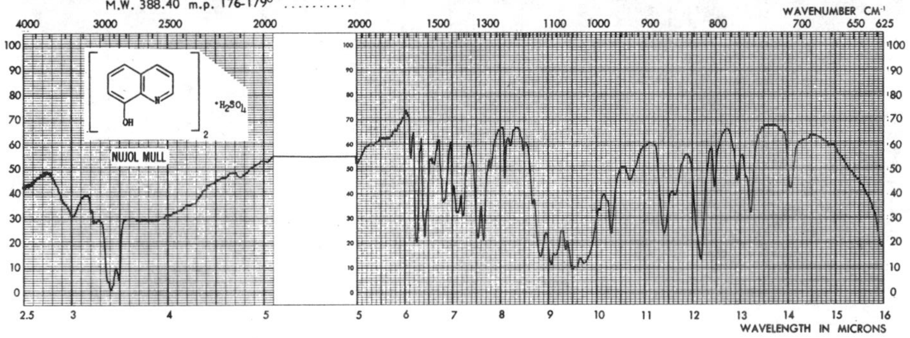

NUJOL MULL

F

10,895-2 **8-Hydroxyquinoline** (8-quinolinol), **magnesium salt**
M.W. 312.61 m.p. > 300°

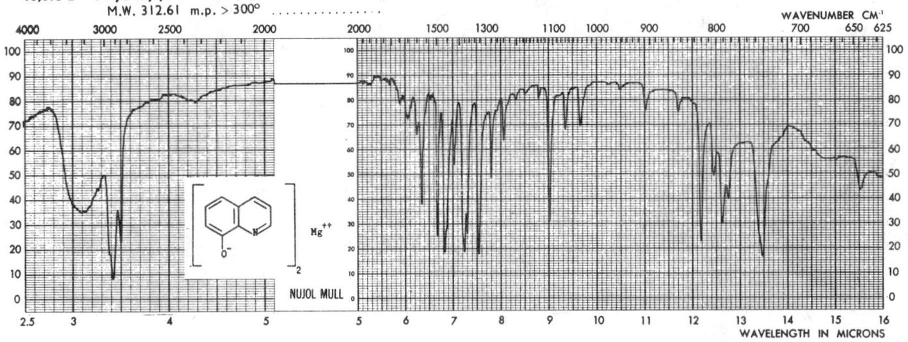

NUJOL MULL

G

10,896-0 **8-Hydroxyquinoline** (8-quinolinol), **zinc salt**
M.W. 353.68 m.p. > 300°

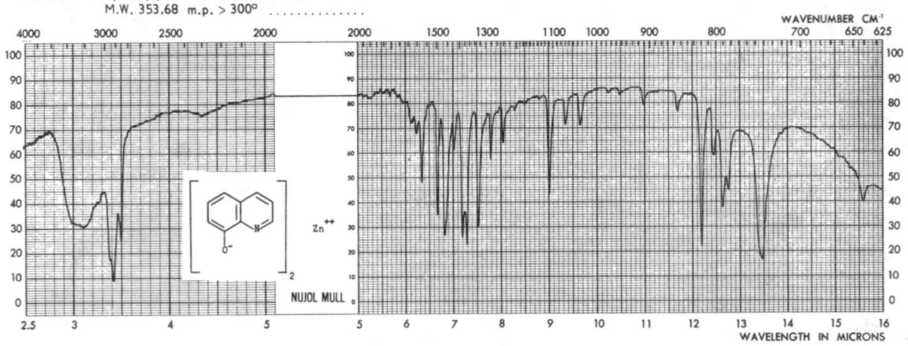

NUJOL MULL

H

10,806-5 **8-Hydroxyquinoline benzoate** (8-quinolinol)
M.W. 267.28 m.p. 56-58°

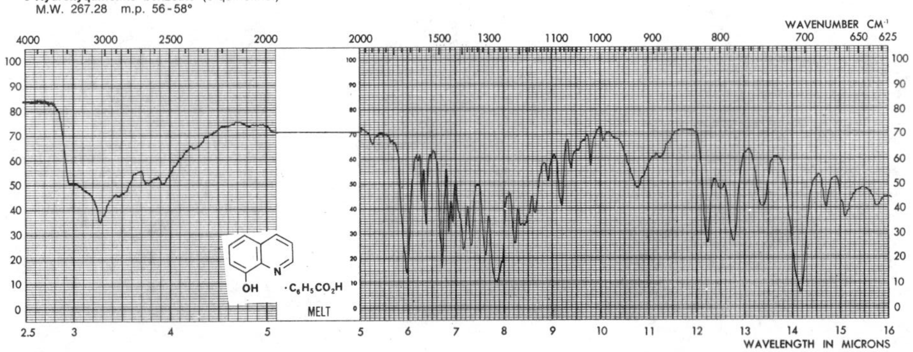

MELT

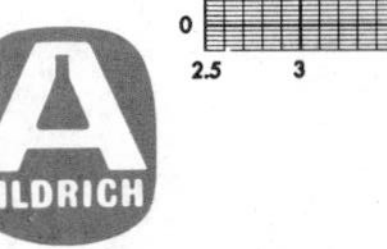

6 MEMBERED FUSED AROMATIC HETEROCYCLES

A H5760-2 **8-Hydroxyquinaldine** (2-methyl-8-quinolinol)
M.W. 159.19 m.p. 72-73°

B H4,380-6
4-Hydroxy-2-methylquinoline, 98.5% (2-methyl-4-quinolinol)
M.W. 159.19 m.p. 234-236° Beil. **21**,104

C 18,421-7
7-(Trifluoromethyl)-4-quinolinol, 97%
M.W. 213.16 m.p. 266-269°

D C4700-0 **5-Chloro-8-hydroxyquinoline** (5-chloro-8-quinolinol)
M.W. 179.61 m.p. 125°

E 13,541-0 **5-Bromo-8-hydroxyquinoline** (5-bromo-8-quinolinol)
M.W. 224.06 m.p. 126-127°

F D6460-0 **5,7-Dichloro-8-hydroxyquinoline** (5,7-dichloro-8-quinolinol)
M.W. 214.05 m.p. 174-176°

G 19,336-4
7-Bromo-5-chloro-8-hydroxyquinoline, tech., 90+%
(7-bromo-5-chloro-8-quinolinol)
FW 258.51 mp 177-179° *Beil.* **21**(1),222
Disp. C

H D4160-0 **5,7-Dibromo-8-hydroxyquinoline** (5,7-dibromo-8-quinolinol)
M.W. 302.96 m.p. 200-201°

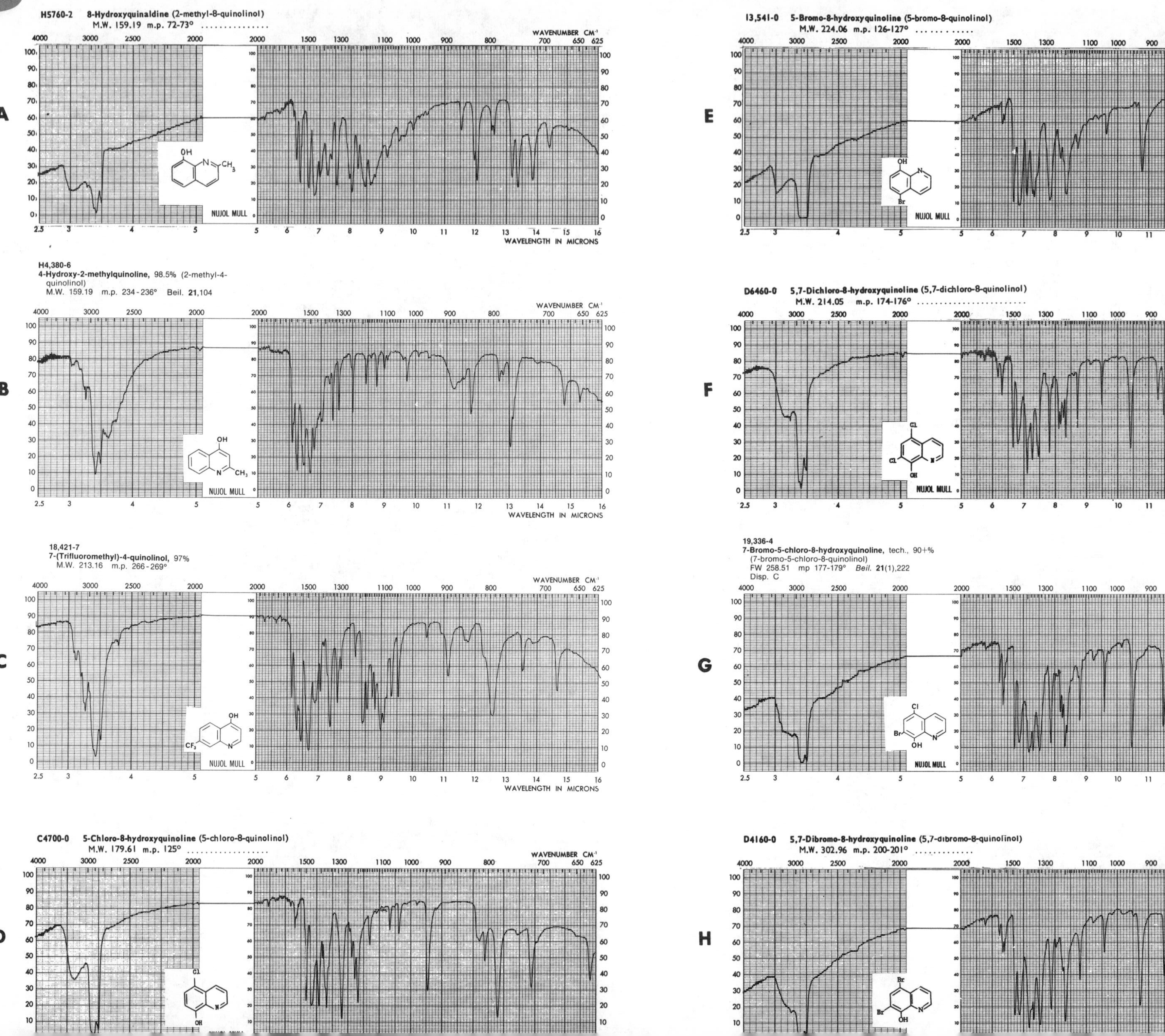

A

FW 305.50 mp 171-174° *Beil.* **21**,98 Disp. C

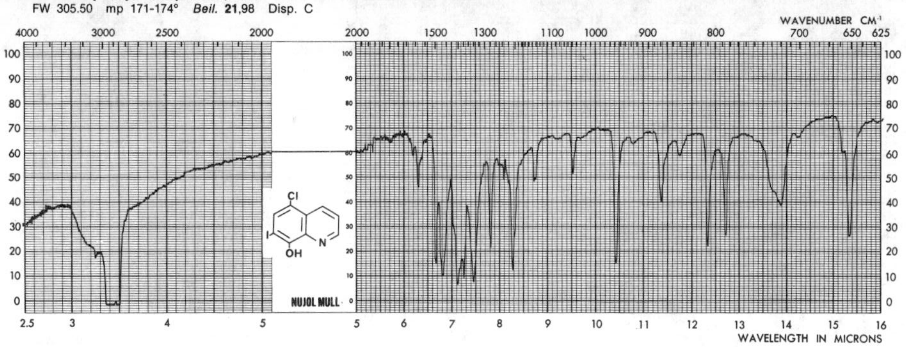

NUJOL MULL

B

D12,360-9 5,7-Diiodo-8-hydroxyquinoline (5,7-diiodo-8-quinolinol)
M.W. 396.95 m.p. 205-208°

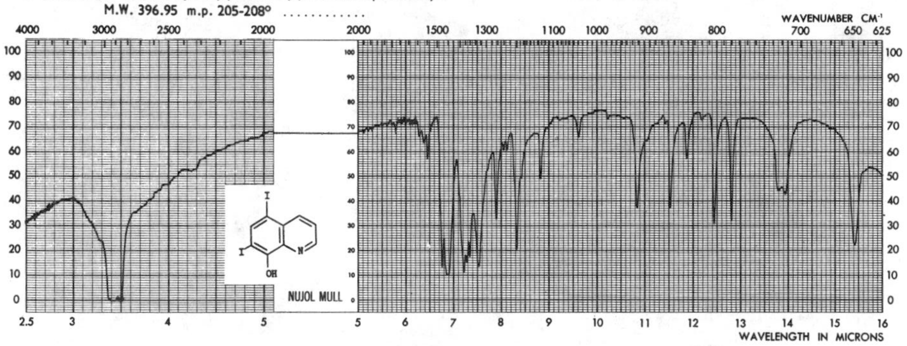

NUJOL MULL

C

13,053-2 5,7-Dichloro-8-hydroxyquinaldine (5,7-dichloro-8-quinaldinol)
M.W. 228.08 m.p. 107-109°

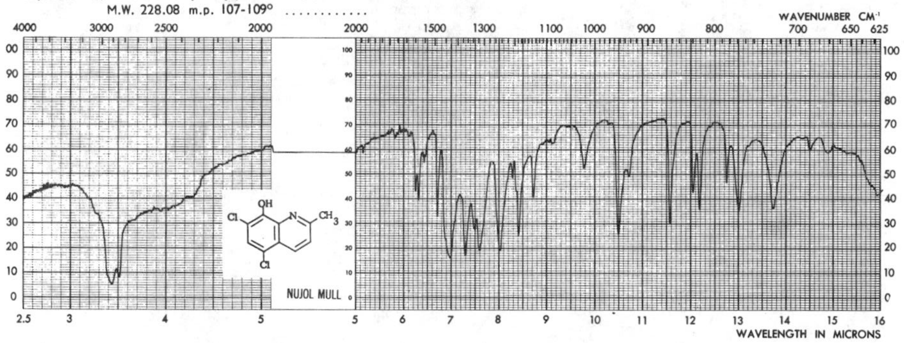

NUJOL MULL

D

13,548-8 5,7-Diiodo-8-hydroxy-2-methylquinoline (5,7-diiodo-2-methyl-8-quinolinol)
M.W. 410.98 m.p. 143-144°

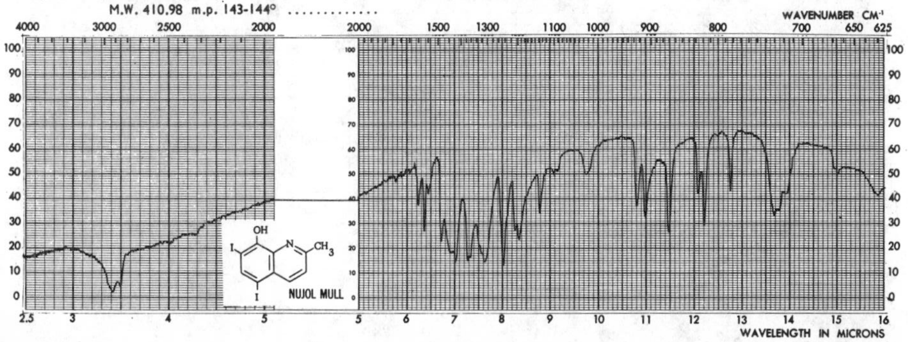

NUJOL MULL

E

11,627-0 2-Quinolinethiol
M.W. 161.23 m.p. 174-176°

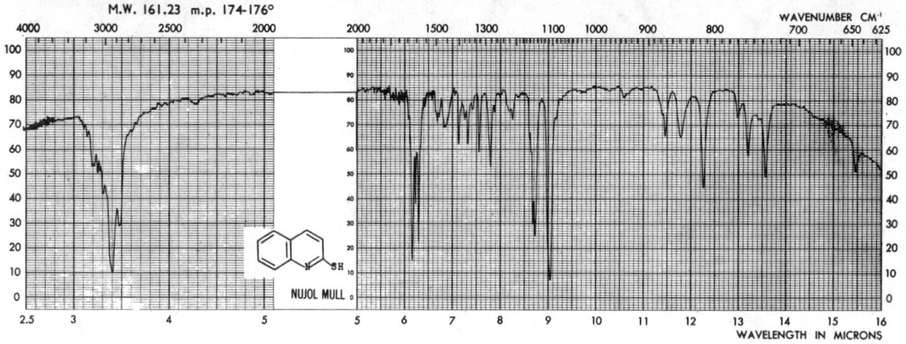

NUJOL MULL

F

18,668-6
7-Trifluoromethyl-4-quinolinethiol, tech.
FW 229.23 mp 222-225° Disp. C

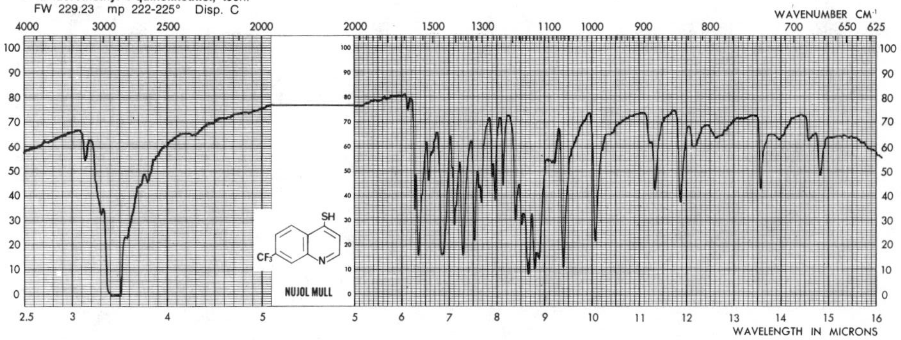

NUJOL MULL

G

A7920-5 5-Aminoquinoline
M.W. 144.18 m.p. 102.5-108°

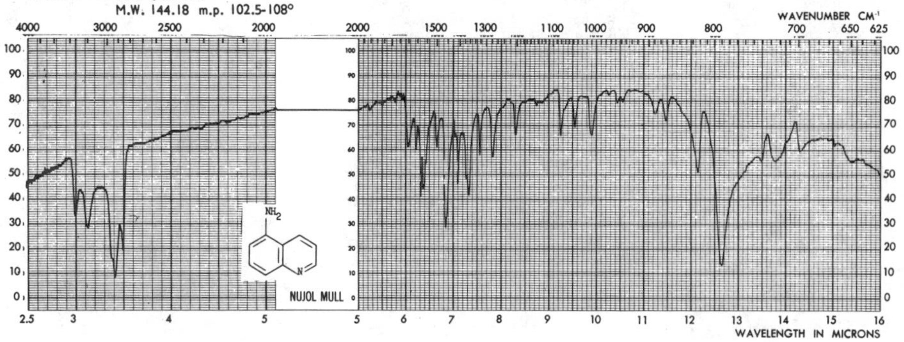

NUJOL MULL

H

A7900-0 4-Aminoquinaldine
M.W. 158.20 m.p. 167-169°

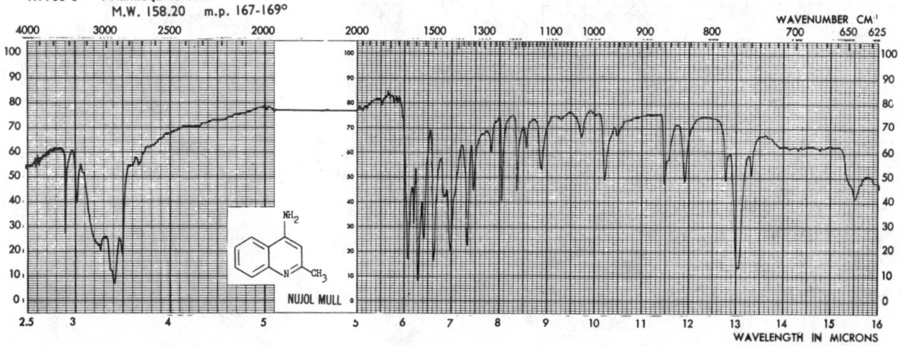

NUJOL MULL

ALDRICH

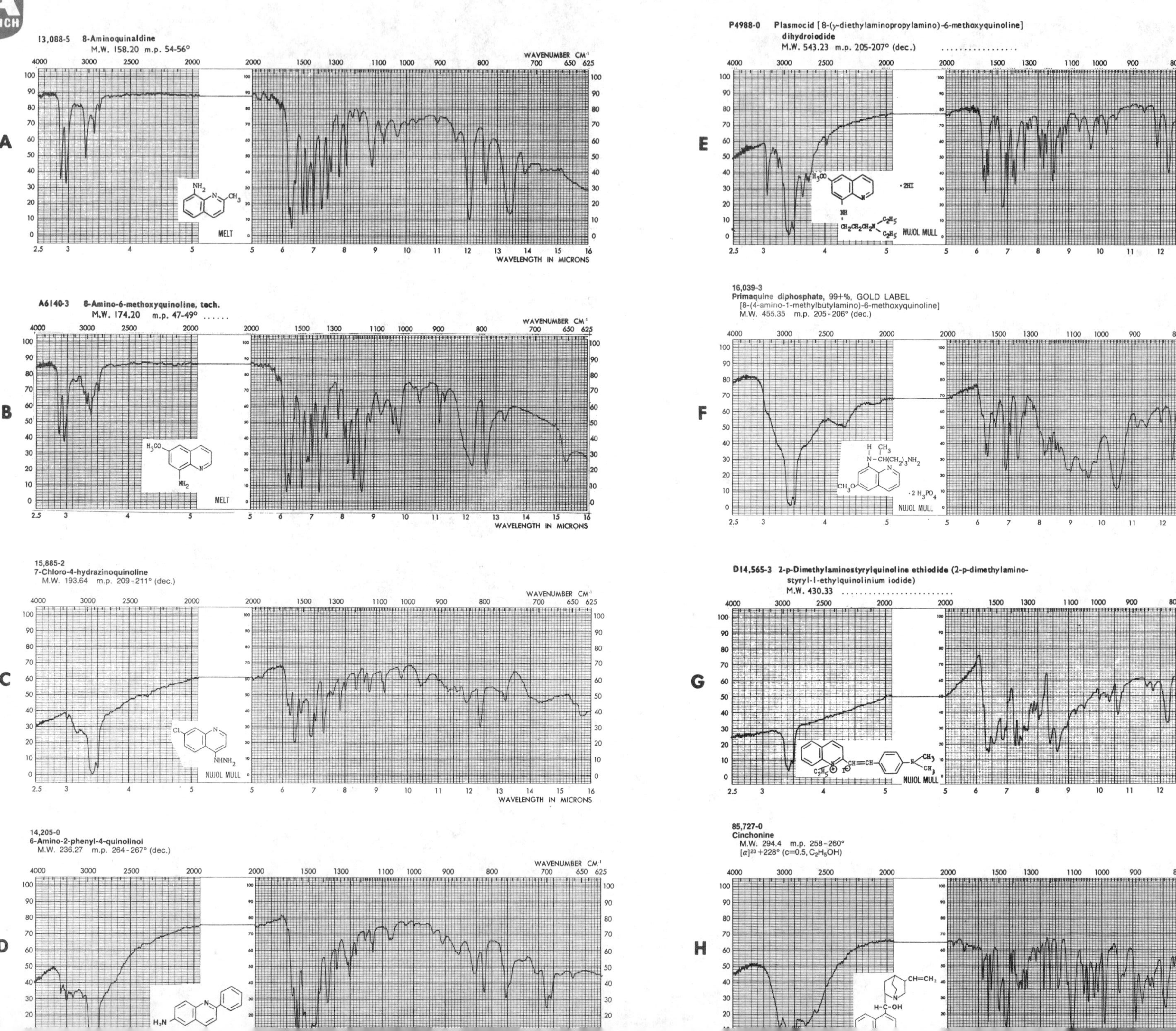

A — 13,088-5 8-Aminoquinaldine
M.W. 158.20 m.p. 54-56°
MELT

B — A6140-3 8-Amino-6-methoxyquinoline, tech.
M.W. 174.20 m.p. 47-49°
MELT

C — 15,885-2
7-Chloro-4-hydrazinoquinoline
M.W. 193.64 m.p. 209-211° (dec.)
NUJOL MULL

D — 14,205-0
6-Amino-2-phenyl-4-quinolinol
M.W. 236.27 m.p. 264-267° (dec.)

E — P4988-0 Plasmocid [8-(γ-diethylaminopropylamino)-6-methoxyquinoline] dihydroiodide
M.W. 543.23 m.p. 205-207° (dec.)
NUJOL MULL

F — 16,039-3
Primaquine diphosphate, 99+%, GOLD LABEL
[8-(4-amino-1-methylbutylamino)-6-methoxyquinoline]
M.W. 455.35 m.p. 205-206° (dec.)
NUJOL MULL

G — D14,565-3 2-p-Dimethylaminostyrylquinoline ethiodide (2-p-dimethylamino-styryl-1-ethylquinolinium iodide)
M.W. 430.33
NUJOL MULL

H — 85,727-0
Cinchonine
M.W. 294.4 m.p. 258-260°
$[\alpha]^{23}$ +228° (c=0.5, C_2H_5OH)

A

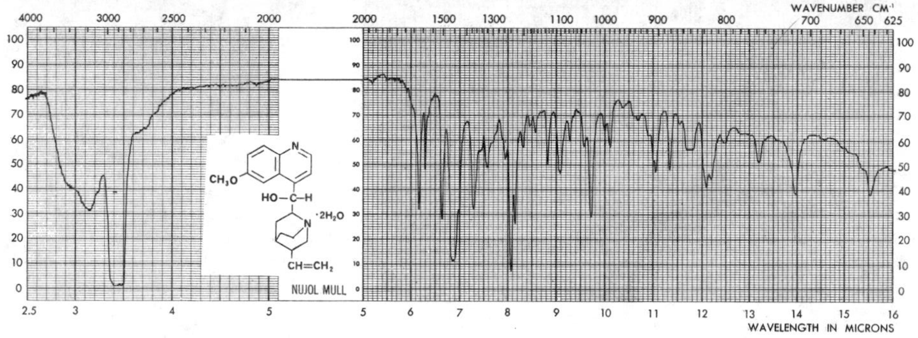

14,592-0
Quinine monohydrochloride dihydrate
M.W. 396.92 m.p. 115-116° (dec.)
$[\alpha]^{25}$ - 146° (c=2, C_2H_5OH)

B

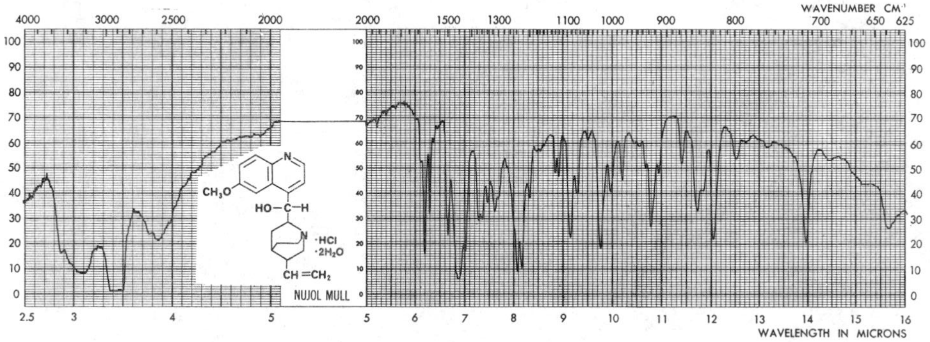

16,132-2
Quinine dihydrochloride monohydrate
M.W. 415.36 m.p. 238-240° (dec.)
$[\alpha]^{23}$ - 184° (c=2, CH_3OH)

C

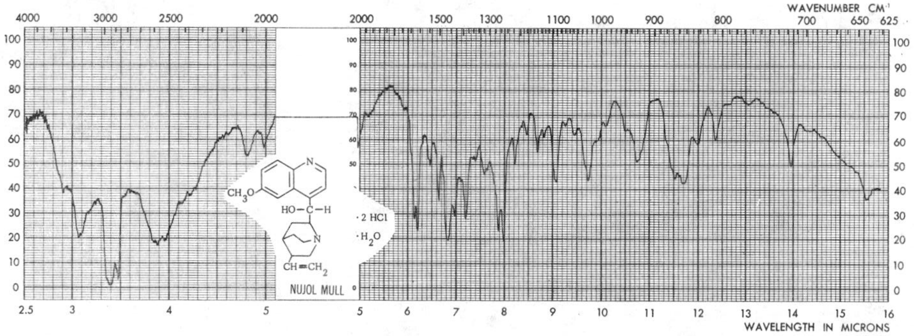

14,591-2
Quinine sulfate dihydrate
M.W. 782.96 m.p. 233-235° (dec.)
$[\alpha]^{15}$ - 222° (c=5, 0.5N HCl)

D

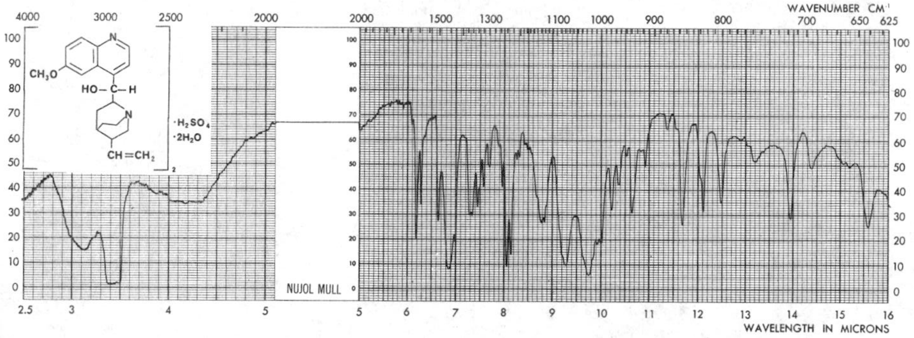

M.W. 342.45 m.p. 166-169°
$[\alpha]_D^{20}$ + 256° (c=1, C_2H_5OH)

E

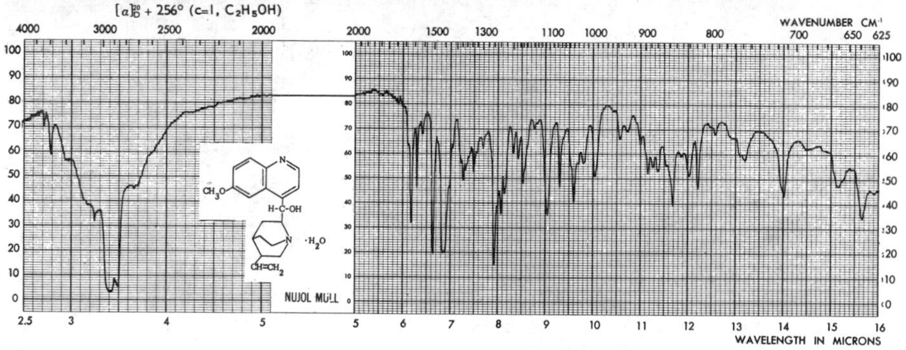

14,589-0 Quinidine sulfate dihydrate
M.W. 782.96 m.p. 212-214° (dec.)
$[\alpha]_D^{25}$ + 220° (c=1.1, C_2H_5OH) ....

F

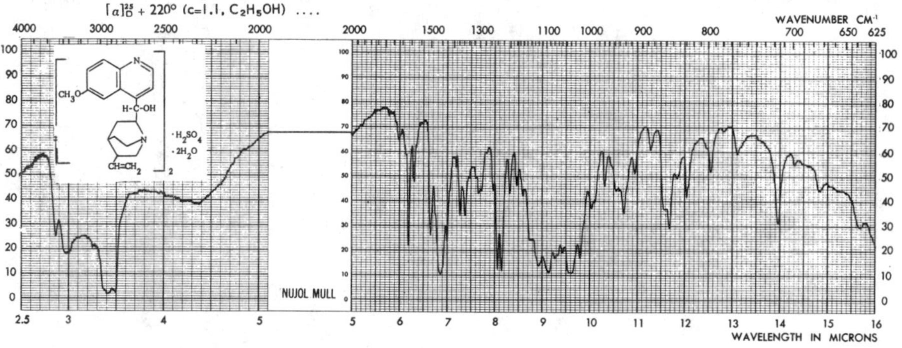

15,018-5 2-Pyridinecarboxaldehyde 2-quinolylhydrazone
M.W. 248.29 m.p. 203-206° ....

G

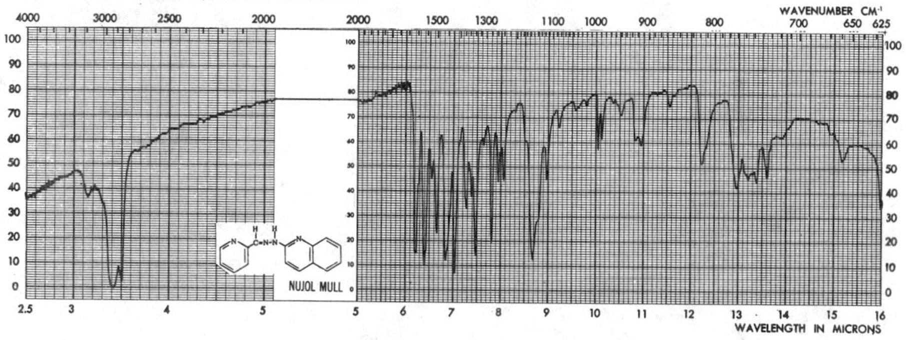

A7990-6 9-Amino-1,2,3,4-tetrahydroacridine (tetrahydroaminacrine)
M.W. 198.27 m.p. 181-183.5° ....

H

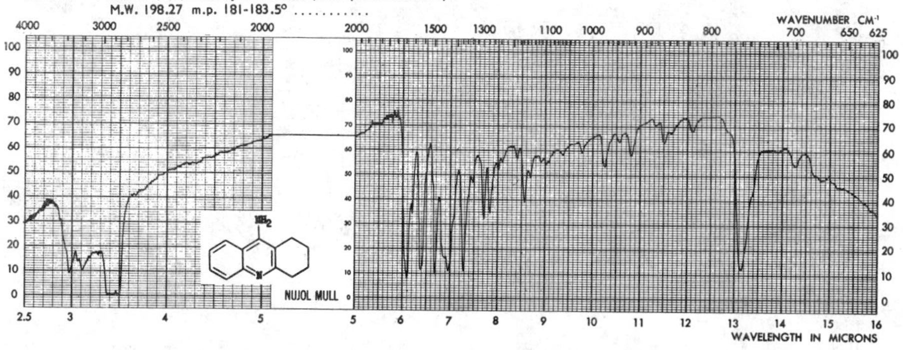

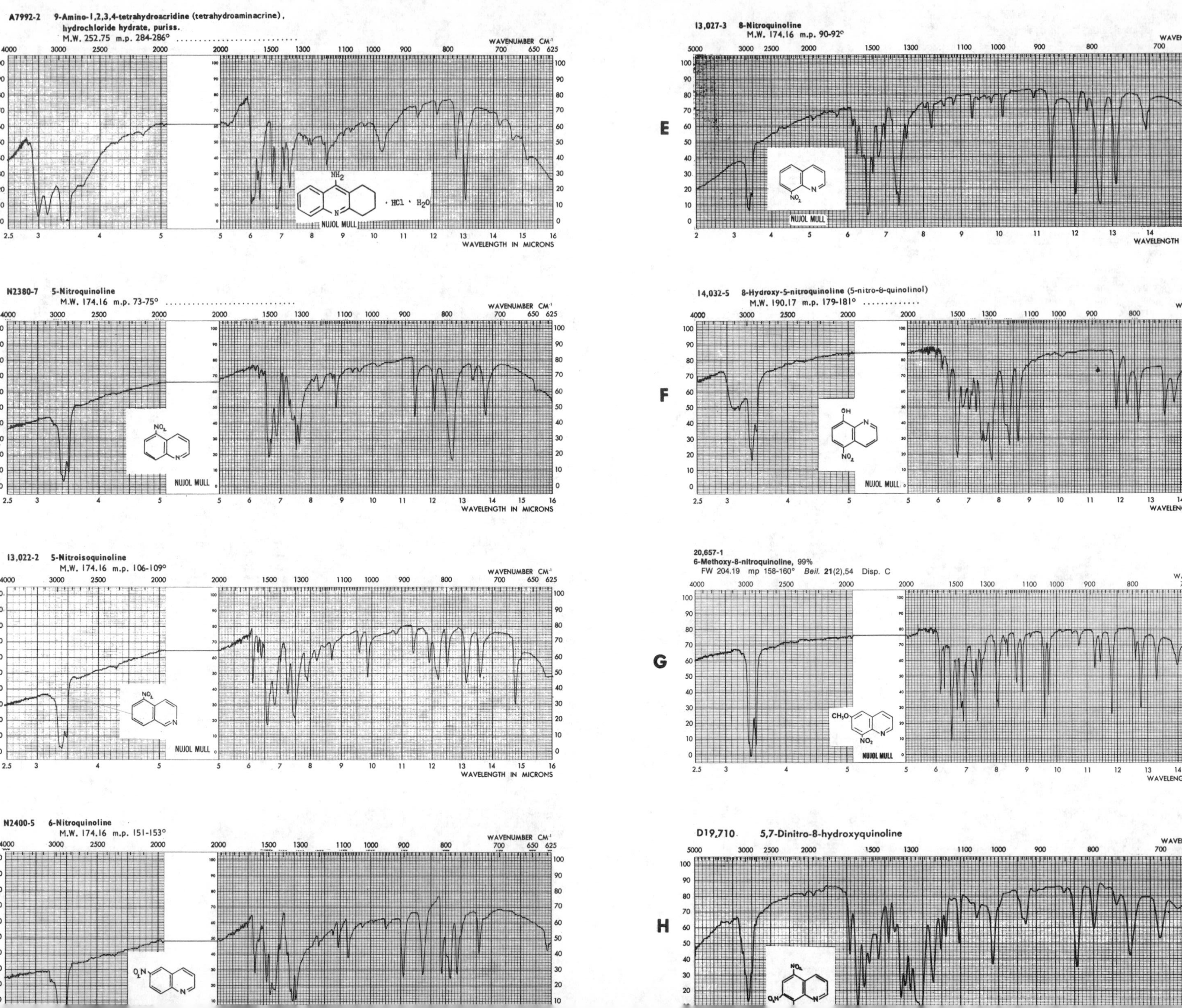
ALDRICH
A
A7992-2 9-Amino-1,2,3,4-tetrahydroacridine (tetrahydroaminacrine), hydrochloride hydrate, puriss.
M.W. 252.75 m.p. 284-286°
· HCl · H2O
NUJOL MULL
B
N2380-7 5-Nitroquinoline
M.W. 174.16 m.p. 73-75°
NUJOL MULL
C
13,022-2 5-Nitroisoquinoline
M.W. 174.16 m.p. 106-109°
NUJOL MULL
D
N2400-5 6-Nitroquinoline
M.W. 174.16 m.p. 151-153°
E
13,027-3 8-Nitroquinoline
M.W. 174.16 m.p. 90-92°
NUJOL MULL
F
14,032-5 8-Hydroxy-5-nitroquinoline (5-nitro-8-quinolinol)
M.W. 190.17 m.p. 179-181°
NUJOL MULL
G
20,657-1
6-Methoxy-8-nitroquinoline, 99%
FW 204.19 mp 158-160° Beil. 21(2),54 Disp. C
NUJOL MULL
H
D19,710 5,7-Dinitro-8-hydroxyquinoline
WAVENUMBER CM⁻¹
WAVELENGTH IN MICRONS

A

14,273-5 **6-Nitro-2-phenyl-4-quinolinol**
M.W. 266.26 m.p. > 300°

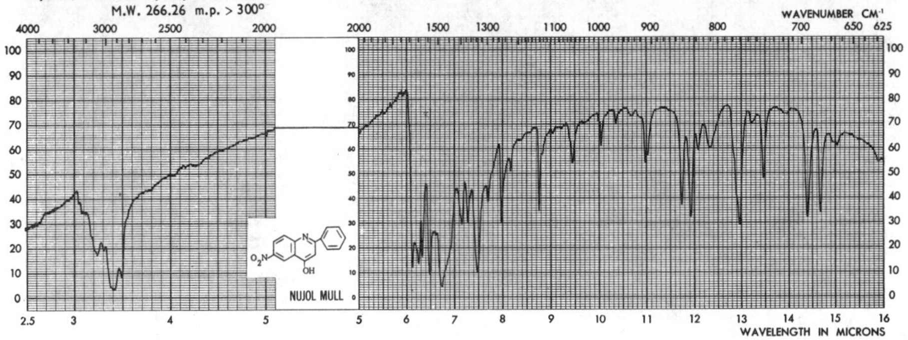

NUJOL MULL

B

14,502-5 **5-Amino-6-nitroquinoline**
M.W. 189.18 m.p. 272° (dec.)

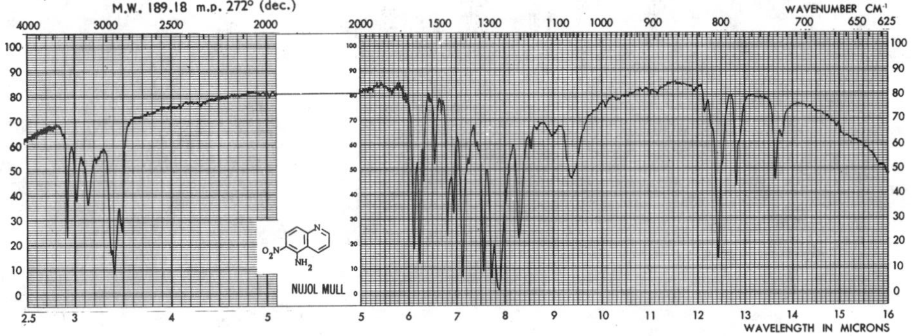

NUJOL MULL

C

H4920-0 **8-Hydroxy-5-nitrosoquinoline** (5-nitroso-8-quinolinol)
M.W. 174.16 m.p. 253° (dec.)

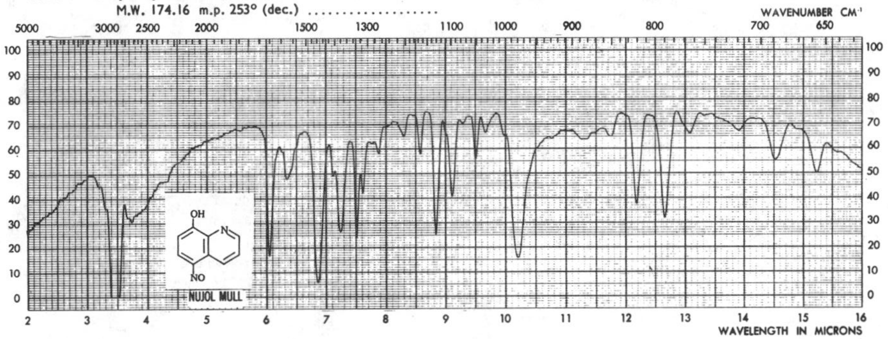

NUJOL MULL

D

I-620-2 **Indo-oxine** [5,8-quinolinequinone-5-(8-hydroxyquinolyl-5-imide)], **sodium salt**
M.W. 323.29 m.p. > 330°

NUJOL MULL

E

3-Quinolinecarboxaldehyde, 98%
M.W. 157.17 m.p. 70-72°

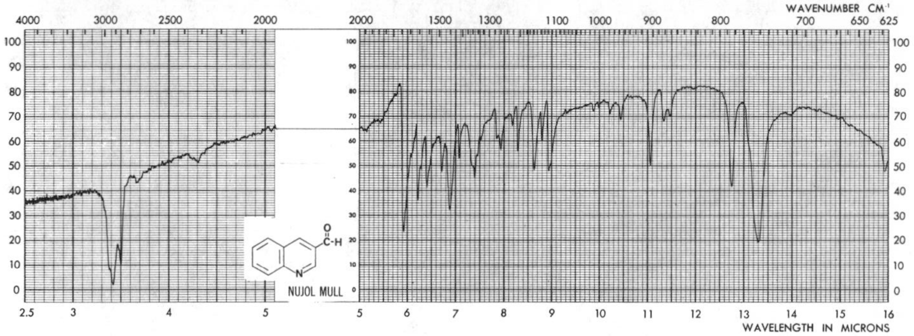

NUJOL MULL

F

17,696-6
4-Quinolinecarboxaldehyde, 98% (cinchoninaldehyde)
M.W. 157.17 m.p. 50-52°

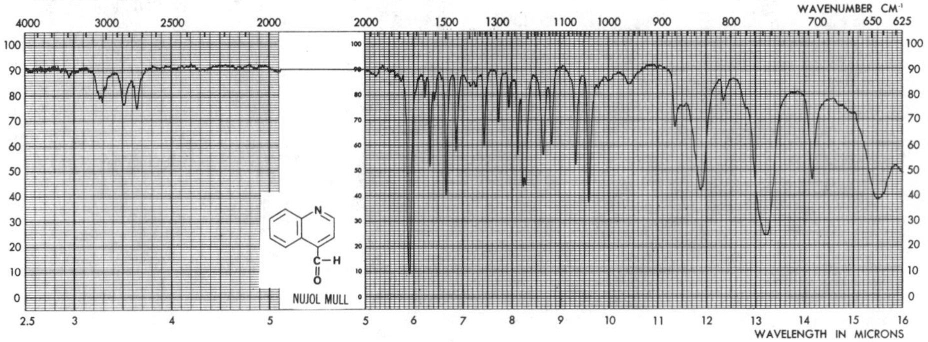

NUJOL MULL

G

16,066-0
Quinaldic acid, 99% (2-quinolinecarboxylic acid)
M.W. 173.17 m.p. 157-159° Beil. **22**,71

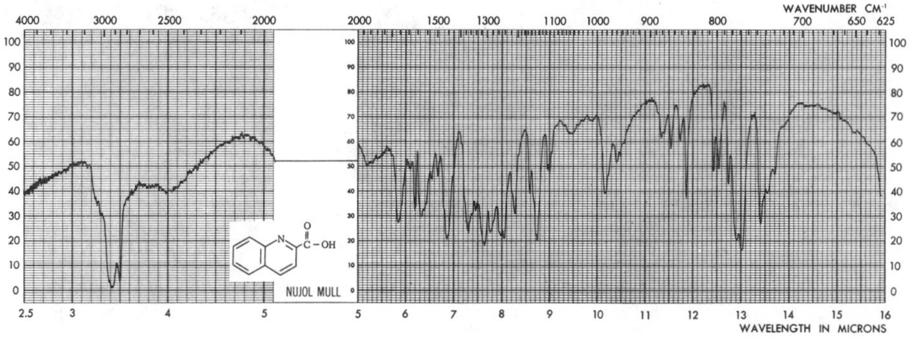

NUJOL MULL

H

17,714-8
3-Quinolinecarboxylic acid, 98%
M.W. 173.17 m.p. 277-280° Beil. **22**(2),56

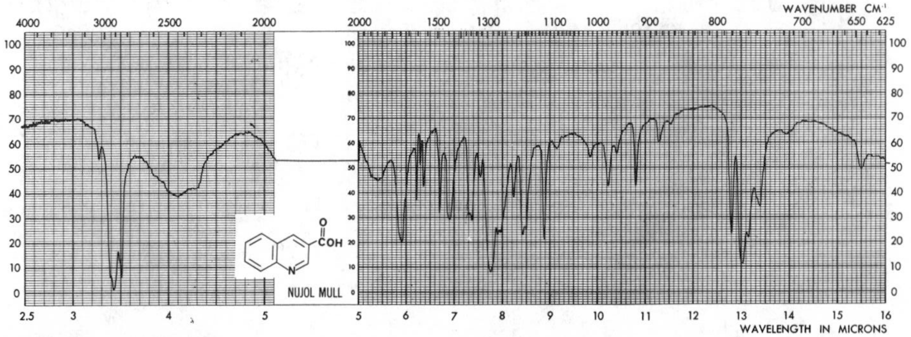

NUJOL MULL

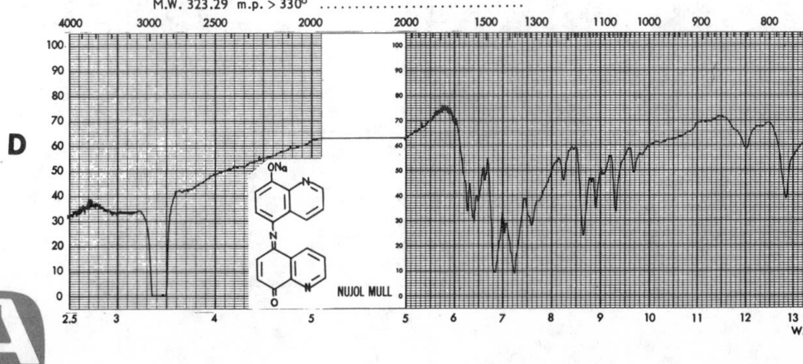

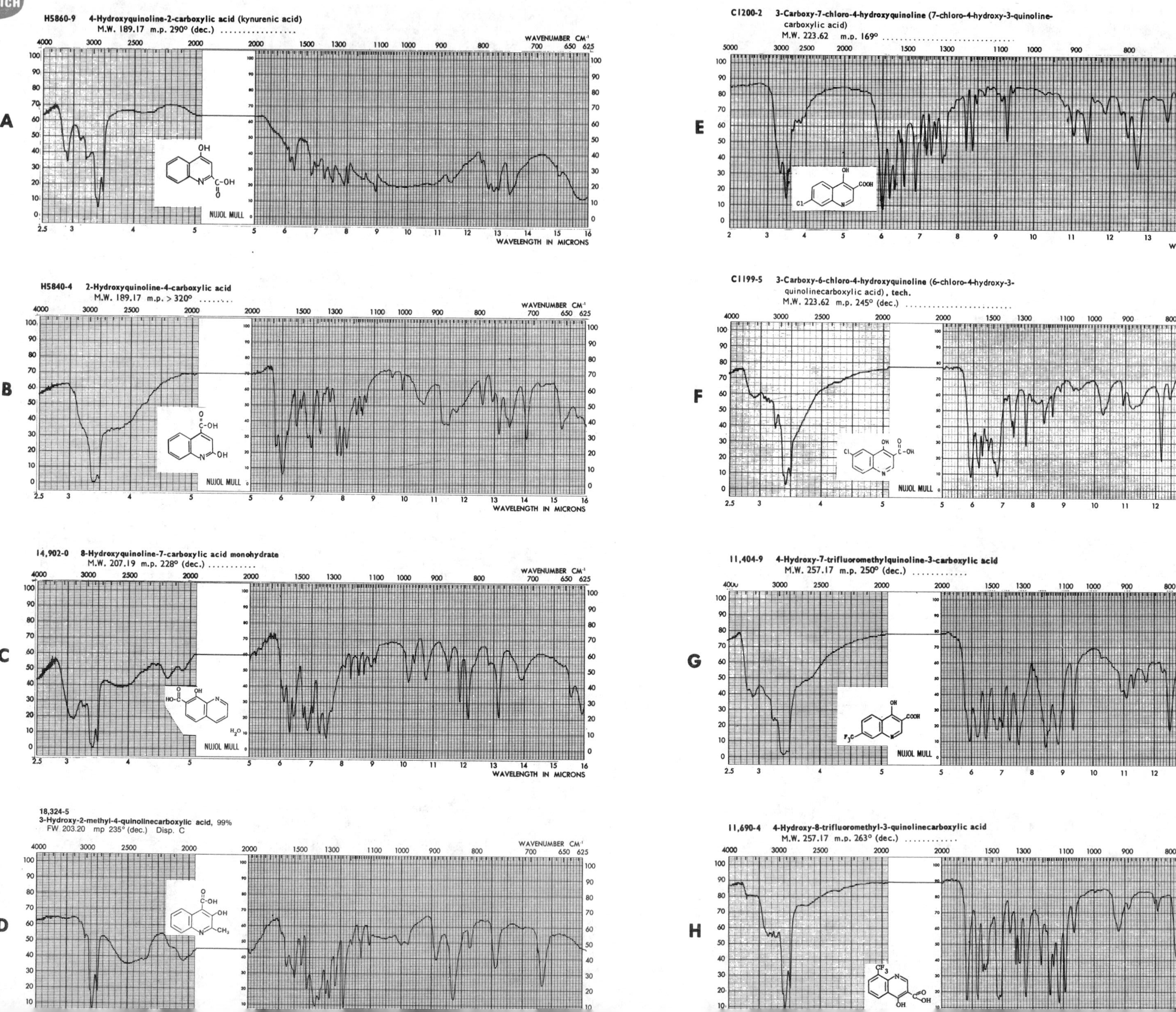

A
H5860-9 4-Hydroxyquinoline-2-carboxylic acid (kynurenic acid)
M.W. 189.17 m.p. 290° (dec.)
NUJOL MULL
B
H5840-4 2-Hydroxyquinoline-4-carboxylic acid
M.W. 189.17 m.p. > 320°
NUJOL MULL
C
14,902-0 8-Hydroxyquinoline-7-carboxylic acid monohydrate
M.W. 207.19 m.p. 228° (dec.)
NUJOL MULL
D
18,324-5
3-Hydroxy-2-methyl-4-quinolinecarboxylic acid, 99%
FW 203.20 mp 235° (dec.) Disp. C
E
C1200-2 3-Carboxy-7-chloro-4-hydroxyquinoline (7-chloro-4-hydroxy-3-quinolinecarboxylic acid)
M.W. 223.62 m.p. 169°
F
C1199-5 3-Carboxy-6-chloro-4-hydroxyquinoline (6-chloro-4-hydroxy-3-quinolinecarboxylic acid), tech.
M.W. 223.62 m.p. 245° (dec.)
NUJOL MULL
G
11,404-9 4-Hydroxy-7-trifluoromethylquinoline-3-carboxylic acid
M.W. 257.17 m.p. 250° (dec.)
NUJOL MULL
H
11,690-4 4-Hydroxy-8-trifluoromethyl-3-quinolinecarboxylic acid
M.W. 257.17 m.p. 263° (dec.)
WAVENUMBER CM⁻¹
WAVELENGTH IN MICRONS

A

M.W. 219.20 m.p. 266° (dec.) ....

B

D12,080-4 4,8-Dihydroxyquinoline-2-carboxylic acid (xanthurenic acid)
M.W. 205.17 m.p. 297-298° (dec.) ....

C

14,233-6 4-Hydroxy-6-nitro-3-quinolinecarboxylic acid (3-carboxy-4-hydroxy-6-nitroquinoline), tech.
M.W. 234.17 m.p. 280° (dec.) ....

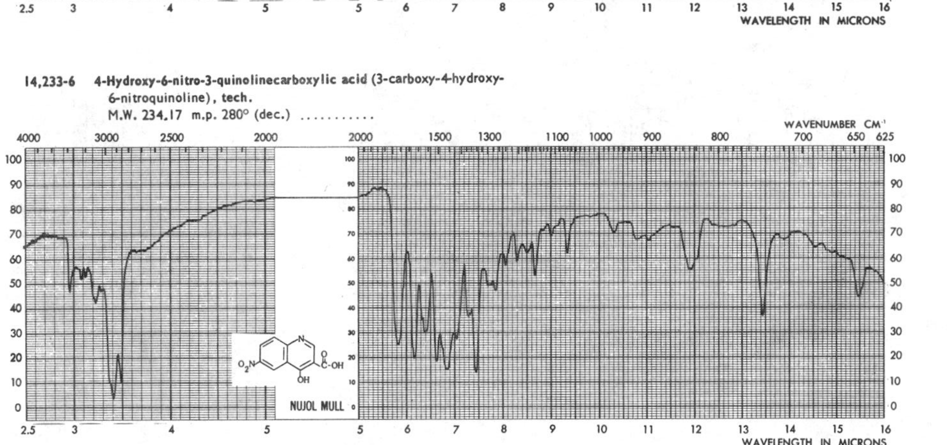

D

14,392-8 2-Piperidinocinchoninic acid (2-piperidino-4-quinolinecarboxylic acid)
M.W. 256.31 m.p. 228-230° ....

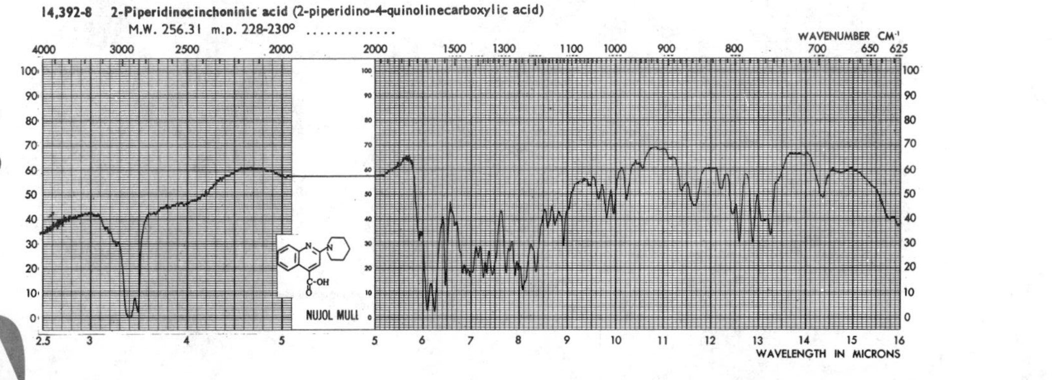

E

H5870-6 8-Hydroxyquinoline glucuronide trihydrate, puriss.
M.W. 375.33 m.p. 130° (dec.) ....

F

P3470-0 2-Phenylquinoline-4-carboxylic acid
M.W. 249.27 m.p. 212-215° ......

G

D5990-9 6,8-Dichlorocinchophen (6,8-dichloro-2-phenylquinoline-4-carboxylic acid)
M.W. 318.16 m.p. 255-257° (dec.) ....

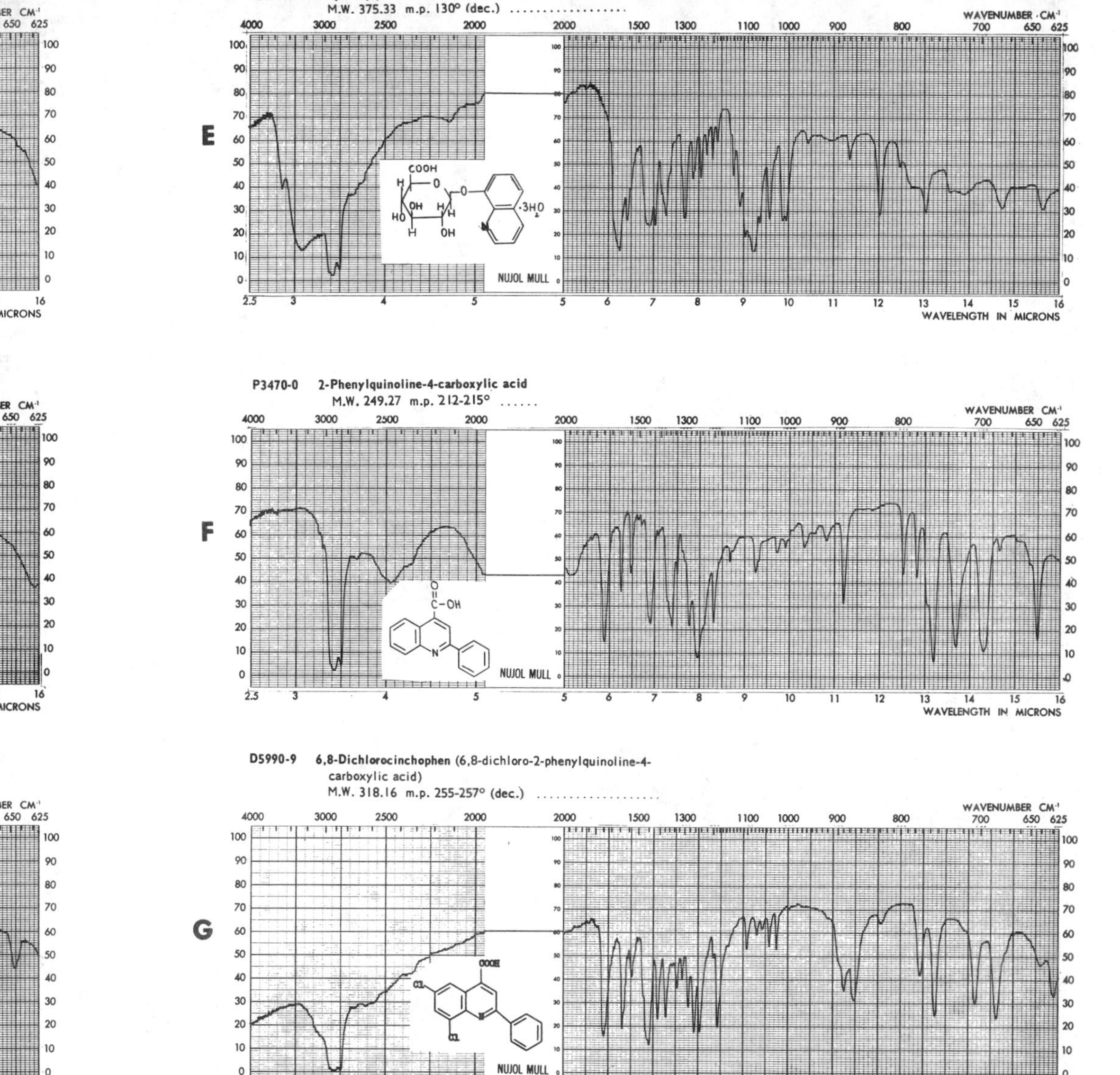

H

11,697-1 Ethyl 8-chloro-4-hydroxy-3-quinolinecarboxylate
M.W. 251.67 m.p. 247-250° ....

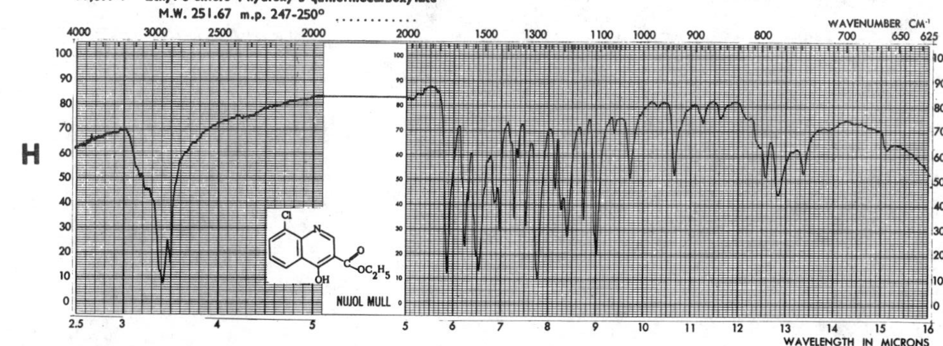

A

10,551-1 Ethyl 4-hydroxy-7-trifluoromethyl-3-quinolinecarboxylate
M.W. 285.23 m.p. > 300°

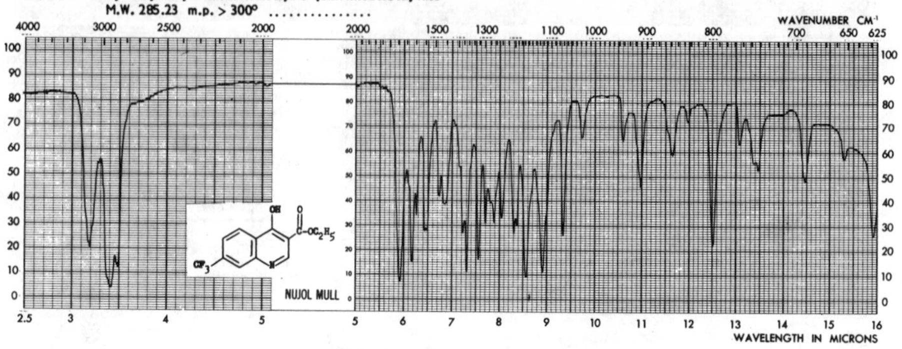

NUJOL MULL

B

11,693-9 Ethyl 4-hydroxy-8-trifluoromethyl-3-quinolinecarboxylate
M.W. 285.23 m.p. 206-208°

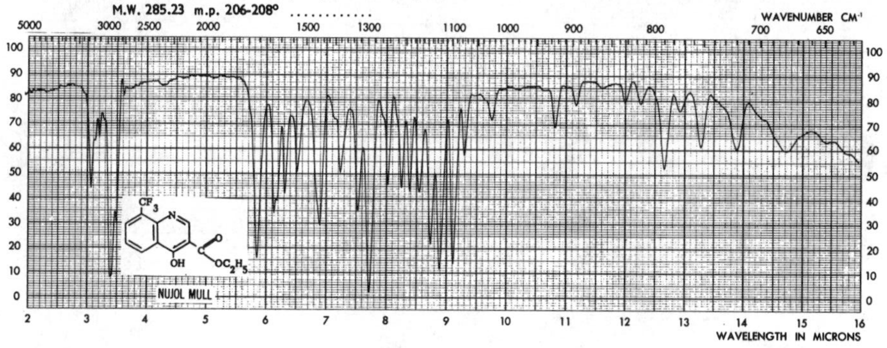

NUJOL MULL

C

11,694-7 Ethyl 4-hydroxy-7-nitro-3-quinolinecarboxylate, tech.
M.W. 262.22 m.p. > 310°

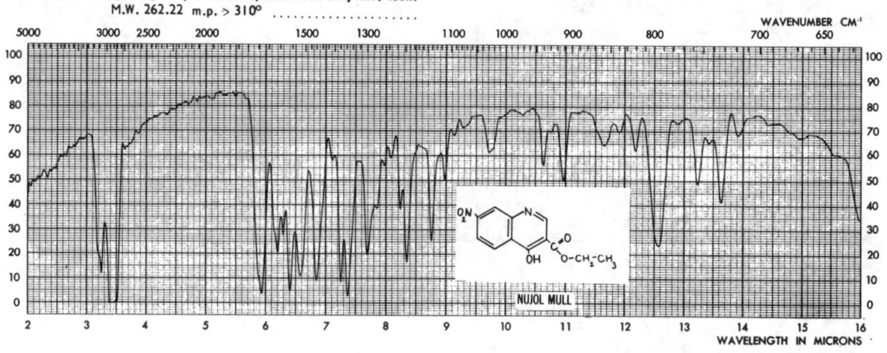

NUJOL MULL

D

15,367-2 Methyl 2-phenyl-4-quinolinecarboxylate
M.W. 263.30 m.p. 57-60°

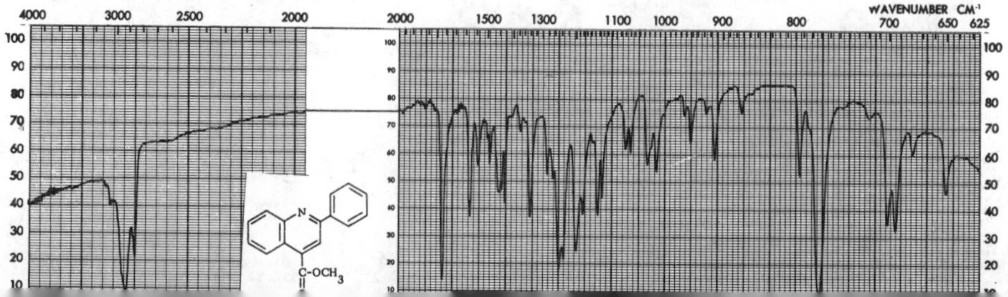

E

11,904-0 Ethyl 6,8-dichloro-2-phenyl-4-quinolinecarboxylate, tech.
M.W. 346.21

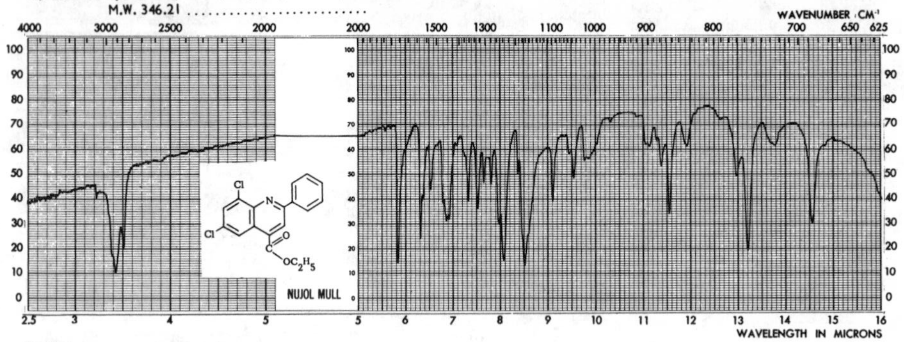

NUJOL MULL

F

17,824-1
IIDQ (2-isobutoxy-1-isobutoxycarbonyl-1,2-dihydroquinoline, isobutyl 1,2-dihydro-2-isobutoxy-1-quinolinecarboxylate)
M.W. 303.4 b.p. 140-142°/0.2mm. n_D^{20} 1.5230
d 1.022

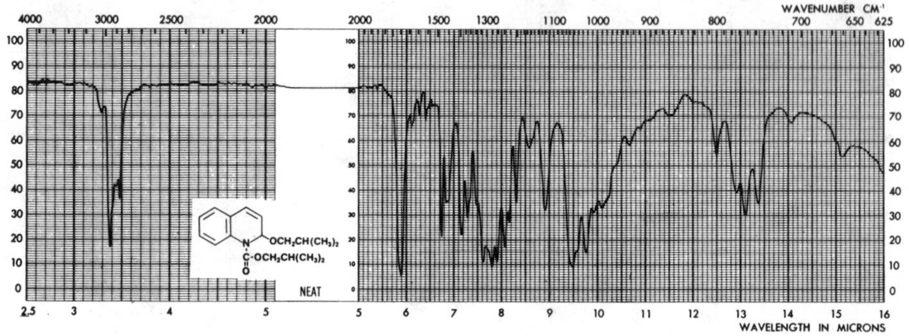

NEAT

G

17,715-6
3-Quinolinecarbonitrile, 98%
M.W. 154.17 m.p. 108-110°

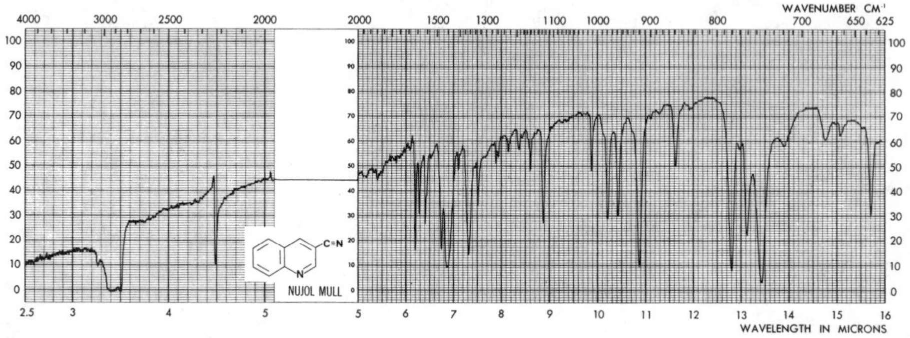

NUJOL MULL

H

Q140-9 8-Quinolinesulfonic acid
M.W. 209.22 m.p. > 300°

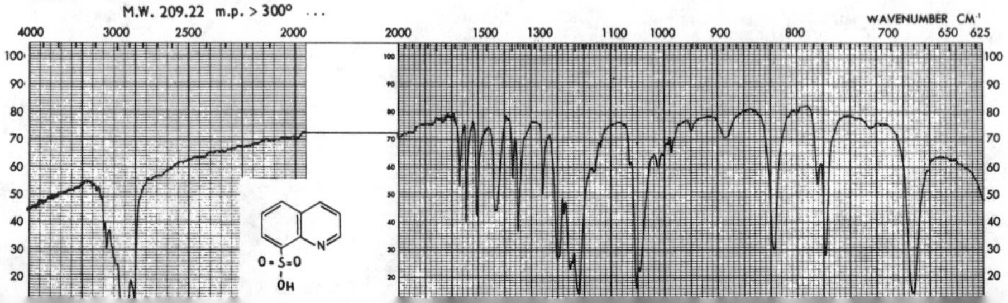

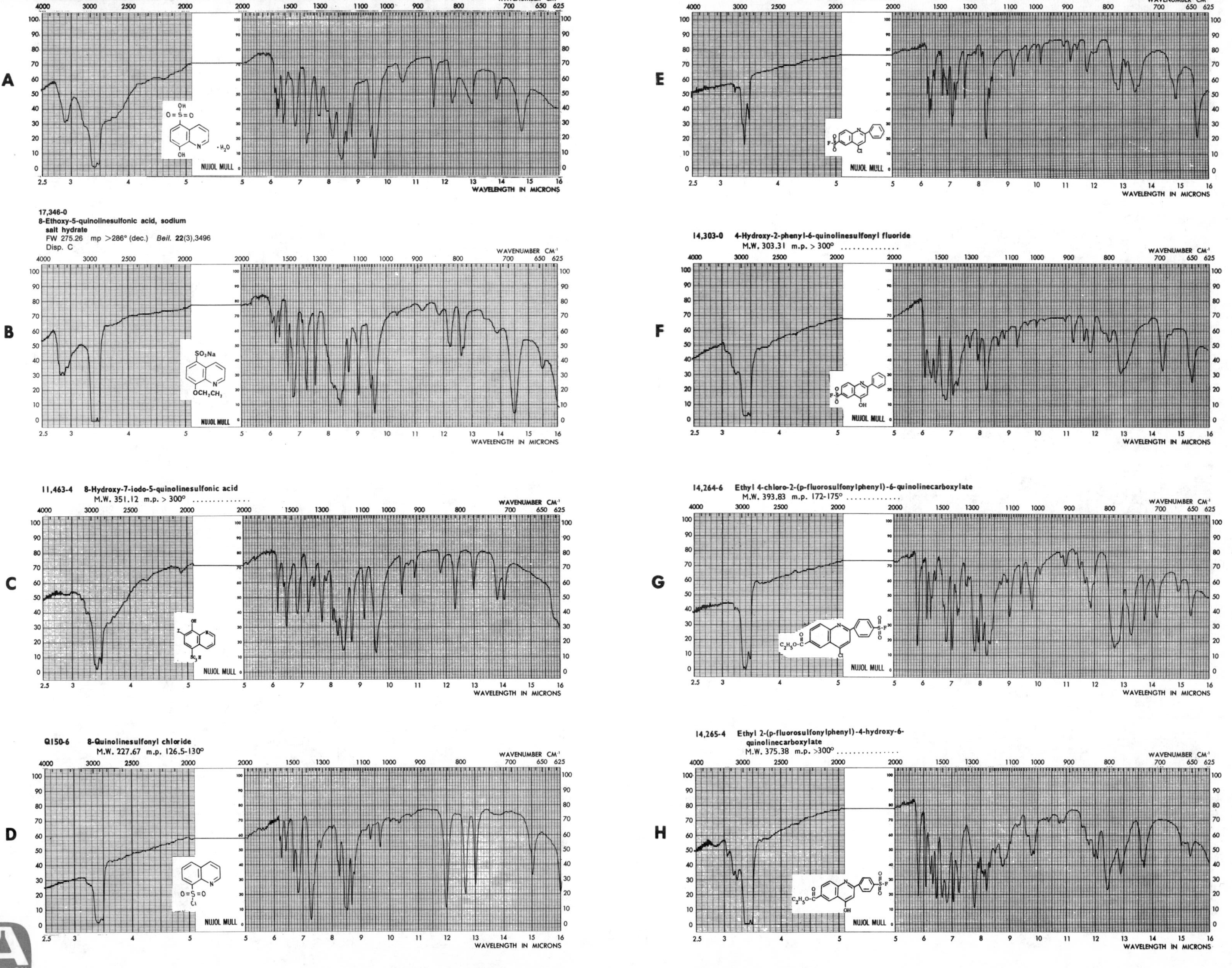

17,346-0
8-Ethoxy-5-quinolinesulfonic acid, sodium salt hydrate
FW 275.26 mp >286° (dec.) *Beil.* **22**(3),3496
Disp. C

11,463-4 8-Hydroxy-7-iodo-5-quinolinesulfonic acid
M.W. 351.12 m.p. > 300°

Q150-6 8-Quinolinesulfonyl chloride
M.W. 227.67 m.p. 126.5-130°

M.W. 321.76 m.p. 126-128°

14,303-0 4-Hydroxy-2-phenyl-6-quinolinesulfonyl fluoride
M.W. 303.31 m.p. > 300°

14,264-6 Ethyl 4-chloro-2-(p-fluorosulfonylphenyl)-6-quinolinecarboxylate
M.W. 393.83 m.p. 172-175°

14,265-4 Ethyl 2-(p-fluorosulfonylphenyl)-4-hydroxy-6-quinolinecarboxylate
M.W. 375.38 m.p. >300°

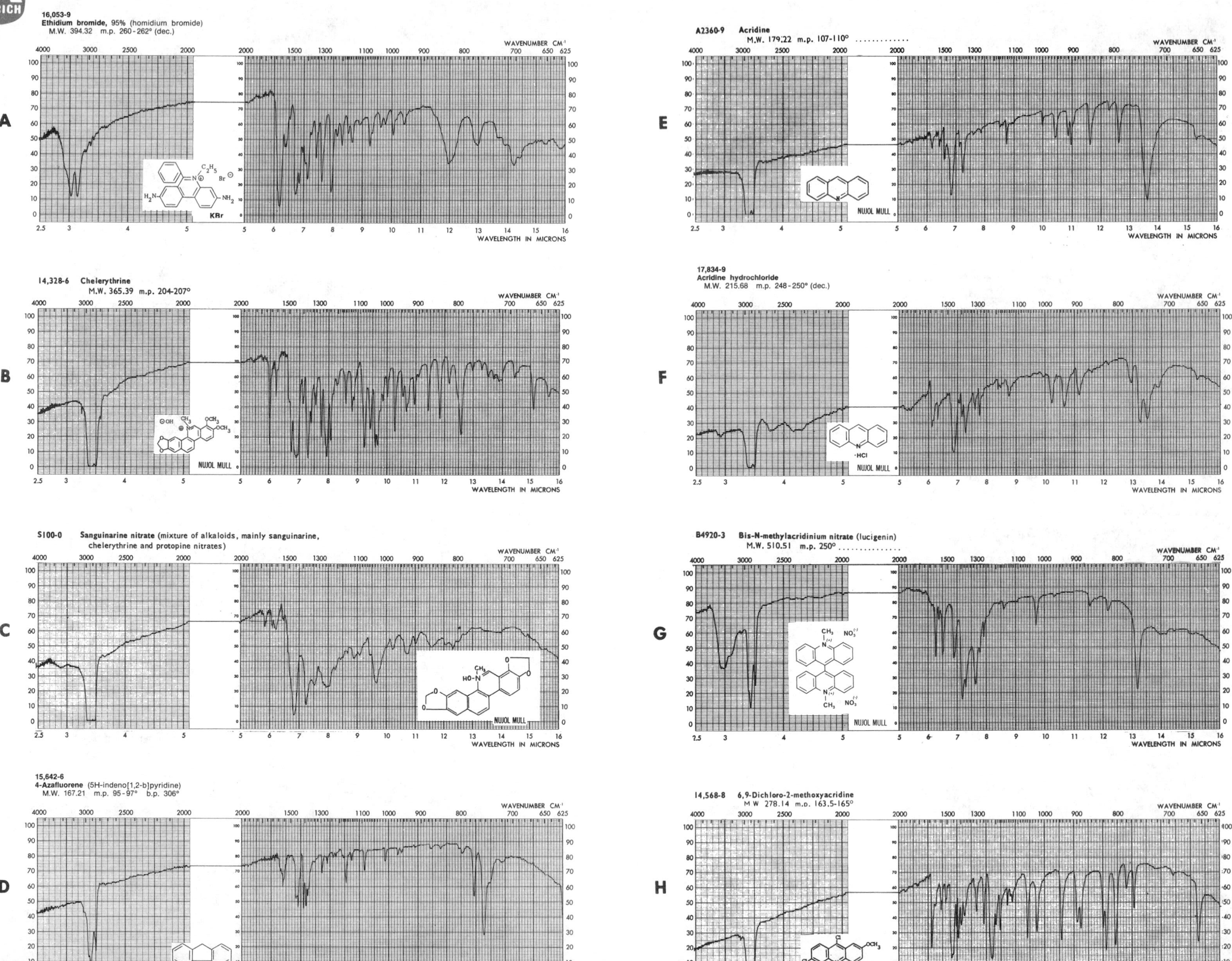
ALDRICH
A
16,053-9
Ethidium bromide, 95% (homidium bromide)
M.W. 394.32 m.p. 260-262° (dec.)
KBr
B
14,328-6 Chelerythrine
M.W. 365.39 m.p. 204-207°
NUJOL MULL
C
S100-0 Sanguinarine nitrate (mixture of alkaloids, mainly sanguinarine, chelerythrine and protopine nitrates)
NUJOL MULL
D
15,642-6
4-Azafluorene (5H-indeno[1,2-b]pyridine)
M.W. 167.21 m.p. 95-97° b.p. 306°
E
A2360-9 Acridine
M.W. 179.22 m.p. 107-110°
NUJOL MULL
F
17,834-9
Acridine hydrochloride
M.W. 215.68 m.p. 248-250° (dec.)
·HCl
NUJOL MULL
G
B4920-3 Bis-N-methylacridinium nitrate (lucigenin)
M.W. 510.51 m.p. 250°
NUJOL MULL
H
14,568-8 6,9-Dichloro-2-methoxyacridine
M.W. 278.14 m.p. 163.5-165°
WAVENUMBER CM⁻¹
WAVELENGTH IN MICRONS

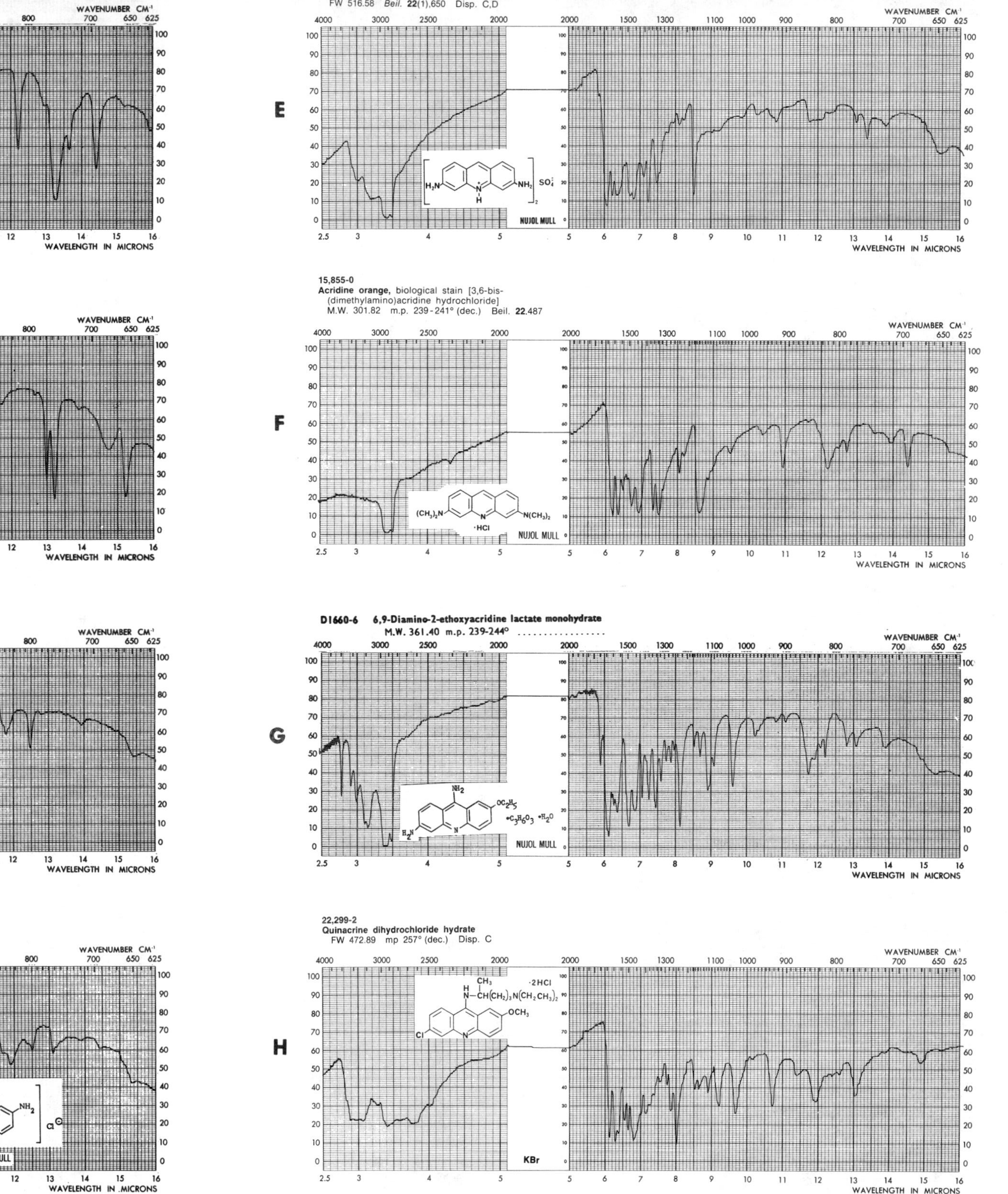

A M.W. 225.25 m.p. 284-289° ....

NUJOL MULL

B A3840-1 9-Aminoacridine hydrochloride
M.W. 230.70 m.p. > 350°

NUJOL MULL

C 13,110-5 3,6-Diaminoacridine, 90+%
M.W. 209.25 m.p. 267-270°

NUJOL MULL

D 12,126-6 Acriflavine (3,6-diamino-10-methylacridinium chloride)
M.W. 259.74 m.p. 265° (dec.) ....

NUJOL MULL

E FW 516.58 *Beil.* **22**(1),650 Disp. C,D

NUJOL MULL

F 15,855-0
Acridine orange, biological stain [3,6-bis-(dimethylamino)acridine hydrochloride]
M.W. 301.82 m.p. 239-241° (dec.) Beil. **22**,487

NUJOL MULL

G D1660-6 6,9-Diamino-2-ethoxyacridine lactate monohydrate
M.W. 361.40 m.p. 239-244° ....

NUJOL MULL

H 22,299-2
Quinacrine dihydrochloride hydrate
FW 472.89 mp 257° (dec.) Disp. C

KBr

ALDRICH

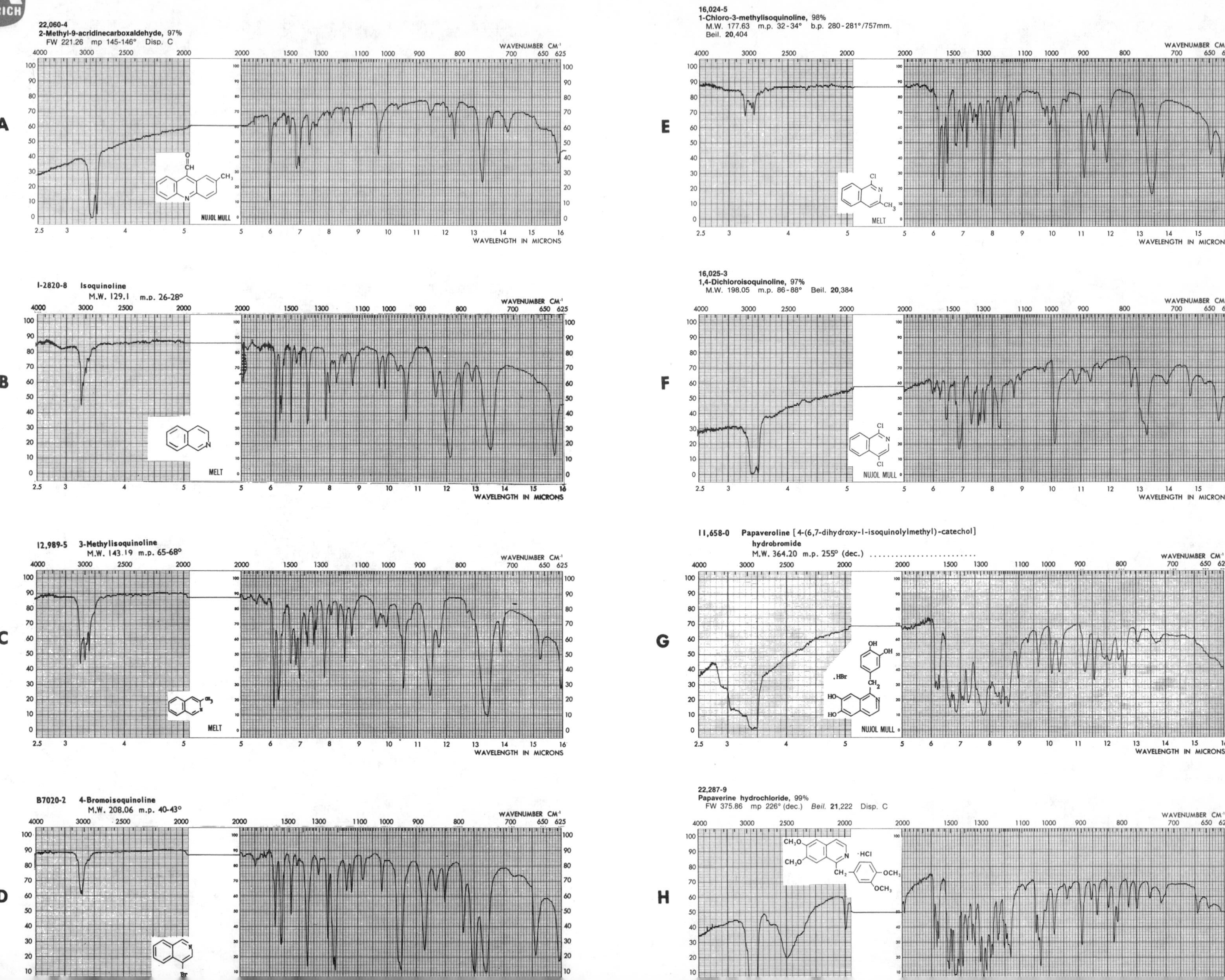
ALDRICH
A
22,060-4
2-Methyl-9-acridinecarboxaldehyde, 97%
FW 221.26 mp 145-146° Disp. C
NUJOL MULL
B
I-2820-8 Isoquinoline
M.W. 129.1 m.p. 26-28°
MELT
C
12,989-5 3-Methylisoquinoline
M.W. 143.19 m.p. 65-68°
MELT
D
B7020-2 4-Bromoisoquinoline
M.W. 208.06 m.p. 40-43°
E
16,024-5
1-Chloro-3-methylisoquinoline, 98%
M.W. 177.63 m.p. 32-34° b.p. 280-281°/757mm.
Beil. 20,404
MELT
F
16,025-3
1,4-Dichloroisoquinoline, 97%
M.W. 198.05 m.p. 86-88° Beil. 20,384
NUJOL MULL
G
11,658-0 Papaveroline [4-(6,7-dihydroxy-1-isoquinolylmethyl)-catechol] hydrobromide
M.W. 364.20 m.p. 255° (dec.)
NUJOL MULL
H
22,287-9
Papaverine hydrochloride, 99%
FW 375.86 mp 226° (dec.) Beil. 21,222 Disp. C
WAVENUMBER CM⁻¹
WAVELENGTH IN MICRONS

A

NUJOL MULL

E

M.W. 144.18 m.p. 120-122° Beil. **22**,640

NUJOL MULL

B

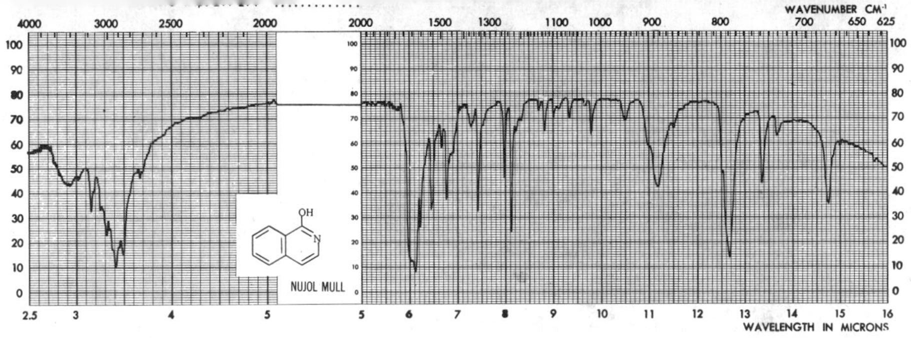

H3,320-7
5-Hydroxyisoquinoline, tech., 90% (5-isoquinolinol)
M.W. 145.16 Beil. **21**,102

NUJOL MULL

F

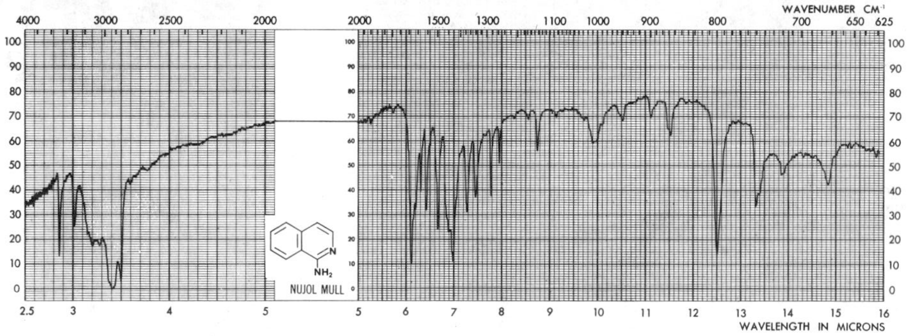

13,610-7 5-Aminoisoquinoline
M.W. 144.18 ....

NUJOL MULL

C

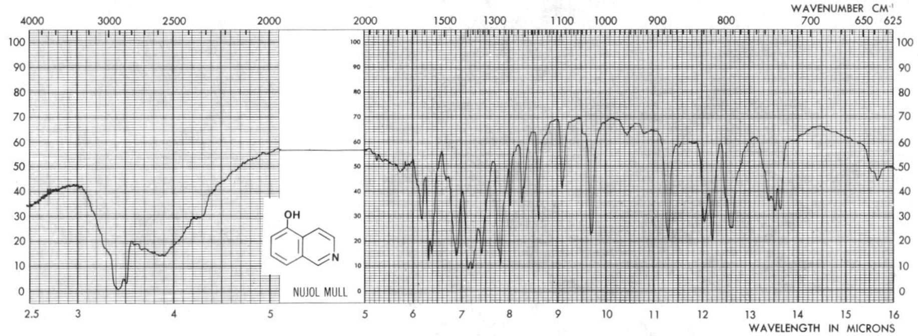

15,920-4
3-Methylisocarbostyril, 98% (3-methyl-1-isoquinolinol)
M.W. 159.19 m.p. 213-215° (dec.) Beil. **21**,113

NUJOL MULL

G

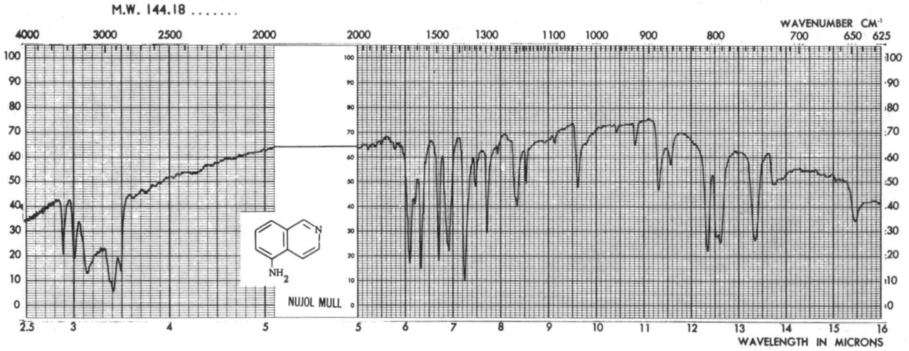

16,026-1
1-Chloro-4-nitroisoquinoline, 97%
M.W. 208.6 m.p. 123-125°

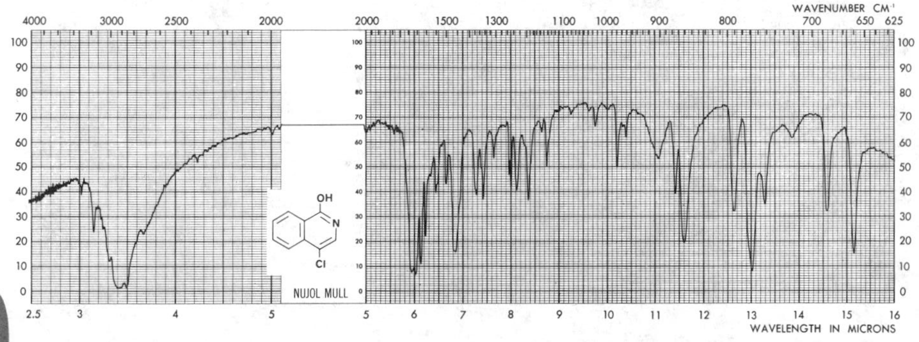

NUJOL MULL

D

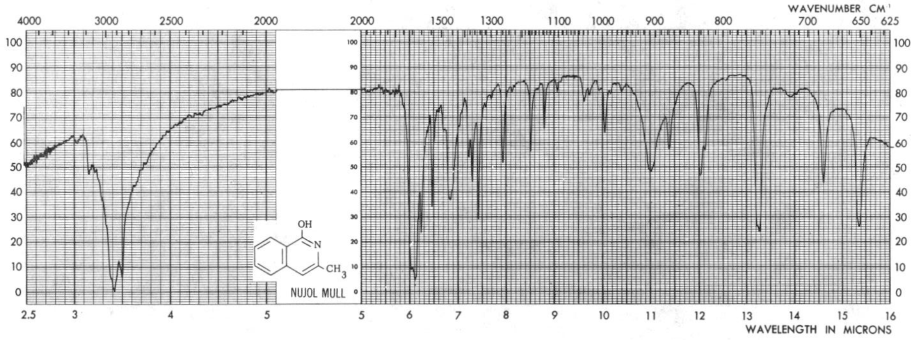

15,673-6
4-Chloroisocarbostyril
M.W. 179.61 m.p. 237-239°

NUJOL MULL

H

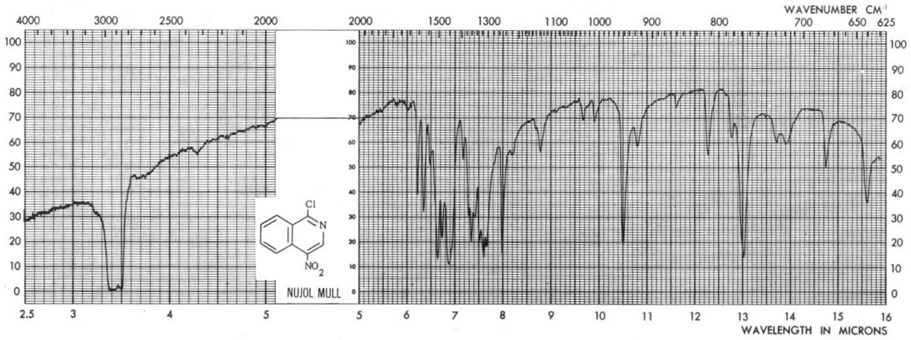

15,919-0
4-Nitroisocarbostyril (4-nitro-1-isoquinolinol)
M.W. 190.16 m.p. 236-238° (dec.)

NUJOL MULL

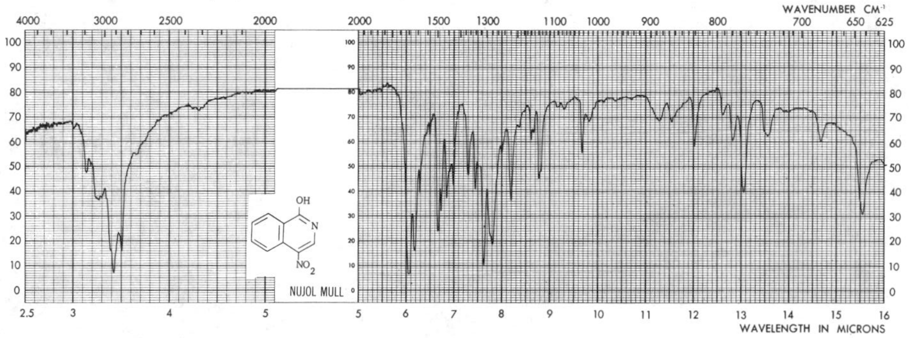

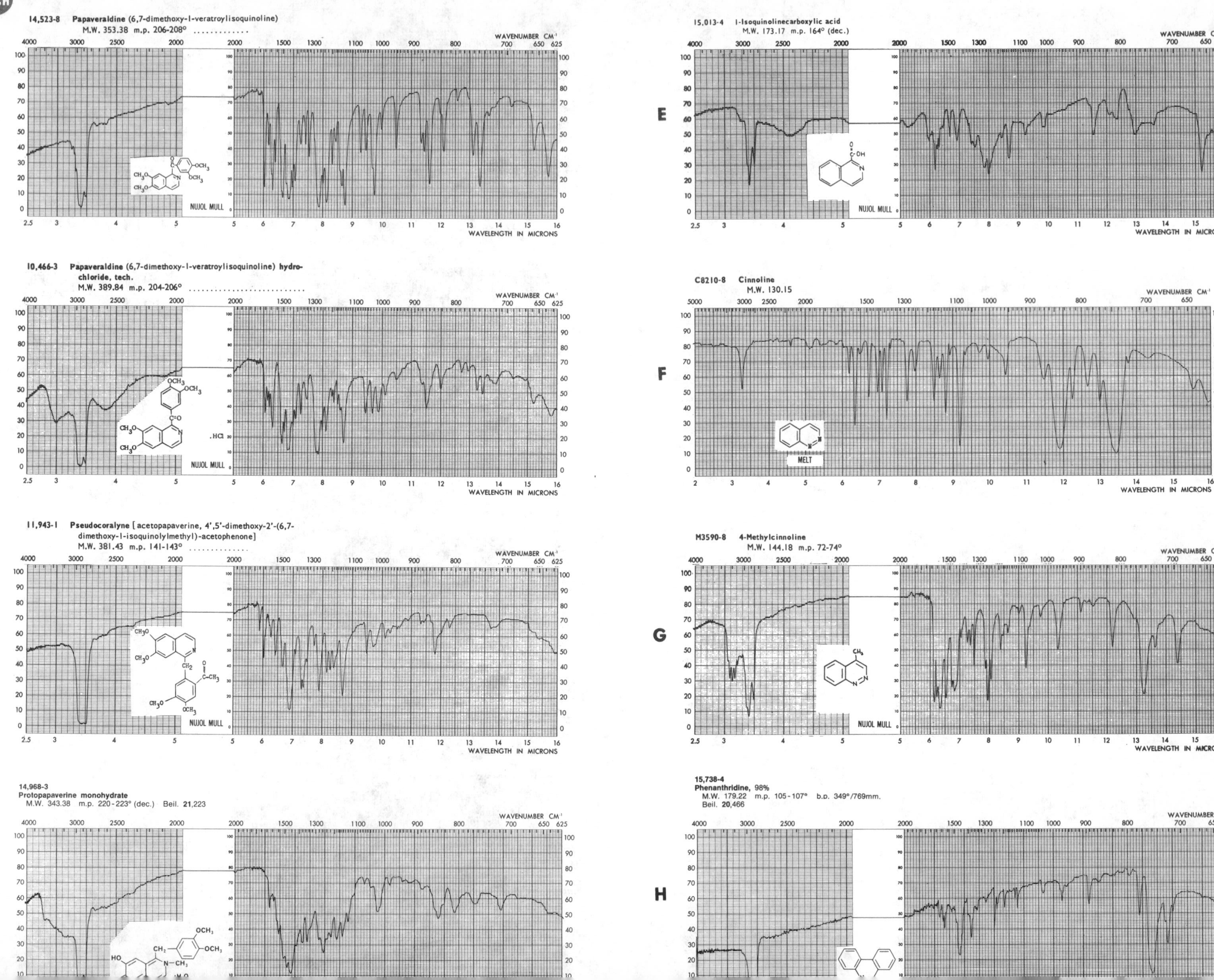
ALDRICH
A
14,523-8 Papaveraldine (6,7-dimethoxy-1-veratroylisoquinoline)
M.W. 353.38 m.p. 206-208°
NUJOL MULL
B
10,466-3 Papaveraldine (6,7-dimethoxy-1-veratroylisoquinoline) hydrochloride, tech.
M.W. 389.84 m.p. 204-206°
.HCl
NUJOL MULL
C
11,943-1 Pseudocoralyne [acetopapaverine, 4',5'-dimethoxy-2'-(6,7-dimethoxy-1-isoquinolylmethyl)-acetophenone]
M.W. 381.43 m.p. 141-143°
NUJOL MULL
D
14,968-3
Protopapaverine monohydrate
M.W. 343.38 m.p. 220-223° (dec.) Beil. 21,223
E
15,013-4 1-Isoquinolinecarboxylic acid
M.W. 173.17 m.p. 164° (dec.)
NUJOL MULL
F
C8210-8 Cinnoline
M.W. 130.15
MELT
G
M3590-8 4-Methylcinnoline
M.W. 144.18 m.p. 72-74°
NUJOL MULL
H
15,738-4
Phenanthridine, 98%
M.W. 179.22 m.p. 105-107° b.p. 349°/769mm.
Beil. 20,466
WAVENUMBER CM⁻¹
WAVELENGTH IN MICRONS

A

M.W. 180.21 m.p. 157-159°

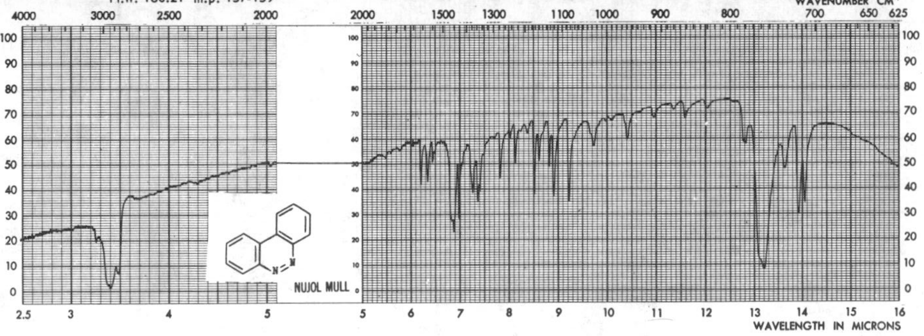

NUJOL MULL

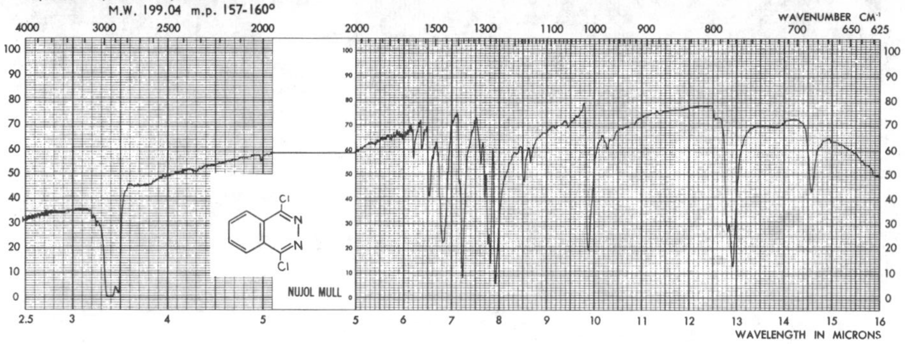

B

11,773-0 3-Cinnolinecarboxaldehyde
M.W. 158.16 m.p. 115-119°

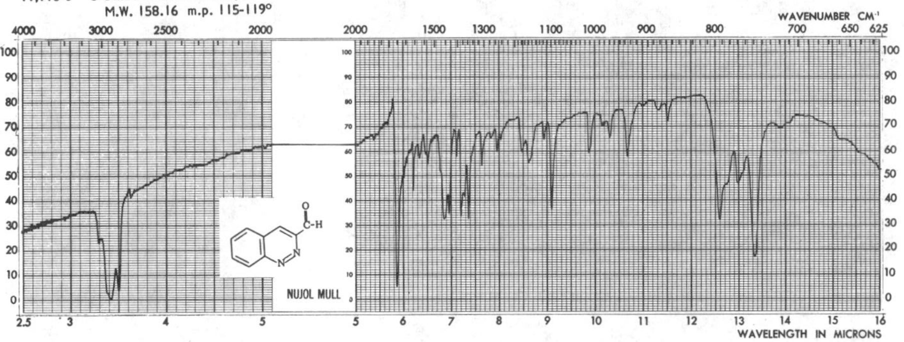

NUJOL MULL

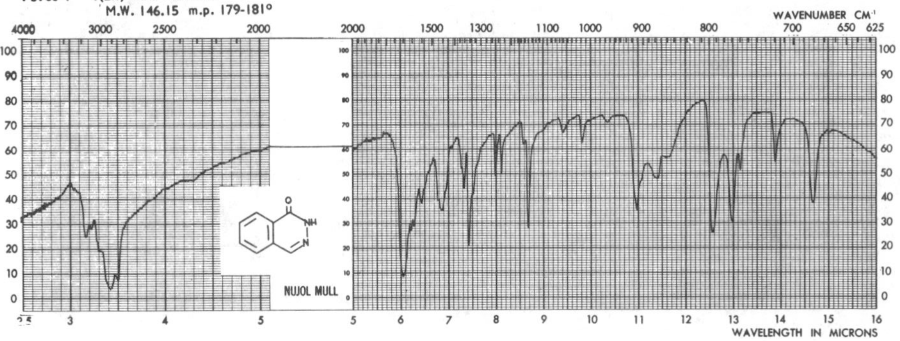

C

C8215-9 Cinnoline-4-carboxylic acid
M.W. 174.16 m.p. 196° (dec.)

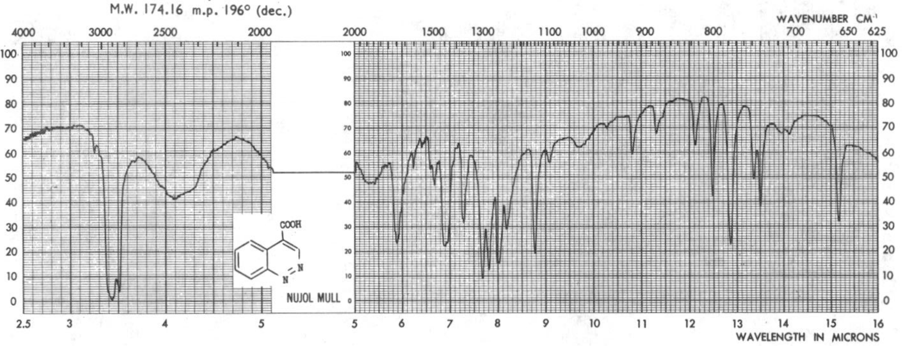

NUJOL MULL

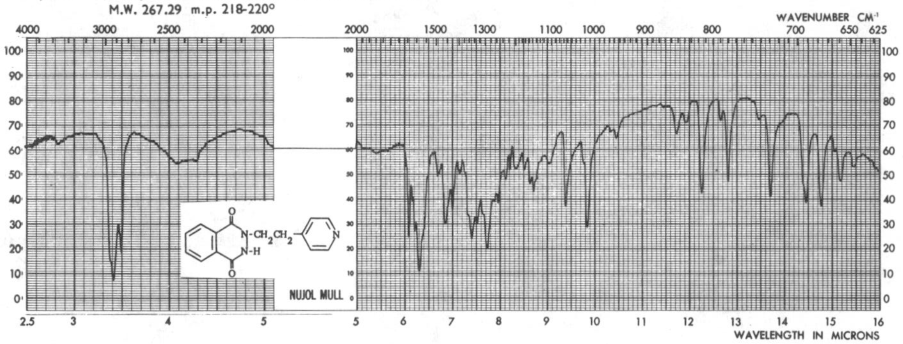

D

P3870-6 Phthalazine
M.W. 130.15 m.p. 89-92° ...

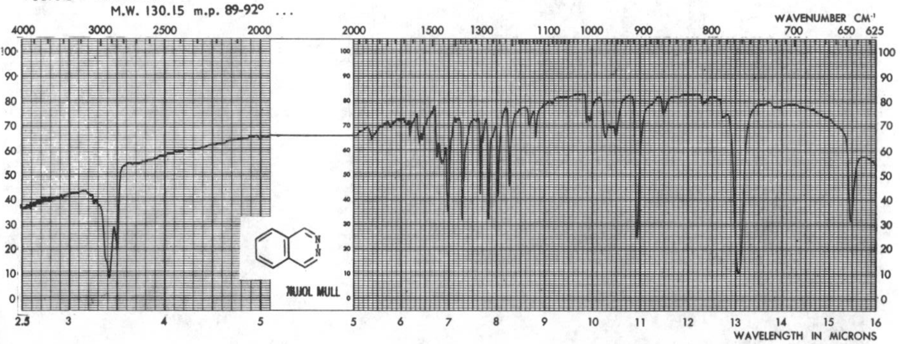

NUJOL MULL

E

[illegible] 1,4-Dichlorophthalazine
M.W. 199.04 m.p. 157-160°

NUJOL MULL

F

P3900-1 1(2H)-Phthalazinone
M.W. 146.15 m.p. 179-181°

NUJOL MULL

G

11,367-0 2,3-Dihydro-2-[2-(4-pyridyl)-ethyl]-1,4-phthalazinedione
M.W. 267.29 m.p. 218-220°

NUJOL MULL

H

D10,430-2 1,4-Dihydrazinophthalazine sulfate dihydrate
M.W. 324.32 m.p. 251-252° (dec.) ....

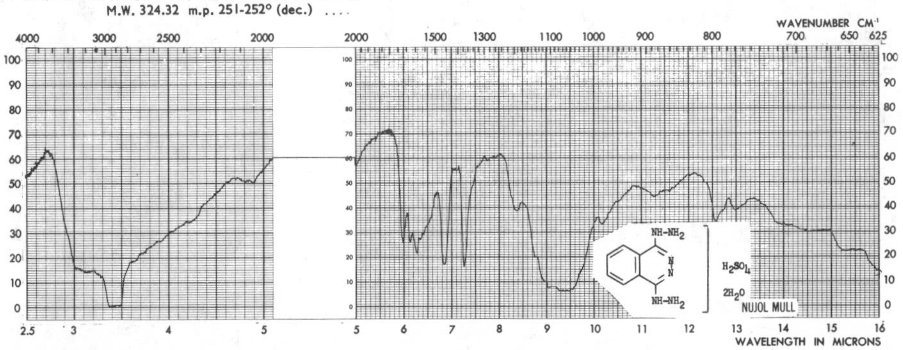

NUJOL MULL

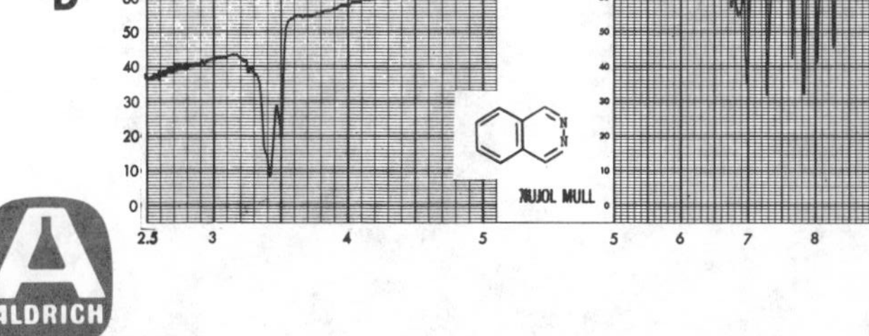

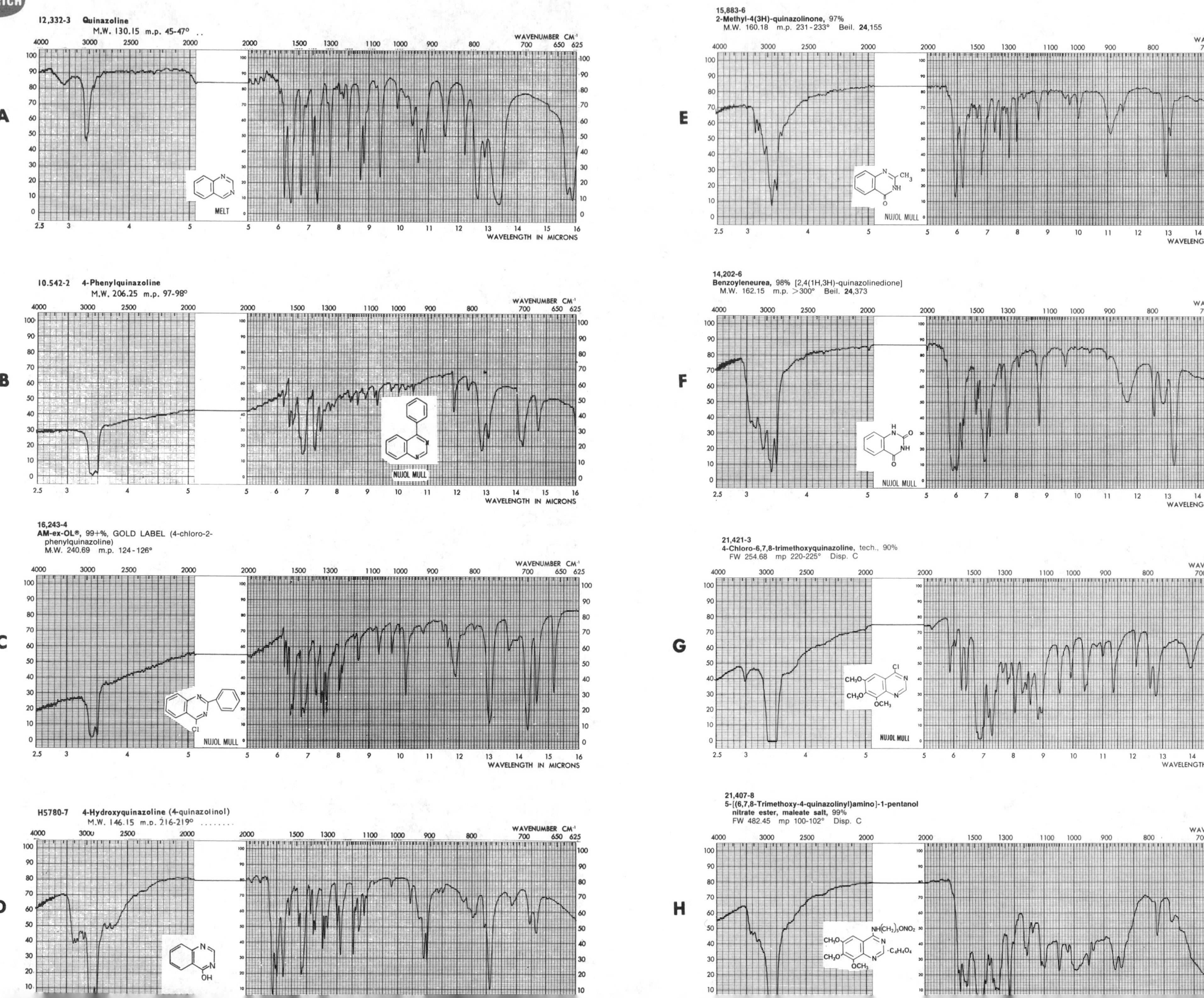
ALDRICH
A
12,332-3 Quinazoline
M.W. 130.15 m.p. 45-47°
MELT
B
10.542-2 4-Phenylquinazoline
M.W. 206.25 m.p. 97-98°
NUJOL MULL
C
16,243-4
AM-ex-OL®, 99+%, GOLD LABEL (4-chloro-2-phenylquinazoline)
M.W. 240.69 m.p. 124-126°
NUJOL MULL
D
H5780-7 4-Hydroxyquinazoline (4-quinazolinol)
M.W. 146.15 m.p. 216-219°
E
15,883-6
2-Methyl-4(3H)-quinazolinone, 97%
M.W. 160.18 m.p. 231-233° Beil. 24,155
NUJOL MULL
F
14,202-6
Benzoyleneurea, 98% [2,4(1H,3H)-quinazolinedione]
M.W. 162.15 m.p. >300° Beil. 24,373
NUJOL MULL
G
21,421-3
4-Chloro-6,7,8-trimethoxyquinazoline, tech., 90%
FW 254.68 mp 220-225° Disp. C
NUJOL MULL
H
21,407-8
5-[(6,7,8-Trimethoxy-4-quinazolinyl)amino]-1-pentanol nitrate ester, maleate salt, 99%
FW 482.45 mp 100-102° Disp. C
WAVENUMBER CM⁻¹
WAVELENGTH IN MICRONS

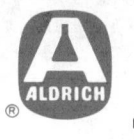

A
M.W. 178.21 m.p. >300° Beil. 24,379
NUJOL MULL

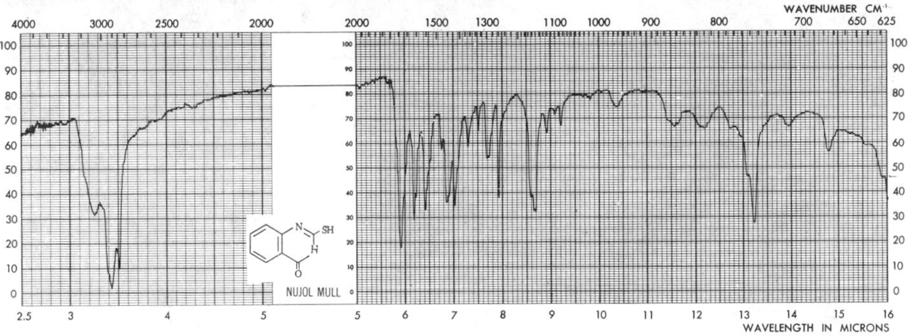

B
14,459-2 2-Trichloromethyl-4(3H)-quinazolinone
M.W. 263.51 m.p. 211-213°
NUJOL MULL

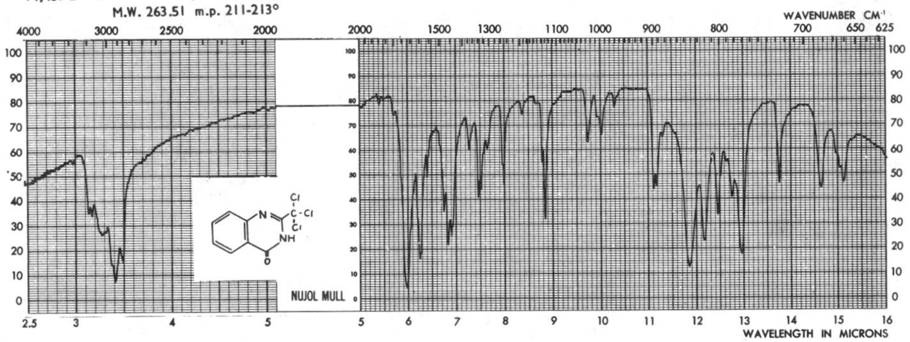

C
22,265-8
4,4'-(1,3-Propanediyldi-4,1-piperidinediyl)-bis[7-nitro-quinazoline], 98%
FW 556.63 mp 187-190° Disp. C
NUJOL MULL

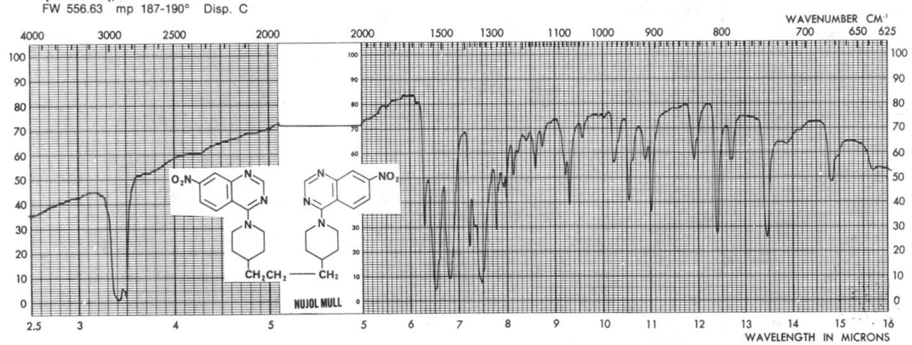

D
10,497-3 2-Guanidino-4-methylquinazoline hydrochloride
M.W. 237.69 m.p. 330-331° (dec.)
NUJOL MULL

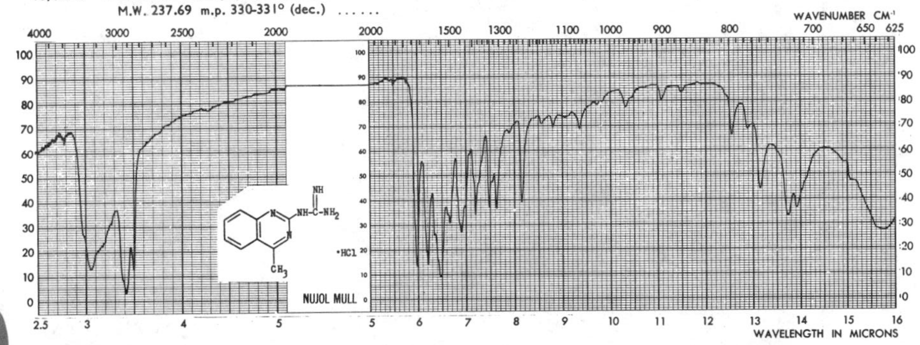

E
10,835-9 Perimidine (1H-benzo[de]quinazoline)
M.W. 168.20 m.p. 232-235°
NUJOL MULL

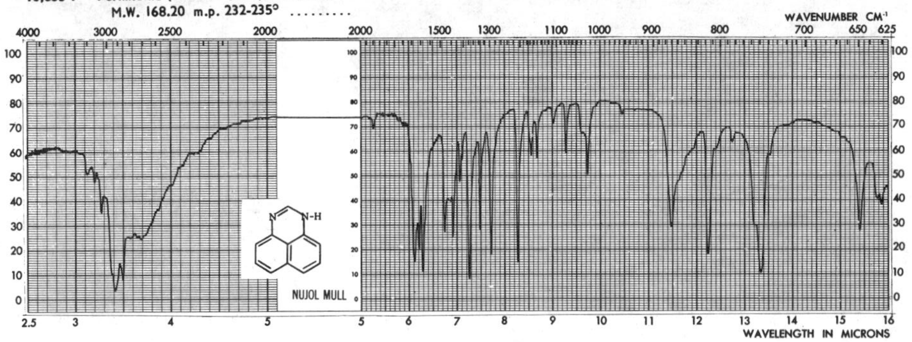

F
10,539-2 3-Guanidino-1-methylbenzo[f]quinazoline hydrochloride
M.W. 287.75 m.p. 314-316° (dec.)
NUJOL MULL

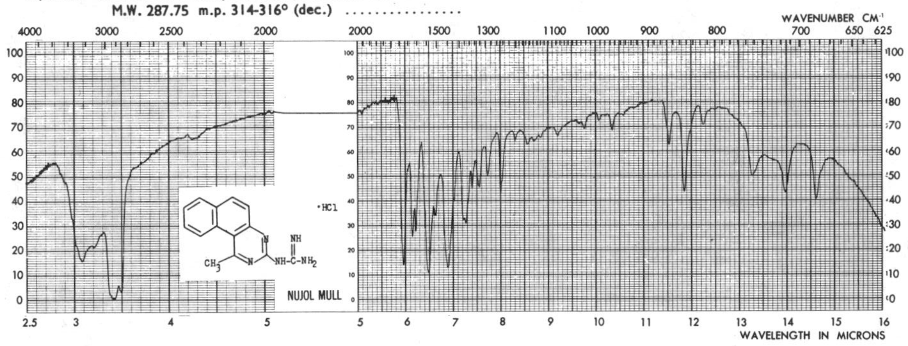

G
Q160-3 Quinoxaline
M.W. 130.15 m.p. 29-32°
MELT

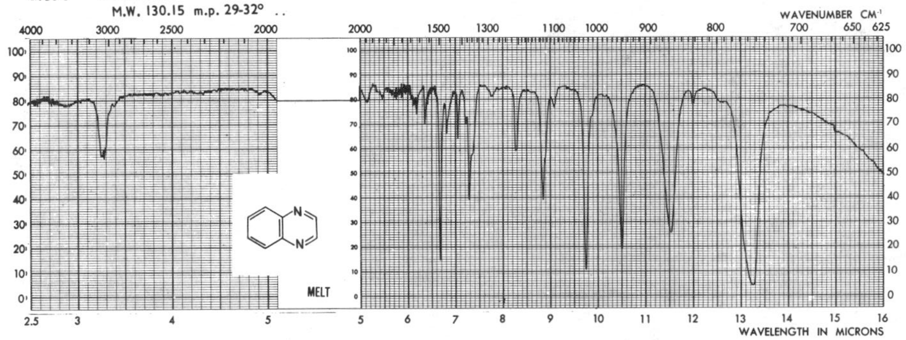

H
M8020-2 2-Methylquinoxaline
M.W. 144.18 n_D^{20} 1.6156 b.p. 245-247°
NEAT

ALDRICH

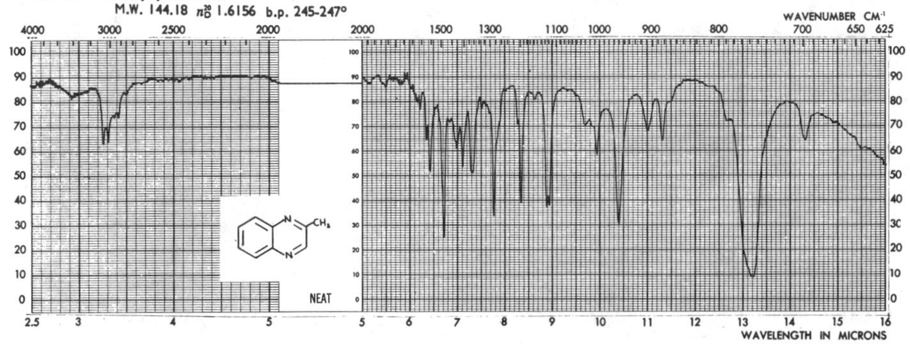

A

D18,497-7 2,3-Dimethylquinoxaline
M.W. 158.20 m.p. 106-107°

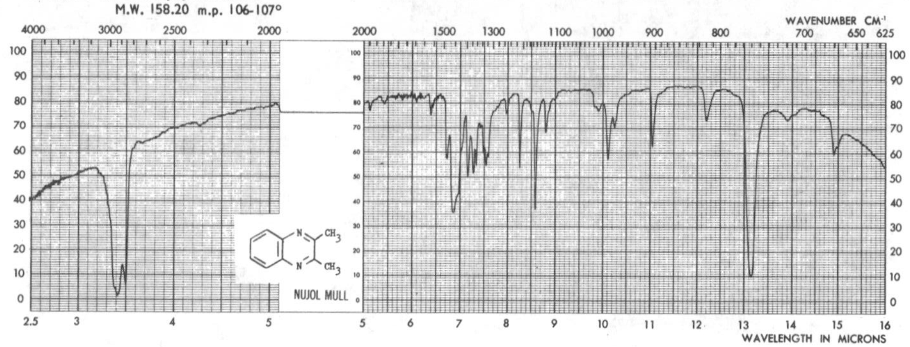

NUJOL MULL

B

14,548-3 2,3-Diphenylquinoxaline
M.W. 282.35 m.p. 125-127°

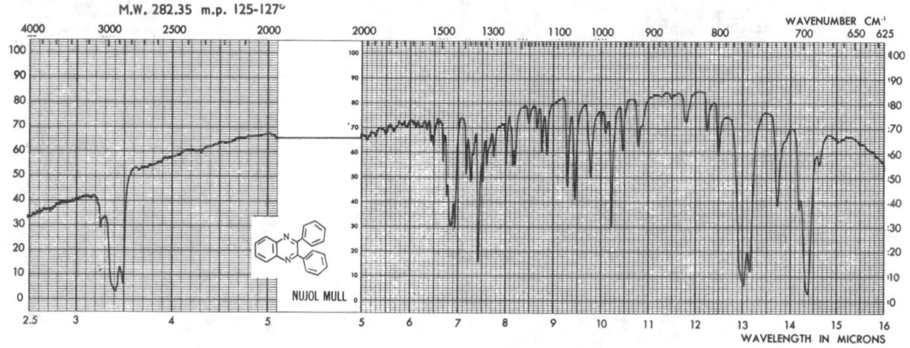

NUJOL MULL

C

12,646-2 6,7-Dimethyl-2,3-di-(2-pyridyl)-quinoxaline
M.W. 312.38 m.p. 191-195°

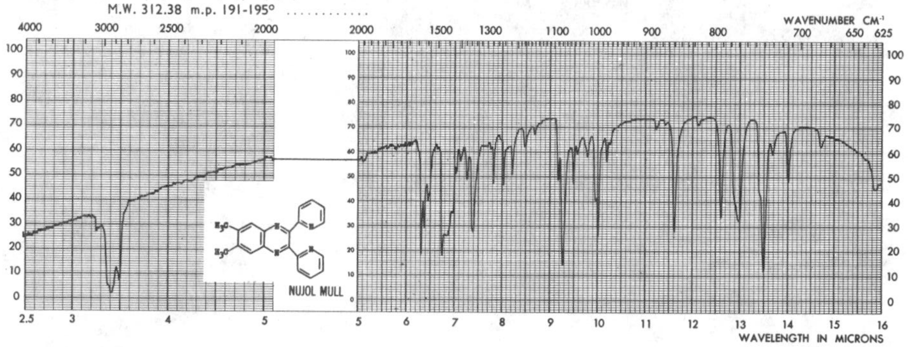

NUJOL MULL

D

19,704-1
Pyrrolo[1,2-a]quinoxaline, 98+%
FW 168.20 mp 132-135° Disp. C

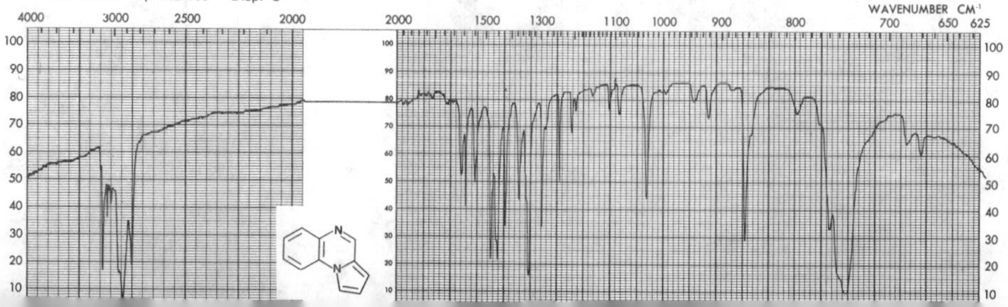

E

P1320-7 Phenazine
M.W. 180.21 m.p. 174-177°

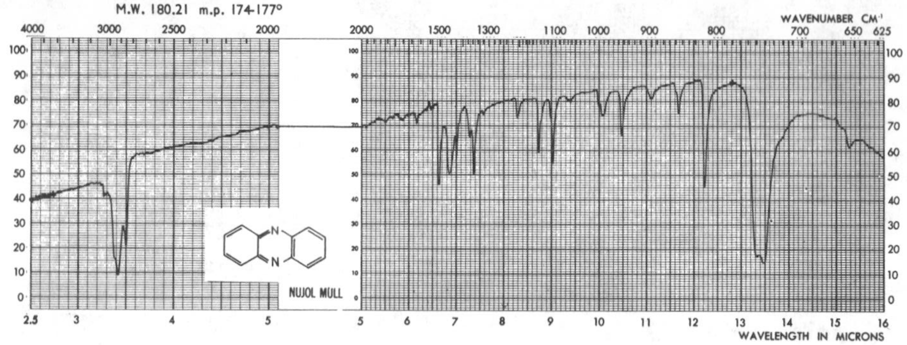

NUJOL MULL

F

P1340-1 Phenazine methosulfate (N-methylphenazonium methosulfate)
M.W. 306.34 m.p. 149-152°

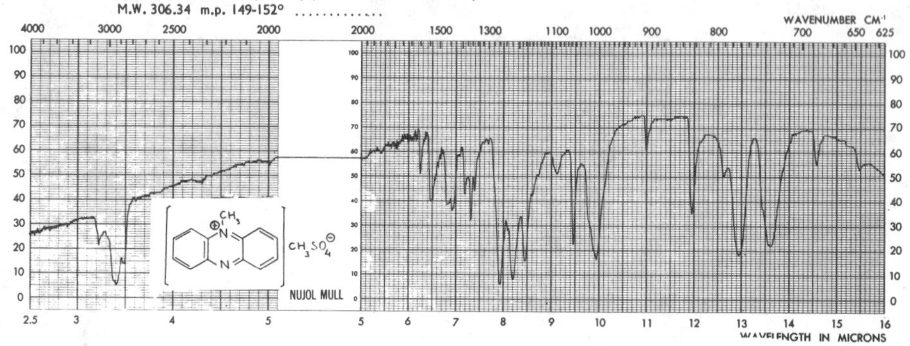

NUJOL MULL

G

D3200-8 Dibenzo[a,c]phenazine
M.W. 280.33 m.p. 216-220°

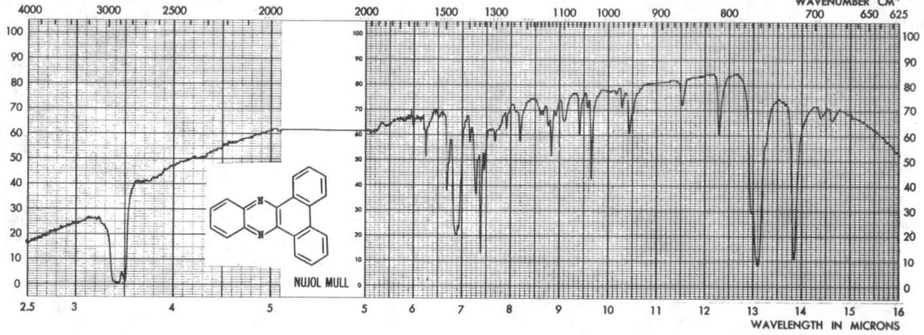

NUJOL MULL

H

T4620-5 1,2,3,4,6,7-Tribenzophenazine
M.W. 330.39 m.p. 274-276°

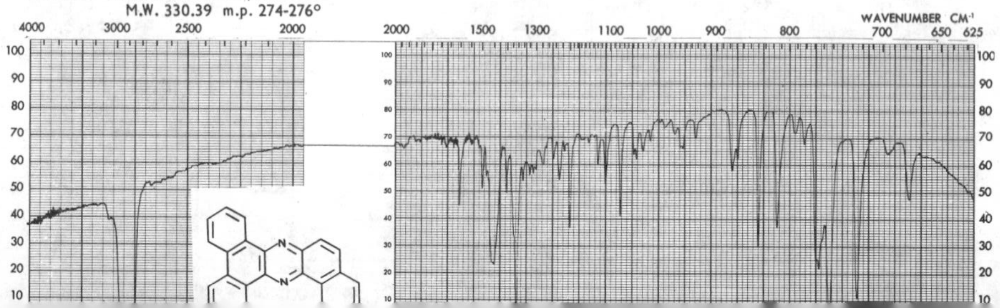

A 13,630-1 2-Chloroquinoxaline
M.W. 164.60 m.p. 46-48°
MELT

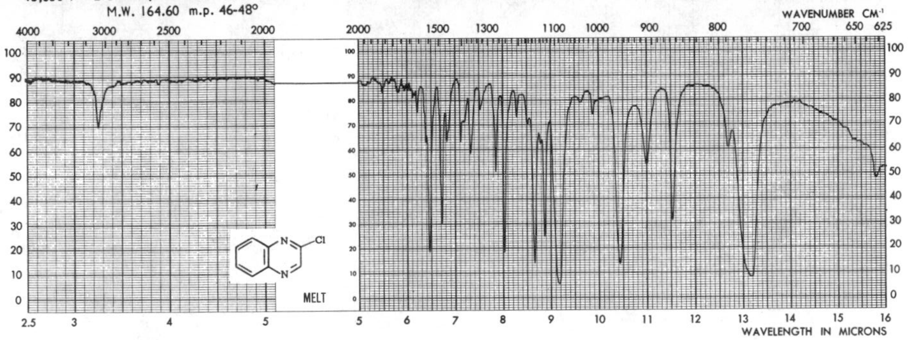

B 14,468-1 2-Chloro-3-methylquinoxaline
M.W. 178.62 m.p. 84-86°
NUJOL MULL

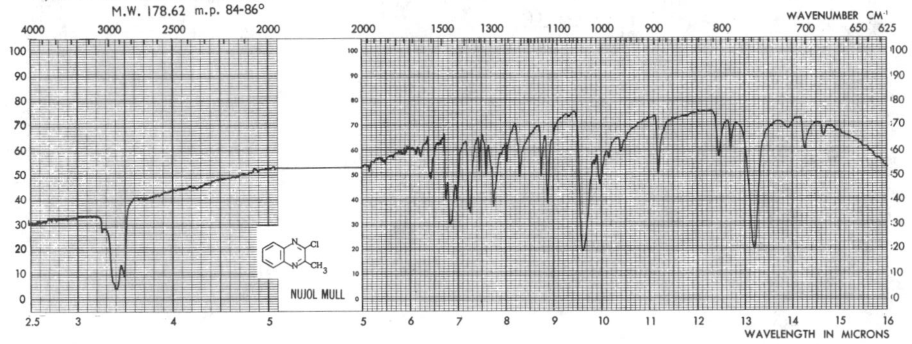

C 14,452-5 2,3-Dichloroquinoxaline
M.W. 199.04 m.p. 152-154°
NUJOL MULL

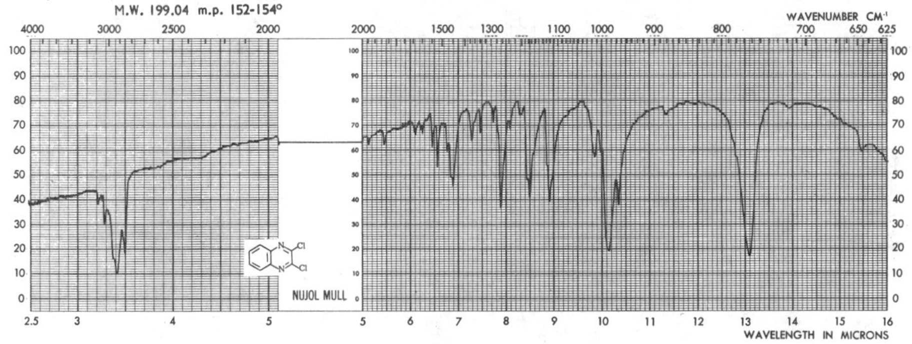

D 10,912-6 2,3,6-Trichloroquinoxaline
M.W. 233.49 m.p. 144-146°
NUJOL MULL

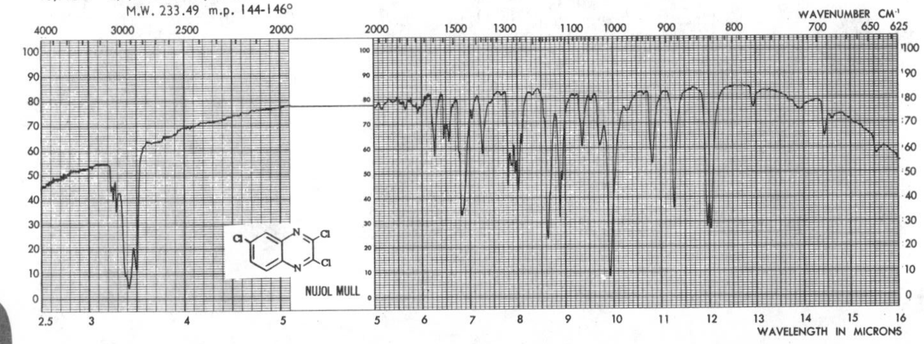

E B3715-9 2,3-Bis-(bromomethyl)-quinoxaline
M.W. 316.01 m.p. 153-156° ....
NUJOL MULL

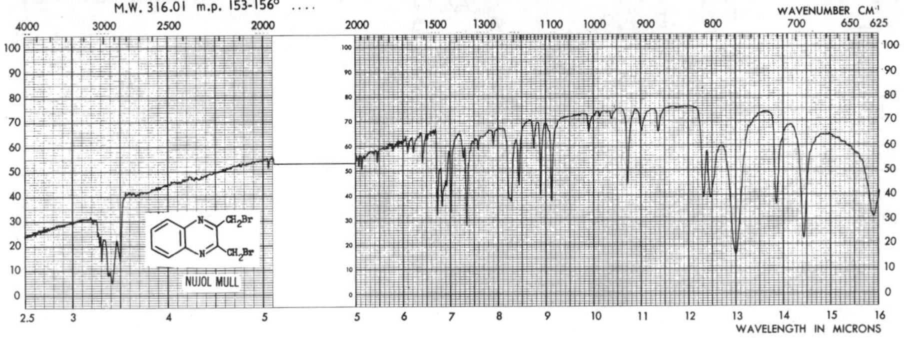

F 14,446-0 3-Methyl-2-quinoxalinol
M.W. 160.18 m.p. 249° (dec.)
NUJOL MULL

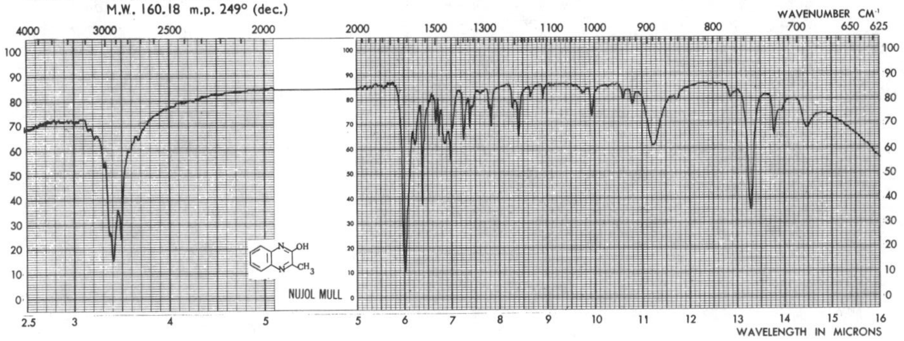

G D12,120-7
2,3-Dihydroxyquinoxaline, 99+%, GOLD LABEL
(2,3-quinoxalinediol)
M.W. 162.15 m.p. >340° Beil. 24,380
NUJOL MULL

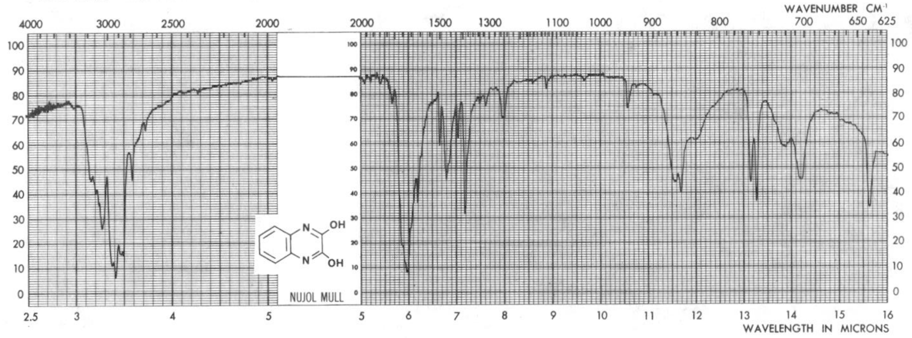

H 10,675-5 2-(o-Aminophenyl)-3-hydroxyquinoxaline
M.W. 237.26 m.p. 258-260° ....
NUJOL MULL

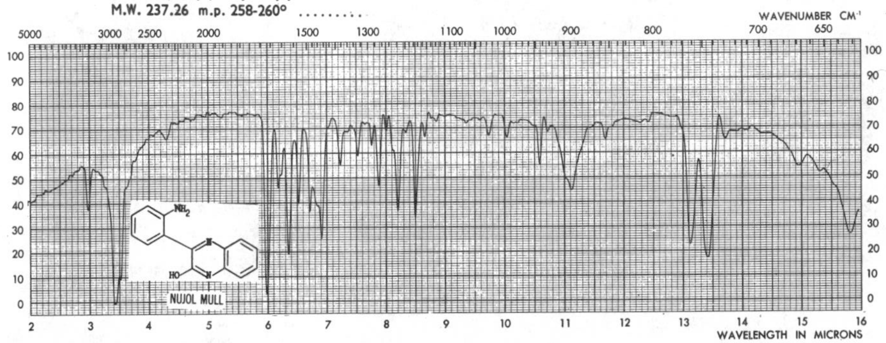

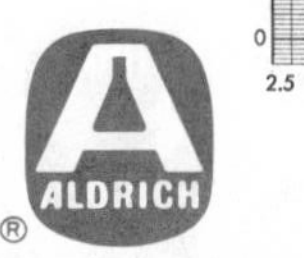

A

10,834-0 **3-Hydroxy-2-quinoxalinecarboxylic acid**
M.W. 190.17 m.p. 267-268°

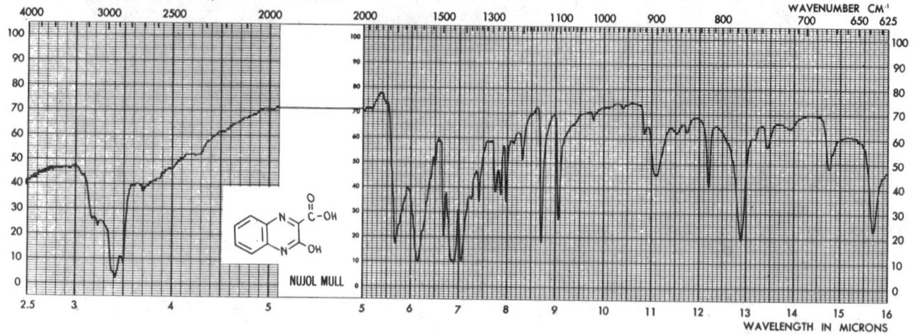

NUJOL MULL

B

16,022-9
Ethyl 3-hydroxy-2-quinoxalineacetate, 99%
M.W. 232.24 m.p. 212-214° (dec.)

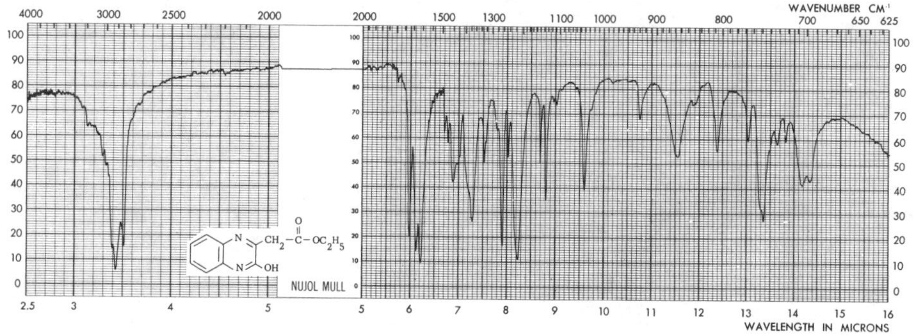

NUJOL MULL

C

14,599-8 **2-Quinoxaloyl chloride** (2-quinoxalinecarbonyl chloride)
M.W. 192.61 m.p. 113-115°

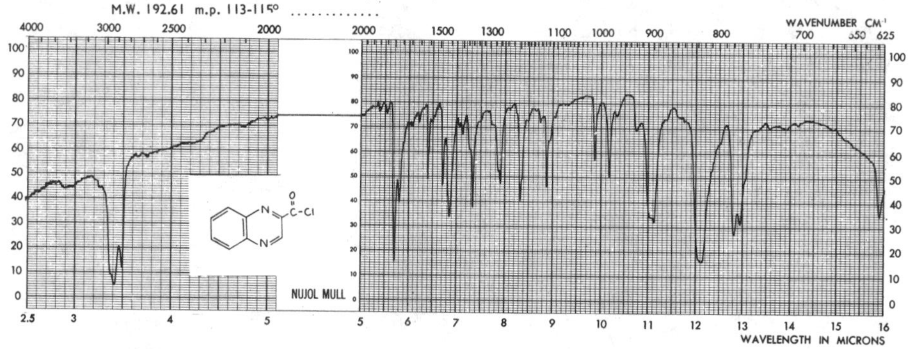

NUJOL MULL

D

12,882-1 **Phenosafranine** (3,7-diamino-5-phenylphenazinium chloride)
M.W. 322.80 m.p. > 300°

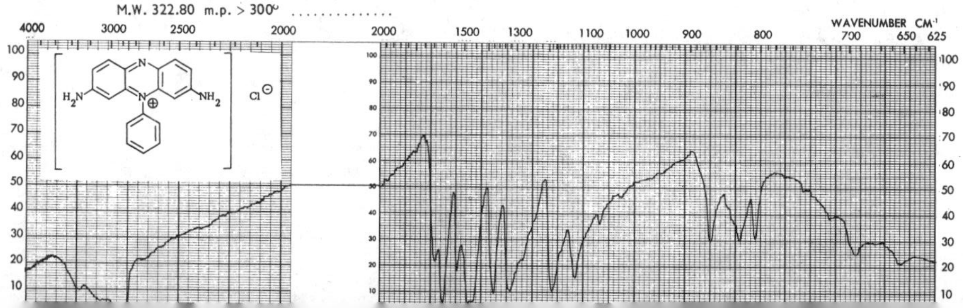

E

10,214-8 **Safranine O** (3,7-diamino-2,8-dimethyl-5-phenylphenazinium chloride)
M.W. 350.85 m.p. > 330°

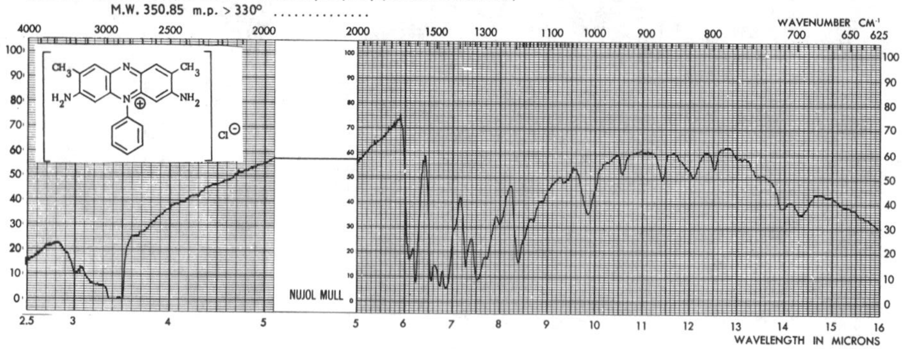

NUJOL MULL

F

A6512-3 **8-Amino-7-methyl-2-phenazinol**
M.W. 225.25 m.p. > 330°

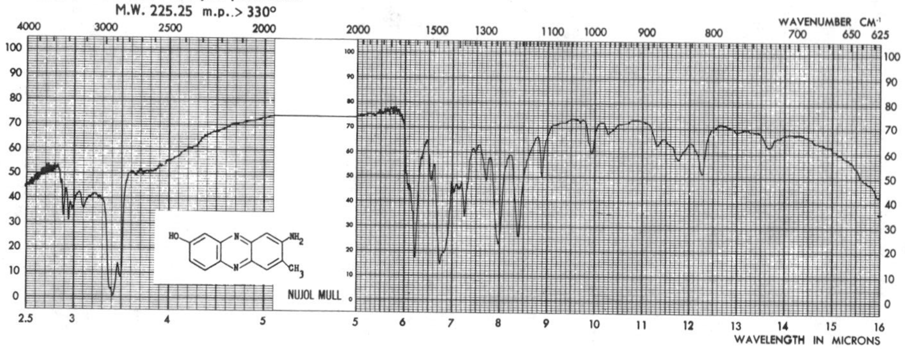

NUJOL MULL

G

13,808-8 **2,3-Dihydroxy-1,4-phenazinedione** (2,3-dihydroxy-1,4-phenazinequinone)
M.W. 242.19 m.p. > 310°

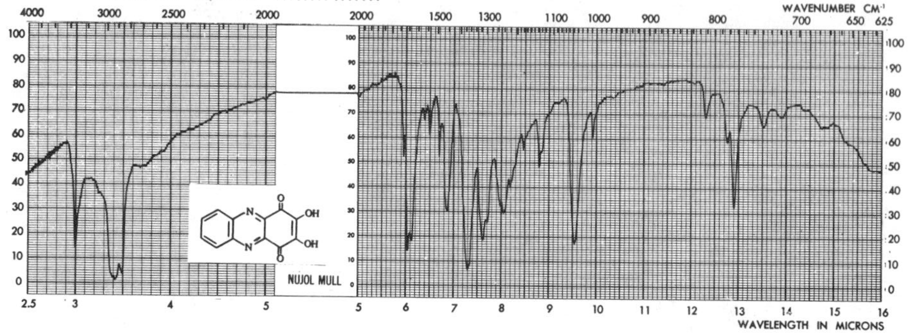

NUJOL MULL

H

M4490-7 **Methylene blue, U.S.P. crystals**
M.W. 373.90 m.p. 195° (dec.)

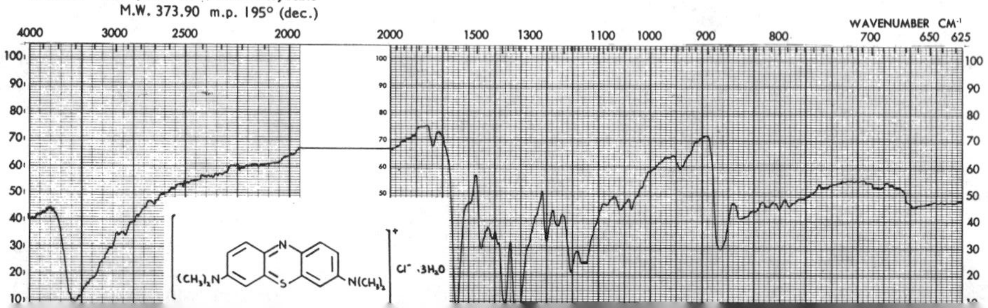

WAVENUMBER CM⁻¹ / WAVELENGTH IN MICRONS

M.W. 300.27

A

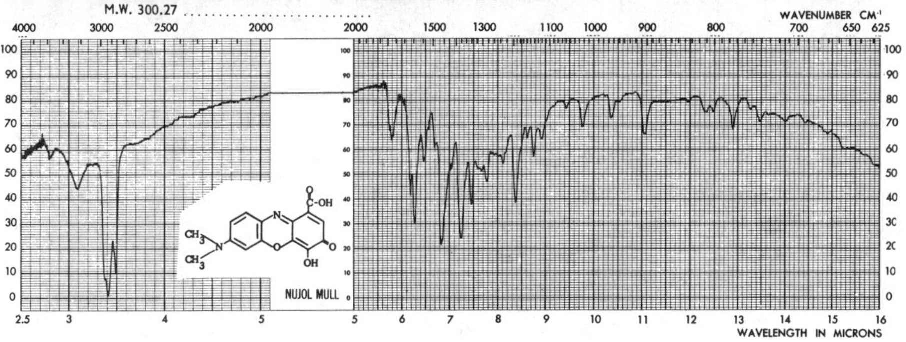

NUJOL MULL

14,027-9 **5,7-Dimethyl-1,8-naphthyridin-2-ol** (5,7-dimethyl-2-hydroxy-1,8-naphthyridine)
M.W. 174.20 m.p. 253-255°

B

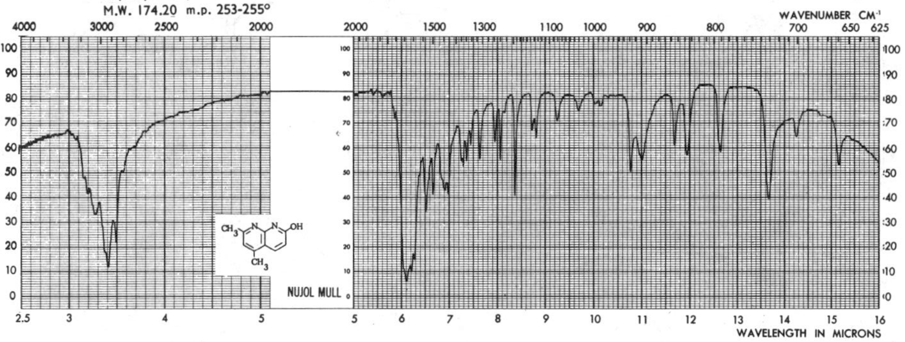

NUJOL MULL

12,048-0 **4-Methyl-1,8-naphthyridine-2,7-diol**
M.W. 176.18 m.p. > 300°

C

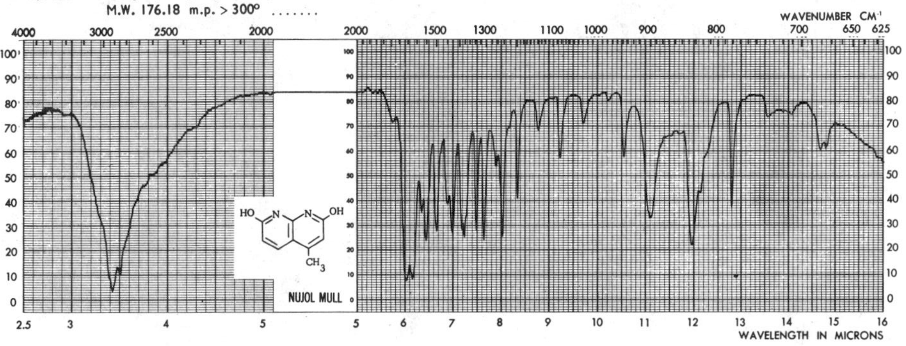

NUJOL MULL

12,001-4 **7-Amino-2,4-dimethyl-1,8-naphthyridine** (2-amino-5,7-dimethyl-1,8-naphthyridine)
M.W. 173.22 m.p. 212-216°

D

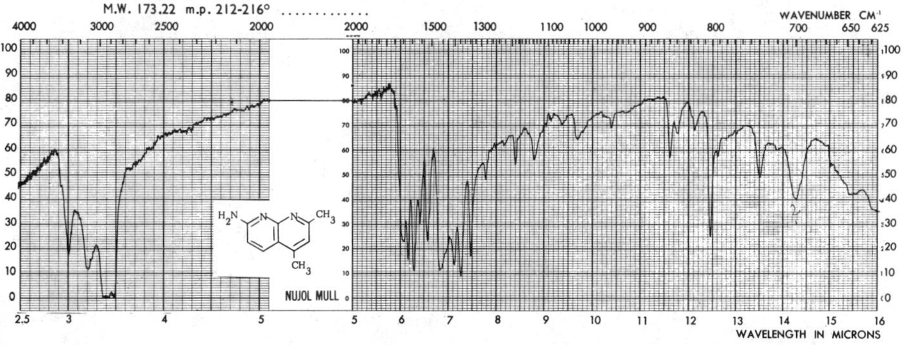

NUJOL MULL

1,8-naphthyridine)
M.W. 175.19 m.p. > 300°

E

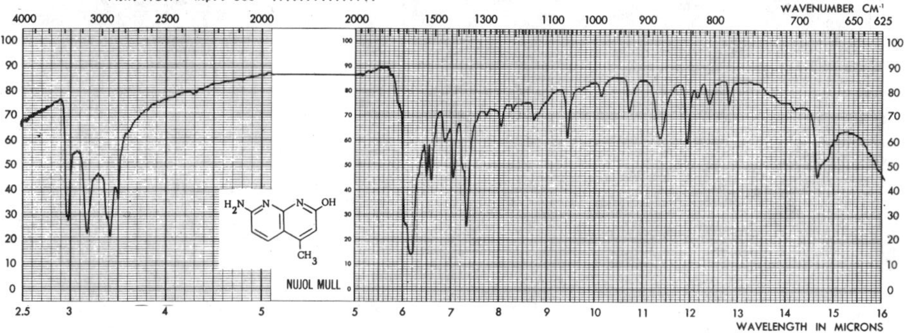

NUJOL MULL

14,173-9 **4-Hydroxy-7-methyl-1,8-naphthyridine-3-carboxylic acid, tech.**
M.W. 204.19 m.p. 266° (dec.)

F

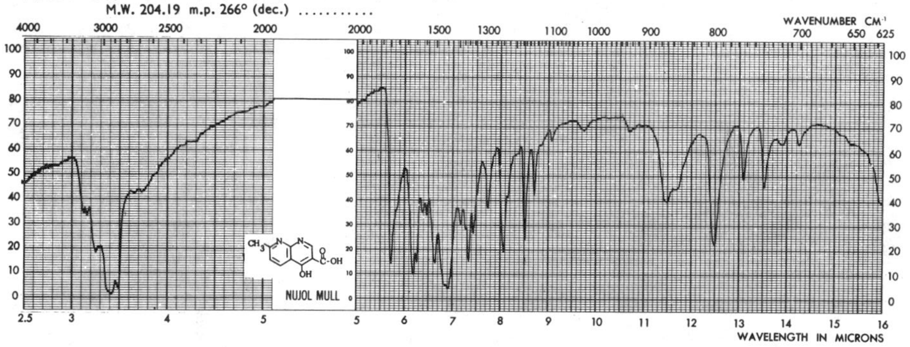

NUJOL MULL

15,854-2
Nalidixic acid (1,4-dihydro-1-ethyl-7-methyl-4-oxo-1,8-naphthyridine-3-carboxylic acid)
M.W. 232.24 m.p. 227-229°

G

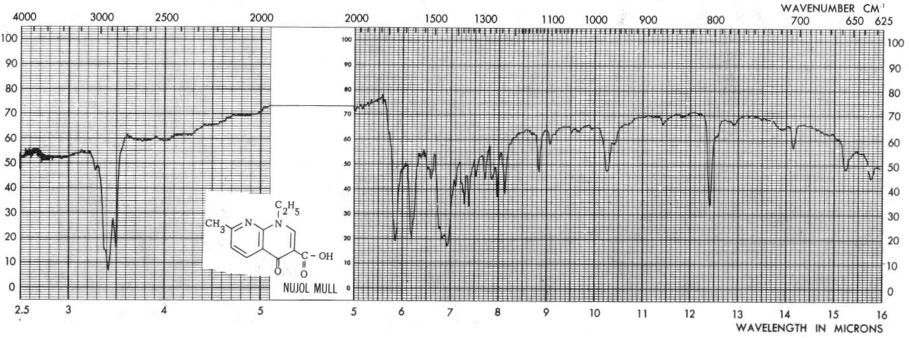

NUJOL MULL

13,137-7 **1,10-Phenanthroline**
M.W. 180.21 m.p. 114-117°

H

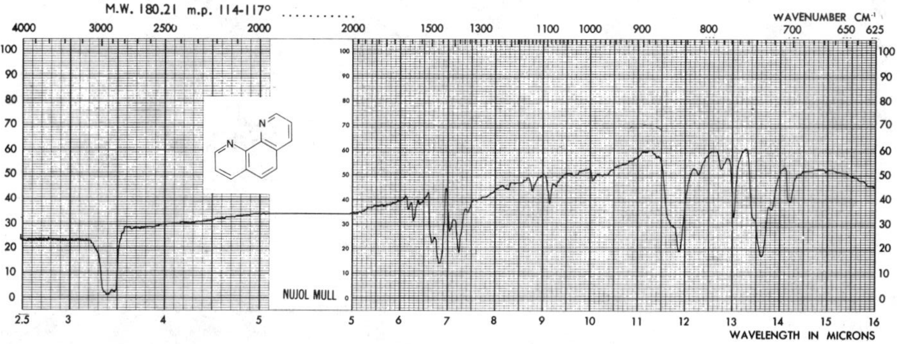

NUJOL MULL

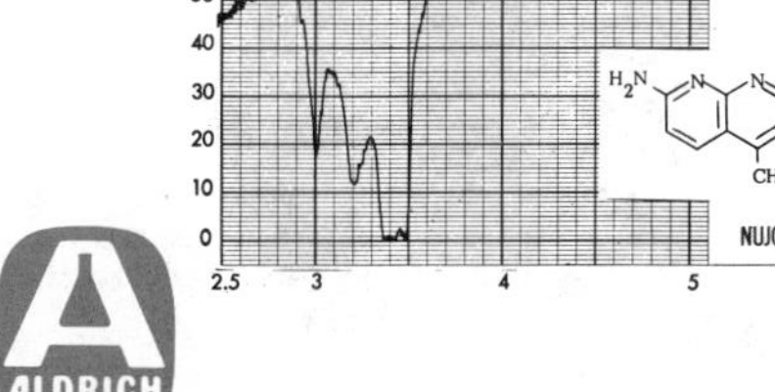

ALDRICH

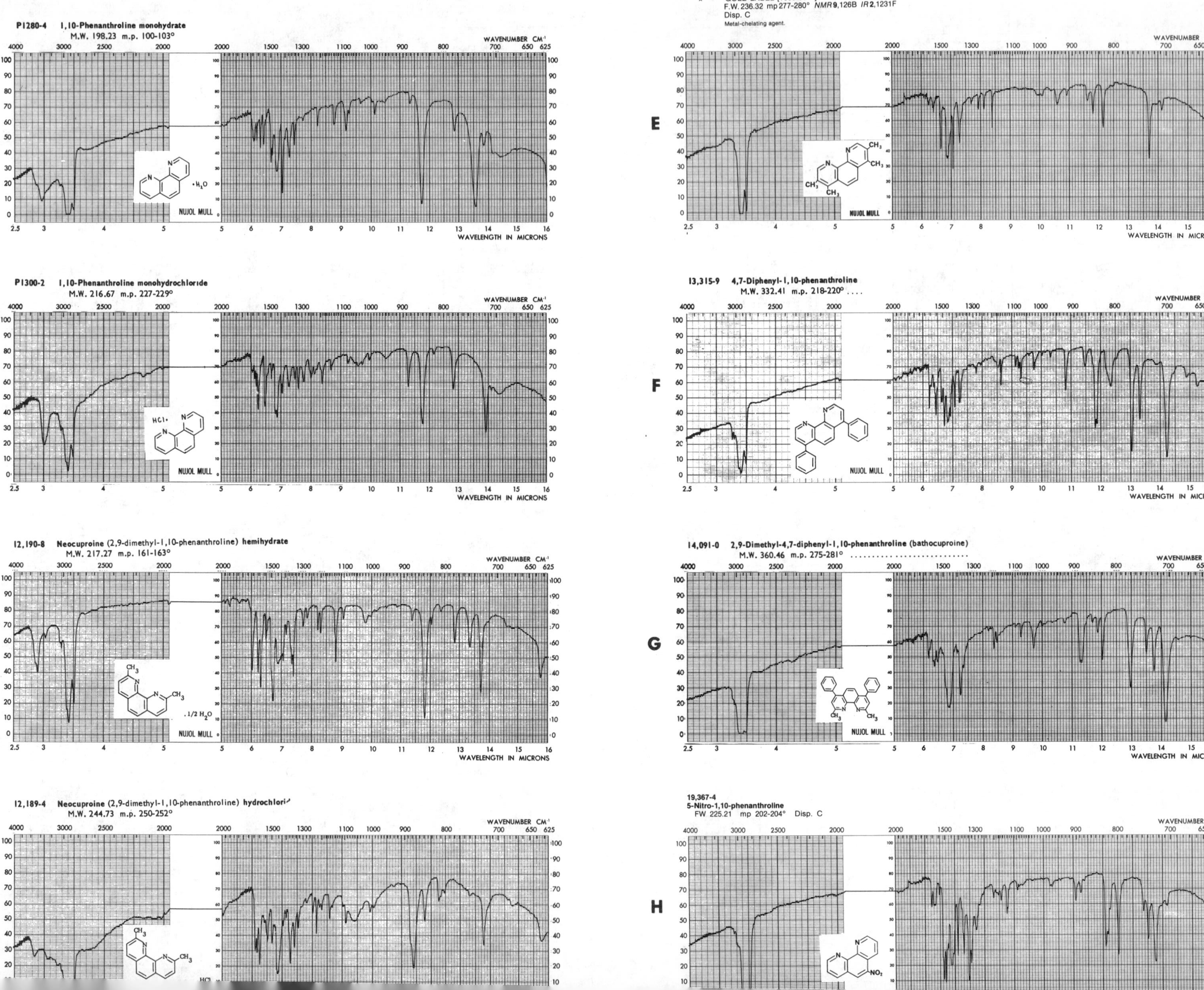
A
P1280-4 1,10-Phenanthroline monohydrate
M.W. 198.23 m.p. 100-103°
NUJOL MULL
B
P1300-2 1,10-Phenanthroline monohydrochloride
M.W. 216.67 m.p. 227-229°
NUJOL MULL
C
12,190-8 Neocuproine (2,9-dimethyl-1,10-phenanthroline) hemihydrate
M.W. 217.27 m.p. 161-163°
NUJOL MULL
D
12,189-4 Neocuproine (2,9-dimethyl-1,10-phenanthroline) hydrochlori-
M.W. 244.73 m.p. 250-252°
E
16,288-4 3,4,7,8-Tetramethyl-1,10-phenanthroline, 99+%
GOLD LABEL [1660-93-1]
F.W. 236.32 mp 277-280° NMR 9,126B IR 2,1231F
Disp. C
Metal-chelating agent.
NUJOL MULL
F
13,315-9 4,7-Diphenyl-1,10-phenanthroline
M.W. 332.41 m.p. 218-220°
NUJOL MULL
G
14,091-0 2,9-Dimethyl-4,7-diphenyl-1,10-phenanthroline (bathocuproine)
M.W. 360.46 m.p. 275-281°
NUJOL MULL
H
19,367-4
5-Nitro-1,10-phenanthroline
FW 225.21 mp 202-204° Disp. C
WAVENUMBER CM⁻¹
WAVELENGTH IN MICRONS

A

M.W. 536.50 (anhydrous) m.p. >300°

NUJOL MULL

B

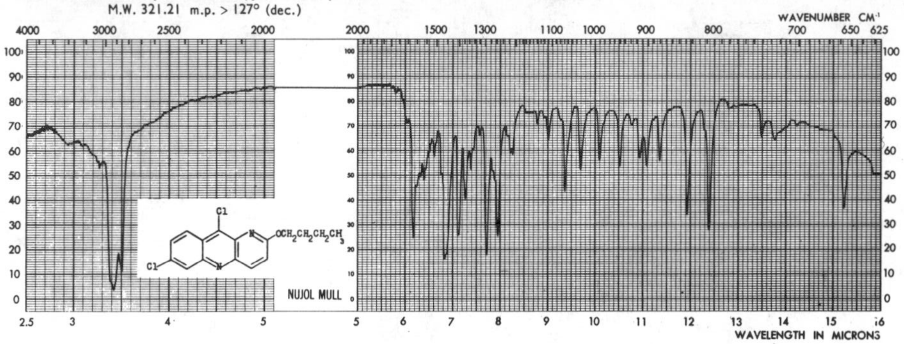

14,662-5 **Bathocuproinedisulfonic acid (2,9-dimethyl-4,7-diphenyl-1,10-phenanthroline disulfonic acid), disodium salt**
M.W. 564.55 m.p. >300°

NUJOL MULL

C

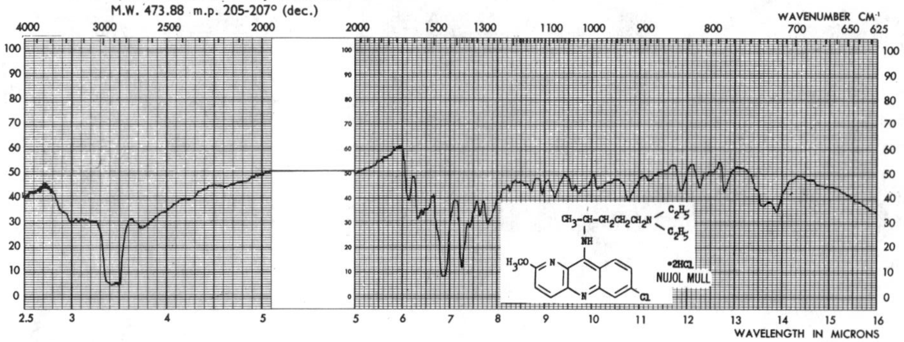

N690-0 **1,5-Naphthyridine monohydrate**
M.W. 130.15 m.p. 70-72°

MELT

D

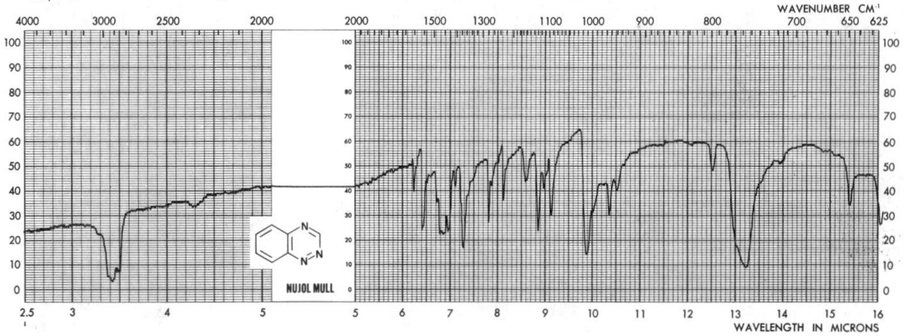

11,385-9 **7,10-Dichloro-2-methoxypyrido[3,2-b]quinoline**
M.W. 279.13 m.p. 182-184°

NUJOL MULL

E

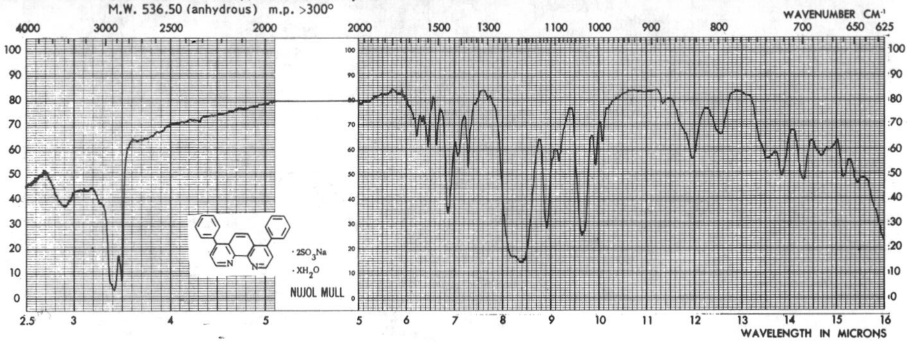

11,384-0 **2-n-Butoxy-7,10-dichloropyrido[3,2-b]quinoline**
M.W. 321.21 m.p. > 127° (dec.)

NUJOL MULL

F

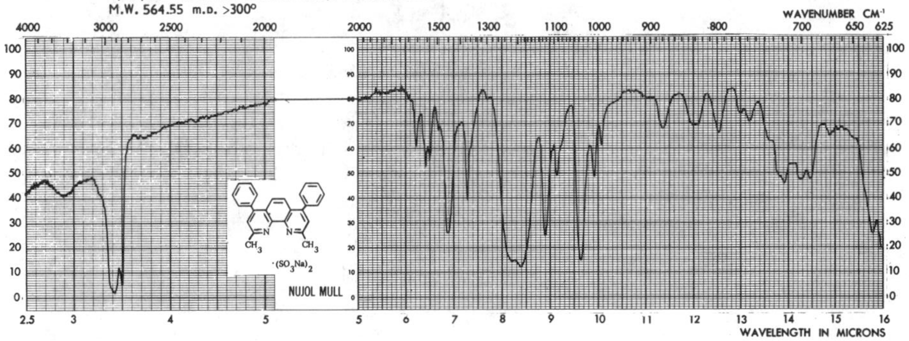

C3380-8 **6-Chloro-9-(4'-diethylamino-1'-methylbutylamino)-2-methoxy-1,10-diazaanthracene dihydrochloride**
M.W. 473.88 m.p. 205-207° (dec.)

NUJOL MULL

G

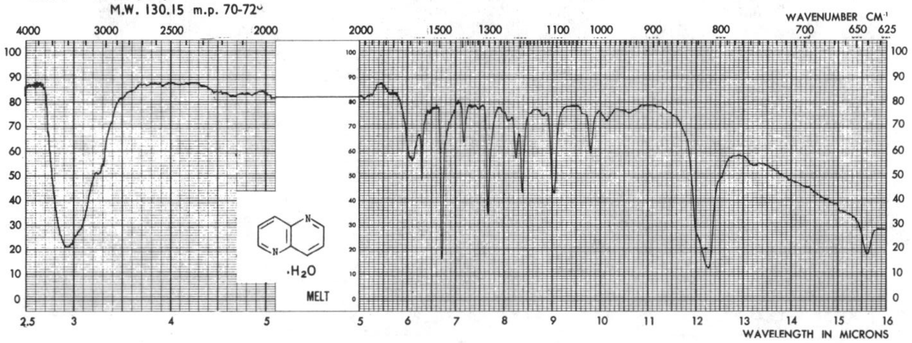

19,460-3
1,2,4-Benzotriazine, 98%
FW 131.14 mp 72-76° bp 235-240° *Beil.* 26,67
Disp. C

NUJOL MULL

H

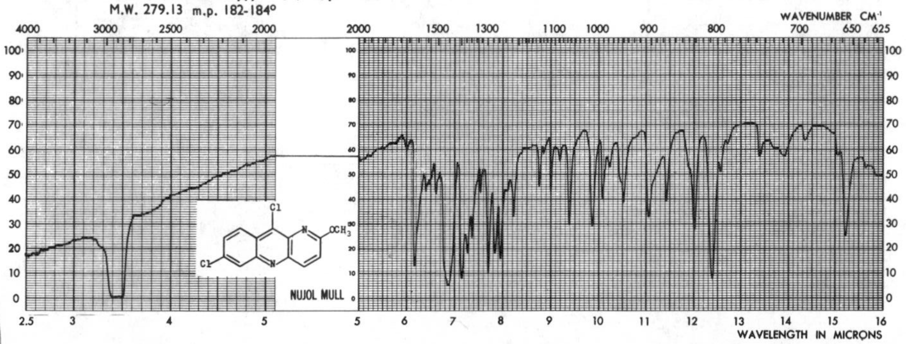

10,413-2 **Pyrido[2,3-b]pyrazine (1,4,5-triazanaphthalene)**
M.W. 131.14 m.p. 139-140°

NUJOL MULL

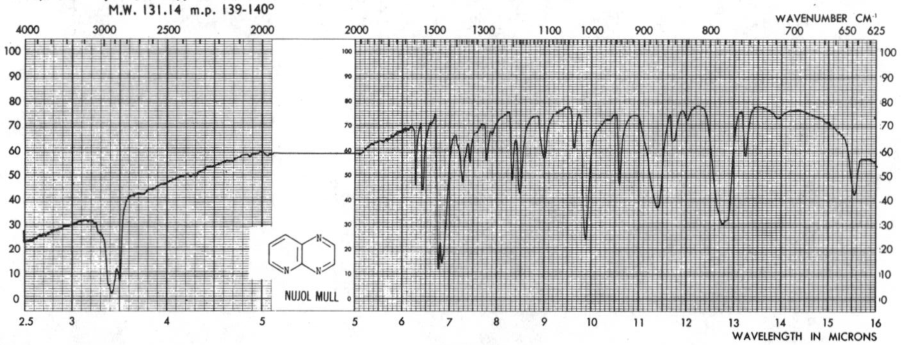

A

P6550-9 **Pyrido[2,3-b]pyrazine-2,3-diol** (2,3-dihydroxy-1,4,5-triaza-naphthalene)
M.W. 163.14 m.p. > 300°

NUJOL MULL

B

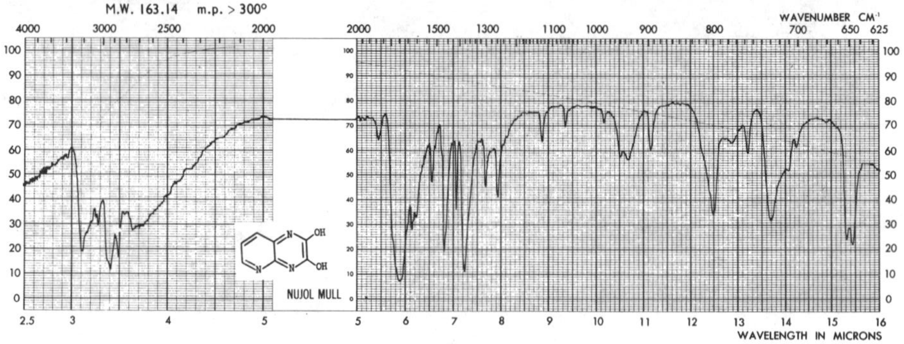

C6970-5 **2-Chloropyridazino[3,2-b]quinazol-10-one**
M.W. 231.64 m.p. 225-228°

NUJOL MULL

C

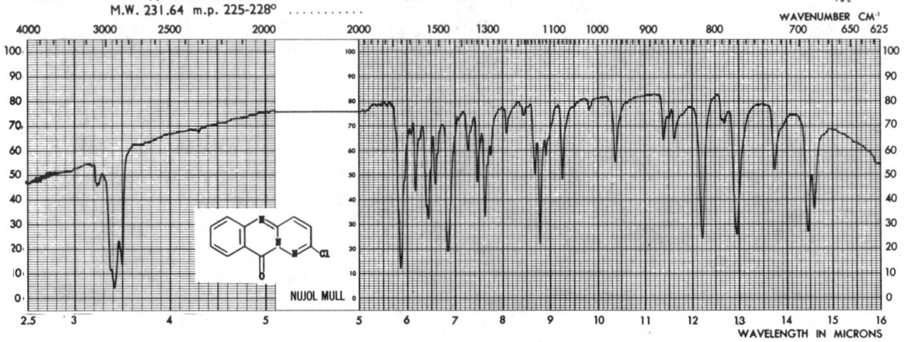

D16,400 **5,7-Dimethyl-4-hydroxy-2-mercaptopyrido[2,3-d]pyrimidine**

NUJOL MULL

D

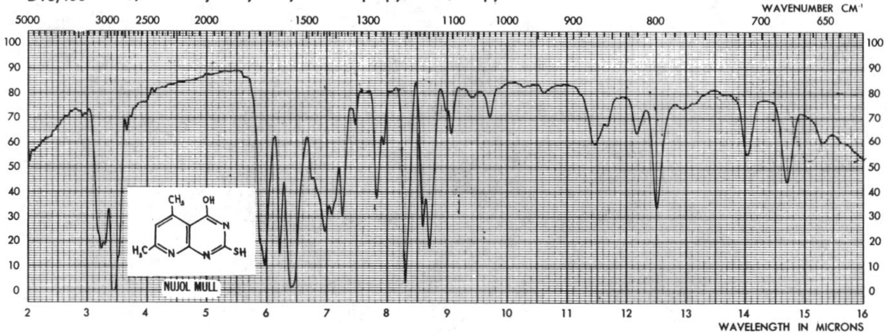

A7880-2 **4-Aminopyrimido[4,5-d]pyrimidine**
M.W. 147.14 m.p. > 340°

E

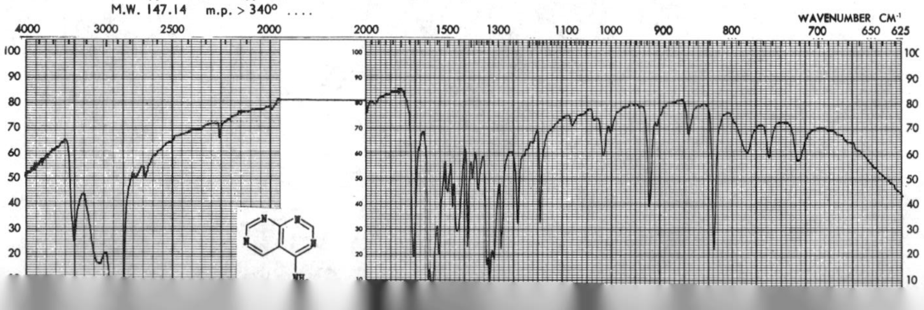

H5650-9 **4-Hydroxypteridine** (4-pteridinol)
M.W. 148.13 m.p. > 310°

NUJOL MULL

F

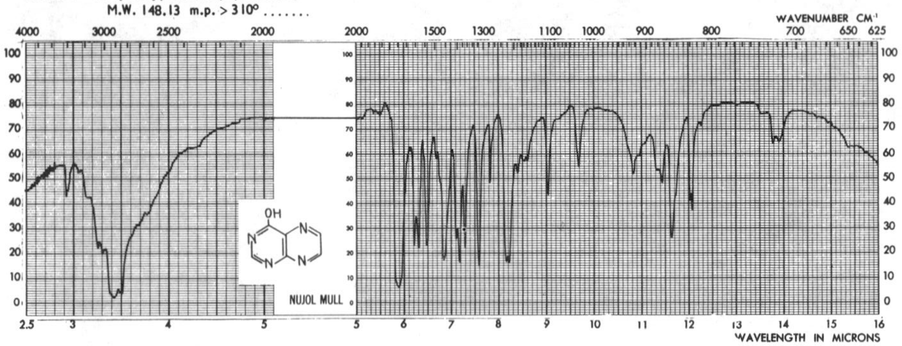

L330-7 **Lumazine** (2,4-pteridinediol)
M.W. 164.12 m.p. 355° (dec.)

NUJOL MULL

G

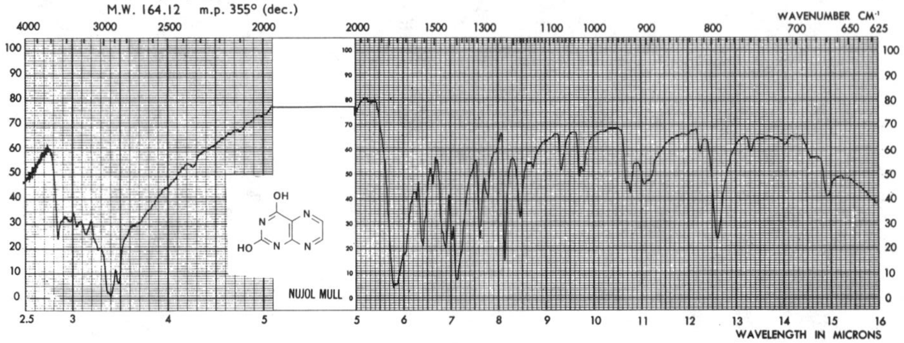

H2,530-1
4-Hydroxy-6,7-dimethylpteridine (6,7-dimethyl-4-pteridinol)
M.W. 176.18 m.p. 355° (dec.)

NUJOL MULL

H

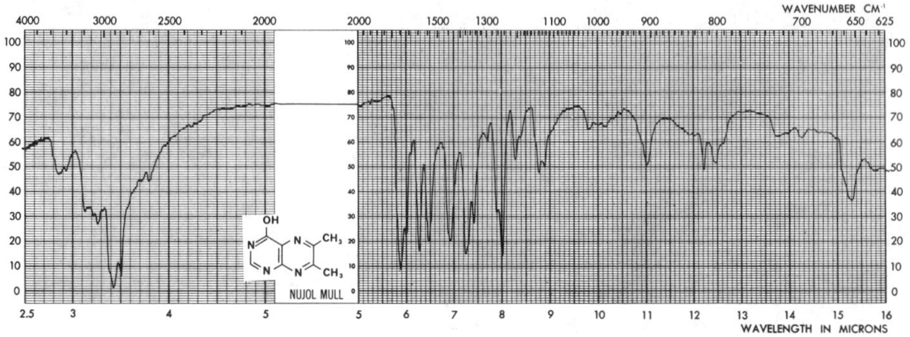

12,214-9 **6,7-Dimethyllumazine** (6,7-dimethyl-2,4-pteridinediol)
M.W. 163.38 m.p. > 300°

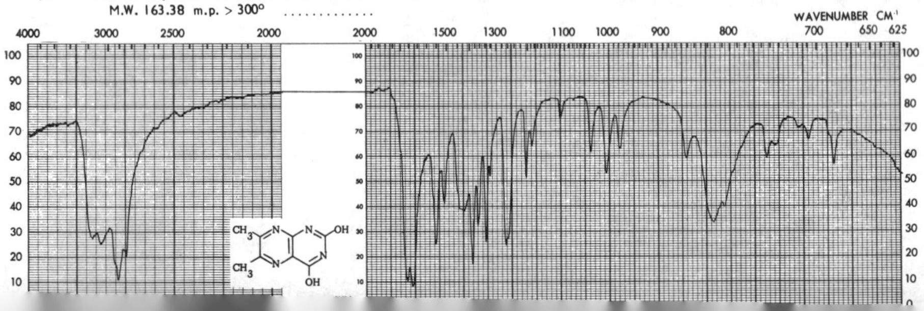

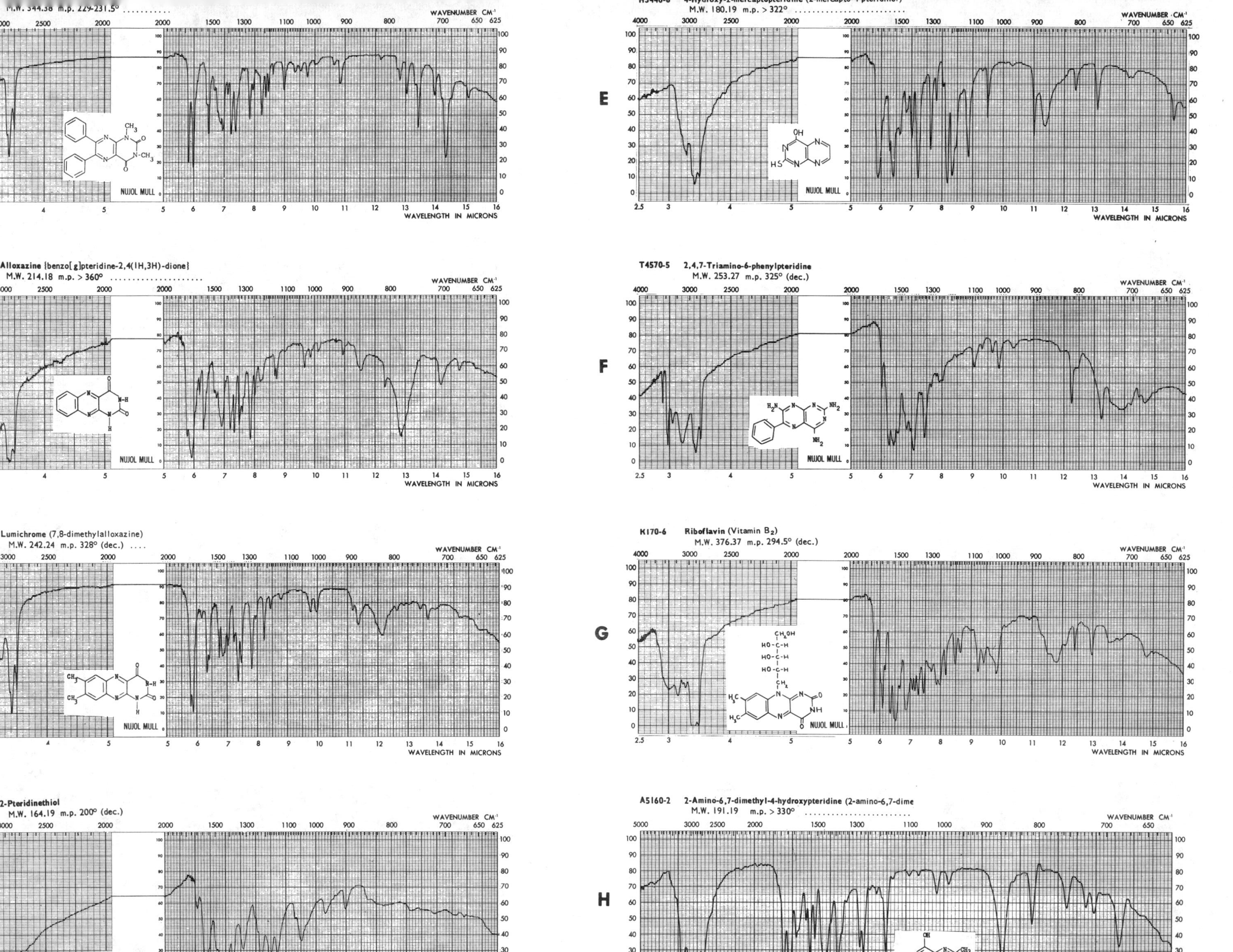

A
M.W. 344.38 m.p. 229-231.5° ....
NUJOL MULL
B
A2865-1 Alloxazine [benzo[g]pteridine-2,4(1H,3H)-dione]
M.W. 214.18 m.p. > 360° ....
NUJOL MULL
C
10,321-7 Lumichrome (7,8-dimethylalloxazine)
M.W. 242.24 m.p. 328° (dec.) ....
NUJOL MULL
D
12,747-7 2-Pteridinethiol
M.W. 164.19 m.p. 200° (dec.)
NUJOL MULL
E
4-Hydroxy-2-mercaptopteridine (2-mercapto-4-pteridinol)
M.W. 180.19 m.p. > 322° ....
NUJOL MULL
F
T4570-5 2,4,7-Triamino-6-phenylpteridine
M.W. 253.27 m.p. 325° (dec.)
NUJOL MULL
G
K170-6 Riboflavin (Vitamin B2)
M.W. 376.37 m.p. 294.5° (dec.)
NUJOL MULL
H
A5160-2 2-Amino-6,7-dimethyl-4-hydroxypteridine (2-amino-6,7-dime
M.W. 191.19 m.p. > 330° ....
NUJOL MULL
WAVENUMBER CM⁻¹
WAVELENGTH IN MICRONS
ALDRICH

6 MEMBERED FUSED AROMATIC HETEROCYCLES

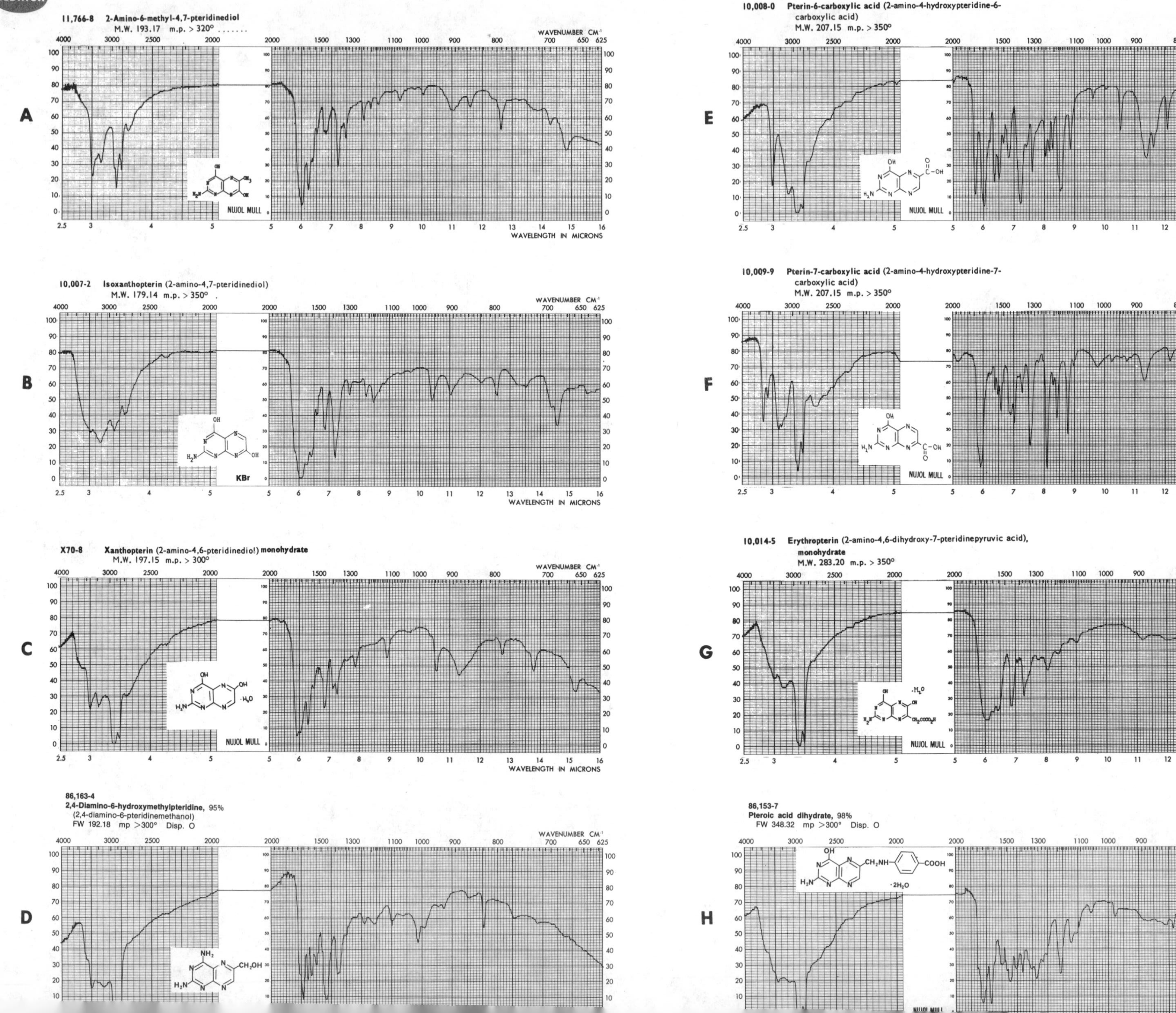

11,766-8 **2-Amino-6-methyl-4,7-pteridinediol**
M.W. 193.17 m.p. > 320°

10,007-2 **Isoxanthopterin** (2-amino-4,7-pteridinediol)
M.W. 179.14 m.p. > 350°

X70-8 **Xanthopterin** (2-amino-4,6-pteridinediol) **monohydrate**
M.W. 197.15 m.p. > 300°

86,163-4
2,4-Diamino-6-hydroxymethylpteridine, 95%
(2,4-diamino-6-pteridinemethanol)
FW 192.18 mp >300° Disp. O

10,008-0 **Pterin-6-carboxylic acid** (2-amino-4-hydroxypteridine-6-carboxylic acid)
M.W. 207.15 m.p. > 350°

10,009-9 **Pterin-7-carboxylic acid** (2-amino-4-hydroxypteridine-7-carboxylic acid)
M.W. 207.15 m.p. > 350°

10,014-5 **Erythropterin** (2-amino-4,6-dihydroxy-7-pteridinepyruvic acid), **monohydrate**
M.W. 283.20 m.p. > 350°

86,153-7
Pteroic acid dihydrate, 98%
FW 348.32 mp >300° Disp. O

mp 270 (dec.) Disp. C,O

A

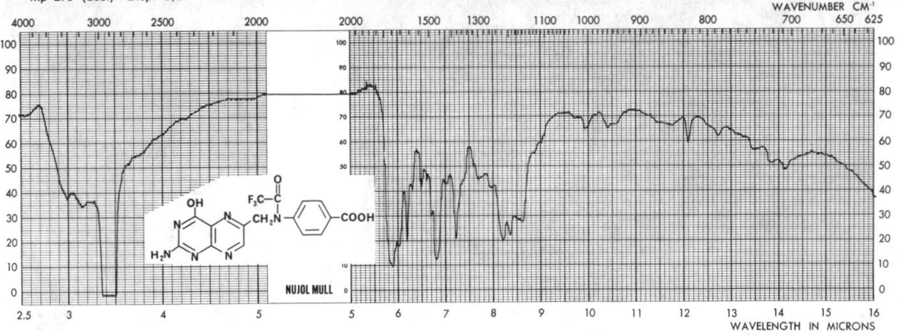

NUJOL MULL

86,158-8
4-[N-(2,4-Diamino-6-pteridinylmethyl)amino]benzoic acid, sodium salt monohydrate, 98%
FW 351.30 mp >300° *Fieser* 7,82 Disp. O

B

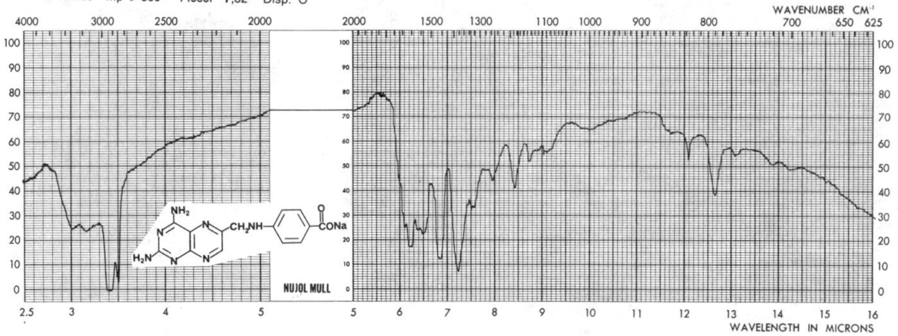

NUJOL MULL

86,155-3
4-[N-(2,4-Diamino-6-pteridinylmethyl)-N-methylamino]-benzoic acid hemihydrochloride dihydrate, 98%
FW 379.59 mp 255° (dec.) Disp. C,O

C

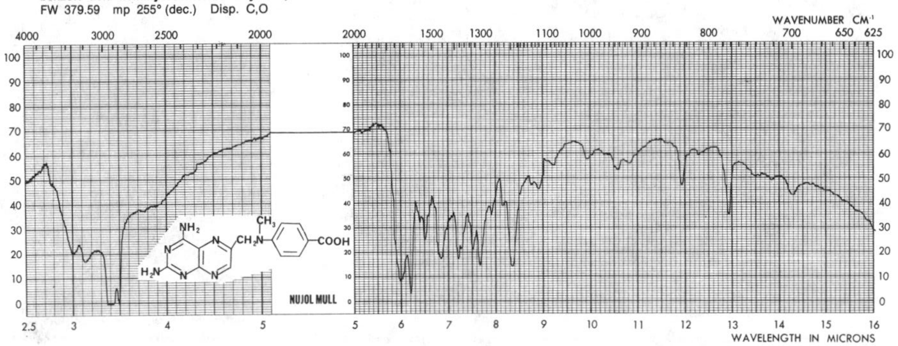

NUJOL MULL

10,013-7 **Fervenulin [6,8-dimethylpyrimido[5,4-e]-as-triazine-5,7(6H,8H)-dione]**
M.W. 193.17 m.p. 178-179°

D

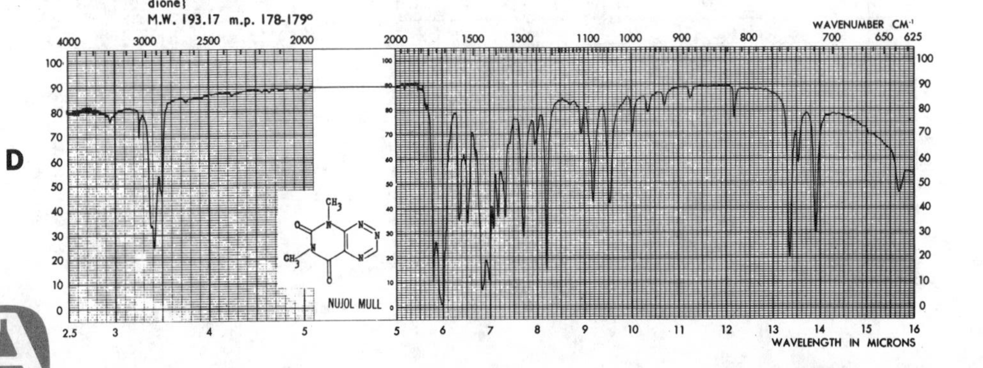

FW 137.10 Disp. F

E

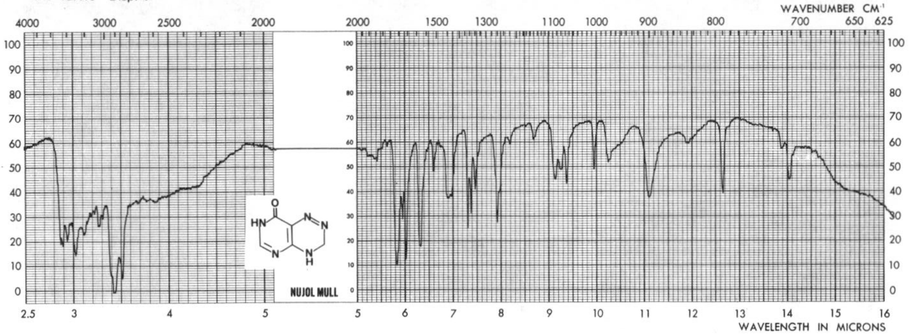

NUJOL MULL

19,469-7
DL-Amethopterin hydrate (DL-4-amino-N^{10}-methylpteroylglutamic acid)
FW 454.45 mp 195° (dec.) Disp. C

F

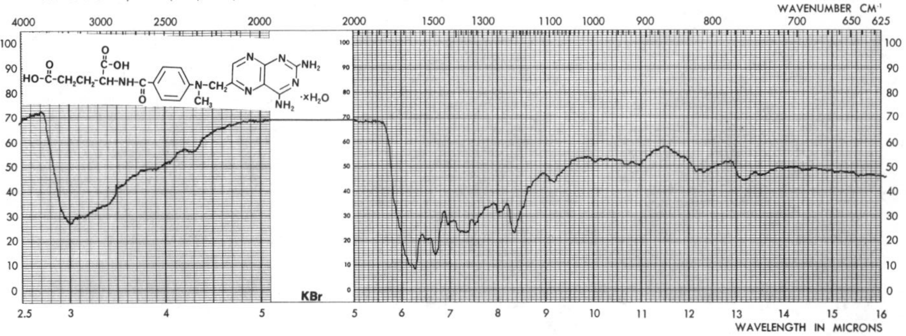

KBr

22,395-6
D-(-)-Amethopterin (D-(-)-4-amino-N^{10}-methylpteroylglutamic acid)
FW 454.45 mp 195° (dec.)
$[\alpha]_D^{25}$ -19.4° (c=2, 0.1 *N* NaOH) Disp. C

G

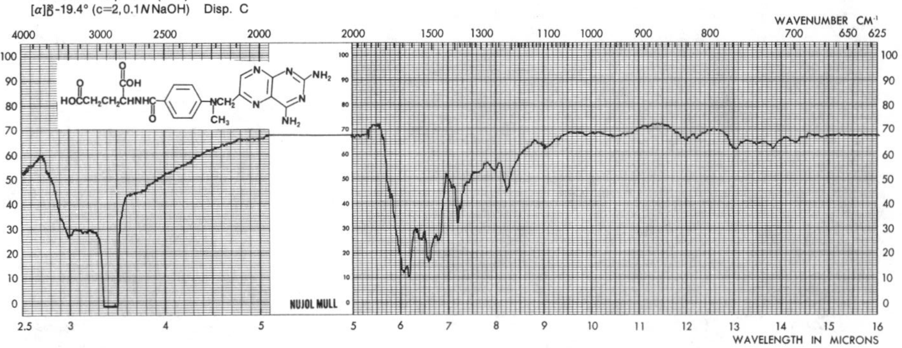

NUJOL MULL

22,394-8
L-(+)-Amethopterin dihydrate (L-(+)-4-amino-N^{10}-methylpteroylglutamic acid, methotrexate, MTX)
FW 490.48 mp 195° (dec.)
$[\alpha]_D^{25}$ +20° (c=1, 0.05 *M* Na_2CO_3) Disp. C

H

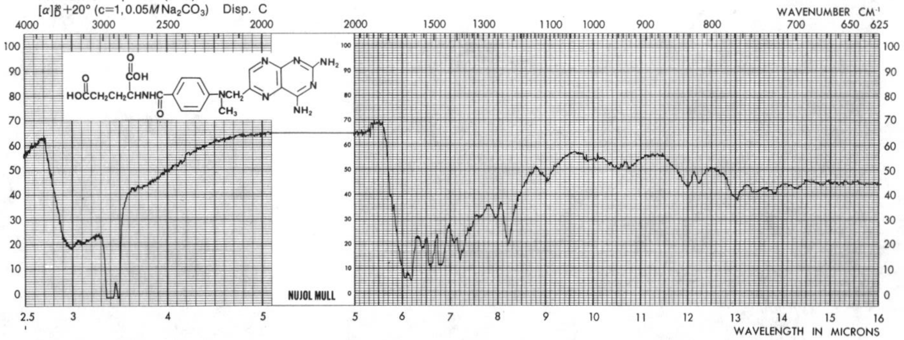

NUJOL MULL

11,968-7 6,7-Diphenyldibenzo[e,g][1,4]diazocine
M.W. 358.45 m.p. 234-238°

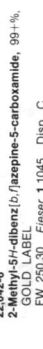

A

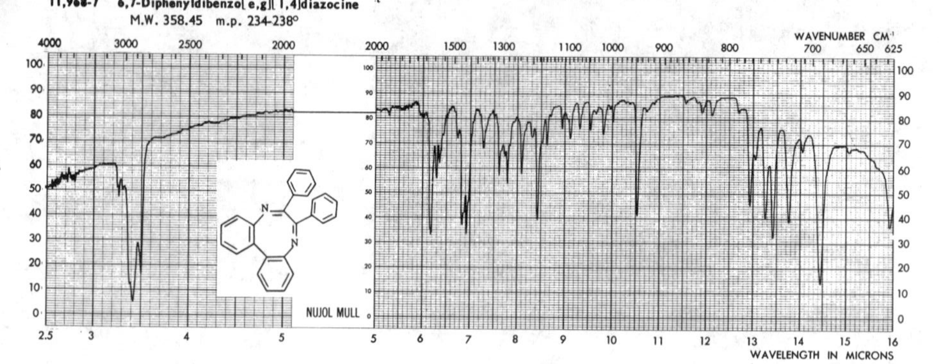

22,042-6
2-Methyl-5*H*-dibenz[*b,f*]azepine-5-carboxamide, 99+%,
GOLD LABEL
FW 250.30 *Fieser* 1,1045 Disp. C

B

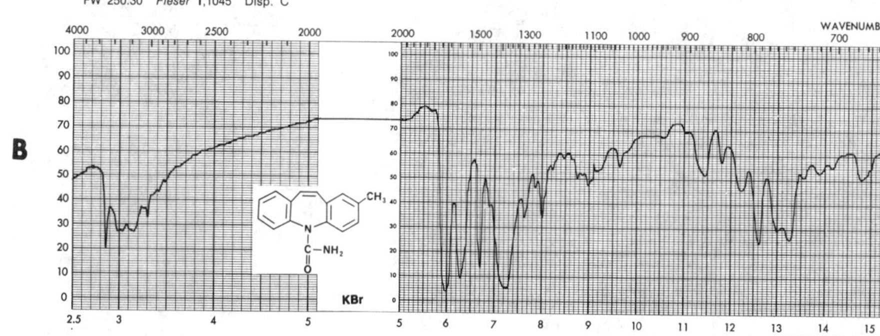

P30-6 Pelargonin chloride
M.W. 631.00

C

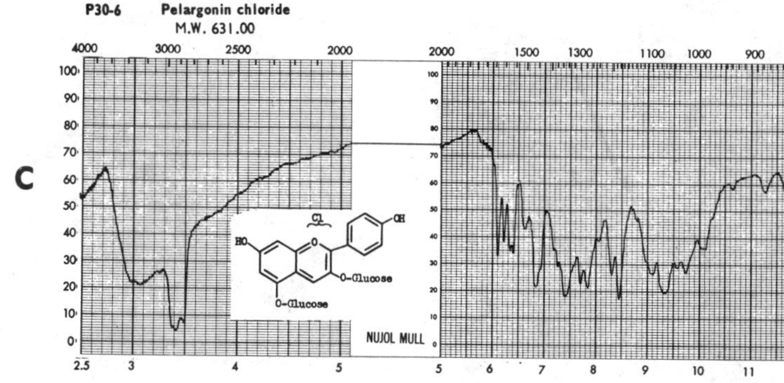

85,837-4
Brilliant cresyl blue, indicator grade
M.W. 332.84 m.p. >300°

D

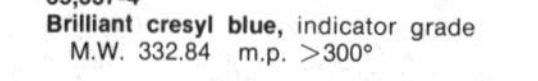

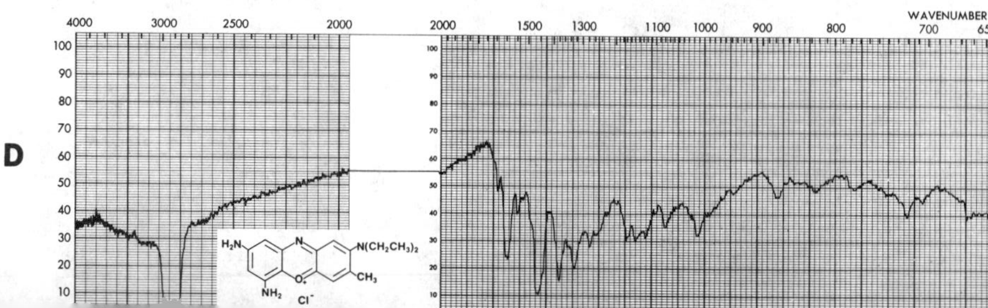

HETEROCYCLIC N-OXIDES

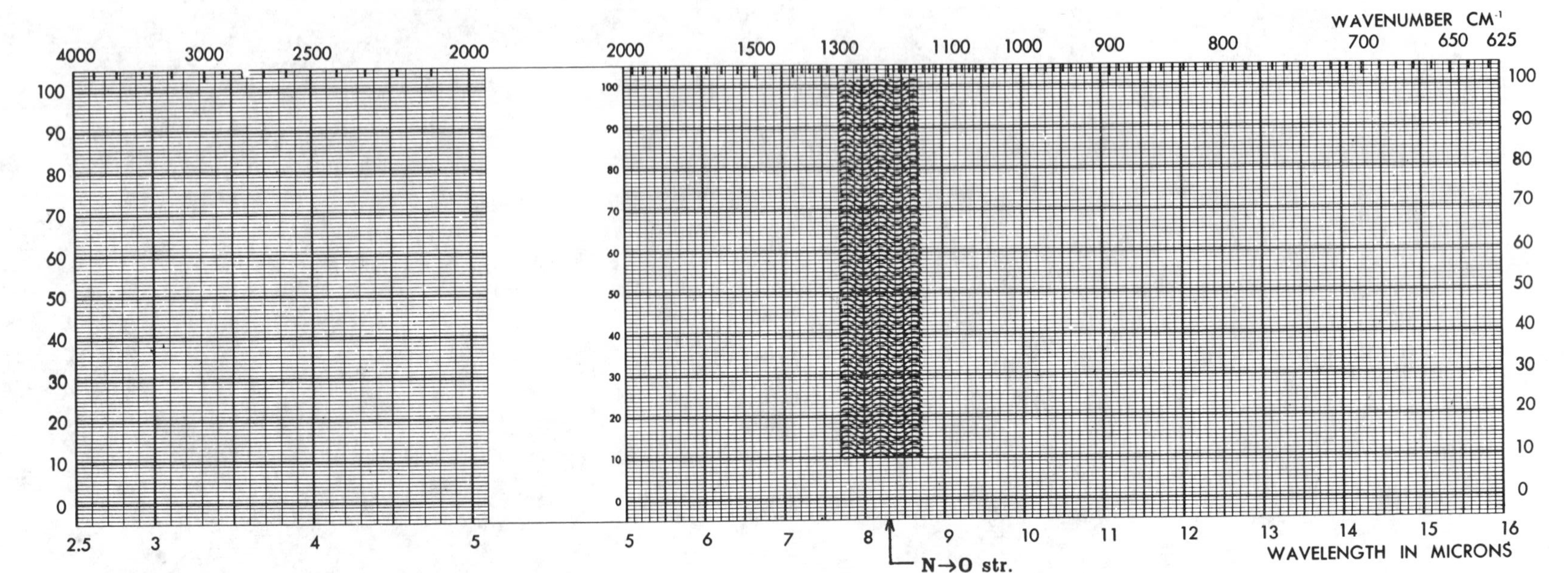

The N→O group absorbs strongly between 7.7 and 8.7 μ (1300–1150 cm^{-1}). The band is usually quite broad and shifts considerably within this region. Its presence in the pyridine series does not alter the substitution pattern of the pyridine ring itself.

In spectrum 1421H, 3-hydroxypyridine-N-oxide, the OH is strongly hydrogen bonded to the N-oxide as can be seen by its broad bands between 3.5 and 6 μ (2855 – 1665 cm^{-1}). This effect of intramolecular bonding is similar in spectrum 1322D, 3-hydroxypyridine.

Many of the pyridine and other heterocyclic N-oxides are extremely hygroscopic. Therefore, absorptions near 3 and 6.1 μ (3335 and 1640 cm^{-1}) due to the presence of moisture are not unusual.

Disp. C

A

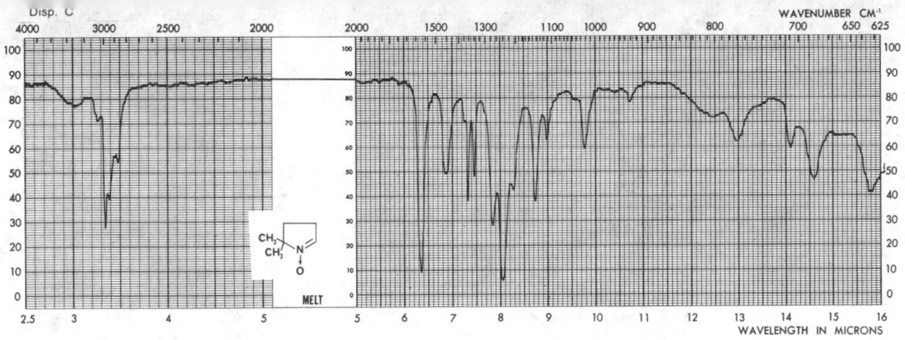

B

22,428-6
N-Methylmorpholine N-oxide monohydrate, 99%
FW 135.16 mp 75-77° *Fieser* 7,244 Disp. C

NUJOL MULL

C

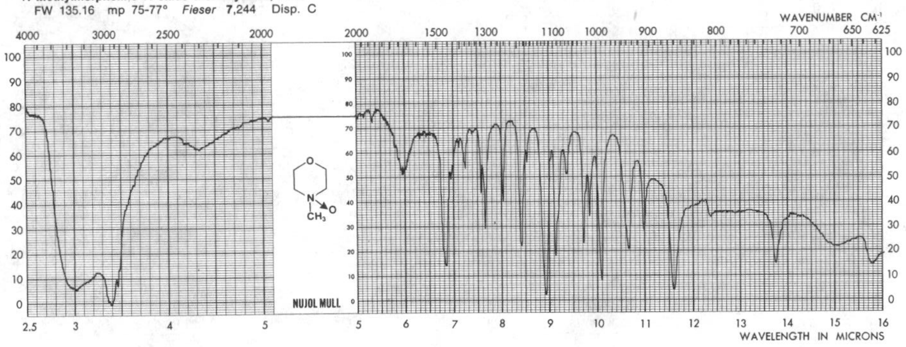

21,400-0
2,2,6,6-Tetramethylpiperidinooxy, free radical, 98% (TEMPO)
FW 156.25 mp 36-38° Disp. C

MELT

D

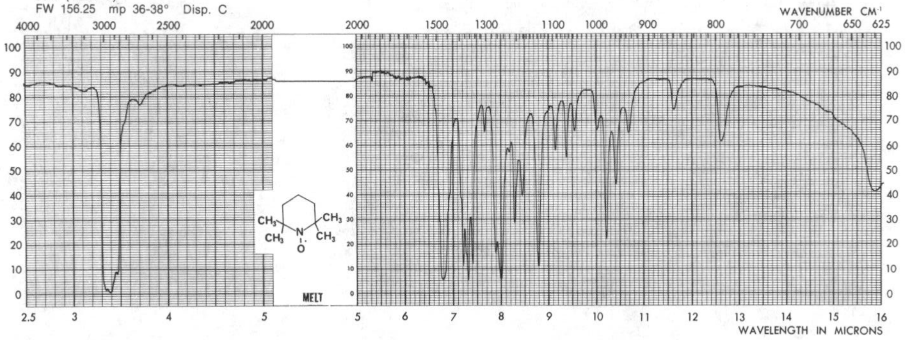

13,165-2 Pyridine-N-oxide
M.W. 95.10 m.p. 62-65°

MELT

E

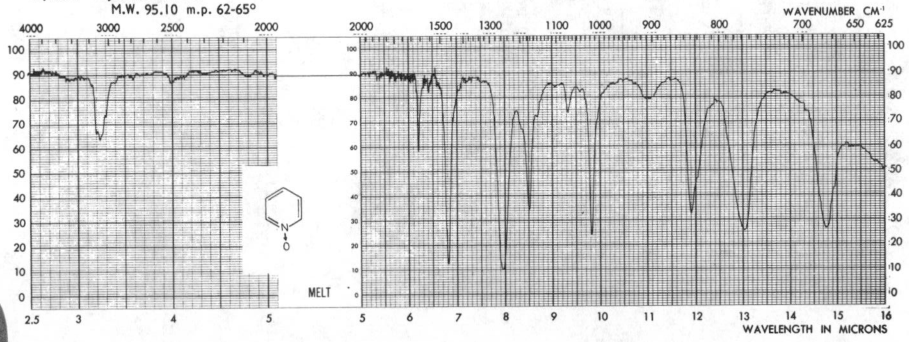

M.W. 109.13 m.p. 48-50°

MELT

F

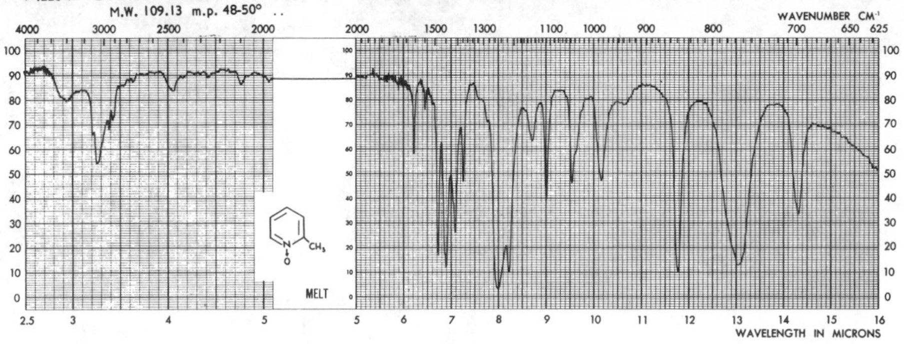

P4240-1 3-Picoline-N-oxide
M.W. 109.13

MELT

G

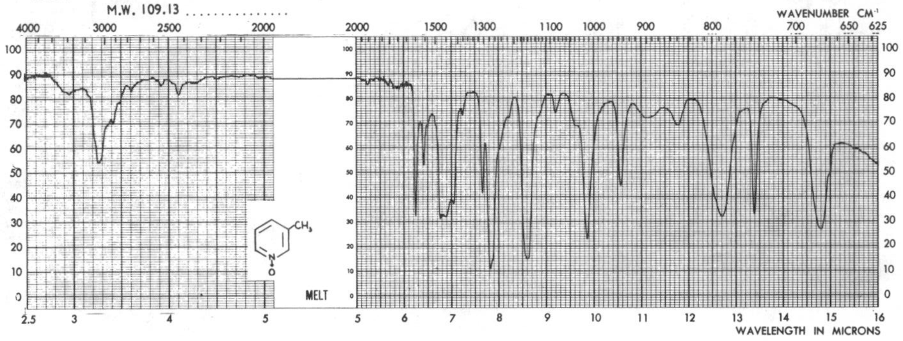

P4260-6 4-Picoline-N-oxide
M.W. 109.13 m.p. 179-183°

NUJOL MULL

H

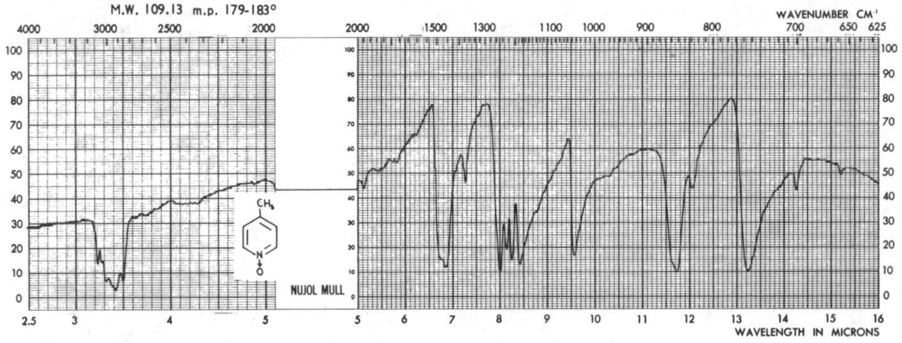

L440-0 2,6-Lutidine-N-oxide (2,6-dimethylpyridine-N-oxide)
M.W. 123.16 n_D^{20} 1.5667

NEAT

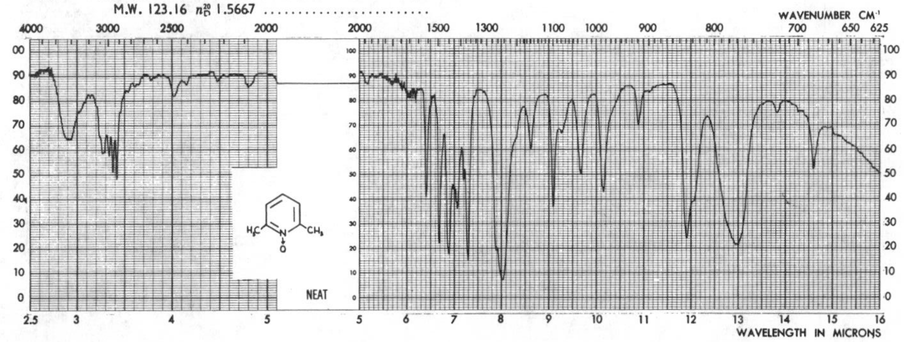

A

18,657-0
2-Chloropyridine-*N*-oxide hydrochloride, 97%
FW 166.01 mp 140-142° *NMR* 9,10C Disp. C

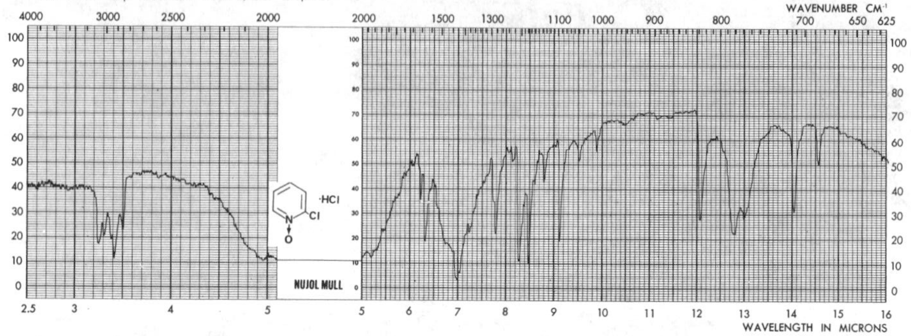

NUJOL MULL

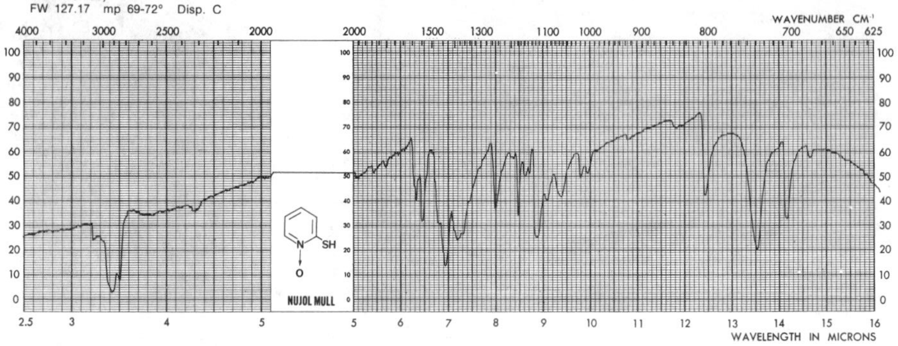

B

19,532-4
2-Bromopyridine-*N*-oxide hydrochloride, 97%
FW 210.46 mp 131-134° Disp. C

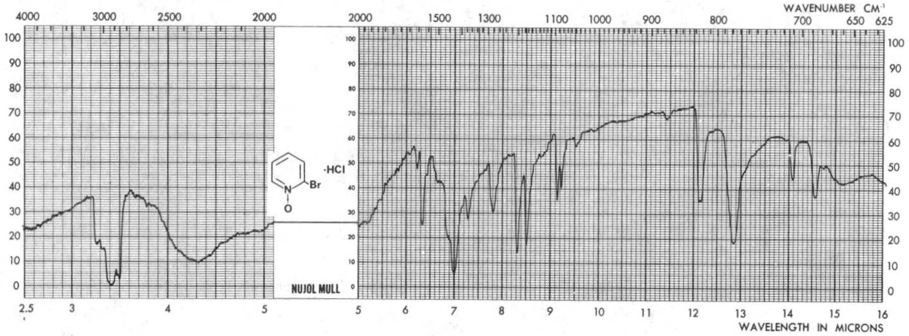

NUJOL MULL

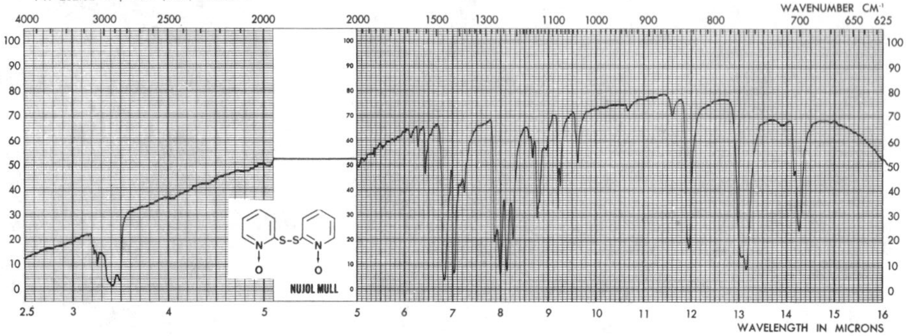

C

17,769-5
2-Picolyl chloride N-oxide hydrochloride, 99%
[2-(chloromethyl)-pyridine-N-oxide]
M.W. 180.04 m.p. 110-112° *HYGROSCOPIC*

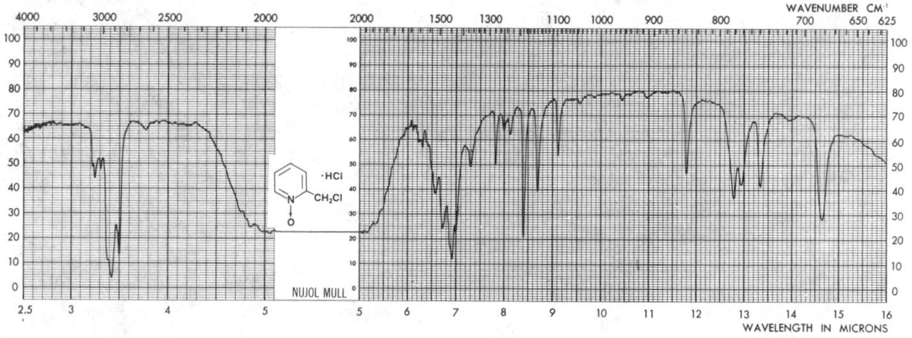

NUJOL MULL

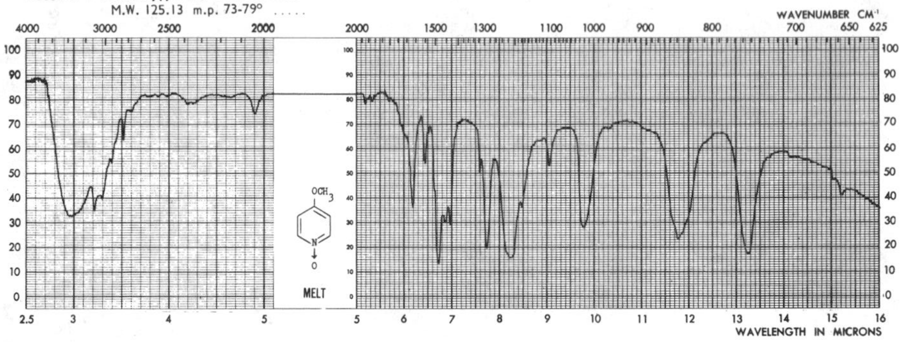

D

19,906-0
2-Hydroxypyridine-*N*-oxide, 97%
(2-pyridinol *N*-oxide)
FW 111.10 mp 149-151° Disp. L

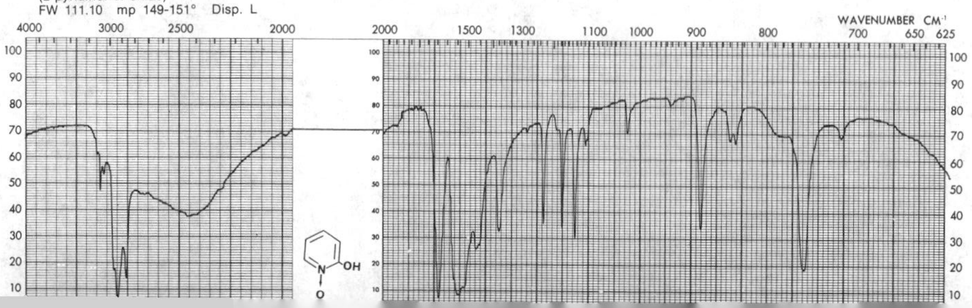

E

18,854-9
2-Mercaptopyridine-*N*-oxide, 99% (2-pyridinethiol 1-oxide)
FW 127.17 mp 69-72° Disp. C

NUJOL MULL

F

19,907-9
2,2′-Dithiobis(pyridine-*N*-oxide), 97%
FW 252.32 mp 205° (dec.) Disp. C

NUJOL MULL

G

M2550-3 **4-Methoxypyridine-N-oxide, tech.**
M.W. 125.13 m.p. 73-79°

MELT

H

12,252-1 **3-Hydroxypyridine-N-oxide** (3-pyridinol N-oxide)
M.W. 111.10 m.p. 190-192.5°

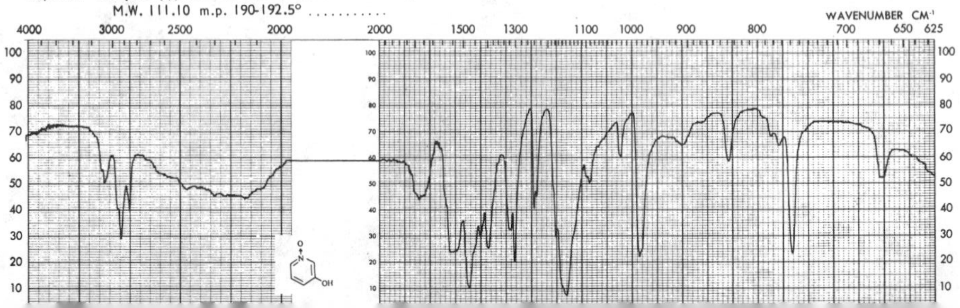

A

M.W. 125.13 m.p. 138-141°

NUJOL MULL

B

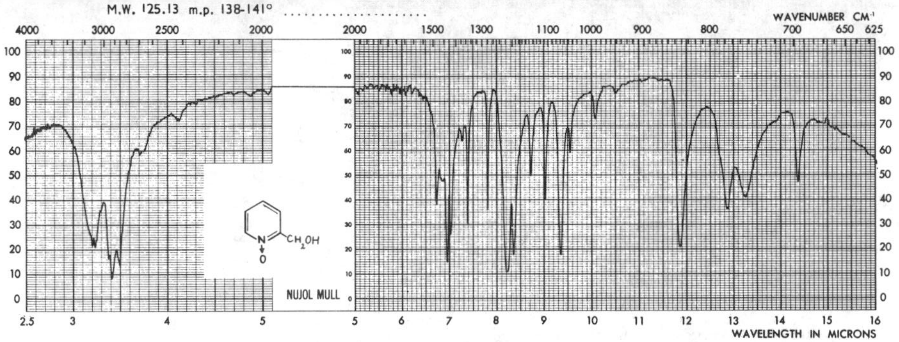

P6740-4 **3-Pyridylcarbinol N-oxide** (3-pyridinemethanol N-oxide)
M.W. 125.13 m.p. 87-89°

NUJOL MULL

C

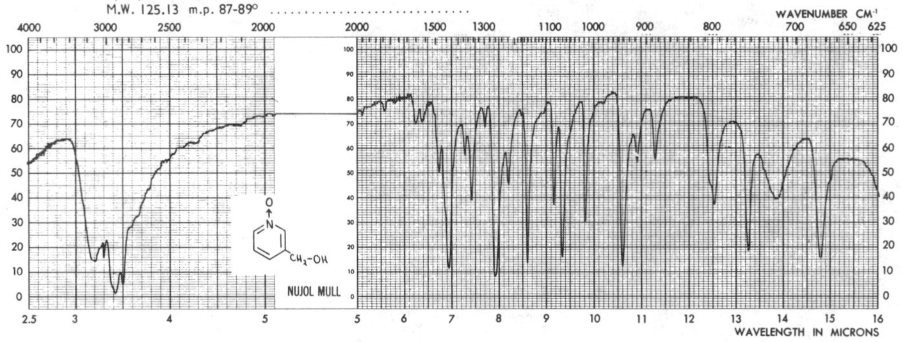

P6760-9 **4-Pyridylcarbinol N-oxide**
M.W. 125.13 m.p. 114-122°

NUJOL MULL

D

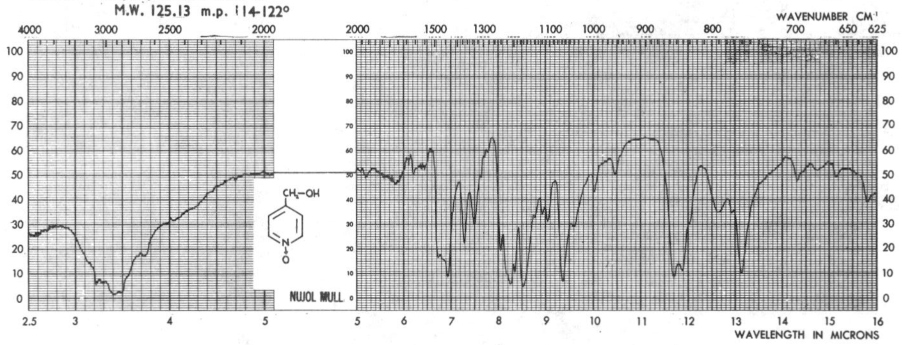

11,777-3 **2-Mercaptopyridine-N-oxide** (1-hydroxy-2-pyridinethione), **sodium salt, tech.**
M.W. 149.15 m.p. 251-253°

NUJOL MULL

E

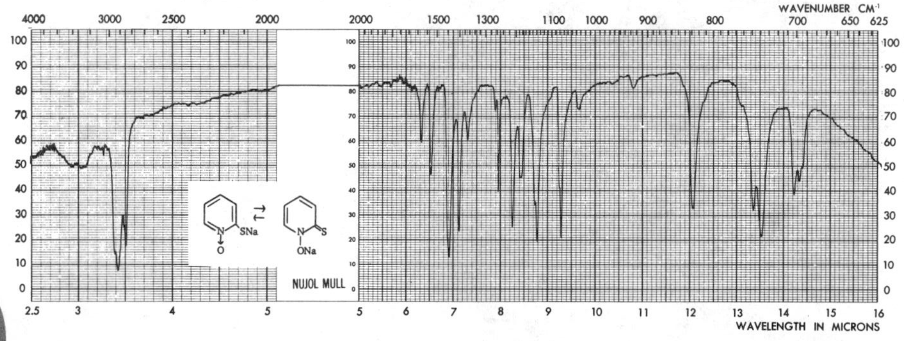

N2299-1 **4-Nitropyridine-N-oxide**
M.W. 140.10 m.p. 159-162°

NUJOL MULL

F

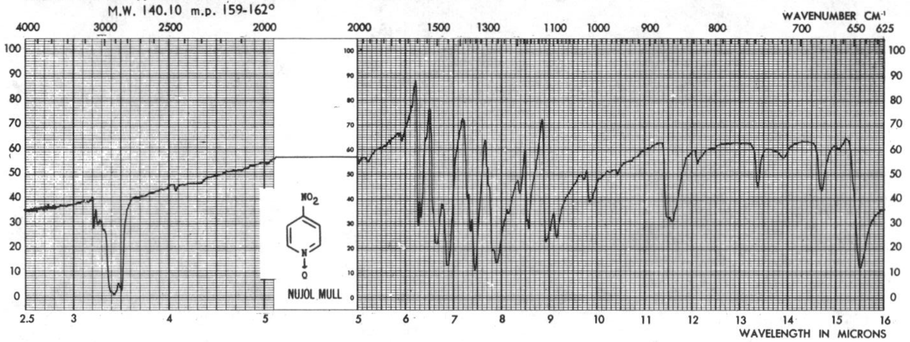

P4300-9 **Picolinic acid N-oxide**
M.W. 139.11 m.p. 152-153°

NUJOL MULL

G

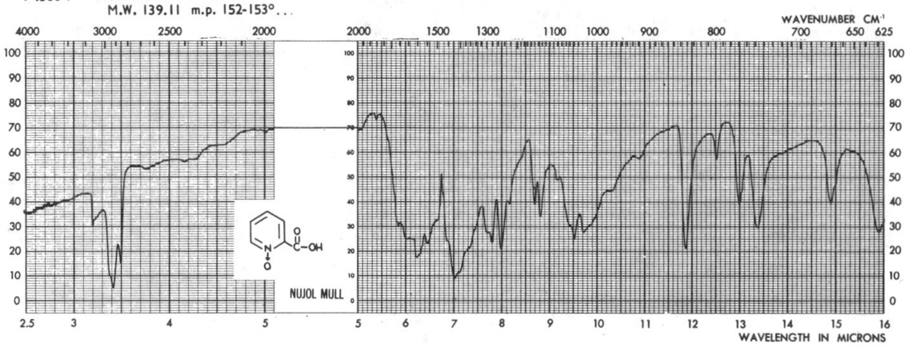

10,619-4 **Nicotinic acid N-oxide**
M.W. 139.11 m.p. 260-262° (dec.)

NUJOL MULL

H

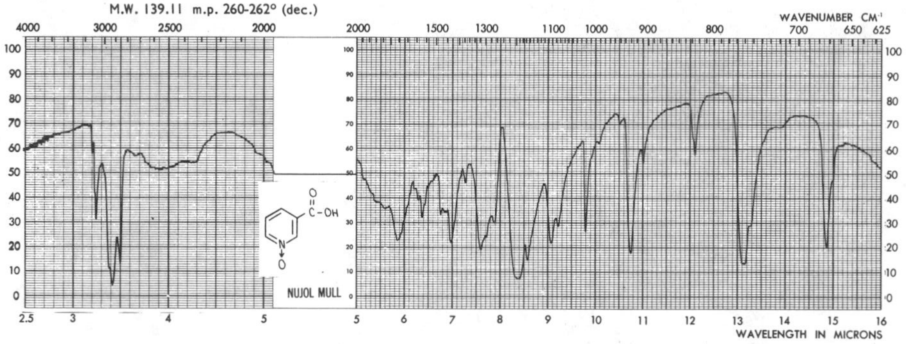

18,713-5
Isonicotinic acid N-oxide, 99%
M.W. 139.11 m.p. 270-271°

NUJOL MULL

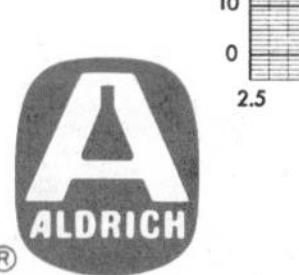

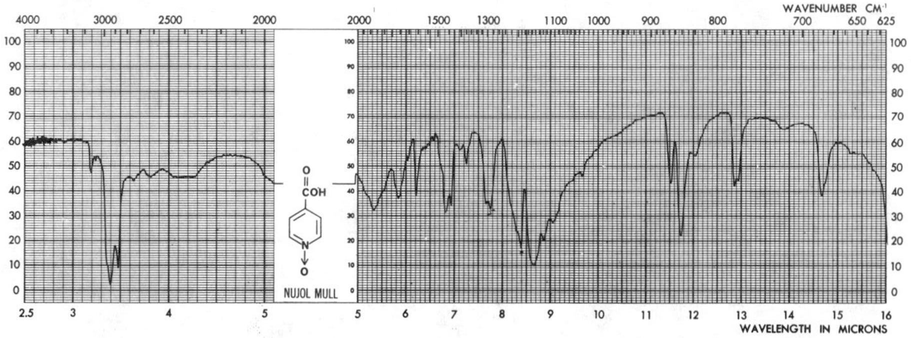

A — N760-5 Nicotinamide-N-oxide
M.W. 138.13 m.p. 291-293°
NUJOL MULL

B — 14,235-2 4-Cyanopyridine-N-oxide (isonicotinonitrile 1-oxide)
M.W. 120.11 m.p. 223-225°
NUJOL MULL

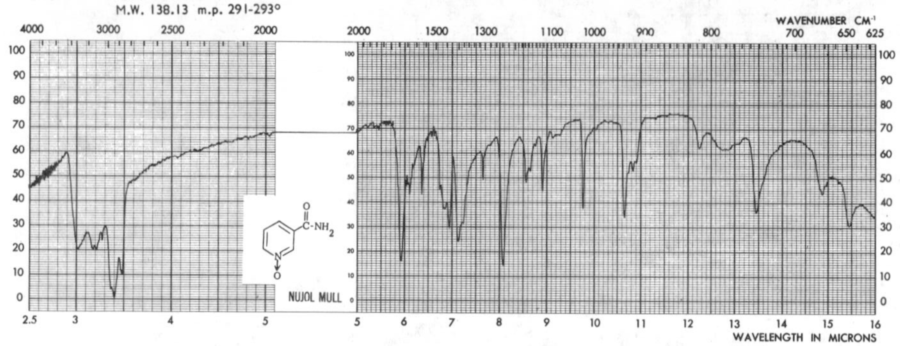

C — 18,349-0
4-Phenylpyridine-N-oxide
M.W. 171.2 m.p. 153-155°
NUJOL MULL

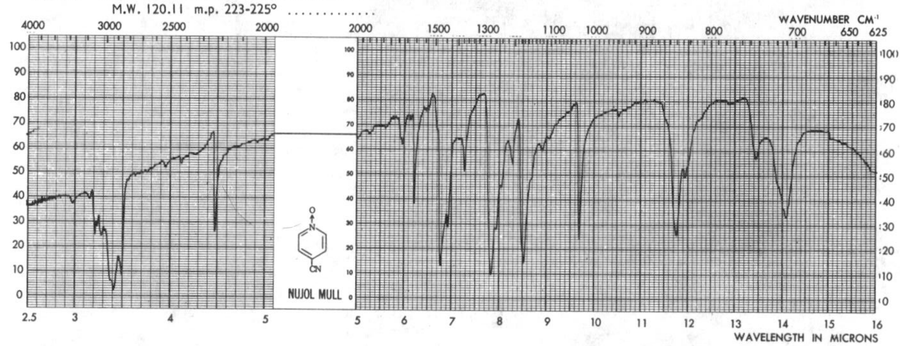

D — 12,248-3 4,4'-Azobis-(pyridine-N-oxide)
M.W. 216.20 (dry) m.p. 240° (dec.)

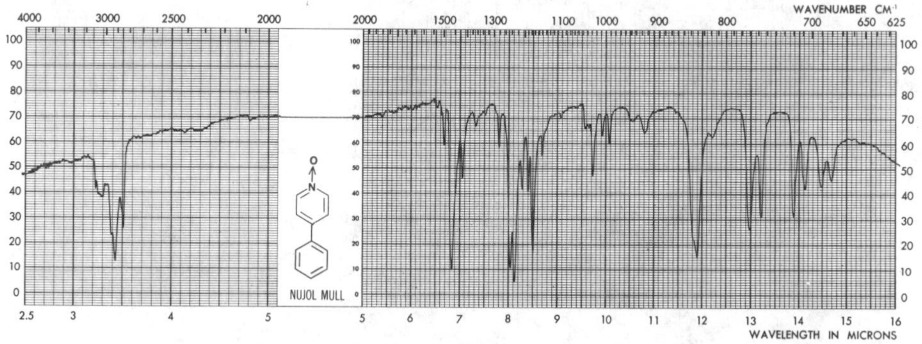

E — 21,543-0
α-(4-Pyridyl 1-oxide)-*N-tert*-butylnitrone, 99% (POBN)
FW 194.24 mp 183-185° Disp. C
NUJOL MULL

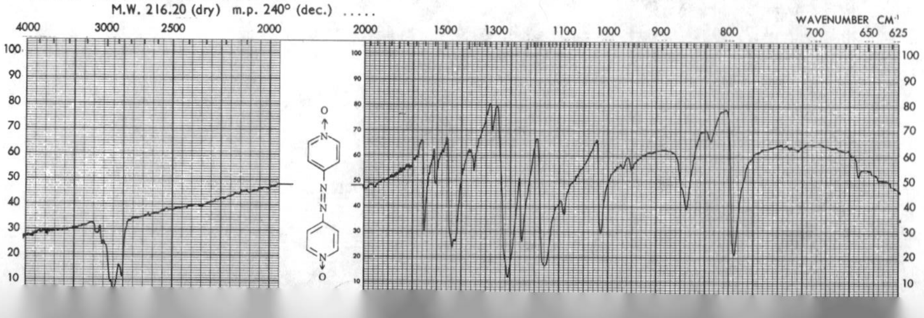

F — 22,113-9
3-Amino-6-(chloromethyl)-2-pyrazinecarbonitrile 4-oxide, 98%
FW 184.59 mp 144-146° Disp. C
NUJOL MULL

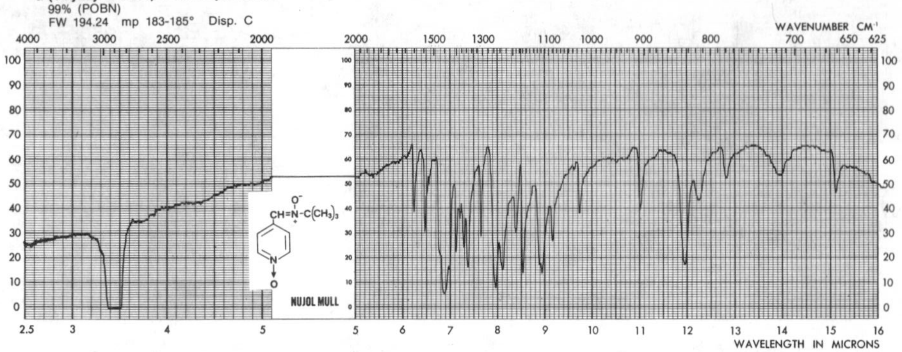

G — 12,232-7 Quinoline-N-oxide hydrate
m.p. 60-64°
MELT

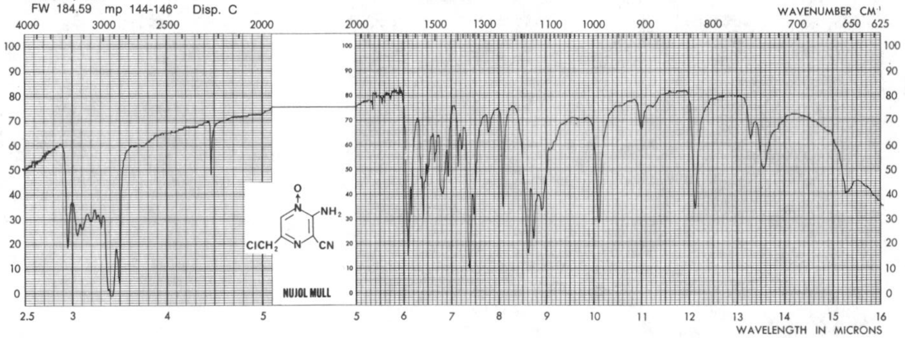

H — 19,269-4
Isoquinoline-*N*-oxide
FW 145.16 mp 105-108° *Beil.* **20**(2),237
Disp. C

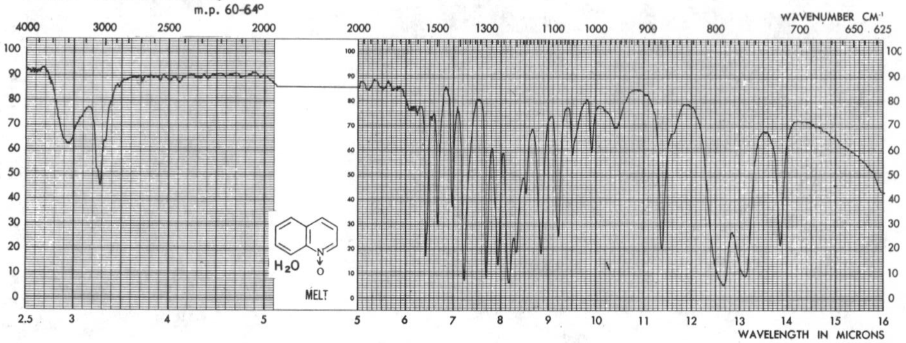

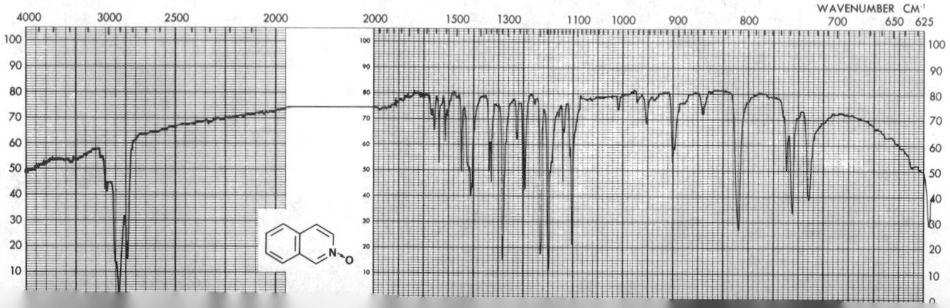

A

12,233-5 8-Hydroxyquinoline-N-oxide (8-quinolinol N-oxide)
M.W. 161.16 m.p. 138-139.5°

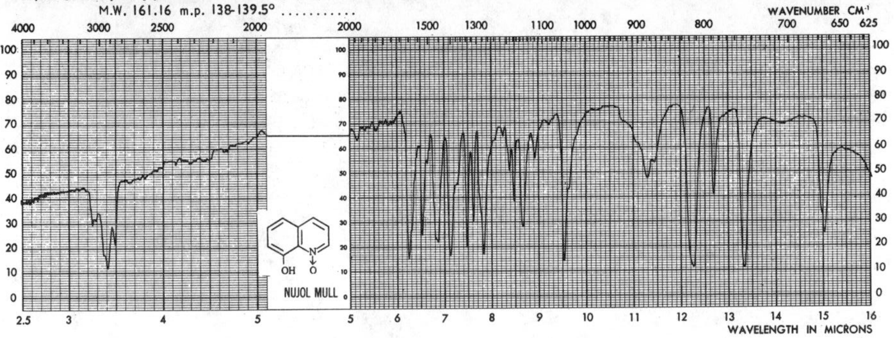

NUJOL MULL

B

M2555-4 6-Methoxyquinoline-N-oxide
M.W. 175.19 m.p. 85-88°

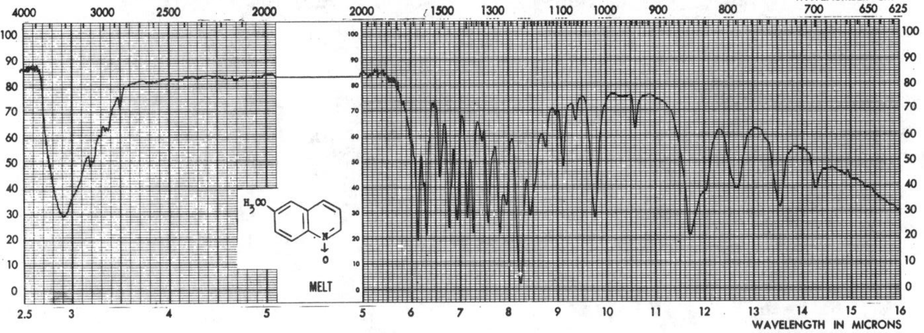

MELT

C

21,844-8
4-Nitroquinoline-N-oxide, 98%
FW 190.16 mp 154-156° Disp. C

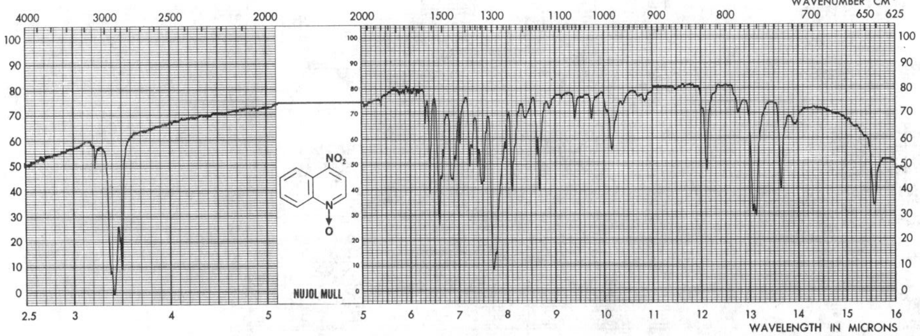

NUJOL MULL

D

15,062-2 Benzofuroxan (benzofurazan 1-oxide)
M.W. 136.11 m.p. 69-71.5°

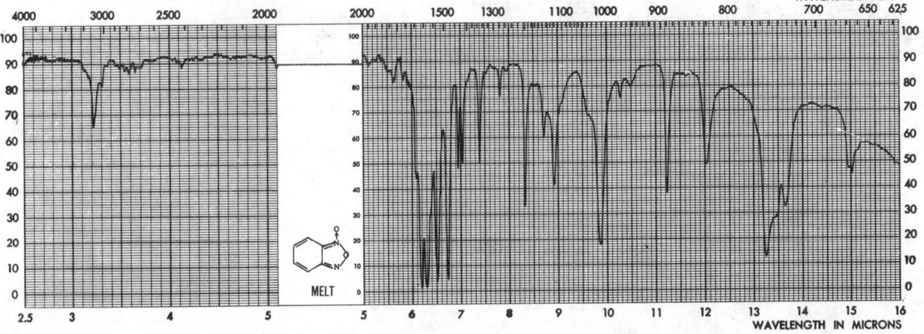

MELT

E

10-oxide, sodium salt)
FW 251.18 *Beil.* **27**,128 Disp. C,D

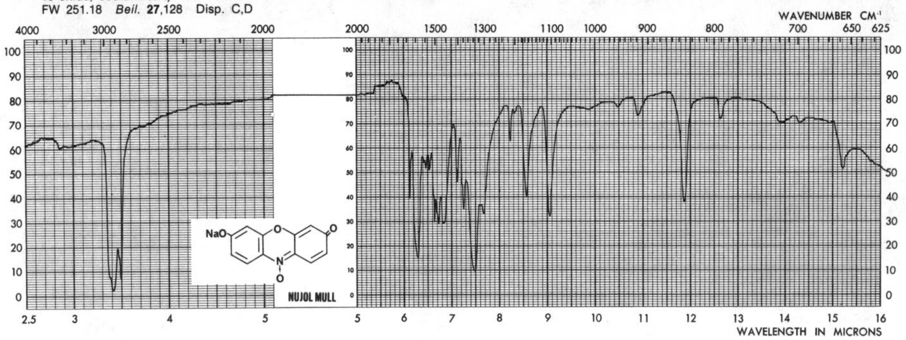

NUJOL MULL

F

85,802-1
Adenine-N¹-oxide
M.W. 151.13 m.p. >300°

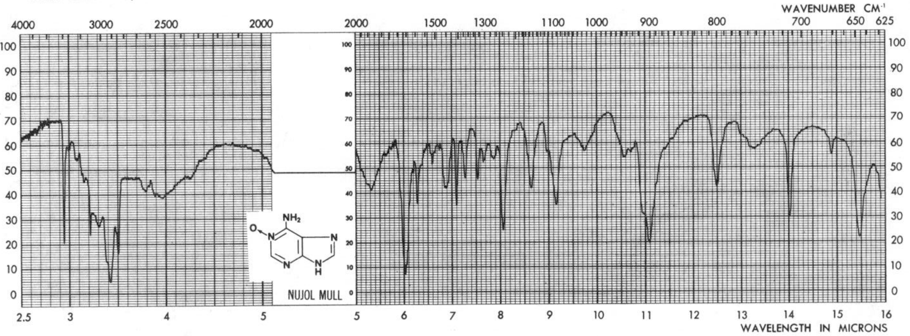

NUJOL MULL

OXIMES

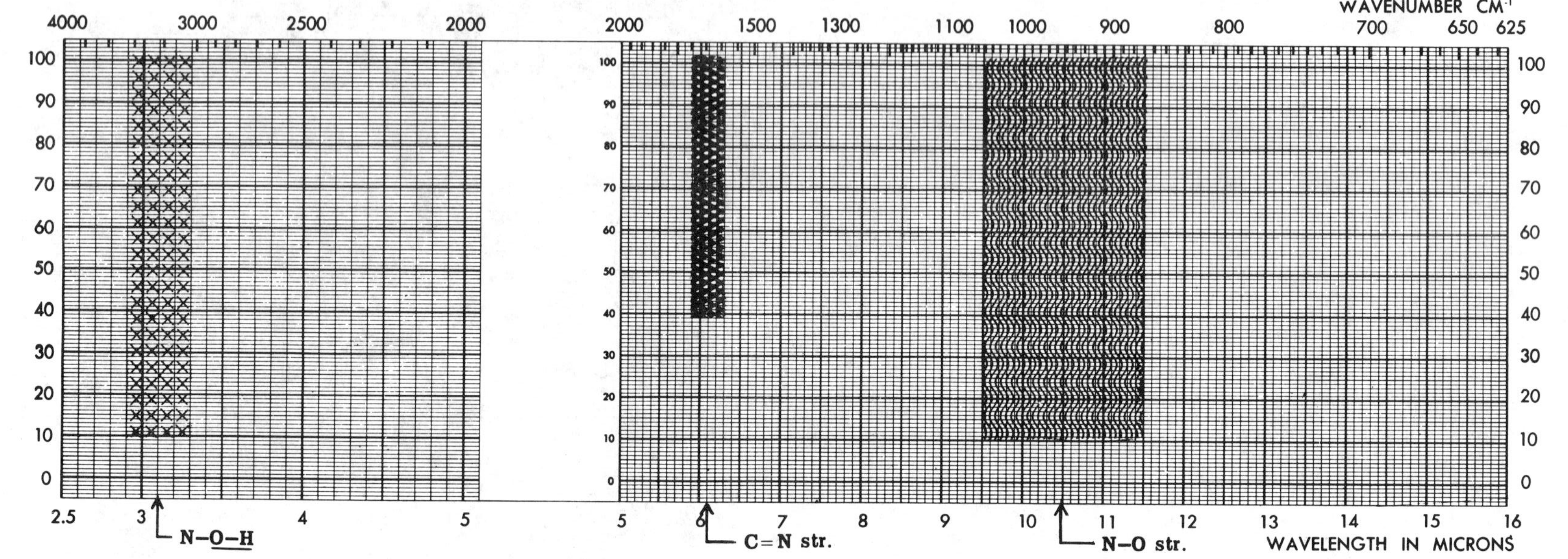

The oxime displays its O–H stretch absorption as a strong broad band between 2.9 and 3.3 μ (3450 – 3030 cm^{-1}). The C=N group absorbs between 5.9 and 6.3 μ (1695 – 1585 cm^{-1}) depending on its conjugation. In the aliphatic oximes (spectra 1426A —1427B), the band is very close to 6 μ (1665 cm^{-1}). In the five-membered ring compounds (spectra 1427C and E), the band appears closer to 5.9 μ (1695 cm^{-1}). In the spectra of the conjugated aromatics, this band, when it does appear, is positioned along with the aromatic ring bands near 6.2 to 6.3 μ (1615 – 1585 cm^{-1}).

The N–O stretch vibration absorbs strongly between 9.5 and 11.5 μ (1055 – 870 cm^{-1}) and is sometimes split into several bands.

A

m.p. 44-46° ....

$H_3C-\overset{H}{C}=N-OH$

NEAT

B

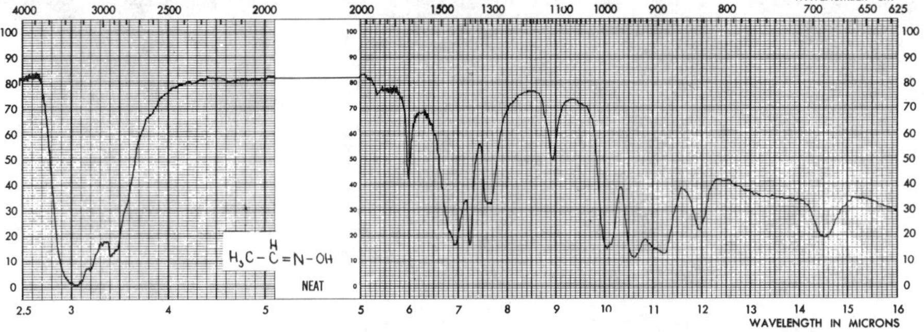

A1050-7 Acetone oxime
$(CH_3)_2C:NOH$ M.W. 73.10 m.p. 60.5-62°

MELT

C

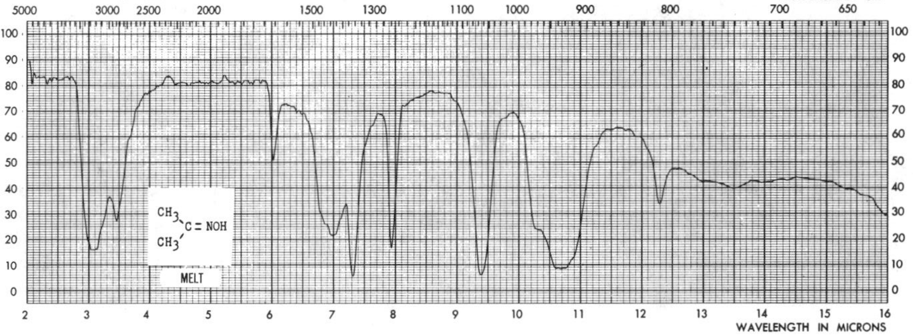

15,903-4
Acetohydroxamic acid, 98%
$CH_3C(=NOH)OH$
M.W. 75.07 m.p. 89-92° Beil. **2**,187
HYGROSCOPIC

NUJOL MULL

D

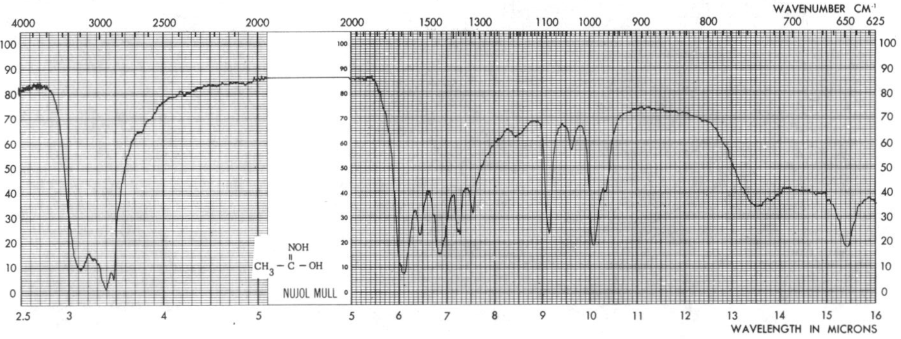

20,892-2
Ethyl *N*-hydroxyacetimidate, 97% (ethyl aceto-hydroximate)
$CH_3C(=NOH)OC_2H_5$ FW 103.12 mp 25-30°
bp 55-58°/6mm. Disp. C

NEAT

E

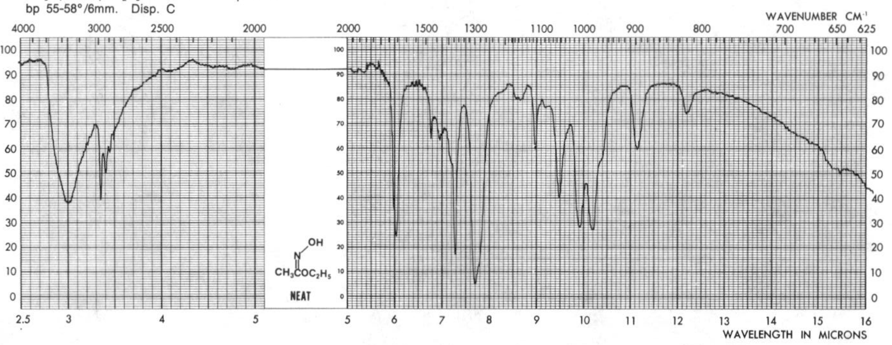

$CH_3C(=NOH)SCH_3$ FW 105.16 mp 94-97°
Disp. C

NUJOL MULL

F

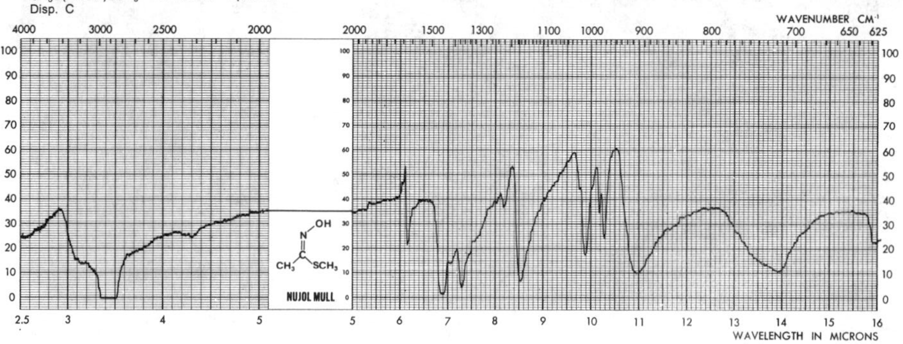

10,970-3 Butyraldoxime
$CH_3CH_2CH_2CH:NOH$ M.W. 87.12
n_D^{20} 1.4363 b.p. 149-152° ....

$H_3C-CH_2-CH_2-\overset{H}{C}=N-OH$

NEAT

G

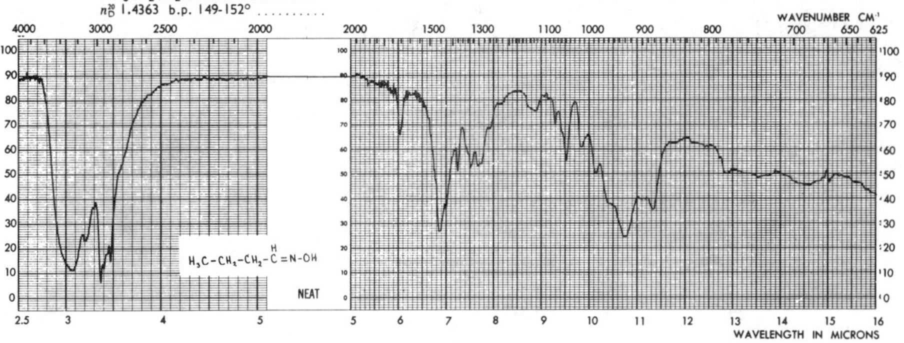

11,213-5 2,3-Butanedione monoxime
$CH_3C(:NOH)COCH_3$ M.W. 101.11 m.p. 77-78°

NUJOL MULL

H

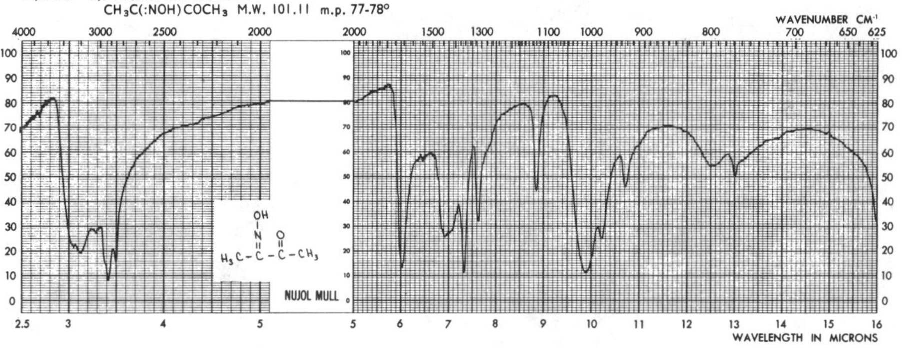

16,257-4
Dimethylglyoxime, 99+%, GOLD LABEL
$CH_3C(=NOH)C(=NOH)CH_3$
M.W. 116.12 m.p. 240-241° Beil. **1**,772

NUJOL MULL

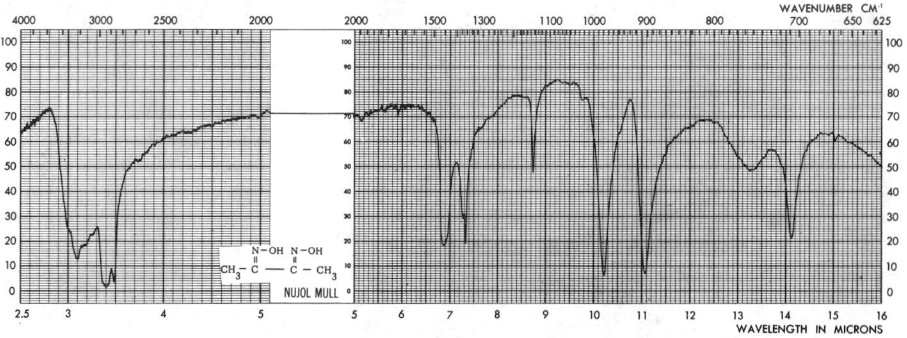

ALDRICH

A

D16,010-5 **Dimethylglyoxime, disodium salt octahydrate**
$CH_3C(:NONa)C(:NONa)CH_3 \cdot 8H_2O$ M.W. 304.20
m.p. > 360°

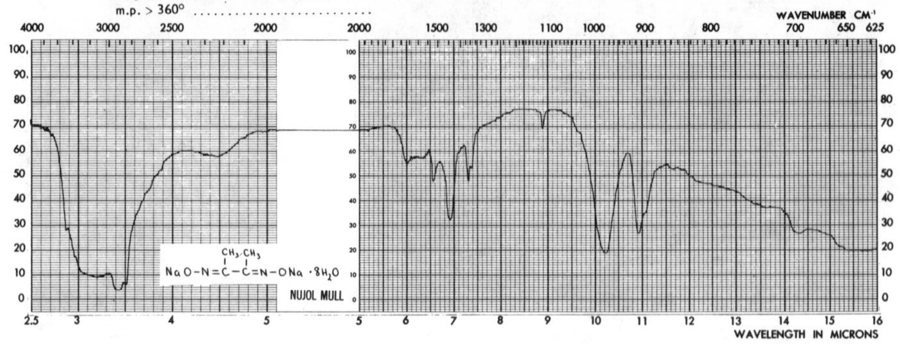

B

16,279-5
1,3-Diisonitrosoacetone, guanidine salt
(mesoxalaldehyde 1,3-dioxime)
$HON{=}CHCOCH{=}NOH \cdot H_2NC({=}NH)NH_2$
M.W. 175.15 m.p. 132-134° (dec.) Beil. **1**,806

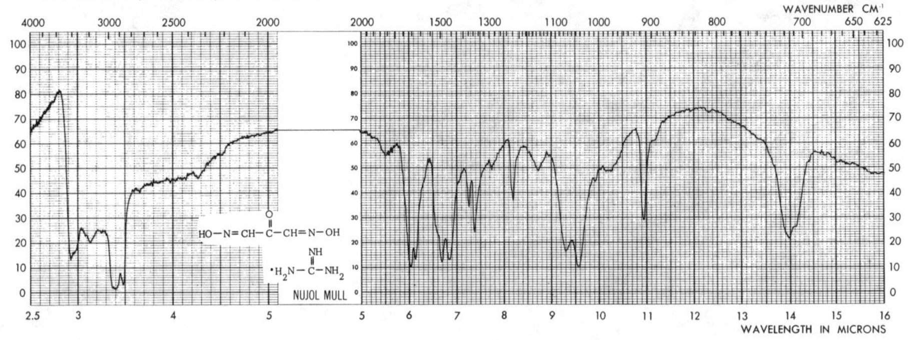

C

C11,243-7 **Cyclopentanone oxime**
$C_5H_8(:NOH)$ M.W. 99.13
m.p. 54-57°

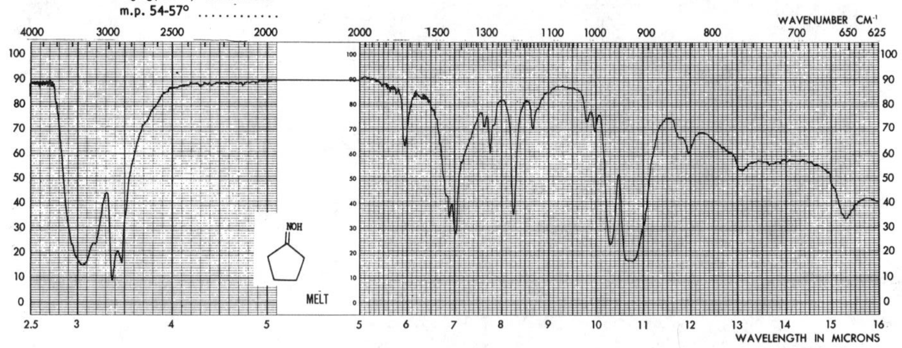

D

C10,220-2 **Cyclohexanone oxime**
$C_6H_{10}(:NOH)$ M.W. 113.16 m.p. 89-91°

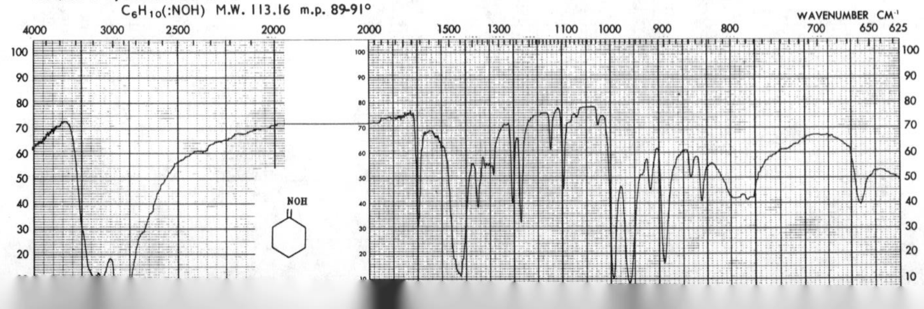

E

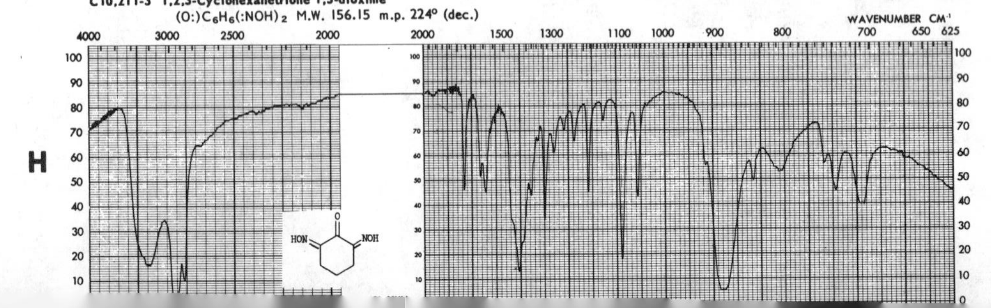

13,123-7 **Norcamphor oxime (2-norbornanone oxime)**
M.W. 125.17 n_D^{20} 1.5185

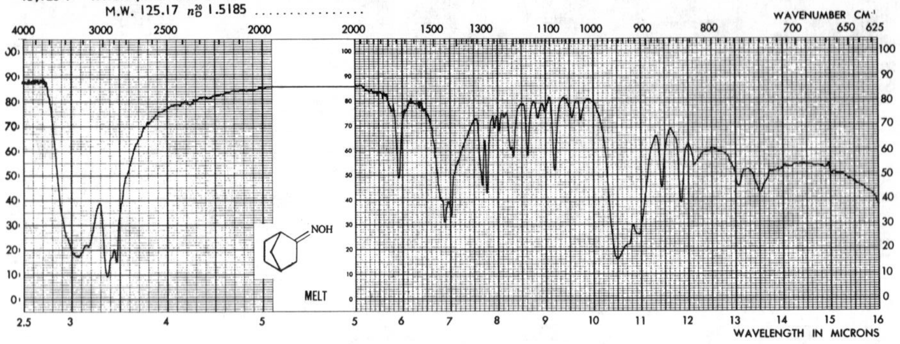

F

C10,200-8 **1,2-Cyclohexanedione dioxime**
$C_6H_8(:NOH)_2$ M.W. 142.16 m.p. 191-195°

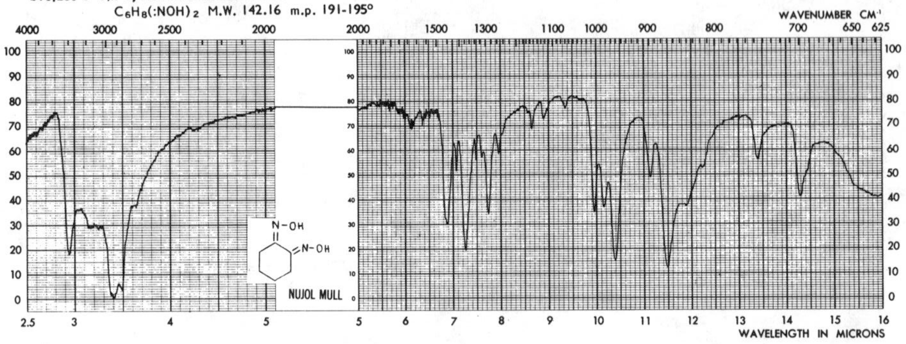

G

15,026-6 **1,2,3-Cyclohexanetrione trioxime**
$C_6H_6(:NOH)_3$ M.W. 171.16
m.p. 183° (dec.)

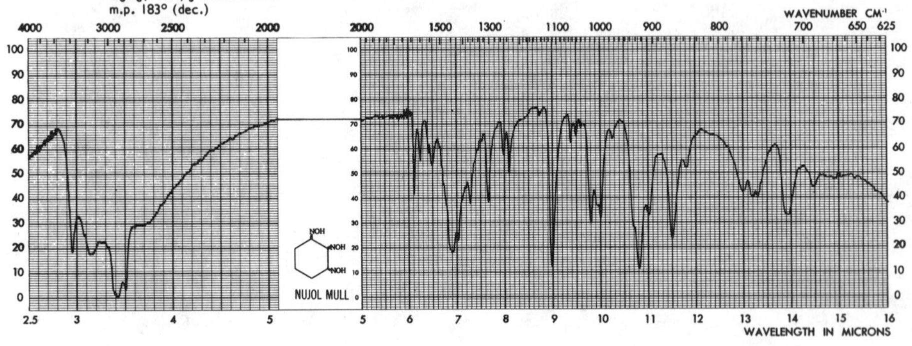

H

C10,211-3 **1,2,3-Cyclohexanetrione 1,3-dioxime**
$(O:)C_6H_6(:NOH)_2$ M.W. 156.15 m.p. 224° (dec.)

FW 185.23 mp 160-162° Disp. C

A

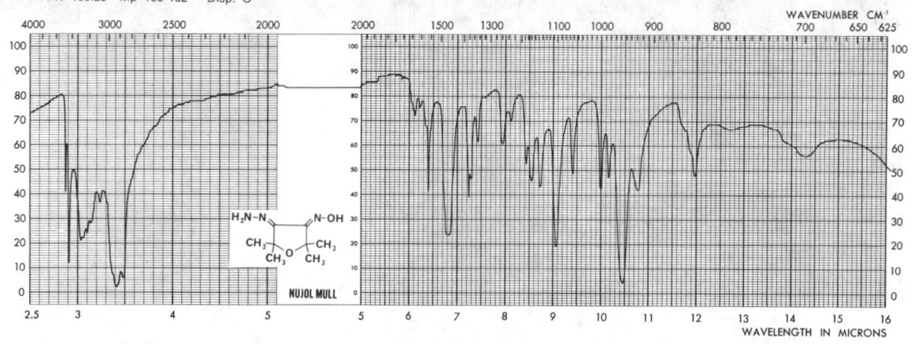

B1040-4 p-Benzoquinone dioxime
$C_6H_4(:NOH)_2$ M.W. 138.13 m.p. 243° (dec.)

B

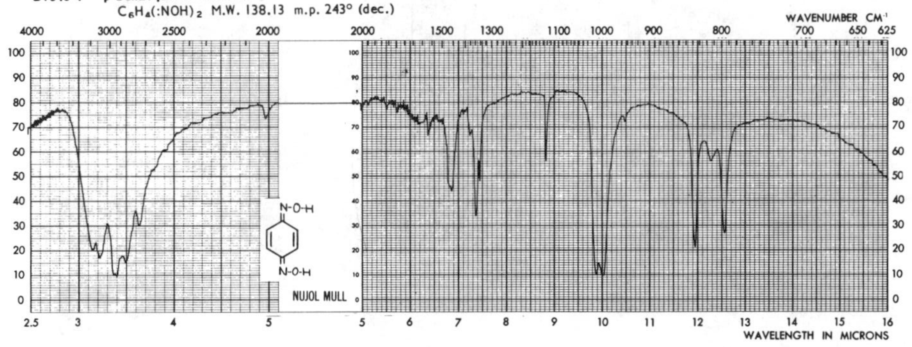

10,417-5 Perillartine (*l*-perillaldehyde α-antioxime)
M.W. 165.24 m.p. 101-103°

C

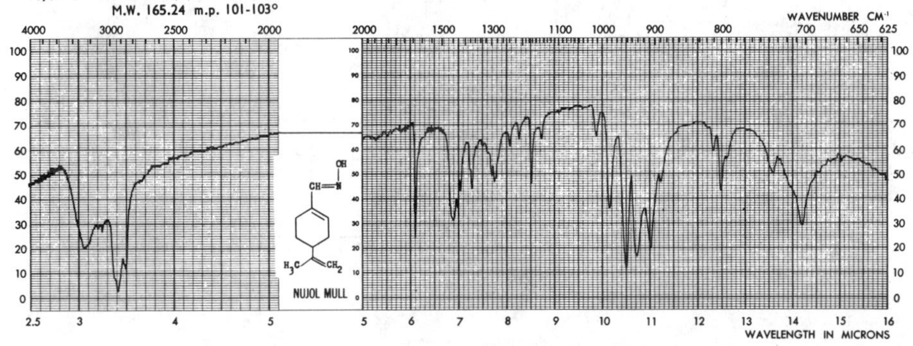

15,040-1 Pinonic acid oxime
$CH_3C(:NOH)C_4H_4(CH_3)_2CH_2CO_2H$ M.W. 199.25
m.p. 145-147° ....

D

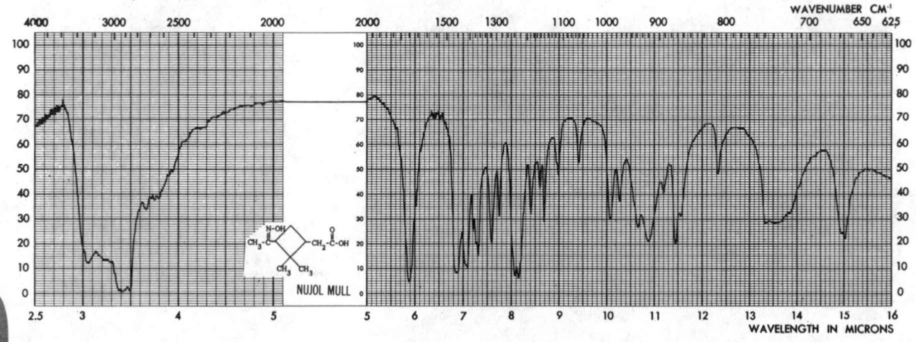

1-Methyl-4-piperidone oxime hydrochloride, 98%
FW 164.64 mp 245° (dec.) Disp. C

E

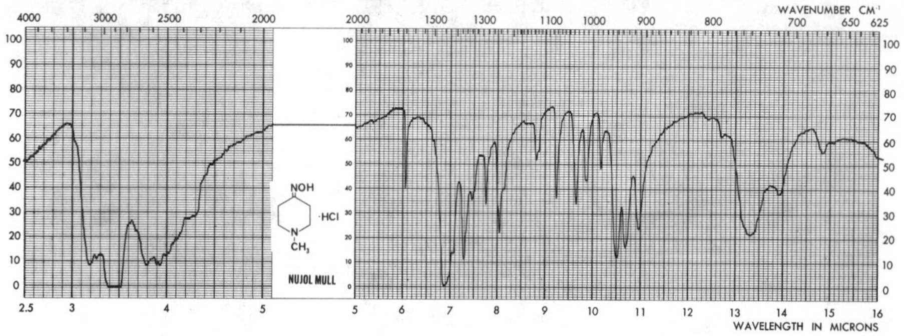

I-1820-2 ω-Isonitrosoacetophenone (phenylglyoxaldoxime)
$C_6H_5COCH:NOH$ M.W. 149.15
m.p. 118-120° ....

F

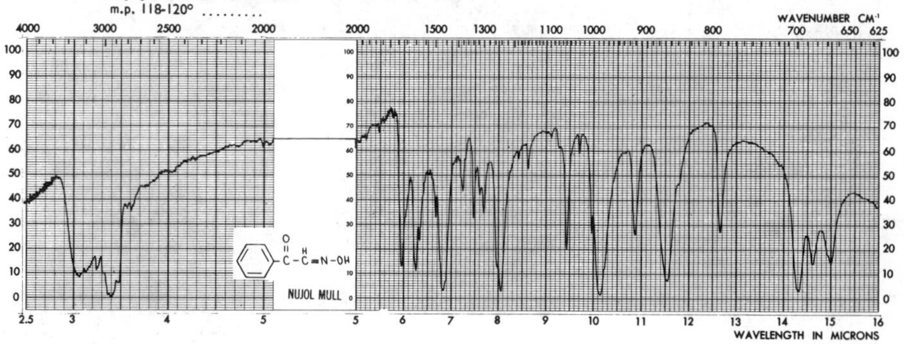

22,009-4
1-Phenyl-1,2-propanedione 2-oxime, 99%
$C_6H_5COC(=NOH)CH_3$ FW 163.18 mp 113-115°
Beil. 7(3),3464 Disp. C

G

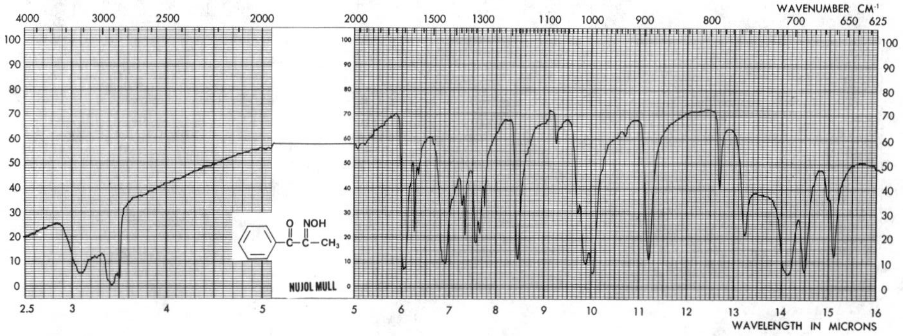

22,307-7
Salicylaldoxime, 98%
$2\text{-}(HO)C_6H_4CH{=}NOH$ FW 137.14 mp 59-61°
Beil. 8,49 Disp. C

H

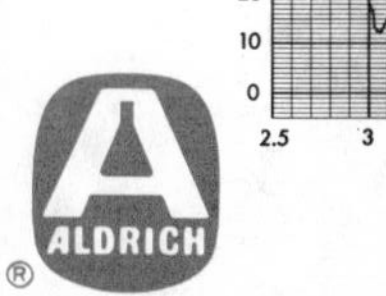

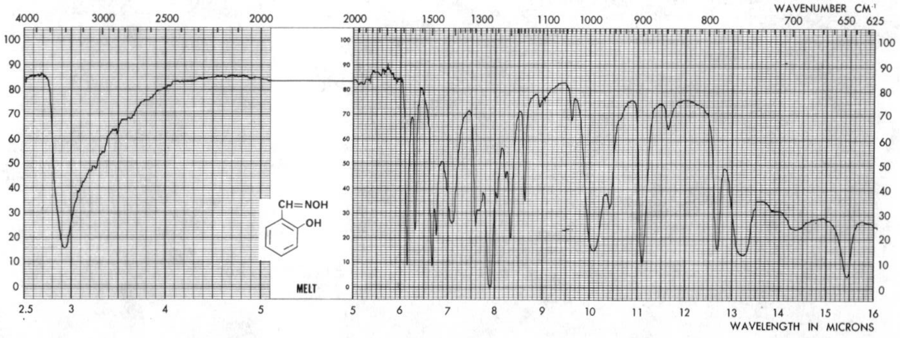

ALDRICH

A

S60-7 **Salicylhydroxamic acid** (2-hydroxybenzohydroxamic acid)
$HOC_6H_4C(:NOH)OH$ M.W. 153.14 m.p. 177° (dec.)

NUJOL MULL

B

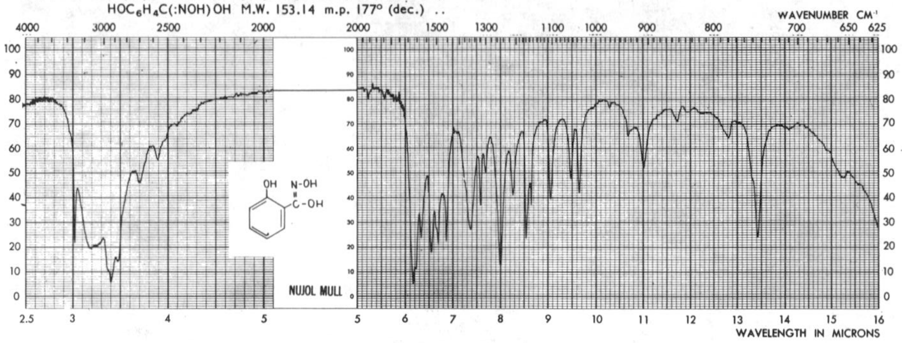

13,825-8 **m-Nitrobenzamidoxime**
$O_2NC_6H_4C(:NOH)NH_2$ M.W. 181.15
m.p. 178-180° (dec.)

NUJOL MULL

C

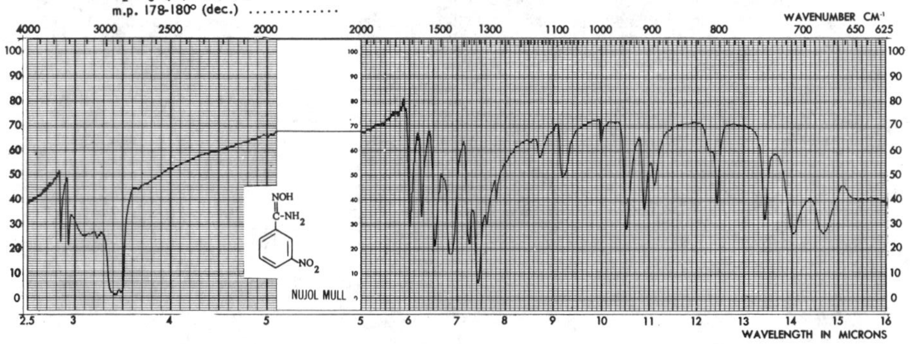

22,263-1
syn-**4-Fluorobenzaldoxime**, 97%
$FC_6H_4CH{=}NOH$ FW 139.13 mp 82-85°
Beil. 7(1),132 Disp. C

NUJOL MULL

D

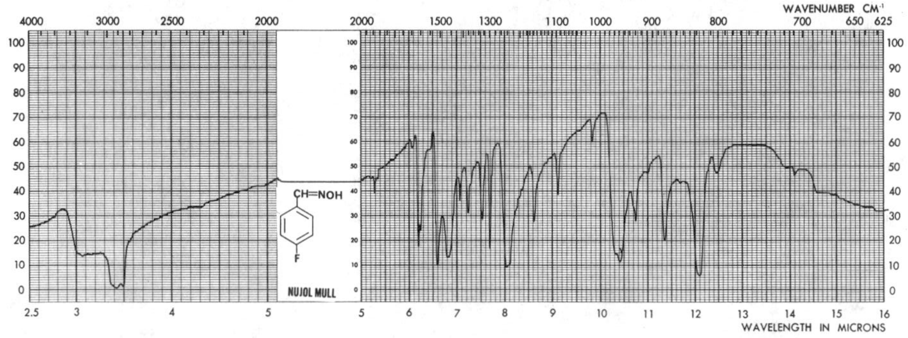

21,989-4
p-**Nitrobenzaldoxime**, 99%
$O_2NC_6H_4CH{=}NOH$ FW 166.14 mp 126-130°
Beil. 7,259 Disp. C

E

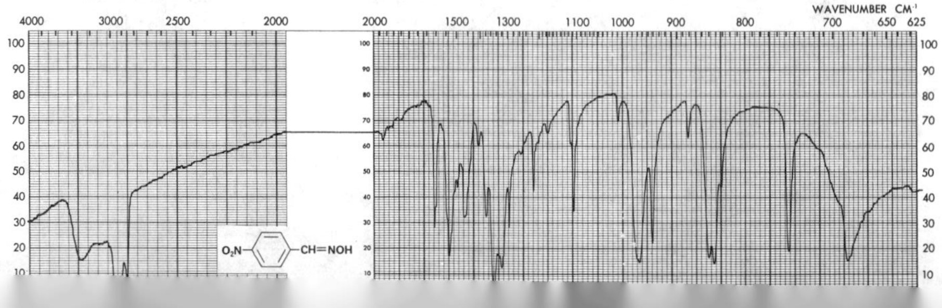

12,096-0 **Palladon** (1-benzoyl-2-methylglyoxime)
$CH_3C(:NOH)C(:NOH)COC_6H_5$ M.W. 206.20
m.p. 173° (dec.)

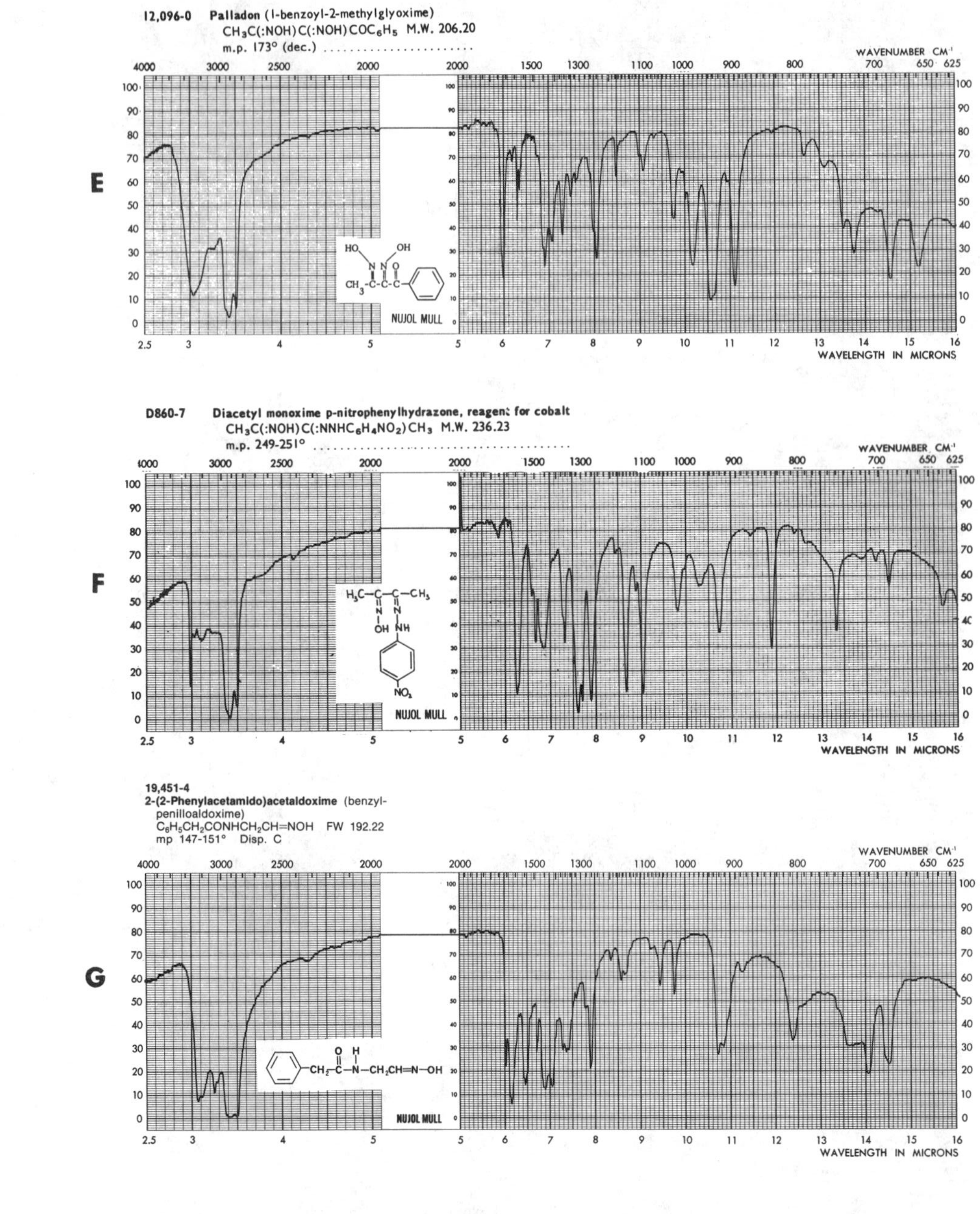

NUJOL MULL

F

D860-7 **Diacetyl monoxime p-nitrophenylhydrazone, reagent for cobalt**
$CH_3C(:NOH)C(:NNHC_6H_4NO_2)CH_3$ M.W. 236.23
m.p. 249-251°

NUJOL MULL

G

19,451-4
2-(2-Phenylacetamido)acetaldoxime (benzylpenilloaldoxime)
$C_6H_5CH_2CONHCH_2CH{=}NOH$ FW 192.22
mp 147-151° Disp. C

NUJOL MULL

H

10,084-6 **4-Biphenylcarboxaldehyde oxime**
$C_6H_5C_6H_4CH:NOH$ M.W. 197.24 m.p. 149-152°

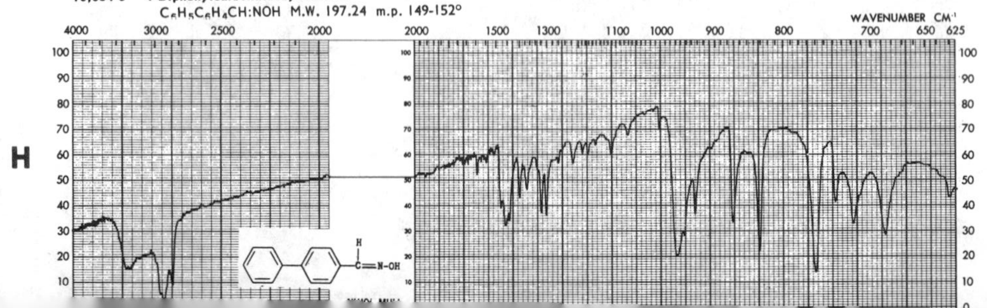

A

m.p. 143-144° ....

NUJOL MULL

B

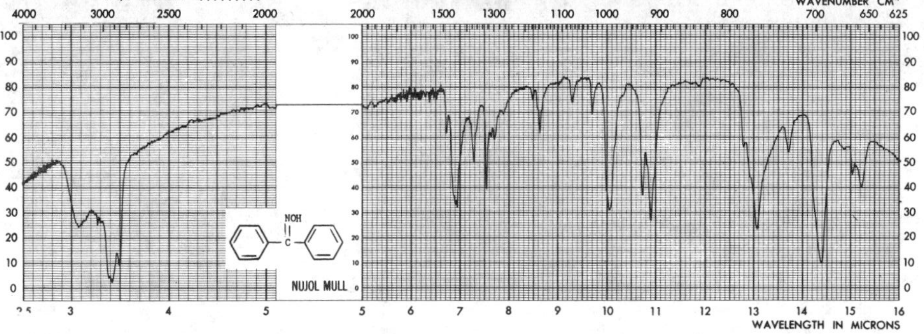

B890-8 **Benzoin oxime**
$C_6H_5CH(OH)C(:NOH)C_6H_5$ M.W. 227.26
m.p. 152-154° ....

NUJOL MULL

C

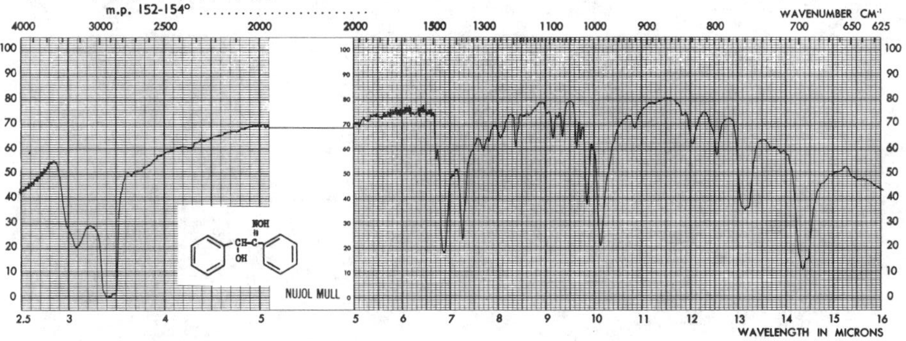

A4557-2 **2-Amino-5-chlorobenzophenone oxime** (mixture of syn and anti isomers)
$H_2NC_6H_3(Cl)C(:NOH)C_6H_5$ M.W. 246.70 ....

NUJOL MULL

D

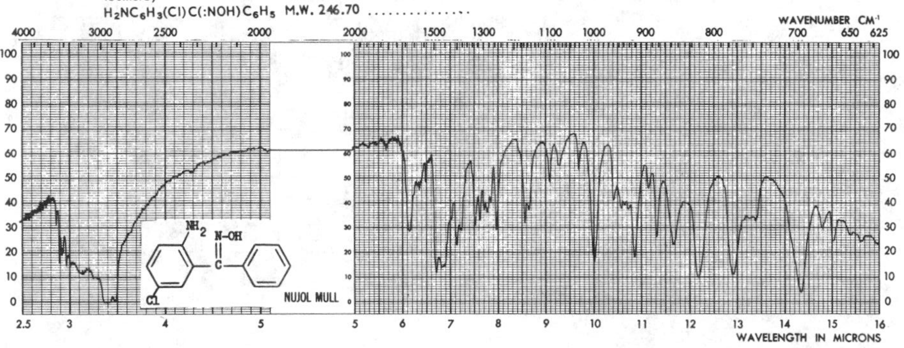

12,618-7 **10,11-Dihydro-5H-dibenzo[a,d]cyclohepten-5-one oxime**
(dibenzosuberone oxime)
M.W. 223.28 m.p. 169-170° ....

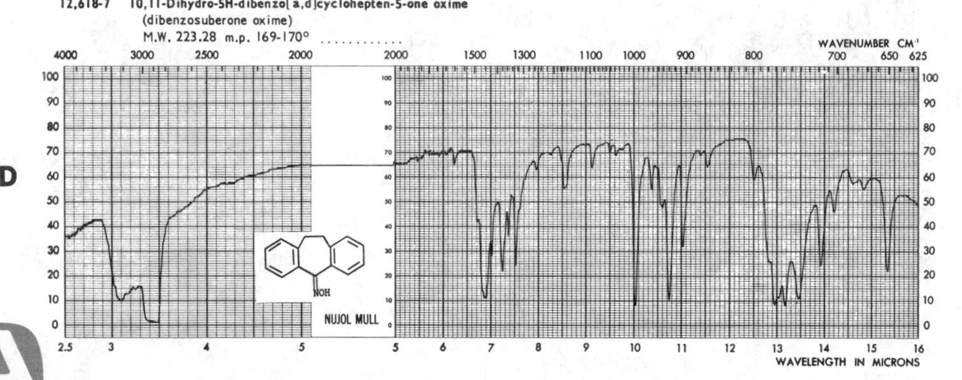

NUJOL MULL

E

D3174-5 **5H-Dibenzo[a,d]cyclohepten-5-one oxime**
M.W. 221.26 m.p. 184-186° ....

NUJOL MULL

F

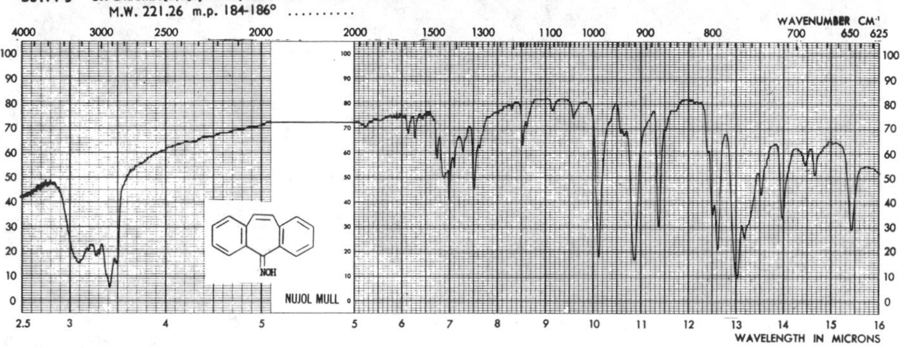

13,317-5 **Thiochroman-4-one oxime**
M.W. 179.24 m.p. 98-100°

NUJOL MULL

G

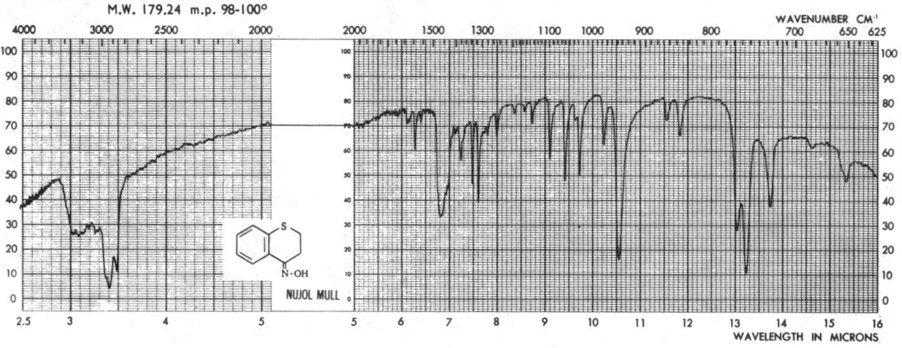

11,462-6 **Isatin-3-oxime**
M.W. 162.15 m.p. 225° (dec.)

NUJOL MULL

H

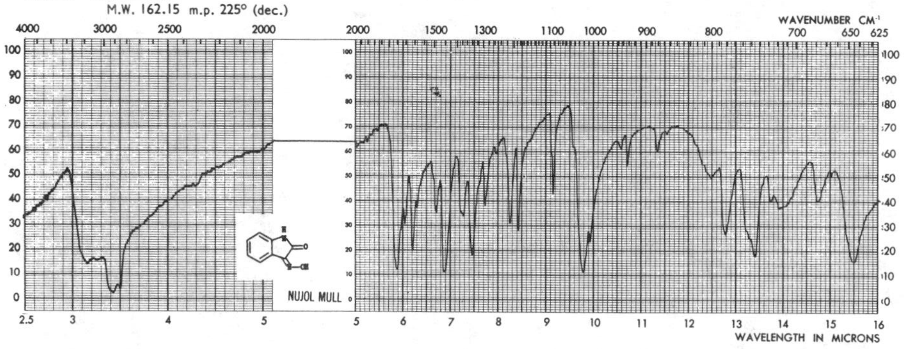

11,179-1 **α-Furil monoxime**
M.W. 205.17 m.p. 95-97°

NUJOL MULL

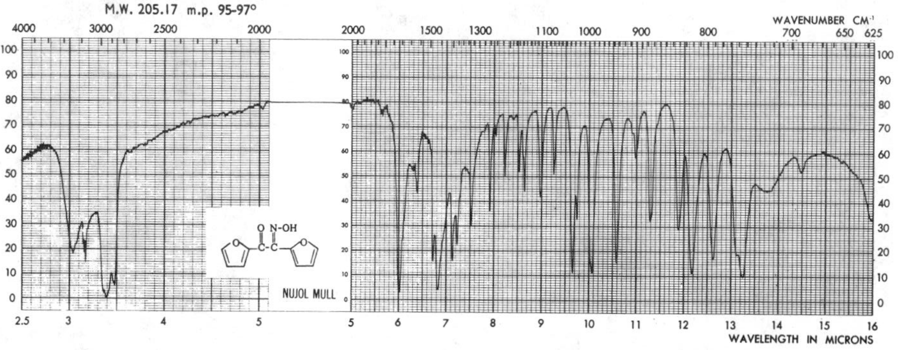

A

21,947-9
α-Furildioxime, mixture of isomers
FW 220.18 mp 161-168° *Beil.* **19**,166 Disp. C

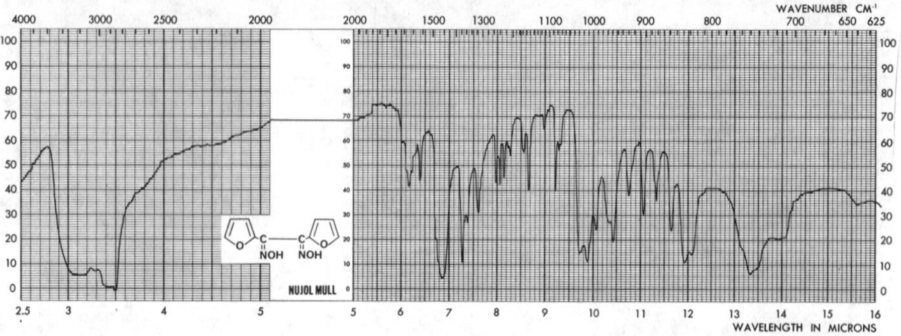

NUJOL MULL

B

11,821-4 **2-Furanpyruvic acid oxime**
M.W. 169.14 m.p. 123° (dec.)

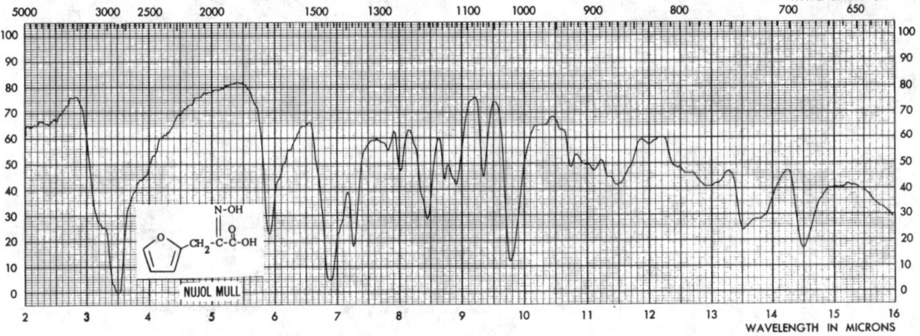

NUJOL MULL

C

P5820-0 **2-Pyridinealdoxime, puriss.**
M.W. 122.13 m.p. 112-113°

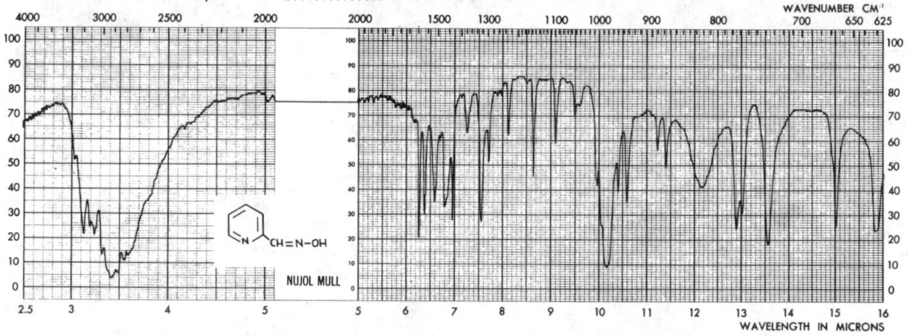

NUJOL MULL

D

16,170-5
Di-2-pyridyl ketone oxime, 99+%, GOLD LABEL
M.W. 199.21 m.p. 142-143°

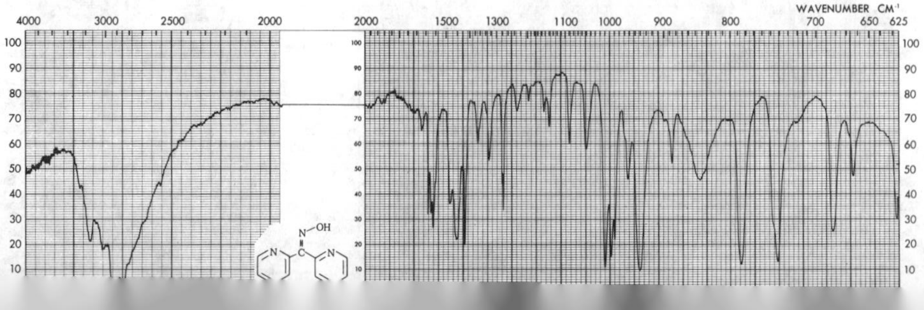

E

13,163-6 **2-Pyridinealdoxime methochloride**
M.W. 172.62 m.p. 228-229° (dec.)

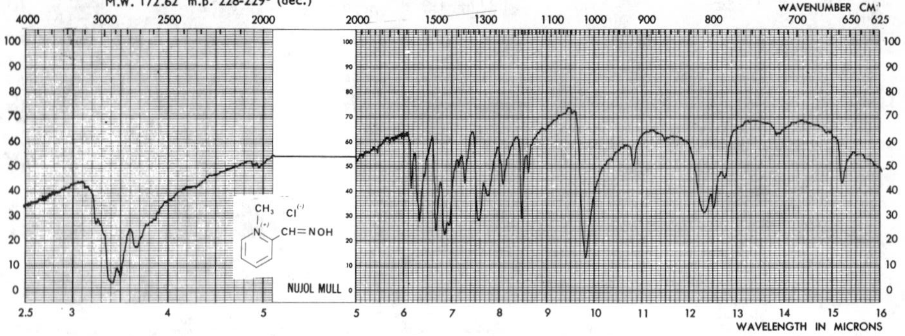

NUJOL MULL

F

P6020-5 **2-Pyridinealdoxime methiodide (2PAM), puriss.**
M.W. 264.07 m.p. 214-215°

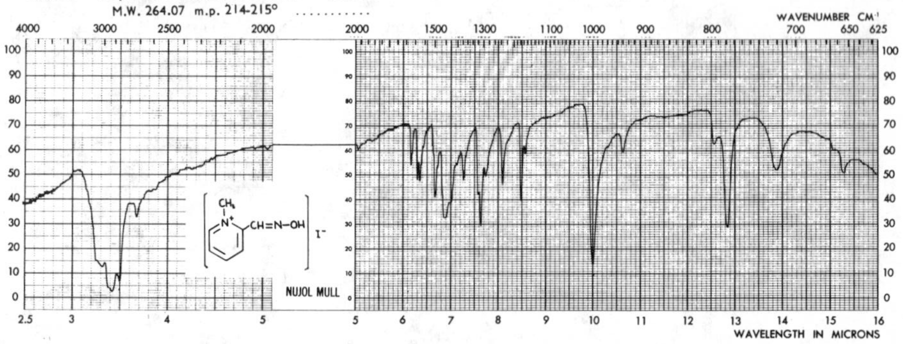

NUJOL MULL

G

P6060-4 **2-Pyridinealdoxime methyl methanesulfonate (P2S)**
M.W. 232.26 m.p. 151-157°

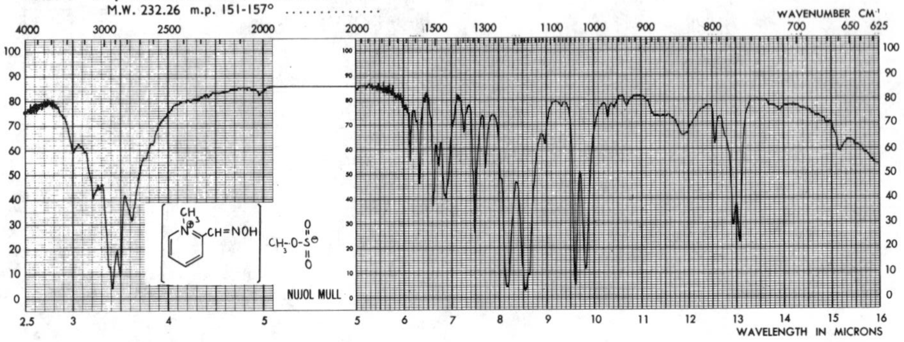

NUJOL MULL

H

P5840-5 **3-Pyridinealdoxime**
M.W. 122.13 m.p. 150-153°

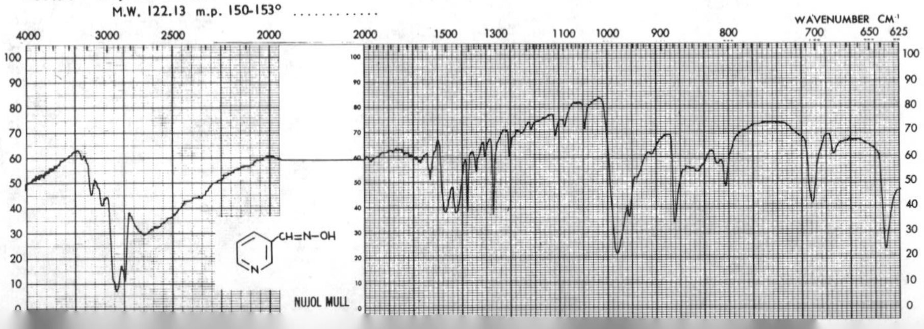

NUJOL MULL

M.W. 122.13 m.p. 130-133°

A

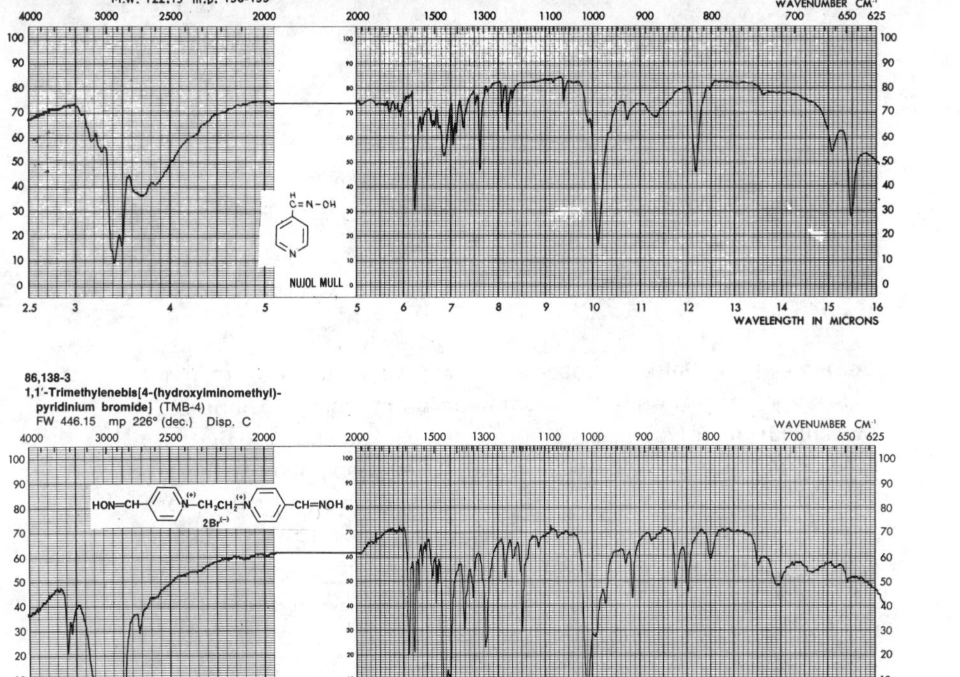

86,138-3
1,1'-Trimethylenebis[4-(hydroxyiminomethyl)-pyridinium bromide] (TMB-4)
FW 446.15 mp 226° (dec.) Disp. C

B

E4730-1 Ethyl 2-pyridylglyoxylate oxime
M.W. 194.19 m.p. 150-152°

C

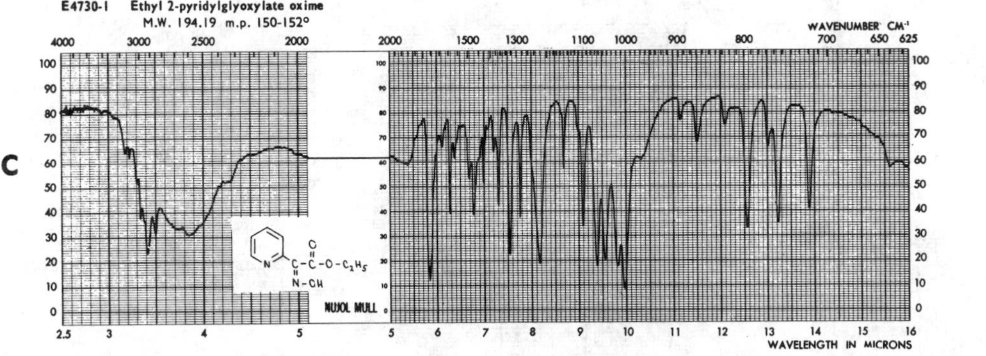

I-480-3 Indole-3-carboxaldehyde oxime
M.W. 160.18 m.p. 198-199°

D

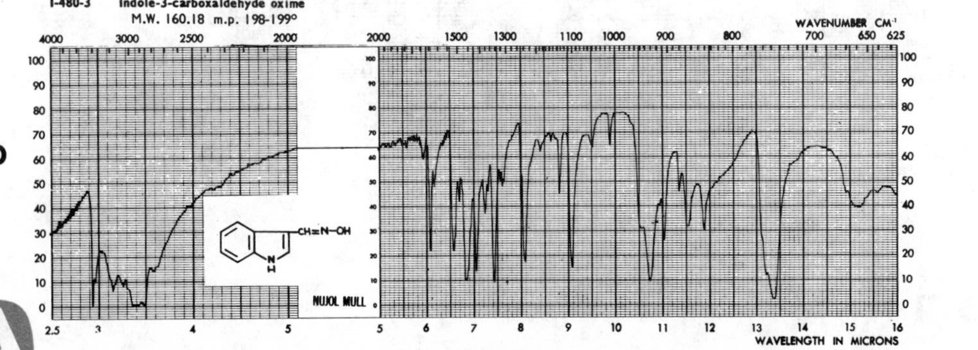

ALKYNES

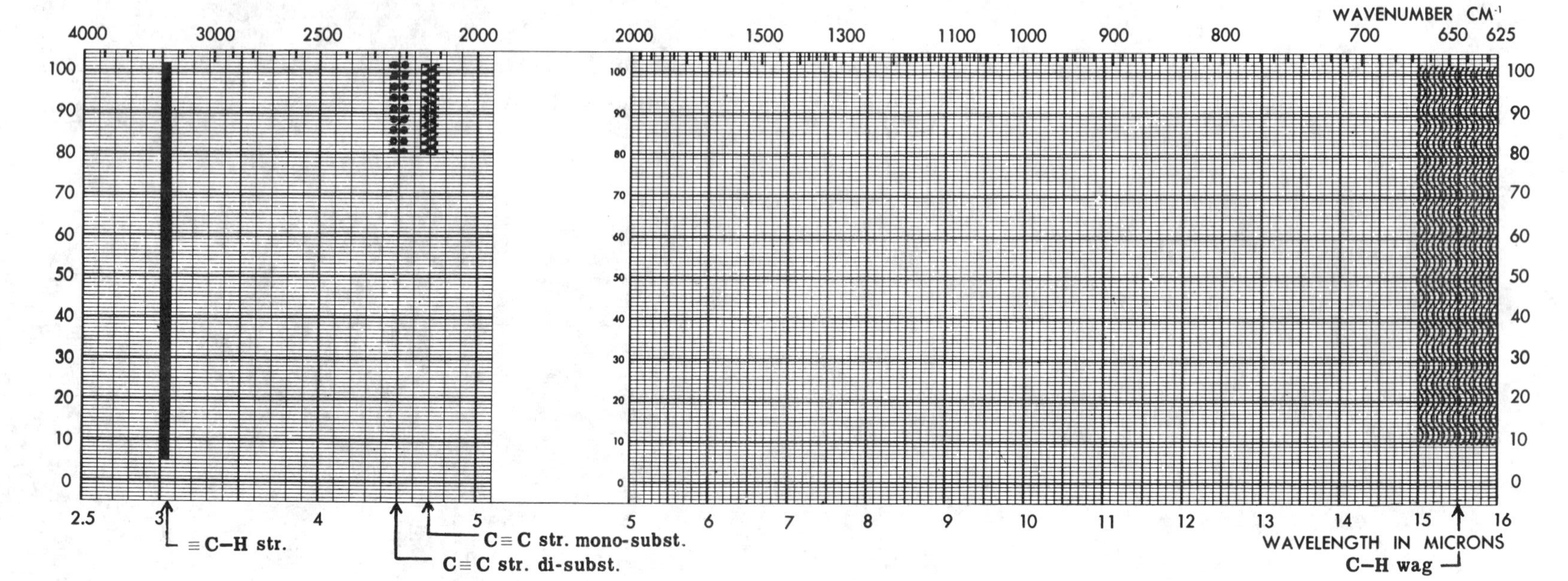

The acetylene triple bond absorption is extremely variable in intensity. When it is monosubstituted, the C≡C stretch appears near 4.7 μ (2130 cm^{-1}). When disubstituted, this band is shifted to 4.5 μ (2220 cm^{-1}). In the various spectra in this section, careful attention should be paid to the molecular configuration determining its intensity which varies from nonexistent in the symmetrically disubstituted acetylenes (spectra 1434H, 1436B and 1437E) to strong when the triple bond is conjugated to a carbonyl (spectra 1438A—B and 1438F). Again, the symmetry of the carbonyl conjugated molecules seen in spectra 1438C and 1438G is responsible for the disappearance of the band near 4.5 μ (2220 cm^{-1}).

The C–H stretch of the ≡C–H group appears as a strong narrow band near 3.02 μ (3310 cm^{-1}) and is accompanied by a very strong and broad CH wag absorption near 15 to 16 μ (665 – 625 cm^{-1}).

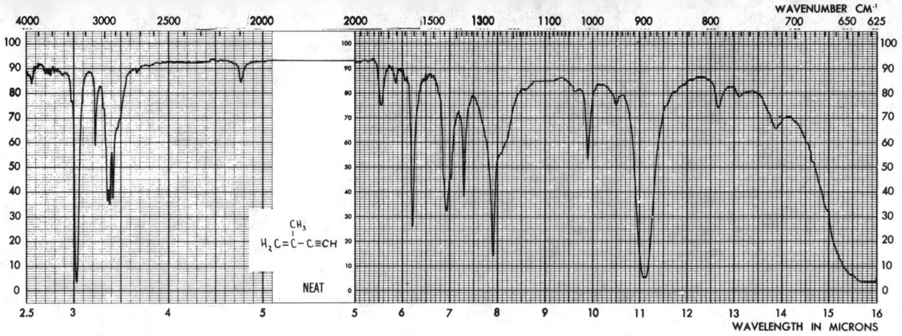

A

$H_2C{=}C(CH_3){-}C{\equiv}CH$ NEAT

16,129-2
1,7-Octadiyne, 99%
$HC{\equiv}C(CH_2)_4C{\equiv}CH$
M.W. 106.17 b.p. 135-136° n_D^{20} 1.4464 d 0.8
Beil. **1**(2),248 *IRRITANT*

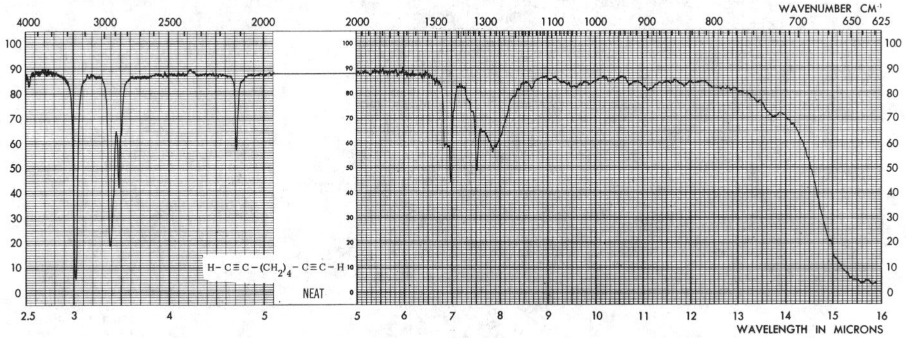

B

$H{-}C{\equiv}C{-}(CH_2)_4{-}C{\equiv}C{-}H$ NEAT

16,130-6
1,8-Nonadiyne, 98%
$HC{\equiv}C(CH_2)_5C{\equiv}CH$
M.W. 120.2 m.p. -21° b.p. 55-55.5°/13mm.
n_D^{20} 1.4492 d 0.799 Beil. **1**(2),248 *STENCH*

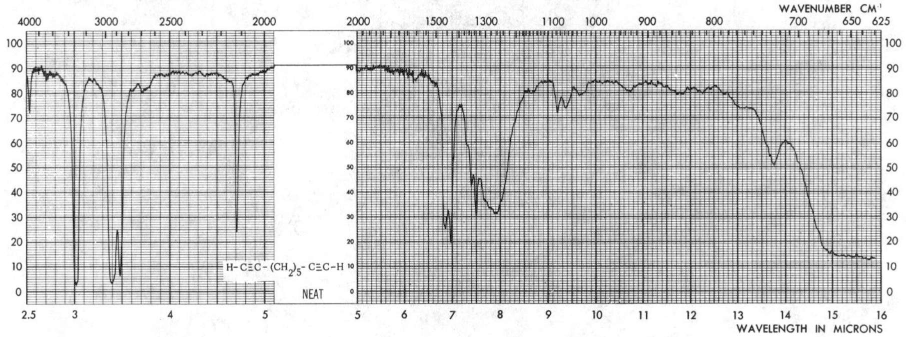

C

$H{-}C{\equiv}C{-}(CH_2)_5{-}C{\equiv}C{-}H$ NEAT

12,921-6 **Cyclohexylacetylene** (ethynylcyclohexane)
$C_6H_{11}C{\equiv}CH$ M.W. 103.18 n_D^{20} 1.4593
b.p. 130-132°

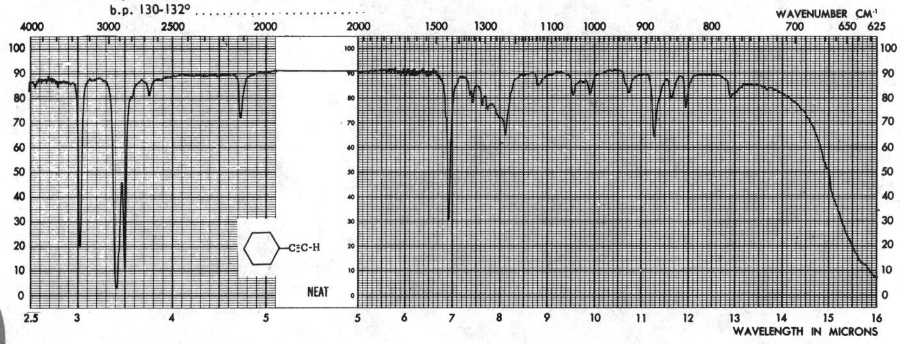

D

$C_6H_{11}{-}C{\equiv}C{-}H$ NEAT

b.p. 56°

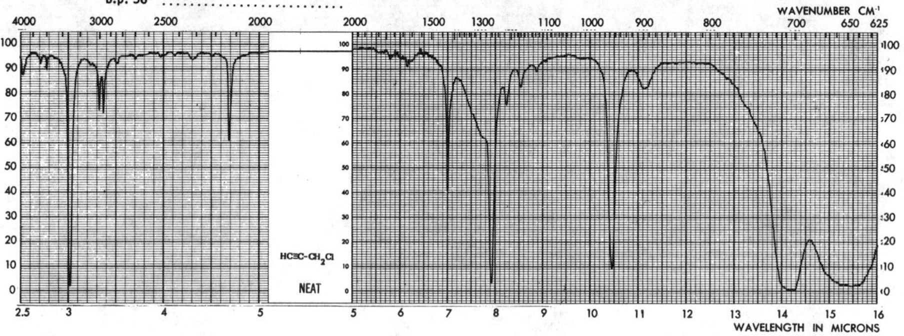

E

$HC{\equiv}C{-}CH_2Cl$ NEAT

19,236-8
3-Chloro-1-butyne, tech., 90+%
$CH_3CH(Cl)C{\equiv}CH$ FW 88.54 bp 68-80°
n_D^{20} 1.4280 d 0.961 *Beil.* **1**(4),970 Disp. C

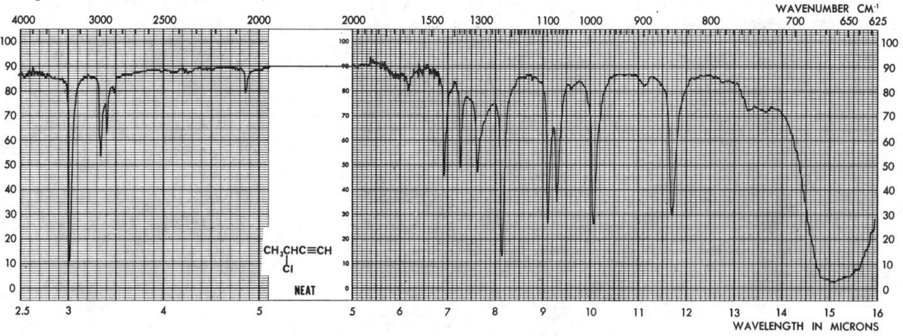

F

$CH_3CH(Cl)C{\equiv}CH$ NEAT

P5100-1 **Propargyl bromide** (3-bromopropyne)
$HC{\equiv}CCH_2Br$ M.W. 118.97 n_D^{20} 1.4922
b.p. 88-90°

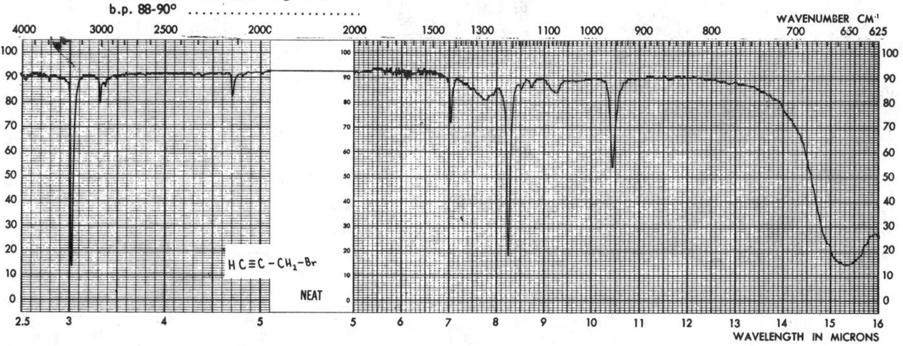

G

$HC{\equiv}C{-}CH_2{-}Br$ NEAT

D5960-7 **1,4-Dichloro-2-butyne**
$ClCH_2C{\equiv}CCH_2Cl$ M.W. 122.98 n_D^{20} 1.5048

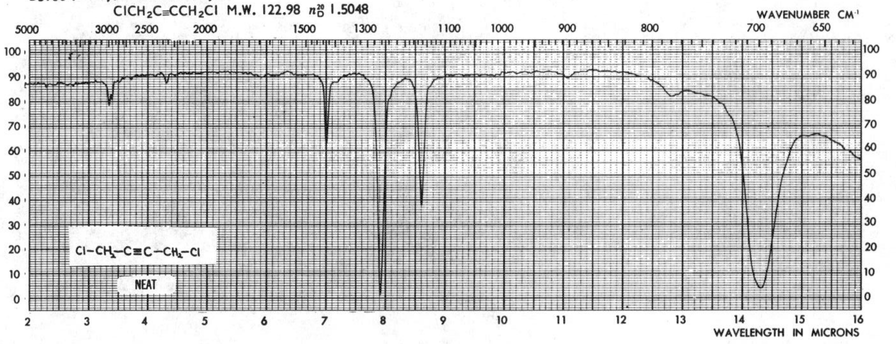

H

$Cl{-}CH_2{-}C{\equiv}C{-}CH_2{-}Cl$ NEAT

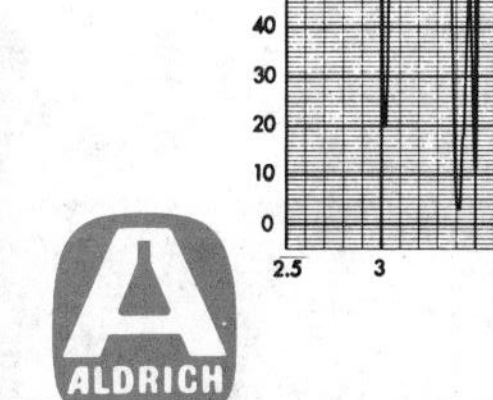

A

M1260-6 **1-Methoxy-1-buten-3-yne** (50% solution in aqueous methanol)
$HC{\equiv}CCH{:}CHOCH_3$ M.W. 82.10 (dry basis)..

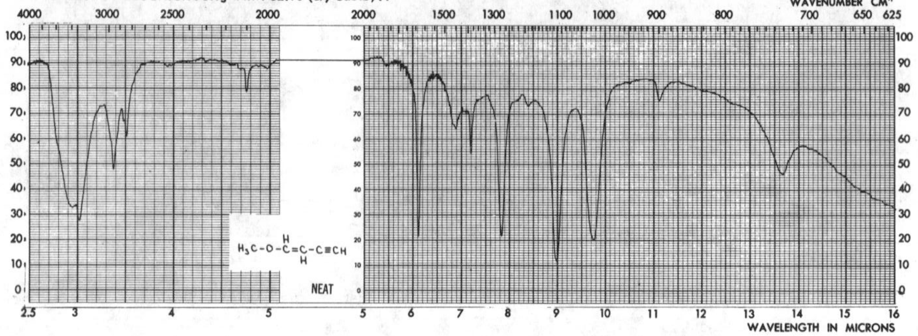

$H_3C{-}O{-}\overset{H}{C}{=}\underset{H}{C}{-}C{\equiv}CH$

NEAT

B

P5080-3 **Propargyl alcohol** (2-propyn-1-ol)
$HC{\equiv}CCH_2OH$ M.W. 56.06 n_D^{20} 1.4322
b.p. 118°

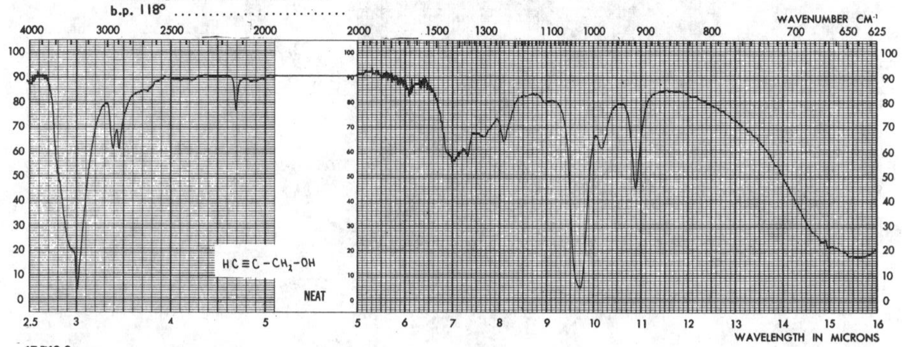

$HC{\equiv}C{-}CH_2{-}OH$

NEAT

C

17,719-9
Methyl propargyl ether, 98% (methyl 2-propynyl ether)
$HC{\equiv}CCH_2OCH_3$
M.W. 70.09 b.p. 61-62° n_D^{20} 1.3961 d 0.83
Beil. 1,454 *LACHRYMATOR*

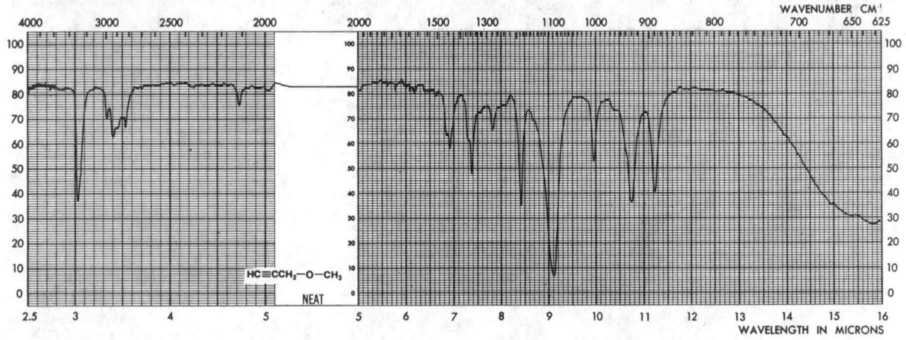

$HC{\equiv}CCH_2{-}O{-}CH_3$

NEAT

D

13,085-0 **3-Butyn-1-ol**
$HC{\equiv}CCH_2CH_2OH$ M.W. 70.09 n_D^{20} 1.4407

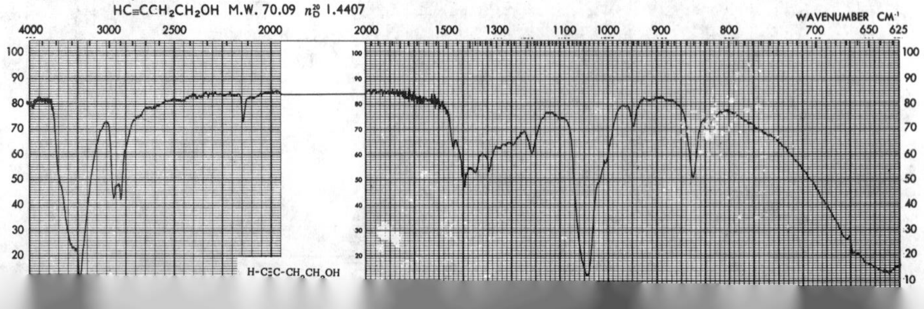

$H{-}C{\equiv}C{-}CH_2CH_2OH$

E

12,976-3 **2-Methyl-3-butyn-2-ol**
$HC{\equiv}CC(CH_3)_2OH$ M.W. 84.12 n_D^{20} 1.4209 b.p. 103-104°

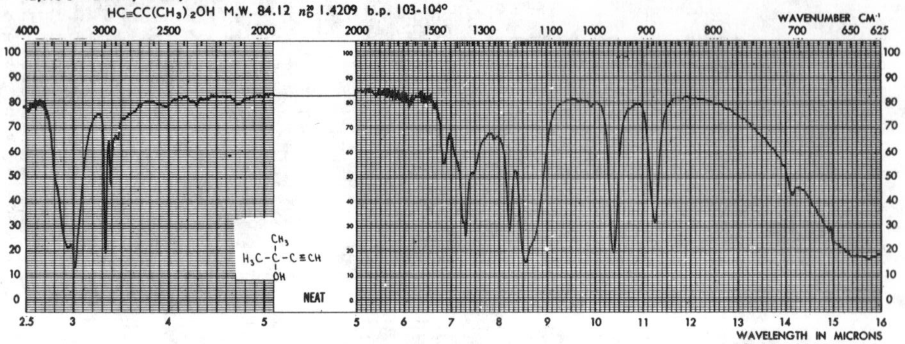

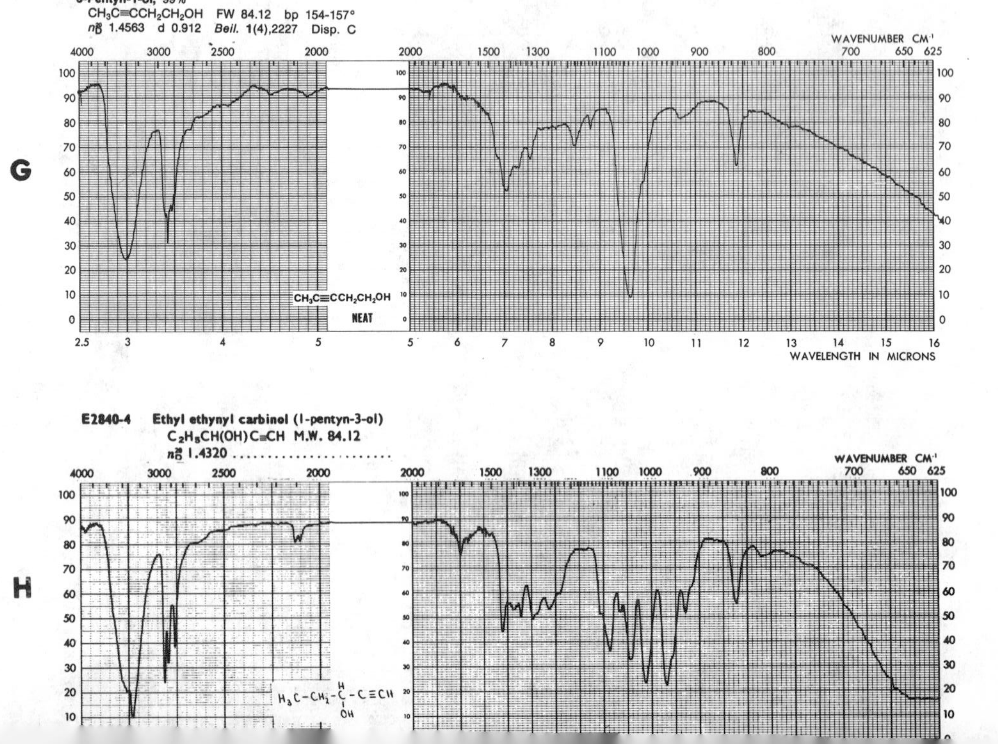

F

13,756-1 **3-Methyl-1-pentyn-3-ol, puriss.**
$C_2H_5C(CH_3)(OH)C{\equiv}CH$ M.W. 98.15 n_D^{20} 1.4311
b.p. 121-122°

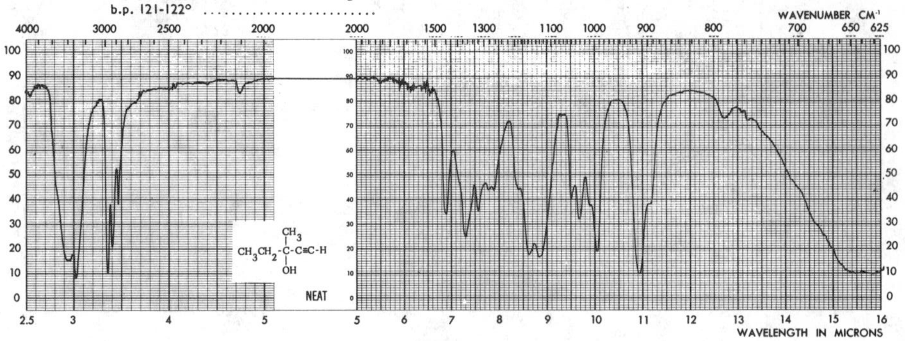

$CH_3CH_2{-}\overset{CH_3}{C}({OH}){-}C{\equiv}C{-}H$

NEAT

G

20,869-8
3-Pentyn-1-ol, 99%
$CH_3C{\equiv}CCH_2CH_2OH$ FW 84.12 bp 154-157°
n_D^{20} 1.4563 d 0.912 *Beil.* 1(4),2227 Disp. C

$CH_3C{\equiv}CCH_2CH_2OH$

NEAT

H

E2840-4 **Ethyl ethynyl carbinol** (1-pentyn-3-ol)
$C_2H_5CH(OH)C{\equiv}CH$ M.W. 84.12
n_D^{20} 1.4320

$H_3C{-}CH_2{-}\overset{H}{C}(OH){-}C{\equiv}CH$

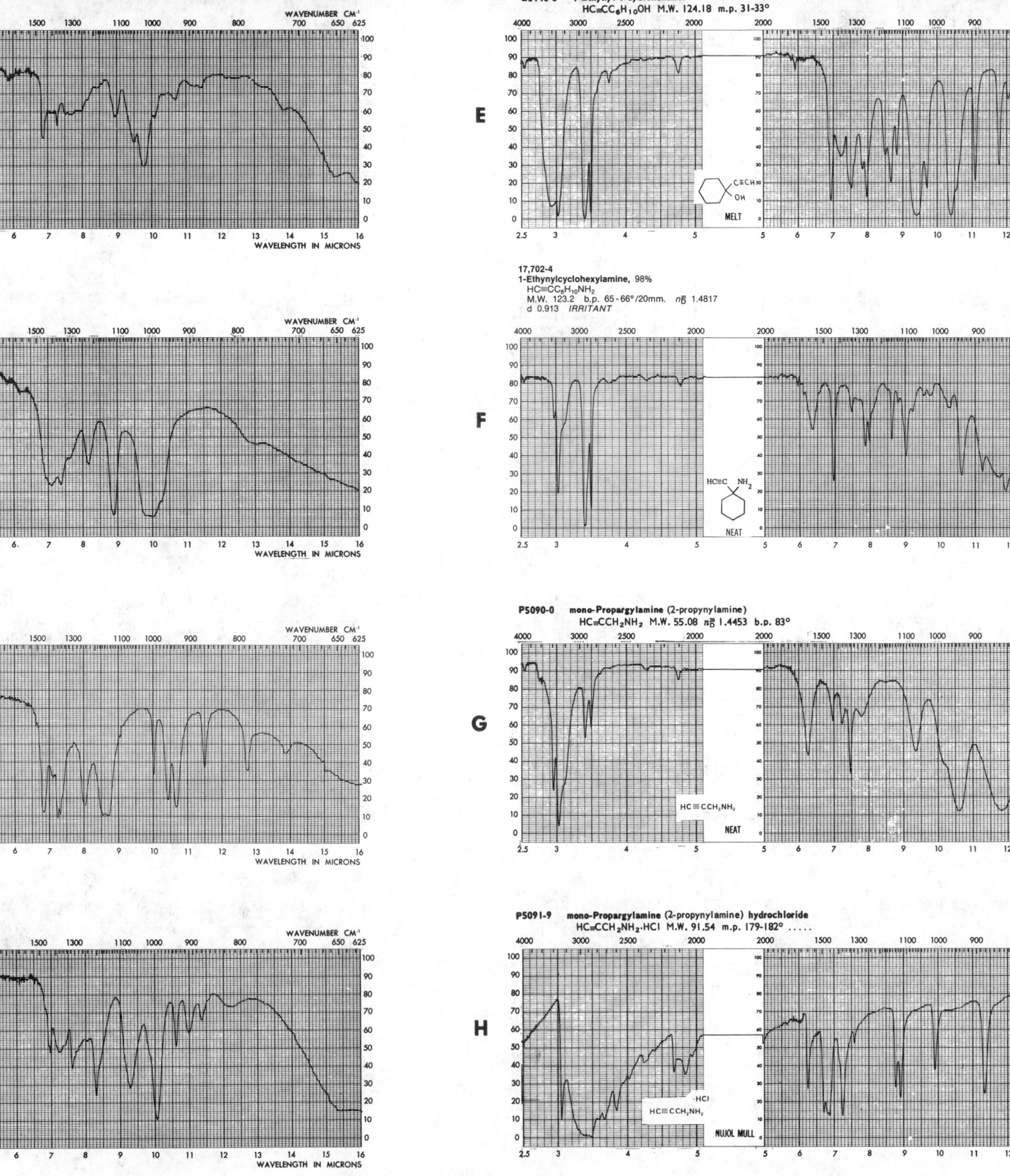

A
n_D^{20} 1.4420 ....

B
B10,320-9 2-Butyne-1,4-diol
$HOCH_2C{\equiv}CCH_2OH$ M.W. 86.09 m.p. 52-54°

C
22,262-3
2,5-Dimethyl-3-hexyne-2,5-diol, 98%
$HOC(CH_3)_2C{\equiv}CC(CH_3)_2OH$ FW 142.20
mp 90-94° bp 121-123°/7mm. *Beil.* 1,501
Disp. C

D
13,086-9 1-Ethynylcyclopentanol
$HC{\equiv}CC_5H_8OH$ M.W. 110.16 n_D^{20} 1.4751

E
E5140-6 1-Ethynyl-1-cyclohexanol
$HC{\equiv}CC_6H_{10}OH$ M.W. 124.18 m.p. 31-33°

F
17,702-4
1-Ethynylcyclohexylamine, 98%
$HC{\equiv}CC_6H_{10}NH_2$
M.W. 123.2 b.p. 65-66°/20mm. n_D^{20} 1.4817
d 0.913 *IRRITANT*

G
P5090-0 mono-Propargylamine (2-propynylamine)
$HC{\equiv}CCH_2NH_2$ M.W. 55.08 n_D^{20} 1.4453 b.p. 83°

H
P5091-9 mono-Propargylamine (2-propynylamine) hydrochloride
$HC{\equiv}CCH_2NH_2{\cdot}HCl$ M.W. 91.54 m.p. 179-182° .....

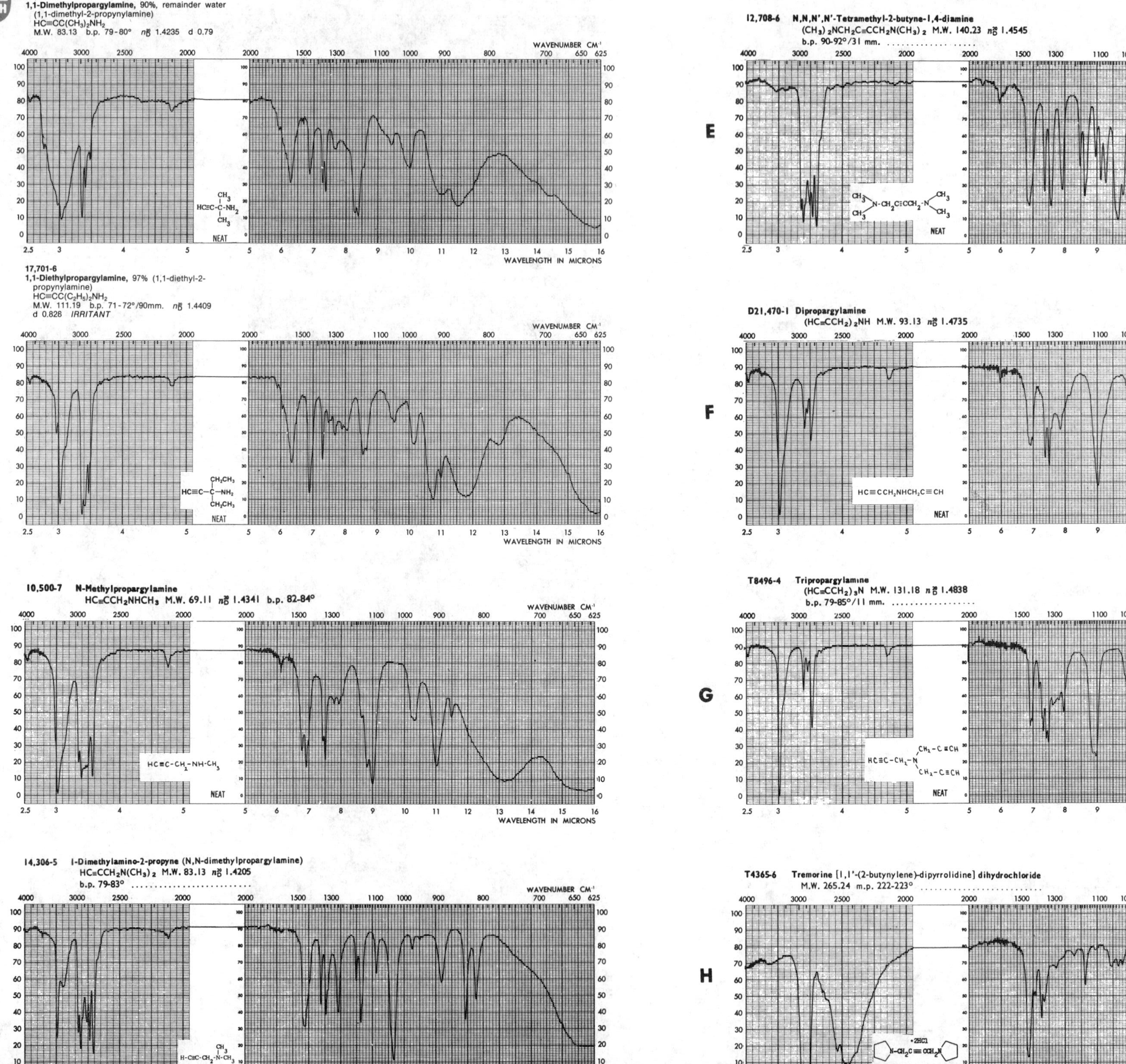
A
17,700-8
1,1-Dimethylpropargylamine, 90%, remainder water
(1,1-dimethyl-2-propynylamine)
HC≡CC(CH3)2NH2
M.W. 83.13 b.p. 79-80° n_D^{20} 1.4235 d 0.79
NEAT
B
17,701-6
1,1-Diethylpropargylamine, 97% (1,1-diethyl-2-propynylamine)
HC≡CC(C2H5)2NH2
M.W. 111.19 b.p. 71-72°/90mm. n_D^{20} 1.4409
d 0.828 IRRITANT
NEAT
C
10,500-7 N-Methylpropargylamine
HC≡CCH2NHCH3 M.W. 69.11 n_D^{20} 1.4341 b.p. 82-84°
HC≡C-CH2-NH-CH3
NEAT
D
14,306-5 1-Dimethylamino-2-propyne (N,N-dimethylpropargylamine)
HC≡CCH2N(CH3)2 M.W. 83.13 n_D^{20} 1.4205
b.p. 79-83°
E
12,708-6 N,N,N',N'-Tetramethyl-2-butyne-1,4-diamine
(CH3)2NCH2C≡CCH2N(CH3)2 M.W. 140.23 n_D^{20} 1.4545
b.p. 90-92°/31 mm.
NEAT
F
D21,470-1 Dipropargylamine
(HC≡CCH2)2NH M.W. 93.13 n_D^{20} 1.4735
HC≡CCH2NHCH2C≡CH
NEAT
G
T8496-4 Tripropargylamine
(HC≡CCH2)3N M.W. 131.18 n_D^{20} 1.4838
b.p. 79-85°/11 mm.
NEAT
H
T4365-6 Tremorine [1,1'-(2-butynylene)-dipyrrolidine] dihydrochloride
M.W. 265.24 m.p. 222-223°
·2HCl
WAVENUMBER CM⁻¹
WAVELENGTH IN MICRONS

LACHRYMATOR

A

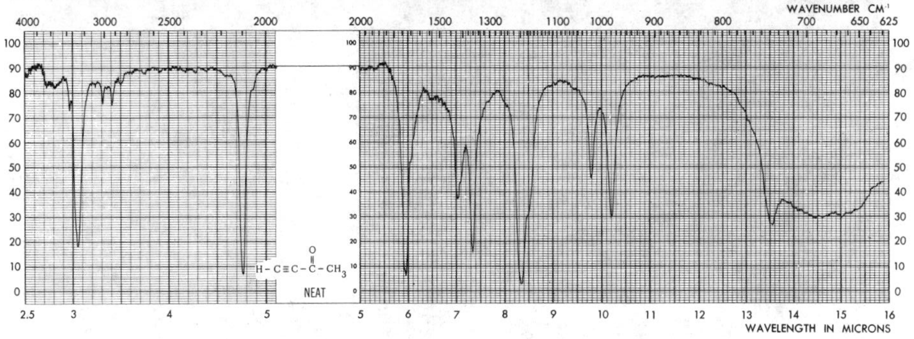

$H-C\equiv C-\overset{O}{\overset{\|}{C}}-CH_3$ NEAT

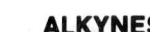

P5140-0 Propiolic acid
$HC\equiv CCO_2H$ M.W. 70.05 n_D^{20} 1.4298
b.p. 55-56°/12 mm. ....

B

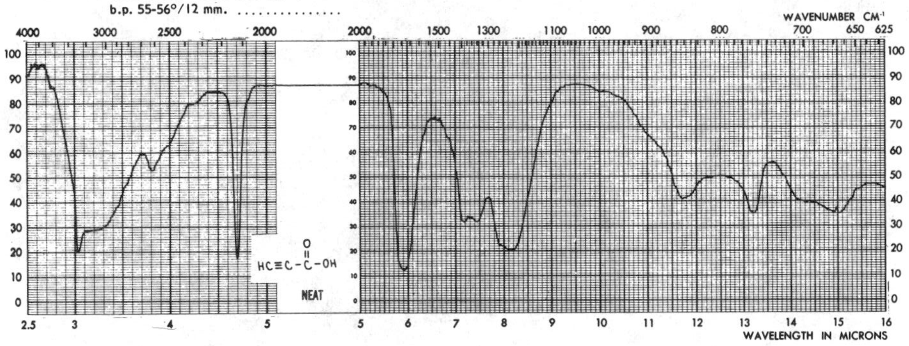

$HC\equiv C-\overset{O}{\overset{\|}{C}}-OH$ NEAT

A1520-7 Acetylenedicarboxylic acid
$HO_2CC\equiv CCO_2H$ M.W. 114.06 m.p. 180° (dec.) ....

C

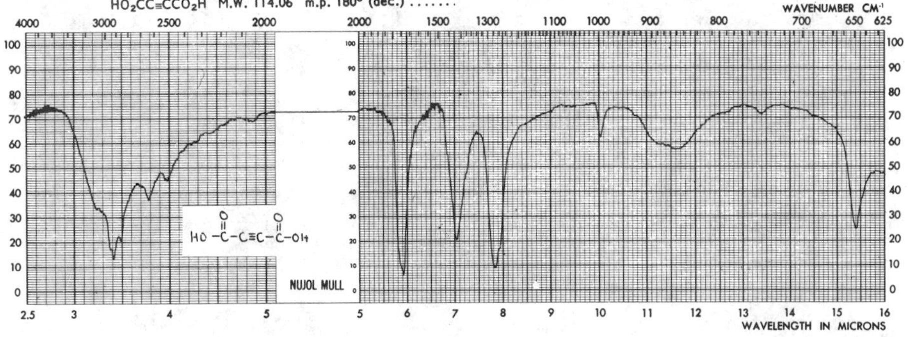

$HO-\overset{O}{\overset{\|}{C}}-C\equiv C-\overset{O}{\overset{\|}{C}}-OH$ NUJOL MULL

A1540-1 Acetylenedicarboxylic acid, monopotassium salt, puriss.
$HO_2CC\equiv CCO_2K$ M.W. 152.15
m.p. 189-190° (dec.) ....

D

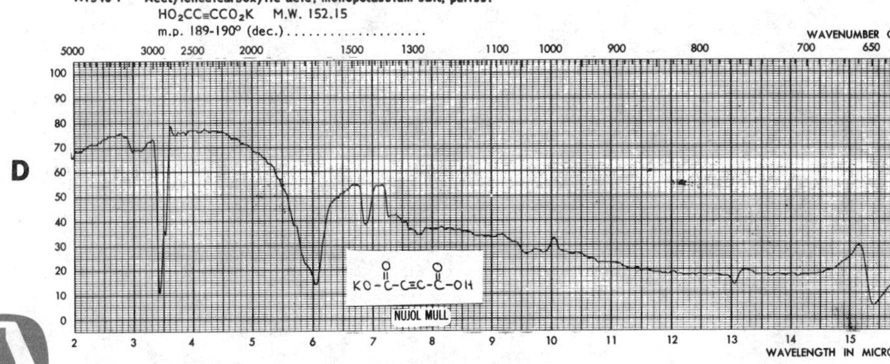
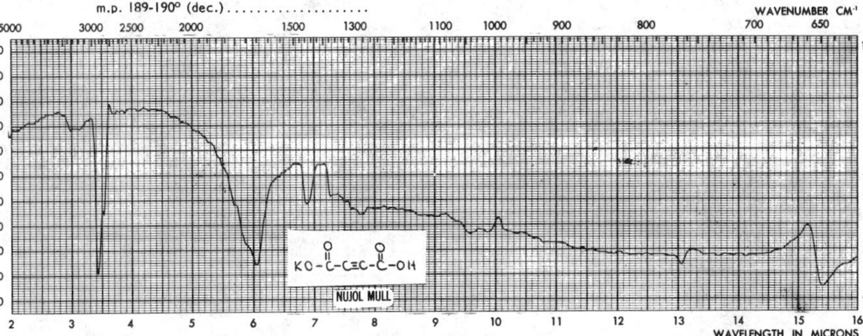

$HC\equiv CCO_2CH_3$ FW 84.07 bp 103-105°
n_D^{20} 1.4080 d 0.945 *Beil.* **2**(1),208 Disp. C

E

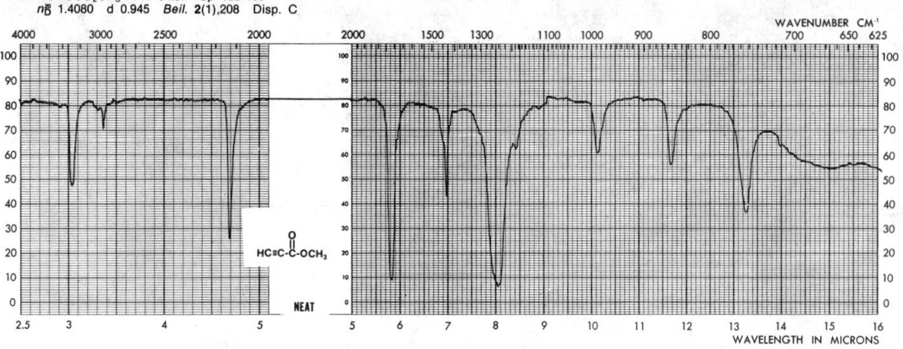

$HC\equiv C-\overset{O}{\overset{\|}{C}}-OCH_3$ NEAT

E4660-7 Ethyl propiolate
$HC\equiv CCO_2C_2H_5$ M.W. 98.10
n_D^{20} 1.4131 ....

F

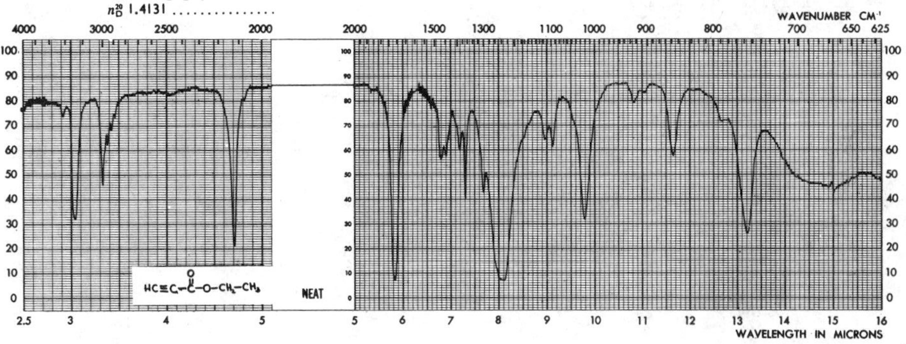

$HC\equiv C-\overset{O}{\overset{\|}{C}}-O-CH_2-CH_3$ NEAT

D13,840-1 Dimethyl acetylenedicarboxylate
$CH_3O_2CC\equiv CCO_2CH_3$ M.W. 142.11
n_D^{20} 1.4540 ....

G

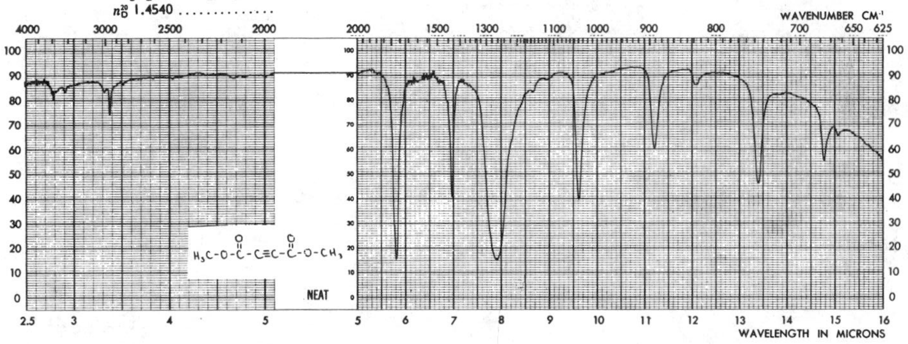

$H_3C-O-\overset{O}{\overset{\|}{C}}-C\equiv C-\overset{O}{\overset{\|}{C}}-O-CH_3$ NEAT

15,944-1
Diethyl acetylenedicarboxylate, 99+%, GOLD LABEL
$C_2H_5O_2CC\equiv CCO_2C_2H_5$
M.W. 170.16 b.p. 107-110°/11mm. n_D^{20} 1.4426
d 1.063 Beil. **2**,803 Fieser **1**,244 **2**,127
LACHRYMATOR

H

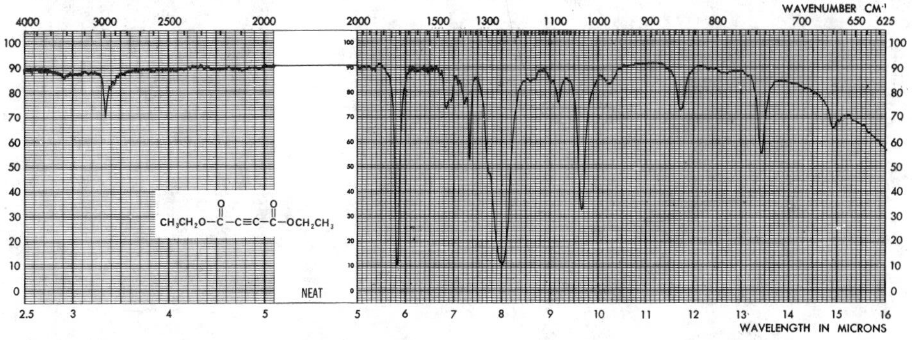

$CH_3CH_2O-\overset{O}{\overset{\|}{C}}-C\equiv C-\overset{O}{\overset{\|}{C}}-OCH_2CH_3$ NEAT

ALDRICH ®

A

B10,325 **2-Butyne-1,4-diol diacetate**

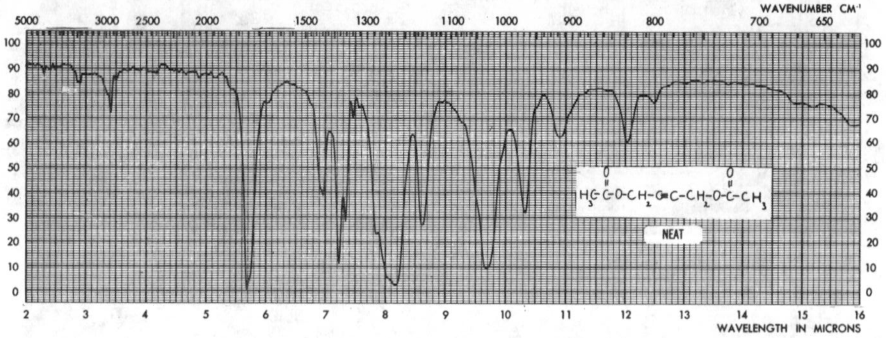

NEAT

B

10,832-4 **Oxotremorine sesquifumarate**
M.W. 380.39 m.p. 102-105°

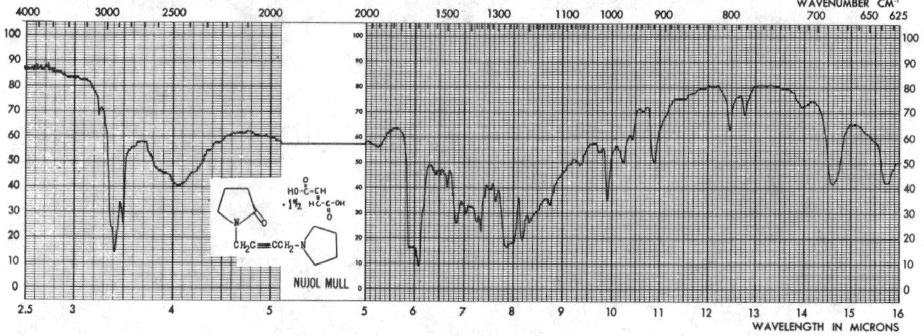

NUJOL MULL

C

11,305-0 **Oxotremorine** [1-[4-(1-pyrrolidinyl)-2-butynyl]-2-pyrrolidinone]
M.W. 206.28 n_D^{20} 1.5145 b.p. 124°/0.1 mm.

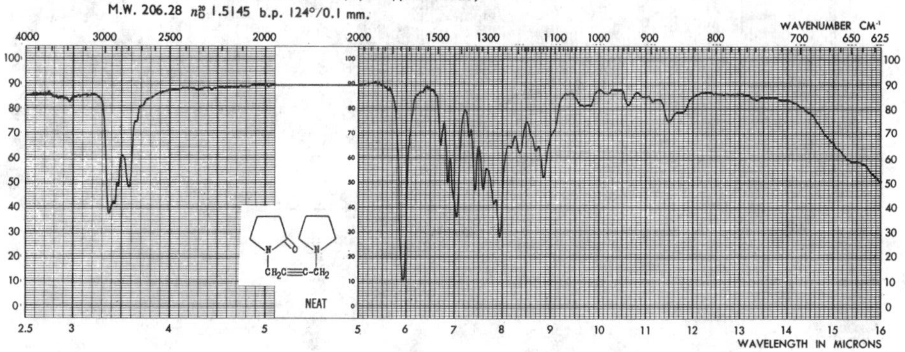

NEAT

D

11,770-6 **Phenylacetylene** (ethynylbenzene)
$C_6H_5C{\equiv}CH$ M.W. 102.14 n_D^{20} 1.5502
b.p. 142-144°

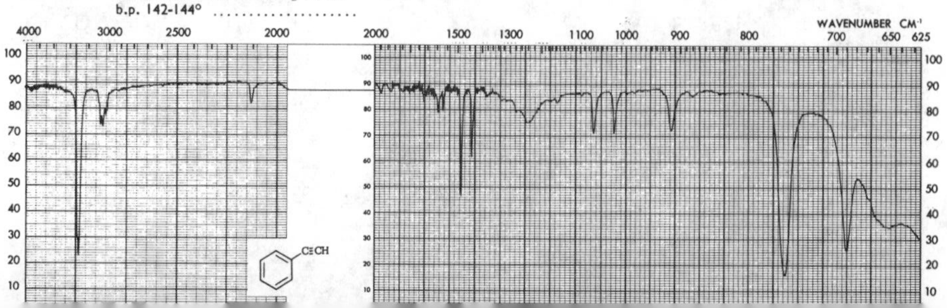

E

16,124-1
1-Phenyl-1-propyne, 99%
$C_6H_5C{\equiv}CCH_3$ FW 116.16 bp 185° n_D^{20} 1.5644
d 0.928 *Beil.* 5,514 Disp. C

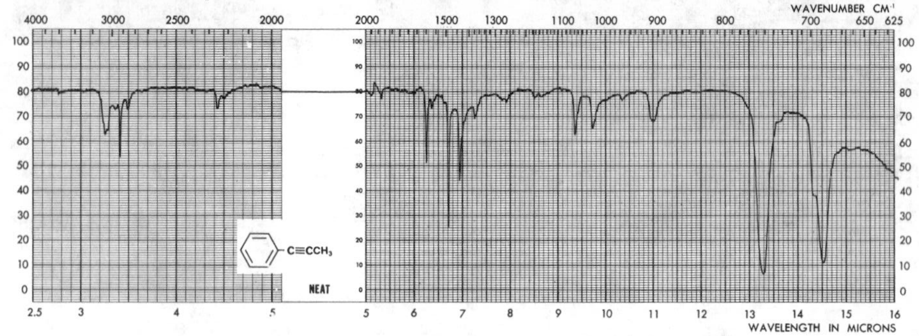

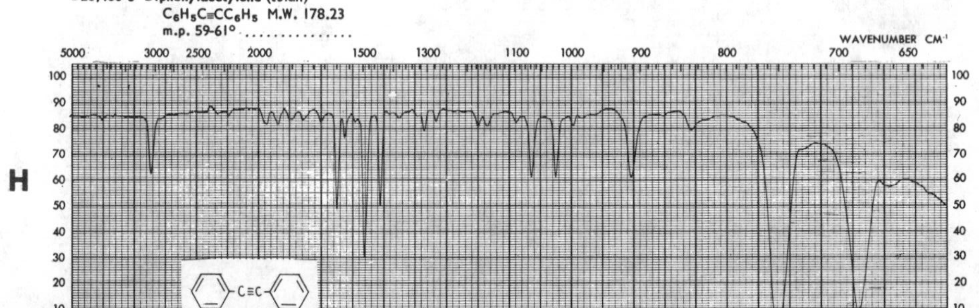

NEAT

F

11,884-2 **5-Phenyl-1-pentyne**
$C_6H_5(CH_2)_3C{\equiv}CH$ M.W. 144.22
n_D^{20} 1.5142

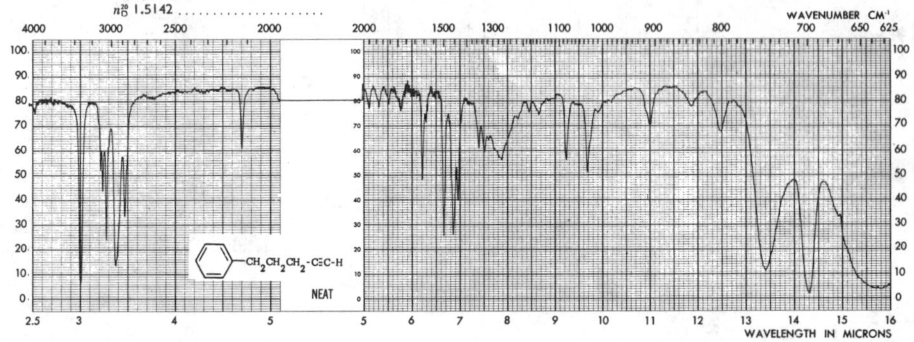

NEAT

G

11,883-4 **6-Phenyl-2-hexyne**
$C_6H_5(CH_2)_3C{\equiv}CCH_3$ M.W. 158.24
n_D^{20} 1.5209

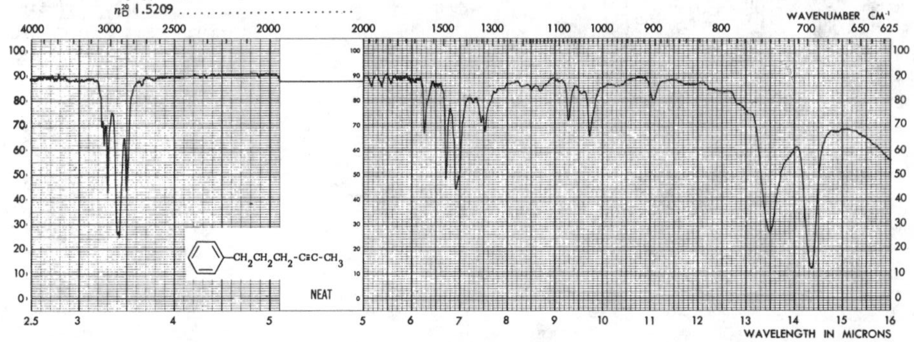

NEAT

H

D20,480-3 **Diphenylacetylene** (tolan)
$C_6H_5C{\equiv}CC_6H_5$ M.W. 178.23
m.p. 59-61°

A

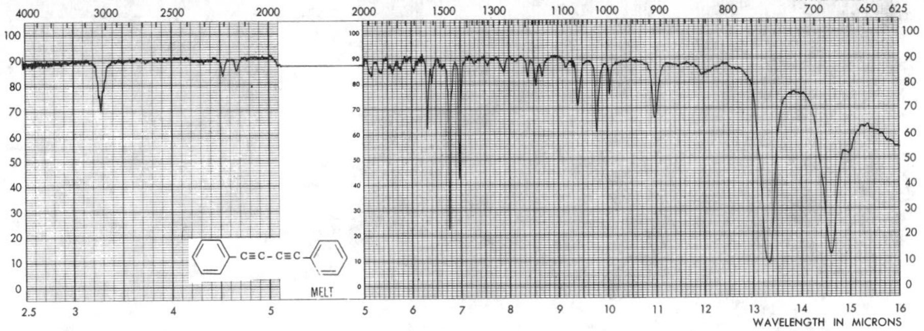

M.W. 202.25 m.p. 86-87° Beil. 5,693

B

21,299-7
2-Phenyl-3-butyn-2-ol, 98+%
$HC{\equiv}CC(C_6H_5)(OH)CH_3$ FW 146.19 mp 47-49°
bp 102-103°/12mm. *Beil.* 6(2),559 Disp. C

C

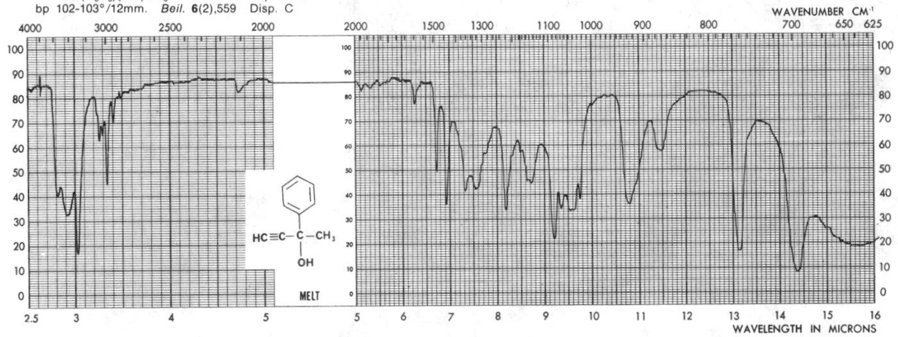

11,500-2 α,α,γ-Triphenylpropargyl alcohol (1,1,3-triphenyl-2-propyn-1-ol)
$C_6H_5C{\equiv}CC(C_6H_5)_2OH$ M.W. 284.36
m.p. 81-82°

D

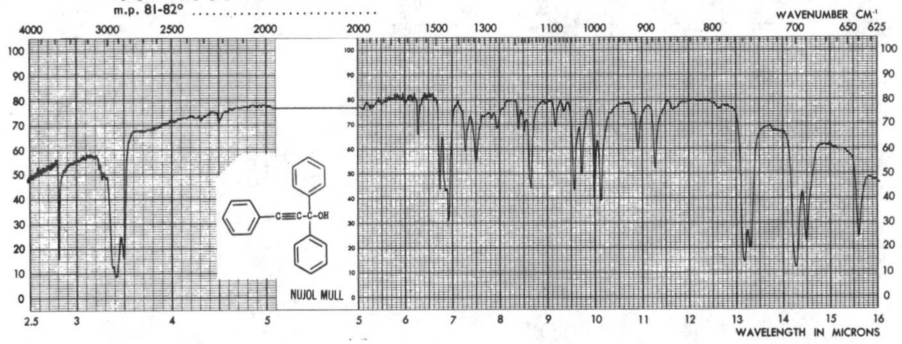

13,465-1 1,1,4,4-Tetraphenyl-2-butyne-1,4-diol
$HOC(C_6H_5)_2C{\equiv}CC(C_6H_5)_2OH$ M.W. 390.48
m.p. 191-193°

E

$C_6H_5C{\equiv}CCH(OC_2H_5)_2$ M.W. 204.27 n_D^{20} 1.5170
b.p. 99-100°/2 mm.

F

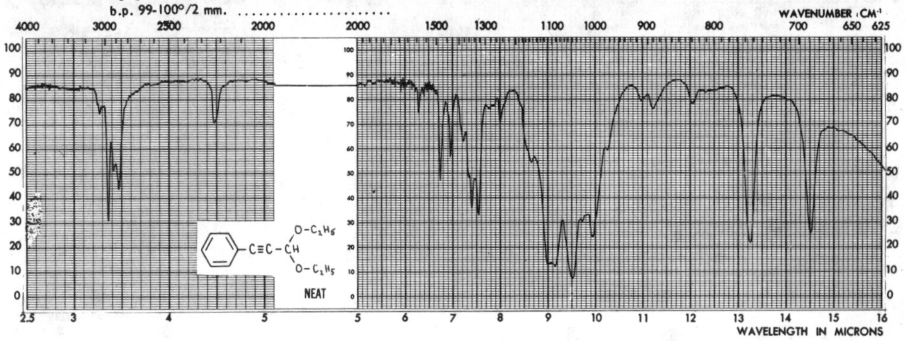

B2990-3 N-Benzylpropargylamine (N-2-propynylbenzylamine)
$C_6H_5CH_2NHCH_2C{\equiv}CH$ M.W. 145.21
n_D^{20} 1.5378

G

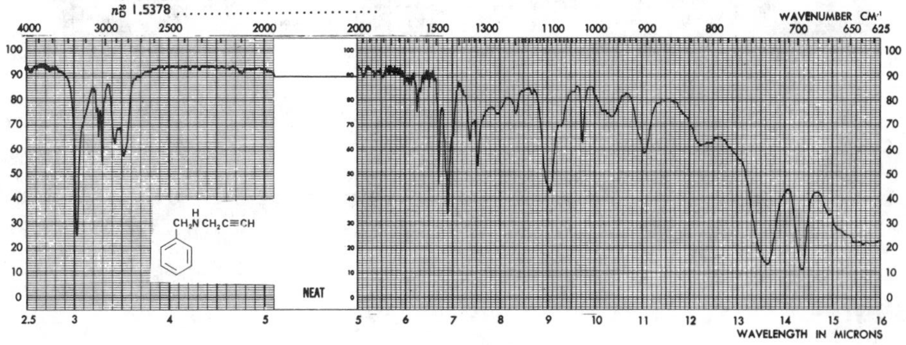

M7425-3 N-Methyl-N-propargylbenzylamine
$C_6H_5CH_2N(CH_3)CH_2C{\equiv}CH$ M.W. 159.23 n_D^{20} 1.5213

H

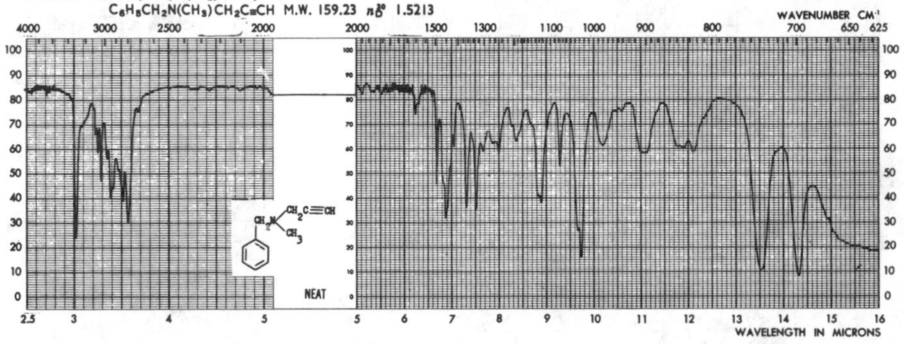

19,173-6
N-Methyl-*N*-propargylbenzylamine hydrochloride, 99%
(pargyline)
$C_6H_5CH_2N(CH_3)CH_2C{\equiv}CH \cdot HCl$ FW 195.69
mp 160-163° Disp. C

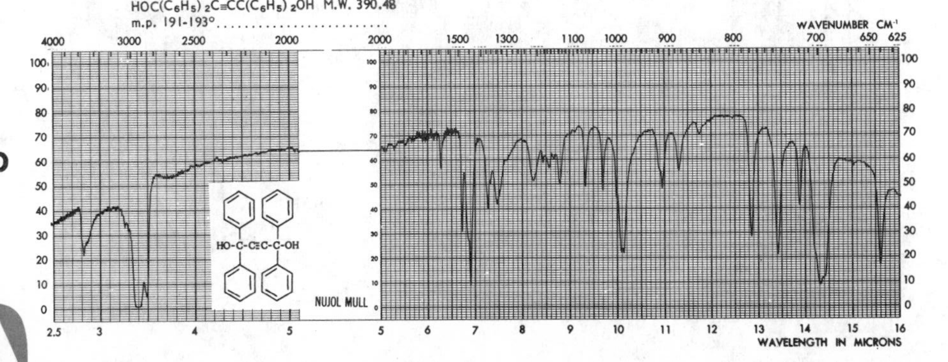

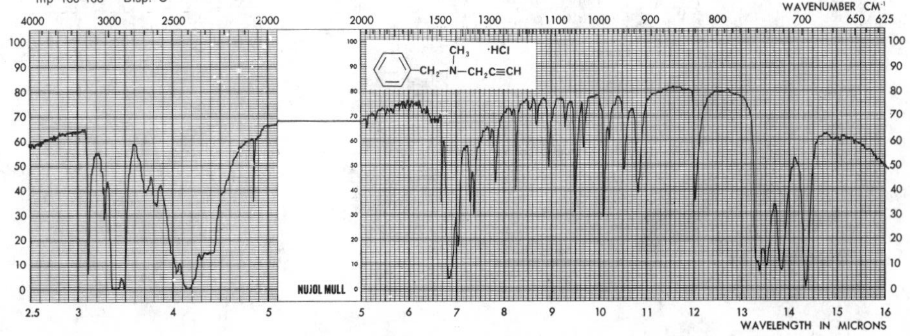

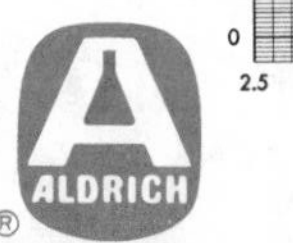

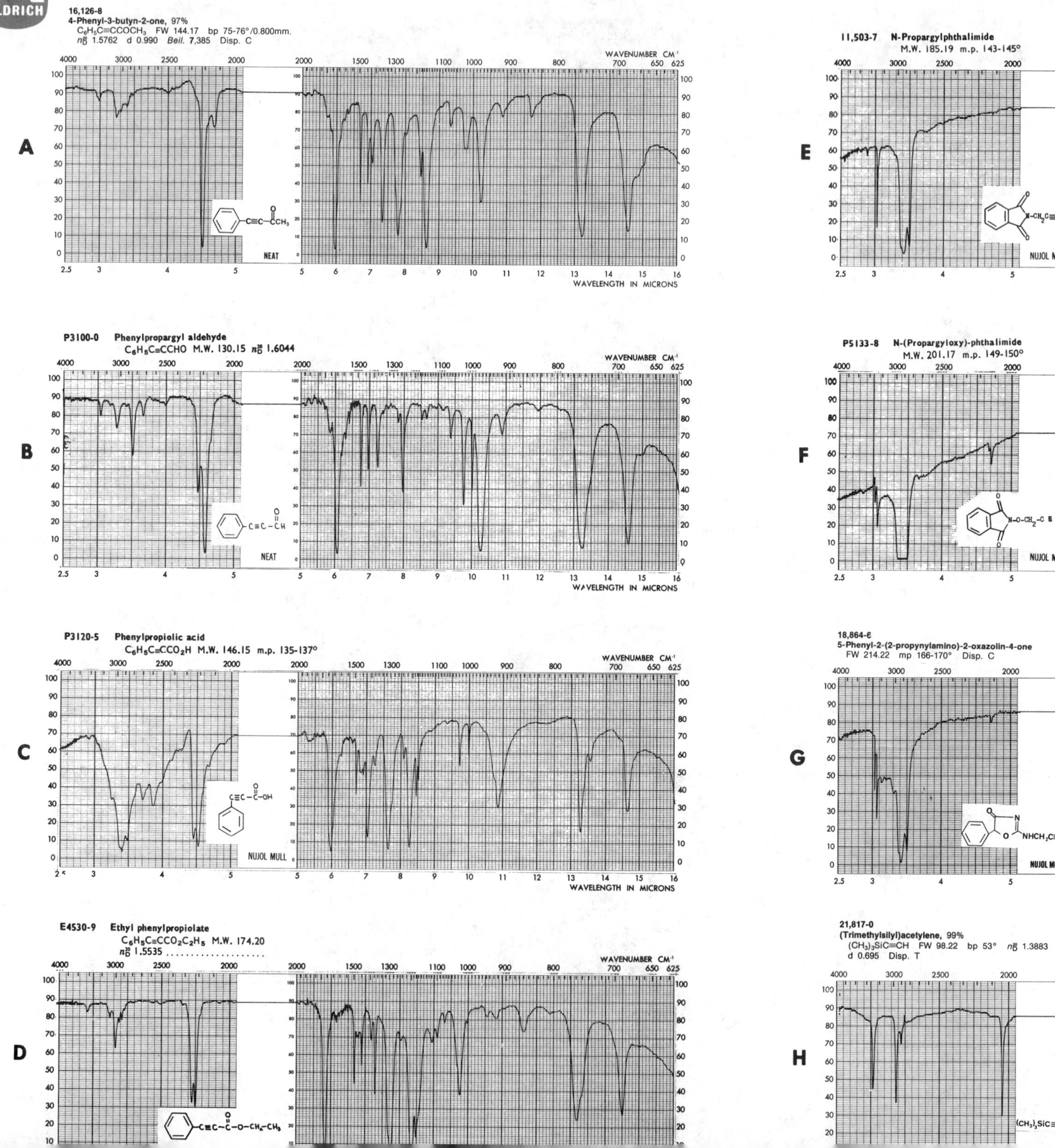

A
16,126-8
4-Phenyl-3-butyn-2-one, 97%
$C_6H_5C{\equiv}CCOCH_3$ FW 144.17 bp 75-76°/0.800mm.
n_D^{20} 1.5762 d 0.990 *Beil.* 7,385 Disp. C
NEAT

B
P3100-0 Phenylpropargyl aldehyde
$C_6H_5C{\equiv}CCHO$ M.W. 130.15 n_D^{20} 1.6044
NEAT

C
P3120-5 Phenylpropiolic acid
$C_6H_5C{\equiv}CCO_2H$ M.W. 146.15 m.p. 135-137°
NUJOL MULL

D
E4530-9 Ethyl phenylpropiolate
$C_6H_5C{\equiv}CCO_2C_2H_5$ M.W. 174.20
n_D^{20} 1.5535

E
11,503-7 N-Propargylphthalimide
M.W. 185.19 m.p. 143-145°
NUJOL MULL

F
P5133-8 N-(Propargyloxy)-phthalimide
M.W. 201.17 m.p. 149-150°
NUJOL MULL

G
18,864-6
5-Phenyl-2-(2-propynylamino)-2-oxazolin-4-one
FW 214.22 mp 166-170° Disp. C
NUJOL MULL

H
21,817-0
(Trimethylsilyl)acetylene, 99%
$(CH_3)_3SiC{\equiv}CH$ FW 98.22 bp 53° n_D^{20} 1.3883
d 0.695 Disp. T

SCHIFF BASES, AZOBENZENES, INDICATORS & DYES

Due to the nature and use of most of the compounds presented in this section, the purities of the compounds vary between 80 and 100%. The common impurities are generally inorganic.

The Schiff bases (spectra 1447C—1449A) display their C=N stretch at the same position as the C=C stretch of the aromatic ring. The group is therefore very difficult to diagnose.

The azo group (N=N) is also difficult to determine by infrared analysis. When the azobenzenes are substituted in the position para to the azo group, strong absorption occurs near 7.3 and 8.7 μ (1370 and 1150 cm^{-1}). There are many bands in compounds of this type throughout the entire region between 6.2 and 10 μ (1615 – 1000 cm^{-1}).

In the spectra (1476A—1482G) of various pairs of sulfonephthalein type indicators and their corresponding sodium salts, it is interesting to note the broadness of the absorption bands in the sodium salt versus the relatively sharp and distinct peaks in the free sulfonephthaleins.

FW 258.34 mp 102-105° Disp. C,D

A

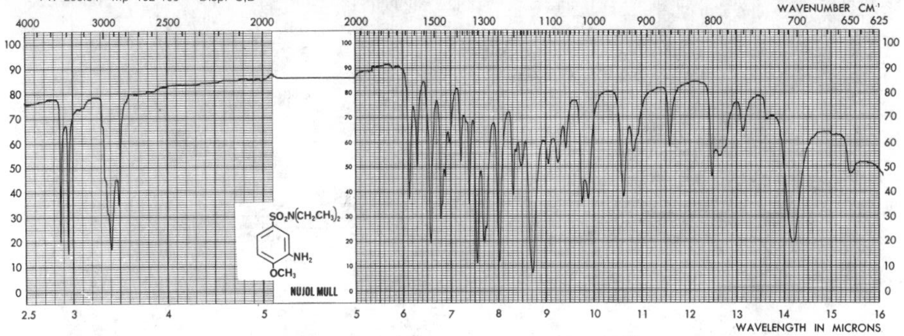

20,152-9
Fast Blue BB (Azoic Diazo No. 20, C.I. 37175)
FW 300.36 mp 98-100° *Beil.* **13**(3),2170
Disp. C,D

B

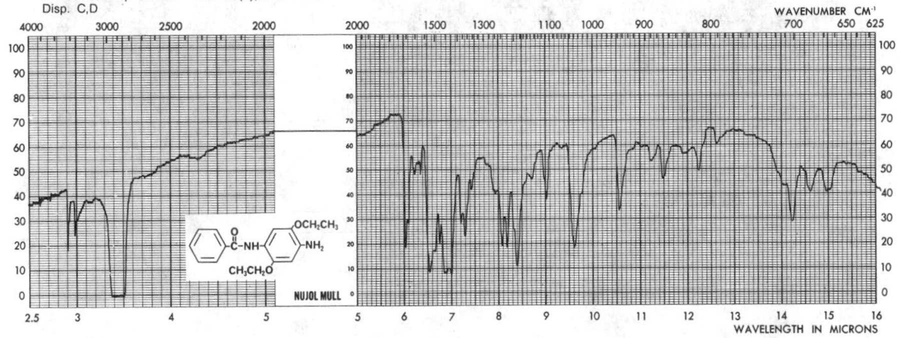

20,154-5
Fast Blue RR (Azoic Diazo No. 24, C.I. 37155)
FW 272.31 mp 165-168° *Beil.* **13**(3),2170
Disp. C,D

C

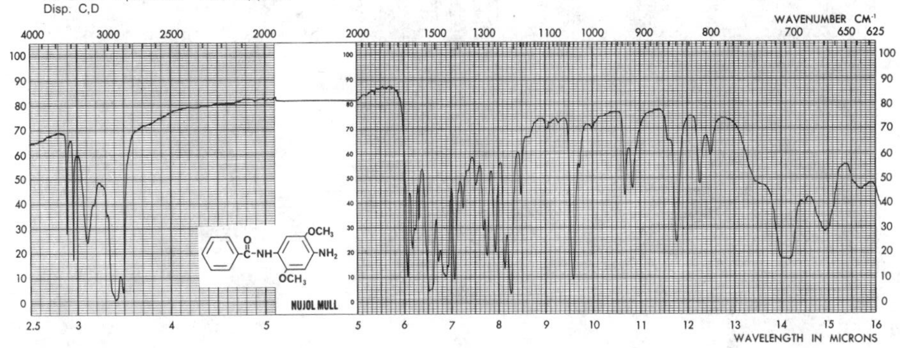

21,225-3
Disperse Yellow 9 [C.I. 10375, *N*-(2,4-dinitrophenyl)-*p*-phenylenediamine]
$(O_2N)_2C_6H_3NHC_6H_4NH_2$ FW 274.24 mp 187-190°
Beil. **13**,79 Disp. C,D

D

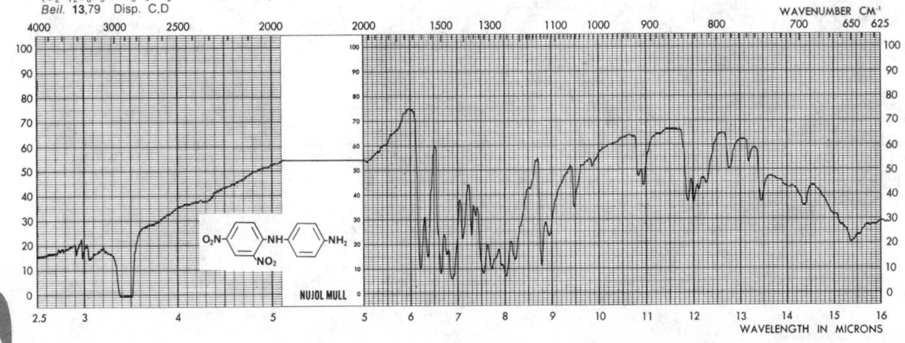

Disperse Yellow 42 (C.I. 10338)
FW 369.40 mp 156-158° *Beil.* **14**,709 Disp. C,D

E

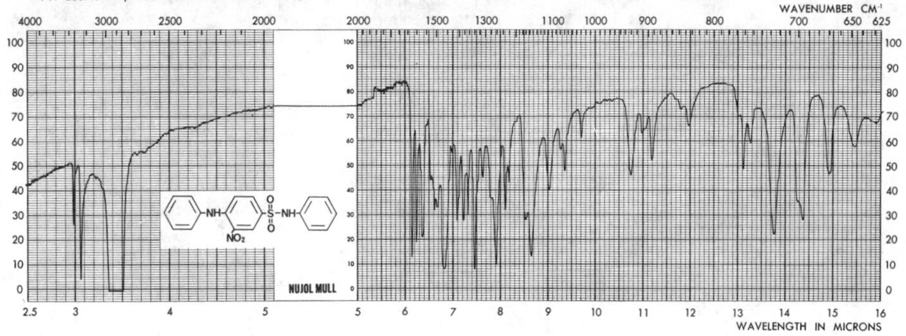

19,962-1
Naphthol Yellow S (Acid Yellow 1, C.I. 10316)
FW 358.20 *Beil.* **11**,275 Disp. C,D

F

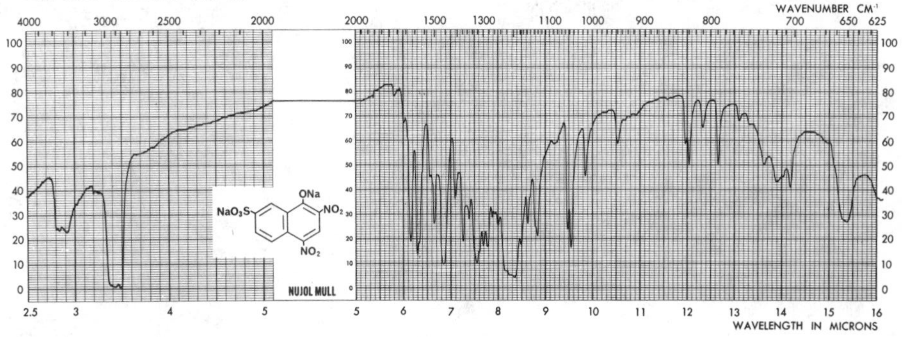

20,158-8
Fast Violet B (Azoic Diazo No. 41, C.I. 37165)
FW 256.31 mp 185-188° *Beil.* **13**(3),1611
Disp. C,D

G

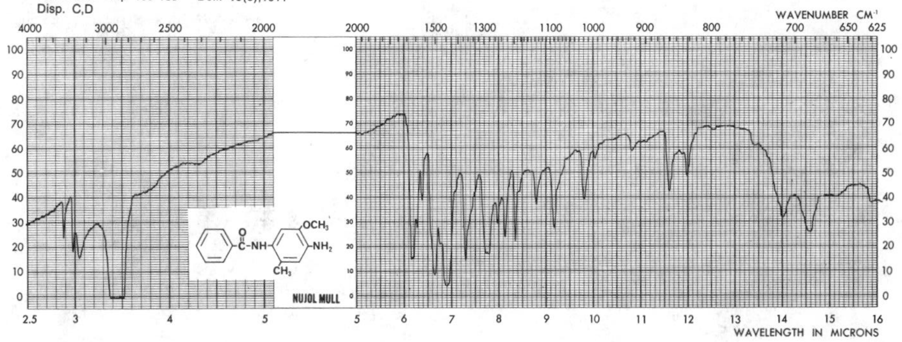

86,118-9
Hematoxylin, certified (C.I. 75290, Natural Black 1)
FW 302.29 mp 245° (dec.) Disp. C,D

H

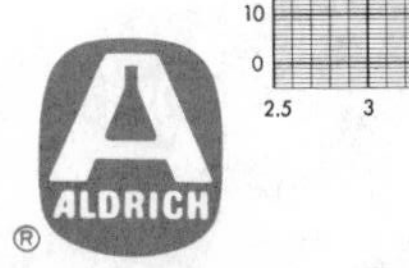

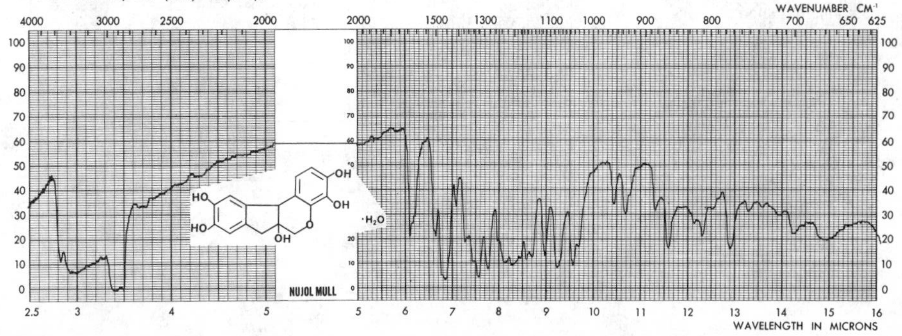

A

21,192-3
Disperse Yellow 42 (C.I. 10338)
FW 369.40 mp 156-158° *Beil.* **14**,709 Disp. C,D

NUJOL MULL

B

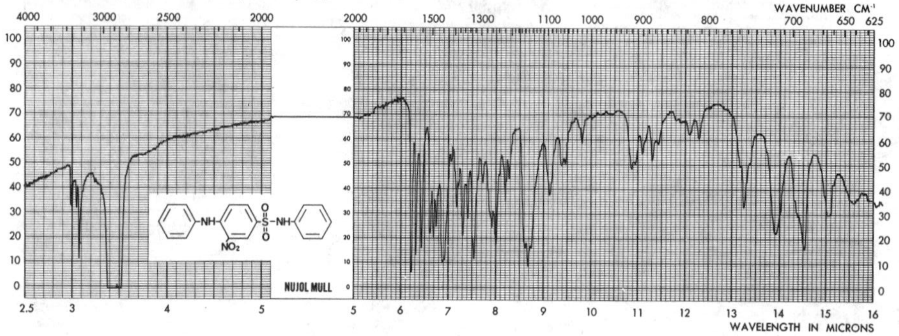

86,150-2
Lucifer Yellow CH
FW 457.25 Disp. C,D

NUJOL MULL

C

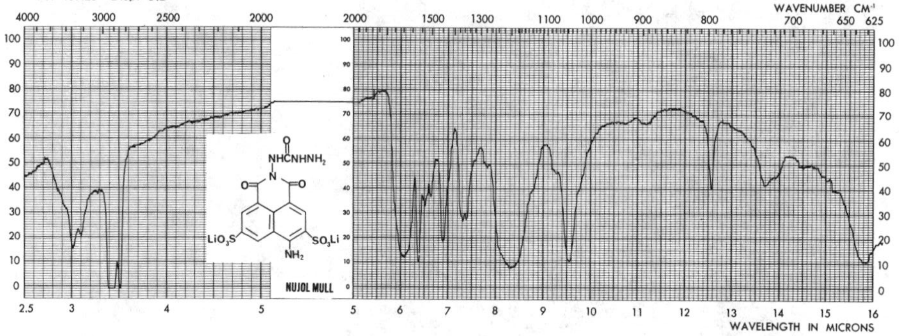

19,829-3
Martius Yellow, biological stain and chemical indicator (2,4-dinitro-1-naphthol)
$(O_2N)_2C_{10}H_5OH$ FW 234.17 mp 130-133°
Beil. **6**,617 Disp. C,D

KBr

D

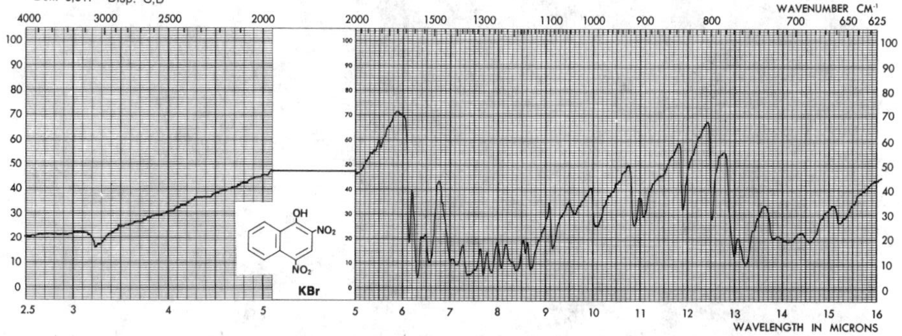

20,146-4
Variamine Blue RT salt (Azoic Diazo No. 22, C.I. 37240)
FW 293.30 *Beil.* **16**,602 Disp. C,D

E

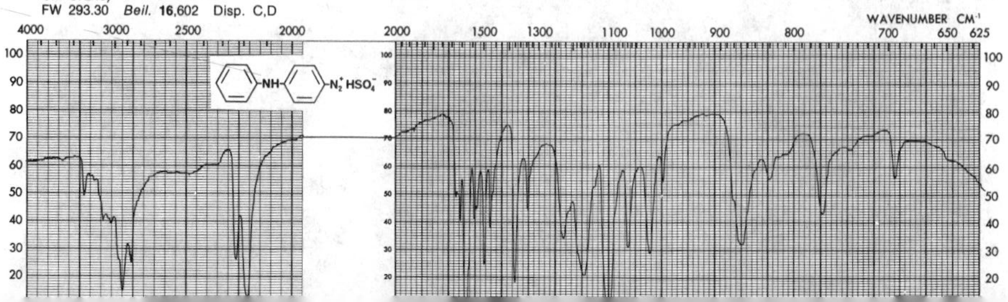

20,123-5
Fast Garnet GBC salt (Azoic Diazo No. 4, C.I. 37210)
FW 334.36 Disp. C,D

NUJOL MULL

F

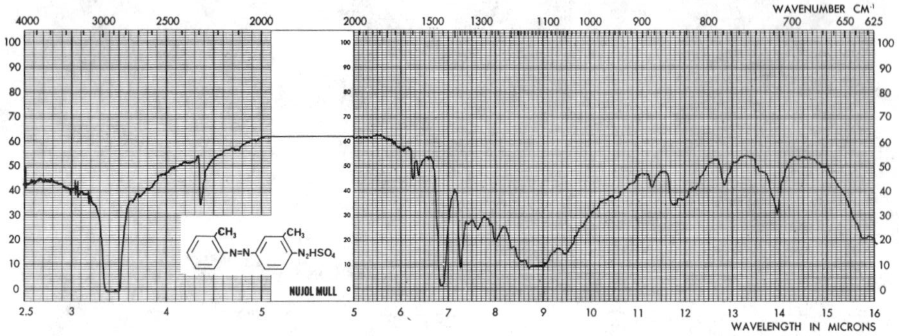

20,135-9
Fast Dark Blue R salt (Azoic Diazo No. 51, C.I. 37195)
FW 486.76 Disp. C,D

NUJOL MULL

G

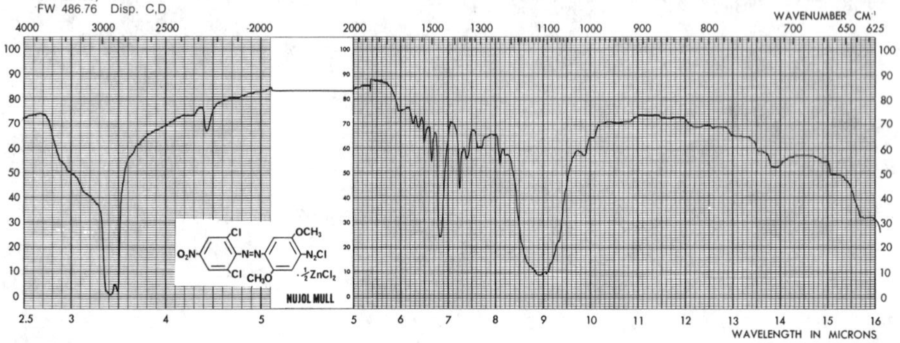

20,151-0
Fast Black K salt (Azoic Diazo No. 38, C.I. 37190)
FW 417.87 mp 150° (dec.) Disp. C,D

KBr

H

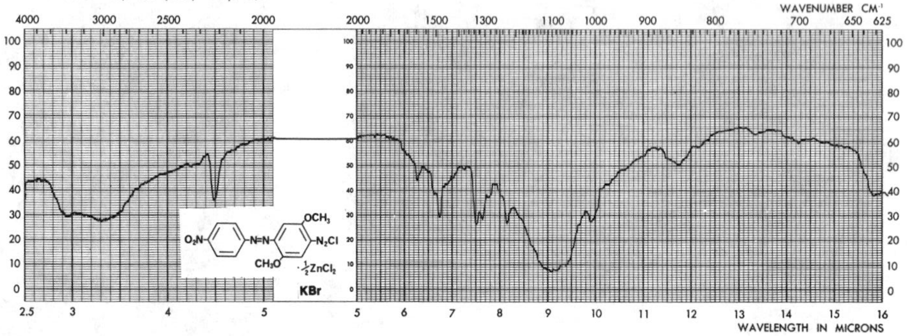

20,147-2
Diazo Red RC (Azoic Diazo No. 10, C.I. 37120, Fast Red RC salt)
FW 273.18 Disp. C,D

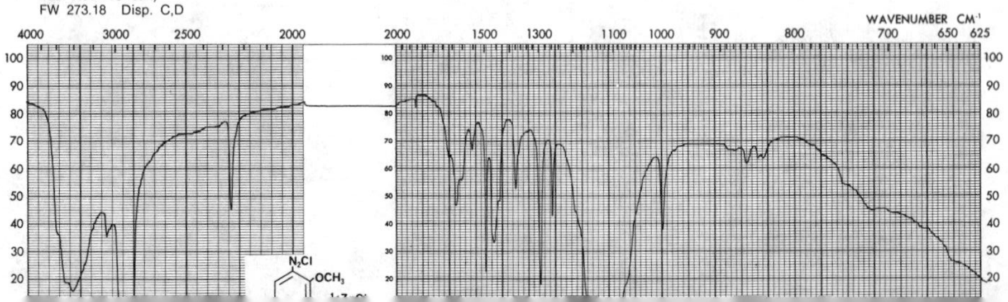

A

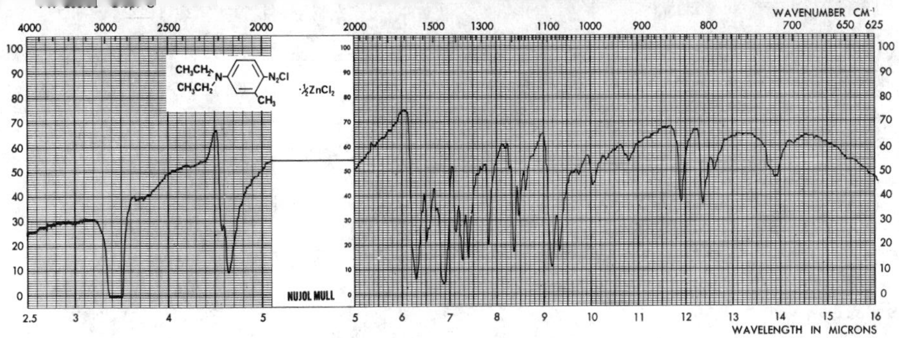

B

20,129-4
Fast Red PDC salt (Azoic Diazo No. 14, C.I. 37151)
FW 373.93 Disp. C,D

C

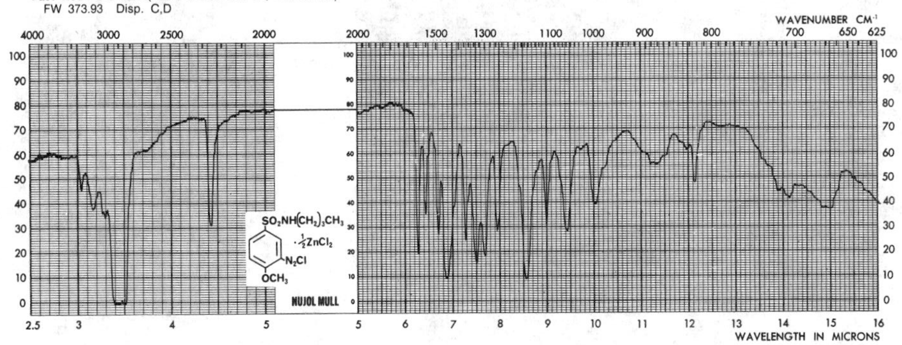

20,127-8
Fast Red ITR salt (Azoic Diazo No. 42, C.I. 37150)
FW 373.92 Disp. C,D

D

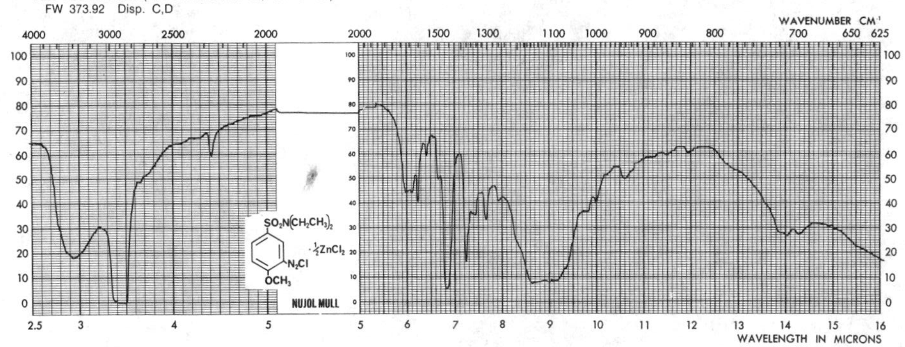

20,142-1
Fast Blue B salt (Azoic Diazo No. 48, C.I. 37235)
FW 475.46 *Beil.* **16**(2),292 Disp. C,D

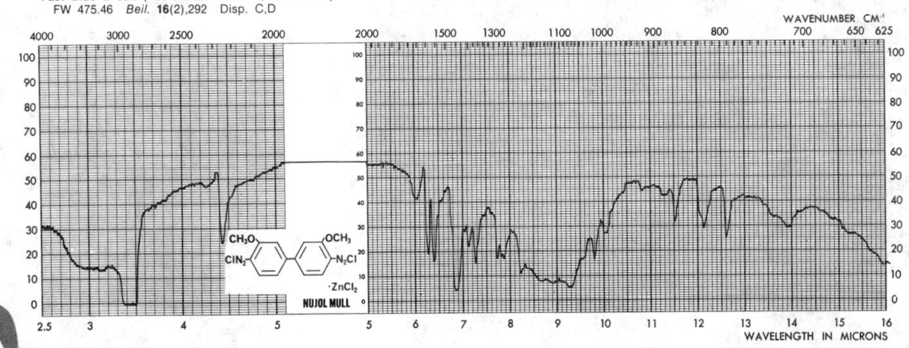

E

...ast Blue BB salt (Azoic Diazo No. 20, C.I. 37175)
FW 415.94 mp 157° (dec.) Disp. C,D

F

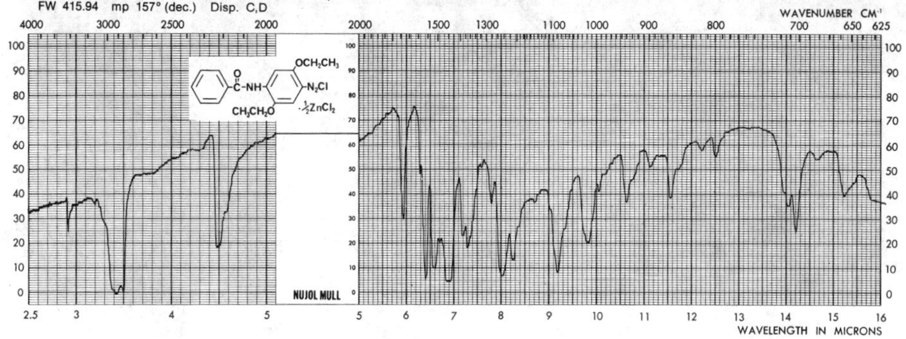

20,159-6
Fast Violet B salt, purified (Azoic Diazo No. 41, C.I. 37165)
FW 371.89 Disp. C,D

G

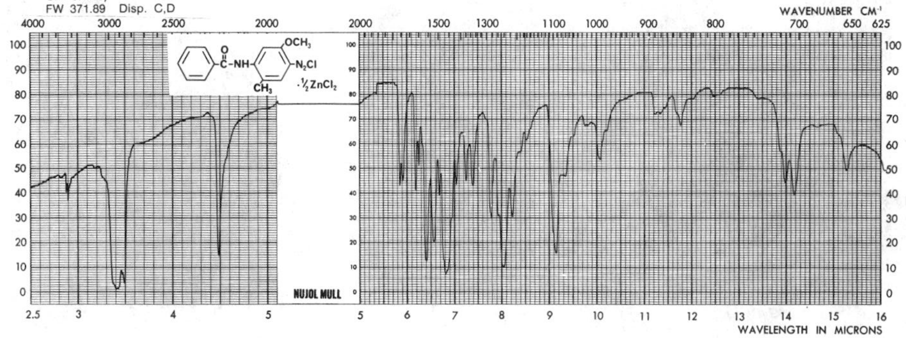

20,122-7
Fast Blue RR salt (Azoic Diazo No. 24, C.I. 37155)
FW 387.89 Disp. C,D

H

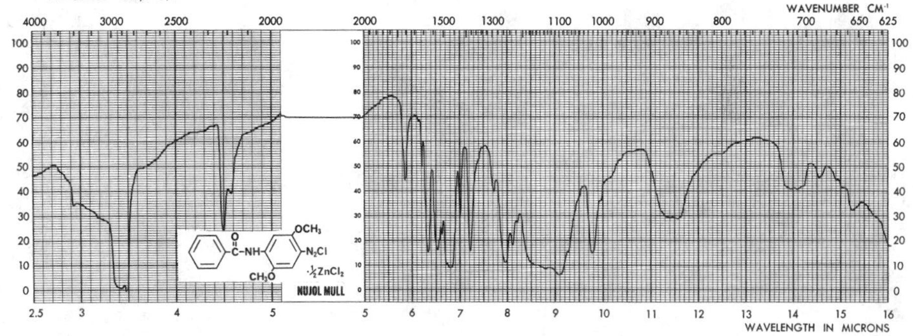

20,155-3
Fast Red TR salt (Azoic Diazo No. 11, C.I. 37085)
FW 440.88 Disp. C,D

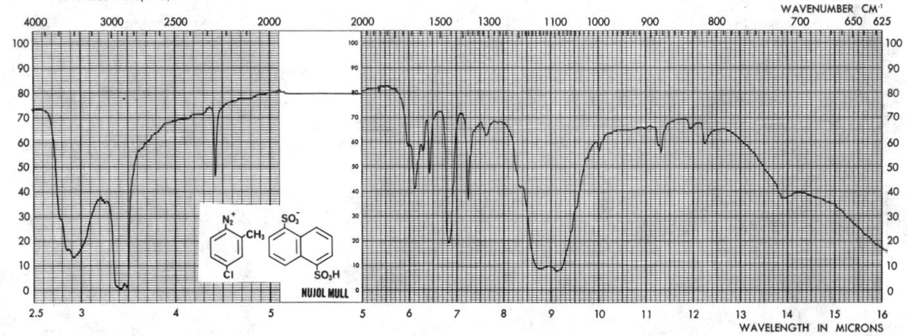

A 20,125-1
Fast Red B salt (Azoic Diazo No. 5, C.I. 37125)
FW 467.44 *Beil.* **16**(2),287 Disp. C,D

B 20,124-3
Fast Red AL salt (Azoic Diazo No. 36, C.I. 37275)
FW 270.68 Disp. C,D

C 18,027-0
N-*tert*.-Butyl-α-phenylnitrone
$C_6H_5CH{=}N(O)C(CH_3)_3$
M.W. 177.25 m.p. 73-74°

D 12,229-7 **N,N'-Terephthalylidenedi-p-toluidine**
C_6H_4-1,4-$(CH{:}NC_6H_4CH_3)_2$ M.W. 312.42
m.p. 184.5-187°, 264-265°

E 13,603-4 **o-(o-Hydroxybenzylideneamino)-phenol** (salicylidene-o-aminophenol)
$HOC_6H_4CH{:}NC_6H_4OH$ M.W. 213.24
m.p. 185-187°

F G1040-7 **Glyoxalbis-(o-hydroxyanil)** [2,2'-(ethanediylidenedinitrilo)-diphenol]
$HOC_6H_4N{:}CHCH{:}NC_6H_4OH$ M.W. 240.26
m.p. 201-205°

G 15,822-4
N-(p-Methoxybenzylidene)-p-butylaniline (MBBA)
$CH_3(CH_2)_3C_6H_4N{=}CHC_6H_4OCH_3$
M.W. 267.37 n_D^{20} 1.5496

H 14,284-0 **α-(4-Bromophenylimino)-4,6-dibromo-o-cresol**
$BrC_6H_4N{:}CHC_6H_2(Br)_2OH$ M.W. 433.94
m.p. 153-156°

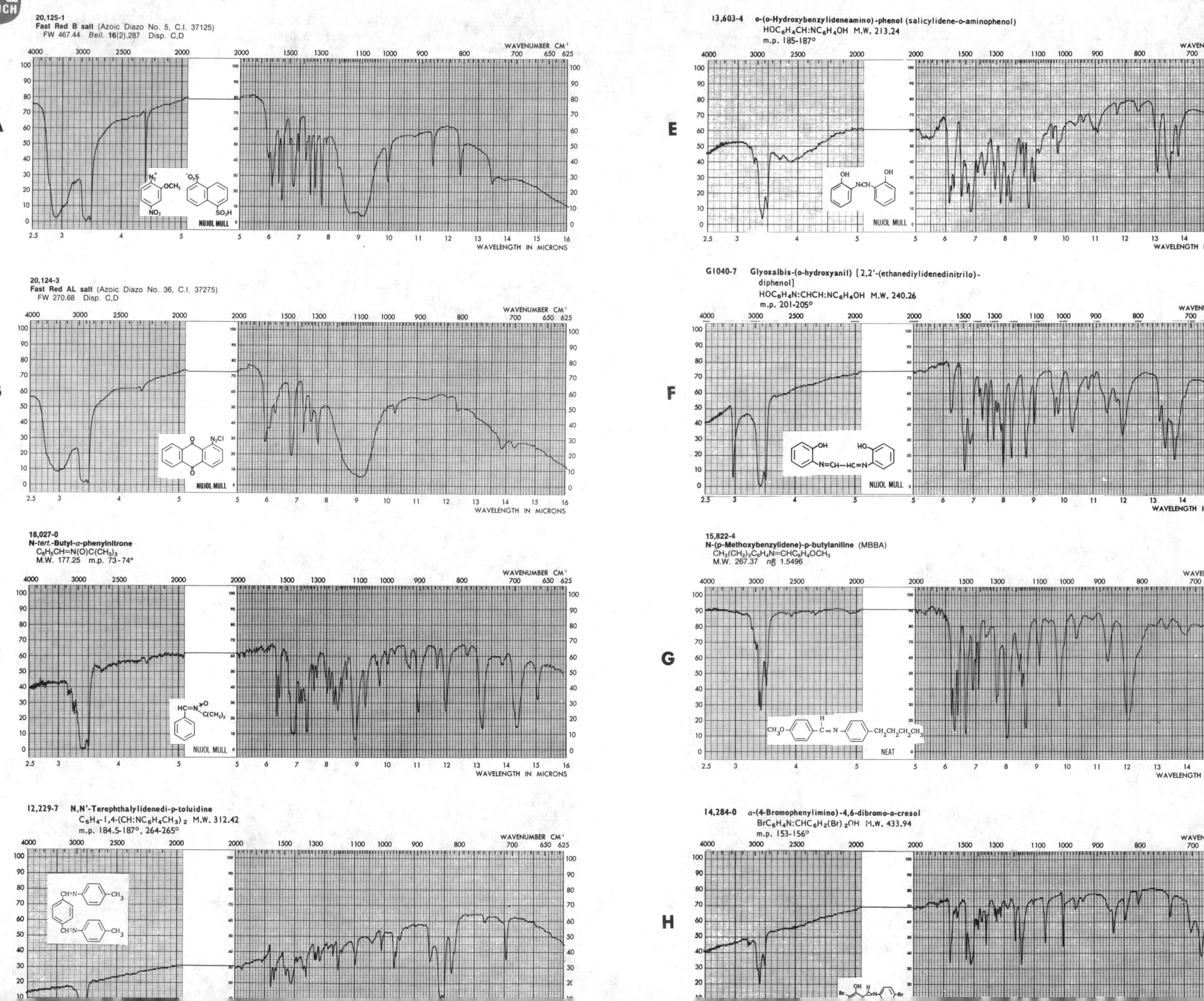

A

12,585-2 Isolar green H
M.W. 581.46 m.p. 219-221°

NUJOL MULL

E

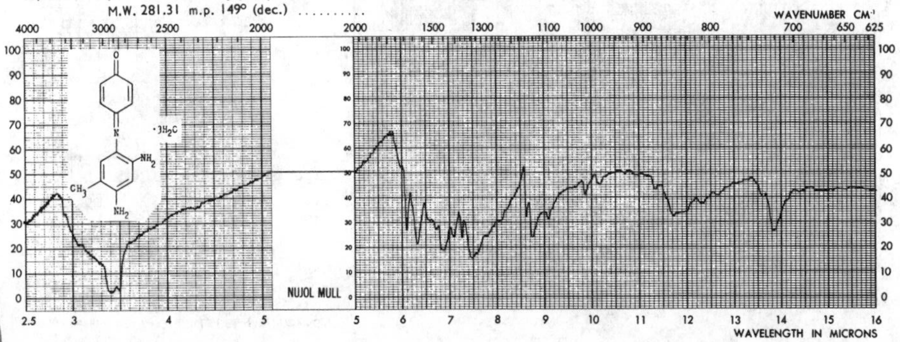

amino)-3-methylsalicyliminodiacetic acid]
M.W. 516.16 m.p. > 300° ....

NUJOL MULL

B

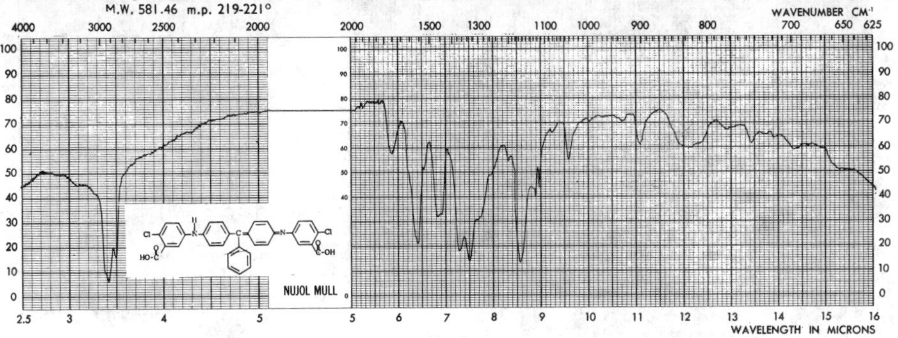

11,981-4 **2,6-Dichloroindophenol, sodium salt**
M.W. 290.08 m.p. > 360°

NUJOL MULL

F

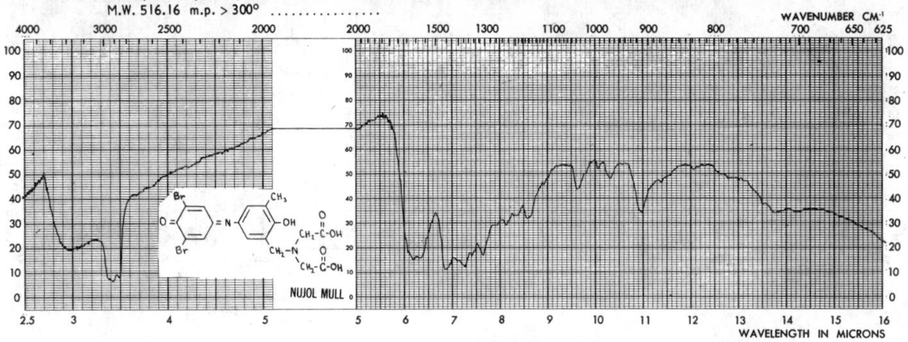

85,734-3
Fuchsine monohydrochloride (rosaniline, C.I. Basic Violet 14)
M.W. 337.86 m.p. 268-270° (dec.)

NUJOL MULL

C

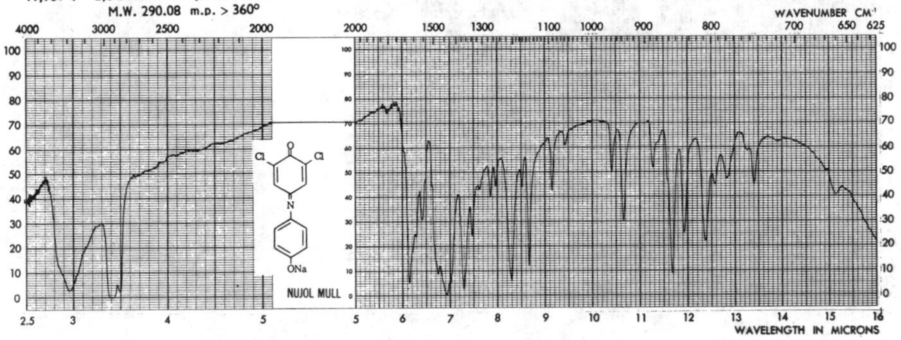

12,090-1 **2,6-Dichloroindo-m-cresol, sodium salt**
M.W. 304.11 m.p. > 300°

NUJOL MULL

G

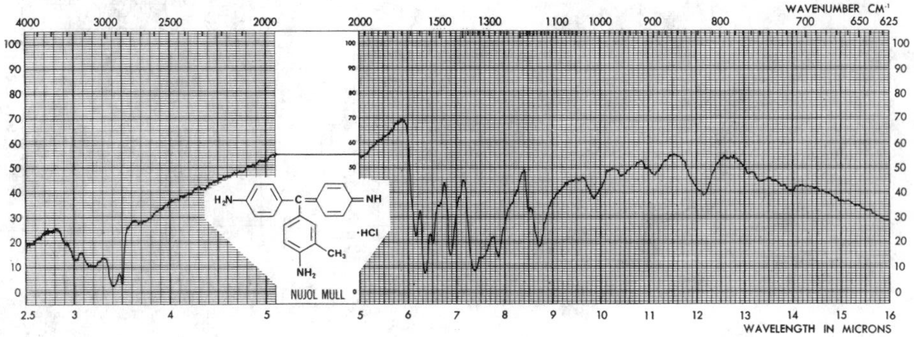

85,840-4
Methyl violet, indicator grade
M.W. 393.96 m.p. 208-210° (dec.)

NUJOL MULL

D

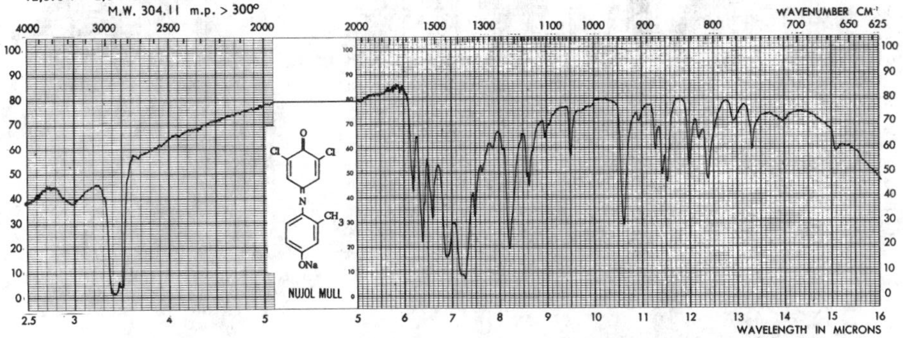

10,628-3 **N-(2,4-Diamino-5-methylphenyl)-p-benzoquinoneimine trihydrate**
M.W. 281.31 m.p. 149° (dec.) ....

NUJOL MULL

H

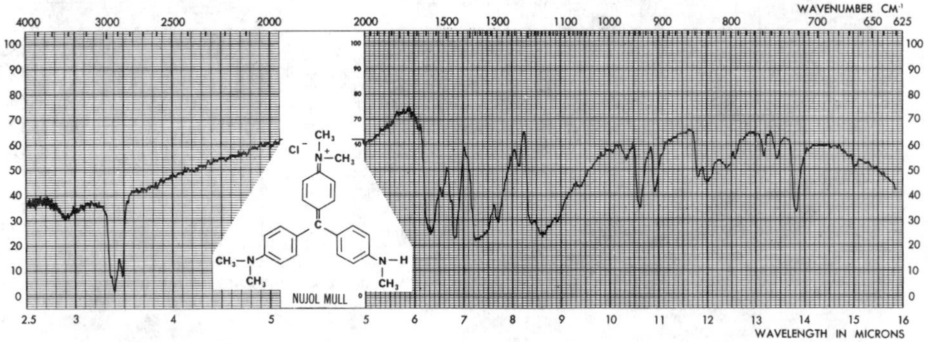

85,740-8
Acid fuchsine (C.I. Acid Violet 19)
M.W. 585.55 m.p. >300°

NUJOL MULL

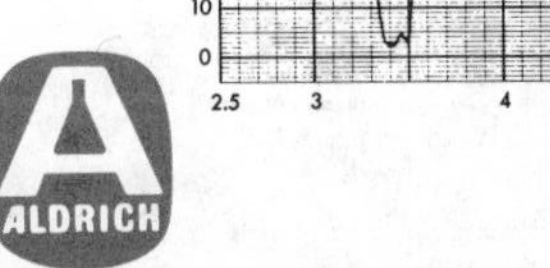

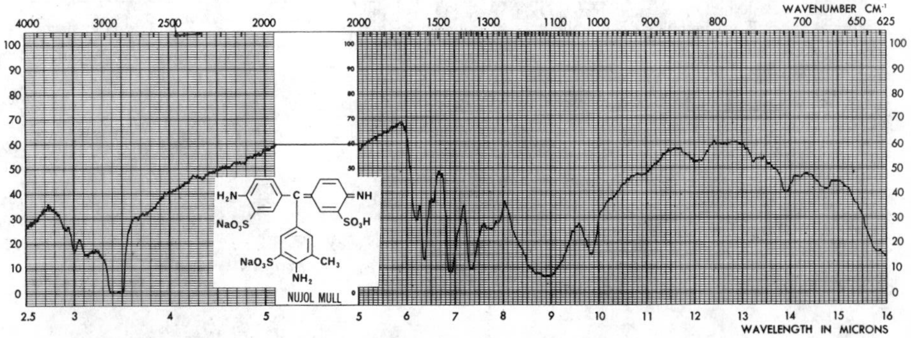

A

17,753-9
Syringaldazine, 99+%, GOLD LABEL (4-hydroxy-3,5-dimethoxybenzaldehyde azine)
$[HOC_6H_2(OCH_3)_2CH{=}N{-}]_2$
M.W. 360.37 m.p. 209-210°

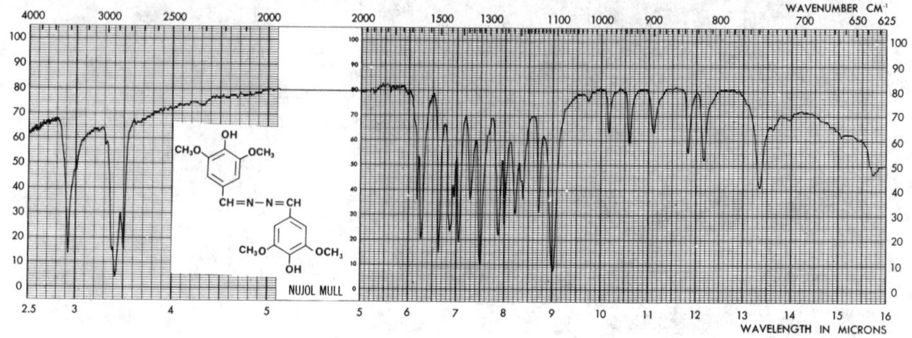

NUJOL MULL

B

15,073-8 **Azobenzene**, zone refined, 99.9 %, GOLD LABEL
$C_6H_5N{:}NC_6H_5$ M.W. 182.23 m.p. 68.30

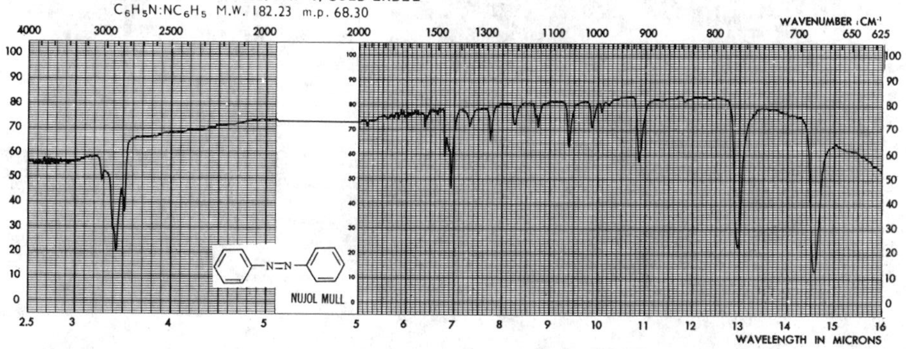

NUJOL MULL

C

18,628-7
Azoxybenzene
$C_6H_5N{=}N(O)C_6H_5$
M.W. 198.23

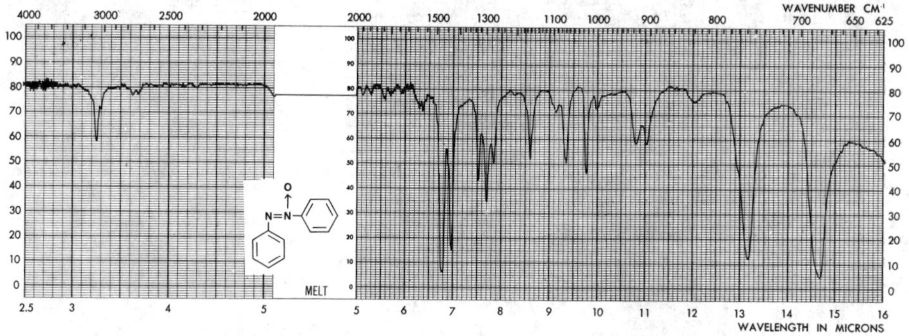

MELT

D

13,567-4 **4,4'-Dichloroazoxybenzene**
$ClC_6H_4N{:}N(O)C_6H_4Cl$ M.W. 267.12
m.p. 158-159°

E

M980-7 **4-Methoxyazobenzene**
$CH_3OC_6H_4N{:}NC_6H_5$ M.W. 212.25 m.p. 50-53°

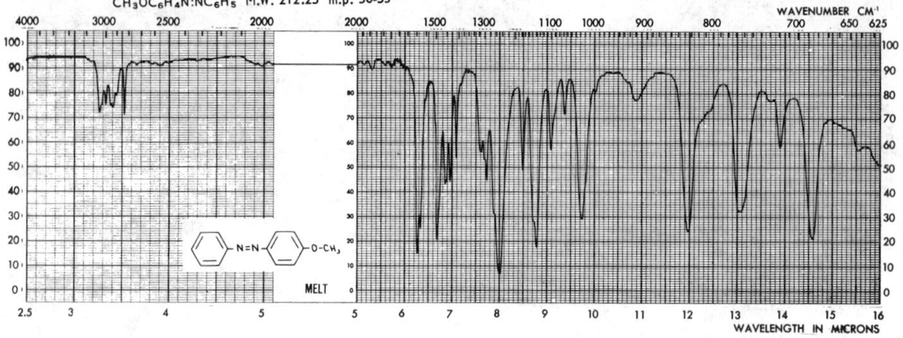

MELT

F

A9700-9 **4,4'-Azoxyanisole (4,4'-azoxydianisole)**
$CH_3OC_6H_4N{:}N(O)C_6H_4OCH_3$ M.W. 258.28
m.p. 118-121°

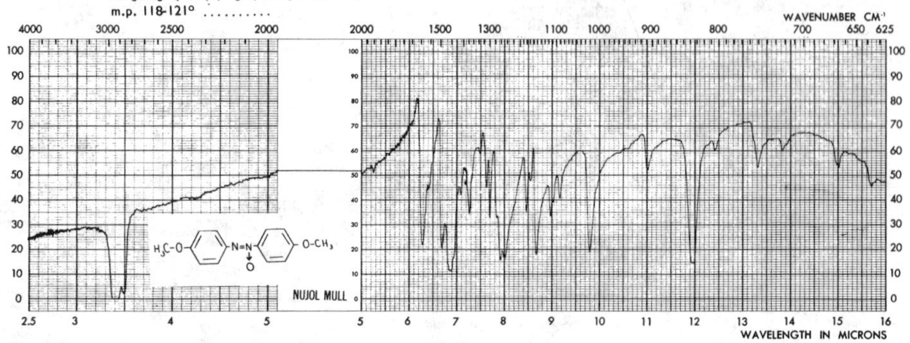

NUJOL MULL

G

13,108-3 **p-Phenylazophenol**
$C_6H_5N{:}NC_6H_4OH$ M.W. 198.23
m.p. 155-157°

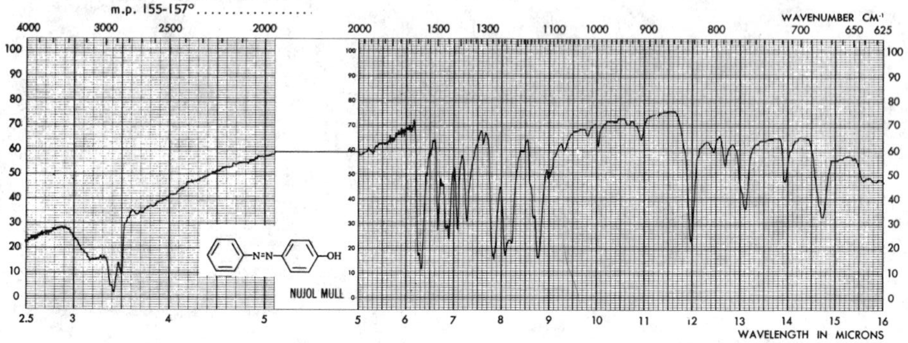

NUJOL MULL

H

11,701-3 **6-Phenylazo-3,4-xylenol**
$C_6H_5N{:}NC_6H_2(CH_3)_2OH$ M.W. 226.28
m.p. 127-129°

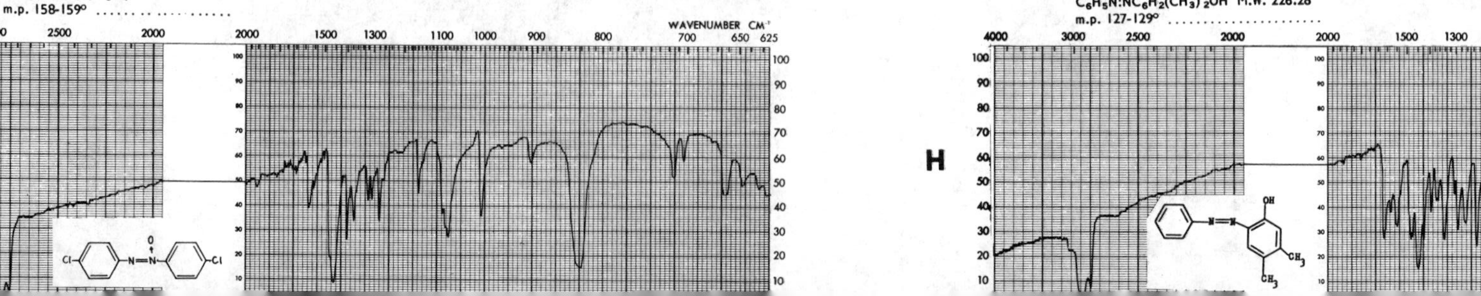

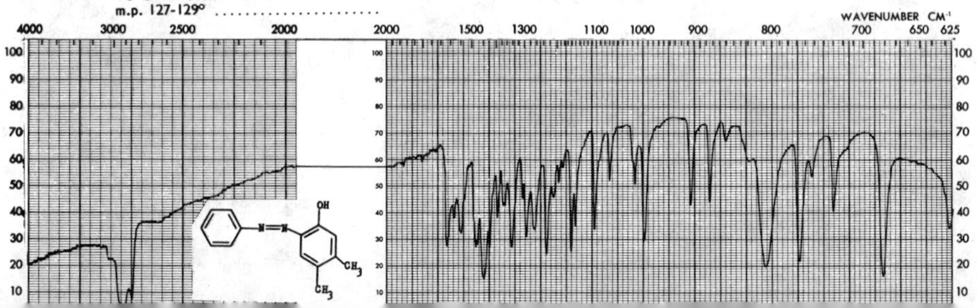

WAVENUMBER CM⁻¹ / WAVELENGTH IN MICRONS

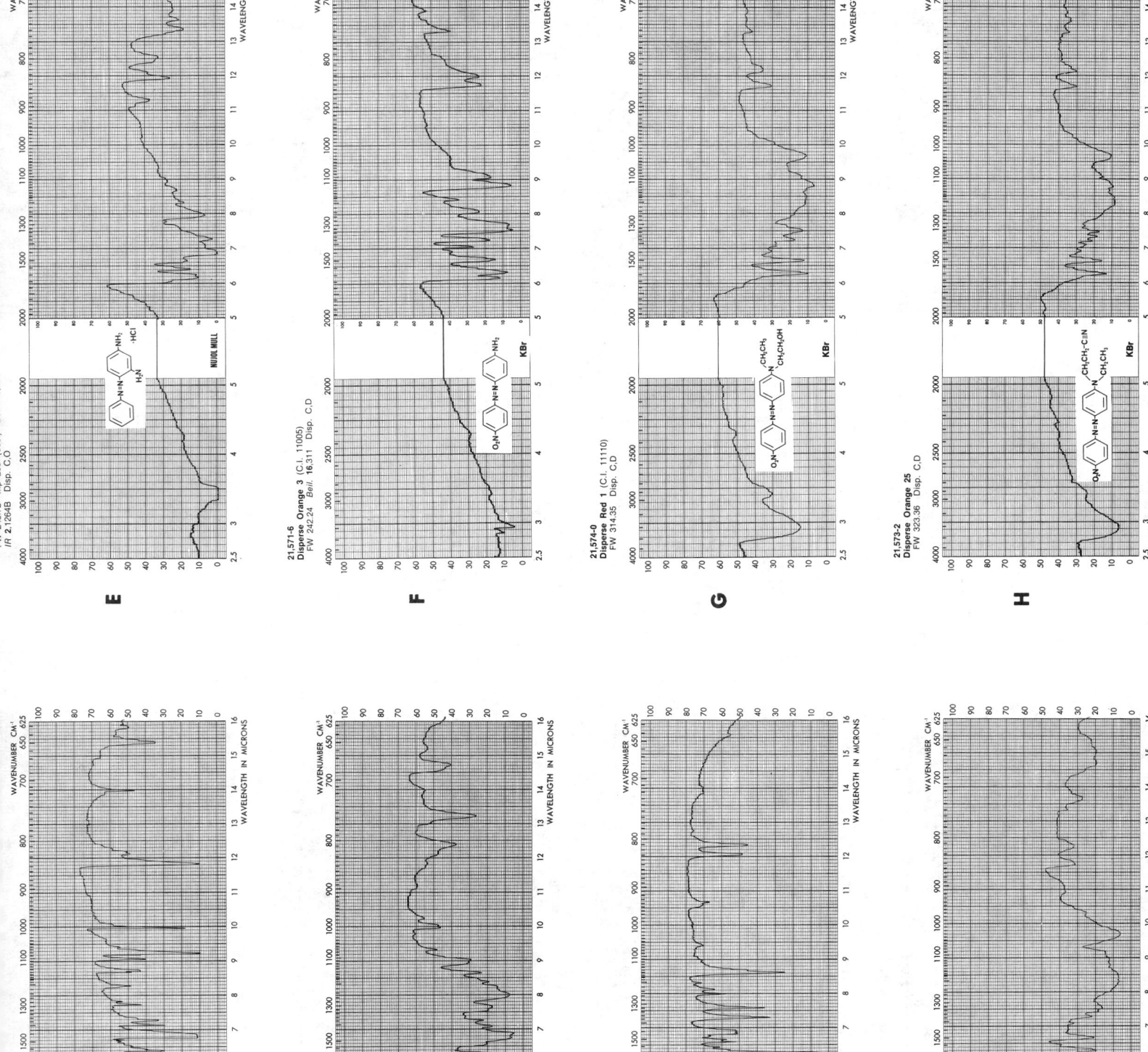

A

19,967-2
Sudan Orange G [C.I. 11920, 4-(phenylazo)-resorcinol, Solvent Orange 1]
$C_6H_5N{=}NC_6H_3$-1,3-$(OH)_2$ FW 214.22
mp 143-146° Disp. C,D

B

22,536-3
***N,N*-Dimethyl-4,4'-azodianiline** [4-amino-4'-(dimethylamino)azobenzene, C.I. 11025, Disperse Black 3]
$(CH_3)_2NC_6H_4N{=}NC_6H_4NH_2$ FW 240.31
mp 189° (dec.) *Beil.* **16**,335 Disp. C,D

C

21,576-7
Disperse Red 19 (C.I. 11130)
FW 330.35 Disp. C,D

D

FW 248.72 mp 235° (dec.) *Beil.* **16**,383
IR **2**,1264B Disp. C,O

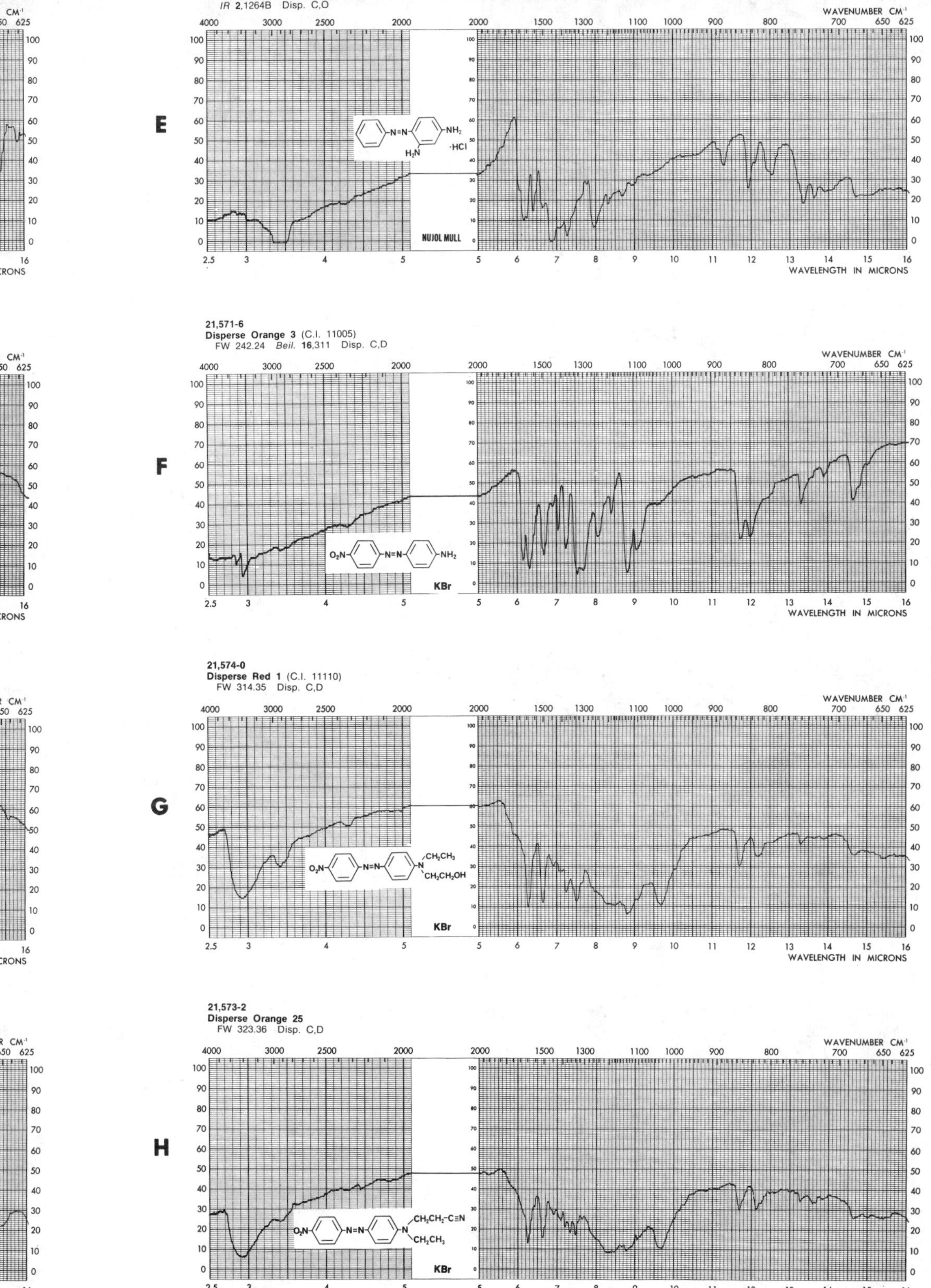

E

21,571-6
Disperse Orange 3 (C.I. 11005)
FW 242.24 *Beil.* **16**,311 Disp. C,D

F

21,574-0
Disperse Red 1 (C.I. 11110)
FW 314.35 Disp. C,D

G

21,573-2
Disperse Orange 25
FW 323.36 Disp. C,D

H

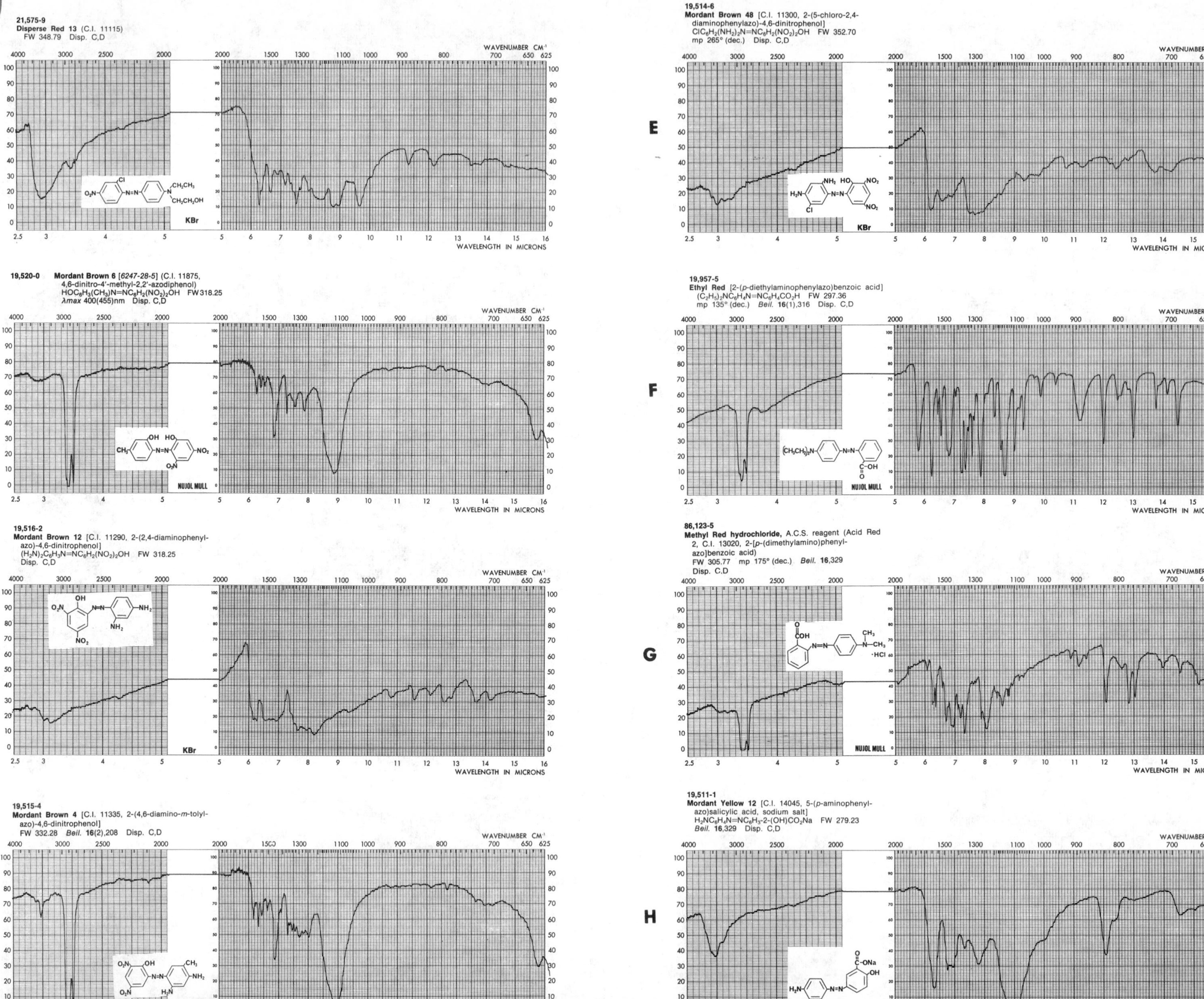

A

21,575-9
Disperse Red 13 (C.I. 11115)
FW 348.79 Disp. C,D

KBr

B

19,520-0 **Mordant Brown 6** [*6247-28-5*] (C.I. 11875, 4,6-dinitro-4'-methyl-2,2'-azodiphenol)
$HOC_6H_3(CH_3)N{=}NC_6H_2(NO_2)_2OH$ FW 318.25
λmax 400(455)nm Disp. C,D

NUJOL MULL

C

19,516-2
Mordant Brown 12 [C.I. 11290, 2-(2,4-diaminophenylazo)-4,6-dinitrophenol]
$(H_2N)_2C_6H_3N{=}NC_6H_2(NO_2)_2OH$ FW 318.25
Disp. C,D

KBr

D

19,515-4
Mordant Brown 4 [C.I. 11335, 2-(4,6-diamino-*m*-tolylazo)-4,6-dinitrophenol]
FW 332.28 *Beil.* **16**(2),208 Disp. C,D

E

19,514-6
Mordant Brown 48 [C.I. 11300, 2-(5-chloro-2,4-diaminophenylazo)-4,6-dinitrophenol]
$ClC_6H_2(NH_2)_2N{=}NC_6H_2(NO_2)_2OH$ FW 352.70
mp 265° (dec.) Disp. C,D

KBr

F

19,957-5
Ethyl Red [2-(*p*-diethylaminophenylazo)benzoic acid]
$(C_2H_5)_2NC_6H_4N{=}NC_6H_4CO_2H$ FW 297.36
mp 135° (dec.) *Beil.* **16**(1),316 Disp. C,D

NUJOL MULL

G

86,123-5
Methyl Red hydrochloride, A.C.S. reagent (Acid Red 2, C.I. 13020, 2-[*p*-(dimethylamino)phenylazo]benzoic acid)
FW 305.77 mp 175° (dec.) *Beil.* **16**,329
Disp. C,D

NUJOL MULL

H

19,511-1
Mordant Yellow 12 [C.I. 14045, 5-(*p*-aminophenylazo)salicylic acid, sodium salt]
$H_2NC_6H_4N{=}NC_6H_3\text{-}2\text{-}(OH)CO_2Na$ FW 279.23
Beil. **16**,329 Disp. C,D

A

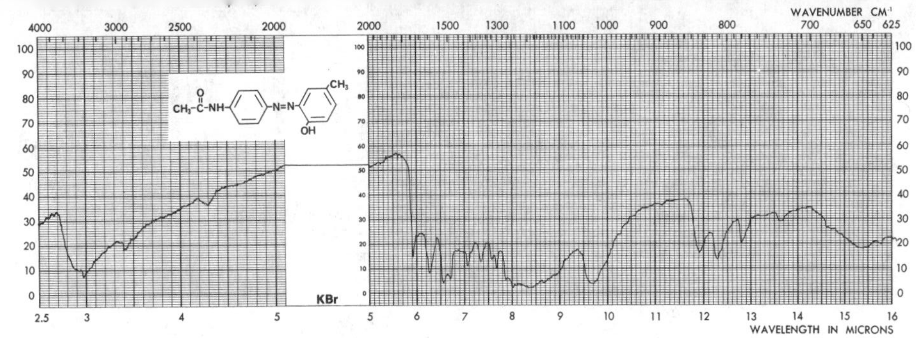

KBr

10,362-4 **Sudan I** (1-phenylazo-2-naphthol)
C_6H_5N:$NC_{10}H_6OH$ M.W. 248.29
m.p. 131-133°

B

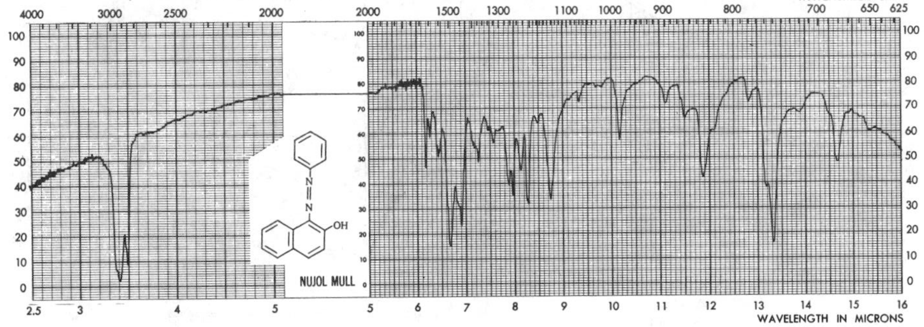

NUJOL MULL

14,779-6 **1-(2-Hydroxyphenylazo)-2-naphthol**
HOC_6H_4N:$NC_{10}H_6OH$ M.W. 264.29
m.p. 192-193°

C

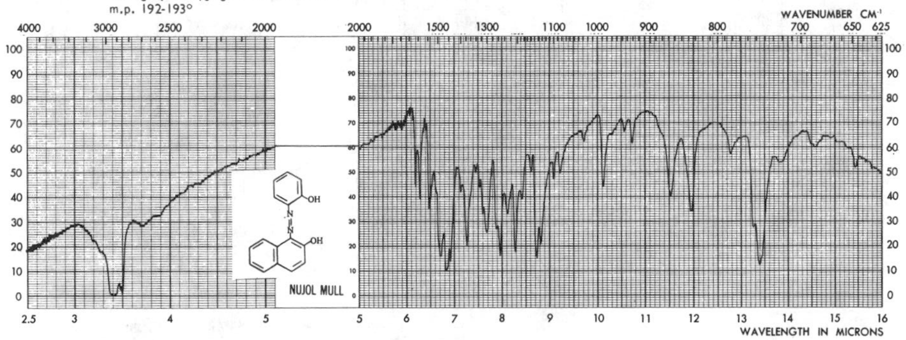

NUJOL MULL

10,430-2 **Sudan II** [1-(2,4-dimethylphenylazo)-2-naphthol]
$(CH_3)_2C_6H_3N$:$NC_{10}H_6OH$ M.W 276.34 m.p. 159-161.5°

D

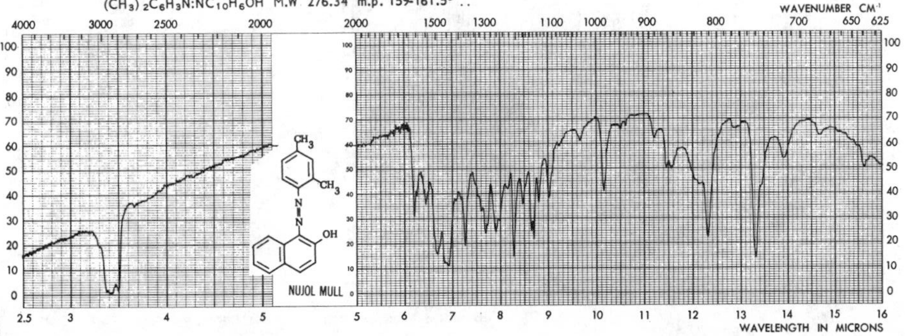

NUJOL MULL

Beil. 16(1),310

E

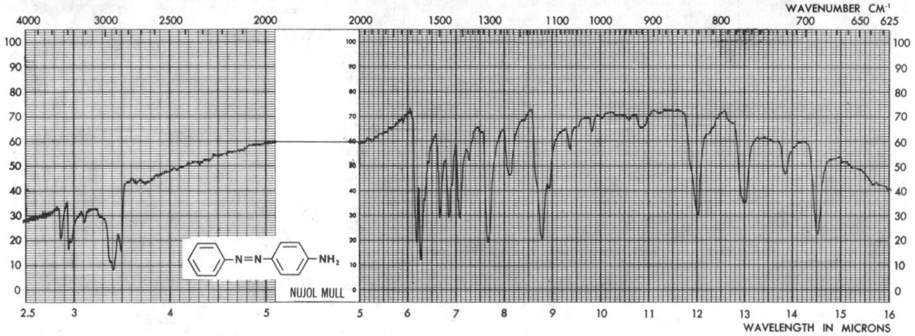

NUJOL MULL

15,006-1 **p-Phenylazoaniline** (p-aminoazobenzene) **hydrochloride, tech.**
C_6H_5N:$NC_6H_4NH_2\cdot HCl$ M.W. 233.70
m.p. 227-228° (anhydrous)

F

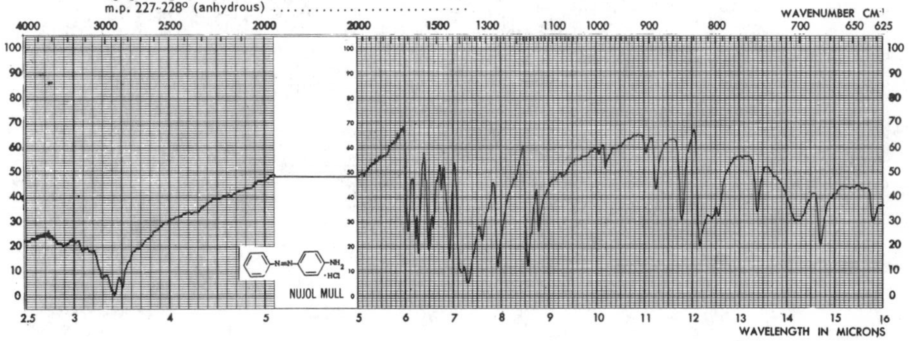

NUJOL MULL

11,449-9 **Methyl yellow** (N,N-dimethyl-p-phenylazoaniline)
C_6H_5N:$NC_6H_4N(CH_3)_2$ M.W. 225.30
m.p. 111° (dec.)

G

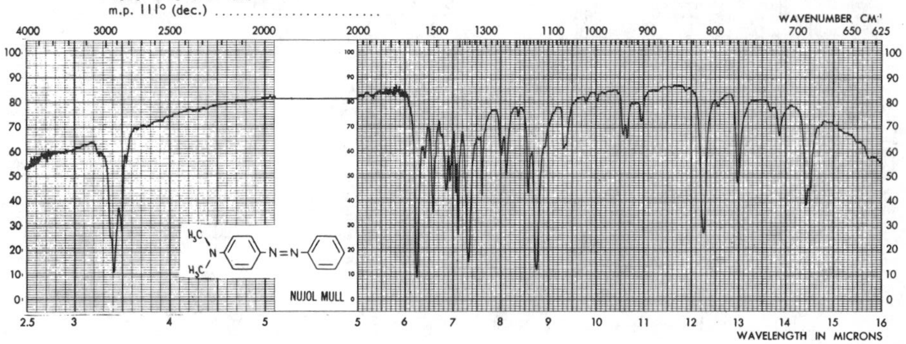

NUJOL MULL

12,898-8 **4-(Diethylamino)-azobenzene** [N,N-diethyl-4-(phenylazo)aniline]
C_6H_5N:$NC_6H_4N(C_2H_5)_2$ M.W. 253.35
m.p. 96-97°

H

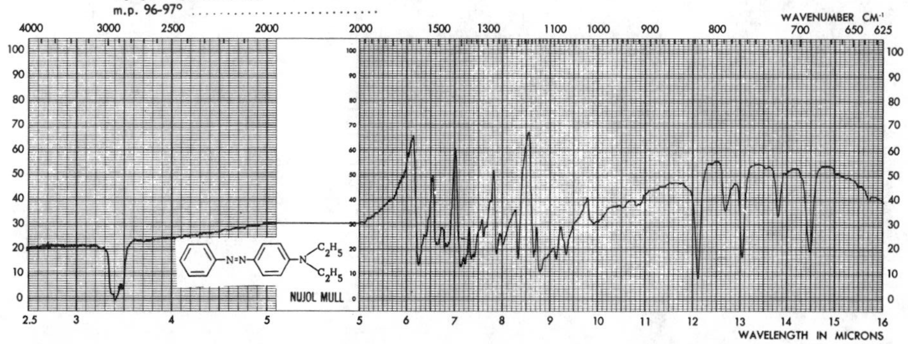

NUJOL MULL

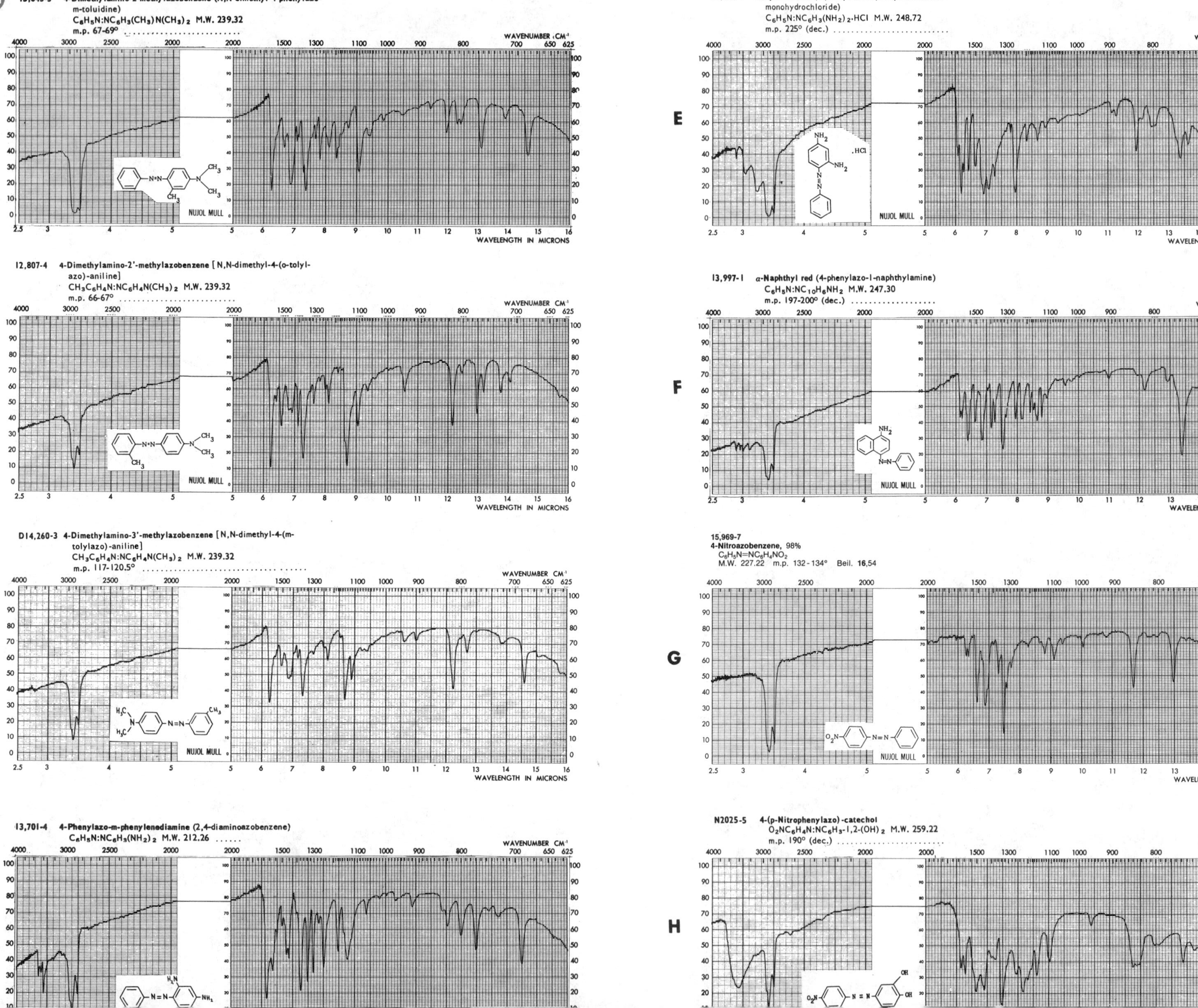

A 13,043-5 **4-Dimethylamino-2-methylazobenzene (N,N-dimethyl-4-phenylazo-m-toluidine)**
$C_6H_5N{:}NC_6H_3(CH_3)N(CH_3)_2$ M.W. 239.32
m.p. 67-69°

B 12,807-4 **4-Dimethylamino-2'-methylazobenzene** [N,N-dimethyl-4-(o-tolylazo)-aniline]
$CH_3C_6H_4N{:}NC_6H_4N(CH_3)_2$ M.W. 239.32
m.p. 66-67°

C D14,260-3 **4-Dimethylamino-3'-methylazobenzene** [N,N-dimethyl-4-(m-tolylazo)-aniline]
$CH_3C_6H_4N{:}NC_6H_4N(CH_3)_2$ M.W. 239.32
m.p. 117-120.5°

D 13,701-4 **4-Phenylazo-m-phenylenediamine** (2,4-diaminoazobenzene)
$C_6H_5N{:}NC_6H_3(NH_2)_2$ M.W. 212.26

E 11,098-1 Chrysoidine G (4-phenylazo-m-phenylenediamine monohydrochloride)
$C_6H_5N{:}NC_6H_3(NH_2)_2{\cdot}HCl$ M.W. 248.72
m.p. 225° (dec.)

F 13,997-1 **α-Naphthyl red (4-phenylazo-1-naphthylamine)**
$C_6H_5N{:}NC_{10}H_6NH_2$ M.W. 247.30
m.p. 197-200° (dec.)

G 15,969-7
4-Nitroazobenzene, 98%
$C_6H_5N{=}NC_6H_4NO_2$
M.W. 227.22 m.p. 132-134° Beil. **16**,54

H N2025-5 **4-(p-Nitrophenylazo)-catechol**
$O_2NC_6H_4N{:}NC_6H_3\text{-}1,2\text{-}(OH)_2$ M.W. 259.22
m.p. 190° (dec.)

A

m.p. 185° (dec.) . . . .

NUJOL MULL

B

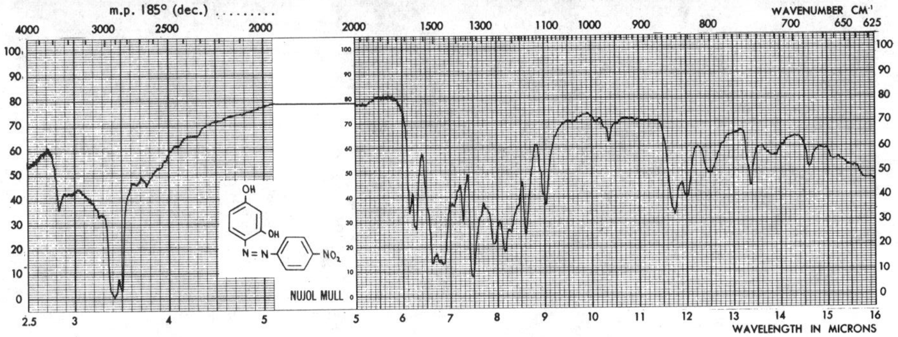

11,467-7 4-(p-Nitrophenylazo)-orcinol
$O_2NC_6H_4N{:}NC_6H_2\text{-}5\text{-}(CH_3)\text{-}1,3\text{-}(OH)_2$ M.W. 273.25
m.p. 210° (dec.) . . . .

NUJOL MULL

C

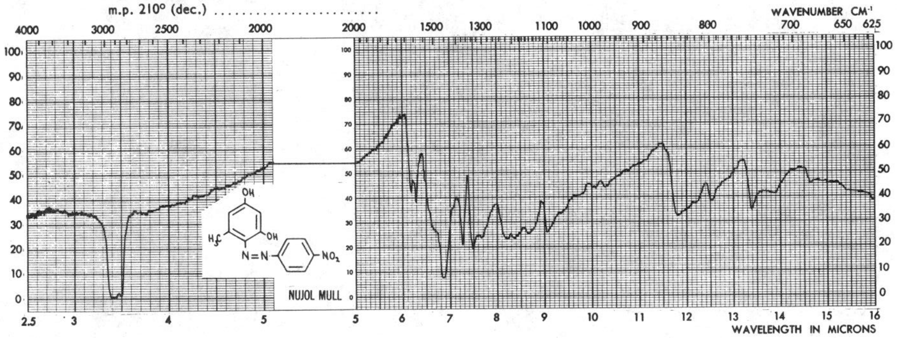

10,099-4 Para red [1-(p-nitrophenylazo)-2-naphthol]
$O_2NC_6H_4N{:}NC_{10}H_6OH$ M.W. 293.28
m.p. 248-252° . . . .

NUJOL MULL

D

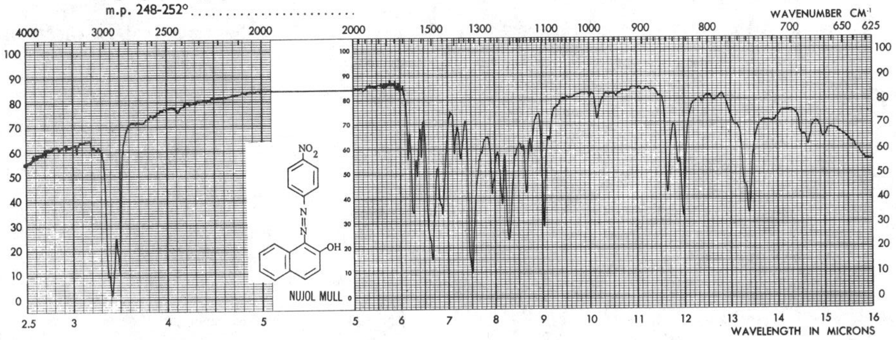

11,465-0 4-(p-Nitrophenylazo)-1-naphthol
$O_2NC_6H_4N{:}NC_{10}H_6OH$ M.W. 293.28
m.p. 272° (dec.) . . . .

NUJOL MULL

E

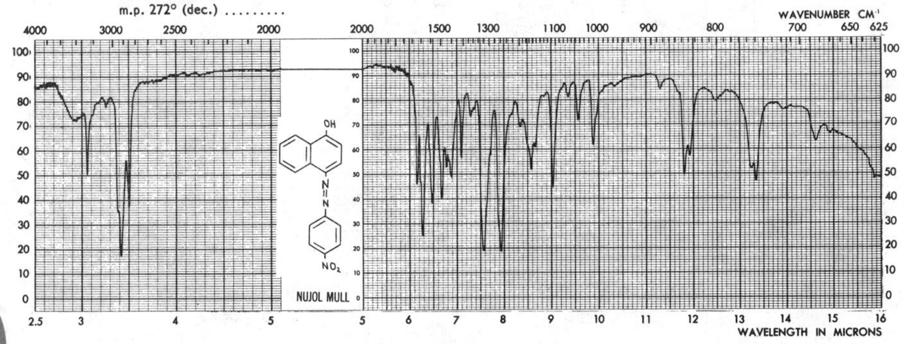

$HOC_6H_4N{:}NC_6H_4CO_2H$ M.W. 242.24
m.p. 205-207° . . .

NUJOL MULL

F

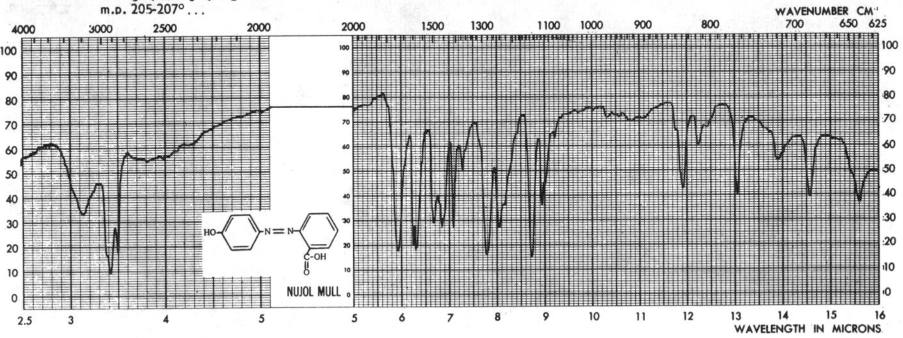

11,450-2 Methyl red, water soluble [2-[p-(dimethylamino)-phenylazo]-benzoic acid, sodium salt]
$(CH_3)_2NC_6H_4N{:}NC_6H_4CO_2Na$
M.W. 291.29 . . . .

NUJOL MULL

G

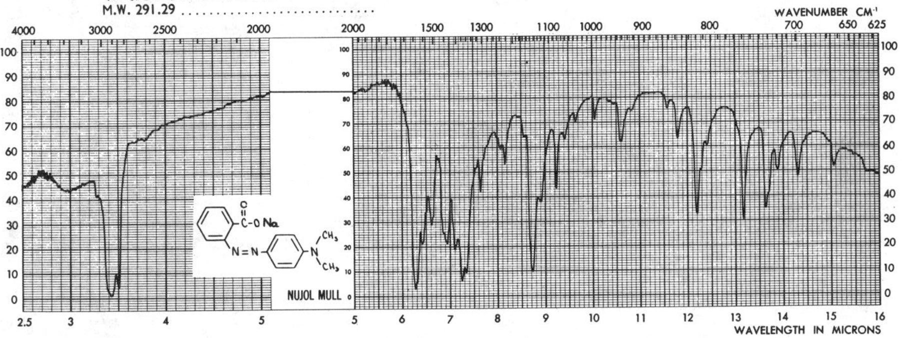

11,997-0 Alizarin yellow GG [metachrome yellow, 5-(m-nitrophenylazo)-salicylic acid, sodium salt]
$O_2NC_6H_4N{:}NC_6H_3\text{-}2\text{-}(OH)CO_2Na$ M.W. 309.22
m.p. > 360° . . . .

NUJOL MULL

H

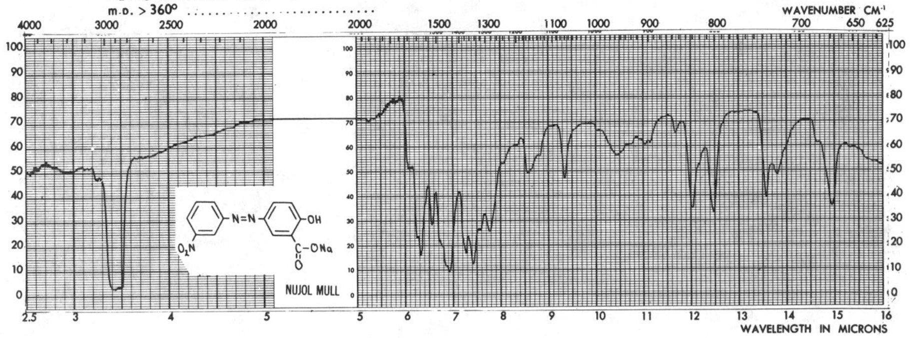

11,988-1 5-(p-Nitrophenylazo)-salicylic acid
$O_2NC_6H_4N{:}NC_6H_3\text{-}2\text{-}(OH)CO_2H$ M.W. 287.23
m.p. 248-251° (dec.) . . . .

NUJOL MULL

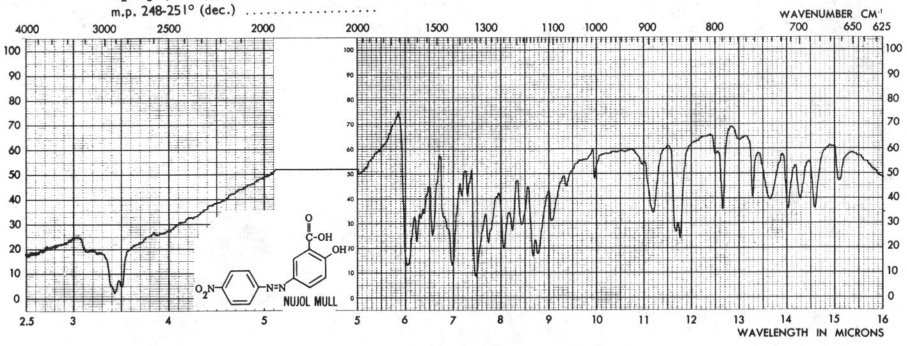

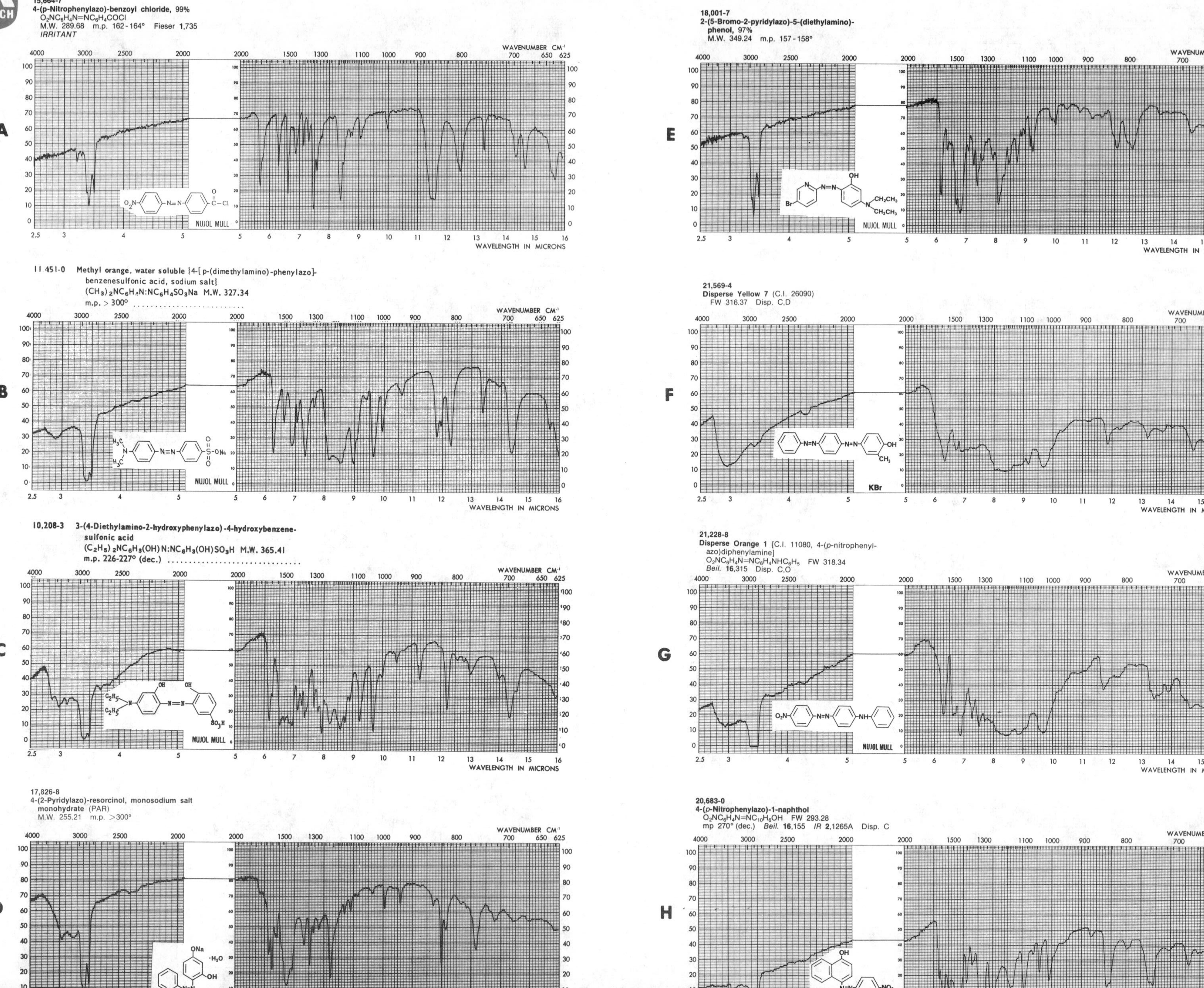

A

15,664-7
4-(p-Nitrophenylazo)-benzoyl chloride, 99%
$O_2NC_6H_4N{=}NC_6H_4COCl$
M.W. 289.68 m.p. 162-164° Fieser 1,735
IRRITANT

NUJOL MULL

B

11 451-0 **Methyl orange, water soluble** [4-[p-(dimethylamino)-phenylazo]-benzenesulfonic acid, sodium salt]
$(CH_3)_2NC_6H_4N{:}NC_6H_4SO_3Na$ M.W. 327.34
m.p. > 300°

NUJOL MULL

C

10,208-3 **3-(4-Diethylamino-2-hydroxyphenylazo)-4-hydroxybenzene-sulfonic acid**
$(C_2H_5)_2NC_6H_3(OH)N{:}NC_6H_3(OH)SO_3H$ M.W. 365.41
m.p. 226-227° (dec.)

NUJOL MULL

D

17,826-8
4-(2-Pyridylazo)-resorcinol, monosodium salt monohydrate (PAR)
M.W. 255.21 m.p. >300°

E

18,001-7
2-(5-Bromo-2-pyridylazo)-5-(diethylamino)-phenol, 97%
M.W. 349.24 m.p. 157-158°

NUJOL MULL

F

21,569-4
Disperse Yellow 7 (C.I. 26090)
FW 316.37 Disp. C,D

KBr

G

21,228-8
Disperse Orange 1 [C.I. 11080, 4-(p-nitrophenylazo)diphenylamine]
$O_2NC_6H_4N{=}NC_6H_4NHC_6H_5$ FW 318.34
Beil. **16**,315 Disp. C,O

NUJOL MULL

H

20,683-0
4-(p-Nitrophenylazo)-1-naphthol
$O_2NC_6H_4N{=}NC_{10}H_6OH$ FW 293.28
mp 270° (dec.) *Beil.* **16**,155 *IR* **2**,1265A Disp. C

A

FW 307.31 mp 270-272° *Beil.* **16**(3),136
Disp. C,D

NUJOL MULL

B

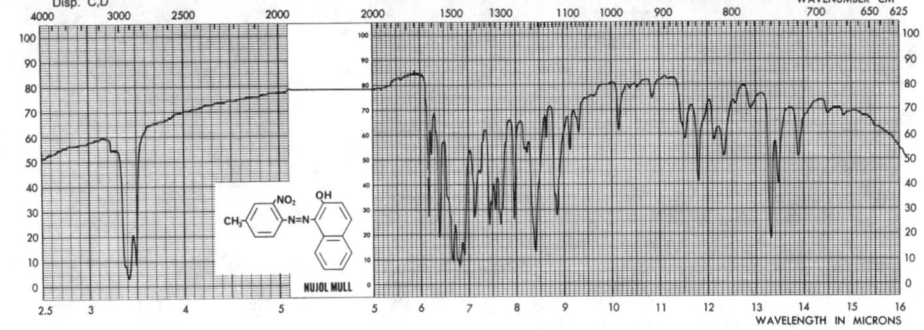

20,161-8
Sudan Red 7B (C.I. 26050, Fat Red 7B, Solvent Red 19)
FW 379.47 *Beil.* **16**,379 Disp. C,D

KBr

C

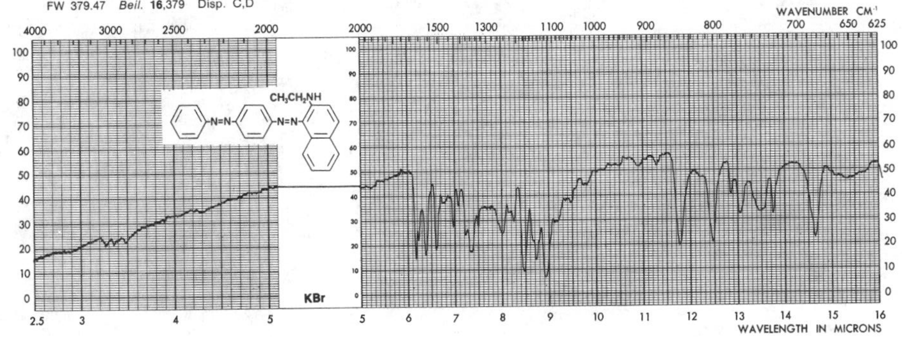

19,811-0
Sudan III, certified (C.I. 26100, Solvent Red 23)
FW 352.40 mp 199° (dec.) Disp. C,D

NUJOL MULL

D

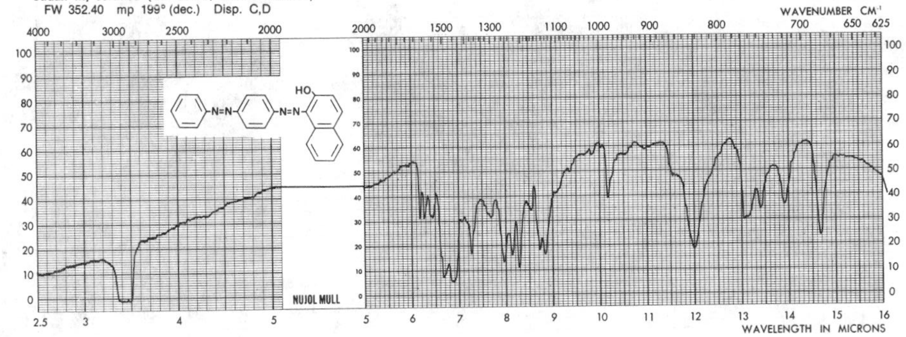

19,819-6
Oil Red O, biological stain (C.I. 26125, Solvent Red 27)
FW 408.51 mp 120° (dec.) *Beil.* **16**(2),75
Disp. C,D

KBr

E

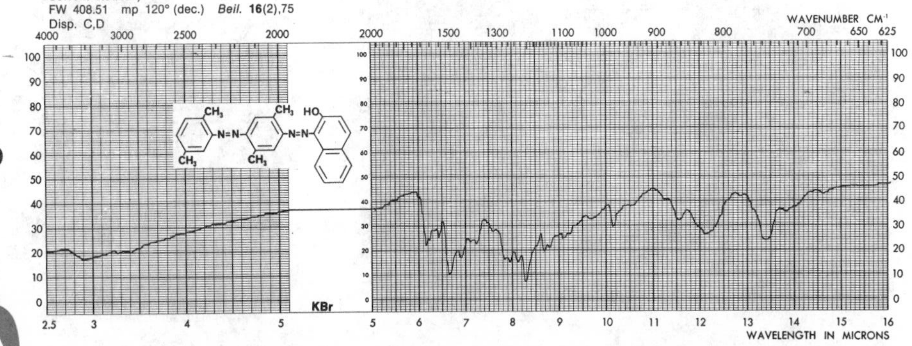

Disperse Orange 13 (C.I. 26080)
FW 352.40 *Beil.* **16**(2),53 Disp. C,D

NUJOL MULL

F

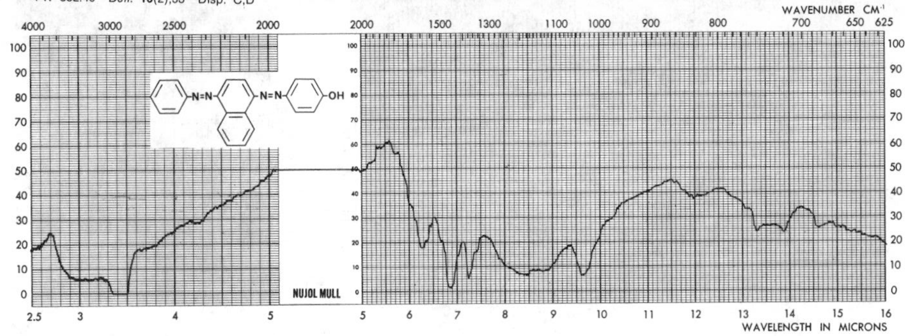

19,965-6
Sudan II (C.I. 12140, Solvent Orange 7)
FW 276.34 mp 156-158° *Beil.* **16**,168 Disp. C,D

NUJOL MULL

G

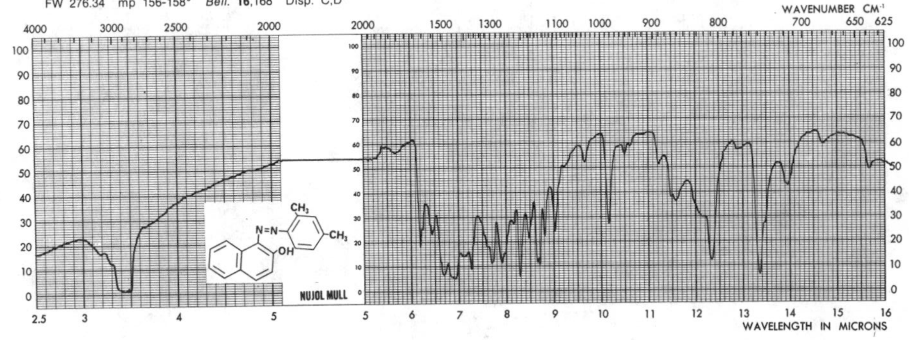

19,819-6
Oil Red O, biological stain (C.I. 26125, Solvent Red 27)
FW 408.51 mp 120° (dec.) *Beil.* **16**(2),75
Disp. C,D

NUJOL MULL

H

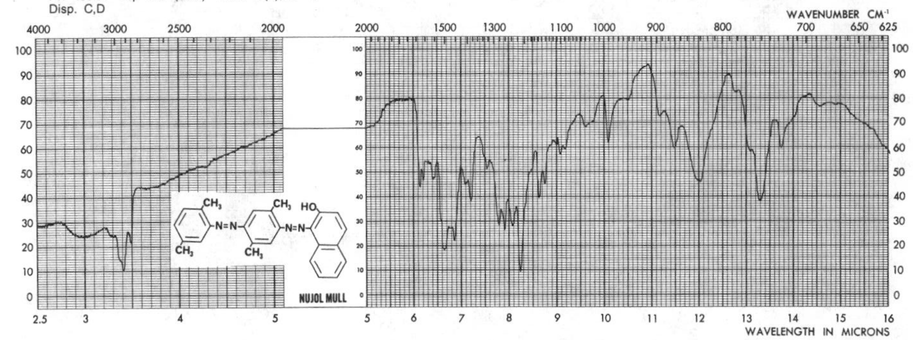

19,810-2
Sudan IV, certified (C.I. 26105, Scarlet Red, Solvent Red 24)
FW 380.45 mp 199° (dec.) *Beil.* **16**(4),148
Disp. C,O

KBr

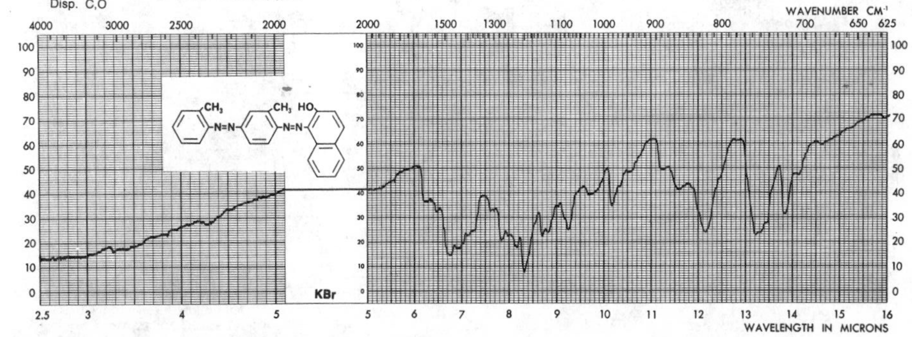

A 19,956-7
Ethyl Orange, indicator grade [4-(*p*-diethylamino-phenylazo)benzenesulfonic acid]
$(C_2H_5)_2NC_6H_4N{=}NC_6H_4SO_3H$ FW 333.41
mp >300° *Beil.* **16**,332 Disp. C,D

B 19,510-3
Mordant Yellow 10 [C.I. 14010, 5-(*p*-sulfophenylazo)-salicylic acid, disodium salt]
$NaO_3SC_6H_4N{=}NC_6H_3$-2-(OH)CO_2Na FW 366.26
Disp. C,D

C 19,968-0
Tropaeolin O (Acid Orange 6, C.I. 14270)
FW 316.27 *Beil.* **16**,275 Disp. C,D

D 19,513-8
Mordant Yellow 7 [3-methyl-5-(*p*-sulfophenylazo)-salicylic acid, disodium salt]
$CH_3C_6H_2(N{=}NC_6H_4SO_3Na)$-2-(OH)$CO_2Na$
FW 380.29 mp 285° (dec.) Disp. C,D

E 19,518-9
Mordant Brown 33 [C.I. 13250, 2,4-diamino-5-(2-hydroxy-5-nitrophenylazo)benzenesulfonic acid, sodium salt]
$HOC_6H_3(NO_2)N{=}NC_6H_2(NH_2)_2SO_3Na$ FW 375.30
Disp. C,D

F 20,180-4
Acid Yellow 99 (C.I. 13900)
FW 496.35 Disp. C,D

G 20,202-9
Metanil Yellow (Acid Yellow 36, C.I. 13065)
FW 375.38 *Beil.* **16**,330 Disp. C,D

H 19,508-1
Mordant Orange 10 (C.I. 26560)
FW 484.40 Disp. C,D

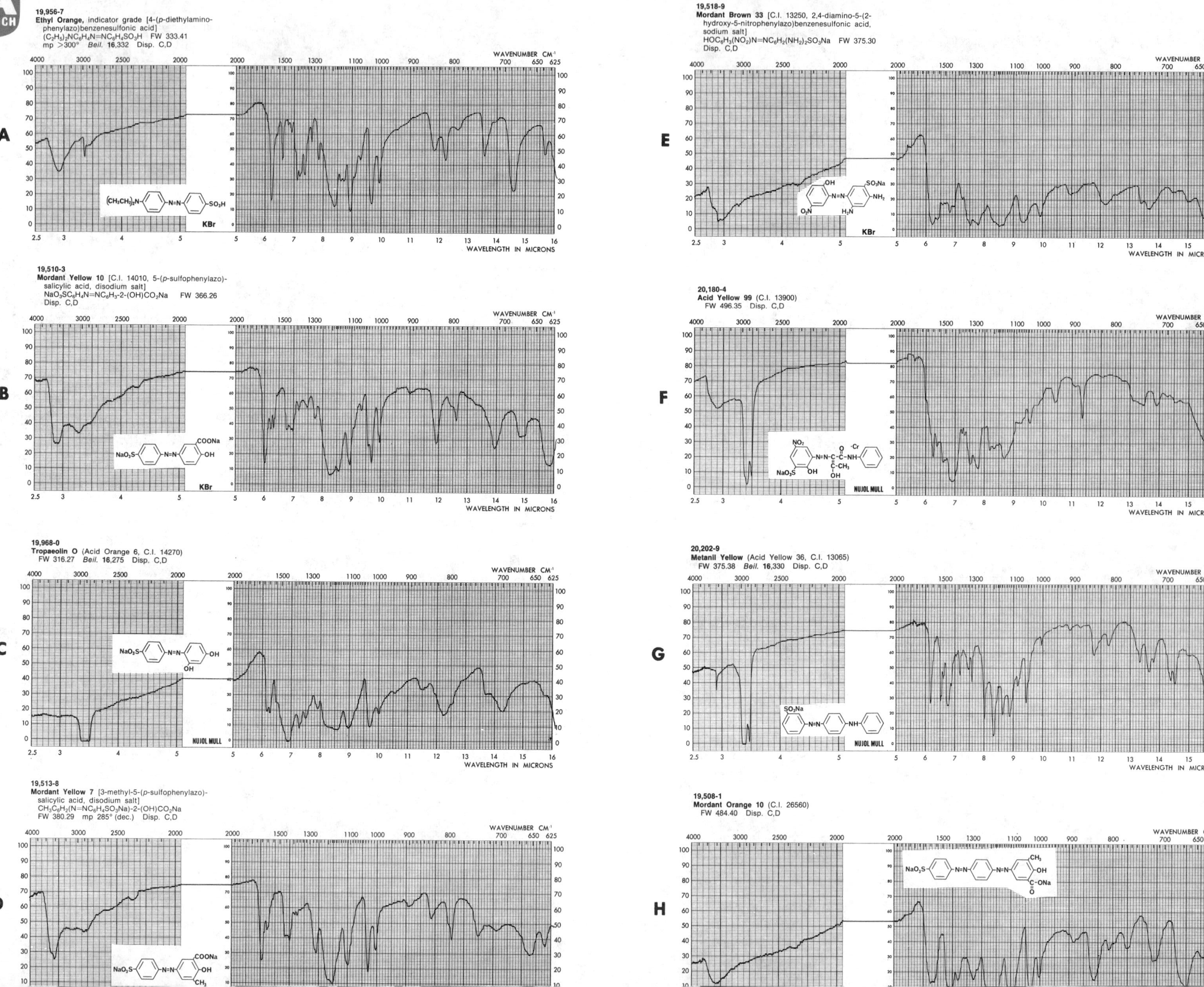

A

FW 484.40 Disp. C,D

KBr

B

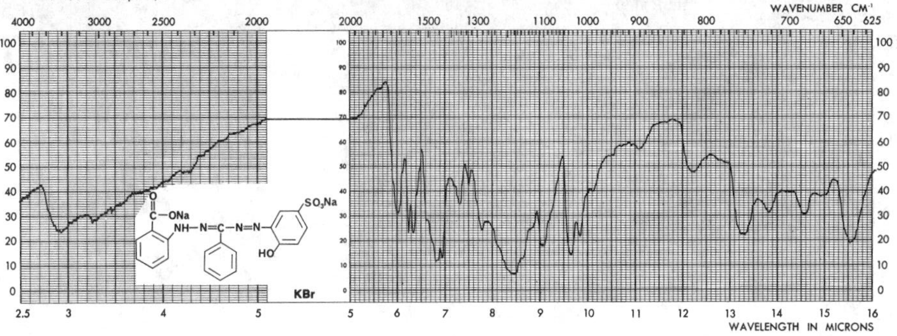

21,460-4
Mordant Orange 6 (C.I. 26520)
FW 470.38 *Beil.* **16**(4),301 Disp. C,D

NUJOL MULL

C

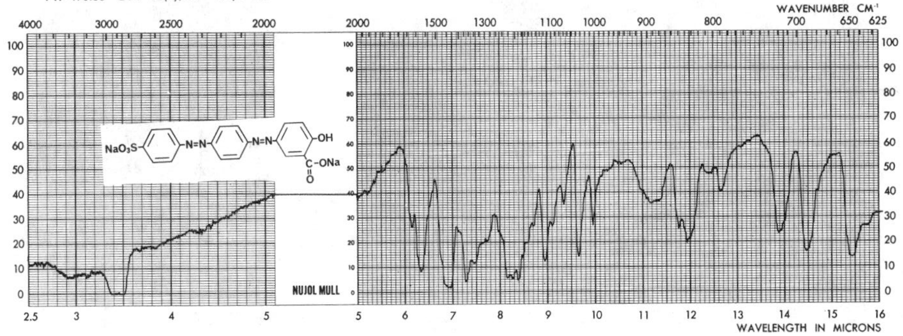

21,222-9
Bismarck Brown R (Basic Brown 4, C.I. 21010)
FW 461.40 mp 222° (dec.) *Beil.* **16**(2),209
Disp. C,D

·2HCl

KBr

D

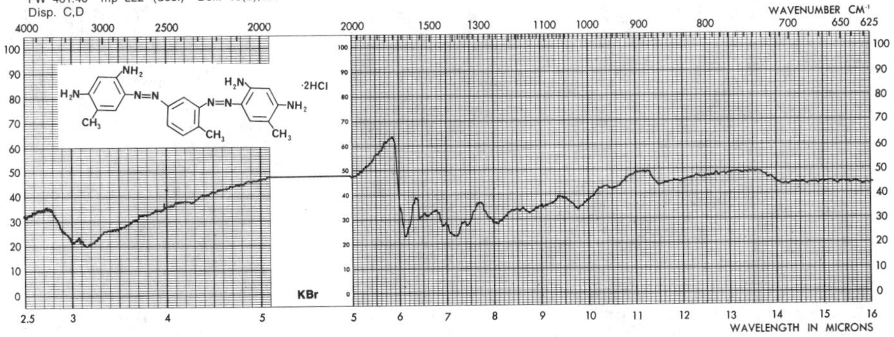

20,137-5
Brilliant Yellow (C.I. 24890, Direct Yellow 4)
FW 624.56 *Beil.* **16**,291 Disp. C,D

NUJOL MULL

E

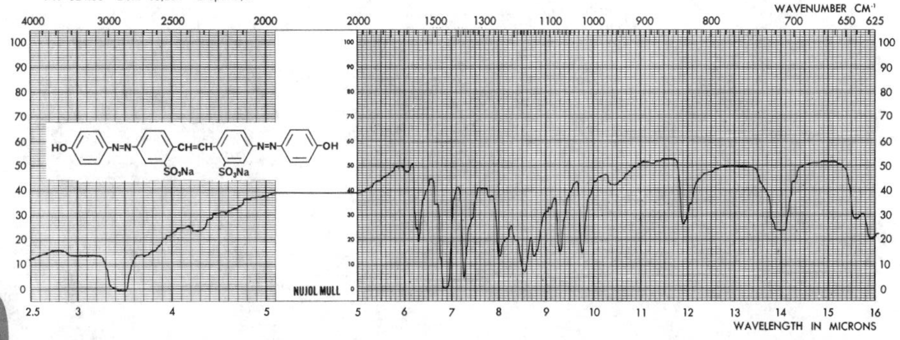

Acid Yellow 65 (C.I. 14170)
FW 590.57 Disp. C,D

KBr

F

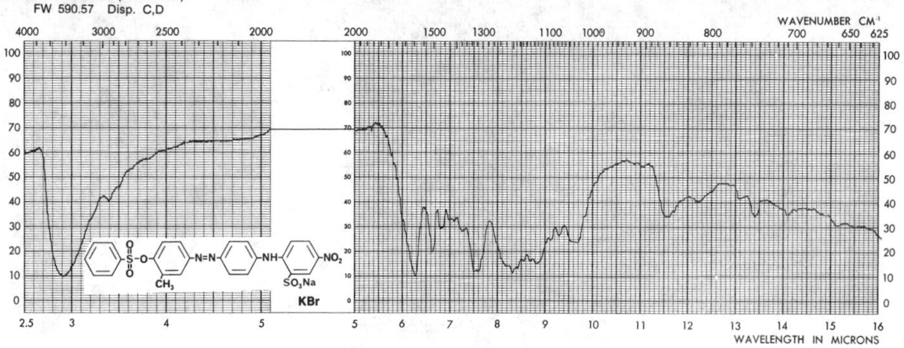

20,190-1
Chrysophenine (C.I. 24895, Direct Yellow 12)
FW 680.67 *Beil.* **16**,292 Disp. C,D

KBr

G

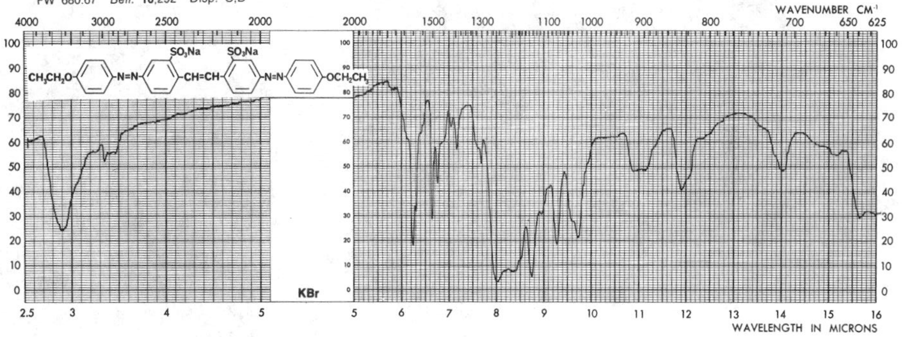

20,194-4
Acid Yellow 38 (C.I. 25135)
FW 686.70 Disp. C,D

KBr

H

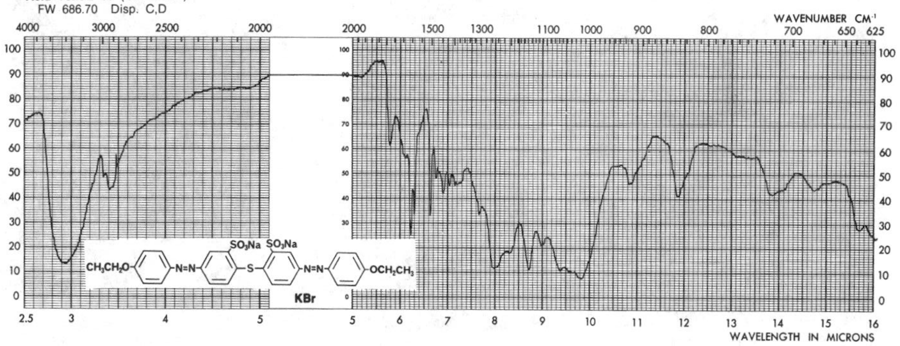

10,935-5 **Cadion S** [4'-(4-nitro-2-sulfophenyldiazoamino)-azobenzene-4-sulfonic acid, disodium salt]
$O_2NC_6H_3(SO_3Na)N{:}NNHC_6H_4N{:}NC_6H_4SO_3Na$ M.W. 550.44
m.p. > 300°

NUJOL MULL

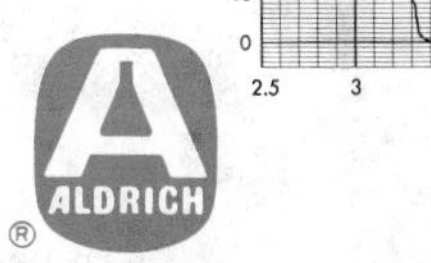

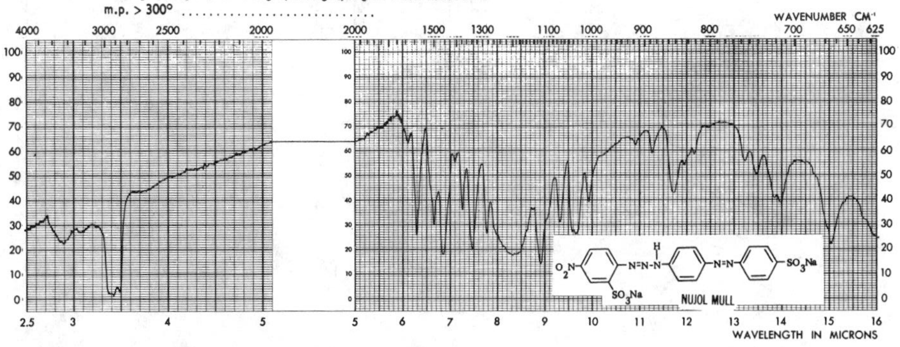

A

11,976-8 **o-{2-[α-(2-Hydroxy-5-sulfophenylazo)-benzylidene]-hydrazino}-benzoic acid** (zincon)
M.W. 440.43 m.p. 203° (dec.)

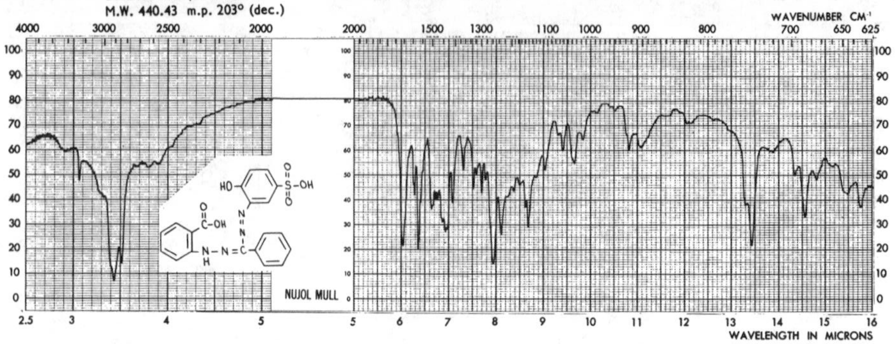

NUJOL MULL

B

19,813-7
Crocein Orange G (Acid Orange 12, C.I. 15970)
FW 350.33 *Beil.* **16**,297 Disp. C,D

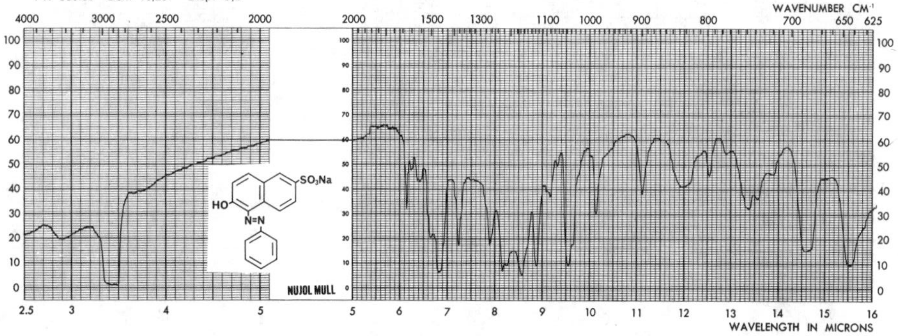

NUJOL MULL

C

21,074-9
Acid Red 4 (C.I. 14710)
FW 380.36 Disp. C,D

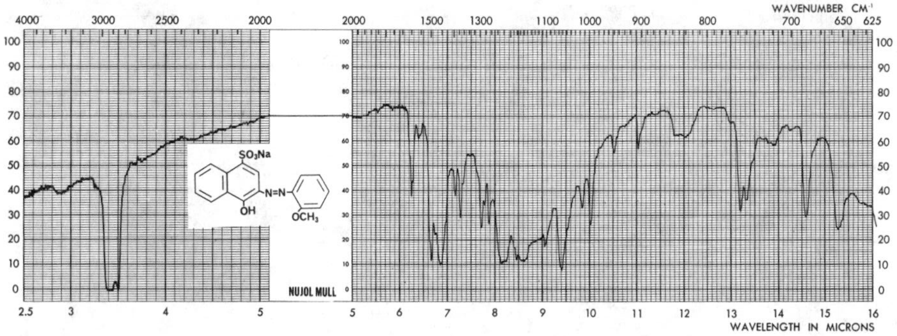

NUJOL MULL

D

21,040-4
Acid Violet 1 (C.I. 17025)
FW 512.39 Disp. C,D

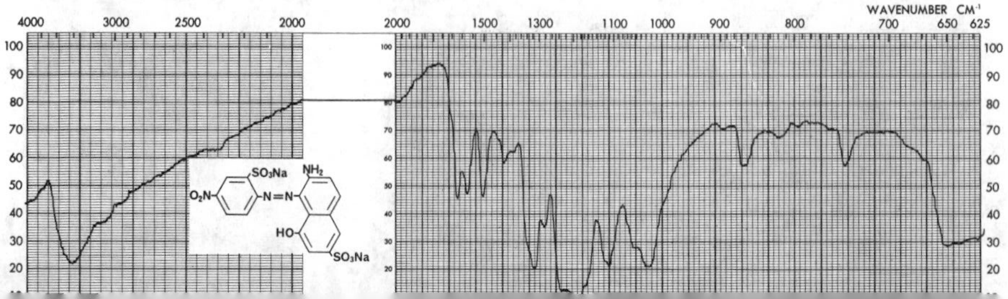

E

21,453-1
Acid Orange 8 (C.I. 15575)
FW 364.36 Disp. C,D

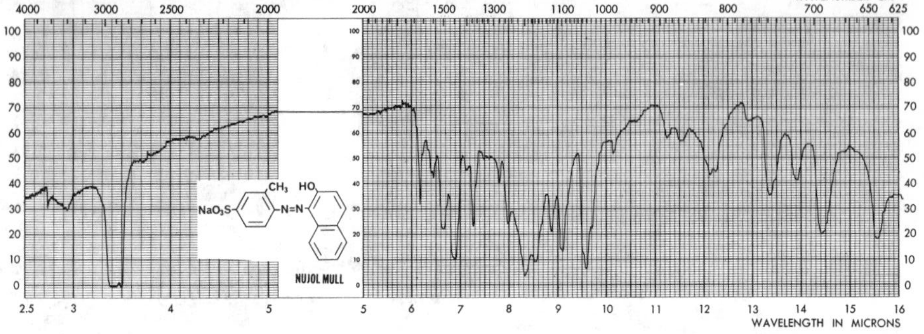

NUJOL MULL

F

21,452-3
Acid Red 8 (C.I. 14900)
FW 480.43 Disp. C,D

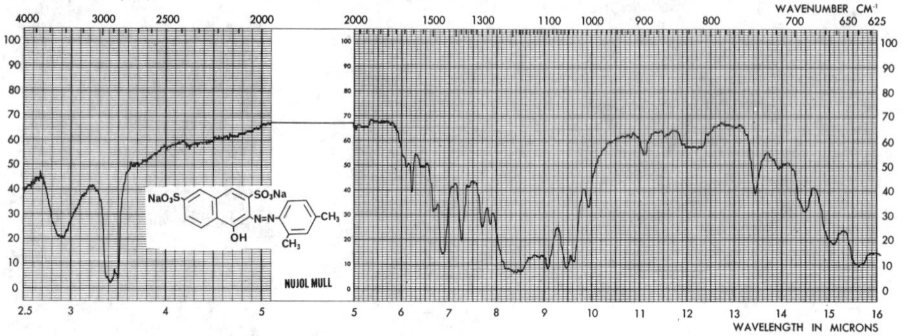

NUJOL MULL

G

19,976-1
Xylidine Ponceau 2R (Acid Red 26, C.I. 16150)
FW 480.43 Disp. C,D

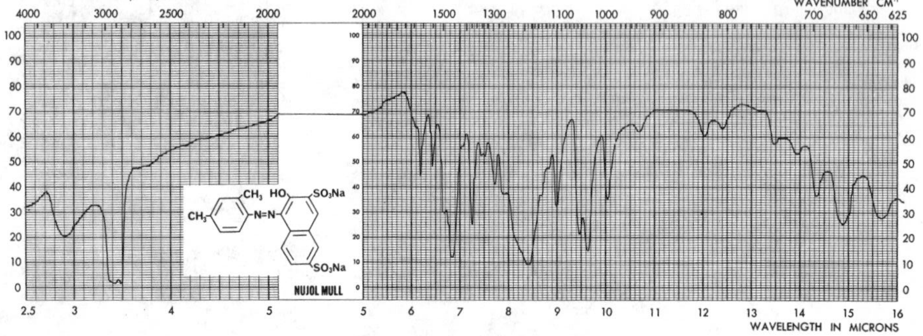

NUJOL MULL

H

19,521-9
Mordant Blue 9 [C.I. 14855, 6-(5-chloro-2-hydroxy-4-sulfophenylazo)-5-hydroxy-1-naphthalenesulfonic acid, disodium salt]
$NaO_3SC_6H_2(Cl)(OH)N{=}NC_{10}H_5(OH)SO_3Na$
FW 502.82 Disp. C,D

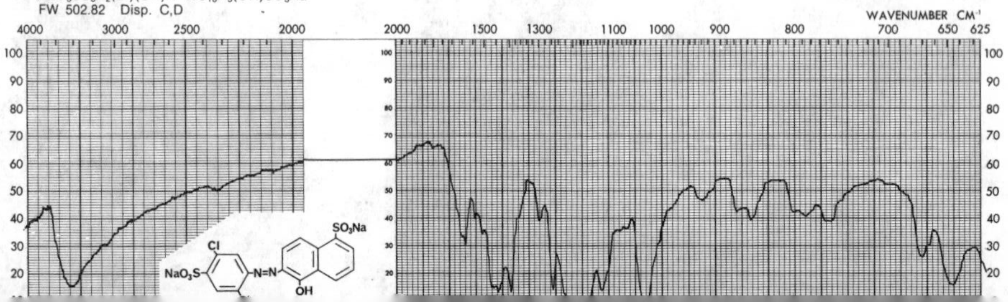

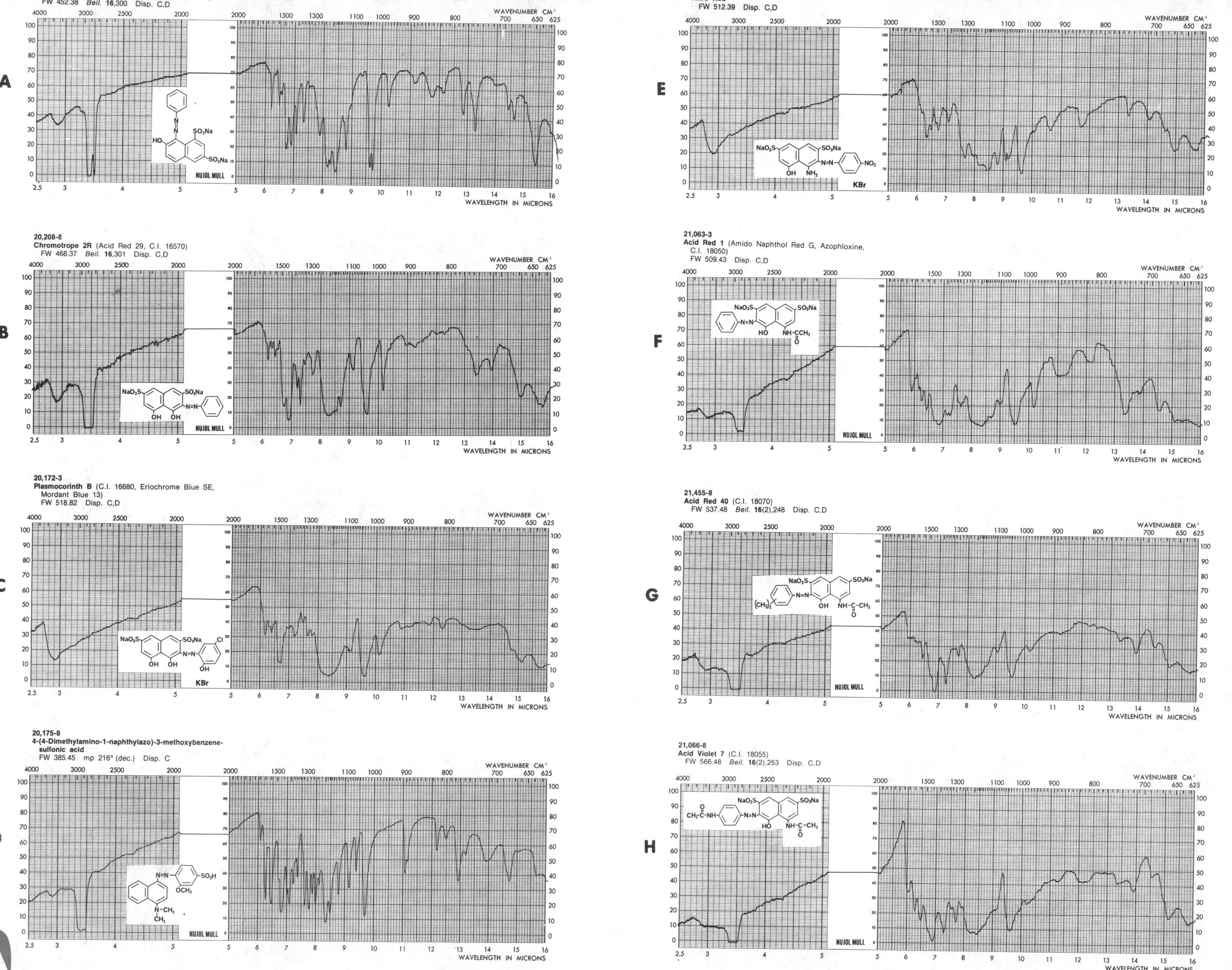
A
Orange G, certified (Acid Orange 10, C.I. 16230)
FW 452.38 *Beil.* **16**,300 Disp. C,D
NUJOL MULL
B
20,208-8
Chromotrope 2R (Acid Red 29, C.I. 16570)
FW 468.37 *Beil.* **16**,301 Disp. C,D
NUJOL MULL
C
20,172-3
Plasmocorinth B (C.I. 16680, Eriochrome Blue SE, Mordant Blue 13)
FW 518.82 Disp. C,D
KBr
D
20,175-8
4-(4-Dimethylamino-1-naphthylazo)-3-methoxybenzene-sulfonic acid
FW 385.45 mp 216° (dec.) Disp. C
NUJOL MULL
E
Nitro Red
FW 512.39 Disp. C,D
KBr
F
21,063-3
Acid Red 1 (Amido Naphthol Red G, Azophloxine, C.I. 18050)
FW 509.43 Disp. C,D
NUJOL MULL
G
21,455-8
Acid Red 40 (C.I. 18070)
FW 537.48 *Beil.* **16**(2),248 Disp. C,D
NUJOL MULL
H
21,066-8
Acid Violet 7 (C.I. 18055)
FW 566.48 *Beil.* **16**(2),253 Disp. C,D
NUJOL MULL
WAVENUMBER CM⁻¹
WAVELENGTH IN MICRONS
ALDRICH

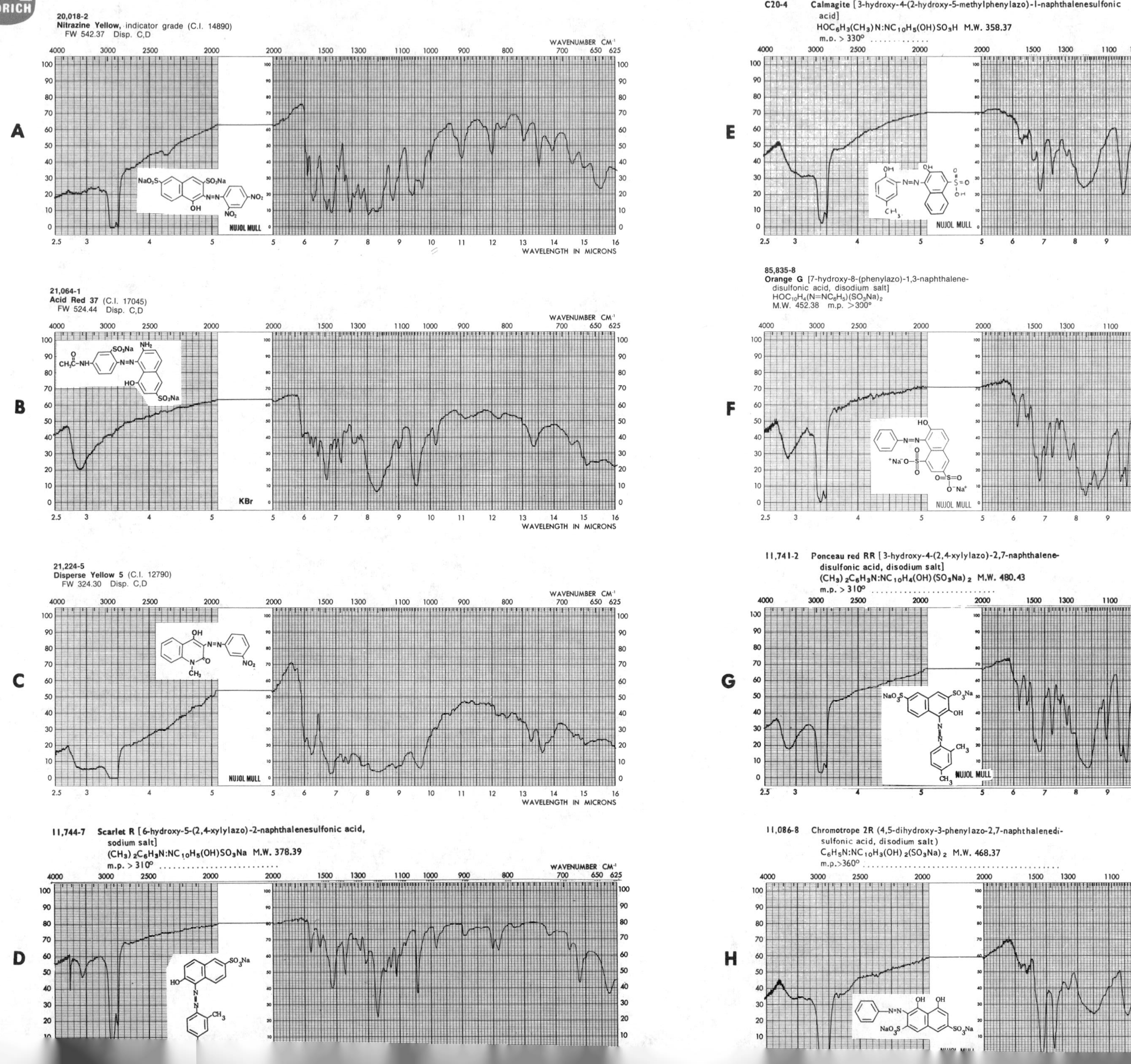
A
20,018-2
Nitrazine Yellow, indicator grade (C.I. 14890)
FW 542.37 Disp. C,D
NUJOL MULL
B
21,064-1
Acid Red 37 (C.I. 17045)
FW 524.44 Disp. C,D
KBr
C
21,224-5
Disperse Yellow 5 (C.I. 12790)
FW 324.30 Disp. C,D
NUJOL MULL
D
11,744-7 Scarlet R [6-hydroxy-5-(2,4-xylylazo)-2-naphthalenesulfonic acid, sodium salt]
$(CH_3)_2C_6H_3N{:}NC_{10}H_5(OH)SO_3Na$ M.W. 378.39
m.p. > 310°
E
C20-4 Calmagite [3-hydroxy-4-(2-hydroxy-5-methylphenylazo)-1-naphthalenesulfonic acid]
$HOC_6H_3(CH_3)N{:}NC_{10}H_5(OH)SO_3H$ M.W. 358.37
m.p. > 330°
NUJOL MULL
F
85,835-8
Orange G [7-hydroxy-8-(phenylazo)-1,3-naphthalenedisulfonic acid, disodium salt]
$HOC_{10}H_4(N{=}NC_6H_5)(SO_3Na)_2$
M.W. 452.38 m.p. >300°
NUJOL MULL
G
11,741-2 Ponceau red RR [3-hydroxy-4-(2,4-xylylazo)-2,7-naphthalenedisulfonic acid, disodium salt]
$(CH_3)_2C_6H_3N{:}NC_{10}H_4(OH)(SO_3Na)_2$ M.W. 480.43
m.p. > 310°
NUJOL MULL
H
11,086-8 Chromotrope 2R (4,5-dihydroxy-3-phenylazo-2,7-naphthalenedisulfonic acid, disodium salt)
$C_6H_5N{:}NC_{10}H_3(OH)_2(SO_3Na)_2$ M.W. 468.37
m.p.>360°
WAVENUMBER CM⁻¹
WAVELENGTH IN MICRONS

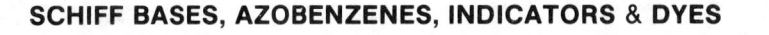

A

m.p. > 300° . . . .

NUJOL MULL

B

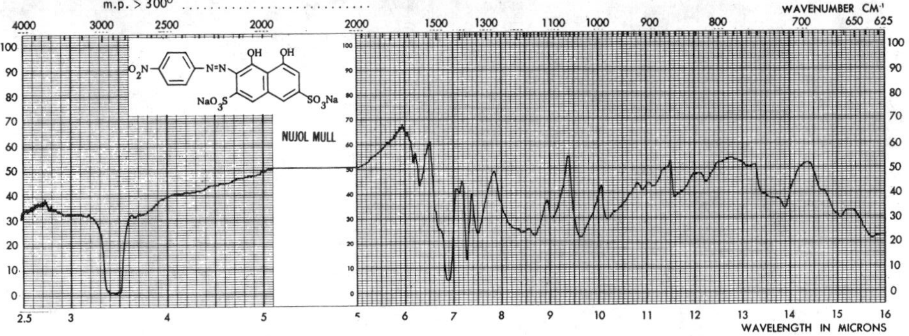

85,833-1
Biebrich scarlet, water soluble (Ponceau BS)
M.W. 556.49 m.p. >300°

NUJOL MULL

C

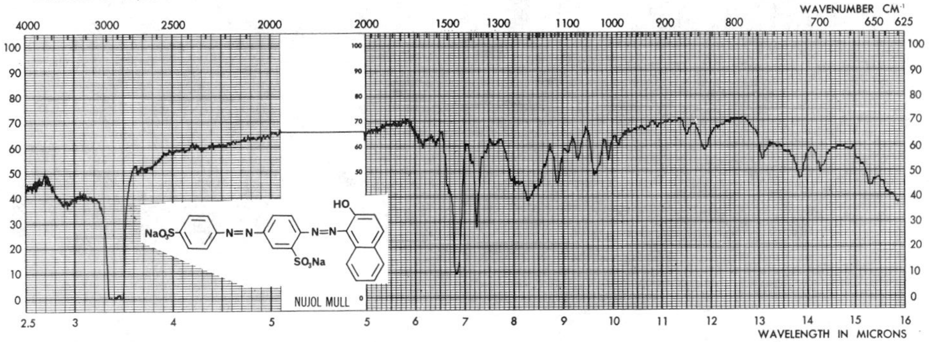

10,215-6 **Sulfonazo III** [3,6-bis-(o-sulfophenylazo)-4,5-dihydroxy-2,7-naphthalenedisulfonic acid]
$(HO_3SC_6H_4N:N)_2C_{10}H_2(OH)_2(SO_3H)_2$ M.W. 688.65
m.p. > 300° . . . .

NUJOL MULL

D

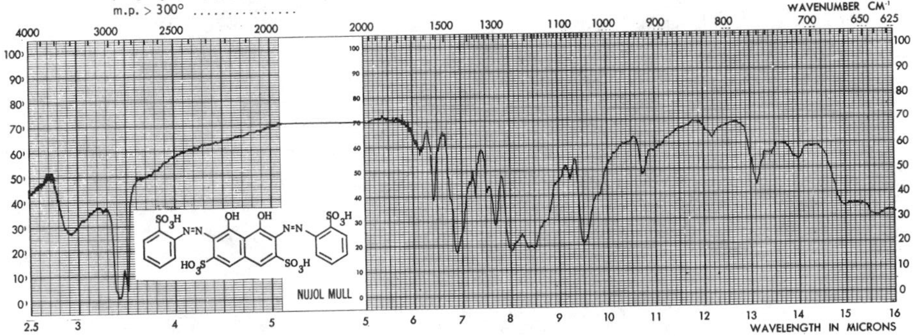

15,335-4 **Methylsulfonazo III, indicator grade**
M.W. 760.67 m.p. > 310° . . . .

NUJOL MULL

E

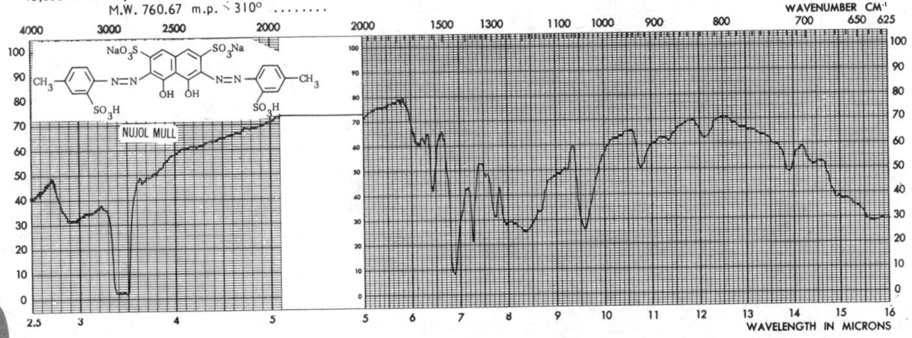

mp 280° (dec.) *Beil.* **16**,287 Disp. C,D

KBr

F

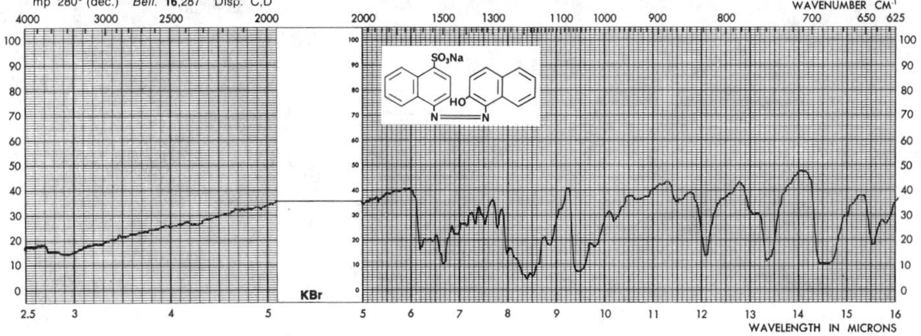

21,673-9
Palatine Chrome Black 6BN (C.I. 15705, Eriochrome Blue Black R, Mordant Black 17)
FW 416.39 *Beil.* **16**,297 Disp. C,D

KBr

G

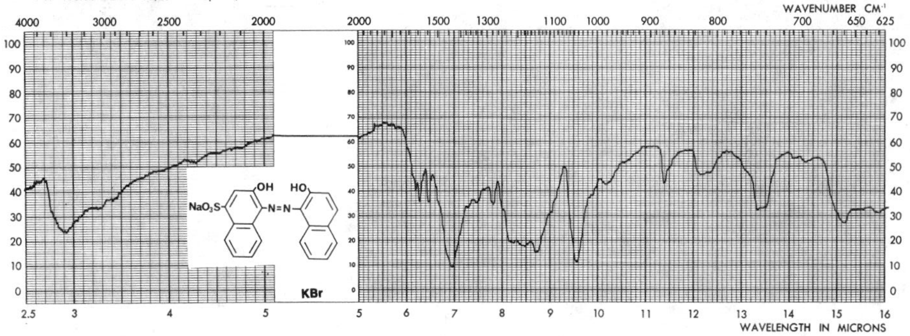

20,183-9
Acid Blue 161 (C.I. 15706)
FW 1353.19 Disp. C,D

KBr

H

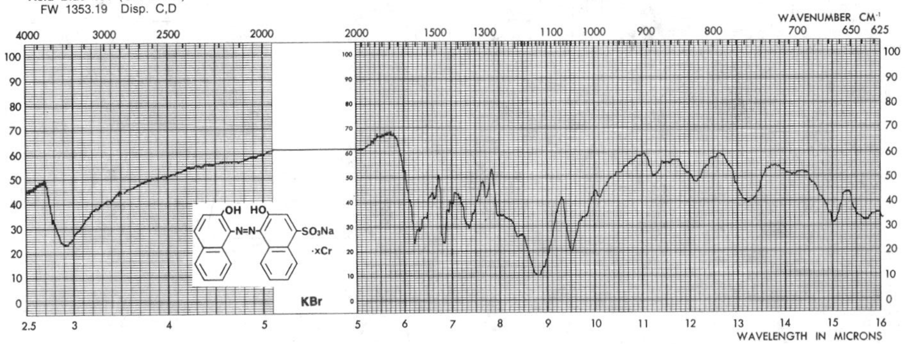

20,149-9
Eriochrome Blue Black B (C.I. 14640, Mordant Black 3)
FW 416.39 *Beil.* **16**,297 Disp. C,D

NUJOL MULL

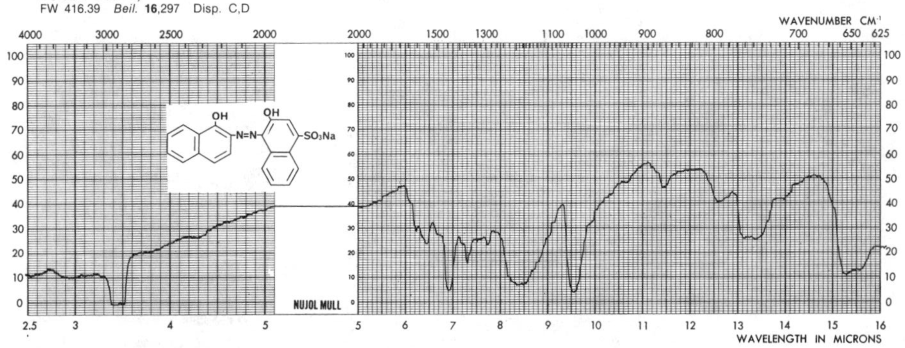

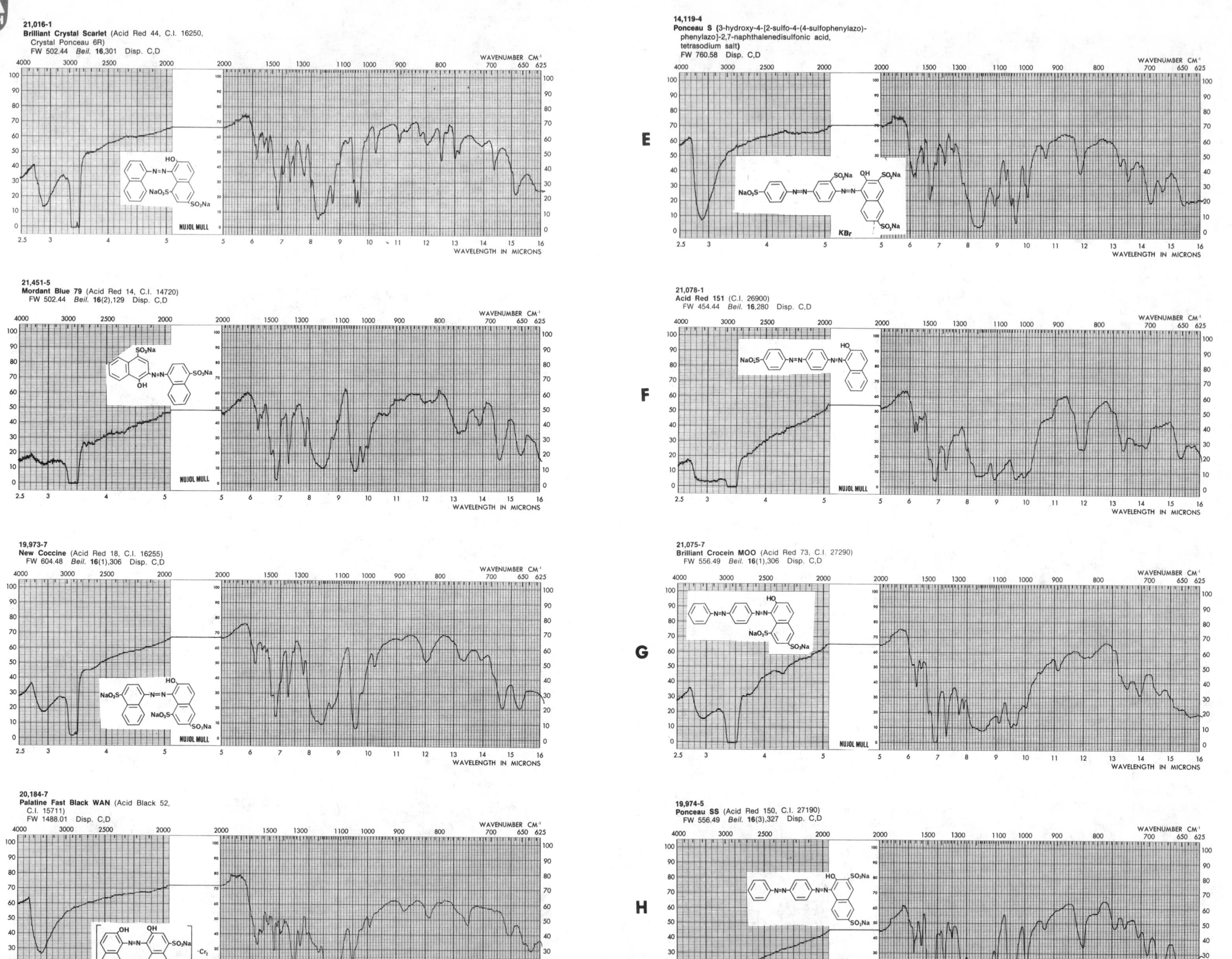

A

21,016-1
Brilliant Crystal Scarlet (Acid Red 44, C.I. 16250, Crystal Ponceau 6R)
FW 502.44 *Beil.* **16**,301 Disp. C,D

NUJOL MULL

B

21,451-5
Mordant Blue 79 (Acid Red 14, C.I. 14720)
FW 502.44 *Beil.* **16**(2),129 Disp. C,D

NUJOL MULL

C

19,973-7
New Coccine (Acid Red 18, C.I. 16255)
FW 604.48 *Beil.* **16**(1),306 Disp. C,D

NUJOL MULL

D

20,184-7
Palatine Fast Black WAN (Acid Black 52, C.I. 15711)
FW 1488.01 Disp. C,D

E

14,119-4
Ponceau S (3-hydroxy-4-[2-sulfo-4-(4-sulfophenylazo)-phenylazo]-2,7-naphthalenedisulfonic acid, tetrasodium salt)
FW 760.58 Disp. C,D

KBr

F

21,078-1
Acid Red 151 (C.I. 26900)
FW 454.44 *Beil.* **16**,280 Disp. C,D

NUJOL MULL

G

21,075-7
Brilliant Crocein MOO (Acid Red 73, C.I. 27290)
FW 556.49 *Beil.* **16**(1),306 Disp. C,D

NUJOL MULL

H

19,974-5
Ponceau SS (Acid Red 150, C.I. 27190)
FW 556.49 *Beil.* **16**(3),327 Disp. C,D

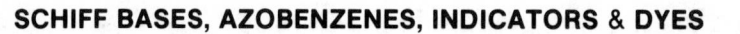

A

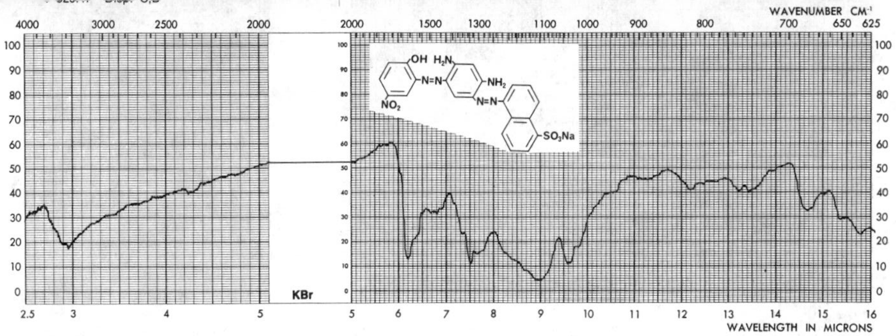

KBr

19,524-3
Acid Black 1 [C.I. 20470, 4-amino-5-hydroxy-3-(*p*-nitrophenylazo)-6-(phenylazo)-2,7-naphthalenedisulfonic acid, disodium salt]
$O_2NC_6H_4N{=}NC_{10}H_2(NH_2)(OH)(N{=}NC_6H_5)(SO_3Na)_2$
FW 616.50 *Beil.* **16**(2),257 Disp. C,D

B

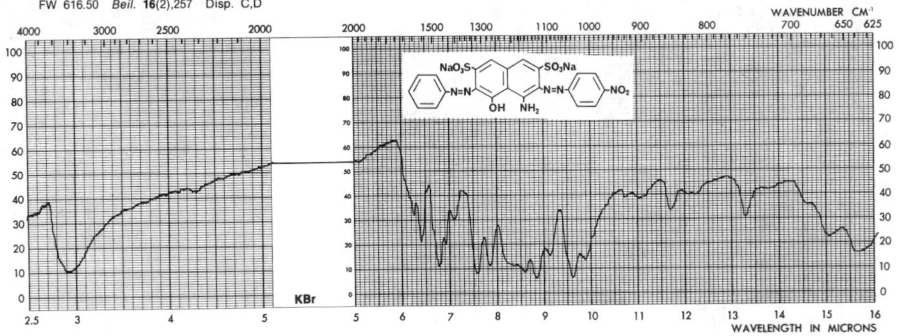

KBr

21,076-5
Acid Red 106 (C.I. 18110)
FW 621.58 Disp. C,D

C

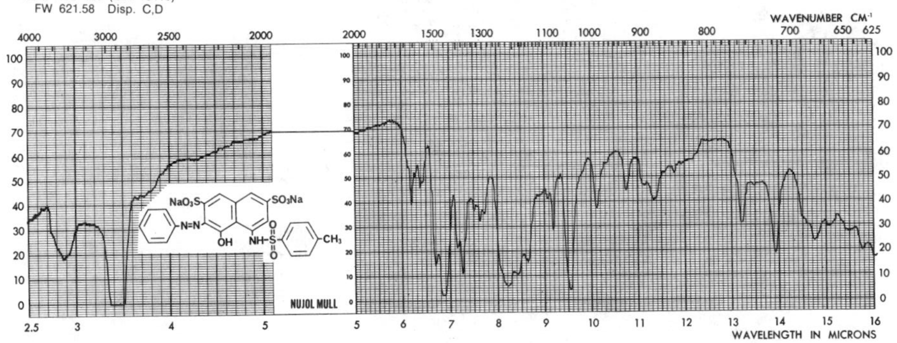

NUJOL MULL

21,080-3
Acid Violet 5 (C.I. 18125)
FW 678.63 Disp. C,D

D

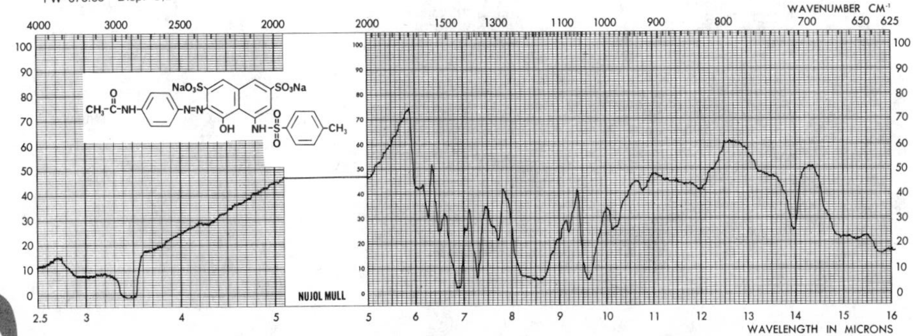

NUJOL MULL

FW 695.59 Disp. C,D

E

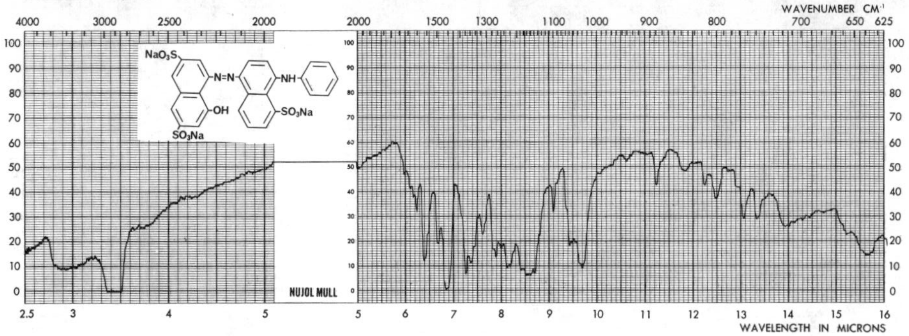

NUJOL MULL

19,966-4
Sudan Black B, certified (C.I. 26150, Solvent Black 3)
FW 456.55 mp 120-124° Disp. C,D

F

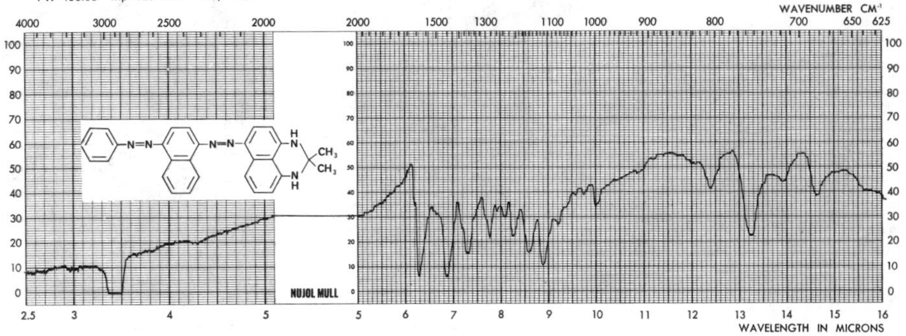

NUJOL MULL

21,043-9
Acid Blue 113 (C.I. 26360)
FW 681.66 mp >300° Disp. C,D

G

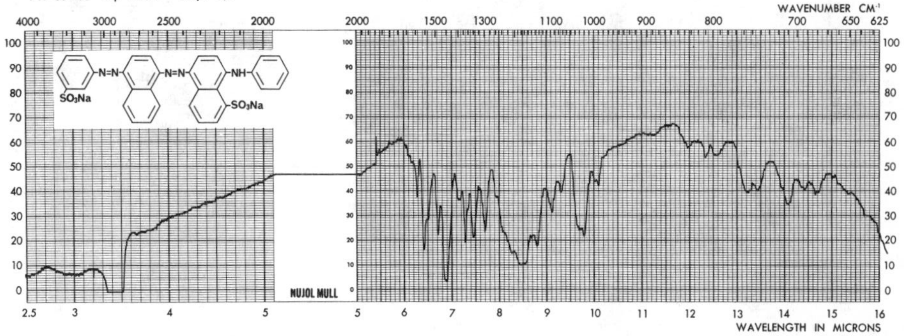

NUJOL MULL

21,044-7
Acid Blue 120 (C.I. 26400)
FW 695.69 mp >300° Disp. C,D

H

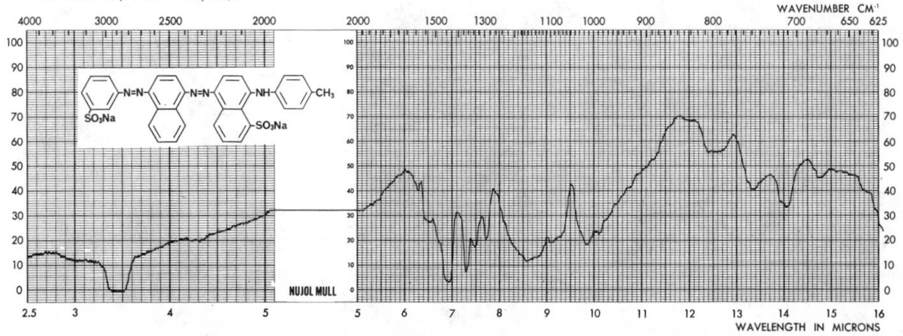

NUJOL MULL

A

21,045-5
Acid Black 24 (C.I. 26370)
FW 731.72 Disp. C,D

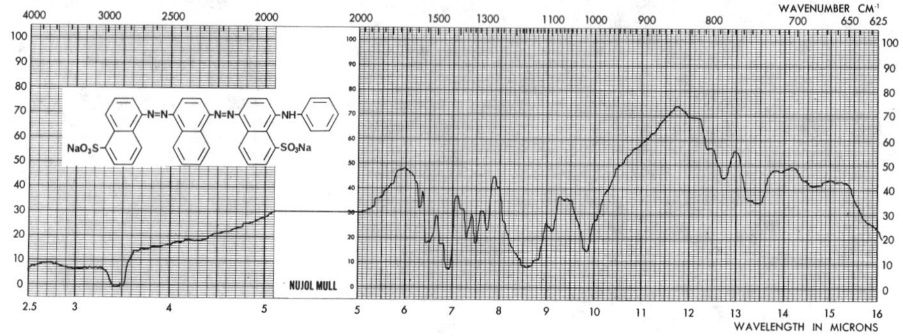

NUJOL MULL

B

20,156-1
Fast Sulphon Black F (Acid Black 32, C.I. 26990)
FW 774.65 *Beil.* **16**(2),132 Disp. C,D

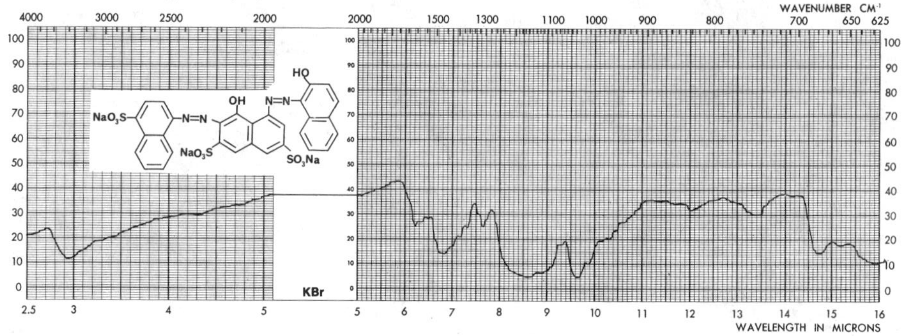

KBr

C

21,240-7
Direct Blue 71 (C.I. 34140)
FW 1029.88 Disp. C,D

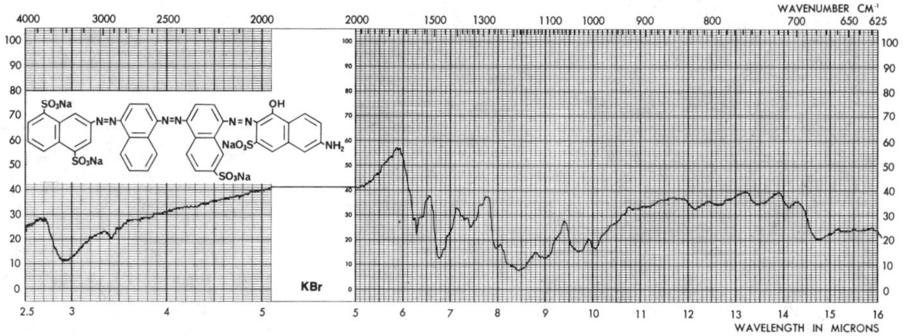

KBr

D

21,459-0
Acid Orange 51 (C.I. 26550)
FW 860.81 Disp. C,D

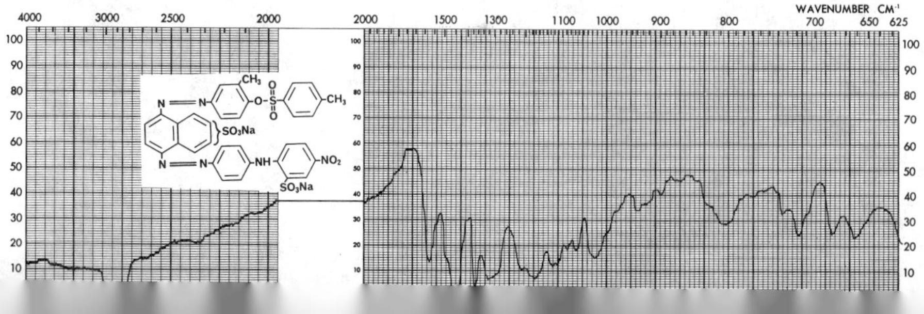

E

21,031-5
Acid Red 114 (C.I. 23635)
FW 830.83 Disp. C,D

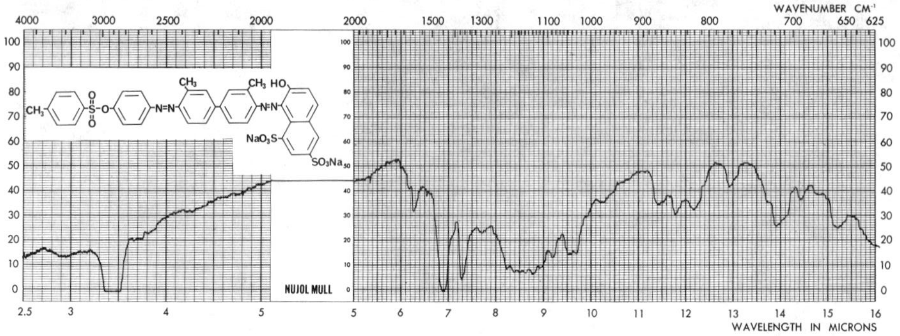

NUJOL MULL

F

86,095-6
Congo Red, certified (C.I. 22120, Direct Red 28)
FW 696.67 *Beil.* **16**,410 Disp. C,D

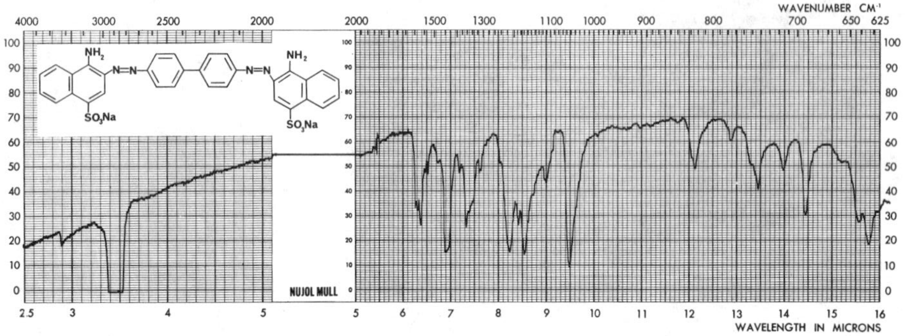

NUJOL MULL

G

21,039-0
Acid Red 97 (C.I. 22890)
FW 698.65 *Beil.* **16**(2),125 Disp. C,D

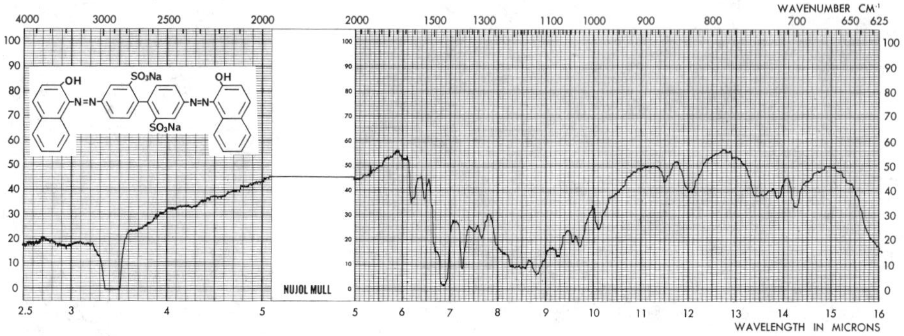

NUJOL MULL

H

19,525-1
Direct Red 81 (C.I. 28160)
FW 675.61 mp 240° (dec.) *Beil.* **16**(2),235
Disp. C,D

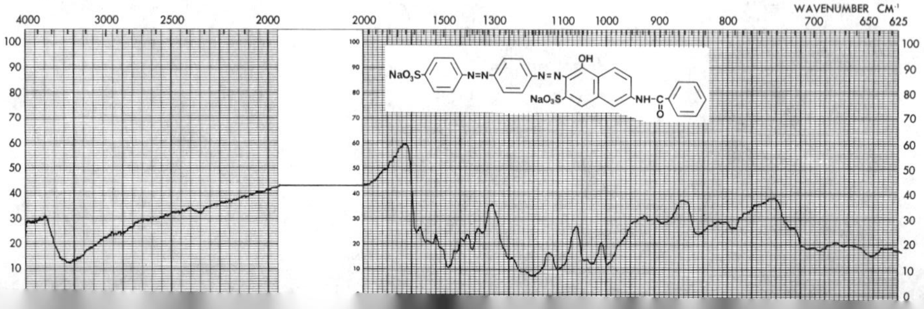

A

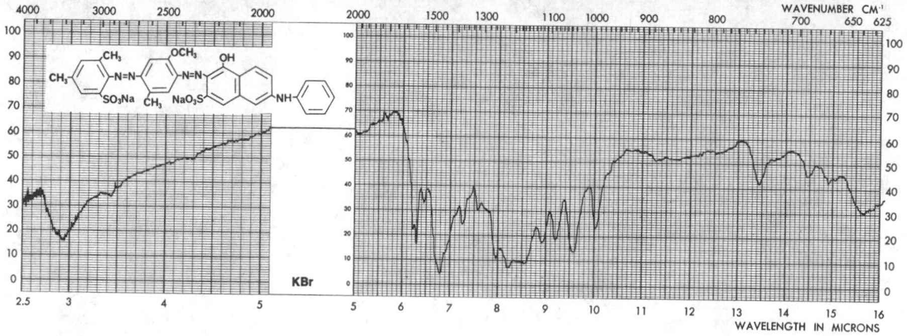

KBr

21,262-8
Direct Black 22 (C.I. 35435)
FW 1083.99 Disp. C,D

B

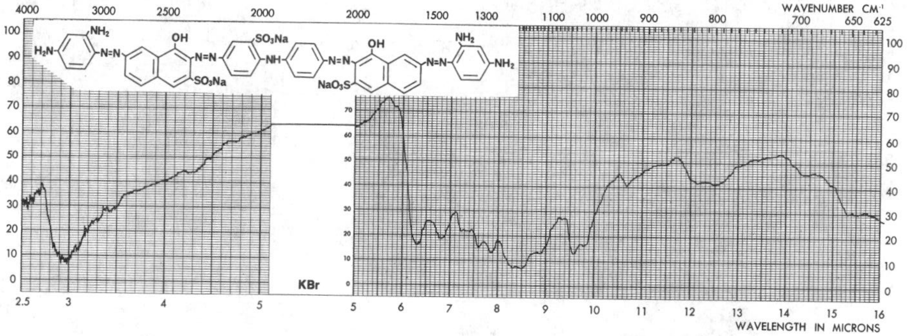

KBr

21,235-0
Direct Red 75 (Benzo Fast Pink 2BL, C.I. 25380)
FW 990.80 Disp. C,D

C

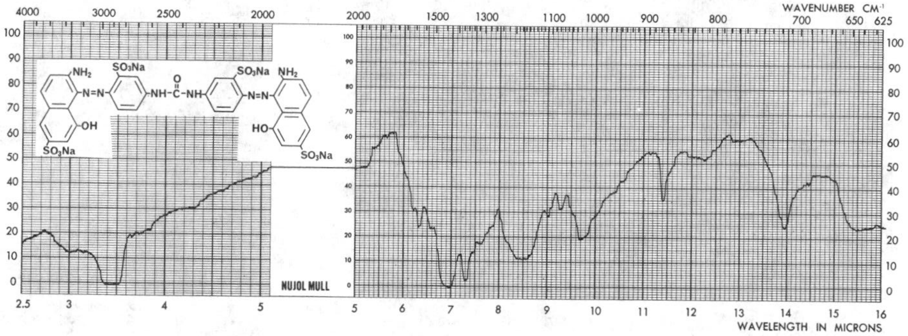

NUJOL MULL

20,189-8
Direct Yellow 50 (C.I. 29025)
FW 956.83 Disp. C,D

D

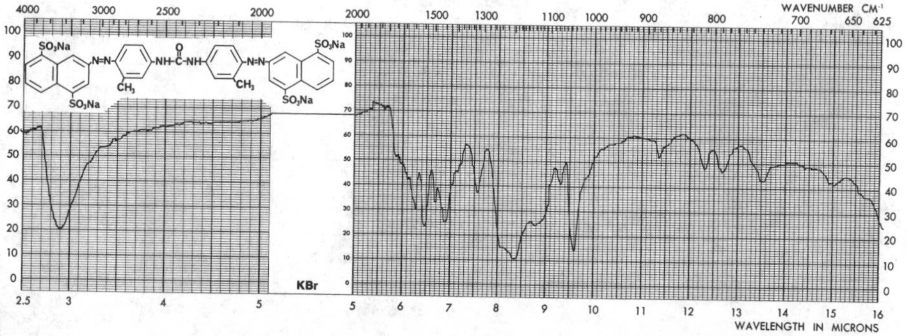

KBr

FW 813.74 Disp. C,D

E

KBr

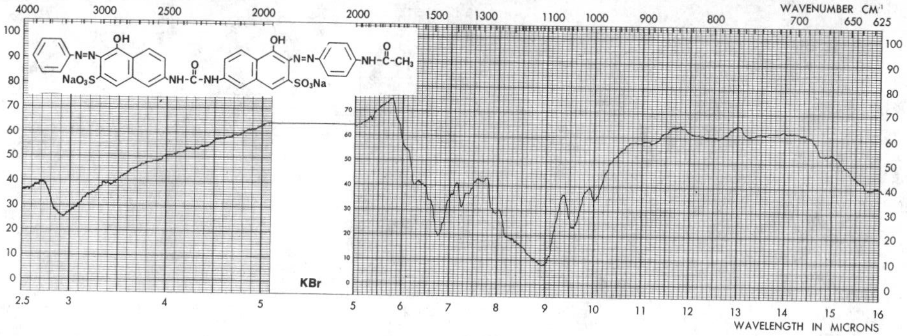

20,633-4
Evans Blue (C.I. 23860)
FW 960.82 *Beil.* **16**(2),259 Disp. C,D

F

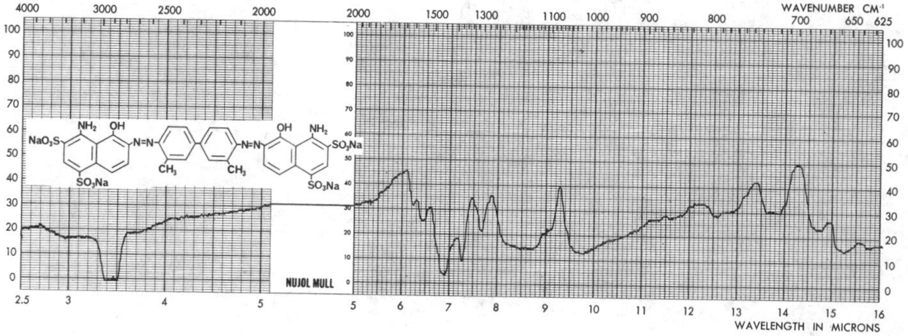

NUJOL MULL

20,138-3
Chicago Sky Blue 6B (C.I. 24410, Direct Blue 1)
FW 992.82 *Beil.* **16**(1),346 Disp. C,D

G

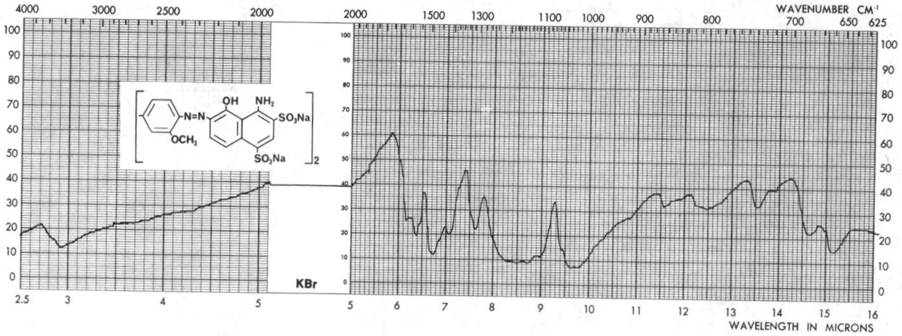

KBr

19,812-9
Trypan Blue (C.I. 23850, Direct Blue 14, Niagara Blue 3B)
FW 960.82 *Beil.* **16**(1),346 Disp. C,D

H

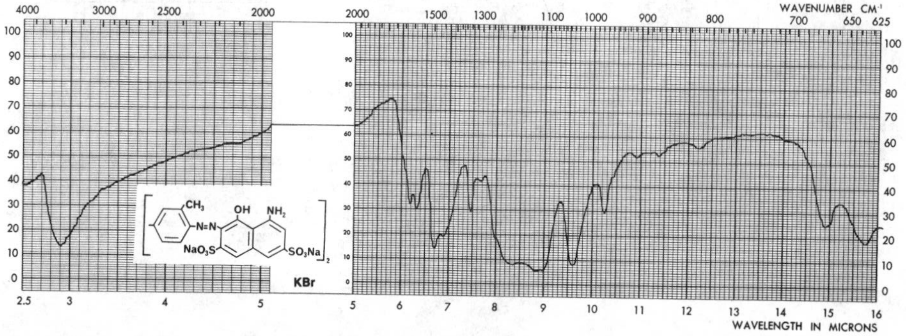

KBr

ALDRICH

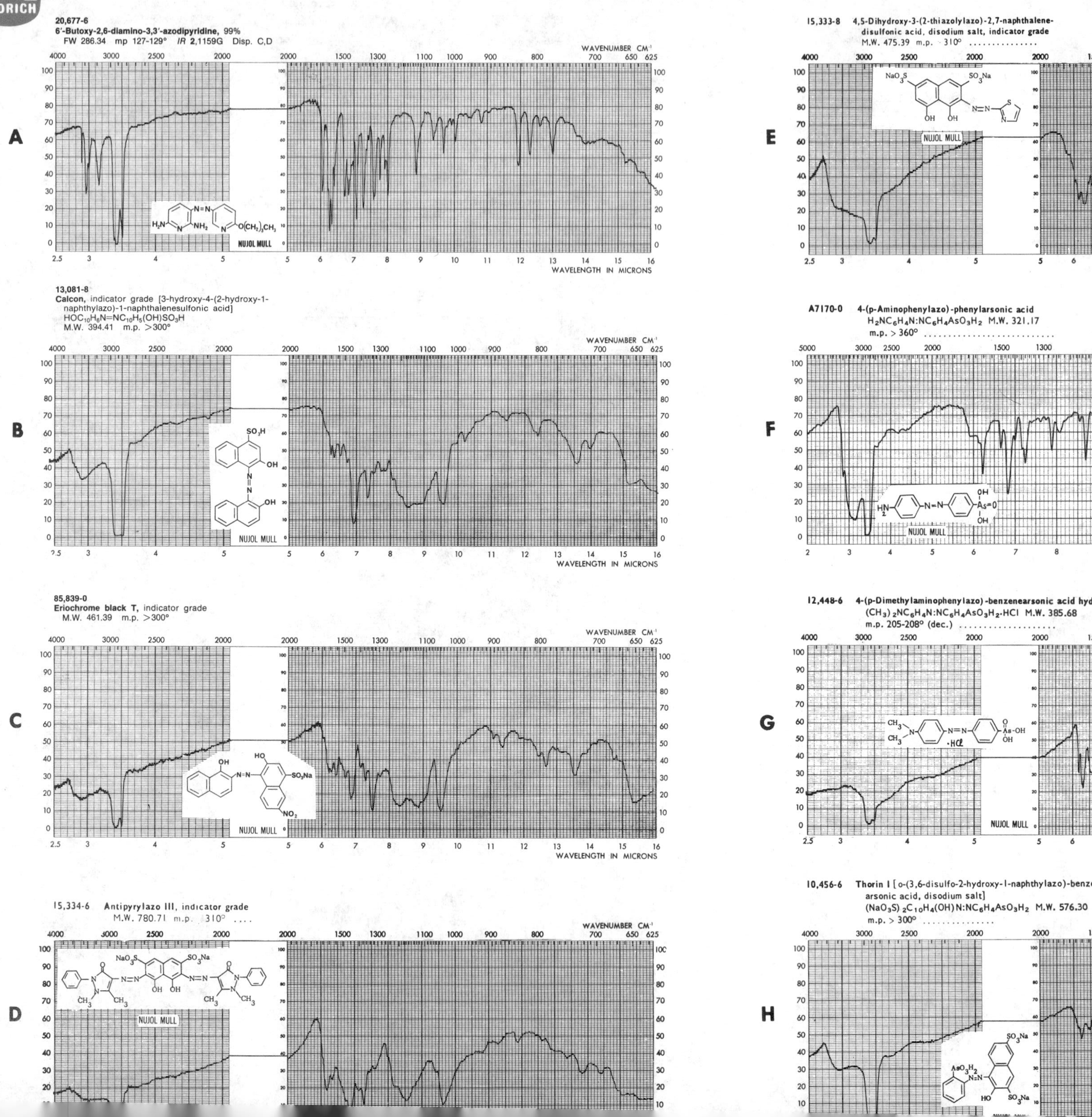
A
20,677-6
6'-Butoxy-2,6-diamino-3,3'-azodipyridine, 99%
FW 286.34 mp 127-129° IR 2,1159G Disp. C,D
NUJOL MULL
B
13,081-8
Calcon, indicator grade [3-hydroxy-4-(2-hydroxy-1-naphthylazo)-1-naphthalenesulfonic acid]
$HOC_{10}H_6N{=}NC_{10}H_5(OH)SO_3H$
M.W. 394.41 m.p. >300°
NUJOL MULL
C
85,839-0
Eriochrome black T, indicator grade
M.W. 461.39 m.p. >300°
NUJOL MULL
D
15,334-6 Antipyrylazo III, indicator grade
M.W. 780.71 m.p. 310° ....
NUJOL MULL
E
15,333-8 4,5-Dihydroxy-3-(2-thiazolylazo)-2,7-naphthalenedisulfonic acid, disodium salt, indicator grade
M.W. 475.39 m.p. 310° ....
NUJOL MULL
F
A7170-0 4-(p-Aminophenylazo)-phenylarsonic acid
$H_2NC_6H_4N{:}NC_6H_4AsO_3H_2$ M.W. 321.17
m.p. > 360° ....
NUJOL MULL
G
12,448-6 4-(p-Dimethylaminophenylazo)-benzenearsonic acid hydrochloride
$(CH_3)_2NC_6H_4N{:}NC_6H_4AsO_3H_2{\cdot}HCl$ M.W. 385.68
m.p. 205-208° (dec.) ....
NUJOL MULL
H
10,456-6 Thorin I [o-(3,6-disulfo-2-hydroxy-1-naphthylazo)-benzenearsonic acid, disodium salt]
$(NaO_3S)_2C_{10}H_4(OH)N{:}NC_6H_4AsO_3H_2$ M.W. 576.30
m.p. > 300° ....
WAVENUMBER CM⁻¹
WAVELENGTH IN MICRONS

M.W. 548.33 m.p. > 300°

A9277-5 **Arsenazo III** [o-(1,8-dihydroxy-3,6-disulfonaphthylene-2,7-bisazo)-bisbenzenearsonic acid]
M.W. 776.37 m.p. > 320°

20,199-5
Flavazin L (Acid Yellow 11, C.I. 18820)
FW 380.36 *Beil.* **24**,337 Disp. C,D

20,200-2
Acid Yellow 34 (C.I. 18890)
FW 414.81 Disp. C,D

FW 430.81 *Beil.* **24**(2),173 Disp. C,D

20,181-2
Acid Orange 74 (C.I. 18745)
FW 493.38 Disp. C,D

20,195-2
Tartrazine (Acid Yellow 23, C.I. 19140)
FW 534.37 *Beil.* **25**,252 Disp. C,D

20,182-0
Acid Red 183 (C.I. 18800)
FW 584.87 mp >300° Disp. C,D

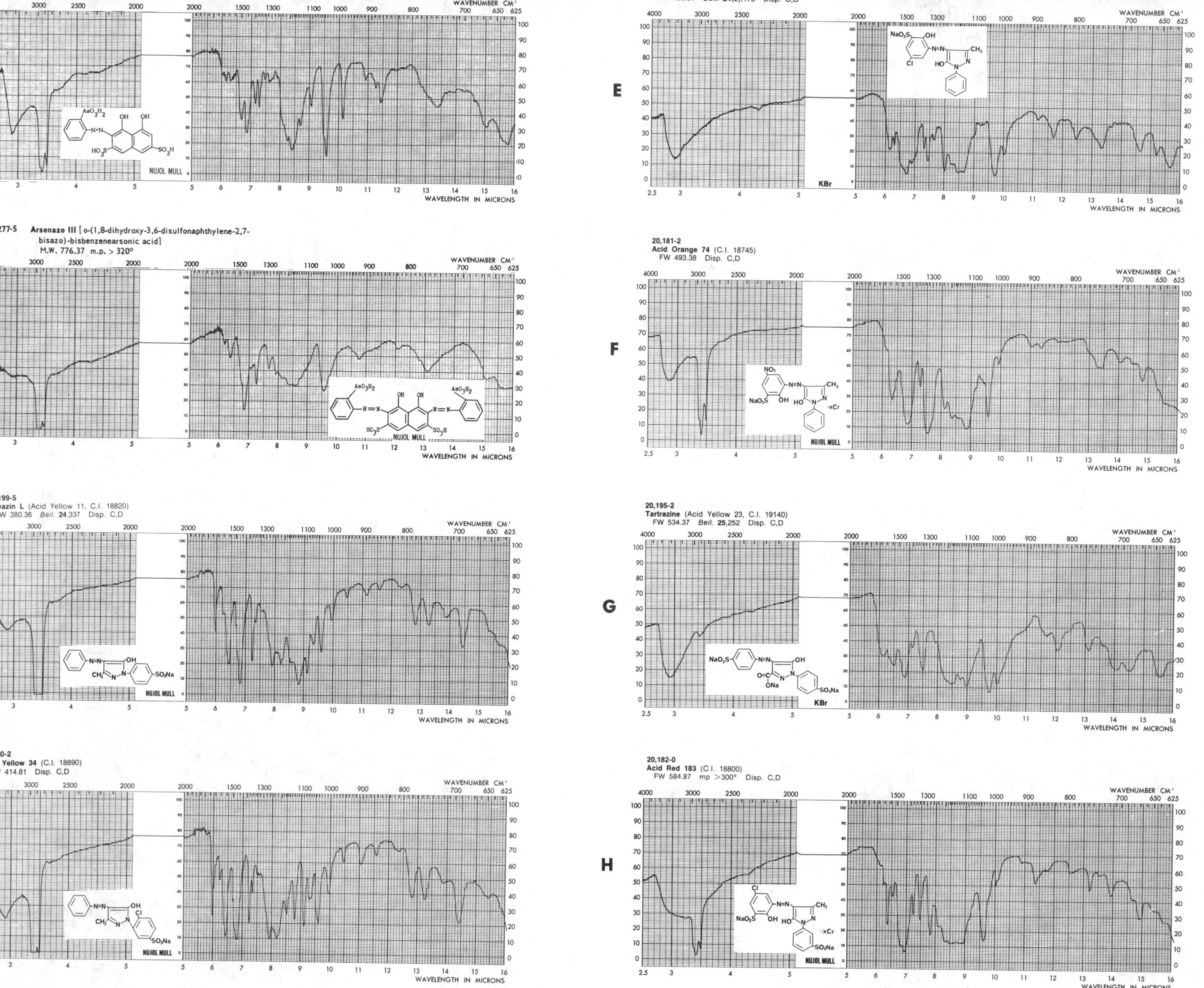

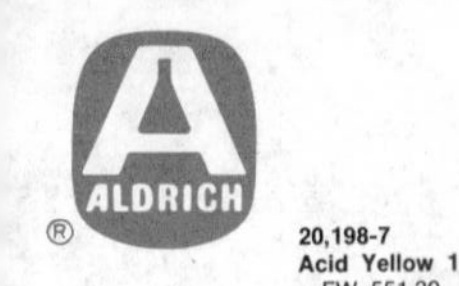

A

20,198-7
Acid Yellow 17 (C.I. 18965)
FW 551.30 *Beil.* **24**,338 Disp. C,D

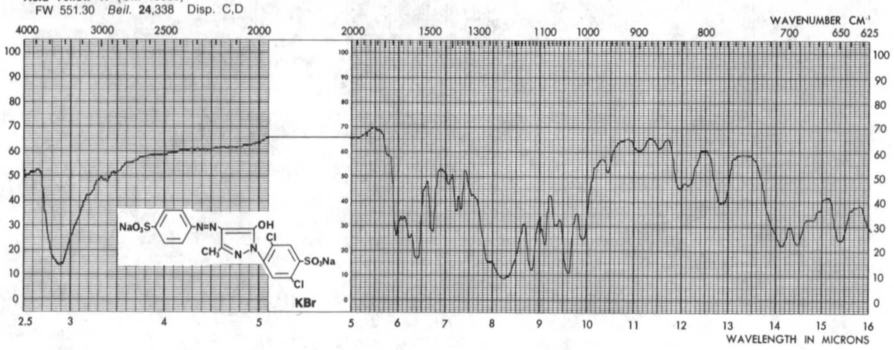

B

20,179-0
Palatine Fast Yellow BLN (Acid Yellow 54, C.I. 19010)
FW 614.44 Disp. C,D

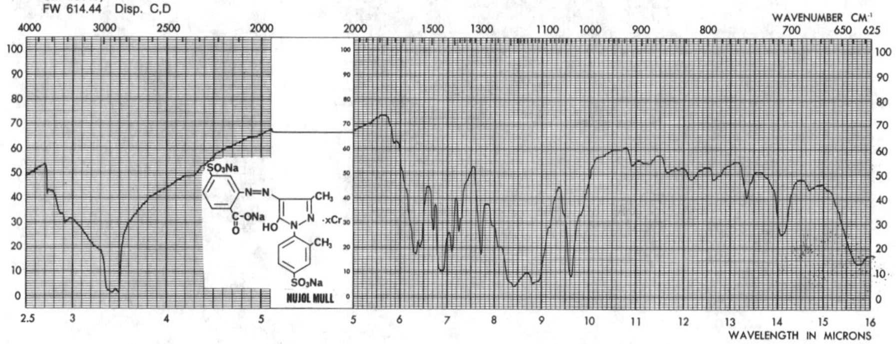

C

20,196-0
Acid Yellow 25 (C.I. 18835)
FW 549.56 Disp. C,D

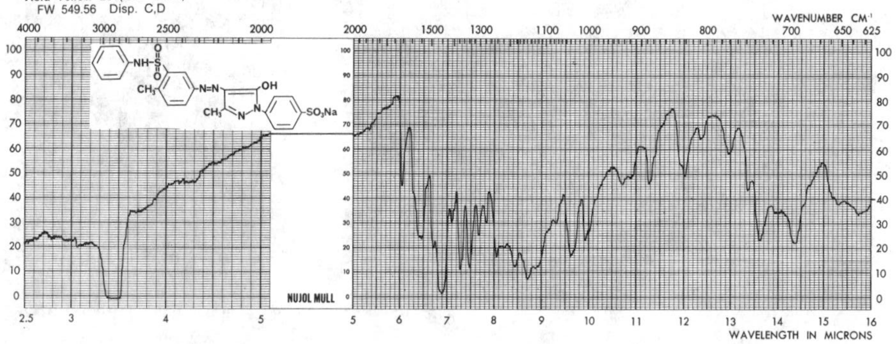

D

21,458-2
Acid Yellow 76 (C.I. 18850)
FW 550.55 Disp. C,D

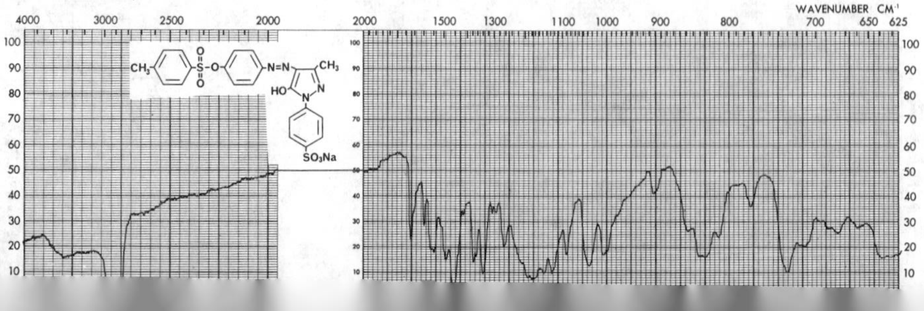

E

20,193-6
Acid Yellow 40 (C.I. 18950)
FW 584.99 mp 147° (dec.) Disp. C,D

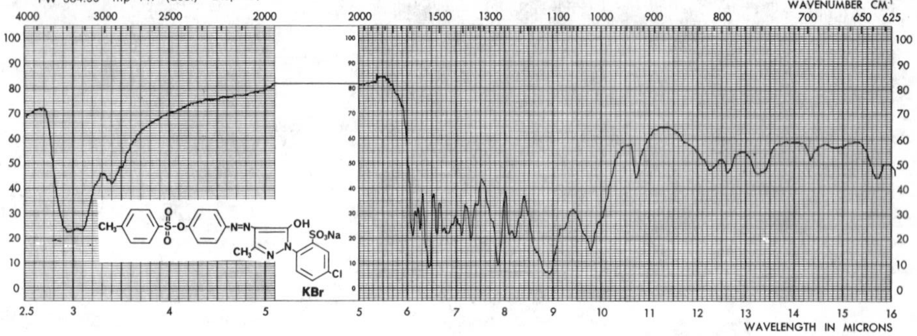

F

21,036-6
Acid Yellow 29 (C.I. 18900)
FW 569.98 mp 238° (dec.) Disp. C,D

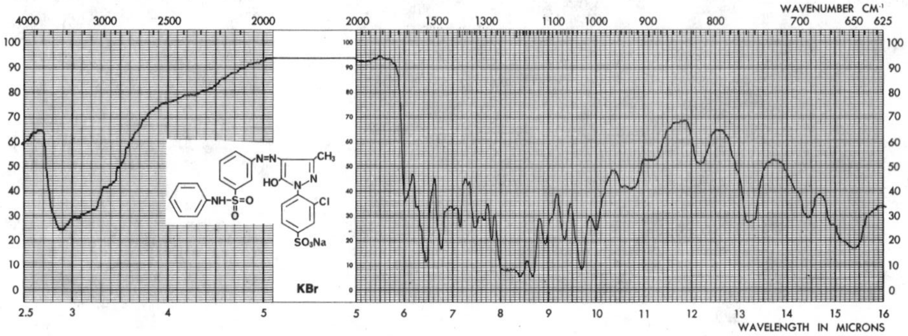

G

21,000-5
Erlochrome Red B (C.I. 18760, Mordant Red 7)
FW 446.42 *Beil.* **24**(2),174 Disp. C,D

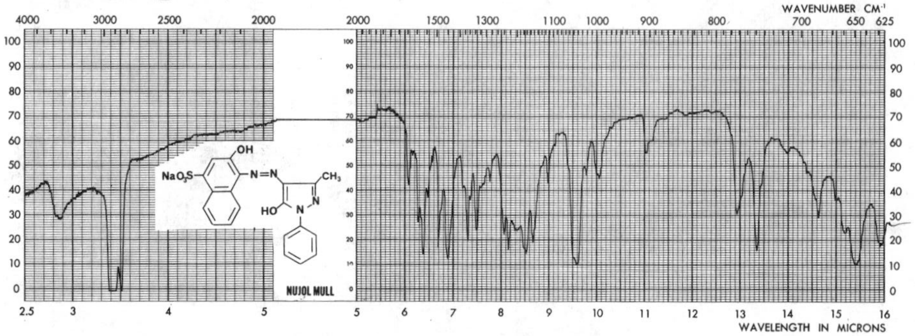

H

21,037-4
Acid Yellow 42 (C.I. 22910)
FW 758.71 mp 263° (dec.) Disp. C,D

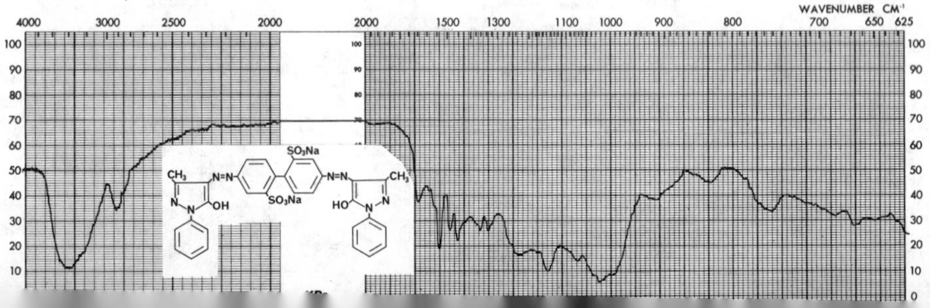

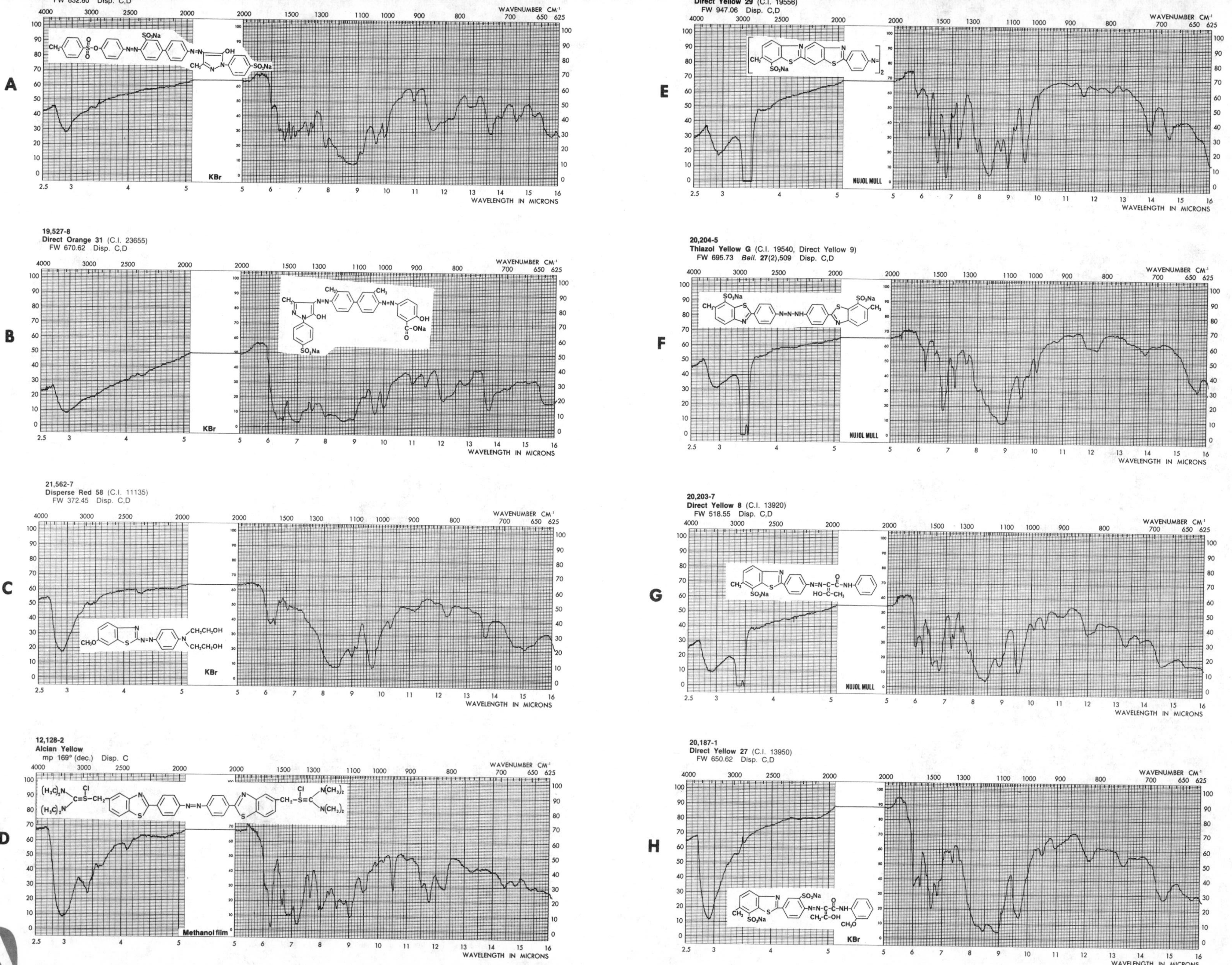
A
FW 832.80 Disp. C,D
KBr
19,527-8
Direct Orange 31 (C.I. 23655)
FW 670.62 Disp. C,D
B
KBr
21,562-7
Disperse Red 58 (C.I. 11135)
FW 372.45 Disp. C,D
C
KBr
12,128-2
Alcian Yellow
mp 169° (dec.) Disp. C
D
Methanol film
Direct Yellow 29 (C.I. 19556)
FW 947.06 Disp. C,D
E
NUJOL MULL
20,204-5
Thiazol Yellow G (C.I. 19540, Direct Yellow 9)
FW 695.73 Beil. 27(2),509 Disp. C,D
F
NUJOL MULL
20,203-7
Direct Yellow 8 (C.I. 13920)
FW 518.55 Disp. C,D
G
NUJOL MULL
20,187-1
Direct Yellow 27 (C.I. 13950)
FW 650.62 Disp. C,D
H
KBr
WAVENUMBER CM⁻¹
WAVELENGTH IN MICRONS
ALDRICH

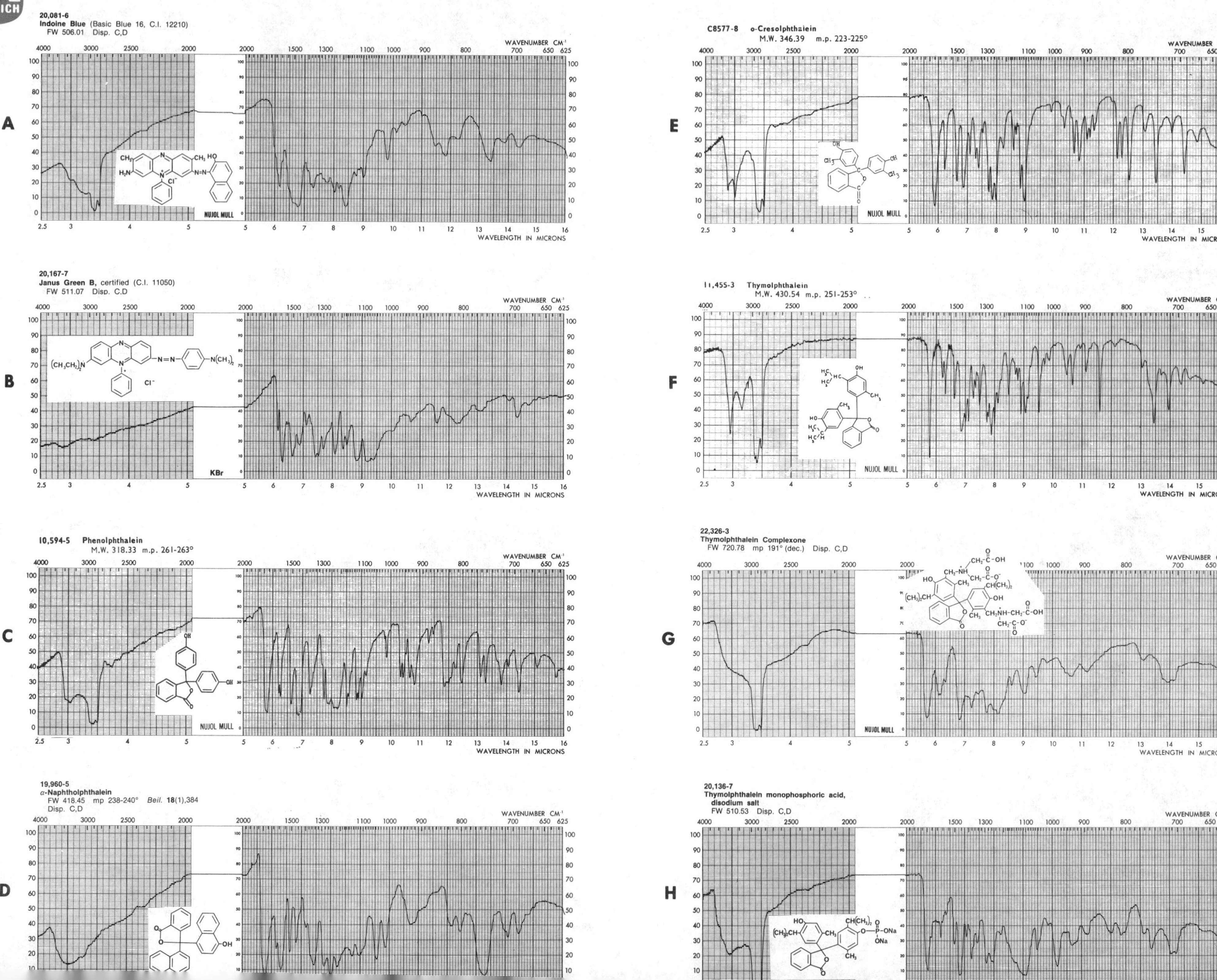
A
20,081-6
Indoine Blue (Basic Blue 16, C.I. 12210)
FW 506.01 Disp. C,D
NUJOL MULL
B
20,167-7
Janus Green B, certified (C.I. 11050)
FW 511.07 Disp. C,D
KBr
C
10,594-5 Phenolphthalein
M.W. 318.33 m.p. 261-263°
NUJOL MULL
D
19,960-5
α-Naphtholphthalein
FW 418.45 mp 238-240° Beil. 18(1),384
Disp. C,D
E
C8577-8 o-Cresolphthalein
M.W. 346.39 m.p. 223-225°
NUJOL MULL
F
11,455-3 Thymolphthalein
M.W. 430.54 m.p. 251-253°
NUJOL MULL
G
22,326-3
Thymolphthalein Complexone
FW 720.78 mp 191° (dec.) Disp. C,D
NUJOL MULL
H
20,136-7
Thymolphthalein monophosphoric acid, disodium salt
FW 510.53 Disp. C,D
WAVENUMBER CM⁻¹
WAVELENGTH IN MICRONS

A

FW 636.62 Disp. C,D

NUJOL MULL

B

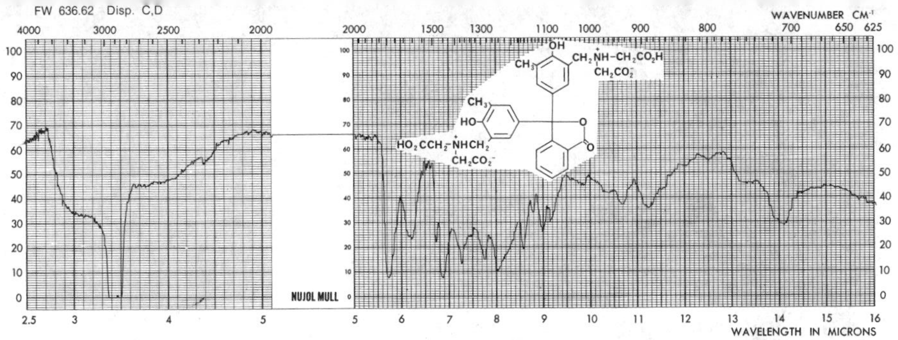

11,477-4 **Tetrabromophenolphthalein ethyl ester, potassium salt**
M.W. 700.08 m.p. 270° (dec.)

NUJOL MULL

C

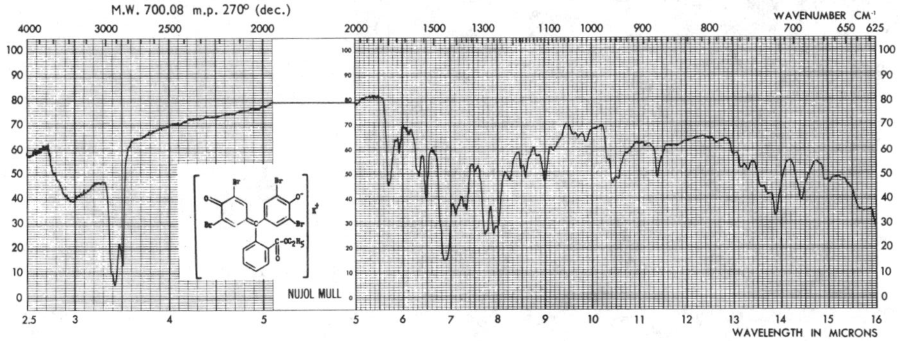

22,498-7
3',3'',5',5''-Tetraiodophenolphthalein, indicator grade
FW 821.92 mp 268° (dec.) *Beil.* **18**,151
Disp. C,D

NUJOL MULL

D

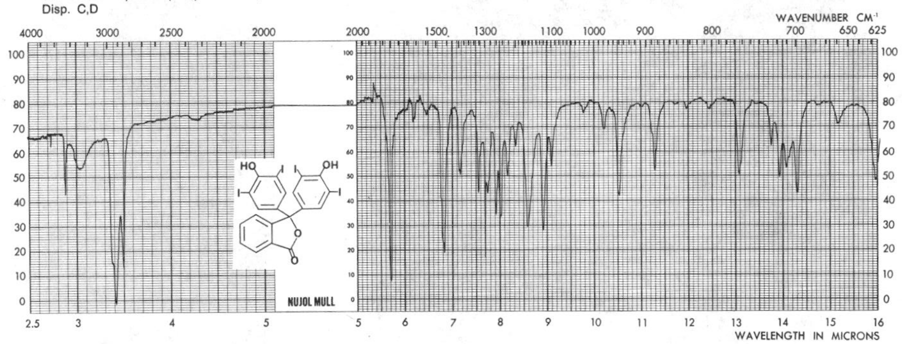

10,212-1 **Phenolphthalexon** [3',3''-bis-[N,N-bis-(carboxymethyl)-amino-methyl]-phenolphthalein, tetrasodium salt]
M.W. 696.49 m.p. > 360°

NUJOL MULL

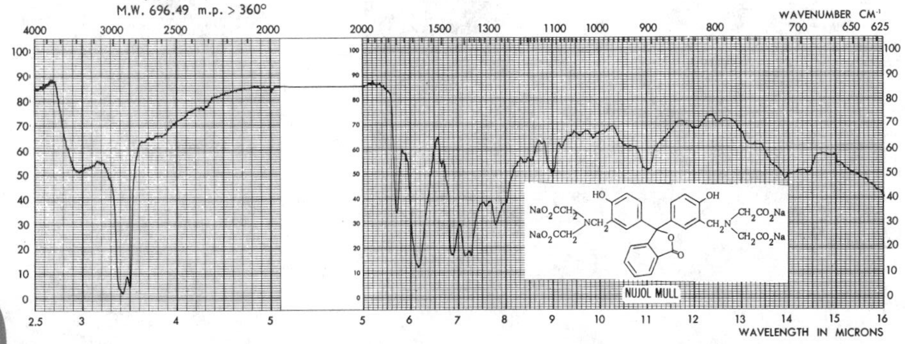

E

NUJOL MULL

F

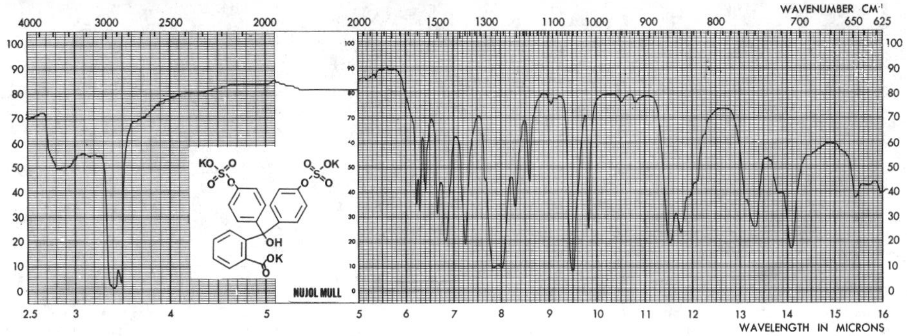

85,604-5
Phenolphthalein diphosphate, tetrasodium salt dihydrate
M.W. 602.25 m.p. >300°

NUJOL MULL

G

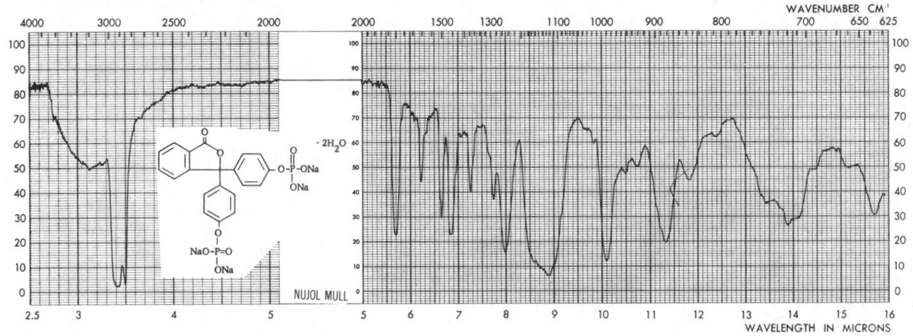

20,176-6
Thymolphthalein monophosphoric acid, magnesium salt
FW 532.83 mp 270° (dec.) Disp. C,D

NUJOL MULL

H

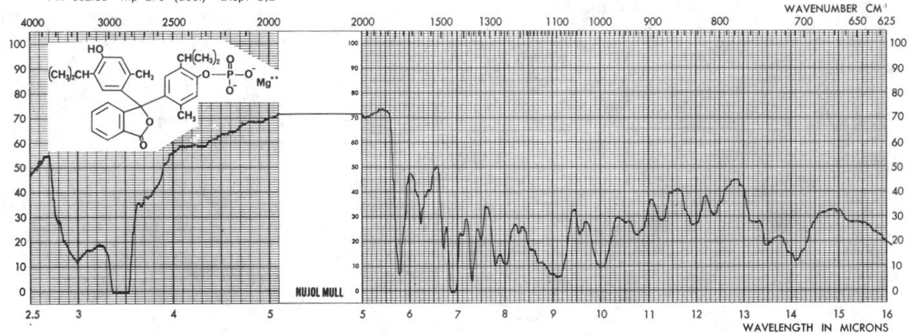

20,165-0
Fluorescamine
FW 278.27 mp 154-156° Disp. C,D

NUJOL MULL

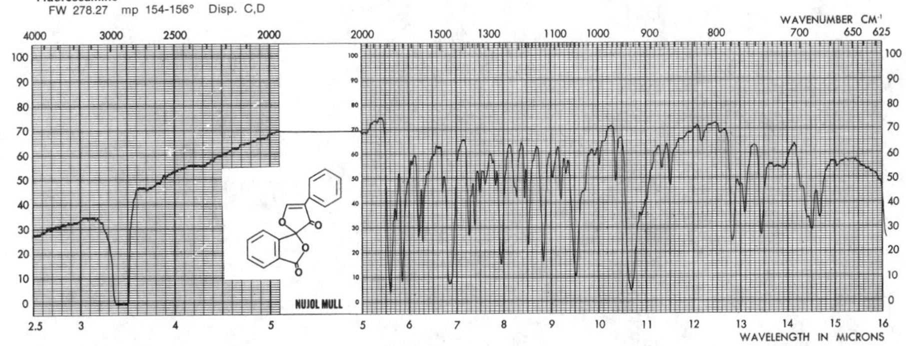

A

F245-6 **Fluorescein**
M.W. 389.39 m.p. > 320°
NUJOL MULL

B

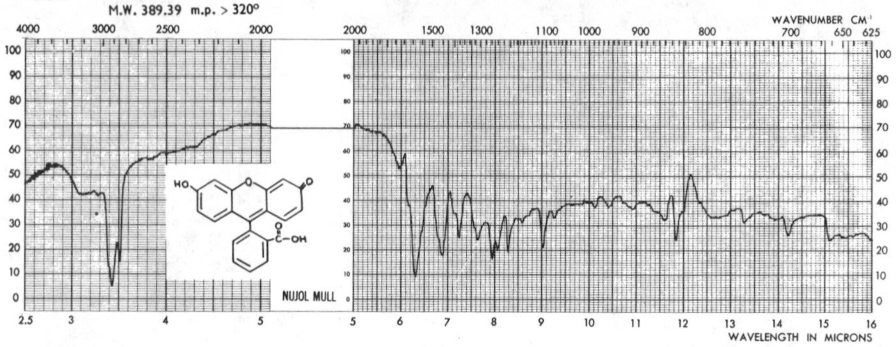

16,630-8
Fluorescein sodium, tech.
M.W. 376.28 m.p. >300°
NUJOL MULL

C

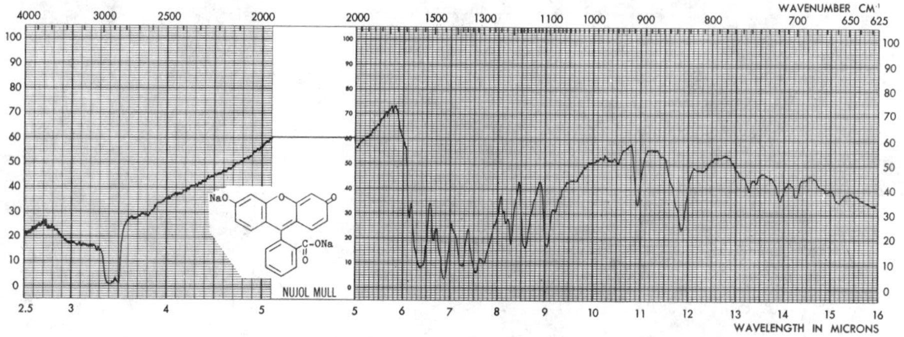

20,164-2
Fluorescein diacetate
FW 416.39 mp 200-203° *Beil.* **19**,227 Disp. C,D
NUJOL MULL

D

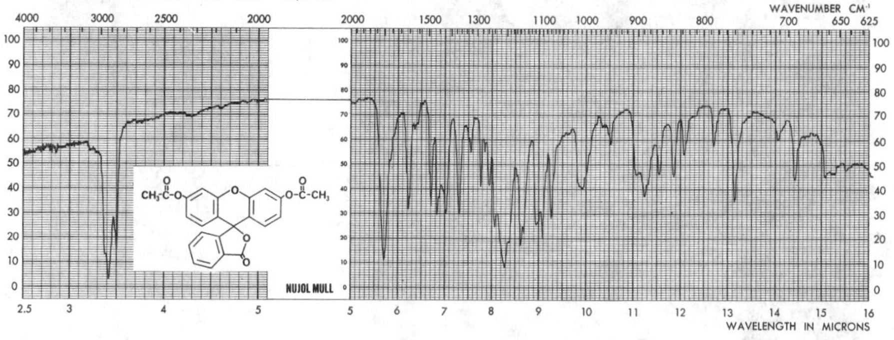

20,148-0
2',7'-Dichlorofluorescein
FW 401.20 *Beil.* **19**(1),722 Disp. C,D

E

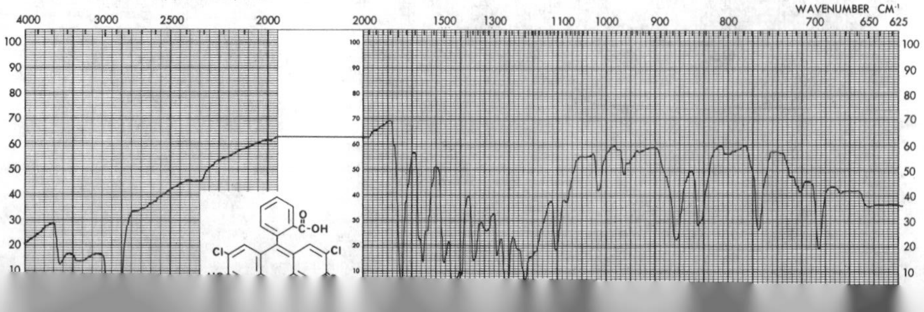

16,490-9
4',5'-Dichlorofluorescein, indicator grade
M.W. 401.2
NUJOL MULL

F

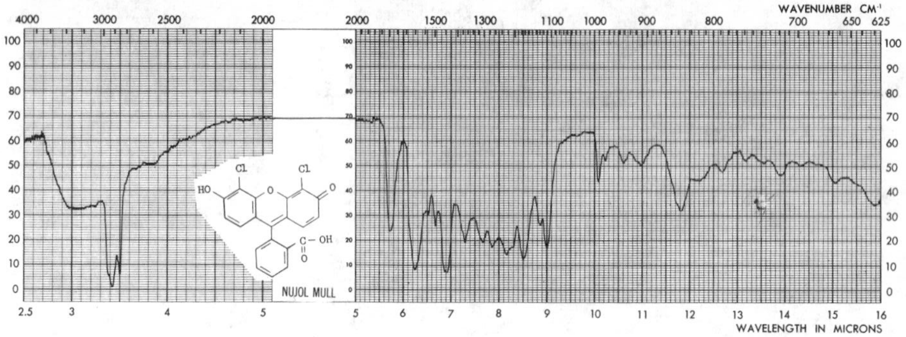

20,680-6
4',5'-Diiodofluorescein
FW 584.10 mp 240° (dec.) *Beil.* **19**(3),2922
Disp. C,D
KBr

G

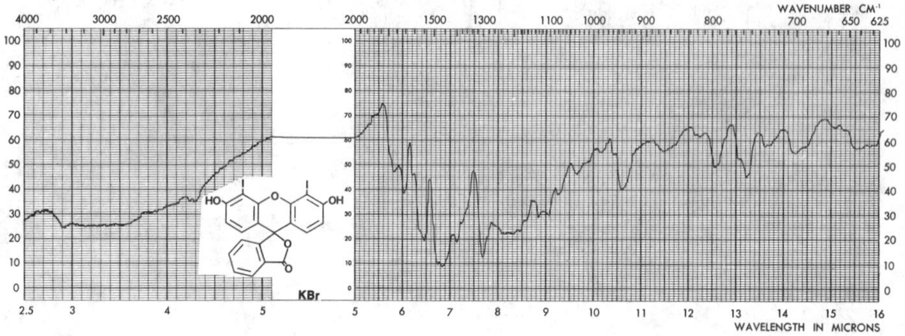

21,672-0
4',5'-Dibromofluorescein (C.I. 45370.1, Solvent Red 72)
FW 490.12 mp 270-273° *Beil.* **19**,228 Disp. C,D
KBr

H

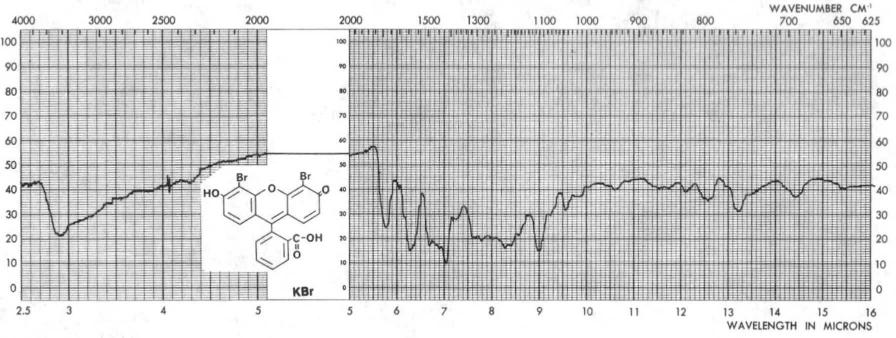

20,680-6
4',5'-Diiodofluorescein
FW 584.10 mp 240° (dec.) *Beil.* **19**(3),2922
Disp. C,D

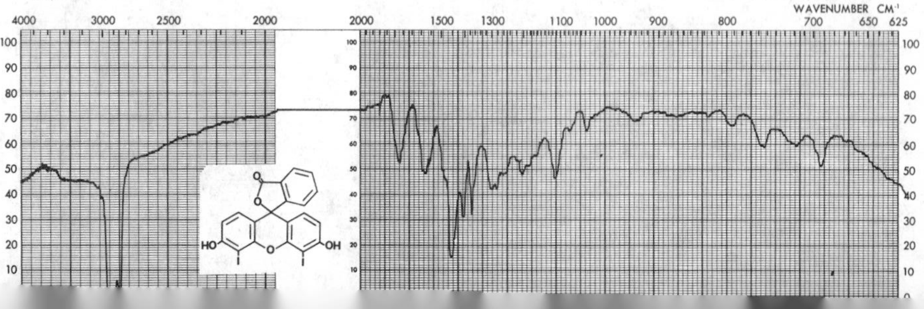

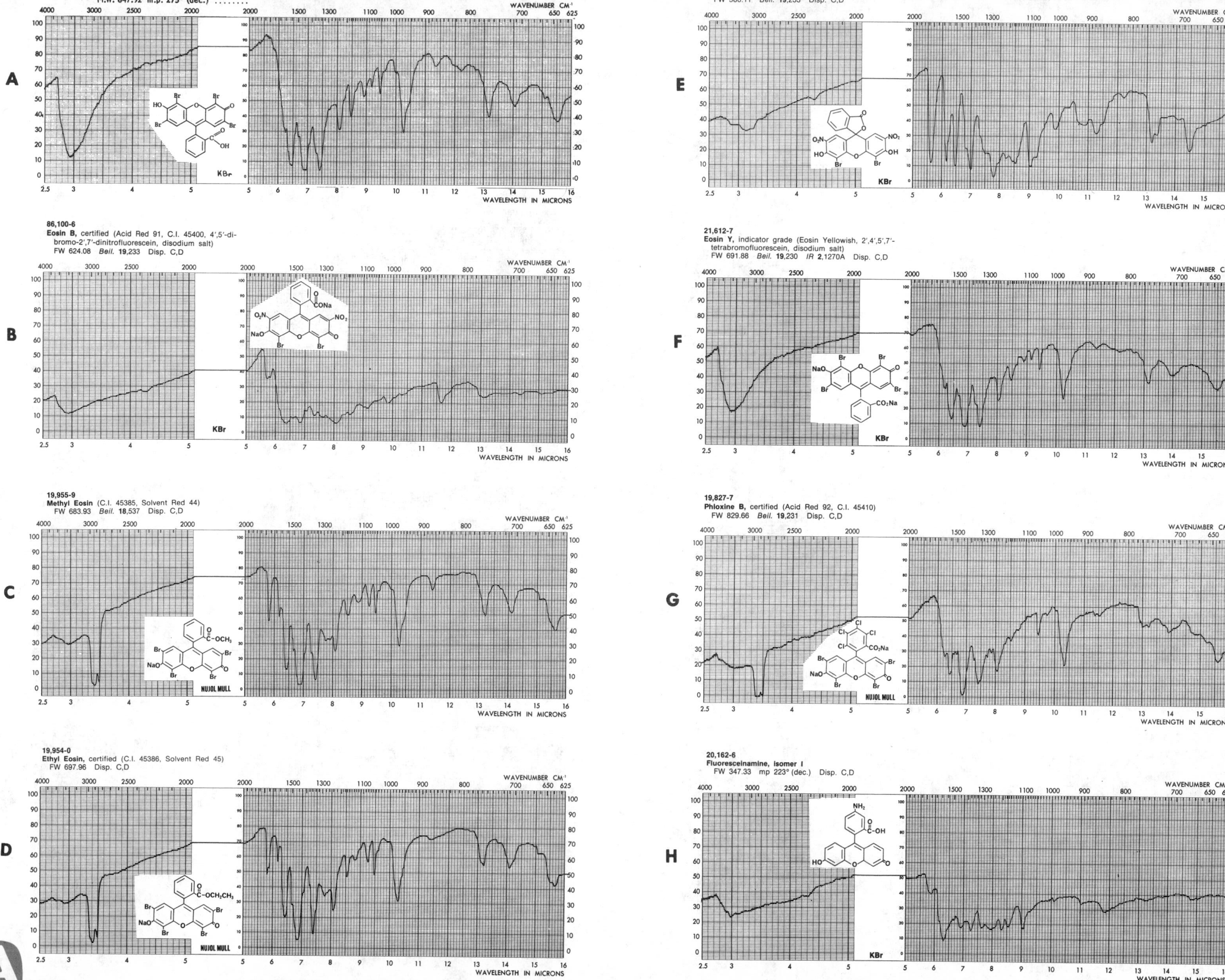

A 11,983-0 **Eosin (2',4',5',7'-tetrabromofluorescein)**
M.W. 647.92 m.p. 275° (dec.) .... KBr

B 86,100-6
Eosin B, certified (Acid Red 91, C.I. 45400, 4',5'-dibromo-2',7'-dinitrofluorescein, disodium salt)
FW 624.08 *Beil.* **19**,233 Disp. C,D KBr

C 19,955-9
Methyl Eosin (C.I. 45385, Solvent Red 44)
FW 683.93 *Beil.* **18**,537 Disp. C,D NUJOL MULL

D 19,954-0
Ethyl Eosin, certified (C.I. 45386, Solvent Red 45)
FW 697.96 Disp. C,D NUJOL MULL

E **Eosin B, spirit soluble** (C.I. 45400)
FW 580.11 *Beil.* **19**,233 Disp. C,D KBr

F 21,612-7
Eosin Y, indicator grade (Eosin Yellowish, 2',4',5',7'-tetrabromofluorescein, disodium salt)
FW 691.88 *Beil.* **19**,230 *IR* **2**,1270A Disp. C,D KBr

G 19,827-7
Phloxine B, certified (Acid Red 92, C.I. 45410)
FW 829.66 *Beil.* **19**,231 Disp. C,D NUJOL MULL

H 20,162-6
Fluoresceinamine, isomer I
FW 347.33 mp 223° (dec.) Disp. C,D KBr

A

20,163-4
Fluoresceinamine, isomer II
FW 347.33 mp 285° (dec.) Disp. C,D

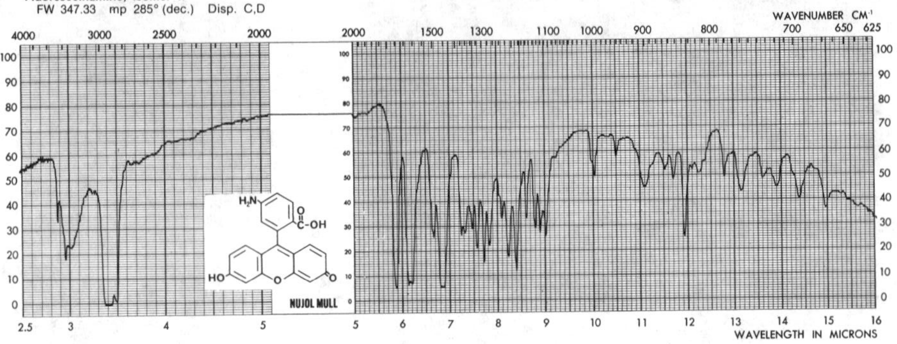

NUJOL MULL

B

20,132-4
Rhodamine 6G (Basic Red 1, C.I. 45160)
FW 479.02 *Beil.* **19**,344 Disp. C,D

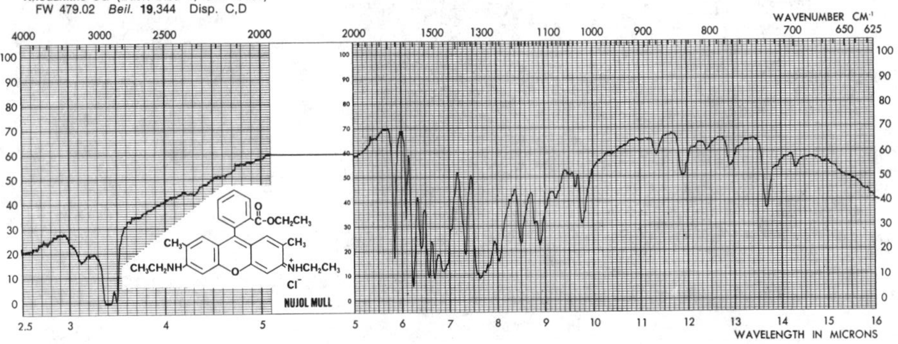

NUJOL MULL

C

12,730-2 **Erythrosin** (2',4',5',7'-tetraiodofluorescein), **disodium salt**
M.W. 879.87 m.p. > 300°

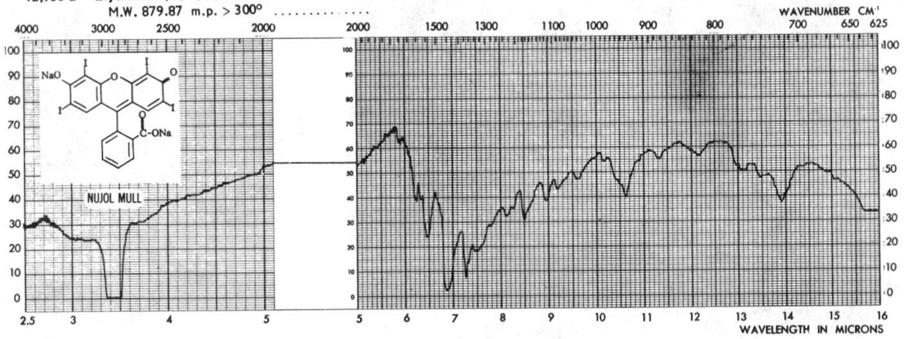

NUJOL MULL

D

19,825-0
Rose Bengal, certified (Acid Red 94, C.I. 45440)
FW 1017.65 *Beil.* **19**(2),261 Disp. C,D

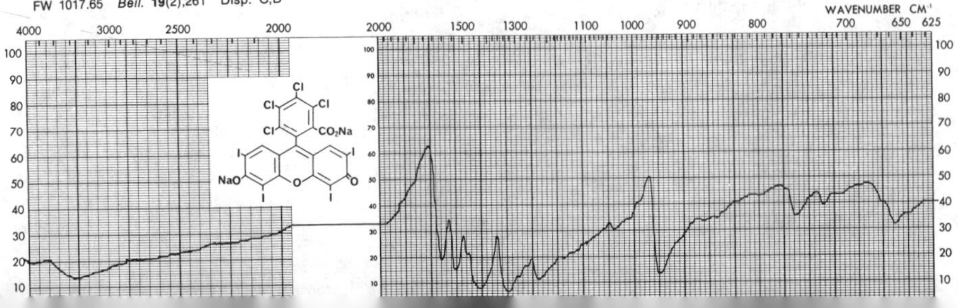

E

20,096-4
Erythrosin B, spirit soluble, 95+%
FW 835.90 mp 303° (dec.) *Beil.* **19**,231
Disp. C,D

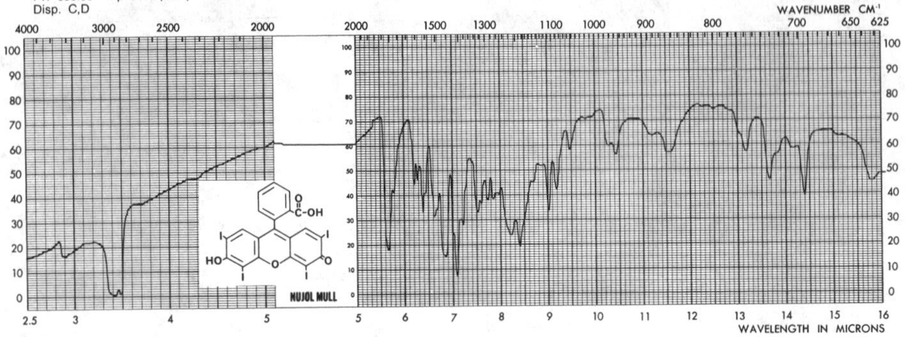

NUJOL MULL

F

R95-3 **Rhodamine B**
M.W. 479.02 m.p. 210-211° (dec.)

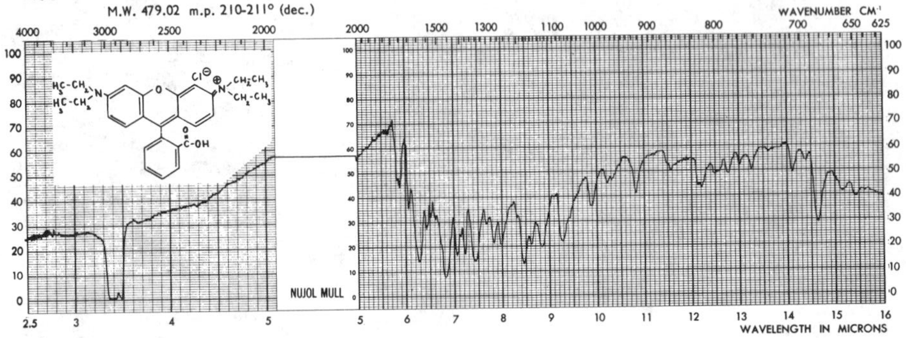

NUJOL MULL

G

11,985-7 **Fluorexon [bis-[N,N-bis-(carboxymethyl)-aminomethyl]-fluorescein, tetrasodium salt]**
M.W. 710.47 m.p. > 300°

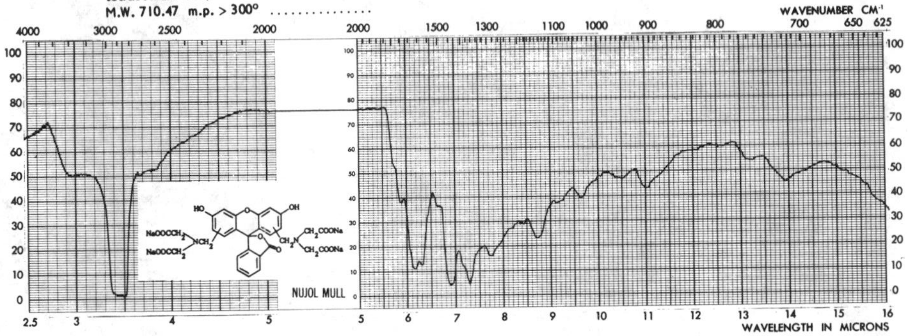

NUJOL MULL

H

19,959-1
Mercurochrome (merbromin)
FW 750.67 Disp. C,D

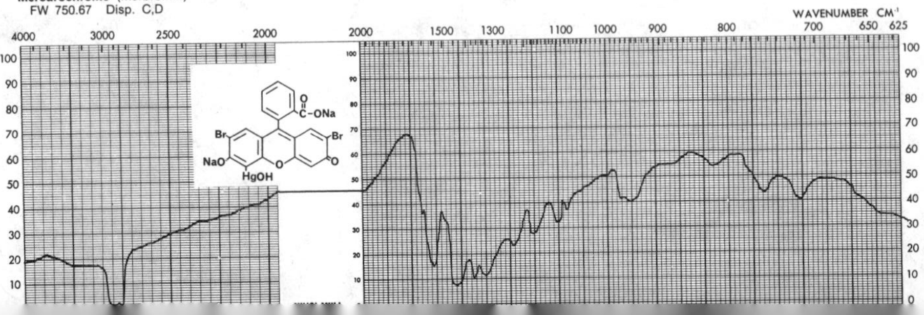

A 11,452-9 **Phenol red** (phenolsulfonephthalein)
M.W. 354.38 m.p. > 300°

NUJOL MULL

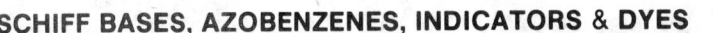

B 11,453-7 **Phenol red, water soluble** (phenolsulfonephthalein, sodium salt)
M.W. 376.36 m.p. 112° (dec.)

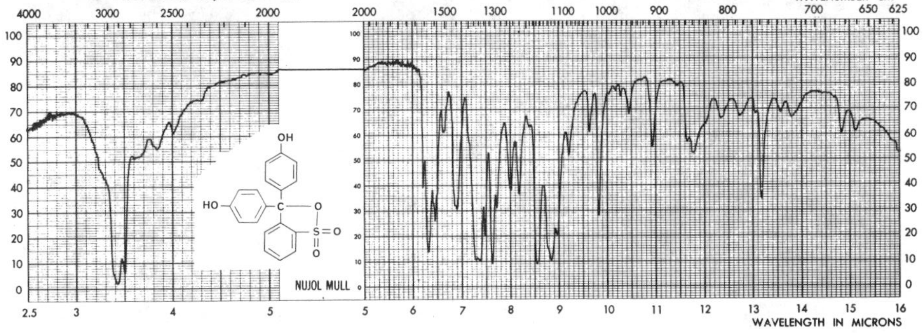

NUJOL MULL

C 11,447-2 **Cresol red** (o-cresolsulfonephthalein)
M.W. 382.43 m.p. > 300°

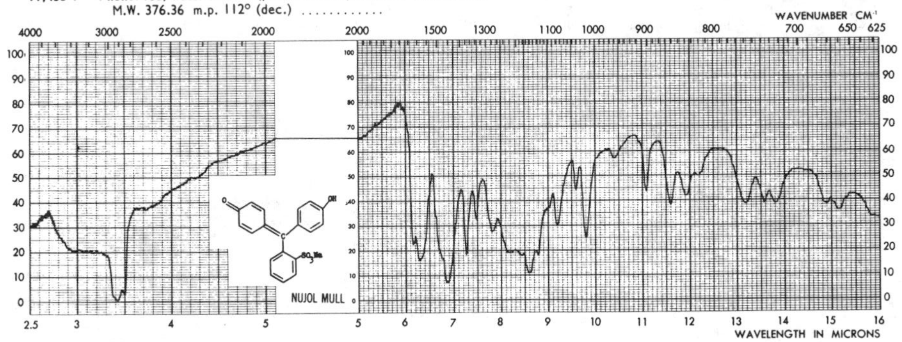

NUJOL MULL

D 11,448-0 **Cresol red, water soluble** (o-cresolsulfonephthalein, sodium salt)
M.W. 404.42 m.p. 123° (dec.)

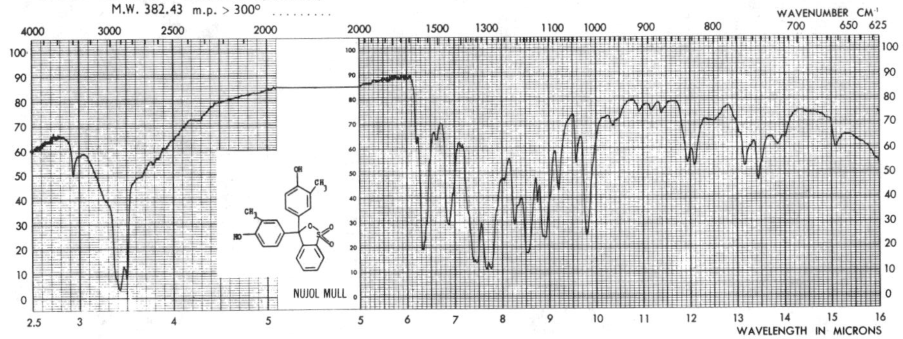

NUJOL MULL

E **Disperse Blue 14** (C.I. 61500)
FW 266.30 *Beil.* **14**,198 Disp. C,D

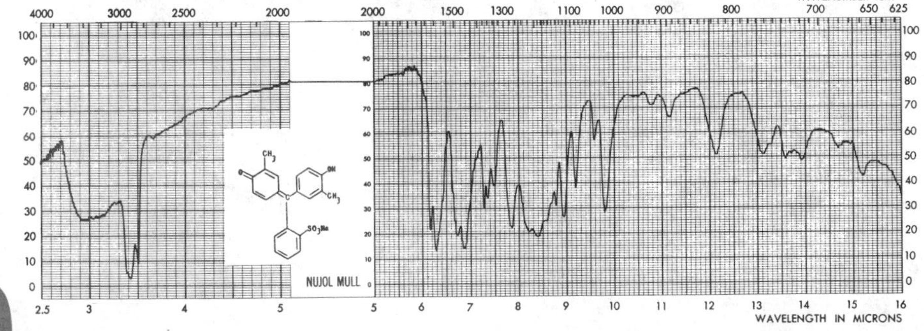

KBr

F 21,709-3
Disperse Orange 11 (C.I. 60700)
FW 237.26 *Beil.* **14**,221 Disp. C,O

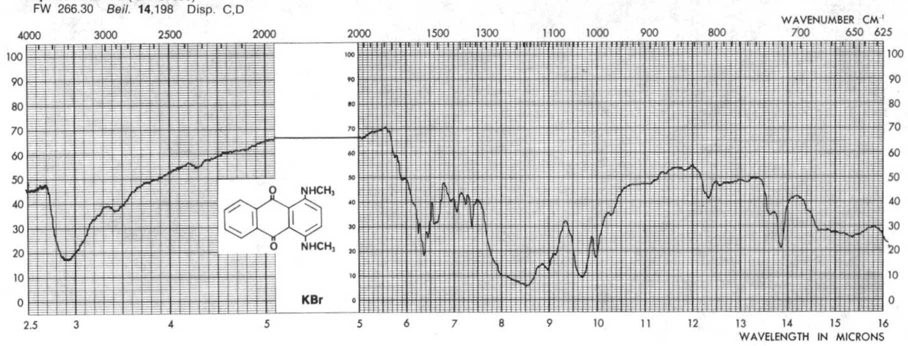

NUJOL MULL

G 20,525-7
Oil Blue N (C.I. 61555, Solvent Blue 14)
FW 378.52 mp 210° (dec.) Disp. C,D

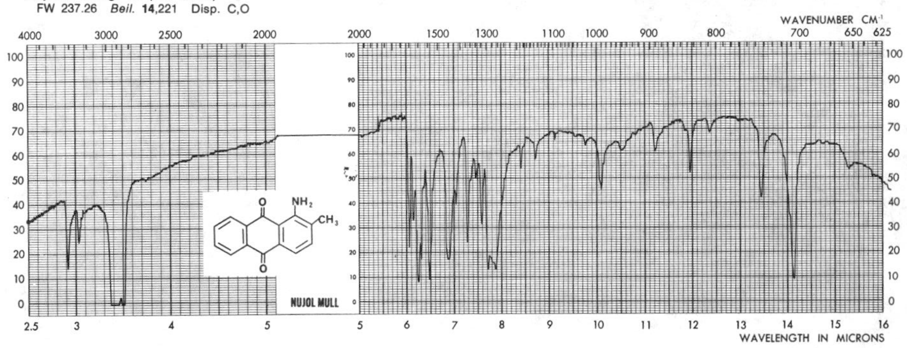

NUJOL MULL

H 21,565-1
Disperse Blue 3 (C.I. 61505)
FW 296.33 *Beil.* **14**(3),447 Disp. C,D

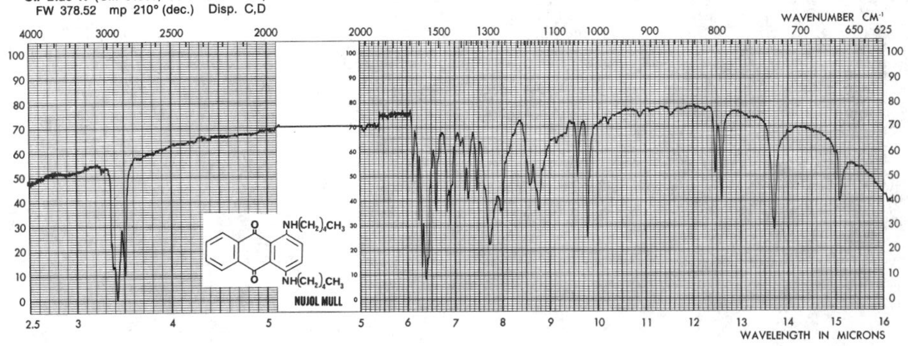

KBr

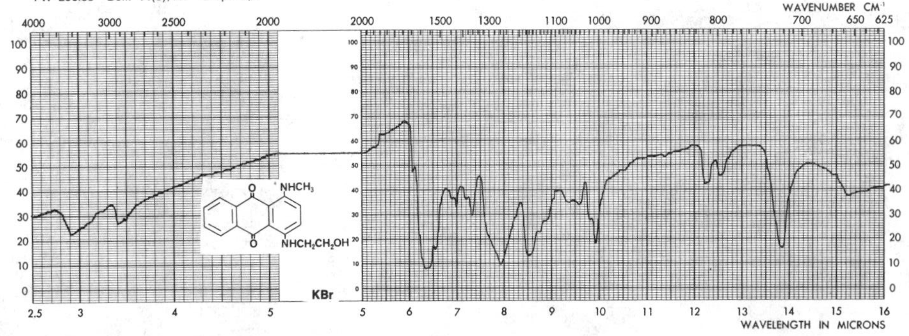

A

21,069-2
Acid Blue 45 (C.I. 63010)
FW 474.34 *Beil.* **14**,874 Disp. C,D

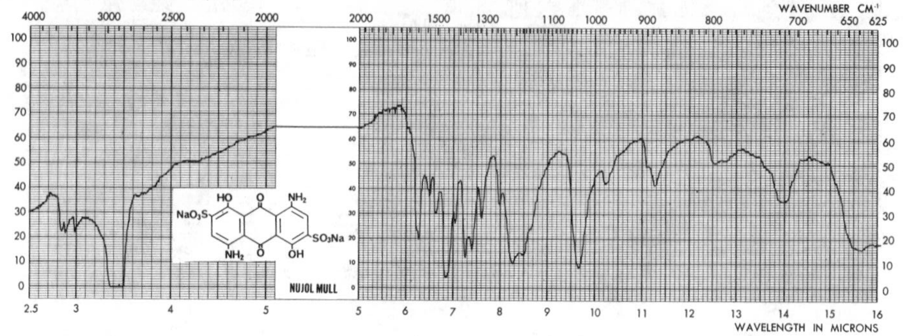

NUJOL MULL

B

21,564-3
Disperse Blue 1 (C.I. 64500)
FW 268.28 *Beil.* **14**,217 Disp. C,D

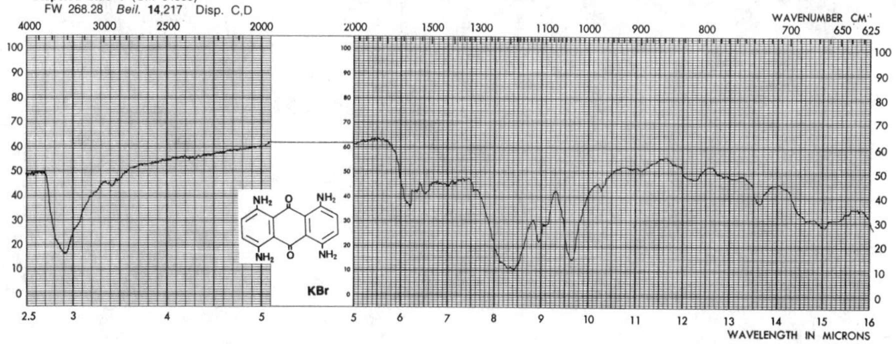

KBr

C

21,068-4
Acid Blue 25 (C.I. 62055)
FW 416.39 *Beil.* **14**(2),517 Disp. C,D

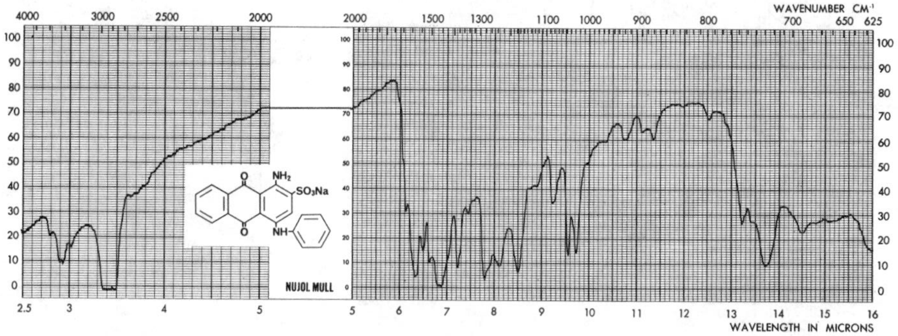

NUJOL MULL

D

21,055-2
Acid Blue 41 (C.I. 62130)
FW 487.47 mp >300° *Beil.* **14**(2),517
Disp. C,D

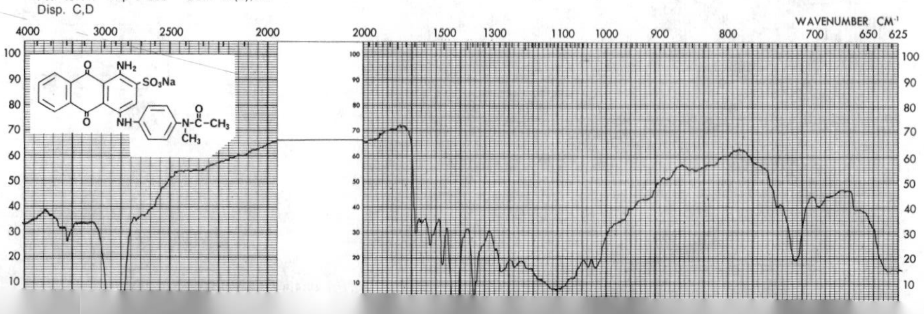

E

21,054-4
Acid Blue 40 (C.I. 62125)
FW 473.44 *Beil.* **14**(2),517 Disp. C,D

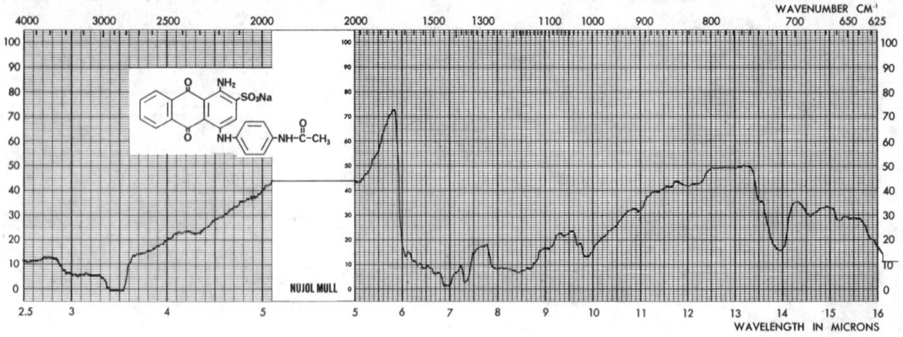

NUJOL MULL

F

22,324-7
Remazol Brilliant Blue R (C.I. 61200)
FW 624.54 Disp. C,D

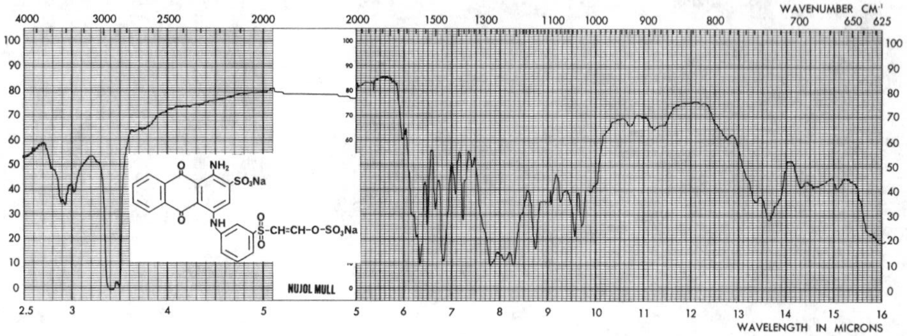

NUJOL MULL

G

21,198-2
Solvent Green 3 (C.I. 61565)
FW 418.50 mp 220-221° *Beil.* **14**,199 Disp. C,D

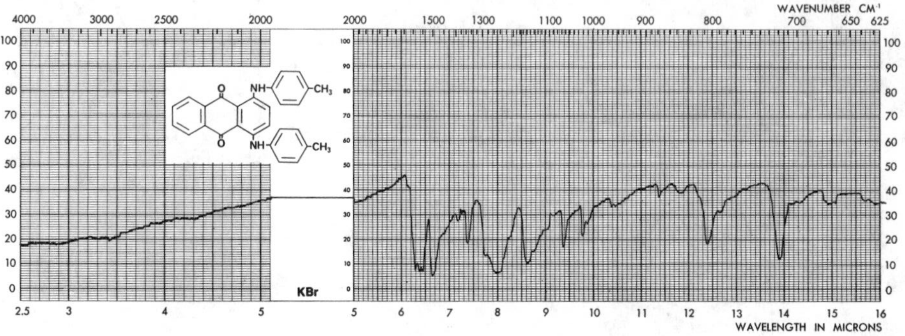

KBr

H

21,456-6
Acid Green 25 (C.I. 61570)
FW 622.59 mp 235-238° *Beil.* **14**,725 Disp. C,D

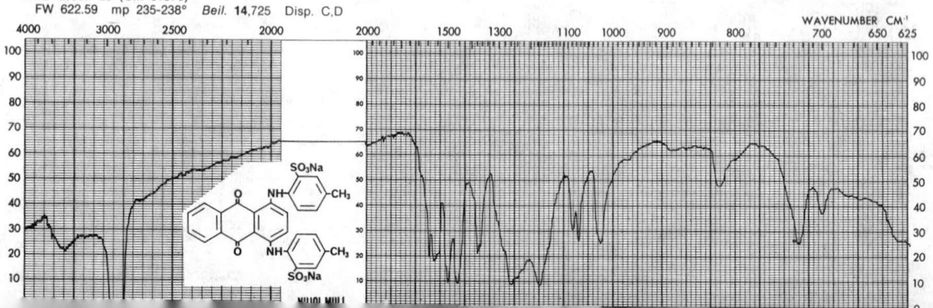

A

FW 706.75 mp 258-260° Disp. C,D

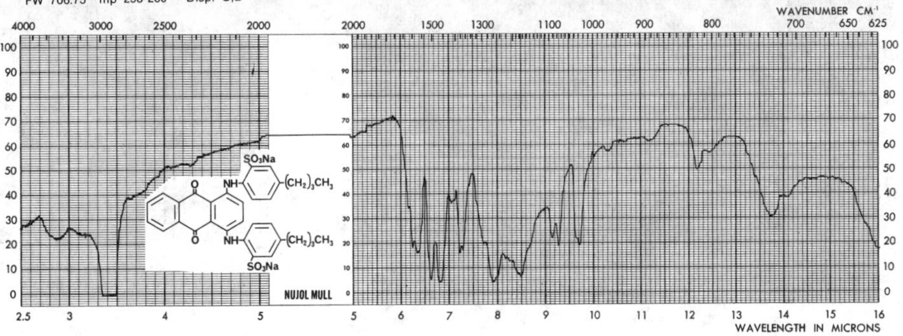

NUJOL MULL

B

21,071-4
Acid Green 41 (C.I. 62560)
FW 654.59 mp 286-290° Disp. C,D

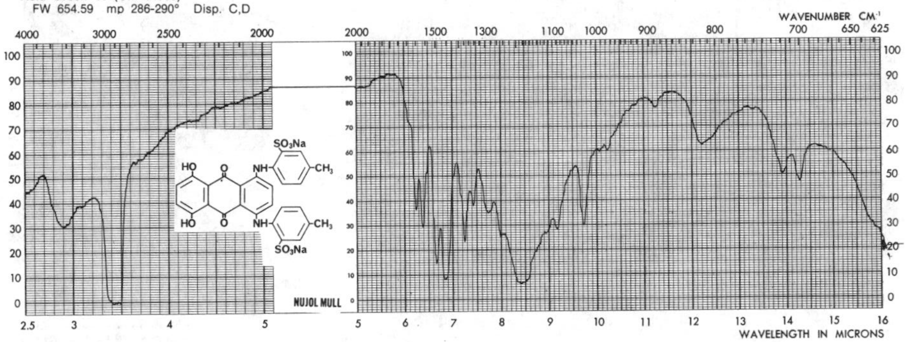

NUJOL MULL

C

21,032-3
Acid Blue 80 (C.I. 61585)
FW 678.70 Disp. C,D

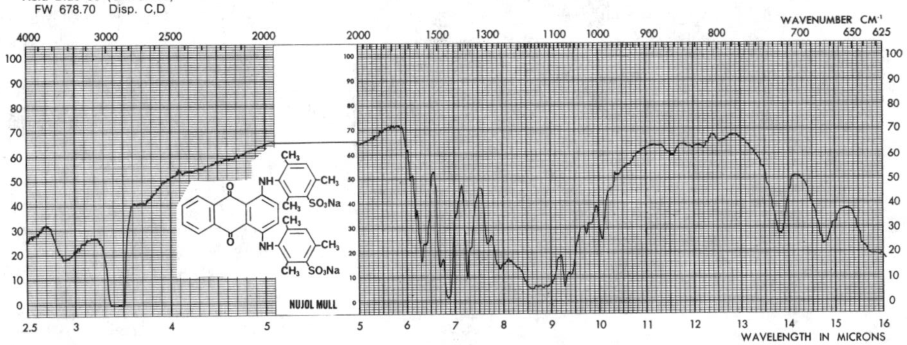

NUJOL MULL

D

19,424-7
Acid Black 48 (Coomassie® Grey 3G, C.I. 65005)
mp 275° (dec.) *Beil.* **14**(2),116 Disp. C

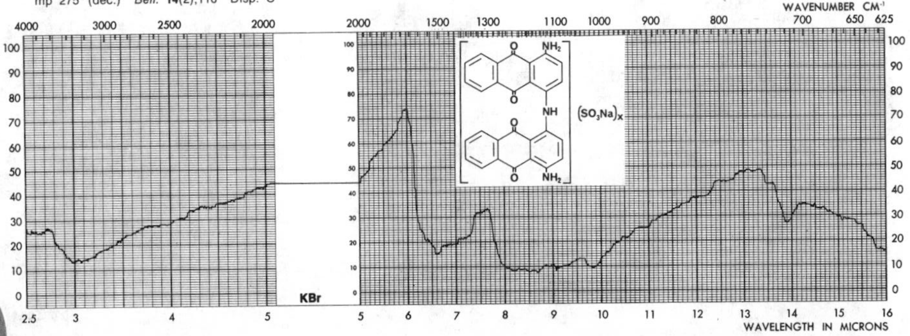

KBr

E

Cochineal (C.I. 75470, Natural Red 4)
Disp. C,D

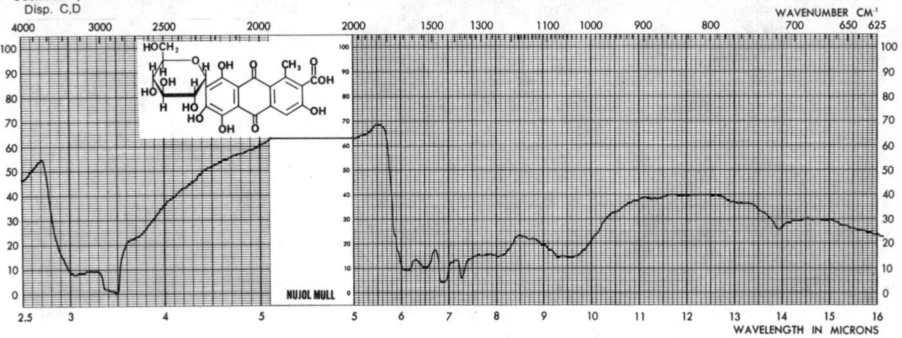

NUJOL MULL

F

20,134-0
Procion Blue HB (C.I. 61211, Reactive Blue 2)
FW 840.12 Disp. C,D

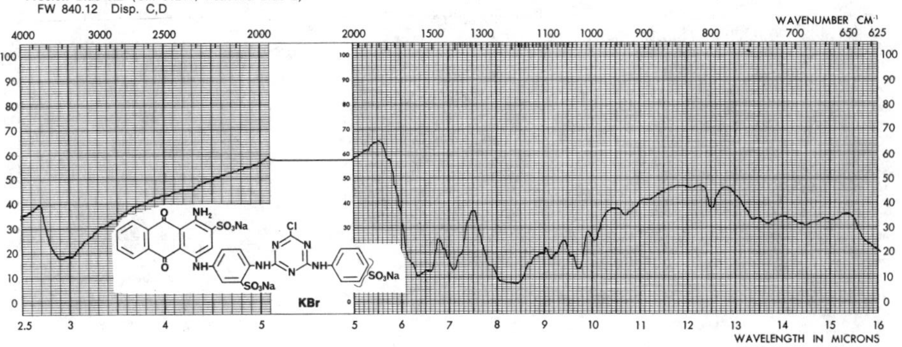

KBr

G

11,445-6 **Cresol purple** (m-cresolsulfonephthalein)
M.W. 382.43 m.p. > 300°

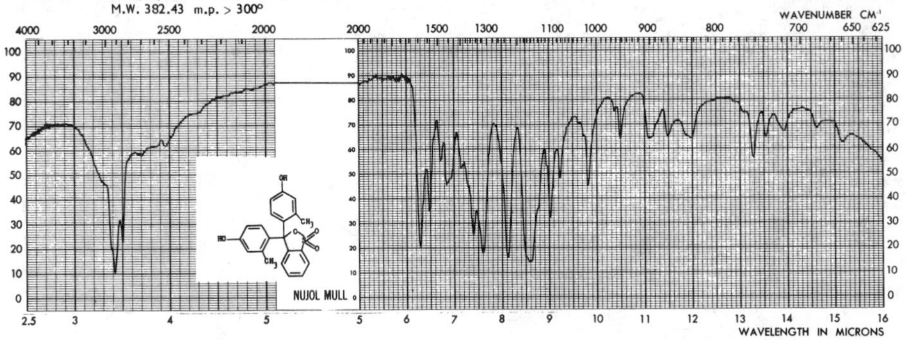

NUJOL MULL

H

11,446-4 **Cresol purple, water soluble** (m-cresolsulfonephthalein, sodium salt)
M.W. 404.42 m.p. 270° (dec.) . . . .

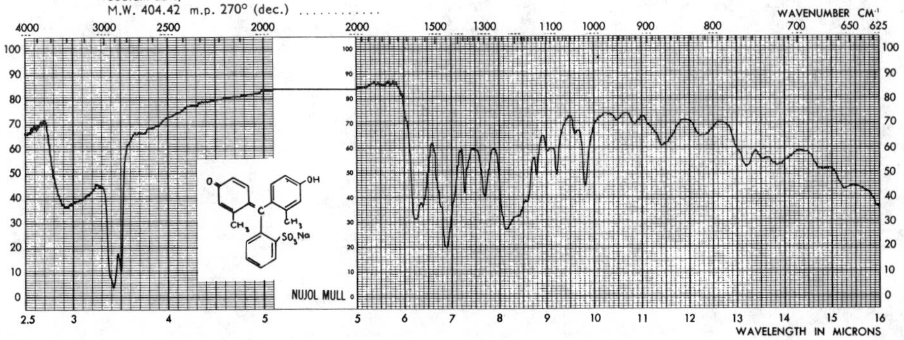

NUJOL MULL

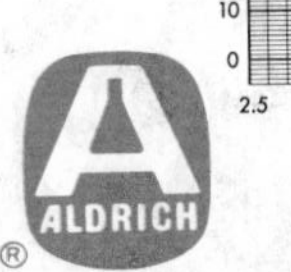

A
85,789-0
m-Cresol Purple, indicator grade (*m*-cresolsulfonephthalein)
FW 382.43 *Beil.* **19**(2),107 Disp. C,D

B
21,176-1
Cresol Purple, water soluble (*m*-cresolsulfonephthalein, sodium salt)
FW 404.42 *Beil.* **19**(2),107 Disp. C,D

C
86,089-1
Bromocresol Purple, water soluble, indicator grade (5',5''-dibromo-o-cresolsulfonephthalein, sodium salt)
FW 562.22 mp 255° (dec.) *Beil.* **19**,91
Disp. C,D

D
X105-9 **Xylenol blue** (p-xylenolsulfonephthalein)
M.W. 410.49 m.p. 263-265° (dec.) ...

E
11,456-1 **Xylenol blue, water soluble** (p-xylenolsulfonephthalein, sodium salt)
M.W. 432.47 m.p. 295° (dec.)

F
11,454-5 **Thymol blue** (thymolsulfonephthalein)
M.W. 466.60 m.p. 221-224° (dec.)

G
10,173-7 **Pyrocatechol violet** (pyrocatecholsulfonephthalein)
M.W. 386.38 ....

H
19,952-4
Chlorophenol Red, indicator grade (3',3''-dichlorophenolsulfonphthalein)
FW 423.28 Disp. C,D

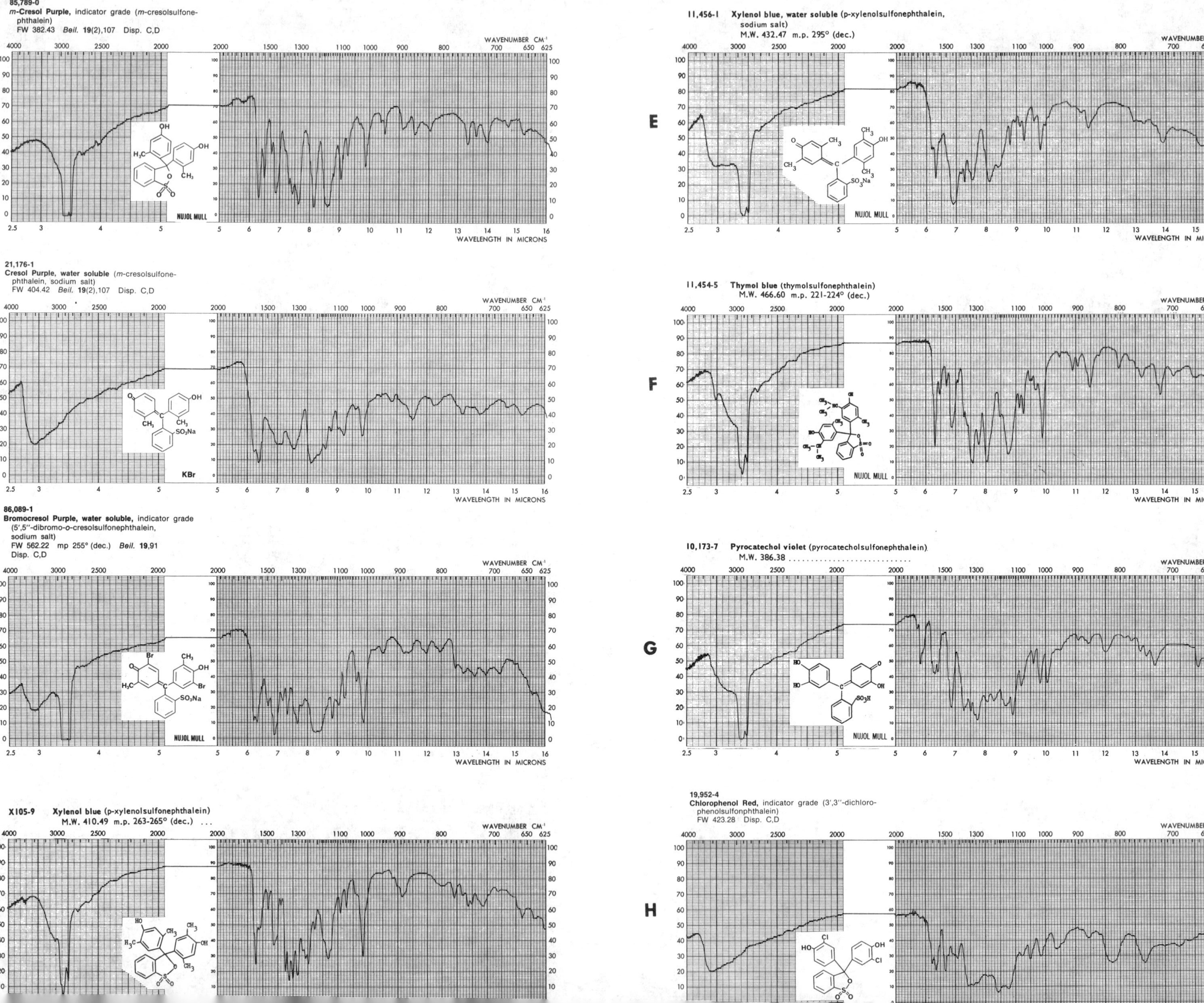

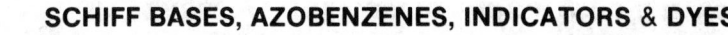

sodium salt)
FW 580.07 Disp. C,D

A

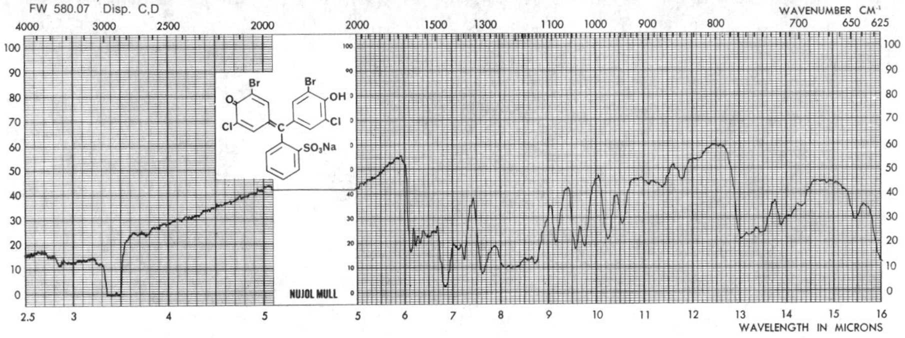

NUJOL MULL

12,881-3 **Bromophenol red** (3',3''-dibromophenolsulfonephthalein)
M.W. 512.19

B

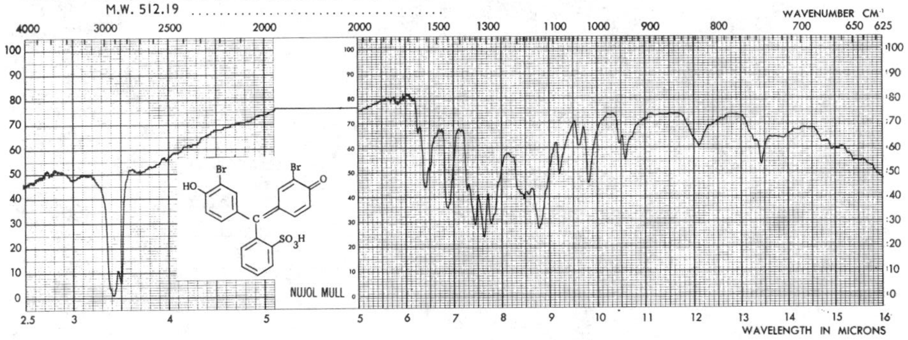

NUJOL MULL

12,195-9 **Bromopyrogallol red** (5',5''-dibromopyrogallolsulfonephthalein)
M.W. 576.18 m.p. > 300°

C

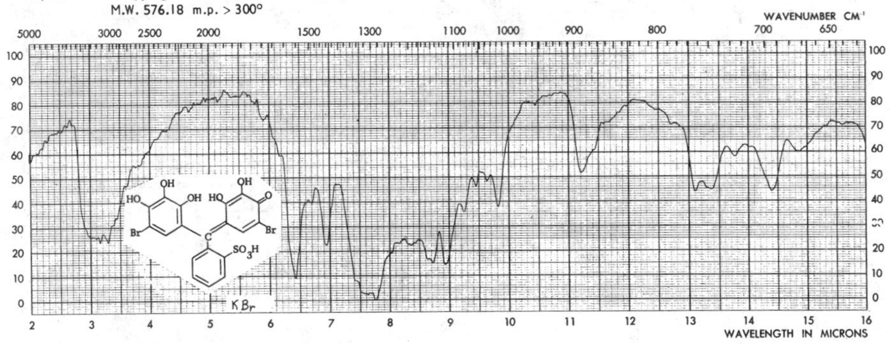

KBr

11,439-1 **Bromophenol blue** (3',3'',5',5''-tetrabromophenolsulfonephthalein)
M.W. 669.98 m.p. 278° (dec.)

D

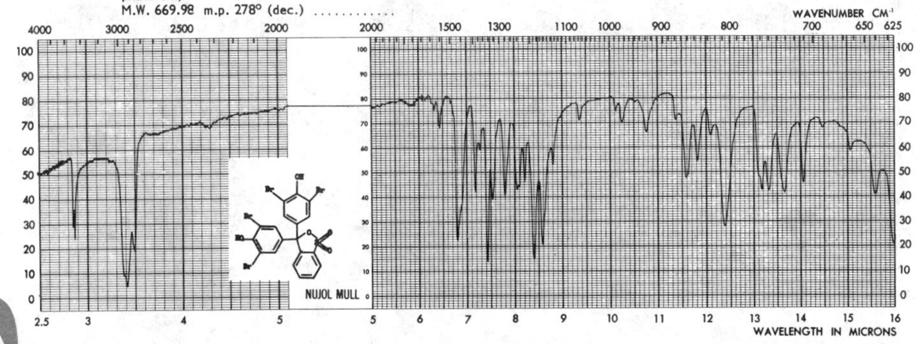

NUJOL MULL

M.W. 691.97 m.p. 289° (dec.)

E

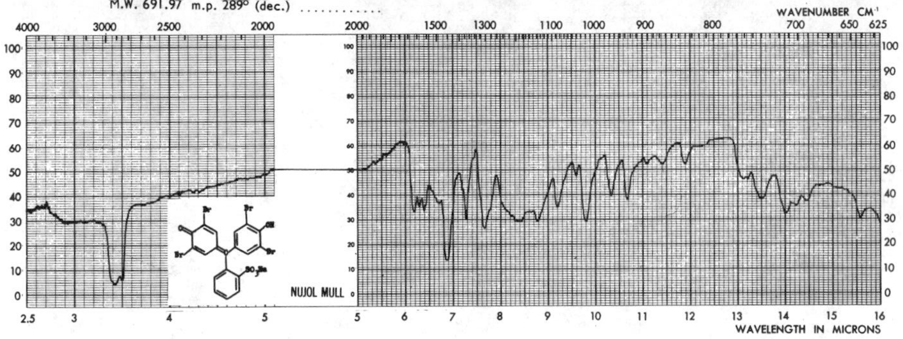

NUJOL MULL

11,435-9 **Bromocresol green** (3',3'',5',5''-tetrabromo-m-cresolsulfonephthalein)
M.W. 698.04 m.p. 226-227° (dec.)

F

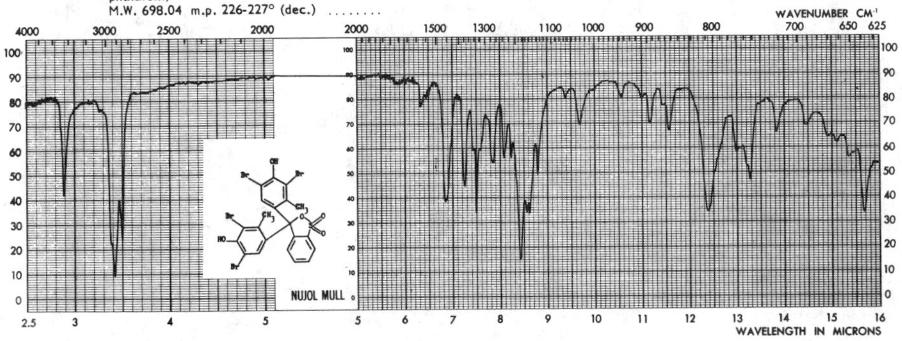

NUJOL MULL

11,436-7 **Bromocresol green, water soluble** (3',3'',5',5''-tetrabromo-m-cresolsulfonephthalein, sodium salt)
M.W. 720.02 m.p. 253° (dec.)

G

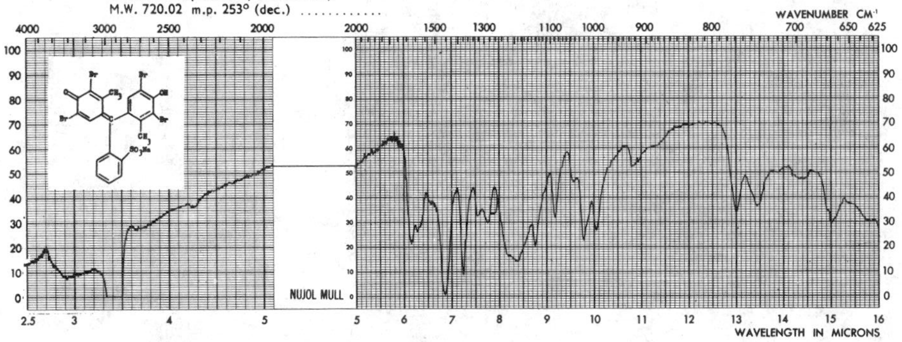

NUJOL MULL

16,720-7
Sulfobromophthalein sodium tetrahydrate
(bromsulfalein)
M.W. 838.03 m.p. >300°

H

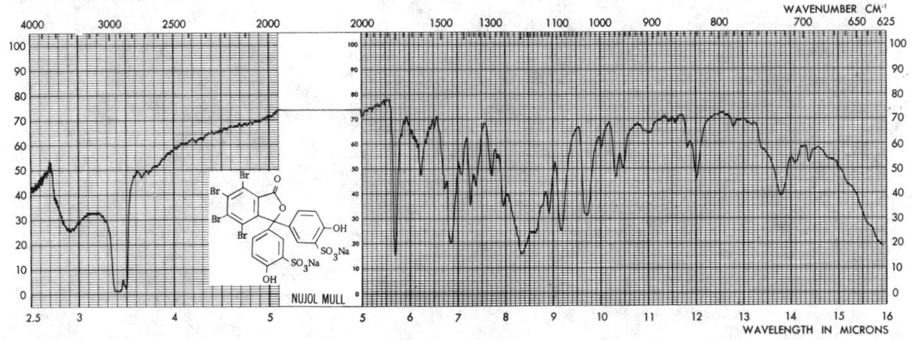

NUJOL MULL

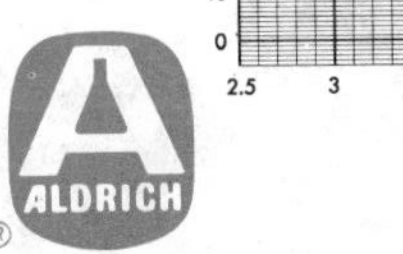

A

T505-2 **Tetrabromophenol blue**
M.W. 987.61

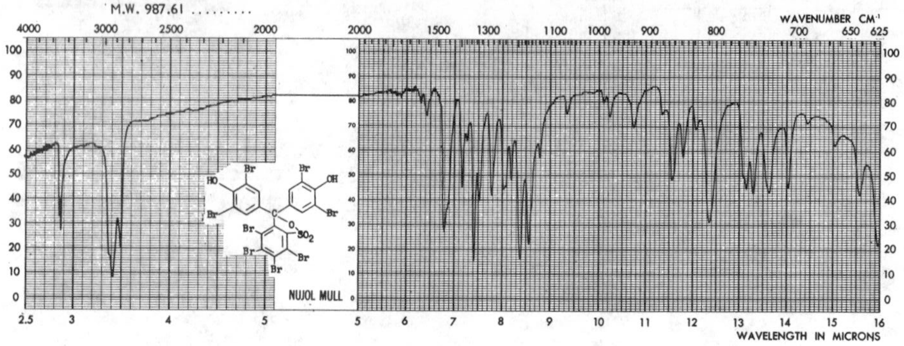

NUJOL MULL

B

11,437-5 **Bromocresol purple** (5',5''-dibromo-o-cresolsulfonephthalein)
M.W. 540.24 m.p. 222° (dec.)

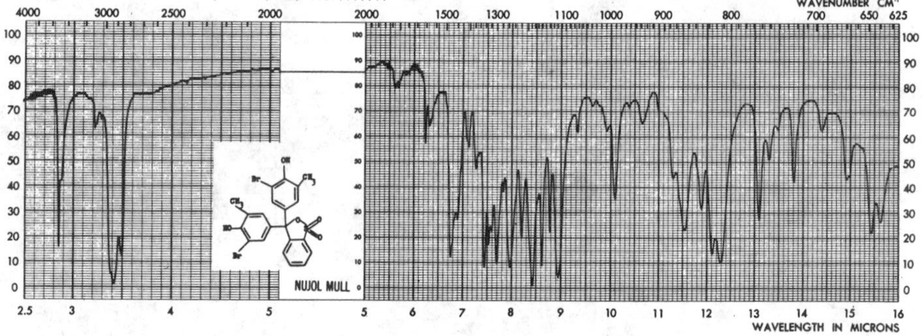

NUJOL MULL

C

11,438-3 **Bromocresol purple, water soluble** (5',5''-dibromo-o-cresolsulfonephthalein, sodium salt)
M.W. 562.22 m.p. 259° (dec.)

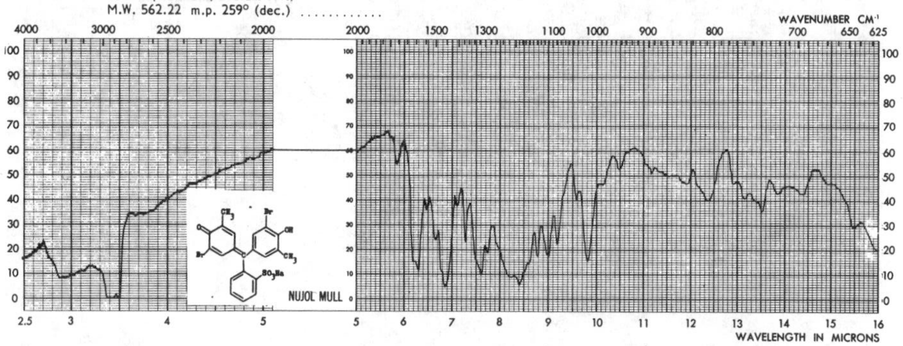

NUJOL MULL

D

B8385-1 **Bromoxylenol blue** (3',3''-dibromo-p-xylenolsulfonephthalein)
M.W. 568.31 m.p. 221° (dec.)

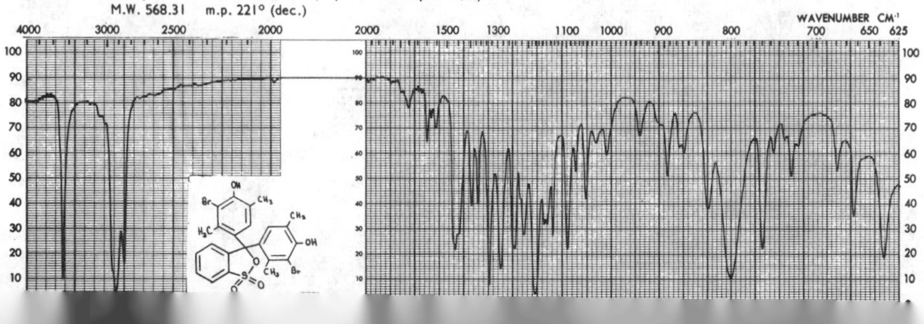

E

11,444-8 **Bromoxylenol blue, water soluble** (3',3''-dibromo-p-xylenolsulfonephthalein, sodium salt)
M.W. 590.27

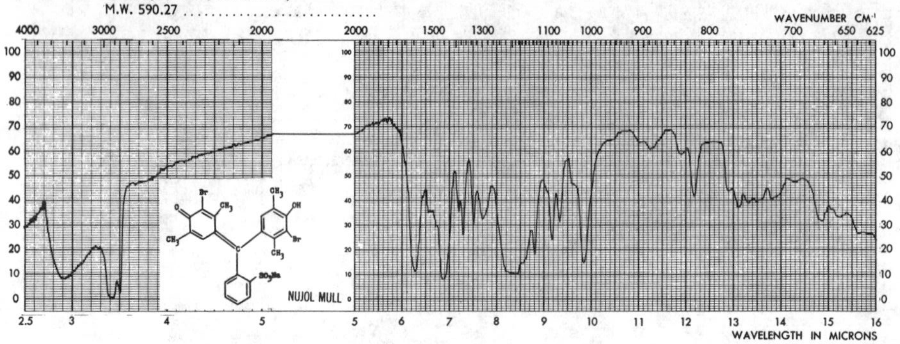

NUJOL MULL

F

86,136-7
Thymol Blue, sodium salt, A.C.S. reagent (thymolsulfonephthalein)
FW 488.58 mp 283-285° (dec.) Disp. C,D

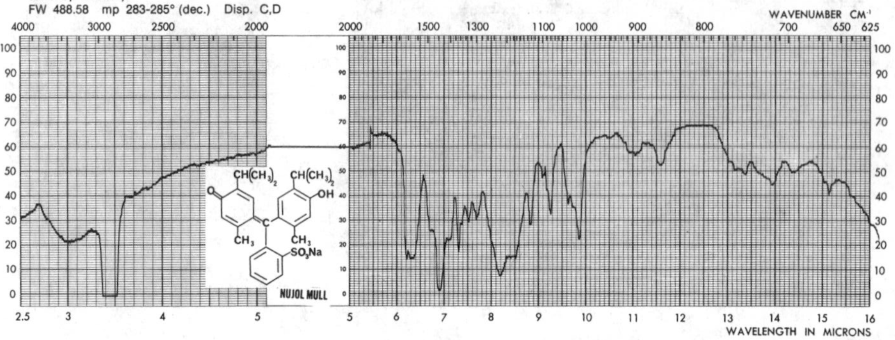

NUJOL MULL

G

11,441-3 **Bromothymol blue** (3',3''-dibromothymolsulfonephthalein)
M.W. 624.40 m.p. 200-202°

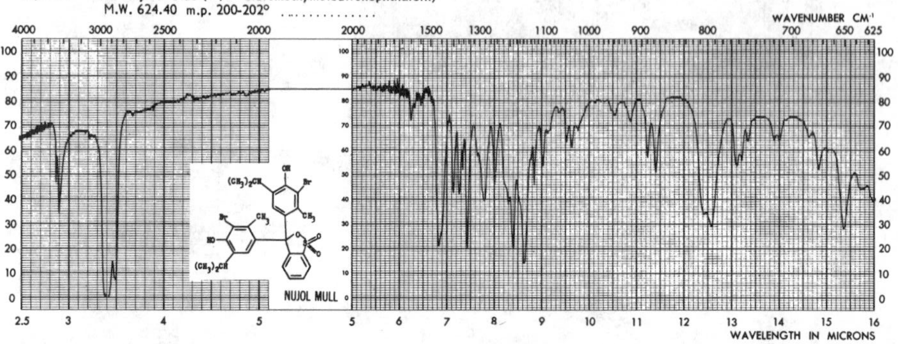

NUJOL MULL

H

11,442-1 **Bromothymol blue, water soluble** (3',3''-dibromothymolsulfonephthalein, sodium salt)
M.W. 646.38 m.p. 265° (dec.)

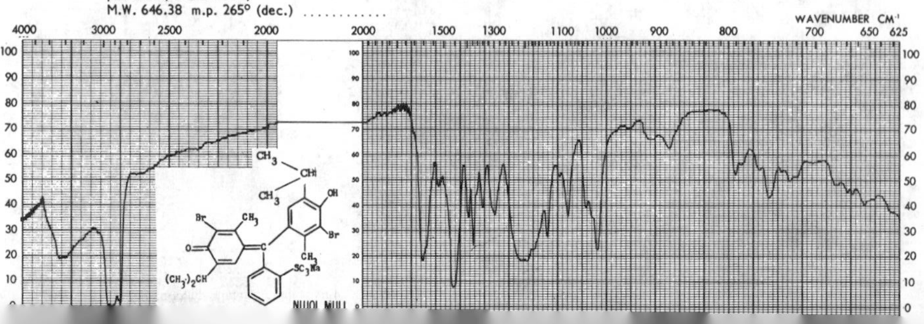

NUJOL MULL

A

10,056-0 **Glycinecresol red** [3',3''-bis-[N-(carboxymethyl)-aminomethyl]-o-cresolsulfonephthalein, sodium salt]
M.W. 578.58 m.p. > 360° ....

B

10,068-4 **Glycinethymol blue** [3',3''-bis-[N-(carboxymethyl)-aminomethyl]-thymolsulfonephthalein, sodium salt]
M.W. 662.74 m.p. > 300° ....

C

12,454-0 **Methylxylenol blue** [3',3''-bis-[N,N-bis-(carboxymethyl)-aminomethyl]-p-xylenolsulfonephthalein, sodium salt]
M.W. 722.21 ....

D

M.W. 760.60

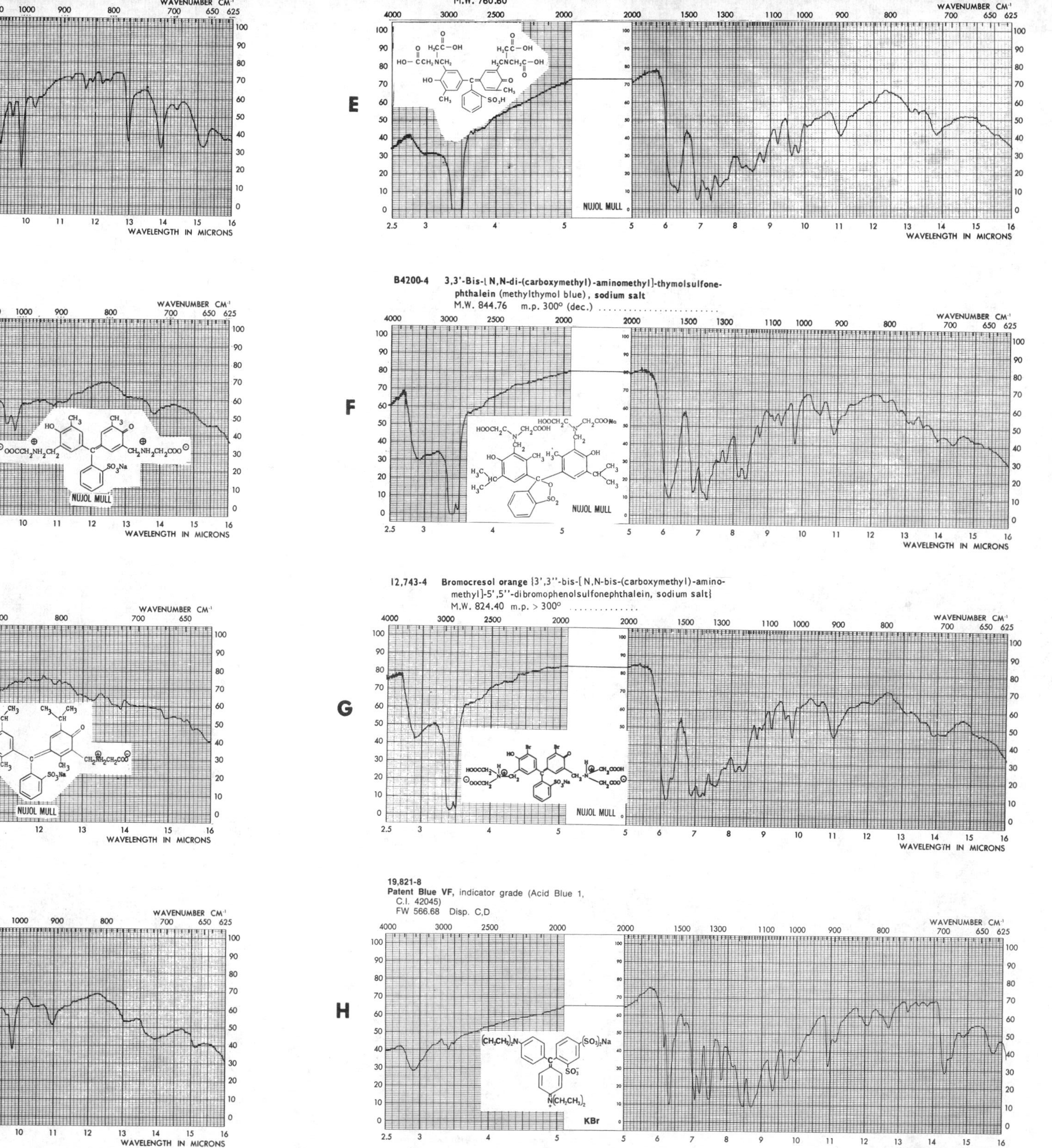

E

B4200-4 **3,3'-Bis-[N,N-di-(carboxymethyl)-aminomethyl]-thymolsulfonephthalein (methylthymol blue), sodium salt**
M.W. 844.76 m.p. 300° (dec.) ....

F

12,743-4 **Bromocresol orange** [3',3''-bis-[N,N-bis-(carboxymethyl)-aminomethyl]-5',5''-dibromophenolsulfonephthalein, sodium salt]
M.W. 824.40 m.p. > 300° ....

G

19,821-8
Patent Blue VF, indicator grade (Acid Blue 1, C.I. 42045)
FW 566.68 Disp. C,D

H

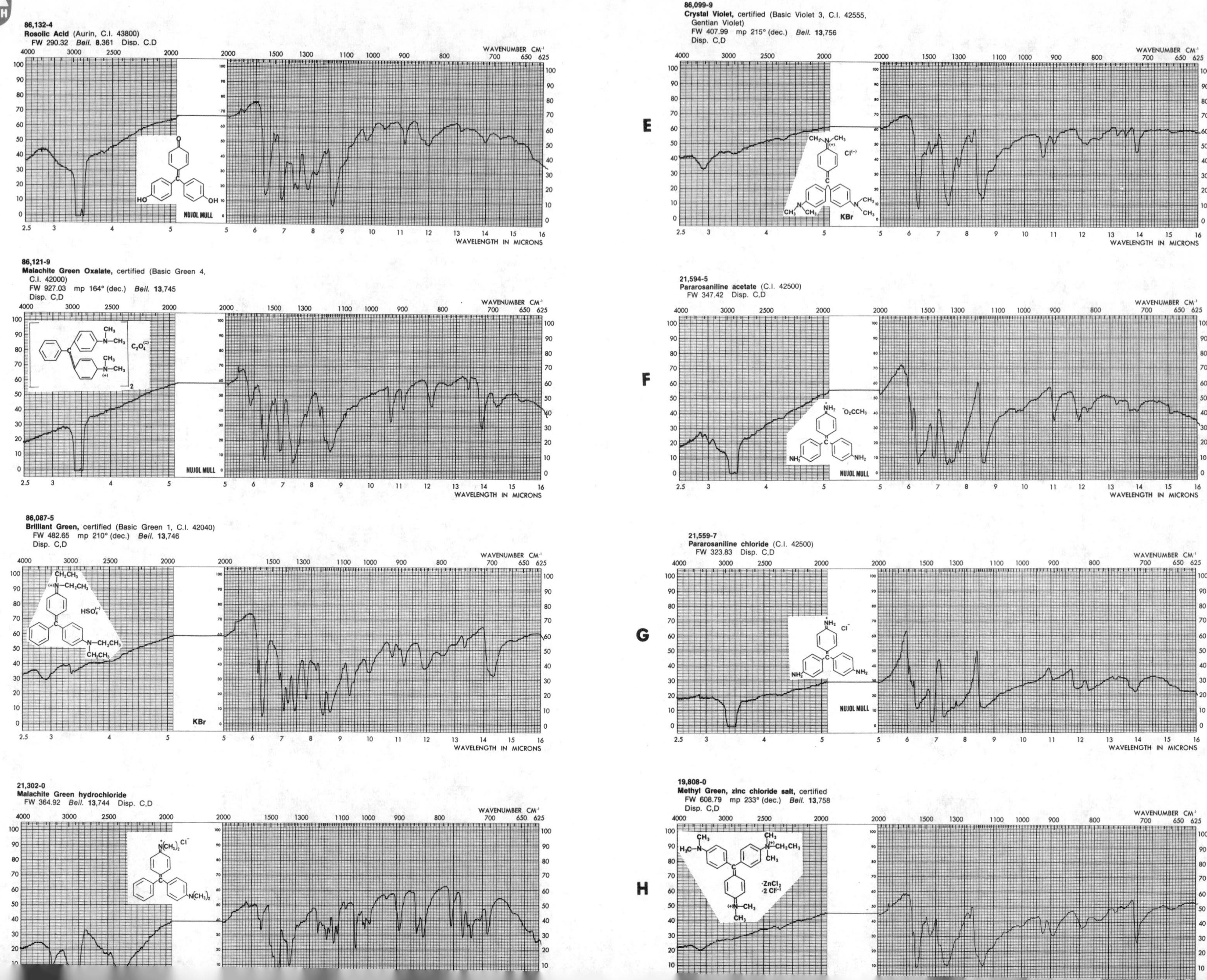

ALDRICH
A
86,132-4
Rosolic Acid (Aurin, C.I. 43800)
FW 290.32 *Beil.* 8,361 Disp. C,D
NUJOL MULL
B
86,121-9
Malachite Green Oxalate, certified (Basic Green 4, C.I. 42000)
FW 927.03 mp 164° (dec.) *Beil.* 13,745
Disp. C,D
NUJOL MULL
C
86,087-5
Brilliant Green, certified (Basic Green 1, C.I. 42040)
FW 482.65 mp 210° (dec.) *Beil.* 13,746
Disp. C,D
KBr
D
21,302-0
Malachite Green hydrochloride
FW 364.92 *Beil.* 13,744 Disp. C,D
E
86,099-9
Crystal Violet, certified (Basic Violet 3, C.I. 42555, Gentian Violet)
FW 407.99 mp 215° (dec.) *Beil.* 13,756
Disp. C,D
KBr
F
21,594-5
Pararosaniline acetate (C.I. 42500)
FW 347.42 Disp. C,D
NUJOL MULL
G
21,559-7
Pararosaniline chloride (C.I. 42500)
FW 323.83 Disp. C,D
NUJOL MULL
H
19,808-0
Methyl Green, zinc chloride salt, certified
FW 608.79 mp 233° (dec.) *Beil.* 13,758
Disp. C,D
WAVENUMBER CM⁻¹
WAVELENGTH IN MICRONS

A

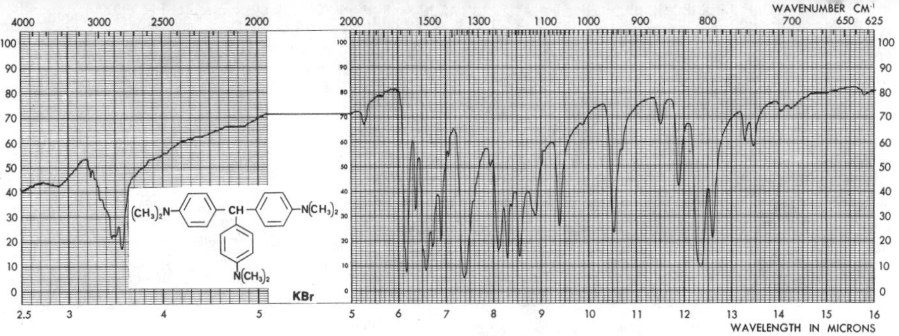

KBr

B

21,057-9
Acid Violet 17 (C.I. 42650)
FW 761.94 Disp. C,D

NUJOL MULL

C

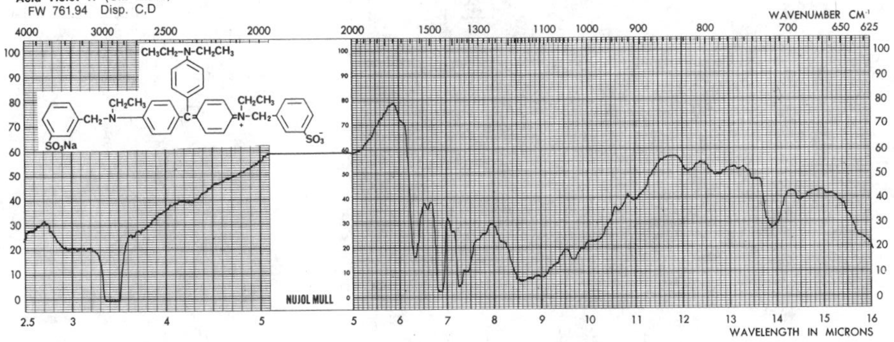

19,969-9
Victoria Blue B (Basic Blue 26, C.I. 44045)
FW 506.10 mp 206° (dec.) Disp. C,D

KBr

D

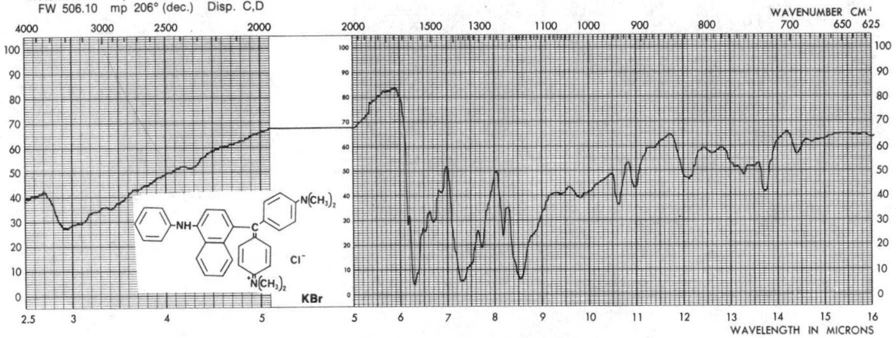

19,814-5
Alphazurine A (Acid Blue 7, C.I. 42080, Patent Blue A)
FW 690.82 mp 290° (dec.) *Beil.* **14**,856
Disp. C,D

KBr

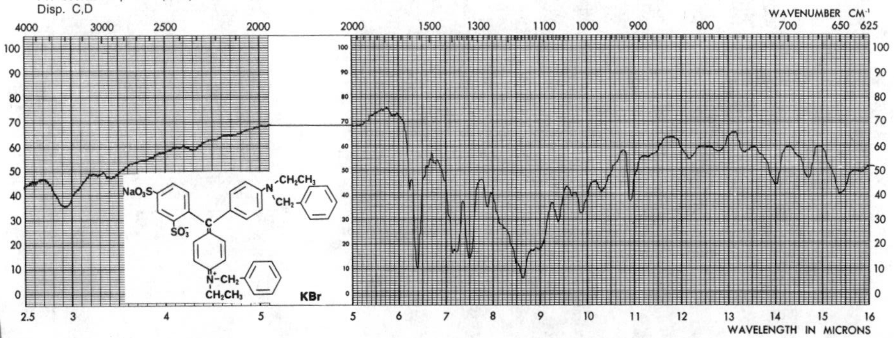

E

KBr

F

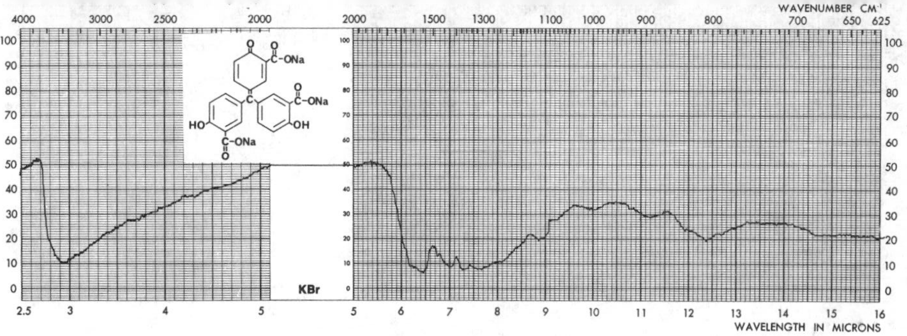

20,682-2
Naphthochrome Green (C.I. 44530)
FW 506.43 *Beil.* **10**(2),762 Disp. C,D

NUJOL MULL

G

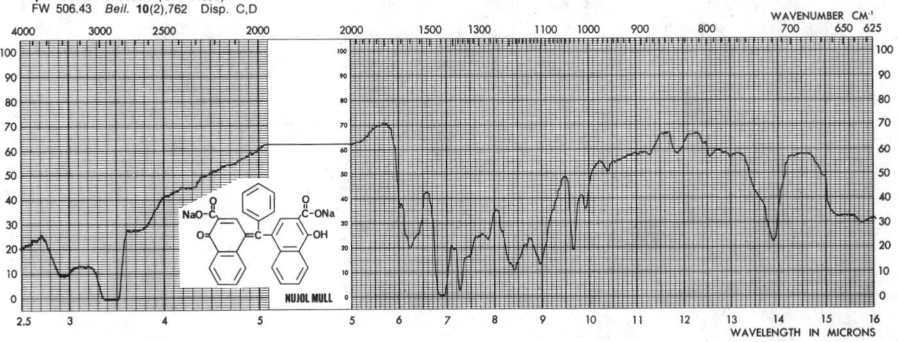

19,958-3
Lissamine Green B (Acid Green 50, C.I. 44090, Wool Green S)
FW 576.63 *Beil.* **14**(2),514 Disp. C,D

NUJOL MULL

H

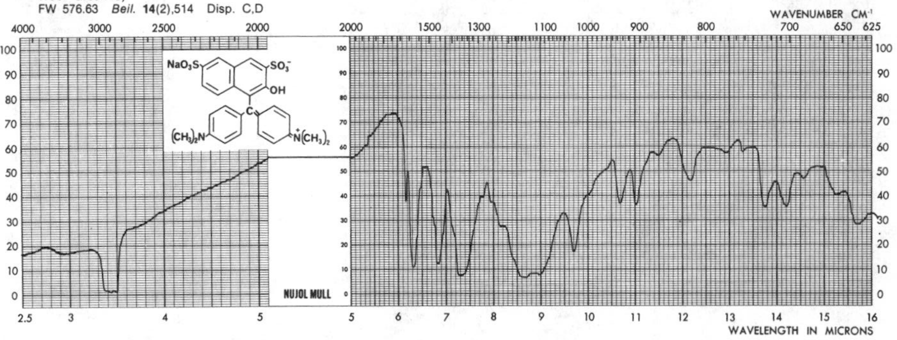

19,953-2
Chrome Azurol S (C.I. 43825, Mordant Blue 29)
FW 605.29 Disp. C,D

NUJOL MULL

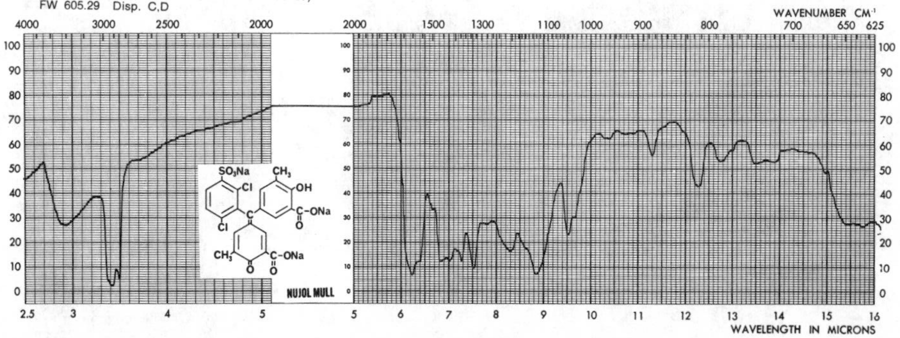

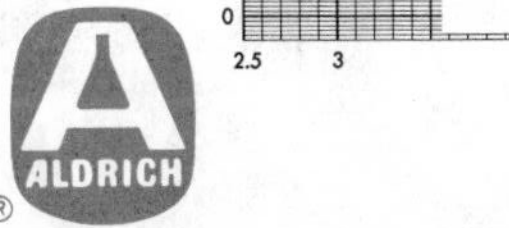

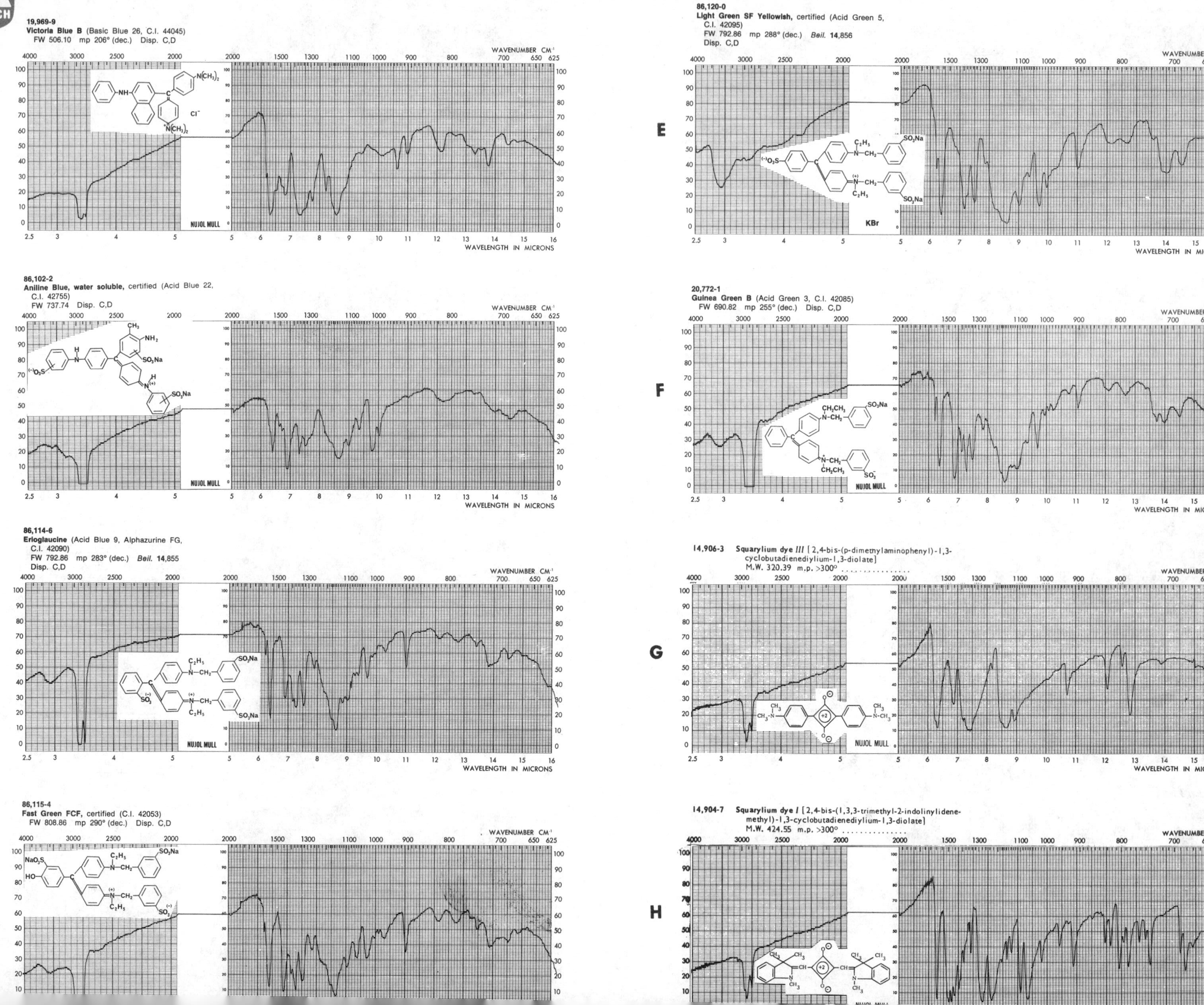
ALDRICH
A
19,969-9
Victoria Blue B (Basic Blue 26, C.I. 44045)
FW 506.10 mp 206° (dec.) Disp. C,D
NUJOL MULL
B
86,102-2
Aniline Blue, water soluble, certified (Acid Blue 22, C.I. 42755)
FW 737.74 Disp. C,D
NUJOL MULL
C
86,114-6
Erioglaucine (Acid Blue 9, Alphazurine FG, C.I. 42090)
FW 792.86 mp 283° (dec.) Beil. 14,855
Disp. C,D
NUJOL MULL
D
86,115-4
Fast Green FCF, certified (C.I. 42053)
FW 808.86 mp 290° (dec.) Disp. C,D
E
86,120-0
Light Green SF Yellowish, certified (Acid Green 5, C.I. 42095)
FW 792.86 mp 288° (dec.) Beil. 14,856
Disp. C,D
KBr
F
20,772-1
Guinea Green B (Acid Green 3, C.I. 42085)
FW 690.82 mp 255° (dec.) Disp. C,D
NUJOL MULL
G
14,906-3 Squarylium dye III [2,4-bis-(p-dimethylaminophenyl)-1,3-cyclobutadienediylium-1,3-diolate]
M.W. 320.39 m.p. >300°
NUJOL MULL
H
14,904-7 Squarylium dye I [2,4-bis-(1,3,3-trimethyl-2-indolinylidene-methyl)-1,3-cyclobutadienediylium-1,3-diolate]
M.W. 424.55 m.p. >300°
WAVENUMBER CM⁻¹
WAVELENGTH IN MICRONS

A

M.W. 420.52 m.p. >300° ....

NUJOL MULL

B

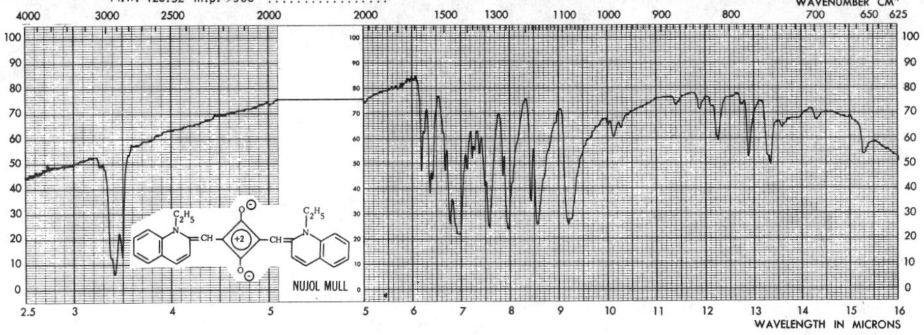

85,739-4
Pyronine G, indicator grade (pyronine Y)
M.W. 302.81 m.p. 228-230° (dec.)

NUJOL MULL

C

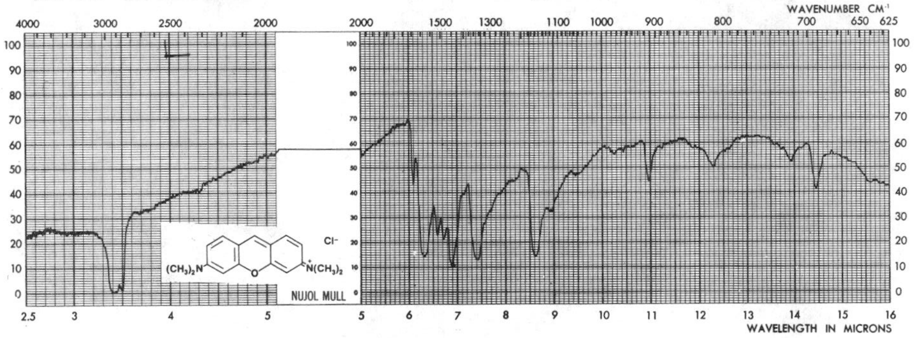

22,255-0
Nile Blue hydrochloride (C.I. 51180)
FW 353.85 *Beil.* **27**,404 Disp. C,D

KBr

D

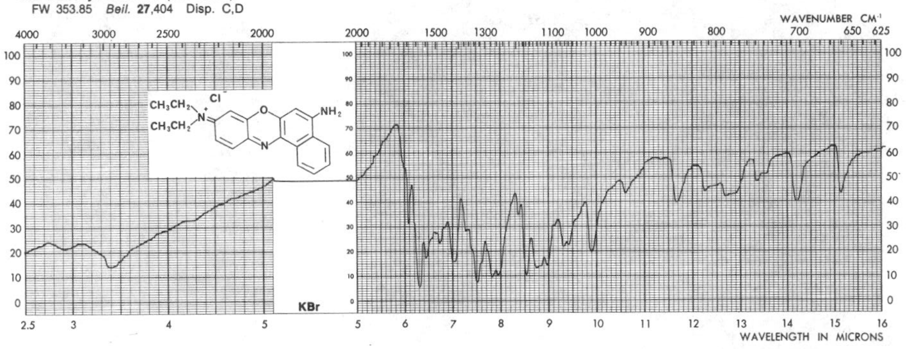

86,098-0
Cresyl Violet acetate, certified
FW 321.34 mp 140-143° Disp. C,D

NUJOL MULL

E

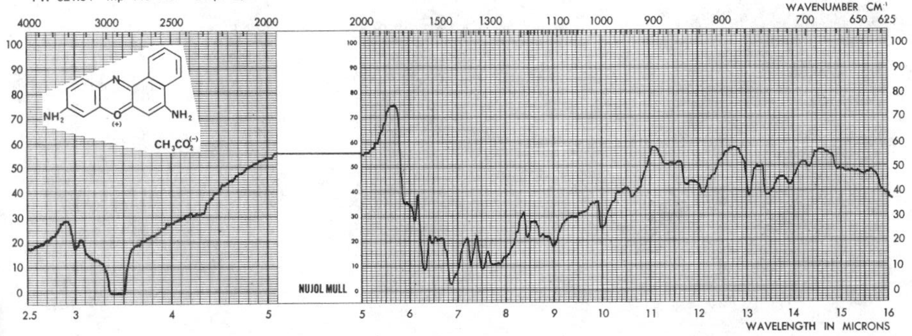

M.W. 500.51 m.p. 210 (dec.)

NUJOL MULL

F

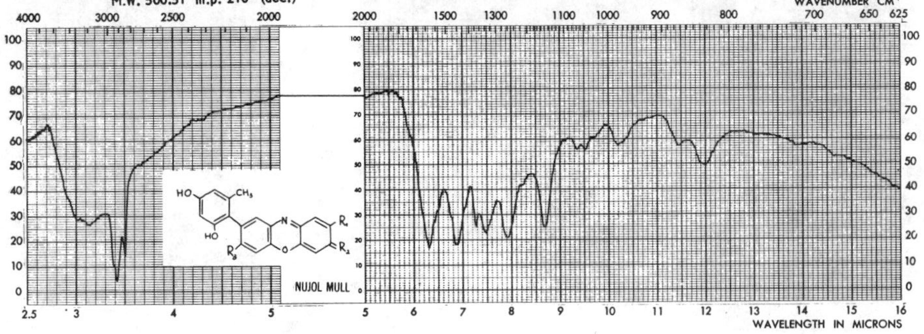

12,139-8
Giemsa Stain, certified
mp 300° Disp. C,D

KBr

G

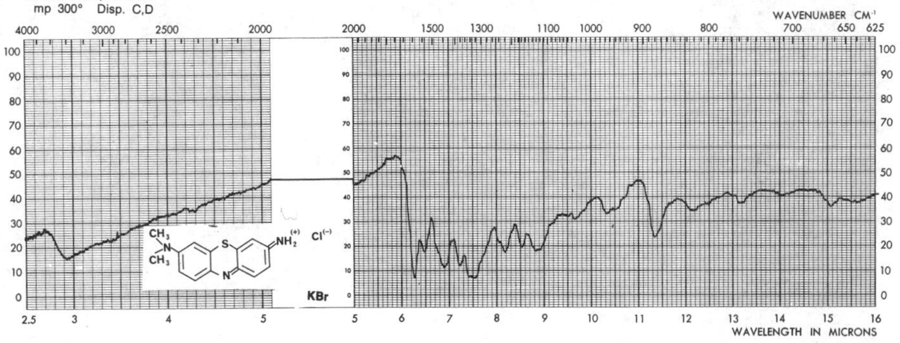

86,104-9
Azure A, certified (C.I. 52005)
FW 291.80 mp 290° (dec.) *Beil.* **27**,392
Disp. C,D

KBr

H

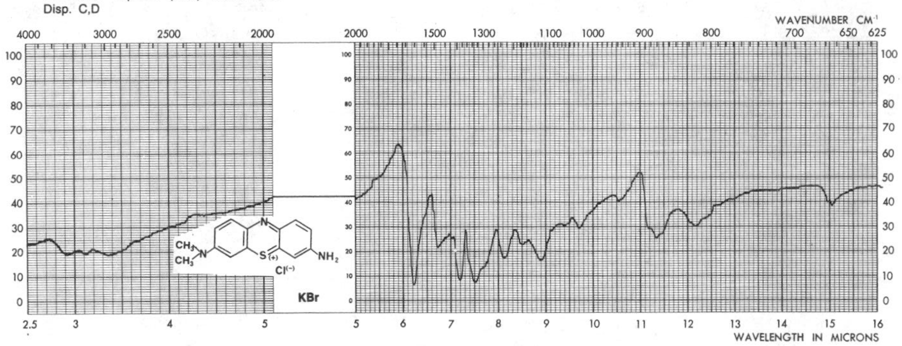

86,134-0
Thionin, certified
FW 287.34 *Beil.* **27**,392 Disp. C,D

NUJOL MULL

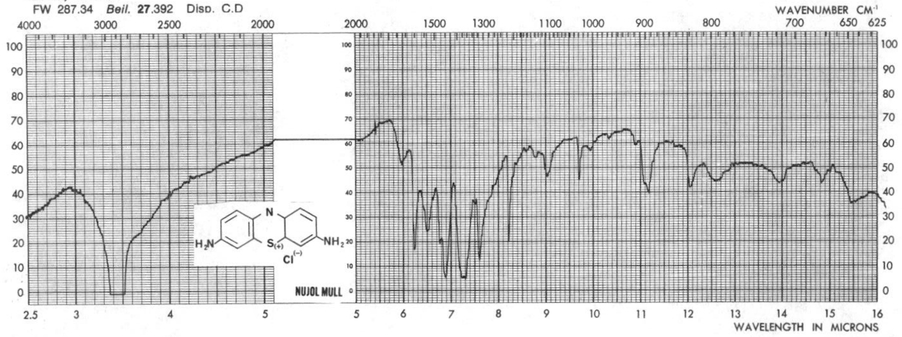

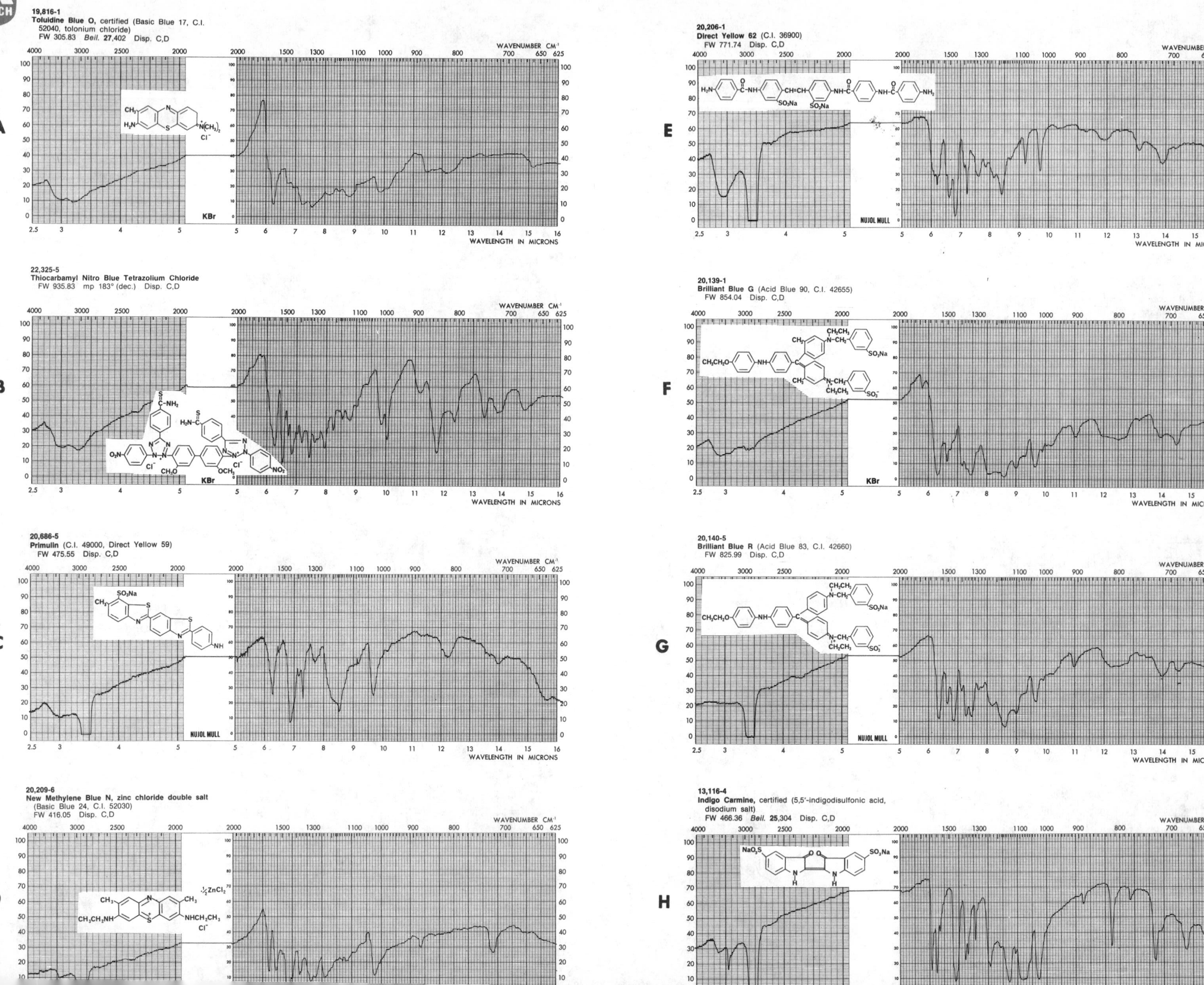
ALDRICH
A
19,816-1
Toluidine Blue O, certified (Basic Blue 17, C.I. 52040, tolonium chloride)
FW 305.83 Beil. 27,402 Disp. C,D
KBr
B
22,325-5
Thiocarbamyl Nitro Blue Tetrazolium Chloride
FW 935.83 mp 183° (dec.) Disp. C,D
KBr
C
20,686-5
Primulin (C.I. 49000, Direct Yellow 59)
FW 475.55 Disp. C,D
NUJOL MULL
D
20,209-6
New Methylene Blue N, zinc chloride double salt
(Basic Blue 24, C.I. 52030)
FW 416.05 Disp. C,D
E
20,206-1
Direct Yellow 62 (C.I. 36900)
FW 771.74 Disp. C,D
NUJOL MULL
F
20,139-1
Brilliant Blue G (Acid Blue 90, C.I. 42655)
FW 854.04 Disp. C,D
KBr
G
20,140-5
Brilliant Blue R (Acid Blue 83, C.I. 42660)
FW 825.99 Disp. C,D
NUJOL MULL
H
13,116-4
Indigo Carmine, certified (5,5'-indigodisulfonic acid, disodium salt)
FW 466.36 Beil. 25,304 Disp. C,D
WAVENUMBER CM⁻¹
WAVELENGTH IN MICRONS

FW 330.34 mp 273° (dec.) Disp. C,D

A

NUJOL MULL

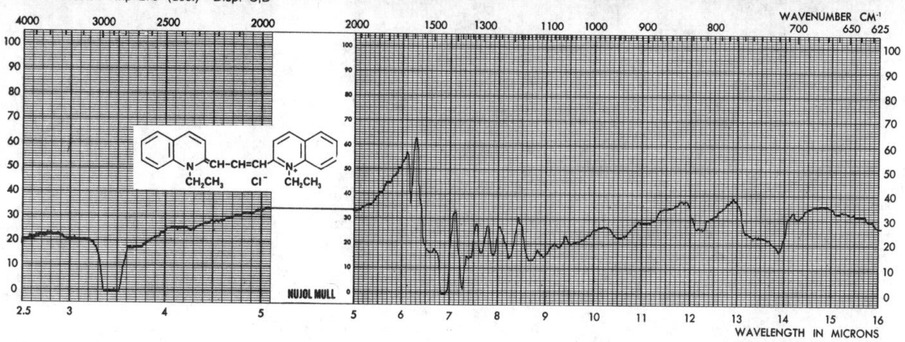

20,634-2
Celestine Blue (C.I. 51050)
FW 363.80 mp 227-230° Disp. C,D

B

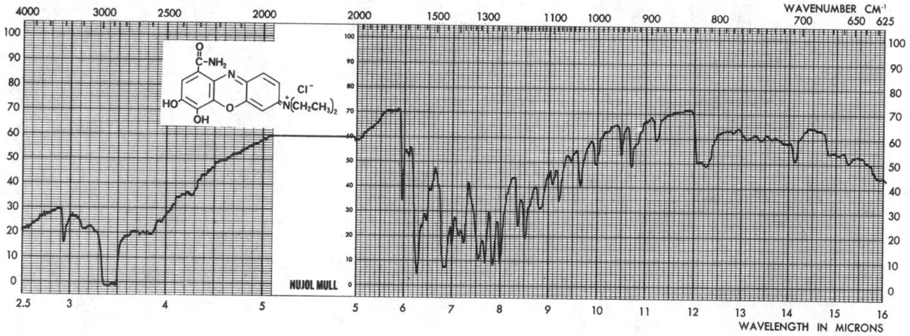

NUJOL MULL

20,186-3
Basic Yellow 11 (C.I. 48055)
FW 372.90 mp 297° (dec.) Disp. C,D

C

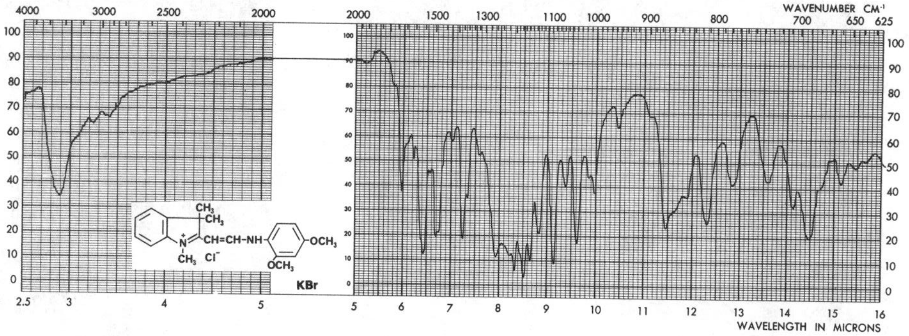

KBr

20,168-5
Methyl Calcein Blue
FW 277.28 mp 100° (dec.) Disp. C,D

D

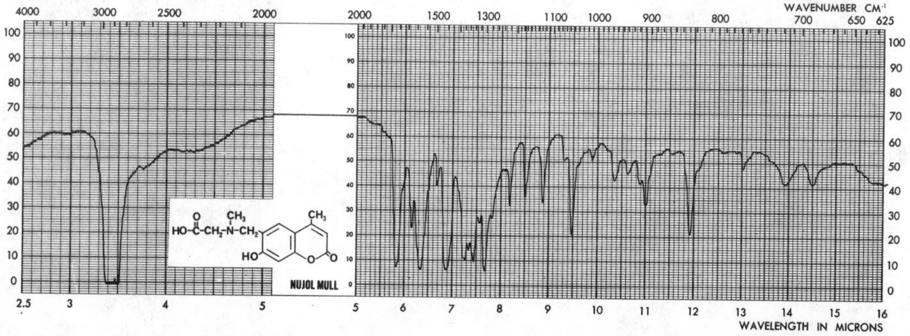

NUJOL MULL

C.I. 50420)
Beil. **12**,130 Disp. C,D

E

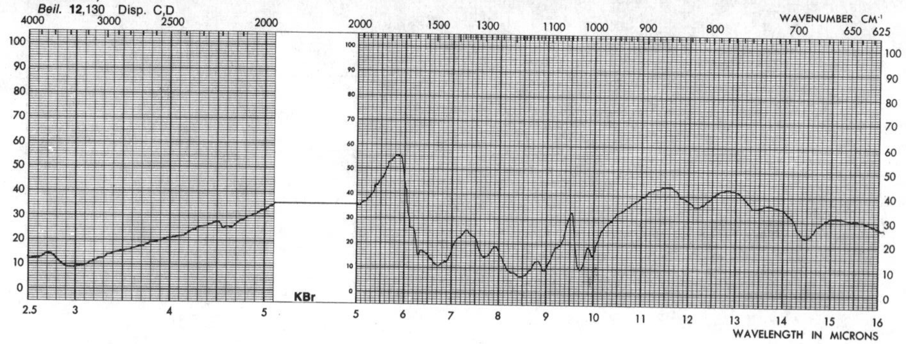

KBr

20,130-8
Pyronin B, certified (C.I. 45010)
FW 358.91 mp 174-176° *Beil.* **18**,596 Disp. C,D

F

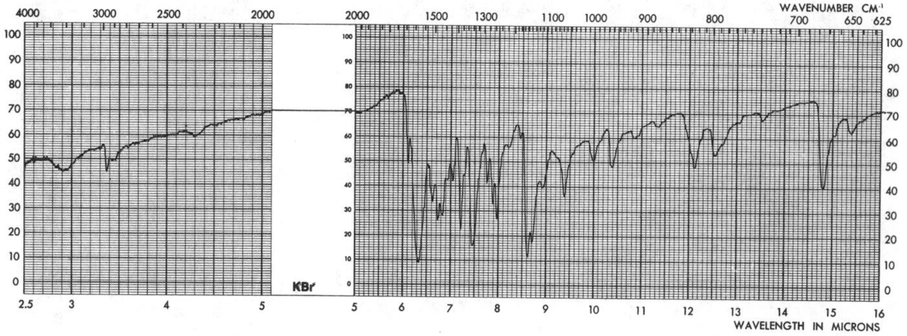

KBr

86,137-5
Wright Stain, certified
Disp. C,D

G

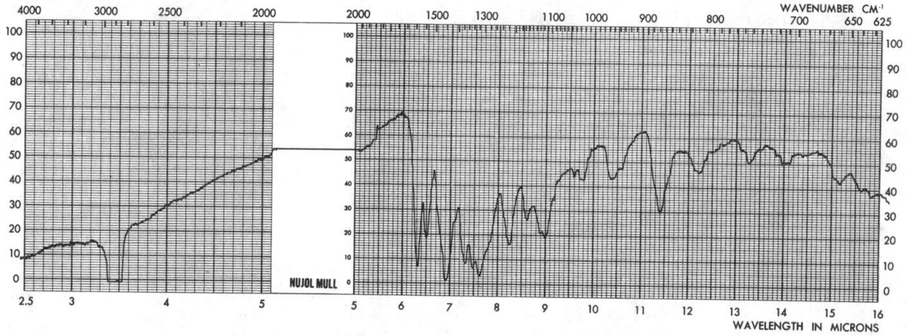

NUJOL MULL

86,108-1
Basic Fuchsin, special for flagella, certified
Disp. C,D

H

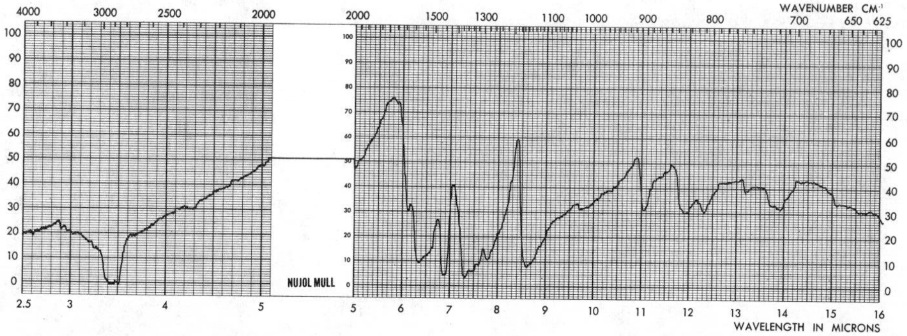

NUJOL MULL

A

21,680-1
Resorcin Crystal Violet
Disp. C,D
NUJOL MULL

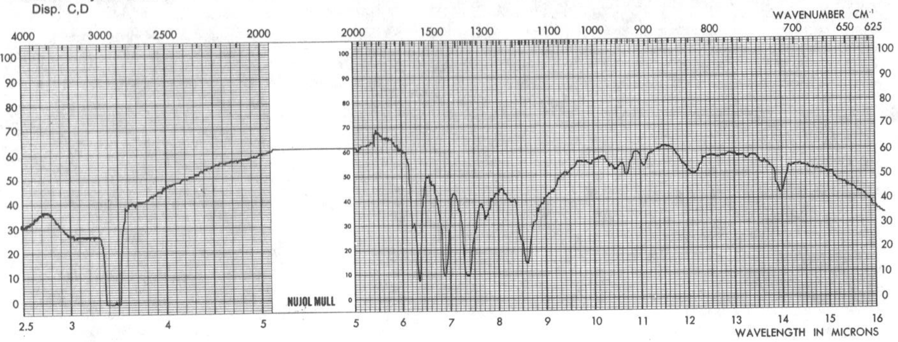

B

21,679-8
Twort Stain
Disp. C,D
NUJOL MULL

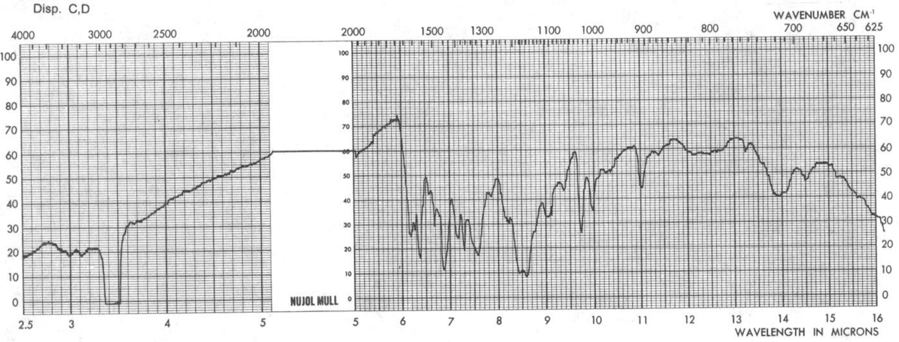

C

20,019-0
Tetrachrome Stain (MacNeal)
Disp. C,D
KBr

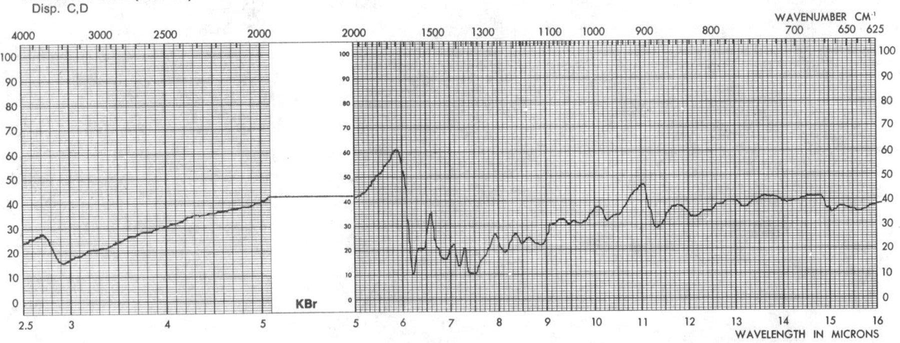

D

20,023-9
Azure B Eosinate
Disp. C,D

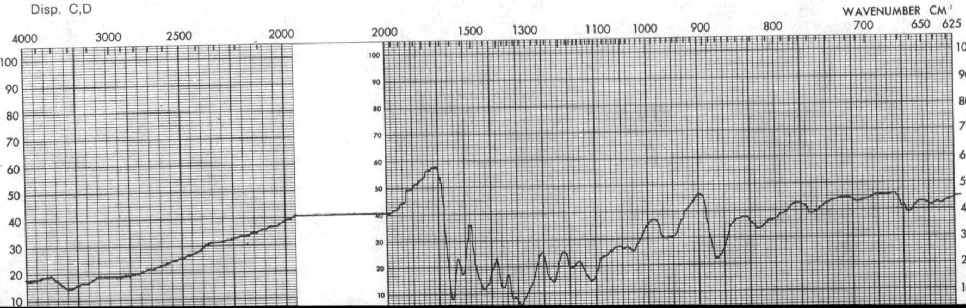

E

20,021-2
Azure A Eosinate
Disp. C,D
KBr

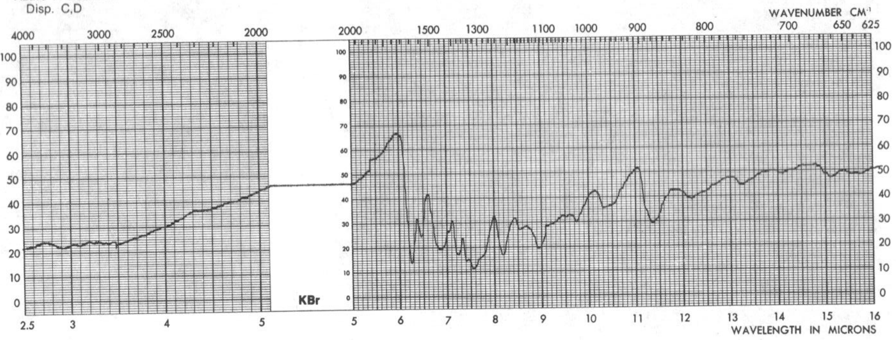

F

20,022-0
Azure II Eosinate
Disp. C,D
NUJOL MULL

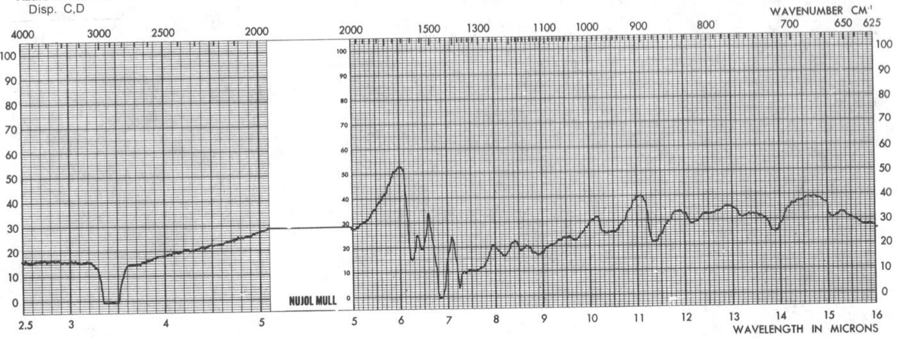

G

20,020-4
Leishman Stain
Disp. C,D
NUJOL MULL

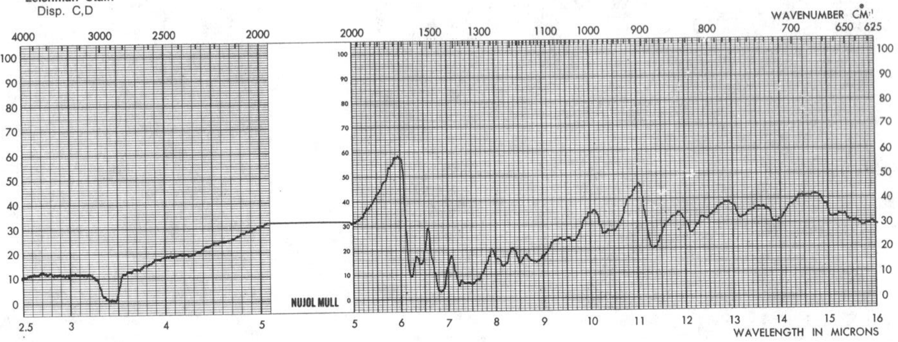

H

19,972-9
Litmus, indicator grade
Disp. C,D

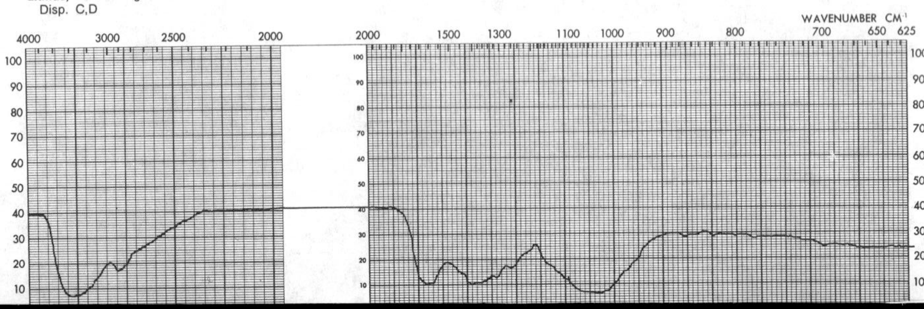

A

19,950-8
Acridine Yellow G (C.I. 46025)
FW 273.77 *Beil.* **22**,488 Disp. C,D

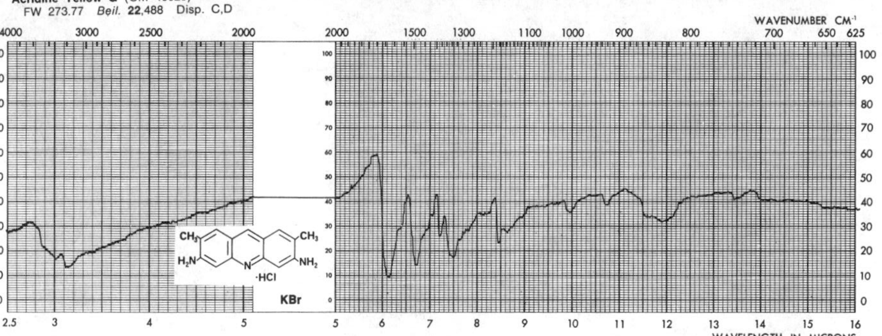

B

20,131-6
Quinaldine Red
FW 430.33 *IR* **2**,1213C Disp. C,D

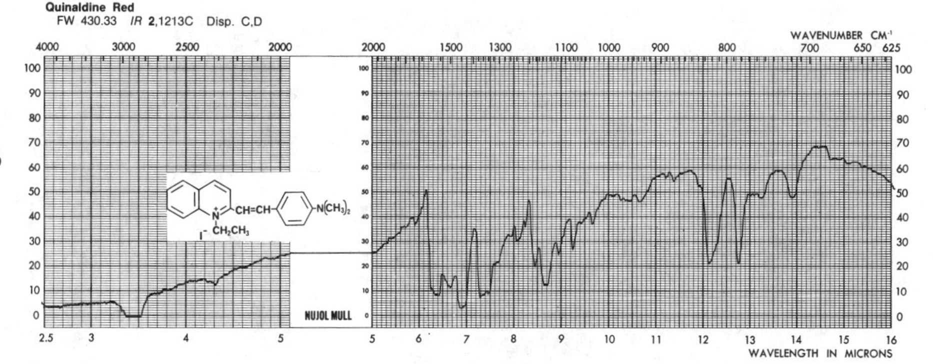

C

86,103-0
Auramine O, certified (Basic Yellow 2, C.I. 41000)
FW 303.84 Disp. C,D

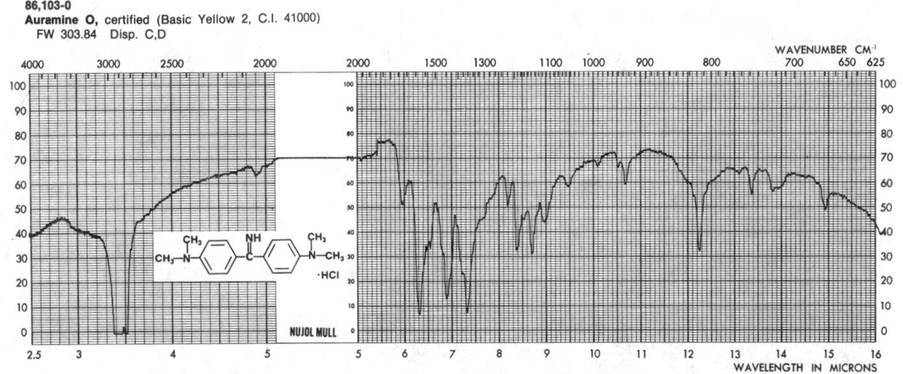

D

19,584-7
Cyssor I [2-methyl-N^1-benzenesulfonyl-N^4-(bromo-acetyl)quinonediimide]
FW 381.26 mp 116-117° Disp. C

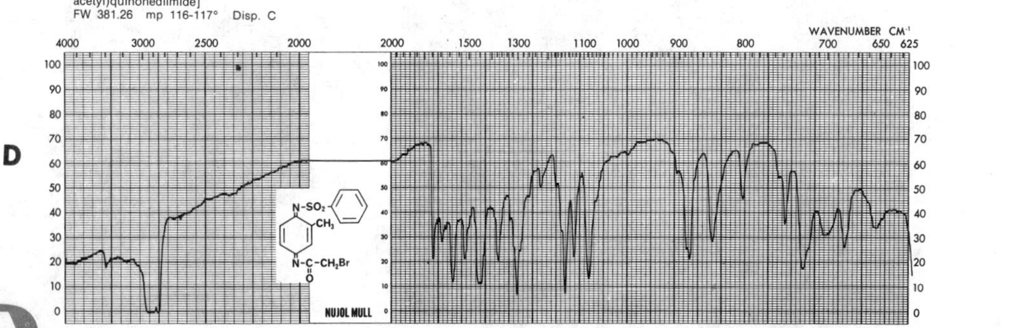

STEROIDS AND INDOLE ALKALOIDS

This section has been prepared primarily for the purpose of providing standard infrared spectra on a number of interesting steroids and indole alkaloids.

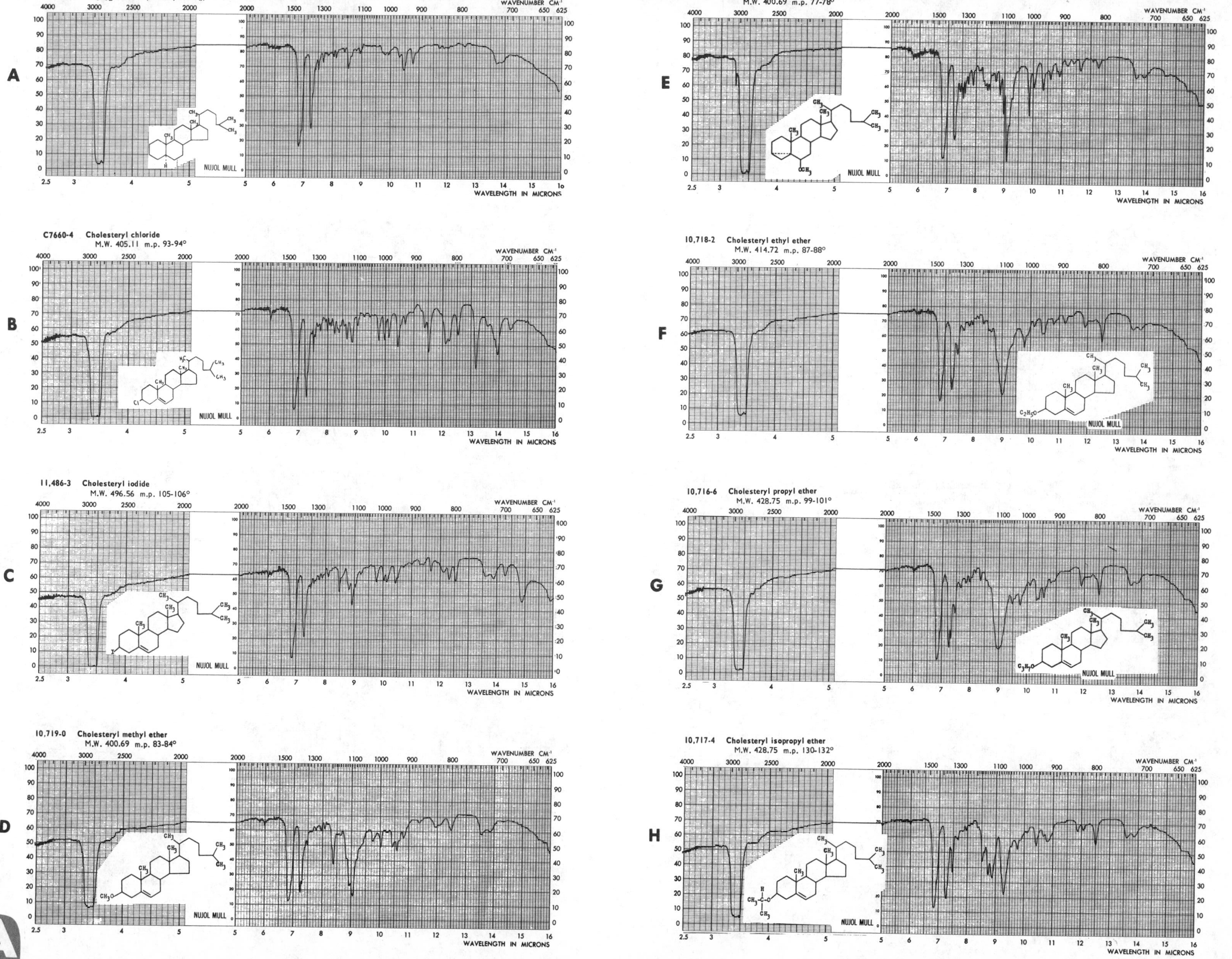
A
M.W. 372.68 m.p. 80-82°
[α]D + 28.7° (c=2.33, CHCl3)
NUJOL MULL
C7660-4 Cholesteryl chloride
M.W. 405.11 m.p. 93-94°
B
NUJOL MULL
11,486-3 Cholesteryl iodide
M.W. 496.56 m.p. 105-106°
C
NUJOL MULL
10,719-0 Cholesteryl methyl ether
M.W. 400.69 m.p. 83-84°
D
NUJOL MULL
11,410-3 i-Cholesteryl methyl ether
M.W. 400.69 m.p. 77-78°
E
NUJOL MULL
10,718-2 Cholesteryl ethyl ether
M.W. 414.72 m.p. 87-88°
F
NUJOL MULL
10,716-6 Cholesteryl propyl ether
M.W. 428.75 m.p. 99-101°
G
NUJOL MULL
10,717-4 Cholesteryl isopropyl ether
M.W. 428.75 m.p. 130-132°
H
NUJOL MULL
WAVENUMBER CM-1
WAVELENGTH IN MICRONS
ALDRICH

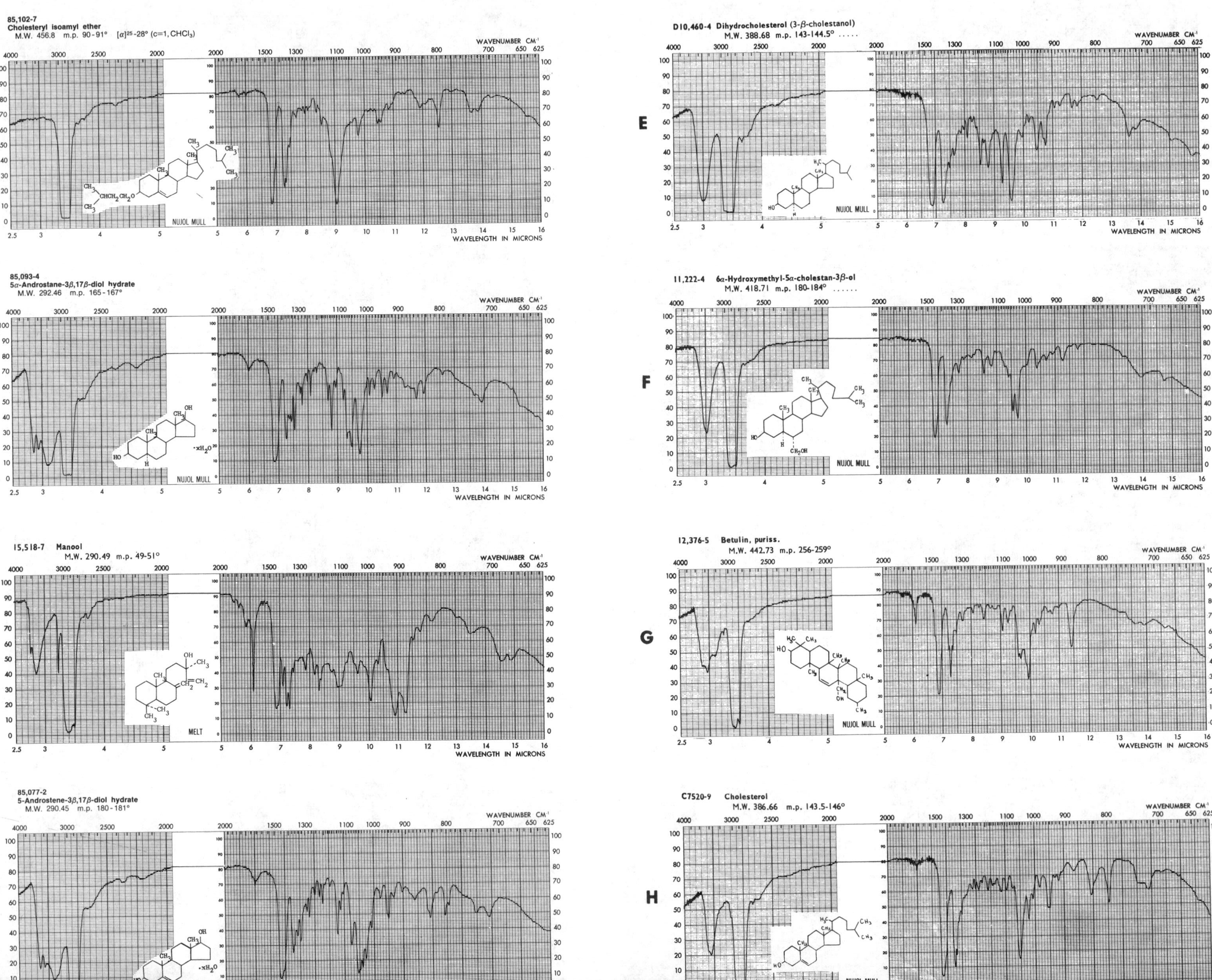
A
85,102-7
Cholesteryl isoamyl ether
M.W. 456.8 m.p. 90-91° [α]25 -28° (c=1, CHCl3)
NUJOL MULL
B
85,093-4
5α-Androstane-3β,17β-diol hydrate
M.W. 292.46 m.p. 165-167°
NUJOL MULL
C
15,518-7 Manool
M.W. 290.49 m.p. 49-51°
MELT
D
85,077-2
5-Androstene-3β,17β-diol hydrate
M.W. 290.45 m.p. 180-181°
E
D10,460-4 Dihydrocholesterol (3-β-cholestanol)
M.W. 388.68 m.p. 143-144.5°
NUJOL MULL
F
11,222-4 6α-Hydroxymethyl-5α-cholestan-3β-ol
M.W. 418.71 m.p. 180-184°
NUJOL MULL
G
12,376-5 Betulin, puriss.
M.W. 442.73 m.p. 256-259°
NUJOL MULL
H
C7520-9 Cholesterol
M.W. 386.66 m.p. 143.5-146°
WAVENUMBER CM⁻¹
WAVELENGTH IN MICRONS

A

$[\alpha]_D^{25}$ - 37° (c=2 in $CHCl_3$) ....

NUJOL MULL

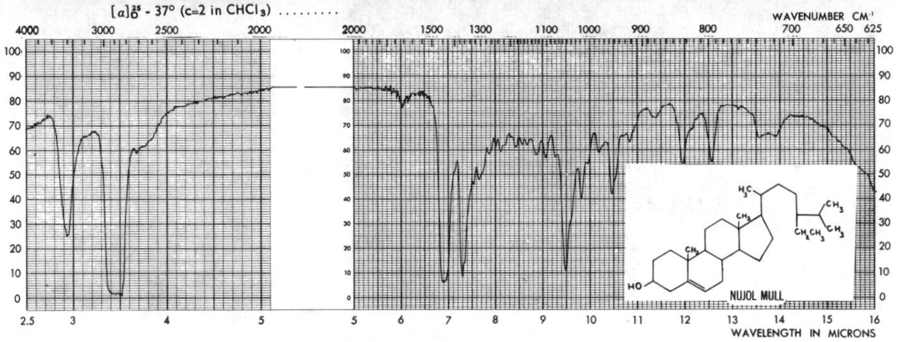

B

21,309-8
Stigmastanol, 99%
FW 416.74 mp 136-138°
$[\alpha]^{22}$ +23.4° (c=1, $CHCl_3$) Disp. C,D

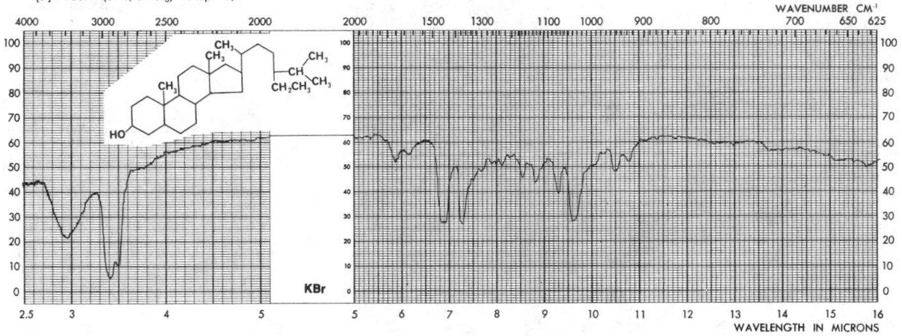

KBr

C

L40-8 Lanosterol (from natural sources, 40-60%)
M.W. 426.73 m.p. 134-136.5° $[\alpha]_D^{20}$ + 60.0° (c=1 in $CHCl_3$)

NUJOL MULL

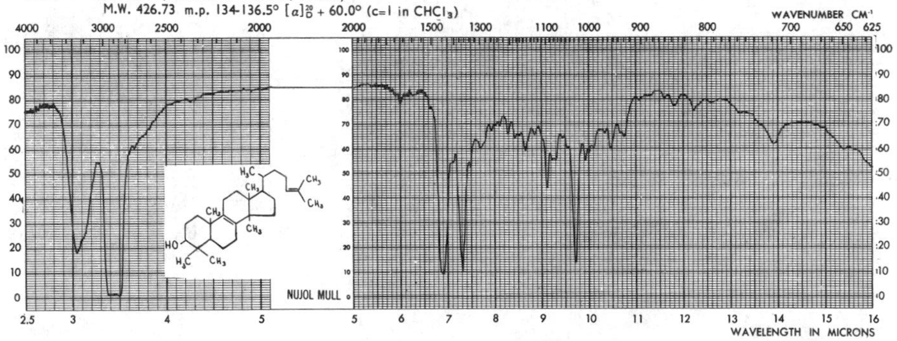

D

D300-1 7-Dehydrocholesterol
M.W. 384.65 ....

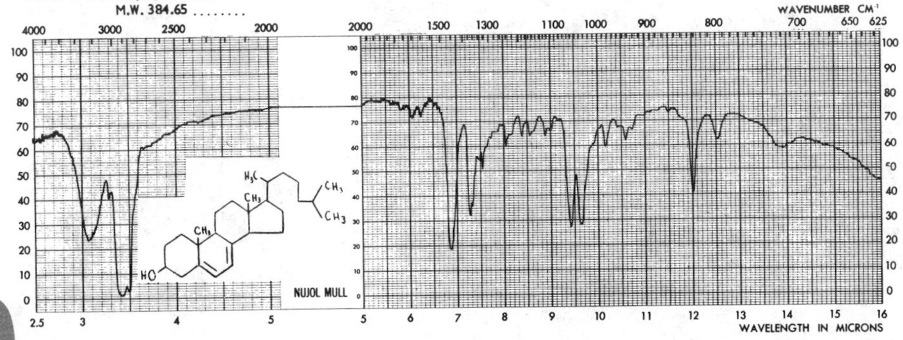

NUJOL MULL

E

L340-4 Lumisterol-3
M.W. 396.66 m.p. 89° (dec.)

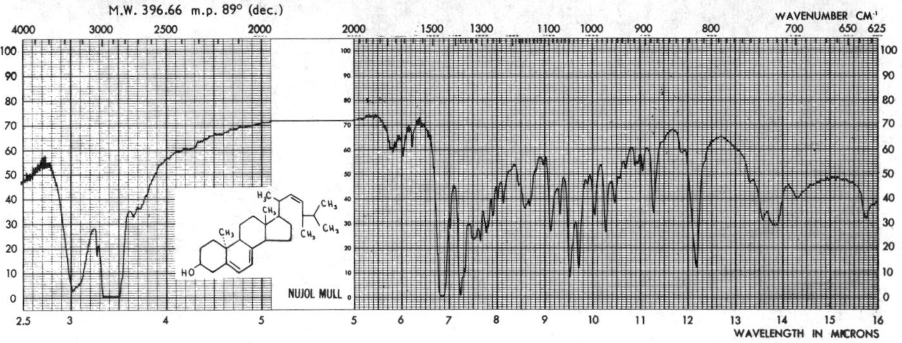

NUJOL MULL

F

E200-0 Ergosterol
M.W. 396.66 m.p. 160-164°

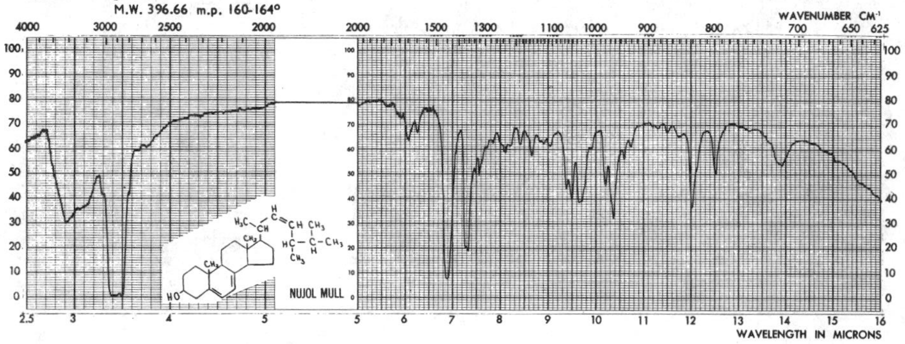

NUJOL MULL

G

V380-8 Vitamin D_3, crystalline, puriss.
M.W. 384.65 m.p. 85-87° ...

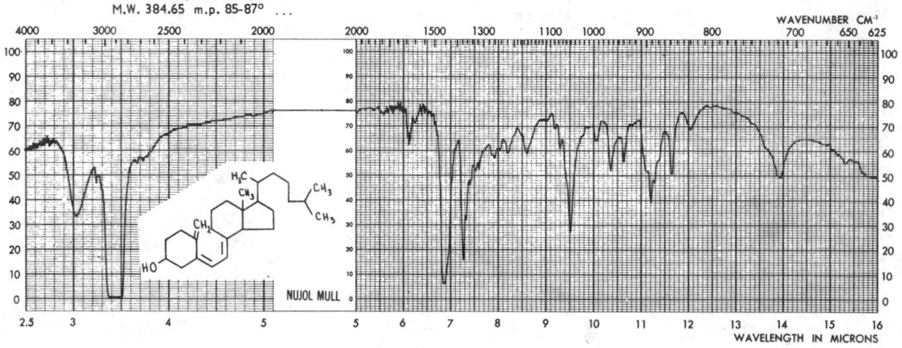

NUJOL MULL

H

13,611-5 Thiocholesterol
M.W. 402.73 m.p. 97-99°

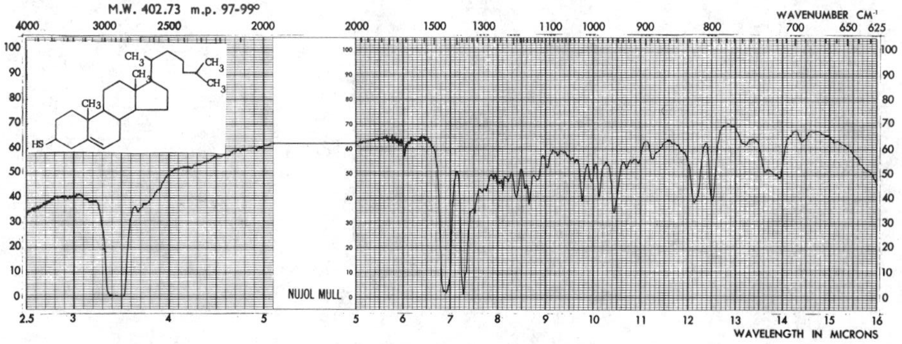

NUJOL MULL

ALDRICH

STEROIDS & INDOLE ALKALOIDS

A V125-2 **Veratramine**
M.W. 409.62 m.p. 206-207°

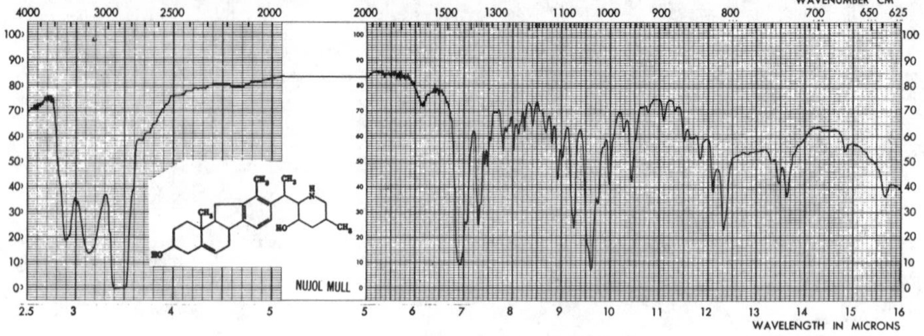

NUJOL MULL

B 10,712-3 **N-Cholesterylaniline**
M.W. 461.78 m.p. 190-192°

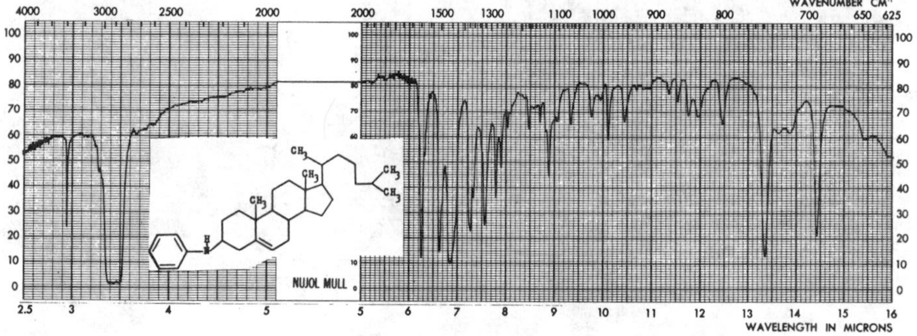

NUJOL MULL

C S360-7 **Solanine**
M.W. 868.07 m.p. 290° (dec.)

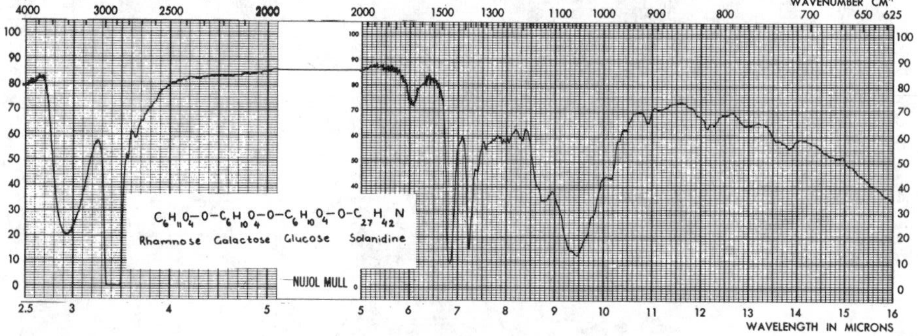

$C_6H_{11}O_4$–O–$C_6H_{10}O_4$–O–$C_6H_{10}O_4$–O–$C_{27}H_{42}N$
Rhamnose Galactose Glucose Solanidine

NUJOL MULL

D C7440-7 **Cholestan-3-one**
M.W. 386.66 m.p. 128-130° $[\alpha]_D^{20}$ + 42° (c=1, $CHCl_3$)

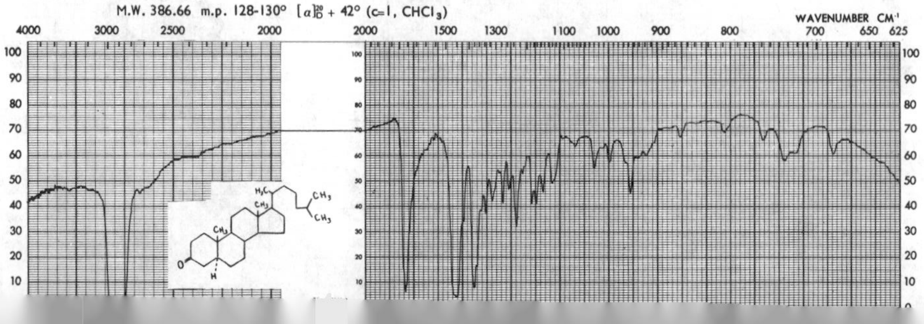

E A8600-7 **Androstanolone** (17β-hydroxy-5α-androstan-3-one)
M.W. 290.45 m.p. 179-183°

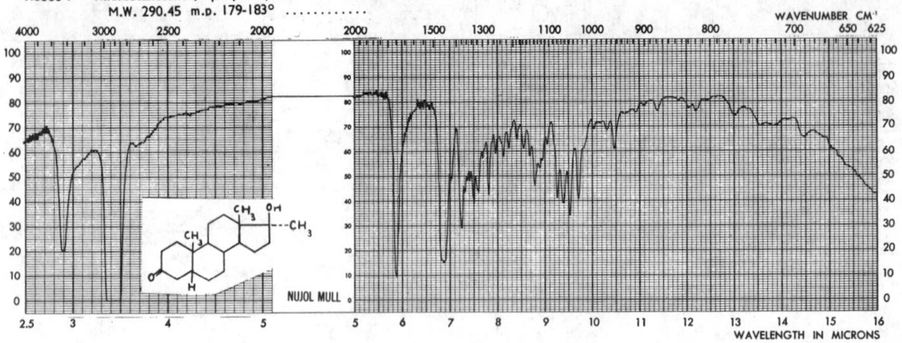

NUJOL MULL

F 12,578-4 **Dehydroisoandrosterone** (3β-hydroxy-5-androsten-17-one)
M.W. 288.43 m.p. 148.5-150.5°

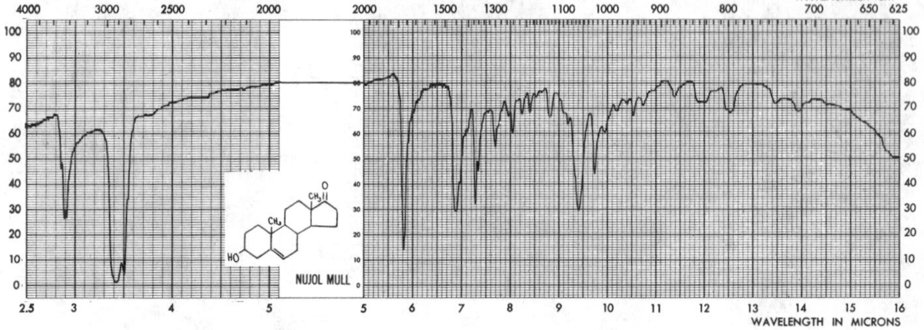

NUJOL MULL

G H4260-5 **17α-Hydroxy-16β-methylpregnenolone** (3β,17α-dihydroxy-16β-methyl-5-pregnen-20-one)
M.W. 346.51 m.p. 227-229°

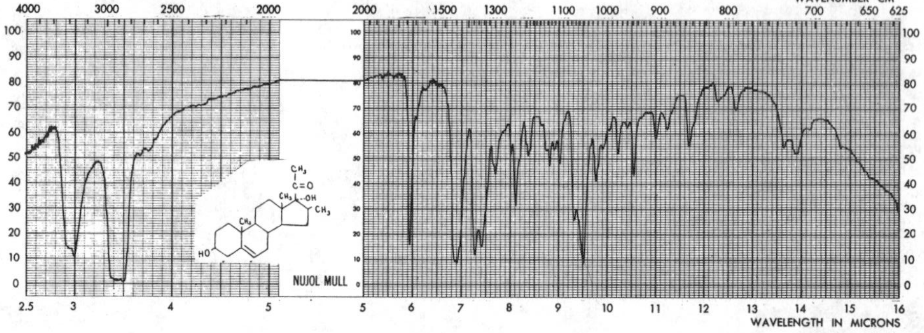

NUJOL MULL

H K60-6 **6-Ketocholestanol**
M.W. 402.66

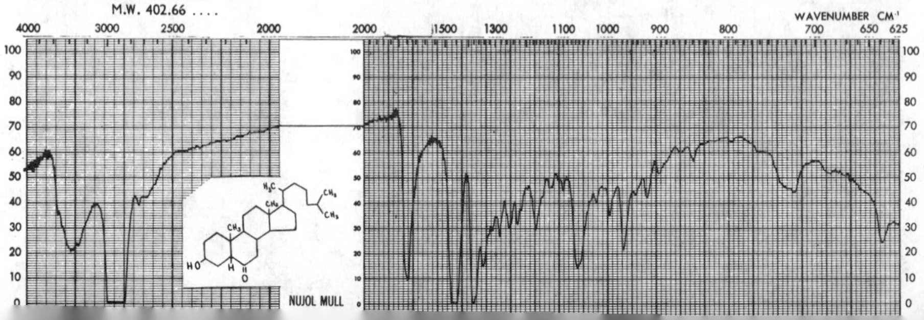

NUJOL MULL

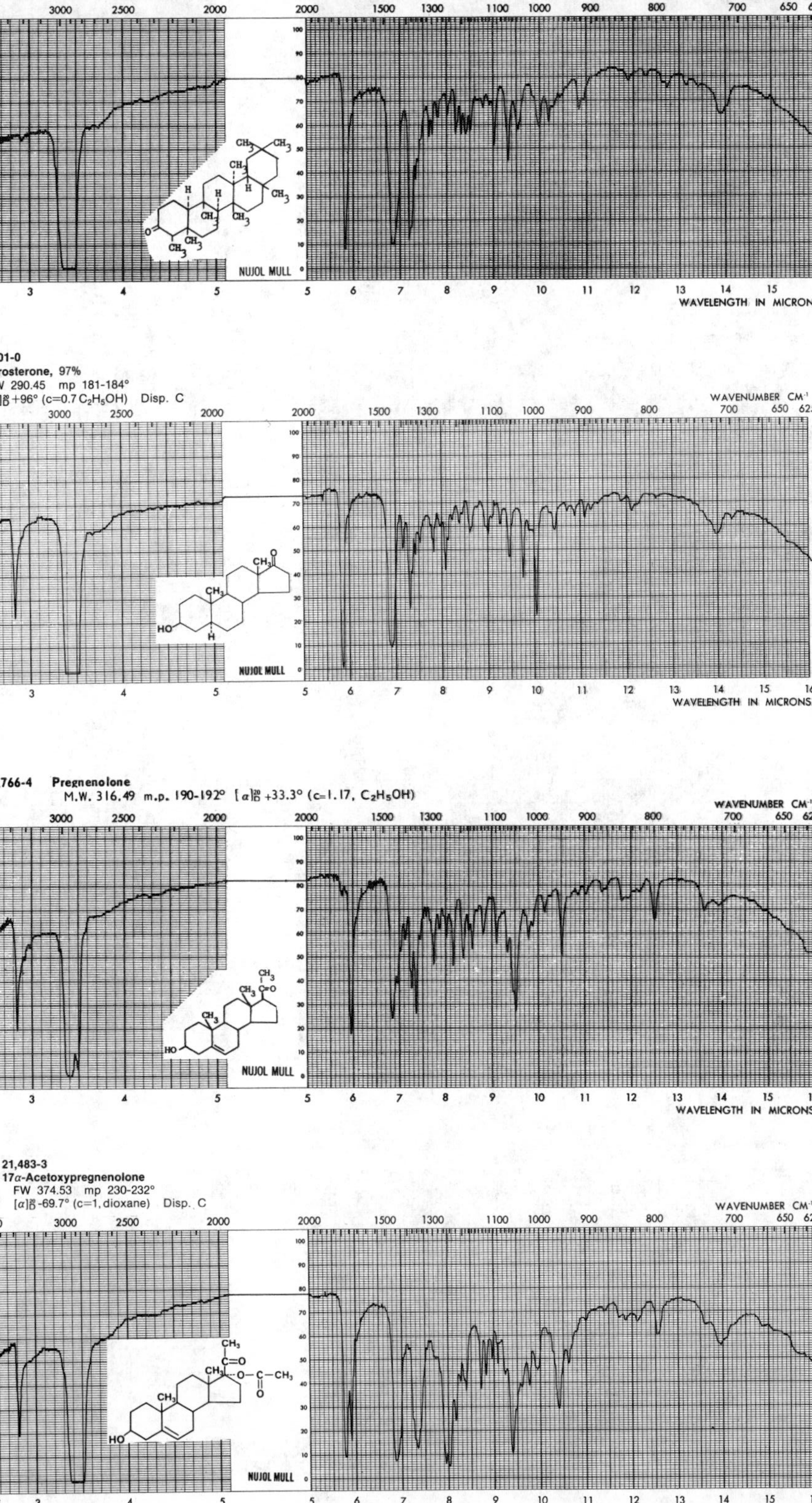

M.W. 426.73 m.p. 262-265°

A

21,901-0
Androsterone, 97%
FW 290.45 mp 181-184°
$[\alpha]^{20}_{D}$ +96° (c=0.7 C_2H_5OH) Disp. C

B

14,766-4 Pregnenolone
M.W. 316.49 m.p. 190-192° $[\alpha]^{20}_{D}$ +33.3° (c=1.17, C_2H_5OH)

C

21,483-3
17α-Acetoxypregnenolone
FW 374.53 mp 230-232°
$[\alpha]^{20}_{D}$ -69.7° (c=1, dioxane) Disp. C

D

16α-Methylpregnenolone
M.W. 330.51 m.p. 184-187°

E

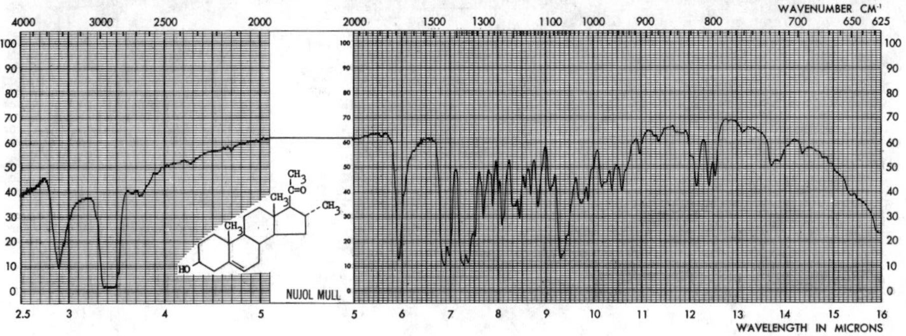

85,045-4
Progesterone
FW 314.47 mp 129-130°
$[\alpha]^{23}$ +182° (c=2, dioxane) Disp. D

F

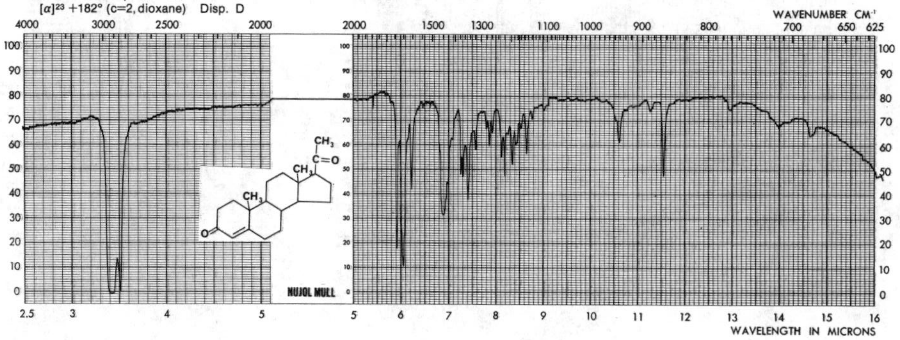

18,817-4
4-Cholesten-3-one
FW 384.65 mp 79-81° Disp. C

G

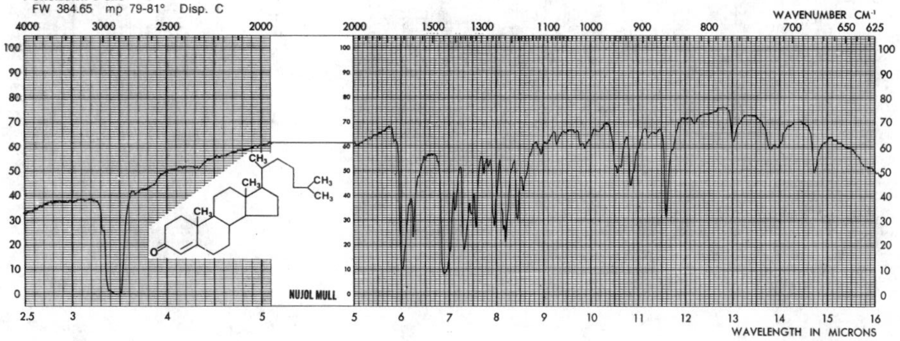

S435-2 4,22-Stigmastadien-3-one
M.W. 410.66 m.p. 123-125°

H

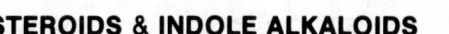

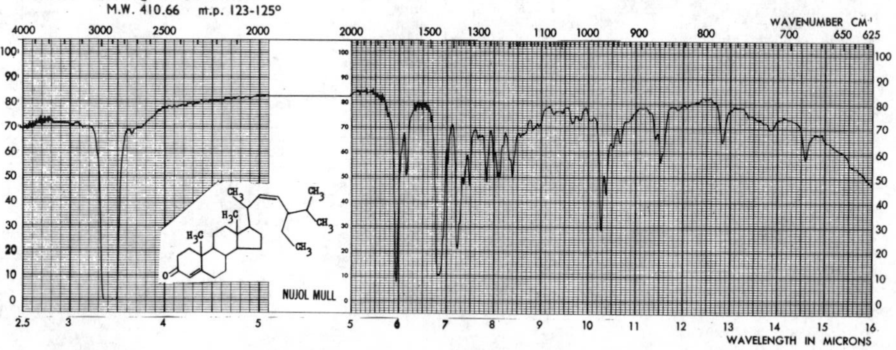

A

14,765-6 Testosterone, N.F.
M.W. 288.43 m.p. 153-155° $[\alpha]^{20}_{D}$ + 115.6° (c=1.11, C_2H_5OH)

NUJOL MULL

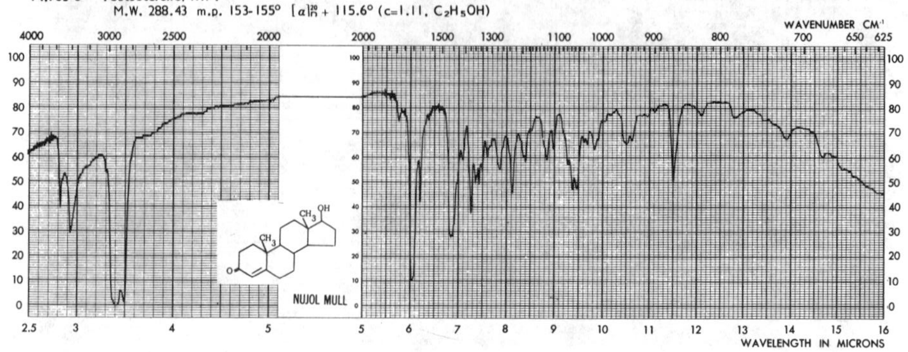

B

21,480-9
1α-Methyltestosterone
FW 302.46 mp 189-193° $[\alpha]_D$ +130° (c=1, $CHCl_3$)
Disp. C

NUJOL MULL

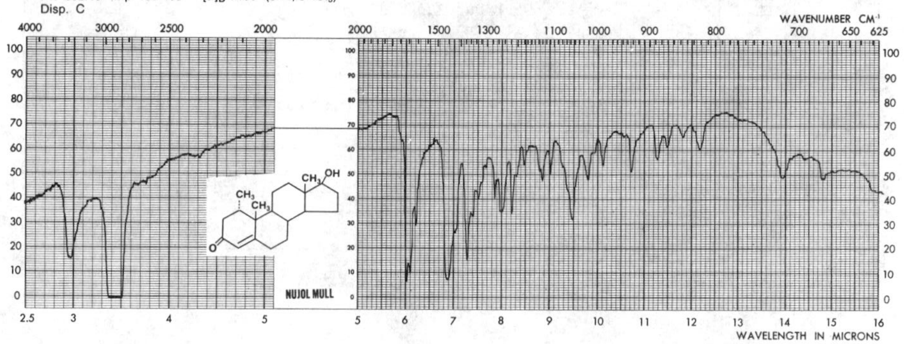

C

85,108-6
11α-Hydroxy-17α-methyltestosterone
M.W. 318.46 m.p. 153-155°

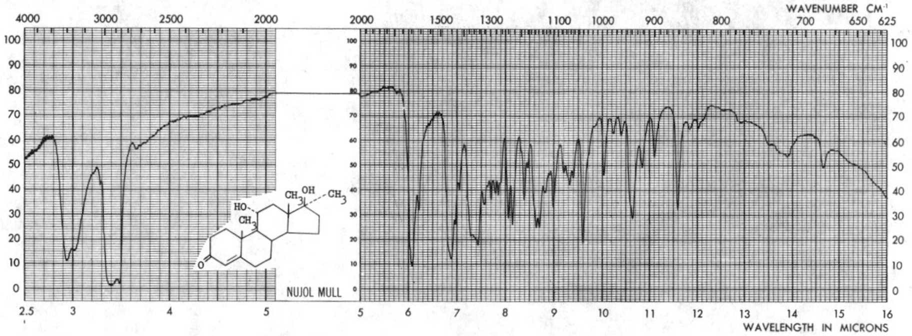

NUJOL MULL

D

85,079-9
17-Methyltestosterone
M.W. 302.46 m.p. 163-165°

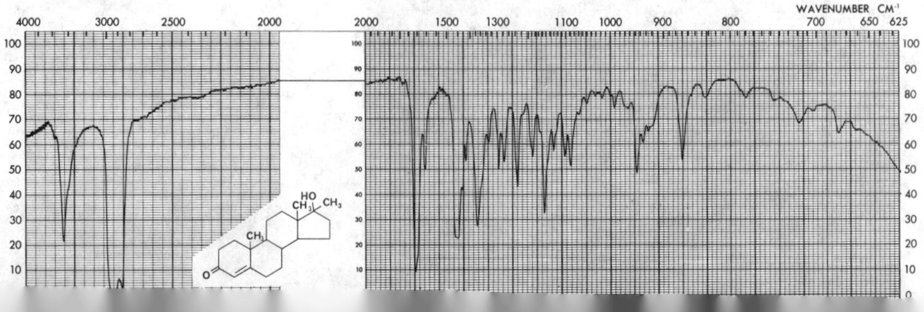

E

21,478-7
20-(Hydroxymethyl)pregna-1,4-dien-3-one
FW 328.50 mp 180-181° $[\alpha]_D$ +29° (c=1, $CHCl_3$)
Disp. C

NUJOL MULL

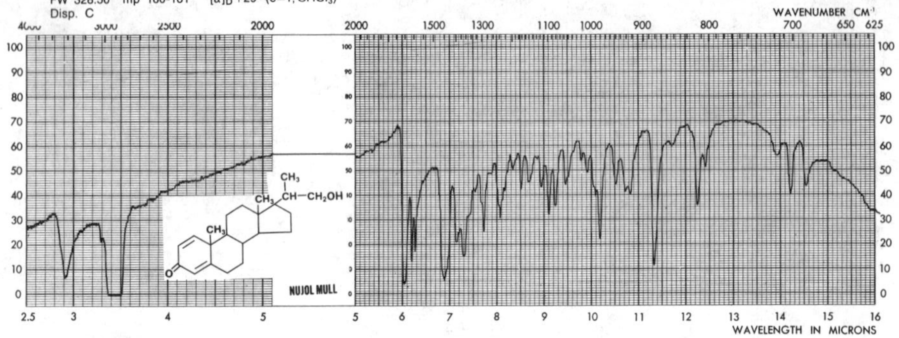

F

14,767-2 Progesterone
M.W. 314.47 m.p. 128-130°

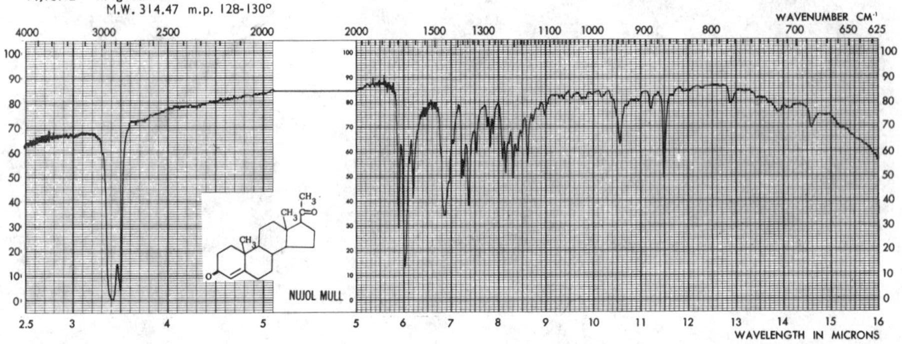

NUJOL MULL

G

H5420-4 11α-Hydroxyprogesterone (11α-hydroxy-4-pregnene-3,20-dione)
M.W. 330.47 m.p. 165-166°

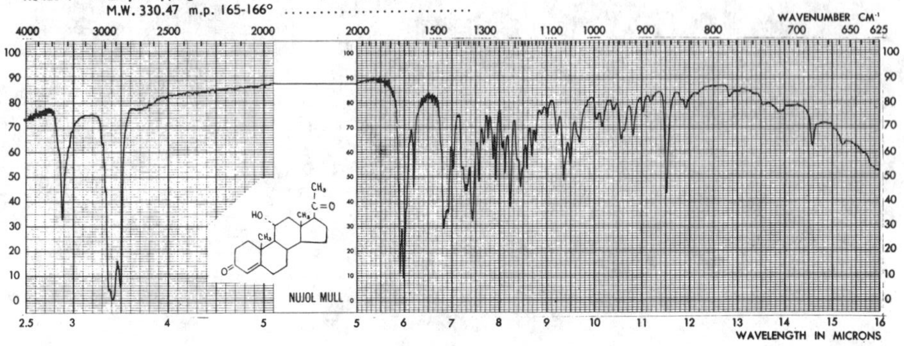

NUJOL MULL

H

14,769-9 Desoxycorticosterone
M.W. 330.47 m.p. 136-138.5° $[\alpha]^{23}_{D}$ + 177° (c=1, dioxane)

NUJOL MULL

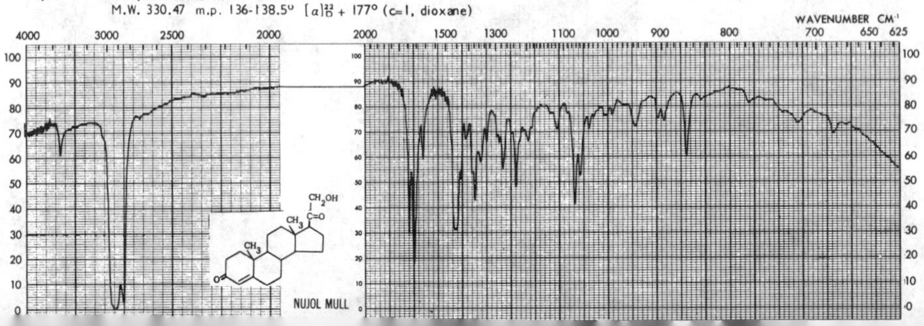

A

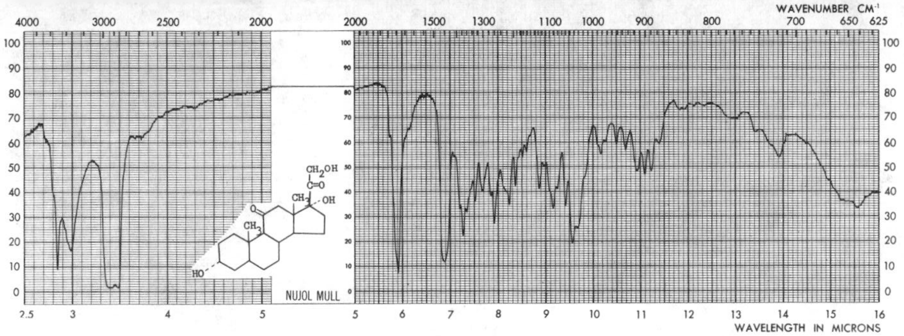

NUJOL MULL

11,964-4 **Cortexolone** (17,21-dihydroxy-4-pregnene-3,20-dione, Reichstein's compound S)
M.W. 346.47 m.p. 208° (dec.)
$[\alpha]_D^{20}$ + 120° ....

B

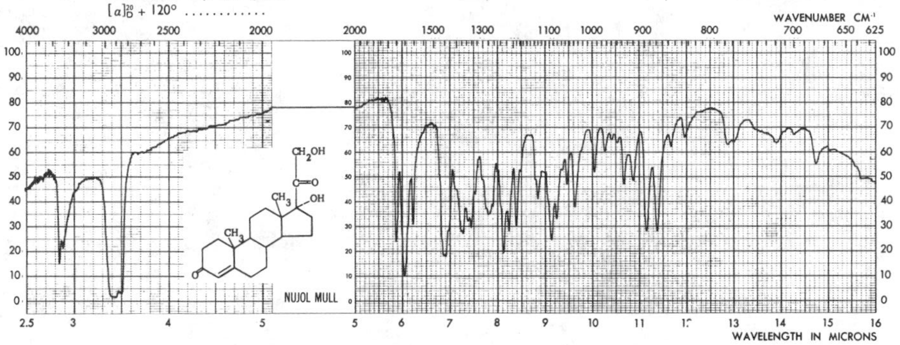

NUJOL MULL

13,213-6 **14α,17α,21-Trihydroxy-4-pregnene-3,20-dione** (14α-hydroxy-compound S)
M.W. 362.47 m.p. 215-217° (dec.) ....

C

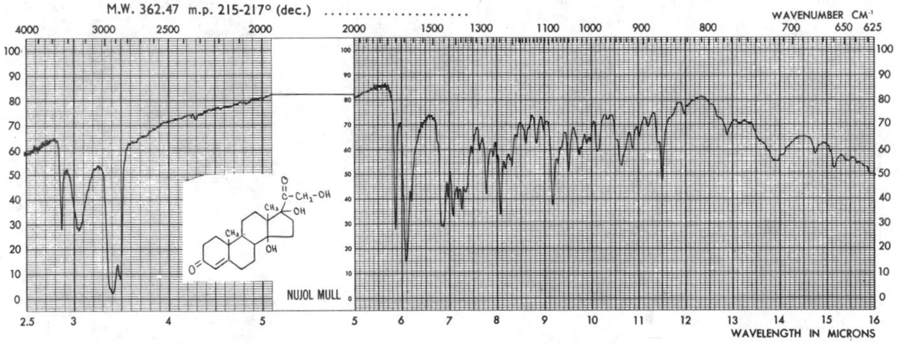

NUJOL MULL

D420-2 **16-Dehydroprogesterone** (4,16-pregnadiene-3,20-dione)
M.W. 312.46 m.p. 185-187° $[\alpha]_D^{20}$ + 155° ..

D

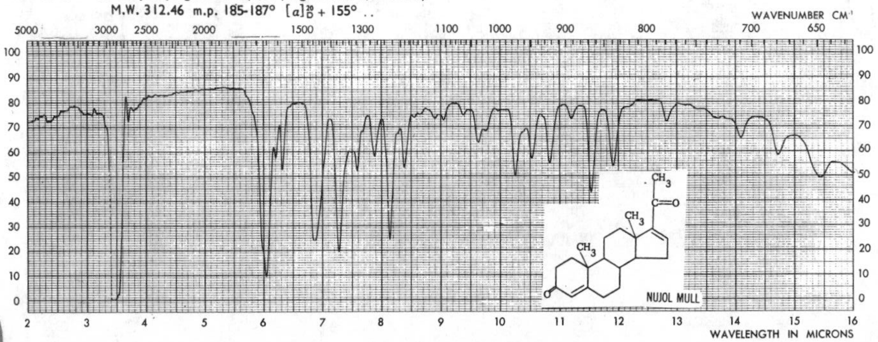

NUJOL MULL

M.W. 284.4 m.p. 138-139°

E

NUJOL MULL

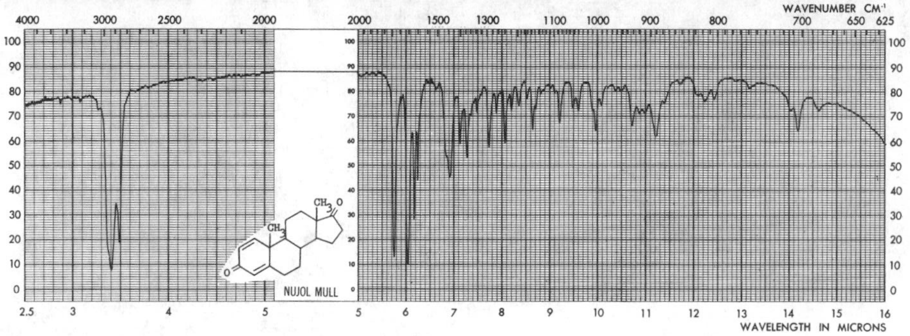

21,627-5
11α-Hydroxy-1,4-androstadiene-3,17-dione
FW 300.40 mp 205-207° $[\alpha]^{21}$ +84° (c=1, $CHCl_3$)
Disp. C

F

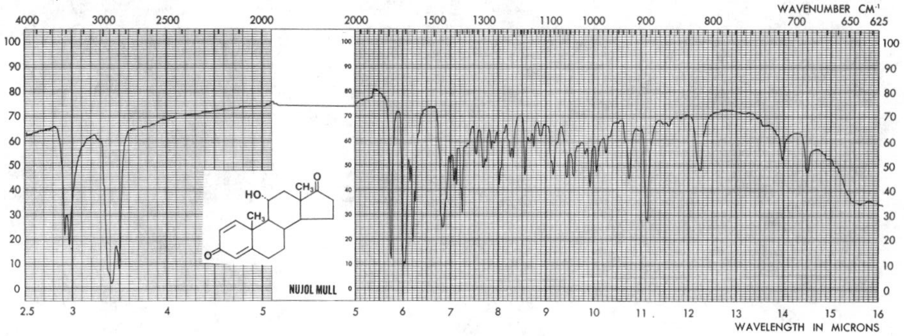

NUJOL MULL

11,659-9 **9-Acetoxyroyleanone**
M.W. 374.48 m.p. 207-209°

G

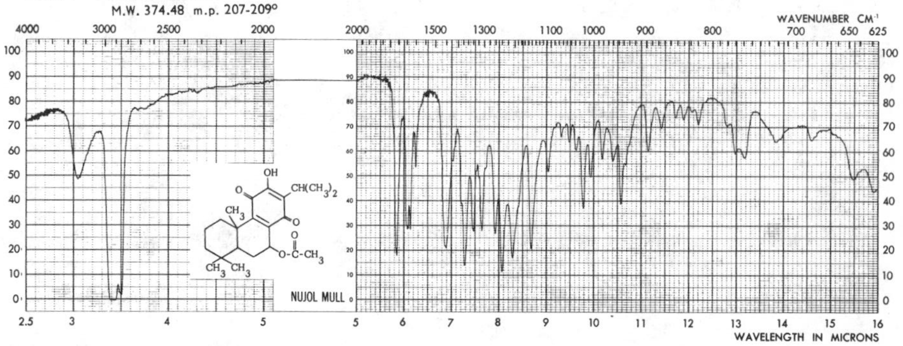

NUJOL MULL

E320-1 **Estrone**
M.W. 270.37 m.p. 235-248° $[\alpha]_D^{28}$ +150.9°

H

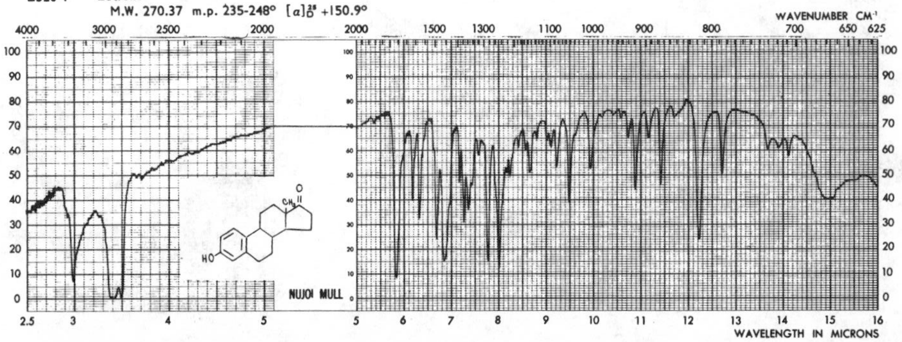

NUJOL MULL

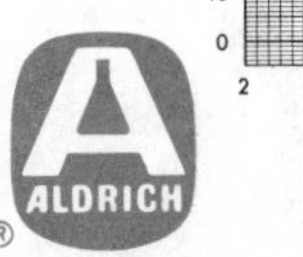

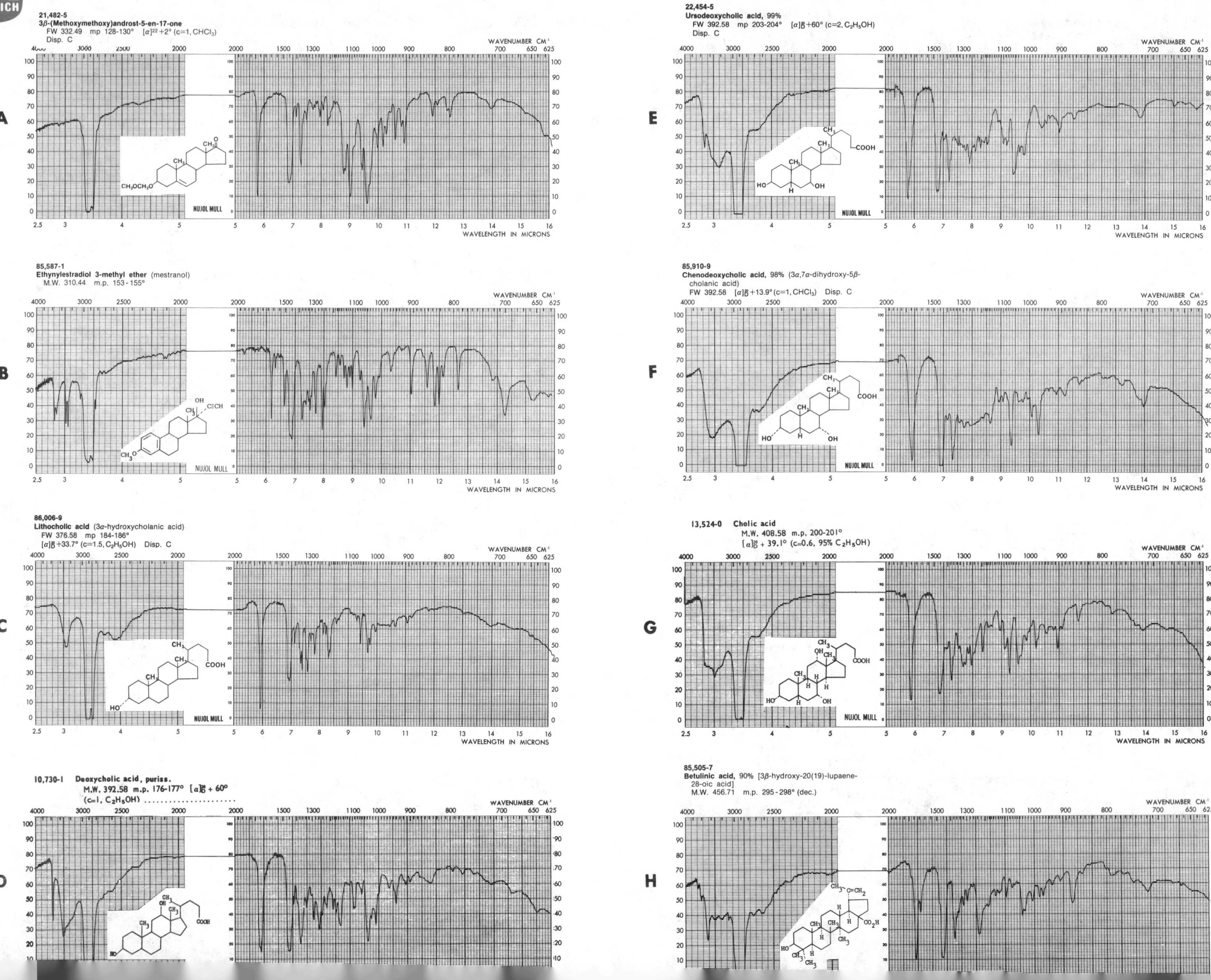
ALDRICH
A
21,482-5
3β-(Methoxymethoxy)androst-5-en-17-one
FW 332.49 mp 128-130° [α]22 +2° (c=1, CHCl3)
Disp. C
B
85,587-1
Ethynylestradiol 3-methyl ether (mestranol)
M.W. 310.44 m.p. 153-155°
C
86,006-9
Lithocholic acid (3α-hydroxycholanic acid)
FW 376.58 mp 184-186°
[α]D +33.7° (c=1.5, C2H5OH) Disp. C
D
10,730-1 Deoxycholic acid, puriss.
M.W. 392.58 m.p. 176-177° [α]D + 60°
(c=1, C2H5OH)
E
22,454-5
Ursodeoxycholic acid, 99%
FW 392.58 mp 203-204° [α]D +60° (c=2, C2H5OH)
Disp. C
F
85,910-9
Chenodeoxycholic acid, 98% (3α,7α-dihydroxy-5β-cholanic acid)
FW 392.58 [α]D +13.9° (c=1, CHCl3) Disp. C
G
13,524-0 Cholic acid
M.W. 408.58 m.p. 200-201°
[α]D + 39.1° (c=0.6, 95% C2H5OH)
H
85,505-7
Betulinic acid, 90% [3β-hydroxy-20(19)-lupaene-28-oic acid]
M.W. 456.71 m.p. 295-298° (dec.)
NUJOL MULL
WAVENUMBER CM⁻¹
WAVELENGTH IN MICRONS

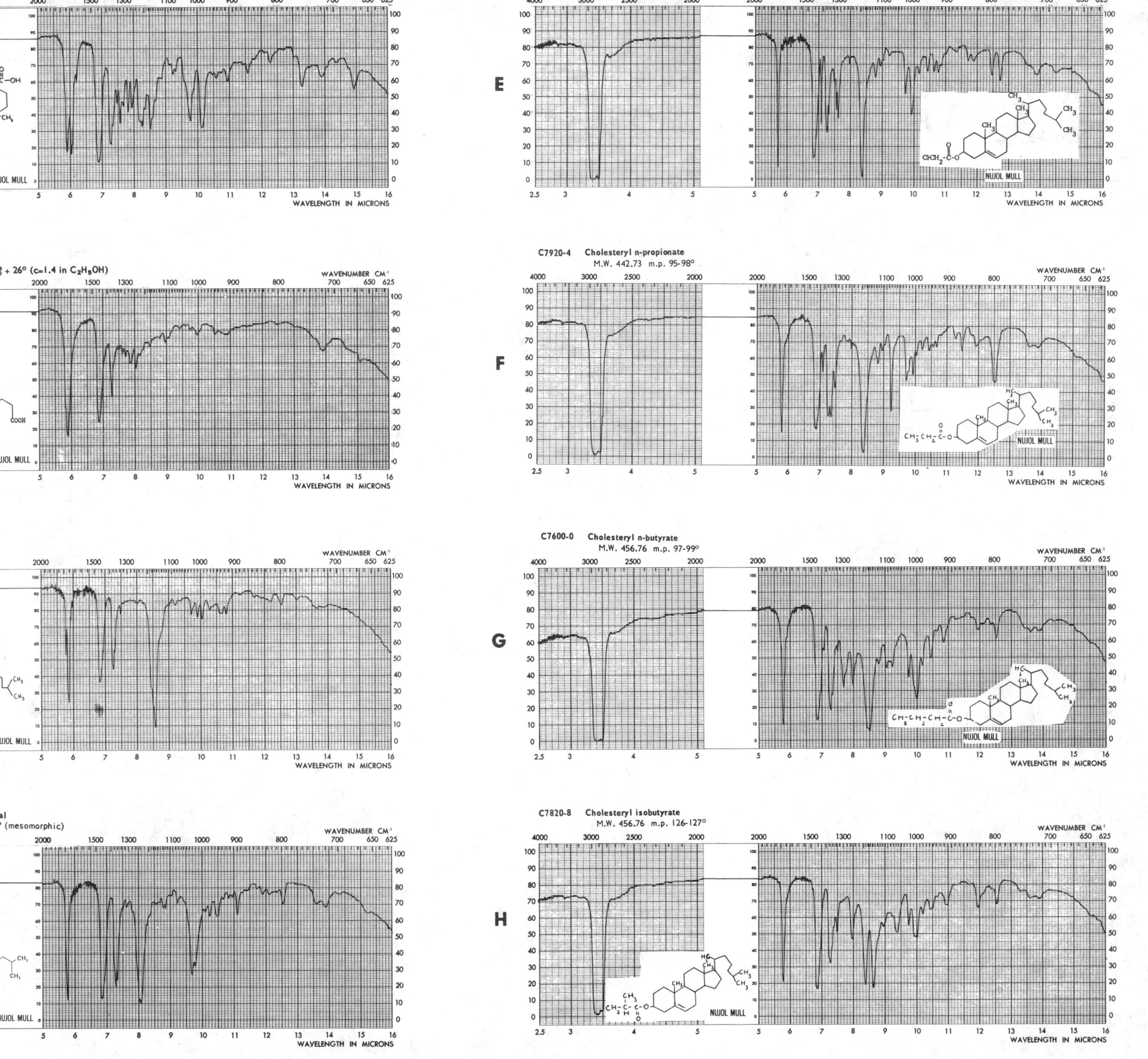

A

B

10,729-8 Dehydrocholic acid
M.W. 402.53 m.p. 233-235° $[\alpha]^{20}_{D}$ + 26° (c=1.4 in C_2H_5OH)

C

C7760-0 Cholesteryl formate
M.W. 414.67 m.p. 94.5-95°

D

15,111-4 Cholesteryl acetate, liquid crystal
M.W. 428.71 m.p. 111.5-113.5° (mesomorphic)

E

F

C7920-4 Cholesteryl n-propionate
M.W. 442.73 m.p. 95-98°

G

C7600-0 Cholesteryl n-butyrate
M.W. 456.76 m.p. 97-99°

H

C7820-8 Cholesteryl isobutyrate
M.W. 456.76 m.p. 126-127°

A

C7960-3 **Cholesteryl n-valerate**
M.W. 470.78 m.p. 96-98°

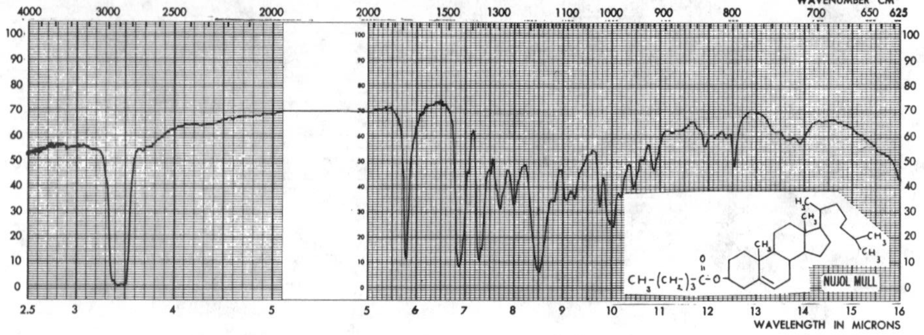

B

C7620-5 **Cholesteryl caproate** (cholesteryl hexanoate)
M.W. 484.81 m.p. 94-96°

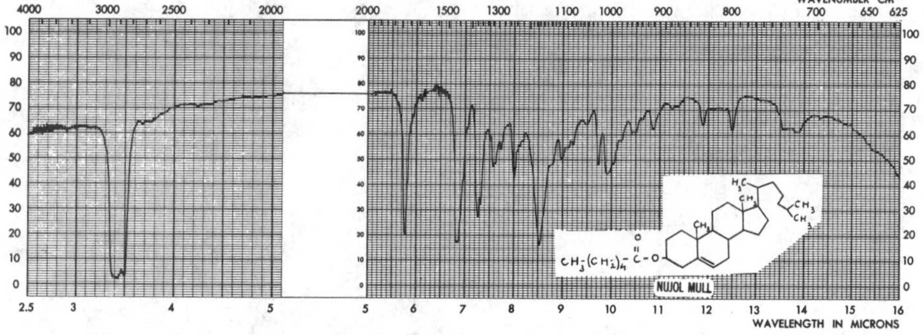

C

C7780-5 **Cholesteryl n-heptylate** (cholesteryl heptanoate)
M.W. 498.84 m.p. 112-113°

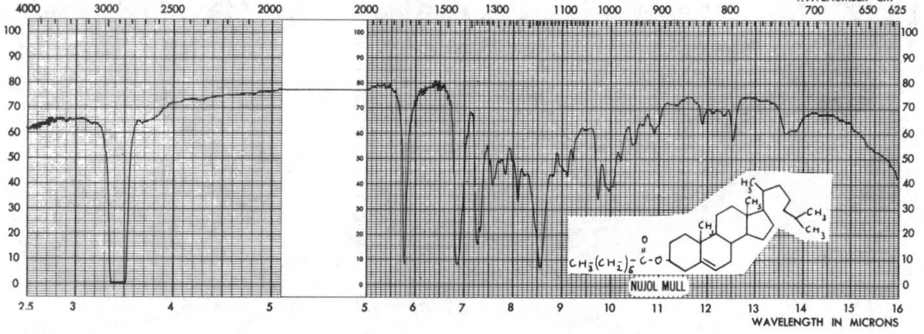

D

12,525-3 **Cholesteryl caprylate** (cholesteryl octanoate)
M.W. 512.86 m.p. 104-106°

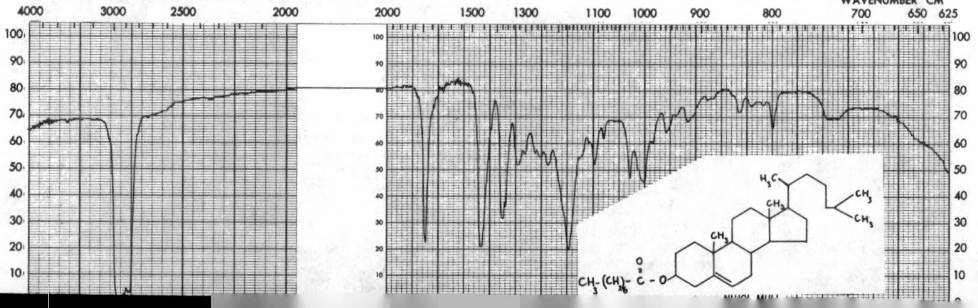

E

C7880-1 **Cholesteryl pelargonate** (cholesteryl nonanoate)
M.W. 526.89 m.p. 78-80°

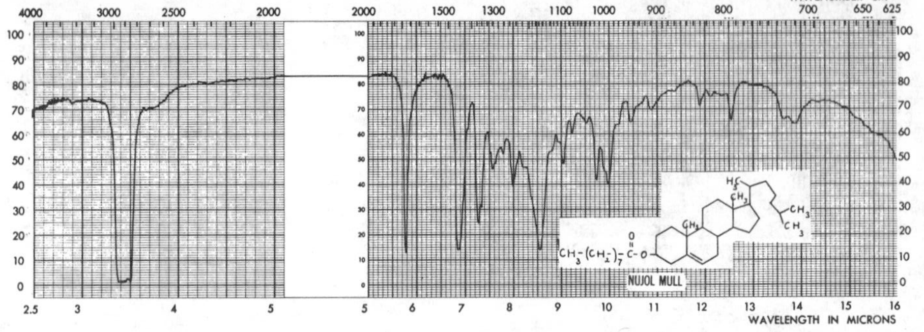

F

C7740-6 **Cholesteryl n-decylate** (cholesteryl decanoate)
M.W. 540.92 m.p. 84-87.5°

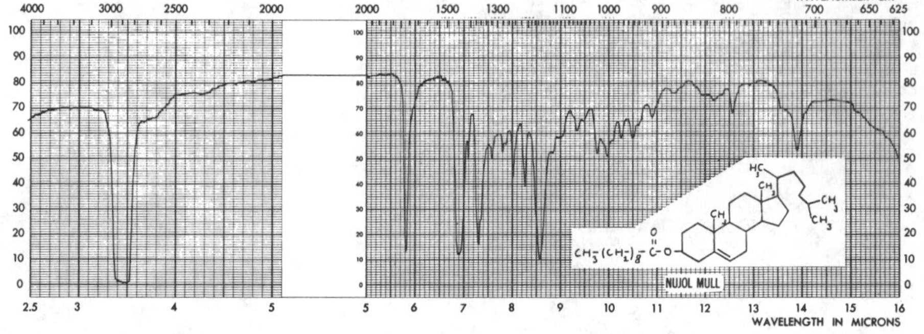

G

C7830-5 **Cholesteryl laurate**
M.W. 568.97 m.p. 91-92.5°

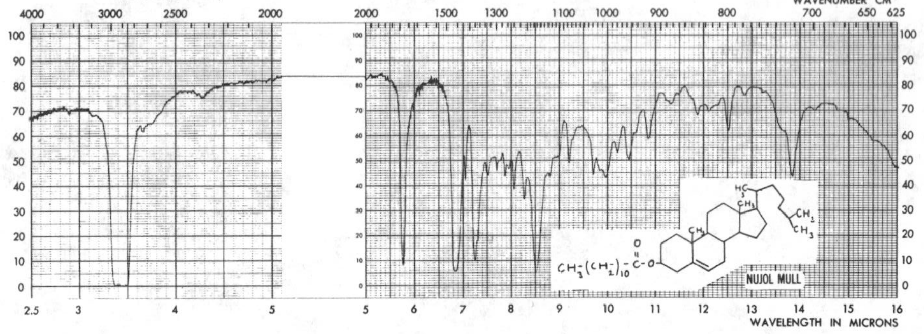

H

15,113-0 **Cholesteryl myristate, liquid crystal**
M.W. 597.03 m.p. 69-84° (mesomorphic)

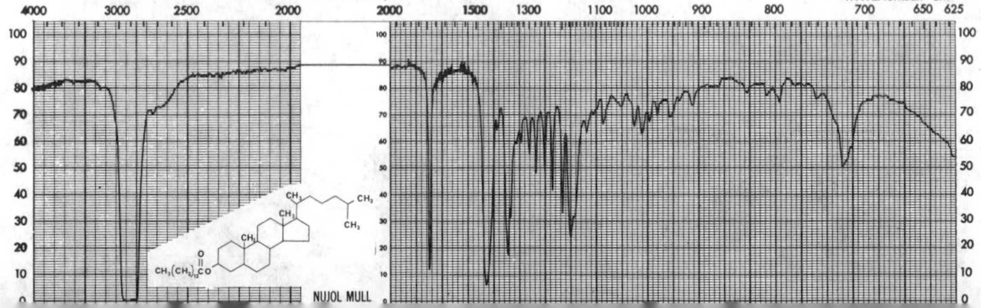

A

M.W. 625.08 m.p. 77-78°

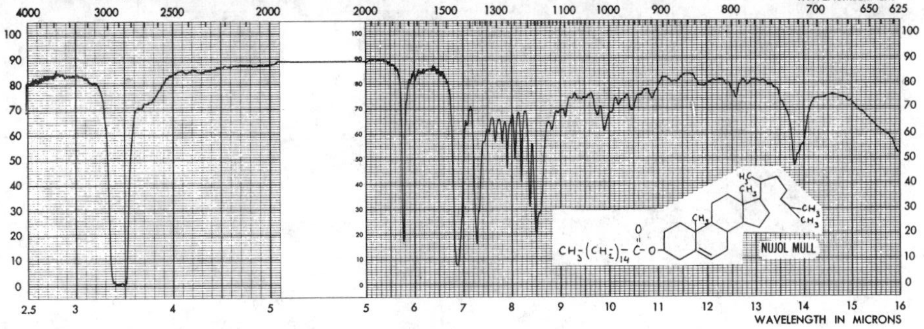

NUJOL MULL

B

C7940-9 Cholesteryl stearate

M.W. 653.13 . . . . .

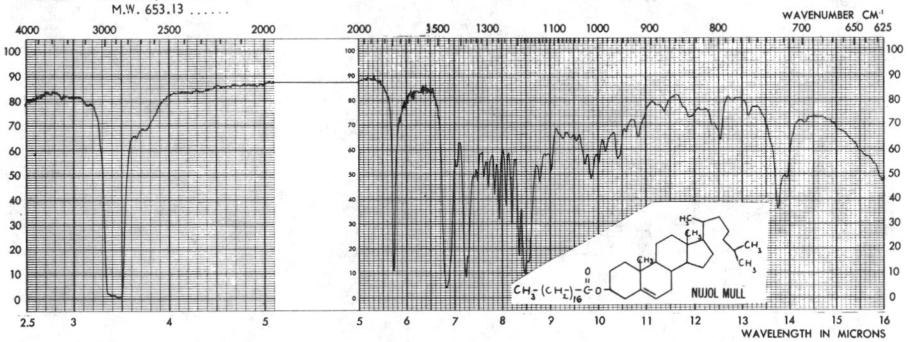

NUJOL MULL

C

15,114-9 Cholesteryl oleate, liquid crystal

M.W. 651.12 m.p. 44-47° (mesomorphic)

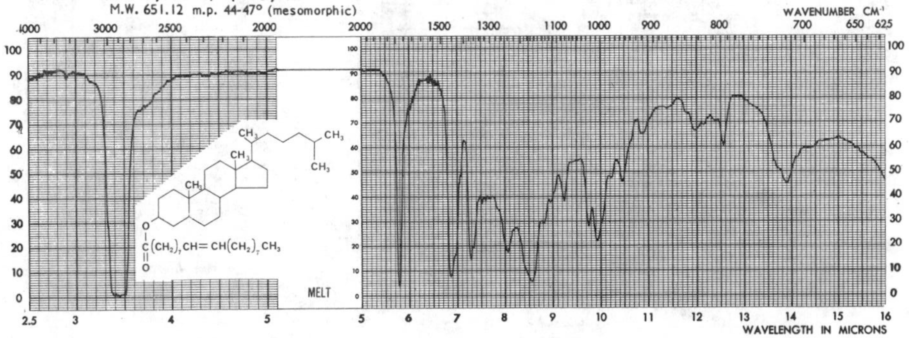

MELT

D

C7540-3 Cholesteryl acetoacetate

M.W. 470.74 m.p. 83-85°

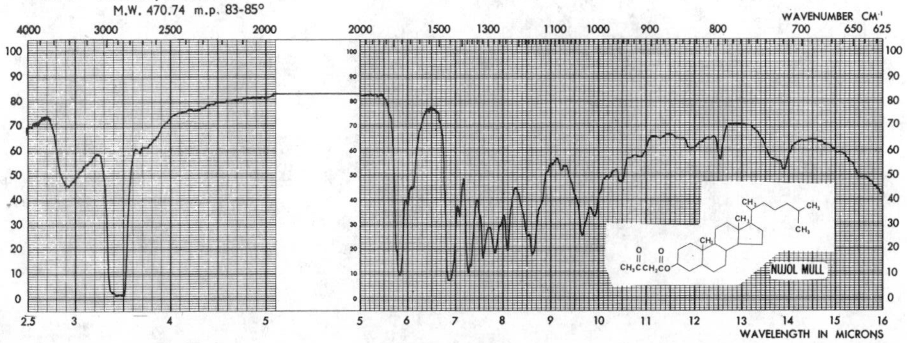

NUJOL MULL

E

M.W. 444.70 m.p. 111-113°

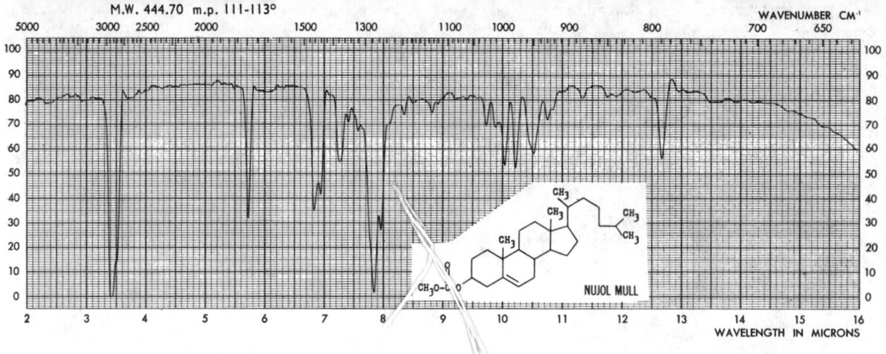

NUJOL MULL

F

10,179-6 Cholesteryl n-propyl carbonate

M.W. 472.75 m.p. 96-98° . . .

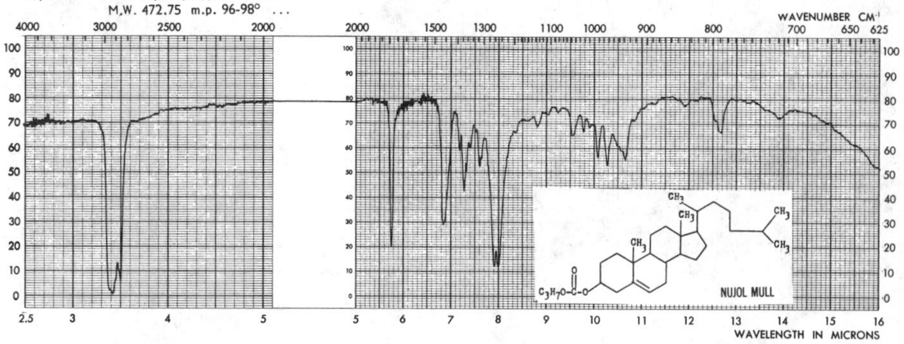

NUJOL MULL

G

15,810-0

Cholesteryl 2-ethylhexyl carbonate

M.W. 542.89 n_D^{20} 1.5007 $[\alpha]^{23}$ -26° (c=2, $CHCl_3$)

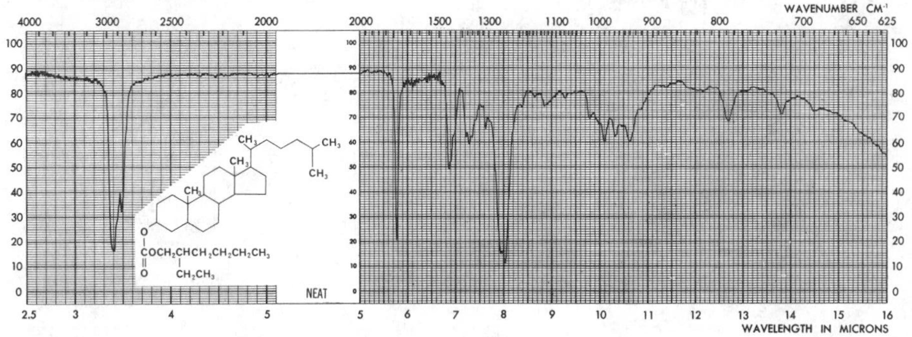

NEAT

H

15,115-7 Cholesteryl oleyl carbonate, liquid crystal

M.W. 681.15 . . . .

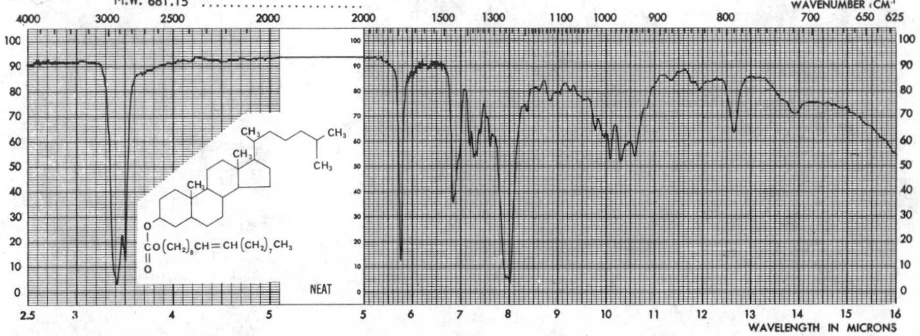

NEAT

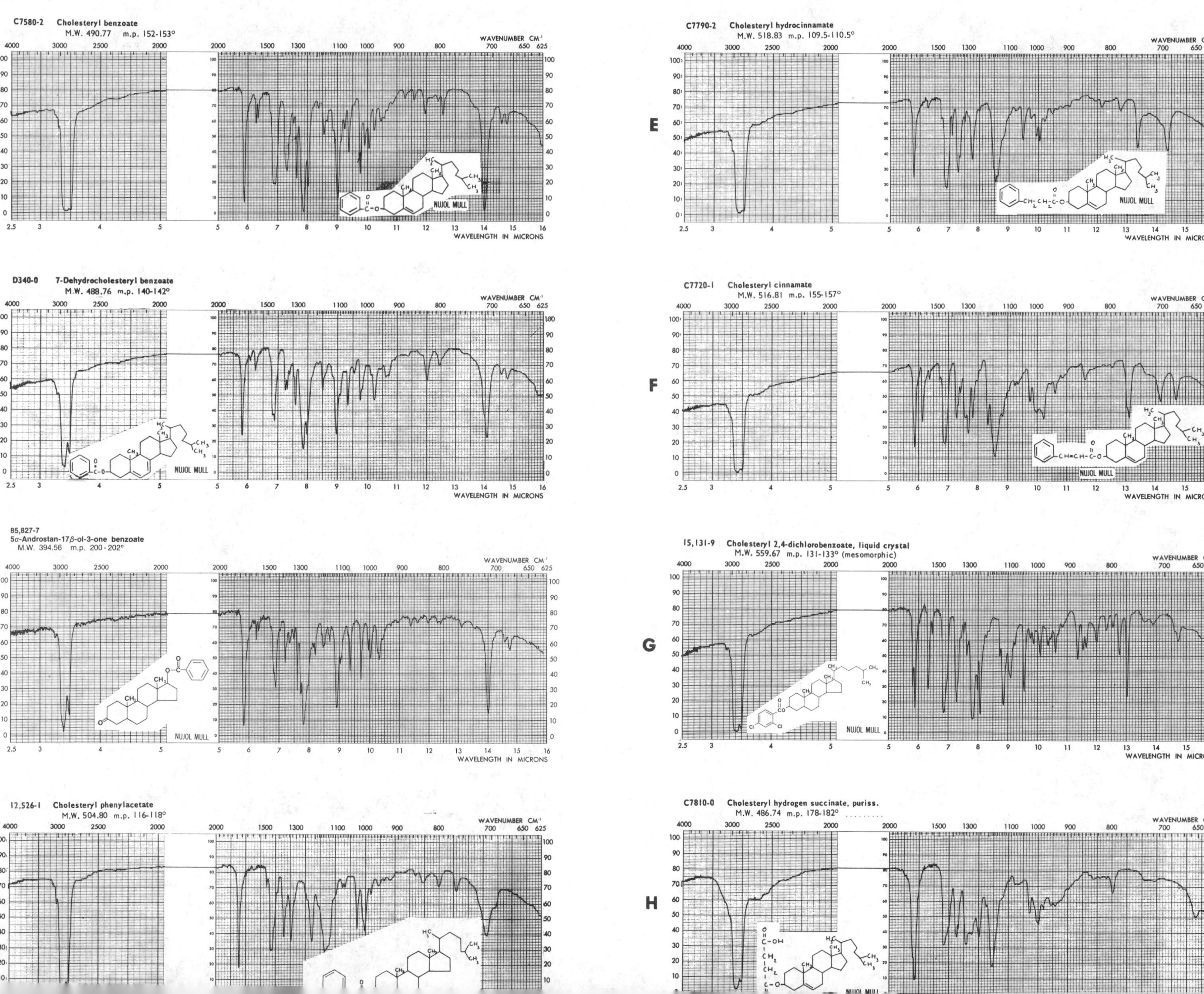
ALDRICH
A
C7580-2 Cholesteryl benzoate
M.W. 490.77 m.p. 152-153°
B
D340-0 7-Dehydrocholesteryl benzoate
M.W. 488.76 m.p. 140-142°
C
85,827-7
5α-Androstan-17β-ol-3-one benzoate
M.W. 394.56 m.p. 200-202°
D
12,526-1 Cholesteryl phenylacetate
M.W. 504.80 m.p. 116-118°
E
C7790-2 Cholesteryl hydrocinnamate
M.W. 518.83 m.p. 109.5-110.5°
F
C7720-1 Cholesteryl cinnamate
M.W. 516.81 m.p. 155-157°
G
15,131-9 Cholesteryl 2,4-dichlorobenzoate, liquid crystal
M.W. 559.67 m.p. 131-133° (mesomorphic)
H
C7810-0 Cholesteryl hydrogen succinate, puriss.
M.W. 486.74 m.p. 178-182°
NUJOL MULL
WAVENUMBER CM⁻¹
WAVELENGTH IN MICRONS

A

M.W. 534.78 m.p. 158-162°

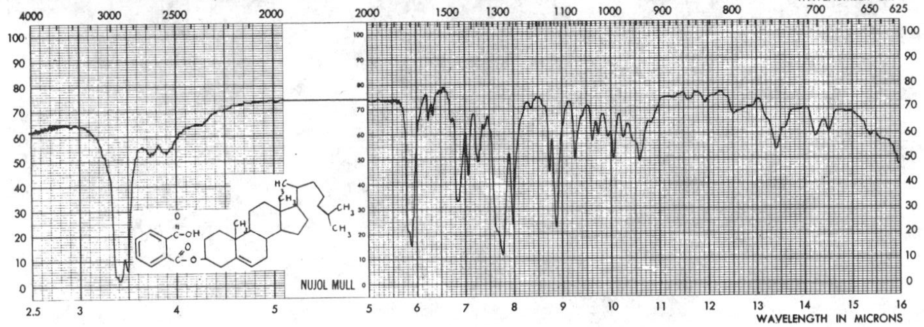

NUJOL MULL

B

P4990-2 Pregnenolone acetate
M.W. 358.52 m.p. 149-152°

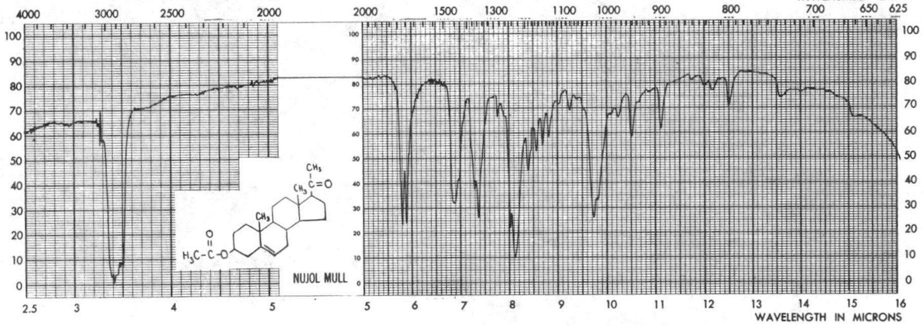

NUJOL MULL

C

85,576-6
21-Acetoxypregnenolone
M.W. 374.52 m.p. 185-188°
$[\alpha]^{24}$ +37° (c=1, $CHCl_3$)

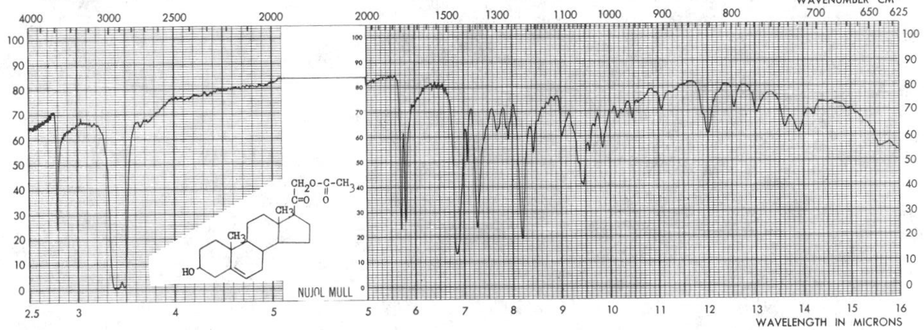

NUJOL MULL

D

85,838-2
16α,17α-Epoxypregnenolone acetate
M.W. 372.51 m.p. 161-163°
$[\alpha]^{23}$ -11.2° (c=2, $CHCl_3$)

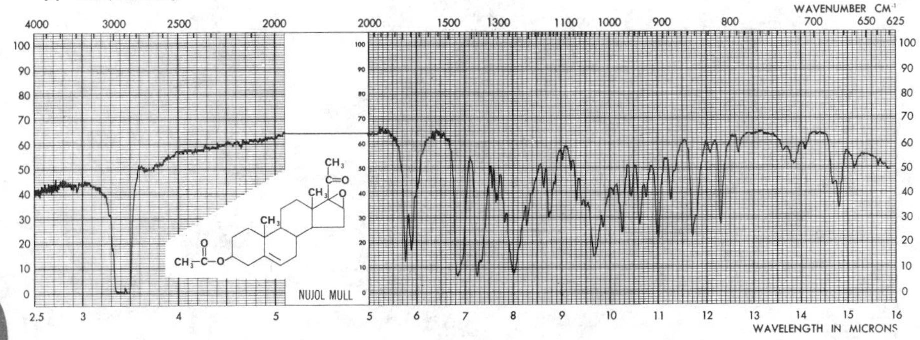

NUJOL MULL

E

M.W. 372.51 m.p. 171-175°

NUJOL MULL

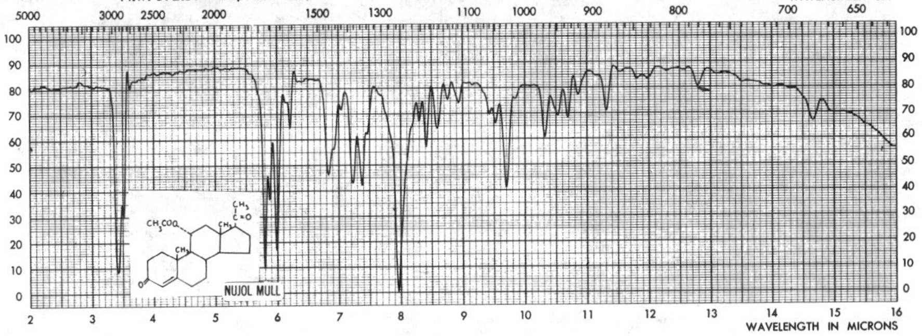

F

85,086-1
17α-Acetoxy-16α-methylprogesterone
M.W. 386.53 m.p. 233-235°

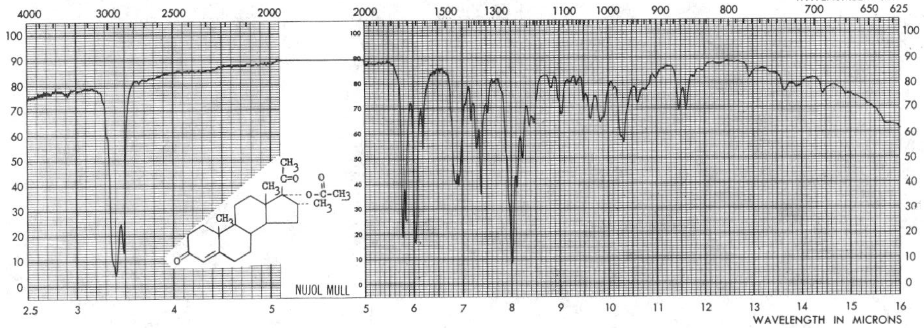

NUJOL MULL

G

14,768-0 Testosterone acetate
M.W. 330.47 m.p. 138-140° $[\alpha]^{25}_{D}$ + 90.5° (c=1.69, dioxane)

NUJOL MULL

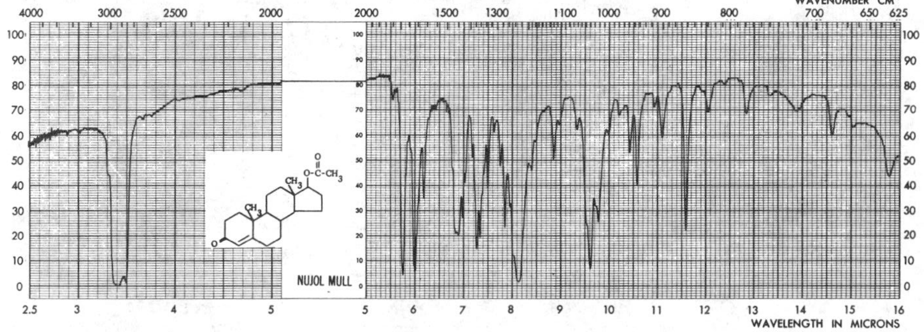

H

12,194-0 3β-Hydroxy-5,16-pregnadien-20-one acetate (16-dehydropregnenolone acetate)
M.W. 356.51 m.p. 166-169°

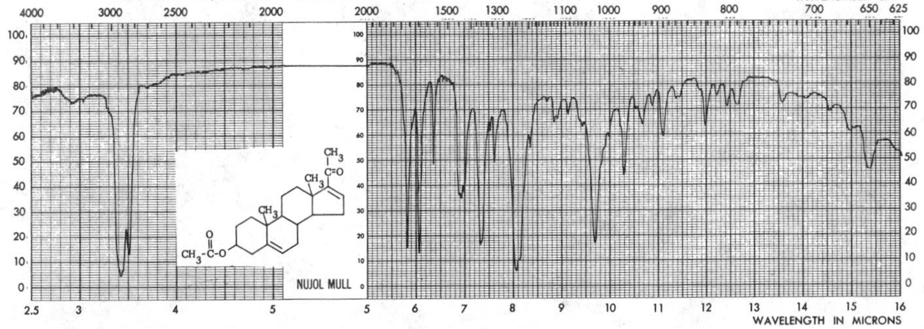

NUJOL MULL

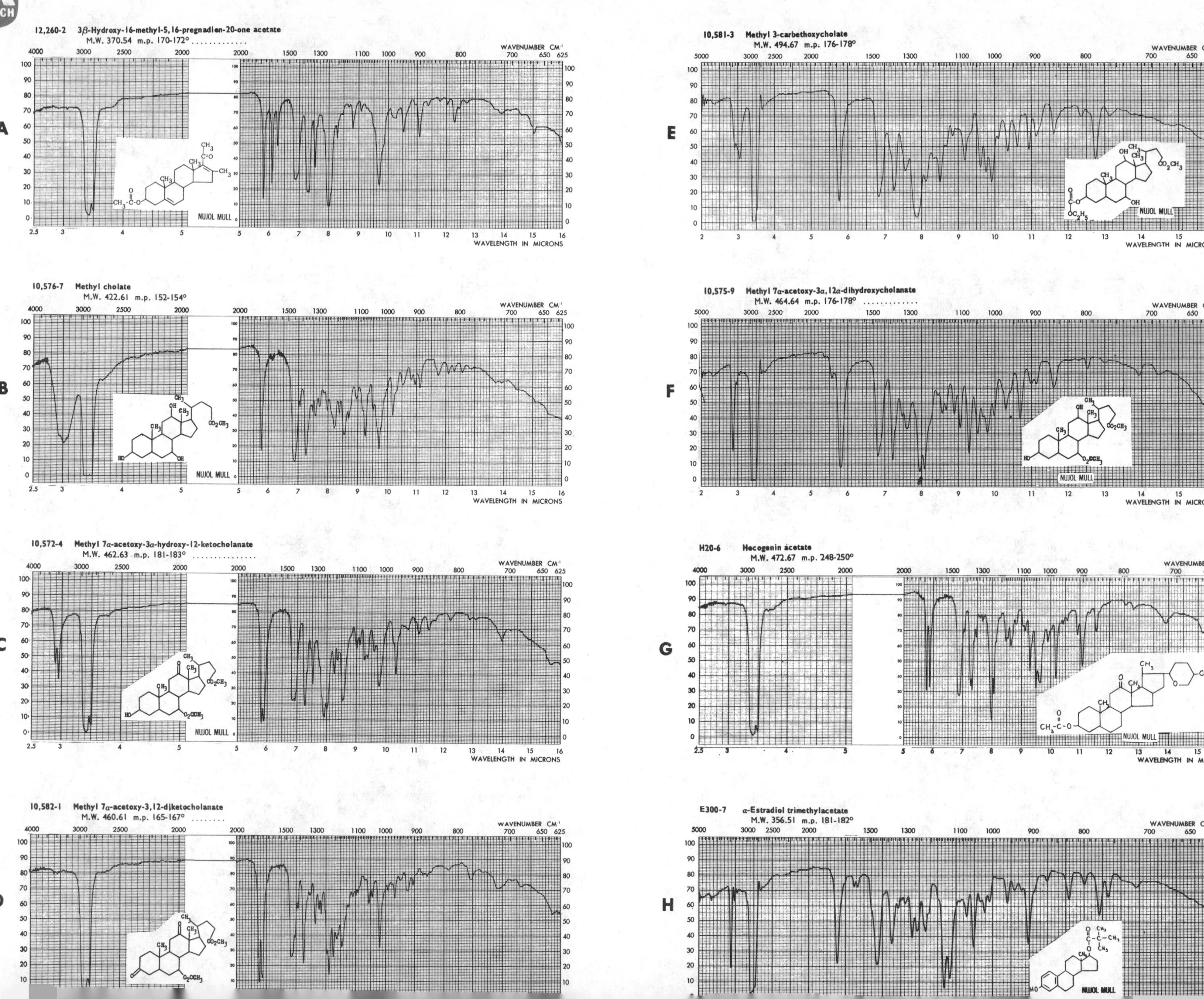
ALDRICH
A
12,260-2 3β-Hydroxy-16-methyl-5,16-pregnadien-20-one acetate
M.W. 370.54 m.p. 170-172°
NUJOL MULL
B
10,576-7 Methyl cholate
M.W. 422.61 m.p. 152-154°
NUJOL MULL
C
10,572-4 Methyl 7α-acetoxy-3α-hydroxy-12-ketocholanate
M.W. 462.63 m.p. 181-183°
NUJOL MULL
D
10,582-1 Methyl 7α-acetoxy-3,12-diketocholanate
M.W. 460.61 m.p. 165-167°
E
10,581-3 Methyl 3-carbethoxycholate
M.W. 494.67 m.p. 176-178°
NUJOL MULL
F
10,575-9 Methyl 7α-acetoxy-3α,12α-dihydroxycholanate
M.W. 464.64 m.p. 176-178°
NUJOL MULL
G
H20-6 Hecogenin acetate
M.W. 472.67 m.p. 248-250°
NUJOL MULL
H
E300-7 α-Estradiol trimethylacetate
M.W. 356.51 m.p. 181-182°
NUJOL MULL
WAVENUMBER CM⁻¹
WAVELENGTH IN MICRONS

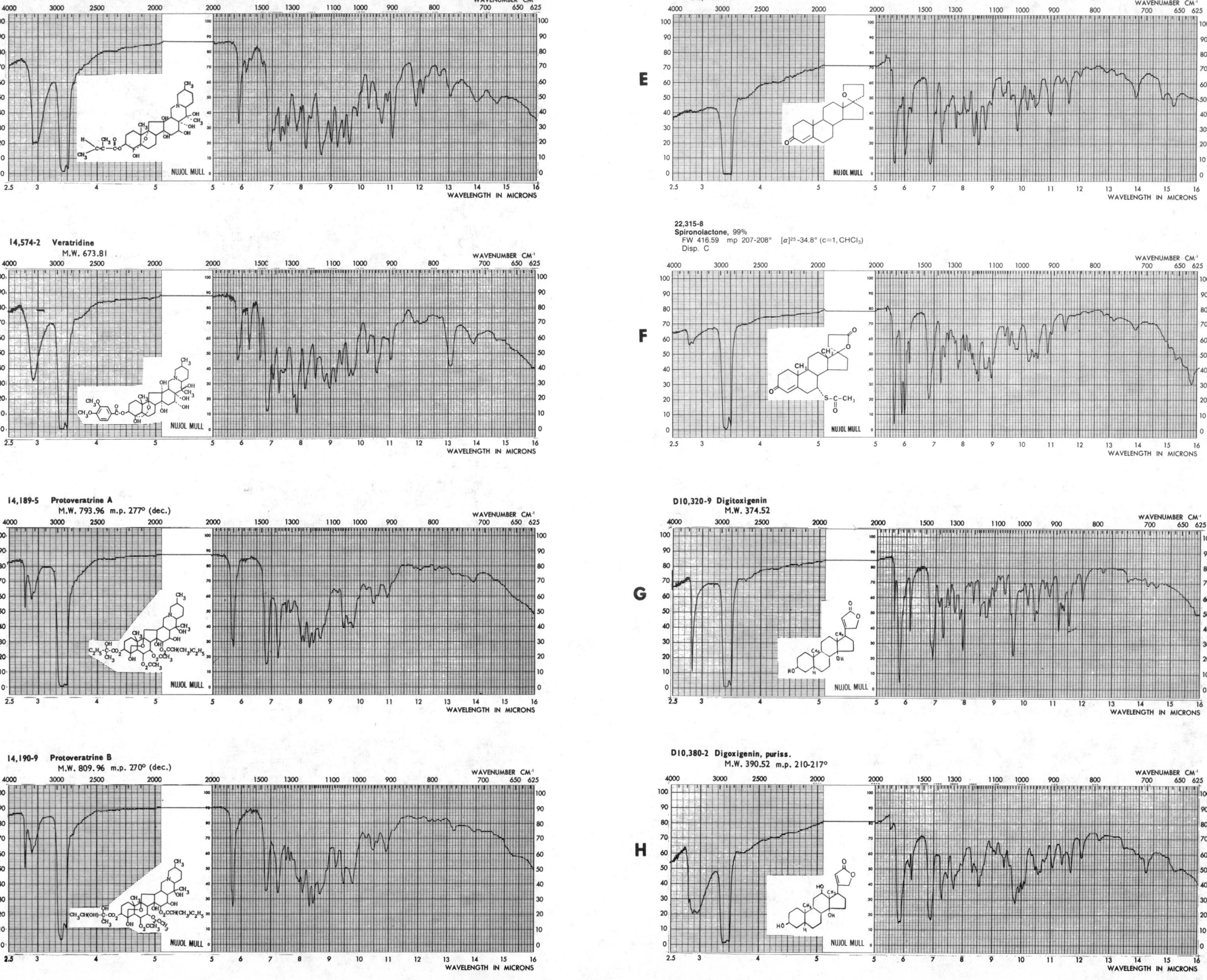
A
M.W. 591.75 m.p. 198-200°
NUJOL MULL
B
14,574-2 Veratridine
M.W. 673.81
NUJOL MULL
C
14,189-5 Protoveratrine A
M.W. 793.96 m.p. 277° (dec.)
NUJOL MULL
D
14,190-9 Protoveratrine B
M.W. 809.96 m.p. 270° (dec.)
NUJOL MULL
E
FW 342.48 mp 156-159° [α]D +73° (c=1, CHCl3)
Disp. C
NUJOL MULL
F
22,315-8
Spironolactone, 99%
FW 416.59 mp 207-208° [α]25 -34.8° (c=1, CHCl3)
Disp. C
NUJOL MULL
G
D10,320-9 Digitoxigenin
M.W. 374.52
NUJOL MULL
H
D10,380-2 Digoxigenin, puriss.
M.W. 390.52 m.p. 210-217°
NUJOL MULL
WAVENUMBER CM⁻¹
WAVELENGTH IN MICRONS
ALDRICH

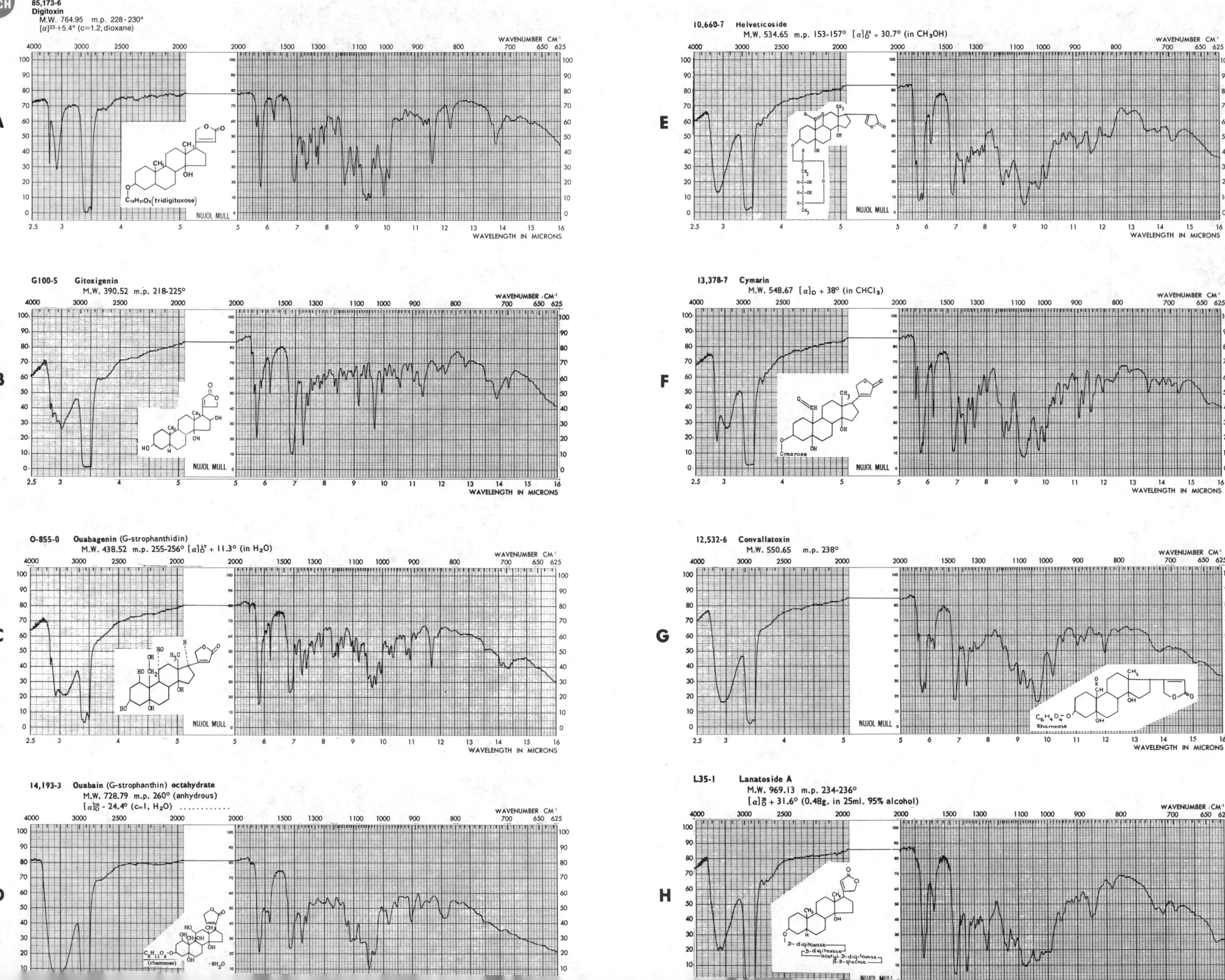
ALDRICH
A
85,173-6
Digitoxin
M.W. 764.95 m.p. 228-230°
[α]²³ +5.4° (c=1.2, dioxane)
$C_{18}H_{31}O_9$(tridigitoxose)
NUJOL MULL
B
G100-5 Gitoxigenin
M.W. 390.52 m.p. 218-225°
NUJOL MULL
C
O-855-0 Ouabagenin (G-strophanthidin)
M.W. 438.52 m.p. 255-256° [α]²⁷_D + 11.3° (in H₂O)
NUJOL MULL
D
14,193-3 Ouabain (G-strophanthin) octahydrate
M.W. 728.79 m.p. 260° (anhydrous)
[α]²⁸_D - 24.4° (c=1, H₂O)
(rhamnose)
·8H₂O
E
10,660-7 Helveticoside
M.W. 534.65 m.p. 153-157° [α]²⁶_D + 30.7° (in CH₃OH)
NUJOL MULL
F
13,378-7 Cymarin
M.W. 548.67 [α]_D + 38° (in CHCl₃)
Cymarose
NUJOL MULL
G
12,532-6 Convallatoxin
M.W. 550.65 m.p. 238°
Rhamnose
NUJOL MULL
H
L35-1 Lanatoside A
M.W. 969.13 m.p. 234-236°
[α]²⁰_D + 31.6° (0.48g. in 25ml. 95% alcohol)
D-digitoxose
D-digitoxose
acetyl-D-digitoxose
β-D-glucose
WAVENUMBER CM⁻¹
WAVELENGTH IN MICRONS

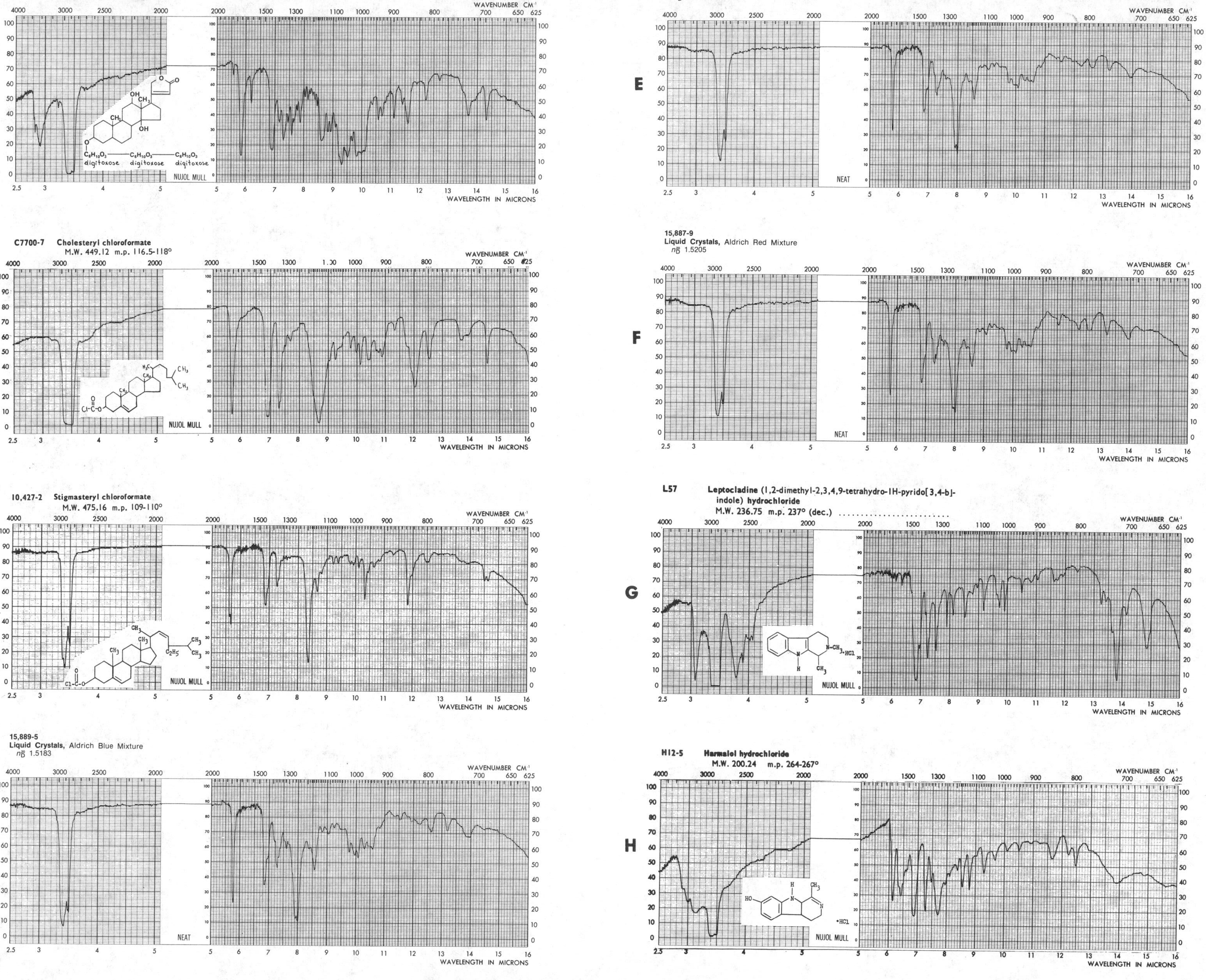
M.W. 780.95 m.p. 248-250° (dec.)
A
NUJOL MULL
digitoxose digitoxose digitoxose
C7700-7 Cholesteryl chloroformate
M.W. 449.12 m.p. 116.5-118°
B
NUJOL MULL
10,427-2 Stigmasteryl chloroformate
M.W. 475.16 m.p. 109-110°
C
NUJOL MULL
15,889-5
Liquid Crystals, Aldrich Blue Mixture
n_D^{20} 1.5183
D
NEAT
Liquid Crystals, Aldrich Gold Mixture
n_D^{20} 1.5195
E
NEAT
15,887-9
Liquid Crystals, Aldrich Red Mixture
n_D^{20} 1.5205
F
NEAT
L57 Leptocladine (1,2-dimethyl-2,3,4,9-tetrahydro-1H-pyrido[3,4-b]-indole) hydrochloride
M.W. 236.75 m.p. 237° (dec.)
G
NUJOL MULL
H12-5 Harmalol hydrochloride
M.W. 200.24 m.p. 264-267°
H
NUJOL MULL
WAVENUMBER CM⁻¹
WAVELENGTH IN MICRONS
ALDRICH

STEROIDS & INDOLE ALKALOIDS

A

H10-9 **Harmaline hydrochloride dihydrate**
M.W. 286.76 m.p. 239-240°

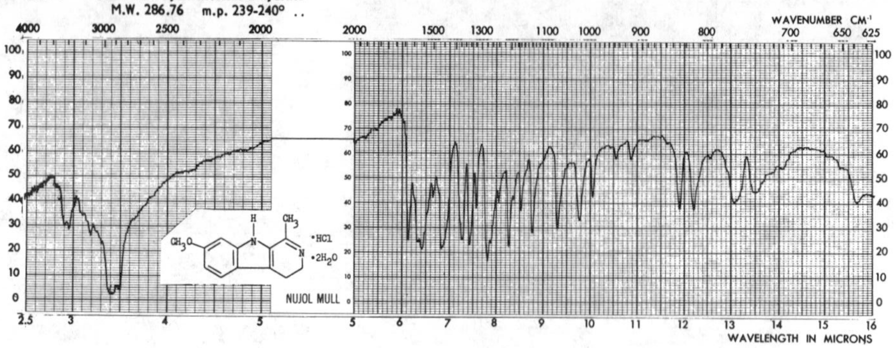

NUJOL MULL

B

14,196-8 **Agroclavine**
M.W. 238.33 m.p. 205-207°

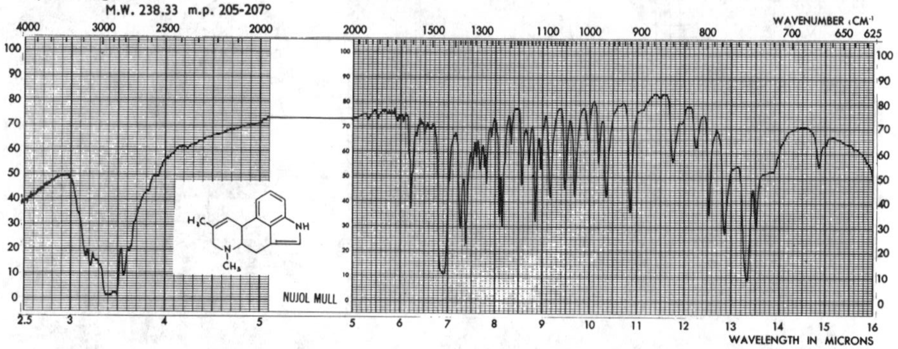

NUJOL MULL

C

14,197-6 **Elymoclavine**
M.W. 254.33 m.p. 245-250° (dec.)

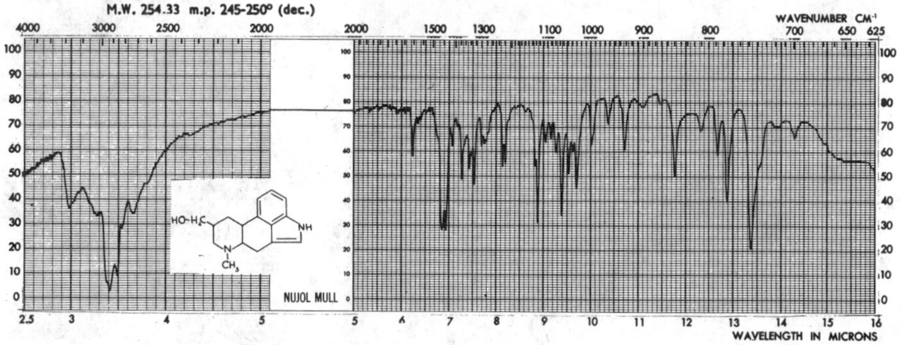

NUJOL MULL

D

I-10-5 **Ibogaine hydrochloride**
M.W. 346.90 m.p. 300-302° $[\alpha]_D^{25}$ - 49° (in H_2O)

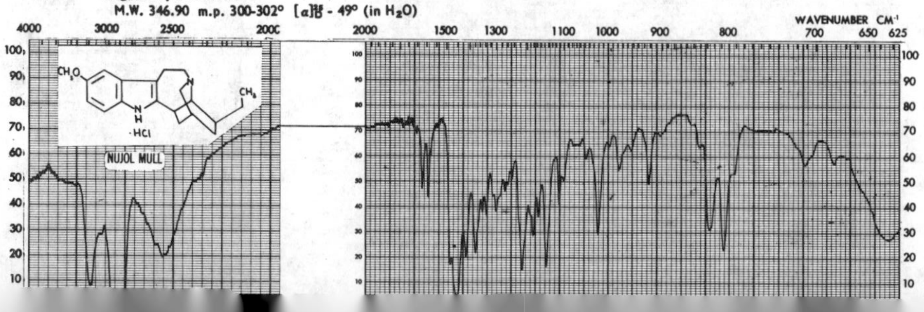

NUJOL MULL

E

21,931-2
Eserine, 99% (physostigmine)
FW 275.35 mp 105-107° $[\alpha]^{25}$ -116° (c=1, C_6H_6)
Beil. 23(2),330 Disp. C

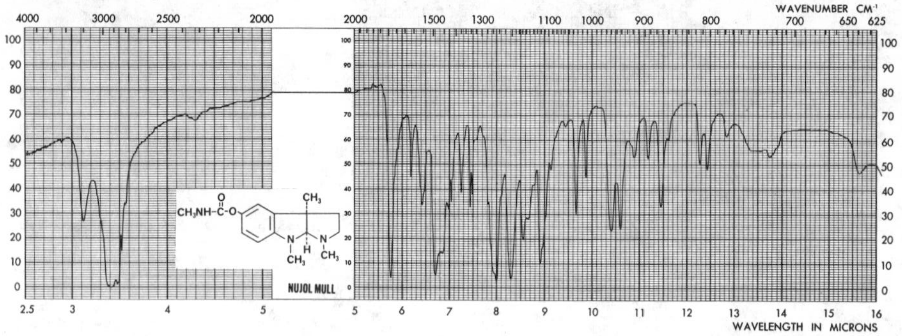

NUJOL MULL

F

85,508-1
Calycanthine
M.W. 346.48 m.p. 247-249°

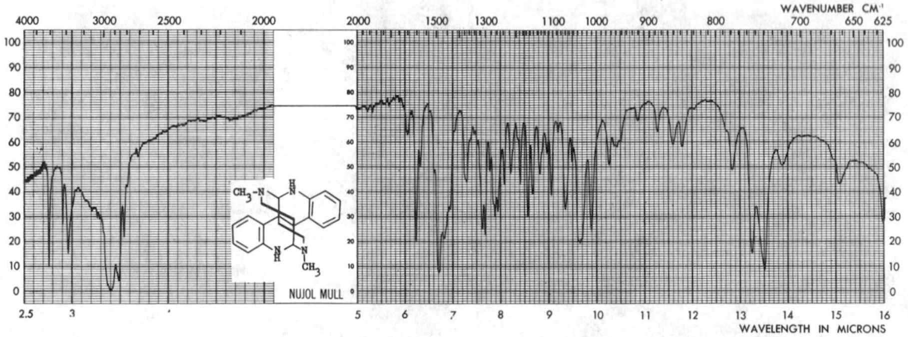

NUJOL MULL

G

13,492-9 *l*-**Strychnine**
M.W. 334.42 m.p. 284-286°

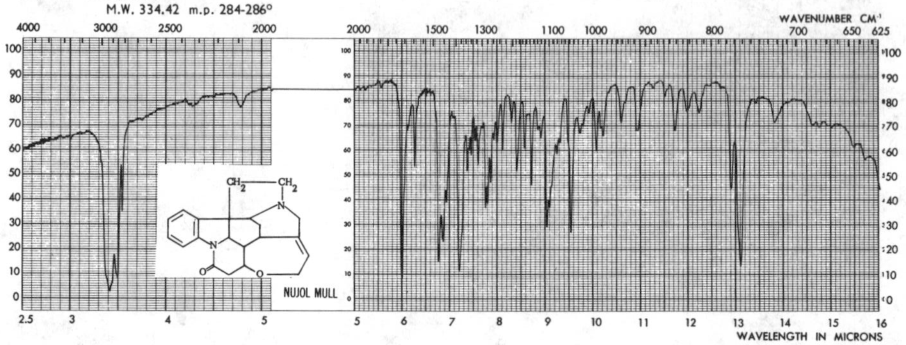

NUJOL MULL

H

19,472-7
(-)-Eburnamonine, 98+%
FW 294.40 mp 174-177°
$[\alpha]^{23}$ -93.7° (c=0.4, $CHCl_3$) Disp. C

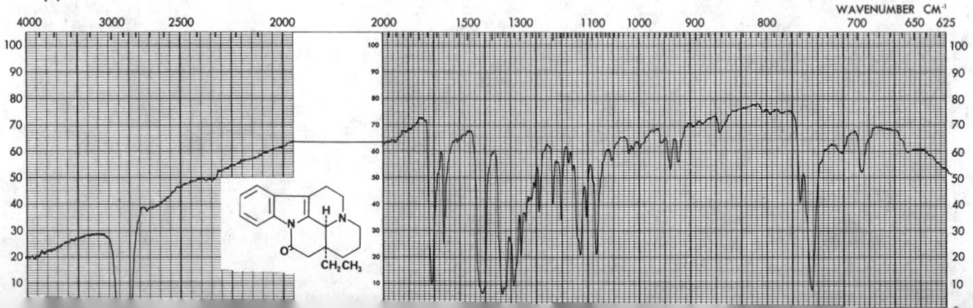

WAVENUMBER CM⁻¹ / WAVELENGTH IN MICRONS

A

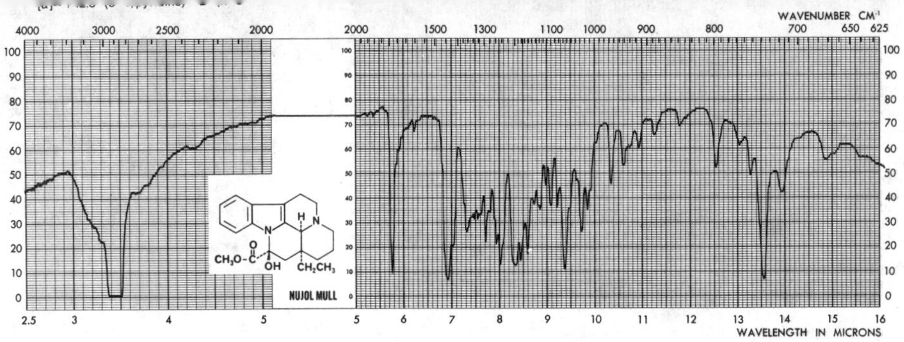

B

14,329-4 **Strychnine-N-oxide (genestrychnine) trihydrate**
M.W. 404.47 m.p. 200° (dec.)

C

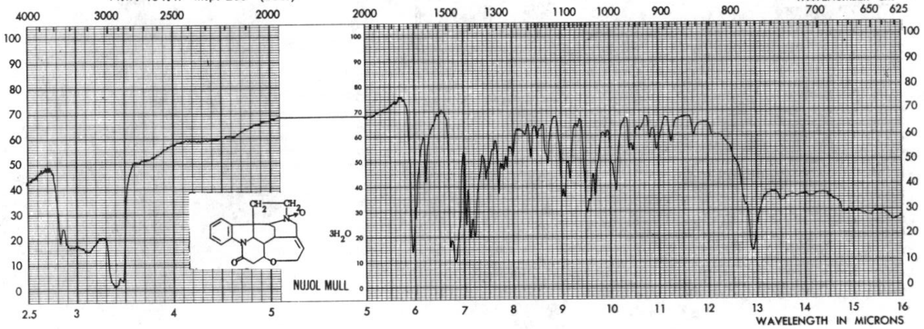

14,974-8 **2-Aminostrychnine**
M.W. 349.44 m.p. 263-268° (dec.)

D

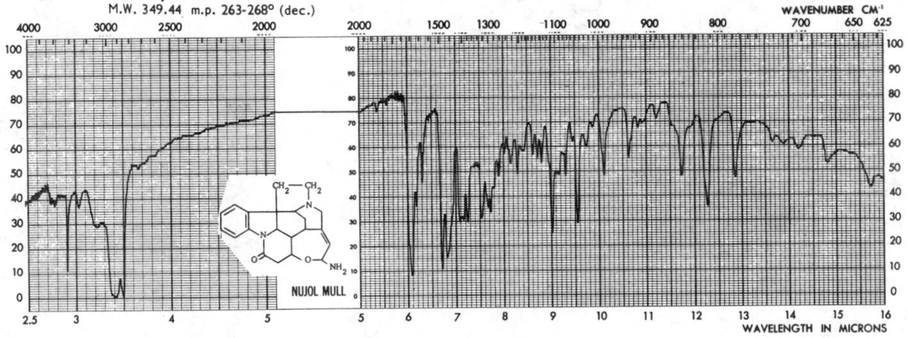

14,967-5 **2-Nitrostrychnine**
M.W. 379.42 m.p. 239-240° (dec.)

E

Bromodesoxyisostrychnine hydrobromide, tech.
M.W. 480.25 m.p. 285-286° (dec.)

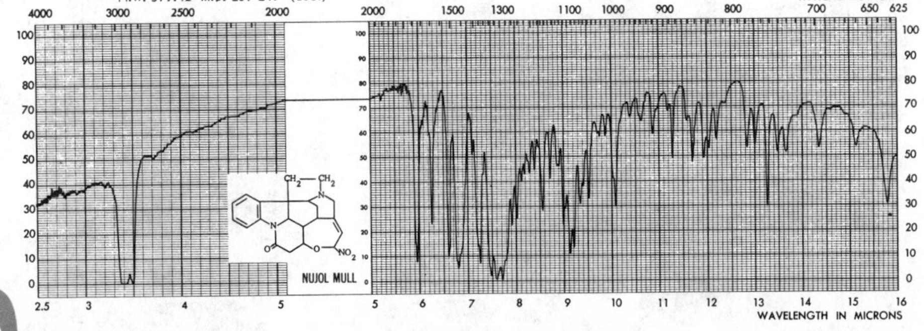

F

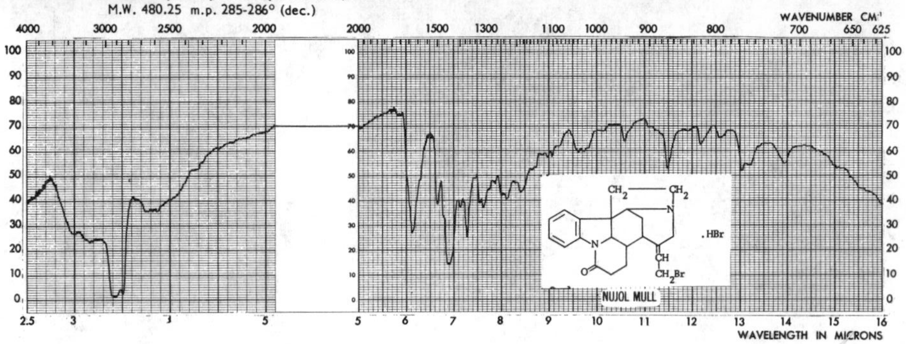

11,937-7 **Genestrychninic acid (N-oxystrychninic acid) monohydrate**
M.W. 386.45 m.p. 210-211° (dec.)

G

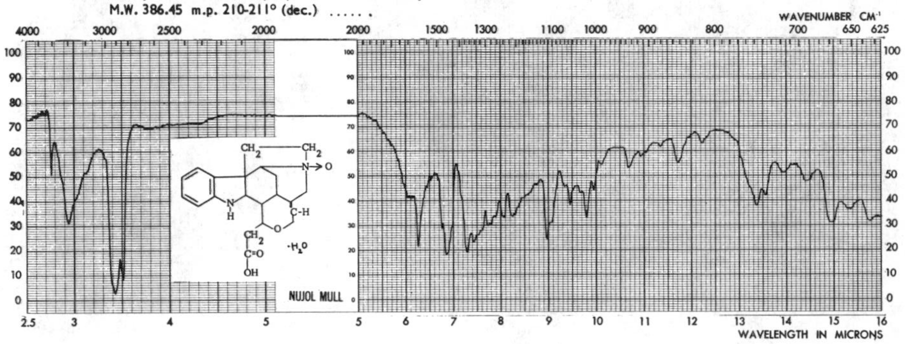

85,169-8
Gelsemine, 90%
M.W. 322.41 m.p. 180-181°
$[\alpha]^{24}$ + 14° (c=1.45, $CHCl_3$)

H

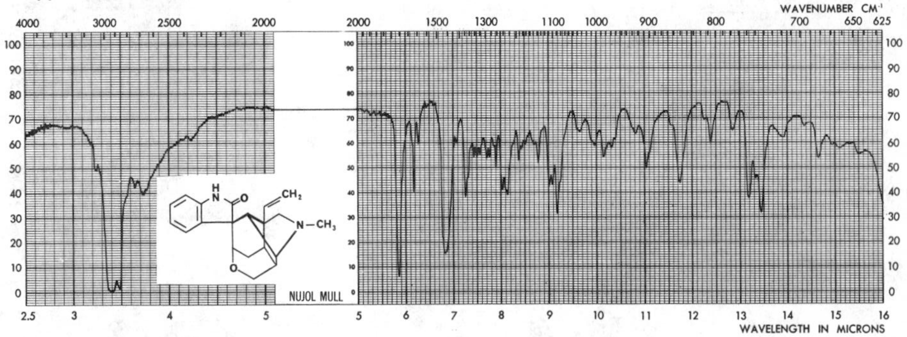

85,536-7
Ajmaline, contains methanol of crystallization
M.W. 358.48 m.p. 135-137° (dec.)
$[\alpha]_D^{25}$ + 138° (c=0.4, $CHCl_3$)

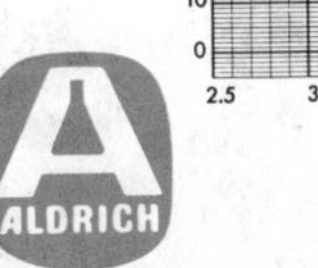

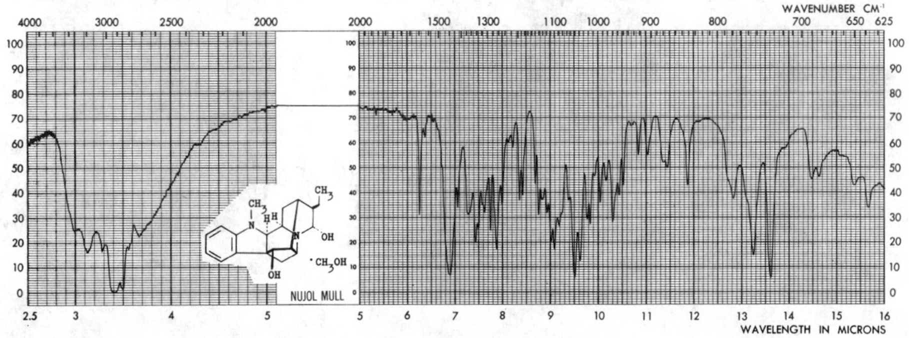

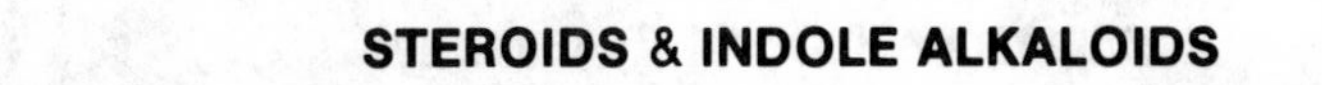

A 14,976-4 **Isostrychnic acid monohydrate**
M.W. 370.45 m.p. 227-230° (dec.)
NUJOL MULL

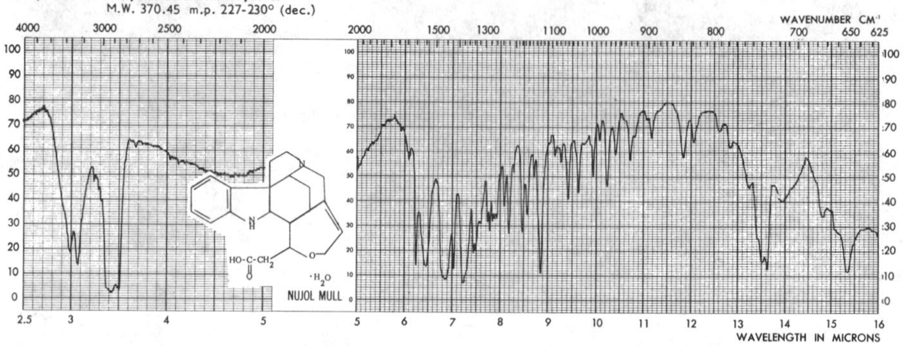

B 14,558-0 **Brucine tetrahydrate**
M.W. 466.53 m.p. 175-177°
$[\alpha]_D^{25}$ - 79.3° (c=1.3, C_2H_5OH)
NUJOL MULL

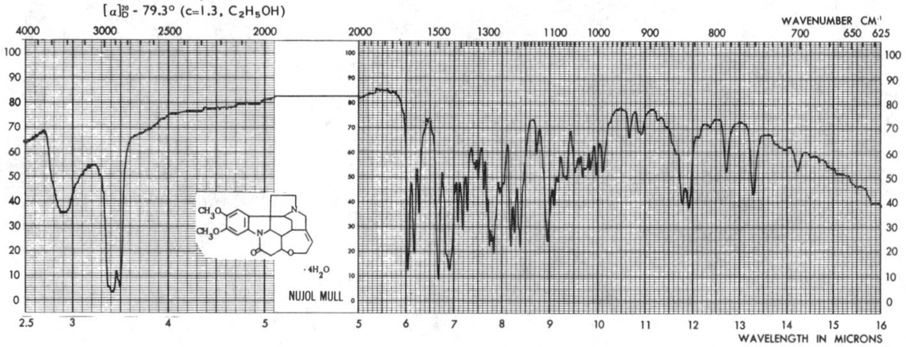

C 14,224-7 **Brucine-N-oxide (genebrucine) hydrate**
M.W. 410.47 (anhydrous) ....
NUJOL MULL

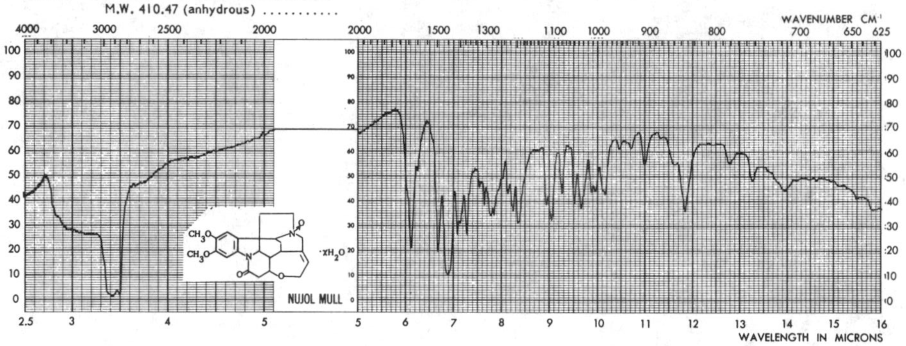

D 85,549-9
Mitomycin C
M.W. 334.33

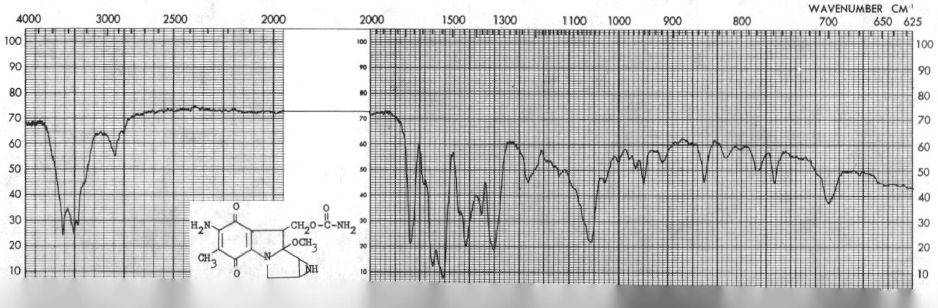

E 15,047-9 **Cacotheline, indicator**
M.W. 427.42 m.p. >300°
NUJOL MULL

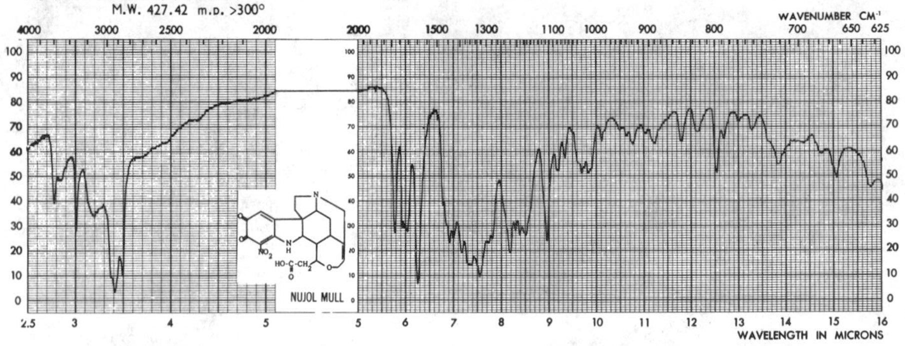

F 14,975-6 **Brucinoquinone perchlorate**
M.W. 464.86 m.p. 280° (dec.)
NUJOL MULL

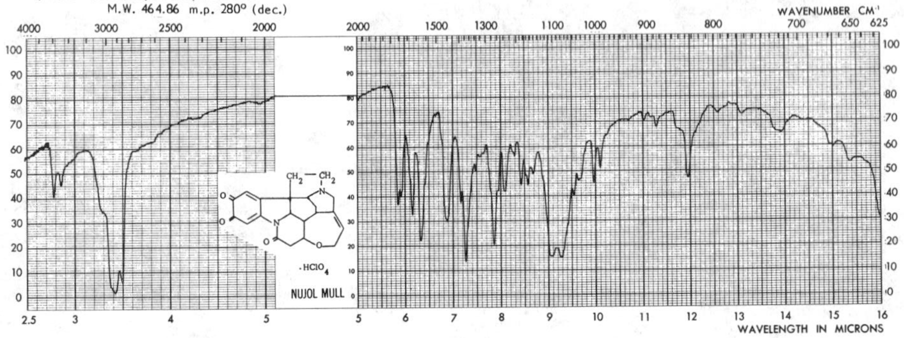

G 21,798-0
Vincristine sulfate
FW 923.06 mp >300° Disp. C
NUJOL MULL

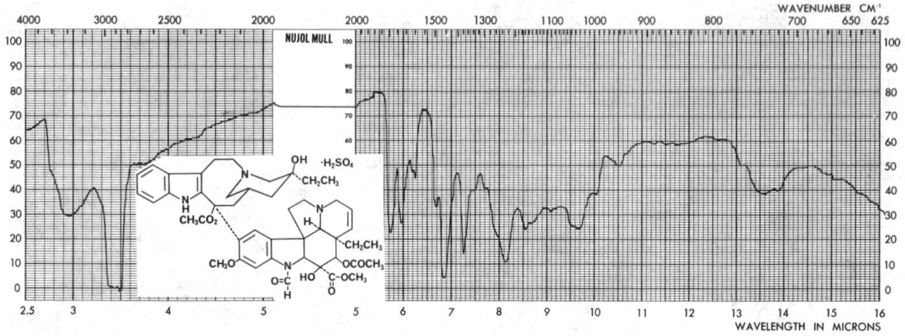

H 21,799-9
Vinblastine sulfate
FW 909.07 mp 267° (dec.)
$[\alpha]^{21}$ -27.1° (c=2, CH_3OH) Disp. C
NUJOL MULL

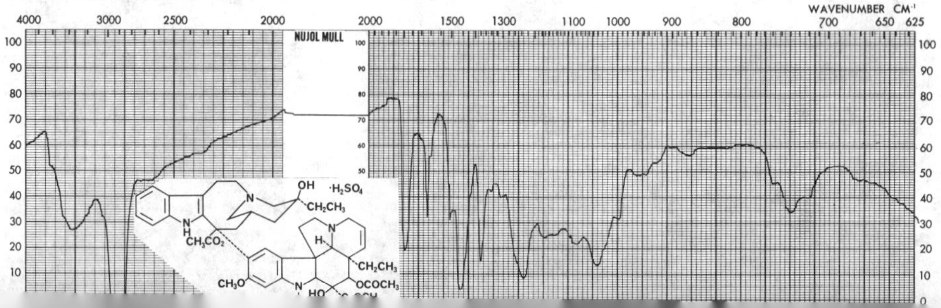

A

M.W. 358.44 m.p. 267-268° (dec.)

NUJOL MULL

B

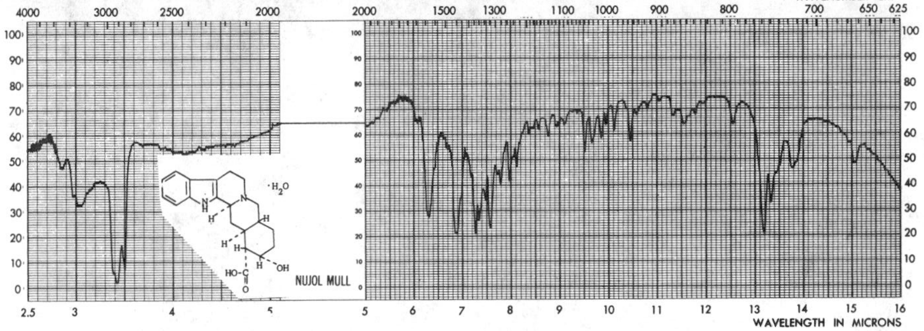

21,887-1
Corynanthine hydrochloride hydrate
FW 408.92 mp 288-290° $[\alpha]^{21}$ -67° (c=1, H_2O)
Beil. **25**(2),208 Disp. C

NUJOL MULL

C

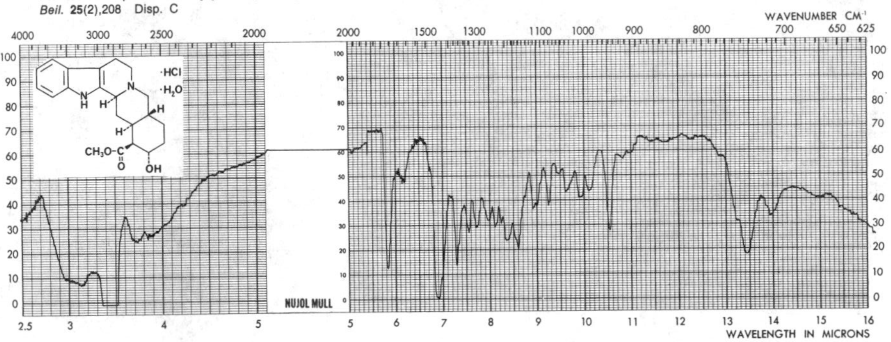

Y20-8 **Yohimbine hydrochloride**
M.W. 390.91 m.p. 288-290° (dec.) $[\alpha]_D^{20}$ + 129°
(c=1 in H_2O)

NUJOL MULL

D

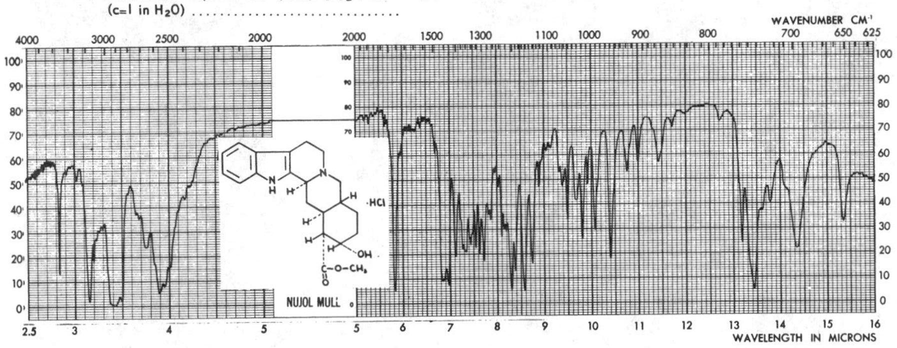

R17-1 **Reserpine**
M.W. 608.69 m.p. 248-250°

NUJOL MULL

E

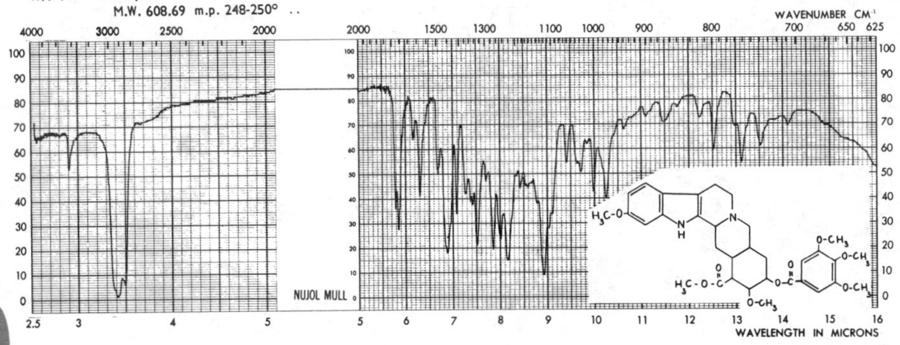

M.W. 634.73 m.p. 234-237

NUJOL MULL

F

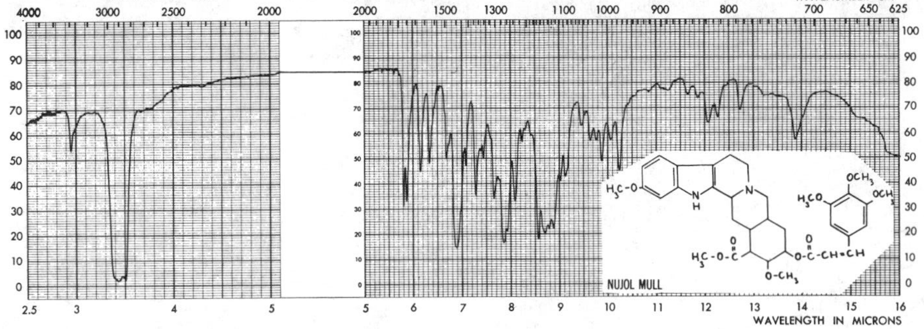

12,487-7 **Dihydroergotamine methanesulfonate**
M.W. 679.80 m.p. 232° (dec.)

NUJOL MULL

G

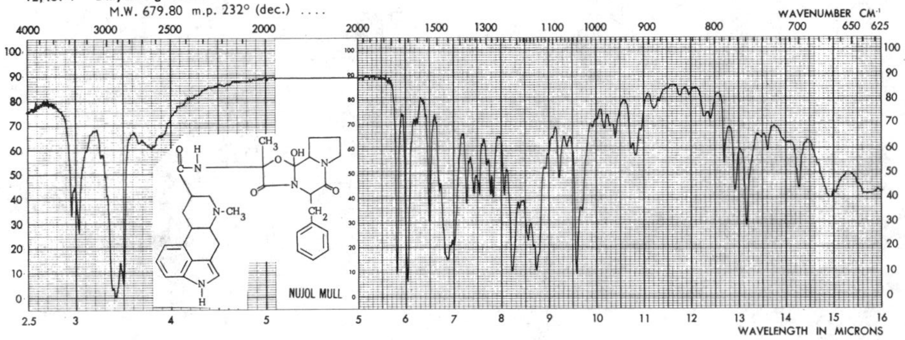

14,192-5
Veratrine, mixture of the alkaloids cevadine, veratridine, cevadilline, sabadine and cevine
m.p. > 130° (dec.) *SEVERE POISON*

NUJOL MULL

H

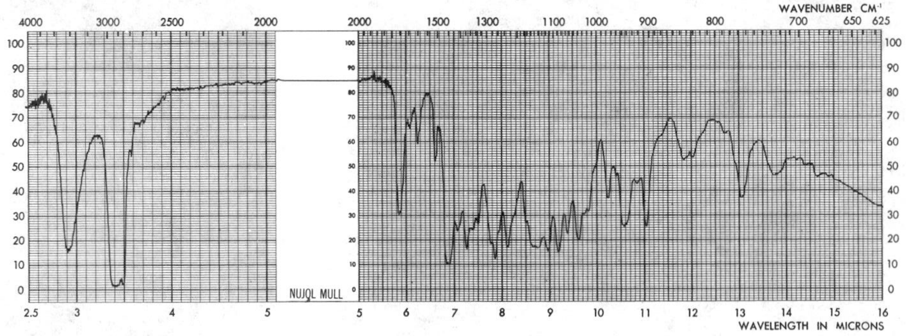

19,342-9
Coralyne chloride hydrate
FW 399.88 mp 215° (dec.) Disp. C

KBr

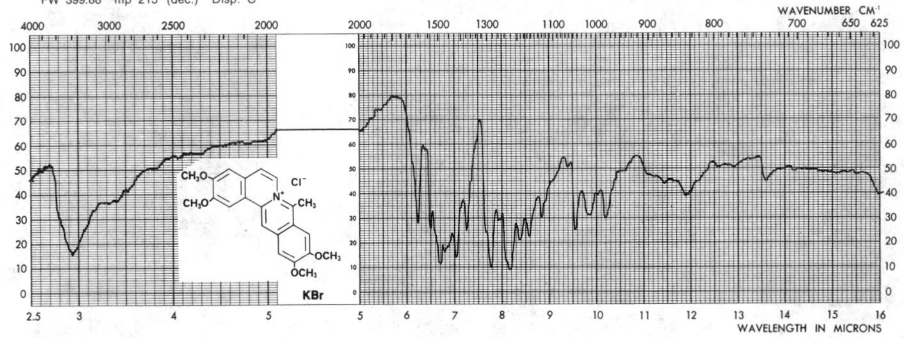

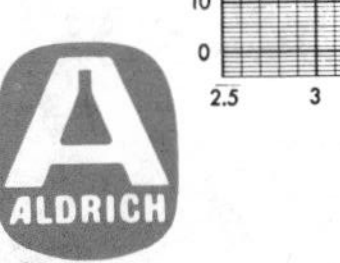

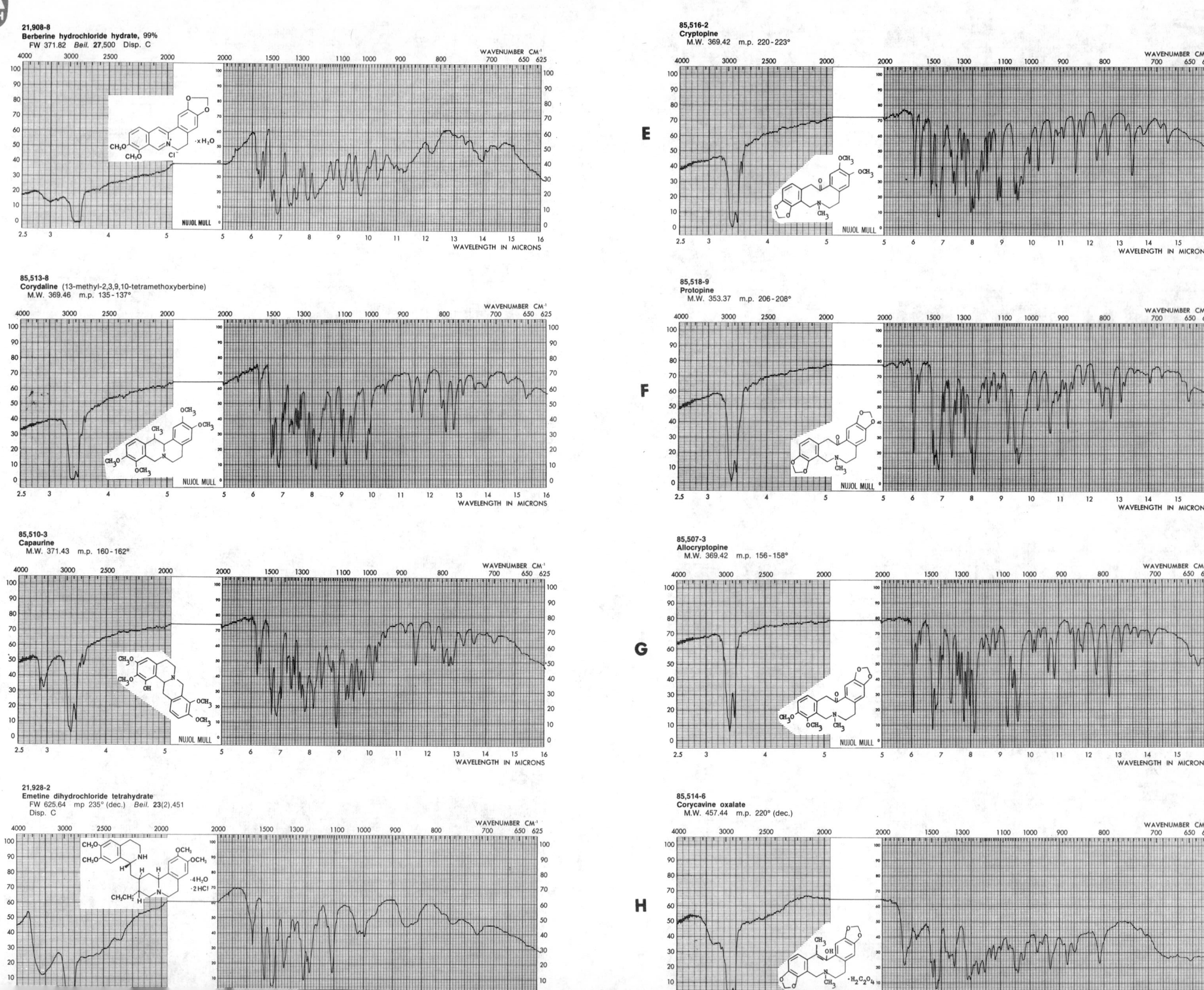

ALDRICH
A
21,908-8
Berberine hydrochloride hydrate, 99%
FW 371.82 Beil. 27,500 Disp. C
B
85,513-8
Corydaline (13-methyl-2,3,9,10-tetramethoxyberbine)
M.W. 369.46 m.p. 135-137°
C
85,510-3
Capaurine
M.W. 371.43 m.p. 160-162°
D
21,928-2
Emetine dihydrochloride tetrahydrate
FW 625.64 mp 235° (dec.) Beil. 23(2),451
Disp. C
E
85,516-2
Cryptopine
M.W. 369.42 m.p. 220-223°
F
85,518-9
Protopine
M.W. 353.37 m.p. 206-208°
G
85,507-3
Allocryptopine
M.W. 369.42 m.p. 156-158°
H
85,514-6
Corycavine oxalate
M.W. 457.44 m.p. 220° (dec.)
NUJOL MULL
WAVENUMBER CM⁻¹
WAVELENGTH IN MICRONS

A

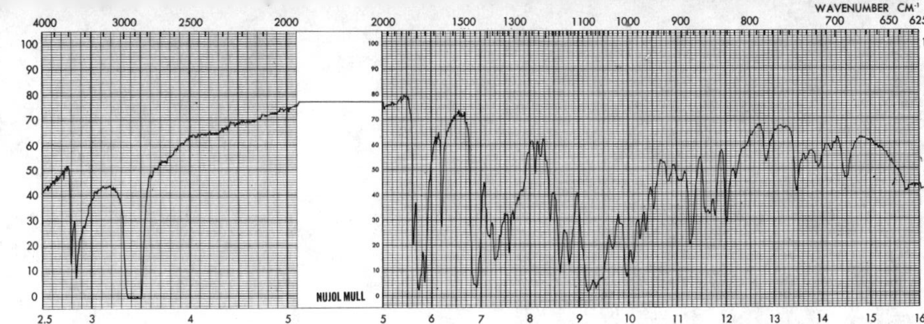
WAVENUMBER CM⁻¹
4000
3000
2500
2000
1500
1300
1100
1000
900
800
700
650
625
NUJOL MULL
WAVELENGTH IN MICRONS

DEUTERATED COMPOUNDS

The following spectra of deuterated compounds appear immediately next to their hydrogen counterparts so that the reader can observe the band shifts to higher wavelengths resulting from the heavier deuterium atom replacing the hydrogen atom.

A

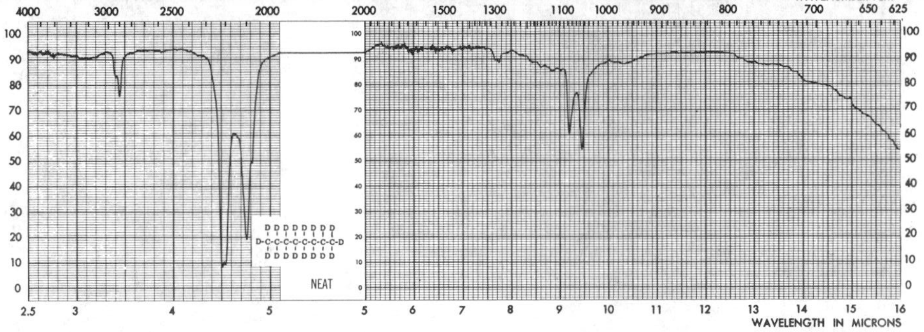

O-325-7 Octane, puriss.
$CH_3(CH_2)_6CH_3$ M.W. 114.23 n_D^{20} 1.3960
b.p. 124-126°

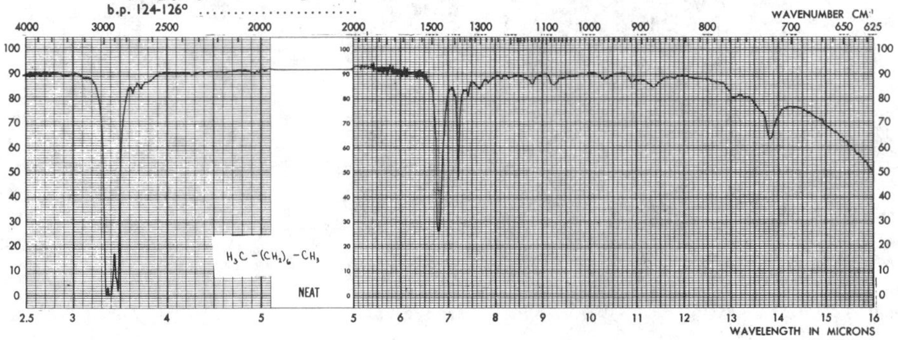

B

15,186-6 Cyclohexane-d_{12}, 99%
C_6D_{12} M.W. 96.26

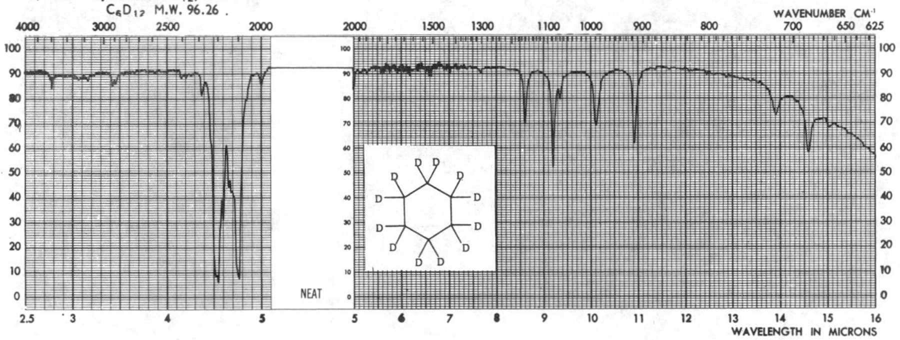

C

C10,030-7 Cyclohexane, 99 + %
C_6H_{12} M.W. 84.16 n_D^{20} 1.4255 m.p. 4-6°

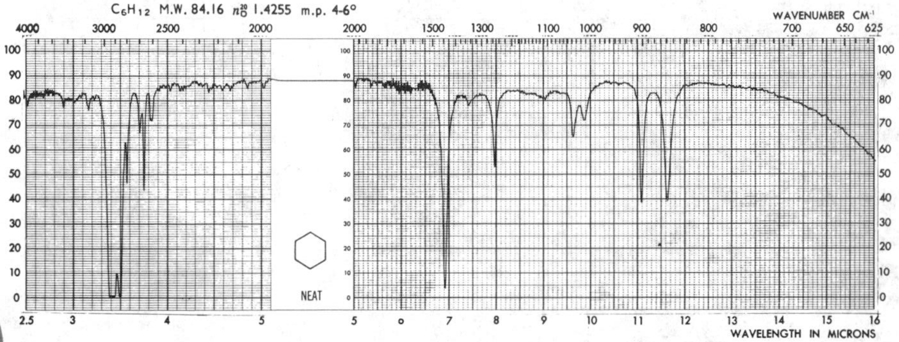

D

Disp. C

E

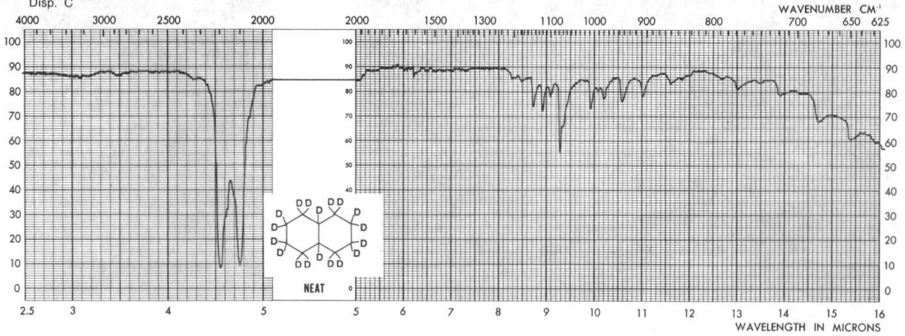

D25-1 Decahydronaphthalene
$C_{10}H_{18}$ M.W. 138.25 n_D^{20} 1.4760

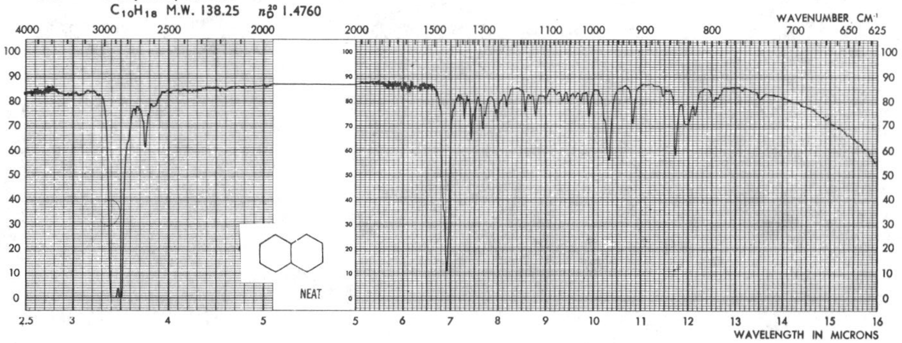

F

17,603-6
Iodomethane-d_3, 99+ atom % D, GOLD LABEL
CD_3I
M.W. 144.96 n_D^{20} 1.5262

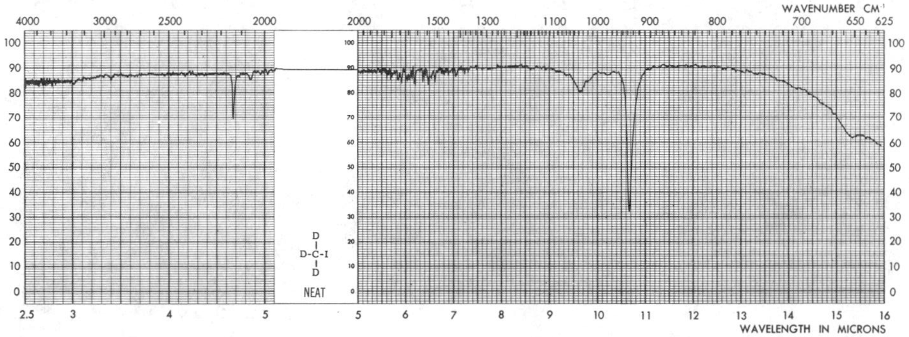

G

I-850-7 Iodomethane (methyl iodide)
CH_3I M.W. 141.94 n_D^{20} 1.5304

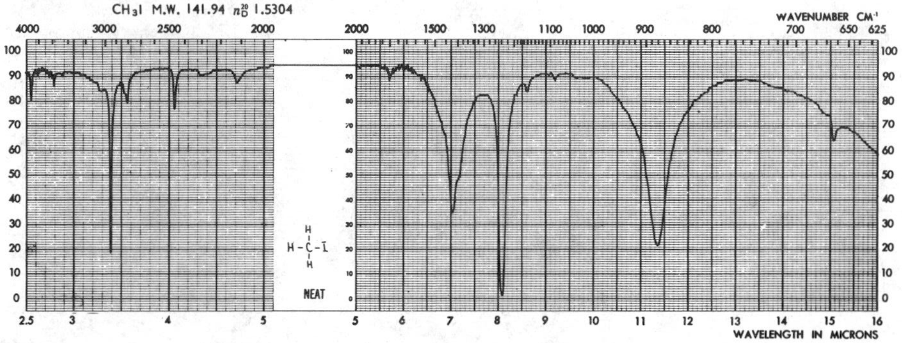

H

ALDRICH

DEUTERATED

A 17,786-5 **Dichloromethane-d_2**, 99+ atom % D, GOLD LABEL (methylene-d_2 chloride) CD_2Cl_2 M.W. 86.95 n_D^{20} 1.4218 NEAT

B D6510-0 **Dichloromethane** (methylene chloride) **A.C.S. reagent** CH_2Cl_2 M.W. 84.93 n_D^{20} 1.4235 NEAT

C 15,185-8 **Chloroform-*d*, 100%** $CDCl_3$ M.W. 120.39 n_D^{20} 1.4450 NEAT

D 15,183-1 **Chloroform-*d*, 99.8%** (contains 1% TMS) $CDCl_3$ M.W. 120.39 n_D^{20} 1.4437

E 13,295-0 **Chloroform, U.S.P.** $CHCl_3$ M.W. 119.38 n_D^{20} 1.4453 b.p. 61.1° NEAT

F 18,594-9 **2-Chloro-2-methylpropane-d_9**, 99 atom % D, GOLD LABEL (*tert*-butyl-d_9 chloride) $(CD_3)_3CCl$ FW 101.64 bp 50° n_D^{20} 1.3819 Disp. C NEAT

G C5635-2 **2-Chloro-2-methylpropane** (tert.-butyl chloride) $(CH_3)_3CCl$ M.W. 92.57 n_D^{20} 1.3848 NEAT

H 15,189-0 **Deuterium oxide, 100%** D_2O M.W. 20.03 NEAT

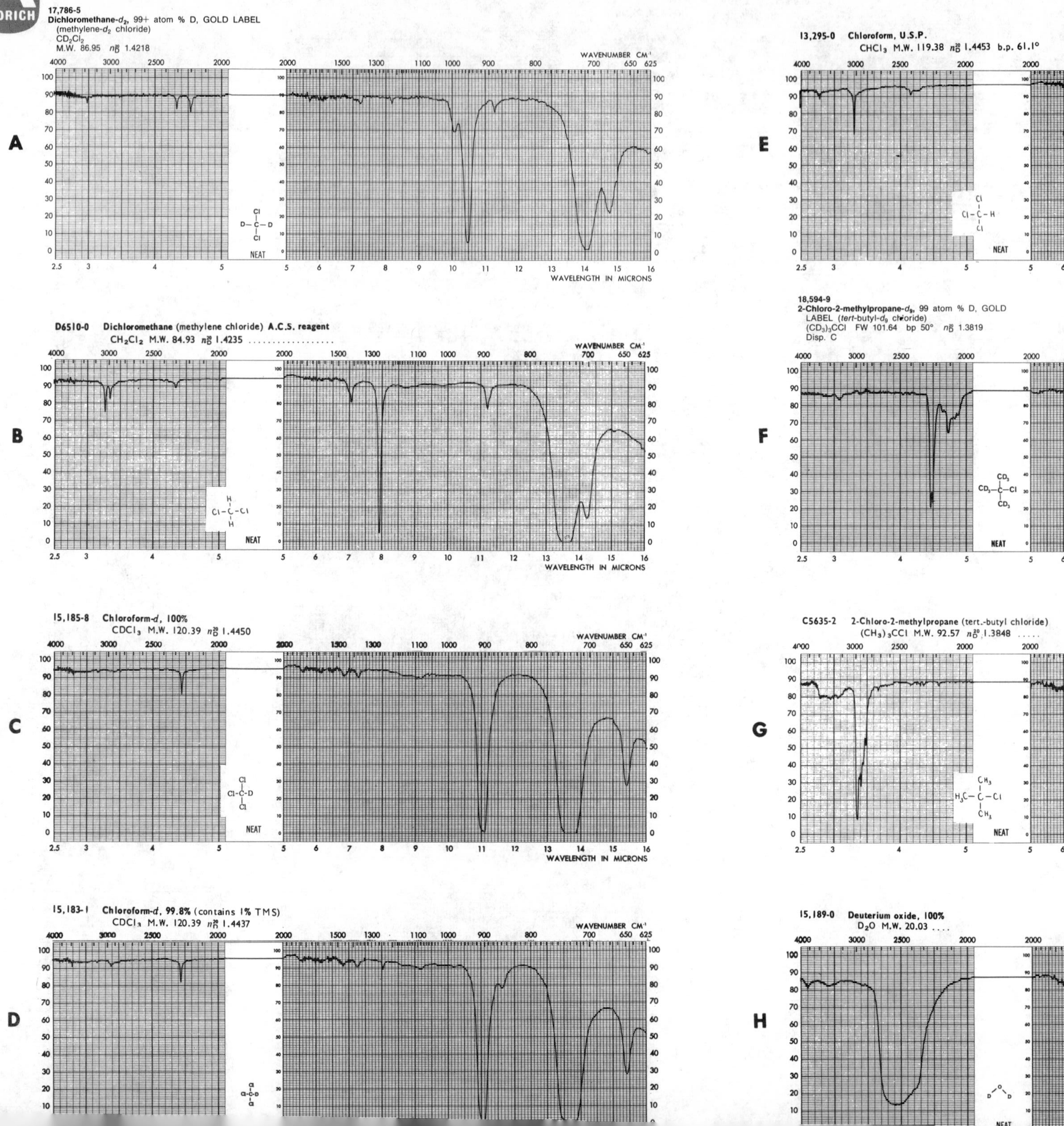

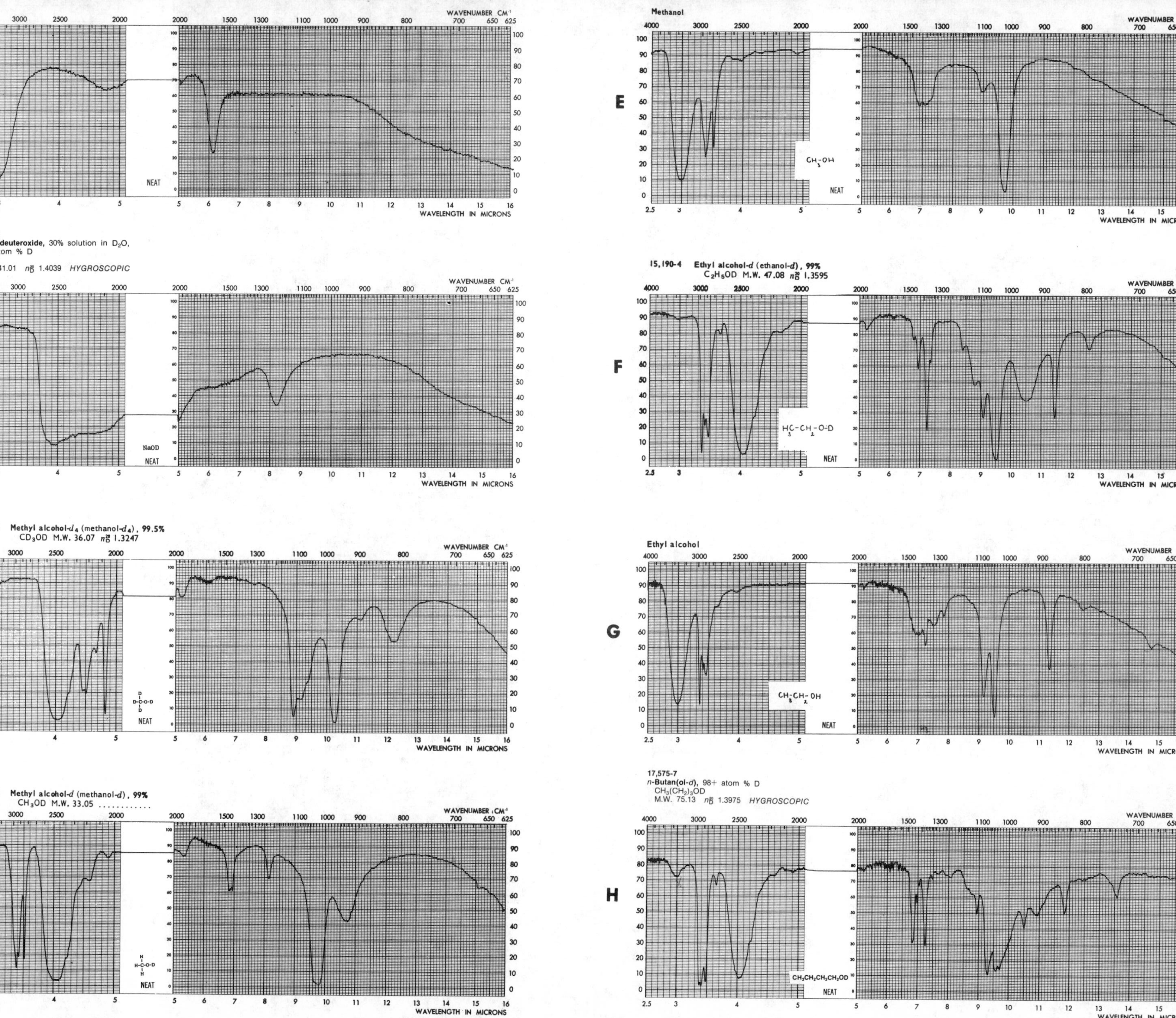

A

16,448-8
Sodium deuteroxide, 30% solution in D_2O, 99+ atom % D
NaOD
M.W. 41.01 n_D^{20} 1.4039 *HYGROSCOPIC*

B

15,194-7 **Methyl alcohol-d_4** (methanol-d_4), 99.5%
CD_3OD M.W. 36.07 n_D^{20} 1.3247

C

15,193-9 **Methyl alcohol-*d*** (methanol-*d*), 99%
CH_3OD M.W. 33.05

D

Methanol

E

15,190-4 **Ethyl alcohol-*d*** (ethanol-*d*), 99%
C_2H_5OD M.W. 47.08 n_D^{20} 1.3595

F

Ethyl alcohol

G

17,575-7
***n*-Butan(ol-*d*)**, 98+ atom % D
$CH_3(CH_2)_3OD$
M.W. 75.13 n_D^{20} 1.3975 *HYGROSCOPIC*

H

ALDRICH

A

15,467-9
n-**Butanol,** spectrophotometric grade, GOLD LABEL
(meets A.C.S. specifications) (*n*-butyl alcohol)
$CH_3(CH_2)_3OH$
M.W. 74.12 m.p. -90 to -80° b.p. 117.7°
n_D^{20} 1.3985 d 0.81 Beil. **1**,367

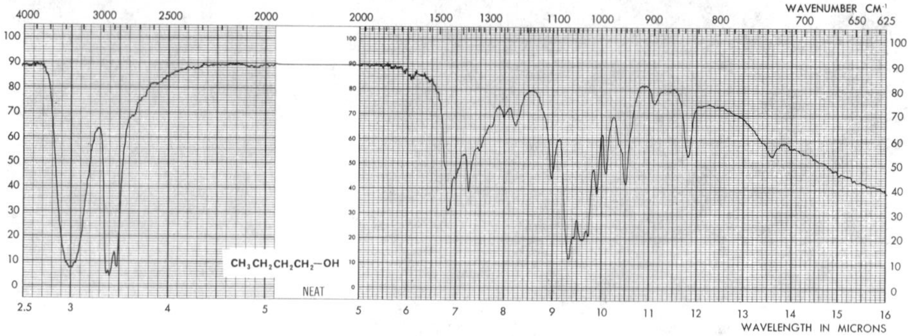

$CH_3CH_2CH_2CH_2$–OH
NEAT

B

17,584-6
Isopropan(ol-*d*), 98+ atom % D
$(CH_3)_2CHOD$
M.W. 61.1 n_D^{20} 1.3752 *HYGROSCOPIC*

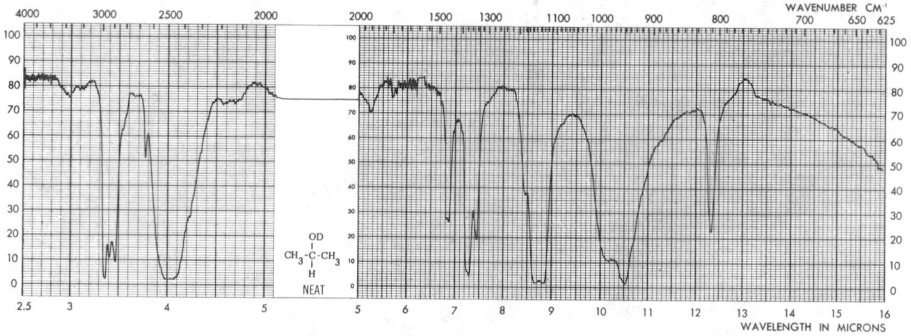

NEAT

C

17,589-7
Isopropanol-d_8, 99+ atom % D, GOLD LABEL
$(CD_3)_2CDOD$
M.W. 68.16 n_D^{20} 1.3728 *HYGROSCOPIC*

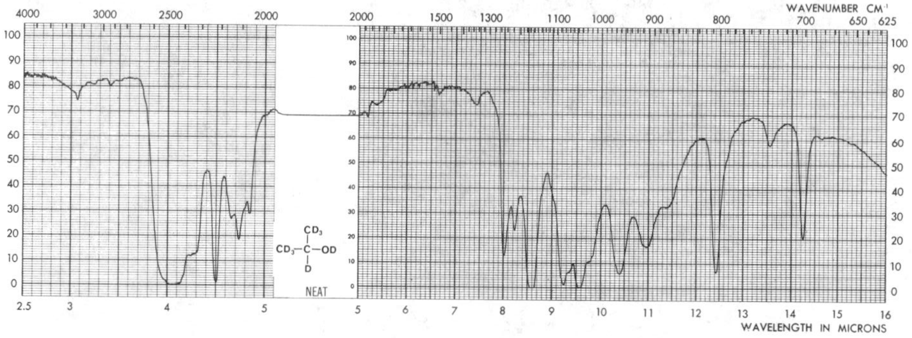

NEAT

D

10,982-7 **Isopropanol** (isopropyl alcohol), **99+%, anhydrous**
$(CH_3)_2CHOH$ M.W. 60.10 n_D^{20} 1.3770
b.p. 82.3°

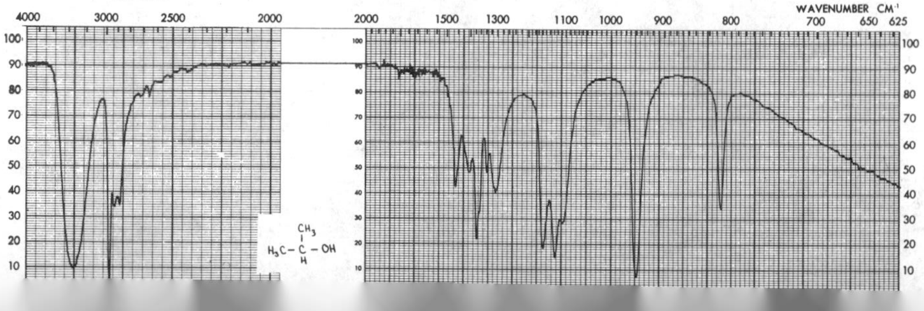

E

17,576-5
tert.-**Butan(ol-*d*),** 98+ atom % D
$(CH_3)_3COD$
M.W. 75.13 n_D^{20} 1.3847 *HYGROSCOPIC*

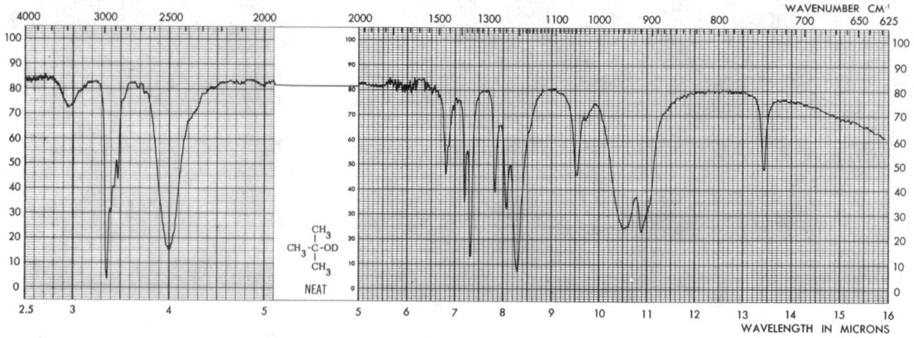

NEAT

F

17,588-9
tert.-**Butanol-d_{10},** 99+ atom % D, GOLD LABEL
$(CD_3)_3COD$
M.W. 84.2 n_D^{20} 1.3835 *HYGROSCOPIC*

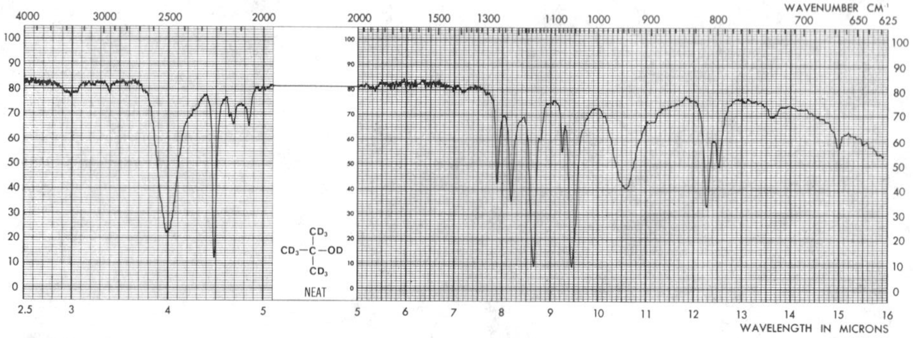

NEAT

G

B8,592-7
tert.-**Butanol,** 99.5% (*tert*.-butyl alcohol)
$(CH_3)_3COH$
M.W. 74.12 m.p. 25-25.5° b.p. 83° n_D^{20} 1.3860
d 0.786 Beil. **1**,379

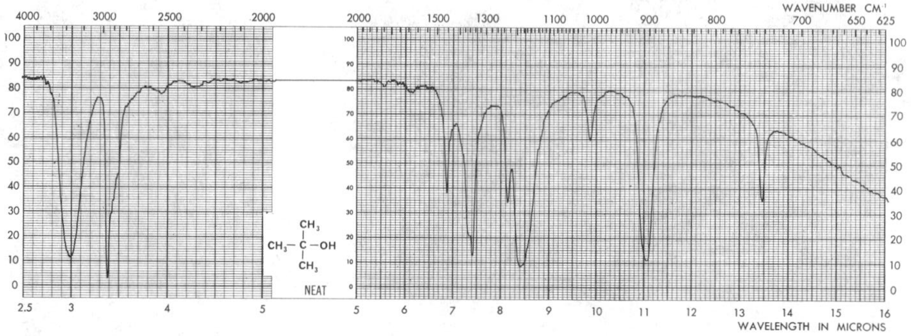

NEAT

H

17,574-9
1,4-Butane(diol-d_2), 98+ atom % D
$DO(CH_2)_4OD$
M.W. 92.13 n_D^{20} 1.4432 *HYGROSCOPIC*

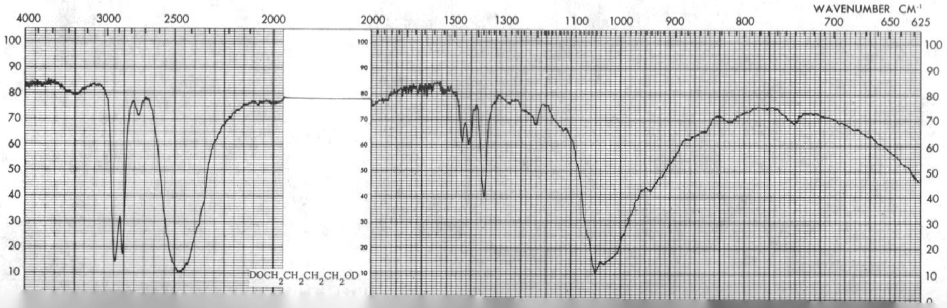

$DOCH_2CH_2CH_2CH_2OD$

$HO(CH_2)_4OH$ M.W. 90.12 n_D^{20} 1.4440 m.p. 15-19°

n_D^{20} 1.4244

17,577-3
Cyclohexanol-d_{12}, 98+ atom % D
$C_6D_{11}OD$
M.W. 112.26 n_D^{20} 1.4608 *HYGROSCOPIC*

18,431-4
Tetrahydrofuran-d_8, 98 atom % D
M.W. 80.17

10,589-9 **Cyclohexanol**
$C_6H_{11}OH$ M.W. 100.16 n_D^{20} 1.4641
m.p. 20-22° b.p. 160-161°

14,722-2 **Tetrahydrofuran** (THF), 99.5+% (stabilized with 0.025% butylated hydroxytoluene)
M.W. 72.11 n_D^{20} 1.4070 b.p. 65.5-66.7°

16,449-6
Carbitol-d_1 [2-(2-ethoxyethoxy)-ethanol-d_1]
$C_2H_5OCH_2CH_2OCH_2CH_2OD$
M.W. 135.18 n_D^{20} 1.4260 *HYGROSCOPIC*

18,640-6
p-Dioxane-d_8, 98.5 atom % D, GOLD LABEL
FW 96.17 n_D^{20} 1.4198 Disp. C

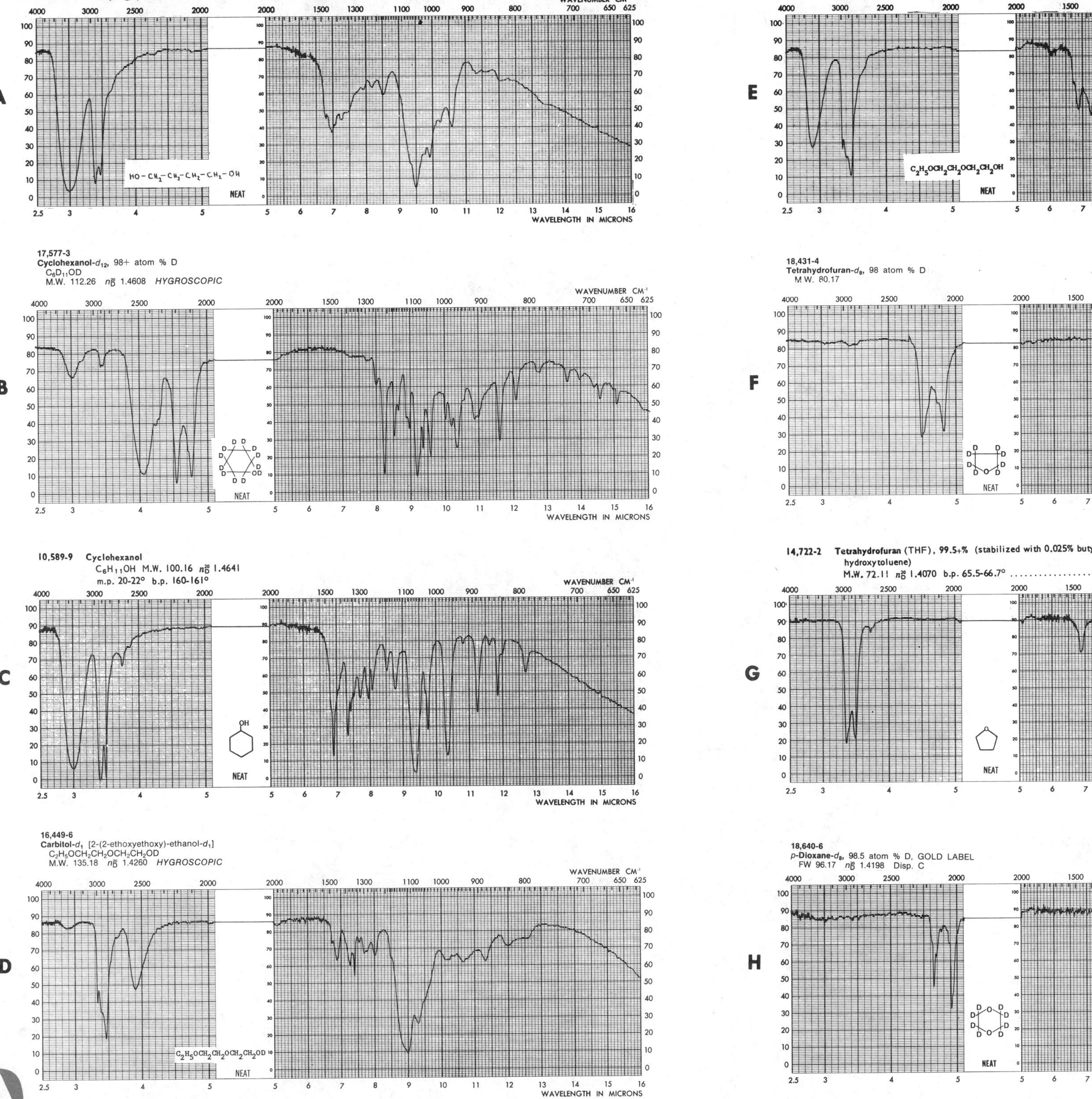

A

D20,186-3 **p-Dioxane**
M.W. 88.11 n_D^{20} 1.4206 m.p. 10-12°

NEAT

B

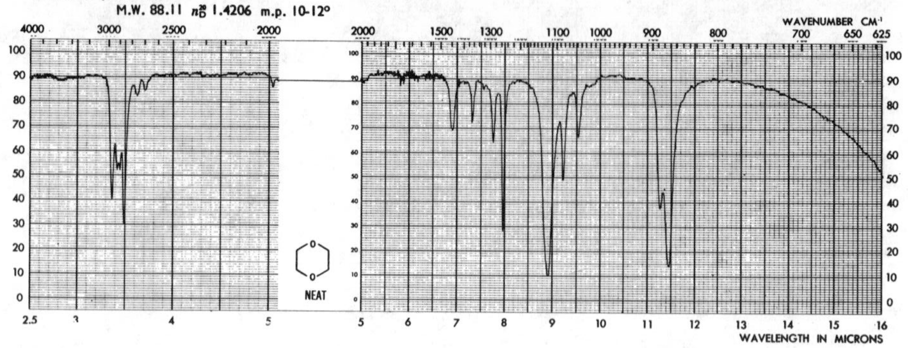

21,607-0
(Methyl sulfide)-d_6, 99+ atom % D, GOLD LABEL
(dimethyl-d_6 sulfide)
$(CD_3)_2S$ FW 68.18 bp 36.5° n_D^{20} 1.4315
d 0.928 Disp. J

CD_3-S-CD_3
NEAT

C

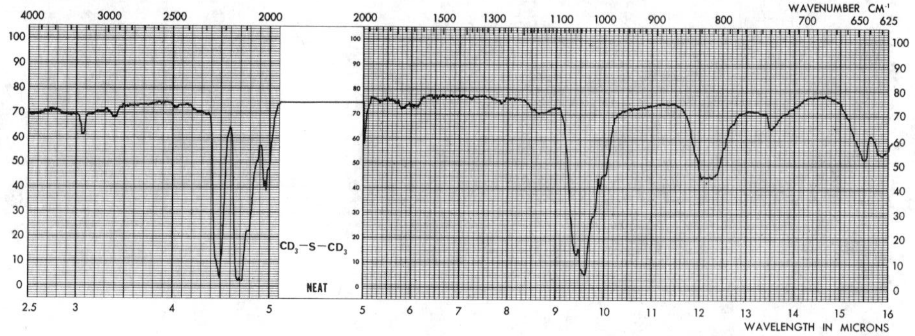

M8163-2 **Methyl sulfide**
$(CH_3)_2S$ M.W. 62.13 n_D^{20} 1.4351

$H_3C-S-CH_3$
NEAT

D

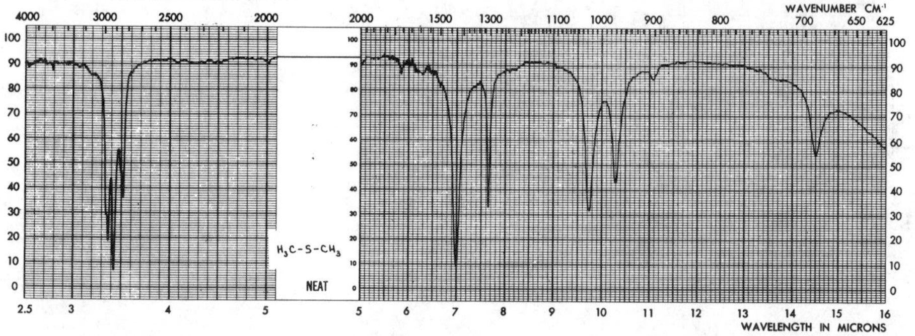

17,567-6
Ammonium-d_4 chloride, 98+ atom % D
ND_4Cl
M.W. 57.52 m.p. >300° *HYGROSCOPIC*

E

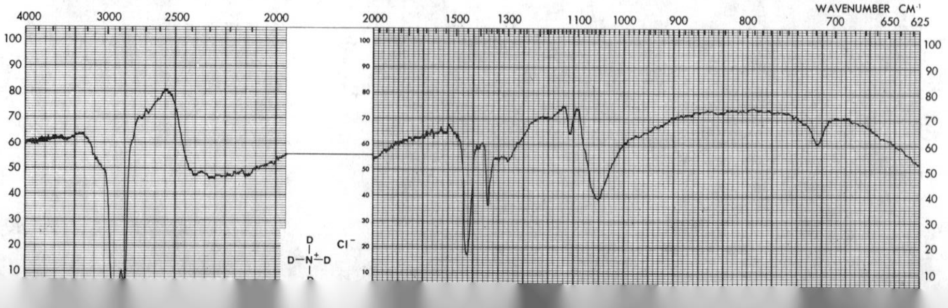

17,568-4
Ammonium-d_4 sulfate, 98+ atom % D
$(ND_4)_2SO_4$
M.W. 140.2 m.p. >300° *HYGROSCOPIC*

NUJOL MULL

F

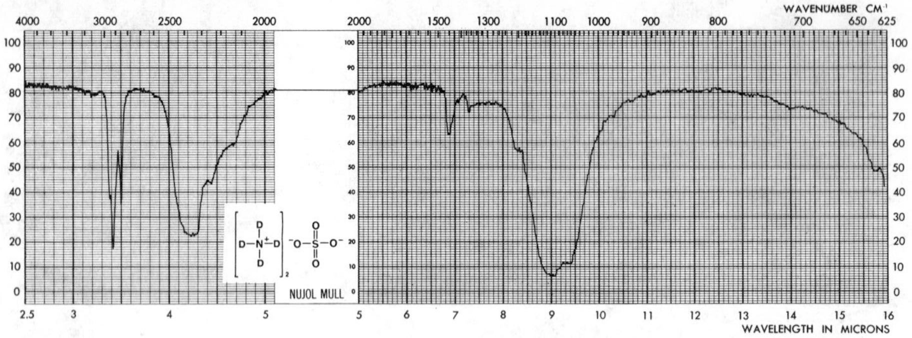

17,658-3
Ammonium-d_4 perchlorate, 98+ atom % D
ND_4ClO_4
M.W. 121.52 m.p. >300° *HYGROSCOPIC*

NUJOL MULL

G

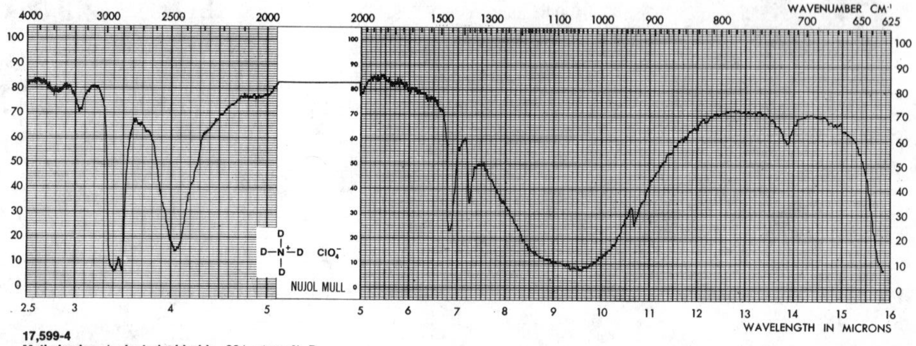

17,599-4
Methylamine-d_2 deuteriochloride, 98+ atom % D
(methylammonium-d_3 chloride)
$CH_3ND_2 \cdot DCl$
M.W. 70.54 m.p. 233-235° (dec.)
HYGROSCOPIC

NUJOL MULL

H

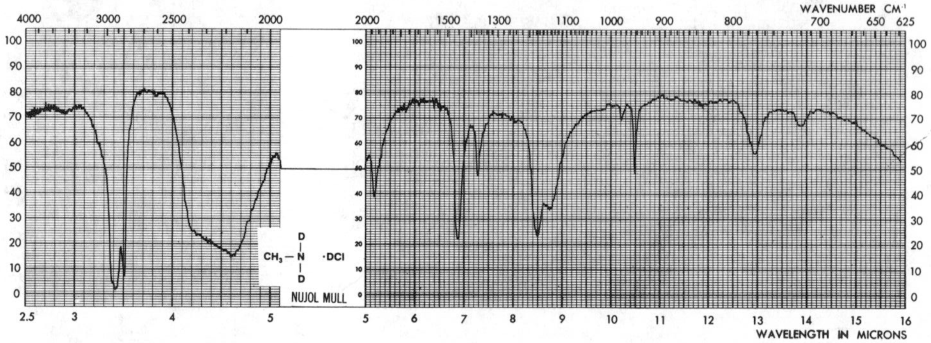

17,600-1
Methyl-d_3-amine hydrochloride, 98+ atom % D
$CD_3NH_2 \cdot HCl$
M.W. 70.54 m.p. 229-232° *HYGROSCOPIC*

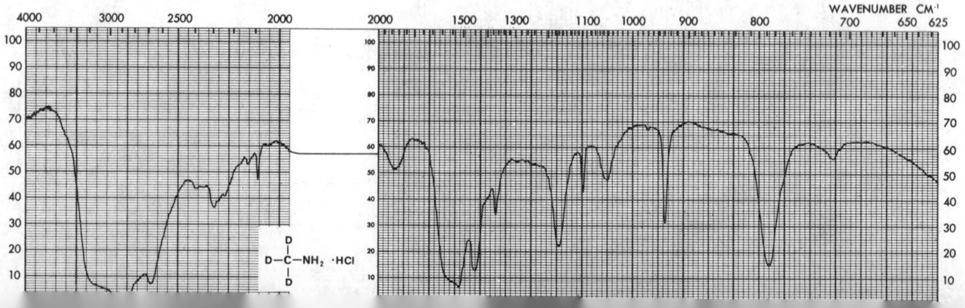

A

$CH_3NH_2 \cdot HCl$ M.W. 67.52 m.p. 233.5-235°

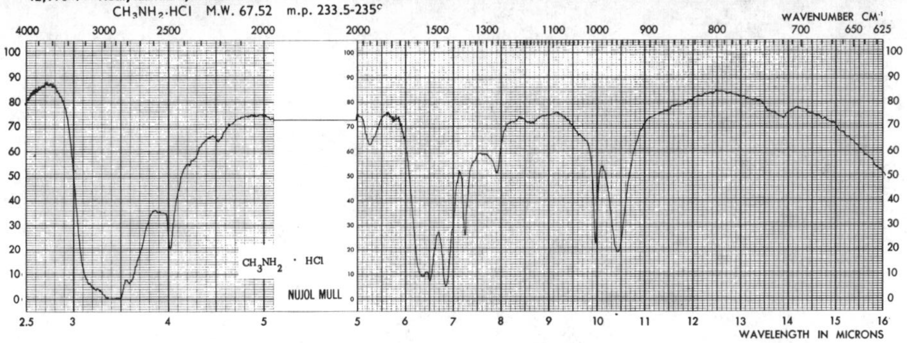

$CH_3NH_2 \cdot HCl$

NUJOL MULL

B

17,602-8
Methylamine-d_5 deuteriochloride, 98+ atom % D
(methylammonium-d_6 chloride)
$CD_3ND_2 \cdot DCl$ FW 73.57 Disp. L

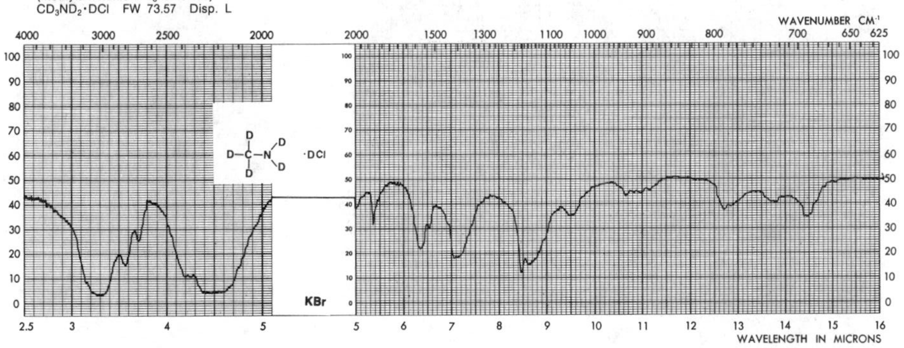

$CD_3ND_2 \cdot DCl$

KBr

C

15,196-3 **Nitromethane-d_3, 99%**
CD_3NO_2 M.W. 64.07

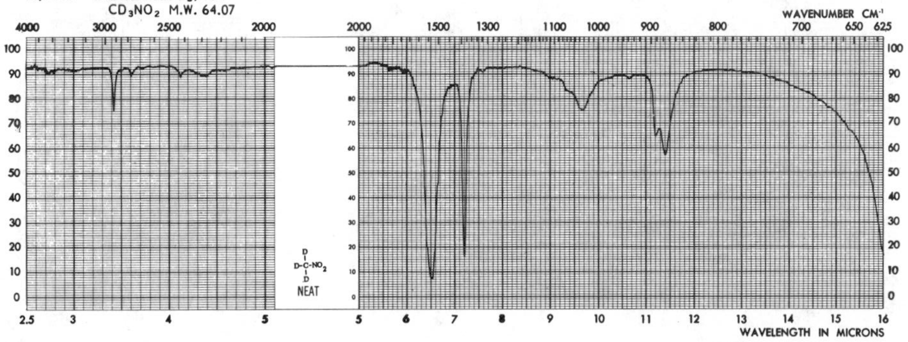

CD_3NO_2

NEAT

D

10,817-0 **Nitromethane**
CH_3NO_2 M.W. 61.04 n_D^{20} 1.3806
b.p. 100-102° . . . .

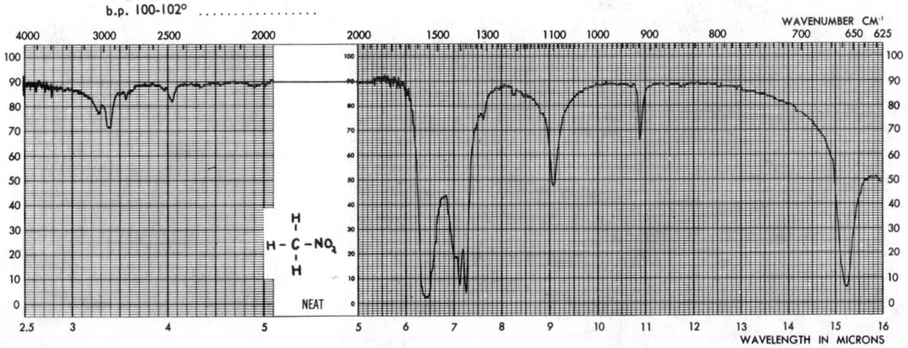

$H-C(H)(H)-NO_2$

NEAT

E

CD_3COCD_3 M.W. 64.13
n_D^{20} 1.3560 . . . .

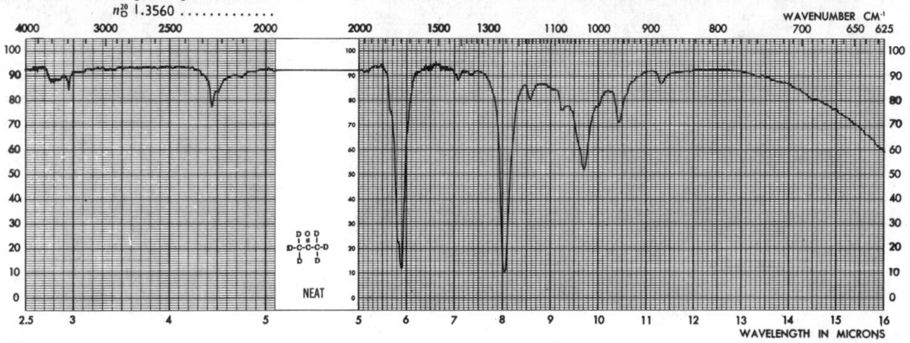

CD_3COCD_3

NEAT

F

15,459-8 **Acetone, spectrophotometric grade, GOLD LABEL**
(meets A.C.S. spectrophotometric requirements)
CH_3COCH_3 M.W. 58.08 b.p. 56°

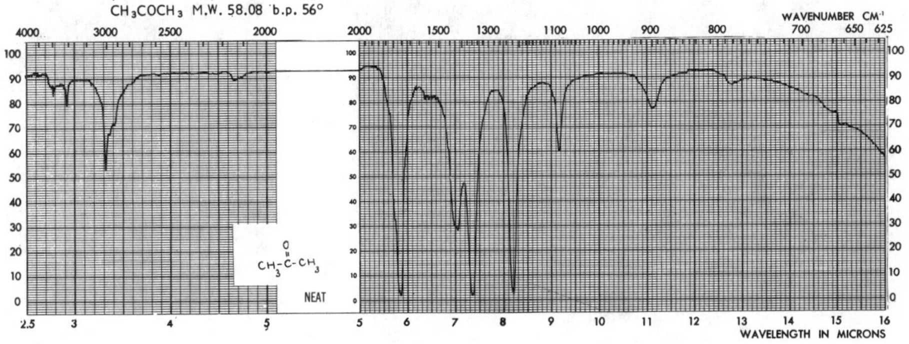

$CH_3-C(=O)-CH_3$

NEAT

G

15,192-0 **Hexafluoroacetone** (hexafluoro-2-propanone) **deuterate, 99.5%**
$CF_3COCF_3 \cdot 1.6D_2O$ M.W. 198.07 . . . .

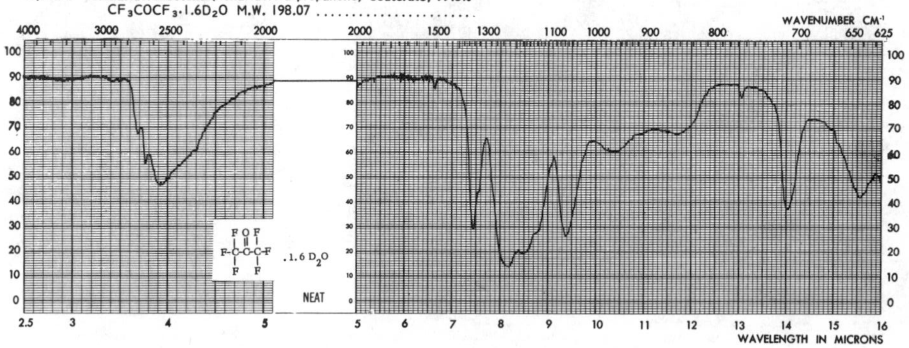

$CF_3COCF_3 \cdot 1.6\,D_2O$

NEAT

H

13,923-8 **Hexafluoroacetone** (hexafluoro-2-propanone) **sesquihydrate**
$CF_3COCF_3 \cdot 1\frac{1}{2}H_2O$ M.W. 193.04 n_D^{20} 1.3079 . . . .

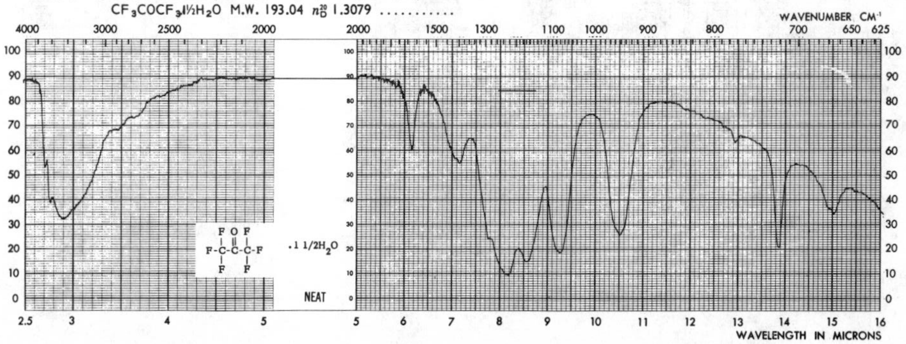

$CF_3COCF_3 \cdot 1\,1/2H_2O$

NEAT

ALDRICH

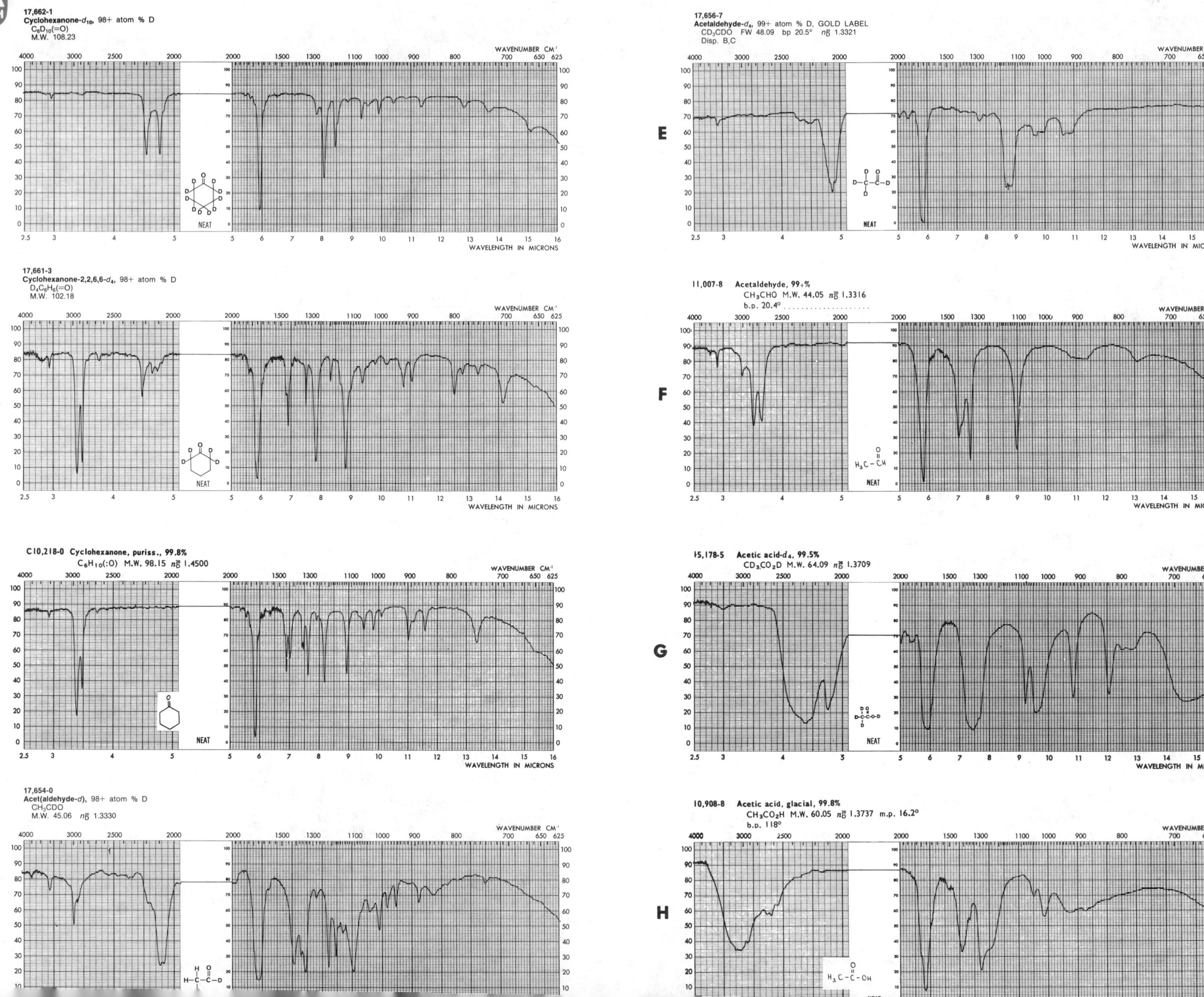

A 17,662-1 **Cyclohexanone-d_{10}**, 98+ atom % D
$C_6D_{10}(=O)$
M.W. 108.23
NEAT

B 17,661-3 **Cyclohexanone-2,2,6,6-d_4**, 98+ atom % D
$D_4C_6H_6(=O)$
M.W. 102.18
NEAT

C C10,218-0 **Cyclohexanone, puriss., 99.8%**
$C_6H_{10}(:O)$ M.W. 98.15 n_D^{20} 1.4500
NEAT

D 17,654-0 **Acet(aldehyde-*d*)**, 98+ atom % D
CH_3CDO
M.W. 45.06 n_D^{20} 1.3330

E 17,656-7 **Acetaldehyde-d_4**, 99+ atom % D, GOLD LABEL
CD_3CDO FW 48.09 bp 20.5° n_D^{20} 1.3321
Disp. B,C
NEAT

F 11,007-8 **Acetaldehyde, 99+%**
CH_3CHO M.W. 44.05 n_D^{20} 1.3316
b.p. 20.4°
NEAT

G 15,178-5 **Acetic acid-d_4, 99.5%**
CD_3CO_2D M.W. 64.09 n_D^{20} 1.3709
NEAT

H 10,908-8 **Acetic acid, glacial, 99.8%**
CH_3CO_2H M.W. 60.05 n_D^{20} 1.3737 m.p. 16.2°
b.p. 118°

A CF$_3$CO$_2$D M.W. 115.03

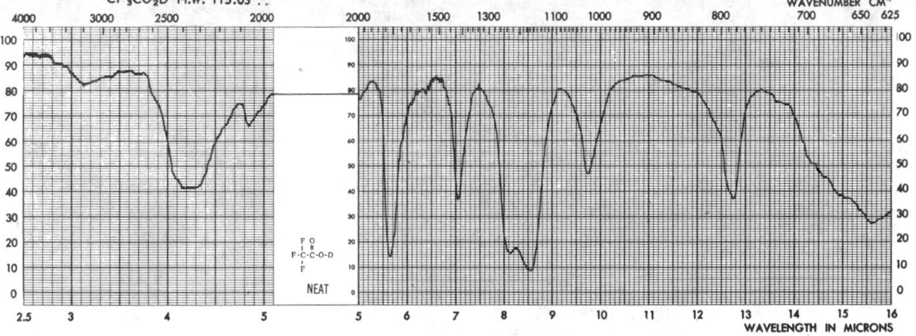

NEAT

B T6220-0 Trifluoroacetic acid
CF$_3$CO$_2$H M.W. 114.02

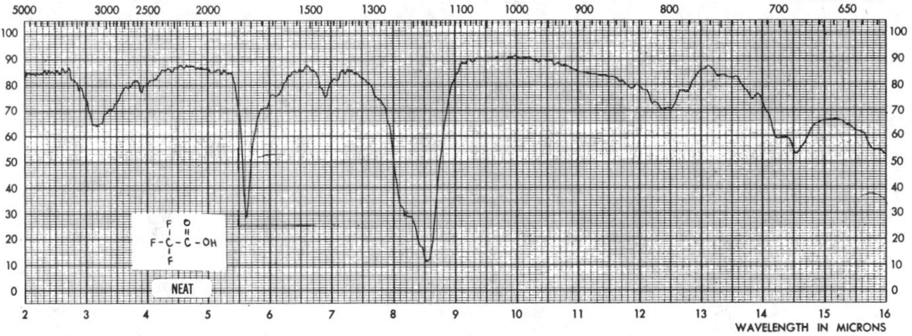

NEAT

C 18,595-7
Oxalic acid-d_2, 99 atom % D, GOLD LABEL
DO$_2$CCO$_2$D FW 92.05 mp 122-127° (dec.)
Disp. I

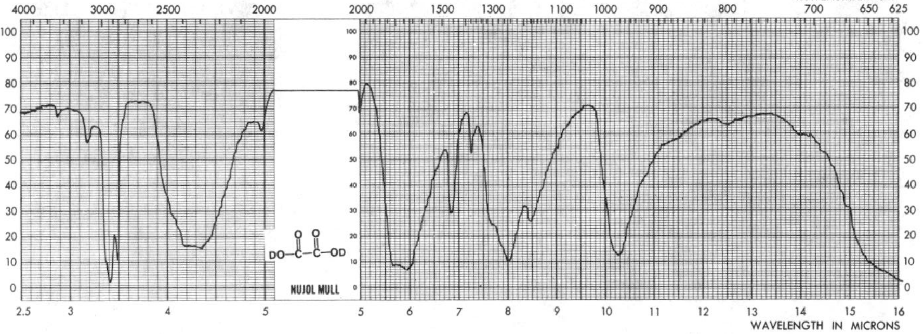

NUJOL MULL

D 0-875-5 Oxalic acid

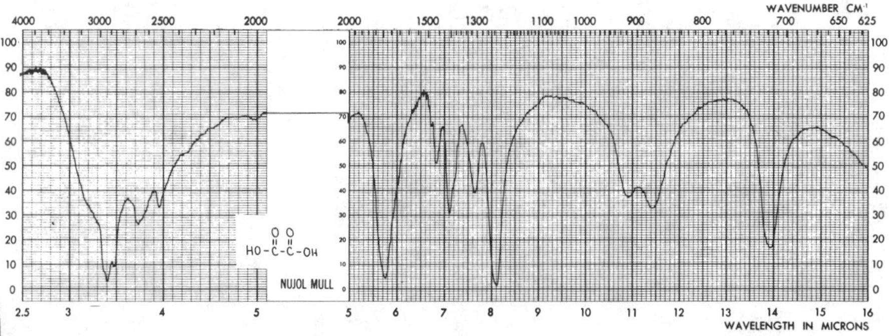

NUJOL MULL

E

NUJOL MULL

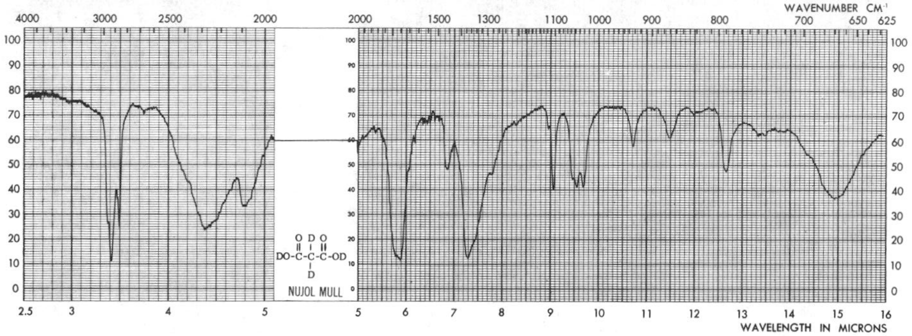

F M129-6 Malonic acid
HO$_2$CCH$_2$CO$_2$H M.W. 104.06 m.p. 135-137°

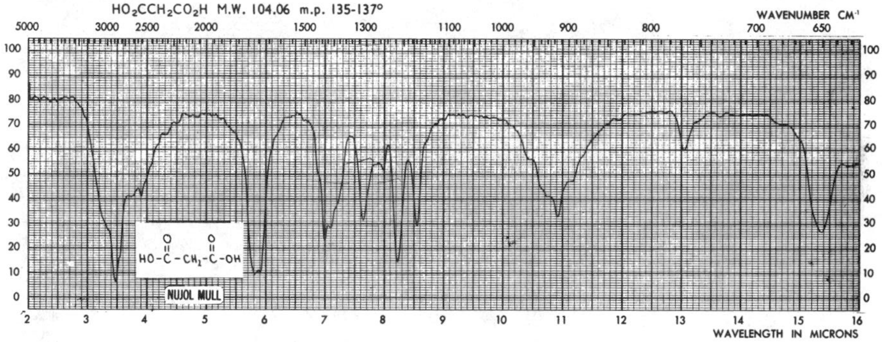

NUJOL MULL

G 17,598-6
(DL-Malic acid)-d_6
DO$_2$CCD$_2$CD(OD)CO$_2$D
M.W. 140.14 m.p. 125-127°

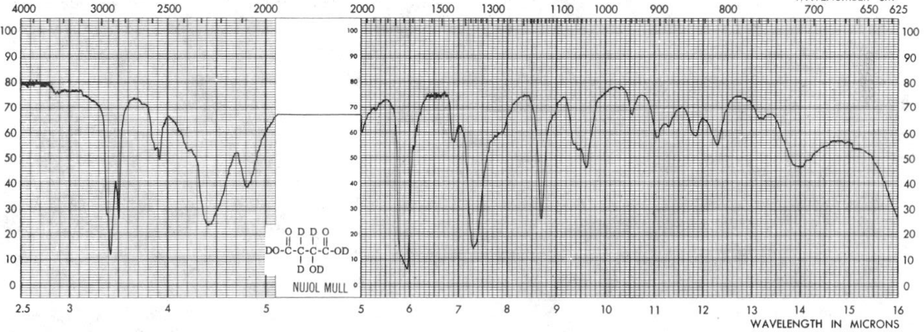

NUJOL MULL

H M121-0 DL-Malic acid (DL-hydroxysuccinic acid)
HO$_2$CCH$_2$CH(OH)CO$_2$H M.W. 134.09
m.p. 128-132°

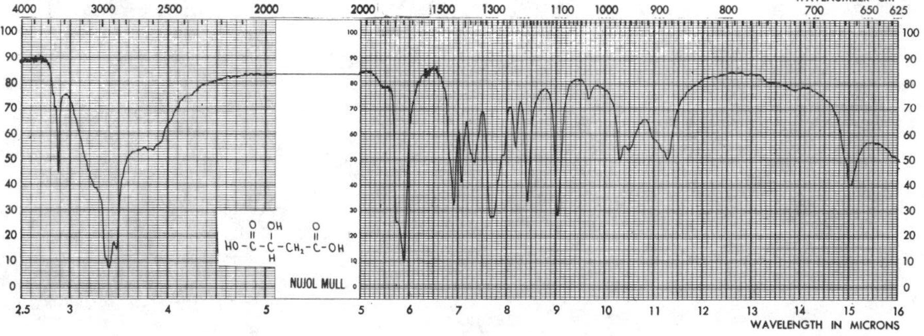

NUJOL MULL

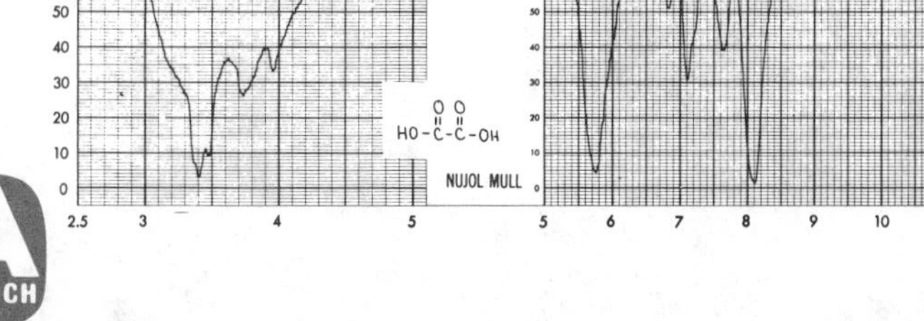

DEUTERATED

®

A 17,607-9
Acetic-d_3 acid, sodium salt, 99+ atom % D,
GOLD LABEL
CD_3CO_2Na
M.W. 85.06 m.p. >300° *IRRITANT*
NUJOL MULL

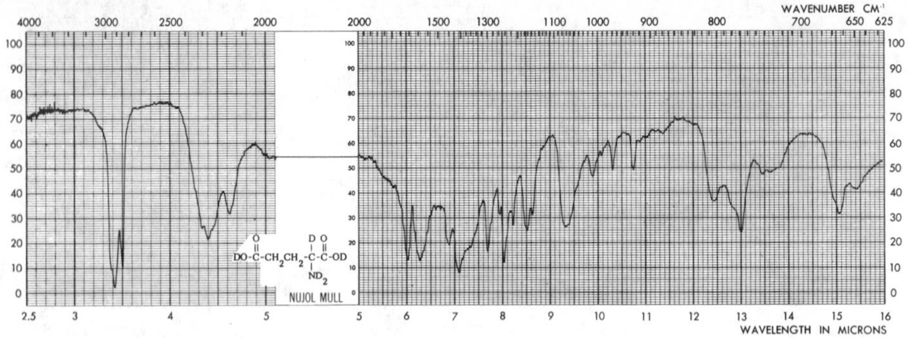

B 11,019-1 **Acetic acid, sodium salt** (sodium acetate), **anhydrous**
CH_3CO_2Na M.W. 82.03 m.p. > 300°
NUJOL MULL

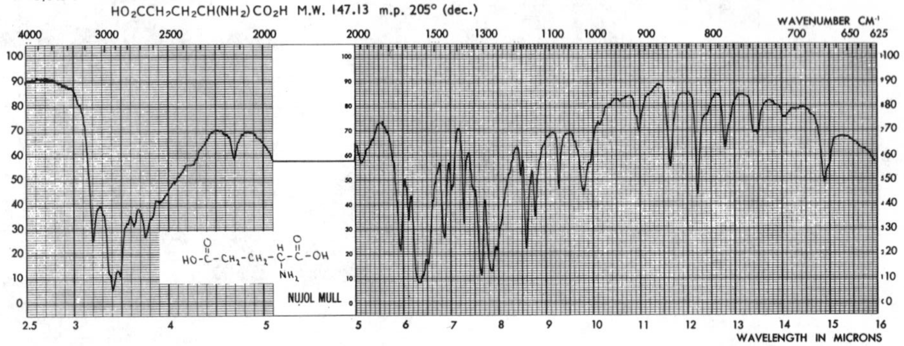

C 17,583-8
Glycine-d_5, 98+ atom % D
$D_2NCD_2CO_2D$
M.W. 80.11 m.p. 248° (dec.)
NUJOL MULL

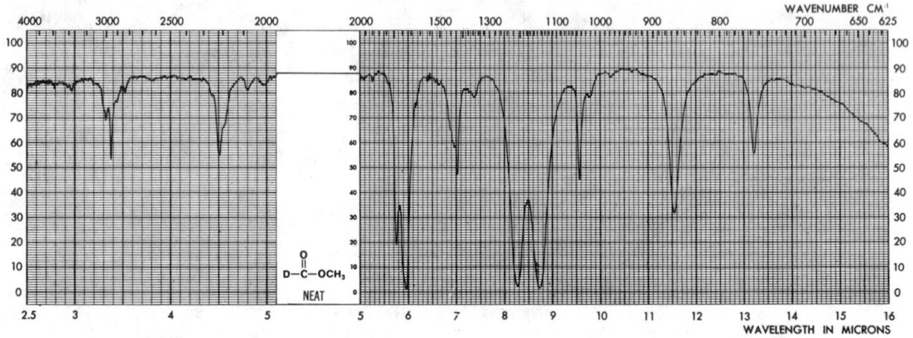

D G620-1 **Glycine**
$H_2NCH_2CO_2H$ M.W. 75.07 m.p. 245° (dec.)

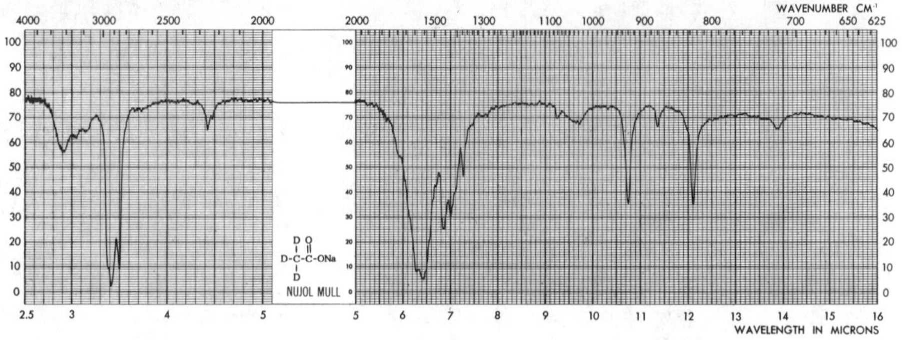

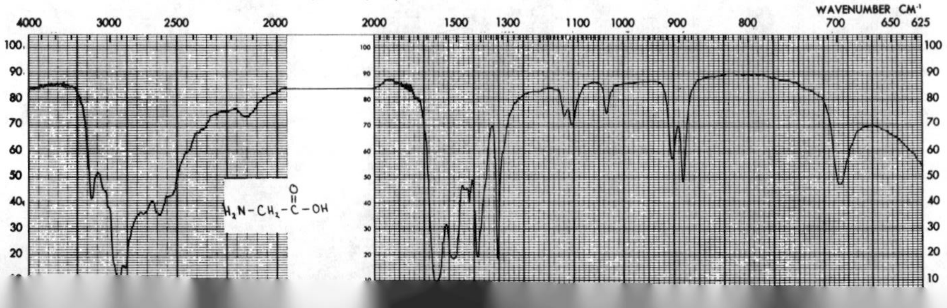

E 17,581-1
L-Glutamic-N,N,2-d_3 acid-d_2, 98+ atom % D
$DO_2CCH_2CH_2CD(ND_2)CO_2D$
M.W. 152.17 m.p. 209-211°
NUJOL MULL

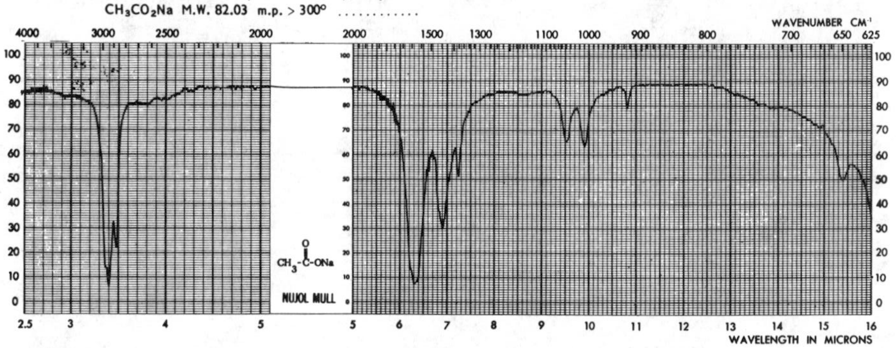

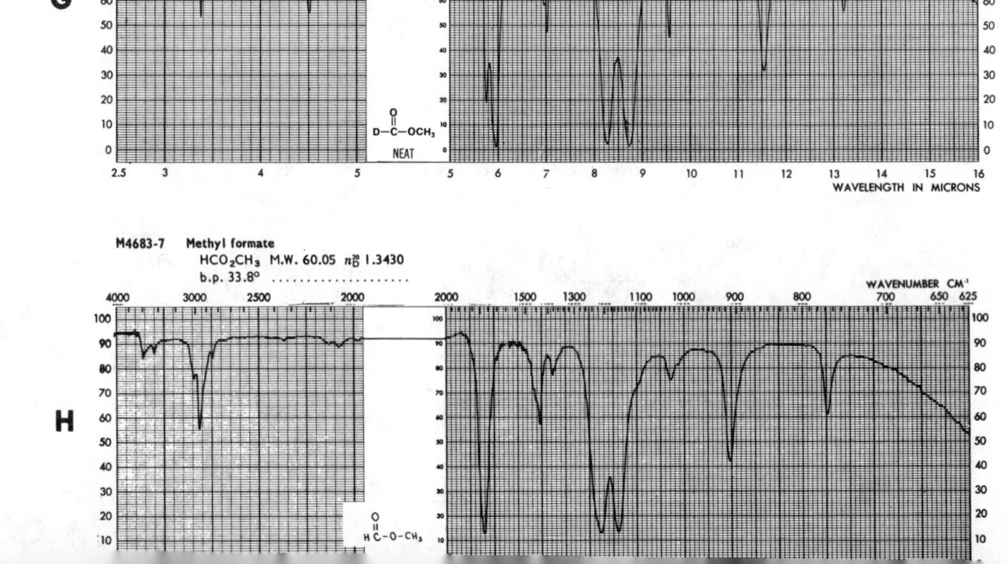

F 12,843-0 **L-Glutamic acid**
$HO_2CCH_2CH_2CH(NH_2)CO_2H$ M.W. 147.13 m.p. 205° (dec.)
NUJOL MULL

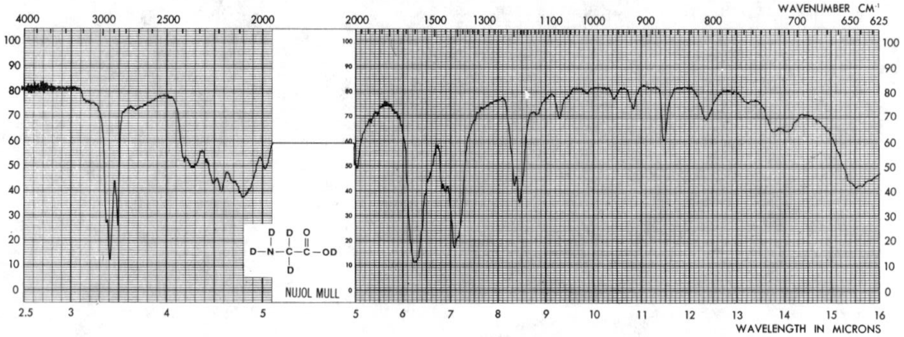

G 17,667-2
Methyl formate-*d*, 98+ atom % D
DCO_2CH_3
M.W. 61.06 n_D^{20} 1.3435
NEAT

H M4683-7 **Methyl formate**
HCO_2CH_3 M.W. 60.05 n_D^{20} 1.3430
b.p. 33.8°

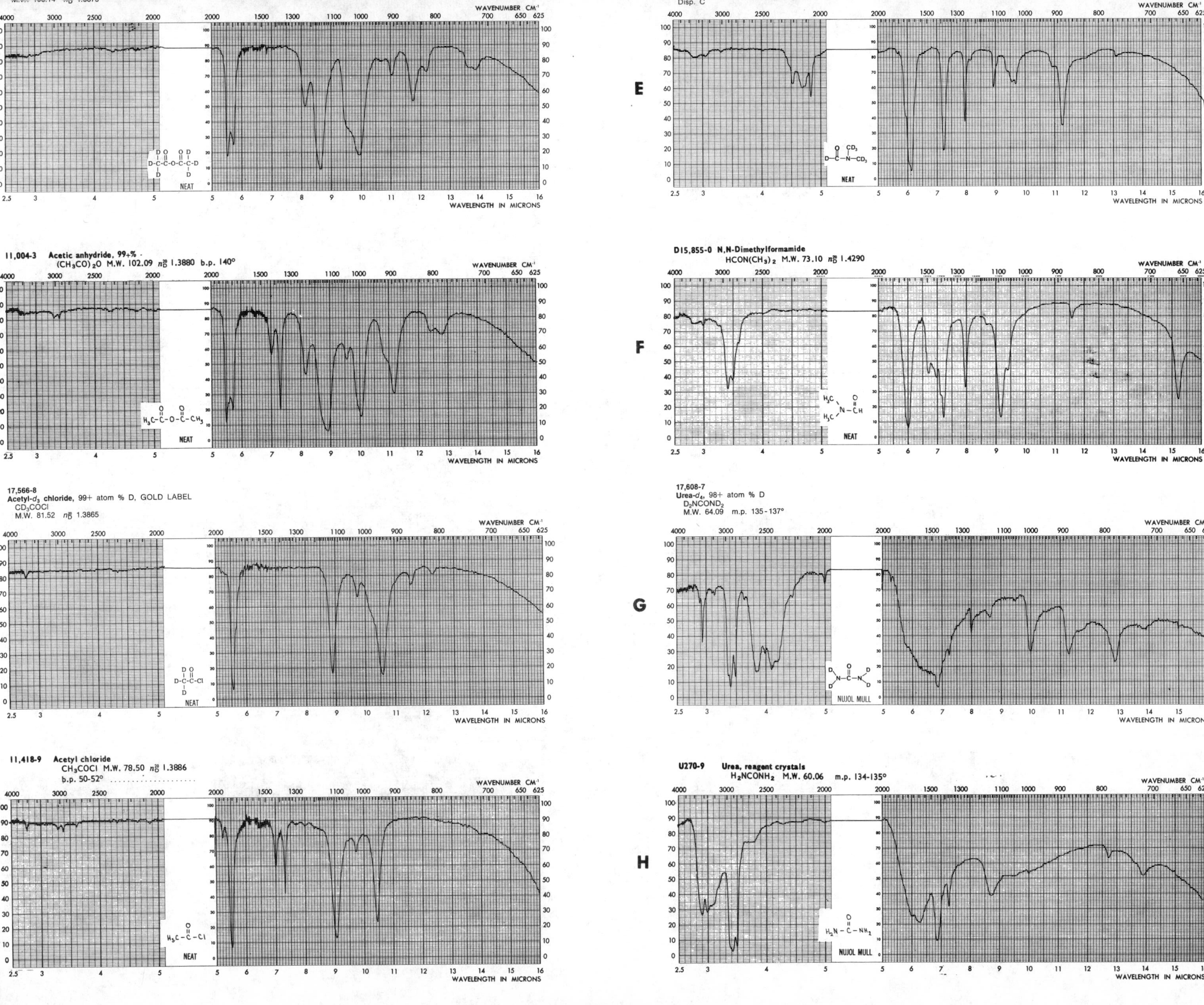

A
NEAT
11,004-3 Acetic anhydride, 99+%
$(CH_3CO)_2O$ M.W. 102.09 n_D^{20} 1.3880 b.p. 140°
B
NEAT
17,566-8
Acetyl-d_3 chloride, 99+ atom % D, GOLD LABEL
CD_3COCl
M.W. 81.52 n_D^{20} 1.3865
C
NEAT
11,418-9 Acetyl chloride
CH_3COCl M.W. 78.50 n_D^{20} 1.3886
b.p. 50-52°
D
NEAT
$DCON(CD_3)_2$ FW 80.15 n_D^{20} 1.4280 d 1.030
Disp. C
E
NEAT
D15,855-0 N,N-Dimethylformamide
$HCON(CH_3)_2$ M.W. 73.10 n_D^{20} 1.4290
F
NEAT
17,608-7
Urea-d_4, 98+ atom % D
D_2NCOND_2
M.W. 64.09 m.p. 135-137°
G
NUJOL MULL
U270-9 Urea, reagent crystals
H_2NCONH_2 M.W. 60.06 m.p. 134-135°
H
NUJOL MULL
WAVENUMBER CM⁻¹
WAVELENGTH IN MICRONS
ALDRICH

DEUTERATED

A

15,180-7 **Acetonitrile-d_3, 99%**
CD_3CN M.W. 44.08 n_D^{20} 1.3483

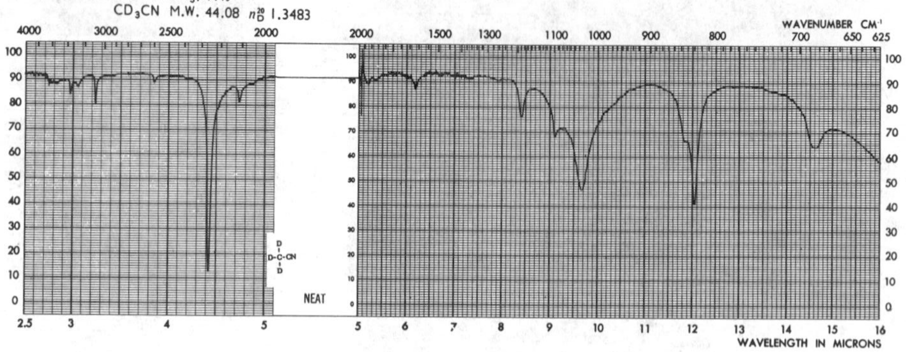

NEAT

B

11,008-6 **Acetonitrile, 99%**
CH_3CN M.W. 41.05 n_D^{20} 1.3440 b.p. 81.6°

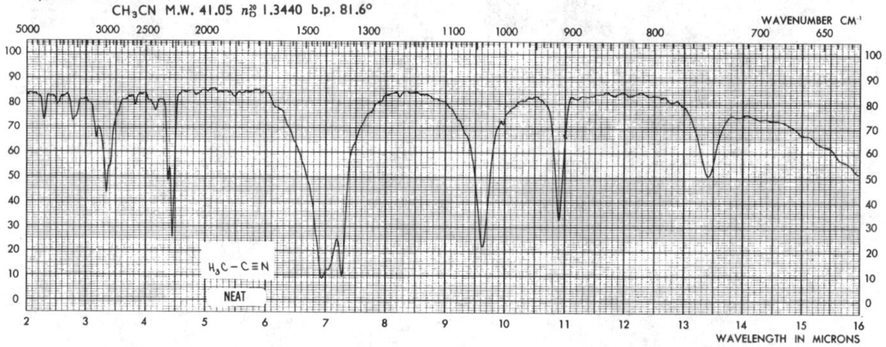

NEAT

C

15,187-4 **Methyl sulfoxide-d_6** (dimethyl sulfoxide-d_6), 99.5%
$(CD_3)_2SO$ M.W. 84.18 .....

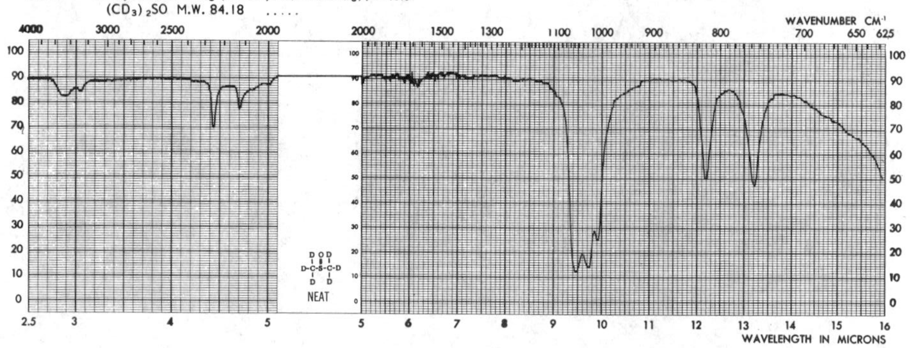

NEAT

D

M8180-2 **Methyl sulfoxide** (dimethyl sulfoxide, DMSO)
$(CH_3)_2SO$ M.W. 78.13 n_D^{20} 1.4770 ....

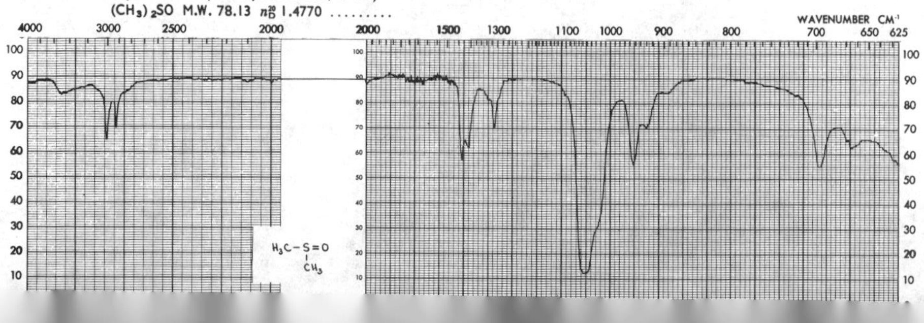

E

16,452-6
Dimethyl-d_6 sulfate, 99+ atom % D, GOLD LABEL
$(CD_3O)_2SO_2$
M.W. 132.18 n_D^{20} 1.3850 *SEVERE POISON*

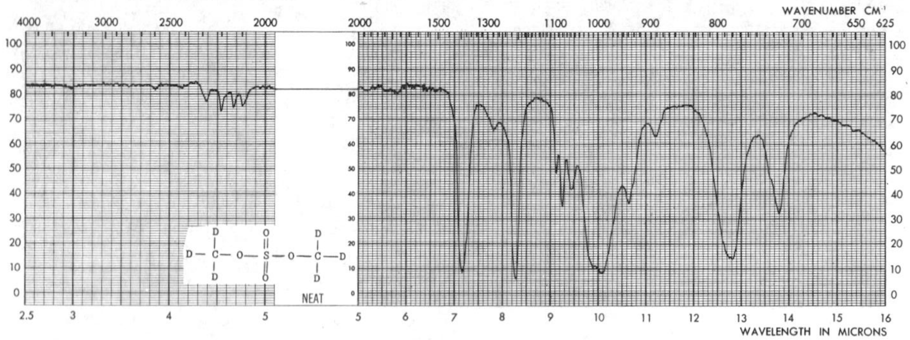

NEAT

F

D18,630-9 **Dimethyl sulfate, puriss.**
$(CH_3O)_2SO_2$ M.W. 126.13 n_D^{20} 1.3865
b.p. 75-77°/15 mm. ....

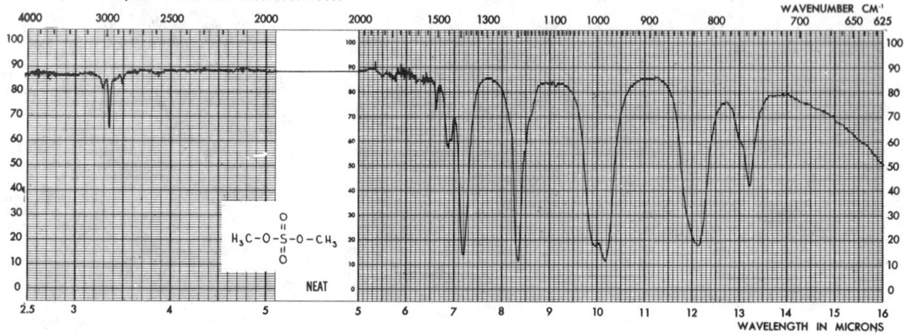

NEAT

G

16,486-0
Triethyl phosphonoacetate-d_2
$(C_2H_5O)_2P(O)CD_2CO_2C_2H_5$
M.W. 226.21 b.p. 110°/0.5mm. n_D^{20} 1.4307

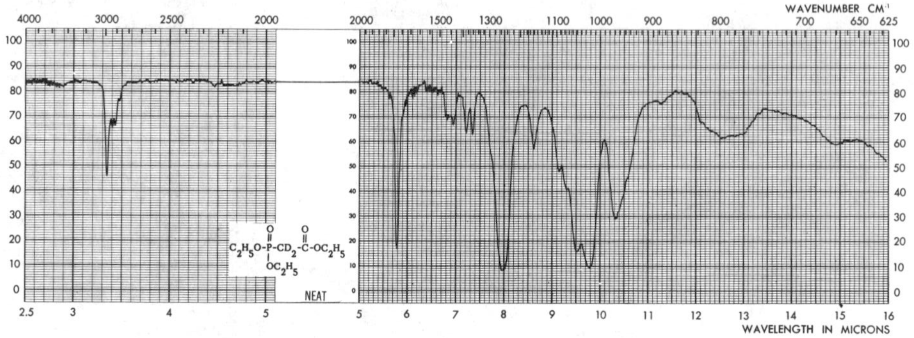

NEAT

H

T6130-1 **Triethyl phosphonoacetate**
$(C_2H_5O)_2P(O)CH_2CO_2C_2H_5$ M.W. 224.19 n_D^{20} 1.4315
b.p. 142.5-145.5°/9 mm. ....

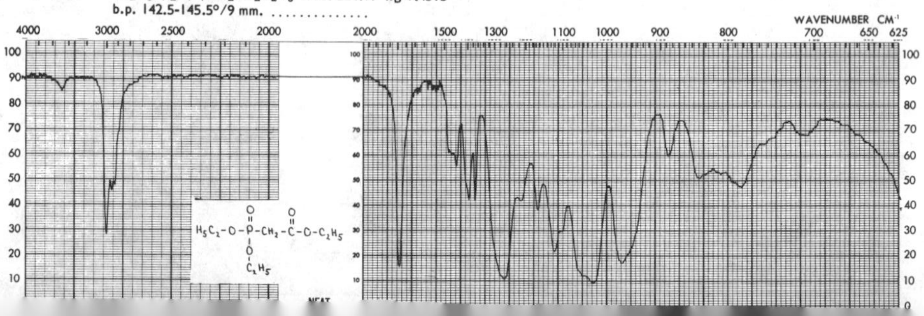

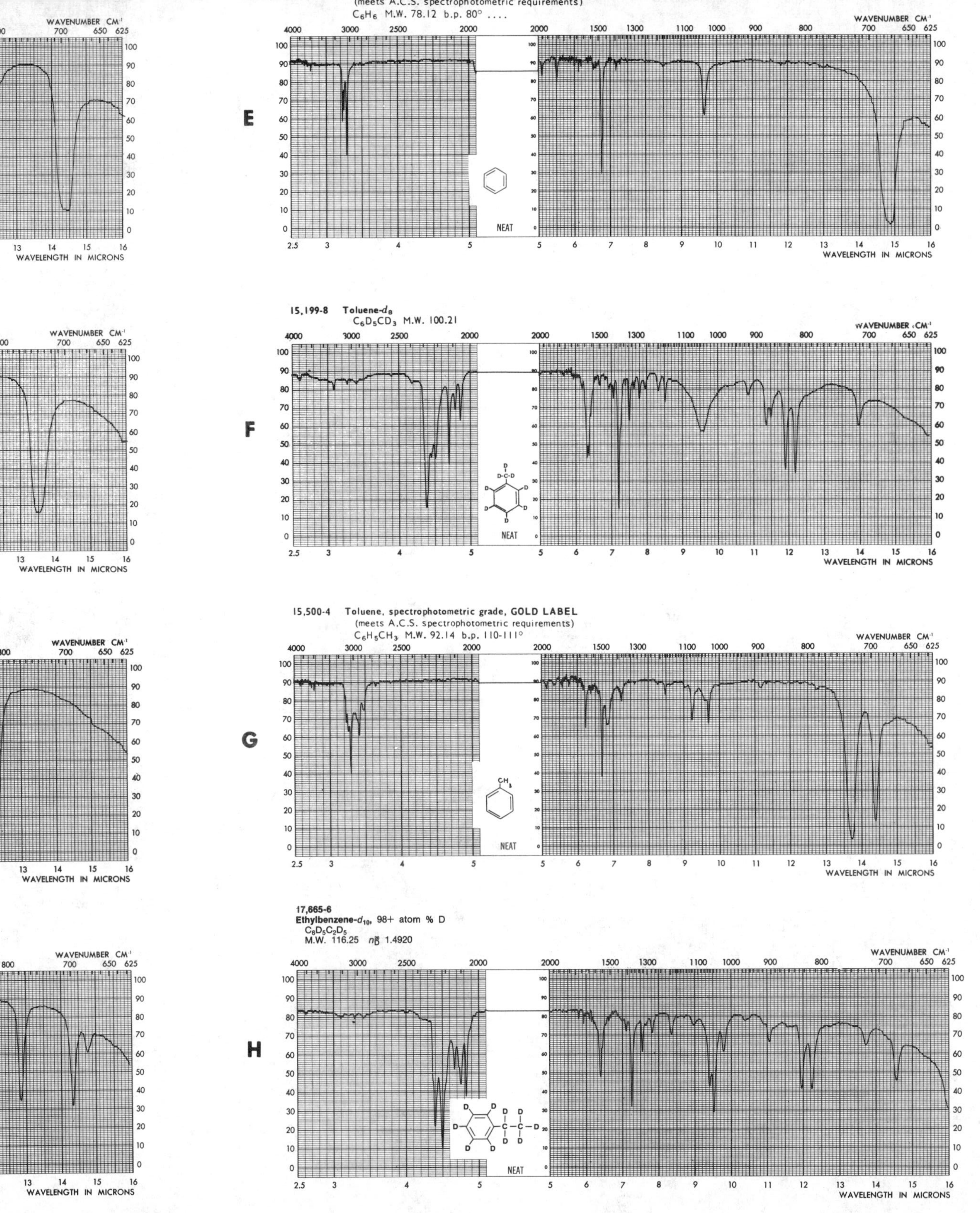

A

GOLD LABEL
$[(CD_3)_2N]_3P(O)$ FW 197.35 n_D^{20} 1.4538 Disp. C

B

H1160-2 **Hexamethylphosphoramide** (hexamethylphosphoric triamide)
$[(CH_3)_2N]_3P(O)$ M.W. 179.20 n_D^{20} 1.4579
b.p. 66°/0.5 mm. ......

C

15,181-5 **Benzene-d_6, 99.5%**
C_6D_6 M.W. 84.16 n_D^{20} 1.4976

D

17,572-2
Benzene-d, 98+ atom % D
C_6H_5D
M.W. 79.12 n_D^{20} 1.4980

E

(meets A.C.S. spectrophotometric requirements)
C_6H_6 M.W. 78.12 b.p. 80° ....

F

15,199-8 **Toluene-d_8**
$C_6D_5CD_3$ M.W. 100.21

G

15,500-4 **Toluene, spectrophotometric grade, GOLD LABEL**
(meets A.C.S. spectrophotometric requirements)
$C_6H_5CH_3$ M.W. 92.14 b.p. 110-111°

H

17,665-6
Ethylbenzene-d_{10}, 98+ atom % D
$C_6D_5C_2D_5$
M.W. 116.25 n_D^{20} 1.4920

A

E1250-8 **Ethylbenzene**
$C_6H_5C_2H_5$ M.W. 106.17 n_D^{20} 1.4952

NEAT

B

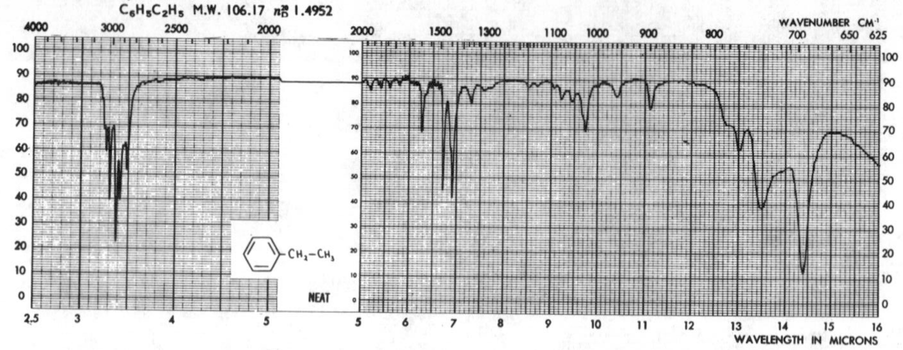

19,556-1
sec-**Butylbenzene-d_{14}**, 98 atom % D
$C_6D_5CD(CD_3)C_2D_5$ FW 148.34 bp 174°
n_D^{20} 1.4870 d 0.954 Disp. C

NEAT

C

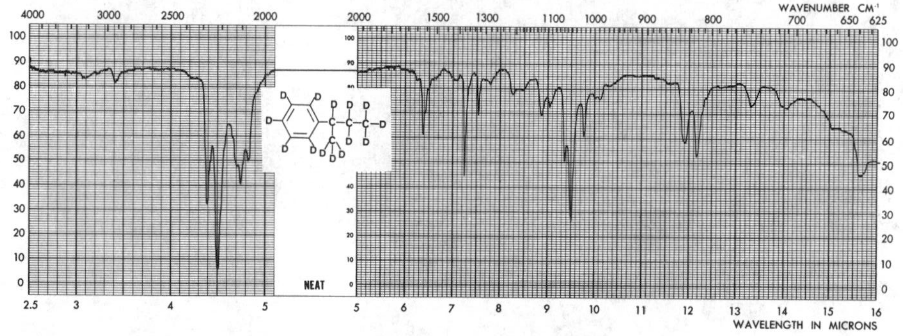

B9040-8 **sec.-Butylbenzene, puriss.**
$C_6H_5CH(CH_3)C_2H_5$ M.W. 134.22 n_D^{20} 1.4890
b.p. 173-174°

NEAT

D

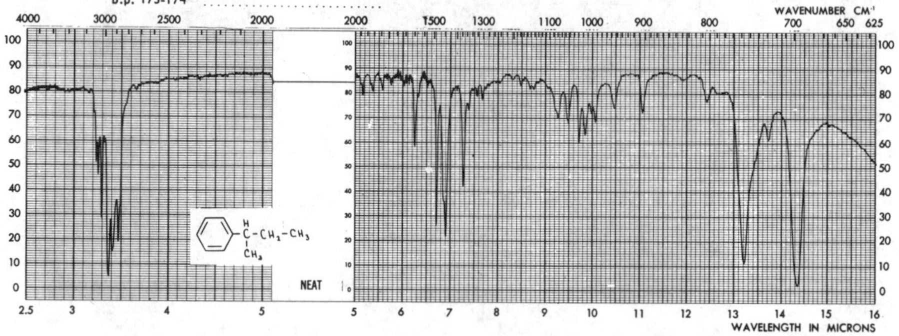

17,590-0
o-Xylene-d_{10}, 99+ atom % D, GOLD LABEL
$C_6D_4(CD_3)_2$
M.W. 116.25 n_D^{20} 1.5016

E

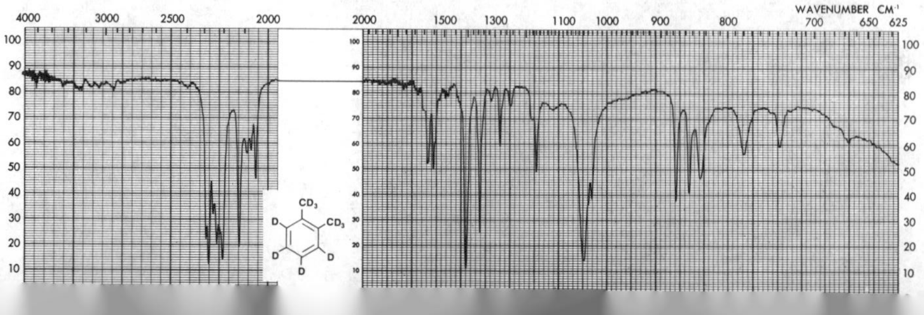

X104-0 **o-Xylene, 99+%**
$C_6H_4(CH_3)_2$ M.W. 106.17 n_D^{20} 1.5027 m.p. -25 to -23°
b.p. 143.5-144.5°

NEAT

F

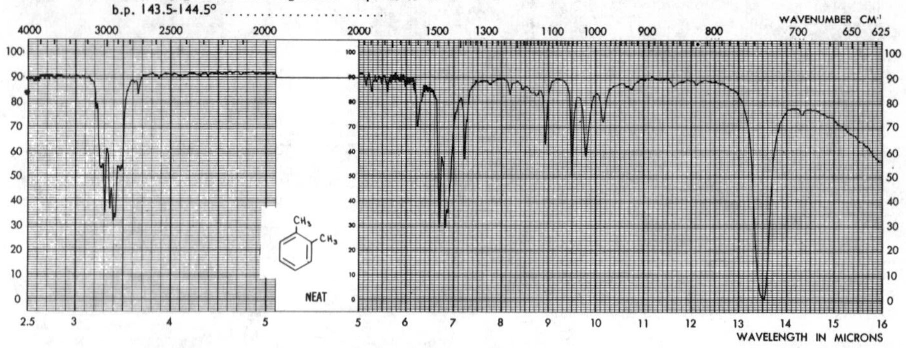

22,708-0 **1,2,3,4-Tetrahydronaphthlene-d_{12}**, 99 atom % D
M.W. 144.30 n_D^{20} 1.5383

NEAT

G

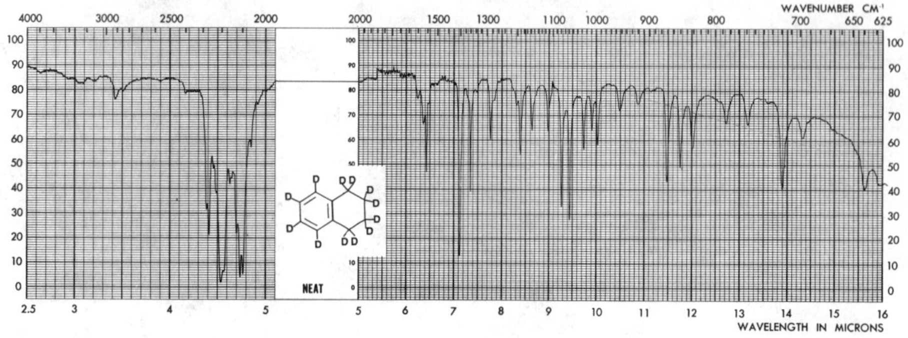

10,241-5 **1,2,3,4-Tetrahydronaphthalene**
$C_{10}H_{12}$ M.W. 132.21 n_D^{20} 1.5411 b.p. 207°

NEAT

H

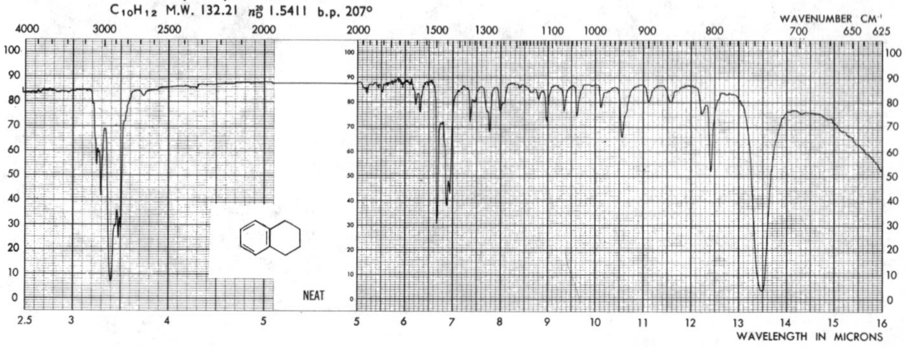

17,592-7
p-Xylene-d_{10}, 99+ atom % D, GOLD LABEL
$C_6D_4(CD_3)_2$
M.W. 116.25 n_D^{20} 1.4920

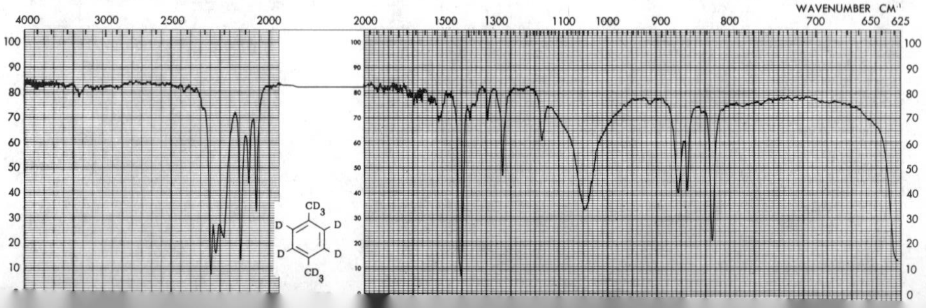

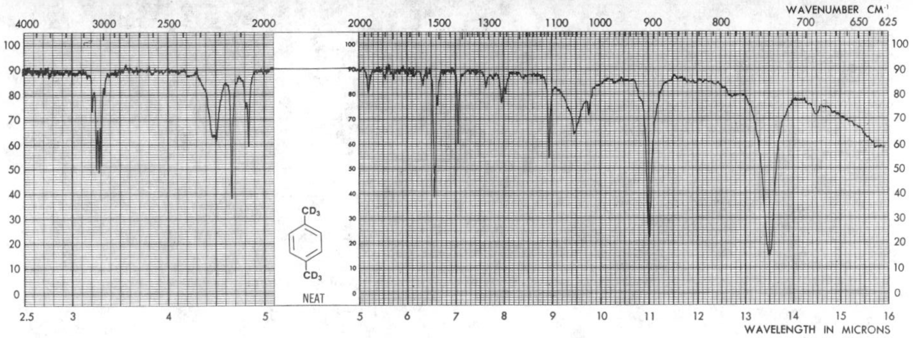

A

13,444-9 p-Xylene
$C_6H_4(CH_3)_2$ M.W. 106.17 n_D^{20} 1.4954 m.p. 12-13°
b.p. 138°

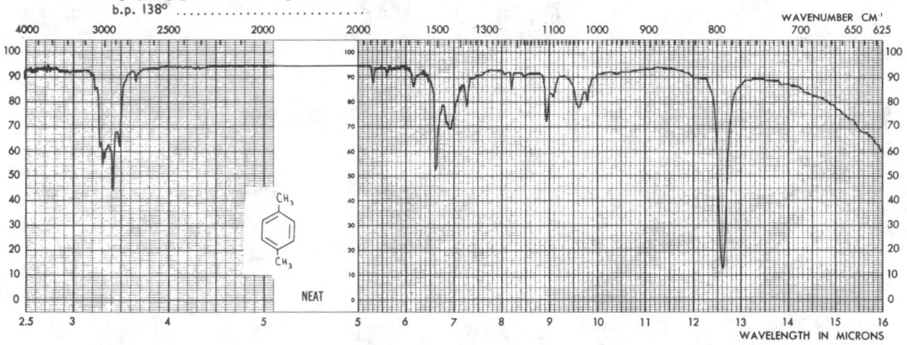

B

17,669-9
Styrene-d_8, 98+ atom % D
$C_6D_5CD{=}CD_2$
M.W. 112.22 n_D^{20} 1.5443

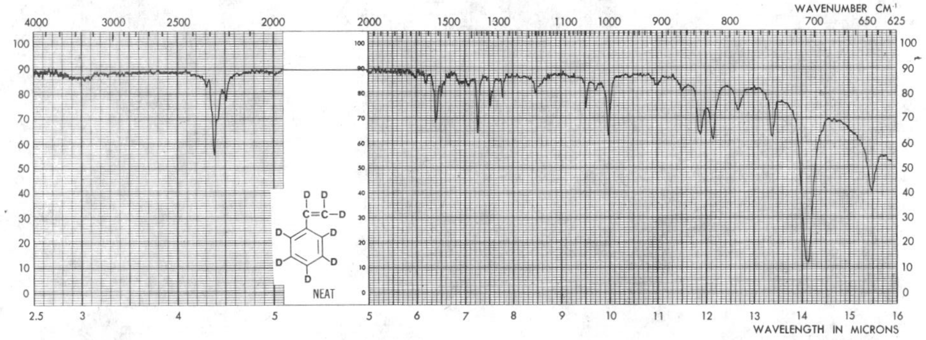

C

S497-2 Styrene
$C_6H_5CH{:}CH_2$ M.W. 104.15 n_D^{20} 1.5458
b.p. 145-146°

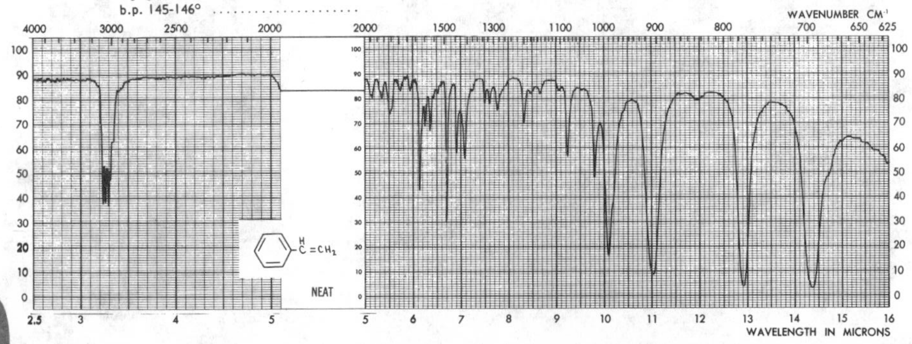

D

M.W. 136.24 m.p. 81-83°

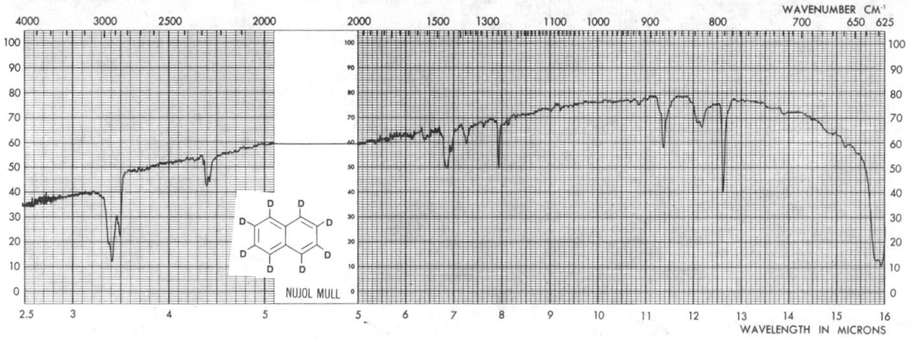

E

11,390-5 Naphthalene, zone refined
$C_{10}H_8$ M.W. 128.18 m.p. 80.20°

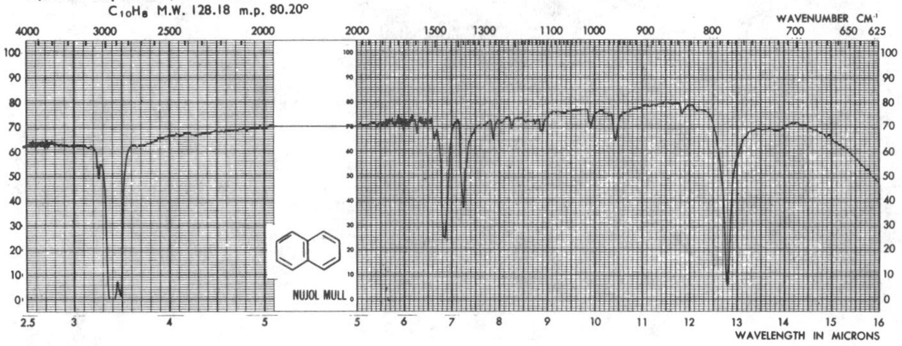

F

17,659-1
Anthracene-d_{10}, 98+ atom % D
M.W. 188.32 m.p. 208-210°

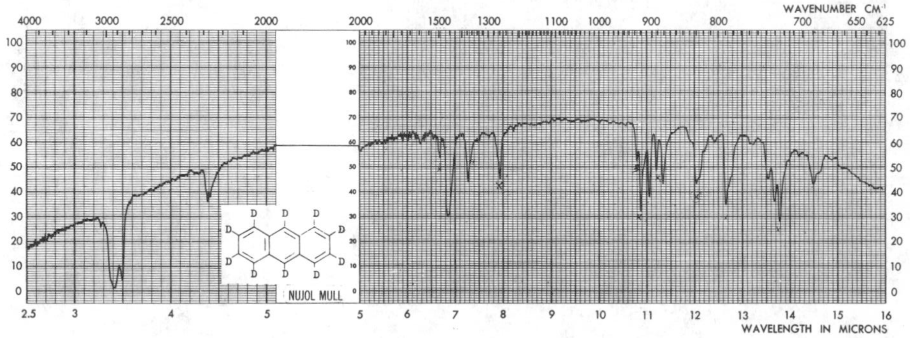

G

15,071-1 **Anthracene, zone refined, 99.9 %, GOLD LABEL**
M.W. 178.23 m.p. 215.62°

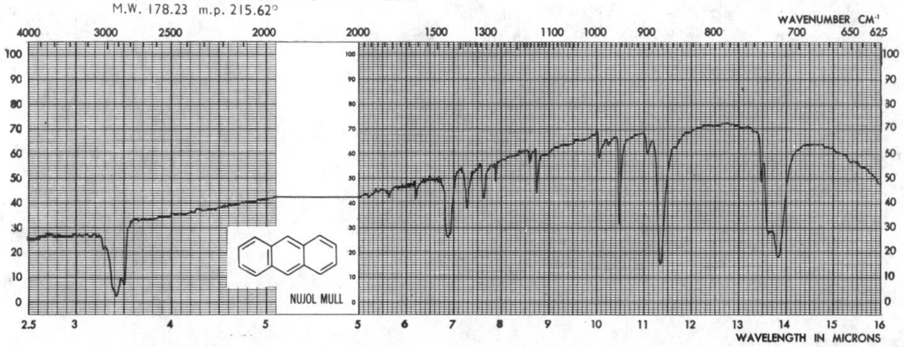

H

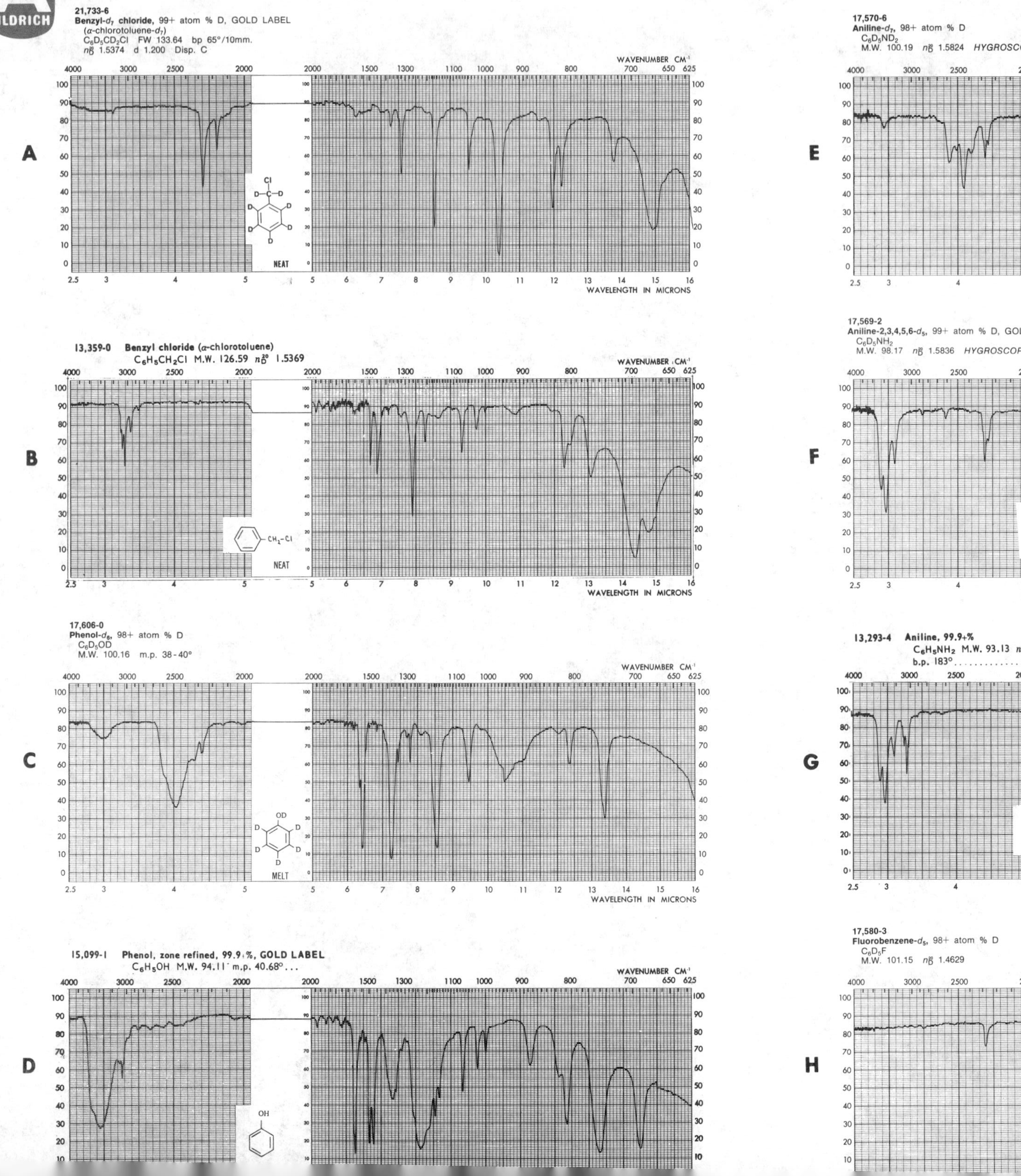

A
21,733-6
Benzyl-d_7 chloride, 99+ atom % D, GOLD LABEL
(α-chlorotoluene-d_7)
$C_6D_5CD_2Cl$ FW 133.64 bp 65°/10mm.
n_D^{20} 1.5374 d 1.200 Disp. C
NEAT
B
13,359-0 **Benzyl chloride** (α-chlorotoluene)
$C_6H_5CH_2Cl$ M.W. 126.59 n_D^{20} 1.5369
NEAT
C
17,606-0
Phenol-d_6, 98+ atom % D
C_6D_5OD
M.W. 100.16 m.p. 38-40°
MELT
D
15,099-1 **Phenol, zone refined, 99.9+%, GOLD LABEL**
C_6H_5OH M.W. 94.11 m.p. 40.68°...
E
17,570-6
Aniline-d_7, 98+ atom % D
$C_6D_5ND_2$
M.W. 100.19 n_D^{20} 1.5824 HYGROSCOPIC
NEAT
F
17,569-2
Aniline-2,3,4,5,6-d_5, 99+ atom % D, GOLD LABEL
$C_6D_5NH_2$
M.W. 98.17 n_D^{20} 1.5836 HYGROSCOPIC
NEAT
G
13,293-4 **Aniline, 99.9+%**
$C_6H_5NH_2$ M.W. 93.13 n_D^{20} 1.5855
b.p. 183°
NEAT
H
17,580-3
Fluorobenzene-d_5, 98+ atom % D
C_6D_5F
M.W. 101.15 n_D^{20} 1.4629
WAVENUMBER CM⁻¹
WAVELENGTH IN MICRONS

n_D^{20} 1.4653 ....

A

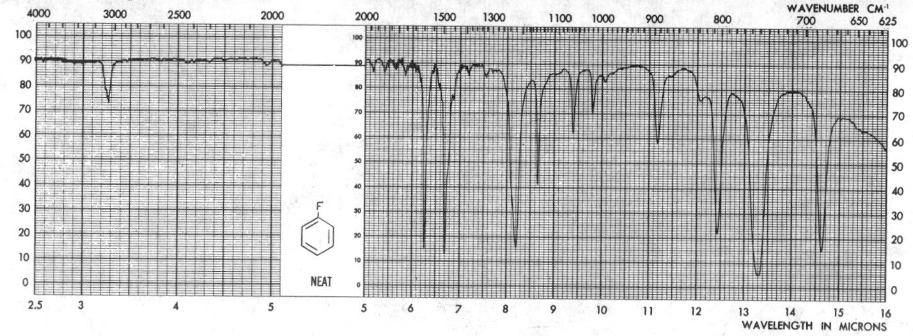

NEAT

17,660-5
Chlorobenzene-d_5, 99+ atom % D, GOLD LABEL
C_6D_5Cl
M.W. 117.6 n_D^{20} 1.5220

B

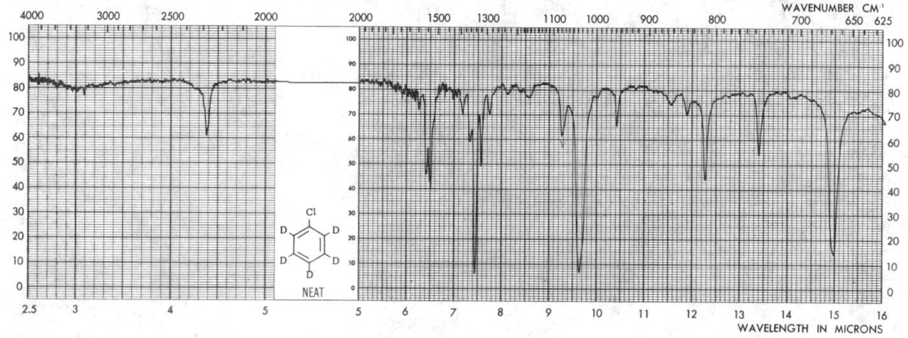

NEAT

10,138-9 **Chlorobenzene**
C_6H_5Cl M.W. 112.56 n_D^{20} 1.5236
b.p. 132° ....

C

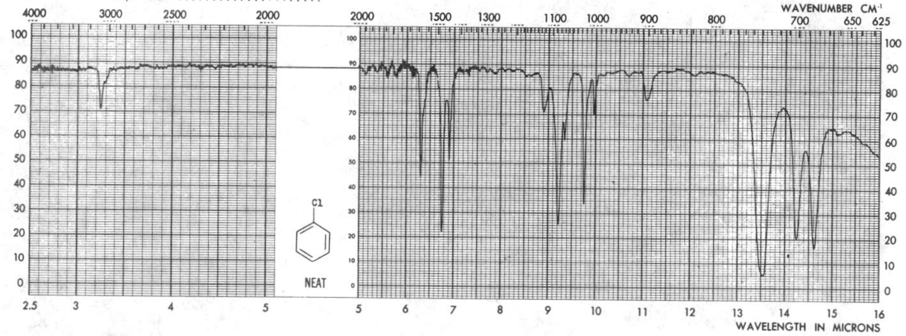

NEAT

17,573-0
Bromobenzene-d_5, 99+ atom % D, GOLD LABEL
C_6D_5Br
M.W. 162.06 n_D^{20} 1.5568

D

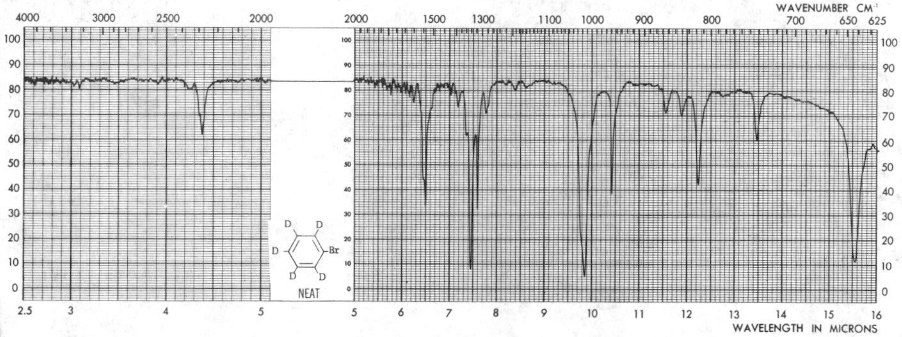

NEAT

Bromobenzene
C_6H_5Br M.W. 157.02 n_D^{20} 1.5580

E

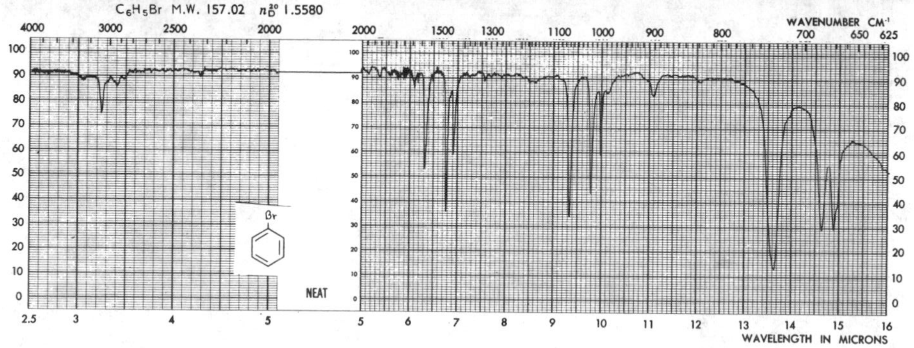

NEAT

15,195-5 **Nitrobenzene-d_5, 99%**
$C_6D_5NO_2$ M.W. 128.15

F

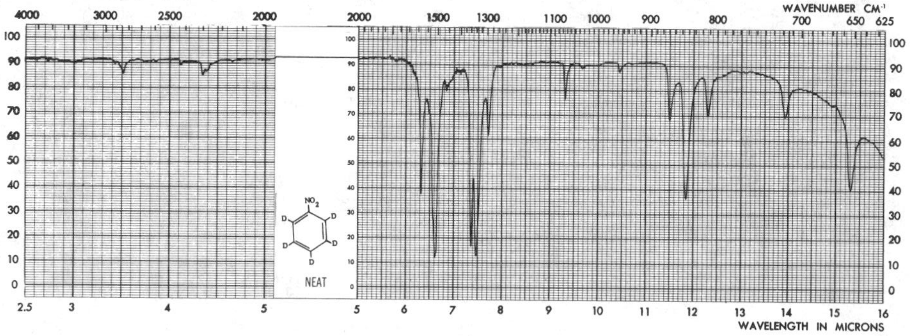

NEAT

N1095-0 **Nitrobenzene**
$C_6H_5NO_2$ M.W. 123.11 n_D^{20} 1.5513 m.p. 5-6°

G

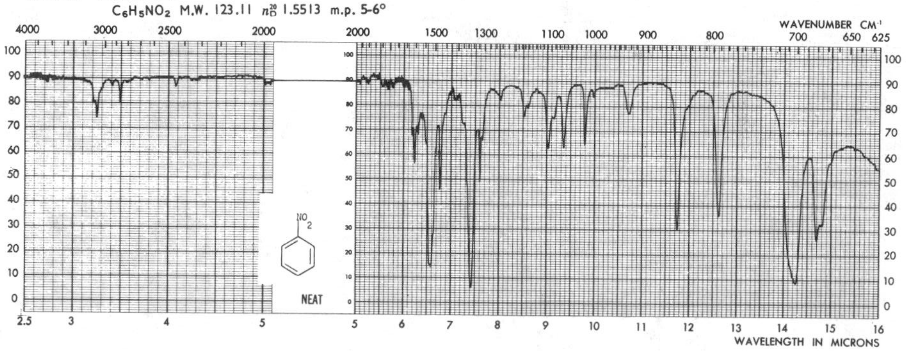

NEAT

17,605-2
1-Nitronaphthalene-d_7
$C_{10}D_7NO_2$
M.W. 180.23 m.p. 58-60°

H

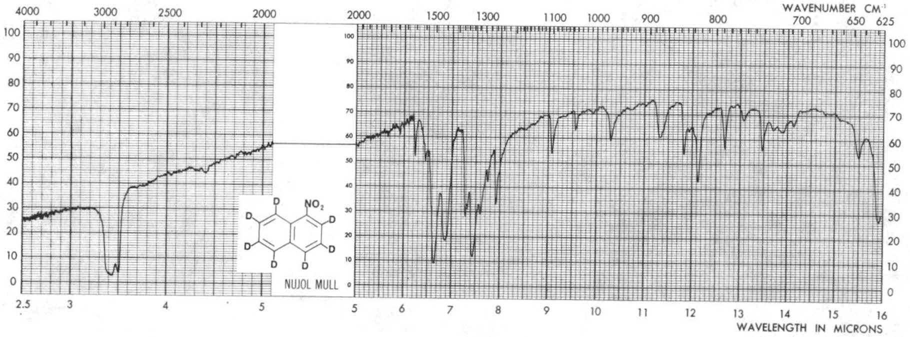

NUJOL MULL

ALDRICH

A

10,359-4 **1-Nitronaphthalene**
$C_{10}H_7NO_2$ M.W. 173.17 m.p. 55-56°

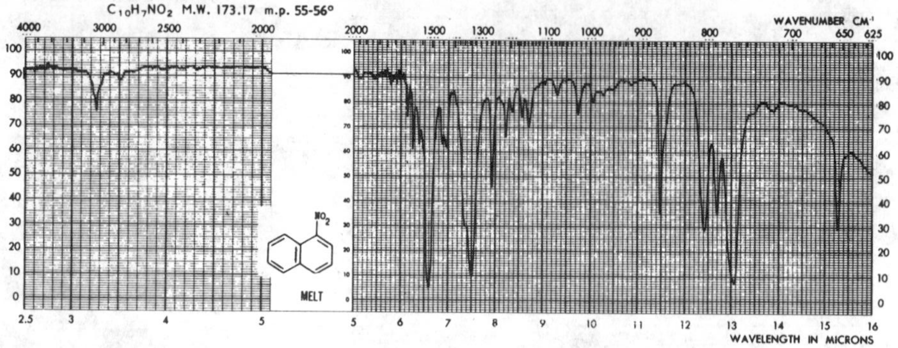

MELT

B

21,715-8
Benzoic-d_5 acid, 99+ atom % D, GOLD LABEL
$C_6D_5CO_2H$ FW 127.17 mp 120-122° Disp. I

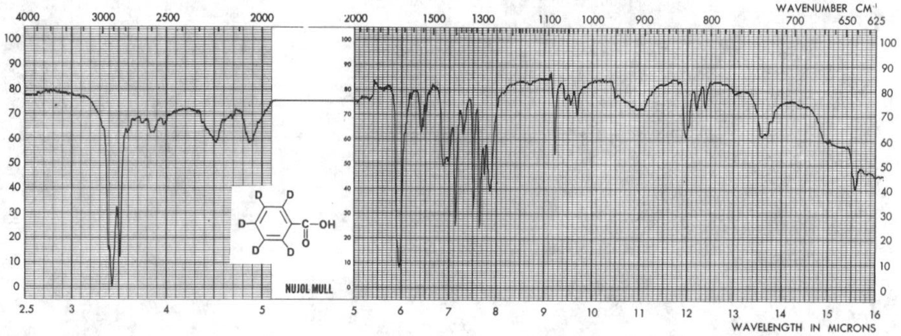

NUJOL MULL

C

10,420-5 **Benzoic acid, zone refined**
$C_6H_5CO_2H$ M.W. 122.12 m.p. 122.39°

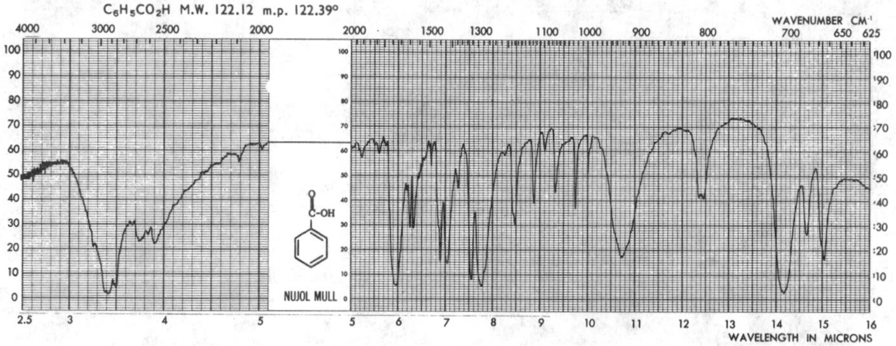

NUJOL MULL

D

19,555-3
Terephthalic-d_4 acid, 98 atom % D
C_6D_4-1,4-$(CO_2H)_2$ FW 170.17 mp >300°
Fieser 7,81 Disp. C

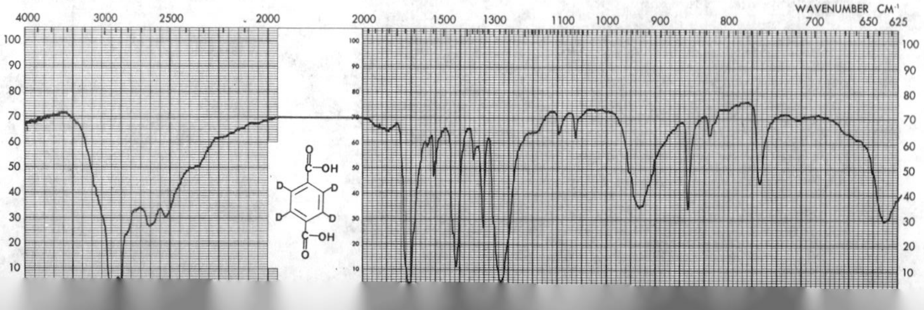

E

T230-4 **Terephthalic acid**
C_6H_4-1,4-$(CO_2H)_2$ M.W. 166.13
m.p. > 320°

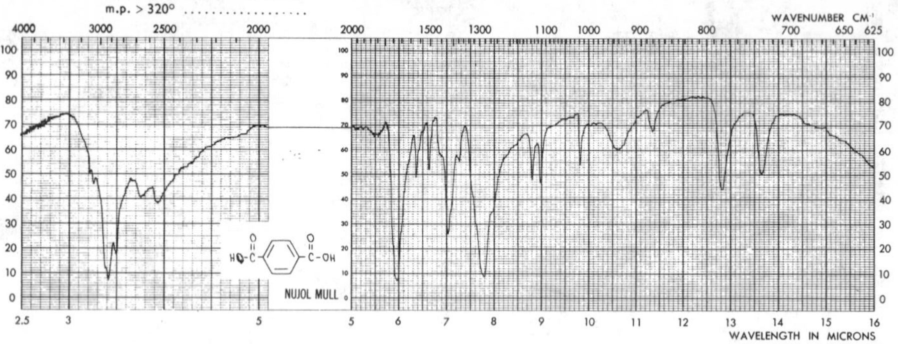

NUJOL MULL

F

16,485-2
(Methyl-d_3)-triphenylphosphonium bromide, 99+ atom % D, GOLD LABEL
$CD_3P(C_6H_5)_3Br$
M.W. 360.26 m.p. 230-232°

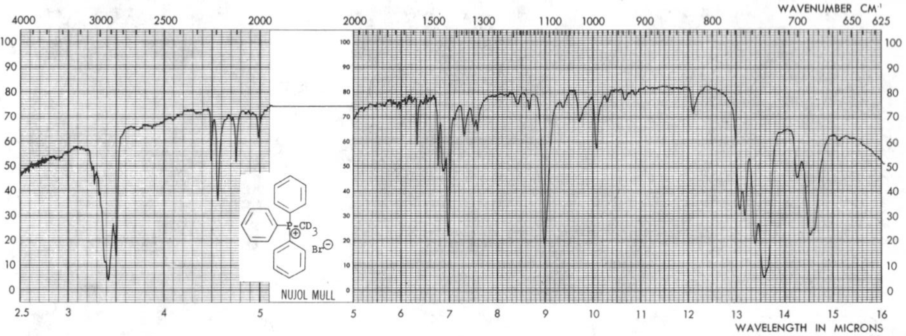

NUJOL MULL

G

13,007-9 **(Methyl)-triphenylphosphonium bromide**
$CH_3P(C_6H_5)_3Br$ M.W. 357.24
m.p. 230-233°

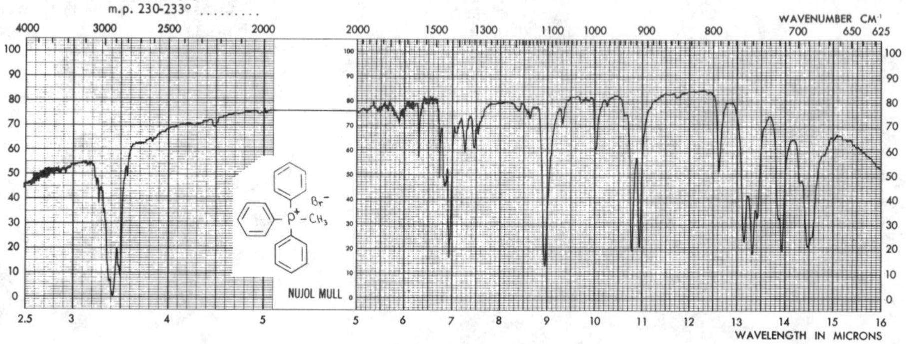

NUJOL MULL

H

15,232-3 **Pyridine-d_5, 99%**
M.W. 84.14

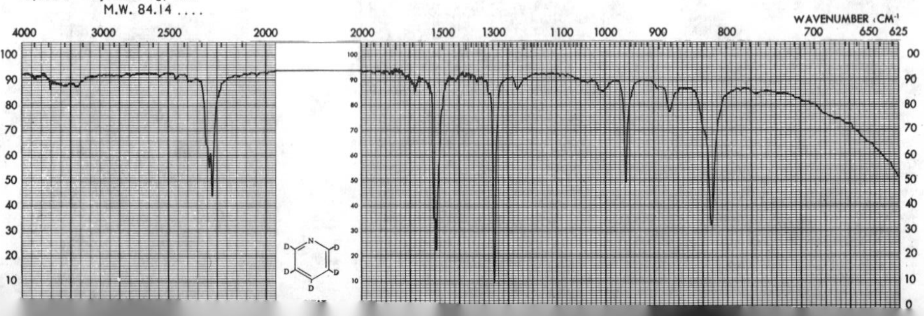

M.W. 79.10 n_D^{20} 1.5075 b.p. 115.2° ....

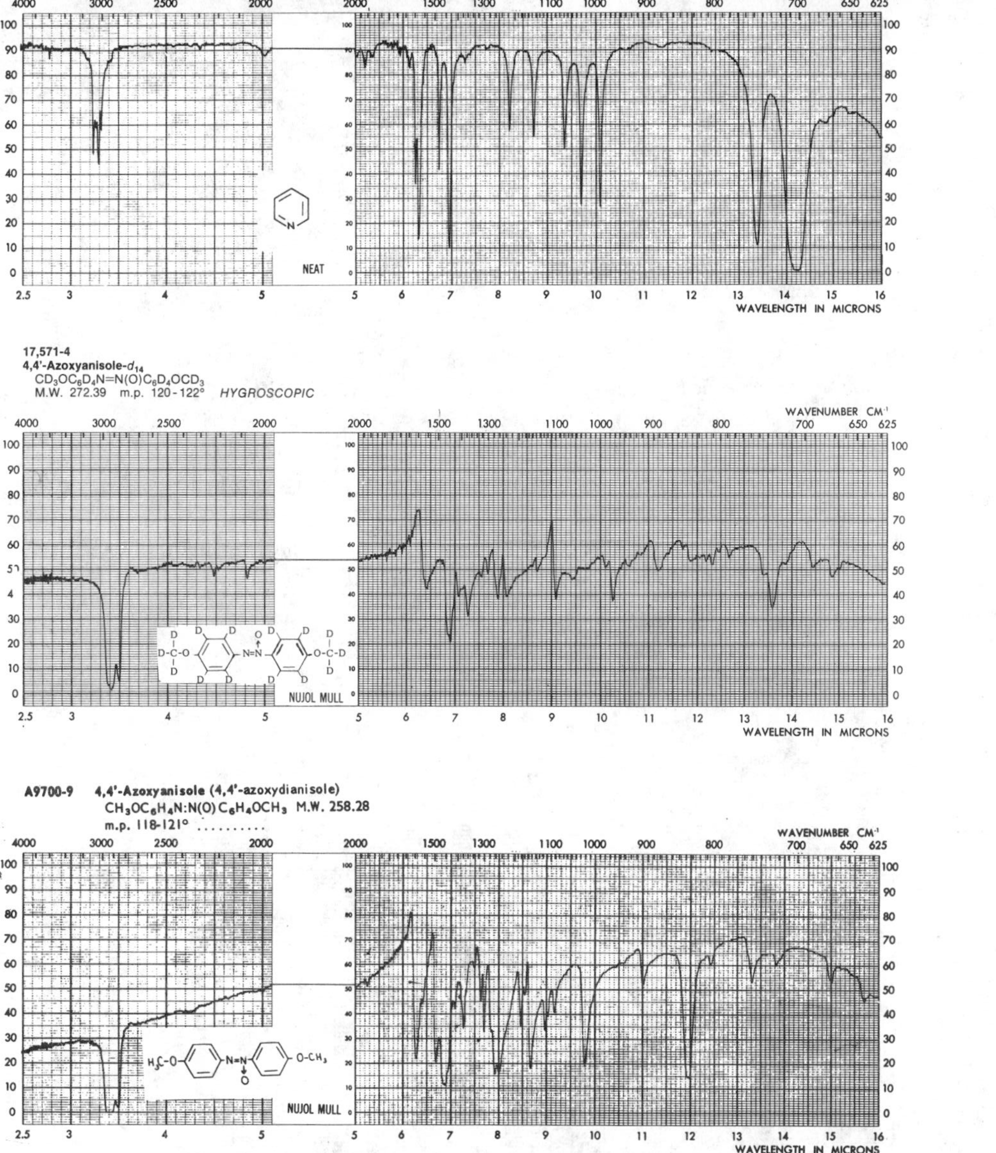

17,571-4
4,4'-Azoxyanisole-d_{14}
$CD_3OC_6D_4N{=}N(O)C_6D_4OCD_3$
M.W. 272.39 m.p. 120-122° *HYGROSCOPIC*

A9700-9 4,4'-Azoxyanisole (4,4'-azoxydianisole)
$CH_3OC_6H_4N{:}N(O)C_6H_4OCH_3$ M.W. 258.28
m.p. 118-121° ....

19,002-0
Sodium cyanoborodeuteride, 98 atom % D
$NaBD_3CN$ FW 65.87 mp >242° (dec.) Disp. C

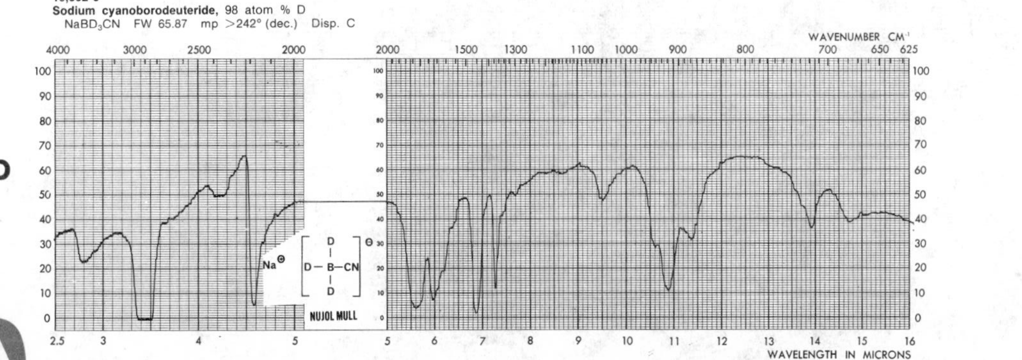

$NaBH_3CN$ M.W. 62.84

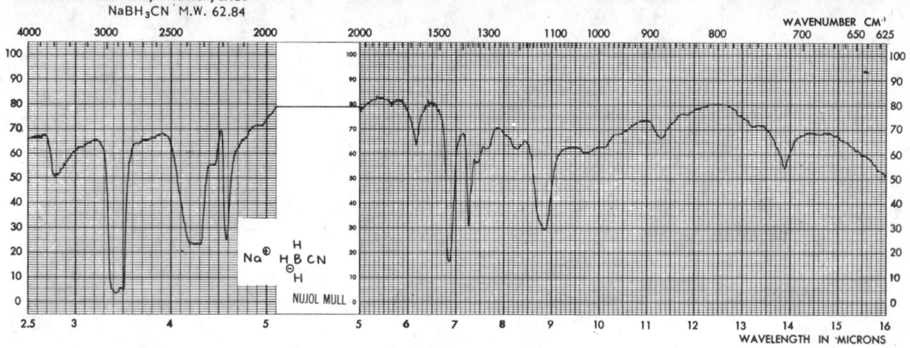

20,559-1
Sodium borodeuteride, 98 atom % D
$NaBD_4$ FW 41.87 mp >300° *Fieser* 3,281
Disp. Y

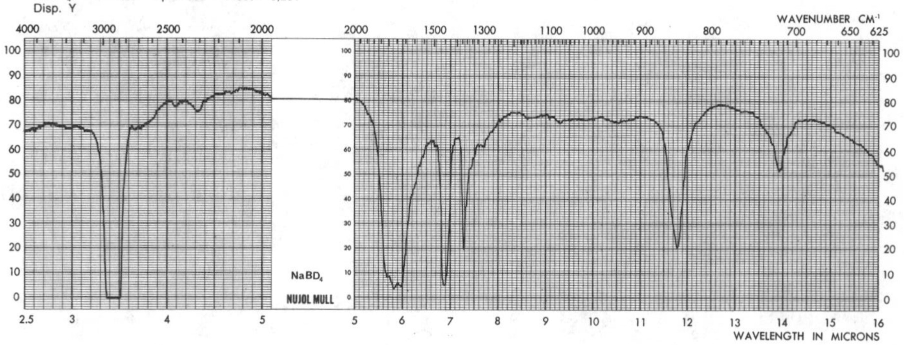

19,807-2
Sodium borohydride, powder, 98+% (sodium tetrahydridoborate)
$NaBH_4$ FW 37.83 mp >300° *Fieser* 1,1049
2,377 3,262 4,443 5,597 6,530 7,329 Disp. Y

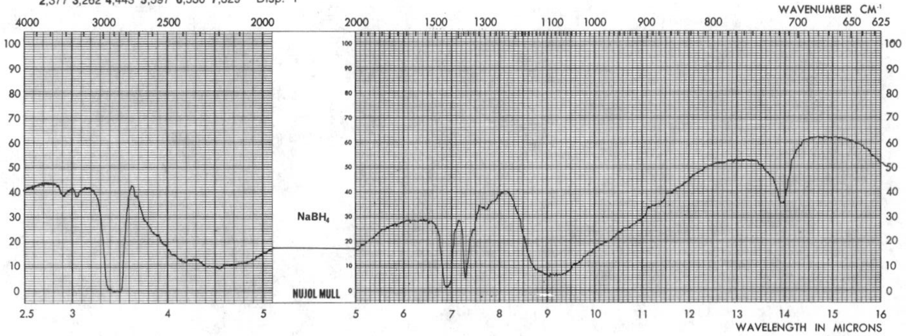

DEUTERATED

SILANES

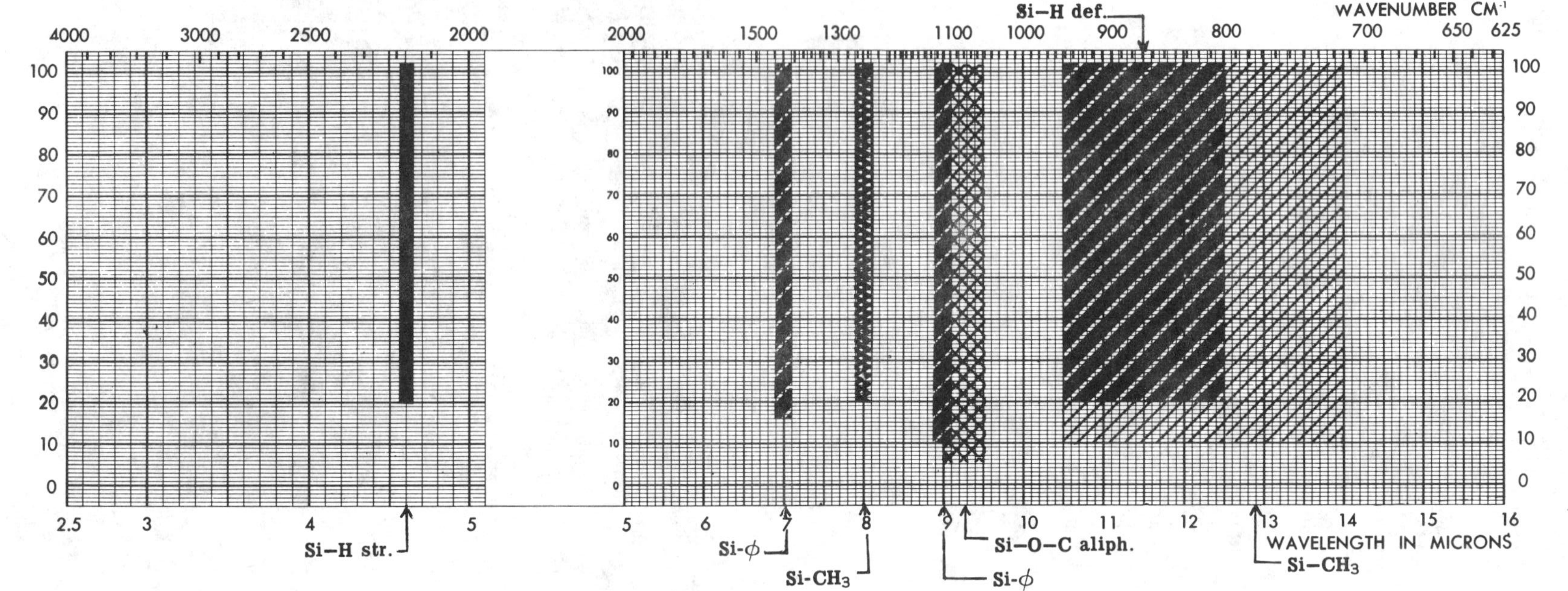

The Si–C (aromatic) group displays bands typified in spectra 1544G—1545B. The positioning of the two bands very close to 7 and 9μ (1430 and 1110 cm^{-1}) is quite characteristic. The band at 8 μ (1250 cm^{-1}) is due to the aliphatic Si–CH_3 group and is accompanied by bands between 11 and 14 μ (910 and 715 cm^{-1}).

The Si–H stretch vibration appears as a strong band near 4.7 μ (2130 cm^{-1}) along with its deformation bands between 10.5 and 12.5 μ (950 – 800 cm^{-1}).

The Si–O–C (aliphatic) group absorbs very strongly in the vicinity of 9 – 9.5 μ (1110 – 1050 cm^{-1}).

The Si–Cl, Si–Cl_2 and Si–Cl_3 groups absorb beyond the 16 μ (625 cm^{-1}) region. Due to the extreme reactivity of this group with moisture, it is difficult to avoid partial hydrolysis. A broad absorption between 9 and 10 μ (1110 – 1000 cm^{-1}) can be observed which is a result of some Si–O–Si formation. (See spectra 1540A—H).

A 10,490-6 **Dimethoxydimethylsilane**
$(CH_3O)_2Si(CH_3)_2$ M.W. 120.22 n_D^{20} 1.3715 b.p. 82°

CH_3–Si(CH_3)(OCH_3)–OCH_3 NEAT

B 10,475-2 **Methyltrimethoxysilane**
$CH_3Si(OCH_3)_3$ M.W. 136.22 n_D^{20} 1.3679 b.p. 103°

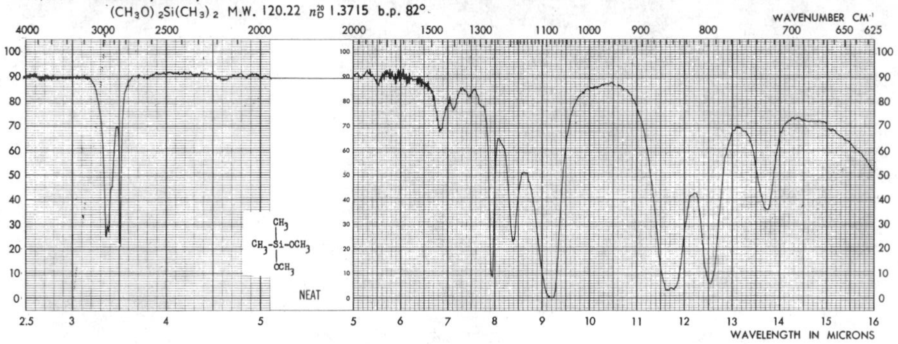

CH_3–Si(OCH_3)(OCH_3)–OCH_3 NEAT

C 21,847-2
Tetramethyl orthosilicate, 99%
$Si(OCH_3)_4$ FW 152.22 mp -4° bp 121-122°
n_D^{20} 1.3680 d 1.023 *Beil.* 1,287 Disp. C

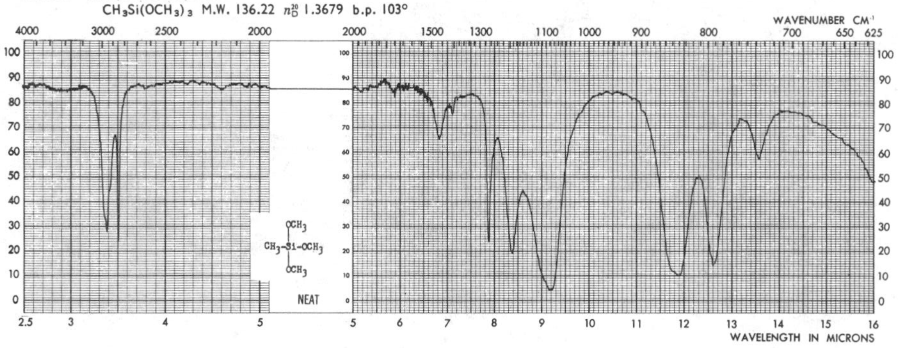

H_3CO–Si(OCH_3)(OCH_3)–OCH_3 NEAT

D 17,561-7
(3-Mercaptopropyl)-trimethoxysilane
$HSCH_2CH_2CH_2Si(OCH_3)_3$
M.W. 196.34 n_D^{20} 1.4416 *IRRITANT*

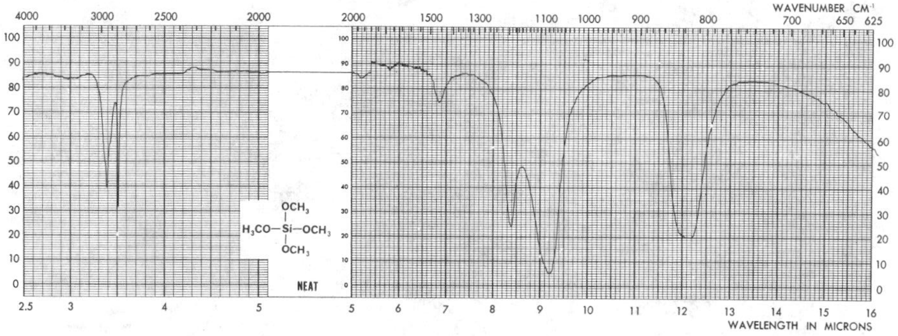

CH_3O–Si(OCH_3)(OCH_3)–$CH_2CH_2CH_2SH$ NEAT

E $(CH_3)_2Si(OC_2H_5)_2$
M.W. 148.28 b.p. 114° n_D^{20} 1.3811 d 0.865

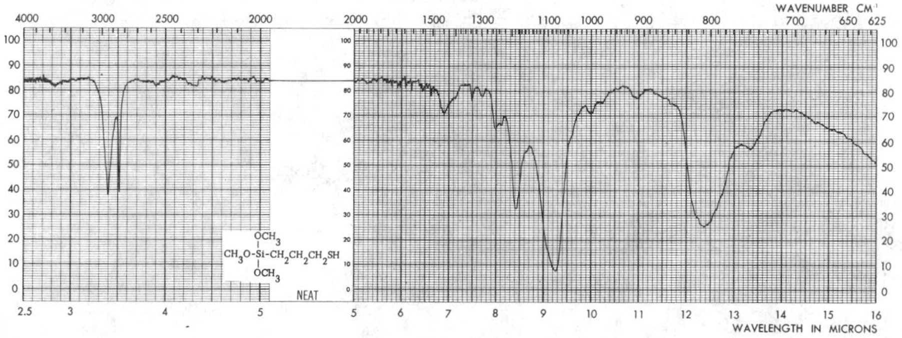

CH_3CH_2O–Si(CH_3)(CH_3)–OCH_2CH_3 NEAT

F 17,557-9
Methyltriethoxysilane, 98%
$CH_3Si(OC_2H_5)_3$
M.W. 178.3 b.p. 141-143° n_D^{20} 1.3845 d 0.895
Beil. 4,629 *IRRITANT*

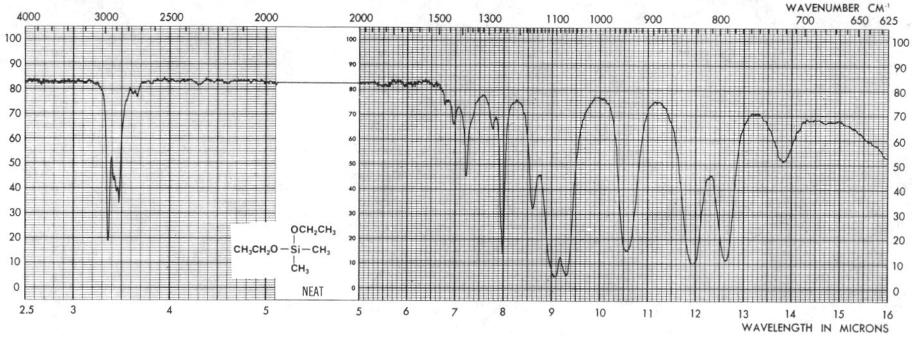

CH_3–Si(OC_2H_5)(OC_2H_5)–OC_2H_5 NEAT

G 14,849-0 **Triethoxysilane**
$(C_2H_5O)_3SiH$ M.W. 164.28 n_D^{20} 1.3762

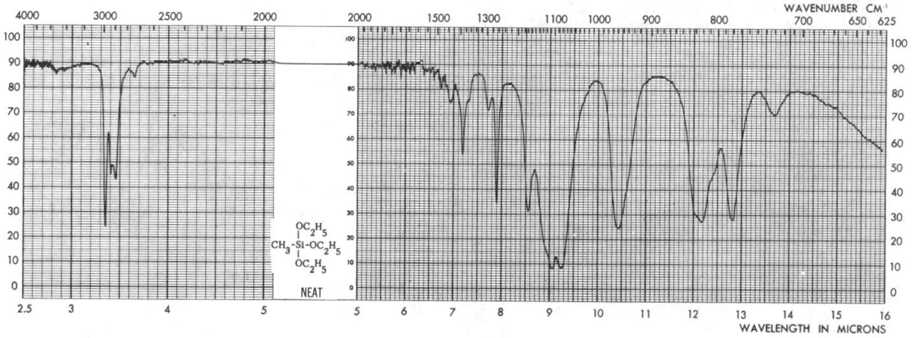

C_2H_5O–SiH(OC_2H_5)–OC_2H_5 NEAT

H 13,190-3 **Tetraethyl orthosilicate**
$Si(OC_2H_5)_4$ M.W. 208.33 n_D^{20} 1.3825

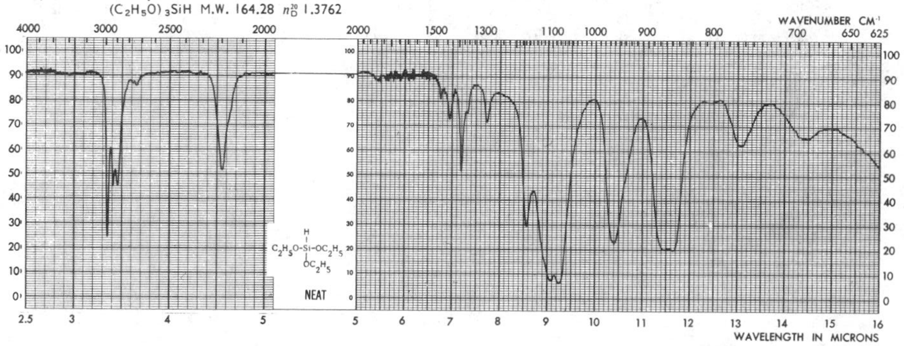

H_5C_2–O–Si(OC_2H_5)(OC_2H_5)–O–C_2H_5 NEAT

WAVENUMBER CM⁻¹ 4000 3000 2500 2000 1500 1300 1100 1000 900 800 700 650 625
WAVELENGTH IN MICRONS 2.5 3 4 5 6 7 8 9 10 11 12 13 14 15 16

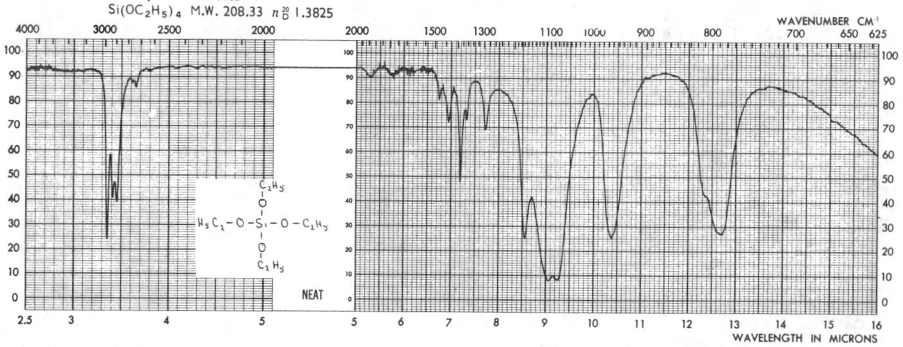

ALDRICH ®

A

T570 **Tetrabutyl orthosilicate**
$Si(OC_4H_9)_4$ M.W. 320.55 n_D^{20} 1.4132

NEAT

B

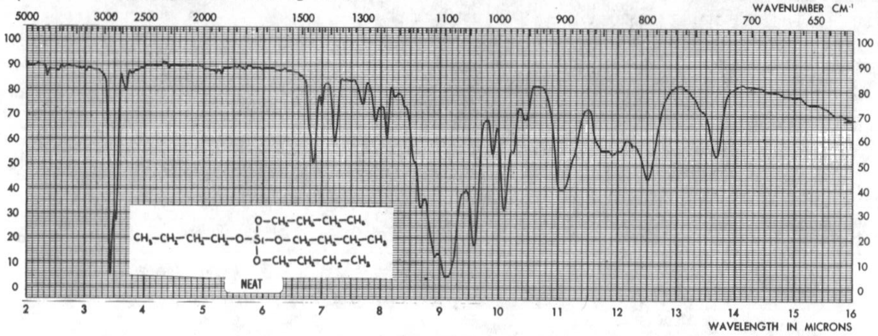

T1190 **Tetrahexyl orthosilicate**
$Si(OC_6H_{13})_4$ M.W. 432.77 n_D^{20} 1.4281

NEAT

C

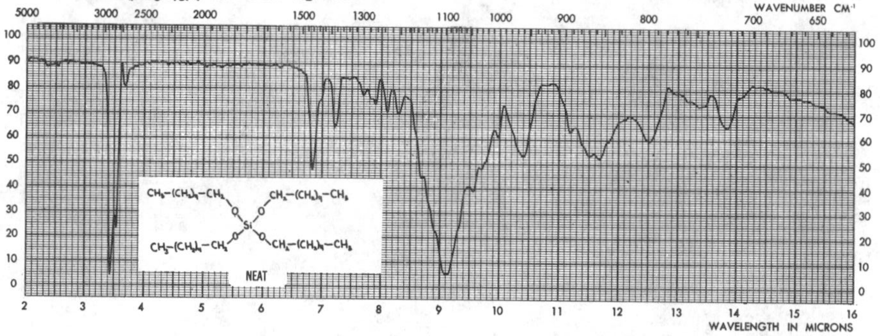

T2510 **Tetraoctyl orthosilicate**
$Si(OC_8H_{17})_4$ M.W. 544.98 n_D^{20} 1.4380

NEAT

D

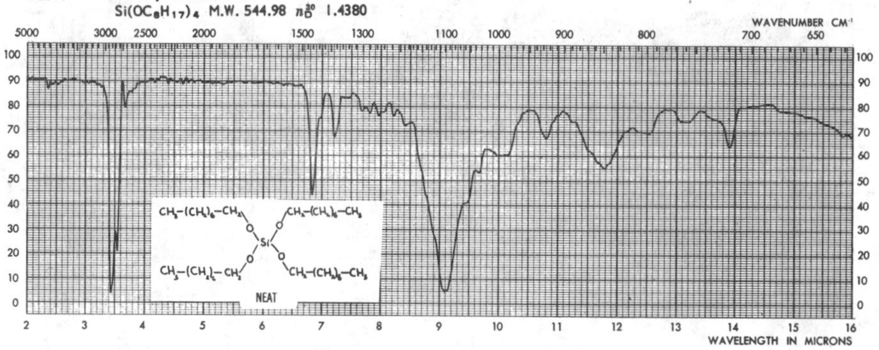

17,620-6
Polymethylhydrosiloxane (PMHS)
$(CH_3)_3SiO[(CH_3)HSiO]xSi(CH_3)_3$
n_D^{20} 1.3979

$(CH_3)_3SiO[(CH_3)HSiO]_xSi(CH_3)_3$ (x~35)

E

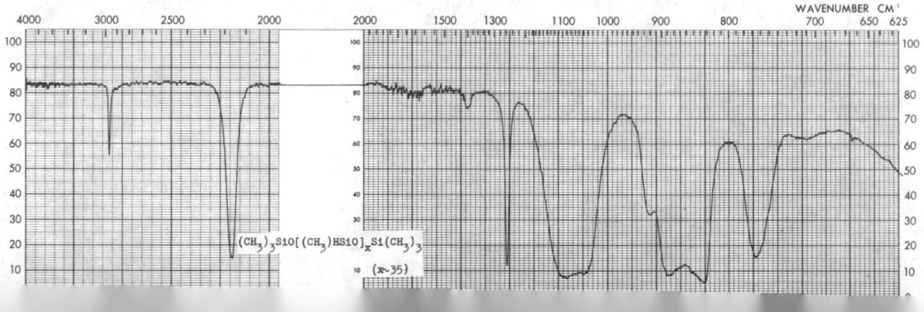

14,615-3 **Silicone oil (for melting point and boiling point apparatus)**
n_D^{20} 1.4040

NEAT

F

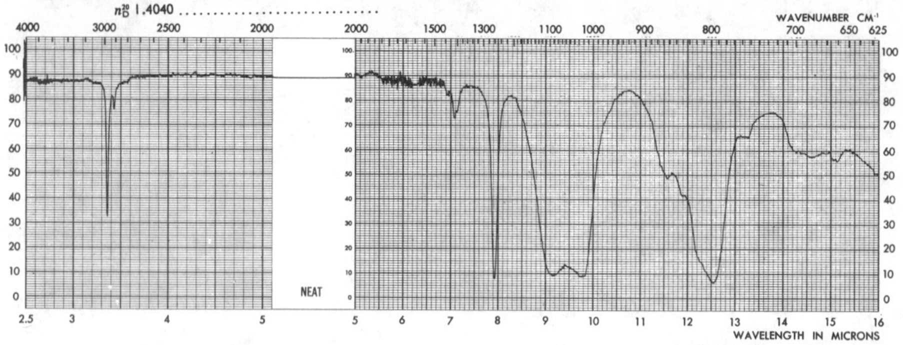

17,563-3
Silicone oil, high temperature
n_D^{20} 1.5040 d 1.019 *CORROSIVE*

NEAT

G

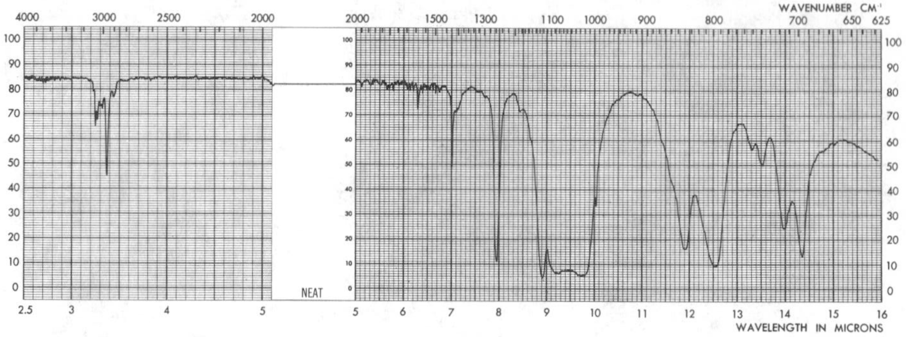

T890 **Tetracyclohexyl orthosilicate**
$Si(OC_6H_{11})_4$ M.W. 424.70 m.p. 83-89°

NUJOL MULL

H

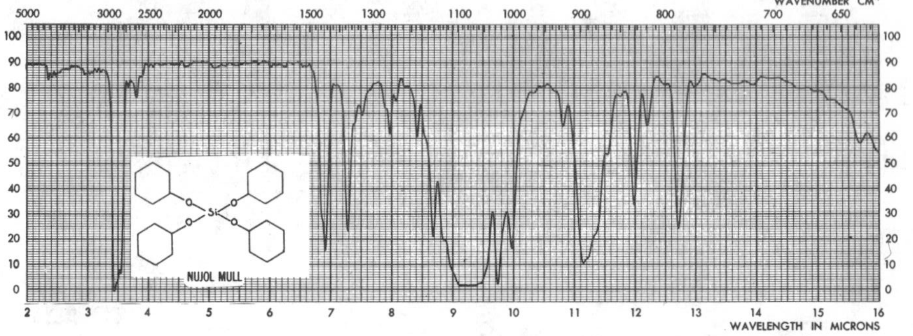

17,556-0
Triethoxyvinylsilane, 99%
$H_2C{=}CHSi(OC_2H_5)_3$
M.W. 190.32 b.p. 160-161° n_D^{20} 1.3978 d 0.903
IRRITANT

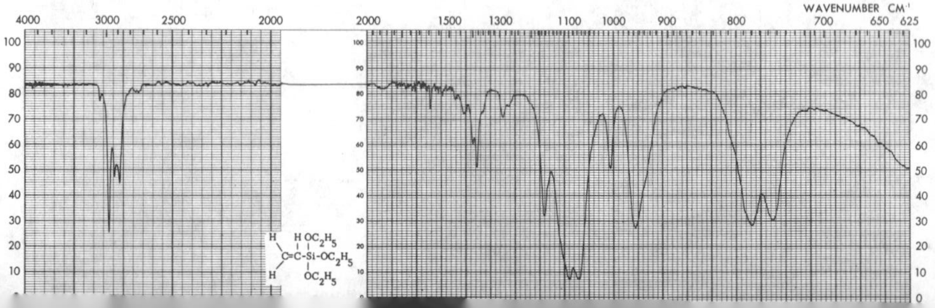

A

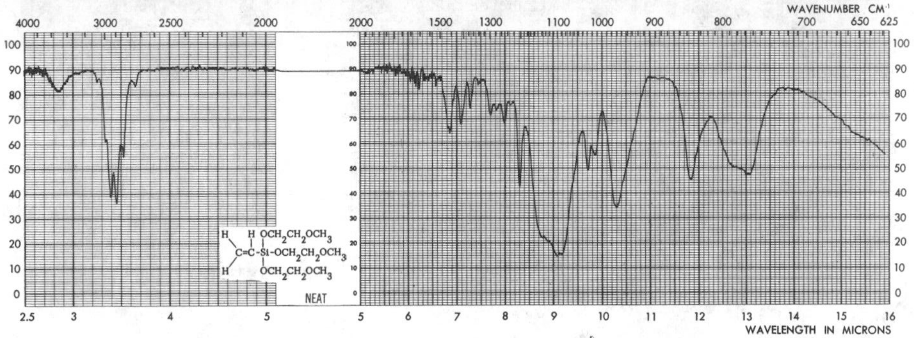

$H_2C{=}C(H)$–Si$(OCH_2CH_2OCH_3)_3$

NEAT

A3630-1 Allyltriethoxysilane
$H_2C{:}CHCH_2Si(OC_2H_5)_3$ M.W. 204.34
n_D^{20} 1.4059

B

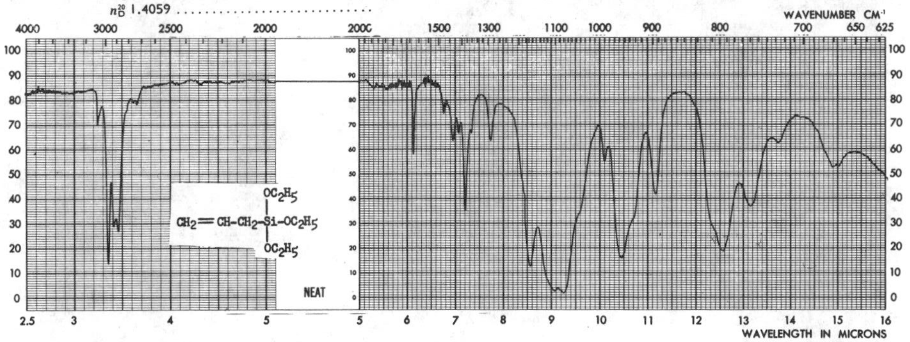

$CH_2{=}CH{-}CH_2{-}Si(OC_2H_5)_3$

NEAT

T6762 Triisopropoxyvinylsilane
$H_2C{:}CHSi[OCH(CH_3)_2]_3$ M.W. 232.40
n_D^{20} 1.3981

C

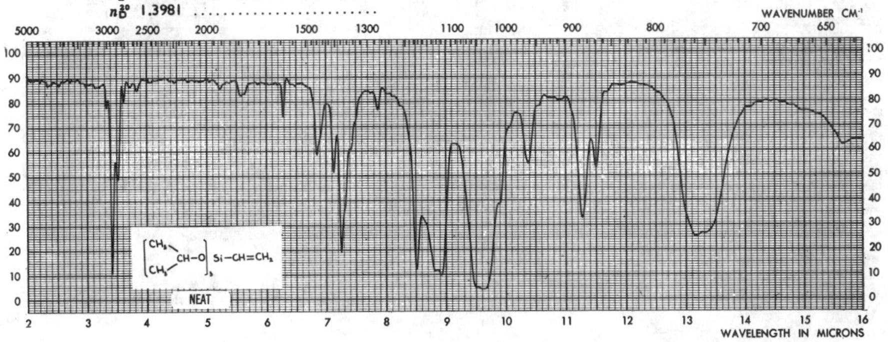

$[(CH_3)_2CH{-}O]_3Si{-}CH{=}CH_2$

NEAT

E930-7 Ethoxytriallylsilane
$(H_2C{:}CHCH_2)_3SiOC_2H_5$ M.W. 196.37
n_D^{20} 1.4540

D

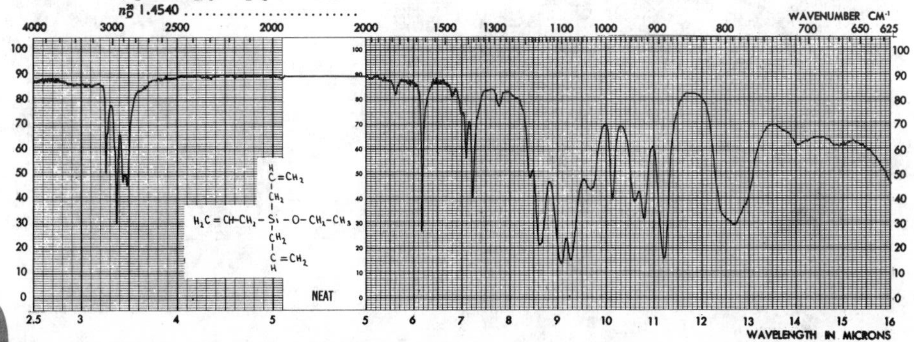

$(H_2C{=}CH{-}CH_2)_3Si{-}O{-}CH_2{-}CH_3$

NEAT

E

$N{\equiv}C{-}CH_2{-}CH_2{-}Si(O{-}C_2H_5)_3$

NEAT

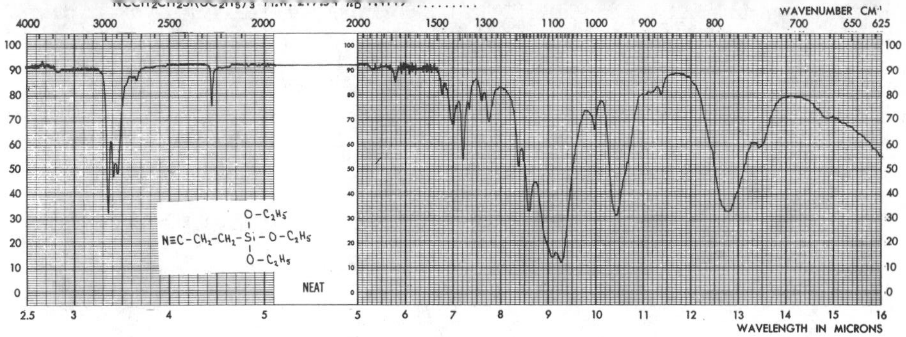

10,492-2 Triacetoxyvinylsilane
$(CH_3CO_2)_3SiCH{:}CH_2$ M.W. 232.26 n_D^{20} 1.4205
b.p. 115°/10 mm.

F

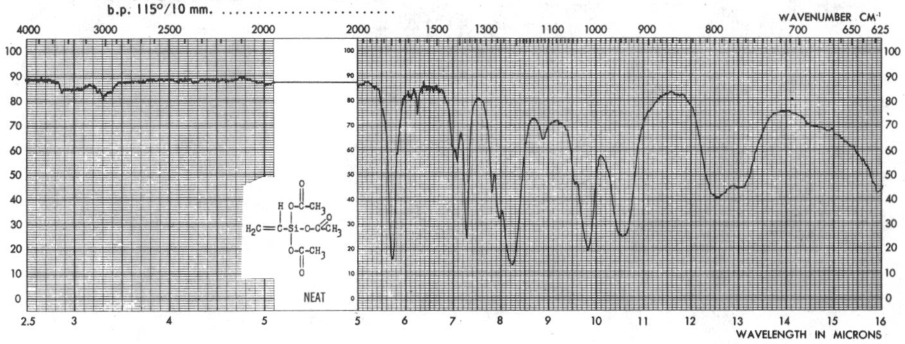

$H_2C{=}C(H){-}Si(O{-}C(=O){-}CH_3)_3$

NEAT

14,481-9
1-Cyclohexenyloxytrimethylsilane, 97%
$C_6H_9OSi(CH_3)_3$
M.W. 170.33 b.p. 64-65°/15mm. n_D^{20} 1.4469

G

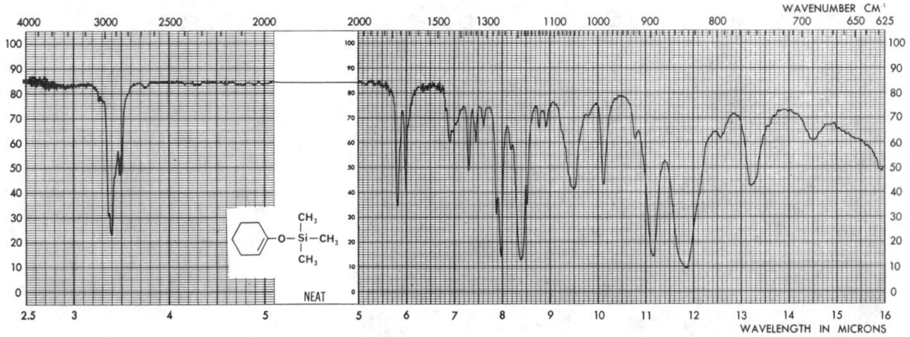

$C_6H_9{-}O{-}Si(CH_3)_3$

NEAT

12,891-0 Bis-(trimethylsilyl)-acetamide (BSA)
$CH_3C[{:}NSi(CH_3)_3]OSi(CH_3)_3$ M.W. 203.43 n_D^{20} 1.4181
b.p. 71-73°/35 mm.

H

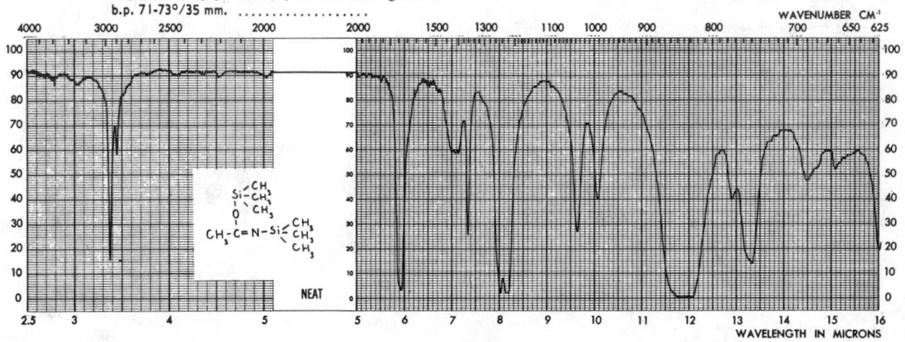

$CH_3{-}C(O{-}Si(CH_3)_3){=}N{-}Si(CH_3)_3$

NEAT

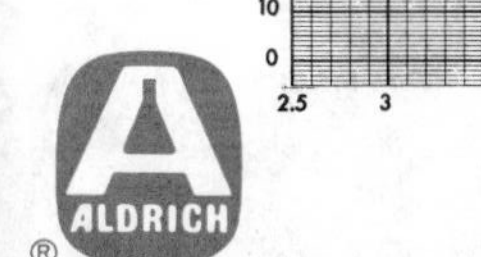

A 15,519-5 **Bis-(trimethylsilyl)-trifluoroacetamide (BSTFA)**
$CF_3C[:NSi(CH_3)_3]OSi(CH_3)_3$ M.W. 257.41 n_D^{20} 1.3839
b.p. 45-50 14 mm.

B T2400-7 **Tetramethylsilane** (NMR grade, 99.9% min.)
$Si(CH_3)_4$ M.W. 88.23 n_D^{20} 1.3571
b.p. 26-28°

C 21,706-9
Hexamethyldisilane, 95%
$(CH_3)_3SiSi(CH_3)_3$ FW 146.38 bp 112-114°
n_D^{20} 1.4221 d 0.715 *Beil.* **4**(1),582 Disp. C

D 20,535-4
Chloromethyltrimethylsilane, 99%
$(CH_3)_3SiCH_2Cl$ FW 122.67 bp 98-99° n_D^{20} 1.4175
d 0.879 *Beil.* **4**(3),1844 Disp. T

E 22,014-0
(Dichloromethyl)trimethylsilane, 97%
$(CH_3)_3SiCHCl_2$ FW 157.12 bp 133°/730mm.
n_D^{20} 1.4455 d 1.040 *Beil.* **4**(3),1846 Disp. C

F 22,106-6
Bis(chloromethyl)dimethylsilane, 95%
$(CH_3)_2Si(CH_2Cl)_2$ FW 157.12 bp 159-160°
n_D^{20} 1.4600 d 1.075 *Beil.* **4**(3),1845 Disp. C

G 22,030-2
(Iodomethyl)trimethylsilane, 99%
$(CH_3)_3SiCH_2I$ FW 214.12 bp 139-141°
n_D^{20} 1.4916 d 1.443 *Beil.* **4**(3),1845 Disp. C

H 17,555-2
Trichlorosilane, 95%
$SiHCl_3$
M.W. 135.45 b.p. 31-32° d 1.342 *CORROSIVE*

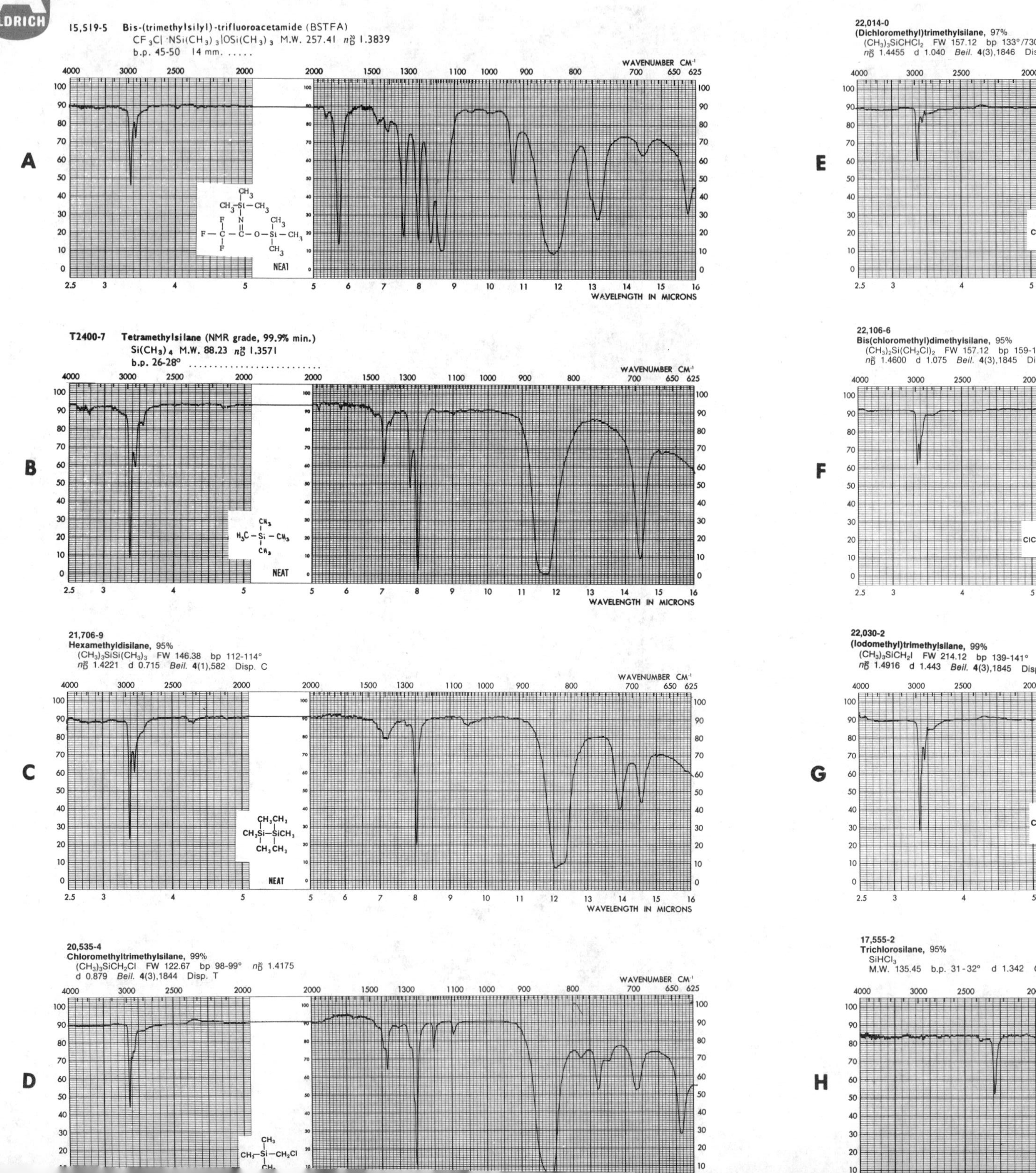

A

$(CH_3)_2SiHCl$ M.W. 94.62 n_D^{20} 1.3827

NEAT

B

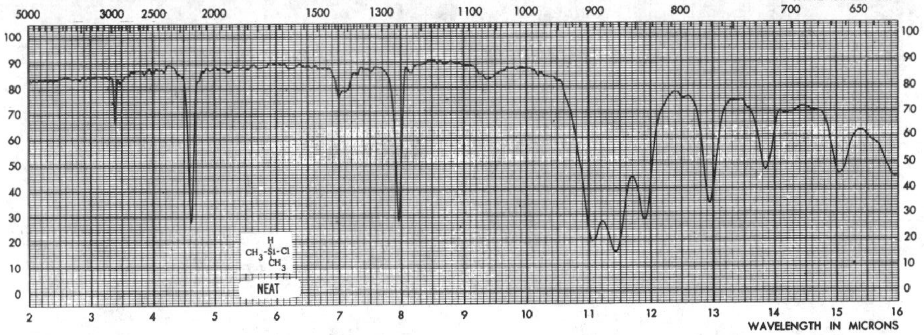

20,538-9
Hexamethyldisiloxane, 98+%
$(CH_3)_3SiOSi(CH_3)_3$ FW 162.38 mp -59° bp 101°
n_D^{20} 1.3775 d 0.764 *Beil.* 4(3),1859 Disp. C

NEAT

C

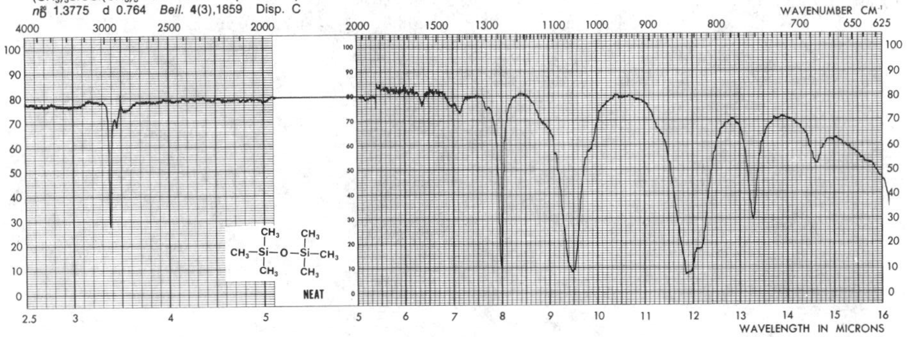

C7285-4 **Chlorotrimethylsilane** (trimethylchlorosilane), tech.
$(CH_3)_3SiCl$ M.W. 108.64 n_D^{20} 1.3887

NEAT

D

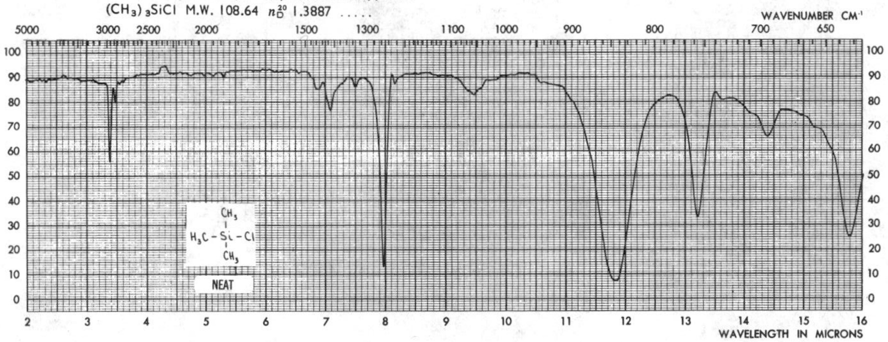

19,440-9
Bromotrimethylsilane, 98% (trimethylsilyl bromide)
$(CH_3)_3SiBr$ FW 153.10 bp 79° n_D^{20} 1.4245
d 1.160 Disp. C

NEAT

E

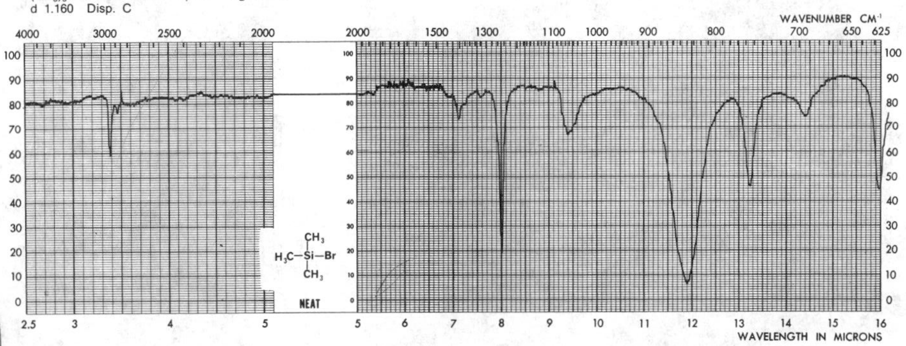

d 1.406 Disp. C

NEAT

F

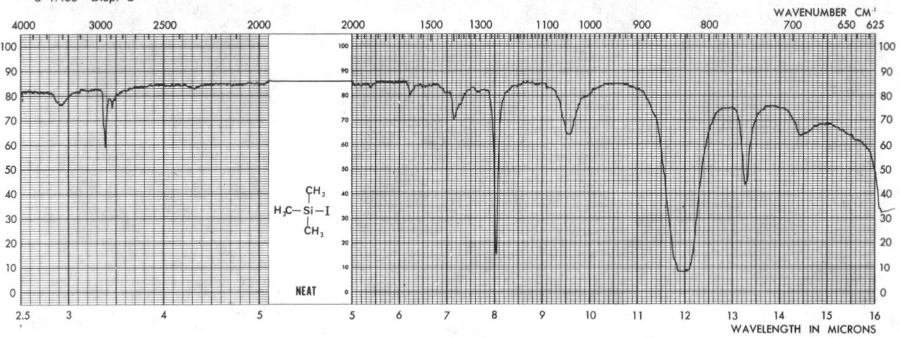

19,050-0
***tert*-Butyldimethylsilyl chloride** (*tert*-butylchlorodimethylsilane)
$(CH_3)_3CSi(CH_3)_2Cl$ FW 150.73 mp 86-89°
bp 125° *Fieser* 4,176 5,74 6,78 Disp. C

NUJOL MULL

G

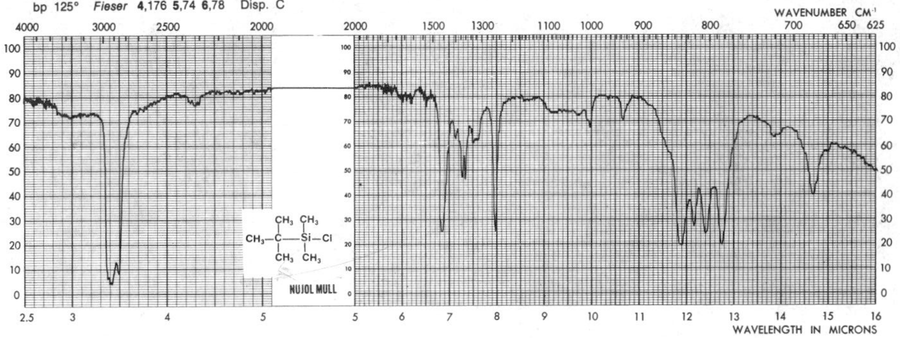

D6082-6 **Dichlorodimethylsilane**
$(CH_3)_2SiCl_2$ M.W. 129.06 n_D^{20} 1.4038

NEAT

H

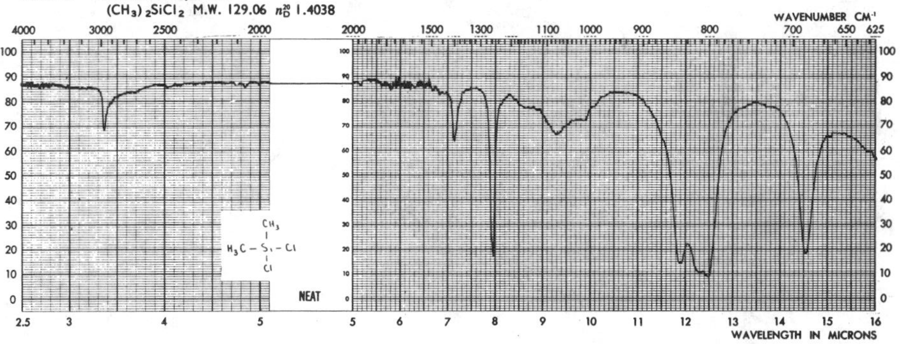

M8530-1 **Methyltrichlorosilane** (trichloromethylsilane), tech.
CH_3SiCl_3 M.W. 149.48 n_D^{20} 1.4098 b.p. 66°

NEAT

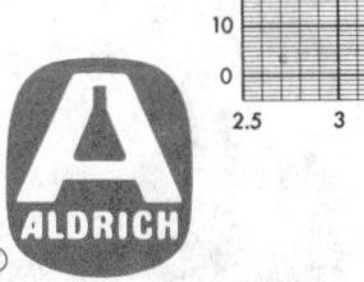

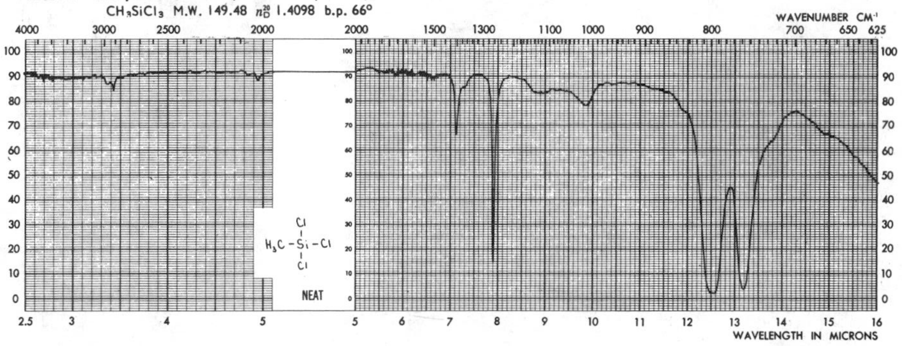

A

10,484-1 **Ethyltrichlorosilane**
$C_2H_5SiCl_3$ M.W. 163.51 n_D^{20} 1.4252 b.p. 99°

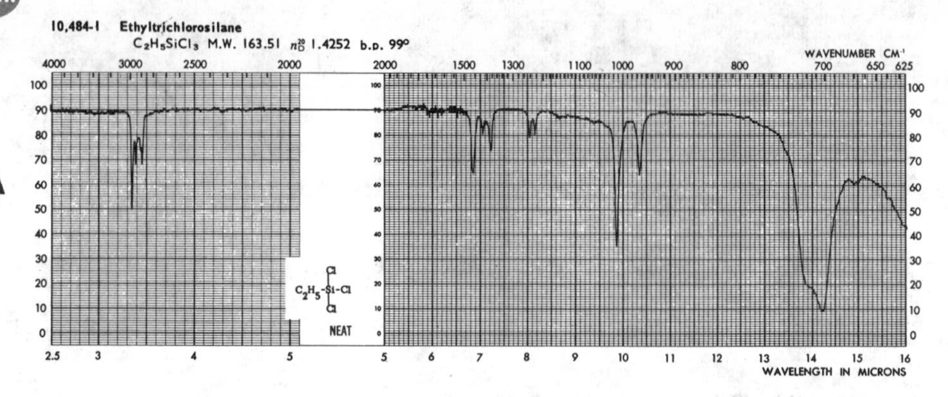

B

10,483-3 **n-Propyltrichlorosilane**
$CH_3CH_2CH_2SiCl_3$ M.W. 177.53 n_D^{20} 1.4320 b.p. 123.5°

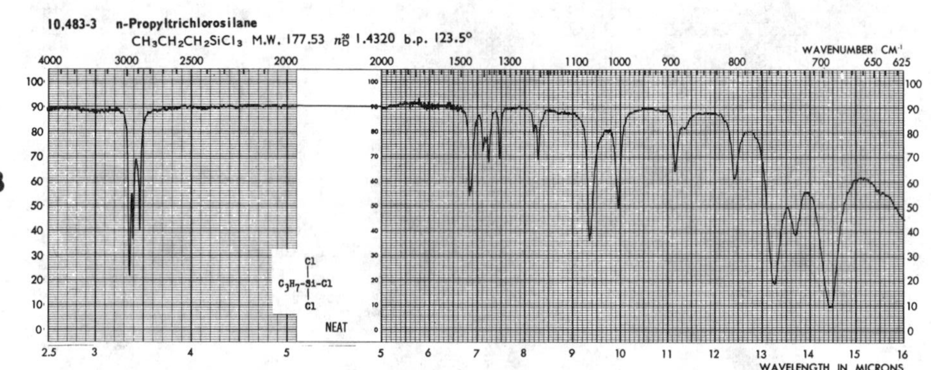

C

10,482-5 **n-Butyltrichlorosilane**
$CH_3(CH_2)_3SiCl_3$ M.W. 191.56 n_D^{20} 1.4373 b.p. 142° ...

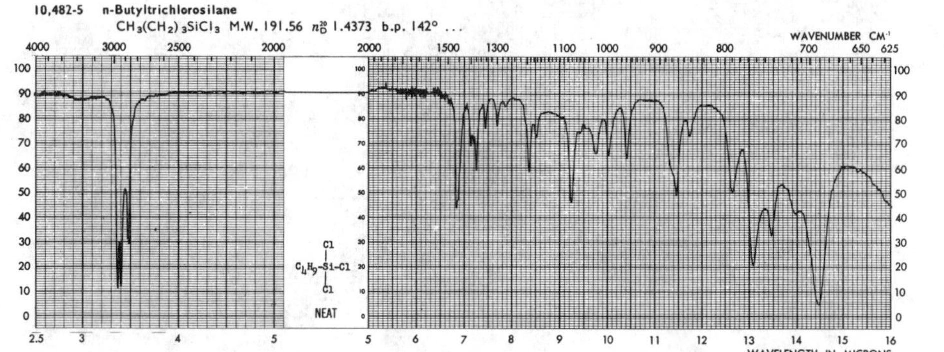

D

10,481-7 **Octadecyltrichlorosilane**
$CH_3(CH_2)_{17}SiCl_3$ M.W. 387.94 n_D^{20} 1.4602 b.p. 223°/10 mm.

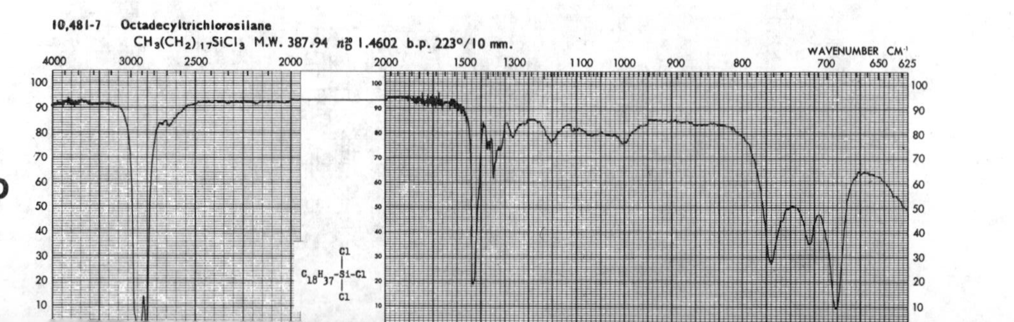

E

21,395-0
Vinyltrimethylsilane, 97% (ethenyltrimethylsilane, trimethylvinylsilane)
$H_2C{=}CHSi(CH_3)_3$ FW 100.24 bp 55° n_D^{20} 1.3920
d 0.649 Disp. C

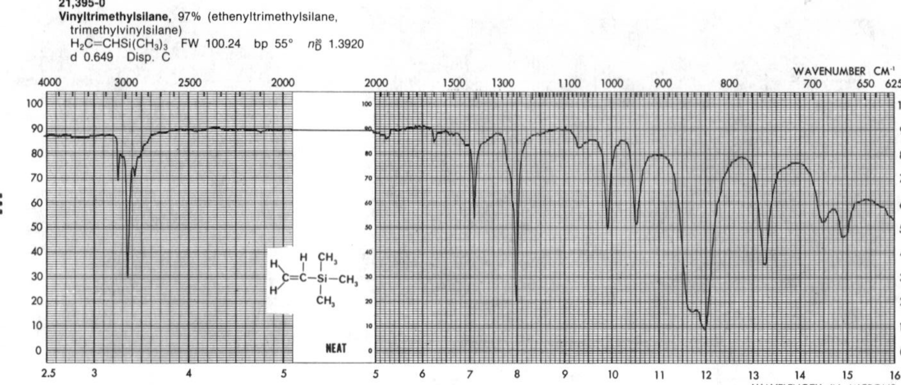

F

10,491-4 **Dichloromethylvinylsilane**
$H_2C{:}CHSi(CH_3)Cl_2$ M.W. 141.07 n_D^{20} 1.4318 b.p. 92°

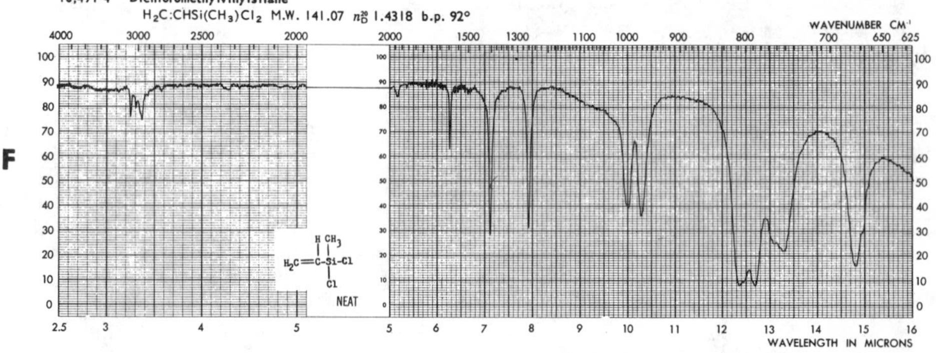

G

10,487-6 **Trichlorovinylsilane**
$H_2C{:}CHSiCl_3$ M.W. 161.49 n_D^{20} 1.4362
b.p. 90.5° ....

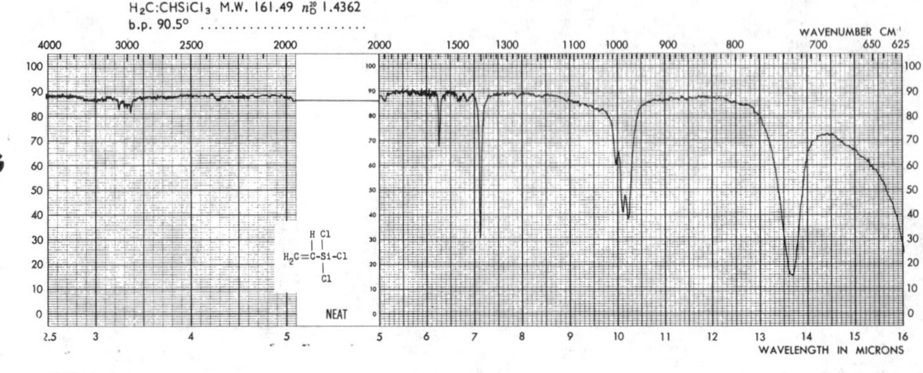

H

10,777-8
Allyltrichlorosilane
$H_2C{=}CHCH_2SiCl_3$
M.W. 175.52 b.p. 116°/750mm. n_D^{20} 1.4450
CORROSIVE

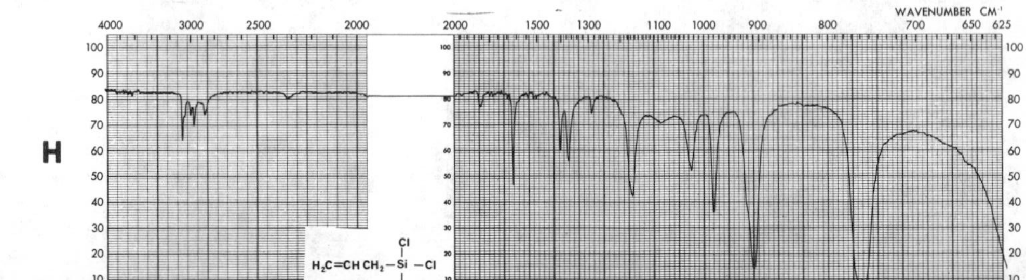

n_D^{20} 1.4056 d 0.719 Disp. C

A

NEAT

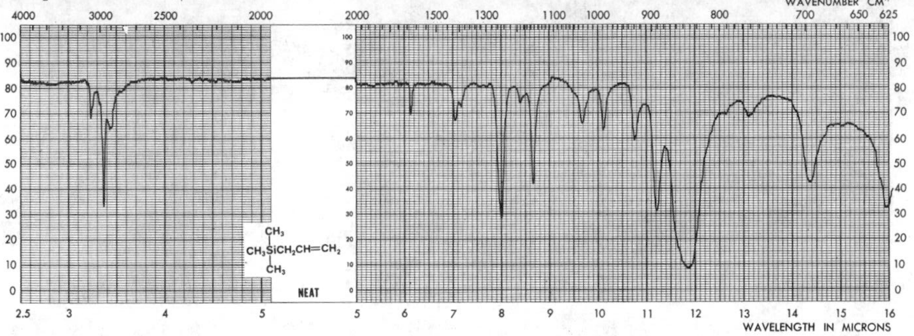

11,339-5 **3-Aminopropyltriethoxysilane** (3-triethoxysilylpropylamine)
$H_2N(CH_2)_3Si(OC_2H_5)_3$ M.W. 413.11 n_D^{20} 1.4201 ....

B

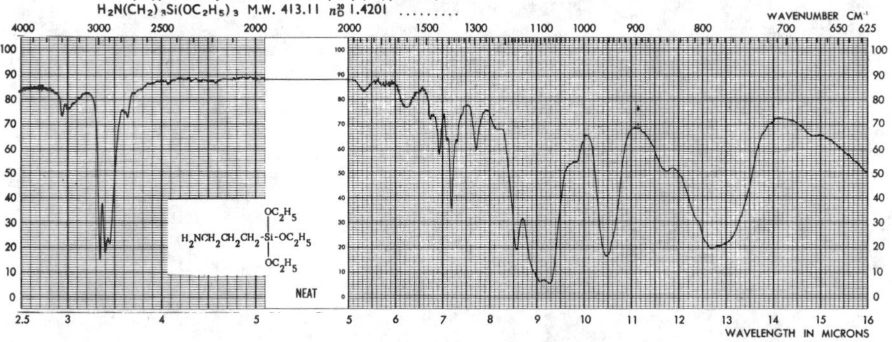

NEAT

13,924-6 **1,1,3,3-Tetramethyldisilazane**
$(CH_3)_2SiHNHSiH(CH_3)_2$ M.W. 133.34
n_D^{20} 1.4044 ....

C

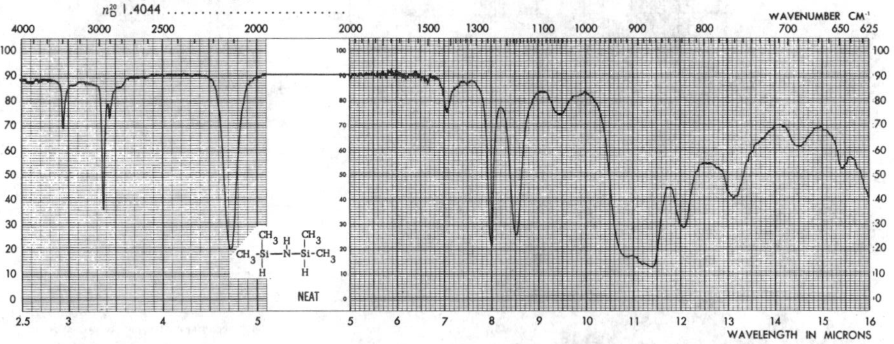

NEAT

H1000-2 **1,1,1,3,3,3-Hexamethyldisilazane**
$(CH_3)_3SiNHSi(CH_3)_3$ M.W. 161.40
n_D^{20} 1.4071 ....

D

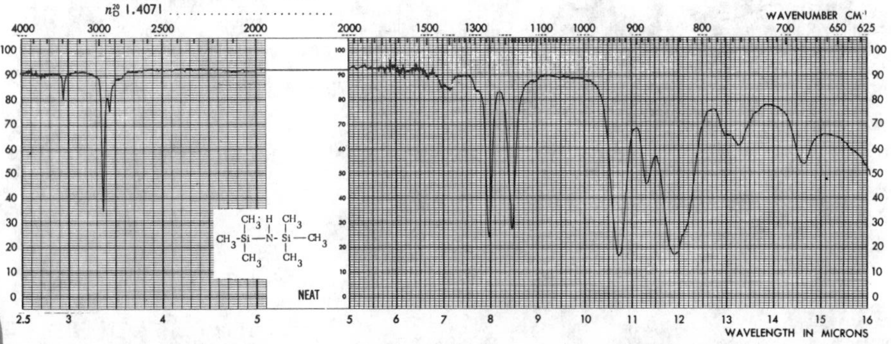

NEAT

b.p. 115-120 ....

E

NEAT

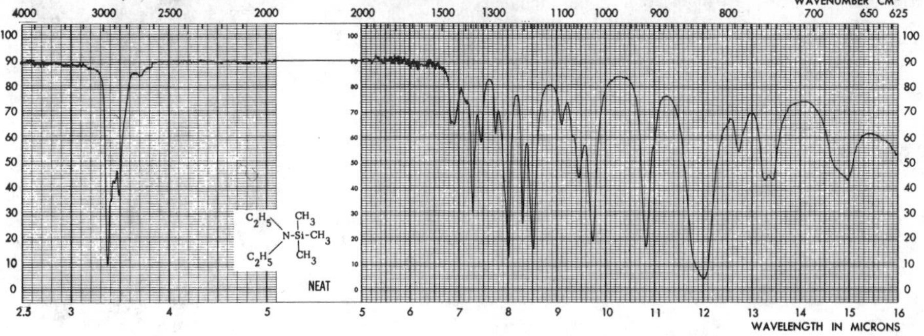

15,507-1
Azidotrimethylsilane (trimethylsilyl azide)
$(CH_3)_3SiN_3$
M.W. 115.21 b.p. 52-53°/175mm. n_D^{20} 1.4142
Fieser 1,1236 3,316

F

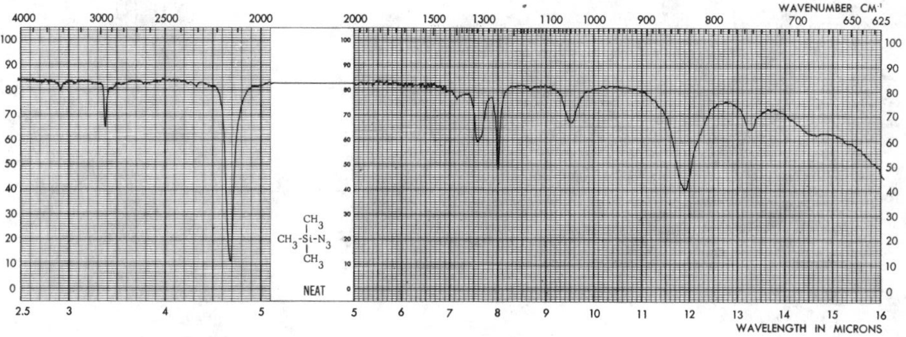

NEAT

22,081-7
2-Trimethylsilyl-1,3-dithiane, 99+%
FW 192.42 bp 54-55°/0.170mm. n_D^{20} 1.5327
d 1.014 Disp. C

G

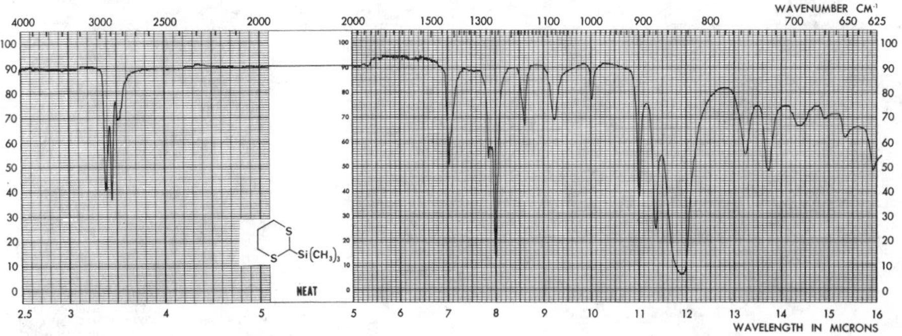

NEAT

18,033-5
3-(Trimethylsilyl)propionic acid, sodium salt, 99+%,
GOLD LABEL
$(CH_3)_3SiCH_2CH_2CO_2Na$
M.W. 168.25 m.p. >300°

H

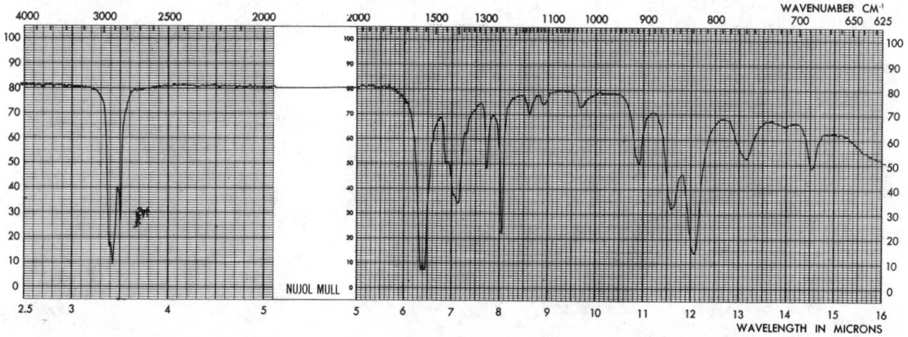

NUJOL MULL

SILANES

ALDRICH

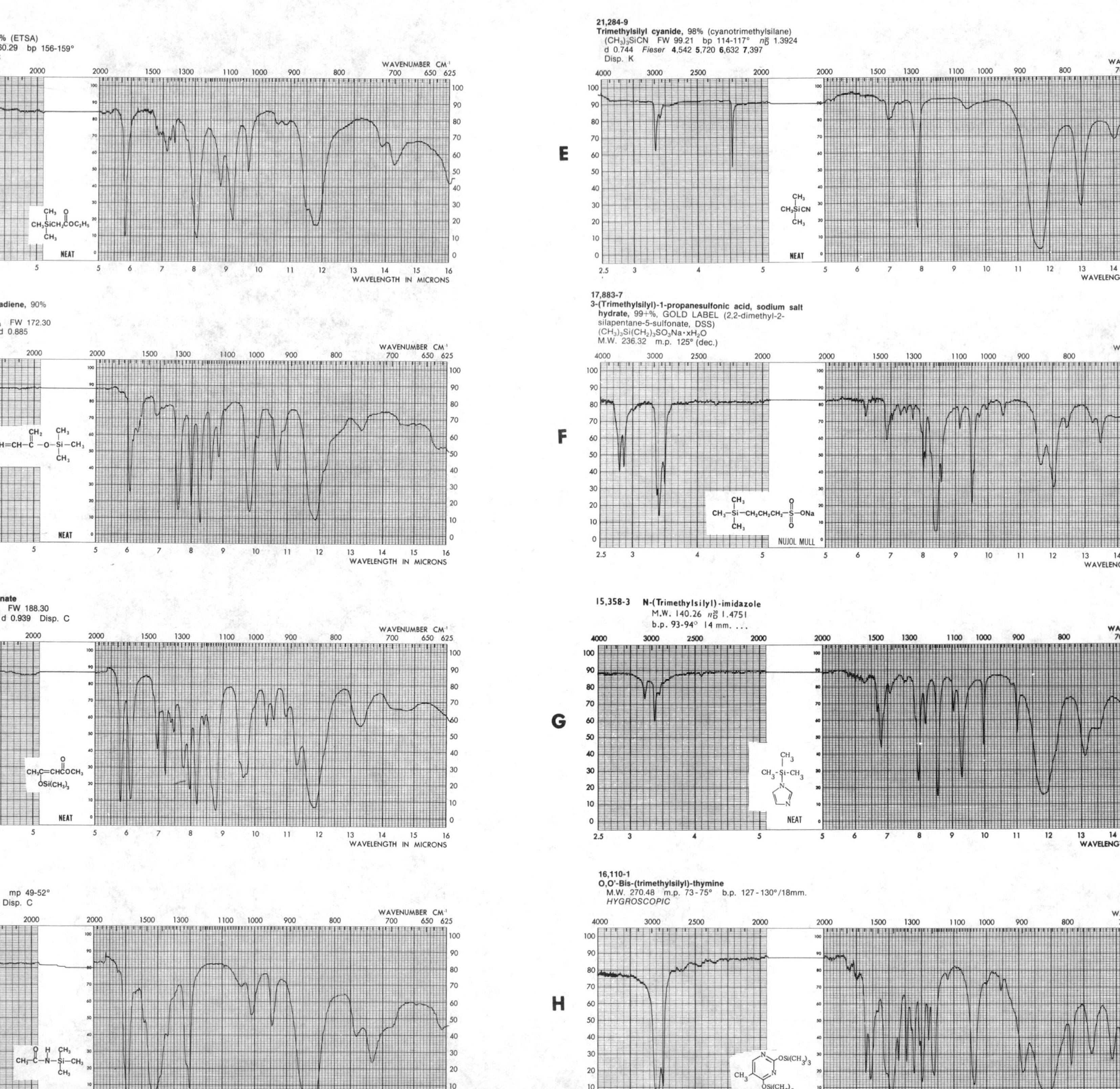

A

20,912-0
Ethyl (trimethylsilyl)acetate, 99% (ETSA)
$(CH_3)_3SiCH_2CO_2C_2H_5$ FW 160.29 bp 156-159°
n_D^{20} 1.4153 d 0.876 Disp. C

B

21,283-0
1-Methoxy-3-(trimethylsilyloxy)butadiene, 90%
(Danishefsky's diene)
$(CH_3)_3SiOC(=CH_2)CH=CHOCH_3$ FW 172.30
bp 68-69°/14mm. n_D^{20} 1.4545 d 0.885
Fieser **6**,370 **7**,233 Disp. C

C

22,375-1
Methyl 3-(trimethylsilyloxy)crotonate
$CH_3C[OSi(CH_3)_3]=CHCO_2CH_3$ FW 188.30
bp 57-59°/9mm. n_D^{20} 1.4435 d 0.939 Disp. C

D

22,329-8
***N*-(Trimethylsilyl)acetamide**, 99%
$CH_3CONHSi(CH_3)_3$ FW 131.25 mp 49-52°
bp 84°/18mm. *Fieser* **1**,1235 Disp. C

E

21,284-9
Trimethylsilyl cyanide, 98% (cyanotrimethylsilane)
$(CH_3)_3SiCN$ FW 99.21 bp 114-117° n_D^{20} 1.3924
d 0.744 *Fieser* **4**,542 **5**,720 **6**,632 **7**,397
Disp. K

F

17,883-7
3-(Trimethylsilyl)-1-propanesulfonic acid, sodium salt hydrate, 99+%, GOLD LABEL (2,2-dimethyl-2-silapentane-5-sulfonate, DSS)
$(CH_3)_3Si(CH_2)_3SO_3Na \cdot xH_2O$
M.W. 236.32 m.p. 125° (dec.)

G

15,358-3 **N-(Trimethylsilyl)-imidazole**
M.W. 140.26 n_D^{20} 1.4751
b.p. 93-94° 14 mm. . . .

H

16,110-1
O,O'-Bis-(trimethylsilyl)-thymine
M.W. 270.48 m.p. 73-75° b.p. 127-130°/18mm.
HYGROSCOPIC

A

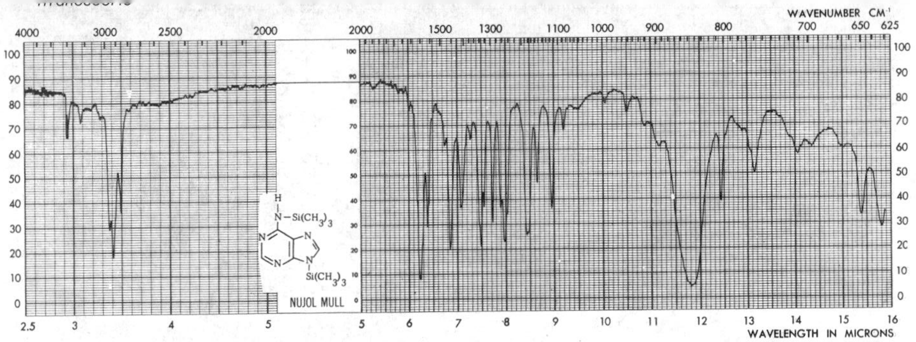

NUJOL MULL

16,112-8
O,O',9-Tris-(trimethylsilyl)-xanthine
M.W. 368.66 m.p. 94-96° b.p. 163°/15mm.

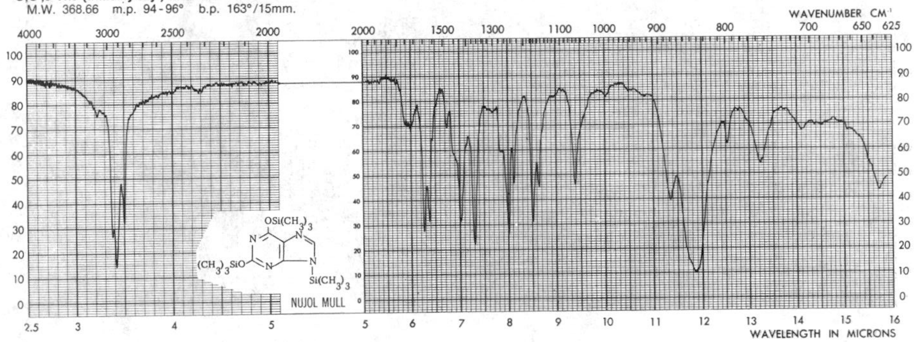

B

NUJOL MULL

18,743-7
Bis(trimethylsilyl)acetylene, 99% (BTMSA)
$(CH_3)_3SiC{\equiv}CSi(CH_3)_3$
M.W. 170.41 d 1.427

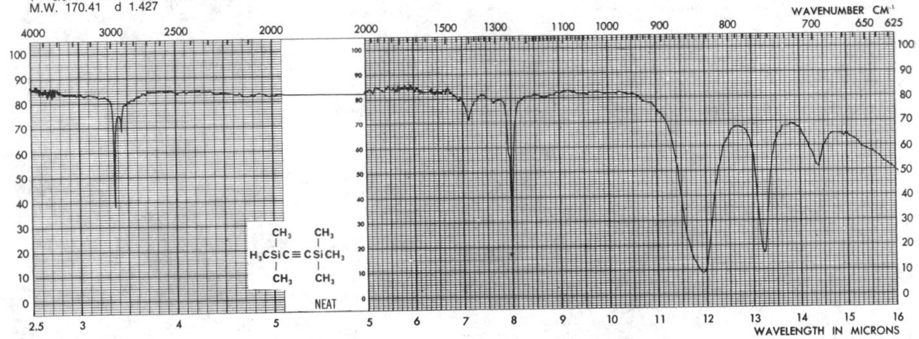

C

NEAT

14,848-2 Diphenylsilane
$(C_6H_5)_2SiH_2$ M.W. 184.32 n_D^{20} 1.5789

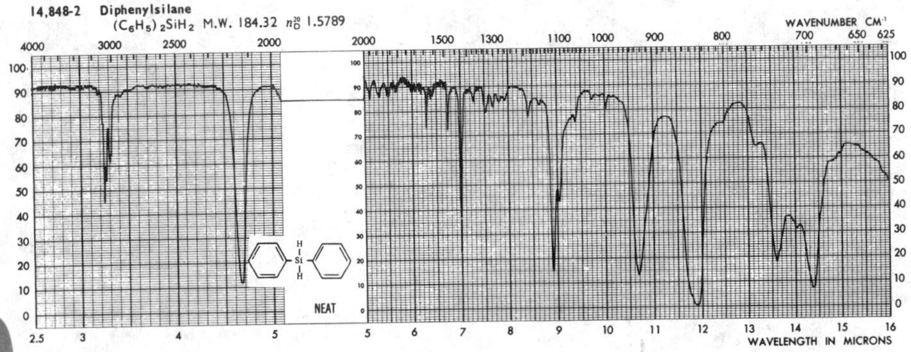

D

NEAT

E

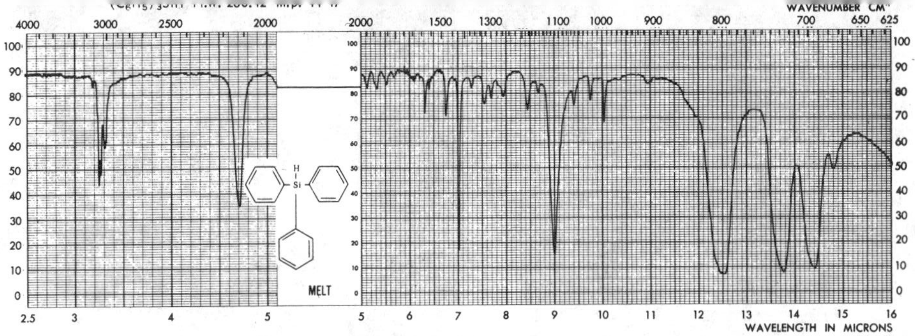

MELT

11,338-7 Benzylchlorodimethylsilane
$C_6H_5CH_2Si(CH_3)_2Cl$ M.W. 376.48 n_D^{20} 1.5107

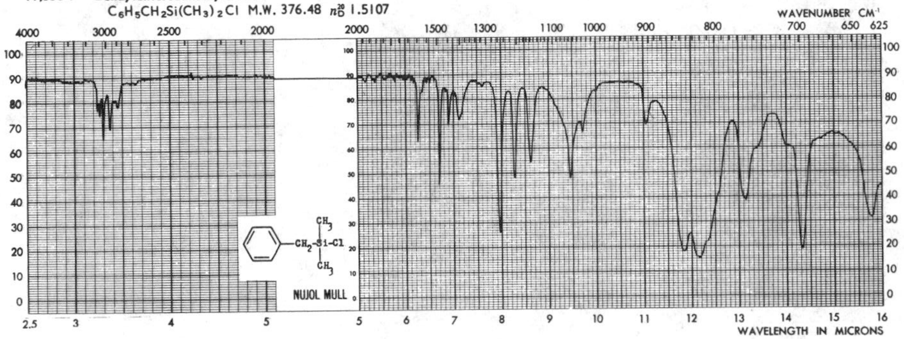

F

NUJOL MULL

11,337-9 Chlorodimethylphenylsilane
$C_6H_5Si(CH_3)_2Cl$ M.W. 362.45 n_D^{20} 1.5090

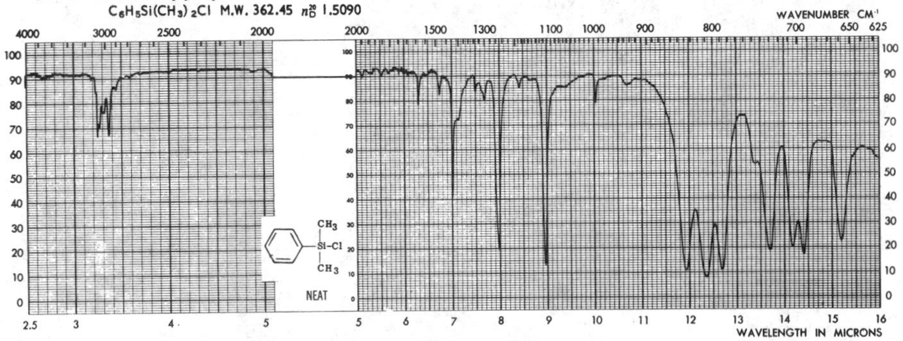

G

NEAT

19,773-4
Phenyltrimethylsilane, 99%
$C_6H_5Si(CH_3)_3$ FW 150.30 bp 168-170°
n_D^{20} 1.4907 d 0.873 *Beil.* **16**(1),525 Disp. C

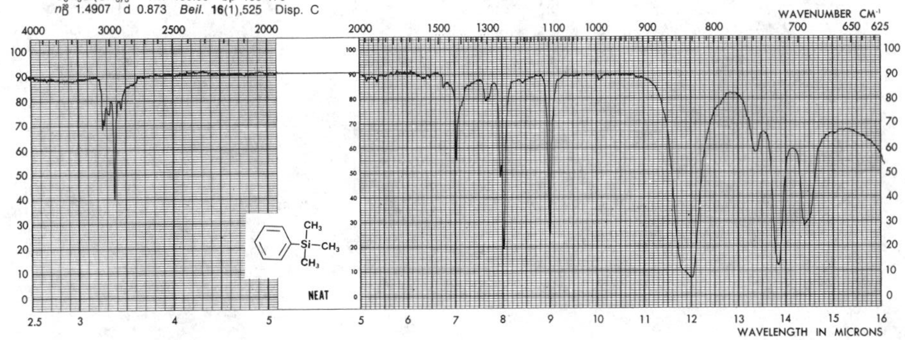

H

NEAT

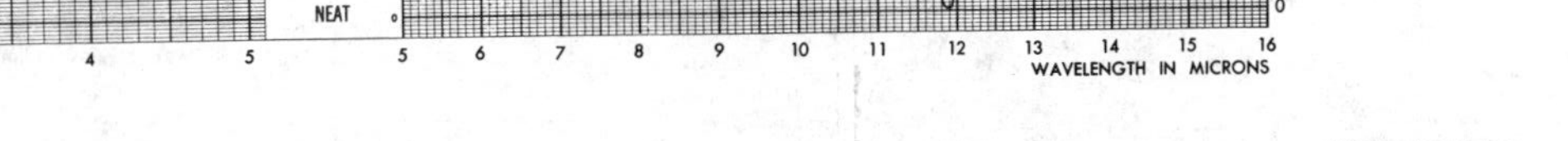

A

19,553-7
tert-**Butylchlorodiphenylsilane**, 98% (*tert*-butyldiphenylsilyl chloride)
$(CH_3)_3CSi(C_6H_5)_2Cl$ FW 274.87 n_D^{20} 1.5675
d 1.057 *Fieser* 6,81 Disp. C

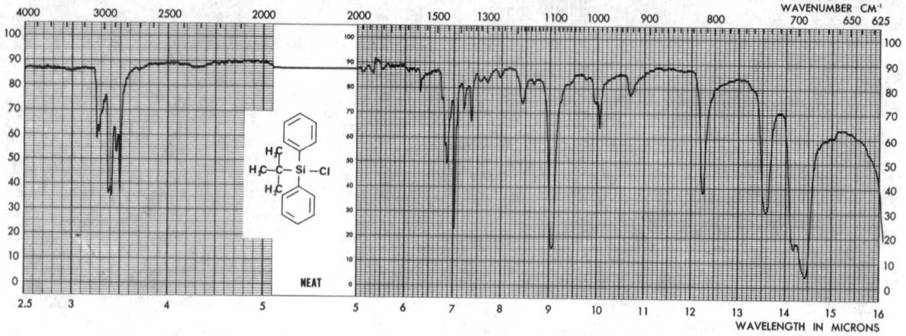

NEAT

B

10,476-0 **Chlorodiphenylmethylsilane**
$CH_3Si(C_6H_5)_2Cl$ M.W. 232.79 n_D^{20} 1.5750 b.p. 152°/10 mm.

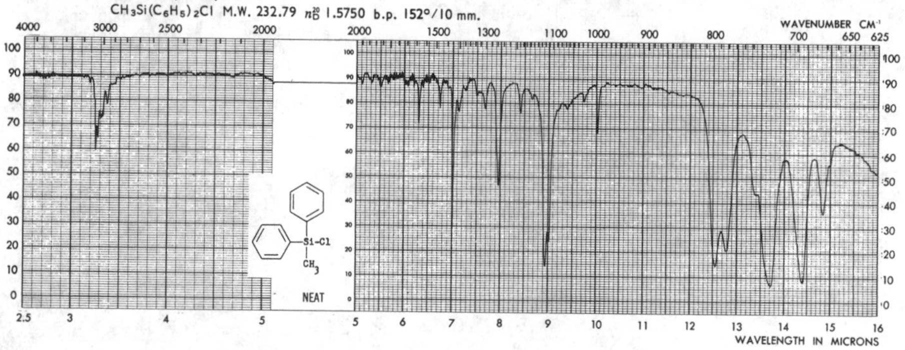

NEAT

C

11,416-2 **Triphenylsilyl chloride** (chlorotriphenylsilane)
$(C_6H_5)_3SiCl$ M.W. 294.86 ....

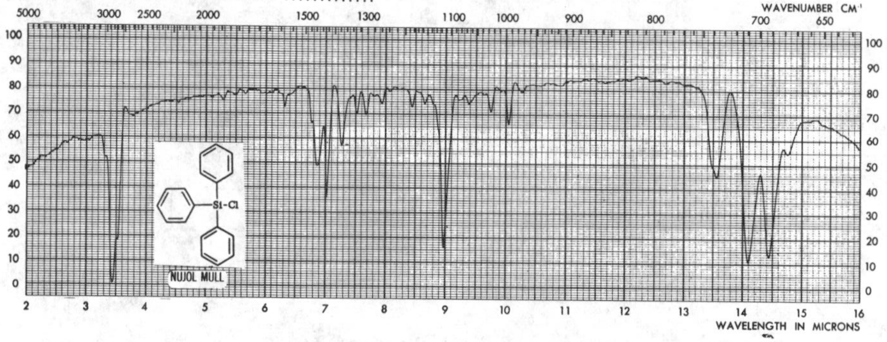

NUJOL MULL

D

D6150-4 **Dichlorodiphenylsilane**
$(C_6H_5)_2SiCl_2$ M.W. 253.20 n_D^{25} 1.5800
b.p. 305° ....

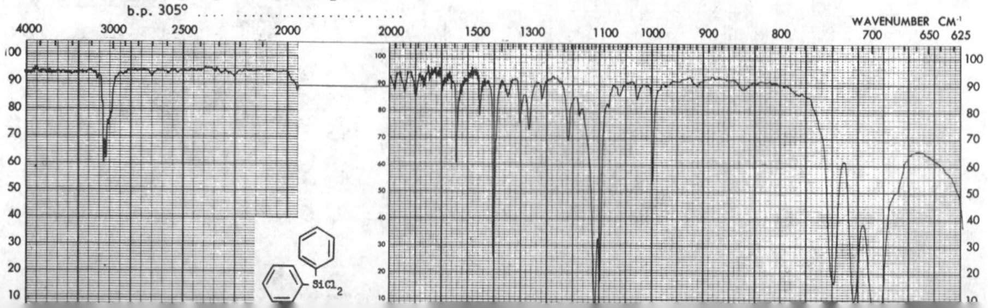

E

10,478-7 **Dichloromethylphenylsilane**
$C_6H_5Si(CH_3)Cl_2$ M.W. 191.13 n_D^{20} 1.5190 b.p. 77°/10 mm.

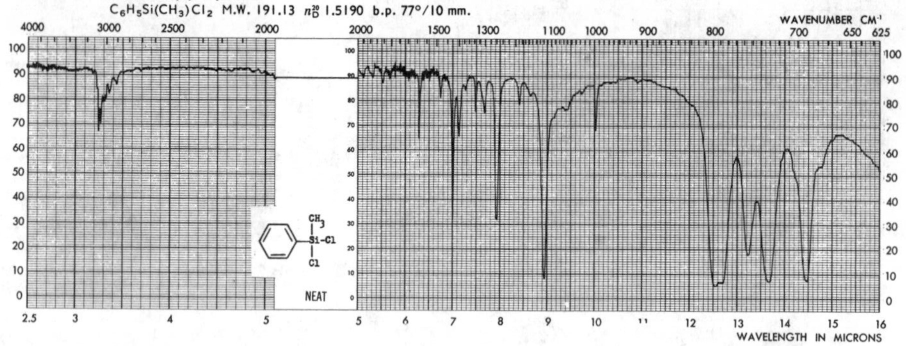

NEAT

F

P3670-3 **Phenyltrichlorosilane** (trichlorophenylsilane)
$C_6H_5SiCl_3$ M.W. 211.55 n_D^{20} 1.5240 b.p. 201°

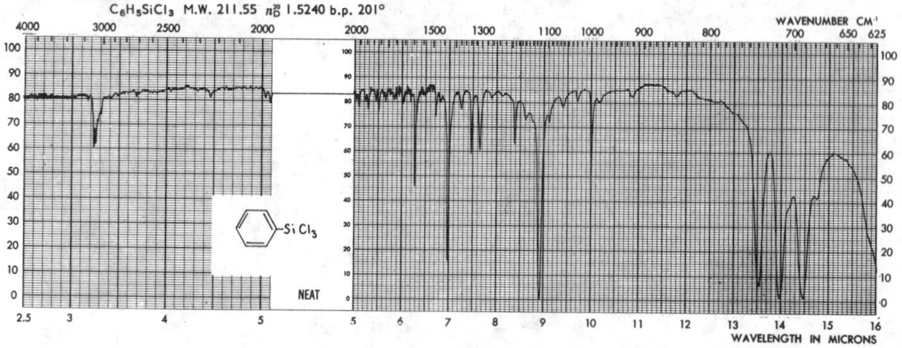

NEAT

G

10,392-6 **Dimethoxymethylphenylsilane**
$C_6H_5Si(OCH_3)_2CH_3$ M.W. 182.30 n_D^{20} 1.4795
b.p. 129°/79 mm. ....

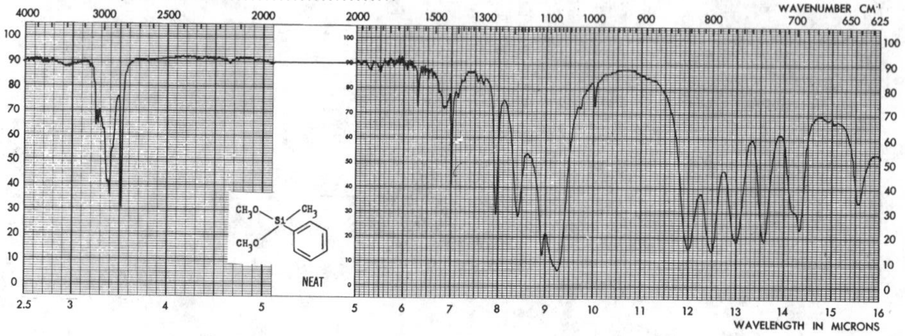

NEAT

H

10,489-2 **Dimethoxydiphenylsilane**
$(C_6H_5)_2Si(OCH_3)_2$ M.W. 244.37 n_D^{20} 1.5426
b.p. 191°/53 mm. ....

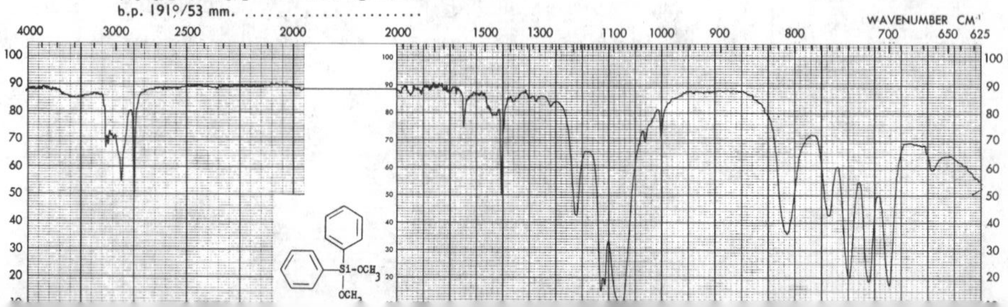

A

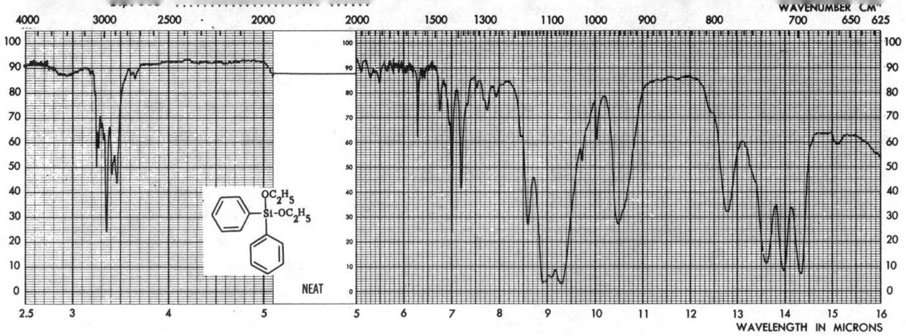

NEAT

10,474-4 Phenyltrimethoxysilane
$C_6H_5Si(OCH_3)_3$ M.W. 198.30 n_D^{20} 1.4730
b.p. 136°/69 mm.

B

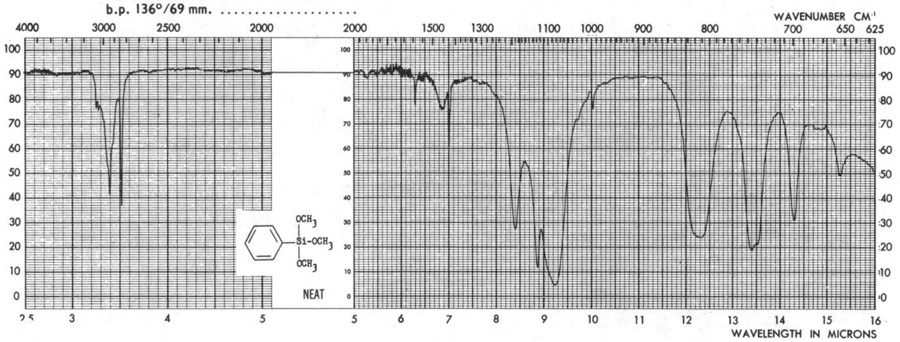

NEAT

17,560-9
Phenyltriethoxysilane, 98%
$C_6H_5Si(OC_2H_5)_3$
M.W. 240.38 b.p. 112-113°/10mm. n_D^{20} 1.4604
d 0.996 Beil. **16**,911 *IRRITANT*

C

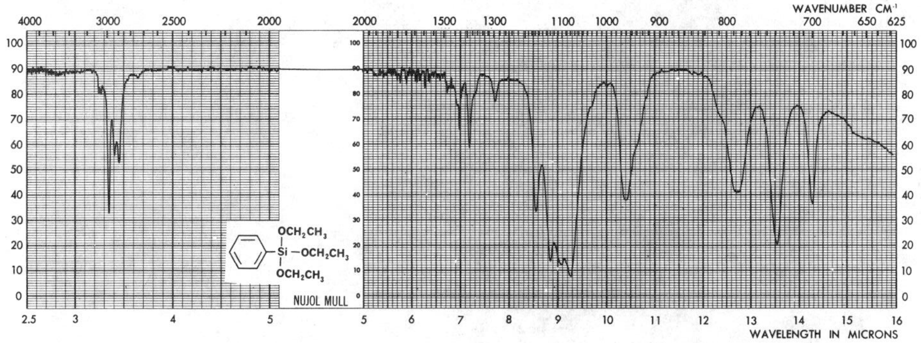

NUJOL MULL

15,000-2 Octaphenylcyclotetrasiloxane
M.W. 793.20 m.p. 196-198°

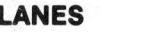

D

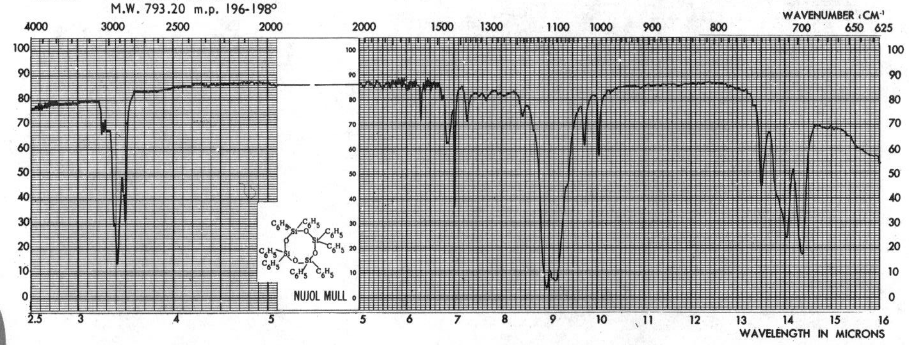

NUJOL MULL

E

NUJOL MULL

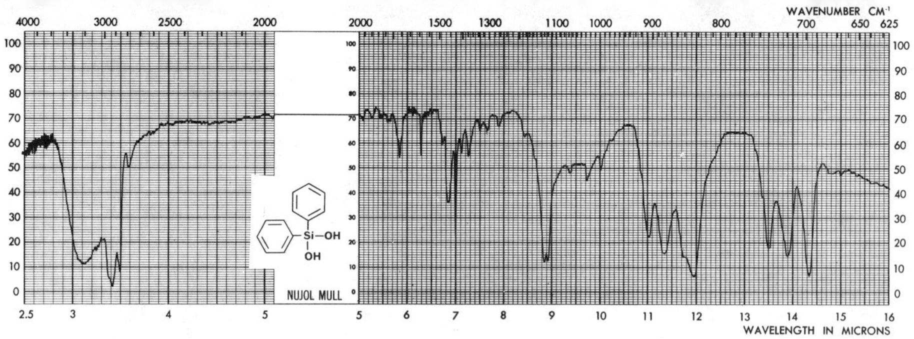

14,372-3 Triphenylsilanol
$(C_6H_5)_3SiOH$ M.W. 276.41
m.p. 148-150° (dec.)

F

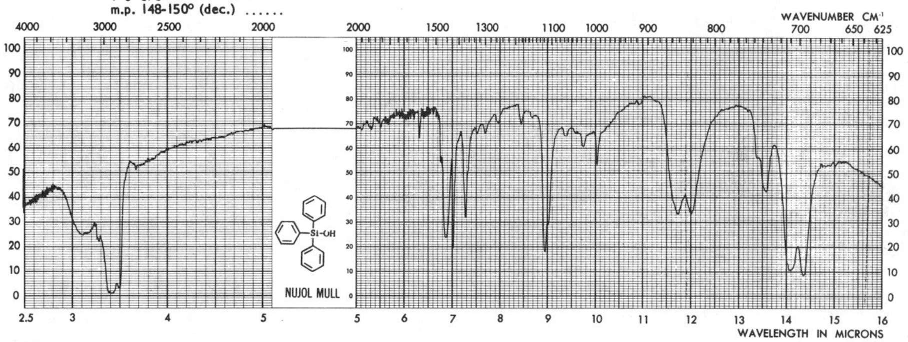

NUJOL MULL

BORANES

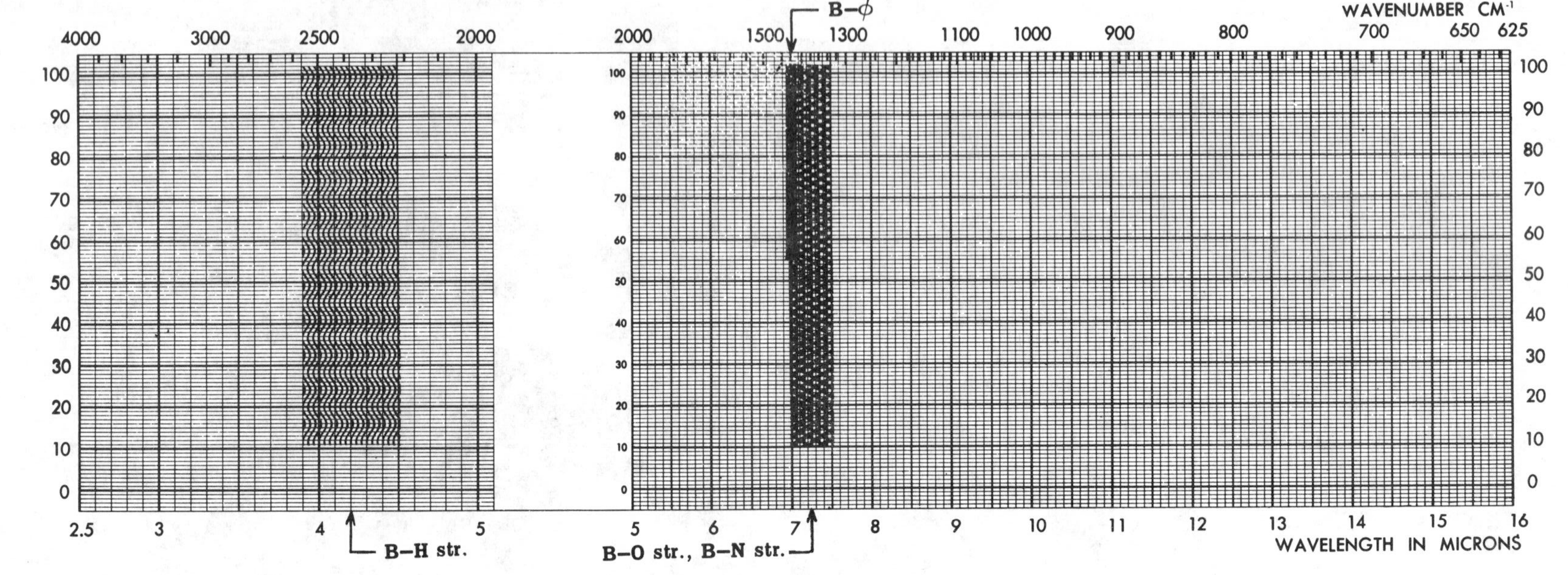

The boron-hydrogen group absorbs strongly between 4 and 4.5 μ (2500 – 2220 cm^{-1}) in the salts seen in spectra 1548B—49B and between 3.9 and 4 μ (2565 – 2500 cm^{-1}) in the borinane compound of spectrum 1549E.

The B–O group absorbs strongly between 7 and 7.5 μ (1430 – 1335 cm^{-1}) as does the boron-nitrogen group.

Boron attached directly to the benzene ring causes the aromatic ring to display an absorption very close to 7 μ (1430 cm^{-1}). This is also true with the phosphorus-phenyl and silicon-phenyl groups and will be seen when arsenic, antimony, tin or lead is attached directly to the aromatic ring (See spectra 1556H—1562B).

A

$NaBH_4$

NUJOL MULL

B

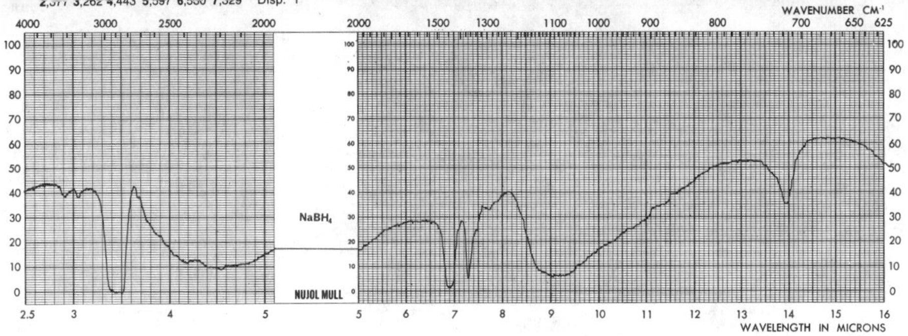

15,615-9 Sodium cyanoborohydride
$NaBH_3CN$ M.W. 62.84

NUJOL MULL

C

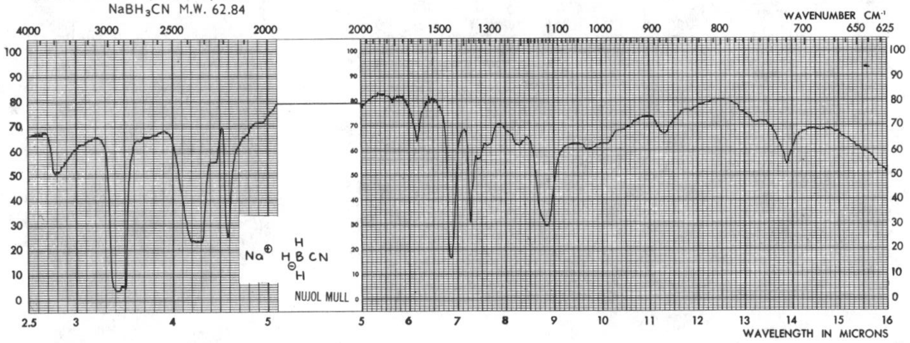

18,021-1
Borane-*tert.*-butylamine complex (*tert.*-butylamineborane)
$(CH_3)_3CNH_2 \cdot BH_3$
M.W. 86.97 m.p. 98-100° (dec.)

NUJOL MULL

D

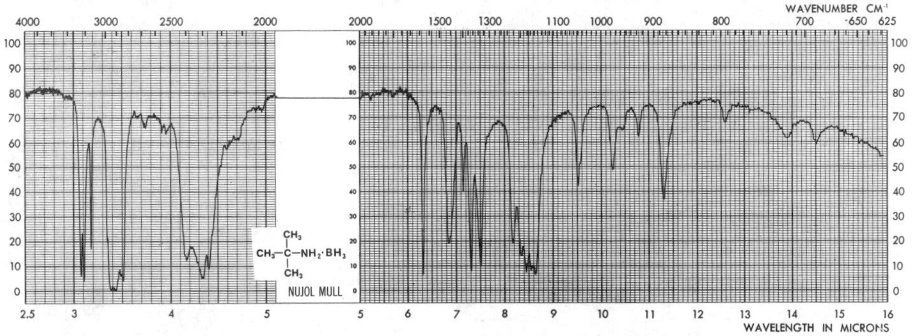

18,023-8
Borane-dimethylamine complex
$(CH_3)_2NH \cdot BH_3$ FW 58.92 mp 36° Disp. C

MELT

E

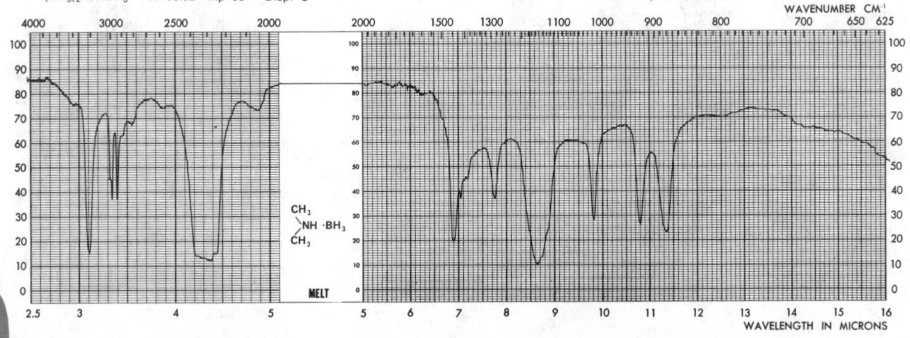

Fieser 1,1229 5,708 Disp. C

NUJOL MULL

F

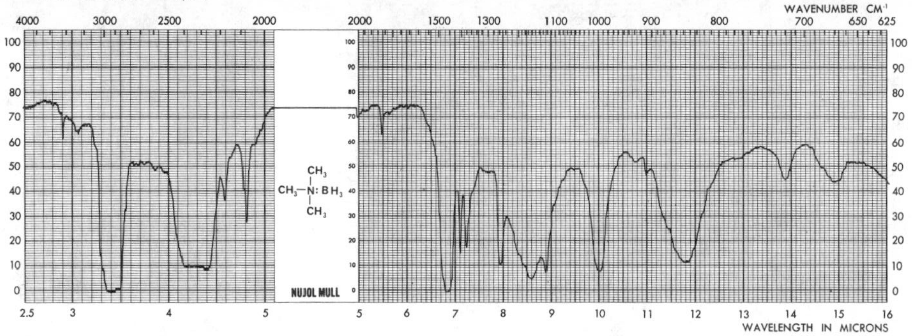

17,897-7
Borane-triethylamine complex
$(C_2H_5)_3N \cdot BH_3$
M.W. 115.03 n_D^{20} 1.4425 / Fieser 3,299

NEAT

G

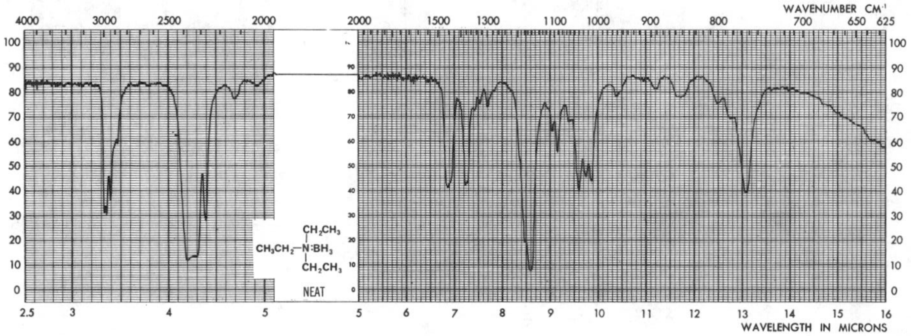

17,904-3
Borane-N,N-diethylaniline complex
$C_6H_5N(C_2H_5)_2 \cdot BH_3$
M.W. 163.07

NEAT

H

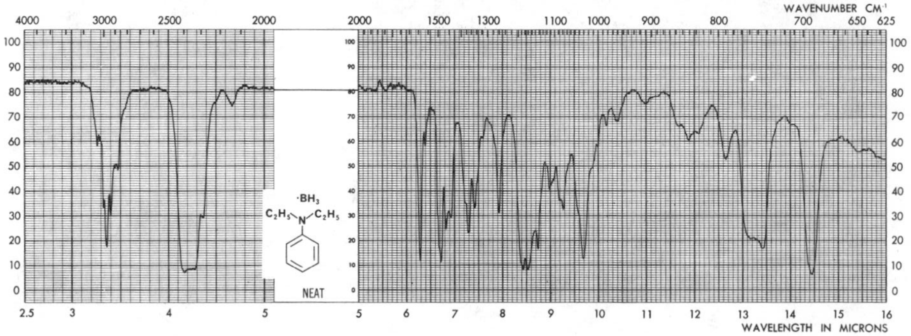

13,424-4 **Morpholineborane**
M.W. 100.96 m.p. 93-96°

NUJOL MULL

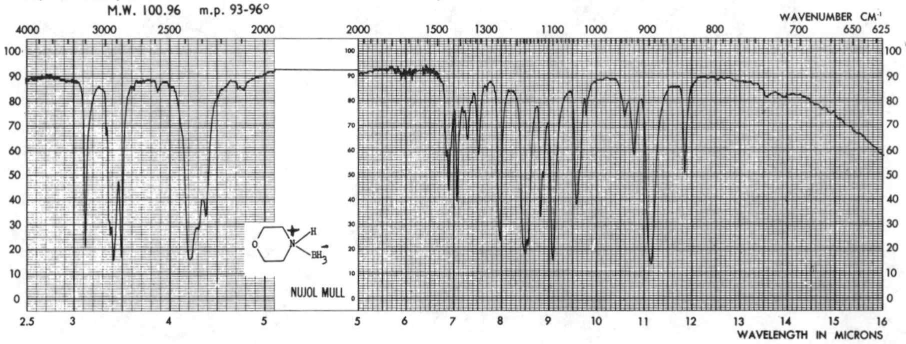

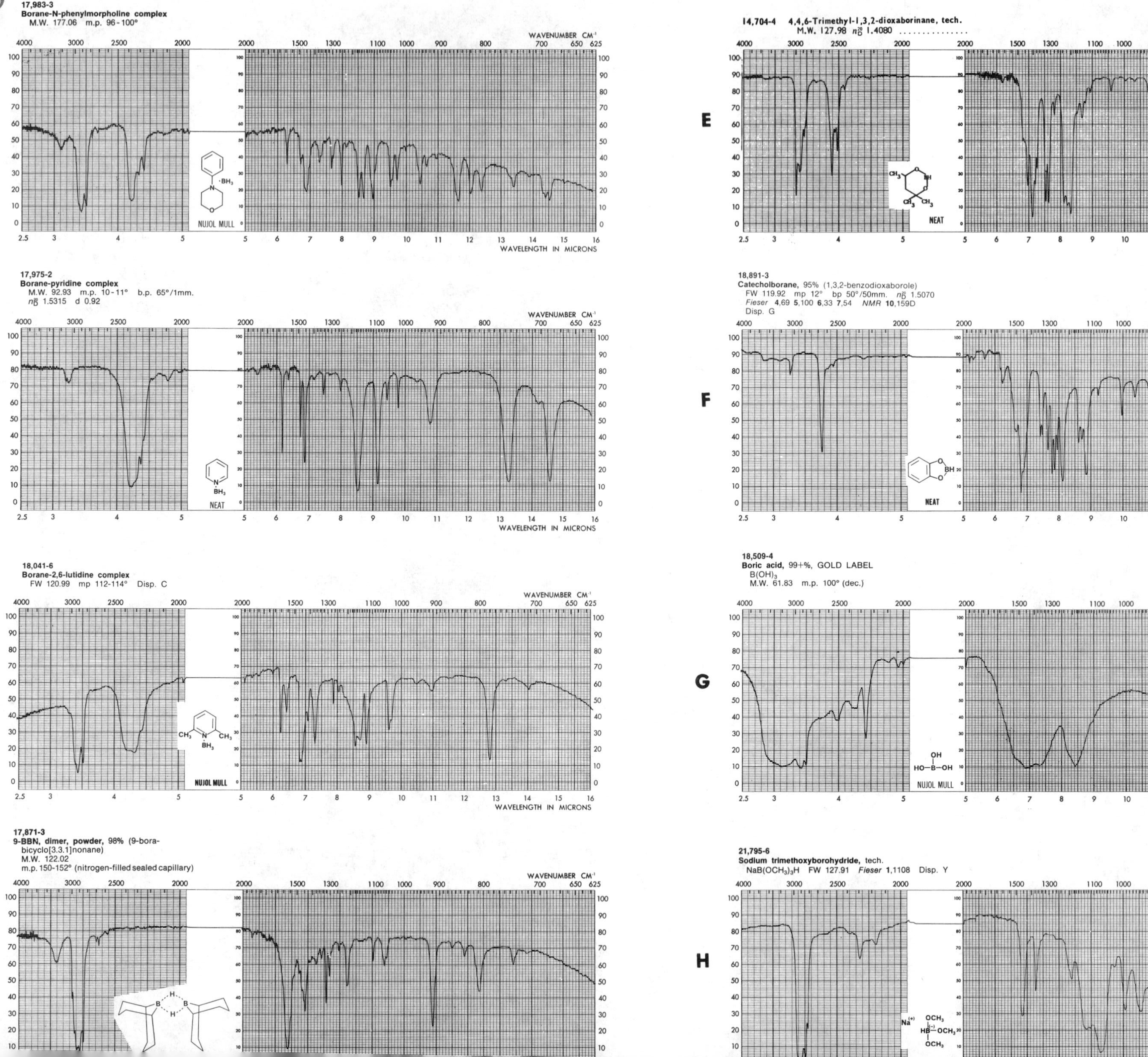

A
17,983-3
Borane-N-phenylmorpholine complex
M.W. 177.06 m.p. 96-100°
NUJOL MULL

B
17,975-2
Borane-pyridine complex
M.W. 92.93 m.p. 10-11° b.p. 65°/1mm.
n_D^{20} 1.5315 d 0.92
NEAT

C
18,041-6
Borane-2,6-lutidine complex
FW 120.99 mp 112-114° Disp. C
NUJOL MULL

D
17,871-3
9-BBN, dimer, powder, 98% (9-borabicyclo[3.3.1]nonane)
M.W. 122.02
m.p. 150-152° (nitrogen-filled sealed capillary)

E
14,704-4 **4,4,6-Trimethyl-1,3,2-dioxaborinane, tech.**
M.W. 127.98 n_D^{20} 1.4080
NEAT

F
18,891-3
Catecholborane, 95% (1,3,2-benzodioxaborole)
FW 119.92 mp 12° bp 50°/50mm. n_D^{20} 1.5070
Fieser **4**,69 **5**,100 **6**,33 **7**,54 *NMR* **10**,159D
Disp. G
NEAT

G
18,509-4
Boric acid, 99+%, GOLD LABEL
$B(OH)_3$
M.W. 61.83 m.p. 100° (dec.)
NUJOL MULL

H
21,795-6
Sodium trimethoxyborohydride, tech.
$NaB(OCH_3)_3H$ FW 127.91 *Fieser* **1**,1108 Disp. Y

Disp. C

A

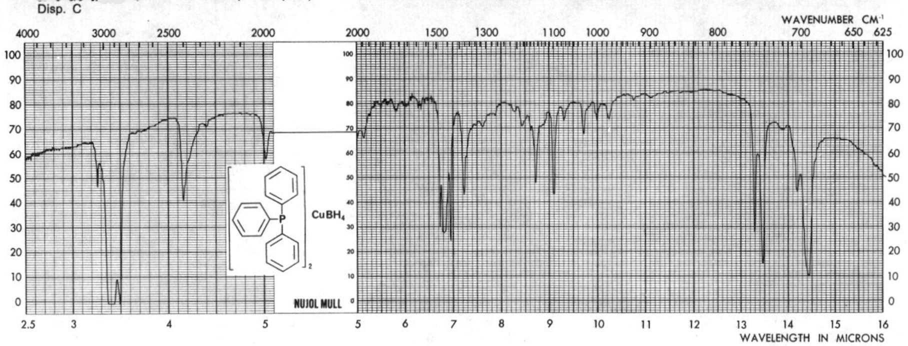

NUJOL MULL

T7565-5 **Trimethyl borate** (methyl borate)
$(CH_3O)_3B$ M.W. 103.91 n_D^{20} 1.3568
b.p. 67-69°

B

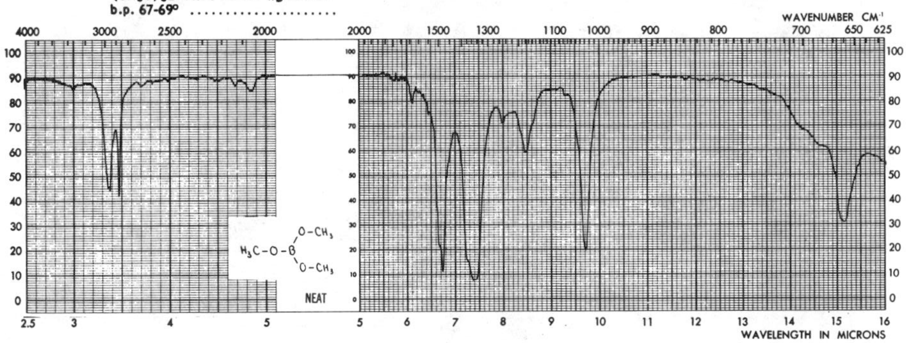

NEAT

14,708-7 Methyl polyborate, tech.
$2(CH_3O)_3B \cdot 3B_2O_3$ M.W. 416.69 n_D^{20} 1.4123

C

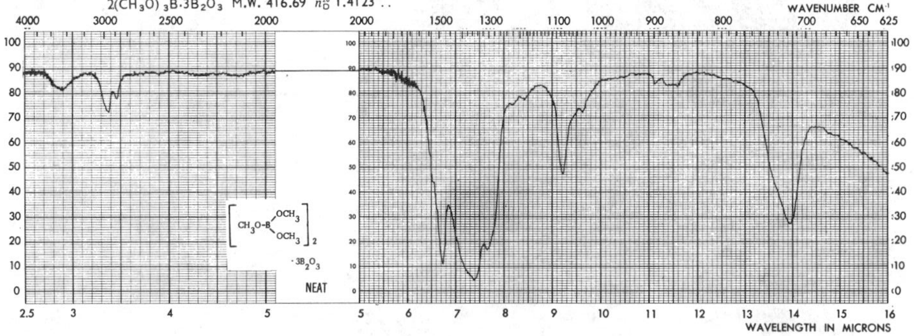

NEAT

T5930-7 **Triethyl borate**
$(C_2H_5O)_3B$ M.W. 145.99 n_D^{20} 1.3749

D

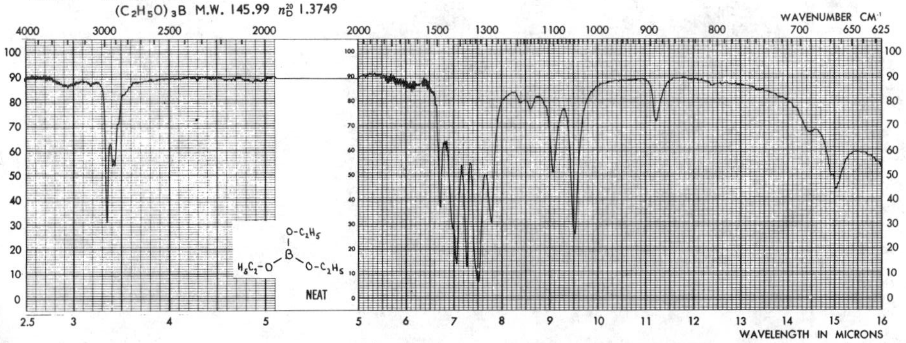

NEAT

$[(CH_3)_2CHO]_3B$ FW 188.08 bp 139-141°
n_D^{20} 1.3764 d 0.815 *Beil.* **1**,363 Disp. C

E

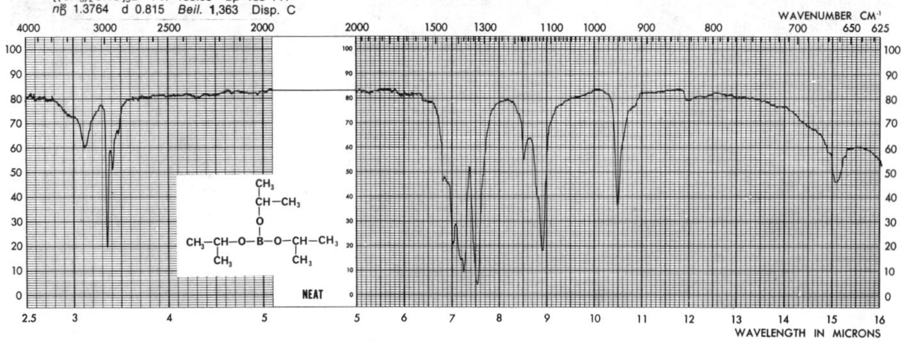

NEAT

14,703-6 Isopropyl polyborate, tech.
$2[(CH_3)_2CHO]_3B \cdot 3B_2O_3$ M.W. 585.02
m.p. 54-57°

F

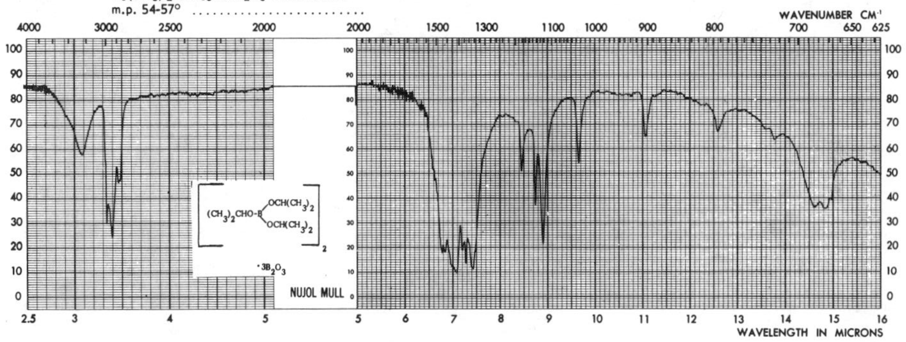

NUJOL MULL

18,000-9
Tributyl borate
$[CH_3(CH_2)_3O]_3B$ FW 230.16 mp -70°
bp 230-235° n_D^{20} 1.4100 d 0.853 *Beil.* **1**(2),398
Disp. C,D

G

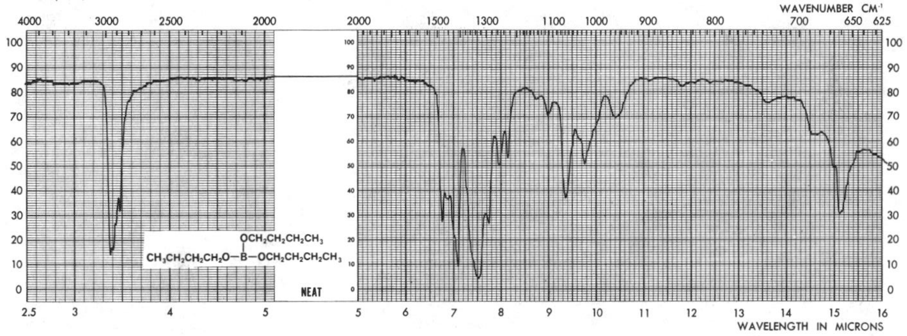

NEAT

18,004-1
Tri-o-tolyl borate
$(CH_3C_6H_4O)_3B$
M.W. 332.21

H

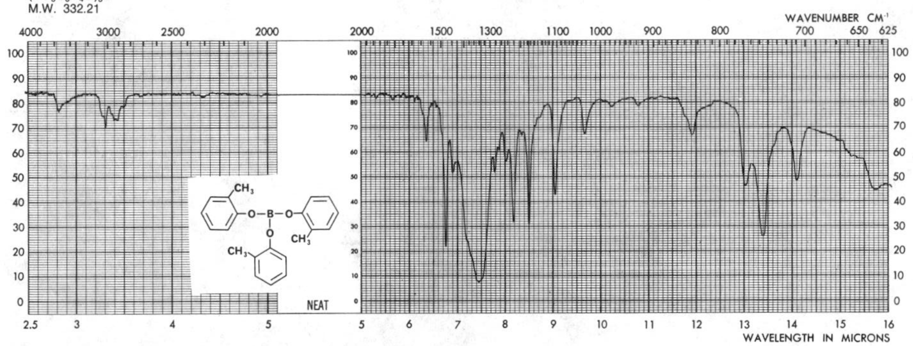

NEAT

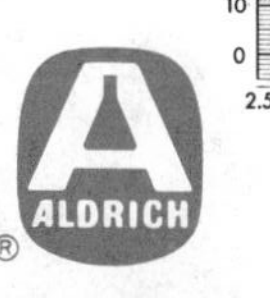

A

T7020-3 Trimethoxyboroxine (trimethoxyboroxole)
M.W. 173.53 n_D^{20} 1.3996
NEAT

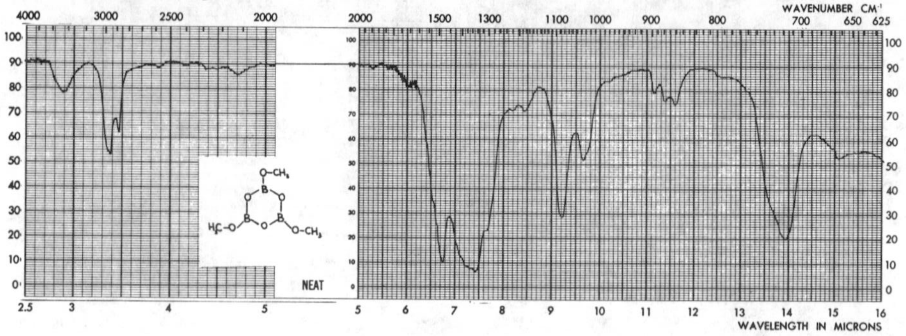

B

14,702-8 Triisopropylboroxine (isopropyl metaborate), **tech.**
M.W. 257.70 m.p. 58-62°
MELT

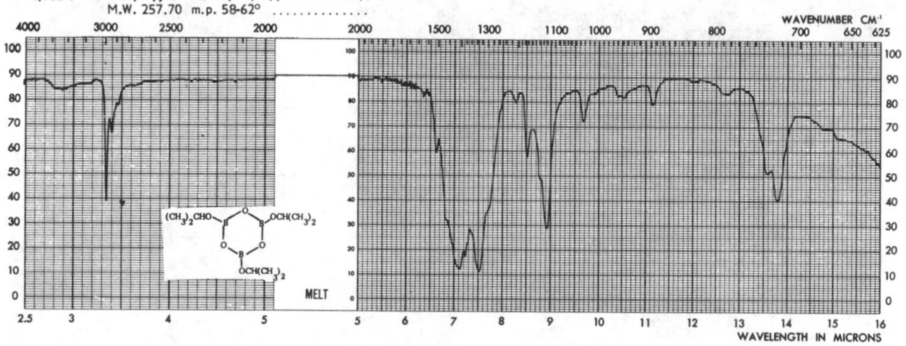

C

19,319-4
Trimethylene borate (1,3-propanediol cyclic ester with boric acid)
FW 243.86 bp 125°/0mm. n_D^{20} 1.4537 d 1.153
Disp. C
NEAT

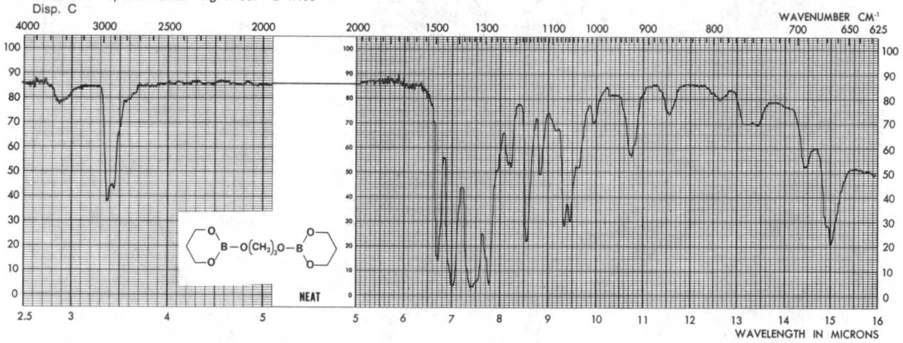

D

14,705-2 4,4,6-Trimethyl-2-vinyl-1,3,2-dioxaborinane
M.W. 154.02 n_D^{20} 1.4290 b.p. 69-70°/35 mm.

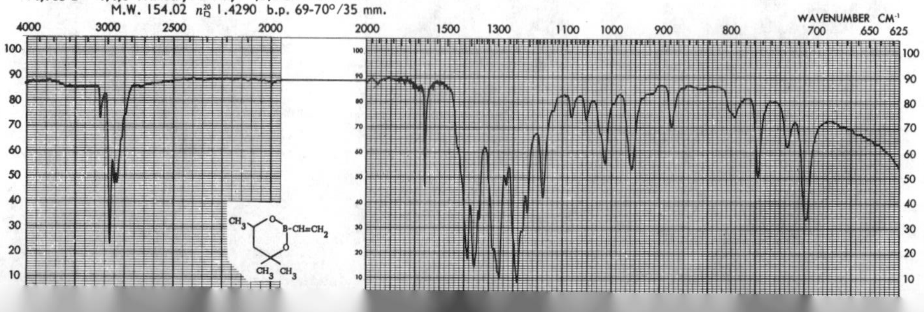

E

14,706-0 2-(2-Dimethylaminoethoxy)-4-methyl-1,3,2-dioxaborinane, tech.
M.W. 187.05 n_D^{20} 1.4392
NEAT

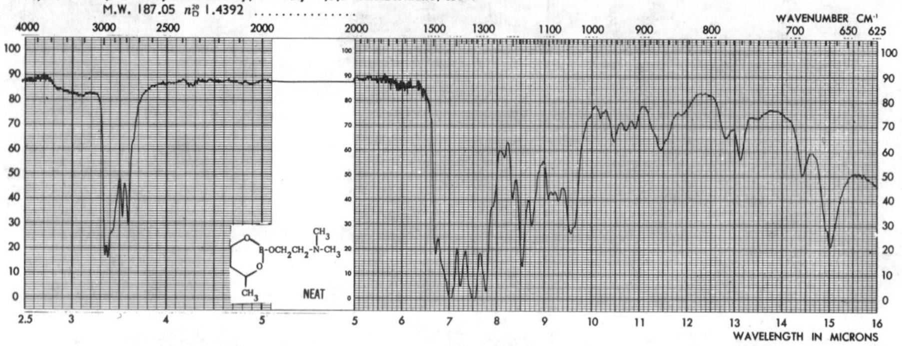

F

T5840-8 Triethanolamine borate (2,2',2''-nitrilotriethyl borate)
M.W. 156.98 m.p. 232-234°
NUJOL MULL

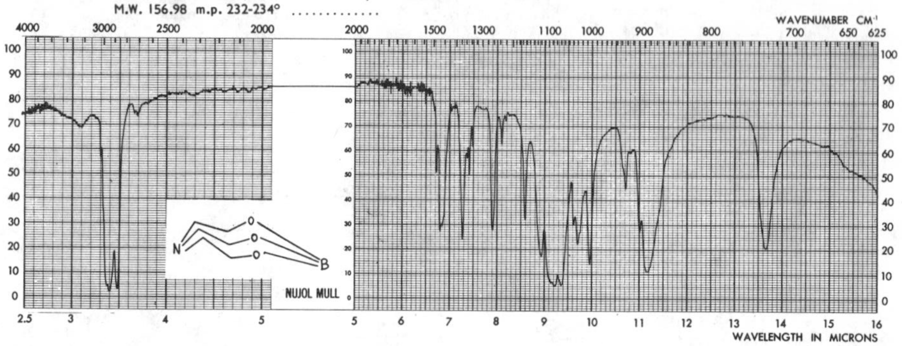

G

T6760-1 Triisopropanolamine borate [1,1',1''-nitrilotri-(2-propanol) borate]
M.W. 199.06 m.p. 151-155°
NUJOL MULL

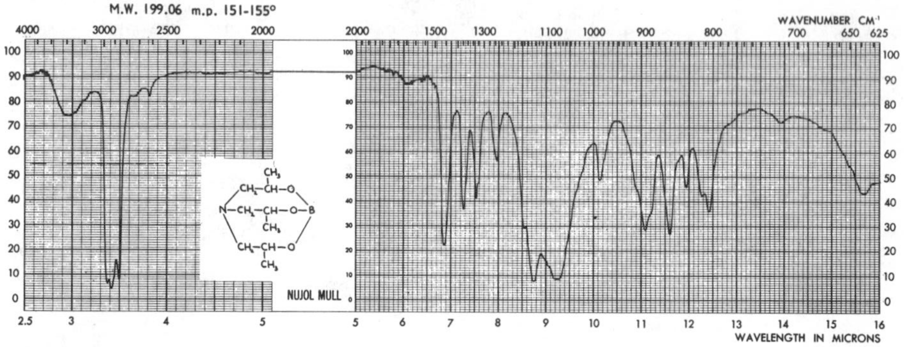

H

18,004-1
Tri-o-tolyl borate
$(CH_3C_6H_4O)_3B$
M.W. 332.21

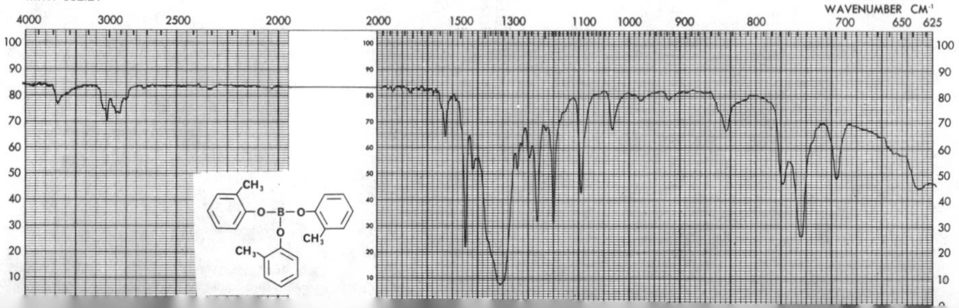

A 14,707-9 **2,4,6-Trichloro-1,3,5-trimethylborazine**
M.W. 225.92 m.p. 154-158° ....

B 13,118-0 **2,4,6-Trichloro-1,3,5-triphenylborazine**
M.W. 412.13 m.p. 289-292° ....

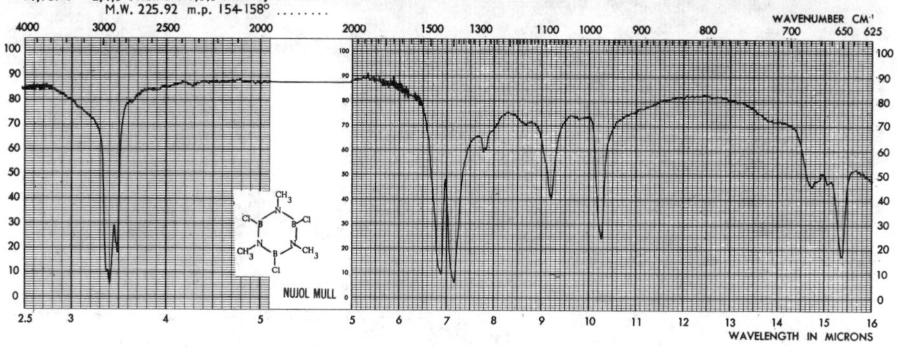

C P1982-5 **2-Phenyl-1,3,2-benzodiazaborole** (2-phenyl-2,1,3-benzoboradiazole)
M.W. 194.05 m.p. 209-213° ....

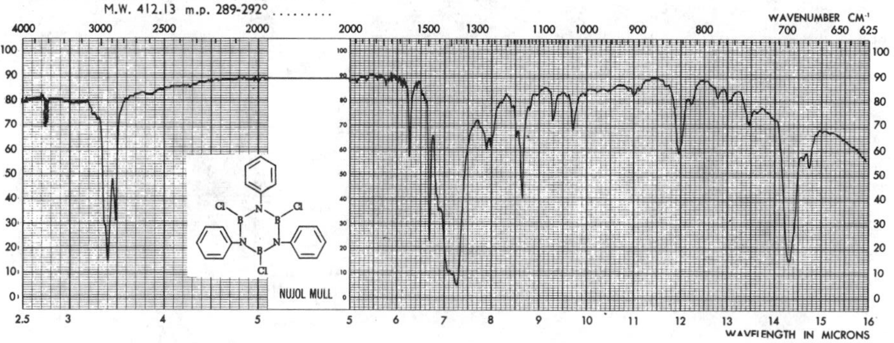

D 10,134-6 **Dichlorophenylborane** (phenylboron dichloride)
$C_6H_5BCl_2$ M.W. 158.82 n_D^{20} 1.5465 b.p. 66°/11 mm.

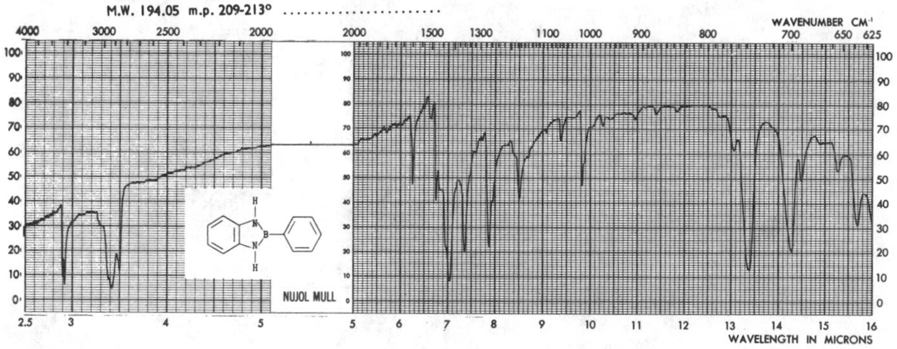

E **diphenylborate, natural product Reagent A)**
$(C_6H_5)_2BOCH_2CH_2NH_2$ M.W. 225.10 m.p. 195-198° .....

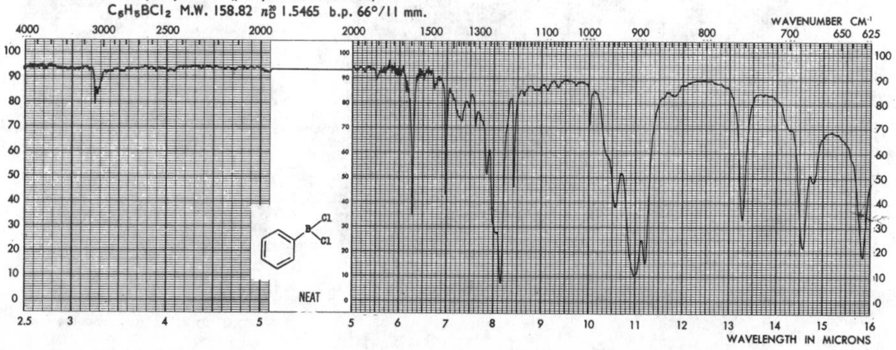

F T8220-1 **Triphenylborine**
$(C_6H_5)_3B$ M.W. 242.13 ..

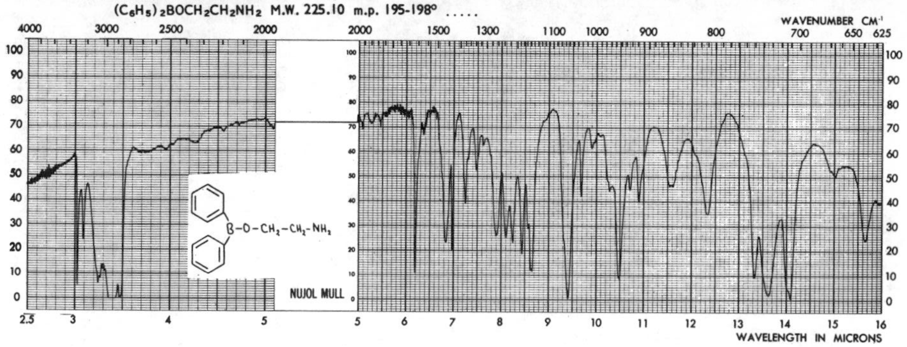

G 22,517-7
Trimesitylborane
$[2,4,6\text{-}(CH_3)_3C_6H_2]_3B$ FW 368.38 mp 193-195°
Fieser 3,308 Disp. C

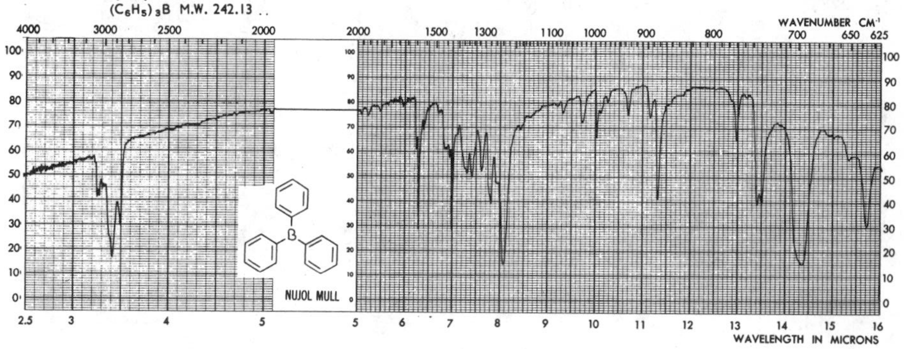

H T2540-2 **Tetraphenylboron sodium** (sodium tetraphenylborate), **puriss.**
$(C_6H_5)_4BNa$ M.W. 342.23 m.p. > 300° ..

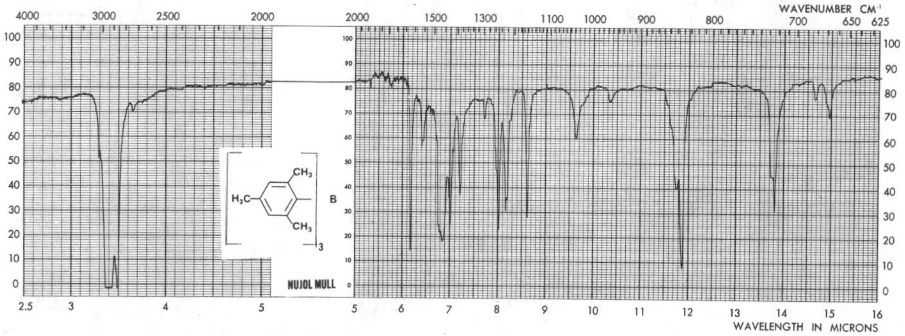

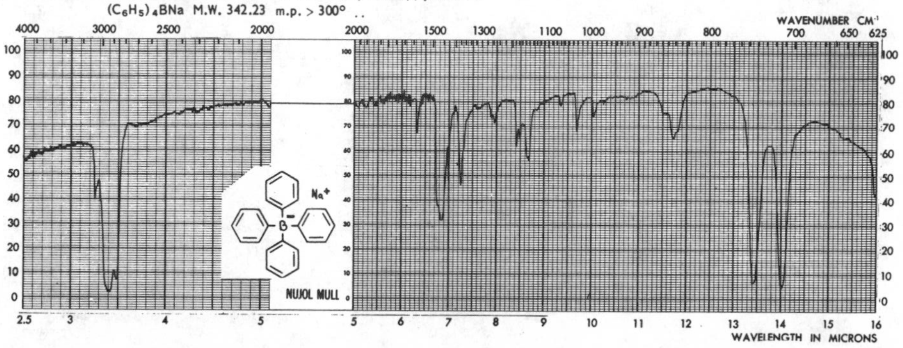

16,324-4
1-Butaneboronic acid, 99+%, GOLD LABEL
(-n-butylboronic acid)
$CH_3(CH_2)_3B(OH)_2$
M.W. 101.94 m.p. 94-96° *HYGROSCOPIC*

A

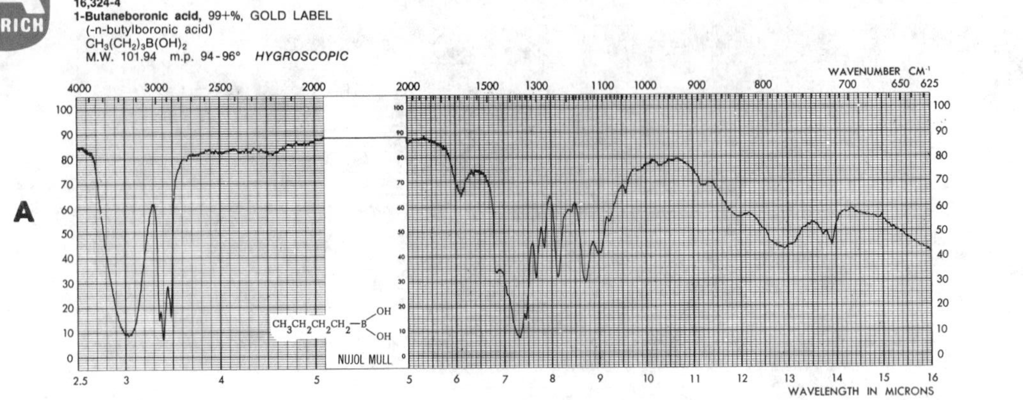

P2000-9 Phenylboric acid (benzeneboronic acid)
$C_6H_5B(OH)_2$ M.W. 121.93 m.p. 217-220°

B

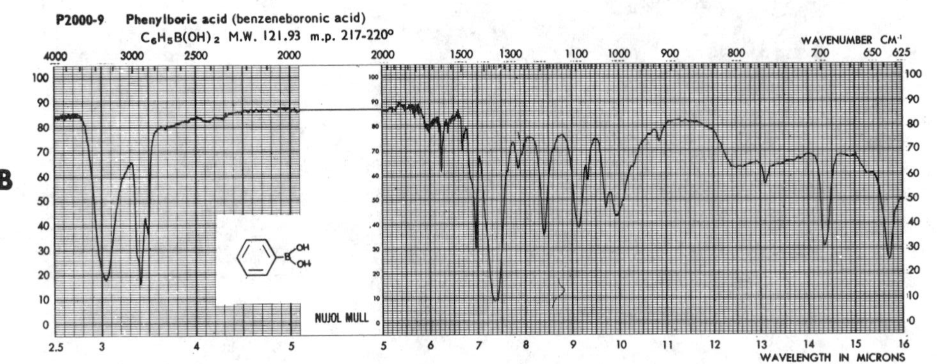

B7595-6 p-Bromophenylboric acid (4-bromobenzeneboronic acid)
$BrC_6H_4B(OH)_2$ M.W. 200.83 m.p. 260-272° ....

C

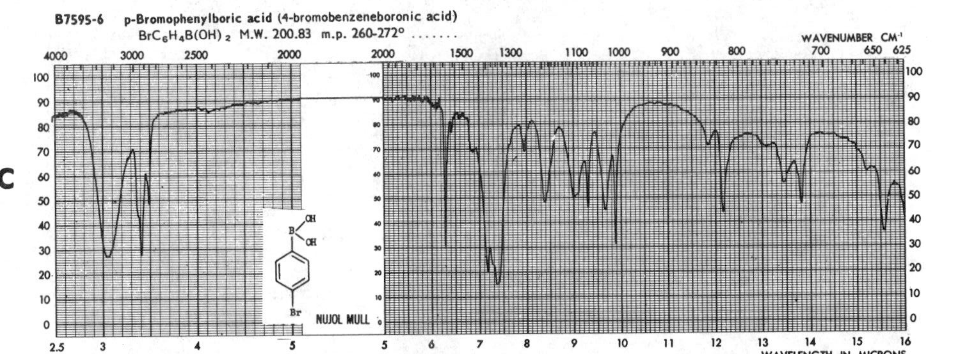

A7175-1 m-Aminophenylboric acid (3-aminobenzeneboronic acid)
hemisulfate
$H_2NC_6H_4B(OH)_2 \cdot \frac{1}{2}H_2SO_4$ M.W. 186.00
m.p. > 300° (dec.) ....

D

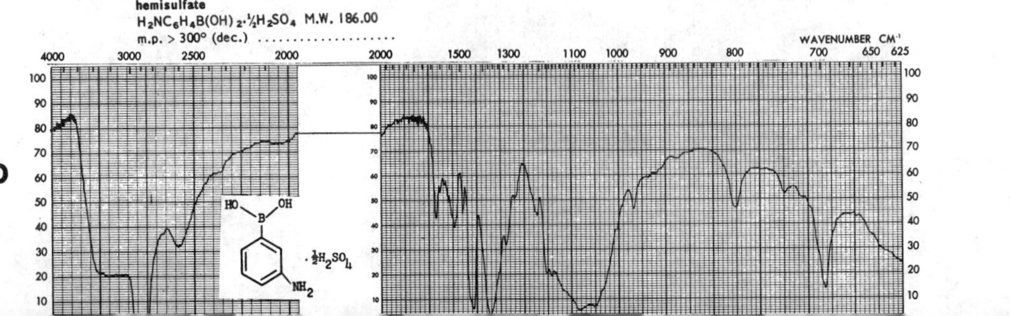

22,398-0
3-(5-Dimethylamino-1-naphthalenesulfonylamino)-benzeneboronic acid hydrate, 98%
$(CH_3)_2NC_{10}H_6SO_2NHC_6H_4B(OH)_2 \cdot xH_2O$ FW 370.24
Disp. C

E

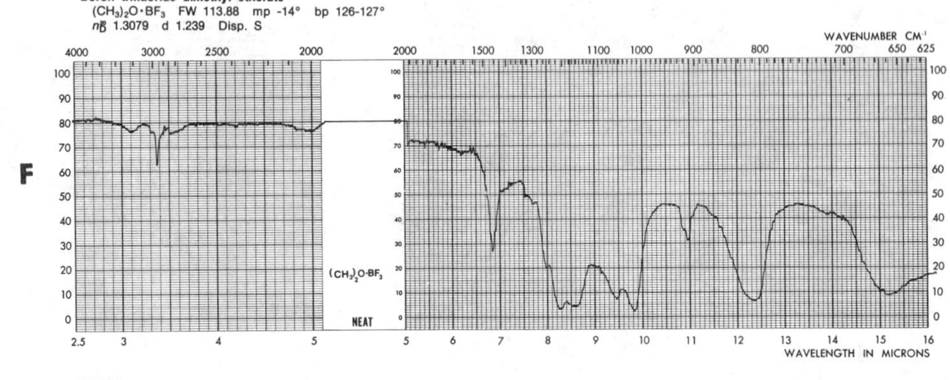

21,884-7
Boron trifluoride dimethyl etherate
$(CH_3)_2O \cdot BF_3$ FW 113.88 mp -14° bp 126-127°
n_D^{20} 1.3079 d 1.239 Disp. S

F

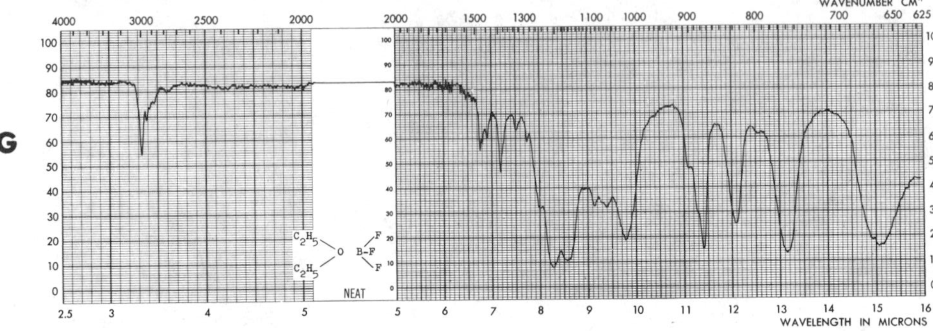

17,550-1
Boron trifluoride etherate
$(C_2H_5)_2O \cdot BF_3$
M.W. 141.93 b.p. 126° n_D^{20} 1.3439 d 1.154
Fieser **1**,70 **2**,35 **3**,33 *CORROSIVE*

G

ALDRICH

ORGANOMETALLIC AND ARSENIC COMPOUNDS

Aside from the influence that the elements arsenic, antimony, tin, lead and mercury have on the aromatic ring absorptions, characteristic bands are not present in the infrared spectra of compounds with these elements. However, sharp bands at 7 and between 9 and 10 μ (1430 and 1110 – 1000 cm^{-1}) can be noted when the above mentioned elements are attached directly to the aromatic ring.

The arsonic acid group displays its broad OH bands between 3 and 5 μ (3335 – 2000 cm^{-1}). In addition it absorbs strongly between 11 and 13.5 μ (910 – 740 cm^{-1}). (See spectra 1558B to 1559B).

In spectra 1559H and 1560A where CH_3 groups are attached directly to the tin atom, strong bands appear near 13 μ (770 cm^{-1}). In the longer chain butyl compounds, a strong absorption is noted between 14 and 15.5 μ (715 – 645 cm^{-1}). (See spectra 1560B—1561B). This band is also present in the tetrabutyllead spectrum 1561E.

In the cyclopentadienyl spectra, 1563C—1565H, the C–H of the ring absorbs at 3.2 μ (3125 cm^{-1}) along with bands between 9 and 10 μ (1110 – 1000 cm^{-1}) and a strong absorption between 11.5 and 12.5 μ (870 – 800 cm^{-1}).

The carbonyl compounds of spectra 1566C through 1567C display their C=O stretch band between 4.8 and 5.7 μ (2085 – 1755 cm^{-1}).

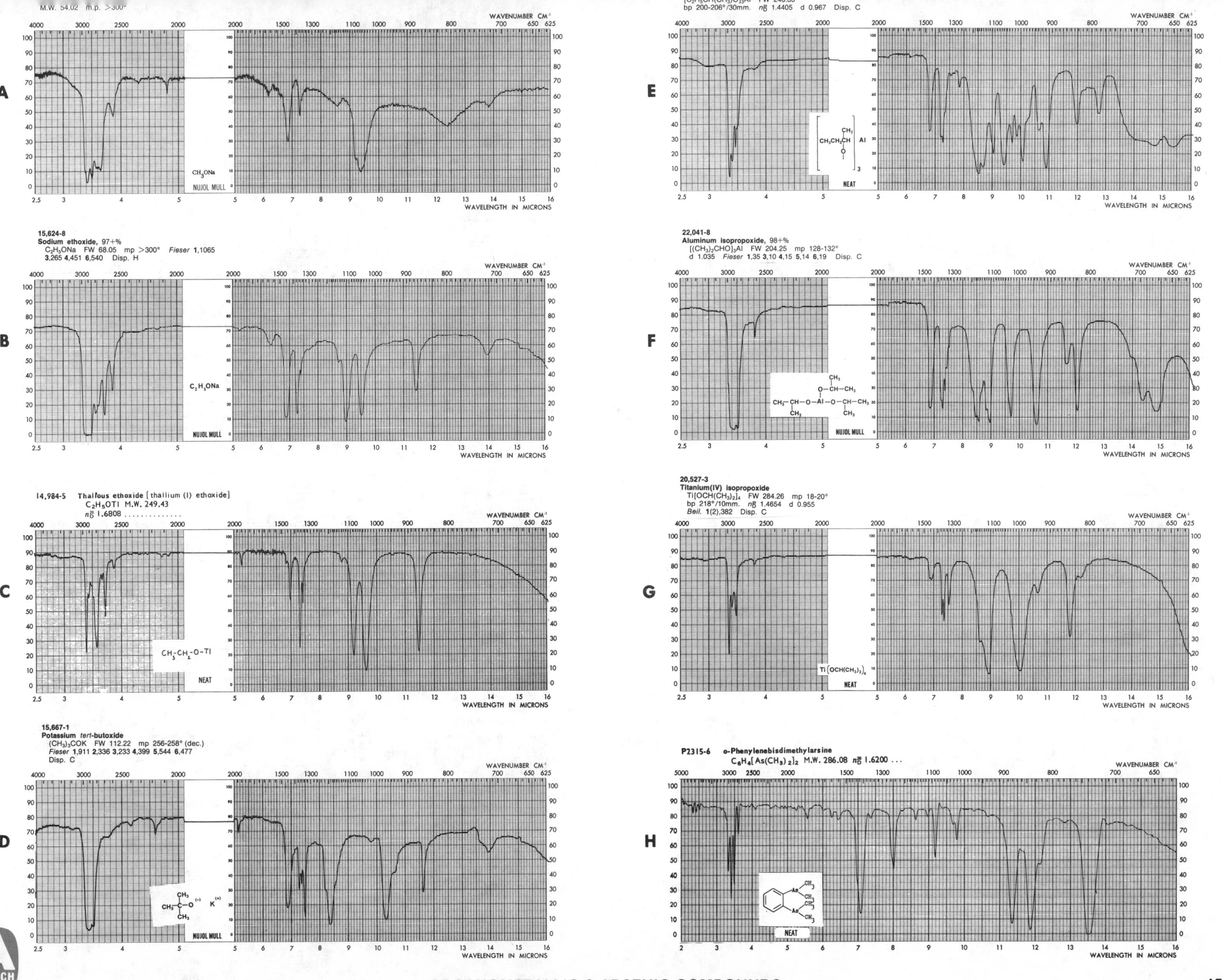

ALDRICH

ORGANOMETALLIC & ARSENIC COMPOUNDS

A

12,755-8 **Methylenebis-(diphenylarsine)**
$(C_6H_5)_2AsCH_2As(C_6H_5)_2$ M.W. 472.30
m.p. 96-98°

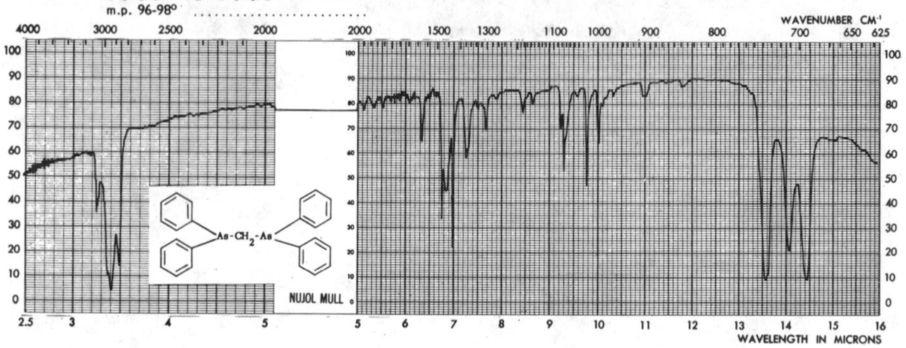

NUJOL MULL

B

11,925-3 **Ethylenebis-(diphenylarsine)**
$(C_6H_5)_2AsCH_2CH_2As(C_6H_5)_2$ M.W. 486.32
m.p. 83-87°

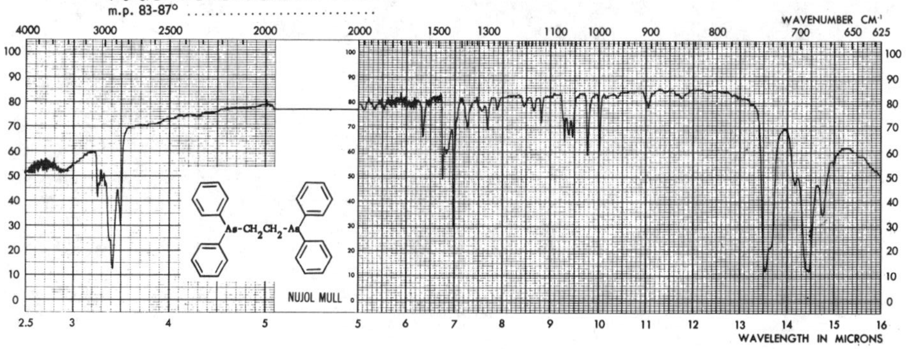

NUJOL MULL

C

T8190-6 **Triphenylarsine**
$(C_6H_5)_3As$ M.W. 306.21 m.p. 60-61.5°

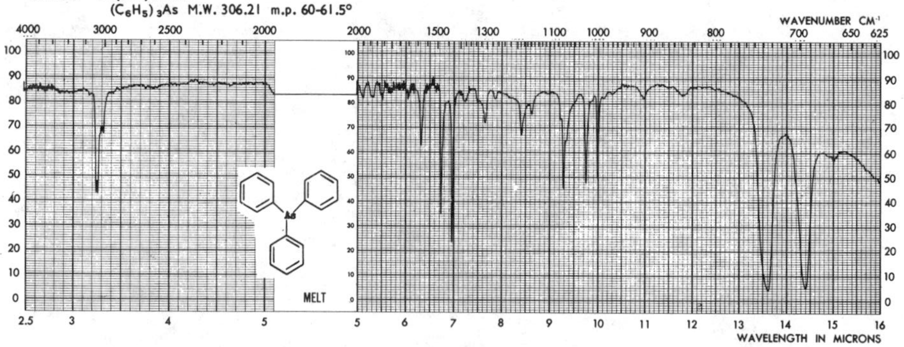

MELT

D

T2530-5 **Tetraphenylarsonium chloride hydrate**
$(C_6H_5)_4AsCl{\cdot}xH_2O$ M.W. 418.80 (anhydrous) m.p. 264-265°

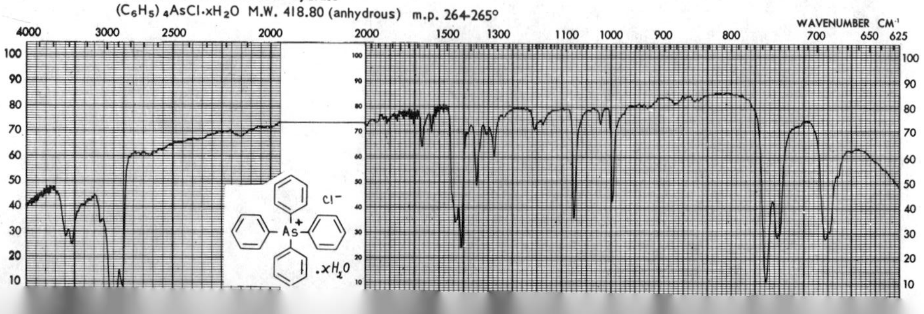

E

14,745-1 **Tetraphenylarsonium chloride hydrochloride dihydrate**
$(C_6H_5)_4AsCl{\cdot}HCl{\cdot}2H_2O$ M.W. 491.29
m.p. 205-209°

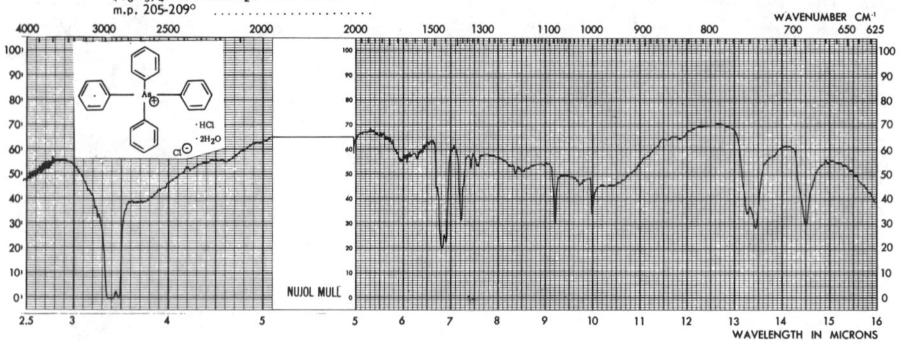

NUJOL MULL

F

13,705-7 **(Methyl)-triphenylarsonium iodide**
$CH_3As(C_6H_5)_3I$ M.W. 448.18 m.p. 175-176° (dec.)

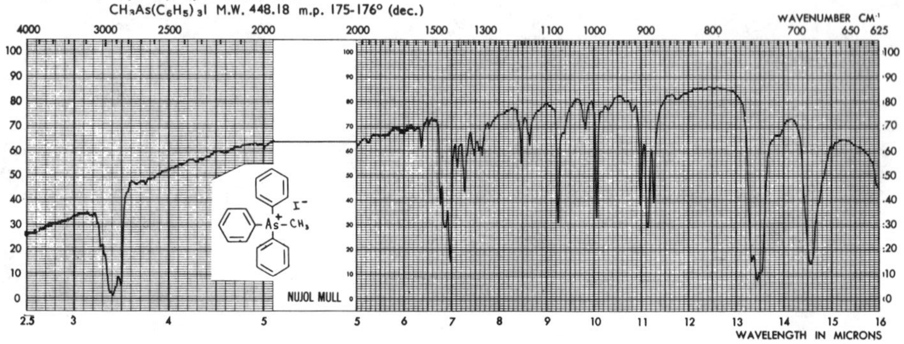

NUJOL MULL

G

18,472-1
Phenylarsine oxide (oxophenylarsine)
$C_6H_5As{=}O$
M.W. 168.03 m.p. 138-141° Beil. 16(1),438

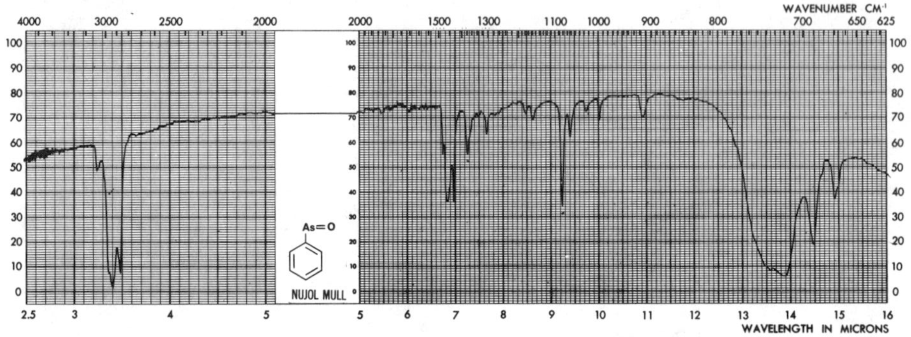

NUJOL MULL

H

11,589-4 **Triphenylarsine oxide hydrate**
$(C_6H_5)_3As(O){\cdot}xH_2O$ M.W. 322.24 (anhydrous)
m.p. 190-192° (anhydrous)

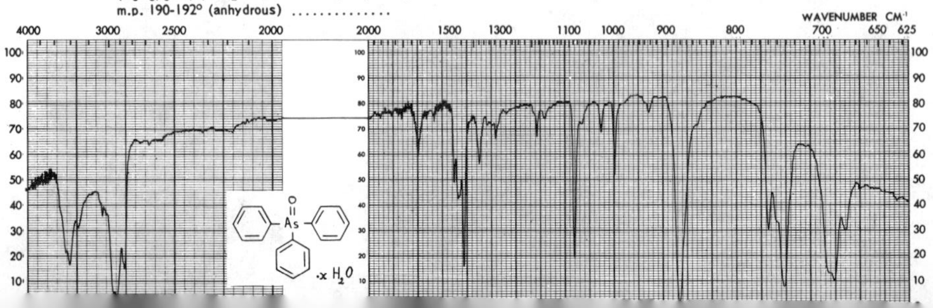

A

M.W. 277.59

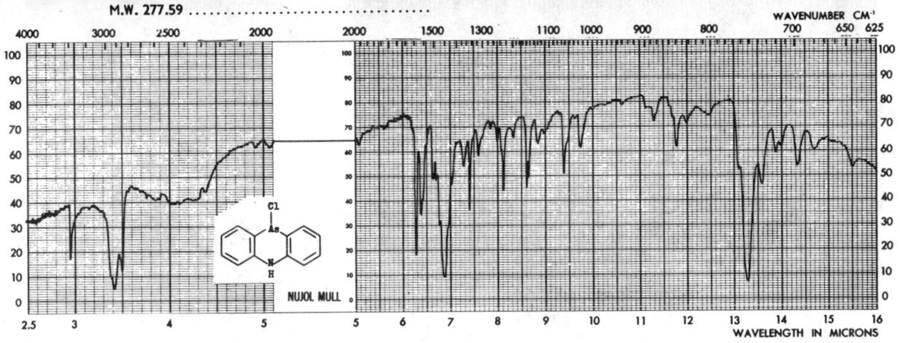

B

11,530-4 Arsonoacetic acid, disodium salt monohydrate
HOAs(O)(ONa)$CH_2CO_2Na \cdot H_2O$ M.W. 245.96
m.p. 207-209°

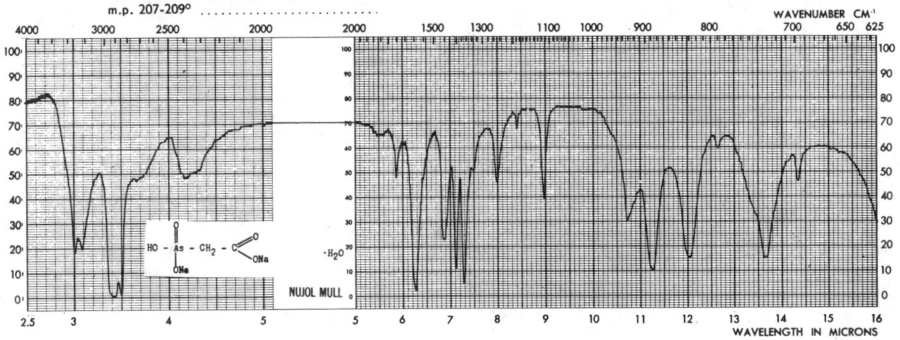

C

11,683-1 o-Phenylenediarsonic acid
$C_6H_4(AsO_3H_2)_2$ M.W. 325.97 m.p. > 330°

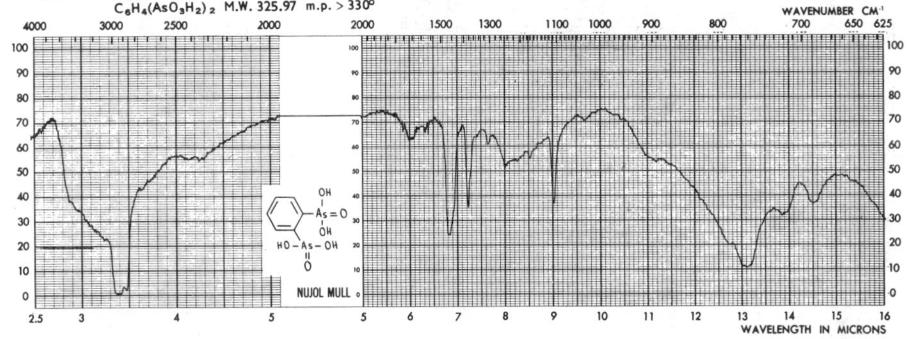

D

C2400-0 4-Chlorobenzenearsonic acid
$ClC_6H_4As(O)(OH)_2$ M.W. 236.49 m.p. > 310°

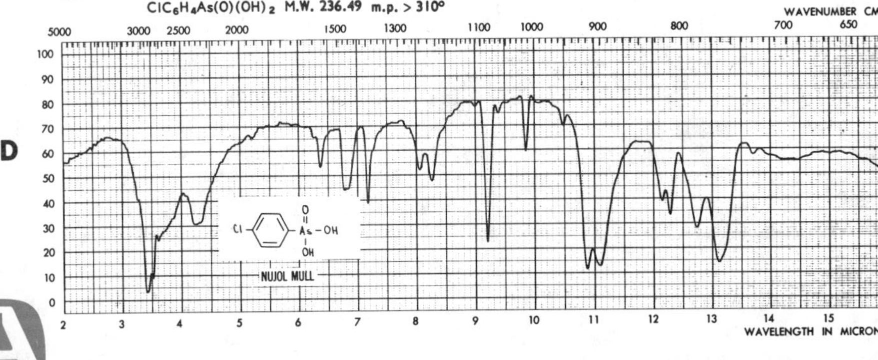

E

11,011-6 p-Hydroxybenzenearsonic acid
$HOC_6H_4AsO_3H_2$ M.W. 218.03 m.p. 181-183° (dec.)

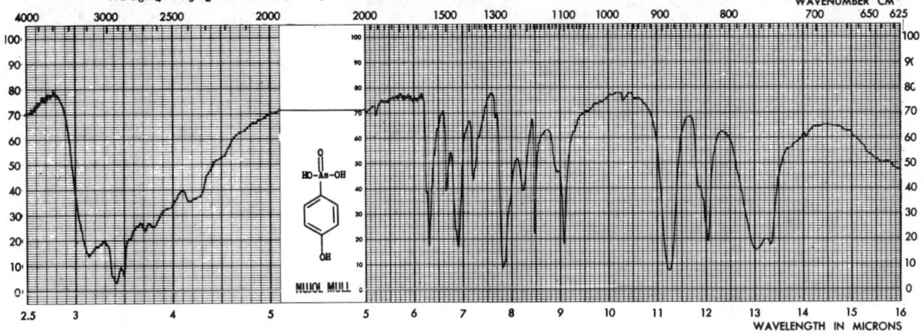

F

13,902-5 o-Arsanilic acid (o-aminobenzenearsonic acid)
$H_2NC_6H_4AsO_3H_2$ M.W. 217.06
m.p. 149-153°

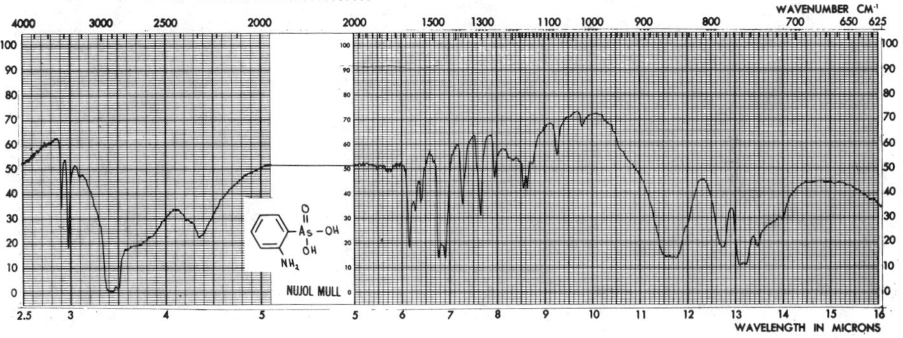

G

A9275-9 p-Arsanilic acid (p-aminobenzenearsonic acid)
$H_2NC_6H_4AsO_3H_2$ M.W. 217.06

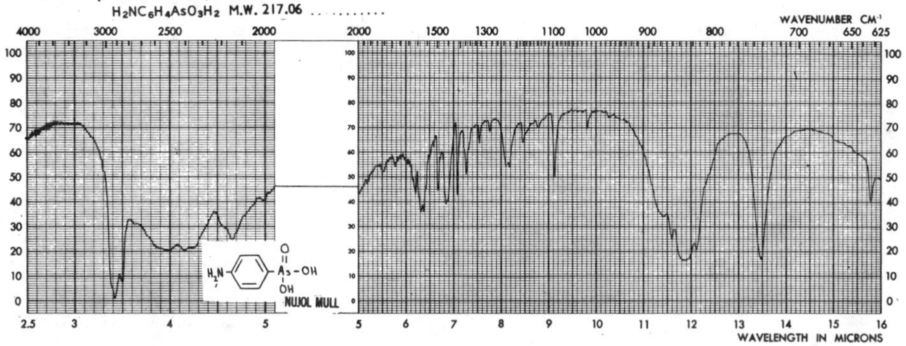

H

N1120-5 p-Nitrobenzenearsonic acid
$O_2NC_6H_4AsO_3H_2$ M.W. 247.04
m.p. > 310°

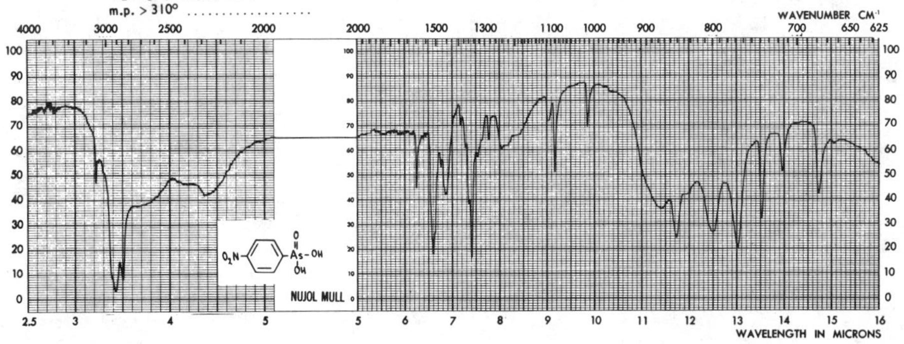

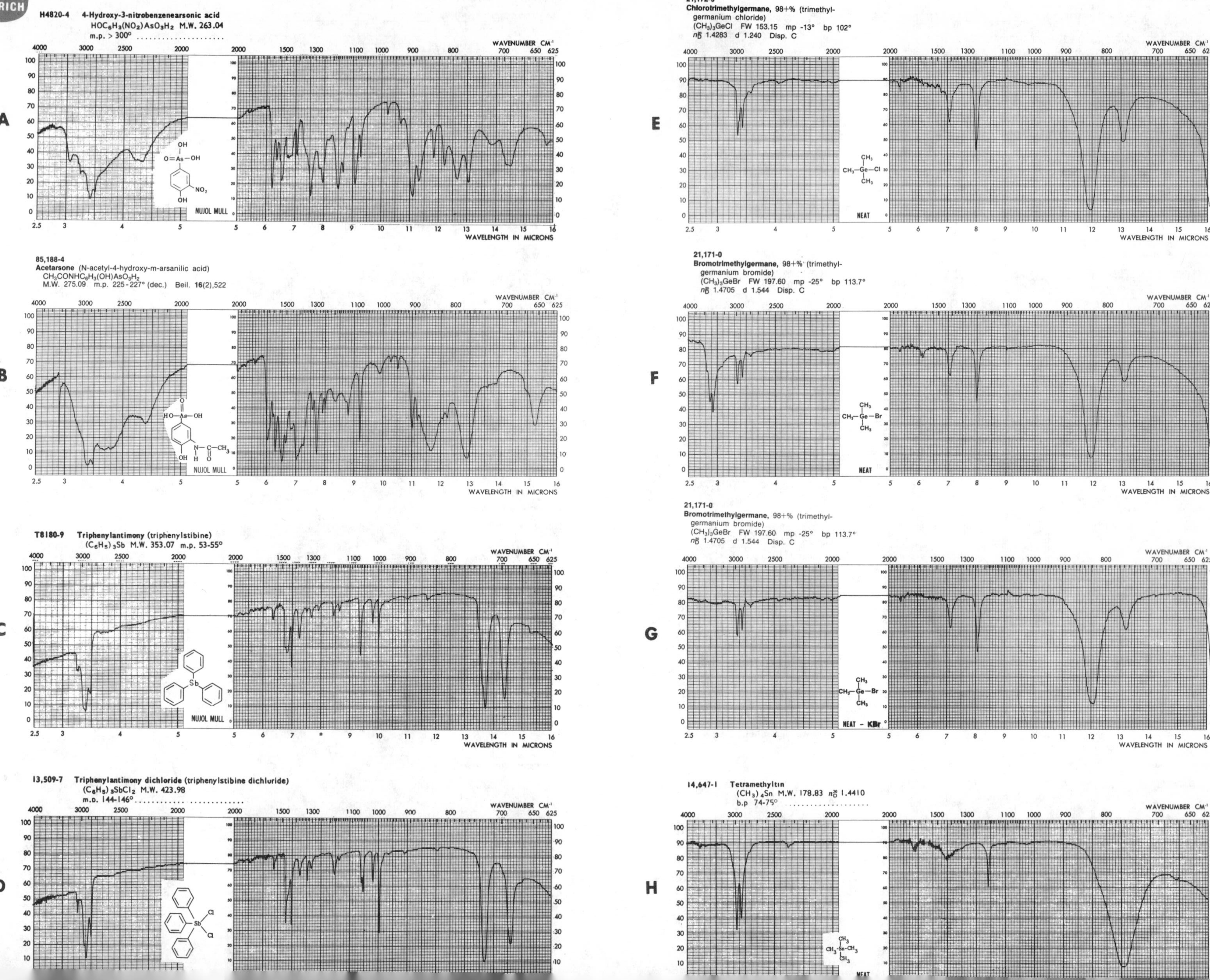
ALDRICH
A
H4820-4 4-Hydroxy-3-nitrobenzenearsonic acid
$HOC_6H_3(NO_2)AsO_3H_2$ M.W. 263.04
m.p. > 300°
NUJOL MULL
B
85,188-4
Acetarsone (N-acetyl-4-hydroxy-m-arsanilic acid)
$CH_3CONHC_6H_3(OH)AsO_3H_2$
M.W. 275.09 m.p. 225-227° (dec.) Beil. 16(2),522
NUJOL MULL
C
T8180-9 Triphenylantimony (triphenylstibine)
$(C_6H_5)_3Sb$ M.W. 353.07 m.p. 53-55°
NUJOL MULL
D
13,509-7 Triphenylantimony dichloride (triphenylstibine dichloride)
$(C_6H_5)_3SbCl_2$ M.W. 423.98
m.p. 144-146°
E
21,172-9
Chlorotrimethylgermane, 98+% (trimethylgermanium chloride)
$(CH_3)_3GeCl$ FW 153.15 mp -13° bp 102°
n_D^{20} 1.4283 d 1.240 Disp. C
NEAT
F
21,171-0
Bromotrimethylgermane, 98+% (trimethylgermanium bromide)
$(CH_3)_3GeBr$ FW 197.60 mp -25° bp 113.7°
n_D^{20} 1.4705 d 1.544 Disp. C
NEAT
G
21,171-0
Bromotrimethylgermane, 98+% (trimethylgermanium bromide)
$(CH_3)_3GeBr$ FW 197.60 mp -25° bp 113.7°
n_D^{20} 1.4705 d 1.544 Disp. C
NEAT - KBr
H
14,647-1 Tetramethyltin
$(CH_3)_4Sn$ M.W. 178.83 n_D^{20} 1.4410
b.p 74-75°
NEAT
WAVENUMBER CM⁻¹
WAVELENGTH IN MICRONS

A

$(CH_3)_3SnCl$ M.W. 199.25 m.p. 37-39.5°

MELT

B

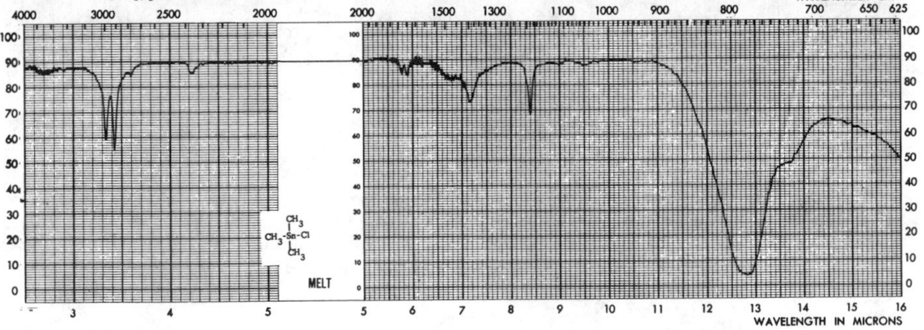

T600-8 **Tetra-n-butyltin**
$[CH_3(CH_2)_3]_4Sn$ M.W. 347.15 n_D^{20} 1.4742

NEAT

C

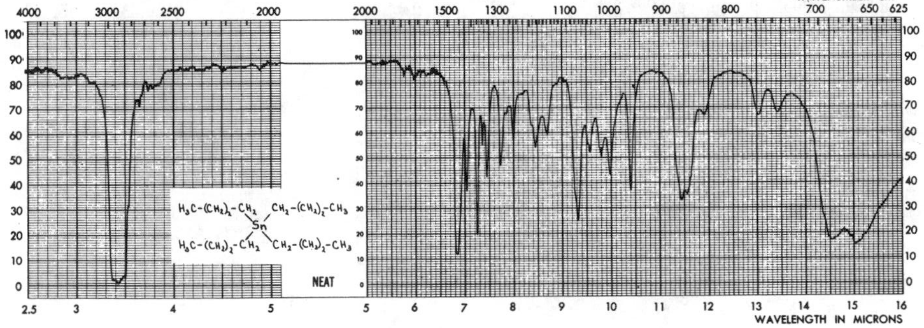

17,621-4
Tetrabutyldiacetoxytin oxide dimer (acetoxydibutyltin oxide dimer)
$[(CH_3CO_2Sn[(CH_2)_3CH_3]_2)_2O]_2$
M.W. 1199.87 m.p. 56-58°

NUJOL MULL

D

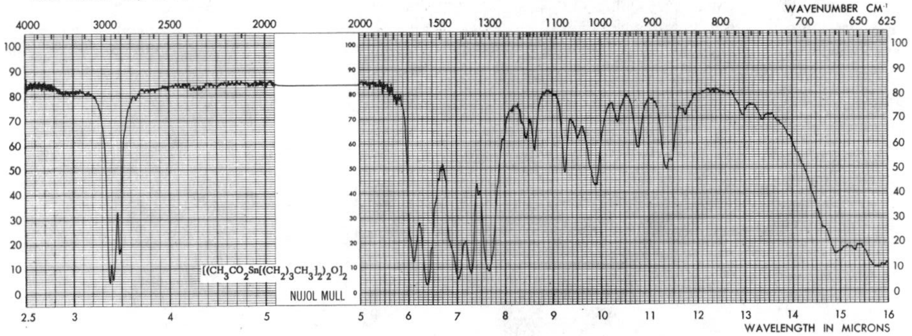

H520-0 **Hexa-n-butylditin**
$[(C_4H_9)_3Sn-]_2$ M.W. 580.08 n_D^{20} 1.5112

NEAT

E

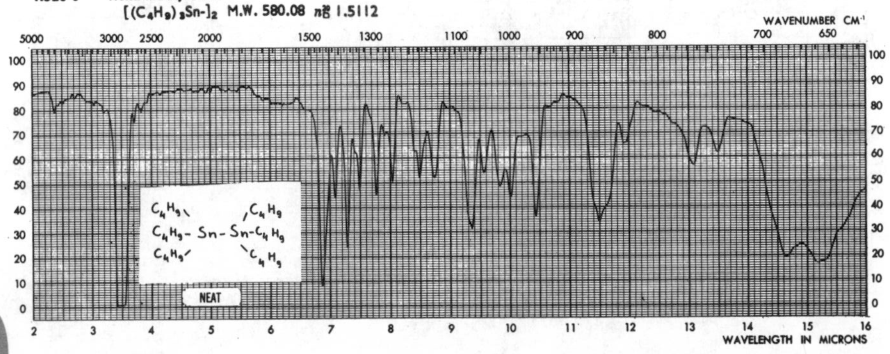

b.p. 171-173°/25 mm.

NEAT

F

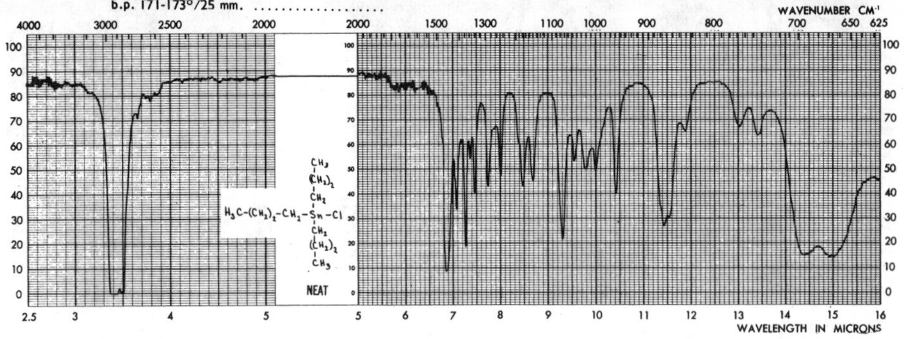

20,105-7
Butyltin trichloride, 95% (butyltrichlorotin)
$CH_3(CH_2)_3SnCl_3$ FW 282.17 bp 93°/10mm.
n_D^{20} 1.5229 d 1.693 Disp. C

NEAT

G

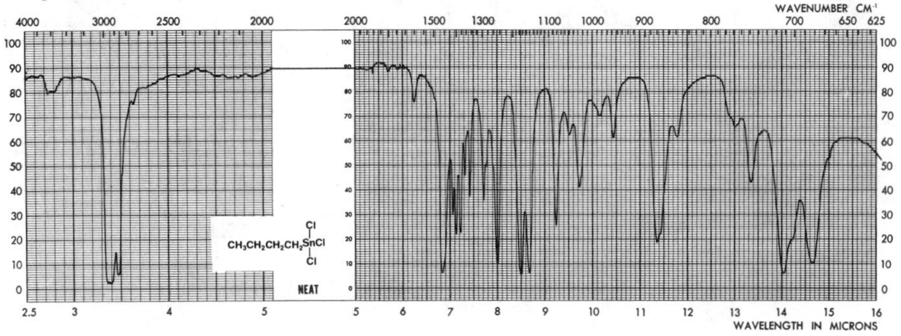

T5120-9 **Tri-n-butyltin methoxide**
$[CH_3(CH_2)_3]_3SnOCH_3$ M.W. 321.07
n_D^{20} 1.4738

NEAT

H

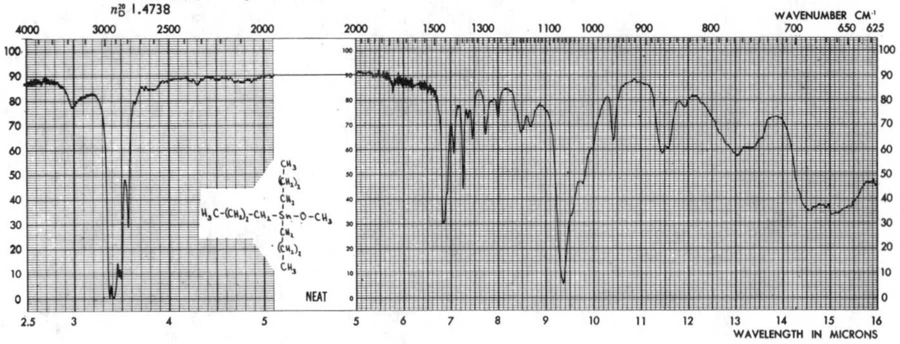

18,308-3
Dibutyltin oxide (dibutyloxotin)
$[CH_3(CH_2)_3]_2Sn(=O)$
M.W. 248.92 m.p. >300° Beil. **4**(1),588

NUJOL MULL

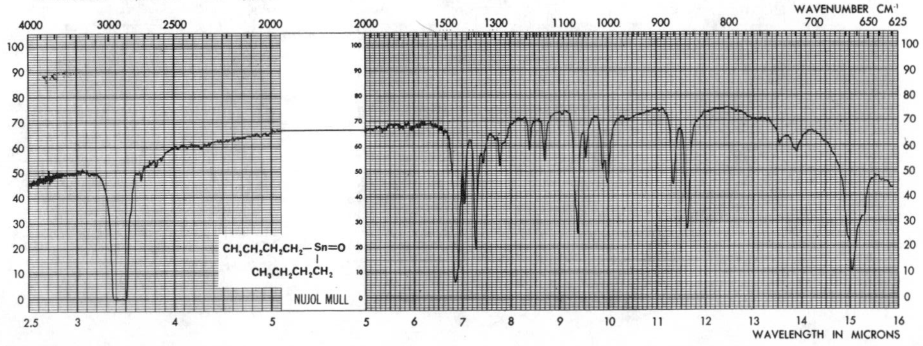

A D4980 Di-n-butyltin dimethoxide
$(C_4H_9)_2Sn(OCH_3)_2$ M.W. 294.99 n_D^{20} 1.5095

B B5338-3 Bis-(tri-n-butyltin)-oxide
$[CH_3(CH_2)_3]_3SnOSn[(CH_2)_3CH_3]_3$ M.W. 596.08
n_D^{20} 1.4864

C 11,361-1 Bis-(triphenyltin) oxide
$[(C_6H_5)_3Sn]_2O$ M.W. 897.67 m.p. 119.5-123°

D T2672-7 Tetraphenyltin
$Sn(C_6H_5)_4$ M.W. 427.11 m.p. 227-230°

E 11,674-2 Tetra-n-butyllead
$[CH_3(CH_2)_3]_4Pb$ M.W. 435.66 n_D^{20} 1.4920

F 11,675-0 Di-n-butyldichlorolead
$[CH_3(CH_2)_3]_2PbCl_2$ M.W. 392.33
m.p. 211° (dec.)

G 11,676-9 (Methylthio)triphenyllead
$(C_6H_5)_3PbSCH_3$ M.W. 485.61
m.p. 105-107°

H T2640-9 Tetraphenyllead
$Pb(C_6H_5)_4$ M.W. 515.61 m.p. 227.5-228°

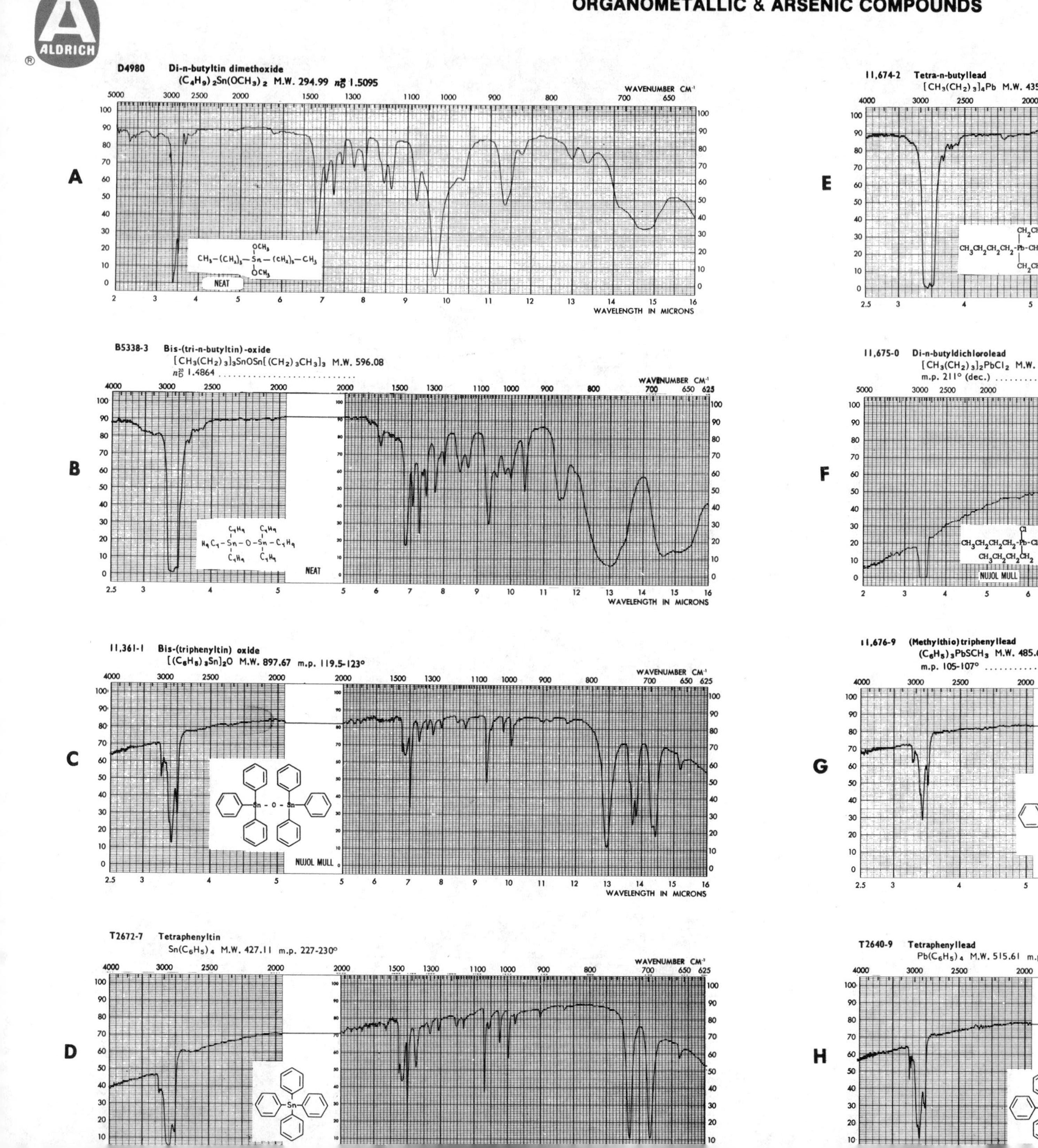

A

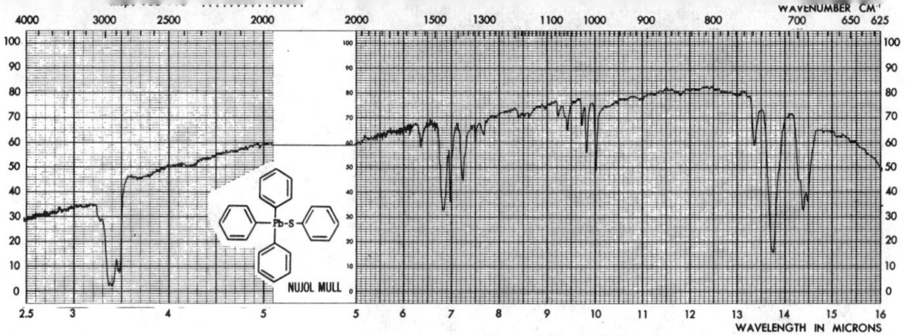

NUJOL MULL

11,921-0 Hexaphenyldilead
$(C_6H_5)_3PbPb(C_6H_5)_3$ M.W. 877.02
m.p. 160° (dec.) ....

B

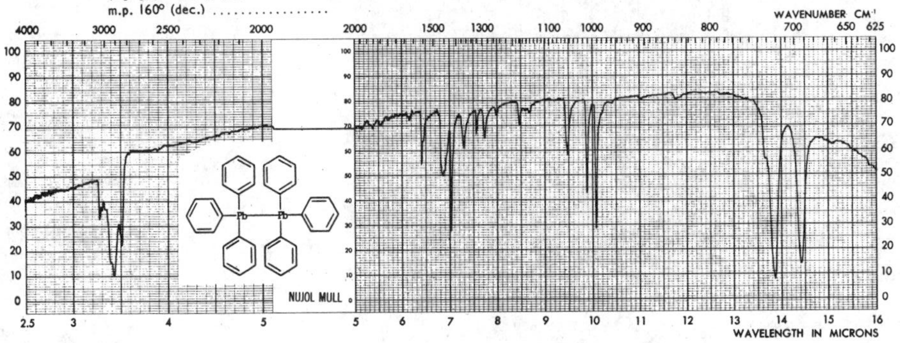

NUJOL MULL

21,666-6
Tetrakis(triphenylphosphine)palladium(0), 99%
$[(C_6H_5)_3P]_4Pd$ FW 1155.58 *Fieser* **6**,571 **7**,357
Disp. R

C

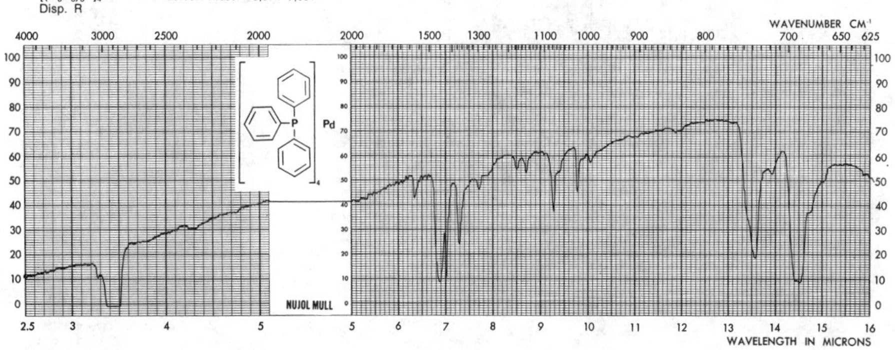

NUJOL MULL

19,998-2
Tris(triphenylphosphine)rhodium(I) chloride
(Wilkinson's catalyst)
$[(C_6H_5)_3P]_3RhCl$ FW 925.24 *Fieser* **1**,140 **3**,325
4,559 **5**,736 **6**,652 **7**,68 Disp. R

D

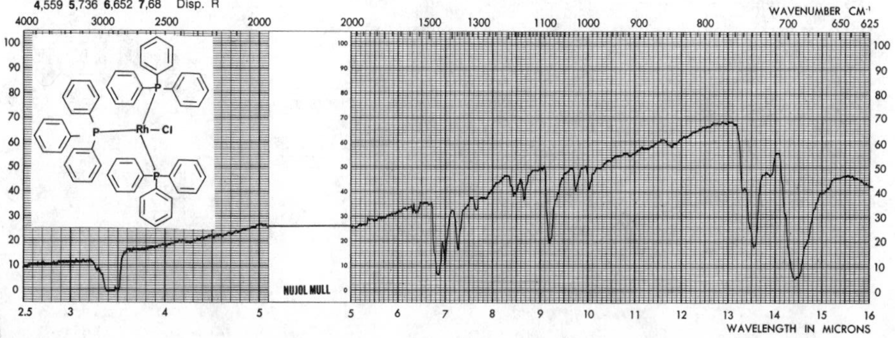

NUJOL MULL

E

NUJOL MULL

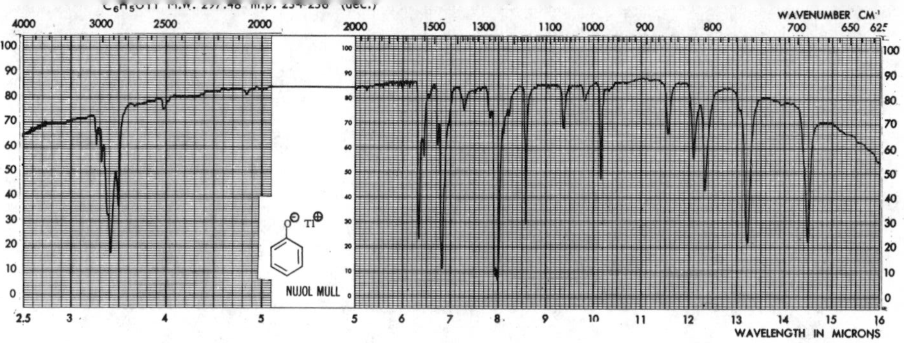

P2714-3 Phenylmercuric hydroxide
C_6H_5HgOH M.W. 294.70 m.p. 197° (dec.)

F

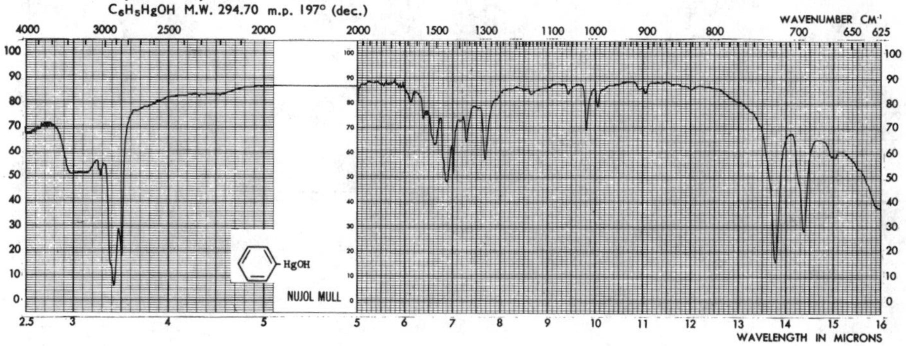

NUJOL MULL

P2713-5 Phenylmercuric chloride
C_6H_5HgCl M.W. 313.15 m.p. 252-253° ..

G

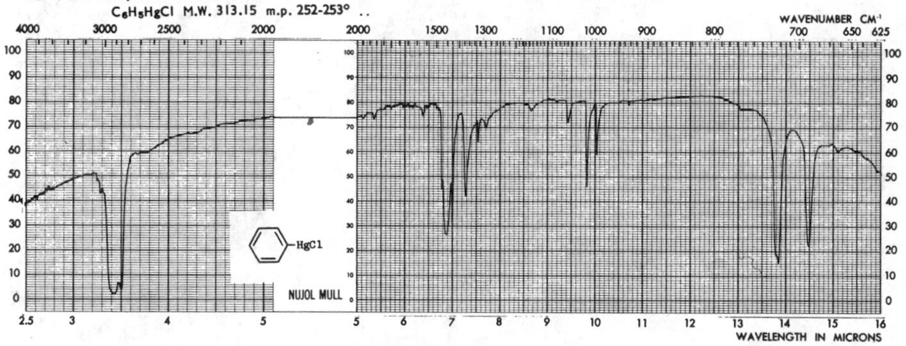

NUJOL MULL

C4960-7 4-Chloromercuribenzoic acid
$ClHgC_6H_4CO_2H$ M.W. 357.16
m.p. 287° (dec.) ....

H

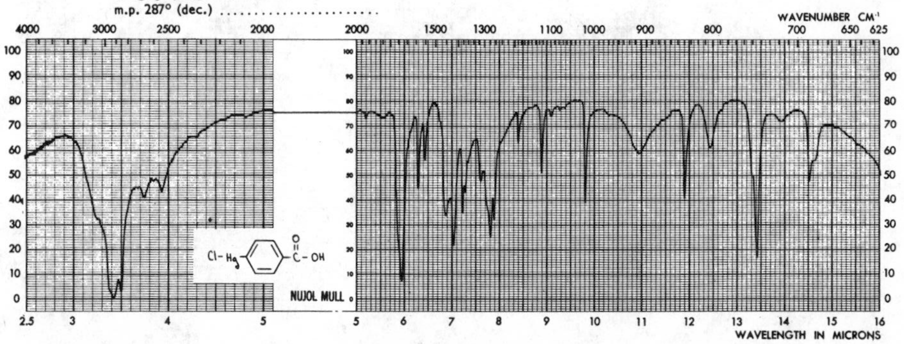

NUJOL MULL

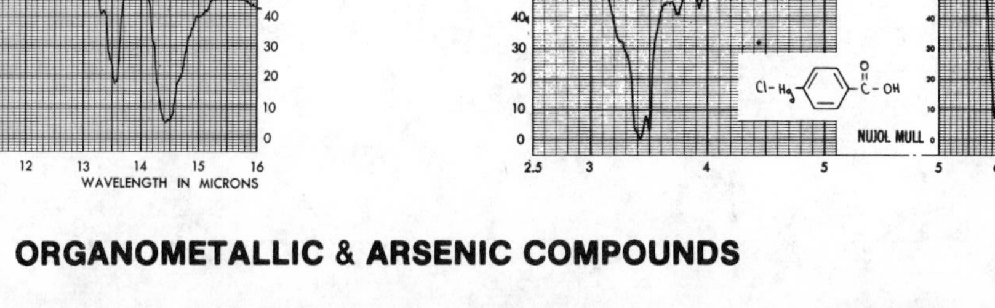

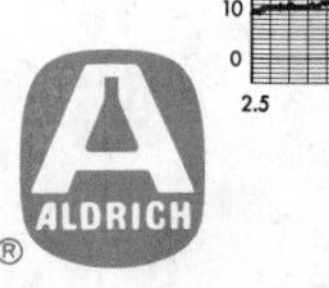

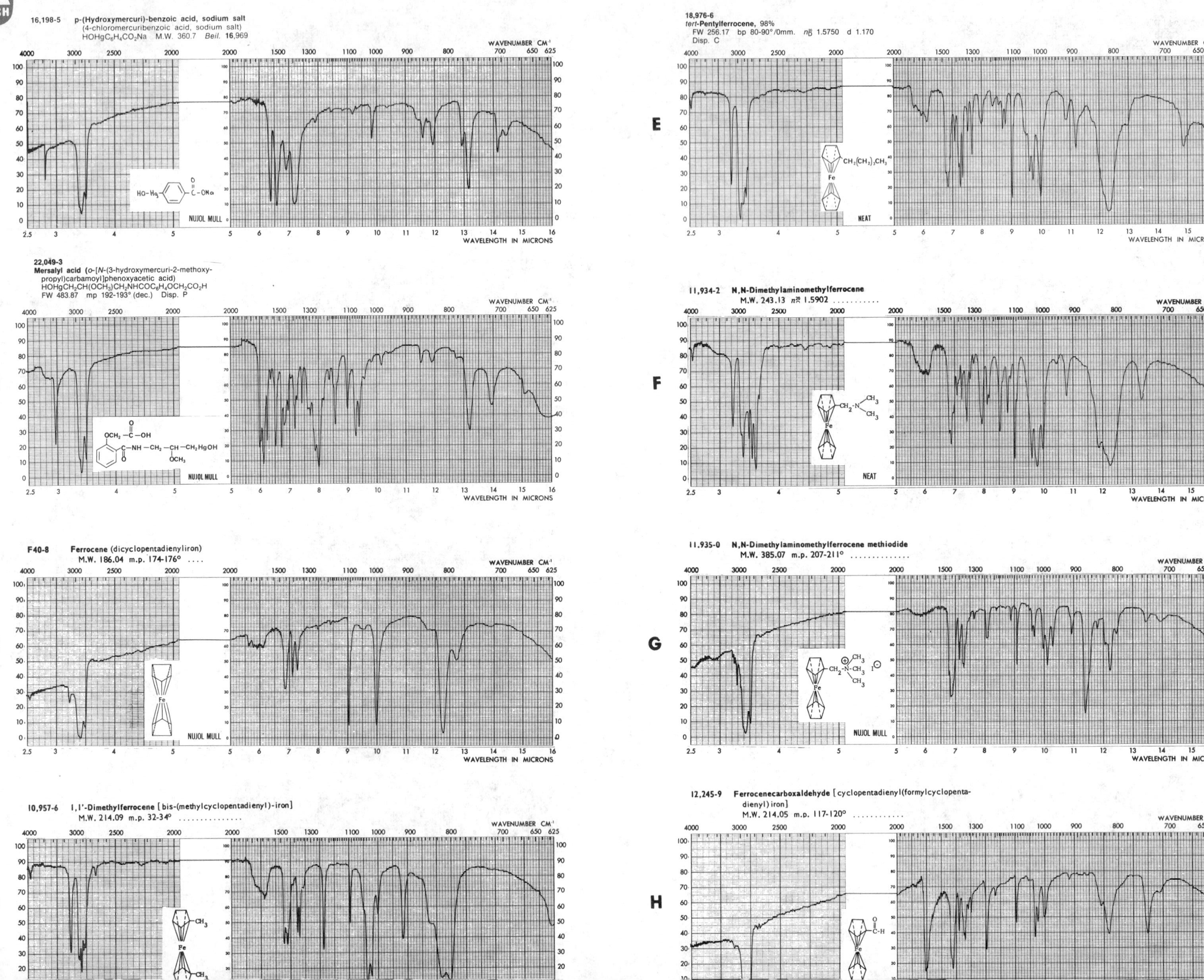
ALDRICH
A
16,198-5 p-(Hydroxymercuri)-benzoic acid, sodium salt
(4-chloromercuribenzoic acid, sodium salt)
$HOHgC_6H_4CO_2Na$ M.W. 360.7 Beil. 16,969
NUJOL MULL
B
22,049-3
Mersalyl acid (o-[N-(3-hydroxymercuri-2-methoxypropyl)carbamoyl]phenoxyacetic acid)
$HOHgCH_2CH(OCH_3)CH_2NHCOC_6H_4OCH_2CO_2H$
FW 483.87 mp 192-193° (dec.) Disp. P
NUJOL MULL
C
F40-8 Ferrocene (dicyclopentadienyliron)
M.W. 186.04 m.p. 174-176°
NUJOL MULL
D
10,957-6 1,1'-Dimethylferrocene [bis-(methylcyclopentadienyl)-iron]
M.W. 214.09 m.p. 32-34°
E
18,976-6
tert-Pentylferrocene, 98%
FW 256.17 bp 80-90°/0mm. n_D^{20} 1.5750 d 1.170
Disp. C
NEAT
F
11,934-2 N,N-Dimethylaminomethylferrocene
M.W. 243.13 n_D^{20} 1.5902
NEAT
G
11,935-0 N,N-Dimethylaminomethylferrocene methiodide
M.W. 385.07 m.p. 207-211°
NUJOL MULL
H
12,245-9 Ferrocenecarboxaldehyde [cyclopentadienyl(formylcyclopentadienyl)iron]
M.W. 214.05 m.p. 117-120°
WAVENUMBER CM⁻¹
WAVELENGTH IN MICRONS

A

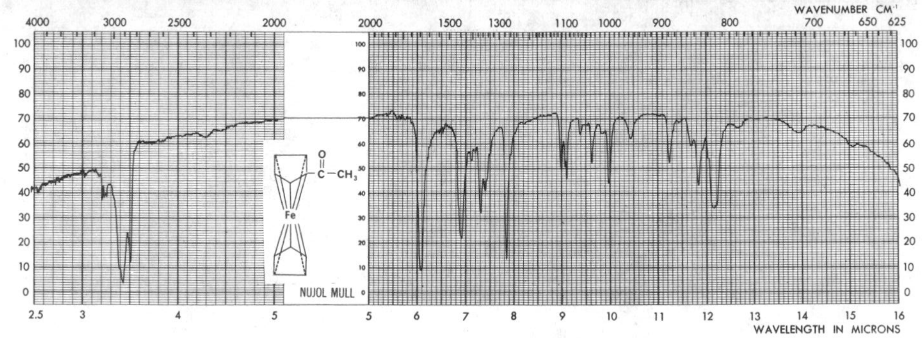

10,687-9
1,1'-Diacetylferrocene [bis-(acetylcyclopentadienyl)-iron]
M.W. 270.11 m.p. 125-127°

B

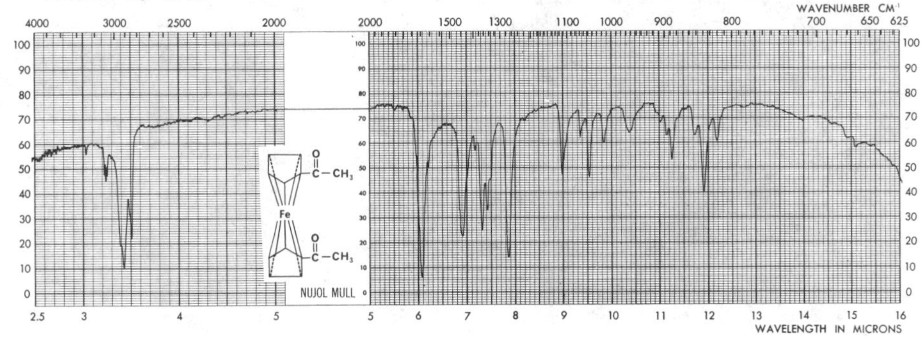

12,246-7 **Benzoylferrocene** [(benzoylcyclopentadienyl)cyclopentadienyl-iron]
M.W. 290.15 m.p. 108-110° ....

C

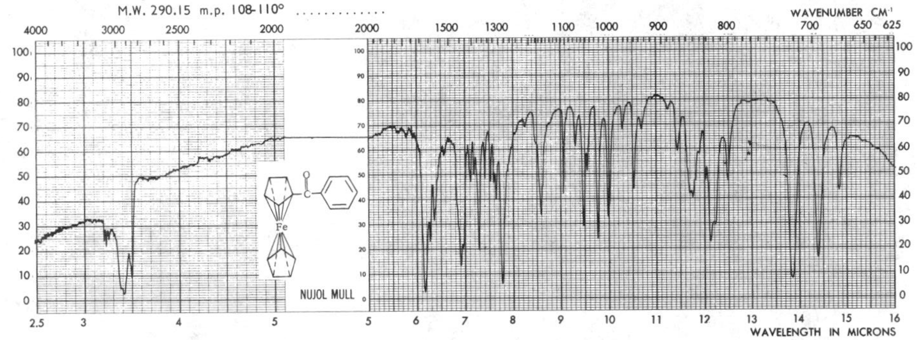

12,247-5 **1,1'-Dibenzoylferrocene** [bis-(benzoylcyclopentadienyl)-iron]
M.W. 394.26 m.p. 103-105° ....

D

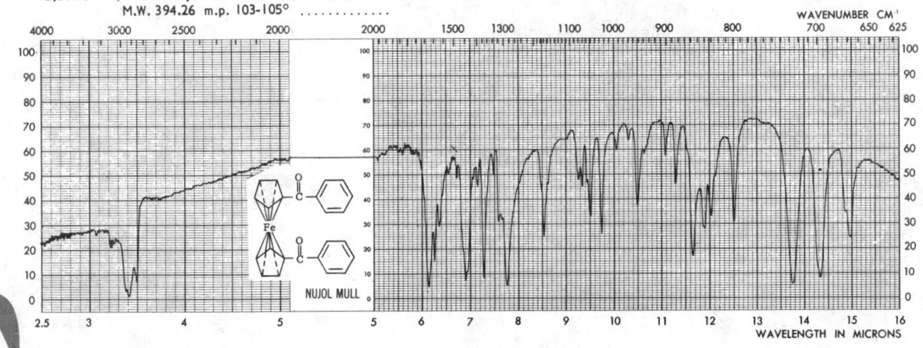

E

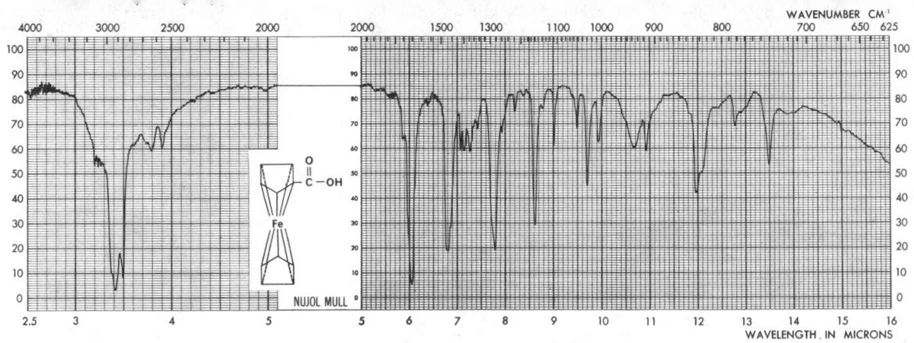

10,689-5
1,1'-Ferrocenedicarboxylic acid [bis-(carboxy-cyclopentadienyl)-iron]
M.W. 274.06 m.p. >300°

F

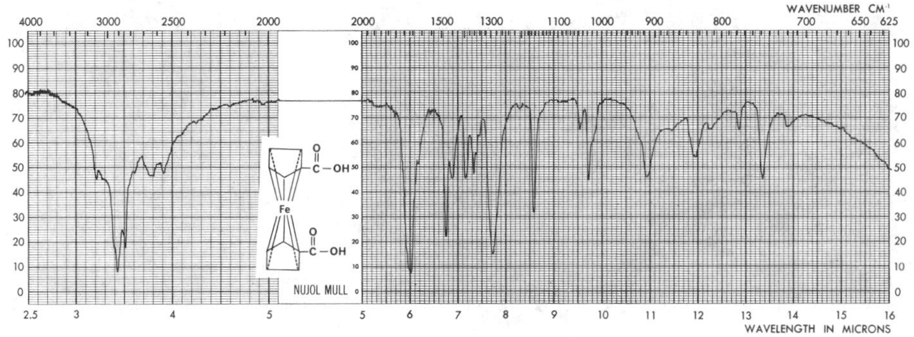

16,476-3
Diferrocenylphenylphosphine, 98%
M.W. 478.14 m.p. 191-194°

G

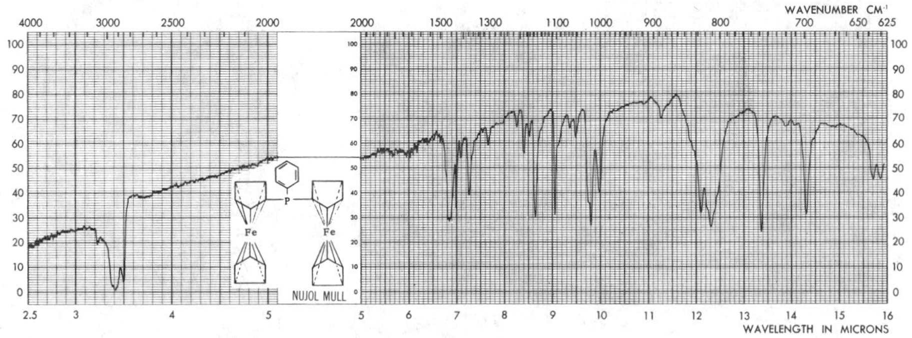

17,726-1
1,1'-Ferrocenebis-(diphenylphosphine), 98%
M.W. 554.39 m.p. 179-182° (dec.)

H

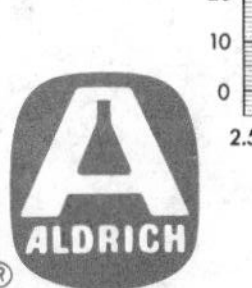

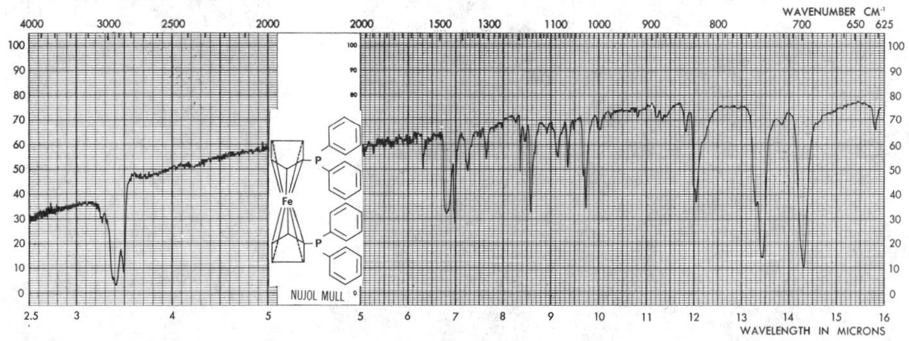

ALDRICH

A — 15,676-0 1-(Chloromercuri)-ferrocene
M.W. 421.07 m.p. 196-198° (dec.)
SEVERE POISON

B — 15,677-9 1,1'-Bis-(chloromercuri)-ferrocene, tech.
M.W. 656.11 m.p. >300°

C — N752-4 Nickelocene (dicyclopentadienylnickel)
M.W. 188.90 m.p. 172.5° (dec.)

D — 15,534-9 Cyclopentadienylthallium
M.W. 269.47 m.p. 300°

E — C8400-3 Cobaltocene (dicyclopentadienylcobalt) (7½% solution in diethylbenzene)
M.W. 189.12 (dry basis)

F — T3543-2 Titanocene dichloride (dichlorodicyclopentadienyltitanium)
M.W. 249.00 m.p. 287-289° (dec.)

G — Z70-0 Zirconocene dichloride (dichlorodicyclopentadienylzirconium)
M.W. 292.32 m.p. 243-245°

H — 11,933-4 Hafnocene dichloride (dichlorodicyclopentadienylhafnium)
M.W. 379.59 m.p. 230-233° (dec.)

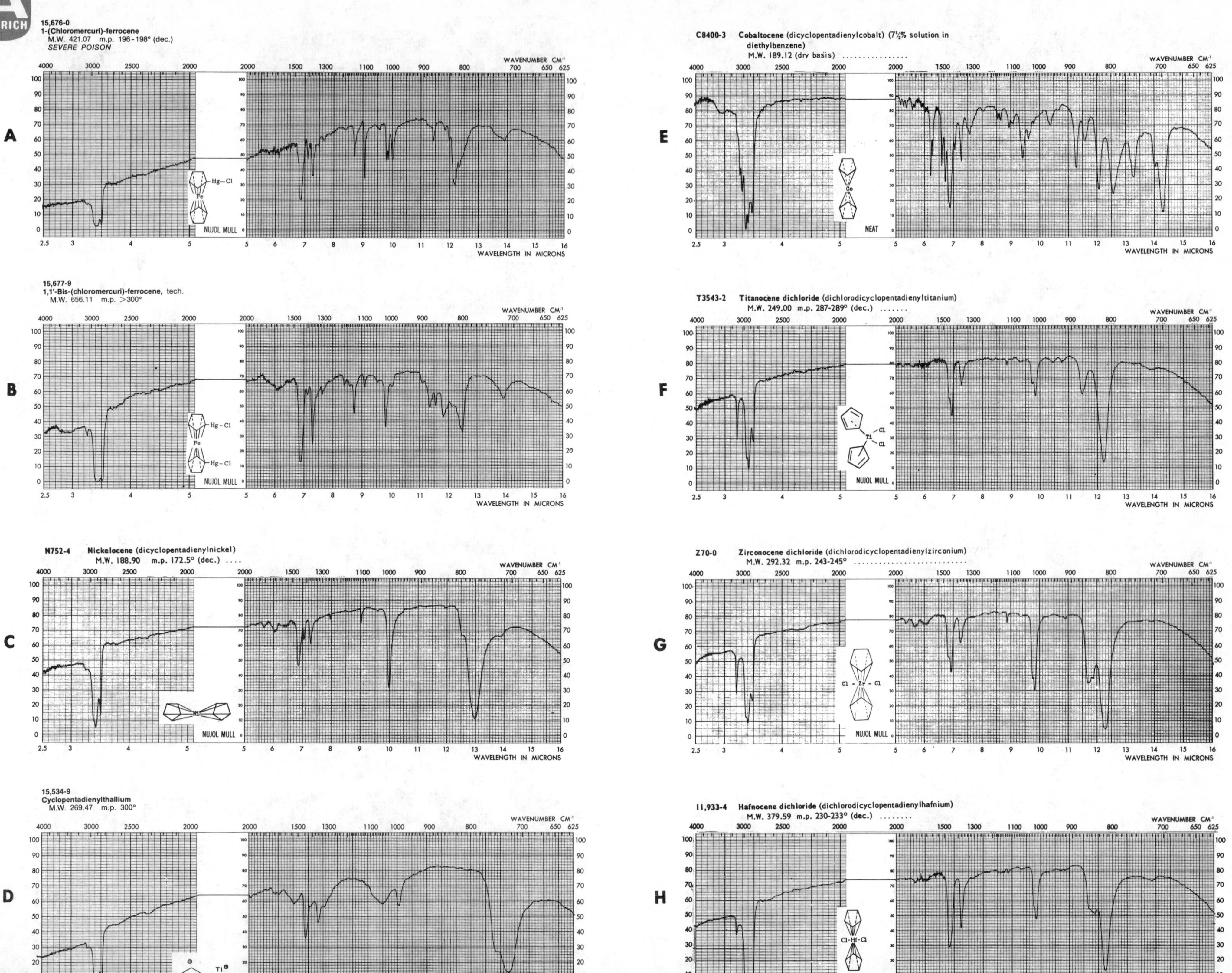

A

M.W. 292.39 ....

NEAT

B

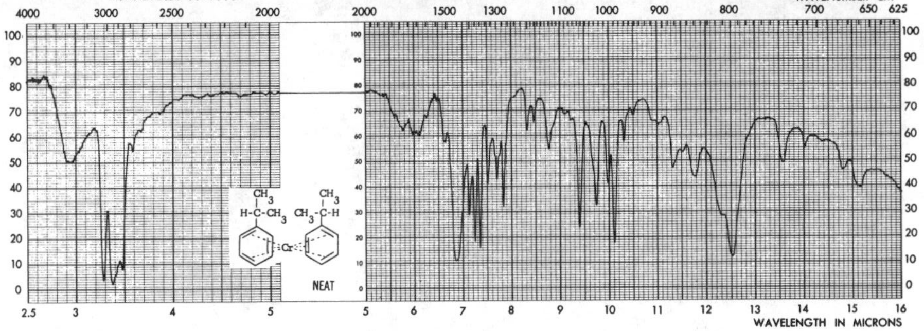

19,573-1
Iron pentacarbonyl (pentacarbonyliron)
$Fe(CO)_5$ FW 195.90 mp -20° bp 103°
n_D^{20} 1.5196 d 1.490 *Fieser* 1,519 2,229 3,167 4,268
5,357 6,304 Disp. C

$Fe(CO)_5$ NEAT

C

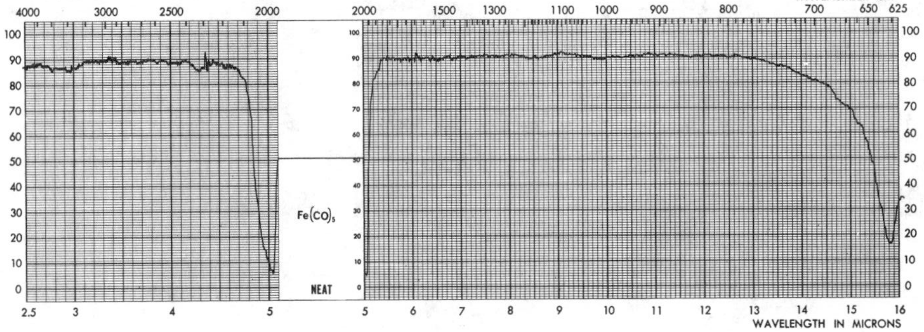

11,929-6 **1,3-Butadiene iron tricarbonyl**
M.W. 193.97 n_D^{20} 1.5730 b.p. 62-66°/13 mm.

NEAT

D

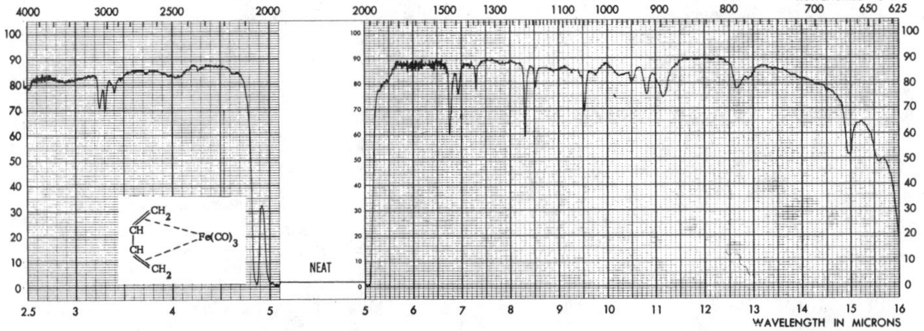

C11,130 **Cyclopentadienyliron dicarbonyl dimer**
(tetracarbonyldicyclopentadienyldiiron)
$[C_5H_5Fe(CO)_2]_2$ M.W. 353.93 m.p. 193-194° (dec.)

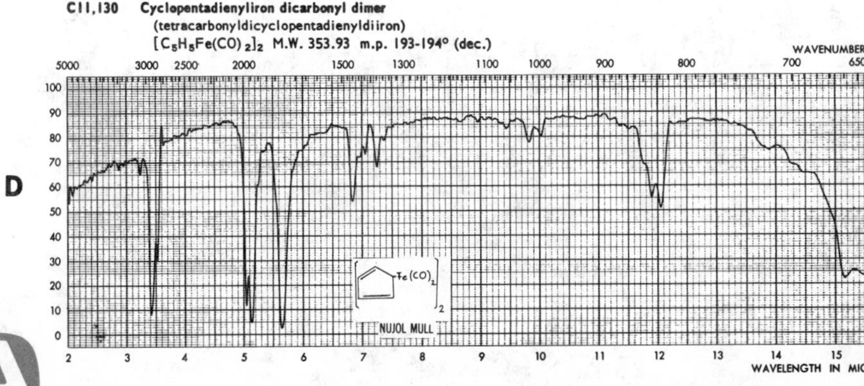

E

$(CH_3)_4N[HFe(CO)_4]$ FW 243.05 Disp. T

NUJOL MULL

F

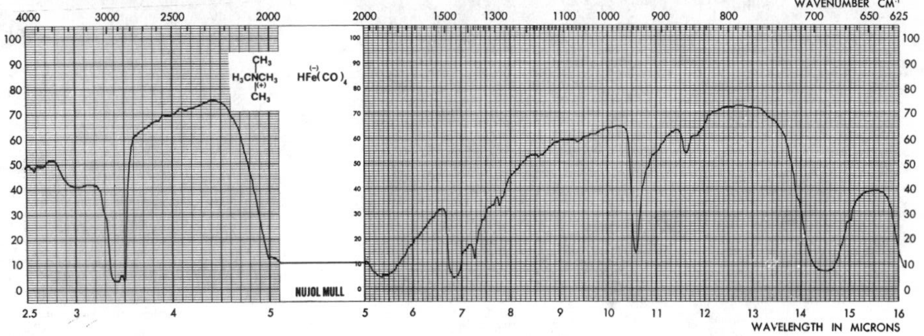

11,932-6 **Bis-(cyclopentadienylchromium tricarbonyl)-mercury**
M.W. 602.83 m.p. 145° (dec.) ....

NUJOL MULL

G

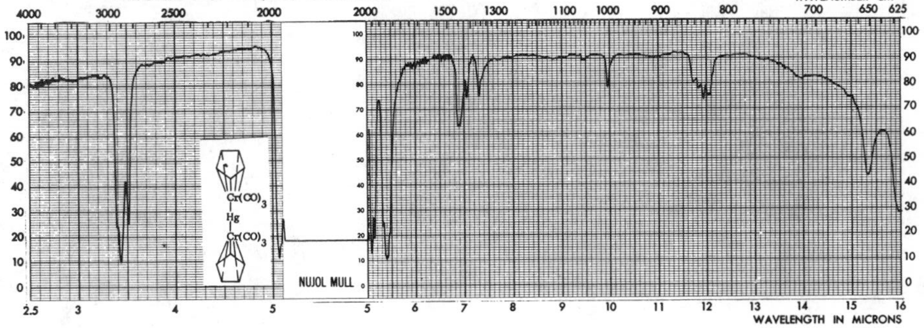

19,995-8
Molybdenum hexacarbonyl (hexacarbonylmolybdenum)
$Mo(CO)_6$ FW 264.00 mp 150° (dec.) bp 156°
d 1.960 *Fieser* 2,287 3,206 4,346 Disp. C

NUJOL MULL

H

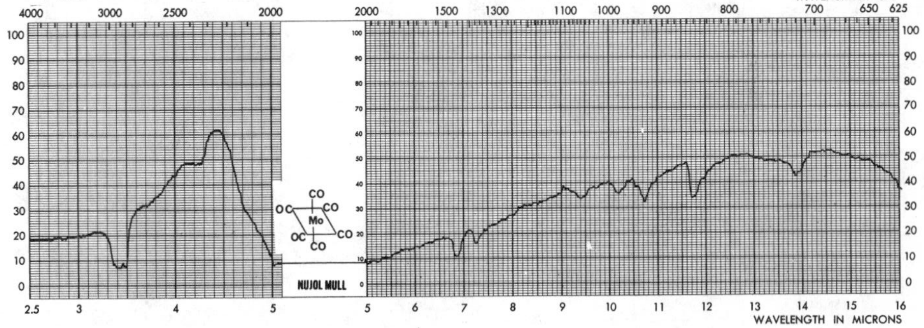

11,760-9 **Cyclopentadienylmolybdenum tricarbonyl dimer**
$[(C_5H_5)Mo(CO)_3]_2$ M.W. 490.13
m.p. 222° (dec.) ....

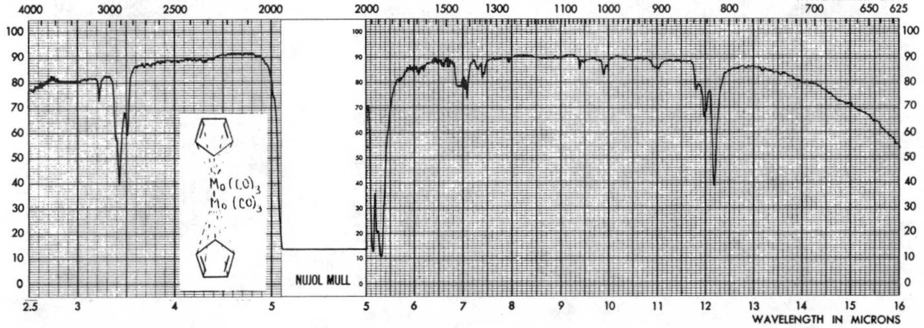

NUJOL MULL

A

11,926-1 **Bicyclo[2.2.1]hepta-2,5-diene molybdenum tetracarbonyl**
M.W. 300.12 m.p. 75-79°

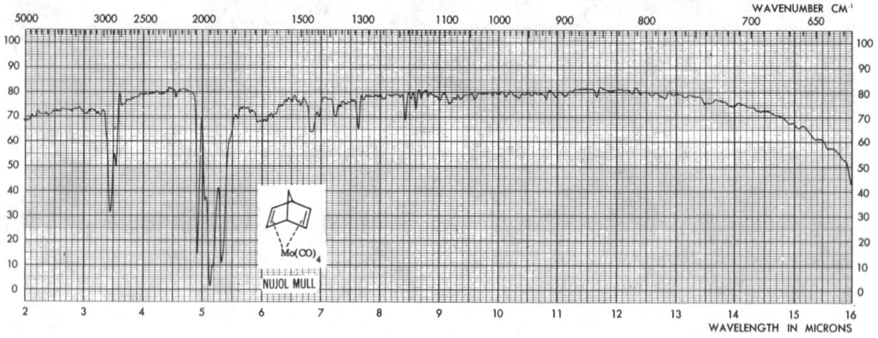

NUJOL MULL

B

11,931-8 **Benzene chromium tricarbonyl**
M.W. 214.14 m.p. 161-164°

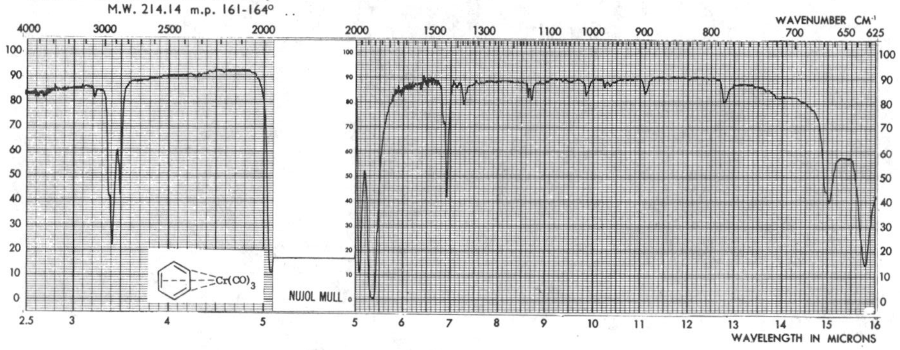

NUJOL MULL

C

11,928-8 **Cycloheptatriene molybdenum tricarbonyl**
M.W. 272.11 m.p. 98-100° (dec.)

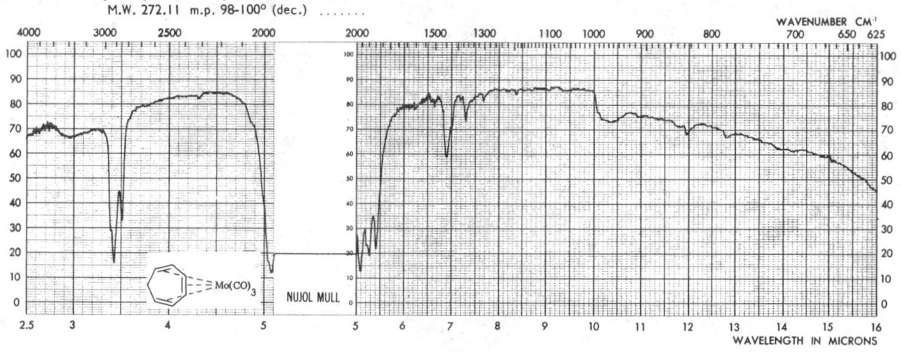

NUJOL MULL

D

11,679-3 **1-(Tri-n-butylplumbyl)-imidazole**
M.W. 445.61 m.p. 47-49°

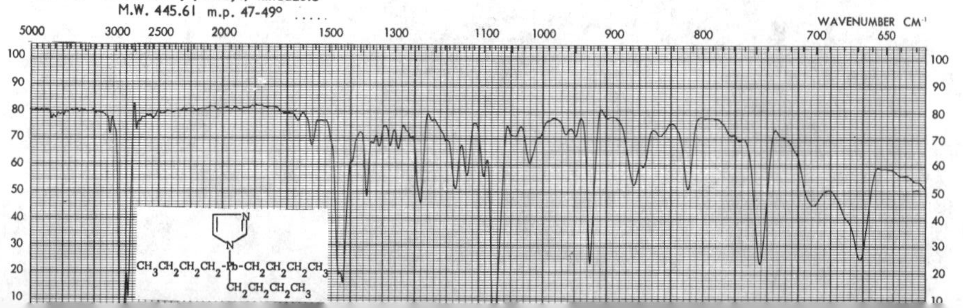

E

17,964-7
Silver carbonate
Ag_2CO_3
M.W. 275.75 m.p. 210° (dec.)

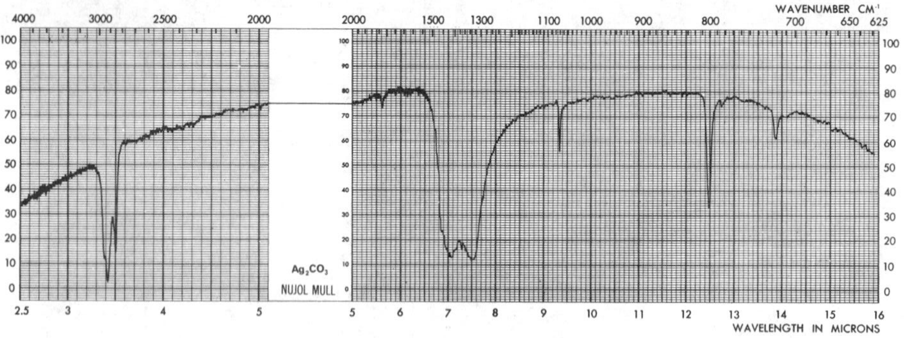

Ag_2CO_3 NUJOL MULL

F

16,152-7
Sodium hydrosulfide hydrate
$NaSH \cdot xH_2O$
M.W. 56.06 m.p. 52-54° Fieser 3,266

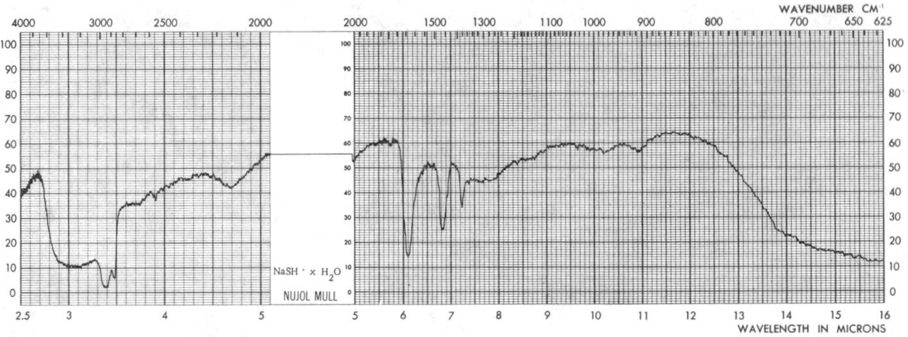

$NaSH \cdot x\ H_2O$ NUJOL MULL

G

15,795-3
Sodium dithionite, 90+% (sodium hydrosulfite)
$Na_2S_2O_4$
M.W. 174.11 m.p. >300° (dec.) Fieser 1,1081

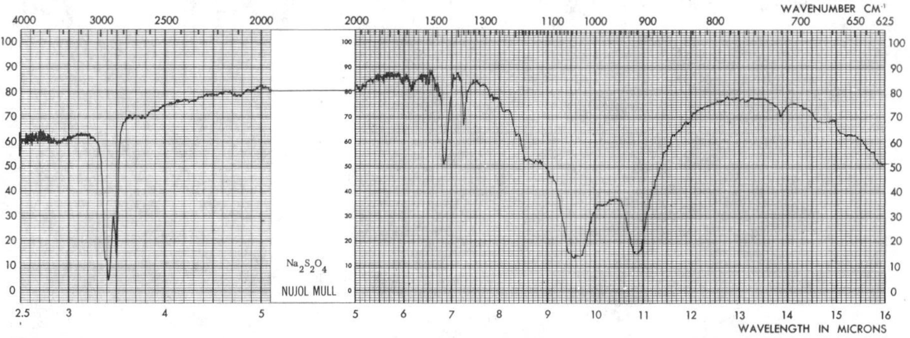

$Na_2S_2O_4$ NUJOL MULL

H

16,151-9
Sodium bisulfite, anhydrous, 97% (sodium metabisulfite)
$Na_2S_2O_5$
M.W. 190.1 m.p. >300° *HYGROSCOPIC*

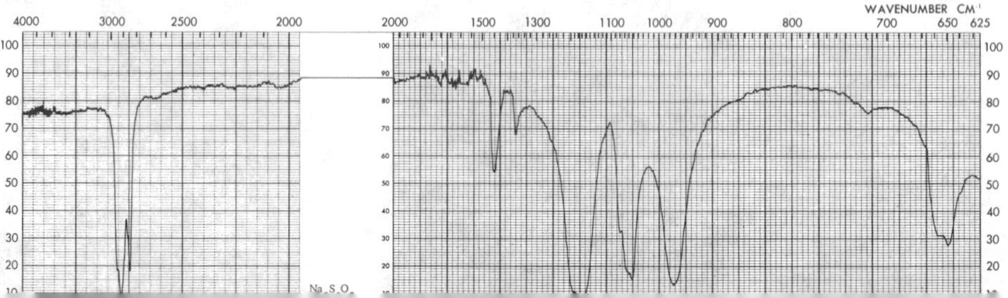

Pb(SCN)$_2$ FW 323.35 mp 190° (dec.) d 3.820
Disp. P

A

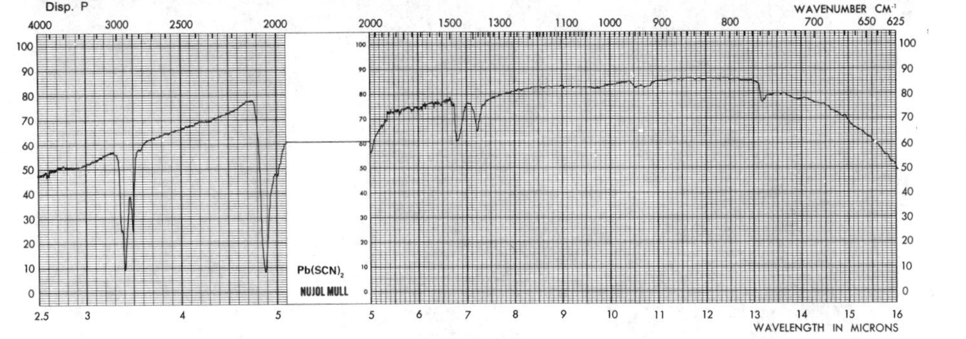

19,993-1
Sodium azide, 99%
NaN$_3$ FW 65.01 d 1.850 *Fieser* **1**,1041 **2**,376
3,259 **4**,440 **5**,593 Disp. F

B

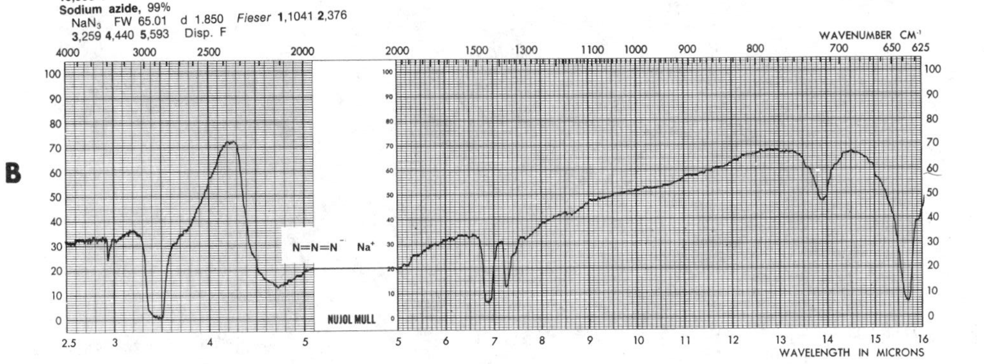

20,173-1
Ruthenium Red
[(NH$_3$)$_5$RuORu(NH$_3$)$_4$ORu(NH$_3$)$_5$]Cl$_6$ FW 786.36
Disp. R

C

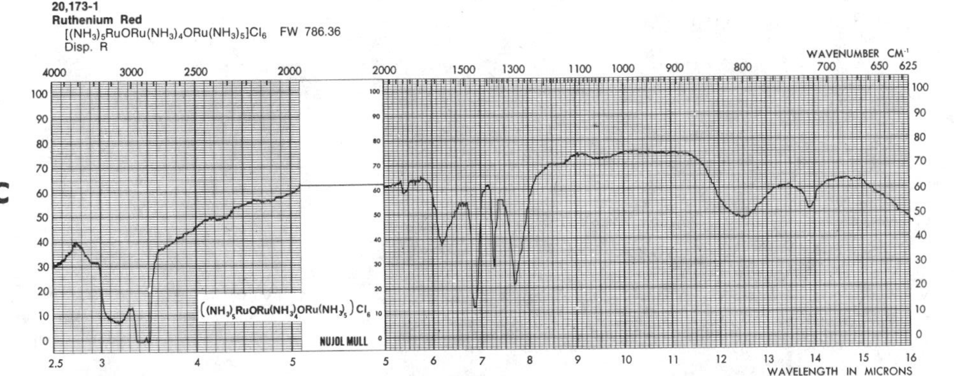

85,856-0
Hemin, bovine, crystalline [chloroprotoporphyrin IX iron(III)]
M.W. 651.96 m.p. >300°

D

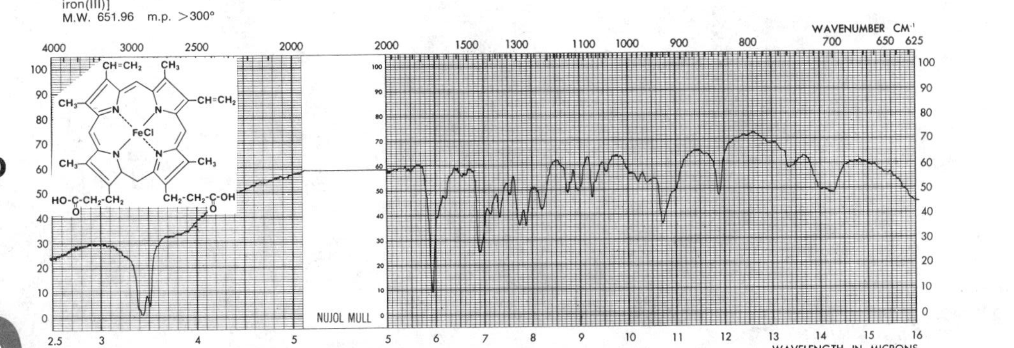

POLYMERS

The polymer spectra were produced as films from appropriate solvents. The polymer was dissolved and then spread on to a NaCl plate. The solvent was then evaporated at ~100° C. and the spectrum run. Some of the spectra do show residual solvent when the solvent used would not totally evaporate.

A

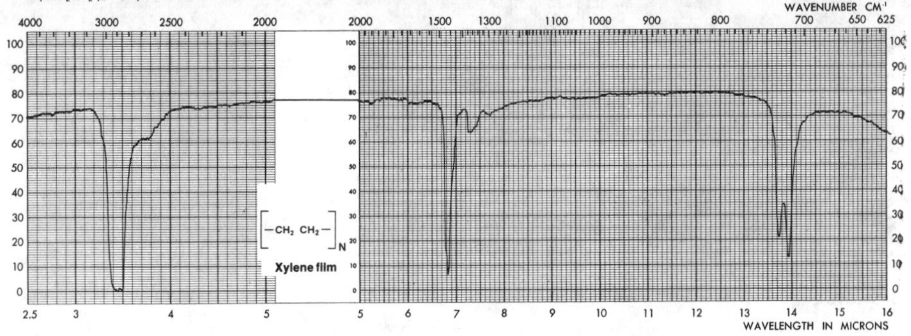

$[-CH_2\ CH_2-]_N$
Xylene film

18,190-0
Poly(ethylene), high density
Pellets

B

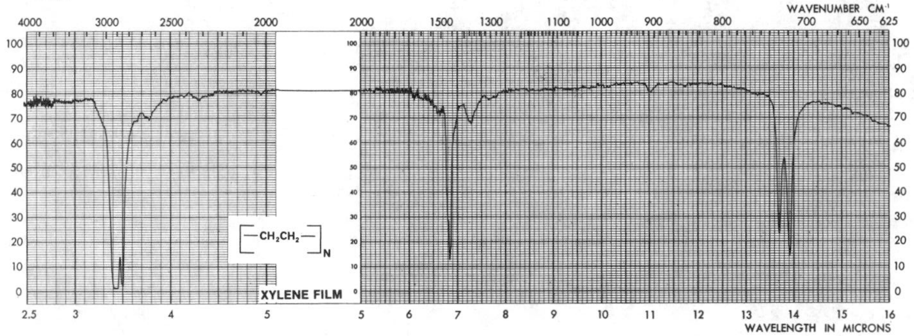

$[-CH_2CH_2-]_N$
XYLENE FILM

19,191-4
Poly(ethylene), oxidized, low molecular weight
Disp. D

C

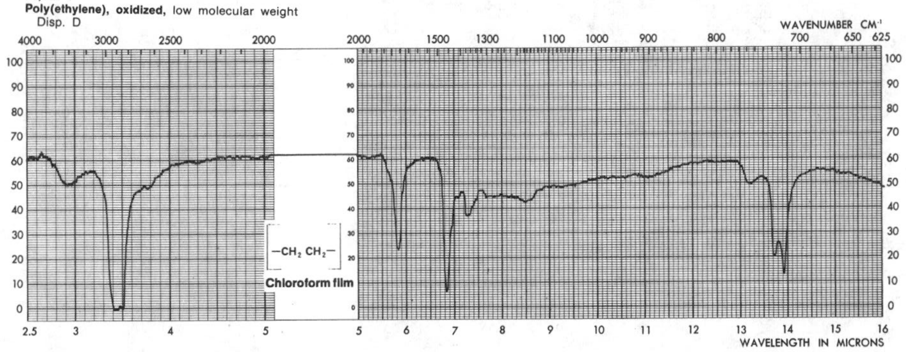

$[-CH_2\ CH_2-]$
Chloroform film

19,192-2
Poly(ethylene), oxidized, high molecular weight
Disp. D

D

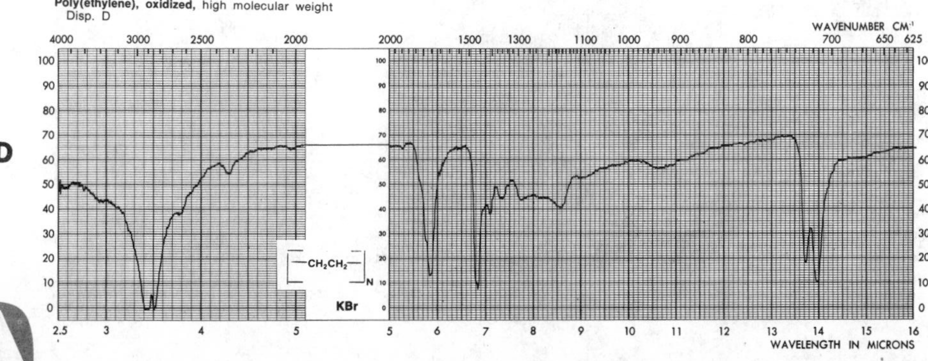

$[-CH_2CH_2-]_N$
KBr

E

$[-CH_2-CH(CH_3)-]_N$
Xylene film

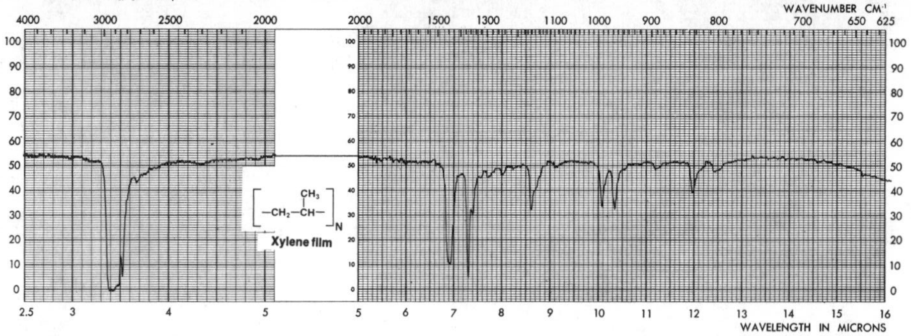

18,962-6
Ethylene/propylene copolymer, low molecular weight
Disp. D

F

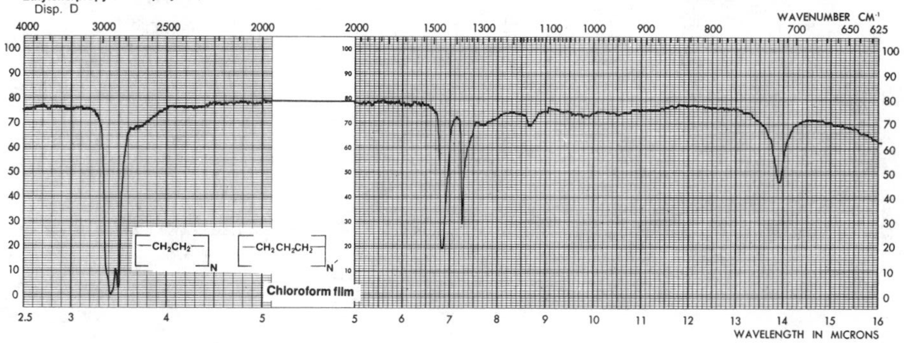

$[-CH_2CH_2-]_N$ $[-CH_2CH_2CH_2-]_{N'}$
Chloroform film

20,051-4
Ethylene/propylene/diene terpolymer
Disp. D

G

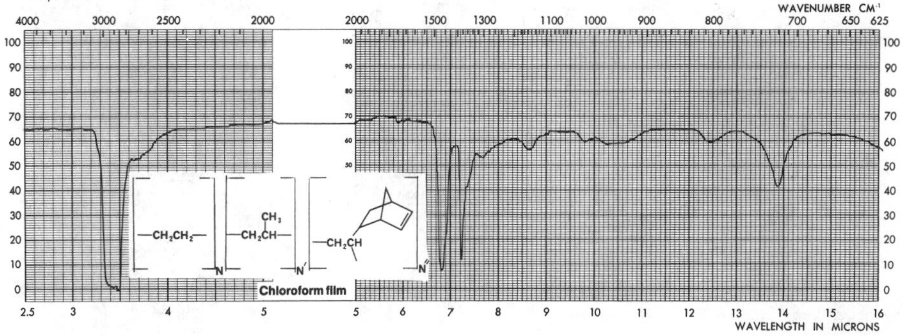

$[-CH_2CH_2-]_N$ $[-CH_2CH(CH_3)-]_{N'}$ $[-CH_2CH<]_{N''}$
Chloroform film

18,963-4
Ethylene/propylene/diene terpolymer, medium molecular weight
Disp. D

H

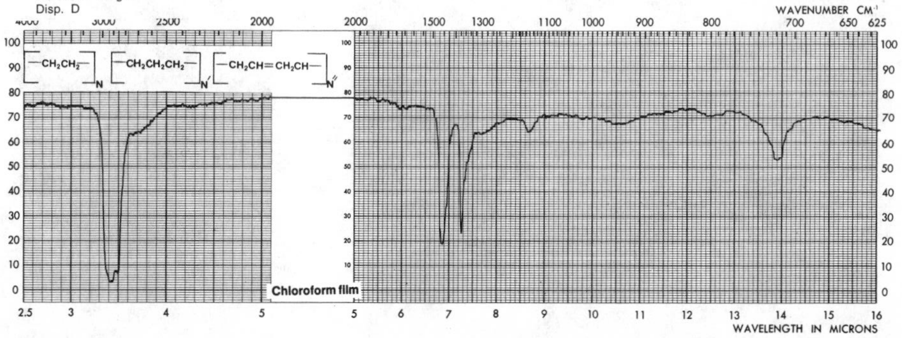

$[-CH_2CH_2-]_N$ $[-CH_2CH_2CH_2-]_{N'}$ $[-CH_2CH=CH_2CH-]_{N''}$
Chloroform film

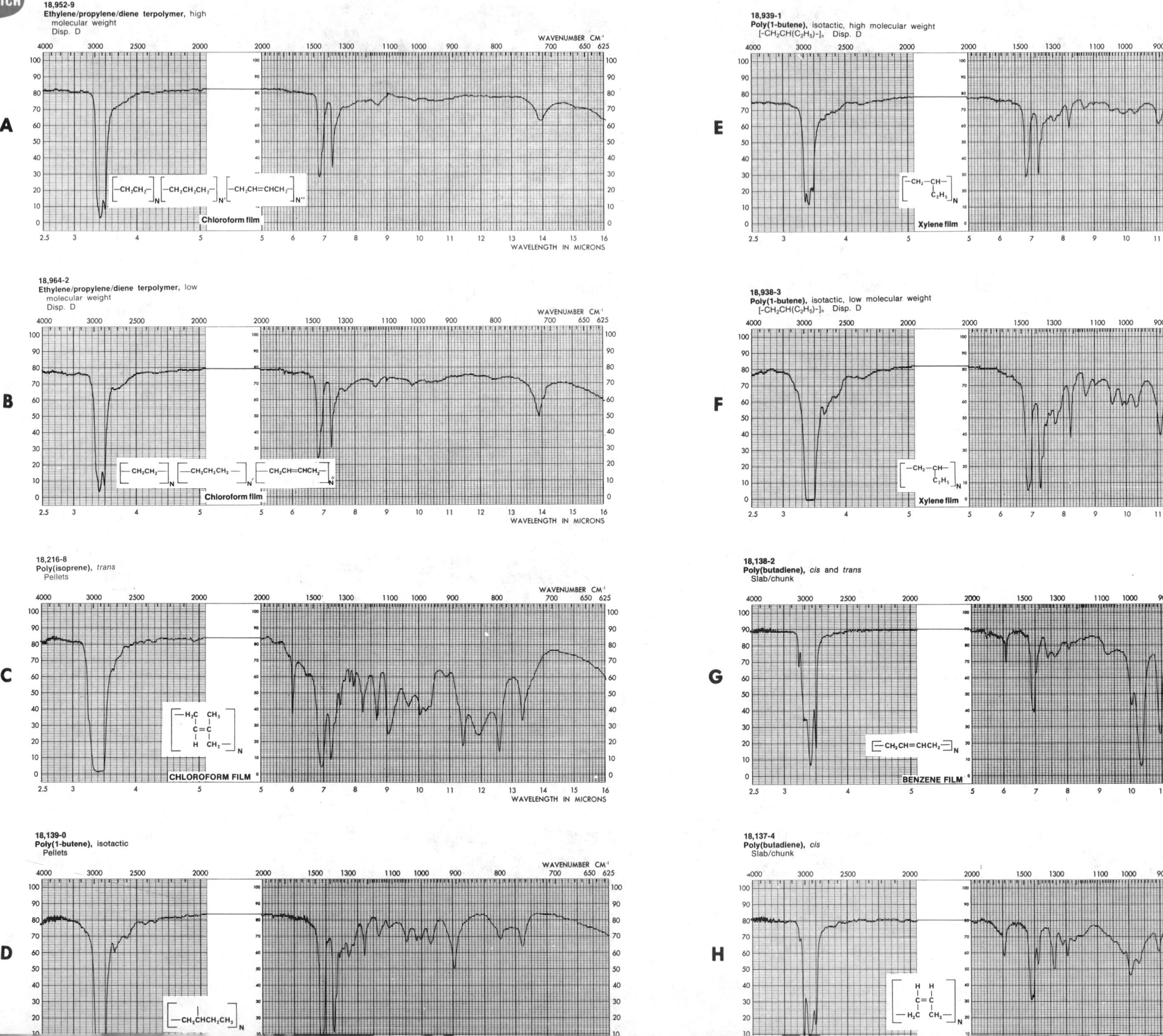
ALDRICH
A
18,952-9
Ethylene/propylene/diene terpolymer, high molecular weight
Disp. D
Chloroform film
B
18,964-2
Ethylene/propylene/diene terpolymer, low molecular weight
Disp. D
Chloroform film
C
18,216-8
Poly(isoprene), trans
Pellets
CHLOROFORM FILM
D
18,139-0
Poly(1-butene), isotactic
Pellets
E
18,939-1
Poly(1-butene), isotactic, high molecular weight
[-CH2CH(C2H5)-]n Disp. D
Xylene film
F
18,938-3
Poly(1-butene), isotactic, low molecular weight
[-CH2CH(C2H5)-]n Disp. D
Xylene film
G
18,138-2
Poly(butadiene), cis and trans
Slab/chunk
BENZENE FILM
H
18,137-4
Poly(butadiene), cis
Slab/chunk
WAVENUMBER CM-1
WAVELENGTH IN MICRONS

Slab/chunk

A

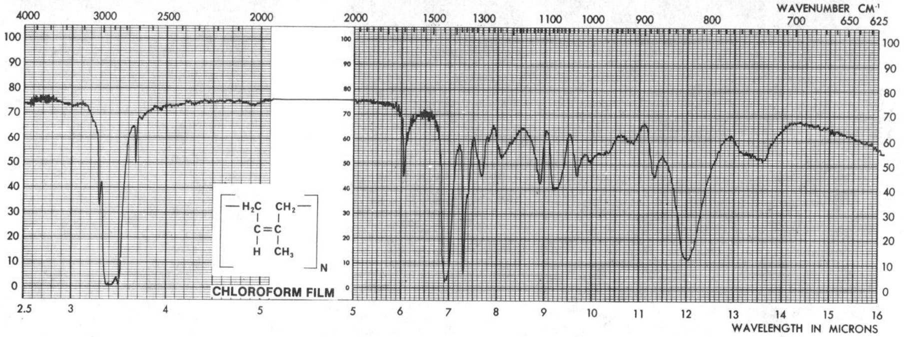

CHLOROFORM FILM

20,228-2 **Poly(butadiene), phenyl terminated**
Disp. D
Viscous liquid. Contains 99% unsaturation, 25% vinyl, 40% *trans*-1,4. Average M.N. 900

B

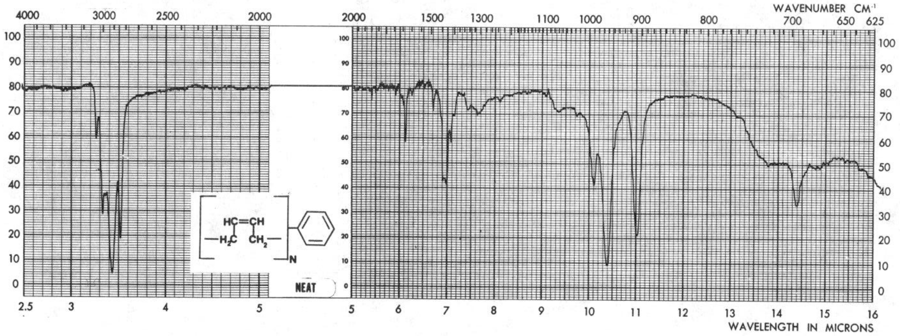

NEAT

20,046-8 **Poly(butadiene), phenyl terminated**
Disp. D
Viscous liquid. Contains 99% unsaturation, (40% vinyl, 30% *trans*-1,4). Average M.N. 1,300. Density 0.89. Flash point 170°C

C

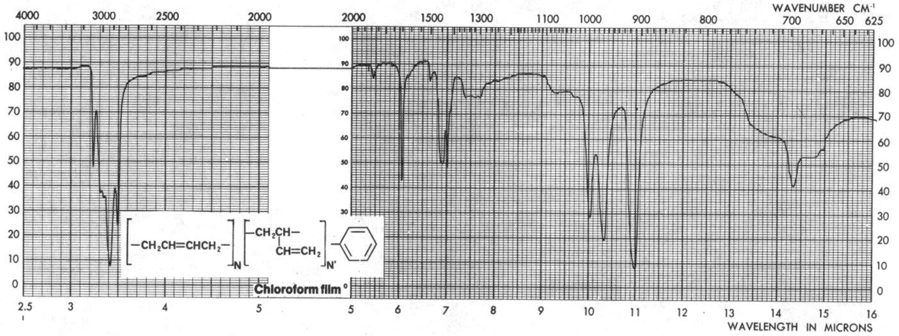

Chloroform film°

18,145-5
Poly(isobutylene), low molecular weight
Slab/chunk

D

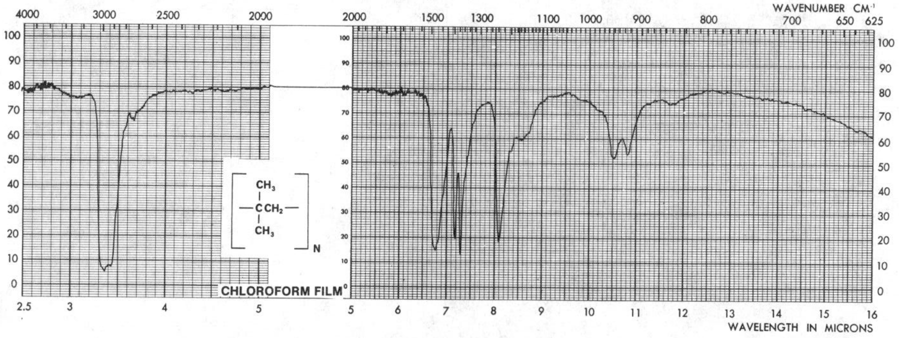

CHLOROFORM FILM°

Poly(isobutylene), medium molecular weight
Slab/chunk

E

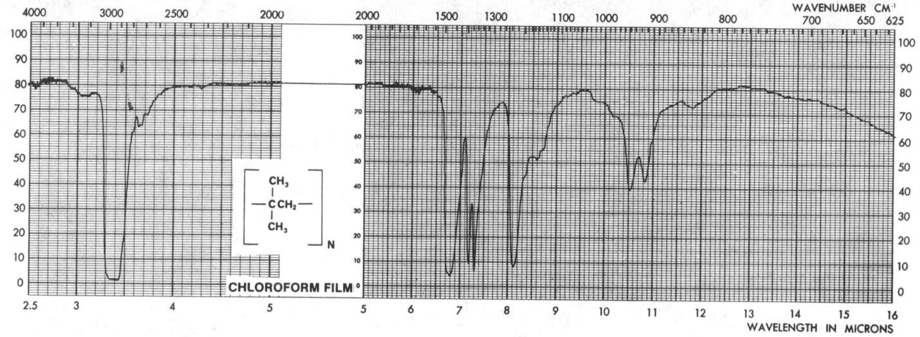

CHLOROFORM FILM°

18,147-1
Poly(isobutylene), medium high molecular weight
Slab/chunk

F

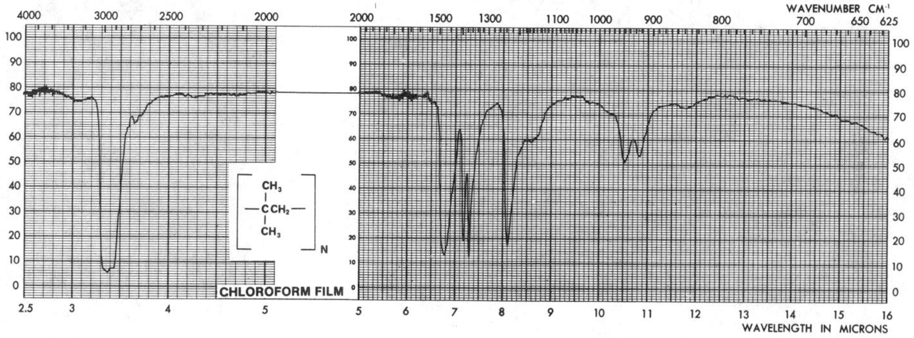

CHLOROFORM FILM°

18,149-8
Poly(isobutylene), high molecular weight
Slab/chunk

G

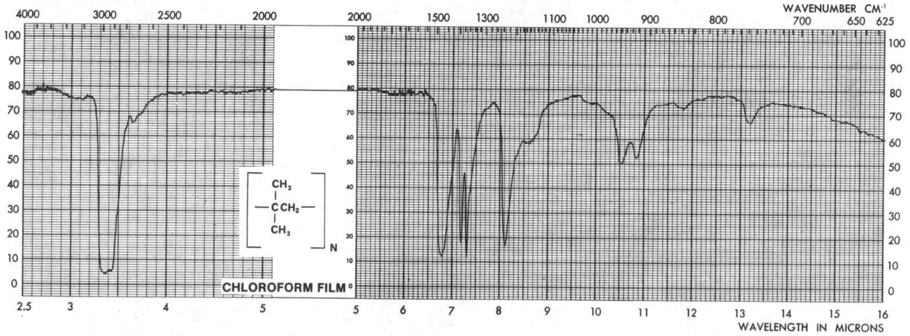

CHLOROFORM FILM°

19,098-5
Poly(4-methyl-1-pentene), low molecular weight
$(-CH_2CH[CH_2CH(CH_3)_2]-)_n$ Disp. D

H

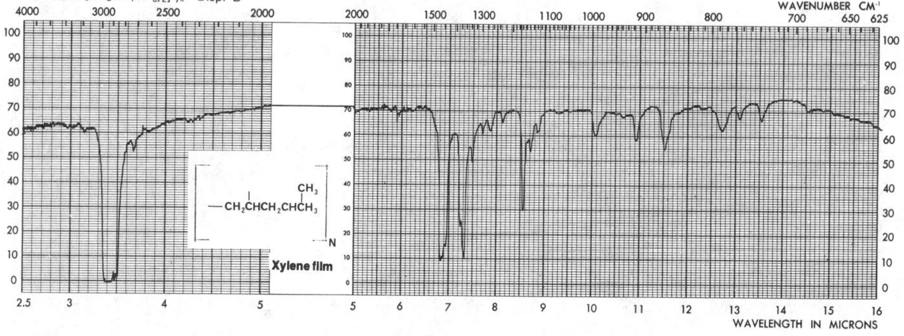

Xylene film

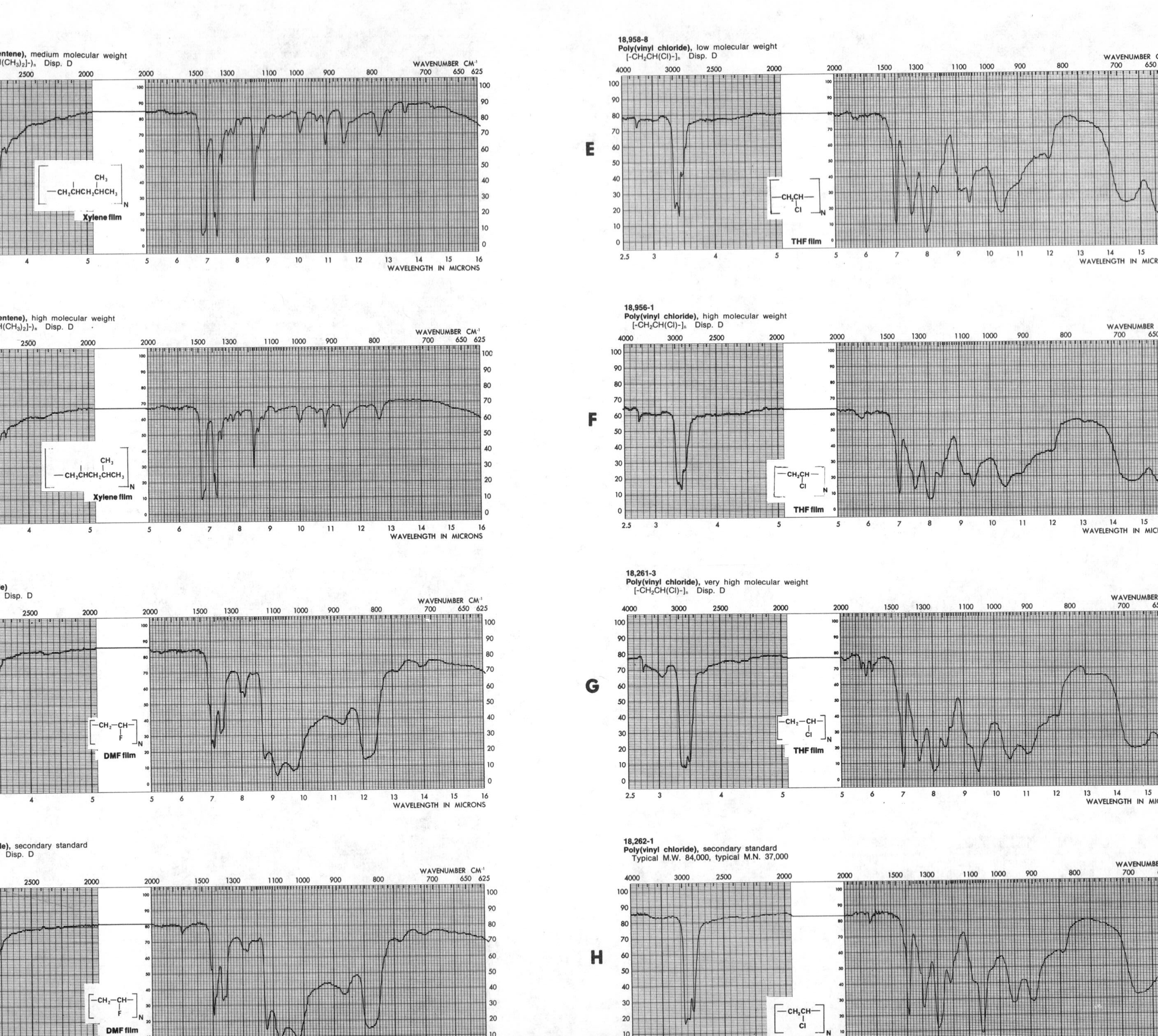
ALDRICH
A
19,099-3
Poly(4-methyl-1-pentene), medium molecular weight
(-CH₂CH[CH₂CH(CH₃)₂]-)ₙ Disp. D
Xylene film
B
19,100-0
Poly(4-methyl-1-pentene), high molecular weight
(-CH₂CH[CH₂CH(CH₃)₂]-)ₙ Disp. D
Xylene film
C
18,266-4
Poly(vinyl fluoride)
[-CH₂CH(F)-]ₙ Disp. D
DMF film
D
18,267-2
Poly(vinyl fluoride), secondary standard
[-CH₂CH(F)-]ₙ Disp. D
DMF film
E
18,958-8
Poly(vinyl chloride), low molecular weight
[-CH₂CH(Cl)-]ₙ Disp. D
THF film
F
18,956-1
Poly(vinyl chloride), high molecular weight
[-CH₂CH(Cl)-]ₙ Disp. D
THF film
G
18,261-3
Poly(vinyl chloride), very high molecular weight
[-CH₂CH(Cl)-]ₙ Disp. D
THF film
H
18,262-1
Poly(vinyl chloride), secondary standard
Typical M.W. 84,000, typical M.N. 37,000
WAVENUMBER CM⁻¹
WAVELENGTH IN MICRONS

A

Fieser 7,100 Disp. D

$[-CH_2CH(Cl)-]_N$ …$CO^{(-)}$

THF film

B

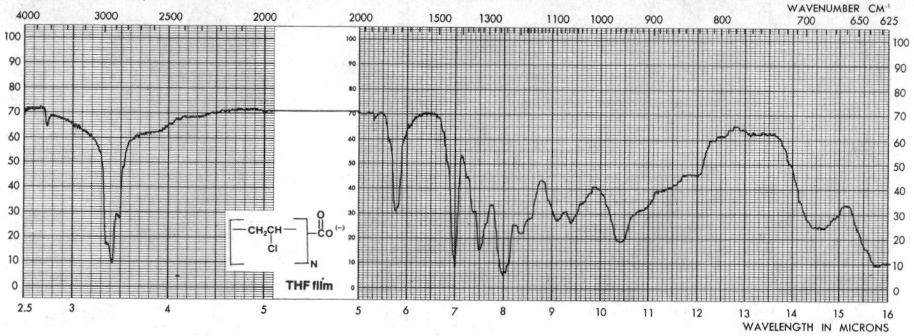

18,270-2
Poly(vinylidene fluoride)
Powder

$[-CH_2CF_2-]_N$

DMF FILM

C

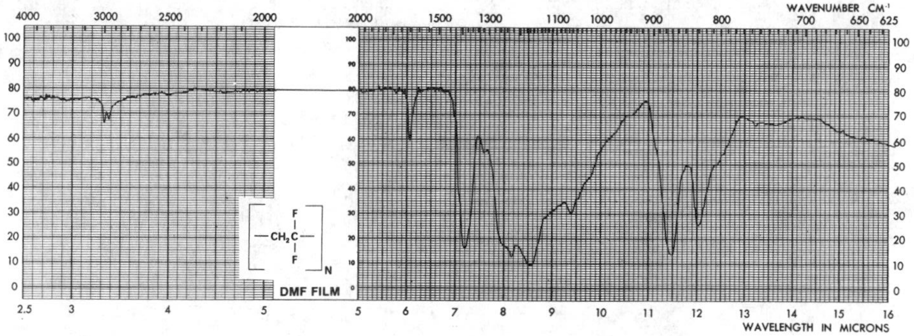

18,247-8
Poly(tetrafluoroethylene)
$(-CF_2CF_2-)_n$ Disp. D

$[-CF_2CF_2-]_N$

MELT

D

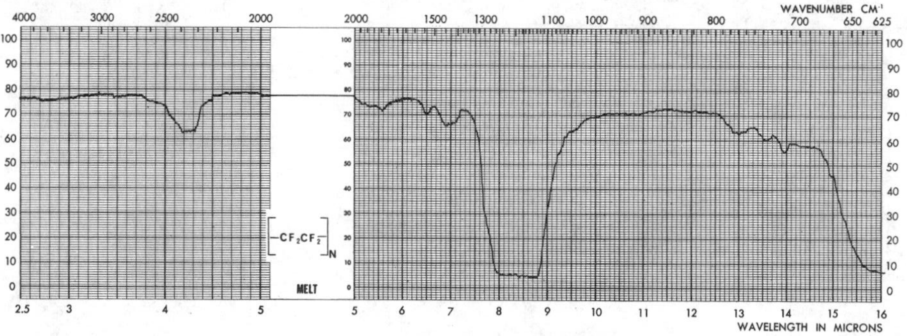

18,168-4
Poly(chloroprene)
Chunks

$[-CH_2C(Cl)=CHCH_2-]_N$

CHLOROFORM FILM

E

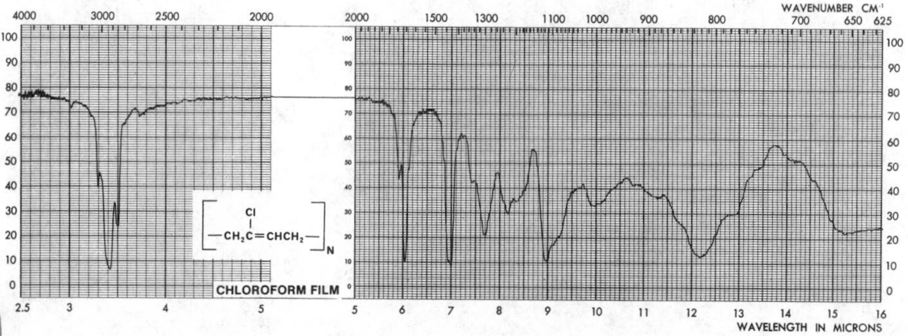

Granular. Chlorine content 36%

XYLENE FILM

F

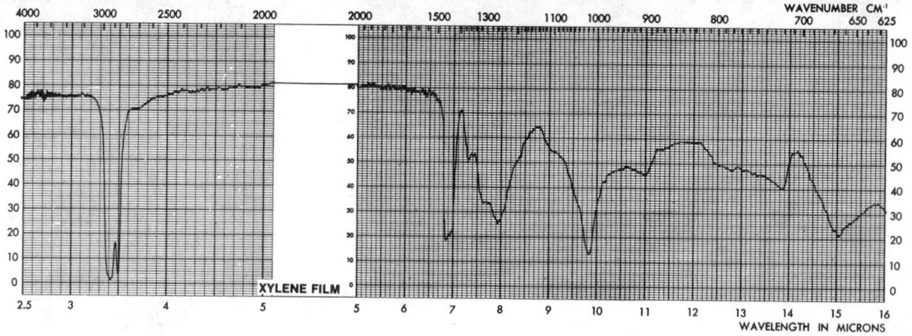

18,194-3
Poly(ethylene), chlorinated
Granular. Chlorine content 42%

CHLOROFORM FILM

G

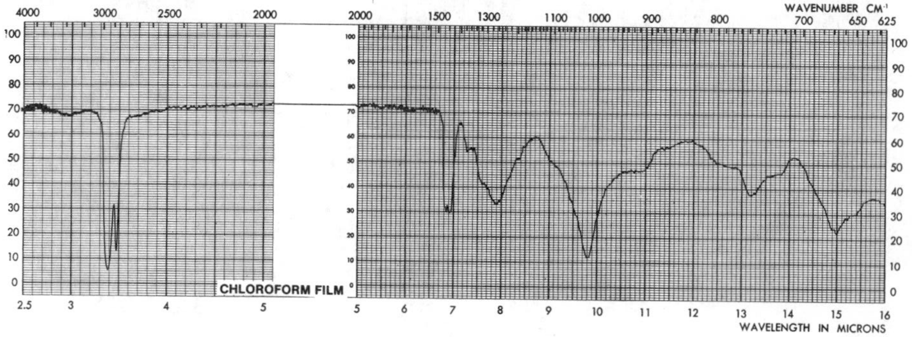

18,195-1
Poly(ethylene), chlorosulfonated
Chunks

CHLOROFORM FILM°

H

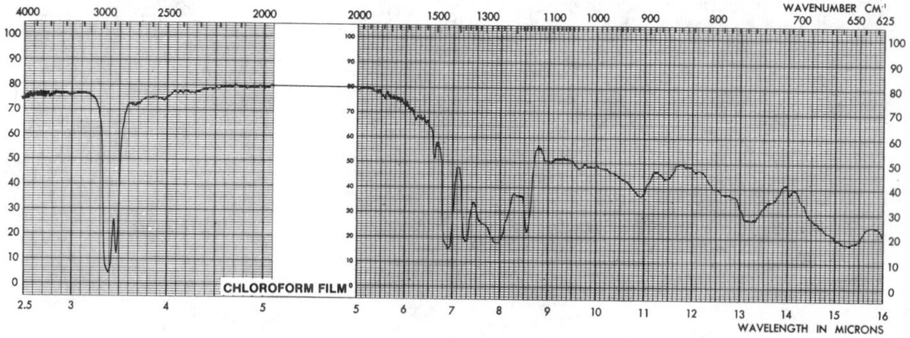

18,239-7
Poly(propylene), chlorinated
Disp. D

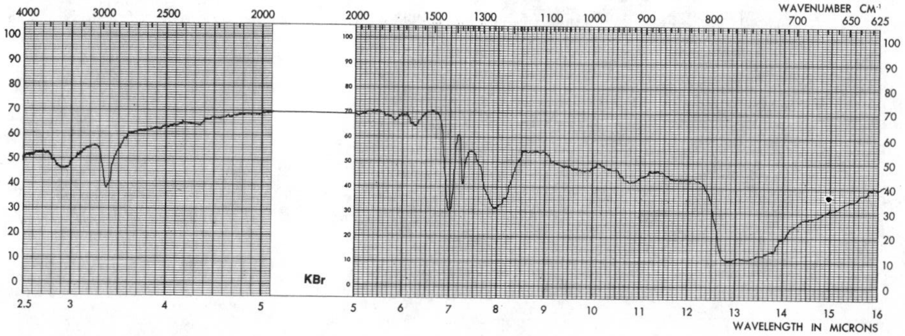

KBr

A

18,273-7
Poly(vinyl methyl ether), secondary standard
Typical M.W. 71,000, typical M.W. 32,000

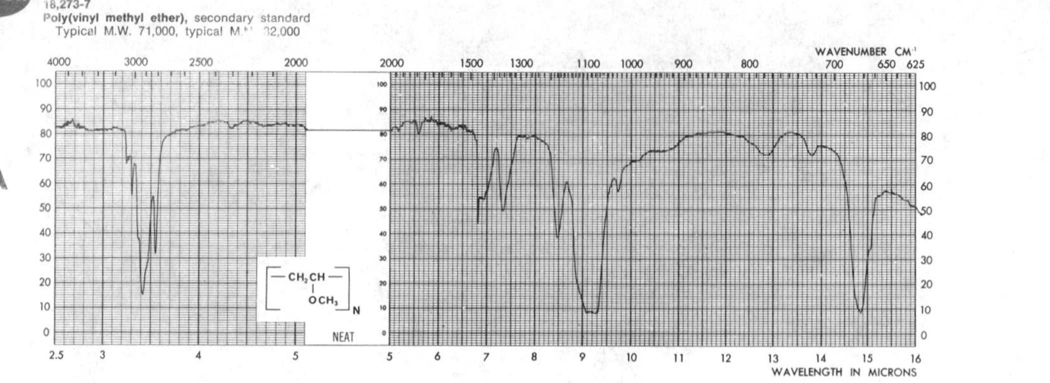

B

18,265-6
Poly(vinyl ethyl ether), low molecular weight
Opaque, viscous liquid

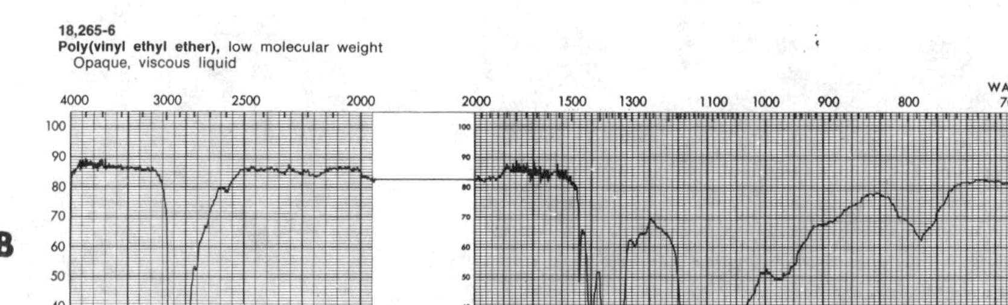

C

18,255-9
Poly(vinyl isobutyl ether), 50 wt. %
solution in xylene
(-CH₂CH[OCH₂CH(CH₃)₂]-)ₙ Disp. D

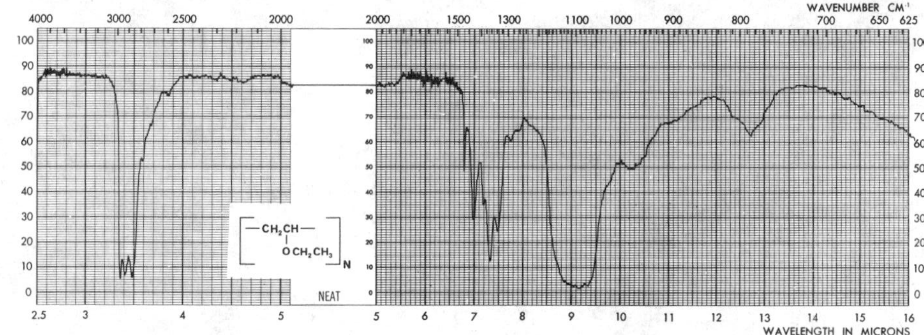

D

18,946-4
Poly(ethylene oxide)
(-CH₂CH₂O-)ₙ Disp. D

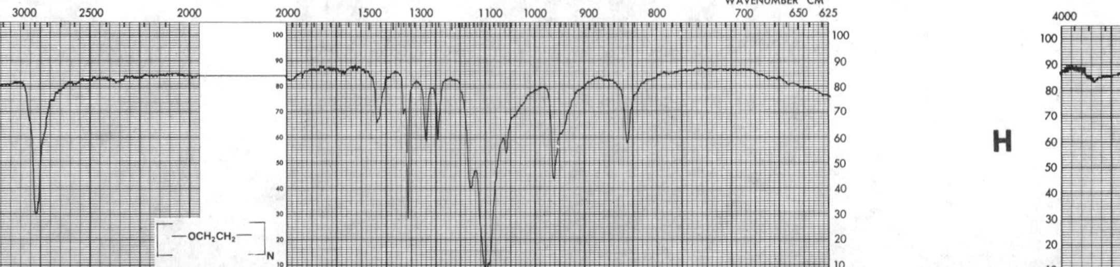

E

18,198-6
Poly(ethylene oxide)
Powder. Average M.W. 100,000

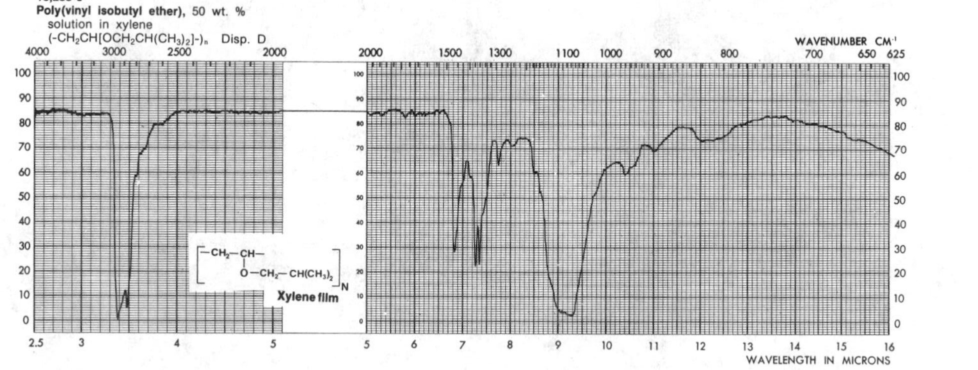

F

18,199-4
Poly(ethylene oxide)
Powder. Average M.W. 200,000

G

18,200-1
Poly(ethylene oxide)
Powder. Average M.W. 300,000

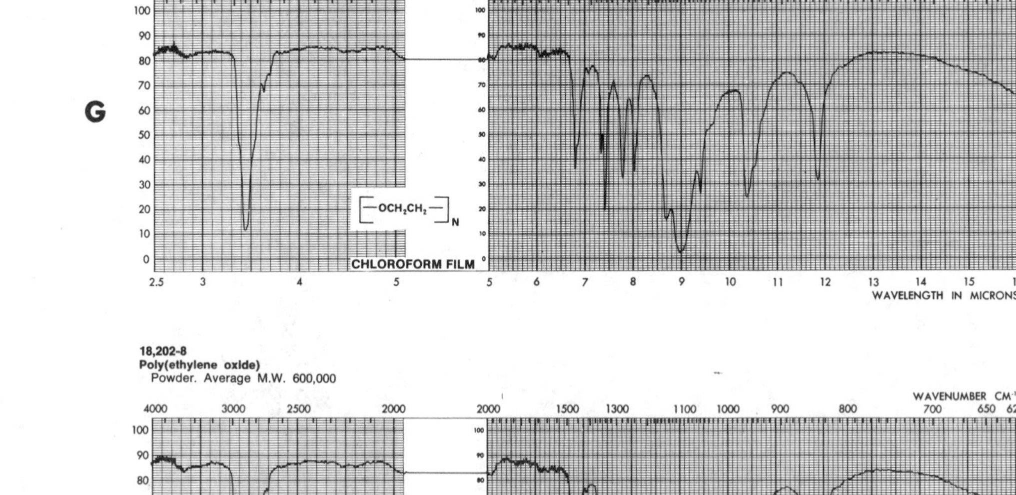

H

18,202-8
Poly(ethylene oxide)
Powder. Average M.W. 600,000

$H(OCH_2CH_2)_nOH$ Disp. D

A

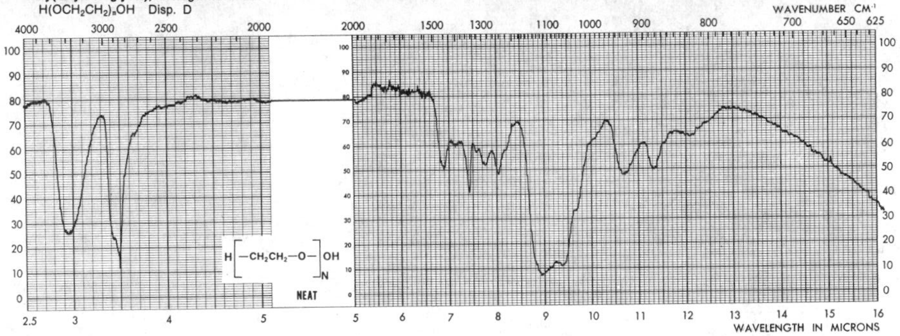

20,233-9
Poly(propylene glycol), average M.W. 2,000
$H[OCH(CH_3)CH_2]_nOH$ Disp. D

B

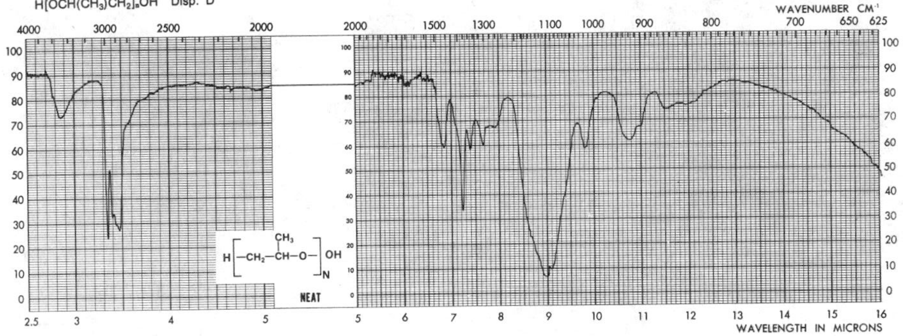

20,248-7
Poly(ethylene glycol methyl ether),
average M.W. 550
$CH_3(OCH_2CH_2)_nOH$ Disp. D

C

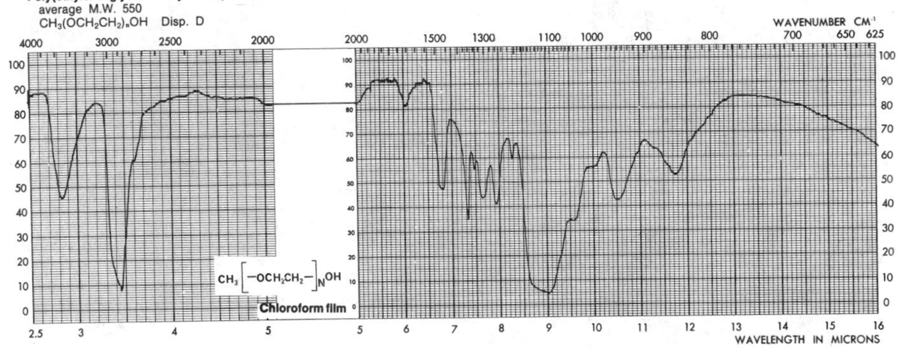

18,186-2
Poly(epichlorohydrin)
Slab/chunk

D

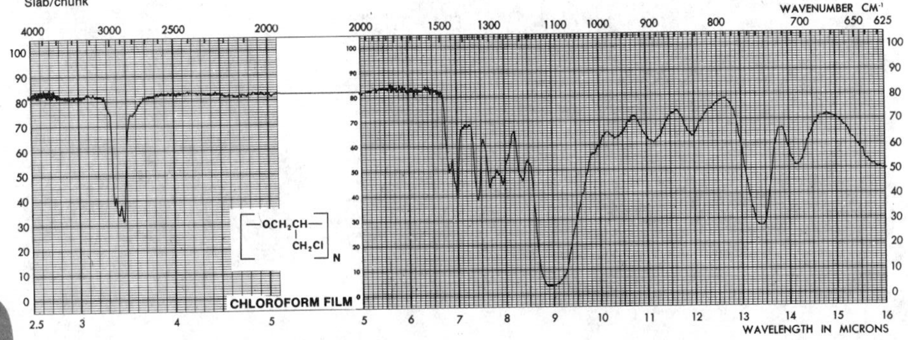

E

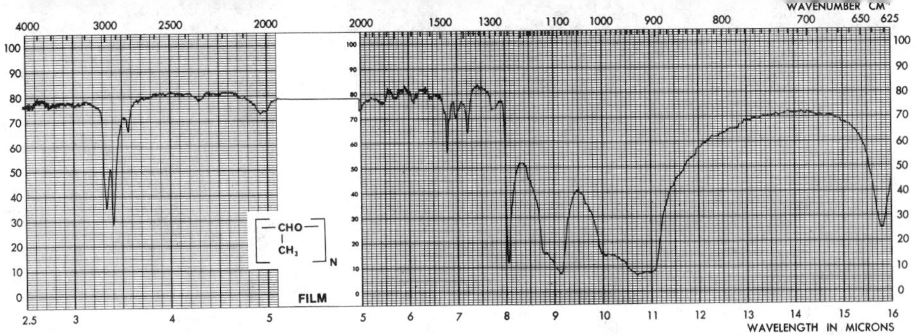

18,269-9
Poly(vinyl formal), secondary standard
Typical M.W. 47,000, typical M.N. 17,000

F

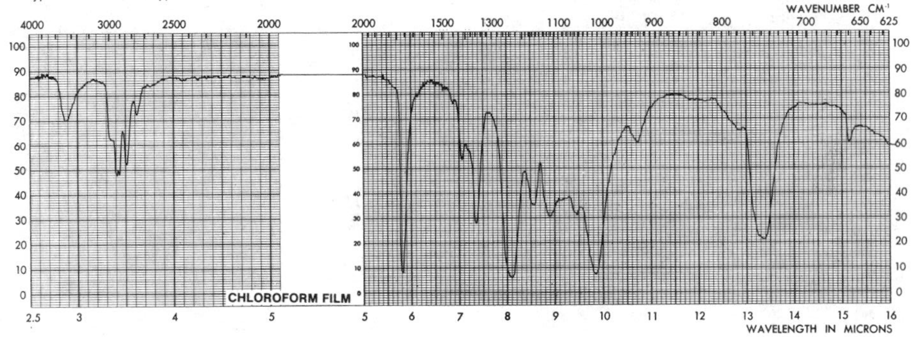

18,268-0
Poly(vinyl formal)
Disp. D

G

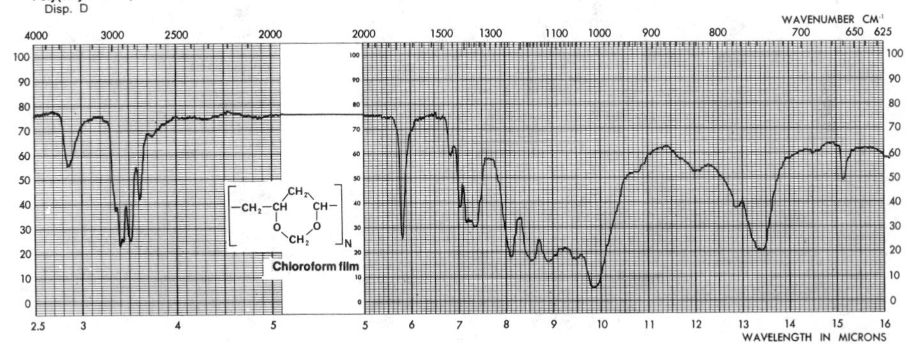

18,257-5
Poly(vinyl butyral), secondary standard
Typical M.W. 49,000, typical M.N. 11,000

H

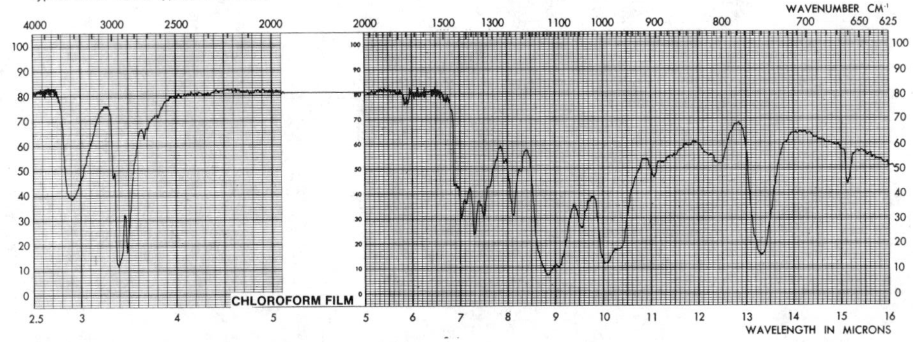

A

19,097-7
Vinyl alcohol/vinyl butyral copolymer
Disp. D

DMF film

B

18,256-7
Poly(vinyl butyral)
Disp. D

Chloroform film

C

18,936-7
Poly(vinyl alcohol), 75% hydrolyzed
$[-CH_2CH(OH)-]_n$ Disp. D

DMF film

D

18,934-0
Poly(vinyl alcohol), 88% hydrolyzed
$[-CH_2CH(OH)-]_n$ Disp. D

E

18,953-7
Poly(vinyl alcohol), 96% hydrolyzed
$[-CH_2CH(OH)-]_n$ Disp. D

DMF film

F

18,967-7
Poly(vinyl alcohol), 98% hydrolyzed
$[-CH_2CH(OH)-]_n$ Disp. D

DMF film

G

18,965-0
Poly(vinyl alcohol), 100% hydrolyzed
$[-CH_2CH(OH)-]_n$ Disp. D

DMF film

H

19,079-9
Poly(butadiene) diol
Disp. D

$HO-[-CH_2CH=CHCH_2-]_N-OH$

A

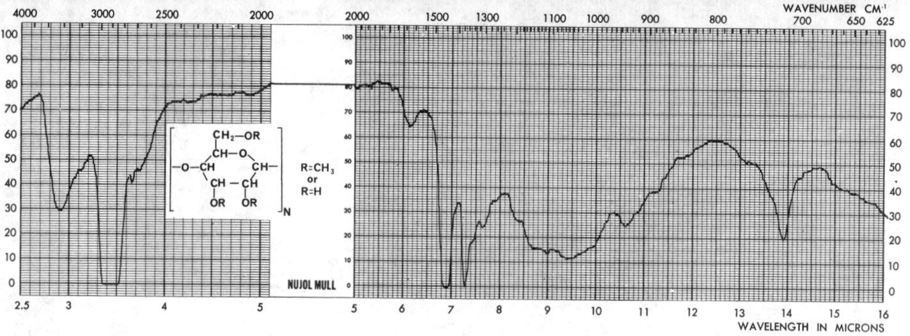

NUJOL MULL

18,102-1
Ethyl cellulose
Powder

B

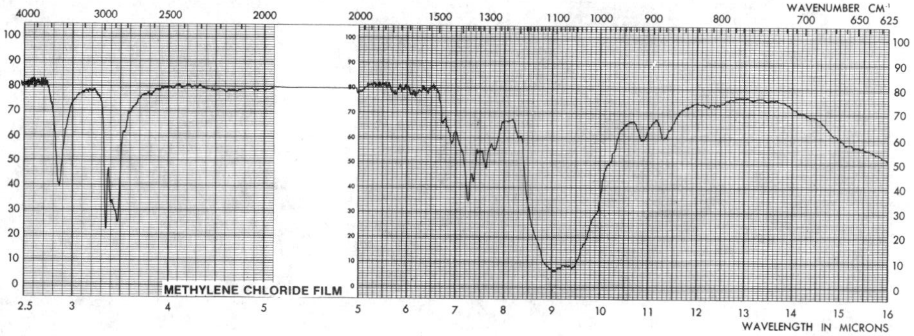

METHYLENE CHLORIDE FILM

19,188-4
Hydroxypropyl cellulose
Disp. D

C

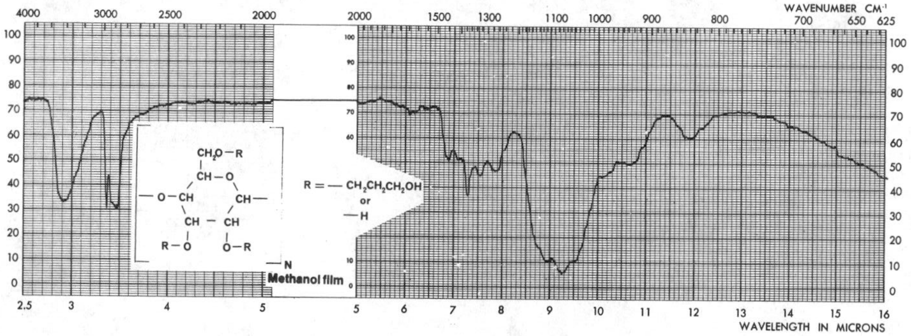

Methanol film

20,032-8
Hydroxypropyl methyl cellulose
Disp. D

D

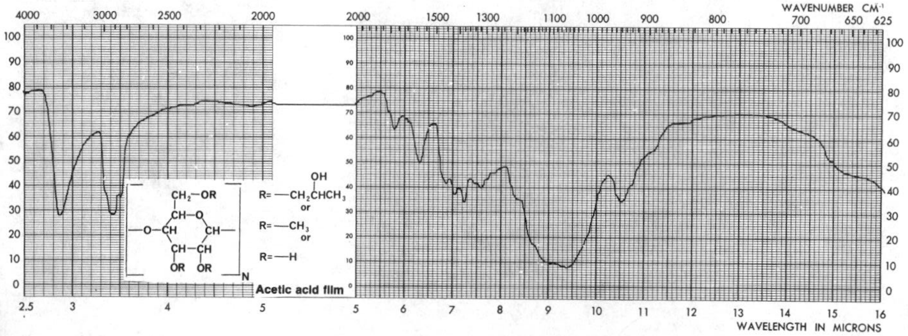

Acetic acid film

E

Acetic acid film

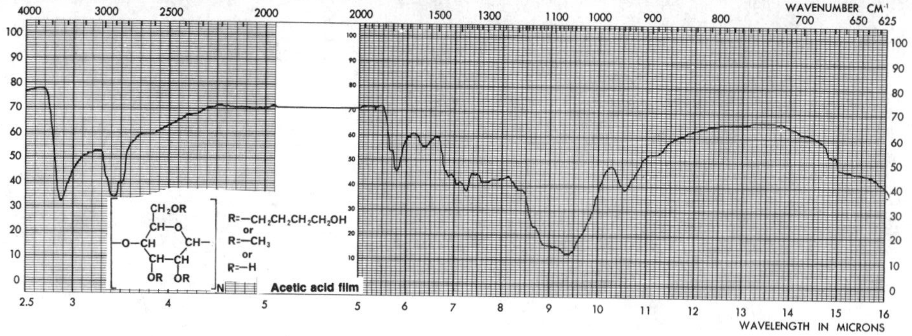

18,465-9
Cellulose, cyanoethylated
Disp. D

F

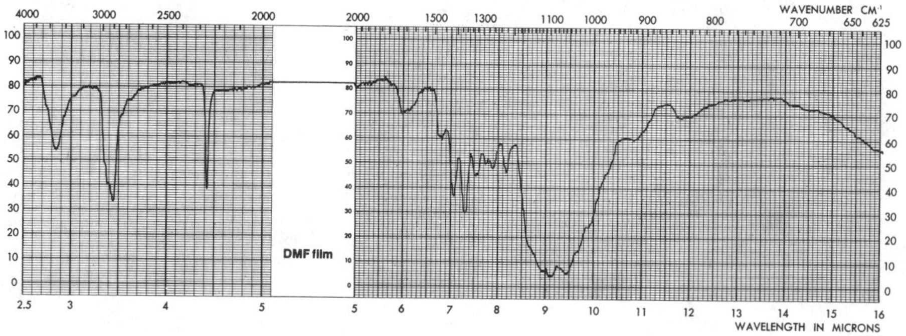

DMF film

18,095-5
Cellulose acetate
Powder. Acetyl content 39.8%, ASTM viscosity 3

G

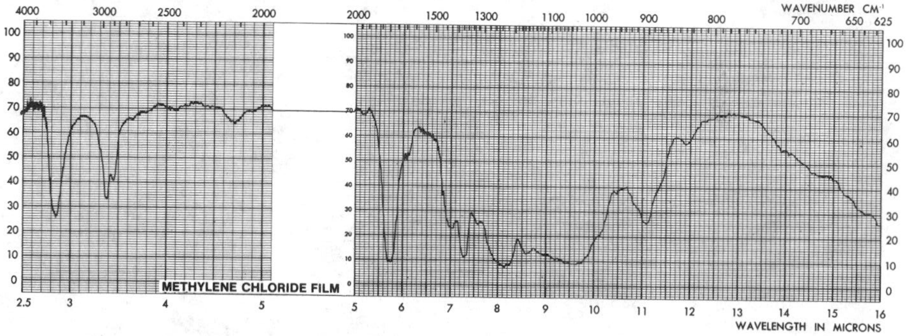

METHYLENE CHLORIDE FILM

18,100-5
Cellulose triacetate
Granular. Soluble in chlorinated solvents.

H

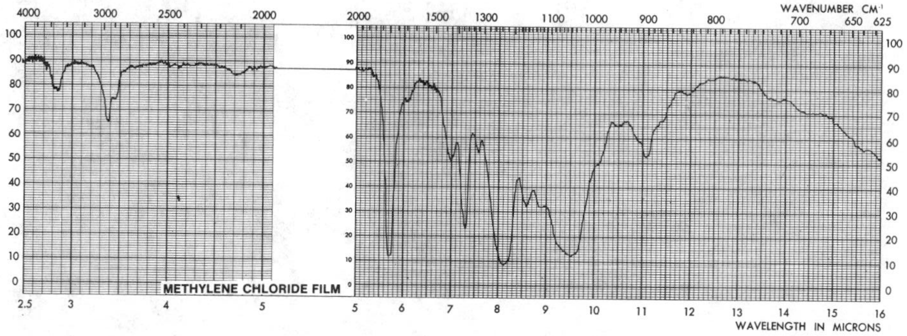

METHYLENE CHLORIDE FILM

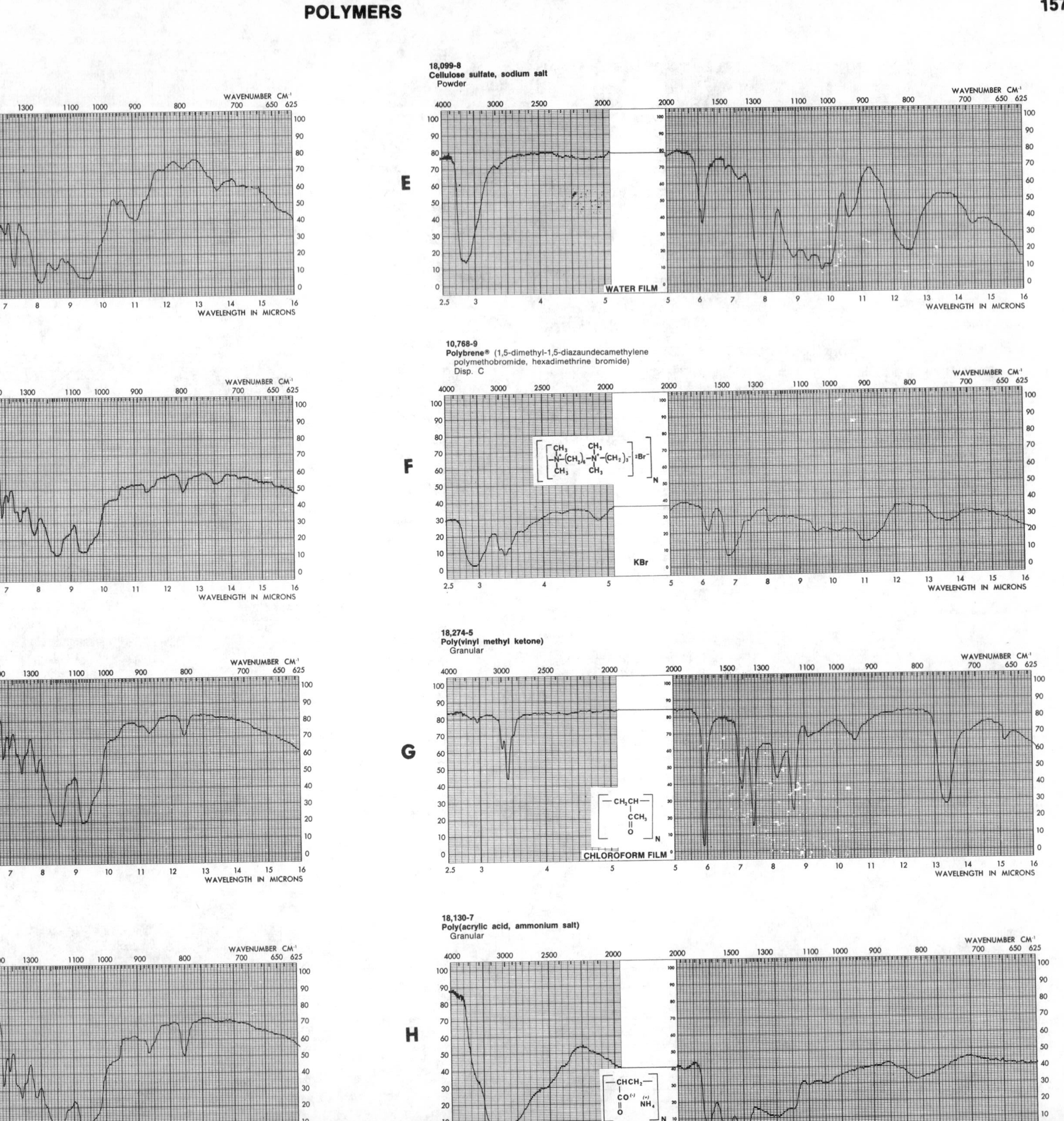
A
18,096-3
Cellulose acetate butyrate
Fluffy solid. Butyryl content 17%, ASTM viscosity 15
METHYLENE CHLORIDE FILM
B
18,461-6
Cellulose propionate, low molecular weight
Disp. D
Acetone film
C
18,097-1
Cellulose propionate, medium molecular weight
Pellets
ACETONE FILM
D
18,462-4
Cellulose propionate, high molecular weight
Disp. D
Acetone film
E
18,099-8
Cellulose sulfate, sodium salt
Powder
WATER FILM
F
10,768-9
Polybrene® (1,5-dimethyl-1,5-diazaundecamethylene polymethobromide, hexadimethrine bromide)
Disp. C
KBr
G
18,274-5
Poly(vinyl methyl ketone)
Granular
CHLOROFORM FILM
H
18,130-7
Poly(acrylic acid, ammonium salt)
Granular
WAVENUMBER CM⁻¹
WAVELENGTH IN MICRONS

A

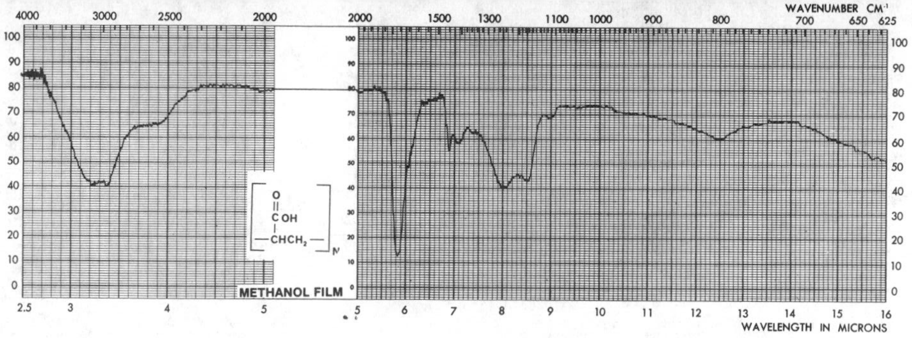

METHANOL FILM

18,128-5
Poly(acrylic acid)
Powder

B

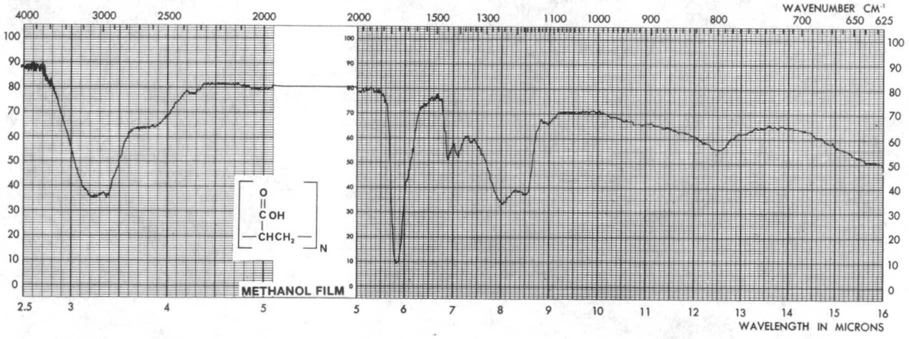

METHANOL FILM

18,949-9
Poly(vinyl acetate), low molecular weight
[-$CH_2CH(O_2CCH_3)$-]$_n$ Disp. D

C

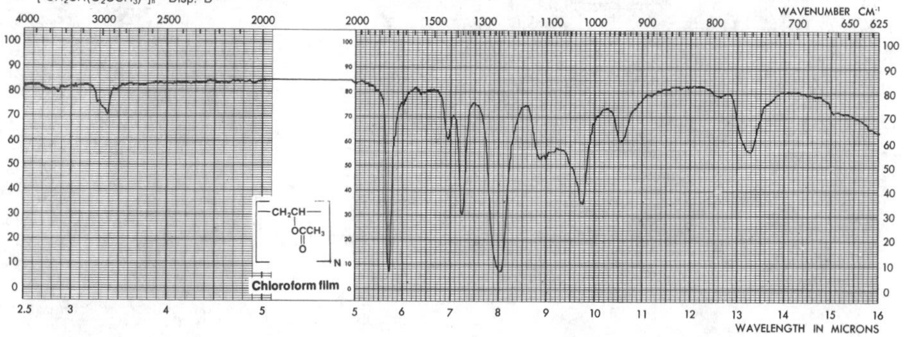

Chloroform film

18,948-0
Poly(vinyl acetate), medium molecular weight
[-$CH_2CH(O_2CCH_3)$-]$_n$ Disp. D

D

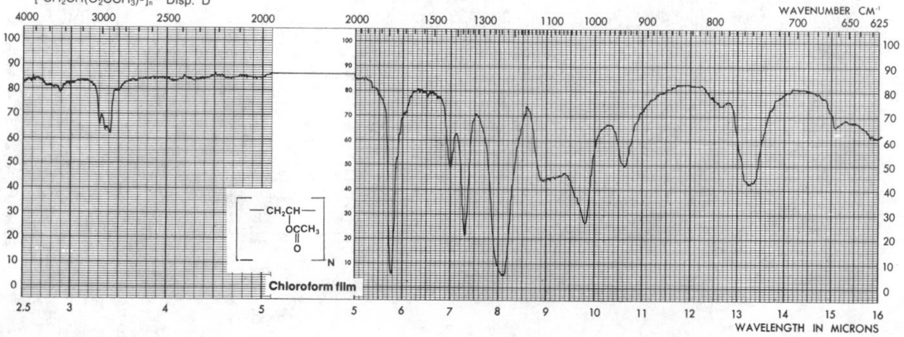

Chloroform film

E

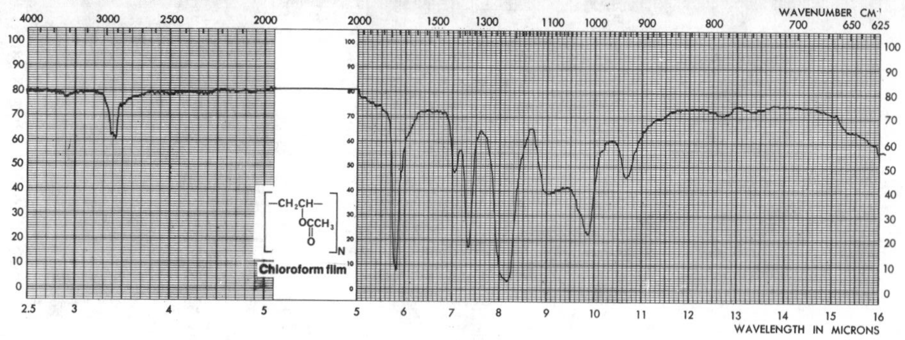

Chloroform film

18,249-4
Poly(vinyl acetate), secondary standard
Typical M.W. 331,000, typical M.N. 83,000

F

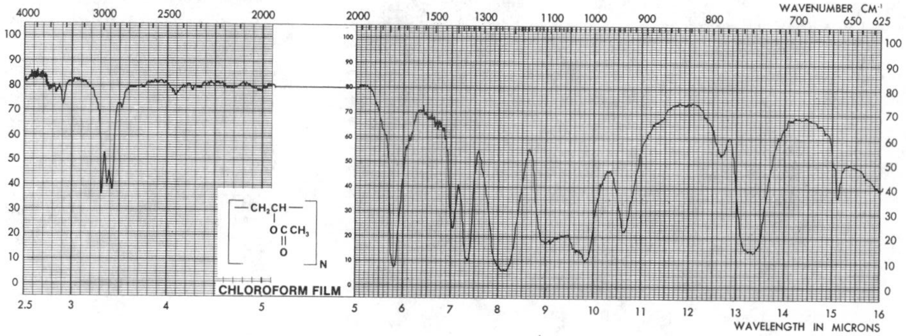

CHLOROFORM FILM

18,278-8
Poly(vinyl propionate)
[-$CH_2CH(O_2CC_2H_5)$-]$_n$ Disp. D

G

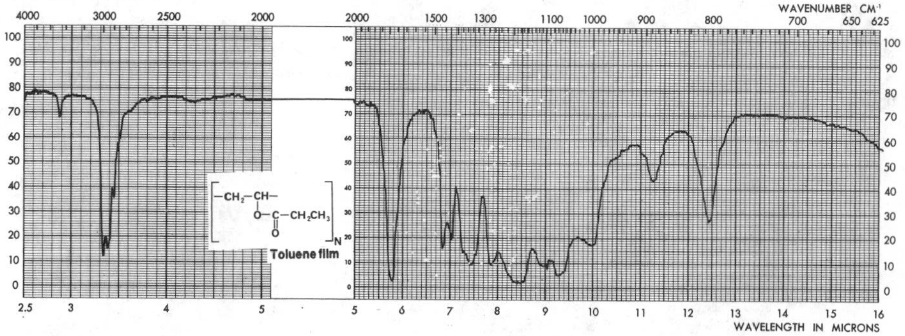

Toluene film

18,258-3
Poly(vinyl butyrate)
[-$CH_2CH(O_2CCH_2CH_2CH_3)$-]$_n$ Disp. D

H

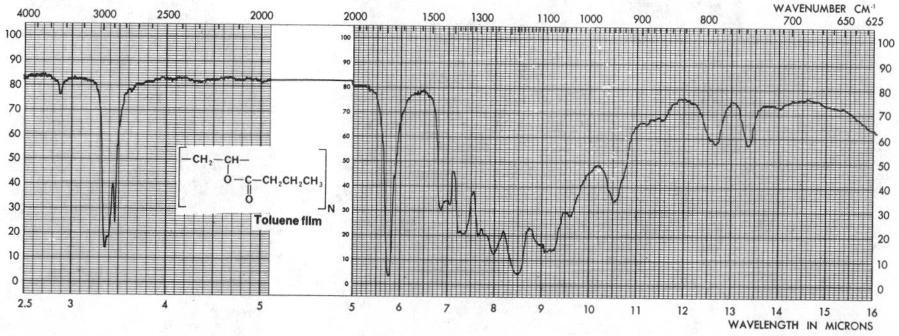

Toluene film

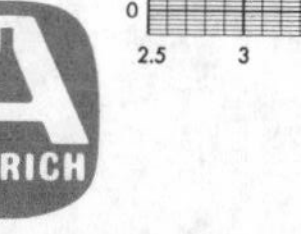

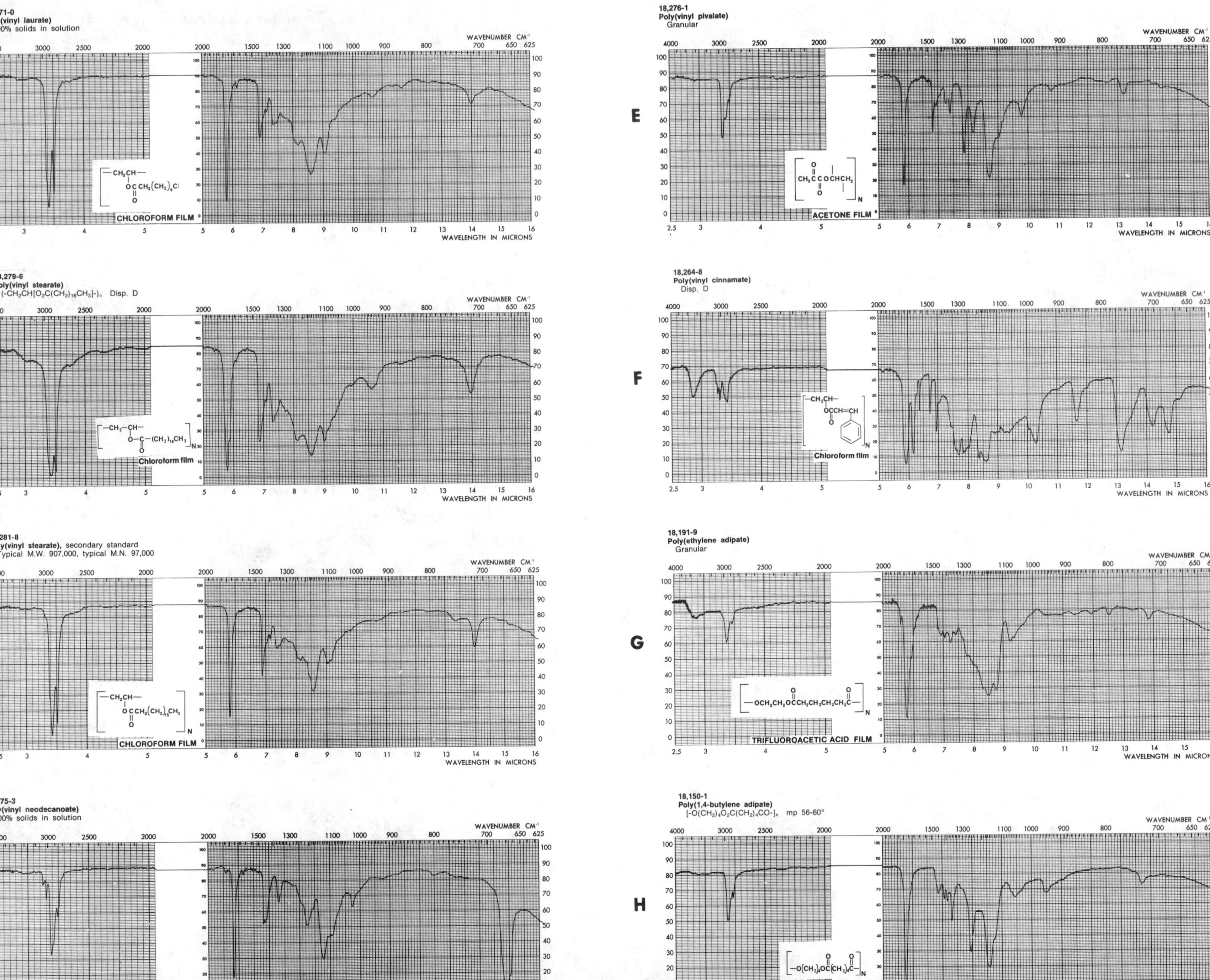
ALDRICH
A
18,271-0
Poly(vinyl laurate)
100% solids in solution
CHLOROFORM FILM
B
18,279-6
Poly(vinyl stearate)
(-CH2CH[O2C(CH2)16CH3]-)n Disp. D
Chloroform film
C
18,281-8
Poly(vinyl stearate), secondary standard
Typical M.W. 907,000, typical M.N. 97,000
CHLOROFORM FILM
D
18,275-3
Poly(vinyl neodecanoate)
100% solids in solution
E
18,276-1
Poly(vinyl pivalate)
Granular
ACETONE FILM
F
18,264-8
Poly(vinyl cinnamate)
Disp. D
Chloroform film
G
18,191-9
Poly(ethylene adipate)
Granular
TRIFLUOROACETIC ACID FILM
H
18,150-1
Poly(1,4-butylene adipate)
[-O(CH2)4O2C(CH2)4CO-]n mp 56-60°
WAVENUMBER CM⁻¹
WAVELENGTH IN MICRONS

A

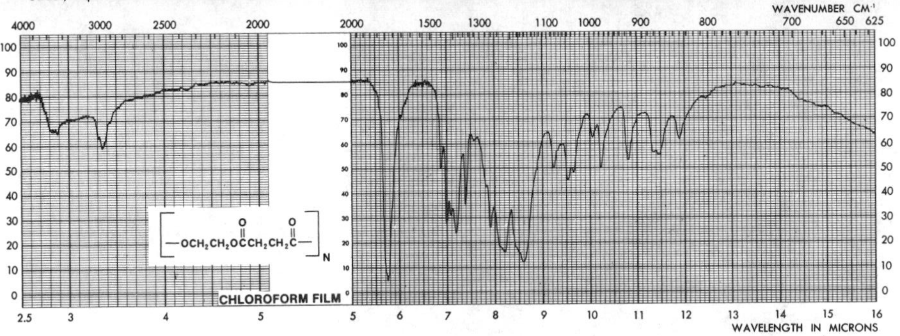

CHLOROFORM FILM

18,181-1
Poly(2,2-dimethyl-1,3-propylene succinate)

B

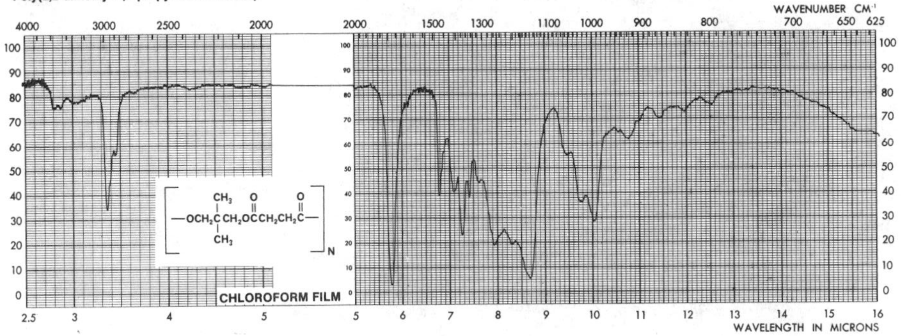

CHLOROFORM FILM

18,211-7
Poly(hexamethylene sebacate)
Powder

C

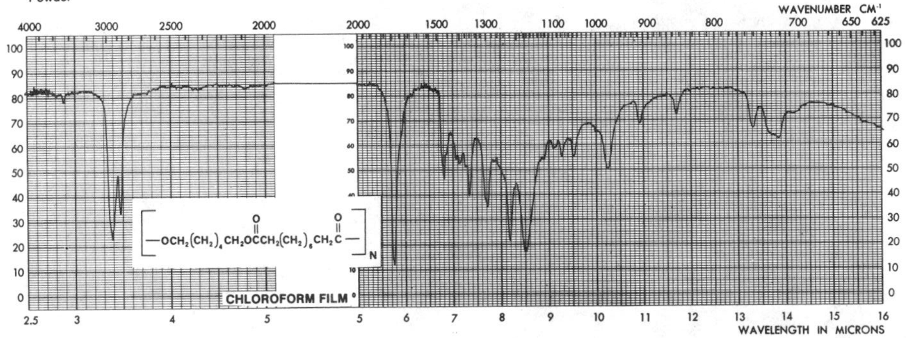

CHLOROFORM FILM

18,222-2
Poly(methyl acrylate), secondary standard
Typical M.W. 70,000, typical M.N. 24,000

D

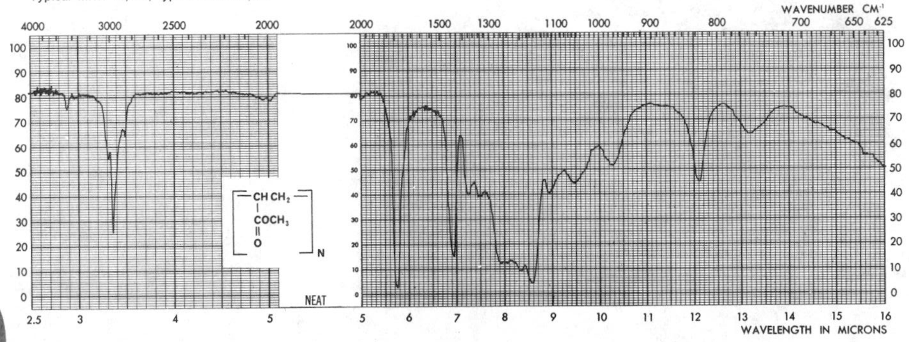

NEAT

E

FILM

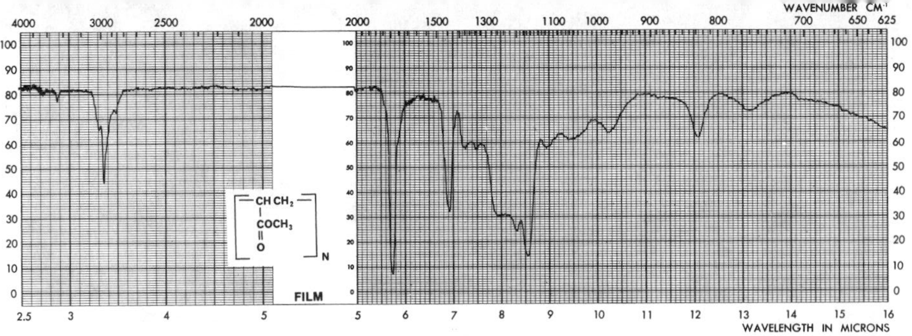

18,187-0
Poly(ethyl acrylate), secondary standard
Typical M.W. 175,000, typical M.N. 37,000

F

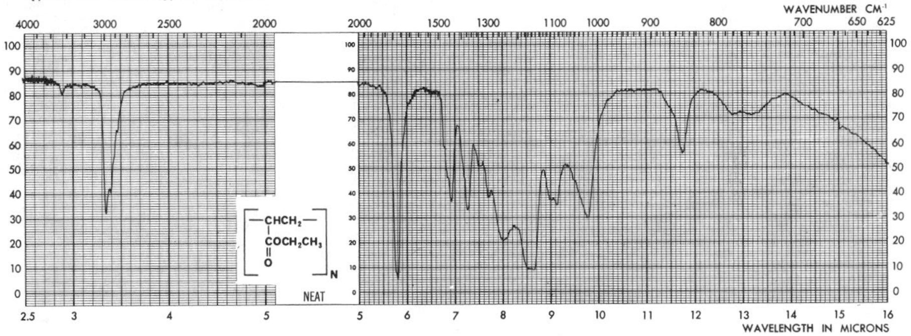

NEAT

18,188-9
Poly(ethyl acrylate)
100% solids in solution

G

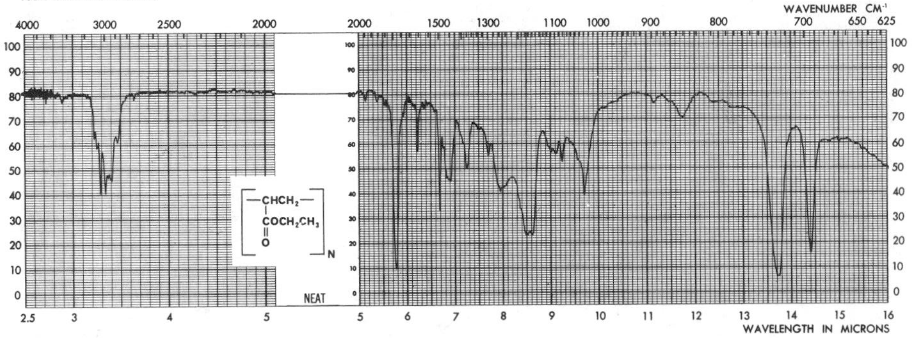

NEAT

18,237-0
Poly(isopropyl acrylate)
100% solids in solution

H

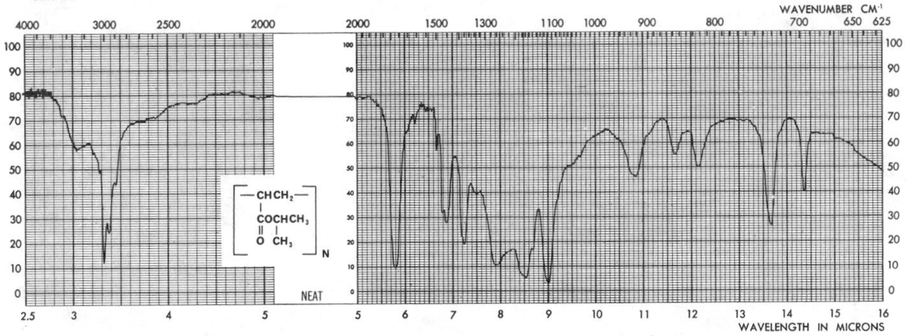

NEAT

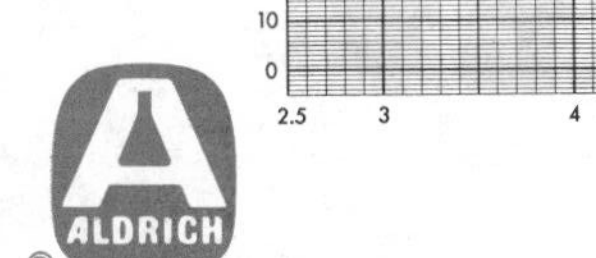

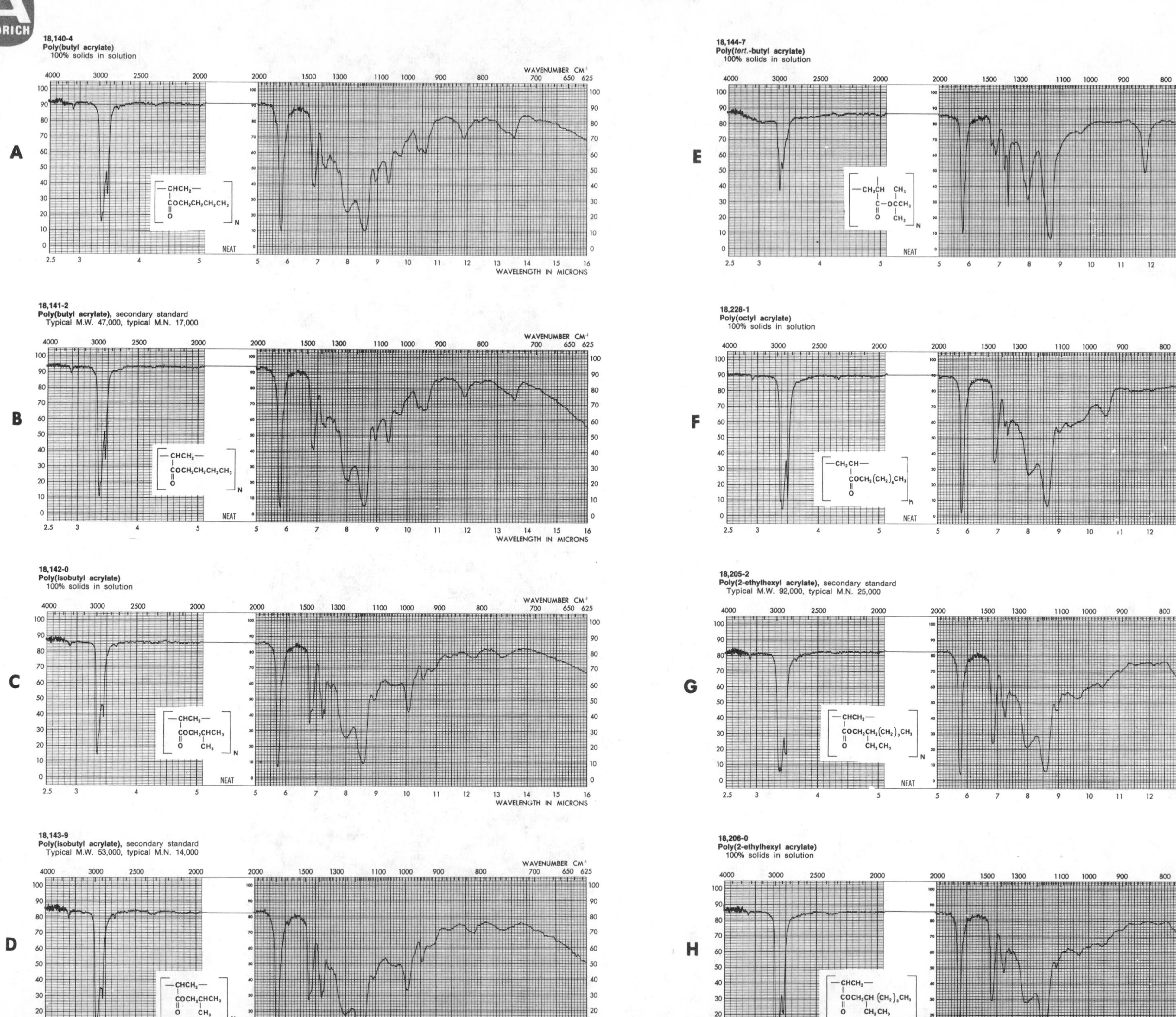
A
18,140-4
Poly(butyl acrylate)
100% solids in solution
NEAT
B
18,141-2
Poly(butyl acrylate), secondary standard
Typical M.W. 47,000, typical M.N. 17,000
NEAT
C
18,142-0
Poly(isobutyl acrylate)
100% solids in solution
NEAT
D
18,143-9
Poly(isobutyl acrylate), secondary standard
Typical M.W. 53,000, typical M.N. 14,000
E
18,144-7
Poly(tert.-butyl acrylate)
100% solids in solution
NEAT
F
18,228-1
Poly(octyl acrylate)
100% solids in solution
NEAT
G
18,205-2
Poly(2-ethylhexyl acrylate), secondary standard
Typical M.W. 92,000, typical M.N. 25,000
NEAT
H
18,206-0
Poly(2-ethylhexyl acrylate)
100% solids in solution
WAVENUMBER CM⁻¹
WAVELENGTH IN MICRONS

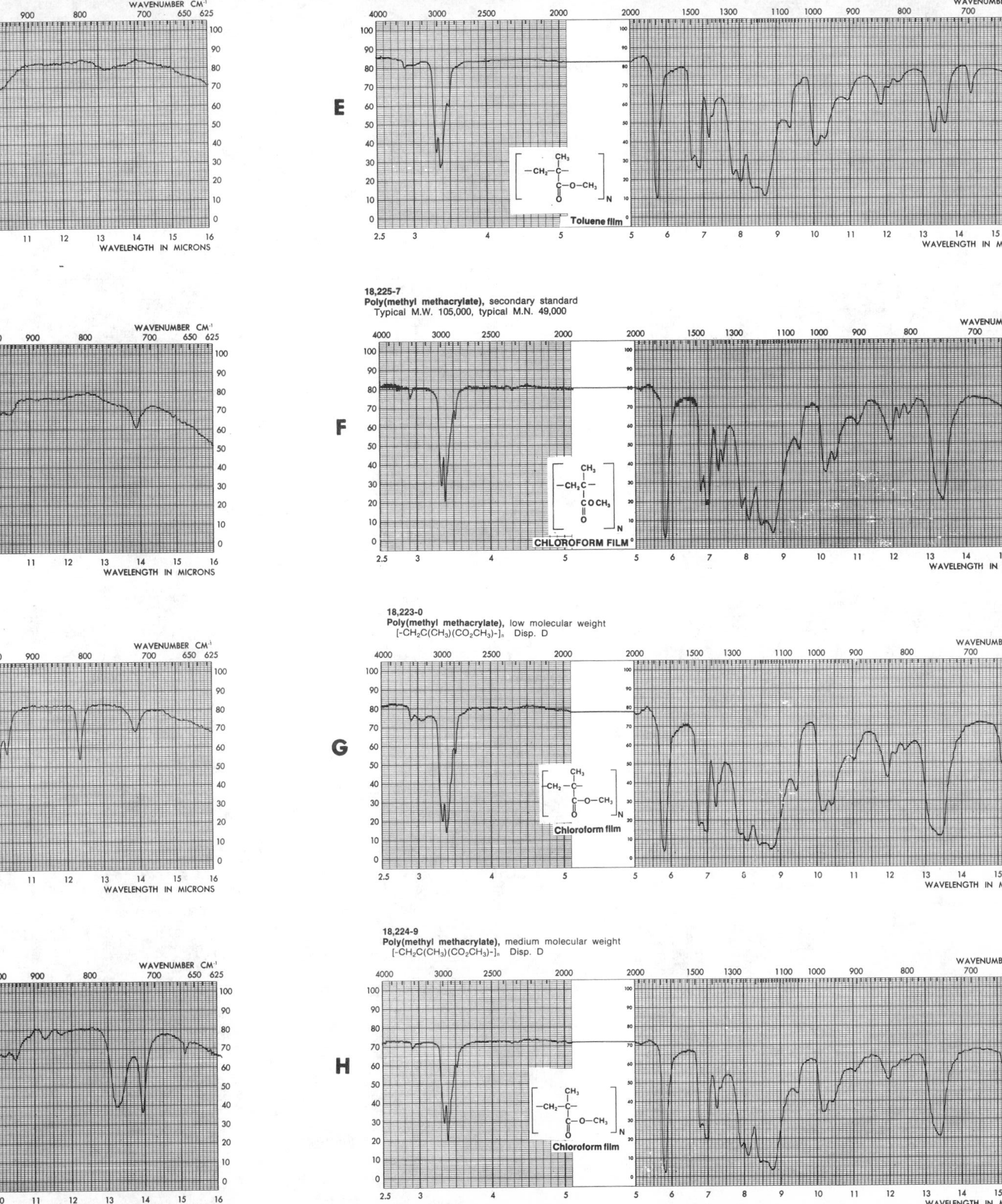

A

100% solids in solution

B

18,217-6
Poly(lauryl acrylate)
100% solids in solution
NEAT

C

18,209-5
Poly(hexadecyl acrylate)
100% solids in solution
NEAT

D

18,231-1
Poly(octadecyl acrylate), secondary standard
Typical M.W. 68,000, typical M.N. 32,000
CHLOROFORM FILM

E

Disp. D
Toluene film

F

18,225-7
Poly(methyl methacrylate), secondary standard
Typical M.W. 105,000, typical M.N. 49,000
CHLOROFORM FILM

G

18,223-0
Poly(methyl methacrylate), low molecular weight
$[-CH_2C(CH_3)(CO_2CH_3)-]_n$ Disp. D
Chloroform film

H

18,224-9
Poly(methyl methacrylate), medium molecular weight
$[-CH_2C(CH_3)(CO_2CH_3)-]_n$ Disp. D
Chloroform film

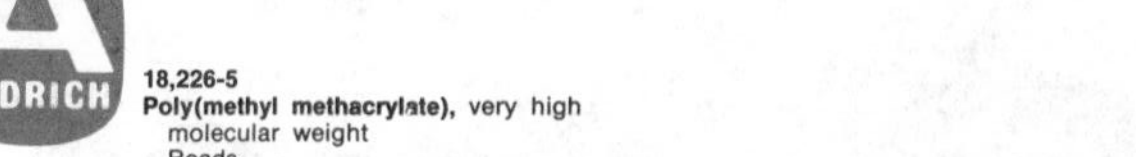

A

18,226-5
Poly(methyl methacrylate), very high molecular weight
Beads

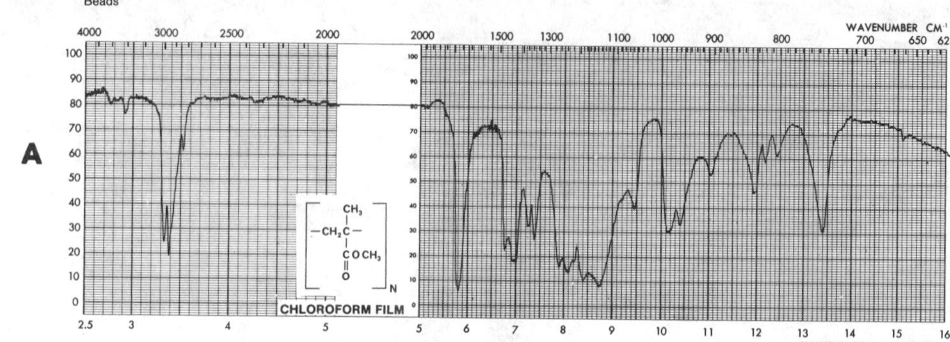

B

18,335-0
Poly(ethyl methacrylate), secondary standard
Typical M.W. 395,000, typical M.N. 144,000

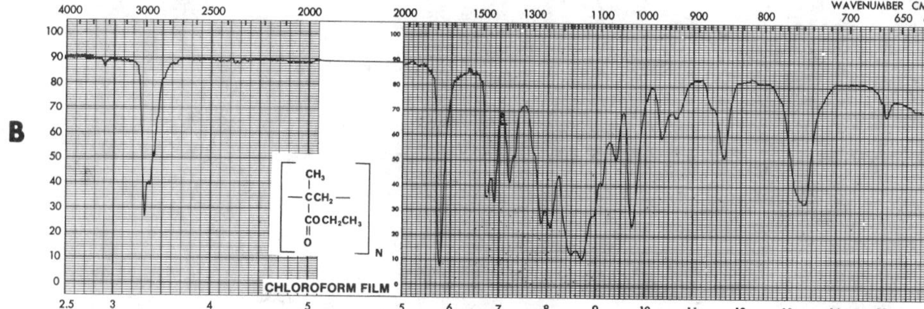

C

18,208-7
Poly(ethyl methacrylate), very high molecular weight
Beads

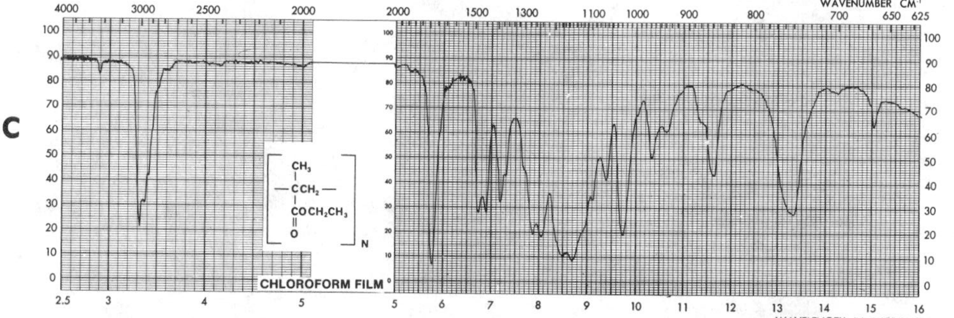

D

18,213-3
Poly(2-hydroxypropyl methacrylate)
$(-CH_2C(CH_3)[CO_2CH_2CH(OH)CH_3]-)_n$ Disp. D

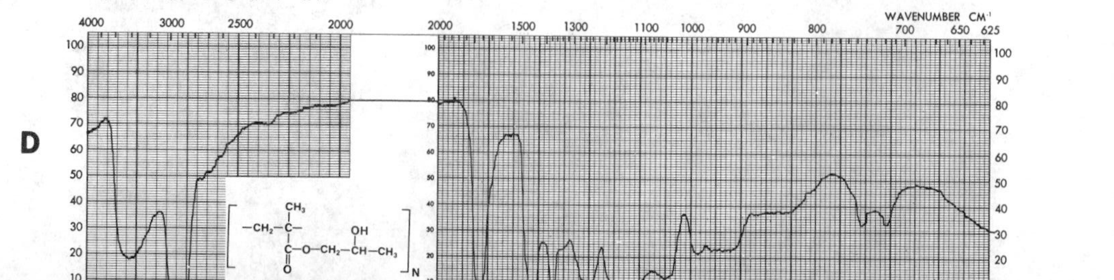

E

18,240-0
Poly(isopropyl methacrylate)
Granular

F

18,152-8
Poly(butyl methacrylate), high molecular weight
BEADS

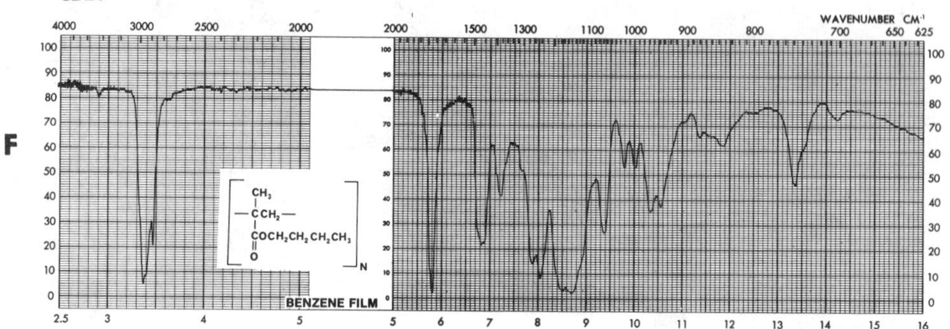

G

18,153-6
Poly(butyl methacrylate), secondary standard
Typical M.W. 214,000, typical M.N. 72,000

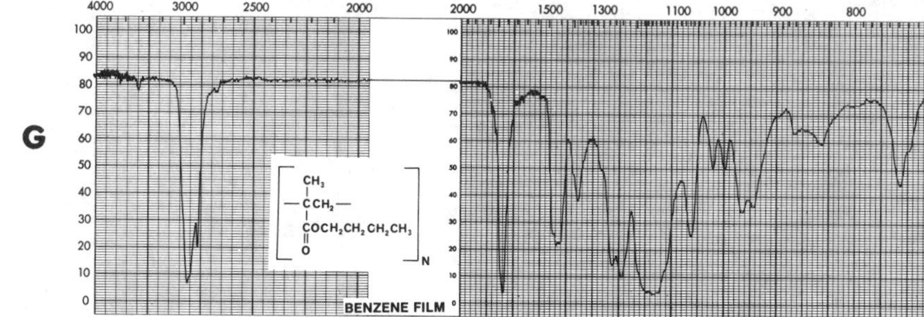

H

18,154-4
Poly(isobutyl methacrylate), high molecular weight
Beads

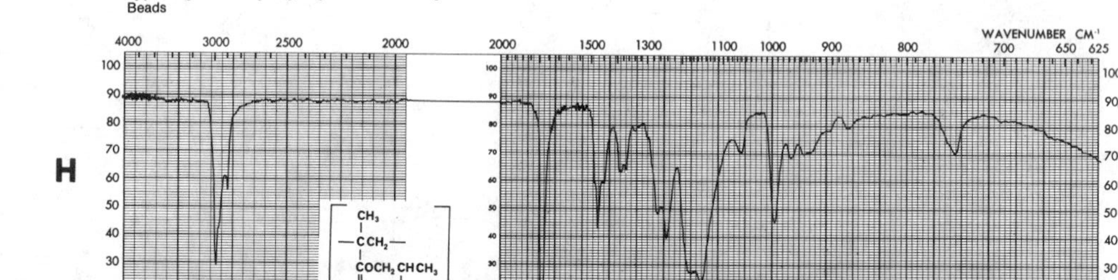

A

Typical M.W. 369,000, typical M.N. 128,000

CHLOROFORM FILM

B

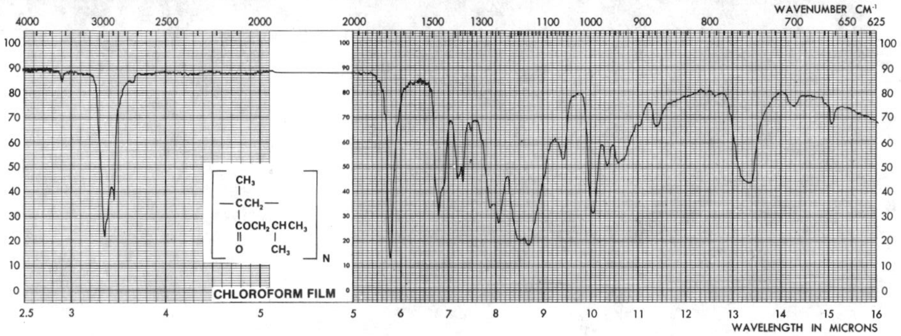

18,157-9
Poly(*sec.*-butyl methacrylate)
Granular

BENZENE FILM

C

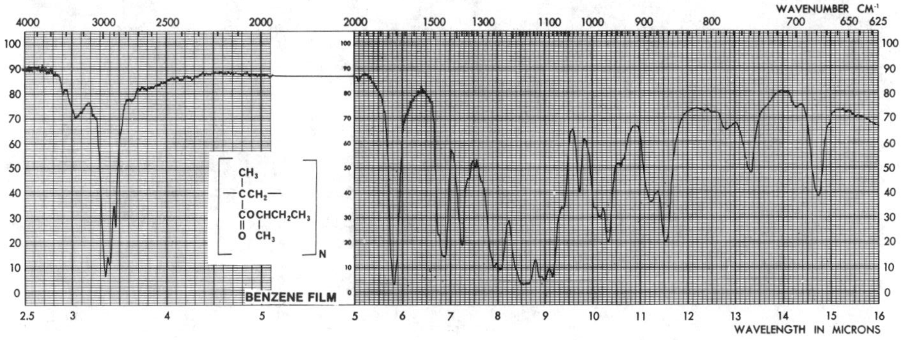

18,158-7
Poly(*tert.*-butyl methacrylate)
Granular

BENZENE FILM

D

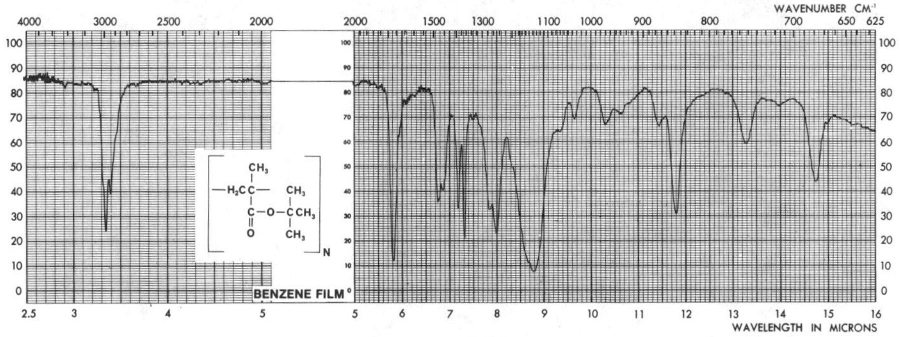

18,212-5
Poly(hexyl methacrylate)
100% solids in solution

NEAT

E

Poly(2-ethylhexyl methacrylate)
100% solids in solution

NEAT

F

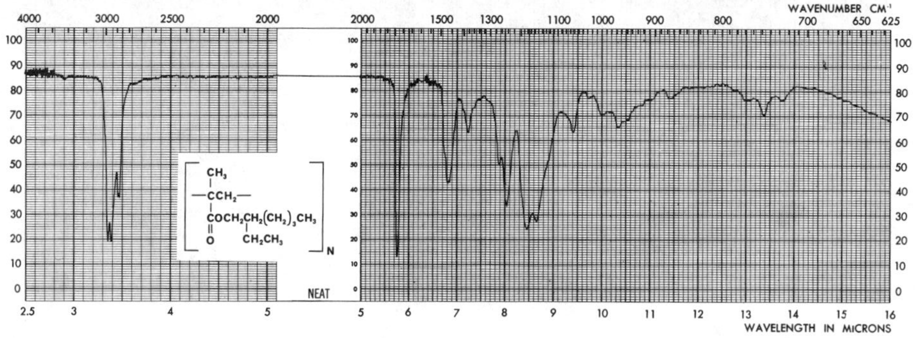

18,174-9
Poly(isodecyl methacrylate)
100% solids in solution

NEAT

G

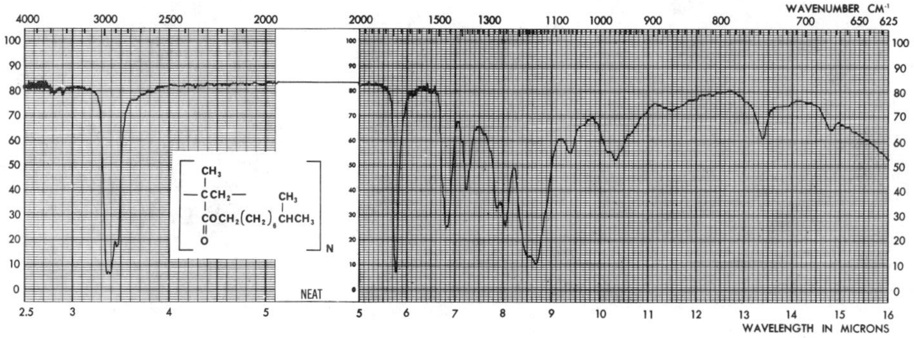

18,219-2
Poly(lauryl methacrylate), secondary standard
Typical M.W. 70,000, typical M.N. 31,000

NEAT

H

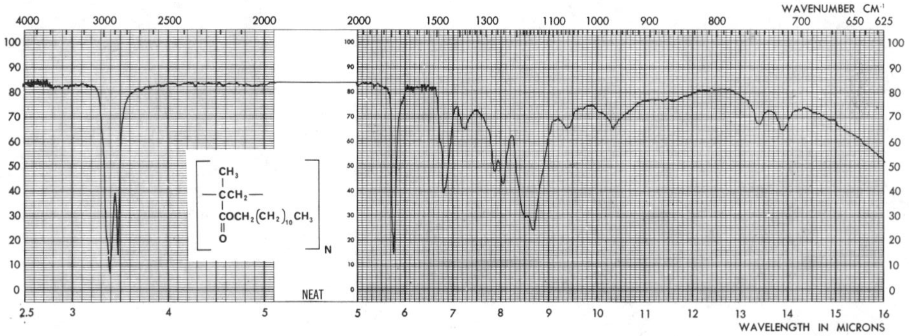

18,218-4
Poly(lauryl methacrylate)
100% solids in solution

NEAT

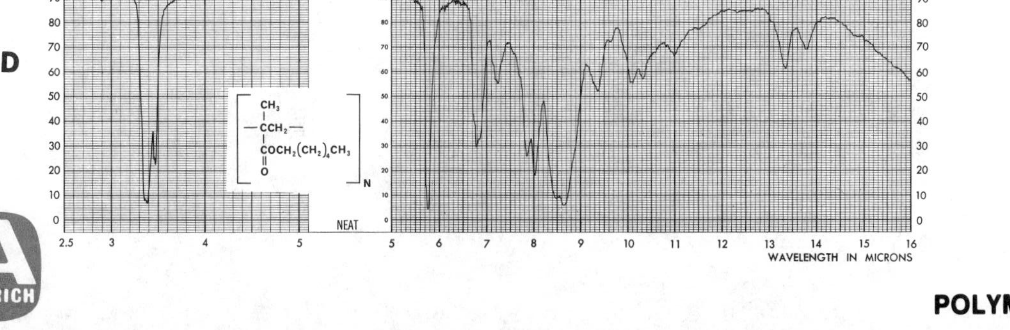

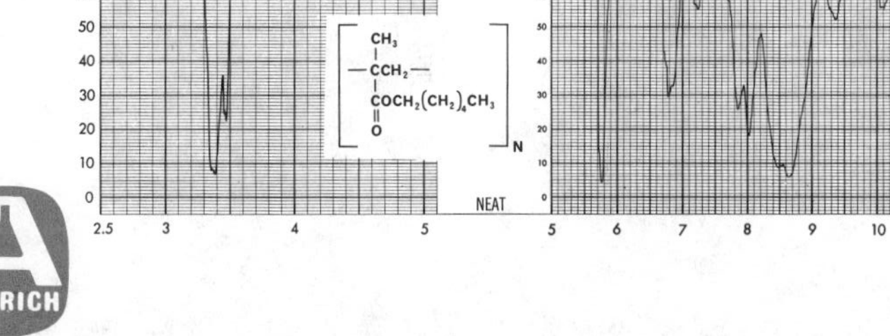

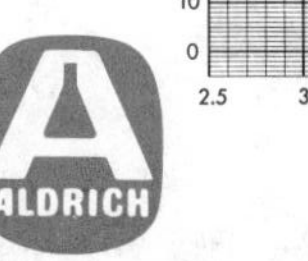

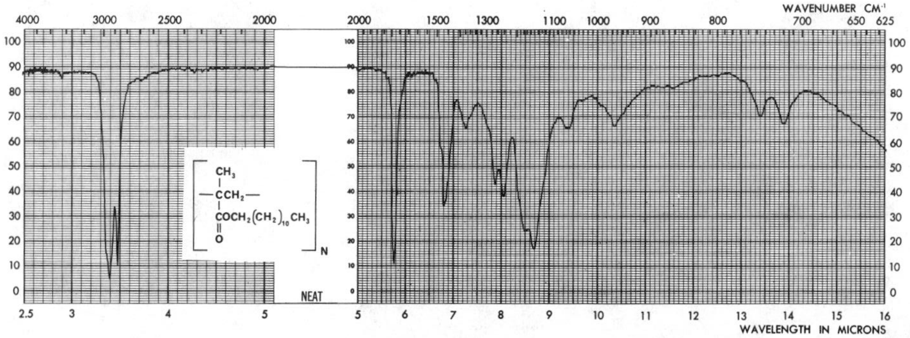

A 18,210-9
Poly(hexadecyl methacrylate)
100% solids in solution
NEAT

B 18,233-8
Poly(octadecyl methacrylate)
$[-CH_2C(CH_3)[CO_2(CH_2)_{17}CH_3]-]_n$ Disp. D
NEAT

C 18,234-6
Poly(octadecyl methacrylate), secondary standard
Typical M.W. 109,000, typical M.N. 44,000
CHLOROFORM FILM

D 19,194-9
Poly(cyclohexyl methacrylate)
$[-CH_2C(CH_3)(CO_2C_6H_{11})-]_n$ Disp. D

E 19,195-7
Poly(isobornyl methacrylate)
Disp. D
KBr

F 19,206-6
Poly(2-hydroxyethyl methacrylate)
$[-CH_2C(CH_3)(CO_2CH_2CH_2OH)-]_n$ Disp. D
DMSO film

G 18,161-7
Poly(caprolactone), secondary standard
Typical M.W. 33,000, typical M.N. 11,000
CHLOROFORM FILM

H 18,160-9
Poly(caprolactone)
Flakes

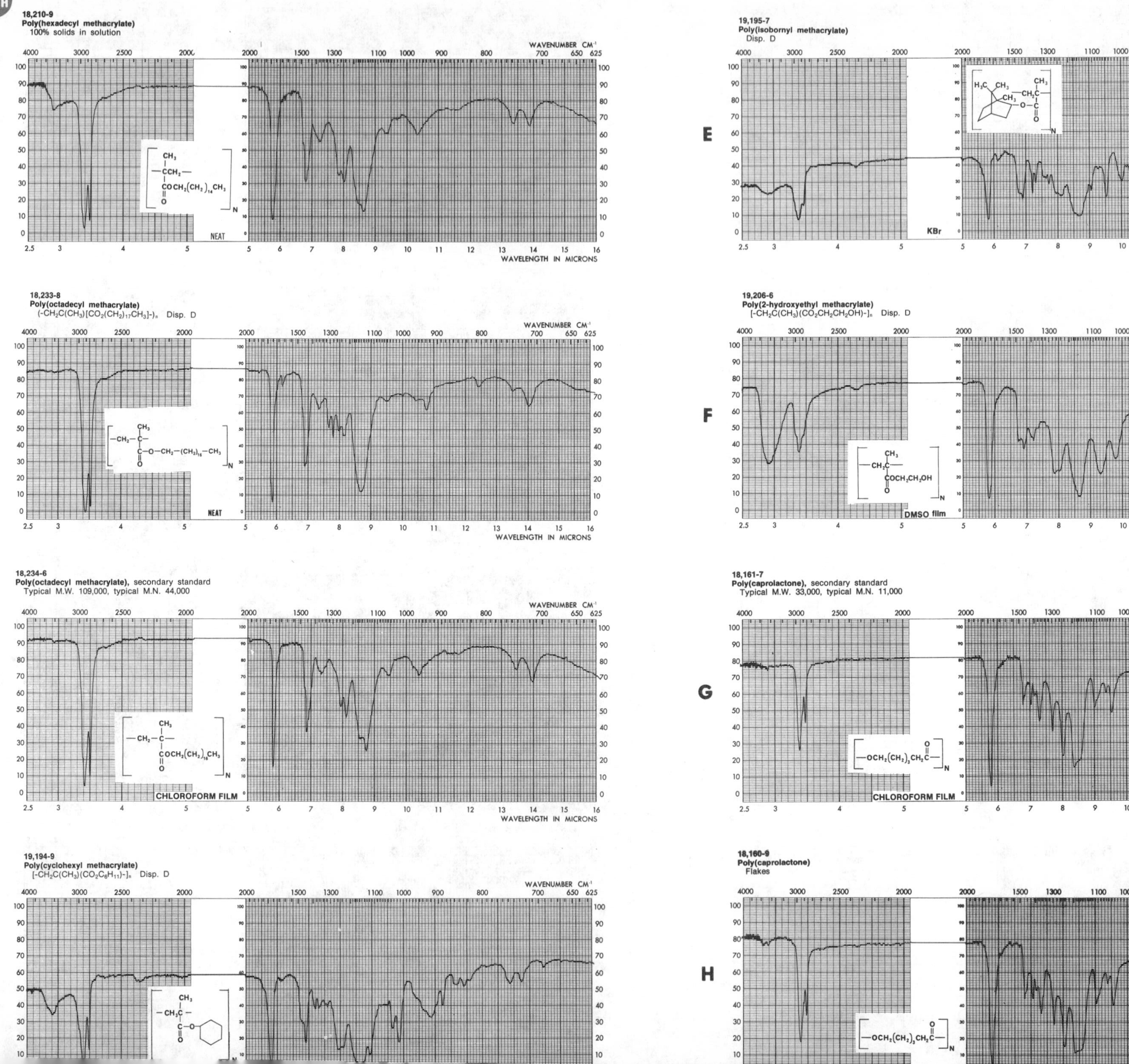

Disp. D *IRRITANT*
Fused mass. Average M.W. 530. Density 1.073. Tm 35°

A

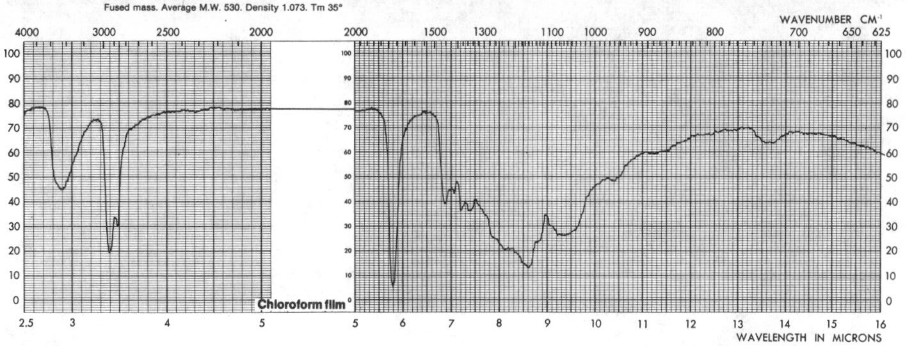

Chloroform film

20,542-7 **Poly(caprolactone) diol**
Disp. D
Viscous liquid. Average M.W. 830. Density 1.073. Tm 40°
Hydroxyl number 135mg KOH/g

B

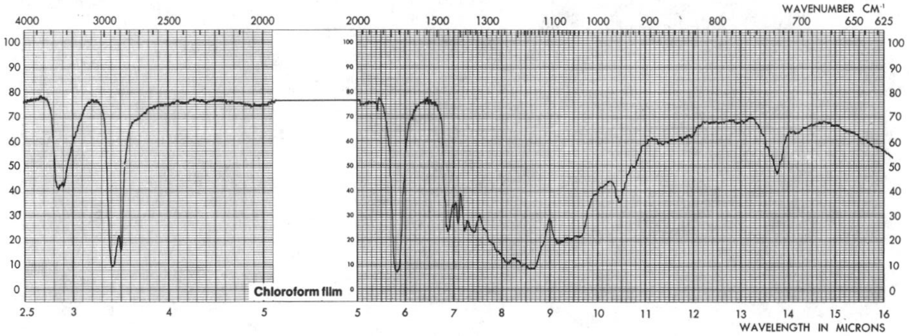

Chloroform film

18,941-3 **Poly(caprolactone) diol**
Disp. D *IRRITANT*
Fused mass. Average M.W. 1,250. Density 1.071. Tm 45°

C

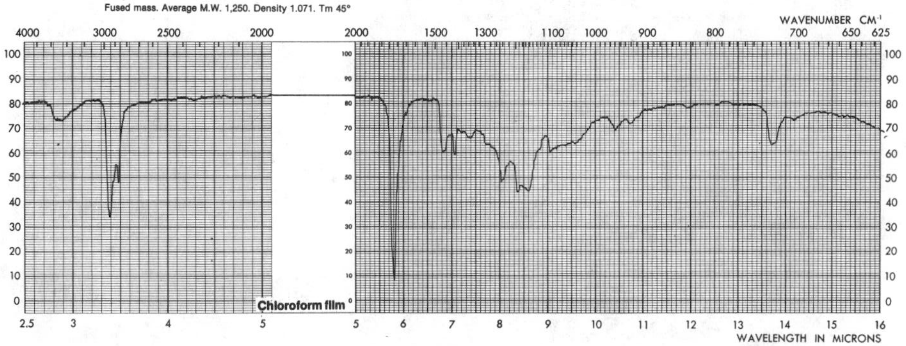

Chloroform film

18,942-1 **Poly(caprolactone) diol**
Disp. D *IRRITANT*
Fused mass. Average M.W. 2,000. Density 1.071. Tm 50°

D

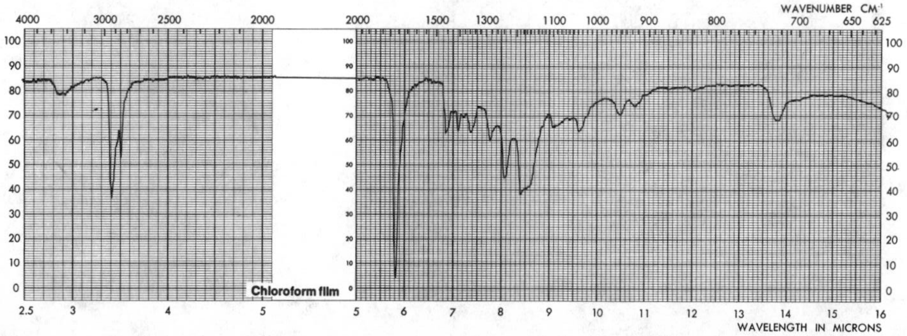

Chloroform film

18,944-8 **Poly(caprolactone) diol**
Fused mass. Average M.W. 3,000.

E

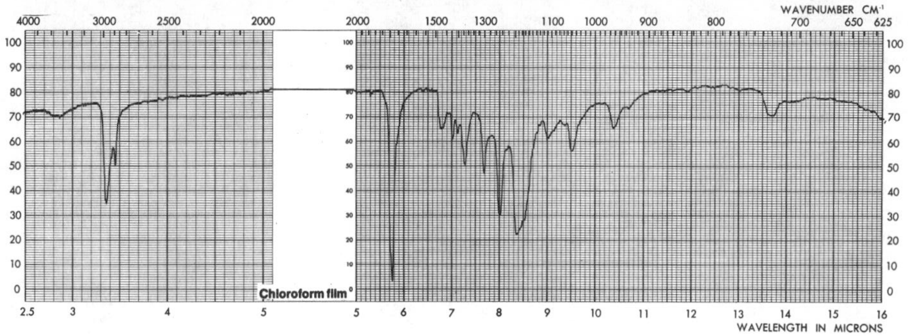

Chloroform film

20,039-5
Poly(caprolactone) triol
Disp. D

F

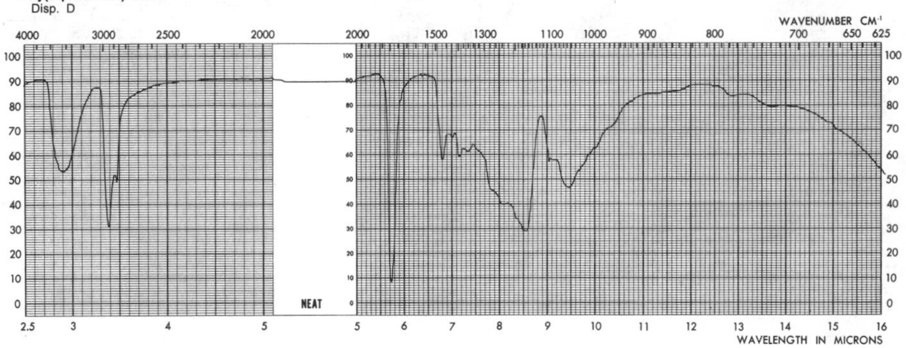

NEAT

18,171-4
Poly(1,4-cyclohexanedimethylene succinate)
Chunks

G

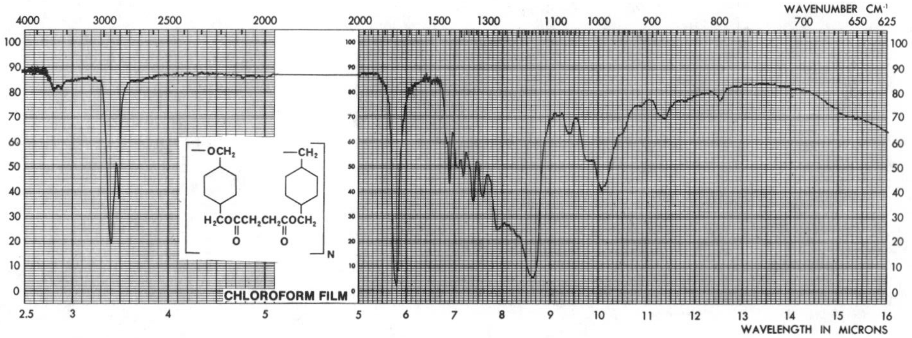

CHLOROFORM FILM

18,172-2
Poly(1,4-cyclohexanedimethylene terephthalate)
Pellets

H

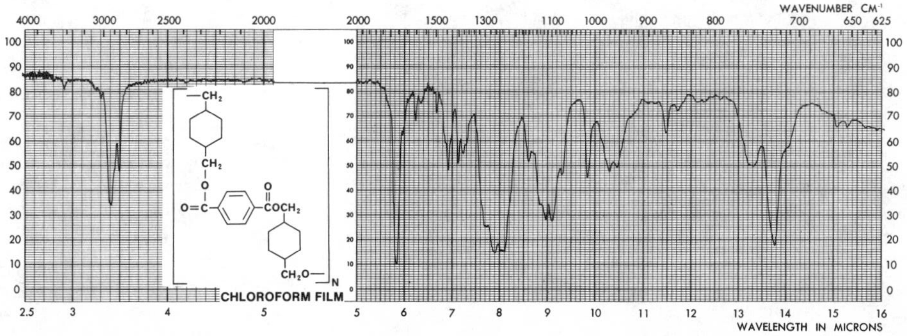

CHLOROFORM FILM

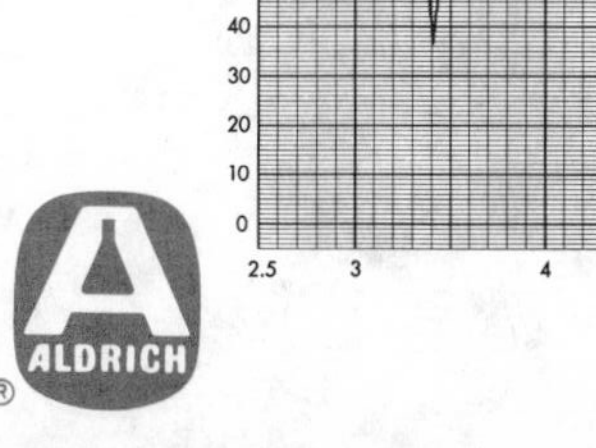

A

18,167-6
Polycarbonate resin, secondary standard, molecular weight series
Typical M.W. 34,000, 38,000, 48,000
Typical M.N. 13,000, 14,000, 18,000
CHLOROFORM FILM

B

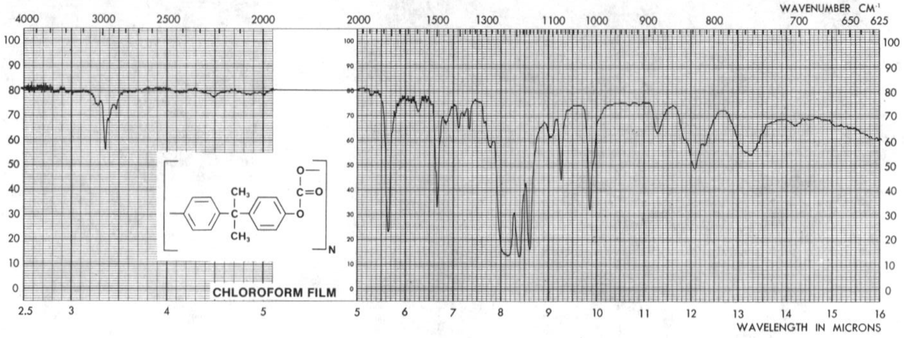

18,164-1
Polycarbonate resin, secondary standard
Typical M.W. 34,000, typical M.N. 13,000
CHLOROFORM FILM

C

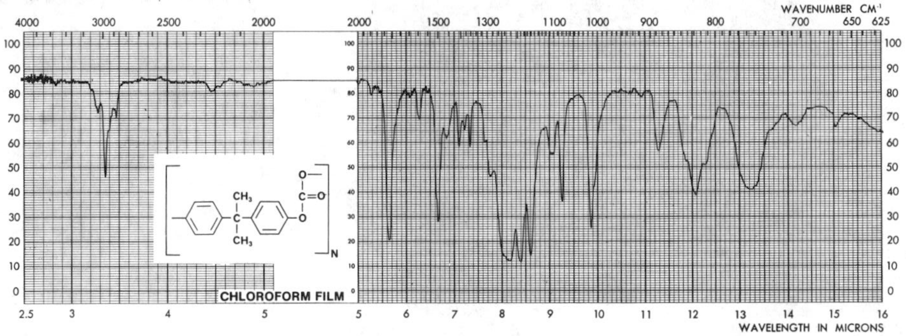

18,162-5
Polycarbonate resin, low molecular weight
Pellets
BENZENE FILM

D

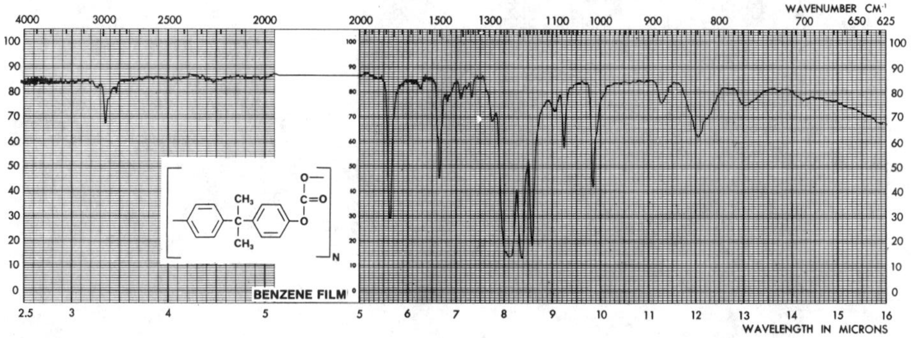

18,163-3
Polycarbonate resin, very high molecular weight
Granular

E

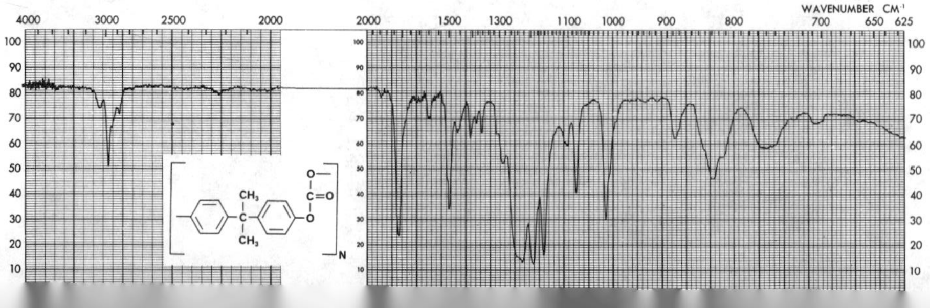

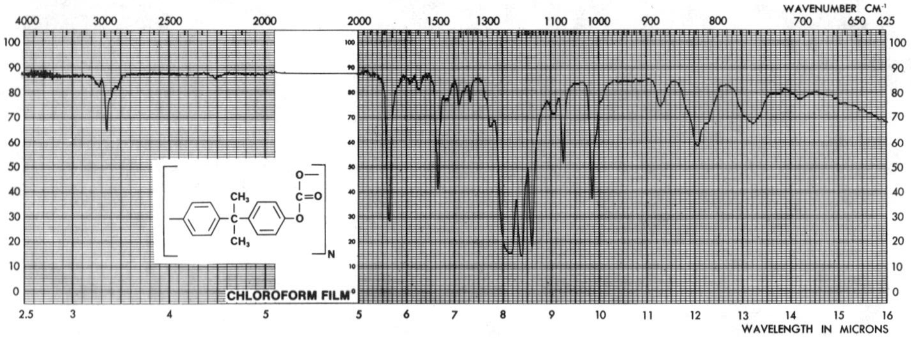

18,166-8
Polycarbonate resin, ultra high molecular weight
Granular
CHLOROFORM FILM

F

18,176-5
Poly(diallyl phthalate)
Powder
CHLOROFORM FILM

G

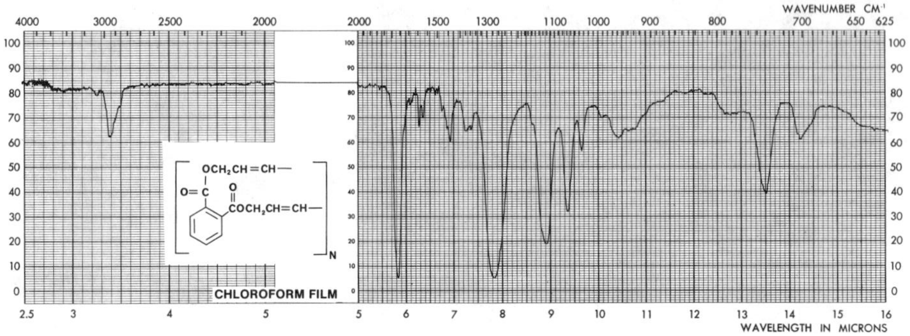

18,175-7
Poly(diallyl isophthalate)
Powder
TOLUENE FILM

H

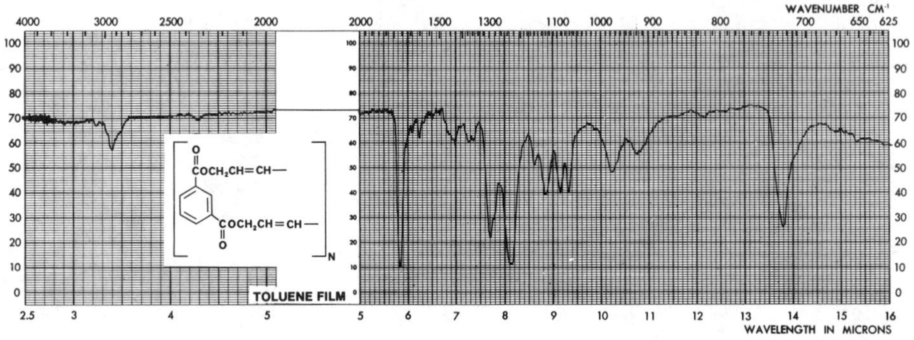

19,094-2
Poly(1,4-butylene terephthalate)
$[-O(CH_2)_4O_2CC_6H_4\text{-}4\text{-}CO]_n$ Disp. D
TFA film

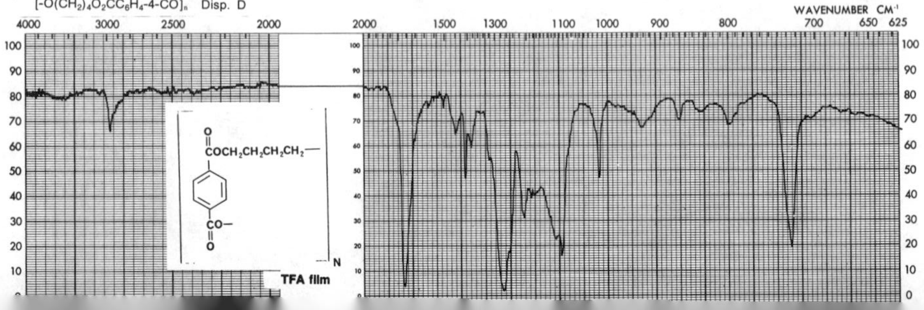

Granular

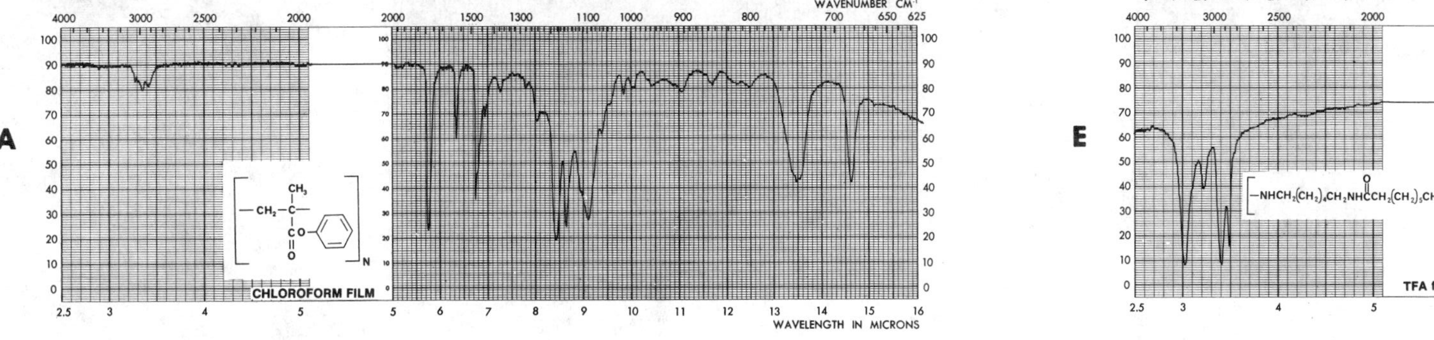

A

CHLOROFORM FILM

18,135-8
Poly(benzyl methacrylate)
Powder

B

BENZENE FILM

18,111-0
Nylon 6 [poly(caprolactam)]
Pellets

C

TRIFLUOROETHANOL FILM

18,112-9
Nylon 6/6 [poly(hexamethylene adipamide)]
Pellets

D

TRIFLUOROACETIC ACID FILM

Nylon 6/9 [poly(hexamethylene nonanediamide)]
[-NH(CH$_2$)$_6$NHCO(CH$_2$)$_7$CO-]$_n$ Disp. D

E

TFA film

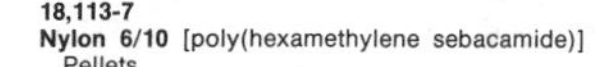

18,113-7
Nylon 6/10 [poly(hexamethylene sebacamide)]
Pellets

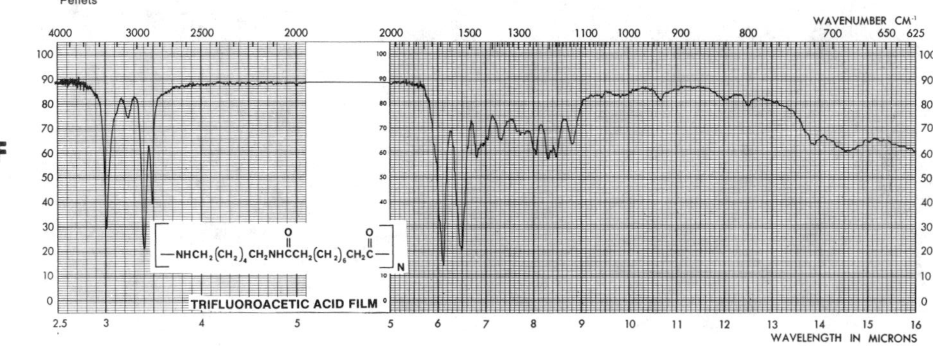

F

TRIFLUOROACETIC ACID FILM

18,114-5
Nylon 6/12 [poly(hexamethylene dodecanediamide)]
Pellets

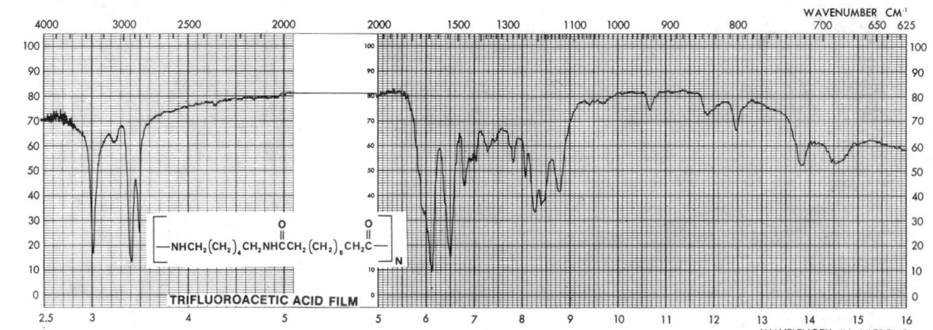

G

TRIFLUOROACETIC ACID FILM

18,808-5
Nylon 6/T [poly(hexamethylene terephthalamide)]
[-NH(CH$_2$)$_6$NHCOC$_6$H$_4$-4-CO-]$_n$ Disp. D

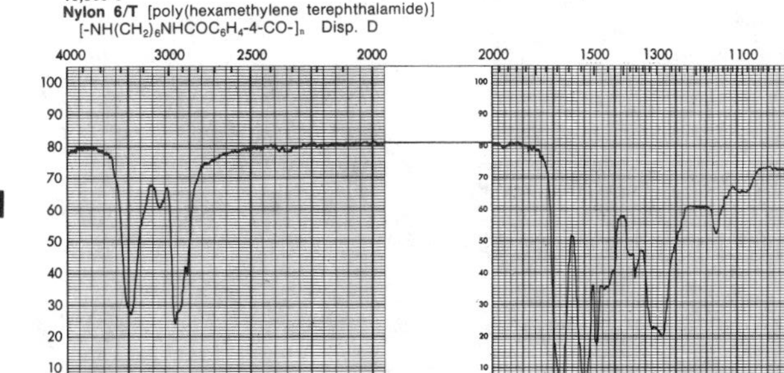

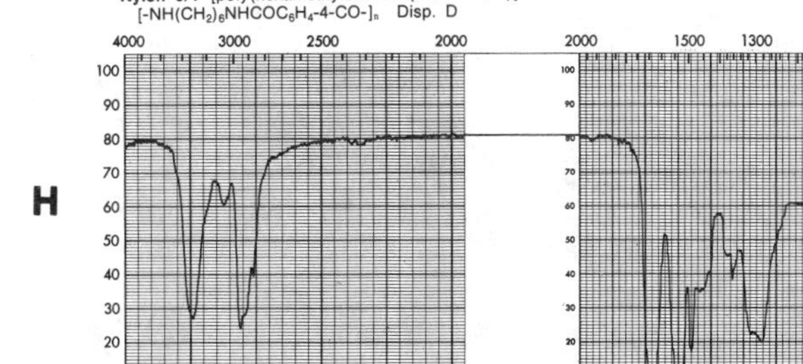

H

DMF film

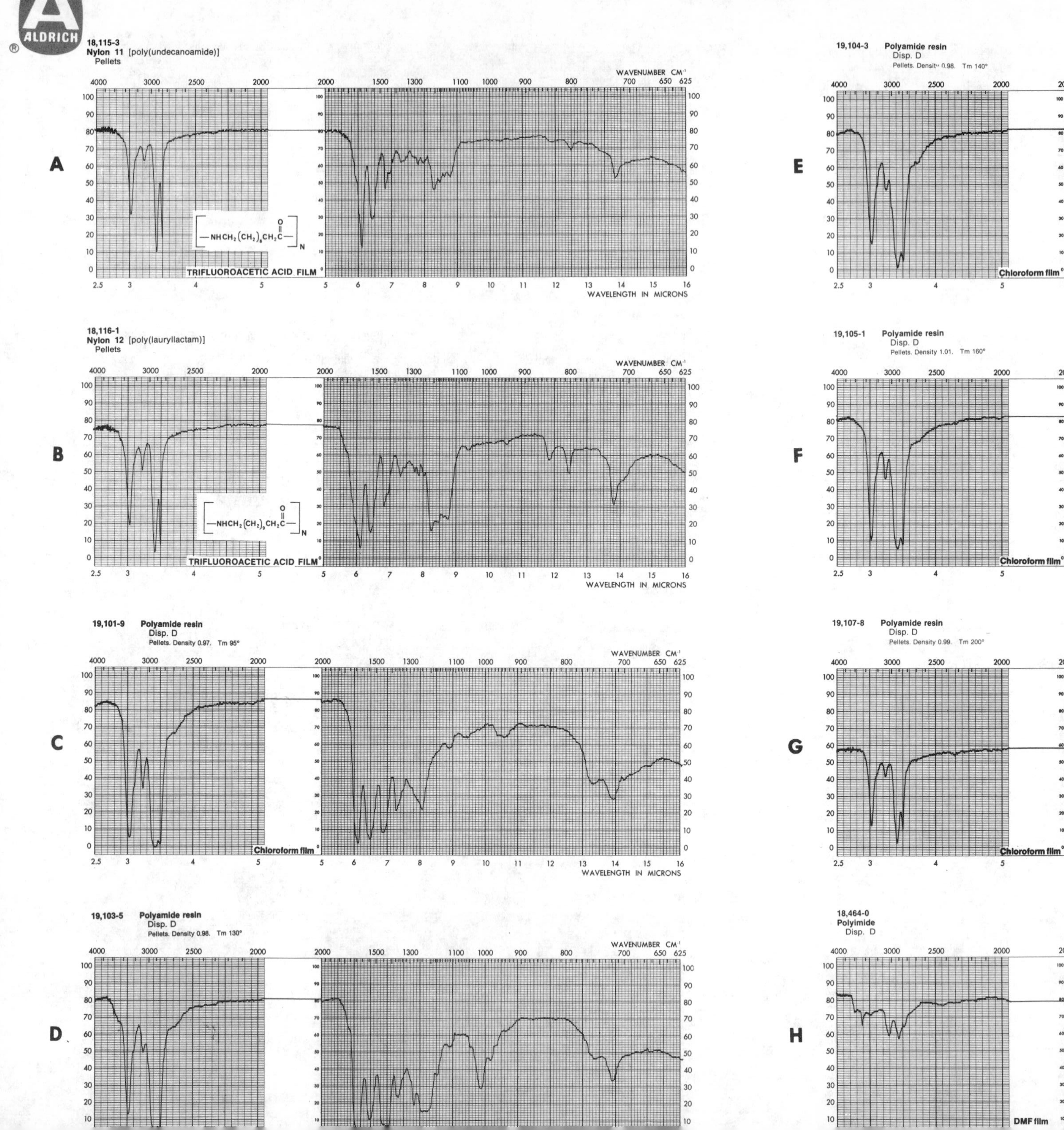
ALDRICH
A
18,115-3
Nylon 11 [poly(undecanoamide)]
Pellets
TRIFLUOROACETIC ACID FILM
B
18,116-1
Nylon 12 [poly(lauryllactam)]
Pellets
TRIFLUOROACETIC ACID FILM
C
19,101-9 Polyamide resin
Disp. D
Pellets. Density 0.97. Tm 95°
Chloroform film
D
19,103-5 Polyamide resin
Disp. D
Pellets. Density 0.98. Tm 130°
E
19,104-3 Polyamide resin
Disp. D
Pellets. Density 0.98. Tm 140°
Chloroform film
F
19,105-1 Polyamide resin
Disp. D
Pellets. Density 1.01. Tm 160°
Chloroform film
G
19,107-8 Polyamide resin
Disp. D
Pellets. Density 0.99. Tm 200°
Chloroform film
H
18,464-0
Polyimide
Disp. D
DMF film
WAVENUMBER CM⁻¹
WAVELENGTH IN MICRONS

Granular

A

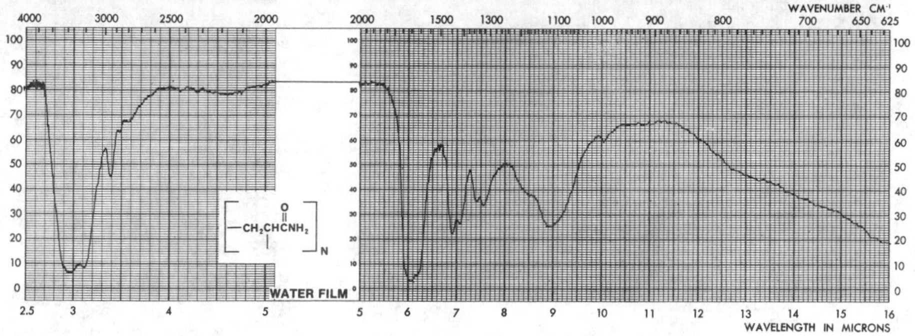

WATER FILM

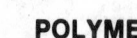

19,092-6
Poly(acrylamide), carboxyl modified, low carboxyl content
Disp. D

B

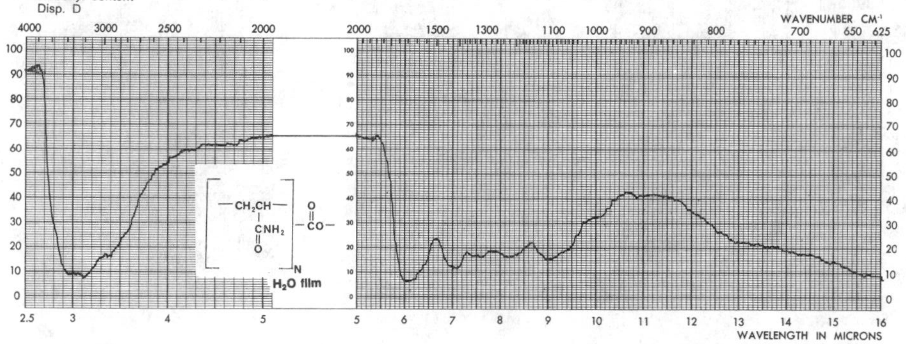

H_2O film

19,093-4
Poly(acrylamide), carboxyl modified, high carboxyl content
Disp. D

C

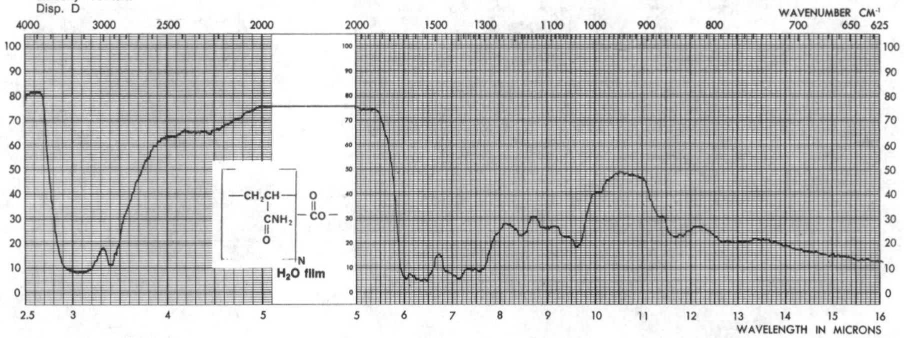

H_2O film

85,647-9
Polyvinylpyrrolidone
Average M.W. 360,000

D

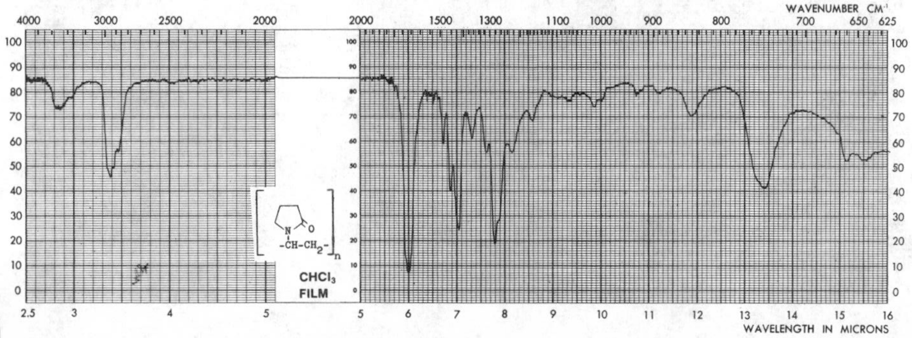

$CHCl_3$ FILM

m.p. 225° (dec.)
Average M.W. 40,000

E

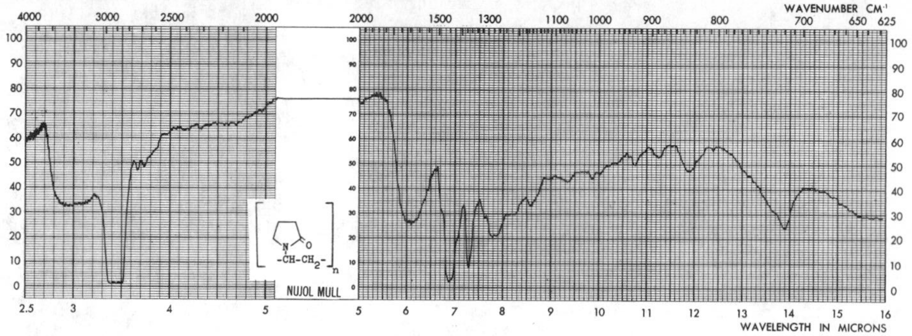

NUJOL MULL

85,645-2
Polyvinylpyrrolidone
Plasma expander.
Average M.W. 10,000

F

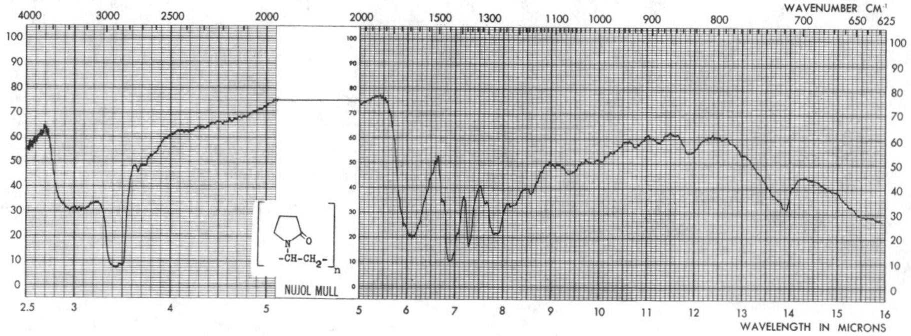

NUJOL MULL

85,648-7
Polyvinylpyrrolidone, cross-linked (polyvinylpolypyrrolidone)
mp >300° Disp. C

G

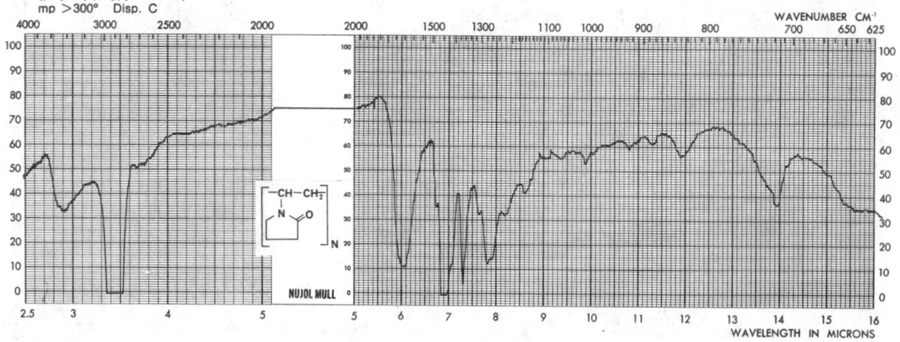

NUJOL MULL

86,056-5
Polyvinylpyrrolidone-iodine complex (PVP-I)
mp 300° (dec.) Disp. D

H

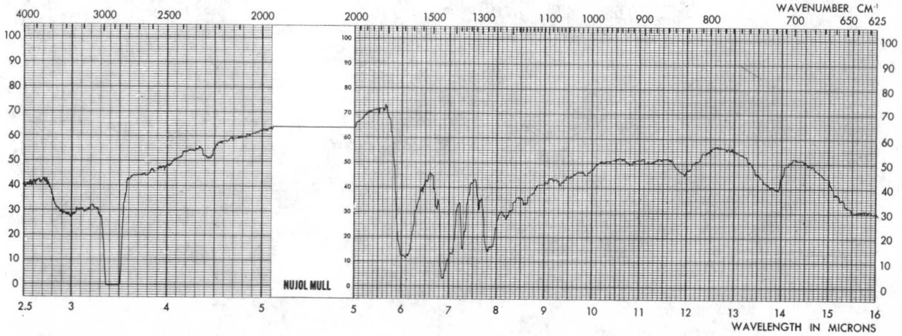

NUJOL MULL

A

19,086-1
N-**Vinylpyrrolidone/styrene copolymer**, 40 wt. % solution in water
Disp. D
Methanol film

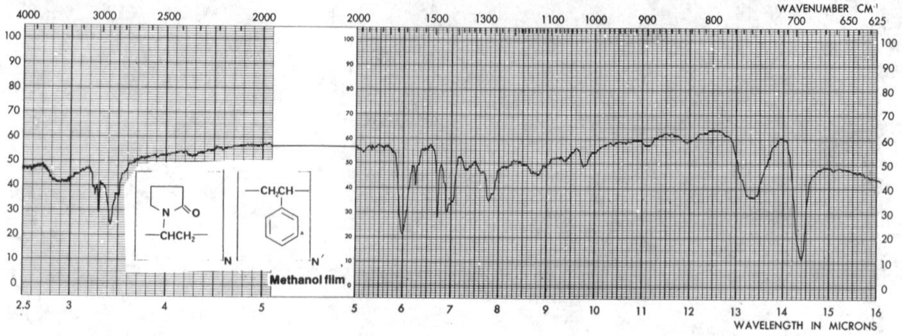

B

19,084-5
N-**Vinylpyrrolidone/vinyl acetate copolymer**
Disp. D
Acetone film

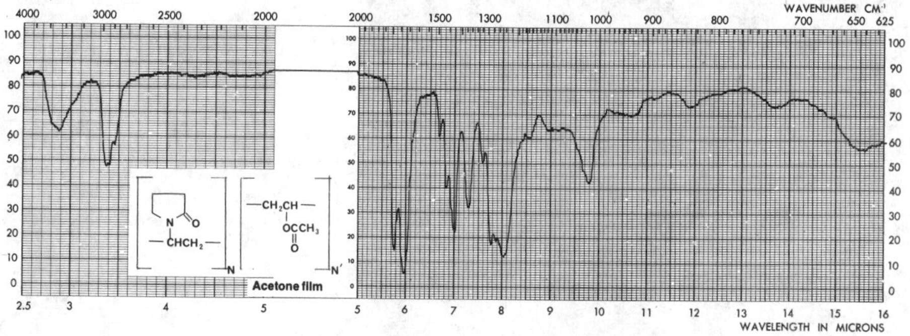

C

19,085-3
N-**Vinylpyrrolidone/ethyl acrylate copolymer**
Disp. D
Methanol film

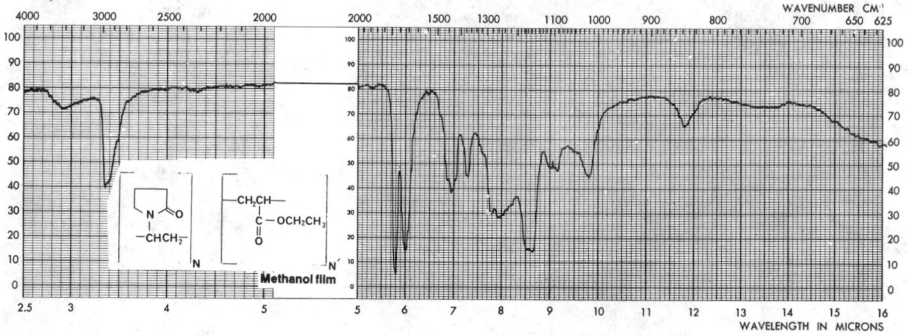

D

18,132-3
Poly(acrylonitrile), secondary standard
Typical M.W. 485,000, typical M.N. 92,000

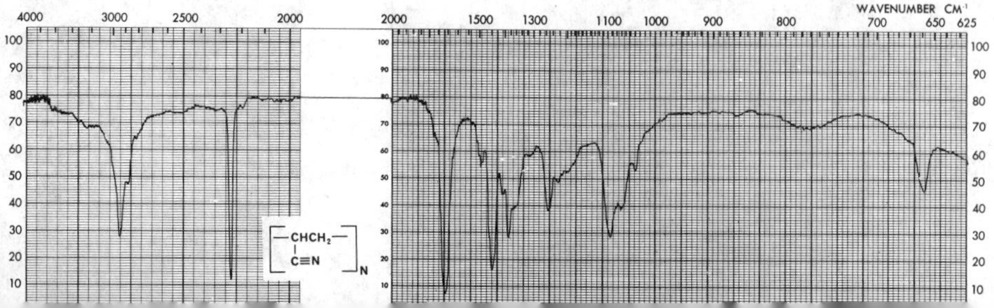

E

18,131-5
Poly(acrylonitrile)
Powder
METHYL SULFOXIDE FILM

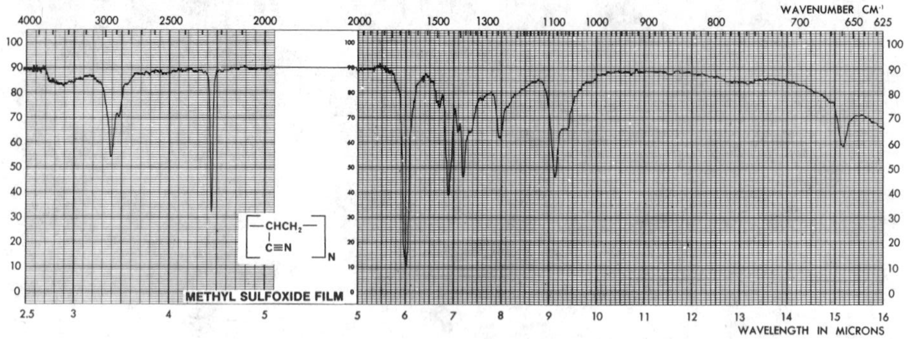

F

18,243-5
Poly(styrene), secondary standard
Typical M.W. 321,000, typical M.N. 85,000
CHLOROFORM FILM

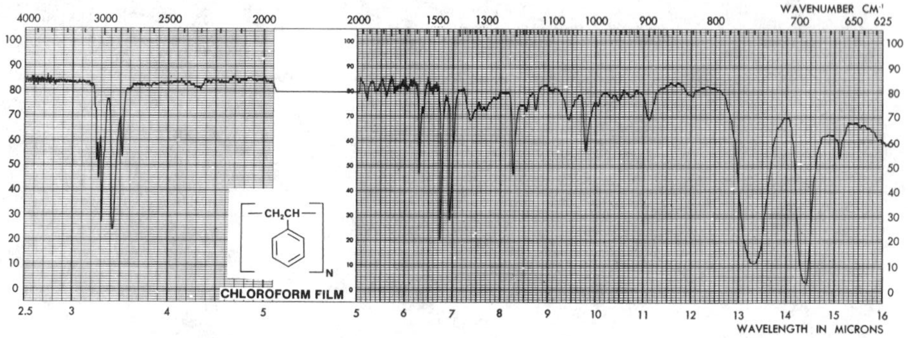

G

18,959-6
Poly(styrene), monocarboxy terminated
Disp. D
Chloroform film

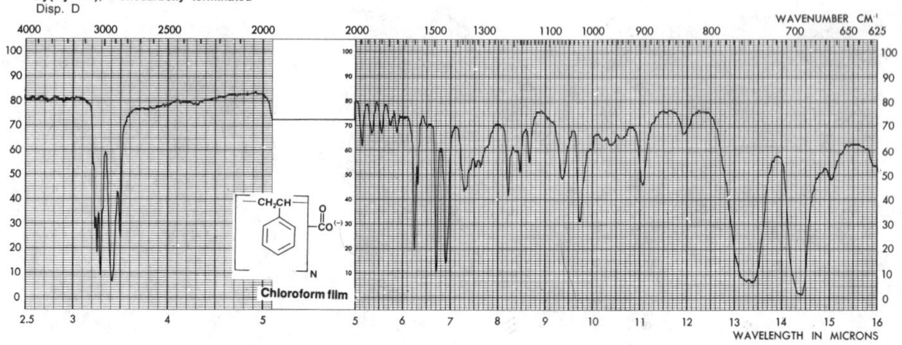

H

18,961-8
Poly(styrene), dicarboxy terminated
Disp. D

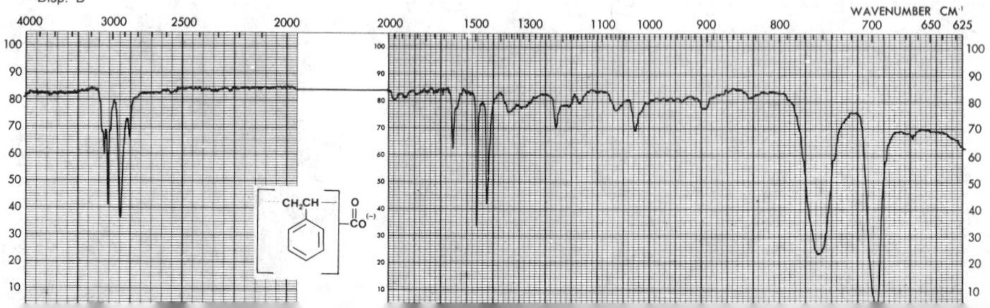

$[-CH_2C(CH_3)(C_6H_5)-]_n$ Disp. D

A — Chloroform film

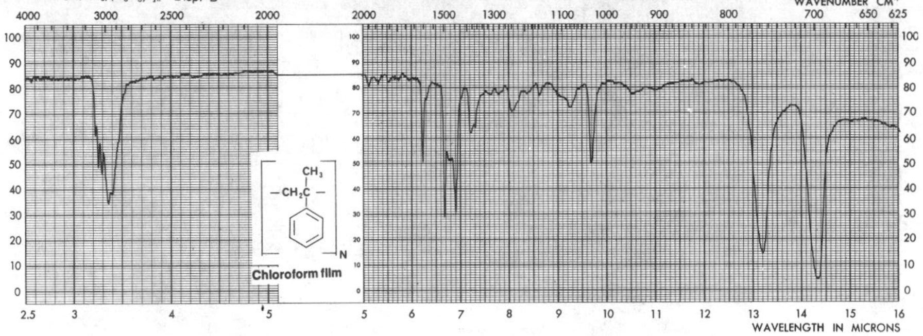

19,183-3
Poly(α-methylstyrene), medium molecular weight
$[-CH_2C(CH_3)(C_6H_5)-]_n$ Disp. D

B — Chloroform film

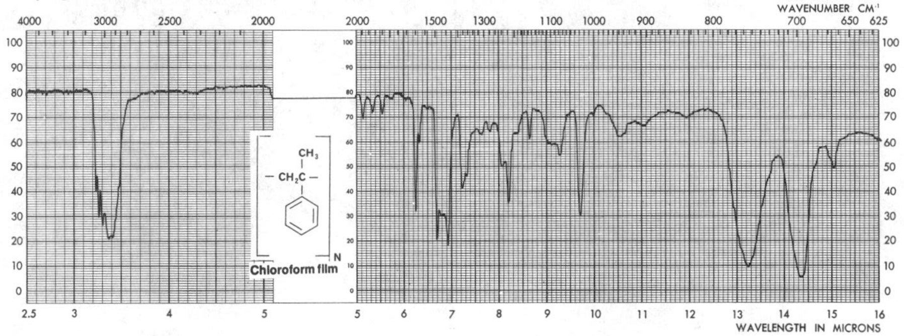

19,184-1
Poly(α-methylstyrene), high molecular weight
$[-CH_2C(CH_3)(C_6H_5)-]_n$ Disp. D

C — Chloroform film

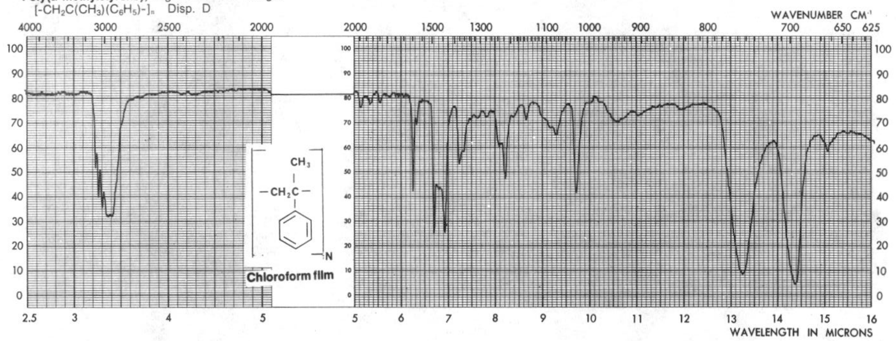

18,227-3
Poly(4-methylstyrene)
Granular

D — CHLOROFORM FILM

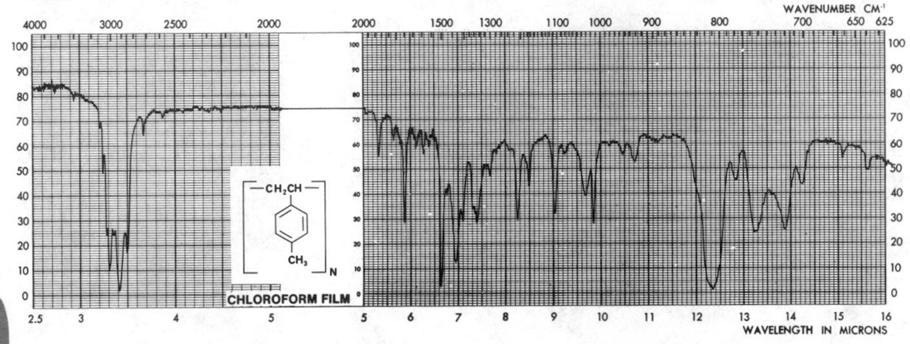

Granular

E — CHLOROFORM FILM

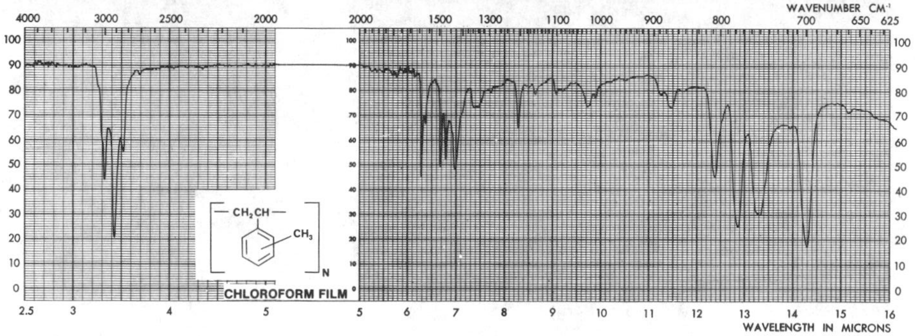

18,241-9
Poly(4-isopropylstyrene)
Granular

F — CHLOROFORM FILM

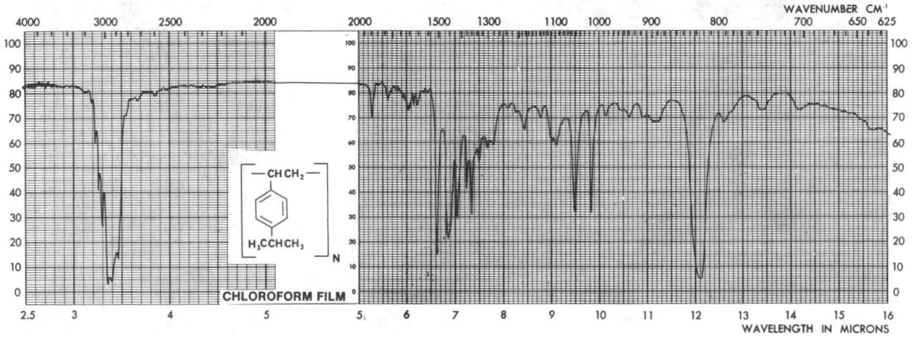

18,159-5
Poly(p-*tert.*-butylstyrene)
Granular

G — BENZENE FILM

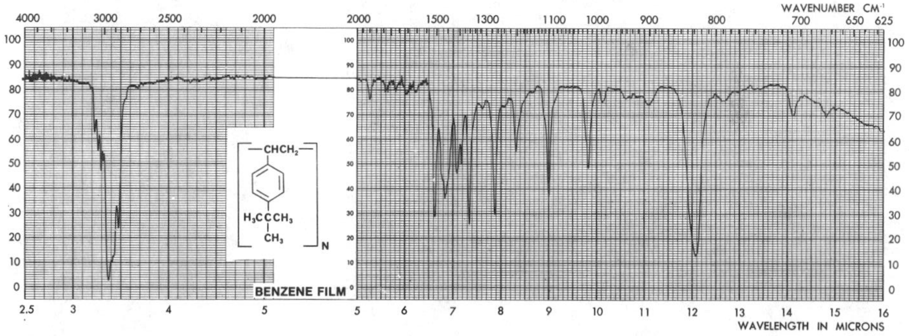

18,254-0
Poly(4-vinylbiphenyl)
Powder

H — CHLOROFORM FILM

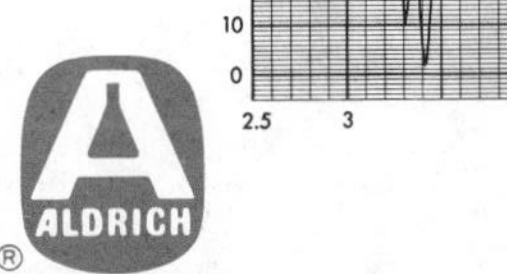

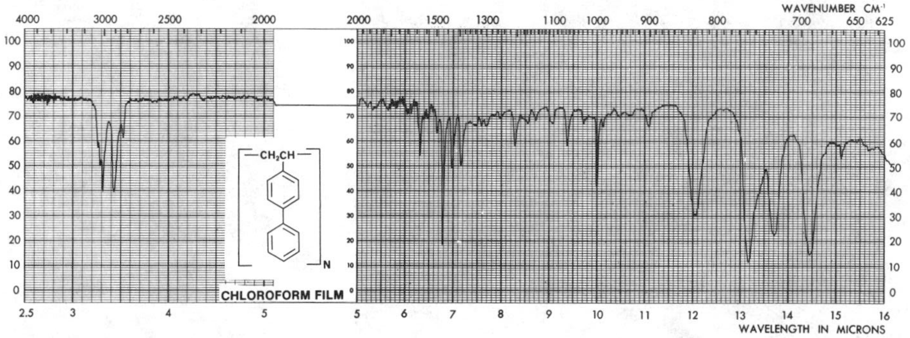

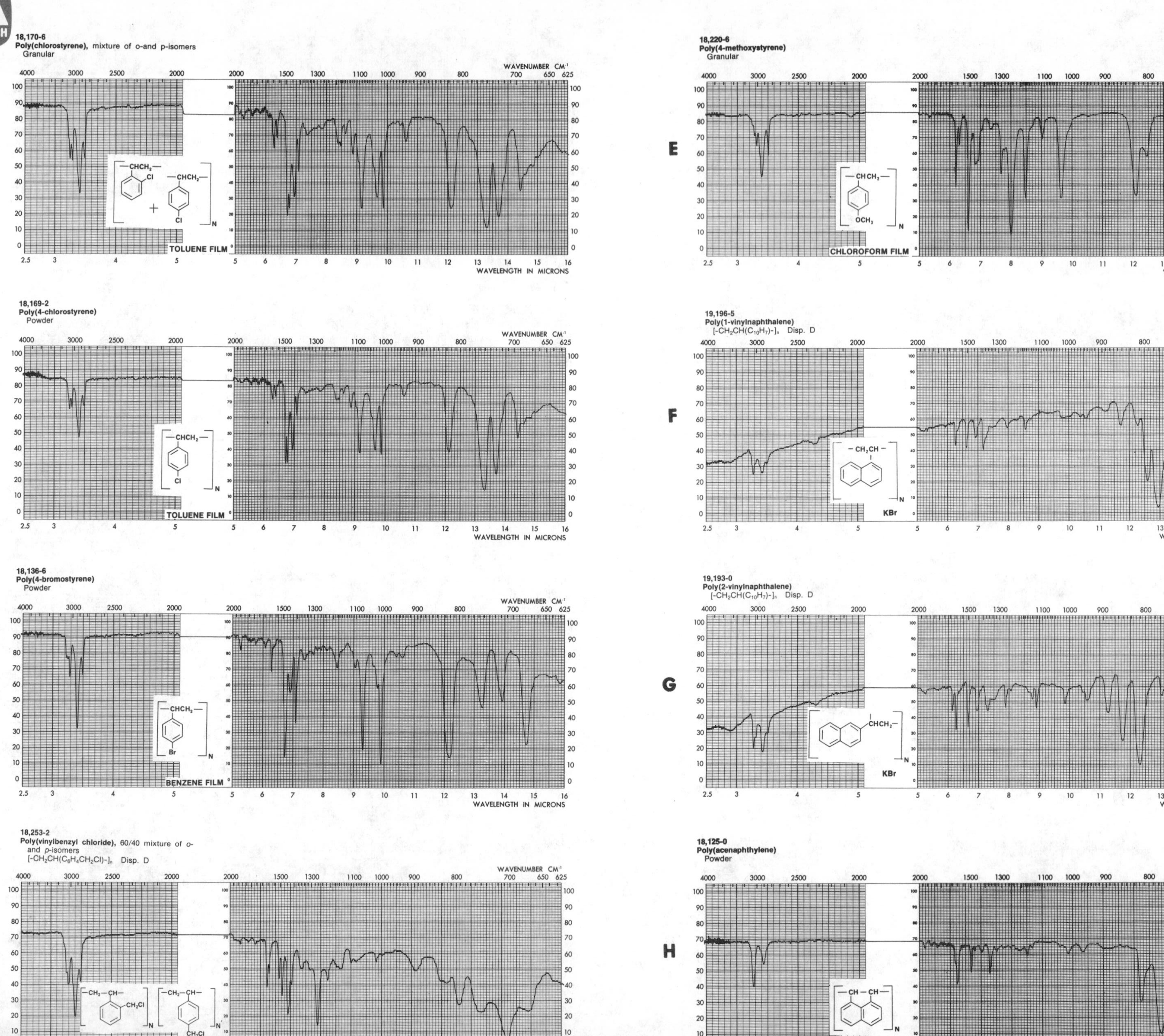

ALDRICH
A
18,170-6
Poly(chlorostyrene), mixture of o-and p-isomers
Granular
TOLUENE FILM
B
18,169-2
Poly(4-chlorostyrene)
Powder
TOLUENE FILM
C
18,136-6
Poly(4-bromostyrene)
Powder
BENZENE FILM
D
18,253-2
Poly(vinylbenzyl chloride), 60/40 mixture of o- and p-isomers
[-CH2CH(C6H4CH2Cl)-]n Disp. D
E
18,220-6
Poly(4-methoxystyrene)
Granular
CHLOROFORM FILM
F
19,196-5
Poly(1-vinylnaphthalene)
[-CH2CH(C10H7)-]n Disp. D
KBr
G
19,193-0
Poly(2-vinylnaphthalene)
[-CH2CH(C10H7)-]n Disp. D
KBr
H
18,125-0
Poly(acenaphthylene)
Powder
WAVENUMBER CM-1
WAVELENGTH IN MICRONS

A

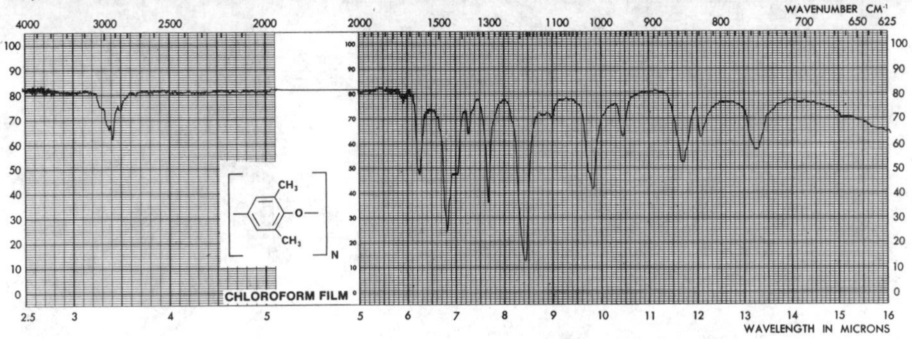

CHLOROFORM FILM

18,178-1
Poly(2,6-dimethyl-p-phenylene oxide)
Powder

B

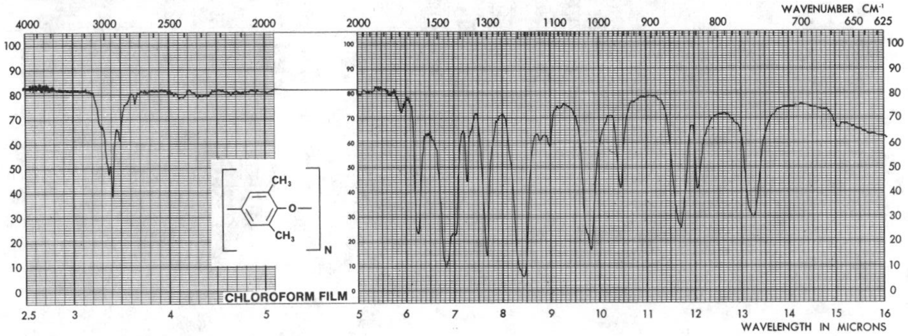

CHLOROFORM FILM

18,235-4
Poly(phenylene sulfide)
Powder

C

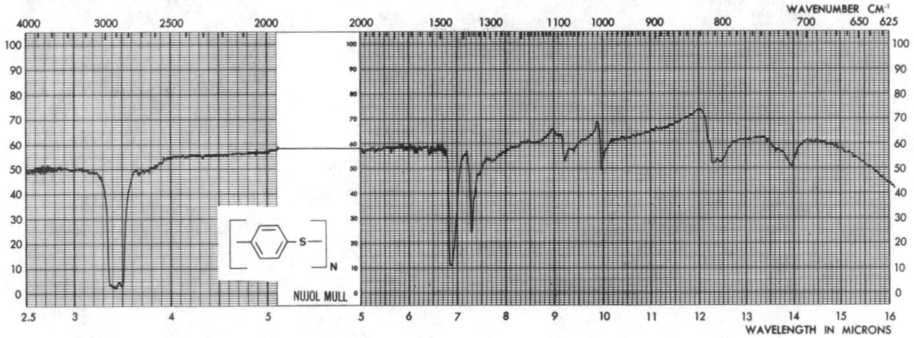

NUJOL MULL

18,950-2
Poly(2-vinylpyridine)
Disp. D

D

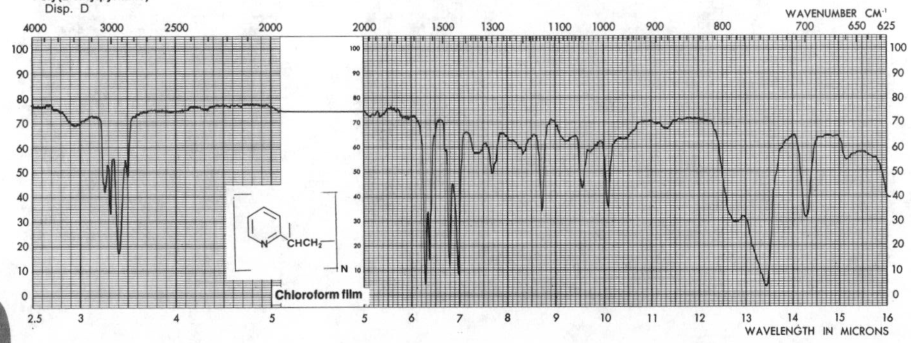

Chloroform film

E

Chloroform film

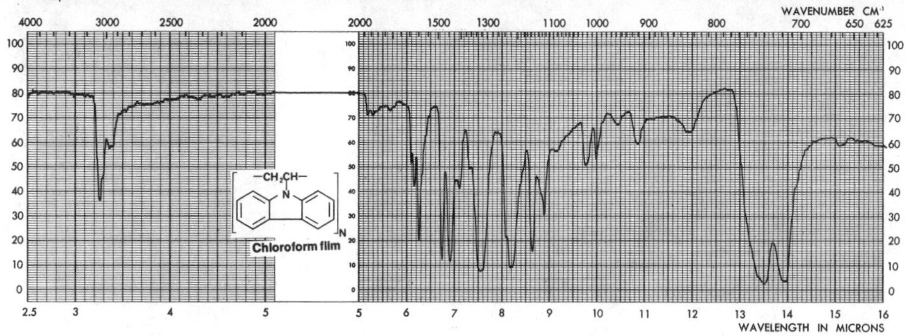

18,259-1
Poly(N-vinylcarbazole), secondary standard
Typical M.W. 1,410,000, typical M.N. 276,000

F

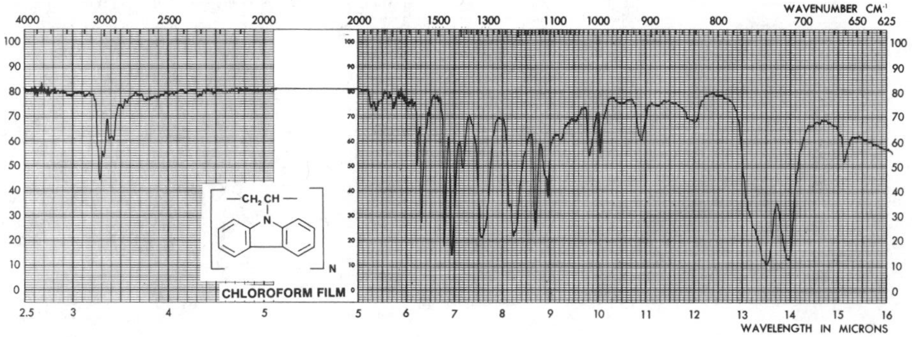

CHLOROFORM FILM

18,184-6
Poly(dimethylsiloxane), secondary standard
Typical M.W. 77,000, typical M.N. 31,000

G

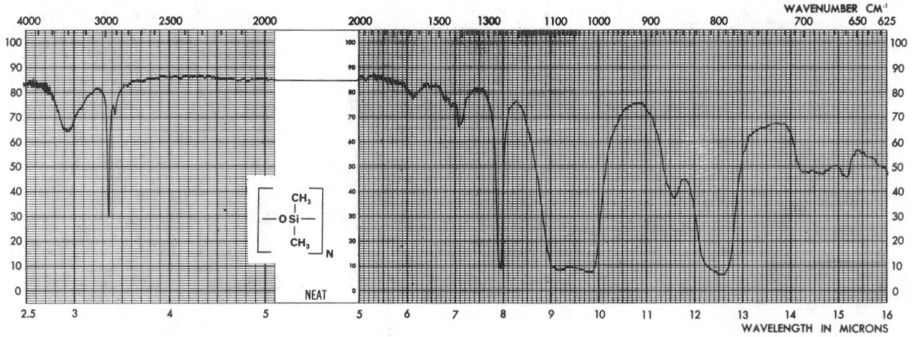

NEAT

18,183-8
Poly(dimethylsiloxane)
Opaque, viscous liquid

H

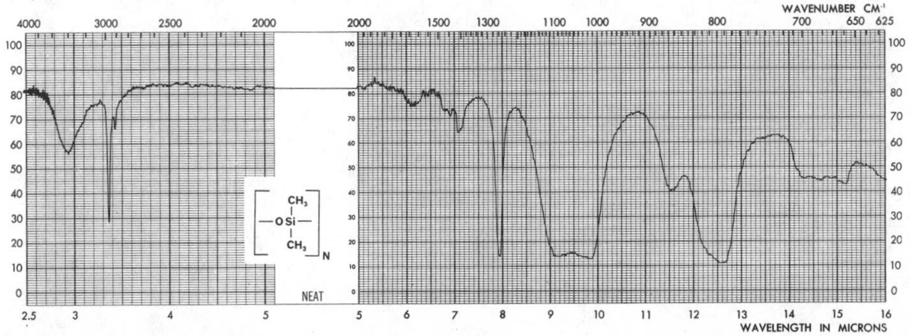

NEAT

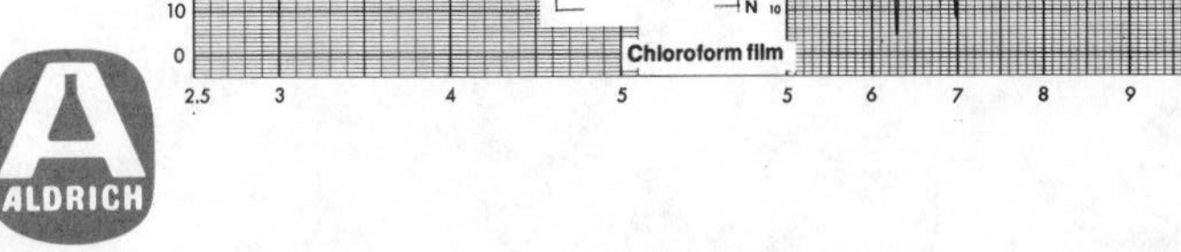

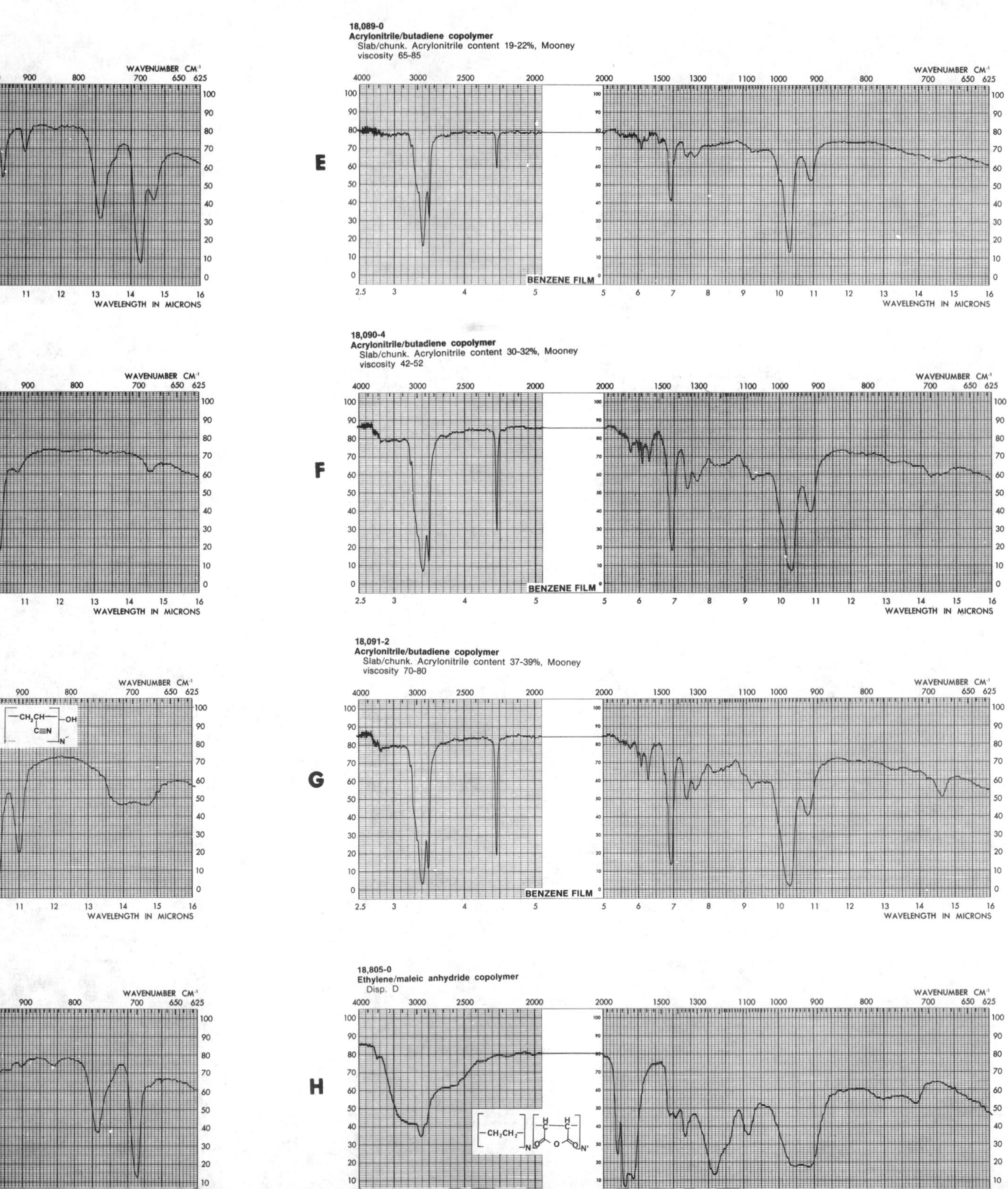

A
18,088-2
Acrylonitrile/butadiene/styrene resin
Beads
BENZENE FILM

B
18,092-0
Acrylonitrile/butadiene copolymer
Slab/chunk. Acrylonitrile content 43-45%, Mooney viscosity 50-70
BENZENE FILM

C
19,081-0
Poly(butadiene-co-acrylonitrile) diol
Disp. D
CH_2Cl_2 film

D
18,093-9
Acrylonitrile/styrene/butyl acrylate
Pellets

E
18,089-0
Acrylonitrile/butadiene copolymer
Slab/chunk. Acrylonitrile content 19-22%, Mooney viscosity 65-85
BENZENE FILM

F
18,090-4
Acrylonitrile/butadiene copolymer
Slab/chunk. Acrylonitrile content 30-32%, Mooney viscosity 42-52
BENZENE FILM

G
18,091-2
Acrylonitrile/butadiene copolymer
Slab/chunk. Acrylonitrile content 37-39%, Mooney viscosity 70-80
BENZENE FILM

H
18,805-0
Ethylene/maleic anhydride copolymer
Disp. D

Disp. D

A

WAVENUMBER CM⁻¹ — WAVELENGTH IN MICRONS

[—CH₂CH—(C₆H₅)]$_N$ [—CH—CH—(CO—O—CO)]$_{N'}$

Acetone film

18,293-1
Styrene/maleic anhydride copolymer
Powder. Average M.W. 50,000

B

WAVENUMBER CM⁻¹ — WAVELENGTH IN MICRONS

[—CH₂CH—(C₆H₅)]$_N$ [—CH—CH—(CO—O—CO)]$_N$

ACETONE FILM

18,458-6
Methyl vinyl ether/maleic anhydride copolymer,
medium molecular weight
Disp. D

C

WAVENUMBER CM⁻¹ — WAVELENGTH IN MICRONS

[—CH₂CH—(OCH₃)]$_N$ [—CH—CH—(CO—O—CO)]$_{N'}$

KBr

18,459-4
Methyl vinyl ether/maleic anhydride copolymer, high
molecular weight
Disp. D

D

WAVENUMBER CM⁻¹ — WAVELENGTH IN MICRONS

[—CH₂CH—(OCH₃)]$_N$ [—CH—CH—(CO—O—CO)]$_{N'}$

KBr

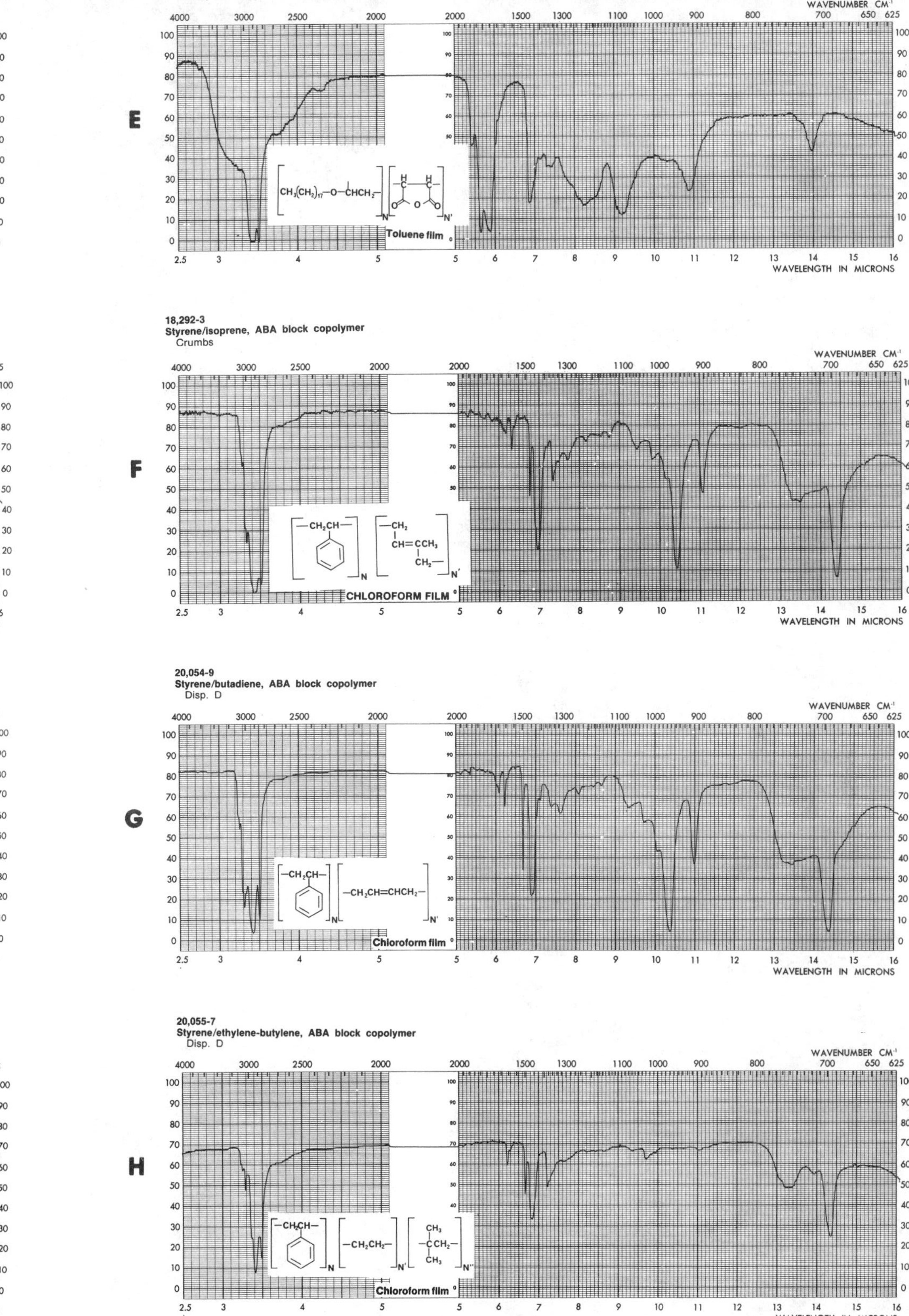

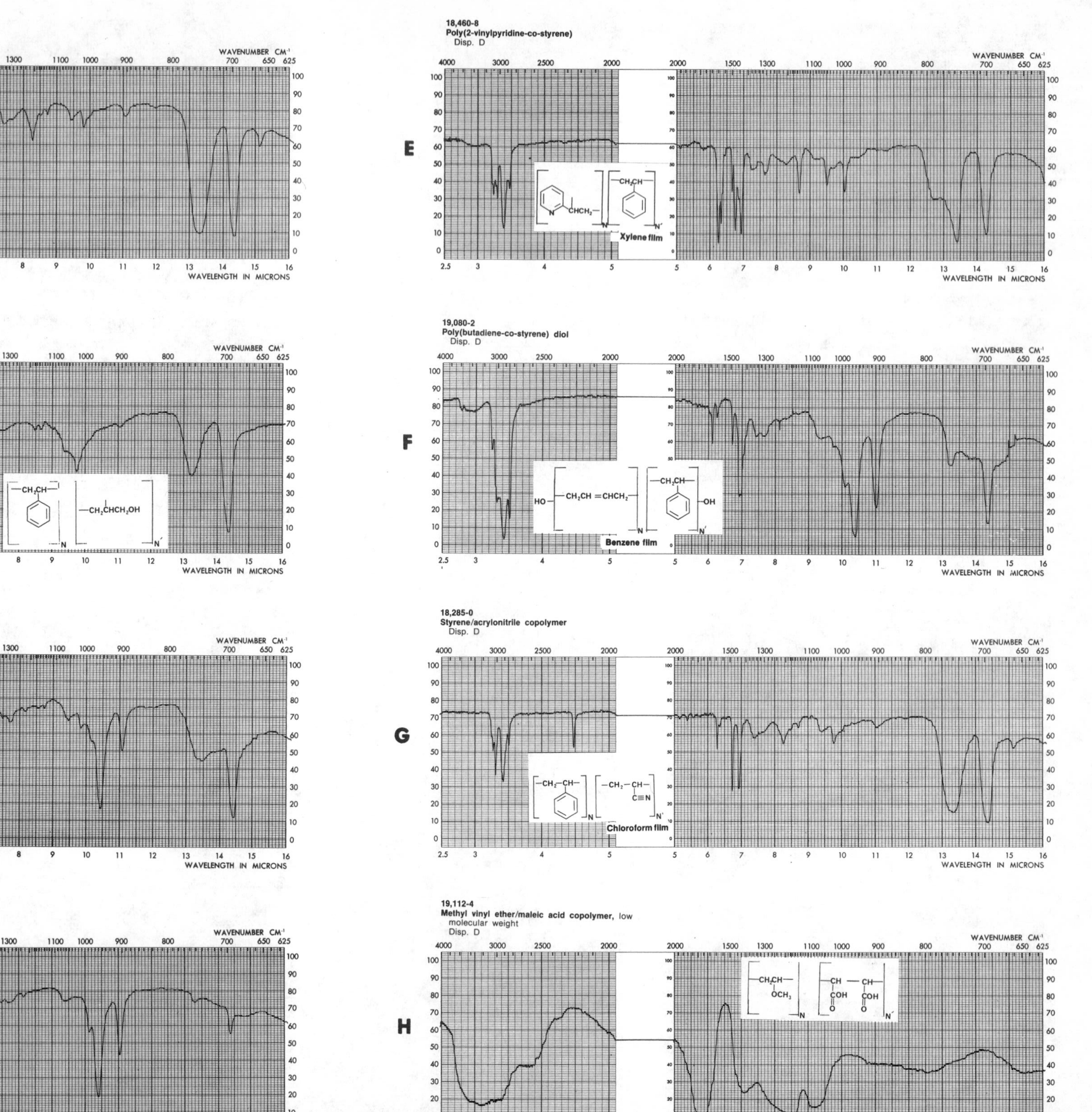
ALDRICH
A
18,286-9
Styrene/acrylonitrile copolymer
Beads. Acrylonitrile content 30%
CHLOROFORM FILM
B
19,110-8
Styrene/allyl alcohol copolymer
Disp. D
KBr
C
18,287-7
Styrene/butadiene, ABA block copolymer
Crumbs
CHLOROFORM FILM
D
18,288-5
Styrene/butadiene copolymer
Slab/chunk. Styrene content 5%
E
18,460-8
Poly(2-vinylpyridine-co-styrene)
Disp. D
Xylene film
F
19,080-2
Poly(butadiene-co-styrene) diol
Disp. D
Benzene film
G
18,285-0
Styrene/acrylonitrile copolymer
Disp. D
Chloroform film
H
19,112-4
Methyl vinyl ether/maleic acid copolymer, low molecular weight
Disp. D
WAVENUMBER CM⁻¹
WAVELENGTH IN MICRONS

Powder

A — WATER FILM

19,091-8
Methyl vinyl ether/maleic acid, monoethyl ester copolymer
Disp. D

B — Isopropanol film

18,110-2
Methyl vinyl ether/maleic anhydride copolymer, low molecular weight
Powder

C — WATER FILM

20,057-3
Ethylene/ethyl acrylate copolymer
Disp. D

D — Toluene film

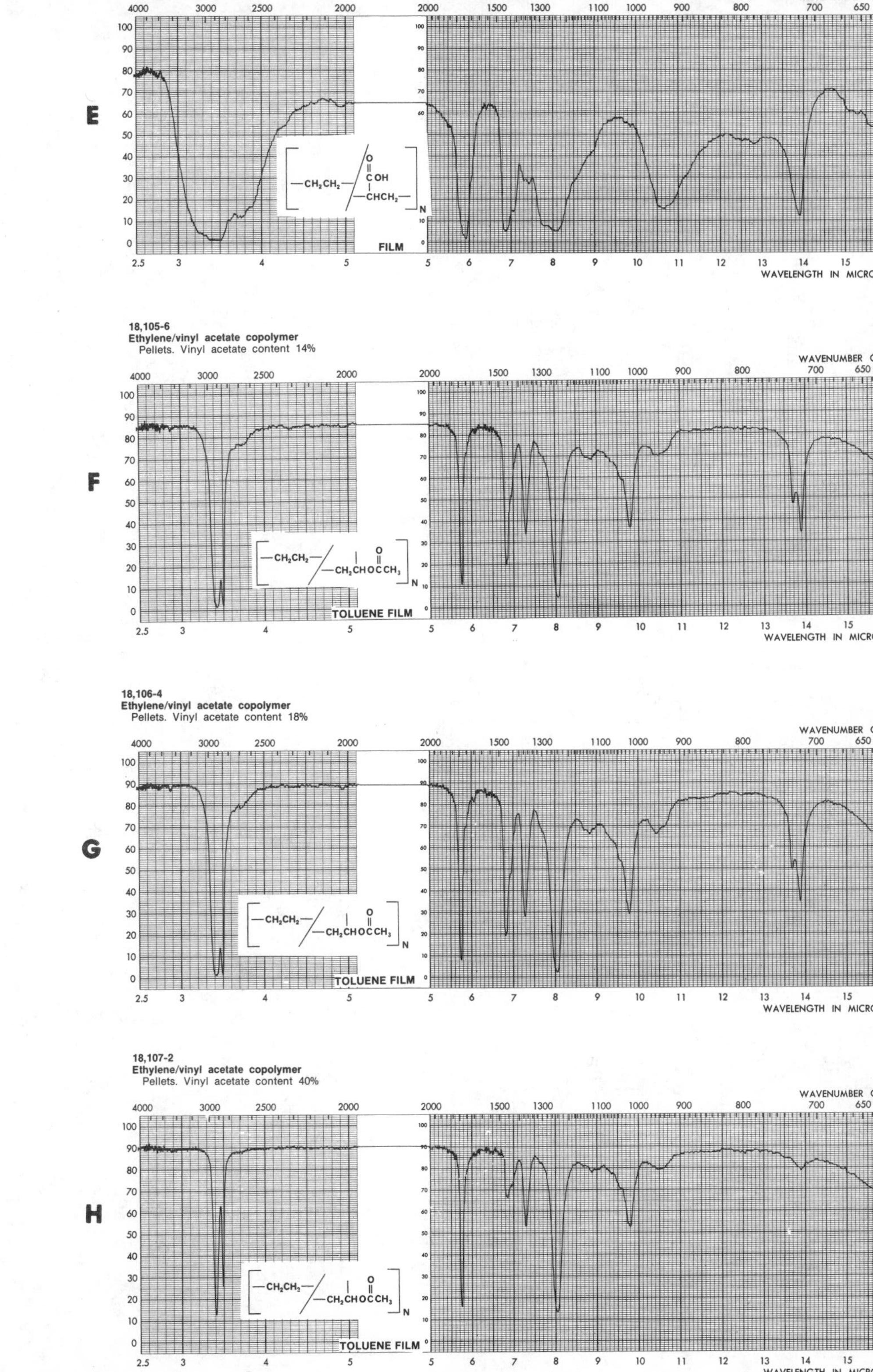

A

18,108-0
Ethylene/vinyl acetate copolymer
Pellets. Vinyl acetate content 28%

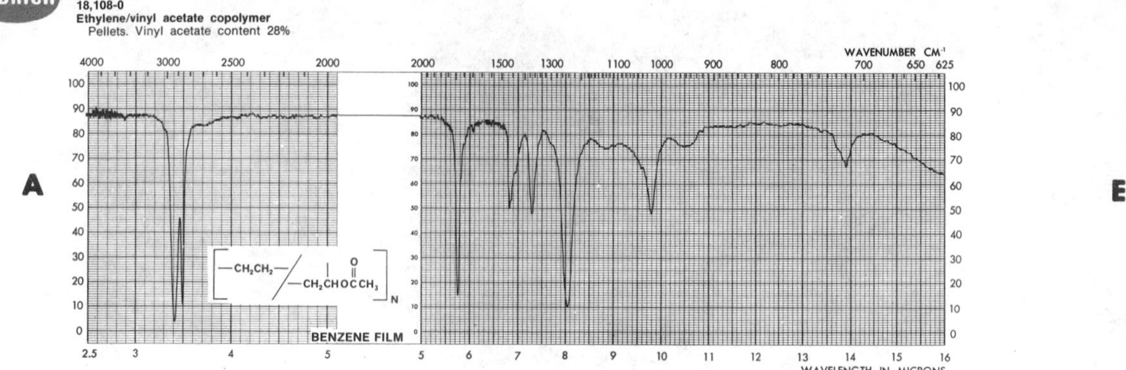

B

18,295-8 **Vinyl chloride/vinyl acetate copolymer** [9003-22-9]
Disp. O *CANCER SUSPECT AGENT*
Powder. Vinyl acetate content 17%. Density 1.33

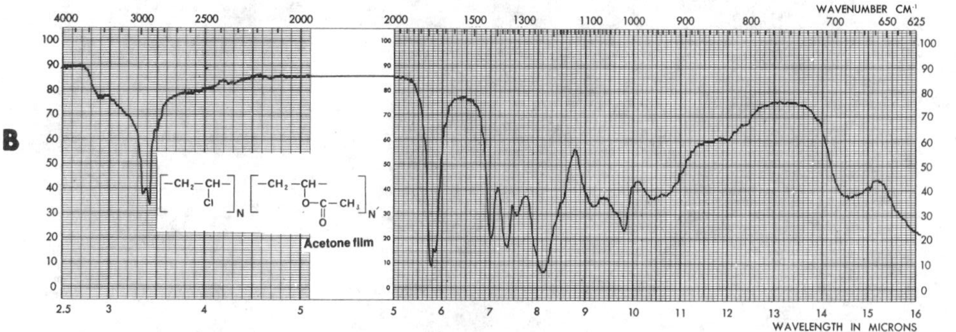

C

18,296-6 **Vinyl chloride/vinyl acetate copolymer** [9003-22-9]
Disp. O *CANCER SUSPECT AGENT*
Powder. Vinyl acetate content 13%. Density 1.37

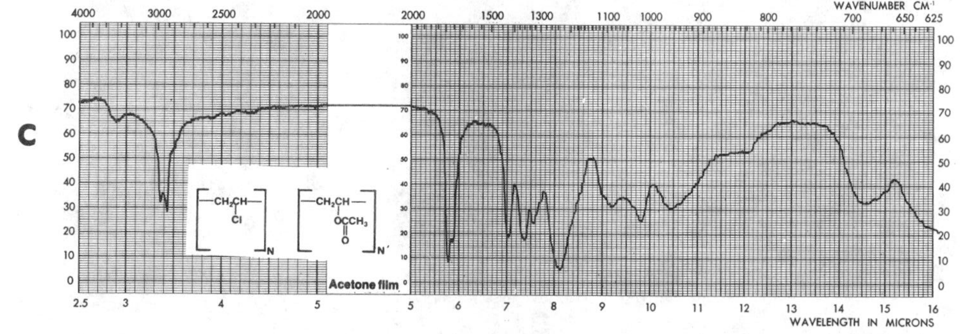

D

18,297-4 **Vinyl chloride/vinyl acetate copolymer** [9003-22-9]
Disp. O *CANCER SUSPECT AGENT*
Powder. Vinyl acetate content 10%. Density 1.36

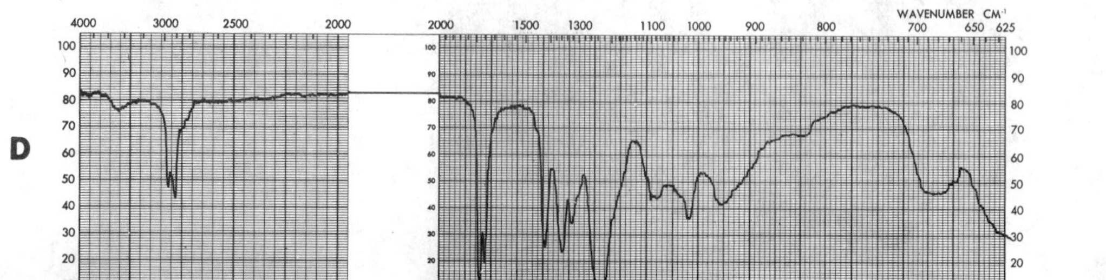

E

18,298-2 **Vinyl chloride/vinyl acetate copolymer** [9003-22-9]
Disp. O *CANCER SUSPECT AGENT*
Powder. Vinyl acetate content 2%. Density 1.39

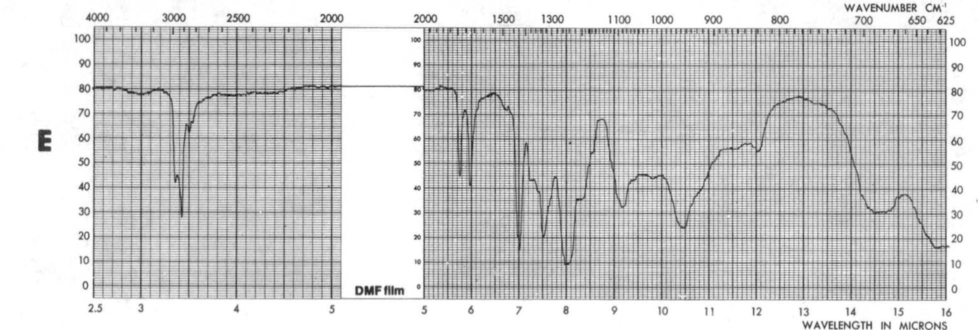

F

20,030-1
Vinyl chloride/vinyl acetate copolymer, carboxylated
Disp. O

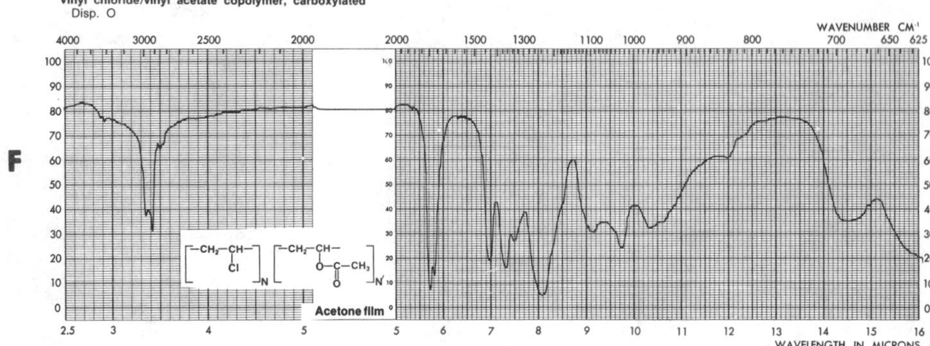

G

18,299-0
Vinyl chloride/vinyl acetate/vinyl alcohol terpolymer
Powder. Vinyl chloride content 91%, vinyl acetate content 3%, vinyl alcohol content 6%

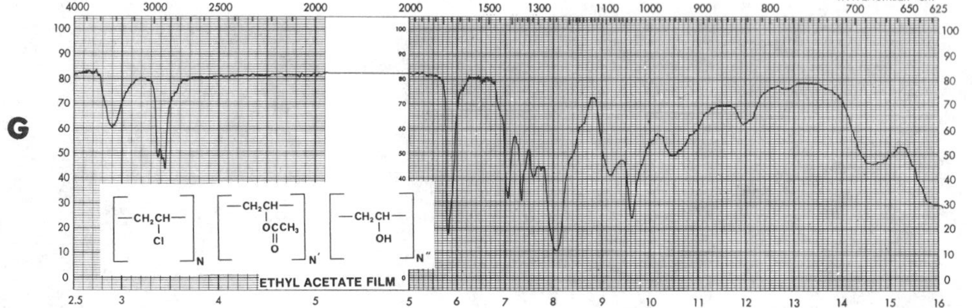

H

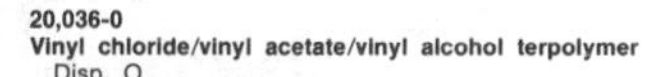

20,036-0
Vinyl chloride/vinyl acetate/vinyl alcohol terpolymer
Disp. O

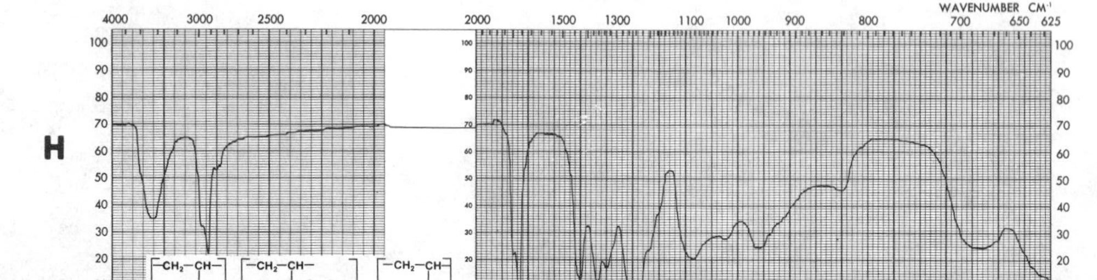

24% solution in toluene. Vinyl acetate content 91%

A

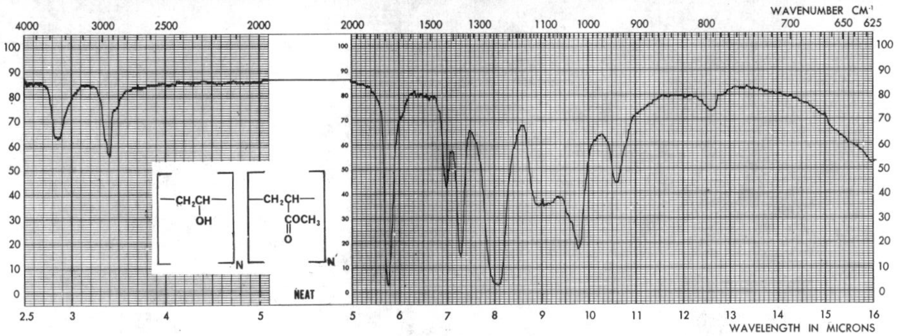

19,096-9 **Vinyl alcohol/vinyl acetate copolymer** [25213-24-5]
★ Fp 14°F(-10°C) Disp. D
28% solution in toluene. Vinyl acetate content 82%

B

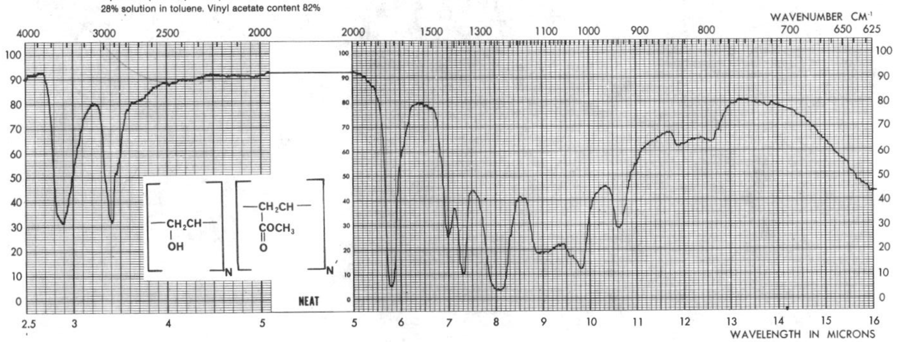

19,180-9
Vinylidene chloride/acrylonitrile copolymer, low molecular weight
Disp. O

C

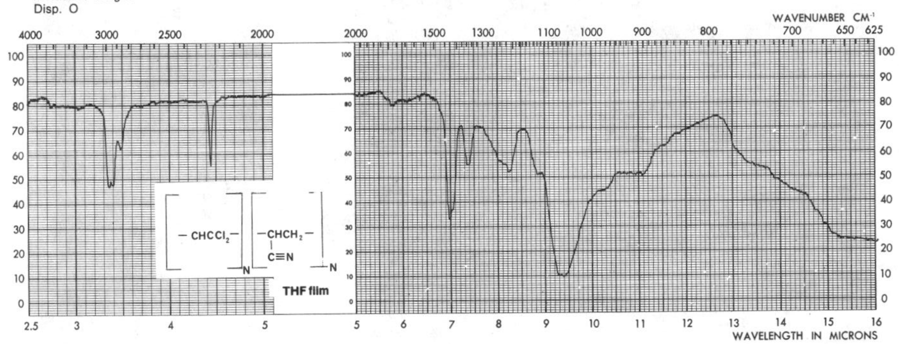

19,181-7
Vinylidene chloride/acrylonitrile copolymer, high molecular weight
Disp. O

D

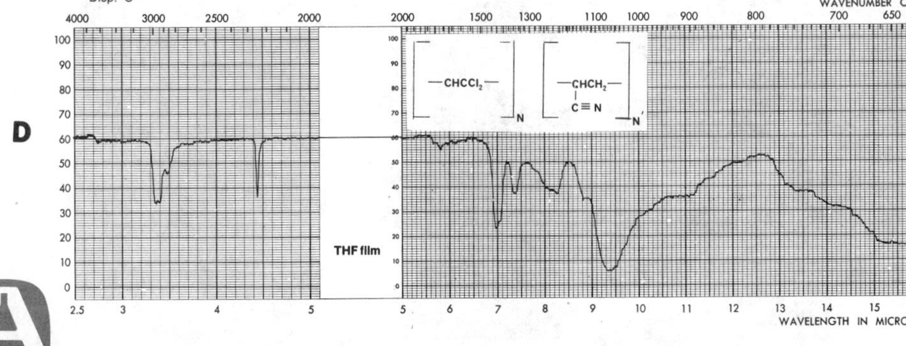
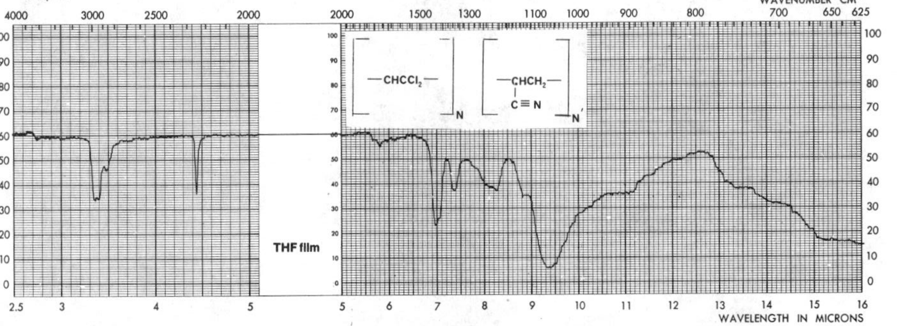

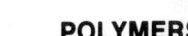

Vinylidene chloride/vinyl chloride copolymer
Disp. O

E

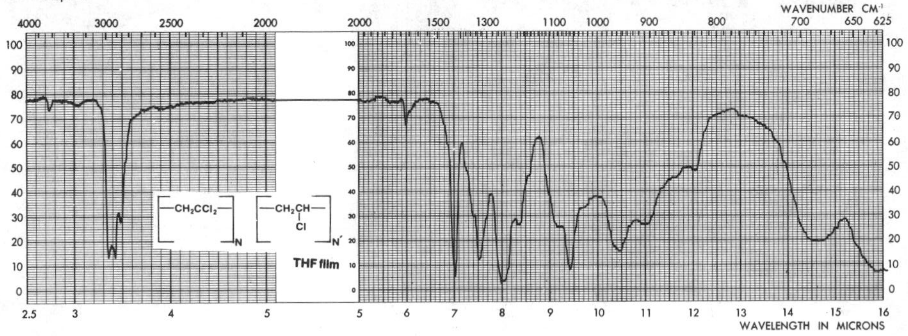

18,156-0
Butyl methacrylate/isobutyl methacrylate copolymer, high molecular weight
Powder

F

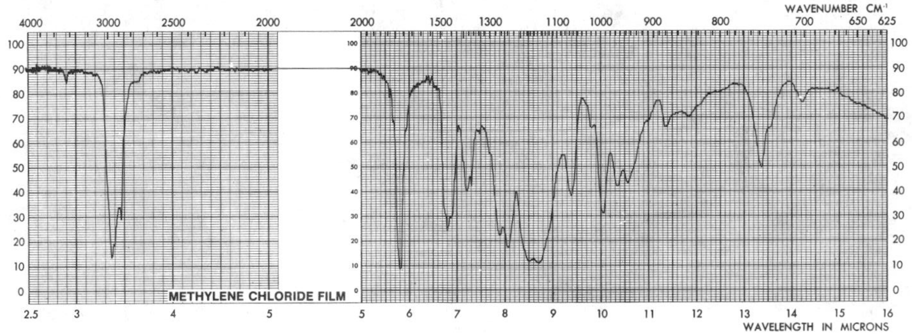

18,101-3
Epichlorohydrin/ethylene oxide copolymer
Slab/chunk

G

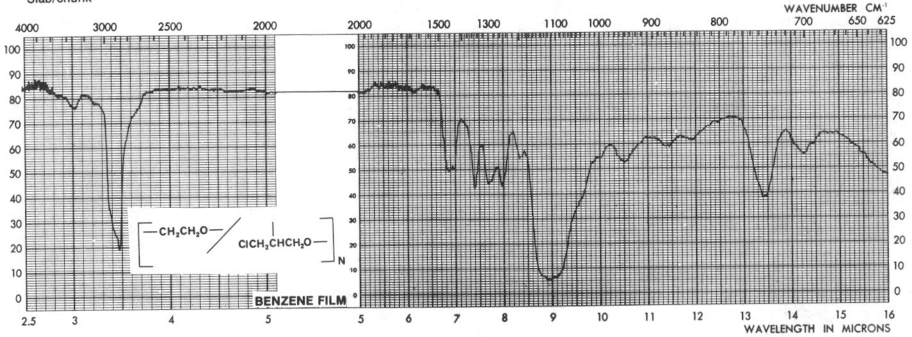

20,035-2
Poly[methylene(polyphenyl isocyanate)]
Disp. D

H

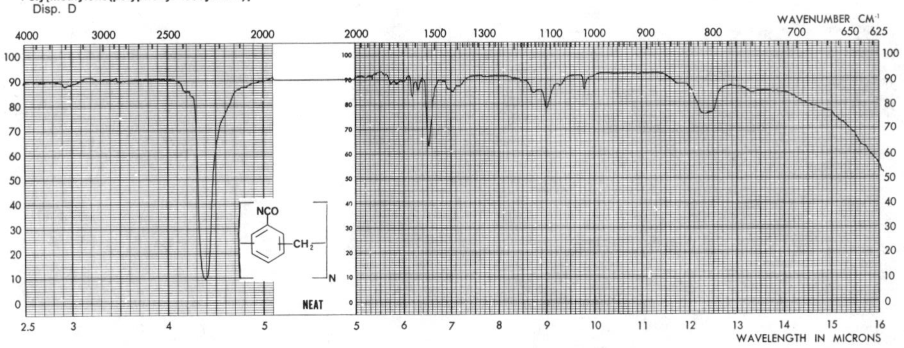

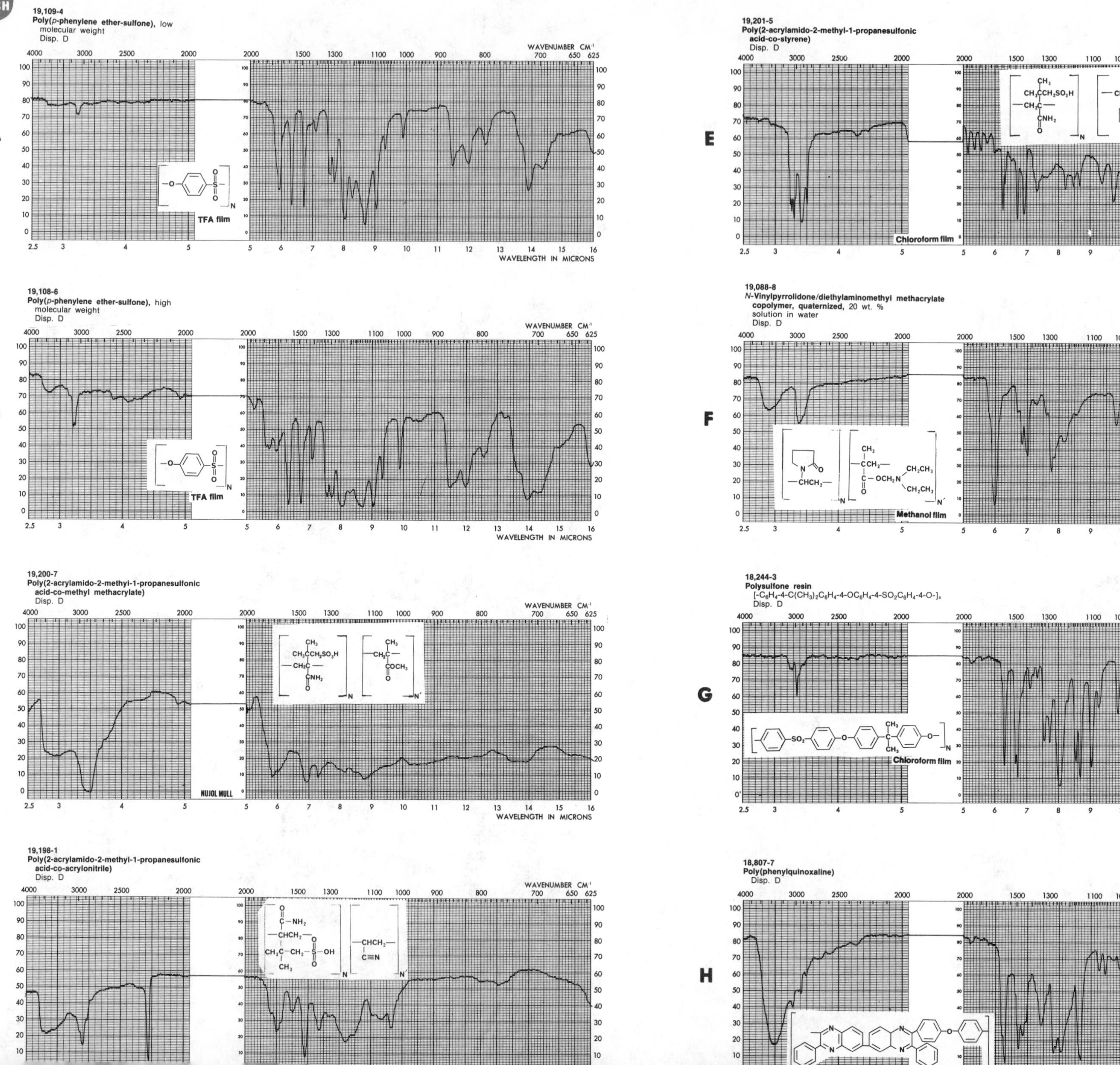
A
19,109-4
Poly(p-phenylene ether-sulfone), low molecular weight
Disp. D
TFA film
B
19,108-6
Poly(p-phenylene ether-sulfone), high molecular weight
Disp. D
TFA film
C
19,200-7
Poly(2-acrylamido-2-methyl-1-propanesulfonic acid-co-methyl methacrylate)
Disp. D
NUJOL MULL
D
19,198-1
Poly(2-acrylamido-2-methyl-1-propanesulfonic acid-co-acrylonitrile)
Disp. D
E
19,201-5
Poly(2-acrylamido-2-methyl-1-propanesulfonic acid-co-styrene)
Disp. D
Chloroform film
F
19,088-8
N-Vinylpyrrolidone/diethylaminomethyl methacrylate copolymer, quaternized, 20 wt. % solution in water
Disp. D
Methanol film
G
18,244-3
Polysulfone resin
[-C6H4-4-C(CH3)2C6H4-4-OC6H4-4-SO2C6H4-4-O-]n
Disp. D
Chloroform film
H
18,807-7
Poly(phenylquinoxaline)
Disp. D
WAVENUMBER CM⁻¹
WAVELENGTH IN MICRONS

A

Acetone film

B

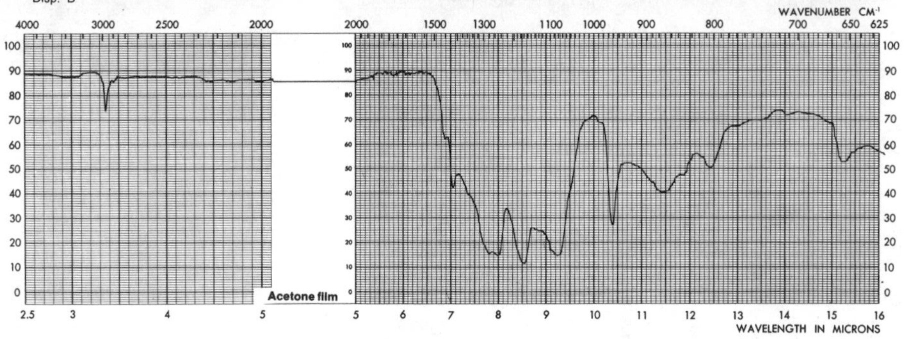

20,029-8
Poly(diphenoxyphosphazene)
Disp. D

Acetone & $CHCl_3$ film

C

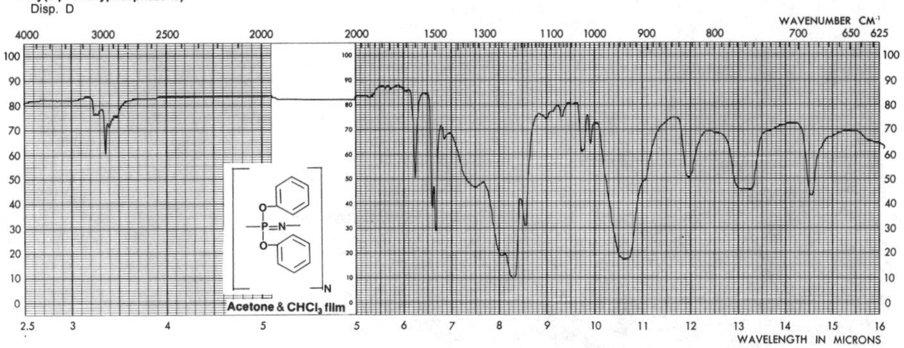

18,122-6
Phenoxy resin, secondary standard
Typical M.W. 50,000, typical M.N. 13,000

ACETONE TOLUENE FILM

D

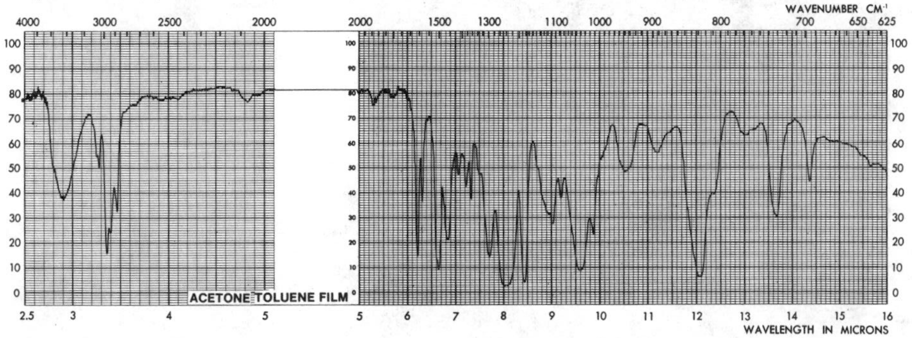

18,119-6
Phenoxy resin, low molecular weight
Pellets

ACETONE TOLUENE FILM

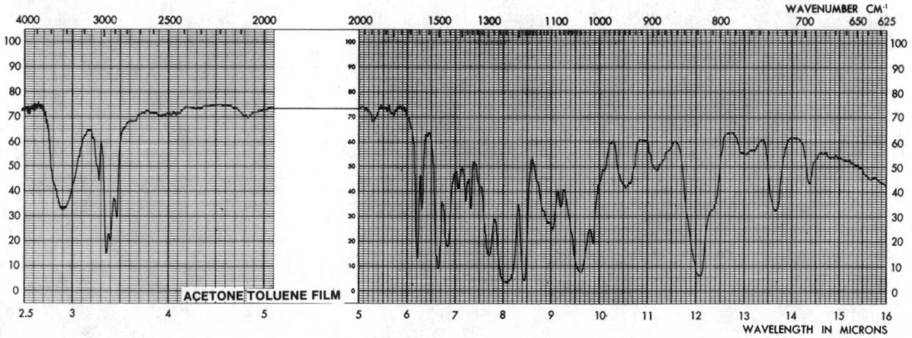

E

ACETONE TOLUENE FILM

F

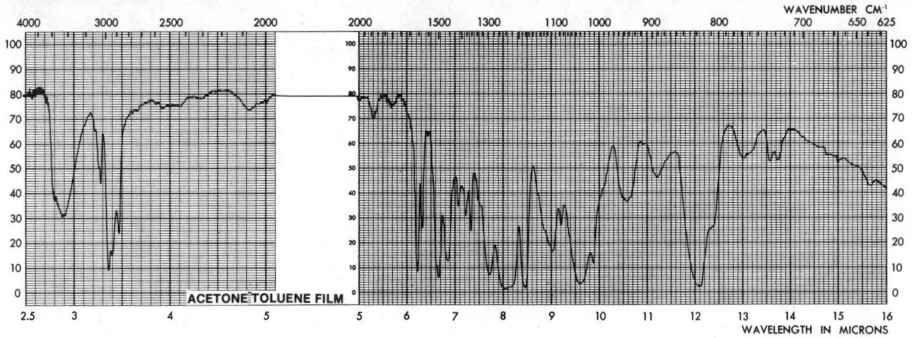

18,123-4
Phenoxy resin, high molecular weight
Pellets

ACETONE TOLUENE FILM

G

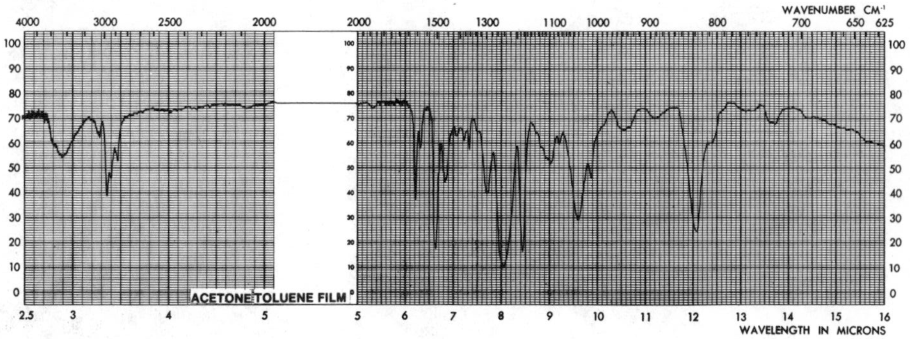

18,245-1
Polysulfone resin, secondary standard
Typical M.W 67,000, typical M.N. 20,000

CHLOROFORM FILM

H

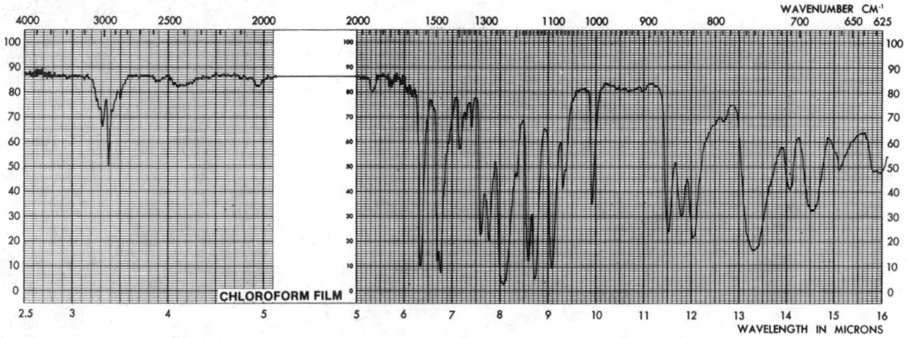

18,283-4
Rubber, chlorinated
Powder

CHLOROFORM FILM

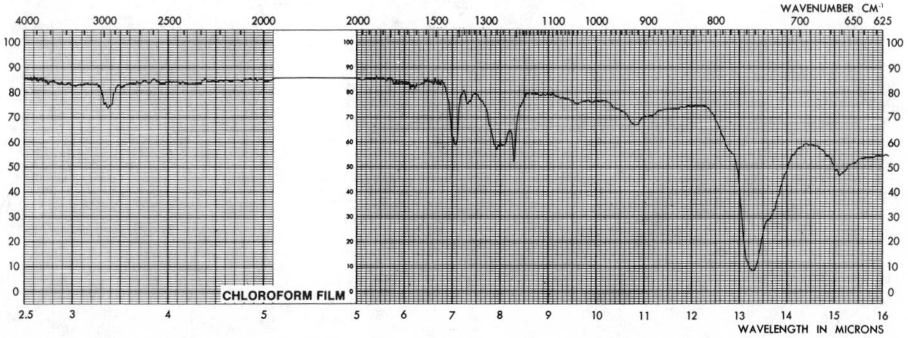

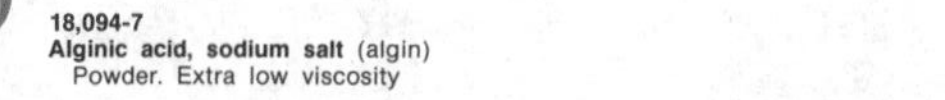

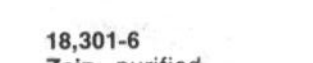

18,094-7
Alginic acid, sodium salt (algin)
Powder. Extra low viscosity

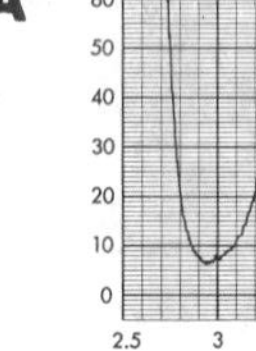

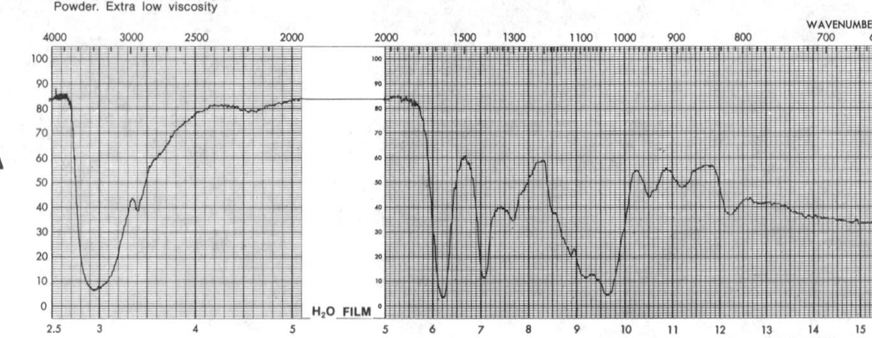

B

18,301-6
Zein, purified

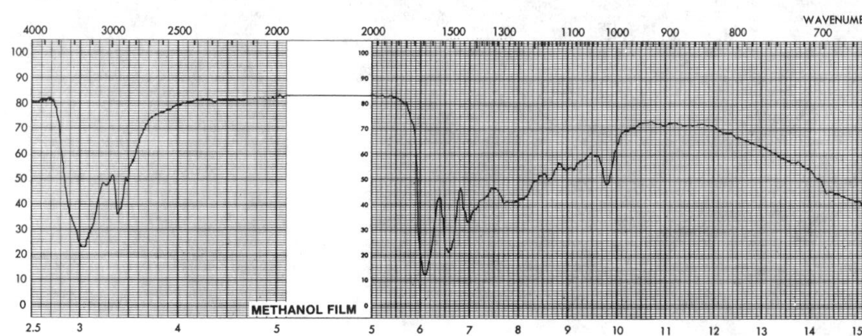

ALPHABETICAL INDEX

MOLECULAR FORMULA INDEX

ALDRICH CATALOG-HANDBOOK NUMBER INDEX

14565-3 1321D
14566-1 302A
14568-8 1399H
14569-6 1360E
14571-8 737E
14572-6 997G
14573-4 291E
14574-2 1506B
14576-9 683H
14577-7 264B
14578-5 44C
14579-3 969A
14580-7 425C
14581-5 1291D
14582-3 749H
14583-1 188E
14585-8 1131A
14586-6 1217C
14588-2 1392E
14589-0 1392F
14590-4 1392A
14591-2 1392D
14592-0 1392B
14593-9 1311E
14594-7 63H
14596-3 1371H
14599-8 1409C
14600-5 176A
14601-3 1282H
14604-8 261C
14605-6 808A
14606-4 342C
14607-2 438F
14608-0 371D
14609-9 202G
14610-2 482C
14611-0 1173D
14614-5 216D
14615-3 1537E
14616-1 969G
14618-8 970H
14619-6 937F
14621-8 1273E
14622-6 319D
14623-4 557E
14624-2 954H
14625-0 1130G
14626-9 834G
14627-7 601C
14628-5 599G
14629-3 1026H
14630-7 1043H
14632-3 231B
14633-1 231A
14635-8 468H
14636-6 469A
14639-0 973F
14640-4 982C
14641-2 103D
14642-0 106B
14643-9 824D
14644-7 1159G
14645-5 276H
14646-3 802H
14647-1 1559H
14649-8 1560A
14650-1 1070B
14653-6 973E
14655-2 796H
14658-7 522F
14659-5 1296E
14660-9 482E
14661-7 1412A
14662-5 1412B
14663-3 236A
14664-1 236D
14666-8 686G
14667-6 1029B
14668-4 782B
14669-2 849B
14670-6 881H
14673-0 983C
14674-9 665H
14675-7 917H
14676-5 520B
14677-3 206A
14678-1 787D
14680-3 1323H
14681-1 1332D
14684-6 1318C
14685-4 1325F
14686-2 919C
14687-0 284G
14700-1 274C
14702-8 1551B
14703-6 1550F
14704-4 1549E
14705-2 1551D
14706-0 1551E
14707-9 1552A
14708-7 1550C
14709-5 1226H
14710-9 1108D
14711-7 796G
14712-5 797A
14716-8 262C
14717-6 319B
14721-4 823H
14722-2 139G
14723-0 292D
14724-9 427A
14725-7 610B
14726-5 690D
14727-3 707E
14728-1 1160C
14730-3 723B
14731-1 815D
14733-8 1125D
14734-6 1127H
14735-4 1127B
14736-2 1127D
14737-0 1126B
14738-9 254B
14739-7 1179A
14740-0 441D
14741-9 1202C
14745-1 1557E
14748-6 636B
14749-4 957F
14750-8 440B
14751-6 318F
14752-4 36G
14753-2 1062H
14754-0 641D
14755-9 682H
14756-7 814E
14757-5 316A
14758-3 36C
14759-1 236B
14760-5 317C
14761-3 1184B
14765-6 1497A
14766-4 1496C
14767-2 1497F
14768-0 1504G
14769-9 1497H
14770-2 514B
14771-0 374A
14774-5 1512A
14775-3 1132B
14776-1 795D
14778-8 1185F
14779-6 1452C
14781-8 745H
14782-6 870H
14783-4 891E
14784-2 744C
14785-0 144G
14786-9 428E
14787-7 300C
14788-5 852D
14789-3 599B
14791-5 980D
14792-3 533B
14793-1 350E
14795-8 663H
14796-6 994H
14797-4 144H
14798-2 71D
14799-0 71C
14800-8 362C
14801-6 185H
14802-4 797G
14803-2 1454E
14805-9 641F
14806-7 641E
14807-5 261F
14808-3 81A
14809-1 627E
14810-5 1302A
14811-3 741F
14812-1 827C
14814-8 834E
14815-6 1175A
14820-2 1324D
14822-9 1106D
14823-7 254H
14824-5 638H
14825-3 511F
14828-8 374C
14829-6 418E
14831-8 641B
14832-6 448E
14847-4 53A
14848-2 1544D
14849-0 1536G
14850-4 1544E
14851-2 1138D
14853-9 638D
14854-7 613D
14856-3 573E
14860-1 1175D
14862-8 1381E
14865-2 729A
14866-0 438D
14867-9 37F
14868-7 38A
14869-5 146E
14873-3 217F
14874-1 1387A
14876-8 307E
14877-6 966B
14878-4 663A
14879-2 663B
14880-6 947D
14881-4 1022H
14882-2 999G
14883-0 702B
14884-9 1000D
14885-7 1000B
14886-5 1023G
14887-3 1073E
14888-1 1023D
14890-3 1052E
14893-8 45E
14894-6 351G
14895-4 363D
14896-2 362G
14897-0 363C
14898-9 363G
14899-7 362D
14900-4 364H
14901-2 369B
14902-0 1395C
14903-9 969H
14904-7 1485H
14906-3 1485G
14907-1 1486A
14909-8 984G
14910-1 752C
14912-8 1103C
14913-6 979D
14914-4 979A
14916-0 626E
14918-7 1039G
14919-5 1090B
14920-9 390B
14921-7 1198B
14922-5 156G
14923-3 247E
14924-1 1103B
14926-8 417D
14927-6 1205C
14928-4 1201H
14929-2 255A
14930-6 129H
14931-4 445G
14932-2 138E
14933-0 1162G
14934-9 891D
14935-7 971F
14936-5 1141A
14937-3 37H
14938-1 727D
14940-3 1161E
14941-1 351E
14943-8 762F
14944-6 210F
14945-4 572B
14946-2 1188G
14947-0 1188F
14948-9 1189B
14949-7 1189A
14967-5 1510D
14968-3 1403D
14969-1 207E
14970-5 1135G
14971-3 618B
14974-8 1510C
14975-6 1511F
14976-4 1511A
14977-2 445H
14978-0 1015A
14979-9 582D
14980-2 782D
14983-7 1091D
14984-5 1556C
14985-3 790B
14986-1 1206B
14989-6 1032C
14991-8 802C
14993-4 418F
14994-2 728D
14995-0 410H
14996-9 254A
14997-7 214H
14998-5 175D
14999-3 201F
15000-2 1546D
15001-0 1162D
15004-5 74D
15005-3 211B
15006-1 1452F
15009-6 831D
15011-8 757B
15012-6 925A
15013-4 1403E
15014-2 928B
15015-0 29A
15017-7 1276B
15018-5 1392G
15019-3 1183F
15020-7 1041G
15021-5 904B
15023-1 1386D
15026-6 1427G
15027-4 106D
15028-2 763H
15029-0 869C
15030-4 764G
15031-2 156A
15032-0 1492A
15033-9 1340G
15034-7 302G
15035-5 960E
15036-3 1198D
15037-1 883A
15040-1 1428D
15042-8 507B
15043-6 23A
15044-4 319A
15045-2 300H
15046-0 155E
15047-9 1511E
15048-7 234A
15049-5 234B
15051-7 29E
15052-5 1167H
15053-3 328A
15054-1 1275C
15056-8 354F
15057-6 506C
15058-4 67B
15059-2 1067B
15060-6 541B
15061-4 269F
15062-2 1424D
15063-0 1379E
15064-9 1365A
15065-7 1365B
15066-5 1364G
15067-3 1369G
15068-1 579A
15070-3 437B
15071-1 579E
15073-8 1449B
15074-6 955A
15076-2 1076F
15078-9 881G
15079-7 1068F
15081-9 262B
15082-7 470D
15083-5 1262D
15084-3 714G
15085-1 651E
15088-6 581C
15089-4 645H
15090-8 1388D
15091-6 1242A
15092-4 956G
15093-2 298B
15097-5 582E
15098-3 1068D
15099-1 644A
15102-5 571H
15104-1 917D
15106-8 917E
15108-4 1197B
15111-4 1500D
15113-0 1501H
15114-9 1502C
15115-7 1502H
15116-5 325E
15117-3 883C
15121-1 289H
15123-8 391G
15125-4 333C
15126-2 1119E
15127-0 1326B
15128-9 605C
15130-0 985H
15131-9 1503G
15132-7 208B
15133-5 1186B
15134-3 927G
15135-1 1312G
15137-8 1152D
15138-6 431B
15139-4 966D
15140-8 974C

15720-1	334H	**15793-7**	551F	**15863-1**	1068B	**15935-2**	1143B	**16015-6**	942C	**16077-6**	1320B	**16158-6**	131A	**16230-2**	590F
15723-6	979H	**15794-5**	1185G	**15865-8**	359C	**15936-0**	1143F	**16016-4**	930H	**16078-4**	828E	**16159-4**	516D	**16231-0**	626H
15726-0	1275E	**15795-3**	1567F	**15872-0**	317B	**15937-9**	1143E	**16017-2**	942D	**16079-2**	932D	**16160-8**	98F	**16232-9**	594A
15727-9	373C	**15796-1**	1235F	**15873-9**	261D	**15938-7**	1143D	**16018-0**	942F	**16080-6**	649G	**16163-2**	810D	**16233-7**	730A
15728-7	517H	**15799-6**	35C	**15875-5**	1186E	**15940-9**	55E	**16019-9**	942E	**16082-2**	508E	**16164-0**	749B	**16234-5**	946H
15729-5	373B	**15800-3**	29G	**15876-3**	552A	**15941-7**	165C	**16020-2**	743F	**16086-5**	1198E	**16165-9**	1068C	**16235-3**	85A
15730-9	1188C	**15801-1**	563E	**15877-1**	1177A	**15944-1**	1438H	**16021-0**	1063D	**16087-3**	1198A	**16166-7**	428F	**16243-4**	1405C
15731-7	547B	**15803-8**	1025A	**15879-8**	1317E	**15949-2**	934D	**16022-9**	1409B	**16088-1**	334C	**16168-3**	253B	**16244-2**	655G
15732-5	629B	**15806-2**	540G	**15880-1**	1138H	**15950-6**	745F	**16024-5**	1401E	**16093-8**	334F	**16169-1**	1041F	**16248-5**	771D
15733-3	627B	**15807-0**	1186A	**15882-8**	1406A	**15951-4**	518F	**16025-3**	1401F	**16096-2**	502E	**16170-5**	1431D	**16249-3**	774A
15734-1	631C	**15808-9**	1179B	**15883-6**	1405E	**15952-2**	249F	**16026-1**	1402G	**16097-0**	1262A	**16171-3**	1061F	**16250-7**	679A
15736-8	632B	**15809-7**	1154D	**15884-4**	227H	**15953-0**	858C	**16028-8**	1265D	**16098-9**	916G	**16172-1**	868E	**16251-5**	677F
15737-6	632C	**15810-0**	1502G	**15885-2**	1391C	**15954-9**	961A	**16029-6**	1265C	**16099-7**	1199H	**16174-8**	755C	**16253-1**	1058F
15738-4	1403H	**15812-7**	125C	**15886-0**	1102A	**15955-7**	655A	**16031-8**	449A	**16101-2**	1327A	**16175-6**	126F	**16255-8**	825A
15739-2	417F	**15813-5**	341A	**15887-9**	1508F	**15956-5**	518E	**16032-6**	891F	**16104-7**	1154A	**16176-4**	155F	**16256-6**	46D
15740-6	426H	**15814-3**	339D	**15888-7**	1508E	**15957-3**	1205F	**16033-4**	947C	**16106-3**	843C	**16177-2**	632G	**16257-4**	1426H
15741-4	426F	**15815-1**	340A	**15889-5**	1508D	**15960-3**	1031F	**16034-2**	109F	**16107-1**	896F	**16178-0**	872G	**16258-2**	683F
15742-2	425G	**15817-8**	341B	**15891-7**	202F	**15961-1**	882A	**16035-0**	62D	**16109-8**	1544A	**16179-9**	1157F	**16260-4**	1136B
15743-0	426B	**15818-6**	339B	**15892-5**	1161C	**15963-8**	687E	**16036-9**	935G	**16110-1**	1543H	**16180-2**	244B	**16261-2**	995A
15744-9	610G	**15819-4**	1336D	**15894-1**	3A	**15964-6**	1104C	**16037-7**	1339E	**16112-8**	1544B	**16181-0**	792E	**16262-0**	1002G
15745-7	268G	**15820-8**	1341D	**15896-8**	115D	**15968-9**	988B	**16038-5**	1100G	**16113-6**	779C	**16182-9**	1158H	**16263-9**	1004B
15746-5	880G	**15821-6**	554F	**15898-4**	858E	**15969-7**	1453G	**16039-3**	1391F	**16114-4**	1063A	**16183-7**	271G	**16264-7**	1003G
15747-3	880F	**15822-4**	1447G	**15899-2**	1166H	**15970-0**	236E	**16040-7**	1021C	**16115-2**	842H	**16184-5**	1151E	**16265-5**	341G
15748-1	881C	**15824-0**	234F	**15901-8**	1037H	**15971-9**	1167G	**16041-5**	1379G	**16116-0**	910H	**16185-3**	506B	**16266-3**	342E
15750-3	855E	**15825-9**	998B	**15902-6**	371E	**15972-7**	856B	**16046-6**	137G	**16117-9**	1285D	**16186-1**	946C	**16267-1**	343B
15753-8	885A	**15826-7**	206H	**15903-4**	1426C	**15973-5**	441B	**16047-4**	1232G	**16118-7**	1287F	**16189-6**	779F	**16269-8**	1255G
15754-6	629G	**15828-3**	1384D	**15904-2**	1027E	**15974-3**	143D	**16048-2**	540C	**16119-5**	826G	**16191-8**	994C	**16270-1**	1315B
15755-4	630G	**15829-1**	888G	**15906-9**	628B	**15988-3**	771F	**16049-0**	1097D	**16123-3**	1440A	**16192-6**	1096F	**16272-8**	344B
15756-2	639B	**15831-3**	1025H	**15907-7**	628A	**15989-1**	773A	**16050-4**	693B	**16124-1**	1439E	**16193-4**	542G	**16273-6**	333H
15757-0	842D	**15832-1**	922C	**15908-5**	1184H	**15990-5**	246A	**16051-2**	1057B	**16126-8**	1441A	**16195-0**	496F	**16274-4**	334A
15758-9	880H	**15834-8**	671A	**15909-3**	815A	**15991-3**	854F	**16052-0**	865C	**16129-2**	1434B	**16196-9**	181C	**16275-2**	334B
15759-7	174B	**15835-6**	1271D	**15910-7**	784B	**15992-1**	854G	**16053-9**	1399A	**16130-6**	1434C	**16197-7**	184B	**16276-0**	1114G
15761-9	672C	**15836-4**	838B	**15911-5**	1215A	**15995-6**	365E	**16054-7**	325F	**16131-4**	1438A	**16198-5**	1563A	**16278-7**	428A
15762-7	782F	**15838-0**	245H	**15912-3**	879F	**15996-4**	1115C	**16055-5**	524H	**16132-2**	1392C	**16200-0**	262G	**16279-5**	1427B
15763-5	504H	**15839-9**	625G	**15913-1**	1289H	**15997-2**	1115F	**16056-3**	451F	**16133-0**	418G	**16201-9**	317A	**16280-9**	953C
15764-3	255F	**15840-2**	146C	**15915-8**	484E	**15998-0**	1115E	**16057-1**	652C	**16135-7**	334G	**16209-4**	821F	**16283-3**	667F
15765-1	535E	**15841-0**	300G	**15916-6**	625C	**15999-9**	1115G	**16059-8**	1227D	**16136-5**	603F	**16212-4**	174A	**16284-1**	667E
15767-8	504E	**15842-9**	47H	**15917-4**	1213A	**16000-8**	1116A	**16060-1**	1380A	**16141-1**	910G	**16214-0**	390H	**16286-8**	903C
15771-6	727E	**15846-1**	1361A	**15918-2**	1212H	**16001-6**	1116C	**16062-8**	281B	**16143-8**	626B	**16215-9**	102D	**16287-6**	484B
15772-4	727C	**15848-8**	642D	**15919-0**	1402H	**16002-4**	1116D	**16063-6**	259G	**16144-6**	1030A	**16216-7**	93H	**16288-4**	1411E
15776-7	541H	**15849-6**	750G	**15920-4**	1402C	**16003-2**	1116E	**16064-4**	1214H	**16145-4**	1096G	**16217-5**	531C	**16289-2**	1224F
15777-5	554E	**15851-8**	932G	**15922-0**	365C	**16004-0**	1116G	**16065-2**	602E	**16146-2**	524E	**16218-3**	531D	**16295-7**	782E
15780-5	541G	**15852-6**	324D	**15923-9**	626C	**16005-9**	1116F	**16066-0**	1394G	**16148-9**	744G	**16219-1**	531F	**16296-5**	127E
15785-6	758B	**15854-2**	1410G	**15924-7**	346A	**16006-7**	1116H	**16067-9**	611A	**16149-7**	733G	**16220-5**	690B	**16297-3**	127F
15786-4	1221B	**15855-0**	1400F	**15925-5**	865E	**16007-5**	930C	**16068-7**	264F	**16150-0**	821G	**16222-1**	1138G	**16302-3**	58C
15787-2	160A	**15856-9**	550E	**15926-3**	509C	**16008-3**	941E	**16069-5**	919D	**16151-9**	1567H	**16224-8**	188G	**16312-0**	827E
15788-0	1028D	**15858-5**	550D	**15927-1**	181H	**16009-1**	941D	**16070-9**	756D	**16152-7**	1567G	**16225-6**	188H	**16314-7**	1324C
15790-2	479D	**15860-7**	548E	**15930-1**	58F	**16010-5**	942B	**16072-5**	787H	**16153-5**	340G	**16226-4**	189A	**16315-5**	385H
15791-0	385A	**15861-5**	556D	**15932-8**	59B	**16011-3**	941F	**16074-1**	813G	**16154-3**	1097A	**16227-2**	37D	**16317-1**	734C
15792-9	1186F	**15862-3**	1056G	**15934-4**	1144A	**16014-8**	941G	**16076-8**	1162A	**16157-8**	455F	**16229-9**	593D	**16319-8**	1382D

NOTES

NOTES

NOTES